Stanley Gibbons
STAMP CATALOGUE

PART 1

# British Commonwealth 1992/93

Including post-independence issues of
Ireland, Fiji and South Africa

Ninety-fifth edition

VOLUME 1

Great Britain and Countries A to I

Stanley Gibbons Publications Ltd
London and Ringwood

*By Appointment to Her Majesty The Queen*
*Stanley Gibbons Ltd, London*
*Philatelists*

*Published by* **Stanley Gibbons Publications Ltd**
Editorial, Sales Offices and Distribution Centre:
5 Parkside, Christchurch Road, Ringwood,
Hants BH24 3SH.



**ISBN: 0-85259-328-7**

**Item No. 2811 (92/93)**

Text assembled by Black Bear Press Limited, Cambridge

Made and Printed in Great Britain by William Clowes Limited, Beccles, Suffolk

# Preface to the 1992/93 Edition

## REORGANIZATION AND REVIVAL

The long-anticipated point when this catalogue could no longer be produced as a single volume was reached with the publication of the 1992 edition. It was then clear to us that the *Part 1* had become physically difficult to use, due to its weight and bulk, and there were other associated problems such as the visibility of the text in columns next to the binding edge.

Plans for this eventuality had already been made. Regular readers may remember the questionnaire included with the 1987 edition and further soundings were taken subsequently. A detailed analysis of the options available to us was given in the January 1992 issue of *Gibbons Stamp Monthly*. After careful consideration of these it was decided that an alphabetical split, of the type which had worked successfully for *Stamps of the World* since 1983, was the best alternative.

It is our firm intention that the division into two volumes will provide easier handling without losing too much of the convenience of a single volume. To achieve this two further innovations, previewed in the preface last year, have been introduced. Readers will now find all issues for a particular country or territory listed under its current name. For example, stamps inscribed "BASUTOLAND" are now included, with their successors, under "LESOTHO" and those of "NORTHERN RHODESIA" precede those for "ZAMBIA". In almost all instances the catalogue and illustration numbers already run-on and there are obvious advantages in having issues listed consecutively. The other alteration is that stamps for previously separate colonies which subsequently united to form a federation are now listed before the issues for the larger country, rather than in alphabetical sequence. The Australian colonies now appear before Australia, the Canadian provinces before Canada and the various territories which combined to form South Africa are listed in the catalogue under "S". Full details of all these relocations will be found in the boxed panel on page xvi.

As the two volumes of the *Part 1* will be available separately it is our intention that each volume will be self-contained. Considerable progress towards this has been made in this edition with the provision of further illustrations and the amendment of cross-references in Volume 2. It is hoped to complete the task in next year's catalogue.

The reorganization of *Part 1* has, to a certain extent, overshadowed important trends elsewhere. The review of prices in this volume shows a stamp market in a far more healthy condition than has been the case for a number of years. There are other pointers to renewed interest in the hobby. Attendance figures for exhibitions and stamp fairs continue to rise, the flow of material for auction is improving and the more restrained approach of many postal administrations to the production of new issues have all combined to indicate that far brighter times are ahead.

## PRICES

It is a relief to report that the era of widespread price reductions appears to have passed. With the exception of commemorative issues from the 1960s and 1970s, where levels are still depressed due to more than adequate stocks, increased demand, coupled with insufficient supplies, has caused prices to rise.

Trends visible in the 1992 edition continue. Some classic issues remain quiet, but rises from the later Queen Victoria issues onwards are substantial. Interest in the stamps of King George VI has grown to a point where there are even rises for some of the Omnibus sets and such movements have extended to the definitive issues of the present reign where some worthwhile increases occur for the first time in many years. Errors and varieties, as always, are still much sought-after, as are used examples of postage due issues.

Some stamps, never available in quantity, are becoming increasingly difficult to find and this is highlighted by extensive repricing for **Batum**, **British Post Office in Siam**, **Burma Japanese Occupation**, **Cameroons** and **Heligoland**.

Elsewhere some Great Britain Used Abroad listings, such as **Ascension** and **Cyprus**, show rises as do a number of the smaller West Indies islands, notably **Bahamas**, **Barbados**, **Belize (British Honduras)**, **Bermuda** (principally King George VI), and **British Virgin Islands**.

The market for **Australia and States** remains difficult. There are rises for the **New South Wales** Sydney Views, **South Australia** officials and high values in general. Activity in **Australia** itself is mainly concentrated on used prices and the surprisingly popular postage due sets. **Cook Islands** used are also marked-up to 1945 as are the similar issues for **Aitutaki** and **Penhryn**. There is also considerable activity for **Gibraltar** issues from King Edward VII onwards and also amongst the pre-independence issues of **British Guiana (Guyana)**. In **India** there is much repricing amongst the Queen Victoria stamps, including the officials, with the **Convention States** also very active. **Ireland** issues since 1945 are also in considerable demand and this is reflected in this edition.

For **Great Britain** used prices for the Queen Victoria line-engraved stamps have increased, but those quoted for mounted mint King Edward VII and King George V stamps have fallen back. Other issues are relatively quiet, but it is clear that there is a very keen market for Decimal Machin stamps only available from booklets and also for obsolete Greetings stamps.

## REVISIONS IN THIS EDITION

The task of listing chalk-surfaced paper varieties has been completed with work on the King George VI issues. Additional listings appear under **Bahamas**, **Bermuda**, **British Virgin Islands**, **Dominica**, **Grenada** and **Hong Kong**.

Further King George VI varieties have been added and the policy of improving the listings has been extended back to earlier issues with the inclusion of the malformed and repaired "S" flaws on the Queen Victoria Key Type (originally brought to our attention by Mr. P. O. Beale) on **Belize** and **Gambia**, the dented frame ("Glover" flaw) on the King Edward VII issues of **Cayman Islands** and **Gambia**, and the split "A" on the King George V stamps of **Gambia**.

Improved postal history notes have been provided for **Antigua**, **Cocos (Keeling) Islands** and the **Japanese Occupation of Hong Kong**.

Listings of butterflies and other insects in this edition have been revised to reflect the work of the Butterfly and Moth Stamp Society for our thematic catalogue *Collect Butterflies and Other Insects on Stamps*. It is worth noting that our listings of fauna and flora subjects often provide more accurate descriptions of species than the stamp captions.

**Antigua.** Watermark sideways varieties from the 1863–67 series are now listed for the first time.

**Australia and States.** The coverage of the popular **Tasmania** pictorials from 1899 onwards has been revised with the help of Mr. K. E. Lancaster. A start has been made on the revision of **Victoria** with the rewriting of the Private Contract period to 1860. It is hoped that the new treatment of these issues, inspired by the highly-recommended handbook *The Stamps of Victoria* by G. Kellow, will attract new collectors to these interesting stamps. For **Australia** itself there are a number of unannounced perforation changes amongst recent definitives which are listed and priced.

**Botswana.** The incorporation of the stamps of **Stellaland** and **Bechuanaland** under this heading has provided the opportunity for a general revision of the pre-independence issues to give more postal history information and details of settings.

**Canada.** Further work has been undertaken on the modern definitives with the help of Mr. P. Harris. There are a number of paper varieties listed for past issues and, hopefully, all the unannounced perforations which have appeared in recent months are now included and, in almost every instance, priced.

**Ghana.** Further work has been done on the 1988–90 surcharges based on information provided by Mr. A. Irani. These locally-produced surcharges show many major errors and even some postal forgeries.

**Guyana.** The information provided for the 1899 British Guiana surcharges on the Jubilee issue has been revised, with a number of new listings, on the advice of Mr. M. Nicholson.

**Hong Kong.** The 1882–96 issues have been rewritten.

**India.** Much interesting information on the postal arrangements for the **International Commission in Indo-China** has been provided, taken, with permission, from an article by Mr. K. Lewis in the *Indo-China Philatelist*. For the Feudatory States the variety positions on the 1890–93 issue of **Bamra** are now given, new basic stamps listed for **Jasdan** and **Soruth** 1864 issue and there are further varieties included for the 1868–75 set from the same state.

**Iraq.** Mr. A. Khalastchy has provided details of his research into the settings of the British Occupation surcharges.

**Ireland.** Mr. B. Warren has continued to provide details of the surprisingly-complex modern definitives.

There are many other alterations elsewhere and, as always, we are most grateful to those collectors, dealers and postal administrations who continue to provide us with invaluable help in the improvement of the listings.

Finally there are two reminders. The second volume of the 1992–93 *Part 1* catalogue, covering countries J to Z, will be published on 2 October 1992. The two-volume *Part 1* catalogue to be published *next* year will be dated 1993, so the pre-dating of editions, which has caused an increasing amount of confusion in recent years, will then be at an end.

David J. Aggersberg

# Stanley Gibbons Addresses

## HEAD OFFICE, 399 STRAND, LONDON WC2R 0LX

**Auction Room and Specialist Departments.** Open Monday-Friday 9.30 a.m. to 5 p.m.

**Shop.** Open Monday 9.30 a.m. to 5.30 p.m., Tuesday-Friday 8.30 a.m. to 5.30 p.m. and Saturday 10 a.m. to 4 p.m.

**Telephone 071 836 8444 and Fax 071 836 7342 for all departments.**

## RINGWOOD OFFICE

**Stanley Gibbons Publications.** 5 Parkside, Christchurch Road, Ringwood, Hants BS24 3SH. Telephone 0425 472363 and Fax 0425 470247.

**Publications Shop** (at above address). Open Monday–Friday 9.30 a.m. to 3.30 p.m.

## OVERSEAS BRANCHES

**Stanley Gibbons Australia Pty. Ltd.** P.O. Box 863J, Melbourne 3001, Australia. Telephone (01 0613) 670 3332 and Telex AA 37223.

**Stanley Gibbons (Singapore) Pte. Ltd.** Raffles City, P.O. Box 1689, Singapore 9117, Republic of Singapore. Telephone (010 65) 336 1998.

## STANLEY GIBBONS PUBLICATIONS LIMITED OVERSEAS REPRESENTATION

Stanley Gibbons Publications Ltd are represented overseas by the following sole distributors (*) and main agents (**).

**Australia***

Lighthouse Philatelic (Aust.) Pty Ltd
PO Box 763
Strawberry Hills
New South Wales 2012
Australia

**Belgium and Luxembourg****

Philac
Rue du Midi 48
Bruxelles
Belgium 1000

**Canada***

Lighthouse Publications (Canada) Ltd
255 Duke Street
Montreal
Quebec
Canada H3C 2M2

**Denmark****

Nordfrim
DK 5450
Otterup
Denmark

**France***

Davo France SARL
25 Rue Monge
75005 Paris
France

**Germany and Austria****

Leuchtturm Albenverlag
Paul Koch KG
Am Spakenberg 45
Postfach 1340
D-2054 Geesthacht
Germany

Ka-Be Briefmarkenalben-Verlag
Daimlerstrasse 15
Volkhardt GMBH
Goppingen
Germany

**Hong Kong****

Po-on Stamp Service
GPO Box 2498
Hong Kong

**Israel****

Capital Stamps
PO Box 3769
Jerusalem 91036
Israel

**Italy***

Secrian Srl
Via Pantelleria 2
1-20156 Milano
Italy

**Japan****

Japan Philatelic Co Ltd
PO Box 2
Suginami-Minami
Tokyo
Japan

**Netherlands***

Davo Publications
PO Box 411
7400 AK Deventer
Netherlands

**New Zealand***

Philatelic Distributors Ltd
PO Box 863
New Plymouth
New Zealand

**Norway****

Wennergren Cappelen AS
Nedre Vollgate 4
PO Box 738
Sentrum N-0105
Oslo 1
Norway

**South Africa****

Stanley Gibbons (Pty) Ltd
PO Box 930
Parklands
RSA 2121

Republic Coin and Stamp Accessories (Pty) Ltd
PO Box 260325
Excom 2023
Johannesburg
RSA

**Sweden***

Chr Winther Sorensen AB
Box 43
S-310 Knared
Sweden

**Switzerland****

Phila Service
Burgstrasse 160
CH 4125 Riehen
Switzerland

**USA***

Lighthouse Publications Inc
PO Box 705
274 Washington Avenue
Hackensack
New Jersey 07602-0705
USA

**West Indies/Caribbean****

Hugh Dunphy
PO Box 413
Kingston 10
Jamaica
West Indies

# Contents


Preface .. iii
Stamps Added and Numbers Altered .. vi
Specialist Philatelic Societies .. vii
General Philatelic Information .. viii
Prices .. viii
Abbreviations .. xvi
Select Bibliography .. xix

GREAT BRITAIN .. GB1
Channel Islands .. GB68
Guernsey .. GB68
Alderney .. GB77
Isle of Man .. GB78
Jersey .. GB86
BRITISH POST OFFICES ABROAD .. GB95
ABU DHABI .. 1
ANGUILLA .. 1
ANTIGUA .. 11
Barbuda .. 28
Redonda .. 37
ASCENSION .. 39
AUSTRALIA .. 48
New South Wales .. 48
Queensland .. 53
South Australia .. 56
Tasmania .. 60
Victoria .. 63
Western Australia .. 72
Commonwealth of Australia .. 74
British Commonwealth Occupation Force (Japan) .. 102
Australian Antarctic Territory .. 103
BAHAMAS .. 105
BAHRAIN .. 116
BANGLADESH .. 117
BARBADOS .. 125
BATUM .. 136
BELIZE .. 136
British Honduras .. 136
Belize .. 140
Cayes of Belize .. 148
BERMUDA .. 149
BOTSWANA .. 160
Stellaland .. 160
British Bechuanaland .. 160
Bechuanaland Protectorate .. 160
Bechuanaland .. 162
Botswana .. 162
BRITISH ANTARCTIC TERRITORY .. 170
BRITISH INDIAN OCEAN TERRITORY .. 173
BRITISH LEVANT .. 175
British Post Offices in Turkish Empire .. 175
British Post Offices in Constantinople and Smyrna .. 177
British Field Office in Salonica .. 177
BRITISH OCCUPATION OF ITALIAN COLONIES .. 177
Middle East Forces .. 177
Cyrenaica .. 178
Eritrea .. 178
Somalia .. 178
Tripolitania .. 179
BRITISH POST OFFICES IN CRETE .. 179
BRITISH POST OFFICE IN SIAM .. 179
BRITISH POSTAL AGENCIES IN EASTERN ARABIA .. 179
BRITISH VIRGIN ISLANDS .. 180
BRUNEI .. 190
Japanese Occupation .. 197
BURMA .. 198
Japanese Occupation .. 199
BUSHIRE .. 201
CAMEROONS .. 201
CANADA .. 201
British Columbia and Vancouver Island .. 201
Colony of Canada .. 201
New Brunswick .. 203
Newfoundland .. 204
Nova Scotia .. 209
Prince Edward Island .. 211
Dominion of Canada .. 211
CAYMAN ISLANDS .. 241
CHRISTMAS ISLAND .. 250
COCOS (KEELING) ISLANDS .. 255
COOK ISLANDS .. 259
Aitutaki .. 273
Penrhyn Island .. 280
CYPRUS .. 286
Turkish Cypriot Posts .. 299
DOMINICA .. 305
EGYPT .. 320
Egyptian Post Offices Abroad .. 322
Ethiopia, Turkish Empire
British Forces in Egypt .. 323
FALKLAND ISLANDS .. 323
FALKLAND ISLANDS DEPENDENCIES .. 333
A. Graham Land .. 333
B. South Georgia .. 333
C. South Orkneys .. 333
D. South Shetlands .. 333
E. Falkland Islands Dependencies .. 333
F. South Georgia .. 333
G. Falkland Islands Dependencies .. 334
FIJI .. 335
GAMBIA .. 346
GHANA .. 359
Gold Coast .. 359
Ghana .. 360
GIBRALTAR .. 378
GILBERT AND ELLICE ISLANDS .. 389
GRENADA .. 392
Grenadines of Grenada .. 413
GUYANA .. 424
British Guiana .. 424
Guyana .. 427
HELIGOLAND .. 455
HONG KONG .. 455
Japanese Occupation .. 466
British Post Offices in China .. 466
British Post Offices in Japan .. 468
INDIA .. 468
India Used Abroad .. 507
China Expeditionary Force .. 508
Indian Expeditionary Forces .. 508
Indian Custodian Forces in Korea .. 508
Indian U.N. Force in Congo .. 508
Indian U.N. Force in Gaza .. 508
International Commission in Indo-China .. 509
Indian National Army .. 509
Japanese Occupation of Andaman and Nicobar Islands .. 509
Indian Convention States .. 509
Chamba, Faridkot, Gwalior, Jind, Nabha, Patiala
Indian Feudatory States .. 516
Alwar, Bamra, Barwani, Bhopal, Bhor, Bijawar, Bundi, Bussahir, Charkhari, Cochin, Dhar, Dungarpur, Duttia, Faridkot, Hyderabad, Idar, Indore, Jaipur, Jammu and Kashmir, Jasdan, Jhalawar, Jind, Kishangarh, Las Bela, Morvi, Nandgaon, Nawanagar, Orchha, Poonch, Rajasthan, Rajpipla, Shahpura, Sirmoor, Soruth, Travancore, Travancore-Cochin, Wadhwan
IONIAN ISLANDS .. 547
IRAQ .. 547
IRELAND .. 549
Addenda .. 567
Index .. 569

# Numbers Added or Changed

## STAMPS ADDED

Excluding new issues which have appeared in Gibbons *Stamp Monthly* Supplements, the following are the Catalogue numbers of stamps listed in this edition for the first time.

**Great Britain.** 35b, 73c, 121b, 210*b*, X910a, X935a, X969a, 948i, 1449a, 1481a, 1506a, 1519a, 1527a, 1531a, 1533a, 1573a, 1588a
**Guernsey.** 301b, 309b

**Antigua.** 7b, 8a
**Barbuda.** 139a

**Ascension.** 12d, 34k

**Australia — Queensland.** 206*c*
**Tasmania.** 142a, 237d, 240ca, 242c, 247db, 250fb/fc, 250gc/gd, 252d, 254c
**Victoria.** 57, 86
**Australia.** 184b, 185b, 200b, 1199a, 1200a, 1269b/ba, 1270a

**Bahamas.** 115a, 155a, 171a, 174a

**Bangladesh.** 262a, O29

**Barbados.** 251ab

**Belize.** 52a, 1060

**Bermuda.** 118g, 120c

**Botswana.** 64a, 89b, 294a, 713B/16B

**British Levant.** 32a, 37b

**British Occupation of Italian Colonies.** M1a, M2a, M3a, M4b, M5a, T3a, T4a, T16a, T17a

**British Virgin Islands.** 42*d*, 110a, 111a, 112a, 113a, 114a, 115a, 116a, 117a, 118a, 119a

**Brunei.** 12b, 35b

**Canada — Colony of Canada.** 26a, 28a
**Newfoundland.** 259b
**Canada.** 556a, 884ba, 885a, 885ca, 1054a, 1055ac, 1056a, 1057a, 1057ba, 1061a, 1067a, 1148b, 1266a, 1269c, 1270ca, 1273ba, 1275c, 1276ca, 1350b/ba, 1351a, 1352a, 1354c

**Cayman Islands.** 3a, 4a, 5a, 6a, 7a, 8a, 9a, 10a, 11a, 12a, 13a, 14a, 15a, 16a, 17a, 18e, 19b, 35b, 85a, 96h, 499a

**Cook Islands.** 60a/b, 207a

**Dominica.** 109a

**Falkland Islands Dependencies.** G9a

**Gambia.** 37a/b, 38a/b, 39a, 40a/b, 41a, 42a, 43a, 44a, 45a, 46a, 47a, 48a, 49a, 50a, 51a, 52a, 53a, 54a, 55a, 56a, 57a, 58a, 59a, 60b, 61a, 62a, 63a, 64a, 65a, 66a, 67a, 68a, 69a, 70b, 72a, 73a, 74a, 75b, 76a, 77a, 78a, 79a, 80a, 81a, 82a, 83a, 84a, 85a, 86c, 87c, 88a, 89a, 90b, 91d, 92d, 93d, 94a, 95a, 96b, 97b, 98a, 99a, 100a, 101a

**Ghana.** 387b, 412c, 414c, 446a, 1031ac, 1246f, 1248/9a, 1251/5i, 1258a, 1259/60a, 1262c, 126[illegible] 1264a, 1392*a*, 1393*a*

**Gibraltar.** 143a, 346a, 347a, 348a

**Grenada.** 152a, 152c, 365b, 499a

**Guyana.** 155a, 157a, 222b/c, 2266a

**Hong Kong.** 136e, 156a, 158a, 160ab

**India.** 923ab, 927ab, 936b, 1211a, 1218a, 1219a, 1220, 1311a, 1320a, O18a, O254a, O256a, O257a, O258a, O259a, O260a, O261a, O262a, O263a, O264a, O265a, O266a
**China Expeditionary Force.** C1b, C2b, C3a, C4a, C5a, C6b, C7b, C8a, C9b, C10a, C14a
**Convention States — Patiala.** 35a
**Feudatory States — Barwani.** 10b, 23a
**Bhopal.** O301a
**Duttia.** 3a
**Jasdan.** 2
**Poonch.** 11a
**Soruth.** 4*a*, 10b, 11a/b, 12b/d, 13a, 14a, 15a/b, 24a
**Travancore-Cochin.** 1dd, 3c, 6ac

**Ireland.** 746a, 753a, 757a, 763a

## CATALOGUE NUMBERS ALTERED

The table below is a cross-reference for those stamps, the Catalogue numbers of which have altered in this edition.

| *Old* | *New* |
|---|---|
| **Great Britain** | |
| X913/21 | X914/22 |
| X936/67 | X937/68 |
| X968/74 | X970/6 |
| X975/83 | X978/86 |
| X984 | X988 |
| X985 | X990 |
| X986 | X992 |
| X987 | X994 |
| X988 | X993 |
| X1016/23 | X1017/24 |
| 1449a/c | 1449b/d |
| **Regionals** | |
| NI47/55 | NI48/56 |
| NI56/8a | NI58/60a |
| NI59/62 | NI62/5 |
| S60/7 | S61/8 |
| S68/70 | S70/2 |
| S71/4 | S74/7 |
| W48/56 | W53/8 |
| W57/9 | W61/3 |
| W60/3 | W65/8 |
| **Guernsey** | |
| 309b/c | 309c/d |
| **Antigua** | |
| 64 | 65 |
| 65/6 | 64/*a* |
| **Australia — Tasmania** | |
| 239*c*/*ca* | 239*d*/da |
| 239d | 239c |
| 242*c*/*f* | 242*d*/*g* |
| 250*e*/ea | 250*f*/fa |
| 250f | 250e |
| **Victoria** | |
| 18/19 | 23/4 |
| 20/5 | 26/31 |
| 26/7 | 48/9 |
| 28/9 | 78/9 |
| 30/4 | 18/22 |
| 35/8 | 36/9 |
| 39 | 25 |
| 40 | 54 |
| 41 | 81 |
| 42 | 40 |
| 43 | 73 |
| 44 | 32 |
| 45 | 53 |
| 46 | 58 |
| 47 | 61 |
| 48 | 60 |
| 49 | 35 |
| 50 | 56 |
| 51 | 82 |
| 52 | 34 |
| 53 | 55 |
| 54 | 33 |
| 55/8 | 41/4 |
| 59 | 46 |
| 60/2 | 50/2 |
| 63 | 74 |
| 64 | 45 |
| 65 | 47 |
| 66 | 77 |
| 67 | 59 |
| 68/71 | 62/5 |
| 72 | 75 |
| 73/4 | 66/8 |
| 75 | 69a |
| 76 | 71 |
| 77 | 80 |
| 78 | 71ca |
| 79/*b* | 69/70*a* |
| 80/1 | 71a/2 |
| 82 | 83a |
| 83 | 76 |
| 84/6*b* | 83/5*a* |
| 87 | 86a |
| 88 | 87a |
| 89/90 | 86b/7 |
| 91 | 76b |
| **Australia** | |
| 1187/8 | 1186/7 |
| **Bangladesh** | |
| 365/73 | 376/81 |
| **Belize** | |
| **MS**1060/96 | **MS**1061/97 |
| **Bermuda** | |
| 120be/d | 120ce/e |
| 622/7 | 624/9 |
| **Botswana** | |
| 24 | 23c |
| 27 | 26a |
| 90 | *Deleted* |
| **British Levant** | |
| 26b | 25a |
| **British Virgin Islands** | |
| 8 | 9 |
| 9 | 8 |
| 22b | 22ab |
| **Canada — Newfoundland** | |
| 80/2 | 91/3 |
| **Canada** | |
| 885*a*/*c* | 885*b*/*d* |
| 1054a | 1054b |
| 1056a | 1056b |
| 1057a | 1057b |
| 1148b | 1148ba |
| 1270ca/cb | 1270cb/cc |
| 1276ca/cb | 1276cb/cc |
| 1353 | 1354 |
| 1354 | 1356 |
| **Christmas Island** | |
| 310/13 | 311/14 |
| **Cocos (Keeling) Islands** | |
| 235 | 234 |
| **Cook Islands — Aitutaki** | |
| O36*a*/40 | O37/41 |
| **Dominica** | |
| 51*ab* | 51b |
| 1383/91 | 1388/6 |
| 1392/6 | 1383/7 |
| **Falkland Islands** | |
| 161*a* | 161*c* |
| **Gambia** | |
| 41*a* | 41*b* |
| **Ghana** | |
| 387b/ba | 387c/ca |
| 1248 | 1250 |
| 1249/51a | 1256/8a |
| 1252/3b | 1261/2b |
| 1254 | 1264 |
| **Grenada** | |
| 152*a* | 152b |
| **Guyana** | |
| 155a/c | 155b/d |
| 157a | 157b |
| 1889/93 | **MS**1889 |
| D1b/c | D1ab/ac |
| D2aa/b | D2a/ac |
| **Hong Kong** | |
| 34/6 | 35/7 |
| 37/9 | 40/2 |
| 40/1 | 38/9 |
| 42/8 | 45/51 |
| 49/50 | 43/4 |
| 51 | 34 |
| 145*a*/*b* | 145*b*/*c* |
| 145c | 145a |
| 153*a* | 153*b* |
| 153*b* | 153a |
| 156*a* | 156b |
| **India** | |
| 1219/20 | 1218/19 |
| **Feudatory States — Barwani** | |
| 23a/*b* | 23*b*/*c* |
| **Bhopal** | |
| O301a/d | O301b/e |
| **Jasdan** | |
| 2/5 | 3/6 |
| **Soruth** | |
| 10*b* | 10*c* |
| **Travancore-Cochin** | |
| 3c/g | 3d/h |
| **Iraq** | |
| 7ca | 7da |
| 116a | 115a |

# Specialist Philatelic Societies

ritish Decimal Stamps Study Circle
ecretary—Mr. P. R. Daniels
0 Moor Park Close, Rainham, Gillingham,
ent ME8 8QT

reat Britain Philatelic Society
Membership Secretary—Mr. D. S. Glover
0 Rockwood Park, Saint Hill, East
rinstead, West Sussex RH19 4JX

reat Britain Decimal Stamp Book Study
ircle
Membership Secretary—Mr. A. J. Wilkins
Buttermere Close, Brierley Hill, West
Midlands DY5 3SD

hannel Islands Specialists Society
Membership Secretary—Mr. B. Cropp
7 Westlands Avenue, Huntercombe,
lough, Berkshire SL1 6AG

---

scension Study Circle
ecretary—Dr. R. C. F. Baker
reys, Tower Road, Whitstable, Kent
T5 2ER

echuanalands and Botswana Society
ecretary—Mr. M. George
.O. Box 108, St. Albans, Hertfordshire
L1 3AD

elize Philatelic Study Circle
ecretary—Mr. C. R. Gambill
730 Collingswood, Corpus Christi, Texas
78412, U.S.A.

Bermuda Collectors Society
Secretary—Mr. T. J. McMahon
Nash Road, Purdy Station, N.Y. 10578,
U.S.A.

Bermuda High (Keyplates)
Editor—Mr. R. W. Dickgiesser
P.O. Box 475, Derby, CT 06418, U.S.A.

British Caribbean Philatelic Study Group
Overseas Director—Mr. R. V. Swarbrick
The Four Winds, 919 Uppingham Road,
Bushby, Leicestershire LE7 9RR

British Society of Australian Philately
Secretary—Mr. T. R. Finlayson
86 Clarence Road, Fleet, Hampshire
GU13 9RS

British West Indies Study Circle
Secretary—Mr. M. Wilson
Timbers, Chequers Road, Tharston,
Norwich, Norfolk NR15 2YA

Burma Philatelic Study Circle
Secretary—Mr. A. Meech
7208-91 Avenue, Edmonton, Alberta,
Canada T6B 0R8

Canadian Philatelic Society of Great Britain
Secretary—Mr. B. T. Stalker
Glaramara, Parc Bryn Coch, Upper Bryn
Coch, Mold, Clwyd

Ceylon Study Circle
Secretary—Mr. R.W.P. Frost
42 Lonsdale Road, Cannington, Bridgwater,
Somerset TA5 2JS

Cyprus Study Circle
Secretary—Dr. R. I. Watson
Hill Cottage, Slinfold, West Sussex
RH13 7SN

East Africa Study Circle
Secretary—Mr. R. Dunstan
Chantry Court, 1 The Close, Warminster,
Wiltshire BA12 9AL

Falklands Islands Study Group
Membership Secretary—Mr. D. W. A.
Jeffery
38 Bradstock Road, Stoneleigh, Epsom,
Surrey KT17 2LH

Gibraltar Philatelic Society
Honorary Secretary—Mr. M. Ramagge
P.O. Box 270, Gibraltar

Gibraltar Study Circle
Membership Secretary—Mr. B. M. Walker
21 Orchard Street, Aberdeen AB2 3DA

Great Britain Overprints Society
Membership Secretary—Mr. A. H. Bishop
The Coach House, Ridgemount Road,
Sunningdale, Berkshire SL5 9RL

Greater Southern Africa Philatelic Society
Representative—Mr. A. H. Murray
Erlesdene Garden Cottage, Greenwalk,
Bowdon, Altrincham, Cheshire WA14 2SL

Hong Kong Study Circle
Membership Secretary—Mr. P. V. Ball
37 Hart Court, Newcastle-under-Lyme,
Staffordshire ST5 2AL

Indian Ocean Study Circle (Western
Islands)
Secretary—Mrs. D. J. Hopson
Field Acre, Hoe Benham, Newbury,
Berkshire RG16 8PD

India Study Circle
Secretary—Dr. W. Fincham
10 Vallis Way, London W13 0DD

Irish Philatelic Circle
General Secretary—Mr. P. J. Wood
21 Loftus Road, London W12 7EH

King George V Silver Jubilee Study Circle
Secretary—Mr. N. Levinge
11 Broadway, Northampton NN1 4SF

King George VI Collectors Society
Secretary—Mr. F. R. Lockyer, OBE
24 Stourwood Road, Southbourne,
Bournemouth, Dorset BH6 3QP

Malaya Study Group
Membership Secretary—Mr. D. Moon
Holly Cottage, Barrows Road, Cheddar,
Somerset BS27 3BD

Malta Study Circle
Membership Secretary—Mr. D. Ward
40 Kingsman Road, Stanford-le-Hope,
Essex SS17 0JW

New Zealand Society of Great Britain
General Secretary—Mrs. M. Frankcom
Queens House, 34a Tarrant Street,
Arundel, West Sussex BN18 9DJ

Orange Free State Study Circle
Secretary—Mr. J. R. Stroud
28 Oxford Street, Burnham-on-Sea,
Somerset TA8 1LQ

Pacific Islands Study Circle of Great Britain
Honorary Secretary—Mr. J. D. Ray
24 Woodvale Avenue, London SE25 4AE

Papuan Philatelic Society
Secretary—Mr. G. Amedro
45A Main Street, Gorebridge, Midlothian
EH23 4BX

Pitcairn Islands Study Group (U.K.)
Honorary Secretary—Mr. A. B. Mears
Ragnall Cottge, Ragnall Lane, Walkley
Wood, Nailsworth, Stroud, Gloucestershire
GL6 0RX

Rhodesian Study Circle
Membership Secretary—Miss B. J. R.
Lashbrook
25 Exe View, Exminster, Devon EX6 8AL

St. Helena, Ascension and Tristan da Cunha
Philatelic Society
Secretary—Mrs. V. W. Finne
P.O. Box 366, Calpella, California 95418,
U.S.A.

Sarawak Specialists Society
Secretary—Dr. J. Higgins
The Stone House, Grimston Road, South
Wootton, Kings Lynn, Norfolk PE30 3NR

South African Collectors' Society
General Secretary—Mr. W. A. Page
138 Chastilian Road, Dartford, Kent
DA1 3LG

Sudan Study Group
Secretary—Mr. J. W. Scott
Bemerton, Lingfield Road, East Grinstead,
West Sussex RH19 2EJ

Tonga and Tin Can Mail Study Circle
Secretary—Mr. T. Jackson
121 Mullingar Ct. 1A, Schaumburg,
IL60193-3258, U.S.A.

Transvaal Study Circle
Secretary—Mr. J. Woolgar
132 Dale Street, Chatham, Kent ME4 6QH

West Africa Study Circle
Secretary—Mr. J. Powell
7 Pebble Moor, Edlesborough, Dunstable,
Bedfordshire LU6 2HZ

# General Philatelic Information

## and Guidelines to the Scope of the Part 1 (British Commonwealth) Catalogue

The notes which follow seek to reflect current practice in compiling the Part 1 (British Commonwealth) Catalogue.

It scarcely needs emphasising that the *Stanley Gibbons Stamp Catalogue* has a very long history and that the vast quantity of information it contains has been carefully built up by successive generations through the work of countless individuals. Philately itself is never static and the Catalogue has evolved and developed during this long time-span. Thus, while these notes are important for today's criteria, they may be less precise the further back in the listings one travels. They are not intended to inaugurate some unwanted series of piecemeal alterations in a widely respected work, but it does seem to us useful that Catalogue users know as exactly as possible the policies currently in operation.

## PRICES

The prices quoted in this Catalogue are the estimated selling prices of Stanley Gibbons Ltd at the time of publication. They are, *unless it is specifically stated otherwise*, for examples in fine condition for the issue concerned. Superb examples are worth more; those of a lower quality considerably less.

All prices are subject to change without prior notice and Stanley Gibbons Ltd may from time to time offer stamps below catalogue price. Individual low value stamps sold at 399, Strand are liable to an additional handling charge.

No guarantee is given to supply all stamps priced, since it is not possible to keep every catalogued item in stock. Commemorative issues may, at times, only be available in complete sets and not as individual values.

**Quotation of prices.** The prices in the left-hand column are for unused stamps and those in the right-hand column are for used.

A dagger (†) denotes that the item listed does not exist in that condition and a blank, or dash, that it exists, or may exist, but no market price is known.

Prices are expressed in pounds and pence sterling. One pound comprises 100 pence (£1 = 100p).

The method of notation is as follows: pence in numerals (e.g. 10 denotes ten pence); pound and pence, up to £100, in numerals (e.g. 4·25 denotes four pounds and twenty-five pence); prices above £100 expressed in whole pounds with the "£" sign shown.

**Unused stamps.** Great Britain and Commonwealth: the prices for unused stamps of Queen Victoria to King George V are for lightly hinged examples. Unused prices for King Edward VIII to Queen Elizabeth II issues are for unmounted mint.

Some stamps from the King George VI period are often difficult to find in unmounted mint condition. In such instances we would expect that collectors would need to pay a high proportion of the price quoted to obtain mounted mint examples. Generally speaking lightly mounted mint stamps from this reign, issued before 1945, are in considerable demand.

Mounted mint stamps from the reign of Queen Elizabeth II are frequently available at lower prices than those quoted for the stamps unmounted.

**Used stamps.** The used prices are normally for stamps postally used but may be for stamps cancelled-to-order where this practice exists.

A pen-cancellation on early issues can sometimes correctly denote postal use. Instances are individually noted in the Catalogue in explanation of the used price given.

Prices quoted for bisects on cover or on large piece are for those dated during the period officially authorised.

Stamps not sold unused to the public (e.g. some official stamps) are priced used only.

The use of "unified" designs, that is stamps inscribed for both postal and fiscal purposes, results in a number of stamps of very high face value. In some instances these may not have been primarily intended for postal purposes, but if they are so inscribed we include them. We only price such items used, however, where there is evidence of normal postal usage.

**Cover prices.** To assist collectors, cover prices are quoted for issues up to 1945 at the beginning of each country.

The system gives a general guide in the form of a factor by which the corresponding used price of the loose stamp should be multiplied when found in fine average condition on cover.

Care is needed in applying the factors and they relate to a cover which bears a single of the denomination listed; strips and blocks would need individual valuation outside the scope. If more than one denomination is present the most highly priced attracts the multiplier and the remainder are priced at the simple figure for used singles in arriving at a total.

The cover should be of non-philatelic origin, bearing the correct postal rate for the period and distance involved and cancelled with the markings normal to the offices concerned. Purely philatelic items have a cover value only slightly greater than the catalogue value for the corresponding used stamps. This applies generally to those high-value stamps used philatelically rather than in the normal course of commerce. Low-value stamps, e.g. ¼d. and ½d., are desirable when used as a single rate on cover and merit an increase in "multiplier" value.

First-day covers in the period up to 1945 are not within the scope of the system and the multiplier should not be used. As a special category of philatelic usage, with wide variations in valuation according to scarcity, they require separate treatment.

Oversized covers, difficult to accommodate on an album page, should be reckoned as worth little more than the corresponding value of the used stamps. The condition of a cover affects its value. Except for "wreck covers", serious damage or soiling reduce the value where the postal markings and stamps are ordinary ones. Conversely, visual appeal adds to the value and this can include freshness of appearance, important addresses, old-fashioned but legible hand-writing, historic town-names, etc.

The multipliers are a base on which further value would be added to take account of the cover's postal historical importance in demonstrating such things as unusual, scarce or emergency cancels, interesting routes, significant postal markings, combination usage, the development of postal rates, and so on.

For *Great Britain*, rather than multiplication factors, the cover price is shown as a third column, following the prices for unused and used stamps. It will be extended beyond King Edward VII in subsequent editions.

**Minimum price.** The minimum price quoted is ten pence. This represents a handling charge rather than a basis for valuing common stamps, for which the 10p price should not be reckoned automatically, since it covers a variation in real scarcity.

**Set prices.** Set prices are generally for one of each value, excluding shades and varieties, but including major colour changes. Where there are alternative shades, etc., the cheapest is usually included. The number of stamps in the set is always stated for clarity. The mint prices for sets containing *se-tenant* pieces are based on the prices quoted for such combinations, and not on those for the individual stamps.

**Specimen stamps.** The pricing of these items explained under that heading.

**Repricing.** Collectors will be aware that th market factors of supply and demand direct influence the prices quoted in this Catalogue Whatever the scarcity of a particular stamp, if ther is no one in the market who wishes to buy it cannot be expected to achieve a high price Conversely, the same item actively sought b numerous potential buyers may cause the price t rise.

All the prices in this Catalogue are examine during the preparation of each new edition b expert staff of Stanley Gibbons and repriced a necessary. They take many factors into accoun including supply and demand, and are in clos touch with the international stamp market and th auction world.

**Commonwealth cover prices and advice on posta history material originally provided by Edward B Proud.**

## GUARANTEE

All stamps are guaranteed genuine originals in the following terms:

If not as described, and returned by the purchaser we undertake to refund the price paid to us in the original transaction. If any stamp is certified as genuine by the Expert Committee of the Roya Philatelic Society, London, or by B.P.A. Expertising Ltd, the purchaser shall not be entitled to make any claim against us for any error, omission or mistake in such certificate.

Consumers' statutory rights are not affected by the above guarantee.

The recognised Expert Committees in this country are those of the Royal Philatelic Society, 41 Devonshire Place, London W1N 1PE, and B.P.A. Expertising Ltd, P.O. Box 137, Leatherhead, Surrey KT22 0RG. They do not undertake valuations under any circumstances and fees are payable for their services.

## THE CATALOGUE IN GENERAL

**Contents.** The Catalogue is confined to adhesive postage stamps, including miniature sheets. For particular categories the rules are:

(*a*) Revenue (fiscal) stamps or telegraph stamps are listed only where they have been expressly authorised for postal duty.

(*b*) Stamps issued only precancelled are included, but normally issued stamps available additionally with precancel have no separate precancel listing unless the face value is changed.

(*c*) Stamps prepared for use but not issued, hitherto accorded full listing, are nowadays footnoted with a price (where possible).

(*d*) Bisects (trisects, etc.) are only listed where such usage was officially authorised.

(*e*) Stamps issued only on first day covers or in presentation packs and not available separately are not listed but may be priced in a footnote.

(*f*) New printings are only included in this Catalogue where they show a major philatelic variety, such as a change in shade, watermark or paper. Further details of modern new printings, including changes in imprint dates, are given in the *Two Reigns Catalogue* series. (Details for the relevant areas are also given in *Collect Channel Islands and Isle of Man Stamps*.)

(*g*) Official and unofficial reprints are dealt with by footnote.

(*h*) Stamps from imperforate printings of modern issues which also occur perforated are covered by footnotes, but are listed where widely available for postal use.

**Exclusions.** The following are excluded: (*a*) non-postal revenue or fiscal stamps; (*b*) postage stamps used fiscally; (*c*) local carriage labels and private local issues; (*d*) telegraph stamps; (*e*) bogus or phantom stamps; (*f*) railway or airline letter fee tamps, bus or road transport company labels; (*g*) cut-outs; (*h*) all types of non-postal labels and ouvenirs; (*i*) documentary labels for the postal service, e.g. registration, recorded delivery, airmail etiquettes, etc.; (*j*) privately applied embellishments to official issues and privately commissioned items generally; (*k*) stamps for training postal officers.

**Full listing.** "Full listing" confers our recognition and implies allotting a catalogue number and (wherever possible) a price quotation.

In judging status for inclusion in the catalogue broad considerations are applied to stamps. They must be issued by a legitimate postal authority, recognised by the government concerned, and must be adhesives valid for proper postal use in the class of service for which they are inscribed. Stamps, with the exception of such categories as postage dues and officials, must be available to the general public, at face value, in reasonable quantities without any artificial restrictions being imposed on their distribution.

We record as abbreviated Appendix entries, without catalogue numbers or prices, stamps from countries which either persist in having far more issues than can be justified by postal need or have failed to maintain control over their distribution so that they have not been available to the public in reasonable quantities at face value. Miniature sheets and imperforate stamps are not mentioned in these entries.

The publishers of this catalogue have observed, with concern, the proliferation of "artificial" stamp-issuing territories. On several occasions this has resulted in separately inscribed issues for various component parts of otherwise united states or territories.

Stanley Gibbons Publications Ltd have decided that where such circumstances occur, they will not, in the future, list these items in the SG catalogue without first satisfying themselves that the stamps represent a genuine political, historical or postal division within the country concerned. Any such issues which do not fulfil this stipulation will be recorded in the Catalogue Appendix only.

For errors and varieties the criterion is legitimate (albeit inadvertent) sale through a postal administration in the normal course of business. Details of provenance are always important; printers' waste and fraudulently manufactured material is excluded.

**Certificates.** In assessing unlisted items due weight is given to Certificates from recognised Expert Committees and, where appropriate, we will usually ask to see them.

**New issues.** New issues are listed regularly in the Catalogue Supplement published in *Gibbons Stamp Monthly,* whence they are consolidated into the next available edition of the Catalogue.

**Date of issue.** Where local issue dates differ from dates of release by agencies, "date of issue" is the local date. Fortuitous stray usage before the officially intended date is disregarded in listing. For ease of reference, the Catalogue displays in the top corner the date of issue of the first set listed on each page.

**Catalogue numbers.** Stamps of each country are catalogued chronologically by date of issue. Subsidiary classes are placed at the end of the country, as separate lists, with a distinguishing letter prefix to the catalogue number, e.g. D for postage due, O for official and E for express delivery stamps.

The catalogue number appears in the extreme left column. The boldface Type numbers in the next column are merely cross-references to illustrations. Catalogue numbers in the *Gibbons Stamp Monthly* Supplement are provisional only and may need to be altered when the lists are consolidated. For the numbering of miniature sheets and sheetlets *see* section below.

Once published in the Catalogue, numbers are changed as little as possible; really serious renumbering is reserved for the occasions when a complete country or an entire issue is being rewritten. The edition first affected includes cross-reference tables of old and new numbers.

Our catalogue numbers are universally recognised in specifying stamps and as a hallmark of status.

**Illustrations.** Stamps are illustrated at three-quarters linear size. Stamps not illustrated are the same size and format as the value shown, unless otherwise indicated. Stamps issued only as miniature sheets have the stamp alone illustrated but sheet size is also quoted. Overprints, surcharges and watermarks are normally actual size. Illustrations of varieties are often enlarged to show the detail.

**Designers.** Designers' names are quoted where known, though space precludes naming every individual concerned in the production of a set. In particular, photographers supplying material are usually named only where they also make an active contribution in the design stage; posed photographs of reigning monarchs are, however, an exception to this rule.

## CONTACTING THE CATALOGUE EDITOR

The editor is always interested in hearing from people who have new information which will improve or correct the Catalogue. As a general rule he must see and examine the actual stamps before they can be considered for listing; photographs or photocopies are insufficient evidence.

Submissions should be made in writing to the Catalogue Editor, Stanley Gibbons Publications Ltd. at the Ringwood office. The cost of return postage for items submitted is appreciated, and this should include the registration fee if required.

Where information is solicited purely for the benefit of the enquirer, the editor cannot undertake to reply if the answer is already contained in these published notes or if return postage is omitted. Written communications are greatly preferred to enquiries by telephone and the editor regrets that he or his staff cannot see personal callers without a prior appointment being made. Correspondence may be subject to delay during the production period of each new edition.

The editor welcomes close contact with study circles and is interested, too, in finding reliable local correspondents who will verify and supplement official information in countries where this is deficient.

**We regret we do not give opinions as to the genuineness of stamps, nor do we identify stamps or number them by our Catalogue.**

## TECHNICAL MATTERS

The meanings of the technical terms used in the catalogue will be found in our *Philatelic Terms Illustrated* (3rd edition), (*price* £7.50 *plus postage and packing charge*).

References below to "more specialised" listings are to be taken to indicate, as appropriate, the Stanley Gibbons *Great Britain Specialised Catalogue* in 5 volumes; the *Great Britain, Australia* or *New Zealand Concise Catalogues* and (for Commonwealth stamps from 1937) the *Two Reigns Stamp Catalogue* series.

### 1. Printing

**Printing errors.** Errors in printing are of major interest to the Catalogue. Authenticated items meriting consideration would include: background, centre or frame inverted or omitted; centre or subject transposed; error of colour; error or omission of value; double prints and impressions; printed both sides; and so on. Designs *tête-bêche,* whether intentionally or by accident, are listable. *Se-tenant* arrangements of stamps are recognised in the listings or footnotes. Gutter pairs (a pair of stamps separated by blank margin) are not included in this volume. Colours only partially omitted are not listed. Stamps with embossing omitted and (for Commonwealth countries) stamps printed on the gummed side are reserved for our more specialised listings.

**Printing varieties.** Listing is accorded to major changes in the printing base which lead to completely new types. In recess-printing this could be a design re-engraved; in photogravure or photolithography a screen altered in whole or in part. It can also encompass flat-bed and rotary printing if the results are readily distinguishable.

To be considered at all, varieties must be constant.

Early stamps, produced by primitive methods, were prone to numerous imperfections: the lists reflect this, recognising re-entries, retouches, broken frames, misshapen letters, and so on. Printing technology has, however, radically improved over the years, during which time photogravure and lithography have become predominant. Varieties nowadays are more in the nature of flaws and these, being too specialised for this general catalogue, are almost always outside the scope. The development of our range of specialised catalogues allows us now to list those items which have philatelic significance in their appropriate volume.

In no catalogue, however, do we list such items as: dry prints, kiss prints, doctor-blade flaws, colour shifts or registration flaws (unless they lead to the complete omission of a colour from an individual stamp), lithographic ring flaws, and so on. Neither do we recognise fortuitous happenings like paper creases or confetti flaws.

**Overprints (and surcharges).** Overprints of different types qualify for separate listing. These include overprints in different colours; overprints from different printing processes such as litho and typo; overprints in totally different typefaces, etc. Major errors in machine-printed overprints are important and listable. They include: overprint inverted or omitted; overprint double (treble, etc.); overprint diagonal; overprint double, one inverted; pairs with one overprint omitted, e.g. from a radical shift to an adjoining stamp; error of colour; error of type fount; letters inverted or omitted, etc. If the overprint is handstamped, few of these would qualify and a distinction is drawn. We continue, however, to list pairs of stamps where one has a handstamped overprint and the other has not.

Varieties occurring in overprints will often take the form of broken letters, slight differences in spacing, rising spaces, etc. Only the most important would be considered for footnote mention.

**Sheet positions.** If space permits we quote sheet positions of listed varieties and authenticated data is solicited for this purpose.

**De La Rue plates.** The Catalogue classifies the general plates used by De La Rue for printing British Colonial stamps as follows:

*VICTORIAN KEY TYPE*

**Die I**

1. The ball of decoration on the second point of the crown appears as a dark mass of lines.
2. Dark vertical shading separates the front hair from the bun.
3. The vertical line of colour outlining the front of the throat stops at the sixth line of shading on the neck.

4. The white space in the coil of the hair above the curl is roughly the shape of a pin's head.

**Die II**

1. There are very few lines of colour in the ball and it appears almost white.
2. A white vertical strand of hair appears in place of the dark shading.
3. The line stops at the eighth line of shading.
4. The white space is oblong, with a line of colour partially dividing it at the left end.

Plates numbered 1 and 2 are both Die I. Plates 3 and 4 are Die II.

*GEORGIAN KEY TYPE*

**Die I**

A. The second (thick) line below the name of the country is cut slanting, conforming roughly to the shape of the crown on each side.
B. The labels of solid colour bearing the words "POSTAGE" and "& REVENUE" are square at the inner top corners.
C. There is a projecting "bud" on the outer spiral of the ornament in each of the lower corners.

**Die II**

A. The second line is cut vertically on each side of the crown.
B. The labels curve inwards at the top.
C. There is no "bud" in this position.

Unless otherwise stated in the lists, all stamps with watermark Multiple Crown CA (w **8**) are Die I while those with watermark Multiple Crown Script CA (w **9**) are Die II. The Georgian Die II was introduced in April 1921 and was used for Plates 10 to 22 and 26 to 28. Plates 23 to 25 were made from Die I by mistake.

## 2. Paper

All stamps listed are deemed to be on "ordinary" paper of the wove type and white in colour; only departures from this are normally mentioned.

**Types.** Where classification so requires we distinguish such other types of paper as, for example, vertically and horizontally laid; wove and laid bâtonné; card(board); carton; cartridge; glazed; granite; native; pelure; porous; quadrillé; ribbed; rice; and silk thread.

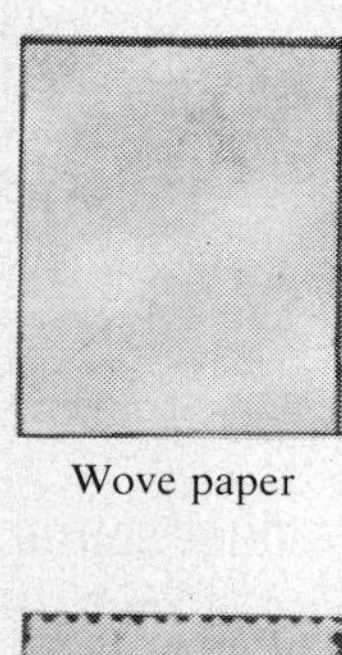

Wove paper

Laid paper

Granite paper

Quadrillé paper

Burelé band

The various makeshifts for normal paper are listed as appropriate. The varieties of double paper and joined paper are recognised. The security device of a printed burelé band on the back of a stamp, as in early Queensland, qualifies for listing.

**Descriptive terms.** The fact that a paper is handmade (and thus probably of uneven thickness) is mentioned where necessary. Such descriptive terms as "hard" and "soft"; "smooth" and 'rough"; "thick", "medium" and "thin" are applied where there is philatelic merit in classifying papers. We do not, for example, even in more specialised listings, classify paper thicknesses in the Wilding and Machin definitives of Great Britain. Weight standards for the paper apply to complete reels only, so that differences on individual stamps are acceptable to the printer provided the reel conforms overall.

**Coloured, very white and toned papers.** A coloured paper is one that is coloured right through (front and back of the stamp). In the Catalogue the colour of the paper is given in *italics,* thus:

black/*rose* = black design on rose paper.

Papers have been made specially white in recent years by, for example, a very heavy coating of chalk. We do not classify shades of whiteness of paper as distinct varieties. There does exist, however, a type of paper from early days called toned. This is off-white, often brownish or buffish, but it cannot be assigned any definite colour. A toning effect brought on by climate, incorrect storage or gum staining is disregarded here, as this was not the state of the paper when issued.

**Modern developments.** Two modern developments also affect the listings: printing on self-adhesive paper and the use of metallic foils. For self-adhesive stamps *see* under "Gum", below. Care should be taken not to damage the embossi[ng] on stamps impressed on metallic foils, [such as] Sierra Leone 1965–67, by subjecting the albu[m] pages to undue pressure. The possibility of fake "missing gold heads" is noted at the appropria[te] places in the listing of modern Great Britain.

**"Ordinary" and "Chalk-surfaced" papers.** Th[e] availability of many postage stamps for revenu[e] purposes made necessary some safeguard again[st] the illegitimate re-use of stamps with removab[le] cancellations. This was at first secured by usi[ng] fugitive inks and later by printing on chal[k]-surfaced paper, both of which made it difficult t[o] remove any form of obliteration without als[o] damaging the stamp design.

This catalogue now lists these chalk-surface[d] paper varieties from their introduction in 190[5]. Where no indication is given, the paper [is] "ordinary".

Our chalk-surfaced paper is specifically on[e] which shows a black mark when touched with [a] silver wire. The paper used during the Secon[d] World War for high values, as in Bermuda, th[e] Leeward Islands, etc., was thinly coated with som[e] kind of surfacing which does not react to silver an[d] is therefore regarded (and listed) as "ordinary". Stamps on chalk-surfaced paper can easily lose th[e] coating through immersion in water.

Another paper introduced during the War as [a] substitute for chalk-surfaced is rather thick, ver[y] white and glossy and shows little or no watermark nor does it show a black line when touched wit[h] silver. In the Bahamas high values this paper migh[t] be mistaken for the chalk-surfaced (which [is] thinner and poorer-looking) but for the silver test.

**Glazed paper.** In 1969 the Crown Agent[s] introduced a new general-purpose paper for use i[n] conjunction with all current printing processes. [It] generally has a marked glossy surface but th[e] degree varies according to the process used, bein[g] more marked in recess-printing stamps. As it doe[s] not respond to the silver test this presents a furthe[r] test where previous printings were on chalk[y] paper. A change of paper to the glazed variet[y] merits separate listing.

**Green and yellow papers.** Issues of the Firs[t] World War and immediate postwar period occu[r] on green and yellow papers and these are give[n] separate Catalogue listing. The original coloure[d] papers (coloured throughout) gave way to surface-coloured papers, the stamps having "white backs"; other stamps show one colour on the front and [a] different one at the back. Because of the numerous variations a grouping of colours is adopted a[s] follows:

*YELLOW PAPERS*

(1) The original *yellow* paper (throughout), usually bright in colour. The gum is often sparse of harsh consistency and dull-looking.

(2) The *white backs.*

(3) A bright *lemon* paper. The colour must have a pronounced greenish tinge, different from the "yellow" in (1). As a rule, the gum on stamps using this lemon paper is plentiful, smooth and shiny, and the watermark shows distinctly. Care is needed with stamps printed in green on yellow paper (1) as it may appear that the paper is this lemon.

(4) An *orange-buff* paper. The colour must have a distinct brownish tinge. It is not to be confused with a muddy yellow (1) nor the misleading appearance (on the surface) of stamps printed in red on yellow paper where an engraved plate has been insufficiently wiped.

(5) A *pale yellow* paper that has a creamy tone to the yellow.

*GREEN PAPERS*

(6) The original "green" paper, varying considerably through shades of *blue-green* and *yellow-green,* the front and back sometimes differing.

(7) The *white backs.*

(8) A paper blue-green on the surface with *pale olive* back. The back must be markedly paler than the front and this and the pronounced olive tinge to the back distinguish it from (6).

(9) Paper with a vivid green surface, commonly called *emerald-green*; it has the olive back of (8).

(10) Paper with *emerald-green* both back and front.

### 3. Perforation and Rouletting

**Perforation gauge.** The gauge of a perforation is the number of holes in a length of 2 cm. For correct classification the size of the holes (large or small) may need to be distinguished; in a few cases the actual number of holes on each edge of the stamp needs to be quoted.

**Measurement.** The Gibbons *Instanta* gauge is the standard for measuring perforations. The stamp is viewed against a dark background with the transparent gauge put on top of it. Though the gauge measures to decimal accuracy, perforations read from it are generally quoted in the Catalogue to the nearest half. For example:

| | |
|---|---|
| Just over perf 12¾ to just under 13¼ | = perf 13 |
| Perf 13¼ exactly, rounded up | = perf 13½ |
| Just over perf 13¼ to just under 13¾ | = perf 13½ |
| Perf 13¾ exactly, rounded up | = perf 14 |

However, where classification depends on it, actual quarter-perforations are quoted.

**Notation.** Where no perforation is quoted for an issue it is imperforate. Perforations are usually abbreviated (and spoken) as follows, though sometimes they may be spelled out for clarity. This notation for rectangular stamps (the majority) applies to diamond shapes if "top" is read as the edge to the top right.

*P* 14: perforated alike on all sides (read: "perf 14").

*P* 14 × 15: the first figure refers to top and bottom, the second to left and right sides (read: "perf 14 by 15"). This is a compound perforation. For an upright triangular stamp the first figure refers to the two sloping sides and second to the base. In inverted triangulars the base is first and the second figure refers to the sloping sides.

*P* 14–15: perforation measuring anything between 14 and 15: the holes are irregularly spaced, thus the gauge may vary along a single line or even along a single edge of the stamp (read: "perf 14 to 15").

*P* 14 *irregular*: perforated 14 from a worn perforator, giving badly aligned holes irregularly spaced (read: "irregular perf 14").

*P comp(ound)* 14 × 15: two gauges in use but not necessarily on opposite sides of the stamp. It could be one side in one gauge and three in the other; or two adjacent sides with the same gauge. (Read: "perf compound of 14 and 15".) For three gauges or more, abbreviated as "*P* 14, 14½, 15 *or compound*" for example.

*P* 14, 14½: perforated approximately 14¼ (read: "perf 14 or 14½"). It does *not* mean two stamps, one perf 14 and the other perf 14½. This obsolescent notation is gradually being replaced in the Catalogue.

*Imperf*: imperforate (not perforated).

*Imperf* × *P* 14: imperforate at top and bottom and perf 14 at sides.

Perf × imperf

*P* 14 × *imperf*: perf 14 at top and bottom and imperforate at sides.

Such headings as "*P* 13 × 14 (*vert*) and *P* 14 × 13 (*horiz*)" indicate which perforations apply to which stamp format—vertical or horizontal.

Some stamps are additionally perforated so that a label or tab is detachable; others have been perforated suitably for use as two halves. Listings are normally for whole stamps, unless stated otherwise.

**Other terms.** Perforation almost always gives circular holes; where other shapes have been used they are specified, e.g. square holes; lozenge perf. Interrupted perfs are brought about by the omission of pins at regular intervals. Perforations merely simulated by being printed as part of the design are of course ignored. With few exceptions, privately applied perforations are not listed.

In the nineteenth century perforations are often described as clean cut (clean, sharply incised holes), intermediate or rough (rough holes, imperfectly cut, often the result of blunt pins).

**Perforation errors and varieties.** Authenticated errors, where a stamp normally perforated is accidentally issued imperforate, are listed provided no traces of perforation (blind holes or indentations) remain. They must be provided as pairs, both stamps wholly imperforate, and are only priced in that form.

In Great Britain, numerous of these part-perforated stamps have arisen from the introduction of the Jumelle Press. This has a rotary perforator with rows of pins on one drum engaging with holes on another. Engagement is only gradual when the perforating unit is started up or stopped, giving rise to perforations "fading out", a variety mentioned above as not listed.

Stamps imperforate between stamp and sheet margin are not listed in this catalogue, but such errors on Great Britain stamps will be found in the *Great Britain Specialised Catalogue*.

Pairs described as "imperforate between" have the line of perforations between the two stamps omitted.

*Imperf between* (*horiz pair*): a horizontal pair of stamps with perfs all around the edges but none between the stamps.

*Imperf between* (*vert pair*): a vertical pair of stamps with perfs all around the edges but none between the stamps.

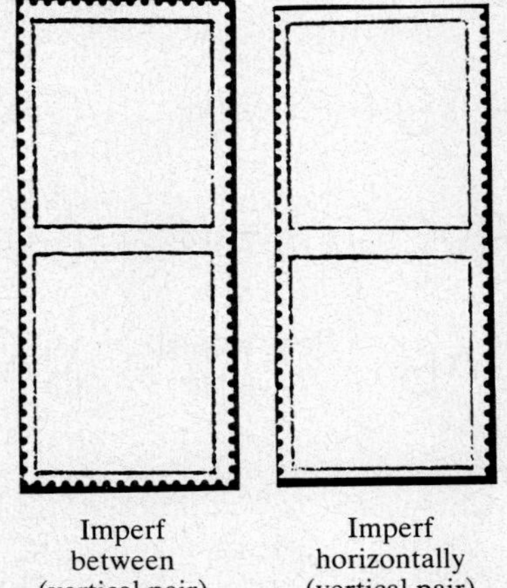

Imperf between (vertical pair) — Imperf horizontally (vertical pair)

Where several of the rows have escaped perforation the resulting varieties are listable. Thus:

*Imperf vert* (*horiz pair*): a horizontal pair of stamps perforated top and bottom; all three vertical directions are imperf—the two outer edges and between the stamps.

*Imperf horiz* (*vert pair*): a vertical pair perforated at left and right edges; all three horizontal directions are imperf—the top, bottom and between the stamps.

**Straight edges.** Large sheets cut up before issue to post offices can cause stamps with straight edges, i.e. imperf on one side or on two sides at right angles. They are not usually listable in this condition and are worth less than corresponding stamps properly perforated all round. This does not, however, apply to certain stamps, mainly from coils and booklets, where straight edges on various sides are the manufacturing norm affecting every stamp. The listings and notes make clear which sides are correctly imperf.

**Malfunction.** Varieties of double, misplaced or partial perforation caused by error or machine malfunction are not listable, neither are freaks, such as perforations placed diagonally from paper folds, nor missing holes caused by broken pins.

**Centering.** Well-centred stamps have designs surrounded by equal opposite margins. Where this condition affects the price the fact is stated.

**Types of perforating.** Where necessary for classification, perforation types are distinguished. These include:

*Line perforation* from one line of pins punching single rows of holes at a time.

*Comb perforation* from pins disposed across the sheet in comb formation, punching out holes at three sides of the stamp a row at a time.

*Harrow perforation* applied to a whole pane or sheet at one stroke.

*Rotary perforation* from toothed wheels operating across a sheet, then crosswise.

*Sewing-machine perforation*. The resultant condition, clean-cut or rough, is distinguished where required.

*Pin-perforation* is the commonly applied term for pin-roulette in which, instead of being punched out, round holes are pricked by sharp-pointed pins and no paper is removed.

*Mixed perforation* occurs when stamps with defective perforations are re-perforated in a different gauge.

**Punctured stamps.** Perforation holes can be punched into the face of the stamp. Patterns of small holes, often in the shape of initial letters, are privately applied devices against pilferage. These "perfins" are outside the scope except for Australia, Papua and Sudan where they were used as official stamps by the national administration. Identification devices, when officially inspired, are listed or noted; they can be shapes, or letters or words formed from holes, sometimes converting one class of stamp into another.

**Rouletting.** In rouletting the paper is cut, for ease of separation, but none is removed. The gauge is measured, when needed, as for perforations. Traditional French terms descriptive of the type of cut are often used and types include:

*Arc roulette* (*percé en arc*). Cuts are minute, spaced arcs, each roughly a semicircle.

*Cross roulette* (*percé en croix*). Cuts are tiny diagonal crosses.

*Line roulette* (*percé en ligne* or *en ligne droite*). Short straight cuts parallel to the frame of the stamp. The commonest basic roulette. Where not further described, "roulette" means this type.

*Rouletted in colour* or *coloured roulette* (*percé en lignes colorées* or *en lignes de couleur*). Cuts with coloured edges, arising from notched rule inked simultaneously with the printing plate.

*Saw-tooth roulette* (*percé en scie*). Cuts applied zigzag fashion to resemble the teeth of a saw.

*Serpentine roulette* (*percé en serpentin*). Cuts as sharply wavy lines.

*Zigzag roulette* (*percé en zigzags*). Short straight cuts at angles in alternate directions, producing sharp points on separation. U.S. usage favours "serrate(d) roulette" for this type.

Pin-roulette (originally *percé en points* and now *perforés trous d'epingle*) is commonly called pin-perforation in English.

### 4. Gum

All stamps listed are assumed to have gum of some kind; if they were issued without gum this is stated. Original gum (o.g.) means that which was present on the stamp as issued to the public. Deleterious climates and the presence of certain chemicals can cause gum to crack and, with early stamps, even make the paper deteriorate. Unscrupulous fakers are adept in removing it and regumming the stamp to meet the unreasoning demand often made for "full o.g." in cases where such a thing is virtually impossible.

The gum normally used on stamps has been gum arabic until the late 1960s when synthetic adhesives were introduced. Harrison and Sons Ltd for instance use *polyvinyl alcohol,* known to philatelists as PVA. This is almost invisible except for a slight yellowish tinge which was incorporated to make it possible to see that the stamps have been gummed. It has advantages in hot countries, as stamps do not curl and sheets are less likely to stick together. Gum arabic and PVA are not distinguished in the lists except that where a stamp exists with both forms this is indicated in footnotes. Our more specialised catalogues provide separate listing of gums for Great Britain.

Self-adhesive stamps are issued on backing paper, from which they are peeled before affixing to mail. Unused examples are priced as for backing paper intact, in which condition they are recommended to be kept. Used examples are best collected on cover or on piece.

### 5. Watermarks

Stamps are on unwatermarked paper except where the heading to the set says otherwise.

**Detection.** Watermarks are detected for Catalogue description by one of four methods: (1) holding stamps to the light; (2) laying stamps face down on a dark background; (3) adding a few drops of petroleum ether 40/60 to the stamp laid face down in a watermark tray; (4) by use of the Morley-Bright Detector, or other equipment, which work by revealing the thinning of the paper at the watermark (Note that petroleum ether is highly inflammable in use and can damage photogravure stamps.)

**Listable types.** Stamps occurring on both watermarked and unwatermarked papers are different types and both receive full listing.

*Single watermarks* (devices occurring once on every stamp) can be modified in size and shape as between different issues; the types are noted but not usually separately listed. Fortuitous absence of watermark from a single stamp or its gross displacement would not be listable.

To overcome registration difficulties the device may be repeated at close intervals (a *multiple watermark*), single stamps thus showing parts of several devices. Similarly, a large *sheet watermark* (or *all-over watermark*) covering numerous stamps can be used. We give informative notes and illustrations for them. The designs may be such that numbers of stamps in the sheet automatically lack watermark: this is not a listable variety. Multiple and all-over watermarks sometimes undergo modifications, but if the various types are difficult to distinguish from single stamps notes are given but not separate listings.

*Papermakers' watermarks* are noted where known but not listed separately, since most stamps in the sheet will lack them. Sheet watermarks which are nothing more than officially adopted papermakers' watermarks are, however, given normal listing.

*Marginal watermarks,* falling outside the pane of stamps, are ignored except where misplacement caused the adjoining row to be affected, in which case they are footnoted.

**Watermark errors and varieties.** Watermark errors are recognised as of major importance. They comprise stamps intended to be on unwatermarked paper but issued watermarked by mistake, or stamps printed on paper with the wrong watermark. Watermark varieties, on the other hand, such as broken or deformed bits on the dandy roll, are not listable.

Watermark positions. The diagram shows how watermark position is described in the Catalogue. Paper has a side intended for printing and watermarks are usually impressed so that they read normally when looked through from that printed side. However, since philatelists customarily detect watermarks by looking at the back of the stamp the watermark diagram also makes clear what is actually seen.

Illustrations in the Catalogue are of watermarks in normal positions (from the front of the stamps) and are actual size where possible.

Differences in watermark position are collectable as distinct varieties. In this Catalogue, however, only normal and sideways watermarks are listed (and "sideways inverted" is treated as "sideways"). Inverted and reversed watermarks have always been outside its scope: in the early days of flat-bed printing sheets of watermarked paper were fed indiscriminately through the press and the resulting watermark positions had no particular philatelic significance. Similarly, the special make-up of sheets for booklets can in some cases give equal quantities of normal and inverted watermarks.

Collectors are reminded that inverted and reversed watermarks are listed in the *Great Britain Specialised Catalogue, Great Britain, Australia* or *New Zealand Concise Catalogues* and (for Commonwealth stamps from 1937) in the *Two Reigns Catalogue* series.

Where a watermark comes indiscriminately in various positions our policy is to cover this by a general note: we do not give separate listings because the watermark position in these circumstances has no particular philatelic importance. There is a general note of this sort in modern Cyprus, for example. Issues printed since 1962 by Aspioti-Elka occur with the vertical stamps having the watermark normal or inverted, while horizontal stamps are likewise found with the watermark reading upwards or downwards.

| AS DESCRIBED (Read through front of stamp) | | AS SEEN DURING WATERMARK DETECTION (Stamp face down and back examined) |
|---|---|---|
| GvR | Normal | |
| | Inverted | |
| | Reversed | GvR |
| | Reversed and inverted | |
| | Sideways | |
| | Sideways inverted | |

**Standard types of watermark.** Some watermarks have been used generally for various British possessions rather than exclusively for a single colony. To avoid repetition the Catalogue classifies 17 general types, as under, with references in the headings throughout the listings being given either in words or in the form "*W* w **14**" (meaning "watermark type w **14**"). In those cases where watermark illustrations appear in the listings themselves, the respective reference reads for example, *W* **153**, thus indicating that the watermark will be found in the normal sequence of illustrations as (type) **153**.

The general types are as follows, with an example of each quoted.

| *W* | *Description* | *Example* |
|---|---|---|
| w **1** | Large Star | St. Helena No. 1 |
| w **2** | Small Star | Turks Is. No. 4 |
| w **3** | Broad (pointed) Star | Grenada No. 24 |
| w **4** | Crown (over) CC, small stamp | Antigua No. 13 |
| w **5** | Crown (over) CC, large stamp | Antigua No. 31 |
| w **6** | Crown (over) CA, small stamp | Antigua No. 21 |
| w **7** | Crown CA (CA over Crown), large stamp | Sierra Leone No. 54 |
| w **8** | Multiple Crown CA | Antigua No. 41 |
| w **9** | Multiple Crown Script CA | Seychelles No. 158 |
| w **9*a*** | do. Error | Seychelles No. 158a |
| w **9*b*** | do. Error | Seychelles No. 158b |
| w **10** | V over Crown | N.S.W. No. 327 |
| w **11** | Crown over A | N.S.W. No. 347 |
| w **12** | Multiple St. Edward's Crown Block CA | Antigua No. 149 |
| w **13** | Multiple PTM | Johore No. 166 |
| w **14** | Multiple Crown CA Diagonal | Antigua No. 426 |
| w **15** | Multiple POST OFFICE | Kiribati No. 141 |
| w **16** | Multiple Crown Script CA Diagonal | Ascension No. 376 |
| w **17** | Multiple CARTOR | Brunei No. 357 |

CC in these watermarks is an abbreviation for "Crown Colonies" and CA for "Crown Agents". Watermarks w **1**, w **2** and w **3** are on stamps printed by Perkins, Bacon; w **4** onwards on stamps from De La Rue and other printers.

w **1**
Large Star

w **2**
Small Star

w **3**
Broad (pointed) Star

Watermark w **1**, *Large Star,* measures 15 to 16 mm across the star from point to point and about 27 mm from centre to centre vertically between stars in the sheet. It was made for long stamps like Ceylon 1857 and St. Helena 1856.

Watermark w **2**, *Small Star,* is of similar design but measures 12 to 13½ mm from point to point and 24 mm from centre to centre vertically. It was for use with ordinary-size stamps such as Grenada 1863–71.

When the Large Star watermark was used with the smaller stamps it only occasionally comes in the centre of the paper. It is frequently so misplaced as to show portions of two stars above and below and this eccentricity will very often help in determining the watermark.

Watermark w **3**, *Broad (pointed) Star*, resembles w **1** but the points are broader.

w **4**
Crown (over) CC

w **5**
Crown (over) CC

Two *Crown (over) CC* watermarks were used: w **4** was for stamps of ordinary size and w **5** for those of larger size.

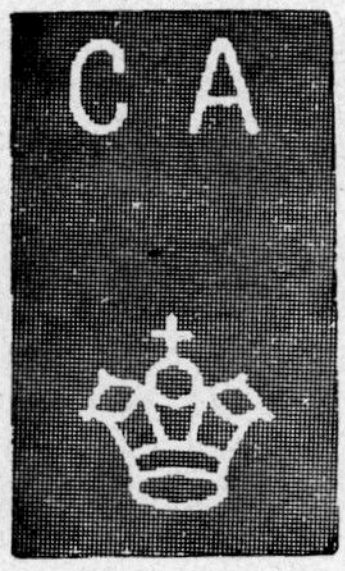

w **6**
Crown (over) CA

w **7**
CA over Crown

Two watermarks of *Crown CA* type were used, w **6** being for stamps of ordinary size. The other, w **7**, is properly described as *CA over Crown*. It was specially made for paper on which it was intended to print long fiscal stamps: that some were used postally accounts for the appearance of w **7** in the Catalogue. The watermark occupies twice the space of the ordinary Crown CA watermark, w **6**. Stamps of normal size printed on paper with w **7** watermark show it *sideways*; it takes a horizontal pair of stamps to show the entire watermark.

w **8**
Multiple Crown CA

w **9**
Multiple Crown Script CA

Multiple watermarks began in 1904 with w **8**, *Multiple Crown CA*, changed from 1921 to w **9**, *Multiple Crown Script CA*. On stamps of ordinary size portions of two or three watermarks appear and on the large-sized stamps a greater number can be observed. The change to letters in script character with w **9** was accompanied by a Crown of distinctly different shape.

w **9a**: Error,
Crown missing

w **9b**: Error,
St. Edward's Crown

The *Multiple Crown Script CA* watermark, w **9**, is known with two errors recurring among the 1950–52 printings of several territories. In the first a crown has fallen away from the dandy-roll that impresses the watermark into the paper pulp. It gives w **9a**, *Crown missing*, but this omission has been found in both "Crown only" (*illustrated*) and "Crown CA" rows. The resulting faulty paper was used for Seychelles, Johore and the postage due stamps of nine colonies.

When the omission was noticed a second mishap occurred, which was to insert a wrong crown in the space, giving w **9b**, *St. Edward's Crown*. This produced varieties in Bahamas, St. Kitts-Nevis and Singapore and the incorrect crown likewise occurs in "Crown only" and "Crown CA" rows.

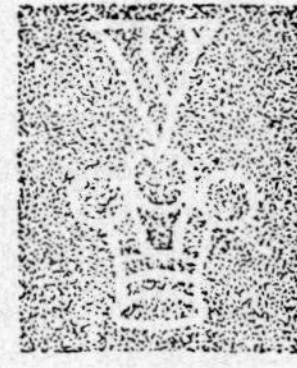

w **10**
V over Crown

w **11**
Crown over A

Resuming the general types, two watermarks found in issues of several Australian States are: w **10**, *V over Crown*, and w **11**, *Crown over A*.

w **12**
Multiple St. Edward's Crown Block CA

The *Multiple St. Edward's Crown Block CA* watermark, w **12**, was introduced in 1957 and besides the change in the Crown (from that used in *Multiple Crown Script CA*, w **9**) the letters reverted to block capitals. The new watermark began to appear sideways in 1966 and these stamps are generally listed as separate sets.

w **13**
Multiple PTM

The watermark w **13**, *Multiple PTM*, was introduced for new Malayan issues in November 1961.

w **14**
Multiple Crown CA Diagonal

By 1974 the two dandy-rolls (the "upright" and the "sideways") for w **12** were wearing out; the Crown Agents therefore discontinued using the sideways-watermark one and retained the other only as a stand-by. A new dandy-roll with the pattern of w **14**, *Multiple Crown CA Diagonal*, was introduced and first saw use with some Churchill Centenary issues.

The new watermark has the design arranged in gradually spiralling rows. It is improved in design to allow smooth passage over the paper (the gaps between letters and rows had caused jolts in previous dandy-rolls) and the sharp corners and angles, where fibres used to accumulate, have been eliminated by rounding.

This watermark has no "normal" sideways position amongst the different printers using it. To avoid confusion our more specialised listings do not rely on such terms as "sideways inverted" but describe the direction in which the watermark points.

w **15**
Multiple POST OFFICE

During 1981 w **15**, *Multiple POST OFFICE*, was introduced for certain issues prepared by Philatelists Ltd, acting for various countries in the Indian Ocean, Pacific and West Indies.

w **16**
Multiple Crown Script CA Diagonal

A new Crown Agents watermark was introduced during 1985, w **16**, *Multiple Crown Script CA Diagonal*. This was very similar to the previous w **14**, but showed "CA" in script rather than block letters. It was first used on the omnibus series of stamps commemorating the Life and Times of Queen Elizabeth the Queen Mother.

w **17**
Multiple CARTOR

Watermark w **17**, *Multiple CARTOR*, was used from 1985 for issues printed by this French firm for countries which did not normally use the Crown Agents watermark.

In recent years the use of watermarks has, to a small extent, been superseded by fluorescent security markings. These are often more visible from the reverse of the stamp (Cook Islands from 1970 onwards), but have occurred printed over the design (Hong Kong Nos. 415/30). In 1982 the Crown Agents introduced a new stock paper, without watermark, known as "C-Kurity" on which a fluorescent pattern of blue rosettes is visible on the reverse, beneath the gum. This paper was used for issues from Gambia and Norfolk Island.

### 6. Colours

Stamps in two or three colours have these named in order of appearance, from the centre moving outwards. Four colours or more are usually listed as multicoloured.

In compound colour names the second is the predominant one, thus:

orange-red = a red tending towards orange;

red-orange = an orange containing more red than usual.

**Standard colours used.** The 200 colours most used for stamp identification are given in the Stanley Gibbons Stamp Colour Key. The Catalogue has used the Stamp Colour Key as standard for describing new issues for some years. The names are also introduced as lists are rewritten, though exceptions are made for those early issues where traditional names have become universally established.

**Determining colours.** When comparing actual stamps with colour samples in the Stamp Colour Key, view in a good north daylight (or its best substitute: fluorescent "colour-matching" light). Sunshine is not recommended. Choose a solid portion of the stamp design; if available, marginal markings such as solid bars of colour or colour check dots are helpful. Shading lines in the design can be misleading as they appear lighter than solid colour. Postmarked portions of a stamp appear darker than normal. If more than one colour is present, mask off the extraneous ones as the eye tends to mix them.

**Errors of colour.** Major colour errors in stamps or overprints which qualify for listing are: wrong colours; one colour inverted in relation to the rest; albinos (colourless impressions), where these have Expert Committee certificates; colours completely omitted, but only on unused stamps (if found on used stamps the information is footnoted) and with good credentials, missing colours being frequently faked.

Colours only partially omitted are not recognised. Colour shifts, however spectacular, are not listed.

**Shades.** Shades in philately refer to variations in the intensity of a colour or the presence of differing amounts of other colours. They are particularly significant when they can be linked to specific printings. In general, shades need to be quite marked to fall within the scope of this Catalogue; it does not favour nowadays listing the often numerous shades of a stamp, but chooses a single applicable colour name which will indicate particular groups of outstanding shades. Furthermore, the listings refer to colours as issued: they may deteriorate into something different through the passage of time.

Modern colour printing by lithography is prone to marked differences of shade, even within a single run, and variations can occur within the same sheet. Such shades are not listed.

**Aniline colours.** An aniline colour meant originally one derived from coal-tar; it now refers more widely to colour of a particular brightness suffused on the surface of a stamp and showing through clearly on the back.

**Colours of overprints and surcharges.** All overprints and surcharges are in black unless stated otherwise in the heading or after the description of the stamp.

### 7. Specimen Stamps

Originally, stamps overprinted SPECIMEN were circulated to postmasters or kept in official records, but after the establishment of the Universal Postal Union supplies were sent to Berne for distribution to the postal administrations of member countries.

During the period 1884 to 1928 most of the stamps of British Crown Colonies required for this purpose were overprinted SPECIMEN in various shapes and sizes by their printers from typeset formes. Some locally produced provisionals were handstamped locally, as were sets prepared for presentation. From 1928 stamps were punched with holes forming the word SPECIMEN, each firm of printers using a different machine or machines. From 1948 the stamps supplied for U.P.U. distribution were no longer punctured.

Stamps of some other Commonwealth territories were overprinted or handstamped locally, while stamps of Great Britain and those overprinted for use in overseas postal agencies (mostly of the higher denominations) bore SPECIMEN overprints and handstamps applied by the Inland Revenue or the Post Office.

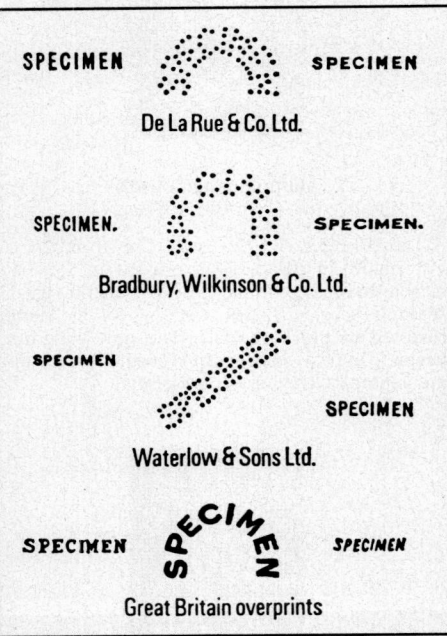

SPECIMEN SPECIMEN
De La Rue & Co. Ltd.

SPECIMEN. SPECIMEN.
Bradbury, Wilkinson & Co. Ltd.

SPECIMEN SPECIMEN
Waterlow & Sons Ltd.

SPECIMEN SPECIMEN SPECIMEN
Great Britain overprints

Some of the commoner types of overprints or punctures are illustrated here. Collectors are warned that dangerous forgeries of the punctured type exist.

The *Part 1 (British Commonwealth) Catalogue* records those Specimen overprints or perforations intended for distribution by the U.P.U. to member countries. In addition the Specimen overprints of Australia and its dependent territories, which were sold to collectors by the Post Office, are also included.

All other Specimens are outside the scope of this volume. The *Two Reigns Catalogue* series contains details of modern Specimen overprints issued for publicity purposes.

Specimens are not quoted in Great Britain as they are fully listed in the Stanley Gibbons *Great Britain Specialised Catalogue*.

In specifying type of specimen for individual high-value stamps, "H/S" means handstamped, "Optd" is overprinted and "Perf" is punctured. Some sets occur mixed, e.g. "Optd/Perf". If unspecified, the type is apparent from the date or it is the same as for the lower values quoted as a set.

**Prices.** Prices for stamps up to £1 are quoted in sets; higher values are priced singly after the colours, thus "(S. £20)". Where specimens exist in more than one type the price quoted is for the cheapest. Specimen stamps have rarely survived even as pairs; these and strips of three, four or five are worth considerably more than singles.

### 8. Luminescence

Machines which sort mail electronically have been introduced in recent years. In consequence some countries have issued stamps on fluorescent or phosphorescent papers, while others have marked their stamps with phosphor bands.

The various papers can only be distinguished by ultraviolet lamps emitting particular wavelengths. They are separately listed only when the stamps have some other means of distinguishing them, visible without the use of these lamps. Where this is not so, the papers are recorded in footnotes or headings.

For this Catalogue we do not consider it appropriate that collectors be compelled to have use of an ultraviolet lamp before being able to identify stamps by our listings. Some experience will also be found necessary in interpreting the results given by ultraviolet. Collectors using the lamps, nevertheless, should exercise great care in their use as exposure to their light is extremely dangerous to the eyes.

Phosphor bands are listable, since they are visible to the naked eye (by holding stamps at an angle to the light and looking along them, the bands appear dark). Stamps existing with and without phosphor bands or with differing numbers of bands are given separate listings. Varieties such as double bands, bands omitted, misplaced or printed on the back are not listed.

Detailed descriptions appear at appropriate places in the listings in explanation of luminescent papers; *see*, for example, Australia above No. 308, Canada above Nos. 472 and 611, Cook Is. above No. 249, etc.

For Great Britain, where since 1959 phosphors have played a prominent and intricate part in stamp issues, the main notes above Nos. 599, 723 and after the Decimal Machin issue (No. X841 onwards) should be studied, as well as the footnotes to individual listings where appropriate. In general the classification is as follows.

Stamps with *phosphor bands* are those where a separate cylinder applies the phosphor after the stamps are printed. Issues with "all-over" phosphor have the "band" covering the entire stamp. Parts of the stamp covered by phosphor bands, or the entire surface for "all-over" phosphor versions, appear matt. Stamps on *phosphorised paper* have the phosphor added to the paper coating before the stamps are printed. Issues on this paper have a completely shiny surface.

Further particularisation of phosphor—their methods of printing and the colours they exhibit under ultraviolet—is outside the scope. The more specialised listings should be consulted for this information.

### 9. Coil Stamps

Stamps issued only in coil form are given full listing. If stamps are issued in both sheets and coils the coil stamps are listed separately only where there is some feature (e.g. perforation or watermark sideways) by which singles can be distinguished. Coil strips containing different stamps *se-tenant* are also listed.

Coil join pairs are too random and too easily faked to permit of listing; similarly ignored are coil stamps which have accidentally suffered an extra row of perforations from the claw mechanism in a malfunctioning vending machine.

### 10. Booklet Stamps

Stamp booklets are outside the scope of this Catalogue.

Single stamps from booklets are listed if they are distinguishable in some way (such as watermark or perforation) from similar sheet stamps.

Booklet panes are listed where they contain stamps of different denominations *se-tenant*, where stamp-size labels are included, or where such panes are otherwise identifiable. Booklet panes are placed in the listing under the lowest denomination present.

Particular perforations (straight edges) are covered by appropriate notes.

### 11. Miniature Sheets and Sheetlets

We distinguish between "miniature sheets" and "sheetlets" and this affects the catalogue numbering. An item in sheet form that is postally valid, containing a single stamp, pair, block or set of stamps, with wide, inscribed and/or decorative margins, is a *miniature sheet* if it is sold at post offices as an indivisible entity. As such the Catalogue allots a single **MS** number and describes what stamps make it up. (*See* Great Britain 1978 Historic Buildings, No. **MS**1058, as an example.) The *sheetlet* or *small sheet* differs in that the individual stamps are intended to be purchased separately for postal purposes. For sheetlets, all the component postage stamps are numbered individually and the composition explained in a footnote. (The 1978 Christmas Island Christmas sheetlet, Nos. 99/107, is an example.) Note that the definitions refer to post office sale—not how items may be subsequently offered by stamp dealers.

Production as sheetlets is a modern marketing development chosen by postal administrations to interest collectors in purchasing the item complete; if he has done so he should, as with all *se-tenant* arrangements, keep the sheetlet intact in his collection.

The Catalogue will in future no longer give full listing to designs, originally issued in normal sheets, which subsequently appear in sheetlets showing changes of colour, perforation, printing process or face value. Such stamps will be covered by footnotes.

### 12. Forgeries and Fakes

**Forgeries.** Where space permits, notes are considered if they can give a concise description that will permit unequivocal detection of a forgery. Generalised warnings, lacking detail, are not nowadays inserted, since their value to the collector is problematic.

**Fakes.** Unwitting fakes are numerous, particularly "new shades" which are colour changelings brought about by exposure to sunlight, soaking in water contaminated with dyes from adherent paper, contact with oil and dirt from a pocketbook, and so on. Fraudulent operators, in addition, can offer to arrange: removal of hinge marks; repairs of thins on white or coloured papers; replacement of missing margins or perforations; reperforating in true or false gauges; removal of fiscal cancellations; rejoining of severed pairs, strips and blocks; and (a major hazard) regumming. Collectors can only be urged to purchase from reputable sources and to insist upon Expert Committee certification where there is any kind of doubt.

The Catalogue can consider footnotes about fakes where these are specific enough to assist in detection.

## 1935 SILVER JUBILEE CROWN COLONY ISSUE

The Crown Colony Windsor Castle design by Harold Fleury is, surely, one of the most impressive produced in the 20th-century and its reproduction in the recess process by three of the leading stamp-printing firms of the era has provided a subject for philatelic research which has yet to be exhausted.

Each of the three, Bradbury, Wilkinson & Co. and Waterlow and Sons, who both produced fifteen issues, together with De La Rue & Co. who printed fourteen, used a series of vignette (centre) plates coupled with individual frame plates for each value. All were taken from dies made by Waterlow. Several worthwhile varieties exist on the frame plates, but most interest has been concentrated on the centre plates, each of which was used to print a considerable number of different stamps.

Sheets printed by Bradbury, Wilkinson were without printed plate numbers, but research has now identified eleven centre plates which were probably used in permanent pairings. A twelfth plate awaits confirmation. Stamps from some of these centre plates have revealed a number of prominent plate flaws, the most famous of which, the extra flagstaff, has been eagerly sought by collectors for many years.

Extra flagstaff (Plate 1" R. 9/1)

Short extra flagstaff (Plate "2" R. 2/1)

Lightning conductor (Plate "3" R. 2/5)

Flagstaff on right-hand turret (Plate "5" R. 7/1)

Double flagstaff (Plate "6" R. 5/2)

De La Rue sheets were initially printed with plate numbers, but in many instances these were subsequently trimmed off. Surviving examples do, however, enable a positive identification of six centre plates, 2A, 2B, (2A), (2B), 4 and 4/ to be made. The evidence of sheet markings and plate flaws clearly demonstrates that there were two different pairs of plates numbered 2A 2B. The second pair is designated (2A) (2B) by specialist collectors to avoid further confusion. The number of major plate flaws is not so great as on the Bradbury, Wilkinson sheets, but four examples are included in the catalogue.

Diagonal line by turret (Plate 2A R. 10/2)

Dot to left of chapel (Plate 2B R. 8/3)

Dot by flagstaff (Plate 4 R. 8/4)

Dash by turret (Plate 4/ R. 3/6)

Much less is known concerning the Waterlow centre plate system as the sheets did not show plate numbers. Ten individual plates have, so far, been identified and it is believed that these were used in pairs. The two versions of the kite and log flaw from plate "2" show that this plate exists in two states.

Kite and vertical log (Plate "2A" R. 10/6)

Kite and horizontal log (Plate "2B" R. 10/6)

# Abbreviations

**Printers**

| | |
|---|---|
| A.B.N. Co | American Bank Note Co, New York. |
| A. & M. | Alden & Mowbray Ltd, Oxford. |
| Ashton-Potter | Ashton-Potter Ltd, Toronto. |
| Aspioti-Elka (Aspiotis) | Aspioti-Elka, Greece. |
| B.A.B.N. | British American Bank Note Co, Ottawa. |
| B.D.T. | B.D.T. International Security Printing Ltd, Dublin, Ireland. |
| B.W. | Bradbury Wilkinson & Co, Ltd. |
| Cartor | Cartor S.A., L'Aigle, France |
| C.B.N. | Canadian Bank Note Co, Ottawa. |
| Continental B.N. Co | Continental Bank Note Co. |
| Courvoisier | Imprimerie Courvoisier S.A., La-Chaux-de-Fonds, Switzerland. |
| D.L.R. | De La Rue & Co, Ltd, London, and (from 1961) Bogota, Colombia. |
| Edila | Editions de l'Aubetin, S.A. |
| Enschedé | Joh. Enschedé en Zonen, Haarlem, Netherlands. |
| Format | Format International Security Printers, Ltd, London. |
| Harrison | Harrison & Sons, Ltd, London |
| Heraclio Fournier | Heraclio Fournier S.A., Vitoria, Spain. |
| J.W. | John Waddington Security Print Ltd., Leeds |
| P.B. | Perkins Bacon Ltd, London. |
| Questa | Questa Colour Security Printers, Ltd., London |
| Ueberreuter | Ueberreuter (incorporating Bruder Rosenbaum), Korneuburg, Austria. |
| Walsall | Walsall Security Printers, Ltd. |
| Waterlow | Waterlow & Sons, Ltd, London. |

**General Abbreviations**

| | |
|---|---|
| Alph | Alphabet |
| Anniv | Anniversary |
| Comp | Compound (perforation) |
| Des | Designer; designed |
| Diag | Diagonal; diagonally |
| Eng | Engraver; engraved |
| F.C. | Fiscal Cancellation |
| H/S | Handstamped |
| Horiz | Horizontal; horizontally |
| Imp, Imperf | Imperforate |
| Inscr | Inscribed |
| L | Left |
| Litho | Lithographed |
| mm | Millimetres |
| MS | Miniature sheet |
| N.Y. | New York |
| Opt(d) | Overprint(ed) |
| P or P-c | Pen-cancelled |
| P, Pf or Perf | Perforated |
| Photo | Photogravure |
| Pl | Plate |
| Pr | Pair |
| Ptd | Printed |
| Ptg | Printing |
| R | Right |
| R. | Row |
| Recess | Recess-printed |
| Roto | Rotogravure |
| Roul | Rouletted |
| S | Specimen (overprint) |
| Surch | Surcharge(d) |
| T.C. | Telegraph Cancellation |
| T | Type |
| Typo | Typographed |
| Un | Unused |
| Us | Used |
| Vert | Vertical; vertically |
| W or wmk | Watermark |
| Wmk s | Watermark sideways |

(†)=Does not exist.

(—) (or blank price column)=Exists, or may exist, but no market price is known.

/ between colours means "on" and the colour following is that of the paper on which the stamp is printed.

**Colours of Stamps**

Bl (blue); blk (black); brn (brown); car, carm (carmine); choc (chocolate); clar (claret); emer (emerald); grn (green); ind (indigo); mag (magenta); mar (maroon); mult (multicoloured); mve (mauve); ol (olive); orge (orange); pk (pink); pur (purple); scar (scarlet); sep (sepia); turq (turquoise); ultram (ultramarine); verm (vermilion); vio (violet); yell (yellow).

**Colour of Overprints and Surcharges**

(B.) = blue, (Blk.) = black, (Br.) = brown, (C.) = carmine, (G.) = green, (Mag.) = magenta, (Mve.) = mauve, (Ol.) = olive, (O.) = orange, (P.) = purple, (Pk.) = pink, (R.)=red, (Sil.) = silver, (V.) = violet, (Vm.) or (Verm.) = vermilion, (W.) = white, (Y.) = yellow.

**Arabic Numerals**

As in the case of European figures, the details of the Arabic numerals vary in different stamp designs, but they should be readily recognised with the aid of this illustration.

| ٠ | ١ | ٢ | ٣ | ٤ | ٥ | ٦ | ٧ | ٨ | ٩ |
|---|---|---|---|---|---|---|---|---|---|
| 0 | 1 | 2 | 3 | 4 | 5 | 6 | 7 | 8 | 9 |

## COUNTRIES RELOCATED IN THIS EDITION

Aden *see* SOUTH ARABIAN FEDERATION
Aden Protectorate States *see* SOUTH ARABIAN FEDERATION
Basutoland *see* LESOTHO
Bechuanaland *see* BOTSWANA
British Columbia & Vancouver Island *see* CANADA
British East Africa *see* KENYA, UGANDA AND TANGANYIKA
British Guiana *see* GUYANA
British Honduras *see* BELIZE
Cape of Good Hope *see* SOUTH AFRICA
Ceylon *see* SRI LANKA
Gilbert Islands *see* KIRIBATI
Gold Coast *see* GHANA
Griqualand West *see* SOUTH AFRICA
Labuan *see* MALAYSIA
Lagos *see* NIGERIA
Natal *see* SOUTH AFRICA
New Brunswick *see* CANADA
Newfoundland *see* CANADA
New Guinea *see* PAPUA NEW GUINEA
New Hebrides *see* VANUATU
New Republic *see* SOUTH AFRICA
New South Wales *see* AUSTRALIA
Niger Coast Protectorate *see* NIGERIA
Niger Company Territories *see* NIGERIA
North Borneo *see* MALAYSIA
Northern Nigeria *see* NIGERIA
Northern Rhodesia *see* ZAMBIA
Nova Scotia *see* CANADA
Nyasaland *see* MALAWI
Orange Free State *see* SOUTH AFRICA
Papua (British New Guinea) *see* PAPUA NEW GUINEA
Prince Edward Island *see* CANADA
Queensland *see* AUSTRALIA
Rhodesia (from No. 351) *see* ZIMBABWE
Sabah *see* MALAYSIA
Sarawak *see* MALAYSIA
South Australia *see* AUSTRALIA
Southern Nigeria *see* NIGERIA
Southern Rhodesia *see* ZIMBABWE
South West Africa *see* NAMIBIA
Stellaland *see* BOTSWANA
Tanganyika *see* TANZANIA
Tasmania *see* AUSTRALIA
Transvaal *see* SOUTH AFRICA
Victoria *see* AUSTRALIA
Western Australia *see* AUSTRALIA
Zanzibar *see* TANZANIA
Zululand *see* SOUTH AFRICA

# Stanley Gibbons Stamp Catalogue
# Complete List of Parts

**1 British Commonwealth**
(Annual in two volumes)

**2 Austria & Hungary** (4th edition, 1988)
Austria, Bosnia & Herzegovina, U.N. (Vienna), Hungary

**3 Balkans** (3rd edition, 1987)
Albania, Bulgaria, Greece & Islands, Rumania, Yugoslavia

**4 Benelux** (3rd edition, 1988)
Belgium & Colonies, Netherlands & Colonies, Luxembourg

**5 Czechoslovakia & Poland** (4th edition, 1991)
Czechoslovakia, Bohemia & Moravia, Slovakia, Poland

**6 France** (3rd edition, 1987)
France, Colonies, Post Offices, Andorra, Monaco

**7 Germany** (4th edition, 1992)
Germany, States, Colonies, Post Offices

**8 Italy & Switzerland** (3rd edition, 1986)
Italy & Colonies, Fiume, San Marino, Vatican City, Trieste, Liechtenstein, Switzerland, U.N. (Geneva)

**9 Portugal & Spain** (3rd edition, 1991)
Andorra, Portugal & Colonies, Spain & Colonies

**10 Russia** (4th edition, 1991)
Russia, Baltic States, Mongolia, Tuva

**11 Scandinavia** (3rd edition, 1988)
Aland Island, Denmark, Faroe Islands, Finland, Greenland, Iceland, Norway, Sweden

**12 Africa since Independence A-E** (2nd edition, 1983)
Algeria, Angola, Benin, Bophuthatswana, Burundi, Cameroun, Cape Verde, Central African Republic, Chad, Comoro Islands, Congo, Djibouti, Equatorial Guinea, Ethiopia

**13 Africa since Independence F-M** (1st edition, 1981)
Gabon, Guinea, Guinea-Bissau, Ivory Coast, Liberia, Libya, Malagasy Republic, Mali, Mauritania, Morocco, Mozambique

**14 Africa since Independence N-Z** (1st edition, 1981)
Niger Republic, Rwanda, St. Thomas & Prince, Senegal, Somalia, Sudan, Togo, Transkei, Tunisia, Upper Volta, Venda, Zaire

**15 Central America** (2nd edition, 1984)
Costa Rica, Cuba, Dominican Republic, El Salvador, Guatemala, Haiti, Honduras, Mexico, Nicaragua, Panama

**16 Central Asia** (2nd edition, 1983)
Afghanistan, Iran, Turkey

**17 China** (4th edition, 1989)
China, Taiwan, Tibet, Foreign P.O.s

**18 Japan & Korea** (3rd edition, 1992)
Japan, Ryukyus, Korean Empire, South Korea, North Korea

**19 Middle East** (4th edition, 1990)
Bahrain, Egypt, Iraq, Israel, Jordan, Kuwait, Lebanon, Oman, Qatar, Saudi Arabia, Syria, U.A.E., Yemen A.R., Yemen P.D.R.

**20 South America** (3rd edition, 1989)
Argentina, Bolivia, Brazil, Chile, Colombia, Ecuador, Paraguay, Peru, Surinam, Uruguay, Venezuela

**21 South-East Asia** (2nd edition, 1985)
Bhutan, Burma, Indonesia, Kampuchea, Laos, Nepal, Philippines, Thailand, Vietnam

**22 United States** (3rd edition, 1990)
U.S. & Possessions, Canal Zone, Marshall Islands, Micronesia, Palau, U.N. (New York, Geneva, Vienna)

---

## GREAT BRITAIN SPECIALISED CATALOGUES

Volume 1 **Queen Victoria** (10th edition, 1992)
Volume 2 **King Edward VII to King George VI** (8th edition, 1989)
Volume 3 **Queen Elizabeth II Pre-decimal Issues** (8th edition, 1990)
Volume 4 **Queen Elizabeth II Decimal Definitive Issues** (6th edition, 1991)
Volume 5 **Queen Elizabeth II Decimal Special Issues** (2nd edition, 1991)

## THEMATIC CATALOGUES

**Collect Birds on Stamps** (3rd edition forthcoming)
**Collect Mammals on Stamps** (1st edition, 1986)
**Collect Railways on Stamps** (2nd edition, 1990)
**Collect Ships on Stamps** (2nd edition forthcoming)
**Collect Fungi on Stamps** (1st edition, 1991)
**Collect Butterflies and Other Insects on Stamps** (1st edition, 1991)
**Collect Chess on Stamps** (forthcoming)
**Collect Aircraft on Stamps** (forthcoming)

# Select Bibliography

The literature on British Commonwealth stamps is vast, but works are often difficult to obtain once they are out of print. The selection of books below has been made on the basis of authority together with availability to the general reader, either as new or secondhand. Very specialised studies, and those covering aspects of postal history to which there are no references in the catalogue, have been excluded.

The following abbreviations are used to denote publishers:
CRL–Christie's Robson Lowe; HH–Harry Hayes; PB–Proud Bailey Co. Ltd.; PC–Philip Cockrill; RPSL–Royal Philatelic Society, London; SG–Stanley Gibbons Ltd.

Where no publisher is quoted, the book is published by its author.


**GENERAL.** *Encyclopaedia of British Empire Postage Stamps. Vols 1–6.* Edited Robson Lowe. (CRL, 1951–1991)

*The Commemorative Stamps of the British Commonwealth.* H.D.S. Haverbeck. (Faber, 1955)

*Specimen Stamps of the Crown Colonies 1857–1948.* Marcus Samuel. (RPSL, 1976 and 1984 Supplement)

*U.P.U. Specimen Stamps.* J. Bendon. (1988)

*Silver Jubilee of King George V Stamps Handbook.* A.J. Ainscough. (Ainwheel Developments, 1985)

*The Printings of King George VI Colonial Stamps.* W.J.W. Potter & Lt-Col R.C.M. Shelton. (1952)

*King George VI Large Key Type Stamps of Bermuda, Leeward Islands, Nyasaland.* R.W. Dickgiesser and E.P. Yendall. (Triad Publications, 1985)

**GREAT BRITAIN.** For extensive bibliographies see *G.B. Specialised Catalogues. Vols 1–5.*

**Channel Islands.** *Stamps and Postal History of the Channel Islands.* W. Newport. (Heineman, 1972)

**ADEN.** *The Postal History of British Aden 1839–67.* Major R.W. Pratt (PB, 1985)

**ASCENSION.** *Ascension. The Stamps and Postal History.* J.H. Attwood. (CRL, 1981)

**BAHAMAS.** *The Postage Stamps and Postal History of the Bahamas.* H.G.D. Gisburn. (SG, 1950)

**BARBADOS.** *The Stamps of Barbados.* E.A. Bayley. (1989)

**BASUTOLAND.** *The Cancellations and Postal Markings of Basutoland/Lesotho Post Offices.* A.H. Scott. (Collectors Mail Auctions (Pty) Ltd, 1980)

**BATUM.** *British Occupation of Batum.* P.T. Ashford. (1989)

**BRITISH EAST AFRICA.** *British East Africa. The Stamps and Postal Stationery.* J. Minns. (RPSL, 1982 and 1990 Supplement)

**BRITISH GUIANA.** *The Postage Stamps and Postal History of British Guiana.* W.A. Townsend and F.G. Howe. (RPSL, 1970)

**BRITISH OCCUPATION OF GERMAN COLONIES.** *G.R.I.* R.M. Gibbs. (CRL, 1989)

**BRITISH POSTAL AGENCIES IN EASTERN ARABIA.** *The Postal Agencies in Eastern Arabia and the Gulf.* N. Donaldson. (HH, 1975)

**BRITISH WEST AFRICA.** *The Postal History and Handstamps of British West Africa.* C. McCaig. (CRL, 1978)

**BRUNEI.** *Brunei. The Definitive Issues and Postal Cancellations to 1974.* E. Thorndike. (PC, 1983)

**BURMA.** *Burma Postal History.* G. Davis and D. Martin. (CRL, 1971 and 1987 Supplement)

**CANADA.** *Stamps of British North America.* F. Jarrett. (Quarterman Publications Inc, 1975)

*The Postage Stamps and Postal History of Canada.* W.S. Boggs. (Quarterman Publications Inc, 1974)

*The Edward VII Issue of Canada.* G.C. Marler. (National Postal Museum, Canada, 1975)

*The Admiral Issue of Canada.* G.C. Marler. (American Philatelic Society, 1982)

**CAPE OF GOOD HOPE.** *Postmarks of the Cape of Good Hope.* R. Goldblatt. (Reijger Publishers (Pty) Ltd, 1984)

**CAYMAN ISLANDS.** *The Postal History of the Cayman Islands.* T.E. Giraldi and P.P. McCann. (Triad Publications, 1989)

**COCOS (KEELING) ISLANDS.** *Cocos (Keeling) Islands. A Philatelic and Postal History to 1979.* P. Collas & J. Hill. (B. & K. Philatelic Publishing, 1991)

**COOK ISLANDS.** *The Early Cook Islands Post Office.* A.R. Burge. (Hawthorn Press, 1978)

**CYPRUS.** *Cyprus 1353–1986.* W. Castle. (CRL, 3rd edition, 1987)

**FALKLAND ISLANDS.** *The Postage Stamps of the Falkland Islands and Dependencies.* B.S.H. Grant. (SG, 1952)

*The De La Rue Definitives of the Falkland Islands 1901–29.* J.P. Bunt. (1986)

*The Falkland Islands. Printings of the Pictorial Issue of 1938–49.* C.E. Glass. (CRL, 1979)

**FIJI.** *The Postal History of Fiji 1911–1952.* J.G. Rodger. (Pacific Islands Study Circle, 1991)

**GAMBIA.** *The Stamps and Postal History of the Gambia.* Edited J.O. Andrew. (CRL, 1985)

**GIBRALTAR.** *Posted in Gibraltar.* W. Hine-Haycock. (CRL, 1978)

**HONG KONG.** *The Philatelic History of Hong Kong. Vol 1.* (Hong Kong Study Circle, 1984)

*Cancellations of the Treaty Ports of Hong Kong.* H. Schoenfeld. (1988)

**INDIA.** *India Used Abroad.* V.S. Dastur. (Mysore Philatelics, 1982)

*A Handbook on Gwalior Postal History and Stamps.* V.K. Gupta. (1980)

**LABUAN.** *A Concise Guide to the Queen Issues of Labuan.* R. Price.

**MALAYSIA.** *The Postal History of British Malaya. Vols 1–3.* E.B. Proud. (PB, 1982–84)

*The Postage Stamps of Federated Malay States.* W.A. Reeves. (Malaya Study Group, 1978)

**MALTA.** *Malta. The Postal History and Postage Stamps.* Edited R.E. Martin. (CRL, 1980 and 1985 Supplement)

**MAURITIUS.** *The Postal History and Stamps of Mauritius.* P. Ibbotson. (RPSL, 1991)

**MOROCCO AGENCIES.** *British Post Offices and Agencies in Morocco 1857–1907 and Local Posts 1891–1914.* R.K. Clough. (Gibraltar Study Circle, 1984).

**NEWFOUNDLAND.** *The Postage Stamps and Postal History of Newfoundland.* W.S. Boggs. (Quarterman Publications, 1975)

**NEW SOUTH WALES.** *The Postal History of New South Wales 1788–1901.* Edited J.S. White. (Philatelic Assoc of New South Wales, 1988)

**NEW ZEALAND.** *The Postage Stamps of New Zealand. Vols I–VII.* (Royal Philatelic Society of New Zealand, 1939–88)

*The Postal History and Postage Stamps of the Tokelau/Union Islands.* A.H. Burgess. (Pacific Islands Study Circle, 1977)

**NORTH BORNEO.** *The Stamps and Postal History of North Borneo. Parts 1–3.* L.H. Shipman and P.K. Cassells. (Sarawak Specialists Society, 1976–88)

**ORANGE FREE STATE.** *Stamps of the Orange Free State. Parts 1–3.* G.D. Buckley & W.B. Marriott. (Orange Free State Study Circle, 1967–80)

**PAPUA.** *The Postal History of British New Guinea and Papua 1885–1942.* R. Lee. (CRL, 1983)

**RHODESIA.** *Mashonaland. A Postal History 1890–96.* A. Drysdall and D. Collis (CRL, 1990)

*Rhodesia. A Postal History.* R.C. Smith. (1967 and 1970 Supplement)

**ST. HELENA.** *St. Helena. Postal History and Stamps.* E. Hibbert. (CRL, 1979)

**SAMOA.** *A Postal History of the Samoan Islands (Parts I and II).* Edited R. Burge. (Royal Philatelic Society of New Zealand, 1987–89)

**SARAWAK.** *The Stamps and Postal History of Sarawak.* W.A. Forrester-Wood. (Sarawak Specialists Society, 1959 & 1970 Supplement)

*Sarawak: The Issues of 1871 and 1875.* W. Batty-Smith & W. Watterson.

**SIERRA LEONE.** *The Postal Service of Sierra Leone.* P.O. Beale. (RPSL, 1988)

**SOLOMON ISLANDS.** *British Solomon Islands Protectorate. Its Postage Stamps and Postal History.* H.G.D. Gisburn. (T. Sanders (Philatelist) Ltd., 1956)

**SOUTH AUSTRALIA.** *The Departmental Stamps of South Australia.* A.R. Butler. (RPSL, 1978)

**SOUTH WEST AFRICA.** *The Overprinted Stamps of South West Africa to 1930.* N. Becker. (Philatelic Holdings (Pty) Ltd, 1990)

**SUDAN.** *Sudan. The Stamps and Postal Stationery of 1867 to 1970.* E.C.W. Stagg. (HH, 1977)

**TANGANYIKA.** *The Postal History of Tanganyika. 1915–1961.* E.B. Proud. (PB, 1989)

**TASMANIA.** *Stamps and Postal History of Tasmania.* W.E. Tinsley. (RPSL, 1986)

*The Pictorial Stamps of Tasmania 1899–1912.* K.E. Lancaster. (Royal Philatelic Society of Victoria, 1986)

**TRANSVAAL.** *Transvaal Philately.* Edited I.B. Mathews. (Reijger Publishers (Pty) Ltd, 1986)

**TRISTAN DA CUNHA.** *The History and Postal History of Tristan da Cunha.* G. Crabb. (1980)

**TURKS AND CAICOS ISLANDS.** *Turks Islands and Caicos Islands to 1950.* J.J. Challis. (Roses Caribbean Philatelic Society, 1983)

**TUVALU.** *Tuvalu. A Philatelic Handbook.* M. Forand. (Tuvalu Philatelic Society, 1982)

**VICTORIA.** *The Stamps of Victoria.* G. Kellow. (B. & K. Philatelic Publishing, 1990)

**WESTERN AUSTRALIA.** *Western Australia. The Stamps and Postal History.* Edited M. Hamilton and B. Pope. (Western Australia Study Group, 1979)

*Postage Stamps and Postal History of Western Australia. Vols 1–3.* M. Juhl. (1981–83)

STANLEY GIBBONS STAMP CATALOGUE

# Part 1: BRITISH COMMONWEALTH

VOLUME 1: GREAT BRITAIN AND COUNTRIES A TO I

95th EDITION—1992/93

## Great Britain

Great Britain Postage Stamps, GB 1
Regional Issues—
I. Northern Ireland, GB 64
II. Scotland, GB 64
III. Wales, GB 64
Postage Due Stamps, GB 66
Official Stamps, GB 66
Postal Fiscal Stamps, GB 67
Channel Islands General Issue, GB 68
Guernsey, GB 68
Alderney, GB 77
Isle of Man, GB 78
Jersey, GB 86
British Post Offices Abroad, GB 95

STAMPS ON COVER. Prices are quoted, as a third price column, for those Victorian and Edwardian issues usually found used on cover. In general these prices refer to the cheapest version of each basic stamp with other shades, plates or varieties, together with unusual frankings and postmarks, being worth more.

### QUEEN VICTORIA
### 20 June 1837—22 January 1901

MULREADY ENVELOPES AND LETTER SHEETS, so called from the name of the designer, William Mulready, were issued concurrently with the first British adhesive stamps.

**1d. black**

| | |
|---|---|
| Envelopes: | £125 *unused*; £175 *used.* |
| Letter Sheets: | £110 *unused*; £145 *used.* |

**2d. blue**

| | |
|---|---|
| Envelopes: | £200 *unused*; £600 *used.* |
| Letter Sheets: | £175 *unused*; £575 *used.* |

### LINE-ENGRAVED ISSUES

**GENERAL NOTES**

Brief notes on some aspects of the line-engraved stamps follow, but for further information and a full specialist treatment of these issues collectors are recommended to consult Volume 1 of the Stanley Gibbons *Great Britain Specialised Catalogue.*

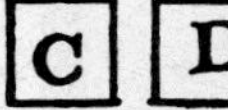
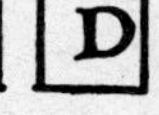

Alphabet I

Alphabet II

Alphabet III

Alphabet IV

Typical Corner Letters of the four Alphabets

**Alphabets.** Four different letterings were used for the corner letters on stamps prior to the issue with letters in all four corners, these being known to collectors as:

*Alphabet I.* Used for all plates made from 1840 to the end of 1851. Letters small.

*Alphabet II.* Plates from 1852 to mid-1855. Letters larger, heavier and broader.

*Alphabet III.* Plates from mid-1855 to end of period. Letters tall and more slender.

*Alphabet IV.* 1861. 1d. Die II, Plates 50 and 51 only. Letters were hand-engraved instead of being punched on the plate. They are therefore inconsistent in shape and size but generally larger and outstanding.

While the general descriptions and the illustrations of typical letters given above may be of some assistance, only long experience and published aids can enable every stamp to be allocated to its particular Alphabet without hesitation, as certain letters in each are similar to those in one of the others.

**Blue Paper.** The blueing of the paper of the earlier issues is believed to be due to the presence of prussiate of potash in the printing ink, or in the paper, which, under certain conditions, tended to colour the paper when the sheets were damped for printing. An alternative term is bleuté paper.

**Corner Letters.** The corner letters on the early British stamps were intended as a safeguard against forgery, each stamp in the sheet having a different combination of letters. Taking the first 1d. stamp, printed in 20 horizontal rows of 12, as an example, the lettering is as follows:

Row 1. A A, A B, A C, etc. to A L.

Row 2. B A, B B, B C, etc. to B L.

and so on to

Row 20. T A, T B, T C, etc. to T L.

On the stamps with four corner letters, those in the upper corners are in the reverse positions to those in the lower corners. Thus in a sheet of 240 (12 × 20) the sequence is:

Row 1. AA/AA BA/AB CA/AC etc. to LA/AL

Row 2. AB/BA BB/BB CB/BC etc. to LB/BL

and so on to

Row 20. AT/TA BT/TB CT/TC etc. to LT/TL

Placing letters in all four corners was not only an added precaution against forgery but was meant to deter unmarked parts of used stamps being pieced together and passed off as an unused whole.

**Dies.** The first die of the 1d. was used for making the original die of the 2d., both the No Lines and White Lines issues. In 1855 the 1d. Die I was amended by retouching the head and deepening the lines on a transferred impression of the original. This later version, known to collectors as Die II, was used for making the dies for the 1d. and 2d. with letters in all four corners and also for the 1½d.

The two dies are illustrated above No. 17 in the catalogue.

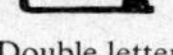

Double letter

Guide line in corner

Guide line through value

**Double Corner Letters.** These are due to the workman placing his letter-punch in the wrong position at the first attempt, when lettering the plate, and then correcting the mistake; or to a slight shifting of the punch when struck. If a wrong letter was struck in the first instance, traces of a wrong letter may appear in a corner in addition to the correct one. A typical example is illustrated.

**Guide Lines and Dots.** When laying down the impressions of the design on the early plates, fine vertical and horizontal guide lines were marked on the plates to assist the operative. These were usually removed from the gutter margins, but could not be removed from the stamp impressions without damage to the plate, so that in such cases they appear on the printed stamps, sometimes in the corners, sometimes through "POSTAGE" or the value. Typical examples are illustrated.

Guide dots or cuts were similarly made to indicate the spacing of the guide lines. These too sometimes appear on the stamps.

Ivory Head

**"Ivory Head."** The so-called "ivory head" variety is one in which the Queen's Head shows white on the back of the stamp. It arises from the comparative absence of ink in the head portion of the design, with consequent absence of blueing. (*See* "Blued Paper" note above.)

**Line-engraving.** In this context "line-engraved" is synonymous with recess-printing, in which the engraver cuts recesses in a plate and printing (the coloured areas) is from these recesses. "Line-engraved" is the traditional philatelic description for these stamps; other equivalent terms found are "engraving in *taille-douce*" (French) or "in *intaglio*" (Italian).

**Plates.** Until the introduction of the stamps with letters in all four corners, the number of the plate was not indicated in the design of the stamp, but was printed on the sheet margin. By long study of identifiable blocks and the minor variations in the design, coupled with the position of the corner letters, philatelists are now able to allot many of these stamps to their respective plates. Specialist collectors often endeavour to obtain examples of a given stamp printed from its different plates and our catalogue accordingly reflects this depth of detail.

Maltese Cross — Type of Town postmark

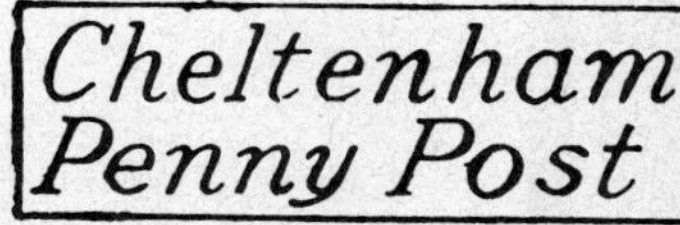


Type of Penny Post cancellation

Example of 1844 type postmark

**Postmarks.** The so-called "Maltese Cross" design was the first employed for obliterating British postage stamps and was in use from 1840 to 1844. Being hand-cut, the obliterating stamps varied greatly in detail and some distinctive types can be allotted to particular towns or offices. Local types, such as those used at Manchester, Norwich, Leeds, etc., are keenly sought. A red ink was first employed, but was superseded by black, after some earlier experiments, in February 1841. Maltese Cross obliterations in other colours are rare.

Obliterations of this type, numbered 1 to 12 in the centre, were used at the London Chief Office in 1843 and 1844.

Some straight-line cancellations were in use in 1840 at the Penny Post receiving offices, normally applied on the envelope, the adhesives then being obliterated at the Head Office. They are nevertheless known, with or without Maltese Cross, on the early postage stamps.

In 1842 some offices in S.W. England used dated postmarks in place of the Maltese Cross, usually on the back of the letter since they were not originally intended as obliterators. These town postmarks have likewise been found on adhesives.

In 1844 the Maltese Cross design was superseded by numbered obliterators of varied type, one of which is illustrated. They are naturally comparatively scarce on the first 1d. and 2d. stamps. Like the Maltese Cross they are found in various colours, some of which are rare.

Re-entry

"Union Jack" re-entry

**Re-entries.** Re-entries on the plate show as a doubling of part of the design of the stamp generally at top or bottom. Many re-entries are very slight while others are most marked. A typical one is illustrated.

The "*Union Jack*" *re-entry*, so called owing to the effect of the re-entry on the appearance of the corner stars (*see illustration*) occurs on stamp L K of Plate 75 of the 1d. red, Die I.



SGBCPGB1 00 000008170 0236 00142

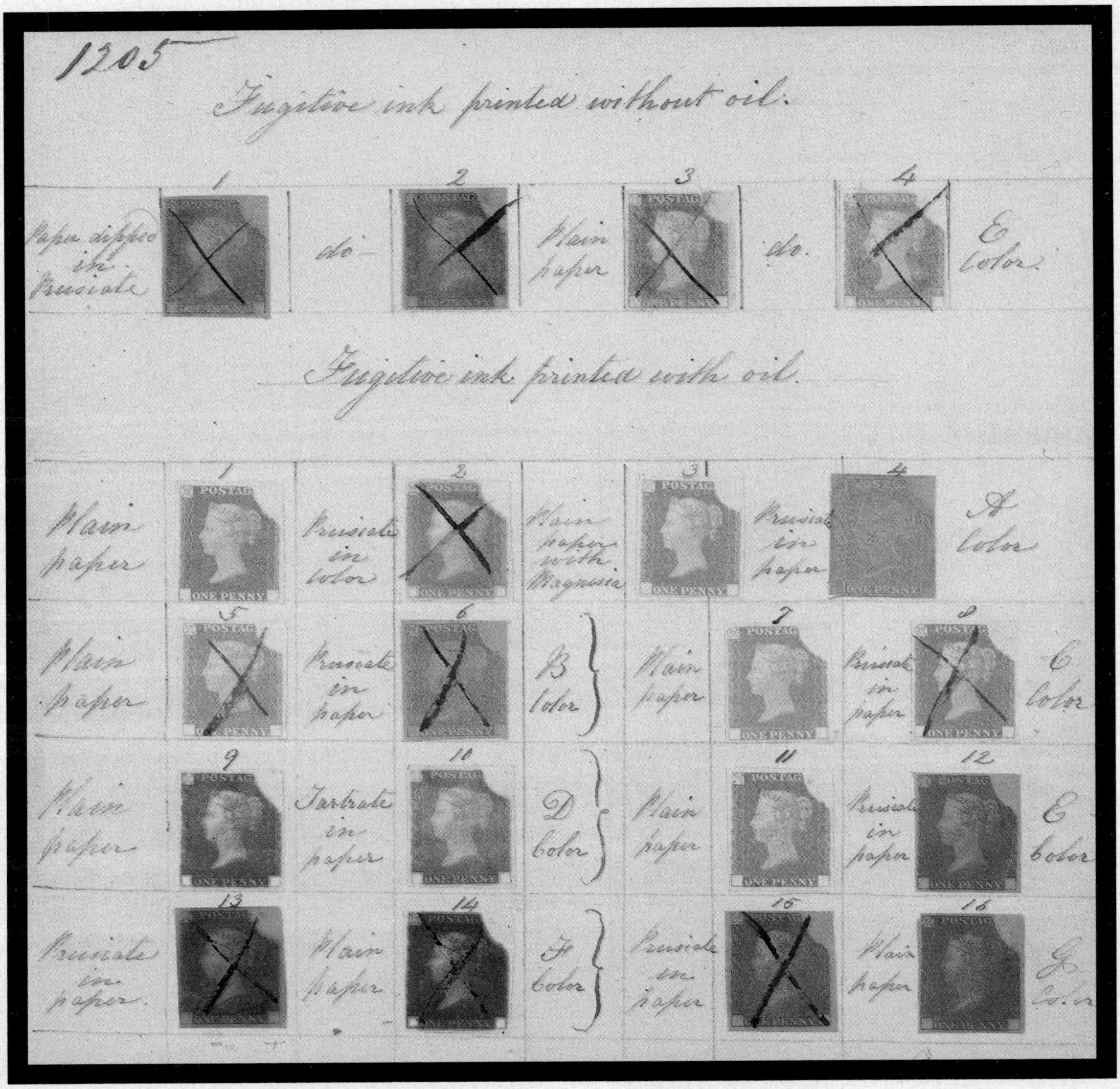

T A (T L) M A (M L)
Varieties of Large Crown Watermark

I Two states of Large Crown Watermark II

**Watermarks.** Two watermark varieties, as illustrated, consisting of crowns of entirely different shape, are found in sheets of the Large Crown paper and fall on stamps lettered M A and T A (or M L and T L when the paper is printed on the wrong side). Both varieties are found on the 1d. rose-red of 1857, while the M A (M L) variety comes also on some plates of the 1d. of 1864 (Nos. 43, 44) up to about Plate 96. On the 2d. the T A (T L) variety is known on plates 8 and 9, and the M A (M L) on later prints of plate 9. These varieties may exist inverted, or inverted reversed on stamps lettered A A and A L and H A and H L, and some are known.

In 1861 a minor alteration was made in the Large Crown watermark by the removal of the two vertical strokes, representing *fleurs-de-lis*, which projected upwards from the uppermost of the three horizontal curves at the base of the Crown. Hence two states are distinguishable, as illustrated.

## CONDITION—IMPERFORATE LINE-ENGRAVED ISSUES

The prices quoted for the 1840 and 1841 imperforate Line-engraved issues are for "fine" examples. As condition is most important in assessing the value of a stamp, the following definitions will assist collectors in the evaluation of individual examples.

Four main factors are relevant when considering quality.

(a) **Impression.** This should be clean and the surface free of any rubbing or unnatural blurring which would detract from the appearance.

(b) **Margins.** This is perhaps the most difficult factor to evaluate. Stamps described as "fine", the standard adopted in this catalogue for pricing purposes, should have margins of the recognised width, defined as approximately one half of the distance between two adjoining unsevered stamps. Stamps described as "very fine" or "superb" should have margins which are proportionately larger than those of a "fine" stamp. Examples with close margins should not, generally, be classified as "fine".

(c) **Cancellation.** On a "fine" stamp this should be reasonably clear and not noticeably smudged. A stamp described as "superb" should have a neat cancellation, preferably centrally placed or to the right.

(d) **Appearance.** Stamps, at the prices quoted, should always be without any tears, creases, bends or thins and should not be toned on either the front or back. Stamps with such defects are worth only a proportion of the catalogue price.

Good

Fine

Very Fine

Superb

The above actual size illustrations of 1840 1d. blacks show the various grades of quality. When comparing these illustrations it should be assumed that they are all from the same plate and that they are free of any hidden defects.



**PRINTERS.** Nos. 1/53*a* were recess-printed by Perkins, Bacon & Petch, known from 1852 as Perkins, Bacon & Co.

1

1*a*

2 Small Crown

(Eng Charles and Frederick Heath)

**1840** (6–8 May). *Letters in lower corners. Wmk Small Crown. W* **2**. *Imperf.*

| *No.* | *Type* | | *Un* | *Used* | *Used on cover* |
|---|---|---|---|---|---|
| 1 | 1 | 1d. intense black .. .. .. | £3500 | £200 | |
| 2 | | 1d. black .. .. .. .. | £3000 | £150 | £250 |
| 3 | | 1d. grey-black (worn plate) .. | £3000 | £200 | |
| 4 | 1*a* | 2d. deep full blue (8.5.40) .. | £7000 | £400 | |
| 5 | | 2d. blue .. .. .. .. | £5500 | £300 | £650 |
| 6 | | 2d. pale blue .. .. .. .. | £7000 | £375 | |

The 1d. stamp in black was printed from Plates 1 to 11. Plate 1 exists in two states (known to collectors as 1*a* and 1*b*), the latter being the result of extensive repairs.

Repairs were also made to Plates 2, 5, 6, 8, 9, 10 and 11, and certain impressions exist in two or more states.

The so-called "Royal reprint" of the 1d. black was made in 1864, from Plate 66, Die II, on paper with Large Crown watermark, inverted. A printing was also made in carmine, on paper with the same watermark, normal.

For 1d. black with "VR" in upper corners *see* No. V1 under Official Stamps.

The 2d. stamps were printed from Plates 1 and 2.

**Plates of 1d. black**

| *Plate* | *Un* | *Used* |
|---|---|---|
| 1*a* .. .. .. .. .. | £4500 | £180 |
| 1*b* .. .. .. .. .. | £3000 | £150 |
| 2 .. .. .. .. .. | £3000 | £150 |
| 3 .. .. .. .. .. | £3500 | £190 |
| 4 .. .. .. .. .. | £3000 | £160 |
| 5 .. .. .. .. .. | £3000 | £150 |
| 6 .. .. .. .. .. | £3000 | £150 |
| 7 .. .. .. .. .. | £3250 | £180 |
| 8 .. .. .. .. .. | £3500 | £200 |
| 9 .. .. .. .. .. | £4000 | £250 |
| 10 .. .. .. .. .. | £4500 | £325 |
| 11 .. .. .. .. .. | £4500 | £1600 |

**Varieties of 1d. black**

| | | *Un* | *Used* |
|---|---|---|---|
| a. | On *bleuté* paper (Plates 1 to 8) .. *from* | — | £200 |
| b. | Double letter in corner .. *from* | £3000 | £180 |
| bb. | Re-entry .. .. .. .. | £3250 | £200 |
| bc. | "PB" re-entry (Plate 5, 3rd state) .. | — | £4000 |
| cc. | Large letters in each corner (E J, I L, J C and P A) (Plate 1*b*) .. .. .. *from* | £3500 | £325 |
| c. | Guide line in corner .. .. .. | £3000 | £180 |
| d. | ,, ,, through value .. .. | £3000 | £180 |
| e. | Watermark inverted .. .. .. | £3750 | £350 |
| g. | Obliterated by Maltese Cross | | |
| | In red | — | £150 |
| | In black | — | £150 |
| | In blue | — | £1400 |
| | In magenta | — | £600 |
| | In yellow | — | £3250 |
| h. | Obliterated by Maltese Cross with number in centre | | |
| | No. 1 | — | £2250 |
| | No. 2 | — | £1250 |
| | No. 3 | — | £1250 |
| | No. 4 | — | £1250 |
| | No. 5 | — | £1250 |
| | No. 6 | — | £1250 |
| | No. 7 | — | £1250 |
| | No. 8 | — | £1250 |
| | No. 9 | — | £1250 |
| | No. 10 | — | £1250 |
| | No. 11 | — | — |
| | No. 12 | — | £1250 |
| i. | Obliterated "Penny Post" in black .. *from* | — | £1200 |
| j. | Obliterated by town postmark (without Maltese Cross) | | |
| | In black *from* | — | £1000 |
| | In yellow *from* | — | £4000 |
| | In red *from* | — | £1100 |
| k. | Obliterated by 1844 type postmark in black *from* | — | £450 |

**Plates of 2d. blue**

| *Plate* | | *Un* | *Used* |
|---|---|---|---|
| 1 .. .. | *Shades from* | £5500 | £300 |
| 2 .. .. | *Shades from* | £6500 | £375 |

**Varieties of 2d. blue**

| | | *Un* | *Used* |
|---|---|---|---|
| a. | Double letter in corner .. .. .. .. | — | £425 |
| aa. | Re-entry .. .. .. .. .. | — | £475 |
| b. | Guide line in corner .. .. .. .. | — | £375 |
| c. | ,, ,, through value .. .. .. | — | £375 |
| d. | Watermark inverted .. .. .. .. | £7000 | £650 |
| e. | Obliterated by Maltese Cross | | |
| | In red | — | £300 |
| | In black | — | £300 |
| | In blue | — | £2250 |
| | In magenta | — | £2000 |
| f. | Obliterated by Maltese Cross with number in centre | | |
| | No. 1 | — | £2500 |
| | No. 2 | — | £2500 |
| | No. 3 | — | — |
| | No. 4 | — | £2500 |
| | No. 5 | — | £2500 |
| | No. 6 | — | £2750 |
| | No. 7 | — | £2500 |
| | No. 8 | — | £2500 |
| | No. 9 | — | £3000 |
| | No. 10 | — | £2750 |
| | No. 11 | — | £2750 |
| | No. 12 | — | £2500 |
| g. | Obliterated "Penny Post" in black .. *from* | — | £1400 |
| h. | Obliterated by town postmark (without Maltese Cross) in black .. *from* | — | £1200 |
| i. | Obliterated by 1844 type postmark | | |
| | In black *from* | — | £700 |
| | In blue *from* | — | £2000 |

**1841** (10 Feb). *Printed from "black" plates. Wmk W* **2**. *Paper more or less blued. Imperf.*

| *No.* | *Type* | | *Un* | *Used* | *Used on cover* |
|---|---|---|---|---|---|
| 7 | 1 | 1d. red-brown (*shades*) .. .. | £450 | 40·00 | 70·00 |
| | | a. "PB" re-entry (Plate 5, 3rd state) .. .. | — | £1200 | |

The first printings of the 1d. in red-brown were made from Plates 1*b*, 2, 5 and 8 to 11 used for the 1d. black.

**1d. red-brown from "black" plates**

| *Plate* | *Un* | *Used* |
|---|---|---|
| 1*b* .. .. .. .. .. | £3000 | £150 |
| 2 .. .. .. .. .. | £1750 | £100 |
| 5 .. .. .. .. .. | £650 | 50·00 |
| 8 .. .. .. .. .. | £500 | 40·00 |
| 9 .. .. .. .. .. | £450 | 40·00 |
| 10 .. .. .. .. .. | £475 | 40·00 |
| 11 .. .. .. .. .. | £500 | 40·00 |

**1841** (late Feb). *Plate 12 onwards. Wmk W* **2**. *Paper more or less blued. Imperf.*

| | | | *Un* | *Used* | *Used on cover* |
|---|---|---|---|---|---|
| 8 | 1 | 1d. red-brown .. .. .. | £130 | 3·50 | 8·00 |
| 8*a* | | 1d. red-brown on very blue paper | £150 | 3·50 | |
| 9 | | 1d. pale red-brown (worn plates) | £200 | 10·00 | |
| 10 | | 1d. deep red-brown .. .. | £150 | 7·00 | |
| 11 | | 1d. lake-red .. .. .. | £600 | £200 | |
| 12 | | 1d. orange-brown .. .. | £300 | 50·00 | |

*Error. No letter "A" in right lower corner (Stamp* B(A), *Plate* 77)

| | | | | |
|---|---|---|---|---|
| 12*a* | 1 | 1d. red-brown .. .. .. .. | — | £4500 |

The error "No letter A in right corner" was due to the omission to insert this letter on stamp B A of Plate 77. The error was discovered some months after the plate was registered and was then corrected.

There are innumerable variations in the colour and shade of the 1d. "red" and those given in the above list represent colour groups each covering a wide range.

**Varieties of 1d. red-brown, etc.**

| | | *Un* | *Used* |
|---|---|---|---|
| b. | Re-entry .. .. .. .. .. *from* | — | 22·00 |
| c. | Double letter in corner .. .. *from* | — | 12·00 |
| d. | Double Star (Plate 75) "Union Jack" re-entry | — | £450 |
| e. | Guide line in corner .. .. .. .. | — | 6·00 |
| f. | ,, ,, through value .. .. .. | — | 12·00 |
| g. | Thick outer frame to stamp .. .. .. | — | 12·00 |
| h. | Ivory head .. .. .. .. .. | £180 | 6·00 |
| i. | Watermark inverted .. .. .. .. | £350 | 35·00 |
| j. | Left corner letter "S" inverted (Plates 78, 105, 107) .. .. .. .. *from* | — | 40·00 |
| k. | P converted to R (Plates 30, 33, 83, 86) *from* | — | 30·00 |
| l. | Obliterated by Maltese Cross | | |
| | In red | — | £800 |
| | In black | — | 8·00 |
| | In blue | — | £110 |
| m. | Obliterated by Maltese Cross with number in centre | | |
| | No. 1 | — | 30·00 |
| | No. 2 | — | 30·00 |
| | No. 3 | — | 40·00 |
| | No. 4 | — | £100 |
| | No. 5 | — | 30·00 |
| | No. 6 | — | 25·00 |
| | No. 7 | — | 22·00 |
| | No. 8 | — | 22·00 |
| | No. 9 | — | 30·00 |
| | No. 10 | — | 40·00 |
| | No. 11 | — | 50·00 |
| | No. 12 | — | 70·00 |
| n. | Obliterated "Penny Post" in black .. .. | — | £200 |
| o. | Obliterated by town postmark (without Maltese Cross) | | |
| | In black *from* | — | £100 |
| | In blue *from* | — | £225 |
| | In green *from* | — | £375 |
| | In yellow *from* | — | £3500 |
| | In red *from* | — | £2000 |
| p. | Obliterated by 1844 type postmark | | |
| | In blue *from* | — | 30·00 |
| | In red *from* | — | £800 |
| | In green *from* | — | 90·00 |
| | In violet *from* | — | £500 |
| | In black *from* | — | 3·50 |

Stamps with thick outer frame to the design are from plates on which the frame-lines have been strengthened or recut, particularly Plates 76 and 90.

For "Union Jack" re-entry *see* General Notes to Line-engraved Issues.

In "P converted to R" the corner letter "R" is formed from the "P", the distinctive long tail having been hand-cut.

## KEY TO LINE-ENGRAVED ISSUES

| S.G. Nos. | Description | Date | Wmk | Perf | Die | Alphabet |
|---|---|---|---|---|---|---|
| | **THE IMPERFORATE ISSUES** | | | | | |
| 1/3 | 1d. black | 6.5.40 | SC | Imp | I | I |
| 4/6 | 2d. no lines | 8.5.40 | SC | Imp | I | I |
| | PAPER MORE OR LESS BLUED | | | | | |
| 7 | 1d. red-brown | 10.2.41 | SC | Imp | I | I |
| 8/12 | 1d. red-brown | Feb 41 | SC | Imp | I | I |
| 8/12 | 1d. red-brown | 6.2.52 | SC | Imp | I | II |
| 13/15 | 2d. white lines | 13.3.41 | SC | Imp | I | I |
| | **THE PERFORATED ISSUES** | | | | | |
| | ONE PENNY VALUE | | | | | |
| 16*a* | 1d. red-brown | 1848 | SC | Roul | I | I |
| 16*b* | 1d. red-brown | 1850 | SC | 16 | I | I |
| 16*c* | 1d. red-brown | 1853 | SC | 16 | I | II |
| 16*d* | 1d. red-brown | 1854 | SC | 14 | I | I |
| 17/18 | 1d. red-brown | Feb 1854 | SC | 16 | I | II |
| 22 | 1d. red-brown | Jan 1855 | SC | 14 | I | II |
| 24/5 | 1d. red-brown | 28.2.55 | SC | 14 | II | II |
| 21 | 1d. red-brown | 1.3.55 | SC | 16 | II | II |
| 26 | 1d. red-brown | 15.5.55 | LC | 16 | II | II |
| 29/33 | 1d. red-brown | Aug 1855 | LC | 14 | II | III |
| | NEW COLOURS ON WHITE PAPER | | | | | |
| 37/41 | 1d. rose-red | Nov 1856 | LC | 14 | II | III |
| 36 | 1d. rose-red | 26.12.57 | LC | 16 | II | III |
| 42 | 1d. rose-red | 1861 | LC | 14 | II | IV |
| | TWO PENCE VALUE | | | | | |
| 19, 20 | 2d. blue | 1.3.54 | SC | 16 | I | I |
| 23 | 2d. blue | 22.2.55 | SC | 14 | I | I |
| 23*a* | 2d. blue | 5.7.55 | SC | 14 | I | II |
| 20*a* | 2d. blue | 18.8.55 | SC | 16 | I | II |
| 27 | 2d. blue | 20.7.55 | LC | 16 | I | II |
| 34 | 2d. blue | 20.7.55 | LC | 14 | I | II |
| 35 | 2d. blue | 2.7.57 | LC | 14 | I | III |
| 36*a* | 2d. blue | 1.2.58 | LC | 16 | I | III |
| | **LETTERS IN ALL FOUR CORNERS** | | | | | |
| 48/9 | ½d. rose-red | 1.10.70 | W 9 | 14 | — | |
| 43/4 | 1d. rose-red | 1.4.64 | LC | 14 | II | |
| 53*a* | 1½d. rosy mauve | 1860 | LC | 14 | II | |
| 51/3 | 1½d. rose-red | 1.10.70 | LC | 14 | II | |
| 45 | 2d. blue | July 1858 | LC | 14 | II | |
| 46/7 | 2d. thinner lines | 7.7.69 | LC | 14 | II | |

*Watermarks*: SC = Small Crown, T **2**.
LC = Large Crown, T **4**.
*Dies*: *See* notes above No. 17 in the catalogue.
*Alphabets*: *See* General Notes to this section.

**3** White lines added

**1841** (13 Mar)–**51**. *White lines added. Wmk W* **2**. *Paper more or less blued. Imperf.*

| | | | Un | Used | Used on cover |
|---|---|---|---|---|---|
| 13 | **3** | 2d. pale blue | £1300 | 45·00 | |
| 14 | | 2d. blue | £1000 | 35·00 | £140 |
| 15 | | 2d. deep full blue | £1300 | 50·00 | |
| 15*aa* | | 2d. violet-blue (1851) | £7000 | £475 | |

The 2d. stamp with white lines was printed from Plates 3 and 4.

No. 15*aa* came from Plate 4 and the price quoted is for examples on thicker, lavender tinted paper.

**Plates of 2d. blue**

| *Plate* | | *Un* | *Used* |
|---|---|---|---|
| 3 | *Shades from* | £1000 | 40·00 |
| 4 | *Shades from* | £1200 | 35·00 |

**Varieties of 2d. blue**

| | | | *Un* | *Used* |
|---|---|---|---|---|
| a. | Guide line in corner | | — | 38·00 |
| b. | ,, ,, through value | | £1500 | 38·00 |
| bb. | Double letter in corner | | — | 45·00 |
| be. | Re-entry | | £1800 | 60·00 |
| c. | Ivory head | | £1600 | 40·00 |
| d. | Watermark inverted | | £2250 | £200 |
| e. | Obliterated by Maltese Cross | | | |
| | | In red | — | £3500 |
| | | In black | — | 55·00 |
| | | In blue | — | £750 |
| f. | Obliterated by Maltese Cross with number in centre | | | |
| | | No. 1 | — | £160 |
| | | No. 2 | — | £160 |
| | | No. 3 | — | £160 |
| | | No. 4 | — | £150 |
| | | No. 5 | — | £200 |
| | | No. 6 | — | £150 |
| | | No. 7 | — | £300 |
| | | No. 8 | — | £200 |
| | | No. 9 | — | £300 |
| | | No. 10 | — | £350 |
| | | No. 11 | — | £200 |
| | | No. 12 | — | £110 |
| g. | Obliterated by town postmark (without Maltese Cross) | | | |
| | | In black *from* | — | £350 |
| | | In blue *from* | — | £600 |
| h. | Obliterated by 1844 type postmark | | | |
| | | In black *from* | — | 35·00 |
| | | In blue *from* | — | £325 |
| | | In red *from* | — | £3500 |
| | | In green *from* | — | £450 |

**1841** (April). *Trial printing (unissued) on Dickinson silk-thread paper. Imperf.*

16 **1** 1d. red-brown (Plate 11) .. .. £1500

Eight sheets were printed on this paper, six being gummed, two ungummed, but we have only seen examples without gum.

**1848**. *Wmk Small Crown, W* **2**. *Rouletted approx* 11½ *by Henry Archer.*

16*a* **1** 1d. red-brown (Plates 70, 71) .. .. £4000

**1850**. *Wmk Small Crown, W* **2**. *P* 16 *by Henry Archer.*

16*b* **1** 1d. red-brown (Alph 1) (from Plates 71, 79, 90–101, 105 and 107. Also Plate 8, unused only) .. .. *from* £500 £150

Stamp on cover, dated prior to February 1854 (*price* £350); dated February and after 1854 (*price* £250).

**1853**. *Government Trial Perforations. Wmk Small Crown, W* **2**.

16*c* **1** 1d. red-brown (*p* 16) (Alph II) (*on cover*) † £4750
16*d* 1d. red-brown (*p* 14) (Alph I) .. .. £3750

**SEPARATION TRIALS.** Although the various trials of machines for rouletting and perforating were unofficial, Archer had the consent of the authorities in making his experiments, and sheets so experimented upon were afterwards used by the Post Office.

As Archer ended his experiments in 1850 and plates with corner letters Alphabet II did not come into issue until 1852, perforated stamps with corner letters of Alphabet I may safely be assumed to be Archer productions, if genuine.

The Government trial perforations were done on Napier machines in 1853. As Alphabet II was by that time in use, the trials can only be distinguished from the perforated stamps listed below by being dated prior to 28 January 1854, the date when the perforated stamps were officially issued.

Die I

Die II

**4** Large Crown

Die I: The features of the portrait are lightly shaded and consequently lack emphasis.

Die II (Die I retouched): The lines of the features have been deepened and appear stronger.

The eye is deeply shaded and made more lifelike. The nostril and lips are more clearly defined, the latter appearing much thicker. A strong downward stroke of colour marks the corner of the mouth. There is a deep indentation of colour between lower lip and chin. The band running from the back of the ear to the chignon has a bolder horizontal line below it than in Die I.

The original die (Die I) was used to provide roller dies for the laying down of all the line-engraved stamps from 1840 to 1855. In that year a new master die was laid down (by means of a Die I roller die) and the impression was retouched by hand engraving by William Humphrys. This retouched die, always known to philatelists as Die II, was from that time used for preparing all new roller dies.

*One Penny*. The numbering of the 1d. plates recommenced at 1 on the introduction of Die II. Plates 1 to 21 were Alphabet II from which a scarce plum shade exists. Corner letters of Alphabet III appear on Plate 22 and onwards.

As an experiment, the corner letters were engraved by hand on Plates 50 and 51 in 1856, instead of being punched (Alphabet IV), but punching was again resorted to from Plate 52 onwards. Plates 50 and 51 were not put into use until 1861.

*Two Pence*. Unlike the 1d. the old sequence of plate numbers continued. Plates 3 and 4 of the 2d. had corner letters of Alphabet I, Plate 5 Alphabet II and Plate 6 Alphabet III. In Plate 6 the white lines are thinner than before.

**1854–57**. *Paper more or less blued. (a) Wmk Small Crown, W* **2**. *P* 16.

| | | | Un | Used | ★ Used on cover |
|---|---|---|---|---|---|
| 17 | **1** | 1d. red-brown (Die I) (2.54) | £125 | 3·50 | 10·00 |
| 18 | | 1d. yellow-brown (Die I) | £150 | 10·00 | |
| 19 | **3** | 2d. deep blue (Plate 4) (1.3.54) | £1300 | 35·00 | 55·00 |
| | | a. Imperf three sides (horiz pair) | † | — | |
| 20 | | 2d. pale blue (Plate 4) | £1300 | 45·00 | |
| 20*a* | | 2d. blue (Plate 5) (18.8.55) | £1800 | £130 | £200 |
| 21 | **1** | 1d. red-brown (Die I) (1.3.55) | £150 | 12·00 | 22·00 |
| | | a. Imperf | | | |
| | | *(b) Wmk Small Crown, W* **2**. *P* 14 | | | |
| 22 | **1** | 1d. red-brown (Die I) (1.55) | £250 | 18·00 | 35·00 |
| 23 | **3** | 2d. blue (Plate 4) (22.2.55) | £1800 | £120 | £160 |
| 23*a* | | 2d. blue (Plate 5) (5.7.55) | £1800 | £120 | £150 |
| | | b. Imperf (Plate 5) | | | |
| 24 | **1** | 1d. red-brown (Die II) (28.2.55) | £225 | 16·00 | 25·00 |
| 24*a* | | 1d. deep red-brown (very blue paper) (Die II) | £250 | 20·00 | |
| 25 | | 1d. orange-brown (Die II) | £575 | 45·00 | |
| | | *(c) Wmk Large Crown, W* **4**. *P* 16 | | | |
| 26 | **1** | 1d. red-brown (Die II) (15.5.55) | £450 | 35·00 | 50·00 |
| | | a. Imperf (Plate 7) | | | |
| 27 | **3** | 2d. blue (Plate 5) (20.7.55) | £2000 | £130 | £200 |
| | | a. Imperf | — | £2500 | |
| | | *(d) Wmk Large Crown, W* **4**. *P* 14 | | | |
| 29 | **1** | 1d. red-brown (Die II) (18.8.55) | £100 | 1·00 | 5·50 |
| | | a. Imperf (*shades*) (Plates 22, 24, 25, 32, 43) | £950 | £750 | |
| 30 | | 1d. brick-red (Die II) | £140 | 12·00 | |
| 31 | **1** | 1d. plum (Die II) (2.56) | £800 | £275 | |
| 32 | | 1d. brown-rose (Die II) | £160 | 14·00 | |
| 33 | | 1d. orange-brown (Die II) (3.57) | £250 | 17·00 | |
| 34 | **3** | 2d. blue (Plate 5) (20.7.55) | £1000 | 25·00 | 70·00 |
| 35 | | 2d. blue (Plate 6) (2.7.57) | £1100 | 22·00 | 60·00 |
| | | a. Imperf | — | £2750 | |
| | | b. Imperf horiz (vert pair) | † | — | |
| ★17/35a | | **For well-centred, lightly used** | +125% | | |

**1856–58**. *Paper no longer blued. (a) Wmk Large Crown, W* **4**. *P* 16.

| | | | | | |
|---|---|---|---|---|---|
| 36 | **1** | 1d. rose-red (Die II) (26.12.57) | £550 | 22·00 | 40·00 |
| 36*a* | **3** | 2d. blue (Plate 6) (1.2.58) | £3000 | £130 | £200 |
| | | *(b) (Die II) Wmk Large Crown, W* **4**. *P* 14 | | | |
| 37 | **1** | 1d. red-brown (11.56) | £225 | 50·00 | |
| 38 | | 1d. pale red (9.4.57) | 40·00 | 2·00 | |
| | | a. Imperf | £500 | £425 | |
| 39 | | 1d. pale rose (3.57) | 40·00 | 6·00 | |
| 40 | | 1d. rose-red (9.57) | 25·00 | 1·00 | 2·00 |
| | | a. Imperf | £550 | £425 | |
| 41 | | 1d. deep-rose-red (7.57) | 40·00 | 2·00 | |

**1861**. *Letters engraved on plate instead of punched (Alphabet IV).*

| | | | | | |
|---|---|---|---|---|---|
| 42 | **1** | 1d. rose-red (Die II) (Plates 50 and 51) | £110 | 8·00 | 22·00 |
| | | a. Imperf | — | £1800 | |
| ★36/42a | | **For well-centred, lightly used** | +125% | | |

In both values, varieties may be found as described in the preceding issues—ivory heads, inverted watermarks, re-entries, and double letters in corners.

The change of perforation from 16 to 14 was decided upon late in 1854 since the closer holes of the former gauge tended to cause the sheets of stamps to break up when handled, but for a time both gauges were in concurrent use. Owing to faulty alignment of the impressions on the plates and to shrinkage of the paper when damped, badly perforated stamps are plentiful in the line-engraved issues.

**5**

**6**

Showing position of the plate number on the 1d. and 2d. values. (Plate 170 shown)

**1858–79**. *Letters in all four corners. Wmk Large Crown, W* **4**. *Die* II (*1d. and 2d.*). *P* 14.

| | | | Un | Used | ★ Used on cover |
|---|---|---|---|---|---|
| 43 | **5** | 1d. rose-red (1.4.64) | 4·50 | 50 | 1·50 |
| 44 | | 1d. lake-red | 4·50 | 50 | |
| | | a. Imperf .. .. *from* | £750 | £600 | |
| ★43/4a | | **For well-centred, lightly used** | +125% | | |

| *Plate* | *Un* | *Used* | *Plate* | *Un* | *Used* |
|---|---|---|---|---|---|
| 71 | 12·00 | 2·00 | 133 | 45·00 | 6·00 |
| 72 | 18·00 | 2·50 | 134 | 4·50 | 50 |
| 73 | 12·00 | 2·00 | 135 | 50·00 | 20·00 |
| 74 | 10·00 | 50 | 136 | 50·00 | 15·00 |
| 76 | 20·00 | 50 | 137 | 8·00 | 90 |
| 77 | £50000 | £30000 | 138 | 6·00 | 50 |
| 78 | 50·00 | 50 | 139 | 16·00 | 11·00 |
| 79 | 15·00 | 50 | 140 | 6·00 | 50 |
| 80 | 10·00 | 75 | 141 | 75·00 | 6·00 |
| 81 | 30·00 | 1·00 | 142 | 25·00 | 18·00 |
| 82 | 60·00 | 2·50 | 143 | 15·00 | 10·00 |
| 83 | 70·00 | 4·00 | 144 | 50·00 | 15·00 |
| 84 | 30·00 | 1·00 | 145 | 4·50 | 1·00 |
| 85 | 12·00 | 1·00 | 146 | 5·00 | 3·50 |
| 86 | 15·00 | 2·50 | 147 | 9·00 | 2·00 |
| 87 | 4·50 | 50 | 148 | 10·00 | 1·50 |
| 88 | 80·00 | 5·50 | 149 | 7·50 | 3·50 |
| 89 | 20·00 | 50 | 150 | 4·50 | 50 |
| 90 | 14·00 | 50 | 151 | 13·00 | 6·00 |
| 91 | 20·00 | 3·50 | 152 | 9·00 | 3·25 |
| 92 | 7·00 | 50 | 153 | 35·00 | 6·00 |
| 93 | 20·00 | 50 | 154 | 7·50 | 50 |
| 94 | 20·00 | 3·00 | 155 | 8·00 | 75 |
| 95 | 12·00 | 50 | 156 | 7·50 | 50 |
| 96 | 14·00 | 50 | 157 | 7·50 | 50 |
| 97 | 8·00 | 1·75 | 158 | 4·50 | 50 |
| 98 | 8·00 | 3·50 | 159 | 4·50 | 50 |
| 99 | 12·00 | 3·00 | 160 | 4·50 | 50 |
| 100 | 18·00 | 1·25 | 161 | 15·00 | 4·00 |
| 101 | 25·00 | 6·00 | 162 | 8·00 | 4·00 |
| 102 | 10·00 | 55 | 163 | 7·50 | 1·50 |
| 103 | 10·00 | 1·50 | 164 | 7·50 | 2·00 |
| 104 | 14·00 | 3·00 | 165 | 10·00 | 50 |
| 105 | 35·00 | 4·00 | 166 | 7·50 | 3·50 |
| 106 | 15·00 | 55 | 167 | 5·00 | 50 |
| 107 | 20·00 | 3·75 | 168 | 6·00 | 5·50 |
| 108 | 15·00 | 1·00 | 169 | 15·00 | 4·00 |
| 109 | 38·00 | 1·75 | 170 | 6·00 | 50 |
| 110 | 10·00 | 6·00 | 171 | 4·50 | 50 |
| 111 | 18·00 | 1·00 | 172 | 4·50 | 90 |
| 112 | 30·00 | 1·00 | 173 | 25·00 | 6·00 |
| 113 | 8·00 | 7·50 | 174 | 4·50 | 40 |
| 114 | £175 | 8·00 | 175 | 18·00 | 1·75 |
| 115 | 50·00 | 1·00 | 176 | 13·00 | 90 |
| 116 | 38·00 | 6·00 | 177 | 5·00 | 50 |
| 117 | 8·00 | 50 | 178 | 7·50 | 2·00 |
| 118 | 12·00 | 50 | 179 | 8·00 | 1·00 |
| 119 | 5·00 | 75 | 180 | 8·00 | 3·00 |
| 120 | 4·50 | 50 | 181 | 7·50 | 50 |
| 121 | 20·00 | 6·00 | 182 | 50·00 | 3·00 |
| 122 | 4·50 | 50 | 183 | 13·00 | 1·50 |
| 123 | 6·00 | 75 | 184 | 4·50 | 75 |
| 124 | 6·00 | 50 | 185 | 7·50 | 1·50 |
| 125 | 8·00 | 1·00 | 186 | 15·00 | 1·00 |
| 127 | 17·00 | 1·00 | 187 | 6·00 | 50 |
| 129 | 6·00 | 5·00 | 188 | 10·00 | 7·00 |
| 130 | 9·00 | 1·00 | 189 | 18·00 | 4·00 |
| 131 | 38·00 | 11·00 | 190 | 7·00 | 3·50 |
| 132 | 50·00 | 16·00 | 191 | 4·50 | 4·00 |

| Plate | | Un | Used | Plate | | Un | Used |
|---|---|---|---|---|---|---|---|
| 92 | .. .. | 13·00 | 50 | 209 | .. .. | 7·50 | 6·00 |
| 93 | .. .. | 4·50 | 50 | 210 | .. .. | 10·00 | 8·00 |
| 94 | .. .. | 7·50 | 5·00 | 211 | .. .. | 22·00 | 15·00 |
| 95 | .. .. | 7·50 | 5·00 | 212 | .. .. | 7·50 | 7·50 |
| 96 | .. .. | 5·00 | 3·00 | 213 | .. .. | 7·50 | 7·50 |
| 97 | .. .. | 8·00 | 6·00 | 214 | .. .. | 13·00 | 13·00 |
| 98 | .. .. | 4·50 | 3·50 | 215 | .. .. | 13·00 | 13·00 |
| 99 | .. .. | 10·00 | 3·50 | 216 | .. .. | 13·00 | 13·00 |
| 00 | .. .. | 10·00 | 50 | 217 | .. .. | 10·00 | 4·00 |
| 01 | .. .. | 4·50 | 3·00 | 218 | .. .. | 6·00 | 5·00 |
| 02 | .. .. | 7·50 | 5·00 | 219 | .. .. | 30·00 | 50·00 |
| 03 | .. .. | 4·50 | 10·00 | 220 | .. .. | 4·50 | 3·50 |
| 04 | .. .. | 6·00 | 75 | 221 | .. .. | 15·00 | 10·00 |
| 05 | .. .. | 6·00 | 2·00 | 222 | .. .. | 25·00 | 25·00 |
| 06 | .. .. | 6·00 | 6·00 | 223 | .. .. | 30·00 | 40·00 |
| 07 | .. .. | 6·00 | 6·00 | 224 | .. .. | 35·00 | 35·00 |
| 08 | .. .. | 6·00 | 10·00 | 225 | .. .. | £1000 | £300 |

*Error. Imperf.* Issued at Cardiff (Plate 116)

| | | | Un | Used |
|---|---|---|---|---|
| 4*b* | **5** | 1d. rose-red (18.1.70) .. .. .. | £1500 | £1000 |

The following plate numbers are also known imperf and used (No. 4a); 72,79, 80, 81, 82, 83, 86, 87, 88, 90, 91, 92, 93, 96, 97, 100, 102, 03, 104, 105, 107, 108, 109, 112, 114, 117, 120, 121, 122, 136, 137, 42, 146, 148, 158, 162, 164, 166, 171, 174, 191 and 202.

The numbering of this series of 1d. red plates follows after that of e previous 1d. stamp, last printed from Plate 68.

Plates 69, 70, 75, 126 and 128 were prepared for this issue but ejected owing to defects, and stamps from these plates do not exist, o that specimens which appear to be from these plates (like many of ose which optimistic collectors believe to be from Plate 77) bear ther plate numbers. Owing to faulty engraving or printing it is not lways easy to identify the plate number. Plate 77 was also rejected ut some stamps printed from it were used. One specimen is in the apling Collection and six or seven others are known. Plates 226 to 28 were made but not used.

Specimens from most of the plates are known with inverted atermark. The variety of watermark described in the General otes to this section occurs on stamp M A (or M L) on plates up to bout 96 (*Prices from* £110 *used*).

Re-entries in this issue are few, the best being on stamps M K and K of Plate 71 and on S L and T L, Plate 83.

| | | | Un | ★ Used | Used on cover |
|---|---|---|---|---|---|
| 5 | **6** | 2d. blue (thick lines) (7.58) .. | £160 | 4·00 | 15·00 |
| | | a. Imperf (Plate 9) .. .. | — | £3000 | |
| | | *Plate* | | | |
| | | 7 .. .. .. .. | £400 | 18·00 | |
| | | 8 .. .. .. .. | £450 | 14·00 | |
| | | 9 .. .. .. .. | £160 | 4·00 | |
| | | 12 .. .. .. .. | £700 | 40·00 | |
| 6 | | 2d. blue (thin lines) (1.7.69) .. | £150 | 6·00 | 16·00 |
| 7 | | 2d. deep blue (thin lines) .. | £150 | 6·00 | |
| | | a. Imperf (Plate 13) .. .. | £1800 | | |
| | | *Plate* | | | |
| | | 13 .. .. .. .. | £180 | 6·00 | |
| | | 14 .. .. .. .. | £200 | 8·00 | |
| | | 15 .. .. .. .. | £150 | 8·00 | |
| 45/7 | | **For well-centred, lightly used** .. | | +125% | |

Plates 10 and 11 of the 2d. were prepared but rejected. Plates 13 to 5 were laid down from a new roller impression on which the white nes were thinner.

There are some marked re-entries and repairs, particularly on lates 7, 8, 9 and 12.

Stamps with inverted watermark may be found and also the T A T L) and M A (M L) watermark varieties (*see* General Notes to this ection).

Though the paper is normally white, some printings showed lueing and stamps showing the "ivory head" may therefore be ound.

7

Showing the plate number (9)

9

**370** (1 Oct). *Wmk W* **9**, *extending over three stamps. P* 14.

| | | | Un | ★ Used | Used on cover |
|---|---|---|---|---|---|
| 8 | **7** | ½d. rose-red .. .. .. | 45·00 | 6·00 | 24·00 |
| 9 | | ½d. rose .. .. .. .. | 45·00 | 6·00 | |
| | | a. Imperf (Plates 1, 4, 5, 6, 8, 14) .. .. .. *from* | £950 | £600 | |
| | | *Plate* | | | |
| | | 1 .. .. .. .. | 95·00 | 40·00 | |
| | | 3 .. .. .. .. | 60·00 | 14·00 | |
| | | 4 .. .. .. .. | 75·00 | 8·00 | |
| | | 5 .. .. .. .. | 55·00 | 6·00 | |
| | | 6 .. .. .. .. | 45·00 | 6·00 | |
| | | 8 .. .. .. .. | 85·00 | 40·00 | |
| | | 9 .. .. .. .. | £2250 | £300 | |
| | | 10 .. .. .. .. | 75·00 | 6·00 | |
| | | 11 .. .. .. .. | 45·00 | 6·00 | |
| | | 12 .. .. .. .. | 45·00 | 6·00 | |
| | | 13 .. .. .. .. | 45·00 | 6·00 | |
| | | 14 .. .. .. .. | 45·00 | 6·00 | |
| | | 15 .. .. .. .. | 60·00 | 9·00 | |
| | | 19 .. .. .. .. | 90·00 | 18·00 | |
| | | 20 .. .. .. .. | 95·00 | 30·00 | |
| 49/9a | | **For well-centred, lightly used** .. | | +200% | |

The ½d. was printed in sheets of 480 (24 × 20) so that the check tters run from AA XT to AA TX.

Plates 2, 7, 16, 17 and 18 were not completed while Plates 21 and 2, though made, were not used.

Owing to the method of perforating, the outer side of stamps in either the A or X row (i e the left or right side of the sheet) is imperf.

Stamps may be found with watermark inverted or reversed, or without watermark, the latter due to misplacement of the paper when printing.

8

Position of plate Number

**1870** (1 Oct). *Wmk W* **4**. *P* 14.

| | | | Un | ★ Used | Used on cover |
|---|---|---|---|---|---|
| 51 | **8** | 1½d. rose-red .. .. .. | £150 | 18·00 | £130 |
| 52 | | 1½d. lake-red .. .. .. | £150 | 18·00 | |
| | | a. Imperf (Plates 1 and 3) *from* | £1900 | † | |
| | | *Plate* | | | |
| | | (1) .. .. .. .. | £350 | 25·00 | |
| | | 3 .. .. .. .. | £150 | 18·00 | |

*Error of lettering.* OP-PC *for* CP-PC (*Plate* 1)

| | | | Un | Used |
|---|---|---|---|---|
| 53 | **8** | 1½d. rose-red .. .. | £3750 | £600 |
| ★51/3 | | **For well-centred, lightly used** .. | | +125% |

**1860.** *Prepared for use but not issued; blued paper. Wmk W* **4**. *P* 14.

| | | | Un | Used |
|---|---|---|---|---|
| 53*a* | **8** | 1½d. rosy mauve (Plate 1) .. .. | £1800 | |
| | | b. Error of lettering, OP-PC for CP-PC | | |

Owing to a proposed change in the postal rates, 1½d. stamps were first printed in 1860, in rosy mauve, No. 53*a*, but the change was not approved and the greater part of the stock was destroyed.

In 1870 a 1½d. stamp was required and was issued in rose-red.

Plate 1 did not have the plate number in the design of the stamps, but on stamps from Plate 3 the number will be found in the frame as shown above.

Plate 2 was defective and was not used.

The error of lettering OP-PC on Plate 1 was apparently not noticed by the printers, and therefore not corrected.

## EMBOSSED ISSUES

Volume 1 of the Stanley Gibbons *Great Britain Specialised Catalogue* gives further detailed information on the embossed issues.

**PRICES.** The prices quoted are for cut-square stamps with average to fine embossing. Stamps with exceptionally clear embossing are worth more.

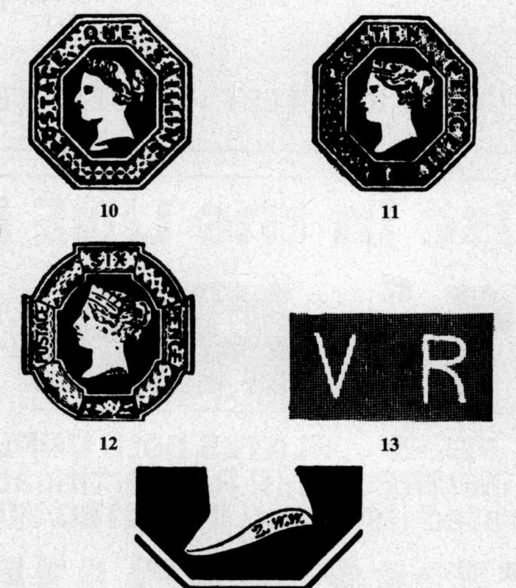


10 11 12 13

Position of die number

(Primary die engraved at the Royal Mint by William Wyon. Stamps printed at Somerset House)

**1847–54.** *Imperf.* (For paper and wmk see footnote.)

| | | | Un | Used | Used on cover |
|---|---|---|---|---|---|
| 54 | **10** | 1s. pale green (11.9.47) .. | £2750 | £350 | £450 |
| 55 | | 1s. green .. .. .. | £2750 | £400 | |
| 56 | | 1s. deep green .. .. | £3250 | £450 | |
| | | Die 1 (1847) .. .. | £2750 | £350 | |
| | | Die 2 (1854) .. .. | £3250 | £400 | |
| 57 | **11** | 10d. brown (6.11.48) .. | £2250 | £575 | £900 |
| | | Die 1 (1848) .. .. | £2500 | £625 | |
| | | Die 2 (1850) .. .. | £2250 | £575 | |
| | | Die 3 (1853) .. .. | £2250 | £575 | |
| | | Die 4 (1854) .. .. | £2500 | £625 | |
| | | Die 5 .. .. .. | £16000 | | |
| 58 | **12** | 6d. mauve (1.3.54) .. | £2500 | £425 | |
| 59 | | 6d. dull lilac .. .. | £2500 | £400 | £500 |
| 60 | | 6d. purple .. .. | £2500 | £400 | |
| 61 | | 6d. violet .. .. | £3250 | £600 | |

The 1s. and 10d. are on "Dickinson" paper with "silk" threads (actually a pale blue twisted cotton yarn). The 6d. is on paper watermarked V R in single-lined letters, W **13**, which may be found in four ways—upright, inverted, upright reversed, and inverted reversed; upright reversed being the most common.

The die numbers are indicated on the base of the bust. Only Die 1 (1 WW) of the 6d. was used for the adhesive stamps. The 10d. is from Die 1 (W.W.1 on stamps), and Dies 2 to 5 (2 W.W., 3 W.W., 4 W.W. and 5 W.W.) but the number and letters on stamps from Die 1 are seldom clear and many specimens are known without any trace of them. Because of this the stamp we previously listed as "No die number" has been deleted. That they are from Die 1 is proved by the existence of blocks showing stamps with and without the die number The 1s. is from Dies 1 and 2 (W.W.1, W.W.2).

The normal arrangement of the "silk" threads in the paper was in pairs running down each vertical row of the sheet, the space between the threads of each pair being approximately 5 mm and between pairs of threads 20 mm. Varieties due to misplacement of the paper in printing show a single thread on the first stamp from the sheet margin and two threads 20 mm apart on the other stamps of the row. Faulty manufacture is the cause of stamps with a single thread in the middle.

Through bad spacing of the impressions, which were handstruck, all values may be found with two impressions more or less overlapping. Owing to the small margin allowed for variation of spacing, specimens with good margins on all sides are not common.

Double impressions are known of all values.

Later printings of the 6d. had the gum tinted green to enable the printer to distinguish the gummed side of the paper.

## SURFACE-PRINTED ISSUES

### GENERAL NOTES

Volume 1 of the Stanley Gibbons *Great Britain Specialised Catalogue* gives further detailed information on the surface-printed issues.

**"Abnormals".** The majority of the great rarities in the surface-printed group of issues are the so-called "abnormals", whose existence is due to the practice of printing six sheets from every plate as soon as made, one of which was kept for record purposes at Somerset House, while the others were perforated and usually issued. If such plates were not used for general production or if, before they came into full use, a change of watermark or colour took place, the six sheets originally printed would differ from the main issue in plate, colour or watermark and, if issued, would be extremely rare.

The abnormal stamps of this class listed in this Catalogue and distinguished, where not priced, by an asterisk (*), are:

| *No.* | | |
|---|---|---|
| 78 | 3d. | Plate 3 (with white dots) |
| 152 | 4d. | vermilion, Plate 16 |
| 153 | 4d. | sage-green, Plate 17 |
| 109 | 6d. | mauve, Plate 10 |
| 123/*a* | 6d. | chestnut and 6d. pale chestnut, Plate 12 |
| 145 | 6d. | pale buff, Plate 13 |
| 88 | 9d. | Plate 3 (hair lines) |
| 98 | 9d. | Plate 5 (*see* footnote to No. 98) |
| 113 | 10d. | Plate 2 |
| 91 | 1s. | Plate 3 ("Plate 2") |
| 148/50 | 1s. | green, Plate 14 |
| 120 | 2s. | blue, Plate 3 |

Those which may have been issued, but of which no specimens are known, are 2½d. wmk Anchor, Plates 4 and 5; 3d. wmk Emblems, Plate 5; 3d. wmk Spray, Plate 21; 6d. grey, wmk Spray, Plate 18; 8d. orange, Plate 2; 1s. wmk Emblems, Plate 5. 5s. wmk Maltese Cross, Plate 4.

The 10d. Plate 1, wmk Emblems (No. 99), is sometimes reckoned among the abnormals, but was an error, due to the use of the wrong paper.

**Corner Letters.** With the exception of the 4d., 6d. and 1s. of 1855–57, the ½d., 1½d., 2d. and 5d. of 1880, the 1d. lilac of 1881 and the £5 (which had letters in lower corners only, and in the reverse order to the normal), all the surface-printed stamps issued prior to 1887 had letters in all four corners, as in the later line-engraved stamps. The arrangement is the same, the letters running in sequence right across and down the sheets, whether these were divided into panes or not. The corner letters existing naturally depend on the number of stamps in the sheet and their arrangement.

**Imprimaturs and Imperforate Stamps.** The Post Office retained in their records (now in the National Postal Museum) one imperforate sheet from each plate, known as the Imprimatur (or officially approved) sheet. Some stamps were removed from time to time for presentation purposes and have come on to the market, but these imperforates are not listed as they were not issued. Full details can be found in Volume I of the *Great Britain Specialised Catalogue*.

However, other imperforate stamps are known to have been issued and these are listed where it has been possible to prove that they do not come from the Imprimatur sheets. It is therefore advisable to purchase these only when acccompanied by an Expert Committee certificate of genuineness.

**Plate Numbers.** All stamps from No. 75 to No. 163 bear in their designs either the plate number or, in one or two earlier instances, some other indication by which one plate can be distinguished from another. With the aid of these and of the corner letters it is thus possible to "reconstruct" a sheet of stamps from any plate of any issue or denomination.

**Surface-printing.** In this context the traditional designation "surface-printing" is synonymous with typo(graphy)—a philatelic term—or letterpress—the printers' term—as meaning printing from (the surface of) raised type. It is also called relief-printing, as the image is in relief (in French, *en épargne*), unwanted parts of the design having been cut away. Duplicate impressions can be electrotyped or stereotyped from an original die, the resulting *clichés* being locked together to form the printing plate.

**Wing Margins.** As the vertical gutters (spaces) between the panes, into which sheets of stamps of most values were divided until the introduction of the Imperial Crown watermark, were perforated through the centre with a single row of holes, instead of each vertical row of stamps on the inner side of the panes having its own line of perforation as is now usual, a proportion of the stamps in each sheet have what is called a "wing margin" about 5 mm wide on one or other side.

The stamps with "wing margins" are the watermark Emblems and Spray of Rose series (3d. 6d. 9d. 10d. 1s. and 2s.) with letters D, E, H or I in S.E. corner, and the watermark Garter series (4d. and 8d.) with letters F or G in S.E. corner. Knowledge of this lettering will enable collectors to guard against stamps with wing margin cut down and re-perforated, but note that wing margin stamps of Nos. 62 to 73 are also to be found re-perforated.

**PRINTERS.** The issues of Queen Victoria, Nos. 62/214, were typo by Thomas De La Rue & Co.

**PERFORATIONS.** All the surface-printed issues of Queen Victoria are Perf 14, with the exception of Nos. 126/9.

## *ALTERED CATALOGUE NUMBERS*

Any Catalogue numbers altered from the last edition are shown as a list in the introductory pages.

# SIMON ANDREWS
AT
## CECIL COURT STAMPS

6 Cecil Court, London WC2H 4HE, England
Tel: 071–240 1051 Fax: 071–379 1477

*For specialised GB stamps, covers & booklets, pre–1840 to 1950*

**London's newest and oldest stamp shop (No. 6 Cecil Court has been a stamp shop since the early 20's) offers collectors, whether visiting in person or via the post, phone or fax, a fine selection of high quality G.B. stamps, covers and early booklets.**
In addition, we can supply philatelic literature & reference books, old auction catalogues, accessories, album pages, FDC's, current catalogues, etc. etc., – in fact practically anything the collector of G.B. could possible want.
For browsers, Commonwealth & GB on album pages and in the Tarifolds.

**STAMPS**
Fine mint and used material of the highest quality, including Trials, Essays, etc., plus a very good selection of Mint and Used Officials.

**COVERS**
Fine and scarce Victorian covers, both Line Engraved and Surface Printed. High quality Postal History, Blacks and Reds with distinctive crosses and coloured cancels, and there is always a wide choice of Mulready's. I also stock a good selection of Irish Covers and Postal History, while the Surface Printed Cover stock concentrates on high quality and scarce destinations.

**EARLY BOOKLETS (Buying & Selling)**
Always a good selection, 1904–1954

**PLUS . . .**
A good mint and used selection of Edward VII and George V (specialised and shades), plus definitive & commemorative sets to date.

ESSAY

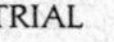
TRIAL

SG011 (A GREAT RARITY)

EXPERIMENTAL

UNOFFICIAL

PROPAGANDA

VERY RARE . . .

QUALITY

SUPERB

**VISIT LONDON'S NEWEST* STAMP SHOP**

**And oldest! There has been a stamp shop at No. 6 Cecil Court since the early 1920's.*

SEND FOR A FREE COPY OF OUR LATEST ILLUSTRATED LIST

---

# We specialise in the LINE ENGRAVED

# 1d RED

We have good stocks of **IMPERFS, PERFS** + **PLATES** both **UNPLATED** and **PLATED** including the **RARER PLATES** 175, 176 and 177 **IMPERF** with R.P.S. certificates as well as The **GARDNER HILL** collection of the First Perforated issue and **INVERTED WMKS** from the whole range

# ERIC PAUL

**Stephens Buildings, 62 Market St., Manchester M1 1PW. Tel. No. 061–427 2101**

*If you share our interest contact us either by POST or TELEPHONE*

Members: P.T.S., B.P.F., M + D.P.T.A., G.B.P.S.

---

# THINKING OF SELLING?

★ WE URGENTLY REQUIRE COLLECTIONS, STOCKS, AND GOOD SINGLE ITEMS
★ BEST PRICES PAID ★ PRIVATE TREATY SALES FACILITIES ★ HOME VISITS CAN BE ARRANGED
★ WRITE, OR PHONE FOR IMMEDIATE ATTENTION

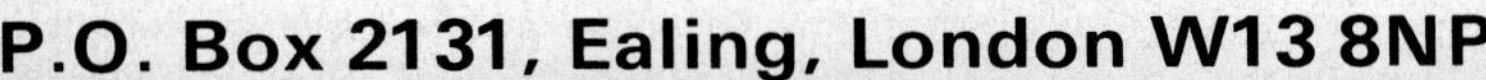
P.O. Box 2131, Ealing, London W13 8NP

TEL: 081–991 1872
FAX: 081–566 7997

## KEY TO SURFACE-PRINTED ISSUES 1855–83

| *S.G. Nos.* | *Description* | *Watermark* | *Date of Issue* |
|---|---|---|---|
| | **NO CORNER LETTERS** | | |
| 62 | 4d. carmine | Small Garter | 31.7.55 |
| 63/5 | 4d. carmine | Medium Garter | 25.2.56 |
| 66/*a* | 4d. carmine | Large Garter | Jan 1857 |
| 69/70 | 6d. lilac | Emblems | 21.10.56 |
| 71/3 | 1s. green | Emblems | 1.11.56 |
| | **SMALL WHITE CORNER LETTERS** | | |
| 75/7 | 3d. carmine | Emblems | 1.5.62 |
| 78 | 3d. carmine (dots) | Emblems | Aug 1862 |
| 79/82 | 4d. red | Large Garter | 15.1.62 |
| 83/5 | 6d. lilac | Emblems | 1.12.62 |
| 86/8 | 9d. bistre | Emblems | 15.1.62 |
| 89/91 | 1s. green | Emblems | 1.12.62 |
| | **LARGE WHITE CORNER LETTERS** | | |
| 92 | 3d. rose | Emblems | 1.3.65 |
| 102/3 | 3d. rose | Spray | July 1867 |
| 93/5 | 4d. vermilion | Large Garter | 4.7.65 |
| 96/7 | 6d. lilac | Emblems | 7.3.65 |
| 104/7 | 6d. lilac | Spray | 21.6.67 |
| 108/9 | 6d. lilac | Spray | 8.3.69 |
| 122/4 | 6d. chestnut | Spray | 12.4.72 |
| 125 | 6d. grey | Spray | 24.4.73 |
| 98 | 9d. straw | Emblems | 30.10.65 |
| 110/11 | 9d. straw | Spray | 3.10.67 |
| 99 | 10d. brown | Emblems | 11.11.67 |
| 112/14 | 10d. brown | Spray | 1.7.67 |
| 101 | 1s. green | Emblems | Feb 1865 |
| 115/17 | 1s. green | Spray | 13.7.67 |
| 118/20*b* | 2s. blue | Spray | 1.7.67 |
| 121 | 2s. brown | Spray | 27.2.80 |
| 126/7 | 5s. rose | Cross | 1.7.67 |
| 128 | 10s. grey | Cross | 26.9.78 |
| 129 | £1 brown-lilac | Cross | 26.9.78 |
| 130, 134 | 5s. rose | Anchor | 25.11.82 |
| 131, 135 | 10s. grey-green | Anchor | Feb 1883 |
| 132, 136 | £1 brown-lilac | Anchor | Dec 1882 |
| 133, 137 | £5 orange | Anchor | 21.3.82 |
| | **LARGE COLOURED CORNER LETTERS** | | |
| 166 | 1d. Venetian red | Crown | 1.1.80 |
| 138/9 | 2½d. rosy mauve | Anchor | 1.7.75 |
| 141 | 2½d. rosy mauve | Orb | 1.5.76 |
| 142 | 2½d. blue | Orb | 5.2.80 |
| 157 | 2½d. blue | Crown | 23.3.81 |
| 143/4 | 3d. rose | Spray | 5.7.73 |
| 158 | 3d. rose | Crown | Jan 1881 |
| 159 | 3d. on 3d. lilac | Crown | 1.1.83 |
| 152 | 4d. vermilion | Large Garter | 1.3.76 |
| 153 | 4d. sage-green | Large Garter | 12.3.77 |
| 154 | 4d. brown | Large Garter | 15.8.80 |
| 160 | 4d. brown | Crown | 9.12.80 |
| 145 | 6d. buff | Spray | 15.3.73 |
| 146/7 | 6d. grey | Spray | 20.3.74 |
| 161 | 6d. grey | Crown | 1.1.81 |
| 162 | 6d. on 6d. lilac | Crown | 1.1.83 |
| 156*a* | 8d. purple-brown | Large Garter | July 1876 |
| 156 | 8d. orange | Large Garter | 11.9.76 |
| 148/50 | 1s. green | Spray | 1.9.73 |
| 151 | 1s. brown | Spray | 14.10.80 |
| 163 | 1s. brown | Crown | 29.5.81 |

| *Watermarks:* | | |
|---|---|---|
| | Anchor | W **40, 47** |
| | Cross | W **39** |
| | Crown | W **49** |
| | Emblems | W **20** |
| | Large Garter | W **17** |
| | Medium Garter | W **16** |
| | Orb | W **48** |
| | Small Garter | W **15** |
| | Spray | W **33** |

**14**

**15** Small Garter

**16** Medium Garter

**17** Large Garter

**1855–57.** *No corner letters.*

(*a*) *Wmk Small Garter, W* **15**. *Highly glazed, deeply blued paper* (31 July 1855)

| | | | Un | ★ Used | Used on cover |
|---|---|---|---|---|---|
| 62 | **14** | 4d. carmine (*shades*) | £2250 | £170 | £275 |
| | | a. Paper slightly blued | £2500 | £160 | |
| | | b. White paper | £3000 | £350 | |

(*b*) *Wmk Medium Garter, W* **16**

(i) *Thick, blued highly glazed paper* (25 February 1856)

| | | | | | |
|---|---|---|---|---|---|
| 63 | **14** | 4d. carmine (*shades*) | £2750 | £160 | £250 |
| | | a. White paper | £2500 | | |

(ii) *Ordinary thin white paper* (September 1856)

| | | | | | |
|---|---|---|---|---|---|
| 64 | **14** | 4d. pale carmine | £1800 | £150 | £225 |
| | | a. Stamp printed double | † | — | |

(iii) *Ordinary white paper, specially prepared ink* (1 November 1856)

| | | | | | |
|---|---|---|---|---|---|
| 65 | **14** | 4d. rose *or* deep rose | £1800 | £160 | £250 |

(*c*) *Wmk Large Garter, W* **17**. *Ordinary white paper* (January 1857)

| | | | | | |
|---|---|---|---|---|---|
| 66 | **14** | 4d. rose-carmine | £700 | 38·00 | 70·00 |
| | | *a. Rose* | £600 | 38·00 | |
| | | b. Thick glazed paper | £1700 | 90·00 | |

★62/6b **For well-centred, lightly used** .. **+125%**

**18**

**19**

**20** Emblems wmk (normal)

**20*a*** Wmk error, three roses and shamrock

**20*b*** Wmk error, three roses and thistle

(*d*) *Wmk Emblems, W* **20**

| | | | Un | ★ Used | Used on cover |
|---|---|---|---|---|---|
| 69 | **18** | 6d. deep lilac (21.10.56) | £550 | 55·00 | |
| 70 | | 6d. pale lilac | £500 | 40·00 | 75·00 |
| | | a. Azure paper | £2500 | £350 | |
| | | b. Thick paper | £750 | £125 | |
| | | c. Error. Wmk W **20*a*** | | | |
| 71 | **19** | 1s. deep green (1.11.56) | £1200 | £150 | |
| 72 | | 1s. green | £650 | £140 | £160 |
| 73 | | 1s. pale green | £650 | £140 | |
| | | a. Azure paper | — | £500 | |
| | | b. Thick paper | — | £160 | |
| | | c. Imperf | | | |

★69/73b **For well-centred, lightly used** .. **+125%**

**21**

**22**

**23**

**24**

**25** Plate 2

A. White dots added

B. Hair lines

**1862–64.** *A small uncoloured letter in each corner, the 4d. wmk Large Garter. W* **17**, *the others Emblems, W* **20**.

| | | | Un | ★ Used | Used on cover |
|---|---|---|---|---|---|
| 75 | **21** | 3d. deep carmine-rose (Plate 2) (1.5.62) | £1100 | £130 | |
| 76 | | 3d. bright carmine-rose | £700 | £110 | £225 |
| 77 | | 3d. pale carmine-rose | £700 | £100 | |
| | | b. Thick paper | — | £160 | |
| 78 | | 3d. rose (with white dots, Type A, Plate 3) (8.62) | * | £2500 | |
| | | a. Imperf (Plate 3) | £2000 | | |
| 79 | **22** | 4d. bright red (Plate 3) (15.1.62) | £750 | 50·00 | |
| 80 | | 4d. pale red | £500 | 35·00 | 85·00 |
| 81 | | 4d. bright red (Hair lines, Type B, Plate 4) (16.10.63) | £650 | 38·00 | |
| 82 | | 4d. pale red (Hair lines, Type B, Plate 4) | £550 | 28·00 | 75·00 |
| | | a. Imperf (Plate 4) | £1500 | | |
| 83 | **23** | 6d. deep lilac (Plate 3) (1.12.62) | £750 | 50·00 | |
| 84 | | 6d. lilac | £650 | 30·00 | 65·00 |
| | | a. Azure paper | — | £300 | |
| | | b. Thick paper | — | 65·00 | |
| | | c. Error. Wmk W **20*b*** (stamp TF) | | | |
| 85 | | 6d. lilac (Hair lines, Plate 4) (20.4.64) | £800 | 50·00 | £120 |
| | | a. Imperf | £1100 | | |
| | | c. Thick paper | £1200 | 80·00 | |
| 86 | **24** | 9d. bistre (Plate 2) (15.1.62) | £1100 | £140 | £250 |
| 87 | | 9d. straw | £1100 | £130 | |
| | | a. On azure paper | | | |
| | | b. Thick paper | £1700 | £175 | |
| 88 | | 9d. bistre (Hair lines, Plate 3) (5.62) | £6000 | £1800 | |
| 89 | **25** | 1s. deep green (Plate No. 1 = Plate 2) (1.12.62) | £800 | £110 | |
| 90 | | 1s. green (Plate No. 1 = Plate 2) | £700 | 65·00 | £130 |
| | | a. "K" in lower left corner in white circle (stamp KD) | £4250 | £500 | |
| | | aa. "K" normal (stamp KD) | — | £750 | |
| | | b. On azure paper | | | |
| | | c. Thick paper | — | £160 | |
| | | ca. Thick paper, "K" in circle as No. 90a | — | £1000 | |
| 91 | | 1s. deep green (Plate No. 2 = Plate 3) | £11000 | * | |
| | | a. Imperf | £1500 | | |

★75/91 **For well-centred, lightly used** .. **+125%**

The 3d. as Type **21**, but with network background in the spandrels which is found overprinted SPECIMEN, was never issued.

The plates of this issue may be distinguished as follows:

3d. Plate 2. No white dots.
 Plate 3. White dots as Illustration A.
4d. Plate 3. No hair lines. Roman I next to lower corner letters.
 Plate 4. Hair lines in corners. (Illustration B.). Roman II.
6d. Plate 3. No hair lines.
 Plate 4. Hair lines in corners.
9d. Plate 2. No hair lines.
 Plate 3. Hair lines in corners. Beware of faked lines.
1s. Plate 2. Numbered 1 on stamps.
 Plate 3. Numbered 2 on stamps and with hair lines.

The 9d. on azure paper (No. 87a) is very rare, only one confirmed example being known.

The variety "K" in circle, No. 90a, is believed to be due to a damaged letter having been cut out and replaced. It is probable that the punch was driven in too deeply, causing the flange to penetrate the surface, producing an indentation showing as an uncoloured circle.

The watermark variety "three roses and a shamrock" illustrated in W **20*a*** was evidently due to the substitution of an extra rose for the thistle in a faulty watermark bit. It is found on stamp T A of Plates 2 and 4 of the 3d., Plates 1 (No. 70c), 3, 5 and 6 of the 6d., Plate 4 of the 9d. and Plate 4 of the 1s.

A similar variety, W **20*b***, but showing three roses and a thistle is found on stamp T F of the 6d. (No. 84) and 9d. (No. 98).

**26**

**27**

**28** (with hyphen)

**28*a*** (without hyphen)

**29**

**30**

**31**

**1865–67.** *Large uncoloured corner letters. Wmk Large Garter* (4*d.*); *others Emblems.*

| | | | Un | ★ Used | Used on cover |
|---|---|---|---|---|---|
| 92 | **26** | 3d. rose (Plate 4) (1.3.65) | £375 | 40·00 | 95·00 |
| | | a. Error. Wmk W **20*a*** | £900 | £275 | |
| | | b. Thick paper | £500 | 50·00 | |
| 93 | **27** | 4d. dull vermilion (4.7.65) | £225 | 15·00 | 35·00 |
| 94 | | 4d. vermilion | £225 | 15·00 | |
| | | a. Imperf (Plates 11, 12) | £500 | | |
| 95 | | 4d. deep vermilion | £225 | 20·00 | |
| | | *Plate* | | | |
| | | 7 (1865) | £300 | 19·00 | |
| | | 8 (1866) | £250 | 19·00 | |
| | | 9 (1867) | £250 | 15·00 | |
| | | 10 (1868) | £300 | 30·00 | |
| | | 11 (1869) | £250 | 15·00 | |
| | | 12 (1870) | £225 | 15·00 | |
| | | 13 (1872) | £250 | 17·00 | |
| | | 14 (1873) | £300 | 35·00 | |
| 96 | **28** | 6d. deep lilac (with hyphen) (7.3.65) | £400 | 38·00 | |
| 97 | | 6d. lilac (with hyphen) | £350 | 28·00 | 65·00 |
| | | a. Thick paper | £450 | 50·00 | |
| | | b. Stamp doubly printed (Plate 6) | — | £4000 | |
| | | c. Error. Wmk W **20*a*** (Pl 5, 6) .. *from* | — | £300 | |
| | | *Plate* | | | |
| | | 5 (1865) | £350 | 28·00 | |
| | | 6 (1867) | £1000 | 55·00 | |

| No. | Type | Description | Un | Used | Used on cover |
|---|---|---|---|---|---|
| 98 | 29 | 9d. straw (Plate 4) (30.10.65) | £700 | £200 | £300 |
| | | a. Thick paper | £950 | £325 | |
| | | b. Error. Wmk W **20a** | — | £375 | |
| | | c. Error. Wmk W **20b** (stamp T F) | | | |
| 99 | 30 | 10d. red-brown (Plate 1) (11.11.67) | † | £12000 | |
| 101 | 31 | 1s. green (Plate 4) (26.1.65) | £650 | 65·00 | £110 |
| | | a. Error. Wmk W **20a** | — | £350 | |
| | | b. Thick paper | £750 | £120 | |
| | | c. Imperf between (vert pair) | — | £4000 | |

★92/101c **For well-centred, lightly used** .. +100%

From mid-1866 to about the end of 1871 4d. stamps of this issue appeared generally with watermark inverted.

Unused examples of No. 98 from Plate 5 exist, but this was never put to press and all evidence points to the existing stamps being from a portion of the Imprimatur sheet which was perforated by De La Rue in 1887 for insertion in albums to be presented to members of the Stamp Committee (*Price* £10000 *un*).

The 10d. stamps, No. 99, were printed in *error* on paper watermarked "Emblems" instead of on "Spray of Rose".

**32**   **33** Spray of Rose   **34**

**1867–80.** *Wmk Spray of Rose, W* **33**.

| No. | Type | Description | Un | Used | ★ Used on cover |
|---|---|---|---|---|---|
| 102 | 26 | 3d. deep rose (12.7.67) | £225 | 18·00 | |
| 103 | | 3d. rose | £200 | 12·00 | 38·00 |
| | | a. Imperf (Plates 5, 6, 8) *from* | £700 | | |
| | | *Plate* | | | |
| | | 4 (1867) | £300 | 50·00 | |
| | | 5 (1868) | £200 | 14·00 | |
| | | 6 (1870) | £225 | 12·00 | |
| | | 7 (1871) | £275 | 15·00 | |
| | | 8 (1872) | £250 | 14·00 | |
| | | 9 (1872) | £250 | 20·00 | |
| | | 10 (1873) | £275 | 42·00 | |
| 104 | 28 | 6d. lilac (with hyphen) (Plate 6) (21.6.67) | £550 | 30·00 | 90·00 |
| | | a. Imperf | | | |
| 105 | | 6d. deep lilac (with hyphen) (Plate 6) | £550 | 30·00 | |
| 106 | | 6d. purple (with hyphen) (Pl 6) | £550 | 45·00 | |
| 107 | | 6d. bright violet (with hyphen) (Plate 6) (22.7.68) | £550 | 32·00 | |
| 108 | 28a | 6d. dull violet (without hyphen) (Plate 8) (18.3.69) | £325 | 25·00 | |
| 109 | | 6d. mauve (without hyphen) | £275 | 25·00 | 55·00 |
| | | a. Imperf (Plate Nos. 8 and 9) | £750 | £650 | |
| | | *Plate* | | | |
| | | 8 (1869, mauve) | £275 | 25·00 | |
| | | 9 (1870, mauve) | £275 | 25·00 | |
| | | 10 (1869, mauve) | * | £12000 | |
| 110 | 29 | 9d. straw (Plate No. 4) (3.10.67) | £600 | £100 | £200 |
| 111 | | 9d. pale straw (Plate No. 4) | £600 | £100 | |
| | | a. Imperf (Plate 4) | £1900 | | |
| 112 | 30 | 10d. red-brown (1.7.67) | £1000 | £130 | £325 |
| 113 | | 10d. pale red-brown | £1000 | £140 | |
| 114 | | 10d. deep red-brown | £1200 | £160 | |
| | | a. Imperf (Plate 1) | £1800 | | |
| | | *Plate* | | | |
| | | 1 (1867) | £1000 | £130 | |
| | | 2 (1867) | £12000 | £2500 | |
| 115 | 31 | 1s. deep green (13.7.67) | £425 | 10·00 | |
| 117 | | 1s. green | £350 | 10·00 | 20·00 |
| | | a. Imperf between (horiz pair) (Plate 7) | | | |
| | | b. Imperf (Plate 4) | £1000 | £600 | |
| | | *Plate* | | | |
| | | 4 (1867) | £350 | 15·00 | |
| | | 5 (1871) | £400 | 12·00 | |
| | | 6 (1872) | £550 | 10·00 | |
| | | 7 (1873) | £550 | 30·00 | |
| 118 | 32 | 2s. dull blue (1.7.67) | £950 | 60·00 | £325 |
| 119 | | 2s. deep blue | £950 | 60·00 | |
| | | a. Imperf (Plate 1) | £1800 | | |
| 120 | | 2s. pale blue | £1500 | 95·00 | |
| | | aa. Imperf (Plate 1) | £1800 | | |
| 120a | | 2s. cobalt | £5000 | £900 | |
| 120b | | 2s. milky blue | £3000 | £400 | |
| | | *Plate* | | | |
| | | 1 (1867) | £950 | 60·00 | |
| | | 3 (1868) | * | £3000 | |
| 121 | | 2s. brown (Plate No. 1) (27.2.80) | £6000 | £1000 | |
| | | a. Imperf | £4000 | | |
| | | b. No watermark | † | — | |

★102/21 **For well-centred, lightly used** .. +75%

Examples of the 1s. from Plates 5 and 6 *without* watermark are postal forgeries used at the Stock Exchange Post Office in the early 1870's.

**1872–73.** *Uncoloured letters in corners. Wmk Spray, W* **33**.

| No. | Type | Description | Un | Used | ★ Used on cover |
|---|---|---|---|---|---|
| 122 | 34 | 6d. deep chestnut (12.4.72) | £425 | 18·00 | 50·00 |
| 123 | | 6d. chestnut (22.5.72) | £350 | 18·00 | |
| 123a | | 6d. pale chestnut (1872) | * | £1300 | |
| 124 | | 6d. pale buff (25.10.72) | £400 | 30·00 | £130 |
| | | *Plate* | | | |
| | | 11 (1872, deep chestnut) | £425 | 18·00 | |
| | | 11 (1872, chestnut) | £350 | 18·00 | |
| | | 11 (1872, pale buff) | £400 | 30·00 | |
| | | 12 (1872 pale chestnut) | * | £1300 | |
| | | 12 (1872 chestnut) | * | £1300 | |
| | | 12 (1872 pale buff) | £750 | 50·00 | |
| 125 | | 6d. grey (Plate No. 12) (24.4.73) | £600 | 75·00 | £130 |
| | | a. Imperf. | £1300 | | |

★122/5 **For well-centred, lightly used** .. +50%

**35**

**36**

**37**

**38**

**39** Maltese Cross

**40** Large Anchor

**1867–83.** *Uncoloured letters in corners.*

(*a*) *Wmk Maltese Cross, W* **39**. *P* 15½ × 15

| No. | Type | Description | Un | ★ Used |
|---|---|---|---|---|
| 126 | 35 | 5s. rose (1.7.67) | £2500 | £250 |
| 127 | | 5s. pale rose | £2750 | £250 |
| | | a. Imperf (Plate 1) | £4000 | |
| | | *Plate* | | |
| | | 1 (1867) | £2500 | £250 |
| | | 2 (1874) | £3500 | £325 |
| 128 | 36 | 10s. greenish grey (Plate 1) (26.9.78) | £18000 | £850 |
| 129 | 37 | £1 brown-lilac (Plate 1) (26.9.78) | £22000 | £1200 |
| | | (*b*) *Wmk Anchor, W* **40**. *P* 14. (i) *Blued paper* | | |
| 130 | 35 | 5s. rose (Plate 4) (25.11.82) | £5000 | £850 |
| 131 | 36 | 10s. grey-green (Plate 1) (2.83) | £20000 | £1100 |
| 132 | 37 | £1 brown-lilac (Plate 1) (12.82) | £27000 | £2000 |
| 133 | 38 | £5 orange (Plate 1) (21.3.82) | £15000 | £3000 |
| | | (ii) *White paper* | | |
| 134 | 35 | 5s. rose (Plate 4) | £4500 | £850 |
| 135 | 36 | 10s. greenish grey (Plate 1) | £22000 | £1100 |
| 136 | 37 | £1 brown-lilac (Plate 1) | £32000 | £2000 |
| 137 | 38 | £5 orange (Plate 1) | £4250 | £1200 |

★126/37 **For well-centred, lightly used** .. +75%

**41**

**42**

**43**

**44**   **45**

**46**

**47** Small Anchor

**48** Orb

**1873–80.** *Large coloured letters in the corners.*

(*a*) *Wmk Anchor, W* **47**

| No. | Type | Description | Un | Used | ★ Used on cover |
|---|---|---|---|---|---|
| 138 | 41 | 2½d. rosy mauve (*blued paper*) (1.7.75) | £375 | 35·00 | |
| | | a. Imperf | | | |
| 139 | | 2½d. rosy mauve (*white paper*) | £225 | 25·00 | 50·00 |
| | | *Plate* | | | |
| | | 1 (*blued paper*) (1875) | £375 | 35·00 | |
| | | 1 (*white paper*) (1875) | £225 | 25·00 | |
| | | 2 (*blued paper*) (1875) | £3000 | £500 | |
| | | 2 (*white paper*) (1875) | £225 | 25·00 | |
| | | 3 (*white paper*) (1875) | £400 | 30·00 | |
| | | 3 (*blued paper*) (1875) | — | £2250 | |
| | | *Error of Lettering* L H—F L *for* L H—H L (*Plate* 2) | | | |
| 140 | 41 | 2½d. rosy mauve | £7000 | £700 | |
| | | (*b*) *Wmk Orb, W* **48** | | | |
| 141 | 41 | 2½d. rosy mauve (1.5.76) | £225 | 14·00 | 35·00 |
| | | *Plate* | | | |
| | | 3 (1876) | £500 | 30·00 | |
| | | 4 (1876) | £225 | 14·00 | |
| | | 5 (1876) | £225 | 18·00 | |
| | | 6 (1876) | £225 | 14·00 | |
| | | 7 (1877) | £225 | 14·00 | |
| | | 8 (1877) | £225 | 18·00 | |
| | | 9 (1877) | £225 | 14·00 | |
| | | 10 (1878) | £250 | 19·00 | |
| | | 11 (1878) | £225 | 14·00 | |
| | | 12 (1878) | £225 | 18·00 | |
| | | 13 (1878) | £225 | 18·00 | |
| | | 14 (1879) | £225 | 14·00 | |
| | | 15 (1879) | £225 | 14·00 | |
| | | 16 (1879) | £225 | 14·00 | |
| | | 17 (1880) | £550 | 90·00 | |
| 142 | | 2½d. blue (5.2.80) | £180 | 10·00 | 15·00 |
| | | *Plate* | | | |
| | | 17 (1880) | £180 | 20·00 | |
| | | 18 (1880) | £200 | 12·00 | |
| | | 19 (1880) | £180 | 10·00 | |
| | | 20 (1880) | £180 | 10·00 | |
| | | (*c*) *Wmk Spray, W* **33** | | | |
| 143 | 42 | 3d. rose (5.7.73) | £200 | 12·00 | 35·00 |
| 144 | | 3d. pale rose | £200 | 12·00 | |
| | | *Plate* | | | |
| | | 11 (1873) | £200 | 12·00 | |
| | | 12 (1873) | £225 | 14·00 | |
| | | 14 (1874) | £250 | 15·00 | |
| | | 15 (1874) | £200 | 14·00 | |
| | | 16 (1875) | £200 | 14·00 | |
| | | 17 (1875) | £225 | 14·00 | |
| | | 18 (1875) | £225 | 14·00 | |
| | | 19 (1876) | £200 | 14·00 | |
| | | 20 (1879) | £200 | 30·00 | |
| 145 | 43 | 6d. pale buff (Plate 13) (15.3.73) | * | £4500 | |
| 146 | | 6d. deep grey (20.3.74) | £225 | 20·00 | 40·00 |
| 147 | | 6d. grey | £225 | 20·00 | |
| | | *Plate* | | | |
| | | 13 (1874) | £225 | 22·00 | |
| | | 14 (1875) | £225 | 22·00 | |
| | | 15 (1876) | £225 | 20·00 | |
| | | 16 (1878) | £225 | 20·00 | |
| | | 17 (1880) | £300 | 38·00 | |
| 148 | 44 | 1s. deep green (1.9.73) | £325 | 35·00 | |
| 150 | | 1s. pale green | £250 | 28·00 | 50·00 |
| | | *Plate* | | | |
| | | 8 (1873) | £325 | 35·00 | |
| | | 9 (1874) | £325 | 35·00 | |
| | | 10 (1874) | £300 | 35·00 | |
| | | 11 (1875) | £300 | 35·00 | |
| | | 12 (1875) | £250 | 28·00 | |
| | | 13 (1876) | £250 | 28·00 | |
| | | 14 (—) | * | £10000 | |
| 151 | | 1s. orange-brown (Plate 13) (14.10.80) | £1100 | £170 | £275 |
| | | (*d*) *Wmk Large Garter, W* **17** | | | |
| 152 | 45 | 4d. vermilion (1.3.76) | £600 | £140 | £275 |
| | | *Plate* | | | |
| | | 15 (1876) | £600 | £140 | |
| | | 16 (1877) | * | £10000 | |
| 153 | | 4d. sage-green (12.3.77) | £400 | 85·00 | £180 |
| | | *Plate* | | | |
| | | 15 (1877) | £450 | 90·00 | |
| | | 16 (1877) | £400 | 85·00 | |
| | | 17 (1877) | * | £6000 | |
| 154 | | 4d. grey-brown (Plate 17) (15.8.80) | £600 | £140 | £225 |
| | | a. Imperf | £2000 | | |
| 156 | 46 | 8d. orange (Plate 1) (11.9.76) | £550 | £110 | £200 |

★138/56 **For well-centred, lightly used** .. +100%

**1876** (July). *Prepared for use but not issued.*

| No. | Type | Description | Un |
|---|---|---|---|
| 156a | 46 | 8d. purple-brown (Plate 1) | £3000 |

**49** Imperial Crown

3d ..
**(50)**

**1880–83.** *Wmk Imperial Crown, W* **49**.

| No. | Type | Description | Un | Used | ★ Used on cover |
|---|---|---|---|---|---|
| 157 | 41 | 2½d. blue (23.3.81) | £180 | 8·00 | 20·00 |
| | | *Plate* | | | |
| | | 21 (1881) | £225 | 9·00 | |
| | | 22 (1881) | £180 | 8·00 | |
| | | 23 (1881) | £180 | 8·00 | |
| 158 | 42 | 3d. rose (3.81) | £200 | 30·00 | 38·00 |
| | | *Plate* | | | |
| | | 20 (1881) | £250 | 45·00 | |
| | | 21 (1881) | £200 | 30·00 | |

PTS

Stanley Gibbons
Great Britain
Queen Victoria
Great Britain
King Edward VII to King George VI
Great Britain
Queen Elizabeth Pre-decimal Issues
Great Britain
Elizabeth II Definitive Issues
Great Britain
Queen Elizabeth II Decimal Special Issues

| No. | Type | Description | Un | Used | Used on cover |
|---|---|---|---|---|---|
| 159 | **42** | 3d. on 3d. lilac (T **50**) (C.) (Plate 21) (1.1.83) | £225 | 70·00 | £225 |
| 160 | **45** | 4d. grey-brown (8.12.80) | £180 | 25·00 | 70·00 |
| | | *Plate* | | | |
| | | 17 (1880) | £180 | 25·00 | |
| | | 18 (1882) | £180 | 25·00 | |
| 161 | **43** | 6d. grey (1.1.81) | £150 | 22·00 | 45·00 |
| | | *Plate* | | | |
| | | 17 (1881) | £180 | 22·00 | |
| | | 18 (1882) | £150 | 22·00 | |
| 162 | | 6d. on 6d. lilac (as T **50**) (C.) (Plate 18) (1.1.83) | £200 | 65·00 | £140 |
| | | a. Slanting dots (various) *from* | £250 | 80·00 | |
| | | b. Opt double | — | £4000 | |
| 163 | **44** | 1s. orange-brown (29.5.81) | £225 | 45·00 | 90·00 |
| | | *Plate* | | | |
| | | 13 (1881) | £275 | 45·00 | |
| | | 14 (1881) | £225 | 45·00 | |
| ★157/63 | | **For well-centred, lightly used** | | +75% | |

The 1s. Plate 14 (line perf 14) exists in purple, but was not issued in this shade (*Price £2500 unused*). Examples were included in a few of the Souvenir Albums prepared for members of the "Stamp Committee of 1884".

52

53

54

55

56

**1880–81.** *Wmk Imperial Crown, W* **49**.

| No. | Type | Description | Un | ★ Used | Used on cover |
|---|---|---|---|---|---|
| 164 | **52** | ½d. deep green (14.10.80) | 15·00 | 3·00 | 6·00 |
| | | a. Imperf | £600 | | |
| 165 | | ½d. pale green | 17·00 | 5·00 | |
| 166 | **53** | 1d. Venetian red (1.1.80) | 5·00 | 2·00 | 4·00 |
| | | a. Imperf | £600 | | |
| 167 | **54** | 1½d. Venetian red (14.10.80) | 80·00 | 14·00 | 60·00 |
| 168 | **55** | 2d. pale rose (8.12.80) | 95·00 | 30·00 | 60·00 |
| 168*a* | | 2d. deep rose | 95·00 | 30·00 | |
| 169 | **56** | 5d. indigo (15.3.81) | £350 | 40·00 | £125 |
| | | a. Imperf | £1100 | | |
| ★164/9 | | **For well-centred, lightly used** | | +75% | |

Die I

57

Die II

**1881.** *Wmk Imperial Crown, W* **49**. (*a*) 14 *dots in each corner, Die* I (12 July).

| No. | Type | Description | Un | ★ Used | Used on cover |
|---|---|---|---|---|---|
| 170 | **57** | 1d. lilac | 75·00 | 12·00 | 20·00 |
| 171 | | 1d. pale lilac | 75·00 | 12·00 | |
| | | (*b*) 16 *dots in each corner, Die* II (12 December) | | | |
| 172 | **57** | 1d. lilac | 1·00 | 40 | 1·10 |
| 172*a* | | 1d. bluish lilac | £180 | 45·00 | |
| 173 | | 1d. deep purple | 1·00 | 30 | |
| | | a. Printed both sides | £400 | † | |
| | | b. Frame broken at bottom | £475 | £180 | |
| | | c. Printed on gummed side | £375 | † | |
| | | d. Imperf three sides (pair) | £1800 | † | |
| | | e. Printed both sides but impression on back inverted | £400 | † | |
| | | f. No watermark | £250 | † | |
| | | g. Blued paper | £1500 | | |
| 174 | | 1d. mauve | 1·00 | 40 | |
| | | a. Imperf (pair) | £900 | | |
| ★170/4 | | **For well-centred, lightly used** | | +50% | |

1d. stamps with the words "PEARS SOAP" printed on back in *orange, blue* or *mauve* price *from* £300, *unused*.

The variety "frame broken at bottom" (No. 173b) shows a white space just inside the bottom frame-line from between the "N" and "E" of "ONE" to below the first "N" of "PENNY", breaking the pearls and cutting into the lower part of the oval below "PEN".

## MINIMUM PRICE

The minimum price quote is 10p which represents a handling charge rather than a basis for valuing common stamps. For further notes about prices see introductory pages.

## KEY TO SURFACE-PRINTED ISSUES 1880–1900

| *S.G. Nos.* | *Description* | *Date of Issue* |
|---|---|---|
| 164/5 | ½d. green | 14.10.80 |
| 187 | ½d. slate-blue | 1.4.84 |
| 197/d | ½d. vermilion | 1.1.87 |
| 213 | ½d. blue-green | 17.4.1900 |
| 166 | 1d. Venetian red | 1.1.80 |
| 170/1 | 1d. lilac, Die I | 12.7.81 |
| 172/4 | 1d. lilac, Die II | 12.12.81 |
| 167 | 1½d. Venetian red | 14.10.80 |
| 188 | 1½d. lilac | 1.4.84 |
| 198 | 1½d. purple and green | 1.1.87 |
| 168/*a* | 2d. rose | 8.12.80 |
| 189 | 2d. lilac | 1.4.84 |
| 199/200 | 2d. green and red | 1.1.87 |
| 190 | 2½d. lilac | 1.4.84 |
| 201 | 2½d. purple on blue paper | 1.1.87 |
| 191 | 3d. lilac | 1.4.84 |
| 202/4 | 3d. purple on yellow paper | 1.1.87 |
| 192 | 4d. dull green | 1.4.84 |
| 205/*a* | 4d. green and brown | 1.1.87 |
| 206 | 4½d. green and carmine | 15.9.92 |
| 169 | 5d. indigo | 15.3.81 |
| 193 | 5d. dull green | 1.4.84 |
| 207 | 5d. purple and blue, Die I | 1.1.87 |
| 207*a* | 5d. purple and blue, Die II | — |
| 194 | 6d. dull green | 1.4.84 |
| 208/*a* | 6d. purple on rose-red paper | 1.1.87 |
| 195 | 9d. dull green | 1.8.83 |
| 209 | 9d. purple and blue | 1.1.87 |
| 210 | 10d. purple and carmine | 24.2.90 |
| 196 | 1s. dull green | 1.4.84 |
| 211 | 1s. green | 1.1.87 |
| 214 | 1s. green and carmine | 11.7.1900 |
| 175 | 2s. 6d. lilac on blued paper | 2.7.83 |
| 178/9 | 2s. 6d. lilac | 1884 |
| 176 | 5s. rose on blued paper | 1.4.84 |
| 180/1 | 5s. rose | 1884 |
| 177/*a* | 10s. ultramarine on blued paper | 1.4.84 |
| 182/3*a* | 10s. ultramarine | 1884 |
| 185 | £1 brown-lilac, wmk Crowns | 1.4.84 |
| 186 | £1 brown-lilac, wmk Orbs | 1.2.88 |
| 212 | £1 green | 27.1.91 |

Note that the £5 value used with the above series is listed as Nos. 133 and 137.

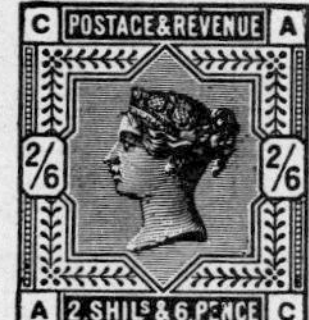
58

59

60

**1883–84.** *Coloured letters in the corners. Wmk Anchor, W* **40**.

| No. | Type | Description | Un | ★ Used |
|---|---|---|---|---|
| | | (*a*) *Blued paper* | | |
| 175 | **58** | 2s. 6d. lilac (2.7.83) | £2000 | £475 |
| 176 | **59** | 5s. rose (1.4.84) | £3500 | £950 |
| 177 | **60** | 10s. ultramarine (1.4.84) | £12000 | £2000 |
| 177*a* | | 10s. cobalt (5.84) | £14000 | £3750 |
| | | (*b*) *White paper* | | |
| 178 | **58** | 2s. 6d. lilac | £200 | 60·00 |
| 179 | | 2s. 6d. deep lilac | £200 | 60·00 |
| | | a. Deep lilac, blued paper | £1600 | £475 |
| 180 | **59** | 5s. rose | £400 | 75·00 |
| 181 | | 5s. crimson | £400 | 75·00 |
| 182 | **60** | 10s. cobalt | £13000 | £3250 |
| 183 | | 10s. ultramarine | £750 | £225 |
| 183*a* | | 10s. pale ultramarine | £750 | £225 |
| ★175/83*a* | | **For well-centred, lightly used** | | +50% |

For No. 180 perf 12 *see* second note below No. 196.

61

Broken frames, Plate 2

**1884** (1 April). *Wmk Three Imperial Crowns, W* **49**.

| No. | Type | Description | Un | ★ Used |
|---|---|---|---|---|
| 185 | **61** | £1 brown-lilac | £10000 | £850 |
| | | a. Frame broken | £17500 | £1500 |

**1888** (1 Feb). *Wmk Three Orbs, W* **48**.

| No. | Type | Description | Un | Used |
|---|---|---|---|---|
| 186 | **61** | £1 brown-lilac | £16000 | £1300 |
| | | a. Frame broken | £25000 | £2250 |
| ★185/6a | | **For well-centred, lightly used** | | +50% |

The broken-frame varieties, Nos. 185a and 186a, are on Plate 2 stamps JC and TA, as illustrated. *See also* No. 212a.

62

63

64

65

66

**1883** (1 Aug) (9*d.*) or **1884** (1 April) (*others*). *Wmk Imperial Crown, W* **49** (*sideways on horiz designs*).

| No. | Type | Description | Un | ★ Used | Used on cover |
|---|---|---|---|---|---|
| 187 | **52** | ½d. slate-blue | 8·00 | 1·50 | 5·00 |
| | | a. Imperf | £450 | | |
| 188 | **62** | 1½d. lilac | 55·00 | 18·00 | 55·00 |
| | | a. Imperf | £450 | | |
| 189 | **63** | 2d. lilac | 70·00 | 30·00 | 60·00 |
| | | a. Imperf | £500 | | |
| 190 | **64** | 2½d. lilac | 40·00 | 5·00 | 12·00 |
| | | a. Imperf | £500 | | |
| 191 | **65** | 3d. lilac | 90·00 | 40·00 | 60·00 |
| | | a. Imperf | £500 | | |
| 192 | **66** | 4d. dull green | £225 | 90·00 | £130 |
| | | a. Imperf | £550 | | |
| 193 | **62** | 5d. dull green | £225 | 90·00 | £120 |
| | | a. Imperf | £550 | | |
| 194 | **63** | 6d. dull green | £250 | 95·00 | £140 |
| | | a. Imperf | £550 | | |
| 195 | **64** | 9d. dull green (1.8.83) | £475 | £225 | £600 |
| 196 | **65** | 1s. dull green | £350 | £130 | £250 |
| | | a. Imperf | £1200 | | |
| ★187/96 | | **For well-centred, lightly used** | | +100% | |

The above prices are for stamps in the true dull green colour. Stamps which have been soaked, causing the colour to run, are virtually worthless.

Stamps of the above set and No. 180 are also found perf 12; these are official perforations, but were never issued. A second variety of the 5d. is known with a line instead of a stop under the "d" in the value; this was never issued and is therefore only known *unused* (*Price £5000*).

71

72

73

74

75

76

77

78

79

80

81

82

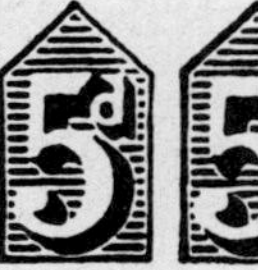

Die I Die II

Die I: Square dots to right of "d".
Die II: Thin vertical lines to right of "d".

**1887** (1 Jan)–**1892.** *"Jubilee" issue. New types. The bicoloured stamps have the value tablets, or the frames including the value tablets, in the second colour. Wmk Imperial Crown, W* **49** *(Three Crowns on £1).*

| | | | Un | Used | ★ Used on cover |
|---|---|---|---|---|---|
| 197 | **71** | ½d. vermilion | 1·00 | 50 | 5·00 |
| | | a. Printed on gummed side | £700 | † | |
| | | b. Printed both sides | | | |
| | | c. Doubly printed | £1800 | | |
| | | d. Imperf | £475 | | |
| 197*e* | | ½d. orange-vermilion | 1·00 | 50 | |
| 198 | **72** | 1½d. dull purple and pale green | 10·00 | 4·00 | 18·00 |
| | | a. Purple part of design double | — | £3000 | |
| 199 | **73** | 2d. green and scarlet | £275 | £130 | |
| 200 | | 2d. grey-green and carmine | 15·00 | 6·00 | 18·00 |
| 201 | **74** | 2½d. purple/*blue* | 10·00 | 75 | 5·00 |
| | | a. Printed on gummed side | — | † | |
| | | b. Imperf three sides | £1200 | | |
| | | c. Imperf | | | |
| 202 | **75** | 3d. purple/*yellow* | 15·00 | 1·50 | 20·00 |
| | | a. Imperf | £3000 | | |
| 203 | | 3d. deep purple/*yellow* | 15·00 | 1·50 | |
| 204 | | 3d. purple/*orange* (1890) | £400 | £130 | |
| 205 | **76** | 4d. green and purple-brown | 18·00 | 7·25 | 18·00 |
| | | aa. Imperf | | | |
| 205*a* | | 4d. green and deep brown | 18·00 | 7·25 | |
| 206 | **77** | 4½d. green & carmine (15.9.92) | 5·00 | 20·00 | 55·00 |
| 206*a* | | 4½d. green & deep brt carmine | £450 | £300 | |
| 207 | **78** | 5d. dull purple & blue (Die I) | £350 | 30·00 | 60·00 |
| 207*a* | | 5d. dull purple & blue (Die II) (1888) | 18·00 | 6·00 | 22·00 |
| 208 | **79** | 6d. purple/*rose-red* | 18·00 | 7·50 | 15·00 |
| 208*a* | | 6d. deep purple/*rose-red* | 18·00 | 7·50 | |
| 209 | **80** | 9d. dull purple and blue | 40·00 | 25·00 | 50·00 |
| 210 | **81** | 10d. dull purple and carmine (*shades*) (24.2.90) | 35·00 | 22·00 | 60·00 |
| | | aa. Imperf | £3250 | | |
| 210*a* | | 10d. dull mauve & deep carmine | £350 | £150 | |
| 210*b* | | 10d. dull purple and dull scarlet | 45·00 | 28·00 | |
| 211 | **82** | 1s. dull green | £130 | 30·00 | 75·00 |
| 212 | **61** | £1 green (28.1.91) | £2000 | £350 | |
| | | a. Frame broken | £4500 | £800 | |
| **★197/212a** | | **For well-centred, lightly used** | **+50%** | | |

The broken-frame varieties, No. 212a, are on Plate 2 stamps JC or TA, as illustrated above No. 185.

½d. stamps with "PEARS SOAP" printed on the back in *orange, blue* or *mauve*, price *from* £300 each.

**1900.** *Colours changed. Wmk Imperial Crown, W* **49**.

| | | | Un | Used | ★ Used on cover |
|---|---|---|---|---|---|
| 213 | **71** | ½d. blue-green (17.4) | 1·00 | 60 | 5·00 |
| | | a. Printed on gummed side | — | † | |
| | | b. Imperf | £1500 | | |
| 214 | **82** | 1s. green and carmine (11.7) | 45·00 | 80·00 | £225 |
| 197/214 | | *Set of* 14 | £325 | £190 | |
| **★213/14** | | **For well-centred, lightly used** | **+50%** | | |

The ½d. No. 213, in bright blue, is a colour changeling.

## KING EDWARD VII
## 22 January 1901–6 May 1910

**PRINTINGS.** Distinguishing De La Rue printings from the provisional printings of the same values made by Harrison & Sons Ltd. or at Somerset House may prove difficult in some cases. For very full guidance Volume 2 of the Stanley Gibbons *Great Britain Specialised Catalogue* should prove helpful.

Note that stamps perforated 15 × 14 must be Harrison; the 2½d., 3d. and 4d. in this perforation are useful reference material, their shades and appearance in most cases matching the Harrison perf 14 printings.

Except for the 6d. value, all stamps on chalk-surfaced paper were printed by De La Rue.

Of the stamps on ordinary paper, the De La Rue impressions are usually clearer and of a higher finish than those of the other printers. The shades are markedly different except in some printings of the 4d., 6d. and 7d. and in the 5s., 10s. and £1.

Used stamps in good, clean, unrubbed condition and with dated postmarks can form the basis of a useful reference collection, the dates often assisting in the assignment to the printers.

**USED STAMPS.** For well-centred, lightly used examples of King Edward VII stamps, add the following percentages to the used prices quoted below:

De La Rue printings (Nos. 215/66)—3d. values +35%, 4d. orange +100%, 6d. +75%, 7d. and 1s. +25%, all other values +50%.

Harrison printings (Nos. 267/86)—all values and perforations +75%

Somerset House printings (Nos. 287/320)—1s. values +25%, all other values +50%.

83

84

85

86

87

88

89

90

91

92

93

94

95

96

97

(Des E. Fuchs)

**1902** (1 Jan)–**10.** *Printed by De La Rue & Co. Wmk Imperial Crown (½d. to 1s.); Anchor (2s. 6d. to 10s.); Three Crowns (£1). Ordinary paper. P 14.*

| | | | Un | Used | Used on cover |
|---|---|---|---|---|---|
| 215 | **83** | ½d. dull blue-green (1.1.02) | 50 | 30 | 60 |
| 216 | | ½d. blue-green | 50 | 30 | |
| 217 | | ½d. pale yellowish green (26.11.04) | 40 | 30 | 30 |
| 218 | | ½d. yellowish green | 40 | 30 | |
| | | a. Booklet pane. Five stamps plus St. Andrew's Cross label (6.06) | £150 | | |
| | | b. Doubly printed (bottom row on one pane) (Control H9) | £9750 | | |
| 219 | | 1d. scarlet (1.1.02) | 40 | 30 | 1·50 |
| 220 | | 1d. bright scarlet | 40 | 30 | |
| | | a. Imperf (pair) | £7500 | | |
| 221 | **84** | 1½d. dull purple & grn (21.3.02) | 12·00 | 6·00 | |
| 222 | | 1½d. slate-purple and green | 12·00 | 4·75 | 12·00 |
| 223 | | 1½d. pale dull pur & grn (*chalk-surfaced paper*) (8.05) | 15·00 | 5·50 | |
| 224 | | 1½d. slate-purple & bluish green (*chalk-surfaced paper*) | 15·00 | 4·25 | |
| 225 | **85** | 2d. yellowish green & carmine-red (25.3.02) | 15·00 | 4·00 | 12·00 |
| 226 | | 2d. grey-green & carmine-red (1904) | 15·00 | 4·00 | |
| 227 | | 2d. pale grey-green & carmine-red (*chalk-surfaced paper*) (4.06) | 15·00 | 6·00 | |
| 228 | | 2d. pale grey-grn & scar (*chalk-surfaced paper*) (1909) | 15·00 | 6·00 | |
| 229 | | 2d. dull bl-grn & carm (*chalk-surfaced paper*) (1907) | 35·00 | 20·00 | |
| 230 | **86** | 2½d. ultramarine (1.1.02) | 4·00 | 2·50 | 10·00 |
| 231 | | 2½d. pale ultramarine | 4·00 | 2·50 | |
| 232 | **87** | 3d. dull pur/*orge-yell* (20.3.02) | 15·00 | 2·50 | 20·00 |
| | | a. Chalk-surfaced paper | 65·00 | 18·00 | |
| 232*b* | | 3d. deep purple/*orange-yellow* | 15·00 | 2·50 | |
| 232*c* | | 3d. pale reddish purple/*orge-yell* (*chalk-surfaced paper*) (3.06) | 60·00 | 15·00 | |
| 233 | | 3d. dull reddish pur/*yell* (*lemon back*) (*chalk-surfaced paper*) | 60·00 | 28·00 | |
| 233*b* | | 3d. pale purple/*lemon* (*chalk-surfaced paper*) | 12·00 | 6·00 | |
| 234 | | 3d. pur/*lemon* (*chalk-surfaced paper*) | 12·00 | 6·00 | |
| 235 | **88** | 4d. green & grey-brn (27.3.02) | 20·00 | 11·00 | |
| 236 | | 4d. green & chocolate-brown | 20·00 | 12·00 | |
| | | a. Chalk-surfaced paper (1.06) | 15·00 | 7·00 | 25·00 |
| 238 | | 4d. dp green & chocolate-brown (*chalk-surfaced paper*) | 15·00 | 8·50 | |
| 239 | | 4d. brown-orange (1.11.09) | 90·00 | 80·00 | |
| 240 | | 4d. pale orange (12.09) | 7·50 | 6·50 | 20·00 |
| 241 | | 4d. orange-red (12.09) | 7·50 | 7·00 | |
| 242 | **89** | 5d. dull purple & ultramarine (14.5.02) | 15·00 | 6·00 | 30·00 |
| | | a. Chalk-surfaced paper (5.06) | 15·00 | 8·00 | |
| 244 | | 5d. slate-purple and ultramarine (*chalk-surfaced paper*) | 15·00 | 8·00 | |

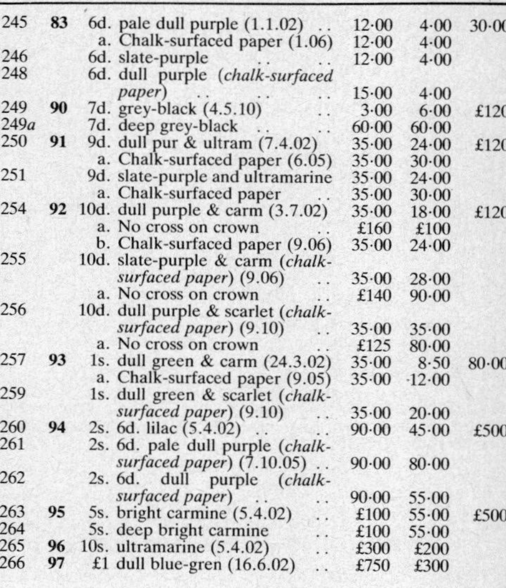

| | | | Un | Used | Used on cover |
|---|---|---|---|---|---|
| 245 | **83** | 6d. pale dull purple (1.1.02) | 12·00 | 4·00 | 30·00 |
| | | a. Chalk-surfaced paper (1.06) | 12·00 | 4·00 | |
| 246 | | 6d. slate-purple | 12·00 | 4·00 | |
| 248 | | 6d. dull purple (*chalk-surfaced paper*) | 15·00 | 4·00 | |
| 249 | **90** | 7d. grey-black (4.5.10) | 3·00 | 6·00 | £120 |
| 249*a* | | 7d. deep grey-black | 60·00 | 60·00 | |
| 250 | **91** | 9d. dull pur & ultram (7.4.02) | 35·00 | 24·00 | £120 |
| | | a. Chalk-surfaced paper (6.05) | 35·00 | 30·00 | |
| 251 | | 9d. slate-purple and ultramarine | 35·00 | 24·00 | |
| | | a. Chalk-surfaced paper | 35·00 | 30·00 | |
| 254 | **92** | 10d. dull purple & carm (3.7.02) | 35·00 | 18·00 | £120 |
| | | a. No cross on crown | £160 | £100 | |
| | | b. Chalk-surfaced paper (9.06) | 35·00 | 24·00 | |
| 255 | | 10d. slate-purple & carm (*chalk-surfaced paper*) (9.06) | 35·00 | 28·00 | |
| | | a. No cross on crown | £140 | 90·00 | |
| 256 | | 10d. dull purple & scarlet (*chalk-surfaced paper*) (9.10) | 35·00 | 35·00 | |
| | | a. No cross on crown | £125 | 80·00 | |
| 257 | **93** | 1s. dull green & carm (24.3.02) | 35·00 | 8·50 | 80·00 |
| | | a. Chalk-surfaced paper (9.05) | 35·00 | 12·00 | |
| 259 | | 1s. dull green & scarlet (*chalk-surfaced paper*) (9.10) | 35·00 | 20·00 | |
| 260 | **94** | 2s. 6d. lilac (5.4.02) | 90·00 | 45·00 | £500 |
| 261 | | 2s. 6d. pale dull purple (*chalk-surfaced paper*) (7.10.05) | 90·00 | 80·00 | |
| 262 | | 2s. 6d. dull purple (*chalk-surfaced paper*) | 90·00 | 55·00 | |
| 263 | **95** | 5s. bright carmine (5.4.02) | £100 | 55·00 | £500 |
| 264 | | 5s. deep bright carmine | £100 | 55·00 | |
| 265 | **96** | 10s. ultramarine (5.4.02) | £300 | £200 | |
| 266 | **97** | £1 dull blue-gren (16.6.02) | £750 | £300 | |

97*a*

**1910** (May). *Prepared for use, but not issued.*

| | | | Un |
|---|---|---|---|
| 266*a* | **97*a*** | 2d. Tyrian plum | £10000 |

One example of this stamp is known used, but it was never issued to the public.

**1911.** *Printed by Harrison & Sons. Ordinary paper. Wmk Imperial Crown. (a) P 14.*

| | | | Un | Used | Used on cover |
|---|---|---|---|---|---|
| 267 | **83** | ½d. dull yellow-green (3.5.11) | 90 | 40 | 3·00 |
| 268 | | ½d. dull green | 1·25 | 40 | |
| 269 | | ½d. deep dull green | 5·00 | 2·00 | |
| 270 | | ½d. pale bluish green | 20·00 | 22·00 | |
| | | a. Booklet pane. Five stamps plus St. Andrew's Cross label | £195 | | |
| | | b. Wmk sideways | — | £10000 | |
| | | c. Imperf (pair) | £9500 | | |
| 271 | | ½d. bright green (fine impression) (6.11) | £150 | £110 | |
| 272 | | 1d. rose-red (3.5.11) | 1·75 | 4·00 | 6·00 |
| | | a. No wmk | 35·00 | 35·00 | |
| 273 | | 1d. deep rose-red | 2·75 | 4·00 | |
| 274 | | 1d. rose-carmine | 25·00 | 9·00 | |
| 275 | | 1d. aniline pink (5.11) | £250 | £110 | |
| 275*a* | | 1d. aniline rose | 80·00 | 75·00 | |
| 276 | **86** | 2½d. bright blue (10.7.11) | 20·00 | 10·00 | 18·00 |
| 277 | **87** | 3d. purple/*lemon* (12.9.11) | 30·00 | £120 | £400 |
| 277*a* | | 3d. grey/*lemon* | £2750 | | |
| 278 | **88** | 4d. bright orange (13.7.11) | 30·00 | 30·00 | £100 |
| | | *(b) P 15 × 14* | | | |
| 279 | **83** | ½d. dull green (30.10.11) | 18·00 | 25·00 | 65·00 |
| 279*a* | | ½d. deep dull green | 20·00 | 20·00 | |
| 280 | | 1d. rose-red (5.10.11) | 15·00 | 10·00 | |
| 281 | | 1d. rose-carmine | 6·50 | 5·00 | 15·00 |
| 282 | | 1d. pale rose-carmine | 8·00 | 3·00 | |
| 283 | **86** | 2½d. bright blue (14.10.11) | 10·00 | 5·00 | 12·00 |
| 284 | | 2½d. dull blue | 10·00 | 5·00 | |
| 285 | **87** | 3d. purple/*lemon* (22.9.11) | 15·00 | 3·50 | 15·00 |
| 285*a* | | 3d. grey/*lemon* | £2250 | | |
| 286 | **88** | 4d. bright orange (11.11.11) | 10·00 | 6·00 | 40·00 |
| 279/86 | | *Set of* 5 | 55·00 | 40·00 | |

**1911–13.** *Printed at Somerset House. Ordinary paper. Wmk as 1902–10. P 14.*

| | | | Un | Used | Used on cover |
|---|---|---|---|---|---|
| 287 | **84** | 1½d. reddish purple and bright green (13.7.11) | 20·00 | 9·50 | |
| 288 | | 1½d. dull purple and green | 10·00 | 6·00 | 30·00 |
| 289 | | 1½d. slate-purple & grn (9.12) | 12·00 | 10·00 | |
| 290 | **85** | 2d. dp dull grn & red (8.8.11) | 10·00 | 4·50 | 30·00 |
| 291 | | 2d. deep dull green & carmine | 10·00 | 4·50 | |
| 292 | | 2d. grey-green & bright carmine (carmine shows clearly on back) (11.3.12) | 10·00 | 6·00 | |
| 293 | **89** | 5d. dull reddish purple and bright blue (7.8.11) | 12·00 | 4·75 | 50·00 |
| 294 | | 5d. deep dull reddish purple and bright blue | 10·00 | 4·75 | |
| 295 | **83** | 6d. royal purple (31.10.11) | 25·00 | 40·00 | |
| 296 | | 6d. bright magenta (*chalk-surfaced paper*) (31.10.11) | £1750 | | |
| 297 | | 6d. dull purple | 12·00 | 6·00 | 60·00 |
| 298 | | 6d. reddish purple (11.11) | 12·00 | 8·00 | |
| | | a. No cross on crown (*various shades*) | £175 | | |
| 299 | | 6d. very dp reddish pur (11.11) | 20·00 | 18·00 | |
| 300 | | 6d. dark purple (3.12) | 15·00 | 15·00 | |
| 301 | | 6d. dull purple ("Dickinson" coated paper*) (3.13) | 95·00 | 80·00 | |
| 303 | | 6d. deep plum (7.13) | 10·00 | 35·00 | |
| | | a. No cross on crown | £200 | | |
| 305 | **90** | 7d. slate-grey (1.8.12) | 4·00 | 8·50 | 85·00 |
| 306 | **91** | 9d. reddish purple and light blue (24.7.11) | 45·00 | 30·00 | |

| No. | Type | Description | Un | Used | |
|---|---|---|---|---|---|
| 306*a* | **91** | 9d. deep dull reddish purple & deep bright blue (9.11) | 45·00 | 32·00 | |
| 307 | | 9d. dull reddish purple and blue (10.11) | 30·00 | 22·00 | 85·00 |
| 307*a* | | 9d. deep plum and blue (7.13) | 30·00 | 30·00 | |
| 308 | | 9d. slate-purple & cobalt-blue (3.12) | 60·00 | 35·00 | |
| 309 | **92** | 10d. dull pur & scar (9.10.11) | 35·00 | 25·00 | |
| 310 | | 10d. dull reddish purple and aniline pink | £150 | £110 | |
| 311 | | 10d. dull reddish purple and carmine (5.12) | 30·00 | 20·00 | 85·00 |
| | | a. No cross on crown | £450 | | |
| 312 | **93** | 1s. dark green & scar (13.7.11) | 55·00 | 25·00 | |
| 313 | | 1s. dp green & scarlet (9.10.11) | 35·00 | 9·00 | 85·00 |
| 314 | | 1s. green and carmine (15.4.12) | 25·00 | 8·00 | |
| 315 | **94** | 2s. 6d. dull greyish purple (27.9.11) | £250 | £150 | |
| 316 | | 2s. 6d. dull reddish pur (10.11) | 95·00 | 55·00 | |
| 317 | | 2s. 6d. dark purple | 95·00 | 55·00 | |
| 318 | **95** | 5s. carmine (29.2.12) | £125 | 55·00 | |
| 319 | **96** | 10s. blue (14.1.12) | £275 | £200 | |
| 320 | **97** | £1 deep green (3.9.11) | £750 | £300 | |
| 215/314 | | *Set of* 15 (*to* 1s. *and inc* ½d. (2)) | £160 | 90·00 | |

*No. 301 was on an experimental coated paper which does not respond to the silver test.

## KING GEORGE V
### 6 May 1910–20 January 1936

Further detailed information on the issues of King George V will be found in Volume 2 of the Stanley Gibbons *Great Britain Specialised Catalogue*.

**PRINTERS.** Types **98** to **102** were typographed by Harrison & Sons Ltd, with the exception of certain preliminary printings made at Somerset House and distinguishable by the controls "A.11", B.11" or "B.12" (the Harrison printings do not have a full stop after the letter). The booklet stamps, Nos. 334/7, and 344/5 were printed by Harrisons only.

**WATERMARK VARIETIES.** Many British stamps to 1967 exist without watermark owing to misplacement of the paper, and with either inverted, reversed, or inverted and reversed watermarks. A proportion of the low-value stamps issued in booklets have the watermark inverted in the normal course of printing.

Low values with *watermark sideways* are normally from stamp rolls used in machines with sideways delivery or, from June 1940, certain booklets.

**STAMPS WITHOUT WATERMARK.** Stamps found without watermark, due to misplacement of the sheet in relation to the dandy roll, are not listed here, but will be found in the *Great Britain Specialised Catalogue*.

The 1½d. and 5d. 1912–22, and 2d. and 2½d., 1924–26, listed here, are from *whole* sheets completely without watermark.

98

99

For type differences with T **101/2** *see* notes below the latter.

Die A

Die B

**Dies of Halfpenny**

Die A. The three upper scales on the body of the right hand dolphin form a triangle; the centre jewel of the cross inside the crown is suggested by a comma.

Die B. The three upper scales are incomplete; the centre jewel is suggested by a crescent.

Die A

Die B

**Dies of One Penny**

Die A. The second line of shading on the ribbon to the right of the crown extends right across the wreath; the line nearest to the crown on the right hand ribbon shows as a short line at the bottom of the ribbon.

Die B. The second line of shading is broken in the middle; the first line is little more than a dot.

(Des Bertram Mackennal and G. W. Eve. Head from photograph by W. & D. Downey. Die eng J. A. C. Harrison)

**1911–12.** *Wmk Imperial Crown, W* **49**. *P* 15 × 14.

| No. | Type | Description | *Un* | *Used* |
|---|---|---|---|---|
| 321 | **98** | ½d. pale green (Die A) (22.6.11) | 3·00 | 1·00 |
| 322 | | ½d. green (Die A) (22.6.11) | 2·50 | 1·00 |
| | | a. Error. Perf 14 | — | £250 |
| 323 | | ½d. bluish green (Die A) | £225 | £130 |
| 324 | | ½d. yellow-green (Die B) | 4·00 | 60 |
| 325 | | ½d. bright green (Die B) | 4·00 | 60 |
| | | a. Wmk sideways | — | £1700 |
| 326 | | ½d. bluish green (Die B) | £140 | 70·00 |
| 327 | **99** | 1d. carmine-red (Die A) (22.6.11) | 2·25 | 1·00 |
| | | a. Error. Perf 14 | | |
| | | b. Experimental ptg on chalk-surfaced paper (Control A.11) | £175 | |
| | | c. Wmk sideways | † | — |
| 328 | | 1d. pale carmine (Die A) (22.6.11) | 8·00 | 1·25 |
| | | a. No cross on crown | £250 | £150 |
| 329 | | 1d. carmine (Die B) | 4·00 | 1·00 |
| 330 | | 1d. pale carmine (Die B) | 4·00 | 1·00 |
| | | a. No cross on crown | £350 | £250 |
| 331 | | 1d. rose-pink (Die B) | 60·00 | 20·00 |
| 332 | | 1d. scarlet (Die B) (6.12) | 13·00 | 9·00 |
| 333 | | 1d. aniline scarlet (Die B) | 95·00 | 55·00 |

For note on the aniline scarlet No. 333 *see* below No. 343.

**100** Simple Cypher

**1912** (Aug). *Booklet stamps. Wmk Royal Cypher ("Simple"), W* **100**. *P* 15 × 14.

| No. | Type | Description | Un | Used |
|---|---|---|---|---|
| 334 | **98** | ½d. pale green (Die B) | 20·00 | 22·00 |
| 335 | | ½d. green (Die B) | 20·00 | 22·00 |
| 336 | **99** | 1d. scarlet (Die B) | 12·00 | 12·00 |
| 337 | | 1d. bright scarlet (Die B) | 12·00 | 12·00 |

**101**

**102**

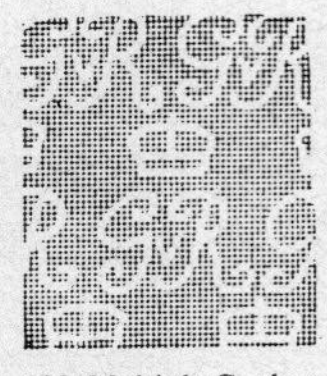
**103** Multiple Cypher

**Type differences**

½d. In T **98** the ornament above "P" of "HALFPENNY" has two thin lines of colour and the beard is undefined. In T **101** the ornament has one thick line and the beard is well defined.

1d. In T **99** the body of the lion is unshaded and in T **102** it is shaded.

**1912** (1 Jan). *Wmk Imperial Crown, W* **49**. *P* 15 × 14.

| No. | Type | Description | Un | Used |
|---|---|---|---|---|
| 338 | **101** | ½d. deep green | 7·00 | 3·00 |
| 339 | | ½d. green | 3·00 | 50 |
| 340 | | ½d. yellow-green | 3·00 | 75 |
| | | a. No cross on crown | 50·00 | 15·00 |
| 341 | **102** | 1d. bright scarlet | 1·25 | 50 |
| | | a. No cross on crown | 40·00 | 15·00 |
| | | b. Printed double, one albino | 95·00 | |
| 342 | | 1d. scarlet | 1·50 | 50 |
| 343 | | 1d. aniline scarlet* | £100 | 55·00 |
| | | a. No cross on crown | £600 | |

* Our prices for the aniline scarlet 1d. stamps, Nos. 333 and 343, are for specimens in which the colour is suffused on the surface of the stamp and shows through clearly on the back. Specimens without these characteristics but which show "aniline" reactions under the quartz lamp are relatively common.

**1912** (Aug). *Wmk Royal Cypher ("Simple"), W* **100**. *P* 15 × 14.

| No. | Type | Description | Un | Used |
|---|---|---|---|---|
| 344 | **101** | ½d. green | 2·50 | 70 |
| | | a. No cross on crown | 60·00 | 15·00 |
| 345 | **102** | 1d. scarlet | 4·00 | 50 |
| | | a. No cross on crown | 50·00 | 15·00 |

**1912** (Sept–Oct). *Wmk Royal Cypher ("Multiple"), W* **103**. *P* 15 × 14.

| No. | Type | Description | Un | Used |
|---|---|---|---|---|
| 346 | **101** | ½d. green (Oct) | 5·00 | 4·00 |
| | | a. No cross on crown | 60·00 | 20·00 |
| | | b. Imperf | 75·00 | |
| | | c. Wmk sideways | † | £1000 |
| | | d. Printed on gummed side | — | † |
| 347 | | ½d. yellow-green | 5·00 | 4·50 |
| 348 | | ½d. pale green | 6·00 | 4·00 |
| 349 | **102** | 1d. bright scarlet | 6·00 | 4·50 |
| 350 | | 1d. scarlet | 5·00 | 4·50 |
| | | a. No cross on crown | 65·00 | 16·00 |
| | | b. Imperf | 65·00 | |
| | | c. Wmk sideways | 65·00 | 75·00 |
| | | d. Wmk sideways. No cross on crown | £450 | |

**104**

**105**

**106**

No. 357a

No. 357ab

No. 357ac

**107**

**108**

Die I

Die II

**Dies of 2d.**

Die I.— Inner frame-line at top and sides close to solid of background. *Four* complete lines of shading between top of head and ova frame-line. These four lines do *not* extend to the oval itself White line round "TWOPENCE" thin.

Die II.— Inner frame-line farther from solid of background. *Thre* lines between top of head and extending to the oval. Whit line round "TWOPENCE" thicker.

(Des Bertram Mackennal (heads) and G. W. Eve (frames). Coinag head (½, 1½, 2, 3 and 4d.); large medal head (1d., 2½d.); intermediat medal head (5d. to 1s.); small medal head used for fiscal stamps Dies eng J. A. C. Harrison)

(Typo by Harrison & Sons Ltd., except the 6d. printed by th Stamping Department of the Board of Inland Revenue, Somerse House. The latter also made printings of the following which ca only be distinguished by the controls: ½d. B.13; 1½d. A.12; 2c C.13; 2½d. A.12; 3d. A.12, B.13, C.13; 4d. B.13; 5d. B.13; 7c C.13; 8d. C.13; 9d. agate B.13; 10d. C.13; 1s. C.13)

**1912–24.** *Wmk Royal Cypher, W* **100**. *Chalk-surfaced paper* (6d.) *P* 15×14.

| No. | Type | Description | Un | Used |
|---|---|---|---|---|
| 351 | **105** | ½d. green (1.13) | 30 | 2 |
| | | a. Doubly printed | £9500 | |
| 352 | | ½d. bright green | 30 | 2 |
| 353 | | ½d. deep green | 2·25 | 1·0 |
| 354 | | ½d. yellow-green | 3·50 | 1·2 |
| 355 | | ½d. very yellow (Cyprus) grn (1914) | £1750 | |
| 356 | | ½d. blue-green | 20·00 | 12·0 |
| 357 | **104** | 1d. bright scarlet (10.12) | 30 | 2 |
| | | a. "Q" for "O" (R.1/4) (Control E14) | £125 | 75·0 |
| | | ab. "Q" for "O" (R.4/11) (Control T22) | £175 | £10 |
| | | ac. Reversed "Q" for "O" (R.15/9) (Control T22) | £225 | £13 |
| | | ad. Inverted "Q" for "O" (R.20/3) | £300 | £15 |
| | | b. *Tête-bêche* (pair) | £45000 | |
| 358 | | 1d. vermilion | 1·50 | 6 |
| 359 | | 1d. pale rose-red | 6·00 | 5 |
| 360 | | 1d. carmine-red | 4·00 | 2·2 |
| 361 | | 1d. scarlet-vermilion | 70·00 | 20·0 |
| | | a. Printed on back† | £175 | |
| 362 | **105** | 1½d. red-brown (10.12) | 1·00 | 2 |
| | | a. "PENCF" (R.15/12) | £180 | £12 |
| | | b. Booklet pane. Four stamps plus two printed labels (2.24) | £225 | |
| 363 | | 1½d. chocolate-brown | 2·00 | 3 |
| | | a. Without wmk | 90·00 | |
| 364 | | 1½d. chestnut | 1·50 | 2 |
| | | a. "PENCF" (R.15/12) | 95·00 | 75·0 |
| 365 | | 1½d. yellow-brown | 8·00 | 9·0 |
| 366 | **106** | 2d. orange-yellow (Die I) (8.12) | 4·00 | 1·5 |
| 367 | | 2d. reddish orange (Die I) (11.13) | 1·25 | 5 |
| 368 | | 2d. orange (Die I) | 1·00 | 5 |
| 369 | | 2d. bright orange (Die I) | 1·50 | 7 |
| 370 | | 2d. orange (Die II) (9.21) | 2·00 | 1·7 |
| 371 | **104** | 2½d. cobalt-blue (10.12) | 4·50 | 1·0 |
| 371*a* | | 2½d. bright blue (1914) | 4·50 | 1·0 |
| 372 | | 2½d. blue | 4·50 | 1·0 |
| 373 | | 2½d. indigo-blue* (1920) | £750 | £55 |
| 373*a* | | 2½d. dull Prussian blue* (1921) | £475 | £35 |
| 374 | **106** | 3d. dull reddish violet (10.12) | 6·00 | 1·0 |
| 375 | | 3d. violet | 2·00 | 7 |
| 376 | | 3d. bluish violet (11.13) | 2·75 | 9 |
| 377 | | 3d. pale violet | 4·00 | 9 |
| 378 | | 4d. deep grey-green (1.13) | 15·00 | 3·5 |
| 379 | | 4d. grey-green | 4·00 | 7 |
| 380 | | 4d. pale grey-green | 10·00 | 2·0 |
| 381 | **107** | 5d. brown (6.13) | 3·50 | 3·0 |
| 382 | | 5d. yellow-brown | 4·50 | 3·0 |
| | | a. Without wmk | £350 | |
| 383 | | 5d. bistre-brown | 65·00 | 25·0 |
| 384 | | 6d. dull purple (8.13) | 12·00 | 3·0 |
| 385 | | 6d. reddish purple | 6·00 | 1·5 |
| | | a. Perf 14 (10.20) | 60·00 | 85·0 |
| 386 | | 6d. deep reddish purple | 12·00 | 1·5 |
| 387 | | 7d. olive (8.13) | 6·00 | 3·7 |
| 388 | | 7d. bronze-green (1915) | 35·00 | 12·0 |
| 389 | | 7d. sage-green (1917) | 35·00 | 6·0 |
| 390 | | 8d. black/*yellow* (8.13) | 15·00 | 6·5 |
| 391 | | 8d. black/*yellow-buff* (*granite*) (5.17) | 15·00 | 8·0 |
| 392 | **108** | 9d. agate (6.13) | 5·00 | 2·2 |
| 393 | | 9d. deep agate | 10·00 | 2·7 |
| 393*a* | | 9d. olive-green (9.22) | 65·00 | 15·0 |
| 393*b* | | 9d. pale olive-green | 65·00 | 15·0 |
| 394 | | 10d. turquoise-blue (8.13) | 9·00 | 12·0 |
| 394*a* | | 10d. deep turquoise-blue | 30·00 | 15·0 |

| No. | Type | Description | Unused | Used |
|---|---|---|---|---|
| 395 | **108** | 1s. bistre (8.13) | 7·50 | 1·00 |
| 396 | | 1s. bistre-brown | 18·00 | 5·00 |
| 351/95 | | *Set of* 15 | £120 | 45·00 |

Imperf stamps of this issue exist but may be war-time colour trials.

† The impression of No. 361a is set sideways and is very pale.

* No. 373 comes from Control O 20 and also exists on toned paper. No. 373*a* comes from Control R 21 and also exists on toned paper, but both are unlike the rare Prussian blue shade of the 1935 2½d. Jubilee issue.

See also Nos. 418/29.

For the 2d., T **106** bisected, see note under Guernsey, War Occupation Issues.

**1913** (Aug). *Wmk Royal Cypher* ("*Multiple*"), *W* **103**. *P* 15 × 14.

| No. | Type | Description | Unused | Used |
|---|---|---|---|---|
| 397 | **105** | ½d. bright green | 50·00 | 95·00 |
| 398 | **104** | 1d. dull scarlet | £110 | £130 |

Both these stamps were originally issued in rolls only. Subsequently sheets were found, so that horizontal pairs and blocks are known but are of considerable rarity.

**109**

A

**110** Single Cypher

**Major Re-entries on 2s. 6d.**

Nos. 400a and 408a

No. 415b

(Des Bertram Mackennal. Dies eng J. A. C. Harrison. Recess)

*High values, so-called "Sea Horses" design: T* **109**. *Background around portrait consists of horizontal lines, Type A. Wmk Single Cypher, W* **110**. *P* 11 × 12.

**1913** (30 June–Aug). *Printed by Waterlow Bros & Layton.*

| No. | Description | Unused | Used |
|---|---|---|---|
| 399 | 2s. 6d. deep sepia-brown | 95·00 | 65·00 |
| 400 | 2s. 6d. sepia-brown | 95·00 | 60·00 |
| | a. Re-entry (R.2/1) | £650 | £400 |
| 401 | 5s. rose-carmine (4 July) | £200 | £130 |
| 402 | 10s. indigo-blue (1 Aug) | £275 | £225 |
| 403 | £1 green (1 Aug) | £950 | £600 |
| 404 | £1 dull blue-green (1 Aug) | £950 | £650 |
| ★399/404 | **For well-centred, lightly used** | | **+25%** |

**1915** (Dec)–**18**. *Printed by De La Rue & Co.*

| No. | Description | Unused | Used |
|---|---|---|---|
| 405 | 2s. 6d. deep yellow-brown | £125 | 70·00 |
| 406 | 2s. 6d. yellow-brown | £125 | 65·00 |
| 407 | 2s. 6d. pale brown (worn plate) | £110 | 65·00 |
| 408 | 2s. 6d. sepia (seal-brown) | £125 | 70·00 |
| | a. Re-entry (R.2/1) | £550 | £400 |
| 409 | 5s. bright carmine | £200 | £140 |
| 410 | 5s. pale carmine (worn plate) | £225 | £140 |
| 411 | 10s. deep blue | £750 | £300 |
| 412 | 10s. blue | £550 | £250 |
| 413 | 10s. pale blue | £550 | £250 |
| ★405/13 | **For well-centred, lightly used** | | **+25%** |

**1918** (Dec)–**19**. *Printed by Bradbury, Wilkinson & Co, Ltd.*

| No. | Description | Unused | Used |
|---|---|---|---|
| 413*a* | 2s. 6d. olive-brown | 70·00 | 25·00 |
| 414 | 2s. 6d. chocolate-brown | 70·00 | 30·00 |
| 415 | 2s. 6d. reddish brown | 75·00 | 30·00 |
| 415*a* | 2s. 6d. pale brown | 75·00 | 25·00 |
| | b. Major re-entry (R.1/2) | £450 | £250 |
| 416 | 5s. rose-red (1.19) | £125 | 45·00 |
| 417 | 10s. dull grey-blue (1.19) | £175 | 80·00 |
| 399/417 | *Set of* 4 | £1250 | £700 |
| ★413*a*/17 | **For well-centred, lightly used** | | **+25%** |

**DISTINGUISHING PRINTINGS.** Note that the £1 value was only printed by Waterlow.

Waterlow and De La Rue stamps measure exactly 22 mm vertically. In the De La Rue printings the gum is usually patchy and yellowish, and the colour of the stamp, particularly in the 5s., tends to show through the back. The holes of the perforation are smaller than those of the other two printers.

In the Bradbury Wilkinson printings the height of the stamp is 22¾ or 23 mm. On most of the 22¾ mm high stamps a minute coloured guide dot appears in the margin just above the middle of the upper frame-line.

For (1934) re-engraved Waterlow printings *see* Nos. 450/2.

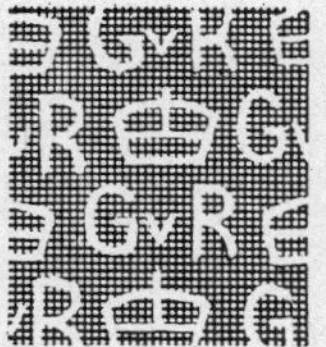

**111** Block Cypher **111*a***

The watermark Type **111*a***, as compared with Type **111,** differs as follows: Closer spacing of horizontal rows (12½ mm instead of 14½ mm). Letters shorter and rounder. Watermark thicker.

(Typo by Waterlow & Sons, Ltd (all values except 6d.) and later, 1934–35, by Harrison & Sons, Ltd (all values). Until 1934 the 6d. was printed at Somerset House where a printing of the 1½d. was also made in 1926 (identifiable only by control E.26). Printings by Harrisons in 1934–35 can be identified, when in mint condition, by the fact that the gum shows a streaky appearance vertically, the Waterlow gum being uniformly applied, but Harrisons also used up the balance of the Waterlow "smooth gum" paper)

**1924** (Feb)–**26**. *Wmk Block Cypher, W* **111**. *P* 15×14.

| No. | Type | Description | Unused | Used |
|---|---|---|---|---|
| 418 | **105** | ½d. green | 15 | 25 |
| | | a. Wmk sideways (5.24) | 5·00 | 2·50 |
| | | b. Doubly printed | £6500 | |
| 419 | **104** | 1d. scarlet | 15 | 25 |
| | | a. Wmk sideways | 10·00 | 10·00 |
| | | b. Experimental paper, W **111*a*** (10.24) | 20·00 | |
| | | c. Inverted "Q" for "O" (R.20/3) | £275 | |
| 420 | **105** | 1½d. red-brown | 15 | 25 |
| | | a. *Tête-bêche* (pair) | £275 | £500 |
| | | b. Wmk sideways (8.24) | 4·25 | 2·25 |
| | | c. Printed on the gummed side | £250 | † |
| | | d. Booklet pane. Four stamps plus two printed labels (6.24) | 60·00 | |
| | | e. Ditto. Wmk sideways | £2000 | |
| | | f. Experimental paper. W **111*a*** (10.24) | 35·00 | |
| | | g. Double impression | £4500 | |
| 421 | **106** | 2d. orange (Die II) (9.24) | 75 | 80 |
| | | a. No wmk | £300 | |
| | | b. Wmk sideways (7.26) | 45·00 | 55·00 |
| | | c. Doubly printed | £10000 | |
| 422 | **104** | 2½d. blue (10.24) | 3·00 | 1·25 |
| | | a. No wmk | £400 | |
| | | b. Wmk sideways | † | — |
| 423 | **106** | 3d. violet (10.24) | 4·00 | 1·00 |
| 424 | | 4d. grey-green (11.24) | 6·00 | 1·00 |
| | | a. Printed on the gummed side | £850 | † |
| 425 | **107** | 5d. brown (11.24) | 10·00 | 1·60 |
| 426 | | 6d. reddish purple (*chalk-surfaced paper*) (9.24) | 5·00 | 1·50 |
| 426*a* | | 6d. purple (6.26) | 1·50 | 50 |
| 427 | **108** | 9d. olive-green (12.24) | 5·00 | 2·25 |
| 428 | | 10d. turquoise-blue (11.24) | 15·00 | 16·00 |
| 429 | | 1s. bistre-brown (10.24) | 10·00 | 1·00 |
| 418/29 | | *Set of* 12 | 50·00 | 23·00 |

There are numerous shades in this issue.

The 6d. on both chalk-surfaced and ordinary papers was printed by both Somerset House and Harrisons. The Harrisons printings have streaky gum, differ slightly in shade, and that on chalk-surfaced paper is printed in a highly fugitive ink. The prices quoted are for the commonest (Harrison) printing in each case.

**112**

(Des H. Nelson. Eng J. A. C. Harrison. Recess Waterlow)

**1924–25.** *British Empire Exhibition. W* **111**. *P* 14.

(*a*) *Dated* "1924" (23.4.24)

| No. | Type | Description | Unused | Used |
|---|---|---|---|---|
| 430 | **112** | 1d. scarlet | 5·00 | 6·00 |
| 431 | | 1½d. brown | 7·50 | 11·00 |

(*b*) *Dated* "1925" (9.5.25)

| No. | Type | Description | Unused | Used |
|---|---|---|---|---|
| 432 | **112** | 1d. scarlet | 8·00 | 17·00 |
| 433 | | 1½d. brown | 25·00 | 50·00 |

**113**

**114**

**115**

**116** St. George and the Dragon

**117**

(Des J. Farleigh (T **113** and **115**), E. Linzell (T **114**) and H. Nelson (T **116**). Eng C. G. Lewis (T **113**), T. E. Storey (T **115**), both at the Royal Mint; J. A. C. Harrison, of Waterlow (T **114** and **116**). Typo by Waterlow from plates made at the Royal Mint, except T **116**, recess by Bradbury, Wilkinson from die and plate of their own manufacture)

**1929** (10 May). *Ninth U.P.U. Congress, London.*

(*a*) *W* **111**. *P* 15×14

| No. | Type | Description | Unused | Used |
|---|---|---|---|---|
| 434 | **113** | ½d. green | 1·50 | 1·50 |
| | | a. Wmk sideways | 25·00 | 32·00 |
| 435 | **114** | 1d. scarlet | 1·50 | 1·50 |
| | | a. Wmk sideways | 45·00 | 45·00 |
| 436 | | 1½d. purple-brown | 1·00 | 1·00 |
| | | a. Wmk sideways | 25·00 | 21·00 |
| | | b. Booklet pane. Four stamps plus two printed labels | £150 | |
| 437 | **115** | 2½d. blue | 7·50 | 9·00 |

(*b*) *W* **117**. *P* 12

| No. | Type | Description | Unused | Used |
|---|---|---|---|---|
| 438 | **116** | £1 black | £500 | £400 |
| 434/7 | | *Set of* 4 (*to* 2½*d*.) | 10·00 | 11·50 |

**PRINTERS.** All subsequent issues were printed in photogravure by Harrison and Sons, Ltd, *except where otherwise stated*.

**118** **119** **120** **121** **122**

**1934–36.** *W* **111**. *P* 15 × 14.

| No. | Type | Description | Unused | Used |
|---|---|---|---|---|
| 439 | **118** | ½d. green (19.11.34) | 10 | 25 |
| | | a. Wmk sideways | 6·00 | 3·00 |
| | | b. Imperf three sides | £750 | |
| 440 | **119** | 1d. scarlet (24.9.34) | 10 | 25 |
| | | a. Imperf (pair) | £750 | |
| | | b. Printed on the gummed side | £375 | † |
| | | c. Wmk sideways | 8·00 | 3·25 |
| | | d. Double impression | † | £9500 |
| | | e. Imperf between (pair) | £1100 | |
| | | f. Imperf three sides (pair) | £750 | |
| 441 | **118** | 1½d. red-brown (20.8.34) | 10 | 25 |
| | | a. Imperf (pair) | £250 | |
| | | b. Imperf three sides (lower stamp in vert pair) | £450 | |
| | | c. Imperf between (horiz pair) | | |
| | | d. Wmk sideways | 5·00 | 3·00 |
| | | e. Booklet pane. Four stamps plus two printed labels (1.35) | 50·00 | |
| 442 | **120** | 2d. orange (21.1.35) | 25 | 25 |
| | | a. Imperf (pair) | £950 | |
| | | b. Wmk sideways | 45·00 | 45·00 |
| 443 | **119** | 2½d. ultramarine (18.3.35) | 75 | 60 |
| 444 | **120** | 3d. violet (18.3.35) | 75 | 50 |
| 445 | | 4d. deep grey-green (2.12.35) | 1·00 | 55 |
| 446 | **121** | 5d. yellow-brown (17.2.36) | 3·50 | 1·50 |
| 447 | **122** | 9d. deep olive-green (2.12.35) | 6·00 | 1·60 |
| 448 | | 10d. turquoise-blue (24.2.36) | 6·00 | 8·00 |
| 449 | | 1s. bistre-brown (24.2.36) | 8·00 | 50 |
| | | a. Double impression | | |
| 439/49 | | *Set of* 11 | 24·00 | 11·00 |

Owing to the need for wider space for the perforations the size of the designs of the ½d. and 2d. were once, and the 1d. and 1½d. twice reduced from that of the first printings.

There are also numerous minor variations, due to the photographic element in the process.

The ½d. imperf three sides, No. 439b, is known in a block of four, from a sheet, in which the bottom pair is imperf at top and sides.

For No. 442 bisected, see Guernsey, War Occupation Issues.

B

123

(Eng J. A. C. Harrison. Recess Waterlow)

**1934** (Oct). *T* **109** *(re-engraved). Background around portrait consists of horizontal and diagonal lines, Type* B. *W* **110.** *P* 11 × 12.

| | | | | |
|---|---|---|---|---|
| 450 | **109** | 2s. 6d. chocolate-brown .. .. .. | 40·00 | 15·00 |
| 451 | | 5s. bright rose-red .. .. .. | 85·00 | 40·00 |
| 452 | | 10s. indigo .. .. .. | £200 | 40·00 |
| 450/2 | | .. .. .. .. *Set of* 3 | £275 | 85·00 |

There are numerous other minor differences in the design of this issue.

(Des B. Freedman)

**1935** (7 May). *Silver Jubilee. W* **111.** *P* 15 × 14.

| | | | | |
|---|---|---|---|---|
| 453 | **123** | ½d. green .. .. .. .. | 25 | 20 |
| 454 | | 1d. scarlet .. .. .. .. | 50 | 1·00 |
| 455 | | 1½d. red-brown .. .. .. .. | 25 | 20 |
| 456 | | 2½d. blue .. .. .. .. | 4·00 | 3·00 |
| 456*a* | | 2½d. Prussian blue .. .. .. | £2500 | £2750 |
| 453/6 | | .. .. .. .. *Set of* 4 | 4·50 | 6·00 |

The 1½d. and 2½d. values differ from T **123** in the emblem in the panel at right.

No. 456*a*, from three sheets printed with the wrong ink, was issued at a P.O. in Edmonton, North London.

## KING EDWARD VIII
### 20 January–10 December 1936

Further detailed information on the stamps of King Edward VIII will be found in Volume 2 of the Stanley Gibbons *Great Britain Specialised Catalogue.*

124

125

(Des from photo by Hugh Cecil)

**1936.** *W* **125.** *P* 15 × 14.

| | | | | |
|---|---|---|---|---|
| 457 | **124** | ½d. green (1.9.36) .. .. .. | 20 | 15 |
| | | a. Double impression .. .. | | |
| 458 | | 1d. scarlet (14.9.36) .. .. .. | 50 | 20 |
| 459 | | 1½d. red-brown (1.9.36) .. .. | 25 | 15 |
| | | a. Booklet pane. Four stamps plus two printed labels .. .. .. | 35·00 | |
| 460 | | 2½d. bright blue (1.9.36) .. .. | 25 | 60 |
| 457/60 | | .. .. .. .. *Set of* 4 | 1·00 | 1·00 |

## KING GEORGE VI
### 11 December 1936–6 February 1952

Further detailed information on the stamps of King George VI will be found in Volume 2 of the Stanley Gibbons *Great Britain Specialised Catalogue.*

**126** King George VI and Queen Elizabeth

(Des E. Dulac)

**1937** (13 May). *Coronation. W* **127.** *P* 15 × 14.

| | | | | |
|---|---|---|---|---|
| 461 | **126** | 1½d. maroon .. .. .. .. | 40 | 25 |

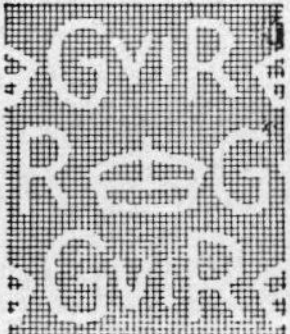

127

128

129

130

King George VI and National Emblems

(Des T **128/9,** E. Dulac (head) and E. Gill (frames). T **130,** E. Dulac (whole stamp))

**1937–47.** *W* **127.** *P* 15 × 14.

| | | | | |
|---|---|---|---|---|
| 462 | **128** | ½d. green (10.5.37) .. .. .. | 10 | 15 |
| | | a. Wmk sideways (1.38) .. .. | 25 | 25 |
| | | ab. Booklet pane of 4 .. .. .. | 15·00 | |
| 463 | | 1d. scarlet (10.5.37) .. .. .. | 10 | 15 |
| | | a. Wmk sideways (2.38) .. .. | 18·00 | 4·00 |
| | | ab. Booklet pane of 4 .. .. .. | 40·00 | |
| 464 | | 1½d. red-brown (30.7.37) .. .. | 20 | 15 |
| | | a. Wmk sideways (2.38) .. .. | 90 | 70 |
| | | b. Booklet pane. Four stamps plus two printed labels .. .. .. | 35·00 | |
| | | c. Imperf three sides (pair) .. .. | | |
| 465 | | 2d. orange (31.1.38) .. .. .. | 1·25 | 35 |
| | | a. Wmk sideways (2.38) .. .. | 80·00 | 25·00 |
| | | b. Bisected (on cover) .. .. | † | 20·00 |
| 466 | | 2½d. ultramarine (10.5.37) .. .. | 25 | 15 |
| | | a. Wmk sideways (6.40) .. .. | 75·00 | 15·00 |
| | | b. *Tête-bêche* (horiz pair) .. .. | | |
| 467 | | 3d. violet (31.1.38) .. .. .. | 6·00 | 60 |
| 468 | **129** | 4d. grey-green (21.11.38) .. .. | 35 | 30 |
| | | a. Imperf (pair) .. .. .. | £1200 | |
| | | b. Imperf three sides (horiz pair) .. | £1500 | |
| 469 | | 5d. brown (21.11.38) .. .. | 2·50 | 35 |
| | | a. Imperf (pair) .. .. .. | £1300 | |
| | | b. Imperf three sides (horiz pair) .. | £1000 | |
| 470 | | 6d. purple (30.1.39) .. .. | 1·75 | 25 |
| 471 | **130** | 7d. emerald-green (27.2.39) .. | 5·00 | 35 |
| | | a. Imperf three sides (horiz pair) .. | £1000 | |
| 472 | | 8d. bright carmine (27.2.39) .. .. | 5·00 | 40 |
| 473 | | 9d. deep olive-green (1.5.39) .. .. | 6·50 | 40 |
| 474 | | 10d. turquoise-blue (1.5.39) .. .. | 6·50 | 45 |
| | | aa. Imperf (pair) .. .. .. | £2000 | |
| 474*a* | | 11d. plum (29.12.47) .. .. .. | 3·00 | 1·25 |
| 475 | | 1s. bistre-brown (1.5.39) .. .. | 7·50 | 25 |
| 462/75 | | .. .. .. .. *Set of* 15 | 42·00 | 5·00 |

For later printings of the lower values in apparently lighter shades and different colours, see Nos. 485/90 and 503/8.

No. 465b was authorised for use in Guernsey. See notes on War Occupation Issues.

Nos. 468b and 469b are perforated at foot only and each occurs in the same sheet as Nos. 468a and 469a.

No. 471a is also perforated at foot only, but occurs on the top row of a sheet.

**131** King George VI

**132** King George VI

133

(Des E. Dulac (T **131**) and Hon. G. R. Bellew (T **132**). Eng J. A. C. Harrison. Recess Waterlow)

**1939–48.** *W* **133.** *P* 14.

| | | | | |
|---|---|---|---|---|
| 476 | **131** | 2s. 6d. brown (4.9.39) .. .. | 40·00 | 6·50 |
| 476*a* | | 2s. 6d. yellow-green (9.3.42) .. .. | 9·00 | 75 |
| 477 | | 5s. red (21.8.39) .. .. .. | 18·00 | 1·00 |
| 478 | **132** | 10s. dark blue (30.10.39) .. .. | £130 | 15·00 |
| 478*a* | | 10s. ultramarine (30.11.42) .. .. | 40·00 | 3·50 |
| 478*b* | | £1 brown (1.10.48) .. .. .. | 15·00 | 19·00 |
| 476/8*b* | | .. .. .. .. .. *Set of* 6 | £225 | 40·00 |

**134** Queen Victoria and King George VI.

(Des H. L. Palmer)

**1940** (6 May). *Centenary of First Adhesive Postage Stamps. W* **127.** *P* 14½ × 14.

| | | | | |
|---|---|---|---|---|
| 479 | **134** | ½d. green .. .. .. .. | 30 | 20 |
| 480 | | 1d. scarlet .. .. .. .. | 90 | 40 |
| 481 | | 1½d. red-brown .. .. .. .. | 30 | 30 |
| 482 | | 2d. orange .. .. .. .. | 50 | 40 |
| | | a. Bisected (on cover) .. .. | † | 16·00 |
| 483 | | 2½d. ultramarine .. .. .. | 1·90 | 80 |
| 484 | | 3d. violet .. .. .. .. | 4·00 | 4·00 |
| 479/84 | | .. .. .. .. *Set of* 6 | 7·00 | 5·50 |

No. 482a was authorised for use in Guernsey. See notes on War Occupation Issues.

**1941–42.** *Head as Nos.* 462/7, *but lighter background. W* **127.** *P* 15 × 14.

| | | | | |
|---|---|---|---|---|
| 485 | **128** | ½d. pale green (1.9.41) .. .. | 15 | 10 |
| | | a. *Tête-bêche* (horiz pair) .. .. | £2500 | |
| | | b. Imperf (pair) .. .. .. | £1200 | |
| 486 | | 1d. pale scarlet (11.8.41) .. .. | 15 | 10 |
| | | a. Wmk sideways (10.42) .. .. | 4·50 | 5·00 |
| | | b. Imperf (pair) .. .. .. | £1500 | |
| | | c. Imperf three sides (horiz pair) .. | £1000 | |
| | | d. Imperf between (vert pair) .. | | |
| 487 | **128** | 1½d. pale red-brown (28.9.42) .. .. | 75 | 45 |
| 488 | | 2d. pale orange (6.10.41) .. .. | 50 | 40 |
| | | a. Wmk sideways (6.42) .. .. | 20·00 | 12·00 |
| | | b. *Tête-bêche* (horiz pair) .. .. | £1500 | |
| | | c. Imperf (pair) .. .. .. | £1500 | |
| | | d. Imperf pane* .. .. .. | | |
| 489 | | 2½d. light ultramarine (21.7.41) .. | 15 | 10 |
| | | a. Wmk sideways (8.42) .. .. | 12·00 | 8·00 |
| | | b. *Tête-bêche* (horiz pair) .. .. | £1300 | |
| | | c. Imperf (pair) .. .. .. | £2000 | |
| | | d. Imperf pane* .. .. .. | £2500 | |
| 490 | | 3d. pale violet (3.11.41) .. .. | 1·50 | 50 |
| 485/90 | | .. .. .. .. *Set of* 6 | 2·75 | 1·50 |

The *tête-bêche* varieties are from defectively made-up stamp booklets.

No. 486c is perforated at foot only and occurs in the same sheet as No. 486b.

*BOOKLET ERRORS. Those listed as "imperf panes" show one row of perforations either at the top or at the bottom of the pane of 6.

**WATERMARK VARIETIES.** Please note that *inverted watermarks* are outside the scope of this Catalogue but are fully listed in the *Great Britain Specialised Catalogue*. See also the notes about watermarks at the beginning of the King George V section.

135

**136** Symbols of Peace and Reconstruction

(Des H. L. Palmer (T **135**) and R. Stone (T **136**))

**1946** (11 June). *Victory. W* **127.** *P* 15 × 14.

| | | | | |
|---|---|---|---|---|
| 491 | **135** | 2½d. ultramarine .. .. .. | 25 | 15 |
| 492 | **136** | 3d. violet .. .. .. .. | 25 | 15 |

137

**138** King George VI and Queen Elizabeth

(Des G. Knipe and Joan Hassall from photographs by Dorothy Wilding)

**1948** (26 Apr). *Royal Silver Wedding. W* **127.** *P* 15 × 14 (2½*d.*) *or* 14 × 15 (£1).

| | | | | |
|---|---|---|---|---|
| 493 | **137** | 2½d. ultramarine .. .. .. | 30 | 30 |
| 494 | **138** | £1 blue .. .. .. .. | 32·00 | 30·00 |

**1948** (10 May). Stamps of 1d. and 2½d. showing seaweed-gathering were on sale at eight Head Post Offices in Great Britain, but were primarily for use in the Channel Islands and are listed there (see after Great Britain Postal Fiscals).

**139** Globe and Laurel Wreath

**140** "Speed"

**141** Olympic Symbol

**142** Winged Victory

(Des P. Metcalfe (T **139**), A. Games (T **140**), S. D. Scott (T **141**) and E. Dulac (T **142**))

**1948** (29 July). *Olympic Games. W* **127.** *P* 15 × 14.

| | | | | | |
|---|---|---|---|---|---|
| 495 | **139** | 2½d. | ultramarine .. .. .. | 10 | 10 |
| 496 | **140** | 3d. | violet .. .. .. .. | 30 | 30 |
| 497 | **141** | 6d. | bright purple .. .. .. | 60 | 30 |
| 498 | **142** | 1s. | brown .. .. .. .. | 1·25 | 1·50 |
| 495/8 | | | .. .. .. .. .. *Set of* 4 | 2·00 | 2·00 |

**143** Two Hemispheres

**144** U.P.U. Monument, Berne

**145** Goddess Concordia, Globe and Points of Compass

**146** Posthorn and Globe

(Des Mary Adshead (T **143**), P. Metcalfe (T **144**), H. Fleury (T **145**) and Hon. G. R. Bellew (T **146**))

**1949** (10 Oct). *75th Anniv of Universal Postal Union. W* **127.** *P* 15 × 14.

| | | | | | |
|---|---|---|---|---|---|
| 499 | **143** | 2½d. | ultramarine .. .. .. | 10 | 10 |
| 500 | **144** | 3d. | violet .. .. .. .. | 30 | 40 |
| 501 | **145** | 6d. | bright purple .. .. .. | 60 | 75 |
| 502 | **146** | 1s. | brown .. .. .. .. | 1·25 | 1·50 |
| 499/502 | | | .. .. .. .. .. *Set of* 4 | 2·00 | 2·75 |

**1950–52.** 4*d. as Nos.* 468 *and others as Nos.* 485/9, *but colours changed.*

| | | | | | |
|---|---|---|---|---|---|
| 503 | **128** | ½d. | pale orange (3.5.51) .. .. | 10 | 15 |
| | | a. | Imperf (pair) .. .. .. | | |
| | | b. | *Tête-bêche* (horiz pair) .. .. | £2000 | |
| | | c. | Imperf pane* .. .. .. | | |
| 504 | | 1d. | light ultramarine (3.5.51) .. .. | 15 | 15 |
| | | a. | Wmk sideways (5.51) .. .. | 40 | 45 |
| | | b. | Imperf (pair) .. .. .. | £1100 | |
| | | c. | Imperf three sides (horiz pair) .. | £1000 | |
| | | d. | Booklet pane. Three stamps plus three printed labels (3.52) .. | 14·00 | |
| | | e. | Ditto. Partial *tête-bêche* pane .. | £1750 | |
| 505 | | 1½d. | pale green (3.5.51) .. .. | 25 | 30 |
| | | a. | Wmk sideways (9.51) .. .. | 2·00 | 2·50 |
| 506 | | 2d. | pale red-brown (3.5.51) .. .. | 25 | 20 |
| | | a. | Wmk sideways (5.51) .. .. | 80 | 1·10 |
| | | b. | *Tête-bêche* (horiz pair) .. .. | £2000 | |
| | | c. | Imperf three sides (horiz pair) .. | £900 | |
| 507 | | 2½d. | pale scarlet (3.5.51) .. .. | 20 | 15 |
| | | a. | Wmk sideways (5.51) .. .. | 80 | 90 |
| | | b. | *Tête-bêche* (horiz pair) .. .. | | |
| 508 | **129** | 4d. | light ultramarine (2.10.50) .. | 1·50 | 1·10 |
| | | a. | Double impression .. .. | † | — |
| 503/8 | | | .. .. .. .. *Set of* 6 | 2·25 | 1·75 |

No. 504c is perforated at foot only and occurs in the same sheet as No. 504b.

No. 506c is also perforated at foot only.

*BOOKLET ERRORS. Those listed as "imperf panes" show one row of perforations either at the top or at the bottom of the pane of 6.

**147** H.M.S. *Victory*

**148** White Cliffs of Dover

**149** St. George and the Dragon

**150** Royal Coat of Arms

(Des Mary Adshead (T **147/8**), P. Metcalfe (T **149/50**). Recess Waterlow)

**1951** (3 May). *W* **133.** *P* 11 × 12.

| | | | | | |
|---|---|---|---|---|---|
| 509 | **147** | 2s. | 6d. yellow-green .. .. .. | 8·00 | 75 |
| 510 | **148** | 5s. | red .. .. .. .. .. | 30·00 | 1·50 |
| 511 | **149** | 10s. | ultramarine .. .. .. | 18·00 | 10·00 |
| 512 | **150** | £1 | brown .. .. .. .. | 40·00 | 14·00 |
| 509/12 | | | .. .. .. .. *Set of* 4 | 85·00 | 22·00 |

**151** "Commerce and Prosperity"

**152** Festival Symbol

(Des E. Dulac (T **151**), A. Games (T **152**))

**1951** (3 May). *Festival of Britain. W* **127.** *P* 15 × 14.

| | | | | | |
|---|---|---|---|---|---|
| 513 | **151** | 2½d. | scarlet .. .. .. .. | 25 | 15 |
| 514 | **152** | 4d. | ultramarine .. .. .. | 50 | 45 |

## QUEEN ELIZABETH II
### 6 February 1952

Further detailed information on the stamps of Queen Elizabeth II will be found in volumes 3, 4 and 5 of the Stanley Gibbons *Great Britain Specialised Catalogue.*

**USED PRICES.** For Nos. 515 onwards the used prices quoted are for examples with circular dated postmarks.

**153** Tudor Crown

**154**

**155**

**156**

**157**

**158** **159** **160**

Queen Elizabeth II and National Emblems

I

II

Types of 2½d. Type I:—In the frontal cross of the diadem, the top line is only half the width of the cross.

Type II:—The top line extends to the full width of the cross and there are signs of strengthening in other parts of the diadem.

(Des Enid Marx (T **154**), M. Farrar-Bell (T **155/6**), G. Knipe (T **157**), Mary Adshead (T **158**), E. Dulac (T **159/60**). Portrait by Dorothy Wilding)

**1952–54.** *W* **153.** *P* 15 × 14.

| | | | | | |
|---|---|---|---|---|---|
| 515 | **154** | ½d. | orange-red (31.8.53) .. .. | 10 | 15 |
| 516 | | 1d. | ultramarine (31.8.53) .. .. | 20 | 20 |
| | | a. | Booklet pane. Three stamps plus three printed labels .. .. | 20·00 | |
| 517 | | 1½d. | green (5.12.52) .. .. .. | 10 | 15 |
| | | a. | Wmk sideways (15.10.54) .. | 35 | 60 |
| | | b. | Imperf pane* .. .. .. | | |
| 518 | | 2d. | red-brown (31.8.53) .. .. | 20 | 15 |
| | | a. | Wmk sideways (8.10.54) .. .. | 80 | 1·25 |
| 519 | **155** | 2½d. | carmine-red (Type I) (5.12.52) .. | 10 | 15 |
| | | a. | Wmk sideways (15.11.54) .. | 8·00 | 7·50 |
| | | b. | Type II (Booklets) (5.53) .. .. | 1·00 | 70 |
| 520 | | 3d. | deep lilac (18.1.54) .. .. | 1·00 | 30 |
| 521 | **156** | 4d. | ultramarine (2.11.53) .. .. | 3·00 | 80 |
| 522 | **157** | 5d. | brown (6.7.53) .. .. .. | 90 | 2·00 |
| 523 | | 6d. | reddish purple (18.1.54) .. .. | 3·00 | 60 |
| | | a. | Imperf three sides (pair) .. .. | | |
| 524 | | 7d. | bright green (18.1.54) .. .. | 10·00 | 3·50 |
| 525 | **158** | 8d. | magenta (6.7.53) .. .. .. | 1·00 | 60 |
| 526 | | 9d. | bronze-green (8.2.54) .. .. | 22·00 | 3·00 |
| 527 | | 10d. | Prussian blue (8.2.54) .. .. | 18·00 | 3·00 |
| 528 | | 11d. | brown-purple (8.2.54) .. .. | 35·00 | 16·00 |
| 529 | **159** | 1s. | bistre-brown (6.7.53) .. .. | 1·00 | 40 |
| 530 | **160** | 1s. | 3d. green (2.11.53) .. .. | 5·00 | 2·00 |
| 531 | **159** | 1s. | 6d. grey-blue (2.11.53) .. .. | 12·00 | 2·25 |
| 515/31 | | | .. .. .. .. .. *Set of* 17 | £100 | 28·00 |

See also Nos. 540/56, 561/6, 570/94 and 599/618*a*.

*BOOKLET ERRORS.—This pane of 6 stamps is *completely* imperf (see No. 540*a*, etc.).

**161**

**162**

**163**

**164**

(Des E. Fuller (2½d.), M. Goaman (4d.), E. Dulac (1s. 3d.), M. Farrar-Bell (1s. 6d.), Portrait (except 1s. 3d.) by Dorothy Wilding)

**1953** (3 June). *Coronation. W* **153.** *P* 15 × 14.

| | | | | | |
|---|---|---|---|---|---|
| 532 | **161** | 2½d. | carmine-red .. .. .. | 10 | 10 |
| 533 | **162** | 4d. | ultramarine .. .. .. | 30 | 70 |
| 534 | **163** | 1s. | 3d. deep yellow-green .. .. | 4·00 | 4·00 |
| 535 | **164** | 1s. | 6d. deep grey-blue .. .. | 6·75 | 7·00 |
| 532/5 | | | .. .. .. .. .. *Set of* 4 | 10·00 | 10·00 |

**165** St. Edward's Crown

**166** Carrickfergus Castle

**167** Caernarvon Castle

**168** Edinburgh Castle

**169** Windsor Castle

(Des L. Lamb. Portrait by Dorothy Wilding. Recess Waterlow (until 31.12.57) and De La Rue (subsequently))

**1955–58.** *W* **165.** *P* 11 × 12.

| No. | Type | Description | | |
|---|---|---|---|---|
| 536 | **166** | 2s. 6d. black-brown (23.9.55) | 10·00 | 2·00 |
| | | a. De La Rue printing (17.7.58) | 28·00 | 2·50 |
| 537 | **167** | 5s. rose-carmine (23.9.55) | 40·00 | 3·50 |
| | | a. De La Rue printing (30.4.58) | 85·00 | 6·50 |
| 538 | **168** | 10s. ultramarine (1.9.55) | 95·00 | 11·00 |
| | | a. De La Rue printing. *Dull ultramarine* (25.4.58) | £160 | 19·00 |
| 539 | **169** | £1 black (1.9.55) | £160 | 28·00 |
| | | a. De La Rue printing (28.4.58) | £325 | 50·00 |
| 536/9 | | *Set of* 4 | £275 | 40·00 |
| 536a/9a | | *Set of* 4 | £550 | 70·00 |

See also Nos. 595/8a and 759/62.

On 1 January 1958, the contract for printing the high values, T **166** to **169** was transferred to De La Rue & Co, Ltd.

The work of the two printers is very similar, but the following notes will be helpful to those attempting to identify Waterlow and De La Rue stamps of the W **165** issue.

The De La Rue sheets are printed in pairs and have a ⊣ or ⊢ shaped guide-mark at the centre of one side-margin, opposite the middle row of perforations, indicating left- and right-hand sheets respectively.

The Waterlow sheets have a small circle (sometimes crossed) instead of a "⊢" and this is present in both side-margins opposite the 6th row of stamps, though one is sometimes trimmed off. Short dashes are also present in the perforation gutter between the marginal stamps marking the middle of the four sides and a cross is at the centre of the sheet. The four corners of the sheet have two lines forming a right-angle as trimming marks, but some are usually trimmed off. All these gutter marks and sheet-trimming marks are absent in the De La Rue printings.

De La Rue used the Waterlow die and no alterations were made to it, so that no difference exists in the design or its size, but the making of new plates at first resulted in slight but measurable variations in the width of the gutters between stamps, particularly the horizontal, as follows:

| | W. | D.L.R. |
|---|---|---|
| Horiz gutters, mm | 3.8 to 4.0 | 3.4 to 3.8 |

Later D.L.R. plates were however less distinguishable in this respect.

For a short time in 1959 the D.L.R. 2s. 6d. appeared with one dot in the bottom margin below the first stamp.

It is possible to sort singles with reasonable certainty by general characteristics. The individual lines of the D.L.R. impression are cleaner and devoid of the whiskers of colour of Waterlow's, and the whole impression lighter and softer.

Owing to the closer setting of the horizontal rows the strokes of the perforating comb are closer; this results in the topmost tooth on each side of De La Rue stamps being narrower than the corresponding teeth in Waterlow's which were more than normally broad.

Shades also help. The 2s. 6d. D.L.R. is a warmer, more chocolate shade than the blackish brown of W.; the 5s. a lighter red with less carmine than W's; the 10s. more blue and less ultramarine; the £1 less intense black.

The paper of D.L.R. printings is uniformly white, identical with that of W. printings from February 1957 onwards, but earlier W. printings are on paper which is creamy by comparison.

In this and later issues of T **166/9** the dates of issue given for changes of watermark or paper are those on which supplies were first sent by the Supplies Department to Postmasters.

**1955–58.** *W* **165.** *P* 15 × 14.

| No. | Type | Description | | |
|---|---|---|---|---|
| 540 | **154** | ½d. orange-red (booklets 8.55, sheets 12.12.55) | 10 | 15 |
| | | a. Part perf pane* | £800 | |
| 541 | | 1d. ultramarine (19.9.55) | 25 | 15 |
| | | a. Booklet pane. Three stamps plus three printed labels | 11·00 | |
| | | b. *Tête-bêche* (horiz pair) | £500 | |
| 542 | | 1½d. green (booklets 8.55, sheets 11.10.55) | 10 | 15 |
| | | a. Wmk sideways (7.3.56) | 15 | 75 |
| | | b. *Tête-bêche* (horiz pair) | £900 | |
| 543 | | 2d. red-brown (6.9.55) | 20 | 20 |
| | | aa. Imperf between (vert pair) | £1500 | |
| | | a. Wmk sideways (31.7.56) | 20 | 60 |
| | | ab. Imperf between (wmk sideways) (horiz pair) | £1500 | |
| 543*b* | | 2d. light red-brown (17.10.56) | 20 | 15 |
| | | ba. *Tête-bêche* (horiz pair) | £600 | |
| | | bb. Imperf pane* | £800 | |
| | | bc. Part perf pane* | £850 | |
| | | d. Wmk sideways (5.3.57) | 9·00 | 5·50 |
| 544 | **155** | 2½d. carmine-red (Type I) (28.9.55) | 20 | 15 |
| | | a. Wmk sideways (Type I) (23.3.56) | 1·25 | 1·10 |
| | | b. Type II (booklets 9.55, sheets 1957) | 25 | 40 |
| | | ba. *Tête-bêche* (horiz pair) | £750 | |
| | | bb. Imperf pane* | £900 | |
| | | bc. Part perf pane* | £750 | |
| 545 | | 3d. deep lilac (17.7.56) | 20 | 15 |
| | | aa. *Tête-bêche* (horiz pair) | £750 | |
| | | a. Imperf three sides (pair) | £500 | |
| | | b. Wmk sideways (22.11.57) | 14·00 | 10·00 |
| 546 | **156** | 4d. ultramarine (14.11.55) | 1·40 | 40 |
| 547 | **157** | 5d. brown (21.9.55) | 5·00 | 3·50 |
| 548 | | 6d. reddish purple (20.12.55) | 4·00 | 75 |
| | | aa. Imperf three sides (pair) | £400 | |
| | | *a. Deep claret* (8.5.58) | 3·50 | 80 |
| | | ab. Imperf three sides (pair) | £400 | |
| 549 | | 7d. bright green (23.4.56) | 48·00 | 7·50 |
| 550 | **158** | 8d. magenta (21.12.55) | 5·50 | 1·00 |
| 551 | | 9d. bronze-green (15.12.55) | 17·00 | 1·50 |
| 552 | | 10d. Prussian blue (22.9.55) | 12·00 | 1·50 |
| 553 | | 11d. brown-purple (28.10.55) | 40 | 1·00 |
| 554 | **159** | 1s. bistre-brown (3.11.55) | 15·00 | 40 |
| 555 | **160** | 1s. 3d. green (27.3.56) | 17·00 | 1·25 |
| 556 | **159** | 1s. 6d. grey-blue (27.3.56) | 16·00 | 1·00 |
| 540/56 | | *Set of* 18 | £120 | 18·00 |

The dates given for Nos. 540/556 are those on which they were first issued by the Supplies Dept to postmasters.

In December 1956 a completely imperforate sheet of No. 543*b* was noticed by clerks in a Kent post office, one of whom purchased it against P.O. regulations. In view of this irregularity we do not consider it properly issued.

Types of 2½d. In this issue, in 1957, Type II formerly only found in stamps from booklets, began to replace Type I on sheet stamps.

*BOOKLET ERRORS. Those listed as "imperf panes" show one row of perforations either at top or bottom of the booklet pane; those as "part perf panes" have one row of 3 stamps imperf on three sides.

**170** Scout Badge and "Rolling Hitch"

**171** "Scouts coming to Britain"

**172** Globe within a Compass

(Des Mary Adshead (2½d.), P. Keely (4d.), W. H. Brown (1s. 3d.))

**1957** (1 Aug). *World Scout Jubilee Jamboree. W* **165.** *P* 15 × 14.

| No. | Type | Description | | |
|---|---|---|---|---|
| 557 | **170** | 2½d. carmine-red | 15 | 10 |
| 558 | **171** | 4d. ultramarine | 50 | 40 |
| 559 | **172** | 1s. 3d. green | 5·00 | 5·00 |
| 557/9 | | *Set of* 3 | 5·00 | 5·00 |

**173**

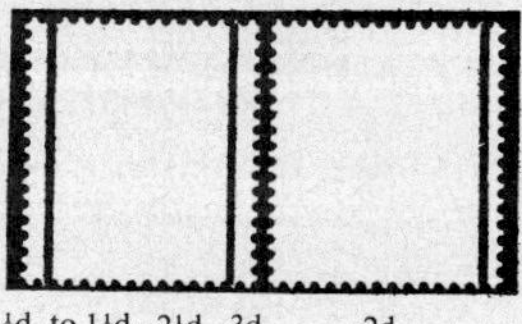

½d. to 1½d., 2½d., 3d. 2d.

Graphite-line arrangements (Stamps viewed from back)

**1957** (12 Sept). *46th Inter-Parliamentary Union Conference. W* **165.** *P* 15 × 14.

| No. | Type | Description | | |
|---|---|---|---|---|
| 560 | **173** | 4d. ultramarine | 1·10 | 1·10 |

**GRAPHITE-LINED ISSUES.** These were used in connection with automatic sorting machinery, first introduced experimentally at Southampton in December 1957.

The graphite lines were printed in black on the back, beneath the gum; two lines per stamp, except for the 2d.

In November 1959 phosphor bands were introduced (see notes after No. 598).

**1957** (19 Nov). *Graphite-lined issue. Two graphite lines on the back, except 2d. value, which has one line. W* **165.** *P* 15 × 14.

| No. | Type | Description | | |
|---|---|---|---|---|
| 561 | **154** | ½d. orange-red | 20 | 30 |
| 562 | | 1d. ultramarine | 20 | 35 |
| 563 | | 1½d. green | 40 | 1·25 |
| | | a. Both lines at left | £750 | £350 |
| 564 | | 2d. light red-brown | 3·00 | 1·50 |
| | | a. Line at left | £500 | £175 |
| 565 | **155** | 2½d. carmine-red (Type II) | 7·00 | 8·00 |
| 566 | | 3d. deep lilac | 50 | 50 |
| 561/6 | | *Set of* 6 | 10·00 | 11·00 |

No. 564a results from a misplacement of the line and horizontal pairs exist showing one stamp without line. No. 563a results from a similar misplacement.

See also Nos. 587/94.

**176** Welsh Dragon

**177** Flag and Games Emblem

**178** Welsh Dragon

(Des R. Stone (3d.), W. H. Brown (6d.), P. Keely (1s. 3d.))

**1958** (18 July). *Sixth British Empire and Commonwealth Games, Cardiff. W* **165.** *P* 15 × 14.

| No. | Type | Description | | |
|---|---|---|---|---|
| 567 | **176** | 3d. deep lilac | 15 | 10 |
| 568 | **177** | 6d. reddish purple | 25 | 20 |
| 569 | **178** | 1s. 3d. green | 2·75 | 2·00 |
| 567/9 | | *Set of* 3 | 2·75 | 2·10 |

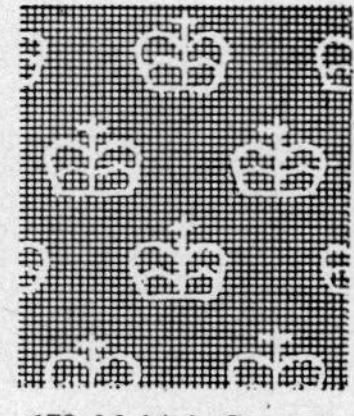

**179** Multiple Crowns

**1958–65.** *W* **179.** *P* 15 × 14.

| No. | Type | Description | | |
|---|---|---|---|---|
| 570 | **154** | ½d. orange-red (25.11.58) | 10 | 10 |
| | | a. Wmk sideways (26.5.61) | 10 | 15 |
| | | c. Part perf pane* | £800 | |
| | | k. Chalk-surfaced paper (15.7.63) | 2·00 | 2·25 |
| | | l. Booklet pane. No. 570k×3 *se-tenant* with 574k | 6·00 | |
| | | m. Booklet pane. No. 570a×2 *se-tenant* with 574l×2 (1.7.64) | 1·25 | |
| 571 | | 1d. ultramarine (booklets 11.58, sheets 24.3.59) | 10 | 10 |
| | | aa. Imperf (vert pair from coil) | £900 | |
| | | a. Wmk sideways (26.5.61) | 60 | 40 |
| | | b. Part perf pane* | £700 | |
| | | c. Imperf pane | £1100 | |
| | | l. Booklet pane. No. 571a×2 *se-tenant* with 575a×2 (16.8.65) | 4·50 | |
| 572 | | 1½d. grn (booklets 12.58, sheets 30.8.60) | 10 | 15 |
| | | a. Imperf three sides (horiz strip of 3) | £1200 | |
| | | b. Wmk sideways (26.5.61) | 8·00 | 3·50 |
| 573 | | 2d. light red-brown (4.12.58) | 10 | 10 |
| | | a. Wmk sideways (3.4.59) | 25 | 65 |
| 574 | **155** | 2½d. carmine-red (Type II) (booklets 11.58, sheets 15.9.59) | 10 | 10 |
| | | a. Imperf strip of 3 | £225 | |
| | | b. *Tête-bêche* (horiz pair) | £600 | |
| | | c. Imperf pane | £1100 | |
| | | d. Wmk sideways (Type I) (10.11.60) | 20 | 30 |
| | | e. Type I (wmk upright) (4.10.61) | 15 | 35 |
| | | ea. Imperf strip of 6 | | |
| | | k. Chalk-surfaced paper (Type II) (15.7.63) | 20 | 45 |
| | | l. Wmk sideways (Type II) Ord paper (1.7.64) | 40 | 75 |
| 575 | | 3d. deep lilac (booklets 11.58, sheets 8.12.58) | 10 | 10 |
| | | a. Wmk sideways (24.10.58) | 15 | 25 |
| | | b. Imperf pane* | £850 | |
| | | c. Part perf pane* | £750 | |
| | | d. Phantom "R" (Cyl 41 no dot) | £250 | |
| | | e. Phantom "R" (Cyl 37 no dot) | 25·00 | |
| 576 | **156** | 4d. ultramarine (29.10.58) | 50 | 20 |
| | | *a. Deep ultramarine*†† (28.4.65) | 15 | 10 |
| | | ab. Wmk sideways (31.5.65) | 45 | 35 |
| | | ac. Imperf pane* | £950 | |
| | | ad. Part perf pane* | £650 | |
| 577 | | 4½d. chestnut (9.2.59) | 10 | 15 |
| 578 | **157** | 5d. brown (10.11.58) | 25 | 20 |
| 579 | | 6d. deep claret (23.12.58) | 25 | 15 |
| | | a. Imperf three sides (pair) | £450 | |
| | | b. Imperf (pair) | £550 | |
| 580 | | 7d. bright green (26.11.58) | 40 | 20 |
| 581 | **158** | 8d. magenta (24.2.60) | 40 | 15 |
| 582 | | 9d. bronze-green (24.3.59) | 40 | 15 |
| 583 | | 10d. Prussian blue (18.11.58) | 1·00 | 15 |
| 584 | **159** | 1s. bistre-brown (30.10.58) | 40 | 15 |
| 585 | **160** | 1s. 3d. green (17.6.59) | 25 | 15 |
| 586 | **159** | 1s. 6d. grey-blue (16.12.58) | 6·00 | 40 |
| 570/86 | | *Set of* 17 | 9·00 | 2·10 |

*BOOKLET ERRORS. See note after No. 556.

†Booklet pane No. 571l comes in two forms, with the 1d. stamps on the left or on the right.

††This "shade" was brought about by making more deeply etched cylinders, resulting in apparent depth of colour in parts of the design. There is no difference in the colour of the ink.

Sideways watermark. The 2d., 2½d., 3d. and 4d. come from coils and the ½d., 1d., 1½d., 2½d., 3d. and 4d. come from booklets. In *coil* stamps the sideways watermark shows the top of the watermark to the left. In the *booklet* stamps it comes equally to the left or right.

Nos. 570k and 574k only come from 2s. "Holiday Resort" Experimental undated booklets issued in 1963, in which one page contained 1 × 2½d. *se-tenant* with 3 × ½d. (*See* No. 570l).

No. 574l comes from coils, and the "Holiday Resort" Experimental booklets dated "1964" comprising four panes each containing two of these 2½d. stamps *se-tenant* vertically with two ½d. No. 570a. (*See* No. 570m.)

2½d. imperf. No. 574aa comes from a booklet with watermark upright. No. 574ba is from a coil with sideways watermark.

No. 574b comes from *sheets* bearing cylinder number 42 and is also known on vertical delivery coils.

Nos. 575d and 615a occurred below the last stamp of the sheet from Cyl 41 (no dot), where an incomplete marginal rule revealed an "R". The cylinder was later twice retouched. The stamps listed show the original, unretouched "R". The rare variety, No. 575d, is best collected in a block of 4 or 6 with full margins in order to be sure that it is not No. 615a with phosphor lines removed.

No. 575e is a similar variety but from Cyl. 37 (no dot). The marginal rule is much narrower and only a very small part of the "R" is revealed. The cylinder was later retouched. The listed variety is for the original, unretouched state.

**WHITER PAPER.** On 18 May 1962 the Post Office announced that a whiter paper was being used for the current issue (including Nos. 595/8). This is beyond the scope of this catalogue, but the whiter papers are listed in Vol. 3 of the Stanley Gibbons *Great Britain Specialised Catalogue*.

**1958** (24 Nov)–**61.** *Graphite-lined issue. Two graphite lines on the back, except 2d. value, which has one line. W* **179.** *P* 15 × 14.

| No. | Type | | Description | Unused | Used |
|---|---|---|---|---|---|
| 587 | **154** | ½d. | orange-red (15.6.59)† | 1·25 | 2·25 |
| 588 | | 1d. | ultramarine (18.12.58) | 1·00 | 1·25 |
| | | a. | Misplaced graphite lines (7.61)* | 60 | 90 |
| 589 | | 1½d. | green (4.8.59)† | 40·00 | 40·00 |
| 590 | | 2d. | light red-brown (24.11.58) | 7·00 | 4·00 |
| 591 | **155** | 2½d. | carmine-red (Type II) (9.6.59) | 12·00 | 10·00 |
| 592 | | 3d. | deep lilac (24.11.58) | 40 | 40 |
| | | a. | Misplaced graphite lines (5.61)* | £375 | £350 |
| 593 | **156** | 4d. | ultramarine (29.4.59) | 4·00 | 4·50 |
| | | a. | Misplaced graphite lines (1961)* | £1400 | |
| 594 | | 4½d. | chestnut (3.6.59) | 5·00 | 4·00 |
| 587/94 | | | *Set of* 8 | 65·00 | 60·00 |

Nos. 587/9 were only issued in booklets or coils (587/8).

*No. 588a (in coils), and Nos. 592a and 593a (both in sheets) result from the use of a residual stock of graphite-lined paper. As the use of graphite lines had ceased, the register of the lines in relation to the stamps was of no importance and numerous misplacements occurred—two lines close together, one line only, etc. No. 588a refers to two lines at left or at right; No. 592a refers to stamps with two lines only at left and both clear of the perforations and No. 593a to stamps with two lines at left (with left line down perforations) and traces of a third line down the opposite perforations.

†The prices quoted are for stamps with the watermark inverted. (*Prices for upright watermark* ½*d.* £6 *un,* £3 *us;* 1½*d.* £90 *un,* £60 *us.*)

(Recess D.L.R. (until 31.12.62), then B.W.)

**1959–68.** *W* **179.** *P* 11 × 12.

| No. | Type | | Description | Unused | Used |
|---|---|---|---|---|---|
| 595 | **166** | 2s. | 6d. black-brown (22.7.59) | 10·00 | 75 |
| | | a. | B.W. printing (1.7.63) | 50 | 30 |
| | | k. | Chalk-surfaced paper (30.5.68) | 50 | 1·10 |
| 596 | **167** | 5s. | scarlet-vermilion (15.6.59) | 55·00 | 2·00 |
| | | a. | B.W. ptg. *Red (shades)* (3.9.63) | 1·00 | 60 |
| | | ab. | Printed on the gummed side | £750 | |
| 597 | **168** | 10s. | blue (21.7.59) | 35·00 | 5·00 |
| | | a. | B.W. ptg. *Bright ultram* (16.10.63) | 2·50 | 3·00 |
| 598 | **169** | £1 | black (23.6.59) | 85·00 | 12·00 |
| | | a. | B.W. printing (14.11.63) | 10·00 | 5·00 |
| 595/8 | | | *Set of* 4 | £150 | 17·00 |
| 595a/8a | | | *Set of* 4 | 13·00 | 8·00 |

The B.W. printings have a marginal Plate Number. They are generally more deeply engraved than the D.L.R., showing more of the Diadem detail and heavier lines on Her Majesty's face. The vertical perf is 11.9 to 12 as against D.L.R. 11.8.

See also Nos. 759/62.

**PHOSPHOR BAND ISSUES.** These are printed on the front and are wider than graphite lines. They are not easy to see but show as broad vertical bands at certain angles to the light.

Values representing the rate for printed papers (and when this was abolished in 1968 for second class mail) have one band and others two, three or four bands as stated, according to the size and format.

In the small size stamps the bands are on each side with the single band at left (*except where otherwise stated*). In the large-size commemorative stamps the single band may be at left, centre or right, varying in different designs. The bands are vertical on both horizontal and vertical designs *except where otherwise stated*.

The phosphor was originally applied typographically but later usually by photogravure and sometimes using flexography, a typographical process using rubber cylinders.

Three different types of phosphor have been used, distinguishable by the colour emitted under an ultra-violet lamp, the first being green, then blue and now violet. Different sized bands are also known. All these are fully listed in Vol. 3 of the Stanley Gibbons *Great Britain Specialised Catalogue*.

Varieties. Misplaced and missing phosphor bands are known but such varieties are beyond the scope of this Catalogue.

**1959** (18 Nov). *Phosphor-Graphite issue. Two phosphor bands on front and two graphite lines on back, except 2d. value, which has one band on front and one line on back. P* 15 × 14. (*a*) *W* **165.**

| No. | Type | | Description | Unused | Used |
|---|---|---|---|---|---|
| 599 | **154** | ½d. | orange-red | 4·00 | 5·00 |
| 600 | | 1d. | ultramarine | 6·00 | 4·50 |
| 601 | | 1½d. | green | 2·50 | 4·50 |

(*b*) W **179**

| No. | Type | | Description | Unused | Used |
|---|---|---|---|---|---|
| 605 | **154** | 2d. | light red-brown (1 band) | 5·00 | 4·50 |
| | | a. | Error. W **165** | £150 | £150 |
| 606 | **155** | 2½d. | carmine-red (Type II) | 22·00 | 11·00 |
| 607 | | 3d. | deep lilac | 11·00 | 7·50 |
| 608 | **156** | 4d. | ultramarine | 12·00 | 27·00 |
| 609 | | 4½d. | chestnut | 28·00 | 18·00 |
| 599/609 | | | *Set of* 8 | 80·00 | 75·00 |

**1960** (22 June)–**67.** *Phosphor issue. Two phosphor bands on front, except where otherwise stated. W* **179.** *P* 15 × 14.

| No. | Type | | Description | Unused | Used |
|---|---|---|---|---|---|
| 610 | **154** | ½d. | orange-red | 10 | 15 |
| | | a. | Wmk sideways (26.5.61) | 9·00 | 8·00 |
| 611 | | 1d. | ultramarine | 10 | 10 |
| | | a. | Wmk sideways (14.7.61) | 35 | 40 |
| | | l. | Booklet pane. No. 611a × 2 *se-tenant* with 615d × 2† (16.8.65) | 7·50 | |
| | | m. | Booklet pane. No. 611a × 2 *se-tenant* with 615b × 2†† (11.67) | 3·50 | |
| 612 | | 1½d. | green | 10 | 20 |
| | | a. | Wmk sideways (14.7.61) | 9·00 | 9·00 |
| 613 | | 2d. | light red-brown (1 band) | 22·00 | 20·00 |
| 613*a* | | 2d. | lt red-brown (two bands) (4.10.61) | 10 | 10 |
| | | aa. | Imperf three sides*** | | |
| | | ab. | Wmk sideways (6.4.67) | 15 | 60 |
| 614 | **155** | 2½d. | carmine-red (Type II) (2 bands)* | 10 | 40 |
| 614*a* | | 2½d. | carmine-red (Type II) (1 band) (4.10.61) | 40 | 75 |
| 614*b* | | 2½d. | carmine-red (Type I) (1 band) (7.11.61) | 35·00 | 27·00 |
| 615 | | 3d. | deep lilac (2 bands) | 60 | 45 |
| | | a. | Phantom "R" (Cyl 41 no dot) | 20·00 | |
| | | b. | Wmk sideways (14.7.61) | 1·25 | 90 |
| 615*c* | | 3d. | deep lilac (1 side band) (29.4.65) | 35 | 60 |
| | | d. | Wmk sideways (16.8.65) | 4·50 | 3·50 |
| | | e. | One centre band (8.12.66) | 25 | 40 |
| | | ea. | Wmk sideways (19.6.67) | 25 | 60 |
| 616 | **156** | 4d. | ultramarine | 3·00 | 2·50 |
| | | *a.* | *Deep ultramarine* (28.4.65) | 15 | 15 |
| | | aa. | Part perf pane** | £650 | |
| | | ab. | Wmk sideways (16.8.65) | 15 | 25 |
| 616*b* | | 4½d. | chestnut (13.9.61) | 15 | 25 |
| 616*c* | **157** | 5d. | brown (9.6.67) | 20 | 25 |
| 617 | | 6d. | deep claret (27.6.60) | 40 | 20 |
| 617*a* | | 7d. | bright green (15.2.67) | 60 | 25 |
| 617*b* | **158** | 8d. | magenta (28.6.67) | 20 | 25 |
| 617*c* | | 9d. | bronze-green (29.12.66) | 60 | 25 |
| 617*d* | | 10d. | Prussian blue (30.12.66) | 80 | 35 |
| 617*e* | **159** | 1s. | bistre-brown (28.6.67) | 40 | 20 |
| 618 | **160** | 1s. | 3d. green | 1·75 | 2·50 |
| 618*a* | **159** | 1s. | 6d. grey-blue (12.12.66) | 2·00 | 1·00 |
| 610/618*a* | | | *Set of* 17 | 7·00 | 6·00 |

The automatic facing equipment was brought into use on 6 July 1960 but the phosphor stamps may have been released a few days earlier.

The stamps with watermark sideways are from booklets except Nos. 613ab and 615ea which are from coils. No. 616ab comes from both booklets and coils.

No. 615a. See footnote after No. 586.

*No. 614 with two bands on the creamy paper was originally from cylinder 50 dot and no dot. When the change in postal rates took place in 1965 it was reissued from cylinder 57 dot and no dot on the whiter paper. Some of these latter were also released in error in districts of S.E. London in September 1964. The shade of the reissue is slightly more carmine.

**Booklet error. Two stamps at bottom left imperf on three sides and the third imperf on two sides.

***This comes from the bottom row of a sheet which is imperf at bottom and both sides.

†Booklet pane No. 611l comes in two forms, with the 1d. stamps on the left or on the right. This was printed in this manner to provide for 3d. stamps with only one band.

††Booklet pane No. 611m comes from 2s. booklets of January and March 1968. The two bands on the 3d. stamp thus created are intentional because of the technical difficulty of producing a single band on one stamp *se-tenant* with a two-banded stamp, as this requires perfect registration of the bands.

Unlike previous one-banded phosphor stamps, No. 615*c* has a broad band extending over two stamps so that alternate stamps have the band at left or right (same prices either way).

**180** Postboy of 1660

**181** Posthorn of 1660

(Des R. Stone (3d.), Faith Jaques (1s. 3d.))

**1960** (7 July). *Tercentenary of Establishment of General Letter Office. W* **179** (*sideways on* 1*s.* 3*d.*). *P* 15 × 14 (3*d.*) *or* 14 × 15 (1*s.* 3*d.*).

| No. | Type | | Description | Unused | Used |
|---|---|---|---|---|---|
| 619 | **180** | 3d. | deep lilac | 20 | 10 |
| 620 | **181** | 1s. | 3d. green | 4·50 | 4·25 |

**182** Conference Emblem

(Des R. Stone (emblem, P. Rahikainen))

**1960** (19 Sept). *First Anniv of European Postal and Telecommunications Conference. Chalk-surfaced paper. W* **179.** *P* 15 × 14.

| No. | Type | | Description | Unused | Used |
|---|---|---|---|---|---|
| 621 | **182** | 6d. | bronze-green and purple | 40 | 60 |
| 622 | | 1s. | 6d. brown and blue | 6·50 | 5·50 |

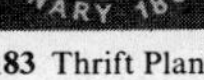

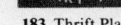

**183** Thrift Plant

**184** "Growth of Savings"

**185** Thrift Plant

(Des P. Gauld (2½d.), M. Goaman (others))

**1961** (28 Aug). *Centenary of Post Office Saving Bank. Chalk-surfaced paper. W* **179** (*sideways on* 2½*d.*) *P* 14 × 15 (2½*d.*) *or* 15 × 14 (*others*).

I. "TIMSON" Machine
II. "THRISSELL" Machine

| No. | Type | | Description | I Unused | I Used | II Unused | II Used |
|---|---|---|---|---|---|---|---|
| 623 | **183** | 2½d. | black and red | 10 | 10 | 2·00 | 1·75 |
| | | a. | Black omitted | £6000 | — | † | |
| 624 | **184** | 3d. | orange-brown & vio | 10 | 10 | 25 | 25 |
| | | a. | Orange-brn omitted | £130 | — | £250 | — |
| | | x. | Perf through side sheet margin | 20·00 | — | † | |
| | | xa. | Orange-brn omitted | £400 | — | † | |
| 625 | **185** | 1s. | 6d. red and blue | 2·50 | 2·00 | † | |
| 623/5 | | | *Set of* 3 | 2·50 | 2·00 | | |

2½d. TIMSON. Cyls 1E–1F. Deeply shaded portrait (brownish black).

2½d. THRISSELL. Cyls 1D–1B or 1D (dot)–1B (dot). Lighter portrait (grey-black).

3d. TIMSON. Cyls 3D–3E. Clear, well-defined portrait with deep shadows and bright highlights.

3d. THRISSELL. Cyls 3C–3B or 3C (dot)–3B (dot). Dull portrait, lacking in contrast.

Sheet marginal examples *without* single extension perf hole on the short side of the stamp are always "Timson", as are those with large punch-hole *not* coincident with printed three-sided box guide mark.

The 3d. "Timson" perforated completely through the right-hand side margin comes from a relatively small part of the printing perforated on a sheet-fed machine.

Normally the "Timsons" were perforated in the reel, with three large punch-holes in both long margins and the perforations completely through both short margins. Only one punch-hole coincides with the guide-mark.

The "Thrissells" have one large punch-hole in one long margin, coinciding with guide-mark and one short margin imperf (except sometimes for encroachments).

**186** C.E.P.T. Emblem

**187** Doves and Emblem

**188** Doves and Emblem

(Des M. Goaman (doves T. Kurpershoek))

**1961** (18 Sept). *European Postal and Telecommunications* (*C.E.P.T.*) *Conference, Torquay. Chalk-surfaced paper. W* **179.** *P* 15 × 14.

| No. | Type | | Description | Unused | Used |
|---|---|---|---|---|---|
| 626 | **186** | 2d. | orange, pink and brown | 10 | 10 |
| 627 | **187** | 4d. | buff, mauve and ultramarine | 20 | 10 |
| 628 | **188** | 10d. | turquoise, pale green & Prussian bl | 40 | 25 |
| | | a. | Pale green omitted | £3000 | |
| | | b. | Turquoise omitted | £2500 | |
| 626/8 | | | *Set of* 3 | 60 | 40 |

**189** Hammer Beam Roof, Westminster Hall

**190** Palace of Westminster

(Des Faith Jaques)

**1961** (25 Sept). *Seventh Commonwealth Parliamentary Conference. Chalk-surfaced paper. W* **179** (*sideways on* 1*s.* 3*d.*). *P* 15 × 14 (6*d.*) *or* 14 × 15 (1*s.* 3*d.*).

| No. | Type | | Description | Unused | Used |
|---|---|---|---|---|---|
| 629 | **189** | 6d. | purple and gold | 25 | 20 |
| | | a. | Gold omitted | £400 | |
| 630 | **190** | 1s. | 3d. green and blue | 2·75 | 2·00 |
| | | a. | Blue (Queen's head) omitted | £3000 | |

**191** "Units of Productivity"

**192** "National Productivity"

**193** "Unified Productivity"

(Des D. Gentleman)

**1962** (14 Nov). *National Productivity Year. Chalk-surfaced paper. W* **179** *(inverted on 2½d. and 3d.). P* 15 × 14.

| No. | Type | Description | Unused | Used |
|---|---|---|---|---|
| 631 | **191** | 2½d. myrtle-green & carm-red (*shades*) | 20 | 10 |
| | | p. One phosphor band .. .. | 1·00 | 40 |
| 632 | **192** | 3d. light blue and violet (*shades*) .. | 25 | 10 |
| | | a. Light blue (Queen's head) omitted | £900 | |
| | | p. Three phosphor bands .. .. | 1·00 | 50 |
| 633 | **193** | 1s. 3d. carmine, light blue & dp green | 2·50 | 1·60 |
| | | a. Light blue (Queen's head) omitted | £3500 | |
| | | p. Three phosphor bands .. .. | 24·00 | 21·00 |
| 631/3 | | .. .. .. .. *Set of* 3 | 2·75 | 1·60 |
| 631p/3p | | .. .. .. .. *Set of* 3 | 24·00 | 21·00 |

**194** Campaign Emblem and Family

**195** Children of Three Races

(Des M. Goaman)

**1963** (21 Mar). *Freedom from Hunger. Chalk-surfaced paper. W* **179** *(inverted). P* 15 × 14.

| No. | Type | Description | Unused | Used |
|---|---|---|---|---|
| 634 | **194** | 2½d. crimson and pink .. .. .. | 10 | 10 |
| | | p. One phosphor band .. .. | 1·00 | 1·00 |
| 635 | **195** | 1s. 3d. bistre-brown and yellow .. | 2·75 | 2·50 |
| | | p. Three phosphor bands .. .. | 24·00 | 22·00 |

**196** "Paris Conference"

(Des R. Stone)

**1963** (7 May). *Paris Postal Conference Centenary. Chalk-surfaced paper. W* **179** *(inverted). P* 15 × 14.

| No. | Type | Description | Unused | Used |
|---|---|---|---|---|
| 636 | **196** | 6d. green and mauve .. .. .. | 60 | 40 |
| | | a. Green omitted .. .. .. | £2000 | |
| | | p. Three phosphor bands .. .. | 6·50 | 6·50 |

**197** Posy of Flowers

**198** Woodland Life

(Des S. Scott (3d.), M. Goaman (4½d.))

**1963** (16 May). *National Nature Week. Chalk-surfaced paper. W* **179**. *P* 15 × 14.

| No. | Type | Description | Unused | Used |
|---|---|---|---|---|
| 637 | **197** | 3d. yellow, green, brown and black .. | 20 | 20 |
| | | p. Three phosphor bands .. .. | 50 | 50 |
| 638 | **198** | 4½d. black, blue, yellow, mag & brn-red | 40 | 40 |
| | | p. Three phosphor bands .. .. | 3·50 | 3·00 |

**199** Rescue at Sea

**200** 19th-century Lifeboat

**201** Lifeboatmen

(Des D. Gentleman)

**1963** (31 May). *Ninth International Lifeboat Conference, Edinburgh. Chalk-surfaced paper. W* **179**. *P* 15 × 14.

| No. | Type | Description | Unused | Used |
|---|---|---|---|---|
| 639 | **199** | 2½d. blue, black and red .. .. | 10 | 10 |
| | | p. One phosphor band .. .. | 40 | 50 |
| 640 | **200** | 4d. red, yellow, brown, black and blue | 40 | 30 |
| | | p. Three phosphor bands .. .. | 20 | 50 |
| 641 | **201** | 1s. 6d. sepia, yellow and grey-blue .. | 4·50 | 4·00 |
| | | p. Three phosphor bands .. .. | 32·00 | 28·00 |
| 639/41 | | .. .. .. .. *Set of* 3 | 4·50 | 4·00 |
| 639p/41p | | .. .. .. .. *Set of* 3 | 32·00 | 28·00 |

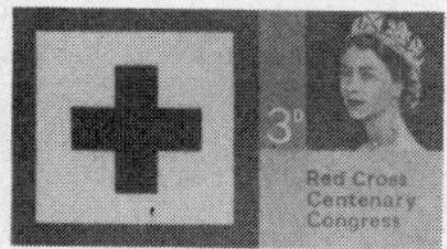


**202** Red Cross

**203**

**204**

(Des H. Bartram)

**1963** (15 Aug). *Red Cross Centenary Congress. Chalk-surfaced paper. W* **179**. *P* 15 × 14.

| No. | Type | Description | Unused | Used |
|---|---|---|---|---|
| 642 | **202** | 3d. red and deep lilac .. .. .. | 10 | 10 |
| | | a. Red omitted .. .. .. | £2500 | |
| | | p. Three phosphor bands .. .. | 60 | 60 |
| | | pa. Red omitted .. .. .. | £5500 | |
| 643 | **203** | 1s. 3d. red, blue and grey .. .. | 3·25 | 2·75 |
| | | p. Three phosphor bands .. .. | 35·00 | 35·00 |
| 644 | **204** | 1s. 6d. red, blue and bistre .. .. | 3·25 | 2·75 |
| | | p. Three phosphor bands .. .. | 26·00 | 20·00 |
| 642/4 | | .. .. .. .. *Set of* 3 | 6·00 | 5·00 |
| 642p/4p | | .. .. .. .. *Set of* 3 | 55·00 | 50·00 |

**205** Commonwealth Cable

(Des P. Gauld)

**1963** (3 Dec). *Opening of COMPAC (Trans-Pacific Telephone Cable). Chalk-surfaced paper. W* **179**. *P* 15 × 14.

| No. | Type | Description | Unused | Used |
|---|---|---|---|---|
| 645 | **205** | 1s. 6d. blue and black .. .. .. | 3·25 | 3·25 |
| | | a. Black omitted .. .. .. | £3250 | |
| | | p. Three phosphor bands .. .. | 18·00 | 20·00 |

**206** Puck and Bottom (*A Midsummer Night's Dream*)

**207** Feste (*Twelfth Night*)

**208** Balcony Scene (*Romeo and Juliet*)

**209** "Eve of Agincourt" (*Henry V*)

**210** Hamlet contemplating Yorick's Skull (*Hamlet*) and Queen Elizabeth II

(Des D. Gentleman. Photo Harrison & Sons (3d., 6d., 1s. 3d., 1s. 6d.). Des C. and R. Ironside. Recess B.W. (2s. 6d.))

**1964** (23 April). *Shakespeare Festival. Chalk-surfaced paper. W* **179**. *P* 11 × 12 *(2s. 6d.) or* 15 × 14 *(others).*

| No. | Type | Description | Unused | Used |
|---|---|---|---|---|
| 646 | **206** | 3d. yell-bistre, blk & dp vio-bl (*shades*) | 10 | 10 |
| | | p. Three phosphor bands .. .. | 20 | 30 |
| 647 | **207** | 6d. yellow, orge, blk & yell-ol (*shades*) | 20 | 20 |
| | | p. Three phosphor bands .. .. | 60 | 70 |
| 648 | **208** | 1s. 3d. cerise, bl-grn, blk & sep (*shades*) | 1·00 | 1·25 |
| | | p. Three phosphor bands .. .. | 5·75 | 7·25 |
| 649 | **209** | 1s. 6d. violet, turq, blk & blue (*shades*) | 1·25 | 1·25 |
| | | p. Three phosphor bands .. .. | 11·00 | 7·25 |
| 650 | **210** | 2s. 6d. deep slate-purple (*shades*) .. | 2·00 | 2·00 |
| 646/50 | | .. .. .. .. *Set of* 5 | 4·25 | 4·25 |
| 646p/9p | | .. .. .. .. *Set of* 4 | 15·00 | 14·00 |

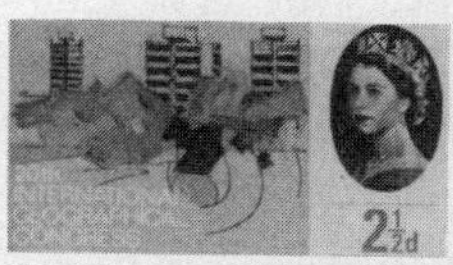


**211** Flats near Richmond Park ("Urban Development")

**212** Shipbuilding Yards, Belfast ("Industrial Activity")

**213** Beddgelert Forest Park, Snowdonia ("Forestry")

**214** Nuclear Reactor, Dounreay ("Technological Development")

(Des D. Bailey)

**1964** (1 July). *20th International Geographical Congress, London. Chalk-surfaced paper. W* **179**. *P* 15 × 14.

| No. | Type | Description | Unused | Used |
|---|---|---|---|---|
| 651 | **211** | 2½d. blk, olive-yellow, ol-grey & turq-bl | 10 | 10 |
| | | p. One phosphor band .. .. | 50 | 40 |
| 652 | **212** | 4d. orge-brn, red-brn, rose, blk & vio | 25 | 25 |
| | | a. Violet omitted .. .. .. | £200 | |
| | | b. Red-brown omitted .. .. | | |
| | | c. Violet and red-brown omitted .. | £200 | |
| | | p. Three phosphor bands .. .. | 90 | 70 |
| 653 | **213** | 8d. yellow-brown, emerald, grn & blk | 50 | 50 |
| | | a. Green (lawn) omitted .. .. | £3500 | |
| | | p. Three phosphor bands .. .. | 2·00 | 1·75 |
| 654 | **214** | 1s. 6d. yell-brn, pale pink, blk & brn | 4·00 | 3·75 |
| | | p. Three phosphor bands .. .. | 24·00 | 24·00 |
| 651/4 | | .. .. .. .. *Set of* 4 | 4·50 | 4·25 |
| 651p/4p | | .. .. .. .. *Set of* 4 | 24·00 | 24·00 |

**215** Spring Gentian

**216** Dog Rose

**217** Honeysuckle

**218** Fringed Water Lily

(Des M. and Sylvia Goaman)

**1964** (5 Aug). *Tenth International Botanical Congress, Edinburgh. Chalk-surfaced paper. W* **179**. *P* 15 × 14.

| | | | | |
|---|---|---|---|---|
| 655 | **215** | 3d. violet, blue and sage-green .. | 10 | 10 |
| | | a. Blue omitted .. .. .. | £3500 | |
| | | p. Three phosphor bands .. .. | 20 | 20 |
| 656 | **216** | 6d. apple-green, rose, scarlet and green | 20 | 20 |
| | | p. Three phosphor bands .. .. | 1·25 | 1·40 |
| 657 | **217** | 9d. lemon, green, lake and rose-red .. | 2·25 | 2·25 |
| | | a. Green (leaves) omitted .. .. | £3500 | |
| | | p. Three phosphor bands .. .. | 3·75 | 5·00 |
| 658 | **218** | 1s. 3d. yellow, emerald, reddish violet and grey-green .. .. .. | 3·00 | 2·10 |
| | | a. Yellow (flowers) omitted .. .. | £7500 | |
| | | p. Three phosphor bands .. .. | 22·00 | 22·00 |
| 655/8 .. | | .. .. .. .. *Set of* 4 | 5·00 | 4·25 |
| 655p/8p . | | .. .. .. .. *Set of* 4 | 24·00 | 24·00 |

**219** Forth Road Bridge

**220** Forth Road and Railway Bridges

(Des A. Restall)

**1964** (4 Sept). *Opening of Forth Road Bridge. Chalk-surfaced paper. W* **179**. *P* 15 × 14.

| | | | | |
|---|---|---|---|---|
| 659 | **219** | 3d. black, blue and reddish violet .. | 15 | 10 |
| | | p. Three phosphor bands .. .. | 50 | 50 |
| 660 | **220** | 6d. black, light blue and carmine-red | 45 | 40 |
| | | a. Light blue omitted .. .. .. | £2000 | £1500 |
| | | p. Three phosphor bands .. .. | 5·00 | 5·50 |

**221** Sir Winston Churchill

(Des D. Gentleman and Rosalind Dease, from photograph by Karsh)

**1965** (8 July). *Churchill Commemoration. Chalk-surfaced paper. W* **179**. *P* 15 × 14.

I. "REMBRANDT" Machine

| | | | | |
|---|---|---|---|---|
| 661 | **221** | 4d. black and olive-brown .. .. | 15 | 10 |
| | | p. Three phosphor bands .. .. | 30 | 30 |

II. "TIMSON" Machine

| | | | | |
|---|---|---|---|---|
| 661*a* | **221** | 4d. black and olive-brown .. .. | 25 | 25 |

III. "L. & M. 4" Machine

| | | | | |
|---|---|---|---|---|
| 662 | – | 1s. 3d. black and grey .. .. .. | 45 | 30 |
| | | p. Three phosphor bands .. .. | 3·00 | 3·50 |

The 1s. 3d. shows a closer view of Churchill's head.

4d. REMBRANDT. Cyls 1A–1B dot and no dot. Lack of shading detail on Churchill's portrait. Queen's portrait appears dull and coarse. This is a rotary machine which is sheet-fed.

4d. TIMSON. Cyls 5A–6B no dot. More detail on Churchill's portrait—furrow on forehead, his left eyebrow fully drawn and more shading on cheek. Queen's portrait lighter and sharper. This is a reel-fed, two-colour 12-in. wide rotary machine and the differences in impression are due to the greater pressure applied by this machine.

1s. 3d. Cyls 1A–1B no dot. The "Linotype and Machinery No. 4" machine is an ordinary sheet-fed rotary press machine. Besides being used for printing the 1s. 3d. stamps it was also employed for overprinting the phosphor bands on both values.

Two examples of the 4d. value exist with the Queen's head omitted, one due to something adhering to the cylinder and the other due to a paper fold. The stamp also exists with Churchill's head omitted, also due to a paper fold.

**222** Simon de Montfort's Seal

**223** Parliament Buildings (after engraving by Hollar, 1647)

(Des S. Black (6d.), R. Guyatt (2s. 6d.))

**1965** (19 July). *700th Anniv of Simon de Montfort's Parliament. Chalk-surfaced paper. W* **179**. *P* 15 × 14.

| | | | | |
|---|---|---|---|---|
| 663 | **222** | 6d. olive-green .. .. .. .. .. | 10 | 10 |
| | | p. Three phosphor bands .. .. | 40 | 40 |
| 664 | **223** | 2s. 6d. black, grey and pale drab .. | 1·25 | 1·25 |

**224** Bandsmen and Banner

**225** Three Salvationists

(Des M. Farrar-Bell (3d.), G. Trenaman (1s. 6d.))

**1965** (9 Aug). *Salvation Army Centenary. Chalk-surfaced paper. W* **179**. *P* 15 × 14.

| | | | | |
|---|---|---|---|---|
| 665 | **224** | 3d. indigo, grey-blue, cerise, yell & brn | 10 | 10 |
| | | p. One phosphor band .. .. | 40 | 40 |
| 666 | **225** | 1s. 6d. red, blue, yellow and brown .. | 1·00 | 1·00 |
| | | p. Three phosphor bands .. .. | 3·50 | 4·25 |

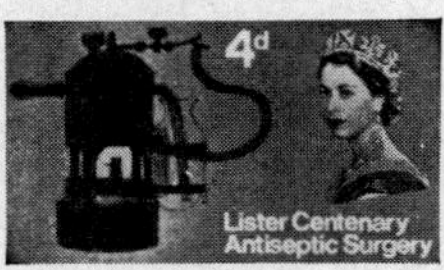


**226** Lister's Carbolic Spray

**227** Lister and Chemical Symbols

(Des P. Gauld (4d.), F. Ariss (1s.))

**1965** (1 Sept). *Centenary of Joseph Lister's Discovery of Antiseptic Surgery. Chalk-surfaced paper. W* **179**. *P* 15 × 14.

| | | | | |
|---|---|---|---|---|
| 667 | **226** | 4d. indigo, brown-red and grey-black | 10 | 10 |
| | | a. Brown-red (tube) omitted .. .. | £200 | 75·00 |
| | | b. Indigo omitted .. .. .. | £1500 | |
| | | p. Three phosphor bands .. .. | 15 | 20 |
| | | pa. Brown-red (tube) omitted .. .. | £1100 | |
| 668 | **227** | 1s. black, purple and new blue .. | 1·00 | 1·25 |
| | | p. Three phosphor bands .. .. | 1·60 | 1·60 |

**228** Trinidad Carnival Dancers

**229** Canadian Folk-dancers

(Des D. Gentleman and Rosalind Dease)

**1965** (1 Sept). *Commonwealth Arts Festival. Chalk-surfaced paper. W* **179**. *P* 15 × 14.

| | | | | |
|---|---|---|---|---|
| 669 | **228** | 6d. black and orange .. .. .. | 10 | 10 |
| | | p. Three phosphor bands .. .. | 30 | 30 |
| 670 | **229** | 1s. 6d. black and light reddish violet .. | 1·40 | 1·40 |
| | | p. Three phosphor bands .. .. | 2·25 | 2·25 |

**230** Flight of Spitfires

**231** Pilot in Hurricane

**232** Wing-tips of Spitfire and Messerschmitt "ME-109"

**233** Spitfires attacking Heinkel "HE-111" Bomber

**234** Spitfire attacking Stuka Dive-bomber

**235** Hurricanes over Wreck of Dornier "DO-17z2" Bomber

**236** Anti-aircraft Artillery in Action

**237** Air-battle over St. Paul's Cathedral

(Des D. Gentleman and Rosalind Dease (4d. × 6 and 1s. 3d.), A. Restall (9d.))

**1965** (13 Sept). *25th Anniv of Battle of Britain. Chalk-surfaced paper. W* **179**. *P* 15 × 14.

| | | | | |
|---|---|---|---|---|
| 671 | **230** | 4d. yellow-olive and black .. .. | 30 | 35 |
| | | a. Block of 6. Nos. 671/6 .. .. | 5·00 | 5·00 |
| | | p. Three phosphor bands .. .. | 40 | 50 |
| | | pa. Block of 6. Nos. 671p/6p .. .. | 9·50 | 8·00 |
| 672 | **231** | 4d. yellow-olive, olive-grey and black | 30 | 35 |
| | | p. Three phosphor bands .. .. | 40 | 50 |
| 673 | **232** | 4d. red, new blue, yell-ol, ol-grey & blk | 30 | 35 |
| | | p. Three phosphor bands .. .. | 40 | 50 |
| 674 | **233** | 4d. olive-grey, yellow-olive and black | 30 | 35 |
| | | p. Three phosphor bands .. .. | 40 | 50 |
| 675 | **234** | 4d. olive-grey, yellow-olive and black | 30 | 35 |
| | | p. Three phosphor bands .. .. | 40 | 50 |
| 676 | **235** | 4d. olive-grey, yell-olive, new blue & blk | 30 | 35 |
| | | a. New blue omitted .. .. .. | — | £3000 |
| | | p. Three phosphor bands .. .. | 40 | 50 |

| | | | | |
|---|---|---|---|---|
| 677 | **236** | 9d. bluish violet, orange and slate-purple | 1·25 | 1·25 |
| | | p. Three phosphor bands .. .. | 80 | 80 |
| 678 | **237** | 1s. 3d. light grey, deep grey, black, light blue and bright blue .. .. | 1·25 | 1·25 |
| | | p. Three phosphor bands .. .. | 80 | 80 |
| 671/8 | | .. .. .. .. *Set of* 8 | 6·50 | 4·25 |
| 671p/8p | | .. .. .. .. *Set of* 8 | 10·00 | 4·25 |

Nos. 671/6 were issued together *se-tenant* in blocks of 6 (3×2) within the sheet.

**238** Tower and Georgian Buildings **239** Tower and "Nash" Terrace, Regent's Park

(Des C. Abbott)

**1965** (8 Oct). *Opening of Post Office Tower. Chalk-surfaced paper. W* **179** (*sideways on 3d.*). *P* 14×15 (*3d.*) *or* 15×14 (*1s. 3d.*).

| | | | | |
|---|---|---|---|---|
| 679 | **238** | 3d. olive-yell, new blue & bronze-green | 10 | 10 |
| | | a. Olive-yellow (Tower) omitted .. | £750 | |
| | | p. One phosphor band .. .. | 10 | 10 |
| 680 | **239** | 1s. 3d. bronze-green, yellow-green & bl | 65 | 75 |
| | | p. Three phosphor bands .. .. | 50 | 50 |

The one phosphor band on No. 679p was produced by printing broad phosphor bands across alternate vertical perforations. Individual stamps show the band at right or left (same prices either way).

**240** U.N. Emblem

**241** I.C.Y. Emblem

(Des J. Matthews)

**1965** (25 Oct). *20th Anniv of U.N.O. and International Co-operation Year. Chalk-surfaced paper. W* **179**. *P* 15×14.

| | | | | |
|---|---|---|---|---|
| 681 | **240** | 3d. black, yellow-orange and light blue | 15 | 20 |
| | | p. One phosphor band .. .. | 25 | 25 |
| 682 | **241** | 1s. 6d. black, bright purple and lt blue | 1·10 | 90 |
| | | p. Three phosphor bands .. .. | 2·50 | 2·50 |

**242** Telecommunications Network

**243** Radio Waves and Switchboard

(Des A. Restall)

**1965** (15 Nov). *I.T.U. Centenary. Chalk-surfaced paper. W* **179**. *P* 15×14.

| | | | | |
|---|---|---|---|---|
| 683 | **242** | 9d. red, ultram, dp slate, vio, blk & pk | 20 | 20 |
| | | p. Three phosphor bands .. .. | 60 | 50 |
| 684 | **243** | 1s. 6d. red, greenish bl, ind, blk & lt pk | 1·40 | 1·10 |
| | | a. Light pink omitted .. .. | £1100 | |
| | | p. Three phosphor bands .. .. | 6·00 | 6·00 |

Originally scheduled for issue on 17 May 1965, supplies from the Philatelic Bureau were sent in error to reach a dealer on that date and another dealer received his supply on 27 May.

**244** Robert Burns (after Skirving chalk drawing)

**245** Robert Burns (after Nasmyth portrait)

(Des G. Huntly)

**1966** (25 Jan). *Burns Commemoration. Chalk-surfaced paper. W* **179**. *P* 15×14.

| | | | | |
|---|---|---|---|---|
| 685 | **244** | 4d. black, deep violet-blue and new blue | 15 | 15 |
| | | p. Three phosphor bands .. .. | 25 | 25 |
| 686 | **245** | 1s. 3d. black, slate-blue & yellow-orge | 70 | 70 |
| | | p. Three phosphor bands .. .. | 1·00 | 1·00 |

**246** Westminster Abbey

**247** Fan Vaulting, Henry VII Chapel

(Des Sheila Robinson. Photo Harrison (3d.). Des and eng Bradbury, Wilkinson. Recess (2s. 6d.))

**1966** (28 Feb). *900th Anniv of Westminster Abbey. Chalk-surfaced paper (3d.). W* **179**. *P* 15×14 (*3d.*) *or* 11×12 (*2s. 6d.*).

| | | | | |
|---|---|---|---|---|
| 687 | **246** | 3d. black, red-brown and new blue .. | 15 | 10 |
| | | p. One phosphor band .. .. | 30 | 30 |
| 688 | **247** | 2s. 6d. black .. .. .. .. | 85 | 90 |

**248** View near Hassocks, Sussex

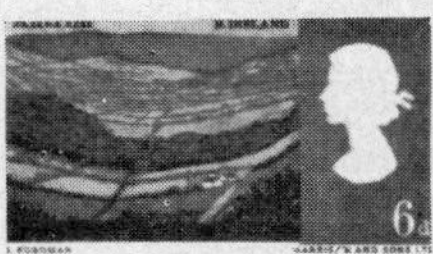


**249** Antrim, Northern Ireland

**250** Harlech Castle, Wales

**251** Cairngorm Mountains, Scotland

(Des L. Rosoman. Queen's portrait, adapted by D. Gentleman from coinage)

**1966** (2 May). *Landscapes. Chalk-surfaced paper. W* **179**. *P* 15×14.

| | | | | |
|---|---|---|---|---|
| 689 | **248** | 4d. black, yellow-green and new blue | 15 | 15 |
| | | p. Three phosphor bands .. .. | 15 | 15 |
| 690 | **249** | 6d. black, emerald and new blue .. | 15 | 15 |
| | | p. Three phosphor bands .. .. | 25 | 25 |
| 691 | **250** | 1s. 3d. blk, greenish yell & greenish bl | 35 | 35 |
| | | p. Three phosphor bands .. .. | 35 | 35 |
| 692 | **251** | 1s. 6d. black, orange and Prussian blue | 50 | 50 |
| | | p. Three phosphor bands .. .. | 50 | 50 |
| 689/92 | | .. .. .. .. *Set of* 4 | 1·00 | 1·00 |
| 689p/92p | | .. .. .. .. *Set of* 4 | 1·00 | 1·00 |

**252** Players with Ball

**253** Goalmouth Mêlée

**254** Goalkeeper saving Goal

(Des D. Gentleman (4d.), W. Kempster (6d.), D. Caplan (1s. 3d.). Queen's portrait adapted by D. Gentleman from coinage)

**1966** (1 June). *World Cup Football Competition Chalk-surfaced paper. W* **179** (*sideways on 4d.*). *P* 14×15 (*4d.*) *or* 15×14 (*others*).

| | | | | |
|---|---|---|---|---|
| 693 | **252** | 4d. red, reddish pur, brt bl, flesh & blk | 15 | 10 |
| | | p. Two phosphor bands .. .. | 15 | 10 |
| 694 | **253** | 6d. black, sepia, red, apple-green & blue | 20 | 20 |
| | | a. Black omitted .. .. .. | 85·00 | |
| | | b. Apple-green omitted .. .. | £1800 | |
| | | c. Red omitted .. .. .. | £1800 | |
| | | p. Three phosphor bands .. .. | 20 | 20 |
| | | pa. Black omitted .. .. .. | £500 | |
| 695 | **254** | 1s. 3d. black, blue, yell, red & lt yell-ol | 50 | 50 |
| | | a. Blue omitted .. .. .. | £200 | |
| | | p. Three phosphor bands .. .. | 50 | 50 |
| 693/5 | | .. .. .. .. *Set of* 3 | 75 | 75 |
| 693p/5p | | .. .. .. .. *Set of* 3 | 75 | 75 |

**255** Black-headed Gull

**256** Blue Tit

**257** European Robin

**258** Blackbird

(Des J. Norris Wood)

**1966** (8 Aug). *British Birds. Chalk-surfaced paper. W* **179**. *P* 15×14.

| | | | | |
|---|---|---|---|---|
| 696 | **255** | 4d. grey, black, red, emerald-green, brt blue, greenish yellow and bistre .. | 10 | 15 |
| | | a. Block of 4. Nos. 696/9 .. .. | 1·00 | 1·00 |
| | | ab. Black (value), etc. omitted* (*block of four*) .. .. .. .. | £4000 | |
| | | ac. Black only omitted* .. .. | | |
| | | p. Three phosphor bands .. .. | 10 | 15 |
| | | pa. Block of 4. Nos. 696p/9p .. | 1·00 | 1·00 |
| 697 | **256** | 4d. black, greenish yellow, grey, emerald-green, bright blue and bistre .. | 10 | 15 |
| | | p. Three phosphor bands .. .. | 10 | 15 |
| 698 | **257** | 4d. red, greenish yellow, black, grey, bistre, reddish brown & emerald-grn | 10 | 15 |
| | | p. Three phosphor bands .. .. | 10 | 15 |
| 699 | **258** | 4d. black, reddish brown, greenish yellow, grey and bistre** .. | 10 | 15 |
| | | p. Three phosphor bands .. .. | 10 | 15 |
| 696/9 | | .. .. .. .. *Set of* 4 | 1·00 | 50 |
| 696p/9p | | .. .. .. .. *Set of* 4 | 1·00 | 50 |

Nos. 696/9 were issued together *se-tenant* in blocks of four within the sheet.

* In No. 696ab the blue, bistre and reddish brown are also omitted but in No. 696ac only the black is omitted.

** On No. 699 the black was printed over the bistre.

Other colours omitted, and the stamps affected:

| | | |
|---|---|---|
| d. | Greenish yellow (Nos. 696/9) .. .. | £300 |
| e. | Red (Nos. 696 and 698) .. .. | £400 |
| f. | Emerald-green (Nos. 696/8) .. .. | 60·00 |
| pf. | Emerald-green (Nos. 696p/8p) .. .. | 60·00 |
| g. | Bright blue (Nos. 696/7) .. .. | £150 |
| pg. | Bright blue (Nos. 696p/7p) .. .. | £180 |
| h. | Bistre (Nos. 696/9) .. .. | 75·00 |
| ph. | Bistre (Nos. 696p/9p) .. .. | 75·00 |
| j. | Reddish brown (Nos. 698/9) .. .. | 75·00 |
| pj. | Reddish brown (Nos. 698p/9p) .. .. | £100 |

The prices quoted are for each stamp.

## NEW INFORMATION

The editor is always interested to correspond with people who have new information that will improve or correct the Catalogue.

**259** Cup Winners

**1966** (18 Aug). *England's World Cup Football Victory. Chalk-surfaced paper. W* **179** *(sideways). P* 14 × 15.
700 **259** 4d. red, reddish pur, brt bl, flesh & blk . . . 20 20

These stamps were only put on sale at post offices in England, the Channel Islands and the Isle of Man, and at the Philatelic Bureau in London and also, on 22 August, in Edinburgh on the occasion of the opening of the Edinburgh Festival as well as at Army post offices at home and abroad.

**260** Jodrell Bank Radio Telescope

**261** British Motor-cars

**262** "SRN 6" Hovercraft

**263** Windscale Reactor

(Des D. and A. Gillespie (4d., 6d.), A. Restall (others))

**1966** (19 Sept). *British Technology. Chalk-surfaced paper. W* **179.** *P* 15 × 14.

| | | | | |
|---|---|---|---|---|
| 701 | **260** | 4d. black and lemon . . | 15 | 15 |
| | | p. Three phosphor bands . . | 15 | 15 |
| 702 | **261** | 6d. red, deep blue and orange . . | 15 | 15 |
| | | a. Red (Mini-cars) omitted . . | £3500 | |
| | | b. Deep blue (Jaguar and inscr) omitted | £3000 | |
| | | p. Three phosphor bands . . | 15 | 15 |
| 703 | **262** | 1s. 3d. black, orange-red, slate and light greenish blue . . | 30 | 40 |
| | | p. Three phosphor bands . . | 45 | 50 |
| 704 | **263** | 1s. 6d. black, yellow-green, bronze-green, lilac and deep blue . . | 50 | 45 |
| | | p. Three phosphor bands . . | 65 | 60 |
| 701/4 | | . . *Set of* 4 | 1·00 | 1·00 |
| 701p/4p | | . . *Set of* 4 | 1·25 | 1·25 |

**264**

**265**

**266**

**267**

**268**

**269**

All the above show battle scenes and they were issued together *se-tenant* in horizontal strips of six within the sheet.

**270** Norman Ship

**271** Norman Horsemen attacking Harold's Troops

(All the above are scenes from the Bayeux Tapestry)

(Des D. Gentleman. Photo, Queen's head die-stamped (6d., 1s. 3d.))

**1966** (14 Oct). *900th Anniv of Battle of Hastings. Chalk-surfaced paper. W* **179** *(sideways on* 1s. 3d.*). P* 15 × 14.

| | | | | |
|---|---|---|---|---|
| 705 | **264** | 4d. black, olive-green, bistre, deep blue, orange, mag, grn, blue and grey . . | 10 | 15 |
| | | a. Strip of 6. Nos. 705/10 . . | 2·00 | 2·00 |
| | | p. Three phosphor bands . . | 10 | 25 |
| | | pa. Strip of 6. Nos. 705p/10p . . | 2·00 | 2·00 |
| 706 | **265** | 4d. black, olive-green, bistre, deep blue, orange, mag, grn, blue and grey . . | 10 | 15 |
| | | p. Three phosphor bands . . | 10 | 25 |
| 707 | **266** | 4d. black, olive-green, bistre, deep blue, orange, mag, grn, blue and grey . . | 10 | 15 |
| | | p. Three phosphor bands . . | 10 | 25 |
| 708 | **267** | 4d. black, olive-green, bistre, deep blue, magenta, green, blue and grey . . | 10 | 15 |
| | | p. Three phosphor bands . . | 10 | 25 |
| 709 | **268** | 4d. black, olive-green, bistre, deep blue, orange, mag, grn, blue and grey . . | 10 | 15 |
| | | p. Three phosphor bands . . | 10 | 25 |
| 710 | **269** | 4d. black, olive-green, bistre, deep blue, orange, mag, grn, blue and grey . . | 10 | 15 |
| | | p. Three phosphor bands . . | 10 | 25 |
| 711 | **270** | 6d. black, olive-grn, vio, bl, grn & gold | 10 | 10 |
| | | p. Three phosphor bands . . | 10 | 10 |
| 712 | **271** | 1s. 3d. black, lilac, bronze-green, rosine, bistre-brown and gold . . | 20 | 20 |
| | | a. Lilac omitted . . | £450 | |
| | | p. Four phosphor bands . . | 20 | 20 |
| | | pa. Lilac omitted . . | £650 | |
| 705/12 | | . . *Set of* 8 | 2·00 | 1·10 |
| 705p/12p | | . . *Set of* 8 | 2·00 | 1·60 |

Other colours omitted on the 4d. values and the stamps affected:

| | |
|---|---|
| b. Olive-green (Nos. 705/10) . . | 25·00 |
| pb. Olive-green (Nos. 705p/10p) . . | 25·00 |
| c. Bistre (Nos. 705/10) . . | 25·00 |
| pc. Bistre (Nos. 705p/10p) . . | 30·00 |
| d. Deep blue (Nos. 705/10) . . | 35·00 |
| pd. Deep blue (Nos. 705p/10p) . . | 35·00 |
| e. Orange (Nos. 705/7 and 709/10) . . | 25·00 |
| pe. Orange (Nos. 705p/7p and 709p/10p) . . | 20·00 |
| f. Magenta (Nos. 705/10) . . | 30·00 |
| pf. Magenta (Nos. 705p/10p) . . | 30·00 |
| g. Green (Nos. 705/10) . . | 25·00 |
| pg. Green (Nos. 705p/10p) . . | 25·00 |
| h. Blue (Nos. 705/10) . . | 20·00 |
| ph. Blue (Nos. 705p/10p) . . | 35·00 |
| j. Grey (Nos. 705/10) . . | 20·00 |
| pj. Grey (Nos. 705p/10p) . . | 20·00 |
| pk. Magenta and green (Nos. 705p/10p) . . | |

The prices quoted are for each stamp.

Nos. 705 and 709, with grey and blue omitted, have been seen commercially used, posted from Middleton-in-Teesdale.

Three examples of No. 712 in a right-hand top corner block of 10 (2 × 5) are known with the Queen's head omitted as a result of a double paper fold prior to die-stamping. The perforation is normal. Of the other seven stamps, four have the Queen's head misplaced and three are normal.

**MISSING GOLD HEADS.** The 6d and 1s. 3d. were also issued with the die-stamped gold head omitted but as these can also be removed by chemical means we are not prepared to list them unless a way is found of distinguishing the genuine stamps from the fakes which will satisfy the Expert Committees.

The same remarks apply to Nos. 713/14.

**272** King of the Orient

**273** Snowman

(Des Tasveer Shemza (3d.), J. Berry (1s. 6d.) (winners of children's design competition). Photo, Queen's head die-stamped)

**1966** (1 Dec). *Christmas. Chalk-surfaced paper. W* **179** *(sideways on* 3d.*). P* 14 × 15.

| | | | | |
|---|---|---|---|---|
| 713 | **272** | 3d. black, blue, green, yell, red & gold | 10 | 10 |
| | | a. Queen's head double . . | | |
| | | b. Green omitted . . | — | £150 |
| | | p. One phosphor band . . | 10 | 10 |
| 714 | **273** | 1s. 6d. blue, red, pink, black and gold | 35 | 35 |
| | | a. Pink (hat) omitted . . | £1100 | |
| | | p. Two phosphor bands . . | 35 | 35 |

See note below Nos. 679/80 which also applies to No. 713p.

**274** Sea Freight

**275** Air Freight

(Des C. Abbott)

**1967** (20 Feb). *European Free Trade Association (EFTA). Chalk-surfaced paper. W* **179.** *P* 15 × 14.

| | | | | |
|---|---|---|---|---|
| 715 | **274** | 9d. deep blue, red, lilac, green, brown, new blue, yellow and black . . | 15 | 15 |
| | | a. Black (Queen's head, etc.), brown, new blue and yellow omitted . . | £800 | |
| | | b. Lilac omitted . . | 60·00 | |
| | | c. Green omitted . . | 40·00 | |
| | | d. Brown omitted . . | 45·00 | |
| | | e. New blue omitted . . | 42·00 | |
| | | f. Yellow omitted . . | 42·00 | |
| | | p. Three phosphor bands . . | 15 | 15 |
| | | pb. Lilac omitted . . | 75·00 | |
| | | pc. Green omitted . . | 45·00 | |
| | | pd. Brown omitted . . | 45·00 | |
| | | pe. New blue omitted . . | 45·00 | |
| | | pf. Yellow omitted . . | 75·00 | |
| 716 | **275** | 1s. 6d. violet, red, deep blue, brown, green, blue-grey, new bl, yell & blk | 30 | 30 |
| | | a. Red omitted . . | | |
| | | b. Deep blue omitted . . | £225 | |
| | | c. Brown omitted . . | 45·00 | |
| | | d. Blue-grey omitted . . | 45·00 | |
| | | e. New blue omitted . . | 45·00 | |
| | | f. Yellow omitted . . | 45·00 | |
| | | p. Three phosphor bands . . | 30 | 30 |
| | | pa. Red omitted . . | | |
| | | pb. Deep blue omitted . . | £200 | |
| | | pc. Brown omitted . . | 45·00 | |
| | | pd. Blue-grey omitted . . | 45·00 | |
| | | pf. New blue omitted . . | 45·00 | |

**276** Hawthorn and Bramble

**277** Larger Bindweed and Viper's Bugloss

**278** Ox-eye Daisy, Coltsfoot and Buttercup

**279** Bluebell, Red Campion and Wood Anemone

The above were issued together *se-tenant* in blocks of four within the sheet.

**280** Dog Violet

**281** Primroses

(Des Rev. W. Keble Martin (T **276/9**), Mary Grierson (others))

**1967** (24 Apr). *British Wild Flowers. Chalk-surfaced paper.* *W* **179.** *P* 15 × 14.

| | | | | |
|---|---|---|---|---|
| 717 | **276** | 4d. grey, lemon, myrtle-green, red, agate and slate-purple .. .. | 15 | 10 |
| | | a. Block of 4. Nos. 717/20 .. .. | 1·25 | 1·25 |
| | | b. Grey double* .. .. .. | | |
| | | c. Red omitted .. .. .. .. | £1500 | |
| | | p. Three phosphor bands .. .. | 10 | 10 |
| | | pa. Block of 4. Nos. 717p/20p .. .. | 1·00 | 1·00 |
| | | pd. Agate omitted .. .. .. | £900 | |
| | | pf. Slate-purple omitted .. .. | £150 | |
| 718 | **277** | 4d. grey, lemon, myrtle-green, red, agate and violet .. .. .. | 15 | 10 |
| | | b. Grey double* .. .. .. | | |
| | | p. Three phosphor bands .. .. | 10 | 10 |
| | | pd. Agate omitted .. .. .. | £450 | |
| | | pe. Violet omitted .. .. .. | | |
| 719 | **278** | 4d. grey, lemon, myrtle-green, red and agate .. .. .. .. .. | 15 | 10 |
| | | b. Grey double* .. .. .. | | |
| | | p. Three phosphor bands .. .. | 10 | 10 |
| | | pd. Agate omitted .. .. .. | £450 | |
| 720 | **279** | 4d. grey, lemon, myrtle-green, reddish purple, agate and violet .. .. | 15 | 10 |
| | | b. Grey double* .. .. .. | | |
| | | c. Reddish purple omitted .. .. | £950 | |
| | | p. Three phosphor bands .. .. | 10 | 10 |
| | | pd. Agate omitted .. .. .. | £450 | |
| | | pe. Violet omitted .. .. .. | | |
| 721 | **280** | 9d. lavender-grey, green, reddish violet and orange-yellow .. .. .. | 15 | 10 |
| | | p. Three phosphor bands .. .. | 10 | 10 |
| 722 | **281** | 1s. 9d. lavender-grey, green, greenish yellow and orange .. .. .. | 20 | 20 |
| | | p. Three phosphor bands .. .. | 30 | 20 |
| 717/22 | | .. .. .. .. .. *Set of* 6 | 1·40 | 65 |
| 717p/22p | | .. .. .. .. *Set of* 6 | 1·25 | 65 |

* The double impression of the grey printing affects the Queen's head, value and inscription.

**PHOSPHOR BANDS**. Issues from No. 723 are normally with phosphor bands only, except for the high values. However, most stamps have appeared with the phosphor bands omitted in error, but they are outside the scope of this catalogue. They are listed in Volumes 3, 4 and 5 of the Stanley Gibbons *Great Britain Specialised Catalogue*.

See also further notes after No. X1026.

**PHOSPHORISED PAPER**. Following the adoption of phosphor bands the Post Office started a series of experiments involving the addition of the phosphor to the paper coating before the stamps were printed. No. 743c was the first of these experiments to be issued for normal postal use. See also notes after No. X1026.

**PVA GUM.** Polyvinyl alcohol was introduced by Harrisons in place of gum Arabic in 1968. It is almost invisible except that a small amount of pale yellowish colouring matter was introduced to make it possible to see that the stamps had been gummed. Although this can be distinguished from gum arabic in unused stamps there is, of course, no means of detecting it in used examples. Such varieties are outside the scope of this catalogue, but they are listed in the *Great Britain Concise Catalogue*. See further notes *re* gum after Nos. 744 and 762.

**282** **282*a***

I II

Two types of the 2d.

I. Value spaced away from left side of stamp (cylinders 1 no dot and dot).

II. Value close to left side from new multipositive used for cylinders 5 no dot and dot onwards. The portrait appears in the centre, thus conforming to the other values.

(Des after plaster cast by Arnold Machin)

**1967** (5 June)–**70.** *Chalk-surfaced paper. Two phosphor bands except where otherwise stated. No wmk. P* 15 × 14.

| | | | | |
|---|---|---|---|---|
| 723 | **282** | ½d. orange-brown (5.2.68) .. .. | 10 | 20 |
| 724 | | 1d. lt olive (*shades*) (2 bands) (5.2.68) | 10 | 10 |
| | | a. Imperf (coil strip)† .. | £750 | |
| | | b. Part perf pane* .. .. .. | | |
| | | c. Imperf pane* .. .. .. | £3750 | |
| | | d. Uncoated paper** .. .. | 85·00 | |
| | | l. Booklet pane. No. 724×2 *se-tenant* with 730×2 (6.4.68) .. .. | 2·75 | |
| | | m. Booklet pane. No. 724×4 *se-tenant* with 734×2 (6.1.69) .. .. | 3·25 | |
| | | n. Booklet pane. No. 724×6, 734×6 and 735×3 *se-tenant* (1.12.69) .. | 11·00 | |
| | | na. Uncoated paper** .. .. | £900 | |
| 725 | | 1d. yellowish olive (1 centre band) (16.9.68) .. .. .. | 25 | 30 |
| | | l. Booklet pane. No. 725×4 *se-tenant* with 732×2 .. .. .. | 3·75 | |
| | | m. Coil strip. No. 728×2 *se-tenant* with 729, 725 and 733 (27.8.69) .. | 1·25 | |
| 726 | | 2d. lake-brown (Type I) (2 bands) (5.2.68) .. .. .. .. | 10 | 15 |
| 727 | | 2d. lake-brn (Type II) (2 bands) (1969) | 15 | 15 |
| 728 | | 2d. lake-brown (Type II) (1 centre band) (27.8.69) .. .. .. | 40 | 50 |
| 729 | | 3d. violet (*shades*) (1 centre band) (8.8.67) .. .. .. .. | 10 | 10 |
| | | a. Imperf (pair) .. .. .. | £475 | |
| 730 | | 3d. violet (2 bands) (6.4.68) .. | 30 | 30 |
| | | a. Uncoated paper** .. .. | £900 | |
| 731 | | 4d. deep sepia (*shades*) (2 bands) .. | 10 | 10 |
| | | b. Part perf pane* .. .. .. | £550 | |
| 732 | | 4d. dp olive-brown (*shades*) (1 centre band) (16.9.68) .. .. .. | 10 | 10 |
| | | a. Part perf pane* .. .. .. | £450 | |
| | | l. Booklet pane. Two stamps plus two printed labels .. .. | 75 | |
| 733 | | 4d. brt verm (1 centre band) (6.1.69) | 10 | 10 |
| | | a. *Tête-bêche* (horiz pair) .. .. | £2500 | |
| | | b. Uncoated paper** .. .. | 8·00 | |
| | | l. Booklet pane. Two stamps plus two printed labels (3.3.69) .. | 80 | |
| 734 | **282** | 4d. brt vermilion (1 side band) (6.1.69) | 1·40 | 1·60 |
| | | a. Uncoated paper** .. .. | £150 | |
| 735 | | 5d. royal blue (*shades*) (1.7.68) .. | 10 | 10 |
| | | a. Imperf pane* .. .. .. | £450 | |
| | | b. Part perf pane* .. .. .. | £400 | |
| | | c. Imperf (pair)†† .. .. .. | £100 | |
| | | d. Uncoated paper** .. .. | 15·00 | |
| 736 | | 6d. brt reddish pur (*shades*) (5.2.68) | 20 | 20 |
| 737 | **282*a*** | 7d. bright emerald (1.7.68) .. .. | 40 | 30 |
| 738 | | 8d. bright vermilion (1.7.68) .. | 15 | 30 |
| 739 | | 8d. light turquoise-blue (6.1.69) .. | 45 | 50 |
| 740 | | 9d. myrtle-green (8.8.67) .. .. | 50 | 30 |
| 741 | **282** | 10d. drab (1.7.68) .. .. .. | 45 | 50 |
| | | a. Uncoated paper** .. .. | 25·00 | |
| 742 | | 1s. light bluish violet (*shades*) .. | 40 | 30 |
| 743 | | 1s. 6d. greenish blue and deep blue (*shades*) (8.8.67) .. .. | 50 | 30 |
| | | a. Greenish blue omitted .. .. | £100 | |
| | | c. Phosphorised paper. *Prussian blue and indigo* (10.12.69) .. .. | 75 | 90 |
| | | ca. Prussian blue omitted .. .. | £225 | |
| 744 | | 1s. 9d. dull orange and black (*shades*) | 40 | 30 |
| 723/44 | | .. .. .. .. *Set of* 16 | 3·00 | 3·25 |

*BOOKLET ERRORS. See note after No. 556.

** Uncoated paper. This does not respond to the chalky test, and may be further distinguished from the normal chalk-surfaced paper by the fibres which clearly show on the surface, resulting in the printing impression being rougher, and by the screening dots which are not so evident. The 1d., 4d. and 5d. come from the £1 "Stamps for Cooks" Booklet (1970); and the 3d. and 10d. from sheets (1969). The 20p. and 50p. high values (Nos. 830/1) exist with similar errors.

† No. 724a occurs in a vertical strip of four, top stamp perforated on three sides, bottom stamp imperf three sides and the two middle stamps completely imperf.

†† No. 735c comes from the original state of cylinder 15 which is identifiable by the screening dots which extend through the gutters of the stamps and into the margins of the sheet. This must not be confused with imperforate stamps from cylinder 10, a large quantity of which was stolen from the printers early in 1970.

The 1d. with centre band (725) only came in the September 1968 booklets (PVA gum) and the coil strip (725m) (gum arabic); the 2d. with centre band (728) was only issued in the coil strip (725m); the 3d. (No. 730) appeared in booklets on 6.4.68, from coils during December 1968 and from sheets in January 1969; and the 4d. with one side band (734) only in 10s. and £1 booklets.

Gum. The 1d. (725), 3d. (729), 4d. (731 and 733), 9d., 1s., 1s. 6d. and 1s. 9d. exist with gum arabic as well as the PVA gum; the 2d. (728) and coil strip (725m) exist only with gum arabic; and the remainder exist with PVA gum only.

The 4d. (731) in shades of washed-out grey are colour changelings which we understand are caused by the concentrated solvents used in modern dry cleaning methods.

For decimal issue, see Nos. X841/1026.

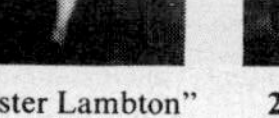

**283** "Master Lambton" (Sir Thomas Lawrence) **284** "Mares and Foals in a Landscape" (George Stubbs)

**285** "Children Coming Out of School" (L. S. Lowry)

**1967** (10 July). *British Paintings. Chalk-surfaced paper. Two phosphor bands. No wmk. P* 14 × 15 (*4d.*) *or* 15 × 14 (*others*).

| | | | | |
|---|---|---|---|---|
| 748 | **283** | 4d. rose-red, lemon, brown, black, new blue and gold .. .. .. | 10 | 10 |
| | | a. Gold (value and Queen's head) omitted .. .. .. .. | £180 | |
| | | b. New blue omitted .. .. .. | £2500 | |
| 749 | **284** | 9d. Venetian red, ochre, grey-black, new blue, greenish yellow and black | 20 | 20 |
| | | a. Black (Queen's head and value) omitted .. .. .. .. | £400 | |
| | | b. Greenish yellow omitted .. .. | £1200 | |
| 750 | **285** | 1s. 6d. greenish yellow, grey, rose, new blue, grey-black and gold .. .. | 35 | 25 |
| | | a. Gold (Queen's head) omitted .. | £750 | |
| | | b. New blue omitted .. .. .. | £140 | |
| | | c. Grey omitted.. .. .. .. | 85·00 | |
| 748/50 | | .. .. .. .. .. *Set of* 3 | 50 | 50 |

**286** *Gypsy Moth IV*

(Des M. and Sylvia Goaman)

**1967** (24 July). *Sir Francis Chichester's World Voyage. Chalk-surfaced paper. Three phosphor bands. No wmk. P* 15 × 14.

| | | | | |
|---|---|---|---|---|
| 751 | **286** | 1s. 9d. black, brown-red, lt emer & blue | 25 | 25 |

**287** Radar Screen

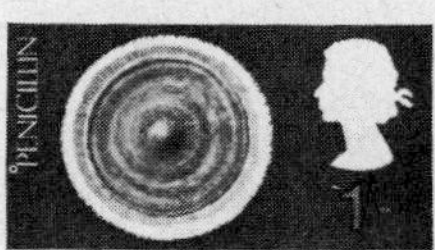


**288** *Penicillium notatum*

**289** "VC-10" Jet Engines **290** Television Equipment

(Des C. Abbott (4d., 1s.), Negus-Sharland team (others))

**1967** (19 Sept). *British Discovery and Invention. Chalk-surfaced paper. Three phosphor bands* (*4d.*) *or two phosphor bands* (*others*). *W* **179** (*sideways on 1s. 9d.*). *P* 14 × 15 (*1s. 9d.*) *or* 15 × 14 (*others*).

| | | | | |
|---|---|---|---|---|
| 752 | **287** | 4d. greenish yellow, black and vermilion | 10 | 10 |
| 753 | **288** | 1s. blue-green, light greenish blue, slate-purple and bluish violet .. .. | 10 | 10 |
| 754 | **289** | 1s. 6d. black, grey, royal blue, ochre and turquoise-blue .. .. .. | 25 | 15 |
| 755 | **290** | 1s. 9d. black, grey-blue, pale olive-grey, violet and orange .. .. .. | 30 | 20 |
| | | a. Grey-blue omitted .. .. | | |
| 752/5 | | .. .. .. .. .. *Set of* 4 | 60 | 50 |

**WATERMARK.** All issues from this date are on unwatermarked paper.

**291** "The Adoration of the Shepherds" (School of Seville) **292** "Madonna and Child" (Murillo)

**293** "The Adoration of the Shepherds" (Louis le Nain)

**1967.** *Christmas. Chalk-surfaced paper. One phosphor band (3d.) or two phosphor bands (others). P 15 × 14 (1s. 6d.) or 14 × 15 (others).*

756 **291** 3d. ol-yell, rose, bl, blk & gold (27.11) .. 10 10
 a. Gold (value and Queen's head) omitted .. .. .. .. .. 60·00
 b. Printed on the gummed side .. £300
 c. Rose omitted .. .. ..
757 **292** 4d. bright purple, greenish yellow, new blue, grey-black and gold (18.10) .. 10 10
 a. Gold (value and Queen's head) omitted .. .. .. .. .. 60·00
 b. Yellow (Child, robe and Madonna's face) omitted .. .. ..
758 **293** 1s. 6d. brt purple, bistre, lemon, black, orange-red, ultram & gold (27.11) 35 35
 a. Gold (value and Queen's head) omitted .. .. .. .. .. £200
 b. Ultramarine omitted .. .. £300
756/8 .. .. .. .. .. *Set of 3* 50 50

Distinct shades exist of the 4d. value but are not listable as there are intermediate shades. Stamps emanating from one machine show a darker background and give the appearance of the yellow colour being omitted but this is not so and these should not be confused with the true missing yellow No. 757b.

(Recess Bradbury, Wilkinson)

**1967–68.** *No wmk. White paper. P 11 × 12.*

759 **166** 2s. 6d. black-brown (1.7.68) .. .. 40 50
760 **167** 5s. red (10.4.68) .. .. .. 1·00 1·00
761 **168** 10s. bright ultramarine (10.4.68) .. 5·00 5·50
762 **169** £1 black (4.12.67) .. .. .. 4·00 4·00
759/62 .. .. .. .. .. *Set of 4* 9·00 10·00

**PVA GUM.** All the following issues from this date have PVA gum *except where footnotes state otherwise.*

**294** Tarr Steps, Exmoor

**295** Aberfeldy Bridge

**296** Menai Bridge

**297** M4 Viaduct

(Des A. Restall (9d.), L. Rosoman (1s. 6d.), J. Matthews (others))

**1968** (29 Apr). *British Bridges. Chalk-surfaced paper. Two phosphor bands. P 15 × 14.*

763 **294** 4d. black, bluish violet, turq-bl & gold 10 10
 a. Printed on gummed side .. .. 25·00
764 **295** 9d. red-brown, myrtle-green, ultramarine, olive-brown, black and gold .. 10 10
 a. Gold (Queen's head) omitted .. £150
 b. Ultramarine omitted .. .. † £3000
765 **296** 1s. 6d. olive-brown, red-orange, bright green, turquoise-green and gold .. 20 15
 a. Gold (Queen's head) omitted .. £150
 b. Red-orange omitted .. .. £225
766 **297** 1s. 9d. olive-brown, greenish yellow, dull green, deep ultramarine & gold 25 30
 a. Gold (Queen's head) omitted .. £200
763/6 .. .. .. .. .. *Set of 4* 60 60

No. 764b is only known on first day covers posted from Canterbury.

**298** "T U C" and Trades Unionists

**299** Mrs. Emmeline Pankhurst (statue)

**300** Sopwith "Camel" and "Lightning" Fighters

**301** Captain Cook's *Endeavour* and Signature

(Des D. Gentleman (4d.), C. Abbott (others))

**1968** (29 May). *British Anniversaries. Events described on stamps. Chalk-surfaced paper. Two phosphor bands. P 15 × 14.*

767 **298** 4d. emerald, olive, blue and black .. 10 10
768 **299** 9d. reddish violet, bluish grey and black 10 10
769 **300** 1s. olive-brown, bl, red, slate-bl & blk 20 20
770 **301** 1s. 9d. yellow-ochre and blackish brown 25 25
767/70 .. .. .. .. .. *Set of 4* 60 60

**302** "Queen Elizabeth I" (unknown artist) **303** "Pinkie" (Lawrence)

**304** "Ruins of St. Mary Le Port" (Piper) **305** "The Hay Wain" (Constable)

**1968** (12 Aug). *British Paintings. Queen's head embossed. Chalk-surfaced paper. Two phosphor bands. P 15 × 14 (1s. 9d.) or 14 × 15 (others).*

771 **302** 4d. blk, verm, greenish yell, grey & gold 10 10
 a. Gold (value and Queen's head) omitted .. .. .. .. .. £150
 b. Vermilion omitted* .. .. £200
772 **303** 1s. mauve, new blue, greenish yellow, black, magenta and gold .. .. 15 15
 a. Gold (value and Queen's head) omitted .. .. .. .. .. £180
773 **304** 1s. 6d. slate, orange, black, mauve, greenish yellow, ultramarine & gold 20 20
 a. Gold (value and Queen's head) omitted .. .. .. .. .. £180
774 **305** 1s. 9d. greenish yellow, black, new blue, red and gold .. .. .. 25 25
 a. Gold (value and Queen's head) and embossing omitted .. .. .. £450
 b. Red omitted .. .. .. .. £2000
771/4 .. .. .. .. .. *Set of 4* 60 60

*The effect of this is to leave the face and hands white and there is more yellow and olive in the costume.

The 4d. and 1s. are known with the embossing only omitted. No. 774a is only known with the phosphor also omitted. No. 772a exists both with or without embossing or phosphor bands.

**306** Boy and Girl with Rocking Horse

**307** Girl with Doll's House **308** Boy with Train Set

(Des Rosalind Dease. Head printed in gold and then embossed)

**1968** (25 Nov). *Christmas. Chalk-surfaced paper. One centre phosphor band (4d.) or two phosphor bands (others). P 15 × 14 (4d.) or 14 × 15 (others).*

775 **306** 4d. black, orange, vermilion, ultramarine, bistre and gold .. .. 10 10
 a. Gold omitted .. .. .. .. £1500
 b. Vermilion omitted* .. .. .. £140
 c. Ultramarine omitted .. .. £150
776 **307** 9d. yellow-olive, black, brown, yellow, magenta, orange, turq-green & gold 15 15
 a. Yellow omitted .. .. .. 60·00
777 **308** 1s. 6d. ultramarine, yellow-orange, brt purple, blue-green, black and gold 25 25
775/7 .. .. .. .. .. *Set of 3* 50 50

*The effect of the missing vermilion is shown on the rocking horse, saddle and faces which appear orange instead of red.

A single used example of the 4d. exists with the bistre omitted.

No. 775c is only known with the phosphor also omitted. All values exist with the embossing of Queen's head omitted.

**309** R.M.S. *Queen Elizabeth 2*

**310** Elizabethan Galleon

**311** East Indiaman

**312** *Cutty Sark*

**313** S.S. *Great Britain*

**314** R.M.S. *Mauretania*

(Des D. Gentleman)

**1969** (15 Jan). *British Ships. Chalk-surfaced paper. Two vertical phosphor bands at right (1s.), one horizontal phosphor band (5d.) or two phosphor bands (9d.). P 15 × 14.*

778 **309** 5d. black, grey, red and turquoise .. 10 10
a. Black (Queen's head, value, hull and inscr) omitted .. .. .. £750
b. Grey (decks, etc.) omitted .. £110
c. Red omitted .. .. .. 50·00
779 **310** 9d. red, blue, ochre, brown, blk & grey 10 15
a. Strip of 3. Nos. 779/81 .. .. 85 85
ab. Red and blue omitted .. .. £1000
ac. Blue omitted .. .. £1000
780 **311** 9d. ochre, brown, black and grey .. 10 15
781 **312** 9d. ochre, brown, black and grey .. 10 15
782 **313** 1s. brn, black, grey, grn & greenish yell 25 25
a. Pair. Nos. 782/3 .. .. .. 90 85
ab. Greenish yellow omitted .. .. £2000
783 **314** 1s. red, black, brown, carmine and grey 25 25
a. Carmine (hull overlay) omitted ..
778/83 .. .. .. .. *Set of* 6 1·60 90

The 9d. and 1s. values were arranged in horizontal strips of three and pairs respectively throughout the sheet.

No. 779b is known only with the phosphor also omitted.

**315** "Concorde" in Flight

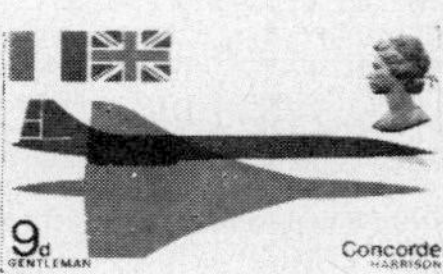


**316** Plan and Elevation Views

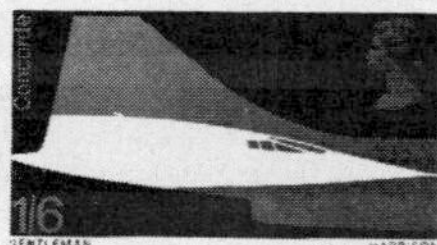


**317** "Concorde's" Nose and Tail

(Des M. and Sylvia Goaman (4d.), D. Gentleman (9d., 1s. 6d.))

**1969** (3 Mar). *First Flight of "Concorde". Chalk-surfaced paper. Two phosphor bands. P 15 × 14.*

784 **315** 4d. yellow-orange, violet, greenish blue, blue-green and pale green .. 10 10
a. Violet (value, etc.) omitted .. £300
b. Yellow-orange omitted .. .. £130
785 **316** 9d. ultramarine, emerald, red & grey-bl 20 20
786 **317** 1s. 6d. deep blue, silver-grey & lt blue 30 30
a. Silver-grey omitted .. .. £275
784/6 .. .. .. .. .. *Set of* 3 50 50

No. 786a affects the Queen's head which appears in the light blue colour.

**318** Queen Elizabeth II. (See also Type **357**)

(Des after plaster cast by Arnold Machin. Recess Bradbury, Wilkinson)

**1969** (5 Mar). *P 12.*

787 **318** 2s. 6d. brown .. .. .. .. 50 30
788 5s. crimson-lake .. .. .. 2·25 60
789 10s. deep ultramarine .. .. .. 7·00 7·50
790 £1 bluish black .. .. .. 3·00 1·60
787/90 .. .. .. .. .. *Set of* 4 11·50 9·00

For decimal issue, see Nos. 829/31*b* and notes after No. 831*b*.

**319** Page from *Daily Mail*, and Vickers "Vimy" Aircraft

**320** Europa and CEPT Emblems

**321** ILO Emblem

**322** Flags of NATO Countries

**323** Vickers "Vimy" Aircraft and Globe showing Flight

(Des P. Sharland (5d., 1s., 1s. 6d.), M. and Sylvia Goaman (9d., 1s. 9d.)

**1969** (2 Apr). *Anniversaries. Events described on stamps. Chalk-surfaced paper. Two phosphor bands. P 15 × 14.*

791 **319** 5d. black, pale sage-grn, chest & new bl 10 10
792 **320** 9d. pale turq, dp bl, lt emer-green & blk 20 20
793 **321** 1s. bright purple, deep blue and lilac 20 20
794 **322** 1s. 6d. red, royal blue, yellow-green, black, lemon and new blue .. 20 20
e. Black omitted .. .. .. 60·00
f. Yellow-green omitted .. .. 48·00
795 **323** 1s. 9d. yellow-olive, greenish yellow and pale turquoise-green .. .. 25 25
a. Uncoated paper* .. .. .. £200
791/5 .. .. .. .. .. *Set of* 5 85 85

*Uncoated paper. The second note after No. 744 also applies here.

**324** Durham Cathedral

**325** York Minster

**326** St. Giles' Cathedral, Edinburgh

**327** Canterbury Cathedral

**328** St. Paul's Cathedral

**329** Liverpool Metropolitan Cathedral

(Des P. Gauld)

**1969** (28 May). *British Architecture. Cathedrals. Chalk-surfaced paper. Two phosphor bands. P 15 × 14.*

796 **324** 5d. grey-blk, orge, pale bluish vio & blk 10 10
a. Block of 4. Nos. 796/9 .. .. 85 1·00
b. Pale bluish violet omitted .. .. £1750
797 **325** 5d. grey-black, pale bluish violet, new blue and black .. .. .. 10 10
b. Pale bluish violet omitted .. £1750
798 **326** 5d. grey-black, purple, green and black 10 10
c. Green omitted* .. .. .. 40·00
799 **327** 5d. grey-black, green, new blue & black 10 10
800 **328** 9d. grey-blk, ochre, pale drab, vio & blk 15 15
a. Black (value) omitted .. .. £100
801 **329** 1s. 6d. grey-black, pale turquoise, pale reddish violet, pale yellow-ol & blk 15 15
a. Black (value) omitted .. £2500
b. Black (value) double .. ..
796/801 .. .. .. .. *Set of* 6 1·00 55

The 5d. values were issued together *se-tenant* in blocks of four throughout the sheet.

*The missing green on the roof top is known on R. 2/5, R. 8/5 and R. 10/5, but all from different sheets, and it only occurred in part of the printing, being "probably caused by a batter on the impression cylinder". Examples are also known with the green partly omitted.

**330** The King's Gate, Caernarvon Castle

**331** The Eagle Tower, Caernarvon Castle

**332** Queen Eleanor's Gate, Caernarvon Castle

**333** Celtic Cross, Margam Abbey

**334** H.R.H. The Prince of Wales (after photo by G. Argent)

(Des D. Gentleman)

**1969** (1 July). *Investiture of H.R.H. The Prince of Wales. Chalk-surfaced paper. Two phosphor bands. P 14 × 15.*

802 **330** 5d. deep olive-grey, light olive-grey, deep grey, light grey, red, pale turquoise-green, black and silver .. 10 10
a. Strip of 3. Nos. 802/4 .. 70 75
b. Black (value and inscr) omitted .. £200
c. Red omitted* .. .. .. £250
d. Deep grey omitted** .. .. 90·00
e. Pale turquoise-green omitted .. £250
803 **331** 5d. deep olive-grey, light olive-grey, deep grey, light grey, red, pale turquoise-green, black and silver .. 10 10
b. Black (value and inscr) omitted .. £200
c. Red omitted* .. .. .. £250
d. Deep grey omitted** .. .. 90·00
e. Pale turquoise-green omitted .. £250
804 **332** 5d. deep olive-grey, light olive-grey, deep grey, light grey, red, pale turquoise-green, black and silver .. 10 10
b. Black (value and inscr) omitted .. £200
c. Red omitted* .. .. .. £250
d. Deep grey omitted** .. .. 90·00
e. Pale turquoise-green omitted .. £250
805 **333** 9d. deep grey, light grey, black and gold 20 10
806 **334** 1s. blackish yellow-olive and gold .. 20 10
802/6 .. .. .. .. .. *Set of* 5 1·00 45

The 5d. values were issued together, *se-tenant*, in strips of three throughout the sheet.

*The 5d. value is also known with the red misplaced downward and where this occurs the red printing does not take very well on the silver background and in some cases is so faint that it could be mistaken for a missing red. However, the red can be seen under a magnifying glass and caution should therefore be exercised when purchasing copies of Nos. 802/4c.

**The deep grey affects the dark portions of the windows and doors.

**335** Mahatma Gandhi

(Des B. Mullick)

**1969** (13 Aug). *Gandhi Centenary Year. Chalk-surfaced paper. Two phosphor bands. P* 15 × 14.
807 **335** 1s. 6d. black, green, red-orange & grey .. 30 30
a. Printed on the gummed side .. £300

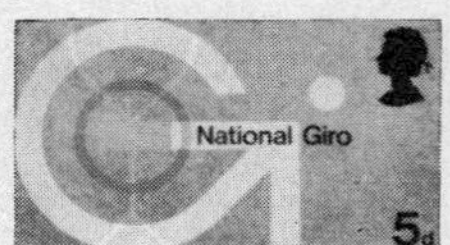

**336** National Giro "G" Symbol

**337** Telecommunications—International Subscriber Dialling

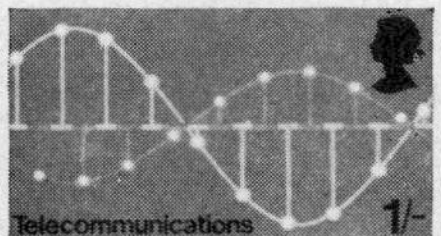

**338** Telecommunications—Pulse Code Modulation

**339** Postal Mechanisation—Automatic Sorting

(Des D. Gentleman. Litho De La Rue)

**1969** (1 Oct). *Post Office Technology Commemoration. Chalk-surfaced paper. Two phosphor bands. P* 13½ × 14.
808 **336** 5d. new bl, greenish bl, lavender & blk 10 10
809 **337** 9d. emerald, violet-blue and black .. 15 15
810 **338** 1s. emerald, lavender and black .. 15 15
811 **339** 1s. 6d. brt purple, lt blue, grey-bl & blk 40 40
808/11 .. .. .. .. .. *Set of* 4 70 70

**340** Herald Angel

**341** The Three Shepherds

**342** The Three Kings

(Des F. Wegner. Queen's head (and stars 4d., 5d. and scroll-work 1s. 6d.) printed in gold and then embossed)

**1969** (26 Nov). *Christmas. Chalk-surfaced paper. Two phosphor bands* (5*d.*, 1*s.* 6*d.*) *or one centre band* (4*d.*). *P* 15 × 14.
812 **340** 4d. vermilion, new blue, orange, bright purple, light green, bluish violet, blackish brown and gold .. .. 10 10
a. Gold (Queen's head etc.) omitted .. £2000
813 **341** 5d. magenta, light blue, royal blue, olive-brown, green, greenish yellow, red and gold .. .. .. .. 10 10
a. Light blue (sheep, etc.) omitted .. 60·00
b. Red omitted* .. .. .. £500
c. Gold (Queen's head) omitted .. £400
d. Green omitted .. .. .. £225
814 **342** 1s. 6d. greenish yellow, bright purple, bluish violet, deep slate, orange, green, new blue and gold .. .. 30 30
a. Gold (Queen's head etc.) omitted .. £100
b. Deep slate (value) omitted .. .. £300
c. Greenish yellow omitted .. .. £130
d. Bluish violet omitted .. .. £300
e. New blue omitted .. .. .. 75·00
812/14 .. .. .. .. .. *Set of* 3 45 45

*The effect of the missing red is shown on the hat, leggings and purse which appear as dull orange.

The 5d. and 1s. 6d. values are known with the embossing omitted.

Used copies of the 5d. have been seen with the olive-brown or greenish yellow omitted.

**343** Fife Harling

**344** Cotswold Limestone

**345** Welsh Stucco

**346** Ulster Thatch

(Des D. Gentleman (5d., 9d.), Sheila Robinson (1s., 1s. 6d.))

**1970** (11 Feb). *British Rural Architecture. Chalk-surfaced paper. Two phosphor bands. P* 15 × 14.
815 **343** 5d. grey, grey-black, black, lemon, greenish bl, orge-brn, ultram & grn 10 10
a. Lemon omitted .. .. .. 60·00
b. Grey (Queen's head and cottage shading) omitted .. .. .. £4000
816 **344** 9d. orange-brown, olive-yellow, bright green, black, grey-black and grey .. 20 20
817 **345** 1s. dp blue, reddish lilac, drab & new bl 20 20
a. New blue omitted .. .. .. 45·00
818 **346** 1s. 6d. greenish yell, blk, turq-bl & lilac 35 35
a. Turquoise-blue omitted .. .. £3500
815/18 .. .. .. .. .. *Set of* 4 75 75

Used examples of the 5d. have been seen with the grey-black or greenish blue colours omitted.

**347** Signing the Declaration of Arbroath

**348** Florence Nightingale attending Patients

**349** Signing of International Co-operative Alliance

**350** Pilgrims and *Mayflower*

**351** Sir William Herschel, Francis Baily, Sir John Herschel and Telescope

(Des F. Wegner (5d., 9d., and 1s. 6d.), Marjorie Saynor (1s., 1s. 9d.). Queen's head printed in gold and then embossed)

**1970** (1 Apr). *Anniversaries. Events described on stamps. Chalk-surfaced paper. Two phosphor bands. P* 15 × 14.
819 **347** 5d. blk, yell-olive, blue, emer, greenish yellow, rose-red, gold & orange-red 10 10
a. Gold (Queen's head) omitted .. £400
b. Emerald omitted .. .. .. 50·00
820 **348** 9d. ochre, deep blue, carmine, black, blue-green, yellow-olive, gold & bl 15 15
a. Ochre omitted .. .. .. £150
821 **349** 1s. green, greenish yellow, brown, black, cerise, gold and light blue .. 25 15
a. Gold (Queen's head) omitted .. 50·00
c. Green omitted .. .. .. £110
d. Brown omitted .. .. .. £130
822 **350** 1s. 6d. greenish yellow, carmine, deep yellow-olive, emerald, black, blue gold and sage-green .. .. .. 30 30
a. Gold (Queen's head) omitted .. 90·00
b. Emerald omitted .. .. .. 40·00
823 **351** 1s. 9d. blk, slate, lemon, gold & brt pur 30 30
819/23 .. .. .. .. .. *Set of* 5 1·00 90

The 9d., 1s. and 1s. 6d. are known with the embossing omitted. No. 821c also exists with embossing omitted.

The 1s. 9d. with the lemon colour omitted has been seen used on a First Day Cover.

**352** "Mr. Pickwick and Sam" (*Pickwick Papers*)

**353** "Mr. and Mrs. Micawber" (*David Copperfield*)

**354** "David Copperfield and Betsy Trotwood" (*David Copperfield*)

**355** "Oliver asking for more" (*Oliver Twist*)

**356** "Grasmere" (from engraving by J. Farrington, R.A.)

T **352/5** were issued together *se-tenant* in blocks of four throughout the sheet.

(Des Rosalind Dease. Queen's head printed in gold and then embossed)

**1970** (3 June). *Literary Anniversaries. Death Centenary of Charles Dickens* (*novelist*) (5*d.* × 4) *and Birth Bicentenary of William Wordsworth* (*poet*) (1*s.* 6*d.*). *Chalk-surfaced paper. Two phosphor bands. P* 14 × 15.
824 **352** 5d. black, orange, silver, gold and mag 10 10
a. Block of 4. Nos. 824/7 .. .. 90 90
ab. Imperf (block of four) .. .. £600
825 **353** 5d. black, magenta, silver, gold & orge 10 10
826 **354** 5d. black, light greenish blue, silver, gold and yellow-bistre .. .. 10 10
b. Yellow-bistre (value) omitted .. £1200
827 **355** 5d. black, yellow-bistre, silver, gold and light greenish blue .. .. .. 10 10
b. Yellow-bistre (background) omitted £3000
c. Light greenish blue (value) omitted* £300
828 **356** 1s. 6d. light yellow-olive, black, silver, gold and bright blue .. .. 20 20
a. Gold (Queen's head) omitted .. £225
b. Silver ("Grasmere") omitted .. 60·00
824/8 .. .. .. .. .. *Set of* 5 1·00 55

*No 827c (unlike No. 827b) comes from a sheet on which the colour was only partially omitted so that, although No. 827 was completely without the light greenish blue colour, it was still partially present on No. 826.

The 1s. 6d. is known with embossing omitted.

**357** (Value redrawn)

(Des after plaster cast by Arnold Machin. Recess B.W.)

**1970** (17 June)–**72**. *Decimal Currency. Chalk-surfaced paper or phosphorised paper* (10*p.*). *P* 12.
829 **357** 10p. cerise .. .. .. .. 1·00 75
830 20p. olive-green .. .. .. .. 70 15
831 50p. deep ultramarine .. .. .. 1·50 40
831*b* £1 bluish black (6.12.72) .. .. 3·50 75
829/31*b* .. .. .. .. .. *Set of* 4 6·00 1·75

The 20p. and 50p. exist on thinner, uncoated paper and are listed in the *Great Britain Concise Catalogue*.

A whiter paper was introduced in 1973. The £1 appeared on 27 Sept. 1973, the 20p. on 30 Nov. 1973 and the 50p. on 20 Feb. 1974.

The 50p. was issued on 1 Feb. 1973 on phosphorised paper. This cannot be distinguished from No. 831 with the naked eye.

The £1, T **318**, was also issued, on 17 June 1970, in sheets of 100 (10 × 10) instead of panes of 40 (8 × 5) but it is not easy to distinguish from No. 790 in singles. It can be readily differentiated when in large strips or marginal pieces showing sheet markings or plate numbers.

**358** Runners

**359** Swimmers

**360** Cyclists

(Des A. Restall. Litho D.L.R.)

**1970** (15 July). *Ninth British Commonwealth Games. Chalk-surfaced paper. Two phosphor bands. P* 13½ × 14.

832 **358** 5d. pk, emer, greenish yell & dp yell-grn .. 10 10
 a. Greenish yellow omitted .. .. £3500
833 **359** 1s. 6d. light greenish blue, lilac, bistre-brown and Prussian blue .. 50 50
834 **360** 1s. 9d. yellow-orange, lilac, salmon and deep red-brown .. .. 50 50
832/4 .. .. .. .. .. *Set of* 3 1·00 1·00

**361** 1d. Black (1840)



**362** 1s. Green (1847)

**363** 4d. Carmine (1855)

(Des D. Gentleman)

**1970** (18 Sept). *"Philympia 70" Stamp Exhibition. Chalk-surfaced paper. Two phosphor bands. P* 14 × 14½.

835 **361** 5d. grey-black, brownish bistre, black and dull purple .. .. 10 10
836 **362** 9d. light drab, bluish green, stone, black and dull purple .. .. 35 35
837 **363** 1s. 6d. carmine, lt drab, blk & dull pur 40 40
835/7 .. .. .. .. .. *Set of* 3 75 75

**364** Shepherds and Apparition of the Angel

**365** Mary, Joseph, and Christ in the Manger

**366** The Wise Men bearing gifts

(Des Sally Stiff after De Lisle Psalter. Queen's head printed in gold and then embossed)

**1970** (25 Nov). *Christmas. Chalk-surfaced paper. One centre phosphor band* (4d.) *or two phosphor bands* (*others*). *P* 14 × 15.

838 **364** 4d. brown-red, turquoise-green, pale chestnut, brn, grey-blk, gold & verm 10 10
839 **365** 5d. emerald, gold, blue, brown-red, ochre, grey-black and violet .. 10 10
 a. Gold (Queen's head) omitted .. † £2500
 b. Emerald omitted .. .. .. 60·00
 c. Imperf (pair) .. .. .. £250
840 **366** 1s. 6d. gold, grey-black, pale turq-grn, salmon, ultram, ochre & yellow-grn 35 35
 a. Salmon omitted .. .. .. £130
 b. Ochre omitted .. .. .. 65·00
838/40 .. .. .. .. .. *Set of* 3 50 50

The 4d. and 5d. are known with embossing omitted, and the 1s. 6d. is known with embossing and phosphor omitted.

**(New Currency. 100 new pence = £1)**

**"X" NUMBERS.** The following definitive series has been allocated "X" prefixes to the catalogue numbers to avoid re-numbering all subsequent issues.

**367**

**367*a***

**NO VALUE INDICATED.** Stamps as Types **367**/*a* inscribed "2nd" or "1st" are listed as Nos. 1445/52 and 1511/16.

**PRINTING PROCESSES**

Litho Photo

(*Illustrations enlarged* ×6)

Litho. Clear outlines to value and frame of stamp.

Photo. Uneven lines to value and frame formed by edges of screen.

Two types of the 3p., 10p. and 26p. (Nos. X930/c, X886/b and X971/a).

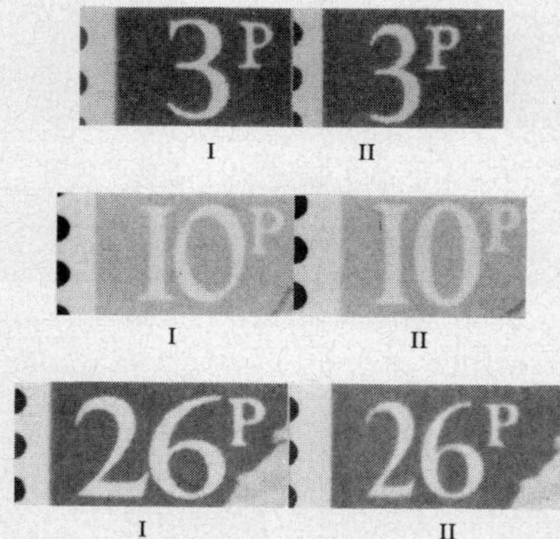


Figures of face value as I (all ptgs of 3p. bright magenta except multi-value coil No. 930cl and sheets from 21.1.92 onwards, 10p. orange-brown except 1984 "Christian Heritage" £4 booklet and 26p. rosine except 1987 £1.04 "window" booklet).

Figures of face value narrower as in II (from coil No. X930cl and in sheets from 21.1.92 (3p.), 1984 "Christian Heritage" £4 booklet (10p.) or 1987 £1.04 "window" booklet (26p.)).

This catalogue includes changes of figure styles on those stamps where there is no other listable difference. Similar changes have also taken place on other values, but only in conjunction with listed colour, paper or perforation differences.

(Des from plaster cast by Arnold Machin)

**1971** (15 Feb)–**92**. *Decimal Currency. T* **367**. *Chalk-surfaced paper.*

(*a*) *Photo Harrison* (*except for printings of Nos.* X879 *and* X913 *in sheets produced by Enschedé in* 1979 (8*p.*) *and* 1991 (18*p.*)). *With phosphor bands. P* 15×14.

X841 ½p. turquoise-blue (2 bands) .. .. 10 10
 a. Imperf (pair)† .. .. .. £900
 l. Booklet pane. No. X841 × 2 *se-tenant* vert with X849 × 2 .. .. .. 5·50
 la. Ditto, *se-tenant* horiz (14.7.71) .. 75
 m. Booklet pane. No. X841×5 plus label 2·25
 n. Coil strip. No. X849, X841×2 and X844×2 .. .. .. .. 35
 o. Booklet pane. No. X841 × 3, X851 × 3 and X852 × 6 (24.5.72) .. .. 10·00
 p. Booklet pane. No. X841 × 3, X842 and X852 × 2 (24.5.72) .. .. .. 70·00
 q. Coil strip. No. X870, X849, X844 and X841 × 2 (3.12.75) .. .. .. 80
 r. Booklet pane. No. X841 × 2, X844 × 3 and X870 (10.3.76) .. .. .. 60
 s. Booklet pane. No. X841 × 2, X844 × 2, X873 × 2 and X881 × 4 (8½p. values at right) (26.1.77) .. .. 2·50
 sa. Ditto. 8½p. values at left .. .. 2·50
 t. Booklet pane. No. X841, X844, X894 × 3 and X902 (14p. value at right) (26.1.81) .. .. .. .. 2·25
 ta. Ditto. 14p. value at left .. .. 2·25
 u. Booklet pane. No. X841, X857 × 4 and X899 × 3 (12½p. values at left) (1.2.82) 2·75
 ua. Ditto. 12½p. values at right .. .. 2·75
X842 ½p. turquoise-blue (1 side band) (24.5.72) 60·00 25·00
X843 ½p. turquoise-bl (1 centre band) (14.12.77) 30 20
 l. Coil strip. No. X843 × 2, X875 and X845 × 2 (14.12.77) .. .. .. 55
 m. Booklet pane. No. X843 × 2, X845 × 2 and X875 plus label (8.2.78) .. 60
X844 1p. crimson (2 bands) .. .. .. 10 10
 a. Imperf (vert coil) .. .. ..
 b. Pair, one imperf 3 sides (vert coil) ..
 c. Imperf (pair) .. .. .. ..
 l. Booklet pane. No. X844 × 2 *se-tenant* vert with X848 × 2 .. .. .. 5·50
 m. Ditto, *se-tenant* horiz (14.7.71) .. 75
 n. Booklet pane. No. X844 × 2, X876 × 3 and X883 × 3 (9p. values at right) (13.6.77) .. .. .. .. 4·00
 na. Ditto. 9p. values at left .. .. 2·50
X845 1p. crimson (1 centre band) (14.12.77) .. 20 20
 l. Booklet pane. No. X879 and X845 × 2 plus label (17.10.79) .. .. .. 50
 m. Coil strip. No. X879 and X845 × 2 plus 2 labels (16.1.80) .. .. .. 45
 n. Booklet pane. No. X845 × 2, X860 and X898 each × 3 (5.4.83) .. .. 5·00
 p. Booklet pane. No. X845× 3, X863 × 2 and X900 × 3 (3.9.84) .. .. 4·00
 q. Booklet pane. No. X845 × 2 and X896 × 4 (29.7.86) .. .. .. 8·00
 s. Booklet pane. No. X845, X867 × 2 and X900 × 3 (20.10.86) .. .. 4·00
 sa. Ditto, but with vert edges of pane imperf (29.9.87) .. .. .. 3·00
X846 1p. crimson ("all-over") (10.10.79) .. 20 20
X847 1p. crimson (1 side band) (20.10.86) .. 75 90
 l. Booklet pane. X847, X901 and X912 ×2 .. .. .. .. .. 3·00
 m. Booklet pane. No. X847, X901×2, X912×5 and X918 with margins all round (3.3.87) .. .. .. 8·50
X848 1½p. black (2 bands) .. .. .. 20 15
 a. Uncoated paper (1971)* .. .. £110
 b. Imperf (pair) .. .. ..
 c. Imperf 3 sides (horiz pair) .. ..
X849 2p. myrtle-green (face value as T **367**) (2 bands) .. .. .. .. 20 10
 a. Imperf (horiz pair) .. .. ..
 l. Booklet pane. No. X849×2, X880×2 and X886×3 plus label (10p. values at right) (28.8.79) .. .. .. 2·00
 la. Ditto. 10p. values at left .. .. 2·00
 m. Booklet pane. No. X849×3, X889×2 and X895×2 plus label (12p. values at right) (4.2.80) .. .. .. 2·00
 ma. Ditto. 12p. values at left .. .. 2·00
 n. Booklet pane. No. X849, X888×3, X889 and X895×4 with margins all round (16.4.80) .. .. .. 3·00
 o. Booklet pane. No. X849×6 with margins all round (16.4.80) .. .. 60
 p. Booklet pane. No. X849, X857, X898 and X899×6 with margins all round (19.5.82) .. .. .. .. 6·50
X850 2p. myrtle-green (face value as T **367**) ("all-over") (10.10.79) .. .. 20 15
X851 2½p. magenta (1 centre band) .. .. 15 10
 a. Imperf (pair)† .. .. .. £225
 l. Booklet pane. No. X851 × 5 plus label 3·50
 m. Booklet pane. No. X851 × 4 plus two labels .. .. .. .. 4·00
 n. Booklet pane. No. X851 × 3, X852 × 3 and X855 × 6 (24.5.72) .. .. 10·00
X852 2½p. magenta (1 side band) .. .. 1·75 1·75
 l. Booklet pane. No. X852 × 2 and X855 × 4 .. .. .. .. .. 4·50
X853 2½p. magenta (2 bands) (21.5.75) .. 20 30
X854 2½p. rose-red (2 bands) (26.8.81) .. 40 40
 l. Booklet pane. No. X854 × 3, X862 × 2 and X894 × 3 (11½p. values at left) .. 4·50
 la. Ditto. 11½p. values at right .. .. 6·50
X855 3p. ultramarine (2 bands) .. .. 20 10
 a. Imperf (coil strip of 5) .. .. £1000
 b. Imperf (pair)† .. .. .. £225
 c. Uncoated paper (1972)* .. .. 40·00
 l. Booklet pane. No. X855 × 5 plus label 2·25
X856 3p. ultramarine (1 centre band) (10.9.73) 20 25
 a. Imperf (pair)† .. .. .. £250
 b. Imperf between (vert pair)† .. £375
 c. Imperf horiz (vert pair)† .. .. £150
X857 3p. bright magenta (Type I) (2 bands) (1.2.82) .. .. .. .. 30 25

| No. | Description | | |
|---|---|---|---|
| X858 | 3½p. olive-grey (*shades*) (2 bands) | 30 | 30 |
| | a. Imperf (pair) | £350 | |
| X859 | 3½p. olive-grey (1 centre band) (24.6.74) | 30 | 15 |
| X860 | 3½p. purple-brown (1 centre band) (5.4.83) | 1·75 | 1·25 |
| X861 | 4p. ochre-brown (2 bands) | 20 | 20 |
| | a. Imperf (pair)† | £450 | |
| X862 | 4p. greenish blue (2 bands) (26.8.81) | 2·00 | 1·75 |
| X863 | 4p. greenish blue (1 centre band) (3.9.84) | 1·00 | 1·00 |
| X864 | 4p. greenish blue (1 side band) (8.1.85) | 1·50 | 1·50 |
| | l. Booklet pane. No. X864×2, X901×4, X909×2 and X920 with margins all round | 9·50 | |
| X865 | 4½p. grey-blue (2 bands) (24.10.73) | 20 | 25 |
| | a. Imperf (pair) | £250 | |
| X866 | 5p. pale violet (2 bands) | 20 | 10 |
| X867 | 5p. claret (1 centre band) (20.10.86) | 1·25 | 1·00 |
| X868 | 5½p. violet (2 bands) (24.10.73) | 25 | 25 |
| X869 | 5½p. violet (1 centre band) (17.3.75) | 20 | 20 |
| | a. Uncoated paper* | £350 | |
| X870 | 6p. light emerald (2 bands) | 30 | 15 |
| | a. Uncoated paper* | 15·00 | |
| X871 | 6½p. greenish blue (2 bands) (4.9.74) | 45 | 45 |
| X872 | 6½p. greenish blue (1 centre band) (24.9.75) | 30 | 15 |
| | a. Imperf (vert pair) | £300 | |
| | b. Uncoated paper* | £160 | |
| X873 | 6½p. greenish blue (1 side band) (26.1.77) | 60 | 55 |
| X874 | 7p. purple-brown (2 bands) (15.1.75) | 35 | 25 |
| | a. Imperf (pair) | £250 | |
| X875 | 7p. purple-brown (1 centre band) (13.6.77) | 35 | 20 |
| | a. Imperf (pair) | £100 | |
| | l. Booklet pane. No. X875 × 10 and X883 × 10 (15.11.78) | 4·50 | |
| X876 | 7p. purple-brown (1 side band) (13.6.77) | 60 | 75 |
| X877 | 7½p. pale chestnut (2 bands) | 30 | 25 |
| X878 | 8p. rosine (2 bands) (24.10.73) | 25 | 20 |
| | a. Uncoated paper* | 10·00 | |
| X879 | 8p. rosine (1 centre band) (20.8.79) | 25 | 15 |
| | a. Uncoated paper* | £550 | |
| | b. Imperf (pair) | £550 | |
| | l. Booklet pane. No. X879 and X886, each × 10 (14.11.79) | 5·00 | |
| X880 | 8p. rosine (1 side band) (28.8.79) | 60 | 60 |
| X881 | 8½p. light yellowish green (*shades*) (2 bands) (24.9.75) | 35 | 20 |
| | a. Imperf (pair) | £750 | |
| X882 | 9p. yellow-orange and black (2 bands) | 60 | 30 |
| X883 | 9p. deep violet (2 bands) (25.2.76) | 45 | 25 |
| | a. Imperf (pair) | £180 | |
| X884 | 9½p. purple (2 bands) (25.2.76) | 45 | 30 |
| X885 | 10p. orge-brown & chest (2 bands) (11.8.71) | 40 | 30 |
| | a. Orange-brown omitted | £150 | |
| | b. Imperf (horiz pair) | £2000 | |
| X886 | 10p. orange-brn (Type I) (2 bands) (25.2.76) | 40 | 20 |
| | a. Imperf (pair) | £250 | |
| | b. Type II (4.9.84) | 6·00 | 6·00 |
| | bl. Booklet pane. No. X886b, X901 and X909 × 7, with margins all round | 9·50 | |
| X887 | 10p. orange-brown (Type I) ("all-over") (3.10.79) | 30 | 45 |
| X888 | 10p. orange-brown (Type I) (1 centre band) (4.2.80) | 30 | 20 |
| | a. Imperf (pair) | £225 | |
| | l. Booklet pane. No. X888×9 with margins all round (16.4.80) | 2·75 | |
| | m. Booklet pane. No. X888 and X895, each × 10 (12.11.80) | 6·00 | |
| X889 | 10p. orange-brown (Type I) (1 side band) (4.2.80) | 60 | 60 |
| X890 | 10½p. yellow (2 bands) (25.2.76) | 40 | 30 |
| X891 | 10½p. deep dull blue (2 bands) (26.4.78) | 60 | 45 |
| X892 | 11p. brown-red (2 bands) (25.2.76) | 60 | 25 |
| | a. Imperf (pair) | £1500 | |
| X893 | 11½p. drab (1 centre band) (14.1.81) | 45 | 30 |
| | a. Imperf (pair) | £180 | |
| | l. Booklet pane. No. X893 and X902, each × 10 (11.11.81) | 7·00 | |
| X894 | 11½p. drab (1 side band) (26.1.81) | 60 | 60 |
| | l. Booklet pane. No. X894 × 4 and X902 × 6 (6.5.81) | 5·00 | |
| X895 | 12p. yellowish green (2 bands) (4.2.80) | 60 | 40 |
| | l. Booklet pane. No. X895 × 9 with margins all round (16.4.80) | 3·50 | |
| X896 | 12p. brt emerald (1 centre band) (29.10.85) | 60 | 40 |
| | l. Booklet pane. No. X896 × 9 with margins all round (18.3.86) | 4·50 | |
| X897 | 12p. bright emerald (1 side band) (14.1.86) | 75 | 75 |
| | l. Booklet pane. No. X897×4 and X909×6 (12p. values at left) | 6·00 | |
| | la. Ditto. 12p. values at right | 6·00 | |
| | m. Booklet pane. No. X897×6, X909×2 and X919 with margins all round (18.3.86) | 8·50 | |
| X898 | 12½p. light emerald (1 centre band) (27.1.82) | 45 | 25 |
| | a. Imperf (pair) | £100 | |
| | l. Booklet pane. No. X898 and X907 each × 10 (10.11.82) | 9·50 | |
| X899 | 12½p. light emerald (1 side band) (1.2.82) | 60 | 60 |
| | l. Booklet pane. No. X899 × 4 and X907 × 6 (1.2.82) | 5·00 | |
| | m. Booklet pane. No. X899 × 6 with margins all round (19.5.82) | 2·25 | |
| | n. Booklet pane. No. X899 × 4 and X908 × 6 (12½p. values at left) (5.4.83) | 8·00 | |
| | na. Ditto. 12½p. values at right | 8·00 | |
| X900 | 13p. pale chestnut (1 centre band) (28.8.84) | 50 | 35 |
| | a. Imperf (pair) | £400 | |
| | l. Booklet pane. No. X900 × 9 with margins all round (8.1.85) | 4·00 | |
| | m. Booklet pane. No. X900 × 6 with margins all round (3.3.87) | 2·50 | |
| | n. Booklet pane. No. X900 × 4 with margins all round (4.8.87) | 2·50 | |
| | o. Booklet pane. No. X900 × 10 with margins all round (4.8.87) | 6·00 | |
| X901 | 13p. pale chestnut (1 side band) (3.9.84) | 60 | 60 |
| | l. Booklet pane. No. X901×4 and X909×6 (13p. values at left) | 6·00 | |
| | la. Ditto. 13p. values at right | 7·00 | |
| | m. Booklet pane. No. X901×6 with margins all round (4.9.84) | 5·00 | |
| | n. Booklet pane. No. X901 and X912×5 (20.10.86) | 5·00 | |
| | na. Ditto, but with vert edges of pane imperf (29.9.87) | 5·00 | |
| X902 | 14p. grey-blue (2 bands) (26.1.81) | 50 | 45 |
| X903 | 14p. deep blue (1 centre band) (23.8.88) | 45 | 40 |
| | a. Imperf (pair) | | |
| | l. Booklet pane. No. X903 × 4 with margins all round | 3·75 | |
| | m. Booklet pane. No. X903 × 10 with margins all round | 6·00 | |
| | n. Booklet pane. No. X903 × 4 with horiz edges of pane imperf (11.10.88) | 3·75 | |
| | p. Booklet pane. No. X903 × 10 with horiz edges of pane imperf (11.10.88) | 8·00 | |
| | q. Booklet pane. No. X903×4 with three edges of pane imperf (24.1.89) | 4·00 | |
| X904 | 14p. deep blue (1 side band) (5.9.88) | 1·25 | 1·25 |
| | l. Booklet pane. No. X904 and X914×2 plus label | 3·00 | |
| | m. Booklet pane. No. X904×2 and X914×4 with vert edges of pane imperf | 4·00 | |
| X905 | 15p. bright blue (1 centre band) (26.9.89) | 25 | 20 |
| | a. Imperf (pair) | £250 | |
| X906 | 15p. bright blue (1 side band) (2.10.89) | 1·25 | 1·25 |
| | l. Booklet pane. No. X906×2 and X916 plus label | 4·00 | |
| | m. Booklet pane. No. X906, X916, X922, 1446, 1448, 1468, 1470 and 1472 plus label with margins all round (20.3.90) | 8·00 | |
| X907 | 15½p. pale violet (2 bands) (1.2.82) | 45 | 45 |
| | l. Booklet pane. No. X907×6 with margins all round (19.5.82) | 3·00 | |
| | m. Booklet pane. No. X907×9 with margins all round (19.5.82) | 4·00 | |
| X908 | 16p. olive-drab (2 bands) (5.4.83) | 1·50 | 1·75 |
| X909 | 17p. grey-blue (2 bands) (3.9.84) | 75 | 75 |
| | l. Booklet pane. No. X909×3 plus label (4.11.85) | 3·00 | |
| X910 | 17p. deep blue (1 centre band) (4.9.90) | 30 | 30 |
| | a. Imperf (pair) | | |
| X911 | 17p. deep blue (1 side band) (4.9.90) | 30 | 30 |
| | l. Booklet pane. No. X911×3 plus label | 1·75 | |
| | m. Booklet pane. No. X911×2, X917×3 plus 3 labels with vert edges of pane imperf | 2·75 | |
| X912 | 18p. deep olive-grey (2 bands) (20.10.86) | 75 | 75 |
| X913 | 18p. bright green (1 centre band) (10.9.91) | 30 | 35 |
| X914 | 19p. bright orange-red (2 bands) (5.9.88) | 1·00 | 1·00 |
| X915 | 20p. dull purple (2 bands) (25.2.76) | 75 | 40 |
| X916 | 20p. brownish black (2 bands) (2.10.89) | 85 | 85 |
| X917 | 22p. bright orange-red (2 bands) (4.9.90) | 75 | 35 |
| X918 | 26p. rosine (Type I) (2 bands) (3.3.87) | 5·50 | 5·50 |
| X919 | 31p. purple (2 bands) (18.3.86) | 5·50 | 5·50 |
| X920 | 34p. ochre-brown (2 bands) (8.1.85) | 5·50 | 5·50 |
| X921 | 50p. ochre-brown (2 bands) (2.2.77) | 1·75 | 40 |
| X922 | 50p. ochre (2 bands) (20.3.90) | 4·50 | 4·50 |

(*b*) *Photo Harrison. On phosphorised paper.* P 15×14.

| No. | Description | | |
|---|---|---|---|
| X924 | ½p. turquoise-blue (10.12.80) | 10 | 10 |
| | a. Imperf (pair) | £130 | |
| | l. Coil strip. No. X924 and X932×3 (30.12.81) | 45 | |
| X925 | 1p. crimson (12.12.79) | 10 | 10 |
| | a. Imperf (pair) | | |
| | l. Coil strip. No. X925 and X932×3 (14.8.84) | 60 | |
| | m. Booklet pane. No. X925 and X969, each × 2 (10.9.91) | 75 | |
| X926 | 2p. myrtle-green (face value as T **367**) (12.12.79) | 10 | 10 |
| | a. Imperf (pair) | | |
| X927 | 2p. deep green (face value as T **367*a***) (26.7.88) | 10 | 10 |
| | a. Imperf (pair) | | |
| | l. Booklet pane. No. X927×2 and X969×4 plus 2 labels with vert edges of pane imperf (10.9.91) | 1·50 | |
| X928 | 2p. myrtle-green (face value as T **367*a***) (5.9.88) | 75 | 25 |
| | l. Coil strip. No. X928 and X932×3 | 1·00 | |
| X929 | 2½p. rose-red (14.1.81) | 20 | 20 |
| | l. Coil strip. No. X929 and X930×3 (6.81) | 75 | |
| X930 | 3p. bright magenta (Type I) (22.10.80) | 20 | 20 |
| | a. Imperf (horiz pair) | | |
| | b. Booklet pane. No. X930, X931×2 and X949×6 with margins all round (14.9.83) | 6·00 | |
| | c. Type II (10.10.89) | 30 | 30 |
| | cl. Coil strip. No. X930c and X933×3 | 1·25 | |
| X931 | 3½p. purple-brown (30.3.83) | 45 | 30 |
| X932 | 4p. greenish blue (30.12.81) | 25 | 20 |
| X933 | 4p. new blue (26.7.88) | 10 | 10 |
| | l. Coil strip. No. X933×3 and X935 (27.11.90) | 1·00 | |
| | m. Coil strip. No. X933 and X935, each × 2 (1.10.91) | 30 | |
| X934 | 5p. pale violet (10.10.79) | 30 | 25 |
| X935 | 5p. dull red-brown (26.7.88) | 10 | 10 |
| | a. Imperf (pair) | | |
| X936 | 6p. olive-yellow (10.9.91) | 10 | 15 |
| X937 | 7p. brownish red (29.10.85) | 2·00 | 1·50 |
| X938 | 8½p. yellowish green (24.3.76) | 30 | 55 |
| X939 | 10p. orange-brown (Type I) (11.79) | 15 | 20 |
| X940 | 10p. dull orange (Type II) (4.9.90) | 15 | 15 |
| X941 | 11p. brown-red (27.8.80) | 60 | 75 |
| X942 | 11½p. ochre-brown (15.8.79) | 50 | 45 |
| X943 | 12p. yellowish green (30.1.80) | 45 | 40 |
| X944 | 13p. olive-grey (15.8.79) | 60 | 45 |
| X945 | 13½p. purple-brown (30.1.80) | 65 | 60 |
| X946 | 14p. grey-blue (14.1.81) | 50 | 40 |
| X947 | 15p. ultramarine (15.8.79) | 50 | 40 |
| X948 | 15½p. pale violet (14.1.81) | 50 | 40 |
| | a. Imperf (pair) | £300 | |
| X949 | 16p. olive-drab (30.3.83) | 60 | 30 |
| | a. Imperf (pair) | £160 | |
| | l. Booklet pane. No. X949×9 with margins all round (14.9.83) | 3·75 | |
| X950 | 16½p. pale chestnut (27.1.82) | 85 | 75 |
| X951 | 17p. light emerald (30.1.80) | 70 | 40 |
| X952 | 17p. grey-blue (30.3.83) | 50 | 40 |
| | a. Imperf (pair) | £225 | |
| | l. Booklet pane. No. X952×6 with margins all round (4.9.84) | 3·00 | |
| | m. Booklet pane. No. X952×9 with margins all round (8.1.85) | 4·50 | |
| X953 | 17½p. pale chestnut (30.1.80) | 80 | 80 |
| X954 | 18p. deep violet (14.1.81) | 70 | 75 |
| X955 | 18p. deep olive-grey (28.8.84) | 70 | 60 |
| | a. Imperf (pair) | £160 | |
| | l. Booklet pane. No. X955×9 with margins all round (3.3.87) | 5·50 | |
| | m. Booklet pane. No. X955×4 with margins all round (4.8.87) | 3·00 | |
| | n. Booklet pane. No. X955×10 with margins all round (4.8.87) | 6·50 | |
| X956 | 19p. bright orange-red (23.8.88) | 30 | 35 |
| | a. Imperf (pair) | £225 | |
| | l. Booklet pane. No. X956×4 with margins all round | 4·50 | |
| | m. Booklet pane. No. X956×10 with margins all round | 7·00 | |
| | n. Booklet pane. No. X956×4 with horiz edges of pane imperf (11.10.88) | 3·50 | |
| | o. Booklet pane. No. X956×10 with horiz edges of pane imperf (11.10.88) | 11·00 | |
| | q. Booklet pane. No. X956×4 with three edges of pane imperf (24.1.89) | 4·00 | |
| X957 | 19½p. olive-grey (27.1.82) | 2·00 | 1·50 |
| X958 | 20p. dull purple (10.10.79) | 80 | 20 |
| X959 | 20p. turquoise-green (23.8.88) | 30 | 35 |
| X960 | 20p. brownish black (26.9.89) | 30 | 30 |
| | a. Imperf (pair) | | |
| | l. Booklet pane. No. X960×5 plus label with vert edges of pane imperf (2.10.89) | 3·25 | |
| X961 | 20½p. ultramarine (30.3.83) | 1·10 | 85 |
| | a. Imperf (pair) | £750 | |
| X962 | 22p. blue (22.10.80) | 80 | 45 |
| | a. Imperf (pair) | £150 | |
| X963 | 22p. yellow-green (28.8.84) | 60 | 55 |
| | a. Imperf (horiz pair) | £950 | |
| X964 | 22p. bright orange-red (4.9.90) | 35 | 35 |
| X965 | 23p. brown-red (30.3.83) | 1·40 | 60 |
| | a. Imperf (horiz pair) | £750 | |
| X966 | 23p. bright green (23.8.88) | 70 | 40 |
| X967 | 24p. violet (28.8.84) | 1·40 | 85 |
| X968 | 24p. Indian red (26.9.89) | 40 | 45 |
| | a. Imperf (horiz pair) | | |
| X969 | 24p. chestnut (10.9.91) | 40 | 45 |
| | a. Imperf (pair) | | |
| X970 | 25p. purple (14.1.81) | 90 | 90 |
| X971 | 26p. rosine (Type I) (27.1.82) | 90 | 30 |
| | a. Type II (4.8.87) | 4·50 | 3·75 |
| | al. Booklet pane. No. X970a×4 with margins all round | 15·00 | |
| X972 | 26p. drab (4.9.90) | 40 | 40 |
| X973 | 27p. chestnut (23.8.88) | 1·00 | 85 |
| | l. Booklet pane. No. X973×4 with margins all round | 5·00 | |
| | m. Booklet pane. No. X973×4 with horiz edges of pane imperf (11.10.88) | 8·00 | |
| X974 | 27p. violet (4.9.90) | 45 | 45 |
| X975 | 28p. deep violet (30.3.83) | 75 | 60 |
| | a. Imperf (pair) | £1000 | |
| X976 | 28p. ochre (23.8.88) | 45 | 50 |
| X977 | 28p. deep bluish grey (10.9.91) | 45 | 50 |
| X978 | 29p. ochre-brown (27.1.82) | 2·50 | 1·25 |
| X979 | 29p. deep mauve (26.9.89) | 45 | 50 |
| X980 | 30p. deep olive-grey (26.9.89) | 45 | 50 |
| X981 | 31p. purple (30.3.83) | 1·25 | 80 |
| | a. Imperf (pair) | £1000 | |
| X982 | 31p. ultramarine (4.9.90) | 50 | 50 |
| X983 | 32p. greenish blue (23.8.88) | 50 | 55 |
| | a. Imperf (pair) | | |
| X984 | 33p. light emerald (4.9.90) | 50 | 50 |
| X985 | 34p. ochre-brown (28.8.84) | 1·10 | 80 |
| X986 | 34p. deep bluish grey (26.9.89) | 1·00 | 80 |
| X987 | 34p. deep mauve (10.9.91) | 55 | 60 |
| X988 | 35p. sepia (23.8.88) | 1·25 | 75 |
| | a. Imperf (pair) | | |
| X989 | 35p. yellow (10.9.91) | 55 | 60 |
| X990 | 37p. rosine (26.9.89) | 60 | 65 |
| X991 | 39p. bright mauve (10.9.91) | 60 | 65 |

(*c*) *Photo Harrison. On ordinary paper.* P 15×14

| No. | Description | | |
|---|---|---|---|
| X992 | 50p. ochre-brown (21.5.80) | 1·50 | 45 |
| | a. Imperf (pair) | £400 | |
| X993 | 75p. grey-black (face value as T **367*a***) (26.7.88) | 1·10 | 1·25 |

(*d*) *Photo Harrison. On ordinary or phosphorised paper.* P 15×14

| No. | Description | | |
|---|---|---|---|
| X994 | 50p. ochre (13.3.90) | 75 | 45 |

(*e*) *Litho J.W.* P 14

| No. | Description | | |
|---|---|---|---|
| X996 | 4p. greenish blue (2 phosphor bands) (30.1.80) | 20 | 25 |
| X997 | 4p. greenish blue (phosphorised paper) (11.81) | 25 | 20 |
| X998 | 20p. dull pur (2 phosphor bands) (21.5.80) | 1·00 | 40 |
| X999 | 20p. dull pur (phosphorised paper) (11.81) | 1·00 | 40 |

(*f*) *Litho Questa.* P 14 (*Nos.* X1000, X1003/4 *and* X1018) *or* 15×14 (*others*)

| No. | Description | | |
|---|---|---|---|
| X1000 | 2p. emerald-green (face value as T **367**) (phosphorised paper) (21.5.80) | 20 | 20 |
| | a. Perf 15×14 (10.7.84) | 30 | 20 |
| X1001 | 2p. bright green & dp green (face value as T **367*a***) (phosphorised paper) (23.2.88) | 25 | 25 |
| X1002 | 4p. greenish blue (phosphorised paper) (13.5.86) | 30 | 20 |
| X1003 | 5p. lt violet (phosphorised paper) (21.5.80) | 40 | 20 |
| X1004 | 5p. claret (phosphorised paper) (27.1.82) | 50 | 20 |
| | a. Perf 15×14 (21.2.84) | 40 | 35 |
| X1005 | 13p. pale chestnut (1 centre band) (9.2.88) | 70 | 70 |
| | l. Booklet pane. No. X1005×6 with margins all round | 3·00 | |
| X1006 | 13p. pale chestnut (1 side band) (9.2.88) | 60 | 60 |
| | l. Booklet pane. No. X1006×6, X1010, X1013 and X1017 with margins all round | 11·00 | |
| X1007 | 14p. deep blue (1 centre band) (11.10.88) | 1·00 | 50 |
| X1008 | 17p. deep blue (1 centre band) (19.3.91) | 60 | 50 |
| | l. Booklet pane. No. X1008×6 with margins all round | 1·50 | |
| X1009 | 18p. deep olive-grey (phosphorised paper) (9.2.88) | 60 | 60 |
| | l. Booklet pane. No. X1009×9 with margins all round | 4·50 | |
| | m. Booklet pane. No. X1009×6 with margins all round | 3·00 | |

X1010 18p. dp ol-grey (2 phosphor bands) (9.2.88) 4·00 4·00
X1011 19p. brt orange-red (phosphorised paper) (11.10.88) .. .. .. .. .. 1·25 90
X1012 20p. dull purple (phosphorised paper) (13.5.86) .. .. .. .. .. 1·00 70
X1013 22p. yell-grn (2 phosphor bands) (9.2.88) 4·00 4·00
X1014 22p. brt orange-red (phosphorised paper) (19.3.91) .. .. .. .. .. 35 35
l. Booklet pane. No. 1014×9 with margins all round .. .. .. 3·00
m. Booklet pane. No. 1014×6, X1015×2 and central label with margins all round 3·00
X1015 33p. light emerald (phosphorised paper) (19.3.91) .. .. .. .. .. 50 50
X1016 33p. lt emer (2 phosphor bands) (25.2.92) 1·10 1·10
X1017 34p. ochre-brn (2 phosphor bands) (9.2.88) 3·50 3·50
X1018 75p. black (face value as T **367**) (ordinary paper) (30.1.80) .. .. .. .. 3·00 1·50
a. Perf 15×14 (21.2.84) .. .. .. 3·00 1·50
X1019 75p. brownish grey and black (face value as T **367***a*) (ordinary paper) (23.2.88) .. 6·50 3·50

(*g*) *Litho Walsall. P* 14

X1020 14p. deep blue (1 side band) (25.4.89) .. 3·00 3·00
l. Booklet pane. No. X1020×2 and X1021×4 with vert edges of pane imperf .. .. .. .. .. 10·00
X1021 19p. bright orange-red (2 phosphor bands) (25.4.89) .. .. .. .. .. 1·00 1·00
X1022 29p. dp mve (2 phosphor bands) (2.10.89) 3·50 3·00
l. Booklet pane. No. X1022×4 with three edges of pane imperf .. .. 14·00
X1023 29p. deep mauve (phosphorised paper) (17.4.90) .. .. .. .. .. 3·50 3·00
l. Booklet pane. No. X1023×4 with three edges of pane imperf .. .. 14·00
X1024 31p. ultram (phosphorised paper) (17.9.90) 50 50
l. Booklet pane. No. X1024×4 with horiz edges of pane imperf .. .. 1·90
X1025 33p. light emerald (phosphorised paper) (16.9.91) .. .. .. .. .. 50 55
l. Booklet pane. Nos. X1025×4 with horiz edges of pane imperf .. .. 2·00
X1026 39p. bright mauve (phosphorised paper) (16.9.91) .. .. .. .. .. 60 65
l. Booklet pane. No. X1026×4 with horiz edges of pane imperf .. .. 2·40

*See footnote after No. 744.
†These come from sheets with gum arabic.

Nos. X842, X847, X852, X854, X857, X860, X864, X867, X873, X876, X880, X889, X894/5, X897, X899, X901, X904, X906, X911/12, X914, X916, X918/20, X922, X1005/11, X1013/17 and X1020/6 come from booklets; Nos. X843 and X845 come from booklets or coils; Nos. X928 and X932 come from coils; Nos. X852, X864, X873, X876, X880, X889, X894, X897, X899, X901, X911 and X1006 were each issued with the phosphor band at the right or the left from the same booklet, usually in equal quantities. Nos. X847 and X906 also exist with phosphor band at the left or right, but these come from different booklets.

No. X1016 comes from the *se-tenant* pane in the Wales £6 booklet which is listed under No. W49a in the Wales Regional Section.

Nos. X844a/b come from a strip of eight of the vertical coil. It comprises two normals, one imperforate at sides and bottom, one completely imperforate, one imperforate at top, left and bottom and partly perforated at right due to the bottom three stamps being perforated twice. No. X844b is also known from another strip having one stamp imperforate at sides and bottom.

Nos. X848b/c come from the same sheet, the latter having perforations at the foot of the stamps only.

Multi-value coil strips Nos. X9241, X9251, X9281, X9291 and X9331/m were produced by the Post Office for a large direct mail marketing firm. Use of the first coil strip, No. X9291, is known from June 1981. From 2 September 1981 No. X9291 was available from the Philatelic Bureau, Edinburgh and, subsequently, from a number of other Post Office counters.

Later coil strips were sold at the Philatelic Bureau and Post Office philatelic counters.

**PART-PERFORATED SHEETS.** Since the introduction of the "Jumelle" press in 1972 a number of part-perforated sheets, both definitive and commemoratives, have been discovered. It is believed that these occur when the operation of the press is interrupted. Such sheets invariably show a number of "blind" perforations, where the pins have failed to cut the paper. Our listings of imperforate errors from these sheets are for pairs showing no trace whatsoever of the perforations. Examples showing "blind" perforations are outside the scope of this catalogue.

In cases where perforation varieties affect *se-tenant* stamps fuller descriptions will be found in Vol. 4 of the *G.B. Specialised Catalogue*,

**WHITE PAPER.** From 1972 printings appeared on fluorescent white paper giving a stronger chalk reaction than the original ordinary cream paper.

**GUM ARABIC.** The following exist with gum arabic as well as PVA gum (with or without added dextrin): Nos. X841, X841n, X851, X855, X856, X861 and X870. See notes after No. 722.

**DEXTRIN GUM.** From 1973 printings in photogravure appeared with PVA gum to which dextrin had been added. As the resulting gum was virtually colourless bluish green colouring matter was added to distinguish it from the previous PVA. Questa printings in lithography from 1988 onwards used PVA gum with dextrin, but did not show the colouring agent.

**"ALL-OVER" PHOSPHOR.** To improve mechanised handling most commemoratives from the 1972 Royal Silver Wedding 3p. value to the 1979 Rowland Hill Death Centenary set had the phosphor applied by printing cylinder across the entire surface of the stamp, giving a matt effect. Printing of the 1, 2 and 10p. definitives, released in October 1979, also had "all-over" phosphor, but these were purely a temporary expedient pending the adoption of phosphorised paper. Nos. X883, X890 and X921 have been discovered with "all over" phosphor in addition to the normal phosphor bands. These error are outside the scope of this catalogue.

**PHOSPHORISED PAPER.** Following the experiments on Nos. 743b and 829 a printing of the 4½p. definitive was issued on 13 November 1974, which had, in addition to the normal phosphor bands, phosphor included in the paper coating. Because of difficulties in identifying the phosphorised paper with the naked eye this printing is not listed separately in this catalogue.

No. X938 was the first value printed on phosphorised paper without phosphor bands and was a further experimental issue to test the efficacy of this system. From 15 August 1979 phosphorised paper was accepted for use generally, the paper replacing phosphor bands on values other than those required in the second-class rate.

Stamps on phosphorised paper show a shiny surface instead of the matt areas of those printed with phosphor bands.

**VARNISH COATING.** Nos. X841 and X883 exist with and without a varnish coating. This cannot easily be detected without the use of an ultra-violet lamp as it merely reduces the fluorescent paper reaction.

**UNDERPRINTS.** From 1982 various values appeared with underprints, printed on the reverse, in blue, over the gum. These were usually from special stamp booklets, sold at a discount by the Post Office, but in 1985 surplus stocks of such underprinted paper were used for other purposes.

The following Decimal Machin stamps exist with underprints:
12p. bright emerald (1 centre band)—double-lined star underprint from sheet printing (also exists without)
12½p. light emerald (1 centre band)—star with central dot underprint from booklet pane X898l
12½p. light emerald (1 centre band)—double-lined star underprint from booklet pane of 20
13p. pale chestnut (1 centre band)—double-lined star underprint from booklet pane of 10 (also exists without)
15½p. pale violet (2 bands)—star with central dot underprint from booklet pane X898l
16p. olive-drab (phosphorised paper)—double-lined D underprint from booklet pane of 10 (also exists without)
17p. grey-blue (2 bands)—double-lined star underprint from booklet pane X909l
17p. grey-blue (phosphorised paper)—double-lined D underprint from booklet pane of 10 (also exists without)

**DECIMAL MACHIN CATALOGUE NUMBER CHANGES**

| 1992 Edition | 1992/93 Edition |
|---|---|
| X913/21 | X914/22 |
| X936/67 | X937/68 |
| X968/74 | X970/6 |
| X975/83 | X978/86 |
| X984 | X988 |
| X985 | X990 |
| X986 | X992 |
| X987 | X994 |
| X988 | X993 |
| X1016/23 | X1017/24 |

**368** "A Mountain Road" (T. P. Flanagan)

**369** "Deer's Meadow" (Tom Carr)

**370** "Slieve na brock" (Colin Middleton)

(Layout des Stuart Rose)

**1971** (16 June). *"Ulster 1971" Paintings. Chalk-surfaced paper. Two phosphor bands. P* 15 × 14.

| No. | Type | Description | | |
|---|---|---|---|---|
| 881 | **368** | 3p. yellow-buff, pale yellow, Venetian red, black, blue and drab .. | 10 | 10 |
| 882 | **369** | 7½p. olive-brown, brownish grey, pale olive-grey, dp bl, cobalt & grey-bl | 75 | 80 |
| | | a. Pale olive-grey omitted* .. .. | 60·00 | |
| 883 | **370** | 9p. greenish yellow, orange, grey, lavender-grey, bistre, black, pale ochre-brown, and ochre-brown .. | 75 | 80 |
| | | a. Orange omitted .. .. .. | £500 | |
| 881/3 | | .. .. .. .. .. *Set of* 3 | 1·40 | 1·50 |

A used example of the 3p. has been seen with the Venetian red omitted.

**371** John Keats (150th Death Anniv)

**372** Thomas Gray (Death Bicentenary)

**373** Sir Walter Scott (Birth Bicentenary)

(Des Rosalind Dease. Queen's head printed in gold and then embossed)

**1971** (28 July). *Literary Anniversaries. Chalk-surfaced paper. Two phosphor bands. P* 15 × 14.

| No. | Type | Description | | |
|---|---|---|---|---|
| 884 | **371** | 3p. black, gold and greyish blue .. | 10 | 10 |
| | | a. Gold (Queen's head) omitted .. | 75·00 | |
| 885 | **372** | 5p. black, gold and yellow-olive .. | 75 | 80 |
| | | a. Gold (Queen's head) omitted .. | £160 | |
| 886 | **373** | 7½p. black, gold and yellow-brown .. | 75 | 80 |
| 884/6 | | .. .. .. .. .. *Set of* 3 | 1·40 | 1·50 |

The 7½p. exists with embossing omitted.

**374** Servicemen and Nurse of 1921

**375** Roman Centurion

**376** Rugby Football, 1871

(Des F. Wegner)

**1971** (25 Aug). *British Anniversaries. Events described on stamps. Chalk-surfaced paper. Two phosphor bands. P* 15 × 14.

| No. | Type | Description | | |
|---|---|---|---|---|
| 887 | **374** | 3p. red-orange, grey, deep blue, olive-grn, olive-brn, blk, rosine & vio-bl | 10 | 10 |
| | | a. Deep blue omitted* .. .. .. | £600 | |
| | | b. Red-orange (nurse's cloak) omitted | £275 | |
| | | c. Olive-brown (faces, etc.) omitted | £160 | |
| | | d. Black omitted .. .. .. .. | £10000 | |
| 888 | **375** | 7½p. grey, yellow-brown, vermilion, mauve, grey-black, black, silver, gold and ochre .. .. .. | 75 | 75 |
| | | a. Grey omitted .. .. .. .. | 75·00 | |
| | | b. Yellow-brown (shading on horse, walls, etc) omitted .. .. | | |
| 889 | **376** | 9p. new blue, myrtle-green, grey-blk, lemon, olive-brown, mag & yell-ol | 75 | 75 |
| | | a. Olive-brown omitted .. .. | £110 | |
| | | b. New blue omitted .. .. | £1750 | |
| | | c. Myrtle-green omitted .. .. | £2000 | |
| 887/9 | | .. .. .. .. .. *Set of* 3 | 1·40 | 1·40 |

*The effect of the missing deep blue is shown on the sailor's uniform, which appears as grey.

A used example has been seen of the 3p. with grey omitted.

**377** Physical Sciences Building, University College of Wales, Aberystwyth

**378** Faraday Building, Southampton University

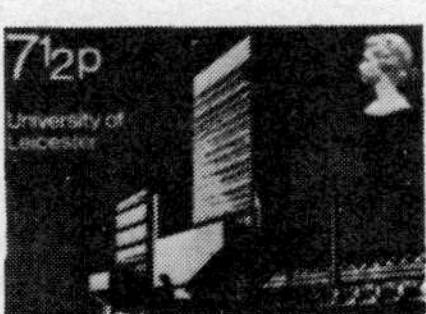


**379** Engineering Department, Leicester University

**380** Hexagon Restaurant, Essex University

(Des N. Jenkins)

**1971** (22 Sept). *British Architecture. Modern University Buildings. Chalk-surfaced paper. Two phosphor bands. P* 15 × 14.

| No. | Type | Description | | |
|---|---|---|---|---|
| 890 | **377** | 3p. olive-brn, ochre, lem, blk & yell-ol | 10 | 10 |
| | | a. Lemon omitted .. .. .. | | |
| | | b. Black (windows) omitted .. | £4500 | |
| 891 | **378** | 5p. rose, black, chestnut and lilac .. | 20 | 25 |
| 892 | **379** | 7½p. ochre, black and purple-brown .. | 80 | 80 |
| 893 | **380** | 9p. pale lilac, black, sepia-brn & dp bl | 1·60 | 1·60 |
| 890/3 | | .. .. .. .. .. *Set of* 4 | 2·50 | 2·50 |

**381** "Dream of the Wise Men"

**382** "Adoration of the Magi"

**383** "Ride of the Magi"

(Des Clarke-Clements-Hughes design team, from stained-glass windows, Canterbury Cathedral. Queen's head printed in gold and then embossed)

**1971** (13 Oct). *Christmas. Ordinary paper. One centre phosphor band* (2½p.) *or two phosphor bands (others). P* 15 × 14.

| No. | Type | Description | | |
|---|---|---|---|---|
| 894 | **381** | 2½p. new blue, black, lemon, emerald, reddish violet, carmine-red, carmine-rose and gold .. .. | 10 | 10 |
| | | a. Imperf (pair) .. .. .. | £450 | |
| 895 | **382** | 3p. black, reddish violet, lemon, new bl, carm-rose, emer, ultram & gold | 10 | 10 |
| | | a. Gold (Queen's head) omitted .. | £350 | |
| | | b. Carmine-rose omitted .. .. | £1750 | |
| | | c. Lemon omitted .. .. .. | 60·00 | |
| | | d. New blue omitted .. .. .. | † | — |
| 896 | **383** | 7½p. black, lilac, lemon, emerald, new blue, rose, green and gold .. | 90 | 1·00 |
| | | a. Gold (Queen's head) omitted .. | 90·00 | |
| | | b. Lilac omitted .. .. .. | £400 | |
| | | c. Emerald omitted .. .. | £200 | |
| 894/6 | | .. .. .. .. .. *Set of* 3 | 1·00 | 1·10 |

The 3p. exists with embossing omitted; used copies have been seen with reddish violet and embossing omitted, with lemon and carmine-rose omitted. The 7½p. is known with embossing omitted and embossing double.

**WHITE CHALK-SURFACED PAPER.** From No. 897 all issues, with the exception of Nos. 904/8, were printed on fluorescent white paper, giving a stronger chalk reaction than the original cream paper.

**384** Sir James Clark Ross **385** Sir Martin Frobisher

**386** Henry Hudson **387** Capt. Scott

(Des Marjorie Saynor. Queen's head printed in gold and then embossed)

**1972** (16 Feb). *British Polar Explorers. Two phosphor bands. P* 14 × 15.

| No. | Type | Description | | |
|---|---|---|---|---|
| 897 | **384** | 3p. yellow-brown, indigo, slate-black, flesh, lemon, rose, brt blue & gold | 10 | 10 |
| | | a. Gold (Queen's head) omitted .. | 60·00 | |
| | | b. Slate-black (hair, etc.) omitted .. | £1500 | |
| | | c. Lemon omitted .. .. .. | | |
| 898 | **385** | 5p. salmon, flesh, purple-brown, ochre, black and gold .. .. | 20 | 20 |
| | | a. Gold (Queen's head) omitted .. | 90·00 | |
| 899 | **386** | 7½p. reddish violet, blue, deep slate, yellow-brown, buff, black and gold | 65 | 65 |
| | | a. Gold (Queen's head) omitted .. | £200 | |

900 **387** 9p. dull blue, ultramarine, black, greenish yell, pale pink, rose-red & gold .. 1·10 1·10
897/900 .. .. .. .. .. *Set of* 4 1·75 1·75

The 3p. and 5p. are known with embossing omitted and the 3p. also exists with gold and embossing omitted. An example of the 3p. is known used on piece with the flesh colour omitted.

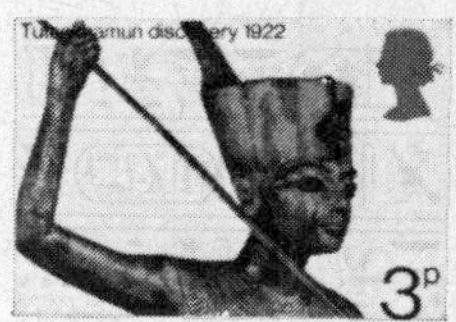


**388** Statuette of Tutankhamun

**389** 19th-century Coastguard

**390** Ralph Vaughan Williams and Score

(Des Rosalind Dease (3p.), F. Wegner (7½p.), C. Abbott (9p.). Queen's head printed in gold and then embossed (7½p., 9p.))

**1972** (26 Apr). *General Anniversaries. Events described on stamps. Two phosphor bands. P* 15 × 14.

901 **388** 3p. black, grey, gold, dull bistre-brown, blackish brn, pale stone & lt brn .. 10 10
902 **389** 7½p. pale yellow, new blue, slate-blue, violet-blue, slate and gold .. 70 80
903 **390** 9p. bistre-brown, black, sage-green, dp slate, yellow-ochre, brown & gold .. 70 65
a. Gold (Queen's head) omitted .. £1250
b. Brown (facial features) omitted .. £1000
c. Deep slate omitted .. £7500
901/3 .. .. .. .. .. *Set of* 3 1·25 1·40

The 7½p. exists with embossing omitted.

**391** St. Andrew's, Greensted-juxta-Ongar, Essex

**392** All Saints, Earls Barton, Northants

**393** St. Andrew's, Letheringsett, Norfolk

**394** St. Andrew's, Helpringham, Lincs

**395** St. Mary the Virgin, Huish Episcopi, Somerset

(Des R. Maddox. Queen's head printed in gold and then embossed)

**1972** (21 June). *British Architecture. Village Churches. Ordinary paper. Two phosphor bands. P* 14 × 15.

904 **391** 3p. violet-blue, black, lt yellow-olive, emerald-green, orange-verm & gold 10 10
a. Gold (Queen's head) omitted .. 75·00
905 **392** 4p. deep yellow-olive, black, emerald, violet-blue, orge-vermilion & gold 20 20
a. Gold (Queen's head) omitted .. £2000
b. Violet-blue omitted .. .. £110
906 **393** 5p. deep emerald, black, royal blue, lt yellow-olive, orange-verm & gold 20 25
a. Gold (Queen's head) omitted .. £150
907 **394** 7½p. orange-red, black, deep yellow-ol, royal blue, lt emerald & gold .. 1·00 1·10
908 **395** 9p. new blue, black, emerald-green, dp yellow-olive, orange-verm & gold 1·25 1·40
904/8 .. .. .. .. .. *Set of* 5 2·50 2·75

The 3p., 4p., 5p. and 9p. exist with embossing omitted.

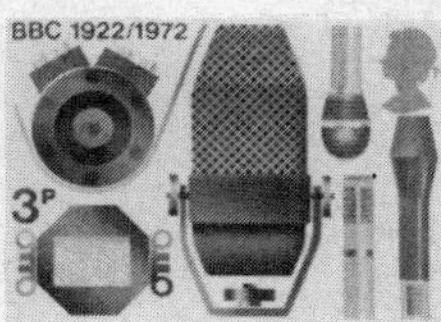


**396** Microphones, 1924–69

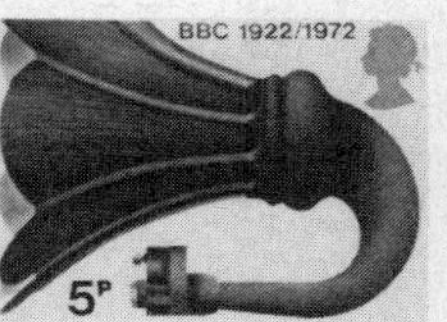


**397** Horn Loudspeaker

**398** T.V. Camera, 1972

**399** Oscillator and Spark Transmitter, 1897

(Des D. Gentleman)

**1972** (13 Sept). *Broadcasting Anniversaries. 75th Anniv of Marconi and Kemp's Radio Experiments* (9p.), *and 50th Anniv of Daily Broadcasting by the B.B.C.* (*others*). *Two phosphor bands. P* 15 × 14.

909 **396** 3p. pale brown, black, grey, greenish yellow and brownish slate .. 10 10
a. Greenish yellow (terminals) omitted .. .. .. £1200
910 **397** 5p. brownish slate, lake-brown, salmon, lt brown, black & red-brn 15 20
911 **398** 7½p. light grey, slate, brownish slate, magenta and black .. .. 1·00 1·00
a. Brownish slate (Queen's head) omitted .. .. .. .. † —
912 **399** 9p. lemon, brown, brownish slate, deep brownish slate, bluish slate & blk 1·00 1·00
a. Brownish slate (Queen's head) omitted .. .. .. .. £1300
909/12 .. .. .. .. .. *Set of* 4 2·00 2·00

No. 911a is only known on first day covers posted from the Philatelic Bureau in Edinburgh.

**400** Angel holding Trumpet

**401** Angel playing Lute

**402** Angel playing Harp

(Des Sally Stiff. Photo and embossed)

**1972** (18 Oct). *Christmas. One centre phosphor band* (2½p.) *or two phosphor bands* (*others*). *P* 14 × 15.

913 **400** 2½p. cerise, pale reddish brown, yellow-orange, orange-vermilion, lilac, gold, red-brown and deep grey .. 10 15
a. Gold omitted .. .. .. £250
c. Deep grey omitted .. .. ..
914 **401** 3p. ultramarine, lavender, light turquoise-blue, bright green, gold, red-brown and bluish violet .. 10 15
a. Red-brown omitted .. .. £500
b. Bright green omitted .. .. 70·00
c. Bluish violet omitted .. .. 75·00
915 **402** 7½p. deep brown, pale lilac, light cinnamon, ochre, gold, red-brown and blackish violet .. .. .. 90 80
a. Ochre omitted .. .. .. 55·00
913/15 .. .. .. .. .. *Set of* 3 1·00 1·00

All three values exist with embossing omitted.

**403** Queen Elizabeth and Duke of Edinburgh

**404** "Europe"

(Des J. Matthews from photo by N. Parkinson)

**1972** (20 Nov). *Royal Silver Wedding. "All-over" phosphor* (3p.) *or without phosphor* (20p.). *P* 14 × 15.

I. "REMBRANDT" Machine

916 **403** 3p. brownish black, dp blue & silver 20 20
a. Silver omitted .. .. .. £300
917 20p. brownish blk, reddish pur & silver 80 80

II. "JUMELLE" Machine

918 **403** 3p. brownish black, deep blue & silver 20 25

The 3p. "JUMELLE" has a lighter shade of the brownish black than the 3p. "Rembrandt". It also has the brown cylinders less deeply etched, which can be distinguished in the Duke's face which is slightly lighter, and in the Queen's hair where the highlights are sharper.

3p. "REMBRANDT". Cyls. 3A-1B-11C no dot. Sheets of 100 (10 × 10).

3p. "JUMELLE". Cyls. 1A–1B–3C dot and no dot. Sheets of 100 (two panes 5 × 10, separated by gutter margin).

(Des P. Murdoch)

**1973** (3 Jan). *Britain's Entry into European Communities. Two phosphor bands. P* 14 × 15.

919 **404** 3p. dull orange, bright rose-red, ultramarine, light lilac and black .. 10 10
920 5p. new blue, bright rose-red, ultramarine, cobalt-blue and black .. .. 25 35
a. Pair. Nos. 920/1 .. .. 1·50 1·60
921 5p. light emerald-green, bright rose-red, ultramarine, cobalt-blue and black 25 35
919/21 .. .. .. .. .. *Set of* 3 1·50 70

Nos. 920/1 were printed horizontally *se-tenant* throughout the sheet.

**405** Oak Tree

(Des D. Gentleman)

**1973** (28 Feb). *Tree Planting Year. British Trees* (1*st issue*). *Two phosphor bands. P* 15 × 14.

922 **405** 9p. brownish black, apple-green, deep olive, sepia, blackish green and brownish grey .. .. .. 50 45
a. Brownish black (value and inscr) omitted .. .. .. .. £450
b. Brownish grey (Queen's head) omitted .. .. .. .. £300

See also No. 949.

**CHALK-SURFACED PAPER.** The following issues are printed on chalk-surfaced paper but where "all-over" phosphor has been applied there is no chalk reaction except in the sheet margins outside the phosphor area.

**406** David Livingstone **407** H. M. Stanley

(T **406/7** were printed together, horizontally *se-tenant* within the sheet)

**408** Sir Francis Drake **409** Walter Raleigh

**410** Charles Sturt

(Des Marjorie Saynor. Queen's head printed in gold and then embossed)

**1973** (18 Apr). *British Explorers. "All-over" phosphor. P* 14 × 15.

923 **406** 3p. orange-yellow, light orange-brown, grey-black, light turquoise-blue, turquoise-blue and gold .. .. 25 20
a. Pair. Nos. 923/4 .. .. .. 1·60 1·75
b. Gold (Queen's head) omitted .. 32·00
c. Turquoise-blue (background and inscr) omitted .. .. .. £450
d. Light orange-brown omitted .. £350

924 **407** 3p. orange-yellow, light orange-brown, grey-black, light turquoise-blue, turquoise-blue and gold .. .. 25 20
b. Gold (Queen's head) omitted .. 32·00
c. Turquoise-blue (background and inscr) omitted .. .. .. £450
d. Light orange-brown omitted .. £350

925 **408** 5p. light flesh, chrome-yellow, orange-yellow, sepia, brownish grey, grey-black, violet-blue and gold .. 30 30
a. Gold (Queen's head) omitted .. 90·00
b. Grey-black omitted .. .. £550
c. Sepia omitted .. .. £450

926 **409** 7½p. light flesh, reddish brown, sepia, ultram, grey-blk, brt lilac & gold 35 30
a. Gold (Queen's head) omitted .. £1500
b. Ultramarine (eyes) omitted .. £1300

927 **410** 9p. flesh, pale stone, grey-blue, grey-black, brown-grey, Venetian red, brown-red and gold .. .. 40 40
a. Gold (Queen's head) omitted .. 90·00
b. Brown-grey printing double *from* £800
c. Grey-black omitted .. .. £1000

923/7 .. .. .. .. .. .. *Set of* 5 2·50 1·25

Caution is needed when buying missing gold heads in this issue as they can be removed by using a hard eraser, etc., but this invariably affects the "all-over" phosphor. Genuine examples have the phosphor intact. Used examples off cover cannot be distinguished as much of the phosphor is lost in the course of floating.

In the 5p. value the missing grey-black affects the doublet, which appears as brownish grey, and the lace ruff, which is entirely missing. The missing sepia affects only Drake's hair, which appears much lighter.

The double printing of the brown-grey (cylinder 1F) on the 9p. is a most unusual type of error to occur in a multicoloured photogravure issue. Two sheets are known and it is believed that they stuck to the cylinder and went through a second time. This would result in the following two sheets missing the colour but at the time of going to press this error has not been reported. The second print is slightly askew and more prominent in the top half of the sheets. Examples from the upper part of the sheet showing a clear double impression of the facial features are worth a substantial premium over the price quoted.

The 3p values, the 5p. and the 9p. exist with embossing omitted.

**411** **412**

**413**

(T **411/13** show sketches of W. G. Grace by Harry Furniss)

(Des E. Ripley. Queen's head printed in gold and then embossed)

**1973** (16 May). *County Cricket* 1873–1973. *"All-over" phosphor. P* 14 × 15.

928 **411** 3p. black, ochre and gold .. .. 10 10
a. Gold (Queen's head) omitted .. £2500
929 **412** 7½p. black, light sage-green and gold .. 1·25 1·40
930 **413** 9p. black, cobalt and gold .. .. 1·50 1·40
928/30 .. .. .. .. .. *Set of* 3 2·50 2·50

All three values exist with embossing omitted.

**414** "Self-portrait" (Reynolds) **415** "Self-portrait" (Raeburn)

**416** "Nelly O'Brien" (Reynolds) **417** "Rev. R. Walker (The Skater)" (Raeburn)

(Des S. Rose. Queen's head printed in gold and then embossed)

**1973** (4 July). *British Paintings. 250th Birth Anniv of Sir Joshua Reynolds and 150th Death Anniv of Sir Henry Raeburn. "All-over" phosphor. P* 14 × 15.

931 **414** 3p. rose, new blue, jet-black, magenta, greenish yellow, blk, ochre & gold 10 10
a. Gold (Queen's head) omitted .. 60·00
932 **415** 5p. cinnamon, greenish yellow, new blue, lt mag, blk, yell-olive & gold 20 25
a. Gold (Queen's head) omitted .. 75·00
b. Greenish yellow omitted .. .. £350
933 **416** 7½p. greenish yellow, new blue, light magenta, black, cinnamon and gold 70 70
a. Gold (Queen's head) omitted .. 75·00
b. Cinnamon omitted .. .. £3500
934 **417** 9p. brownish rose, black, dull rose, pale yell, brownish grey, pale bl & gold 90 90
b. Brownish rose omitted .. .. 30·00
931/4 .. .. .. .. .. *Set of* 4 1·60 1·75

No. 931a is also known with the embossing also omitted or misplaced.

The 5p. and 7½p. are known with the embossing omitted.

The 9p. is known with the embossing and phosphor both omitted.

**418** Court Masque Costumes

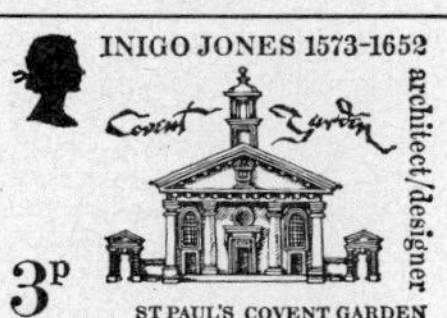


**419** St. Paul's Church, Covent Garden

**420** Prince's Lodging, Newmarket

**421** Court Masque Stage Scene

T **418/19** and T **420/1** were printed horizontally *se-tenant* within the sheet

(Des Rosalind Dease. Litho and typo B.W.)

**1973** (15 Aug). *400th Birth Anniv of Inigo Jones (architect and designer). "All-over" phosphor. P* 15 × 14.

935 **418** 3p. deep mauve, black and gold .. 10 15
a. Pair. Nos. 935/6 .. .. .. 35 40
936 **419** 3p. deep brown, black and gold .. 10 15
937 **420** 5p. blue, black and gold .. .. 40 45
a. Pair. Nos. 937/8 .. .. .. 1·90 1·50
938 **421** 5p. grey-olive, black and gold .. 40 45
935/8 .. .. .. .. .. *Set of* 4 2·00 1·10

**422** Palace of Westminster seen from Whitehall **423** Palace of Westminster seen from Millbank

(Des R. Downer. Recess and typo B.W.)

**1973** (12 Sept). *19th Commonwealth Parliamentary Conference. "All-over" phosphor. P* 15 × 14.

939 **422** 8p. black, brownish grey and stone .. 50 60
940 **423** 10p. gold and black .. .. .. 50 40

**424** Princess Anne and Capt. Mark Phillips.

(Des C. Clements and E. Hughes from photo by Lord Litchfield)

**1973** (14 Nov). *Royal Wedding. "All-over" phosphor. P* 15 × 14.

941 **424** 3½p. dull violet and silver .. .. 10 10
a. Imperf (pair) .. .. £900
942 20p. deep brown and silver .. .. 90 1·00
a. Silver omitted .. .. .. £900

**425**

**426**

**427**

428

429

**T 425/9** depict the carol "Good King Wenceslas" and were printed horizontally *se-tenant* within the sheet.

**430** "Good King Wenceslas, the Page and Peasant"

(Des D. Gentleman)

**1973** (28 Nov). *Christmas. One centre phosphor band* (3p.) *or "all-over" phosphor* (3½p.). *P* 15 × 14.

| No. | Type | Value | Description | Unused | Used |
|---|---|---|---|---|---|
| 943 | **425** | 3p. | grey-black, blue, brownish grey, light brown, bright rose-red, turq-green, salmon-pink and gold .. | 15 | 15 |
| | | a. | Strip of 5. Nos. 943/7 .. .. | 3·00 | 2·75 |
| | | b. | Imperf (horiz strip of 5) .. .. | £1000 | |
| 944 | **426** | 3p. | grey-black, violet-blue, slate, brown, rose-red, rosy mauve, turq-green, salmon-pink and gold .. | 15 | 15 |
| | | a. | Rosy mauve omitted .. .. | £625 | |
| 945 | **427** | 3p. | grey-black, violet-blue, slate, brown, rose-red, rosy mauve, turq-green, salmon-pink and gold .. | 15 | 15 |
| | | a. | Rosy mauve omitted .. .. | £625 | |
| 946 | **428** | 3p. | grey-black, violet-blue, slate, brown, rose-red, rosy mauve, turq-green, salmon-pink and gold .. | 15 | 15 |
| | | a. | Rosy mauve omitted .. .. | £625 | |
| 947 | **429** | 3p. | grey-black, violet-blue, slate, brown, rose-red, rosy mauve, turq-green, salmon-pink and gold .. | 15 | 15 |
| | | a. | Rosy mauve omitted .. .. | £625 | |
| 948 | **430** | 3½p. | salmon-pink, grey-black, red-brown, blue, turquoise-green, bright rose-red, rosy mauve, lavender-grey and gold .. .. | 15 | 15 |
| | | a. | Imperf (pair) .. .. .. | £450 | |
| | | b. | Grey-black (value and inscr, etc) omitted .. .. .. .. | 75·00 | |
| | | c. | Salmon-pink omitted .. .. | 70·00 | |
| | | d. | Blue (leg, robes) omitted .. .. | £130 | |
| | | e. | Rosy mauve (robe at right) omitted | 80·00 | |
| | | f. | Blue and rosy mauve omitted .. | £250 | |
| | | g. | Bright rose-red (King's robe) omitted .. .. .. .. | 75·00 | |
| | | h. | Red-brown (logs, basket, etc) omitted .. .. .. .. | | |
| | | i. | Turquoise-green (leg, robe, etc) omitted .. .. .. .. | | |
| 943/8 | | | .. .. .. .. *Set of* 6 | 3·00 | 80 |

An example of the 3½p. with the gold background colour omitted has been seen used on cover; and another example with the lavender-grey omitted used on piece.

The 3p. and 3½p. are normally with PVA gum with added dextrin but the 3½p. also exists with normal PVA gum and the 3p. with gum arabic.

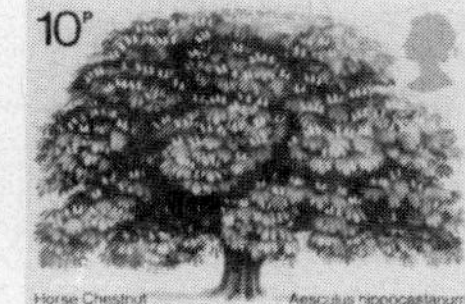


**431** Horse Chestnut

(Des. D. Gentleman)

**1974** (27 Feb). *British Trees* (*2nd issue*). *"All-over" phosphor. P* 15 × 14.

| No. | Type | Value | Description | Unused | Used |
|---|---|---|---|---|---|
| 949 | **431** | 10p. | light emerald, bright green, greenish yellow, brown-olive, black and brownish grey .. .. .. | 50 | 50 |

**432** First Motor Fire-engine, 1904

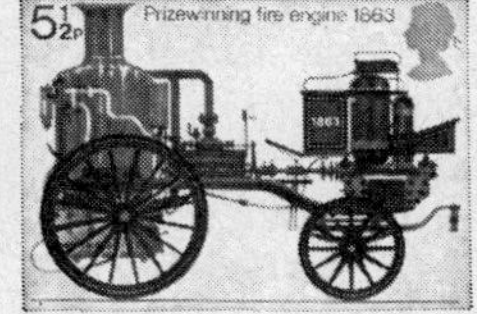


**433** Prize-winning Fire-engine, 1863

**434** First Steam Fire-engine, 1830

**435** Fire-engine, 1766

(Des D. Gentleman)

**1974** (24 Apr). *Bicentenary of the Fire Prevention* (*Metropolis*) *Act. "All-over" phosphor. P* 15 × 14.

| No. | Type | Value | Description | Unused | Used |
|---|---|---|---|---|---|
| 950 | **432** | 3½p. | grey-black, orange-yellow, greenish yellow, dull rose, ochre and grey | 10 | 10 |
| | | a. | Imperf (pair) .. .. .. | £850 | |
| 951 | **433** | 5½p. | greenish yellow, deep rosy magenta, orange-yellow, light emerald, grey-black and grey .. .. | 25 | 25 |
| 952 | **434** | 8p. | greenish yellow, light blue-green, light greenish blue, light chestnut, grey-black and grey .. .. | 60 | 65 |
| 953 | **435** | 10p. | grey-black, pale reddish brown, lt brown, orange-yellow and grey .. | 80 | 85 |
| 950/3 | | | .. .. .. .. .. *Set of* 4 | 1·50 | 1·60 |

The 3½p. exists with ordinary PVA gum.

**436** P & O Packet, *Peninsular*, 1888

**437** Farman Biplane, 1911

**438** Airmail-blue Van and Postbox, 1930

**439** Imperial Airways "C" Class Flying-boat, 1937

(Des Rosalind Dease)

**1974** (12 June). *Centenary of Universal Postal Union. "All-over" phosphor. P* 15 × 14.

| No. | Type | Value | Description | Unused | Used |
|---|---|---|---|---|---|
| 954 | **436** | 3½p. | deep brownish grey, bright mauve, grey-black and gold .. .. | 10 | 10 |
| 955 | **437** | 5½p. | pale orge, lt emer, grey-blk & gold | 20 | 25 |
| 956 | **438** | 8p. | cobalt, brown, grey-black and gold | 30 | 35 |
| 957 | **439** | 10p. | deep brownish grey, orange, grey-black and gold .. .. .. | 50 | 40 |
| 954/7 | | | .. .. .. .. .. *Set of* 4 | 1·00 | 1·00 |

**440** Robert the Bruce

**441** Owain Glyndŵr

**442** Henry the Fifth

**443** The Black Prince

(Des F. Wegner)

**1974** (10 July). *Medieval Warriors. "All-over" phosphor. P* 15 × 14.

| No. | Type | Value | Description | Unused | Used |
|---|---|---|---|---|---|
| 958 | **440** | 4½p. | greenish yellow, vermilion, slate-blue, red-brown, reddish brown, lilac-grey and gold .. .. | 10 | 10 |
| 959 | **441** | 5½p. | lemon, vermilion, slate-blue red-brn, reddish brn, ol-drab & gold | 20 | 25 |
| 960 | **442** | 8p. | deep grey, vermilion, greenish yellow, new blue, red-brown, deep cinnamon and gold .. .. | 70 | 65 |
| 961 | **443** | 10p. | vermilion, greenish yellow, new blue, red-brown, reddish brown, light blue and gold .. .. | 70 | 70 |
| 958/61 | | | .. .. .. .. .. *Set of* 4 | 1·50 | 1·50 |

**444** Churchill in Royal Yacht Squadron Uniform

**445** Prime Minister, 1940

**446** Secretary for War and Air, 1919

**447** War Correspondent, South Africa, 1899

(Des C. Clements and E. Hughes)

**1974** (9 Oct). *Birth Centenary of Sir Winston Churchill. "All-over" phosphor. P* 14 × 15.

| No. | Type | Value | Description | Unused | Used |
|---|---|---|---|---|---|
| 962 | **444** | 4½p. | Prussian blue, pale turquoise-green and silver .. .. .. .. | 15 | 15 |
| 963 | **445** | 5½p. | sepia, brownish grey and silver .. | 20 | 25 |
| 964 | **446** | 8p. | crimson, light claret and silver .. | 50 | 50 |
| 965 | **447** | 10p. | light brown, stone and silver .. | 50 | 50 |
| 962/5 | | | .. .. .. .. .. *Set of* 4 | 1·25 | 1·25 |

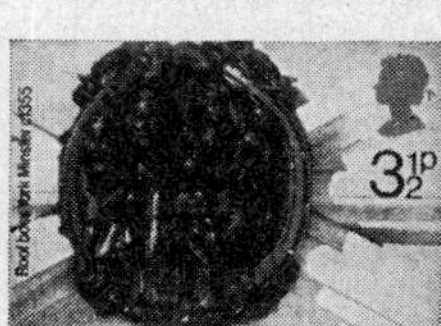


**448** "Adoration of the Magi" (York Minster, *circa* 1355)

**449** "The Nativity" (St. Helen's Church, Norwich, *circa* 1480)

**450** "Virgin and Child" (Ottery St. Mary Church, *circa* 1350)

**451** "Virgin and Child" (Worcester Cathedral, *circa* 1224)

(Des Peter Hatch Partnership)

**1974** (27 Nov). *Christmas. Church Roof Bosses. One phosphor band (3½p.) or "all-over" phosphor (others). P* 15 × 14.

966 **448** 3½p. gold, light new blue, light brown, grey-black and light stone .. 10 10
 a. Light stone (background shading) omitted .. .. .. .. .. £8000
967 **449** 4½p. gold, yellow-orange, rose-red, light brown, grey-black, & lt new blue 10 10
968 **450** 8p. blue, gold, light brown, rose-red, dull green and grey-black .. 45 45
969 **451** 10p. gold, dull rose, grey-black, light new blue, pale cinnamon and light brown .. .. .. .. .. 50 50
966/9 .. .. .. .. .. *Set of* 4 1·00 1·00

The phosphor band on the 3½p. was first applied down the centre of the stamp but during the printing this was deliberately placed to the right between the roof boss and the value; however, intermediate positions, due to shifts, are known.

**452** Invalid in Wheelchair

(Des P. Sharland)

**1975** (22 Jan). *Health and Handicap Funds. "All-over" phosphor. P* 15 × 14.

970 **452** 4½p. + 1½p. azure and grey-blue .. 25 25

**453** "Peace—Burial at Sea"

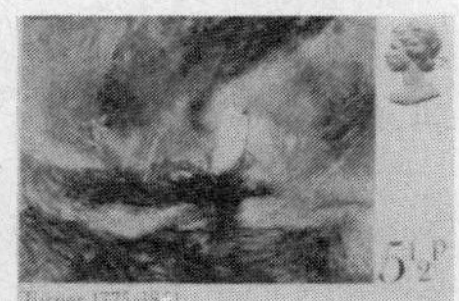


**454** "Snowstorm—Steamer off a Harbour's Mouth"

**455** "The Arsenal, Venice"

**456** "St. Laurent"

(Des S. Rose)

**1975** (19 Feb). *Birth Bicentenary of J. M. W. Turner (painter). "All-over" phosphor. P* 15 × 14.

971 **453** 4½p. grey-blk, salmon, stone, bl & grey 10 10
972 **454** 5½p. cobalt, greenish yellow, light yellow-brown, grey-black and rose 15 15
973 **455** 8p. pale yellow-orange, greenish yellow, rose, cobalt and grey-black 55 55
974 **456** 10p. deep blue, light yellow-ochre, light brown, deep cobalt and grey-black 60 60
971/4 .. .. .. .. .. *Set of* 4 1·25 1·25

**457** Charlotte Square, Edinburgh

**458** The Rows, Chester

T **457/8** were printed horizontally *se-tenant* within the sheet.

**459** Royal Observatory, Greenwich

**460** St. George's Chapel, Windsor

**461** National Theatre, London

(Des P. Gauld)

**1975** (23 Apr). *European Architectural Heritage Year. "All-over" phosphor. P* 15 × 14.

975 **457** 7p. greenish yellow, bright orange, grey-black, red-brown, new blue, lavender and gold .. .. 30 30
 a. Pair. Nos. 975/6 .. .. 90 90
976 **458** 7p. grey-black, greenish yellow, new blue, brt orange, red-brown & gold 30 30
977 **459** 8p. magenta, deep slate, pale magenta, lt yellow-olive, grey-black & gold 20 25
978 **460** 10p. bistre-brown, greenish yellow, deep slate, emer-green, grey-blk & gold 25 25
979 **461** 12p. grey-blk, new bl, pale mag & gold 30 35
975/9 .. .. .. .. .. *Set of* 5 1·50 1·25

**462** Sailing Dinghies

**463** Racing Keel Yachts

**464** Cruising Yachts

**465** Multihulls

(Des A. Restall. Recess and photo)

**1975** (11 June). *Sailing "All-over" phosphor. P* 15 × 14.

980 **462** 7p. black, bluish violet, scarlet, orange-vermilion, orange and gold .. 20 20
981 **463** 8p. black, orange-vermilion, orange, lavender, bright mauve, bright blue, deep ultramarine and gold .. 30 30
 a. Black omitted .. .. .. 55·00
982 **464** 10p. black, orange, bluish emerald, light olive-drab, chocolate and gold .. 35 35
983 **465** 12p. black, ultramarine, turquoise-blue, rose, grey, steel-blue and gold .. 55 55
980/3 .. .. .. .. .. *Set of* 4 1·25 1·25

On No. 981a the recess-printed black colour is completely omitted.

**466** Stephenson's *Locomotion*, 1825

**467** *Abbotsford*, 1876

**468** *Caerphilly Castle*, 1923

**469** High Speed Train, 1975

(Des B. Craker)

**1975** (13 Aug). *150th Anniv of Public Railways. "All-over" phosphor. P* 15 × 14.

984 **466** 7p. red-brown, grey-black, greenish yellow, grey and silver .. .. 30 35
985 **467** 8p. brown, orange-yellow, vermilion, grey-black, grey and silver .. 30 40
986 **468** 10p. emerald-green, grey-black, yellow-orange, vermilion, grey and silver 40 45
987 **469** 12p. grey-black, pale lemon, vermilion, blue, grey and silver .. .. 50 60
984/7 .. .. .. .. .. *Set of* 4 1·40 1·60

**470** Palace of Westminster

(Des R. Downer)

**1975** (3 Sept). *62nd Inter-Parliamentary Union Conference. "All-over" phosphor. P* 15 × 14.

988 **470** 12p. light new blue, black, brownish grey and gold .. .. .. 50 50

471 "Emma and Mr. Woodhouse" (*Emma*)

472 "Catherine Morland" (*Northanger Abbey*)

473 "Mr. Darcy" (*Pride and Prejudice*)

474 "Mary and Henry Crawford" (*Mansfield Park*)

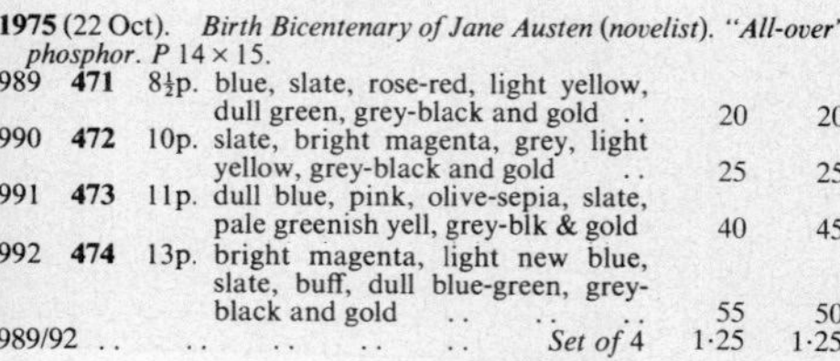

(Des Barbara Brown)

**1975** (22 Oct). *Birth Bicentenary of Jane Austen (novelist). "All-over" phosphor. P* 14 × 15.

| No. | Type | Value | Description | Unused | Used |
|---|---|---|---|---|---|
| 989 | **471** | 8½p. | blue, slate, rose-red, light yellow, dull green, grey-black and gold .. | 20 | 20 |
| 990 | **472** | 10p. | slate, bright magenta, grey, light yellow, grey-black and gold .. | 25 | 25 |
| 991 | **473** | 11p. | dull blue, pink, olive-sepia, slate, pale greenish yell, grey-blk & gold | 40 | 45 |
| 992 | **474** | 13p. | bright magenta, light new blue, slate, buff, dull blue-green, grey-black and gold .. .. .. | 55 | 50 |
| 989/92 | | | .. .. .. .. .. *Set of* 4 | 1·25 | 1·25 |

475 Angels with Harp and Lute

476 Angel with Mandolin

477 Angel with Horn

478 Angel with Trumpet

(Des R. Downer)

**1975** (26 Nov). *Christmas. One phosphor band (6½p.), phosphor-inked background (8½p.), "all-over" phosphor (others). P* 15 × 14.

| No. | Type | Value | Description | Unused | Used |
|---|---|---|---|---|---|
| 993 | **475** | 6½p. | bluish violet, bright reddish violet, light lavender and gold .. .. | 20 | 15 |
| 994 | **476** | 8½p. | turquoise-green, bright emerald-green, slate, lt turq-green & gold | 20 | 20 |
| 995 | **477** | 11p. | vermilion, cerise, pink and gold .. | 50 | 50 |
| 996 | **478** | 13p. | drab, brn, brt orge, buff & gold .. | 50 | 55 |
| 993/6 | | | .. .. .. .. .. *Set of* 4 | 1·25 | 1·25 |

479 Housewife

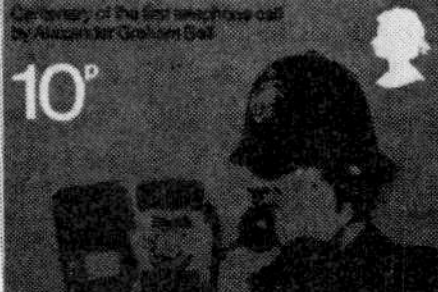

480 Policeman

481 District Nurse

482 Industrialist

(Des P. Sharland)

**1976** (10 Mar). *Telephone Centenary. "All-over" phosphor. P* 15 × 14.

| No. | Type | Value | Description | Unused | Used |
|---|---|---|---|---|---|
| 997 | **479** | 8½p. | greenish blue, dp rose, black & bl | 20 | 20 |
| | | | a. Deep rose omitted .. .. .. | £2250 | |
| 998 | **480** | 10p. | greenish blue, black & yellow-ol | 25 | 25 |
| 999 | **481** | 11p. | greenish blue, deep rose, black and bright mauve .. .. | 40 | 45 |
| 1000 | **482** | 13p. | olive-brn, dp rose, blk & orge-red | 55 | 50 |
| 997/1000 | | | .. .. .. .. *Set of* 4 | 1·25 | 1·25 |

483 Hewing Coal (Thomas Hepburn)

484 Machinery (Robert Owen)

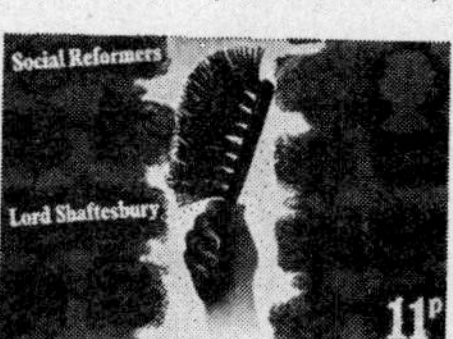

485 Chimney Cleaning (Lord Shaftesbury)

486 Hands clutching Prison Bars (Elizabeth Fry)

(Des D. Gentleman)

**1976** (28 Apr). *Social Reformers. "All-over" phosphor. P* 15 × 14.

| No. | Type | Value | Description | Unused | Used |
|---|---|---|---|---|---|
| 1001 | **483** | 8½p. | lavender-grey, grey-black, black and slate-grey .. .. .. | 20 | 20 |
| 1002 | **484** | 10p. | lavender-grey, grey-black, grey and slate-violet .. .. .. | 25 | 25 |
| 1003 | **485** | 11p. | black, slate-grey and drab .. | 40 | 50 |
| 1004 | **486** | 13p. | slate-grey, black & deep dull grn | 55 | 45 |
| 1001/4 | | | .. .. .. .. .. *Set of* 4 | 1·25 | 1·25 |

## NEW INFORMATION

The editor is always interested to correspond with people who have new information that will improve or correct the Catalogue.

487 Benjamin Franklin (bust by Jean-Jacques Caffieri)

(Des P. Sharland)

**1976** (2 June). *Bicentenary of American Revolution. "All-over" phosphor. P* 14 × 15.

| No. | Type | Value | Description | Unused | Used |
|---|---|---|---|---|---|
| 1005 | **487** | 11p | pale bistre, slate-violet, pale blue-green, black and gold .. .. | 50 | 50 |

488 "Elizabeth of Glamis"

489 "Grandpa Dickson"

490 "*Rosa Mundi*"

491 "Sweet Briar"

(Des Kristin Rosenberg)

**1976** (30 June). *Centenary of Royal National Rose Society. "All-over" phosphor. P* 14 × 15.

| No. | Type | Value | Description | Unused | Used |
|---|---|---|---|---|---|
| 1006 | **488** | 8½p. | bright rose-red, greenish yellow, emerald, grey-black and gold .. | 20 | 20 |
| 1007 | **489** | 10p. | greenish yellow, bright green, red-dish brown, grey-black and gold | 30 | 30 |
| 1008 | **490** | 11p. | bright magenta, greenish yellow, emerald, grey-blue, grey-black and gold .. .. .. .. | 45 | 50 |
| 1009 | **491** | 13p. | rose-pink, lake-brown, yellow-green, pale greenish yellow, grey-black and gold .. .. .. | 45 | 40 |
| | | | a. Value omitted* .. .. .. | | |
| 1006/9 | | | .. .. .. .. .. *Set of* 4 | 1·25 | 1·25 |

*During printing the value was obscured on one position (R. 1/9) of the cylinder, but the error was discovered before issue and most examples were removed from the sheets.

492 Archdruid

493 Morris Dancing

494 Scots Piper

495 Welsh Harpist

(Des Marjorie Saynor)

**1976** (4 Aug). *British Cultural Traditions. "All-over" phosphor. P* 14 × 15.

| No. | Type | Value | Description | Unused | Used |
|---|---|---|---|---|---|
| 1010 | **492** | 8½p. | yellow, sepia, bright rose, dull ultramarine, black and gold .. | 20 | 20 |
| 1011 | **493** | 10p. | dull ultramarine, bright rose-red, sepia, greenish yellow, blk & gold | 30 | 30 |
| 1012 | **494** | 11p. | bluish green, yellow-brown, yell-orge, blk, brt rose-red & gold .. | 45 | 50 |
| 1013 | **495** | 13p. | dull violet-blue, yellow-orange, yell-brn, blk, bluish grn & gold | 45 | 40 |
| 1010/13 | | | .. .. .. .. *Set of* 4 | 1·25 | 1·25 |

The 8½p. and 13p. commemorate the 800th Anniv of the Royal National Eisteddfod.

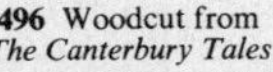

**496** Woodcut from *The Canterbury Tales*

**497** Extract from *The Tretyse of Love*

**498** Woodcut from *The Game and Playe of Chesse*

**499** Early Printing Press

(Des R. Gay. Queen's head printed in gold and then embossed)

**976** (29 Sept). 500*th Anniv of British Printing. "All-over" phosphor. P* 14 × 15.

| | | | | | |
|---|---|---|---|---|---|
| 014 | **496** | 8½p. | black, light new blue and gold .. | 20 | 20 |
| 015 | **497** | 10p. | black, olive-green and gold .. | 25 | 30 |
| 016 | **498** | 11p. | black, brownish grey and gold .. | 45 | 45 |
| 017 | **499** | 13p. | chocolate, pale ochre and gold .. | 50 | 45 |
| 014/17 .. | | | .. .. .. .. *Set of* 4 | 1·25 | 1·25 |

**500** Virgin and Child

**501** Angel with Crown

**502** Angel appearing to Shepherds

**503** The Three Kings

(Des Enid Marx)

**976** (24 Nov). *Christmas. English Medieval Embroidery. One phosphor band* (6½*p.*), *"all-over" phosphor* (*others*). *P* 15 × 14.

| | | | | | |
|---|---|---|---|---|---|
| 018 | **500** | 6½p. | bl, bistre-yell, brn & brt orange | 15 | 15 |
| | | a. | Imperf (pair) .. .. .. | £450 | |
| 019 | **501** | 8½p. | sage-green, yellow, brown-ochre, chestnut and olive-black .. | 20 | 20 |
| 020 | **502** | 11p. | deep magenta, brown-orange, new blue, black and cinnamon .. | 50 | 50 |
| | | a. | Uncoated paper* .. .. | 70·00 | 30·00 |
| 021 | **503** | 13p. | bright purple, new blue, cinnamon, bronze-green and olive-grey | 55 | 55 |
| 018/21 .. | | | .. .. .. .. *Set of* 4 | 1·25 | 1·25 |

* See footnote after No. 744.

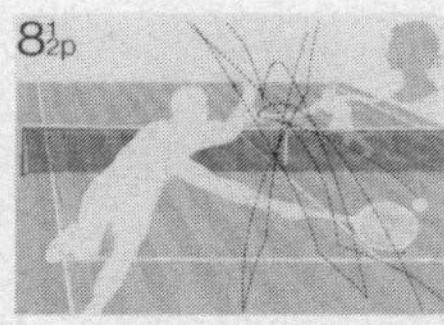

**504** Lawn Tennis

**505** Table Tennis

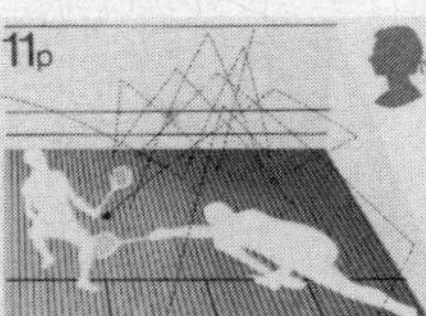

**506** Squash

**507** Badminton

(Des A. Restall)

**1977** (12 Jan). *Racket Sports. Phosphorised paper. P* 15 × 14.

| | | | | | |
|---|---|---|---|---|---|
| 1022 | **504** | 8½p. | emer-grn, blk, grey & bluish grn | 20 | 20 |
| | | a. | Imperf (horiz pair) .. .. | £850 | |
| 1023 | **505** | 10p. | myrtle-green, black, grey-black and deep blue-green .. .. | 30 | 30 |
| 1024 | **506** | 11p. | orange, pale yellow, black, slate-black and grey .. .. .. | 45 | 50 |
| 1025 | **507** | 13p. | brown, grey-black, grey and bright reddish violet .. .. .. | 45 | 40 |
| 1022/5 .. | | | .. .. .. .. *Set of* 4 | 1·25 | 1·25 |

**508**

(Des after plaster cast by Arnold Machin)

**1977** (2 Feb)–**87**. *P* 14 × 15.

| | | | | | |
|---|---|---|---|---|---|
| 1026 | **508** | £1 | brt yellow-green & blackish olive | 3·00 | 20 |
| | | a. | Imperf (pair) .. .. .. | £650 | |
| 1026*b* | | | £1.30, pale drab and deep greenish blue (3.8.83) .. .. .. | 8·00 | 8·00 |
| 1026*c* | | | £1.33, pale mve & grey-blk (28.8.84) | 8·00 | 8·00 |
| 1026*d* | | | £1.41, pale drab and deep greenish blue (17.9.85) .. .. .. | 7·50 | 7·50 |
| 1026*e* | | | £1.50, pale mauve & grey-blk (2.9.86) | 6·00 | 4·00 |
| 1026*f* | | | £1.60 pale drab and deep greenish blue (15.9.87) .. .. .. | 6·00 | 6·00 |
| 1027 | | | £2 light emerald and purple-brown .. | 5·50 | 75 |
| 1028 | | | £5 salmon and chalky blue .. .. | 13·00 | 2·00 |
| | | a. | Imperf (vert pair) .. .. | | |
| 1026/8 .. | | | .. .. .. *Set of* 8 | 50·00 | 30·00 |

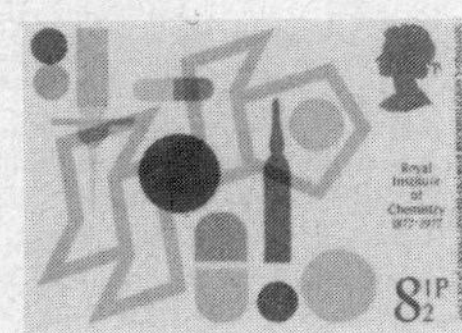

**509** Steroids—Conformational Analysis

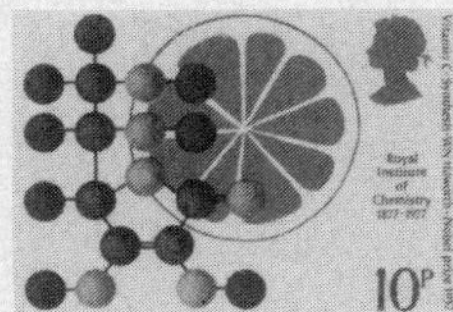

**510** Vitamin C—Synthesis

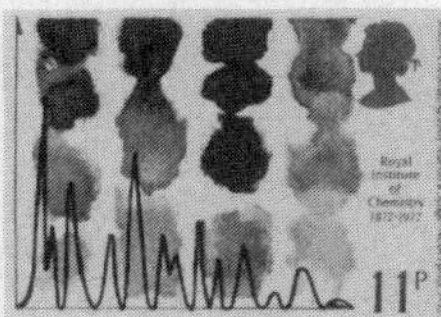

**511** Starch—Chromatography

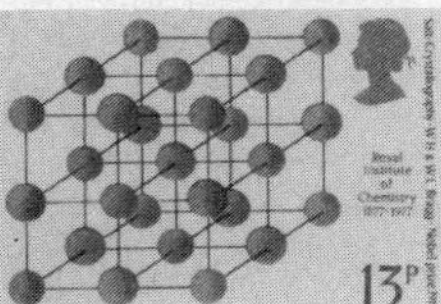

**512** Salt—Crystallography

(Des J. Karo)

**1977** (2 Mar). *Royal Institute of Chemistry Centenary. "All-over" phosphor. P* 15 × 14.

| | | | | | |
|---|---|---|---|---|---|
| 1029 | **509** | 8½p. | rosine, new blue, olive-yellow, brt mauve, yellow-brown, blk & gold | 20 | 20 |
| | | a. | Imperf (horiz pair) .. .. | £850 | |
| 1030 | **510** | 10p. | bright orange, rosine, new blue, bright blue, black and gold .. | 30 | 30 |
| 1031 | **511** | 11p. | rosine, greenish yellow, new blue, deep violet, black and gold .. | 45 | 50 |
| 1032 | **512** | 13p. | new blue, brt green, black & gold | 45 | 40 |
| 1029/32 | | | .. .. .. .. *Set of* 4 | 1·25 | 1·25 |

**513**

**514**

**515**

**516**

T **513/16** differ in the decorations of "ER".

(Des R. Guyatt)

**1977** (11 May–15 June). *Silver Jubilee. "All-over" phosphor. P* 15 × 14.

| | | | | | |
|---|---|---|---|---|---|
| 1033 | **513** | 8½p. | blackish green, black, silver, olive-grey and pale turquoise-green .. | 20 | 20 |
| | | a. | Imperf (pair) .. .. .. | £750 | |
| 1034 | | 9p. | maroon, black, silver, olive-grey and lavender (15 June) .. .. | 25 | 25 |
| 1035 | **514** | 10p. | blackish blue, black, silver, olive-grey and ochre .. .. .. | 25 | 30 |
| | | a. | Imperf (horiz pair) .. .. | | |
| 1036 | **515** | 11p. | brown-purple, black, silver, olive-grey and rose-pink .. .. | 30 | 35 |
| | | a. | Imperf (horiz pair) .. .. | £1300 | |
| 1037 | **516** | 13p. | sepia, black, silver, olive-grey and bistre-yellow .. .. .. | 40 | 40 |
| | | a. | Imperf (pair) .. .. .. | £1300 | |
| 1033/7 .. | | | .. .. .. .. *Set of* 5 | 1·25 | 1·40 |

**517** "Gathering of Nations"

(Des P. Murdoch. Recess and photo)

**1977** (8 June). *Commonwealth Heads of Government Meeting, London. "All-over" phosphor. P* 14 × 15.

| | | | | | |
|---|---|---|---|---|---|
| 1038 | **517** | 13p. | black, blackish green, rose-car and silver .. .. .. | 50 | 50 |

**518** Hedgehog

**519** Brown Hare

**520** Red Squirrel

**521** Otter

**522** Badger

T **518/22** were printed horizontally *se-tenant* within the sheet.

(Des P. Oxenham)

**1977** (5 Oct). *British Wildlife. "All-over" phosphor. P* 14 × 15.

| | | | | |
|---|---|---|---|---|
| 1039 | **518** | 9p. reddish brown, grey-black, pale lemon, brt turq-bl, brt mag & gold | 25 | 20 |
| | | a. Horiz strip of 5. Nos. 1039/43 .. | 1·75 | 1·75 |
| | | b. Imperf (vert pair) .. .. | | |
| | | c. Imperf (horiz pair, Nos. 1039/40) .. | | |
| 1040 | **519** | 9p. reddish brown, grey-black, pale lemon, brt turq-bl, brt mag & gold | 25 | 20 |
| 1041 | **520** | 9p. reddish brown, grey-black, pale lemon, brt turq-bl, brt mag & gold | 25 | 20 |
| 1042 | **521** | 9p. reddish brown, grey-black, pale lemon, brt turq-bl, brt mag & gold | 25 | 20 |
| 1043 | **522** | 9p. grey-black, reddish brown, pale lemon, brt turq-bl, brt mag & gold | 25 | 20 |
| 1039/43 | | .. .. .. .. *Set of* 5 | 1·75 | 90 |

**523** "Three French Hens, Two Turtle Doves and a Partridge in a Pear Tree"

**524** "Six Geese a-laying, Five Gold Rings, Four Colly Birds"

**525** "Eight Maids a-milking, Seven Swans a-swimming"

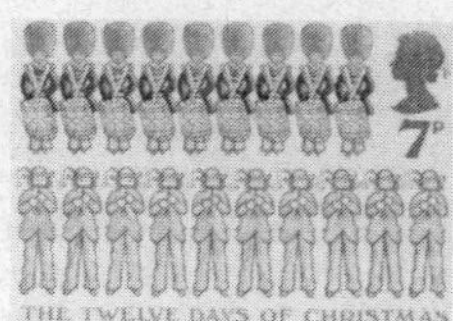


**526** "Ten Pipers piping, Nine Drummers drumming"

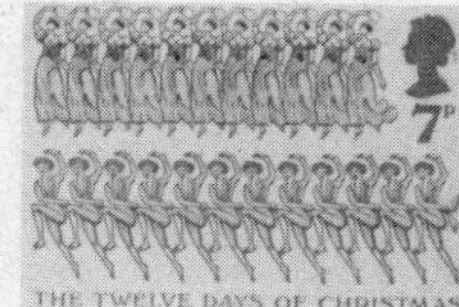


**527** "Twelve Lords a-leaping, Eleven Ladies dancing"

T **523/7** depict the carol "The Twelve Days of Christmas" and were printed horizontally *se-tenant* within the sheet.

**528** "A Partridge in a Pear Tree"

(Des D. Gentleman)

**1977** (23 Nov). *Christmas. One centre phosphor band* (7*p.*) *or "all-over" phosphor* (9*p.*). *P* 15 × 14.

| | | | | |
|---|---|---|---|---|
| 1044 | **523** | 7p. slate, grey, bright yellow-green, new blue, rose-red and gold .. .. | 15 | 15 |
| | | a. Horiz strip of 5. Nos. 1044/8 .. | 1·00 | 1·10 |
| | | ab. Imperf (strip of 5, Nos. 1044/8) .. | £1100 | |
| 1045 | **524** | 7p. slate, brt yellow-grn, new bl & gold | 15 | 15 |
| 1046 | **525** | 7p. slate, grey, bright yellow-green, new blue, rose-red and gold .. .. | 15 | 15 |
| 1047 | **526** | 7p. slate, grey, bright yellow-green, new blue, rose-red and gold .. .. | 15 | 15 |
| 1048 | **527** | 7p. slate, grey, bright yellow-green, new blue, rose-red and gold .. .. | 15 | 15 |
| 1049 | **528** | 9p. pale brown, pale orange, brt emer, pale greenish yell, slate-blk & gold | 20 | 20 |
| | | a. Imperf (pair) .. .. .. .. | £850 | |
| 1044/9 | | .. .. .. .. *Set of* 6 | 1·10 | 85 |

**529** Oil—North Sea Production Platform

**530** Coal—Modern Pithead

**531** Natural Gas—Flame Rising from Sea

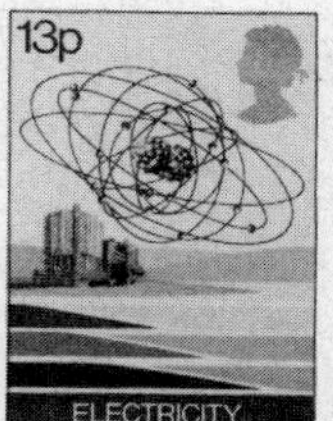


**532** Electricity—Nuclear Power Station and Uranium Atom

(Des P. Murdoch)

**1978** (25 Jan). *Energy Resources. "All-over" phosphor. P* 14 × 15.

| | | | | |
|---|---|---|---|---|
| 1050 | **529** | 9p. deep brown, orange-vermilion, grey-black, greenish yellow, rose-pink, new blue and silver .. | 25 | 20 |
| 1051 | **530** | 10½p. light emerald-green, grey-black, red-brown, slate-grey, pale apple-green and silver .. .. | 25 | 35 |
| 1052 | **531** | 11p. greenish blue, bright violet, violet-blue, blackish brown, grey-black and silver .. .. .. | 35 | 45 |
| 1053 | **532** | 13p. orange-vermilion, grey-black, deep brown, greenish yellow, light brown, light blue and silver .. | 55 | 40 |
| 1050/3 | | .. .. .. .. *Set of* 4 | 1·25 | 1·25 |

**533** The Tower of London

**534** Holyroodhouse

**535** Caernarvon Castle

**536** Hampton Court Palace

(Des R. Maddox (stamps), J. Matthews (miniature sheet))

**1978** (1 Mar). *British Architecture. Historic Buildings. "All-over" phosphor. P* 15 × 14.

| | | | | |
|---|---|---|---|---|
| 1054 | **533** | 9p. black, olive-brown, new blue, brt green, lt yellow-olive & rose-red | 25 | 20 |
| 1055 | **534** | 10½p. black, brown-olive, orange-yell, brt grn, lt yell-olive & vio-bl .. | 25 | 30 |
| 1056 | **535** | 11p. black, brown-olive, violet-blue, brt green, lt yellow-olive & dull bl | 45 | 35 |
| 1057 | **536** | 13p. black, orange-yellow, lake-brown, bright green and light yellow-olive | 50 | 55 |
| 1054/7 | | .. .. .. .. *Set of* 4 | 1·25 | 1·25 |
| **MS**1058 | | 121 × 89 mm. Nos. 1054/7 (*sold at* 53½*p.*) | 1·50 | 1·60 |
| | | a. Imperforate .. .. .. | £4000 | |
| | | b. Light yellow-olive (Queen's head) omitted .. .. .. .. | £3000 | |
| | | c. Rose-red (Union Jack on 9p.) omitted .. .. .. .. | £1750 | |
| | | d. Orange-yellow omitted .. .. | £1750 | |

The premium on No. **MS**1058 was used to support the London 1980 International Stamp Exhibition.

**537** State Coach

**538** St. Edward's Crown

**539** The Sovereign's Orb

**540** Imperial State Crown

(Des J. Matthews)

**1978** (31 May). *25th Anniv of Coronation. "All-over" phosphor. P* 14 × 15.

| | | | | |
|---|---|---|---|---|
| 1059 | **537** | 9p. gold and royal blue .. .. | 20 | 20 |
| 1060 | **538** | 10½p. gold and brown-lake .. .. | 25 | 30 |
| 1061 | **539** | 11p. gold and deep dull green .. | 45 | 50 |
| 1062 | **540** | 13p. gold and reddish violet .. .. | 50 | 40 |
| 1059/62 | | .. .. .. .. *Set of* 4 | 1·25 | 1·25 |

**541** Shire Horse

**542** Shetland Pony

**543** Welsh Pony

**544** Thoroughbred

(Des P. Oxenham)

**1978** (5 July). *Horses. "All-over" phosphor. P* 15 × 14.

| | | | | | |
|---|---|---|---|---|---|
| 1063 | **541** | 9p. | black, pale reddish brown, grey-black, greenish yellow, light blue, vermilion and gold .. .. | 20 | 25 |
| 1064 | **542** | 10½p. | pale chestnut, magenta, brownish grey, greenish yellow, greenish blue, grey-black and gold .. | 25 | 30 |
| 1065 | **543** | 11p. | reddish brown, black, light green, greenish yellow, bistre, grey-black and gold .. .. .. .. .. | 45 | 35 |
| 1066 | **544** | 13p. | reddish brown, pale reddish brown, emerald, greenish yellow, grey-black and gold | 50 | 50 |
| 1063/6 .. | | | .. .. .. .. *Set of* 4 | 1·25 | 1·25 |

**545** "Penny-farthing" and 1884 Safety Bicycle

**546** 1920 Touring Bicycles

**547** Modern Small-wheel Bicycles

**548** 1978 Road-racers

(Des F. Wegner)

**978** (2 Aug). *Centenaries of Cyclists Touring Club and British Cycling Federation. "All-over" phosphor. P* 15 × 14.

| | | | | | |
|---|---|---|---|---|---|
| 067 | **545** | 9p. | brown, deep dull blue, rose-pink, pale olive, grey-black and gold .. | 20 | 20 |
| | | a. | Imperf (pair) .. .. .. | £350 | |
| 068 | **546** | 10½p. | olive, pale yellow-orange, orange-vermilion, rose-red, light brown, grey-black and gold .. .. | 25 | 35 |
| 069 | **547** | 11p. | orange-vermilion, greenish blue, light brown, pale greenish yellow, deep grey, grey-black and gold .. | 45 | 45 |
| 070 | **548** | 13p. | new blue, orange-vermilion, light brn, olive-grey, grey-black & gold | 50 | 40 |
| | | a. | Imperf (pair) .. .. .. .. | £750 | |
| 067/70 .. | | | .. .. .. .. *Set of* 4 | 1·25 | 1·25 |

**549** Singing Carols round the Christmas Tree

**550** The Waits

**551** 18th-century Carol Singers

**552** "The Boar's Head Carol"

(Des Faith Jaques)

**1978** (22 Nov). *Christmas. One centre phosphor band* (7p.) *or "all-over" phosphor* (*others*). *P* 15 × 14.

| | | | | | |
|---|---|---|---|---|---|
| 1071 | **549** | 7p. | bright green, greenish yellow, magenta, new blue, black and gold | 20 | 20 |
| | | a. | Imperf (vert pair) .. .. | £350 | |
| 1072 | **550** | 9p. | magenta, greenish yellow, new blue, sage-green, black and gold | 25 | 25 |
| | | a. | Imperf (horiz pair) .. .. | | |
| 1073 | **551** | 11p. | magenta, new blue, greenish yellow, yellow-brown, black and gold | 45 | 50 |
| | | a. | Imperf (horiz pair) .. .. | | |
| 1074 | **552** | 13p. | salmon-pink, new blue, greenish yellow, magenta, black and gold | 50 | 45 |
| 1071/4 .. | | | .. .. .. .. *Set of* 4 | 1·25 | 1·25 |

**553** Old English Sheepdog

**554** Welsh Springer Spaniel

**555** West Highland Terrier

**556** Irish Setter

(Des P. Barrett)

**1979** (7 Feb). *Dogs. "All-over" phosphor. P* 15 × 14.

| | | | | | |
|---|---|---|---|---|---|
| 1075 | **553** | 9p. | grey-black, sepia, turquoise-green, pale greenish yellow, pale greenish blue and grey .. .. | 20 | 25 |
| 1076 | **554** | 10½p. | grey-black, lake-brown, apple-green, pale greenish yellow, pale greenish blue and grey .. .. | 30 | 35 |
| 1077 | **555** | 11p. | grey-black, claret, yellowish grn, pale greenish yell, cobalt & grey | 45 | 40 |
| | | a. | Imperf (horiz pair) .. .. | £850 | |
| 1078 | **556** | 13p. | grey-black, lake-brown, green, pale greenish yellow & dp turq-bl | 45 | 40 |
| 1075/8 .. | | | .. .. .. .. *Set of* 4 | 1·25 | 1·25 |

**557** Primrose

**558** Daffodil

**559** Bluebell

**560** Snowdrop

(Des P. Newcombe)

**1979** (21 Mar). *Spring Wild Flowers. "All-over" phosphor. P* 14 × 15.

| | | | | | |
|---|---|---|---|---|---|
| 1079 | **557** | 9p. | slate-black, deep brown, pale greenish yellow, deep olive, pale new blue and silver .. .. | 20 | 20 |
| | | a. | Imperf (pair) .. .. .. | £400 | |
| 1080 | **558** | 10½p. | greenish yellow, grey-green, steel-blue, slate-blk, new blue & silver | 30 | 35 |
| | | a. | Imperf (vert pair) .. .. | £1500 | |
| 1081 | **559** | 11p. | slate-black, deep brown, ultramarine, light greenish blue, pale greenish yellow and silver .. | 45 | 45 |
| | | a. | Imperf (horiz pair) .. .. | £1200 | |
| 1082 | **560** | 13p. | slate-black, indigo, grey-green, sepia, ochre and silver .. .. | 45 | 40 |
| | | a. | Imperf (horiz pair) .. .. | £750 | |
| 1079/82 | | | .. .. .. .. *Set of* 4 | 1·25 | 1·25 |

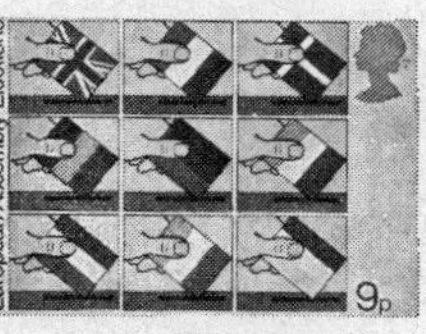


**561**

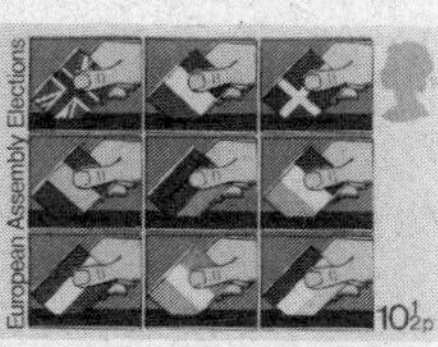


**562**

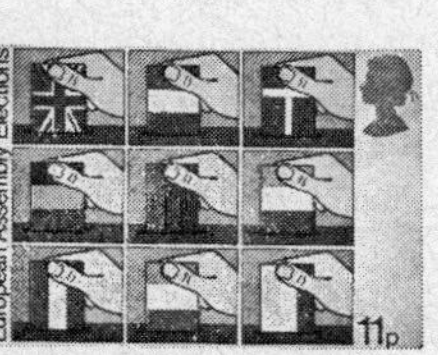


**563**

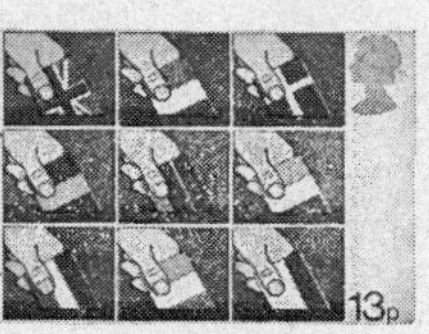


**564**

T **561/4** show Hands placing National Flags in Ballot Boxes.

(Des S. Cliff)

**1979** (9 May). *First Direct Elections to European Assembly. Phosphorised paper. P* 15 × 14.

| | | | | | |
|---|---|---|---|---|---|
| 1083 | **561** | 9p. | grey-black, vermilion, cinnamon, pale greenish yellow, pale turq-green and dull ultramarine .. | 20 | 20 |
| 1084 | **562** | 10½p. | grey-black, vermilion, cinnamon, pale greenish yellow, dull ultramarine, pale turq-grn & chestnut | 30 | 35 |
| 1085 | **563** | 11p. | grey-black, vermilion, cinnamon, pale greenish yellow, dull ultramarine, pale turq-grn & grey-grn | 45 | 45 |
| 1086 | **564** | 13p. | grey-black, vermilion, cinnamon, pale greenish yellow, dull ultramarine, pale turq-grn & brown | 45 | 40 |
| 1083/6 .. | | | .. .. .. .. *Set of* 4 | 1·25 | 1·25 |

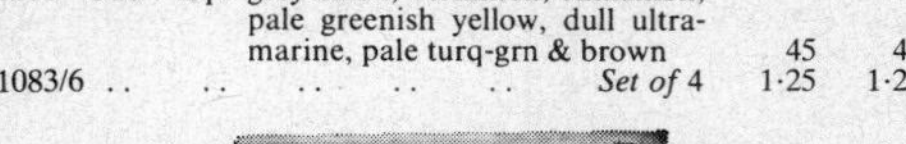

**565** "Saddling 'Mahmoud' for the Derby, 1936" (Sir Alfred Munnings)

**566** "The Liverpool Great National Steeple Chase, 1839" (aquatint by F. C. Turner)

**567** "The First Spring Meeting, Newmarket, 1793" (J. N. Sartorius)

**568** "Racing at Dorsett Ferry, Windsor, 1684" (Francis Barlow)

(Des S. Rose)

**1979** (6 June). *Horseracing Paintings. Bicentenary of the Derby* (9p.). *"All-over" phosphor. P* 15 × 14.

| | | | | | |
|---|---|---|---|---|---|
| 1087 | **565** | 9p. | light blue, red-brown, rose-pink, pale greenish yellow, grey-black and gold .. .. .. .. | 25 | 25 |
| 1088 | **566** | 10½p. | bistre-yellow, slate-blue, salmon-pink, lt blue, grey-black and gold | 30 | 30 |
| 1089 | **567** | 11p. | rose, vermilion, pale greenish yellow, new blue, grey-black and gold | 35 | 50 |
| 1090 | **568** | 13p. | bistre-yellow, rose, turquoise, grey-black and gold .. .. | 50 | 55 |
| 1087/90.. | | | .. .. .. .. *Set of* 4 | 1·25 | 1·40 |

**569** *The Tale of Peter Rabbit* (Beatrix Potter)

**570** *The Wind in the Willows* (Kenneth Grahame)

**571** *Winnie-the-Pooh* (A. A. Milne)

**572** *Alice's Adventures in Wonderland* (Lewis Carroll)

(Des E. Hughes)

**1979** (11 July). *International Year of the Child. Children's Book Illustrations. "All-over" phosphor. P* 14 × 15.

| | | | | | |
|---|---|---|---|---|---|
| 1091 | **569** | 9p. | deep bluish green, grey-black, bistre-brown, bright rose, greenish yellow and silver .. .. | 45 | 20 |
| 1092 | **570** | 10½p. | dull ultramarine, grey-black, ol-brown, bright rose, yellow-orge, pale greenish yellow and silver .. | 50 | 35 |
| 1093 | **571** | 11p. | drab, grey-black, greenish yellow, new bl, yell-orge, agate & silver | 55 | 40 |
| 1094 | **572** | 13p. | pale greenish yellow, grey-black, bright rose, deep bluish green, olive-brown, new blue and silver | 60 | 55 |
| 1091/4 .. | | | .. .. .. .. *Set of* 4 | 1·90 | 1·40 |

**573** Sir Rowland Hill

**574** Postman, *circa* 1839

**575** London Postman, *circa* 1839

**576** Woman and Young Girl with Letters, 1840

(Des E. Stemp)

**1979** (22 Aug–24 Oct). *Death Centenary of Sir Rowland Hill. "All-over" phosphor. P* 14 × 15.

| | | | | | |
|---|---|---|---|---|---|
| 1095 | **573** | 10p. | grey-black, brown-ochre, myrtle-green, pale greenish yellow, rosine, bright blue and gold .. | 25 | 25 |
| 1096 | **574** | 11½p. | grey-black, brown-ochre, bright blue, rosine, bistre-brown, pale greenish yellow and gold .. | 30 | 35 |
| 1097 | **575** | 13p. | grey-black, brown-ochre, bright blue, rosine, bistre-brown, pale greenish yellow and gold .. | 35 | 40 |
| 1098 | **576** | 15p. | grey-black, brown-ochre, myrtle-green, bistre-brown, rosine, pale greenish yellow and gold .. | 50 | 40 |
| 1095/8 .. | | | .. .. .. .. *Set of* 4 | 1·25 | 1·25 |
| **MS**1099 | | | 89 × 121 mm. Nos. 1095/8 (*sold at* 59½*p.*) (24 Oct) .. .. .. .. .. | 1·25 | 1·25 |
| | | | a. Imperforate .. .. .. | £1100 | |
| | | | b. Brown-ochre (15p. background, etc) omitted .. .. | £750 | |
| | | | c. Gold (Queen's head) omitted .. | £225 | |
| | | | d. Brown-ochre, myrtle-green and gold omitted .. .. .. | £3000 | |
| | | | e. Bright blue (13p. background, etc) omitted .. .. .. | £950 | |
| | | | f. Myrtle-green (10p. (background), 15p.) omitted .. .. | £1300 | |
| | | | g. Pale greenish yellow omitted .. | £160 | |
| | | | h. Rosine omitted .. .. .. | £600 | |
| | | | i. Bistre-brown omitted .. .. | £750 | |

The premium on No. **MS**1099 was used to support the London 1980 International Stamp Exhibition.

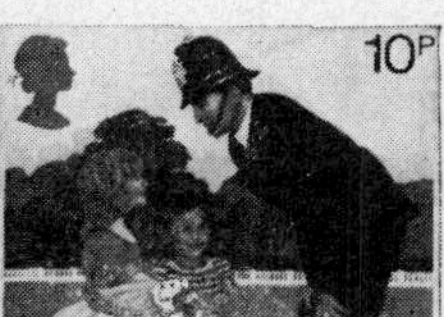


**577** Policeman on the Beat

**578** Policeman directing Traffic

**579** Mounted Policewoman

**580** River Patrol Boat

(Des B. Sanders)

**1979** (26 Sept). *150th Anniv of Metropolitan Police. Phosphorised paper. P* 15 × 14.

| | | | | | |
|---|---|---|---|---|---|
| 1100 | **577** | 10p. | grey-black, red-brown, emerald, greenish yellow, brt blue & mag | 25 | 25 |
| 1101 | **578** | 11½p. | grey-black, bright orange, purple-brown, ultramarine, greenish yellow and deep bluish green .. | 30 | 35 |
| 1102 | **579** | 13p. | grey-black, red-brown, magenta, ol-grn, greenish yell & dp dull bl | 35 | 40 |
| 1103 | **580** | 15p. | grey-black, magenta, brown, slate-bl, dp brown & greenish blk | 50 | 40 |
| 1100/3 .. | | | .. .. .. .. *Set of* 4 | 1·25 | 1·25 |

**581** The Three Kings

**582** Angel appearing to the Shepherds

**583** The Nativity

**584** Mary and Joseph travelling to Bethlehem

**585** The Annunciation

(Des F. Wegner)

**1979** (21 Nov). *Christmas. One centre phosphor band* (8p.) *or phosphorised paper* (*others*). *P* 15 × 14.

| | | | | | |
|---|---|---|---|---|---|
| 1104 | **581** | 8p. | blue, grey-black, ochre, slate-violet and gold .. .. .. | 20 | 20 |
| | | | a. Imperf (pair) .. .. .. | £550 | |
| 1105 | **582** | 10p. | bright rose-red, grey-black, chestnut, chrome-yell, dp vio & gold | 25 | 25 |
| | | | a. Imperf between (vert pair) .. | £450 | |
| | | | b. Imperf (pair) .. .. .. | £600 | |
| 1106 | **583** | 11½p. | orange-vermilion, steel-bl, drab, grey-black, deep blue-grn & gold | 30 | 35 |
| 1107 | **584** | 13p. | bright blue, orange-vermilion, bistre, grey-black and gold .. | 40 | 40 |
| 1108 | **585** | 15p. | orange-vermilion, blue, bistre, grey-black, green and gold .. | 50 | 45 |
| 1104/8 .. | | | .. .. .. .. *Set of* 5 | 1·50 | 1·50 |

## *MINIMUM PRICE*

The minimum price quote is 10p which represents a handling charge rather than a basis for valuing common stamps. For further notes about prices see introductory pages.

**586** Common Kingfisher

**587** Dipper

**588** Moorhen

**589** Yellow Wagtails

(Des M. Warren)

**1980** (16 Jan). *Centenary of Wild Bird Protection Act. Phosphorised paper. P* 14 × 15.

| | | | | | |
|---|---|---|---|---|---|
| 1109 | **586** | 10p. | bright blue, bright yellow-green, vermilion, pale greenish yellow, grey-black and gold .. .. | 25 | 25 |
| 1110 | **587** | 11½p. | sepia, grey-black, dull ultramarine, vermilion, grey-green, pale greenish yellow and gold .. | 30 | 35 |
| 1111 | **588** | 13p. | emerald-green, grey-black, bright bl, verm, pale greenish yell & gold | 55 | 45 |
| 1112 | **589** | 15p. | greenish yellow, brown, light green, slate-bl, grey-blk & gold | 60 | 50 |
| 1109/12.. | | | .. .. .. .. *Set of* 4 | 1·50 | 1·40 |

**590** "Rocket" approaching Moorish Arch, Liverpool

**591** First and Second Class Carriages passing through Olive Mount cutting

**592** Third Class Carriage and Cattle Truck crossing Chat Moss

**593** Horsebox and Carriage Truck near Bridgewater Canal

**594** Goods Truck and Mail-Coach at Manchester

T **590/4** were printed together, *se-tenant*, in horizontal strips of 5 throughout the sheet.

(Des D. Gentleman)

**1980** (12 Mar). *150th Anniv of Liverpool and Manchester Railway. Phosphorised paper. P* 15 × 14.

| | | | | | |
|---|---|---|---|---|---|
| 1113 | **590** | 12p. | lemon, light brown, rose-red, pale blue and grey-black .. .. | 25 | 25 |
| | | a. | Strip of 5. Nos. 1113/17 .. .. | 1·50 | 1·60 |
| | | ab. | Imperf (horiz strip of 5. Nos. 1113/17) .. .. .. .. | £1200 | |
| | | ac. | Lemon omitted (horiz strip of 5. Nos. 1113/17) .. .. .. | | |
| 1114 | **591** | 12p. | rose-red, light brown, lemon, pale blue and grey-black .. .. | 25 | 25 |
| 1115 | **592** | 12p. | pale blue, rose-red, lemon, light brown and grey-black .. .. | 25 | 25 |
| 1116 | **593** | 12p. | light brown, lemon, rose-red, pale blue and grey-black .. .. | 25 | 25 |
| 1117 | **594** | 12p. | light brown, rose-red, pale blue, lemon and grey-black .. .. | 25 | 25 |
| 1113/17 .. | | | .. .. .. *Set of* 5 | 1·50 | 1·10 |

**595** Montage of London Buildings

(Des J. Matthews. Recess)

**1980** (9 Apr–7 May). *"London 1980" International Stamp Exhibition. Phosphorised paper. P* 14½ × 14.

| | | | | | |
|---|---|---|---|---|---|
| 1118 | **595** | 50p. | agate .. .. .. .. .. | 1·50 | 1·50 |
| **MS**1119 | | | 90 × 123 mm. No. 1118 (*sold at* 75*p*.) (7 May) .. .. .. .. .. | 1·50 | 1·50 |
| | | a. | Error. Imperf .. .. .. | £700 | |

**596** Buckingham Palace

**597** The Albert Memorial

**598** Royal Opera House

**599** Hampton Court

**600** Kensington Palace

(Des Sir Hugh Casson)

**1980** (7 May). *London Landmarks. Phosphorised paper. P* 14 × 15.

| | | | | | |
|---|---|---|---|---|---|
| 1120 | **596** | 10½p. | grey, pale blue, rosine, pale greenish yell, yellowish green & silver | 25 | 25 |
| 1121 | **597** | 12p. | grey-black, bistre, rosine, yellowish green, pale greenish yellow and silver .. .. .. | 30 | 30 |
| | | a. | Imperf (vert pair) .. .. | £550 | |
| 1122 | **598** | 13½p. | grey-black, pale salmon, pale olgreen, slate-blue and silver .. | 35 | 35 |
| | | a. | Imperf (pair) .. .. .. | £550 | |
| 1123 | **599** | 15p. | grey-black, pale salmon, slateblue, dull yellowish green, oliveyellow and silver .. .. | 50 | 45 |
| 1124 | **600** | 17½p. | grey, slate-blue, red-brown, sepia, yellowish green, pale greenish yellow and silver .. .. .. | 60 | 55 |
| | | a. | Silver (Queen's head) omitted .. | £250 | |
| 1120/4 .. | | | .. .. .. .. *Set of* 5 | 1·75 | 1·75 |

No. 1124a shows the Queen's head in pale greenish yellow, this colour being printed beneath the silver for technical reasons.

**601** Charlotte Brontë (*Jane Eyre*)

**602** George Eliot (*The Mill on the Floss*)

**603** Emily Brontë (*Wuthering Heights*)

**604** Mrs. Gaskell (*North and South*)

T **601/4** show authoresses and scenes from their novels. T **601/2** also include the "Europa" C.E.P.T. emblem.

(Des Barbara Brown)

**1980** (9 July). *Famous Authoresses. Phosphorised paper. P* 15 × 14.

| | | | | | |
|---|---|---|---|---|---|
| 1125 | **601** | 12p. | red-brown, bright rose, bright bl, greenish yellow, grey and gold | 30 | 30 |
| 1126 | **602** | 13½p. | red-brown, dull vermilion, pale bl, pale greenish yell, grey & gold | 35 | 35 |
| | | a. | Pale blue omitted .. .. | £1500 | |
| 1127 | **603** | 15p. | red-brown, vermilion, blue, lemon, grey and gold .. | 40 | 45 |
| 1128 | **604** | 17½p. | dull vermilion, slate-blue, ultram, pale greenish yell, grey and gold | 60 | 60 |
| | | a. | Imperf and slate-blue omitted (pair) .. .. .. .. | £700 | |
| 1125/8 .. | | | .. .. .. *Set of* 4 | 1·50 | 1·50 |

**605** Queen Elizabeth the Queen Mother

(Des J. Matthews from photograph by N. Parkinson)

**1980** (4 Aug). *80th Birthday of Queen Elizabeth the Queen Mother. Phosphorised paper. P* 14 × 15.

| | | | | | |
|---|---|---|---|---|---|
| 1129 | **605** | 12p. | bright rose, greenish yellow, new blue, grey and silver .. .. | 50 | 50 |
| | | a. | Imperf (horiz pair) .. .. | £1200 | |

**606** Sir Henry Wood

**607** Sir Thomas Beecham

**608** Sir Malcolm Sargent

**609** Sir John Barbirolli

(Des P. Gauld)

**1980** (10 Sept). *British Conductors. Phosphorised paper. P* 14 × 15.

| No. | Type | Value | Description | Unused | Used |
|---|---|---|---|---|---|
| 1130 | **606** | 12p. | slate, rose-red, greenish yellow, bistre and gold | 30 | 30 |
| 1131 | **607** | 13½p. | grey-black, vermilion, greenish yellow, pale carmine-rose and gold | 35 | 40 |
| 1132 | **608** | 15p. | grey-black, bright rose-red, greenish yellow, turquoise-grn & gold | 45 | 45 |
| 1133 | **609** | 17½p. | black, bright rose-red, greenish yellow, dull violet-blue and gold | 55 | 50 |
| 1130/3 | | | *Set of* 4 | 1·50 | 1·50 |

**610** Running

**611** Rugby

**612** Boxing

**613** Cricket

(Des R. Goldsmith. Litho Questa)

**1980** (10 Oct). *Sport Centenaries. Phosphorised paper. P* 14 × 14½.

| No. | Type | Value | Description | Unused | Used |
|---|---|---|---|---|---|
| 1134 | **610** | 12p. | pale new blue, greenish yellow, magenta, light brown, reddish purple and gold | 30 | 30 |
| | | a. | Gold (Queen's head) omitted | | |
| 1135 | **611** | 13½p. | pale new blue, olive-yellow, bright purple, orange-vermilion, blackish lilac and gold | 35 | 40 |
| 1136 | **612** | 15p. | pale new blue, greenish yellow, bright purple, chalky blue & gold | 40 | 40 |
| | | a. | Gold (Queen's head) omitted | | |
| 1137 | **613** | 17½p. | pale new blue, greenish yellow, magenta, dp ol, grey-brn & gold | 60 | 55 |
| 1134/7 | | | *Set of* 4 | 1·50 | 1·50 |

Centenaries:—12p. Amateur Athletics Association; 13½p. Welsh Rugby Union; 15p. Amateur Boxing Association; 17½p. First England–Australia Test Match.

No. 1134a was caused by a paper fold.

**614** Christmas Tree

**615** Candles

**616** Apples and Mistletoe

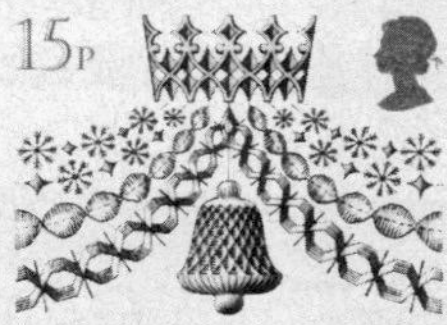


**617** Crown, Chains and Bell

**618** Holly

(Des J. Matthews)

**1980** (19 Nov). *Christmas. One centre phosphor band* (10*p.*) *or phosphorised paper* (*others*). *P* 15 × 14.

| No. | Type | Value | Description | Unused | Used |
|---|---|---|---|---|---|
| 1138 | **614** | 10p. | black, turquoise-green, greenish yellow, vermilion and blue | 25 | 25 |
| | | a. | Imperf (horiz pair) | | |
| 1139 | **615** | 12p. | grey, magenta, rose-red, greenish grey and pale orange | 30 | 35 |
| 1140 | **616** | 13½p. | grey-black, dull yellow-green, brown, greenish yellow and pale olive-bistre | 35 | 40 |
| 1141 | **617** | 15p. | grey-black, bistre-yellow, bright orange, magenta and new blue | 50 | 45 |
| 1142 | **618** | 17½p. | black, vermilion, dull yellowish green and greenish yellow | 55 | 50 |
| 1138/42 | | | *Set of* 5 | 1·75 | 1·75 |

**619** St. Valentine's Day

**620** Morris Dancers

**621** Lammastide

**622** Medieval Mummers

T **619/20** also include the "Europa" C.E.P.T. emblem.

(Des F. Wegner)

**1981** (6 Feb). *Folklore. Phosphorised paper. P* 15 × 14.

| No. | Type | Value | Description | Unused | Used |
|---|---|---|---|---|---|
| 1143 | **619** | 14p. | cerise, green, yellow-orange, salmon-pink, black and gold | 35 | 35 |
| 1144 | **620** | 18p. | dull ultramarine, lemon, lake-brown, brt green, black & gold | 45 | 50 |
| 1145 | **621** | 22p. | chrome-yellow, rosine, brown, new blue, black and gold | 60 | 60 |
| 1146 | **622** | 25p. | brt blue, red-brown, brt rose-red, greenish yellow, black and gold | 75 | 70 |
| 1143/6 | | | *Set of* 4 | 2·00 | 2·00 |

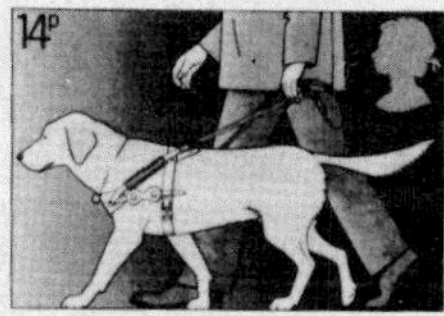


**623** Blind Man with Guide Dog

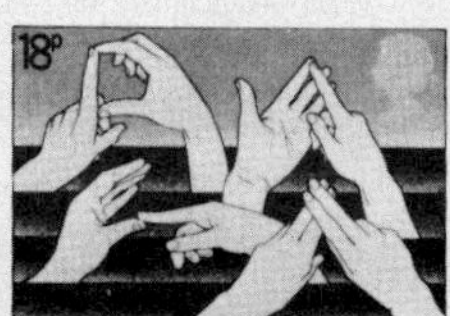


**624** Hands spelling "Deaf" in Sign Language

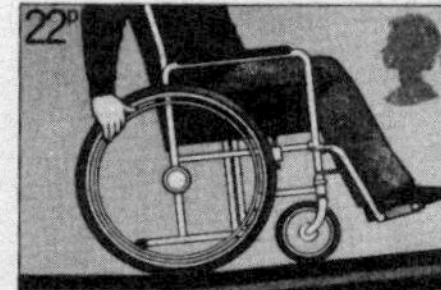


**625** Disabled Man in Wheelchair

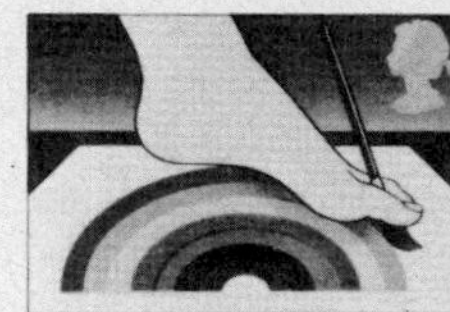

**626** Disabled Artist painting with Foot

(Des J. Gibbs)

**1981** (25 Mar). *International Year of the Disabled. Phosphorised paper. P* 15 × 14.

| No. | Type | Value | Description | Unused | Used |
|---|---|---|---|---|---|
| 1147 | **623** | 14p. | drab, greenish yellow, bright rose-red, dull purple and silver | 35 | 35 |
| | | a. | Imperf (pair) | £750 | |
| 1148 | **624** | 18p. | deep blue-green, brt orange, dull vermilion, grey-black and silver | 45 | 50 |
| 1149 | **625** | 22p. | brown-ochre, rosine, purple-brn, greenish blue, black and silver | 60 | 60 |
| 1150 | **626** | 25p. | vermilion, lemon, pale salmon, olive-brn, new blue, blk & silver | 75 | 70 |
| 1147/50 | | | *Set of* 4 | 2·00 | 2·00 |

All known examples of No. 1147a are creased.

**627** *Aglais urticae*

**628** *Maculinea arion*

**629** *Inachis io*

**630** *Carterocephalus palaemon*

(Des G. Beningfield)

**1981** (13 May). *Butterflies. Phosphorised paper. P* 14 × 15.

| No. | Type | Value | Description | Unused | Used |
|---|---|---|---|---|---|
| 1151 | **627** | 14p. | greenish yellow, yellow-green, brt rose, brt blue, emerald & gold | 35 | 35 |
| | | a. | Imperf (pair) | £950 | |
| 1152 | **628** | 18p. | black, greenish yellow, dull yellowish green, bright mauve, bright blue, bright green and gold | 50 | 50 |
| 1153 | **629** | 22p. | black, greenish yell, bronze-grn, rosine, ultramarine, lt grn & gold | 60 | 65 |
| 1154 | **630** | 25p. | black, greenish yellow, bronze-green, bright rose-red, ultramarine, bright emerald and gold | 70 | 75 |
| 1151/4 | | | *Set of* 4 | 2·00 | 2·00 |

**631** Glenfinnan, Scotland

**632** Derwentwater, England

**633** Stackpole Head, Wales

**634** Giant's Causeway, Northern Ireland

**635** St. Kilda, Scotland

(Des M. Fairclough)

**1981** (24 June). *50th Anniv of National Trust for Scotland. British Landscapes. Phosphorised paper. P* 15 × 14.

| No. | Type | Value | Description | Un. | Used |
|---|---|---|---|---|---|
| 1155 | **631** | 14p. | lilac, dull blue, reddish brown, bistre-yellow, black and gold .. | 40 | 40 |
| 1156 | **632** | 18p. | bottle green, bright blue, brown, bistre-yellow, black and gold .. | 50 | 55 |
| 1157 | **633** | 20p. | deep turq-blue, dull blue, greenish yellow, reddish brn, black & gold | 55 | 60 |
| 1158 | **634** | 22p. | chrome-yellow, reddish brn, new blue, yellow-brown, black & gold | 60 | 60 |
| 1159 | **635** | 25p. | ultramarine, new blue, olive-green, olive-grey and gold .. | 75 | 70 |
| 1155/9 .. | | | .. .. .. .. *Set of* 5 | 2·50 | 2·50 |

**636** Prince Charles and Lady Diana Spencer

(Des J. Matthews from photograph by Lord Snowdon)

**1981** (22 July). *Royal Wedding. Phosphorised paper. P* 14 × 15.

| No. | Type | Value | Description | Un. | Used |
|---|---|---|---|---|---|
| 1160 | **636** | 14p. | grey-blk, greenish yellow, brt rose-red, ultram, pale bl, blue & silver | 35 | 35 |
| 1161 | | 25p. | drab, greenish yellow, bright rose-red, ultramarine, grey-brown, grey-black and silver .. .. | 90 | 90 |

**637** "Expeditions"

**638** "Skills"

**639** "Service"

**640** "Recreation"

(Des P. Sharland. Litho J.W.)

**1981** (12 Aug). *25th Anniv of Duke of Edinburgh Award Scheme. Phosphorised paper. P* 14.

| No. | Type | Value | Description | Un. | Used |
|---|---|---|---|---|---|
| 1162 | **637** | 14p. | greenish yellow, magenta, pale new blue, black, emerald & silver | 35 | 35 |
| 1163 | **638** | 18p. | greenish yellow, magenta, pale new blue, black, cobalt and gold | 50 | 50 |
| 1164 | **639** | 22p. | greenish yellow, magenta, pale new blue, black, red-orge & gold | 60 | 60 |
| 1165 | **640** | 25p. | bright orange, mauve, pale new blue, black, flesh and bronze .. | 70 | 70 |
| 1162/5 .. | | | .. .. .. .. *Set of* 4 | 2·00 | 2·00 |

**641** Cockle-dredging

**642** Hauling in Trawl Net

**643** Lobster Potting

**644** Hoisting Seine Net

(Des B. Sanders)

**1981** (23 Sept). *Fishing Industry. Phosphorised paper. P* 15 × 14.

| No. | Type | Value | Description | Un. | Used |
|---|---|---|---|---|---|
| 1166 | **641** | 14p. | slate, greenish yellow, magenta, new blue, orange-brown, olive-grey and bronze-green .. .. | 35 | 35 |
| 1167 | **642** | 18p. | slate, greenish yellow, brt crimson, ultramarine, blk & greenish slate | 50 | 50 |
| 1168 | **643** | 22p. | grey, greenish yellow, bright rose, dull ultram, reddish lilac & black | 60 | 60 |
| 1169 | **644** | 25p. | grey, greenish yellow, bright rose, cobalt and black .. .. .. | 70 | 65 |
| 1166/9 .. | | | .. .. .. .. *Set of* 4 | 2·00 | 2·00 |

Nos. 1166/9 were issued on the occasion of the centenary of the Royal National Mission to Deep Sea Fishermen.

**645** Father Christmas

**646** Jesus Christ

**647** Flying Angel

**648** Joseph and Mary arriving at Bethlehem

**649** Three Kings approaching Bethlehem

(Des Samantha Brown (11½p.), Tracy Jenkins (14p.), Lucinda Blackmore (18p.), Stephen Moore (22p.), Sophie Sharp (25p.))

**1981** (18 Nov). *Christmas. Children's Pictures. One phosphor band* (11½*p.*) *or phosphorised paper* (*others*). *P* 15 × 14.

| No. | Type | Value | Description | Un. | Used |
|---|---|---|---|---|---|
| 1170 | **645** | 11½p. | ultramarine, black, red, olive-bistre, bright green and gold .. | 30 | 30 |
| 1171 | **646** | 14p. | bistre-yellow, brt magenta, blue, greenish blue, brt grn, blk & gold | 40 | 40 |
| 1172 | **647** | 18p. | pale blue-green, bistre-yellow, brt magenta, ultramarine, blk & gold | 50 | 50 |
| 1173 | **648** | 22p. | deep turquoise-blue, lemon, magenta, black and gold .. .. | 60 | 60 |
| 1174 | **649** | 25p. | royal blue, lemon, bright magenta, black and gold .. .. .. | 70 | 70 |
| 1170/4 .. | | | .. .. .. .. *Set of* 5 | 2·25 | 2·25 |

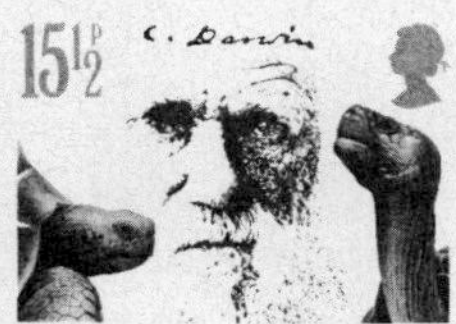


**650** Charles Darwin and Giant Tortoises

**651** Darwin and Marine Iguanas

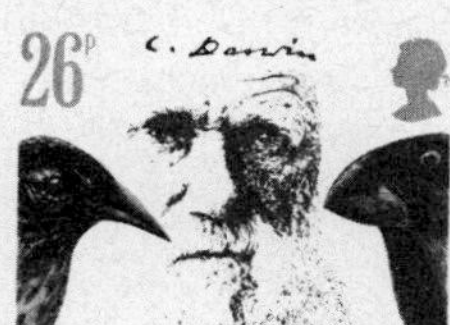


**652** Darwin, Cactus Ground Finch and Large Ground Finch

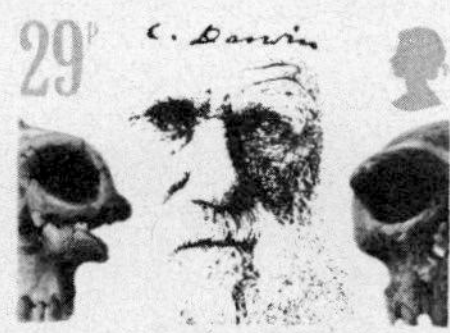


**653** Darwin and Prehistoric Skulls

(Des D. Gentleman)

**1982** (10 Feb). *Death Centenary of Charles Darwin. Phosphorised paper. P* 15 × 14.

| No. | Type | Value | Description | Un. | Used |
|---|---|---|---|---|---|
| 1175 | **650** | 15½p. | dull purple, drab, bistre, black and grey-black .. .. .. | 35 | 35 |
| 1176 | **651** | 19½p. | violet-grey, bistre-yellow, slate-black, red-brown, grey-blk & blk | 60 | 60 |
| 1177 | **652** | 26p. | sage green, bistre-yellow, orange, chalky bl, grey-blk, red-brn & blk | 70 | 70 |
| 1178 | **653** | 29p. | grey-brown, yellow-brn, brown-ochre, black and grey-black .. | 75 | 75 |
| 1175/8 .. | | | .. .. .. .. *Set of* 4 | 2·25 | 2·25 |

**654** Boys' Brigade

**655** Girls' Brigade

**656** Boy Scout Movement **657** Girl Guide Movement

(Des B. Sanders)

**1982** (24 Mar). *Youth Organizations. Phosphorised paper. P* 15 × 14.

| No. | Type | Value | Description | Unused | Used |
|---|---|---|---|---|---|
| 1179 | **654** | 15½p. | gold, greenish yellow, pale orange, mauve, dull blue and grey-black | 35 | 35 |
| 1180 | **655** | 19½p. | gold, greenish yellow, pale orange, bright rose, deep ultramarine, olive-bistre and grey-black . . | 70 | 70 |
| 1181 | **656** | 26p. | gold, greenish yellow, olive-sepia, rosine, deep blue, deep dull green and grey-black . . . . . . | 90 | 90 |
| 1182 | **657** | 29p. | gold, yellow, dull orange, cerise, dull ultram, chestnut & grey-blk | 1·00 | 1·00 |
| 1179/82 | | | . . . . . . . . *Set of* 4 | 2·75 | 2·75 |

Nos. 1179/82 were issued on the occasion of the 75th anniversary of the Boy Scout Movement; the 125th birth anniversary of Lord Baden-Powell and the centenary of the Boys' Brigade (1983).

**658** Ballerina **659** "Harlequin"

**660** "Hamlet" **661** Opera Singer

(Des A. George)

**1982** (28 Apr). *Europa. British Theatre. Phosphorised paper. P* 15 × 14.

| No. | Type | Value | Description | Unused | Used |
|---|---|---|---|---|---|
| 1183 | **658** | 15½p. | carm-lake, greenish bl, greenish yell, grey-blk, bottle grn & silver | 35 | 35 |
| 1184 | **659** | 19½p. | rosine, new blue, greenish yellow, black, ultramarine and silver | 70 | 70 |
| 1185 | **660** | 26p. | carmine-red, bright rose-red, greenish yellow, black, dull ultramarine, lake-brown and silver . . | 90 | 90 |
| 1186 | **661** | 29p. | rose-red, greenish yellow, bright blue, grey-black and silver . . | 1·00 | 1·00 |
| 1183/6 | | | . . . . . . . . *Set of* 4 | 2·75 | 2·75 |

**662** Henry VIII and *Mary Rose*

**663** Admiral Blake and *Triumph*

**664** Lord Nelson and H.M.S. *Victory*

**665** Lord Fisher and H.M.S. *Dreadnought*

**666** Viscount Cunningham and H.M.S *Warspite*

(Des Marjorie Saynor. Eng C. Slania. Recess and photo)

**1982** (16 June). *Maritime Heritage. Phosphorised paper. P* 15 × 14.

| No. | Type | Value | Description | Unused | Used |
|---|---|---|---|---|---|
| 1187 | **662** | 15½p. | black, lemon, bright rose, pale orange, ultramarine and grey . . | 35 | 35 |
| | | a. | Imperf (pair) . . . . . . | £750 | |
| 1188 | **663** | 19½p. | black, greenish yellow, bright rose-red, pale orange, ultram and grey . . . . . . . . | 60 | 60 |
| 1189 | **664** | 24p. | black, orange-yellow, bright rose-red, lake-brown, dp ultram & grey | 70 | 70 |
| 1190 | **665** | 26p. | black, orange-yellow, bright rose, lemon, ultramarine and grey . . | 80 | 80 |
| | | a. | Imperf (pair) . . . . . . | | |
| 1191 | **666** | 29p. | black, olive-yellow, bright rose, orange-yellow, ultram & grey . . | 90 | 80 |
| 1187/91 | | | . . . . . . . . *Set of* 5 | 3·00 | 3·00 |

Nos. 1187/91 were issued on the occasion of Maritime England Year, the Bicentenary of the Livery Grant by City of London to Worshipful Company of Shipwrights and the raising of *Mary Rose* from Portsmouth Harbour.

Several used examples of the 15½p. have been seen with the black recess (ship and waves) omitted.

**667** "Strawberry Thief" (William Morris) **668** Untitled (Steiner and Co)

**669** "Cherry Orchard" (Paul Nash) **670** "Chevron" (Andrew Foster)

(Des Peter Hatch Partnership)

**1982** (23 July). *British Textiles. Phosphorised paper. P* 14 × 15.

| No. | Type | Value | Description | Unused | Used |
|---|---|---|---|---|---|
| 1192 | **667** | 15½p. | blue, olive-yellow, rosine, deep blue-green, bistre & Prussian blue | 35 | 35 |
| | | a. | Imperf (horiz pair) . . . . | £950 | |
| 1193 | **668** | 19½p. | olive-grey, greenish yellow, bright magenta, dull grn, yell-brn & blk | 70 | 70 |
| | | a. | Imperf (vert pair) . . . . | £1500 | |
| 1194 | **669** | 26p. | bright scarlet, dull mauve, dull ultramarine and bright carmine | 70 | 70 |
| 1195 | **670** | 29p. | bronze-green, orange-yellow, turq-green, stone, chestnut & sage-grn | 1·00 | 1·00 |
| 1192/5 | | | . . . . . . . . *Set of* 4 | 2·50 | 2·50 |

Nos. 1192/5 were issued on the occasion of the 250th birth anniversary of Sir Richard Arkwright (inventor of spinning machine).

**671** Development of Communications

**672** Modern Technological Aids

(Des Delaney and Ireland)

**1982** (8 Sept). *Information Technology. Phosphorised paper. P* 14 × 15.

| No. | Type | Value | Description | Unused | Used |
|---|---|---|---|---|---|
| 1196 | **671** | 15½p. | black, greenish yellow, bright rose-red, bistre-brn, new bl & lt ochre | 45 | 50 |
| | | a. | Imperf (pair) . . . . . . | £250 | |
| 1197 | **672** | 26p. | black, greenish yellow, bright rose-red, ol-bistre, new bl & lt ol-grey | 80 | 85 |
| | | a. | Imperf (pair) . . . . . . | £1300 | |

**673** Austin "Seven" and "Metro"

**674** Ford "Model T" and "Escort"

**675** Jaguar "SS 1" and "XJ6"

**676** Rolls-Royce "Silver Ghost" and "Silver Spirit"

(Des S. Paine. Litho Questa)

**1982** (13 Oct). *British Motor Cars. Phosphorised paper. P* 14½ × 14.

| No. | Type | Value | Description | Unused | Used |
|---|---|---|---|---|---|
| 1198 | **673** | 15½p. | slate, orange-vermilion, bright orange, drab, yellow-green, olive-yellow, bluish grey and black . . | 50 | 50 |
| 1199 | **674** | 19½p. | slate, brt orange, olive-grey, rose-red, dull vermilion, grey & black | 1·00 | 1·10 |
| 1200 | **675** | 26p. | slate, red-brown, bright orange, turquoise-green, myrtle-green, dull blue-green, grey and olive . . | 1·10 | 1·25 |
| 1201 | **676** | 29p. | slate, bright orange, carmine-red, reddish purple, grey and black . . | 1·25 | 1·40 |
| 1198/201 | | | . . . . . . . . *Set of* 4 | 3·50 | 3·75 |

**677** "While Shepherds Watched"

**678** "The Holly and the Ivy"

**679** "I Saw Three Ships"

**680** "We Three Kings"

**681** "Good King Wenceslas"

(Des Barbara Brown)

**1982** (17 Nov). *Christmas. Carols. One phosphor band* (12½p.) *or phosphorised paper* (*others*). *P* 15 × 14.

| | | | | | |
|---|---|---|---|---|---|
| 1202 | **677** | 12½p. | black, greenish yellow, brt scar, steel blue, red-brown & gold .. | 30 | 30 |
| 1203 | **678** | 15½p. | black, bistre-yellow, brt rose-red, bright blue, bright green & gold | 55 | 55 |
| | | a. | Imperf (pair) .. .. .. | | |
| 1204 | **679** | 19½p. | black, bistre-yellow, brt rose-red, dull blue, deep brown & gold .. | 80 | 80 |
| | | a. | Imperf (pair) .. .. .. | £1300 | |
| 1205 | **680** | 26p. | black, bistre-yellow, brt magenta, brt blue, choc, gold & orange-red | 80 | 80 |
| 1206 | **681** | 29p. | black, bistre-yellow, magenta, brt blue, chestnut, gold and brt mag | 90 | 90 |
| 202/6 | | | .. .. .. .. *Set of* 5 | 3·00 | 3·00 |

**682** Salmon

**683** Pike

**684** Trout

**685** Perch

(Des A. Jardine)

**983** (26 Jan). *British River Fishes. Phosphorised paper. P* 15 × 14.

| | | | | | |
|---|---|---|---|---|---|
| 207 | **682** | 15½p. | grey-black, bistre-yellow, bright purple, new blue and silver .. | 35 | 35 |
| | | a. | Imperf (pair) .. .. .. .. | £1300 | |
| 208 | **683** | 19½p. | black, bistre-yellow, olive-bistre, dp claret, silver & dp bluish green | 70 | 70 |
| 209 | **684** | 26p. | grey-black, bistre-yell, chrome-yellow, magenta, silver & pale bl | 80 | 80 |
| | | a. | Imperf (pair) .. .. .. | £850 | |
| 210 | **685** | 29p. | black, greenish yellow, bright carmine, new blue and silver .. | 90 | 90 |
| 207/10 | | | .. .. .. .. *Set of* 4 | 2·50 | 2·50 |

All known examples of No. 1209a are creased.

**686** Tropical Island

**687** Desert

**688** Temperate Farmland **689** Mountain Range

(Des D. Fraser)

**1983** (9 Mar). *Commonwealth Day. Geographical Regions. Phosphorised paper. P* 14 × 15.

| | | | | | |
|---|---|---|---|---|---|
| 1211 | **686** | 15½p. | greenish blue, greenish yellow, bright rose, light brown, grey-black, deep claret and silver .. | 35 | 35 |
| 1212 | **687** | 19½p. | brt lilac, greenish yell, mag, dull blue, grey-blk, dp dull-bl & silver | 70 | 70 |
| 1213 | **688** | 26p. | lt blue, greenish yellow, brt mag, new blue, grey-blk, vio & silver | 80 | 80 |
| 1214 | **689** | 29p. | dull vio-bl, reddish vio, slate-lilac, new blue, myrtle-grn, blk & silver | 90 | 90 |
| 1211/14 | | | .. .. .. .. .. *Set of* 4 | 2·50 | 2·50 |

**690** Humber Bridge

**691** Thames Flood Barrier

**692** *Iolair* (oilfield emergency support vessel)

(Des. M. Taylor)

**1983** (25 May). *Europa. Engineering Achievements. Phosphorised paper. P* 15 × 14.

| | | | | | |
|---|---|---|---|---|---|
| 1215 | **690** | 16p. | silver, orange-yellow, ultramarine, black and grey .. .. | 55 | 55 |
| 1216 | **691** | 20½p. | silver, greenish yellow, bright purple, blue, grey-black and grey .. | 1·25 | 1·25 |
| 1217 | **692** | 28p. | silver, lemon, brt rose-red, chestnut, dull ultramarine, blk & grey | 1·25 | 1·25 |
| 1215/17 | | | .. .. .. .. .. *Set of* 3 | 2·75 | 2·75 |

**693** Musketeer and Pikeman, The Royal Scots (1633)

**694** Fusilier and Ensign, The Royal Welch Fusiliers (mid-18th century)

**695** Riflemen, 95th Rifles (The Royal Green Jackets) (1805)

**696** Sergeant (khaki service uniform) and Guardsman (full dress), The Irish Guards (1900)

**697** Paratroopers, The Parachute Regiment (1983)

(Des E. Stemp)

**1983** (6 July). *British Army Uniforms. Phosphorised paper. P* 14 × 15.

| | | | | | |
|---|---|---|---|---|---|
| 1218 | **693** | 16p. | black, buff, deep brown, slate-black, rose-red, gold & new blue | 40 | 40 |
| 1219 | **694** | 20½p. | black, buff, greenish yellow, slate-blk, brn-rose, gold & brt bl | 70 | 70 |
| 1220 | **695** | 26p. | black, buff, slate-purple, green, bistre and gold .. .. .. | 80 | 80 |
| | | a. | Imperf (pair) .. .. .. | £1300 | |
| 1221 | **696** | 28p. | black, buff, light brown, grey, dull rose, gold and new blue .. | 80 | 80 |
| 1222 | **697** | 31p. | black, buff, olive-yellow, grey, deep magenta, gold and new blue | 90 | 90 |
| 1218/22 | | | .. .. .. .. *Set of* 5 | 3·25 | 3·25 |

Nos. 1218/22 were issued on the occasion of the 350th anniversary of the Royal Scots, the senior line regiment of the British Army.

**698** 20th-century Garden, Sissinghurst

**699** 19th-century Garden, Biddulph Grange

**700** 18th-century Garden, Blenheim

**701** 17th-century Garden, Pitmedden

(Des Liz Butler, Litho J.W.)

**1983** (24 Aug). *British Gardens. Phosphorised paper. P* 14.

| | | | | | |
|---|---|---|---|---|---|
| 1223 | **698** | 16p. | greenish yellow, brt purple, new blue, black, bright green & silver | 50 | 40 |
| 1224 | **699** | 20½p. | greenish yellow, brt purple, new blue, black, bright green & silver | 60 | 65 |
| 1225 | **700** | 28p. | greenish yellow, brt purple, new blue, black, bright green & silver | 95 | 1·00 |
| 1226 | **701** | 31p. | greenish yellow, brt purple, new blue, black, bright green & silver | 1·00 | 1·00 |
| 1223/6 | | | .. .. .. .. .. *Set of* 4 | 2·75 | 2·75 |

Nos. 1223/6 were issued on the occasion of the death bicentenary of "Capability" Brown (landscape gardener)

**702** Merry-go-round

**703** Big Wheel, Helter-Skelter and Performing Animals

**704** Side Shows

**705** Early Produce Fair

(Des A. Restall)

**1983** (5 Oct). *British Fairs. Phosphorised paper. P* 15 × 14.

| | | | | | |
|---|---|---|---|---|---|
| 1227 | **702** | 16p. | grey-black, greenish yellow, orge-red, ochre & turquoise-blue . . | 50 | 40 |
| 1228 | **703** | 20½p. | grey-black, yellow-ochre, yellow-orange, brt magenta, violet & blk | 60 | 65 |
| 1229 | **704** | 28p. | grey-black, bistre-yellow, orange-red, violet and yellow-brown . . | 95 | 1·00 |
| 1230 | **705** | 31p. | grey-black, greenish yellow, red, dp turq-green, slate-violet & brn | 1·00 | 1·00 |
| 1227/30 | | | . . . . . . . . . . *Set of* 4 | 2·75 | 2·75 |

**706** "Christmas Post" (pillar-box)

**707** "The Three Kings" (chimney-pots)

**708** "World at Peace" (Dove and Blackbird)

**709** "Light of Christmas" (street lamp)

**710** "Christmas Dove" (hedge sculpture)

(Des T. Meeuwissen)

**1983** (16 Nov). *Christmas. One phosphor band* (12½p.) *or phosphorised paper* (*others*). *P* 15 × 14.

| | | | | | |
|---|---|---|---|---|---|
| 1231 | **706** | 12½p. | black, greenish yellow, bright rose-red, bright blue, gold and grey-black . . . . . . | 30 | 30 |
| | | a. | Imperf (horiz pair) . . . . | £750 | |
| 1232 | **707** | 16p. | black, greenish yellow, bright rose, pale new blue, gold & brown-pur | 45 | 45 |
| | | a. | Imperf (pair) . . . . . . | £850 | |
| 1233 | **708** | 20½p. | black, greenish yellow, bright rose, new blue, gold and blue . . . . | 70 | 70 |
| 1234 | **709** | 28p. | black, lemon, bright carmine, bluish violet, gold, deep turquoise-green and purple . . . . | 90 | 90 |
| 1235 | **710** | 31p. | black, greenish yellow, brt rose, new blue, gold, green & brn-olive | 1·00 | 1·00 |
| 1231/5 | | | . . . . . . . . . . *Set of* 5 | 3·00 | 3·00 |

**711** Arms of the College of Arms

**712** Arms of King Richard III (founder)

**713** Arms of the Earl Marshal of England

**714** Arms of the City of London

(Des J. Matthews)

**1984** (17 Jan). *500th Anniv of College of Arms. Phosphorised paper. P* 14½.

| | | | | | |
|---|---|---|---|---|---|
| 1236 | **711** | 16p. | black, chrome-yellow, reddish brn, scar-verm, brt bl & grey-blk | 40 | 40 |
| 1237 | **712** | 20½p. | black, chrome-yellow, rosine, bright blue and grey-black . . | 70 | 70 |
| 1238 | **713** | 28p. | black, chrome-yellow, rosine, brt blue, dull green and grey-black | 1·00 | 1·00 |
| 1239 | **714** | 31p. | black, chrome-yellow, rosine, brt blue and grey-black . . . . | 1·25 | 1·25 |
| | | a. | Imperf (horiz pair) . . . . | £1800 | |
| 1236/9 | | | . . . . . . . . *Set of* 4 | 3·00 | 3·00 |

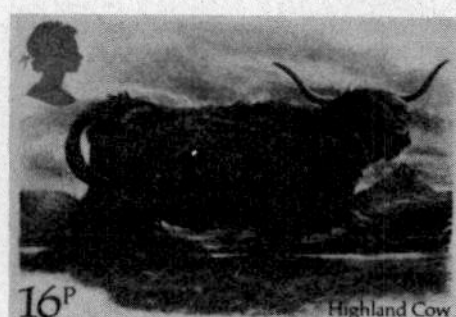


**715** Highland Cow

**716** Chillingham Wild Bull

**717** Hereford Bull

**718** Welsh Black Bull

**719** Irish Moiled Cow

(Des B. Driscoll)

**1984** (6 Mar). *British Cattle. Phosphorised paper. P* 15 × 14.

| | | | | | |
|---|---|---|---|---|---|
| 1240 | **715** | 16p. | grey-black, bistre-yellow, rosine, yellow-orge, new bl & pale drab | 40 | 40 |
| 1241 | **716** | 20½p. | grey-black, greenish yellow, magenta, bistre, dull blue-green, pale drab and light green . . . . | 65 | 65 |
| 1242 | **717** | 26p. | black, chrome-yellow, rosine, reddish brown, new blue & pale drab | 70 | 70 |
| 1243 | **718** | 28p. | black, greenish yellow, bright carmine, orange-brown, deep dull blue and pale drab . . . . | 85 | 85 |
| 1244 | **719** | 31p. | grey-black, bistre-yellow, rosine, red-brown, light blue & pale drab | 1·00 | 1·00 |
| 1240/4 | | | . . . . . . . . . . *Set of* 5 | 3·25 | 3·25 |

Nos. 1240/4 were issued on the occasion of the centenary of the Highland Cattle Society and the bicentenary of the Royal Highland and Agricultural Society of Scotland.

**720** Liverpool Garden Festival Hall

**721** Milburngate Centre, Durham

**722** Bush House, Bristol

**723** Commercial Street Development, Perth

(Des R. Maddox and Trickett and Webb Ltd)

**1984** (10 Apr). *Urban Renewal. Phosphorised paper. P* 15 × 14.

| | | | | | |
|---|---|---|---|---|---|
| 1245 | **720** | 16p. | bright emerald, greenish yellow, cerise, steel-bl, blk, silver & flesh | 40 | 40 |
| 1246 | **721** | 20½p. | bright orange, greenish yellow, deep dull blue, yellowish green, azure, black and silver | 70 | 70 |
| | | a. | Imperf (horiz pair) . . . . | £1000 | |
| 1247 | **722** | 28p. | rosine, greenish yellow, Prussian blue, pale blue-green, blk & silver | 95 | 95 |
| 1248 | **723** | 31p. | blue, greenish yell, cerise, grey-blue, bright green, black & silver | 1·00 | 1·00 |
| | | a. | Imperf (pair) . . . . . . | £1000 | |
| 1245/8 | | | . . . . . . . . . . *Set of* 4 | 2·75 | 2·75 |

Nos. 1245/8 were issued on the occasion of 150th anniversaries of the Royal Institute of British Architects and the Chartered Institute of Building, and to commemorate the first International Gardens Festival, Liverpool.

**ROYAL MAIL POSTAGE LABELS**

These imperforate labels, printed in red on phosphorised paper with grey-green background design, were issued on 1 May 1984 as an experiment by the Post Office. Special microprocessor controlled machines were installed at post offices in Cambridge, London, Shirley, (Southampton) and Windsor to provide an after-hours sales service to the public. The machines printed and dispensed the labels according to the coins inserted and the buttons operated by the customer. Values were initially available in ½p steps to 16p and in addition, the labels were sold at philatelic counters in two packs containing either 3 values (3½, 12½, 16p) or 32 values (½p to 16p).

From 28 August 1984 the machines were adjusted to provide values up to 17p. After 31 December 1984 labels including ½p values were withdrawn. The machines were withdrawn from service on 30 April 1985.

**724** C.E.P.T. 25th Aniversary Logo **725** Abduction of Europa

(Des J. Larrivière (T **724**), F. Wegner (T **725**)

**984** (15 May). *25th Anniv of C.E.P.T. ("Europa") (T* **724***) and Second Elections to European Parliament (T* **725***). Phosphorised paper. P* 15 × 14.

| | | | | | |
|---|---|---|---|---|---|
| 249 | **724** | 16p. greenish slate, deep blue and gold | | 60 | 60 |
| | | a. Horiz pair. Nos. 1249/50 | .. | 1·25 | 1·25 |
| | | ab. Imperf (horiz pair) | .. .. | £1300 | |
| 250 | **725** | 16p. greenish slate, deep blue, black and gold | .. .. .. | 60 | 60 |
| 251 | **724** | 20½p. Venetian red, dp magenta & gold | | 1·00 | 1·00 |
| | | a. Horiz pair. Nos. 1251/2 | .. | 2·00 | 2·00 |
| | | ab. Imperf (horiz pair) | .. | | |
| 252 | **725** | 20½p. Venetian red, deep magenta, black and gold | .. .. | 1·00 | 1·00 |
| 249/52 | | .. .. .. .. *Set of* 4 | | 3·00 | 3·00 |

Nos. 1249/50 and 1251/2 were each printed together, *se-tenant*, in horizontal pairs throughout the sheets.

**726** Lancaster House

(Des P. Hogarth)

**984** (5 June). *London Economic Summit Conference. Phosphorised paper. P* 14 × 15.

| | | | | | |
|---|---|---|---|---|---|
| 253 | **726** | 31p. silver, bistre-yellow, brown-ochre, black, rosine, bright blue and reddish lilac | .. .. .. .. | 1·25 | 1·25 |

**727** View of Earth from "Apollo 11" **728** Navigational Chart of English Channel

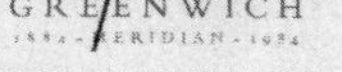

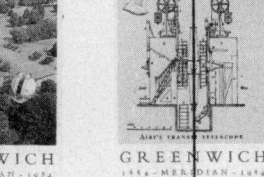

**729** Greenwich Observatory **730** Sir George Airy's Transit Telescope

(Des. H. Waller. Litho Questa)

**984** (26 June). *Centenary of the Greenwich Meridian. Phosphorised paper. P* 14 × 14½.

| | | | | | |
|---|---|---|---|---|---|
| 254 | **727** | 16p. new blue, greenish yellow, magenta, black, scarlet and blue-black | .. .. | 40 | 40 |
| 255 | **728** | 20½p. olive-sepia, light brown, pale buff, black and scarlet | .. .. .. | 65 | 65 |
| 256 | **729** | 28p. new blue, greenish yellow, scarlet, black and bright purple | .. .. | 1·10 | 1·10 |
| 257 | **730** | 31p. deep blue, cobalt, scarlet and black | .. | 1·25 | 1·25 |
| 254/7 | | .. .. .. .. .. *Set of* 4 | | 3·00 | 3·00 |

On Nos. 1254/7 the Meridian is represented by a scarlet line.

**731** Bath Mail Coach, 1784

**732** Attack on Exeter Mail, 1816

**733** Norwich Mail in Thunderstorm, 1827

**734** Holyhead and Liverpool Mails leaving London, 1828

**735** Edinburgh Mail Snowbound, 1831

(Des K. Bassford and S. Paine. Eng C. Slania. Recess and photo)

**1984** (31 July). *Bicentenary of First Mail Coach Run Bath and Bristol to London. Phosphorised paper. P* 15 × 14.

| | | | | | |
|---|---|---|---|---|---|
| 1258 | **731** | 16p. pale stone, black, grey-black and bright scarlet | .. .. | 65 | 65 |
| | | a. Horiz strip of 5 Nos. 1258/62 | .. | 3·00 | 3·00 |
| 1259 | **732** | 16p. pale stone, black, grey-black and bright scarlet | .. .. | 65 | 65 |
| 1260 | **733** | 16p. pale stone, black, grey-black and bright scarlet | .. .. | 65 | 65 |
| 1261 | **734** | 16p. pale stone, black, grey-black and bright scarlet | .. .. | 65 | 65 |
| 1262 | **735** | 16p. pale stone, black, grey-black and bright scarlet | .. .. | 65 | 65 |
| 1258/62 | | .. .. .. .. .. *Set of* 5 | | 3·00 | 3·00 |

Nos. 1258/62 were printed together, *se-tenant*, in horizontal strips of 5 throughout the sheet.

**736** Nigerian Clinic

**737** Violinist and Acropolis, Athens

**738** Building Project, Sri Lanka

**739** British Council Library, Middle East

(Des F. Newell and J. Sorrell)

**1984** (25 Sept). *50th Anniv of the British Council. Phosphorised paper. P* 15 × 14.

| | | | | | |
|---|---|---|---|---|---|
| 1263 | **736** | 17p. grey-green, greenish yellow, bright purple, dull blue, black, pale green and yellow-green | .. .. .. | 50 | 50 |
| 1264 | **737** | 22p. crimson, greenish yellow, bright rose-red, dull green, black, pale drab and slate-purple | .. .. .. .. | 75 | 75 |
| 1265 | **738** | 31p. sepia, olive-bistre, red, black, pale stone and olive-brown | .. .. | 1·10 | 1·10 |
| 1266 | **739** | 34p. steel blue, yellow, rose-red, new blue, black, azure and pale blue | .. .. | 1·25 | 1·25 |
| 1263/6 | | .. .. .. .. .. *Set of* 4 | | 3·25 | 3·25 |

**740** The Holy Family

**741** Arrival in Bethlehem

**742** Shepherd and Lamb

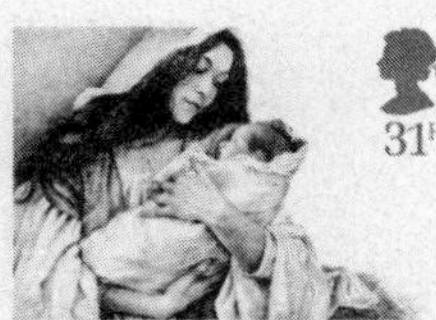


**743** Virgin and Child

**744** Offering of Frankincense

(Des Yvonne Gilbert)

**1984** (20 Nov). *Christmas. One phosphor band* (13*p.*) *or phosphorised paper (others). P* 15 × 14.

| | | | | | |
|---|---|---|---|---|---|
| 1267 | **740** | 13p. pale cream, grey-black, bistre-yellow, magenta, red-brown and lake-brown | | 30 | 30 |
| 1268 | **741** | 17p. pale cream, grey-black, yellow, magenta, dull blue and deep dull blue | | 50 | 50 |
| 1269 | **742** | 22p. pale cream, grey-black, olive-yellow, bright magenta, bright blue and brownish grey | .. .. .. | 70 | 70 |
| 1270 | **743** | 31p. pale cream, grey-black, bistre-yellow, magenta, dull blue and light brown | | 1·10 | 1·10 |
| 1271 | **744** | 34p. pale cream, olive-grey, bistre-yellow, magenta, turquoise-green and brown-olive | .. .. .. .. .. | 1·25 | 1·25 |
| 1267/71 | | .. .. .. .. .. *Set of* 5 | | 3·50 | 3·50 |

Examples of No. 1267 from the Christmas £2.30 discount stamp booklet show a blue underprint of a double-lined star printed on the reverse over the gum.

**745** "The Flying Scotsman"

**746** "The Golden Arrow"

**747** "The Cheltenham Flyer"

**748** "The Royal Scot"

**749** "The Cornish Riviera"

(Des T. Cuneo)

**1985** (22 Jan). *Famous Trains. Phosphorised paper. P* 15 × 14.

1272 **745** 17p. black, lemon, magenta, dull glue, grey-black and gold .. .. 60 60
a. Imperf (pair) .. .. .. £1800
1273 **746** 22p. black, greenish yellow, bright rose, dp dull blue, grey-blk & gold 90 90
1274 **747** 29p. black, greenish yellow, magneta, blue, grey-black and gold .. 1·25 1·25
1275 **748** 31p. black, bistre-yellow, bright magenta, new blue slate-black & gold 1·25 1·25
1276 **749** 34p. black, greenish yellow, bright rose, blue, slate-black and gold .. 1·60 1·60
1272/6 .. .. .. .. .. *Set of* 5 5·00 5·00

Nos. 1272/6 were issued on the occasion of the 150th anniversary of the Great Western Railway Company.

**750** *Bombus terrestris* (bee)

**751** *Coccinella septempunctata* (ladybird)

**752** *Decticus verrucivorus* (bush-cricket)

**753** *Lucanus cervus* (stag beetle)

**754** *Anax imperator* (dragonfly)

(Des G. Beningfield)

**1985** (12 Mar). *Insects. Phosphorised paper. P* 14 × 15.

1277 **750** 17p. black, greenish yellow, magenta, blue, azure, gold and slate-black .. .. 50 55
1278 **751** 22p. black, greenish yellow, bright rose-red, dull blue-green, slate-black and gold 70 70
1279 **752** 29p. black, greenish yellow, bright rose, greenish blue, grey-black, gold and bistre-yellow.. .. .. .. .. 90 90
1280 **753** 31p. black, greenish yellow, rose, pale new blue and gold .. .. .. 1·10 1·10
1281 **754** 34p. black, greenish yellow, magenta, greenish blue, grey-black and gold .. 1·10 1·10
1277/81 .. .. .. .. .. *Set of* 5 4·00 4·00

Nos. 1277/81 were issued on the occasion of the centenaries of the Royal Entomological Society of London's Royal Charter, and of the Selborne Society.

**755** "Water Music" (George Frideric Handel)

**756** "The Planets" Suite (Gustav Holst)

**757** "The First Cuckoo" (Frederick Delius)

**758** "Sea Pictures" (Edward Elgar)

(Des W. McLean)

**1985** (14 May). *Europa. European Music Year. British Composers. Phosphorised paper. P* 14 × 14½.

1282 **755** 17p. black, brt yellow-grn, dp magenta, new blue, grey-black & gold .. 75 75
a. Imperf (vert pair) .. ..
1283 **756** 22p. black, greenish yellow, brt mag, new blue, grey-black and gold .. 1·00 1·00
a. Imperf (pair) .. .. .. £1300
1284 **757** 31p. black, greenish yellow, magenta, greenish blue, grey-black and gold 1·40 1·40
1285 **758** 34p. black, olive-yellow, bistre, turq-blue, slate and gold .. .. 1·60 1·60
1282/5 .. .. .. .. .. *Set of* 5 4·25 4·25

Nos. 1282/5 were issued on the occasion of the 300th birth anniversary of Handel.

**759** R.N.L.I. Lifeboat and Signal Flags

**760** Beachy Head Lighthouse and Chart

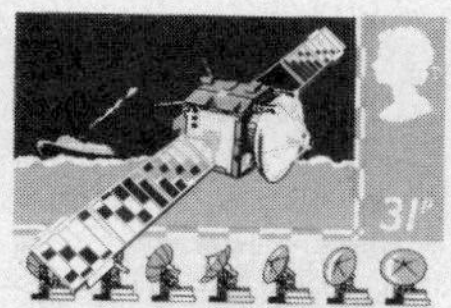

**761** "Marecs A" Communications Satellite and Dish Aerials

**762** Buoys

(Des F. Newell and J. Sorrel. Litho J.W.)

**1985** (18 June). *Safety at Sea. Phosphorised paper. P* 14.

1286 **759** 17p. black, azure, emerald, ultramarine, orange-yellow, vermilion, bright blue, and chrome-yellow .. .. .. 50 50
1287 **760** 22p. black, azure, emerald, ultramarine, orange-yellow, vermilion, bright blue and chrome-yellow .. .. .. 75 75
1288 **761** 31p. black, azure, emerald, ultramarine, orange-yellow, vermilion, and bright blue .. .. .. .. .. 1·10 1·10
1289 **762** 34p. black, azure, emerald, ultramarine, orange-yellow, vermilion, bright blue and chrome-yellow .. .. .. 1·25 1·25
1286/9 .. .. .. .. .. *Set of* 4 3·25 3·25

Nos. 1286/9 were issued on the occasion of the Bicentenary of the unimmersible lifeboat and the 50th anniversary of radar.

**763** Datapost Motorcyclist, City of London

**764** Rural Postbus

**765** Parcel Delivery in Winter

**766** Town Letter Delivery

(Des P. Hogarth)

**1985** (30 July). 350 *Years of Royal Mail Public Postal Service. Phosphorised paper. P* 14 × 15.

1290 **763** 17p. black, greenish yellow, bright carmine, greenish blue, yellow-brown, grey-black and silver .. 50 50
a. Imperf on 3 sides (vert pair) .. £1300
1291 **764** 22p. black, greenish yellow, cerise, steel blue, lt grn, grey-blk & silver 75 75
1292 **765** 31p. black, greenish yellow, brt carm, dull blue, drab, grey-blk & silver 1·10 1·10
a. Imperf (vert pair).. .. .. £1300
1293 **766** 34p. black, greenish yellow, cerise, ultram, lt brown, grey-blk & silver 1·25 1·25
1290/3 .. .. .. .. .. *Set of* 4 3·25 3·25

Examples of No. 1290 from the commemorative £1.53 discount stamp booklet show a blue underprint of a double-lined D printed on the reverse over the gum.

No. 1290a shows perforation indentations at right, but is imperforate at top, bottom and on the left-hand side.

**767** King Arthur and Merlin

**768** Lady of the Lake

**769** Queen Guinevere and Sir Lancelot

**770** Sir Galahad

(Des Yvonne Gilbert)

**1985** (3 Sept). *Arthurian Legends. Phosphorised paper.* P 15×14.

| No. | Type | Value | Description | Unused | Used |
|---|---|---|---|---|---|
| 1294 | **767** | 17p. | grey-black, lemon, brown-lilac, ultramarine, grey-black and silver | 50 | 50 |
| | | | a. Imperf (pair) .. .. .. .. | £1800 | |
| 1295 | **768** | 22p. | black, lemon, brown-lilac, pale blue, grey-black, silver & grey-blk | 75 | 75 |
| 1296 | **769** | 31p. | black, lemon, magenta, turquoise-blue, grey-black, silver & grey-blk | 1·25 | 1·25 |
| 1297 | **770** | 34p. | grey, lemon, magenta, new blue, grey-black, silver and grey-black. . | 1·40 | 1·40 |
| 1294/7 | | | .. .. .. .. .. *Set of* 4 | 3·50 | 3·50 |

Nos. 1294/7 were issued on the occasion of the 500th anniversary of the printing of Sir Thomas Malory's *Morte d'Arthur*.

**771** Peter Sellers (from photo by Bill Brandt)

**772** David Niven (from photo by Cornell Lucas)

**773** Charlie Chaplin (from photo by Lord Snowdon)

**774** Vivien Leigh (from photo by Angus McBean)

**775** Alfred Hitchcock (from photo by Howard Coster)

(Des K. Bassford)

**1985** (8 Oct). *British Film Year. Phosphorised paper.* P 14½.

| No. | Type | Value | Description | Unused | Used |
|---|---|---|---|---|---|
| 1298 | **771** | 17p. | grey-black, ol-grey, gold & silver | 50 | 50 |
| 1299 | **772** | 22p. | black, brown, gold and silver .. | 85 | 90 |
| 1300 | **773** | 29p. | black, lavender, gold and silver .. | 1·40 | 1·40 |
| 1301 | **774** | 31p. | black, pink, gold and silver .. | 1·40 | 1·40 |
| 1302 | **775** | 34p. | black, greenish blue, gold & silver | 1·40 | 1·40 |
| 1298/302 | | | .. .. .. .. .. *Set of* 5 | 5·00 | 5·00 |

**776** Principal Boy

**777** Genie

**778** Dame

**779** Good Fairy

**780** Pantomine Cat

(Des A. George)

**1985** (19 Nov). *Christmas. Pantomine Characters. One phosphor band* (12p.) *or phosphorised paper (others).* P 15×14.

| No. | Type | Value | Description | Unused | Used |
|---|---|---|---|---|---|
| 1303 | **776** | 12p. | new blue, greenish yellow, bright rose, gold, grey-black and silver | 45 | 45 |
| | | | a. Imperf (pair) .. .. .. .. | £1300 | |
| 1304 | **777** | 17p. | emerald, greenish yellow, bright rose, new blue, blk, gold & silver | 55 | 55 |
| | | | a. Imperf (pair) .. .. .. .. | £1800 | |
| 1305 | **778** | 22p. | bright carmine, greenish yellow, pale new blue, grey, gold & silver | 85 | 85 |
| 1306 | **779** | 31p. | bright orange, lemon, rose, slate-purple, silver and gold .. .. | 1·10 | 1·10 |
| 1307 | **780** | 34p. | brt reddish violet, brt blue, brt rose, blk, grey-brn, gold & silver | 1·25 | 1·25 |
| 1303/7 | | | .. .. .. .. .. *Set of* 5 | 3·75 | 3·75 |

Examples of No. 1303 from the Christmas £2.40 stamp booklet show a blue underprint of a double-lined star printed on the reverse over the gum.

**781** Light Bulb and North Sea Oil Drilling Rig (Energy)

**782** Thermometer and Pharmaceutical Laboratory (Health)

**783** Garden Hoe and Steelworks (Steel)

**784** Loaf of Bread and Cornfield (Agriculture)

(Des K. Bassford. Litho Questa)

**1986** (14 Jan). *Industry Year. Phosphorised paper.* P 14½×14.

| No. | Type | Value | Description | Unused | Used |
|---|---|---|---|---|---|
| 1308 | **781** | 17p. | gold, black, magenta, greenish yellow and new blue .. .. | 45 | 45 |
| 1309 | **782** | 22p. | gold, pale turquoise-green, black, magenta, greenish yellow and blue | 70 | 70 |
| 1310 | **783** | 31p. | gold, black, magenta, greenish yellow and new blue .. .. | 1·10 | 1·10 |
| 1311 | **784** | 34p. | gold, black, magenta, greenish yellow and new blue .. .. | 1·10 | 1·10 |
| 1308/11 | | | .. .. .. .. .. *Set of* 4 | 3·00 | 3·00 |

**785** Dr. Edmond Halley as Comet

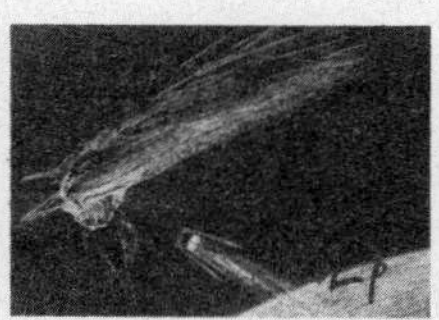

**786** *Giotto* Spacecraft approaching Comet

**787** "Twice in a Lifetime"

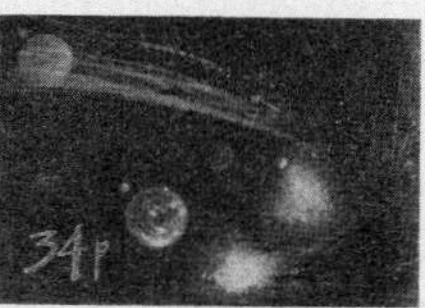


**788** Comet orbiting Sun and Planets

(Des R. Steadman)

**1986** (18 Feb). *Appearance of Halley's Comet. Phosphorised paper.* P 15×14.

| No. | Type | Value | Description | Unused | Used |
|---|---|---|---|---|---|
| 1312 | **785** | 17p. | black, bistre, rosine, blue, grey-black, gold and deep brown .. | 45 | 45 |
| 1313 | **786** | 22p. | orange-vermilion, greenish yellow, brt purple, new bl, blk & gold | 90 | 90 |
| 1314 | **787** | 31p. | black, greenish yellow, brt purple dp turquoise-blue, grey-blk & gold | 1·25 | 1·25 |
| 1315 | **788** | 34p. | blue, greenish yellow, magenta, deep turquoise-blue, black & gold | 1·25 | 1·25 |
| 1312/15 | | | .. .. .. .. .. *Set of* 4 | 3·50 | 3·50 |

**789** Queen Elizabeth II in 1928, 1942 and 1952

**790** Queen Elizabeth II in 1958, 1973 and 1982

(Des J. Matthews)

**1986** (21 Apr). *60th Birthday of Queen Elizabeth II. Phosphorised paper.* P 15×14.

| No. | Type | Value | Description | Unused | Used |
|---|---|---|---|---|---|
| 1316 | **789** | 17p. | grey-black, turquoise-green, bright green, green and dull blue. . | 75 | 75 |
| | | | a. Horiz pair. Nos. 1316/17. . | 1·50 | 1·50 |
| 1317 | **790** | 17p. | grey-black, dull blue, greenish blue and indigo .. .. .. | 75 | 75 |
| 1318 | **789** | 34p. | grey-black, deep dull purple, yellow-orange and red .. .. | 1·50 | 1·50 |
| | | | a. Horiz pair. Nos. 1318/19. . | 3·00 | 3·00 |
| 1319 | **790** | 34p. | grey-black, olive-brown, yellow-brown, olive-grey and red .. | 1·50 | 1·50 |
| 1316/19 | | | .. .. .. .. .. *Set of* 4 | 4·00 | 4·00 |

Nos. 1316/17 and 1318/19 were printed together, *se-tenant*, in horizontal pairs throughout the sheets.

## NEW INFORMATION

The editor is always interested to correspond with people who have new information that will improve or correct the Catalogue.

**791** Barn Owl

**792** Pine Marten

**793** Wild Cat

**794** Natterjack Toad

(Des K. Lilly)

**1986** (20 May). *Europa. Nature Conservation. Endangered Species. Phosphorised paper. P* 14½ × 14.

1320 **791** 17p. gold, greenish yellow, rose, yellow-brown, olive-grey, new blue & blk 50 50
1321 **792** 22p. gold, greenish yellow, reddish brn, ol-yell, turq-bl, grey-blk & blk 90 90
1322 **793** 31p. gold, brt yellow-green, magenta, lt brown, ultramarine, ol-brn & blk 1·40 1·40
1323 **794** 34p. gold, greenish yellow, bright rose-red, brt green, grey-black & black 1·40 1·40
1320/3 .. .. .. .. .. .. *Set of* 4 3·75 3·75

**795** Peasants working in Fields

**796** Freemen working at Town Trades

**797** Knight and Retainers

**798** Lord at Banquet

(Des Tayburn Design Consultancy)

**1986** (17 June). *900th Anniv of Domesday Book. Phosphorised paper. P* 15 × 14.

1324 **795** 17p. yell-brn, verm, lemon, brt emer, orge-brn, grey & brownish grey 50 50
1325 **796** 22p. yellow-ochre, red, greenish blue, chestnut, grey-blk & brownish grey 90 90
1326 **797** 31p. yellow-brown, verm, grn, Indian red, grey-blk & brownish grey 1·40 1·40
1327 **798** 34p. yellow-ochre, brt scar, grey-brn, new bl, lake-brn, grey-blk & grey 1·40 1·40
1324/7 .. .. .. .. .. .. *Set of* 4 3·75 3·75

## MINIMUM PRICE

The minimum price quote is 10p which represents a handling charge rather than a basis for valuing common stamps. For further notes about prices see introductory pages.

**799** Athletics

**800** Rowing

**801** Weightlifting

**802** Rifle Shooting

**803** Hockey

(Des N. Cudworth)

**1986** (15 July). *Thirteenth Commonwealth Games, Edinburgh and World Hockey Cup for Men, London* (34*p.*). *Phosphorised paper. P* 15 × 14.

1328 **799** 17p. black, greenish yellow, orange-vermilion, ultram, chestnut & emer 45 50
1329 **800** 22p. black, lemon, scarlet, new blue, royal blue, chestnut & dp ultram 90 60
1330 **801** 29p. grey-black, greenish yellow, scarlet, new blue, brown-ochre, brown-rose and pale chestnut .. 1·25 1·25
1331 **802** 31p. black, greenish yellow, rose, blue, dull yell-grn, chestnut & yell-grn 1·25 1·25
1332 **803** 34p. black, lemon, scarlet, brt blue, brt emerald, red-brown & vermilion 1·25 1·10
a. Imperf (pair) .. .. .. £1300
1328/32 .. .. .. .. .. .. *Set of* 5 4·50 4·00

No. 1332 also commemorates the Centenary of the Hockey Association.

**804** **805**
Prince Andrew and Miss Sarah Ferguson (from photo by Gene Nocon)

(Des J. Matthews)

**1986** (22 July). *Royal Wedding. One phosphor band* (12*p.*) *or phosphorised paper* (17*p.*). *P* 14 × 15.

1333 **804** 12p. lake, greenish yellow, cerise, ultramarine, black and silver .. .. 60 60
1334 **805** 17p. steel blue, greenish yellow, cerise, ultramarine, black and gold .. 90 90
a. Imperf (pair) .. .. .. .. £850

**806** Stylised Cross on Ballot Paper

(Des J. Gibbs. Litho Questa)

**1986** (19 Aug). *32nd Commonwealth Parliamentary Association Conference. Phosphorised paper. P* 14 × 14½.

1335 **806** 34p. pale grey-lilac, black, vermilion, yellow and ultramarine .. .. 1·50 1·50

**807** Lord Dowding and Hawker "Hurricane"

**808** Lord Tedder and Hawker "Typhoon"

**809** Lord Trenchard and De Havilland "DH 9A"

**810** Sir Arthur Harris and Avro "Lancaster"

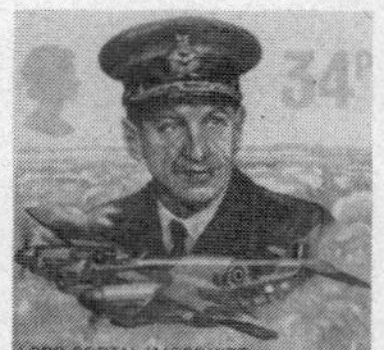


**811** Lord Portal and De Havilland "Mosquito"

(Des B. Sanders)

**1986** (16 Sept). *History of the Royal Air Force. Phosphorised paper. P* 14½.

1336 **807** 17p. pale blue, greenish yellow, bright rose, blue, black and grey-black 45 40
a. Imperf (pair) .. .. .. £950
1337 **808** 22p. pale turquoise-green, greenish yell, mag, new bl, blk & grey-blk 1·00 90
a. Face value omitted* .. .. £400
b. Queen's head omitted* .. .. £400
1338 **809** 29p. pale drab, olive-yellow, magenta, blue, grey-black and black .. 1·25 1·10
1339 **810** 31p. pale flesh, greenish yellow, magenta, ultram, blk & grey-blk 1·40 1·25
1340 **811** 34p. buff, greenish yellow, magenta, blue, grey-black and black .. 1·50 1·25
1336/40 .. .. .. .. .. *Set of* 5 5·00 4·50

*Nos. 1337a/b come from three consecutive sheets on which the stamps in the first vertical row are without the face value and those in the second vertical row the Queen's head.

Nos. 1336/40 were issued to celebrate the 50th anniversary of the first R.A.F. Commands.

**812** The Glastonbury Thorn

**813** The Tanad Valley Plygain

**814** The Hebrides Tribute

**815** The Dewsbury Church Knell

**816** The Hereford Boy Bishop

(Des Lynda Gray)

**1986** (18 Nov–2 Dec). *Christmas. One phosphor band* (12*p*., 13*p*.) *or phosphorised paper* (*others*). *P* 15 × 14.

| | | | | | |
|---|---|---|---|---|---|
| 1341 | **812** | 12p. | gold, greenish yellow, vermilion, dp brown, emerald & dp bl (2.12) | 75 | 75 |
| | | a. | Imperf (pair) | | |
| 1342 | | 13p. | deep blue, greenish yellow, verm, deep brown, emerald and gold .. | 40 | 40 |
| 1343 | **813** | 18p. | myrtle-green, yellow, vermilion, dp blue, black, reddish brn & gold | 55 | 55 |
| 1344 | **814** | 22p. | vermilion, olive-bistre, dull blue, deep brown, deep green and gold | 75 | 75 |
| 1345 | **815** | 31p. | deep brown, yellow, vermilion, violet, dp dull green, black & gold | 1·00 | 1·00 |
| 1346 | **816** | 34p. | violet, lemon, vermilion, deep dull blue, reddish brown and gold .. | 1·00 | 1·00 |
| 1341/6 | | | .. .. .. .. *Set of* 6 | 4·00 | 4·00 |

No. 1341 represented a discount of 1p., available between 2 and 24 December 1986, on the current second class postage rate.

Examples of the 13p. value from special folders, containing 36 stamps and sold for £4.30, show a blue underprint of double-lined stars printed on the reverse over the gum.

**817** North American Blanket Flower

**818** Globe Thistle

**819** *Echeveria*

**820** Autumn Crocus

(Adapted J. Matthews)

**1987** (20 Jan). *Flower Photographs by Alfred Lammer. Phosphorised paper. P* 14½ × 14.

| | | | | | |
|---|---|---|---|---|---|
| 1347 | **817** | 18p. | silver, greenish yellow, rosine, deep green and black .. .. | 50 | 50 |
| 1348 | **818** | 22p. | silver, greenish yellow, new blue, greenish blue and black .. | 80 | 80 |
| 1349 | **819** | 31p. | silver, greenish yellow, scarlet, blue-green, deep green and black | 1·25 | 1·25 |
| | | a. | Imperf (pair) .. .. .. | £1600 | |
| 1350 | **820** | 34p. | silver, greenish yellow, magenta, dull blue, deep green and black .. | 1·40 | 1·40 |
| 1347/50 | | | .. .. .. .. *Set of* 4 | 3·50 | 3·50 |

## OMNIBUS ISSUES

Details, together with prices for complete sets, of the various Omnibus issues from the 1935 Silver Jubilee series to date are included in a special section following Zimbabwe at the end of Volume 2.

**821** *The Principia Mathematica*

**822** *Motion of Bodies in Ellipses*

**823** *Optick Treatise*

**824** *The System of the World*

(Des Sarah Godwin)

**1987** (24 Mar). *300th Anniv of* The Principia Mathematica *by Sir Isaac Newton. Phosphorised paper. P* 14 × 15.

| | | | | | |
|---|---|---|---|---|---|
| 1351 | **821** | 18p. | black, greenish yellow, cerise, blue-green, grey-black and silver .. | 50 | 50 |
| 1352 | **822** | 22p. | black, greenish yellow, brt orange, blue, brt emer, silver & bluish vio | 80 | 80 |
| 1353 | **823** | 31p. | black, greenish yellow, scar, new bl, bronze-grn, silver & slate-grn | 1·25 | 1·25 |
| 1354 | **824** | 34p. | black, greenish yellow, red, bright blue, grey-black and silver .. | 1·40 | 1·40 |
| 1351/4 | | | .. .. .. .. *Set of* 4 | 3·50 | 3·50 |

**825** Willis Faber & Dumas Building, Ipswich

**826** Pompidou Centre, Paris

**827** Staatsgalerie, Stuttgart

**828** European Investment Bank, Luxembourg

(Des Brian Tattersfield)

**1987** (12 May). *Europa. British Architects in Europe. Phosphorised paper. P* 15 × 14.

| | | | | | |
|---|---|---|---|---|---|
| 1355 | **825** | 18p. | black, bistre-yellow, cerise, bright blue, deep grey and grey-black .. | 50 | 50 |
| 1356 | **826** | 22p. | black, greenish yellow, carmine, bright blue, dp grey & grey-black | 80 | 80 |
| 1357 | **827** | 31p. | grey-black, bistre-yellow, cerise, brt blue, brt green, black & dull vio | 1·25 | 1·25 |
| | | a. | Imperf (horiz pair) .. .. | £1000 | |
| 1358 | **828** | 34p. | black, greenish yellow, cerise, bright blue, grey-black & deep grey | 1·40 | 1·40 |
| 1355/8 | | | .. .. .. .. *Set of* 4 | 3·50 | 3·50 |

**829** Brigade Members with Ashford Litter, 1887

**830** Bandaging Blitz Victim, 1940

**831** Volunteer with fainting Girl, 1965

**832** Transport of Transplant Organ by Air Wing, 1987

(Des Debbie Cook. Litho Questa)

**1987** (16 June). *Centenary of St. John Ambulance Brigade. Phosphorised paper. P* 14 × 14½.

| | | | | | |
|---|---|---|---|---|---|
| 1359 | **829** | 18p. | new blue, greenish yellow, magenta, black, silver and pink .. | 50 | 50 |
| 1360 | **830** | 22p. | new blue, greenish yellow, magenta, black, silver and cobalt | 80 | 80 |
| 1361 | **831** | 31p. | new blue, greenish yellow, magenta, black, silver & bistre-brn | 1·25 | 1·25 |
| 1362 | **832** | 34p. | new blue, greenish yellow, mag, blk, silver & greenish grey | 1·40 | 1·40 |
| 1359/62 | | | .. .. .. .. *Set of* 4 | 3·50 | 3·50 |

**833** Arms of the Lord Lyon King of Arms

**834** Scottish Heraldic Banner of Prince Charles

**835** Arms of Royal Scottish Academy of Painting, Sculpture and Architecture

**836** Arms of Royal Society of Edinburgh

(Des J. Matthews)

**1987** (21 July). *300th Anniv of Revival of Order of the Thistle. Phosphorised paper. P* 14½.

| | | | | | |
|---|---|---|---|---|---|
| 1363 | **833** | 18p. | black, lemon, scarlet, blue, deep green, slate and brown .. .. | 50 | 50 |
| 1364 | **834** | 22p. | black, greenish yellow, carmine, new blue, dp grn, grey & lake-brn | 80 | 80 |
| 1365 | **835** | 31p. | black, greenish yellow, scarlet, new blue, dull grn, grey & grey-blk | 1·25 | 1·25 |
| 1366 | **836** | 34p. | black, greenish yellow, scarlet, dp ultram, dull grn, grey & yell-brn | 1·40 | 1·40 |
| 1363/6 | | | .. .. .. .. *Set of* 4 | 3·50 | 3·50 |

**837** Crystal Palace, "Monarch of the Glen" (Landseer) and Grace Darling

**838** *Great Eastern, Beeton's Book of Household Management* and Prince Albert

**839** Albert Memorial, Ballot Box and Disraeli

**840** Diamond Jubilee Emblem, Newspaper Placard for Relief of Mafeking and Morse Key

(Des M. Dempsey. Eng C. Slania. Recess and photo)

**1987** (8 Sept). *150th Anniv of Queen Victoria's Accession. Phosphorised paper. P* 15 × 14.

| | | | | | |
|---|---|---|---|---|---|
| 1367 | **837** | 18p. | pale stone, dp blue, lemon, rose, greenish bl, brn-ochre & grey-blk | 50 | 50 |
| 1368 | **838** | 22p. | pale stone, deep brown, lemon, rose, grey-black and brown-ochre | 80 | 80 |
| 1369 | **839** | 31p. | pale stone, dp lilac, lemon, cerise, brn-ochre, greenish bl & grey-blk | 1·25 | 1·25 |
| 1370 | **840** | 34p. | pale stone, myrtle-green, yellow-ochre, reddish brown & brn-ochre | 1·40 | 1·40 |
| 1367/70 | | | *Set of* 4 | 3·50 | 3·50 |

**841** Pot by Bernard Leach

**842** Pot by Elizabeth Fritsch

**843** Pot by Lucie Rie

**844** Pot by Hans Coper

(Des T. Evans)

**1987** (13 Oct). *Studio Pottery. Phosphorised paper. P* 14½ × 14.

| | | | | | |
|---|---|---|---|---|---|
| 1371 | **841** | 18p. | gold, lemon, light red-brown, chestnut, light grey and black | 50 | 50 |
| 1372 | **842** | 26p. | blue over silver, yellow-orange, bright purple, lavender, bluish violet, grey-brown and black | 80 | 80 |
| 1373 | **843** | 31p. | rose-lilac over silver, greenish yellow, cerise, new bl, grey-lilac & blk | 1·25 | 1·25 |
| 1374 | **844** | 34p. | copper, yellow-brown, reddish brown, grey-lilac and black | 1·40 | 1·40 |
| 1371/4 | | | *Set of* 4 | 3·50 | 3·50 |

**845** Decorating the Christmas Tree

**846** Waiting for Father Christmas

**847** Sleeping Child and Father Christmas in Sleigh

**848** Child reading

**849** Child playing Recorder and Snowman

(Des M. Foreman)

**1987** (17 Nov). *Christmas. One phosphor band* (13p.) *or phosphorised paper* (*others*). *P* 15 × 14.

| | | | | | |
|---|---|---|---|---|---|
| 1375 | **845** | 13p. | gold, greenish yellow, rose, greenish blue and black | 50 | 50 |
| 1376 | **846** | 18p. | gold, greenish yellow, bright purple, greenish blue, brt blue & blk | 60 | 60 |
| 1377 | **847** | 26p. | gold, greenish yellow, bright purple, new blue, bright blue and black | 90 | 90 |
| 1378 | **848** | 31p. | gold, greenish yellow, scarlet, brt mag, dull rose, greenish bl & blk | 1·10 | 1·10 |
| 1379 | **849** | 34p. | gold, greenish yellow, dull rose, greenish blue, bright blue & black | 1·10 | 1·10 |
| 1375/9 | | | *Set of* 5 | 3·75 | 3·75 |

**850** Bull-rout (Jonathan Couch)

**851** Yellow Waterlily (Major Joshua Swatkin)

**852** Bewick's Swan (Edward Lear)

**853** *Morchella esculenta* (James Sowerby)

(Des E. Hughes)

**1988** (19 Jan). *Bicentenary of Linnean Society. Archive Illustrations. Phosphorised paper. P* 15 × 14.

| | | | | | |
|---|---|---|---|---|---|
| 1380 | **850** | 18p. | grey-black, stone, orange-yellow, bright purple, olive-bistre & gold | 45 | 45 |
| 1381 | **851** | 26p. | black, stone, bistre-yellow, dull orange, greenish bl, gold & pale bis | 85 | 85 |
| 1382 | **852** | 31p. | black, stone, greenish yellow, rose-red, dp blue, gold & olive-bis | 1·10 | 1·10 |
| | | | a. Imperf (horiz pair) | £1300 | |
| 1383 | **853** | 34p. | black, stone, yellow, pale bistre, olive-grey, gold and olive-bistre | 1·25 | 1·25 |
| 1380/3 | | | *Set of* 4 | 3·25 | 3·25 |

**854** Revd William Morgan (Bible translator, 1588)

**855** William Salesbury (New Testament translator, 1567)

**856** Bishop Richard Davies (New Testament translator, 1567)

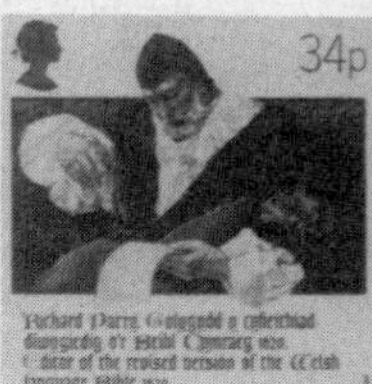

**857** Bishop Richard Parry (editor of Revised Welsh Bible, 1620)

(Des K. Bowen)

**1988** (1 Mar). *400th Anniv of Welsh Bible. Phosphorised paper. P* 14½ × 14.

| | | | | | |
|---|---|---|---|---|---|
| 1384 | **854** | 18p. | grey-black, greenish yellow, cerise, blue, black and emerald | 45 | 45 |
| | | | a. Imperf (pair) | £1300 | |
| 1385 | **855** | 26p. | grey-black, yellow, bright rose-red, turquoise-blue, black & orge | 85 | 85 |
| 1386 | **856** | 31p. | black, chrome-yellow, carmine, new blue, grey-black and blue | 1·10 | 1·10 |
| 1387 | **857** | 34p. | grey-black, greenish yellow, cerise, turquoise-grn, blk & brt vio | 1·25 | 1·25 |
| 1384/7 | | | *Set of* 4 | 3·25 | 3·25 |

**858** Gymnastics (Centenary of British Amateur Gymnastics Association)

**859** Downhill Skiing (Ski Club of Great Britain)

**860** Tennis (Centenary of Lawn Tennis Association)

**861** Football (Centenary of Football League)

(Des J. Sutton)

**1988** (22 Mar). *Sports Organizations. Phosphorised paper. P* 14½.

| | | | | | |
|---|---|---|---|---|---|
| 1388 | **858** | 18p. | violet-blue, greenish yellow, rosine, brt rose, new blue & silver | 45 | 45 |
| 1389 | **859** | 26p. | violet-blue, greenish yellow, vermilion, carmine, yell-orge & silver | 85 | 85 |
| 1390 | **860** | 31p. | violet-bl, greenish yell, rose, bl, pale greenish bl, silver & brt orge | 1·10 | 1·10 |
| 1391 | **861** | 34p. | violet-blue, greenish yellow, vermilion, bl, brt emer, silver & pink | 1·25 | 1·25 |
| 1388/91 | | | *Set of* 4 | 3·25 | 3·25 |

**862** *Mallard* and Mailbags on Pick-up Arms

**863** Loading Transatlantic Mail on Liner *Queen Elizabeth*

**864** Glasgow Tram No. 1173 and Pillar Box

**865** Imperial Airways Handley Page "HP 24" and Airmail Van

(Des M. Dempsey)

**1988** (10 May). *Europa. Transport and Mail Services in* 1930's. *Phosphorised paper. P* 15 × 14.

| | | | | |
|---|---|---|---|---|
| 1392 | **862** | 18p. brown, yellow, rose-red, dull blue, dp brown, reddish vio & blk | 50 | 50 |
| 1393 | **863** | 26p. brown, yellow, orange-vermilion, dull blue, violet-bl, brt emer & blk | 80 | 80 |
| 1394 | **864** | 31p. brown, yellow-orange, carmine, dull purple, vio-bl, brt grn & blk | 1·10 | 1·10 |
| 1395 | **865** | 34p. brown, orange-yellow, carmine-rose, bluish vio, brt bl, sepia & blk | 1·25 | 1·25 |
| 1392/5 | | *Set of* 4 | 3·25 | 3·25 |

**866** Early Settler and Sailing Clipper

**867** Queen Elizabeth II with British and Australian Parliament Buildings

**868** W. G. Grace (cricketer) and Tennis Racquet

**869** Shakespeare, John Lennon (entertainer) and Sydney Landmarks

(Des G. Emery. Litho Questa)

**1988** (21 June). *Bicentenary of Australian Settlement. Phosphorised paper. P* 14½.

| | | | | |
|---|---|---|---|---|
| 1396 | **866** | 18p. deep ultramarine, orange-yellow, scarlet, black, bluish grey & emerald | 60 | 60 |
| | | a. Horiz pair. Nos. 1396/7 | 1·25 | 1·25 |
| 1397 | **867** | 18p. deep ultramarine, orange-yellow, black, bluish grey and emerald | 60 | 60 |
| 1398 | **868** | 34p. deep ultramarine, orange-yellow, scarlet, black, bluish grey & emerald | 1·10 | 1·10 |
| | | a. Horiz pair. Nos. 1398/9 | 2·40 | 2·40 |
| 1399 | **869** | 34p. deep ultramarine, orange-yellow, black, bluish grey and emerald | 1·10 | 1·10 |
| 1396/9 | | *Set of* 4 | 3·25 | 3·25 |

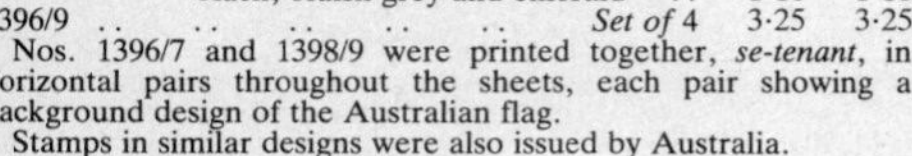

Nos. 1396/7 and 1398/9 were printed together, *se-tenant*, in horizontal pairs throughout the sheets, each pair showing a background design of the Australian flag.

Stamps in similar designs were also issued by Australia.

**870** Spanish Galeasse off The Lizard

**871** English Fleet leaving Plymouth

**872** Engagement off Isle of Wight

**873** Attack of English Fire-ships, Calais

**874** Armada in Storm, North Sea

(Des G. Everndon)

**1988** (19 July). 400*th Anniv of Spanish Armada. Phosphorised paper. P* 15 × 14.

| | | | | |
|---|---|---|---|---|
| 1400 | **870** | 18p. slate-black, yellow-orange, bright carm, brt bl, turq-bl, yell-grn & gold | 65 | 65 |
| | | a. Horiz strip of 5. Nos. 1400/4 | 2·75 | 2·75 |
| 1401 | **871** | 18p. slate-black, yellow-orange, bright carm, brt bl, turq-bl, yell-grn & gold | 65 | 65 |
| 1402 | **872** | 18p. slate-black, yellow-orange, bright carm, brt bl, turq-bl, yell-grn & gold | 65 | 65 |
| 1403 | **873** | 18p. slate-black, yellow-orange, bright carm, brt bl, turq-bl, yell-grn & gold | 65 | 65 |
| 1404 | **874** | 18p. slate-black, yellow-orange, bright carm, brt bl, turq-bl, yell-grn & gold | 65 | 65 |
| 1400/4 | | *Set of* 5 | 2·75 | 2·75 |

Nos. 1400/4 were printed together, *se-tenant*, in horizontal strips of 5 throughout the sheet, forming a composite design.

**875** "The Owl and the Pussy-cat"

**876** "Edward Lear as a Bird" (self-portrait)

**877** "Cat" (from alphabet book)

35P
There was a Young Lady whose bonnet,
Came untied when the birds sate upon it;
EDWARD LEAR • 1812-1888


**878** "There was a Young Lady whose Bonnet .." (limerick)

(Des M. Swatridge and S. Dew)

**1988** (6–27 Sept). *Death Centenary of Edward Lear (artist and author). Phosphorised paper. P* 15 × 14.

| | | | | |
|---|---|---|---|---|
| 1405 | **875** | 19p black, pale cream and carmine | 50 | 50 |
| 1406 | **876** | 27p black, pale cream and yellow | 80 | 80 |
| 1407 | **877** | 32p black, pale cream and emerald | 1·10 | 1·10 |
| 1408 | **878** | 35p black, pale cream and blue | 1·25 | 1·25 |
| 1405/8 | | *Set of* 4 | 3·25 | 3·25 |
| **MS**1409 | | 122 × 90 mm. Nos. 1405/8 (*sold at* £1.35) (27 Sept) | 12·00 | 10·00 |

The premium on No. **MS**1409 was used to support the "Stamp World London 90" International Stamp Exhibition.

**879** Carrickfergus Castle

**880** Caernarfon Castle

**881** Edinburgh Castle

**882** Windsor Castle

(Des from photos by Prince Andrew, Duke of York. Eng C. Matthews. Recess Harrison)

**1988** (18 Oct). *Ordinary paper. P* 15 × 14.

| | | | | |
|---|---|---|---|---|
| 1410 | **879** | £1 deep green | 1·50 | 50 |
| 1411 | **880** | £1.50, maroon | 2·25 | 1·00 |
| 1412 | **881** | £2 indigo | 3·00 | 1·50 |
| 1413 | **882** | £5 deep brown | 7·50 | 3·00 |
| 1410/13 | | *Set of* 4 | 13·00 | 5·50 |

For similar designs, but with silhouette Queen's head see Nos. 1611/14.

**883** Journey to Bethlehem

**884** Shepherds and Star

**885** Three Wise Men

**886** Nativity

**887** The Annunciation

(Des L. Trickett)

**1988** (15 Nov). *Christmas. Christmas Cards. One phosphor band (14p.) or phosphorised paper (others). P* 15 × 14.

1414 **883** 14p. gold, orange-yellow, bright mauve, bluish violet, brt blue & grey-black .. 35 35
a. Error. "13p." instead of "14p." .. £3500
b. Imperf (pair) .. .. .. .. .. £600
1415 **884** 19p. gold, yell-orange, brt violet, ultram, rose-red, grey-black & bright blue .. 50 50
a. Imperf (pair) .. .. .. .. .. £600
1416 **885** 27p. gold, red, deep lavender, deep lilac, emerald, grey-black and bright blue 80 80
1417 **886** 32p. gold, orange-yellow, bright rose, dp mauve, violet, grey-black & brt blue 1·10 1·10
1418 **887** 35p. gold, green, reddish violet, bright blue, bright purple and grey-black .. 1·25 1·25
1414/18 .. .. .. .. *Set of* 5 3·50 3·50

Examples of No. 1414a were found in some 1988 Post Office Yearbooks.

**888** Puffin

**889** Avocet

**890** Oystercatcher

**891** Gannet

(Des D. Cordery)

**1989** (17 Jan). *Centenary of Royal Society for the Protection of Birds. Phosphorised paper. P* 14 × 15.

1419 **888** 19p. grey, orange-yellow, orange-red, dull ultramarine, grey-black and silver .. 50 50
1420 **889** 27p. grey, bistre, rose, steel-blue, lavender, silver and grey-black .. 1·10 1·10
1421 **890** 32p. grey, bistre, scarlet, orange-red, lavender, silver and black .. .. 1·25 1·25
1422 **891** 35p. grey, lemon, rose-carmine, green, new blue, silver and black .. .. 1·10 1·10
1419/22 .. .. .. .. *Set of* 4 3·25 3·25

**892** Rose

**893** Cupid

**894** Yachts

**895** Fruit

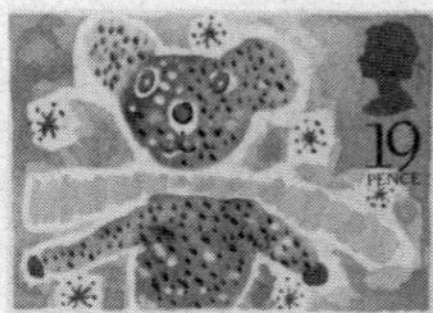


**896** Teddy Bear

(Des P. Sutton)

**1989** (31 Jan). *Greetings Stamps. Phosphorised paper. P* 15 × 14.

1423 **892** 19p. black, greenish yellow, bright rose, red, new blue, light green and gold .. 3·00 2·00
a. Booklet pane. Nos. 1423/7 × 2 plus 12 half stamp-size labels .. .. 28·00
1424 **893** 19p. black, greenish yellow, bright rose, red, new blue, light green and gold .. 3·00 2·00
1425 **894** 19p. black, greenish yellow, bright rose, red, new blue, light green and gold .. 3·00 2·00
1426 **895** 19p. black, greenish yellow, bright rose, red, new blue, light green and gold .. 3·00 2·00
1427 **896** 19p. black, greenish yellow, bright rose, red, new blue, light green and gold .. 3·00 2·00
1423/7 .. .. .. .. *Set of* 5 14·00 9·00

Nos. 1423/7 were only issued in £1.90 booklets.

**897** Fruit and Vegetables

**898** Meat Products

**899** Dairy Produce

**900** Cereal Products

(Des Sedley Place Ltd)

**1989** (7 Mar). *Food and Farming Year. Phosphorised paper. P* 14 × 14½.

1428 **897** 19p. brownish grey, greenish yellow, rose, new blue, black, pale grey & emerald 50 50
1429 **898** 27p. brownish grey, greenish yellow, bright carmine, new blue, black, pale grey and bright orange .. .. 80 80
1430 **899** 32p. brownish grey, greenish yellow, rose-red, new blue, black, pale grey and bistre-yellow .. .. .. 1·10 1·10
1431 **900** 35p. brownish grey, greenish yellow, bright carmine, new blue, black, pale grey and brown-red .. .. 1·25 1·25
1428/31 .. .. .. .. *Set of* 4 3·25 3·25

**901** Mortar Board (150th Anniv of Public Education in England)

**902** Cross on Ballot Paper (3rd Direct Elections to European Parliament)

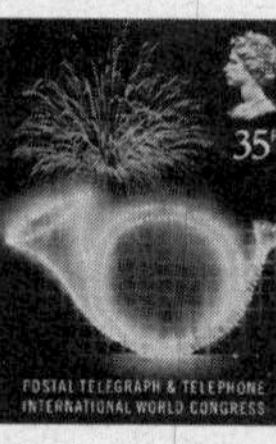


**903** Posthorn (26th Postal, Telegraph and Telephone International Congress, Brighton)

**904** Globe(Inter–Parliamentary Union Centenary Conference, London)

(Des Lewis Moberly from firework set-pieces. Litho Questa)

**1989** (11 Apr). *Anniversaries. Phosphorised paper. P* 14 × 14½.

1432 **901** 19p. new blue, greenish yellow, mag & blk 55 55
a. Horiz pair. Nos. 1432/3 .. .. 1·10 1·10
1433 **902** 19p. new blue, greenish yellow, mag & blk 55 55
1434 **903** 35p. new blue, greenish yellow, mag & blk 1·10 1·10
a. Horiz pair. Nos. 1434/5 .. .. 2·25 2·25
1435 **904** 35p. new blue, greenish yellow, mag & blk 1·10 1·10
1432/5 .. .. .. .. *Set of* 4 3·00 3·00

Nos. 1432/3 and 1434/5 were each printed together, *se-tenant*, in horizontal pairs throughout the sheets.

**905** Toy Train and Airplane

**906** Building Bricks

**907** Dice and Board Games

**908** Toy Robot, Boat and Doll's House

(Des D. Fern)

**1989** (16 May). *Europa. Games and Toys. Phosphorised paper. P* 14 × 15.

1436 **905** 19p. black, greenish yellow, vermilion, blue-green, blue, gold and pale ochre 50 50
1437 **906** 27p. black, greenish yellow, reddish orange, blue-green, blue and gold .. 80 80
1438 **907** 32p. black, greenish yellow, orange-red, blue-green, blue, gold and pale ochre 1·10 1·10
1439 **908** 35p. black, greenish yellow, reddish orange, blue-green, bl, gold & stone 1·25 1·25
1436/9 .. .. .. .. *Set of* 4 3·25 3·25

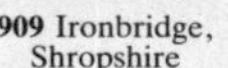


**909** Ironbridge, Shropshire

**910** Tin Mine, St. Agnes Head, Cornwall

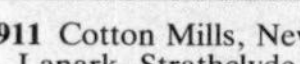


**911** Cotton Mills, New Lanark, Strathclyde

**912** Pontcysyllte Aqueduct, Clwyd

(Des R. Maddox)

**1989** (4–25 July). *Industrial Archaeology. Phosphorised paper. P* 14×15.

1440 **909** 19p. black, bistre-yellow, rose-red, apple-green, lt blue, grey-black & emerald 50 50
1441 **910** 27p. black, bistre-yellow, rose-red, apple-green, lt blue, grey-black & dull blue 80 80
1442 **911** 32p. black, yellow-orange, apple-green, yellow, dull blue, grey-black and deep reddish violet .. .. 1·00 1·00
1443 **912** 35p. black, yellow, bright rose, apple-green, dull blue, grey-black & verm 1·10 1·10
1440/3 .. .. .. .. *Set of* 4 3·00 3·00
**MS**1444 122×90 mm. 19p., 27p., 32p., 35p. each black, olive-yellow, bright rose-red, dull blue, apple-green, grey-black and vermilion. P 15×14 (*sold at* £1.40) (25 July) .. .. .. 8·00 6·00

The stamps in No. **MS**1444 are horizontal versions of Nos. 1440/3 with each design continuing onto the sheet margins.

The premium on No. **MS**1444 was used to support "Stamp World London 90" International Stamp Exhibition.

## *MINIMUM PRICE*

The minimum price quote is 10p which represents a handling charge rather than a basis for valuing common stamps. For further notes about prices see introductory pages.

**913**

**914**

**1989** (22 Aug)–**92**. *Booklet Stamps.*

(*a*) *Photo Harrison. P* 15×14

1445 **913** (2nd) bright blue (1 centre band) .. 45 45
a. Booklet pane. No. 1445×10 with horiz edges of pane imperf .. 6·00
b. Booklet pane. No. 1445×4 with three edges of pane imperf (28.11.89) .. .. .. 3·50
1446 (2nd) bright blue (1 side band) (20.3.90) 4·00 4·00
1447 **914** (1st) brownish black (phosphorised paper) .. .. .. .. 1·00 1·00
a. Booklet pane. No. 1447×10 with horiz edges of pane imperf .. 10·00
b. Booklet pane. No. 1447×4 with three edges of pane imperf (5.12.89) .. .. .. 8·00
1448 (1st) brownish black (2 bands) (20.3.90) 4·00 4·00

(*b*) *Litho Walsall. P* 14

1449 **913** (2nd) bright blue (1 centre band) .. 30 35
a. Imperf between (vert pair) ..
b. Booklet pane. No. 1449×4 with three edges of pane imperf .. 3·00
c. Booklet pane. No. 1449×4 with horiz edges of pane imperf (6.8.91) .. .. .. 1·25
d. Booklet pane. No. 1449×10 with horiz edges of pane imperf (6.8.91) .. .. .. 2·75
1450 **914** (1st) blackish brown (2 bands) .. 1·50 1·50
a. Booklet pane. No. 1450×4 with three edges of pane imperf .. 6·00

(*c*) *Litho Questa. P* 15×14

1451 **913** (2nd) brt blue (1 centre band) (19.9.89) 30 35
1451*a* (2nd) brt blue (1 side band) (25.2.92) 2·10 2·10
1452 **914** (1st) brownish black (phosphorised paper) (19.9.89) .. .. 1·10 1·10

Nos. 1445, 1447, 1449/51 and 1452 were initially sold at 14p. (2nd) and 19p. (1st), but these prices were later increased to reflect new postage rates.

Nos. 1446 and 1448 come from the *se-tenant* pane in the 1990 London Life £5 booklet: This pane is listed as No. X906m.

No. 1449a occurred on a miscut example of pane No. 1449d which showed an additional vertical pair beneath the last stamp in the bottom row.

No. 1451a comes from the *se-tenant* pane in the Wales £6 booklet. This pane is listed under No. W49a in the Wales Regional Section.

For illustrations showing the difference between photogravure and lithography see beneath Type **367**.

For similar designs, but in changed colours see Nos. 1511/16.

**915** Snowflake (×10)

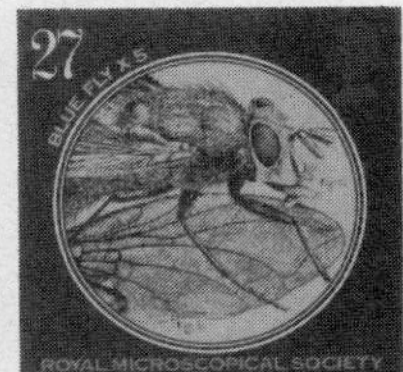


**916** *Calliphora erythrocephala* (×5) (fly)

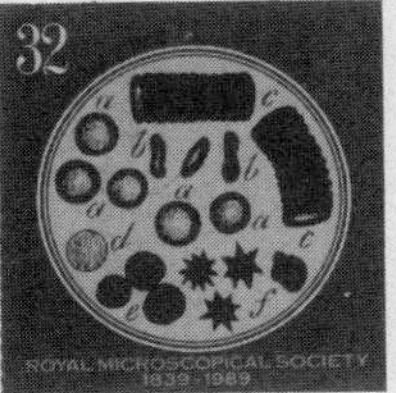


**917** Blood Cells (×500)

**918** Microchip (×600)

(Des K. Bassford. Litho Questa)

**1989** (5 Sept). 150*th Anniv of Royal Microscopical Society. Phosphorised paper. P* 14½×14.

1453 **915** 19p. gold, lemon, pale blue, grey, black and grey-black .. .. .. 50 50
1454 **916** 27p. gold, lemon, drab, black & grey-blk 85 85
1455 **917** 32p. gold, lemon, orange-vermilion, flesh, black and grey-black .. .. 1·00 1·00
1456 **918** 35p. gold, lemon, blk, brt grn & grey-blk 1·00 1·00
1453/6 .. .. .. .. *Set of* 4 3·00 3·00

**919** Royal Mail Coach

**920** Escort of Blues and Royals

**921** Lord Mayor's Coach

**922** Coach Team passing St. Pauls

**923** Blues and Royals Drum Horse

(Des P. Cox)

**1989** (17 Oct). *Lord Mayor's Show, London. Phosphorised paper. P* 14×15.

1457 **919** 20p. gold, lemon, rose, orge, pale bl & blk 60 60
a. Horiz strip of 5. Nos. 1457/61 .. 2·75 2·75
ab. Imperf (horiz strip of 5. Nos. 1457/61) .. .. .. ..
ac. Imperf (horiz strip of 4. Nos. 1457/60) .. .. .. ..
ad. Imperf (horiz strip of 3. Nos. 1457/9)
1458 **920** 20p. gold, lemon, rose, orge, pale bl & blk 60 60
1459 **921** 20p. gold, lemon, rose, orge, pale bl & blk 60 60
1460 **922** 20p. gold, lemon, rose, orge, pale bl & blk 60 60
1461 **923** 20p. gold, lemon, rose, orge, pale bl & blk 60 60
1457/61 .. .. .. .. *Set of* 5 2·75 2·75

This issue commemorates the 800th anniversary of the installation of the first Lord Mayor of London.

Nos. 1457/61 were printed together, *se-tenant*, in horizontal strips of 5 throughout the sheet.

Nos. 1457ab/ad come from a sheet partly imperforate at left.

**924** 14th-century Peasants from Stained-glass Window

**925** Arches and Roundels, West Front

**926** Octagon Tower

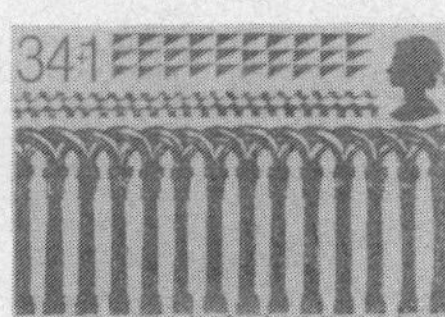


**927** Arcade from West Transept

**928** Triple Arch from West Front

(Des D. Gentleman)

**1989** (14 Nov). *Christmas. 800th Anniversary of Ely Cathedral. One phosphor band* (15*p.*, 15*p.*+1*p.*) *or phosphorised paper* (*others*). *P* 15×14.

1462 **924** 15p. gold, silver and blue .. .. 35 35
1463 **925** 15p. + 1p. gold, silver and blue .. 50 50
a. Imperf (pair) .. .. .. £1300
1464 **926** 20p. + 1p. gold, silver and rosine .. 60 60
a. Imperf (pair) .. .. .. £1300
1465 **927** 34p. + 1p. gold, silver and emerald .. 1·10 1·10
1466 **928** 37p. + 1p. gold, silver and yellow-olive 1·10 1·10
1462/6 .. .. .. .. *Set of* 5 3·25 3·25

**929** Queen Victoria and Queen Elizabeth II

(Des J. Matthews (from plaster casts by Wyon and Machin))

**1990** (10 Jan–12 June). 150*th Anniv of the Penny Black.*

(*a*) *Photo Harrison. P* 15×14

1467 **929** 15p. bright blue (1 centre band) .. 55 55
a. Imperf (pair) .. .. ..
l. Booklet pane. No. 1467×10 with horiz edges of pane imperf (30.1.90) 5·50
1468 15p. bright blue (1 side band) (30.1.90) 1·25 1·25
l. Booklet pane. No. 1468×2 and 1470 plus label .. .. .. 4·00
1469 20p. brownish black and cream (phosphorised paper) .. 75 75
l. Booklet pane. No. 1469×5 plus label with vert sides of pane imperf (30.1.90) .. .. .. 3·25
m. Booklet pane. No. 1469×10 with horiz edges of pane imperf (30.1.90) 8·00
n. Booklet pane. No. 1469×6 with margins all round (20.3.90) .. 2·50
r. Booklet pane. No. 1469×4 with three edges of pane imperf (17.4.90) .. 1·25
1470 20p. brownish black and cream (2 bands) (30.1.90) .. .. .. 1·10 1·10
1471 29p. deep mauve (phosphorised paper) 1·00 1·10
1472 29p. deep mauve (2 bands) (20.3.90) 4·50 4·50
1473 34p. dp bluish grey (phosphorised paper) 1·25 1·40
1474 37p. rosine (phosphorised paper) .. 1·40 1·50

(*b*) *Litho Walsall. P* 14

1475 **929** 15p. bright blue (1 centre band) (30.1.90) 75 75
l. Booklet pane. No. 1475×4 with three edges of pane imperf .. 3·00
m. Booklet pane. No. 1475×10 with three edges of pane imperf (12.6.90) 7·50
1476 20p. brownish black and cream (phosphorised paper) (30.1.90) .. 1·25 1·25
l. Booklet pane. No. 1476×5 plus label with vertical edges of pane imperf .. .. .. 6·00
m. Booklet pane. No. 1476×4 with three edges of pane imperf .. 5·00
n. Booklet pane. No. 1476×10 with three edges of pane imperf (12.6.90) 12·50

(*c*) *Litho Questa. P* 15×14

1477 **929** 15p. bright blue (1 centre band) (17.4.90) 1·00 1·00
1478 20p. brownish black (phosphorised paper) (17.4.90) .. .. .. 1·00 1·00

Nos. 1468, 1470, 1472 and 1475/8 come from booklets. No. 1468 exists with the phosphor band at left or right. Nos. 1468 (band at right), 1470 and 1472 occur in the *se-tenant* pane from the 1990 London Life £5 booklet. This pane is listed as No. X906m.

For illustrations showing the difference between photogravure and lithography see beneath Type **367**.

For No. 1469 in miniature sheet see No. **MS**1501.

**930** Kitten

**931** Rabbit

**932** Duckling

**933** Puppy

(Des T. Evans. Litho Questa)

**1990** (23 Jan). *150th Anniv of Royal Society for Prevention of Cruelty to Animals. Phosphorised paper. P* 14×14½.

1479 **930** 20p. new blue, greenish yellow, bright magenta, black and silver .. .. 50 50
 a. Silver (Queen's head and face value) omitted .. .. .. .. £200
1480 **931** 29p. new blue, greenish yellow, bright magenta, black and silver .. .. 80 80
 a. Imperf (horiz pair) .. ..
1481 **932** 34p. new blue, greenish yellow, bright magenta, black and silver .. 1·00 1·00
 a. Silver (Queen's head and face value) omitted .. .. .. .. £350
1482 **933** 37p. new blue, greenish yellow, bright magenta, black and silver .. 1·10 1·10
1479/82 .. .. .. .. *Set of* 4 3·00 3·00

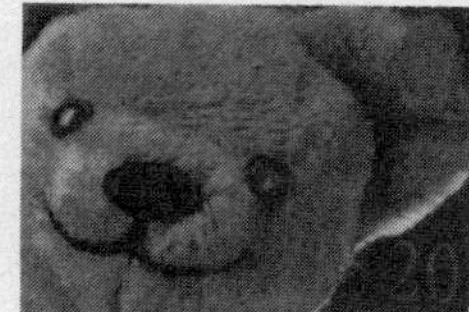

**934** Teddy Bear

**935** Dennis the Menace

**936** Punch

**937** Cheshire Cat

**938** The Man in the Moon

**939** The Laughing Policeman

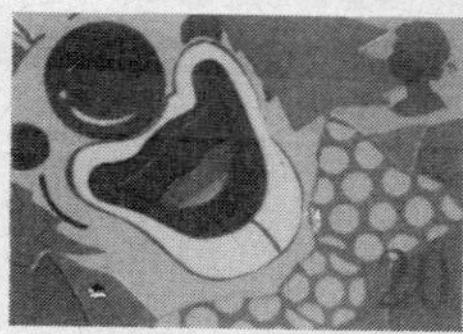

**940** Clown

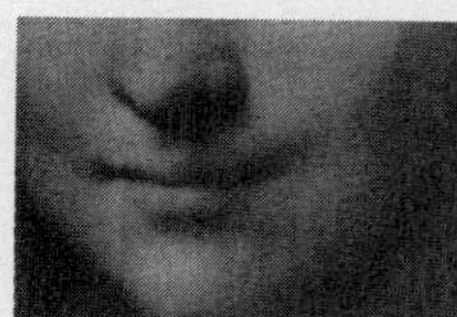

**941** Mona Lisa

**942** Queen of Hearts

**943** Stan Laurel (comedian)

(Des Michael Peters and Partners Ltd)

**1990** (6 Feb). *Greetings Stamps. "Smiles". Two phosphor bands. P* 15×14.

1483 **934** 20p. gold, greenish yellow, bright rose-red, new blue and grey-black .. 75 75
 a. Booklet pane. Nos. 1483/92 with margins all round .. .. 6·75
1484 **935** 20p. gold, greenish yellow, brt rose-red, new blue, deep blue and grey-black 75 75
1485 **936** 20p. gold, greenish yellow, brt rose-red, new blue, deep blue and grey-black 75 75
1486 **937** 20p. gold, greenish yellow, brt rose-red, new blue and grey-black .. .. 75 75
1487 **938** 20p. gold, greenish yellow, brt rose-red, new blue and grey-black .. .. 75 75
1488 **939** 20p. gold, greenish yellow, brt rose-red, new blue and grey-black .. .. 75 75
1489 **940** 20p. gold, greenish yellow, brt rose-red, new blue and grey-black .. .. 75 75
1490 **941** 20p. gold, greenish yellow, bright rose-red, and grey-black .. .. 75 75
1491 **942** 20p. gold, greenish yellow, bright rose-red, new blue and grey-black .. 75 75
1492 **943** 20p. gold and grey-black .. .. 75 75
1483/92 .. .. .. .. *Set of* 10 6·75 6·75

Nos. 1483/92 were only issued in £2 booklets. The designs of Nos. 1483, 1485/7, 1489 and 1492 extend onto the pane margin.

For these designs with the face value expressed as "1st" see Nos. 1550/9.

**944** Alexandra Palace ("Stamp World London 90" Exhibition)

**945** Glasgow School of Art

**946** British Philatelic Bureau, Edinburgh

**947** Templeton Carpet Factory, Glasgow

(Des P. Hogarth)

**1990** (6–20 Mar). *Europa* (*Nos.* 1493 *and* 1495) *and "Glasgow* 1990 *European City of Culture"* (*Nos.* 1494 *and* 1496). *Phosphorised paper. P* 14×15.

1493 **944** 20p. silver, lemon, flesh, grey-brown, blue, grey-black and black .. 50 50
 a. Booklet pane. No. 1493×4 with margins all round (20 March) .. 2·75
1494 **945** 20p. silver, greenish yellow, dull orange, blue, grey-black and black .. 50 50
1495 **946** 29p. silver, stone, orange, olive-sepia, grey-blue, grey-black and black .. 1·00 1·00
1496 **947** 37p. silver, greenish yellow, brt emerald, salmon, olive-sepia, brt blue & black 1·10 1·10
1493/6 .. .. .. .. *Set of* 4 2·75 2·75

**948** Export Achievement Award

**949** Technological Achievement Award

(Des S. Broom. Litho Questa)

**1990** (10 Apr). *25th Anniv of Queen's Awards for Export and Technology. Phosphorised paper. P* 14×14½.

1497 **948** 20p. new blue, greenish yellow, magenta, black and silver .. .. .. 55 55
 a. Horiz pair. Nos. 1497/8 .. .. 1·10 1·10
1498 **949** 20p. new blue, greenish yellow, magenta, black and silver .. .. .. 55 55
1499 **948** 37p. new blue, greenish yellow, magenta, black and silver .. .. .. 1·10 1·10
 a. Horiz pair. Nos. 1499/500 .. 2·25 2·25
1500 **949** 37p. new blue, greenish yellow, magenta, black and silver .. .. .. 1·10 1·10
1497/500 .. .. .. .. *Set of* 4 3·00 3·00

Nos. 1497/8 and 1499/500 were each printed together, *se-tenant*, in horizontal pairs throughout the sheets.

(Des J. Matthews and Sedley Place Design Ltd. Eng C. Matthews. Recess and photo)

**1990** (3 May). *"Stamp World London 90" International Stamp Exhibition, London. Sheet,* 122×90 *mm., containing No.* 1469. *Phosphorised paper. P* 15×14.

**MS**1501 **929** 20p. brownish blk & cream (*sold at* £1) 3·25 3·25
 a. Error. Imperf .. ..
 b. Black (recess printing) omitted
 c. Black (recess printing) inverted

The premium on No. **MS**1501 was used to support the "Stamp World London 90" International Stamp Exhibition.

On examples of No. **MS**1501b the 1d. black and seahorse background are omitted due to a printer's sheet becoming attached to the underside before the recess part of the design was printed. There is an albino impression visible on the reverse.

No. **MS**1501c shows the recess part of the design inverted in relation to the photogravure printing of Type **929**.

**950** Cycad and Sir Joseph Banks Building

**951** Stone Pine and Princess of Wales Conservatory

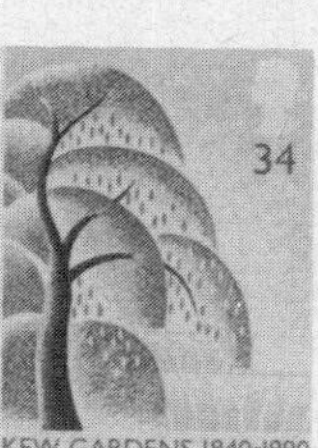


**952** Willow Tree and Palm House

**953** Cedar Tree and Pagoda

(Des P. Leith)

**1990** (5 June). *150th Anniv of Kew Gardens. Phosphorised paper. P* 14×15.

1502 **950** 20p. black, brt emerald, pale turquoise-green, light brown and lavender .. 50 50
1503 **951** 29p. black, brt emerald, turquoise-green, reddish orange and grey-black .. 80 80
1504 **952** 34p. Venetian red, brt green, cobalt, dull purple, turquoise-grn & yellow-green 1·10 1·25
1505 **953** 37p. pale violet-blue, bright emerald, red-brown, steel-blue and brown-rose .. 1·25 1·40
1502/5 .. .. .. .. *Set of* 4 3·25 3·50

**954** Thomas Hardy and Clyffe Clump, Dorset

(Des J. Gibbs)

**1990** (10 July). *150th Birth Anniv of Thomas Hardy (author). Phosphorised paper. P* 14×15.

| | | | | | |
|---|---|---|---|---|---|
| 1506 | **954** | 20p. | vermilion, greenish yellow, pale lake-brown, deep brown, light red-brown and black .. .. | 60 | 70 |
| | | | a. Imperf (pair) .. .. .. | | |

**955** Queen Elizabeth the Queen Mother

**956** Queen Elizabeth

**957** Elizabeth, Duchess of York

**958** Lady Elizabeth Bowes-Lyon

(Des J. Gorham from photographs by N. Parkinson (20p.), Dorothy Wilding (29p.), B. Park (34p.), Rita Martin (37p.))

**1990** (2 Aug). *90th Birthday of Queen Elizabeth the Queen Mother. Phosphorised paper. P* 14×15.

| | | | | | |
|---|---|---|---|---|---|
| 1507 | **955** | 20p. | silver, greenish yellow, magenta, turquoise-blue and grey-black .. | 50 | 50 |
| 1508 | **956** | 29p. | silver, indigo and grey-blue .. | 80 | 80 |
| 1509 | **957** | 34p. | silver, lemon, red, new blue and grey-black .. .. .. | 1·10 | 1·25 |
| 1510 | **958** | 37p. | silver, sepia and stone .. .. | 1·25 | 1·40 |
| 1507/10 | | | .. .. .. .. *Set of* 4 | 3·25 | 3·50 |

**1990** (7 Aug)–**92**. *Booklet Stamps. As T* **913/14**, *but colours changed.*

(*a*) *Photo Harrison. P* 15×14

| | | | | | |
|---|---|---|---|---|---|
| 1511 | **913** | (2nd) | deep blue (1 centre band) .. | 45 | 45 |
| | | | a. Booklet pane. No. 1511×10 with horiz edges of pane imperf .. | 4·00 | |
| 1512 | **914** | (1st) | brt orge-red (phosphorised paper) | 30 | 35 |
| | | | a. Booklet pane. No. 1512×10 with horiz edges of pane imperf .. | 3·00 | |

(*b*) *Litho Questa. P* 15×14

| | | | | | |
|---|---|---|---|---|---|
| 1513 | **913** | (2nd) | deep blue (1 centre band) .. | 45 | 45 |
| 1514 | **914** | (1st) | brt orge-red (phosphorised paper) | 30 | 35 |
| 1514*a* | | (1st) | brt orange-red (2 bands) (25.2.92) | 2·25 | 2·25 |

(*c*) *Litho Walsall. P* 14

| | | | | | |
|---|---|---|---|---|---|
| 1515 | **913** | (2nd) | deep blue (1 centre band) .. | 50 | 50 |
| | | | a. Booklet pane. No. 1515×4 with horiz edges of pane imperf .. | 1·75 | |
| | | | b. Booklet pane. No. 1515×10 with horiz edges of pane imperf .. | 4·00 | |
| 1516 | **914** | (1st) | brt orge-red (phosphorised paper) | 30 | 35 |
| | | | a. Booklet pane. No. 1516×4 with horiz edges of pane imperf .. | 1·25 | |
| | | | b. Booklet pane. No. 1516×10 with horiz edges of pane imperf .. | 3·00 | |
| | | | c. Error. Perf 13 .. .. .. | 2·00 | 2·00 |
| | | | ca. Booklet pane. No. 1516c×4 with horiz edges of pane imperf .. | 8·00 | |

Nos. 1511/14 and 1515/16 were initially sold at 15p. (2nd) and 20p. (1st), but these prices were later increased to reflect new postage rates.

No. 1514*a* comes from the *se-tenant* pane in the Wales £6 booklet. This pane is listed under No. W49a in the Wales Regional Section.

For illustrations showing the difference between photogravure and lithography see beneath Type **367**.

**959** Victoria Cross

**960** George Cross

**961** Distinguished Service Cross and Distinguished Service Medal

**962** Military Cross and Military Medal

**963** Distinguished Flying Cross and Distinguished Flying Medal

(Des J. Gibbs and J. Harwood)

**1990** (11 Sept). *Gallantry Awards. Phosphorised paper. P* 14×15 (*vert*) *or* 15×14 (*horiz*).

| | | | | | |
|---|---|---|---|---|---|
| 1517 | **959** | 20p. | grey-black, pale stone, stone, bistre-brown and bright carmine .. | 65 | 65 |
| 1518 | **960** | 20p. | grey-black, pale stone, flesh, grey and ultramarine .. .. .. | 65 | 65 |
| 1519 | **961** | 20p. | grey-black, pale stone, flesh, pale blue and ultramarine .. .. | 65 | 65 |
| | | | a. Imperf (pair) .. .. .. | | |
| 1520 | **962** | 20p. | grey-black, pale stone, ochre, pale blue, ultramarine, scarlet and violet | 65 | 65 |
| 1521 | **963** | 20p. | grey-black, pale stone, yellow-brown, bluish grey and purple .. | 65 | 65 |
| 1517/21 | | | .. .. .. .. *Set of* 5 | 3·00 | 3·00 |

**964** Armagh Observatory, Jodrell Bank Radio Telescope and La Palma Telescope

**965** Newton's Moon and Tides Diagram with Early Telescopes

**966** Greenwich Old Observatory and Early Astronomical Equipment

**967** Stonehenge, Gyroscope and Navigating by Stars

(Des J. Fisher. Litho Questa)

**1990** (16 Oct). *Astronomy. Phosphorised paper. P* 14×14½.

| | | | | | |
|---|---|---|---|---|---|
| 1522 | **964** | 22p. | cream, grey, dull blue-grn, slate-bl, blue-grn, orange-red, gold & black | 50 | 40 |
| | | | a. Gold (Queen's head) omitted .. | | |
| 1523 | **965** | 26p. | black, yellow, dull purple, pale cream, brown-rose, new blue, greenish yellow, vermilion & gold | 80 | 90 |
| 1524 | **966** | 31p. | black, cream, pale cream, yellow-orge, salmon, lemon, verm & gold | 1·00 | 1·00 |
| 1525 | **967** | 37p. | black, pale buff, olive-bistre, pale cream, pale flesh, flesh, grey, rose-red and gold .. .. | 1·10 | 1·10 |
| 1522/5 | | | .. .. .. .. *Set of* 4 | 3·00 | 3·00 |

Nos. 1522/5 commemorate the Centenary of the British Astronomical Association and the Bicentenary of the Armagh Observatory.

**968** Building a Snowman

**969** Fetching the Christmas Tree

**970** Carol Singing

**971** Tobogganing

**972** Ice-skating

(Des J. Gorham and A. Davidson)

**1990** (13 Nov). *Christmas. One phosphor band* (17*p*) *or phosphorised paper* (*others*). *P* 15×14.

| | | | | | |
|---|---|---|---|---|---|
| 1526 | **968** | 17p. | gold, greenish yellow, rose, new blue and grey-black .. .. | 45 | 35 |
| | | | a. Booklet pane of 20 .. .. | 9·00 | |
| 1527 | **969** | 22p. | gold, greenish yellow, magenta, new blue and black .. .. .. | 55 | 65 |
| | | | a. Imperf (horiz pair) .. .. | | |
| 1528 | **970** | 26p. | gold, olive-yellow, pale magenta, agate, new blue, dull violet-bl & blk | 80 | 80 |
| 1529 | **971** | 31p. | gold, greenish yellow, bright rose-red, dull mauve, new blue, turquoise-blue and grey-black .. | 1·00 | 1·00 |
| 1530 | **972** | 37p. | gold, greenish yellow, rose, new blue and slate-green .. .. | 1·10 | 1·10 |
| 1526/30 | | | .. .. .. .. *Set of* 5 | 3·50 | 3·50 |

Booklet pane No. 1526a comes from a special £3.40 Christmas booklet and has the horizontal edges of the pane imperforate.

**973** "King Charles Spaniel"

**974** "A Pointer"

**975** "Two Hounds in a Landscape"

**976** "A Rough Dog"

**977** "Fino and Tiny"

(Des Carroll Dempsey & Thirkell Ltd)

**1991** (8 Jan). *Dogs. Paintings by George Stubbs. Phosphorised paper. P* 14×14½.

1531 **973** 22p. gold, greenish yellow, magenta, new blue black and drab . . . . 60 60
a. Imperf (pair) . . . . . . . .
1532 **974** 26p. gold, greenish yellow, magenta, new blue, black and drab . . . . 70 70
1533 **975** 31p. gold, greenish yellow, magenta, new blue, black and drab . . . . 80 80
a. Imperf (pair) . . . . . . . .
1534 **976** 33p. gold, greenish yellow, magenta, new blue, black and drab . . . . 85 85
1535 **977** 37p. gold, greenish yellow, magenta, new blue, black and drab . . . . 1·00 1·00
1531/5 . . . . . . . . *Set of* 5 3·50 3·50

**978** Thrush's Nest

**979** Shooting Star and Rainbow

**980** Magpies and Charm Bracelet

**981** Black Cat

**982** Kingfisher with Key

**983** Duck and Frog

**984** Four-leaf Clover in Boot and Match Box

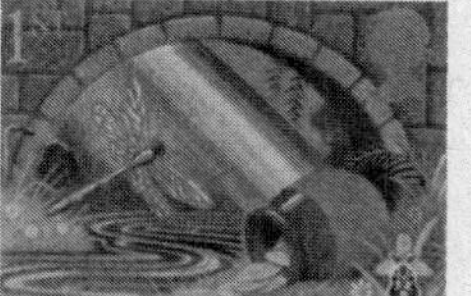

**985** Pot of Gold at End of Rainbow

**986** Heart-shaped Butterflies

**987** Wishing Well and Sixpence

(Des T. Meeuwissen)

**1991** (5 Feb). *Greetings Stamps. "Good Luck". Two phosphor bands. P* 15×14.

1536 **978** (1st) silver, greenish yellow, magenta new blue, olive-brown and black . . 60 60
a. Booklet pane. Nos. 1536/45 plus 12 half stamp-size labels with margins on 3 sides . . . . . . 5·50
1537 **979** (1st) silver, greenish yellow, magenta new blue, olive-brown and black . . 60 60
1538 **980** (1st) silver, greenish yellow, magenta new blue, olive-brown and black . . 60 60
1539 **981** (1st) silver, greenish yellow, magenta new blue, olive-brown and black . . 60 60
1540 **982** (1st) silver, greenish yellow, magenta new blue, olive-brown and black . . 60 60
1541 **983** (1st) silver, greenish yellow, magenta new blue, olive-brown and black . . 60 60
1542 **984** (1st) silver, greenish yellow, magenta new blue, olive-brown and black . . 60 60
1543 **985** (1st) silver, greenish yellow, magenta new blue, olive-brown and black . . 60 60
1544 **986** (1st) silver, greenish yellow, magenta new blue, olive-brown and black . . 60 60
1545 **987** (1st) silver, greenish yellow, magenta new blue, olive-brown and black . . 60 60
1536/45 . . . . . . *Set of* 10 5·50 5·50

Nos. 1536/45 were initially sold at 22p. each and were only issued in £2.20 booklets. It is intended that the price will be increased to reflect future alterations in postage rates. The backgrounds of the stamps form a composite design.

**988** Michael Faraday (inventor of electric motor) (Birth Bicentenary)

**989** Charles Babbage (computer science pioneer) (Birth Bicentenary)

**990** Radar Sweep of East Anglia (50th anniv of operational radar network)

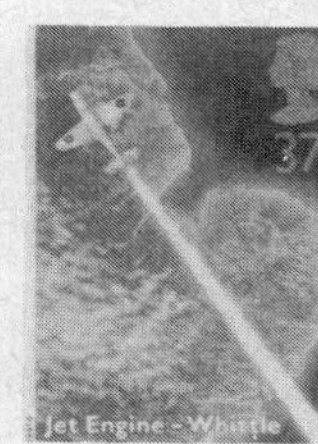


**991** Gloster E28/39 Aircraft over East Anglia (50th anniv of first flight of Sir Frank Whittle's jet engine)

(Des P. Till (Nos. 1546/7), J. Harwood (Nos. 1548/9))

**1991** (5 Mar). *Scientific Achievements. Phosphorised paper. P* 14×15.

1546 **988** 22p. silver, olive-brown greenish yellow, magenta, slate-blue, grey and black 60 60
a. Imperf (pair) . . . . . .
1547 **989** 22p. silver, chrome yellow, red, grey-black, brownish grey and sepia . . 60 60
1548 **990** 31p. silver, deep turquoise-green, violet-blue, steel blue and deep dull blue 85 85
1549 **991** 37p. silver, olive-bistre, rose-red, turq-blue, new blue and grey-black . . 95 95
1546/9 . . . . . . . . *Set of* 4 2·75 2·75

**992** Teddy Bear

**1991** (26 Mar). *Greetings Stamps. "Smiles". As Nos.* 1483/92, *but inscr* "1st" *as in T* **992**. *Two phosphor bands. P* 15×14.

1550 **992** (1st) gold, greenish yellow, bright rose-red, new blue and grey-black . . 35 40
a. Booklet pane. Nos. 1550/9 plus 12 half stamp-size labels with margins on 3 sides . . . . . . 3·25
1551 **935** (1st) gold, greenish yellow, brt rose-red, new blue, deep blue & grey-black 35 40
1552 **936** (1st) gold, greenish yellow, brt rose-red, new blue, deep blue & grey-black 35 40
1553 **937** (1st) gold, greenish yellow, bright rose-red, new blue and grey-black . . 35 40
1554 **938** (1st) gold, greenish yellow, bright rose-red, new blue and grey-black . . 35 40
1555 **939** (1st) gold, greenish yellow, bright rose-red, new blue and grey-black . . 35 40
1556 **940** (1st) gold, greenish yellow, bright rose-red, new blue and grey-black . . 35 40
1557 **941** (1st) gold, greenish yellow, bright rose-red and grey-black . . . . 35 40
1558 **942** (1st) gold, greenish yellow, bright rose-red, new blue and grey-black . . 35 40
1559 **943** (1st) gold and grey-black . . . . 35 40
1550/9 . . . . . . . . *Set of* 10 3·25 3·50

Nos. 1550/9 were initially sold at 22p. each and were only issued in £2.20 booklets. It is intended that the price will be increased to reflect future alterations in postage rates. The designs of Nos. 1550, 1552/4, 1555 and 1559 extend onto the pane margin.

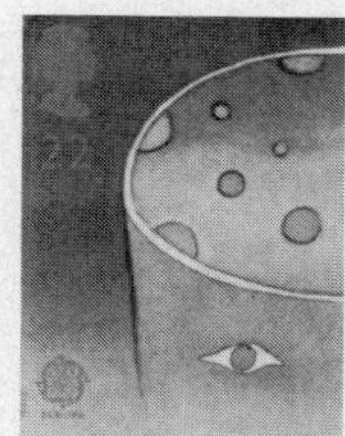

**993** Man looking at Space **994**

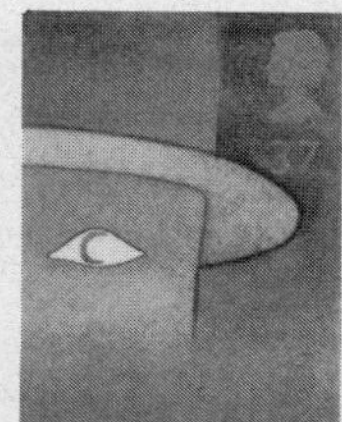

**995** Space looking at Man **996**

(Des J.-M. Folon)

**1991** (23 Apr). *Europa. Europe in Space. Phosphorised paper. P* 14×15.

1560 **993** 22p. silver-mauve, greenish yellow, scar, violet-blue, brt blue, brt green & blk 55 55
a. Horiz pair. Nos. 1560/1 . . . . 1·10 1·10
1561 **994** 22p. silver-mauve, greenish yellow, scar, violet-blue, bright blue and black 55 55
1562 **995** 37p. silver-mauve, bistre-yellow, dull vermilion, blue and black . . 1·00 1·00
a. Horiz pair. Nos. 1562/3 . . . . 2·00 2·00
1563 **996** 37p. silver-mauve, bistre-yellow, dull vermilion, blue and black . . 1·00 1·00
1560/3 . . . . . . . . *Set of* 4 2·75 2·75

Nos. 1560/1 and 1562/3 were each printed together, *se-tenant*, in horizontal pairs throughout the sheets, each pair forming a composite design.

**997** Fencing

**998** Hurdling

**999** Diving

**1000** Rugby

(Des Huntley Muir)

**1991** (11 June). *World Student Games, Sheffield* (*Nos.* 1564/6) *and World Cup Rugby Championship* (*No.* 1567). *Phosphorised paper. P* 14½×14.

1564 **997** 22p. black, greenish yellow, vermilion, bright orange, ultramarine and grey 50 50
1565 **998** 26p. pale blue, greenish yellow, red, bright blue and black .. .. 70 70
1566 **999** 31p. bright blue, bistre-yellow, rose, vermilion, new blue and black .. 85 85
1567 **1000** 37p. yellow-orange, greenish yellow, rose, bright blue, emerald & black 1·00 1·00
1564/7 .. .. .. .. *Set of* 4 2·75 2·75

**1001** "Silver Jubilee"

**1002** "Mme Alfred Carrière"

**1003** *Rosa moyesii*

**1004** "Harvest Fayre"

**1005** "Mutabilis"

(Des Yvonne Skargon. Litho Questa)

**1991** (16 July). *9th World Congress of Roses, Belfast. Phosphorised paper. P* 14½×14.

1568 **1001** 22p. new blue, greenish yellow, magenta, black and silver .. 50 50
1569 **1002** 26p. new blue, greenish yellow, magenta, black and silver .. 60 60
1570 **1003** 31p. new blue, greenish yellow, magenta, black and silver .. 70 70
1571 **1004** 33p. new blue, greenish yellow, magenta, black and silver .. 80 80
1572 **1005** 37p. new blue, greenish yellow, magenta, black and silver 1·00 1·00
1568/72 .. .. .. .. *Set of* 5 3·25 3·25

**1006** Iguanodon

**1007** Stegosaurus

**1008** Tyrannosaurus

**1009** Protoceratops

**1010** Triceratops

(Des B. Kneale)

**1991** (20 Aug). *150th Anniv of Dinosaurs' Identification by Owen. Phosphorised paper. P* 14½×14.

1573 **1006** 22p. grey, pale blue, magenta, bright blue, dull violet and grey-black .. 35 40
a. Imperf (pair) .. .. ..
1574 **1007** 26p. grey, greenish yellow, pale emerald, bright blue-green, pale bright blue, grey-black and black 40 45
1575 **1008** 31p. grey, light blue, magenta, brt blue, pale blue, brown and grey-black .. 50 55
1576 **1009** 33p. grey, dull rose, pale brt bl, brt rose-red, yellow-orge, grey-blk & blk 50 55
1577 **1010** 37p. grey, greenish yellow, turquoise-blue, dull violet, yellow-brn & blk 60 65
1573/7 .. .. .. .. *Set of* 5 2·10 2·40

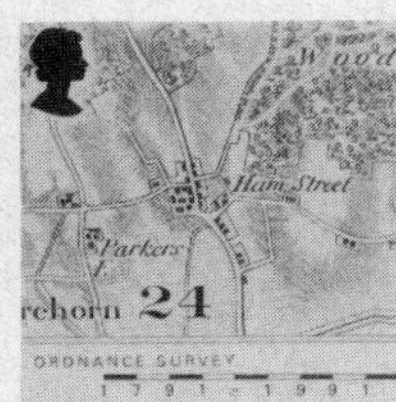


**1011** Map of 1816

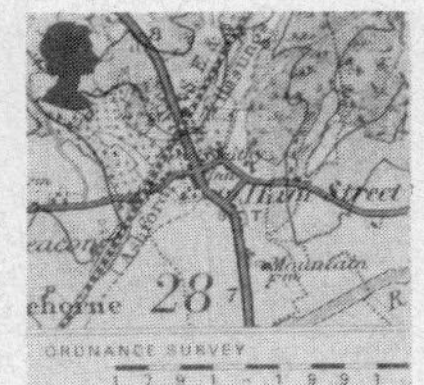


**1012** Map of 1906

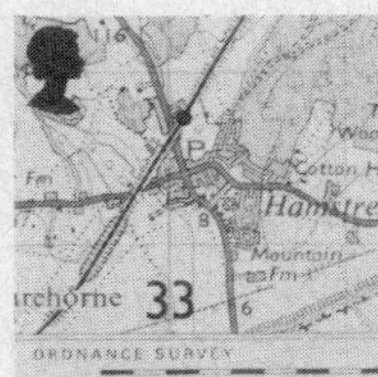


**1013** Map of 1959

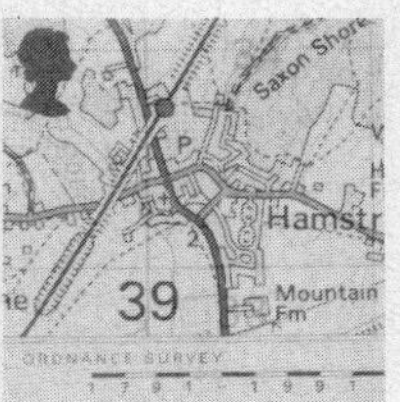


**1014** Map of 1991

(Des H. Brown. Recess and litho Harrison (24p.), Litho Harrison (28p.), Questa (33p., 39p.))

**1991** (17 Sept). *Bicentenary of Ordnance Survey. Maps of Hamstreet, Kent. Phosphorised paper. P* 14½×14.

1578 **1011** 24p. black, magenta, and cream .. 40 45
1579 **1012** 28p. blk, brt yellow-grn, new bl, reddish orge, magenta, olive-sepia & cream 45 50
1580 **1013** 33p. dull blue-green, orange-brown, magenta, olive-grey, greenish yellow, verm, greenish grey, pale bl, bl, dull orge, apple grn & blk 50 55
1581 **1014** 39p. black, mag, greenish yell & new bl 60 65
1578/81 .. .. .. .. *Set of* 4 1·75 1·90

**1015** Adoration of the Magi

**1016** Mary and Baby Jesus in the Stable

**1017** The Holy Family and Angel

**1018** The Annunciation

**1019** The Flight into Egypt

(Des D. Driver)

**1991** (12 Nov). *Christmas. Illuminated Letters from "Acts of Mary and Jesus" Manuscript in Bodleian Library, Oxford. One phosphor band* (18p.) *or phosphorised paper* (*others*). *P* 15×14.

1582 **1015** 18p. steel-blue, greenish yellow, rose-red, orange-red, black and gold .. 30 35
a. Booklet pane of 20 .. .. 5·50
1583 **1016** 24p. bright rose-red, greenish yellow, vermilion, slate-blue, yellow-green, grey-black and gold .. .. 40 45
1584 **1017** 28p. reddish brn, bistre-yellow, orange-vermilion, orange-red, deep dull blue, grey-black and gold .. 45 50
1585 **1018** 33p. green, greenish yell, red, orange-red, blue, grey and gold .. 50 55
1586 **1019** 39p. orange-red, greenish yell, orange-vermilion, deep dull blue, olive-sepia, black and gold .. .. 60 65
1582/6 .. .. .. .. *Set of* 5 2·00 2·25

Booklet pane No. 1582a comes from special £3.60 Christmas booklet and has margins at left, top and bottom.

**1020** Fallow Deer in Scottish Forest

**1021** Hare on North Yorkshire Moors

**1022** Fox in the Fens

**1023** Redwing and Home Counties Village

**1024** Welsh Mountain Sheep in Snowdonia

(Des J. Gorham and K. Bowen)

**1992** (14 Jan–25 Feb). *The Four Seasons. Wintertime. One phosphor band* (18p.) *or phosphorised paper (others). P* 15×14.

1587 **1020** 18p. silver, greenish yellow, grey, dull rose, new blue and black . . . . 30 35
1588 **1021** 24p. silver, lemon, rose, blue & grey-blk 40 45
a. Imperf (pair) . . . . . .
1589 **1022** 28p. silver, greenish yellow, bright rose, steel-blue and grey black . . . . 45 50
1590 **1023** 33p. silver, greenish yellow, brt orange, brt purple, greenish blue & grey 50 55
1591 **1024** 39p. silver, yellow, yellow-orange, grey, vermilion, new blue and black . . 60 65
a. Booklet pane. No. 1591×4 with margins all round (25 Feb) . . 2·50
1587/91 . . . . . . . . *Set of* 5 2·00 2·25

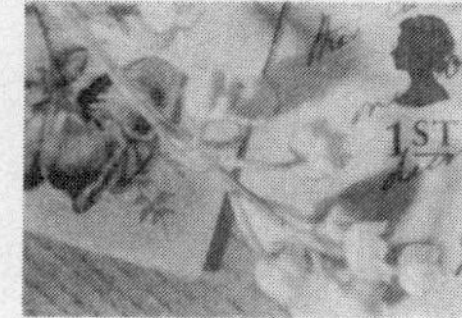


**1025** Flower Spray

**1026** Double Locket

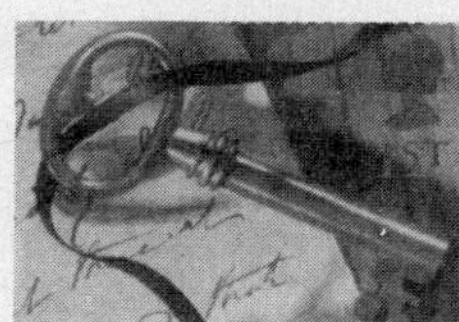


**1027** Key

**1028** Model Car and Cigarette Cards

**1029** Compass and Map

**1030** Pocket Watch

**1031** 1858–79 1d. Red Stamp and Pen

**1032** Pearl Necklace

**1033** Marbles

**1034** Bucket, Spade and Starfish

(Des Trickett and Webb Ltd)

**1992** (28 Jan). *Greetings Stamps. "Memories". Two phosphor bands. P* 15×14.

1592 **1025** (1st) gold, greenish yellow, magenta, ochre, light blue and grey-black . . 40 45
a. Booklet pane. Nos. 1592/1601 plus 12 half stamp-size labels with margins on 3 sides . . . . 3·50
1593 **1026** (1st) gold, greenish yellow, magenta, ochre, light blue and grey-black . . 40 45
1594 **1027** (1st) gold, greenish yellow, magenta, ochre, light blue and grey-black . . 40 45
1595 **1028** (1st) gold, greenish yellow, magenta, ochre, light blue and grey-black . . 40 45
1596 **1029** (1st) gold, greenish yellow, magenta, ochre, light blue and grey-black . . 40 45
1597 **1030** (1st) gold, greenish yellow, magenta, ochre, light blue and grey-black . . 40 45
1598 **1031** (1st) gold, greenish yellow, magenta, ochre, light blue and grey-black . . 40 45
1599 **1032** (1st) gold, greenish yellow, magenta, ochre, light blue and grey-black . . 40 45
1600 **1033** (1st) gold, greenish yellow, magenta, ochre, light blue and grey-black . . 40 45
1601 **1034** (1st) gold, greenish yellow, magenta, ochre, light blue and grey-black . . 40 45
1592/1601 . . . . . . . . *Set of* 10 3·50 4·00

Nos. 1592/1601 were only issued in £2.40 booklets. The backgrounds of the stamps form a composite design.

**1035** Queen Elizabeth in Coronation Robes and Parliamentary Emblem

**1036** Queen Elizabeth in Garter Robes and Archiepiscopal Arms

**1037** Queen Elizabeth with Baby Prince Andrew and Royal Arms

**1038** Queen Elizabeth at Trooping the Colour and Service Emblems

**1039** Queen Elizabeth and Commonwealth Emblem

(Des Why Not Associates. Litho Questa)

**1992** (6 Feb). *40th Anniv of Accession. Two phosphor bands. P* 14½×14.

1602 **1035** 24p. new blue, greenish yellow, magenta, black, silver and gold . . 40 45
a. Horiz strip of 5. Nos. 1602/6 . . 1·75 2·00
1603 **1036** 24p. new blue, greenish yellow, magenta, black, silver and gold . . 40 45
1604 **1037** 24p. new blue, greenish yellow, magenta, black and silver . . 40 45
1605 **1038** 24p. new blue, greenish yellow, magenta, black, silver and gold . . 40 45
1606 **1039** 24p. new blue, greenish yellow, magenta, black, silver and gold . . 40 45
1602/6 . . . . . . . . *Set of* 5 1·75 2·00

Nos. 1602/6 were printed together, *se-tenant,* in horizontal strips of five throughout the sheet.

**1040** Tennyson in 1888 and "The Beguiling of Merlin" (Sir Edward Burne-Jones)

**1041** Tennyson in 1864 and "I am Sick of the Shadows" (John Waterhouse)

**1042** Tennyson in 1856 and "April Love" (Arthur Hughes)

**1043** Tennyson as a Young Man and "Mariana" (Dante Gabriel Rossetti)

(Des Irene von Treskow)

**1992** (10 Mar). *Death Centenary of Alfred, Lord Tennyson (poet). Phosphorised paper. P* 14½×14.

1607 **1040** 24p. gold, greenish yellow, magenta, new blue and black . . . . 40 45
1608 **1041** 28p. gold, greenish yellow, magenta, new blue and black . . . . 45 50
1609 **1042** 33p. gold, greenish yellow, magenta, new blue and black . . . . 50 55
1610 **1043** 39p. gold, greenish yellow, magenta, new blue, bistre and black . . 60 65
1607/10 . . . . . . . . *Set of* 4 1·75 1·90

**1044** Carrickfergus Castle

Oval hole in vertical perforations

(Des from photos by Prince Andrew, Duke of York. Eng C. Matthews. Recess Harrison)

**1992** (24 Mar). *Designs as Nos.* 1410/13, *but showing Queen's head in silhouette as T* **1044**. *P* 15×14*.

1611 **1044** £1 bottle green and gold † . . . . 1·50 1·50
1612 **880** £1.50, maroon and gold † . . . . 2·25 2·25
1613 **881** £2 indigo and gold † . . . . 3·00 3·00
1614 **882** £5 deep brown and gold † . . . . 7·50 7·50
1611/14 . . . . . . . . *Set of* 4 13·00 13·00

*These stamps show a larger oval-shaped perforation hole at the centre of each vertical edge.

†The Queen's head on these stamps is printed in optically variable ink which changes colour from gold to green when viewed from different angles.

**1045** British Olympic Association Logo (Olympic Games, Barcelona)

**1046** British Paralympic Association Symbol (Paralympics '92, Barcelona)

**1047** *Santa Maria* (500th Anniv of Discovery of America by Columbus)

**1048** *Kaisei* (cadet sailing ship) (Grand Regatta Columbus, 1992)

**1049** British Pavilion, "Expo '92", Seville

(Des K. Bassford (Nos. 1615/16, 1619), K. Bassford and S. Paine, Eng. C. Matthews (Nos. 1617/18). Litho Questa (Nos. 1615/16, 1619) or recess and litho Harrison (Nos. 1617/18))

**1992** (7 Apr). *Europa. International Events. Phosphorised paper. P* 14×14½.

| | | | | | |
|---|---|---|---|---|---|
| 1615 | **1045** | 24p. | new blue, lemon, magenta & black | 40 | 45 |
| | | | a. Horiz pair. Nos. 1615/16 .. | 80 | 90 |
| 1616 | **1046** | 24p. | new blue, lemon, magenta & black | 40 | 45 |
| 1617 | **1047** | 24p. | black, grey, carmine, cream & gold | 40 | 45 |
| 1618 | **1048** | 39p. | black, grey, carmine, cream & gold | 60 | 65 |
| 1619 | **1049** | 39p. | new blue, lemon, magenta & black | 60 | 65 |
| 1615/19 | | | .. .. .. .. *Set of* 5 | 2·10 | 2·50 |

Nos. 1615/16 were printed together, *se-tenant*, throughout the sheet.

**1050** Pikeman

**1051** Drummer

**1052** Musketeer

**1053** Standard Bearer

(Des J. Sancha)

**1992** (16 June). *350th Anniv of the Civil War. Phosphorised paper. P* 14½×14.

| | | | | | |
|---|---|---|---|---|---|
| 1620 | **1050** | 24p. | black, stone, bistre, scarlet, indigo, grey-green and yellow-ochre .. | 40 | 45 |
| 1621 | **1051** | 28p. | black, yellow-ochre, ochre, rose-pink, bl, dull yell-grn & slate-lilac | 45 | 50 |
| 1622 | **1052** | 33p. | black, ochre, pale orange, lemon, reddish orange, new bl & olive-grn | 50 | 55 |
| 1623 | **1053** | 39p. | black, yellow-ochre, yell, greenish yell, verm, ind & orge-brn .. | 60 | 65 |
| 1620/3 | | | .. .. .. .. *Set of* 4 | 1·75 | 2·00 |

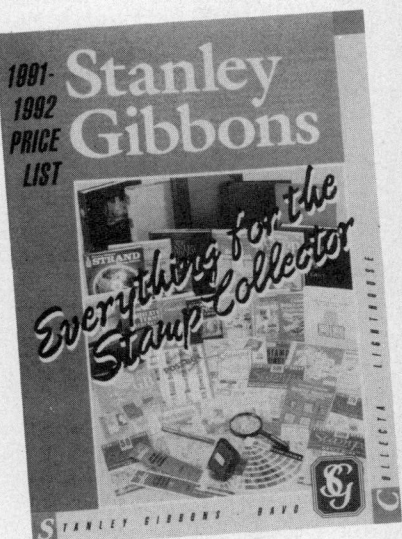

## REGIONAL ISSUES

For Regional Issues of Guernsey, Jersey and the Isle of Man, *see* after Great Britain Postal Fiscals.

Printers (£ s. d. stamps of all regions):—Photo Harrison & Sons. Portrait by Dorothy Wilding Ltd.

**DATES OF ISSUE.** Conflicting dates of issue have been announced for some of the regional issues, partly explained by the stamps being released on different dates by the Philatelic Bureau in Edinburgh or the Philatelic Counter in London and in the regions. We have adopted the practice of giving the earliest known dates, since once released the stamps could have been used anywhere in the U.K.

### I. NORTHERN IRELAND

N 1

N 2

N 3

(Des W. Hollywood (3d., 4d., 5d.), L. Pilton (6d., 9d.), T. Collins (1s. 3d., 1s. 6d.))

**1958–67.** *W* **179.** *P* 15 × 14.
NI1 N 1 3d. deep lilac (18.8.58) .. .. 20 10
p. One centre phosphor band (9.6.67) 20 15
NI2 4d. ultramarine (7.2.66) .. .. 20 15
p. Two phosphor bands (10.67) .. 20 15
NI3 N 2 6d. deep claret (29.9.58) .. .. 20 20
NI4 9d. bronze-green (2 phosphor bands) (1.3.67) .. .. .. .. 30 50
NI5 N 3 1s. 3d. green (29.9.58) .. .. 30 50
NI6 1s. 6d. grey-blue (2 phosphor bands) (1.3.67) .. .. .. .. 30 50

**1968–69.** *No wmk. Chalk-surfaced paper. One centre phosphor band (Nos.* NI8/9) *or two phosphor bands (others). P* 15 × 14.
NI 7 N 1 4d. deep bright blue (27.6.68) .. 20 15
NI 8 4d. olive-sepia (4.9.68) .. .. 20 15
NI 9 4d. bright vermilion (26.2.69) .. 20 20
NI10 5d. royal blue (4.9.68) .. .. 20 20
NI11 N 3 1s. 6d. grey-blue (20.5.69) .. 2·50 3·00

No. NI7 was only issued in Northern Ireland with gum arabic. After it had been withdrawn from Northern Ireland but whilst still on sale at the philatelic counters elsewhere, about fifty sheets with PVA gum were sold over the London Philatelic counter on 23 October 1968, and some were also on sale at the British Philatelic Exhibition Post Office in October, without any prior announcement. The other values exist with PVA gum only.

N 4

(Des J. Matthews after plaster cast by Arnold Machin)

**1971** (7 July)–**91.** *Decimal Currency. Chalk-surfaced paper. Type* **N 4.** (*a*) *Photo Harrison. With phosphor bands. P* 15×14.
NI12 2½p. bright magenta (1 centre band) 75 25
NI13 3p. ultramarine (2 bands) .. .. 40 15
NI14 3p. ultramarine (1 centre band) (23.1.74) 20 15
NI15 3½p. olive-grey (2 bands) (23.1.74) .. 20 20
NI16 3½p. olive-grey (1 centre band) (6.11.74) .. 20 25
NI17 4½p. grey-blue (2 bands) (6.11.74) .. 25 25
NI18 5p. reddish violet (2 bands) .. .. 1·50 1·50
NI19 5½p. violet (2 bands) (23.1.74) .. .. 20 20
NI20 5½p. violet (1 centre band) (21.5.75) .. 20 20
NI21 6½p. greenish blue (1 centre band) (14.1.76) 20 20
NI22 7p. purple-brown (1 centre band) (18.1.78) 35 25
NI23 7½p. chestnut (2 bands) .. .. 2·50 2·50
NI24 8p. rosine (2 bands) (23.1.74) .. .. 30 30
NI25 8½p. yellow-green (2 bands) (14.1.76) .. 30 30
NI26 9p. deep violet (2 bands) (18.1.78) .. 30 30
NI27 10p. orange-brown (2 bands) (20.10.76) .. 35 35
NI28 10p. orange-brown (1 centre band) (23.7.80) 35 35
NI29 10½p. steel-blue (2 bands) (18.1.78) .. 40 40
NI30 11p. scarlet (2 bands) (20.10.76) .. .. 40 40

(*b*) *Photo Harrison. On phosphorised paper. P* 15 × 14.
NI31 12p. yellowish green (23.7.80) .. .. 50 45
NI32 13½p. purple-brown (23.7.80) .. .. 60 70
NI33 15p. ultramarine (23.7.80) .. .. 60 50

(*c*) *Litho Questa. One side phosphor band* (11½p., 12p., 12½p., 13p.), *one centre band* (14p. (*No.* NI39), 15p., 17p. (*No.* NI44), 18p. (*No.* NI47)) *or on phosphorised paper* (*others*). *P* 14 (11½p., 12½p., 14p. (*No.* NI38), 15½p., 16p., 18p. (*No.* NI45), 19½p., 20½p., 22p. (*No.* NI52), 26p. (*No.* NI58), 28p (*No.* NI60)) *or* 15×14 (*others*).
NI34 11½p. drab (8.4.81) .. .. .. 1·00 60
NI35 12p. bright emerald (7.1.86) .. .. 50 50
NI36 12½p. light emerald (24.2.82) .. .. 50 40
a. Perf 15×14 (28.2.84) .. .. 4·00 4·00
NI37 13p. pale chestnut (23.10.84) .. .. 60 35
NI38 14p. grey-blue (8.4.81) .. .. .. 70 50
NI39 14p. deep blue (8.11.88) .. .. 40 35
NI40 15p. bright blue (28.11.89) .. .. 45 30
NI41 15½p. pale violet (24.2.82) .. .. 1·00 65
NI42 16p. drab (27.4.83) .. .. .. 1·00 1·00
a. Perf 15×14 (28.2.84) .. .. 7·00 1·00
NI43 17p. grey-blue (23.10.84) .. .. 80 40
NI44 17p. deep blue (4.12.90) .. .. 30 35
NI45 18p. deep violet (8.4.81) .. .. 80 80
NI46 18p. olive-grey (6.1.87) .. .. .. 80 70
NI47 18p. bright green (3.12.91) .. .. 30 35
NI48 19p. bright orange-red (8.11.88) .. .. 60 60
NI49 19½p. olive-grey (24.2.82) .. .. 2·00 2·00
NI50 20p. brownish black (28.11.89) .. .. 30 30
NI51 20½p. ultramarine (27.4.83) .. .. 4·00 4·00
NI52 22p. blue (8.4.81) .. .. .. 90 1·10
NI53 22p. yellow-green (23.10.84) .. .. 85 85
NI54 22p. bright orange-red (4.12.90) .. .. 85 40
NI55 23p. bright green (8.11.88) .. .. 80 80
NI56 24p. Indian red (28.11.89) .. .. 70 70
NI57 24p. chestnut (3.12.91) .. .. .. 40 45
NI58 26p. rosine (24.2.82) .. .. .. 90 90
a. Perf 15×14 (27.1.87) .. .. 1·50 1·50
NI59 26p. drab (4.12.90) .. .. .. 40 45
NI60 28p. deep violet-blue (27.4.83) .. .. 1·00 1·00
a. Perf 15×14 (27.1.87) .. .. 80 80
NI61 28p. deep bluish grey (3.12.91) .. .. 45 50
NI62 31p. bright purple (23.10.84) .. .. 1·10 1·10
NI63 32p. greenish blue (8.11.88) .. .. 1·10 1·10
NI64 34p. deep bluish grey (28.11.89) .. .. 1·00 1·00
NI65 37p. rosine (4.12.90) .. .. .. 60 65
NI66 39p. bright mauve (3.12.91) .. .. 60 65

From 1972 printings were made on fluorescent white paper and from 1973 printings had dextrin added to the PVA gum (see notes after No. X1026 of Great Britain).

### II. SCOTLAND

S 1

S 2

S 3

(Des G. Huntly (3d., 4d., 5d), J. Fleming (6d., 9d.), A. Imrie (1s. 3d., 1s. 6d.))

**1958–67.** *W* **179.** *P* 15 × 14.
S1 S 1 3d. deep lilac (18.8.58) .. .. .. 20 15
p. Two phosphor bands (29.1.63) .. 15·00 1·00
pa. One side phosphor band (30.4.65) .. 20 25
pb. One centre phosphor band (9.11.67) 20 15
S2 4d. ultramarine (7.2.66) .. .. .. 20 10
p. Two phosphor bands .. .. 20 20
S3 S 2 6d. deep claret (29.9.58) .. .. 20 15
p. Two phosphor bands (29.1.63) .. 20 25
S4 9d. bronze-green (2 phosphor bands) (1.3.67) .. .. .. .. 30 30
S5 S 3 1s. 3d. green (29.9.58) .. .. 30 30
p. Two phosphor bands (29.1.63) .. 30 30
S6 1s. 6d. grey-blue (2 phosphor bands) (1.3.67) .. .. .. .. 35 30

The one phosphor band on No. S1pa was produced by printing broad phosphor bands across alternate vertical perforations. Individual stamps show the band at right or left (same prices either way).

**1967–70.** *No wmk. Chalk-surfaced paper. One centre phosphor band* (S7, S9/10) *or two phosphor bands (others). P* 15 × 14.
S 7 S 1 3d. deep lilac (16.5.68) .. .. .. 10 15
S 8 4d. deep bright blue (28.11.67) .. .. 10 15
S 9 4d. olive-sepia (4.9.68) .. .. .. 10 10
S10 4d. bright vermilion (26.2.69) .. .. 10 10
S11 5d. royal blue (4.9.68) .. .. .. 20 10
S12 S 2 9d. bronze-green (28.9.70) .. .. 5·00 5·50
S13 S 3 1s. 6d. grey-blue (12.12.68) .. .. 1·40 1·00

Nos. S7/8 exist with both gum arabic and PVA gum; others with PVA gum only.

S 4

(Des J. Matthews after plaster cast by Arnold Machin)

**1971** (7 July)–**91.** *Decimal Currency. Chalk-surfaced paper. Type* **S 4.**

(*a*) *Photo Harrison. With phosphor bands. P* 15 × 14
S14 2½p. bright magenta (1 centre band) .. 25 15
S15 3p. ultramarine (2 bands) .. .. 30 15
a. Imperf (pair)† .. .. .. £400
S16 3p. ultramarine (1 centre band) (23.1.74) .. 15 15
S17 3½p. olive-grey (2 bands) (23.1.74) .. 20 20
S18 3½p. olive-grey (1 centre band) (6.11.74) .. 20 20
S19 4½p. grey-blue (2 bands) (6.11.74) .. 25 20
S20 5p. reddish violet (2 bands) .. .. 1·50 1·50
S21 5½p. violet (2 bands) (23.1.74) .. .. 20 20
S22 5½p. violet (1 centre band) (21.5.75) .. 20 20
a. Imperf (pair) .. .. .. £350
S23 6½p. greenish blue (1 centre band) (14.1.76) 20 20
S24 7p. purple-brown (1 centre band) (18.1.78) 25 25
S25 7½p. chestnut (2 bands) .. .. 2·00 2·00
S26 8p. rosine (2 bands) (23.1.74) .. .. 30 40
S27 8½p. yellow-green (2 bands) (14.1.76) .. 30 30
S28 9p. deep violet (2 bands) (18.1.78) .. 30 30
S29 10p. orange-brown (2 bands) (20.10.76) .. 35 30
S30 10p. orange-brown (1 centre band) (23.7.80) 35 35
S31 10½p. steel-blue (2 bands) (18.1.78) .. 45 35
S32 11p. scarlet (2 bands) (20.10.76) .. .. 45 35

(*b*) *Photo Harrison. On phosphorised paper. P* 15 × 14
S33 12p. yellowish green (23.7.80) .. .. 50 30
S34 13½p. purple-brown (23.7.80) .. .. 60 65
S35 15p. ultramarine (23.7.80) .. .. 60 45

(*c*) *Litho J.W. One side phosphor band* (11½p., 12p., 12½p., 13p.) *or phosphorised paper* (*others*). *P* 14
S36 11½p. drab (8.4.81) .. .. .. 85 60
S37 12p. bright emerald (7.1.86) .. .. 80 70
S38 12½p. light emerald (24.2.82) .. .. 50 40
S39 13p. pale chestnut (23.10.84) .. .. 60 30
S40 14p. grey-blue (8.4.81) .. .. .. 60 50
S41 15½p. pale violet (24.2.82) .. .. 70 65
S42 16p. drab (27.4.83) .. .. .. 70 45
S43 17p. grey-blue (23.10.84) .. .. 3·25 2·00
S44 18p. deep violet (8.4.81) .. .. 1·00 90
S45 19½p. olive-grey (24.2.82) .. .. 2·00 2·25
S46 20½p. ultramarine (27.4.83) .. .. 3·75 3·75
S47 22p. blue (8.4.81) .. .. .. 80 1·10
S48 22p. yellow-green (23.10.84) .. .. 1·00 80
S49 26p. rosine (24.2.82) .. .. .. 90 80
S50 28p. deep violet-blue (27.4.83) .. .. 1·00 80
S51 31p. bright purple (23.10.84) .. .. 1·40 1·10

(*d*) *Litho Questa. P* 15×14
S52 12p. bright emerald (1 side band) (29.4.86) 60 60
S53 13p. pale chestnut (1 side band) (4.11.86) .. 60 30
S54 14p. deep blue (1 centre band) (8.11.88) .. 40 30
l. Booklet pane. No. S54×6 with margins all round (21.3.89) .. .. .. 2·50
S55 14p. deep blue (1 side band) (21.3.89) .. 80 80
l. Booklet pane. No. S55×5, S62×2, S67 and centre label with margins all round 9·00
la. Error. Booklet pane imperf .. ..
S56 15p. bright blue (1 centre band) (28.11.89) 50 30
a. Imperf three sides (block of 4) ..
S57 17p. grey-bl (phosphorised paper) (29.4.86) 3·50 2·00
S58 17p. deep blue (1 centre band) (4.12.90) .. 30 35
S59 18p. ol-grey (phosphorised paper) (6.1.87) 1·00 90
S60 18p. bright green (1 centre band) (3.12.91) 30 35
S61 19p. bright orange-red (phosphorised paper) (8.11.88) .. .. .. .. 60 45
l. Booklet pane. No. S61×9 with margins all round (21.3.89) .. .. .. 5·00
m. Booklet pane. No. S61×6 with margins all round (21.3.89) .. .. .. 3·00
S62 19p. bright orange-red (2 bands) (21.3.89) 1·40 1·40
S63 20p. brownish black (phosphorised paper) (28.11.89) .. .. .. .. 60 30
S64 22p. yell-grn (phosphorised paper) (27.1.87) 80 80
S65 22p. bright orange-red (phosphorised paper) (4.12.90) .. .. .. .. 90 40
S66 23p. brt grn (phosphorised paper) (8.11.88) 90 80
S67 23p. bright green (2 bands) (21.3.89) .. 3·75 3·75
S68 24p. Indian red (phosphorised paper) (28.11.89) .. .. .. .. 70 70
S69 24p. chestnut (phosphorised paper) (3.12.91) .. .. .. .. 40 45
S70 26p. rosine (phosphorised paper) (27.1.87) 1·50 1·10
S71 26p. drab (phosphorised paper) (4.12.90) .. 40 45
S72 28p. deep violet-blue (phosphorised paper) (27.1.87) .. .. .. .. 85 75
S73 28p. deep bluish grey (phosphorised paper) (3.12.91) .. .. .. .. 45 50
S74 31p. brt pur (phosphorised paper) (29.4.86) 1·50 1·10
S75 32p. greenish blue (phosphorised paper) (8.11.88) .. .. .. .. 1·10 90
S76 34p. deep bluish grey (phosphorised paper) (28.11.89) .. .. .. .. 1·00 90
S77 37p. rosine (phosphorised paper) (4.12.90) 60 65
S78 39p. brt mve (phosphorised paper) (3.12.91) 60 65

† Exists only with gum arabic.

Nos. S55, S62 and S67 were only issued in the £5 sponsored stamp booklet of 21 March 1989.

No. S56a occurred in the second vertical row on two sheets. The error is best collected as a block of four to include the left-hand vertical pair imperforate on three sides.

From 1972 printings were on fluorescent white paper. Nos. S14/15 exist with PVA and gum arabic and the remainder with PVA only. From 1973 printings had extra dextrin added (see notes after No. X1026 of Great Britain).

### III. WALES

From the inception of the Regional stamps, the Welsh versions were tendered to members of the public at all Post Offices within the former County of Monmouthshire but the English alternatives were available on request. Offices with a Monmouthshire postal address but situated outside the County, namely Beachley, Brockweir, Redbrook, Sedbury, Tutshill, Welsh Newton and Woodcroft, were not supplied with the Welsh Regional stamps.

With the re-formation of Counties, Monmouthshire became known as Gwent and was also declared to be part of Wales. From 1 July 1974, therefore, except for the offices mentioned above, only Welsh Regional stamps were available at the offices under the jurisdiction of Newport, Gwent.

W 1

W 2

W 3

(Des R. Stone)

**1958–67.** *W* **179.** *P* 15 × 14.
W1 W 1 3d. deep lilac (18.8.58) .. .. 20 10
p. One centre phosphor band (16.5.67) .. .. .. .. 20 15
W2 4d. ultramarine (7.2.66) .. .. 20 15
p. Two phosphor bands (10.67) .. 20 15
W3 W 2 6d. deep claret (29.9.58) .. .. 40 20
W4 9d. bronze-green (2 phosphor bands) (1.3.67) .. .. .. .. 30 35
W5 W 3 1s. 3d. green (29.9.58) .. .. 30 30
W6 1s. 6d. grey-blue (2 phosphor bands) (1.3.67) .. .. .. .. 35 30

**1967–69.** *No wmk. Chalk-surfaced paper. One centre phosphor band* (W7, W9/10) *or two phosphor bands (others). P* 15 × 14.
W 7 W 1 3d. deep lilac (6.12.67) .. .. 20 10
W 8 4d. deep bright blue (21.6.68) .. 20 10
W 9 4d. olive-sepia (4.9.68) .. .. 20 10
W10 4d. bright vermilion (26.2.69) .. 20 20
W11 5d. royal blue (4.9.68) .. .. 20 10
W12 W 3 1s. 6d. grey-blue (1.8.69) .. .. 3·00 3·00

The 3d. exists with gum arabic only; the remainder with PVA gum only.

W 4

(Des J. Matthews after plaster cast by Arnold Machin)

**1971** (7 July)–**92**. *Decimal Currency. Chalk-surfaced paper. Type* W **4**. (*a*) *Photo Harrison. With phosphor bands. P* 15×14

W13 2½p. bright magenta (1 centre band) .. 20 15
W14 3p. ultramarine (2 bands) .. .. .. 25 15
W15 3p. ultramarine (1 centre band) (23.1.74) .. 20 20
W16 3½p. olive-grey (2 bands) (23.1.74) .. .. 20 25
W17 3½p. olive-grey (1 centre band) (6.11.74) .. 20 25
W18 4½p. grey-blue (2 bands) (6.11.74) .. .. 25 20
W19 5p. reddish violet (2 bands) .. .. 1·50 1·50
W20 5½p. violet (2 bands) (23.1.74) .. .. 20 25
W21 5½p. violet (1 centre band) (21.5.75) .. 20 25
a. Imperf (pair) .. .. .. .. £400
W22 6½p. greenish blue (1 centre band) (14.1.76) 20 20
W23 7p. purple-brown (1 centre band) (18.1.78) 25 25
W24 7½p. chestnut (2 bands) .. .. .. 2·00 2·25
W25 8p. rosine (2 bands) (23.1.74) .. .. 30 30
W26 8½p. yellow-green (2 bands) (14.1.76) .. 30 30
W27 9p. deep violet (2 bands) (18.1.78) .. 30 30
W28 10p. orange-brown (2 bands) (20.10.76) .. 35 30
W29 10p. orange-brown (1 centre band) (23.7.80) 35 30
W30 10½p. steel-blue (2 bands) (18.1.78) .. .. 40 35
W31 11p. scarlet (2 bands) (20.10.76) .. .. 40 45

(*b*) *Photo Harrison. On phosphorised paper. P* 15 × 14

W32 12p. yellowish green (23.7.80) .. .. 50 45
W33 13½p. purple-brown (23.7.80) .. .. 60 70
W34 15p. ultramarine (23.7.80) .. .. .. 60 50

(*c*) *Litho Questa. P* 14 (11½*p.*, 12½*p.*, 14*p.* (*No.* W39), 15½*p.*, 16*p.*, 18*p.* (*No.* W46), 19½*p.*, 20½*p.*, 22*p.* (*No.* W54), 26*p.* (*No.* W61), 28*p.* (*No.* W63)) *or* 15×14 (*others*).

W35 11½p. drab (1 side band) (8.4.81) .. .. 85 60
W36 12p. bright emerald (1 side band) (7.1.86) 1·40 1·10
W37 12½p. light emerald (1 side band) (24.2.82) 60 60
a. Perf 15×14 (10.1.84) .. .. 6·00 4·50
W38 13p. pale chestnut (1 side band) (23.10.84) 50 35
W39 14p. grey-bl (phosphorised paper) (8.4.81) 65 50
W40 14p. deep blue (1 centre band) (8.11.88) 45 30
W41 15p. bright blue (1 centre band) (28.11.89) 45 30
W42 15½p. pale violet (phosphorised paper) (24.2.82) .. .. .. .. 80 65
W43 16p. drab (phosphorised paper (27.4.83) 1·50 1·25
a. Perf 15×14 (10.1.84) .. .. 1·50 1·25
W44 17p. grey-blue (phosphorised paper) (23.10.84) .. .. .. .. 70 55
W45 17p. deep blue (1 centre band) (4.12.90) 30 35
W46 18p. deep violet (8.4.81) .. .. .. 80 75
W47 18p. deep olive-grey (phosphorised paper) (6.1.87) .. .. .. .. 1·00 45
W48 18p. bright green (1 centre band) (3.12.91) 30 35
a. Booklet pane. No. W48×6 with margins all round (25.2.92) .. .. 1·90
W49 18p. bright green (1 side band) (25.2.92) 1·10 1·10
a. Booklet pane. No. X1016×2, 1451*a*, 1514*a*, W49×2, W60×2 and centre label with margins all round .. .. 9·00
W50 19p. bright orange-red (phosphorised paper) (8.11.88) .. .. .. 60 45
W51 19½p. olive-grey (phosphorised paper) (24.2.82) .. .. .. .. 2·00 2·00
W52 20p. brownish black (phosphorised paper) (28.11.89) .. .. .. .. 60 50
W53 20½p. ultram (phosphorised paper) (27.4.83) 3·75 3·75
W54 22p. blue (phosphorised paper) (8.4.81) .. 1·00 1·10
W55 22p. yellow-green (phosphorised paper) (23.10.84) .. .. .. .. 80 50
W56 22p. bright orange-red (phosphorised paper) (4.12.90) .. .. .. 35 40
W57 23p. brt grn (phosphorised paper) (8.11.88) 80 70
W58 24p. Indian red (phosphorised paper) (28.11.89) .. .. .. .. 70 70
W59 24p. chestnut (phosphorised paper) (3.12.91) .. .. .. .. 40 45
a. Booklet pane. No. W59×6 with margins all round (25.2.92) .. .. 2·50
W60 24p. chestnut (2 bands) (25.2.92) .. .. 1·10 1·10
W61 26p. rosine (phosphorised paper) (24.2.82) 90 80
a. Perf 15×14 (27.1.87) .. .. 3·00 2·50
W62 26p. drab (phosphorised paper) (4.12.90) 40 45
W63 28p. deep violet-blue (phosphorised paper) (27.4.83) .. .. .. .. 1·00 80
a. Perf 15×14 (27.1.87) .. .. 80 75
W64 28p. deep bluish grey (phosphorised paper) (3.12.91) .. .. .. .. 45 50
W65 31p. bright purple (phosphorised paper) (23.10.84) .. .. .. .. 1·00 70
W66 32p. greenish blue (phosphorised paper) (8.11.88) .. .. .. .. 1·10 75
W67 34p. deep bluish grey (phosphorised paper) (28.11.89) .. .. .. .. 1·00 85
W68 37p. rosine (phosphorised paper) (4.12.90) 60 65
W69 39p. bright mauve (phosphorised paper) (3.12.91) .. .. .. .. 60 65

*Exists only with gum arabic.

From 1972 printings were on fluorescent white paper. Nos. W13/14 exist with PVA and gum arabic and the remainder with PVA only. From 1973 printings had dextrin added (see notes after No. X1026 of Great Britain).

## POSTAGE DUE STAMPS

**PERFORATIONS.** All postage due stamps are perf 14 × 15.

D 1

D 2

(Typo by Somerset House (early trial printings of ½d., 1d., 2d. and 5d.; all printings of 1s.) and by Harrison (later printings of all values except 1s.). Not easily distinguishable except by the control)

**1914** (20 Apr)–**23.** *W* **100** (*Simple Cypher*) *sideways.*

| | | | | |
|---|---|---|---|---|
| D1 | D 1 | ½d. emerald | 50 | 50 |
| D2 | | 1d. carmine | 50 | 50 |
| | | *a. Pale carmine* | 75 | 75 |
| D3 | | 1½d. chestnut (1923) | 40·00 | 15·00 |
| D4 | | 2d. agate | 50 | 40 |
| D5 | | 3d. violet (1918) | 2·00 | 1·00 |
| | | *a. Bluish violet* | 3·50 | 3·50 |
| D6 | | 4d. dull grey-green (12.20) | 25·00 | 3·00 |
| D7 | | 5d. brownish cinnamon | 5·00 | 2·00 |
| D8 | | 1s. bright blue (1915) | 25·00 | 2·50 |
| | | *a. Deep bright blue* | 25·00 | 2·50 |
| D1/8 | | *Set of* 8 | 60·00 | 20·00 |

The 1d. is known bisected and used to make up a 1½d. rate on understamped letters from Ceylon (1921) and the 2d. bisected and used as 1d. at West Kensington and at Streatham both in the same year.

**1924.** *As* 1914–23, *but on thick chalk-surfaced paper.*

| | | | | |
|---|---|---|---|---|
| D9 | D 1 | 1d. carmine | 2·25 | 3·00 |

(Typo Waterlow and (from 1934) Harrison)

**1924–31.** *W* **111** (*Block Cypher*) *sideways.*

| | | | | |
|---|---|---|---|---|
| D10 | D 1 | ½d. emerald (6.25) | 50 | 30 |
| D11 | | 1d. carmine (4.25) | 50 | 30 |
| D12 | | 1½d. chestnut (10.24) | 35·00 | 15·00 |
| D13 | | 2d. agate (7.24) | 1·00 | 40 |
| D14 | | 3d. dull violet (10.24) | 1·50 | 40 |
| | | a. Printed on gummed side | 60·00 | † |
| | | b. Experimental paper W **111***a* | 35·00 | 30·00 |
| D15 | | 4d. dull grey-green (10.24) | 8·00 | 2·00 |
| D16 | | 5d. brownish cinnamon (1.31) | 20·00 | 20·00 |
| D17 | | 1s. deep blue (9.24) | 5·00 | 75 |
| D18 | D 2 | 2s. 6d. purple/*yellow* (10.24) | 20·00 | 1·75 |
| D10/18 | | *Set of* 9 | 80·00 | 40·00 |

**1936–37.** *W* **125** (E 8 R) *sideways.*

| | | | | |
|---|---|---|---|---|
| D19 | D 1 | ½d. emerald (6.37) | 8·00 | 6·00 |
| D20 | | 1d. carmine (5.37) | 1·50 | 1·60 |
| D21 | | 2d. agate (5.37) | 8·00 | 6·00 |
| D22 | | 3d. dull violet (3.37) | 1·50 | 1·60 |
| D23 | | 4d. dull grey-green (12.36) | 18·00 | 17·00 |
| D24 | | 5d. brownish cinnamon (11.36) | 38·00 | 22·00 |
| | | *a. Yellow-brown* (1937) | 12·00 | 17·00 |
| D25 | | 1s. deep blue (12.36) | 10·00 | 4·75 |
| D26 | D 2 | 2s. 6d. purple/*yellow* (5.37) | £190 | 8·50 |
| D19/26 | | *Set of* 8 (*cheapest*) | £225 | 60·00 |

The 1d. is known bisected (Solihull, 3 July 1937).

**1937–38.** *W* **127** (G VI R) *sideways.*

| | | | | |
|---|---|---|---|---|
| D27 | D 1 | ½d. emerald (1938) | 8·00 | 3·25 |
| D28 | | 1d. carmine (1938) | 2·50 | 40 |
| D29 | | 2d. agate (1938) | 2·50 | 40 |
| D30 | | 3d. violet (1938) | 10·00 | 40 |
| D31 | | 4d. dull grey-green (1937) | 60·00 | 7·50 |
| D32 | | 5d. yellow-brown (1938) | 10·00 | 1·00 |
| D33 | | 1s. deep blue (1937) | 55·00 | 1·00 |
| D34 | D 2 | 2s. 6d. purple/*yellow* (1938) | 55·00 | 3·00 |
| D27/34 | | *Set of* 8 | £180 | 15·00 |

The 2d. is known bisected in June 1951 (Harpenden and St. Albans) and on 30 October 1954 (Harpenden).

**DATES OF ISSUE.** The dates for Nos. D35/68 are those on which stamps were first issued by the Supplies Department to postmasters.

**1951–52.** *Colours changed and new value* (1½*d.*). *W* **127** (G VI R) *sideways.*

| | | | | |
|---|---|---|---|---|
| D35 | D 1 | ½d. orange (18.9.51) | 1·75 | 2·00 |
| D36 | | 1d. violet-blue (6.6.51) | 1·10 | 75 |
| D37 | | 1½d. green (11.2.52) | 1·75 | 1·75 |
| D38 | | 4d. blue (14.8.51) | 28·00 | 9·00 |
| D39 | | 1s. ochre (6.12.51) | 28·00 | 4·00 |
| D35/9 | | *Set of* 5 | 55·00 | 16·00 |

The 1d. is known bisected (Dorking, 1952, and Camberley, 6 April 1954).

**1954–55.** *W* **153** (*Mult Tudor Crown and* E 2 R) *sideways.*

| | | | | |
|---|---|---|---|---|
| D40 | D 1 | ½d. orange (8.6.55) | 4·00 | 2·50 |
| D41 | | 2d. agate (28.7.55) | 2·00 | 2·00 |
| D42 | | 3d. violet (4.5.55) | 42·00 | 25·00 |
| D43 | | 4d. blue (14.7.55) | 15·00 | 16·00 |
| | | a. Imperf (pair) | £225 | |
| D44 | | 5d. yellow-brown (19.5.55) | 20·00 | 6·50 |
| D45 | D 2 | 2s. 6d. purple/*yellow* (11.54) | £120 | 3·00 |
| D40/5 | | *Set of* 6 | £180 | 50·00 |

**1955–57.** *W* **165** (*Mult St. Edward's Crown and* E 2 R) *sideways.*

| | | | | |
|---|---|---|---|---|
| D46 | D 1 | ½d. orange (16.7.56) | 1·50 | 2·25 |
| D47 | | 1d. violet-blue (7.6.56) | 4·00 | 1·25 |
| D48 | | 1½d. green (13.2.56) | 3·75 | 3·75 |
| D49 | | 2d. agate (22.5.56) | 35·00 | 3·00 |
| D50 | | 3d. violet (5.3.56) | 4·50 | 1·25 |
| D51 | | 4d. blue (24.4.56) | 18·00 | 3·00 |
| D52 | | 5d. brown-ochre (23.3.56) | 27·00 | 2·00 |
| D53 | | 1s. ochre (22.11.55) | 65·00 | 1·25 |
| D54 | D 2 | 2s. 6d. purple/*yellow* (28.6.57) | £160 | 7·50 |
| D55 | | 5s. scarlet/*yellow* (25.11.55) | 90·00 | 19·00 |
| D46/55 | | *Set of* 10 | £375 | 40·00 |

The 2d. is known bisected (June 1956), and also the 4d. (Poplar, London, April 1959).

**1959–63.** *W* **179** (*Mult St Edward's Crown*) *sideways.*

| | | | | |
|---|---|---|---|---|
| D56 | D 1 | ½d. orange (18.10.61) | 10 | 45 |
| D57 | | 1d. violet-blue (9.5.60) | 10 | 15 |
| D58 | | 1½d. green (5.10.60) | 90 | 1·50 |
| D59 | | 2d. agate (14.9.59) | 1·25 | 30 |
| D60 | | 3d. violet (24.3.59) | 40 | 15 |
| D61 | | 4d. blue (17.12.59) | 40 | 20 |
| D62 | | 5d. yellow-brown (6.11.61) | 45 | 45 |
| D63 | | 6d. purple (29.3.62) | 60 | 30 |
| D64 | | 1s. ochre (11.4.60) | 1·40 | 25 |
| D65 | D 2 | 2s. 6d. purple/*yellow* (11.5.61) | 4·00 | 45 |
| D66 | | 5s. scarlet/*yellow* (8.5.61) | 7·50 | 70 |
| D67 | | 10s. blue/*yellow* (2.9.63) | 9·00 | 3·75 |
| D68 | | £1 black/*yellow* (2.9.63) | 45·00 | 7·00 |
| D56/68 | | *Set of* 13 | 60·00 | 14·00 |

*Whiter paper.* The note after No. 586 also applies to Postage Due stamps.

The 1d. is known bisected (Newbury, Dec. 1962).

**1968–69.** *Typo. No wmk. Chalk-surfaced paper.*

| | | | | |
|---|---|---|---|---|
| D69 | D 1 | 2d. agate (11.4.68) | 40 | 40 |
| D70 | | 3d. violet (9.9.68) | 25 | 40 |
| D71 | | 4d. blue (6.5.68) | 25 | 40 |
| D72 | | 5d. orange-brown (3.1.69) | 4·50 | 5·25 |
| D73 | | 6d. purple (9.9.68) | 80 | 60 |
| D74 | | 1s. ochre (19.11.68) | 80 | 1·00 |
| D69/74 | | *Set of* 6 | 6·50 | 7·00 |

The 2d. and 4d. exist with gum arabic and PVA gum; remainder with PVA gum only.

**1968–69.** *Photo. No wmk. Chalk-surfaced paper. PVA gum. P* 14 × 15.

| | | | | |
|---|---|---|---|---|
| D75 | D 1 | 4d. blue (12.6.69) | 5·00 | 5·00 |
| D76 | | 8d. red (3.10.68) | 1·25 | 75 |

Nos. D75/6 are smaller, 21½ × 17½ mm.

D 3

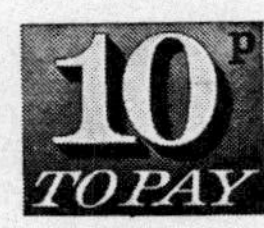

D 4

(Des J. Matthews. Photo Harrison)

**1970** (17 June)–**75.** *Decimal Currency. Chalk-surfaced paper. P* 14 × 15.

| | | | | |
|---|---|---|---|---|
| D77 | D 3 | ½p. turquoise-blue (15.2.71) | 10 | 20 |
| D78 | | 1p. deep reddish purple (15.2.71) | 10 | 15 |
| D79 | | 2p. myrtle-green (15.2.71) | 10 | 15 |
| D80 | | 3p. ultramarine (15.2.71) | 15 | 15 |
| D81 | | 4p. yellow-brown (15.2.71) | 15 | 15 |
| D82 | | 5p. violet (15.2.71) | 20 | 20 |
| D83 | | 7p. red-brown (21.8.74) | 35 | 45 |
| D84 | D 4 | 10p. carmine | 30 | 20 |
| D85 | | 11p. slate-green (18.6.75) | 50 | 60 |
| D86 | | 20p. olive-brown | 60 | 50 |
| D87 | | 50p. ultramarine | 1·50 | 40 |
| D88 | | £1 black | 2·75 | 60 |
| D89 | | £5 orange-yellow and black (2.4.73) | 20·00 | 2·00 |
| D77/89 | | *Set of* 13 | 25·00 | 5·00 |

Later printings were on fluorescent white paper, some with dextrin added to the PVA gum (see notes after X1023 of Great Britain).

D 5

D 6

(Des Sedley Place Design Ltd. Photo Harrison)

**1982** (9 June). *Chalk-surfaced paper. P* 14 × 15.

| | | | | |
|---|---|---|---|---|
| D 90 | D 5 | 1p. lake | 10 | 10 |
| D 91 | | 2p. bright blue | 10 | 10 |
| D 92 | | 3p. deep mauve | 10 | 15 |
| D 93 | | 4p. deep blue | 10 | 20 |
| D 94 | | 5p. sepia | 10 | 20 |
| D 95 | D 6 | 10p. light brown | 15 | 25 |
| D 96 | | 20p. olive-green | 30 | 30 |
| D 97 | | 25p. deep greenish blue | 40 | 70 |
| D 98 | | 50p. grey-black | 75 | 1·00 |
| D 99 | | £1 red | 1·50 | 80 |
| D100 | | £2 turquoise-blue | 3·00 | 2·00 |
| D101 | | £5 dull orange | 7·50 | 1·50 |
| D90/101 | | *Set of* 12 | 12·50 | 6·50 |

## OFFICIAL STAMPS

In 1840 the 1d. black (Type **1**), with "V R" in the upper corners, was prepared for official use, but never issued for postal purposes. Obliterated specimens are those which were used for experimental trials of obliterating inks, or those that passed through the post by oversight.

V 1

**1840.** *Prepared for use but not issued; "V" "R" in upper corners. Imperf.*

| | | | Un | Used | Used on cover |
|---|---|---|---|---|---|
| V1 | V 1 | 1d. black | £6000 | £5000 | £15000 |

The following Official stamps would be more correctly termed Departmental stamps as they were exclusively for the use of certain government departments. Until 1882 official mail used ordinary postage stamps purchased at post offices, the cash being refunded once a quarter.

Later the government departments obtained Official stamps by requisition.

Official stamps were on sale to the public for a short time at Somerset House but they were not sold from post offices. The system of only supplying the Government departments was open to abuse so that all Official stamps were withdrawn on 14 May 1904.

**OVERPRINTS, PERFORATIONS, WATERMARKS.** All Official stamps were overprinted by Thomas De La Rue & Co. and are perf 14. They are on Crown watermarked paper unless otherwise stated.

### INLAND REVENUE

These stamps were used by revenue officials in the provinces, mail to and from Head Office passing without a stamp. The London Office used these stamps only for foreign mail.

**I.R.**

**OFFICIAL**

(O 1)

**I. R.**

**OFFICIAL**

(O 2)

*Optd with Types* O **1** (½*d. to* 1*s.*) *or* O **2** (*others*)

**1882–1901.** *Stamps of Queen Victoria.* (*a*) *Issues of* 1880–81.

| | | *Un* | *Used* | ★ *Used on cover* |
|---|---|---|---|---|
| O 1 | ½d. green (1.11.82) | 12·00 | 3·00 | 40·00 |
| O 3 | 1d. lilac (Die II) (1.10.82) | 1·50 | 65 | 10·00 |
| | a. Optd in blue-black | 60·00 | 35·00 | |
| | b. "OFFICIAL" omitted | — | £2250 | |
| O 4 | 6d. grey (Plate 18) (3.11.82) | 75·00 | 20·00 | |

No. O3 with the lines ot the overprint transposed is an essay.

(*b*) *Issues of* 1884–88

| | | | | |
|---|---|---|---|---|
| O 5 | ½d. slate-blue (8.5.85) | 25·00 | 15·00 | 75·00 |
| O 6 | 2½d. lilac (12.3.85) | £110 | 35·00 | £500 |
| O 7 | 1s. green (12.3.85) | £2500 | £450 | |
| O 8 | 5s. rose (*blued paper*) (12.3.85) | £2750 | £475 | |
| O 9 | 5s. rose (3.90) | £1300 | £400 | |
| | a. Raised stop after "R" | £1600 | £325 | |
| | b. Optd in blue-black | £2000 | £450 | |
| O 9*c* | 10s. cobalt (*blued paper*) (12.3.85) | £5000 | £700 | |
| O 9*d* | 10s. ultram (*blued paper*) (12.3.85) | £5000 | £1400 | |
| O10 | 10s. ultramarine (3.90) | £2250 | £475 | |
| | a. Raised stop after "R" | £3000 | £500 | |
| | b. Optd in blue-black | £3500 | £700 | |
| O11 | £1 brown-lilac (wmk Crowns) (12.3.85) | £18000 | | |
| | a. Frame broken | £22000 | | |
| O12 | £1 brown-lilac (wmk Orbs) (3.90) | £25000 | | |
| | a. Frame broken | £27000 | | |

(*c*) *Issues of* 1887–92

| | | | | |
|---|---|---|---|---|
| O13 | ½d. vermilion (5.88) | 1·50 | 50 | 20·00 |
| | a. Without "I.R." | £1500 | | |
| | b. Imperf | £850 | | |
| | c. Opt double (imperf) | £1000 | | |
| O14 | 2½d. purple/*blue* (2.92) | 50·00 | 4·00 | £150 |
| O15 | 1s. green (9.89) | £200 | 20·00 | £1000 |
| O16 | £1 green (6.92) | £3750 | £450 | |
| | a. No stop after "R" | — | £800 | |
| | b. Frame broken | £5500 | £900 | |

Nos. O3, O13, O15 and O16 may be found with two varieties of overprint, namely, 1887 printings, *thin* letters, and 1894 printings, *thicker* letters.

(*d*) *Issues of* 1887 *and* 1900

| | | | | |
|---|---|---|---|---|
| O17 | ½d. blue-green (4.01) | 4·00 | 3·00 | 85·00 |
| O18 | 6d. purple/*rose-red* (1.7.01) | £100 | 22·00 | |
| O19 | 1s. green and carmine (12.01) | £600 | £100 | |
| ★O1/19 | **For well-centred, lightly used** | | +35% | |

**1902–04.** *Stamps of King Edward VII. Ordinary paper.*

| | | | | |
|---|---|---|---|---|
| O20 | ½d. blue-green (4.2.02) | 17·00 | 1·50 | 80·00 |
| O21 | 1d. scarlet (4.2.02) | 10·00 | 70 | 40·00 |
| O22 | 2½d. ultramarine (19.2.02) | £400 | 60·00 | |
| O23 | 6d. dull purple (14.3.04) | £85000 | £65000 | |
| O24 | 1s. green and carmine (29.4.02) | £500 | 65·00 | |
| O25 | 5s. carmine (29.4.02) | £4000 | £1300 | |
| | a. Raised stop after "R" | £4500 | £1500 | |
| O26 | 10s. ultramarine (29.4.02) | £15000 | £9500 | |
| | a. Raised stop after "R" | £17000 | £11000 | |
| O27 | £1 dull blue-green (29.4.02) | £12000 | £6000 | |

### OFFICE OF WORKS

These were issued to Head and Branch (local) offices in London and to Branch (local) offices at Birmingham, Bristol, Edinburgh, Glasgow, Leeds, Liverpool, Manchester and Southampton. The overprints on stamps of value 2d. and upwards were created later in 1902, the 2d. for registration fees and the rest for overseas mail.

**O. W.**

**OFFICIAL**

(O 3)

*Optd with Type* O **3**

**1896** (24 Mar)–**02.** *Stamps of Queen Victoria.*

| | | | | |
|---|---|---|---|---|
| O31 | ½d. vermilion | 90·00 | 40·00 | £180 |
| O32 | ½d. blue-green (2.02) | £150 | 75·00 | |
| O33 | 1d. lilac (Die II) | £150 | 40·00 | £200 |
| O34 | 5d. dull purple and blue (II) (29.4.02) | £750 | £150 | |
| O35 | 10d. dull purple and carmine (28.5.02) | £1300 | £225 | |

**1902** (11 Feb)–**03**. *Stamps of King Edward VII. Ordinary paper.*

| No. | Description | Un | Used |
|---|---|---|---|
| O36 | ½d. blue-green (8.02) | £350 | 80·00 |
| O37 | 1d. scarlet | £350 | 80·00 |
| O38 | 2d. green and carmine (29.4.02) | £600 | 75·00 |
| O39 | 2½d. ultramarine, (29.4.02) | £700 | £200 |
| O40 | 10d. purple and carmine (18.5.03) | £5000 | £1500 |
| ★O31/40 | **For well-centred, lightly used** | | +25% |

### ARMY

Letters to and from the War Office in London passed without postage. The overprinted stamps were distributed to District and Station Paymasters nationwide, including Cox and Co., the Army Agents, who were paymasters to the Household Division.

ARMY OFFICIAL (O 4)  ARMY OFFICIAL (O 5)  ARMY OFFICIAL (O 6)

**1896** (1 Sept)–**01**. *Stamps of Queen Victoria optd with Type* O **4** (*½d., 1d.*) *or* O **5** (*2½d., 6d.*).

| No. | Description | Un | Used | Used on cover |
|---|---|---|---|---|
| O41 | ½d. vermilion | 1·50 | 75 | 20·00 |
| | a. "OFFICIAI" (R. 13/7) | 35·00 | 16·00 | |
| | b. Lines of opt transposed | £1000 | | |
| O42 | ½d. blue-green (6.00) | 1·75 | 4·00 | |
| O43 | 1d. lilac (Die II) | 1·50 | 75 | 30·00 |
| | a. "OFFICIAI" (R. 13/7) | 35·00 | 16·00 | |
| O44 | 2½d. purple/*blue* | 4·00 | 3·00 | £250 |
| O45 | 6d. purple/*rose-red* (9.01) | 16·00 | 10·00 | £450 |

Nos. O41a and O43a occur on sheets overprinted by Forme 1.

**1902–03**. *Stamps of King Edward VII optd with Type* O **4** (*Nos.* O48/50) *or Type* O **6** (*No.* O52). *Ordinary paper.*

| No. | Description | Un | Used | Used on cover |
|---|---|---|---|---|
| O48 | 1d. blue-green (11.2.02) | 2·00 | 65 | 50·00 |
| O49 | 1d. scarlet (11.2.02) | 1·50 | 55 | 50·00 |
| | a. "ARMY" omitted | | | |
| O50 | 6d. dull purple (23.8.02) | 60·00 | 32·00 | |
| O52 | 6d. dull purple (12.03) | £850 | £275 | |

### GOVERNMENT PARCELS

These stamps were issued to all departments, including the Head Office, for use on parcels weighing over 3 lb. Below this weight government parcels were sent by letter post to avoid the 55% of the postage paid from accruing to the railway companies, as laid down by parcel-post regulations. Most government parcels stamps suffered heavy postmarks in use.

GOVT PARCELS (O 7)

*Optd as Type* O **7**

**1883** (1 July)–**86**. *Stamps of Queen Victoria.*

| No. | Description | Un | ★ Used |
|---|---|---|---|
| O61 | 1½d. lilac (30.4.86) | £100 | 25·00 |
| | a. No dot under "T" | £130 | 28·00 |
| | b. Dot to left of "T" | £100 | 28·00 |
| O62 | 6d. dull green (30.4.86) | £800 | £275 |
| O63 | 9d. dull green (1.8.83) | £650 | £180 |
| O64 | 1s. orange-brown (wmk Crown, Pl 13) | £425 | 70·00 |
| | a. No dot under "T" | £475 | 80·00 |
| | b. Dot to left of "T" | £475 | 80·00 |
| O64*c* | 1s. orange-brown (Pl 14) | £750 | £110 |
| | ca. No dot under "T" | £825 | £100 |
| | cb. Dot to left of "T" | | |

**1887–90**. *Stamps of Queen Victoria.*

| No. | Description | Un | Used |
|---|---|---|---|
| O65 | 1½d. dull purple and pale green (29.10.87) | 14·00 | 2·00 |
| | a. No dot under "T" | 18·00 | 6·00 |
| | b. Dot to right of "T" | 16·00 | 5·00 |
| | c. Dot to left of "T" | 16·00 | 5·00 |
| O66 | 6d. purple/*rose-red* (19.12.87) | 28·00 | 10·00 |
| | a. No dot under "T" | 30·00 | 12·00 |
| | b. Dot to right of "T" | 30·00 | 12·00 |
| | c. Dot to left of "T" | 30·00 | 11·00 |
| O67 | 9d. dull purple and blue (21.8.88) | 55·00 | 15·00 |
| O68 | 1s. dull green (25.3.90) | £120 | 70·00 |
| | a. No dot under "T" | £140 | 75·00 |
| | b. Dot to right of "T" | £140 | 75·00 |
| | c. Dot to left of "T" | £160 | 80·00 |
| | d. Optd in blue-black | | |

**1891–1900**. *Stamps of Queen Victoria.*

| No. | Description | Un | Used |
|---|---|---|---|
| O69 | 1d. lilac (Die II) (6.97) | 28·00 | 8·00 |
| | a. No dot under "T" | 30·00 | 20·00 |
| | b. Dot to left of "T" | 30·00 | 20·00 |
| | c. Opt inverted | £800 | £600 |
| | d. Ditto. Dot to left of "T" | £900 | £500 |
| O70 | 2d. grey-green and carmine (24.10.91) | 45·00 | 7·00 |
| | a. No dot under "T" | 50·00 | 8·00 |
| | b. Dot to left of "T" | 50·00 | 9·00 |
| O71 | 4½d. green and carmine (9.92) | £100 | 75·00 |
| | b. Dot to right of "T" | | |
| O72 | 1s. green and carmine (11.00) | £160 | 50·00 |
| | a. Opt inverted | — | £3750 |
| ★O61/72 | **For well-centred lightly used** | | +100% |

The "no dot under T" variety occurred on R.12/3 and 20/2. The "dot to left of T" comes four times in the sheet on R.2/7, 6/7, 7/9 and 12/9. The best example of the "dot to right of T" is on R.20/1. All three varieties were corrected around 1897.

**1902**. *Stamps of King Edward VII. Ordinary paper.*

| No. | Description | Un | Used |
|---|---|---|---|
| O74 | 1d. scarlet (30.10.02) | 17·00 | 6·00 |
| O75 | 2d. green and carmine (29.4.02) | 65·00 | 18·00 |
| O76 | 6d. dull purple (19.2.02) | £100 | 18·00 |
| | a. Opt double, one albino | £3500 | |
| O77 | 9d. purple and ultramarine (28.8.02) | £225 | 50·00 |
| O78 | 1s. green and carmine (17.12.02) | £350 | 85·00 |

### BOARD OF EDUCATION

BOARD OF EDUCATION (O 8)

*Optd with Type* O **8**

**1902** (19 Feb). *Stamps of Queen Victoria.*

| No. | Description | Un | Used |
|---|---|---|---|
| O81 | 5d. dull purple and blue (II) | £525 | £100 |
| O82 | 1s. green and carmine | £950 | £375 |

**1902–04**. *Stamps of King Edward VII. Ordinary paper.*

| No. | Description | Un | Used |
|---|---|---|---|
| O83 | ½d. blue-green (19.2.02) | 18·00 | 6·00 |
| O84 | 1d. scarlet (19.2.02) | 18·00 | 5·00 |
| O85 | 2½d. ultramarine (19.2.02) | £500 | 50·00 |
| O86 | 5d. purple and blue (6.2.04) | £2000 | £950 |
| O87 | 1s. green and carmine (23.2.02) | £35000 | £25000 |

### ROYAL HOUSEHOLD

R.H. OFFICIAL (O 9)

**1902**. *Stamps of King Edward VII optd with Type* O **9**. *Ordinary paper.*

| No. | Description | Un | Used | Used on cover |
|---|---|---|---|---|
| O91 | ½d. blue-green (29.4.02) | £150 | 95·00 | £400 |
| O92 | 1d. scarlet (19.2.02) | £130 | 85·00 | £300 |

### ADMIRALTY

ADMIRALTY OFFICIAL (O 10)  ADMIRALTY OFFICIAL (O 11)

**1903** (3 Mar). *Stamps of King Edward VII optd with Type* O **10**. *Ordinary paper.*

| No. | Description | Un | Used | Used on cover |
|---|---|---|---|---|
| O101 | ½d. blue-green | 10·00 | 4·00 | £225 |
| O102 | 1d. scarlet | 5·00 | 2·50 | 50·00 |
| O103 | 1½d. purple and green | 60·00 | 45·00 | |
| O104 | 2d. green and carmine | £100 | 50·00 | |
| O105 | 2½d. ultramarine | £120 | 40·00 | |
| O106 | 3d. purple/*yellow* | £100 | 38·00 | |

**1903–04**. *Stamps of King Edward VII optd with Type* O **11**. *Ordinary paper.*

| No. | Description | Un | Used | Used on cover |
|---|---|---|---|---|
| O107 | ½d. blue-green (9.03) | 7·00 | 4·00 | £250 |
| O108 | 1d. scarlet (11.03) | 6·50 | 3·50 | 50·00 |
| O109 | 1½d. purple and green (2.04) | £180 | 50·00 | |
| O110 | 2d. green and carmine (3.04) | £400 | £100 | |
| O111 | 2½d. ultramarine (3.04) | £450 | £225 | |
| O112 | 3d. purple/*yellow* (2.04) | £350 | 85·00 | |

Stamps of various issues perforated with a Crown and initials ("H.M.O.W.", "O.W.", "B.T." or "S.O.") or with initials only ("H.M.S.O." or "D.S.I.R.") have also been used for official purposes, but these are outside the scope of the catalogue.

## POSTAL FISCAL STAMPS

**PRICES.** Prices in the used column are for stamps with genuine postal cancellations dated from the time when they were authorised for use as postage stamps. Beware of stamps with fiscal cancellations removed and fraudulent postmarks applied.

**VALIDITY.** The 1d. Surface-printed stamps were authorised for postal use from 1 June 1881 and the 3d. and 6d. values, together with the Embossed issues, from 1 January 1883.

### SURFACE-PRINTED ISSUES

(Typo Thomas De La Rue & Co)

F 1
Rectangular Buckle

F 2 DRAFT ONE PENNY

F 3
Octagonal Buckle

F 4

F 5
Double-lined Anchor

F 6
Single-lined Anchor

**1853–57**. *P* 15½ × 15. (*a*) *Wmk* F **5** (*inverted*) (1853–55).

| No. | Type | Description | Un | Used | Used on cover |
|---|---|---|---|---|---|
| F1 | F **1** | 1d. light blue (10.10.53) | 12·00 | 16·00 | 75·00 |
| F2 | F **2** | 1d. ochre (10.53) | 50·00 | 35·00 | £150 |
| | | a. *Tête-bêche* (in block of four) | £8000 | | |
| F3 | F **3** | 1d. pale turquoise-blue (12.53) | 15·00 | 15·00 | £130 |
| F4 | | 1d. light blue/*blue* (1854) | 30·00 | 22·00 | £150 |
| F5 | F **4** | 1d. reddish lilac/*blue glazed paper* (25.3.55) | 45·00 | 11·00 | £100 |

Only one example is known of No. F2a outside the National Postal Museum and the Royal Collection.

(*b*) *Wmk* F **6** (1856–57)

| No. | Type | Description | Un | Used | Used on cover |
|---|---|---|---|---|---|
| F6 | F **4** | 1d. reddish lilac (*shades*) | 5·50 | 4·00 | 80·00 |
| F7 | | 1d. reddish lilac/*bluish* (*shades*) (1857) | 5·50 | 4·00 | 80·00 |

INLAND REVENUE

(F 7)

**1860** (3 Apr). *No.* F7 *optd with Type* F **7**, *in red.*

| No. | Type | Description | Un | Used | Used on cover |
|---|---|---|---|---|---|
| F8 | F **4** | 1d. dull reddish lilac/*blue* | £350 | £300 | £500 |

**BLUE PAPER.** In the following issues we no longer distinguish between bluish and white paper. There is a range of papers from white or greyish to bluish.

F 8

F 9

F 10

**1860–67**. *Bluish to white paper. P* 15½ × 15. (*a*) *Wmk* F **6** (1860).

| No. | Type | Description | Un | Used | Used on cover |
|---|---|---|---|---|---|
| F 9 | F **8** | 1d. reddish lilac (May) | 6·00 | 6·00 | 80·00 |
| F10 | F **9** | 3d. reddish lilac (June) | £225 | 80·00 | £150 |
| F11 | F **10** | 6d. reddish lilac (Oct) | 85·00 | 60·00 | £180 |

(*b*) *W* **40**. (*Anchor* 16 *mm high*) (1864)

| No. | Type | Description | Un | Used | Used on cover |
|---|---|---|---|---|---|
| F12 | F **8** | 1d. pale reddish lilac (Nov) | 4·75 | 4·75 | 65·00 |
| F13 | F **9** | 3d. pale reddish lilac | 75·00 | 55·00 | |
| F14 | F **10** | 6d. pale reddish lilac | 75·00 | 55·00 | £150 |

(*c*) *W* **40** (*Anchor* 18 *mm high*) (1867)

| No. | Type | Description | Un | Used | Used on cover |
|---|---|---|---|---|---|
| F15 | F **8** | 1d. reddish lilac | 13·00 | 6·00 | £130 |
| F16 | F **9** | 3d. reddish lilac | 60·00 | 60·00 | £160 |
| F17 | F **10** | 6d. reddish lilac | 70·00 | 35·00 | £150 |

For stamps perf 14, see Nos. F24/7.

F 11

F 12

**Four Dies of Type F 12**

Die 1. Corner ornaments small and either joined or broken; heavy shading under chin

Die 2. Ornaments small and always broken; clear line of shading under chin

Die 3. Ornaments larger and joined; line of shading under chin extended half way down neck

Die 4. Ornaments much larger; straight line of shading continued to bottom of neck

**1867–81.** *White to bluish paper. P* 14. (*a*) *W* **47** (*Small Anchor*).

| No. | Type | Description | | | |
|---|---|---|---|---|---|
| F18 | **F 11** | 1d. purple (1.9.67) | 8·00 | 5·00 | 60·00 |
| F19 | **F 12** | 1d. purple (Die 1) (6.68) | 1·75 | 1·50 | 40·00 |
| F20 | | 1d. purple (Die 2) (6.76) | 10·00 | 10·00 | £180 |
| F21 | | 1d. purple (Die 3) (3.77) | 4·00 | 4·00 | 75·00 |
| F22 | | 1d. purple (Die 4) (7.78) | 3·00 | 2·50 | 65·00 |
| | | (*b*) *W* **48** (*Orb*) | | | |
| F23 | **F 12** | 1d. purple (Die 4) (1.81) | 2·00 | 1·50 | 40·00 |

**1881.** *White to bluish paper. P* 14.

| No. | Type | Description | | | |
|---|---|---|---|---|---|
| | | (*a*) *W* **40** (*Anchor* 18 *mm high*) (Jan) | | | |
| F24 | **F 9** | 3d. reddish lilac | £325 | £200 | £325 |
| F25 | **F 10** | 6d. reddish lilac | £170 | 50·00 | £150 |
| | | (*b*) *W* **40** (*Anchor* 20 *mm high*) (May) | | | |
| F26 | **F 9** | 3d. reddish lilac | £250 | 55·00 | £150 |
| F27 | **F 10** | 6d. reddish lilac | £110 | 75·00 | £250 |

### ISSUES EMBOSSED IN COLOUR

(Made at Somerset House)

The embossed stamps were struck from dies not appropriated to any special purpose on paper which had the words "INLAND REVENUE" previously printed, and thus became available for payment of any duties for which no special stamps had been provided.

The die letters are included in the embossed designs and holes were drilled for the insertion of plugs showing figures indicating dates of striking.

F 13

F 14

INLAND
REVENUE

(F 15)

INLAND
REVENUE

(F 16)

**1860** (3 Apr)–**71.** *Types* F **13**/**14** *and similar types embossed on bluish paper. Underprint Type* F **15**. *No wmk. Imperf.*

| No. | Description | *Un* | *Used* |
|---|---|---|---|
| F28 | 2d. pink (Die A) (1.1.71) | £120 | £120 |
| F29 | 3d. pink (Die C) | 90·00 | 80·00 |
| | a. *Tête-bêche* (vert pair) | £1000 | |
| F30 | 3d. pink (Die D) | £325 | |
| F31 | 6d. pink (Die T) | £650 | |
| F32 | 6d. pink (Die U) | 95·00 | 80·00 |
| | a. *Tête-bêche* (vert pair) | £1200 | |
| F33 | 9d. pink (Die C) (1.1.71) | £225 | |
| F34 | 1s. pink (Die E) (28.6.61) | £325 | £130 |
| F35 | 1s. pink (Die F) (28.6.61) | £110 | 90·00 |
| | a. *Tête-bêche* (vert pair) | £500 | |
| F36 | 2s. pink (Die K) (6.8.61) | £250 | £150 |
| F37 | 2s. 6d. pink (Die N) (28.6.61) | £750 | |
| F38 | 2s. 6d. pink (Die O) (28.6.61) | 75·00 | 65·00 |

**1861–71.** *As last but perf* 12½.

| No. | Description | *Un* | *Used* |
|---|---|---|---|
| F39 | 2d. pink (Die A) (8.71) | £225 | £110 |
| F40 | 3d. pink (Die C) | | |
| F41 | 3d. pink (Die D) | | |
| F42 | 9d. pink (Die C) (8.71) | £250 | £120 |
| F43 | 1s. pink (Die E) (8.71) | £190 | £110 |
| F44 | 1s. pink (Die F) (8.71) | £170 | 85·00 |
| F45 | 2s. 6d. pink (Die O) (8.71) | £100 | 50·00 |

**1874** (Nov). *Types as before embossed on white paper. Underprint Type* F **16**, *in green. W* **47** (*Small Anchor*). *P* 12½.

| No. | Description | *Un* | *Used* |
|---|---|---|---|
| F46 | 2d. pink (Die A) | — | £150 |
| F47 | 9d. pink (Die C) | | |
| F48 | 1s. pink (Die F) | £170 | 90·00 |
| F49 | 2s. 6d. pink (Die O) | — | £130 |

**1875** (Nov)–**80.** *As last but colour changed and on white or bluish paper.*

| No. | Description | *Un* | *Used* |
|---|---|---|---|
| F50 | 2d. vermilion (Die A) (1880) | £250 | 85·00 |
| F51 | 9d. vermilion (Die C) (1876) | £250 | £120 |
| F52 | 1s. vermilion (Die E) | £150 | 55·00 |
| F53 | 1s. vermilion (Die F) | £150 | 55·00 |
| F54 | 2s. 6d. vermilion (Die O) (1878) | £190 | 85·00 |

**1882** (Oct). *As last but W* **48** (*Orbs*).

| No. | Description | *Un* | *Used* |
|---|---|---|---|
| F55 | 2d. vermilion (Die A) | | |
| F56 | 9d. vermilion (Die C) | | |
| F57 | 1s. vermilion (Die E) | | |
| F58 | 2s. 6d. vermilion (Die O) | £400 | £190 |

The sale of Inland Revenue stamps up to the 2s. value ceased from 30 December 1882 and stocks were called in and destroyed. The 2s. 6d. value remained on sale until 2 July 1883 when it was replaced by the 2s. 6d. "Postage & Revenue" stamp. Inland Revenue stamps still in the hands of the public continued to be accepted for revenue and postal purposes.

**CONTROLS.** Since the 1967 edition of the Part 1 Catalogue the priced lists of stamps with control letters have been transferred to Volumes 1 and 2 of the Stanley Gibbons *Great Britain Specialised Catalogue*.

**TELEGRAPH STAMPS.** A priced listing of the Post Office telegraph stamps appears in Volume 1 of the Stanley Gibbons *Great Britain Specialised Catalogue*. The last listing for the private telegraph companies in the Part 1 Catalogue was in the 1940 edition and for military telegraphs the 1941 edition.

## ISLAND ISSUES

Several islands off the coast of Great Britain have issued local stamps (usually termed British Private Local Issues or Local Carriage Labels) ostensibly to cover the cost of ferrying mail to the nearest mainland post office. No official post offices operate on most of these islands. As these stamps are not recognised as valid for national or international mail they are not listed here. The following islands are known to operate (or have operated) a local postal service and issued stamps from the dates shown:

*Bardsey*, Gwynedd (from 1979); *Bernera*, Hebrides (from 1977); *Brecqhou*, Channel Is. (1969); *Caldey*, Dyfed (from 1973); *Calf of Man*, Isle of Man (1962–73); *Calve*, Hebrides (from 1984); *Canna*, Hebrides (from 1958); *Carn Iar*, Hebrides (1961–62); *Davaar*, Argyllshire (from 1964); *Drake's Island*, Devon (1973–82); *Easdale*, Argyllshire (from 1988); *Eynhallow*, Orkney (from 1973); *Gairsay*, Orkney (from 1980); *Gruney*, Shetland (from 1981); *Gugh*, Isles of Scilly (1972–80); *Herm*, Channel Is. (1949–69); *Heston*, Wigtownshire (1960s); *Hilbre*, Cheshire (1960s); *Inchcolm*, Fife (1961, unissued); *Jethou*, Channel Is. (1960–69); *Lihou*, Channel Is. (1966–69); *Lundy*, Devon (from 1929); *Pabay*, Skye (1962–70, 1972–81 and from 1982); *St. Kilda*, Hebrides (1968–71); *Sanda*, Argyllshire (from 1962); *Shuna*, Argyllshire (from 1949); *Soay*, Skye (1965–67); *Staffa*, Hebrides (from 1969); *Steep Holm*, Avon (1980–87); *Stroma*, Caithness (1962–70) and *Summer Isles*, Hebrides (from 1970). Those issued for Soay have been declared bogus by a committee of the Philatelic Traders Society.

Issues of the *Commodore Shipping Co* (1950–69), the *Alderney Shipping Co* (1969–75) and the *Isle of Sark Shipping Co* (from 1969) were/are for use on parcels carried by ship between Guernsey and Alderney and Sark. They are not valid for the carriage of letters and postcards.

Issues inscribed Alderney (1975–83) were issued in conjunction with an internal parcel delivery service. They were not valid for use on letters or postcards.

## CHANNEL ISLANDS

### GENERAL ISSUE

C 1 Gathering Vraic

C 2 Islanders gathering Vraic

(Des J. R. R. Stobie (1d.) or from drawing by E. Blampied (2½d.). Photo Harrison)

**1948** (10 May). *Third Anniv of Liberation. W* **127** *of Great Britain. P* 15 × 14.

| No. | Type | Description | | |
|---|---|---|---|---|
| C1 | **C 1** | 1d. scarlet | 20 | 20 |
| C2 | **C 2** | 2½d. ultramarine | 30 | 30 |

## GUERNSEY

Further detailed information on the stamps of Guernsey will be found in the Stanley Gibbons *Channel Islands Specialised Catalogue*.

### WAR OCCUPATION ISSUES

Stamps issued under British authority during the German Occupation.

**BISECTS.** On 24 December 1940 authority was given, by Post Office notice, that prepayment of penny postage could be effected by using half a British 2d. stamp, diagonally bisected. Such stamps were first used on 27 December 1940.

The 2d. stamps generally available were those of the Postal Centenary issue, 1940 (S.G. 482) and the first colour of the King George VI issue (S.G. 465). These are listed under Nos. 482a and 465b. A number of the 2d. King George V, 1912–22, and of the King George V photogravure stamp (S.G. 442) which were in the hands of philatelists, were also bisected and used.

1

**1***a* Loops (*half actual size*)

(Des E. W. Vaudin. Typo Guernsey Press Co Ltd)

**1941–44.** *Rouletted.* (*a*) *White paper. No wmk.*

| No. | Type | Description | | |
|---|---|---|---|---|
| 1 | **1** | ½d. light green (7.4.41) | 3·00 | 2·75 |
| | | *a. Emerald-green* (6.41) | 3·00 | 2·75 |
| | | *b. Bluish green* (11.41) | 48·00 | 28·00 |
| | | *c. Bright green* (2.42) | 24·00 | 12·00 |
| | | *d. Dull green* (9.42) | 4·50 | 3·50 |
| | | *e. Olive-green* (2.43) | 25·00 | 22·00 |
| | | *f. Pale yellowish green* (7.43 and later) (*shades*) | 3·00 | 2·50 |
| | | g. Imperf (pair) | £150 | |
| | | h. Imperf between (horiz pair) | £600 | |
| | | i. Imperf between (vert pair) | £700 | |
| 2 | | 1d. scarlet (18.2.41) | 2·25 | 1·25 |
| | | *a. Pale vermilion* (7.43) (etc.) | 2·00 | 2·00 |
| | | *b. Carmine* (1943) | 4·00 | 3·50 |
| | | c. Imperf (pair) | £150 | 75·00 |
| | | d. Imperf between (horiz pair) | £600 | |
| | | da. Imperf vert (centre stamp of horiz strip of 3) | | |
| | | e. Imperf between (vert pair) | £700 | |
| | | f. Printed double (scarlet shade) | 75·00 | |
| 3 | | 2½d. ultramarine (12.4.44) | 6·00 | 6·00 |
| | | *a. Pale ultramarine* (7.44) | 6·00 | 4·50 |
| | | b. Imperf (pair) | £350 | |
| | | c. Imperf between (horiz pair) | £800 | |
| | | (*b*) *Bluish French bank-note paper. W* **1***a* (*sideways*) | | |
| 4 | **1** | ½d. bright green (11.3.42) | 16·00 | 20·00 |
| 5 | | 1d. scarlet (9.4.42) | 9·00 | 24·00 |

The dates given for the shades of Nos. 1/3 are the months in which they were printed as indicated on the printer's imprints. Others are issue dates.

### REGIONAL ISSUES

**DATES OF ISSUE.** Conflicting dates of issue have been announced for some of the regional issues, partly explained by the stamps being released on different dates by the Philatelic Bureau in Edinburgh or the Philatelic Counter in London and in the regions. We have adopted the practice of giving the earliest known dates, since once released the stamps could have been used anywhere in the U.K.

2

3

(Des E. A. Piprell. Portrait by Dorothy Wilding Ltd. Photo Harrison & Sons)

**1958** (18 Aug)–**67.** *W* **179** *of Great Britain. P* 15 × 14.

| No. | Type | Description | | |
|---|---|---|---|---|
| 6 | **2** | 2½d. rose-red (8.6.64) | 35 | 40 |
| 7 | **3** | 3d. deep lilac | 35 | 30 |
| | | p. One centre phosphor band (24.5.67) | 20 | 20 |
| 8 | | 4d. ultramarine (7.2.66) | 25 | 30 |
| | | p. Two phosphor bands (24.10.67) | 20 | 20 |
| 6/8p. | | *Set of* 3 | 50 | 75 |

**968–69.** *No wmk. Chalk-surfaced paper. PVA gum*. One centre phosphor band (Nos. 10/11) or two phosphor bands (others). P 15 × 14.*

9 **3** 4d. pale ultramarine (16.4.68) .. .. 10 25
0 4d. olive-sepia (4.9.68) .. .. 15 20
1 4d. bright vermilion (26.2.69) .. .. 15 30
2 5d. royal blue (4.9.68) .. .. 15 30
9/12 .. .. .. .. .. *Set of* 4 40 95

No. 9 was not issued in Guernsey until 22 April.

* PVA Gum. See note after No. 722 of Great Britain.

## INDEPENDENT POSTAL ADMINISTRATION

**4** Castle Cornet and Edward the Confessor

**5** View of Sark

Two Types of 1d. and 1s. 6d.:

I. Latitude inscr "40° 30′ N".
II. Corrected to "49° 30′ N".

(Des R. Granger Barrett. Photo Harrison (½d. to 2s. 6d.); Delrieu (others))

**1969** (1 Oct)–**70.** *Designs as T* **4/5.** *P* 14 (½*d. to* 2*s.* 6*d.*) *or* 12½ (*others*).

3 ½d. deep magenta and black .. .. 10 10
4 1d. bright blue and black (I) .. .. 10 10
4*b* 1d. bright blue and black (II) (12.12.69) .. 50 60
c. Booklet stamp with blank margins .. 55 55
5 1½d. yellow-brown and black .. .. 10 10
6 2d. gold, bright red, deep blue and black .. 10 10
7 3d. gold, pale greenish yellow, orge-red & blk 15 15
a. Error. Wmk w **12** .. .. .. £1100
18 4d. multicoloured .. .. .. 25 25
a. Booklet stamp with blank margins (12.12.69) .. .. .. .. 35 35
ab. Yellow omitted .. .. .. .. £225
ac. Emerald (stem) omitted .. .. £100
9 5d. gold, brt vermilion, bluish violet & black 25 15
a. Booklet stamp with blank margins (12.12.69) .. .. .. .. 35 35
b. Gold (inscr etc.) omitted (booklets) .. £450
20 6d. gold, pale greenish yellow, light bronze-green and black .. .. .. .. 30 35
21 9d. gold, bright red, crimson and black .. 70 60
22 1s. gold, bright vermilion, bistre and black 55 45
23 1s. 6d. turquoise-green and black (I) .. 40 50
23*b* 1s. 6d. turquoise-green and black (II) (4.2.70) 6·50 1·90
24 1s. 9d. multicoloured .. .. .. 2·50 3·00
a. Emerald (stem) omitted .. .. £300
25 2s. 6d. bright reddish violet and black .. 10·00 4·50
26 5s. multicoloured .. .. .. 4·00 6·00
27 10s. multicoloured .. .. .. 25·00 28·00
a. Perf 13 (4.3.70) .. .. .. 65·00 60·00
28 £1 multicoloured .. .. .. 4·00 4·00
a. Perf 13 (4.3.70) .. .. .. 2·00 2·00
3/28 .. .. .. .. *Set of* 16 50·00 40·00

Designs: *Horiz as T* **4**—1d. (*both*), 1s. 6d. (*both*), Map and William I; 1½d. Martello Tower and Henry II; 2d. Arms of Sark and King John; 3d. Arms of Alderney and Edward III; 4d. Guernsey Lily and Henry V; 5d. Arms of Guernsey and Elizabeth I; 6d. Arms of Alderney and Charles II; 9d. Arms of Sark and George III; 1s. Arms of Guernsey and Queen Victoria; 1s. 9d. Guernsey Lily and Elizabeth I; 2s. 6d. Martello Tower and King John. *Horiz as T* **5**—10s. View of Alderney; £1, View of Guernsey.

The booklet panes consist of single perforated stamps with wide margins all round intended to fit automatic machines designed for the Great Britain 2s. booklets. They are therefore found with three margins when detached from booklets or four margins when complete.

There was no postal need for the ½d. and 1½d. values as the ½d. coin had been withdrawn prior to their issue in anticipation of decimalisation. These values were only on sale at the Philatelic Bureau and the Crown Agents as well as in the U.S.A.

Nos. 14*b* and 23*b* are known only on thin paper and Nos. 13, 14, 16, 17, 20, 21, 22, 23, 24 and 25 also exist on thin paper.

**19** Isaac Brock as Colonel

**23** Landing Craft entering St. Peter's Harbour

(Litho Format)

**1969** (1 Dec). *Birth Bicentenary of Sir Isaac Brock. T* **19** *and similar multicoloured designs. P* 13½ × 14 (2*s.* 6*d.*) *or* 14 × 13½ (*others*).

29 4d. Type **19** .. .. .. .. .. 30 30
30 5d. Sir Isaac Brock as Major-General .. 30 30
31 1s. 9d. Isaac Brock as Ensign .. .. 2·75 2·50
32 2s. 6d. Arms and flags (*horiz*) .. .. 2·75 2·50
29/32 .. .. .. .. .. *Set of* 4 5·50 5·00

(Des and photo Courvoisier)

**1970** (9 May). *25th Anniv of Liberation. T* **23** *and similar designs. Granite paper. P* 11½.

33 4d. blue and pale blue .. .. .. 35 50
34 5d. brown-lake and pale grey .. .. 35 50
35 1s. 6d. bistre-brown and buff .. .. 4·75 3·00
33/5 .. .. .. .. *Set of* 3 5·00 4·00

Designs: *Horiz*—5d. British ships entering St. Peter's Port. *Vert*—1s. 6d. Brigadier Snow reading Proclamation.

**26** Guernsey "Toms" **32** St. Peter Church, Sark

(Des and photo Courvoisier)

**1970** (12 Aug). *Agriculture and Horticulture. T* **26** *and similar horiz designs. Multicoloured. Granite paper. P* 11½.

36 4d. Type **26** .. .. .. .. .. 1·00 30
37 5d. Guernsey Cow .. .. .. .. 1·10 30
38 9d. Guernsey Bull .. .. .. .. 14·00 3·25
39 1s. 6d. Freesias .. .. .. .. 16·00 3·75
36/9 .. .. .. .. *Set of* 4 28·00 7·00

(Des and photo Courvoisier)

**1970** (11 Nov). *Christmas. Guernsey Churches* (1*st series*). *T* **32** *and similar multicoloured designs. Granite paper. P* 11½.

40 4d. St. Anne's Church, Alderney (*horiz*) .. 50 20
41 5d. St. Peter's Church (*horiz*) .. .. 60 25
42 9d. Type **32** .. .. .. .. .. 3·00 2·00
43 1s. 6d. St. Tugual Chapel, Herm .. .. 3·75 2·00
40/3 .. .. .. .. *Set of* 4 7·00 4·00

See also Nos. 63/6.

**INVALIDATION.** The regional issues for Guernsey were invalidated for use in Guernsey and Jersey on 1 November 1969 but remained valid for use in the rest of the United Kingdom. Nos. 13/43 (except Nos. 28/a) and Nos. D1/7 were invalidated on 14 February 1972.

**34** Martello Tower and King John

(Photo Harrison (½p. to 10p.), Delrieu (others))

**1971** (6 Jan)–**73.** *Decimal Currency. Designs as Nos.* 13/27 *but values inscr in decimal currency as in T* **34.** *Chalk-surfaced paper. P* 14 (½*p. to* 10*p.*) *or* 13 (20*p.*, 50*p.*).

44 ½p. deep magenta and black (15.2.71) .. 10 15
a. Booklet stamp with margins (*glazed, ordinary paper*) .. .. .. .. 15 20
ab. Ditto. Chalk-surfaced paper (2.4.73) .. 15 20
45 1p. bright blue and black (II) (15.2.71) .. 10 10
46 1½p. yellow-brown and black (15.2.71) .. 15 15
47 2p. multicoloured (15.2.71) .. .. 15 15
a. Booklet stamp with margins (*glazed, ordinary paper*) .. .. .. .. 20 20
ab. Ditto. Chalk-surfaced paper (2.4.73) .. 20 20
ac. Emerald (stem) omitted .. .. £1100
b. Glazed, ordinary paper (15.2.71) .. 20 20
48 2½p. gold, brt verm, bluish vio & blk (15.2.71) 15 10
a. Bright vermilion omitted .. .. £450
b. Booklet stamp with margins (*glazed, ordinary paper*) .. .. .. .. 20 20
ba. Ditto. Chalk-surfaced paper (2.4.73) .. 20 20
49 3p. gold, pale greenish yellow, orange-red and black (15.2.71) .. .. .. 20 20
50 3½p. mult (*glazed, ordinary paper*) (15.2.71) .. 25 25
51 4p. multicoloured (15.2.71) .. .. 35 25
52 5p. turquoise-green and black (II) (15.2.71) 30 25
53 6p. gold, pale greenish yellow, light bronze-green and black (15.2.71) .. .. 30 35
54 7½p. gold, brt verm, bistre & black (15.2.71) 40 45
55 9p. gold, brt red, crimson & black (15.2.71) 1·00 1·25
56 10p. bright reddish violet and black .. .. 1·60 2·00
a. Ordinary paper. *Bright reddish violet and deep black* (1.9.72) .. .. .. 1·00 1·50
57 20p. multicoloured (*glazed, ordinary paper*) .. 1·00 1·10
*a. Shade** (25.1.73) .. .. .. 80 75
58 50p. multicoloured (*glazed, ordinary paper*) .. 2·00 3·25
44/58 .. .. .. .. *Set of* 15 7·00 8·00

*No. 57 has the sky in a pale turquoise-blue; on No. 57*a* it is pale turquoise-green.

**35** Hong Kong 2 c. of 1862

(Des and recess D.L.R.)

**1971** (2 June). *Thomas De La Rue Commemoration. T* **35** *and similar horiz designs. P* 14 × 13½.

59 2p. dull purple to brown-purple* .. .. 50 30
60 2½p. carmine-red .. .. .. .. 50 30
61 4p. deep bluish green .. .. .. 4·00 3·00
62 7½p. deep blue .. .. .. .. 4·00 3·00
59/62 .. .. .. .. *Set of* 4 8·00 8·00

Designs: (each incorporating portraits of Queen Elizabeth II and Thomas De La Rue as in T **35**)—2½p. Great Britain 4d. of 1855–7; 4p. Italy 5 c. of 1862; 7½p. Confederate States 5 c. of 1862.

* These colours represent the extreme range of shades of this value. The majority of the printing, however, is in an intermediate shade.

**36** Ebenezer Church, St. Peter Port

(Des and photo Courvoisier)

**1971** (27 Oct). *Christmas. Guernsey Churches* (2*nd series*). *T* **36** *and similar multicoloured designs. Granite paper. P* 11½.

63 2p. Type **36** .. .. .. .. .. 45 25
64 2½p. Church of St. Pierre du Bois .. .. 50 25
65 5p. St. Joseph's Church, St. Peter Port (*vert*) 3·25 2·00
66 7½p. Church of St. Philippe de Torteval (*vert*) 3·50 2·00
63/6 .. .. .. .. *Set of* 4 7·00 4·00

**37** *Earl of Chesterfield* (1794)

(Des and photo Courvoisier)

**1972** (10 Feb). *Mail Packet Boats* (1*st series*). *T* **37** *and similar horiz designs. Multicoloured. Granite paper. P* 11½.

67 2p. Type **37** .. .. .. .. .. 25 15
68 2½p. *Dasher* (1827) .. .. .. .. 25 20
69 7½p. *Ibex* (1891) .. .. .. .. 75 75
70 9p. *Alberta* (1900) .. .. .. .. 1·00 85
67/70 .. .. .. .. *Set of* 4 2·00 1·75

See also Nos. 80/3



**38** Guernsey Bull

(Photo Courvoisier)

**1972** (22 May). *World Conference of Guernsey Breeders, Guernsey. Granite paper. P* 11½.

71 **38** 5p. multicoloured .. .. .. 1·00 1·00

**39** Bermuda Buttercup **40** Angels adoring Christ

(Des and photo Courvoisier)

**1972** (24 May). *Wild Flowers. T* **39** *and similar multicoloured designs. Granite paper. P* 11½.

72 2p. Type **39** .. .. .. .. .. 15 20
73 2½p. Heath Spotted Orchid (*vert*) .. .. 15 20
74 7½p. Kaffir Fig .. .. .. .. 80 80
75 9p. Scarlet Pimpernel (*vert*) .. .. 1·10 1·10
72/5 .. .. .. .. *Set of* 4 2·00 2·00

(Des and photo Courvoisier)

**1972** (20 Nov). *Royal Silver Wedding and Christmas. T* **40** *and similar vert designs showing stained-glass windows from Guernsey Churches. Multicoloured. Granite paper. P* 11½.

76 2p. Type **40** .. .. .. .. .. 10 10
77 2½p. The Epiphany .. .. .. .. 15 15
78 7½p. The Virgin Mary .. .. .. .. 75 75
79 9p. Christ .. .. .. .. .. 80 80
76/9 .. .. .. .. *Set of* 4 1·60 1·60

See also Nos. 89/92.

(Des and photo Courvoisier)

**1973** (9 Mar). *Mail Packet Boats (2nd series). Multicoloured designs as T* **37**. *Granite paper. P* 11½.

| No. | Value | Description | Unused | Used |
|---|---|---|---|---|
| 80 | 2½p. | *St. Julien* (1925) | 10 | 10 |
| 81 | 3p. | *Isle of Guernsey* (1930) | 20 | 20 |
| 82 | 7½p. | *St. Patrick* (1947) | 65 | 60 |
| 83 | 9p. | *Sarnia* (1961) | 85 | 75 |
| 80/3 | | *Set of* 4 | 1·60 | 1·50 |

**41** Supermarine "Sea Eagle" **42** "The Good Shepherd"

(Des and photo Courvoisier)

**1973** (4 July). *50th Anniv of Air Service. T* **41** *and similar horiz designs. Multicoloured. Granite paper. P* 11½.

| No. | Value | Description | Unused | Used |
|---|---|---|---|---|
| 84 | 2½p. | Type **41** | 10 | 10 |
| 85 | 3p. | Westland "Wessex" | 15 | 15 |
| 86 | 5p. | De Havilland "Rapide" | 25 | 25 |
| 87 | 7½p. | Douglas "Dakota" | 55 | 50 |
| 88 | 9p. | Vickers "Viscount" | 60 | 55 |
| 84/8 | | *Set of* 5 | 1·50 | 1·40 |

(Des and photo Courvoisier)

**1973** (24 Oct). *Christmas. T* **42** *and similar vert designs showing stained-glass windows from Guernsey Churches. Multicoloured. Granite paper. P* 11½.

| No. | Value | Description | Unused | Used |
|---|---|---|---|---|
| 89 | 2½p. | Type **42** | 10 | 10 |
| 90 | 3p. | Christ at the well of Samaria | 10 | 10 |
| 91 | 7½p. | St. Dominic | 30 | 30 |
| 92 | 20p. | Mary and the Child Jesus | 60 | 60 |
| 89/92 | | *Set of* 4 | 1·00 | 1·00 |

**43** Princess Anne and Capt. Mark Phillips

(Des G. Anderson. Photo Courvoisier)

**1973** (14 Nov). *Royal Wedding. Granite paper. P* 11½.

| No. | Value | Description | Unused | Used |
|---|---|---|---|---|
| 93 **43** | 25p. | multicoloured | 85 | 80 |

**44** *John Lockett*, 1875

(Des and photo Courvoisier)

**1974** (15 Jan). *150th Anniv of Royal National Lifeboat Institution. T* **44** *and similar horiz designs. Multicoloured. Granite paper. P* 11½.

| No. | Value | Description | Unused | Used |
|---|---|---|---|---|
| 94 | 2½p. | Type **44** | 10 | 10 |
| 95 | 3p. | *Arthur Lionel*, 1912 | 10 | 10 |
| 96 | 8p. | *Euphrosyne Kendal*, 1954 | 45 | 45 |
| 97 | 10p. | *Arun*, 1972 | 45 | 45 |
| 94/7 | | *Set of* 4 | 1·00 | 1·00 |

**45** Private, East Regt, 1815 **46** Driver, Field Battery, Royal Guernsey Artillery, 1848

(Photo Courvoisier (½ to 10p.) or Delrieu (others))

**1974** (2 Apr)–**78**. *Designs as T* **45/6**. *Multicoloured.*

(*a*) *Vert designs as T* **45**. *Granite paper. P* 11½

| No. | Value | Description | Unused | Used |
|---|---|---|---|---|
| 98 | ½p. | Type **45** | 10 | 10 |
| | | a. Booklet strip of 8 (98 × 5 and 102 × 3)† | 50 | |
| | | b. Booklet pane of 16 (98 × 4, 102 × 6 and 103 × 6)† | 1·75 | |
| 99 | 1p. | Officer, 2nd North Regt, 1825 | 10 | 10 |
| | | a. Booklet strip of 8 (99 × 4, 103, 105 × 2 and 105*a*) (8.2.77)† | 85 | |
| | | b. Booklet strip of 4 (99, 101 × 2 and 105*a*) (7.2.78)† | 50 | |
| 100 | 1½p. | Gunner, Guernsey Artillery, 1787 | 10 | 10 |
| 101 | 2p. | Gunner, Guernsey Artillery, 1815 | 10 | 10 |
| 102 | 2½p. | Corporal, Royal Guernsey Artillery, 1868 | 10 | 10 |
| 103 | 3p. | Field Officer, Royal Guernsey Artillery, 1895 | 10 | 10 |
| 104 | 3½p. | Sergeant, 3rd Regt, 1867 | 10 | 10 |
| 105 | 4p. | Officer, East Regt, 1822 | 15 | 15 |
| 105*a* | 5p. | Field Officer, Royal Guernsey Artillery, 1895 (29.5.76) | 15 | 15 |
| 106 | 5½p. | Colour-Sergeant of Grenadiers, East Regt, 1833 | 20 | 25 |
| 107 | 6p. | Officer, North Regt, 1832 | 20 | 25 |
| 107*a* | 7p. | Officer, East Regt, 1822 (29.5.76) | 25 | 25 |
| 108 | 8p. | Field Officer, Rifle Company, 1868 | 25 | 30 |
| 109 | 9p. | Private, 4th West Regt, 1785 | 30 | 35 |
| 110 | 10p. | Field Officer, 4th West Regt, 1824 | 30 | 35 |

(*b*) *Size as T* **46**. *P* 13 × 13½ (20, 50*p*.) *or* 13½ × 13 (£1)

| No. | Value | Description | Unused | Used |
|---|---|---|---|---|
| 111 | 20p. | Type **46** (1.4.75) | 55 | 55 |
| 112 | 50p. | Officer, Field Battery, Royal Guernsey Artillery, 1868 (1.4.75) | 1·50 | 1·40 |
| 113 | £1 | Cavalry Trooper, Light Dragoons, 1814 (*horiz*) (1.4.75) | 3·00 | 2·75 |
| 98/113 | | *Set of* 18 | 6·75 | 6·75 |

The ½p. and 2½p. with the red colour omitted are chemically produced fakes.

† Nos. 98a/b come from special booklet sheets of 88 (8 × 11), and Nos. 99a/b from separate booklet sheets of 80 (2 panes 8 × 5). These sheets were put on sale in addition to the normal sheets. The strips and panes have the left-hand selvedge stuck into booklet covers, except for No. 99b which was loose, and then folded and supplied in plastic wallets.

**47** Badge of Guernsey and U.P.U. Emblem

(Photo Courvoisier)

**1974** (7 June). *U.P.U. Centenary. T* **47** *and similar horiz designs. Multicoloured. Granite paper. P* 11½.

| No. | Value | Description | Unused | Used |
|---|---|---|---|---|
| 114 | 2½p. | Type **47** | 10 | 10 |
| 115 | 3p. | Map of Guernsey | 10 | 10 |
| 116 | 8p. | U.P.U. Building, Berne, and Guernsey flag | 45 | 45 |
| 117 | 10p. | "Salle des Etats" | 45 | 45 |
| 114/17 | | *Set of* 4 | 1·00 | 1·00 |

**48** "Cradle Rock" **49** Guernsey Spleenwort

(Des and photo Delrieu)

**1974** (21 Sept). *Renoir Paintings. T* **48** *and similar multicoloured designs. P* 13.

| No. | Value | Description | Unused | Used |
|---|---|---|---|---|
| 118 | 3p. | Type **48** | 10 | 10 |
| 119 | 5½p. | "Moulin Huet Bay" | 15 | 15 |
| 120 | 8p. | "Au Bord de la Mer" (*vert*) | 40 | 40 |
| 121 | 10p. | Self-portrait (*vert*) | 45 | 45 |
| 118/21 | | *Set of* 4 | 1·00 | 1·00 |

(Des and photo Courvoisier)

**1975** (7 Jan). *Guernsey Ferns. T* **49** *and similar vert designs. Multicoloured. Granite paper. P* 11½.

| No. | Value | Description | Unused | Used |
|---|---|---|---|---|
| 122 | 3½p. | Type **49** | 10 | 10 |
| 123 | 4p. | Sand Quillwort | 10 | 10 |
| 124 | 8p. | Guernsey Quillwort | 40 | 40 |
| 125 | 10p. | Least Adder's Tongue | 50 | 50 |
| 122/5 | | *Set of* 4 | 1·00 | 1·00 |

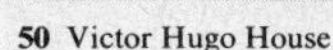

**50** Victor Hugo House **51** Globe and Seal of Bailiwick

(Des and photo Courvoisier)

**1975** (6 June). *Victor Hugo's Exile in Guernsey. T* **50** *and similar multicoloured designs. Granite paper. P* 11½.

| No. | Value | Description | Unused | Used |
|---|---|---|---|---|
| 126 | 3½p. | Type **50** | 10 | 10 |
| 127 | 4p. | Candie Gardens (*vert*) | 10 | 10 |
| 128 | 8p. | United Europe Oak, Hauteville (*vert*) | 40 | 40 |
| 129 | 10p. | Tapestry Room, Hauteville | 50 | 50 |
| 126/9 | | *Set of* 4 | 1·00 | 1·00 |
| **MS**130 | | 114 × 143 mm. Nos. 126/9 | 1·00 | 1·00 |

(Des and photo Delrieu)

**1975** (7 Oct). *Christmas. Multicoloured designs each showing Globe as T* **51**. *P* 13.

| No. | Value | Description | Unused | Used |
|---|---|---|---|---|
| 131 | 4p. | Type **51** | 10 | 10 |
| 132 | 6p. | Guernsey flag | 15 | 15 |
| 133 | 10p. | Guernsey flag and Alderney shield (*horiz*) | 35 | 35 |
| 134 | 12p. | Guernsey flag and Sark shield (*horiz*) | 50 | 50 |
| 131/4 | | *Set of* 4 | 1·00 | 1·00 |

**52** Les Hanois

(Des and photo Courvoisier)

**1976** (10 Feb). *Lighthouses. T* **52** *and similar horiz designs. Multicoloured. Granite paper. P* 11½.

| No. | Value | Description | Unused | Used |
|---|---|---|---|---|
| 135 | 4p. | Type **52** | 10 | 10 |
| 136 | 6p. | Les Casquets | 15 | 15 |
| 137 | 11p. | Quesnard | 40 | 35 |
| 138 | 13p. | Point Robert | 45 | 50 |
| 135/8 | | *Set of* 4 | 1·00 | 1·00 |

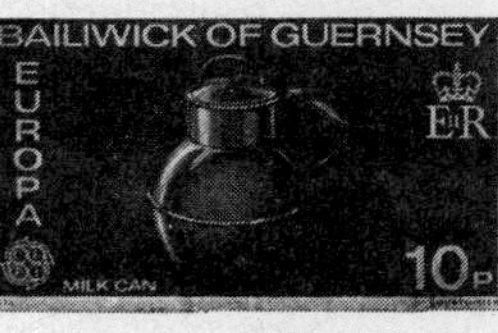

**53** Milk Can

(Des and photo Courvoisier)

**1976** (29 May). *Europa. T* **53** *and similar horiz design. Granite paper. P* 11½.

| No. | Value | Description | Unused | Used |
|---|---|---|---|---|
| 139 | 10p. | chestnut and greenish black | 30 | 30 |
| 140 | 25p. | slate and deep dull blue | 70 | 70 |

Design:—25p. Christening Cup.

**54** Pine Forest, Guernsey

(Des and photo Courvoisier)

**1976** (3 Aug). *Bailiwick Views. T* **54** *and similar multicoloured designs. Granite paper. P* 11½.

| No. | Value | Description | Unused | Used |
|---|---|---|---|---|
| 141 | 5p. | Type **54** | 15 | 10 |
| 142 | 7p. | Herm and Jethou | 15 | 15 |
| 143 | 11p. | Grand Greve Bay, Sark (*vert*) | 40 | 35 |
| 144 | 13p. | Trois Vaux Bay, Alderney (*vert*) | 40 | 50 |
| 141/4 | | *Set of* 4 | 1·00 | 1·00 |

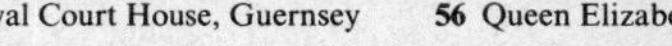

**55** Royal Court House, Guernsey **56** Queen Elizabeth II

(Des and photo Courvoisier)

**1976** (14 Oct). *Christmas. Buildings. T* **55** *and similar horiz designs. Multicoloured. Granite paper. P* 11½.

| No. | Value | Description | Unused | Used |
|---|---|---|---|---|
| 145 | 5p. | Type **55** | 15 | 10 |
| 146 | 7p. | Elizabeth College, Guernsey | 15 | 15 |
| 147 | 11p. | La Seigneurie, Sark | 40 | 35 |
| 148 | 13p. | Island Hall, Alderney | 40 | 50 |
| 145/8 | | *Set of* 4 | 1·00 | 1·00 |

(Des R. Granger Barrett. Photo Courvoisier)

**1977** (8 Feb). *Silver Jubilee. T* **56** *and similar vert design. Multicoloured. Granite paper. P* 11½.

| No. | Value | Description | Unused | Used |
|---|---|---|---|---|
| 149 | 7p. | Type **56** | 20 | 20 |
| 150 | 35p. | Queen Elizabeth (half-length portrait) | 80 | 80 |

## OMNIBUS ISSUES

Details, together with prices for complete sets, of the various Omnibus issues from the 1935 Silver Jubilee series to date are included in a special section following Zimbabwe at the end of Volume 2.

**57** Woodland, Talbot's Valley **58** Statue-menhir, Castel

(Des and photo Courvoisier)

**977** (17 May). *Europa. T* **57** *and similar horiz design. Multicoloured. Granite paper. P* 11½.
51 7p. Type **57** .. .. .. .. .. 25 25
52 25p. Pastureland, Talbot's Valley .. .. 75 75

(Des and photo Courvoisier)

**977** (2 Aug). *Prehistoric Monuments. T* **58** *and similar multicoloured designs. Granite paper. P* 11½.
53 5p. Type **58** .. .. .. .. .. .. 10 10
54 7p. Megalithic tomb, St. Saviour (*horiz*) .. 15 15
55 11p. Cist, Tourgis (*horiz*) .. .. .. 40 35
56 13p. Statue-menhir, St. Martin .. .. 50 50
53/6 .. .. .. .. .. *Set of* 4 1·00 1·00

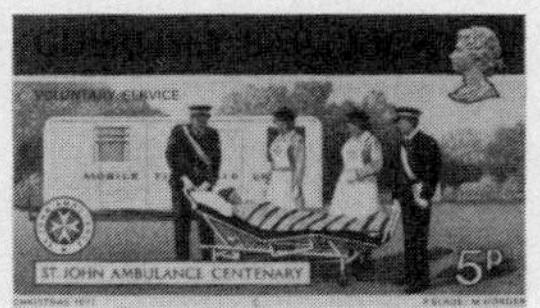


**59** Mobile First Aid Unit

(Des P. Slade and M. Horder. Photo Courvoisier)

**977** (25 Oct). *Christmas and St. John Ambulance Centenary. T* **59** *and similar multicoloured designs. Granite paper. P* 11½.
57 5p. Type **59** .. .. .. .. .. .. 10 10
58 7p. Mobile radar unit .. .. .. .. 15 15
59 11p. Marine Ambulance *Flying Christine II* (*vert*) .. .. .. .. .. .. 40 35
60 13p. Cliff rescue (*vert*) .. .. .. .. 50 50
57/60 .. .. .. .. .. *Set of* 4 1·00 1·00

**60** View from Clifton, *circa* 1830

(Des, recess and litho D.L.R.)

**978** (7 Feb). *Old Guernsey Prints* (1*st series*). *T* **60** *and similar horiz designs. P* 14 × 13½.
61 5p. black and pale apple-green .. .. 10 10
62 7p. black and stone .. .. .. .. 15 15
63 11p. black and light pink .. .. .. 40 35
64 13p. black and light azure .. .. .. 50 50
61/4 .. .. .. .. .. *Set of* 4 1·00 1·00
Designs:—7p. Market Square, St. Peter Port, *circa* 1838; 11p. Petit-Bo Bay, *circa* 1839; 13p. The Quay, St. Peter Port, *circa* 1830.
See also Nos. 249/52.

**61** *Prosperity* Memorial **62** Queen Elizabeth II

(Des R. Granger Barrett. Litho Questa)

**978** (2 May). *Europa. T* **61** *and similar vert design. Multicoloured. P* 14½.
65 5p. Type **61** .. .. .. .. .. .. 35 35
66 7p. Victoria Monument .. .. .. .. 40 40

Des R. Granger Barrett from bust by Arnold Machin. Photo Courvoisier)

**978** (2 May). *25th Anniv of Coronation. Granite paper. P* 11½.
67 **62** 20p. black, grey and bright blue .. .. 60 60

**1978** (28 June). *Royal Visit. Design as No.* 167 *but inscr.* "VISIT OF H.M. THE QUEEN AND H.R.H. THE DUKE OF EDINBURGH JUNE 28–29, 1978 TO THE BAILIWICK OF GUERNSEY".
168 **62** 7p. black, grey and bright green .. .. 25 25

**63** Northern Gannet

(Des J.W. Photo Courvoisier)

**1978** (29 Aug). *Birds. T* **63** *and similar horiz designs. Multicoloured. Granite paper. P* 11½.
169 5p. Type **63** .. .. .. .. .. .. 15 15
170 7p. Firecrest .. .. .. .. .. .. 25 25
171 11p. Dartford Warbler .. .. .. .. 35 35
172 13p. Spotted Redshank .. .. .. .. 40 40
169/72 .. .. .. .. .. *Set of* 4 1·00 1·00

**64** Solanum

(Des and photo Courvoisier)

**1978** (31 Oct). *Christmas. T* **64** *and similar designs. Granite paper. P* 11½.
173 5p. multicoloured .. .. .. .. .. 10 10
174 7p. multicoloured .. .. .. .. .. 20 20
175 11p. multicoloured .. .. .. .. .. 40 30
176 13p. dp blue-green, grey & greenish yellow 50 50
173/6 .. .. .. .. .. *Set of* 4 1·10 1·00
Designs: *Horiz*—7p. Christmas Rose. *Vert*—11p. Holly; 13p. Mistletoe.

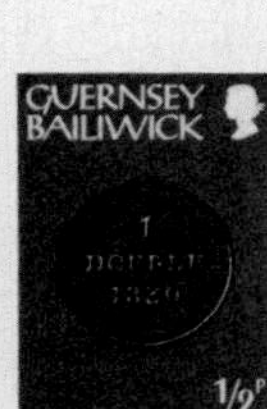

**65** One Double Coin, 1830 **66** Ten Shillings William I Commemorative Coin, 1966

**66a** Seal of the Bailiwick

(Des R. Reed and Courvoisier (£5). Photo Courvoisier)

**1979** (13 Feb)–**83**. *Designs as T* **65/6a**. *Granite paper. P* 11½.
177 ½p. multicoloured .. .. .. .. .. 10 10
a. Booklet pane of 10. Nos. 177 × 2, 178 × 3, 179 × 2, 181, 183 and 187 (6.5.80) .. 1·00
b. Booklet pane of 10. Nos. 177 × 2, 178, 179 × 2, 183 × 2 and 187 × 3 (6.5.80) .. 1·50
178 1p. multicoloured .. .. .. .. .. 10 10
a. Booklet strip of 4. Nos. 178 × 2, 179 and 182 .. .. .. .. .. .. 40
179 2p. multicoloured .. .. .. .. .. 10 10
a. Booklet strip of 5. Nos. 179, 182 × 2 and 184 × 2 .. .. .. .. .. .. 90
180 4p. multicoloured .. .. .. .. .. 10 10
a. Booklet pane of 10. Nos. 180 and 184, each × 5 (24.2.81) .. .. .. .. 1·75
b. Booklet pane of 15. Nos. 180, 184 and 190, each × 5 (24.2.81) .. .. .. 3·50
c. Booklet pane of 10. Nos. 180 × 2, 185 × 3 and 191 × 5 (14.3.83) .. .. .. 3·00
d. Booklet pane of 15. Nos. 180, 185 and 191 each × 5 (14.3.83) .. .. .. 4·50
181 5p. grey-black, silver & chestnut (*shades*) .. 15 10
b. Booklet pane. Nos. 181 × 5, 184 × 4 and 191 (2.2.82) .. .. .. .. .. 2·00
c. Booklet pane. Nos. 181, 184 and 191 each × 5 (2.2.82) .. .. .. .. .. 3·75
182 6p. grey-black, silver and brown-red .. 15 15
183 7p. grey-black, silver and green .. .. 15 20
184 8p. grey-black, silver and brown .. .. 20 20
185 9p. multicoloured .. .. .. .. .. 25 20
186 10p. multicoloured (green background) .. 50 50
187 10p. mult (orange background) (5.2.80) .. 35 30
188 11p. multicoloured .. .. .. .. .. 25 30
189 11½p. multicoloured (5.2.80) .. .. .. 25 30
190 12p. multicoloured .. .. .. .. .. 30 30
191 13p. multicoloured .. .. .. .. .. 30 30
192 14p. grey-black, silver and dull blue .. 30 30
193 15p. grey-black, silver and bistre .. .. 35 35
194 20p. grey-black, silver and dull brown .. 50 45
195 50p. grey-black, orange-red and silver (5.2.80) 1·25 1·25
196 £1 grey-blk, yellowish grn & silver (5.2.80) 2·40 2·40
197 £2 grey-black, new blue and silver (5.2.80) 4·75 4·75
198 £5 multicoloured (22.5.81) .. .. .. 10·00 10·50
177/98 .. .. .. .. .. *Set of* 22 19·00 20·00
Coins: *Vert as T* **65**—1p. Two doubles, 1899; 2p. Four doubles, 1902; 4p. Eight doubles 1959; 5p. Three pence, 1956; 6p. Five new pence, 1968; 7p. Fifty new pence, 1969; 8p. Ten new pence, 1970; 9p. Half new penny, 1971; 10p. (*both*), One new penny, 1971; 11p. Two new pence, 1971; 11½p. Half penny, 1979; 12p. One penny, 1977; 13p. Two pence, 1977; 14p. Five pence, 1977; 15p. Ten pence, 1977; 20p. Twenty-five pence, 1972. *Horiz as T* **66**—£1 Silver Jubilee commemorative crown, 1977; £2 Royal Silver Wedding crown, 1972.
Nos. 177a/b, 178a, 179a, 180a/d and 181b/c come from special booklet sheets of 40 (8 × 5) (Nos. 177a and 178a); 30 (6 × 5) (Nos. 177b, 180a/b, 180d and 181 b/c), 25 (5 × 5) (No. 179a) or 20 (4 × 5) No. 180c). These were put on sale in addition to the normal sheets, being first separated into strips, then folded and either affixed by the selvedge to booklet covers or supplied loose in plastic wallets.

**67** Pillar-box and Postmark, 1853, Mail Van and Postmark, 1979 **68** Steam Tram, 1879

(Des R. Granger Barrett. Photo Courvoisier)

**1979** (8 May). *Europa. Communications. T* **67** *and similar vert design. Multicoloured. Granite paper. P* 11½.
201 6p. Type **67** .. .. .. .. .. .. 30 30
202 8p. Telephone, 1897 and telex machine, 1979 30 30

(Photo Courvoisier)

**1979** (7 Aug). *History of Public Transport. T* **68** *and similar horiz designs. Multicoloured. Granite paper. P* 11½.
203 6p. Type **68** .. .. .. .. .. .. 15 15
204 8p. Electric tram, 1896 .. .. .. .. 20 20
205 11p. Motor bus, 1911 .. .. .. .. 40 35
206 13p. Motor bus, 1979 .. .. .. .. 50 45
203/6 .. .. .. .. .. *Set of* 4 1·10 1·00

**69** Bureau and Postal Headquarters **70** Major-General Le Marchant

(Des R. Granger Barrett. Photo Courvoisier)

**1979** (1 Oct). *Christmas and 10th Anniv of Guernsey Postal Administration. T* **69** *and similar horiz designs. Multicoloured. Granite paper. P* 11½.
207 6p. Type **69** .. .. .. .. .. .. 15 15
208 8p. "Mails and telegrams" .. .. .. 25 15
209 13p. "Parcels" .. .. .. .. .. 30 35
210 15p. "Philately" .. .. .. .. .. 40 45
207/10 .. .. .. .. .. *Set of* 4 1·00 1·00
**MS**211 120 × 80 mm. Nos. 207/10 .. .. .. 1·00 70
One copy of a pre-release sample as No. 210, but with a face value of 11p., is known. Such stamps were not sold for postal purposes.

(Des and photo Courvoisier)

**1980** (6 May). *Europa. Personalities. T* **70** *and similar vert design. Multicoloured. Granite paper. P* 11½.
212 10p. Type **70** .. .. .. .. .. .. 35 35
213 13½p. Admiral Lord De Saumarez .. .. 45 45

**71** Policewoman with Lost Child

(Litho J.W.)

**1980** (6 May). *60th Anniv of Guernsey Police Force. T* **71** *and similar horiz designs. Multicoloured. P* 13½ × 14.
214 7p. Type **71** .. .. .. .. .. .. 15 15
215 15p. Police motorcyclist escorting lorry .. 60 45
216 17½p. Police dog-handler .. .. .. .. 65 50
214/16 .. .. .. .. .. *Set of* 3 1·25 1·00

**72** Golden Guernsey Goat

(Des P. Lambert. Photo Delrieu)

**1980** (5 Aug). *Golden Guernsey Goats. T* **72** *and similar horiz designs showing goats. P* 13.

| | | | | |
|---|---|---|---|---|
| 217 | 7p. | multicoloured | 20 | 20 |
| 218 | 10p. | multicoloured | 40 | 35 |
| 219 | 15p. | multicoloured | 60 | 45 |
| 220 | 17½p. | multicoloured | 75 | 60 |
| 217/20 | | *Set of* 4 | 1·75 | 1·40 |

**73** "Sark Cottage"

(Photo Courvoisier)

**1980** (15 Nov). *Christmas. Peter le Lievre Paintings. T* **73** *and similar multicoloured designs. Granite paper. P* 11½.

| | | | | |
|---|---|---|---|---|
| 221 | 7p. | Type **73** | 30 | 20 |
| 222 | 10p. | "Moulin Huet" | 35 | 25 |
| 223 | 13½p. | "Boats at Sea" | 40 | 30 |
| 224 | 15p. | "Cow Lane" (*vert*) | 50 | 40 |
| 225 | 17½p. | "Peter le Lievre" (*vert*) | 55 | 50 |
| 221/5 | | *Set of* 5 | 2·00 | 1·50 |

**74** *Polyommatus icarus*

**75** Sailors paying respect to "Le Petit Bonhomme Andriou" (rock resembling head of a man)

(Photo Harrison)

**1981** (24 Feb). *Butterflies. T* **74** *and similar horiz designs. Multicoloured. P* 14.

| | | | | |
|---|---|---|---|---|
| 226 | 8p. | Type **74** | 25 | 25 |
| 227 | 12p. | *Vanessa atalanta* | 40 | 40 |
| 228 | 22p. | *Aglais urticae* | 75 | 70 |
| 229 | 25p. | *Lasiommata megera* | 85 | 90 |
| 226/9 | | *Set of* 4 | 2·00 | 2·00 |

(Des C. Abbott. Litho Questa)

**1981** (22 May). *Europa. Folklore. T* **75** *and similar vert design. P* 14½.

| | | | | |
|---|---|---|---|---|
| 230 | 12p. | gold, red-brown and cinnamon | 45 | 45 |
| 231 | 18p. | gold, indigo and azure | 55 | 55 |

Design:—18p. Fairies and Guernsey Lily.

**76** Prince Charles

**77** Sark Launch

(Des C. Abbott. Litho Questa)

**1981** (29 July). *Royal Wedding. T* **76** *and similar multicoloured designs. P* 14½.

| | | | | |
|---|---|---|---|---|
| 232 | 8p. | Type **76** | 20 | 20 |
| | a. | Horiz strip of 3. Nos. 232/4 | 75 | 75 |
| 233 | 8p. | Prince Charles and Lady Diana Spencer | 20 | 20 |
| 234 | 8p. | Lady Diana | 20 | 20 |
| 235 | 12p. | Type **76** | 30 | 30 |
| | a. | Horiz strip of 3. Nos. 235/7 | 1·25 | 1·10 |
| 236 | 12p. | As No. 233 | 30 | 30 |
| 237 | 12p. | As No. 234 | 30 | 30 |
| 238 | 25p. | Royal family (49 × 32 *mm*) | 75 | 75 |
| 232/8 | | *Set of* 7 | 2·50 | 2·00 |
| **MS**239 | | 104 × 127 mm. Nos. 232/8. P 14 | 2·50 | 2·50 |

The 8 and 12p. values were each printed together, *se-tenant*, in horizontal strips of 3 throughout the sheets.

(Des and photo Courvoisier)

**1981** (25 Aug). *Inter-island Transport. T* **77** *and similar horiz designs. Multicoloured. Granite paper. P* 11½.

| | | | | |
|---|---|---|---|---|
| 240 | 8p. | Type **77** | 20 | 20 |
| 241 | 12p. | "Trislander" aeroplane | 40 | 40 |
| 242 | 18p. | Hydrofoil | 60 | 60 |
| 243 | 22p. | Herm catamaran | 75 | 75 |
| 244 | 25p. | *Sea Trent* (coaster) | 85 | 85 |
| 240/4 | | *Set of* 5 | 2·50 | 2·50 |

**78** Rifle Shooting

**79** Sir Edgar MacCulloch (founder-president) and Guille-Allès Library, St. Peter Port

(Des P. le Vasseur. Litho Questa)

**1981** (17 Nov). *International Year for Disabled Persons. T* **78** *and similar horiz designs. Multicoloured. P* 14½.

| | | | | |
|---|---|---|---|---|
| 245 | 8p. | Type **78** | 20 | 20 |
| 246 | 12p. | Riding | 50 | 40 |
| 247 | 22p. | Swimming | 75 | 65 |
| 248 | 25p. | "Work" | 80 | 70 |
| 245/8 | | *Set of* 4 | 2·00 | 1·75 |

(Des, recess and litho D.L.R.)

**1982** (2 Feb). *Old Guernsey Prints* (2*nd series*). *Prints from sketches by T. Compton. Horiz designs as T* **60**. *P* 14 × 13½.

| | | | | |
|---|---|---|---|---|
| 249 | 8p. | black and pale blue | 20 | 20 |
| 250 | 12p. | black and pale turquoise-green | 50 | 50 |
| 251 | 22p. | black and pale yellow-brown | 75 | 75 |
| 252 | 25p. | black and pale rose-lilac | 80 | 80 |
| 249/52 | | *Set of* 4 | 2·00 | 2·00 |

Designs:—8p. Jethou; 12p. Fermain Bay; 22p. The Terres; 25p. St. Peter Port.

(Des G. Drummond. Photo Courvoisier)

**1982** (28 Apr). *Centenary of La Société Guernesiaise. T* **79** *and similar horiz designs. Multicoloured. Granite paper. P* 11½.

| | | | | |
|---|---|---|---|---|
| 253 | 8p. | Type **79** | 20 | 20 |
| 254 | 13p. | French invasion fleet crossing English Channel, 1066 ("History") | 45 | 45 |
| 255 | 20p. | H.M.S. *Crescent*, 1793 ("History") | 55 | 55 |
| 256 | 24p. | Dragonfly ("Entomology") | 70 | 70 |
| 257 | 26p. | Common Snipe caught for ringing ("Ornithology") | 75 | 75 |
| 258 | 29p. | Samian Bowl, 160–200 A.D. ("Archaeology") | 80 | 80 |
| 253/8 | | *Set of* 6 | 3·25 | 3·25 |

The 13 and 20p. values also include the Europa C.E.P.T. emblem in the designs.

**80** "Sea Scouts"

**81** Midnight Mass

(Des W.L.G. Creative Services Ltd. Litho Questa)

**1982** (13 July). *75th Anniv of Boy Scout Movement. T* **80** *and similar vert designs. Multicoloured. P* 14½ × 14.

| | | | | |
|---|---|---|---|---|
| 259 | 8p. | Type **80** | 20 | 25 |
| 260 | 13p. | "Scouts" | 50 | 50 |
| 261 | 26p. | "Cub Scouts" | 80 | 80 |
| 262 | 29p. | "Air Scouts" | 1·00 | 1·00 |
| 259/62 | | *Set of* 4 | 2·25 | 2·25 |

(Des Lynette Hemmant. Photo Harrison)

**1982** (12 Oct). *Christmas. T* **81** *and similar horiz designs. Multicoloured. P* 14½.

| | | | | |
|---|---|---|---|---|
| 263 | 8p. | Type **81** | 20 | 20 |
| | a. | Black (Queen's head, value and inscr) omitted | | |
| 264 | 13p. | Exchanging gifts | 40 | 40 |
| 265 | 24p. | Christmas meal | 80 | 80 |
| 266 | 26p. | Exchanging cards | 80 | 80 |
| 267 | 29p. | Queen's Christmas message | 85 | 85 |
| 263/7 | | *Set of* 5 | 2·75 | 2·75 |

**82** Flute Player and Boats

**83** Building Albert Pier Extension, 1850s

(Des Sally Stiff. Photo Harrison)

**1983** (18 Jan). *Centenary of Boys' Brigade. T* **82** *and similar horiz designs. Multicoloured. P* 14.

| | | | | |
|---|---|---|---|---|
| 268 | 8p. | Type **82** | 25 | 25 |
| 269 | 13p. | Cymbal player and tug 'o' war | 45 | 45 |
| 270 | 24p. | Trumpet player and bible class | 75 | 75 |
| 271 | 26p. | Drummer and cadets marching | 85 | 85 |
| 272 | 29p. | Boys' Brigade band | 95 | 95 |
| 268/72 | | *Set of* 5 | 3·00 | 3·00 |

(Des C. Abbott. Photo Courvoisier)

**1983** (14 Mar). *Europa. Development of St. Peter Port Harbour. T* **8**[3] *and similar horiz designs. Multicoloured. Granite paper. P* 11½.

| | | | | |
|---|---|---|---|---|
| 273 | 13p. | Type **83** | 35 | 3 |
| | a. | Horiz pair. Nos. 273/4 | 70 | 7 |
| 274 | 13p. | St. Peter Port Harbour, 1983 | 35 | 3 |
| 275 | 20p. | St. Peter Port, 1680 | 75 | 7 |
| | a. | Horiz pair. Nos. 275/6 | 1·50 | 1·5 |
| 276 | 20p. | Artist's impression of future development scheme | 75 | 7 |
| 273/6 | | *Set of* 4 | 2·00 | 2·0 |

The two designs of each value were issued together, *se-tenant*, in horizontal pairs throughout the sheets.

**84** "View at Guernsey" (Renoir)

(Des and photo Courvoisier)

**1983** (6 Sept). *Centenary of Renoir's Visit to Guernsey. T* **84** *and similar multicoloured designs, showing paintings. Granite paper. P* 11 × 11½ (13*p*.) *or* 11½ (*others*).

| | | | | |
|---|---|---|---|---|
| 277 | 9p. | Type **84** | 25 | 2 |
| 278 | 13p. | "Children on the Seashore" (25 × 39 *mm*) | 45 | 4 |
| 279 | 26p. | "Marine, Guernesey" | 80 | 8 |
| 280 | 28p. | "La Baie du Moulin Huet à travers les Arbres" | 85 | 8 |
| 281 | 31p. | "Brouillard à Guernesey" | 95 | 9 |
| 277/81 | | *Set of* 5 | 3·00 | 3·0 |

**85** Launching *Star of the West*, 1869, and Capt. J. Lenfestey

(Des R. Granger Barrett. Litho Questa)

**1983** (15 Nov). *Guernsey Shipping* (1*st series*). *"Star of the West" (brigantine). T* **85** *and similar horiz designs. Multicoloured. P* 14

| | | | | |
|---|---|---|---|---|
| 282 | 9p. | Type **85** | 25 | 25 |
| 283 | 13p. | Leaving St. Peter Port | 40 | 40 |
| 284 | 26p. | Off Rio Grande Bar | 80 | 80 |
| 285 | 28p. | Off St. Lucia | 85 | 85 |
| 286 | 31p. | Map of 1879–80 voyage | 95 | 95 |
| 282/6 | | *Set of* 5 | 3·00 | 3·00 |

See also Nos. 415/19.

**86** Dame of Sark as Young Woman

(Des Jennifer Toombs. Litho Questa)

**1984** (7 Feb). *Birth Centenary of Sibyl Hathaway, Dame of Sark. T* **86** *and similar horiz designs. Multicoloured. P* 14½.

| | | | | |
|---|---|---|---|---|
| 287 | 9p. | Type **86** | 25 | 25 |
| 288 | 13p. | German occupation, 1940–45 | 40 | 45 |
| 289 | 26p. | Royal Visit, 1957 | 90 | 90 |
| 290 | 28p. | Chief Pleas | 95 | 95 |
| 291 | 31p. | The Dame of Sark rose | 1·10 | 1·10 |
| 287/91 | | *Set of* 5 | 3·25 | 3·25 |

**87** C.E.P.T. 25th Anniversary Logo

(Des J. Larrivière and C. Abbott. Litho Questa)

**1984** (10 Apr). *Europa. P* 15 × 14½.

| | | | | |
|---|---|---|---|---|
| 292 **87** | 13p. | cobalt, dull ultramarine and black | 50 | 50 |
| 293 | 20½p. | emerald, deep dull green and black | 75 | 75 |

**88** The Royal Court and St. George's Flag

**89** St. Apolline Chape[l]

(Des C. Abbott. Litho Questa)

**1984** (10 Apr). *Links with the Commonwealth. T* **88** *and similar horiz design. Multicoloured. P* 14 × 14½.
294 9p. Type **88** .. .. .. .. .. 30 30
295 31p. Castle Cornet and Union flag .. .. 1·10 1·10

(Des C. Abbott. Litho Questa)

**1984** (18 Sept)–**91**. *Views. T* **89** *and similar multicoloured designs. Chalk-surfaced paper. P* 14½.
296 1p. Little Chapel (23.7.85) .. .. 10 10
297 2p. Fort Grey (*horiz*) (23.7.85) .. .. 10 10
a. Booklet pane. Nos. 297×2, 299×4, 300×2 and 305×2 (2.12.85) .. .. 1·60
298 3p. Type **89** .. .. .. .. 10 10
a. Booklet pane. Nos. 298, 299×2, 306×4 and 309×3 (30.3.87) .. .. 1·75
299 4p. Petit Port (*horiz*) .. .. .. 10 10
a. Booklet pane. Nos. 299×2, 304×3 and 307×5 .. .. .. .. 4·00
b. Booklet pane. Nos. 299, 304 and 307, each × 5 .. .. .. .. 4·50
c. Booklet pane. Nos. 299×4, 306*b*×3 and 309*c*×3 (28.3.88) .. .. 1·75
d. Booklet pane. Nos. 299, 301, 306*b*×3 and 309*d*×3 (28.2.89) .. .. 1·75
300 5p. Little Russel (*horiz*) (23.7.85) .. 10 10
a. Booklet pane. Nos. 300×2, 301×2, 309×3 and 310*b*×3 (2.4.91) .. .. 2·50
301 6p. The Harbour, Herm (*horiz*) (23.7.85) 10 15
a. Booklet pane. Nos. 301×4, 308×4 and 310×2 (27.12.89) .. .. .. 2·40
b. Uncoated paper .. .. ..
302 7p. Saints (*horiz*) (23.7.85) .. .. 15 20
303 8p. St. Saviour (23.7.85) .. .. 15 20
304 9p. New jetty (inscr "Cambridge Berth") (*horiz*) .. .. .. .. 20 25
a. Booklet pane. Nos. 304×4 and 308×6 (19.3.85) .. .. .. .. 3·50
b. Booklet pane. Nos. 304×2 and 308×8 (19.3.85) .. .. .. .. 4·00
305 10p. Belvoir, Herm (*horiz*) .. .. 20 25
a. Booklet pane. Nos. 305 and 308, each × 5 (1.4.86) .. .. .. 2·10
306 11p. La Seigneurie, Sark (*horiz*) (23.7.85) 20 25
a. Booklet pane. Nos. 306 and 309, each × 5 (30.3.87) .. .. .. 2·25
306*b* 12p. Petit Bot (28.3.88) .. .. 25 30
ba. Booklet pane. Nos. 306*b* and 309*c*, each × 5 .. .. .. .. 2·50
bb. Booklet pane. Nos. 306*b* and 309*d*, each × 4 (28.2.89) .. .. 2·10
307 13p. St. Saviours reservoir (*horiz*) .. 25 30
308 14p. St. Peter Port .. .. .. 30 35
a. Booklet pane. Nos. 308 and 310, each × 5 (27.12.89) .. .. .. 3·50
b. Uncoated paper .. .. ..
309 15p. Havelet (23.7.85) .. .. .. 30 35
a. Booklet pane. Nos. 309 and 310*b*, each × 5 (2.4.91) .. .. .. 3·50
b. Imperf at sides and foot (horiz pair)
309*c* 16p. Hostel of St. John (*horiz*) (28.3.88) 30 35
309*d* 18p. Le Variouf (28.2.89) .. .. 35 40
310 20p. La Coupee, Sark (*horiz*) .. .. 40 45
a. Uncoated paper .. .. ..
310*b* 21p. King's Mills (*horiz*) (2.4.91) .. .. 40 45
310*c* 26p. Town Church (2.4.91) .. .. 50 55
311 30p. Grandes Rocques (*horiz*) (23.7.85) .. 60 65
312 40p. Torteval church .. .. .. 80 85
313 50p. Bordeaux (*horiz*) .. .. .. 1·00 1·10
314 £1 Albecq (*horiz*) .. .. .. 2·00 2·10
315 £2 L'Ancresse (*horiz*) (23.7.85) .. 4·00 4·25
296/315 .. .. .. .. *Set of* 25 11·50 12·50

Booklet panes Nos. 297a, 298a, 299a/c, 304a/b, 305a, 306a and 306ba have margins all round and were issued, folded and loose, within the booklet covers.

Booklet panes Nos. 299d, 300a, 301a, 306bb, 308a and 309a have the outer edges imperforate on three sides and were also issued loose within the booklet covers.

The uncoated errors, Nos. 301b, 308b and 310a, come from examples of booklet panes Nos. 301a and 308a.

For 11p., 12p., 15p. and 16p. stamps in a smaller size see Nos. 398/9*a*.

**90** "A Partridge in a Pear Tree' **91** Sir John Doyle and Coat of Arms

(Des R. Downer. Litho Questa)

**1984** (20 Nov). *Christmas. "The Twelve Days of Christmas". T* **90** *and similar vert designs. Multicoloured. P* 14½.
316 5p. Type **90** .. .. .. .. 20 20
a. Sheetlet of 12. Nos. 316/27 .. .. 2·50
317 5p. "Two turtle doves" .. .. .. 20 20
318 5p. "Three French hens" .. .. .. 20 20
319 5p. "Four colly birds" .. .. .. 20 20
320 5p. "Five gold rings" .. .. .. 20 20
321 5p. "Six geese a-laying" .. .. .. 20 20
322 5p. "Seven swans a-swimming" .. .. 20 20
323 5p. "Eight maids a-milking" .. .. 20 20
324 5p. "Nine drummers drumming" .. .. 20 20
325 5p. "Ten pipers piping" .. .. .. 20 20
326 5p. "Eleven ladies dancing" .. .. 20 20
327 5p. "Twelve lords a-leaping" .. .. 20 20
316/27 .. .. .. .. *Set of* 12 2·50 2·50

Nos. 316/27 were printed, *se-tenant*, in sheetlets of 12.

(Des E. Stemp. Photo Courvoisier)

**1984** (20 Nov). *150th Death Anniv of Lieut-General Sir John Doyle. T* **91** *and similar multicoloured designs. Granite paper. P* 11½.
328 13p. Type **91** .. .. .. .. 40 40
329 29p. Battle of Germantown, 1777 (*horiz*) .. 1·00 1·00
330 31p. Reclamation of Braye du Valle, 1806 (*horiz*) 1·10 1·10
331 34p. Mail for Alderney, 1812 (*horiz*) .. .. 1·10 1·10
328/31 .. .. .. .. *Set of* 4 3·25 3·25

**92** Cuckoo Wrasse **93** Dove

(Des P. Barrett. Photo Courvoisier)

**1985** (22 Jan). *Fishes. T* **92** *and similar horiz designs. Multicoloured. Granite paper. P* 11½.
332 9p. Type **92** .. .. .. .. .. 40 40
333 13p. Red Gurnard .. .. .. .. 60 60
334 29p. Red Mullet .. .. .. .. 1·50 1·10
335 31p. Mackerel .. .. .. .. 1·50 1·10
336 34p. Sunfish .. .. .. .. 1·60 1·25
332/6 .. .. .. .. *Set of* 5 5·00 4·00

(Des C. Abbott. Litho Questa)

**1985** (9 May). *40th Anniv of Peace in Europe. P* 14 × 14½.
337 **93** 22p. multicoloured .. .. .. 1·00 1·00

**94** I.Y.Y. Emblem and Young People of Different Races **95** Stave of Music enclosing Flags

(Des Suzanne Brehaut (9p.), Mary Harrison (31p.). Litho Questa)

**1985** (14 May). *International Youth Year. T* **94** *and similar square design. Multicoloured. P* 14.
338 9p. Type **94** .. .. .. .. 40 40
339 31p. Girl Guides cooking over campfire .. 1·00 1·00

(Des Fiona Sloan (14p.), Katie Lillington (22p.). Litho Questa)

**1985** (14 May). *Europa. European Music Year. T* **95** *and similar horiz design. Multicoloured. P* 14 × 14½.
340 14p. Type **95** .. .. .. .. 45 40
341 22p. Stave of music and musical instruments .. .. .. .. .. 95 1·00

**96** Guide Leader, Girl Guide and Brownie **97** Santa Claus

(Des Karon Mahy. Litho Questa)

**1985** (14 May). *75th Anniv of Girl Guide Movement. P* 14.
342 **96** 34p. multicoloured .. .. .. 1·25 1·25

(Des C. Abbott. Photo Courvoisier)

**1985** (19 Nov). *Christmas. Gift-bearers. T* **97** *and similar vert designs. Multicoloured. Granite paper. P* 12½.
343 5p. Type **97** .. .. .. .. 25 25
a. Sheetlet of 12. Nos. 343/54 .. .. 3·00
344 5p. Lussibruden (Sweden) .. .. 25 25
345 5p. King Balthazar .. .. .. 25 25
346 5p. Saint Nicholas (Netherlands) .. .. 25 25
347 5p. La Befana (Italy) .. .. .. 25 25
348 5p. Julenisse (Denmark) .. .. .. 25 25
349 5p. Christkind (Germany) .. .. .. 25 25
350 5p. King Wenceslas (Czechoslovakia) .. 25 25
351 5p. Shepherd of Les Baux (France) .. .. 25 25
352 5p. King Caspar .. .. .. .. 25 25
353 5p. Baboushka (Russia) .. .. .. 25 25
354 5p. King Melchior .. .. .. .. 25 25
343/54 .. .. .. .. *Set of* 12 3·00 3·00

Nos. 343/54 were printed, *se-tenant*, in sheetlets of 12.

**98** "Vraicing"

(Des and photo Harrison)

**1985** (19 Nov). *Paintings by Paul Jacob Naftel. T* **98** *and similar horiz designs. Multicoloured. P* 15 × 14.
355 9p. Type **98** .. .. .. .. 40 40
356 14p. "Castle Cornet" .. .. .. 50 50
357 22p. "Rocquaine Bay" .. .. .. 1·00 1·00
358 31p. "Little Russel" .. .. .. 1·50 1·50
359 34p. "Seaweedgatherers" .. .. .. 1·60 1·60
355/9 .. .. .. .. *Set of* 5 4·50 4·50

**99** Squadron off Nargue Island, 1809 **100** Profile of Queen Elizabeth II (after R. Maklouf)

(Des T. Thompson. Photo Courvoisier)

**1986** (4 Feb). *150th Death Anniv of Admiral Lord De Saumarez. T* **99** *and similar horiz designs. Multicoloured. Granite paper. P* 11½.
360 9p. Type **99** .. .. .. .. 40 40
361 14p. Battle of the Nile, 1798 .. .. 60 60
362 29p. Battle of St. Vincent, 1797 .. .. 1·50 1·50
363 31p. H.M.S. *Crescent* off Cherbourg, 1793 .. 1·50 1·50
364 34p. Battle of the Saints, 1782 .. .. 1·60 1·60
360/4 .. .. .. .. *Set of* 5 5·00 5·00

(Des C. Abbott. Litho Questa)

**1986** (21 Apr). *60th Birthday of Queen Elizabeth II. P* 14.
365 **100** 60p. multicoloured .. .. .. 2·25 2·25

**101** Northern Gannet and Nylon Net ("Operation Gannet") **102** Prince Andrew and Miss Sarah Ferguson

(Des P. Newcombe. Photo Courvoisier)

**1986** (22 May). *Europa. Nature and Environmental Protection. T* **101** *and similar vert designs. Multicoloured. Granite paper. P* 11½.
366 10p. Type **101** .. .. .. .. 45 45
367 14p. Loose-flowered Orchid .. .. 65 65
368 22p. Guernsey Elm .. .. .. 85 85
366/8 .. .. .. .. *Set of* 3 1·75 1·75

(Des C. Abbott. Litho Questa)

**1986** (23 July). *Royal Wedding. T* **102** *and similar multicoloured design. P* 14 (14*p*.) *or* 13½ × 14 (34*p*.).
369 14p. Type **102** .. .. .. .. 60 60
370 34p. Prince Andrew and Miss Sarah Ferguson (*different*) (47 × 30 *mm*) .. .. 1·40 1·40

**103** Bowls **104** Guernsey Museum and Art Gallery, Candie Gardens

(Des R. Goldsmith. Litho Questa)

**1986** (24 July). *Sport in Guernsey. T* **103** *and similar multicoloured designs. P* 14½.
371 10p. Type **103** .. .. .. .. 30 30
372 14p. Cricket .. .. .. .. 50 50
373 22p. Squash .. .. .. .. 75 75
374 29p. Hockey .. .. .. .. 1·10 1·10
375 31p. Swimming (*horiz*) .. .. .. 1·25 1·25
376 34p. Rifle-shooting (*horiz*) .. .. 1·40 1·40
371/6 .. .. .. .. *Set of* 6 4·75 4·75

(Des Sir Hugh Casson. Litho Questa)

**1986** (18 Nov). *Centenary of Guernsey Museums. T* **104** *and similar horiz designs. Multicoloured. P* 14½.
377 14p. Type **104** .. .. .. .. 60 60
378 29p. Fort Grey Maritime Museum .. .. 1·10 1·10
379 31p. Castle Cornet .. .. .. 1·10 1·10
380 34p. National Trust of Guernsey Folk Museum .. .. .. .. .. 1·40 1·40
377/80 .. .. .. .. *Set of* 4 3·75 3·75

**105** "While Shepherds Watched their Flocks by Night"

(Des Wendy Bramall. Photo Courvoisier)

**1986** (18 Nov). *Christmas. Carols. T* **105** *and similar vert designs. Multicoloured. Granite paper. P* 12½.

381 6p. Type **105** .. 25 25
 a. Sheetlet of 12. Nos. 381/92 .. 2·75
382 6p. "In The Bleak Mid-Winter" .. 25 25
383 6p. "O Little Town of Bethlehem" .. 25 25
384 6p. "The Holly and the Ivy" .. 25 25
385 6p. "O Little Christmas Tree" .. 25 25
386 6p. "Away in a Manger" .. 25 25
387 6p. "Good King Wenceslas" .. 25 25
388 6p. "We Three Kings of Orient Are" .. 25 25
389 6p. "Hark the Herald Angels Sing" .. 25 25
390 6p. "I Saw Three Ships" .. 25 25
391 6p. "Little Donkey" .. 25 25
392 6p. "Jingle Bells" .. 25 25
381/92 .. *Set of* 12 2·75 2·75

Nos. 381/92 were printed, *se-tenant*, in sheetlets of 12.

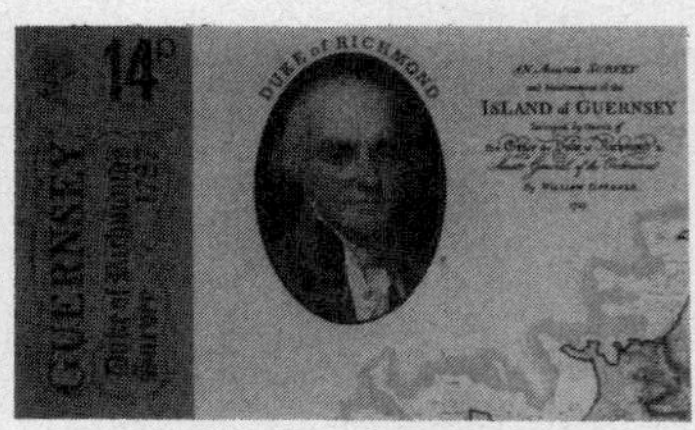

**106** Duke of Richmond and Portion of Map

(Des J. Cooter. Litho Questa)

**1987** (10 Feb). *Bicentenary of Duke of Richmond's Survey of Guernsey. Sheet* 134 × 103 *mm containing T* **106** *and similar horiz designs showing sections of map. Multicoloured. P* 14½ × 14.

**MS**393 14p. Type **106**; 29p. North-east; 31p. South-west; 34p. South-east .. 3·50 3·75

The stamps within No. **MS**393 show a composite design of the Duke of Richmond's map of Guernsey.

**107** Post Office Headquarters **108** Sir Edmund Andros and La Plaiderie, Guernsey

(Des R. Reed. Litho Cartor, France)

**1987** (5 Mar). *Europa. Modern Architecture. T* **107** *and similar vert designs. Multicoloured. P* 13 × 13½.

394 15p. Type **107** .. 55 55
 a. Horiz pair. Nos. 394/5 .. 1·10 1·10
395 15p. Architect's elevation of Post Office Headquarters .. 55 55
396 22p. Guernsey Grammar School .. 80 80
 a. Horiz pair. Nos. 396/7 .. 1·75 1·75
397 22p. Architect's elevation of Grammar School 80 80
394/7 .. *Set of* 4 2·50 2·50

Nos. 394/5 and 396/7 were each printed together, *se-tenant*, in horizontal pairs throughout the sheets.

(Photo Harrison)

**1987** (15 May)–**88**. *Coil Stamps. Designs as Nos.* 306, 306*b and* 309/*a, but smaller. P* 14 × 14½ (11*p*., 16*p*.) *or* 14½ × 14 (12*p*., 15*p*.).

398 11p. La Seigneurie, Sark (22 × 18 *mm*) .. 30 30
398*a* 12p. Petit Bot (18 × 22 *mm*) (28.3.88) .. 20 25
399 15p. Havelet (18 × 22 *mm*) .. 45 45
399*a* 16p. Hospital of St. John (22 × 18 *mm*) (28.3.88) .. 30 35
398/9*a* .. *Set of* 4 1·10 1·25

(Des B. Sanders. Photo Courvoisier)

**1987** (7 July). *350th Birth Anniv of Sir Edmund Andros (colonial administrator). T* **108** *and similar horiz designs, each showing portrait. Multicoloured. Granite paper. P* 12.

400 15p. Type **108** .. 45 45
401 29p. Governor's Palace, Virginia .. 1·00 1·00
402 31p. Governor Andros in Boston .. 1·10 1·10
403 34p. Map of New Amsterdam (New York), 1661 .. 1·40 1·40
400/3 .. *Set of* 4 3·50 3·50

**109** The Jester's Warning to Young William **110** John Wesley preaching on the Quay, Alderney

(Des P. le Vasseur. Litho Cartor, France)

**1987** (9 Sept). *900th Death Anniv of William the Conqueror. T* **109** *and similar vert designs. Multicoloured. P* 13½ × 14.

404 11p. Type **109** .. 45 45
405 15p. Hastings battlefield .. 60 60
 a. Horiz pair. Nos. 405/6 .. 1·25 1·25
406 15p. Norman soldier with pennant .. 60 60
407 22p. William the Conqueror .. 95 95
 a. Horiz pair. Nos. 407/8 .. 1·90 1·90
408 22p. Queen Matilda and Abbaye aux Dames, Caen .. 95 95
409 34p. William's Coronation regalia and Halley's Comet .. 1·40 1·40
404/9 .. *Set of* 6 4·50 4·50

Nos. 405/6 and 407/8 were each printed together, *se-tenant*, in horizontal pairs throughout the sheets.

(Des R. Geary. Litho Questa)

**1987** (17 Nov). *Bicentenary of John Wesley's Visit to Guernsey. T* **110** *and similar horiz designs. Multicoloured. P* 14½.

410 7p. Type **110** .. 30 30
411 15p. Wesley preaching at Mon Plaisir, St. Peter Port .. 45 45
412 29p. Preaching at Assembly Rooms .. 1·25 1·25
413 31p. Wesley and La Ville Baudu (early Methodist meeting place) .. 1·25 1·25
414 34p. Wesley and first Methodist Chapel, St. Peter Port .. 1·25 1·25
410/14 .. *Set of* 5 4·00 4·00

**111** *Golden Spur* off St. Sampson Harbour

(Des R. Granger Barrett. Litho B.D.T.)

**1988** (9 Feb). *Guernsey Shipping (2nd series). "Golden Spur" (full-rigged ship). T* **111** *and similar horiz designs. Multicoloured. P* 13½.

415 11p. Type **111** .. 35 35
416 15p. *Golden Spur* entering Hong Kong harbour .. 50 50
417 29p. Anchored off Macao .. 1·25 1·25
418 31p. In China Tea Race .. 1·25 1·25
419 34p. *Golden Spur* and map showing voyage of 1872–74 .. 1·25 1·25
415/19 .. *Set of* 5 4·00 4·00

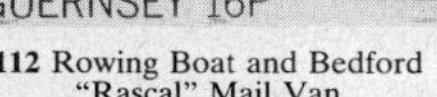

**112** Rowing Boat and Bedford "Rascal" Mail Van **113** Frederick Corbin Lukis and Lukis House, St. Peter Port

(Des C. Abbott. Litho Questa)

**1988** (10 May). *Europa. Transport and Communications. T* **112** *and similar horiz designs. Multicoloured. P* 14½.

420 16p. Type **112** .. 55 55
 a. Horiz pair. Nos. 420/1 .. 1·10 1·10
421 16p. Rowing boat and "Viscount" mail plane .. 55 55
422 22p. Postman on bicycle and horse-drawn carriages, Sark .. 85 85
 a. Horiz pair. Nos. 422/3 .. 1·75 1·75
423 22p. Postmen on bicycles and carriage .. 85 85
420/3 .. *Set of* 4 2·50 2·50

Nos. 420/1 and 422/3 were each printed together, *se-tenant*, in horizontal pairs throughout the sheets, the two stamps of each value forming a composite design.

(Des Wendy Bramall. Photo Courvoisier)

**1988** (12 July). *Birth Bicentenary of Frederick Corbin Lukis (archaeologist). T* **113** *and similar horiz designs. Multicoloured. Granite paper. P* 12½.

424 12p. Type **113** .. 40 40
425 16p. Natural history books and reconstructed pot .. 50 50
426 29p. Lukis directing excavation of Le Creux ès Faies and prehistoric beaker .. 1·10 1·10
427 31p. Lukis House Observatory and garden .. 1·10 1·10
428 34p. Prehistoric artifacts .. 1·10 1·10
424/8 .. *Set of* 5 3·75 3·75

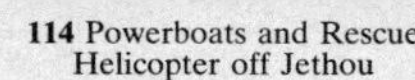

**114** Powerboats and Rescue Helicopter off Jethou **115** Joshua Gosselin and Herbarium

(Des and photo Courvoisier)

**1988** (6 Sept). *World Offshore Powerboat Championships. T* **114** *and similar multicoloured designs. Granite paper. P* 12.

429 16p. Type **114** .. 60 60
430 30p. Powerboats in Gouliot Passage .. 1·10 1·10
431 32p. Start of race at St. Peter Port (*vert*) .. 1·10 1·10
432 35p. Admiralty chart showing course (*vert*) .. 1·40 1·40
429/32 .. *Set of* 4 3·75 3·75

(Des M. Oxenham. Litho Cartor, France)

**1988** (15 Nov). *Bicentenary of Joshua Gosselin's* Flora Sarniensis. *T* **115** *and similar vert designs. Multicoloured. P* 13½ × 14.

433 12p. Type **115** .. 40 40
434 16p. Hares-tail Grass .. 55 55
 a. Horiz pair. Nos. 434/5 .. 1·10 1·10
435 16p. Dried Hares-tail Grass .. 55 55
436 23p. Variegated Catchfly .. 75 75
 a. Horiz pair. Nos. 436/7 .. 1·50 1·50
437 23p. Dried Variegated Catchfly .. 75 75
438 35p. Rock Sea Lavender .. 1·25 1·25
433/8 .. *Set of* 6 3·75 3·75

Nos. 434/5 and 436/7 were each printed together, *se-tenant*, in horizontal pairs throughout the sheets.

**116** Coutances Cathedral, France **117** Lé Cat (Tip Cat)

(Des R. Downer. Litho Questa)

**1988** (15 Nov). *Christmas. Ecclesiastical Links. T* **116** *and similar vert designs. Multicoloured. P* 14½.

439 8p. Type **116** .. 25 25
 a. Sheetlet of 12. Nos. 439/50 .. 3·00
440 8p. Interior of Notre Dame du Rosaire Church, Guernsey .. 25 25
441 8p. Stained glass, St. Sampson's Church, Guernsey .. 25 25
442 8p. Dol-de-Bretagne Cathedral, France .. 25 25
443 8p. Bishop's throne, Town Church, Guernsey 25 25
444 8p. Winchester Cathedral .. 25 25
445 8p. St. John's Cathedral, Portsmouth .. 25 25
446 8p. High altar, St. Joseph's Church, Guernsey 25 25
447 8p. Mont Saint-Michel, France .. 25 25
448 8p. Chancel, Vale Church, Guernsey .. 25 25
449 8p. Lychgate, Forest Church, Guernsey .. 25 25
450 8p. Marmoutier Abbey, France .. 25 25
439/50 .. *Set of* 12 3·00 3·00

Nos. 439/50 were printed, *se-tenant*, in sheetlets of 12.

(Des P. le Vasseur. Litho Cartor, France)

**1989** (28 Feb). *Europa. Children's Toys and Games. T* **117** *and similar horiz designs. Multicoloured. P* 13½.

451 12p. Type **117** .. 40 40
452 16p. Girl with Cobo Alice doll .. 50 50
453 23p. Lé Colimachaön (hopscotch) .. 80 80
451/3 .. *Set of* 3 1·50 1·50

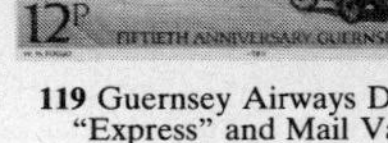

**118** Outline Map of Guernsey **119** Guernsey Airways DH86 "Express" and Mail Van

(Photo Harrison)

**1989** (3 Apr–27 Dec). *Coil Stamps. No value expressed. P* 14½ × 14.

454 **118** (–) ultramarine (27.12.89) .. 30 35
455 (–) emerald .. 40 45

No. 454 is inscribed "MINIMUM BAILIWICK POSTAGE PAID" and No. 455 "MINIMUM FIRST CLASS POSTAGE TO UK PAID". They were initially sold at 14p. and 18p., but it is intended that this will change in line with future postage rate rises.

In these coils every fifth stamp is numbered on the reverse.

(Des N. Foggo. Litho B.D.T.)

**1989** (5 May). *50th Annivs of Guernsey Airport (Nos. 456, 458 and 460) and 201 Squadron's Affiliation with Guernsey (Nos. 457, 459 and 461). T* **119** *and similar horiz designs. Multicoloured. P* 13½.

456 12p. Type **119** .. 40 40
 a. Booklet pane. No. 456 × 6 .. 2·50
457 12p. Supermarine "Southampton" flying boat at mooring .. 40 40
458 18p. B.E.A. DH89 "Rapide" .. 55 55
 a. Booklet pane. No. 458 × 6 .. 2·75
459 18p. Sunderland "Mk V" flying boat taking off 55 55
460 35p. Air U.K. BAe "146" .. 1·00 1·00
 a. Booklet pane. No. 460 × 6 .. 5·50
461 35p. Shackleton "Mk 3" .. 1·00 1·00
456/61 .. *Set of* 6 3·50 3·50

Each booklet pane has margins all round with text printed at the foot.

120 "Queen Elizabeth II" (June Mendoza)

121 *Ibex* at G.W.R. Terminal, St. Peter Port

(Des A. Theobald. Litho B.D.T.)

**1989** (23 May). *Royal Visit. P* 15 × 14.
462 **120** 30p. multicoloured .. .. .. 1·00 1·00

(Des C. Jaques. Litho B.D.T.)

**1989** (5 Sept). *Centenary of Great Western Railway Steamer Service to Channel Islands. T* **121** *and similar horiz designs. Multicoloured. P* 13½.
463 12p. Type **121** .. .. .. .. .. 30 30
464 18p. *Great Western* (paddle-steamer) in Little Russel .. .. .. .. .. 65 65
465 29p. *St. Julien* passing Casquets Light .. 90 90
466 34p. *Roebuck* off Portland .. .. 1·10 1·10
467 37p. *Antelope* and boat train at Weymouth quay .. .. .. .. .. 1·25 1·25
463/7 .. .. .. .. *Set of* 5 3·75 3·75
**MS**468 115×117 mm. Nos. 463/7 .. .. 3·75 3·75

122 Two-toed Sloth

123 Star

(Des Anne Farncombe. Litho Cartor, France)

**1989** (17 Nov). *10th Anniv of Guernsey Zoological Trust. Animals of the Rainforest. T* **122** *and similar vert designs. Multicoloured. P* 13½×14.
469 18p. Type **122** .. .. .. .. .. 90 90
a. Horiz strip of 5. Nos. 469/73 .. .. 4·00
470 29p. Capuchin Monkey .. .. .. 90 90
471 32p. White-lipped Tamarin .. .. .. 90 90
472 34p. Common Squirrel-Monkey .. .. 90 90
473 37p. Common Gibbon .. .. .. 90 90
469/73 .. .. .. .. *Set of* 5 4·00 4·00

Nos. 469/73 were printed together, *se-tenant*, in horizontal strips of five throughout the sheet.

(Des Wendy Bramall. Litho B.D.T.)

**1989** (17 Nov). *Christmas. Christmas Tree Decorations. T* **123** *and similar square designs. Multicoloured. P* 13.
474 10p. Type **123** .. .. .. .. 30 30
a. Sheetlet. Nos. 474/85 .. .. 3·25
475 10p. Fairy .. .. .. .. .. 30 30
476 10p. Candles .. .. .. .. .. 30 30
477 10p. Bird .. .. .. .. .. 30 30
478 10p. Present .. .. .. .. .. 30 30
479 10p. Carol-singer .. .. .. .. 30 30
480 10p. Christmas cracker .. .. .. 30 30
481 10p. Bauble .. .. .. .. .. 30 30
482 10p. Christmas stocking .. .. .. 30 30
483 10p. Bell .. .. .. .. .. 30 30
484 10p. Fawn .. .. .. .. .. 30 30
485 10p. Church .. .. .. .. .. 30 30
474/85 .. .. .. .. *Set of* 12 3·25 3·25

Nos. 474/85 were printed, *se-tenant*, in sheetlets of 12.

124 Sark Post Office, *c.* 1890

(Des C. Abbott. Litho Enschedé)

**1990** (27 Feb). *Europa. Post Office Buildings. T* **124** *and similar horiz designs. P* 13½×14.
486 20p. blackish brown, sepia and pale cinnamon 60 60
487 20p. multicoloured .. .. .. .. 60 60
488 24p. blackish brown, sepia and pale cinnamon 75 75
489 24p. multicoloured .. .. .. .. 75 75
486/9 .. .. .. .. *Set of* 4 2·50 2·50

Designs:—No. 487, Sark Post Office, 1990; 488, Arcade Post Office counter, St. Peter Port, *c.* 1840; 489, Arcade Post Office counter, St. Peter Port, 1990.

125 Penny Black and Mail Steamer off St. Peter Port, 1840

(Des Jennifer Toombs. Litho Questa)

**1990** (3 May). *150th Anniv of the Penny Black. T* **125** *and similar horiz designs. Multicoloured. P* 14.
490 14p. Type **125** .. .. .. .. .. 45 45
491 20p. Penny Red, 1841, and pillar box of 1853 60 60
492 32p. Bisected 2d., 1940, and German Army band .. .. .. .. .. 90 90
493 34p. Regional 3d., 1958, and Guernsey emblems .. .. .. .. .. 95 95
494 37p. Independent postal administration 1½d., 1969, and queue outside Main Post Office 1·00 1·00
490/4 .. .. .. .. *Set of* 5 3·50 3·50
**MS**495 151×116 mm. Nos. 490/4 .. .. 3·50 3·50

No. **MS**495 also commemorates "Stamp World London 90" International Stamp Exhibition. It was reissued on 24 August 1990 overprinted for "NEW ZEALAND 1980" and sold at this international stamp exhibition in Auckland.

126 Lt. Philip Saumarez writing Log Book

(Des R. Granger Barrett. Litho Enschedé)

**1990** (26 July). *250th Anniv of Anson's Circumnavigation. T* **126** *and similar horiz designs. Multicoloured. P* 13½×14.
496 14p. Type **126** .. .. .. .. .. 45 45
497 20p. Anson's squadron leaving Portsmouth, 1740 .. .. .. .. .. 60 60
498 29p. Ships at St. Catherine's Island, Brazil .. 90 90
499 34p. H.M.S. *Tryal* (sloop) dismasted, Cape Horn, 1741 .. .. .. .. .. 95 95
500 37p. Crew of H.M.S. *Centurion* on Juan Fernandez .. .. .. .. .. 1·00 1·00
496/500 .. .. .. .. *Set of* 5 3·50 3·50

127 Grey Seal and Pup

128 Blue Tit and Great Tit

(Des Jennifer Toombs. Litho Questa)

**1990** (16 Oct). *Marine Life. T* **127** *and similar horiz designs. Multicoloured. P* 14½.
501 20p Type **127** .. .. .. .. .. 60 60
502 26p Bottle-nosed Dolphin .. .. .. 80 80
503 31p Basking Shark .. .. .. .. 85 85
504 37p Common Porpoise .. .. .. 1·10 1·10
501/4 .. .. .. .. *Set of* 4 3·00 3·00

(Des Wendy Bramall. Litho B.D.T.)

**1990** (16 Oct). *Christmas. Winter Birds. T* **128** *and similar square designs. Multicoloured. P* 13.
505 10p. Type **128** .. .. .. .. .. 25 25
a. Sheetlet of 12. Nos. 505/16 .. .. 3·00
506 10p. Snow Bunting .. .. .. .. 25 25
507 10p. Common Kestrel .. .. .. .. 25 25
508 10p. Common Starling .. .. .. .. 25 25
509 10p. Greenfinch .. .. .. .. 25 25
510 10p. European Robin .. .. .. .. 25 25
511 10p. Winter Wren .. .. .. .. 25 25
512 10p. Barn Owl .. .. .. .. .. 25 25
513 10p. Mistle Thrush .. .. .. .. 25 25
514 10p. Grey Heron .. .. .. .. 25 25
515 10p. Chaffinch .. .. .. .. .. 25 25
516 10p. Common Kingfisher .. .. .. 25 25
505/16 .. .. .. .. *Set of* 12 3·00 3·00

Nos. 505/16 were printed, *se-tenant*, in sheetlets of 12.

129 Air Raid and 1941 ½d. Stamp

(Des C. Abbott. Litho B.D.T.)

**1991** (18 Feb). *50th Anniv of First Guernsey Stamps. T* **129** *and similar square designs. Multicoloured. P* 13½.
517 37p. Type **129** .. .. .. .. .. 1·10 1·10
a. Booklet pane. Nos. 517/19 .. .. 3·25
518 53p. 1941 1d. stamp .. .. .. .. 1·25 1·10
519 57p. 1941 2½d. stamp .. .. .. .. 1·25 1·10
517/19 .. .. .. .. *Set of* 3 3·25 3·00

Booklet pane No. 517a exists in three versions which differ in the order of the stamps from left to right and in the information printed on the pane margins.

130 Visit of Queen Victoria to Guernsey, and Discovery of Neptune, 1846

(Des Jennifer Toombs. Litho Enschedé)

**1991** (30 Apr). *Europa. Europe in Space. T* **130** *and similar horiz designs. Multicoloured. P* 13½×14.
520 21p. Type **130** .. .. .. .. .. 50 50
521 21p. Visit of Queen Elizabeth II and Prince Philip to Sark, and "Sputnik" (first artificial satellite), 1957 .. .. .. 50 50
522 26p. Maiden voyage of *Sarnia* (ferry), and "Vostok 1" (first manned space flight), 1961 .. .. .. .. .. .. 60 60
523 26p. Cancelling Guernsey stamps, and first manned landing on Moon, 1969 .. 60 60
520/3 .. .. .. .. *Set of* 4 2·00 2·00

131 Children in Guernsey Sailing Trust "GP14" Dinghy

132 Pair of Oystercatchers

(Des C. Abbott. Litho B.D.T.)

**1991** (2 July). *Centenary of Guernsey Yacht Club. T* **131** *and similar vert designs. Multicoloured. P* 14.
524 15p. Type **131** .. .. .. .. .. 30 35
525 21p. Guernsey Regatta .. .. .. .. 40 45
526 26p. Lombard Channel Islands Challenge race 50 55
527 31p. Rolex Swan Regatta .. .. .. 60 65
528 37p. Old Gaffers' Association gaff-rigged yacht 75 80
524/8 .. .. .. .. *Set of* 5 2·25 2·50
**MS**529 163×75 mm. Nos. 524/8 .. .. 2·50 2·75

(Des Wendy Bramall. Litho Questa)

**1991** (15 Oct). *Nature Conservation. L'Eree Shingle Bank Reserve. T* **132** *and similar horiz designs. Multicoloured. P* 14½.
530 15p. Type **132** .. .. .. .. .. 30 35
a. Horiz strip of 5. Nos 530/4 .. .. 1·50
531 15p. Three Turnstones .. .. .. .. 30 35
532 15p. Dunlins and Turnstones .. .. .. 30 35
533 15p. Curlew and Turnstones .. .. .. 30 35
534 15p. Ringed Plover with Chicks .. .. 30 35
535 21p. Gull and wild flowers .. .. .. 40 45
a. Horiz strip of 5. Nos. 535/9 .. .. 2·00
536 21p. Yellow Horned Poppy .. .. .. 40 45
537 21p. Pair of Stone Chats and wild flowers .. 40 45
538 21p. Wild flowers on shingle .. .. .. 40 45
539 21p. Sea Kale on shore .. .. .. 40 45
530/9 .. .. .. .. *Set of* 10 3·25 3·50

Nos. 530/4 and 535/9 were each printed together, *se-tenant*, in horizontal strips of 5, throughout sheets of 20, with the backgrounds forming composite designs which continue onto the sheet margins.

133 "Rudolph the Red-nosed Reindeer" (Melanie Sharpe)

134 Queen Elizabeth II in 1952

(Litho B.D.T.)

**1991** (15 Oct). *Christmas. Children's Paintings. T* **133** *and similar square designs. Multicoloured. P* 13½×13.

| No. | Value | Description | Unused | Used |
|---|---|---|---|---|
| 540 | 12p. | Type **133** | 25 | 30 |
| | | a. Sheetlet of 12. Nos. 540/51 | 2·75 | |
| 541 | 12p. | "Christmas Pudding" (James Quinn) | 25 | 30 |
| 542 | 12p. | "Snowman" (Lisa Guille) | 25 | 30 |
| 543 | 12p. | "Snowman in Top Hat" (Jessica Ede-Golightly) | 25 | 30 |
| 544 | 12p. | "Robins and Christmas Tree" (Sharon Le Page) | 25 | 30 |
| 545 | 12p. | "Shepherds and Angels" (Anna Coquelin) | 25 | 30 |
| 546 | 12p. | "Nativity" (Claudine Lihou) | 25 | 30 |
| 547 | 12p. | "Three Wise Men" (Jonathan Le Noury) | 25 | 30 |
| 548 | 12p. | "Star of Bethlehem and Angels" (Marcia Mahy) | 25 | 30 |
| 549 | 12p. | "Christmas Tree" (Laurel Garfield) | 25 | 30 |
| 550 | 12p. | "Santa Claus" (Rebecca Driscoll) | 25 | 30 |
| 551 | 12p. | "Snowman and Star" (Ian Lowe) | 25 | 30 |
| 540/51 | | *Set of* 12 | 2·75 | 3·25 |

Nos. 540/51 were printed, *se-tenant*, in sheetlets of 12.

(Des C. Abbott. Litho Questa)

**1992** (6 Feb). *40th Anniv of Accession. T* **134** *and similar vert designs. Multicoloured. P* 14.

| No. | Value | Description | Unused | Used |
|---|---|---|---|---|
| 552 | 23p. | Type **134** | 45 | 50 |
| 553 | 28p. | Queen Elizabeth in 1977 | 55 | 60 |
| 554 | 33p. | Queen Elizabeth in 1986 | 65 | 70 |
| 555 | 39p. | Queen Elizabeth in 1991 | 75 | 80 |
| 552/5 | | *Set of* 4 | 2·10 | 2·25 |

**135** Christopher Columbus

(Des R. Ollington. Litho Walsall)

**1992** (6 Feb). *Europa. 500th Anniv of Discovery of America by Columbus. T* **135** *and similar horiz designs. Multicoloured. P* 13½×14.

| No. | Value | Description | Unused | Used |
|---|---|---|---|---|
| 556 | 23p. | Type **135** | 45 | 50 |
| 557 | 23p. | Examples of Columbus's signature | 45 | 50 |
| 558 | 28p. | *Santa Maria* | 55 | 60 |
| 559 | 28p. | Map of first voyage | 55 | 60 |
| 556/9 | | *Set of* 4 | 1·75 | 2·00 |
| **MS**560 | | 157×77 mm. Nos. 556/9 | 2·00 | 2·25 |

POSTAGE DUE STAMPS

D 1 Castle Cornet

D 2 St. Peter Port

(Des R. Granger Barrett. Photo Delrieu)

**969** (1 Oct). *Value in black; background colour given. No wmk. P* 12½ × 12.
)1 D 1 1d. plum .. .. .. .. .. .. 2·50 1·25
)2 2d. bright green .. .. .. .. .. 2·50 1·25
)3 3d. vermilion .. .. .. .. .. 4·00 4·00
)4 4d. ultramarine .. .. .. .. .. 5·00 5·00
)5 5d. yellow-ochre .. .. .. .. .. 6·00 6·00
)6 6d. turquoise-blue .. .. .. .. 9·00 8·00
)7 1s. lake-brown .. .. .. .. .. 21·00 20·00
)1/7 .. .. .. .. *Set of* 7 45·00 40·00

**971** (15 Feb)–**76**. *As Type* D 1 *but values in decimal currency.*
) 8 D 1 ½p. plum .. .. .. .. .. 10 10
) 9 1p. bright green .. .. .. .. 10 10
)10 2p. vermilion .. .. .. .. .. 10 10
)11 3p. ultramarine .. .. .. .. 10 15
)12 4p. yellow-ochre .. .. .. .. 15 15
)13 5p. turquoise-blue .. .. .. .. 15 15
)14 6p. violet (10.2.76) .. .. .. 20 20
)15 8p. light yellow-orange (7.10.75) .. 25 20
)16 10p. lake-brown .. .. .. .. 30 30
)17 15p. grey (10.2.76) .. .. .. .. 40 40
)8/17 .. .. .. .. *Set of* 10 1·50 1·60

(Photo Delrieu)

**977** (2 Aug)–**80**. *Face value in black; background colour given. P* 13.
)18 D 2 ½p. lake-brown .. .. .. .. 10 10
)19 1p. bright purple .. .. .. .. 10 10
)20 2p. bright orange .. .. .. .. 10 10
)21 3p. vermilion .. .. .. .. 10 10
)22 4p. turquoise-blue .. .. .. .. 15 15
)23 5p. yellow-green .. .. .. .. 15 15
)24 6p. turquoise-green .. .. .. .. 20 20
)25 8p. brown-ochre .. .. .. .. 25 25
)26 10p. ultramarine .. .. .. .. 30 30
)27 14p. green (5.2.80) .. .. .. 35 35
)28 15p. bright violet .. .. .. .. 35 35
)29 16p. rose-red (5.2.80) .. .. .. 45 45
)18/29 .. .. .. .. *Set of* 12 2·10 2·10

D 3 Milking Cow

(Litho Questa)

**982** (13 July). *Guernsey Scenes, circa 1900. Horiz designs as Type* D 3. *P* 14½.
)30 1p. indigo, blue-black and bright green .. 10 10
)31 2p. sepia, yellow-brown and azure .. 10 10
)32 3p. blackish green, black and lilac .. 10 10
)33 4p. bottle-green, black and dull orange .. 10 10
)34 5p. dp violet-blue, blue-black & turq-grn .. 10 10
)35 16p. deep grey-blue, deep blue and cobalt .. 30 35
)36 18p. steel-blue, indigo and apple-green .. 35 40
)37 20p. brown-olive, agate and pale blue .. 40 45
)38 25p. Prussian blue, blue-black and rose-pink 50 55
)39 30p. dp bluish grn, blackish ol & bistre-yell 60 65
)40 50p. olive-brown, sepia and dull violet-blue 1·00 1·10
)41 £1 light brown, brown and pale brown .. 2·00 2·10
)30/41 .. .. .. .. *Set of* 12 5·00 5·25

Designs:—2p. Vale Mill; 3p. Sark cottage; 4p. Quay-side, St. Peter ort; 5p. Well, Water Lane, Moulin Huet; 16p. Seaweed gathering; 8p. Upper Walk, White Rock; 20p. Cobo Bay; 25p. Saint's Bay; )p. La Coupee, Sark; 50p. Old Harbour, St. Peter Port; £1 reenhouses, Doyle Road, St. Peter Port.

## ALDERNEY

The following issues are provided by the Guernsey Post Office for se on Alderney. They are also valid for postal purposes throughout e rest of the Bailiwick of Guernsey.

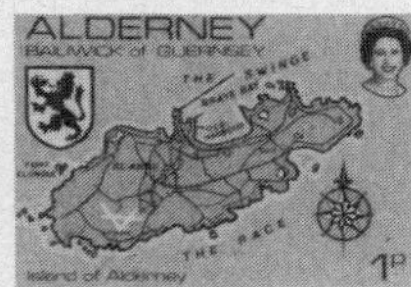


A 1 Island Map

(Des G. Drummond. Litho B.D.T. (20p., 21p., 23p.). Photo Courvoisier (others))

**983** (14 June)–**92**. *Island Scenes. Type* A 1 *and similar horiz designs. Multicoloured. Granite paper (Nos.* A1/12). *P* 15×14 (20p., 21p., 23p.) *or* 11½ (*others*).
1 1p. Type A **1** .. .. .. .. .. 10 10
2 4p. Hanging Rock .. .. .. .. 10 10
3 9p. States' Building, St. Anne .. .. 20 25
4 10p. St. Anne's Church .. .. .. 20 25
5 11p. Yachts in Braye Bay .. .. .. 20 25
6 12p. Victoria St., St. Anne .. .. .. 25 30
7 13p. Map of Channel .. .. .. .. 25 30
8 14p. Fort Clonque .. .. .. .. 30 35
9 15p. Corblets Bay and Fort .. .. .. 30 35
A10 16p. Old Tower, St. Anne .. .. .. 30 35
A11 17p. Golf course and Essex Castle .. .. 35 40
A12 18p. Old Harbour .. .. .. .. 35 40
A12*a* 20p. Quesnard Lighthouse (38×27 *mm*) (27.12.89) .. .. .. .. .. 40 45
A12*b* 21p. Braye Harbour (38×27 *mm*) (2.4.91) 40 45
A12*c* 23p. Island Hall (38×27 *mm*) (6.12.92) .. 45 50
A1/12*c* .. .. .. .. *Set of* 15 3·50 4·00

A2 Oystercatcher

(Des and photo Harrison)

**1984** (12 June). *Birds. Type* **A2** *and similar horiz designs. Multicoloured. P* 14½.
A13 9p. Type **A2** .. .. .. .. .. .. 2·00 1·75
A14 13p. Turnstone .. .. .. .. .. 2·75 2·50
A15 26p. Ringed Plover .. .. .. .. 8·00 5·00
A16 28p. Dunlin .. .. .. .. .. 8·50 5·50
A17 31p. Curlew .. .. .. .. .. 10·00 6·00
A13/17 .. .. .. .. *Set of* 5 28·00 18·00

A 3 Wessex Helicopter of the Queen's Flight

A 4 Royal Engineers, 1890

(Des A. Theobald. Photo Courvoisier)

**1985** (19 Mar). *50th Anniv of Alderney Airport. Type* **A 3** *and similar horiz designs. Multicoloured. Granite paper. P* 11½.
A18 9p. Type A **3** .. .. .. .. .. 3·50 2·50
A19 13p. Britten-Norman "Trislander" .. .. 4·00 3·50
A20 29p. De Havilland "Heron" .. .. .. 8·00 4·75
A21 31p. De Havilland "Dragon Rapide" .. 8·50 8·50
A22 34p. Saro "Windhover" .. .. .. 9·50 6·00
A18/22 .. .. .. .. *Set of* 5 30·00 20·00

(Des E. Stemp. Litho Harrison)

**1985** (24 Sept). *Regiments of the Alderney Garrison. Type* A **4** *and similar vert designs. Multicoloured. P* 14½.
A23 9p. Type A **4** .. .. .. .. .. 75 75
A24 14p. Duke of Albany's Own Highlanders (72nd Highland Regt), 1856 .. .. 1·50 1·25
A25 29p. Royal Artillery, 1855 .. .. .. 2·00 2·25
A26 31p. South Hampshire Regiment, 1810 .. 2·75 2·75
A27 34p. Royal Irish Regiment, 1782 .. .. 3·00 3·00
A23/7 .. .. .. .. *Set of* 5 9·00 9·00

No. A24 shows the tartan and insignia of the 78th Highland Regiment in error.

A 5 Fort Grosnez

A 6 *Liverpool* (full-rigged ship) 1902

(Des R. Reed. Litho Cartor, France)

**1986** (23 Sept). *Alderney Forts. Type* A **5** *and similar vert designs. Multicoloured. P* 13 × 13½.
A28 10p. Type A **5** .. .. .. .. .. 1·50 1·50
A29 14p. Fort Tourgis .. .. .. .. 2·25 2·25
A30 31p. Fort Clonque .. .. .. .. 5·25 5·25
A31 34p. Fort Albert .. .. .. .. 5·50 5·50
A28/31 .. .. .. .. *Set of* 4 13·00 13·00

(Des C. Jaques. Litho Questa)

**1987** (5 May). *Alderney Shipwrecks. Type* A **6** *and similar horiz designs. Multicoloured. P* 14 × 14½.
A32 11p. Type A **6** .. .. .. .. .. 1·75 1·25
A33 15p. *Petit Raymond* (schooner), 1906 .. 2·50 1·60
A34 29p. *Maina* (yacht), 1910 .. .. .. 4·50 4·50
A35 31p. *Burton* (steamer), 1911 .. .. .. 5·25 5·00
A36 34p. *Point Law* (oil tanker), 1975 .. .. 6·00 5·50
A32/6 .. .. .. .. *Set of* 5 18·00 16·00

***NEW INFORMATION***

The editor is always interested to correspond with people who have new information that will improve or correct the Catalogue.

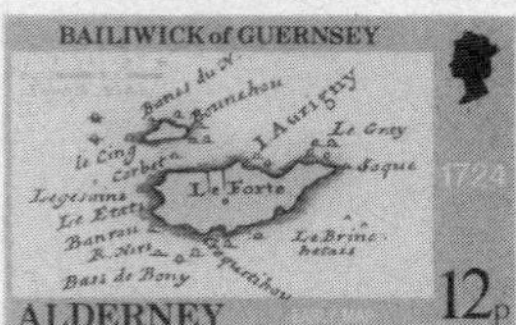


A 7 Moll's Map of 1724

(Des J. Cooter. Litho Enschedé)

**1989** (7 July). *250th Anniv of Bastide's Survey of Alderney. Type* A **7** *and similar horiz designs. P* 13½×14.
A37 12p. multicoloured .. .. .. .. 45 45
A38 18p. black, greenish blue and orange-brown 60 60
A39 27p. black, greenish blue & dull yellow-green 1·10 1·10
A40 32p. black, greenish blue and bright rose-red 1·10 1·10
A41 35p. multicoloured .. .. .. .. 1·25 1·25
A37/41 .. .. .. .. *Set of* 5 4·00 4·00

Designs:—18p. Bastide's survey of 1739; 27p. Goodwin's map of 1831; 32p. General Staff map of 1943; 35p. Ordnance Survey map, 1988.

A 8 H.M.S. *Alderney* (bomb ketch), 1738

(Des A. Theobald. Litho B.D.T.)

**1990** (3 May). *Royal Navy Ships named after Alderney. Type* A **8** *and similar horiz designs. P* 13½.
A42 14p. black and olive-bistre .. .. .. 45 45
A43 20p. black and orange-brown .. .. 60 60
A44 29p. black and cinnamon .. .. .. 1·10 1·10
A45 34p. black and pale turquoise-blue .. .. 1·10 1·10
A46 37p. black and cobalt .. .. .. 1·25 1·25
A42/6 .. .. .. .. *Set of* 5 4·00 4·00

Designs:—20p. H.M.S. *Alderney* (sixth rate), 1742; 29p. H.M.S. *Alderney* (sloop), 1755; 34p. H.M.S. *Alderney* (submarine), 1945; 37p. H.M.S. *Alderney* (fishery protection vessel), 1979.

A 9 Wreck of H.M.S. *Victory*, 1744

(Des A. Theobald. Litho Cartor, France)

**1991** (30 Apr). *Automation of The Casquets Lighthouse. Type* A **9** *and similar horiz designs. Multicoloured. P* 14×13½.
A47 21p. Type A **9** .. .. .. .. .. 50 50
A48 26p. Lighthouse keeper's daughter rowing back to the Casquets .. .. .. 60 60
A49 31p. Helicopter leaving pad on St. Thomas Tower .. .. .. .. .. 70 70
A50 37p. Migrating birds over lighthouse .. 1·00 1·00
A51 50p. Trinity House vessel *Patricia* and arms 1·40 1·40
A47/51 .. .. .. .. *Set of* 5 3·75 3·75

# ISLE OF MAN

## REGIONAL ISSUES

Although specifically issued for use in the Isle of Man, these issues were also valid for use throughout Great Britain.

**DATES OF ISSUE:** The note at the beginning of Guernsey also applies here.

Nos. 8/11 and current stamps of Great Britain were withdrawn from sale on the island from 5 July 1973 when the independent postal administration was established but remained valid for use there until 5 August 1973. They also remained on sale at the Philatelic Sales counters in the United Kingdom until 4 July 1974.

1

2

3

(Des J. Nicholson. Portrait by Dorothy Wilding Ltd. Photo Harrison)

**1958** (18 Aug)–**68**. *W* **179**. *P* 15 × 14.
1 **1** 2½d. carmine-red (8.6.64) .. .. 45 80
2 **2** 3d. deep lilac .. .. .. 20 10
a. Chalk-surfaced paper (17.5.63) .. 16·00 11·00
p. One centre phosphor band (27.6.68) 20 30
3 4d. ultramarine (7.2.66) .. .. 1·50 1·10
p. Two phosphor bands (5.7.67) .. 20 15
1/3p .. .. .. .. .. *Set of* 3 55 90

No. 2a was released in London sometime after 17 May 1963, this being the date of issue in Douglas.

**1968–69**. *No wmk. Chalk-surfaced paper. PVA gum. One centre phosphor band* (*Nos.* 5/6) *or two phosphor bands* (*others*). *P* 15 × 14.
4 **2** 4d. blue (24.6.68) .. .. .. .. 20 25
5 4d. olive-sepia (4.9.68) .. .. .. 20 30
6 4d. bright vermilion (26.2.69) .. .. 45 60
7 5d. royal blue (4.9.68) .. .. .. 45 60
4/7 .. .. .. .. .. *Set of* 4 1·00 1·60

(Des J. Matthews. Portrait after plaster cast by Arnold Machin. Photo Harrison)

**1971** (7 July). *Decimal Currency. Chalk-surfaced paper. One centre phosphor band* (2½p.) *or two phosphor bands* (*others*). *P* 15 × 14.
8 **3** 2½p. bright magenta .. .. .. 20 15
9 3p. ultramarine .. .. .. .. 20 15
10 5p. reddish violet .. .. .. 70 75
11 7½p. chestnut .. .. .. .. 70 90
8/11 .. .. .. .. .. *Set of* 4 1·50 1·75

All values exist with PVA gum on ordinary cream paper and the 2½p. and 3p. also on fluorescent white paper.

## INDEPENDENT POSTAL ADMINISTRATION

4 Castletown

5 Manx Cat

(Des J. Nicholson. Photo Courvoisier)

**1973** (5 July)–**75**. *Horiz designs as T* **4** (½p. *to* 9p., 11p. *and* 13p.) *or vert designs as T* **5** (*others*). *Multicoloured. Granite paper. P* 11½.
12 ½p. Type **4** .. .. .. .. .. 10 10
13 1p. Port Erin .. .. .. .. .. 10 10
14 1½p. Snaefell .. .. .. .. .. 10 10
15 2p. Laxey .. .. .. .. .. 10 10
16 2½p. Tynwald Hill .. .. .. .. 10 10
17 3p. Douglas Promenade .. .. .. 10 10
18 3½p. Port St. Mary .. .. .. .. 15 15
19 4p. Fairy Bridge .. .. .. .. 15 15
20 4½p. As 2½p. (8.1.75) .. .. .. 20 20
21 5p. Peel .. .. .. .. .. 20 20
22 5½p. As 3p. (28.5.75) .. .. .. 25 25
23 6p. Cregneish .. .. .. .. .. 25 25
24 7p. As 2p. (28.5.75) .. .. .. 30 30
25 7½p. Ramsey Bay .. .. .. .. 25 25
26 8p. As 7½p. (8.1.75) .. .. .. 35 35
27 9p. Douglas Bay .. .. .. .. 30 35
28 10p. Type **5** .. .. .. .. .. 30 35
29 11p. Monk's Bridge, Ballasalla (29.10.75) .. 45 50
30 13p. Derbyhaven (29.10.75) .. .. 55 50
31 20p. Manx Loaghtyn Ram .. .. .. 65 65
32 50p. Manx Shearwater .. .. .. 1·60 1·60
33 £1 Viking longship .. .. .. 3·25 3·25
12/33 .. .. .. .. *Set of* 22 9·00 9·00

Some printings from late 1973 have invisible gum.

6 Viking landing on Man, A.D. 938

7 *Sutherland*

(Des J. Nicholson. Photo Harrison)

**1973** (5 July). *Inauguration of Postal Independence. P* 14.
34 **6** 15p. multicoloured .. .. .. .. 80 80

(Des J. Nicholson. Photo Harrison)

**1973** (4 Aug). *Steam Railway Centenary. T* **7** *and similar horiz designs showing steam locomotives. Multicoloured. P* 15 × 14.
35 2½p. Type **7** .. .. .. .. .. 20 20
36 3p. *Caledonia* .. .. .. .. .. 20 20
37 7½p. *Kissack* .. .. .. .. .. 1·40 1·50
38 9p. *Pender* .. .. .. .. .. 1·50 1·50
35/8 .. .. .. .. .. *Set of* 4 3·00 3·00

8 Leonard Randles, First Winner, 1923

(Des J. Nicholson. Litho J.W.)

**1973** (4 Sept). *Golden Jubilee of the Manx Grand Prix. T* **8** *and similar horiz design. Multicoloured. P* 14.
39 3p. Type **8** .. .. .. .. .. 30 20
40 3½p. Alan Holmes, Double Winner, 1957 .. 30 20

9 Princess Anne and Capt. Mark Phillips

(Des A. Larkins. Recess and litho D.L.R.)

**1973** (14 Nov). *Royal Wedding. P* 13½.
41 **9** 25p. multicoloured .. .. .. 1·00 90

10 Badge, Citation and Sir William Hillary (Founder)

(Des J. Nicholson. Photo Courvoisier)

**1974** (4 Mar). *150th Anniv of Royal National Lifeboat Institution. T* **10** *and similar horiz designs. Multicoloured. Granite paper. P* 11½.
42 3p. Type **10** .. .. .. .. .. 10 10
43 3½p. Wreck of *St. George*, 1830 .. .. 15 15
44 8p. R.N.L.B. *Manchester & Salford*, 1868–87 60 65
45 10p. R.N.L.B. *Osman Gabriel* .. .. 60 65
42/5 .. .. .. .. .. *Set of* 4 1·25 1·40

11 Stanley Woods, 1935

(Des J. Nicholson. Litho D.L.R.)

**1974** (29 May). *Tourist Trophy Motor-cycle Races* (1*st issue*). *T* **11** *and similar horiz designs. Multicoloured. P* 13 × 13½.
46 3p. Type **11** .. .. .. .. .. 10 10
47 3½p. Freddy Frith, 1937 .. .. .. 10 10
48 8p. Max Deubel and Emil Horner, 1961 .. 45 45
49 10p. Mike Hailwood, 1961 .. .. .. 55 45
46/9 .. .. .. .. .. *Set of* 4 1·10 1·00

See also Nos. 63/6.

12 Rushen Abbey and Arms

(Des J. Nicholson from ideas by G. Kneale. Litho Questa (3½p., 10p.) or J.W. (others))

**1974** (18 Sept). *Historical Anniversaries. T* **12** *and similar horiz designs. Multicoloured. P* 14.
50 3½p. Type **12** .. .. .. .. .. 10 10
51 4½p. Magnus Haraldson rows King Edgar on the Dee .. .. .. .. .. 10 10
52 8p. King Magnus and Norse fleet .. .. 40 40
53 10p. Bridge at Avignon and bishop's mitre .. 50 50
50/3 .. .. .. .. .. *Set of* 4 1·00 1·00

Nos. 50 and 53 mark the 600th Death Anniv of William Russell, Bishop of Sodor and Man, and Nos. 51/2 the 1000th Anniv of the rule of King Magnus Haraldson.

13 Churchill and Bugler Dunne at Colenso, 1899

(Des G. Kneale. Photo Courvoisier)

**1974** (22 Nov). *Birth Centenary of Sir Winston Churchill. T* **13** *and similar horiz designs. Multicoloured. Granite paper. P* 11½.
54 3½p. Type **13** .. .. .. .. .. 10 10
55 4½p. Churchill and Government Buildings, Douglas .. .. .. .. .. 10 10
56 8p. Churchill and Manx ack-ack crew .. 25 35
57 20p. Churchill as Freeman of Douglas .. 65 55
54/7 .. .. .. .. .. *Set of* 4 1·00 1·00
**MS**58 121 × 91 mm. Nos. 54/7 .. .. .. 1·00 1·00

No. **MS**58 is inscribed "30th Nov. 1974".

14 Cabin School and Names of Pioneers

(Des J. Nicholson. Photo Courvoisier)

**1975** (14 Mar). *Manx Pioneers in Cleveland, Ohio. T* **14** *and similar horiz designs. Multicoloured. Granite paper. P* 11½.
59 4½p. Type **14** .. .. .. .. .. 10 10
60 5½p. Terminal Tower Building, J. Gill and R. Carran .. .. .. .. .. 15 10
61 8p. Clague House Museum, and Robert and Margaret Clague .. .. .. .. 35 40
62 10p. S.S. *William T. Graves* and Thomas Quayle 50 50
59/62 .. .. .. .. .. *Set of* 4 1·00 1·00

15 Tom Sheard, 1923

(Des J. Nicholson. Litho J.W.)

**1975** (28 May). *Tourist Trophy Motor-cycle Races* (2*nd issue*). *T* **15** *and similar horiz designs. Multicoloured. P* 13½.
63 5½p. Type **15** .. .. .. .. .. 10 15
64 7p. Walter Handley, 1925 .. .. .. 20 20
65 10p. Geoff Duke, 1955 .. .. .. .. 40 30
66 12p. Peter Williams, 1973 .. .. .. 40 45
63/6 .. .. .. .. .. *Set of* 4 1·00 1·00

16 Sir George Goldie and Birthplace

17 Title Page of Manx Bible

(Des G. Kneale. Photo Courvoisier)

**1975** (9 Sept). *50th Death Anniv of Sir George Goldie. T* **16** *and similar multicoloured designs. Granite paper. P* 11½.
67 5½p. Type **16** .. .. .. .. .. 10 15
68 7p. Goldie and map of Africa (*vert*) .. 20 20
69 10p. Goldie as President of Geographical Society (*vert*) .. .. .. .. .. 40 30
70 12p. River scene on the Niger .. .. 40 45
67/70 .. .. .. .. .. *Set of* 4 1·00 1·00

(Des J. Nicholson. Litho Questa)

**1975** (29 Oct). *Christmas and Bicentenary of Manx Bible. T* **17** *and similar horiz designs. Multicoloured. P* 14.
71 5½p. Type **17** .. .. .. .. .. 15 15
72 7p. Rev. Philip Moore and Ballaugh Old Church .. .. .. .. .. 20 20
73 11p. Bishop Hildesley and Bishops Court .. 40 35
74 13p. John Kelly saving Bible manuscript .. 45 40
71/4 .. .. .. .. .. *Set of* 4 1·10 1·00

**18** William Christian listening to Patrick Henry   **19** First Horse Tram, 1876

(Des and litho J.W.)

**976** (12 Mar). *Bicentenary of American Revolution. T* **18** *and similar vert designs. Multicoloured. P* 13½.
'5 5½p. Type **18** .. .. .. .. .. .. 15 15
'6 7p. Conveying the Fincastle Resolutions .. 20 20
'7 13p. Patrick Henry and William Christian .. 35 35
'8 20p. Christian as an Indian fighter .. .. 50 50
'5/8 .. .. .. .. .. *Set of* 4 1·10 1·10
**MS**79 153 × 89 mm. Nos. 75/8. P 14 .. .. 1·90 2·50

(Des J. Nicholson. Photo Courvoisier)

**976** (26 May). *Douglas Horse Trams Centenary. T* **19** *and similar horiz designs. Multicoloured. Granite paper. P* 11½.
30 5½p. Type **19** .. .. .. .. .. .. 10 15
31 7p. "Toast-rack" tram, 1890 .. .. .. 15 15
32 11p. Horse-bus, 1895 .. .. .. .. .. 45 35
33 13p. Royal tram, 1972 .. .. .. .. 50 45
30/3 .. .. .. .. .. *Set of* 4 1·10 1·00

**20** Barroose Beaker   **21** Diocesan Banner

(Des J. Nicholson. Photo Courvoisier)

**976** (28 July). *Europa. Ceramic Art. T* **20** *and similar multicoloured designs. Granite paper. P* 11½.
34 5p. Type **20** .. .. .. .. .. 20 25
a. Strip of 3. Nos. 84/6 .. .. .. 75 75
35 5p. Souvenir teapot .. .. .. .. 20 25
36 5p. Laxey jug .. .. .. .. .. 20 25
37 10p. Cronk Aust food vessel (*horiz*) .. .. 40 45
a. Strip of 3. Nos. 87/9 .. .. .. 1·50 1·50
38 10p. Sansbury bowl (*horiz*) .. .. .. 40 45
39 10p. Knox urn (*horiz*) .. .. .. .. 40 45
34/9 .. .. .. .. .. *Set of* 6 2·00 2·00
Nos. 84/6 and 87/9 were each printed in sheets of 9 (3 × 3) the three esigns being horizontally and vertically *se-tenant*.

(Des G. Kneale. Litho Questa)

**976** (14 Oct). *Christmas and Centenary of Mothers' Union. T* **21** *and similar vert designs. Multicoloured. P* 14½.
90 6p. Type **21** .. .. .. .. .. 15 15
91 7p. Onchan banner .. .. .. .. 15 15
92 11p. Castletown banner .. .. .. 40 35
93 13p. Ramsey banner .. .. .. .. 40 45
90/3 .. .. .. .. .. *Set of* 4 1·00 1·00

**22** Queen Elizabeth II

(Des A. Larkins. Litho and recess D.L.R.)

**977** (1 Mar). *Silver Jubilee. T* **22** *and similar multicoloured designs. P* 14 × 13 (*7p.*) *or* 13 × 14 (*others*).
94 6p. Type **22** .. .. .. .. .. 20 20
95 7p. Queen Elizabeth and Prince Philip (*vert*) 20 20
96 25p. Queen Elizabeth .. .. .. .. 80 70
94/6 .. .. .. .. .. *Set of* 3 1·10 1·00
The 25p. is similar to T **22** but has the portrait on the right.

**23** Carrick Bay from "Tom-the-Dipper"

(Des J. Nicholson. Litho Questa)

**977** (26 May). *Europa. Landscapes. T* **23** *and similar horiz design. Multicoloured. P* 13½ × 14.
97 6p. Type **23** .. .. .. .. .. 20 20
98 10p. View from Ramsey .. .. .. .. 30 30

**24** F. A. Applebee, 1912

(Des J. Nicholson. Litho J.W.)

**1977** (26 May). *Linked Anniversaries. T* **24** *and similar horiz designs. Multicoloured. P* 13½.
99 6p. Type **24** .. .. .. .. .. 15 15
100 7p. St. John Ambulance Brigade at Governor's Bridge, *c.* 1938 .. .. .. 15 20
101 11p. Scouts working scoreboard .. .. 40 40
102 13p. John Williams, 1976 .. .. .. 40 40
99/102 .. .. .. .. .. *Set of* 4 1·00 1·00
The events commemorated are: 70th Anniv of Manx TT; 70th Anniv of Boy Scouts; Centenary of St John Ambulance Brigade.

**25** Old Summer House, Mount Morrison, Peel

(Des and photo Courvoisier)

**1977** (19 Oct). *Bicentenary of the First Visit of John Wesley. T* **25** *and similar horiz designs. Multicoloured. Granite paper. P* 11½.
103 6p. Type **25** .. .. .. .. .. 15 15
104 7p. Wesley preaching in Castletown Square 20 20
105 11p. Wesley preaching outside Braddan Church .. .. .. .. .. 35 35
106 13p. New Methodist Church, Douglas .. 40 40
103/6 .. .. .. .. .. *Set of* 4 1·00 1·00
Nos. 104/5 are larger, 38 × 26 mm.

**26** H.M.S. *Ben-My-Chree* and Short "Type 184" Seaplane, 1915

(Des A. Theobald. Litho J.W.)

**1978** (28 Feb). *R.A.F. Diamond Jubilee. T* **26** *and similar horiz designs. Multicoloured. P* 13½ × 14.
107 6p. Type **26** .. .. .. .. .. 15 15
108 7p. H.M.S. *Vindex* and Bristol "Scout", 1915 20 20
109 11p. Boulton Paul "Defiant" over Douglas Bay, 1941 .. .. .. .. .. 40 35
110 13p. "Jaguar" over Ramsey, 1977 .. .. 45 40
107/10 .. .. .. .. .. *Set of* 4 1·10 1·00

**27** Watch Tower, Langness   **27a** Queen Elizabeth II

(Des J. Nicholson (½p. to £1), G. Kneale (£2). Litho Questa (½p. to 16p.). Photo Courvoisier (20p. to £2))

**1978** (28 Feb)–**81**. *Various multicoloured designs.*

(*a*) *As T* **27**. A. *P* 14. B. *P* 14½

| No. | | | A | | B | |
|---|---|---|---|---|---|---|
| 111 | ½p. | Type **27** | 20 | 10 | 40 | 40 |
| 112 | 1p. | Jurby Church | 20 | 10 | 30 | 30 |
| 113 | 6p. | Government Buildings | 30 | 25 | † | |
| 114 | 7p. | Tynwald Hill | 35 | 30 | 4·00 | 2·50 |
| 115 | 8p. | Milner's Tower | 35 | 30 | 50 | 30 |
| 116 | 9p. | Laxey Wheel | 35 | 35 | 50 | 30 |
| 117 | 10p. | Castle Rushen | 35 | 35 | 50 | 30 |
| 118 | 11p. | St. Ninian's Church | 40 | 40 | 50 | 40 |
| 119 | 12p. | Tower of Refuge | 45 | 45 | 40 | 30 |
| 120 | 13p. | St. German's Cathedral | 50 | 50 | 40 | 30 |
| 121 | 14p. | Point of Ayre Lighthouse | 50 | 50 | 50 | 40 |
| 122 | 15p. | Corrin's Tower | 60 | 60 | 50 | 30 |
| 123 | 16p. | Douglas Head Lighthouse | 75 | 65 | 27·00 | 20·00 |

(*b*) *As T* **27** *but size* 25 × 31 *mm. Granite paper. P* 11½ (18.10.78)
124 20p. Fuchsia .. .. .. .. .. 60 50
125 25p. Manx cat .. .. .. .. .. 75 65
126 50p. Chough .. .. .. .. .. 1·25 1·25
127 £1 Viking warrior .. .. .. .. 2·50 2·50

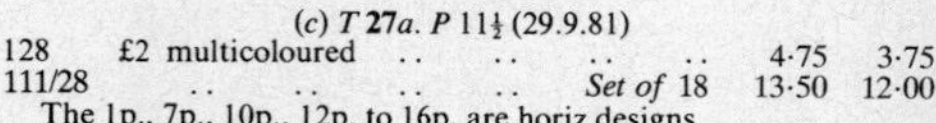

(*c*) *T* **27a**. *P* 11½ (29.9.81)
128 £2 multicoloured .. .. .. .. 4·75 3·75
111/28 .. .. .. .. *Set of* 18 13·50 12·00
The 1p., 7p., 10p., 12p. to 16p. are horiz designs.

**28** Queen Elizabeth in Coronation Regalia   **29** Wheel-headed Cross-slab

(Des G. Kneale. Litho Questa)

**1978** (24 May). *25th Anniv of Coronation. P* 14½ × 14.
132 **28** 25p. multicoloured .. .. .. .. 75 75

(Des J. Nicholson. Photo Courvoisier)

**1978** (24 May). *Europa. Sculpture. T* **29** *and similar vert designs showing Celtic and Norse Crosses. Multicoloured. Granite paper. P* 11½.
133 6p. Type **29** .. .. .. .. .. 15 15
a. Strip of 3. Nos. 133/5 .. .. .. 40 50
134 6p. Celtic wheel-cross .. .. .. .. 15 15
135 6p. Keeil Chiggyrt Stone .. .. .. 15 15
136 11p. Olaf Liotulfson Cross .. .. .. 25 30
a. Strip of 3. Nos. 136/8 .. .. .. 80 90
137 11p. Odd's and Thorleif's Crosses .. .. 25 30
138 11p. Thor Cross .. .. .. .. .. 25 30
133/8 .. .. .. .. .. *Set of* 6 1·10 1·25
Nos. 133/5 and 136/8 were each printed together, *se-tenant*, in horizontal and vertical strips of 3 throughout the sheet.

**30** J. K. Ward and Ward Library, Peel   **31** Hunt the Wren

(Des J.W. (7p.), G. Kneale (11p.), J. Nicholson (others). Litho J.W.)

**1978** (10 June). *Anniversaries and Events. T* **30** *and similar horiz designs. Multicoloured. Invisible gum. P* 13½.
139 6p. Type **30** .. .. .. .. .. 15 15
140 7p. Swimmer, cyclist and walker (42 × 26 *mm*) .. .. .. .. .. .. 20 20
141 11p. American Bald Eagle, Manx arms and maple leaf (42 × 26 *mm*) .. .. .. 35 35
142 13p. Lumber camp at Three Rivers, Quebec 40 40
139/42 .. .. .. .. .. *Set of* 4 1·00 1·00
Commemorations:—6, 13p. James Kewley Ward (Manx pioneer in Canada); 7p. Commonwealth Games, Edmonton; 11p. 50th anniversary of North American Manx Association.

(Des J. Nicholson. Litho J.W.)

**1978** (18 Oct). *Christmas. P* 13.
143 **31** 5p. multicoloured .. .. .. .. 30 25

**32** P. M. C. Kermode (founder) and *Nassa kermodei*   **33** Postman, 1859

(Des J. Nicholson. Litho Questa)

**1979** (27 Feb). *Centenary of Natural History and Antiquarian Society. T* **32** *and similar horiz designs. Multicoloured. P* 14.
144 6p. Type **32** .. .. .. .. .. 15 15
145 7p. Peregrine Falcon .. .. .. .. 20 20
146 11p. Fulmar .. .. .. .. .. 35 35
147 13p. *Epitriptus cowini* (fly) .. .. .. 40 40
144/7 .. .. .. .. .. *Set of* 4 1·00 1·00

(Des A. Theobald. Litho Questa)

**1979** (16 May). *Europa. Communications. T* **33** *and similar vert design. Multicoloured. P* 14½.
148 6p. Type **33** .. .. .. .. .. 20 20
149 11p. Postman, 1979 .. .. .. .. 30 30

**34** Viking Longship Emblem

**35** Viking Raid at Garwick

Two types of No. 150:

Type I. Wrongly inscribed "INSULAREM". "1979" imprint date.

Type II. Inscription corrected to "INSULARUM". "1980" imprint date.

(Des J. Nicholson. Litho Harrison (3, 4p.), J.W. (others))

**1979** (16 May)–**80**. *Millenium of Tynwald. Multicoloured.*

(*a*) *Vert designs as T* **34**. *P* 14½ × 14

150 3p. Type **34** (Type I) .. .. .. .. 15 15
 a. Booklet pane. Nos. 150 × 4, 151 × 2 (4p. stamps at top) .. .. .. .. 80
 ab. Ditto (4p. stamps in centre) .. .. 1·00
 b. Type II (29.9.80) .. .. .. .. 10 10
 ba. Booklet pane. Nos. 150b × 4, 151 × 2 (4p. stamps at bottom) .. .. .. 75
151 4p. "Three Legs of Man" emblem .. .. 15 15

(*b*) *Horiz designs as T* **35**. *P* 13

152 6p. Type **35** .. .. .. .. 15 15
153 7p. 10th-century meeting of Tynwald .. 20 20
154 11p. Tynwald Hill and St. John's Church .. 30 30
155 13p. Procession to Tynwald Hill .. .. 45 35
150/5 .. .. .. .. .. *Set of* 6 1·25 1·10

See also Nos. 188/9.

The 3 and 4p. values were printed in sheets containing ten blocks of 6 and five blocks of 4 separated by blank margins. The blocks of 6 contained four 3p. values and two 4p., *se-tenant*, with the 4p. in either the top or centre rows. The blocks of 4 contain the 4p. value only.

For details of No. 150ba see after No. 189.

**36** Queen and Court on Tynwald Hill

(Des G. Kneale. Litho Questa)

**1979** (5 July). *Royal Visit. T* **36** *and similar horiz design. Multicoloured. P* 14½.

156 7p. Type **36** .. .. .. .. .. 30 20
157 13p. Queen and procession from St. John's Church to Tynwald Hill .. .. .. 40 40

**37** *Odin's Raven*

(Des J. Nicholson. Litho Questa)

**1979** (19 Oct). *Voyage of "Odin's Raven". P* 14 × 14½.

158 **37** 15p. multicoloured .. .. .. .. 50 50

**38** John Quilliam seized by the Press Gang

**39** Young Girl with Teddybear and Cat

(Des A. Theobald. Litho Questa)

**1979** (19 Oct). *150th Death Anniv of Captain John Quilliam. T* **38** *and similar horiz designs. Multicoloured. P* 14.

159 6p. Type **38** .. .. .. .. .. 15 15
160 8p. Steering H.M.S. *Victory*, Battle of Trafalgar .. .. .. .. .. 20 20
161 13p. Capt. John Quilliam and H.M.S. *Spencer* 50 40
162 15p. Capt. John Quilliam (member of the House of Keys) .. .. .. .. 55 45
159/62 .. .. .. .. .. *Set of* 4 1·25 1·10

(Des Mrs E. Moore. Litho J.W.)

**1979** (19 Oct). *Christmas. International Year of the Child. T* **39** *and similar vert design. Multicoloured. P* 13.

163 5p. Type **39** .. .. .. .. .. 25 25
164 7p. Father Christmas with young children 35 35

**40** Conglomerate Arch, Langness

(Des J. Nicholson. Litho Questa)

**1980** (5 Feb). *150th Anniv of Royal Geographical Society. T* **40** *and similar horiz designs. Multicoloured. P* 14½.

165 7p. Type **40** .. .. .. .. .. 20 20
166 8p. Braaid Circle .. .. .. .. .. 20 20
167 12p. Cashtal-yn-Ard .. .. .. .. 30 30
168 13p. Volcanic Rocks at Scarlett .. .. 45 40
169 15p. Sugar-loaf Rock .. .. .. .. 55 45
165/9 .. .. .. .. .. *Set of* 5 1·50 1·40

**41** *Mona's Isle I*

(Des J. Nicholson. Photo Courvoisier)

**1980** (6 May). *150th Anniv of Isle of Man Steam Packet Company. T* **41** *and similar horiz designs. Multicoloured. Granite paper. P* 11½.

170 7p. Type **41** .. .. .. .. .. 20 20
171 8p. *Douglas I* .. .. .. .. .. 20 20
172 11½p. H.M.S. *Mona's Queen II* sinking U-boat 30 30
173 12p. H.M.S. *King Orry* at surrender of German fleet .. .. .. .. .. 30 30
174 13p. *Ben-My-Chree IV* .. .. .. .. 35 35
175 15p. *Lady of Mann II* .. .. .. .. 55 40
170/5 .. .. .. .. .. *Set of* 6 1·75 1·60
**MS**176 180 × 125 mm. Nos. 170/5 .. .. .. 1·75 1·75

No. **MS**176 was issued to commemorate the "London 1980" International Stamp Exhibition.

**42** Stained Glass Window, T. E. Brown Room, Manx Museum

(Des G. Kneale. Photo Courvoisier)

**1980** (6 May). *Europa. Personalities. Thomas Edward Brown (poet and scholar) Commemoration. T* **42** *and similar horiz design. Multicoloured. Granite paper. P* 11½.

177 7p. Type **42** .. .. .. .. .. 20 20
178 13½p. Clifton College, Bristol .. .. .. 40 40

**43** King Olav V

(Des J. Nicholson. Litho Questa)

**1980** (13 June). *Visit of King Olav of Norway, August* 1979. *P* 14 × 14½.

179 **43** 12p. multicoloured .. .. .. .. 50 50
**MS**180 125 × 157 mm. Nos. 158 and 179 .. .. 1·00 1·00

No. **MS**180 also commemorates the "NORWEX 80" Stamp Exhibition, Oslo.

**44** Winter Wren and View of Calf of Man

(Des J. Nicholson. Litho J.W.)

**1980** (29 Sept). *Christmas and Wildlife Conservation Year. T* **44** *and similar horiz design. Multicoloured. P* 13½ × 14.

181 6p. Type **44** .. .. .. .. .. 30 30
182 8p. European Robin and view of Port Erin Marine Biological Station .. .. .. 45 45

**45** William Kermode and Brig *Robert Quayle*, 1819

**46** Peregrine Falcon

(Des A. Theobald. Litho Questa)

**1980** (29 Sept). *Kermode Family in Tasmania Commemoration. T* **45** *and similar horiz designs. Multicoloured. P* 14½.

183 7p. Type **45** .. .. .. .. .. 20 20
184 9p. "Mona Vale", Van Diemen's Land, 1834 25 25
185 13½p. Ross Bridge, Tasmania .. .. .. 40 35
186 15p. "Mona Vale", Tasmania (completed 1868) .. .. .. .. .. 45 40
187 17½p. Robert Q. Kermode and Parliament Buildings, Tasmania .. .. .. .. 50 45
183/7 .. .. .. .. .. *Set of* 5 1·60 1·50

(Des J. Nicholson. Litho Harrison)

**1980** (29 Sept). *Booklet stamps. Vert designs as T* **46**. *Multicoloured. P* 14½ × 14.

188 1p. Type **46** .. .. .. .. .. 25 25
 a. Booklet pane. Nos. 151, 188 and 189 each × 2 .. .. .. .. .. 75
189 5p. Loaghtyn Ram .. .. .. .. 40 40

In addition to 40p. and 80p. booklets Nos. 188/9 also come from special booklet sheets of 60. These sheets contained No. 150ba and 188a, each × 5.

**47** Luggers passing Red Pier, Douglas

(Des J. Nicholson. Litho Questa)

**1981** (24 Feb). *Centenary of Royal National Mission to Deep Sea Fishermen. T* **47** *and similar horiz designs. Multicoloured. P* 14.

190 8p. Type **47** .. .. .. .. .. 25 25
191 9p. Peel Lugger *Wanderer* rescuing survivors from the *Lusitania* .. .. .. .. 30 30
192 18p. Nickeys leaving Port St. Mary Harbour 55 45
193 20p. Nobby entering Ramsey Harbour .. 55 50
194 22p. Nickeys *Sunbeam* and *Zebra* at Port Erin 60 50
190/4 .. .. .. .. .. *Set of* 5 2·00 1·75

**48** "Crosh Cuirn" Superstition

(Des J. Nicholson. Litho Questa)

**1981** (22 May). *Europa. Folklore. T* **48** *and similar horiz design. Multicoloured. P* 14½.

195 8p. Type **48** .. .. .. .. .. 25 25
196 18p. "Bollan Cross" superstition .. .. 55 55

**49** Lt. Mark Wilks (Royal Manx Fencibles) and Peel Castle

(Des A. Theobald. Litho Questa)

**981** (22 May). 150*th Death Anniv of Colonel Mark Wilks. T* **49** *and similar horiz designs. Multicoloured. P* 14.

97 8p. Type **49** .. .. .. .. .. .. 25 25
98 20p. Ensign Mark Wilks and Fort St. George, Madras .. .. .. .. .. 50 50
99 22p. Governor Mark Wilks and Napoleon, St. Helena .. .. .. .. .. 70 55
.00 25p. Col. Mark Wilks (Speaker of the House of Keys) and estate, Kirby .. .. 80 80
97/200 .. .. .. .. .. *Set of* 4 2·00 1·90

**50** Miss Emmeline Goulden (Mrs. Pankhurst) and Mrs. Sophia Jane Goulden

(Des A. Theobald. Litho Questa)

**981** (22 May). *Centenary of Manx Women's Suffrage. P* 14.

01 **50** 9p. black, olive-grey and stone .. .. 35 30

**51** Prince Charles and Lady Diana Spencer

(Des G. Kneale. Litho Harrison)

**981** (29 July). *Royal Wedding. P* 14.

02 **51** 9p. black, bright blue and pale blue .. 25 25
03 25p. black, bright blue and pink .. 75 75
**AS204** 130 × 183 mm. Nos. 202/3 × 2 .. .. 2·40 2·40

**52** Douglas War Memorial, Poppies and Commemorative Inscription

(Des A. Theobald. Photo Courvoisier)

**981** (29 Sept). 60*th Anniv of The Royal British Legion. T* **52** *and similar horiz designs. Multicoloured. Granite paper. P* 11½.

205 8p. Type **52** .. .. .. .. .. 25 25
206 10p. Major Robert Cain (war hero) .. .. 30 35
207 18p. Festival of Remembrance, Royal Albert Hall .. .. .. .. .. 55 45
208 20p. T.S.S. *Tynwald* at Dunkirk, May 1940 60 50
05/8 .. .. .. .. .. *Set of* 4 1·50 1·40

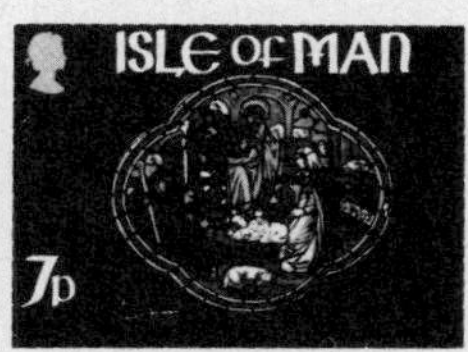


**53** Nativity Scene (stained-glass window, St. George's Church)

(Des J.W. (7p.), G. Kneale (9p.). Litho J.W.)

**981** (29 Sept). *Christmas. T* **53** *and similar multicoloured design. P* 14.

09 7p. Type **53** .. .. .. .. .. .. 20 20
10 9p. Children from Special School performing nativity play (48 × 30 *mm*) .. .. 25 25

The 7p. value also commemorates the bicentenary of St. George's Church, Douglas and the 9p. the International Year for Disabled Persons.

**54** Joseph and William Cunningham (founders of Isle of Man Boy Scout Movement) and Cunningham House Headquarters

(Des G. Kneale. Litho Questa)

**1982** (23 Feb). 75*th Anniv of Boy Scout Movement and* 125*th Birth Anniv of Lord Baden-Powell. T* **54** *and similar multicoloured designs. P* 14 × 14½ (19½*p.*) *or* 13½ × 14 (*others*).

211 9p. Type **54** .. .. .. .. .. 30 30
212 10p. Baden-Powell visiting Isle of Man, 1911 30 30
213 19½p. Baden-Powell and Scout emblem (40 × 31 *mm*) .. .. .. .. .. 55 55
214 24p. Scouts and Baden-Powell's last message 75 75
215 29p. Scout salute, handshake, emblem and globe .. .. .. .. .. 95 95
211/15 .. .. .. .. .. *Set of* 5 2·50 2·50

**55** *The Principals and Duties of Christianity* (Bishop T. Wilson) (first book printed in Manx, 1707)

(Des A. Theobald. Photo Courvoisier)

**1982** (1 June). *Europa. Historic Events. T* **55** *and similar horiz design. Multicoloured. Granite paper. P* 12 × 12½.

216 9p. Type **55** .. .. .. .. .. 25 25
217 19½p. Landing at Derbyhaven (visit of Thomas, 2nd Earl of Derby, 1507) .. 50 50

**56** Charlie Collier (first TT race (single cylinder) winner) and Tourist Trophy Race, 1907

(Des J. Nicholson. Litho Questa)

**1982** (1 June). 75*th Anniv of Tourist Trophy Motorcycle Racing. T* **56** *and similar horiz designs. Multicoloured. P* 14.

218 9p. Type **56** .. .. .. .. .. 20 20
219 10p. Freddie Dixon (Sidecar and Junior TT winner) and Junior TT race, 1927 .. 25 25
220 24p. Jimmie Simpson (TT winner and first to lap at 60, 70 and 80 mph) and Senior TT, 1932 .. .. .. .. .. .. 70 70
221 26p. Mike Hailwood (winner of fourteen TT's) and Senior TT, 1961 .. .. 90 80
222 29p. Jock Taylor (Sidecar TT winner, 1978, 1980 and 1981) and Sidecar TT (with Benga Johansson), 1980 .. .. 1·00 90
218/22 .. .. .. .. .. *Set of* 5 2·75 2·50

**57** *Mona I*

(Des J. Nicholson. Litho Questa)

**1982** (5 Oct). 150*th Anniv of Isle of Man Steam Packet Company Mail Contract. T* **57** *and similar horiz design. Multicoloured. P* 13½ × 14.

223 12p. Type **57** .. .. .. .. .. 40 40
224 19½p. *Manx Maid II* .. .. .. .. .. 60 60

**58** Three Wise Men bearing Gifts

**59** Princess Diana with Prince William

(Des and litho J.W.)

**1982** (5 Oct). *Christmas. T* **58** *and similar multicoloured design. P* 13 × 13½ (8*p.*) *or* 13½ × 13 (11*p.*).

225 8p. Type **58** .. .. .. .. .. 30 30
226 11p. Christmas snow scene (*vert*) .. .. 40 40

(Des G. Kneale. Litho Questa)

**1982** (12 Oct). 21*st Birthday of Princess of Wales and Birth of Prince William. Sheet* 100 × 83 *mm. P* 14½ × 14.

**MS**227 **59** 50p. multicoloured .. .. .. 2·00 2·00

**60** Opening of Salvation Army Citadel, and T.H. Cannell, J.P.

(Des A. Theobald. Photo Courvoisier)

**1983** (15 Feb). *Centenary of Salvation Army in Isle of Man. T* **60** *and similar horiz designs. Multicoloured. Granite paper. P* 11½.

228 10p. Type **60** .. .. .. .. .. 30 30
229 12p. Early meeting place and Gen. William Booth .. .. .. .. .. .. 40 40
230 19½p. Salvation Army band .. .. .. .. 60 60
231 26p. Treating lepers and Lt.-Col. Thomas Bridson .. .. .. .. .. 90 90
228/31 .. .. .. .. .. *Set of* 4 2·00 2·00

**61** Atlantic Puffins

**61a** "Queen Elizabeth II" (Ricardo Macarron)

(Des Colleen Corlett (£5), J. Nicholson (others). Litho Questa)

**1983** (15 Feb)–**85**. *Horiz designs as T* **61**, *showing sea birds, and T* **61a**. *Multicoloured. P* 14 (20*p.* to £1), 14 × 13½ (£5) *or* 14½ (*others*).

232 1p. Type **61** .. .. .. .. .. 15 15
233 2p. Northern Gannets .. .. .. .. 15 15
234 5p. Lesser Black-backed Gulls .. .. 30 30
235 8p. Common Cormorants .. .. .. 30 30
236 10p. Kittiwakes .. .. .. .. .. 35 35
237 11p. Shags .. .. .. .. .. 35 35
238 12p. Grey Herons .. .. .. .. 40 40
239 13p. Herring Gulls .. .. .. .. 40 40
240 14p. Razorbills .. .. .. .. .. 40 40
241 15p. Great Black-backed Gulls .. .. 50 50
242 16p. Common Shelducks .. .. .. 50 50
243 18p. Oystercatchers .. .. .. .. 60 60
244 20p. Arctic Terns (14.9.83) .. .. .. 75 75
245 25p. Common Guillemots (14.9.83) .. .. 1·00 1·00
246 50p. Redshanks (14.9.83) .. .. .. 1·75 1·75
247 £1 Mute Swans (14.9.83) .. .. .. 3·00 3·00
248 £5 Type **61a** (31.1.85) .. .. .. 10·00 10·50
232/48 .. .. .. .. .. *Set of* 17 18·00 18·00

Nos. 244/7 are larger, 39 × 26 mm.

**62** Design Drawings by Robert Casement for the Great Laxey Wheel

(Des J. Nicholson. Litho Questa)

**1983** (18 May). *Europa. The Great Laxey Wheel. T* **62** *and similar horiz design. P* 14.

249 10p. black, azure and buff .. .. .. .. 40 35
250 20½p. multicoloured .. .. .. .. .. 70 70

Design:—20½p. Robert Casement and the Great Laxey Wheel.

**63** Nick Keig (international yachtsman) and Trimaran *Three Legs of Man III*

**64** New Post Office Headquarters, Douglas

(Des J. Nicholson (10p., 31p.), Colleen Corlett (12p., 28p.). Photo Courvoisier)

**1983** (18 May). 150*th Anniv of King William's College. T* **63** *and similar horiz designs. Multicoloured. Granite paper. P* 11½.

251 10p. Type **63** .. .. .. .. .. .. 30 30
252 12p. King William's College, Castletown .. 40 40
253 28p. Sir William Bragg (winner of Nobel Prize for Physics) and spectrometer .. 90 90
254 31p. General Sir George White V.C. and action at Charasiah .. .. .. 1·10 1·10
251/4 .. .. .. .. .. *Set of* 4 2·40 2·40

(Des Colleen Corlett (10p.), J. Nicholson (15p.). Litho Questa)

**1983** (5 July). *World Communications Year and 10th Anniv of Isle of Man Post Office Authority. T* **64** *and similar vert design. Multicoloured. P* 14½.

255 10p. Type **64** .. .. .. .. .. .. 40 30
256 15p. As Type **6**, but inscr "POST OFFICE DECENNIUM 1983" .. .. .. 60 50

**65** Shepherds

(Des Colleen Corlett. Litho J.W.)

**1983** (14 Sept). *Christmas. T* **65** *and similar horiz design. Multicoloured. P* 13.

257 9p. Type **65** .. .. .. .. .. .. 50 50
258 12p. Three Kings .. .. .. .. .. 50 50

**66** *Manx King* (full-rigged ship)   **67** C.E.P.T. 25th Anniversary Logo

(Des J. Nicholson (10p. to 31p.); Colleen Corlett, J. Nicholson and J. Smith (miniature sheet). Litho Questa)

**1984** (14 Feb). *The Karran Fleet. T* **66** *and similar horiz designs. Multicoloured. P* 14.

259 10p. Type **66** .. .. .. .. .. .. 35 35
260 13p. *Hope* (barque) .. .. .. .. .. 45 45
261 20½p. *Rio Grande* (brig) .. .. .. .. 70 70
262 28p. *Lady Elizabeth* (barque) .. .. .. 85 85
263 31p. *Sumatra* (barque) .. .. .. .. 95 95
259/63 .. .. .. .. .. .. *Set of* 5 3·00 3·00
**MS**264 103×94 mm. 28p. As No. 262, 31p. *Lady Elizabeth* (as shown on Falkland Islands No. 417) (*sold at* 60p.) .. .. .. .. .. .. 2·75 2·75

No. **MS**264 was issued to commemorate links between the Isle of Man and Falkland Islands.

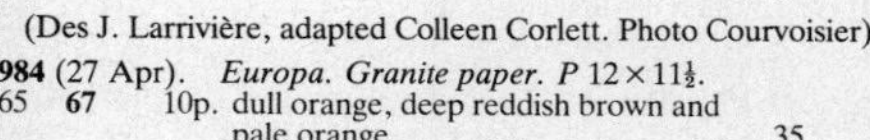

(Des J. Larrivière, adapted Colleen Corlett. Photo Courvoisier)

**1984** (27 Apr). *Europa. Granite paper. P* 12×11½.

265 **67** 10p. dull orange, deep reddish brown and pale orange .. .. .. .. 35 35
266 20½p. light blue, deep blue and pale blue 70 70

**68** Railway Air Services "D.H.84"   **69** Window from Glencrutchery House, Douglas

(Des A. Theobald. Litho Questa)

**1984** (27 Apr). (27 Apr). *50th Anniv of First Official Airmail to the Isle of Man and 40th Anniv of International Civil Aviation Organization. T* **68** *and similar horiz designs. Multicoloured. P* 14.

267 11p. Type **68** .. .. .. .. .. .. 35 35
268 13p. West Coast Air Services "D.H.86" .. .. 40 40
269 26p. B.E.A. "DC-3" .. .. .. .. .. 85 85
270 28p. B.E.A. Vickers "Viscount" .. .. .. 95 95
271 31p. Telair "Islander" .. .. .. .. .. 1·10 1·10
267/71 .. .. .. .. .. .. *Set of* 5 3·25 3·25

(Des D. Swinton. Litho J.W.)

**1984** (21 Sept). *Christmas. Stained-glass Windows. T* **69** *and similar vert design. Multicoloured. P* 14.

272 10p. Type **69** .. .. .. .. .. .. 50 50
273 13p. Window from Lonan Old Church.. .. .. 50 50

**70** William Cain's Birthplace, Ballasalla

(Des J. Nicholson. Litho Questa)

**1984** (21 Sept). *William Cain (civic leader, Victoria) Commemoration. T* **70** *and similar horiz designs. Multicoloured. P* 14½ × 14.

274 11p. Type **70** .. .. .. .. .. .. 30 30
275 22p. The *Anna* leaving Liverpool, 1852 .. .. 65 65
276 28p. Early Australian railway .. .. .. .. 90 90
277 30p. William Cain as Mayor of Melbourne, and Town Hall .. .. .. .. .. 1·00 1·00
278 33p. Royal Exhibition Building, Melbourne .. 1·10 1·10
274/8 .. .. .. .. .. .. *Set of* 5 3·50 3·50

**71** Queen Elizabeth II and Commonwealth Parliamentary Association Badge

(Des and litho J.W.)

**1984** (21 Sept). *Links with the Commonwealth. 30th Commonwealth Parliamentary Association Conference. T* **71** *and similar horiz design. Multicoloured. P* 14.

279 14p. Type **71** .. .. .. .. .. .. 45 45
280 33p. Queen Elizabeth II and Manx emblem .. 1·00 1·00

**72** Cunningham House Headquarters, and Mrs. Willie Cunningham and Mrs. Joseph Cunningham (former Commissioners)

(Des Colleen Corlett. Photo Courvoisier)

**1985** (31 Jan). *75th Anniv of Girl Guide Movement. T* **72** *and similar horiz designs. Multicoloured. Granite paper. P* 11½.

281 11p. Type **72** .. .. .. .. .. .. 45 45
282 14p. Princess Margaret, Isle of Man standard and guides .. .. .. .. .. .. 70 70
283 29p. Lady Olave Baden-Powell opening Guide Headquarters, 1955 .. .. .. .. 1·10 1·10
284 31p. Guide uniforms from 1910 to 1985 .. .. 1·25 1·25
285 34p. Guide handclasp, salute and early badge .. 1·50 1·50
281/5 .. .. .. .. .. .. *Set of* 5 4·50 4·50

**73** Score of Manx National Anthem

(Des D. Swinton. Photo Courvoisier)

**1985** (24 Apr). *Europa. European Music Year. T* **73** *and similar horiz designs. Granite paper. P* 11½.

286 12p. black, orange-brown and chestnut .. .. 45 45
a. Horiz pair. Nos. 286/7 .. .. .. .. 90 90
287 12p. black, orange-brown and chestnut .. .. 45 45
288 22p. black, bright new blue and new blue .. 95 95
a. Horiz pair. Nos. 288/9 .. .. .. .. 1·90 1·90
289 22p. black, bright new blue and new blue .. 95 95
286/9 .. .. .. .. .. .. *Set of* 4 2·50 2·50

Designs:—No. 287, William H. Gill (lyricist); 288, Score of hymn "Crofton"; 289, Dr. John Clague (composer).

Nos. 286/7 and 288/9 were printed together, *se-tenant*, in horizontal pairs throughout the sheets.

**74** Charles Rolls in 20 h.p. Rolls-Royce (1906 Tourist Trophy Race)

(Des A. Theobald. Litho Questa)

**1985** (25 May). *Century of Motoring. T* **74** *and similar horiz designs. Multicoloured. P* 14.

290 12p. Type **74** .. .. .. .. .. .. 40 40
a. Horiz pair. Nos. 290/1 .. .. .. .. 85 85
291 12p. W. Bentley in 3 litre Bentley (1922 Tourist Trophy Race) .. .. .. .. 40 40
292 14p. F. Gerrard in E.R.A. (1950 British Empire Trophy Race) .. .. .. .. 55 55
a. Horiz pair. Nos. 292/3 .. .. .. .. 1·10 1·10
293 14p. Brian Lewis in Alfa Romeo (1934 Mannin Moar Race) .. .. .. .. .. 55 55
294 31p. Jaguar "XJ-SC" ("Roads Open" car, 1984 Motor Cycle T.T. Races) .. .. 1·25 1·25
a. Horiz pair. Nos. 294/5 .. .. .. .. 2·50 2·50
295 31p. Tony Pond and Mike Nicholson in Vauxhall "Chevette" (1981 Rothmans International Rally) .. .. .. .. .. 1·25 1·25
290/5 .. .. .. .. .. .. *Set of* 6 4·00 4·00

Nos. 290/1, 292/3 and 294/5 were printed together, *se-tenant*, in horizontal pairs throughout the sheets.

**75** Queen Alexandra and Victorian Sergeant with Wife

(Des Colleen Corlett. Litho Questa)

**1985** (4 Sept). *Centenary of the Soldiers', Sailors' and Airmen's Families Association. T* **75** *and similar horiz designs showing Association Presidents. Multicoloured. P* 14.

296 12p. Type **75** .. .. .. .. .. .. 55 55
297 15p. Queen Mary and Royal Air Force family 70 70
298 29p. Earl Mountbatten and Royal Navy family 1·25 1·25
299 34p. Prince Michael of Kent and Royal Marine with parents, 1982 .. .. .. .. 1·40 1·40
296/9 .. .. .. .. .. .. *Set of* 4 3·50 3·50

**76** Kirk Maughold (Birthplace)

(Des A. Theobald. Litho Questa)

**1985** (2 Oct). *Birth Bicentenary of Lieutenant-General Sir Mark Cubbon (Indian administrator). T* **76** *and similar multicoloured designs. P* 14.

300 12p. Type **76** .. .. .. .. .. .. 45 45
301 22p. Lieutenant-General Sir Mark Cubbon (*vert*) .. .. .. .. .. .. 85 85
302 45p. Memorial Statue, Bangalore, India (*vert*) 1·75 1·75
300/2 .. .. .. .. .. .. *Set of* 3 2·75 2·75

**77** St. Peter's Church, Onchan

(Des A. Theobald. Litho J.W.)

**1985** (2 Oct). *Christmas. Manx Churches. T* **77** *and similar horiz designs. Multicoloured. P* 13×13½.

303 11p. Type **77** .. .. .. .. .. .. 45 45
304 14p. Royal Chapel of St. John, Tynwald .. .. 55 55
305 31p. Bride Parish Church .. .. .. .. 1·25 1·25
303/5 .. .. .. .. .. .. *Set of* 3 2·00 2·00

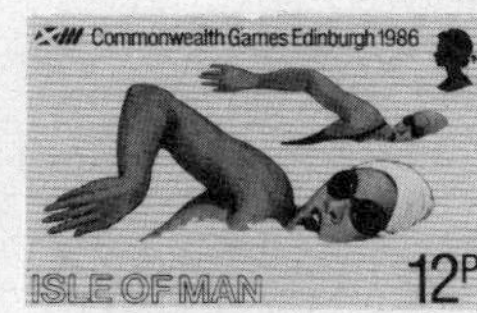


**78** Swimming

(Des C. Abbott. Litho Questa)

**1986** (5 Feb). *Commonwealth Games, Edinburgh. T* **78** *and similar horiz designs. Multicoloured. P* 14.

306 12p. Type **78** .. .. .. .. .. .. 50 50
307 15p. Race walking .. .. .. .. .. 60 60
308 31p. Rifle-shooting .. .. .. .. .. 1·40 1·40
309 34p. Cycling .. .. .. .. .. .. 1·40 1·40
306/9 .. .. .. .. .. .. *Set of* 4 3·50 3·50

No. 309 also commemorates the 50th anniversary of Manx International Cycling Week.

**79** Viking Necklace and Peel Castle   **80** Viking Longship

(Des J. Nicholson. Litho Questa)

**1986** (5 Feb). *Centenary of the Manx Museum. T* **79** *and similar multicoloured designs. P* 14.

310 12p. Type **79** .. .. .. .. .. .. 45 45
311 15p. Meayll Circle, Rushen .. .. .. .. 55 55
312 22p. Skeleton of Great Deer and Manx Museum (*vert*) .. .. .. .. .. 85 85
313 26p. Viking longship model (*vert*) .. .. 95 95
314 29p. Open Air Museum, Cregneash .. .. 1·10 1·10
310/14 .. .. .. .. .. .. *Set of* 5 3·50 3·50

(Des Colleen Corlett. Litho Harrison)

**1986** (10 Apr). *Manx Heritage Year. Booklet stamps. T* **80** *and similar vert design. P* 14½ × 14.

315 2p. multicoloured .. .. .. .. .. 25 25
  a. Booklet pane. Nos. 315×2 and 316×4 .. 2·50
316 10p. black, apple green and brownish grey .. 75 75
  a. Booklet pane. No. 316×3 and 3 stamp-size labels .. .. .. .. .. 2·50

Design:—10p. Celtic cross logo.

In addition to 50p. and £1.14 booklets Nos. 315/16 also come from special booklet sheets of 50 containing five each of Nos. 315a and 316a.

**81** *Usnea articulata* (lichen) and *Neotinea intacta* (orchid), The Ayres

**82** Ellanbane (home of Myles Standish)

(Des J. Nicholson and Nancy Corkish. Photo Courvoisier)

**1986** (10 Apr). *Europa. Protection of Nature and the Environment. T* **81** *and similar horiz designs. Multicoloured. Granite paper. P* 11½.

317 12p. Type **81** .. .. .. .. .. .. 45 45
  a. Horiz pair. Nos. 317/18 .. .. .. 90 90
318 12p. Hen Harrier, Calf of Man .. .. 45 45
319 22p. Manx Stoat, Eary Cushlin .. .. 80 80
  a. Horiz pair. Nos. 319/20 .. .. .. 1·60 1·60
320 22p. *Stenobothus stigmaticus* (grasshopper), St. Michael's Isle .. .. .. .. 80 80
317/20 .. .. .. .. .. *Set of* 4 2·25 2·25

The two designs of each value were printed together, *se-tenant*, in horizontal pairs throughout the sheets.

(Des C. Abbott. Litho Cartor, France)

**1986** (22 May). *"Ameripex '86" International Stamp Exhibition, Chicago. Captain Myles Standish of the "Mayflower". T* **82** *and similar vert designs. Multicoloured. P* 13½.

321 12p. Type **82** .. .. .. .. .. 35 35
322 15p. *Mayflower* crossing the Atlantic, 1620 .. 55 55
323 31p. Pilgrim Fathers landing at Plymouth, 1620 .. .. .. .. .. 1·10 1·10
324 34p. Captain Myles Standish .. .. .. 1·40 1·40
321/4 .. .. .. .. .. *Set of* 4 3·00 3·00
**MS**325 100×75 mm. Nos. 323/4. P 12½ .. .. 2·50 2·50

No. **MS**325 also commemorates the 75th anniversary of the World Manx Association.

**83** Prince Andrew in Naval Uniform and Miss Sarah Ferguson

**84** Prince Philip (from photo by Karsh)

(Des Colleen Corlett. Litho B.D.T.)

**1986** (23 July). *Royal Wedding. T* **83** *and similar horiz design. Multicoloured. P* 15 × 14.

326 15p. Type **83** .. .. .. .. .. 60 60
327 40p. Engagement photograph .. .. .. 1·40 1·40

(Des Colleen Corlett. Photo Courvoisier)

**1986** (28 Aug). *Royal Birthdays. T* **84** *and similar multicoloured designs. Granite paper. P* 11½.

328 15p. Type **84** .. .. .. .. .. 60 60
  a. Horiz pair. Nos. 328/9 .. .. .. 1·25 1·25
329 15p. Queen Elizabeth II (from photo by Karsh) .. .. .. .. .. 60 60
330 34p. Queen Elizabeth and Prince Philip (from photo by Karsh) (48×35 *mm*) .. .. 1·50 1·50
328/30 .. .. .. .. .. *Set of* 3 2·50 2·50

Nos. 328/9 were printed together, *se-tenant*, in horizontal pairs throughout the sheet.

Nos. 328/30 also commemorate "Stockholmia '86" International Stamp Exhibition, Sweden and the 350th anniversary of the Swedish Post Office and are so inscribed on the margins of the sheet of twelve (Nos. 328/9) and six (No. 330).

**85** European Robins on Globe and "Peace and Goodwill" in Braille

**86** North Quay

(Des Colleen Corlett. Litho Questa)

**1986** (25 Sept). *Christmas. International Peace Year. T* **85** *and similar vert designs. Multicoloured. P* 14.

331 11p. Type **85** .. .. .. .. .. 50 50
332 14p. Hands releasing peace dove .. .. 55 55
333 31p. Clasped hands and "Peace" in sign language .. .. .. .. .. 1·25 1·25
331/3 .. .. .. .. .. *Set of* 3 2·00 2·00

(Des A. Theobald. Litho Questa)

**1987** (21 Jan–26 Mar). *Victorian Douglas. T* **86** *and similar horiz designs. Multicoloured. P* 14 × 14½.

334 2p. Type **86** .. .. .. .. .. 10 10
  a. Booklet pane. Nos. 334×2, 335×2 and 336×4 (2p. stamps at top) (26.3) .. 1·40
  ab. Ditto, but 2p. stamps at bottom (26.3) .. 1·40
  b. Booklet pane. Nos. 334/7, each×2 (26.3) 1·75
335 3p. Old Fishmarket .. .. .. .. 10 10
336 10p. The Breakwater .. .. .. .. 35 35
337 15p. Jubilee Clock .. .. .. .. 50 50
338 31p. Loch Promenade .. .. .. .. 1·25 1·25
339 34p. Beach .. .. .. .. .. 1·40 1·40
334/9 .. .. .. .. .. *Set of* 6 3·25 3·25

**87** "The Old Fishmarket and Harbour, Douglas"

(Des A. Theobald. Litho Cartor, France)

**1987** (18 Feb). *Paintings by John Miller Nicholson. T* **87** *and similar horiz designs. Multicoloured. P* 13½.

340 12p. Type **87** .. .. .. .. .. 35 35
341 26p. "Red Sails at Douglas" .. .. .. 80 80
342 29p. "The Double Corner, Peel" .. .. 95 95
343 34p. "Peel Harbour" .. .. .. .. 1·25 1·25
340/3 .. .. .. .. .. *Set of* 4 3·00 3·00

**88** Sea Terminal, Douglas

(Des R. Maddox. Litho B.D.T.)

**1987** (29 Apr). *Europa. Architecture. T* **88** *and similar horiz designs. Multicoloured. P* 13½.

344 12p. Type **88** .. .. .. .. .. 45 45
  a. Horiz pair. Nos. 344/5 .. .. .. 95 95
345 12p. Tower of Refuge, Douglas .. .. 45 45
346 22p. Gaiety Theatre, Douglas .. .. .. 85 85
  a. Horiz pair. Nos. 346/7 .. .. .. 1·75 1·75
347 22p. Villa Marina, Douglas .. .. .. 85 85
344/7 .. .. .. .. .. *Set of* 4 2·50 2·50

Nos. 344/5 and 346/7 were each printed, *se-tenant*, in horizontal pairs throughout the sheets.

**89** Supercharged BMW 500cc Motor Cycle, 1939

(Des B. Dix. Litho Cartor, France)

**1987** (27 May). *80th Anniv of Tourist Trophy Motor Cycle Races. T* **89** *and similar horiz designs. Multicoloured. P* 13½ × 13.

348 12p. Type **89** .. .. .. .. .. 40 40
349 15p. Manx "Kneeler" Norton 350cc, 1953 .. 60 60
350 29p. MV Agusta 500cc 4, 1956 .. .. 1·00 1·00
351 31p. Guzzi 500cc V8, 1957 .. .. .. 1·10 1·10
352 34p. Honda 250cc 6, 1967 .. .. .. 1·40 1·40
348/52 .. .. .. .. .. *Set of* 5 4·00 4·00
**MS**353 150×140 mm. Nos. 348/52. P 14×13½ .. 4·00 4·00

Nos. 348/53 also commemorate the Centenary of the St. John Ambulance Brigade and the miniature sheet also carries the logo of "Capex '87" International Stamp Exhibition, Toronto, on its margin.

**90** Fuchsia and Wild Roses

**91** Stirring the Christmas Pudding

(Des Nancy Corkish. Litho Enschedé)

**1987** (9 Sept). *Wild Flowers. T* **90** *and similar vert designs. Multicoloured. P* 14½ × 13.

354 16p. Type **90** .. .. .. .. .. 50 50
355 29p. Field Scabious and Ragwort .. .. 90 90
356 31p. Wood Anemone and Celandine .. .. 1·00 1·00
357 34p. Violets and Primroses .. .. .. 1·25 1·25
354/7 .. .. .. .. .. *Set of* 4 3·25 3·25

(Des Colleen Corlett. Litho Questa)

**1987** (16 Oct). *Christmas. Victorian Scenes. T* **91** *and similar vert designs. Multicoloured. P* 14.

358 12p. Type **91** .. .. .. .. .. 50 50
359 15p. Bringing home the Christmas tree .. 65 65
360 31p. Decorating the Christmas tree .. .. 1·10 1·10
358/60 .. .. .. .. .. *Set of* 3 2·00 2·00

**92** Russell Brookes in Vauxhall Opel (Manx Rally winner, 1985)

(Des C. Abbott. Litho Enschedé)

**1988** (10 Feb). *Motor Sport. T* **92** *and similar horiz designs. Multicoloured. P* 13½ × 14½.

361 13p. Type **92** .. .. .. .. .. 60 60
362 26p. Ari Vatanen in Ford "Escort" (Manx Rally winner, 1976) .. .. .. .. 90 90
363 31p. Terry Smith in Repco "March 761" (Hill Climb winner, 1980) .. .. .. .. 1·00 1·00
364 34p. Nigel Mansell in Williams/Honda (British Grand Prix winner, 1986 and 1987) .. 1·10 1·10
361/4 .. .. .. .. .. *Set of* 4 3·25 3·25

**93** Horse Tram Terminus, Douglas Bay Tramway

**93*a*** Queen Elizabeth II taking Salute at Trooping the Colour

(Des Colleen Corlett (£2), A. Theobald (others). Litho B.D.T. (1p. to 19p., 21p., 23p.). Questa (20p. and 25p. to £2))

**1988** (10 Feb)–**92**. *Manx Railways and Tramways. Horiz designs as T* **93**, *and T* **93*a***. *Multicoloured. P* 13 *(1p. to 19p., 21p., 23p.),* 14½×15 *(20p., 25p. to £1) or* 14½ *(£2).*

365 1p. Type **93** .. .. .. .. 10 10
366 2p. Snaefell Mountain Railway .. .. 10 10
367 3p. Marine Drive Tramway .. .. .. 10 10
  a. Booklet pane. Nos. 367×2, 370 and 373×2 (16.3.88) .. .. .. 1·25
  b. Booklet pane. Nos. 367×2, 371×2 and 374 (16.10.89) .. .. .. 1·25
367*c* 4p. Douglas Cable Tramway (9.1.91) .. 10 10
  ca. Booklet pane. Nos. 367*c*×3, 374 and 377*a* .. .. .. .. .. 1·00
  cb. Booklet pane. Nos. 367*c*×3, 374×4 and 377*a* .. .. .. .. 2·00
368 5p. Douglas Head Incline Railway .. .. 10 10
369 10p. Manx Electric Railway train at Maughold Head .. .. .. .. 20 25
370 13p. As 4p. .. .. .. .. .. 25 30
  a. Booklet pane. Nos. 370×4 and 373×6 (16.3.88) .. .. .. .. 3·50
371 14p. Manx Northern Railway No. 4, *Caledonia*, at Gob-y-Deigan .. .. .. 30 35
  a. Booklet pane. Nos. 371×4 and 374×6 (16.10.89) .. .. .. .. 3·75
372 15p. Laxey Mine Railway Lewin locomotive *Ant* .. .. .. .. .. 30 35
  a. Booklet pane. Nos. 372 and 376×2 (14.2.90) .. .. .. .. 1·25
  b. Booklet pane. Nos. 372×4 and 376×6 (14.2.90) .. .. .. .. 4·00
373 16p. Port Erin Breakwater Tramway locomotive *Henry B. Loch* .. .. .. 30 35
374 17p. Ramsey Harbour Tramway .. .. .. 35 40
375 18p. Locomotive No. 7, *Tynwald*, on Foxdale line .. .. .. .. .. 35 40
375*a* 18p. T.P.O. Special leaving Douglas, 3 July 1991 (8.1.92) .. .. .. .. 35 40
  ab. Booklet pane. Nos. 375*a*×3 and 377*b*×2 .. .. .. .. .. 2·00
  ac. Booklet pane. Nos. 375*a*×6 and 377*b*×4 .. .. .. .. .. 4·00
376 19p. Baldwin Reservoir Tramway steam locomotive *Injebreck* .. .. .. .. 40 45
377 20p. I.M.R. No. 13, *Kissack*, near St. Johns (21.9.88) .. .. .. .. .. 40 45
377*a* 21p. As 14p. (9.1.91) .. .. .. .. 40 45
377*b* 23p. Double-decker horse tram, Douglas (8.1.92) .. .. .. .. .. 45 50
378 25p. I.M.R. No. 12, *Hutchinson*, leaving Douglas (21.9.88) .. .. .. .. 50 55
379 50p. Groudle Glen Railway locomotive *Polar Bear* (21.9.88) .. .. .. 1·00 1·10
380 £1 I.M.R. No. 11, *Maitland*, pulling Royal Train, 1963 (21.9.88) .. .. 2·00 2·10

380*a* £2 Type **93***a* (14.2.90) .. .. .. .. 4·00 4·25
365/80*a* .. .. .. .. .. *Set of* 21 10·50 11·50

In addition to stamp booklets Nos. 367a/b, 370a, 371a, 372a/b and 375ab/ac also come from special booklet sheets of 50 containing either ten examples of the strips of five or five examples of the strips of ten.

Nos. 367*c* and 377*a* show the Queen's head in white. The 4p. value was only issued in 50p and £1 stamp booklets or in special booklet sheets of 50 containing five vertical strips of No. 367cb and five extra examples of both Nos. 367*c* and 377*a*. The 17p. from these booklets shows a 1991 imprint date.

For miniature sheet containing Nos. 367*c* and 377*a* see No. **MS**484.

**94** Laying Isle of Man—U.K. Submarine Cable

(Des C. Abbott. Litho Cartor, France)

**1988** (14 Apr). *Europa. Transport and Communications. T* **94** *and similar horiz designs. Multicoloured. P* 14 × 13½.

381 13p. Type **94** .. .. .. .. .. 40 40
a. Horiz pair. Nos. 381/2 .. .. .. 85 85
382 13p. *Flex Service 3* (cable ship) .. .. 40 40
383 22p. Earth station, Braddan .. .. .. 70 70
a. Horiz pair. Nos. 383/4 .. .. .. 1·40 1·40
384 22p. "INTELSAT 5" satellite .. .. .. 70 70
381/4 .. .. .. .. .. *Set of* 4 2·00 2·00

Nos. 381/2 and 383/4 were each printed together, *se-tenant*, in horizontal pairs throughout the sheets. Nos. 381/2 form a composite design.

**95** *Euterpe* (full-rigged ship) off Ramsey, 1863

**96** "Magellanica"

(Des J. Nicholson. Litho Questa)

**1988** (11 May). *Manx Sailing Ships. T* **95** *and similar horiz designs. Multicoloured. P* 14.

385 16p. Type **95** .. .. .. .. .. 50 50
386 29p. *Vixen* (topsail schooner) leaving Peel for Australia, 1853 .. .. .. .. 85 85
387 31p. *Ramsey* (full-rigged ship) off Brisbane, 1870 .. .. .. .. .. 90 90
388 34p. *Star of India* (formerly *Euterpe*) (barque) off San Diego, 1976 .. .. .. 1·10 1·10
385/8 .. .. .. .. .. *Set of* 4 3·00 3·00
**MS**389 110 × 85 mm. Nos. 385 and 388 .. .. 1·75 1·75

Nos. 386/7 also commemorate the Bicentenary of Australian Settlement.

(Des Colleen Corlett. Litho Enschedé)

**1988** (21 Sept). *50th Anniv of British Fuchsia Society. T* **96** *and similar vert designs. Multicoloured. P* 13½ × 14.

390 13p. Type **96** .. .. .. .. .. 40 40
391 16p. "Pink Cloud" .. .. .. .. 50 50
392 22p. "Leonora" .. .. .. .. 70 70
393 29p. "Satellite" .. .. .. .. 1·00 1·00
394 31p. "Preston Guild" .. .. .. .. 1·10 1·10
395 34p. "Thalia" .. .. .. .. 1·25 1·25
390/5 .. .. .. .. .. *Set of* 6 4·50 4·50

**97** Long-eared Owl

(Des Audrey North. Litho Questa)

**1988** (12 Oct). *Christmas. Manx Birds. T* **97** *and similar horiz designs. Multicoloured. P* 14.

396 12p. Type **97** .. .. .. .. .. 50 50
397 15p. European Robin .. .. .. .. 65 65
398 31p. Grey Partridge .. .. .. .. 1·10 1·10
396/8 .. .. .. .. .. *Set of* 3 2·00 2·00

**98** Ginger Cat

**99** Tudric Pewter Clock, *c.* 1903

(Des P. Layton. Litho Questa)

**1989** (8 Feb). *Manx Cats. T* **98** *and similar horiz designs. Multicoloured. P* 14.

399 16p. Type **98** .. .. .. .. .. 50 50
400 27p. Black and white cat .. .. .. 90 90
401 30p. Tortoiseshell and white cat .. .. 1·10 1·10
402 40p. Tortoiseshell cat .. .. .. .. 1·40 1·40
399/402 .. .. .. .. .. *Set of* 4 3·50 3·50

(Des Colleen Corlett. Litho Cartor, France)

**1989** (8 Feb). *125th Birth Anniv of Archibald Knox (artist and designer). T* **99** *and similar multicoloured designs. P* 13.

403 13p. Type **99** .. .. .. .. .. 35 35
404 16p. "Celtic Cross" watercolour .. .. .. 45 45
405 23p. Silver cup and cover, 1902-03 .. .. 75 75
406 32p. Gold and silver brooches from Liberty's Cymric range (*horiz*) .. .. .. 1·10 1·10
407 35p. Silver jewel box, 1900 (*horiz*) .. .. 1·25 1·25
403/7 .. .. .. .. .. *Set of* 5 3·50 3·50

**100** William Bligh and Old Church, Onchan

(Des C. Abbott. Litho B.D.T.)

**1989** (28 Apr). *Bicentenary of the Mutiny on the Bounty. T* **100** *and similar horiz designs. Multicoloured. P* 14.

408 13p. Type **100** .. .. .. .. .. 25 30
a. Booklet pane. Nos. 408/10 and 412/14 .. 3·00
b. Booklet pane. Nos. 408/9 and 411/14 .. 3·00
409 16p. Bligh and loyal crew cast adrift .. .. 30 35
410 23p. Pitcairn Islands 1989 Settlement Bicentary 90 c., No. 345 .. .. .. .. 80 85
a. Booklet pane. Nos. 410/11, each × 3 .. 3·00
411 27p. Norfolk Island 1989 Bicentenary 39 c., No. 461 .. .. .. .. .. 90 95
412 30p. Midshipman Peter Heywood and Tahiti .. 70 70
413 32p. H.M.S. *Bounty* anchored off Pitcairn Island .. .. .. .. .. 75 75
414 35p. Fletcher Christian and Pitcairn Island .. 80 80
408/14 .. .. .. .. .. *Set of* 7 4·00 4·25
**MS**415 110 × 85 mm. Nos. 410/11 and 414 .. .. 2·25 2·25

Nos. 410/11 were only issued in £5.30 booklets and as part of No. **MS**415.

Booklet panes Nos. 408a/b and 410a each contain two vertical rows of three stamps, separated by a central gutter.

**101** Skipping and Hopscotch

**102** Atlantic Puffin

(Des Colleen Corlett. Litho Enschedé)

**1989** (17 May). *Europa. Children's Games. T* **101** *and similar horiz designs. Multicoloured. P* 13½.

416 13p. Type **101** .. .. .. .. .. 50 50
a. Horiz pair. Nos. 416/17 .. .. .. 1·00 1·00
417 13p. Wheelbarrow, leapfrog and piggyback .. 50 50
418 23p. Completing model house and blowing bubbles .. .. .. .. .. 75 75
a. Horiz pair. Nos. 418/19 .. .. .. 1·50 1·50
419 23p. Girl with doll and doll's house .. .. 75 75
416/19 .. .. .. .. .. *Set of* 4 2·25 2·25

Nos. 416/17 and 418/19 were printed together, *se-tenant* as composite designs, in horizontal pairs throughout the sheets.

(Des W. Oliver. Litho Questa)

**1989** (20 Sept). *Sea Birds. T* **102** *and similar vert designs. Multicoloured. P* 14.

420 13p. Type **102** .. .. .. .. .. 40 40
a. Strip of 4. Nos. 420/3 .. .. .. 1·60
421 13p. Black Guillemot .. .. .. .. 40 40
422 13p. Common Cormorant .. .. .. .. 40 40
423 13p. Kittiwake .. .. .. .. .. 40 40
420/3 .. .. .. .. .. *Set of* 4 1·60 1·60

Nos. 420/3 were printed together, *se-tenant*, in horizontal and vertical strips of 4 throughout the sheet. The sheet exists with or without perforations across the side margins.

**103** Red Cross Cadets learning Resuscitation

**104** Mother with Baby, Jane Crookall Maternity Home

(Des A. Theobald. Litho Questa)

**1989** (16 Oct). *125th Anniversary of International Red Cross and Centenary of Noble's Hospital, Isle of Man. T* **103** *and similar horiz designs. P* 14.

424 14p. multicoloured .. .. .. .. 30 35
425 17p. grey and orange-vermilion .. .. .. 50 45
426 23p. multicoloured .. .. .. .. 75 75
427 30p. multicoloured .. .. .. .. 95 95
428 35p. multicoloured .. .. .. .. 1·10 1·10
424/8 .. .. .. .. .. *Set of* 5 3·25 3·25

Designs:—17p. Anniversary logo; 23p. Signing Geneva Convention, 1864; 30p. Red Cross ambulance; 35p. Henri Dunant (founder).

(Des Colleen Corlett. Litho Questa)

**1989** (16 Oct). *Christmas. 50th Anniversary of Jane Crookall Maternity Home and 75th Anniversary of St. Ninian's Church, Douglas. T* **104** *and similar vert designs. Multicoloured. P* 14½.

429 13p. Type **104** .. .. .. .. .. 35 35
430 16p. Mother with child .. .. .. .. 45 45
431 34p. Madonna and Child .. .. .. .. 90 90
432 37p. Baptism, St. Ninian's Church .. .. 1·10 1·10
429/32 .. .. .. .. .. *Set of* 4 2·50 2·50

**105** "The Isle of Man Express going up a Gradient"

**106** Modern Postman

(Des D. Swinton. Litho B.D.T.)

**1990** (14 Feb). *Isle of Man Edwardian Postcards. T* **105** *and similar horiz designs. Multicoloured. P* 14.

433 15p. Type **105** .. .. .. .. .. 30 35
434 19p. "A way we have in the Isle of Man" .. 50 45
435 32p. "Douglas–waiting for the male boat" .. 75 75
436 34p. "The last toast rack home, Douglas Parade" .. .. .. .. .. 95 95
437 37p. "The last Isle of Man boat" .. .. .. 1·10 1·10
433/7 .. .. .. .. .. *Set of* 5 3·25 3·25

(Des A. Kellett. Litho Cartor, France)

**1990** (18 Apr). *Europa. Post Office Buildings. T* **106** *and similar multicoloured designs. P* 13½.

438 15p. Type **106** .. .. .. .. .. 35 35
a. Horiz pair. Nos. 438/9 .. .. .. 70 70
439 15p. Ramsey Post Office, 1990 (40×26 *mm*) .. 35 35
440 24p. Postman, 1890 .. .. .. .. 60 60
a. Horiz pair. Nos. 440/1 .. .. .. 1·25 1·25
441 24p. Douglas Post Office, 1890 (40×26 *mm*) .. 60 60
438/41 .. .. .. .. .. *Set of* 4 1·75 1·75

Nos. 438/9 and 440/1 were each printed together, *se-tenant*, in horizontal pairs throughout the sheets.

**107** Penny Black

**108** Queen Elizabeth the Queen Mother

(Des Colleen Corlett. Eng Inge Madle (No. **MS**447). Recess and litho (No. **MS**447) or litho (others) Enschedé)

**1990** (3 May). *150th Anniv of the Penny Black. T* **107** *and similar vert designs. P* 14×13½.

442 1p. black, buff and gold .. .. .. 10 10
a. Sheetlet. Horiz strip of 5. Nos. 442/6 .. 3·00
b. Sheetlet. No. 442×25 .. .. .. 1·00
c. Booklet pane. No. 442×8 with margins all round .. .. .. .. .. 25
443 19p. gold, black and buff .. .. .. 55 55
a. Booklet pane. Nos. 443/46×2 with margins all round .. .. .. .. 6·50
444 32p. multicoloured .. .. .. .. 85 85
445 34p. multicoloured .. .. .. .. 90 90
446 37p. multicoloured .. .. .. .. 95 95
442/6 .. .. .. .. .. *Set of* 5 3·00 3·00
**MS**447 100×71 mm. £1 black, gold and buff (50×60 *mm*) .. .. .. .. .. 2·50 2·50

Designs:—19p. Wyon Medal, 1837; 32p. Wyon's stamp essay; 34p. Perkins Bacon engine-turned essay, 1839; 37p. Twopence Blue, 1840; £1 Block of four Penny Black stamps lettered IM–JN.

Sheetlet No. 442a was reissued on 24 August 1990 overprinted "From STAMP WORLD LONDON '90 to NEW ZEALAND 1990" for sale at the New Zealand exhibition.

The Penny Black stamps shown on Nos. 442b/c each have different corner letters at foot. The sheetlet of 25 was issued in conjunction with a special postal concession which allowed hand-addressed personal mail for the island to be posted for 1p. between 10 am. and 12 noon on 6 May 1990.

No. **MS**447 also commemorates "Stamp World London 90" International Stamp Exhibition, London.

(Des Colleen Corlett. Litho B.D.T.)

**1990** (4 Aug). *90th Birthday of Queen Elizabeth the Queen Mother. P* 13×13½.

448 **108** 90p. multicoloured . . . . . . 2·25 2·25

No. 448 was printed in sheets of ten stamps and ten *se-tenant* inscribed labels.

**109** Hurricane, Blenheim and Home Defence

(Des A. Theobald. Litho Questa)

**1990** (5 Sept). *50th Anniv of Battle of Britain. T* **109** *and similar horiz designs. Multicoloured. P* 14.

449 15p. Type **109** . . . . . . 35 35
a. Horiz pair. Nos. 449/50 . . . . 70 70
450 15p. Spitfire with rescue aircraft and launch 35 35
451 24p. Rearming fighters . . . . 70 70
a. Horiz pair. Nos. 451/2 . . . . 1·40 1·40
452 24p. Ops room and scramble . . . . 70 70
453 29p. Civil Defence personnel . . . . 75 75
a. Horiz pair. Nos. 453/4 . . . . 1·50 1·50
454 29p. Anti-aircraft battery . . . . 75 75
449/54 . . . . *Set of* 6 3·25 3·25

The two designs of each value were printed together, *se-tenant*, in horizontal pairs throughout the sheets of 8.

**110** Churchill with Freedom of Douglas Casket

**111** Boy on Toboggan and Girl posting Letter

(Des C. Abbott. Litho Cartor, France)

**1990** (5 Sept). *25th Death Anniv of Sir Winston Churchill. T* **110** *and similar horiz designs. Multicoloured. P* 13½.

455 19p. Type **110** . . . . 55 55
456 32p. Churchill and London blitz . . . . 85 85
457 34p. Churchill and searchlights over Westminster . . . . 95 95
458 37p. Churchill with R.A.F. fighters . . . . 1·00 1·00
455/8 . . . . *Set of* 4 3·00 3·00

(Des C. Abbott. Litho B.D.T)

**1990** (10 Oct). *Christmas. T* **111** *and similar vert designs. Multicoloured. P* 13×13½.

459 14p. Type **111** . . . . 40 40
460 18p. Girl on toboggan and skaters . . . . 45 45
461 34p. Boy with snowman . . . . 95 95
462 37p. Children throwing snowballs . . . . 1·00 1·00
459/62 . . . . *Set of* 4 2·50 2·50
**MS**463 123×55 mm. As Nos. 459/62, but face values in black . . . . 2·50 2·50

**112** Henry Bloom Noble and Orphans (Marshall Wane)

**113** Lifeboat *Sir William Hillary*, Douglas

(Des Colleen Corlett. Litho Walsall)

**1991** (9 Jan). *Manx Photography. T* **112** *and similar horiz designs. P* 14.

464 17p. blackish brown, pale brownish grey & blk 35 40
465 21p. deep brown and ochre . . . . 50 45
466 26p. blackish brown, stone and brownish black 70 70
467 31p. agate, pale grey-brown and black . . 95 95
468 40p. multicoloured . . . . 1·10 1·10
464/8 . . . . *Set of* 5 3·25 3·25

Designs:—21p. Douglas (Frederick Frith); 26p. Studio portrait of three children (Hilda Newby); 31p. Cashtal yn Ard (Christopher Killip); 40p. Peel Castle (Colleen Corlett).

(Des A. Peck. Litho Questa)

**1991** (13 Feb). *Manx Lifeboats. T* **113** *and similar horiz designs. Multicoloured. P* 14.

469 17p. Type **113** . . . . 35 40
470 21p. *Osman Gabriel*, Port Erin . . . . 50 50
471 26p. *James & Ann Ritchie*, Ramsey . . 70 70
472 31p. *The Gough Ritchie*, Port St. Mary . . 95 95
473 37p. *John Batstone*, Peel . . . . 1·10 1·10
469/73 . . . . *Set of* 5 3·25 3·25

No. 469 is inscribed "HILARY" in error.

**114** "Intelsat" Communications Satellite

**115** Oliver Godfrey with Indian 500cc at Start, 1911

(Des D. Miller. Litho B.D.T.)

**1991** (24 Apr). *Europa. Europe in Space. T* **114** *and similar vert designs. Multicoloured. P* 14.

474 17p. Type **114** . . . . 50 50
a. Vert pair. Nos. 474/5 . . . . 1·00 1·00
475 17p. "Ariane" rocket launch and fishing boats in Douglas harbour . . . . 50 50
476 26p. Weather satellite and space station . . 75 75
a. Vert pair. Nos. 476/7 . . . . 1·50 1·50
477 26p. Ronaldsway Airport, Manx Radio transmitter and Space shuttle launch . . 75 75
474/7 . . . . *Set of* 4 2·25 2·25

Nos. 474/5 and 476/7 were each printed together, *se-tenant*, in vertical pairs throughout the sheets, each pair forming a composite design.

(Des A. Theobald. Litho Enschedé)

**1991** (30 May). *80th Anniv of Tourist Trophy Mountain Course. T* **115** *and similar horiz designs. Multicoloured. P* 14½×13.

478 17p. Type **115** . . . . 40 40
479 21p. Freddie Dixon on Douglas "banking" sidecar, 1923 . . . . 50 50
480 26p. Bill Ivy on Yamaha 125cc, 1968 . . 70 70
481 31p. Giacomo Agostini on MV Agusta 500cc, 1972 . . . . 95 95
482 37p. Joey Dunlop on RVF Honda 750cc, 1985 1·10 1·10
478/82 . . . . *Set of* 5 3·25 3·25
**MS**483 149×144 mm. Nos. 478/82 . . . . 3·25 3·25

(Des Colleen Corlett. Litho B.D.T.)

**1991** (1 July). *9th Conference of Commonwealth Postal Administrations, Douglas. Sheet* 119×77 *mm containing Nos.* 367*c and* 377*a, each* × 2. *Multicoloured. P* 13.

**MS**484 Nos. 367c and 377a, each × 2 . . . . 1·00 1·10

**116** Laxey Hand-cart, 1920

**117** Mute Swans, Douglas Harbour

(Des C. Abbott. Litho Questa)

**1991** (18 Sept). *Fire Engines. T* **116** *and similar square designs. Multicoloured. P* 14½.

485 17p. Type **116** . . . . 35 40
486 21p. Horse-drawn steamer, Douglas, 1909 . . 40 45
487 30p. Merryweather "Hatfield" pump, 1936 . . 60 65
488 33p. Dennis "F8" pumping appliance, Peel, 1953 . . . . 65 70
489 37p. Volvo turntable ladder, Douglas, 1989 . . 75 80
485/9 . . . . *Set of* 5 2·50 2·75

(Des Colleen Corlett. Litho Cartor, France)

**1991** (18 Sept). *Swans. T* **117** *and similar horiz designs. Multicoloured. P* 13.

490 17p. Type **117** . . . . 35 40
a. Horiz pair. Nos. 490/1 . . . . 70 80
491 17p. Black Swans, Curraghs Wildlife Park . . 35 40
492 26p. Whooper Swans, Bishop's Dub, Ballaugh 50 55
a. Horiz pair. Nos. 492/3 . . . . 1·00 1·10
493 26p. Bewick's Swans, Eairy Dam, Foxdale . . 50 55
494 37p. Coscaroba Swans, Curraghs Wildlife Park 75 80
a. Horiz pair. Nos. 494/5 . . . . 1·50 1·60
495 37p. Trumpeter Swans, Curraghs Wildlife Park 75 80
490/5 . . . . *Set of* 6 3·00 3·25

The two designs of each value were printed together, *se-tenant*, in horizontal pairs throughout the sheets with the backgrounds forming composite designs.

**118** The Three Kings

**119** North African and Italian Campaigns, 1942–43

(Des D. Swinton. Litho Walsall)

**1991** (14 Oct). *Christmas. Paper Sculptures. T* **118** *and similar square designs. Multicoloured. (a) Sheet stamps. P* 14×14½.

496 16p. Type **118** . . . . 30 35
497 20p. Mary with manger . . . . 40 45
498 26p. Shepherds with sheep . . . . 50 55
499 37p. Choir of angels . . . . 75 80
496/9 . . . . *Set of* 4 1·75 1·90

*(b) Booklet stamps. Self-adhesive. Stamps die-cut*

500 16p. Type **118** . . . . 30 35
a. Booklet pane. Nos. 500×8 and 501×4 . . 4·00
501 20p. As No. 497 . . . . 40 45

(Des A. Theobald. Litho Questa)

**1992** (6 Feb). *50th Anniv of Parachute Regiment. T* **119** *and similar horiz designs. Multicoloured. P* 14.

502 23p. Type **119** . . . . 45 50
a. Horiz pair. Nos. 502/3 . . . . 90 1·00
503 23p. D-Day, 1944 . . . . 45 50
504 28p. Arnhem, 1944 . . . . 55 60
a. Horiz pair. Nos. 504/5 . . . . 1·10 1·25
505 28p. Rhine crossing, 1945 . . . . 55 60
506 39p. Operations in Near, Middle and Far East, 1945–68 . . . . 80 85
a. Horiz pair. Nos. 506/7 . . . . 1·60 1·75
507 39p. Liberation of Falkland Islands, 1982 . . 80 85
502/7 . . . . *Set of* 6 3·25 3·50

The two designs of each value were printed together, *se-tenant*, in horizontal pairs throughout the sheets of 8.

**120** Queen Elizabeth II at Coronation, 1953

(Des D. Miller. Litho B.D.T.)

**1992** (6 Feb). *40th Anniv of Accession. T* **120** *and similar vert designs. Multicoloured. P* 14.

508 18p. Type **120** . . . . 35 40
509 23p. Queen visiting Isle of Man, 1979 . . 45 50
510 28p. Queen in evening dress . . . . 55 60
511 33p. Queen visiting Isle of Man, 1989 . . 70 75
512 39p. Queen arriving for film premiere, 1990 . . 80 85
508/12 . . . . *Set of* 5 2·50 3·00

POSTAGE DUE STAMPS

D 1

D 2

D 3

(Litho Questa)

**1973** (5 July). *P* 13½ × 14.

D1 **D 1** ½p. red, black and bistre-yellow . . 2·25 1·40
D2 1p. red, black and cinnamon . . 75 55
D3 2p. red, black and light apple-green . . 15 20
D4 3p. red, black and grey . . 25 25
D5 4p. red, black and carmine-rose . . 35 30
D6 5p. red, black and cobalt . . 40 35
D7 10p. red, black and light lavender . . 50 45
D8 20p. red, black and pale turquoise-green 90 70
D1/8 . . . . *Set of* 8 5·00 3·75

A second printing of all values was put on sale by the Philatelic Bureau from 1 September 1973, although examples are known used from mid-August onwards. These can be distinguished by the addition of a small "A" after the date "1973" in the bottom left margin of the stamps. Spurious examples of the second printing exist with the "A" removed.

Prices quoted above are for the second printing. *Prices for set of* 8 *original printing £40 mint; £40 used.*

(Des and litho Questa)

**1975** (8 Jan). *Arms and inscriptions in black and red; background colour given. P* 14 × 13½.

D 9 **D 2** ½p. greenish yellow . . . . 10 10
D10 1p. flesh . . . . 10 10
D11 4p. rose-lilac . . . . 10 10
D12 7p. light greenish blue . . . . 20 20
D13 9p. brownish grey . . . . 25 25
D14 10p. bright mauve . . . . 30 30
D15 50p. orange-yellow . . . . 1·40 1·40
D16 £1 turquoise-green . . . . 2·00 2·00
D9/16 . . . . *Set of* 8 4·00 4·00

(Litho B.D.T.)

**1982** (5 Oct). *P* 15 × 14.

D17 **D 3** 1p. multicoloured . . . . 10 10
D18 2p. multicoloured . . . . 10 10
D19 5p. multicoloured . . . . 10 10
D20 10p. multicoloured . . . . 20 25
D21 20p. multicoloured . . . . 40 45
D22 50p. multicoloured . . . . 1·00 1·10
D23 £1 multicoloured . . . . 2·00 2·10
D24 £2 multicoloured . . . . 4·00 4·25
D17/24 . . . . *Set of* 8 7·00 7·50

## JERSEY

Further detailed information on the stamps of Jersey will be found in the Stanley Gibbons *Channel Islands Specialised Catalogue*.

### WAR OCCUPATION ISSUES

Stamps issued under British authority during the German Occupation

1

(Des Major N. V. L. Rybot. Typo *Jersey Evening Post*, St. Helier)

**1941–43**. *White paper* (*thin to thick*). *No wmk. P* 11.

| | | | | |
|---|---|---|---|---|
| 1 | **1** | ½d. bright green (29.1.42) | 3·75 | 2·50 |
| | | a. Imperf between (vert pair) | £650 | |
| | | b. Imperf between (horiz pair) | £550 | |
| | | c. Imperf (pair) | £180 | |
| | | d. On greyish paper (1.43) | 5·00 | 6·50 |
| 2 | | 1d. scarlet (1.4.41) | 4·00 | 2·75 |
| | | a. Imperf between (vert pair) | £650 | |
| | | b. Imperf between (horiz pair) | £550 | |
| | | c. Imperf (pair) | £200 | |
| | | d. On chalk-surfaced paper | 38·00 | 40·00 |
| | | e. On greyish paper (1.43) | 4·50 | 6·50 |

**2** Old Jersey Farm

**3** Portelet Bay

**4** Corbière Lighthouse

**5** Elizabeth Castle

**6** Mont Orgueil Castle

**7** Gathering Vraic (seaweed)

(Des E. Blampied. Eng H. Cortot. Typo French Govt Works, Paris)

**1943–44.** *No wmk. P* 13½.

| | | | | |
|---|---|---|---|---|
| 3 | **2** | ½d. green (1 June) | 7·00 | 5·50 |
| | | a. Rough, grey paper (6.10.43) | 8·50 | 9·00 |
| 4 | **3** | 1d. scarlet (1 June) | 1·50 | 50 |
| | | a. On newsprint (28.2.44) | 2·00 | 2·75 |
| 5 | **4** | 1½d. brown (8 June) | 3·00 | 3·00 |
| 6 | **5** | 2d. orange-yellow (8 June) | 3·00 | 2·25 |
| 7 | **6** | 2½d. blue (29 June) | 1·50 | 1·50 |
| | | a. On newsprint (25.2.44) | 1·00 | 2·00 |
| | | ba. Thin paper* | £180 | |
| 8 | **7** | 3d. violet (29 June) | 1·00 | 2·75 |
| 3/8 | | *Set of* 6 | 14·00 | 12·50 |

*On No. 7ba the design shows clearly through the back of the stamp.

### REGIONAL ISSUES

**DATES OF ISSUE.** The note at the beginning of the Guernsey Regional Issues also applies here.

8

9

(Des E. Blampied (T **8**), W. Gardner (T **9**). Portrait by Dorothy Wilding Ltd. Photo Harrison & Sons)

**1958** (18 Aug)–**67.** *W* **179** *of Great Britain. P* 15 × 14.

| | | | | |
|---|---|---|---|---|
| 9 | **8** | 2½d. carmine-red (8.6.64) | 35 | 50 |
| | | a. Imperf three sides (pair) | £1800 | |
| 10 | **9** | 3d. deep lilac | 35 | 30 |
| | | p. One centre phosphor band (9.6.67) | 20 | 20 |
| 11 | | 4d. ultramarine (7.2.66) | 25 | 30 |
| | | p. Two phosphor bands (5.9.67) | 20 | 25 |
| 9/11p | | *Set of* 3 | 60 | 85 |

**1968–69.** *No wmk. Chalk-surfaced paper. PVA gum**. *One centre phosphor band* (*4d. values*) *or two phosphor bands* (*5d.*). *P* 15 × 14.

| | | | | |
|---|---|---|---|---|
| 12 | **9** | 4d. olive-sepia (4.9.68) | 20 | 25 |
| 13 | | 4d. bright vermilion (26.2.69) | 20 | 30 |
| 14 | | 5d. royal blue (4.9.68) | 20 | 40 |
| 12/14 | | *Set of* 3 | 50 | 85 |

*PVA Gum. See note after No. 722 of Great Britain.

### INDEPENDENT POSTAL ADMINISTRATION

**10** Elizabeth Castle

**11** Queen Elizabeth II (after Cecil Beaton)

**13** Queen Elizabeth II (after Cecil Beaton)

**12** Jersey Airport

(Des V. Whiteley. Photo Harrison (½d. to 1s. 9d.); Courvoisier (others))

**1969** (1 Oct). *T* **10/13** *and similar horiz designs as T* **10** (*½d. to* 1*s.* 6*d.*) *or T* **12** (5*s.*, 10*s.*, £1). *Multicoloured. Granite paper* (2*s.* 6*d. to* £1). *P* 14 (*½d. to* 1*s.* 9*d.*) *or* 12 (*others*).

| | | | |
|---|---|---|---|
| 15 | ½d. Type **10** | 10 | 60 |
| 16 | 1d. La Hougue Bie (prehistoric tomb) (*shades*) | 15 | 20 |
| | a. Booklet stamp with blank margins | 55 | 60 |
| 17 | 2d. Portelet Bay | 10 | 15 |
| 18 | 3d. La Corbière Lighthouse | 20 | 15 |
| | b. Orange omitted | £110 | |
| 19 | 4d. Mont Orgueil Castle by night | 15 | 10 |
| | a. Booklet stamp with blank margins | 30 | 35 |
| 20 | 5d. Arms and Royal Mace | 15 | 10 |
| 21 | 6d. Jersey Cow | 30 | 40 |
| 22 | 9d. Chart of English Channel | 55 | 90 |
| 23 | 1s. Mont Orgueil Castle by day | 90 | 90 |
| 24 | 1s. 6d. As 9d. | 1·75 | 1·75 |
| 25 | 1s. 9d. Type **11** | 1·75 | 1·75 |
| 26 | 2s. 6d. Type **12** | 3·75 | 2·50 |
| 27 | 5s. Legislative Chamber | 15·00 | 7·50 |
| 28 | 10s. The Royal Court | 30·00 | 22·00 |
| | a. Error. Green border* | £4000 | |
| 29 | £1 Type **13** (*shades*) | 2·00 | 1·50 |
| 15/29 | *Set of* 15 | 50·00 | 35·00 |

*During the final printing of the 10s. a sheet was printed in the colours of the 50p., No. 56, i.e. green border instead of slate.

The 3d. is known with the orange omitted.

There was no postal need for the ½d. value as the ½d. coin had been withdrawn prior to its issue in anticipation of decimalisation.

Nos. 16a and 19a come from 2s. booklets for the automatic machines formerly used for the Great Britain 2s. booklets (see also note after Guernsey No. 28).

Various papers were used by Harrisons. The ½d. and 1d. exist on much thicker paper from 2s. booklets and the 2d. to 1s. 9d. exist on thinner paper having white instead of creamy gum.

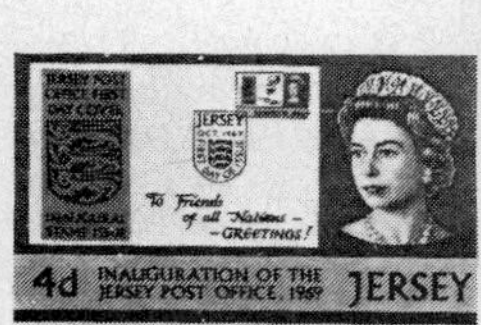


**24** First Day Cover

**25** Lord Coutanche, former Bailiff of Jersey

(Des R. Sellar. Photo Harrison)

**1969** (1 Oct). *Inauguration of Post Office. P* 14.

| | | | | |
|---|---|---|---|---|
| 30 | **24** | 4d. multicoloured | 25 | 30 |
| 31 | | 5d. multicoloured | 50 | 60 |
| 32 | | 1s. 6d. multicoloured | 2·50 | 4·00 |
| 33 | | 1s. 9d. multicoloured | 2·50 | 4·00 |
| 30/3 | | *Set of* 4 | 5·00 | 8·00 |

(Des Rosalind Dease. Photo Courvoisier)

**1970** (9 May). 25*th Anniv of Liberation. T* **25** *and similar multicoloured designs. Granite paper P* 11½.

| | | | |
|---|---|---|---|
| 34 | 4d. Type **25** | 25 | 25 |
| 35 | 5d. Sir Winston Churchill | 35 | 25 |
| 36 | 1s. 6d. "Liberation" (Edmund Blampied) (*horiz*) | 3·00 | 2·00 |
| 37 | 1s. 9d. S.S. *Vega* (*horiz*) | 3·00 | 2·00 |
| 34/7 | *Set of* 4 | 6·00 | 4·00 |

**29** "A Tribute to Enid Blyton"

(Des Jennifer Toombs. Photo Courvoisier)

**1970** (28 July). "*Battle of Flowers*" *Parade. T* **29** *and similar horiz designs. Multicoloured. Granite paper. P* 11½.

| | | | |
|---|---|---|---|
| 38 | 4d. Type **29** | 25 | 35 |
| 39 | 5d. "Rags to Riches" (Cinderella and pumpkin) | 40 | 45 |
| 40 | 1s. 6d. "Gourmet's Delight" (lobster and cornucopia) | 13·00 | 3·50 |
| 41 | 1s. 9d. "We're the Greatest" (ostriches) | 13·00 | 3·50 |
| 38/41 | *Set of* 4 | 24·00 | 7·00 |

**INVALIDATION.** The regional issues for Jersey were invalidated for use in Jersey and Guernsey on 1 November 1969 but remained valid for use in the rest of the United Kingdom. Nos. 15/41 (except No. 29) and Nos. D1/6 were invalidated on 14 February 1972.

**33** Jersey Airport

(Des V. Whiteley. Photo Harrison (½ to 9p.); Courvoisier (others))

**1970** (1 Oct)–**74.** *Decimal Currency. Designs as Nos.* 15/28, *but with values inscr in decimal currency as in T* **33**, *and new horiz design as T* **10** (6*p.*). *Chalk-surfaced paper* (4½, 5½, 8*p.*), *granite paper* (10, 20, 50*p.*).

| | | | |
|---|---|---|---|
| 42 | ½p. Type **10** (15.2.71) | 10 | 10 |
| | a. Booklet stamp with blank margins | 40 | 40 |
| 43 | 1p. La Corbière Lighthouse (*shades*) (15.2.71) | 10 | 10 |
| | a. Orange omitted | | |
| 44 | 1½p. Jersey Cow (15.2.71) | 10 | 10 |
| 45 | 2p. Mont Orgueil Castle by night (15.2.71) | 10 | 10 |
| | a. Booklet stamp with blank margins | 1·10 | 1·10 |
| 46 | 2½p. Arms and Royal Mace (15.2.71) | 10 | 10 |
| | a. Booklet stamp with blank margins | 70 | 70 |
| | ab. Gold (Mace) omitted | £350 | |
| | ac. Gold (Mace) printed double | £275 | |
| 47 | 3p. La Hougue Bie (prehistoric tomb) (15.2.71) | 10 | 10 |
| | a. Booklet stamp with blank margins (1.12.72) | 90 | 60 |
| 48 | 3½p. Portelet Bay (15.2.71) | 15 | 15 |
| | a. Booklet stamp with blank margins (1.7.74) | 1·10 | 70 |
| 49 | 4p. Chart of English Channel (15.2.71) | 15 | 15 |
| 49*a* | 4½p. Arms and Royal Mace (1.11.74) | 20 | 20 |
| | ab. Uncoated paper | £350 | |
| 50 | 5p. Mont Orgueil Castle by day (15.2.71) | 10 | 15 |
| 50*a* | 5½p. Jersey Cow (1.11.74) | 40 | 25 |
| 51 | 6p. Martello Tower, Archirondel (15.2.71) | 25 | 30 |
| 52 | 7½p. Chart of English Channel (15.2.71) | 30 | 40 |
| 52*a* | 8p. Mont Orgueil Castle by night (1.11.74) | 25 | 25 |
| 53 | 9p. Type **11** (15.2.71) | 30 | 30 |
| 54 | 10p. Type **33** | 30 | 55 |
| 55 | 20p. Legislative Chamber | 60 | 75 |
| 56 | 50p. The Royal Court | 1·25 | 1·25 |
| 42/56 | *Set of* 18 | 4·00 | 4·50 |

Original printings of the ½p. to 4p., 5p. and 6p. to 9p. were with PVA gum; printings from 1974 (including original printings of the 4½p. and 5½p.) have dextrin added (see notes after 1971 Great Britain Decimal Machin issue). The 10p. to 50p. have gum arabic.

The border of No. 56 has been changed from turquoise-blue to dull green.

**34** White Eared-pheasant

(Des Jennifer Toombs. Photo Courvoisier)

**1971** (12 Mar). *Wildlife Preservation Trust* (1*st series*). *T* **34** *and similar multicoloured designs. Granite paper. P* 11½.

| | | | |
|---|---|---|---|
| 57 | 2p. Type **34** | 75 | 25 |
| 58 | 2½p. Thick-billed Parrot (*vert*) | 75 | 25 |
| 59 | 7½p. Western Black and White Colobus Monkey (*vert*) | 11·50 | 4·25 |
| 60 | 9p. Ring-tailed Lemur | 11·50 | 4·25 |
| 57/60 | *Set of* 4 | 22·00 | 8·00 |

See also Nos. 73/6, 217/21, 324/9 and 447/51.

**35** Poppy Emblem and Field

**36** "Tante Elizabeth" (E. Blampied)

(Des G. Drummond. Litho Questa)

**1971** (15 June). *50th Anniv of Royal British Legion. T* **35** *and similar horiz designs. Multicoloured. P* 14.

| | | | | |
|---|---|---|---|---|
| 61 | 2p. | Royal British Legion Badge | 40 | 35 |
| 62 | 2½p. | Type **35** | 40 | 35 |
| 63 | 7½p. | Jack Counter, V.C., and Victoria Cross | 3·50 | 3·00 |
| 64 | 9p. | Crossed Tricolour and Union Jack | 3·50 | 3·00 |
| 61/4 | | *Set of 4* | 7·00 | 6·00 |

(Des and photo Courvoisier)

**1971** (5 Oct). *Paintings. T* **36** *and similar multicoloured designs. Granite paper. P* 11½.

| | | | | |
|---|---|---|---|---|
| 65 | 2p. | Type **36** | 15 | 15 |
| 66 | 2½p. | "English Fleet in the Channel" (P. Monamy) (*horiz*) | 20 | 20 |
| 67 | 7½p. | "The Boyhood of Raleigh" (Millais) (*horiz*) | 4·25 | 3·25 |
| 68 | 9p. | "The Blind Beggar" (W. W. Ouless) | 4·25 | 3·25 |
| 65/8 | | *Set of 4* | 8·00 | 6·00 |

See also Nos. 115/18 and 213/16.

**37** Jersey Fern

**38** Artillery Shako

(Des G. Drummond. Photo Courvoisier)

**1972** (18 Jan). *Wild Flowers of Jersey. T* **37** *and similar vert designs. Multicoloured. Granite paper. P* 11½.

| | | | | |
|---|---|---|---|---|
| 69 | 3p. | Type **37** | 25 | 15 |
| 70 | 5p. | Jersey Thrift | 60 | 50 |
| 71 | 7½p. | Jersey Orchid | 3·25 | 3·00 |
| 72 | 9p. | Jersey Viper's Bugloss | 3·25 | 3·00 |
| 69/72 | | *Set of 4* | 7·50 | 6·00 |

(Des Jennifer Toombs. Photo Courvoisier)

**1972** (17 Mar). *Wildlife Preservation Trust* (2*nd series*). *Multicoloured designs similar to T* 34. *Granite paper. P* 11½.

| | | | | |
|---|---|---|---|---|
| 73 | 2½p. | Cheetah | 75 | 20 |
| 74 | 3p. | Rothschild's Mynah (*vert*) | 40 | 35 |
| 75 | 7½p. | Spectacled Bear | 2·00 | 2·50 |
| 76 | 9p. | Tuatara | 2·40 | 2·50 |
| 73/6 | | *Set of 4* | 5·00 | 5·00 |

(Des and photo Courvoisier)

**1972** (27 June). *Royal Jersey Militia. T* **38** *and similar vert designs. Multicoloured. Granite paper. P* 11½.

| | | | | |
|---|---|---|---|---|
| 77 | 2½p. | Type **38** | 15 | 20 |
| 78 | 3p. | Shako (2nd North Regt) | 20 | 20 |
| 79 | 7½p. | Shako (5th South-West Regt) | 1·10 | 1·10 |
| 80 | 9p. | Helmet (3rd Jersey Light Infantry) | 1·25 | 1·25 |
| 77/80 | | *Set of 4* | 2·50 | 2·50 |

**39** Princess Anne

**40** Armorican Bronze Coins

(Des G. Drummond from photographs by D. Groves. Photo Courvoisier)

**1972** (1 Nov). *Royal Silver Wedding. T* **39** *and similar multicoloured designs. Granite paper. P* 11½.

| | | | | |
|---|---|---|---|---|
| 81 | 2½p. | Type **39** | 10 | 10 |
| 82 | 3p. | Queen Elizabeth and Prince Philip (*horiz*) | 10 | 10 |
| 83 | 7½p. | Prince Charles | 40 | 40 |
| 84 | 20p. | The Royal Family (*horiz*) | 50 | 50 |
| 81/4 | | *Set of 4* | 1·00 | 1·00 |

(Des G. Drummond. Photo Courvoisier)

**1973** (23 Jan). *Centenary of La Société Jersiaise. T* **40** *and similar multicoloured designs. Granite paper. P* 11½.

| | | | | |
|---|---|---|---|---|
| 85 | 2½p. | Silver cups | 10 | 10 |
| 86 | 3p. | Gold torque (*vert*) | 10 | 10 |
| 87 | 7½p. | Royal Seal of Charles II (*vert*) | 50 | 40 |
| 88 | 9p. | Type **40** | 50 | 50 |
| 85/8 | | *Set of 4* | 1·10 | 1·00 |

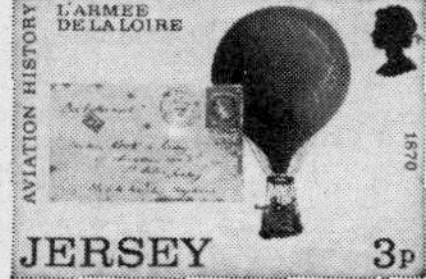


**41** Balloon and Letter

**42** *North Western*

(Des and photo Courvoisier)

**1973** (16 May). *Jersey Aviation History* (1st *series*). *T* **41** *and similar horiz designs. Multicoloured. Granite paper. P* 11½.

| | | | | |
|---|---|---|---|---|
| 89 | 3p. | Type **41** | 10 | 10 |
| 90 | 5p. | Seaplane "Astra" | 15 | 15 |
| 91 | 7½p. | Supermarine "Sea Eagle" | 50 | 60 |
| 92 | 9p. | De Havilland "Express" | 50 | 60 |
| 89/92 | | *Set of 4* | 1·10 | 1·25 |

See also Nos. 340/3.

(Des G. Drummond. Photo Courvoisier)

**1973** (6 Aug). *Centenary of Jersey Eastern Railway. T* **42** *and similar designs showing early locomotives. Multicoloured. Granite paper. P* 11½.

| | | | | |
|---|---|---|---|---|
| 93 | 2½p. | Type **42** | 10 | 10 |
| 94 | 3p. | *Calvados* | 10 | 10 |
| 95 | 7½p. | *Carteret* | 50 | 40 |
| 96 | 9p. | *Caesarea* | 50 | 50 |
| 93/6 | | *Set of 4* | 1·10 | 1·00 |

**43** Princess Anne and Capt. Mark Phillips

(Des and photo Courvoisier)

**1973** (14 Nov). *Royal Wedding. Granite paper. P* 11½.

| | | | | |
|---|---|---|---|---|
| 97 | **43** | 3p. multicoloured | 10 | 10 |
| 98 | | 20p. multicoloured | 90 | 90 |

**44** Spider Crab

**45** Freesias

(Des Jennifer Toombs. Photo Courvoisier)

**1973** (15 Nov). *Marine Life. T* **44** *and similar horiz designs. Multicoloured. Granite paper. P* 11½.

| | | | | |
|---|---|---|---|---|
| 99 | 2½p. | Type **44** | 10 | 10 |
| 100 | 3p. | Conger eel | 10 | 10 |
| 101 | 7½p. | Lobster | 35 | 35 |
| 102 | 20p. | Ormer | 55 | 55 |
| 99/102 | | *Set of 4* | 1·00 | 1·00 |

(Des G. Drummond. Photo Courvoisier)

**1974** (13 Feb). *Spring Flowers. T* **45** *and similar vert designs. Multicoloured. Granite paper. P* 11½.

| | | | | |
|---|---|---|---|---|
| 103 | 3p. | Type **45** | 10 | 10 |
| 104 | 5½p. | Anemones | 10 | 10 |
| 105 | 8p. | Carnations and Gladioli | 40 | 40 |
| 106 | 10p. | Daffodils and Iris | 50 | 50 |
| 103/6 | | *Set of 4* | 1·00 | 1·00 |

**46** First Letter-Box and Contemporary Cover

**47** John Wesley

(Des G. Drummond. Photo Courvoisier)

**1974** (7 June). *U.P.U. Centenary. T* **46** *and similar horiz designs. Multicoloured. Granite paper. P* 11½.

| | | | | |
|---|---|---|---|---|
| 107 | 2½p. | Type **46** | 10 | 10 |
| 108 | 3p. | Postmen, 1862 and 1969 | 10 | 10 |
| 109 | 5½p. | Letter-box and letter, 1974 | 25 | 30 |
| 110 | 20p. | R.M.S. *Aquila* (1874) and aeroplane (1974) | 70 | 60 |
| 107/10 | | *Set of 4* | 1·00 | 1·00 |

(Des, recess and litho D.L.R.)

**1974** (31 July). *Anniversaries. T* **47** *and similar vert designs. P* 13 × 14.

| | | | | |
|---|---|---|---|---|
| 111 | 3p. | agate and light cinnamon | 10 | 10 |
| 112 | 3½p. | blackish violet and light azure | 10 | 10 |
| 113 | 8p. | blue-black and pale rose-lilac | 30 | 35 |
| 114 | 20p. | black and pale buff | 70 | 65 |
| | | a. Pale buff (background) omitted | | |
| 111/14 | | *Set of 4* | 1·00 | 1·00 |

Portraits and events:—3p. Type **47** (Bicentenary of Methodism in Jersey); 3½p. Sir William Hillary, founder (150th Anniv of R.N.L.I.); 8p. Cannon Wace, poet and historian (800th Death Anniv); 20p. Sir Winston Churchill (Birth Centenary).

**48** Royal Yacht

**49** Potato Digger

(Des and photo Courvoisier)

**1974** (22 Nov). *Marine Paintings by Peter Monamy. T* **48** *and similar multicoloured designs. Granite paper. P* 11½.

| | | | | |
|---|---|---|---|---|
| 115 | 3½p. | Type **48** | 10 | 10 |
| 116 | 5½p. | French two-decker | 15 | 15 |
| 117 | 8p. | Dutch vessel (*horiz*) | 25 | 30 |
| 118 | 25p. | Battle of Cap La Hague, 1692 (55 × 27 *mm*) | 65 | 60 |
| 115/18 | | *Set of 4* | 1·00 | 1·00 |

(Des G. Drummond. Photo Courvoisier)

**1975** (25 Feb). *19th-Century Farming. T* **49** *and similar horiz designs. Multicoloured. Granite paper. P* 11½.

| | | | | |
|---|---|---|---|---|
| 119 | 3p. | Type **49** | 10 | 10 |
| 120 | 3½p. | Cider crusher | 10 | 15 |
| 121 | 8p. | Six-horse plough | 35 | 35 |
| 122 | 10p. | Hay cart | 55 | 50 |
| 119/22 | | *Set of 4* | 1·00 | 1·00 |

**50** H.M. Queen Elizabeth, the Queen Mother (photograph by Cecil Beaton)

**51** Shell

(Des and photo Courvoisier)

**1975** (30 May). *Royal Visit. Granite paper. P* 11½.

| | | | | |
|---|---|---|---|---|
| 123 | **50** | 20p. multicoloured | 75 | 75 |

(Des A. Games. Photo Courvoisier)

**1975** (6 June). *Jersey Tourism. T* **51** *and similar vert designs based on holiday posters. Multicoloured. Granite paper. P* 11½.

| | | | | |
|---|---|---|---|---|
| 124 | 5p. | Type **51** | 10 | 10 |
| 125 | 8p. | Parasol | 15 | 15 |
| 126 | 10p. | Deckchair | 35 | 35 |
| 127 | 12p. | Sandcastle with flags of Jersey and the U.K. | 50 | 50 |
| 124/7 | | *Set of 4* | 1·00 | 1·00 |
| **MS**128 | | 146 × 68 mm. Nos. 124/7 | 1·00 | 1·10 |

**52** Common Tern

**53** Siskin "3-A"

(Des Jennifer Toombs. Photo Courvoisier)

**1975** (28 July). *Sea Birds. T* **52** *and similar vert designs. Multicoloured. Granite paper. P* 11½.

| | | | | |
|---|---|---|---|---|
| 129 | 4p. | Type **52** | 15 | 15 |
| 130 | 5p. | British Storm Petrel | 15 | 15 |
| 131 | 8p. | Brent Geese | 30 | 35 |
| 132 | 25p. | Shag | 60 | 55 |
| 129/32 | | *Set of 4* | 1·10 | 1·10 |

(Des A. Theobald. Photo Courvoisier)

**1975** (30 Oct). *50th Anniv of Royal Air Forces Association, Jersey Branch. T* **53** *and similar horiz designs. Multicoloured. Granite paper. P* 11½.

| | | | | |
|---|---|---|---|---|
| 133 | 4p. | Type **53** | 10 | 10 |
| 134 | 5p. | "Southampton" flying-boat | 15 | 15 |
| 135 | 10p. | Mk. I "Spitfire" | 30 | 30 |
| 136 | 25p. | Folland "Gnat" | 60 | 60 |
| 133/6 | | *Set of 4* | 1·00 | 1·00 |

**54** Map of Jersey Parishes

**55** Parish Arms and Island Scene

(Des Courvoisier (£2). G. Drummond (others). Litho Questa (½ to 15p.). Photo Courvoisier (others))

**1976–80.** *Various multicoloured designs as T* **54/5**.

(*a*) *Parish Arms and Views as T* **54**. *P* 14½. (29 Jan)

137 ½p. Type **54** .. .. .. .. .. 10 10
138 1p. Zoological Park .. .. .. .. .. 10 10
a. Booklet pane of 2 plus 2 *se-tenant* labels (5.4.76) .. .. .. .. 1·75
b. Booklet pane of 4 (5.4.76) .. .. .. 1·50
139 5p. St. Mary's Church .. .. .. 15 15
a. Booklet pane of 4 (5.4.76) .. .. 60
140 6p. Seymour Tower .. .. .. .. 15 15
a. Booklet pane of 4 (28.2.78) .. .. 1·25
141 7p. La Corbière Lighthouse .. .. 20 20
a. Booklet pane of 4 (5.4.76) .. .. 75
142 8p. St. Saviour's Church .. .. .. 20 20
a. Booklet pane of 4 (28.2.78) .. .. 1·50
143 9p. Elizabeth Castle .. .. .. 25 25
a. Booklet pane of 4 (6.5.80) .. .. 1·25
144 10p. Gorey Harbour .. .. .. .. 25 25
145 11p. Jersey Airport .. .. .. .. 30 25
146 12p. Grosnez Castle .. .. .. .. 30 30
147 13p. Bonne Nuit Harbour .. .. .. 35 35
148 14p. Le Hocq Tower .. .. .. .. 35 40
149 15p. Morel Farm .. .. .. .. 40 45

(*b*) *Emblems as T* **55**. *Granite paper. P* 12 (20 Aug 1976–16 Nov 1977)

150 20p. Type **55** .. .. .. .. .. 50 50
151 30p. Flag and map .. .. .. .. 75 75
152 40p. Postal H.Q. and badge .. .. .. 1·00 1·00
153 50p. Parliament, Royal Court and arms .. 1·25 1·25
154 £1 Lieutenant-Governor's flag and Government House .. .. .. .. 2·50 2·50
155 £2 Queen Elizabeth II (photograph by Alex Wilson) (*vert*) (16.11.77) .. .. 4·00 4·25
137/55 .. .. .. .. *Set of* 19 11·50 12·00

Nos. 156/9 are vacant.

**56** Sir Walter Ralegh and Map of Virginia

(Des M. Orbell. Photo Courvoisier)

**1976** (29 May). *"Links with America". T* **56** *and similar horiz designs. Multicoloured. Granite paper. P* 11½.

160 5p. Type **56** .. .. .. .. .. 10 10
161 7p. Sir George Carteret and map of New Jersey .. .. .. .. .. 15 15
162 11p. Philippe Dauvergne and Long Island Landing .. .. .. .. .. 40 35
163 13p. John Copley and sketch .. .. 45 50
160/3 .. .. .. .. .. *Set of* 4 1·00 1·00

**57** Dr. Grandin and Map of China

**58** Coronation, 1953 (photographed by Cecil Beaton)

(Des Jennifer Toombs. Photo Courvoisier)

**1976** (25 Nov). *Birth Centenary of Dr. Lilian Grandin (medical missionary). T* **57** *and similar horiz designs. Granite paper. P* 11½.

164 5p. multicoloured .. .. .. .. .. 10 10
165 7p. light yellow, yellow-brown and black .. 15 15
166 11p. multicoloured .. .. .. .. .. 50 35
167 13p. multicoloured .. .. .. .. .. 50 50
164/7 .. .. .. .. .. *Set of* 4 1·10 1·00

Designs:—7p. Sampan on the Yangtze; 11p. Overland trek; 13p. Dr. Grandin at work.

(Des G. Drummond. Photo Courvoisier)

**1977** (7 Feb). *Silver Jubilee. T* **58** *and similar vert designs. Multicoloured. Granite paper. P* 11½.

168 5p. Type **58** .. .. .. .. .. 15 15
169 7p. Visit to Jersey, 1957 .. .. .. 30 20
170 25p. Queen Elizabeth II (photo by Peter Grugeon) .. .. .. .. .. 80 80
168/70 .. .. .. .. .. *Set of* 3 1·10 1·00

**59** Coins of 1871 and 1877

(Des D. Henley. Litho Questa)

**1977** (25 Mar). *Centenary of Currency Reform. T* **59** *and similar horiz designs. Multicoloured. P* 14.

171 5p. Type **59** .. .. .. .. .. 10 10
172 7p. One-twelfth shilling, 1949 .. .. 15 15
173 11p. Silver Crown, 1966 .. .. .. 40 35
174 13p. £2 piece, 1972 .. .. .. .. 45 50
171/4 .. .. .. .. .. *Set of* 4 1·00 1·00

**60** Sir William Weston and *Santa Anna*, 1530

(Des A. Theobald. Litho Questa)

**1977** (24 June). *St. John Ambulance Centenary. T* **60** *and similar horiz designs each showing a Grand Prior of the Order. Multicoloured. P* 14 × 13½.

175 5p. Type **60** .. .. .. .. .. 10 10
176 7p. Sir William Drogo and ambulance, 1877 15 15
177 11p. Duke of Connaught and ambulance, 1917 .. .. .. .. .. 40 35
178 13p. Duke of Gloucester and stretcher-team, 1977 .. .. .. .. .. 45 50
175/8 .. .. .. .. .. *Set of* 4 1·00 1·00

**61** Arrival of Queen Victoria, 1846

(Des R. Granger Barrett. Litho Questa)

**1977** (29 Sept). *125th Anniv of Victoria College. T* **61** *and similar multicoloured designs. P* 14½.

179 7p. Type **61** .. .. .. .. .. 20 20
180 10½p. Victoria College, 1852 .. .. .. 25 20
181 11p. Sir Galahad statue, 1924 (*vert*) .. 30 35
182 13p. College Hall (*vert*) .. .. .. 35 35
179/82 .. .. .. .. .. *Set of* 4 1·00 1·00

**62** Harry Vardon Statuette and Map of Royal Jersey Course

(Des Jennifer Toombs. Litho Questa)

**1978** (28 Feb). *Centenary of Royal Jersey Golf Club. T* **62** *and similar horiz designs. Multicoloured. P* 14.

183 6p. Type **62** .. .. .. .. .. 15 15
184 8p. Harry Vardon's grip and swing .. 20 20
185 11p. Harry Vardon's putt .. .. .. 35 35
186 13p. Golf trophies and book by Harry Vardon 40 40
183/6 .. .. .. .. .. *Set of* 4 1·00 1·00

**63** Mont Orgueil Castle

**64** "Gaspé Basin" (P. J. Ouless)

(Des from paintings by Thomas Phillips. Photo Courvoisier)

**1978** (1 May). *Europa. Castles. T* **63** *and similar horiz designs. Multicoloured. Granite paper. P* 11½.

187 6p. Type **63** .. .. .. .. .. 20 20
188 8p. St. Aubin's Fort .. .. .. .. 40 40
189 10½p. Elizabeth Castle .. .. .. .. 50 50
187/9 .. .. .. .. .. *Set of* 3 1·00 1·00

(Des R. Granger Barrett. Litho Questa)

**1978** (9 June). *Links with Canada. T* **64** *and similar horiz designs. Multicoloured. P* 14½.

190 6p. Type **64** .. .. .. .. .. 15 15
191 8p. Map of Gaspé Peninsula .. .. .. 20 20
192 10½p. *Century* (brigantine) .. .. .. 25 25
193 11p. Early map of Jersey .. .. .. 30 30
194 13p. St. Aubin's Bay, town and harbour .. 35 35
190/4 .. .. .. .. .. *Set of* 5 1·10 1·10

**65** Queen Elizabeth and Prince Philip

**66** Mail Cutter, 1778–1827

(Des and photo Courvoisier)

**1978** (26 June). *25th Anniv of Coronation. T* **65** *and similar vert design. Granite paper. P* 11½.

195 8p. silver, black and cerise .. .. .. 30 30
196 25p. silver, black and new blue .. .. 70 70

Design:—25p. Hallmarks of 1953 and 1977.

(Des Jersey P.O. Litho Harrison)

**1978** (18 Oct). *Bicentenary of England-Jersey Government Mail Packet Service. T* **66** *and similar horiz designs. P* 14½ × 14.

197 6p. black, yellow-brown and greenish yellow 15 15
198 8p. black, dull yellowish grn & pale yell-grn 20 20
199 10½p. black, ultramarine and cobalt .. .. 30 30
200 11p. black, purple and pale rose-lilac .. 35 35
201 13p. black, Venetian red and pink .. .. 45 45
197/201 .. .. .. .. *Set of* 5 1·25 1·25

Designs:—8p. *Flamer*, 1831–37; 10½p. *Diana*, 1877–90; 11p. *Ibex*, 1891–1925; 13p. *Caesarea*, 1960–75.

**67** Jersey Calf

**68** Jersey Pillar Box, *circa* 1860

(Des Jersey P.O. and Questa. Litho Questa)

**1979** (1 Mar). *9th World Jersey Cattle Bureau Conference. T* **67** *and similar horiz design. Multicoloured. P* 13½.

202 6p. Type **67** .. .. .. .. .. 20 20
203 25p. "Ansom Designette" (cow presented to the Queen, 27 June 1978) (46 × 29 *mm*) 80 80

(Des Jennifer Toombs. Litho Questa)

**1979** (1 Mar). *Europa. T* **68** *and similar vert designs. Multicoloured.* A. *P* 14. B. *P* 14½.

| | | | A | | B | |
|---|---|---|---|---|---|---|
| 204 | 8p. | Type **68** .. .. | 20 | 25 | 20 | 25 |
| | a. | Horiz pair. Nos. 204/5 | 40 | 50 | 40 | 50 |
| 205 | 8p. | Clearing a modern Jersey post box .. .. | 20 | 25 | 20 | 25 |
| 206 | 10½p. | Telephone switchboard, *circa* 1900 .. | 25 | 30 | 25 | 30 |
| | a. | Horiz pair, Nos. 206/7 | 55 | 65 | 55 | 65 |
| 207 | 10½p. | Modern S.P.C. telephone system .. .. | 25 | 30 | 25 | 30 |
| 204/7 .. | | *Set of* 4 | 1·00 | 1·10 | 1·00 | 1·10 |

Nos. 204/5 and 206/7 were each printed together, *se-tenant*, in horizontal pairs throughout the sheets.

**69** Percival "Mew Gull"

**70** "My First Sermon"

(Des A. Theobald. Photo Courvoisier)

**1979** (24 Apr). *25th Anniv of International Air Rally. T* **69** *and similar horiz designs. Multicoloured. Granite paper. P* 11½.

208 6p. Type **69** .. .. .. .. .. 15 15
209 8p. De Havilland "Chipmunk" .. .. 20 20
210 10½p. Druine "Turbulent" .. .. .. 30 30
211 11p. De Havilland "Tiger Moth" .. .. 45 35
212 13p. North American "Harvard" Mk. 4 .. 50 40
208/12 .. .. .. .. .. *Set of* 5 1·40 1·25

(Des Jersey P.O. and Courvoisier. Photo Courvoisier)

**1979** (13 Aug). *International Year of the Child and 150th Birth Anniv of Millais. Paintings. T* **70** *and similar multicoloured designs. Granite paper. P* 12 × 12½ (25p.) *or* 12 × 11½ (*others*).

213 8p. Type **70** .. .. .. .. .. 25 25
214 10½p. "Orphans" .. .. .. .. .. 30 30
215 11p. "The Princes in the Tower" .. .. 40 40
216 25p. "Christ in the House of His Parents" (50 × 32 *mm*) .. .. .. .. 65 65
213/16 .. .. .. .. .. *Set of* 4 1·40 1·40

(Des Jennifer Toombs. Photo Courvoisier)

**1979** (8 Nov). *Wildlife Preservation Trust (3rd series). Multicoloured designs as T* **34**. *Granite paper. P* 11½.

| No. | Description | | |
|---|---|---|---|
| 217 | 6p. Pink Pigeon (*vert*) | 15 | 15 |
| 218 | 8p. Orang-Utan (*vert*) | 20 | 20 |
| 219 | 11½p. Waldrapp | 40 | 35 |
| 220 | 13p. Lowland Gorilla (*vert*) | 45 | 40 |
| 221 | 15p. Rodriguez Flying Fox (*vert*) | 60 | 45 |
| 217/21 | *Set of* 5 | 1·60 | 1·40 |

**71** Plan of Mont Orgueil

(Litho Enschedé)

**1980** (5 Feb). *Fortresses. T* **71** *and similar multicoloured designs showing drawings by Thomas Phillips. P* 13 × 13½ (25*p*.) *or* 13½ × 13 (*others*).

| No. | Description | | |
|---|---|---|---|
| 222 | 8p. Type **71** | 25 | 25 |
| 223 | 11½p. Plan of La Tour de St. Aubin | 30 | 30 |
| 224 | 13p. Plan of Elizabeth Castle | 45 | 35 |
| 225 | 25p. Map of Jersey showing fortresses (38 × 27 *mm*) | 80 | 70 |
| 222/5 | *Set of* 4 | 1·60 | 1·40 |

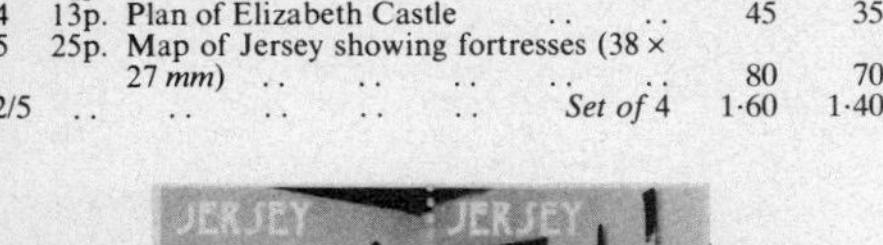

**72** Sir Walter Raleigh and Paul Ivy (engineer) discussing Elizabeth Castle

(Des Jersey Post Office and Questa. Litho Questa)

**1980** (6 May). *Europa. Personalities. Links with Britain. T* **72** *and similar vert design. Multicoloured. P* 14.

| No. | Description | | |
|---|---|---|---|
| 226 | 9p. } Type **72** | 20 | 20 |
| 227 | 9p. } | 20 | 20 |
| | a. Horiz pair. Nos. 226/7 | 50 | 50 |
| 228 | 13½p. } Sir George Carteret receiving rights to Smith's Island, Virginia from King Charles II | 40 | 35 |
| 229 | 13½p. } | 40 | 35 |
| | a. Horiz pair. Nos. 228/9 | 80 | 70 |
| 226/9 | *Set of* 4 | 1·25 | 1·10 |

Nos. 226/7 and 228/9 were each printed together, *se-tenant*, in horizontal pair throughout the sheet, forming composite designs.

**73** Planting

**74** Three Lap Event

(Des R. Granger Barrett. Litho Questa)

**1980** (6 May). *Centenary of Jersey Royal Potato. T* **73** *and similar vert designs. Multicoloured. P* 14.

| No. | Description | | |
|---|---|---|---|
| 230 | 7p. Type **73** | 15 | 15 |
| 231 | 15p. Digging | 45 | 35 |
| 232 | 17½p. Weighbridge | 65 | 60 |
| 230/2 | *Set of* 3 | 1·10 | 1·00 |

(Des A. Theobald. Photo Courvoisier)

**1980** (24 July). *60th Anniv of Jersey Motor-cycle and Light Car Club. T* **74** *and similar horiz designs. Multicoloured. Granite paper. P* 11½.

| No. | Description | | |
|---|---|---|---|
| 233 | 7p. Type **74** | 25 | 25 |
| 234 | 9p. Jersey International Road Race | 25 | 25 |
| 235 | 13½p. Scrambling | 40 | 40 |
| 236 | 15p. Sand racing (saloon cars) | 45 | 45 |
| 237 | 17½p. National Hill Climb | 50 | 50 |
| 233/7 | *Set of* 5 | 1·60 | 1·60 |

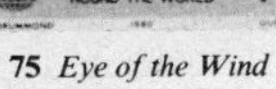

**75** *Eye of the Wind*

**76** Detail of "The Death of Major Peirson"

(Des G. Drummond. Litho Questa)

**1980** (1 Oct). *"Operation Drake" Round the World Expedition and 150th Anniv of Royal Geographical Society* (14*p*.). *P* 14.

| No. | Description | | |
|---|---|---|---|
| 238 | 7p. Type **75** | 20 | 20 |
| 239 | 9p. Diving from inflatable dinghy | 25 | 25 |
| 240 | 13½p. Exploration of Papua New Guinea | 45 | 35 |
| 241 | 14p. Captain Scott's *Discovery* | 45 | 35 |
| 242 | 15p. Using aerial walkways, Conservation Project, Sulawesi | 45 | 35 |
| 243 | 17½p. *Eye of the Wind* and Goodyear airship | 45 | 45 |
| 238/43 | *Set of* 6 | 2·00 | 1·75 |

(Photo Courvoisier)

**1981** (6 Jan). *Bicentenary of Battle of Jersey. Painting "The Death of Major Peirson" by J. S. Copley. T* **76** *and similar vert designs showing details of the work. Granite paper. P* 12½ × 12.

| No. | Description | | |
|---|---|---|---|
| 244 | 7p. multicoloured | 25 | 25 |
| 245 | 10p. multicoloured | 30 | 30 |
| 246 | 15p. multicoloured | 50 | 50 |
| 247 | 17½p. multicoloured | 55 | 55 |
| 244/7 | *Set of* 4 | 1·40 | 1·40 |
| **MS**248 | 144 × 97 mm. Nos. 244/7 | 1·75 | 1·50 |

Stamps from No. **MS**248 are without white margins.

**77** De Bagot

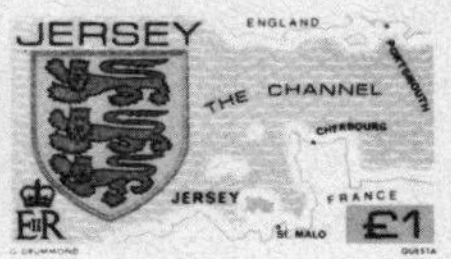

**78** Jersey Crest and Map of Channel

**78a** "Queen Elizabeth II" (Norman Hepple)

(Des and photo Courvoisier (£5). Des G. Drummond. Litho Questa (others))

**1981** (24 Feb)–**88**. *Arms of Jersey Families. T* **77** *and similar designs in black, silver and turquoise-green* (½*p*.), *black, silver and mauve* (4*p*.), *black, silver and lemon* (20*p*.), *black and dull blue* (25*p*.), *black, silver and carmine* (26*p*.) *or multicoloured* (*others*) *with T* **78/a**. *Granite paper* (£5). *P* 12½×12 (£5), 15×14 (16*p*., 17*p*., 18*p*., 19*p*., 26*p*., 75*p*.) *or* 14 (*others*).

| No. | Description | | |
|---|---|---|---|
| 249 | ½p. Type **77** | 10 | 10 |
| 250 | 1p. De Carteret | 10 | 10 |
| | a. Booklet pane of 6 | 20 | |
| | b. Perf 15 × 14 (12.1.88) | 10 | 10 |
| 251 | 2p. La Cloche | 10 | 10 |
| | a. Booklet pane of 6 (1.12.81) | 40 | |
| | b. Perf 15 × 14 (15.11.84) | 10 | 10 |
| | ba. Booklet pane of 6 (1.4.86) | 20 | |
| 252 | 3p. Dumaresq | 10 | 10 |
| | a. Booklet pane of 6 | 55 | |
| | b. Perf 15 × 14 (27.4.84) | 10 | 10 |
| | ba. Booklet pane of 6 | 55 | |
| 253 | 4p. Payn | 15 | 15 |
| | a. Perf 15 × 14 (4.3.86) | 10 | 10 |
| | ab. Booklet pane of 6 (6.4.87) | 40 | |
| 254 | 5p. Janvrin | 15 | 15 |
| | a. Perf 15 × 14 (4.3.86) | 15 | 15 |
| 255 | 6p. Poingdestre | 20 | 20 |
| | a. Perf 15 × 14 (4.3.86) | 20 | 20 |
| 256 | 7p. Pipon | 20 | 20 |
| | a. Booklet pane of 6 | 1·40 | |
| 257 | 8p. Marett | 25 | 25 |
| | a. Booklet pane of 6 (19.4.83) | 1·50 | |
| 258 | 9p. Le Breton | 30 | 30 |
| | a. Perf 15 × 14 (27.4.84) | 30 | 30 |
| | ab. Booklet pane of 6 | 1·75 | |
| 259 | 10p. Le Maistre | 30 | 30 |
| | a. Booklet pane of 6 | 1·75 | |
| | b. Perf 15 × 14 (1.4.86) | 20 | 25 |
| | ba. Booklet pane of 6 | 1·10 | |
| 260 | 11p. Bisson (28.7.81) | 35 | 35 |
| | a. Booklet pane of 6 (19.4.83) | 2·00 | |
| | b. Perf 15 × 14 (6.4.87) | 50 | 45 |
| | ba. Booklet pane of 6 | 1·25 | |
| 261 | 12p. Robin (28.7.81) | 40 | 40 |
| | a. Perf 15 × 14 (27.4.84) | 20 | 25 |
| | ab. Booklet pane of 6 | 1·25 | |
| 262 | 13p. Herault (28.7.81) | 40 | 40 |
| | a. Perf 15 × 14 (15.11.84) | 25 | 30 |
| 263 | 14p. Messervy (28.7.81) | 45 | 45 |
| | a. Perf 15 × 14 (15.11.84) | 25 | 30 |
| | ab. Booklet pane of 6 (1.4.86) | 1·50 | |
| 264 | 15p. Fiott (28.7.81) | 45 | 45 |
| | a. Perf 15 × 14 (6.4.87) | 45 | 45 |
| | ab. Booklet pane of 6 | 1·60 | |
| 265 | 16p. Malet (25.10.85) | 30 | 35 |
| | a. Booklet pane of 6 (17.5.88) | 1·75 | |
| 266 | 17p. Mabon (25.10.85) | 50 | 50 |
| 266*a* | 18p. De St. Martin (26.4.88) | 55 | 55 |
| 266*b* | 19p. Hamptonne (26.4.88) | 60 | 60 |
| 267 | 20p. Badier (28.7.81) | 60 | 60 |
| | a. Perf 15 × 14 (4.3.86) | 60 | 60 |
| 268 | 25p. L'Arbalestier (23.2.82) | 45 | 50 |
| 268*a* | 26p. Type **77** (26.4.88) | 45 | 50 |
| 269 | 30p. Journeaux (23.2.82) | 90 | 90 |
| | a. Perf 15 × 14 (4.3.86) | 50 | 55 |
| 270 | 40p. Lempriere (23.2.82) | 1·25 | 1·25 |
| | a. Perf 15 × 14 (6.4.87) | 1·00 | 1·00 |
| 271 | 50p. D'Auvergene (23.2.82) | 1·50 | 1·50 |
| | a. Perf 15 × 14 (6.4.87) | 1·25 | 1·25 |
| 272 | 75p. Remon (23.4.87) | 2·00 | 1·75 |
| 273 | £1 Type **78** (23.2.82) | 3·00 | 3·00 |
| 274 | £5 Type **78a** (17.11.83) | 10·00 | 10·50 |
| 249/74 | *Set of* 29 | 19·00 | 20·00 |

No. 258a only occurs in the £2.16 stamp booklet issued 27 April 1984, No. 259b from the £3.12 booklet of 1 April 1986, No. 260b from the £3.60 booklet of 6 April 1987 and No. 261a from the £2.16 booklet of 27 April 1984 and the £3.84 booklet of 17 May 1988.

**79** Knight of Hambye slaying Dragon

(Des Jennifer Toombs. Litho Questa)

**1981** (7 Apr). *Europa. Folklore. T* **79** *and similar horiz designs. Multicoloured. P* 14½.

| No. | Description | | |
|---|---|---|---|
| 275 | 10p. Type **79** | 25 | 25 |
| | a. Horiz pair. Nos. 275/6 | 55 | 55 |
| 276 | 10p. Servant slaying Knight of Hambye, and awaiting execution | 25 | 25 |
| 277 | 18p. St. Brelade celebrating Easter on island | 50 | 50 |
| | a. Horiz pair. Nos. 277/8 | 1·10 | 1·10 |
| 278 | 18p. Island revealing itself as a huge fish | 50 | 50 |
| 275/8 | *Set of* 4 | 1·50 | 1·40 |

Legends:—10p. (*both*), Slaying of the Dragon of Lawrence by the Knight of Hambye; 18p. (*both*), Voyages of St. Brelade.

Nos. 275/6 and 277/8 were each printed together, *se-tenant*, in horizontal pairs throughout the sheet.

**80** The Harbour by Gaslight

**81** Prince Charles and Lady Diana Spencer

(Des R. Granger Barrett. Photo Courvoisier)

**1981** (22 May). *150th Anniv of Gas Lighting in Jersey. T* **80** *and similar horiz designs showing Jersey by gaslight. Multicoloured. Granite paper. P* 11½.

| No. | Description | | |
|---|---|---|---|
| 279 | 7p. Type **80** | 25 | 25 |
| 280 | 10p. The Quay | 30 | 30 |
| 281 | 18p. Royal Square | 55 | 45 |
| 282 | 22p. Halkett Place | 65 | 55 |
| 283 | 25p. Central Market | 75 | 65 |
| 279/83 | *Set of* 5 | 2·25 | 2·00 |

(Des Jersey P.O. and Courvoisier. Photo Courvoisier)

**1981** (28 July). *Royal Wedding. Granite paper. P* 11½.

| No. | Description | | |
|---|---|---|---|
| 284 | **81** 10p. multicoloured | 55 | 25 |
| 285 | 25p. multicoloured | 1·25 | 1·25 |

**82** Christmas Tree in Royal Square

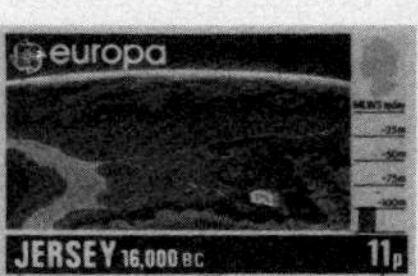

**83** Jersey, 16,000 B.C.

(Des A. Copp. Litho Questa)

**1981** (29 Sept). *Christmas. T* **82** *and similar vert designs. Multicoloured. P* 14½.

| No. | Description | | |
|---|---|---|---|
| 286 | 7p. Type **82** | 25 | 25 |
| 287 | 10p. East window, Parish Church, St. Helier | 40 | 40 |
| 288 | 18p. Boxing Day meet of Jersey Drag Hunt | 60 | 60 |
| 286/8 | *Set of* 3 | 1·10 | 1·10 |

(Des A. Copp. Litho Questa)

**1982** (20 Apr). *Europa. Historic Events. Formation of Jersey. T* **83** *and similar multicoloured designs. P* 14½.

| No. | Description | | |
|---|---|---|---|
| 289 | 11p. Type **83** | 30 | 30 |
| 290 | 11p. Jersey, 10,000 B.C. (*vert*) | 30 | 30 |
| 291 | 19½p. 7,000 B.C. (*vert*) | 60 | 60 |
| 292 | 19½p. 4,000 B.C. | 60 | 60 |
| 289/92 | *Set of* 4 | 1·60 | 1·60 |

**84** Duke Rollo of Normandy, William the Conqueror and "Clameur de Haro" (traditional procedure for obtaining justice)

(Des R. Granger Barrett. Litho Questa)

**1982** (11 June–7 Sept). *Links with France. T* **84** *and similar horiz designs. Multicoloured. P* 14.

293 8p. Type **84** .. .. .. .. .. .. 30 30
a. Horiz pair. Nos. 293/4 .. .. .. 60 60
b. Booklet pane. Nos. 293 and 294 each × 2 (7 Sept) .. .. .. .. .. 1·40
294 8p. John of England, Philippe Auguste of France and Siege of Rouen .. .. 30 30
295 11p. Jean Martell (brandy merchant), early still and view of Cognac .. .. 40 40
a. Horiz pair. Nos. 295/6 .. .. .. 80 80
b. Booklet pane. Nos. 295 and 296 each × 2 (7 Sept) .. .. .. .. .. 1·60
296 11p. Victor Hugo, "Le Rocher des Proscrits" (rock where he used to meditate) and Marine Terrace .. .. .. 40 40
297 19½p. Pierre Teilhard de Chardin (philosopher) and "Maison Saint Louis" (science institute) .. .. .. .. 70 70
a. Horiz pair. Nos. 297/8 .. .. .. 1·40 1·40
b. Booklet pane. Nos. 297 and 298 each × 2 (7 Sept) .. .. .. .. .. 2·75
298 19½p. Père Charles Rey (scientist), anemotachymeter and The Observatory, St. Louis .. .. .. .. .. 70 70
293/8 .. .. .. .. .. *Set of* 6 2·50 2·50

The two designs of each value were printed together, *se-tenant*, in horizontal pairs throughout the sheet.

Nos. 293b, 295b and 297b were printed with either a French or an English inscription on the selvedge.

**85** Sir William Smith, Founder of Boys' Brigade

**86** H.M.S. *Tamar* with H.M.S. *Dolphin* at Port Egmont

(Des A. Theobald. Photo Courvoisier)

**1982** (18 Nov). *75th Anniv of Boy Scout Movement* (*Nos.* 301/3) *and Centenary of Boys' Brigade* (*Nos.* 299/301). *T* **85** *and similar multi-coloured designs. Granite paper. P* 11½.

299 8p. Type **85** .. .. .. .. .. .. 25 25
300 11p. Boys' Brigade "Old Boys" band, Liberation Parade, 1945 (*vert*) .. .. 35 35
301 24p. William Smith and Lord Baden-Powell at Royal Albert Hall, 1903 .. .. 75 75
302 26p. Lord and Lady Baden-Powell in St. Helier, 1924 (*vert*) .. .. .. 90 90
303 29p. Scouts at "Westward Ho" campsite, St. Ouen's Bay .. .. .. .. 1·10 1·10
299/303.. .. .. .. .. *Set of* 5 3·00 3·00

(Des R. Granger Barrett. Litho Questa)

**1983** (15 Feb). *Jersey Adventurers* (1*st series*). *250th Birth Anniv of Philippe de Carteret. T* **86** *and similar horiz designs. Multi-coloured. P* 14 × 14½.

304 8p. Type **86** .. .. .. .. .. .. 25 25
305 11p. H.M.S. *Dolphin* and H.M.S. *Swallow* off Magellan Strait .. .. .. 35 35
306 19½p. Discovering Pitcairn Island .. .. 60 60
307 24p. Carteret taking possession of English Cove, New Ireland .. .. .. 85 85
308 26p. H.M.S. *Swallow* sinking a pirate, Macassar Strait .. .. .. .. 90 90
309 29p. H.M.S. *Endymion* leading convoy from West Indies .. .. .. .. 1·00 1·00
304/9 .. .. .. .. .. *Set of* 6 3·50 3·50

See also Nos. 417/21 and 573/8.

**87** 1969 5s. Legislative Chamber Definitive

(Des G. Drummond. Litho Questa)

**1983** (19 Apr). *Europa. T* **87** *and similar multicoloured designs. P* 14½.

310 11p. Type **87** .. .. .. .. .. 50 50
a. Horiz pair. Nos. 310/11 .. .. .. 1·00 1·00
311 11p. Royal Mace (23 × 32 *mm*) .. .. 50 50
312 19½p. 1969 10s. Royal Court definitive showing green border error .. .. .. 85 85
a. Horiz pair. Nos. 312/13 .. .. .. 1·75 1·75
313 19½p. Bailiff's Seal (23 × 32 *mm*) .. .. 85 85
310/13 .. .. .. .. *Set of* 4 2·50 2·50

The two designs of each value were issued together, *se-tenant*, in horizontal pairs throughout the sheets.

**88** Charles Le Geyt and Battle of Minden (1759)

(Des A. Copp. Litho Questa)

**1983** (21 June). *World Communications Year and 250th Birth Anniv of Charles Le Geyt* (*first Jersey postmaster*). *T* **88** *and similar horiz designs. Multicoloured. P* 14.

314 8p. Type **88** .. .. .. .. .. 25 25
315 11p. London to Weymouth mail coach .. 35 35
316 24p. P.O. Mail Packet *Chesterfield* attacked by French privateer .. .. .. 75 75
317 26p. Mary Godfray and the Hue Street Post Office .. .. .. .. .. 90 90
318 29p. Mail steamer leaving St. Helier harbour 1·10 1·10
314/18 .. .. .. .. .. *Set of* 5 3·00 3·00

**89** Assembly Emblem

**90** "Cardinal Newman"

(Des A. Copp. Litho Questa)

**1983** (21 June). *13th General Assembly of the A.I.P.L.F.* (*Association Internationale des Parlementaires de Langue Francaise*), *Jersey. P* 14½.

319 **89** 19½p. multicoloured .. .. .. 90 90

(Des and photo Courvoisier)

**1983** (20 Sept). *50th Death Anniv of Walter Ouless* (*artist*). *T* **90** *and similar multicoloured designs, showing paintings. Granite paper. P* 11½.

320 8p. Type **90** .. .. .. .. .. 25 25
321 11p. "Incident in the French Revolution" .. 45 45
322 20½p. "Thomas Hardy" .. .. .. .. 85 85
323 31p. "David with the head of Goliath" (38 × 32 *mm*) .. .. .. .. 1·25 1·25
320/3 .. .. .. .. .. *Set of* 4 2·50 2·50

**91** Golden Lion Tamarin

**92** C.E.P.T. 25th Anniversary Logo

(Des W. Oliver. Litho Questa)

**1984** (17 Jan). *Wildlife Preservation Trust* (*4th series*). *T* **91** *and similar vert designs. Multicoloured. P* 13½ × 14.

324 9p. Type **91** .. .. .. .. .. 30 30
325 12p. Snow Leopard .. .. .. .. 40 40
326 20½p. Jamaican Boa .. .. .. .. 65 65
327 26p. Round Island Gecko .. .. .. 80 80
328 28p. Coscoroba Swan .. .. .. .. 90 90
329 31p. St. Lucia Amazon .. .. .. 1·00 1·00
324/9 .. .. .. .. *Set of* 6 3·75 3·75

(Des J. Larrivière. Litho Questa)

**1984** (12 Mar). *Europa. P* 14½ × 15.

330 **92** 9p. cobalt, dull ultramarine and black 30 30
331 12p. light green, green and black .. 40 40
332 20½p. rose-lilac, deep magenta and black 70 70
330/2 .. .. .. .. .. *Set of* 3 1·25 1·25

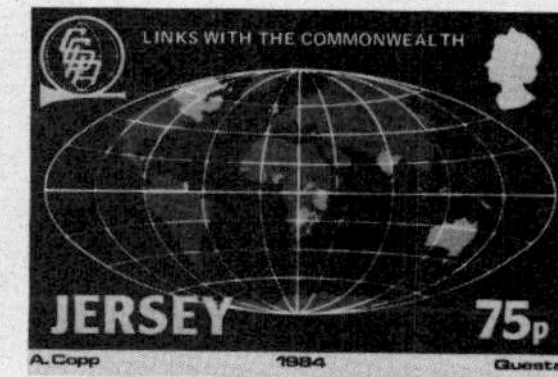


**93** Map showing Commonwealth

(Des A. Copp. Litho Questa)

**1984** (12 Mar). *Links with the Commonwealth. Sheet* 108 × 74 *mm. P* 15 × 14½.

MS333 **93** 75p. multicoloured .. .. .. 2·75 2·75

**94** *Sarah Bloomshoft* at Demie de Pas Light, 1906

(Des G. Palmer. Litho Questa)

**1984** (1 June). *Centenary of the Jersey R.N.L.I. Lifeboat Station T* **94** *and similar horiz designs showing famous rescues. Multicoloured. P* 14½.

334 9p. Type **94** .. .. .. .. .. 30 30
335 9p. *Hearts of Oak* and *Maurice Georges*, 1949 30 30
336 12p. *Elizabeth Rippon* and *Hanna*, 1949 .. 40 40
337 12p. *Elizabeth Rippon* and *Santa Maria*, 1951 40 40
338 20½p. *Elizabeth Rippon* and *Bacchus*, 1973 .. 65 65
339 20½p. *Thomas James King* and *Cythara*, 1983 .. 65 65
334/9 .. .. .. .. .. *Set of* 6 2·50 2·50

**95** Bristol "Type 170" Freighter

(Des G. Drummond. Litho Questa)

**1984** (24 July). *Jersey Aviation History* (*2nd series*). *T* **95** *and similar horiz designs. Multicoloured. P* 14.

340 9p. Type **95** .. .. .. .. .. 30 30
341 12p. Airspeed "A.S.57 Ambassador 2" .. 40 40
342 26p. De Havilland "D.H.114 Heron 1B" .. 90 90
343 31p. De Havilland "D.H.89A Dragon Rapide" 1·10 1·10
340/3 .. .. .. .. .. *Set of* 4 2·50 2·50

**96** "Robinson Crusoe leaves the Wreck"

**97** "B.L.C. St Helier" Orchid

(Des R. Granger Barrett. Photo Courvoisier)

**1984** (21 Sept). *Links with Australia. Paintings by John Alexander Gilfillan. T* **96** *and similar horiz designs. Multicoloured. Granite paper. P* 11½ × 12.

344 9p. Type **96** .. .. .. .. .. 30 30
345 12p. "Edinburgh Castle" .. .. .. 40 40
346 20½p. "Maori Village" .. .. .. .. 75 75
347 26p. "Australian Landscape" .. .. .. 90 90
348 28p. "Waterhouse's Corner, Adelaide" .. 1·00 1·00
349 31p. "Captain Cook at Botany Bay" .. 1·10 1·10
344/9 .. .. .. .. .. *Set of* 6 4·00 4·00

(Photo Courvoisier)

**1984** (15 Nov). *Christmas. Jersey Orchids* (*1st series*). *T* **97** *and similar vert design. Multicoloured. Granite paper. P* 12 × 11½.

350 9p. Type **97** .. .. .. .. .. 45 45
351 12p. "Oda Mt Bingham" .. .. .. 75 75

See also Nos. 433/7.

**98** "*Hebe* off Corbiere, 1874"

(Photo Harrison)

**1985** (26 Feb). *Death Centenary of Philip John Ouless* (*artist*). *T* **98** *and similar horiz designs. Multicoloured. P* 14 × 15.

352 9p. Type **98** .. .. .. .. .. 30 30
353 12p. "The *Gaspe* engaging the *Diomede*" .. 40 40
354 22p. "The Paddle-steamer *London* entering Naples, 1856" .. .. .. .. 80 80
355 31p. "The *Rambler* entering Cape Town, 1840" .. .. .. .. .. 1·10 1·10
356 34p. "St. Aubin's Bay from Mount Bingham, 1872" .. .. .. .. .. 1·25 1·25
352/6 .. .. .. .. .. *Set of* 5 3·50 3·50

**99** John Ireland (composer) and Faldouet Dolmen

**100** Girls' Brigade

(Des Jennifer Toombs. Litho Questa)

**1985** (23 Apr). *Europa. European Music Year. T* **99** *and similar horiz designs. Multicoloured. P* 14.

357 10p. Type **99** .. .. .. .. .. 40 45
358 13p. Ivy St. Helier (actress) and His Majesty's Theatre, London .. .. .. .. 55 60
359 22p. Claude Debussy (composer) and Elizabeth Castle .. .. .. .. .. 90 95
357/9 .. .. .. .. .. *Set of* 3 1·60 1·75

(Des A. Theobald. Litho Questa)

**1985** (30 May). *International Youth Year. T* **100** *and similar vert designs. Multicoloured. P* 14½ × 14.

360 10p. Type **100** .. .. .. .. .. 30 30
361 13p. Girl Guides (75th anniversary) .. .. .. 50 50
362 29p. Prince Charles and Jersey Youth Service Activities Base .. .. .. .. .. 1·00 1·00
363 31p. Sea Cadet Corps .. .. .. .. 1·00 1·00
364 34p. Air Training Corps .. .. .. .. 1·10 1·10
360/4 .. .. .. .. .. *Set of* 5 3·50 3·50

**101** *Duke of Normandy* at Cheapside

(Des G. Palmer. Photo Courvoisier)

**1985** (16 July). *The Jersey Western Railway. T* **101** *and similar horiz designs. Multicoloured. Granite paper. P* 11½.

365 10p. Type **101** .. .. .. .. .. 40 40
366 13p. Saddletank at First Tower .. .. .. 50 50
367 22p. *La Moye* at Millbrook .. .. .. 90 90
368 29p. *St. Heliers* at St. Aubin .. .. .. 1·00 1·00
369 34p. *St. Aubyns* at Corbière .. .. .. 1·10 1·10
365/9 .. .. .. .. .. *Set of* 5 3·50 3·50

**102** Memorial Window to Revd. James Hemery (former Dean) and St. Helier Parish Church

(Des R. Granger Barrett. Litho Questa)

**1985** (10 Sept). *300th Anniv of Huguenot Immigration. T* **102** *and similar horiz designs. Multicoloured. P* 14.

370 10p. Type **102** .. .. .. .. .. 20 30
a. Booklet pane of 4.. .. .. .. .. 80
371 10p. Judge Francis Jeune, Baron St. Helier, and Houses of Parliament .. .. .. 20 30
a. Booklet pane of 4.. .. .. .. .. 80
372 13p. Silverware by Pierre Amiraux .. .. .. 25 45
a. Booklet pane of 4.. .. .. .. .. 1·00
373 13p. Francis Voisin (merchant) and Russian port.. .. .. .. .. .. 25 45
a. Booklet pane of 4.. .. .. .. .. 1·00
374 22p. Robert Brohier, Schweppes carbonation plant and bottles .. .. .. .. 45 75
a. Booklet pane of 4.. .. .. .. .. 1·75
375 22p. George Ingouville, V.C., R.N., and attack on Viborg .. .. .. .. 45 75
a. Booklet pane of 4.. .. .. .. .. 1·75
370/5 .. .. .. .. .. *Set of* 6 1·60 2·75

Each booklet pane has margins all round and text printed on the binding selvedge.

**103** Howard Davis Hall, Victoria College

(Des A. Copp. Litho Cartor, France)

**1985** (25 Oct). *Thomas Benjamin Davis (philanthropist) Commemoration. T* **103** *and similar horiz designs. Multicoloured. P* 13½.

376 10p. Type **103** .. .. .. .. .. 40 40
377 13p. Racing schooner *Westward* .. .. .. 60 60
378 31p. Howard Davis Park, St. Helier .. .. .. 1·10 1·10
379 34p. Howard Davis Experimental Farm, Trinity .. .. .. .. .. .. 1·25 1·25
376/9 .. .. .. .. .. *Set of* 4 3·00 3·00

**104** "Amaryllis belladonna" (Pandora Sellars)

**105** King Harold, William of Normandy and Halley's Comet, 1066 (from Bayeux Tapestry)

(Des C. Abbott. Litho Questa)

**1986** (28 Jan). *Jersey Lilies. T* **104** *and similar multicoloured design. P* 15 × 14½.

380 13p. Type **104** .. .. .. .. .. 50 50
381 34p. "A Jersey Lily" (Lily Langtry) (Sir John Millais) (30 × 48 *mm*) .. .. .. 1·25 1·25
**MS**382 140 × 96 mm. Nos. 380 × 4 and 381 .. 3·25 3·25

(Des Jennifer Toombs. Litho Cartor, France)

**1986** (4 Mar). *Appearance of Halley's Comet. T* **105** *and similar horiz designs. Multicoloured. P* 13½ × 13.

383 10p. Type **105** .. .. .. .. .. 40 40
384 22p. Lady Carteret, Edmond Halley, map and Comet .. .. .. .. .. .. 85 85
385 31p. Aspects of communications in 1910 and 1986 on TV screen .. .. .. 1·25 1·25
383/5 .. .. .. .. .. *Set of* 3 2·25 2·25

**106** Dwarf Pansy

**107** Queen Elizabeth II (from photo by Karsh)

(Des Pandora Sellars. Litho Questa)

**1986** (21 Apr). *Europa. Environmental Conservation. T* **106** *and similar vert designs. Multicoloured. P* 14½ × 14.

386 10p. Type **106** .. .. .. .. .. 35 35
387 14p. Sea Stock .. .. .. .. .. 65 65
388 22p. Sand Crocus .. .. .. .. .. 95 95
386/8 .. .. .. .. .. *Set of* 3 1·75 1·75

(Photo Courvoisier)

**1986** (21 Apr). *60th Birthday of Queen Elizabeth II. Granite paper. P* 11½.

389 **107** £1 multicoloured .. .. .. .. 2·75 2·75

No. 389 was retained in use as part of the current definitive series until replaced by No. 500.

For a £2 value in this design see No. 491*b*.

**108** Le Rât Cottage

**109** Prince Andrew and Miss Sarah Ferguson

(Des A. Copp. Litho Cartor, France)

**1986** (17 June). *50th Anniv of National Trust for Jersey. T* **108** *and similar horiz designs. Multicoloured. P* 13½ × 13.

390 10p. Type **108** .. .. .. .. .. 30 30
391 14p. The Elms (Trust headquarters) .. .. .. 45 45
392 22p. Morel Farm .. .. .. .. .. 80 80
393 29p. Quétivel Mill .. .. .. .. .. 1·00 1·10
394 31p. La Vallette .. .. .. .. .. 1·10 1·25
390/4 .. .. .. .. .. *Set of* 5 3·25 3·50

(Des A. Copp. Litho Cartor, France)

**1986** (23 July). *Royal Wedding. P* 13½.

395 **109** 14p. multicoloured .. .. .. .. 50 50
396 40p. multicoloured .. .. .. .. 1·50 1·50

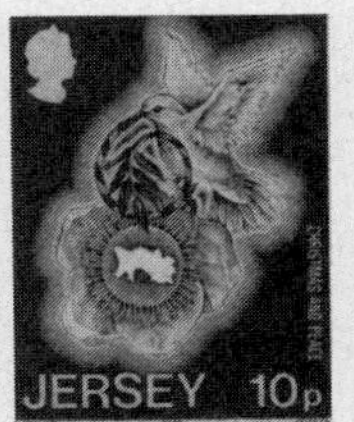


**110** "Gathering Vraic"

**111** Island Map on Jersey Lily, and Dove holding Olive Branch

(Des A. Copp. Litho Questa)

**1986** (28 Aug). *Birth Centenary of Edmund Blampied (artist). T* **110** *and similar vert designs. P* 14.

397 10p. multicoloured .. .. .. .. .. 30 30
398 14p. black, light blue and brownish grey .. 50 50
399 29p. multicoloured .. .. .. .. .. 1·00 1·00
400 31p. black, pale orange and brownish grey .. 1·25 1·10
401 34p. multicoloured .. .. .. .. .. 1·40 1·25
397/401 .. .. .. .. .. *Set of* 5 4·00 3·75

Designs:—14p. "Driving Home in the Rain"; 29p. "The Miller"; 31p. "The Joy Ride"; 34p. "Tante Elizabeth".

(Des G. Taylor. Litho Questa)

**1986** (4 Nov). *Christmas. International Peace Year. T* **111** *and similar vert designs. Multicoloured. P* 14½.

402 10p. Type **111** .. .. .. .. .. 40 40
403 14p. Mistletoe wreath encircling robin and dove .. .. .. .. .. .. 60 60
404 34p. Christmas cracker releasing dove .. .. 1·25 1·25
402/4 .. .. .. .. .. *Set of* 3 2·00 2·00

**112** *Westward* under Full Sail

(Des A. Copp. Litho Cartor, France)

**1987** (15 Jan). *Racing Schooner "Westward". T* **112** *and similar horiz designs. Multicoloured. P* 13½.

405 10p. Type **112** .. .. .. .. .. 40 40
406 14p. T. B. Davis at the helm .. .. .. 60 60
407 31p. *Westward* overhauling *Britannia* .. .. 1·10 1·10
408 34p. *Westward* fitting-out at St. Helier .. .. 1·25 1·25
405/8 .. .. .. .. .. *Set of* 4 3·00 3·00

**113** De Havilland "DH86" *Belcroute Bay*

(Des G. Palmer. Litho Questa)

**1987** (3 Mar). *50th Anniv of Jersey Airport. T* **113** *and similar horiz designs. Multicoloured. P* 14.

409 10p. Type **113** .. .. .. .. .. 30 30
410 14p. Boeing "757" and Douglas "DC 9" .. .. 40 40
411 22p. Britten Norman "Trislander" and "2A Islander" .. .. .. .. .. .. 70 70
412 29p. Short "SD330" and Vickers "Viscount 800" .. .. .. .. .. .. 1·00 1·00
413 31p. BAC "1-11" and HPR "7 Dart Herald" .. 1·25 1·25
409/13 .. .. .. .. .. *Set of* 5 3·25 3·25

**114** St. Mary and St. Peter's Roman Catholic Church

(Des A. Copp. Litho Questa)

**1987** (23 Apr). *Europa. Modern Architecture. T* **114** *and similar horiz designs. Multicoloured. P* 15 × 14.

414 11p. Type **114** .. .. .. .. .. 35 35
415 15p. Villa Devereux, St. Brelade .. .. .. 65 65
416 22p. Fort Regent Leisure Centre, St. Helier (57 × 29 *mm*) .. .. .. .. .. 90 90
414/16 .. .. .. .. .. *Set of* 3 1·75 1·75

**115** H.M.S. *Racehorse* (bomb-ketch) trapped in Arctic

(Des R. Granger Barrett. Litho Questa)

**1987** (9 July). *Jersey Adventurers (2nd series). Philippe D'Auvergne. T* **115** *and similar horiz designs. Multicoloured. P* 14.

417 11p. Type **115** .. .. .. .. .. 40 40
418 15p. H.M.S. *Alarm* on fire, Rhode Island .. .. 50 50
419 29p. H.M.S. *Arethusa* wrecked off Ushant .. 90 90
420 31p. H.M.S. *Rattlesnake* stranded on Isle de Trinidad .. .. .. .. .. .. 1·00 1·00
421 34p. Mont Orgueil Castle and fishing boats .. 1·10 1·10
417/21 .. .. .. .. .. *Set of* 5 3·50 3·50

See also Nos. 501/6 and 539/44.

**116** Grant of Lands to Normandy, 911 and 933

(Des Jennifer Toombs. Litho Cartor, France)

**1987** (9 Sept–16 Oct). *900th Death Anniv of William the Conqueror. T* **116** *and similar horiz designs. Multicoloured. P* 13½.

422 11p. Type **116** .. .. .. .. .. 40 40
a. Booklet pane of 4 (16 Oct) .. .. .. 1·60
423 15p. Edward the Confessor and Duke Robert I of Normandy landing on Jersey, 1030 .. 45 45
a. Booklet pane of 4 (16 Oct) .. .. .. 1·75

424 22p. King William's coronation, 1066, and fatal fall, 1087 .. .. .. .. .. 70 70
a. Booklet pane of 4 (16 Oct) .. .. 2·75
425 29p. Death of William Rufus, 1100, and Battle of Tinchebrai, 1106 .. .. .. .. 85 85
a. Booklet pane of 4 (16 Oct) .. .. 3·25
426 31p. Civil war between Matilda and Stephen, 1135–41 .. .. .. .. .. 95 95
a. Booklet pane of 4 (16 Oct) .. .. 3·75
427 34p. Henry inherits Normandy, 1151; John asserts ducal rights in Jersey, 1213 .. 1·10 1·10
a. Booklet pane of 4 (16 Oct) .. .. 4·25
422/7 .. .. .. .. .. *Set of* 6 4·00 4·00

Each booklet pane has margins all round and text printed on the binding selvedge.

**117** "Grosnez Castle"

(Photo Courvoisier)

**1987** (3 Nov). *Christmas. Paintings by John Le Capelain. T* **117** *and similar horiz designs. Multicoloured. Granite paper. P* 11½.
428 11p. Type **117** .. .. .. .. .. 40 40
429 15p. "St. Aubin's Bay" .. .. .. .. 60 60
430 22p. "Mont Orgueil Castle" .. .. .. 80 80
431 31p. "Town Fort and Harbour, St. Helier" .. 1·00 1·00
432 34p. "The Hermitage" .. .. .. .. 1·10 1·10
428/32 .. .. .. .. .. *Set of* 5 3·50 3·50

**118** *Cymbidium pontac*

(Litho Questa)

**1988** (12 Jan). *Jersey Orchids (2nd series). T* **118** *and similar multicoloured designs. P* 14.
433 11p. Type **118** .. .. .. .. .. 40 40
434 15p. *Odontioda Eric Young (vert)* .. .. 50 50
435 29p. *Lycaste auburn* "Seaford" and "Ditchling" .. .. .. .. .. 90 90
436 31p. *Odontoglossum St. Brelade (vert)* .. 1·00 1·00
437 34p. *Cymbidium mavourneen* "Jester" .. 1·10 1·10
433/7 .. .. .. .. .. *Set of* 5 3·50 3·50

**119** Labrador Retriever

(Des P. Layton. Litho Questa)

**1988** (2 Mar). *Centenary of Jersey Dog Club. T* **119** *and similar horiz designs. Multicoloured. P* 14.
438 11p. Type **119** .. .. .. .. .. 40 40
439 15p. Wire-haired Dachshund .. .. .. 60 60
440 22p. Pekinese .. .. .. .. .. 80 80
441 31p. Cavalier King Charles Spaniel .. .. 1·00 1·00
442 34p. Dalmatian .. .. .. .. .. 1·10 1·10
438/42 .. .. .. .. .. *Set of* 5 3·50 3·50

**120** D.H. "Dash 7" Aircraft, London Landmarks and Jersey Control Tower

**121** Rodriguez Fody

(Des A. Copp. Litho Cartor, France)

**1988** (26 Apr). *Europa. Transport and Communications. T* **120** *and similar multicoloured designs. P* 14×13½ *(horiz) or* 13½×14 *(vert).*
443 16p. Type **120** .. .. .. .. .. 50 50
444 16p. Weather radar and Jersey airport landing system *(vert)* .. .. .. .. 50 50
445 22p. Hydrofoil, St. Malo and Elizabeth Castle, St. Helier .. .. .. .. 90 90
446 22p. Port control tower and Jersey Radio maritime communication centre, La Moye *(vert)* .. .. .. .. .. 90 90
443/6 .. .. .. .. .. *Set of* 4 2·50 2·50

(Des W. Oliver. Litho Cartor, France)

**1988** (6 July). *Wildlife Preservation Trust (5th series). T* **121** *and similar multicoloured designs. P* 13½ × 14 *(vert) or* 14 × 13½ *(horiz).*
447 12p. Type **121** .. .. .. .. .. 50 50
448 16p. Volcano Rabbit *(horiz)* .. .. .. 60 60
449 29p. White-faced Marmoset .. .. .. 1·00 1·00
450 31p. Ploughshare Tortoise *(horiz)* .. .. 1·10 1·10
451 34p. Mauritius Kestrel .. .. .. .. 1·25 1·25
447/51 .. .. .. .. .. *Set of* 5 4·00 3·75

**122** Rain Forest Leaf Frog, Costa Rica

**123** St. Clement Parish Church

(Des V. Ambrus. Photo Courvoisier)

**1988** (27 Sept). *Operation Raleigh. T* **122** *and similar horiz designs. Multicoloured. Granite paper. P* 12.
452 12p. Type **122** .. .. .. .. .. 45 45
453 16p. Archaeological survey, Peru .. .. 55 55
454 22p. Climbing glacier, Chile .. .. .. 70 70
455 29p. Red Cross Centre, Solomon Islands .. 80 80
456 31p. Underwater exploration, Australia .. 85 85
457 34p. *Zebu* (brigantine) returning to St. Helier 1·10 1·10
452/7 .. .. .. .. .. *Set of* 6 4·00 4·00

(Des P. Layton. Litho B.D.T.)

**1988** (15 Nov). *Christmas. Jersey Parish Churches (1st series). T* **123** *and similar horiz designs. Multicoloured. P* 13½.
458 12p. Type **123** .. .. .. .. .. 35 35
459 16p. St. Ouen .. .. .. .. .. 60 60
460 31p. St. Brelade .. .. .. .. .. 1·00 1·00
461 34p. St. Lawrence .. .. .. .. .. 1·10 1·10
458/61 .. .. .. .. .. *Set of* 4 2·75 2·75

See also Nos. 535/8.

**124** Talbot "Type 4 CT Tourer", 1912

**125** Belcroute Bay

(Des A. Copp. Litho Questa)

**1989** (31 Jan). *Vintage Cars. T* **124** *and similar horiz designs. Multicoloured. P* 14.
462 12p. Type **124** .. .. .. .. .. 45 35
463 16p. De Dion "Bouton Type 1-D", 1920 .. 55 40
464 23p. Austin 7 "Chummy", 1926 .. .. 80 55
465 30p. Ford "Model T", 1926 .. .. .. 95 80
466 32p. Bentley 8 litre, 1930 .. .. .. 1·10 1·00
467 35p. Cadillac "452A -V16 Fleetwood Sports Phaeton", 1931 .. .. .. .. 1·25 1·10
462/7 .. .. .. .. .. *Set of* 6 4·50 3·75

(Des and photo Courvoisier (£2). Des G. Drummond. Litho B.D.T. (others))

**1989** (21 May)–**91**. *Jersey Scenes. Horiz design as T* **125** *and Queen's portrait as T* **107**. *Multicoloured. P* 11½×12 *(£2) or* 13×13½ *(others).*
468 1p. Type **125** .. .. .. .. .. 10 10
469 2p. High Street, St. Aubin .. .. .. 10 10
470 4p. Royal Jersey Golf Course .. .. .. 10 10
a. Booklet pane of 6 with margins all round (3.5.90) .. .. .. .. .. 40
471 5p. Portelet Bay .. .. .. .. .. 10 10
a. Booklet pane of 6 with margins all round (12.2.91) .. .. .. .. .. 50
472 10p. Les Charrières D'Anneport .. .. 20 25
473 13p. St Helier Marina .. .. .. .. 25 30
474 14p. Sand yacht racing, St. Ouen's Bay .. 30 35
a. Booklet pane of 6 with margins all round (3.5.90) .. .. .. .. .. 1·75
475 15p. Rozel Harbour .. .. .. .. 30 35
a. Booklet pane of 6 with margins all round (12.2.91) .. .. .. .. .. 1·75
476 16p. St. Aubin's Harbour .. .. .. .. 30 35
477 17p. Jersey Airport .. .. .. .. 35 40
478 18p. Corbière Lighthouse .. .. .. .. 35 40
a. Booklet pane of 6 with margins all round (3.5.90) .. .. .. .. .. 2·10
479 19p. Val de Mare .. .. .. .. .. 40 45
480 20p. Elizabeth Castle .. .. .. .. 40 45
a. Booklet pane of 6 with margins all round (12.2.91) .. .. .. .. .. 2·40
481 21p. Greve de Lecq (16.1.90) .. .. .. 40 45
482 22p. Samarès Manor (16.1.90) .. .. .. 45 50
483 23p. Bonne Nuit Harbour (16.1.90) .. .. 45 50
484 24p. Grosnez Castle (16.1.90) .. .. .. 50 55
485 25p. Augrès Manor (16.1.90) .. .. .. 50 55
486 26p. Central Market (16.1.90) .. .. .. 50 55
487 27p. St. Brelade's Bay (16.1.90) .. .. 55 60
488 30p. St. Ouen's Manor (13.3.90) .. .. 60 65
489 40p. La Hougue Bie (13.3.90) .. .. .. 80 85
490 50p. Mont Orgueil Castle (13.3.90) .. .. 1·00 1·10
491 75p. Royal Square, St Helier (13.3.90) .. 1·50 1·60
491*b* £2 Type **107** (19.3.91) .. .. .. 4·00 4·25
468/91*b* .. .. .. .. *Set of* 25 13·00 14·00

**126** Agile Frog

**127** Toddlers' Toys

(Des W. Oliver. Litho Cartor, France)

**1989** (25 Apr). *Endangered Jersey Fauna. T* **126** *and similar multicoloured designs. P* 13½×13 *(Nos. 492 and 495),* 13×13½ *(No. 493) or* 13½×14 *(No. 494).*
492 13p. Type **126** .. .. .. .. .. 40 35
493 13p. *Heteropterus morpheus* (butterfly) *(vert)* 40 35
494 17p. Barn Owl *(vert)* .. .. .. .. 65 50
495 17p. Green Lizard .. .. .. .. .. 65 50
492/5 .. .. .. .. .. *Set of* 4 1·75 1·50

(Des Clare Luke. Litho Questa)

**1989** (25 Apr). *Europa. Children's Toys and Games. T* **127** *and similar square designs showing clay plaques. Multicoloured. P* 14.
496 17p. Type **127** .. .. .. .. .. 50 50
497 17p. Playground games .. .. .. .. 50 50
498 23p. Party games .. .. .. .. .. 90 90
499 23p. Teenage sports .. .. .. .. 90 90
496/9 .. .. .. .. .. *Set of* 4 2·50 2·50

**128** Queen Elizabeth II and Royal Yacht *Britannia* in Elizabeth Harbour

(Des A. Copp. Litho Questa)

**1989** (24 May). *Royal Visit. P* 14½.
500 **128** £1 multicoloured .. .. .. .. 2·00 2·10

No. 500 was retained in use as part of the current definitive series.

**129** Philippe D'Auvergne presented to Louis XVI, 1786

(Des V. Ambrus. Litho Cartor, France)

**1989** (7 July). *Bicentenary of the French Revolution. Philippe D'Auvergne. T* **129** *and similar horiz designs. Multicoloured. P* 13½.
501 13p. Type **129** .. .. .. .. .. 35 35
a. Booklet pane of 4 .. .. .. .. 1·40
502 17p. Storming the Bastille, 1789 .. .. 55 45
a. Booklet pane of 4 .. .. .. .. 2·25
503 23p. Marie de Bouillon and revolutionaries, 1790 .. .. .. .. .. .. 65 55
a. Booklet pane of 4 .. .. .. .. 2·75
504 30p. Auvergne's headquarters at Mont Orgueil, 1795 .. .. .. .. .. 1·10 1·00
a. Booklet pane of 4 .. .. .. .. 4·50
505 32p. Landing arms for Chouan rebels, 1796 .. 1·10 1·00
a. Booklet pane of 4 .. .. .. .. 4·50
506 35p. The last Chouan revolt, 1799 .. .. 1·25 1·10
a. Booklet pane of 4 .. .. .. .. 5·00
501/6 .. .. .. .. .. *Set of* 6 4·50 4·00

Each booklet pane has margins all round and text printed on the binding selvedge.

See also Nos. 539/44.

**130** *St. Helier* off Elizabeth Castle

(Des G. Palmer. Litho Questa)

**1989** (5 Sept). *Centenary of Great Western Railway Steamer Service to Channel Islands. T* **130** *and similar horiz designs. Multicoloured. P* 13½×14.
507 13p. Type **130** .. .. .. .. .. 50 50
508 17p. *Caesarea II* off Corbière Lighthouse .. 60 60
509 27p. *Reindeer* in St. Helier harbour .. .. 1·00 95
510 32p. *Ibex* racing *Frederica* off Portelet .. 1·10 1·10
511 35p. *Lynx* off Noirmont .. .. .. .. 1·25 1·10
507/11 .. .. .. .. .. *Set of* 5 4·00 3·75

**131** "Gorey Harbour"

**132** Head Post Office, Broad Street, 1969

(Litho Enschedé)

**1989** (24 Oct). *150th Birth Anniv of Sarah Louisa Kilpack (artist). T* **131** *and similar horiz designs. Multicoloured. P* 13×12½.

|  |  |  | | |
|---|---|---|---|---|
| 512 | 13p. | Type **131** | 50 | 45 |
| 513 | 17p. | "La Corbière" | 60 | 55 |
| 514 | 23p. | "Grève de Lecq" | 1·00 | 95 |
| 515 | 32p. | "Bouley Bay" | 1·10 | 1·10 |
| 516 | 35p. | "Mont Orgueil" | 1·25 | 1·10 |
| 512/16 | | *Set of* 5 | 4·00 | 3·75 |

(Des P. Layton. Litho Cartor, France)

**1990** (13 Mar). *Europa. Post Office Buildings. T* **132** *and similar multicoloured designs. P* 13½×14 (*vert*) *or* 14×13½ (*horiz*).

|  |  |  | | |
|---|---|---|---|---|
| 517 | 18p. | Type **132** | 45 | 45 |
| 518 | 18p. | Postal Headquarters, Mont Millais, 1990 | 45 | 45 |
| 519 | 24p. | Hue Street Post Office, 1815 (*horiz*) | 65 | 65 |
| 520 | 24p. | Head Post Office, Halkett Place, 1890 (*horiz*) | 65 | 65 |
| 517/20 | | *Set of* 4 | 2·00 | 2·00 |

**133** "Battle of Flowers" Parade

**134** Early Printing Press and Jersey Newspaper Mastheads

(Des A. Copp. Litho Enschedé)

**1990** (3 May). *Festival of Tourism. T* **133** *and similar vert designs. Multicoloured. P* 14×13½.

|  |  |  | | |
|---|---|---|---|---|
| 521 | 18p. | Type **133** | 50 | 50 |
| 522 | 24p. | Sports | 65 | 65 |
| 523 | 29p. | Mont Orgueil Castle and German Underground Hospital Museum | 80 | 80 |
| 524 | 32p. | Salon Culinaire | 85 | 85 |
| 521/4 | | *Set of* 4 | 2·50 | 2·50 |
| **MS**525 | | 151×100 mm. Nos. 521/4 | 2·50 | 2·50 |

(Des A. Copp. Litho Cartor, France)

**1990** (26 June). *International Literacy Year. Jersey News Media. T* **134** *and similar horiz designs. Multicoloured. P* 13½.

|  |  |  | | |
|---|---|---|---|---|
| 526 | 14p. | Type **134** | 45 | 45 |
| 527 | 18p. | Modern press, and offices of *Jersey Evening Post* in 1890 and 1990 | 50 | 50 |
| 528 | 34p. | Radio Jersey broadcaster | 90 | 90 |
| 529 | 37p. | Channel Television studio cameraman | 95 | 95 |
| 526/9 | | *Set of* 4 | 2·50 | 2·50 |

**135** BAe Hawk

**136** "Landsat 5" and Thematic Mapper Image over Jersey

(Des G. Palmer. Litho Questa)

**1990** (4 Sept). *50th Anniv of Battle of Britain. T* **135** *and similar horiz designs. Multicoloured. P* 14.

|  |  |  | | |
|---|---|---|---|---|
| 530 | 14p. | Type **135** | 45 | 45 |
| 531 | 18p. | Supermarine Spitfire | 50 | 50 |
| 532 | 24p. | Hawker Hurricane | 65 | 65 |
| 533 | 34p. | Vickers Wellington | 85 | 85 |
| 534 | 37p. | Avro Lancaster | 90 | 90 |
| 530/4 | | *Set of* 5 | 3·00 | 3·00 |

(Des P. Layton. Litho B.D.T.)

**1990** (13 Nov). *Christmas. Jersey Parish Churches (2nd series). Horiz designs as T* **123**. *Multicoloured. P* 13½.

|  |  |  | | |
|---|---|---|---|---|
| 535 | 14p. | St. Helier | 40 | 40 |
| 536 | 18p. | Grouville | 45 | 45 |
| 537 | 34p. | St. Saviour | 95 | 95 |
| 538 | 37p. | St. John | 1·00 | 1·00 |
| 535/8 | | *Set of* 4 | 2·50 | 2·50 |

(Des V. Ambrus. Litho Cartor, France)

**1991** (22 Jan). *175th Death Anniv of Philippe d'Auvergne. Horiz designs as T* **129**. *Multicoloured. P* 13½.

|  |  |  | | |
|---|---|---|---|---|
| 539 | 15p. | Prince's Tower, La Hougue Bie | 40 | 40 |
| 540 | 20p. | Auvergne's arrest in Paris | 55 | 55 |
| 541 | 26p. | Auvergne plotting against Napoleon | 65 | 65 |
| 542 | 31p. | Execution of George Cadoudal | 90 | 90 |
| 543 | 37p. | H.M. Cutter *Surly* attacking enemy convoy | 1·00 | 1·00 |
| 544 | 44p. | Auvergne's last days in London | 1·25 | 1·25 |
| 539/44 | | *Set of* 6 | 4·25 | 4·25 |

(Des A. Copp. Litho Enschedé)

**1991** (19 Mar). *Europa. Europe in Space. T* **136** *and similar vert designs. Multicoloured. P* 14½×13.

|  |  |  | | |
|---|---|---|---|---|
| 545 | 20p. | Type **136** | 40 | 45 |
| 546 | 20p. | "ERS-1" earth resources remote sensing satellite | 40 | 45 |
| 547 | 26p. | "Meteosat" weather satellite | 50 | 55 |
| 548 | 26p. | "Olympus" direct broadcasting satellite | 50 | 55 |
| 545/8 | | *Set of* 4 | 1·50 | 1·75 |

**137** 1941 1d. Stamp (50th anniv of first Jersey postage stamp)

**138** *Melitaea cinxia*

(Des A. Copp. Litho Cartor, France)

**1991** (16 May). *Anniversaries. T* **137** *and similar vert designs. Multicoloured. P* 13½.

|  |  |  | | |
|---|---|---|---|---|
| 549 | 15p. | Type **137** | 40 | 40 |
| 550 | 20p. | Steam train (centenary of Jersey Eastern Railway extension to Gorey Pier) | 50 | 50 |
| 551 | 26p. | Jersey cow and Herd Book (125th anniv of Jersey Herd Book) | 60 | 60 |
| 552 | 31p. | Stone-laying ceremony (from painting by P. J. Ouless) (150th anniv of Victoria Harbour) | 70 | 70 |
| 553 | 53p. | Marie Bartlett and hospital (250th anniv of Marie Bartlett's hospital bequest) | 1·40 | 1·40 |
| 549/53 | | *Set of* 5 | 3·25 | 3·25 |

(Des W. Oliver. Litho Enschedé)

**1991** (9 July). *Butterflies and Moths. T* **138** *and similar horiz designs. Multicoloured. P* 13×12½.

|  |  |  | | |
|---|---|---|---|---|
| 554 | 15p. | Type **138** | 30 | 35 |
| 555 | 20p. | *Euplagia quadripunctaria* | 40 | 45 |
| 556 | 37p. | *Deilephilia porcellus* | 75 | 80 |
| 557 | 57p. | *Inachis io* | 1·10 | 1·25 |
| 554/7 | | *Set of* 4 | 2·50 | 2·75 |

**139** Drilling for Water, Ethiopia

**140** "This is the Place for Me"

(Des A. Theobald. Litho B.D.T.)

**1991** (3 Sept). *Overseas Aid. T* **139** *and similar horiz designs. Multicoloured. P* 13½×14.

|  |  |  | | |
|---|---|---|---|---|
| 558 | 15p. | Type **139** | 30 | 35 |
| 559 | 20p. | Building construction, Rwanda | 40 | 45 |
| 560 | 26p. | Village polytechnic, Kenya | 50 | 55 |
| 561 | 31p. | Treating leprosy, Tanzania | 60 | 65 |
| 562 | 37p. | Ploughing, Zambia | 75 | 80 |
| 563 | 44p. | Immunisation clinic, Lesotho | 90 | 95 |
| 558/63 | | *Set of* 6 | 3·00 | 3·50 |

(Litho Questa)

**1991** (5 Nov). *Christmas. Illustrations by Edmund Blampied for J.M. Barrie's* Peter Pan. *T* **140** *and similar vert designs. Multicoloured. P* 14.

|  |  |  | | |
|---|---|---|---|---|
| 564 | 15p. | Type **140** | 30 | 35 |
| 565 | 20p. | "The Island Come True" | 40 | 45 |
| 566 | 37p. | "The Never Bird" | 75 | 80 |
| 567 | 53p. | "The Great White Father" | 1·10 | 1·25 |
| 564/7 | | *Set of* 4 | 2·25 | 2·50 |

***MINIMUM PRICE***

The minimum price quote is 10p which represents a handling charge rather than a basis for valuing common stamps. For further notes about prices see introductory pages.

**141** Pied Wagtail

**142** Shipping at Shanghai, 1860

(Des W. Oliver. Litho Cartor)

**1992** (7 Jan). *Winter Birds. T* **141** *and similar vert designs. Multicoloured. P* 13½×14.

|  |  |  | | |
|---|---|---|---|---|
| 568 | 16p. | Type **141** | 30 | 35 |
| 569 | 22p. | Firecrest | 45 | 50 |
| 570 | 28p. | Snipe | 55 | 60 |
| 571 | 39p. | Lapwing | 80 | 85 |
| 572 | 57p. | Fieldfare | 1·10 | 1·25 |
| 568/72 | | *Set of* 5 | 3·00 | 3·25 |

(Des V. Ambrus. Litho Cartor, France)

**1992** (25 Feb). *Jersey Adventurers (3rd series). 150th Birth Anniv of William Mesny. T* **142** *and similar horiz designs. Multicoloured. P* 13½.

|  |  |  | | |
|---|---|---|---|---|
| 573 | 16p. | Type **142** | 30 | 35 |
| | | a. Booklet pane of 4 | 1·25 | |
| 574 | 16p. | Mesny's junk running Taiping blockade, 1862 | 30 | 35 |
| | | a. Booklet pane of 4 | 1·25 | |
| 575 | 22p. | General Mesny outside river gate, 1874 | 45 | 50 |
| | | a. Booklet pane of 4 | 1·75 | |
| 576 | 22p. | Mesny in Burma, 1877 | 45 | 50 |
| | | a. Booklet pane of 4 | 1·75 | |
| 577 | 33p. | Mesny and Governor Chang, 1882 | 65 | 70 |
| | | a. Booklet pane of 4 | 2·50 | |
| 578 | 33p. | Mesny in mandarin's sedan chair, 1886 | 65 | 70 |
| | | a. Booklet pane of 4 | 2·50 | |
| 573/8 | | *Set of* 6 | 2·50 | 2·75 |

Each booklet pane has margins all round and text printed on the binding selvedge.

**143** *Tickler* (brig)

(Des A. Copp. Litho Questa)

**1992** (14 Apr). *Jersey Ship Building. T* **143** *and similar horiz designs. Multicoloured. P* 14.

|  |  |  | | |
|---|---|---|---|---|
| 579 | 16p. | Type **143** | 30 | 35 |
| 580 | 22p. | *Hebe* (snow) | 45 | 50 |
| 581 | 50p. | *Gemini* (barque) | 1·00 | 1·10 |
| 582 | 57p. | *Percy Douglas* (full-rigged ship) | 1·10 | 1·25 |
| 579/82 | | *Set of* 4 | 2·50 | 2·75 |
| **MS**583 | | 148×98 mm. Nos. 579/82 | 2·75 | 3·00 |

**144** John Bertram (ship owner) and Columbus

(Des V. Ambrus. Litho Questa)

**1992** (14 Apr). *Europa. 500th Anniv of Discovery of America by Columbus. T* **144** *and similar horiz designs. P* 14×14½.

|  |  |  | | |
|---|---|---|---|---|
| 584 | 22p. | Type **144** | 45 | 50 |
| 585 | 28p. | Sir George Carteret (founder of New Jersey) | 55 | 60 |
| 586 | 39p. | Sir Walter Ralegh (founder of Virginia) | 80 | 85 |
| 584/6 | | *Set of* 3 | 1·60 | 1·75 |

POSTAGE DUE STAMPS

D **1**

D **2** Map

(Des F. Guénier. Litho Bradbury, Wilkinson)

**1969** (1 Oct). *P* 14×13½.

|  |  |  |  | | |
|---|---|---|---|---|---|
| D1 | D **1** | 1d. | bluish violet | 2·50 | 1·90 |
| D2 | | 2d. | sepia | 3·50 | 2·00 |
| D3 | | 3d. | magenta | 5·00 | 3·25 |
| D4 | D **2** | 1s. | bright emerald | 13·00 | 8·50 |
| D5 | | 2s. 6d. | olive-grey | 25·00 | 22·00 |
| D6 | | 5s. | vermilion | 35·00 | 40·00 |
| D1/6 | | | *Set of* 6 | 75·00 | 70·00 |

**1971** (15 Feb)–**75**. *As Type* D **2** *but values in decimal currency.*

| | | | | |
|---|---|---|---|---|
| D 7 | ½p. black | | 10 | 10 |
| D 8 | 1p. violet-blue | | 10 | 10 |
| D 9 | 2p. olive-grey | | 10 | 10 |
| D10 | 3p. reddish purple | | 10 | 10 |
| D11 | 4p. pale red | | 10 | 10 |
| D12 | 5p. bright emerald | | 15 | 15 |
| D13 | 6p. yellow-orange (12.8.74) | | 15 | 15 |
| D14 | 7p. bistre-yellow (12.8.74) | | 15 | 15 |
| D15 | 8p. light greenish blue (1.5.75) | | 25 | 25 |
| D16 | 10p. pale olive-grey | | 35 | 35 |
| D17 | 11p. ochre (1.5.75) | | 35 | 40 |
| D18 | 14p. violet | | 40 | 45 |
| D19 | 25p. myrtle-green (12.8.74) | | 80 | 90 |
| D20 | 50p. dull purple (1.5.75) | | 1·40 | 1·50 |
| D7/20 | | *Set of* 14 | 4·00 | 4·25 |

D 3 Arms of St. Clement and Dovecote at Samares

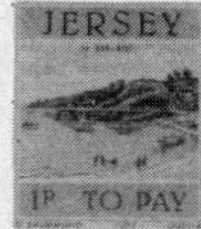

D 4 St. Brelade

(Des G. Drummond. Litho Questa)

**1978** (17 Jan). *Type* D **3** *and similar horiz designs showing the Parish Arms given. P* 14.

| | | | | |
|---|---|---|---|---|
| D21 | 1p. blue-green and black | | 10 | 10 |
| D22 | 2p. orange-yellow and black (St. Lawrence) | | 10 | 10 |
| D23 | 3p. lake-brown and black (St. John) | | 10 | 10 |
| D24 | 4p. orange-vermilion and black (St. Ouen) | | 15 | 15 |
| D25 | 5p. ultramarine and black (St. Peter) | | 15 | 20 |
| D26 | 10p. brown-olive and black (St. Martin) | | 25 | 30 |
| D27 | 12p. greenish blue and black (St. Helier) | | 30 | 35 |
| D28 | 14p. red-orange and black (St. Saviour) | | 30 | 40 |
| D29 | 15p. bright magenta and black (St. Brelade) | | 35 | 40 |
| D30 | 20p. yellow-green and black (Grouville) | | 45 | 50 |
| D31 | 50p. deep brown and black (St. Mary) | | 1·25 | 1·40 |
| D32 | £1 chalky blue and black (Trinity) | | 2·50 | 2·50 |
| D21/32 | | *Set of* 12 | 5·25 | 6·00 |

Parish Views shown:—2p. Handois Reservoir; 3p. Sorel Point; 4p. Pinnacle Rock; 5p. Quetivel Mill; 10p. St. Catherine's Breakwater; 12p. St. Helier Harbour; 14p. Highlands College; 15p. Beauport Bay; 20p. La Hougue Bie; 50p. Perry Farm; £1 Bouley Bay.

(Des G. Drummond. Litho Questa)

**1982** (7 Sept). *Type* D **4** *and similar vert designs depicting Jersey Harbours. P* 14.

| | | | | |
|---|---|---|---|---|
| D33 | 1p. bright turquoise-green and black | | 10 | 10 |
| D34 | 2p. chrome-yellow and black | | 10 | 10 |
| D35 | 3p. lake-brown and black | | 10 | 10 |
| D36 | 4p. red and black | | 10 | 10 |
| D37 | 5p. bright blue and black | | 10 | 10 |
| D38 | 6p. yellow-olive and black | | 10 | 15 |
| D39 | 7p. bright reddish mauve and black | | 15 | 20 |
| D40 | 8p. bright orange-red and black | | 15 | 20 |
| D41 | 9p. bright green and black | | 20 | 25 |
| D42 | 10p. turquoise-blue and black | | 20 | 25 |
| D43 | 20p. apple-green and black | | 40 | 45 |
| D44 | 30p. bright purple and black | | 60 | 65 |
| D45 | 40p. dull orange and black | | 80 | 85 |
| D46 | £1 bright reddish violet and black | | 2·00 | 2·10 |
| D33/46 | | *Set of* 14 | 4·50 | 5·00 |

Designs:—2p. St. Aubin; 3p. Rozel; 4p. Greve de Lecq; 5p. Bouley Bay; 6p. St. Catherine; 7p. Gorey; 8p. Bonne Nuit; 9p. La Roque; 10p. St. Helier; 20p. Ronez; 30p. La Collette; 40p. Elizabeth Castle; £1 Upper Harbour Marina.

# British Post Offices Abroad

The origins of the network of Post Offices, Postal Agencies and Packet Agents can be recognised from the 18th century, but the system did not become established until the expansion of trade, following the end of the Napoleonic Wars in 1815.

Many offices were provided in newly acquired dependent territories, and were then, eventually, transferred from the control of the British Post Office to the evolving local administrations.

Those in foreign countries, nearly always based on existing British Consular appointments, were mostly connected to the network of British Packet lines which had been re-established in 1814. They tended to survive until the country in which they were situated established its own efficient postal service or joined the U.P.U. The term "Post Office Agent" was employed by the British G.P.O. and "Packet Agent" by the shipping lines to describe similar functions.

Listed in this section are the Crowned-circle handstamps and G.B. stamps used in the Post Offices and Agencies situated in foreign countries. Those for the territories within the scope of this catalogue will be found under the following headings:


| | Page |
|---|---|
| Antigua | 11 |
| Ascension | 39 |
| Bahamas | 105 |
| Barbados | 125 |
| Bermuda | 149 |
| British Guiana | *see* Guyana 424 |
| British Honduras | *see* Belize 136 |
| British Levant | 175 |
| British Virgin Islands | 180 |
| Canada | 203 |
| Cyprus | 286 |
| Dominica | 305 |
| Egypt | 320 |
| Gibraltar | 379 |
| Grenada | 392 |
| Hong Kong | 455 |
| Ionian Islands | 547 |
| Jamaica | *see* Vol. 2 |
| Lagos | *see* Nigeria *in* Vol. 2 |
| Malta | *see* Vol. 2 |
| Mauritius | *see* Vol. 2 |
| Montserrat | *see* Vol. 2 |
| Newfoundland | *see* Canada 204 |
| New Zealand | *see* Vol. 2 |
| Niger Coast | *see* Nigeria *in* Vol. 2 |
| Niger Company Territories | *see* Nigeria *in* Vol. 2 |
| Nova Scotia | *see* Canada 209 |
| St. Kitts-Nevis | *see* Vol. 2 |
| St. Lucia | *see* Vol. 2 |
| St. Vincent | *see* Vol. 2 |
| Seychelles | *see* Vol. 2 |
| Trinidad and Tobago | *see* Vol. 2 |
| Turks Islands | *see* Turks and Caicos Islands *in* Vol. 2 |


**Prices.** Catalogue prices quoted in this section, and throughout the volume, covering Crowned-circle handstamps and stamps of Great Britain used abroad are for fine used examples with the cancellation or handstamp clearly legible. Poor impressions of the cancellations and handstamps are worth much less than the prices quoted.

## CROWNED-CIRCLE HANDSTAMPS

Following the introduction, in 1840, of adhesive stamps in Great Britain there was considerable pressure from a number of the dependent territories for the British Post Office to provide something similar for their use.

Such suggestions were resisted, however, because of supposed operational problems, but the decision was taken, in connection with an expansion of the Packet Service, to issue a uniform series of handstamps and date stamps to the offices abroad, both in the dependent territories and in foreign countries.

Under the regulations circulated in December 1841, letters and packets forwarded through these offices to the United Kingdom or any of its territories were to be sent unpaid, the postage being collected on delivery. Where this was not possible, for example from a British colony to a foreign country or between two foreign ports, then a *crowned-circle handstamp* was to be applied with the postage, paid in advance, noted alongside in manuscript.

Examples of these handstamps were supplied over twenty years from 1842, but many continued to fulfil other functions long after the introduction of adhesive stamps in the colony concerned.

Our listings cover the use of these handstamps for their initial purpose and the prices quoted are for examples used on cover during the pre-adhesive period.

In most instances the dates quoted are those on which the handstamp appears in the G.P.O. Record Books, but it seems to have been normal for the handstamps to be sent to the office concerned immediately following this registration.

Many of the handstamps were individually cut by hand, so that each has its own characteristics, but for the purposes of the listing they have been grouped into nine Types as shown in the adjacent column. No attempt has been made to identify them by anything but the most major differences, so that minor differences in size and in the type of the crown have been ignored.

DOUBLE CIRCLE

CC 1

CC 1a

Curved "PAID"

CC 1b

CC 1c

Curved "PAID"

CC 2

Straight "PAID"

SINGLE CIRCLE

CC 3

CC 4

Straight "PAID"

CC 5

Curved "PAID"

CC 6

Straight "PAID"

CC 7

Curved "PAID"

## GREAT BRITAIN STAMPS USED ABROAD

Prices quoted are for single stamps not on cover unless otherwise stated. Stamps on cover are worth considerably more in most cases.

In many instances obliterators allocated to post offices abroad were, at a later date re-allocated to offices at home. Postmarks on issues later than those included in our lists can therefore safely be regarded as *not* having been "used abroad".

### INDEX


| | Page |
|---|---|
| A01 Kingston (Jamaica) | *see* Vol. 2 |
| A02 St. John's (Antigua) | 11 |
| A03–A04 Georgetown and New Amsterdam (Guyana) | 424 |
| A05 Nassau (Bahamas) | 105 |
| A06 Belize | 136 |
| A07 Dominica | 305 |
| A08 Montserrat | *see* Vol. 2 |
| A09 Charlestown, Nevis (St. Kitts-Nevis) | *see* Vol. 2 |
| A10 Kingstown (St. Vincent) | *see* Vol. 2 |
| A11 Castries (St. Lucia) | *see* Vol. 2 |
| A12 Basse-Terre, St. Christopher (St. Kitts-Nevis) | *see* Vol. 2 |
| A13 Tortola (British Virgin Islands) | 180 |
| A14 Scarborough, Tobago (Trinidad and Tobago) | *see* Vol. 2 |
| A15 St. George (Grenada) | 392 |
| A18 English Harbour (Antigua) | 11 |
| A25 Malta | *see* Vol. 2 |
| A26 Gibraltar | 379 |
| A27–A78 Jamaica | *see* Vol. 2 |
| A80–A99 | see note on page GB101 |
| Abutshi, Niger Company Territories (Nigeria) | *see* Vol. 2 |
| Akassa, Niger Company Territories (Nigeria) | *see* Vol. 2 |
| Ascension | 39 |
| B01 Alexandria (Egypt) | 320 |
| B02 Suez (Egypt) | 320 |
| B03, B12, B56, B57 | see note on page GB101 |
| B32 Buenos Ayres (Argentine Republic) | GB97 |
| B53 Mauritius | *see* Vol. 2 |
| B62 Hong Kong | see note on page 455 |
| B64 Seychelles | *see* Vol. 2 |
| Benin and Benin River, Niger Coast Protectorate (Nigeria) | *see* Vol. 2 |
| Bonny and Bonny River, Niger Coast Protectorate (Nigeria) | *see* Vol. 2 |
| Brass River, Niger Coast Protectorate (Nigeria) | *see* Vol. 2 |
| Burutu, Niger Company Territories (Nigeria) | *see* Vol. 2 |
| C Constantinople (British Levant) | 175 |
| C28 Montevideo (Uruguay) | GB101 |
| C30 Valparaiso (Chile) | GB97 |
| C35 Panama (Colombia) | GB98 |
| C36 Arica (Peru) | GB100 |
| C37 Caldera (Chile) | GB97 |
| C38 Callao (Peru) | GB100 |
| C39 Cobija (Bolivia) | GB97 |
| C40 Coquimbo (Chile) | GB97 |
| C41 Guayaquil (Ecuador) | GB99 |
| C42 Islay (Peru) | GB100 |
| C43 Paita (Peru) | GB100 |
| C51 St. Thomas (Danish West Indies) | GB98 |
| C56 (or 65) Carthagena (Colombia) | GB98 |
| C57 Greytown (Nicaragua) | GB99 |
| C58 Havana (Cuba) | GB98 |
| C59 Jacmel (Haiti) | GB99 |
| C60 La Guayra (Venezuela) | GB101 |
| C61 San Juan (Porto Rico) | GB101 |
| C62 Santa Martha (Colombia) | GB98 |
| C63 Tampico (Mexico) | GB99 |
| C65 (see C56) | GB98 |
| C79 | See note on page GB101 |
| C81 Bahia (Brazil) | GB97 |
| C82 Pernambuco (Brazil) | GB97 |
| C83 Rio de Janeiro (Brazil) | GB97 |
| C86 Porto Plata (Dominican Republic) | GB99 |
| C87 St. Domingo (Dominican Republic) | GB99 |
| C88 St. Jago de Cuba (Cuba) | GB98 |
| Crimea (Army) | GB101 |
| D22 Ciudad Bolivar (Venezuela) | GB101 |
| D26 Spanish Mail (St. Thomas, Danish West Indies) | GB99 |
| D47 Polymedia (Cyprus) | 286 |
| D48 Army H.Q. (Cyprus) | 286 |
| D65 Pisagua? (Peru) | GB100 |
| D74 Pisco and Chincha Islands (Peru) | GB100 |
| D87 Iquique (Peru) | GB100 |
| E53 Port-au-Prince (Haiti) | GB99 |
| E88 Colon (Colombia) | GB98 |
| Egypt (Army) | GB102 |
| F69 Savanilla (Colombia) | GB98 |
| F83 Arroyo (Porto Rico) | GB100 |
| F84 Aguadilla (Porto Rico) | GB100 |
| F85 Mayaguez (Porto Rico) | GB101 |
| F87 Smyrna (British Levant) | 175 |
| F88 Ponce (Porto Rico) | GB101 |
| Forcados River (Niger Coast Protectorate) | *see* Vol. 2 |
| G Gibraltar | 379 |
| G06 Beyrout (British Levant) | 175 |
| Ionian Islands | 547 |
| Lokoja, Niger Company Territories (Nigeria) | *see* Vol. 2 |
| M Malta | *see* Vol. 2 |
| Old Calabar River, Niger Coast Protectorate (Nigeria) | *see* Vol. 2 |
| Opobo River, Niger Coast Protectorate (Nigeria) | *see* Vol. 2 |
| S. Stamboul (British Levant) | 175 |
| South Africa (Army) | GB102 |
| Salonica (British Levant) | 175 |
| Sudan (Army) | GB102 |
| 247 Fernando Poo | GB99 |
| 582 Naguabo (Porto Rico) | GB101 |
| 942, 969, 974, 975, 981, 982 Cyprus | 286 |
| Wavy lines Malta | *see* Vol. 2 |


### ALTERED CATALOGUE NUMBERS

Any Catalogue numbers altered from the last edition are shown as a list in the introductory pages.

## TYPES OF OBLITERATOR FOR GREAT BRITAIN STAMPS USED ABROAD

### HORIZONTAL OVAL

(1)

(2)

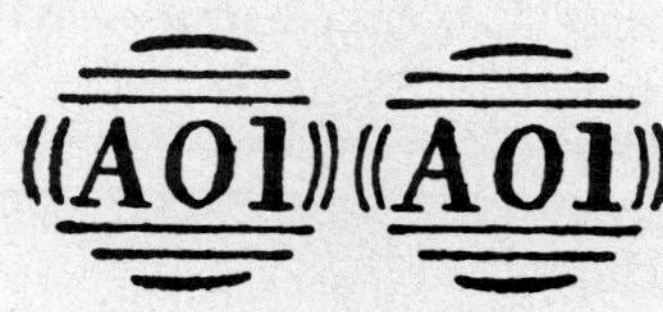

(3)

(4)

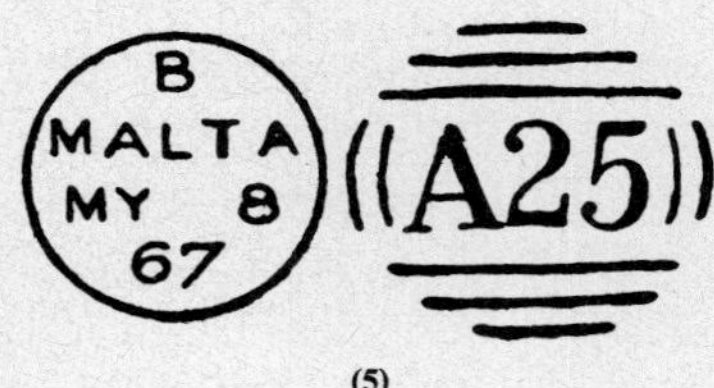

(5)

(6)

(7)

### VERTICAL OVAL

(8)

(9)

(10)

(11)

(12)

(13)

(14)

(15)

### CIRCULAR DATE STAMPS

(16)

(17)

(18)

(19)

(20)

## ARGENTINE REPUBLIC

### BUENOS AYRES

The first regular monthly British mail packet service was introduced in 1824, replacing a private arrangement which had previously existed for some years.

Great Britain stamps were used from 1860 until the office closed at the end of June 1873. Until 1878 the British Consul continued to sell stamps which were used in combination with an Argentine value prepaying the internal rate. The British stamps on such covers were cancelled on arrival in England.

CROWNED-CIRCLE HANDSTAMPS

CC1 CC 7 BUENOS AYRES (R.) (5.1.1851) *Price on cover* £650

*Stamps of* GREAT BRITAIN *cancelled* "B 32" *as in Types* **2, 12** *or* **13.**

**1860** *to* **1873.**

Z 1 1d. rose-red (1857)
Z 2 1d. rose-red (1864) *From* 10·00
Plate Nos. 71, 72, 73, 74, 76, 78, 79, 80, 81, 82, 85, 87, 89, 90, 91, 92, 93, 94, 95, 96, 97, 99, 101, 103, 104, 107, 108, 110, 112, 113, 114, 117, 118, 119, 120, 121, 123, 125, 127, 129, 130, 131, 135, 136, 138, 139, 140, 142, 143, 145, 147, 149, 150, 151, 155, 159, 163, 164, 166, 169, 172.
Z 3 2d. blue (1858–69) *From* 20·00
Plate Nos. 8, 9, 12, 13, 14.
Z 4 3d. carmine-rose (1862) £150
Z 5 3d. rose (1865) (Plate No. 4) 60·00
Z 6 3d. rose (1867–73) *From* 30·00
Plate Nos. 4, 5, 6, 7, 8, 9, 10.
Z 7 4d. rose (1857) 50·00
Z 8 4d. red (1862) (Plate Nos. 3, 4) 60·00
Z 9 4d. vermilion (1865–73) *From* 30·00
Plate Nos. 7, 8, 9, 10, 11, 12, 13.
Z10 6d. lilac (1856) 55·00
Z11 6d. lilac (1862) (Plate Nos. 3, 4)
Z12 6d. lilac (1865–67) (Plate Nos. 5, 6) *From* 45·00
Z13 6d. lilac (1867) (Plate No. 6) 70·00
Z14 6d. violet (1867–70) (Plate Nos. 6, 8, 9) *From* 40·00
Z15 6d. buff (1872) (Plate No. 11) 60·00
Z16 6d. chestnut (1872) (Plate No. 11) 35·00
Z17 9d. bistre (1862) £225
Z18 9d. straw (1862) £180
Z19 9d. straw (1865) £275
Z20 9d. straw (1867) £180
Z21 10d. red-brown (1867) £200
Z22 1s. green (1856) £140
Z23 1s. green (1862) £130
Z24 1s. green (1865) (Plate No. 4) 80·00
Z25 1s. green (1867–73) (Plate Nos. 4, 5, 6, 7) *From* 20·00
Z26 1s. green (1873–77) (Plate No. 8)
Z27 2s. blue (1867) £110
Z28 5s. rose (1867) (Plate No. 1) £300

A "B 32" obliteration was later used by Mauritius on its own stamps.

## AZORES

### ST. MICHAELS (SAN MIGUEL)

A British Postal Agency existed at Ponta Delgada, the chief port of the island, to operate with the services of the Royal Mail Steam Packet Company.

CROWNED-CIRCLE HANDSTAMPS

CC1 CC **1b** ST. MICHAELS (27.5.1842)

## BOLIVIA

### COBIJA

It is believed that the British Postal Agency opened in 1852. The stamps of Great Britain were used between 1865 and 1878. The Agency closed in 1881, the town having been occupied by Chile in 1879.

CROWNED-CIRCLE HANDSTAMPS

CC1 CC 4 COBIJA (29.3.1862) *Price on cover* £4000

*Stamps of* GREAT BRITAIN *cancelled* "C 39" *as Types* **4, 8** *or* **12.**

**1865** *to* **1878.**

Z 1 1d. rose-red (Plate Nos. 93, 95)
Z 2 2d. blue (1858–69) (Plate No. 14)
Z 3 3d. rose (1867–73) (Plate No. 6)
Z 4 3d. rose (1873–76) (Plate Nos. 16, 19)
Z 5 4d. sage-green (1877) (Plate No. 15)
Z 6 6d. violet (1867–70) (Plate No. 9) £350
Z 7 6d. buff (1872) (Plate No. 11)
Z 8 6d. grey (1874–76) (Plate Nos. 13, 14, 15, 16) £275
Z 9 1s. green (1867–73) (Plate Nos. 4, 5)
Z10 1s. green (1873–77) (Plate Nos. 10, 11, 12, 13) £275
Z11 2s. blue (1867) £450
Z12 5s. rose (1867–74) (Plate No. 2)

## BRAZIL

The first British packets ran to Brazil in 1808 when the Portuguese royal family went into exile at Rio de Janeiro. The Agencies at Bahia and Pernambuco did not open until 1851. All three agencies used the stamps of Great Britain from 1866, and were closed in 1874.

### BAHIA

CROWNED-CIRCLE HANDSTAMPS

CC1 CC 7 BAHIA (B., G. *or* R.) (6.1.1851) *Price on cover* £1500

*Stamps of* GREAT BRITAIN *cancelled* "C 81" *as Type* **12.**

**1866** *to* **1874.**

Z 1 1d. rose-red (1864–79) *From* 30·00
Plate Nos. 90, 93, 96, 108, 113, 117, 135, 140, 147, 155.
Z 2 1½d. lake-red (1870–74) (Plate No. 3) 75·00
Z 3 2d. blue (1858–69) (Plate Nos. 9, 12, 13, 14) 55·00
Z 4 3d. rose (1865) (Plate No. 4)
Z 5 3d. rose (1867–73) (Plate Nos. 4, 6, 8, 9, 10) 45·00
Z 6 3d. rose (1873–79) (Plate No. 11)
Z 7 4d. vermilion (1865–73) *From* 30·00
Plate Nos. 8, 9, 10, 11, 12, 13.
Z 8 6d. lilac (1865–67) (Plate No. 5)
Z 9 6d. lilac (1867) (Plate No. 6) 65·00
Z10 6d. violet (1867–70) (Plate Nos. 6, 8, 9) *From* 45·00
Z11 6d. buff (1872–73) (Plate Nos. 11, 12) *From* 85·00
Z12 6d. chestnut (1872) (Plate No. 11)
Z13 6d. grey (1873) (Plate No. 12)
Z14 6d. grey (1874–76) (Plate No. 13)
Z15 9d. straw (1865) £350
Z16 9d. straw (1867) £150
Z17 1s. green (1865) (Plate No. 4) 80·00
Z18 1s. green (1867–73) (Plate Nos. 4, 5, 6, 7) *From* 30·00
Z19 1s. green (1873–77) (Plate Nos. 8, 9) *From* 50·00
Z20 2s. blue (1867) £180
Z21 5s. rose (1867) (Plate No. 1) £350

### PERNAMBUCO

CROWNED-CIRCLE HANDSTAMPS

CC2 CC 7 PERNAMBUCO (Black *or* R.) (6.1.1851) *Price on cover* £1500

*Stamps of* GREAT BRITAIN *cancelled* "C 82" *as Type* **12.**

**1866** *to* **1874.**

Z22 1d. rose-red (1864–79) *From* 30·00
Plate Nos. 85, 108, 111, 130, 131, 132, 149, 157, 159, 160, 187.
Z23 2d. blue (1858–69) (Plate Nos. 9, 12, 13, 14) *From* 40·00
Z24 3d. rose (1867–73) (Plate Nos. 4, 5, 6, 7, 10) 35·00
Z25 3d. rose (1873–77) (Plate No. 11)
Z26 4d. vermilion (1865–73) *From* 25·00
Plate Nos. 9, 10, 11, 12, 13, 14.
Z27 6d. lilac (1865–67) (Plate Nos. 5, 6)
Z28 6d. lilac (1867) (Plate No. 6) 55·00
Z29 6d. violet (1867–70) (Plate Nos. 8, 9) *From* 35·00
Z30 6d. buff (1872–73) (Plate Nos. 11, 12) 45·00
Z31 6d. chestnut (1872) (Plate No. 11) 35·00
Z32 6d. grey (1873) (Plate No. 12)
Z33 9d. straw (1865) £350
Z34 9d. straw (1867) £130
Z35 10d. red-brown (1867) £180
Z36 1s. green (1865) (Plate No. 4) 65·00
Z37 1s. green (1867–73) (Plate Nos. 4, 5, 6, 7) 28·00
Z38 2s. blue (1867) £225
Z39 5s. rose (1867–74) (Plate Nos. 1, 2) £400

### RIO DE JANEIRO

CROWNED-CIRCLE HANDSTAMPS

CC3 CC 7 RIO DE JANEIRO (Black, B., G. *or* R.) (6.1.1851) *Price on cover* £400

*Stamps of* GREAT BRITAIN *cancelled* "C 83" *as Type* **12.**

**1866** *to* **1874.**

Z40 1d. rose-red (1857) 38·00
Z41 1d. rose-red (1864–79) *From* 20·00
Plate Nos. 71, 76, 80, 82, 86, 94, 103, 113, 117, 119, 123, 130, 132, 134, 135, 146, 148, 159, 161, 166, 185, 200, 204.
Z42 2d. blue (1858–69) (Plate Nos. 9, 12, 13, 14) *From* 22·00
Z43 3d. rose (1867–73) (Plate Nos. 4, 5, 6, 7, 8) *From* 28·00
Z44 3d. rose (1873–77) (Plate No. 11)
Z45 4d. vermilion (1865–73) *From* 25·00
Plate Nos. 8, 9, 10, 11, 12, 13, 14.
Z46 6d. lilac (1865–67) (Plate No. 5)
Z47 6d. lilac (1867) (Plate No. 6) 55·00
Z48 6d. violet (1867–70) (Plate Nos. 6, 8, 9) *From* 30·00
Z49 6d. buff (1872) (Plate No. 11) 45·00
Z50 6d. chestnut (1872) (Plate No. 11) 35·00
Z51 6d. grey (1873) (Plate No. 12)
Z52 9d. straw (1865) £250
Z53 9d. straw (1867) £110
Z54 10d. red-brown (1867) £140
Z55 1s. green (1865) (Plate No. 4) 70·00
Z56 1s. green (1867–73) (Plate Nos. 4, 5, 6, 7) *From* 15·00
Z57 1s. green (1873–77) (Plate Nos. 8, 9) 35·00
Z58 2s. blue (1867) 90·00
Z59 5s. rose (1867–74) (Plate Nos. 1, 2) *From* £200

## CAPE VERDE ISLANDS

The British Packet Agency at St. Vincent opened in 1851 as part of the revised service to South America. The agency was closed by 1880.

CROWNED-CIRCLE HANDSTAMPS

CC1 CC **6** ST. VINCENT C.DE.V. (6.1.1851) *Price on cover* £4000

## CHILE

The British Postal Agency at Valparaiso opened in 1846, to be followed by further offices at Caldera (1862) and Coquimbo (1863). The stamps of Great Britain were introduced in 1865 and all three offices closed on 31 March 1881 when Chile joined the U.P.U.

### CALDERA

*Stamps of* GREAT BRITAIN *cancelled* "C 37" *as in Type* **4.**

**1865** *to* **1881.**

Z 1 1d. rose-red (1864–79) *From* 25·00
Plate Nos. 71, 72, 88, 90, 95, 160, 195.
Z 2 1½d. lake-red (1870–74) (Plate No. 3)
Z 3 2d. blue (1858–69) (Plate No. 9) 35·00
Z 4 3d. rose (1865) (Plate No. 4) 65·00
Z 5 3d. rose (1867–73) (Plate Nos. 5, 7)
Z 6 3d. rose (1873–76) *From* 25·00
Plate Nos. 11, 12, 16, 17, 18, 19.
Z 7 4d. red (1862) (Plate No. 4)
Z 8 4d. vermilion (1865–73) *From* 40·00
Plate Nos. 8, 11, 12, 13, 14.
Z 9 4d. sage-green (1877) (Plate No. 16)
Z10 6d. lilac (1862) (Plate No. 4) 80·00
Z11 6d. lilac (1865–67) (Plate Nos. 5, 6)
Z12 6d. violet (1867–70) (Plate Nos. 6, 8, 9) *From* 40·00
Z13 6d. buff (1872) (Plate No. 11)
Z14 6d. chestnut (1872) (Plate No. 11)
Z15 6d. grey (1873) (Plate No. 12)
Z16 6d. grey (1874–80) *From* 30·00
Plate Nos. 13, 14, 15, 16, 17.
Z17 8d. orange (1876) £250
Z18 9d. straw (1867) £140
Z19 10d. red-brown (1867) £200
Z20 1s. green (1865) (Plate No. 4)
Z21 1s. green (1867–73) (Plate Nos. 4, 5, 6) *From* 22·00
Z22 1s. green (1873–77) *From* 40·00
Plate Nos. 8, 10, 11, 12, 13.
Z23 2s. blue (1867) £200
Z23*a* 2s. cobalt (1867)
Z24 2s. brown (1880) £1200
Z25 5s. rose (1867–74) (Plate No. 2) £400

### COQUIMBO

*Stamps of* GREAT BRITAIN *cancelled* "C 40" *as in Type* **4.**

**1865** *to* **1881.**

Z26 ½d. rose-red (1870–79) (Plate No. 14)
Z27 1d. rose-red (1857)
Z28 1d. rose-red (1864–79) (Plate Nos. 85, 204)
Z29 2d. blue (1858–69) (Plate Nos. 9, 14)
Z30 3d. rose (1865)
Z31 3d. rose (1872) (Plate No. 8)
Z32 3d. rose (1873–76) (Plate Nos. 18, 19) *From* 25·00
Z33 4d. red (1863) (Plate No. 4) 50·00
Z34 4d. vermilion (1865–73) (Plate Nos. 12, 14)
Z35 4d. sage-green (1877) (Plate Nos. 15, 16) £120
Z36 6d. lilac (1862) (Plate Nos. 3, 4) 60·00
Z37 6d. lilac (1865–67) (Plate No. 5)
Z38 6d. lilac (1867) (Plate No. 6) 60·00
Z39 6d. violet (1867–70) (Plate Nos. 6, 8, 9) *From* 32·00
Z40 6d. buff (1872–73) (Plate Nos. 11, 12) *From* 55·00
Z41 6d. chestnut (1872) (Plate No. 11)
Z42 6d. grey (1873) (Plate No. 12) 80·00
Z43 6d. grey (1874–76) (Plate Nos. 13, 14, 15, 16) *From* 25·00
Z44 8d. orange (1876)
Z45 9d. straw (1862) £200
Z46 9d. straw (1867) £140
Z47 10d. red-brown (1867)
Z48 1s. green (1865) (Plate No. 4) 65·00
Z49 1s. green (1867–73) (Plate Nos. 4, 5, 6) 22·00
Z50 1s. green (1873–77) *From* 30·00
Plate Nos. 8, 10, 11, 12, 13.
Z51 2s. blue (1867) £130
Z51*a* 2s. cobalt (1867)
Z52 2s. brown (1880) £1300
Z53 5s. rose (1867–74) (Plate Nos. 1, 2) £325

### VALPARAISO

CROWNED-CIRCLE HANDSTAMPS

CC1 CC **2** VALPARAISO (R.) (13.1.1846) *Price on cover* £375
CC2 CC **1** VALPARAISO (R.) (16.7.1846) *Price on cover* £475

*Stamps of* GREAT BRITAIN *cancelled* "C 30", *as in Types* **12** *and* **14** *or circular date stamp as Type* **16.**

**1865** *to* **1881.**

Z54 ½d. rose-red (1870–79) *From* 50·00
Plate Nos. 6, 11, 12, 13, 14.
Z55 1d. rose-red (1864–79) *From* 15·00
Plate Nos. 80, 84, 85, 89, 91, 101, 106, 113, 116, 122, 123, 138, 140, 141, 146, 148, 149, 152, 157, 158, 162, 167, 175, 178, 181, 185, 186, 187, 189, 190, 195, 197, 198, 199, 200, 201, 207, 209, 210, 211, 212, 213, 214, 215, 217.
Z56 1½d. lake-red (1870–74) (Plate Nos. 1, 3) *From* 55·00
Z57 2d. blue (1858–69) (Plate Nos. 9, 13, 14, 15) 35·00
Z58 2½d. rosy mauve (1875), white paper (Plate No. 2) 60·00
Z59 2½d. rosy mauve (1876) (Plate Nos. 4, 8) 50·00
Z60 3d. carmine-rose (1862)
Z61 3d. rose (1865) (Plate No. 4)
Z62 3d. rose (1867–73) *From* 20·00
Plate Nos. 5, 6, 7, 8, 9, 10.
Z63 3d. rose (1873–76) *From* 20·00
Plate Nos. 11, 12, 14, 16, 17, 18, 19.
Z63*a* 4d. red (1862) (Plate No. 4)
Z63*b* 4d. red (1863) (Plate No. 4) (*Hair lines*)
Z64 4d. vermilion (1865–73) *From* 25·00
Plate Nos. 9, 10, 11, 12, 13, 14.
Z65 4d. vermilion (1876) (Plate No. 15) £140
Z66 4d. sage-green (1877) (Plate Nos. 15, 16) 85·00
Z67 4d. grey-brown (1880) *wmk* Large Garter
Plate No. 17.
Z68 6d. lilac (1862) (Plate Nos. 3, 4) *From* 50·00
Z69 6d. lilac (1865) (Plate Nos. 5, 6)
Z70 6d. lilac (1867) (Plate No. 6)
Z71 6d. violet (1867–70) (Plate Nos. 6, 8, 9) *From* 30·00
Z72 6d. buff (1872–73) (Plate Nos. 11, 12) *From* 40·00
Z73 6d. chestnut (1872) (Plate Nos. 11, 12) 25·00
Z74 6d. grey (1873) (Plate No. 12) 80·00
Z75 6d. grey (1874–80) *From* 22·00
Plate Nos. 13, 14, 15, 16, 17.
Z76 6d. grey (1881) (Plate No. 17)
Z77 8d. orange (1876) £150
Z78 9d. straw (1862)
Z79 9d. straw (1865)
Z80 9d. straw (1867) £120
Z81 10d. red-brown (1867) £130
Z82 1s. green (1865) (Plate No. 4)
Z83 1s. green (1867–73) (Plate Nos. 4, 5, 6, 7) *From* 12·00
Z84 1s. green (1873–77) *From* 30·00
Plate Nos. 8, 9, 10, 11, 12, 13.
Z85 1s. orange-brown (1880) (Plate No. 13) £180
Z86 2s. blue (1867) 80·00
Z86*a* 2s. cobalt (1867) £800
Z87 2s. brown (1880) £1100
Z88 5s. rose (1867–74) (Plate Nos. 1, 2) *From* £200
Z89 10s. grey-green (1878) (*wmk* Cross) £1500
Z90 £1 brown-lilac (1878) (*wmk* Cross) £2500

**1880.**

Z91 1d. Venetian red
Z92 1½d. Venetian red

## COLOMBIA

The system of British Postal Agencies in the area was inaugurated by the opening of the Carthagena office in 1825. In 1842 agencies at Chagres, Panama and Santa Martha were added to the system. A further office opened at Colon in 1852, this port also being known as Aspinwall. During 1872 the system was further enlarged by an office at Savanilla, although this agency was later, 1878, transferred to Barranquilla.

Stamps of Great Britain were supplied to Carthagena, Panama and Santa Martha in 1865, Colon in 1870 and Savanilla in 1872.

All offices, except Chagres which had ceased to operate in 1855, closed for public business on 30 June 1881. Colon and Panama continued to exist as transit offices to deal with the mail across the isthmus. Both finally closed on 31 March 1921.

### CARTHAGENA

CROWNED-CIRCLE HANDSTAMPS

CC1 CC **1b** CARTHAGENA (R.) (15.1.1841) *Price on cover* £750
CC2 CC **1** CARTHAGENA (1.7.1846) .. *Price on cover* £650

*Stamps of* GREAT BRITAIN *cancelled* "C 56" *as in Type* **4**.

**1865** *to* **1881.**
Z 1 ½d. rose-red (1870–79) (Plate No. 10) .. ..
Z 2 1d. rose-red (1864–79) .. .. .. *From* 30·00
Plate Nos. 78, 87, 100, 111, 113, 117, 119, 125, 172, 189, 217.
Z 3 2d. blue (1858–69) (Plate Nos. 9, 14) .. *From* 26·00
Z 4 3d. rose (1865) (Plate No. 4) .. ..
Z 5 3d. rose (1865–68) (Plate Nos. 4, 5) .. ..
Z 6 3d. rose (1873–79) (Plate Nos. 12, 17, 18) .. *From* 38·00
Z 7 4d. vermilion (1865–73) .. .. .. *From* 26·00
Plate Nos. 7, 8, 9, 10, 11, 12, 13, 14.
Z 8 4d. vermilion (1876) (Plate No. 15) .. .. .. £150
Z 9 4d. sage-green (1877) (Plate Nos. 15, 16) .. *From* £120
Z10 6d. lilac (1865–67) (Plate Nos. 5, 6) .. ..
Z11 6d. violet (1867–70) (Plate Nos. 6, 8) .. *From* 42·00
Z12 6d. grey (1873) (Plate No. 12) .. .. .. 80·00
Z13 6d. grey (1874–76) (Plate Nos. 13, 14, 15, 16) *From* 30·00
Z14 8d. orange (1876) .. .. .. .. .. £150
Z15 9d. straw (1865) .. .. .. .. ..
Z16 1s. green (1865) .. .. .. .. ..
Z17 1s. green (1867–73) (Plate Nos. 4, 5, 7) .. .. 32·00
Z18 1s. green (1873–77) (Plate Nos. 8, 9, 10, 11, 12, 13) 32·00
Z19 1s. orange-brown (1880) .. .. .. ..
Z20 2s. blue (1867) .. .. .. .. .. £170
Z21 5s. rose (1867) (Plate No. 1) .. .. .. £325

*Cancelled* "C 65" (*incorrect handstamp, supplied in error*) *as T* **12**.

**1866** *to* **1881.**
Z22 ½d. rose-red (1870–79) (Plate No. 10) .. ..
Z23 1d. rose-red (1864–79) (Plate Nos. 100, 106, 111, 123) .. .. .. .. *From* 40·00
Z23*a* 1½d. lake-red (1870) (Plate No. 3) .. ..
Z24 2d. blue (1858–69) (Plate No. 9) .. .. .. 38·00
Z25 2d. rose (1880) .. .. .. .. ..
Z26 2½d. blue (1880) (Plate No. 19) .. .. ..
Z27 3d. rose (1867–73) (Plate No. 9) .. .. ..
Z28 3d. rose (1873–79) (Plate Nos. 14, 17, 19, 20) ..
Z29 4d. vermilion (1865–73) .. .. .. *From* 35·00
Plate Nos. 7, 8, 9, 11, 12, 13, 14.
Z30 4d. vermilion (1876) (Plate No. 15) .. .. £180
Z31 4d. sage-green (1877) (Plate Nos. 15, 16) .. *From* £130
Z32 6d. violet (1867–70) (Plate Nos. 6, 8) .. .. 80·00
Z33 6d. pale buff (1872) (Plate No. 11) .. ..
Z34 6d. grey (1873) (Plate No. 12) .. .. .. 80·00
Z35 6d. grey (1874–80) (Plate Nos. 13, 15, 16, 17) .. 40·00
Z36 8d. orange (1876) .. .. .. .. .. £250
Z37 9d. straw (1865) .. .. .. .. .. £250
Z38 1s. green (1865) (Plate No. 4) .. .. .. 70·00
Z39 1s. green (1867) (Plate Nos. 4, 5, 6, 7) .. .. 28·00
Z40 1s. green (1873–77) (Plate Nos. 8, 11, 12, 13) *From* 32·00
Z41 1s. orange-brown (1880) .. .. .. ..
Z42 2s. blue (1867) .. .. .. .. .. £350
Z43 2s. brown (1880) .. .. .. .. .. £1200
Z44 5s. rose (1867) (Plate Nos. 1, 2) .. .. .. £375

### CHAGRES

CROWNED-CIRCLE HANDSTAMPS

CC3 CC **1** CHAGRES (16.9.1846) .. .. ..

### COLON

CROWNED-CIRCLE HANDSTAMPS

CC4 CC **5** COLON (R.) (21.6.1854) .. *Price on cover* £3250

*Stamps of* GREAT BRITAIN *cancelled* "E 88" *as in Type* **12**.

**1870** *to* **1881.**
Z45 1d. rose-red (1864–79) .. .. .. *From* 23·00
Plate Nos. 107, 121, 122, 123, 125, 127, 130, 131, 133, 136, 138, 142, 150, 151, 152, 153, 155, 156, 157, 158, 160, 169, 170, 171, 174, 176, 178, 179, 184, 187, 188, 194, 195, 201, 209, 213, 214, 217.
Z46 1d. Venetian red (1880) .. .. .. ..
Z47 1½d. lake-red (1870–74) (Plate No. 3) .. .. 90·00
Z48 2d. blue (1858–69) (Plate Nos. 14, 15) .. .. 28·00
Z49 2d. pale rose (1880) .. .. .. ..
Z50 3d. rose (1867–73) (Plate Nos. 6, 9) .. ..
Z51 3d. rose (1873–76) .. .. .. .. 35·00
Plate Nos. 11, 12, 16, 18, 19, 20.
Z52 4d. vermilion (1865–73) .. .. .. *From* 30·00
Plate Nos. 10, 11, 12, 13, 14.
Z53 4d. vermilion (1876) (Plate No. 15) .. ..
Z54 4d. sage-green (1877) (Plate Nos. 15, 16) .. .. £120
Z55 4d. grey-brown (1880) *wmk* Large Garter .. .. £150
Plate No. 17.
Z56 4d. grey-brown (1880) *wmk* Crown (Plate No. 17)
Z57 6d. violet (1867–70) (Plate Nos. 6, 8, 9) .. ..
Z58 6d. buff (1872) (Plate No. 11) .. ..
Z59 6d. chestnut (1872) (Plate No. 11) .. .. 50·00
Z60 6d. grey (1873) (Plate No. 12) .. ..
Z61 6d. grey (1874–80) .. .. .. *From* 28·00
Plate Nos. 13, 14, 15, 16, 17.
Z62 8d. orange (1876) .. .. .. .. ..
Z63 9d. straw (1867) .. .. .. .. .. £130
Z63*a* 10d. red-brown (1867) .. .. .. ..
Z64 1s. green (1867–73) (Plate Nos. 4, 5, 6, 7) .. 25·00
Z65 1s. green (1873–77) .. .. .. *From* 27·00
Plate Nos. 8, 9, 10, 11, 12, 13.
Z66 1s. orange-brown (1880) (Plate 13) .. .. £225
Z67 1s. orange-brown (1881) (Plate 13) .. .. 60·00
Z68 2s. blue (1867) .. .. .. .. .. £120
Z69 2s. brown (1880) .. .. .. .. .. £1500
Z70 5s. rose (1867) (Plate Nos. 1, 2) .. .. .. £350

### PANAMA

CROWNED-CIRCLE HANDSTAMPS

CC5 CC **1** PANAMA (R.) (24.8.1846) .. *Price on cover* £1000

*Stamps of* GREAT BRITAIN *cancelled* "C 35" *as in Types* **4, 11** *or* **14**.

**1865** *to* **1881.**
Z 71 ½d. rose-red (1870–79) .. .. .. *From* 27·00
Plate Nos. 10, 11, 12, 13, 14, 15, 19.
Z 72 1d. rose-red (1864–79) .. .. .. *From* 16·00
Plate Nos. 71, 72, 76, 81, 85, 87, 88, 89, 93, 95, 96, 101, 104, 114, 124, 130, 138, 139, 142, 159, 168, 171, 172, 174, 177, 179, 180, 184, 185, 187, 189, 191, 192, 193, 196, 197, 200, 203, 204, 205, 207, 208, 209, 210, 211, 213, 214, 215, 218, 224.
Z 73 1½d. lake-red (1870–74) (Plate No. 3) .. .. 40·00
Z 74 2d. blue (1858–69) .. .. .. *From* 22·00
Plate Nos. 9, 12, 13, 14, 15.
Z 75 2½d. rosy mauve (1875) (Plate No. 1) .. ..
Z 76 2½d. rosy mauve (1876–80) (Plate Nos. 4, 12, 16) ..
Z 77 2½d. blue (1880) (Plate No. 19) .. .. ..
Z 78 2½d. blue (1881) (Plate Nos. 22, 23) .. ..
Z 79 3d. carmine-red (1862) .. .. .. .. £110
Z 80 3d. rose (1865) (Plate No. 4) .. .. ..
Z 81 3d. rose (1867–73) .. .. .. *From* 20·00
Plate Nos. 4, 5, 6, 7, 8, 9.
Z 82 3d. rose (1873–76) .. .. .. *From* 20·00
Plate Nos. 12, 14, 15, 16, 17, 18, 19, 20.
Z 83 3d. rose (1881) (Plate Nos. 20, 21) .. ..
Z 84 4d. red (1863) (Plate No. 4) .. .. .. 65·00
Z 85 4d. vermilion (1865–73) .. .. *From* 25·00
Plate Nos. 7, 8, 9, 10, 11, 12, 13, 14.
Z 86 4d. vermilion (1876) (Plate No. 15) .. .. £160
Z 87 4d. sage-green (1877) (Plate Nos. 15, 16) .. .. £100
Z 88 4d. grey-brown (1880) *wmk* Crown .. *From* 45·00
Plate Nos. 17, 18.
Z 89 6d. lilac (1862) (Plate Nos. 3, 4) .. *From* 55·00
Z 90 6d. lilac (1865–67) (Plate Nos. 5, 6) .. *From* 30·00
Z 91 6d. lilac (1867) (Plate No. 6) .. ..
Z 92 6d. violet (1867–70) (Plate Nos. 6, 8, 9) .. .. 28·00
Z 93 6d. buff (1872–73) (Plate Nos. 11, 12) .. *From* 42·00
Z 94 6d. chestnut (Plate No. 11) .. .. .. 25·00
Z 95 6d. grey (1873) (Plate No. 12) .. .. .. 80·00
Z 96 6d. grey (1874–80) .. .. .. *From* 28·00
Plate Nos. 13, 14, 15, 16, 17.
Z 97 6d. grey (1881) (Plate No. 17) .. .. .. 60·00
Z 98 8d. orange (1876) .. .. .. .. £140
Z 99 9d. straw (1862) .. .. .. .. £150
Z100 9d. straw (1867) .. .. .. .. £200
Z101 10d. red-brown (1867) .. .. .. .. £175
Z102 1s. green (1865) (Plate No. 4) .. .. .. 65·00
Z103 1s. green (1867–73) (Plate Nos. 4, 5, 6, 7) *From* 16·00
Z104 1s. green (1873–77) .. .. .. *From* 27·00
Plate Nos. 8, 9, 10, 11, 12, 13.
Z105 1s. orange-brown (1880) (Plate No. 13) .. .. £180
Z106 1s. orange-brown (1881) (Plate No. 13) .. .. 50·00
Z107 2s. blue (1867) .. .. .. .. .. 80·00
Z108 2s. brown (1880) .. .. .. .. .. £1200
Z109 5s. rose (1867–74) (Plate Nos. 1, 2) .. *From* £250

**1880.**
Z110 1d. Venetian red .. .. .. .. .. 15·00
Z111 2d. rose .. .. .. .. .. .. 35·00
Z112 5d. indigo .. .. .. .. .. .. 75·00

Later stamps cancelled "C 35" are believed to originate from sailors' letters or other forms of maritime mail.

### SANTA MARTHA

CROWNED-CIRCLE HANDSTAMPS

CC6 CC **1b** SANTA MARTHA (R.) (15.12.1841) *Price on cover* £900

*Stamps of* GREAT BRITAIN *cancelled* "C 62" *as in Type* **4**.

**1865** *to* **1881.**
Z113 ½d. rose-red (1870–79) (Plate No. 6) .. .. 70·00
Z114 1d. rose-red (1864–79) (Plate No. 106) .. .. 50·00
Z115 2d. blue (1858–69) (Plate No. 9) .. .. 70·00
Z116 4d. vermilion (1865–73) .. .. *From* 30·00
Plate Nos. 7, 8, 9, 11, 12, 13, 14.
Z117 4d. sage-green (1877) (Plate No. 15) .. .. £110
Z118 4d. grey-brown (1880) *wmk* Large Garter .. .. £160
Plate No. 17.
Z119 4d. grey-brown (1880) *wmk* Crown (Plate No. 17) 55·00
Z120 6d. lilac (1865–67) (Plate No. 5) .. .. 55·00
Z121 6d. grey (1873) (Plate No. 12) .. ..
Z122 6d. grey (1874–76) (Plate No. 14) .. ..
Z123 8d. orange (1876) .. .. .. .. £200
Z123*a* 9d. bistre (1862) .. .. .. ..
Z124 1s. green (1865) (Plate No. 4) .. .. .. 75·00
Z125 1s. green (1867–73) (Plate Nos. 5, 7) .. .. 50·00
Z126 1s. green (1873–77) (Plate No. 8) .. ..
Z127 2s. blue (1867) .. .. .. .. £275
Z128 5s. rose (1867) (Plate No. 2) .. .. .. £375

### SAVANILLA (BARRANQUILLA)

*Stamps of* GREAT BRITAIN *cancelled* "F 69" *as in Type* **12**.

**1872** *to* **1881.**
Z129 ½d. rose-red (1870–79) (Plate No. 6) .. .. 55·00
Z130 1d. rose-red (1864–79) (Plate Nos. 122, 171) .. 50·00
Z131 1½d. lake-red (1870–74) (Plate No. 3) .. .. 90·00
Z132 3d. rose (1867–73) (Plate No. 7) .. ..
Z133 3d. rose (1873–76) (Plate No. 20) .. .. 85·00
Z134 3d. rose (1881) (Plate No. 20) .. .. .. 85·00
Z135 4d. vermilion (1865–73) (Plate Nos. 12, 13, 14) .. 30·00
Z136 4d. vermilion (1876) (Plate No. 15) .. .. £160
Z137 4d. sage-green (1877) (Plate Nos. 15, 16) .. .. £110
Z138 4d. grey-brown (1880) *wmk* Large Garter .. £150
Plate No. 17.
Z139 4d. grey-brown (1880) *wmk* Crown (Plate No. 17) 50·00
Z140 6d. buff (1872) (Plate No. 11) .. ..
Z141 6d. grey (1878) (Plate No. 16) .. .. .. 60·00
Z142 8d. orange (1876) .. .. .. .. £200
Z143 1s. green (1867–73) (Plate Nos. 5, 7) .. .. 40·00
Z144 1s. green (1873–77) (Plate Nos. 8, 11, 12, 13) .. 45·00
Z145 1s. orange-brown (1880) .. .. .. £200
Z146 2s. blue (1867) .. .. .. .. .. £170
Z147 5s. rose (1867–74) (Plate No. 2) .. .. .. £350

## CUBA

The British Postal Agency at Havana opened in 1762, the island then being part of the Spanish Empire. A further office, at St. Jago de Cuba, was added around 1840.

Great Britain stamps were supplied to these offices in 1865 and continued in use until they closed on 30 May 1877.

### HAVANA

CROWNED-CIRCLE HANDSTAMPS

CC1 CC **1b** HAVANA (13.11.1841) .. .. *Price on cover* £850
CC2 CC **1c** HAVANA (1848) .. .. *Price on cover* £850
CC3 CC **2** HAVANA (14.7.1848) .. .. *Price on cover* £750

*Stamps of* GREAT BRITAIN *cancelled* "C 58" *as in Types* **4, 12** *or* **14**.

**1865** *to* **1877.**
Z 1 ½d. rose-red (1870) (Plate Nos. 6, 12) .. .. 50·00
Z 2 1d. rose-red (1864–79) .. .. .. .. 30·00
Plate Nos. 86, 90, 93, 115, 120, 123, 144, 146, 171, 174, 208.
Z 3 2d. blue (1858–69) (Plate Nos. 9, 14, 15) .. .. 35·00
Z 4 3d. rose (1867–73) (Plate No. 4) .. .. 75·00
Z 5 3d. rose (1873–76) (Plate Nos. 18, 19) .. ..
Z 6 4d. vermilion (1865–73) .. .. .. *From* 30·00
Plate Nos. 7, 8, 10, 11, 12, 13, 14.
Z 7 4d. vermilion (1876) (Plate No. 15) .. ..
Z 8 6d. lilac (1865) (with hyphen) (Plate No. 5) ..
Z 9 6d. grey (1874–76) (Plate No. 15) .. ..
Z10 8d. orange (1876) .. .. .. .. ..
Z11 9d. straw (1867) .. .. .. .. .. £180
Z12 10d. red-brown (1867) .. .. .. .. £250
Z13 1s. green (1865) (Plate No. 4) .. .. .. 70·00
Z14 1s. green (1867–73) (Plate Nos. 4, 5, 7) .. *From* 35·00
Z15 1s. green (1873–77) (Plate Nos. 10, 12, 13) *From* 40·00
Z16 2s. blue (1867) .. .. .. .. .. £160
Z17 5s. rose (1867–74) (Plate Nos. 1, 2) .. .. £375

### ST. JAGO DE CUBA

CROWNED-CIRCLE HANDSTAMPS

CC4 CC **1b** ST. JAGO-DE-CUBA (R.) (15.12.1841) *Price on cover* £4500

*Stamps of* GREAT BRITAIN *cancelled* "C 88" *as Type* **12**.

**1865** *to* **1877.**
Z18 ½d. rose-red (1870–79) (Plate Nos. 4, 6, 14) ..
Z19 1d. rose-red (1864–79) .. .. .. *From* 60·00
Plate Nos. 100, 105, 106, 109, 111, 120, 123, 138, 144, 146, 147, 148, 171, 208.
Z20 1½d. lake-red (1870–74) (Plate No. 3) .. ..
Z21 2d. blue (1858–69) (Plate Nos. 9, 12, 13, 14) ..
Z22 3d. rose (1867) (Plate No. 5) .. .. ..
Z23 4d. vermilion (1865–73) .. .. .. *From* 60·00
Plate Nos. 9, 10, 11, 12, 13, 14.
Z24 4d. vermilion (1876) (Plate No. 15) .. .. £175
Z25 6d. violet (1867–70) (Plate Nos. 6, 8, 9) .. *From* £200
Z26 6d. buff (Plate No. 11) .. .. .. ..
Z27 9d. straw (1865) .. .. .. .. ..
Z27*a* 9d. straw (1867) .. .. .. .. ..
Z28 10d. red-brown (1867) .. .. .. .. £275
Z29 1s. green (1867–73) (Plate Nos. 4, 5, 6) .. *From* £200
Z30 1s. green (1873–77) (Plate Nos. 9, 10, 12, 13) ..
Z31 2s. blue (1867) .. .. .. .. ..
Z32 5s. rose (1867) (Plate 1) .. .. .. ..

## DANISH WEST INDIES

### ST. THOMAS

The British Postal Agency at St. Thomas opened in January 1809 and by 1825 was the office around which many of the packet routes were organised.

Great Britain stamps were introduced on 3 July 1865.

Following a hurricane in October 1867 the main British packet office was moved to Colon in Colombia.

The British Post Office at St. Thomas closed to the public on 1 September 1877, but continued to operate as a transit office for a further two years.

CROWNED-CIRCLE HANDSTAMPS

CC1 CC **1** ST. THOMAS (R.) (1850) *Price on cover* £500
CC2 CC **6** ST. THOMAS (R.) (1.5.1855) *Price on cover* £1000

*Stamps of* GREAT BRITAIN *cancelled* "C 51" *as in Types* **4, 12** *or* **14**.

**1865** *to* **1879.**
Z 1 ½d. rose-red (1870–79) .. .. .. .. 30·00
Plate Nos. 5, 6, 8, 10, 11, 12.
Z 2 1d. rose-red (1857) .. .. .. ..
Z 3 1d. rose-red (1864–79) .. .. .. *From* 18·00
Plate Nos. 71, 72, 79, 81, 84, 85, 86, 87, 88, 89, 90, 93, 94, 95, 96, 97, 98, 99, 100, 101, 102, 105, 106, 107, 108, 109, 110, 111, 112, 113, 114, 116, 117, 118, 119, 120, 121, 122, 123, 124, 125, 127, 129, 130, 131, 133, 134, 136, 137, 138, 139, 140, 141, 142, 144, 145, 146, 147, 148, 149, 150, 151, 152, 154, 155, 156, 157, 158, 159, 160, 161, 162, 163, 164, 165, 166, 167, 169, 170, 171, 172, 173, 174, 175, 176, 177, 178, 179, 180, 181, 182, 184, 185, 186, 187, 189, 190, 197.
Z 4 1½d. lake-red (1870–74) (Plate Nos. 1, 3) .. .. 45·00
Z 5 2d. blue (1858–69) .. .. .. *From* 25·00
Plate Nos. 9, 12, 13, 14, 15.
Z 6 3d. rose (1865) (Plate No. 4) .. .. .. 55·00
Z 7 3d. rose (1867–73) .. .. .. *From* 25·00
Plate Nos. 4, 5, 6, 7, 8, 9, 10.
Z 8 3d. rose (1873–76) .. .. .. *From* 25·00
Plate Nos. 11, 12, 14, 15, 16, 17, 18, 19.
Z 9 4d. red (1862) (Plate Nos. 3, 4) .. .. 45·00
Z10 4d. vermilion (1865–73) .. .. .. *From* 28·00
Plate Nos. 7, 8, 9, 10, 11, 12, 13, 14.
Z11 4d. vermilion (1876) (Plate No. 15) .. .. £160
Z12 4d. sage-green (1877) (Plate Nos. 15, 16) .. *From* £110
Z13 4d. grey-brown (1880) *wmk* Large Garter .. £150
Plate No. 17.
Z14 6d. lilac (1864) (Plate No. 4) .. .. .. £100
Z15 6d. lilac (1865–67) (Plate Nos. 5, 6) .. *From* 35·00
Z16 6d. lilac (1867) (Plate No. 6) .. .. .. 35·00
Z17 6d. violet (1867–70) (Plate Nos. 6, 8, 9) .. *From* 30·00
Z18 6d. buff (1872–73) (Plate Nos. 11, 12) .. *From* 60·00
Z19 6d. chestnut (1872) (Plate No. 11) .. .. 26·00
Z20 6d. grey (1873) (Plate No. 12) .. .. .. 80·00
Z21 6d. grey (1874–76) (Plate Nos. 13, 14, 15, 16) .. 30·00

Z22 8d. orange (1876) £150
Z23 9d. straw (1862) £150
Z24 9d. bistre (1862) £140
Z25 9d. straw (1865) £250
Z26 9d. straw (1867) £120
Z27 10d. red-brown (1867) £180
Z28 1s. green (1865) (Plate No. 4) 70·00
Z29 1s. green (1867–73) (Plate Nos. 4, 5, 6, 7) *From* 17·00
Z30 1s. green (1873–77) *From* 25·00
Plate Nos. 8, 9, 10, 11, 12, 13.
Z31 2s. blue (1867) £120
Z32 5s. rose (1867–74) (Plate Nos. 1, 2) *From* £250

*Stamps of* GREAT BRITAIN *cancelled "D 26" as Type* **12** *(used by British postal clerks on Spanish mail packets between St. Thomas, Cuba, Dominican Republic and Porto Rico).*

**1868** *to* **1871**.
Z33 1d. rose-red (1864)
Plate Nos. 98, 125.
Z34 4d. vermilion (1865–73) (Plate Nos. 9, 10, 11) £600
Z35 6d. violet (1867–70) (Plate No. 8)
Z36 1s. green (1867) (Plate No. 4)

## DOMINICAN REPUBLIC

British Postal Agencies may have existed in the area before 1866, but it is only from that year that details can be found concerning offices at Porto Plata and St. Domingo.

Great Britain stamps were supplied in 1869, but both agencies did not operate between 1870 and 1876. Both finally closed in 1881.

### PORTO PLATA

*Stamps of* GREAT BRITAIN *cancelled "C 86" or circular date stamp as in Types* **8** *or* **17**.

**1869/70** *and* **1876** *to* **1881**.
Z 1 ½d. rose-red (1870–79) (Plate Nos. 10, 12, 14) *From* 50·00
Z 2 1d. rose-red (1864–79) *From* 30·00
Plate Nos. 123, 130, 136, 146, 151, 178, 199, 200, 205, 217.
Z 3 1½d. lake-red (1870–74) (Plate No. 3) 75·00
Z 4 2d. blue (1858–69) (Plate Nos. 14, 15) 35·00
Z 5 2½d. rosy mauve (1876–79) (Plate Nos. 13, 14) *From* £130
Z 6 3d. rose (1873–76) (Plate No. 18) 75·00
Z 7 4d. vermilion (1873) (Plate No. 14) 75·00
Z 8 4d. vermilion (1876) (Plate No. 15) £180
Z 9 4d. sage-green (1877) (Plate No. 15) £130
Z10 6d. violet (1867–70) (Plate No. 8)
Z11 6d. grey (1874–76) (Plate No. 15) 60·00
Z12 8d. orange (1876) £250
Z13 1s. green (1867–73) (Plate Nos. 4, 7) *From* 35·00
Z14 1s. green (1873–77) (Plate Nos. 11, 12, 13) *From* 30·00
Z15 2s. blue (1867) £200
Z15*a* 5s. rose (1867–83) (Plate No. 2)

### ST. DOMINGO

*Stamps of* GREAT BRITAIN *cancelled "C 87" or circular date stamp as in Types* **12** *or* **16**.

**1869/70** *and* **1876** *to* **1881**.
Z16 ½d. rose-red (1870–79) *From* 50·00
Plate Nos. 5, 6, 8, 10, 11, 13.
Z17 1d. rose-red (1864–79) *From* 38·00
Plate Nos. 146, 154, 171, 173, 174, 176, 178, 186, 190, 197, 220.
Z18 1½d. lake-red (1870–74) (Plate No. 3) 75·00
Z19 2d. blue (1858–69) (Plate Nos. 13, 14) 60·00
Z20 3d. rose (1873–76) (Plate No. 18)
Z21 4d. vermilion (1865–73) *From* 40·00
Plate Nos. 11, 12, 14.
Z22 4d. vermilion (1876) (Plate No. 15) £200
Z23 4d. sage-green (1877) (Plate No. 15) £130
Z24 6d. grey (1874–76) (Plate No. 15)
Z25 9d. straw (1867)
Z26 1s. green (1867) (Plate No. 4)
Z27 1s. green (1873–77) *From* 60·00
Plate Nos. 10, 11, 12, 13.
Z28 2s. blue (1867)

## ECUADOR

### GUAYAQUIL

The first British Postal Agent in Guayaquil was appointed during 1849.

Great Britain stamps were supplied in 1865 and continued to be used until the agency closed in 1880.

*Stamps of* GREAT BRITAIN *cancelled "C 41" as Type* **4**.

**1865** *to* **1880**.
Z 1 ½d. rose-red (1870–79) (Plate Nos. 5, 6) 55·00
Z 2 1d. rose-red (1857)
Z 3 1d. rose-red (1864–79) *From* 27·00
Plate Nos. 74, 78, 85, 92, 94, 105, 110, 115, 133, 140, 145, 166, 174, 180, 216.
Z 4 1½d. lake-red (1870–74) (Plate No. 3) 75·00
Z 5 2d. blue (1858–69) (Plate Nos. 9, 13, 14) *From* 30·00
Z 6 3d. carmine-rose (1862) £175
Z 7 3d. rose (1865) (Plate No. 4) 50·00
Z 8 3d. rose (1867–73) (Plate Nos. 6, 7, 9, 10) *From* 25·00
Z 9 3d. rose (1873–76) *From* 25·00
Plate Nos. 11, 12, 15, 16, 17, 18, 19, 20.
Z10 4d. red (1862) (Plate Nos. 3, 4) 65·00
Z11 4d. vermilion (1865–73) *From* 26·00
Plate Nos. 7, 8, 9, 10, 11, 12, 13, 14.
Z12 4d. vermilion (1876) (Plate No. 15) £150
Z13 4d. sage-green (1877) (Plate Nos. 15, 16) £120
Z14 6d. lilac (1864) (Plate No. 4) 70·00
Z15 6d. lilac (1865–67) (Plate Nos. 5, 6) 35·00
Z16 6d. lilac (1867) (Plate No. 6)
Z17 6d. violet (1867–70) (Plate Nos. 6, 8, 9) *From* 32·00
Z18 6d. buff (1872–73) (Plate Nos. 11, 12) 70·00
Z19 6d. chestnut (1872)
Z20 6d. grey (1873) (Plate No. 12)
Z21 6d. grey (1874–76) (Plate Nos. 13, 14, 15, 16) *From* 30·00
Z22 8d. orange (1876) £180
Z23 9d. straw (1862) £190
Z24 9d. straw (1867) £130
Z25 10d. red-brown (1867) £150
Z26 1s. green (1865) (Plate No. 4) 80·00
Z27 1s. green (1867–73) (Plate Nos. 4, 5, 6, 7) *From* 24·00
Z28 1s. green (1873–77) *From* 40·00
Plate Nos. 8, 9, 10, 11, 12, 13.
Z29 2s. blue (1867) £120
Z30 2s. brown (1880) £1300
Z31 5s. rose (1867–74) (Plate Nos. 1, 2) *From* £350

## FERNANDO PO

The British Consulate in this Spanish colony was a centre of British influence in the area before the growth of interest in Nigeria. The first British Post Office Agent (the resident Consul) was appointed in 1859.

Great Britain stamps were supplied in 1874 and the office remained open until 1877.

### CROWNED-CIRCLE HANDSTAMPS

CC1 CC **4** FERNANDO-PO (R.) (19.2.1859) *Price on cover* £3500

*Stamps of* GREAT BRITAIN *cancelled "247" as Type* **9**.

**1874** *to* **1877**.
Z1 4d. vermilion (1865–72) (Plate Nos. 13, 14) £700
Z2 4d. vermilion (1876) (Plate No. 15)
Z3 6d. grey (1874–76) (Plate Nos. 13, 14, 15, 16) £600

## GUADELOUPE

A British Packet Agency was established on Guadeloupe in April 1850 and continued to function until 1874.

No. CC1 is often found used in conjunction with French Colonies (General Issues) adhesive stamps.

A similar packet agency existed on Martinique from 1848 until 1870, but no crowned-circle handstamp was issued for it.

### CROWNED-CIRCLE HANDSTAMPS

CC1 CC **1** GUADALOUPE (R., B. *or* Black) (9.3.1849) *Price on cover* £900

## HAITI

The original British Postal Agencies in Haiti date from 1830 when it is known a Packet Agency was established at Jacmel. An office at Port-au-Prince followed in 1842, both these agencies remaining in operation until 30 June 1881.

During this period short-lived agencies also operated in the following Haitian towns: Aux Cayes (1859 to 1863), Cap Haitien (1842 to 1863), Gonaives (1849 to 1857) and St. Marc (1854 to 1861). A further agency may have operated at Le Mole around the year 1841.

Great Britain stamps were supplied to Jacmel in 1865 and to Port-au-Prince in 1869.

### CAP HAITIEN

CROWNED-CIRCLE HANDSTAMPS

CC1 CC **1b** CAPE-HAITIEN (R.) (31.12.1841) *Price on cover* £2750

### JACMEL

CROWNED-CIRCLE HANDSTAMPS

CC2 CC **1b** JACMEL (R.) (29.6.1843) *Price on cover* £900

*Stamps of* GREAT BRITAIN *cancelled "C 59" as Type* **4**.

**1865** *to* **1881**.
Z 1 ½d. rose-red (1870–79) *From* 32·00
Plate Nos. 4, 5, 6, 10, 11, 12, 14, 15.
Z 2 1d. rose-red (1864–79) *From* 25·00
Plate Nos. 74, 81, 84, 87, 95, 106, 107, 109, 122, 136, 137, 139, 148, 150, 151, 152, 156, 157, 159, 160, 162, 164, 166, 167, 170, 171, 179, 181, 183, 184, 186, 187, 189, 192, 194, 198, 200, 204, 206, 215, 219.
Z 3 1½d. lake-red (1870–74) (Plate No. 3) 48·00
Z 4 2d. blue (1858–69) (Plate Nos. 9, 13, 14, 15) 30·00
Z 5 2½d. rosy mauve (1876) (Plate No. 4)
Z 6 3d. rose (1867–73) (Plate Nos. 5, 6, 7, 8, 9, 10) *From* 30·00
Z 7 3d. rose (1873–76) 30·00
Plate Nos. 11, 12, 14, 16, 17, 18, 19.
Z 8 4d. red (1863) (Plate No. 4) (*Hair lines*) 75·00
Z 9 4d. vermilion (1865–73) *From* 30·00
Plate Nos. 7, 8, 9, 10, 11, 12, 13, 14.
Z10 4d. vermilion (1876) (Plate No. 15) £180
Z11 4d. sage-green (1877) (Plate Nos. 15, 16) £120
Z12 4d. grey-brown (1880) *wmk* Large Garter £150
Plate No. 17.
Z13 4d. grey-brown (1880) *wmk* Crown (Plate No. 17) 30·00
Z14 6d. lilac (1867) (Plate Nos. 5, 6) 35·00
Z15 6d. violet (1867–70) (Plate Nos. 8, 9) 30·00
Z16 6d. buff (1872–73) (Plate Nos. 11, 12) *From* 55·00
Z17 6d. chestnut (1872) (Plate No. 11)
Z18 6d. grey (1873) (Plate No. 12)
Z19 6d. grey (1874–76) *From* 30·00
Plate Nos. 13, 14, 15, 16, 17.
Z20 8d. orange (1876) £180
Z21 9d. straw (1862) £150
Z22 9d. straw (1867) £130
Z23 10d. red-brown (1867) £130
Z24 1s. green (1865) (Plate No. 4) 80·00
Z25 1s. green (1867–73) (Plate Nos. 4, 5, 6, 7) *From* 22·00
Z26 1s. green (1873–77) *From* 30·00
Plate Nos. 8, 9, 10, 11, 12, 13.
Z27 1s. orange-brown (1880) (Plate No. 13) £150
Z28 2s. blue (1867) £100
Z29 2s. brown (1880) £1300
Z30 5s. rose (1867–74) (Plate Nos. 1, 2) *From* £250

**1880**.
Z31 ½d. green (1880) 25·00
Z32 1d. Venetian red 22·00
Z33 1½d. Venetian red 38·00
Z34 2d. rose 50·00

### PORT-AU-PRINCE

CROWNED-CIRCLE HANDSTAMPS

CC3 CC **1b** PORT-AU-PRINCE (R.) (29.6.1843) *Price on cover* £1500

*Stamps of* GREAT BRITAIN *cancelled "E 53" as in Types* **8** *or* **12**.

**1869** *to* **1881**.
Z35 ½d. rose-red (1870–79) *From* 38·00
Plate Nos. 5, 6, 10, 11, 12, 13, 14.
Z36 1d. rose-red (1864–79) *From* 24·00
Plate Nos. 87, 134, 154, 167, 171, 173, 174, 183, 187, 189, 193, 199, 200, 201, 202, 206, 209, 210, 218, 219.
Z37 1½d. lake-red (1870–74) (Plate No. 3) 48·00
Z38 2d. blue (1858–69) (Plate Nos. 9, 14, 15) 35·00
Z40 2½d. rosy mauve (1876–79) (Plate Nos. 3, 9) 70·00
Z41 3d. rose (1867–73) (Plate Nos. 6, 7)
Z42 3d. rose (1873–79) (Plate Nos. 17, 18, 20) 28·00
Z43 4d. vermilion (1865–73) *From* 27·00
Plate Nos. 11, 12, 13, 14.
Z44 4d. vermilion (1876) (Plate No. 15) £175
Z45 4d. sage-green (1877) (Plate Nos. 15, 16) *From* £100
Z46 4d. grey-brown (1880) *wmk* Large Garter £150
Plate No. 17.
Z47 4d. grey-brown (1880) *wmk* Crown (Plate No. 17) 30·00
Z48 6d. grey (1874–76) (Plate Nos. 15, 16)
Z49 8d. orange (1876) £170
Z50 1s. green (1867–73) (Plate Nos. 4, 5, 6, 7) *From* 22·00
Z51 1s. green (1873–77) *From* 32·00
Plate Nos. 8, 9, 10, 11, 12, 13.
Z52 1s. orange-brown (1880) (Plate No. 13) £150
Z53 1s. orange-brown (1881) (Plate No. 13) 50·00
Z54 2s. blue (1867) £100
Z55 2s. brown (1880) £1300
Z56 5s. rose (1867–74) (Plate Nos. 1, 2) £325
Z57 10s. greenish grey (1878) £1900

**1880**.
Z58 ½d. green 35·00
Z59 1d. Venetian red 26·00
Z60 1½d. Venetian red 38·00
Z61 2d. rose

## MACAO

Some form of British Postal Agency was operating in this Portuguese territory as early as 1838, its existence being confirmed by a cover of that year. The Agency continued to function, in conjunction with the Hong Kong Post Office, until Portugal joined the U.P.U. in 1884.

### CROWNED-CIRCLE HANDSTAMPS

CC1 CC **2** PAGO EM MACAO (1870) *Price on cover* £10000

What may be a locally-cut variation is known from the 1843–44 period. This shows a Crown over an oval 20 mm wide, inscribed "PAID AT MACAO". Three examples are said to exist, all struck in red (*Price* £14000).

## MADEIRA

The British Packet Agency on this Portuguese island was opened in 1767 and was of increased importance from 1808 following the exile of the Portuguese royal family to Brazil. The South American packets ceased to call in 1858. It appears to have closed sometime before 1880.

### CROWN-CIRCLE HANDSTAMPS

CC1 CC **1b** MADEIRA (R.) (28.2.1842) *Price on cover* £2500

## MEXICO

The British Postal Agency at Vera Cruz opened in 1825, following the introduction of the Mexican Packet service. No handstamps were supplied, however, until 1842, when a similar agency at Tampico was set up.

Great Britain stamps were used at Tampico from 1867, but, apparently, were never sent to the Vera Cruz office. The Agency at Vera Cruz closed in 1874 and that at Tampico in 1876.

### TAMPICO

CROWNED-CIRCLE HANDSTAMPS

CC1 CC **1b** TAMPICO (R.) (13.11.1841) *Price on cover* £1300

No. CC1 may be found on cover, used in conjunction with Mexico adhesive stamps.

*Stamps of* GREAT BRITAIN *cancelled "C 63" as Type* **4**.

**1867** *to* **1876**.
Z 1 1d. rose-red (1864–79) *From* 80·00
Plate Nos. 81, 89, 103, 117, 139, 147.
Z 2 2d. blue (1858–69) (Plate Nos. 9, 14) £100
Z 3 4d. vermilion (1865–73) *From* 50·00
Plate Nos. 7, 8, 10, 11, 12, 13, 14.
Z 4 1s. green (1867–73) (Plate Nos. 4, 5, 7, 8) 70·00
Z 5 2s. blue (1867) £350

### VERA CRUZ

CROWNED-CIRCLE HANDSTAMPS

CC2 CC **1b** VERA CRUZ (R.) (13.11.1841) *Price on cover* £1500
CC3 VERA CRUZ (Black) (*circa* 1845) *Price on cover* £700

No. CC3 can also be found used in conjunction with Mexico adhesive stamps.

## NICARAGUA

### GREYTOWN

British involvement on the Mosquito Coast of Nicaragua dates from 1655 when contacts were first made with the indigenous Misquito Indians. A formal alliance was signed in 1740 and the area was considered as a British dependency until the Spanish authorities negotiated a withdrawal in 1786.

The Misquitos remained under British protection, however, and, following the revolutionary period in the Spanish dominions, this eventually led to the appropriation, by the Misquitos with British backing, of the town of San Juan del Norte, later renamed Greytown.

The port was included in the Royal West Indian Mail Steam Packet Company's mail network from January 1842, forming part of the Jamaica District. This arrangement only lasted until September of that year, however, although packets were once again calling at Greytown by November 1844. Following the discovery of gold in California the office increased in importance, owing to the overland traffic, although the first distinctive postmark is not recorded in use until February 1856.

A subsidiary agency, without its own postmark, operated at Bluefields from 1857 to 1863.

The British Protectorate over the Misquitos ended in 1860, but the British Post Office at Greytown continued to operate, being supplied with Great Britain stamps in 1865. These are occasionally found used in combination with Nicaragua issues, which had only internal validity.

The British Post Office at Greytown closed in May 1882 when the Republic of Nicaragua joined the U.P.U.

CROWNED-CIRCLE HANDSTAMPS

Z 1

CC1 **Z 1** GREYTOWN (R.) (14.4.1859)

Z 2 Z 4

Z 3

*Stamps of* GREAT BRITAIN *cancelled* "C 57" *as in Types* Z **2** (*issued* 1865), Z **3** (*issued* 1875), *or with circular postmark as Type* Z **4** (*issued* 1864).

**1865** *to* **1882**.

| No. | Description | Price |
|---|---|---|
| Z 1 | ½d. rose-red (1870–79) (Plate Nos. 5, 10, 11) | 50·00 |
| Z 2 | 1d. rose-red (1864–79) (Plate Nos. 180, 197, 210) | 30·00 |
| Z 3 | 1½d. lake-red (1870) (Plate No. 3) | 50·00 |
| Z 4 | 2d. blue (1858–69) (Plate Nos. 9, 14, 15) | |
| Z 5 | 3d. rose (1873–76) (Plate Nos. 17, 18, 19, 20) | 40·00 |
| Z 6 | 3d. rose (1881) (Plate No. 20) | |
| Z 7 | 4d. vermilion (1865–73) *From* Plate Nos. 8, 10, 11, 12, 13, 14. | 32·00 |
| Z 8 | 4d. vermilion (1876) (Plate No. 15) | £180 |
| Z 9 | 4d. sage-green (1877) (Plate Nos. 15, 16) | £110 |
| Z10 | 4d. grey-brown (1880) *wmk* Large Garter Plate No. 17. | £150 |
| Z11 | 4d. grey-brown (1880) *wmk* Crown (Plate No. 17) | 85·00 |
| Z12 | 6d. grey (1874–76) (Plate Nos. 14, 15, 16) | 50·00 |
| Z13 | 8d. orange (1876) | |
| Z14 | 1s. green (1865) (Plate No. 4) | |
| Z15 | 1s. green (1867–73) (Plate Nos. 6, 7) | |
| Z16 | 1s. green (1873–77) (Plate Nos. 8, 12, 13) | 35·00 |
| Z17 | 1s. orange-brown (1880) (Plate No. 13) | £200 |
| Z18 | 1s. orange-brown (1881) (Plate No. 13) | 65·00 |
| Z19 | 2s. blue (1867) | £150 |
| Z20 | 2s. brown (1880) | £1300 |
| Z21 | 5s. rose (1867–74) (Plate Nos. 1, 2) | £250 |
| Z22 | 5s. rose (1882) (Plate No. 4), blue *paper* | £1000 |
| Z23 | 10s. greenish grey (1878) | £1500 |

**1880**.

| No. | Description | Price |
|---|---|---|
| Z24 | 1d. Venetian red | |
| Z25 | 1½d. Venetian red | 38·00 |

## PERU

British Agencies in Peru date from 1846 when offices were established at Arica and Callao. The network was later expanded to include agencies at Paita and Pisco (both 1848), and Iquique and Islay (both 1869). This last office was transferred to Mollendo in 1871.

It is believed that a further agency existed at Pisagua, but no details exist.

Great Britain stamps were supplied from 1865. The Postal Agency at Pisco closed in 1870 and the remainder in 1879, the towns of Arica, Iquique and Pisagua passing to Chile by treaty in 1883.

### ARICA

CROWNED-CIRCLE HANDSTAMPS

CC1 **CC 1** ARICA (R.) (5.11.1850) *Price on cover* £2500

*Stamps of* GREAT BRITAIN *cancelled* "C 36" *as in Types* **4, 12** *or* **14**.

**1865** *to* **1879**.

| No. | Description | Price |
|---|---|---|
| Z 1 | ½d. rose-red (1870–79) *From* Plate Nos. 5, 6, 10, 11, 13. | 45·00 |
| Z 2 | 1d. rose-red (1864–79) *From* Plate Nos. 102, 139, 140, 163, 167. | 30·00 |
| Z 3 | 1½d. lake-red (1870–74) (Plate No. 3) | |
| Z 4 | 2d. blue (1858–69) (Plate No. 14) | 65·00 |
| Z 5 | 3d. rose (1867–73) (Plate Nos. 5, 9) | |
| Z 6 | 3d. rose (1873–76) *From* Plate Nos. 11, 12, 17, 18, 19. | 24·00 |
| Z 7 | 4d. vermilion (1865–73) *From* Plate Nos. 10, 11, 12, 13, 14. | 27·00 |
| Z 8 | 4d. vermilion (1876) (Plate No. 15) | |
| Z 9 | 4d. sage-green (1877) (Plate Nos. 15, 16) | £110 |
| Z10 | 6d. lilac (1862) (Plate Nos. 3, 4) | |
| Z11 | 6d. lilac (1865–67) (Plate No. 5) | |
| Z12 | 6d. violet (1867–70) (Plate Nos. 6, 8, 9) | 32·00 |
| Z13 | 6d. buff (1872) (Plate No. 11) | 75·00 |
| Z14 | 6d. chestnut (1872) (Plate No. 11) | |
| Z15 | 6d. grey (1873) (Plate No. 12) | 80·00 |
| Z16 | 6d. grey (1874–76) (Plate Nos. 13, 14, 15, 16) *From* | 24·00 |
| Z17 | 8d. orange (1876) | |
| Z18 | 9d. straw (1862) | |
| Z19 | 9d. straw (1865) | |
| Z20 | 9d. straw (1867) | £130 |
| Z21 | 10d. red-brown (1867) | |
| Z22 | 1s. green (1862) | |
| Z23 | 1s. green (1865) | |
| Z24 | 1s. green (1867–73) (Plate Nos. 4, 5, 6, 7) *From* | 20·00 |
| Z25 | 1s. green (1873–77) *From* Plate Nos. 8, 9, 10, 11, 12, 13. | 40·00 |
| Z26 | 2s. blue (1867) | £150 |
| Z27 | 5s. rose (1867–74) (Plate Nos. 1, 2) | £300 |

### CALLAO

CROWNED-CIRCLE HANDSTAMPS

CC2 **CC 2** CALLAO (R.) (13.1.1846) *Price on cover* £1100
CC3 **CC 1** CALLAO (R.) (16.7.1846) *Price on cover* £600

*Stamps of* GREAT BRITAIN *cancelled* "C 38" *as in Types* **4, 12** *or with circular date stamp as Type* **5**.

**1865** *to* **1879**.

| No. | Description | Price |
|---|---|---|
| Z28 | ½d. rose-red (1870–79) *From* Plate Nos. 5, 6, 10, 11, 12, 13, 14. | 30·00 |
| Z29 | 1d. rose-red (1864–79) *From* Plate Nos. 74, 88, 89, 93, 94, 97, 108, 123, 127, 128, 130, 134, 137, 139, 140, 141, 143, 144, 145, 146, 148, 149, 156, 157, 160, 163, 167, 171, 172, 173, 175, 176, 180, 181, 182, 183, 185, 187, 190, 193, 195, 198, 199, 200, 201, 204, 206, 209, 210, 212, 213, 215. | 14·00 |
| Z30 | 1½d. lake-red (1870–74) (Plate No. 3) | |
| Z31 | 2d. blue (1858–69) *From* Plate Nos. 9, 12, 13, 14, 15. | 18·00 |
| Z32 | 3d. carmine-rose (1862) | |
| Z33 | 3d. rose (1865) (Plate No. 4) | 50·00 |
| Z34 | 3d. rose (1867–73) *From* Plate Nos. 5, 6, 7, 8, 9, 10. | 22·00 |
| Z35 | 3d. rose (1873–76) *From* Plate Nos. 11, 12, 14, 15, 16, 17, 18, 19. | 27·00 |
| Z36 | 4d. red (1862) (Plate Nos. 3, 4) | |
| Z37 | 4d. vermilion (1865–73) *From* Plate Nos. 8, 10, 11, 12, 13, 14. | 25·00 |
| Z38 | 4d. vermilion (1876) (Plate No. 15) | £150 |
| Z39 | 4d. sage-green (1877) (Plate Nos. 15, 16) | £110 |
| Z40 | 6d. lilac (1862) (Plate Nos. 3, 4) | |
| Z40*a* | 6d. lilac (1865) (Plate No. 5) | |
| Z41 | 6d. lilac (1867) | |
| Z42 | 6d. violet (1867–70) (Plate Nos. 6, 8, 9) *From* | 38·00 |
| Z43 | 6d. buff (1872–73) (Plate Nos. 11, 12) *From* | 48·00 |
| Z44 | 6d. chestnut (1872) (Plate No. 11) | 28·00 |
| Z45 | 6d. grey (1873) (Plate No. 12) | 80·00 |
| Z46 | 6d. grey (1874–80) (Plate Nos. 13, 14, 15, 16) *From* | 28·00 |
| Z47 | 8d. orange (1876) | £150 |
| Z48 | 9d. straw (1862) | |
| Z49 | 9d. straw (1865) | £250 |
| Z50 | 9d. straw (1867) | £120 |
| Z51 | 10d. red-brown (1867) | £150 |
| Z52 | 1s. green (1865) | |
| Z53 | 1s. green (1867–73) (Plate Nos. 4, 5, 6, 7) *From* | 20·00 |
| Z54 | 1s. green (1873–77) *From* Plate Nos. 8, 9, 10, 11, 12, 13. | 24·00 |
| Z55 | 2s. blue (1867) | £110 |
| Z56 | 5s. rose (1867–74) (Plate Nos. 1, 2) *From* | £225 |

### IQUIQUE

*Stamps of* GREAT BRITAIN *cancelled* "D 87" *as Type* **12**.

**1865** *to* **1879**.

| No. | Description | Price |
|---|---|---|
| Z57 | ½d. rose-red (1870–79) (Plate Nos. 5, 6, 13, 14) | 60·00 |
| Z58 | 1d. rose-red (1864–79) (Plate Nos. 76, 179, 185, 205) | 40·00 |
| Z59 | 2d. blue (1858–69) (Plate Nos. 9, 12, 13, 14) | |
| Z60 | 3d. rose (1867–73) (Plate Nos. 5, 6, 7, 8, 9) *From* | 38·00 |
| Z61 | 3d. rose (1873–76) (Plate Nos. 12, 18, 19) | 50·00 |
| Z62 | 4d. vermilion (1865–73) (Plate Nos. 12, 13, 14) | 35·00 |
| Z63 | 4d. vermilion (1876) (Plate No. 15) | £175 |
| Z64 | 4d. sage-green (1877) (Plate Nos. 15, 16) *From* | £125 |
| Z65 | 6d. mauve (1869) (Plate Nos. 8, 9) | |
| Z66 | 6d. buff (1872–73) (Plate Nos. 11, 12) *From* | 80·00 |
| Z67 | 6d. chestnut (1872) (Plate No. 11) | |
| Z68 | 6d. grey (1873) (Plate No. 12) | 80·00 |
| Z69 | 6d. grey (1874–76) (Plate Nos. 13, 14, 15, 16) | |
| Z70 | 8d. orange (1876) | £200 |
| Z71 | 9d. straw (1867) | £140 |
| Z72 | 10d. red-brown (1867) | |
| Z73 | 1s. green (1867–73) (Plate Nos. 4, 6, 7) *From* | 38·00 |
| Z74 | 1s. green (1873–77) *From* Plate Nos. 8, 9, 10, 11, 12, 13. | 40·00 |
| Z75 | 2s. blue (1867) | |

### ISLAY (*later* MOLLENDO)

CROWNED-CIRCLE HANDSTAMPS

CC4 **CC 1** ISLAY (R.) (23.10.1850)

*Stamps of* GREAT BRITAIN *cancelled* "C 42" *as Types* **4** *or* **12**.

**1865** *to* **1879**.

| No. | Description | Price |
|---|---|---|
| Z76 | 1d. rose-red (1864–79) *From* Plate Nos. 78, 84, 87, 88, 96, 103, 125, 134. | 30·00 |
| Z77 | 1½d. lake-red (1870–74) (Plate No. 3) | |
| Z78 | 2d. blue (1858–69) (Plate Nos. 9, 13, 15) | 24·00 |
| Z79 | 3d. carmine-rose (1862) | |
| Z80 | 3d. rose (1865) | 60·00 |
| Z81 | 3d. rose (1867–73) (Plate Nos. 4, 5, 6, 10) | 32·00 |
| Z82 | 4d. red (1862) (Plate Nos. 3, 4) | 65·00 |
| Z83 | 4d. vermilion (1867–73) *From* Plate Nos. 9, 10, 11, 12, 13. | 30·00 |
| Z84 | 4d. vermilion (1876) (Plate No. 15) | |
| Z85 | 4d. sage-green (1877) (Plate Nos. 15, 16) | £110 |
| Z86 | 6d. lilac (1862) (Plate Nos. 3, 4) | 80·00 |
| Z87 | 6d. lilac (1865) (Plate No. 5) | 50·00 |
| Z88 | 6d. violet (1867–70) (Plate Nos. 6, 8, 9) *From* | 45·00 |
| Z89 | 6d. buff (1873) (Plate No. 12) | |
| Z90 | 6d. grey (1873) (Plate No. 12) | |
| Z91 | 6d. grey (1874–76) (Plate Nos. 13, 14, 15, 16) *From* | 30·00 |
| Z92 | 9d. straw (1865) | £225 |
| Z93 | 9d. straw (1867) | £130 |
| Z94 | 10d. red-brown (1867) | £160 |
| Z95 | 1s. green (1865) (Plate No. 4) | |
| Z96 | 1s. green (1867–73) (Plate Nos. 4, 5, 6, 7) *From* | 28·00 |
| Z97 | 1s. green (1873–77) (Plate Nos. 8, 10, 12, 13) *From* | 30·00 |
| Z98 | 2s. blue (1867) | |
| Z99 | 5s. rose (1867) (Plate No. 1) | |

### PAITA

CROWNED-CIRCLE HANDSTAMPS

CC5 **CC 1** PAITA (Black *or* R.) (5.11.1850) *Price on cover* £3500

*Stamps of* GREAT BRITAIN *cancelled* "C 43" *as Type* **4**.

**1865** *to* **1879**.

| No. | Description | Price |
|---|---|---|
| Z100 | 1d. rose-red (1864–79) (Plate Nos. 127, 147) | |
| Z101 | 2d. blue (1858–69) (Plate Nos. 9, 14) | |
| Z102 | 3d. rose (1867–73) (Plate Nos. 5, 6) | 38·00 |
| Z103 | 3d. rose (1876) (Plate Nos. 17, 18, 19) | 38·00 |
| Z104 | 4d. vermilion (1865–73) *From* Plate Nos. 10, 11, 12, 13, 14. | 35·00 |
| Z105 | 4d. sage-green (1877) (Plate No. 15) | |
| Z106 | 6d. lilac (1862) (Plate No. 3) | 70·00 |
| Z107 | 6d. lilac (1865–67) (Plate Nos. 5, 6) | 45·00 |
| Z108 | 6d. violet (1867–70) (Plate Nos. 6, 8, 9) | 40·00 |
| Z109 | 6d. buff (1872–73) (Plate Nos. 11, 12) *From* | 60·00 |
| Z110 | 6d. chestnut (Plate No. 11) | 38·00 |
| Z111 | 6d. grey (1873) | |
| Z112 | 6d. grey (1874–76) (Plate Nos. 13, 14, 15) | |
| Z113 | 9d. straw (1862) | |
| Z114 | 10d. red-brown (1867) | £200 |
| Z115 | 1s. green (1865) (Plate No. 4) | |
| Z116 | 1s. green (1867–73) (Plate No. 4) | 38·00 |
| Z117 | 1s. green (1873–77) (Plate Nos. 8, 9, 10, 13) | 38·00 |
| Z118 | 2s. blue (1867) | £150 |
| Z119 | 5s. rose (1867) (Plate No. 1) | £350 |

### PISAGUA(?)

*Stamp of* GREAT BRITAIN *cancelled* "D 65" *as Type* **12**.

| No. | Description | Price |
|---|---|---|
| Z120 | 2s. blue (1867) | |

### PISCO AND CHINCHA ISLANDS

*Stamps of* GREAT BRITAIN *cancelled* "D 74" *as Type* **12**.

**1865** *to* **1870**.

| No. | Description | Price |
|---|---|---|
| Z121 | 2d. blue (1858–69) (Plate No. 9) | |
| Z122 | 4d. vermilion (1865–73) (Plate Nos. 10, 12) | £180 |
| Z123 | 6d. violet (1868) (Plate No. 6) | £750 |
| Z124 | 1s. green (1867) (Plate No. 4) | |
| Z125 | 2s. blue (1867) | £650 |

## PORTO RICO

A British Postal Agency operated at San Juan from 1844. In 1872 further offices were opened at Aguadilla, Arroyo, Mayaguez and Ponce, with Naguabo added three years later.

Great Britain stamps were used during 1865–66 and from 1873 to 1877. All the British Agencies closed in 1877.

### AGUADILLA

*Stamps of* GREAT BRITAIN *cancelled* "F 84" *as Type* **8**.

**1873** *to* **1877**.

| No. | Description | Price |
|---|---|---|
| Z 1 | ½d. rose-red (1870) (Plate No. 6) | 70·00 |
| Z 2 | 1d. rose-red (1864–79) Plate Nos. 119, 122, 139, 149, 156, 160. | 40·00 |
| Z 3 | 2d. blue (1858–69) (Plate No. 14) | |
| Z 4 | 3d. rose (1867–73) (Plate Nos. 7, 8, 9) | |
| Z 5 | 3d. rose (1873–76) (Plate No. 12) | |
| Z 6 | 4d. vermilion (1865–73) (Plate Nos. 12, 13, 14) | 40·00 |
| Z 7 | 4d. vermilion (1876) (Plate No. 15) | £175 |
| Z 7*a* | 6d. pale buff (1872–73) (Plate No. 11) | |
| Z 8 | 6d. grey (1874–76) (Plate Nos. 13, 14) | |
| Z 9 | 9d. straw (1867) | £225 |
| Z10 | 10d. red-brown (1867) | £150 |
| Z11 | 1s. green (1867–73) (Plate Nos. 4, 5, 6, 7) *From* | 35·00 |
| Z12 | 1s. green (1873–77) *From* Plate Nos. 8, 9, 10, 11, 12. | 40·00 |
| Z13 | 2s. blue (1867) | £225 |

### ARROYO

*Stamps of* GREAT BRITAIN *cancelled* "F 83" *as Type* **8**.

**1873** *to* **1877**.

| No. | Description | Price |
|---|---|---|
| Z14 | ½d. rose-red (1870) (Plate No. 5) | 55·00 |
| Z15 | 1d. rose-red (1864–79) Plate Nos. 149, 150, 151, 156, 164, 174, 175. | 45·00 |
| Z16 | 1½d. lake-red (1870) (Plate Nos. 1, 3) | |
| Z17 | 2d. blue (1858–69) (Plate No. 14) | |
| Z18 | 3d. rose (1867–73) (Plate Nos. 5, 7, 10) | 40·00 |
| Z19 | 3d. rose (1873–76) (Plate Nos. 11, 12, 14, 16, 18) | 45·00 |
| Z20 | 4d. vermilion (1865–73) (Plate Nos. 12, 13, 14) | 38·00 |
| Z21 | 4d. vermilion (1876) (Plate No. 15) | £150 |
| Z22 | 6d. chestnut (1872) (Plate No. 11) | 50·00 |
| Z23 | 6d. pale-buff (1872) (Plate No. 11) | 55·00 |
| Z23*a* | 6d. grey (1873) (Plate No. 12) | |
| Z24 | 6d. grey (1874–76) (Plate Nos. 13, 14, 15) | 50·00 |

Z25 9d. straw (1867) .. .. .. .. .. .. £225
Z26 10d. red-brown (1867) .. .. .. .. .. £150
Z27 1s. green (1865) (Plate No. 4) .. ..
Z28 1s. green (1867–73) (Plate Nos. 4, 5, 6, 7) .. .. 40·00
Z29 1s. green (1873–77) .. .. .. .. .. .. 40·00
Plate Nos. 8, 9, 10, 11, 12, 13.
Z30 2s. blue (1867) .. .. .. .. .. .. £180
Z31 5s. rose (1867–74) (Plate No. 2) .. .. ..

### MAYAGUEZ

*Stamps of* GREAT BRITAIN *cancelled* "F 85" *as Type* **8**.

**1873** *to* **1877**.
Z32 ½d. rose-red (1870) .. .. .. .. *From* 45·00
Plate Nos. 4, 5, 6, 8, 10, 11.
Z33 1d. rose-red (1864–79) .. .. .. *From* 22·00
Plate Nos. 76, 120, 121, 122, 124, 134, 137, 140, 146, 149, 150, 151, 154, 155, 156, 157, 160, 167, 170, 171, 174, 175, 176, 178, 180, 182, 185, 186, 189.
Z34 1½d. lake-red (1870–74) (Plate Nos. 1, 3) .. .. 40·00
Z35 2d. blue (1858–69) (Plate Nos. 13, 14, 15) .. .. 38·00
Z36 3d. rose (1867–73) (Plate Nos. 7, 8, 9, 10) .. .. 28·00
Z37 3d. rose (1873–76) .. .. .. .. .. 28·00
Plate Nos. 11, 12, 14, 15, 16, 17, 18, 19.
Z38 4d. vermilion (1865–73) (Plate Nos. 11, 12, 13, 14) 30·00
Z39 4d. vermilion (1876) (Plate No. 15) .. .. £150
Z40 4d. sage-green (1877) (Plate No. 15) .. ..
Z41 6d. mauve (1870) (Plate No. 9) .. .. ..
Z42 6d. buff (1872) (Plate No. 11) .. .. .. 70·00
Z43 6d. chestnut (1872) (Plate No. 11) .. .. .. 60·00
Z44 6d. grey (1873) (Plate No. 12) .. .. ..
Z45 6d. grey (1874–80) (Plate Nos. 13, 14, 15, 16) .. 38·00
Z46 8d. orange (1876) .. .. .. .. .. £150
Z47 9d. straw (1867) .. .. .. .. .. £130
Z48 10d. red-brown (1867) .. .. .. .. .. £130
Z49 1s. green (1867–73) (Plate Nos. 4, 5, 6, 7) .. 25·00
Z50 1s. green (1873–77) .. .. .. .. *From* 35·00
Plate Nos. 8, 9, 10, 11, 12.
Z51 2s. blue (1867) .. .. .. .. .. £160
Z52 5s. rose (1867–74) (Plate Nos. 1, 2) .. ..

### NAGUABO

*Stamps of* GREAT BRITAIN *cancelled* "582" *as Type* **9**.

**1875** *to* **1877**.
Z53 ½d. rose-red (1870–79) (Plate Nos. 5, 12, 14) ..
Z54 1d. rose-red (1864–70) (Plate Nos. 159, 165) ..
Z55 3d. rose (1873–76) (Plate Nos. 17, 18) .. .. £400
Z56 4d. vermilion (1872–73) (Plate Nos. 13, 14) *From* £375
Z57 4d. vermilion (1876) (Plate No. 15) .. ..
Z58 6d. grey (1874–76) (Plate Nos. 14, 15) .. ..
Z59 9d. straw (1867) .. .. .. .. ..
Z60 10d. red-brown (1867) .. .. .. .. £800
Z61 1s. green (1873–77) (Plate Nos. 11, 12) .. ..
Z62 2s. dull blue (1867) (Plate No. 1) .. .. £600

### PONCE

*Stamps of* GREAT BRITAIN *cancelled* "F 88" *as Type* **8**.

**1873** *to* **1877**.
Z63 ½d. rose-red (1870) (Plate Nos. 5, 10, 12) .. .. 45·00
Z64 1d. rose-red (1864–79) .. .. .. *From* 22·00
Plate Nos. 120, 121, 122, 123, 124, 146, 148, 154, 156, 157, 158, 160, 167, 171, 174, 175, 179, 186, 187.
Z65 1½d. lake-red (1870–74) (Plate No. 3) .. .. £100
Z66 2d. blue (1858–69) (Plate Nos. 13, 14) .. .. 40·00
Z67 3d. rose (1867–73) (Plate Nos. 7, 8, 9) .. ..
Z68 3d. rose (1873–76) (Plate Nos. 12, 16, 17, 18, 19) .. 35·00
Z69 4d. vermilion (1865–73) .. .. .. *From* 32·00
Plate Nos. 8, 9, 12, 13, 14.
Z70 4d. vermilion (1876) (Plate No. 15) .. .. £150
Z71 4d. sage-green (1877) (Plate Nos. 15, 16) .. .. £110
Z72 6d. buff (1872–73) (Plate Nos. 11, 12) .. .. 65·00
Z73 6d. chestnut (1872) (Plate No. 11) .. .. .. 45·00
Z74 6d. grey (1873) (Plate No. 12) .. .. ..
Z75 6d. grey (1874–76) (Plate Nos. 13, 14, 15) .. *From* 35·00
Z76 9d. straw (1867) .. .. .. .. .. £180
Z77 10d. red-brown (1867) .. .. .. .. £130
Z78 1s. green (1867–73) (Plate Nos. 4, 6, 7) .. .. 28·00
Z79 1s. green (1873–77) .. .. .. .. *From* 35·00
Plate Nos. 8, 9, 10, 11, 12, 13.
Z80 2s. blue (1867) .. .. .. .. ..
Z81 5s. rose (1867–74) (Plate Nos. 1, 2) .. *From* £300

### SAN JUAN

CROWNED-CIRCLE HANDSTAMPS

CC1 CC **1** SAN JUAN PORTO RICO (R. *or* Black) (25.5.1844) .. .. .. *Price on cover* £750

No. CC1 may be found on cover, used in conjunction with Spanish colonial adhesive stamps.

*Stamps of* GREAT BRITAIN *cancelled* "C 61" *as in Types* **4**, **8** *or* **14**.

**1865** *to* **1866** *and* **1873** *to* **1877**.
Z 82 ½d. rose-red (1870) (Plate Nos. 5, 10, 15) .. *From* 30·00
Z 83 1d. rose-red (1857) .. .. .. .. ..
Z 84 1d. rose-red (1864–79) .. .. .. *From* 18·00
Plate Nos. 73, 74, 81, 84, 90, 94, 100, 101, 102, 107, 117, 122, 124, 125, 127, 130, 137, 138, 139, 140, 145, 146, 149, 153, 156, 159, 160, 162, 163, 169, 171, 172, 173, 174, 175, 179, 180, 182, 186.
Z 85 1½d. lake-red (1870–74) (Plate Nos. 1, 3) .. *From* 60·00
Z 86 2d. blue (1858–69) (Plate Nos. 9, 13, 14) .. *From* 25·00
Z 87 3d. rose (1865) (Plate No. 4) .. .. .. 50·00
Z 88 3d. rose (1867–73) .. .. .. .. *From* 25·00
Plate Nos. 5, 6, 7, 8, 9, 10.
Z 89 3d. rose (1873–76) .. .. .. .. *From* 25·00
Plate Nos. 11, 12, 14, 15, 16, 17, 18.
Z 90 4d. vermilion (1865–73) .. .. .. *From* 24·00
Plate Nos. 7, 8, 9, 10, 11, 12, 13, 14.
Z 91 4d. vermilion (1876) (Plate No. 15) .. .. £150
Z 92 6d. lilac (1865–67) (Plate Nos. 5, 6) .. *From* 35·00
Z 93 6d. lilac (1867) (Plate No. 6) .. .. .. 38·00
Z 94 6d. violet (1867–70) (Plate Nos. 6, 8, 9) .. *From* 30·00
Z 95 6d. buff (1872–73) (Plate Nos. 11, 12) .. .. 55·00
Z 96 6d. chestnut (1872) (Plate No. 11) .. .. .. 35·00
Z 97 6d. grey (1873) (Plate No. 12) .. .. ..
Z 98 6d. grey (1874–76) (Plate Nos. 13, 14, 15) .. *From* 24·00
Z 99 9d. straw (1862) .. .. .. .. .. £140
Z100 9d. straw (1865) .. .. .. .. .. £250
Z101 9d. straw (1867) .. .. .. .. .. £120
Z102 10d. red-brown (1867) .. .. .. .. £130
Z103 1s. green (1865) (Plate No. 4) .. .. .. 75·00
Z104 1s. green (1867–73) (Plate Nos. 4, 5, 6, 7) .. *From* 22·00
Z105 1s. green (1873–77) .. .. .. .. *From* 35·00
Plate Nos. 8, 9, 10, 11, 12, 13.
Z106 2s. blue (1867) .. .. .. .. .. £110
Z107 5s. rose (1867) (Plate Nos. 1, 2) .. .. *From* £250

## SPAIN

Little is known about the operation of British Packet Agencies in Spain, other than the dates recorded for the various postal markings in the G.P.O. Proof Books. The Agency at Corunna is said to date from the late 17th century. Teneriffe became a port-of-call for the South American packets in 1817 and this arrangement continued until 1858.

Both appear to have closed by the late 1850s.

### CORUNNA

CROWNED-CIRCLE HANDSTAMPS

CC1 CC **1b** CORUNNA (28.2.1842) .. .. ..

Although recorded in the G.P.O. Proof Books no example of No. CC1 on cover is known.

### TENERIFFE (CANARY ISLANDS)

CROWNED-CIRCLE HANDSTAMPS

CC2 CC **7** TENERIFFE (6.1.1851) .. *Price on cover* £2500
CC3 CC **4** TENERIFFE (23.10.1857) .. *Price on cover* £2500

## UNITED STATES OF AMERICA

The network of British Packet Agencies, to operate the trans-Atlantic Packet system, was re-established in 1814 after the War of 1812.

The New York Agency opened in that year to be followed by further offices at Boston, Charleston (South Carolina), New Orleans, Savannah (Georgia) (all in 1842), Mobile (Alabama) (1848) and San Francisco (1860). Of these agencies Charleston and Savannah closed the same year (1842) as did New Orleans, although the latter was re-activated from 1848 to 1850. Mobile closed 1850, Boston in 1865, New York in 1882 and San Francisco, for which no postal markings have been recorded, in 1883.

Although recorded in the G.P.O. Proof Books no actual examples of the Crowned-circle handstamps for Charleston, Mobile, New Orleans and Savannah are known on cover.

The G.P.O. proof books record, in error, a Crowned-circle handstamp for St. Michaels, Maryland. This handstamp was intended for the agency on San Miguel in the Azores.

### CHARLESTON

CROWNED-CIRCLE HANDSTAMPS

CC1 CC **1b** CHARLESTON (15.12.1841) .. ..

### MOBILE

CROWNED-CIRCLE HANDSTAMPS

CC2 CC **1b** MOBILE (15.12.1841) .. .. ..

### NEW ORLEANS

CROWNED-CIRCLE HANDSTAMPS

CC3 CC **1b** NEW ORLEANS (15.12.1841) .. ..
CC4 CC **1** NEW ORLEANS (27.4.1848) .. ..

### NEW YORK

CROWNED-CIRCLE HANDSTAMPS

CC5 CC **1b** NEW YORK (R.) (15.12.1841) *Price on cover* £8500

### SAVANNAH

CROWNED-CIRCLE HANDSTAMPS

CC6 CC **1b** SAVANNAH (15.12.1841) .. ..

## URUGUAY

### MONTEVIDEO

British packets commenced calling at Montevideo in 1824 on passage to and from Buenos Aires.

Great Britain stamps were in use from 1864. The agency was closed by 1872.

CROWNED-CIRCLE HANDSTAMPS

CC1 CC **5** MONTEVIDEO (Black *or* R.) (6.1.1851) *Price on cover* £750

*Stamps of* GREAT BRITAIN *cancelled* "C 28" *as in Types* **4** *or* **12**.

**1864** *to* **1872**.
Z 1 1d. rose-red (1864) .. .. .. .. .. 45·00
Plate Nos. 73, 92, 93, 94, 119, 148, 154, 157, 171.
Z 2 2d. blue (1858–69) (Plate Nos. 9, 13) .. .. 38·00
Z 3 3d. rose (1865) (Plate No. 4) .. ..
Z 4 3d. rose (1867–71) (Plate Nos. 4, 5, 7) .. .. 38·00
Z 6 4d. rose (1857) .. .. .. .. ..
Z 7 4d. red (1862) (Plate No. 4) .. .. ..
Z 8 4d. vermilion (1865–70) .. .. .. *From* 32·00
Plate Nos. 7, 8, 9, 10, 11, 12.
Z 9 6d. lilac (1856) .. .. .. .. ..
Z10 6d. lilac (1862) (Plate No. 4) .. .. ..
Z11 6d. lilac (1865–67) (Plate Nos. 5, 6) .. .. 48·00
Z12 6d. lilac (1867) (Plate No. 6) .. .. ..
Z13 6d. violet (1867–70) (Plate Nos. 8, 9) .. *From* 38·00
Z14 6d. buff (1872) .. .. .. .. ..
Z15 6d. chestnut (1872) .. .. .. .. ..
Z16 9d. straw (1862) .. .. .. .. ..
Z17 9d. straw (1865) .. .. .. .. ..
Z18 9d. straw (1867) .. .. .. .. £150
Z19 10d. red-brown (1867) .. .. .. .. £130
Z20 1s. green (1862) .. .. .. .. .. £120
Z21 1s. green (1865) (Plate No. 4) .. .. .. 70·00
Z22 1s. green (1867–73) (Plate Nos. 4, 5) .. .. 30·00
Z23 2s. blue (1867) .. .. .. .. .. 95·00
Z24 5s. rose (1867) (Plate No. 1) .. .. .. £250

## VENEZUELA

British Postal Agencies were initially opened at La Guayra and Porto Cabello in 1841. Further offices were added at Maracaibo in 1842 and Ciudad Bolivar during 1868. All agencies closed in 1880.

Great Britain stamps were used at La Guayra from 1865 and at Ciudad Bolivar from its establishment in 1868.

### CIUDAD BOLIVAR

*Stamps of* GREAT BRITAIN *cancelled* "D 22" *as Type* **12**, *or circular date stamp as Type* **17**.

**1868** *to* **1880**.
Z 1 1d. rose-red (1864–79) (Plate No. 133) .. .. 75·00
Z 2 2d. blue (1858–69) (Plate No. 13) .. ..
Z 3 3d. rose (1867–73) (Plate No. 5) .. ..
Z 4 3d. rose (1873–79) (Plate No. 11) .. .. £130
Z 5 4d. vermilion (1865–73) (Plate Nos. 9, 12, 14) .. 45·00
Z 6 4d. sage-green (1877) (Plate Nos. 15, 16) .. *From* £130
Z 7 4d. grey-brown (1880) *wmk* Crown (Plate No. 17)
Z 8 9d. straw (1867) .. .. .. .. ..
Z 9 10d. red-brown (1867) .. .. .. ..
Z10 1s. green (1867–73) (Plate Nos. 4, 5, 7) .. *From* 95·00
Z11 1s. green (1873–77) (Plate Nos. 10, 12, 13) .. 70·00
Z12 2s. blue (1867) .. .. .. .. .. £300
Z13 5s. rose (1867–74) (Plate Nos. 1, 2) .. .. £400

### LA GUAYRA

CROWNED-CIRCLE HANDSTAMPS

CC1 CC **1b** LA GUAYRA (R.) (15.12.1841) *Price on cover* £850

*Stamps of* GREAT BRITAIN *cancelled* "C 60" *as Type* **4**, *circular date stamp as Type* **16** *or with No.* CC1.

**1865** *to* **1880**.
Z14 ½d. rose-red (1870) (Plate No. 6) .. .. ..
Z15 1d. rose-red (1864–79) .. .. .. *From* 35·00
Plate Nos. 81, 92, 96, 98, 111, 113, 115, 131, 138, 144, 145, 154, 177, 178, 180, 196.
Z16 1½d. lake-red (1870–74) (Plate No. 3) .. ..
Z17 2d. blue (1858–69) (Plate Nos. 13, 14) .. .. 40·00
Z18 3d. rose (1873–76) .. .. .. .. *From* 48·00
Plate Nos. 14, 15, 17, 18, 19.
Z19 4d. vermilion (1865–73) .. .. .. *From* 30·00
Plate Nos. 7, 9, 11, 12, 13, 14.
Z20 4d. vermilion (1876) (Plate No. 15) .. .. £150
Z21 4d. sage-green (1877) (Plate Nos. 15, 16) .. .. £110
Z22 6d. lilac (1865) (Plate No. 5) .. .. ..
Z23 6d. violet (1867–70) (Plate Nos. 6, 8) .. ..
Z24 6d. buff (1872–73) (Plate Nos. 11, 12) .. *From* 85·00
Z25 6d. grey (1873) (Plate No. 12) .. .. .. 80·00
Z26 6d. grey (1874–76) (Plate Nos. 13, 14, 15, 16) .. 40·00
Z27 8d. orange (1876) .. .. .. .. .. £170
Z28 9d. straw (1862) .. .. .. .. ..
Z29 9d. straw (1867) .. .. .. .. ..
Z30 10d. red-brown (1867) .. .. .. ..
Z31 1s. green (1865) (Plate No. 4) .. .. .. 80·00
Z32 1s. green (1867–73) (Plate Nos. 4, 7) .. ..
Z33 1s. green (1873–77) .. .. .. .. *From* 32·00
Plate Nos. 8, 9, 10, 11, 12, 13.
Z34 2s. blue (1867) .. .. .. .. .. £200
Z35 5s. rose (1867–74) (Plate No. 1, 2) .. .. *From* £350

### MARACAIBO

CROWNED-CIRCLE HANDSTAMPS

CC2 CC **1b** MARACAIBO (31.12.1841) .. ..

No examples of No. CC2 on cover have been recorded.

### PORTO CABELLO

CROWNED-CIRCLE HANDSTAMPS

CC3 CC **1b** PORTO-CABELLO (R.) (15.12.1841) *Price on cover* £1500

## MAIL BOAT OBLITERATIONS

For many years it was supposed that obliterations numbered A 80 to A 99, B 03, B 12, B 56, B 57 and C 79 were used on mail boats or at Naval Stations abroad (the whereabouts of which were not known), owing to the fact that they are almost invariably found on sailors' letters.

It is definitely known that these obliterations were allotted to mail boats and they are therefore omitted from this Catalogue.

## ARMY FIELD OFFICES

**1854** *to* **1857**. **CRIMEA.**

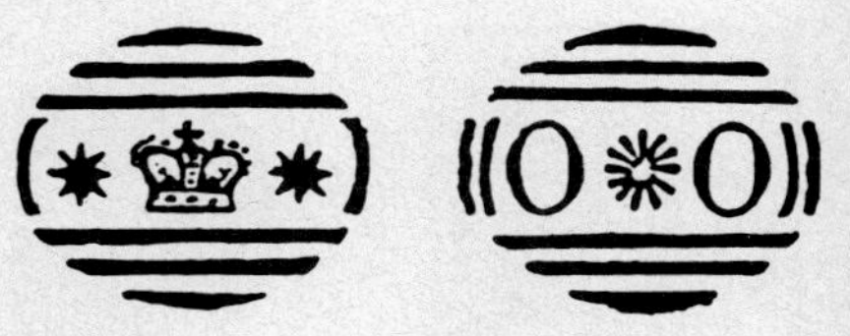

*Crown between Stars*
Z 1 1d. red-brown (1841), *imperf* .. .. .. £375
Z 2 1d. red-brown (1854), Die I, *wmk* Small Crown, *perf* 16 .. .. .. .. .. ..
Z 3 1d. red-brown (1855), Die II, *wmk* Small Crown, *perf* 16 .. .. .. .. .. £100
Z 4 1d. red-brown, Die I, *wmk* Small Crown, *perf* 14 ..
Z 5 1d. red-brown (1855), Die II, Small Crown, *perf* 14
Z 6 2d. blue (1841) *imperf* .. .. .. .. £700
Z 7 2d. blue, Small Crown (1854), *perf* 16 (Plate No. 4)
Z 8 1s. green (1847), embossed .. .. .. .. £1000

*Star between Cyphers*
Z 9 1d. red-brown (1841), *imperf* .. .. ..
Z10 1d. red-brown (1854), Die I, *wmk* Small Crown, *perf* 16 .. .. .. .. .. 50·00

Z11 1d. red-brown (1855), Die II, *wmk* Small Crown, *perf* 16 .. .. .. .. .. .. .. 50·00
Z12 1d. red-brown (1855), Die I, *wmk* Small Crown, *perf* 14 .. .. .. .. .. .. .. 50·00
Z13 1d. red-brown (1855), Die II, *wmk* Small Crown, *perf* 14 .. .. .. .. .. .. .. 50·00
Z14 1d. red-brown (1855), Die II, *wmk* Large Crown, *perf* 16 .. .. .. .. .. .. .. 75·00
Z15 1d. red-brown (1855), Die II, *wmk* Large Crown, *perf* 14 .. .. .. .. .. .. .. 30·00
Z16 2d. blue (1841), *imperf* .. .. .. .. .. £800
Z17 2d. blue (1854) *wmk* Small Crown, *perf* 16 *From* £100
Plate Nos. 4, 5.
Z18 2d. blue (1855) *wmk* Small Crown, *perf* 14 .. £150
Plate No. 4.
Z19 2d. blue (1855), *wmk* Large Crown, *perf* 16 .. £175
Plate No. 5.
Z20 2d. blue (1855), *wmk* Large Crown, *perf* 14 .. 90·00
Plate No. 5.
Z21 4d. rose (1857) .. .. .. .. .. £600
Z22 6d. violet (1854), embossed .. .. .. .. .. £800
Z23 1s. green (1847), embossed .. .. .. .. .. £850

**1882. EGYPT.** *Tel-el-Kebir Campaign.*

Z24 ½d. rose-red (Plate No. 20) .. .. .. .. ..
Z25 ½d. green (1880) .. .. .. .. .. £300
Z26 1d. Venetian red (1880) .. .. .. .. ..
Z27 1d. lilac (1881) .. .. .. .. .. £175
Z28 2½d. blue (1881) (Plate Nos. 21, 22, 23) .. .. £100

**1885. SUDAN.** *Suakin Campaign.*

Z29 1d. lilac (1881) .. .. .. .. .. £300
Z30 2½d. lilac (1884) .. .. .. .. .. £225
Z31 5d. green (1884) .. .. .. .. .. £500

**1899 *to* 1902. SOUTH AFRICA.**

Z32 to Z45*a* ½d., 1d., 1½d., 2d., 2½d., 3d., 4d., 4½d., 5d., 6d., 9d., 10d., 1s., 5s., £1 (1881–92) *From* 14·00
Z46–Z47 ½d., 1s. (1900) .. .. .. .. *From* 20·00
Z48 *to* Z59 ½d., 1d., 1½d., 2d., 2½d., 3d., 4d., 5d., 6d., 9d., 10d., 1s. (1902) .. .. .. *From* 18·00

Many types of cancellation exist besides those shown.

ARMY OFFICIAL

Z60 ½d. vermilion .. .. .. .. .. .. £100
Z61 ½d. green .. .. .. .. .. .. £100
Z62 1d. lilac .. .. .. .. .. .. 85·00
Z63 6d. purple/*red* .. .. .. .. .. ..

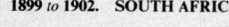

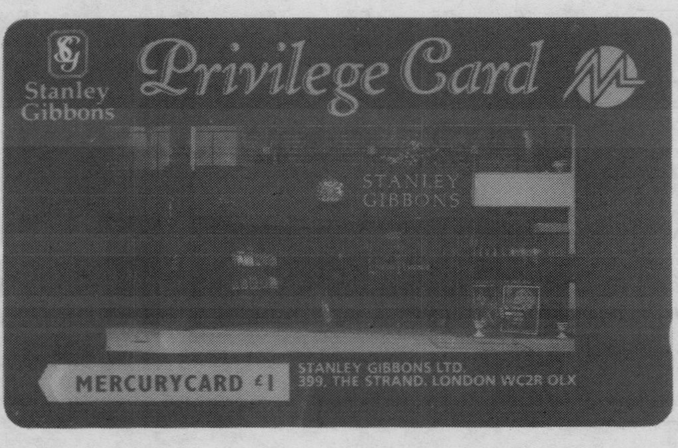

# Stanley Gibbons Great Britain Luxury Hingeless Album

With a space for each stamp and crystal-clear protective mounts already affixed for the immediate insertion of your stamps, this really is the album to give your Great Britain collection a touch of class.

The leaves which are of finest quality paper, have been expertly arranged and include selected illustrations and descriptions for your guidance. Handsomely bound in navy blue leatherette, the deeply padded binders are richly embossed with the coat of arms and crest of the country on the cover and spine and each is presented in its own matching slip case to keep both binder and collection in pristine condition.

An album of this quality and craftsmanship will give real distinction to every collection and at the same time offers the security and protection which your stamps demand.

Now presented in three volumes: Volume 1, 1840–1970 (pre-decimal); Volume 2, 1970 – date and Volume 3. (binder and slip case only).

There is also a special Queen Elizabeth Volume which takes all issues from 1952 to date. Annual supplements available in the spring of each year.

**Item 5484 Great Britain Luxury Hingless Album Volume 1 1840–1970**

**Item 5285 Great Britain Luxury Hingeless Album Volume 2 1971–date**

**Item 5290 Great Britain Luxury Hingeless binder and slipcase – Volume 3**

**Item 5546 Great Britain Luxury Hingless Album, Queen Elizabeth Volume 1952–date**

*For further details visit your favourite stamp shop or write to:*

**Stanley Gibbons Publications Ltd.,**
**5 Parkside, Christchurch Road,**
**Ringwood, Hampshire BH24 3SH**
**Telephone 0425 472363**

# The Stanley Gibbons GREAT BRITAIN SPECIALISED Stamp Catalogue

Whether you collect line-engraved or Machin cylinder blocks, the Stanley Gibbons Great Britain Specialised Catalogue provides you with the information you need for the in-depth study of your stamps.

The winner of several international awards, this detailed and authoritative handbook/catalogue is now split into five convenient volumes, each clearly laid out with thousands of illustrations and explanatory notes to cover every aspect of the postage stamps of Great Britain.

Each new edition is thoroughly revised in order not only to ensure that prices are in line with the current market, but that the most up-to-date information and research are included.

Volumes 1 and 2 available either casebound or paperback – remaining volumes paperback only.

**Item 0285** Volume 1 Queen Victoria
**Item 0286** Volume 2 King Edward VII to King George VI
**Item 2810** Volume 3 Queen Elizabeth Pre-decimal Issues
**Item 2820** Volume 4 Queen Elizabeth Decimal Definitive Issues
**Item 2891** Volume 5 Queen Elizabeth Decimal Special Issues

*For further details visit your favourite stamp shop or write to:*

**Stanley Gibbons Publications Ltd.,**
**5 Parkside, Christchurch Road,**
**Ringwood, Hampshire BH24 3SH**
**Telephone 0425 472363**

# Abu Dhabi

Stamps of the BRITISH POSTAL AGENCIES IN EASTERN ARABIA were used from the oil installation on Das Island from December 1960 onwards, being postmarked at Bahrain. A British postal agency, using the same issues, postmarked "ABU DHABI" or "DAS ISLAND", operated in the shaikdom from 30 March 1963 until the introduction of Abu Dhabi issues in 1964.

An independent Arab Shaikhdom (one of the Trucial States), with a British postal administration until 31 December 1966.

**1** Shaikh Shakhbut bin Sultan

**3** Ruler's Palace

(Des M. Farrar Bell. Photo Harrison (5 n.p. to 75 n.p.). Des C. T. Kavanagh (1, 2 r.), Miss P. M. Goth (5, 10 r.). Recess B.W.)

**1964** (30 Mar). *T* **1, 3** *and similar designs. P* 14½ (5 *to* 75 *n.p.*) *or* 13 × 13½ (*others*).

| | | | | |
|---|---|---|---|---|
| 1 | **1** | 5 n.p. green | 80 | 60 |
| 2 | | 15 n.p. red-brown | 1·25 | 55 |
| 3 | | 20 n.p. ultramarine | 1·40 | 55 |
| 4 | | 30 n.p. red-orange | 1·40 | 90 |
| 5 | – | 40 n.p. reddish violet | 2·75 | 20 |
| 6 | – | 50 n.p. bistre | 2·50 | 55 |
| 7 | – | 75 n.p. black | 2·75 | 1·00 |
| 8 | **3** | 1 r. emerald | 3·75 | 90 |
| 9 | | 2 r. black | 5·50 | 2·50 |
| 10 | – | 5 r. carmine-red | 13·00 | 7·00 |
| 11 | – | 10 r. deep ultramarine | 18·00 | 13·00 |
| 1/11 | | *Set of* 11 | 48·00 | 25·00 |

Designs: *As Type* **1** – 40, 50, 75 n.p. Mountain Gazelle. *As Type* **3** – 5, 10 r. Oil rig and camels.

**5**

**6**

**7**

Saker Falcon

(Des V. Whiteley. Photo Harrison)

**1965** (30 Mar). *Falconry. P* 14½.

| | | | | |
|---|---|---|---|---|
| 12 | **5** | 20 n.p. light brown and grey-blue | 5·50 | 80 |
| 13 | **6** | 40 n.p. light brown and blue | 7·00 | 2·00 |
| 14 | **7** | 2 r. sepia and turquoise-green | 13·00 | 8·50 |
| 12/14 | | *Set of* 3 | 23·00 | 10·00 |

**(New Currency. 1,000 fils = 1 dinar)**

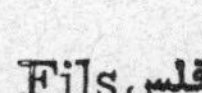

Fils فلس

**(8)**

**1966** (1 Oct). *Nos.* 1/11 *such as T* 8 ("FILS" *only on* 40 *f. to* 70 *f.*) *with new value expressed on remainder), by Arabian Printing and Publishing House, Bahrain. P* 13 × 13½ (20 *f.*), *others as before.*

| | | | | |
|---|---|---|---|---|
| 15 | **1** | 5 f. on 5 n.p. green | 4·50 | 4·00 |
| 16 | | 15 f. on 15 n.p. red-brown | 4·50 | 2·00 |
| 17 | | 20 f. on 20 n.p. ultramarine | 4·50 | 3·25 |
| | | a. Surch inverted | £180 | £250 |
| | | b. Perf 14½ | | |
| 18 | | 30 f. on 30 n.p. red-orange | 6·00 | 6·00 |
| | | a. Arabic "2" for "3" in surch | £1600 | |
| 19 | – | 40 f. on 40 n.p. reddish violet | 9·00 | 75 |
| 20 | – | 50 f. on 50 n.p. bistre | 13·00 | 12·00 |
| 21 | – | 75 f. on 75 n.p. black | 13·00 | 12·00 |
| 22 | **3** | 100 f. on 1 r. emerald | 13·00 | 3·25 |
| 23 | | 200 f. on 2 r. black | 18·00 | 12·00 |
| 24 | – | 500 f. on 5 r. carmine-red | 30·00 | 35·00 |
| 25 | – | 1 d. on 10 r. deep ultramarine | 40·00 | 65·00 |
| 15/25 | | *Set of* 11 | £140 | £140 |

The Abu Dhabi Post Department took over the postal services on 1 January 1967. Later stamp issues will be found in Part 19 (*Middle East*) of this Catalogue.

# Aden
## *see* South Arabian Federation

# Anguilla

St. Christopher, Nevis and Anguilla were granted Associated Statehood on 27 February 1967, but, following a referendum, Anguilla declared her independence on 30 May 1967 and the St. Christopher authorities withdrew. The following stamps were issued by the governing Council and have been accepted for international mail. On 7 July 1969 the Anguilla post office was officially recognised by the Government of St. Christopher, Nevis and Anguilla and normal postal communications via St. Christopher were resumed. By the Anguilla Act of 27 July 1971, Anguilla was restored to direct British control.

A degree of internal self-government with an Executive Council was introduced on 10 February 1976 and the links with St. Kitts-Nevis were officially severed on 18 December 1980.

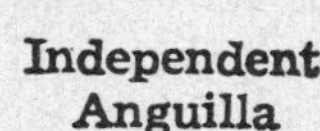

Independent Anguilla

**(1)**

**2** Mahogany Tree, The Quarter

**1967** (4 Sept). *Nos.* 129/44 *of St. Christopher, Nevis and Anguilla optd as T* **1**, *by Island Press Inc, St. Thomas, U.S. Virgin Islands.*

| | | | |
|---|---|---|---|
| 1 | ½ c. New lighthouse, Sombrero | 20·00 | 18·00 |
| 2 | 1 c. Loading sugar cane, St. Kitts | 22·00 | 6·50 |
| 3 | 2 c. Pall Mall Square, Basseterre | 24·00 | 1·25 |
| 4 | 3 c. Gateway, Brimstone Hill Fort, St. Kitts | 24·00 | 4·50 |
| 5 | 4 c. Nelson's Spring, Nevis | 24·00 | 5·50 |
| 6 | 5 c. Grammar School, St. Kitts | 90·00 | 18·00 |
| 7 | 6 c. Crater, Mt. Misery, St. Kitts | 40·00 | 9·00 |
| 8 | 10 c. Hibiscus | 24·00 | 6·50 |
| 9 | 15 c. Sea Island cotton, Nevis | 50·00 | 11·00 |
| 10 | 20 c. Boat building, Anguilla | 85·00 | 12·00 |
| 11 | 25 c. White-crowned Pigeon | 70·00 | 20·00 |
| 12 | 50 c. St. George's Church Tower, Basseterre | — | £450 |
| 13 | 60 c. Alexander Hamilton | — | £850 |
| 14 | $1 Map of St. Kitts-Nevis | — | £400 |
| 15 | $2.50, Map of Anguilla | — | £300 |
| 16 | $5 Arms of St. Christopher, Nevis and Anguilla | — | £300 |
| 1/16 | *Set of* 16 | £8000 | £2250 |

Owing to the limited stocks available for overprinting, the sale of the above stamps was personally controlled by the Postmaster and no orders from the trade were accepted.

(Des John Lister Ltd. Litho A. & M.)

**1967** (27 Nov)–**68**. *T* **2** *and similar horiz designs. P* 12½ × 13.

| | | | |
|---|---|---|---|
| 17 | 1 c. dull green, bistre-brown and pale orange | 10 | 20 |
| 18 | 2 c. bluish green and black (21.3.68) | 10 | 20 |
| 19 | 3 c. black and light emerald (10.2.68) | 10 | 10 |
| 20 | 4 c. cobalt-blue and black (10.2.68) | 10 | 10 |
| 21 | 5 c. multicoloured | 10 | 10 |
| 22 | 6 c. light vermilion and black (21.3.68) | 10 | 10 |
| 23 | 10 c. multicoloured | 15 | 10 |
| 24 | 15 c. multicoloured (10.2.68) | 30 | 20 |
| 25 | 20 c. multicoloured | 40 | 20 |
| 26 | 25 c. multicoloured | 50 | 20 |
| 27 | 40 c. apple green, light greenish blue and black | 80 | 25 |
| 28 | 60 c. multicoloured (10.2.68) | 1·50 | 1·25 |
| 29 | $1 multicoloured (10.2.68) | 1·75 | 2·00 |
| 30 | $2.50, multicoloured (21.3.68) | 2·00 | 2·00 |
| 31 | $5 multicoloured (10.2.68) | 3·50 | 3·75 |
| 17/31 | *Set of* 15 | 10·00 | 9·50 |

Designs:—2 c. Sombrero Lighthouse; 3 c. St. Mary's Church; 4 c. Valley Police Station; 5 c. Old Plantation House, Mt. Fortune; 6 c. Valley Post Office; 10 c. Methodist Church, West End; 15 c. Wall-Blake Airport; 20 c. Aircraft over Sandy Ground; 25 c. Island Harbour; 40 c. Map of Anguilla; 60 c. Hermit Crab and Starfish; $1 Hibiscus; $2.50, Local scene; $5, Spiny Lobster.

On 9 January 1969 Anguilla reaffirmed her independence from St. Kitts and issued Nos. 17/31 overprinted in black "INDEPENDENCE JANUARY 1969" in two lines. These are outside the scope of this catalogue.

**17** Yachts in Lagoon

**18** Purple-throated Carib

(Des John Lister Ltd. Litho A. & M.)

**1968** (11 May). *Anguillan Ships. T* **17** *and similar horiz designs. Multicoloured. P* 14.

| | | | |
|---|---|---|---|
| 32 | 10 c. Type **17** | 15 | 10 |
| 33 | 15 c. Boat on beach | 20 | 10 |
| 34 | 25 c. *Warspite* (schooner) | 30 | 15 |
| 35 | 40 c. *Atlantic Star* (schooner) | 35 | 20 |
| 32/5 | *Set of* 4 | 90 | 40 |

(Des John Lister Ltd. Litho A. & M.)

**1968** (8 July). *Anguillan Birds. T* **18** *and similar multicoloured designs. P* 14.

| | | | |
|---|---|---|---|
| 36 | 10 c. Type **18** | 75 | 15 |
| 37 | 15 c. Bananaquit | 95 | 20 |
| 38 | 25 c. Black-necked Stilt (*horiz*) | 1·25 | 20 |
| 39 | 40 c. Royal Tern (*horiz*) | 1·50 | 30 |
| 36/9 | *Set of* 4 | 4·00 | 75 |

**19** Guides' Badge and Anniversary Years

(Des John Lister Ltd. Litho A. & M.)

**1968** (14 Oct). *35th Anniv of Anguillan Girl Guides. T* **19** *and similar multicoloured designs. P* 13 × 13½ (10, 25 *c.*) *or* 13½ × 13 (*others*).

| | | | |
|---|---|---|---|
| 40 | 10 c. Type **19** | 10 | 10 |
| 41 | 15 c. Badge and silhouettes of Guides (*vert*) | 15 | 10 |
| 42 | 25 c. Guides' badge and Headquarters | 20 | 15 |
| 43 | 40 c. Association and Proficiency badges (*vert*) | 25 | 15 |
| 40/3 | *Set of* 4 | 65 | 35 |

**20** The Three Kings

(Des John Lister Ltd. Litho A. & M.)

**1968** (18 Nov). *Christmas. T* **20** *and similar designs. P* 13.

| | | | |
|---|---|---|---|
| 44 | 1 c. black and cerise | 10 | 10 |
| 45 | 10 c. black and light greenish blue | 10 | 10 |
| 46 | 15 c. black and chestnut | 15 | 10 |
| 47 | 40 c. black and blue | 15 | 10 |
| 48 | 50 c. black and dull green | 20 | 15 |
| 44/8 | *Set of* 5 | 55 | 30 |

Designs: *Vert*—10 c. The Wise Men; 15 c. Holy Family and manger. *Horiz*—40 c. The Shepherds; 50 c. Holy Family and donkey.

**21** Bagging Salt

**22** "The Crucifixion" (Studio of Massys)

(Des John Lister Ltd. Litho A. & M.)

**1969** (4 Jan). *Anguillan Salt Industry. T* **21** *and similar horiz designs. Multicoloured. P* 13.

| | | | |
|---|---|---|---|
| 49 | 10 c. Type **21** | 10 | 10 |
| 50 | 15 c. Packing salt | 15 | 10 |
| 51 | 40 c. Salt pond | 20 | 10 |
| 52 | 50 c. Loading salt | 20 | 10 |
| 49/52 | *Set of* 4 | 50 | 25 |

(Des John Lister Ltd. Litho Format)

**1969** (31 Mar). *Easter Commemoration. T* **22** *and similar vert design. P.* 13½.

| | | | |
|---|---|---|---|
| 53 | 25 c. multicoloured | 15 | 10 |
| 54 | 40 c. multicoloured | 20 | 15 |

Design:—40 c. "The Last Supper" (ascribed to Roberti).

**23** Amaryllis

(Des John Lister Ltd. Litho Format)

**1969** (10 June). *Flowers of the Caribbean. T* **23** *and similar horiz designs. Multicoloured. P* 14.

55 10 c. Type **23** .. .. .. .. .. 20 10
56 15 c. Bougainvillea .. .. .. .. 25 10
57 40 c. Hibiscus .. .. .. .. .. 45 20
58 50 c. *Cattleya* orchid .. .. .. .. 85 40
55/8 .. .. .. .. .. *Set of* 4 1·60 70

24 Turbans and Star Shells

(Des John Lister Ltd. Litho A. & M.)

**1969** (22 Sept). *Sea Shells. T* **24** *and similar horiz designs. Multicoloured. P* 14.

59 10 c. Type **24** .. .. .. .. .. 20 10
60 15 c. Spiny oysters .. .. .. .. 20 10
61 40 c. Scotch, Royal and Smooth Scotch bonnets 30 15
62 50 c. Triton trumpet .. .. .. .. 40 20
59/62 .. .. .. .. .. *Set of* 4 1·00 45

(25)

(26)

(27)

(28)

(29)

**1969** (Oct). *Christmas. Nos.* 17, 25/8 *optd with T* **25/29**.

63 1 c. dull green, bistre-brown & light orange 10 10
64 20 c. multicoloured .. .. .. .. 20 10
65 25 c. multicoloured .. .. .. .. 20 10
66 40 c. apple-green, light greenish blue & black 25 15
67 60 c. multicoloured .. .. .. .. 40 20
63/7 .. .. .. .. .. *Set of* 5 1·00 45

30 Red Goatfish

31 "Morning Glory"

(Des John Lister Ltd. Litho A. & M.)

**1969** (1 Dec). *Fishes. T* **30** *and similar horiz designs. Multicoloured. P* 14.

68 10 c. Type **30** .. .. .. .. .. 30 15
69 15 c. Blue Striped grunts .. .. .. 45 15
70 40 c. Mutton grouper .. .. .. .. 55 20
71 50 c. Banded Butterfly fish .. .. .. 65 20
68/71 .. .. .. .. .. *Set of* 4 1·75 65

(Des John Lister Ltd. Litho A. & M.)

**1970** (23 Feb). *Flowers. T* **31** *and similar vert designs. Multicoloured, P* 14.

72 10 c. Type **31** .. .. .. .. .. 25 10
73 15 c. Blue Petrea .. .. .. .. 40 10
74 40 c. Hibiscus .. .. .. .. .. 60 15
75 50 c. "Flame Tree" .. .. .. .. 70 20
72/5 .. .. .. .. .. *Set of* 4 1·75 45

32 "Deposition" (Rosso Fiorentino)

33 Scout Badge and Map

(Des John Lister Ltd. Litho Format)

**1970** (26 Mar). *Easter. T* **32** *and similar multicoloured designs. P* 13½.

76 10 c. "The Ascent to Calvary" (Tiepolo) (*horiz*) 20 10
77 20 c. "The Crucifixion" (Masaccio) .. .. 30 10
78 40 c. Type **32** .. .. .. .. .. 35 15
79 60 c. "The Ascent to Calvary" (Murillo) (*horiz*) 40 15
76/9 .. .. .. .. .. *Set of* 4 1·10 40

(Des John Lister Ltd. Litho A. & M.)

**1970** (10 Aug). *40th Anniv of Scouting in Anguilla. T* **33** *and similar horiz designs. Multicoloured. P* 13.

80 10 c. Type **33** .. .. .. .. .. 15 10
81 15 c. Scout camp and cubs practising first-aid 20 10
82 40 c. Monkey Bridge .. .. .. .. 25 15
83 50 c. Scout H.Q. Building and Lord Baden-Powell .. .. .. .. .. 35 15
80/3 .. .. .. .. .. *Set of* 4 85 45

34 Boatbuilding

(Des John Lister Ltd. Litho Format)

**1970** (23 Nov). *Various horiz designs as T* **34**. *Multicoloured. P* 14.

84 1 c. Type **34** .. .. .. .. .. 10 20
85 2 c. Road Construction .. .. .. 10 20
86 3 c. Quay, Blowing Point .. .. .. 10 15
87 4 c. Broadcaster, Radio Anguilla .. .. 10 30
88 5 c. Cottage Hospital Extension .. .. 10 30
89 6 c. Valley Secondary School .. .. 10 30
90 10 c. Hotel Extension .. .. .. .. 15 30
91 15 c. Sandy Ground .. .. .. .. 20 30
92 20 c. Supermarket and Cinema .. .. 35 30
93 25 c. Bananas and Mangoes .. .. .. 35 60
94 40 c. Wall Blake Airport .. .. .. 45 70
95 60 c. Sandy Ground Jetty .. .. .. 65 90
96 $1 Administration Buildings .. .. 1·25 1·40
97 $2.50, Livestock .. .. .. .. 1·50 3·00
98 $5 Sandy Hill Bay .. .. .. .. 2·50 3·75
84/98 .. .. .. .. .. *Set of* 15 7·00 11·50

35 "The Adoration of the Shepherds" (Reni)

36 "Ecce Homo" (detail, Correggio)

(Des John Lister Ltd. Litho Questa)

**1970** (11 Dec). *Christmas. T* **35** *and similar vert designs. Multicoloured. P* 13½.

99 1 c. Type **35** .. .. .. .. .. 10 10
100 20 c. "The Virgin and Child" (Gozzoli) .. 30 15
101 25 c. "Mystic Nativity" (detail, Botticelli) .. 30 15
102 40 c. "The Santa Margherita Madonna" (detail, Mazzola) .. .. .. .. 40 20
103 50 c. "The Adoration of the Magi" (detail, Tiepolo) .. .. .. .. 40 20
99/103 .. .. .. .. .. *Set of* 5 1·25 65

(Des John Lister Ltd. Litho Format)

**1971** (29 Mar). *Easter. T* **36** *and similar designs. P* 13½.

104 10 c. multicoloured .. .. .. .. 15 10
105 15 c. multicoloured .. .. .. .. 25 10
106 40 c. multicoloured .. .. .. .. 30 10
107 50 c. multicoloured .. .. .. .. 30 15
104/7 .. .. .. .. .. *Set of* 4 90 25

Designs: *Vert*—15 c. "Christ appearing to St. Peter" (detail, Carracci). *Horiz*—40 c. "Angels weeping over the Dead Christ" (detail, Guercino); 50 c. "The Supper at Emmaus" (detail, Caravaggio).

37 *Hypolimnas misippus*

38 *Magnanime* and *Amiable* in Battle

(Des John Lister Ltd. Litho Questa)

**1971** (21 June). *Butterflies. T* **37** *and similar horiz designs. Multicoloured. P* 14 × 14½.

108 10 c. Type **37** .. .. .. .. .. 80 70
109 15 c. *Junonia evarete* .. .. .. .. 1·00 80
110 40 c. *Agraulis vanillae* .. .. .. 1·60 1·25
111 50 c. *Danaus plexippus* .. .. .. 1·90 1·50
108/11 .. .. .. .. .. *Set of* 4 4·75 3·75

(Des John Lister Ltd. Litho Format)

**1971** (30 Aug). *Sea-battles of the West Indies. T* **38** *and similar vert designs. Multicoloured. P* 14.

112 10 c. Type **38** .. .. .. .. .. 70 70
a. Horiz strip of 5. Nos. 112/16 .. 5·25
113 15 c. H.M.S. *Duke*, *Glorieux* and H.M.S. *Agamemnon* .. .. .. .. 85 85
114 25 c. H.M.S. *Formidable* and H.M.S. *Namur* against *Ville de Paris* .. .. 1·25 1·25
115 40 c. H.M.S. *Canada* .. .. .. .. 1·40 1·40
116 50 c. H.M.S. *St. Albans* and wreck of *Hector* 1·60 1·60
112/16 .. .. .. .. .. *Set of* 5 5·25 5·25

Nos. 112/16 were issued in horizontal *se-tenant* strips within the sheet, to form a composite design in the order listed.

## ADMINISTRATION BY BRITISH COMMISSION

39 "The Ansidei Madonna" (detail, Raphael)

40 Map of Anguilla and St. Martins by Thomas Jefferys (1775)

(Des John Lister Ltd. Litho Questa)

**1971** (29 Nov). *Christmas. T* **39** *and similar vert designs. P* 13½.

117 20 c. multicoloured .. .. .. .. 20 20
118 25 c. multicoloured .. .. .. .. 20 20
119 40 c. multicoloured .. .. .. .. 30 30
120 50 c. multicoloured .. .. .. .. 35 35
117/20 .. .. .. .. .. *Set of* 4 95 95

Designs:—25 c. "Mystic Nativity" (detail, Botticelli); 40 c. "Adoration of the Shepherds" (detail; ascr to Murillo); 50 c. "The Madonna of the Iris" (detail; ascr to Dürer).

(Litho Format)

**1972** (24 Jan). *Maps. T* **40** *and similar multicoloured designs showing maps by the cartographers given. P* 14.

121 10 c. Type **40** .. .. .. .. .. 20 10
122 15 c. Samuel Fahlberg (1814) .. .. 30 15
123 40 c. Thomas Jefferys (1775) (*horiz*) .. 40 25
124 50 c. Capt. E. Barnett (1847) (*horiz*) .. 50 25
121/4 .. .. .. .. .. *Set of* 4 1·25 65

41 "Jesus Buffeted"

42 Loblolly Tree

(Des John Lister Ltd. Litho Format)

**1972** (14 Mar). *Easter. Stained Glass Windows from Church of St. Michael, Bray, Berkshire. T* **41** *and similar vert designs. Multicoloured. P* 14 × 13½.

125 10 c. Type **41** .. .. .. .. .. 25 2
a. Horiz strip of 5. Nos. 125/9 .. 1·40
126 15 c. "The Way of Sorrows" .. .. .. 30 3
127 25 c. "The Crucifixion" .. .. .. .. 30 3
128 40 c. "Descent from the Cross" .. .. 35 3
129 50 c. "The Burial" .. .. .. .. 40 4
125/9 .. .. .. .. .. *Set of* 5 1·40 1·4

Nos. 125/9 were printed horizontally *se-tenant* within the sheet.

(Litho Questa ($10), Format (others))

**1972** (30 Oct)–**75**. *T* **42** *and similar multicoloured designs (horiz except* 2, 4 *and* 6 *c.). P* 13½.

130 1 c. Spear fishing .. .. .. .. 10 3
131 2 c. Type **42** .. .. .. .. .. 10 3
132 3 c. Sandy Ground .. .. .. .. 10 3
133 4 c. Ferry at Blowing Point .. .. .. 15 2
134 5 c. Agriculture .. .. .. .. .. 15 3
135 6 c. St. Mary's Church .. .. .. 25 2
136 10 c. St. Gerard's Church .. .. .. 25 3
137 15 c. Cottage Hospital extension .. .. 25 3
138 20 c. Public library .. .. .. .. 30 3

139 25 c. Sunset at Blowing Point .. .. 40 50
140 40 c. Boat building .. .. .. .. 1·50 1·50
141 60 c. Hibiscus .. .. .. .. 4·00 3·00
142 $1 Magnificent Frigate Bird .. .. 8·00 5·50
143 $2.50, Frangipani .. .. .. .. 6·00 6·50
144 $5 Brown Pelican .. .. .. .. 13·00 12·00
144*a* $10 Green-back turtle (20.5.75) .. .. 18·00 18·00
130/44*a* .. .. .. .. *Set of* 16 48·00 45·00

43 *Malcolm Miller* (schooner) and Common Dolphin

(Des (from photograph by D. Groves) and photo Harrison)

**1972** (20 Nov). *Royal Silver Wedding. Multicoloured; background colour given.* W w **12**. *P* 14 × 14½.
145 **43** 25 c. yellow-olive (*shades*) .. .. 1·00 1·50
146 40 c. chocolate .. .. .. .. 1·10 1·75

44 Flight into Egypt 45 "The Betrayal of Christ"

(Des John Lister Ltd. Litho Questa)

**1972** (4 Dec). *Christmas. T* **44** *and similar vert designs. Multicoloured. P* 13½.
147 1 c. Type **44** .. .. .. .. 10 10
148 20 c. Star of Bethlehem .. .. .. 25 20
a. Vert strip of 4. Nos. 148/51 .. .. 1·10
149 25 c. Holy Family .. .. .. .. 25 20
150 40 c. Arrival of the Magi .. .. .. 30 25
151 50 c. Adoration of the Magi .. .. .. 30 25
147/51 .. .. .. .. *Set of* 5 1·10 85
Nos. 148/51 were printed vertically *se-tenant* within a sheet of 20 stamps.

(Des John Lister Ltd. Litho Questa)

**1973** (26 Mar). *Easter. T* **45** *and similar vert designs. Multicoloured; bottom panel in gold and black. P* 13½.
152 1 c. Type **45** .. .. .. .. 10 10
153 10 c. "The Man of Sorrows" .. .. .. 10 10
a. Vert strip of 5. Nos. 153/7 .. .. 70
154 20 c. "Christ bearing the Cross" .. .. 15 15
155 25 c. "The Crucifixion" .. .. .. 15 15
156 40 c. "The Descent from the Cross" .. .. 15 15
157 50 c. "The Resurrection" .. .. .. 20 20
152/7 .. .. .. .. *Set of* 6 70 70
**MS**158 140 × 141 mm. Nos. 152/7. Bottom panel in gold and mauve .. .. .. .. 70 80
Nos. 153/7 were printed within one sheet, vertically *se-tenant*.

46 *Santa Maria* 47 Princess Anne and Captain Mark Phillips

(Des John Lister Ltd. Litho Questa)

**1973** (10 Sept). *Columbus Discovers the West Indies. T* **46** *and similar horiz designs. Multicoloured. P* 13½.
159 1 c. Type **46** .. .. .. .. 10 10
160 20 c. Early map .. .. .. .. 75 75
a. Horiz strip of 4. Nos. 160/3 .. .. 5·00
161 40 c. Map of voyages .. .. .. 90 90
162 70 c. Sighting land .. .. .. 1·50 1·50
163 $1.20, Landing of Columbus .. .. 2·25 2·25
159/63 .. .. .. .. *Set of* 5 5·00 5·00
**MS**164 193 × 93 mm. Nos. 159/63 .. .. 6·00 7·00
Nos. 160/3 were printed horizontally *se-tenant* within the sheet.

(Des PAD Studio. Litho Questa)

**1973** (14 Nov). *Royal Wedding. Centre multicoloured.* W w **12** (*sideways*). *P* 13½.
165 **47** 60 c. turquoise-green .. .. .. 20 10
166 $1.20, deep mauve .. .. .. 30 15

48 "The Adoration of the Shepherds" (Reni) 49 "The Crucifixion" (Raphael)

(Des John Lister Ltd. Litho Questa)

**1973** (2 Dec). *Christmas. T* **48** *and similar horiz designs. Multicoloured. P* 13½.
167 1 c. Type **48** .. .. .. .. 10 10
168 10 c. "The Madonna and Child with Saints Jerome and Dominic" (Lippi) .. .. 10 10
a. Horiz strip of 5. Nos. 168/72 .. .. 75
169 20 c. "The Nativity" (Master of Brunswick) .. 15 15
170 25 c. "Madonna of the Meadow" (Bellini) .. 15 15
171 40 c. "Virgin and Child" (Cima) .. .. 20 20
172 50 c. "Adoration of the Kings" (Geertgen) .. 20 20
167/72 .. .. .. .. *Set of* 6 75 75
**MS**173 148 × 149 mm. Nos. 167/72 .. .. 80 1·40
Nos. 168/72 were printed within the sheet, horizontally *se-tenant*.

(Des John Lister Ltd. Litho Questa)

**1974** (30 Mar). *Easter. T* **49** *and similar vert designs showing various details of Raphael's "Crucifixion". P* 13½.
174 1 c. multicoloured .. .. .. .. 10 10
175 15 c. multicoloured .. .. .. .. 15 10
a. Vert strip of 5. Nos. 175/9 .. .. 95
176 20 c. multicoloured .. .. .. .. 20 15
177 25 c. multicoloured .. .. .. .. 20 15
178 40 c. multicoloured .. .. .. .. 20 15
179 $1 multicoloured .. .. .. .. 25 25
174/9 .. .. .. .. *Set of* 6 95 70
**MS**180 123 × 141 mm. Nos. 174/9 .. .. 95 1·25
Nos. 175/9 were printed vertically *se-tenant* within one sheet.

50 Churchill making "Victory" Sign

(Des John Lister Ltd. Litho Questa)

**1974** (24 June). *Birth Centenary of Sir Winston Churchill. T* **50** *and similar horiz designs. Multicoloured. P* 13½.
181 1 c. Type **50** .. .. .. .. 10 10
182 20 c. Churchill with Roosevelt .. .. 30 20
a. Horiz strip of 5. Nos. 182/6 .. .. 2·00
183 25 c. Wartime broadcast .. .. .. 30 20
184 40 c. Birthplace, Blenheim Palace .. .. 40 30
185 60 c. Churchill's statue .. .. .. 50 35
186 $1.20, Country residence, Chartwell .. 70 55
181/6 .. .. .. .. *Set of* 6 2·00 1·50
**MS**187 195 × 96 mm. Nos. 181/6 .. .. 2·25 2·25
Nos. 182/6 were printed horizontally *se-tenant* within the sheet.

51 U.P.U. Emblem

(Des John Lister Ltd. Litho Questa)

**1974** (27 Aug). *Centenary of Universal Postal Union. P* 13½*.
188 **51** 1 c. black and bright blue .. .. 10 10
189 20 c. black and pale orange .. .. 15 15
a. Horiz strip of 5. Nos. 189/93 .. 1·40
190 25 c. black and light yellow .. .. 15 15
191 40 c. black and bright mauve .. .. 25 25
192 60 c. black and light emerald .. .. 40 40
193 $1.20, black and light blue .. .. 60 60
188/93 .. .. .. .. *Set of* 6 1·40 1·40
**MS**194 195 × 96 mm. Nos. 188/93 .. .. 1·60 2·00
Nos. 189/93 were printed horizontally *se-tenant* within the sheet.
*In No. **MS**194 the lower row of three stamps, 40 c., 60 c. and $1.20 values, are line-perforated 15 at foot, the remaining 3 stamps being comb-perforated 13½.

52 Anguillan pointing to Star 53 "Mary, John and Mary Magdalene" (Matthias Grünewald)

(Litho Questa)

**1974** (16 Dec). *Christmas. T* **52** *and similar horiz designs. Multicoloured. P* 14.
195 1 c. Type **52** .. .. .. .. 10 10
196 20 c. Child in Manger .. .. .. 15 15
a. Horiz strip of 5. Nos. 196/200 .. .. 95
197 25 c. King's offering .. .. .. 15 15
198 40 c. Star over Map of Anguilla .. .. 15 15
199 60 c. Family looking at star .. .. 20 20
200 $1.20, Angels of Peace .. .. .. 30 30
195/200 .. .. .. .. *Set of* 6 95 95
**MS**201 177 × 85 mm. Nos. 195/200 .. .. 1·40 1·75
Nos. 196/200 were printed horizontally *se-tenant* within the sheet.

(Litho Questa)

**1975** (25 Mar). *Easter. T* **53** *and similar multicoloured designs showing details of the Isenheim altarpiece. P* 14.
202 1 c. Type **53** .. .. .. .. 10 10
203 10 c. "The Crucifixion" .. .. .. 10 10
a. Horiz strip of 5. Nos. 203/7 .. .. 85
204 15 c. "St. John the Baptist" .. .. .. 10 10
205 20 c. "St. Sebastian and Angels" .. .. 15 15
206 $1 "The Entombment" .. .. .. 25 25
207 $1.50, "St. Anthony the Hermit" .. .. 35 35
202/7 .. .. .. .. *Set of* 6 85 85
**MS**208 134 × 127 mm. Nos. 202/7. Imperf. .. .. 1·00 1·75
Nos. 203/7 were printed horizontally *se-tenant* within the sheet.

54 Statue of Liberty 55 "Madonna, Child and the Infant John the Baptist" (Raphael)

(Des John Lister Ltd. Litho Questa)

**1975** (10 Nov). *Bicentenary of American Revolution. T* **54** *and similar horiz designs. Multicoloured. P* 13½*.
209 1 c. Type **54** .. .. .. .. 10 10
210 10 c. The Capitol .. .. .. .. 15 10
a. Horiz strip of 5. Nos. 210/14 .. .. 1·60
211 15 c. "Congress voting for Independence" (Pine and Savage) .. .. .. .. 20 15
212 20 c. Washington and map .. .. .. 20 15
213 $1 Boston Tea Party .. .. .. 50 40
214 $1.50, Bicentenary logo .. .. .. 70 60
209/14 .. .. .. .. *Set of* 6 1·60 1·25
**MS**215 198 × 97 mm. Nos. 209/14 .. .. 2·00 2·50
Nos. 210/14 were printed horizontally *se-tenant* within the sheet.
*In No. **MS**215 the lower row of three stamps, 20 c., $1 and $1.50 values, are line-perforated 15 at foot, the remaining 3 stamps being comb-perforated 13½.

(Des John Lister Ltd. Litho Questa)

**1975** (8 Dec). *Christmas. T* **55** *and similar vert designs showing the "Madonna and Child". Multicoloured. P* 13½.
216 1 c. Type **55** .. .. .. .. 10 10
217 10 c. Cima .. .. .. .. 15 10
a. Horiz strip of 5. Nos. 217/21 .. .. 1·25
218 15 c. Dolci .. .. .. .. 20 15
219 20 c. Dürer .. .. .. .. 20 15
220 $1 Bellini .. .. .. .. 35 25
221 $1.50, Botticelli .. .. .. .. 45 35
216/21 .. .. .. .. *Set of* 6 1·25 90
**MS**222 130 × 145 mm. Nos. 216/21 .. .. 2·00 2·25
Nos. 217/21 were printed horizontally *se-tenant* within the sheet.

## PRICES OF SETS

Set prices are given for many issues, generally those containing three stamps or more. Definitive sets include one of each value or major colour change, but do not cover different perforations, die types or minor shades. Where a choice is possible the set prices are based on the cheapest versions of the stamps included in the listings.

## EXECUTIVE COUNCIL

NEW
CONSTITUTION
1976

(56)

57 Almond

TION

Italic second "O" in "CONSTITUTION". Occurs on Row 2/2 (Nos. 226, 228, 232, 235, 239), Row 3/2 (Nos. 230/1, 233/4, 236/8), Row 4/5 (Nos. 223/4, 240) or Row 5/2 (Nos. 225, 227, 229).

**1976** (10 Feb–1 July). *New Constitution. Nos.* 130 *etc. optd with T* **56** *or surch also.*

223 1 c. Spear fishing .. .. .. .. 15 20
a. Italic "O" .. .. .. .. 1·00
224 2 c. on 1 c. Spear fishing .. .. .. 15 20
a. Italic "O" .. .. .. .. 1·10
225 2 c. Type **42** (1.7.76) .. .. .. 1·75 90
a. Italic "O" .. .. .. .. 5·00
226 3 c. on 40 c. Boat building .. .. .. 15 30
a. "3 c" omitted .. .. ..
b. Typo. "3 c"* .. .. .. .. 2·75 3·50
c. Italic "O" .. .. .. .. 1·10
227 4 c. Ferry at Blowing Point .. .. .. 15 30
a. Italic "O" .. .. .. .. 1·10
228 5 c. on 40 c. Boat building .. .. .. 15 30
a. Italic "O" .. .. .. .. 1·10
229 6 c. St. Mary's Church .. .. .. 15 30
a. Italic "O" .. .. .. .. 1·25
230 10 c. on 20 c. Public Library .. .. .. 15 35
a. Italic "O" .. .. .. .. 1·40
231 10 c. St. Gerard's Church (1.7.76) .. .. 2·50 1·00
a. Italic "O" .. .. .. .. 7·00
232 15 c. Cottage Hospital extension .. .. 25 50
a. Italic "O" .. .. .. .. 1·50
233 20 c. Public Library .. .. .. 25 40
a. Italic "O" .. .. .. .. 1·75
234 25 c. Sunset at Blowing Point .. .. .. 25 40
a. Italic "O" .. .. .. .. 2·40
235 40 c. Boat building .. .. .. .. 45 70
a. Italic "O" .. .. .. .. 2·40
236 60 c. Hibiscus .. .. .. .. 70 70
a. Italic "O" .. .. .. .. 3·00
237 $1 Magnificent Frigate Bird .. .. .. 2·75 2·00
a. Italic "O" .. .. .. .. 7·50
238 $2.50, Frangipani .. .. .. .. 2·25 2·25
a. Italic "O" .. .. .. .. 8·00
239 $5 Brown Pelican .. .. .. .. 5·00 6·00
a. Italic "O" .. .. .. .. 15·00
240 $10 Green-back turtle .. .. .. .. 4·00 6·00
a. Italic "O" .. .. .. .. 15·00
223/40 .. .. .. .. *Set of* 18 18·00 20·00

*No. 226a/b occur on R. 5/2, the "3 c" having been omitted during the normal litho surcharging.

(Des John Lister Ltd. Litho Questa)

**1976** (16 Feb). *Flowering Trees. T* **57** *and similar horiz designs. Multicoloured. P* 13½.

241 1 c. Type **57** .. .. .. .. .. 10 10
242 10 c. Autograph .. .. .. .. .. 10 10
a. Horiz strip of 5. Nos. 242/6 .. .. 1·10
243 15 c. Calabash .. .. .. .. .. 15 15
244 20 c. Cordia .. .. .. .. .. 15 15
245 $1 Papaya .. .. .. .. .. 35 45
246 $1.50, Flamboyant .. .. .. .. 45 55
241/6 .. .. .. .. *Set of* 6 1·10 1·25
**MS**247 194 × 99 mm. Nos. 241/6 .. .. .. 1·50 2·00

Nos. 242/6 were printed horizontally *se-tenant* within the sheet.

58 The Three Marys

59 French Ships approaching Anguilla

(Litho Questa)

**1976** (5 Apr). *Easter. T* **58** *and similar multicoloured designs showing portions of the Altar Frontal Tapestry, Rheinau. P* 13½.

248 1 c. Type **58** .. .. .. .. .. 10 10
249 10 c. The Crucifixion .. .. .. .. 10 10
a. Horiz strip of 5. Nos. 249/53 .. .. 1·75
250 15 c. Two Soldiers .. .. .. .. 15 15
251 20 c. The Annunciation .. .. .. .. 15 15
252 $1 The complete tapestry (*horiz*) .. .. 65 65
253 $1.50, The Risen Christ .. .. .. 80 80
248/53 .. .. .. .. *Set of* 6 1·75 1·75
**MS**254 138 × 130 mm. Nos. 248/53. Imperf .. 1·75 2·10

Nos. 249/53 were printed horizontally *se-tenant* within the sheet.

(Des John Lister Ltd. Litho Questa)

**1976** (8 Nov). *Battle for Anguilla, 1796. T* **59** *and similar horiz designs. Multicoloured. P* 13½.

255 1 c. Type **59** .. .. .. .. .. 10 10
256 3 c. Sailing boat leaving Anguilla .. .. 50 35
a. Horiz strip of 5. Nos. 256/60 .. .. 4·25
257 15 c. Capture of *Le Desius* .. .. .. 75 55
258 25 c. *La Vaillante* forced aground .. .. 1·10 80
259 $1 H.M.S. *Lapwing* .. .. .. .. 1·50 1·25
260 $1.50, *Les Desius* burning .. .. .. 2·00 1·75
255/60 .. .. .. .. *Set of* 6 5·25 4·25
**MS**261 205 × 103 mm. Nos. 255/60 .. .. 6·00 6·00

Nos. 256/60 were printed horizontally *se-tenant* within the sheet.

60 "Christmas Carnival" (A. Richardson)

(Litho Questa)

**1976** (22 Nov). *Christmas. T* **60** *and similar horiz designs showing children's paintings. Multicoloured. P* 13½.

262 1 c. Type **60** .. .. .. .. .. 10 10
263 3 c. "Dreams of Christmas Gifts" (J. Connor) 10 10
a. Horiz strip of 5, Nos. 263/7 .. .. 1·25
264 15 c. "Carolling" (P. Richardson) .. .. 15 15
265 25 c. "Candle-light Procession" (A. Mussington) .. .. .. .. .. 20 20
266 $1 "Going to Church" (B. Franklin) .. .. 40 30
267 $1.50, "Coming Home for Christmas" (E. Gumbs) .. .. .. .. .. 50 40
262/7 .. .. .. .. *Set of* 6 1·25 1·10
**MS**268 232 × 147 mm. Nos. 262/7 .. .. 1·50 1·75

Nos. 263/7 were printed horizontally *se-tenant* within the sheet.

61 Prince Charles and H.M.S. *Minerva*

(Des John Lister Ltd. Litho Questa)

**1977** (9 Feb). *Silver Jubilee. T* **61** *and similar horiz designs. Multicoloured. P* 13½.

269 25 c. Type **61** .. .. .. .. .. 15 10
270 40 c. Prince Philip landing at Road Bay, 1964 20 15
271 $1.20, Coronation scene .. .. .. 35 25
272 $2.50, Coronation regalia and map of Anguilla .. .. .. .. .. 50 40
269/72 .. .. .. .. *Set of* 4 1·10 80
**MS**273 145 × 96 mm. Nos. 269/72 .. .. .. 1·10 1·50

62 Yellow-crowned Night Heron

(Des John Lister Ltd. Litho Questa)

**1977** (18 Apr)–78. *T* **62** *and similar horiz designs. Multicoloured. P* 13½.

274 1 c. Type **62** .. .. .. .. .. 15 20
275 2 c. Great Barracuda .. .. .. .. 15 20
276 3 c. Queen Conch .. .. .. .. 30 30
277 4 c. Spanish Bayonet .. .. .. .. 20 15
278 5 c. Trunkfish .. .. .. .. 30 10
279 6 c. Cable and Wireless Building .. .. 15 15
280 10 c. American Kestrel (20.2.78) .. .. 1·75 70
281 15 c. Ground orchid (20.2.78) .. .. 2·00 80
282 20 c. Parrotfish (20.2.78) .. .. .. 1·75 75
283 22 c. Lobster fishing boat (20.2.78) .. .. 35 45
284 35 c. Boat race (20.2.78) .. .. .. 40 45
285 50 c. Sea Bean (20.2.78) .. .. .. 70 45
286 $1 Sandy Island (20.2.78) .. .. .. 60 45
287 $2.50, Manchineel (20.2.78) .. .. .. 1·00 1·00
288 $5 Ground Lizard (20.2.78) .. .. .. 2·00 1·75
289 $10 Red-billed Tropic Bird .. .. .. 7·00 4·25
274/89 .. .. .. .. *Set of* 16 17·00 11·00

63 "The Crucifixion" (Massys)

(Des John Lister Ltd. Litho Questa)

**1977** (25 Apr). *Easter. T* **63** *and similar horiz designs showing paintings by Castagno* ($1.50) *or Ugolino (others). Multicoloured. P* 13½.

291 1 c. Type **63** .. .. .. .. .. 10 10
292 3 c. "The Betrayal" .. .. .. .. 10 10
a. Horiz strip of 5. Nos. 292/6 .. .. 1·60
293 22 c. "The Way to Calvary" .. .. .. 20 20
294 30 c. "The Deposition" .. .. .. .. 25 25
295 $1 "The Resurrection" .. .. .. 50 50
296 $1.50, "The Crucifixion" .. .. .. 65 65
291/6 .. .. .. .. *Set of* 6 1·60 1·60
**MS**297 192 × 126 mm. Nos. 291/6 .. .. 1·60 1·75

Nos. 292/6 were printed horizontally *se-tenant* within the sheet.

ROYAL VISIT
TO WEST INDIES

(64)

65 "Le Chapeau de Paille"

**1977** (26 Oct). *Royal Visit. Nos.* 269/**MS**273 *optd with T* **64**.

298 25 c. Type **61** .. .. .. .. .. 15 1
299 40 c. Prince Philip landing at Road Bay, 1964 20 2
300 $1.20, Coronation scene .. .. .. 30 3
301 $2.50, Coronation regalia and map of Anguilla .. .. .. .. .. 50 5
298/301 .. .. .. .. *Set of* 4 1·00 1·0
**MS**302 145 × 96 mm. Nos. 298/301 .. .. 1·00 1·7

(Des John Lister Ltd. Litho Questa)

**1977** (1 Nov). *400th Birth Anniv of Rubens. T* **65** *and similar ver designs. Multicoloured. P* 13½.

303 25 c. Type **65** .. .. .. .. .. 15 1
304 40 c. "Helène Fourment and her Two Children" 20 2
305 $1.20, "Rubens and his Wife" .. .. 60 6
306 $2.50, "Marchesa Brigida Spinola-Doria" .. 75 9
303/6 .. .. .. .. *Set of* 4 1·50 1·7
**MS**307 93 × 145 mm. Nos. 303/6 .. .. 1·75 2·1

Each value was issued in sheets of 5 stamps and 1 label.

5c

(66)

EASTER 1978

(67)

**1977** (14 Nov). *Christmas. Nos.* 262/8 *with old date blocked ou and additionally inscr* "1977", *some surch also as T* **66**.

308 1 c. Type **60** .. .. .. .. .. 10 1
309 5 c. on 3 c. "Dreams of Christmas Gifts" .. 10 1
a. Horiz strip of 5. Nos. 309/13 .. .. 1·75
310 12 c. on 15 c. "Carolling" .. .. .. 15 1
311 18 c. on 25 c. "Candle-light Procession" .. 20 2
312 $1 "Going to Church" .. .. .. 45 4
313 $2.50 on $1.50, "Coming Home for Christmas" 90 9
308/13 .. .. .. .. *Set of* 6 1·75 1·7
**MS**314 232 × 147 mm. Nos. 308/13 .. .. 2·50 3·

**1978** (6 Mar). *Easter. Nos.* 303/7 *optd with T* **67**, *in gold.*

315 25 c. Type **65** .. .. .. .. .. 20 2
316 40 c. "Helène Fourment and her Two Children" 25 2
317 $1.20, "Rubens and his Wife" .. .. 50 5
318 $2.50, "Marchesa Brigida Spinola-Doria" .. 85 8
315/18 .. .. .. .. *Set of* 4 1·60 1·
**MS**319 93 × 145 mm. Nos. 315/18 .. .. .. 1·75 2·

68 Coronation Coach at Admiralty Arch

VALLEY
SECONDARY
SCHOOL
1953-1978

(69)

(70)

(Des John Lister Ltd. Litho Questa)

**1978** (6 Apr). *25th Anniv of Coronation. T* **68** *and similar horiz designs. Multicoloured. P* 14.

320 22 c. Buckingham Palace .. .. .. .. 10 10
321 50 c. Type **68** .. .. .. .. .. 15 15
322 $1.50, Balcony scene .. .. .. .. 25 20
323 $2.50, Royal coat of arms .. .. .. 40 30
320/3 .. .. .. .. .. *Set of* 4 80 60
**MS**324 138 × 92 mm. Nos. 320/3 .. .. .. 80 1·00

**1978** (14 Aug). *Anniversaries. Nos.* 283/8 *optd as T* **69** *or surch as T* **70**.

325 22 c. Lobster fishing boat .. .. .. .. 20 15
a. Opt double .. .. .. .. .. £130
b. "C" omitted from "SECONDARY" .. 3·00
326 35 c. Boat race .. .. .. .. .. 30 20
a. "C" omitted from "SECONDARY" .. 3·00
327 50 c. Sea Bean .. .. .. .. .. 40 30
a. "I" omitted from "METHODIST" .. 3·25
328 $1 Sandy Island .. .. .. .. .. 50 40
a. "I" omitted from "METHODIST" .. 3·50
329 $1.20 on $5 Ground Lizard .. .. .. 60 45
a. "I" omitted from "METHODIST" .. 4·00
330 $1.50 on $2.50, Manchineel .. .. .. 75 55
a. "C" omitted from "SECONDARY" .. 5·00
325/30 .. .. .. .. .. *Set of* 6 2·50 1·75

The 22, 35 c. and $1.50 values commemorate the 25th anniversary of Valley Secondary School; the other values commemorate the Centenary of Road Methodist Church.

Nos. 325b, 326a and 330a occur on R. 4/1 and Nos. 327a, 328a and 329a on R. 2/4.

71 Mother and Child

(Des and litho Questa)

**1978** (11 Dec). *Christmas. Children's Paintings. T* **71** *and similar horiz designs. Multicoloured. P* 13½.

331 5 c. Type **71** .. .. .. .. .. 10 10
332 12 c. Christmas masquerade .. .. .. 10 10
333 18 c. Christmas dinner .. .. .. .. 10 10
334 22 c. Serenading .. .. .. .. .. 10 10
335 $1 Child in manger .. .. .. .. 45 20
336 $2.50, Family going to church .. .. 90 40
331/6 .. .. .. .. .. *Set of* 6 1·40 70
**MS**337 191 × 101 mm. Nos. 331/6 .. .. .. 1·60 1·75

**1979** (15 Jan). *International Year of the Child. As Nos.* 331/7 *but additionally inscr with emblem and* "1979 INTERNATIONAL YEAR OF THE CHILD". *Borders in different colours.*

338 5 c. Type **71** .. .. .. .. .. 10 10
339 12 c. Christmas masquerade .. .. .. 10 10
340 18 c. Christmas dinner .. .. .. .. 15 15
341 22 c. Serenading .. .. .. .. .. 15 15
342 $1 Child in manger .. .. .. .. 60 60
343 $2.50, Family going to church .. .. 90 90
338/43 .. .. .. .. .. *Set of* 6 1·75 1·75
**MS**344 205 × 112 mm. Nos. 338/43 .. .. .. 2·25 2·50

(72) 73 Valley Methodist Church

**1979** (12 Feb). *Nos.* 274/7 *and* 279/80 *surch as T* **72**.

345 12 c. on 2 c. Great Barracuda .. .. .. 50 40
346 14 c. on 4 c. Spanish Bayonet .. .. .. 40 40
a. Surch inverted .. .. .. .. .. 45·00
347 18 c. on 3 c. Queen Conch .. .. .. 70 45
348 25 c. on 6 c. Cable and Wireless Building .. 55 40
349 38 c. on 10 c. American Kestrel .. .. 1·00 60
350 40 c. on 1 c. Type **62** .. .. .. .. 1·00 60
345/50 .. .. .. .. .. *Set of* 6 3·75 2·50

(Des John Lister Ltd. Litho Questa)

**1979** (30 Mar). *Easter. Church Interiors. T* **73** *and similar horiz designs. Multicoloured. P* 14.

351 5 c. Type **73** .. .. .. .. .. 10 10
a. Horiz strip of 6. Nos. 351/6 .. .. 1·60
352 12 c. St. Mary's Anglican Church, The Valley 10 10
353 18 c. St. Gerard's Roman Catholic Church, The Valley .. .. .. .. .. .. 15 15
354 22 c. Road Methodist Church .. .. .. 15 15
355 $1.50, St. Augustine's Anglican Church, East End .. .. .. .. .. .. 60 60
356 $2.50, West End Methodist Church .. .. 75 75
351/6 .. .. .. .. .. *Set of* 6 1·60 1·60
**MS**357 190 × 105 mm. Nos. 351/6 .. .. .. 1·75 2·25

Nos. 351/6 were printed together horizontally *se-tenant*, within the sheet.

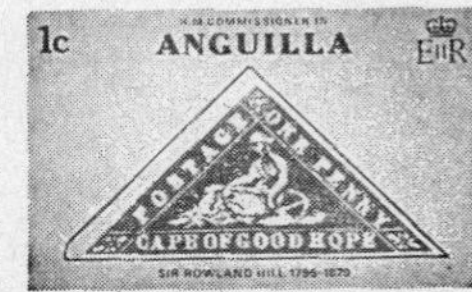


74 Cape of Good Hope 1d. "Woodblock" of 1881

(Des Stanley Gibbons Ltd. Litho Questa)

**1979** (23 Apr). *Death Centenary of Sir Rowland Hill. T* **74** *and similar horiz designs showing stamps. Multicoloured. P* 14.

358 1 c. Type **74** .. .. .. .. .. 10 10
359 1 c. U.S.A. "inverted Jenny" of 1918 .. .. 10 10
360 22 c. Penny Black ("V.R. Official") .. .. 15 15
361 35 c. Germany 2 m. *Graf Zeppelin* of 1928 .. 20 20
362 $1.50, U.S.A. $5 Columbus of 1893 .. .. 60 60
363 $2.50, Great Britain £5 orange of 1882 .. 95 95
358/63 .. .. .. .. .. *Set of* 6 1·75 1·75
**MS**364 187 × 123 mm. Nos. 358/63 .. .. 1·75 2·10

75 Wright *Flyer I* (1st powered flight, 1903)

(Des John Lister Ltd. Litho Questa)

**1979** (21 May). *History of Powered Flight. T* **75** *and similar horiz designs. Multicoloured. P* 14.

365 5 c. Type **75** .. .. .. .. .. 10 10
366 12 c. Louis Blériot at Dover after Channel crossing, 1909 .. .. .. .. .. 15 10
367 18 c. Vickers "Vimy" (1st non-stop crossing of Atlantic, 1919) .. .. .. .. 20 15
368 22 c. *Spirit of St. Louis* (1st solo Atlantic flight by Charles Lindbergh, 1927) .. .. 20 20
369 $1.50, "LZ 127" *Graf Zeppelin*, 1928 .. .. 70 60
370 $2.50, "Concorde", 1979 .. .. .. 1·50 90
365/70 .. .. .. .. .. *Set of* 6 2·50 1·75
**MS**371 200 × 113 mm. Nos. 365/70 .. .. 2·50 2·50

76 Sombrero Island

(Des John Lister Ltd. Litho Questa)

**1979** (20 Aug). *Outer Islands. T* **76** *and similar horiz designs. Multicoloured. P* 14.

372 5 c. Type **76** .. .. .. .. .. 10 10
373 12 c. Anguillita Island .. .. .. .. 15 15
374 18 c. Sandy Island .. .. .. .. .. 20 20
375 25 c. Prickly Pear Cays .. .. .. .. 25 25
376 $1 Dog Island .. .. .. .. .. 50 50
377 $2.50, Scrub Island .. .. .. .. 90 90
372/7 .. .. .. .. .. *Set of* 6 1·90 1·90
**MS**378 180 × 91 mm. Nos. 372/7 .. .. .. 1·90 2·00

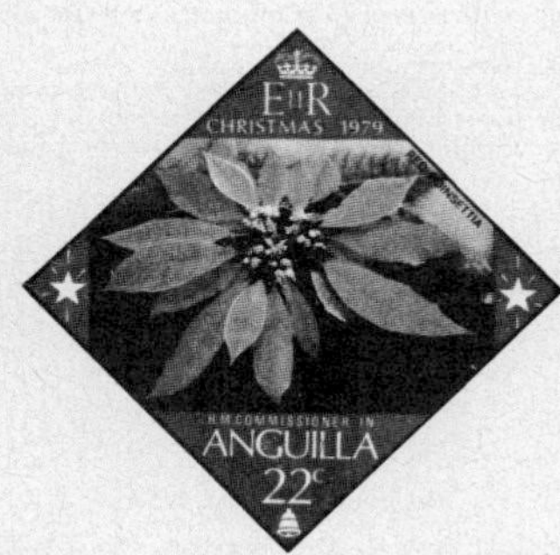


77 Red Poinsettia

(Des John Lister Ltd. Litho Format)

**1979** (22 Oct). *Christmas. Flowers. T* **77** *and similar diamond-shaped designs. Multicoloured. P* 14½.

379 22 c. Type **77** .. .. .. .. .. 40 30
380 35 c. Kalanchoe .. .. .. .. .. 50 40
381 $1.50, Cream Poinsettia .. .. .. 90 80
382 $2.50, White Poinsettia .. .. .. 1·25 1·25
379/82 .. .. .. .. .. *Set of* 4 2·75 2·50
**MS**383 146 × 164 mm. Nos. 379/82 .. .. 3·00 3·25

78 Exhibition Scene

(Des R. Granger Barrett. Litho Format)

**1979** (10 Dec). *"London 1980" International Stamp Exhibition (1st issue). T* **78** *and similar horiz designs. Multicoloured. A. P* 13 *(from sheets of* 20*). B. P* 14½ *(from booklets except* **MS**388B*)*

| | | A | | B | |
|---|---|---|---|---|---|
| 384 | 35 c. Type **78** .. .. .. | 15 | 20 | 15 | 20 |
| 385 | 50 c. Earls Court Exhibition Centre .. .. .. | 20 | 25 | 20 | 25 |
| 386 | $1.50, Penny Black and Two-penny Blue stamps .. .. | 55 | 60 | 55 | 60 |
| 387 | $2.50, Exhibition logo .. .. | 90 | 95 | 90 | 95 |
| 384/7 | .. .. .. *Set of* 4 | 1·60 | 1·75 | 1·60 | 1·75 |
| **MS**388 | 150 × 94 mm. Nos. 384/7 .. | 2·25 | 2·40 | 2·25 | 2·40 |

Nos. 384B/7B also exist from uncut booklet sheets of 10.

See also Nos. 407/10.

79 Games Site

(Des John Lister Ltd. Litho Format)

**1980** (14 Jan). *Winter Olympic Games, Lake Placid, U.S.A. T* **79** *and similar horiz designs. Multicoloured. P* 13.

389 5 c. Type **79** .. .. .. .. .. 10 10
390 18 c. Ice-hockey .. .. .. .. .. 10 10
391 35 c. Ice-skating .. .. .. .. .. 15 20
392 50 c. Bobsleighing .. .. .. .. .. 20 25
393 $1 Skiing .. .. .. .. .. 40 45
394 $2.50, Luge-tobogganing .. .. .. 90 95
389/94 .. .. .. .. .. *Set of* 6 1·60 1·90
**MS**395 136 × 128 mm. Nos. 389/94 .. .. 1·90 2·00

Nos. 389/94 also exist perforated 14½ (*Price for set of* 6 £1.60 *mint*, £1.90 *used*) from additional sheetlets of 10. Stamps perforated 13 are from normal sheets of 40.

50th Anniversary Scouting 1980 75th Anniversary Rotary 1980

80 Salt ready for Reaping (81) (82)

(Des John Lister Ltd. Litho Questa)

**1980** (14 Apr). *Salt Industry. T* **80** *and similar horiz designs. Multicoloured. P* 14.

396 5 c. Type **80** .. .. .. .. .. 10 10
397 12 c. Tallying salt .. .. .. .. .. 15 15
398 18 c. Unloading salt flats .. .. .. .. 20 15
399 22 c. Salt storage heap .. .. .. .. 20 15
400 $1 Salt for bagging and grinding .. .. 50 40
401 $2.50, Loading salt for export .. .. 70 70
396/401 .. .. .. .. *Set of* 6 1·60 1·40
**MS**402 180 × 92 mm. Nos. 396/401 .. .. 1·60 1·75

Nos. 396/7, 398/9 and 400/1 were each printed in the same sheet, but with the values in separate panes.

**1980** (16 Apr). *Anniversaries. Nos.* 280, 282 *and* 287/8 *optd with T* **81** *(10 c., $2.50) or* **82** *(others).*

403 10 c. American Kestrel .. .. .. .. 30 10
404 20 c. Parrotfish .. .. .. .. .. 35 15
405 $2.50, Manchineel .. .. .. .. 1·25 1·00
406 $5 Ground Lizard .. .. .. .. 2·00 1·90
403/6 .. .. .. .. .. *Set of* 4 3·50 2·75

Commemorations:—10 c., $2.50, 50th anniversary of Anguilla Scout Movement; others, 75th anniversary of Rotary International.

83 Palace of Westminster and Great Britain 1970 9d. "Philympia" Commemorative 84 Queen Elizabeth the Queen Mother

(Des Stamp Magazine. Litho Rosenbaum Bros, Vienna)

**1980** (6 May). *"London 1980" International Stamp Exhibition (2nd issue). T* **83** *and similar horiz designs showing famous landmarks and various international stamp exhibition commemorative stamps. Multicoloured. P* 13½.

407 50 c. Type **83** .. .. .. .. .. 35 30
408 $1.50, City Hall, Toronto and Canada 1978 $1.50, "CAPEX" .. .. .. .. 60 55
409 $2.50, Statue of Liberty and U.S.A. 1976 13 c. "Interphil" .. .. .. .. 80 85
407/9 .. .. .. .. .. *Set of* 3 1·60 1·50
**MS**410 157 × 130 mm. Nos. 407/9 .. .. .. 1·60 1·75

(Des R. Granger Barrett from photograph by N. Parkinson. Litho Rosenbaum Bros, Vienna)

**1980** (4 Aug). *80th Birthday of Queen Elizabeth the Queen Mother. P* 13½.

411 **84** 35 c. multicoloured .. .. .. .. 25 20
412 50 c. multicoloured .. .. .. .. 35 25
413 $1.50, multicoloured .. .. .. .. 75 65
414 $3 multicoloured .. .. .. .. 2·75 1·40
411/14 .. .. .. .. .. *Set of* 4 3·50 2·25
**MS**415 160 × 110 mm. Nos. 411/14 .. .. .. 4·00 3·00

85 Brown Pelicans

SEPARATION 1980

(86)

(Des John Lister Ltd. Litho Questa)

**1980** (13 Nov). *Christmas. Birds. T* **85** *and similar vert designs. Multicoloured. P* 13½.
416 5 c. Type **85** .. .. .. .. .. 30 10
417 22 c. Great Blue Heron .. .. .. .. 75 20
418 $1.50, Barn Swallow .. .. .. .. 1·75 60
419 $3 Ruby-throated Hummingbird .. .. 2·25 1·40
416/19 .. .. .. .. *Set of* 4 4·50 2·10
**MS**420 126×160 mm. Nos. 416/19 .. .. 5·00 3·75

**1980** (18 Dec). *Separation of Anguilla from St. Kitts-Nevis. Nos.* 274, 277, 279/89, 341 *and* 418/19 *optd as T* **86** *or surch also.*
421 1 c. Type **62** .. .. .. .. .. 10 20
422 2 c. on 4 c. Spanish Bayonet .. .. .. 10 20
423 5 c. on 15 c. Ground orchid .. .. .. 15 25
424 5 c. on $1.50, Barn Swallow .. .. .. 15 25
425 5 c. on $3 Ruby-throated Hummingbird .. 15 25
426 10 c. American Kestrel .. .. .. .. 20 30
427 12 c. on $1 Sandy Island .. .. .. 20 30
428 14 c. on $2.50, Manchineel .. .. .. 20 30
429 15 c. Ground orchid .. .. .. .. 25 30
430 18 c. on $5 Ground Lizard .. .. .. 25 30
431 20 c. Parrotfish .. .. .. .. .. 25 30
432 22 c. Lobster fishing boat .. .. .. 25 30
433 25 c. on 15 c. Ground orchid .. .. .. 30 35
434 35 c. Boat race .. .. .. .. .. 30 35
435 38 c. on 22 c. Serenading .. .. .. 30 35
436 40 c. on 1 c. Type **62** .. .. .. .. 30 35
437 50 c. Sea Bean .. .. .. .. .. 35 40
438 $1 Sandy Island .. .. .. .. 50 70
439 $2.50, Manchineel .. .. .. .. 1·00 1·40
440 $5 Ground Lizard .. .. .. .. 2·25 2·75
441 $10 Red-billed Tropic Bird .. .. .. 5·00 5·50
442 $10 on 6 c. Cable and Wireless Building .. 5·00 5·50
421/42 .. .. .. .. .. *Set of* 22 16·00 18·00

87 First Petition for Separation, 1825

(Des John Lister Ltd. Litho Format)

**1980** (18 Dec). *Separation of Anguilla from St. Kitts-Nevis. T* **87** *and similar horiz designs. Multicoloured. P* 14.
443 18 c. Type **87** .. .. .. .. .. 10 10
444 22 c. Referendum ballot paper, 1967 .. .. 10 10
445 35 c. Airport blockade, 1967 .. .. .. 15 15
446 50 c. Anguilla flag .. .. .. .. 20 20
447 $1 Separation celebrations, 1980 .. .. 35 35
443/7 .. .. .. .. .. *Set of* 5 85 85
**MS**448 178 × 92 mm. Nos. 443/7 .. .. .. 90 1·25

Nos. 443/4 and 445/6 were each printed in the same sheet with the two values in separate panes.

88 "Nelson's Dockyard" (R. Granger Barrett)

89 Minnie Mouse being chased by Bees

(Litho Rosenbaum Bros, Vienna)

**1981** (2 Mar). *175th Death Anniv of Lord Nelson. Paintings. T* **88** *and similar horiz designs. Multicoloured. P* 14.
449 22 c. Type **88** .. .. .. .. .. 45 15
450 35 c. "Ships in which Nelson served" (Nicholas Pocock) .. .. .. .. .. 55 25
451 50 c. "H.M.S. *Victory*" (Monamy Swaine) .. 70 30
452 $3 "Battle of Trafalgar" (Clarkson Stanfield) 1·75 1·50
449/52 .. .. .. .. *Set of* 4 3·00 2·00
**MS**453 82 × 63 mm. $5 "Horatio Nelson" (L. F. Abbott) and coat of arms .. .. .. .. 3·00 3·25

(Litho Questa)

**1981** (30 Mar). *Easter. Walt Disney Cartoon Characters. T* **89** *and similar vert designs. Multicoloured. P* 13½ × 14.
454 1 c. Type **89** .. .. .. .. .. 10 10
455 2 c. Pluto laughing at Mickey Mouse .. .. 10 10
456 3 c. Minnie Mouse tying ribbon round Pluto's neck .. .. .. .. .. 10 10
457 5 c. Minnie Mouse confronted by love-struck bird who fancies her bonnet .. .. 10 10
458 7 c. Dewey and Huey admiring themselves in mirror .. .. .. .. .. 10 10
459 9 c. Horace Horsecollar and Clarabelle Cow out for a stroll .. .. .. .. 10 10
460 10 c. Daisy Duck with hat full of Easter eggs 10 10
461 $2 Goofy unwrapping Easter hat .. .. 1·90 1·40
462 $3 Donald Duck in his Easter finery .. 2·25 1·60
454/62 .. .. .. .. .. *Set of* 9 3·75 3·00
**MS**463 134 × 108 mm. $5 Chip and Dale making off with hat .. .. .. .. .. .. 2·75 2·75

90 Prince Charles, Lady Diana Spencer and St. Paul's Cathedral

Extra flagstaff at right of Windsor Castle (R. 1/5).

(Des R. Granger Barrett. Litho Rosenbaum Bros, Vienna)

**1981** (15 June). *Royal Wedding. T* **90** *and similar horiz designs showing Prince Charles, Lady Diana Spencer and buildings. Multicoloured. P* 14. (a) *No wmk.*
464 50 c. Type **90** .. .. .. .. .. 25 25
465 $2.50, Althorp .. .. .. .. .. 65 75
466 $3 Windsor Castle .. .. .. .. 70 90
a. Extra flagstaff .. .. .. .. 8·50
464/6 .. .. .. .. *Set of* 3 1·40 1·75
**MS**467 90 x 72 mm. $5 Buckingham Palace .. 1·50 1·75

(*b*) *Booklet stamps. W w* **15** (*sideways*)
468 50 c. Type **90** .. .. .. .. .. 25 45
a. Booklet pane of 4 .. .. .. .. 90
ab. Black printed twice .. .. .. .. 7·00
469 $3 As No. 466 .. .. .. .. 1·25 1·75
a. Booklet pane of 4 .. .. .. .. 4·50
ab. Black printed twice .. .. .. .. 7·00

Nos 464/6 also exist from additional sheetlets of two stamps and one label with changed background colours (*Price for set of* 3 £2 *mint or used*).

Nos. 468/9 come from $14 stamp booklets.

Nos. 468ab and 469ab show the black features of the portraits strengthened by a further printing applied by typography. This is particularly visible on the Prince's suit and on the couple's hair.

91 Children playing in Tree

(Des Susan Csomer. Litho Rosenbaum Bros, Vienna)

**1981** (31 July–30 Sept). *35th Anniv of U.N.I.C.E.F. T* **91** *and similar horiz designs. Multicoloured. P* 14.
470 5 c. Type **91** .. .. .. .. .. 10 10
471 10 c. Children playing by pool .. .. .. 10 10
472 15 c. Children playing musical instruments .. 10 10
473 $3 Children playing with pets (30 Sept) .. 1·40 1·40
470/3 .. .. .. .. .. *Set of* 4 1·40 1·40
**MS**474 78 × 106 mm. $4 Children playing football (*vert*) (30 Sept) .. .. .. .. 2·75 2·25

(Litho Questa)

**1981** (2 Nov). *Christmas. Horiz designs as T* **89** *showing scenes from Walt Disney's cartoon film "The Night before Christmas". P* 13½.
475 1 c. multicoloured .. .. .. .. .. 10 10
476 2 c. multicoloured .. .. .. .. .. 10 10
477 3 c. multicoloured .. .. .. .. .. 10 10
478 5 c. multicoloured .. .. .. .. .. 10 10
479 7 c. multicoloured .. .. .. .. .. 10 10
480 10 c. multicoloured .. .. .. .. .. 10 10
481 12 c. multicoloured .. .. .. .. .. 10 10
482 $2 multicoloured .. .. .. .. .. 1·90 1·25
483 $3 multicoloured .. .. .. .. .. 1·90 1·60
475/83 .. .. .. .. .. *Set of* 9 3·50 2·75
**MS**484 130 × 105 mm. $5 multicoloured .. .. 3·25 2·75

## NEW INFORMATION

The editor is always interested to correspond with people who have new information that will improve or correct the Catalogue.

92 Red Grouper

50c

(93)

(Des R. Granger Barrett. Litho Questa)

**1982** (1 Jan). *Horiz designs as T* **92**. *Multicoloured. P* 13½ × 14.
485 1 c. Type **92** .. .. .. .. .. 15 1
486 5 c. Ferry service, Blowing Point .. .. 15 1
487 10 c. Racing boats .. .. .. .. 15 1
488 15 c. Majorettes .. .. .. .. 15 1
489 20 c. Launching boat, Sandy Hill .. .. 25 1
490 25 c. Corals .. .. .. .. .. 55 2
491 30 c. Little Bay cliffs .. .. .. .. 25 1
492 35 c. Fountain Cave interior .. .. .. 1·00 4
493 40 c. Sunset over Sandy Island .. .. 30 2
494 45 c. Landing at Sombrero .. .. .. 50 4
495 60 c. Seine fishing .. .. .. .. 1·75 7
496 75 c. Boat race at sunset, Sandy Ground .. 70 5
497 $1 Bagging lobster at Island Harbour .. 1·75 1·0
498 $5 Brown Pelicans .. .. .. .. 9·50 5·0
499 $7.50, Hibiscus .. .. .. .. 8·00 5·0
500 $10 Queen Triggerfish .. .. .. 10·00 8·5
485/500 .. .. .. .. *Set of* 16 32·00 20·0

**1982** (22 Mar). *No.* 494 *surch with T* **93**.
501 50 c. on 45 c. Landing at Sombrero .. .. 35 35

94 Anthurium and *Heliconius charithonia*

95 Lady Diana Spencer in 1961

(Des R. Granger Barrett. Litho Questa)

**1982** (5 Apr). *Easter. Flowers and Butterflies. T* **94** *and simila[r] vert designs. Multicoloured. P* 14.
502 10 c. Type **94** .. .. .. .. .. 15 1
503 35 c. Bird of Paradise and *Junonia evarete* 25 2
504 75 c. Allamanda and *Danaus plexippus* .. 45 4
505 $3 Orchid Tree and *Biblis hyperia* .. 1·60 1·6
502/5 .. .. .. .. *Set of* 4 2·25 2·1
**MS**506 65×79 mm. $5 Amaryllis and *Dryas julia* 2·75 3·0

(Des R. Granger Barrett. Litho C. Ueberreuter Security Printing, Vienna)

**1982** (17 May–30 Aug). *21st Birthday of Princess of Wales. T* **9[5]** *and similar vert designs. Multicoloured. P* 14.
507 10 c. Type **95** .. .. .. .. .. 10 1
a. Booklet pane of 4 (30 Aug) .. .. 40
508 30 c. Lady Diana Spencer in 1968 .. .. 20 2
509 40 c. Lady Diana in 1970 .. .. .. 25 2
a. Booklet pane of 4 (30 Aug) .. .. 1·00
510 60 c. Lady Diana in 1974 .. .. .. 35 3
a. Booklet pane of 4 (30 Aug) .. .. 1·40
511 $2 Lady Diana in 1981 .. .. .. 1·10 1·1
a. Booklet pane of 4 (30 Aug) .. .. 4·25
512 $3 Lady Diana in 1981 (*different*) .. .. 1·40 1·4
507/12 .. .. .. .. .. *Set of* 6 3·00 3·0
**MS**513 72 × 90 mm. $5 Princess of Wales .. .. 2·75 3·0
**MS**514 125 × 125 mm. As Nos. 507/12, but with buff borders .. .. .. .. .. .. 3·00 3·5

96 Pitching Tent

(Litho C. Ueberreuter Security Printing, Vienna)

**1982** (5 July). *75th Anniv of Boy Scout Movement. T* **96** *an[d] similar horiz designs. Multicoloured. P* 14.
515 10 c. Type **96** .. .. .. .. .. 35 1
516 35 c. Scout band .. .. .. .. .. 70 4
517 75 c. Yachting .. .. .. .. .. 95 7
518 $3 On parade .. .. .. .. .. 2·50 2·5
515/18 .. .. .. .. *Set of* 4 4·00 3·5
**MS**519 90 × 72 mm. $5 Cooking .. .. .. 3·75 4·0

(Litho Format)

**1982** (3 Aug). *World Cup Football Championship, Spain. Hori[z] designs as T* **89** *showing scenes from Walt Disney's cartoon fil[m] "Bedknobs and Broomsticks". P* 11.
520 1 c. multicoloured .. .. .. .. .. 10 1
521 3 c. multicoloured .. .. .. .. .. 10 1
522 4 c. multicoloured .. .. .. .. .. 10 1
523 5 c. multicoloured .. .. .. .. .. 10 1
524 7 c. multicoloured .. .. .. .. .. 10 1
525 9 c. multicoloured .. .. .. .. .. 10 1
526 10 c. multicoloured .. .. .. .. .. 10 1
527 $2.50 multicoloured .. .. .. .. 1·25 1·2
528 $3 multicoloured .. .. .. .. .. 1·50 1·5
520/8 .. .. .. .. .. *Set of* 9 2·75 2·7
**MS**529 126 × 101 mm. $5 multicoloured. P 14 × 13½ .. .. .. .. .. .. 2·75 3·0

**COMMONWEALTH GAMES 1982**

(97)

**1982** (18 Oct). *Commonwealth Games, Brisbane. Nos.* 487, 495/6 *and* 498 *optd with T* **97**.
530 10 c. Racing boats .. .. .. 10 10
a. "S" omitted from "GAMES" .. .. 1·00
531 60 c. Seine fishing .. .. .. 35 35
a. "S" omitted from "GAMES" .. .. 1·50
532 75 c. Boat race at sunset, Sandy Ground .. 45 45
a. "S" omitted from "GAMES" .. .. 1·50
533 $5 Brown Pelicans .. .. .. 2·75 2·75
a. "S" omitted from "GAMES" .. .. 4·50
530/3 .. .. .. .. .. *Set of* 4 3·25 3·25

The "S" omitted variety occurs on R.2/2 of the right-hand pane for all values.

(Litho Questa)

**1982** (29 Nov). *Birth Centenary of A. A. Milne (author). Horiz designs as T* **89** *showing scenes from various "Winnie the Pooh" stories. P* 14 × 13½.
534 1 c. multicoloured .. .. .. 10 10
535 2 c. multicoloured .. .. .. 10 10
536 3 c. multicoloured .. .. .. 10 10
537 5 c. multicoloured .. .. .. 10 10
538 7 c. multicoloured .. .. .. 15 10
539 10 c. multicoloured .. .. .. 20 10
540 12 c. multicoloured .. .. .. 20 10
541 20 c. multicoloured .. .. .. 25 15
542 $5 multicoloured .. .. .. 3·25 2·75
534/42 .. .. .. .. *Set of* 9 3·75 3·00
**MS**543 120 × 93 mm. $5 multicoloured .. .. 3·50 3·50

**98** Culture

**99** "I am the Lord Thy God"

(Des R. Granger Barrett. Litho Ueberreuter)

**1983** (28 Feb). *Commonwealth Day. T* **98** *and similar horiz designs. Multicoloured. P* 14.
544 10 c. Type **98** .. .. .. 10 10
545 35 c. Anguilla and British flags .. .. 30 30
546 75 c. Economic co-operation .. .. 60 50
547 $2.50, Salt industry (salt pond) .. .. 3·00 1·75
544/7 .. .. .. .. *Set of* 4 3·50 2·40
**MS**548 76 × 61 mm. $5 World map showing position of Commonwealth countries .. .. .. 4·00 3·00

(Litho Questa)

**1983** (31 Mar). *Easter. The Ten Commandments. T* **99** *and similar vert designs. Multicoloured. P* 14.
549 1 c. Type **99** .. .. .. 10 10
550 2 c. "Thou shalt not make any graven image" 10 10
551 3 c. "Thou shalt not take My Name in vain" 10 10
552 10 c. "Remember the Sabbath Day" .. 15 10
553 35 c. "Honour thy father and mother" .. 30 20
554 60 c. "Thou shalt not kill" .. .. 50 35
555 75 c. "Thou shalt not commit adultery" .. 60 40
556 $2 "Thou shalt not steal" .. .. 1·50 1·00
557 $2.50, "Thou shalt not bear false witness" .. 1·75 1·25
558 $5 "Thou shalt not covet" .. .. 2·75 2·50
549/58 .. .. .. .. *Set of* 10 7·00 5·50
**MS**559 126 × 102 mm. $5 "Moses receiving the Tablets" (16th-century woodcut) .. .. 2·50 2·50

**100** Leatherback Turtle

**101** Montgolfier Hot Air Balloon, 1783

(Des R. Granger Barrett. Litho Questa)

**1983** (10 Aug). *Turtles. T* **100** *and similar horiz designs. Multicoloured. A. P* 13½. *B. P* 12.

| | | A | | B | |
|---|---|---|---|---|---|
| 560 | 10 c. Type **100** .. .. | 35 | 20 | 35 | 20 |
| 561 | 35 c. Hawksbill Turtle .. .. | 60 | 35 | 75 | 55 |
| 562 | 75 c. Green Turtle .. .. | 1·00 | 55 | 1·25 | 90 |
| 563 | $1 Loggerhead Turtle .. .. | 1·25 | 85 | 1·50 | 1·00 |
| 560/3 | .. .. *Set of* 4 | 3·00 | 1·75 | 3·50 | 2·40 |
| **MS**564 | 93 × 72 mm. $5 Leatherback Turtle (*different*) .. .. | 2·75 | 3·00 | † | |

(Des R. Granger Barrett. Litho Questa)

**1983** (22 Aug). *Bicentenary of Manned Flight. T* **101** *and similar vert designs. Multicoloured. P* 13½.
565 10 c. Type **101** .. .. .. .. 20 10
566 60 c. Blanchard and Jeffries crossing English Channel by balloon, 1785 .. .. 55 35
567 $1 Henri Giffard's steam driven airship, 1852 .. .. .. .. 70 50
568 $2.50, Otto Lilienthal and glider, 1890–96 1·60 1·25
565/8 .. .. .. .. *Set of* 4 2·75 2·00
**MS**569 72 × 90 mm. $5 Wilbur Wright flying round Statue of Liberty, 1909 .. .. .. 2·50 3·00

**102** Boys' Brigade Band and Flag

(Des R. Granger Barrett. Litho Questa)

**1983** (12 Sept). *Centenary of Boys' Brigade. T* **102** *and similar horiz design. Multicoloured. P* 13½.
570 10 c. Type **102** .. .. .. 15 15
571 $5 Brigade members marching .. .. 2·75 2·75
**MS**572 96 × 115 mm. Nos. 570/1 .. .. .. 2·75 3·25

**150TH ANNIVERSARY ABOLITION OF SLAVERY ACT**

(103)

**1983** (24 Oct). *150th Anniv of the Abolition of Slavery. Nos.* 487, 493 *and* 497/8 *optd with T* **103**.
573 10 c. Racing boats .. .. .. 10 10
a. Opt inverted .. .. .. 35·00
574 40 c. Sunset over Sandy Island .. .. 20 25
575 $1 Bagging lobster at Island Harbour .. 45 50
576 $5 Brown Pelicans .. .. .. 2·50 2·75
573/6 .. .. .. .. *Set of* 4 2·75 3·25

**104** Jiminy on Clock (*Cricket on the Hearth*)

(Litho Format)

**1983** (14 Nov). *Christmas. Walt Disney Cartoon Characters. T* **104** *and similar vert designs depicting scenes from Dickens' Christmas stories. Multicoloured. P* 13½.
577 1 c. Type **104** .. .. .. 10 10
578 2 c. Jiminy with fiddle (*Cricket on the Hearth*) 10 10
579 3 c. Jiminy among toys (*Cricket on the Hearth*) 10 10
580 4 c. Mickey as Bob Cratchit (*A Christmas Carol*) .. .. .. .. 10 10
581 5 c. Donald Duck as Scrooge (*A Christmas Carol*) .. .. .. .. 10 10
582 6 c. Mini and Goofy in *The Chimes* .. 10 10
583 10 c. Goofy sees an imp appearing from bells (*The Chimes*) .. .. .. 10 10
584 $2 Donald Duck as Mr. Pickwick (*The Pickwick Papers*) .. .. .. 2·00 1·25
585 $3 Disney characters as Pickwickians (*The Pickwick Papers*) .. .. .. 2·25 1·60
577/85 .. .. .. .. *Set of* 9 4·25 3·00
**MS**586 130 × 104 mm. $5 Donald Duck as Mr. Pickwick with gifts (*The Pickwick Papers*) .. 3·75 3·50

**105** 100 Metres Race

(Litho Questa)

**1984** (20 Feb–24 Apr). *Olympic Games, Los Angeles. T* **105** *and similar horiz designs showing Mickey Mouse in Decathlon events. Multicoloured. A. Inscr.* "1984 Los Angeles". *P* 14 × 13½. *B. Inscr.* "1984 Olympics Los Angeles" *and Olympic emblem. P* 14 × 13½ (**MS**596B) *or* 12 (*others*) (24 April).

| | | A | | B | |
|---|---|---|---|---|---|
| 587 | 1 c. Type **105** .. .. | 10 | 10 | 10 | 10 |
| 588 | 2 c. Long jumping .. .. | 10 | 10 | 10 | 10 |
| 589 | 3 c. Shot-putting .. .. | 10 | 10 | 10 | 10 |
| 590 | 4 c. High jumping .. .. | 10 | 10 | 10 | 10 |
| 591 | 5 c. 400 metres race .. .. | 10 | 10 | 10 | 10 |
| 592 | 6 c. Hurdling .. .. | 10 | 10 | 10 | 10 |
| 593 | 10 c. Discus-throwing .. .. | 10 | 10 | 10 | 10 |
| 594 | $1 Pole-vaulting .. .. | 1·00 | 80 | 1·00 | 80 |
| 595 | $4 Javelin-throwing .. .. | 3·00 | 2·50 | 3·00 | 2·50 |
| 587/95 | .. .. *Set of* 9 | 4·00 | 3·50 | 4·00 | 3·50 |
| **MS**596 | 117 × 93 mm. $5 1500 metres race .. .. | 3·50 | 2·75 | 2·75 | 2·75 |

Nos. 587B/95B were each printed in small sheets of 6 stamps including one *se-tenant* stamp-size label in position 2.

35c

**106** "Justice" (**107**)

(Des and litho Questa)

**1984** (19 Apr). *Easter. T* **106** *and similar vert designs showing details from "La Stanza della Segnatura" by Raphael. Multicoloured. P* 13½ × 14.
597 10 c. Type **106** .. .. .. 15 10
598 25 c. "Poetry" .. .. .. 20 20
599 35 c. "Philosophy" .. .. .. 30 30
600 40 c. "Theology" .. .. .. 30 30
601 $1 "Abraham and Paul" .. .. 75 70
602 $2 "Moses and Matthew" .. .. 1·40 1·40
603 $3 "John and David" .. .. 2·00 1·90
604 $4 "Peter and Adam" .. .. 2·25 2·25
597/604 .. .. .. *Set of* 8 6·50 6·50
**MS**605 83 × 110 mm. $5 "Astronomy" .. .. 2·50 3·00

**1984** (24 Apr–17 May). *Nos.* 485, 491 *and* 498/500 *surch as T* **107**.
606 25 c. on $7.50, Hibiscus (17 May) .. .. 20 20
607 35 c. on 30 c. Little Bay cliffs .. .. 25 25
608 60 c. on 1 c. Type **92** .. .. .. 45 45
609 $2.50 on $5 Brown Pelicans.. .. .. 1·40 1·50
a. Surch at left with decimal point* .. 18·00
610 $2.50 on $10 Queen Triggerfish .. .. 1·40 1·50
a. Surch at right without decimal point* .. 18·00
606/10 .. .. .. *Set of* 5 3·25 3·50

*The surcharge on No. 609 shows the figures at right of the design and without a decimal point. On No. 610 they are to the left and include a decimal point. No 609a shows, in error, the surcharge for No. 610 and No. 610a that intended for No. 609.

**108** Australia 1913 1d. Kangaroo Stamp

(Des K. Cato. Litho Leigh-Mardon Ltd, Melbourne)

**1984** (16 July). *"Ausipex 84" International Stamp Exhibition, Melbourne. T* **108** *and similar horiz designs showing Australian stamps. Multicoloured. P* 13½ × 14.
611 10 c. Type **108** .. .. .. 15 15
612 75 c. 1914 6d. Laughing Kookaburra.. .. 70 60
613 $1 1932 2d. Sydney Harbour Bridge .. 95 80
614 $2.50, 1938 10s. King George VI .. 2·00 1·75
611/14 .. .. .. *Set of* 4 3·50 3·00
**MS**615 95 × 86 mm. $5 £1 Bass and £2 Admiral King .. .. .. .. 3·00 3·50

**109** Thomas Fowell Buxton

(Des R. Granger Barrett. Litho Questa)

**1984** (1 Aug). *150th Anniv of Abolition of Slavery. T* **109** *and similar horiz designs. Multicoloured. P* 14.
616 10 c. Type **109** .. .. .. 10 10
617 25 c. Abraham Lincoln .. .. .. 25 25
618 35 c. Henri Christophe .. .. .. 35 35
619 60 c. Thomas Clarkson .. .. .. 50 50
620 75 c. William Wilberforce .. .. 60 60
621 $1 Olaudah Equiano .. .. .. 70 70
622 $2.50, General Charles Gordon .. .. 1·60 1·60
623 $5 Granville Sharp .. .. .. 3·00 3·00
616/23 .. .. .. *Set of* 8 6·50 6·50
**MS**624 150 × 121 mm. Nos. 616/23. P 12 .. .. 6·50 7·50

**U.P.U. CONGRESS HAMBURG 1984** (**110**)

**PRINCE HENRY BIRTH 15.9.84** (**111**)

**1984** (13 Aug). *Universal Postal Union Congress, Hamburg. Nos. 486/7 and 498 optd as T* **110** *or surch also (No. 626).*
625 5 c. Ferry service, Blowing Point .. .. 10 10
626 20 c. on 10 c. Racing boats .. .. 15 15
627 $5 Brown Pelicans .. .. .. .. 3·50 3·50
625/7 .. .. .. .. .. *Set of* 3 3·50 3·50

**1984** (31 Oct). *Birth of Prince Henry. Nos. 507/14 optd as T* **111**.
628 10 c. Type **95** .. .. .. .. 10 10
a. Booklet pane of 4 .. .. .. 35
629 30 c. Lady Diana Spencer in 1968 .. .. 20 25
630 40 c. Lady Diana in 1970 .. .. .. 25 30
a. Booklet pane of 4 .. .. .. 1·00
631 60 c. Lady Diana in 1974 .. .. .. 40 45
a. Booklet pane of 4 .. .. .. 1·60
632 $2 Lady Diana in 1981 .. .. .. 1·25 1·40
a. Booklet pane of 4 .. .. .. 5·00
633 $3 Lady Diana in 1981 (*different*) .. 1·50 2·25
628/33 .. .. .. .. *Set of* 6 3·25 4·25
**MS**634 72×90 mm. $5 Princess of Wales .. 2·25 2·75
**MS**635 125×125 mm. As Nos. 628/33, but with buff borders .. .. .. .. .. 4·00 5·50
On No. **MS**634 the lines of overprint are larger, being placed vertically each side of the portrait.

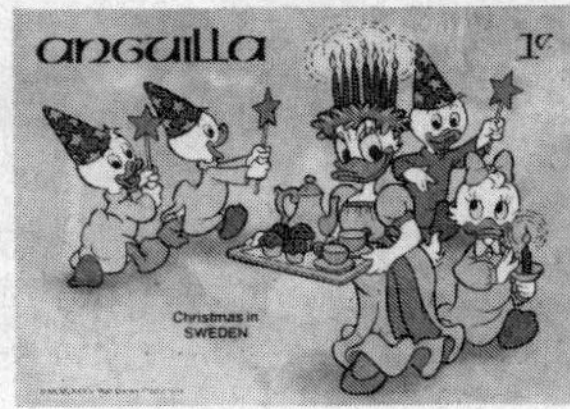


**112** Christmas in Sweden

(Litho Questa)

**1984** (12 Nov). *Christmas. Walt Disney Cartoon Characters. T* **112** *and similar horiz designs showing national scenes. Multicoloured. P* 12 *($2) or* 14 × 13½ *(others).*
636 1 c. Type **112** .. .. .. .. 10 10
637 2 c. Italy .. .. .. .. .. 10 10
638 3 c. Holland .. .. .. .. 10 10
639 4 c. Mexico .. .. .. .. 10 10
640 5 c. Spain .. .. .. .. 10 10
641 10 c. Disneyland, U.S.A. .. .. .. 10 10
642 $1 Japan .. .. .. .. .. 1·50 65
643 $2 Anguilla .. .. .. .. 2·00 1·10
644 $4 Germany .. .. .. .. 3·25 2·25
636/44 .. .. .. .. *Set of* 9 6·50 3·75
**MS**645 126 × 102 mm. $5 England .. .. 4·00 3·50
No. 643 was printed in sheetlets of 8 stamps.

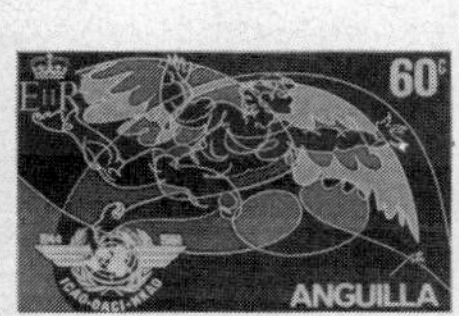

**113** Icarus in Flight **114** Barn Swallow

(Des H. Herni (60 c.), S. Diouf (75 c.), adapted R. Granger Barrett. Litho Ueberreuter)

**1984** (3 Dec). *40th Anniv of International Civil Aviation Organization. T* **113** *and similar multicoloured designs. P* 14.
646 60 c. Type **113** .. .. .. .. 35 45
647 75 c. "Solar Princess" (abstract) .. .. 45 60
648 $2.50, I.C.A.O. emblem (*vert*) .. .. 1·50 1·75
646/8 .. .. .. .. *Set of* 3 2·10 2·50
**MS**649 65 × 49 mm. $5 Map of air routes serving Anguilla .. .. .. .. .. 3·00 3·50

(Litho Questa)

**1985** (29 Apr). *Birth Bicentenary of John J. Audubon (ornithologist). T* **114** *and similar multicoloured designs. P* 14.
650 10 c. Type **114** .. .. .. .. 15 10
651 60 c. American Wood Stork .. .. .. 45 40
652 75 c. Roseate Tern .. .. .. .. 50 45
653 $5 Osprey .. .. .. .. 2·75 3·00
650/3 .. .. .. .. *Set of* 4 3·50 3·50
**MS**654 Two sheets, each 73 × 103 mm. (a) $4 Western Tanager (*horiz*); (b) $4 Solitary Vireo (*horiz*) .. .. .. *Set of 2 sheets* 4·50 5·00
Nos. 650/3 were each issued in sheetlets of five stamps and one stamp-size label, which appears in the centre of the bottom row.

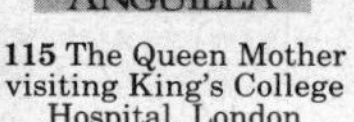

**115** The Queen Mother visiting King's College Hospital, London **116** White-tailed Tropic Bird

(Des J.W. Litho Questa)

**1985** (2 July). *Life and Times of Queen Elizabeth the Queen Mother. T* **115** *and similar vert designs. Multicoloured. P* 14.
655 10 c. Type **115** .. .. .. .. 10 10
656 $2 The Queen Mother inspecting Royal Marine Volunteer Cadets, Deal .. .. 1·10 1·25
657 $3 The Queen Mother outside Clarence House .. .. .. .. .. 1·60 1·75
655/7 .. .. .. .. *Set of* 3 2·50 2·75
**MS**658 56 × 85 mm. $5 At Ascot, 1979 .. .. 2·75 3·00
Nos. 655/7 also exist perforated 12 × 12½ from additional sheetlets of five stamps and one label (*Price for set of* 3 *£2.50 mint, £2.75 used*).

(Des R. Granger Barrett. Litho Questa)

**1985** (22 July)–**86**. *Birds. T* **116** *and similar horiz designs. Multicoloured. P* 13½ × 14.
659 5 c. Brown Pelican (11.11.85) .. .. 30 30
660 10 c. Mourning Dove (11.11.85) .. .. 30 30
661 15 c. Magnificent Frigate Bird (inscr "Man-o-War") (11.11.85) .. .. .. 30 30
662 20 c. Antillean Crested Hummingbird (11.11.85) .. .. .. .. 30 30
663 25 c. Type **116** .. .. .. .. 30 30
664 30 c. Caribbean Elaenia (11.11.85) .. .. 30 30
665 35 c. Black-whiskered Vireo (11.11.85) .. 1·75 1·40
665*a* 35 c. Lesser Antillean Bullfinch (10.3.86) .. 30 35
666 40 c. Yellow-crowned Night Heron (11.11.85) 40 50
667 45 c. Pearly-eyed Thrasher (30.9.85) .. 30 40
668 50 c. Laughing Gull (30.9.85) .. .. 30 40
669 65 c. Brown Booby .. .. .. 35 50
670 80 c. Grey Kingbird (30.9.85) .. .. 55 60
671 $1 Audubon's Shearwater (30.9.85) .. 75 75
672 $1.35, Roseate Tern .. .. .. 75 1·00
673 $2.50, Bananaquit (11.11.85) .. .. 2·00 2·00
674 $5 Belted Kingfisher .. .. .. 2·50 3·00
675 $10 Green Heron (30.9.85) .. .. 4·50 6·00
659/75 .. .. .. .. *Set of* 18 14·00 17·00

GIRL GUIDES 75TH ANNIVERSARY
1910–1985

(**117**)

**1985** (14 Oct). *75th Anniv of Girl Guide Movement. Nos. 486, 491, 496 and 498 optd with T* **117**.
676 5 c. Ferry service, Blowing Point .. .. 15 10
677 30 c. Little Bay cliffs .. .. .. 35 25
678 75 c. Boat race at sunset, Sandy Ground .. 50 70
679 $5 Brown Pelicans .. .. .. 3·75 3·50
a. Opt double .. .. .. .. 85·00
676/9 .. .. .. .. *Set of* 4 4·50 4·00

**118** Goofy as Huckleberry Finn Fishing

(Des Walt Disney Productions. Litho Questa)

**1985** (11 Nov). *150th Birth Anniv of Mark Twain (author). T* **118** *and similar horiz designs showing Walt Disney cartoon characters in scenes from "Huckleberry Finn". Multicoloured. P* 12 *($1) or* 14 × 13½ *(others).*
680 10 c. Type **118** .. .. .. .. 15 15
681 60 c. Pete as Pap surprising Huck .. .. 60 60
682 $1 "Multiplication tables" .. .. .. 85 85
683 $3 The Duke reciting Shakespeare .. .. 2·25 2·25
680/3 .. .. .. .. *Set of* 4 3·50 3·50
**MS**684 127×102 mm. $5 "In school but out" 3·00 3·50
No. 682 was printed in sheetlets of 8 stamps.

**119** Hansel and Gretel (Mickey and Minnie Mouse) awakening in Forest

(Des Walt Disney Productions. Litho Questa)

**1985** (11 Nov). *Birth Bicentenaries of Grimm Brothers (folklorists). T* **119** *and similar horiz designs showing Walt Disney cartoon characters in scenes from "Hansel and Gretel". Multicoloured. P* 12 *(90 c.) or* 14 × 13½ *(others).*
685 5 c. Type **119** .. .. .. .. 10 10
686 50 c. Hansel and Gretel find the gingerbread house .. .. .. .. .. 25 30
687 90 c. Hansel and Gretel meeting the Witch .. 45 50
688 $4 Hansel and Gretel captured by the Witch .. .. .. .. .. 2·00 2·10
685/8 .. .. .. .. *Set of* 4 2·50 2·75
**MS**689 126×101 mm. $5 Hansel and Gretel riding on swan .. .. .. .. 2·50 3·00
No. 687 was printed in sheetlets of 8 stamps.

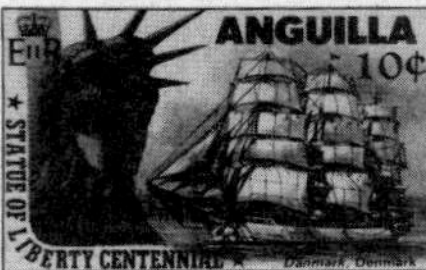


**120** Statue of Liberty and *Danmark* (Denmark)

(Litho Format)

**1985** (14 Nov). *Centenary of the Statue of Liberty (1986). T* **120** *and similar multicoloured designs showing the Statue of Liberty and cadet ships. P* 15.
690 10 c. Type **120** .. .. .. .. 40 40
691 20 c. *Eagle* (U.S.A.) .. .. .. 55 55
692 60 c. *Amerigo Vespucci* (Italy) .. .. 1·00 1·00
693 75 c. *Sir Winston Churchill* (Great Britain) .. 1·25 1·25
694 $2 *Nippon Maru* (Japan) .. .. .. 2·00 2·00
695 $2.50, *Gorch Fock* (West Germany) .. 2·25 2·25
690/5 .. .. .. .. *Set of* 6 6·75 6·75
**MS**696 96 × 69 mm. $5 Statue of Liberty (*vert*) .. 4·50 4·50

(**121**)

(**122**)

**1985** (18 Nov). *80th Anniv of Rotary (10, 35 c.) and International Youth Year (others). Nos. 487, 491 and 497 surch or optd as T* **121** *(10 c., 35 c.) or* **122** *(others).*
697 10 c. Racing boats .. .. .. .. 10 10
698 35 c. on 30 c. Little Bay cliffs .. .. 25 25
699 $1 Bagging lobster at Island Harbour .. 70 70
700 $5 on 30 c. Little Bay cliffs .. .. 3·50 3·50
697/700 .. .. .. .. *Set of* 4 4·00 4·00

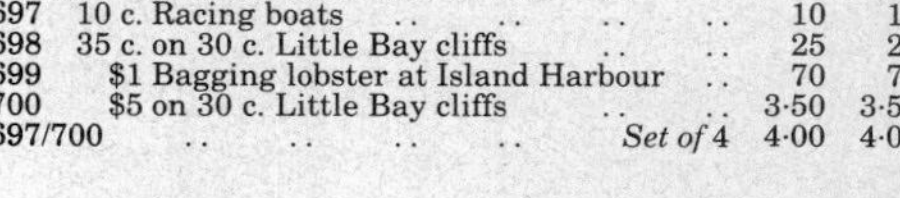

**123** Johannes Hevelius (astronomer) and Mayan Temple Observatory **124** The Crucifixion

(Des W. Hanson. Litho Questa)

**1986** (17 Mar). *Appearance of Halley's Comet. T* **123** *and similar horiz designs. Multicoloured. P* 14.
701 5 c. Type **123** .. .. .. .. 20 20
702 10 c. "Viking Lander" space vehicle on Mars, 1976 .. .. .. .. .. 20 20
703 60 c. Comet in 1664 (from *Theatri Cosmicum*, 1668) .. .. .. .. 70 70
704 $4 Comet over Mississippi riverboat, 1835 (150th birth anniv of Mark Twain) .. 3·00 3·00
701/4 .. .. .. .. *Set of* 4 3·75 3·75
**MS**705 101×70 mm. $5 Halley's Comet over Anguilla .. .. .. .. .. 2·75 3·2

(Des R. Granger Barrett. Litho Questa)

**1986** (27 Mar). *Easter. T* **124** *and similar designs showing stained glass windows from Chartres Cathedral. P* 14 × 13½.
706 10 c. multicoloured .. .. .. .. 15 15
707 25 c. multicoloured .. .. .. .. 25 25
708 45 c. multicoloured .. .. .. .. 45 45
709 $4 multicoloured .. .. .. .. 2·75 2·75
706/9 .. .. .. .. *Set of* 4 3·25 3·25
**MS**710 93×75 mm. $5 multicoloured (*horiz*). P 13½ × 14 .. .. .. .. .. 3·75 4·25

**125** Princess Elizabeth inspecting Guards, 1946

AMERIPEX 1986

(**126**)

(Litho Questa)

**1986** (21 Apr). *60th Birthday of Queen Elizabeth II. T* **125** *and similar vert designs. P 14.*

711 20 c. black and yellow 15 15
712 $2 multicoloured 1·25 1·25
713 $3 multicoloured 1·75 1·75
711/13 *Set of* 3 2·75 2·75
**MS**714 120×85 mm. $5 black and grey-brown 2·75 3·25

Designs:—$2 Queen at Garter Ceremony; $3 At Trooping the Colour; $5 Duke and Duchess of York with baby Princess Elizabeth, 1926.

**1986** (22 May). *"Ameripex" International Stamp Exhibition, Chicago. Nos. 659, 667, 671, 673 and 675 optd with T* **126**.

715 5 c. Brown Pelican 10 10
716 45 c. Pearly-eyed Thrasher 35 35
717 $1 Audubon's Shearwater 65 65
718 $2.50, Bananaquit 1·50 1·50
719 $10 Green Heron 5·50 5·50
715/19 *Set of* 5 7·25 7·25

**127** Prince Andrew and Miss Sarah Ferguson

INTERNATIONAL YEAR OF PEACE

(**128**)

(Des and litho Questa)

**1986** (23 July). *Royal Wedding. T* **127** *and similar vert designs. Multicoloured. A. P 14. B. P 12.*

| | | A | | B | |
|---|---|---|---|---|---|
| 720 | 10 c. Type **127** | 10 | 10 | 10 | 10 |
| 721 | 35 c. Prince Andrew | 20 | 25 | 20 | 25 |
| 722 | $2 Miss Sarah Ferguson | 1·00 | 1·10 | 1·00 | 1·10 |
| 723 | $3 Prince Andrew and Miss Sarah Ferguson (*different*) | 1·50 | 1·60 | 1·50 | 1·60 |
| 720/3 | *Set of* 4 | 2·50 | 2·75 | 2·50 | 2·75 |
| **MS**724 | 119×90 mm. $6 Westminster Abbey | 3·50 | 4·00 | 3·50 | 4·00 |

**1986** (29 Sept). *International Peace Year. Nos. 616/24 optd with T* **128**.

725 10 c. Type **109** 10 10
726 25 c. Abraham Lincoln 20 20
727 35 c. Henri Christophe 30 30
728 60 c. Thomas Clarkson 45 45
729 75 c. William Wilberforce 50 50
730 $1 Olaudah Equiano 65 65
731 $2.50, General Gordon 1·50 1·50
732 $5 Granville Sharp 2·75 2·75
725/32 *Set of* 8 5·75 5·75
**MS**733 150×121 mnm. Nos. 725/32 6·50 7·50

**129** Trading Sloop

**130** Christopher Columbus with Astrolabe

(Des R. Granger Barrett. Litho Questa)

**1986** (25 Nov). *Christmas. Ships. T* **129** *and similar multicoloured designs. P 14.*

734 10 c. Type **129** 30 30
735 45 c. *Lady Rodney* (cargo liner) 75 75
736 80 c. *West Derby* (19th-century sailing ship) 90 90
737 $3 *Warspite* (local sloop) 2·75 2·75
734/7 *Set of* 4 4·25 4·25
**MS**738 130×100 mm. $6 Boat race day (*vert*) 5·50 6·00

(Des Mary Walters. Litho Questa)

**1986** (22 Dec). *500th Anniv of Discovery of America* (1992). *T* **130** *and similar multicoloured designs. P 14.*

739 5 c. Type **130** 10 10
740 10 c. Columbus on board ship 15 15
741 35 c. *Santa Maria* 60 60
742 80 c. King Ferdinand and Queen Isabella of Spain (*horiz*) 80 80
743 $4 Caribbean Indians smoking tobacco (*horiz*) 2·75 2·75
739/43 *Set of* 5 4·00 4·00
**MS**744 Two sheets, each 96×66 mm. (a) $5 Caribbean Manatee (*horiz*). (b) $5 Dragon Tree *Set of* 2 *sheets* 8·00 9·00

## *NEW INFORMATION*

The editor is always interested to correspond with people who have new information that will improve or correct the Catalogue.

**131** *Danaus plexippus*

(Des R. Vigurs. Litho Questa)

**1987** (14 Apr). *Easter. Butterflies. T* **131** *and similar horiz designs. Multicoloured. P 14.*

745 10 c. Type **131** 20 20
746 80 c. *Anartia jatrophae* 70 70
747 $1 *Heliconius charithonia* 90 90
748 $2 *Junonia evarete* 1·50 1·50
745/8 *Set of* 4 3·00 3·00
**MS**749 90×69 mm. $6 *Dryas julia* 5·50 6·00

**132** Old Goose Iron and Modern Electric Iron

CAPEX'87

(**133**)

(Des R. Vigurs. Litho Questa)

**1987** (25 May). *20th Anniv of Separation from St. Kitts–Nevis. T* **132** *and similar horiz designs. Multicoloured. P 14.*

750 10 c. Type **132** 10 10
751 35 c. Old East End School and Albena Lake-Hodge Comprehensive College 15 20
752 45 c. Past and present markets 20 25
753 80 c. Previous sailing ferry and new motor ferry, Blowing Point 35 40
754 $1 Original mobile office and new telephone exchange 45 50
755 $2 Open-air meeting, Burrowes Park, and House of Assembly in session 90 95
750/5 *Set of* 6 1·90 2·10
**MS**756 159×127 mm. Nos. 750/5 3·00 3·50

**1987** (13 June). *"Capex '87" International Stamp Exhibition, Toronto. Nos. 665a, 667, 670 and 675 optd with T* **133** *in red.*

757 35 c. Lesser Antillean Bullfinch 20 20
758 45 c. Pearly-eyed Thrasher 25 25
759 80 c. Grey Kingbird 40 40
760 $10 Green Heron 5·00 5·00
757/60 *Set of* 4 5·25 5·25

20 YEARS OF PROGRESS

1967 – 1987

(**134**)

**1987** (4 Sept). *20th Anniv of Independence. Nos. 659, 661/4 and 665a/75 optd as T* **134** *in red or surch additionally in black (No. 762).*

761 5 c. Brown Pelican 15 20
762 10 c. on 15 c. Magnificent Frigate Bird 15 20
763 15 c. Magnificent Frigate Bird 15 20
764 20 c. Antillean Crested Hummingbird 20 25
765 25 c. Type **116** 20 25
766 30 c. Caribbean Elaenia 30 35
767 35 c. Lesser Antillean Bullfinch 35 40
768 40 c. Yellow-crowned Night Heron 35 40
769 45 c. Pearly-eyed Thrasher 40 50
 a. Opt double, one albino 42·00
770 50 c. Laughing Gull 40 50
771 65 c. Brown Booby 45 55
772 80 c. Grey Kingbird 55 65
773 $1 Audubon's Shearwater 65 75
774 $1.35, Roseate Tern 80 90
775 $2.50, Bananaquit 1·50 1·75
776 $5 Belted Kingfisher 2·75 3·25
777 $10 Green Heron 5·50 7·00
761/77 *Set of* 17 13·50 16·00

**135** Wicket Keeper and Game in Progress

(Des R. Granger Barrett. Litho Questa)

**1987** (5 Oct). *Cricket World Cup. T* **135** *and similar horiz designs. Multicoloured. P* 13½×14.

778 10 c. Type **135** 25 20
779 35 c. Batsman and local Anguilla team 45 40
780 45 c. Batsman and game in progress 55 50
781 $2.50, Bowler and game in progress 1·75 1·90
778/81 *Set of* 4 2·75 2·75
**MS**782 100×75 mm. $6 Batsman and game in progress (*different*) 5·50 5·75

**136** West Indian Top Shell

(Des R. Granger Barrett. Litho Questa)

**1987** (2 Nov). *Christmas. Sea Shells and Crabs. T* **136** *and similar horiz designs. Multicoloured. P* 13½×14.

783 10 c. Type **136** 10 10
784 35 c. Ghost Crab 25 25
785 50 c. Spiny Caribbean Vase 40 40
786 $2 Great Land Crab 1·25 1·25
783/6 *Set of* 4 1·75 1·75
**MS**787 101×75 mm. $6 Queen Conch 3·00 3·50

40TH WEDDING ANNIVERSARY

H.M. QUEEN ELIZABETH II

H.R.H. THE DUKE OF EDINBURGH

(**137**)

**1987** (16 Dec). *Royal Ruby Wedding. Nos. 665a, 671/2 and 675 optd with T* **137** *in carmine.*

788 35 c. Lesser Antillean Bullfinch 15 20
789 $1 Audubon's Shearwater 45 50
790 $1.35, Roseate Tern 60 65
791 $10 Green Heron 4·50 4·75
788/91 *Set of* 4 5·00 5·50

**138** *Crinum erubescens*

**139** Relay Racing

(Des R. Vigurs. Litho Questa)

**1988** (28 Mar). *Easter. Lilies. T* **138** *and similar vert designs. Multicoloured. P* 14×13½.

792 30 c. Type **138** 15 15
793 45 c. Spider Lily 25 25
794 $1 *Crinum macowanii* 50 50
795 $2.50, Day Lily 1·25 1·25
792/5 *Set of* 4 1·90 1·90
**MS**796 100×75 mm. $6 Easter Lily 2·75 3·25

(Des R. Vigurs. Litho Questa)

**1988** (25 July). *Olympic Games, Seoul. T* **139** *and similar vert designs. Multicoloured. P* 14×13½.

797 35 c. Type **139** 30 30
798 45 c. Windsurfing 40 40
799 50 c. Tennis 50 50
800 80 c. Basketball 70 70
797/800 *Set of* 4 1·75 1·75
**MS**801 104×78 mm. $6 Athletics 3·00 3·50

**140** Common Sea Fan

(Des R. Vigurs. Litho Questa)

**1988** (28 Nov). *Christmas. Marine Life. T* **140** *and similar horiz designs. Multicoloured. P* 13½ × 14.

802 35 c. Type **140** 15 20
803 80 c. Coral Crab 40 45
804 $1 Grooved Brain Coral 45 50
805 $1.60, Queen Triggerfish 70 70
802/5 *Set of* 4 1·50 1·60
**MS**806 103 x 78 mm. $6 West Indies Spiny Lobster 2·50 2·75

H.R.H. PRINCESS ALEXANDRA'S VISIT NOVEMBER 1988

(**141**)

**1988** (14 Dec). *Visit of Princess Alexandra. Nos. 665a, 670/1 and 673 optd with T* **141**.

807 35 c. Lesser Antillean Bullfinch 25 25
808 80 c. Grey Kingbird 55 55
809 $1 Audubon's Shearwater 65 65
810 $2.50, Bananaquit 1·40 1·40
807/10 *Set of* 4 2·50 2·50

142 Wood Slave

143 "Christ Crowned with Thorns" (detail) (Bosch)

(Des R. Vigurs. Litho Questa)

**1989** (20 Feb). *Lizards. T* **142** *and similar horiz designs. Multicoloured. P* 13½ × 14.

| | | | |
|---|---|---|---|
| 811 | 45 c. Type **142** | 20 | 25 |
| 812 | 80 c. Slippery Back | 40 | 45 |
| 813 | $2.50, *Iguana delicatissima* | 1·25 | 1·40 |
| 811/13 | *Set of* 3 | 1·60 | 1·90 |
| **MS**814 | 101 × 75 mm. $6 Tree Lizard | 2·75 | 3·00 |

(Des R. Vigurs. Litho Questa)

**1989** (23 Mar). *Easter. Religious Paintings. T* **143** *and similar vert designs. Multicoloured. P* 14 × 13½.

| | | | |
|---|---|---|---|
| 815 | 35 c. Type **143** | 15 | 20 |
| 816 | 80 c. "Christ bearing the Cross" (detail) (Gerard David) | 40 | 45 |
| 817 | $1 "The Deposition" (detail) (Gerard David) | 45 | 50 |
| 818 | $1.60, "Pietà" (detail) (Rogier van der Weyden) | 75 | 80 |
| 815/18 | *Set of* 4 | 1·60 | 1·75 |
| **MS**819 | 103 × 77 mm. $6 "Crucified Christ with the Virgin Mary and Saints" (detail) (Raphael) | 2·75 | 3·00 |

144 University Arms

20th
ANNIVERSARY
MOON
LANDING

(145)

(Des R. Vigurs. Litho Questa)

**1989** (24 Apr). *40th Anniv of University of the West Indies. P* 14 × 13½.

| | | | |
|---|---|---|---|
| 820 | **144** $5 multicoloured | 2·40 | 2·50 |

**1989** (31 July). *20th Anniv of First Manned Landing on Moon. Nos.* 670/2 *and* 674 *optd with T* **145**.

| | | | |
|---|---|---|---|
| 821 | 80 c. Grey Kingbird | 40 | 45 |
| 822 | $1 Audubon's Shearwater | 45 | 50 |
| 823 | $1.35, Roseate Tern | 65 | 70 |
| 824 | $5 Belted Kingfisher | 2·40 | 2·50 |
| 821/4 | *Set of* 4 | 3·50 | 3·75 |

146 Lone Star House, 1930

(Des J. Vigurs. Litho Questa)

**1989** (11 Dec). *Christmas. Historic Houses. T* **146** *and similar horiz designs. Multicoloured. P* 13½×14.

| | | | |
|---|---|---|---|
| 825 | 5 c. Type **146** | 10 | 10 |
| 826 | 35 c. Whitehouse, 1906 | 15 | 20 |
| 827 | 45 c. Hodges House | 20 | 25 |
| 828 | 80 c. Warden's Place | 40 | 45 |
| 825/8 | *Set of* 4 | 75 | 90 |
| **MS**829 | 102×77 mm. $6 Wallblake House, 1787 | 2·75 | 3·00 |

147 Blear Eye

148 The Last Supper

(Des J. Vigurs. Litho Questa)

**1990** (2 Apr). *Fishes. T* **147** *and similar horiz designs. Multicoloured. P* 13½×14.

| | | | |
|---|---|---|---|
| 830 | 5 c. Type **147** | 10 | 10 |
| 831 | 10 c. Redman | 10 | 10 |
| 832 | 15 c. Speckletail | 10 | 10 |
| 833 | 25 c. Grunt | 10 | 15 |
| 834 | 30 c. Amber Jack | 10 | 15 |
| 835 | 35 c. Red Hind | 15 | 20 |
| 836 | 40 c. Goatfish | 15 | 20 |
| 837 | 45 c. Old Wife | 20 | 25 |
| 838 | 50 c. Butter Fish | 20 | 25 |
| 839 | 65 c. Shell Fish | 25 | 30 |
| 840 | 80 c. Yellowtail Snapper | 35 | 40 |
| 841 | $1 Katy | 40 | 45 |
| 842 | $1.35, Mutton Grouper | 55 | 60 |
| 843 | $2.50, Doctor Fish | 1·00 | 1·10 |
| 844 | $5 Angelfish | 2·10 | 2·25 |
| 845 | $10 Barracuda | 4·25 | 4·50 |
| 830/45 | *Set of* 16 | 9·00 | 9·75 |

(Des M. Pollard. Litho Questa)

**1990** (2 Apr). *Easter. T* **148** *and similar vert designs. Multicoloured. P* 14×13½.

| | | | |
|---|---|---|---|
| 846 | 35 c. Type **148** | 15 | 20 |
| 847 | 45 c. The Trial | 20 | 25 |
| 848 | $1.35, The Crucifixion | 55 | 60 |
| 849 | $2.50, The Empty Tomb | 1·00 | 1·10 |
| 846/9 | *Set of* 4 | 1·75 | 1·90 |
| **MS**850 | 114×84 mm. $6 The Resurrection | 3·00 | 3·25 |

149 G.B. 1840 Penny Black

WORLD CUP FOOTBALL
CHAMPIONSHIPS 1990

(150)

(Litho Questa)

**1990** (30 Apr). *"Stamp World London 90" International Stamp Exhibition. T* **149** *and similar multicoloured designs showing stamps. P* 14.

| | | | |
|---|---|---|---|
| 851 | 25 c. Type **149** | 10 | 10 |
| 852 | 50 c. G.B. 1840 Twopenny Blue | 20 | 25 |
| 853 | $1.50, Cape of Good Hope 1861 1d. "woodblock" (*horiz*) | 60 | 65 |
| 854 | $2.50, G.B. 1882 £5 (*horiz*) | 1·00 | 1·10 |
| 851/4 | *Set of* 4 | 1·60 | 1·90 |
| **MS**855 | 86×71 mm. $6 Penny Black and Twopence Blue (*horiz*) | 2·75 | 3·00 |

**1990** (24 Sept). *Anniversaries and Events. Nos.* 841/4 *optd as T* **150**.

| | | | |
|---|---|---|---|
| 856 | $1 Katy (optd "EXPO '90") | 40 | 45 |
| 857 | $1.35, Mutton Grouper (optd "1990 INTERNATIONAL LITERACY YEAR") | 55 | 60 |
| 858 | $2.50, Doctor Fish (optd with T **150**) | 1·00 | 1·10 |
| 859 | $5 Angel Fish (optd "90TH BIRTHDAY H.M. THE QUEEN MOTHER") | 2·00 | 2·10 |
| 856/9 | *Set of* 4 | 3·50 | 3·75 |

151 Mermaid Flag

(Des R. Vigurs. Litho Questa)

**1990** (5 Nov). *Island Flags. T* **151** *and similar horiz designs. Multicoloured. P* 13½×14.

| | | | |
|---|---|---|---|
| 860 | 50 c. Type **151** | 20 | 25 |
| 861 | 80 c. New Anguilla official flag | 30 | 35 |
| 862 | $1 Three Dolphins flag | 40 | 45 |
| 863 | $5 Governor's official flag | 2·00 | 2·10 |
| 860/3 | *Set of* 4 | 2·50 | 2·75 |

152 Laughing Gulls

1991

(153)

(Des R. Vigurs. Litho Questa)

**1990** (26 Nov). *Christmas. Sea Birds. T* **152** *and similar horiz designs. Multicoloured. P* 13½×14.

| | | | |
|---|---|---|---|
| 864 | 10 c. Type **152** | 15 | 15 |
| 865 | 35 c. Brown Booby | 25 | 25 |
| 866 | $1.50, Bridled Tern | 85 | 85 |
| 867 | $3.50, Brown Pelican | 1·75 | 1·75 |
| 864/7 | *Set of* 4 | 2·75 | 2·75 |
| **MS**868 | 101×76 mm. $6 Little Tern | 3·25 | 3·25 |

**1991** (30 Apr). *Easter. Nos.* 846/50 *optd with T* **153**.

| | | | |
|---|---|---|---|
| 869 | 35 c. Type **148** | 15 | 20 |
| 870 | 45 c. The Trial | 20 | 25 |
| 871 | $1.35, The Crucifixion | 55 | 60 |
| 872 | $2.50, The Empty Tomb | 1·00 | 1·10 |
| 869/72 | *Set of* 4 | 1·75 | 1·90 |
| **MS**873 | 114 × 84 mm. $6 The Resurrection | 2·50 | 2·75 |

On No. **MS**873 the "1990" inscription on the sheet margin has also been obliterated.

# Antigua

The first mention of a local postmaster for Antigua is in 1760 and the earliest straight-line mark is not known before 1780. Mail services before 1850 were somewhat haphazard, until St. John's was made a branch office of the British G.P.O. in 1850. A second office, at English Harbour, opened in 1857.

The stamps of Great Britain were used between May 1858 and the end of April 1860, when the island postal service became the responsibility of the local colonial authorities. In the interim period, between the take-over and the appearance of Antiguan stamps, the crowned-circle handstamps were again utilised and No. CC1 can be found used as late as 1869.

For illustrations of the handstamp and postmark types see BRITISH POST OFFICES ABROAD notes, following GREAT BRITAIN.

### ST. JOHN'S

CROWNED-CIRCLE HANDSTAMPS

CC1 CC 1 ANTIGUA (St. John's) (9.3.1850)(R.)
*Price on cover* £550

*Stamps of* GREAT BRITAIN *cancelled* "A 02" *as Type* **2**.

**1858** *to* **1860**.
Z1 1d. rose-red (1857), *perf* 14 .. .. .. £475
Z2 2d. blue (1855), *perf* 14 (Plate No. 6) .. .. £900
Z3 2d. blue (1858) (Plate Nos. 7, 8, 9) .. .. .. £550
Z4 4d. rose (1857) .. .. .. .. £450
Z5 6d. lilac (1856) .. .. .. .. £160
Z6 1s. green (1856) .. .. .. .. £1500

### ENGLISH HARBOUR

CROWNED-CIRCLE HANDSTAMPS

CC2 CC 3 ENGLISH HARBOUR (10.12.1857)
*Price on cover* £4250

*Stamps of* GREAT BRITAIN *cancelled* "A 18" *as Type* **2**.

**1858** to **1860**.
Z7 2d. blue (1858) (Plate No. 7) .. .. .. £5000
Z8 4d. rose (1857) .. .. .. .. £5000
Z9 6d. lilac .. .. .. .. £2000
Z10 1s. green (1856) .. .. .. ..

**PRICES FOR STAMPS ON COVER TO 1945**

| | |
|---|---|
| No. 1 | *from* × 5 |
| Nos. 2/4 | † |
| Nos. 5/10 | *from* × 15 |
| Nos 13/14 | *from* × 20 |
| No. 15 | *from* × 50 |
| Nos. 16/18 | *from* × 30 |
| Nos. 19/23 | *from* × 10 |
| No. 24 | *from* × 40 |
| Nos. 25/30 | *from* × 10 |
| Nos. 31/51 | *from* × 3 |
| Nos. 52/4 | *from* × 5 |
| Nos. 55/61 | *from* × 4 |
| Nos. 62/80 | *from* × 3 |
| Nos. 81/90 | *from* × 4 |
| Nos. 91/4 | *from* × 3 |
| Nos. 95/7 | *from* × 4 |
| Nos. 98/109 | *from* × 3 |

### CROWN COLONY

1

3 (Die I)

(Eng C. Jeens after drawing by Edward Corbould. Recess P.B.)

**1862** (Aug). *No wmk. (a) Rough perf* 14 *to* 16.
1 1 6d. blue-green .. .. .. .. £800 £500

*(b) P* 11 *to* 12½
2 1 6d. blue-green .. .. .. .. £3500

*(c) P* 14 *to* 16 × 11 *to* 12½
3 1 6d. blue-green .. .. .. .. £2500

*(d) P* 14 *to* 16 *compound with* 11 *to* 12½
4 1 6d. blue-green .. .. .. .. £2750

Nos. 2/4 may be trial perforations. They are not known used.

**1863** (Jan)–**67**. *Wmk Small Star. W w* **2** *(sideways on 6d.). Rough perf* 14 *to* 16.
5 1 1d. rosy mauve .. .. .. .. £110 40·00
6 1d. dull rose (1864) .. .. .. .. 90·00 35·00
a. Imperf between (vert pair) .. .. £11000
7 1d. vermilion (1867) .. .. .. £120 22·00
a. Imperf between (horiz pair) .. .. £13000
b. Wmk sideways .. .. ..
8 6d. green (*shades*) .. .. .. £325 22·00
a. Wmk upright .. .. ..
9 6d. dark green .. .. .. .. £275 22·00
10 6d. yellow-green .. .. .. .. £2500 60·00

Caution is needed in buying No. 10 as some of the shades of No. 8 verge on yellow-green.

The 1d. rosy mauve exists showing trial perforations of 11 to 12½ and 14 to 16.

(Recess D.L.R. from P.B. plates)

**1872.** *Wmk Crown CC. P* 12½.
13 1 1d. lake .. .. .. .. 75·00 15·00
14 1d. scarlet .. .. .. .. 95·00 15·00
15 6d. blue-green .. .. .. .. £500 6·00

**1876.** *Wmk Crown CC. P* 14.
16 1 1d. lake .. .. .. .. 80·00 9·00
a. Bisected (½d.) (1883) (on cover) .. † £2250
17 1d. lake-rose .. .. .. .. 80·00 9·00
18 6d. blue-green .. .. .. .. £300 11·00

(Recess (T 1); typo (T 3) De La Rue & Co)

**1879.** *Wmk Crown CC. P* 14.
19 3 2½d. red-brown .. .. .. .. £600 £160
a. Large "2" in "2½" with slanting foot £7000 £2250
20 4d. blue .. .. .. .. £250 14·00

**1882.** *Wmk Crown CA. P* 14.
21 3 ½d. dull green .. .. .. .. 1·40 10·00
22 2½d. red-brown .. .. .. .. £130 45·00
a. Large "2" in "2½" with slanting foot £2250 £1100
23 4d. blue .. .. .. .. £275 15·00

**1884.** *Wmk Crown CA. P* 12.
24 1 1d. carmine-red .. .. .. 48·00 15·00

The 1d. scarlet is a colour changeling.

**1884–86.** *Wmk Crown CA. P* 14.
25 1 1d. carmine-red .. .. .. .. 80 2·25
26 1d. rose .. .. .. .. 48·00 12·00
27 3 2½d. ultramarine (1886) .. .. .. 5·00 11·00
a. Large "2" in "2½" with slanting foot £160 £250
28 4d. chestnut (1886) .. .. .. 1·25 2·00
29 1 6d. deep green .. .. .. .. 55·00 £120
30 3 1s. mauve (1886) .. .. .. £160 £120
27/28, 30 Optd "Specimen" .. *Set of* 3 £150

Nos. 25 and 26 postmarked "A 12" in place of "A 02" were used in St. Christopher.

**2½ 2½ 2½**
A B C

The variety "Large '2' in '2½' with slanting foot" occurs on the first stamp of the seventh row in both left (A) and right (B) panes (in which positions the "NN" of "PENNY" have three vertical strokes shortened) and on the first stamp of the third row of the right-hand pane (C). The "2" varies slightly in each position.

From 31 October 1890 until July 1903 Leeward Islands general issues were used. Subsequently both general issues and the following separate issues were in concurrent use until July 1956, when the general Leewards Island stamps were withdrawn.

4

5

(Typo D.L.R.)

**1903** (July)–**09**. *Wmk Crown CC. Ordinary paper. P* 14.
31 4 ½d. grey-black and grey-green .. .. 2·00 3·50
32 1d. grey-black and rose-red .. .. 3·75 40
a. Bluish paper (1909) .. .. .. 70·00 70·00
33 2d. dull purple and brown .. .. 6·00 22·00
34 2½d. grey-black and blue .. .. .. 8·00 10·00
a. Chalk-surfaced paper (1907) .. 9·00 16·00
35 3d. grey-green and orange-brown .. 9·50 20·00
36 6d. purple and black .. .. .. 24·00 45·00
37 1s. blue and dull purple .. .. .. 23·00 42·00
a. Chalk-surfaced paper (1907) .. 20·00 48·00
38 2s. grey-green and pale violet .. .. 48·00 60·00
39 2s. 6d. grey-black and purple .. .. 16·00 42·00
40 5 5s. grey-green and violet .. .. 60·00 70·00
a. Chalk-surfaced paper (1907) .. 60·00 70·00
31/40 .. .. .. .. *Set of* 10 £160 £275
31/40 Optd "Specimen" .. .. *Set of* 10 £150

**1908–17.** *Wmk Mult Crown CA. Chalk-surfaced paper (2d., 3d. to 2s.). P* 14.
41 4 ½d. green .. .. .. .. 1·00 2·50
42 ½d. blue-green (1917) .. .. .. 1·50 3·75
43 1d. red (1909) .. .. .. .. 2·50 1·40
44 1d. scarlet (5.8.15) .. .. .. 2·25 2·50
45 2d. dull purple and brown (1912) .. 3·25 18·00
46 2½d. ultramarine .. .. .. .. 6·00 13·00
*a. Blue* .. .. .. .. 11·00 17·00
47 3d. grey-green and orange-brown (1912) 6·00 15·00
48 6d. purple and black (1911) .. .. 7·50 26·00
49 1s. blue and dull purple .. .. .. 14·00 55·00
50 2s. grey-green and violet (1912) .. .. 42·00 65·00
41/50 .. .. .. .. *Set of* 8 75·00 £170
41, 43, 46 Optd "Specimen" .. .. *Set of* 3 65·00

**1913.** *As T* **5**, *but portrait of King George V. Wmk Mult Crown CA. Chalk-surfaced paper. P* 14.
51 5s. grey-green and violet (Optd S. £60) .. 60·00 85·00

**WAR STAMP**
(7)

8

**1916** (Sept)–**17**. *No.* 41 *optd in London with T* **7**.
52 4 ½d. green (Bk.) .. .. .. .. 40 65
53 ½d. green (R.) (1.10.17) .. .. .. 40 65

**1918** (July). *Optd with T* **7**. *Wmk Mult Crown CA. P* 14.
54 4 1½d. orange .. .. .. .. 35 60
52/4 Optd "Specimen" .. .. *Set of* 3 70·00

(Typo D.L.R.)

**1921–29.** *P* 14. *(a) Wmk Mult Crown CA. Chalk-surfaced paper.*
55 8 3d. purple/*pale yellow* .. .. .. 3·50 11·00
56 4d. grey-black and red/*pale yellow* (1922) 1·25 5·00
57 1s. black/*emerald* .. .. .. 3·75 6·00
58 2s. purple and blue/*blue* .. .. 7·50 17·00
59 2s. 6d. black and red/*blue* .. .. 11·00 32·00
60 5s. green and red/*pale yellow* (1922) .. 8·00 25·00
61 £1 purple and black/*red* (1922) .. .. £170 £225
55/61 .. .. .. .. *Set of* 7 £190 £275
55/61 Optd "Specimen" .. .. *Set of* 7 £190

*(b) Wmk Mult Script CA. Chalk-surfaced paper (3d. to 4s.).*
62 8 ½d. dull green .. .. .. .. 35 20
63 1d. carmine-red .. .. .. .. 75 20
64 1d. bright violet (1923) .. .. .. 1·25 1·50
*a. Mauve* .. .. .. .. 4·75 5·00
65 1d. bright scarlet (1929) .. .. .. 2·75 90
67 1½d. dull orange (1922) .. .. .. 1·50 7·00
68 1½d. carmine-red (1926) .. .. .. 1·25 1·75
69 1½d. pale red-brown (1929) .. .. .. 1·50 60
70 2d. grey (1922) .. .. .. .. 1·00 75
a. Wmk sideways .. .. ..
71 2½d. bright blue (1922) .. .. .. 6·00 12·00
72 2½d. ultramarine (1927) .. .. .. 3·00 5·50
73 2½d. orange-yellow (1929) .. .. .. 1·25 15·00
74 3d. purple/*pale yellow* (1925) .. .. 4·00 8·50
75 6d. dull and bright purple (1922) .. .. 2·75 5·00
76 1s. black/*emerald* (1929) .. .. .. 7·00 8·00
77 2s. purple and blue/*blue* (1927) .. .. 10·00 30·00
78 2s. 6d. black and red/*blue* (1927) .. .. 15·00 20·00
79 3s. green and violet (1922) .. .. .. 18·00 45·00
80 4s. grey-black and red (1922) .. .. 42·00 48·00
62/80 .. .. .. .. *Set of* 16 95·00 £180
62/80 Optd/Perf "Specimen" .. .. *Set of* 18 £325

**9** Old Dockyard, English Harbour

**10** Government House, St. John's

(Des Mrs. J. Goodwin (5s.), Waterlow (others). Recess Waterlow)

**1932** (27 Jan). *Tercentenary. T* **9/10** *and similar designs. Wmk Mult Script CA. P* 12½.
81 9 ½d. green .. .. .. .. 1·50 3·75
82 1d. scarlet .. .. .. .. 2·00 2·00
83 1½d. brown .. .. .. .. 3·00 3·75
84 10 2d. grey .. .. .. .. 3·75 14·00
85 2½d. deep blue .. .. .. .. 3·75 7·50
86 3d. orange .. .. .. .. 3·75 12·00
87 – 6d. violet .. .. .. .. 11·00 12·00
88 – 1s. olive-green .. .. .. .. 14·00 24·00
89 – 2s. 6d. claret .. .. .. .. 40·00 48·00
90 – 5s. black and chocolate .. .. .. 80·00 £110
81/90 .. .. .. .. *Set of* 10 £140 £200
81/90 Perf "Specimen" .. .. *Set of* 10 £250

Designs: *Horiz*—6d., 1s., 2s. 6d. Nelson's *Victory*. *Vert*—5s. Sir Thomas Warner's *Concepcion*.

**13** Windsor Castle

(Des H. Fleury. Recess D.L.R.)

**1935** (6 May). *Silver Jubilee. Wmk Mult Script CA. P* 13½ × 14.
91 13 1d. deep blue and carmine .. .. 1·50 1·00
f. Diagonal line by turret .. .. 40·00
92 1½d. ultramarine and grey .. .. 1·75 45
93 2½d. brown and deep blue .. .. 3·75 1·00
g. Dot to left of chapel .. .. 65·00
94 1s. slate and purple .. .. .. 7·50 11·00
91/4 .. .. .. .. *Set of* 4 13·00 12·00
91/4 Perf "Specimen" .. .. *Set of* 4 70·00

For illustrations of plate varieties see Catalogue Introduction.

**14** King George VI and Queen Elizabeth

(Des D.L.R.. Recess B.W.)

**1937** (12 May). *Coronation. Wmk Mult Script CA. P* 11×11½.
95 14 1d. carmine .. .. .. .. 50 35
96 1½d. yellow-brown .. .. .. .. 60 30
97 2½d. blue .. .. .. .. 1·75 75
95/7 .. .. .. .. *Set of* 3 2·50 1·25
95/7 Perf "Specimen" .. .. *Set of* 3 50·00

15 English Harbour

16 Nelson's Dockyard

(Recess Waterlow)

**1938** (15 Nov)–**51**. *T* **15**, **16** *and similar designs. Wmk Mult Script CA. P* 12½.

98 **15** ½d. green .. .. .. .. .. 15 40
99 **16** 1d. scarlet .. .. .. .. .. 1·50 70
*a. Red* (8.42 and 11.47) .. .. 50 40
100 1½d. chocolate-brown .. .. .. 2·00 40
*a. Dull reddish brown* (12.43) .. 1·25 75
*b. Lake-brown* (7.49) .. .. .. 16·00 12·00
101 **15** 2d. grey .. .. .. .. .. 30 30
*a. Slate-grey* (6.51) .. .. .. 2·00 1·50
102 **16** 2½d. deep ultramarine .. .. .. 30 45
103 – 3d. orange .. .. .. .. .. 30 30
104 – 6d. violet .. .. .. .. .. 60 30
105 – 1s. black and brown .. .. .. 1·25 45
*a. Black and red-brown* (7.49) .. 24·00 9·50
ab. Frame ptd double, once albino .. £2500
106 – 2s. 6d. brown-purple .. .. .. 23·00 5·50
*a. Maroon* (8.42) .. .. .. 16·00 4·50
107 – 5s. olive-green .. .. .. .. 11·00 7·00
108 **16** 10s. magenta (1.4.48) .. .. .. 16·00 23·00
109 – £1 slate-green (1.4.48) .. .. 22·00 28·00
98/109 .. .. .. .. *Set of* 12 60·00 60·00
98/109 Perf "Specimen" .. .. *Set of* 12 £200

Designs: *Horiz*—3d., 2s. 6d., £1 Fort James. *Vert*—6d., 1s., 5s. St. John's Harbour.

17 Houses of Parliament, London

(Des and recess D.L.R.)

**1946** (1 Nov). *Victory. Wmk Mult Script CA. P* 13½×14.

110 **17** 1½d. brown .. .. .. .. 15 10
111 3d. red-orange .. .. .. .. 15 20
110/111 Perf "Specimen" .. .. *Set of* 2 50·00

18

19

King George VI and Queen Elizabeth

(Des and photo Waterlow (T **18**). Design recess; name typo B.W. (T **19**))

**1949** (3 Jan). *Royal Silver Wedding. Wmk Mult Script CA.*

112 **18** 2½d. ultramarine (*p* 14×15) .. .. 20 30
113 **19** 5s. grey-olive (*p* 11½×11) .. .. 7·50 4·25

20 Hermes, Globe and Forms of Transport

21 Hemispheres, Aeroplane and Steamer

22 Hermes and Globe

23 U.P.U. Monument

(Recess Waterlow (T **20**, **23**). Designs recess, name typo B.W. (T **21**/**2**))

**1949** (10 Oct). *75th Anniv of Universal Postal Union. Wmk Mult Script CA.*

114 **20** 2½d. ultramarine (*p* 13½–14) .. .. 40 50
115 **21** 3d. orange (*p* 11 × 11½) .. .. 80 75
116 **22** 6d. purple (*p* 11 × 11½) .. .. 80 75
117 **23** 1s. red-brown (*p* 13½–14) .. .. 80 75
114/17 .. .. .. .. *Set of* 4 2·50 2·50

**(New Currency. 100 cents = 1 dollar)**

24 Arms of University

25 Princess Alice

(Recess Waterlow)

**1951** (16 Feb). *Inauguration of B.W.I. University College. Wmk Mult Script CA. P* 14×14½.

118 **24** 3 c. black and brown .. .. .. 35 20
119 **25** 12 c. black and violet .. .. .. 45 40

26 Queen Elizabeth II

27 Martello Tower

(Des and eng B.W. Recess D.L.R.)

**1953** (2 June). *Coronation. Wmk Mult Script CA. P* 13½×13.

120 **26** 2 c. black and deep yellow-green .. 10 30

(Recess Waterlow until 1961, then D.L.R.)

**1953** (2 Nov)–**62**. *Designs previously used for King George VI issue, but with portrait of Queen Elizabeth II as in T* **27**. *Wmk Mult Script CA. P* 13×13½ (*horiz*) *or* 13½×13 (*vert*).

120*a* – ½ c. brown (3.7.56) .. .. .. 20 20
121 – 1 c. slate-grey .. .. .. .. 15 10
*a. Slate* (7.11.61) .. .. .. 65 30
122 – 2 c. green .. .. .. .. .. 10 10
123 – 3 c. black and orange-yellow .. .. 20 10
*a. Black and yellow-orange* (5.12.61) 75 60
124 – 4 c. scarlet .. .. .. .. 50 10
*a. Brown-red* (11.12.62) .. .. 45 10
125 – 5 c. black and slate-lilac .. .. 1·00 20
126 – 6 c. yellow-ochre .. .. .. 70 10
*a. Dull yellow-ochre* (5.12.61) .. 1·90 40
127 **27** 8 c. deep blue .. .. .. .. 1·00 10
128 – 12 c. violet .. .. .. .. 1·00 10
129 – 24 c. black and chocolate .. .. 1·50 15
130 **27** 48 c. purple and deep blue .. .. 3·25 1·25
131 – 60 c. maroon .. .. .. .. 4·00 80
132 – $1.20, olive-green .. .. .. 2·00 70
*a. Yellowish olive* (10.8.55) .. .. 1·50 70
133 – $2.40, bright reddish purple .. .. 7·50 12·00
134 – $4.80, slate-blue .. .. .. 8·50 16·00
120*a*/134 .. .. .. .. *Set of* 15 28·00 30·00

Designs: *Horiz*—½ c., 6 c., 60 c., $4.80, Fort James; 2 c., 3 c., 5 c., $2.40, Nelson's Dockyard. *Vert*—1 c., 4 c., English Harbour; 12 c., 24 c., $1.20, St. John's Harbour.

See also Nos. 149/58.

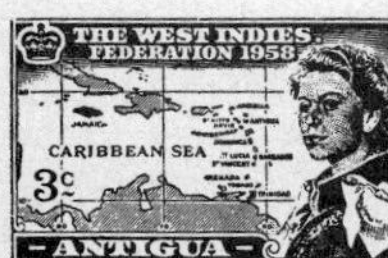
28 Federation Map

COMMEMORATION
ANTIGUA
CONSTITUTION
1960
**(29)**

(Recess B.W.)

**1958** (22 Apr). *Inauguration of British Caribbean Federation. W* w **12**. *P* 11½ × 11.

135 **28** 3 c. deep green .. .. .. .. 60 25
136 6 c. blue .. .. .. .. .. 80 70
137 12 c. scarlet .. .. .. .. 90 40
135/7 .. .. .. .. *Set of* 3 2·10 1·25

**MINISTERIAL GOVERNMENT**

**1960** (1 Jan). *New Constitution. Nos.* 123 *and* 128 *optd with T* **29**.

138 3 c. black and orange-yellow (R.) .. .. 15 15
139 12 c. violet .. .. .. .. .. 15 15

30 Nelson's Dockyard and Admiral Nelson

31 Stamp of 1862 and R.M.S.P. *Solent* at English Harbour

(Recess B.W.)

**1961** (14 Nov). *Restoration of Nelson's Dockyard. W* w **12**. *P* 11½ × 11.

140 **30** 20 c. purple and brown .. .. .. 50 40
141 30 c. green and blue .. .. .. 60 40

(Des A. W. Morley. Recess B.W.)

**1962** (1 Aug). *Stamp Centenary. W* w **12**. *P* 13½.

142 **31** 3 c. purple and deep green .. .. 30 10
143 10 c. blue and deep green .. .. 40 10
144 12 c. deep sepia and deep green .. .. 45 10
145 50 c. orange-brown and deep green .. 1·10 55
142/5 .. .. .. .. *Set of* 4 2·00 70

32 Protein Foods

33 Red Cross Emblem

(Des M. Goaman. Photo Harrison)

**1963** (4 June). *Freedom from Hunger. W* w **12**. *P* 14×14½.

146 **32** 12 c. bluish green .. .. .. 15 15

(Des V. Whiteley. Litho B.W.)

**1963** (2 Sept). *Red Cross Centenary. W* w **12**. *P* 13½.

147 **33** 3 c. red and black .. .. .. 20 30
148 12 c. red and blue .. .. .. 50 70

(Recess D.L.R.)

**1963** (16 Sept)–**65**. *As* 1953–61 *but wmk* w **12**.

149 – ½ c. brown (13.4.65) .. .. .. 60 75
150 – 1 c. slate (13.4.65) .. .. .. 70 1·00
151 – 2 c. green .. .. .. .. 35 15
152 – 3 c. black and yellow-orange .. .. 30 20
153 – 4 c. brown-red .. .. .. .. 30 10
154 – 5 c. black and slate-lilac .. .. 20 10
*a. Black and reddish violet* (15.1.65) 20 10
155 – 6 c. yellow-ochre .. .. .. 40 30
156 **27** 8 c. deep blue .. .. .. .. 30 15
157 – 12 c. violet .. .. .. .. 30 15
158 – 24 c. black and deep chocolate .. .. 70 70
*a. Black and chocolate-brown* (28.4.65) 2·50 1·50
149/158 .. .. .. .. *Set of* 10 3·75 3·25

34 Shakespeare and Memorial Theatre, Stratford-upon-Avon

= =
**15c.**
**(35)**

(Des R. Granger Barrett. Photo Harrison)

**1964** (23 April). *400th Birth Anniv of William Shakespeare. W* w **12**. *P* 14 × 14½.

164 **34** 12 c. orange-brown .. .. .. 15 10

**1965** (1 April). *No.* 157 *surch with T* **35**.

165 15 c. on 12 c. violet .. .. .. .. 10 10

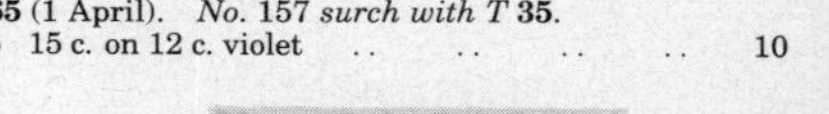

36 I.T.U. Emblem

(Des M. Goaman. Litho Enschedé)

**1965** (17 May). *I.T.U. Centenary. W* w **12**. *P* 11 × 11½.

166 **36** 2 c. light blue and light red .. .. 20 1
167 50 c. orange-yellow and ultramarine .. 1·25 8

37 I.C.Y. Emblem

(Des V. Whiteley. Litho Harrison)

**1965** (25 Oct). *International Co-operation Year. W* w **12**. *P* 14½.

168 **37** 4 c. reddish purple and turquoise-green 15 10
169 15 c. deep bluish green and lavender .. 25 20

## NEW INFORMATION

The editor is always interested to correspond with people who have new information that will improve or correct the Catalogue.

**38** Sir Winston Churchill, and St. Paul's Cathedral in Wartime

(Des Jennifer Toombs. Photo Harrison)

**1966** (24 Jan). *Churchill Commemoration. Printed in black, cerise and gold and with background in colours stated.* W w **12**. *P* 14.

| No. | Type | Description | Unused | Used |
|---|---|---|---|---|
| 170 | **38** | ½ c. new blue | 10 | 10 |
| | | a. Value omitted | £250 | |
| 171 | | 4 c. deep green | 30 | 10 |
| 172 | | 25 c. brown | 65 | 30 |
| 173 | | 35 c. bluish violet | 75 | 40 |
| 170/3 | | *Set of* 4 | 1·60 | 75 |

No. 170a was caused by misplacement of the gold and also shows "ANTIGUA" moved to the right.

**39** Queen Elizabeth II and Duke of Edinburgh

(Des H. Baxter. Litho B.W.)

**1966** (4 Feb). *Royal Visit.* W w **12**. *P* 11 × 12.

| No. | Type | Description | Unused | Used |
|---|---|---|---|---|
| 174 | **39** | 6 c. black and ultramarine | 1·75 | 1·10 |
| 175 | | 15 c. black and magenta | 2·00 | 1·40 |

**40** Footballer's Legs, Ball and Jules Rimet Cup

(Des V. Whiteley. Litho Harrison)

**1966** (1 July). *World Football Cup Championships.* W w **12** (*sideways*). *P* 14.

| No. | Type | Description | Unused | Used |
|---|---|---|---|---|
| 176 | **40** | 6 c. violet, yellow-green, lake & yell-brn | 15 | 15 |
| 177 | | 35 c. chocolate, blue-grn, lake & yell-brn | 50 | 25 |

**41** W.H.O. Building

(Des M. Goaman. Litho Harrison)

**1966** (20 Sept). *Inauguration of W.H.O. Headquarters, Geneva.* W w **12** (*sideways*). *P* 14.

| No. | Type | Description | Unused | Used |
|---|---|---|---|---|
| 178 | **41** | 2 c. black, yellow-green and light blue | 15 | 15 |
| 179 | | 15 c. black, light purple and yellow-brown | 70 | 25 |

**42** Nelson's Dockyard

(Des, eng and recess B.W.)

**1966** (1 Nov)–**68**. *Horiz designs as T* **42**. W w **12**. *P* 11½×11.

| No. | Description | Unused | Used |
|---|---|---|---|
| 180 | ½ c. green and turquoise-blue | 10 | 20 |
| 181 | 1 c. purple and cerise | 10 | 20 |
| 182 | 2 c. slate-blue and yellow-orange | 10 | 15 |
| 183 | 3 c. rose-red and black | 10 | 15 |
| 184 | 4 c. slate-violet and brown | 30 | 10 |
| 185 | 5 c. ultramarine and yellow-olive | 10 | 10 |
| 186 | 6 c. salmon and purple | 15 | 10 |
| 187 | 10 c. emerald and rose-red | 15 | 10 |
| 188 | 15 c. brown and new blue | 30 | 10 |
| 189 | 25 c. slate-blue and sepia | 35 | 20 |
| 190 | 35 c. cerise and blackish brown | 1·50 | 55 |
| 191 | 50 c. dull green and black | 1·50 | 2·25 |
| 192 | 75 c. greenish blue and ultramarine | 1·50 | 2·50 |
| 193 | $1 cerise and yellow-olive | 2·50 | 2·50 |
| | *a. Carmine and yellow-olive* (14.5.68) | 7·00 | 7·50 |
| 194 | $2.50, black and cerise | 3·00 | 4·75 |
| 195 | $5 olive-green and slate-violet | 5·00 | 6·50 |
| 180/195 | *Set of* 16 | 15·00 | 18·00 |

Designs:—1 c. Old Post Office, St. John's; 2 c. Health Centre; 3 c. Teachers' Training College; 4 c. Martello Tower, Barbuda; 5 c. Ruins of Officers' Quarters, Shirley Heights; 6 c. Government House, Barbuda; 10 c. Princess Margaret School; 15 c. Air Terminal building; 25 c. General Post Office; 35 c. Clarence House; 50 c. Government House, St. John's; 75 c. Administration Building; $1, Courthouse, St. John's; $2.50, Magistrates' Court; $5, St. John's Cathedral.

See also Nos. 234/48.

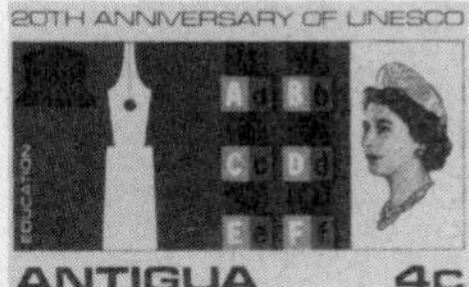


**54** "Education"

**55** "Science"

**56** "Culture"

(Des Jennifer Toombs. Litho Harrison)

**1966** (1 Dec). *20th Anniv of U.N.E.S.C.O.* W w **12** (*sideways*). *P* 14.

| No. | Type | Description | Unused | Used |
|---|---|---|---|---|
| 196 | **54** | 4 c. slate-violet, red, yellow and orange | 15 | 10 |
| 197 | **55** | 25 c. orange-yellow, violet and deep olive | 35 | 10 |
| 198 | **56** | $1 black, bright purple and orange | 1·75 | 1·75 |
| 196/8 | | *Set of* 3 | 2·00 | 1·75 |

**ASSOCIATED STATEHOOD**

**57** State Flag and Maps

(Des W. D. Cribbs. Photo Harrison)

**1967** (27 Feb). *Statehood. T* **57** *and similar horiz designs. Multicoloured.* W w **12** (*sideways*). *P* 14.

| No. | Description | Unused | Used |
|---|---|---|---|
| 199 | 4 c. Type **57** | 10 | 10 |
| 200 | 15 c. State Flag | 10 | 10 |
| 201 | 25 c. Premier's Office and State Flag | 10 | 10 |
| 202 | 35 c. As 15 c. | 15 | 15 |
| 199/202 | *Set of* 4 | 30 | 30 |

**60** Gilbert Memorial Church

(Des G. Drummond (from sketches by W. D. Cribbs). Photo Harrison)

**1967** (18 May). *Attainment of Autonomy by the Methodist Church. T* **60** *and similar horiz designs.* W w **12**. *P* 14½ × 13½.

| No. | Description | Unused | Used |
|---|---|---|---|
| 203 | 4 c. black and orange-red | 10 | 10 |
| 204 | 25 c. black and bright green | 15 | 15 |
| 205 | 35 c. black and bright blue | 15 | 15 |
| 203/5 | *Set of* 3 | 30 | 30 |

Designs:—25 c. Nathaniel Gilbert's House; 35 c. Caribbean and Central American map.

**63** Coat of Arms

**64** Settlers' Ship

(Des V. Whiteley (from sketches by W. D. Cribbs). Photo Harrison)

**1967** (21 July). *300th Anniv of Treaty of Breda and Grant of New Arms.* W w **12** (*sideways*). *P* 14½ × 14.

| No. | Type | Description | Unused | Used |
|---|---|---|---|---|
| 206 | **63** | 15 c. multicoloured | 15 | 10 |
| 207 | | 35 c. multicoloured | 15 | 10 |

(Des and recess B.W.)

**1967** (14 Dec). *300th Anniv of Barbuda Settlement. T* **64** *and similar horiz design.* W w **12**. *P* 11½ × 11.

| No. | Type | Description | Unused | Used |
|---|---|---|---|---|
| 208 | **64** | 4 c. deep ultramarine | 10 | 10 |
| 209 | – | 6 c. purple | 10 | 10 |
| 210 | **64** | 25 c. emerald | 15 | 10 |
| 211 | – | 35 c. black | 15 | 15 |
| 208/11 | | *Set of* 4 | 45 | 30 |

Design:—6, 35 c. Blaeu's map of 1665.

**66** Tracking Station

**70** Limbo-dancing

(Des G. Vasarhelyi. Photo Harrison)

**1968** (29 Mar). *N.A.S.A. Apollo Project. Inauguration of Dow Hill Tracking Station. T* **66** *and similar vert designs in deep blue, orange-yellow and black.* W w **12** (*sideways*). *P* 14½ × 14.

| No. | Description | Unused | Used |
|---|---|---|---|
| 212 | 4 c. Type **66** | 10 | 10 |
| 213 | 15 c. Antenna and spacecraft taking off | 20 | 10 |
| 214 | 25 c. Spacecraft approaching Moon | 20 | 10 |
| 215 | 50 c. Re-entry of space capsule | 30 | 20 |
| 212/15 | *Set of* 4 | 70 | 30 |

(Des and photo Harrison)

**1968** (1 July). *Tourism. T* **70** *and similar horiz designs. Multicoloured.* W w **12**. *P* 14½ × 14.

| No. | Description | Unused | Used |
|---|---|---|---|
| 216 | ½ c. Type **70** | 10 | 10 |
| 217 | 15 c. Water-skiing and bathers | 15 | 10 |
| 218 | 25 c. Yachts and beach | 20 | 10 |
| 219 | 35 c. Underwater swimming | 20 | 10 |
| 220 | 50 c. Type **70** | 30 | 35 |
| 216/20 | *Set of* 5 | 80 | 50 |

**74** Old Harbour in 1768

(Des R. Granger Barrett. Recess B.W.)

**1968** (31 Oct). *Opening of St. John's Deep Water Harbour. T* **74** *and similar horiz designs.* W w **12**. *P* 13.

| No. | Description | Unused | Used |
|---|---|---|---|
| 221 | 2 c. light blue and carmine | 10 | 10 |
| 222 | 15 c. light yellow-green and sepia | 20 | 10 |
| 223 | 25 c. olive-yellow and blue | 25 | 10 |
| 224 | 35 c. salmon and emerald | 30 | 10 |
| 225 | $1 black | 70 | 45 |
| 221/5 | *Set of* 5 | 1·40 | 65 |

Designs:—15 c. Old Harbour in 1829; 25 c. Freighter and chart of New Harbour; 35 c. New Harbour, 1968; $1, Type **74**.

**78** Parliament Buildings

(Des R. Granger Barrett. Photo Harrison)

**1969** (3 Feb). *Tercentenary of Parliament. T* **78** *and similar square designs. Multicoloured.* W w **12** (*sideways*). *P* 12½.

| No. | Description | Unused | Used |
|---|---|---|---|
| 226 | 4 c. Type **78** | 10 | 10 |
| 227 | 15 c. Antigua Mace and bearer | 15 | 10 |
| 228 | 25 c. House of Representatives' Room | 15 | 10 |
| 229 | 50 c. Coat of arms and Seal of Antigua | 25 | 35 |
| 226/9 | *Set of* 4 | 55 | 45 |

**82** Freight Transport

(Des Jennifer Toombs. Litho D.L.R.)

**1969** (14 Apr). *1st Anniv of CARIFTA (Caribbean Free Trade Area). T* **82** *and similar design.* W w **12** (*sideways on* 4 c., 15 c). *P* 13.

| No. | Description | Unused | Used |
|---|---|---|---|
| 230 | 4 c. black and reddish purple | 10 | 10 |
| 231 | 15 c. black and turquoise-blue | 15 | 10 |
| 232 | 25 c. chocolate, black and yellow-ochre | 15 | 15 |
| 233 | 35 c. chocolate, black and yellow-brown | 15 | 15 |
| 230/3 | *Set of* 4 | 45 | 30 |

Designs: *Horiz*—4, 15 c. Type **82**. *Vert*—25, 35 c. Crate of cargo.

**1969–70**. *As Nos.* 180/91 *and* 193/5 *but perf* 13½.
A. *Ordinary paper* (24.6.69).
B. *Glazed paper* (30.9.69 *or* 6.4.70 (4 c.))

| | | A | | B | |
|---|---|---|---|---|---|
| 234 | ½ c. green and turquoise-blue .. | 10 | 20 | † | |
| 235 | 1 c. purple and cerise .. .. | 10 | 15 | 20 | 15 |
| 236 | 2 c. slate-blue & yellow-orange | 10 | 10 | 30 | 10 |
| 237 | 3 c. rose-red and black.. .. | 15 | 15 | † | |
| 238 | 4 c. slate-violet and brown .. | 15 | 15 | 12·00 | 9·00 |
| 239 | 5 c. ultramarine & yellow-olive | 15 | 10 | 30 | 10 |
| 240 | 6 c. salmon and purple .. | 15 | 15 | † | |
| 241 | 10 c. emerald and rose-red .. | 15 | 15 | 65 | 15 |
| 242 | 15 c. brown and new blue .. | † | | 55 | 35 |
| 243 | 25 c. slate-blue and sepia .. | † | | 45 | 35 |
| 244 | 35 c. cerise & blackish brown .. | † | | 60 | 1·00 |
| 245 | 50 c. dull green and black .. | † | | 70 | 2·00 |
| 246 | $1 cerise and yellow-olive .. | † | | 1·25 | 3·50 |
| 247 | $2.50, black and cerise .. | † | | 2·00 | 8·00 |
| 248 | $5 olive-green & slate-violet .. | † | | 14·00 | 24·00 |
| 234/41A .. .. .. | *Set of* 8 | 90 | 1·00 | † | |
| 235/48B .. .. .. | *Set of* 12 | † | | 30·00 | 45·00 |

**84** Island of Redonda (Chart)

(Des R. Granger Barrett. Photo Enschedé)

**1969** (1 Aug). *Centenary of Redonda Phosphate Industry. T* **84** *and similar horiz design. W* w **12** (*sideways*). *P* 13 × 13½.

| | | | |
|---|---|---|---|
| 249 | 15 c. Type **84** .. .. .. .. | 20 | 10 |
| 250 | 25 c. Redonda from the sea .. .. | 20 | 10 |
| 251 | 50 c. Type **84** .. .. .. .. | 45 | 45 |
| 249/51 | .. .. .. *Set of* 3 | 75 | 60 |

**86** "The Adoration of the Magi" (Marcillat)

20¢

(**88**)

(Des adapted by V. Whiteley. Litho Enschedé)

**1969** (15 Oct). *Christmas. Stained-glass Windows. T* **86** *and similar vert design. Multicoloured. W* w **12** (*sideways*). *P* 13 × 14.

| | | | |
|---|---|---|---|
| 252 | 6 c. Type **86** .. .. .. .. | 10 | 10 |
| 253 | 10 c. "The Nativity" (unknown German artist, 15th-century) .. .. .. | 10 | 10 |
| 254 | 35 c. Type **86** .. .. .. .. | 15 | 10 |
| 255 | 50 c. As 10 c. .. .. .. .. | 35 | 30 |
| 252/5 .. | .. .. .. *Set of* 4 | 55 | 45 |

**1970** (2 Jan). *No.* 189 *surch with T* **88**.

| | | | |
|---|---|---|---|
| 256 | 20 c. on 25 c. slate-blue and sepia .. .. | 10 | 10 |

**89** Coat of Arms

**90** Sikorsky "S–38"

(Des and photo Harrison)

**1970–73**. *Coil Stamps. W* w **12**. *P* 14½ × 14.
A. *Chalk-surfaced paper. Wmk upright* (30.1.70).
B. *Glazed paper. Wmk sideways* (8.3.73).

| | | | A | | B | |
|---|---|---|---|---|---|---|
| 257 | **89** | 5 c. blue .. .. .. | 10 | 10 | 25 | 30 |
| 258 | | 10 c. emerald .. .. | 10 | 15 | 30 | 40 |
| 259 | | 25 c. crimson .. .. | 20 | 25 | 60 | 70 |
| 257/9 | .. .. | *Set of* 3 | 35 | 45 | 1·00 | 1·25 |

For 10 c. with watermark W w **14** (inverted), see No. 541*a*.

(Des R. Granger Barrett. Litho J.W.)

**1970** (16 Feb). *40th Anniv of Antiguan Air Services. T* **90** *and similar designs. Multicoloured. W* w **12** (*sideways*). *P* 14½.

| | | | |
|---|---|---|---|
| 260 | 5 c. Type **90** .. .. .. .. | 20 | 10 |
| 261 | 20 c. Dornier "DO–X" .. .. .. | 35 | 10 |
| 262 | 35 c. Hawker Siddeley "HS–748" .. .. | 45 | 10 |
| 263 | 50 c. Douglas "C–124C Globemaster II" | 60 | 60 |
| 264 | 75 c. Vickers "VC–10" .. .. .. | 80 | 1·00 |
| 260/4 | .. .. .. *Set of* 5 | 2·25 | 1·60 |

## COVER PRICES

Cover factors are quoted at the beginning of each country for most issues to 1945. An explanation of the system can be found on page x. The factors quoted do not, however, apply to philatelic covers.

**91** Dickens and Scene from *Nicholas Nickleby*

(Des Jennifer Toombs. Litho Walsall Security Printers Ltd)

**1970** (19 May). *Death Centenary of Charles Dickens. T* **91** *and similar horiz designs. W* w **12** (*sideways*). *P* 14.

| | | | |
|---|---|---|---|
| 265 | 5 c. bistre, sepia and black .. .. | 10 | 10 |
| 266 | 20 c. light turquoise-blue, sepia and black .. | 10 | 10 |
| 267 | 35 c. violet-blue, sepia and black .. .. | 15 | 10 |
| 268 | $1 rosine, sepia and black .. .. | 45 | 50 |
| 265/8 .. | .. .. .. *Set of* 4 | 65 | 60 |

Designs:—20 c. Dickens and Scene from *Pickwick Papers*; 35 c. Dickens and Scene from *Oliver Twist*; $1 Dickens and Scene from *David Copperfield*.

**92** Carib Indian and War Canoe

**93** "The Small Passion" (detail) (Dürer)

(Des J. W. Litho Questa)

**1970** (19 Aug)–**75**. *Horiz designs as T* **92**. *Multicoloured. Toned paper. W* w **12** (*sideways*). *P* 14.

| | | | |
|---|---|---|---|
| 269 | ½ c. Type **92** .. .. .. .. | 10 | 30 |
| 270 | 1 c. Columbus and *Nina* .. .. .. | 25 | 25 |
| 271 | 2 c. Sir Thomas Warner's emblem and *Concepcion* .. .. .. .. | 40 | 25 |
| | a. Whiter paper (20.10.75) .. .. | 1·50 | 2·75 |
| 272 | 3 c. Viscount Hood and H.M.S. *Barfleur* .. | 40 | 30 |
| 273 | 4 c. Sir George Rodney and H.M.S. *Formidable* .. .. .. | 40 | 35 |
| 274 | 5 c. Nelson and H.M.S. *Boreas* .. .. | 50 | 30 |
| 275 | 6 c. William IV and H.M.S. *Pegasus*. .. | 50 | 40 |
| 276 | 10 c. "Blackbeard" and pirate ketch .. .. | 65 | 35 |
| 277 | 15 c. Captain Collingwood and H.M.S. *Pelican* | 2·00 | 1·00 |
| 278 | 20 c. Nelson and H.M.S. *Victory* .. .. | 1·25 | 60 |
| 279 | 25 c. R.M.S.P. *Solent* .. .. .. .. | 1·25 | 60 |
| 280 | 35 c. George V (when Prince George) and H.M.S. *Canada* .. .. .. | 1·60 | 70 |
| 281 | 50 c. H.M.S. *Renown* (battle cruiser) .. | 3·50 | 2·00 |
| 282 | 75 c. *Federal Maple* (freighter) .. .. | 4·75 | 4·50 |
| 283 | $1 *Sol Quest* (yacht) and class emblem .. | 5·00 | 2·00 |
| 284 | $2.50, H.M.S. *London* (destroyer).. .. | 5·00 | 6·50 |
| 285 | $5 *Pathfinder* (tug).. .. .. .. | 7·00 | 7·50 |
| 269/85 | .. .. .. .. *Set of* 17 | 30·00 | 25·00 |

See also Nos. 323/34 and 426.

(Des G. Drummond. Recess and litho D.L.R.)

**1970** (28 Oct). *Christmas. T* **93** *and similar vert design. W* w **12**. *P* 13½ × 14.

| | | | | |
|---|---|---|---|---|
| 286 | **93** | 3 c. black and turquoise-blue .. .. | 10 | 10 |
| 287 | – | 10 c. dull purple and pink .. .. | 10 | 10 |
| 288 | **93** | 35 c. black and rose-red .. .. | 20 | 10 |
| 289 | – | 50 c. black and lilac .. .. | 30 | 30 |
| 286/9 .. | | .. .. *Set of* 4 | 50 | 35 |

Design:—10 c., 50 c. "Adoration of the Magi" (detail) (Dürer).

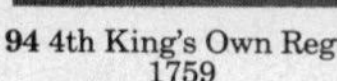

**94** 4th King's Own Regt, 1759

**95** Market Woman casting Vote

(Des P. W. Kingsland. Litho Questa)

**1970** (14 Dec). *Military Uniforms* (1*st series*). *T* **94** *and similar vert designs. Multicoloured. W* w **12**. *P* 14 × 13½.

| | | | |
|---|---|---|---|
| 290 | ½ c. Type **94** .. .. .. .. | 10 | 10 |
| 291 | 10 c. 4th West India Regiment, 1804 .. .. | 50 | 10 |
| 292 | 20 c. 60th Regiment, The Royal American, 1809 .. .. .. .. | 90 | 25 |
| 293 | 35 c. 93rd Regiment, Sutherland Highlanders, 1826–34 .. .. .. .. | 1·25 | 30 |
| 294 | 75 c. 3rd West India Regiment, 1851 .. .. | 2·25 | 2·25 |
| 290/4 .. | .. .. .. *Set of* 5 | 4·50 | 2·50 |
| **MS**295 | 128 × 146 mm. Nos. 290/4 . .. .. | 7·50 | 11·00 |

See also Nos. 303/8, 313/18, 353/8 and 380/5.

(Des Sylvia Goaman. Photo Harrison)

**1971** (1 Feb). *20th Anniversary of Adult Suffrage. T* **95** *and similar vert designs. W* w **12** (*sideways*). *P* 14½ × 14.

| | | | |
|---|---|---|---|
| 296 | 5 c. brown .. .. .. .. .. | 10 | 10 |
| 297 | 20 c. deep olive .. .. .. .. | 10 | 10 |
| 298 | 35 c. reddish purple .. .. .. .. | 10 | 10 |
| 299 | 50 c. ultramarine .. .. .. .. | 15 | 30 |
| 296/9 .. | .. .. .. *Set of* 4 | 30 | 40 |

People voting:—20 c. Executive; 35 c. Housewife; 50 c. Artisan.

**96** "The Last Supper"

**97** "Madonna and Child" (detail, Veronese)

(Des Jennifer Toombs. Litho Questa)

**1971** (7 Apr). *Easter. Works by Dürer. T* **96** *and similar vert designs. W* w **12**. *P* 14 × 13½.

| | | | |
|---|---|---|---|
| 300 | 5 c. black, grey and scarlet .. .. .. | 10 | 10 |
| 301 | 35 c. black, grey and bluish violet .. .. | 10 | 10 |
| 302 | 75 c. black, grey and gold .. .. .. | 20 | 30 |
| 300/2 .. | .. .. .. *Set of* 3 | 30 | 35 |

Designs:—35 c. The Crucifixion; 75 c. The Resurrection.

(Des J. W. Litho Questa)

**1971** (12 July). *Military Uniforms* (2*nd series*). *Multicoloured designs as T* **94**. *W* w **12**. *P* 13½.

| | | | |
|---|---|---|---|
| 303 | ½ c. Private, 12th Regiment, The Suffolk (1704) .. .. .. .. | 10 | 10 |
| 304 | 10 c. Grenadier, 38th Regiment, South Staffs (1751) .. .. .. .. | 35 | 15 |
| 305 | 20 c. Light Company, 5th Regiment, Royal Northumberland Fusiliers (1778) .. | 55 | 20 |
| 306 | 35 c. Private, 48th Regiment, The Northamptonshire (1793) .. .. | 1·00 | 40 |
| 307 | 75 c. Private, 15th Regiment, East Yorks (1805) .. .. .. .. | 2·25 | 2·75 |
| 303/7 .. | .. .. .. *Set of* 5 | 3·75 | 3·25 |
| **MS**308 | 127 × 144 mm. Nos. 303/7. .. .. | 5·50 | 6·50 |

(Des Jennifer Toombs. Litho Questa)

**1971** (4 Oct). *Christmas. T* **97** *and similar vert design. Multicoloured. W* w **12**. *P* 13½.

| | | | |
|---|---|---|---|
| 309 | 3 c. Type **97** .. .. .. .. | 10 | 10 |
| 310 | 5 c. "Adoration of the Shepherds" (detail, Veronese) .. .. .. | 10 | 10 |
| 311 | 35 c. Type **97** .. .. .. .. | 20 | 10 |
| 312 | 50 c. As 5 c. .. .. .. .. | 30 | 30 |
| 309/12 | .. .. .. *Set of* 4 | 55 | 40 |

(Des J.W. Litho Questa)

**1972** (1 July). *Military Uniforms* (3*rd series*). *Multicoloured designs as T* **94**. *W* w **12** (*sideways*). *P* 14 × 13½.

| | | | |
|---|---|---|---|
| 313 | ½ c. Battalion Company Officer, 25th Foot, 1815 .. .. .. .. | 10 | 10 |
| 314 | 10 c. Sergeant, 14th Foot, 1837 .. .. | 35 | 10 |
| 315 | 20 c. Private, 67th Foot, 1853 .. .. .. | 60 | 15 |
| 316 | 35 c. Officer, Royal Artillery, 1854 .. .. | 1·00 | 20 |
| 317 | 75 c. Private, 29th Foot, 1870 .. .. .. | 1·60 | 1·75 |
| 313/17 | .. .. .. *Set of* 5 | 3·25 | 2·00 |
| **MS**318 | 125 × 141 mm. Nos. 313/17 .. .. | 7·00 | 8·00 |

**98** Cowrie-Helmet

(Des J.W. Litho Questa)

**1972** (1 Aug). *Shells. T* **98** *and similar horiz designs. Multicoloured. W* w **12** (*sideways*). *P* 14½.

| | | | |
|---|---|---|---|
| 319 | 3 c. Type **98** .. .. .. .. | 15 | 10 |
| 320 | 5 c. Measled Cowrie .. .. .. | 15 | 10 |
| 321 | 35 c. West Indian Fighting Conch .. .. | 55 | 10 |
| 322 | 50 c. Hawk-wing Conch .. .. .. | 1·10 | 95 |
| 319/22 | .. .. .. *Set of* 4 | 1·75 | 1·10 |

**1972–74.** *As No.* 269 *etc., but W* w **12** (*upright*) *and whiter paper.*

| | | | |
|---|---|---|---|
| 323 | ½ c. Type **92** .. .. .. .. | 15 | 30 |
| 324 | 1 c. Columbus and *Nina* .. .. .. | 30 | 30 |
| 325 | 3 c. Viscount Hood and H.M.S. *Barfleur* .. | 35 | 30 |
| 326 | 4 c. Sir George Rodney and H.M.S. *Formidable* .. .. .. .. | 35 | 40 |
| 327 | 5 c. Nelson and H.M.S. *Boreas* .. .. | 50 | 30 |
| 328 | 6 c. William IV and H.M.S. *Pegasus*. .. | 50 | 60 |
| 329 | 10 c. "Blackbeard" and pirate ketch .. .. | 55 | 30 |
| 330 | 15 c. Collingwood and H.M.S. *Pelican* .. | 3·50 | 75 |
| 331 | 75 c. *Federal Maple* (freighter) .. .. | 5·50 | 3·00 |
| 332 | $1 *Sol Quest* (yacht) and class emblem .. | 4·50 | 1·75 |
| 333 | $2.50, H.M.S. *London* (destroyer) .. .. | 4·50 | 6·50 |
| 334 | $5 *Pathfinder* (tug) .. .. .. .. | 6·50 | 11·00 |
| 323/34 | .. .. .. *Set of* 12 | 24·00 | 23·00 |

Dates of issue:—2.11.72, ½ c., 15 c., 75 c., $1, $5; 2.1.74, 1 to 10 c.; 25.2.74, $2.50.

See also No. 426.

**99** St. John's Cathedral, Side View

(Des J.W. Litho Format)

**1972** (6 Nov). *Christmas and 125th Anniversary of St. John's Cathedral. T* **99** *and similar horiz designs. Multicoloured. W w* **12**. *P* 14.

335 35 c. Type **99** .. .. .. .. .. 20 10
336 50 c. Cathedral interior .. .. .. 25 20
337 75 c. St. John's Cathedral .. .. .. 30 50
335/7 .. .. .. .. *Set of* 3 65 65
**MS**338 165 × 102 mm. Nos. 335/7. P 15 .. .. 65 1·00

**100** Floral Pattern

(Des (from photograph by D. Groves) and photo Harrison)

**1972** (20 Nov). *Royal Silver Wedding. Multicoloured; background colour given. W w* **12**. *P* 14 × 14½.

339 **100** 20 c. bright blue .. .. .. .. 15 15
340 35 c. turquoise-blue .. .. .. .. 15 15

**101** Batsman and Map

(Des G. Vasarhelyi. Litho Questa)

**1972** (15 Dec). *50th Anniv of Rising Sun Cricket Club. T* **101** *and similar horiz designs. Multicoloured. W w* **12**. *P* 13½.

341 5 c. Type **101** .. .. .. .. .. 45 25
342 35 c. Batsman and wicket-keeper .. .. 1·40 1·25
343 $1 Club badge .. .. .. .. 2·75 3·50
341/3 .. .. .. .. *Set of* 3 4·25 4·50
**MS**344 88 × 130 mm. Nos. 341/3 .. .. .. 5·50 7·50

**102** Yacht and Map

**103** "Episcopal Coat of Arms"

(Des M. and G. Shamir. Litho Format)

**1972** (29 Dec). *Sailing Week and Inauguration of Tourist Office, New York. T* **102** *and similar square designs. Multicoloured. W w* **12**. *P* 14½.

345 35 c. Type **102** .. .. .. .. .. 15 10
346 50 c. Yachts .. .. .. .. .. 20 15
347 75 c. St. John's G.P.O. .. .. .. .. 25 30
348 $1 Statue of Liberty .. .. .. .. 30 35
345/8 .. .. .. .. *Set of* 4 80 75
**MS**349 100 × 94 mm. Nos. 346, 348 .. .. 1·00 1·50

(Des PAD Studio. Litho Format)

**1973** (16 Apr). *Easter. T* **103** *and similar vert designs showing stained-glass windows from St. John's Cathedral. Multicoloured. W w* **12** *(sideways). P* 13½.

350 5 c. Type **103** .. .. .. .. .. 10 10
351 35 c. "The Crucifixion" .. .. .. .. 10 10
352 75 c. "Arms of 1st Bishop of Antigua" .. .. 20 30
350/2 .. .. .. .. *Set of* 3 30 35

(Des J.W. Litho Questa)

**1973** (1 July). *Military Uniforms* (4th series). *Multicoloured designs as T* **94**. *W w* **12** *(sideways). P* 13½.

353 ½ c. Private, Zacharia Tiffin's Regiment of Foot, 1701 .. .. .. .. .. 10 10
354 10 c. Private, 63rd Regiment of Foot, 1759 .. 20 10
355 20 c. Light Company Officer, 35th Regiment of Foot, 1828 .. .. .. .. .. 30 15
356 35 c. Private, 2nd West India Regiment, 1853 55 15
357 75 c. Sergeant, 49th Regiment, 1858 .. .. 1·25 1·00
353/7 .. .. .. .. *Set of* 5 2·10 1·25
**MS**358 127 × 145 mm. Nos. 353/7 .. .. .. 2·75 3·25

**104** Butterfly Costumes

(Des G. Vasarhelyi. Litho Format)

**1973** (30 July). *Carnival. T* **104** *and similar horiz designs. Multicoloured. P* 13½.

359 5 c. Type **104** .. .. .. .. .. 10 10
360 20 c. Carnival street scene .. .. .. .. 15 10
361 35 c. Carnival troupe .. .. .. .. 20 10
362 75 c. Carnival Queen .. .. .. .. 30 30
359/62 .. .. .. .. *Set of* 4 65 35
**MS**363 134 × 95 mm. Nos. 359/62 .. .. .. 65 1·00

**105** "Virgin of the Milk Porridge" (Gerard David)

**106** Princess Anne and Captain Mark Phillips

(Des G. Vasarhelyi. Litho Format)

**1973** (15 Oct). *Christmas. T* **105** *and similar vert designs. Multicoloured. P* 14½.

364 3 c. Type **105** .. .. .. .. .. 10 10
365 5 c. "Adoration of the Magi" (Stomer) .. .. 10 10
366 20 c. "The Granducal Madonna" (Raphael) .. 20 10
367 35 c. "Nativity with God the Father and Holy Ghost" (Battista) .. .. .. .. 30 10
368 $1 "Madonna and Child" (Murillo) .. .. 60 60
364/8 .. .. .. .. *Set of* 5 1·10 70
**MS**369 130 × 128 mm. Nos. 364/8 .. .. .. 1·10 1·75

(Des G. Drummond. Litho Format)

**1973** (14 Nov). *Royal Wedding. T* **106** *and similar horiz design. P* 13½.

370 **106** 35 c. multicoloured .. .. .. .. 15 10
371 – $2 multicoloured .. .. .. .. 35 25
**MS**372 78 × 100 mm. Nos. 370/1 .. .. .. 50 40

The $2 is as T **106** but has a different border.

Nos. 370/1 were each issued in small sheets of five stamps and one stamp-size label.

HONEYMOON
VISIT

DECEMBER 16th
1973

(107)

**1973** (15 Dec). *Honeymoon Visit of Princess Anne and Captain Phillips. Nos. 370/MS372 optd with T* **107** *by lithography.**

373 **106** 35 c. multicoloured .. .. .. .. 15 10
a. Typo opt .. .. .. .. 95 95
374 – $2 multicoloured .. .. .. .. 40 40
a. Typo opt .. .. .. .. 2·75 2·75
**MS**375 78 × 100 mm. Nos. 373/4 .. .. .. 55 55
a. Typo opt .. .. .. .. 7·00 9·00

*The litho overprints can be distinguished from the typo by the latter being less clear, less intense, and showing through on the reverse.

**108** Coats of Arms of Antigua and University

(Des PAD Studio. Litho D.L.R.)

**1974** (18 Feb). *25th Anniv of University of West Indies. T* **108** *and similar horiz designs. Multicoloured. W w* **12**. *P* 13.

376 5 c. Type **108** .. .. .. .. .. 10 10
377 20 c. Extra-mural art .. .. .. .. 10 10
378 35 c. Antigua campus .. .. .. .. 10 10
379 75 c. Antigua chancellor .. .. .. .. 20 25
376/9 .. .. .. .. *Set of* 4 30 30

(Des J.W. Litho Questa)

**1974** (1 May). *Military Uniforms* (5th series). *Multicoloured designs as T* **94**. *W w* **12** *(sideways). P* 13½.

380 ½ c. Officer, 59th Foot, 1797 .. .. .. 10 10
381 10 c. Gunner, Royal Artillery, 1800 .. .. 30 10
a. Error. Wmk T **55** of Malawi .. .. 90·00
382 20 c. Private, 1st West India Regiment, 1830 40 10
383 35 c. Officer, 92nd Foot, 1843 .. .. .. 55 10
384 75 c. Private, 23rd Foot, 1846 .. .. .. 90 60
380/4 .. .. .. .. *Set of* 5 2·00 80
**MS**385 127 × 145 mm. Nos. 380/4 .. .. .. 2·00 2·00

**109** English Postman, Mailcoach and Helicopter

**110** Traditional Player

(Des G. Vasarhelyi. Litho Format)

**1974** (15 July). *Centenary of Universal Postal Union. T* **109** *and similar horiz designs. Multicoloured. P* 14½.

386 ½ c. Type **109** .. .. .. .. .. 10 10
387 1 c. Bellman, mail steamer *Orinoco* and satellite .. .. .. .. .. 10 10
388 2 c. Train guard, post-bus and hydrofoil .. 10 10
389 5 c. Swiss messenger, Wells Fargo coach and "Concorde" .. .. .. .. .. 10 10
390 20 c. Postillion, Japanese postmen and carrier pigeon .. .. .. .. .. 30 10
391 35 c. Antiguan postman, flying-boat and tracking station .. .. .. .. 45 15
392 $1 Medieval courier, American express train and Boeing "747" .. .. .. 1·50 1·10
386/92 .. .. .. .. *Set of* 7 2·25 1·25
**MS**393 141 × 164 mm. Nos. 386/92 plus label. P 13 2·25 2·50

On the ½ c. "English" is spelt "Enlish", and on the 2 c. "Postal" is spelt "Fostal".

(Des C. Abbott. Litho Questa)

**1974** (1 Aug). *Antiguan Steel Bands. T* **110** *and similar designs. W w* **12** *(sideways on 5 c., 75 c. and* **MS**398*). P* 13.

394 5 c. rose-red, carmine and black .. .. 10 10
395 20 c. brown-ochre, chestnut and black .. .. 10 10
396 35 c. light sage-green, blue-green and black .. 10 10
397 75 c. dull blue, dull ultramarine and black .. 20 20
394/7 .. .. .. .. *Set of* 4 30 30
**MS**398 115 × 108 mm. Nos. 394/7 .. .. .. 35 65

Designs: *Horiz*—20 c. Traditional band; 35 c. Modern band. *Vert*—75 c. Modern player.

**111** Footballers

EARTHQUAKE
RELIEF

(112)

(Des G. Vasarhelyi. Litho Format)

**1974** (23 Sept). *World Cup Football Championships. T* **111** *and similar vert designs showing footballers. P* 14½.

399 **111** 5 c. multicoloured .. .. .. .. 10 10
400 – 35 c. multicoloured .. .. .. .. 10 10
401 – 75 c. multicoloured .. .. .. .. 25 30
402 – $1 multicoloured .. .. .. .. 30 40
399/402 .. .. .. .. *Set of* 4 55 70
**MS**403 135 × 130 mm. Nos. 399/402 plus two labels. P 13 .. .. .. .. .. 60 90

Nos. 399/402 were each issued in small sheets of five stamps and one stamp-size label.

**1974** (16 Oct). *Earthquake Relief Fund. Nos. 400/2 and 397 optd with T* **112**, *No. 397 surch also.*

404 35 c. multicoloured .. .. .. .. 20 10
405 75 c. multicoloured .. .. .. .. 30 25
406 $1 multicoloured .. .. .. .. 40 30
407 $5 on 75 c. dull blue, dull ultram & black 1·50 2·00
404/7 .. .. .. .. *Set of* 4 2·25 2·40

**113** Churchill as Schoolboy and School College Building, Harrow

**114** "Madonna of the Trees" (Bellini)

(Des V. Whiteley. Litho Format)

**1974** (20 Oct). *Birth Centenary of Sir Winston Churchill. T* **113** *and similar horiz designs. Multicoloured. P* 14½.

408 5 c. Type **113** .. .. .. .. .. 10 10
409 35 c. Churchill and St. Paul's Cathedral .. .. 20 10
410 75 c. Coat of arms and catafalque .. .. 30 35
411 $1 Churchill, "reward" notice and South African escape route .. .. .. 50 60
408/11 .. .. .. .. *Set of* 4 1·00 1·00
**MS**412 1007 × 82 mm. Nos. 408/11. P 13 .. .. 1·00 1·50

(Des M. Shamir. Litho Format)

**1974** (18 Nov). *Christmas. T* **114** *and similar vert designs showing "Madonna and Child" by the artists given. Multicoloured. P* 14½.
413 ½ c. Type **114** .. .. .. .. .. 10 10
414 1 c. Raphael .. .. .. .. .. 10 10
415 2 c. Van der Weyden .. .. .. .. 10 10
416 3 c. Giorgione .. .. .. .. .. 10 10
417 5 c. Mantegna .. .. .. .. .. 10 10
418 20 c. Vivarini .. .. .. .. .. 15 10
419 35 c. Montagna .. .. .. .. .. 25 10
420 75 c. Lorenzo Costa .. .. .. .. 45 60
413/20 .. .. .. .. *Set of* 8 95 90
**MS**421 139 × 126 mm. Nos. 417/20. P 13 .. .. 95 1·40

$10
(115)

116 Carib War Canoe, English Harbour, 1300

**1975** (14 Jan). *Nos.* 331 *and* 390/2 *surch as T* **115**.
422 50 c. on 20 c. multicoloured .. .. .. 1·50 2·00
423 $2.50, on 35 c. multicoloured .. .. .. 3·50 6·00
424 $5 on $1 multicoloured .. .. .. 5·00 8·00
425 $10 on 75 c. multicoloured .. .. .. 5·50 8·50
422/5 .. .. .. .. *Set of* 4 14·00 22·00

**1975** (21 Jan). *As No.* 334, *but W w* 14 *(sideways).*
426 $5 *Pathfinder* (tug) .. .. .. 4·50 10·00

(Des G. Drummond. Litho Format)

**1975** (17 Mar). *Nelson's Dockyard. T* **116** *and similar horiz designs. Multicoloured. P* 14½.
427 5 c. Type **116** .. .. .. .. .. 15 10
428 15 c. Ship of the line, English Harbour, 1770 50 10
429 35 c. H.M.S. *Boreas* at anchor, and Lord Nelson, 1787 .. .. .. .. 80 15
430 50 c. Yachts during "Sailing Week", 1974 .. 85 40
431 $1 Yacht Anchorage, Old Dockyard, 1970 .. 1·25 1·10
427/31 .. .. .. .. *Set of* 5 3·25 1·75
**MS**432 130 × 134 mm. As Nos. 427/31, but in larger format, 43 × 28 mm. P 13½ .. .. 3·25 2·50

117 Lady of the Valley Church

(Des R. Vigurs. Litho Format)

**1975** (19 May). *Antiguan Churches. T* **117** *and similar horiz designs. Multicoloured. P* 14½.
433 5 c. Type **117** .. .. .. .. .. 10 10
434 20 c. Gilbert Memorial .. .. .. 10 10
435 35 c. Grace Hill Moravian .. .. .. 15 10
436 50 c. St. Phillips .. .. .. .. 20 20
437 $1 Ebenezer Methodist .. .. .. 35 50
433/7 .. .. .. .. *Set of* 5 65 75
**MS**438 91 × 101 mm. Nos. 435/7. P 13 .. .. 65 1·25

118 Map of 1721 and Sextant of 1640

(Des PAD Studio. Litho Questa)

**1975** (21 July). *Maps of Antigua. T* **118** *and similar horiz designs. Multicoloured. W w* 14 *(sideways). P* 14.
439 5 c. Type **118** .. .. .. .. .. 15 10
440 20 c. Map of 1775 and galleon .. .. .. 35 10
441 35 c. Maps of 1775 and 1955 .. .. .. 45 15
442 $1 1973 maps of Antigua and English Harbour .. .. .. .. .. 1·10 1·25
439/42 .. .. .. .. *Set of* 4 1·90 1·40
**MS**443 130 × 89 mm. Nos. 439/42 .. .. 1·90 1·75

119 Scout Bugler

(Des G. Vasarhelyi. Litho Questa)

**1975** (26 Aug). *World Scout Jamboree, Norway. T* **119** *and similar horiz designs. Multicoloured. P* 14.
444 15 c. Type **119** .. .. .. .. .. 25 15
445 20 c. Scouts in camp .. .. .. .. 30 15
446 35 c. "Lord Baden-Powell" (D. Jagger) .. 50 20
447 $2 Scout dancers from Dahomey .. .. 1·50 1·75
444/7 .. .. .. .. *Set of* 4 2·25 2·00
**MS**448 145 × 107 mm. Nos. 444/7 .. .. 3·00 3·00

120 *Eurema elathea*

121 "Madonna and Child" (Correggio)

(Des. G. Vasarhelyi. Litho Questa)

**1975** (30 Oct). *Butterflies. T* **120** *and similar horiz designs. Multicoloured. P* 14.
449 ½ c. Type **120** .. .. .. .. 10 10
450 1 c. *Danaus plexippus* .. .. .. 10 10
451 2 c. *Phoebis philea* .. .. .. 10 10
452 5 c. *Hypolimnas misippus* .. .. .. 15 10
453 20 c. *Eurema proterpia* .. .. .. 60 60
454 35 c. *Battus polydamas* .. .. .. 90 90
455 $2 *Cynthia cardui* .. .. .. 4·00 7·00
449/55 .. .. .. .. *Set of* 7 5·50 8·00
**MS**456 147×94 mm. Nos 452/5 .. .. .. 6·00 8·50
No. 452 is incorrectly captioned "Marpesia petreus thetys".

(Des G. Vasarhelyi. Litho Questa)

**1975** (17 Nov). *Christmas. T* **121** *and similar vert designs showing "Madonna and Child". Multicoloured. P* 14.
457 ½ c. Type **121** .. .. .. .. 10 10
458 1 c. El Greco .. .. .. .. 10 10
459 2 c. Dürer .. .. .. .. 10 10
460 3 c. Antonello .. .. .. .. 10 10
461 5 c. Bellini .. .. .. .. 10 10
462 10 c. Dürer (*different*) .. .. .. 10 10
463 35 c. Bellini (*different*) .. .. .. 30 10
464 $2 Dürer (*different*) .. .. .. 85 70
457/64 .. .. .. .. *Set of* 8 1·25 85
**MS**465 138 × 119 mm. Nos. 461/4 .. .. 1·25 1·60

122 Vivian Richards

123 Antillean Crested Hummingbird

(Des G. Vasarhelyi. Litho Format)

**1975** (15 Dec). *World Cup Cricket Winners. T* **122** *and similar multicoloured designs. P* 13½.
466 5 c. Type **122** .. .. .. .. 80 20
467 35 c. Andy Roberts .. .. .. .. 1·75 60
468 $2 West Indies team (*horiz*) .. .. 4·50 6·00
466/8 .. .. .. .. *Set of* 3 6·50 6·25

(Des G. Vasarhelyi. Litho Format)

**1976** (19 Jan)–**78**. *Various multicoloured designs as T* **123**. A. *Without imprint* (19.1.76). B. *With imprint date at foot* (1978).

(*a*) *Size as T* **123**. *P* 14½

| | | A | | B | |
|---|---|---|---|---|---|
| 469 | ½ c. Type **123** .. | 20 | 30 | 35 | 35 |
| 470 | 1 c. Imperial Amazon .. | 30 | 30 | 45 | 35 |
| 471 | 2 c. Zenaida Dove .. | 30 | 30 | 45 | 35 |
| 472 | 3 c. Loggerhead Kingbird .. | 30 | 30 | 45 | 35 |
| 473 | 4 c. Red-necked Pigeon .. | 30 | 30 | 45 | 35 |
| 474 | 5 c. Rufous-throated Solitaire .. | 40 | 10 | 50 | 30 |
| 475 | 6 c. Orchid Tree .. | 30 | 30 | 30 | 30 |
| 476 | 10 c. Bougainvillea .. | 30 | 10 | 30 | 20 |
| 477 | 15 c. Geiger Tree .. | 35 | 10 | 30 | 20 |
| 478 | 20 c. Flamboyant .. | 35 | 20 | 30 | 30 |
| 479 | 25 c. Hibiscus .. | 40 | 15 | 35 | 30 |
| 480 | 35 c. Flame of the Wood .. | 40 | 20 | 35 | 30 |
| 481 | 50 c. Cannon at Fort James .. | 55 | 40 | 50 | 50 |
| 482 | 75 c. Premier's Office .. | 60 | 65 | 55 | 70 |
| 483 | $1 Potworks Dam .. | 75 | 80 | 75 | 80 |
| | (*b*) *Size* 44 × 28 *mm*. *P* 13½ | | | | |
| 484 | $2.50, Irrigation Scheme, Diamond Estate .. | 2·00 | 2·00 | 4·00 | 4·50 |
| 485 | $5 Government House .. | 3·50 | 3·50 | 4·00 | 4·75 |
| 486 | $10 Coolidge Airport .. | 4·50 | 6·00 | 9·00 | 9·50 |
| 469/86 | .. *Set of* 18 | 14·00 | 14·00 | 21·00 | 22·00 |

Nos. 474 and 476/7 exist imperforate from stock dispersed by the liquidator of Format International Security Printers Ltd.

***PRICES OF SETS***

Set prices are given for many issues, generally those containing three stamps or more. Definitive sets include one of each value or major colour change, but do not cover different perforations, die types or minor shades. Where a choice is possible the set prices are based on the cheapest versions of the stamps included in the listings.

124 Privates, Clark's Illinois Regt

125 High Jump

(Des J.W. Litho Format)

**1976** (17 Mar). *Bicentenary of American Revolution. T* **124** *and similar vert designs. Multicoloured. P* 14½.
487 ½ c. Type **124** .. .. .. .. 10 10
488 1 c. Riflemen, Pennsylvania Militia .. .. 10 10
489 2 c. Powder horn .. .. .. .. 10 10
a. Imperf (pair) .. .. .. .. £160
490 5 c. Water bottle .. .. .. .. 10 10
491 35 c. American flags .. .. .. .. 35 10
492 $1 Privateer *Montgomery* .. .. .. 1·00 55
493 $5 Sloop *Ranger* .. .. .. .. 3·50 3·50
487/93 .. .. .. .. *Set of* 7 4·50 3·75
**MS**494 71 × 84 mm. $2.50 Congress flag. P 13 .. 2·25 3·00

(Des J.W. Litho Format)

**1976** (17 July). *Olympic Games, Montreal. T* **125** *and similar horiz designs. P* 14½.
495 ½ c. orange-brown, bistre-yellow and black .. 10 10
496 1 c. light reddish violet, bright blue & black 10 10
497 2 c. light green and black .. .. .. 10 10
498 15 c. bright blue and black .. .. .. 10 10
499 30 c. olive-brown, yellow-ochre and black .. 15 15
500 $1 red-orange, Venetian red and black .. 40 40
501 $2 rosine and black .. .. .. 70 80
495/501 .. .. .. .. *Set of* 7 1·25 1·40
**MS**502 88 × 138 mm. Nos. 498/501. P 13½ .. 1·75 2·25
Designs:—1 c. Boxing; 2 c. Pole vault; 15 c. Swimming; 30 c. Running; $1 Cycling; $2 Shot put.

126 Water Skiing

(Des J.W. Litho Questa)

**1976** (26 Aug). *Water Sports. T* **126** *and similar horiz designs. Multicoloured. P* 14.
503 ½ c. Type **126** .. .. .. .. 10 10
504 1 c. Sailing .. .. .. .. 10 10
505 2 c. Snorkeling .. .. .. .. 10 10
506 20 c. Deep sea fishing .. .. .. 15 10
507 50 c. Scuba diving .. .. .. .. 35 35
508 $2 Swimming .. .. .. .. 1·00 1·25
503/8 .. .. .. .. *Set of* 6 1·40 1·60
**MS**509 89 × 114 mm. Nos. 506/8 .. .. 1·40 1·75

127 French Angelfish

128 The Annunciation

(Des G. Drummond. Litho Questa)

**1976** (4 Oct). *Fishes. T* **127** *and similar horiz designs. Multicoloured. W w* 14 *(sideways). P* 13½.
510 15 c. Type **127** .. .. .. .. 25 15
511 30 c. Yellowfin Grouper .. .. .. 40 30
512 50 c. Yellowtail Snappers .. .. .. 55 50
513 90 c. Shy Hamlet .. .. .. .. 80 80
510/13 .. .. .. .. *Set of* 4 1·75 1·60

(Des J.W. Litho Walsall)

**1976** (15 Nov). *Christmas. T* **128** *and similar vert designs. Multicoloured. P* 13½.
514 8 c. Type **128** .. .. .. .. 10 10
515 10 c. The Holy Family .. .. .. 10 10
516 15 c. The Magi .. .. .. .. 10 10
517 50 c. The Shepherds .. .. .. 20 25
518 $1 Epiphany scene .. .. .. 30 50
514/18 .. .. .. .. *Set of* 5 60 75

**129** Mercury and U.P.U. Emblem   **130** Royal Family

(Des BG Studio. Litho Questa)

**1976** (28 Dec). *Special Events, 1976. T* **129** *and similar horiz designs. Multicoloured. P* 14.
519 ½ c. Type **129** .. 10 10
520 1 c. Alfred Nobel 10 10
521 10 c. Space satellite 20 10
522 50 c. Viv Richards and Andy Roberts 1·75 1·00
523 $1 Bell and telephones 1·75 1·60
524 $2 Yacht *Freelance* 2·50 2·75
519/24 *Set of* 6 5·75 5·00
**MS**525 127 × 101 mm. Nos. 521/4 6·00 8·50

Events:—½ c. 25th Anniv of U.N. Postal Administration; 1 c. 75th Anniv of Nobel Prize; 10 c. "Viking" Space Mission; 50 c. Cricketing achievements; $1 Telephone Centenary; $2 "Operation Sail", U.S. Bicentennial.

(Des J. W. Litho Questa (Nos. 526/31); Manufactured by Walsall (Nos. 532/3))

**1977** (7 Feb–26 Sept). *Silver Jubilee. T* **130** *and similar vert designs. Multicoloured.* (a) *Sheet stamps. P* 14 (7 Feb).
526 10 c. Type **130** .. 10 10
527 30 c. Royal Visit, 1966 10 10
528 50 c. The Queen enthroned 15 15
529 90 c. The Queen after Coronation 25 20
530 $2.50, Queen and Prince Charles 45 35
526/30 *Set of* 5 75 70
**MS**531 116×78 mm. $5 Queen and Prince Philip 1·00 1·10
a. Error. Imperf £350

(b) *Booklet stamps. Roul* 5 × *imperf* (50 c.) *or imperf* ($5).* *Self-adhesive* (26 Sept)
532 50 c. Design as No. 529 (24 × 42 *mm*) 35 60
a. Booklet pane of 6.. 1·90
533 $5 Design as stamp from No. **MS**531 (24 × 42 *mm*) 2·50 3·50
a. Booklet pane of 1.. 2·50

*No. 532 was separated by various combinations of rotary knife (giving a straight edge) and roulette. No. 533 exists only with straight edges.

Stamps as Nos. 526/30 but perforated 11½ × 12, come from sheets of 5 stamps and 1 label. These were not placed on sale by the Antigua Post Office.

**131** Making Camp   **132** Carnival Costume

(Des J.W. Litho Questa)

**1977** (23 May). *Caribbean Scout Jamboree, Jamaica. T* **131** *and similar horiz designs. Multicoloured. P* 14.
534 ½ c. Type **131** 10 10
535 1 c. Hiking 10 10
536 2 c. Rock-climbing 10 10
537 10 c. Cutting logs 10 10
538 30 c. Map and sign reading 20 10
539 50 c. First aid 35 20
540 $2 Rafting 1·50 1·50
534/40 *Set of* 7 2·00 1·75
**MS**541 127 × 114 mm. Nos. 538/40 2·25 2·75

**1977.** *Coil Stamp. W w* **14** (*inverted*). *P* 14½×14.
541*a* **89** 10 c. emerald — 30

(Des C. Abbott. Litho Walsall)

**1977** (18 July). *21st Anniv of Carnival. T* **132** *and similar vert designs. Multicoloured. P* 14.
542 10 c. Type **132** .. 10 10
543 30 c. Carnival Queen 20 10
544 50 c. Butterfly costume 25 15
545 90 c. Queen of the band 35 25
546 $1 Calypso King and Queen 35 30
542/6 *Set of* 5 1·10 70
**MS**547 140×120 mm. Nos. 542/6 1·10 1·60

### MINIMUM PRICE

The minimum price quote is 10p which represents a handling charge rather than a basis for valuing common stamps. For further notes about prices see introductory pages.

ROYAL VISIT
28th OCTOBER 1977
(133)

**134** "Virgin and Child Enthroned" (Tura)

**1977** (17 Oct). *Royal Visit. Nos.* 526/531 *optd with T* **133**. *P* 14.
548 10 c. Type **130** .. 10 10
549 30 c. Royal Visit, 1966 10 10
550 50 c. The Queen enthroned 15 10
551 90 c. The Queen after Coronation 25 20
552 $2.50, Queen and Prince Charles 45 35
548/52 *Set of* 5 80 65
**MS**553 116 × 78 mm. $5 Queen and Prince Philip 1·00 1·25
a. Opt double 50·00

Nos. 548/52 also exist perf 11½ × 12 (*Price for set of* 5 £1 *mint or used*) from additional sheetlets of five stamps and one label.

(Des M. Shamir. Litho Questa)

**1977** (21 Nov). *Christmas. T* **134** *and similar vert designs showing "Virgin and Child" by the artists given. Multicoloured. P* 14.
554 ½ c. Type **134** .. 10 10
555 1 c. Crivelli 10 10
556 2 c. Lotto 10 10
557 8 c. Pontormo 10 10
558 10 c. Tura (*different*) 10 10
559 25 c. Lotto (*different*) 20 10
560 $2 Crivelli (*different*) 75 60
554/60 *Set of* 7 1·00 75
**MS**561 144 × 118 mm. Nos. 557/60 1·00 1·60

**135** Pineapple

(Des and litho J.W.)

**1977** (29 Dec). *Tenth Anniv of Statehood. T* **135** *and similar horiz designs. Multicoloured. P* 13.
562 10 c. Type **135** .. 10 10
563 15 c. State flag 10 10
564 50 c. Police band 50 20
565 90 c. Premier V. C. Bird 35 30
566 $2 State Coat of Arms 60 60
562/6 *Set of* 5 1·50 1·10
**MS**567 126 × 99 mm. Nos. 563/6. P 14 1·50 1·90

**136** *Glider III*, 1902

(Des PAD Studio. Litho Questa)

**1978** (23 Mar). *75th Anniv of Powered Flight. T* **136** *and similar multicoloured designs. P* 14.
568 ½ c. Type **136** .. 10 10
569 1 c. *Flyer I*, 1903 10 10
570 2 c. Launch system and engine 10 10
571 10 c. Orville Wright (*vert.*) 10 10
572 50 c. *Flyer III*, 1905 35 15
573 90 c. Wilbur Wright (*vert*) 50 30
574 $2 Wright "Model B", 1910 80 80
568/74 *Set of* 7 1·75 1·25
**MS**575 90 × 75 mm. $2.50, *Flyer I* on launch system 1·60 2·50

**137** Sunfish Regatta

(Des G. Drummond. Litho Format)

**1978** (27 Apr). *Sailing Week. T* **137** *and similar horiz designs. Multicoloured. P* 15.
576 10 c. Type **137** .. 15 10
577 50 c. Fishing and work boat race 35 20
578 90 c. Curtain Bluff race 60 35
579 $2 Power boat rally 1·25 1·25
576/9 *Set of* 4 2·10 1·75
**MS**580 110 × 77 mm. $2.50, Guadeloupe–Antigua race 1·90 2·50

Nos. 576/9 exist imperforate from stock dispersed by the liquidator of Format International Security Printers Ltd.

**138** Queen Elizabeth and Prince Philip   **139** Glass Coach

(Des J.W. Litho Questa (Nos. 581/6); Manufactured by Walsall (Nos. 587/9))

**1978** (2 June). *25th Anniv of Coronation. Multicoloured.* (a) *Sheet stamps. Vert designs as T* **138**. *P* 14.
581 10 c. Type **138** .. 10 10
582 30 c. Crowning 10 10
583 50 c. Coronation procession 15 10
584 90 c. Queen seated in St. Edward's Chair 20 15
585 $2.50, Queen wearing Imperial State Crown 40 40
581/5 *Set of* 5 65 65
**MS**586 114 × 104 mm. $5 Queen and Prince Philip 1·00 1·10

(b) *Booklet stamps. Horiz design as T* **139** *showing State Coaches. Imperf* ($5) *or roul* 5 × *imperf*. Self-adhesive.*
587 25 c. Type **139** .. 15 30
a. Booklet pane. Nos. 587/8 × 3 1·25
588 50 c. Irish State Coach 25 50
589 $5 Coronation Coach 2·50 3·00
a. Booklet pane of 1.. 2·50
587/9 *Set of* 3 2·50 3·50

Nos. 581/5 also exist perf 12 (*Price for set of* 5 £1 *mint or used*) from additional sheetlets of three stamps and one label. These stamps have changed background colours.

*Nos. 587/8 were separated by various combinations of rotary-knife (giving a straight edge) and roulette. No. 589 exists only with straight edges.

**140** Player running with Ball   **141** Petrea

(Des BG Studio. Litho Format)

**1978** (17 Aug). *World Cup Football Championship, Argentina. T* **140** *and similar vert designs. Multicoloured. P* 14½.
590 10 c. Type **140** .. 10 10
591 15 c. Players in front of goal 10 10
592 $3 Referee and player 2·00 1·75
590/2 *Set of* 3 2·00 1·75
**MS**593 126 × 88 mm. 25 c. Player crouching with ball; 30 c. Players heading ball; 50 c. Players running with ball; $2 Goalkeeper diving. (*All horiz*) 2·25 2·50

Nos. 590/2 were each printed in small sheets of 6 including 1 *se-tenant* stamp-size label.

Nos. 590/2 exist imperforate from stock dispersed by the liquidator of Format International Security Printers Ltd.

(Des G. Drummond. Litho Questa)

**1978** (5 Oct). *Flowers. T* **141** *and similar vert designs. Multicoloured. P* 14.
594 25 c. Type **141** .. 25 10
595 50 c. Sunflower 35 20
596 90 c. Frangipani 60 30
597 $2 Passion Flower 1·25 1·10
594/7 *Set of* 4 2·25 1·40
**MS**598 118 × 85 mm. $2.50, Hibiscus 1·40 1·60

**142** "St Ildefonso receiving the Chasuble from the Virgin" (Rubens)   **143** 1d. Stamp of 1863

(Des BG Studio. Litho Questa)

**1978** (30 Oct). *Christmas Paintings. T* **142** *and similar horiz designs. Multicoloured. P* 14.
599 8 c. Type **142** .. 10 10
600 25 c. "The Flight of St. Barbara" (Rubens) 20 10
601 $2 "Madonna and Child, with St. Joseph, John the Baptist and Donor" (Sebastiano del Piombo*) 95 55
599/601 *Set of* 3 1·10 60
**MS**602 170 × 113 mm. $4 "The Annunciation" (Rubens) 2·00 2·75

*The work is incorrectly attributed to Rubens on the stamp.

(Des G. Vasarhelyi. Litho Questa)

**1979** (12 Feb). *Death Centenary of Sir Rowland Hill. T* **143** *and similar vert designs. Multicoloured. P* 14.

| | | | |
|---|---|---|---|
| 603 | 25 c. Type **143** | 10 | 10 |
| 604 | 50 c. Penny Black | 25 | 15 |
| 605 | $1 Stage-coach and woman posting letter, *circa* 1840 | 45 | 30 |
| 606 | $2 Modern mail transport | 1·00 | 75 |
| 603/6 | *Set of* 4 | 1·60 | 1·10 |
| **MS**607 | 108 × 82 mm. $2.50, Sir Rowland Hill | 80 | 90 |

Nos. 603/6 also exist perf 12 (*Price for set of* 4 £1.60 *mint or used*) from additional sheetlets of five stamps and one label.

**144** "The Deposition from the Cross" (painting)  **145** Toy Yacht and Child's Hand

(Des BG Studio. Litho Questa)

**1979** (15 Mar). *Easter. Works by Dürer. T* **144** *and similar vert designs. P* 14.

| | | | |
|---|---|---|---|
| 608 | 10 c. multicoloured | 10 | 10 |
| 609 | 50 c. multicoloured | 35 | 20 |
| 610 | $4 black, magenta and greenish yellow | 1·50 | 90 |
| 608/10 | *Set of* 3 | 1·75 | 1·00 |
| **MS**611 | 114 × 99 mm. $2.50, multicoloured | 65 | 80 |

Designs:—50 c., $2.50, "Christ on the Cross—The Passion" (wood engravings) (*both different*); $4 "Man of Sorrows with Hands Raised" (wood engraving).

(Des M. Rubin. Litho Questa)

**1979** (9 Apr). *International Year of the Child. T* **145** *and similar vert designs showing toys and hands of children of different races. Multicoloured. P* 14.

| | | | |
|---|---|---|---|
| 612 | 25 c. Type **145** | 10 | 10 |
| 613 | 50 c. Rocket | 25 | 15 |
| 614 | 90 c. Car | 40 | 25 |
| 615 | $2 Train | 1·00 | 90 |
| 612/15 | *Set of* 4 | 1·60 | 1·25 |
| **MS**616 | 80 × 112 mm. $5 Aeroplane | 1·75 | 2·00 |

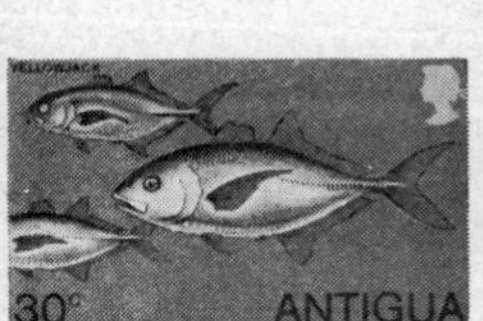

**146** Yellowjack  **147** Cook's Birthplace, Marton

(Des P. Powell. Litho Questa)

**1979** (14 May). *Fishes. T* **146** *and similar horiz designs. Multicoloured. P* 14½ × 14.

| | | | |
|---|---|---|---|
| 617 | 30 c. Type **146** | 30 | 15 |
| 618 | 50 c. Bluefin Tuna | 40 | 25 |
| 619 | 90 c. Sailfish | 60 | 40 |
| 620 | $3 Wahoo | 2·00 | 1·75 |
| 617/20 | *Set of* 4 | 3·00 | 2·25 |
| **MS**621 | 122 × 75 mm. $2.50, Barracuda | 1·25 | 1·40 |

(Des J.W. Litho Questa)

**1979** (2 July). *Death Bicentenary of Captain Cook. T* **147** *and similar vert designs. Multicoloured. P* 14.

| | | | |
|---|---|---|---|
| 622 | 25 c. Type **147** | 45 | 30 |
| 623 | 50 c. H.M.S. *Endeavour* | 65 | 65 |
| 624 | 90 c. Marine chronometer | 80 | 80 |
| 625 | $3 Landing at Botany Bay | 2·00 | 3·00 |
| 622/5 | *Set of* 4 | 3·50 | 4·25 |
| **MS**626 | 110 × 85 mm. $2.50, H.M.S. *Resolution* | 2·25 | 2·50 |

**148** The Holy Family  **149** Javelin Throwing

(Des J.W. Litho Questa)

**1979** (1 Oct). *Christmas. T* **148** *and similar vert designs. Multicoloured. P* 14.

| | | | |
|---|---|---|---|
| 627 | 8 c. Type **148** | 10 | 10 |
| 628 | 25 c. Virgin and Child on Ass | 15 | 10 |
| 629 | 50 c. Shepherd and star | 30 | 30 |
| 630 | $4 Wise Men with gifts | 1·40 | 1·75 |
| 627/30 | *Set of* 4 | 1·75 | 2·00 |
| **MS**631 | 113 × 94 mm. $3 Angel with trumpet. P 12 | 1·00 | 1·50 |

(Des Design Images Inc. Litho Questa)

**1980** (18 Feb). *Olympic Games, Moscow. T* **149** *and similar multicoloured designs. P* 14.

| | | | |
|---|---|---|---|
| 632 | 10 c. Type **149** | 10 | 10 |
| 633 | 25 c. Running | 15 | 10 |
| 634 | $1 Pole vaulting | 40 | 40 |
| 635 | $2 Hurdling | 65 | 75 |
| 632/5 | *Set of* 4 | 1·10 | 1·25 |
| **MS**636 | 127 × 96 mm. $3 Boxing (*horiz*) | 65 | 90 |

**LONDON 1980**

**150** Mickey Mouse and Aeroplane  (**151**)

(Litho Format)

**1980** (24 Mar). *International Year of the Child* (1979). *Walt Disney Cartoon Characters. T* **150** *and similar multicoloured designs showing characters and transport. P* 11.

| | | | |
|---|---|---|---|
| 637 | ½ c. Type **150** | 10 | 10 |
| 638 | 1 c. Donald Duck driving car | 10 | 10 |
| 639 | 2 c. Goofy driving taxi | 10 | 10 |
| 640 | 3 c. Mickey Mouse on motorcycle with Minnie Mouse in sidecar | 10 | 10 |
| 641 | 4 c. Huey, Dewey and Louie riding cycle | 10 | 10 |
| 642 | 5 c. Grandma Duck, chickens and pickup truck | 10 | 10 |
| 643 | 10 c. Mickey Mouse driving jeep (*vert*) | 10 | 10 |
| 644 | $1 Chip and Dale in sailing boat | 1·50 | 1·00 |
| 645 | $4 Donald Duck riding toy train (*vert*) | 3·25 | 3·00 |
| 637/45 | *Set of* 9 | 4·75 | 4·00 |
| **MS**646 | 101 × 127 mm. $2.50, Goofy flying biplane. P 14 × 13½ | 3·00 | 2·00 |

See also Nos. 671/80.

**1980** (6 May). *"London 1980" International Stamp Exhibition. Nos. 603/6 optd with T* **151**. *P* 12.

| | | | |
|---|---|---|---|
| 647 | 25 c. Type **143** | 20 | 15 |
| 648 | 50 c. Penny Black | 30 | 30 |
| 649 | $1 Stage-coach and woman posting letter, *circa* 1840 | 55 | 45 |
| 650 | $2 Modern mail transport | 1·75 | 1·75 |
| 647/50 | *Set of* 4 | 2·50 | 2·40 |

**152** "David" (statue, Donatello)  **153** Rotary International 75th Anniversary Emblem and Headquarters, U.S.A.

(Des J.W. Litho Questa)

**1980** (23 June). *Famous Works of Art. T* **152** *and similar multicoloured designs. P* 13½.

| | | | |
|---|---|---|---|
| 651 | 10 c. Type **152** | 10 | 10 |
| 652 | 30 c. "The Birth of Venus" (painting, Sandro Botticelli) (*horiz*) | 25 | 15 |
| 653 | 50 c. "Reclining Couple" (sarcophagus), Cerveteri (*horiz*) | 35 | 35 |
| 654 | 90 c. "The Garden of Earthly Delights" (painting, Hieronymus Bosch) (*horiz*) | 55 | 55 |
| 655 | $1 "Portinari Altarpiece" (painting, Hugo van der Goes) (*horiz*) | 65 | 65 |
| 656 | $4 "Eleanora of Toledo and her Son Giovanni de'Medici" (painting, Agnolo Bronzino) | 2·00 | 2·50 |
| 651/6 | *Set of* 6 | 3·50 | 3·75 |
| **MS**657 | 99 × 124 mm. $5 "The Holy Family" (painting, Rembrandt) | 2·25 | 2·25 |

(Des G. Vasarhelyi. Litho Questa)

**1980** (21 July). *75th Anniv of Rotary International. T* **153** *and similar horiz designs. Multicoloured. P* 14.

| | | | |
|---|---|---|---|
| 658 | 30 c. Type **153** | 30 | 20 |
| 659 | 50 c. Rotary anniversary emblem and Antigua Rotary Club banner | 35 | 30 |
| 660 | 90 c. Map of Antigua and Rotary emblem | 50 | 50 |
| 661 | $3 Paul P. Harris (founder) and Rotary emblem | 1·75 | 2·00 |
| 658/61 | *Set of* 4 | 2·75 | 2·75 |
| **MS**662 | 102 × 78 mm. $5 Antiguan flags and Rotary emblems | 2·00 | 2·50 |

## ALTERED CATALOGUE NUMBERS

Any Catalogue numbers altered from the last edition are shown as a list in the introductory pages.

**154** Queen Elizabeth the Queen Mother  **155** Ringed Kingfisher

(Des G. Vasarhelyi. Litho Questa)

**1980** (4 Aug). *80th Birthday of Queen Elizabeth the Queen Mother. P* 14.

| | | | |
|---|---|---|---|
| 663 | **154** 10 c. multicoloured | 20 | 10 |
| 664 | $2.50, multicoloured | 2·25 | 2·50 |
| **MS**665 | 68 × 90 mm. **154** $3 multicoloured. P 12 | 2·00 | 2·25 |

(Des Jennifer Toombs. Litho Questa)

**1980** (3 Nov). *Birds. T* **155** *and similar vert designs. Multicoloured. P* 14.

| | | | |
|---|---|---|---|
| 666 | 10 c. Type **155** | 35 | 15 |
| 667 | 30 c. Plain Pigeon | 55 | 30 |
| 668 | $1 Green-throated Carib | 1·50 | 1·10 |
| 669 | $2 Black-necked Stilt | 1·75 | 2·00 |
| 666/9 | *Set of* 4 | 3·75 | 3·25 |
| **MS**670 | 73 × 73 mm. $2.50, Roseate Tern | 4·25 | 3·00 |

(Litho Format)

**1980** (23 Dec). *Christmas. Scenes from Walt Disney's Cartoon Film "Sleeping Beauty". Horiz designs as T* **150**. *P* 11.

| | | | |
|---|---|---|---|
| 671 | ½ c. multicoloured | 10 | 10 |
| 672 | 1 c. multicoloured | 10 | 10 |
| 673 | 2 c. multicoloured | 10 | 10 |
| 674 | 4 c. multicoloured | 10 | 10 |
| 675 | 8 c. multicoloured | 10 | 10 |
| 676 | 10 c. multicoloured | 10 | 10 |
| 677 | 25 c. multicoloured | 15 | 15 |
| 678 | $2 multicoloured | 1·90 | 1·75 |
| 679 | $2.50, multicoloured | 2·25 | 2·00 |
| 671/9 | *Set of* 9 | 4·00 | 3·75 |
| **MS**680 | 126 × 101 mm. $4 multicoloured (*vert*) P 13½ × 14 | 3·75 | 2·50 |

**156** Diesel Locomotive No. 15

(Des G. Drummond. Litho Questa)

**1981** (12 Jan). *Sugar Cane Railway Locomotives. T* **156** *and similar horiz designs. Multicoloured. P* 14.

| | | | |
|---|---|---|---|
| 681 | 25 c. Type **156** | 15 | 15 |
| 682 | 50 c. Narrow-gauge steam locomotive | 30 | 30 |
| 683 | 90 c. Diesel locomotives Nos. 1 and 10 | 55 | 55 |
| 684 | $3 Steam locomotive hauling sugar cane | 2·00 | 2·00 |
| 681/4 | *Set of* 4 | 2·75 | 2·75 |
| **MS**685 | 82 × 111 mm. $2.50, Antigua sugar factory, railway yard and sheds | 1·75 | 1·75 |

**"INDEPENDENCE 1981"**

(**157**)

**158** "Pipes of Pan"

**1981** (31 Mar). *Independence. Optd with T* **157**. A. *On Nos.* 475A, 478A, 480A *and* 484A/6A. B. *On Nos.* 475B/6B *and* 478B/86B.

| | | A | | B | |
|---|---|---|---|---|---|
| 686 | 6 c. Orchid Tree | 45 | 45 | 10 | 10 |
| 687 | 10 c. Bougainvillea | † | | 10 | 10 |
| 688 | 20 c. Flamboyant | 45 | 45 | 10 | 10 |
| 689 | 25 c. Hibiscus | † | | 15 | 15 |
| 690 | 35 c. Flame of the Wood | 90 | 90 | 20 | 20 |
| 691 | 50 c. Cannon at Fort James | † | | 35 | 35 |
| 692 | 75 c. Premier's Office | † | | 40 | 40 |
| 693 | $1 Potworks Dam | † | | 55 | 55 |
| 694 | $2.50, Irrigation Scheme, Diamond Estate | 2·50 | 2·75 | 1·25 | 1·25 |
| 695 | $5 Government House | 5·00 | 5·50 | 2·50 | 2·50 |
| 696 | $10 Coolidge Airport | 8·50 | 9·50 | 4·50 | 5·00 |
| 686A/96A | *Set of* 6 | 16·00 | 18·00 | † | |
| 686B/96B | *Set of* 11 | † | | 9·00 | 9·50 |

(Des J.W. Litho Questa)

**1981** (5 May). *Birth Centenary of Picasso. T* **158** *and similar vert designs. Multicoloured. P* 14.

697 10 c. Type **158** . . . . 10 10
698 50 c. "Seated Harlequin" . . . . 30 30
699 90 c. "Paulo as Harlequin" . . . . 55 55
700 $4 "Mother and Child" . . . . 2·50 2·50
697/700 . . . . *Set of* 4 3·00 3·00
**MS**701 115 × 140 mm. $5 "Three Musicians" (detail) . . . . 2·75 2·75

**159** Prince Charles and Lady Diana Spencer

**160** Prince of Wales at Investiture, 1969

(Des J.W. Litho Questa)

**1981** (23 June). *Royal Wedding. T* **159** *and similar vert designs. Multicoloured. P* 14.

702 25 c. Type **159** . . . . 15 10
703 50 c. Glamis Castle . . . . 25 20
704 $4 Prince Charles skiing . . . . 1·25 1·40
702/4 . . . . *Set of* 3 1·50 1·50
**MS**705 96 × 82 mm. $5 Glass Coach . . 1·40 1·75

Nos. 702/4 also exist perforated 12 (*Price for set of* 3 £1·25 *mint or used*) from additional sheetlets of five stamps and one label. These stamps have changed background colours.

(Manufactured by Walsall)

**1981** (23 June). *Royal Wedding. Booklet stamps. T* **160** *and similar vert designs. Multicoloured* ($5) *or black and flesh* (*others*). *Roul* 5 × *imperf*. Self-adhesive.*

706 25 c. Type **160** . . . . 20 20
a. Booklet pane. Nos. 706/11 . . 2·50
707 25 c. Prince Charles as baby, 1948 . . 20 20
708 $1 Prince Charles at R.A.F. College, Cranwell, 1971 . . 40 40
709 $1 Prince Charles attending Hill House School, 1956 . . 40 40
710 $2 Prince Charles and Lady Diana Spencer 75 75
711 $2 Prince Charles at Trinity College, 1967 75 75
712 $5 Prince Charles and Lady Diana (*different*) 1·50 1·50
a. Booklet pane of 1 . . . . 1·50
706/12 . . . . *Set of* 7 3·50 3·50

*The 25 c. to $2 values were each separated by various combinations of rotary knife (giving a straight edge) and roulette. The $5 value exists only with straight edges.

**161** Irene Joshua (founder)

**162** Antigua and Barbuda Coat of Arms

(Des M. Diamond. Litho Format)

**1981** (28 Oct). *50th Anniv of Antigua Girl Guide Movement. T* **161** *and similar horiz designs. Multicoloured. P* 14½.

713 10 c. Type **161** . . . . 10 10
714 50 c. Campfire sing-song . . . . 35 35
715 90 c. Sailing . . . . 65 65
716 $2.50, Animal tending . . . . 1·75 1·75
713/16 . . . . *Set of* 4 2·50 2·50
**MS**717 110 × 85 mm. $5 Raising the flag . . 4·25 3·50

## INDEPENDENT

Nos. 718/22 and 733 onwards are inscribed "ANTIGUA & BARBUDA".

(Des E. Henry. Litho Format)

**1981** (1 Nov). *Independence. T* **162** *and similar multicoloured designs. P* 14½.

718 10 c. Type **162** . . . . 10 10
719 50 c. Pineapple, Antigua flag and map . . 25 15
720 90 c. Prime Minister Vere Bird . . 50 30
721 $2.50, St. John's Cathedral (38 × 25 *mm*) . . 1·00 1·40
718/21 . . . . *Set of* 4 1·75 1·75
**MS**722 105 × 79 mm. $5 Map of Antigua and Barbuda (42 × 42 *mm*) . . 3·25 2·75

## NEW INFORMATION

The editor is always interested to correspond with people who have new information that will improve or correct the Catalogue.

**163** "Holy Night" (Jacques Stella)

**164** Swimming

(Des Clover Mill. Litho Format)

**1981** (16 Nov). *Christmas. Paintings. T* **163** *and similar vert designs. Multicoloured. P* 14½.

723 8 c. Type **163** . . . . 15 10
724 30 c. "Mary with Child" (Julius Schnorr von Carolfeld) . . 30 15
725 $1 "Virgin and Child" (Alonso Cano) . . 80 70
726 $3 "Virgin and Child" (Lorenzo di Credi) . . 2·25 3·00
723/6 . . . . *Set of* 4 3·25 3·50
**MS**727 77 × 111 mm. $5 "Holy Family" (Pieter von Avon) . . 3·75 3·75

(Des M. Diamond. Litho Format)

**1981** (1 Dec). *International Year for Disabled Persons. Sport for the Disabled. T* **164** *and similar horiz designs. Multicoloured. P* 15.

728 10 c. Type **164** . . . . 10 10
729 50 c. Discus throwing . . . . 30 30
730 90 c. Archery . . . . 55 55
731 $2 Baseball . . . . 1·40 1·40
728/31 . . . . *Set of* 4 2·10 2·10
**MS**732 108 × 84 mm. $4 Basketball . . 4·25 2·75

**165** Scene from Football Match

**166** European "A-300 (Airbus)"

(Des Clover Mill. Litho Questa)

**1982** (15 Apr). *World Cup Football Championship, Spain. T* **165** *and similar horiz designs showing scenes from different matches. P* 14.

733 10 c. multicoloured . . . . 15 10
734 50 c. multicoloured . . . . 40 35
735 90 c. multicoloured . . . . 65 60
736 $4 multicoloured . . . . 3·00 3·00
733/6 . . . . *Set of* 4 3·75 3·50
**MS**737 75 × 92 mm. $5 multicoloured . . 4·50 4·50

Nos. 733/6 also exist perforated 12 (*Price for set of* 4, £3·50 *mint or used*) from additional sheetlets of five stamps and one label. These stamps have changed inscription colours.

(Des Clover Mill. Litho Format)

**1982** (17 June). *Coolidge International Airport. T* **166** *and similar multicoloured designs. P* 14½.

738 10 c. Type **166** . . . . 10 10
739 50 c. Hawker-Siddeley "748" . . . . 30 30
740 90 c. De Havilland "DCH6 (Twin Otter)" . . 60 60
741 $2.50, Britten-Norman "Islander" . . 1·50 1·50
738/41 . . . . *Set of* 4 2·25 2·25
**MS**742 99 × 73 mm. $5 Boeing "747 (Jumbo Jet)" (*horiz*) . . 3·75 3·50

**167** Cordia

(Des G. Drummond. Litho Questa)

**1982** (28 June). *Death Centenary of Charles Darwin. Fauna and Flora. T* **167** *and similar multicoloured designs. P* 15.

743 10 c. Type **167** . . . . 15 10
744 50 c. Small Indian Mongoose (*horiz*) . . 45 40
745 90 c. Corallita . . . . 75 75
746 $3 Mexican Bulldog Bat (*horiz*) . . 2·00 2·75
743/6 . . . . *Set of* 4 3·00 3·50
**MS**747 107 × 85 mm. $5 Caribbean Monk Seal 5·50 6·50

**168** Queen's House, Greenwich

**169** Princess of Wales

(Des PAD Studio. Litho Questa)

**1982** (1 July). *21st Birthday of Princess of Wales. T* **168/9** *and similar vert design. Multicoloured. P* 14½ × 14.

748 90 c. Type **168** . . . . 45 45
749 $1 Prince and Princess of Wales . . 50 50
750 $4 Princess Diana (*different*) . . 2·00 2·00
748/50 . . . . *Set of* 3 2·75 2·75
**MS**751 102 × 75 mm. $5 Type **169** . . 2·40 2·50

Nos. 748/50 also exist in sheetlets of 5 stamps and 1 label.

**170** Boy Scouts decorating Streets for Independence Parade

ROYAL BABY
21.6.82

(**171**)

(Des J.W. Litho Questa)

**1982** (15 July). *75th Anniv of Boy Scout Movement. T* **170** *and similar horiz designs. Multicoloured. P* 14.

752 10 c. Type **170** . . . . 15 10
753 50 c. Boy Scout giving helping hand during street parade . . 40 40
754 90 c. Boy Scouts attending Princess Margaret at Independence Ceremony . . 75 75
755 $2.20, Cub Scout giving directions to tourists 1·75 2·25
752/5 . . . . *Set of* 4 2·75 3·00
**MS**756 102 × 72 mm. $5 Lord Baden-Powell . . 5·50 5·00

**1982** (30 Aug). *Birth of Prince William of Wales. Nos.* 748/51 *optd with T* **171**.

757 90 c. Type **168** . . . . 45 45
758 $1 Prince and Princess of Wales . . 50 50
759 $4 Princess Diana (*different*) . . 2·00 2·00
757/9 . . . . *Set of* 3 2·75 2·75
**MS**760 102 × 75 mm. $5 Type **169** . . 2·40 2·50

Nos. 757/9 also exist in sheetlets of 5 stamps and 1 label.

**172** Roosevelt in 1940

(Des PAD Studio. Litho Format)

**1982** (20 Sept). *Birth Centenary of Franklin D. Roosevelt (Nos.* 761, 763, 765/6 *and* **MS**767) *and 250th Birth Anniv of George Washington (others). T* **172** *and similar multicoloured designs. P* 15.

761 10 c. Type **172** . . . . 15 10
762 25 c. Washington as blacksmith . . 30 15
763 45 c. Churchill, Roosevelt and Stalin at Yalta Conference . . 70 25
764 60 c. Washington crossing the Delaware (*vert*) 70 25
765 $1 "Roosevelt Special" train (*vert*) . . 1·25 55
766 $3 Portrait of Roosevelt (*vert*) . . 1·90 1·75
761/6 . . . . *Set of* 6 4·50 2·75
**MS**767 92 × 87 mm. $4 Roosevelt and Wife . . 3·00 2·25
**MS**768 92 × 87 mm. $4 Portrait of Washington (*vert*) . . 3·00 2·25

**173** "Annunciation"

(Des Design Images. Litho Questa)

**1982** (Nov). *Christmas. Religious Paintings by Raphael. T* **173** *and similar horiz designs. Multicoloured. P* 14 × 13½.

769 10 c. Type **173** . . . . 10 10
770 30 c. "Adoration of the Magi" . . 15 15
771 $1 "Presentation at the Temple" . . 50 50
772 $4 "Coronation of the Virgin" . . 2·10 2·25
769/72 . . . . *Set of* 4 2·50 2·75
**MS**773 95 × 124 mm. $5 "Marriage of the Virgin" 2·50 2·50

174 Tritons and Dolphins

175 Pineapple Produce

(Des Design Images. Litho Format)

**1983** (28 Jan). *500th Birth Anniv of Raphael. Details from "Galatea" Fresco. T* **174** *and similar multicoloured designs. P* 14½.

774 45 c. Type **174** .. .. .. .. .. .. 20 25
775 50 c. Sea Nymph carried off by Triton .. 25 30
776 60 c. Winged angel steering Dolphins (*horiz*) 30 35
777 $4 Cupids shooting arrows (*horiz*) .. .. 1·90 2·00
774/7 .. .. .. .. .. *Set of* 4 2·40 2·50
**MS**778 101 × 125 mm. $5 Galatea pulled along by Dolphins .. .. .. .. .. .. .. 2·50 2·75

(Des Artists International. Litho Questa)

**1983** (14 Mar). *Commonwealth Day. T* **175** *and similar horiz designs. Multicoloured. P* 14.

779 25 c. Type **175** .. .. .. .. .. .. 15 15
780 45 c. Carnival .. .. .. .. .. .. 20 25
781 60 c. Tourism .. .. .. .. .. .. 30 35
782 $3 Airport .. .. .. .. .. .. 1·25 1·50
779/82 .. .. .. .. *Set of* 4 1·75 2·00

176 T.V. Satellite Coverage of Royal Wedding

(Des PAD Studio. Litho Questa)

**1983** (5 Apr). *World Communications Year. T* **176** *and similar horiz designs. Multicoloured. P* 14.

783 15 c. Type **176** .. .. .. .. .. .. 40 15
784 50 c. Police communications .. .. .. 1·75 1·00
785 60 c. House-to-train telephone call .. .. 1·75 1·00
786 $3 Satellite earth station with planets Jupiter and Saturn .. .. .. 3·75 4·25
783/6 .. .. .. .. *Set of* 4 7·00 5·75
**MS**787 100 × 90 mm. $5 "Comsat" satellite over West Indies .. .. .. .. .. .. 3·25 3·75

177 Bottle-nosed Dolphin

(Des D. Miller. Litho Format)

**1983** (9 May). *Whales. T* **177** *and similar horiz designs. Multicoloured. P* 14½.

788 15 c. Type **177** .. .. .. .. .. .. 65 20
789 50 c. Fin Whale .. .. .. .. .. .. 1·25 70
790 60 c. Bowhead Whale .. .. .. .. .. 1·50 80
791 $3 Spectacled Porpoise .. .. .. .. 3·25 3·75
788/91 .. .. .. .. *Set of* 4 6·00 5·00
**MS**792 122 × 101 mm. $5 Narwhal .. .. .. 6·50 5·50

178 Cashew Nut

(Des J.W. Litho Questa)

**1983** (11 July)–**85**. *Fruits and Flowers. T* **178** *and similar horiz designs. Multicoloured.* A. *P* 14. B. *P* 12.

| | | A | | B | |
|---|---|---|---|---|---|
| 793 | 1 c. Type **178** .. .. .. | 15 | 20 | 10 | 10 |
| 794 | 2 c. Passion Fruit .. .. | 15 | 20 | 10 | 10 |
| 795 | 3 c. Mango .. .. .. | 15 | 20 | 10 | 10 |
| 796 | 5 c. Grapefruit .. .. | 20 | 15 | 10 | 10 |
| 797 | 10 c. Pawpaw .. .. .. | 30 | 15 | 15 | 10 |
| 798 | 15 c. Breadfruit .. .. | 35 | 15 | 20 | 10 |
| 799 | 20 c. Coconut .. .. .. | 45 | 15 | 25 | 10 |
| 800 | 25 c. Oleander .. .. .. | 55 | 20 | 30 | 10 |
| 801 | 30 c. Banana .. .. .. | 60 | 30 | 40 | 15 |
| 802 | 40 c. Pineapple .. .. .. | 70 | 30 | 40 | 20 |
| 803 | 45 c. Cordia .. .. .. | 80 | 35 | 50 | 30 |
| 804 | 50 c. Cassia .. .. .. | 90 | 40 | 60 | 30 |
| 805 | 60 c. Poui .. .. .. | 1·25 | 70 | 70 | 40 |
| 806 | $1 Frangipani .. .. | 1·75 | 90 | 1·00 | 55 |
| 807 | $2 Flamboyant .. .. | 3·25 | 2·00 | 1·75 | 1·25 |
| 808 | $2.50, Lemon .. .. | 3·50 | 3·25 | 2·00 | 1·50 |
| 809 | $5 Lignum Vitae .. .. | 6·00 | 6·50 | 4·00 | 4·00 |
| 810 | $10 National flag and coat of arms .. .. | 9·00 | 11·00 | 6·50 | 8·50 |
| 793A/810A | .. .. *Set of* 18 | 27·00 | 24·00 | | |
| 793B/810B | .. .. *Set of* 18 | | | 17·00 | 16·00 |

Dates of issue: 11.7.83, Nos. 793A/810A; 3.85, Nos. 793B/806B, 810B; 12.85, 807B/9B.

179 Dornier "Do X" Flying Boat

(Des W. Wright. Litho Format)

**1983** (15 Aug). *Bicentenary of Manned Flight. T* **179** *and similar horiz designs. Multicoloured. P* 14½.

811 30 c. Type **179** .. .. .. .. .. 65 25
812 50 c. Supermarine "S.6B" seaplane .. .. 75 50
813 60 c. Curtiss "9C" biplane and airship U.S.S. *Akron* .. .. .. .. .. .. 90 70
814 $4 *Pro Juventute* balloon .. .. .. 3·25 4·00
811/14 .. .. .. .. *Set of* 4 5·00 5·00
**MS**815 80 × 105 mm. $5 *Graf Zeppelin* .. .. 3·00 3·25

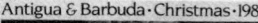

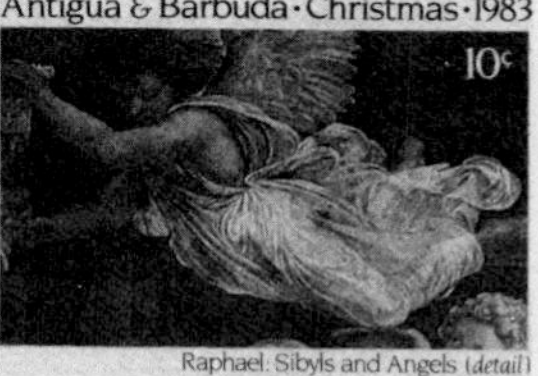

180 "Sibyls and Angels" (detail) (Raphael)

(Des W. Wright. Litho Format)

**1983** (4 Oct). *Christmas. 500th Birth Anniv of Raphael. T* **180** *and similar designs. P* 13½.

816 10 c. multicoloured .. .. .. .. .. 25 20
817 30 c. multicoloured .. .. .. .. .. 55 35
818 $1 multicoloured .. .. .. .. .. 1·25 1·00
819 $4 multicoloured .. .. .. .. .. 3·50 4·25
816/19 .. .. .. .. *Set of* 4 5·00 5·25
**MS**820 101 × 131 mm. $5 multicoloured .. .. 2·75 3·25

Designs: *Horiz*—10 c. to $4 Different details from "Sibyls and Angels". *Vert*—$5 "The Vision of Ezekiel".

181 John Wesley (founder)

182 Discus

(Des M. Diamond. Litho Questa)

**1983** (7 Nov). *Bicentenary of Methodist Church* (1984). *T* **181** *and similar vert designs. Multicoloured. P* 14.

821 15 c. Type **181** .. .. .. .. .. 20 15
822 50 c. Nathaniel Gilbert (founder in Antigua) 60 40
823 60 c. St. John Methodist Church steeple .. 65 55
824 $3 Ebenezer Methodist Church, St. John's .. 2·50 3·50
821/4 .. .. .. .. *Set of* 4 3·50 4·25

(Des Artists International. Litho Format)

**1984** (9 Jan). *Olympic Games, Los Angeles. T* **182** *and similar vert designs. Multicoloured. P* 14½.

825 25 c. Type **182** .. .. .. .. .. 15 15
826 50 c. Gymnastics .. .. .. .. .. 30 30
827 90 c. Hurdling .. .. .. .. .. 55 55
828 $3 Cycling .. .. .. .. .. 2·00 2·25
825/8 .. .. .. .. *Set of* 4 2·75 3·00
**MS**829 82 × 67 mm. $5 Volleyball .. .. .. 2·75 3·00

183 *Booker Vanguard* (freighter)

184 Chenille

(Des Artists International. Litho Format)

**1984** (14 June). *Ships. T* **183** *and similar multicoloured designs. P* 15.

830 45 c. Type **183** .. .. .. .. .. 1·00 55
831 50 c. S.S. *Canberra* (liner) .. .. .. 1·25 70
832 60 c. Sailing boats .. .. .. .. .. 1·50 85
833 $4 *Fairwind* (liner) .. .. .. .. 4·50 5·50
830/3 .. .. .. .. *Set of* 4 7·50 7·00
**MS**834 107 × 80 mm. $5 Eighteenth-century British man-of-war (*vert*) .. .. .. .. 4·50 4·75

(Des J.W. Litho Format)

**1984** (19 June). *Universal Postal Union Congress, Hamburg. T* **184** *and similar vert designs showing flowers. Multicoloured. P* 15.

835 15 c. Type **184** .. .. .. .. .. 30 15
836 50 c. Shell Flower .. .. .. .. .. 80 55
837 60 c. Anthurium .. .. .. .. .. 90 70
838 $3 Angels Trumpet .. .. .. .. 3·75 4·25
835/8 .. .. .. .. *Set of* 4 5·25 5·00
**MS**839 100 × 75 mm. $5 Crown of Thorns .. 4·25 4·50

**$2**

**$2** **$2**

(185) (186)

**1984** (25 June). (*a*) *Nos.* 702/5 *surch with T* **185**

840 $2 on 25 c. Type **159** .. .. .. .. 5·00 5·00
841 $2 on 50 c. Glamis Castle .. .. .. 5·00 5·00
842 $2 on $4 Prince Charles skiing .. .. 5·00 5·00
840/2 .. .. .. .. *Set of* 3 13·50 13·50
**MS**843 96 × 82 mm. $2 on $5 Glass Coach .. 8·00 8·00

(*b*) *Nos.* 748/51 *surch with T* **186**

844 $2 on 90 c. Type **168** (Gold)* .. .. 4·00 3·00
845 $2 on $1 Prince and Princess of Wales (Gold)* .. .. .. .. .. .. 4·00 3·00
846 $2 on $4 Princess Diana (*different*) (Gold)* 4·00 3·00
844/6 .. .. .. .. *Set of* 3 11·00 8·00
**MS**847 102 × 75 mm. $2 on $5 Type **169** (Gold) 7·50 7·50

(*c*) *Nos.* 757/60 *surch with T* **186**

848 $2 on 90 c. Type **168** (Gold)* .. .. 4·00 3·00
849 $2 on $1 Prince and Princess of Wales (Gold)* .. .. .. .. .. .. 4·00 3·00
850 $2 on $4 Princess Diana (*different*) (Gold)* 4·00 3·00
848/50 .. .. .. .. *Set of* 3 11·00 8·00
**MS**851 102 × 75 mm. $2 on $5 Type **169** (Gold) 7·50 7·50

(*d*) *Nos.* 779/82 *surch as T* **185**

852 $2 on 25 c. Type **175** .. .. .. .. 1·25 1·25
853 $2 on 45 c. Carnival .. .. .. .. 1·25 1·25
854 $2 on 60 c. Tourism .. .. .. .. 1·25 1·25
855 $2 on $3 Airport .. .. .. .. 1·25 1·25
852/5 .. .. .. .. *Set of* 4 4·50 4·50

*Nos. 844/6 and 848/50 also exist with similar surcharges in gold or silver on the sheetlets of 5 stamps and 1 label (*price for set of 3 as Nos. 844/6, £12 mint or used*) (*price for set of 3 as Nos. 848/50, £12 mint or used*).

187 Abraham Lincoln

188 View of Moravian Mission

(Des Liane Fried. Litho Questa)

**1984** (18 July). *Presidents of the United States of America. T* **187** *and similar vert designs. Multicoloured. P* 14.

856 10 c. Type **187** .. .. .. .. .. 10 10
857 20 c. Harry Truman .. .. .. .. .. 15 15
858 30 c. Dwight Eisenhower .. .. .. .. 25 25
859 40 c. Ronald Reagan .. .. .. .. .. 30 30
860 90 c. Gettysburg Address, 1863 .. .. .. 70 65
861 $1.10, Formation of N.A.T.O., 1949 .. .. 80 75
862 $1.50, Eisenhower during Second World War 1·10 1·10
863 $2 Reagan and Caribbean Basin Initiative 1·40 1·40
856/63 .. .. .. .. *Set of* 8 4·25 4·00

(Des and litho Questa)

**1984** (1 Aug). *150th Anniv of Abolition of Slavery. T* **188** *and similar horiz designs. Multicoloured. P* 14.

864 40 c. Type **188** .. .. .. .. .. 80 50
865 50 c. Antigua Courthouse, 1823 .. .. .. 90 65
866 60 c. Planting sugar-cane, Monks Hill .. 95 75
867 $3 Boiling house, Delaps' estate .. .. 3·50 4·25
864/7 .. .. .. .. *Set of* 4 5·50 5·50
**MS**868 95 × 70 mm. $5 Loading sugar, Willoughby Bay .. .. .. .. .. .. .. 5·50 4·75

**NEW INFORMATION**

The editor is always interested to correspond with people who have new information that will improve or correct the Catalogue.

189 Rufous-sided Towhee

190 Grass-skiing

(Des Jennifer Toombs. Litho Format)

**1984** (15 Aug). *Songbirds. T* **189** *and similar vert designs. Multicoloured. P* 15.

869 40 c. Type **189** .. .. .. .. .. 1·00 55
870 50 c. Parula Warbler .. .. .. .. 1·10 70
871 60 c. House Wren .. .. .. .. 1·25 80
872 $2 Ruby-crowned Kinglet .. .. .. 2·50 2·75
873 $3 Common Flicker .. .. .. .. 3·50 4·00
869/73 .. .. .. .. .. *Set of* 5 8·50 8·00
**MS**874 76 × 76 mm. $5 Yellow-breasted Chat .. 7·50 6·00

(Des Bonny Redecker. Litho Questa)

**1984** (21 Sept). *"Ausipex" International Stamp Exhibition, Melbourne. Australian Sports. T* **190** *and similar vert designs. Multicoloured. P* 14½.

875 $1 Type **190** .. .. .. .. .. 1·50 1·25
876 $5 Australian Football .. .. .. .. 4·50 4·75
**MS**877 108 × 78 mm. $5 Boomerang-throwing .. 3·50 4·00

191 "The Virgin and Infant with Angels and Cherubs" (Correggio)

192 "The Blue Dancers" (Degas)

(Litho Format)

**1984** (4 Oct). *450th Death Anniv of Correggio (painter). T* **191** *and similar vert designs. Multicoloured. P* 15.

878 25 c. Type **191** .. .. .. .. .. 30 20
879 60 c. "The Four Saints" .. .. .. .. 70 50
880 90 c. "St. Catherine" .. .. .. .. 95 75
881 $3 "The Campori Madonna" .. .. .. 3·00 3·00
878/81 .. .. .. .. .. *Set of* 4 4·50 4·00
**MS**882 90 × 60 mm. $5 "St. John the Baptist" .. 3·25 3·50

(Litho Format)

**1984** (4 Oct). *150th Birth Anniv of Edgar Degas (painter). T* **192** *and similar multicoloured designs. P* 15.

883 15 c. Type **192** .. .. .. .. .. 30 15
884 50 c. "The Pink Dancers" .. .. .. .. 70 50
885 70 c. "Two Dancers" .. .. .. .. 95 75
886 $4 "Dancers at the Bar" .. .. .. 3·75 4·25
883/6 .. .. .. .. .. *Set of* 4 5·25 5·00
**MS**887 90 × 60 mm. $5 "The Folk Dancers" (40 × 27 *mm*) .. .. .. .. .. 3·25 3·50

193 Sir Winston Churchill

194 Donald Duck fishing

(Des J. Iskowitz. Litho Format)

**1984** (19 Nov). *Famous People. T* **193** *and similar multicoloured designs. P* 15.

888 60 c. Type **193** .. .. .. .. .. 1·75 1·50
889 60 c. Mahatma Gandhi .. .. .. .. 1·75 1·50
890 60 c. John F. Kennedy .. .. .. .. 1·75 1·50
891 60 c. Mao Tse-tung .. .. .. .. 1·75 1·50
892 $1 Churchill with General De Gaulle, Paris, 1944 (*horiz*) .. .. .. .. 2·25 2·00
893 $1 Gandhi leaving London by train, 1931 (*horiz*) .. .. .. .. .. 2·25 2·00
894 $1 Kennedy with Chancellor Adenauer and Mayor Brandt, Berlin, 1963 (*horiz*) .. .. .. .. .. 2·25 2·00
895 $1 Mao Tse-tung with Lin Piao, Peking, 1969 (*horiz*) .. .. .. .. 2·25 2·00
888/95 .. .. .. .. .. *Set of* 8 14·50 12·50
**MS**896 114 × 80 mm. $5 Flags of Great Britain, India, the United States and China .. .. 5·50 4·50

(Litho Format)

**1984** (26 Nov). *Christmas. Walt Disney Cartoon Characters. T* **194** *and similar multicoloured designs. P* 11.

897 1 c. Type **194** .. .. .. .. .. 10 10
898 2 c. Donald Duck lying on beach .. .. 10 10
899 3 c. Donald Duck and nephews with fishing rods and fishes .. .. .. .. 10 10
900 4 c. Donald Duck and nephews in boat .. 10 10
901 5 c. Wearing diving masks .. .. .. 10 10
902 10 c. In deckchairs reading books .. .. 10 10
903 $1 With toy shark's fin .. .. .. 1·75 1·10
904 $2 In sailing boat .. .. .. .. 2·50 1·90
905 $5 Attempting to propel boat .. .. 4·25 4·00
897/905 .. .. .. .. .. *Set of* 9 8·00 6·50
**MS**906 Two sheets, each 125 × 100 mm. (a) $5 Nephews with crayon and paintbrushes (*horiz*). P 14 × 13½. (b) $5 Donald Duck in deckchair. P 13½ × 14 .. .. *Set of* 2 *sheets* 9·50 7·50

No. 904 was printed in sheetlets of 8 stamps.

195 Torch from Statue in Madison Square Park, 1885

(Des J. Iskowitz. Litho Format)

**1985** (7 Jan). *Centenary of the Statue of Liberty* (1986) (1*st issue*). *T* **195** *and similar multicoloured designs. P* 15.

907 25 c. Type **195** .. .. .. .. .. 20 20
908 30 c. Statue of Liberty and scaffolding ("Restoration and Renewal") (*vert*) .. 20 20
909 50 c. Frederic Bartholdi (sculptor) supervising construction, 1876 .. .. 30 30
910 90 c. Close-up of Statue .. .. .. 55 55
911 $1 Statue and sailing ship ("Operation Sail", 1976) (*vert*) .. .. .. 60 60
912 $3 Dedication ceremony, 1886 .. .. 1·75 1·75
907/12 .. .. .. .. .. *Set of* 6 3·00 3·00
**MS**913 110 × 80 mm. $5 Port of New York .. 5·00 3·50

See also Nos. 1110/19.

196 Arawak Pot Sherd and Indians making Clay Utensils

(Des N. Waldman. Litho Format)

**1985** (21 Jan). *Native American Artefacts. T* **196** *and similar designs. Multicoloured. P* 15.

914 15 c. Type **196** .. .. .. .. .. 15 10
915 50 c. Arawak body design and Arawak Indians tattooing .. .. .. .. 30 30
916 60 c. Head of the god "Yocahu" and Indians harvesting manioc .. .. .. 40 40
917 $3 Carib war club and Carib Indians going into battle .. .. .. .. 1·75 2·25
914/17 .. .. .. .. .. *Set of* 4 2·40 2·75
**MS**918 97 × 68 mm. $5 Taino Indians worshipping stone idol .. .. .. .. 3·00 3·50

197 Triumph 2hp "Jap", 1903

(Des BG Studio. Litho Questa)

**1985** (7 Mar). *Centenary of the Motorcycle. T* **197** *and similar horiz designs. Multicoloured. P* 14.

919 10 c. Type **197** .. .. .. .. .. 55 15
920 30 c. Indian "Arrow", 1949 .. .. .. 80 30
921 60 c. BMW "R100RS", 1976 .. .. .. 1·25 70
922 $4 Harley-Davidson "Model II", 1916 .. 4·25 4·50
919/22 .. .. .. .. .. *Set of* 4 6·25 5·00
**MS**923 90 × 93 mm. $5 Laverda "Jota", 1975 .. 3·75 4·00

198 Slavonian Grebe

(Litho Questa)

**1985** (25 Mar). *Birth Bicentenary of John J. Audubon (ornithologist)* (1*st issue*). *T* **198** *and similar multicoloured designs showing original paintings. P* 14.

924 90 c. Type **198** .. .. .. .. .. 1·25 75
925 $1 British Storm Petrel .. .. .. 1·40 85
926 $1.50, Great Blue Heron .. .. .. 1·75 1·50
927 $3 Double-crested Cormorant .. .. 3·00 3·25
924/7 .. .. .. .. .. *Set of* 4 6·75 5·75
**MS**928 103 × 72 mm. $5 White-tailed Tropic Bird (*vert*) .. .. .. .. .. 5·00 3·75

Nos. 924/7 were each issued in sheetlets of five stamps and one stamp-size label, which appears in the centre of the bottom row.

See also Nos. 990/4.

199 *Anaea cyanea*

(Des R. Sauber. Litho Questa)

**1985** (16 Apr). *Butterflies. T* **199** *and similar horiz designs. Multicoloured. P* 14.

929 25 c. Type **199** .. .. .. .. .. 85 30
930 60 c. *Leodonta dysoni* .. .. .. .. 1·50 70
931 90 c. *Junea doraete* .. .. .. .. 2·00 85
932 $4 *Prepona pylene* .. .. .. .. 5·50 4·50
929/32 .. .. .. .. .. *Set of* 4 9·00 5·75
**MS**933 132 × 105 mm. $5 *Caerois gerdrudtus* .. 4·50 4·75

200 Cessna "172"

201 Maimonides

(Des A. DiLorenzo. Litho Questa)

**1985** (30 Apr). *40th Anniv of International Civil Aviation Organization. T.* **200** *and similar horiz designs. Multicoloured. P* 14.

934 30 c. Type **200** .. .. .. .. .. 1·00 30
935 90 c. Fokker "DVII" .. .. .. .. 2·00 90
936 $1.50, Spad "VII" .. .. .. .. 2·75 1·50
937 $3 Boeing "747" .. .. .. .. 4·25 4·25
934/7 .. .. .. .. .. *Set of* 4 9·00 6·50
**MS**938 97 × 83 mm. $5 Twin "Otter" .. .. 4·50 5·00

(Des and litho Questa)

**1985** (17 June). *850th Birth Anniv of Maimonides (physician, philosopher and scholar). P* 14.

939 **201** $2 bright green .. .. .. .. 2·25 2·25
**MS**940 70 × 84 mm. **201** $5 reddish brown .. 5·50 4·25

No. 939 was printed in sheetlets of 6 stamps.

202 Young Farmers with Produce

203 The Queen Mother attending Church

(Des Susan David. Litho Questa)

**1985** (1 July). *International Youth Year. T* **202** *and similar horiz designs. Multicoloured. P* 14.

941 25 c. Type **202** .. .. .. .. .. 15 20
942 50 c. Hotel management trainees .. .. 25 30
943 60 c. Girls with goat and boys with football ("Environment") .. .. .. .. 35 40
944 $3 Windsurfing ("Leisure") .. .. .. 1·60 1·75
941/4 .. .. .. .. .. *Set of* 4 2·10 2·40
**MS**945 102 × 72 mm. $5 Young people with Antiguan flags .. .. .. .. .. 2·75 3·00

(Des J.W. Litho Questa)

**1985** (10 July). *Life and Times of Queen Elizabeth the Queen Mother. T* **203** *and similar vert designs. Multicoloured. P* 14.

946 $1 Type **203** .. .. .. .. .. 55 60
947 $1.50, Watching children playing in London garden .. .. .. .. .. 80 85
948 $2.50, The Queen Mother in 1979 .. .. 1·25 1·40
946/8 .. .. .. .. .. *Set of* 3 2·40 2·50
**MS**949 56 × 85 mm. $5 With Prince Edward at Royal Wedding, 1981 .. .. .. .. 3·00 3·00

Stamps as Nos. 946/8, but with face values of 90 c., $1 and $3, exist from additional sheetlets of 5 plus a label issued 13 January 1986. These also have changed background colours and are perforated 12 × 12½ (*price for set of 3 stamps £2.40 mint*).

204 Magnificent Frigate Bird

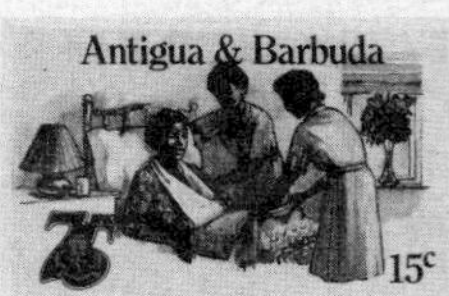


205 Girl Guides Nursing

(Des Mary Walters. Litho Questa)

**1985** (1 Aug). *Marine Life. T* **204** *and similar vert designs. Multicoloured. P* 14.
950 15 c. Type **204** .. .. .. .. .. .. 65 20
951 45 c. Brain Coral .. .. .. .. .. 1·10 60
952 60 c. Cushion Star .. .. .. .. .. 1·50 80
953 $3 Spotted Moray Eel .. .. .. .. 4·50 5·00
950/3 .. .. .. .. .. .. *Set of* 4 7·00 6·00
**MS**954 110×80 mm. $5 Elkhorn Coral .. .. 4·50 5·00

(Des Y. Berry. Litho Questa)

**1985** (22 Aug). *75th Anniv of Girl Guide Movement. T* **205** *and similar horiz designs. Multicoloured. P* 14.
955 15 c. Type **205** .. .. .. .. .. 50 15
956 45 c. Open-air Girl Guide meeting .. .. 1·00 45
957 60 c. Lord and Lady Baden-Powell .. .. 1·25 65
958 $3 Girl Guides gathering flowers .. .. 3·25 3·00
955/8 .. .. .. .. .. .. *Set of* 4 5·50 3·75
**MS**959 67× 96 mm. $5 Barn Swallow (Nature study) .. .. .. .. .. .. 4·25 5·00

206 Bass Trombone

207 Flags of Great Britain and Antigua

(Des Susan David. Litho Questa)

**1985** (26 Aug). *300th Birth Anniv of Johann Sebastian Bach (composer). T* **206** *and similar vert designs. P* 14.
960 25 c. multicoloured .. .. .. .. .. 1·10 40
961 50 c. multicoloured .. .. .. .. .. 1·50 75
962 $1 multicoloured .. .. .. .. .. 2·50 1·40
963 $3 multicoloured .. .. .. .. .. 4·75 5·50
960/3 .. .. .. .. .. .. *Set of* 4 9·00 7·25
**MS**964 104×73 mm. $5 black and brownish grey .. .. .. .. .. .. 4·50 4·75
Designs:—50 c. English horn; $1 Violino piccolo; $3 Bass rackett; $5 Johann Sebastian Bach.

(Des Mary Walters. Litho Format)

**1985** (24 Oct). *Royal Visit. T* **207** *and similar multicoloured designs. P* 14½.
965 60 c. Type **207** .. .. .. .. .. 1·00 45
966 $1 Queen Elizabeth II (*vert*) .. .. .. 1·75 1·00
967 $4 Royal Yacht *Britannia* .. .. .. 4·25 3·75
965/7 .. .. .. .. .. .. *Set of* 3 6·25 4·75
**MS**968 110×83 mm. $5 Map of Antigua .. .. 4·50 4·00

(Des Walt Disney Productions. Litho Questa)

**1985** (4 Nov). *150th Birth Anniv of Mark Twain (author). Horiz designs as T* 118 *of Anguilla showing Walt Disney cartoon characters in scenes from "Roughing It". Multicoloured. P* 14×13½.
969 25 c. Donald Duck and Mickey Mouse meeting Indians .. .. .. .. .. 25 20
970 50 c. Mickey Mouse, Donald Duck and Goofy canoeing .. .. .. .. .. 45 35
971 $1.10, Goofy as Pony Express rider .. .. 80 70
972 $1.50, Donald Duck and Goofy hunting buffalo .. .. .. .. .. .. 1·10 95
973 $2 Mickey Mouse and silver mine .. .. 1·60 1·40
969/73 .. .. .. .. .. *Set of* 5 3·75 3·25
**MS**974 127×101 mm. $5 Mickey Mouse driving stagecoach .. .. .. .. .. .. 3·25 3·50

(Des Walt Disney Productions. Litho Questa)

**1985** (11 Nov). *Birth Bicentenaries of Grimm Brothers (folklorists). Horiz designs as T* **119** *of Anguilla showing Walt Disney cartoon characters in scenes from "Spindle, Shuttle and Needle". Multicoloured. P* 14×13½.
975 30 c. The Prince (Mickey Mouse) searches for a bride .. .. .. .. .. 60 35
a. Error. Wmk w **16** .. .. .. .. £120
976 60 c. The Prince finds the Orphan Girl (Minnie Mouse) .. .. .. .. .. 85 60
977 70 c. The Spindle finds the Prince .. .. 1·00 70
978 $1 The Needle tidies the Girl's House .. 1·50 1·25
979 $3 The Prince proposes .. .. .. 3·25 3·75
975/9 .. .. .. .. .. *Set of* 5 6·50 6·00
**MS**980 125×101 mm. $5 The Orphan Girl and spinning wheel on Prince's horse .. .. 3·75 4·50

208 Benjamin Franklin and U.N. (New York) 1953 U.P.U. 5 c. Stamp

209 "Madonna and Child" (De Landi)

(Litho Walsall)

**1985** (18 Nov). *40th Anniv of United Nations Organization. T* **208** *and similar multicoloured designs showing United Nations (New York) stamps. P* 13½×14.
981 40 c. Type **208** .. .. .. .. .. 75 55
982 $1 George Washington Carver (agricultural chemist) and 1982 Nature Conservation 28 c. stamp .. .. .. .. 1·75 1·50
983 $3 Charles Lindbergh (aviator) and 1978 I.C.A.O. 25 c. stamp .. .. .. .. 3·75 4·25
981/3 .. .. .. .. .. *Set of* 3 5·50 5·75
**MS**984 101×77 mm. $5 Marc Chagall (artist) (*vert*). P 14×13½ .. .. .. .. 4·75 4·75

(Des Mary Walters. Litho Format)

**1985** (30 Dec). *Christmas. Religious Paintings. T* **209** *and similar vert designs. Multicoloured. P* 15.
985 10 c. Type **209** .. .. .. .. .. 25 15
986 25 c. "Madonna and Child" (Berlinghiero) 50 25
987 60 c. "The Nativity" (Fra Angelico) .. .. 80 60
988 $4 "Presentation in the Temple" (Giovanni di Paolo) .. .. .. .. .. 3·75 4·25
985/8 .. .. .. .. .. *Set of* 4 4·75 4·75
**MS**989 113×81 mm. $5 "The Nativity" (Antoniazzo Romano) .. .. .. .. .. 3·75 4·25

(Litho Questa)

**1986** (6 Jan). *Birth Bicentenary of John J. Audubon (ornithologist) (2nd issue). Horiz designs as T* **198** *showing original paintings. Multicoloured. P* 12.
990 60 c. Mallard .. .. .. .. .. .. 1·25 75
991 90 c. North American Black Duck .. .. 1·50 1·00
992 $1.50, Pintail .. .. .. .. .. 2·50 2·50
993 $3 American Wigeon .. .. .. .. 3·75 4·25
990/3 .. .. .. .. .. *Set of* 4 8·00 7·75
**MS**994 102×73 mm. $5 American Eider. P 14 .. 5·00 5·00
Nos. 990/3 were issued in sheetlets of 5 as Nos. 924/7.

210 Football, Boots and Trophy

211 Tug

(Des M. Donk. Litho Questa)

**1986** (17 Mar). *World Cup Football Championship, Mexico. T* **210** *and similar multicoloured designs. P* 14.
995 30 c. Type **210** .. .. .. .. .. 60 30
996 60 c. Goalkeeper (*vert*) .. .. .. .. 85 60
997 $1 Referee blowing whistle (*vert*) .. .. 1·50 1·10
998 $4 Ball in net .. .. .. .. .. 4·00 4·50
995/8 .. .. .. .. .. *Set of* 4 6·50 6·00
**MS**999 87×76 mm. $5 Two players competing for ball .. .. .. .. .. .. .. 6·50 6·50

(Des W. Hanson. Litho Questa)

**1986** (24 Mar). *Appearance of Halley's Comet (1st issue). Horiz designs as T* **123** *of Anguilla. Multicoloured. P* 14.
1000 5 c. Edmond Halley and Old Greenwich Observatory .. .. .. .. .. 10 10
1001 10 c. "Me 163B Komet" (fighter aircraft), 1944 .. .. .. .. .. .. 15 10
1002 60 c. Montezuma (Aztec Emperor) and Comet in 1517 (from "Historias de las Indias de Neuva Espana") .. .. .. 60 45
1003 $4 Pocahontas saving Capt. John Smith and Comet in 1607 .. .. .. .. 2·75 3·00
1000/3 .. .. .. .. .. *Set of* 4 3·25 3·25
**MS**1004 101×70 mm. $5 Halley's Comet over English Harbour, Antigua .. .. .. 3·25 3·75
See also Nos. 1047/51.

(Litho Questa)

**1986** (21 Apr). *60th Birthday of Queen Elizabeth II. Vert designs as T* **125** *of Anguilla. P* 14.
1005 60 c. black and yellow .. .. .. .. 35 35
1006 $1 multicoloured .. .. .. .. .. 55 55
1007 $4 multicoloured .. .. .. .. .. 2·10 2·10
1005/7 .. .. .. .. .. *Set of* 3 2·75 2·75
**MS**1008 120×85 mm. $5 black and grey-brown .. 3·00 3·25
Designs:—60 c. Wedding photograph, 1947; $1 Queen at Trooping the Colour; $4 In Scotland; $5 Queen Mary and Princess Elizabeth, 1927.

(Des A. DiLorenzo. Litho Questa)

**1986** (15 May). *Local Boats. T* **211** *and similar vert designs. Multicoloured. P* 14.
1009 30 c. Type **211** .. .. .. .. .. 25 20
1010 60 c. Game fishing boat .. .. .. .. 45 35
1011 $1 Yacht .. .. .. .. .. .. 75 60
1012 $4 Lugger with auxiliary sail .. .. 2·50 3·00
1009/12 .. .. .. .. .. *Set of* 4 3·50 3·75
**MS**1013 108×78 mm. $5 Boats under construction .. .. .. .. .. .. .. 3·00 4·00

212 "Hiawatha Express"

213 Prince Andrew and Miss Sarah Ferguson

(Des W. Wright. Litho Format)

**1986** (22 May). *"Ameripex '86" International Stamp Exhibition, Chicago. Famous American Trains. T* **212** *and similar horiz designs. Multicoloured. P* 15.
1014 25 c. Type **212** .. .. .. .. .. 70 30
1015 50 c. "Grand Canyon Express" .. .. .. 1·00 65
1016 $1 "Powhattan Arrow Express" .. .. 1·60 1·25
1017 $3 "Empire State Express" .. .. .. 3·75 4·00
1014/17 .. .. .. .. .. *Set of* 4 6·25 5·50
**MS**1018 116×87 mm. $5 "Daylight Express" .. 6·00 6·50

(Des and litho Questa)

**1986** (1 July). *Royal Wedding. T* **213** *and similar vert designs. Multicoloured. P* 14.
1019 45 c. Type **213** .. .. .. .. .. 45 35
1020 60 c. Prince Andrew .. .. .. .. .. 50 45
1021 $4 Prince Andrew with Prince Philip .. 2·50 3·00
1019/21 .. .. .. .. .. *Set of* 3 3·00 3·50
**MS**1022 88×88 mm. $5 Prince Andrew and Miss Sarah Ferguson (*different*) .. .. .. 3·50 4·00

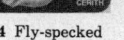

214 Fly-specked Cerith

215 *Nymphaea ampla* (Water Lily)

(Des L. Birmingham. Litho Format)

**1986** (6 Aug). *Sea Shells. T* **214** *and similar multicoloured designs. P* 15.
1023 15 c. Type **214** .. .. .. .. .. 55 20
1024 45 c. Smooth Scotch Bonnet .. .. .. 1·25 70
1025 60 c. West Indian Crown Conch .. .. 1·50 90
1026 $3 Murex Ciboney .. .. .. .. 5·00 5·50
1023/6 .. .. .. .. .. *Set of* 4 7·50 6·50
**MS**1027 109×75 mm. $5 Colourful Atlantic Natica (*horiz*) .. .. .. .. .. .. 6·50 7·50

(Des Mary Walters. Litho Format)

**1986** (25 Aug). *Flowers. T* **215** *and similar horiz designs. Multicoloured. P* 15.
1028 10 c. Type **215** .. .. .. .. .. 15 15
1029 15 c. Queen of the Night .. .. .. .. 20 15
1030 50 c. Cup of Gold .. .. .. .. .. 55 40
1031 60 c. Beach Morning Glory .. .. .. 70 45
1032 70 c. Golden Trumpet .. .. .. .. 80 55
1033 $1 Air Plant .. .. .. .. .. 1·10 75
1034 $3 Purple Wreath .. .. .. .. .. 2·50 2·50
1035 $4 Zephyr Lily .. .. .. .. .. 3·00 3·25
1028/35 .. .. .. .. .. *Set of* 8 8·00 7·50
**MS**1036 Two sheets, each 102×72 mm. (a) $4 Dozakie. (b) $5 Four O'Clock Flower *Set of 2 sheets* 6·00 7·50

WINNERS
Argentina 3
W.Germany 2

(216)

217 *Hygrocybe occidentalis* var. *scarletina*

**1986** (15 Sept). *World Cup Football Championship Winners, Mexico. Nos.* 995/9 *optd as T* **216** *in gold.*
1037 30 c. Type **210** .. .. .. .. .. 30 30
1038 60 c. Goalkeeper (*vert*) .. .. .. .. 50 50
1039 $1 Referee blowing whistle (*vert*) .. .. 75 75
1040 $4 Ball in net .. .. .. .. .. 2·75 3·25
1037/40 .. .. .. .. .. *Set of* 4 4·00 4·25
**MS**1041 87×76 mm. $5 Two players competing for ball .. .. .. .. .. .. .. 3·00 3·50
The overprint on the horizontal designs is in two lines.

(Litho Format)

**1986** (15 Sept). *Mushrooms. T* **217** *and similar vert designs. Multicoloured. P* 15.
1042 10 c. Type **217** 35 15
1043 50 c. *Trogia buccinalis* 1·10 55
1044 $1 *Collybia subpruinosa* 1·75 1·10
1045 $4 *Leucocoprinus brebissonii* 4·50 4·75
1042/5 *Set of* 4 7·00 6·00
**MS**1046 102×82 mm $5 *Pyrrhoglossum pyrrhum* 7·00 7·00
An unissued 3$ and examples of No. 1045 with the face value shown as "4$" exist from stock dispersed by the liquidator of Format International Security Printers Ltd.

(**218**) **219** Auburn "Speedster" (1933)

**1986** (15 Oct). *Appearance of Halley's Comet* (2nd *issue*). *Nos.* 1000/4 *optd with T* **218** (*in silver on* $5).
1047 5 c. Edmond Halley and Old Greenwich Observatory 10 10
1048 10 c. "Me 163B Komet" (fighter aircraft), 1944 10 10
1049 60 c. Montezuma (Aztec Emperor) and Comet in 1517 (from "Historias de las Indias de Neuva Espana") 55 55
1050 $4 Pocahontas saving Capt. John Smith and Comet in 1607 3·00 3·00
1047/50 *Set of* 4 3·25 3·25
**MS**1051 101×70 mm. $5 Halley's Comet over English Harbour, Antigua 4·75 5·50

(Des J. Martin. Litho Questa)

**1986** (20 Oct). *Centenary of First Benz Motor Car. T* **219** *and similar horiz designs. Multicoloured. P* 14.
1052 10 c. Type **219** 10 10
1053 15 c. Mercury "Sable" (1986) 15 10
1054 50 c. Cadillac (1959) 45 30
1055 60 c. Studebaker (1950) 55 45
1056 70 c. Lagonda "V-12" (1939) 70 55
1057 $1 Adler "Standard" (1930) 90 75
1058 $3 DKW (1956) 2·25 2·50
1059 $4 Mercedes "500K" (1936) 2·75 3·00
1052/9 *Set of* 8 7·00 7·00
**MS**1060 Two sheets, each 99×70 mm. (a) $5 Daimler (1896). (b) $5 Mercedes "Knight" (1921) *Set of* 2 *sheets* 5·50 6·50

**220** Young Mickey Mouse playing Santa Claus
**221** Arms of Antigua

(Des Walt Disney Co. Litho Format)

**1986** (4 Nov). *Christmas. T* **220** *and similar horiz designs showing Walt Disney cartoon characters as babies. Multicoloured. P* 11.
1061 25 c. Type **220** 35 35
1062 30 c. Mickey and Minnie Mouse building snowman 40 40
1063 40 c. Aunt Matilda and Goofy baking 45 45
1064 60 c. Goofy and Pluto 65 65
1065 70 c. Pluto, Donald and Daisy Duck carol singing 75 75
1066 $1.50, Donald Duck, Mickey Mouse and Pluto stringing popcorn 1·25 1·25
1067 $3 Grandma Duck and Minnie Mouse 2·50 2·50
1068 $4 Donald Duck and Pete 2·75 2·75
1061/8 *Set of* 8 8·25 8·25
**MS**1069 Two sheets, each 127×102 mm. P 14 × 13½. (a) $5 Goofy, Donald Duck and Minnie Mouse playing reindeer. (b) $5 Mickey Mouse, Donald and Daisy Duck playing with toys. *Set of* 2 *sheets* 9·00 9·00

**1986** (25 Nov). *Coil stamps. T* **221** *and similar vert design. Litho. P* 14.
1070 10 c. new blue 20 20
1071 25 c. orange-vermilion 30 35
Design:—25 c. Flag of Antigua.

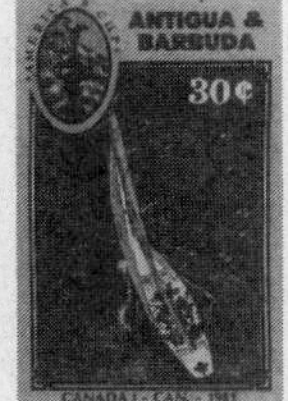

**222** *Canada I* (1981) **223** Bridled Burrfish

(Des J. Iskowitz. Litho Format)

**1987** (5 Feb). *America's Cup Yachting Championship. T* **222** *and similar multicoloured designs. P* 15.
1072 30 c. Type **222** 20 20
1073 60 c. *Gretel II* (1970) 35 35
1074 $1 *Sceptre* (1958) 65 65
1075 $3 *Vigilant* (1893) 1·75 1·75
1072/5 *Set of* 4 2·75 2·75
**MS**1076 113×84 mm. $5 *Australia II* defeating *Liberty* (1983) (*horiz*) 3·50 4·00

(Des G. Drummond. Litho Questa)

**1987** (23 Feb). *Marine Life. T* **223** *and similar horiz designs. Multicoloured. P* 14.
1077 15 c. Type **223** 35 20
1078 30 c. Common Noddy 60 35
1079 40 c. Nassau Grouper 65 45
1080 50 c. Laughing Gull 1·00 70
1081 60 c. French Angelfish 1·00 70
1082 $1 Porkfish 1·25 1·10
1083 $2 Royal Tern 2·50 2·50
1084 $3 Sooty Tern 3·25 3·25
1077/84 *Set of* 8 9·50 8·50
**MS**1085 Two sheets, each 120×94 mm. (a) $5 Banded Butterflyfish. (b) $5 Brown Booby *Set of* 2 *sheets* 8·50 9·00
Nos. 1078, 1080 and 1083/5 are without the World Wildlife Fund logo shown on Type **223**.

**224** Handball **225** "The Profile"

(Litho Questa)

**1987** (23 Mar). *Olympic Games, Seoul* (1988) (1st *issue*). *T* **224** *and similar horiz designs. Multicoloured. P* 14.
1086 10 c. Type **224** 10 10
1087 60 c. Fencing 25 30
1088 $1 Gymnastics 45 50
1089 $3 Football 1·40 1·75
1086/9 *Set of* 4 1·90 2·40
**MS**1090 100×72 mm. $5 Boxing gloves 2·75 3·50
See also Nos. 1222/6.

(Litho Questa)

**1987** (30 Mar). *Birth Centenary of Marc Chagall* (*artist*). *T* **225** *and similar multicoloured designs. P* 13½×14.
1091 10 c. Type **225** 10 10
1092 30 c. "Portrait of the Artist's Sister" 15 15
1093 40 c. "Bride with Fan" 20 25
1094 60 c. "David in Profile" 25 30
1095 90 c. "Fiancee with Bouquet" 40 45
1096 $1 "Self Portrait with Brushes" 45 50
1097 $3 "The Walk" 1·40 1·75
1098 $4 "Three Candles" 1·75 2·00
1091/8 *Set of* 8 4·25 5·00
**MS**1099 Two sheets, each 110×95 mm. (a) $5 "Fall of Icarus" (104×89 *mm*). (b) $5 "Myth of Orpheus" (104×89 *mm*). Imperf *Set of* 2 *sheets* 4·50 5·50

**226** *Spirit of Australia* (fastest powerboat), 1978
**227** Lee Iacocca at Unveiling of Restored Statue

(Des W. Wright. Litho Format)

**1987** (9 Apr). *Milestones of Transportation. T* **226** *and similar horiz designs. Multicoloured. P* 15.
1100 10 c. Type **226** 20 15
1101 15 c. Siemen's electric locomotive, 1879 30 20
1102 30 c. U.S.S. *Triton* (first submerged circumnavigation), 1960 35 25
1103 50 c. Trevithick's steam carriage (first passenger-carrying vehicle), 1801 50 40
1104 60 c. U.S.S. *New Jersey* (battleship), 1942 60 45
1105 70 c. Draisaine bicycle, 1818 60 50
1106 90 c. S.S. *United States* (holder of Blue Riband), 1952 80 65
1107 $1.50, Cierva "C.4" (first autogiro), 1923 1·00 1·00
1108 $2 Curtiss "NC.4" (first transatlantic flight), 1919 1·25 1·25
1109 $3 *Queen Elizabeth 2* (liner), 1969 2·00 2·00
1100/9 *Set of* 10 7·00 6·25

(Litho Questa)

**1987** (23 Apr). *Centenary of Statue of Liberty* (1986) (2*nd issue*). *T* **227** *and similar multicoloured designs. P* 14.
1110 15 c. Type **227** 15 15
1111 30 c. Statue at sunset (side view) 20 20
1112 45 c. Aerial view of head 30 30
1113 50 c. Lee Iacocca and torch 35 35
1114 60 c. Workmen inside head of Statue (*horiz*) 35 35
1115 90 c. Restoration work (*horiz*) 50 50
1116 $1 Head of Statue 55 55
1117 $2 Statue at sunset (front view) 1·00 1·25
1118 $3 Inspecting restoration work (*horiz*) 1·60 1·75
1119 $5 Statue at night 2·50 3·00
1110/19 *Set of* 10 6·75 7·50

**228** Grace Kelly **229** Scouts around Camp Fire and Red Kangaroo

(Des Lynda Bruscheni. Litho Questa)

**1987** (11 May). *Entertainers. T* **228** *and similar vert designs. Multicoloured. P* 14.
1120 15 c. Type **228** 30 20
1121 30 c. Marilyn Monroe 40 35
1122 45 c. Orson Welles 45 40
1123 50 c. Judy Garland 50 45
1124 60 c. John Lennon 75 65
1125 $1 Rock Hudson 85 75
1126 $2 John Wayne 1·40 1·40
1127 $3 Elvis Presley 2·25 2·25
1120/7 *Set of* 8 6·25 5·75

(Litho Format)

**1987** (25 May). *16th World Scout Jamboree, Australia. T* **229** *and similar horiz designs. Multicoloured. P* 15.
1128 10 c. Type **229** 25 10
1129 60 c. Scouts canoeing and Blue-winged Kookaburra 70 40
1130 $1 Scouts on assault course and Ring-tailed Rock Wallaby 1·00 80
1131 $3 Field kitchen and Koala 2·00 2·25
1128/31 *Set of* 4 3·50 3·00
**MS**1132 103×78 mm. $5 Flags of Antigua, Australia and Scout Movement 2·50 3·00

**230** Whistling Frog (**231**)

(Des B. Bundock. Litho Questa)

**1987** (15 June). *"Capex '87" International Stamp Exhibition, Toronto. Reptiles and Amphibians. T* **230** *and similar horiz designs. Multicoloured. P* 14.
1133 30 c. Type **230** 15 15
1134 60 c. Croaking Lizard 25 30
1135 $1 Antiguan Anole 45 50
1136 $3 Red-footed Tortoise 1·40 1·75
1133/6 *Set of* 4 2·00 2·40
**MS**1137 106×76 mm. $5 Ground Lizard 2·25 2·75

**1987** (9 Sept). *10th Death Anniv of Elvis Presley* (*entertainer*). *No.* 1127 *optd with T* **231**.
1138 $3 Elvis Presley 2·00 2·25

**232** House of Burgesses, Virginia ("Freedom of Speech")
**233** "Madonna and Child" (Bernardo Daddi)

(Des and litho Questa)

**1987** (16 Nov). *Bicentenary of U.S. Constitution. T* **232** *and similar multicoloured designs. P* 14.
1139 15 c. Type **232** 10 10
1140 45 c. State Seal, Connecticut 20 25
1141 60 c. State Seal, Delaware 25 30
1142 $4 Gouverneur Morris (Pennsylvania delegate) (*vert*) 1·75 1·90
1139/42 *Set of* 4 2·10 2·25
**MS**1143 105×75 mm. $5 Roger Sherman (Connecticut delegate) (*vert*) 2·25 2·75
Nos. 1139/42 were each issued in sheetlets of five stamps and one stamp-size label, which appears in the centre of the bottom row.

(Litho Questa)

**1987** (1 Dec). *Christmas. Religious Paintings. T* **233** *and similar vert designs. Multicoloured. P* 14.

1144 45 c. Type **233** .. .. .. .. 20 25
1145 60 c. "St. Joseph" (detail, "The Nativity" (Sano di Pietro)) .. .. .. .. 25 30
1146 $1 "Virgin Mary" (detail, "The Nativity" (Sano di Pietro)) .. .. .. 45 50
1147 $4 "Music-making Angel" (Melozzo da Forli) .. .. .. .. 1·75 2·25
1144/7 .. .. .. .. *Set of* 4 2·40 3·00
**MS**1148 99×70 mm. $5 "The Flight into Egypt" (Sano di Pietro) .. .. .. .. .. 2·25 2·75

**234** Wedding Photograph, 1947  **235** Great Blue Heron

(Des and litho Questa)

**1988** (8 Feb). *Royal Ruby Wedding. T* **234** *and similar vert designs. P* 14.

1149 25 c. deep brown, black and bright new blue 15 15
1150 60 c. multicoloured .. .. .. .. 30 30
1151 $2 deep brown, black and light green .. 90 95
1152 $3 multicoloured .. .. .. .. 1·40 1·50
1149/52 .. .. .. .. *Set of* 4 2·50 2·75
**MS**1153 102×77 mm. $5 multicoloured.. .. 2·25 2·75

Designs:—60 c. Queen Elizabeth II; $2 Princess Elizabeth and Prince Philip with Prince Charles at his christening, 1948; $3 Queen Elizabeth (from photo by Tim Graham), 1980; $5 Royal Family, 1952.

(Des W. Wright. Litho Questa)

**1988** (1 Mar). *Birds of Antigua. T* **235** *and similar multicoloured designs. P* 14.

1154 10 c. Type **235** .. .. .. .. 20 15
1155 15 c. Ringed Kingfisher (*horiz*) .. .. 20 15
1156 50 c. Bananaquit (*horiz*) .. .. .. 40 30
1157 60 c. Purple Gallinule (*horiz*) .. .. 40 30
1158 70 c. Blue-hooded Euphonia (*horiz*) .. 50 35
1159 $1 Brown-throated Conure ("Caribbean Parakeet") .. .. .. .. 70 55
1160 $3 Troupial (*horiz*) .. .. .. 2·00 2·25
1161 $4 Purple-throated Carib (*horiz*) .. 2·25 2·75
1154/61 .. .. .. .. *Set of* 8 6·00 6·25
**MS**1162 Two sheets, each 115×86 mm. (a) $5 Greater Flamingo. (b) $5 Brown Pelican *Set of 2 sheets* 4·50 5·50

**236** First Aid at Daycare Centre, Antigua

(Des G. Vasarhelyi. Litho Format)

**1988** (10 Mar). *Salvation Army's Community Service. T* **236** *and similar horiz designs. Multicoloured. P* 14×13½.

1163 25 c. Type **236** .. .. .. .. 35 35
1164 30 c. Giving penicillin injection, Indonesia 35 35
1165 40 c. Children at daycare centre, Bolivia .. 45 45
1166 45 c. Rehabilitation of the handicapped, India .. .. .. .. 45 45
1167 50 c. Training blind man, Kenya .. .. 55 55
1168 60 c. Weighing baby, Ghana .. .. 55 55
1169 $1 Training typist, Zambia .. .. 90 90
1170 $2 Emergency food kitchen, Sri Lanka .. 1·60 1·60
1163/70 .. .. .. .. *Set of* 8 4·75 4·75
**MS**1171 152×83 mm. $5 General Eva Burrows 3·00 3·50

**237** Columbus' Second Fleet, 1493  **238** "Bust of Christ"

(Des I. MacLaury. Litho Questa)

**1988** (16 Mar–16 May). *500th Anniv of Discovery of America by Columbus* (1992) (1*st issue*). *T* **237** *and similar horiz designs. Multicoloured. P* 14.

1172 10 c. Type **237** .. .. .. .. 15 10
1173 30 c. Painos Indian village and fleet (16.5) 20 15
1174 45 c. *Santa Mariagalante* (flagship) and Painos village (16.5) .. .. .. 25 25
1175 60 c. Painos Indians offering Columbus fruit and vegetables (16.5) .. .. 30 30
1176 90 c. Painos Indian and Columbus with parrot .. .. .. .. .. 45 45
1177 $1 Columbus landing on island .. .. 50 50
1178 $3 Spanish soldier and fleet .. .. 1·40 1·50
1179 $4 Fleet under sail (16.5) .. .. 1·75 2·00
1172/9 .. .. .. .. *Set of* 8 4·50 4·75
**MS**1180 Two sheets, each 110×80 mm. (a) $5 Queen Isabella's cross. (b) $5 Gold coin of Ferdinand and Isabella (16.5) *Set of 2 sheets* 5·50 6·50

See also Nos. 1267/71 and 1360/8.

(Litho Questa)

**1988** (11 Apr). *500th Birth Anniv of Titian. T* **238** *and similar vert designs showing paintings. Multicoloured. P* 13½×14.

1181 30 c. Type **238** .. .. .. .. 15 15
1182 40 c. "Scourging of Christ" .. .. 20 25
1183 45 c. "Madonna in Glory with Saints" .. 20 25
1184 50 c. "The Averoldi Polyptych" (detail) .. 25 30
1185 $1 "Christ Crowned with Thorns" .. 45 50
1186 $2 "Christ Mocked" .. .. .. 90 95
1187 $3 "Christ and Simon of Cyrene" .. 1·40 1·50
1188 $4 "Crucifixion with Virgin and Saints" 1·75 2·00
1181/8 .. .. .. .. *Set of* 8 4·75 5·25
**MS**1189 Two sheets, each 110×95 mm. (a) $5 "Ecce Homo" (detail). (b) $5 "Noli me Tangere" (detail) *Set of 2 sheets* 5·00 6·00

**239** Two Yachts rounding Buoy

(Des G. Drummond. Litho Format)

**1988** (18 Apr). *Sailing Week. T* **239** *and similar horiz designs. Multicoloured. P* 15.

1190 30 c. Type **239** .. .. .. .. 25 15
1191 60 c. Three yachts .. .. .. 40 30
1192 $1 British yacht under way .. .. 60 50
1193 $3 Three yachts (*different*) .. .. 1·50 2·00
1190/3 .. .. .. .. *Set of* 4 2·50 2·75
**MS**1194 103×92 mm. $5 Two yachts .. .. 2·75 3·25

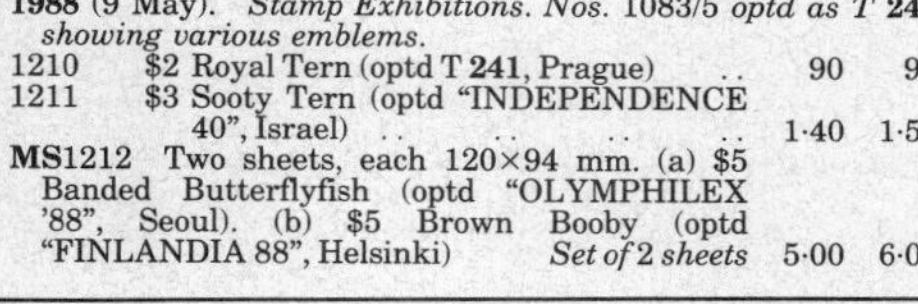

**240** Mickey Mouse and Diver with Porpoise  **(241)**

(Des Walt Disney Co. Litho Questa)

**1988** (3 May). *Disney EPCOT Centre, Orlando, Florida. T* **240** *and similar multicoloured designs showing cartoon characters and exhibits. P* 14×13½ (*horiz*) *or* 13½×14 (*vert*).

1195 1 c. Type **240** .. .. .. .. 10 10
1196 2 c. Goofy and Mickey Mouse with futuristic car (*vert*) .. .. .. 10 10
1197 3 c. Mickey Mouse and Goofy as Atlas (*vert*) .. .. .. .. .. 10 10
1198 4 c. Mickey Mouse and *Edaphosaurus* (prehistoric reptile) .. .. .. 10 10
1199 5 c. Mickey Mouse at Journey into Imagination exhibit .. .. .. 10 10
1200 10 c. Mickey Mouse collecting vegetables (*vert*) .. .. .. .. .. 10 10
1201 25 c. Type **240** .. .. .. .. 15 15
1202 30 c. As 2 c. .. .. .. .. 15 15
1203 40 c. As 3 c. .. .. .. .. 20 25
1204 60 c. As 4 c. .. .. .. .. 25 30
1205 70 c. As 5 c. .. .. .. .. 30 35
1206 $1.50, As 10 c. .. .. .. .. 70 75
1207 $3 Goofy and Mickey Mouse with robot (*vert*) .. .. .. .. .. 1·40 1·50
1208 $4 Mickey Mouse and Clarabelle at Horizons exhibit .. .. .. 1·75 1·90
1195/1208 .. .. .. *Set of* 14 4·75 5·00
**MS**1209 Two sheets, each 125×99 mm. (a) $5 Mickey Mouse and monorail (*vert*). (b) $5 Mickey Mouse flying over EPCOT Centre *Set of 2 sheets* 4·50 5·00

**1988** (9 May). *Stamp Exhibitions. Nos.* 1083/5 *optd as T* **241** *showing various emblems.*

1210 $2 Royal Tern (optd T **241**, Prague) .. 90 95
1211 $3 Sooty Tern (optd "INDEPENDENCE 40", Israel) .. .. .. .. 1·40 1·50
**MS**1212 Two sheets, each 120×94 mm. (a) $5 Banded Butterflyfish (optd "OLYMPHILEX '88", Seoul). (b) $5 Brown Booby (optd "FINLANDIA 88", Helsinki) *Set of 2 sheets* 5·00 6·00

**242** Jacaranda  **243** Gymnastics

(Des Mary Walters. Litho Questa)

**1988** (16 May). *Flowering Trees. T* **242** *and similar vert designs. Multicoloured. P* 14.

1213 10 c. Type **242** .. .. .. .. 20 15
1214 30 c. Cordia .. .. .. .. 25 20
1215 50 c. Orchid Tree .. .. .. .. 40 40
1216 90 c. Flamboyant .. .. .. .. 50 50
1217 $1 African Tulip Tree .. .. .. 55 55
1218 $2 Potato Tree .. .. .. .. 1·10 1·10
1219 $3 Crepe Myrtle .. .. .. 1·40 1·60
1220 $4 Pitch Apple .. .. .. .. 1·75 2·25
1213/20 .. .. .. .. *Set of* 8 5·50 6·00
**MS**1221 Two sheets, each 106×76 mm. (a) $5 Cassia. (b) $5 Chinaberry *Set of 2 sheets* 5·00 6·00

(Des J. Martin. Litho Questa)

**1988** (10 June). *Olympic Games, Seoul* (2*nd issue*). *T* **243** *and similar multicoloured designs. P* 14.

1222 40 c. Type **243** .. .. .. .. 20 25
1223 60 c. Weightlifting .. .. .. .. 25 30
1224 $1 Water polo (*horiz*) .. .. .. 45 50
1225 $3 Boxing (*horiz*) .. .. .. 1·40 1·50
1222/5 .. .. .. .. *Set of* 4 2·10 2·25
**MS**1226 114×80 mm. $5 Runner with Olympic torch .. .. .. .. .. 2·50 3·00

**244** *Danaus plexippus*

(Des S. Heimann. Litho Questa)

**1988** (29 Aug)–**90**. *Caribbean Butterflies. T* **244** *and similar horiz designs. Multicoloured. P* 14.

1227 1 c. Type **144** .. .. .. .. 10 10
1228 2 c. *Greta diaphanus* .. .. .. 10 10
1229 3 c. *Calisto archebates* .. .. .. 10 10
1230 5 c. *Hamadryas feronia* .. .. .. 10 10
1231 10 c. *Mestra dorcas* .. .. .. 10 10
1232 15 c. *Hypolimnas misippus* .. .. 10 10
1233 20 c. *Dione juno* .. .. .. .. 10 10
1234 25 c. *Heliconius charithonia* .. .. 10 15
1235 30 c. *Eurema pyro* .. .. .. 10 15
1236 40 c. *Papilio androgeus* .. .. .. 15 20
1237 45 c. *Anteos maerula* .. .. .. 20 25
1238 50 c. *Aphrissa orbis* .. .. .. 20 25
1239 60 c. *Astraptes xagua* .. .. .. 25 30
1240 $1 *Heliopetes arsalte* .. .. .. 40 45
1241 $2 *Polites baracoa* .. .. .. 85 90
1242 $2.50, *Phocides pigmalion* .. .. 1·00 1·10
1243 $5 *Prepona amphitoe* .. .. .. 2·10 2·25
1244 $10 *Oarisma nanus* .. .. .. 4·25 4·50
1244*a* $20 *Parides lycimenes* (19.2.90) .. 8·50 8·75
1227/44*a* .. .. .. .. *Set of* 19 16·00 17·00

**245** President Kennedy and Family  **246** Minnie Mouse carol singing

(Des J. Iskowitz. Litho Questa)

**1988** (23 Nov). *25th Death Anniv of John F. Kennedy (American statesman). T* **245** *and similar horiz designs, each showing different inset portrait. Multicoloured. P* 14.

1245 1 c. Type **245** .. .. .. .. 10 10
1246 2 c. Kennedy commanding *PT109* .. 10 10
1247 3 c. Funeral cortege .. .. .. 10 10
1248 4 c. In motorcade, Mexico City .. .. 10 10
1249 30 c. As 1 c. .. .. .. .. 15 15
1250 60 c. As 4 c. .. .. .. .. 25 30
1251 $1 As 3 c. .. .. .. .. 45 50
1252 $4 As 2 c. .. .. .. .. 1·60 1·75
1245/52 .. .. .. .. *Set of* 8 2·40 2·50
**MS**1253 105 × 75 mm. $5 Kennedy taking presidential oath of office .. .. 2·50 3·00

(Des Walt Disney Co. Litho Questa)

**1988** (1 Dec). *Christmas. "Mickey's Christmas Chorale". T* **246** *and similar multicoloured designs showing Walt Disney cartoon characters. P* 13½ × 14.
1254 10 c. Type **246** . . . . 10 10
1255 25 c. Pluto . . . . 15 15
1256 30 c. Mickey Mouse playing ukelele . . 15 15
1257 70 c. Donald Duck and nephew . . 35 35
1258 $1 Mordie and Ferdie carol singing . . 45 50
a. Sheetlet. Nos. 1258/65 . . 3·50
1259 $1 Goofy carol singing . . 45 50
1260 $1 Chip n'Dale sliding off roof . . 45 50
1261 $1 Two of Donald Duck's nephews at window . . 45 50
1262 $1 As 10 c. . . 45 50
1263 $1 As 25 c. . . 45 50
1264 $1 As 30 c. . . 45 50
1265 $1 As 70 c. . . 45 50
1254/65 . . *Set of* 12 3·75 4·25
**MS**1266 Two sheets, each 127 × 102 mm. (a) $7 Donald Duck playing trumpet and Mickey and Minnie Mouse in carriage. P 13½ × 14. (b) $7 Mickey Mouse and friends singing carols on roller skates (*horiz*). P 14 × 13½ *Set of* 2 *sheets* 7·00 7·50
Nos. 1258/65 were printed together, *se-tenant* as a composite design, in sheetlets of eight.

**247** Arawak Warriors

**248** De Havilland "Comet 4" Airliner

(Des D. Miller. Litho Questa)

**1989** (16 May). *500th Anniv of Discovery of America by Columbus* (1992) (*2nd issue*). *Pre-Columbian Arawak Society. T* **247** *and similar vert designs. Multicoloured. P* 14.
1267 $1.50, Type **247** . . 65 70
a. Horiz strip of 4. Nos. 1267/70 . . 2·40
1268 $1.50, Whip dancers . . 65 70
1269 $1.50, Whip dancers and chief with pineapple . . 65 70
1270 $1.50, Family and camp fire . . 65 70
1267/70 . . *Set of* 4 2·40 2·50
**MS**1271 71 × 84 mm. $6 Arawak chief . . 2·50 2·75
Nos. 1267/70 were printed together, *se-tenant*, in horizontal strips of 4 throughout the sheet, each strip forming a composite design.

(Des W. Wright. Litho Questa)

**1989** (29 May). *50th Anniv of First Jet Flight. T* **248** *and similar horiz designs. Multicoloured. P* 14.
1272 10 c. Type **248** . . 10 10
1273 30 c. Messerschmitt "Me 262" fighter . . 10 15
1274 40 c. Boeing "707" airliner . . 15 20
1275 60 c. Canadair "F-86 Sabre" fighter . . 25 30
1276 $1 Lockheed "F-104 Starfighter" fighters 40 45
1277 $2 McDonnell Douglas "DC-10" airliner 85 90
1278 $3 Boeing "747" airliner . . 1·25 1·40
1279 $4 McDonnell "F-4 Phantom" fighter . . 1·75 1·90
1272/9 . . *Set of* 8 4·25 4·75
**MS**1280 Two sheets, each 114 × 83 mm. (a) $7 Grumman "F-14 Tomcat" fighter. (b) $7 "Concorde" airliner *Set of* 2 *sheets* 6·00 6·25

**249** *Festivale*

(Des W. Wright. Litho Questa)

**1989** (20 June). *Caribbean Cruise Ships. T* **249** *and similar horiz designs. Multicoloured. P* 14.
1281 25 c. Type **249** . . 10 15
1282 45 c. *Southward* . . 20 25
1283 50 c. *Sagafjord* . . 20 25
1284 60 c. *Daphne* . . 25 30
1285 75 c. *Cunard Countess* . . 30 35
1286 90 c. *Song of America* . . 40 45
1287 $3 *Island Princess* . . 1·25 1·40
1288 $4 *Galileo* . . 1·75 1·90
1281/8 . . *Set of* 8 4·00 4·50
**MS**1289 (a) 113 × 87 mm. $6 *Norway*. (b) 111 × 82 mm. $6 *Oceanic* *Set of* 2 *sheets* 5·00 5·25

**250** "Fish swimming by Duck half-submerged in Stream"

(Litho Questa)

**1989** (1 July). *Japanese Art. Paintings by Hiroshige. T* **250** *and similar horiz designs. Multicoloured. P* 14 × 13½.
1290 25 c. Type **250** . . 10 15
1291 45 c. "Crane and Wave" . . 20 25
1292 50 c. "Sparrows and Morning Glories" . . 20 25
1293 60 c. "Crested Blackbird and Flowering Cherry" . . 25 30
1294 $1 "Great Knot sitting among Water Grass" . . 40 45
1295 $2 "Goose on a Bank of Water" . . 85 90
1296 $3 "Black Paradise Flycatcher and Blossoms" . . 1·25 1·40
1297 $4 "Sleepy Owl perched on a Pine Branch" . . 1·75 1·90
1290/7 . . *Set of* 8 4·50 5·00
**MS**1298 Two sheets, each 102 × 75 mm. (a) $5 "Bullfinch flying near a Clematis Branch". (b) $5 "Titmouse on a Cherry Branch" *Set of* 2 *sheets* 4·25 4·50
Nos. 1290/7 were each printed in sheetlets of 10 containing two horizontal strips of 5 stamps separated by printed labels commemorating Emperor Hirohito.

**251** Mickey and Minnie Mouse in Helicopter over River Seine

(Des Walt Disney Company. Litho Questa)

**1989** (7 July). *"Philexfrance 89" International Stamp Exhibition, Paris. T* **251** *and similar multicoloured designs showing Walt Disney cartoon characters in Paris. P* 14 × 13½.
1299 1 c. Type **251** . . 10 10
1300 2 c. Goofy and Mickey Mouse passing Arc de Triomphe . . 10 10
1301 3 c. Mickey Mouse painting picture of Notre Dame . . 10 10
1302 4 c. Mickey and Minnie Mouse with Pluto leaving Metro station . . 10 10
1303 5 c. Minnie Mouse as model in fashion show . . 10 10
1304 10 c. Daisy Duck, Minnie Mouse and Clarabelle as Folies Bergere dancers 10 10
1305 $5 Mickey and Minnie Mouse shopping in street market . . 2·10 2·25
1306 $6 Mickey and Minnie Mouse, Jose Carioca and Donald Duck at pavement cafe . . 2·50 2·75
1299/1306 . . *Set of* 8 4·50 4·75
**MS**1307 Two sheets, each 127 × 101 mm. (a) $5 Mickey and Minnie Mouse in hot air balloon. P 14 × 13½. (b) $5 Mickey Mouse at Pompidou Centre cafe (*vert*). P 13½ × 14 *Set of* 2 *sheets* 4·25 4·50

**252** Goalkeeper

**253** *Mycena pura*

(Des D. Bruckner. Litho B.D.T.)

**1989** (21 Aug). *World Cup Football Championship, Italy* (1990). *T* **252** *and similar multicoloured designs. P* 14.
1308 15 c. Type **252** . . 10 10
1309 25 c. Goalkeeper moving towards ball . . 10 15
1310 $1 Goalkeeper reaching for ball . . 40 45
1311 $4 Goalkeeper saving goal . . 1·75 1·90
1308/11 . . *Set of* 4 2·10 2·25
**MS**1312 Two sheets, each 75 × 105 mm. (a) $5 Three players competing for ball (*horiz*). (b) $5 Ball and players' legs (*horiz*) *Set of* 2 *sheets* 4·25 4·50

(Litho Questa)

**1989** (12 Oct). *Fungi. T* **253** *and similar multicoloured designs. P* 14.
1313 10 c. Type **253** . . 10 10
1314 25 c. *Psathyrella tuberculata* (*vert*) . . 10 15
1315 50 c. *Psilocybe cubensis* . . 20 25
1316 60 c. *Leptonia caeruleocapitata* (*vert*) . . 25 30
1317 75 c. *Xeromphalina tenuipes* (*vert*) . . 30 35
1318 $1 *Chlorophyllum molybdites* (*vert*) . . 40 45
1319 $3 *Marasmius haematocephalus* . . 1·25 1·40
1320 $4 *Cantharellus cinnabarinus* . . 1·75 1·90
1313/20 . . *Set of* 8 3·75 4·25
**MS**1321 Two sheets, each 88×62 mm. (a) $6 *Leucopaxillus gracillimus* (*vert*). (b) $6 *Volvariella volvacea* . . *Set of* 2 *sheets* 5·00 5·25

## NEW INFORMATION

The editor is always interested to correspond with people who have new information that will improve or correct the Catalogue.

**254** Desmarest's Hutia

**255** Goofy and Old Printing Press

(Des J. Barbaris. Litho B.D.T.)

**1989** (19 Oct). *Local Fauna. T* **254** *and similar multicoloured designs. P* 14.
1322 25 c. Type **254** . . 10 15
1323 45 c. Caribbean Monk Seal . . 20 25
1324 60 c. Mustache Bat (*vert*) . . 25 30
1325 $4 American Manatee (*vert*) . . 1·75 1·90
1322/5 . . *Set of* 4 2·10 2·25
**MS**1326 113×87 mm. $5 West Indies Giant Rice Rat . . 2·10 2·25

(Des Walt Disney Co. Litho Questa)

**1989** (2 Nov). *"American Philately". T* **255** *and similar multicoloured designs, each showing Walt Disney cartoon characters with stamps and the logo of the American Philatelic Society. P* 13½×14.
1327 1 c. Type **255** . . 10 10
1328 2 c. Donald Duck cancelling first day cover for Mickey Mouse . . 10 10
1329 3 c. Donald Duck's nephews reading recruiting poster for Pony Express riders . . 10 10
1330 4 c. Morty and Ferdie as early radio broadcasters . . 10 10
1331 5 c. Donald Duck and water buffalo watching television . . 10 10
1332 10 c. Donald Duck with stamp album . . 10 10
1333 $4 Daisy Duck with computer system . . 1·75 1·90
1334 $6 Donald's nephews with stereo radio, trumpet and guitar . . 2·50 2·75
1327/34 . . *Set of* 8 4·00 4·50
**MS**1335 Two sheets, each 127×102 mm. (a) $5 Donald's nephews donating stamps to charity. P 13½×14. (b) $5 Minnie Mouse flying mailplane upside down (*horiz*). P 14×13½ *Set of* 2 *sheets* 4·25 4·50

**256** Mickey Mouse and Donald Duck with Locomotive *John Bull*, 1831

(Des Walt Disney Co. Litho Questa)

**1989** (17 Nov). *"World Stamp Expo '89" International Stamp Exhibition, Washington* (1*st issue*). *T* **256** *and similar multicoloured designs showing Walt Disney cartoon characters and locomotives. P* 14×13½.
1336 25 c. Type **256** . . 10 15
1337 45 c. Mickey Mouse and friends with *Atlantic*, 1832 . . 20 25
1338 50 c. Mickey Mouse and Goofy with *William Crooks*, 1861 . . 20 25
1339 60 c. Mickey Mouse and Goofy with *Minnetonka*, 1869 . . 25 30
1340 $1 Chip n'Dale with *Thatcher Perkins*, 1863 . . 40 45
1341 $2 Mickey and Minnie Mouse with *Pioneer*, 1848 . . 85 90
1342 $3 Mickey Mouse and Donald Duck with cog railway locomotive *Peppersass*, 1869 . . 1·25 1·40
1343 $4 Mickey Mouse with Huey, Dewey and Louie aboard N.Y. World's Fair *Gimbels Flyer*, 1939 . . 1·75 1·90
1336/43 . . *Set of* 8 4·50 5·00
**MS**1344 Two sheets, each 127×101 mm. (a) $6 Mickey Mouse and Thomas Jefferson, 1835 (*vert*). P 13½×14. (b) $6 Mickey Mouse and friends at "Golden Spike" ceremony, 1869. P 14×13½ . . *Set of* 2 *sheets* 5·00 5·50

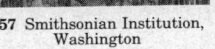

**257** Smithsonian Institution, Washington

**258** Launch of "Apollo 11"

(Des Design Element. Litho Questa)

**1989** (17 Nov). *"World Stamp Expo '89" International Stamp Exhibition, Washington (2nd issue). Sheet 78×61 mm. P 14.*
**MS**1345 **257** $4 multicoloured . . . . . . . . 1·75 1·90

(Des J. Iskowitz. Litho B.D.T.)

**1989** (24 Nov). *20th Anniv of First Manned Landing on Moon. T* **258** *and similar multicoloured designs. P 14.*
1346 10 c. Type **258** . . . . . . . . . . 10 10
1347 45 c. Aldrin on Moon . . . . . . . . 20 25
1348 $1 Module *Eagle* over Moon (*horiz*) . . 40 45
1349 $4 Recovery of "Apollo 11" crew after splashdown (*horiz*) . . . . . . 1·75 1·90
1346/9 . . . . . . . . *Set of* 4 2·25 2·40
**MS**1350 107×77 mm. $5 Astronaut Neil Armstrong . . . . . . . . . . . . 2·10 2·25

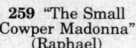

**259** "The Small Cowper Madonna" (Raphael)

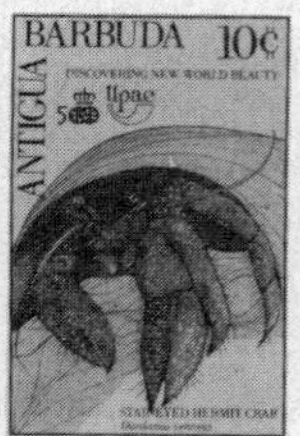

**260** Star-eyed Hermit Crab

(Litho Questa)

**1989** (11 Dec). *Christmas. Paintings by Raphael and Giotto. T* **259** *and similar vert designs. Multicoloured. P 14.*
1351 10 c. Type **259** . . . . . . . . 10 10
1352 25 c. "Madonna of the Goldfinch" (Raphael) 10 15
1353 30 c. "The Alba Madonna" (Raphael) . . 10 15
1354 50 c. Saint (detail, "Bologna Altarpiece") (Giotto) . . . . . . . . 20 25
1355 60 c. Angel (detail, "Bologna Altarpiece") (Giotto) . . . . . . . . 25 30
1356 70 c. Angel slaying serpent (detail, "Bologna Altarpiece") (Giotto) . . 30 35
1357 $4 Evangelist (detail, "Bologna Altarpiece") (Giotto) . . . . . . 1·75 1·90
1358 $5 "Madonna of Foligno" (detail) (Raphael) . . . . . . . . 2·10 2·25
1351/8 . . . . . . . . *Set of* 8 4·25 4·75
**MS**1359 Two sheets, each 71×96 mm. (a) $5 "The Marriage of the Virgin" (detail) (Raphael). (b) $5 Madonna and Child (detail, "Bologna Altarpiece") (Giotto) . . . . *Set of* 2 *sheets* 4·25 4·50

(Des Mary Walters. Litho Questa)

**1990** (26 Mar). *500th Anniv of Discovery of America by Columbus (1992) (3rd issue). New World Natural History – Marine Life. T* **260** *and similar vert designs. Multicoloured. P 14.*
1360 10 c. Type **260** . . . . . . . . 10 10
1361 20 c. Spiny Lobster . . . . . . . . 10 10
1362 25 c. Magnificent Banded Fanworm . . 10 15
1363 45 c. Cannonball Jellyfish . . . . . . 20 25
1364 60 c. Red-spiny Sea Star . . . . . . 25 30
1365 $2 Peppermint Shrimp . . . . . . 85 90
1366 $3 Coral Crab . . . . . . . . 1·25 1·40
1367 $4 Branching Fire Coral . . . . . . 1·75 1·90
1360/7 . . . . . . . . *Set of* 8 4·00 4·50
**MS**1368 Two sheets, each 100×69 mm. (a) $5 Common Sea Fan. (b) $5 Portuguese Man-of-war *Set of* 2 *sheets* 4·25 4·50

**261** *Vanilla mexicana*

**262** Queen Victoria and Queen Elizabeth II

(Des Mary Walters. Litho Questa)

**1990** (17 Apr). *"EXPO 90" International Garden and Greenery Exhibition, Osaka. Orchids. T* **261** *and similar vert designs. Multicoloured. P 14.*
1369 15 c. Type **261** . . . . . . . . 10 10
1370 45 c. *Epidendrum ibaguense* . . . . 20 25
1371 50 c. *Epidendrum secundum* . . . . 20 25
1372 60 c. *Maxillaria conferta* . . . . 25 30
1373 $1 *Oncidium altissimum* . . . . 40 45
1374 $2 *Spiranthes lanceolata* . . . . 85 90
1375 $3 *Tonopsis utricularioides* . . . . 1·25 1·40
1376 $5 *Epidendrum nocturnum* . . . . 2·10 2·25
1369/76 . . . . . . . . *Set of* 8 4·75 5·25
**MS**1377 Two sheets, each 102×70 mm. (a) $5 *Octomeria graminifolia*. (b) $5 *Rodrigueziа lanceolata* . . . . *Set of* 2 *sheets* 4·25 4·50

(Des M. Pollard. Litho B.D.T)

**1990** (3 May). *150th Anniv of the Penny Black. T* **262** *and similar horiz designs. P* 14½×14.
1378 **262** 45 c. blue-green . . . . . . 20 25
1379 – 60 c. magenta . . . . . . . . 25 30
1380 – $5 ultramarine . . . . . . 2·10 2·25
1378/80 . . . . . . . . *Set of* 3 2·25 2·50
**MS**1381 102×80 mm. **262** $6 blackish purple 2·50 2·75
Designs:—60 c, $5 As Type **262**, but with different backgrounds.

**263** *Britannia* (mail steamer), 1840

(Des M. Pollard. Litho B.D.T.)

**1990** (3 May). *"Stamp World London 90" International Stamp Exhibition. T* **263** *and similar horiz designs. P* 13½.
1382 50 c. deep grey-green and scarlet-vermilion 20 25
1383 75 c. purple-brown and scarlet-vermilion 30 35
1384 $4 deep ultramarine & scarlet-vermilion 1·75 1·90
1382/4 . . . . . . . . *Set of* 3 2·00 2·25
**MS**1385 104×81 mm. $6 brownish black and scarlet-vermilion . . . . . . . . 2·50 2·75
Designs:—75 c. Railway sorting carriage, 1892; $4 Imperial Airways flying boat *Centaurus*, 1938; $6 Post Office underground railway, London, 1927.

**264** Flamefish

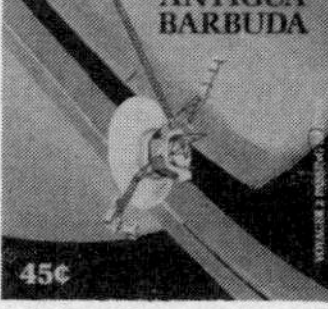

**265** "Voyager 2" passing Saturn

(Des G. Drummond. Litho Questa)

**1990** (21 May). *Reef Fishes. T* **264** *and similar horiz designs. Multicoloured. P 14.*
1386 10 c. Type **264** . . . . . . . . 10 10
1387 15 c. Coney . . . . . . . . . . 10 10
1388 50 c. Squirrelfish . . . . . . . . 20 25
1389 60 c. Sergeant Major . . . . . . 25 30
1390 $1 Yellowtail Snapper . . . . . . 40 45
1391 $2 Rock Beauty . . . . . . . . 85 90
1392 $3 Spanish Hogfish . . . . . . 1·25 1·40
1393 $4 Striped Parrotfish . . . . . . 1·75 1·90
1386/93 . . . . . . . . *Set of* 8 4·25 4·75
**MS**1394 Two sheets, each 99×70 mm. (a) $5 Blackbar Soldierfish. (b) $5 Foureye Butterflyfish . . . . . . . . *Set of* 2 *sheets* 4·25 4·50

(Des K. Gromell. Litho B.D.T)

**1990** (11 June). *Achievements in Space. T* **265** *and similar square designs. Multicoloured. P 14.*
1395 45 c. Type **265** . . . . . . . . 20 25
a. Sheetlet. Nos. 1395/1414 . . . . 3·50
1396 45 c. "Pioneer 11" photographing Saturn 20 25
1397 45 c. Astronaut in transporter . . . . 20 25
1398 45 c. Space shuttle *Columbia* . . . . 20 25
1399 45 c. "Apollo 10" command module on parachutes . . . . . . . . 20 25
1400 45 c. "Skylab" space station . . . . 20 25
1401 45 c. Astronaut Edward White in space . . 20 25
1402 45 c. "Apollo" spacecraft on joint mission . . 20 25
1403 45 c. "Soyuz" spacecraft on joint mission . . 20 25
1404 45 c. "Mariner 1" passing Venus . . . . 20 25
1405 45 c. "Gemini 4" capsule . . . . . . 20 25
1406 45 c. "Sputnik 1" . . . . . . . . 20 25
1407 45 c. Hubble space telescope . . . . 20 25
1408 45 c. "X-15" rocket plane . . . . . . 20 25
1409 45 c. "Bell X-1" aircraft . . . . . . 20 25
1410 45 c. "Apollo 17" astronaut and lunar rock formation . . . . . . . . 20 25
1411 45 c. Lunar Rover . . . . . . . . 20 25
1412 45 c. "Apollo 14" lunar module . . . . 20 25
1413 45 c. Astronaut Buzz Aldrin on Moon . . 20 25
1414 45 c. Soviet "Lunokhod" lunar vehicle . . 20 25
1395/1414 . . . . . . *Set of* 20 3·50 4·50
Nos. 1395/1414 were printed together, *se-tenant*, in sheetlets of 20 forming a composite design.

**266** Queen Mother in Evening Dress

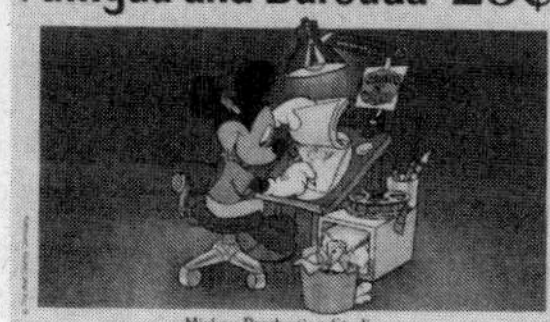

**267** Mickey Mouse as Animator

(Des D. Miller. Litho Questa)

**1990** (27 Aug). *90th Birthday of Queen Elizabeth the Queen Mother. T* **266** *and similar vert designs showing recent photographs of the Queen Mother. P 14.*
1415 15 c. multicoloured . . . . . . . . 10 10
1416 35 c. multicoloured . . . . . . . . 15 20
1417 75 c. multicoloured . . . . . . . . 30 35
1418 $3 multicoloured . . . . . . . . 1·25 1·40
1415/18 . . . . . . . . *Set of* 4 1·60 1·75
**MS**1419 67×98 mm. $6 multicoloured . . 2·50 2·75

(Des Walt Disney Co. Litho Questa)

**1990** (3 Sept). *Mickey Mouse in Hollywood. T* **267** *and similar horiz designs showing Walt Disney cartoon characters. Multicoloured. P* 14×13½.
1420 25 c. Type **267** . . . . . . . . 10 15
1421 45 c. Minnie Mouse learning lines while being dressed . . . . . . . . 20 25
1422 50 c. Mickey Mouse with clapper board . . 20 25
1423 60 c. Daisy Duck making-up Mickey Mouse 25 30
1424 $1 Clarabelle Cow as Cleopatra . . 40 45
1425 $2 Mickey Mouse directing Goofy and Donald Duck . . . . . . . . 85 90
1426 $3 Mickey Mouse directing Goofy as birdman . . . . . . . . 1·25 1·40
1427 $4 Donald Duck and Mickey Mouse editing film . . . . . . . . 1·75 1·90
1420/7 . . . . . . . . *Set of* 8 4·50 5·00
**MS**1428 Two sheets, each 132×95 mm. (a) $5 Minnie Mouse, Daisy Duck and Clarabelle as musical stars. (b) $5 Mickey Mouse on set as director . . . . . . *Set of* 2 *sheets* 4·25 4·50

**268** Men's 20 Kilometres Walk

**269** Huey and Dewey asleep (*Christmas Stories*)

(Des B. Grout. Litho Questa)

**1990** (1 Oct). *Olympic Games, Barcelona (1992). T* **268** *and similar vert designs. Multicoloured. P 14.*
1429 50 c. Type **268** . . . . . . . . 20 25
1430 75 c. Triple jump . . . . . . . . 30 35
1431 $1 Men's 10,000 metres . . . . . . 40 45
1432 $5 Javelin . . . . . . . . . . 2·10 2·25
1429/32 . . . . . . . . *Set of* 4 2·50 2·75
**MS**1433 100×70 mm. $6 Athlete lighting Olympic flame at Los Angeles Olympics . . 2·50 2·75

(Des Walt Disney Co. Litho Questa)

**1990** (15 Oct). *International Literacy Year. T* **269** *and similar vert designs showing Walt Disney cartoon characters illustrating works by Charles Dickens. Multicoloured. P* 13½×14.
1434 15 c. Type **269** . . . . . . . . 10 10
1435 45 c. Donald Duck as Poor Jo looking at grave (*Bleak House*) . . . . . . 20 25
1436 50 c. Dewey as Oliver asking for more (*Oliver Twist*) . . . . . . . . 20 25
1437 60 c. Daisy Duck as The Marchioness (*Old Curiosity Shop*) . . . . . . . . 25 30
1438 $1 Little Nell giving nosegay to her grandfather (*Little Nell*) . . . . 40 45
1439 $2 Scrooge McDuck as Mr. Pickwick (*Pickwick Papers*) . . . . . . 85 90
1440 $3 Minnie Mouse as Florence and Mickey Mouse as Paul (*Dombey and Son*) . . 1·25 1·40
1441 $5 Minnie Mouse as Jenny Wren (*Our Mutual Friend*) . . . . . . . . 2·10 2·25
1434/41 . . . . . . . . *Set of* 8 4·75 5·25
**MS**1442 Two sheets, each 126×102 mm. (a) $6 Artful Dodger picking pocket (*Oliver Twist*). (b) $6 Unexpected arrivals at Mr. Peggoty's (*David Copperfield*) . . . . *Set of* 2 *sheets* 5·00 5·25

**Winners**
**West Germany 1**
**Argentina 0**

(270)

**271** Pearly-eyed Thrasher

**1990** (11 Nov). *World Cup Football Championship Winners, Italy. Nos. 1308/12 optd as T* **270** *by Questa.*
1443 15 c. Type **252** . . . . . . . . 10 10
1444 25 c. Goalkeeper moving towards ball . . 10 10
1445 $1 Goalkeeper reaching for ball . . 40 45
1446 $4 Goalkeeper saving goal . . . . 1·75 1·90
1443/6 . . . . . . . . *Set of* 4 1·90 2·10
**MS**1447 Two sheets, each 75×105 mm. (a) $5 Three players competing for ball (*horiz*). (b) $5 Ball and players' legs (*horiz*) . . *Set of* 2 *sheets* 4·25 4·50
The overprint on No. **MS**1447 is larger and thicker, 31×13 mm.

(Des Jennifer Toombs. Litho B.D.T.)

**1990** (19 Nov). *Birds. T* **271** *and similar horiz designs. Multicoloured. P 14.*
1448 10 c. Type **271** . . . . . . . . 10 10
1449 25 c. Purple-throated Carib . . . . 10 15
1450 50 c. Common Yellowthroat . . . . 20 25
1451 60 c. American Kestrel . . . . . . 25 30
1452 $1 Yellow-bellied Sapsucker . . . . 40 45
1453 $2 Purple Gallinule . . . . . . 85 90
1454 $3 Yellow-crowned Night Heron . . 1·25 1·40
1455 $4 Blue-hooded Euphonia . . . . 1·75 1·90
1448/55 . . . . . . . . *Set of* 8 4·25 4·75
**MS**1456 Two sheets, each 76×60 mm. (a) $6 Brown Pelican. (b) $6 Frigate Bird *Set of* 2 *sheets* 5·00 5·25

**272** "Madonna and Child with Saints" (detail, Sebastiano del Piombo)

(Litho Questa)

**1990** (10 Dec). *Christmas. Paintings by Renaissance Masters. T* **272** *and similar multicoloured designs. P* 14×13½ (*horiz*) *or* 13½×14 (*vert*).

| No. | Value | Description | Unused | Used |
|---|---|---|---|---|
| 1457 | 25 c. | Type **272** | 10 | 15 |
| 1458 | 30 c. | "Virgin and Child with Angels" (detail, Grünewald) (*vert*) | 10 | 15 |
| 1459 | 40 c. | "The Holy Family and a Shepherd" (detail, Titian) | 15 | 20 |
| 1460 | 60 c. | "Virgin and Child" (detail, Lippi) (*vert*) | 25 | 30 |
| 1461 | $1 | "Jesus, St. John and Two Angels" (Rubens) | 40 | 45 |
| 1462 | $2 | "Adoration of the Shepherds" (detail, Vincenzo Catena) | 85 | 90 |
| 1463 | $4 | "Adoration of the Magi" (detail, Giorgione) | 1·75 | 1·90 |
| 1464 | $5 | "Virgin and Child adored by Warrior" (detail, Vincenzo Catena) | 2·10 | 2·25 |
| 1457/64 | | *Set of* 8 | 5·25 | 5·75 |

**MS**1465 Two sheets, each 71×101 mm. (a) $6 "Allegory of the Blessings of Jacob" (detail, Rubens) (*vert*). (b) $6 "Adoration of the Magi" (detail, Fra Angelico) (*vert*) .. *Set of* 2 *sheets* 5·00 5·25

**273** "Rape of the Daughters of Leucippus" (detail)

(Litho Questa)

**1991** (21 Jan). *350th Death Anniv of Rubens. T* **273** *and similar horiz designs. Multicoloured. P* 14×13½.

| No. | Value | Description | Unused | Used |
|---|---|---|---|---|
| 1466 | 25 c. | Type **273** | 10 | 15 |
| 1467 | 45 c. | "Bacchanal" (detail) | 20 | 25 |
| 1468 | 50 c. | "Rape of the Sabine Women" (detail) | 20 | 25 |
| 1469 | 60 c. | "Battle of the Amazons" (detail) | 25 | 30 |
| 1470 | $1 | "Rape of the Sabine Women" (different detail) | 40 | 45 |
| 1471 | $2 | "Bacchanal" (different detail) | 85 | 90 |
| 1472 | $3 | "Rape of the Sabine Women" (different detail) | 1·25 | 1·40 |
| 1473 | $4 | "Bacchanal" (different detail) | 1·75 | 1·90 |
| 1466/73 | | *Set of* 8 | 4·50 | 5·00 |

**MS**1474 Two sheets, each 101×71 mm. (a) $6 "Rape of Hippodameia" (detail). (b) $6 "Battle of the Amazons" (different detail) .. *Set of* 2 *sheets* 5·00 5·25

**274** U.S. Troops cross into Germany, 1944

(Des W. Wright. Litho B.D.T.)

**1991** (11 Mar). *50th Anniv of Second World War. T* **274** *and similar horiz designs. Multicoloured. P* 14.

| No. | Value | Description | Unused | Used |
|---|---|---|---|---|
| 1475 | 10 c. | Type **274** | 10 | 10 |
| 1476 | 15 c. | Axis surrender in North Africa, 1943 | 10 | 10 |
| 1477 | 25 c. | U.S. tanks invade Kwalajalein, 1944 | 10 | 15 |
| 1478 | 45 c. | Roosevelt and Churchill meet at Casablanca, 1943 | 20 | 25 |
| 1479 | 50 c. | Marshal Badoglio, Prime Minister of Italian anti-fascist government, 1943 | 20 | 25 |
| 1480 | $1 | Lord Mountbatten, Supreme Allied Commander South-east Asia, 1943 | 40 | 45 |
| 1481 | $2 | Greek victory at Koritza, 1940 | 85 | 90 |
| 1482 | $4 | Anglo-Soviet mutual assistance pact, 1941 | 1·75 | 1·90 |
| 1483 | $5 | Operation Torch landings, 1942 | 2·10 | 2·25 |
| 1475/83 | | *Set of* 9 | 5·25 | 5·75 |

**MS**1484 Two sheets, each 108 × 80 mm. (a) $6 Japanese attack Pearl Harbour, 1941. (b) $6 U.S.A.A.F. daylight raid on Schweinfurt, 1943 *Set of* 2 *sheets* 5·00 5·25



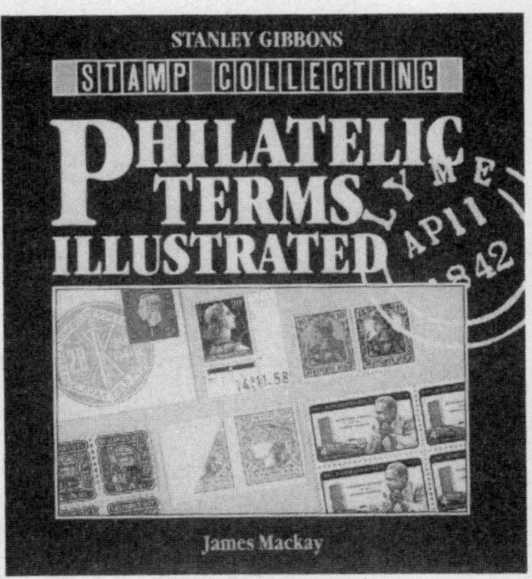

## BARBUDA

DEPENDENCY OF ANTIGUA

PRICES FOR STAMPS ON COVER TO 1945
Nos. 1/11 *from* × 4

**BARBUDA**

(1)

**1922** (13 July). *Stamps of Leeward Islands optd with T* **1**. *All Die II. Chalk-surfaced paper* (3d. *to* 5s.).

| | | | | |
|---|---|---|---|---|
| | | (*a*) *Wmk Mult Script CA* | | |
| 1 | **11** | ½d. deep green | 1·00 | 7·50 |
| 2 | | 1d. bright scarlet | 1·00 | 7·00 |
| 3 | **10** | 2d. slate-grey | 1·00 | 7·00 |
| 4 | **11** | 2½d. bright blue | 1·00 | 7·50 |
| 5 | | 6d. dull and bright purple | 1·50 | 14·00 |
| 6 | **10** | 2s. purple and blue/*blue* | 8·50 | 38·00 |
| 7 | | 3s. bright green and violet | 27·00 | 70·00 |
| 8 | | 4s. black and red (R.) | 35·00 | 70·00 |
| | | (*b*) *Wmk Mult Crown CA* | | |
| 9 | **10** | 3d. purple/*pale yellow* | 1·00 | 8·00 |
| 10 | **12** | 1s. black/*emerald* (R.) | 1·50 | 8·00 |
| 11 | | 5s. green and red/*pale yellow* | 65·00 | £120 |
| 1/11 | | *Set of* 11 | £130 | £300 |
| 1/11 Optd "Specimen" | | *Set of* 11 | £250 | |

Supplies of Nos. 1/8 were exhausted by October 1925 and stamps of Antigua were then used in Barbuda until 1968.

The following issues of Barbuda were also valid for use in Antigua.

2 Map of Barbuda

3 Great Amberjack

(Des R. Granger Barrett. Litho Format)

**1968** (19 Nov)–**70**. *Designs as T* **2/3**. *P* 14.

| | | | |
|---|---|---|---|
| 12 | ½ c. brown, black and pink | 10 | 10 |
| 13 | 1 c. orange, black and flesh | 15 | 10 |
| 14 | 2 c. blackish brown, rose-red and rose | 15 | 10 |
| 15 | 3 c. blackish brown, orange-yellow and lemon | 15 | 10 |
| 16 | 4 c. black, bright green and apple-green | 15 | 10 |
| 17 | 5 c. blue-green, black and pale blue-green | 15 | 10 |
| 18 | 6 c. black, bright purple and pale lilac | 20 | 10 |
| 19 | 10 c. black, ultramarine and cobalt | 20 | 10 |
| 20 | 15 c. black, blue-green and turquoise-green | 20 | 30 |
| 20*a* | 20 c. multicoloured (22.7.70) | 1·50 | 2·00 |
| 21 | 25 c. multicoloured (5.2.69) | 40 | 25 |
| 22 | 35 c. multicoloured (5.2.69) | 40 | 25 |
| 23 | 50 c. multicoloured (5.2.69) | 40 | 45 |
| 24 | 75 c. multicoloured (5.2.69) | 70 | 80 |
| 25 | $1 multicoloured (6.3.69) | 85 | 2·00 |
| 26 | $2.50, multicoloured (6.3.69) | 1·50 | 5·00 |
| 27 | $5 multicoloured (6.3.69) | 3·75 | 7·50 |
| 12/27 | *Set of* 17 | 9·75 | 17·00 |

Designs:—½ to 15 c. Type **2**. *Horiz as T* **3**—20 c. Great Barracuda; 35 c. French Angelfish; 50 c. Porkfish; 75 c. Striped Parrotfish; $1, Longspine Squirrelfish; $2.50, Catalufa; $5, Blue Chromis.

10 Sprinting and Aztec Sun-stone

14 "The Ascension" (Orcagna)

(Des R. Granger Barrett. Litho Format)

**1968** (20 Dec). *Olympic Games, Mexico. T* **10** *and similar horiz designs. Multicoloured. P* 14.

| | | | |
|---|---|---|---|
| 28 | 25 c. Type **10** | 20 | 25 |
| 29 | 35 c. High-jumping and Aztec statue | 25 | 25 |
| 30 | 75 c. Yachting and Aztec lion mask | 40 | 45 |
| 28/30 | *Set of* 3 | 75 | 85 |
| **MS**31 | 85 × 76 mm. $1 Football and engraved plate | 1·00 | 3·25 |

(Des R. Granger Barret. Litho Format)

**1969** (24 Mar). *Easter Commemoration. P* 14.

| | | | | |
|---|---|---|---|---|
| 32 | **14** | 25 c. black and light blue | 15 | 45 |
| 33 | | 35 c. black and deep carmine | 15 | 50 |
| 34 | | 75 c. black and bluish lilac | 15 | 55 |
| 32/4 | | *Set of* 3 | 40 | 1·40 |

15 Scout Enrolment Ceremony

18 "Sistine Madonna" (Raphael)

(Des R. Granger Barrett. Litho Format)

**1969** (7 Aug). *3rd Caribbean Scout Jamboree. T* **15** *and similar horiz designs. Multicoloured. P* 14.

| | | | |
|---|---|---|---|
| 35 | 25 c. Type **15** | 30 | 55 |
| 36 | 35 c. Scouts around camp fire | 45 | 65 |
| 37 | 75 c. Sea Scouts rowing boat | 55 | 85 |
| 35/7 | *Set of* 3 | 1·10 | 1·90 |

(Des. R. Granger Barrett. Litho Format)

**1969** (20 Oct). *Christmas. P* 14.

| | | | | |
|---|---|---|---|---|
| 38 | **18** | ½ c. multicoloured | 10 | 10 |
| 39 | | 25 c. multicoloured | 10 | 15 |
| 40 | | 35 c. multicoloured | 10 | 20 |
| 41 | | 75 c. multicoloured | 20 | 35 |
| 38/41 | | *Set of* 4 | 30 | 60 |

19 William I (1066–87)

20c

(20)

(Des R. Granger Barrett. Litho Format (Nos. 42/9) or Questa (others))

**1970–71**. *English Monarchs. T* **19** *and similar vert designs. Multicoloured. P* 14½ × 14.

| | | | |
|---|---|---|---|
| 42 | 35 c. Type **19** (16.2.70) | 30 | 15 |
| 43 | 35 c. William II (2.3.70) | 15 | 15 |
| 44 | 35 c. Henry I (16.3.70) | 15 | 15 |
| 45 | 35 c. Stephen (1.4.70) | 15 | 15 |
| 46 | 35 c. Henry II (15.4.70) | 15 | 15 |
| 47 | 35 c. Richard I (1.5.70) | 15 | 15 |
| 48 | 35 c. John (15.5.70) | 15 | 15 |
| 49 | 35 c. Henry III (1.6.70) | 15 | 15 |
| 50 | 35 c. Edward I (15.6.70) | 15 | 15 |
| 51 | 35 c. Edward II (1.7.70) | 15 | 15 |
| 52 | 35 c. Edward III (15.7.70) | 15 | 15 |
| 53 | 35 c. Richard II (1.8.70) | 15 | 15 |
| 54 | 35 c. Henry IV (15.8.70) | 15 | 15 |
| 55 | 35 c. Henry V (1.9.70) | 15 | 15 |
| 56 | 35 c. Henry VI (15.9.70) | 15 | 15 |
| 57 | 35 c. Edward IV (1.10.70) | 15 | 15 |
| 58 | 35 c. Edward V (15.10.70) | 15 | 15 |
| 59 | 35 c. Richard III (2.11.70) | 15 | 15 |
| 60 | 35 c. Henry VII (16.11.70) | 15 | 15 |
| 61 | 35 c. Henry VIII (1.12.70) | 15 | 15 |
| 62 | 35 c. Edward VI (15.12.70) | 15 | 15 |
| 63 | 35 c. Lady Jane Grey (2.1.71) | 15 | 15 |
| 64 | 35 c. Mary I (15.1.71) | 15 | 15 |
| 65 | 35 c. Elizabeth I (1.2.71) | 15 | 15 |
| 66 | 35 c. James I (15.2.71) | 15 | 15 |
| 67 | 35 c. Charles I (1.3.71) | 15 | 15 |
| 68 | 35 c. Charles II (15.3.71) | 15 | 15 |
| 69 | 35 c. James II (1.4.71) | 15 | 15 |
| 70 | 35 c. William III (15.4.71) | 15 | 15 |
| 71 | 35 c. Mary II (1.5.71) | 15 | 15 |
| 72 | 35 c. Anne (15.5.71) | 15 | 15 |
| 73 | 35 c. George I (1.6.71) | 15 | 15 |
| 74 | 35 c. George II (15.6.71) | 15 | 15 |
| 75 | 35 c. George III (1.7.71) | 15 | 15 |
| 76 | 35 c. George IV (15.7.71) | 15 | 15 |
| 77 | 35 c. William IV (2.8.71) | 15 | 15 |
| 78 | 35 c. Victoria (16.8.71) | 15 | 15 |
| 42/78 | *Set of* 37 | 5·00 | 5·00 |

See also Nos. 710/15.

**1970** (26 Feb). *No.* 12 *surch with T* **20**.

| | | | | |
|---|---|---|---|---|
| 79 | **2** | 20 c. on ½ c. brown, black and pink | 10 | 20 |
| | | a. Surch inverted | 50·00 | |
| | | b. Surch double | 50·00 | |

21 "The Way to Calvary" (Ugolino)

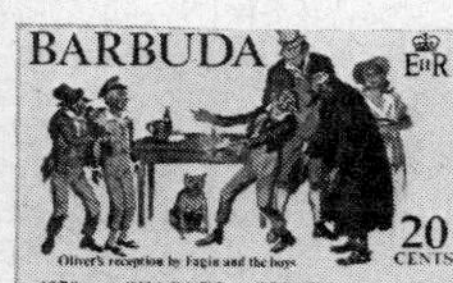


22 Oliver is introduced to Fagin (*Oliver Twist*)

(Des R. Granger Barrett. Litho Questa)

**1970** (16 Mar). *Easter Paintings. T* **21** *and similar vert designs. Multicoloured P* 14.

| | | | |
|---|---|---|---|
| 80 | 25 c. Type **21** | 15 | 3[illegible] |
| | a. Horiz strip of 3. Nos. 80/2 | 40 | |
| 81 | 35 c. "The Deposition from the Cross" (Ugolino) | 15 | 3[illegible] |
| 82 | 75 c. Crucifix (The Master of St. Francis) | 15 | 3[illegible] |
| 80/2 | *Set of* 3 | 40 | 8[illegible] |

Nos. 80/2 were printed together, *se-tenant*, in horizontal strips of 3 throughout the sheet.

(Des R. Granger Barrett. Litho Questa)

**1970** (10 July). *Death Centenary of Charles Dickens. T* **22** *and similar horiz design. Multicoloured. P* 14.

| | | | |
|---|---|---|---|
| 83 | 20 c. Type **22** | 10 | 1[illegible] |
| 84 | 75 c. Dickens and Scene from *The Old Curiosity Shop* | 20 | 4[illegible] |

23 "Madonna of the Meadow" (Bellini)

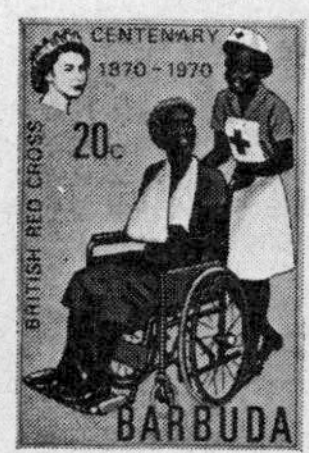


24 Nurse with Patient in Wheelchair

(Des R. Granger Barrett. Litho Questa)

**1970** (15 Oct). *Christmas. T* **23** *and similar horiz designs. Multicoloured. P* 14.

| | | | |
|---|---|---|---|
| 85 | 20 c. Type **23** | 10 | 25 |
| 86 | 50 c. "Madonna, Child and Angels" (from Wilton diptych) | 15 | 30 |
| 87 | 75 c. "The Nativity" (della Francesca) | 15 | 35 |
| 85/7 | *Set of* 3 | 30 | 80 |

(Des R. Granger Barrett. Litho Questa)

**1970** (21 Dec). *Centenary of British Red Cross. T* **24** *and similar multicoloured designs. P* 14.

| | | | |
|---|---|---|---|
| 88 | 20 c. Type **24** | 15 | 30 |
| 89 | 35 c. Nurse giving patient magazines (*horiz*) | 20 | 40 |
| 90 | 75 c. Nurse and mother weighing baby (*horiz*) | 25 | 70 |
| 88/90 | *Set of* 3 | 55 | 1·25 |

25 Angel with Vases

26 Martello Tower

(Des R. Granger Barrett. Litho Questa)

**1971** (7 Apr). *Easter. Details of the "Mond" Crucifixion by Raphael. T* **25** *and similar vert designs. Multicoloured. P* 14.

| | | | |
|---|---|---|---|
| 91 | 35 c. Type **25** | 15 | 65 |
| | a. Horiz strip of 3. Nos. 91/3 | 40 | |
| 92 | 50 c. Christ crucified | 15 | 75 |
| 93 | 75 c. Angel with vase | 15 | 80 |
| 91/3 | *Set of* 3 | 40 | 2·00 |

Nos. 91/3 were issued horizontally *se-tenant* within the sheet.

(Des R. Granger Barrett. Litho Questa)

**1971** (10 May). *Tourism. T* **26** *and similar horiz designs. Multicoloured. P* 14.

| | | | |
|---|---|---|---|
| 94 | 20 c. Type **26** | 10 | 25 |
| 95 | 25 c. Sailing boats | 10 | 30 |
| 96 | 50 c. Hotel bungalows | 15 | 35 |
| 97 | 75 c. Government House and Mystery Stone | 20 | 40 |
| 94/7 | *Set of* 4 | 40 | 1·10 |

27 "The Granducal Madonna" (Raphael)

B
A
R
B
U
D
A

(28)

(Des R. Granger Barrett. Litho Questa)

**1971** (4 Oct). *Christmas. T* **27** *and similar vert designs. Multicoloured. P* 14.

| | | | |
|---|---|---|---|
| 98 | ½ c. Type **27** | 10 | 10 |
| 99 | 35 c. "The Ansidei Madonna" (Raphael) | 10 | 20 |
| 100 | 50 c. "The Madonna and Child" (Botticelli) | 15 | 25 |
| 101 | 75 c. "The Madonna of the Trees" (Bellini) | 15 | 30 |
| 98/101 | *Set of* 4 | 35 | 65 |

The contract with the agency for the distribution of Barbuda tamps was cancelled by the Antiguan Government on 15 August 971 but the above issue was duly authorised. Four stamps (20, 35, 0 and 70 c.) were prepared to commemorate the 500th anniversary f the birth of Albrecht Dürer but their issue was not authorised.
Barbuda ceased to have separate stamps issues in 1972 but again ad stamps of her own on 14 November 1973 with the following ssue.

**973** (14 Nov). *Royal Wedding. Nos.* 370/1 *of Antigua optd with T* **28**.
.02 35 c. multicoloured .. .. .. .. 10·00 4·25
a. Opt inverted .. .. .. .. £100
.03 $2 multicoloured .. .. .. .. 5·00 2·25
a. Opt inverted .. .. .. .. £120
No. **MS**372 of Antigua also exists with this overprint, but was ot placed on sale at post offices. Examples of this sheet are known vith "Specimen" overprint (*Price* £120).

BARBUDA (29) B A R B U D A (30) B A R B U D A (30*a*) B A R B U D A (31)

**973** (26 Nov)–74. *T* **92** *etc. of Antigua optd with T* **29**.

(*a*) *On Nos.* 270 *etc. W w* **12** (*sideways*)
.04 1 c. Columbus and *Nina* .. .. .. 15 20
.05 2 c. Sir Thomas Warner's emblem and *Concepcion* .. .. .. .. 25 25
.06 4 c. Sir George Rodney and H.M.S. *Formidable* .. .. .. .. 30 30
.07 5 c. Nelson and H.M.S. *Boreas* .. .. 40 40
.08 6 c. William IV and H.M.S. *Pegasus* .. .. 40 40
.09 10 c. "Blackbeard" and pirate ketch .. .. 45 45
.10 20 c. Nelson and H.M.S. *Victory* .. .. 55 60
.11 25 c. R.M.S.P. *Solent* .. .. .. .. 55 60
.12 35 c. George V (when Prince George) and H.M.S. *Canada* .. .. .. 55 70
.13 50 c. H.M.S. *Renown* (battle cruiser) .. 55 70
.14 75 c. *Federal Maple* (freighter) .. .. 55 70
.15 $2.50, H.M.S. *London* (destroyer) (18.2.74) 1·50 1·50

(*b*) *On Nos.* 323 *etc. W w* **12** (*upright*). *White paper*
.16 ½ c. Type **92** (11.12.73) .. .. .. 15 20
.17 3 c. Viscount Hood and H.M.S. *Barfleur* (11.12.73) .. .. .. .. 25 25
.18 15 c. Captain Collingwood and H.M.S. *Pelican* (11.12.73) .. .. .. .. 35 50
.19 $1 *Sol Quest* (yacht) and class emblem .. .. .. .. 55 70
.20 $2.50, H.M.S. *London* (destroyer) (18.2.74) 9·00 11·00
.21 $5 *Pathfinder* (tug) (26.11.73) .. .. 1·75 2·50
.04/21 .. .. .. .. *Set of* 18 16·00 19·00

**973** (26 Nov). *Commemorative stamps of Antigua optd.*

(*a*) *Nos.* 353, 355 *and* 357/8 *optd with T* **30**
.22 ½ c. Private, Zacharia Tiffin's Regt of Foot, 1701 .. .. .. .. 10 10
.23 20 c. Light Company Officer, 35th Regt of Foot, 1828 .. .. .. .. 10 10
a. Optd with T **30***a* .. .. .. .. 85 90
.24 75 c. Sergeant, 49th Regt, 1858 .. .. 30 15
.22/4 .. .. .. .. *Set of* 3 40 25
MS125 127 × 145 mm .. .. .. .. 2·00 3·50

(*b*) *Nos* 360/3 *optd with T* **31**, *in red*
.26 20 c. Carnival street scene .. .. .. 10 10
.27 35 c. Carnival troupe .. .. .. .. 10 10
a. Opt inverted .. .. .. .. 30·00
.28 75 c. Carnival Queen .. .. .. .. 20 25
.26/8 .. .. .. .. *Set of* 3 30 40
MS129 134 × 95 mm .. .. .. .. 1·25 2·25
a. Albino opt
b. Opt double .. .. .. .. £275
Type **30***a* is a typographical overprint, applied locally.

B A R B U D A (32) BARBUDA (33) B A R B U D A (34) B A R B U D A (35)

**1973** (11 Dec). *Christmas. Nos.* 364/9 *of Antigua optd with T* **32**.
130 3 c. Type **105** (Sil.) .. .. .. .. 10 10
a. Opt inverted .. .. .. .. 28·00
b. "BABRUDA" (R.4/2) .. .. .. 5·50 5·50
131 5 c. "Adoration of the Magi" (Stomer) (Sil.) 10 10
a. "BABRUDA" (R.4/2) .. .. .. 7·00 7·00
132 20 c. "Granducal Madonna" (Raphael) (Sil.) .. 10 10
a. "BABRUDA" (R.4/2) .. .. .. 9·00 9·00
133 35 c. "Nativity with God the Father and Holy Ghost" (Battista) (R.) .. .. .. 15 15
134 $1 "Madonna and Child" (Murillo) (R.) .. 30 30
a. Opt inverted .. .. .. .. 45·00
130/4 .. .. .. .. *Set of* 5 60 60
**MS**135 130 × 128 mm. Nos. 130/4 (Sil.) .. 6·00 12·00

**1973** (15 Dec). *Honeymoon Visit of Princess Anne and Capt. Phillips. Nos.* 373/5 *of Antigua further optd with T* **33**.
136 35 c. multicoloured .. .. .. .. 40 20
a. Opt double, one albino .. .. 65·00
b. Optd on Antigua No. 373a
137 $2 multicoloured .. .. .. .. 1·25 60
a. Optd on Antigua No. 374a .. ..
**MS**138 78 × 100 mm. Nos. 136/7 .. .. 5·00 7·50

**1974** (18 Feb). *25th Anniv of University of West Indies. Nos.* 376/9 *of Antigua optd with T* **34**.
139 5 c. Coat of arms .. .. .. .. 10 10
a. Opt double, one albino .. .. † —
140 20 c. Extra-mural art .. .. .. 10 10
141 35 c. Antigua campus .. .. .. 15 15
a. Opt double .. .. .. ..
142 75 c. Antigua Chancellor .. .. .. 15 15
139/42 .. .. .. .. *Set of* 4 30 30
No. 139a has only been seen used on first day cover. It shows the "normal" impression misplaced and very faint

**1974** (1 May). *Military Uniforms. Nos.* 380/4 *of Antigua optd with T* **35**.
143 ½ c. Officer, 59th Foot, 1797 .. .. .. 10 10
144 10 c. Gunner, Royal Artillery, 1800 .. .. 10 10
a. Horiz pair, left-hand stamp without opt £120
145 20 c. Private, 1st West India Regt, 1830 .. 20 10
a. Horiz pair, left-hand stamp without opt £120
146 35 c. Officer, 92nd Foot, 1843 .. .. .. 25 10
a. Opt inverted .. .. .. .. 50·00
147 75 c. Private, 23rd Foot, 1846 .. .. .. 45 25
a. Horiz pair, left-hand stamp without opt
143/7 .. .. .. .. *Set of* 5 90 45
Nos. 144a, 145a and 147a come from sheets on which the overprint was so misplaced as to miss the first vertical row completely. Other stamps in these sheets show the overprint at left instead of right.
No. **MS**385 of Antigua also exists with this overprint, but was not placed on sale at post offices.

BARBUDA 13 JULY 1922 (36) BARBUDA 15 SEPT. 1874 G.P.U. (37 "General Postal Union") BARBUDA (38)

**1974** (15 July). *Centenary of Universal Postal Union (1st issue). Nos.* 386/92 *of Antigua optd with T* **36** (*Nos.* 148, 150, 152, 154, 156, 158 *and* 160) *or T* **37** (*others*), *in red.*
148 ½ c. English postman, mailcoach and helicopter .. .. .. .. 10 10
149 ½ c. English postman, mailcoach and helicopter .. .. .. .. 10 10
150 1 c. Bellman, mail steamer *Orinoco* and satellite .. .. .. .. 10 10
151 1 c. Bellman, mail steamer *Orinoco* and satellite .. .. .. .. 10 10
152 2 c. Train guard, post-bus and hydrofoil .. 15 15
153 2 c. Train guard, post-bus and hydrofoil .. 15 15
154 5 c. Swiss messenger, Wells Fargo coach and "Concorde" .. .. .. 15 15
155 5 c. Swiss messenger, Wells Fargo coach and "Concorde" .. .. .. 15 15
156 20 c. Postillion, Japanese postmen and carrier pigeon .. .. .. .. 40 70
157 20 c. Postillion, Japanese postmen and carrier pigeon .. .. .. .. 40 70
158 35 c. Antiguan postman, flying-boat and tracking station .. .. .. 80 1·50
159 35 c. Antiguan postman, flying-boat and tracking station .. .. .. 80 1·50
160 $1 Medieval courier, American express train and Boeing "747" .. .. .. 2·25 4·00
161 $1 Medieval courier, American express train and Boeing "747" .. .. .. 2·25 4·00
148/61 .. .. .. .. *Set of* 14 7·00 12·00
**MS**162 141 × 164 mm. No. **MS**393 of Antigua overprinted with T **38**, in red .. .. .. 3·00 6·00
a. Albino opt
Nos. 148/9, 150/1, 152/3, 154/5, 156/7, 158/9 and 160/1 were each printed together, *se-tenant*, in horizontal pairs throughout the sheet.
See also Nos. 177/80.

**1974** (14 Aug). *Antiguan Steel Bands. Nos.* 394/8 *of Antigua optd with T* **38**.
163 5 c. rose-red, carmine and black .. .. 10 10
164 20 c. brown-ochre, chestnut and black .. 10 10
165 35 c. light sage-green, blue-green and black .. 10 10
166 75 c. dull blue, dull ultramarine and black .. 20 20
163/6 .. .. .. .. *Set of* 4 35 35
**MS**167 115 × 108 mm. Nos. 163/6 .. .. 65 80

39 Footballers

B A R B U D A (40)

(Des G. Drummond. Litho Format)

**1974** (2 Sept). *World Cup Football Championships (1st issue). Various horiz designs as T* **39** *each showing footballers in action. P* 14.
168 **39** 35 c. multicoloured .. .. .. 10 10
169 $1.20, multicoloured .. .. .. 25 35
170 $2.50, multicoloured .. .. .. 35 50
168/70 .. .. .. .. *Set of* 3 60 75
**MS**171 70 × 128 mm. Nos. 168/70 .. .. 85 90

**1974** (23 Sept). *World Cup Football Championships (2nd issue). Nos.* 399/403 *of Antigua optd with T* **40**.
172 5 c. multicoloured .. .. .. .. 10 10
173 35 c. multicoloured .. .. .. .. 10 10
174 75 c. multicoloured .. .. .. .. 15 15
175 $1 multicoloured .. .. .. .. 20 25
172/5 .. .. .. .. *Set of* 4 35 45
**MS**176 135 × 130 mm. Nos. 172/5 .. .. 60 90

41 Ship Letter of 1833

42 Great Amberjack

(Des G. Drummond. Litho Questa)

**1974** (30 Sept). *Centenary of Universal Postal Union (2nd issue). T* **41** *and similar vert designs. Multicoloured. P* 13½.
177 35 c. Type **41** .. .. .. .. 15 15
178 $1.20, Stamps and postmark of 1922 .. 50 75
179 $2.50, Mailplane over map of Barbuda .. 75 1·25
177/9 .. .. .. .. *Set of* 3 1·25 2·00
**MS**180 128 × 97 mm. Nos. 177/9 .. .. 2·00 2·75

(Des G. Drummond. Litho Questa)

**1974** (15 Oct)–75. *Multicoloured designs as T* **42**. *P* 14 × 14½ (½ *c. to* 3 *c.,* 25 *c.*), 14½ × 14 (4 *c. to* 20 *c.,* 35 *c.*), 14 (50 *c. to* $1) *or* 13½ (*others*).
181 ½ c. Oleander, Rose Bay (6.1.75) .. .. 10 30
182 1 c. Blue Petrea (6.1.75) .. .. .. 10 30
183 2 c. Poinsettia (6.1.75) .. .. .. 10 30
184 3 c. Cassia tree (6.1.75) .. .. .. 10 30
185 4 c. Type **42** .. .. .. .. 10 30
186 5 c. Holy Trinity School .. .. .. 15 15
187 6 c. Snorkeling .. .. .. .. 15 20
188 10 c. Pilgrim Holiness Church .. .. 15 20
189 15 c. New Cottage Hospital .. .. .. 15 20
190 20 c. Post Office and Treasury .. .. 15 20
191 25 c. Island jetty and boats .. .. .. 30 30
192 35 c. Martello Tower .. .. .. 30 30
193 50 c. Warden's House (6.1.75) .. .. 30 30
194 75 c. Inter-island aircraft .. .. .. 75 1·00
195 $1 Tortoise (6.1.75) .. .. .. 70 80
196 $2.50, Spiny lobster (6.1.75) .. .. 1·50 2·00
197 $5 Magnificent Frigate Bird (6.1.75) .. 9·00 5·50
a. Perf 14 × 14½ (24.7.75)* .. .. 13·00 19·00
197*b* $10 Hibiscus (19.9.75) .. .. .. 9·00 9·50
181/97*b* .. .. .. *Set of* 18 21·00 20·00
*See footnote below Nos. 227/8.
The 50 c. to $1 are larger, 39 × 25 mm; the $2.50 and $5 are 45 × 29 mm; the $10 is 34 × 48 mm and the ½ c. to 3c. 25 c. and $10 are vert designs.

**1974** (15 Oct). *Birth Centenary of Sir Winston Churchill (1st issue). Nos.* 408/12 *of Antigua optd with T* **38** *in red.*
198 5 c. Churchill as schoolboy, and school college building, Harrow .. .. .. .. 10 10
a. Opt inverted .. .. .. .. 60·00
199 35 c. Churchill and St. Paul's Cathedral .. 20 15
200 75 c. Coat of arms and catafalque .. .. 35 45
201 $1 Churchill, "reward" notice and South African escape route .. .. .. 55 70
a. Opt inverted .. .. .. .. 60·00
198/201 .. .. .. .. *Set of* 4 1·10 1·25
**MS**202 107 × 82 mm. Nos. 198/201 .. .. 8·00 13·00

43 Churchill making Broadcast

BARBUDA (44)

(Des G. Drummond. Litho Questa)

**1974** (20 Nov). *Birth Centenary of Sir Winston Churchill (2nd issue). T* **43** *and similar horiz designs. Multicoloured. P* 13½ × 14.
203 5 c. Type **43** .. .. .. .. 10 10
204 35 c. Churchill and Chartwell .. .. 10 10
205 75 c. Churchill painting .. .. .. 20 20
206 $1 Churchill making "V" sign .. .. 25 30
203/6 .. .. .. .. *Set of* 6 55 60
**MS**207 146 × 95 mm. Nos. 203/6 .. .. 1·40 2·50

**1974** (25 Nov). *Christmas. Nos.* 413/21 *of Antigua optd with T* **33**.
208 ½ c. Bellini .. .. .. .. 10 10
a. Opt inverted .. .. .. .. 45·00
209 1 c. Raphael .. .. .. .. 10 10
210 2 c. Van der Weyden .. .. .. 10 10
211 3 c. Giorgione .. .. .. .. 10 10
212 5 c. Mantegna .. .. .. .. 10 10
213 20 c. Vivarini .. .. .. .. 10 10
214 35 c. Montagna .. .. .. .. 15 15
215 75 c. Lorenzo Costa .. .. .. 30 30
208/15 .. .. .. .. *Set of* 8 60 60
**MS**216 139 × 126 mm. Nos. 208/15 .. .. 80 1·40

**1975** (17 Mar). *Nelson's Dockyard. Nos.* 427/32 *of Antigua optd with T* **44**.
217 5 c. Carib war canoe, English Harbour, 1300 15 15
218 15 c. Ship of the line, English Harbour, 1770 25 25
219 35 c. H.M.S. *Boreas* at anchor, and Lord Nelson, 1787 .. .. .. .. 35 35
220 50 c. Yachts during "Sailing Week", 1974 .. 50 50
221 $1 Yacht Anchorage, Old Dockyard, 1970 .. 80 80
217/21 .. .. .. .. *Set of* 5 1·75 1·75
**MS**222 130 × 134 mm. As Nos. 217/21, but in larger format; 43 × 28 mm .. .. .. 2·25 2·75

**45** Battle of the Saints, 1782

(Des G. Vasarhelyi. Litho Format)

**1975** (30 May). *Sea Battles. T* **45** *and similar horiz designs showing scenes from the Battle of the Saints, 1782. Multicoloured. P* 13½.

| | | | |
|---|---|---|---|
| 223 | 35 c. Type **45** | 2·00 | 85 |
| 224 | 50 c. H.M.S. *Ramillies* | 2·00 | 1·00 |
| 225 | 75 c. Ships firing broadsides | 2·25 | 1·25 |
| 226 | 95 c. Sailors fleeing burning ship | 2·50 | 1·50 |
| 223/6 | *Set of* 4 | 8·00 | 4·25 |

(46)

**1975** (24 July). *"Apollo-Soyuz" Space Project. No.* 197a *optd with T* **46** *and similar ("Soyuz") opt.*

| | | | |
|---|---|---|---|
| 227 | $5 Magnificent Frigate Bird ("Apollo") | 6·50 | 9·00 |
| | a. *Se-tenant* strip of 3. Nos. 227/8 and 197a | 42·00 | |
| 228 | $5 Magnificent Frigate Bird ("Soyuz") | 6·50 | 9·00 |

Nos. 227/8 were issued together *se-tenant* in sheets of 25 (5 × 5), with the "Apollo" opts in the first and third vertical rows and the "Soyuz" opts in the second and fourth vertical rows, the fifth vertical row comprising five unoverprinted stamps (No. 197a).

**47** Officer, 65th Foot, 1763

30TH ANNIVERSARY
UNITED NATIONS
1945 — 1975

(48)

(Des G. Drummond. Litho Questa)

**1975** (17 Sept). *Military Uniforms. T* **47** *and similar vert designs. Multicoloured. P* 13½.

| | | | |
|---|---|---|---|
| 229 | 35 c. Type **47** | 75 | 75 |
| 230 | 50 c. Grenadier, 27th Foot, 1701–10 | 90 | 90 |
| 231 | 75 c. Officer, 21st Foot, 1793–6 | 1·00 | 1·00 |
| 232 | 95 c. Officer, Royal Regt of Artillery, 1800 | 1·25 | 1·25 |
| 229/32 | *Set of* 4 | 3·50 | 3·50 |

**1975** (24 Oct). *30th Anniv of United Nations. Nos.* 203/6 *optd with T* **48**.

| | | | |
|---|---|---|---|
| 233 | 5 c. Churchill making broadcast | 10 | 10 |
| 234 | 35 c. Churchill and Chartwell | 10 | 15 |
| 235 | 75 c. Churchill painting | 15 | 20 |
| 236 | $1 Churchill making "V" sign | 20 | 30 |
| 233/6 | *Set of* 4 | 40 | 60 |

**BARBUDA** (49)     BARBUDA (50)

**1975** (17 Nov). *Christmas. Nos.* 457/65 *of Antigua optd with T* **49**.

| | | | |
|---|---|---|---|
| 237 | ½ c. Correggio | 10 | 10 |
| 238 | 1 c. El Greco | 10 | 10 |
| 239 | 2 c. Dürer | 10 | 10 |
| 240 | 3 c. Antonello | 10 | 10 |
| 241 | 5 c. Bellini | 10 | 10 |
| 242 | 10 c. Dürer | 10 | 10 |
| 243 | 25 c. Bellini | 15 | 20 |
| 244 | $2 Dürer | 60 | 1·00 |
| 237/44 | *Set of* 8 | 95 | 1·50 |
| **MS**245 | 138 × 119 mm. Nos. 241/4 | 1·50 | 2·25 |

**1975** (15 Dec). *World Cup Cricket Winners. Nos.* 466/8 *of Antigua optd with T* **50**.

| | | | |
|---|---|---|---|
| 246 | 5 c. Vivian Richards | 75 | 85 |
| 247 | 35 c. Andy Roberts | 1·50 | 1·75 |
| 248 | $2 West Indies team | 3·25 | 4·00 |
| 246/8 | *Set of* 3 | 5·00 | 6·00 |

**51** "Surrender of Cornwallis at Yorktown" (Trumbull)

(Des G. Vasarhelyi. Litho Format)

**1976** (8 Mar). *Bicentenary of American Revolution. T* **51** *and similar horiz designs. Multicoloured. P* 13½ × 13.

| | | | |
|---|---|---|---|
| 249 | 15 c. } Type **51** | 15 | 15 |
| 250 | 15 c. } | 15 | 15 |
| 251 | 15 c. } | 15 | 15 |
| 252 | 35 c. } "The Battle of Princeton" | 30 | 30 |
| 253 | 35 c. } | 30 | 30 |
| 254 | 35 c. } | 30 | 30 |
| 255 | $1 } "Surrender of General Burgoyne at Saratoga" (W. Mercer) | 60 | 50 |
| 256 | $1 } | 60 | 50 |
| 257 | $1 } | 60 | 50 |
| 258 | $2 } "The Declaration of Independence" (Trumbull) | 90 | 80 |
| 259 | $2 } | 90 | 80 |
| 260 | $2 } | 90 | 80 |
| 249/60 | *Set of* 12 | 5·00 | 4·50 |
| **MS**261 | 140 × 70 mm. Nos. 249/54 and 255/60 (*two sheets*) | 5·00 | 9·00 |

The three designs of each value were printed horizontally *se-tenant* within the sheet to form the composite designs listed. Type **51** shows the left-hand stamp of the 15 c. design.

**52** Bananaquits

(Des G. Drummond. Litho Format)

**1976** (30 June). *Birds. T* **52** *and similar horiz designs. Multicoloured. P* 13½.

| | | | |
|---|---|---|---|
| 262 | 35 c. Type **52** | 2·50 | 70 |
| 263 | 50 c. Blue-hooded Euphonia | 2·75 | 80 |
| 264 | 75 c. Royal Tern | 3·00 | 90 |
| 265 | 95 c. Killdeer | 3·25 | 1·25 |
| 266 | $1.25, Common Cowbird | 4·50 | 1·50 |
| 267 | $2 Purple Gallinule | 6·00 | 2·25 |
| 262/7 | *Set of* 6 | 20·00 | 6·50 |

**1976** (12 Aug). *Royal Visit to the U.S.A. As Nos.* 249/60 *but redrawn and inscr at top* "H.M. QUEEN ELIZABETH ROYAL VISIT 6TH JULY 1976 H.R.H. DUKE OF EDINBURGH".

| | | | |
|---|---|---|---|
| 268 | 15 c. } As Type **51** | 15 | 15 |
| 269 | 15 c. } | 15 | 15 |
| 270 | 15 c. } | 15 | 15 |
| 271 | 35 c. } As Nos. 252/4 | 30 | 30 |
| 272 | 35 c. } | 30 | 30 |
| 273 | 35 c. } | 30 | 30 |
| 274 | $1 } As Nos. 255/7 | 60 | 60 |
| 275 | $1 } | 60 | 60 |
| 276 | $1 } | 60 | 60 |
| 277 | $2 } As Nos. 258/60 | 90 | 90 |
| 278 | $2 } | 90 | 90 |
| 279 | $2 } | 90 | 90 |
| 268/79 | *Set of* 12 | 5·00 | 5·00 |
| **MS**280 | 143 × 81 mm. Nos. 268/73 and 274/9 (*two sheets*) | 5·50 | 8·50 |

The three designs of each value were printed horizontally *se-tenant*, imperf between.

**BARBUDA** (53)     **BARBUDA** (54)

**1976** (2 Dec). *Christmas. Nos.* 514/18 *of Antigua optd with T* **53**.

| | | | |
|---|---|---|---|
| 281 | 8 c. The Annunciation | 10 | 10 |
| 282 | 10 c. The Holy Family | 10 | 10 |
| 283 | 15 c. The Magi | 10 | 10 |
| 284 | 50 c. The Shepherds | 15 | 15 |
| 285 | $1 Epiphany scene | 25 | 30 |
| 281/5 | *Set of* 5 | 45 | 55 |

**1976** (28 Dec). *Olympic Games, Montreal. Nos.* 495/502 *of Antigua optd with T* **54**.

| | | | |
|---|---|---|---|
| 286 | ½ c. High-jump | 10 | 10 |
| 287 | 1 c. Boxing | 10 | 10 |
| 288 | 2 c. Pole-vault | 10 | 10 |
| 289 | 15 c. Swimming | 10 | 10 |
| 290 | 30 c. Running | 10 | 10 |
| 291 | $1 Cycling | 20 | 20 |
| 292 | $2 Shot put | 35 | 35 |
| 286/92 | *Set of* 7 | 60 | 60 |
| **MS**293 | 88 × 138 mm. Nos. 289/92 | 1·50 | 2·40 |

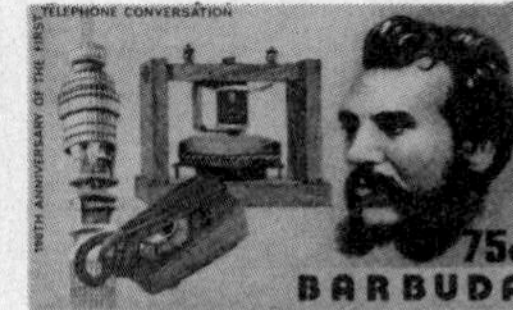


**55** Post Office Tower, Telephones and Alexander Graham Bell

(Des G. Vasarhelyi. Litho Format)

**1977** (31 Jan). *Telephone Centenary* (1976). *T* **55** *and similar horiz designs. Multicoloured. P* 13½.

| | | | |
|---|---|---|---|
| 294 | 75 c. Type **55** | 30 | 35 |
| 295 | $1.25, Dish aerial and television | 45 | 55 |
| 296 | $2 Globe and satellites | 65 | 75 |
| 294/6 | *Set of* 3 | 1·25 | 1·50 |
| **MS**297 | 96 × 144 mm. Nos. 294/6. P 15 | 1·40 | 3·00 |

**56** St. Margaret's Church, Westminster

**1977** (7 Feb). *Silver Jubilee* (1*st issue*). *T* **56** *and similar horiz designs. Multicoloured. Litho. P* 13½ × 13.

| | | | |
|---|---|---|---|
| 298 | 75 c. Type **56** | 15 | 15 |
| 299 | 75 c. Entrance, Westminster Abbey | 15 | 15 |
| 300 | 75 c. Westminster Abbey | 15 | 15 |
| 301 | $1.25, Household Cavalry | 25 | 25 |
| 302 | $1.25, Coronation Coach | 25 | 25 |
| 303 | $1.25, Team of Horses | 25 | 25 |
| 298/303 | *Set of* 6 | 1·10 | 1·10 |
| **MS**304 | 148 × 83 mm. Nos. 298/303. P 15 | 1·10 | 1·75 |

Nos. 298/300 and 301/3 were printed horizontally *se-tenant*, forming composite designs.

See also Nos. 323/30 and 375/8.

**1977** (4 Apr). *Nos.* 469A/86A *of Antigua optd with T* **54**.

| | | | |
|---|---|---|---|
| 305 | ½ c. Antillean Crested Hummingbird | 20 | 20 |
| 306 | 1 c. Imperial Amazon | 30 | 20 |
| 307 | 2 c. Zenaida Dove | 30 | 20 |
| 308 | 3 c. Loggerhead Kingbird | 30 | 20 |
| 309 | 4 c. Red-necked Pigeon | 30 | 20 |
| 310 | 5 c. Rufous-throated Solitaire | 30 | 20 |
| 311 | 6 c. Orchid Tree | 25 | 20 |
| 312 | 10 c. Bougainvillea | 25 | 20 |
| 313 | 15 c. Geiger Tree | 25 | 25 |
| 314 | 20 c. Flamboyant | 30 | 25 |
| 315 | 25 c. Hibiscus | 30 | 25 |
| 316 | 35 c. Flame of the Wood | 35 | 30 |
| 317 | 50 c. Cannon at Fort James | 40 | 40 |
| 318 | 75 c. Premier's Office | 40 | 40 |
| 319 | $1 Potworks Dam | 50 | 60 |
| 320 | $2.50, Irrigation scheme | 1·25 | 1·60 |
| 321 | $5 Government House | 2·75 | 3·25 |
| 322 | $10 Coolidge Airport | 5·50 | 7·50 |
| 305/22 | *Set of* 18 | 13·00 | 15·00 |

**BARBUDA** (57)     **B A R B U D A** (58)     **BARBUDA** (59)

**1977** (4 Apr–20 Dec). *Silver Jubilee* (2*nd issue*).

(*a*) *Sheet stamps. Nos.* 526/31 *of Antigua optd with T* **57**

| | | | |
|---|---|---|---|
| 323 | 10 c. Royal Family | 20 | 25 |
| 324 | 30 c. Royal Visit, 1966 | 40 | 45 |
| 325 | 50 c. Queen enthroned | 60 | 70 |
| 326 | 90 c. Queen after Coronation | 1·10 | 1·40 |
| 327 | $2.50, Queen and Prince Charles | 3·00 | 3·75 |
| 323/7 | *Set of* 5 | 4·75 | 6·00 |
| **MS**328 | 116 × 78 mm. $5 Queen Elizabeth and Prince Philip | 3·25 | 4·00 |
| | a. Error. Imperf | £600 | |
| | b. Opt albino | 25·00 | |
| | c. Opt double | | |

(*b*) *Booklet stamps. Nos.* 532/3 *of Antigua optd with T* **58** *in silver* (50 c.) *or T* **59** *in gold* ($5) (20 Dec)

| | | | |
|---|---|---|---|
| 329 | 50 c. Queen after Coronation | 1·00 | 1·50 |
| | a. Booklet pane of 6 | 6·00 | |
| 330 | $5 The Queen and Prince Philip | 14·00 | 16·00 |
| | a. Booklet pane of 1 | 14·00 | |

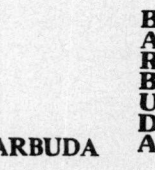

BARBUDA (60)

**61** Royal Yacht *Britannia*

**1977** (13 June). *Caribbean Scout Jamboree, Jamaica. Nos.* 534/41 *of Antigua optd with T* **60**.

| | | | |
|---|---|---|---|
| 331 | ½ c. Making camp | 10 | 10 |
| 332 | 1 c. Hiking | 10 | 10 |
| 333 | 2 c. Rock-climbing | 10 | 10 |
| 334 | 10 c. Cutting logs | 10 | 10 |
| 335 | 30 c. Map and sign reading | 40 | 40 |
| 336 | 50 c. First aid | 55 | 55 |
| 337 | $2 Rafting | 2·00 | 2·00 |
| 331/37 | *Set of* 7 | 2·75 | 2·75 |
| **MS**338 | 127 × 114 mm. Nos. 335/7 | 3·25 | 4·00 |

**1977** (12 Aug). *21st Anniv of Carnival. Nos.* 542/7 *of Antigua optd with T* **60**.

| | | | |
|---|---|---|---|
| 339 | 10 c. Carnival costume | 10 | 10 |
| 340 | 30 c. Carnival Queen | 10 | 10 |
| 341 | 50 c. Butterfly costume | 15 | 20 |
| 342 | 90 c. Queen of the band | 20 | 30 |
| 343 | $1 Calypso King and Queen | 25 | 40 |
| 339/43 | *Set of* 5 | 65 | 90 |
| **MS**344 | 140 × 120 mm. Nos. 339/43 | 1·00 | 1·75 |

(Des G. Drummond. Litho Format)

**1977** (27 Oct). *Royal Visit* (1*st issue*). *T* **61** *and similar horiz designs. Multicoloured. P* 14½.

| | | | |
|---|---|---|---|
| 345 | 50 c. Type **61** | 25 | 20 |
| 346 | $1.50, Jubilee emblem | 40 | 35 |
| 347 | $2.50, Union Jack and flag of Antigua | 60 | 50 |
| 345/7 | *Set of* 3 | 1·10 | 95 |
| **MS**348 | 77 × 124 mm. Nos. 345/7 | 1·60 | 2·75 |

**BARBUDA** (62) **BARBUDA** (63)

64 Zeppelin "LZ1"

**1977** (28 Nov–20 Dec). *Royal Visit (2nd issue). Nos.* 548/**MS**553 *of Antigua optd. A. With T* **57**. *P* 14 (28 Nov). *B. With T* **62**. *P* 11½ × 12 (20 Dec).

| | | A. | | B. | |
|---|---|---|---|---|---|
| 349 | 10 c. Royal Family | 25 | 10 | 15 | 10 |
| | a. Blue opt | | † | 35 | 35 |
| 350 | 30 c. Royal Visit, 1966 | 45 | 20 | 30 | 15 |
| | a. Blue opt | | † | 90 | 95 |
| 351 | 50 c. Queen enthroned | 65 | 35 | 40 | 20 |
| | a. Blue opt | | † | 2·75 | 1·90 |
| 352 | 90 c. Queen after Coronation | 1·25 | 60 | 70 | 30 |
| | a. Blue opt | | † | 5·00 | 3·50 |
| 353 | $2.50, Queen and Prince Charles | 3·25 | 2·25 | 1·75 | 80 |
| | a. Blue opt | | † | 11·00 | 9·50 |
| 349/53 | *Set of* 5 | 5·25 | 3·25 | 3·00 | 1·40 |
| **MS**354 | 116 × 78 mm. $5 Queen and Prince Philip | 4·75 | 5·50 | † | |

Nos. 349B/53B were each printed in small sheets of 6 including one *se-tenant* stamp-size label.

**1977** (28 Nov). *Christmas. Nos.* 554/61 *of Antigua optd with T* **63**. *"Virgin and Child" paintings by the artists given.*

| | | | |
|---|---|---|---|
| 355 | ½ c. Tura | 10 | 10 |
| 356 | 1 c. Crivelli | 10 | 10 |
| 357 | 2 c. Lotto | 10 | 10 |
| 358 | 8 c. Pontormo | 10 | 10 |
| 359 | 10 c. Tura | 10 | 10 |
| 360 | 25 c. Lotto | 15 | 10 |
| 361 | $2 Crivelli | 45 | 45 |
| 355/61 | *Set of* 7 | 70 | 65 |
| **MS**362 | 144 × 118 mm. Nos. 358/61 | 1·00 | 1·75 |

(Des I. Oliver. Litho Format)

**1977** (29 Dec). *Special Events,* 1977. *T* **64** *and similar horiz designs. Multicoloured. P* 14.

| | | | |
|---|---|---|---|
| 363 | 75 c. Type **64** | 50 | 35 |
| | a. Nos 363/6 in *se-tenant* block | 1·75 | |
| 364 | 75 c. German battleship and naval airship "L 31" | 50 | 35 |
| 365 | 75 c. *Graf Zeppelin* in hangar | 50 | 35 |
| 366 | 75 c. Military airship gondola | 50 | 35 |
| 367 | 95 c. "Sputnik 1" | 70 | 35 |
| | a. Nos. 367/70 in *se-tenant* block | 2·50 | |
| 368 | 95 c. "Vostok" | 70 | 35 |
| 369 | 95 c. "Voskhod" | 70 | 35 |
| 370 | 95 c. Space walk | 70 | 35 |
| 371 | $1.25, Fuelling for flight | 1·40 | 45 |
| | a. Nos. 371/4 in *se-tenant* block | 5·00 | |
| 372 | $1.25, Leaving New York | 1·40 | 45 |
| 373 | $1.25, *Spirit of St. Louis* | 1·40 | 45 |
| 374 | $1.25, Welcome in England | 1·40 | 45 |
| 375 | $2 Lion of England | 2·00 | 70 |
| | a. Nos. 375/8 in *se-tenant* block | 7·00 | |
| 376 | $2 Unicorn of Scotland | 2·00 | 70 |
| 377 | $2 Yale of Beaufort | 2·00 | 70 |
| 378 | $2 Falcon of Plantagenets | 2·00 | 70 |
| 379 | $5 "Daniel in the Lion's Den" (Rubens) | 3·00 | 2·00 |
| 380 | $5 | 3·00 | 2·00 |
| 381 | $5 | 3·00 | 2·00 |
| 382 | $5 | 3·00 | 2·00 |
| | a. Nos. 379/82 in *se-tenant* block | 11·00 | |
| 363/82 | *Set of* 20 | 24·00 | 14·00 |
| **MS**383 | 132 × 156 mm. Nos. 363/82 | 24·00 | 32·00 |

Events:—75 c. 75th Anniv of Navigable Airships; 95 c. 20th Anniv of U.S.S.R. Space Programme; $1.25, 50th Anniv of Lindbergh's Transatlantic Flight; $2 Silver Jubilee of Queen Elizabeth II; $5 400th Birth Anniv of Rubens.

Nos. 363/66, 367/70, 371/74, 375/78 and 379/82 were printed in *se-tenant* blocks of four within the sheet.

Nos. 363/83 exist imperforate from stock dispersed by the liquidator of Format International Security Printers Ltd.

**BARBUDA** (65)

66 "Pieta" (sculpture) (detail)

**1978** (15 Feb). *Tenth Anniv of Statehood. Nos.* 562/7 *of Antigua optd with T* **65**.

| | | | |
|---|---|---|---|
| 384 | 10 c. Pineapple | 10 | 10 |
| 385 | 15 c. State flag | 10 | 10 |
| 386 | 50 c. Police band | 20 | 15 |
| 387 | 90 c. Premier V. C. Bird | 20 | 20 |
| 388 | $2 State Coat of Arms | 40 | 40 |
| 384/8 | *Set of* 5 | 80 | 75 |
| **MS**389 | 126 × 99 mm. Nos. 385/88. P 14 | 1·90 | 2·25 |

(Des G. Vasarhelyi. Litho Format)

**1978** (23 Mar). *Easter. Works by Michelangelo. T* **66** *and similar horiz designs. Multicoloured. P* 13½ × 14.

| | | | |
|---|---|---|---|
| 390 | 75 c. Type **66** | 15 | 15 |
| 391 | 95 c. "The Holy Family" (painting) | 20 | 20 |
| 392 | $1.25, "Libyan Sibyl" from Sistine Chapel, Rome | 25 | 25 |
| 393 | $2 "The Flood" from Sistine Chapel | 35 | 35 |
| 390/3 | *Set of* 4 | 85 | 85 |
| **MS**394 | 117 × 85 mm. Nos. 390/3 | 1·60 | 2·00 |

Nos. 390/4 exist imperforate from stock dispersed by the liquidator of Format International Security Printers Ltd.

**BARBUDA** (67)

68 St. Edward's Crown

**1978** (28 Mar). *75th Anniv of Powered Flight. Nos.* 568/75 *of Antigua optd with T* **67**.

| | | | |
|---|---|---|---|
| 395 | ½ c. *Glider III*, 1902 | 10 | 10 |
| 396 | 1 c. *Flyer I*, 1903 | 10 | 10 |
| 397 | 2 c. Launch system and engine | 10 | 10 |
| 398 | 10 c. Orville Wright | 10 | 10 |
| 399 | 50 c. *Flyer III*, 1905 | 25 | 15 |
| 400 | 90 c. Wilbur Wright | 35 | 15 |
| 401 | $2 Wright "Model B", 1910 | 60 | 45 |
| 395/401 | *Set of* 7 | 1·25 | 75 |
| **MS**402 | 90 × 75 mm. $2.50, *Flyer I* on launch system | 1·25 | 2·00 |

**1978** (22 May). *Sailing Week. Nos.* 576/80 *of Antigua optd with T* **67**.

| | | | |
|---|---|---|---|
| 403 | 10 c. Sunfish regatta | 15 | 10 |
| 404 | 50 c. Fishing and work boat race | 35 | 25 |
| 405 | 90 c. Curtain Bluff race | 40 | 35 |
| 406 | $2 Power boat rally | 75 | 75 |
| 403/6 | *Set of* 4 | 1·50 | 1·25 |
| **MS**407 | 110 × 77 mm. $2.50, Guadeloupe–Antigua race | 1·25 | 1·60 |
| | a. Albino opt | † | — |

(Des J. Cooter. Litho)

**1978** (2 June). *25th Anniv of Coronation (1st issue). T* **68** *and similar vert designs. Multicoloured. P* 15.

| | | | |
|---|---|---|---|
| 408 | 75 c. Type **68** | 15 | 15 |
| 409 | 75 c. Imperial State Crown | 15 | 15 |
| 410 | $1.50, Queen Mary's Crown | 25 | 25 |
| 411 | $1.50, Queen Mother's Crown | 25 | 25 |
| 412 | $2.50, Queen Consort's Crown | 45 | 45 |
| 413 | $2.50, Queen Victoria's Crown | 45 | 45 |
| 408/413 | *Set of* 6 | 1·50 | 1·50 |
| **MS**414 | 123 × 117 mm. Nos. 408/13. P 14½ | 2·00 | 2·75 |

The two designs for each value were issued as two *se-tenant* pairs, together with 2 labels, in small sheets of 6.

Examples of the 75 c. and $2.50 values in separate miniature sheets of four exist from stock dispersed by the liquidator of Format International Security Printers Ltd, as do imperforate examples of No. **MS**414.

**1978** (2 June–12 Oct). *25th Anniv of Coronation* (2nd issue).

(*a*) *Sheet stamps. Nos.* 581/6 *of Antigua optd with T* **67**. *P* 14 (2.6)

| | | | |
|---|---|---|---|
| 415 | 10 c. Queen Elizabeth and Prince Philip | 10 | 10 |
| 416 | 30 c. Crowning | 10 | 10 |
| 417 | 50 c. Coronation procession | 15 | 15 |
| 418 | 90 c. Queen seated in St. Edward's Chair | 20 | 20 |
| | a. Opt triple | 85·00 | |
| 419 | $2.50, Queen wearing Imperial State Crown | 50 | 60 |
| 415/19 | *Set of* 5 | 85 | 1·00 |
| **MS**420 | 114 × 103 mm. $5 Queen and Prince Philip (17.7) | 1·50 | 2·00 |
| | a. Albino opt | £250 | |

(*b*) *Booklet stamps. Horiz designs as Nos.* 587/9 *of Antigua but additionally inscr* "BARBUDA". *Multicoloured. Roul* 5 × *imperf**. *Self-adhesive* (12.10)

| | | | |
|---|---|---|---|
| 421 | 25 c. Glass Coach | 1·25 | 1·75 |
| | a. Booklet pane. Nos. 421/2 × 3 | 6·50 | |
| 422 | 50 c. Irish State Coach | 1·25 | 1·75 |
| 423 | $5 Coronation Coach | 3·50 | 4·00 |
| | a. Booklet pane of 1 | 3·50 | |
| 421/3 | *Set of* 3 | 5·50 | 6·75 |

Nos. 415/19 also exist perf 12 (*Price for set of* 5 £1 *mint or used*) from additional sheetlets of three stamps and one label, issued 12 October 1978. These stamps have different background colours from Nos. 415/19.

*The 25 and 50 c. values were separated by various combinations of rotary knife (giving a straight edge) and roulette. The $5 value exists only with straight edges.

**1978** (12 Sept). *World Cup Football Championship, Argentina. Nos.* 590/3 *of Antigua optd with T* **67**.

| | | | |
|---|---|---|---|
| 424 | 10 c. Player running with ball | 10 | 10 |
| 425 | 15 c. Players in front of goal | 10 | 10 |
| 426 | $3 Referee and player | 1·00 | 1·25 |
| 424/6 | *Set of* 3 | 1·00 | 1·25 |
| **MS**427 | 126 × 88 mm. 25 c. Player crouching with ball; 30 c. Players heading ball; 50 c. Players running with ball; $2 Goalkeeper diving | 80 | 90 |

**BARBUDA** (69)

70 Blackbar Soldierfish

**1978** (20 Nov). *Flowers. Nos.* 594/8 *of Antigua optd with T* **69**.

| | | | |
|---|---|---|---|
| 428 | 25 c. Petrea | 25 | 30 |
| 429 | 50 c. Sunflower | 50 | 60 |
| 430 | 90 c. Frangipani | 70 | 80 |
| 431 | $2 Passion Flower | 1·25 | 1·60 |
| 428/31 | *Set of* 4 | 2·40 | 3·00 |
| **MS**432 | 118 × 85 mm. $2.50, Hibiscus | 1·50 | 2·50 |

**1978** (20 Nov). *Christmas. Paintings. Nos.* 599/602 *optd with T* **69** *in silver.*

| | | | |
|---|---|---|---|
| 433 | 8 c. "St. Ildefonso receiving the Chasuble from the Virgin" | 10 | 10 |
| 434 | 25 c. "The Flight of St. Barbara" | 15 | 15 |
| 435 | $2 "Madonna and Child, with St. Joseph, John the Baptist and Donor" | 60 | 1·25 |
| 433/5 | *Set of* 3 | 75 | 1·25 |
| **MS**436 | 170 × 113 mm. $4 "The Annunciation" | 1·75 | 2·25 |

(Litho Format)

**1978** (20 Nov). *Flora and Fauna. T* **70** *and similar horiz designs. Multicoloured. P* 14½.

| | | | |
|---|---|---|---|
| 437 | 25 c. Type **70** | 1·25 | 1·25 |
| 438 | 50 c. *Cynthia cardui* (butterfly) | 2·00 | 2·00 |
| 439 | 75 c. Dwarf Poinciana | 2·50 | 2·50 |
| 440 | 95 c. *Heliconius charithonia* (butterfly) | 3·25 | 3·25 |
| 441 | $1.25, Bougainvillea | 3·25 | 3·25 |
| 437/41 | *Set of* 5 | 11·00 | 11·00 |

71 Footballers and World Cup

72 Sir Rowland Hill

(Des J. Cooter. Litho Format)

**1978** (29 Dec). *Anniversaries and Events. T* **71** *and similar multicoloured designs. P* 14.

| | | | |
|---|---|---|---|
| 442 | 75 c. Type **71** | 65 | 65 |
| 443 | 95 c. Wright brothers and *Flyer I* (*horiz*) | 75 | 75 |
| 444 | $1.25, *Double Eagle II* and map of Atlantic (*horiz*) | 90 | 90 |
| 445 | $2 Prince Philip paying homage to the newly crowned Queen | 2·75 | 2·75 |
| 442/5 | *Set of* 4 | 4·50 | 4·50 |
| **MS**446 | 122 × 90 mm. Nos. 442/5. Imperf | 6·00 | 6·00 |

Events:—75 c. Argentina—Winners of World Cup Football Championship; 95 c. 75th anniversary of powered flight; $1.25 1st Atlantic crossing by balloon; $2 25th anniversary of Coronation.

(Des J. Cooter. Litho Format)

**1979** (4 Apr). *Death Centenary of Sir Rowland Hill (1st issue). T* **72** *and similar multicoloured designs. P* 14.

| | | | |
|---|---|---|---|
| 447 | 75 c. Type **72** | 45 | 50 |
| 448 | 95 c. Mail coach, 1840 (*horiz*) | 55 | 60 |
| 449 | $1.25, London's first pillar box, 1855 (*horiz*) | 60 | 70 |
| 450 | $2 Mail leaving St. Martin's Le Grand Post Office, London | 90 | 95 |
| 447/50 | *Set of* 4 | 2·25 | 2·50 |
| **MS**451 | 129 × 104 mm. Nos. 447/50 Imperf | 2·25 | 2·75 |

Nos. 447/50 were each printed in small sheets of 4 including one *se-tenant* stamp-size label.

**BARBUDA** (73)

74 Passengers alighting from British Airways Boeing "747"

**1979** (4 Apr). *Death Centenary of Sir Rowland Hill (2nd issue). Nos.* 603/7 *of Antigua optd with T* **73** *in blue. P* 14.

| | | | |
|---|---|---|---|
| 452 | 25 c. Antigua 1863 1d. stamp | 15 | 15 |
| 453 | 50 c. Penny Black stamp | 20 | 20 |
| 454 | $1 Stage-coach and woman posting letter, *circa* 1840 | 35 | 30 |
| 455 | $2 Modern mail transport | 80 | 60 |
| 452/5 | *Set of* 4 | 1·40 | 1·10 |
| **MS**456 | 108 × 82 mm. $2.50, Sir Rowland Hill | 75 | 80 |

Nos. 452/5 also exist perf 12 (*Price for set of* 4 £1.75 *mint or used*) from additional sheetlets of four stamps and one label, issued 28 December 1979.

**1979** (12 Apr). *Easter. Works by Dürer. Nos.* 608/11 *of Antigua optd with T* **67**.

| | | | |
|---|---|---|---|
| 457 | 10 c. multicoloured | 10 | 10 |
| 458 | 50 c. multicoloured | 20 | 20 |
| 459 | $4 black, magenta and greenish yellow | 90 | 1·10 |
| 457/9 | *Set of* 3 | 1·00 | 1·25 |
| **MS**460 | 114 × 99 mm. $2.50, multicoloured | 55 | 75 |

(Litho Format)

**1979** (24 May). *30th Anniv of International Civil Aviation Organisation. T* **74** *and similar horiz designs. Multicoloured. P* 13½ × 14.

| | | | |
|---|---|---|---|
| 461 | 75 c. Type **74** | 45 | 80 |
| | a. Block of 4. Nos. 461/3 plus label | 1·40 | |
| 462 | 95 c. Air traffic control | 50 | 90 |
| 463 | $1.25, Ground crew-man directing Boeing "707" on runway | 60 | 1·10 |
| 461/3 | *Set of* 3 | 1·40 | 2·50 |

Nos. 461/3 were either printed in separate sheets, or together with a stamp-size label, *se-tenant*, in blocks of 4, each block divided in the sheet by margins.

**1979** (24 May). *International Year of the Child (1st issue). Nos.* 612/16 *of Antigua optd with T* **67**.

| | | | |
|---|---|---|---|
| 464 | 25 c. Yacht | 20 | 15 |
| 465 | 50 c. Rocket | 35 | 25 |
| 466 | 90 c. Car | 50 | 35 |
| 467 | $2 Train | 1·25 | 60 |
| 464/7 | *Set of* 4 | 2·10 | 1·25 |
| **MS**468 | 80 × 112 mm. $5 Aeroplane | 2·00 | 2·00 |

BARBUDA (75) BARBUDA (76)

**1979** (1 Aug). *Fishes. Nos.* 617/21 *of Antigua optd with T* **75**.
469 30 c. Yellowjack .. .. .. .. .. 20 15
470 50 c. Bluefin Tuna .. .. .. .. .. 30 20
471 90 c. Sailfish .. .. .. .. .. 40 30
472 $3 Wahoo .. .. .. .. .. 1·10 1·10
469/72 .. .. .. .. *Set of* 4 1·75 1·60
**MS**473 122 × 75 mm. $2.50, Barracuda (overprinted with T 73) .. .. .. .. 1·00 1·25
a. Albino opt .. .. .. ..

**1979** (1 Aug). *Death Bicentenary of Captain Cook. Nos.* 622/6 *of Antigua optd with T* **76**.
474 25 c. Cook's Birthplace, Marton .. .. 30 30
475 50 c. H.M.S. *Endeavour* .. .. .. 50 45
476 90 c. Marine chronometer .. .. .. 65 60
477 $3 Landing at Botany Bay .. .. .. 1·75 1·50
474/7 .. .. .. .. *Set of* 4 2·75 2·50
**MS**478 110 × 85 mm. $2.50, H.M.S. *Resolution* (overprinted with T 82) .. .. .. .. 1·25 1·50
a. Albino opt .. .. .. ..

**77** "Virgin with the Pear"

BARBUDA (78)

(Des G. Vasarhelyi. Litho Format)

**1979** (24 Sept). *International Year of the Child* (2*nd issue*). *Details of Paintings by Dürer, showing the infant Jesus. T* **77** *and similar vert designs. Multicoloured. P* 14 × 13½.
479 25 c. Type **77** .. .. .. .. 15 15
480 50 c. "Virgin with the Pink" .. .. .. 25 25
481 75 c. "Virgin with the Pear" (*different*) .. 30 30
482 $1.25, "Nativity" .. .. .. .. 40 40
479/82 .. .. .. .. *Set of* 4 1·00 1·00
**MS**483 86 × 118 mm. Nos. 479/82 .. .. .. 1·25 1·75

**1979** (21 Nov). *Christmas. Nos.* 627/31 *of Antigua optd with T* **78**.
484 8 c. The Holy Family .. .. .. .. 10 10
485 25 c. Virgin and Child on Ass .. .. .. 15 10
486 50 c. Shepherd and star .. .. .. 25 15
487 $4 Wise Men with gifts .. .. .. 1·10 80
484/7 .. .. .. .. *Set of* 4 1·40 1·00
**MS**488 113 × 94 mm. $3 Angel with trumpet .. 80 1·10

**1980** (18 Mar). *Olympic Games, Moscow. Nos.* 632/6 *of Antigua optd with T* **67**.
489 10 c. Javelin throwing .. .. .. .. 10 10
490 25 c. Running .. .. .. .. 10 10
491 $1 Pole vaulting .. .. .. .. 30 20
492 $2 Hurdling .. .. .. .. 55 40
489/92 .. .. .. *Set of* 4 90 65
**MS**493 127 × 96 mm. $3 Boxing .. .. .. 70 1·10

LONDON 1980 (79)

**80** "Apollo 11" Crew Badge

**1980** (6 May). *"London 1980" International Stamp Exhibition. As Nos.* 452/5 *optd with T* **79** *in blue. P* 12.
494 25 c. Antigua 1863 1d. stamp .. .. .. 30 15
495 50 c. Penny Black stamp .. .. .. 40 30
496 $1 Mail coach and woman posting letter, *circa* 1840 .. .. .. .. 75 55
497 $2 Modern mail transport .. .. .. 2·25 1·10
494/7 .. .. .. .. *Set of* 4 3·25 1·90

(Litho Format)

**1980** (21 May). *10th Anniv of Moon Landing. T* **80** *and similar horiz designs. Multicoloured. P* 13½ × 14.
498 75 c. Type **80** .. .. .. .. 25 25
499 95 c. Plaque left on Moon .. .. .. 30 30
500 $1.25, Rejoining mother ship .. .. .. 40 40
501 $2 Lunar Module .. .. .. .. 65 65
498/501 .. .. .. *Set of* 4 1·40 1·40
**MS**502 118 × 84 mm. Nos. 498/501 .. .. .. 1·75 2·50

**81** American Wigeon

(Litho Questa)

**1980** (16 June). *Birds. Multicoloured designs as T* **81**. *P* 14.
503 1 c. Type **81** .. .. .. .. 30 15
504 2 c. Snowy Plover .. .. .. .. 35 15
505 4 c. Rose-breasted Grosbeak .. .. .. 40 20
506 6 c. Mangrove Cuckoo .. .. .. .. 40 20
507 10 c. Adelaide's Warbler .. .. .. 40 20
508 15 c. Scaly-breasted Thrasher .. .. .. 45 25
509 20 c. Yellow-crowned Night Heron .. .. 45 25
510 25 c. Bridled Quail Dove .. .. .. 45 25
511 35 c. Carib Grackle .. .. .. .. 55 30
512 50 c. Pintail .. .. .. .. 65 35
513 75 c. Black-whiskered Vireo .. .. .. 80 45
514 $1 Blue-winged Teal .. .. .. 1·00 70
515 $1.50, Green-throated Carib (*vert*) .. .. 1·25 80
516 $2 Red-necked Pigeon (*vert*) .. .. 2·00 1·25
517 $2.50, Wied's Crested Flycatcher (*vert*) .. 2·50 1·50
518 $5 Yellow-bellied Sapsucker (*vert*) .. .. 3·25 2·50
519 $7.50, Caribbean Elaenia (*vert*) .. .. 4·25 4·00
520 $10 Great Egret (*vert*) .. .. .. 5·00 5·00
503/20 .. .. .. .. *Set of* 18 21·00 17·00

**1980** (29 July). *Famous Works of Art. Nos.* 651/7 *of Antigua optd with T* **67**.
521 10 c. "David" (statue, Donatello) .. .. 10 10
522 30 c. "The Birth of Venus" (painting, Sandro Botticelli) .. .. .. .. 15 15
523 50 c. "Reclining Couple" (sarcophagus), Cerveteri .. .. .. .. 20 20
524 90 c. "The Garden of Earthly Delights" (painting, Hieronymus Bosch) .. 25 25
525 $1 "Portinari Altarpiece" (painting, Hugo van der Goes) .. .. .. 25 25
526 $4 "Eleanora of Toledo and her Son Giovanni de' Medici" (painting, Agnolo Bronzino) 80 80
521/6 .. .. .. .. *Set of* 6 1·50 1·50
**MS**527 99 × 124 mm. $5 "The Holy Family" (painting, Rembrandt) .. .. .. 1·50 1·75

**1980** (8 Sept). *75th Anniv of Rotary International. Nos.* 658/62 *of Antigua optd with T* **67**.
528 30 c. Rotary anniversary emblem and headquarters, U.S.A. .. .. .. .. 15 15
529 50 c. Rotary anniversary emblem and Antigua Rotary Club banner .. .. .. 20 20
530 90 c. Map of Antigua and Rotary emblem .. 25 25
531 $3 Paul P. Harris (founder) and Rotary emblem .. .. .. .. 65 65
528/31 .. .. .. .. *Set of* 4 1·10 1·10
**MS**532 102 × 77 mm. $5 Antigua flags and Rotary emblems .. .. .. .. 1·50 2·25

BARBUDA (82) BARBUDA (83)

**1980** (6 Oct). *80th Birthday of Queen Elizabeth the Queen Mother. Nos.* 663/5 *of Antigua optd with T* **82**.
533 10 c. multicoloured .. .. .. 30 15
a. Opt inverted .. .. .. 38·00
b. Opt double .. .. .. 30·00
534 $2.50, multicoloured .. .. .. 3·00 1·50
**MS**535 68 × 88 mm. $3 multicoloured .. .. 1·75 1·75

**1980** (8 Dec). *Birds. Nos.* 666/70 *of Antigua optd with T* **83**.
536 10 c. Ringed Kingfisher .. .. .. 65 40
537 30 c. Plain Pigeon .. .. .. 1·00 55
538 $1 Green-throated Carib .. .. .. 1·75 1·40
539 $2 Black-necked Stilt .. .. .. 2·50 2·75
536/9 .. .. .. .. *Set of* 4 5·50 4·50
**MS**540 73 × 73 mm. $2.50, Roseate Tern .. .. 1·75 2·00

**1981** (26 Jan). *Sugar Cane Railway Locomotives. Nos.* 681/5 *of Antigua optd with T* **67**.
541 25 c. Diesel Locomotive No. 15 .. .. 80 25
542 50 c. Narrow-gauge steam locomotive .. 1·00 35
543 90 c. Diesel locomotives Nos. 1 and 10 .. 1·25 45
544 $3 Steam locomotive hauling sugar cane .. 2·50 1·40
541/4 .. .. .. .. *Set of* 4 5·00 2·25
**MS**545 82 × 111 mm. $2.50, Antigua sugar factory, railway yard and sheds .. .. .. 1·50 1·75

**84** Florence Nightingale

**85** Goofy in Motor-boat

(Litho Format)

**1981** (9 Mar). *Famous Women. T* **84** *and similar vert designs. P* 14 × 13½.
546 50 c. multicoloured .. .. .. .. 30 30
547 90 c. multicoloured .. .. .. .. 55 55
548 $1 multicoloured .. .. .. .. 60 60
549 $4 black, yellow-brown and rose-lilac .. 1·75 1·75
546/9 .. .. .. .. *Set of* 4 2·75 2·75
Designs:—90 c. Marie Curie; $1 Amy Johnson; $4 Eleanor Roosevelt.

(Litho Format)

**1981** (15 May). *Walt Disney Cartoon Characters. T* **85** *and similar vert designs showing characters afloat. Multicoloured. P* 13½.
550 10 c. Type **85** .. .. .. .. 25 10
551 20 c. Donald Duck reversing car into sea .. 30 15
552 25 c. Mickey Mouse asking tug-boat to take on more than it can handle .. .. .. 40 20
553 30 c. Porpoise turning the tables on Goofy .. 50 25
554 35 c. Goofy in sailing boat .. .. .. 50 25
555 40 c. Mickey Mouse and boat being lifted out of water by fish .. .. .. .. 60 30
556 75 c. Donald Duck fishing for flying-fish with butterfly net .. .. .. .. 75 45
557 $1 Minnie Mouse in brightly decorated sailing boat .. .. .. .. 85 55
558 $2 Chip and Dale on floating ship-in-bottle 1·60 1·10
550/8 .. .. .. .. *Set of* 9 5·25 3·00
**MS**559 127 × 101 mm. $2.50, Donald Duck .. 3·50 2·25

BARBUDA (86)

**1981** (9 June). *Birth Centenary of Picasso. Nos.* 697/701 *of Antigua optd with T* **86**.
560 10 c. "Pipes of Pan" .. .. .. .. 10 10
561 50 c. "Seated Harlequin" .. .. .. 25 25
562 90 c. "Paulo as Harlequin" .. .. .. 45 45
563 $4 "Mother and Child" .. .. .. 1·60 1·60
560/3 .. .. .. .. *Set of* 4 2·10 2·10
**MS**564 115 × 140 mm. $5 "Three Musicians" (detail) .. .. .. .. 2·75 2·75

**87** Buckingham Palace **88**

(Des G. Drummond. Litho Format)

**1981** (27 July). *Royal Wedding (1st issue). Buildings. T* **87**/8 *and similar horiz designs. Each bicoloured**. *P* 11 × 11½.
565 $1 Type **87** .. .. .. .. 70 70
566 $1 Type **88** .. .. .. .. 70 70
a. Sheetlet. Nos. 565/70 .. .. .. 6·50
b. Booklet pane. Nos. 565/6 × 2 in imperf between horiz pairs .. .. .. 2·50
567 $1.50 } Caernarvon Castle .. .. 85 85
568 $1.50 } .. .. 85 85
b. Booklet pane. Nos. 567/8 × 2 in imperf between horiz pairs .. .. .. 3·00
569 $4 } Highgrove House .. .. 1·75 1·75
570 $4 } .. .. 1·75 1·75
b. Booklet pane. Nos. 569/70 × 2 in imperf between horiz pairs .. .. .. 7·00
565/70 .. .. .. .. *Set of* 6 6·00 6·00
**MS**571 75 × 90 mm. $5 black and olive-yellow (St. Paul's Cathedral—26 × 32 *mm*). P 11½ × 11 .. 1·50 2·00

*Nos. 565/70 each exist printed in black with three different background colours, rose-pink, turquoise-green and lavender.

No. 566b was printed only in black and rose-pink. No. 568b black and turquoise-green and No. 570b black and lavender.

Nos. 565/70 were printed together, *se-tenant*, in sheetlets of 6, the two versions of each value forming a composite design.

**1981** (14 Aug). *Royal Wedding (2nd issue). Nos.* 702/5 *of Antigua optd with T* **86**.
572 25 c. Prince Charles and Lady Diana Spencer 25 25
573 50 c. Glamis Castle .. .. .. .. 35 35
a. Opt double .. .. .. 30·00
574 $4 Prince Charles skiing .. .. .. 1·40 1·40
a. Error. Optd on unissued Uganda 20s. as No. 343 .. .. .. .. 60·00
572/4 .. .. .. .. *Set of* 3 1·75 1·75
**MS**575 95 × 85 mm. $5 Glass Coach .. .. 2·00 2·50

Nos. 572/4 also exist perforated 12 (*Price for set of* 3 £1·50 *mint or used*) from additional sheetlets of five stamps and one label. These stamps have changed background colours. One sheetlet of the 25 c. is known with the overprints inverted.

**89** "Integration and Travel"

(Litho Format)

**1981** (14 Sept). *International Year for Disabled Persons. T* **89** *and similar horiz designs. P* 14.
576 50 c. multicoloured .. .. .. .. 65 25
577 90 c. black, red-orange and blue-green .. 85 40
578 $1 black, light blue and bright green .. 95 45
579 $4 black, yellow-ochre and orange-brown .. 2·50 1·75
576/9 .. .. .. .. *Set of* 4 4·50 2·50
Designs:—90 c. Braille and sign language; $1 "Helping hands"; $4 "Mobility aids for disabled".

BARBUDA (90)

**1981** (12 Oct). *Royal Wedding (3rd issue). Booklet stamps. Nos.* 706/12 *of Antigua optd with T* **90** *in silver*.
580 25 c. Prince of Wales at Investiture, 1969 .. 25 25
a. Booklet pane. Nos. 580/5 .. .. 2·75
581 25 c. Prince Charles as baby, 1948 .. .. 25 25
582 $1 Prince Charles at R.A.F. College, Cranwell, 1971 .. .. .. .. 45 45
583 $1 Prince Charles attending Hill House School, 1956 .. .. .. .. 45 45

584 $2 Prince Charles and Lady Diana Spencer 80 80
585 $2 Prince Charles at Trinity College, 1967 80 80
586 $5 Prince Charles and Lady Diana 2·25 3·00
a. Booklet pane of 1 2·25
580/6 *Set of* 7 4·75 5·50

1981 (1 Nov). *Independence. Nos. 686B/96B of Antigua additionally optd with T* **86**.
587 6 c. Orchid Tree 50 15
588 10 c. Bougainvillea 55 15
589 20 c. Flamboyant 70 20
590 25 c. Hibiscus 80 25
591 35 c. Flame of the Wood 90 30
592 50 c. Cannon at Fort James 1·10 45
593 75 c. Premier's Office 1·25 60
594 $1 Potworks Dam 1·50 65
595 $2.50, Irrigation scheme, Diamond Estate 3·50 2·00
596 $5 Government House 4·25 2·75
597 $10 Coolidge International Airport 6·00 4·75
587/97 *Set of* 11 19·00 11·00

**BARBUDA** (91) BARBUDA (92)

1981 (14 Dec). *50th Anniv of Antigua Girl Guide Movement. Nos. 713/17 of Antigua optd with T* **83** *(No.* **MS**602) *or T* **91** *(others).*
598 10 c. Irene Joshua (founder) 45 10
599 50 c. Campfire sing-song 1·00 30
600 90 c. Sailing 1·40 45
601 $2.50, Animal tending 2·75 1·40
598/601 *Set of* 4 5·00 2·00
MS602 110 × 85 mm. $5 Raising the flag 3·25 3·50

1981 (14 Dec). *International Year for Disabled Persons. Sport for the Disabled. Nos. 728/32 of Antigua optd with T* **83** *(No.* **MS**607) *or T* **91** *(others).*
603 10 c. Swimming 30 15
604 50 c. Discus throwing 65 35
605 90 c. Archery 85 60
606 $2 Baseball 1·75 1·60
603/6 *Set of* 4 3·25 2·40
MS607 108 × 84 mm. $4 Basketball 2·75 2·75

1981 (22 Dec). *Christmas. Paintings. Nos. 723/7 of Antigua optd with T* **92**.
608 8 c. "Holy Night" (Jacques Stella) 10 10
609 30 c. "Mary with Child" (Julius Schnorr von Carolfeld) 20 20
610 $1 "Virgin and Child" (Alonso Cano) (S.) 40 40
611 $3 "Virgin and Child" (Lorenzo di Credi) 1·10 1·10
608/11 *Set of* 4 1·60 1·60
MS612 77 × 111 mm. $5 "Holy Family" (Pieter von Avon) 1·75 2·25

*Celebrating the Royal Birth* BARBUDA $1

93 Princess of Wales

*S. Atlantic Fund + 5oc.* (94)

(Des G. Drummond. Litho Format)

1982 (21 June). *Birth of Prince William of Wales (1st issue). T* **93** *and similar vert portraits. W w* **15**. *P* 14.
613 $1 multicoloured 50 50
614 $2.50, multicoloured 1·10 1·10
a. Reddish violet (top inscr) omitted £180
615 $5 multicoloured 2·25 2·25
613/15 *Set of* 3 3·50 3·50
MS616 88 × 108 mm. $4 multicoloured. No wmk 2·00 2·10

Nos. 613/15 were issued in sheets of 10 stamps with 2 undenominated black prints, in positions 9 and 13, and 9 blank labels. These sheets exist in two different formats, with all stamps upright or with 6 stamps and one black print inverted.

1982 (28 June). *South Atlantic Fund. Booklet stamps. Nos. 580/6 surch as T* **94**.
617 25 c. +50 c. Prince of Wales at Investiture, 1969 20 20
a. Booklet pane. Nos. 617/22 2·50
b. Surch double 20·00
618 25 c. +50 c. Prince Charles as baby, 1948 20 20
b. Surch double 20·00
619 $1 +50 c. Prince Charles at R.A.F. College, Cranwell, 1971 45 45
b. Surch double 20·00
620 $1 +50 c. Prince Charles attending Hill House School, 1956 45 45
b. Surch double 20·00
621 $2 +50 c. Prince Charles and Lady Diana Spencer 75 75
b. Surch double 20·00
622 $2 +50 c. Prince Charles at Trinity College, 1967 75 75
b. Surch double 20·00
623 $5 +50 c. Prince Charles and Lady Diana 2·00 2·00
a. Booklet pane of 1 2·00
b. Surch double £150
617/23 *Set of* 7 4·00 4·00

(Des G. Drummond. Litho Format)

1982 (1 July). *21st Birthday of Princess of Wales (1st issue). As Nos. 613/16 but inscribed* "Twenty First Birthday Greetings to H.R.H. The Princess of Wales". *W w* **15**. *P* 14.
624 $1 multicoloured 45 45
625 $2.50, multicoloured 1·25 1·25
626 $5 multicoloured 2·40 2·40
624/6 *Set of* 3 3·75 3·75
MS627 88 × 108 mm. $4 multicoloured. No wmk 2·25 2·25

See note beneath Nos. 613/16.

BARBUDA MAIL (95) BARBUDA MAIL (96)

1982 (30 Aug). *21st Birthday of Princess of Wales (2nd issue). Nos. 748/51 of Antigua optd as T* **95**, *in silver (No. 629) or black (others).*
628 90 c. Queen's House, Greenwich 45 45
629 $1 Prince and Princess of Wales 50 50
630 $4 Princess of Wales 1·50 1·50
628/30 *Set of* 3 2·25 2·25
MS631 102 × 75 mm. $5 Princess of Wales (*different*) 2·25 2·50

The overprint on No. **MS**631 measures 18 × 6 mm.

Nos. 628/30 also exist from additional sheetlets of 5 stamps and 1 label overprinted with a larger overprint, 18 × 6 mm long (*price for set of 3 £3 mint or used*). On the $1 and $4 values the second line of overprint aligns to left.

1982 (12 Oct). *Birth of Prince William of Wales (2nd issue). Nos. 757/60 of Antigua further optd with T* **95**, *in silver ($1, $4) or black (others).*
632 90 c. Queen's House, Greenwich 45 45
633 $1 Prince and Princess of Wales 50 50
634 $4 Princess of Wales 2·00 2·00
632/4 *Set of* 3 2·75 2·75
MS635 102 × 75 mm. $5 Princess of Wales (*different*) 2·40 2·50

The overprint on No. **MS**635 measures 18 × 6 mm.

1982 (6 Dec). *Birth Centenary of Franklin D. Roosevelt (Nos. 636, 638, 640/2) and 250th Birth Anniv of George Washington (others). Nos. 761/8 of Antigua optd as T* **95** *(second line ranged left on No.* **MS**642).
636 10 c. Roosevelt in 1940 15 10
637 25 c. Washington as blacksmith 20 15
638 45 c. Churchill, Roosevelt and Stalin at Yalta conference 35 25
639 60 c. Washington crossing the Delaware 45 35
640 $1 "Roosevelt Special" train 65 55
641 $3 Portrait of Roosevelt 1·75 1·75
636/41 *Set of* 6 3·00 2·75
MS642 92 × 87 mm. $4 Roosevelt and wife 2·00 2·75
MS643 92 × 87 mm. $4 Portrait of Washington 2·00 2·75

1982 (6 Dec). *Christmas. Religious Paintings by Raphael. Nos. 769/73 of Antigua optd with T* **96**.
644 10 c. "Annunciation" 10 10
645 30 c. "Adoration of the Magi" 15 15
646 $1 "Presentation at the Temple" 40 40
647 $4 "Coronation of the Virgin" 1·75 1·75
644/7 *Set of* 4 2·25 2·25
MS648 95 × 124 mm. $5 "Marriage of the Virgin" 2·00 2·75

1983 (14 Mar). *500th Birth Anniv of Raphael. Details from "Galatea" Fresco. Nos. 774/8 of Antigua optd as T* **95** *(45, 50 c. and larger (18 × 6 mm) on* **MS**653) *or T* **96** *(others).*
649 45 c. Tritons and Dolphins 20 20
650 50 c. Sea Nymph carried off by Triton 25 25
651 60 c. Winged angel steering Dolphins (*horiz*) 30 30
652 $4 Cupids shooting arrows (*horiz*) 1·60 1·60
649/52 *Set of* 4 2·10 2·10
MS653 101 × 126 mm. $5 Galatea pulled along by Dolphins 2·25 2·75

1983 (14 Mar). *Commonwealth Day. Nos. 779/82 of Antigua optd as T* **96**.
654 25 c. Pineapple produce 40 50
655 45 c. Carnival 60 70
656 60 c. Tourism 85 95
657 $3 Airport 2·25 3·00
654/7 *Set of* 4 3·75 4·50

1983 (12 Apr). *World Communications Year. Nos. 783/7 of Antigua optd as T* **96** *(Nos. 658/61) or as T* **95** *with second line ranged left (No.* **MS**662).
658 15 c. T.V. satellite coverage of Royal Wedding 40 20
659 50 c. Police communications 1·25 55
660 60 c. House-to-train telephone call 1·25 65
661 $3 Satellite earth station with planets Jupiter and Saturn 2·75 1·75
658/61 *Set of* 4 5·00 2·75
MS662 100 × 90 mm. $5 "Comsat" satellite over West Indies 2·75 3·00

200th Anniversary of Man's First Flight 21 November 1983 Barbuda $1

97 Vincenzo Lunardi's Balloon Flight, London, 1785

= 45c (98)

(Des G. Drummond. Litho)

1983 (13 June). *Bicentenary of Manned Flight (1st issue). T* **97** *and similar vert designs. Multicoloured. P* 14.
663 $1 Type **97** 50 50
664 $1.50, Montgolfier brothers' balloon flight, Paris, 1783 75 75
665 $2.50, Blanchard and Jeffries' Cross-Channel balloon flight, 1785 1·25 1·25
663/5 *Set of* 3 2·25 2·25
MS666 111 × 111 mm. $5 Maiden flight of *Graf Zeppelin*, 1928 2·50 2·75

1983 (4 July). *Whales. Nos. 788/92 of Antigua optd as T* **95** *(Nos. 667/70) or larger, 17 × 5½ mm (No.* **MS**671), *each with the second line ranged left.*
667 15 c. Bottle-nosed Dolphin 65 30
668 50 c. Fin Whale 1·75 90
669 60 c. Bowhead Whale 2·00 1·00
670 $3 Spectacled Porpoise 4·25 2·75
667/70 *Set of* 4 7·75 4·50
MS671 122 × 101 mm. $5 Narwhal 3·75 4·50

1983 (12 Sept). *Bicentenary of Manned Flight (2nd issue). Nos. 811/15 of Antigua optd as T* **96**.
672 30 c. Dornier "Do X" flying boat 50 25
673 50 c. Supermarine "S.6B" seaplane 60 35
674 60 c. Curtiss "9C" biplane and airship U.S.S. *Akron* 75 40
675 $4 *Pro Juventute* balloon 3·50 3·25
672/5 *Set of* 4 4·75 4·00
MS676 80 × 105 mm. $5 *Graf Zeppelin* 3·50 4·25

1983 (21 Oct). *Nos. 565/70 surch as T* **98**. A. *P* 11 × 11½. B. *P* 14½.

| | | A | | B | |
|---|---|---|---|---|---|
| 677 | 45 c. on $1 Type **87** | 55 | 55 | 2·25 | 2·25 |
| | a. Sheetlet. Nos. 677/82 | 3·00 | | 12·00 | |
| | b. Error. 50 c. on $1 | † | | 4·50 | — |
| | c. Surch omitted | † | | 35·00 | — |
| 678 | 45 c. on $1 Type **88** | 55 | 55 | 2·25 | 2·25 |
| | b. Error. 50 c. on $1 | † | | 4·50 | — |
| | c. Surch omitted | † | | 35·00 | — |
| 679 | 50 c. on $1.50, Caernarvon Castle (*left*) | 60 | 60 | 2·25 | 2·25 |
| | b. Error. 45 c. on $1.50 | † | | 4·50 | — |
| | c. Surch omitted | † | | 35·00 | — |
| 680 | 50 c. on $1.50, Caernarvon Castle (*right*) | 60 | 60 | 2·25 | 2·25 |
| | b. Error. 45 c. on $1.50 | † | | 4·50 | — |
| | c. Surch omitted | † | | 35·00 | — |
| 681 | 60 c. on $4 Highgrove House (*left*) | 70 | 70 | 2·25 | 2·25 |
| | c. Surch omitted | † | | 35·00 | — |
| 682 | 60 c. on $4 Highgrove House (*right*) | 70 | 70 | 2·25 | 2·25 |
| | c. Surch omitted | † | | 35·00 | — |
| 677/82 | *Set of* 6 | 3·25 | 3·25 | 12·00 | 12·00 |

Nos. 677b, 678b, 679b and 680b occur on the 14½ perforated sheetlets with rose-pink background.

Examples of No. 677a, and also of the errors, imperforate exist from stock dispersed by the liquidator of Format International Security Printers Ltd.

1983 (28 Oct). *Nos. 793A/810A of Antigua optd with T* **96**.
683 1 c. Cashew Nut 10 10
684 2 c. Passion Fruit 10 10
685 3 c. Mango 10 10
686 5 c. Grapefruit 10 10
687 10 c. Pawpaw 10 10
688 15 c. Breadfruit 15 10
689 20 c. Coconut 20 15
690 25 c. Oleander 20 15
691 30 c. Banana 25 20
692 40 c. Pineapple 30 25
693 45 c. Cordia 35 30
694 50 c. Cassia 40 30
695 60 c. Poui 40 30
696 $1 Frangipani 60 50
697 $2 Flamboyant 1·25 1·25
698 $2.50, Lemon 1·75 1·75
699 $5 Lignum Vitae 2·75 2·75
700 $10 National flag and coat of arms 5·00 5·50
683/700 *Set of* 18 12·50 12·00

BARBUDA MAIL (99)

EDWARD VII 1901 – 1910 $1

100 Edward VII

1983 (28 Oct). *Christmas. 500th Birth Anniv of Raphael. Nos. 816/20 of Antigua optd with T* **99** *or slightly smaller (29 × 4 mm) (*MS*705).*
701 10 c. multicoloured 10 10
702 30 c. multicoloured 15 20
703 $1 multicoloured 45 50
704 $4 multicoloured 1·50 1·75
701/4 *Set of* 4 1·90 2·25
MS705 101 × 131 mm. $5 multicoloured 2·25 2·75

1983 (14 Dec). *Bicentenary of Methodist Church (1984). Nos. 821/4 of Antigua optd with T* **94** *(in silver on 15 c. and 50 c.).*
706 15 c. John Wesley (founder) 20 15
707 50 c. Nathaniel Gilbert (founder in Antigua) 40 30
708 60 c. St. John Methodist Church steeple 45 35
709 $3 Ebenezer Methodist Church, St. John's 1·75 1·75
706/9 *Set of* 4 2·50 2·25

(Des G. Drummond. Litho Format)

1984 (14 Feb). *Members of British Royal Family. T* **100** *and similar vert portraits. Multicoloured. P* 14½.
710 $1 Type **100** 1·25 1·25
711 $1 George V 1·25 1·25
712 $1 George VI 1·25 1·25
713 $1 Elizabeth II 1·25 1·25
714 $1 Charles, Prince of Wales 1·25 1·25
715 $1 Prince William of Wales 1·25 1·25
710/15 *Set of* 6 6·75 6·75

1984 (26 Apr). *Olympic Games, Los Angeles (1st issue). Nos. 825/9 of Antigua optd as T* **99** *(23 × 3 mm in size on Nos. 716/19).*
716 25 c. Discus 15 20
717 50 c. Gymnastics 35 40
718 90 c. Hurdling 50 60
719 $3 Cycling 1·25 1·50
716/19 *Set of* 4 2·00 2·40
MS720 82 × 67 mm. $5 Volleyball 2·75 3·25

**1984** (12 July). *Ships. Nos.* 830/4 *of Antigua optd with T* **95** (**MS**725) *or T* **99** (*others*).
721 45 c. *Booker Vanguard* (freighter) .. .. .. 1·25 45
722 50 c. S.S. *Canberra* (liner) .. .. .. 1·25 50
723 60 c. Sailing boats .. .. .. .. 1·50 60
724 $4 *Fairwind* (liner).. .. .. .. 3·75 2·75
721/4 .. .. .. .. .. *Set of* 4 7·00 3·75
**MS**725 107 × 80 mm. $5 Eighteenth-century British man-of-war (*vert*).. .. .. .. 4·25 4·50

**1984** (12 July). *Universal Postal Union Congress, Hamburg. Nos.* 835/9 *of Antigua optd with T* **95**.
726 15 c. Chenille .. .. .. .. .. 30 15
727 50 c. Shell Flower .. .. .. .. 65 50
728 60 c. Anthurium .. .. .. .. 80 60
729 $3 Angels Trumpet .. .. .. .. 2·00 2·00
726/9 .. .. .. .. .. *Set of* 4 3·25 3·00
**MS**730 100 × 75 mm. $5 Crown of Thorns .. 3·25 3·50

BARBUDA MAIL

101 Olympic Stadium, Athens, 1896 (102)

(Litho Format)

**1984** (27 July). *Olympic Games, Los Angeles (2nd issue). T* **101** *and similar horiz designs. Multicoloured. P* 13½.
731 $1.50, Type **101** .. .. .. .. 1·00 1·10
732 $2.50, Olympic stadium, Los Angeles, 1984 1·50 1·75
733 $5 Athlete carrying Olympic torch .. .. 2·50 2·75
731/3 .. .. .. .. .. *Set of* 3 4·50 5·00
**MS**734 121 × 95 mm. No. 733. P 15 .. .. 2·75 3·50

**1984** (1 Oct). *Presidents of the United States of America. Nos.* 856/63 *of Antigua optd with T* **95** (*in silver on* 10, 90 *c.*, $1.10 *and* $1.50).
735 10 c. Abraham Lincoln .. .. .. 10 10
736 20 c. Harry Truman .. .. .. .. 15 15
737 30 c. Dwight Eisenhower .. .. .. 20 25
738 40 c. Ronald Reagan .. .. .. .. 25 30
739 90 c. Gettysburg Address, 1863 .. .. 50 55
740 $1.10, Formation of N.A.T.O., 1949.. .. 60 65
741 $1.50, Eisenhower during Second World War 80 85
742 $2 Reagan and Caribbean Basin Initiative 1·00 1·25
735/42 .. .. .. .. .. *Set of* 8 3·25 3·75

**1984** (1 Oct). *150th Anniv of Abolition of Slavery. Nos.* 864/8 *of Antigua optd with T* **96** (*Nos.* 743/6) *or as T* **95**, *but* 18 × 6½ *mm* (*No.* **MS**747).
743 40 c. View of Moravian Mission .. .. 30 30
744 50 c. Antigua Courthouse, 1823 .. .. 40 40
745 60 c. Planting sugar-cane, Monks Hill .. 45 45
746 $3 Boiling house, Delaps' Estate .. 1·90 1·90
743/6 .. .. .. .. .. *Set of* 4 2·75 2·75
**MS**747 95 × 70 mm. $5 Loading sugar, Willoughby Bay .. .. .. .. .. .. 3·50 4·00

**1984** (21 Nov). *Songbirds. Nos.* 869/74 *of Antigua optd with T* **95** *or larger* (18 × 7 *mm*) (*No.* **MS**753).
748 40 c. Rufous-sided Towhee .. .. .. 45 45
749 50 c. Parula Warbler .. .. .. .. 50 50
750 60 c. House Wren .. .. .. .. 55 55
751 $2 Ruby-crowned Kinglet .. .. .. 1·50 1·50
752 $3 Common Flicker .. .. .. .. 2·25 2·25
748/52 .. .. .. .. .. *Set of* 5 4·75 4·75
**MS**753 76 × 76 mm. $5 Yellow-breasted Chat .. 4·00 4·50

**1984** (21 Nov). *450th Death Anniv of Correggio (painter). Nos.* 878/82 *of Antigua optd with T* **95** *or larger* (18 × 7 *mm*) *No.* **MS**758), *all in silver.*
754 25 c. "The Virgin and Infant with Angels and Cherubs" .. .. .. .. .. .. 15 20
755 60 c. "The Four Saints" .. .. .. .. 40 45
756 90 c. "St. Catherine" .. .. .. .. 60 65
757 $3 "The Campori Madonna" .. .. 1·75 2·25
754/7 .. .. .. .. .. *Set of* 4 2·50 3·25
**MS**758 90 × 60 mm. $5 "St. John the Baptist" .. 2·75 3·75

**1984** (30 Nov). *"Ausipex" International Stamp Exhibition, Melbourne. Australian Sports. Nos.* 875/7 *of Antigua optd with T* **95** *or larger* (18 × 7 *mm*) (*No.* **MS**761).
759 $1 Grass-skiing .. .. .. .. .. 70 75
760 $5 Australian Football .. .. .. .. 3·00 3·75
**MS**761 108 × 78 mm. $5 Boomerang-throwing 3·00 3·75

**1984** (30 Nov). *150th Birth Anniv of Edgar Degas (painter). Nos.* 883/7 *of Antigua optd with T* **95** (*Nos.* 762/5) *or T* **99** (*No.* **MS**766), *all in silver.*
762 15 c. "The Blue Dancers" .. .. .. .. 10 10
763 50 c. "The Pink Dancers" .. .. .. .. 30 40
764 70 c. "Two Dancers" .. .. .. .. 45 55
765 $4 "Dancers at the Bar" .. .. .. 2·40 3·25
762/5 .. .. .. .. .. *Set of* 4 3·00 3·75
**MS**766 90 × 60 mm. $5 "The Folk Dancers" (40 × 27 *mm*) .. .. .. .. .. .. 2·75 3·25

**1985** (18 Feb). *Famous People. Nos.* 888/96 *of Antigua optd with T* **102** (*horizontally on Nos.* 771/5).
767 60 c. Winston Churchill .. .. .. .. 1·25 80
768 60 c. Mahatma Gandhi .. .. .. .. 1·25 80
769 60 c. John F. Kennedy .. .. .. .. 1·25 80
770 60 c. Mao Tse-tung .. .. .. .. 1·25 80
771 $1 Churchill with General De Gaulle, Paris, 1944 (*horiz*) .. .. .. .. 1·75 1·00
772 $1 Gandhi leaving London by train, 1931 (*horiz*) .. .. .. .. .. .. 1·75 1·00
773 $1 Kennedy with Chancellor Adenauer and Mayor Brandt, Berlin, 1963 (*horiz*) 1·75 1·00
774 $1 Mao Tse-tung with Lin Piao, Peking, 1969 (*horiz*) .. .. .. .. .. 1·75 1·00
767/74 .. .. .. .. .. *Set of* 8 11·00 6·50
**MS**775 114 × 80 mm. $5 Flags of Great Britain, India, the United States and China .. .. 3·50 3·75

103 Lady Elizabeth Bowes-Lyon, 1907, and Camellias — 104 Roseate Tern

(Des G. Drummond. Litho Format)

**1985** (26 Feb). *Life and Times of Queen Elizabeth the Queen Mother (1st issue). T* **103** *and similar vert designs. Multicoloured. P* 14 × 14½.
776 15 c. Type **103**.. .. .. .. .. 10 10
777 45 c. Duchess of York, 1926, and "Elizabeth of Glamis" roses .. .. .. .. 25 30
778 50 c. The Queen Mother after the Coronation, 1937 .. .. .. .. .. 25 30
779 60 c. In Garter robes, 1971, and Dog Roses .. 35 40
780 90 c. Attending Royal Variety show, 1967, and red Hibiscus .. .. .. .. 50 55
781 $2 The Queen Mother in 1982, and blue Plumbago .. .. .. .. .. 1·10 1·25
782 $3 Receiving 82nd birthday gifts from children, and Morning Glory .. .. 1·60 1·75
776/82 .. .. .. .. .. *Set of* 7 3·75 4·00
See also Nos. 826/9.

(Des G. Drummond. Litho Format)

**1985** (4 Apr). *Birth Bicentenary of John J. Audubon (ornithologist) (1st issue). T* **104** *and similar vert designs showing original paintings. Multicoloured. P* 14.
783 45 c. Type **104**.. .. .. .. .. 35 30
784 50 c. Mangrove Cuckoo .. .. .. .. 35 30
785 60 c. Yellow-crowned Night Heron .. .. 45 40
786 $5 Brown Pelican .. .. .. .. 3·00 3·25
783/6 .. .. .. .. .. *Set of* 4 3·75 3·75
See also Nos. 794/8 and 914/17.

**1985** (10 May). *Centenary of the Statue of Liberty* (1986). *Nos.* 907/13 *of Antigua optd horizontally with T* **102**.
787 25 c. Torch from Statue in Madison Square Park, 1885 .. .. .. .. .. 15 20
788 30 c. Statue of Liberty and scaffolding ("Restoration and Renewal") (*vert*) .. .. 15 20
789 50 c. Frederic Bartholdi (sculptor) supervising construction, 1876 .. .. 25 30
790 90 c. Close-up of Statue .. .. .. 50 55
791 $1 Statue and sailing ship ("Operation Sail", 1976) (*vert*) .. .. .. 55 60
792 $3 Dedication ceremony, 1886 (*vert*) .. 1·60 1·75
787/92 .. .. .. .. .. *Set of* 6 2·75 3·00
**MS**793 110 × 80 mm. $5 Port of New York .. 2·75 3·00

BARBUDA MAIL (105) — BARBUDA MAIL (106) — 4TH AUG 1900–1985 (107)

**1985** (18 July). *Birth Bicentenary of John J. Audubon (ornithologist) (2nd issue). Nos.* 924/8 *of Antigua optd with T* **105**.
794 90 c. Slavonian Grebe .. .. .. .. 1·50 1·25
795 $1 British Storm Petrel .. .. .. 1·75 1·40
796 $1.50, Great Blue Heron .. .. .. 2·25 1·75
797 $3 Double-crested Cormorant .. .. 3·25 2·75
794/7 .. .. .. .. .. *Set of* 4 8·00 6·50
**MS**798 103 × 72 mm. $5 White-tailed Tropic Bird (*vert*) .. .. .. .. .. .. 6·50 4·75

**1985** (18 July). *Butterflies. Nos.* 929/33 *of Antigua optd with T* **106**.
799 25 c. *Anaea cyanea*.. .. .. .. 1·25 80
800 60 c. *Leodonta dysoni* .. .. .. 2·00 1·25
801 90 c. *Junea doraete* .. .. .. .. 2·25 1·50
802 $4 *Prepona pylene* .. .. .. .. 5·00 4·25
799/802 .. .. .. .. .. *Set of* 4 9·50 7·00
**MS**803 132 × 105 mm. $5 *Caerois gerdrudtus* .. 6·50 6·50

**1985** (2 Aug). *Centenary of the Motorcycle. Nos.* 919/23 *of Antigua optd with T* **106**.
804 10 c. Triumph 2hp "Jap", 1903 .. .. 30 10
805 30 c. Indian "Arrow", 1949 .. .. .. 50 20
806 60 c. BMW "R100RS", 1976 .. .. .. 75 40
807 $4 Harley-Davidson "Model II", 1916 .. 3·00 2·75
804/7 .. .. .. .. .. *Set of* 4 4·00 3·00
**MS**808 90 × 93 mm. $5 Laverda "Jota", 1975 .. 3·50 4·00

**1985** (2 Aug). *85th Birthday of Queen Elizabeth the Queen Mother. Nos.* 776/82 *optd with T* **107**.
809 15 c. Type **103**.. .. .. .. .. 30 10
a. Red (frame, flowers, etc) omitted .. 32·00
810 45 c. Duchess of York, 1926, and "Elizabeth of Glamis" roses .. .. .. .. 60 30
811 50 c. The Queen Mother after the Coronation, 1937 .. .. .. .. .. 60 30
812 60 c. In Garter robes, 1971, and Dog Roses .. 70 40
813 90 c. Attending Royal Variety show, 1967, and red Hibiscus .. .. .. .. 85 55
814 $2 The Queen Mother in 1982, and blue Plumbago .. .. .. .. .. 1·60 1·25
815 $3 Receiving 82nd birthday gifts from children, and Morning Glory .. .. 2·25 1·75
809/15 .. .. .. .. .. *Set of* 7 6·25 4·00
The 45 c. exists with the yellow omitted from stock dispersed by the liquidator of Format International Security Printers Ltd.

**1985** (30 Aug). *Native American Artefacts. Nos.* 914/18 *of Antigua optd horizontally with T* **102**.
816 15 c. Arawak pot sherd and Indians making clay utensils .. .. .. .. 15 10
817 50 c. Arawak body design and Arawak Indians tattooing .. .. .. .. 30 30
818 60 c. Head of the god "Yocahu" and Indians harvesting manioc .. .. .. .. 40 40
819 $3 Carib war club and Carib Indians going into battle .. .. .. .. .. 1·60 1·75
816/19 .. .. .. .. .. *Set of* 4 2·25 2·25
**MS**820 97 × 68 mm. $5 Taino Indians worshipping stone idol .. .. .. .. .. 3·00 3·50

**1985** (30 Aug). *40th Anniv of International Civil Aviation Organization. Nos.* 934/8 *of Antigua optd with T* **106**.
821 30 c. Cessna "172" .. .. .. .. 20 20
822 90 c. Fokker "DVII" .. .. .. .. 55 55
823 $1.50, Spad "VII" .. .. .. .. 85 85
824 $3 Boeing "747" .. .. .. .. 1·75 1·75
821/4 .. .. .. .. .. *Set of* 4 3·00 3·00
**MS**825 97 × 83 mm. $5 Twin "Otter" .. .. 3·00 3·50

**1985** (8 Nov). *Life and Times of Queen Elizabeth the Queen Mother (2nd issue). Nos.* 946/9 *of Antigua optd with T* **95** (*in silver on Nos.* 826/7 *and* **MS**829).
826 $1 The Queen Mother attending church .. 1·50 1·50
827 $1.50, Watching children playing in London garden .. .. .. .. .. 1·75 1·75
828 $2.50, The Queen Mother in 1979 .. .. 2·25 2·25
826/8 .. .. .. .. .. *Set of* 3 5·00 5·00
**MS**829 56 × 85 mm. $5 With Prince Edward at Royal Wedding, 1981 .. .. .. .. 4·00 4·50
Nos. 826/7 also exist with black and No. 828 with silver overprints (*Price for set of* 3 £50 *mint*).
The stamps from the sheetlets mentioned beneath Antigua No. **MS**949 also exist overprinted with Type **95**.

**1985** (25 Nov). *850th Birth Anniv of Maimonides (physician, philosopher and scholar). Nos.* 939/40 *of Antigua optd with T* **95**.
830 $2 bright green .. .. .. .. .. 2·25 2·25
**MS**831 70 × 84 mm. $5 reddish brown .. .. 3·50 4·00

**1985** (25 Nov). *Marine Life. Nos.* 950/4 *of Antigua optd with T* **95** (*in silver on* 15 *c. and* $3).
832 15 c. Magnificent Frigate Bird .. .. 70 40
833 45 c. Brain Coral .. .. .. .. 1·00 70
834 60 c. Cushion Star .. .. .. .. 1·25 85
835 $3 Spotted Moray Eel .. .. .. 3·75 3·25
832/5 .. .. .. .. .. *Set of* 4 6·00 4·75
**MS**836 110 × 80 mm. $5 Elkhorn Coral .. .. 4·00 4·50

**1986** (17 Feb). *International Youth Year. Nos.* 941/5 *of Antigua optd with T* **95**.
837 25 c. Young farmers with produce .. .. 15 1[illegible]
838 50 c. Hotel management trainees .. .. 25 3[illegible]
839 60 c. Girls with goat and boys with football ("Environment") .. .. .. .. 30 3[illegible]
840 $3 Windsurfing ("Leisure") .. .. 1·50 1·6[illegible]
837/40 .. .. .. .. .. *Set of* 4 2·00 2·1[illegible]
**MS**841 102 × 72 mm. $5 Young people with Antiguan flags .. .. .. .. .. .. 2·75 3·2[illegible]

**1986** (17 Feb). *Royal Visit. Nos.* 965/8 *of Antigua optd wi[th] T* **106**.
842 60 c. Flags of Great Britain and Antigua .. 30 3[illegible]
843 $1 Queen Elizabeth II (*vert*) .. .. 50 5[illegible]
844 $4 Royal Yacht *Britannia* .. .. .. 2·00 2·1[illegible]
842/4 .. .. .. .. .. *Set of* 3 2·50 2·7[illegible]
**MS**845 110 × 83 mm. $5 Map of Antigua .. 2·50 3·0[illegible]

**1986** (10 Mar). *75th Anniv of Girl Guide Movement. Nos.* 955/[9] *of Antigua optd with T* **95**.
846 15 c. Girl Guides nursing .. .. .. 55 4[illegible]
847 45 c. Open-air Girl Guide meeting .. .. 1·25 1·2[illegible]
848 60 c. Lord and Lady Baden-Powell .. .. 1·50 1·5[illegible]
849 $3 Girl Guides gathering flowers.. .. 3·75 3·7[illegible]
846/9 .. .. .. .. .. *Set of* 4 6·50 6·5[illegible]
**MS**850 67 × 96 mm. $5 Barn Swallow (Nature study) .. .. .. .. .. .. 7·50 7·5[illegible]

**1986** (10 Mar). *300th Birth Anniv of Johann Sebastian Bac[h] (composer). Nos.* 960/4 *of Antigua optd with T* **95**.
851 25 c. multicoloured .. .. .. .. 75 6[illegible]
852 50 c. multicoloured .. .. .. .. 1·25 1·1[illegible]
853 $1 multicoloured .. .. .. .. 1·75 1·7[illegible]
854 $3 multiciloured .. .. .. .. 3·75 3·7[illegible]
851/4 .. .. .. .. .. *Set of* 4 6·75 6·7[illegible]
**MS**855 104 × 73 mm. $5 black and brownish grey 7·50 7·5[illegible]

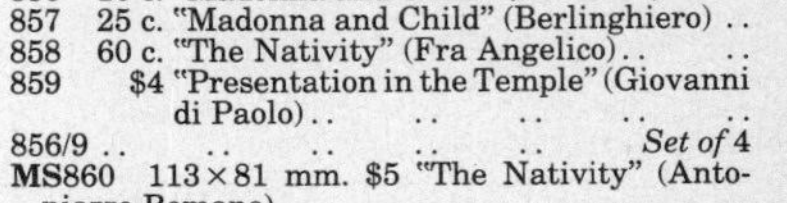

**1986** (4 Apr). *Christmas. Religious Paintings. Nos.* 985/9 *o[f] Antigua optd with T* **106**.
856 10 c. "Madonna and Child" (De Landi) .. 30 2[illegible]
857 25 c. "Madonna and Child" (Berlinghiero) .. 55 4[illegible]
858 60 c. "The Nativity" (Fra Angelico).. .. 1·00 7[illegible]
859 $4 "Presentation in the Temple" (Giovanni di Paolo).. .. .. .. .. .. 3·25 3·7[illegible]
856/9 .. .. .. .. .. *Set of* 4 4·50 4·5[illegible]
**MS**860 113 × 81 mm. $5 "The Nativity" (Antoniazzo Romano) .. .. .. .. .. 4·00 4·7[illegible]

108 Queen Elizabeth II meeting Members of Legislature

(Litho Format)

**1986** (21 Apr). *60th Birthday of Queen Elizabeth II (1st issue). T* **108** *and similar horiz designs. Multicoloured. P* 15.

861 $1 Type **108** .. .. .. .. .. 1·50 1·50
862 $2 Queen with Headmistress of Liberta School .. .. .. .. .. 2·00 2·00
863 $2.50, Queen greeted by Governor-General of Antigua .. .. .. .. .. 2·25 2·25
861/3 .. .. .. .. *Set of* 3 5·25 5·25
**MS**864 95×75 mm. $5 Queen Elizabeth in 1928 and 1986 (33×27 *mm*). *P* 13½×14 .. .. 4·50 4·75

See also Nos. 872/5.

**109** Halley's Comet over Barbuda Beach

(Des and litho Format)

**1986** (10 July). *Appearance of Halley's Comet (1st issue). T* **109** *and similar multicoloured designs. P* 15.

865 $1 Type **109** .. .. .. .. .. 1·75 1·75
866 $2.50, Early telescope and dish aerial (*vert*).. 3·00 3·00
867 $5 Comet and World map .. .. .. 4·75 4·75
865/7 .. .. .. .. *Set of* 3 8·50 8·50

See also Nos. 886/90.

**1986** (12 Aug). *40th Anniv of United Nations Organization. Nos.* 981/4 *of Antigua optd with T* **96** *(Nos.* 868/70) *or T* **95** *(No.* **MS**871).

868 40 c. Benjamin Franklin and U.N. (New York) 1953 U.P.U. 5 c. stamp .. .. 85 85
869 $1 George Washington Carver (agricultural chemist) and 1982 Nature Conservation 28 c. stamp .. .. .. 1·50 1·50
870 $3 Charles Lindbergh (aviator) and 1978 I.C.A.O. 25 c. stamp .. .. .. 2·75 2·75
868/70 .. .. .. .. *Set of* 3 4·50 4·50
**MS**871 101×77 mm. $5 Marc Chagall (artist) (*vert*) .. .. .. .. .. 6·00 6·00

**1986** (12 Aug). *60th Birthday of Queen Elizabeth II (2nd issue). Nos.* 1005/8 *of Antigua optd with T* **95** *in black (No.* **MS**875) *or silver (others)*

872 60 c. black and yellow .. .. .. .. 90 90
873 $1 multicoloured .. .. .. .. 1·50 1·50
874 $4 multicoloured .. .. .. .. 3·25 3·25
872/4 .. .. .. .. *Set of* 3 5·00 5·00
**MS**875 120×85 mm. $5 black and grey-brown .. 4·50 5·00

**1986** (28 Aug). *World Cup Football Championship, Mexico. Nos.* 995/9 *of Antigua optd with T* **96** (30 c., $4) *or T* **95** *(others).*

876 30 c. Football, boots and trophy .. .. 85 85
877 60 c. Goalkeeper (*vert*) .. .. .. 1·40 1·40
878 $1 Referee blowing whistle (*vert*) .. .. 1·90 1·90
879 $4 Ball in net .. .. .. .. 4·25 4·25
876/9 .. .. .. .. *Set of* 4 7·50 7·50
**MS**880 87×76 mm. $5 Two players competing for ball .. .. .. .. .. 7·00 7·00

**1986** (28 Aug). *"Ameripex '86" International Stamp Exhibition, Chicago. Famous American Trains. Nos.* 1014/18 *of Antigua optd with T* **106**.

881 25 c. "Hiawatha Express" .. .. .. 90 90
882 50 c. "Grand Canyon Express" .. .. 1·40 1·40
883 $1 "Powhattan Arrow Express" .. .. 2·25 2·25
884 $3 "Empire State Express" .. .. 4·50 4·50
881/4 .. .. .. .. *Set of* 4 8·00 8·00
**MS**885 116×87 mm. $5 "Daylight Express" .. 6·00 7·00

**1986** (22 Sept). *Appearance of Halley's Comet (2nd issue). Nos.* 1000/4 *of Antigua optd with T* **96** *(Nos.* 886/9) *or T* **95** (**MS**890).

886 5 c. Edmond Halley and Old Greenwich Observatory .. .. .. .. 35 35
887 10 c. "Me 163B Komet" (fighter aircraft), 1944 .. .. .. .. .. 35 35
888 60 c. Montezuma (Aztec Emperor) and Comet in 1517 (from "Historias de las Indias de Neuva Espana") .. .. 1·25 1·25
889 $4 Pocahontas saving Capt. John Smith and Comet in 1607 .. .. .. 4·00 4·00
886/9 .. .. .. .. *Set of* 4 5·50 5·50
**MS**890 101×70 mm. $5 Halley's Comet over English Harbour, Antigua .. .. .. 3·50 4·25

**1986** (22 Sept). *Royal Wedding. Nos.* 1019/22 *of Antigua optd with T* **95** *in silver.*

891 45 c. Prince Andrew and Miss Sarah Ferguson .. .. .. .. .. 45 45
892 60 c. Prince Andrew .. .. .. .. 55 55
893 $4 Prince Andrew with Prince Philip .. 2·75 2·75
891/3 .. .. .. .. *Set of* 3 3·25 3·25
**MS**894 88×88 mm. $5 Prince Andrew and Miss Sarah Ferguson (*different*) .. .. .. 4·25 4·75

**1986** (10 Nov). *Sea Shells. Nos.* 1023/7 *of Antigua optd with T* **106** *(in silver on* 15 c. *to* $3).

895 15 c. Fly-specked Cerith .. .. .. 80 80
896 45 c. Smooth Scotch Bonnet .. .. .. 1·50 1·50
897 60 c. West Indian Crown Conch .. .. 2·00 2·00
898 $3 Murex Ciboney .. .. .. .. 5·00 5·00
895/8 .. .. .. .. *Set of* 4 8·50 8·50
**MS**899 109×75 mm. $5 Colourful Atlantic Natica (*horiz*) .. .. .. .. .. 9·50 9·50

**1986** (10 Nov). *Flowers. Nos.* 1028/36 *of Antigua optd with T* **106**.

900 10 c. *Nymphaea ampla* (water lily) .. .. 20 20
901 15 c. Queen of the Night .. .. .. 30 30
902 50 c. Cup of Gold .. .. .. .. 50 50
903 60 c. Beach Morning Glory .. .. .. 55 55
904 70 c. Golden Trumpet .. .. .. 70 70
905 $1 Air Plant .. .. .. .. 85 85
906 $3 Purple Wreath .. .. .. .. 2·25 2·25
907 $4 Zephyr Lily .. .. .. .. 2·75 2·75
900/7 .. .. .. .. *Set of* 8 7·50 7·50
**MS**908 Two sheets, each 102×72 mm. (a) $4 Dozakie. (b) $5 Four O'Clock Flower *Set of* 2 *sheets* 11·00 12·00

**1986** (28 Nov). *Mushrooms. Nos.* 1042/6 *of Antigua optd with T* **106**.

909 10 c. *Hygrocybe occidentalis* var. *scarletina* 40 30
910 50 c. *Trogia buccinalis* .. .. .. 1·25 1·00
911 $1 *Collybia subpruinosa* .. .. .. 2·00 1·75
912 $4 *Leucocoprinus brebissonii* .. .. 5·00 4·00
909/12 .. .. .. .. *Set of* 4 7·75 6·50
**MS**913 102×82 mm. $5 *Pyrrhoglossum pyrrhum* 8·00 8·00

**1986** (Dec). *Birth Bicentenary of John J. Audubon (ornithologist) (3rd issue). Nos.* 990/3 *of Antigua optd with T* **96** *(in silver on* 60, 90 c.).

914 60 c. Mallard .. .. .. .. .. 50 50
915 90 c. North American Black Duck .. .. 70 70
916 $1.50, Pintail .. .. .. .. 1·25 1·25
917 $3 American Wigeon .. .. .. 2·00 2·00
914/17 .. .. .. .. *Set of* 4 4·00 4·00

**1987** (12 Jan). *Local Boats. Nos.* 1009/13 *of Antigua optd with T* **95**.

918 30 c. Tugboat .. .. .. .. .. 30 30
919 60 c. Game fishing boat .. .. .. 45 45
920 $1 Yacht .. .. .. .. .. 75 75
921 $4 Lugger with auxiliary sail .. .. 2·50 2·50
918/21 .. .. .. .. *Set of* 4 3·50 3·50
**MS**922 108×78 mm. $5 Boats under construction 6·00 6·50

**1987** (12 Jan). *Centenary of First Benz Motor Car. Nos.* 1052/60 *of Antigua optd with T* **95** *(No.* **MS**931) *or T* **96** *(others).*

923 10 c. Auburn "Speedster" (1933) .. .. 15 15
924 15 c. Mercury "Sable" (1986) .. .. 20 20
925 50 c. Cadillac (1959) .. .. .. .. 45 45
926 60 c. Studebaker (1950) .. .. .. 45 45
927 70 c. Lagonda "V-12" (1939) .. .. .. 50 50
928 $1 Adler "Standard" (1930) .. .. 65 65
929 $3 DKW (1956) .. .. .. .. 1·75 1·75
930 $4 Mercedes "500K" (1936) .. .. 2·25 2·25
923/30 .. .. .. .. *Set of* 8 5·75 5·75
**MS**931 Two sheets, each 99×70 mm. (a) $5 Daimler (1896). (b) $5 Mercedes "Knight" (1921) *Set of* 2 *sheets* 6·00 7·00

**1987** (10 Mar). *World Cup Football Championship Winners, Mexico. Nos.* 1037/40 *of Antigua optd with T* **95** (60 c., $1) *or T* **96** (30 c., $4).

932 30 c. Football, boots and trophy .. .. 30 30
933 60 c. Goalkeeper (*vert*) .. .. .. 45 45
934 $1 Referee blowing whistle (*vert*) .. .. 70 70
935 $4 Ball in net .. .. .. .. 2·00 2·00
932/5 .. .. .. .. *Set of* 4 3·00 3·00

**1987** (23 Apr). *America's Cup Yachting Championship. Nos.* 1072/6 *of Antigua optd horizontally as T* **102**.

936 30 c. *Canada I* (1981) .. .. .. .. 20 20
937 60 c. *Gretel II* (1970) .. .. .. .. 35 35
938 $1 *Sceptre* (1958) .. .. .. .. 60 60
939 $3 *Vigilant* (1893) .. .. .. .. 1·75 1·75
936/9 .. .. .. .. *Set of* 4 2·75 2·75
**MS**940 113×84 mm. $5 *Australia II* defeating *Liberty* (1983) (*horiz*) .. .. .. 2·75 3·50

**1987** (1 July). *Marine Life. Nos.* 1077/85 *of Antigua optd with T* **95** *(No.* **MS**949) *or T* **96** *(others).*

941 15 c. Bridled Burrfish .. .. .. 20 20
942 30 c. Common Noddy .. .. .. .. 35 35
943 40 c. Nassau Grouper .. .. .. .. 35 35
944 50 c. Laughing Gull .. .. .. .. 55 55
945 60 c. French Angelfish .. .. .. 55 55
946 $1 Porkfish .. .. .. .. .. 65 65
947 $2 Royal Tern .. .. .. .. 1·50 1·50
948 $3 Sooty Tern .. .. .. .. 2·00 2·00
941/8 .. .. .. .. *Set of* 8 5·50 5·50
**MS**949 Two sheets, each 120×94 mm. (a) $5 Banded Butterflyfish. (b) $5 Brown Booby *Set of* 2 *sheets* 7·00 8·50

**1987** (28 July). *Milestones of Transportation. Nos.* 1100/9 *of Antigua optd with T* **106**.

950 10 c. *Spirit of Australia* (fastest powerboat), 1978 .. .. .. .. .. 25 25
951 15 c. Siemen's electric locomotive, 1879 .. 45 45
952 30 c. U.S.S. *Triton* (first submerged circumnavigation), 1960 .. .. .. .. 55 55
953 50 c. Trevithick's steam carriage (first passenger-carrying vehicle), 1801 .. .. 70 70
954 60 c. U.S.S. *New Jersey* (battleship), 1942 .. 75 75
955 70 c. Draisine bicycle, 1818 .. .. .. 80 80
956 90 c. S.S. *United States* (holder of Blue Riband), 1952 .. .. .. .. 1·00 1·00
957 $1.50, Cierva "C.4" (first autogiro), 1923 .. 1·50 1·50
958 $2 Curtiss "NC.4" (first transatlantic flight), 1919 .. .. .. .. 1·75 1·75
959 $3 *Queen Elizabeth 2* (liner), 1969 .. .. 2·50 2·50
950/9 .. .. .. .. *Set of* 10 9·25 9·25

**110** Shore Crab

(Litho Format)

**1987** (15 Sept). *Marine Life. T* **110** *and similar multicoloured designs. P* 15.

960 5 c. Type **110** .. .. .. .. .. 30 30
961 10 c. Sea Cucumber .. .. .. .. 30 30
962 15 c. Stop Light Parrotfish .. .. .. 40 40
963 25 c. Banded Coral Shrimp .. .. .. 45 45
964 35 c. Spotted Drum .. .. .. .. 50 50
965 60 c. Thorny Starfish .. .. .. .. 75 75
966 75 c. Atlantic Trumpet Triton .. .. 85 85
967 90 c. Feather Star and Yellow Beaker Sponge 1·00 1·00
968 $1 Blue Gorgonian (*vert*) .. .. .. 1·10 1·10
969 $1.25, Slender Filefish (*vert*) .. .. 1·40 1·40
970 $5 Barred Hamlet (*vert*) .. .. .. 4·00 4·00
971 $7.50, Fairy Basslet (*vert*) .. .. .. 6·50 6·50
972 $10 Fire Coral and Butterfly Fish (*vert*) .. 8·00 8·00
960/72 .. .. .. .. *Set of* 13 23·00 23·00

**1987** (12 Oct). *Olympic Games, Seoul (1988). Nos.* 1086/90 *of Antigua optd with T* **95** *(No.* **MS**977) *or T* **96** *in silver (others).*

973 10 c. Handball .. .. .. .. .. 15 10
974 60 c. Fencing .. .. .. .. .. 30 30
975 $1 Gymnastics .. .. .. .. 50 50
976 $3 Football .. .. .. .. .. 1·50 1·60
973/6 .. .. .. .. *Set of* 4 2·25 2·25
**MS**977 100×72 mm. $5 Boxing gloves .. .. 2·50 3·25

**1987** (12 Oct). *Birth Centenary of Marc Chagall (artist). Nos.* 1091/9 *of Antigua optd as T* **95** *(in silver on Nos.* 983, **MS**986b).

978 10 c. "The Profile" .. .. .. .. 10 10
979 30 c. "Portrait of the Artist's Sister" .. .. 15 15
980 40 c. "Bride with Fan" .. .. .. .. 20 25
981 60 c. "David in Profile" .. .. .. 25 30
982 90 c. "Fiancee with Bouquet" .. .. .. 40 45
983 $1 "Self Portrait with Brushes" .. .. 45 50
984 $3 "The Walk" .. .. .. .. 1·40 1·50
985 $4 "Three Candles" .. .. .. .. 1·75 1·90
978/85 .. .. .. .. *Set of* 8 4·25 4·50
**MS**986 Two sheets, each 110×95 mm. (a) $5 "Fall of Icarus" (104×89 *mm*). (b) $5 "Myth of Orpheus" (104×89 *mm*) *Set of* 2 *sheets* 4·50 5·50

**1987** (5 Nov). *Centenary of Statue of Liberty (1986) (2nd issue). Nos* 1110/19 *of Antigua optd with T* **95** (15, 30, 45, 50 c., $1, $2, $5) *or T* **96** (60, 90 c., $3), *in black* (50 c., $3) *or silver (others).*

987 15 c. Lee Iacocca at unveiling of restored Statue .. .. .. .. .. 10 10
988 30 c. Statue at sunset (side view) .. .. 15 15
989 45 c. Aerial view of head .. .. .. 20 25
990 50 c. Lee Iacocca and torch .. .. .. 25 30
991 60 c. Workmen inside head of Statue (*horiz*) 25 30
992 90 c. Restoration work (*horiz*) .. .. 40 45
993 $1 Head of Statue .. .. .. .. 45 50
994 $2 Statue at Sunset (front view) .. .. 90 95
995 $3 Inspecting restoration work (*horiz*) .. 1·40 1·50
996 $5 Statue at night .. .. .. .. 2·25 2·40
987/96 .. .. .. .. *Set of* 10 5·75 6·25

**1987** (5 Nov). *Entertainers. Nos.* 1120/7 *of Antigua optd with T* **95** *(in silver on* $3).

997 15 c. Grace Kelly .. .. .. .. 30 30
998 30 c. Marilyn Monroe .. .. .. .. 45 45
999 45 c. Orson Welles .. .. .. .. 50 50
1000 50 c. Judy Garland .. .. .. .. 65 65
1001 60 c. John Lennon .. .. .. .. 85 85
1002 $1 Rock Hudson .. .. .. .. 90 90
1003 $2 John Wayne .. .. .. .. 1·60 1·60
1004 $3 Elvis Presley .. .. .. .. 2·25 2·25
997/1004 .. .. .. .. *Set of* 8 6·75 6·75

**1987** (5 Nov). *"Capex '87" International Stamp Exhibition, Toronto. Reptiles and Amphibians. Nos.* 1133/7 *of Antigua optd with T* **95** *(No.* **MS**1009) *or T* **96** *(others).*

1005 30 c. Whistling Frog .. .. .. .. 20 20
1006 60 c. Croaking Lizard .. .. .. .. 35 35
1007 $1 Antiguan Anole .. .. .. .. 55 55
1008 $3 Red-footed Tortoise .. .. .. 1·60 1·60
1005/8 .. .. .. .. *Set of* 4 2·40 2·40
**MS**1009 106×76 mm. $5 Ground Lizard .. 3·25 3·75

**1988** (12 Jan). *Christmas. Religious Paintings. Nos.* 1144/8 *of Antigua optd with T* **95**.

1010 45 c. "Madonna and Child" (Bernardo Daddi) .. .. .. .. .. 20 25
1011 60 c. "St. Joseph" (detail, "The Nativity" (Sano di Pietro)) .. .. .. .. 25 30
1012 $1 "Virgin Mary" (detail, "The Nativity" (Sano di Pietro)) .. .. .. .. 45 50
1013 $4 "Music-making Angel" (Melozzo da Forli) .. .. .. .. .. 1·75 1·90
1010/13 .. .. .. .. *Set of* 4 2·40 2·75
**MS**1014 99×70 mm. $5 "The Flight into Egypt" (Sano di Pietro) .. .. .. .. 2·25 2·75

**1988** (25 Mar). *Salvation Army's Community Service. Nos.* 1163/71 *of Antigua optd with T* **106**.

1015 25 c. First aid at daycare centre, Antigua .. 35 35
1016 30 c. Giving penicillin injection, Indonesia 35 35
1017 40 c. Children at daycare centre, Bolivia .. 45 45
1018 45 c. Rehabilitation of the handicapped, India .. .. .. .. .. 45 45
1019 50 c. Training blind man, Kenya .. .. 55 55
1020 60 c. Weighing baby, Ghana .. .. .. 55 55
1021 $1 Training typist, Zambia .. .. .. 85 85
1022 $2 Emergency food kitchen, Sri Lanka .. 1·50 1·50
1015/22 .. .. .. .. *Set of* 8 4·50 4·50
**MS**1023 152×83 mm. $5 General Eva Burrows 4·25 4·50

**1988** (6 May). *Bicentenary of U.S. Constitution. Nos.* 1139/43 *of Antigua optd with T* **95** *($4, $5) or T* **96** *(others), all in silver.*
1024 15 c. House of Burgesses, Virginia ("Freedom of Speech") .. .. 10 10
1025 45 c. State Seal, Connecticut .. .. 20 25
1026 60 c. State Seal, Delaware .. .. 25 30
1027 $4 Gouverneur Morris (Pennsylvania delegate) (*vert*) .. .. 1·75 1·90
1024/7 .. .. .. .. *Set of* 4 2·10 2·25
**MS**1028 105×75 mm. $5 Roger Sherman (Connecticut delegate) (*vert*) .. .. .. 2·75 3·25

**1988** (4 July). *Royal Ruby Wedding. Nos.* 1149/53 *of Antigua optd with T* **95**.
1029 25 c. deep brown, black and bright new blue 20 20
1030 60 c. multicoloured .. .. .. 35 35
1031 $2 deep brown, black and light green .. 1·00 1·00
1032 $3 multicoloured .. .. .. 1·40 1·50
1029/32 .. .. .. .. *Set of* 4 2·75 2·75
**MS**1033 102×77 mm. $5 multicoloured .. 3·00 3·50

**1988** (4 July). *Birds of Antigua. Nos.* 1154/62 *of Antigua optd with T* **95** *(10 c., $1, $5) or T* **96** *(others).*
1034 10 c. Great Blue Heron .. .. .. 25 25
1035 15 c. Ringed Kingfisher (*horiz*) .. .. 25 25
1036 50 c. Bananaquit (*horiz*) .. .. .. 55 55
1037 60 c. Purple Gallinule (*horiz*) .. .. 55 55
1038 70 c. Blue-hooded Euphonia (*horiz*) .. 60 60
1039 $1 Brown-throated Conure ("Caribbean Parakeet") .. .. .. 80 80
1040 $3 Troupial (*horiz*) .. .. .. 1·75 1·75
1041 $4 Purple-throated Carib (*horiz*) .. 2·00 2·00
1034/41 .. .. .. .. *Set of* 8 6·00 6·00
**MS**1042 Two sheets, each 115×86 mm. (a) $5 Greater Flamingo. (b) $5 Brown Pelican *Set of* 2 *sheets* 6·00 7·00

**1988** (25 July–8 Dec). *500th Anniv of Discovery of America by Columbus* (1992) *(1st issue). Nos.* 1172/80 *of Antigua optd with T* **96** *(Nos.* 1043/50*) or T* **95** *(No.* **MS**1051*).*
1043 10 c. Columbus' second fleet, 1493 .. 15 15
1044 30 c. Painos Indian village and fleet .. 20 20
1045 45 c. *Santa Mariagalante* (flagship) and Painos village .. .. .. 35 35
1046 60 c. Painos Indians offering Columbus fruit and vegetables .. .. .. 35 35
1047 90 c. Painos Indian and Columbus with parrot .. .. .. .. 60 60
1048 $1 Columbus landing on island .. .. 65 65
1049 $3 Spanish soldier and fleet .. .. 1·50 1·50
1050 $4 Fleet under sail .. .. .. 2·00 2·00
1043/50 .. .. .. .. *Set of* 8 5·25 5·25
**MS**1051 Two sheets, each 110×80 nn. (a) $5 Queen Isabella's cross. (b) $5 Gold coin of Ferdinand and Isabella (8 Dec) *Set of* 2 *sheets* 4·25 4·75
See also Nos. 1112/16.

**1988** (25 July). *500th Birth Anniv of Titian. Nos.* 1181/9 *of Antigua optd with T* **96** *(Nos.* 1052/9*) or T* **95** *(No.* **MS**1060*), all in silver.*
1052 30 c. "Bust of Christ" .. .. .. 15 15
1053 40 c. "Scourging of Christ" .. .. 20 25
1054 45 c. "Madonna in Glory with Saints" .. 20 25
1055 50 c. "The Averoldi Polyptych" (detail) .. 25 30
1056 $1 "Christ Crowned with Thorns" .. 45 50
1057 $2 "Christ Mocked" .. .. .. 90 95
1058 $3 "Christ and Simon of Cyrene" .. 1·40 1·50
1059 $4 "Crucifixion with Virgin and Saints" 1·75 2·00
1052/9 .. .. .. .. *Set of* 8 4·75 5·25
**MS**1060 Two sheets, each 110×95 mm. (a) $5 "Ecce Homo" (detail). (b) $5 "Noli me Tangere" (detail) *Set of* 2 *sheets* 4·50 5·50

**1988** (25 Aug). *16th World Scout Jamboree, Australia. Nos.* 1128/32 *of Antigua optd with T* **95** *(No.* **MS**1064*) or T* **96** *(others).*
1061 10 c. Scouts around camp fire and Red Kangaroo .. .. .. .. 15 15
1062 60 c. Scouts canoeing and Blue-winged Kookaburra .. .. .. .. 45 45
1063 $1 Scouts on assault course and Ring-tailed Rock Wallaby .. .. 70 70
1064 $3 Field kitchen and Koala .. .. 1·75 1·75
1061/4 .. .. .. .. *Set of* 4 2·75 2·75
**MS**1065 103 × 78 mm. $5 Flags of Antigua, Australia and Scout Movement .. .. 2·50 3·00

**1988** (25 Aug–8 Dec). *Sailing Week. Nos.* 1190/4 *of Antigua optd with T* **95** *(No.* **MS**1070*) or T* **96** *(others).*
1066 30 c. Two yachts rounding buoy .. .. 20 20
1067 60 c. Three yachts .. .. .. 45 45
1068 $1 British yacht under way .. .. 70 70
1069 $3 Three yachts (*different*) .. .. 1·60 1·60
1066/9 .. .. .. .. *Set of* 4 2·75 2·75
**MS**1070 103 × 92 mm. $5 Two yachts (8 Dec) 2·50 3·00

**1988** (16 Sept). *Flowering Trees. Nos.* 1213/21 *of Antigua optd with T* **95**.
1071 10 c. Jacaranda .. .. .. .. 10 10
1072 30 c. Cordia .. .. .. .. 15 15
1073 50 c. Orchid Tree .. .. .. .. 20 25
1074 90 c. Flamboyant .. .. .. .. 40 45
1075 $1 African Tulip Tree .. .. .. 45 50
1076 $2 Potato Tree .. .. .. .. 80 85
1077 $3 Crepe Myrtle .. .. .. .. 1·25 1·40
1078 $4 Pitch Apple .. .. .. .. 1·60 1·75
1071/8 .. .. .. .. *Set of* 8 4·50 5·00
**MS**1079 Two sheets, each 106 × 76 mm. (a) $5 Cassia. (b) $5 Chinaberry .. *Set of* 2 *sheets* 4·25 5·00

**1988** (16 Sept). *Olympic Games, Seoul. Nos.* 1222/6 *of Antigua optd with T* **95** *(Nos.* 1080/1, **MS**1084*) or T* **96** *(Nos.* 1082/3*).*
1080 40 c. Gymnastics .. .. .. .. 20 25
1081 60 c. Weightlifting .. .. .. .. 25 30
1082 $1 Water polo (*horiz*) .. .. .. 45 50
1083 $3 Boxing (*horiz*) .. .. .. 1·25 1·40
1080/3 .. .. .. .. *Set of* 4 1·90 2·25
**MS**1084 114 × 80 mm. $5 Runner with Olympic torch .. .. .. .. .. 2·10 2·40

BARBUDA MAIL

(111)

**1988** (8 Dec)–**90**. *Caribbean Butterflies. Nos.* 1227/44*a of Antigua optd with T* **96** *(Nos.* 1085/1102*) or T* **111** *(No.* 1102*a).*
1085 1 c. *Danaus plexippus* .. .. .. 10 10
1086 2 c. *Greta diaphanus* .. .. .. 10 10
1087 3 c. *Calisto archebates* .. .. .. 10 10
1088 5 c. *Hamadryas feronia* .. .. .. 10 10
1089 10 c. *Mestra dorcas* .. .. .. 10 10
1090 15 c. *Hypolimnas misippus* .. .. .. 10 10
1091 20 c. *Dione juno* .. .. .. .. 10 10
1092 25 c. *Heliconius charithonia* .. .. 10 15
1093 30 c. *Eurema pyro* .. .. .. 10 15
1094 40 c. *Papilio androgeus* .. .. .. 15 20
1095 45 c. *Anteos maerula* .. .. .. 20 25
1096 50 c. *Aphrissa orbis* .. .. .. 20 25
1097 60 c. *Astraptes xagua* .. .. .. 25 30
1098 $1 *Heliopetes arsalte* .. .. .. 40 45
1099 $2 *Polites baracoa* .. .. .. 85 90
1100 $2.50 *Phocides pigmalion* .. .. 1·00 1·10
1101 $5 *Prepona amphitoe* .. .. .. 2·10 2·25
1102 $10 *Oarisma nanus* .. .. .. 4·25 4·50
1102*a* $20 *Parides lycimenes* (4.5.90) .. 8·50 8·75
1085/102*a* .. .. .. *Set of* 19 16·00 17·00

**BARBUDA MAIL**

(112)

BARBUDA MAIL

(113)

**1989** (28 Apr). *25th Death Anniv of John F. Kennedy (American statesman). Nos.* 1245/53 *of Antigua optd with T* **96** *(Nos.* 1103/10*) or T* **112** *(No.* **MS**1111*).*
1103 1 c. President Kennedy and family .. 10 10
1104 2 c. Kennedy commanding *PT109* .. 10 10
1105 3 c. Funeral cortege .. .. .. 10 10
1106 4 c. In motorcade, Mexico City .. .. 10 10
1107 30 c. As 1 c. .. .. .. .. 15 20
1108 60 c. As 4 c. .. .. .. .. 30 35
1109 $1 As 3 c. .. .. .. .. 45 50
1110 $4 As 2 c. .. .. .. .. 1·90 2·00
1103/10 .. .. .. .. *Set of* 8 2·75 3·00
**MS**1111 105 × 75 mm. $5 Kennedy taking presidential oath of office .. .. .. 2·40 3·00

**1989** (24 May). *500th Anniv of Discovery of America by Columbus* (1992) *(2nd issue). Pre-Columbian Arawak Society. Nos.* 1267/71 *of Antigua optd with T* **113**.
1112 $1.50, Arawak warriors .. .. 70 75
a. Horiz strip of 4. Nos. 1112/15 .. 2·50
1113 $1.50, Whip dancers .. .. 70 75
1114 $1.50, Whip dancers and chief with pineapple .. .. .. 70 75
1115 $1.50, Family and camp fire .. .. 70 75
1112/15 .. .. .. .. *Set of* 4 2·50 2·75
**MS**1116 71 × 84 mm. $6 Arawak chief .. 2·75 3·25

**1989** (29 June). *50th Anniv of First Jet Flight. Nos.* 1272/80 *of Antigua optd with T* **111**.
1117 10 c. De Havilland "Comet 4" airliner .. 10 10
1118 30 c. Messerschmitt "Me 262" fighter .. 15 20
1119 40 c. Boeing "707" airliner .. .. 20 25
1120 60 c. Canadair "F-86 Sabre" fighter .. 30 35
1121 $1 Lockheed "F-104 Starfighter" fighters 45 50
1122 $2 McDonnell Douglas "DC-10" airliner 95 1·00
1123 $3 Boeing "747" airliner .. .. 1·50 1·60
1124 $4 McDonnell "F-4 Phantom" fighter 1·90 2·00
1117/24 .. .. .. .. *Set of* 8 5·00 5·50
**MS**1125 Two sheets, each 114×183 mm. (a) $7 Grumman "F-14 Tomcat" fighter. (b) $7 "Concorde" airliner .. .. *Set of* 2 *sheets* 8·50 9·50

BARBUDA MAIL

(114)

**BARBUDA MAIL**

(115)

**1989** (18 Sept). *Caribbean Cruise Ships. Nos.* 1281/9 *of Antigua optd as T* **114**, *but with lines spaced (No.* **MS**1134b*), or with T* **111** *(others).*
1126 25 c. *Festivale* .. .. .. .. 15 15
1127 45 c. *Southward* .. .. .. .. 25 25
1128 50 c. *Sagafjord* .. .. .. .. 30 30
1129 60 c. *Daphne* .. .. .. .. 35 35
1130 75 c. *Cunard Countess* .. .. .. 40 40
1131 90 c. *Song of America* .. .. .. 45 45
1132 $3 *Island Princess* .. .. .. 1·60 1·60
1133 $4 *Galileo* .. .. .. .. 2·00 2·00
1126/33 .. .. .. .. *Set of* 8 5·00 5·00
**MS**1134 (a) 113×187 mm. $6 *Norway*. (b) 111×82 mm. $6 *Oceanic* .. .. *Set of* 2 *sheets* 9·50 10·00

**1989** (14 Dec). *Japanese Art. Paintings by Hiroshige. Nos.* 1290/8 *of Antigua optd with T* **114**.
1135 25 c. "Fish swimming by Duck half-submerged in Stream" .. .. 10 15
1136 45 c. "Crane and Wave" .. .. .. 20 25
1137 50 c. "Sparrows and Morning Glories" .. 25 30
1138 60 c. "Crested Blackbird and Flowering Cherry" .. .. .. .. 30 35
1139 $1 "Great Knot sitting among Water Grass" .. .. .. .. 45 50
1140 $2 "Goose on a Bank of Water" .. 95 1·00
1141 $3 "Black Paradise Flycatcher and Blossoms" .. .. .. 1·50 1·60
1142 $4 "Sleepy Owl perched on a Pine Branch" .. .. .. .. 1·90 2·00
1135/42 .. .. .. .. *Set of* 8 5·00 5·50
**MS**1143 Two sheets, each 102×75 mm. (a) $5 "Bullfinch flying near a Clematis Branch". (b) $5 "Titmouse on a Cherry Branch" .. *Set of* 2 *sheets* 6·50 7·00

**1989** (20 Dec). *World Cup Football Championship, Italy* (1990). *Nos.* 1308/12 *of Antigua optd with T* **115**.
1144 15 c. Goalkeeper .. .. .. .. 10 10
1145 25 c. Goalkeeper moving towards ball .. 10 15
1146 $1 Goalkeeper reaching for ball .. 45 50
1147 $4 Goalkeeper saving goal .. .. 1·90 2·00
1144/7 .. .. .. .. *Set of* 4 2·25 2·40
**MS**1148 Two sheets, each 75×105 mm. (a) $5 Three players competing for ball (*horiz*). (b) $5 Ball and players' legs (*horiz*) .. *Set of* 2 *sheets* 7·00 7·50

**1989** (20 Dec). *Christmas. Paintings by Raphael and Giotto. Nos.* 1351/9 *of Antigua optd with T* **114**.
1149 10 c. "The Small Cowper Madonna" (Raphael) .. .. .. .. 10 10
1150 25 c. "Madonna of the Goldfinch" (Raphael) 10 15
1151 30 c. "The Alba Madonna" (Raphael) .. 15 20
1152 50 c. Saint (detail, "Bologna Altarpiece") (Giotto) .. .. .. .. 25 30
1153 60 c. Angel (detail, "Bologna Altarpiece") (Giotto) .. .. .. .. 30 35
1154 70 c. Angel slaying serpent (detail, "Bologna Altarpiece") (Giotto) .. 35 40
1155 $4 Evangelist (detail, "Bologna Altarpiece") (Giotto) .. .. .. 1·90 2·00
1156 $5 "Madonna of Foligno" (Raphael) .. 2·40 2·50
1149/56 .. .. .. .. *Set of* 8 5·00 5·50
**MS**1157 Two sheets, each 71×96 mm. (a) $5 "The Marriage of the Virgin" (detail) (Raphael). (b) $5 Madonna and Child (detail, "Bologna Altarpiece") (Giotto) .. .. *Set of* 2 *sheets* 6·00 7·00

**1990** (21 Feb). *Fungi. Nos.* 1313/21 *of Antigua optd with T* **111**.
1158 10 c. *Mycena pura* .. .. .. .. 20 20
1159 25 c. *Psathyrella tuberculata* (*vert*) .. 20 20
1160 50 c. *Psilocybe cubensis* .. .. .. 40 40
1161 60 c. *Leptonia caeruleocapitata* (*vert*) .. 45 45
1162 75 c. *Xeromphalina tenuipes* (*vert*) .. 50 50
1163 $1 *Chlorophyllum molybdites* (*vert*) .. 65 65
1164 $3 *Marasmius haematocephalus* .. 1·75 1·75
1165 $4 *Cantharellus cinnabarinus* .. .. 2·00 2·00
1158/65 .. .. .. .. *Set of* 8 5·50 5·50
**MS**1166 Two sheets, each 88×62 mm. (a) $6 *Leucopaxillus gracillimus* (*vert*). (b) $6 *Volvariella volvacea* .. .. *Set of* 2 *sheets* 8·50 8·50

**BARBUDA MAIL**

(116)

**1990** (30 Mar). *Local Fauna. Nos.* 1322/6 *of Antigua optd with T* **116** *(vertically on 60 c., $4).*
1167 25 c. Desmarest's Hutia .. .. .. 25 25
1168 45 c. Caribbean Monk Seal .. .. 45 45
1169 60 c. Mustache Bat (*vert*) .. .. 55 55
1170 $4 American Manatee (*vert*) .. .. 2·25 2·25
1167/70 .. .. .. .. *Set of* 4 3·25 3·25
**MS**1171 113×87 mm. $5 West Indies Giant Rice Rat .. .. .. .. .. 3·25 3·50

**1990** (30 Mar). *20th Anniv of First Manned Landing on Moon. Nos.* 1346/50 *of Antigua optd with T* **116** *(vertically on* 10, *45 c. and $5).*
1172 10 c. Launch of "Apollo 11" .. .. 15 15
1173 45 c. Aldrin on Moon .. .. .. 35 35
1174 $1 Module *Eagle* over Moon (*horiz*) .. 60 60
1175 $4 Recovery of "Apollo 11" crew after splashdown (*horiz*) .. .. .. 2·40 2·40
1172/5 .. .. .. .. *Set of* 4 3·25 3·25
**MS**1176 107×77 mm. $5 Astronaut Neil Armstrong .. .. .. .. .. 3·00 3·25

**1990** (6 June). *500th Anniv of Discovery of America by Columbus* (1992) *(3rd issue). New World Natural History – Marine Life. Nos.* 1360/8 *of Antigua optd as T* **114**, *but with lines spaced.*
1177 10 c. Star-eyed Hermit Crab .. .. 15 15
1178 20 c. Spiny Lobster .. .. .. 20 20
1179 25 c. Magnificent Banded Fanworm .. 20 20
1180 45 c. Cannonball Jellyfish .. .. 35 35
1181 60 c. Red-spiny Sea Star .. .. .. 45 45
1182 $2 Peppermint Shrimp .. .. .. 1·00 1·00
1183 $3 Coral Crab .. .. .. .. 1·40 1·40
1184 $4 Branching Fire Coral .. .. 1·75 1·75
1177/84 .. .. .. .. *Set of* 8 5·00 5·00
**MS**1185 Two sheets, each 101×69 mm. (a) $5 Common Sea Fan. (b) $5 Portuguese Man-of-war *Set of* 2 *sheets* 5·50 6·00

**1990** (12 July). *"EXPO 90" International Garden and Greenery Exhibition, Osaka. Orchids. Nos.* 1369/77 *of Antigua optd as T* **114**, *but with lines spaced.*
1186 15 c. *Vanilla mexicana* .. .. .. 25 2
1187 45 c. *Epidendrum ibaguense* .. .. 45 4
1188 50 c. *Epidendrum secundum* .. .. 45 4
1189 60 c. *Maxillaria conferta* .. .. .. 50 5
1190 $1 *Onicidium altissimum* .. .. 75 7
1191 $2 *Spiranthes lanceolata* .. .. 1·25 1·2
1192 $3 *Tonopsis utricularioides* .. .. 1·75 1·7
1193 $5 *Epidendrum nocturnum* .. .. 2·75 2·7
1186/93 .. .. .. .. *Set of* 8 7·25 7·2
**MS**1194 Two sheets, each 101×69 mm. (a) $6 *Octomeria graminifolia*. (b) $6 *Rodriguezia lanceolata* .. .. *Set of* 2 *sheets* 6·50 6·5

**1990** (14 Aug). *Reef Fishes. Nos.* 1386/94 *of Antigua optd with T* **111**.
1195 10 c. Flamefish .. .. .. .. 15 1
1196 15 c. Coney .. .. .. .. 20 2
1197 50 c. Squirrelfish .. .. .. .. 45 4
1198 60 c. Sergeant Major .. .. .. 50 5
1199 $1 Yellowtail Snapper .. .. .. 70 7
1200 $2 Rock Beauty .. .. .. .. 1·25 1·2
1201 $3 Spanish Hogfish .. .. .. 1·60 1·6
1202 $4 Striped Parrotfish .. .. .. 2·00 2·0
1195/1202 .. .. .. .. *Set of* 8 6·25 6·2
**MS**1203 Two sheets, each 99×70 mm. (a) $5 Blackbar Soldierfish. (b) $5 Foureye Butterflyfish .. .. .. *Set of* 2 *sheets* 6·00 6·0

**$5.00**

**1st Anniversary**
**Hurricane Hugo**
**16th September, 1989-1990**

(117)

**990** (17 Sept). *First Anniv of Hurricane Hugo. Nos.* 971/2 *surch as T* **117**.
204 $5 on $7.50, Fairy Basslet (*vert*) .. 2·25 2·25
205 $7.50 on $10 Fire Coral and Butterfly Fish (*vert*) .. .. .. .. 3·25 3·25

**990** (12 Oct). *90th Birthday of Queen Elizabeth the Queen Mother. Nos.* 1415/19 *of Antigua optd as T* **114**, *but with lines spaced.*
206 15 c. multicoloured .. .. .. .. 15 15
207 35 c. multicoloured .. .. .. .. 20 20
208 75 c. multicoloured .. .. .. .. 35 35
209 $3 multicoloured .. .. .. .. 1·25 1·25
206/9 .. .. .. .. *Set of* 4 1·75 1·75
MS1210 67×98 mm $6 multicoloured .. .. 3·00 3·00

**BARBUDA**
**MAIL**

(118)

119 Troupial

**990** (14 Dec). *Achievements in Space. Nos.* 1395/1414 *of Antigua optd with T* **118** *in silver.*
211 45 c. "Voyager 2" passing Saturn .. .. 25 25
a. Sheetlet. Nos. 1211/30 .. .. 4·50
212 45 c. "Pioneer 11" photographing Saturn .. 25 25
213 45 c. Astronaut in transporter .. .. 25 25
214 45 c. Space shuttle *Columbia* .. .. 25 25
215 45 c. "Apollo 10" command module on parachutes .. .. .. .. 25 25
216 45 c. "Skylab" space station .. .. 25 25
217 45 c. Astronaut Edward White in space .. 25 25
218 45 c. "Apollo" spacecraft on joint mission .. 25 25
219 45 c. "Soyuz" spacecraft on joint mission .. 25 25
220 45 c. "Mariner 1" passing Venus .. .. 25 25
221 45 c. "Gemini 4" capsule .. .. .. 25 25
222 45 c. "Sputnik 1" .. .. .. .. 25 25
223 45 c. Hubble space telescope .. .. 25 25
224 45 c. "X-15" rocket plane .. .. .. 25 25
225 45 c. "Bell X-1" aircraft .. .. .. 25 25
226 45 c. "Apollo 17" astronaut and lunar rock formation .. .. .. .. 25 25
227 45 c. Lunar Rover .. .. .. .. 25 25
228 45 c. "Apollo 14" lunar module .. .. 25 25
229 45 c. Astronaut Buzz Aldrin on Moon .. 25 25
230 45 c. Soviet "Lunokhod" lunar vehicle .. 25 25
211/30 .. .. .. .. *Set of* 20 4·50 4·50

**990** (14 Dec). *Christmas. Paintings by Renaissance Masters. Nos.* 1457/65 *of Antigua optd with T* **111**.
231 25 c. "Madonna and Child with Saints" (detail, Sebastiano del Piombo) .. 10 10
232 30 c. "Virgin and Child with Angels" (detail, Grünewald) (*vert*) .. 10 15
233 40 c. "The Holy Family and a Shepherd" (detail, Titian) .. .. .. 15 20
234 60 c. "Virgin and Child" (detail, Lippi) (*vert*) 25 30
235 $1 "Jesus, St. John and Two Angels" (Rubens) .. .. .. .. 40 45
236 $2 "Adoration of the Shepherds" (detail, Vincenzo Catena) .. .. .. 80 85
237 $4 "Adoration of the Magi" (detail, Giorgione) .. .. .. .. 1·60 1·75
238 $5 "Virgin and Child adored by Warrior" (detail, Vincenzo Catena) .. .. 2·00 2·10
231/8 .. .. .. .. *Set of* 8 4·75 5·25
MS1239 Two sheets, each 71×101 mm. (a) $6 "Allegory of the Blessings of Jacob" (detail, Rubens) (*vert*). (b) $6 "Adoration of the Magi" (detail, Fra Angelico) (*vert*) .. *Set of* 2 *sheets* 4·75 5·00

**991** (4 Feb). *150th Anniv of the Penny Black. Nos.* 1378/81 *of Antigua optd with T* **116**.
240 45 c. blue-green .. .. .. .. 20 25
241 60 c. magenta .. .. .. .. 25 30
242 $5 ultramarine .. .. .. .. 2·00 2·10
240/2 .. .. .. .. *Set of* 3 2·25 2·40
MS1243 102×80 mm. $6 blackish purple .. 2·40 2·50

**991** (4 Feb). *"Stamp World London 90" International Stamp Exhibition. Nos.* 1382/5 *of Antigua optd with T* **116**.
244 50 c. deep grey-green and scarlet-vermilion 20 25
245 75 c. purple-brown and scarlet-vermilion .. 30 35
246 $4 deep ultramarine & scarlet-vermilion 1·60 1·75
244/6 .. .. .. .. *Set of* 3 1·90 2·10
MS1247 104×81 mm. $6 brownish black and scarlet-vermilion .. .. .. .. 2·40 2·50

(Des G. Drummond. Litho Questa)

**1991** (25 Mar). *Wild Birds. T* **119** *and similar vert designs. Multicoloured. P* 14.
1248 60 c. Type **119** .. .. .. .. 25 30
1249 $2 Adelaide's Warbler ("Christmas Bird") 85 90
1250 $4 Rose-breasted Grosbeak .. .. 1·75 1·90
1251 $7 Stolid Flycatcher .. .. .. 3·00 3·25
1248/51 .. .. .. .. *Set of* 4 5·25 5·75

**1991** (23 Apr). *Olympic Games, Barcelona* (1992). *Nos.* 1429/33 *of Antigua optd as T* **114**, *but with lines spaced.*
1252 50 c. Men's 20 kilometres walk .. .. 20 25
1253 75 c. Triple jump .. .. .. .. 30 35
1254 $1 Men's 10,000 metres .. .. 40 45
1255 $5 Javelin .. .. .. .. 2·10 2·25
1252/5 .. .. .. .. *Set of* 4 2·75 3·00
**MS**1256 100 × 70 mm. $6 Athlete lighting Olympic flame at Los Angeles Olympics .. 2·50 2·75

**1991** (23 Apr). *Birds. Nos.* 1448/56 *of Antigua optd with T* **116** *diagonally.*
1257 10 c. Pearly-eyed Thrasher .. .. 10 10
1258 25 c. Purple-throated Carib .. .. 10 15
1259 50 c. Common Yellowthroat .. .. 20 25
1260 60 c. American Kestrel .. .. .. 25 30
1261 $1 Yellow-bellied Sapsucker .. .. 40 45
1262 $2 Purple Gallinule .. .. .. 85 90
1263 $3 Yellow-crowned Night Heron .. 1·25 1·40
1264 $4 Blue-hooded Euphonia .. .. 1·75 1·90
1257/64 .. .. .. .. *Set of* 8 4·25 4·75
**MS**1265 Two sheets, each 76 × 60 mm. (a) $6 Brown Pelican. (b) $6 Frigate Bird *Set of* 2 *sheets* 5·00 5·25

**1991** (21 June). *350th Death Anniv of Rubens. Nos.* 1466/74 *of Antigua optd with T* **111**.
1266 25 c. "Rape of the Daughters of Leucippus" (detail) .. .. .. .. 10 10
1267 45 c. "Bacchanal" (detail) .. .. .. 20 25
1268 50 c. "Rape of the Sabine Women" (detail) 20 25
1269 60 c. "Battle of the Amazons" (detail) .. 25 30
1270 $1 "Rape of the Sabine Women" (different detail) .. .. .. .. 40 45
1271 $2 "Bacchanal" (different detail) .. 85 90
1272 $3 "Rape of the Sabine Women" (different detail) .. .. .. .. 1·25 1·40
1273 $4 "Bacchanal" (different detail) .. 1·75 1·90
1266/73 .. .. .. .. *Set of* 8 4·50 5·00
**MS**1274 Two sheets, each 101 × 71 mm. (a) $6 "Rape of Hippodameia" (detail). (b) $6 "Battle of the Amazons" (different detail) *Set of* 2 *sheets* 5·00 5·25

**1991** (25 July). *50th Anniv of Second World War. Nos.* 1475/84 *of Antigua optd diagonally with T* **116**.
1275 10 c. U.S. troops cross into Germany, 1944 10 10
1276 15 c. Axis surrender in North Africa, 1943 10 10
1277 25 c. U.S. tanks invade Kwalajalein, 1944 10 10
1278 45 c. Roosevelt and Churchill meet at Casablanca, 1943 .. .. .. 20 25
1279 50 c. Marshall Badoglio, Prime Minister of Italian anti-fascist government, 1943 20 25
1280 $1 Lord Mountbatten, Supreme Allied Commander South-east Asia, 1943 .. 40 45
1281 $2 Greek victory at Koritza, 1940 .. 80 85
1282 $4 Anglo-Soviet mutual assistance pact, 1941 .. .. .. .. .. 1·75 1·90
1283 $5 Operation Torch landings, 1942 .. 2·10 2·25
1275/83 .. .. .. .. *Set of* 9 5·25 5·50
**MS**1284 Two sheets, each 108 × 80 mm. (a) $6 Japanese attack Pearl Harbour, 1941. (b) $6 U.S.A.A.F. daylight raid on Schweinfurt, 1943 *Set of* 2 *sheets* 5·00 5·25

## REDONDA

### DEPENDENCY OF ANTIGUA

### Appendix

The following stamps were issued in anticipation of commercial and tourist development, philatelic mail being handled by a bureau in Antigua. Since at the present time the island is uninhabited, we do not list or stock these items. It is understood that the stamps are valid for the prepayment of postage in Antigua. Miniature sheets, imperforate stamps etc., are excluded from this section.

**1979**

*Antigua 1976 definitive issue optd* "REDONDA". 3, 5, 10, 25, 35, 50, 75 c., $1, $2.50, $5, $10.
*Antigua Coronation Anniversary issue optd* "REDONDA". 10, 30, 50, 90 c., $2.50.
*Antigua World Cup Football Championship issue optd* "REDONDA". 10, 15 c., $3.
*Death Centenary of Sir Rowland Hill.* 50, 90 c., $2.50, $3.
*International Year of the Child.* 25, 50 c., $1, $2.
*Christmas. Paintings.* 8, 50, 90 c., $3.

**1980**

*Marine Life.* 8, 25, 50 c., $4.
*75th Anniv of Rotary International.* 25, 50 c., $1, $2.
*Birds of Redonda.* 8, 10, 15, 25, 30, 50 c., $1, $2, $5.
*Olympic Medal Winners, Lake Placid and Moscow.* 8, 25, 50 c., $3.
*80th Birthday of Queen Elizabeth the Queen Mother.* 10 c., $2.50.
*Christmas. Paintings.* 8, 25, 50 c., $4.

**1981**

*Royal Wedding.* 25, 55 c., $4.
*Christmas. Walt Disney Cartoon Characters.* ½, 1, 2, 3, 4, 5, 10 c., $2.50, $3.
*World Cup Football Championship, Spain* (1982). 30 c. × 2, 50 c. × 2, $1 × 2, $2 × 2.

**1982**

*Boy Scout Anniversaries.* 8, 25, 50 c., $3, $5.
*Butterflies.* 8, 30, 50 c., $2.
*21st Birthday of Princess of Wales.* $2, $4.
*Birth of Prince William of Wales. Optd on 21st Birthday of Princess of Wales issue.* $2, $4.
*Christmas. Walt Disney's "One Hundred and One Dalmatians".* ½, 1, 2, 3, 4, 5, 10 c., $2.50, $3.

**1983**

*Easter. 500th Birth Anniv of Raphael.* 10, 50, 90 c., $4.
*Bicentenary of Manned Flight.* 10, 50, 90 c., $2.50.
*Christmas. Walt Disney Cartoon Characters. "Deck the Halls".* ½, 1, 2, 3, 4, 5, 10 c., $2.50, $3.

**1984**

*Easter. Walt Disney Cartoon Characters.* ½, 1, 2, 3, 4, 5, 10 c., $2, $4.
*Olympic Games, Los Angeles.* 10, 50, 90 c., $2.50.
*Christmas. 50th Birthday of Donald Duck.* 45, 60, 90 c., $2, $4.

**1985**

*Birth Bicentenary of John J. Audubon (ornithologist) (1st issue).* 60, 90 c., $1, $3.
*Life and Times of Queen Elizabeth the Queen Mother.* $1, $1.50, $2.50.
*Royal Visit.* 45 c., $1, $4.
*150th Birth Anniv of Mark Twain (author).* 25, 50 c., $1.50, $3.
*Birth Bicentenaries of Grimm Brothers (folklorists). Walt Disney Cartoon Characters.* 30, 60, 70 c., $4.

**1986**

*Birth Bicentenary of John J. Audubon (ornithologist) (2nd issue).* 90 c., $1, $1.50, $3.
*Appearance of Halley's Comet.* 5, 15, 55 c., $4.
*Centenary of Statue of Liberty (1st issue).* 20, 25, 30 c., $4.
*60th Birthday of Queen Elizabeth II.* 50, 60 c., $4.
*Royal Wedding.* 60 c., $1, $4.
*Christmas (1st issue). Disney characters in Hans Andersen Stories.* 30, 60, 70 c., $4.
*Christmas (2nd issue). "Wind in the Willows" (Kenneth Grahame).* 25, 50 c., $1.50, $3.

**1987**

*"Capex '87" International Stamp Exhibition, Toronto. Disney characters illustrating Art of Animation.* 25, 30, 50, 60, 70 c., $1.50, $3, $4.
*Birth Centenary of Marc Chagall (artist).* 10, 30, 40, 60, 90 c., $1, $3, $4.
*Centenary of Statue of Liberty (2nd issue).* 10, 15, 25, 30, 40, 60, 70, 90 c., $1, $2, $3, $4.
*250th Death Anniv of Sir Isaac Newton (scientist).* 20 c., $2.50.
*750th Anniv of Berlin.* $1, $4.
*Bicentenary of U.S. Constitution.* 30 c., $3.
*16th World Scout Jamboree, Australia.* 10 c., $4.

**1988**

*500th Anniv of Discovery of America by Columbus (1992) (1st issue).* 15, 30, 45, 60, 90 c., $1, $2, $3.
*"Finlandia '88" International Stamp Exhibition, Helsinki. Disney characters in Finnish scenes.* 1, 2, 3, 4, 5, 6 c., $5, $6.
*Olympic Games, Seoul.* 25, 60 c., $1.25, $3.
*500th Birth Anniv of Titian.* 10, 25, 40, 70, 90 c., $2, $3, $4.

**1989**

*20th Anniv of First Manned Landing on Moon. Disney characters on Moon.* ½, 1, 2, 3, 4, 5 c., $5, $6.
*500th Anniv of Discovery of America by Columbus (1992) (2nd issue). Pre-Columbian Societies.* 15, 45, 45, 50 c., $2, $2, $3, $3.
*Christmas. Disney characters and Cars of 1950's.* 25, 35, 45, 60 c., $1, $2, $3, $4.

**1990**

*Christmas. Disney characters and Hollywood Cars.* 25, 35, 40, 60 c., $1, $2, $4, $5.

**1991**

*Nobel Prize Winners.* 5, 15, 25, 40, 50 c., $1, $2, $4.

# B. KLEINBERG

## Specialist in BRITISH COMMONWEALTH, 1870–1970

*Fifty years a full time stamp dealer*

EXTENSIVE STOCKS HELD – WANTS LISTS WELCOME

Collections and stocks of British Commonwealth bought. Immediate settlement. I will travel to see worthwhile lots.

*Write to or telephone:*

**B. KLEINBERG**
40 Waxwell Lane
Pinner, Middx HA5 3EN
Tel: 081–866 0993

# TRADITIONAL ALBUMS FOR DISCERNING COLLECTORS

Stanley Gibbons blank leaved springback albums give you the freedom and flexibility you need to arrange your collection exactly as you want it.
Leaves are finely printed with a feint quadrille and most have side and centre markings to aid arrangement.
Albums and binders are now supplied with a sheet of self-adhesive, gold-blocked title panels, a selection of country titles and a run of volume numbers; allowing them to be clearly identifiable on the shelf or left blank if you prefer.

**Tower** (Item 0331) A choice of red, green, or black binder with 100 leaves of white cartridge 11⅛in. × 9⅞in. Boxed.

**Senator Medium** (Item 0384) A very popular 'first' blank leaved album for many years now. 50 leaves 10⅜in. × 8¾in., a choice of three binder colours; black, green or red.

**Senator Standard** (Item 0386) As the Senator Medium but with 100 larger sized leaves (11⅛in. × 9⅞in.). One of our best selling albums!

**Simplex Medium** (Item 3810) Fifty leaves of high quality cream paper with a subtle decorative border (10⅜in. × 8¾in.). Binder choice of green or red.

**Simplex Standard** (Item 3812) 100 larger sized leaves (11⅛in. × 9⅞in.), otherwise the same style as the Simplex Medium. Boxed. Popular with generations of stamp collectors!

**Utile (Item 3821)** 25 white cartridge special double linen-hinged transparent faces leaves (11⅛in. × 9⅞in.) designed to lie flat when album is opened. Attractive binder in choice of green or red.

**Transparent Interleaving** Fine quality glazed transparent paper in packs of 100 sheets for Tower, Senator, Simplex or similar types of loose-leaf springback albums.
Item 3310 Standard size 11in. × 9⅝in.
Item 3311 Medium size 10in. × 8⅛in.

*For further details visit your favourite stamp shop or write to:*

**Stanley Gibbons Publications Ltd.,
5 Parkside, Christchurch Road,
Ringwood, Hampshire BH24 3SH.
Telephone 0425 472363
Telefax 0425 470247**

# Ascension

**DEPENDENCY OF ST. HELENA**

Ascension, first occupied in 1815, was retained as a Royal Navy establishment from 1816 until 20 October 1922 when it became a dependency of St. Helena by Letters Patent.

Under Post Office regulations of 1850 (ratings) and 1854 (officers) mail from men of the Royal Navy serving abroad had the postage prepaid in Great Britain stamps, supplies of which were issued to each ship. Great Britain stamps used on Ascension before 1860 may have been provided by the naval officer in charge of the postal service.

The British G.P.O. assumed responsibility for such matters in 1860, but failed to send any stamps to the island until January 1867.

Until about 1880 naval mail, which made up most early correspondence, did not have the stamps cancelled until arrival in England. The prices quoted for Nos. Z1/3 and Z6 are for examples on cover or large piece showing the Great Britain stamps cancelled on arrival and an Ascension postmark struck elsewhere on the front of the envelope.

The use of British stamps ceased in December 1922.

The following postmarks were used on Great Britain stamps from Ascension:

Z 1 Z 2

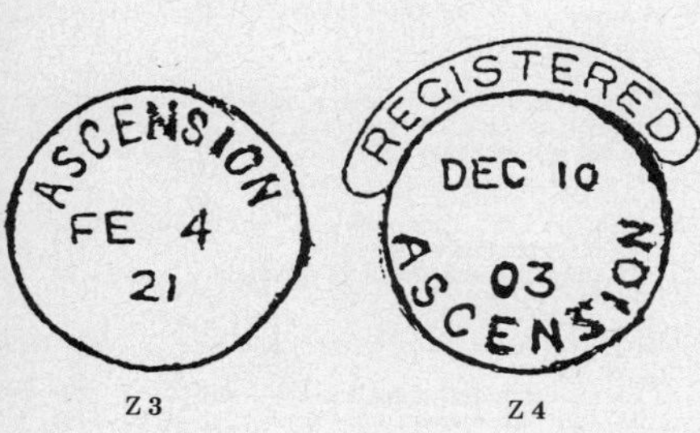


Z 3 Z 4

Z 5

| *Postmark Type* | *Approx Period of Use* | *Diameter* | *Index Letter* |
|---|---|---|---|
| Z 1 | 1858–1862 | 20 mm | A |
| Z 2 | 1864–1872 | 20 mm | A |
| | 1872–1878 | 21½ mm | A |
| | 1879–1889 | 19½ mm | A |
| | 1891–1894 | 21½ mm | C |
| | 1894–1902 | 22 mm | A |
| | 1903–1907 | 20½ mm | A |
| | 1908–1920 | 21 mm | A or none |
| | 1909–1920 | 23 mm | C sideways (1909), none (1910–11), B (1911–20) |
| Z 3 | 1920–1922 | 24 mm | none |
| Z 4 | 1897–1903 Registered | 23 mm | none |
| Z 5 | 1900–1902 Registered | 28 mm | C |
| | 1903–1904 Registered | 29 mm | A |

Forged postmarks exist. Those found most frequently are genuine postmarks of the post-1922 period with earlier date slugs fraudulently inserted, namely a 20 mm postmark as Type Z 2 (because of the shape of the "O" in "ASCENSION" this is often known as the Square O postmark) and a 24 mm postmark as Type Z 3 but with the index letter A.

*Stamps of* GREAT BRITAIN *cancelled with Types* Z 1/5.

*Line-engraved issues.*

| | | |
|---|---|---|
| Z1 | 1d. red-brown (1855) | £1500 |
| Z2 | 1d. rose-red (1864–79) *From* | £900 |
| | Plate Nos. 71, 74, 78, 83, 85, 96, 100, 102, 103, 104, 122, 134, 138, 154, 155, 157, 160, 168, 178 | |

*Surface-printed issues* (1856–1883).

| | | |
|---|---|---|
| Z2a | 6d. lilac (1856) | |
| Z3 | 6d. lilac (1865) (Plate No. 5) | £1800 |
| Z4 | 1s. green (1865) (Plate No. 4) | |
| Z5 | 1s. green (1867) (Plate No. 7) | |
| Z6 | 6d. grey (1874) (Plate Nos. 15, 16, 17) | £1400 |
| Z6a | 6d. on 6d. lilac (1883) | |
| Z7 | 1d. lilac (1881) (16 *dots*) | 22·00 |

**1887–92.**

| | | |
|---|---|---|
| Z 8 | ½d. vermilion | 28·00 |
| Z 9 | 1½d. purple and green | £100 |
| Z10 | 2d. green and carmine | 70·00 |
| Z11 | 2½d. purple/*blue* | 28·00 |
| Z12 | 3d. purple/*yellow* | £100 |
| Z13 | 4d. green and brown | 90·00 |
| Z14 | 4½d. green and carmine | £325 |
| Z15 | 5d. dull purple and blue | 95·00 |
| Z16 | 6d. purple/*rose-red* | 90·00 |
| Z17 | 9d. purple and blue | £180 |
| Z17a | 10d. dull purple and carmine | £250 |
| Z18 | 1s. green | £170 |

**1900.**

| | | |
|---|---|---|
| Z19 | ½d. blue-green | 28·00 |
| Z20 | 1s. green and carmine | £160 |

*King Edward VII issues* (1902–1911).

| | | |
|---|---|---|
| Z21 | ½d. green | 20·00 |
| Z22 | 1d. red | 16·00 |
| Z23 | 1½d. purple and green | 55·00 |
| Z24 | 2d. green and carmine | 45·00 |
| Z25 | 2½d. blue | 45·00 |
| Z26 | 3d. purple/*yellow* | 60·00 |
| Z27 | 4d. green and brown | £160 |
| Z28 | 4d. orange (1909) | 90·00 |
| Z29 | 5d. purple and blue | 95·00 |
| Z30 | 6d. purple | 90·00 |
| Z31 | 7d. grey-black (1910) | £225 |
| Z32 | 9d. purple and blue (1910) | £120 |
| Z32a | 10d. dull purple and scarlet | £170 |
| Z33 | 1s. green and carmine | 55·00 |
| Z33a | 2s. 6d. dull reddish purple (1911) | £500 |
| Z34 | 5s. carmine | £700 |
| Z35 | 10s. ultramarine | £1100 |
| Z35a | £1 green | £2250 |

**1911–12.** *T* **98/9** *of Great Britain.*

| | | |
|---|---|---|
| Z36 | ½d. green (Die A) | 60·00 |
| Z37 | ½d. yellow-green (Die B) | 22·00 |
| Z38 | 1d. scarlet (Die B) | 55·00 |

**1912.** *T* **101/2** *of Great Britain.*

| | | |
|---|---|---|
| Z38a | ½d. green | 55·00 |
| Z38b | 1d. scarlet | 55·00 |

**1912–22.**

| | | |
|---|---|---|
| Z39 | ½d. green (1913) | 18·00 |
| Z40 | 1d. scarlet | 15·00 |
| Z41 | 1½d. red-brown | 22·00 |
| Z42 | 2d. orange (Die I) | 22·00 |
| Z42a | 2d. orange (Die II) (1921) | 95·00 |
| Z43 | 2½d. blue | 25·00 |
| Z44 | 3d. violet | 32·00 |
| Z45 | 4d. grey-green (1913) | 42·00 |
| Z46 | 5d. brown (1913) | 42·00 |
| Z47 | 6d. purple (1913) | 38·00 |
| Z47a | 7d. green (1913) | £250 |
| Z47b | 8d. black/*yellow* (1913) | £225 |
| Z48 | 9d. agate (1913) | £130 |
| Z49 | 9d. olive-green (1922) | £225 |
| Z50 | 10d. turquoise-blue (1913) | £160 |
| Z51 | 1s. bistre (1913) | £110 |
| Z52 | 2s. 6d. brown (1918) | £600 |
| Z53 | 5s. rose-red (1919) | |

Supplies of some values do not appear to have been sent to the island, known examples originating from maritime or philatelic mail.

**PRICES FOR STAMPS ON COVER TO 1945**

| | |
|---|---|
| Nos. 1/34 | *from* × 4 |
| Nos. 35/7 | *from* × 8 |
| Nos. 38/47 | *from* × 5 |

**ASCENSION**

(1)

Line through "P" of "POSTAGE" (R. 3/6)

**1922** (2 Nov). *Stamps of St. Helena, optd with T* 1 *by D.L.R.*

*(a) Wmk Mult Script CA*

| | | | | |
|---|---|---|---|---|
| 1 | **16** | ½d. black and green | 2·75 | 7·00 |
| 2 | **17** | 1d. green | 3·25 | 8·00 |
| 3 | | 1½d. rose-scarlet | 12·00 | 30·00 |
| 4 | **16** | 2d. black and grey | 10·00 | 10·00 |
| | | a. Line through "P" of "POSTAGE" | £120 | |
| 5 | | 3d. bright blue | 10·00 | 14·00 |
| 6 | **17** | 8d. black and dull purple | 24·00 | 28·00 |
| 7 | | 2s. black and blue/*blue* | £100 | £110 |
| 8 | | 3s. black and violet | £150 | £170 |

*(b) Wmk Mult Crown CA*

| | | | | |
|---|---|---|---|---|
| 9 | **16** | 1s. black/*green* (R.) | 24·00 | 29·00 |
| 1/9 | | *Set of* 9 | £300 | £350 |
| 1/9 Optd "Specimen" | | *Set of* 9 | £600 | |

**PLATE FLAWS ON THE 1924–33 ISSUE.** Many constant plate varieties exist on both the vignette and duty plates of this issue.

The three major varieties are illustrated and listed below with prices for mint examples. Fine used stamps showing these flaws are worth a considerable premium over the mint prices quoted.

This issue utilised the same vignette plate as the St. Helena 1922–36 set so that these flaws occur there also.

2 Badge of St. Helena

Broken mainmast. Occurs on R.2/1 of all values.

Torn flag. Occurs on R.4/6 of all values except the 5d. Retouched on sheets of ½d. and 1d. printed after 1927.

Cleft rock. Occurs on R.5/1 of all values.

Broken scroll. Occurs on R. 1/4 of 1½d. only

(Typo D.L.R.)

**1924** (20 Aug)–**33.** *Wmk Mult Script CA. Chalk-surfaced paper. P* 14.

| | | | | |
|---|---|---|---|---|
| 10 | **2** | ½d. grey-black and black | 2·00 | 5·50 |
| | | a. Broken mainmast | 35·00 | |
| | | b. Torn flag | 40·00 | |
| | | c. Cleft rock | 30·00 | |
| 11 | | 1d. grey-black and deep blue-green | 3·25 | 4·50 |
| | | a. Broken mainmast | 40·00 | |
| | | b. Torn flag | 45·00 | |
| | | c. Cleft rock | 35·00 | |
| 11d | | 1d. grey-black & brt blue-green (1933) | 65·00 | £250 |
| | | da. Broken mainmast | £225 | |
| | | dc. Cleft rock | £200 | |
| 12 | | 1½d. rose-red | 4·75 | 14·00 |
| | | a. Broken mainmast | 50·00 | |
| | | b. Torn flag | 50·00 | |
| | | c. Cleft rock | 45·00 | |
| | | d. Broken scroll | 55·00 | |
| 13 | | 2d. grey-black and grey | 5·00 | 3·50 |
| | | a. Broken mainmast | 55·00 | |
| | | b. Torn flag | 55·00 | |
| | | c. Cleft rock | 48·00 | |
| 14 | | 3d. blue | 3·75 | 8·00 |
| | | a. Broken mainmast | 55·00 | |
| | | b. Torn flag | 55·00 | |
| | | c. Cleft rock | 48·00 | |
| 15 | | 4d. grey-black and black/*yellow* | 35·00 | 60·00 |
| | | a. Broken mainmast | £130 | |
| | | b. Torn flag | £130 | |
| | | c. Cleft rock | £110 | |
| 15d | | 5d. purple and olive-green (8.27) | 10·00 | 18·00 |
| | | da. Broken mainmast | 80·00 | |
| | | dc. Cleft rock | 70·00 | |
| 16 | | 6d. grey-black and bright purple | 42·00 | 65·00 |
| | | a. Broken mainmast | £180 | |
| | | b. Torn flag | £180 | |
| | | c. Cleft rock | £150 | |

17 2 8d. grey-black and bright violet .. 10·00 25·00
a. Broken mainmast .. 85·00
b. Torn flag .. 85·00
c. Cleft rock .. 70·00
18 1s. grey-black and brown .. 16·00 30·00
a. Broken mainmast .. 95·00
b. Torn flag .. 95·00
c. Cleft rock .. 80·00
19 2s. grey-black and blue/*blue* .. 55·00 75·00
a. Broken mainmast .. £200
b. Torn flag .. £200
c. Cleft rock .. £180
20 3s. grey-black and black/*blue* .. 80·00 85·00
a. Broken mainmast .. £325
b. Torn flag .. £325
c. Cleft rock .. £300
10/20 .. *Set of* 12 £225 £350
10/20 Optd "Specimen" .. *Set of* 12 £500

3 Georgetown

4 Ascension Island

(Des and recess D.L.R.)

**1934** (2 July). *T* **3/4** *and similar designs. Wmk Mult Script CA. P* 14.
21 3 ½d. black and violet .. 70 80
22 4 1d. black and emerald .. 1·60 1·25
23 – 1½d. black and scarlet .. 1·50 2·00
24 4 2d. black and orange .. 1·75 2·00
25 – 3d. black and ultramarine .. 1·75 1·50
26 – 5d. black and blue .. 2·00 3·00
27 4 8d. black and sepia .. 4·00 4·75
28 – 1s. black and carmine .. 12·00 6·00
29 4 2s. 6d. black and bright purple .. 28·00 32·00
30 – 5s. black and brown .. 45·00 55·00
21/30 .. *Set of* 10 90·00 £100
21/30 Perf "Specimen" .. *Set of* 10 £250
Designs: *Horiz*—1½d. The Pier; 3d. Long Beach; 5d. Three Sisters; 1s. Sooty Tern and Wideawake Fair; 5s. Green Mountain.

**1935** (6 May). *Silver Jubilee. As Nos. 91/4 of Antigua, but ptd by Waterlow. P* 11 × 12.
31 1½d. deep blue and scarlet .. 3·50 3·75
k. Kite and horizontal log .. 60·00
32 2d. ultramarine and grey .. 8·50 13·00
k. Kite and horizontal log .. 90·00
33 5d. green and indigo .. 12·00 13·00
j. Kite and vertical log .. £130
k. Kite and horizontal log .. £150
34 1s. slate and purple .. 18·00 25·00
k. Kite and horizontal log .. £160
31/4 .. *Set of* 4 38·00 50·00
31/4 Perf "Specimen" .. *Set of* 4 £130
For illustrations of plate varieties see Catalogue Introduction.

**1937** (19 May). *Coronation. As Nos. 95/7 of Antigua, but printed by D.L.R. P* 14.
35 1d. green .. 50 50
36 2d. orange .. 1·25 40
37 3d. bright blue .. 1·50 50
35/7 .. *Set of* 3 3·00 1·25
35/7 Perf "Specimen" .. *Set of* 3 £100

10 The Pier

Long centre bar to "E" in "GEORGETOWN" (R. 2/3)

"Davit" flaw (R. 5/1) (all ptgs of 1½d. and 2s. 6d.)

(Recess D.L.R.)

**1938** (12 May)–**53.** *Horiz designs as King George V issue, but modified and with portrait of King George VI as in T* **10**. *Wmk Mult Script CA. P* 13½.
38 3 ½d. black and violet .. 1·00 60
a. Long centre bar to E .. 20·00
b. Perf 13. *Black and bluish violet* (17.5.44) .. 40 65
ba. Long centre bar to E .. 12·00
39 – 1d. black and green .. 48·00 8·00
39*a* – 1d. black and yellow-orange (8.7.40) .. 11·00 11·00
b. Perf 13 (5.42) .. 45 40
c. Perf 14 (17.2.49) .. 70 12·00
39*d* – 1d. black and green, *p* 13 (1.6.49) .. 30 30
40 10 1½d. black and vermilion .. 1·50 1·40
a. Davit flaw .. 45·00
b. Perf 13 (17.5.44) .. 70 80
ba. Davit flaw .. 25·00
c. Perf 14 (17.2.49) .. 4·50 13·00
ca. Davit flaw .. 60·00
40*d* 1½d. black and rose-carmine, *p* 14 (1.6.49) 45 80
da. Davit flaw .. 20·00
db. *Black and carmine* .. 4·00 5·00
dba. Davit flaw .. 55·00
e. Perf 13 (25.2.53) .. 45 5·00
ea. Davit flaw .. 20·00
41 – 2d. black and red-orange .. 2·00 80
a. Perf 13 (17.5.44) .. 80 40
b. Perf 14 (17.2.49) .. 6·00 30·00
41*c* – 2d. black and scarlet, *p* 14 (1.6.49) .. 35 30
42 – 3d. black and ultramarine .. £100 26·00
42*a* – 3d. black and grey (8.7.40) .. 6·50 90
b. Perf 13 (17.5.44) .. 60 50
42*c* – 4d. black and ultramarine (8.7.40) .. 4·50 1·75
d. Perf 13 (17.5.44) .. 3·00 1·75
43 – 6d. black and blue .. 4·75 50
a. Perf 13 (17.5.44) .. 6·50 2·25
44 3 1s. black and sepia .. 6·50 70
a. Perf 13 (17.5.44) .. 3·00 1·25
45 10 2s. 6d. black and deep carmine .. 26·00 7·00
a. Frame printed double, once albino
b. Davit flaw .. £140
c. Perf 13 (17.5.44) .. 26·00 27·00
ca. Davit flaw .. £140
46 – 5s. black and yellow-brown .. 75·00 7·00
a. Perf 13 (17.5.44) .. 30·00 22·00
47 – 10s. black and bright purple .. 95·00 38·00
a. Perf 13 (17.5.44) .. 60·00 48·00
38/47a .. *Set of* 16 £250 85·00
38/47 Perf "Specimen" .. *Set of* 13 £400
Designs: *Horiz*—1d. (Nos. 39/c), 2d., 4d. Green Mountain; 1d. (No. 39*d*), 6d., 10s. Three Sisters; 3d., 5s. Long Beach.

**1946** (21 Oct). *Victory. As Nos. 110/11 of Antigua.*
48 2d. red-orange .. 40 30
49 4d. blue .. 40 30
48/9 Perf "Specimen" .. *Set of* 2 £110

**1948** (20 Oct). *Royal Silver Wedding. As Nos. 112/13 of Antigua.*
50 3d. black .. 50 30
51 10s. bright purple .. 42·00 35·00

**1949** (10 Oct). *75th Anniv of Universal Postal Union. As Nos. 114/17 of Antigua.*
52 3d. carmine .. 1·40 1·00
53 4d. deep blue .. 5·50 1·10
54 6d. olive .. 6·00 2·00
55 1s. blue-black .. 6·00 1·50
52/5 .. *Set of* 4 17·00 5·00

**1953** (2 June). *Coronation. As No. 120 of Antigua.*
56 3d. black and grey-black .. 1·25 1·50

15 Water Catchment

(Recess B.W.)

**1956** (19 Nov). *T* **15** *and similar horiz designs. Wmk Mult Script CA. P* 13.
57 ½d. black and brown .. 10 25
58 1d. black and magenta .. 55 35
59 1½d. black and orange .. 30 35
60 2d. black and carmine-red .. 70 40
61 2½d. black and orange-brown .. 60 55
62 3d. black and blue .. 2·00 1·00
63 4d. black and deep turquoise-green .. 1·25 1·00
64 6d. black and indigo .. 1·25 90
65 7d. black and deep olive .. 1·00 1·00
66 1s. black and vermilion .. 1·00 90
67 2s. 6d. black and deep dull purple .. 24·00 6·50
68 5s. black and blue-green .. 30·00 15·00
69 10s. black and purple .. 48·00 32·00
57/69 .. *Set of* 13 £100 55·00
Designs:—1d. Map of Ascension; 1½d. View of Georgetown; 2d. Map showing cable network; 2½d. Mountain road; 3d. White-tailed Tropic Bird; 4d. Long-finned Tunny; 6d. Rollers on the seashore; 7d. Young turtles; 1s. Land Crab; 2s. 6d. Sooty Tern; 5s. Perfect Crater; 10s. View of Ascension from North-west.

28 Brown Booby

42 Satellite Station

(Des after photos by N. P. Ashmole. Photo Harrison)

**1963** (23 May). *T* **28** *and similar horiz designs. W w* **12.** *P* 14 × 14½.
70 1d. black, lemon and new blue .. 20 15
71 1½d. black, cobalt and ochre .. 35 15
a. Cobalt omitted .. 60·00
72 2d. black, grey and bright blue .. 35 15
73 3d. black, magenta and turquoise-blue .. 45 15
74 4½d. black, bistre-brown and new blue .. 45 20
75 6d. bistre, black and yellow-green .. 45 20
76 7d. black, brown and reddish violet .. 45 20
77 10d. black, greenish yellow and blue-green .. 45 20
78 1s. multicoloured .. 50 20
79 1s. 6d. multicoloured .. 3·25 1·5(
80 2s. 6d. multicoloured .. 4·25 3·0(
81 5s. multicoloured .. 6·00 3·5(
82 10s. multicoloured .. 12·00 4·5(
83 £1 multicoloured .. 22·00 7·0(
70/83 .. *Set of* 14 45·00 19·0(
Designs:—1½d. White-capped Noddy; 2d. White Tern; 3d. Red-billed Tropic Bird; 4½d. Common Noddy; 6d. Sooty Tern; 7d. Ascension Frigate Bird; 10d. Blue-faced Booby; 1s. White-tailed Tropic Bird; 1s. 6d. Red-billed Tropic Bird; 2s. 6d. Madeiran Storm Petrel; 5s. Red-footed Booby (brown phase); 10s. Ascension Frigate Birds; £1 Red-footed Booby (white phase).

**1963** (4 June). *Freedom from Hunger. As No. 146 of Antigua.*
84 1s. 6d. carmine .. 3·00 40

**1963** (2 Sept). *Red Cross Centenary. As Nos. 147/8 of Antigua.*
85 3d. red and black .. 2·50 60
86 1s. 6d. red and blue .. 5·50 2·00

**1965** (17 May). *I.T.U. Centenary. As Nos. 166/7 of Antigua.*
87 3d. magenta and bluish violet .. 1·25 25
88 6d. turquoise-blue and light chestnut .. 1·50 30

**1965** (25 Oct). *International Co-operation Year. As Nos. 168/9 of Antigua.*
89 1d. reddish purple and turquoise-green .. 50 20
90 6d. deep bluish green and lavender .. 1·50 50

**1966** (24 Jan). *Churchill Commemoration. As Nos. 170/3 of Antigua.*
91 1d. new blue .. 50 25
92 3d. deep green .. 2·75 70
93 6d. brown .. 3·50 75
94 1s. 6d. bluish violet .. 4·50 1·25
91/4 .. *Set of* 4 10·00 2·75

**1966** (1 July). *World Cup Football Championships. As Nos. 176/7 of Antigua.*
95 3d. violet, yellow-green, lake and yell-brn .. 1·25 30
96 6d. chocolate, blue-green, lake & yellow-brn 1·50 40

**1966** (20 Sept). *Inauguration of W.H.O. Headquarters, Geneva. As Nos. 178/9 of Antigua.*
97 3d. black, yellow-green and light blue .. 1·75 40
98 1s. 6d. black, light purple and yellow-brown 4·25 1·10

(Des V. Whiteley. Photo Harrison)

**1966** (7 Nov). *Opening of Apollo Communications Satellite Earth Station. W w* **12.** *(sideways). P* 14 × 14½.
99 42 4d. black and reddish violet .. 15 15
100 8d. black and deep bluish green .. 20 15
101 1s. 3d. black and olive-brown .. 25 15
102 2s. 6d. black and turquoise-blue .. 35 20
99/102 .. *Set of* 4 85 60

43 B.B.C. Emblem

44 Human Rights Emblem and Chain Links

(Des B.B.C. staff. Photo, Queen's head and emblem die-stamped Harrison)

**1966** (1 Dec). *Opening of B.B.C. Relay Station. W w* **12.** *P* 14½.
103 43 1d. gold and ultramarine .. 10 1(
104 3d. gold and myrtle-green .. 15 1!
105 6d. gold and reddish violet .. 20 1!
106 1s. 6d. gold and red .. 20 2(
103/6 .. *Set of* 4 60 5(

**1967** (1 Jan). *20th Anniv of U.N.E.S.C.O. As Nos. 196/8 of Antigua.*
107 3d. slate-violet, red, yellow and orange .. 2·25 80
108 6d. orange-yellow, violet and deep olive .. 3·50 1·00
109 1s. 6d. black, bright purple and orange .. 5·50 1·40
107/9 .. .. .. .. .. *Set of* 3 10·00 3·00

(Des and litho Harrison)

**1968** (8 July). *Human Rights Year.* W w **12** (*sideways*). P 14½ × 14.
110 **44** 6d. light orange, red and black .. .. 20 10
111 1s. 6d. light grey-blue, red and black .. 30 15
112 2s. 6d. light green, red and black .. 35 20
110/12 .. .. .. .. *Set of* 3 75 40

45 Ascension Black-Fish

46 H.M.S. *Rattlesnake*

(Des M. Farrar Bell. Litho D.L.R.)

**1968** (23 Oct). *Fishes* (*1st series*). *T* **45** *and similar horiz designs.* W w **12** (*sideways*). P 13.
113 4d. black, slate and turquoise-blue .. .. 60 20
114 8d. multicoloured .. .. .. .. 75 35
115 1s. 9d. multicoloured .. .. .. 1·00 40
116 2s. 3d. multicoloured .. .. .. 1·25 45
113/16 .. .. .. .. *Set of* 4 3·25 1·25
Designs:—8d. Leather-jacket; 1s. 9d. Tunny; 2s. 3d. Mako Shark.
See also Nos. 117/20 and 126/9.

(Des M. Farrar Bell. Litho D.L.R.)

**1969** (3 Mar). *Fishes* (*2nd series*). *Horiz designs as T* **45**. *Multicoloured.* W w **12** (*sideways*). P 13.
117 4d. Sailfish .. .. .. .. .. 90 55
118 6d. Old Wife .. .. .. .. .. 1·25 70
119 1s. 6d. Yellowtail .. .. .. .. 2·00 1·25
120 2s. 11d. Jack .. .. .. .. .. 3·75 2·25
117/20 .. .. .. .. *Set of* 4 7·00 4·25

(Des L. Curtis. Photo Harrison)

**1969** (1 Oct). *Royal Naval Crests* (*1st series*). *T* **46** *and similar vert designs.* W w **12** (*sideways*). P 14 × 14½.
121 4d. multicoloured .. .. .. .. 50 15
122 9d. multicoloured .. .. .. .. 70 15
123 1s. 9d. deep blue, pale blue and gold .. 1·25 25
124 2s. 3d. multicoloured .. .. .. 1·50 30
121/4 .. .. .. .. *Set of* 4 3·50 75
MS125 165 × 105 mm. Nos. 121/4. P 14½ .. 7·50 8·00
Designs:—9d. H.M.S. *Weston*; 1s. 9d. H.M.S. *Undaunted*; 2s. 3d. H.M.S. *Eagle*.
See also Nos. 130/4, 149/53, 154/8 and 166/70.

(Des M. Farrar Bell. Litho D.L.R.)

**1970** (6 Apr). *Fishes* (*3rd series*). *Horiz designs as T* **45**. *Multicoloured.* W w **12** (*sideways*). P 14.
126 4d. Wahoo .. .. .. .. .. 3·50 1·50
127 9d. Coal-fish .. .. .. .. .. 3·50 1·50
128 1s. 9d. Dolphin .. .. .. .. 4·75 2·25
129 2s. 3d. Soldier Fish .. .. .. .. 4·75 2·25
126/9 .. .. .. .. *Set of* 4 15·00 6·75

(Des L. Curtis. Photo D.L.R.)

**1970** (7 Sept). *Royal Naval Crests* (*2nd series*). *Designs as T* **46**. *Multicoloured.* W w **12**. P 12½.
130 4d. H.M.S. *Penelope* .. .. .. .. 1·25 35
131 9d. H.M.S. *Carlisle* .. .. .. .. 1·50 60
132 1s. 6d. H.M.S. *Amphion* .. .. .. 2·00 85
133 2s. 6d. H.M.S. *Magpie* .. .. .. 2·50 1·25
130/3 .. .. .. .. *Set of* 4 6·50 2·75
MS134 153 × 96 mm. Nos. 130/3 .. .. 12·00 9·00

50 Early Chinese Rocket

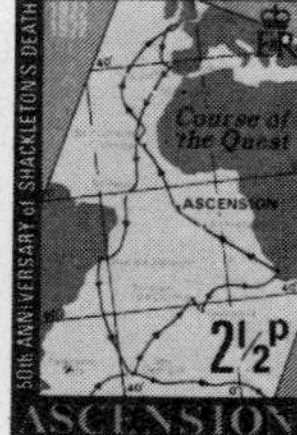


51 Course of the *Quest*

(Des V. Whiteley. Litho Format)

**1971** (15 Feb). *Decimal Currency. The Evolution of Space Travel. T* **50** *and similar multicoloured designs.* W w **12** (*sideways on horiz designs*). P 14.
135 ½p. Type **50** .. .. .. .. .. 15 15
136 1p. Medieval Arab Astronomers .. .. 20 15
137 1½p. Tycho Brahe's Observatory, Quadrant and Supernova .. .. .. .. 30 30
138 2p. Galileo, Moon and Telescope .. .. 40 30
139 2½p. Isaac Newton, Instruments and Apple .. 80 60
140 3½p. Harrison's Chronometer and Ship .. 85 55
141 4½p. Space Rocket taking-off .. .. 1·00 50
142 5p. World's Largest Telescope, Palomar .. 1·00 60
143 7½p. World's largest Radio Telescope, Jodrell Bank .. .. .. .. .. 4·00 1·40
144 10p. Mariner VII and Mars .. .. .. 3·50 1·75
145 12½p. Sputnik II and Space Dog, Laika .. 6·00 2·00
146 25p. Walking in Space .. .. .. .. 7·50 2·25
147 50p. Apollo XI Crew on Moon .. .. .. 4·75 2·50
148 £1 Future Space Research Station .. .. 5·50 4·50
135/48 .. .. .. .. *Set of* 14 32·00 16·00
The ½p., 1p., 4½p. and 25p. are vertical, and the remainder are horizontal.

(Des L. Curtis. Photo D.L.R.)

**1971** (15 Nov). *Royal Naval Crests* (*3rd series*). *Designs as T* **46**. *Multicoloured.* W w **12**. P 13.
149 2p. H.M.S. *Phoenix* .. .. .. .. 1·00 30
150 4p. H.M.S. *Milford* .. .. .. .. 1·50 55
151 9p. H.M.S. *Pelican* .. .. .. .. 1·75 80
152 15p. H.M.S. *Oberon* .. .. .. .. 2·00 1·00
149/52 .. .. .. .. *Set of* 4 5·50 2·40
MS153 151 × 104 mm. Nos. 149/52 .. .. 11·00 12·00

(Des L. Curtis. Litho Questa)

**1972** (29 May). *Royal Naval Crests* (*4th series*). *Multicoloured designs as T* **46**. W w **12** (*sideways*). P 14.
154 1½p. H.M.S. *Lowestoft* .. .. .. 65 50
155 3p. H.M.S. *Auckland* .. .. .. 85 75
156 6p. H.M.S. *Nigeria* .. .. .. .. 1·10 1·25
157 17½p. H.M.S. *Bermuda* .. .. .. 2·25 2·50
154/7 .. .. .. .. *Set of* 4 4·25 4·50
MS158 157 × 93 mm. Nos. 154/7 .. .. 4·75 7·50

(Des J. Cooter. Litho Questa)

**1972** (2 Aug). *50th Anniv of Shackleton's Death. T* **51** *and similar multicoloured designs.* W w **12** (*sideways on 4 and 7½p.*). P 14.
159 2½p. Type **51** .. .. .. .. .. 1·00 60
160 4p. Shackleton and *Quest* (*horiz*) .. .. 1·10 70
161 7½p. Shackleton's cabin and *Quest* (*horiz*) .. 1·25 75
162 11p. Shackleton's statue and memorial .. 1·40 1·00
159/62 .. .. .. .. *Set of* 4 4·25 2·75
MS163 139 × 114 mm. Nos. 159/62 (wmk sideways) 4·50 6·00

52 Land Crab and Mako Shark

(Des (from photograph by D. Groves) and photo Harrison)

**1972** (20 Nov). *Royal Silver Wedding. Multicoloured; background colour given.* W w **12**. P 14 × 14½.
164 **52** 2p. bright bluish violet .. .. .. 15 10
165 16p. rose-carmine .. .. .. 35 30

(Des L. Curtis. Litho J.W.)

**1973** (28 May). *Royal Naval Crests* (*5th series*). *Multicoloured designs as T* **46**. W w **12** (*sideways*). P 14.
166 2p. H.M.S. *Birmingham* .. .. .. 2·50 1·00
167 4p. H.M.S. *Cardiff* .. .. .. .. 3·00 1·00
168 9p. H.M.S. *Penzance* .. .. .. .. 4·00 1·25
169 13p. H.M.S. *Rochester* .. .. .. .. 4·50 1·50
166/9 .. .. .. .. *Set of* 4 12·50 4·25
MS170 109 × 152 mm. Nos. 166/9 .. .. 26·00 10·00

53 Green Turtle

(Des V. Whiteley Studio. Litho Enschedé)

**1973** (28 Aug). *Turtles. T* **53** *and similar triangular designs. Multicoloured.* W w **12**. P 13½.
171 4p. Type **53** .. .. .. .. .. 3·25 1·00
172 9p. Loggerhead turtle .. .. .. .. 3·50 1·50
173 12p. Hawksbill turtle .. .. .. .. 3·75 1·50
171/3 .. .. .. .. *Set of* 3 9·50 3·50

54 Sergeant, R.M. Light Infantry, 1900

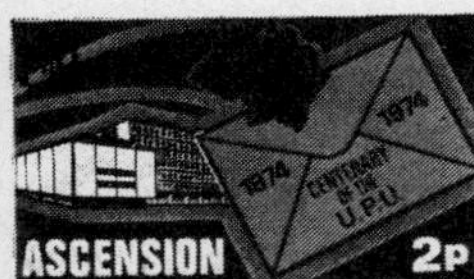


55 Letter and H.Q., Berne

(Des G. Drummond from paintings by C. Stadden. Litho Walsall)

**1973** (31 Oct). *50th Anniv of Departure of Royal Marines from Ascension. T* **54** *and similar vert designs. Multicoloured.* W w **12** (*sideways*). P 14.
174 2p. Type **54** .. .. .. .. .. 2·50 1·25
175 6p. R.M. Private, 1816 .. .. .. 3·50 1·75
176 12p. R.M. Light Infantry Officer, 1880 .. 4·00 2·25
177 20p. R.M. Artillery Colour Sergeant, 1910 .. 4·50 2·50
174/7 .. .. .. .. *Set of* 4 13·00 7·00

**1973** (14 Nov). *Royal Wedding. As Nos. 165/6 of Anguilla. Centre multicoloured.* W w **12** (*sideways*). P 13½.
178 2p. ochre .. .. .. .. .. .. 15 10
179 18p. dull blue-green .. .. .. .. 25 15

(Des PAD Studio. Litho Questa)

**1974** (27 Mar). *Centenary of U.P.U. T* **55** *and similar horiz design. Multicoloured.* W w **12**. P 14½ × 14.
180 2p. Type **55** .. .. .. .. .. 25 30
181 9p. Hermes and U.P.U. monument .. .. 40 45

56 Churchill as a Boy, and Birthplace, Blenheim Palace

(Des J.W. Litho Questa)

**1974** (30 Nov). *Birth Centenary of Sir Winston Churchill. T* **56** *and similar horiz design. Multicoloured. No wmk.* P 14.
182 5p. Type **56** .. .. .. .. .. 40 40
183 25p. Churchill as statesman, and U.N. Building .. .. .. .. .. 1·00 1·00
MS184 93 × 87 mm. Nos. 182/3 .. .. .. 2·50 2·50

57 "Skylab 3" and Photograph of Ascension

(Des PAD Studio. Litho Questa)

**1975** (20 Mar). *Space Satellites. T* **57** *and similar horiz design. Multicoloured.* W w **12** (*sideways*). P 14.
185 2p. Type **57** .. .. .. .. .. 30 30
186 18p. "Skylab 4" command module and photograph .. .. .. .. .. 40 40
The date "11.1.73" given on the 2p. is incorrect, "Skylab 3" was launched in July 1973 and returned to Earth in September 1973.
The date on the 18p. is also incorrect. The photograph was taken on 6 January 1974, three days later than the date given in the caption.

58 U.S.A.F. "Starlifter"

APOLLO-SOYUZ
LINK
1975

(59)

(Des R. Granger Barrett. Litho Questa)

**1975** (19 June). *Wideawake Airfield. T* **58** *and similar horiz designs. Multicoloured.* W w **12** (*sideways*). P 13½.
187 2p. Type **58** .. .. .. .. .. 1·25 65
188 5p. R.A.F. "Hercules" .. .. .. .. 1·75 85
189 9p. Vickers "VC-10" .. .. .. .. 2·00 1·40
190 24p. U.S.A.F. "Galaxy" .. .. .. .. 3·00 2·75
187/90 .. .. .. .. *Set of* 4 7·25 5·00
MS191 144 × 99 mm. Nos. 187/90 .. .. 14·00 16·00

**1975** (18 Aug). *"Apollo–Soyuz" Space Link. Nos. 141 and 145/6 optd with T* **59**.
192 4½p. Space rocket taking-off .. .. .. 15 15
193 12½p. Sputnik II and Space Dog, Laika .. 25 20
194 25p. Walking in Space .. .. .. .. 45 35
192/4 .. .. .. .. *Set of* 3 75 65

60 Arrival of Royal Navy, 1815

(Des J.W. from paintings by Isobel McManus. Litho Walsall)

**1975** (22 Oct). *160th Anniv of Occupation. T* **60** *and similar horiz designs. Multicoloured.* W w **14** (*sideways*). P 14.
195 2p. Type **60** .. .. .. .. .. 35 25
196 5p. Water Supply, Dampiers Drip .. .. 50 40
197 9p. First landing, 1815 .. .. .. .. 60 60
198 15p. The garden on Green Mountain .. .. 75 85
195/8 .. .. .. .. *Set of* 4 2·00 1·90

61 Yellow Canary

62 Boatswain Bird Island Sanctuary

(Des J.W. Litho Questa)

**1976** (26 Apr). *Multicoloured designs as T* **61** *and T* **62**. W w **14** (*sideways on horiz designs*). P 13½ (£2) or 14 (*others*).

199 1p. Type **61** .. .. .. .. .. .. 30 35
200 2p. White Tern .. .. .. .. .. 35 35
201 3p. Common Waxbill .. .. .. .. 35 40
202 4p. White-capped Noddy .. .. .. 35 40
203 5p. Common Noddy .. .. .. .. 50 50
204 6p. Common Mynah .. .. .. .. 50 50
205 7p. Madeiran Storm Petrel .. .. .. 55 55
206 8p. Sooty Tern .. .. .. .. .. 60 60
207 9p. Blue-faced Booby .. .. .. .. 60 65
208 10p. Red-footed Booby .. .. .. .. 60 70
209 15p. Bare-throated Francolin .. .. .. 1·25 1·50
210 18p. Brown Booby .. .. .. .. 1·25 1·50
211 25p. Red-billed Tropic Bird .. .. .. 1·40 1·50
212 50p. White-tailed Tropic Bird .. .. .. 2·25 2·50
213 £1 Ascension Frigate Bird .. .. .. 2·75 3·25
214 £2 Type **62** .. .. .. .. .. 5·50 6·50
199/214 .. .. .. .. .. *Set of* 16 17·00 20·00

The 2, 4, 7, 9, 15, 18p. and £1 are vertical designs.

63 G.B. Penny Red with Ascension Postmark

(Des C. Abbott. Litho J.W.)

**1976** (4 May). *Festival of Stamps, London. T* **63** *and similar designs.* W w **14** (*sideways on 5 and 25p.*). P 13½.

215 5p. rose-red, black and cinnamon .. .. 20 15
216 9p. green, black and greenish stone .. .. 30 20
217 25p. multicoloured .. .. .. .. 50 45
215/17 .. .. .. .. *Set of* 3 90 70

**MS**218 133 × 121 mm. No. 217 with St. Helena 318 and Tristan da Cunha 206 (wmk sideways). P 13 1·50 2·00

Designs: *Vert*—9p. ½d. stamp of 1922. *Horiz*—25p. *Southampton Castle* (liner).

No. **MS**218 was postally valid on each island to the value of 25p.

64 U.S. Base, Ascension

65 Visit of Prince Philip, 1957

(Des V. Whiteley Studio. Litho J.W.)

**1976** (4 July). *Bicentenary of American Revolution. T* **64** *and similar horiz designs. Multicoloured.* W w **14** (*sideways*). P 13.

219 8p. Type **64** .. .. .. .. .. 90 40
220 9p. NASA Station at Devils Ashpit .. .. 90 45
221 25p. "Viking" landing on Mars .. .. 1·50 80
219/21 .. .. .. .. *Set of* 3 3·00 1·50

(Des J. Cooter. Litho Walsall)

**1977** (7 Feb). *Silver Jubilee. T* **65** *and similar horiz designs. Multicoloured.* W w **14** (*sideways on 12 and 25p.*). P 13½.

222 8p. Type **65** .. .. .. .. .. 15 15
223 12p. Coronation Coach leaving Buckingham Palace .. .. .. .. .. 25 20
224 25p. Coronation Coach .. .. .. .. 45 40
222/4 .. .. .. .. .. *Set of* 3 75 65

66 Tunnel carrying Water Pipe

67 Mars Bay Location, 1877

(Des G. Drummond. Litho Harrison)

**1977** (27 June). *Water Supplies. T* **66** *and similar multicoloured designs.* W w **14** (*sideways on 12 and 25p.*). P 14.

225 3p. Type **66** .. .. .. .. .. 20 15
226 5p. Breakneck Valley wells .. .. .. 30 20
227 12p. Break tank (*horiz*) .. .. .. 55 35
228 25p. Water catchment (*horiz*) .. .. .. 90 65
225/8 .. .. .. .. .. *Set of* 4 1·75 1·25

(Des J.W. Litho Questa)

**1977** (3 Oct). *Centenary of Visit of Professor Gill (astronomer). T* **67** *and similar horiz designs. Multicoloured.* W w **14** (*sideways*). P 13½.

229 3p. Type **67** .. .. .. .. .. 25 20
230 8p. Instrument sites, Mars Bay .. .. .. 35 25
231 12p. Sir David and Lady Gill .. .. .. 55 40
232 25p. Maps of Ascension .. .. .. .. 90 70
229/32 .. .. .. .. .. *Set of* 4 1·90 1·40

68 Lion of England

69 Queen Elizabeth II

(Des C. Abbott. Litho Questa)

**1978** (2 June). *25th Anniv of Coronation. T* **68/9** *and similar vert design.* P 15.

233 **68** 25p. yellow, sepia and silver .. .. 60 65
a. Sheetlet. Nos. 233/5 × 2 .. .. 3·25
234 **69** 25p. multicoloured .. .. .. 60 65
235 – 25p. yellow, sepia and silver .. .. 60 65
233/5 .. .. .. .. .. *Set of* 3 1·60 1·75

Design:—No. 235, Green Turtle.

Nos. 233/5 were printed together in small sheets of 6, containing two *se-tenant* strips of 3 with horizontal gutter margin between.

70 Flank of Sisters, Sisters' Red Hill and East Crater

71 "The Resolution" (H. Roberts)

(Des J.W. Litho Questa)

**1978** (4 Sept). *Volcanic Rock Formations of Ascension. T* **70** *and similar horiz designs. Multicoloured.* W w **14**. P 14½.

236 3p. Type **70** .. .. .. .. .. 20 20
a. Horiz strip of 5. Nos. 236/40 .. .. 1·60
237 5p. Holland's Crater (Hollow Tooth) .. .. 30 30
238 12p. Street Crater, Lower Valley Crater and Bear's Back .. .. .. .. .. 40 40
239 15p. Butt Crater, Weather Post and Green Mountain .. .. .. .. .. 45 45
240 25p. Flank of Sisters, Thistle Hill and Two Boats Village .. .. .. .. 50 50
236/40 .. .. .. .. .. *Set of* 5 1·60 1·60
**MS**241 185 × 100 mm. Nos. 236/40, each × 2 .. 4·25 4·50
a. Blue ("Ascension Island") omitted .. £3250

Nos. 236/40 were printed together, *se-tenant*, in horizontal strips of 5 throughout the sheet forming a composite design.

(Des and litho (25p. also embossed) Walsall)

**1979** (19 Feb*). *Bicentenary of Captain Cook's Voyages, 1768–79. T* **71** *and similar vert designs. Multicoloured.* P 11.

242 3p. Type **71** .. .. .. .. .. 45 25
243 8p. Chronometer .. .. .. .. .. 65 40
244 12p. Green Turtle .. .. .. .. .. 75 50
245 25p. Flaxman/Wedgwood medallion of Captain Cook .. .. .. .. .. 1·00 70
242/5 .. .. .. .. .. *Set of* 4 2·50 1·75

*This is the local date of issue; the stamps were released in London on 8 January.

72 St. Mary's Church, Georgetown

73 Landing Cable, Comfortless Cove

(Des Walsall. Litho Format)

**1979** (24 May). *Ascension Day. T* **72** *and similar vert designs. Multicoloured.* W w **14**. P 14.

246 8p. Type **72** .. .. .. .. .. 30 20
247 12p. Map of Ascension .. .. .. .. 40 30
248 50p. "The Ascension" (painting by Rembrandt) 1·00 90
246/8 .. .. .. .. .. *Set of* 3 1·50 1·25

(Des G. Vasarhelyi. Litho Walsall)

**1979** (15 Sept). *80th Anniv of Eastern Telegraph Company's Arrival on Ascension. T* **73** *and similar designs.* W w **14** (*inverted on 12p. or sideways on others*). P 14.

249 3p. black and carmine .. .. .. .. 15 10
250 8p. black and yellowish green .. .. .. 25 20
251 12p. black and yellow .. .. .. .. 30 25
252 15p. black and bright violet .. .. .. 35 35
253 25p. black and orange-brown .. .. .. 50 50
249/53 .. .. .. .. .. *Set of* 5 1·40 1·25

Designs: *Horiz*—8p. C.S. *Anglia*; 15p. C.S. *Seine*; 25p. Cable and Wireless earth station. *Vert*—12p. Map of Atlantic cable network.

74 1938 6d. Stamp

(Des BG Studio. Litho Questa)

**1979** (12 Dec). *Death Centenary of Sir Rowland Hill. T* **74** *and similar designs.* W w **14** (*sideways on 3 and 8p.*). P 14.

254 3p. black, new blue and deep turquoise-blue 10 10
255 8p. black, blue-green and light green .. 20 20
256 12p. black, bright blue and turquoise-blue .. 25 25
257 50p. black, brownish grey and red .. .. 90 90
254/7 .. .. .. .. .. *Set of* 4 1·25 1·25

Designs: *Horiz*—8p. 1956 5s. definitive stamp. *Vert*—12p. 1924 3s. stamp; 50p. Sir Rowland Hill.

75 *Anogramma ascensionis*

76 17th-century Bottle Post

(Des J. Cooter. Litho Format)

**1980** (18 Feb). *Ferns and Grasses. T* **75** *and similar multicoloured designs.* W w **14** (*sideways on 12 to 24p.*). P 14½ × 14 (*3 to 8p.*) *or* 14 × 14½ (*12 to 24p.*).

258 3p. Type **75** .. .. .. .. .. 10 10
259 6p. *Xiphopteris ascensionense* .. .. .. 20 15
260 8p. *Sporobolus caespitosus* .. .. .. 20 15
261 12p. *Sporobolus durus* (*vert*) .. .. .. 30 25
262 18p. *Dryopteris ascensionis* (*vert*) .. .. 40 35
a. Brown (thorns) omitted .. .. .. 60·00
263 24p. *Marattia purpurascens* (*vert*) .. .. 50 50
258/63 .. .. .. .. .. *Set of* 6 1·50 1·25

(Des L. Curtis. Litho Format)

**1980** (1 May). *"London 1980" International Stamp Exhibition. T* **76** *and similar horiz designs. Multicoloured.* W w **14** (*sideways*). P 13½.

264 8p. Type **76** .. .. .. .. .. 25 20
265 12p. 19th-century chance calling ship .. .. 35 25
266 15p. *Garthcastle II* (regular mail service from 1863) .. .. .. .. .. 40 30
267 50p. *St. Helena* (mail services, 1980) .. .. 1·00 90
264/7 .. .. .. .. .. *Set of* 4 1·75 1·50
**MS**268 102 × 154 mm. Nos. 264/7 .. .. 2·10 2·75

77 Queen Elizabeth the Queen Mother

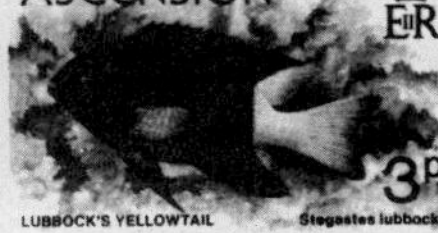


78 Lubbock's Yellowtail

(Des Harrison. Litho Questa)

**1980** (11 Aug)*. *80th Birthday of Queen Elizabeth the Queen Mother.* W w **14** (*sideways*). P 14.

269 **77** 15p. multicoloured .. .. .. .. 40 40

*This was the local release date. The Crown Agents placed stocks on sale in London on 4 August.

(Des G. Drummond. Litho Enschedé)

**1980** (15 Sept). *Fishes. T* **78** *and similar horiz designs. Multicoloured.* W w **14** (*sideways*). P 13 × 13½.

270 3p. Type **78** .. .. .. .. .. 20 15
271 10p. Resplendent Angelfish .. .. .. 35 25
272 25p. Hedgehog Butterflyfish .. .. .. 60 50
273 40p. Marmalade Razorfish .. .. .. 80 65
270/3 .. .. .. .. .. *Set of* 4 1·75 1·40

79 H.M.S. *Tortoise*

(Des D. Bowen. Litho Rosenbaum Bros, Vienna)

**1980** (17 Nov). *150th Anniv of Royal Geographical Society. T* **79** *and similar multicoloured designs.* W w **14** *(sideways)*. P 14 (60p.) or 13½ (*others*).

| No. | Description | Unused | Used |
|---|---|---|---|
| 274 | 10p. Type **79** | 45 | 40 |
| 275 | 15p. "Wideawake Fair" | 55 | 45 |
| 276 | 60p. Mid-Atlantic Ridge (38 × 48 *mm*) | 1·10 | 1·25 |
| 274/6 | *Set of* 3 | 1·90 | 2·00 |

**80** Green Mountain Farm, 1881

(Des C. Abbott. Litho Format)

**1981** (15 Feb). *Green Mountain Farm. T* **80** *and similar horiz designs. Multicoloured.* W w **14** *(sideways)*. P 13½ × 14.

| No. | Description | Unused | Used |
|---|---|---|---|
| 277 | 12p. Type **80** | 45 | 35 |
| 278 | 15p. Two Boats, 1881 | 50 | 40 |
| 279 | 20p. Green Mountain and Two Boats, 1981 | 60 | 50 |
| 280 | 30p. Green Mountain Farm, 1981 | 80 | 70 |
| 277/80 | *Set of* 4 | 2·10 | 1·75 |

**81** Cable and Wireless Earth Station

(Des G. Vasarhelyi and Walsall. Litho Walsall)

**1981** (27 Apr). *"Space Shuttle" Mission and Opening of 2nd Earth Station.* W w **14** *(sideways)*. P 14.

| No. | Description | Unused | Used |
|---|---|---|---|
| 281 **81** | 15p. black, bright blue and pale blue | 30 | 35 |

**82** Poinsettia

**83** Solanum

(Des J. Cooter. Litho J.W.)

**1981** (11 May)–**82**. *Flowers. Designs as T* **82** *(1 to 40p.) or vert as T* **83** *(50p. to £2). Multicoloured.* W w **14** *(sideways on 1, 2, 4, 5, 8, 15, 20, 40, 50p., £1 and £2).* P 13½. A. *Without imprint date.* B. *With imprint date* ("1982") (27.8.82).

| No. | Description | A | | B | |
|---|---|---|---|---|---|
| 282 | 1p. Type **82** | 40 | 30 | † | |
| 283 | 2p. Clustered Wax Flower | 50 | 35 | 50 | 50 |
| 284 | 3p. Kolanchoe (*vert*) | 50 | 35 | 50 | 55 |
| 285 | 4p. Yellow Pops | 55 | 35 | † | |
| 286 | 5p. Camels Foot Creeper | 55 | 35 | † | |
| 287 | 8p. White Oleander | 55 | 40 | † | |
| 288 | 10p. Ascension Lily (*vert*) | 90 | 50 | 45 | 50 |
| 289 | 12p. Coral Plant (*vert*) | 70 | 45 | † | |
| 290 | 15p. Yellow Allamanda | 80 | 55 | 50 | 55 |
| 291 | 20p. Ascension Euphorbia | 80 | 60 | 80 | 60 |
| 292 | 30p. Flame of the Forest (*vert*) | 90 | 80 | † | |
| 293 | 40p. Bougainvillea "King Leopold" | 1·25 | 1·25 | † | |
| 294 | 50p. Type **83** | 1·25 | 1·75 | † | |
| 295 | £1 Ladies Petticoat | 2·00 | 3·00 | 2·00 | 2·75 |
| 296 | £2 Red Hibiscus | 3·75 | 4·75 | † | |
| 282A/96A | *Set of* 15 | 14·00 | 14·00 | † | |
| 283B/95B | *Set of* 6 | † | | 4·25 | 5·00 |

Nos. 283B/95B had the imprint dates printed on the stamps by typography.

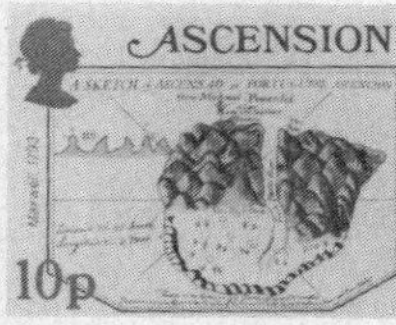

**84** Map by Maxwell, 1793

(Des L. Curtis. Litho Walsall)

**1981** (22 May). *Early Maps of Ascension. T* **84** *and similar horiz designs.* W w **14** *(sideways)*. P 14 × 14½.

| No. | Description | Unused | Used |
|---|---|---|---|
| 297 | 10p. black, gold and pale blue | 40 | 35 |
| 298 | 12p. black, gold and apple-green | 45 | 35 |
| 299 | 15p. black, gold and stone | 50 | 40 |
| 300 | 40p. black, gold and pale greenish yellow | 85 | 85 |
| 297/300 | *Set of* 4 | 2·00 | 1·75 |
| **MS**301 | 79 × 64 mm. 5p. × 4, multicoloured | 60 | 60 |

Designs:—12p. Maxwell, 1793 (*different*); 15p. Ekeberg and Chapman, 1811; 40p. Campbell, 1819; miniature sheet, Linschoten, 1599.

Stamps from No. **MS**301 form a composite design.

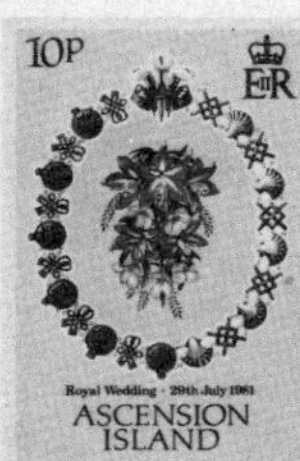

**85** Wedding Bouquet from Ascension

**86** Prince Charles and Lady Diana Spencer

(Des J.W. Litho Questa)

**1981** (22 July). *Royal Wedding. T* **85/6** *and similar vert design. Multicoloured.* W w **14**. P 14.

| No. | Description | Unused | Used |
|---|---|---|---|
| 302 | 10p. Type **85** | 25 | 25 |
| 303 | 15p. Prince Charles in Fleet Air Arm flying kit | 30 | 30 |
| 304 | 50p. Type **86** | 85 | 85 |
| 302/4 | *Set of* 3 | 1·25 | 1·25 |

**87** "Interest"

**88** Scout crossing Rope Bridge

(Des BG Studio. Litho Questa)

**1981** (14 Sept). *25th Anniv of Duke of Edinburgh Award Scheme. T* **87** *and similar vert designs. Multicoloured.* W w **14**. P 14.

| No. | Description | Unused | Used |
|---|---|---|---|
| 305 | 5p. Type **87** | 15 | 15 |
| 306 | 10p. "Physical activities" | 20 | 20 |
| 307 | 15p. "Service" | 25 | 25 |
| 308 | 40p. Duke of Edinburgh | 70 | 70 |
| 305/8 | *Set of* 4 | 1·10 | 1·10 |

(Des A. Theobald. Litho Format)

**1982** (22 Feb). *75th Anniv of Boy Scout Movement. T* **88** *and similar designs.* W w **14** *(sideways)*. P 14.

| No. | Description | Unused | Used |
|---|---|---|---|
| 309 | 10p. black, bright blue and azure | 45 | 35 |
| 310 | 15p. black, orange-brown and greenish yellow | 55 | 50 |
| 311 | 25p. black, bright mauve and pale mauve | 75 | 60 |
| 312 | 40p. black, rosine and pale orange | 1·10 | 85 |
| 309/12 | *Set of* 4 | 2·50 | 2·10 |
| **MS**313 | 121 × 121 mm. 10p., 15p., 25p., 40p. As Nos. 309/12 (*each diamond*, 40 × 40 *mm*). P 14½ | 3·50 | 2·50 |

Designs:—15p. 1st Ascension Scout Group flag; 25p. Scouts learning to use radio; 40p. Lord Baden-Powell.

Stamps from No. **MS**313 have an overall design showing a flag printed on the reverse beneath the gum.

**89** Charles Darwin

(Des L. Curtis. Litho Questa)

**1982** (19 Apr). *150th Anniv of Charles Darwin's Voyage. T* **89** *and similar horiz designs. Multicoloured.* W w **14** *(sideways)*. P 14.

| No. | Description | Unused | Used |
|---|---|---|---|
| 314 | 10p. Type **89** | 50 | 40 |
| 315 | 12p. Darwin's pistols | 55 | 50 |
| 316 | 15p. Rock Crab | 60 | 55 |
| 317 | 40p. H.M.S. *Beagle* | 1·10 | 95 |
| 314/17 | *Set of* 4 | 2·50 | 2·25 |

**90** Fairey "Swordfish"

(Des A. Theobald. Litho Walsall)

**1982** (15 June). *40th Anniv of Wideawake Airfield. T* **90** *and similar horiz designs. Multicoloured.* W w **14** *(sideways)*. P 14.

| No. | Description | Unused | Used |
|---|---|---|---|
| 318 | 5p. Type **90** | 50 | 35 |
| 319 | 10p. North American "B-25C (Mitchell)" | 70 | 40 |
| 320 | 15p. Boeing "EC-135N (Aria)" | 90 | 55 |
| 321 | 50p. Lockheed "Hercules" | 1·50 | 1·10 |
| 318/21 | *Set of* 4 | 3·25 | 2·25 |

**91** Ascension Coat of Arms

**92** Formal Portrait

(Des Jennifer Toombs. Litho Questa)

**1982** (1 July). *21st Birthday of Princess of Wales. T* **91/2** *and similar vert designs. Multicoloured.* W w **14**. P 14 × 14½.

| No. | Description | Unused | Used |
|---|---|---|---|
| 322 | 12p. Type **91** | 35 | 30 |
| 323 | 15p. Lady Diana Spencer in Music Room, Buckingham Palace | 40 | 35 |
| 324 | 25p. Bride and Earl Spencer leaving Clarence House | 65 | 55 |
| 325 | 50p. Type **92** | 1·10 | 1·00 |
| 322/5 | *Set of* 4 | 2·25 | 2·00 |

1st PARTICIPATION
COMMONWEALTH GAMES 1982

(**93**)

**94** Bush House, London

**1982** (29 Oct). *Commonwealth Games, Brisbane. Nos. 290B/1B optd with T* **93**.

| No. | Description | Unused | Used |
|---|---|---|---|
| 326 | 15p. Yellow Allamanda | 30 | 40 |
| 327 | 20p. Ascension Euphorbia | 40 | 45 |

(Des A. Theobald. Litho Questa)

**1982** (1 Dec). *50th Anniv of B.B.C. External Broadcasting. T* **94** *and similar horiz designs. Multicoloured.* W w **14** *(sideways)*. P 14.

| No. | Description | Unused | Used |
|---|---|---|---|
| 328 | 5p. Type **94** | 25 | 25 |
| 329 | 10p. Atlantic relay station | 35 | 35 |
| 330 | 25p. Lord Reith, first director-general | 75 | 75 |
| 331 | 40p. King George V making his first Christmas broadcast, 1932 | 1·00 | 1·00 |
| 328/31 | *Set of* 4 | 2·10 | 2·10 |

**95** *Marasmius echinosphaerus*

**96** Aerial View of Georgetown

(Des Harrison. Litho Questa)

**1983** (1 Mar). *Fungi. T* **95** *and similar vert designs. Multicoloured.* W w **14**. P 14.

| No. | Description | Unused | Used |
|---|---|---|---|
| 332 | 7p. Type **95** | 35 | 25 |
| 333 | 12p. *Chlorophyllum molybdites* | 45 | 35 |
| 334 | 15p. *Leucocoprinus cepaestripes* | 50 | 40 |
| 335 | 20p. *Lycoperdon marginatum* | 65 | 50 |
| 336 | 50p. *Marasmiellus distantifolius* | 1·10 | 1·00 |
| 332/6 | *Set of* 5 | 2·75 | 2·25 |

(Des Jennifer Toombs. Litho Format)

**1983** (12 May). *Island Views (1st series) T* **96** *and similar horiz designs. Multicoloured. W w* **14** *(sideways). P* 14 × 13½.

| No. | Description | Mint | Used |
|---|---|---|---|
| 337 | 12p. Type **96** | 25 | 30 |
| 338 | 15p. Green Mountain farm | 30 | 35 |
| 339 | 20p. Boatswain Bird Island | 40 | 45 |
| 340 | 60p. Telemetry Hill by night | 1·25 | 1·40 |
| 337/40 | *Set of* 4 | 2·00 | 2·25 |

See also Nos. 367/70.

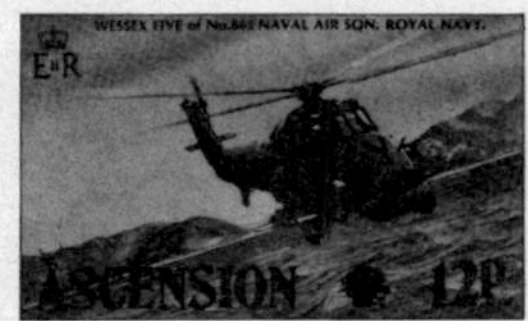


**97** "Wessex 5" Helicopter of No. 845 Naval Air Squadron

(Des D. Hartley-Marjoram. Litho Questa)

**1983** (1 Aug). *Bicentenary of Manned Flight. British Military Aircraft. T* **97** *and similar horiz designs. Multicoloured. W w* **14** *(sideways). P* 13½.

| No. | Description | Mint | Used |
|---|---|---|---|
| 341 | 12p. Type **97** | 60 | 35 |
| 342 | 15p. "Vulcan B2" of No. 44 Squadron | 70 | 40 |
| 343 | 20p. "Nimrod MR2P" of No. 120 Squadron | 85 | 50 |
| 344 | 60p. "Victor K2" of No. 55 Squadron | 1·75 | 1·60 |
| 341/4 | *Set of* 4 | 3·50 | 2·50 |

**98** Iguanid

(Des D. Nockles. Litho Questa)

**1983** (20 Sept). *Introduced Species. T* **98** *and similar horiz designs. Multicoloured. W w* **14** *(sideways). P* 14.

| No. | Description | Mint | Used |
|---|---|---|---|
| 345 | 12p. Type **98** | 30 | 30 |
| 346 | 15p. Rabbit | 35 | 35 |
| 347 | 20p. Cat | 45 | 45 |
| 348 | 60p. Donkey | 1·40 | 1·40 |
| 345/8 | *Set of* 4 | 2·25 | 2·25 |

**99** *Tellina antonii philippi*

**100** 1922 1½d. Stamp

(Des G. Wilby. Litho Format)

**1983** (28 Nov). *Sea Shells. T* **99** *and similar horiz designs. Multicoloured. W w* **14** *(sideways). P* 14½ × 14.

| No. | Description | Mint | Used |
|---|---|---|---|
| 349 | 7p. Type **99** | 20 | 20 |
| 350 | 12p. *Nodipecten nodosus (Linne)* | 30 | 30 |
| 351 | 15p. *Cypraea lurida oceanica sch* | 35 | 35 |
| 352 | 20p. *Nerita ascensionis gmelin* | 45 | 45 |
| 353 | 50p. *Micromelo undatus (bruguiere)* | 1·10 | 1·10 |
| 349/53 | *Set of* 5 | 2·25 | 2·25 |

(Des C. Abbott. Litho Questa)

**1984** (3 Jan). *150th Anniv of St. Helena as a British Colony. T* **100** *and similar vert designs showing stamps of the 1922 issue overprinted on St. Helena. Multicoloured. W w* **14**. *P* 14.

| No. | Description | Mint | Used |
|---|---|---|---|
| 354 | 12p. Type **100** | 35 | 35 |
| 355 | 15p. 1922 2d. stamp | 40 | 40 |
| 356 | 20p. 1922 8d. stamp | 45 | 45 |
| 357 | 60p. 1922 1s. stamp | 1·25 | 1·40 |
| 354/7 | *Set of* 4 | 2·25 | 2·40 |

**101** Prince Andrew

**102** Naval Semaphore

(Des L. Curtis. Litho Questa)

**1984** (10 Apr). *Visit of Prince Andrew. Sheet, 124 × 90 mm, containing vert designs as T* **101**. *W w* **14**. *P* 14½ × 14.

| No. | Description | Mint | Used |
|---|---|---|---|
| **MS**358 | 12p. Type **101**; 70p. Prince Andrew in naval uniform | 1·75 | 1·90 |

(Des D. Hartley-Marjoram. Litho Questa)

**1984** (28 May). *250th Anniv of "Lloyd's List" (newspaper). T* **102** *and similar vert designs. Multicoloured. W w* **14**. *P* 14½ × 14.

| No. | Description | Mint | Used |
|---|---|---|---|
| 359 | 12p. Type **102** | 30 | 30 |
| 360 | 15p. *Southampton Castle* (liner) | 35 | 35 |
| 361 | 20p. Pier Head | 45 | 45 |
| 362 | 70p. *The Dane* (mail ship) | 1·50 | 1·50 |
| 359/62 | *Set of* 4 | 2·40 | 2·40 |

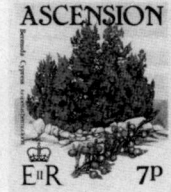

**103** Penny Coin and Yellowfin Tuna

**104** Bermuda Cypress

(Des G. Drummond. Litho Questa)

**1984** (26 July). *New Coinage. T* **103** *and similar horiz designs. Multicoloured. W w* **14** *(sideways). P* 14.

| No. | Description | Mint | Used |
|---|---|---|---|
| 363 | 12p. Type **103** | 50 | 35 |
| 364 | 15p. Twopenny coin and donkey | 60 | 40 |
| 365 | 20p. Fifty pence coin and Green Turtle | 75 | 50 |
| 366 | 70p. Pound coin and Sooty Tern | 2·00 | 1·75 |
| 363/6 | *Set of* 4 | 3·50 | 2·75 |

(Des Jennifer Toombs. Litho B.D.T.)

**1984** (26 Oct). *Island Views (2nd series). Horiz designs as T* **96**. *Multicoloured. W w* **14** *(sideways). P* 13½.

| No. | Description | Mint | Used |
|---|---|---|---|
| 367 | 12p. The Devil's Riding-school | 30 | 30 |
| 368 | 15p. St. Mary's Church | 35 | 35 |
| 369 | 20p. Two Boats Village | 45 | 45 |
| 370 | 70p. Ascension from the sea | 1·50 | 1·50 |
| 367/70 | *Set of* 4 | 2·40 | 2·40 |

(Des N. Shewring. Litho Questa)

**1985** (8 Mar). *Trees. T* **104** *and similar vert designs. Multicoloured. W w* **14**. *P* 14½.

| No. | Description | Mint | Used |
|---|---|---|---|
| 371 | 7p. Type **104** | 45 | 20 |
| 372 | 12p. Norfolk Island Pine | 55 | 30 |
| 373 | 15p. Screwpine | 65 | 35 |
| 374 | 20p. Eucalyptus | 80 | 45 |
| 375 | 65p. Spore Tree | 2·00 | 1·40 |
| 371/5 | *Set of* 5 | 4·00 | 2·40 |

**105** The Queen Mother with Prince Andrew at Silver Jubilee Service

**106** 32 Pdr. Smooth Bore Muzzle-loader, *c* 1820, and Royal Marine Artillery Hat Plate, *c* 1816

(Des A. Theobald (75p.), C. Abbott (others). Litho Questa)

**1985** (7 June). *Life and Times of Queen Elizabeth the Queen Mother. T* **105** *and similar vert designs. Multicoloured. W w* **16**. *P* 14½ × 14.

| No. | Description | Mint | Used |
|---|---|---|---|
| 376 | 12p. With the Duke of York at Balmoral, 1924 | 30 | 30 |
| 377 | 15p. Type **105** | 35 | 35 |
| 378 | 20p. The Queen Mother at Ascot | 45 | 45 |
| 379 | 70p. With Prince Henry at his christening (from photo by Lord Snowdon) | 1·50 | 1·50 |
| 376/9 | *Set of* 4 | 2·40 | 2·40 |
| **MS**380 | 91 × 73 mm. 75p. Visiting the *Queen Elizabeth 2* at Southampton, 1968. Wmk sideways | 1·50 | 1·60 |

(Des W. Fenton. Litho Walsall)

**1985** (19 July). *Guns on Ascension Island. T* **106** *and similar horiz designs. Multicoloured. W w* **14** *(sideways). P* 14 × 14½.

| No. | Description | Mint | Used |
|---|---|---|---|
| 381 | 12p. Type **106** | 50 | 35 |
| 382 | 15p. 7 inch rifled muzzle-loader, *c* 1866, and Royal Cypher on barrel | 60 | 40 |
| 383 | 20p. 7 pdr. rifled muzzle-loader, *c* 1877, and Royal Artillery badge | 70 | 50 |
| 384 | 70p. 5·5 inch gun, 1941, and crest from H.M.S. *Hood* | 2·00 | 1·75 |
| 381/4 | *Set of* 4 | 3·50 | 2·75 |

**107** Guide Flag

**108** *Clerodendrum fragrans*

(Des N. Shewring. Litho Questa)

**1985** (4 Oct). *75th Anniv of Girl Guide Movement and International Youth Year. T* **107** *and similar vert designs. Multicoloured. W w* **14**. *P* 14½ × 14.

| No. | Description | Mint | Used |
|---|---|---|---|
| 385 | 12p. Type **107** | 55 | 45 |
| 386 | 15p. Practising first aid | 65 | 55 |
| 387 | 20p. Camping | 75 | 65 |
| 388 | 70p. Lady Baden-Powell | 2·25 | 2·00 |
| 385/8 | *Set of* 4 | 3·75 | 3·25 |

(Des Josephine Martin. Litho Questa)

**1985** (6 Dec). *Wild Flowers. T* **108** *and similar vert designs. Multicoloured. W w* **16**. *P* 14.

| No. | Description | Mint | Used |
|---|---|---|---|
| 389 | 12p. Type **108** | 45 | 35 |
| 390 | 15p. Shell Ginger | 55 | 40 |
| 391 | 20p. Cape Daisy | 65 | 50 |
| 392 | 70p. Ginger Lily | 2·00 | 1·75 |
| 389/92 | *Set of* 4 | 3·25 | 2·75 |

**109** Newton's Reflector Telescope

**110** Princess Elizabeth in 1926

(Des D. Hartley. Litho B.D.T.)

**1986** (7 Mar). *Appearance of Halley's Comet. T* **109** *and similar vert designs. Multicoloured. W w* **16**. *P* 14.

| No. | Description | Mint | Used |
|---|---|---|---|
| 393 | 12p. Type **109** | 60 | 40 |
| 394 | 15p. Edmond Halley and Old Greenwich Observatory | 70 | 45 |
| 395 | 20p. Short's Gregorian telescope and comet, 1759 | 80 | 55 |
| 396 | 70p. Ascension satellite tracking station and ICE spacecraft | 2·25 | 1·75 |
| 393/6 | *Set of* 4 | 4·00 | 2·75 |

(Des A. Theobald. Litho Format)

**1986** (21 Apr). *60th Birthday of Queen Elizabeth II. T* **110** *and similar vert designs. Multicoloured. W w* **16**. *P* 14 × 14½.

| No. | Description | Mint | Used |
|---|---|---|---|
| 397 | 7p. Type **110** | 15 | 20 |
| 398 | 15p. Queen making Christmas broadcast, 1952 | 30 | 35 |
| 399 | 20p. At Garter ceremony, Windsor Castle, 1983 | 40 | 45 |
| 400 | 35p. In Auckland, New Zealand, 1981 | 70 | 75 |
| 401 | £1 At Crown Agents' Head Office, London, 1983 | 2·00 | 2·10 |
| 397/401 | *Set of* 5 | 3·25 | 3·50 |

**111** 1975 Space Satellites 2p. Stamp

**112** Prince Andrew and Miss Sarah Ferguson

(Des L. Curtis. Litho Walsall)

**1986** (22 May). *"Ameripex '86" International Stamp Exhibition, Chicago. T* **111** *and similar horiz designs showing previous Ascension stamps. Multicoloured. W w* **16** *(sideways). P* 14 × 14½.

| No. | Description | Mint | Used |
|---|---|---|---|
| 402 | 12p. Type **111** | 25 | 30 |
| 403 | 15p. 1980 "London 1980" International Stamp Exhibition 50p. | 30 | 35 |
| 404 | 20p. 1976 Bicentenary of American Revolution 8p. | 40 | 45 |
| 405 | 70p. 1982 40th Anniv of Wideawake Airfield 10p. | 1·40 | 1·50 |
| 402/5 | *Set of* 4 | 2·10 | 2·40 |
| **MS**406 | 60 × 75 mm. 75p. Statue of Liberty | 2·50 | 1·75 |

(Des D. Miller. Litho Questa)

**1986** (23 July). *Royal Wedding. T* **112** *and similar square design. Multicoloured. W w* **16**. *P* 14.

| No. | Description | Mint | Used |
|---|---|---|---|
| 407 | 15p. Type **112** | 35 | 35 |
| 408 | 35p. Prince Andrew aboard H.M.S. *Brazen* | 75 | 75 |

**113** H.M.S. *Ganymede* (*c* 1811)

(Des E. Nisbet. Litho Questa)

**1986** (14 Oct). *Ships of the Royal Navy. T* **113** *and similar horiz designs. Multicoloured. W w* **16** *(sideways). P* 14½.

| No. | Description | Mint | Used |
|---|---|---|---|
| 409 | 1p. Type **113** | 15 | 1 |
| 410 | 2p. H.M.S. *Kangaroo* (*c* 1811) | 15 | 1 |
| 411 | 4p. H.M.S. *Trinculo* (*c* 1811) | 20 | 2 |
| 412 | 5p. H.M.S. *Daring* (*c* 1811) | 20 | 2 |
| 413 | 9p. H.M.S. *Thais* (*c* 1811) | 30 | 3 |
| 414 | 10p. H.M.S. *Pheasant* (1819) | 30 | 3 |
| 415 | 15p. H.M.S. *Myrmidon* (1819) | 40 | 4 |

416 18p. H.M.S. *Atholl* (1825) .. .. .. .. 40 40
417 20p. H.M.S. *Medina* (1830) .. .. .. .. 45 45
418 25p. H.M.S. *Saracen* (1840) .. .. .. .. 60 60
419 30p. H.M.S. *Hydra* (c 1845) .. .. .. .. 70 70
420 50p. H.M.S. *Sealark* (1849) .. .. .. .. 1·25 1·25
421 70p. H.M.S. *Rattlesnake* (1868) .. .. .. 1·75 1·75
422 £1 H.M.S. *Penelope* (1889) .. .. .. .. 2·40 2·40
423 £2 H.M.S. *Monarch* (1897) .. .. .. .. 4·50 4·50
409/23 .. .. .. .. .. *Set of* 15 12·50 12·50

**114** Cape Gooseberry

**115** Ignition of Rocket Motors

(Des R. Gorringe. Litho Walsall)

**1987** (29 Jan). *Edible Bush Fruits. T* **114** *and similar horiz designs. Multicoloured. W w* **16** *(sideways). P* 14.
424 12p. Type **114** .. .. .. .. .. 55 55
425 15p. Prickly Pear .. .. .. .. .. 60 60
426 20p. Guava .. .. .. .. .. 70 70
427 70p. Loquat .. .. .. .. .. 1·75 1·75
424/7 .. .. .. .. .. *Set of* 4 3·25 3·25

(Des D. Hartley. Litho Questa)

**1987** (30 Mar). *25th Anniv of First American Manned Earth Orbit. T* **115** *and similar vert designs. Multicoloured. W w* **16**. *P* 14.
428 15p. Type **115** .. .. .. .. .. 45 45
429 18p. Lift-off .. .. .. .. .. 50 50
430 25p. Re-entry .. .. .. .. .. 65 65
431 £1 Splashdown .. .. .. .. .. 2·25 2·25
428/31 .. .. .. .. *Set of* 4 3·50 3·50
**MS**432 92 × 78 mm. 70p. "Friendship 7" capsule 1·75 2·00

**116** Captains in Full Dress raising Red Ensign

**117** *Cynthia cardui*

(Des C. Collins. Litho Format)

**1987** (29 June). *19th-century Uniforms (1st series). Royal Navy, 1815–20. T* **116** *and similar vert designs. Multicoloured. W w* **16**. *P* 14.
433 25p. Type **116** .. .. .. .. .. 60 60
a. Horiz strip of 5. Nos. 433/7 .. .. 2·75
434 25p. Surgeon and seamen .. .. .. .. 60 60
435 25p. Seaman with water-carrying donkey .. 60 60
436 25p. Midshipman and gun .. .. .. 60 60
437 25p. Commander in undress uniform surveying .. .. .. .. .. 60 60
433/7 .. .. .. .. .. *Set of* 5 2·75 2·75

Nos. 433/7 were printed together, *se-tenant*, in horizontal strips of five throughout the sheet.
See also Nos. 478/82.

(Des I. Loe. Litho Questa)

**1987** (10 Aug). *Insects (1st series). Butterflies. T* **117** *and similar horiz designs. Multicoloured. W w* **16** *(sideways). P* 14 × 14½.
438 15p. Type **117** .. .. .. .. .. 55 55
439 18p. *Danaus chrysippus* .. .. .. .. 60 60
440 25p. *Hypolimnas misippus* .. .. .. .. 75 75
441 £1 *Lampides boeticus* .. .. .. .. 2·25 2·25
438/41 .. .. .. .. .. *Set of* 4 3·75 3·75
See also Nos. 452/5 and 483/6.

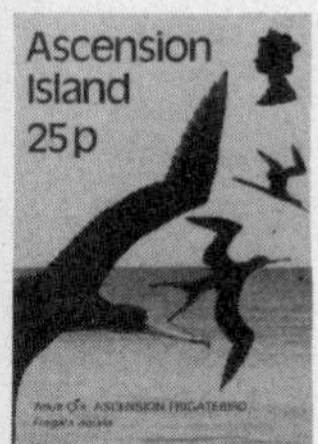


**118** Male Ascension Frigate Birds

40TH WEDDING ANNIVERSARY

(**119**)

(Des N. Arlott. Litho B.D.T.)

**1987** (8 Oct). *Sea Birds (1st series). T* **118** *and similar vert designs. Multicoloured. W w* **16**. *P* 14.
442 25p. Type **118** .. .. .. .. .. 80 80
a. Horiz strip of 5. Nos. 442/6 .. .. 3·50
443 25p. Juvenile Ascension Frigate Bird, Brown Booby and White Boobies .. .. .. 80 80
444 25p. Male Ascension Frigate Bird and White Boobies .. .. .. .. .. 80 80
445 25p. Female Ascension Frigate Bird .. .. 80 80
446 25p. Adult male feeding juvenile Ascension Frigate Bird .. .. .. .. .. 80 80
442/6 .. .. .. .. .. *Set of* 5 3·50 3·50

Nos. 442/6 were printed together, *se-tenant*, in horizontal strips of five throughout the sheet, forming a composite design.
See also Nos. 469/73.

**1987** (9 Dec). *Royal Ruby Wedding. Nos.* 397/401 *optd with T* **119** *in silver*.
447 7p. Type **110** .. .. .. .. .. 15 20
448 15p. Queen making Christmas broadcast, 1952 .. .. .. .. .. 30 35
449 20p. At Garter ceremony, Windsor Castle, 1983 .. .. .. .. .. 40 45
a. Opt double .. .. .. .. .. 75·00
450 35p. In Auckland, New Zealand, 1981 .. 70 75
451 £1 At Crown Agents' Head Office, London, 1983 .. .. .. .. .. 2·00 2·10
447/51 .. .. .. .. *Set of* 5 3·25 3·50

(Des I. Loe. Litho Questa)

**1988** (18 Jan). *Insects (2nd series). Horiz designs as T* **117**. *Multicoloured. W w* **16** *(sideways). P* 14 × 14½.
452 15p. *Gryllus bimaculatus* (field cricket) .. 50 50
453 18p. *Ruspolia differeus* (bush cricket) .. 55 55
454 25p. *Chilomenus lunata* (ladybird) .. .. 70 70
455 £1 *Diachrysia orichalcea* (moth) .. .. 2·25 2·25
452/5 .. .. .. .. .. *Set of* 4 3·50 3·50

**120** Bate's Memorial, St. Mary's Church

(Des S. Noon. Litho Questa)

**1988** (14 Apr). *150th Death Anniv of Captain William Bate (garrison commander, 1828–38). T* **120** *and similar horiz designs. Multicoloured. W w* **16** *(sideways). P* 14.
456 9p. Type **120** .. .. .. .. .. 35 35
457 15p. Commodore's Cottage .. .. .. .. 45 45
458 18p. North East Cottage .. .. .. .. 50 50
459 25p. Map of Ascension .. .. .. .. 70 70
460 70p. Captain Bate and marines .. .. .. 1·75 1·75
456/60 .. .. .. .. .. *Set of* 5 3·25 3·25

**121** H.M.S. *Resolution* (ship of the line), 1667

(Des E. Nisbet. Litho Questa)

**1988** (23 June). *Bicentenary of Australian Settlement. Ships of the Royal Navy. T* **121** *and similar diamond-shaped designs. Multicoloured. W w* **16** *(sideways). P* 14.
461 9p Type **121** .. .. .. .. .. 45 35
462 18p H.M.S. *Resolution* (Captain Cook), 1772 .. .. .. .. .. 65 55
463 25p H.M.S. *Resolution* (battleship), 1892 85 75
464 65p H.M.S. *Resolution* (battleship), 1916 .. 1·50 1·50
461/4 .. .. .. .. .. *Set of* 4 3·00 2·75

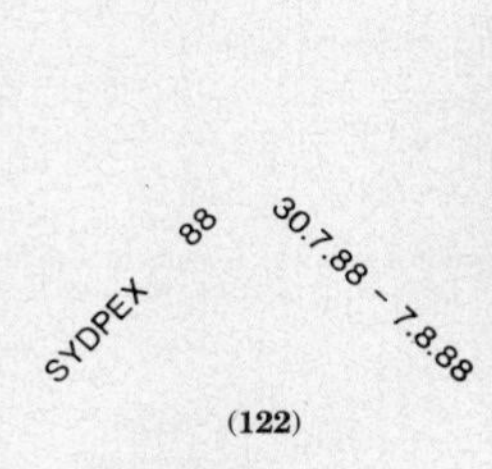


(**122**)

**123** Lloyd's Coffee House, London, 1688

**1988** (30 July). *"Sydpex '88" National Stamp Exhibition, Sydney. Nos.* 461/4 *optd with T* **122**.
465 9p Type **121** .. .. .. .. .. 25 25
466 18p H.M.S. *Resolution* (Captain Cook), 1772 .. .. .. .. .. 40 40
467 25p H.M.S. *Resolution* (battleship), 1892 .. 55 55
468 65p H.M.S. *Resolution* (battleship), 1916 .. 1·40 1·40
465/8 .. .. .. .. .. *Set of* 4 2·40 2·40

(Des N. Arlott. Litho Questa)

**1988** (15 Aug). *Sea Birds (2nd series). Sooty Tern. Vert designs as T* **118**. *Multicoloured. W w* **16**. *P* 14.
469 25p. Pair displaying .. .. .. .. 90 90
a. Horiz strip of 5. Nos. 469/73 .. .. 4·00
470 25p. Turning egg .. .. .. .. .. 90 90
471 25p. Incubating egg .. .. .. .. .. 90 90
472 25p. Feeding chick .. .. .. .. .. 90 90
473 25p. Immature Sooty Tern .. .. .. 90 90
469/73 .. .. .. .. .. *Set of* 5 4·00 4·00

Nos. 469/73 were printed together, *se-tenant*, in horizontal strips of five throughout the sheet, forming a composite design of a nesting colony.

(Des E. Nisbet and D. Miller (8p., 25p.), D. Miller (others). Litho Questa)

**1988** (17 Oct). *300th Anniv of Lloyd's of London. T* **123** *and similar multicoloured designs. W w* **14** *(sideways on* 18, 25*p.). P* 14.
474 8p. Type **123** .. .. .. .. .. 25 25
475 18p. *Alert* (cable ship) *(horiz)* .. .. .. 50 50
476 25p. Satellite recovery in space *(horiz)* .. 70 70
477 65p. *Good Hope Castle* on fire off Ascension, 1973 .. .. .. .. .. 1·50 1·50
474/7 .. .. .. .. .. *Set of* 4 2·75 2·75

(Des C. Collins. Litho B.D.T.)

**1988** (21 Nov). *19th-century Uniforms (2nd series). Royal Marines, 1821–34. Vert designs as T* **116**. *Multicoloured. W w* **14**. *P* 14.
478 25p. Marines landing on Ascension, 1821 .. 90 90
a. Horiz strip of 5. Nos. 478/82 .. .. 4·00
479 25p. Officer and Marine at semaphore station, 1829 .. .. .. .. .. 90 90
480 25p. Sergeant and Marine at Octagonal Tank, 1831 .. .. .. .. .. 90 90
481 25p. Officers at water pipe tunnel, 1833 .. 90 90
482 25p. Officer supervising construction of barracks, 1834 .. .. .. .. 90 90
478/82 .. .. .. .. .. *Set of* 5 4·00 4·00

Nos. 478/82 were printed together, *se-tenant*, in horizontal strips of five throughout the sheet.

(Des I. Loe. Litho Questa)

**1989** (16 Jan). *Insects (3rd series). Horiz designs as T* **117**. *Multicoloured. W w* **16** *(sideways). P* 14 × 14½.
483 15p. *Trichoptilus wahlbergi* (moth) .. .. 40 35
484 18p. *Lucilia sericata* (fly) .. .. .. 45 40
485 25p. *Alceis ornatus* (weevil) .. .. .. 60 55
486 £1 *Polistes fuscatus* (wasp) .. .. .. 2·40 2·10
483/6 .. .. .. .. .. *Set of* 4 3·50 3·00

**124** Two Land Crabs

**125** 1949 75th Anniversary of U. P. U. 1s. Stamp

(Des Doreen McGuiness. Litho Questa)

**1989** (17 Apr). *Ascension Land Crabs* (Gecarcinus lagostoma). *T* **124** *and similar vert designs. Multicoloured. W w* **16**. *P* 14.
487 15p. Type **124** .. .. .. .. .. 40 40
488 18p. Crab with claws raised .. .. .. 45 45
489 25p. Crab on rock .. .. .. .. .. 60 60
490 £1 Crab in surf .. .. .. .. .. 2·25 2·25
487/90 .. .. .. .. *Set of* 4 3·25 3·25
**MS**491 98 × 101 mm. Nos. 487/90 .. .. 3·50 3·75

(Des D. Miller. Litho Walsall)

**1989** (7 July). *"Philexfrance 89" International Stamp Exhibition, Paris, and "World Stamp Expo '89", Washington. Sheet* 104 × 86 *mm. W w* **16**. *P* 14 × 13½.
**MS**492 **125** 75p. multicoloured .. .. .. 1·50 1·75

**126** "Apollo 7" Tracking Station, Ascension

**127** *Queen Elizabeth 2* and Aircraft Carrier in New York Harbour

(Des A. Theobald (£1), D. Miller (others). Litho Questa)

**1989** (20 July). *20th Anniv of First Manned Landing on Moon. T* **126** *and similar multicoloured designs. W w* **16** *(sideways on* 18, 25*p). P* 14 × 13½ (15, 70*p.) or* 14 *(others)*.
493 15p. Type **126** .. .. .. .. .. 30 35
494 18p. Launch of "Apollo 7" (30 × 30 *mm*) .. 35 40
495 25p. "Apollo 7" emblem (30 × 30 *mm*) .. 50 55
496 70p. "Apollo 7" jettisoning expended Saturn rocket .. .. .. .. .. 1·40 1·50
493/6 .. .. .. .. .. *Set of* 4 2·25 2·50
**MS**497 101 × 83 mm. £1 Diagram of "Apollo 11" mission. P 14 × 13½ .. .. .. .. 2·00 2·10

(Des D. Miller. Litho Walsall)

**1989** (21 Aug). *"Philexfrance 89" International Stamp Exhibition, Paris, and "World Stamp Expo '89", Washington. T* **127** *and similar vert designs showing Statue of Liberty and Centenary celebrations. Multicoloured. W w* **14**. *P* 14 × 13½.

| | | | |
|---|---|---|---|
| 498 | 15p. Type **127** | 30 | 35 |
| | a. Sheetlet. Nos. 498/503 | 1·60 | |
| 499 | 15p. Cleaning Statue | 30 | 35 |
| 500 | 15p. Statue of Liberty | 30 | 35 |
| 501 | 15p. Crown of Statue | 30 | 35 |
| 502 | 15p. Warships and New York skyline | 30 | 35 |
| 503 | 15p. French warship and skyscrapers | 30 | 35 |
| 498/503 | *Set of* 6 | 1·60 | 1·90 |

Nos. 498/503 were printed, *se-tenant*, in sheetlets of 6.

**128** Devil's Ashpit Tracking Station

(Des D. Miller. Litho Questa)

**1989** (30 Sept). *Closure of Devil's Ashpit Tracking Station, Ascension. T* **128** *and similar horiz design. Multicoloured. W w* **16** *(sideways). P* 14.

| | | | |
|---|---|---|---|
| 504 | 18p. Type **128** | 45 | 50 |
| | a. Sheetlet. Nos. 504/5, each × 5 | 4·50 | |
| 505 | 25p. Launch of shuttle *Atlantis* | 50 | 55 |

Nos. 504/5 were issued in sheetlets of ten containing vertical strips of five of each design, separated by a central inscribed gutter.

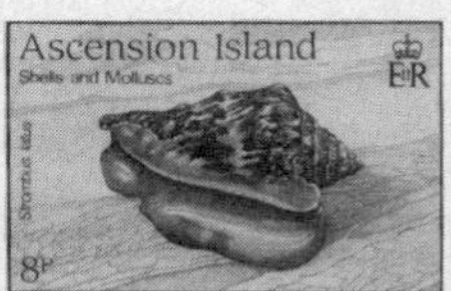

**129** *Strombus latus* **130** Donkeys

(Des I. Loe. Litho Questa)

**1989** (2 Nov). *Sea Shells. T* **129** *and similar horiz designs. Multicoloured. W w* **16** *(sideways). P* 14.

| | | | |
|---|---|---|---|
| 506 | 8p. Type **129** | 25 | 20 |
| 507 | 18p. *Tonna galea* | 45 | 40 |
| 508 | 25p. *Harpa doris* | 60 | 55 |
| 509 | £1 *Charonia variegata* | 2·25 | 2·25 |
| 506/9 | *Set of* 4 | 3·25 | 3·00 |

(Des G. Drummond, adapted N. Harvey. Litho Walsall)

**1989** (17 Nov). *Booklet stamps. T* **130** *and similar vert design. Multicoloured. W w* **16** *(sideways). P* 14.

| | | | |
|---|---|---|---|
| 510 | 18p. Type **130** | 35 | 40 |
| | a. Booklet pane. No. 510×6 | 2·10 | |
| 511 | 25p. Green Turtle | 50 | 55 |
| | a. Booklet pane. No. 511×4 | 2·00 | |

Nos. 510/11 come with either the left or right-hand side imperforate.

**131** Seaman's Pistol, Hat and Cutlass **132** Pair of Ascension Frigate Birds with Young

(Des C. Collins. Litho Questa)

**1990** (12 Feb). *Royal Navy Equipment,* 1815-20. *T* **131** *and similar vert designs. Multicoloured. W w* **16**. *P* 14.

| | | | |
|---|---|---|---|
| 512 | 25p. Type **131** | 60 | 60 |
| | a. Horiz strip of 5. Nos. 512/16 | 2·75 | |
| 513 | 25p. Midshipman's belt plate, button, sword and hat | 60 | 60 |
| 514 | 25p. Surgeon's hat, sword and instrument chest | 60 | 60 |
| 515 | 25p. Captain's hat, telescope and sword | 60 | 60 |
| 516 | 25p. Admiral's epaulette, megaphone, hat and pocket | 60 | 60 |
| 512/16 | *Set of* 5 | 2·75 | 2·75 |

Nos. 512/16 were printed together, *se-tenant*, in horizontal strips of 5 throughout the sheet.

See also Nos. 541/5.

(Des W. Oliver. Litho Questa)

**1990** (5 Mar). *Ascension Frigate Bird. T* **132** *and similar vert designs. Multicoloured. W w* **14**. *P* 14½×14.

| | | | |
|---|---|---|---|
| 517 | 9p. Type **132** | 30 | 30 |
| 518 | 10p. Fledgeling | 35 | 35 |
| 519 | 11p. Adult male in flight | 35 | 35 |
| 520 | 15p. Female and immature birds in flight | 40 | 40 |
| 517/20 | *Set of* 4 | 1·25 | 1·25 |

**133** Penny Black and Twopence Blue

(Des D. Miller. Litho Walsall)

**1990** (3 May). *"Stamp World London 90" International Stamp Exhibition, London. T* **133** *and similar horiz designs. Multicoloured. W w* **14** *(sideways). P* 14.

| | | | |
|---|---|---|---|
| 521 | 9p. Type **133** | 30 | 30 |
| 522 | 18p. Ascension postmarks used on G.B. stamps | 50 | 50 |
| 523 | 25p. Unloading mail at Wideawake Airfield | 75 | 75 |
| 524 | £1 Mail van and Main Post Office | 2·25 | 2·25 |
| 521/4 | *Set of* 4 | 3·50 | 3·50 |

**134** "Queen Elizabeth, 1940" (Sir Gerald Kelly) **135** King George VI and Queen Elizabeth with Bren-gun Carrier

(Des D. Miller. Litho Questa)

**1990** (4 Aug). *90th Birthday of Queen Elizabeth the Queen Mother. W w* **16**. *P* 14×15 (25p.) *or* 14½ (£1).

| | | | | |
|---|---|---|---|---|
| 525 | **134** | 25p. multicoloured | 75 | 75 |
| 526 | **135** | £1 black and deep lilac | 2·25 | 2·25 |

**136** "Madonna and Child" (sculpture, Dino Felici) **137** *Garth Castle* (mail ship), 1910

(Des D. Miller. Litho B.D.T.)

**1990** (24 Oct). *Christmas. Works of Art. T* **136** *and similar vert designs. Multicoloured. W w* **14**. *P* 13½.

| | | | |
|---|---|---|---|
| 527 | 8p. Type **136** | 30 | 30 |
| 528 | 18p. "Madonna and Child" (anon) | 60 | 60 |
| 529 | 25p. "Madonna and Child with St. John" (Johann Gebhard) | 85 | 85 |
| 530 | 65p. "Madonna and Child" (Giacomo Gritti) | 2·00 | 2·00 |
| 527/30 | *Set of* 4 | 3·25 | 3·25 |

(Des L. Curtis. Litho Walsall)

**1990** (27 Nov). *Maiden Voyage of St. Helena II. T* **137** *and similar horiz designs. Multicoloured. W w* **14** *(sideways). P* 14×14½.

| | | | |
|---|---|---|---|
| 531 | 9p. Type **137** | 35 | 35 |
| 532 | 18p. *St. Helena I* during Falkland Islands campaign, 1982 | 55 | 55 |
| 533 | 25p. Launch of *St. Helena II* | 75 | 75 |
| 534 | 70p. Duke of York launching *St. Helena II* | 2·00 | 2·00 |
| 531/4 | *Set of* 4 | 3·25 | 3·25 |
| **MS**535 | 100×100 mm. £1 *St. Helena II* and outline map of Ascension | 2·25 | 2·75 |

No. **MS**535 also contains two imperforate designs of similar stamps from St. Helena and Tristan da Cunha without face values.

BRITISH FOR 175 YEARS

(138)

**139** Queen Elizabeth II at Trooping the Colour

**1991** (5 Feb). *175th Anniv of Occupation. Nos.* 418, 420 *and* 422 *optd with T* **138** *in silver by Cartor, France.*

| | | | |
|---|---|---|---|
| 536 | 25p. H.M.S. *Saracen* (1840) | 75 | 75 |
| 537 | 50p. H.M.S. *Sealark* (1849) | 1·50 | 1·50 |
| 538 | £1 H.M.S. *Penelope* (1889) | 2·50 | 2·50 |
| 536/8 | *Set of* 3 | 4·25 | 4·25 |

(Des D. Miller. Litho Questa)

**1991** (18 June). *65th Birthday of Queen Elizabeth II and 70th Birthday of Prince Philip. T* **139** *and similar vert design. Multicoloured. W w* **16** *(sideways). P* 14½ × 14.

| | | | |
|---|---|---|---|
| 539 | 25p. Type **139** | 75 | 80 |
| | a. Horiz pair. Nos. 539/40 separated by label | 1·50 | 1·60 |
| 540 | 25p. Prince Philip in naval uniform | 75 | 80 |

Nos. 539/40 were printed together, *se-tenant*, in sheetlets of 10 (2 × 5) with designs alternating and the vertical rows separated by inscribed labels.

(Des C. Collins. Litho Questa)

**1991** (1 Aug). *Royal Marines Equipment,* 1821–44. *Vert designs as T* **131**. *Multicoloured. W w* **14**. *P* 14.

| | | | |
|---|---|---|---|
| 541 | 25p. Officer's shako, epaulettes, belt plate and button | 70 | 75 |
| | a. Horiz strip of 5. Nos. 541/5 | 3·25 | |
| 542 | 25p. Officer's cap, sword, epaulettes and belt plate | 70 | 75 |
| 543 | 25p. Drum major's shako and staff | 70 | 75 |
| 544 | 25p. Sergeant's shako, chevrons, belt plate and canteen | 70 | 75 |
| 545 | 25p. Drummer's shako and side-drum | 70 | 75 |
| 541/5 | *Set of* 5 | 3·25 | 3·50 |

Nos. 541/5 were printed together, *se-tenant*, in horizontal strips of 5 throughout the sheet.

**140** B.B.C. World Service Relay Station

(Des D. Miller. Litho Questa)

**1991** (17 Sept). *25th Anniv of B.B.C. Atlantic Relay Station. T* **140** *and similar multicoloured designs. W w* **16** *(sideways on* 15, 18p.). *P* 14½.

| | | | |
|---|---|---|---|
| 546 | 15p. Type **140** | 30 | 35 |
| 547 | 18p. Transmitters at English Bay | 35 | 40 |
| 548 | 25p. Satellite receiving station (*vert*) | 50 | 55 |
| 549 | 70p. Antenna support tower (*vert*) | 1·40 | 1·50 |
| 546/9 | *Set of* 4 | 2·25 | 2·50 |

**141** St. Mary's Church

(Des D. Miller. Litho Questa)

**1991** (1 Oct). *Christmas. Ascension Churches. T* **141** *and similar horiz designs. Multicoloured. W w* **16** *(sideways). P* 14.

| | | | |
|---|---|---|---|
| 550 | 8p. Type **141** | 15 | 20 |
| 551 | 18p. Interior of St. Mary's Church | 35 | 40 |
| 552 | 25p. Our Lady of Ascension Grotto | 50 | 55 |
| 553 | 65p. Interior of Our Lady of Ascension Grotto | 1·25 | 1·40 |
| 550/3 | *Set of* 4 | 2·00 | 2·25 |

**142** Blackfish

(Des G. Drummond. Litho Walsall)

**1991** (10 Dec). *Fishes. T* **142** *and similar horiz designs. Multicoloured. W w* **14** *(sideways). P* 14.

| | | | |
|---|---|---|---|
| 554 | 1p. Type **142** | 10 | 10 |
| 555 | 2p. Five Finger | 10 | 10 |
| 556 | 4p. Resplendent Angelfish | 10 | 10 |
| 557 | 5p. Silver Fish | 10 | 15 |
| 558 | 9p. Gurnard | 20 | 25 |
| 559 | 10p. Blue Dad | 20 | 25 |
| 560 | 15p. Cunning Fish | 30 | 35 |
| 561 | 18p. Grouper | 35 | 40 |
| 562 | 20p. Moray Eel | 40 | 45 |
| 563 | 25p. Hardback Soldierfish | 50 | 55 |
| 564 | 30p. Blue Marlin | 60 | 65 |
| 565 | 50p. Wahoo | 1·00 | 1·10 |
| 566 | 70p. Yellowfin Tuna | 1·40 | 1·50 |
| 567 | £1 Blue Shark | 2·00 | 2·10 |
| 568 | £2.50, Bottlenose Dolphin | 5·00 | 5·25 |
| 554/68 | *Set of* 15 | 11·50 | 12·00 |

**143** Holland's Crater

(Des D. Miller. Litho Questa (70p.), Walsall (others))

**1992** (6 Feb). *40th Anniv of Queen Elizabeth II's Accession. T* **143** *and similar horiz designs. W* w **14** (*sideways*). *P* 14.

| | | | |
|---|---|---|---|
| 569 | 9p. Type **143** | 20 | 25 |
| 570 | 15p. Green Mountain | 30 | 35 |
| 571 | 18p. Boatswain Bird Island | 35 | 40 |
| 572 | 25p. Three portraits of Queen Elizabeth | 50 | 55 |
| 573 | 70p. Queen Elizabeth II | 1·40 | 1·50 |
| 569/73 | *Set of* 5 | 2·50 | 2·75 |

The portraits shown on the 25p. are repeated from the three lower values of the set.

POSTAGE DUE STAMPS

D 1 Outline Map of Ascension

(Des L. Curtis. Litho Questa)

**1986** (9 June). *W* w **16**. *P* 14½×14.

| | | | | |
|---|---|---|---|---|
| D1 | D 1 | 1p. deep brown and cinnamon | 10 | 10 |
| D2 | | 2p. deep brown and bright orange | 10 | 10 |
| D3 | | 5p. deep brown and orange-vermilion | 10 | 10 |
| D4 | | 7p. black and bright reddish violet | 15 | 20 |
| D5 | | 10p. black and violet-blue | 20 | 25 |
| D6 | | 25p. black and pale emerald | 50 | 55 |
| D1/6 | | *Set of* 6 | 95 | 1·10 |

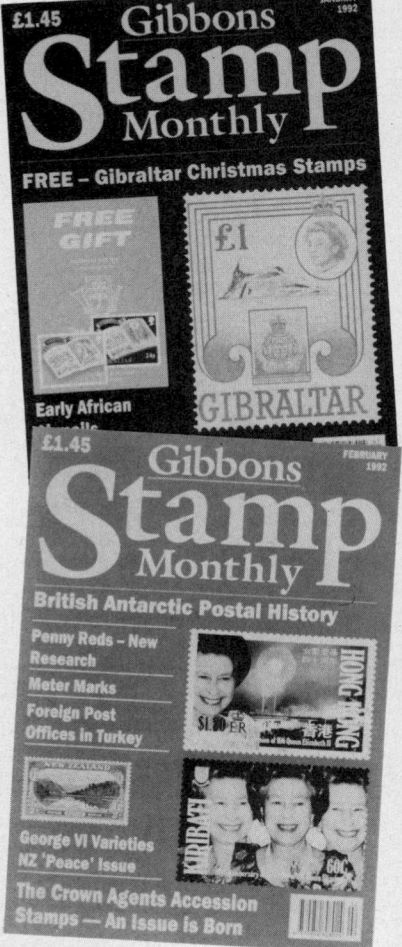

# Australia

The Australian colonies of New South Wales, Queensland, South Australia, Tasmania, Victoria and Western Australia produced their own issues before federation in 1901.

## NEW SOUTH WALES

**PRICES FOR STAMPS ON COVER**

| | |
|---|---|
| Nos. 1/83 | *from* × 2 |
| Nos. 84/108 | *from* × 3 |
| Nos. 109/10 | — |
| No. 110*b* | *from* × 3 |
| Nos. 111/13 | *from* × 2 |
| No. 114 | — |
| Nos. 115/24 | *from* × 2 |
| Nos. 125/6 | — |
| Nos. 127/53 | *from* × 2 |
| Nos. 154/70 | *from* × 3 |
| Nos. 171/2 | — |
| No. 173 | *from* × 2 |
| Nos. 174/81 | — |
| Nos. 186/202 | *from* × 2 |
| Nos. 203/6 | *from* × 10 |
| Nos. 207/21 | *from* × 5 |
| Nos. 222/39 | *from* × 6 |
| Nos. 240/1 | *from* × 2 |
| Nos. 241*a*/3 | *from* × 10 |
| Nos. 244/52 | — |
| Nos. 253/73 | *from* × 10 |
| Nos. 274/80 | — |
| Nos. 281/4 | *from* × 15 |
| Nos. 285/7 | *from* × 10 |
| Nos. 287*c*/*d* | *from* × 2 |
| Nos. 288/97 | *from* × 10 |
| Nos. 298/312 | *from* × 12 |
| Nos. 313/28 | *from* × 10 |
| No. 329 | — |
| Nos. 330/45 | *from* × 12 |
| No. 346 | — |
| Nos. 347/60 | *from* × 12 |
| No. O1 | — |
| Nos. O2/12 | *from* × 4 |
| Nos. O13/18 | — |
| Nos. O19/34 | *from* × 20 |
| Nos. O35/8 | — |
| Nos. O39/47 | *from* × 40 |
| Nos. O48/53 | — |
| Nos. O54/8 | *from* × 20 |
| No. O59 | — |
| Nos. D1/7 | *from* × 50 |
| Nos. D8/10 | — |
| Nos. D11/15 | *from* × 50 |

**PRINTERS.** The early issues of New South Wales were printed on a press supervised by the Inspector of Stamps. On 1 January 1857 this responsibility passed to the Government printer who produced all subsequent issues, *unless otherwise stated.*

**SPECIMEN OVERPRINTS.** Those listed are from U.P.U. distributions between 1892 and 1903. Further "Specimen" overprints exist, but these were used for other purposes. From 1891 examples of some of these Specimens, together with cancelled stamps, were sold to collectors by the N.S.W. Post Office.

1

2

(Eng Robert Clayton, Sydney)

**1850** (1 Jan). *T* **1.** *Plate I. No clouds. (a) Soft yellowish paper.*

| | | | |
|---|---|---|---|
| 1 | 1d. crimson-lake | £4250 | £450 |
| 2 | 1d. carmine | £4000 | £400 |
| 3 | 1d. reddish rose | £3750 | £375 |
| 4 | 1d. brownish red | £4000 | £400 |
| | *(b) Hard bluish paper* | | |
| 5 | 1d. pale red | £3750 | £375 |
| 6 | 1d. dull lake | £3750 | £375 |

**1850** (Aug). *T* **2.** *Plate I, re-engraved by H. C. Jervis, commonly termed Plate II. With clouds. (a) Hard toned white to yellowish paper.*

| | | | |
|---|---|---|---|
| 7 | 1d. vermilion | £2500 | £300 |
| 8 | 1d. dull carmine | £2500 | £300 |
| | a. No trees on hill (R.2/2) | £4500 | £475 |
| | b. Hill unshaded (R.2/3) | £4500 | £475 |
| | c. Without clouds (R.3/5) | £4500 | £475 |
| | *(b) Hard greyish or bluish paper* | | |
| 9 | 1d. crimson-lake | £2500 | £300 |
| 10 | 1d. gooseberry-red | £3000 | £450 |
| 11 | 1d. dull carmine | £2250 | £275 |
| 12 | 1d. brownish red | £2250 | £275 |
| | a. No trees on hill (R.2/2) | £4500 | £475 |
| | b. Hill unshaded (R.2/3) | £4500 | £475 |
| | c. Without clouds (R.3/5) | £4500 | £475 |
| | *(c) Laid paper* | | |
| 13 | 1d. carmine | £4000 | £475 |
| 14 | 1d. vermilion | £4500 | £450 |
| | a. No trees on hill (R.2/2) | — | £800 |
| | b. Hill unshaded (R.2/3) | — | £800 |
| | c. Without clouds (R.3/5) | — | £800 |

The varieties quoted with the letters "a", "b", "c" of course exist in each shade; the prices quoted are for the commonest shade, and the same applies to the following portions of this list.

Nos. 1/14 were printed in sheets of 25 (5×5).

3

4

A (Pl I)

Illustrations A, B, C, and D are sketches of the lower part of the inner circular frame, showing the characteristic variations of each plate.

(Eng John Carmichael)

**1850** (1 Jan). *Plate I. Vertical-lined background. T* **3.**

| | | | |
|---|---|---|---|
| | *(a) Early impressions, full details of clouds, etc.* | | |
| 15 | 2d. greyish blue | £4500 | £350 |
| 16 | 2d. deep blue | — | £400 |
| | a. Double lines on bale (R.2/7) | — | £600 |
| | *(b) Intermediate impressions* | | |
| 16*b* | 2d. greyish blue | £3000 | £275 |
| 16*c* | 2d. deep blue | £3250 | £325 |
| | *(c) Later impressions, clouds, etc., mostly gone, T* **4** | | |
| 17 | 2d. blue | £2250 | £150 |
| 18 | 2d. dull blue | £1800 | £140 |
| | *(d) Stamps in the lower row partially retouched* (end Jan): | | |
| 19 | 2d. blue | £3000 | £275 |
| 20 | 2d. greyish blue | £2750 | £225 |

5

B (Pl II)

C (Pl III)

(Plate entirely re-engraved by H. C. Jervis)

**1850** (Apr). *T* **5.** *Plate II. Horizontal-lined background. Bale on left side supporting the seated figure, dated. Dot in centre of the star in each corner. (a) Early impressions.*

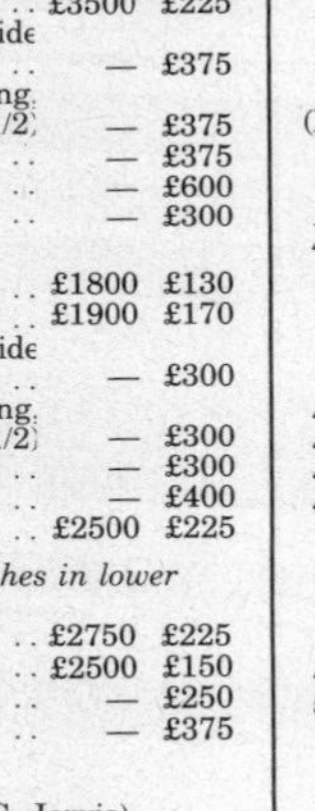

| | | | |
|---|---|---|---|
| 21 | 2d. indigo | £3500 | £275 |
| 22 | 2d. lilac-blue | — | £1000 |
| 23 | 2d. grey-blue | £3500 | £225 |
| 24 | 2d. bright blue | £3500 | £225 |
| | a. Fan as in Pl III, but with shading outside (R.1/1) | — | £375 |
| | b. Fan as in Pl III, but without shading, and inner circle intersects the fan (R.1/2) | — | £375 |
| | c. Pick and shovel omitted (R.1/10) | — | £375 |
| | d. "CREVIT" omitted (R.2/1) | — | £600 |
| | e. No whip (R.1/4, 1/8, 2/8) | — | £300 |
| | *(b) Worn impressions* | | |
| 25 | 2d. dull blue | £1800 | £130 |
| 26 | 2d. Prussian blue | £1900 | £170 |
| | a. Fan as in Pl III, but with shading outside (R.1/1) | — | £300 |
| | b. Fan as in Pl III, but without shading, and inner circle intersects the fan (R.1/2) | — | £300 |
| | c. Pick and shovel omitted (R.1/10) | — | £300 |
| | d. "CREVIT" omitted (R.2/1) | — | £400 |
| | e. No whip (R.1/4, 1/8, 2/8) | £2500 | £225 |
| | *(c) Bottom row retouched with dots and dashes in lower spandrels* (Aug) | | |
| 27 | 2d. Prussian blue | £2750 | £225 |
| 28 | 2d. dull blue | £2500 | £150 |
| | a. No whip (R.2/8) | — | £250 |
| | b. "CREVIT" omitted (R.2/1) | — | £375 |

(Plate re-engraved a second time by H.C. Jervis)

**1850** (Sept). *Plate III. Bale not dated and single-lined, except on No. 30c which is doubled-lined. No dots in stars.*

| | | | |
|---|---|---|---|
| 29 | 2d. ultramarine | £2250 | £160 |
| 30 | 2d. deep blue | £2250 | £160 |
| | a. No whip (R.2/3, 2/7) | — | £250 |
| | b. Fan with 6 segments (R. 2/8) | — | £375 |
| | c. Double lines on bale (R. 1/7, 1/10, 1/12) | — | £225 |

(Plate re-engraved a third time by H. C. Jervis)

**1851** (Jan). *Plate IV. Double-lined bale, and circle in centre of each star. (a) Hard bluish grey wove paper.*

| | | | |
|---|---|---|---|
| 31 | 2d. ultramarine | £2750 | £160 |
| 32 | 2d. Prussian blue | £2250 | £130 |
| 33 | 2d. bright blue | £2500 | £150 |
| | a. Hill not shaded (R.1/12) | — | £225 |
| | b. Fan with 6 segments (R.2/8) | — | £225 |
| | c. No clouds (R.2/10) | — | £225 |
| | d. Retouch (R.2/1) | — | £300 |
| | e. No waves (R.1/9, 2/5) | — | £190 |
| | *(b) Stout yellowish vertically laid paper* | | |
| 34 | 2d. ultramarine | £2750 | £160 |
| 35 | 2d. Prussian blue | £3000 | £160 |
| | a. Hill not shaded (R.1/12) | — | £250 |
| | b. Fan with 6 segments (R.2/8) | — | £250 |
| | c. No clouds (R.2/10) | — | £250 |
| | d. Retouch (R.2/1) | — | £325 |
| | e. No waves (R.1/9, 2/5) | — | £200 |
| | f. "PENOE" (R.2/12) | — | £250 |

The retouch, Nos. 33d and 35d., occurs outside the left margin line on R.2/1.

6

D (Pl V)

7

(Plate re-engraved a fourth time by H. C. Jervis)

**1851** (Apr). *T* **6.** *Plate V. Pearl in fan. (a) Hard greyish wove paper.*

| | | | |
|---|---|---|---|
| 36 | 2d. ultramarine | £2500 | £140 |
| 37 | 2d. dull blue | £2500 | £140 |
| | a. Pick and shovel omitted (R.2/5) | — | £250 |
| | b. Fan with 6 segments (R.2/8) | — | £250 |
| | *(b) Stout yellowish vertically laid paper* | | |
| 38 | 2d. dull ultramarine | £3750 | £300 |
| | a. Pick and shovel omitted (R.2/5) | — | £425 |
| | b. Fan with 6 segments (R.2/8) | — | £425 |

Nos. 15/38 were printed in sheets of 24 (12×2), although the existence of inter-panneau *tête-bêche* pairs from Plate II, and reportedly Plate III, indicates that the printer applied two impressions of the plate to each sheet of paper. The two panes were normally separated before issue. The original plate I was re-cut four times to form Plates II to V. An interesting variety occurs on R.1/9–11 and 2/7 in all five plates. It consists of ten loops of the engine-turning on each side of the design instead of the normal nine loops.

(Eng H. C. Jervis)

**1850.** *T* **7.** *(a) Soft yellowish wove paper.*

| | | | |
|---|---|---|---|
| 39 | 3d. yellow-green | £3000 | £250 |
| 40 | 3d. myrtle-green | £10000 | £1000 |
| 41 | 3d. emerald-green | £3500 | £250 |
| | a. No whip (R.4/3–4) | — | £375 |
| | b. "SIGIIUM" for "SIGILLUM" (R.5/3) | — | £450 |
| | *(b) Bluish to grey wove paper* | | |
| 42 | 3d. yellow-green | £2500 | £225 |
| 43 | 3d. emerald-green | £3000 | £225 |
| | b. No whip (R.4/3–4) | — | £300 |
| | c. "SIGIIUM" for "SIGILLUM" (R.5/3) | — | £375 |
| | *(c) Yellowish to bluish laid paper* | | |
| 43*d* | 3d. bright green | £5500 | £500 |
| 43*e* | 3d. yellowish green | £5000 | £450 |
| | f. No whip (R.4/3–4) | — | £650 |
| | g. "SIGIIUM" for "SIGILLUM" (R.5/3) | — | £750 |

Nos. 39/43*e* were printed in sheets of 25 (5×5).

8

9

(Des A. W. Manning from sketch by W. T. Levine; eng on steel by John Carmichael, Sydney)

**1851** (18 Dec)–**52.** *T* **8.** *Imperf. (a) Thick yellowish wove paper.*

| | | | |
|---|---|---|---|
| 44 | 1d. carmine | £1800 | £190 |
| | a. No leaves right of "SOUTH" | — | £375 |
| | b. Two leaves right of "SOUTH" | — | £450 |
| | c. "WALE" | — | £450 |
| | *(b) Bluish medium wove paper* (1852) | | |
| 45 | 1d. carmine | £1000 | £120 |
| 46 | 1d. scarlet | £1000 | £120 |
| 47 | 1d. vermilion | £900 | £100 |
| 48 | 1d. brick-red | £900 | £100 |
| | a. No leaves right of "SOUTH" (Nos. 7 and 8) | — | £225 |
| | b. Two leaves right of "SOUTH" (No. 15) | — | £300 |
| | c. "WALE" (No. 9) | — | £300 |
| | *(c) Thick vertically laid bluish paper* (1852?) | | |
| 49 | 1d. orange-brown | £3000 | £350 |
| 50 | 1d. claret | £3000 | £350 |
| | a. No leaves right of "SOUTH" | — | £550 |
| | b. Two leaves right of "SOUTH" | — | £650 |
| | c. "WALE" | — | £650 |

(Eng on steel by John Carmichael)

**1851** (24 July). *T* **8.** *Plate I. Imperf. (a) Thick yellowish wove paper.*

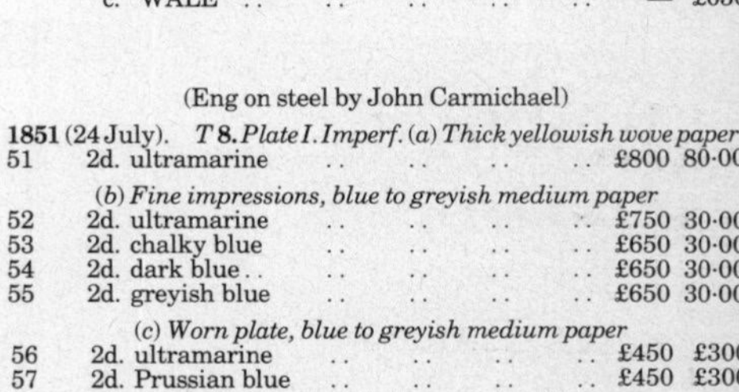

| | | | |
|---|---|---|---|
| 51 | 2d. ultramarine | £800 | 80·00 |
| | *(b) Fine impressions, blue to greyish medium paper* | | |
| 52 | 2d. ultramarine | £750 | 30·00 |
| 53 | 2d. chalky blue | £650 | 30·00 |
| 54 | 2d. dark blue | £650 | 30·00 |
| 55 | 2d. greyish blue | £650 | 30·00 |
| | *(c) Worn plate, blue to greyish medium paper* | | |
| 56 | 2d. ultramarine | £450 | £300 |
| 57 | 2d. Prussian blue | £450 | £300 |
| | *(d) Worn plate, blue wove medium paper* | | |
| 58 | 2d. ultramarine | £350 | 30·00 |
| 59 | 2d. Prussian blue | £325 | 30·00 |

(Plate II eng H. C. Jervis)

**1853** (Oct). *T* **9.** *Plate II. Stars in corners. Imperf.*

| | | | |
|---|---|---|---|
| | *(a) Bluish medium to thick wove paper* | | |
| 60 | 2d. deep ultramarine | £1000 | £110 |
| 61 | 2d. indigo | £1100 | 80·00 |
| | a. "WAEES" (No. 23) | — | £375 |
| | *(b) Worn plate, hard blue wove paper* | | |
| 62 | 2d. deep Prussian blue | £1000 | £100 |
| | a. "WAEES" (No. 23) | — | £375 |

**1855** (Sept). *Plate III, being Plate I re-engraved by H. C. Jervis. Background of crossed lines. Imperf.*

*(a) Medium bluish wove paper*

63 2d. Prussian blue . . £475 55·00
a. "WALES" covered with wavy lines (No. 3) — £190

*(b) Stout white wove paper*

64 2d. Prussian blue . . £475 55·00
a. "WALES" covered with wavy lines (No. 3) — £190

(Eng John Carmichael)

**1852** (3 Dec). *T* **8**. *Imperf. (a) Medium greyish blue wove paper.*

65 3d. deep green . . £1600 £200
66 3d. green . . £1300 £140
67 3d. dull yellow-green . . £1200 £100
a. "WAEES" (No. 37) — £350

*(b) Thick blue wove paper*

69 3d. emerald-green . . £1600 £200
71 3d. blue-green . . £1600 £200
a. "WAEES" (No. 37) — £550

**1852** (Apr). *As T* **8**. *Fine background. Imperf.*

*(a) Medium white wove paper*

72 6d. vandyke-brown . . — £900
a. "WALLS" (No. 8). . — £1500

*(b) Medium bluish grey wove paper*

73 6d. vandyke-brown . . £1700 £250
74 6d. yellow-brown . . £1800 £275
75 6d. chocolate-brown . . £1700 £250
76 6d. grey-brown . . £1600 £250
a. "WALLS" (No. 8). . — £500

**1853** (June). *Plate I re-engraved by H. C. Jervis. Coarse background. Imperf.*

77 6d. brown . . £1800 £300
78 6d. grey-brown . . £1700 £300

(Eng H. C. Jervis)

**1853** (May). *Medium bluish paper. Imperf.*

79 8d. dull yellow . . £3500 £600
80 8d. orange-yellow . . £3500 £600
81 8d. orange . . £3750 £650
a. No bow at back of head (No. 9) . . — £1300
b. No leaves right of "SOUTH" (No. 21) . . — £1300
c. No lines in spandrel (Nos. 12, 22, and 32) — £800

10 13 14

**NOTE.** All watermarked stamps from No. 82 to No. 172 have double-lined figures, as T **10**.

**1854** (Feb). *T* **8**. *Wmk "1", T* **10**. *Imperf. Yellowish wove paper.*

82 1d. red-orange . . £170 15·00
83 1d. orange-vermilion . . £170 15·00
a. No leaves right of "SOUTH" (Nos. 7 and 21) . . £350 85·00
b. Two leaves right of "SOUTH" (No. 15) . . £475 £120
c. "WALE" (No. 9) . . £475 £120

**1854** (Jan). *Plate III. Wmk "2". Imperf.*

84 2d. ultramarine . . £110 10·00
85 2d. Prussian blue . . £110 10·00
86 2d. chalky blue . . £110 7·00
a. "WALES" partly covered . . £425 50·00

**1854** (Mar). *Wmk "3". Imperf.*

87 3d. yellow-green . . £200 25·00
a. "WAEES" (No. 37) . . — £120
b. Error. Wmk "2" . . — £2250

(Eng John Carmichael)

**1856** (1 Jan). *For Registered Letters. T* **13**. *No wmk. Imperf. Soft medium yellowish paper.*

88 (6d.) vermilion and Prussian blue . . £700 £150
a. Frame printed on back. . £2500 £1000
89 (6d.) salmon and indigo . . £700 £170
90 (6d.) orange and Prussian blue . . £700 £200
91 (6d.) orange and indigo . . £700 £180

**1859** (Apr)–**60**. *Hard medium bluish wove paper, with manufacturer's wmk in sans-serif, double-lined capitals across sheet and only showing portions of letters on a few stamps in a sheet.*

*(a) Imperf.*

92 (6d.) orange and Prussian blue . . £700 £130
92*a* (6d.) vermilion and Prussian blue . . £850 £180

*(b) P 12 (2.60)*

93 (6d.) orange and Prussian blue . . £350 40·00
94 (6d.) orange and indigo . . £325 40·00

**1860** (Feb)–**62**. *Coarse yellowish wove paper having the manufacturer's wmk in Roman capitals. (a) P* 12.

95 (6d.) rose-red and Prussian blue . . £250 35·00
96 (6d.) rose-red and indigo . . £325 80·00
97 (6d.) salmon and indigo

*(b) P 13 (1862)*

98 (6d.) rose-red and Prussian blue . . £225 50·00

**1863** (May). *Yellowish wove paper. Wmk "6". P* 13.

99 (6d.) rose-red and Prussian blue . . 90·00 15·00
100 (6d.) rose-red and indigo . . £140 17·00
101 (6d.) rose-red and pale blue . . 65·00 15·00
a. Double impression of frame . . — £1500

(T **14/21** and **24** printed by the New South Wales Govt Ptg Dept from plates engraved by Perkins, Bacon & Co)

Two plates of the 2d. and 6d. were used. On Plate II of the 2d. the stamps are wider apart and more regularly spaced than on Plate I.

**1856** (6 Apr). *Wmk "1". Imperf.*

102 **14** 1d. orange-vermilion . . £130 22·00
a. Error. Wmk "2" . .
103 1d. carmine-vermilion . . £130 22·00
104 1d. orange-red . . £130 22·00
a. Printed on both sides . . — £1400

**1856** (7 Jan). *Plate I. Wmk "2". Imperf.*

105 **14** 2d. light ultramarine . . £140 8·00
106 2d. Prussian blue . . £130 8·00
107 2d. dull blue . . £130 8·00
108 2d. pale blue . . £130 8·00
a. Error. Wmk "1" . . — £4000
b. Error. Wmk "5" . . £450 60·00
c. Error. Wmk "8" . .

**1858.** *Plate I, retouched.*

109 **14** 2d. dull blue . . £1800 £450

**1859** (3 Aug). *Lithographic transfer of Plate I.*

110 **14** 2d. pale cobalt-blue . . — £750
a. Retouched . . — £2500

**1860** (Jan). *Plate II. Recess. Stamps printed wider apart.*

110*b* **14** 2d. blue . . £350 12·00

**1856** (10 Oct). *Wmk "3". Imperf.*

111 **14** 3d. yellow-green . . £700 80·00
112 3d. bluish green . . £750 80·00
113 3d. dull green . . £750 80·00
a. Error, Wmk "2" . . — £3000

In the 3d. the value is in block letters on a white ground.

15 17 19 21

(6d. and 1s. des E. H. Corbould after sketches by T. W. Levinge)

**1855** (1 Dec). *Wmk "5". Imperf.*

114 **15** 5d. dull green . . £1000 £500

**1854** (1 Feb)–**59**. *Wmk "6". Imperf.*

115 **17** 6d. deep slate . . £500 32·00
116 6d. greenish grey . . £400 32·00
117 6d. slate-green . . £400 £100
a. Printed both sides . .
118 6d. bluish grey . . £450 55·00
119 6d. fawn . . £500 95·00
a. Error. Wmk "8" (15.8.59) . . £1600 £120
120 6d. grey . . £450 55·00
121 6d. olive-grey . . £450 32·00
122 6d. greyish brown . . £450 32·00
a. Error. Wmk "8" (15.8.59) . . £1600 £110

**1855** (1 Dec). *Wmk "8". Imperf.*

125 **19** 8d. golden yellow . . £4000 £850
126 8d. dull yellow-orange . . £3500 £800

**1854** (Feb). *Wmk "12". Imperf.*

127 **21** 1s. rosy vermilion . . £750 65·00
a. Error. Wmk "8" (20.6.57) . . £2000 £180
128 1s. pale red . . £750 65·00
129 1s. brownish red . . £800 75·00

**1860** (14 Feb)–**63**. *Wmk double-lined figure of value. P* 12.

131 **14** 1d. orange-red . . £170 16·00
a. Imperf between (pair)
b. Double impression . .
132 1d. scarlet . . £100 16·00
133 2d. cobalt-blue (Pl I) . . £500 £140
a. Retouched . . — £1300
134 2d. greenish blue (Pl II) . . 90·00 10·00
136 2d. Prussian blue (Pl II) . . 90·00 10·00
a. Error. Wmk "1" . . — £2750
b. Retouched (*shades*) . . — £400
137 2d. Prussian blue (Pl I) (3.61) . . £110 11·00
138 2d. dull blue (Pl I) . . £100 10·00
139 3d. yellow-green (1860) . . £1000 55·00
140 3d. blue-green . . £550 42·00
141 **15** 5d. dull green (1863) . . £100 35·00
142 5d. yellowish green (1863) . . £100 35·00
143 **17** 6d. grey-brown . . £275 45·00
144 6d. olive-brown . . £275 55·00
145 6d. greenish grey . . £350 45·00
146 6d. fawn . . £325 65·00
147 6d. mauve . . £300 35·00
148 6d. violet . . £275 16·00
a. Imperf between (pair)
149 **19** 8d. lemon-yellow . . — £1400
150 8d. orange . . £2000 £600
151 8d. red-orange . . £2000 £600
152 **21** 1s. brownish red . . £450 48·00
153 1s. rose-carmine . . £450 48·00
a. Imperf between (pair)

No. 133 was made by perforating a small remaining stock of No. 108. Nos. 137/8 were printed from the original plate after its return from London, where it had been repaired.

**1862–72.** *Wmk double-lined figure of value. (a) P* 13.

154 **14** 1d. scarlet (1862) . . 55·00 8·00
155 1d. dull red . . 55·00 8·00
156 3d. blue-green (12.62) . . 45·00 11·00
157 3d. yellow-green . . 50·00 8·50
a. Error. Wmk "6" (7.72) . . 50·00 12·00
158 3d. dull green . . 50·00 8·00
a. Error. Wmk "6" (7.72) . . 55·00 15·00
160 **15** 5d. bluish green (12.63) . . 35·00 15·00
161 5d. bright yellow-green (8.65) . . 38·00 24·00
162 5d. sea-green (1866) . . 38·00 17·00
162*a* 5d. dark bluish green (11.70) . . 28·00 17·00
163 **17** 6d. reddish purple (Pl I) (7.62) . . 60·00 5·00
164 6d. mauve . . 60·00 5·00
165 6d. purple (Pl II) (1864) . . 55·00 4·50
a. Error. Wmk "5" (7.66) . . £350 25·00
b. Error. Wmk "12" (12.66) . . £275 20·00
166 6d. violet . . 55·00 6·00
167 6d. aniline mauve . . £900 £120
167*a* **19** 8d. red-orange . . £140 55·00
167*b* 8d. yellow-orange . . £140 40·00
167*c* 8d. bright yellow . . £140 40·00
168 **21** 1s. rose-carmine . . 70·00 7·50
169 1s. carmine . . 70·00 8·00
170 1s. crimson-lake . . 70·00 8·00

*(b) Perf compound* 12 × 13

171 **14** 1d. scarlet . . — £1700
172 2d. dull blue . . £2000 £250

23

**1864** (June). *W* **23**. *P* 13.

173 **14** 1d. pale red . . 30·00 12·00

24 25

(Des E. H. Corbould, R.I.)

**1861–88.** *W* **25**. *Various perfs.*

174 **24** 5s. dull violet, *p* 12 (1861) . . £1000 £325
a. Perf 13 (1861) . . £160 28·00
175 5s. royal purple, *p* 13 (1872) . . £275 45·00
176 5s. deep rose-lilac, *p* 13 (1875) . . 95·00 28·00
177 5s. deep purple, *p* 13 (1880) . . £150 40·00
a. Perf 10 (1882) . . £150 45·00
178 5s. rose-lilac, *p* 10 (1883) . . £110 40·00
179 5s. purple, *p* 12 (1885) . . — 45·00
a. Perf 10 × 12 (1885) . . — £120
180 5s. reddish purple, *p* 10 (1886) . . £110 40·00
a. Perf 12 × 10 (1887) . . £275 45·00
181 5s. rose-lilac, *p* 11 (1888) . . — £120

This value was replaced by Nos. 261, etc. in 1888 but reissued in 1897, *see* Nos. 297*c/e*.

26 28 29

(Printed by De La Rue & Co, Ltd, London and perf at Somerset House, London)

**1862–65.** *Surfaced paper. P* 14. (i) *W* **23**.

186 **26** 1d. dull red (Pl I) (4.64) . . 80·00 28·00

*(ii) No wmk*

187 **26** 1d. dull red (Pl II) (1.65) . . 60·00 28·00
188 **28** 2d. pale blue (3.62) . . 60·00 28·00

(Printed from the De La Rue plates in the Colony)

**1862** (12 Apr). *Wmk double-lined "2". P* 13.

189 **28** 2d. blue . . 45·00 7·00
a. Perf 12 . . £120 12·00
b. Perf 12 × 13 . . £400

**1864–65.** *W* **23**. *P* 13.

190 **26** 1d. dark red-brown (Pl I) . . 70·00 14·00
191 1d. brownish red (Pl II) . . 18·00 1·50
192 1d. brick-red (Pl II) . . 18·00 1·50
a. Highly surfaced paper (1865) . . £180
194 **28** 2d. pale blue . . £110 3·50

Plates I and II were made from the same die; they can only be distinguished by the colour or by the marginal inscription.

**1865–66.** *Thin wove paper. No wmk. P* 13.

195 **26** 1d. brick-red .. .. .. .. 90·00 15·00
196 1d. brownish red .. .. .. .. 90·00 15·00
197 **28** 2d. pale blue .. .. .. .. 40·00 3·00

**1863–69.** *W* **29.** *P* 13.

198 **26** 1d. pale red (3.69) .. .. .. 70·00 11·00
199 **28** 2d. pale blue .. .. .. .. 8·50 50
a. Perf 12 .. .. .. ..
200 2d. cobalt-blue .. .. .. .. 8·50 50
201 2d. Prussian blue .. .. .. 21·00 3·50

**1862** (Sept). *Wmk double-lined* "**5**". *P* 13.

202 **28** 2d. dull blue .. .. .. .. 60·00 8·50

32

34

33

35

**1867** (Sept)–**93.** *W* **33** *and* **35.**

203 **32** 4d. red-brown, *p* 13 .. .. .. 32·00 3·00
204 4d. pale red-brown, *p* 13 .. .. .. 32·00 3·00
205 **34** 10d. lilac, *p* 13 (Optd S. £25) .. .. 12·00 3·00
a. Imperf between (pair) .. .. £400
206 10d. lilac, *p* 11 (1893) .. .. .. 13·00 3·00
a. Perf 10 .. .. .. 15·00 4·50
b. Perf 10 and 11, compound .. .. 20·00 7·50
c. Perf 12 × 11 .. .. .. £110 15·00

36

37

38

**NINEPENCE**
(39)

From 1871 to 1903 the 9d. is formed from the 10d. by a *black* surch. (T **39**), 15 mm long on Nos. 219 to 220h, and 13½ mm long on subsequent issues.

**1871–85.** *W* **36.**

207 **26** 1d. dull red, *p* 13 (8.71).. .. .. 5·00 20
a. Imperf vert (horiz pair) .. ..
208 1d. salmon, *p* 13 .. .. .. 5·00 20
a. Perf 10 .. .. .. £250 15·00
b. Perf 13 × 10 .. .. .. 16·00 20
c. *Scarlet.* Perf 10 .. .. .. — £180
209 **28** 2d. Prussian-blue, *p* 13 (11.71).. .. 6·50 20
a. Perf 11 × 12, comb .. .. £250 40·00
b. Imperf vert (horiz pair) .. .. — £500
210 2d. pale blue, *p* 13 .. .. .. 6·50 20
aa. "TWO PENCE" double impression at right .. .. .. — 30·00
a. Perf 10 .. .. .. £250 22·00
b. Perf 13 × 10 .. .. .. 7·00 20
c. Surfaced paper. Perf 13 .. ..
211 **14** 3d. yellow-green (3.74), *p* 13 .. .. 18·00 2·40
a. Perf 10 .. .. .. 65·00 5·50
b. Perf 11 .. .. .. £150 £100
c. Perf 12 .. .. .. — £150
d. Perf 10 × 12 .. .. .. £150 32·00
e. Perf 12 × 11 .. .. .. £120 32·00
212 3d. bright green, *p* 10 .. .. .. £120 11·00
a. Perf 10 × 13 .. .. .. £110 15·00
213 **32** 4d. pale red-brown (8.77), *p* 13.. .. 50·00 6·00
214 4d. red-brown, *p* 13 .. .. .. 50·00 6·00
a. Perf 10 .. .. .. £180 50·00
b. Perf 13 × 10 .. .. .. 75·00 3·50
215 **15** 5d. bluish green (8.84), *p* 10 .. .. 15·00 8·00
a. Perf 12 (5.85) .. .. .. £250 £100
b. Perf 13×10 .. .. ..
c. Perf 10×12 .. .. .. 19·00 9·00
216 **37** 6d. bright mauve (1.72), *p* 13 .. .. 30·00 1·00
a. Imperf between (horiz pair) .. .. — £500
217 6d. pale lilac, *p* 13 .. .. .. 35·00 1·00
a. Perf 10 .. .. .. £180 12·00
b. Perf 13 × 10 .. .. .. 55·00 1·90
c. Imperf between (horiz pair). Perf 13 × 10 .. .. .. — £500
218 **19** 8d. yellow (3.77), *p* 13 .. .. .. 90·00 17·00
a. Perf 10 .. .. .. £250 24·00
b. Perf 13 × 10 .. .. .. £170 22·00
219 **34** 9d. on 10d. pale red-brown (8.71), *p* 13 20·00 4·50
220 9d. on 10d. red-brown, *p* 13 (Optd S. £25) 20·00 6·00
a. Perf 10 .. .. .. 11·00 4·50
b. Perf 12 .. .. .. 11·00 4·50
c. Perf 11 .. .. .. 26·00 7·00
d. Perf 10 × 12 .. .. .. £250 £160
e. Perf 10 × 11 .. .. .. 42·00 9·00
f. Perf 12 × 11 .. .. .. 14·00 5·50
g. Perf 11 × 12, comb .. .. 14·00 5·50
h. In black and blue. Perf 11 .. .. £110

221 **38** 1s. black (4.76), *p* 13 .. .. .. 80·00 2·50
a. Perf 10 .. .. .. £325 12·00
b. Perf 10 × 13 .. .. .. £170 4·50
c. Perf 11 .. .. .. ..
d. Imperf between (horiz pair) .. .. — £750

Collectors should note that the classification of perforations is that adopted by the Royal Philatelic Society, London. "Perf 12" denotes the perforation formerly called "11½, 12" and "perf 13" that formerly called "12½, 13".

40

41

**1882–97.** *W* **40.**

222 **26** 1d. salmon, *p* 10 .. .. .. 9·50 20
a. Perf 13 .. .. ..
b. Perf 10 × 13 .. .. .. 28·00 1·50
223 1d. orange *to* scarlet, *p* 13 .. ..
a. Perf 10 .. .. .. 8·00 20
ab. Imperf between (horiz pair) .. ..
b. Perf 10 × 13 .. .. .. £120 6·00
c. Perf 10 × 12 .. .. .. £250 65·00
d. Perf 10 × 11 .. .. .. £450 £120
e. Perf 12 × 11 .. .. .. — £120
f. Perf 11 × 12, comb .. .. 5·50 25
h. Perf 11 .. .. .. — £130
224 **28** 2d. pale blue, *p* 13 .. .. .. £450 90·00
a. Perf 10 .. .. .. 9·00 25
b. Perf 13 × 10 .. .. .. 65·00 2·00
225 2d. Prussian blue, *p* 10 .. .. .. 17·00 25
a. Perf 13 × 10 .. .. .. 65·00 1·90
b. Perf 12 .. .. .. — £225
c. Perf 11 .. .. .. — £100
d. Perf 12 × 11 .. .. .. — £100
e. Perf 12 × 10 .. .. .. £225 65·00
f. Perf 10 × 11 .. .. .. £450 £100
g. Perf 11 × 12, comb .. .. 12·00 15
226 **14** 3d. yellow-green (1886), *p* 10 .. .. 5·00 80
a. Perf 10 × 12 .. .. .. £160 15·00
b. Perf 11 .. .. .. 5·00 80
c. Perf 11 × 12 or 12 × 11 .. .. 5·00 80
d. Perf 12 .. .. .. 9·00 1·00
e. Imperf between (horiz pair) .. .. £140
f. Imperf (pair) .. .. .. £120
227 3d. bluish green, *p* 10 .. .. .. 5·00 80
a. Perf 11 .. .. .. 5·00 80
b. Perf 10 × 11 .. .. .. 15·00 1·50
c. Perf 12 × 11 .. .. .. 5·00 1·00
d. Perf 12 × 10 .. .. .. 75·00 3·00
228 3d. emerald-green, *p* 10 (1893).. .. 55·00 7·50
a. Perf 10 × 11 .. .. .. 55·00 3·00
b. Perf 12 × 10 .. .. .. 80·00 8·00
229 **32** 4d. red-brown, *p* 10 .. .. .. 32·00 2·00
a. Perf 10 × 12 .. .. .. — £130
b. Perf 11 × 12, comb .. .. 42·00 1·25
230 4d. dark brown, *p* 10 .. .. .. 42·00 2·75
a. Perf 12 .. .. .. — 35·00
b. Perf 10 × 12 .. .. .. — 90·00
c. Perf 11 × 12, comb .. .. 14·00 1·00
231 **15** 5d. dull grn *p* 10 (1890) (Optd S. £25) 12·00 90
a. Perf 11×10 .. .. .. 30·00 2·00
b. Perf 12×10 (4.85) .. .. 80·00 3·50
232 5d. bright green, *p* 10 (4.82) .. .. 32·00 4·50
a. Perf 11 (12.85) .. .. .. — 4·50
b. Perf 10×11 (12.85) .. .. 38·00 4·50
c. Perf 12×10 (4.85) .. .. £150 6·50
233 5d. blue-green, *p* 10 (4.82) .. .. 8·50 90
a. Perf 12 (4.85) .. .. .. 11·00 90
b. Perf 11 (12.85) .. .. .. 8·50 55
c. Perf 10×11 (12.85) .. .. 24·00 1·60
d. Perf 11×12 or 12×11 .. .. 6·50 55
e. Imperf (pair) .. .. .. £275
234 **37** 6d. pale lilac, *p* 10 .. .. .. 30·00 1·00
a. Perf 10×13 or 13×10 .. .. — £300
b. Perf 10×12 or 12×10 .. .. 38·00 1·50
235 6d mauve, *p* 10 .. .. .. 35·00 1·00
a. Perf 12 .. .. .. 80·00 2·50
b. Perf 11 .. .. .. 80·00 8·00
c. Perf 10×12 or 12×10 .. .. 32·00 1·00
ca. Imperf between (horiz pair) .. .. — £650
d. Perf 11×12 or 12×11 .. .. 32·00 1·40
e. Perf 10×11 .. .. .. 55·00 1·00
236 **19** 8d. yellow, *p* 10 (1883) .. .. £100 15·00
a. Perf 12 .. .. .. £150 24·00
b. Perf 11 .. .. .. £100 17·00
c. Perf 10×12 .. .. .. £130 22·00
236*d* **34** 9d. on 10d. red-brown, *p* 11×12 (1897) (Optd S. £25) .. .. .. 8·00 3·75
da. Perf 12 .. .. .. 11·00 5·00
db. Perf 11 .. .. .. 11·00 5·50
dc. Surch double, *p* 11 .. .. £140 £120
236*e* 10d. violet, *p* 11×12 (1897) (Optd S. £25) 12·00 3·25
ea. Perf 12×11½ .. .. .. 12·00 3·25
eb. Perf 12 .. .. .. 15·00 4·00
ec. Perf 11 .. .. .. 15·00 4·00
237 **38** 1s. black, *p* 10 .. .. .. 65·00 2·00
a. Perf 11 .. .. .. £200 9·00
b. Perf 10×12 .. .. ..
c. Perf 10×13 .. .. .. £100 11·00
d. Perf 11×12, comb .. .. 65·00 2·00

**1886–87.** *W* **41.**

238 **26** 1d. scarlet, *p* 10.. .. .. 11·00 3·75
a. Perf 11 × 12, comb .. .. 3·50 90
239 **28** 2d. deep blue, *p* 10 .. .. .. 32·00 5·00
a. Perf 11 × 12, comb .. .. 12·00 95
b. Imperf .. .. ..

**1891** (July). *Wmk* "10" *as T* **35.** *P* 10.

240 **14** 3d. green (Optd S. £25) .. .. 12·00 80·00
241 3d. dark green .. .. .. 5·00 17·00

42

43

**NOTE.** The spacing between the Crown and "NSW" is 1 mm in T **42**, as against 2 mm in T **40**.

**1903–8.** *W* **42.**

241*a* **14** 3d. yellow-green, *p* 11 .. .. 6·00 90
b. Perf 12 .. .. .. 5·00 90
c. Perf 11 × 12 .. .. .. 5·00 90
242 3d. dull green, *p* 12 .. .. .. 19·00 1·75
a. Perf 11 × 12 .. .. .. 7·00 1·00
243 **15** 5d. dark blue-green, *p* 11 × 12 .. .. 5·50 90
a. Perf 11 .. .. .. 12·00 90
b. Perf 12 .. .. .. 19·00 3·50
c. Imperf (pair) .. .. .. £130
d. Wmk sideways .. .. ..

**1885–86.** *W* **41.** (i) *Overprinted* "POSTAGE", *in black.*

244 **43** 5s. green and lilac, *p* 13 .. ..
a. Perf 10 .. .. ..
b. Perf 12 × 10 .. .. .. £325 80·00
245 10s. claret and lilac, *p* 13 .. ..
a. Perf 12 .. .. .. £450 £140
246 £1 claret and lilac, *p* 13 (1886) .. — £2250
a. Perf 12 .. .. .. £2250 £1000

(ii) *Overprinted in blue*

247 **43** 10s. claret and mauve, *p* 10 (Optd S. £60) .. .. .. £550 £160
a. Perf 12 .. .. .. £160 50·00
b. Perf 12 × 11 .. .. .. £275
248 £1 claret and rose-lilac, *p* 12 × 10 .. £2500 £1100

44

**1894.** *Overprinted* "POSTAGE" *in blue. W* **44.**

249 **43** 10s. claret and mauve, *p* 10 .. .. £275 75·00
249*a* 10s. claret and violet, *p* 12 .. .. £160 40·00
b. Perf 11 .. .. .. £250 75·00
c. Perf 12 × 11 .. .. .. £180 50·00
250 10s. aniline crimson & violet, *p* 12 × 11 £160 40·00
a. Perf 12 .. .. .. £200 50·00
250*b* £1 claret and violet, *p* 12 × 11 ..

**1903–04.** *Optd* "POSTAGE" *in blue. Chalk-surfaced paper. W* **44.**

250*c* **43** 10s. aniline crimson & violet, *p* 12 × 11
251 10s. rosine and violet, *p* 12 (1904) .. £140 50·00
a. Perf 11 .. .. .. £140 50·00
b. Perf 12 × 11 .. .. .. £140 40·00
252 10s. claret and violet, *p* 12 × 11 (1904) .. £225 60·00

45 View of Sydney

46 Emu

47 Captain Cook

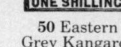

48 Queen Victoria and Arms of Colony

49 Superb Lyrebird

50 Eastern Grey Kangaroo

51 Map of Australia

52 Capt. Arthur Phillip, first Governor and Lord Carrington, Governor in 1888

Des M. Tannenberg (1d., 6d.), Miss Devine (2d., 8d.), H. Barraclough (4d.), Govt Ptg Office (1s.), C. Turner (5s.), Mrs. F. Stoddard (20s.). Eng W. Bell).

**1888** (1 May)–**89.** *Centenary of New South Wales.* (a) *W* **40.** *P* 11×12.
253 **45** 1d. lilac (9.7.88) .. .. .. .. 3·75 10
a. Perf 12×11½ .. .. .. 17·00 90
b. Perf 12 .. .. .. 5·00 10
c. Imperf (pair) .. .. ..
*d. Mauve* .. .. .. 3·75 10
da. Imperf between (pair) ..
da. Perf 12×11½ .. .. .. 6·00 25
dc. Perf 12 .. .. .. 5·50 25
254 **46** 2d. Prussian blue (1.9.88) .. 3·25 10
a. Imperf (pair) .. .. £100
**b. Imperf between (pair) .. £350**
c. Perf 12×11½ .. .. 7·00 10
d. Perf 12 .. .. .. 5·00 10
*e. Chalky blue* .. .. .. 3·25 10
ea. Perf 12×11½ .. ..
eb. Perf 12 .. .. .. 4·25 25
255 **47** 4d. purple-brown (8.10.88) .. 9·00 3·00
a. Perf 12×11½ .. .. .. 28·00 7·50
b. Perf 12 .. .. .. 24·00 3·25
c. Perf 11 .. .. .. £300 90·00
*d. Red-brown* .. .. .. 9·00 3·00
da. Perf 12×11½ .. .. 13·00 2·75
db. Perf 12 .. .. .. 13·00 2·75
*e. Orange-brown, p* 12×11½ .. 13·00 2·75
*f. Yellow-brown, p* 12×11½ .. 10·00 3·00
256 **48** 6d. carmine (26.11.88) .. 20·00 2·50
a. Perf 12×11½ .. .. .. 25·00 3·00
b. Perf 12 .. .. .. 21·00 2·50
257 **49** 8d. lilac-rose (17.1.89) .. 11·00 1·50
a. Perf 12×11½ .. .. .. 35·00 10·00
b. Perf 12 .. .. .. 11·00 1·75
*c. Magenta* .. .. .. 75·00 9·00
ca. Perf 12×11½ .. .. 11·00 1·75
cb. Perf 12 .. .. .. 11·00 2·25
258 **50** 1s. maroon (21.2.89) .. .. 12·00 90
a. Perf 12×11½ .. .. .. 14·00 90
b. Perf 12 .. .. .. 18·00 90
*c. Violet-brown* .. .. .. 12·00 90
ca. Imperf (pair) .. .. £550
cb. Perf 12×11½ .. .. 38·00 1·25
cc. Perf 12 .. .. .. 38·00 90

(b) *W* **41.** *P* 11×12
259 **45** 1d. lilac (1888) .. .. .. 9·00
*a. Mauve* .. .. .. 7·50 10
260 **46** 2d. Prussian blue (1888) .. .. 40·00 3·00

(c) *W* **25.** *P* 10
261 **51** 5s. deep purple (13.3.89) .. .. £225 45·00
*a. Deep violet* .. .. .. £200 42·00
262 **52** 20s. cobalt-blue .. .. .. £300 £110
253/8 Optd "Specimen" .. .. *Set of* 6 £150

Nos. 255c and 261/2 are line perforated, the remainder are comb.

53

54

**1890.** *W* **53** (5s.) *or* **54** (20s.). *P* 10.
263 **51** 5s. lilac .. .. .. .. £150 27·00
a. Perf 11 .. .. .. £225 38·00
ab. Imperf between (horiz pair) ..
b. Perf 12 .. .. .. £300 38·00
c. Perf 10×11 or 11×10 .. £225 27·00
*d. Mauve* .. .. .. £225 27·00
da. Perf 11 .. .. .. £225 38·00
264 **52** 20s. cobalt-blue .. .. .. £225 80·00
a. Perf 11 .. .. .. £300 75·00
b. Perf 11×10 .. .. ..
*c. Ultramarine, p* 11 .. .. £180 75·00
ca. Perf 12 .. .. .. £250 £130
cb. Perf 11×12 or 12×11 .. £180 75·00
263/4 Optd "Specimen" .. .. *Set of* 2 £180

55 Allegorical figure of Australia

**Halfpenny**
(56)

**SEVEN-PENCE**
**HALFPENNY**
(57)

**1890** (22 Dec). *W* **40.**
281 **55** 2½d. ultramarine, *p* 11×12 *comb* (Optd S. £25) .. .. .. 2·00 40
a. Perf 12×11½, comb .. 45·00
b. Perf 12, comb .. .. 7·00 40

**1891** (5 Jan). *Surch as T* **56** *and* **57.** *W* **40.**
282 **26** ½d. on 1d. grey, *p* 11×12 *comb* 1·50 1·75
a. Surch omitted .. ..
b. Surch double .. .. £120
283 **37** 7½d. on 6d. brown, *p* 10 .. 3·50 2·00
a. Perf 11 .. .. .. 3·50 2·00
b. Perf 12 .. .. .. 4·00 3·00
c. Perf 11×12 .. .. 3·75 2·75
d. Perf 10×12 .. .. 4·00 2·75
284 **38** 12½d. on 1s. red, *p* 10 .. .. 7·50 6·50
a. Perf 11 .. .. .. 8·50 6·50
b. Perf 11×12, comb .. 7·50 6·00
c. Perf 12×11½, comb .. 5·00 6·00
d. Perf 12, comb .. .. 9·00 6·00
282/4 Optd "Specimen" .. .. *Set of* 3 70·00

58

Die I

**1892** (21 Mar)–**99.** *T* **58.** *Die I. Narrow "H" in "HALF". W* **40.**
285 ½d. grey, *p* 10 .. .. .. .. 12·00 45
a. Perf 11 .. .. .. 60·00 5·00
b. Perf 10×12 .. .. .. 55·00 7·50
c. Perf 11×12 (Optd S. £20) .. 70·00 10
d. Perf 12 .. .. .. 90·00 10
286 ½d. slate, *p* 11×12 (1897) .. .. 80 10
a. Perf 12×11½ .. .. 80 10
b. Perf 12 .. .. .. 80 10
c. Imperf between (horiz pair). Perf 11×12 £400
287 ½d. bluish green, *p* 11×12 (1899) .. 1·50 10
a. Perf 12×11½ .. .. 70 10
b. Perf 12 .. .. .. 80 10

The perforations 11×12, 12×11½, 12, are from comb machines.

58*a*

58*b*

(Des C. Turner. Typo Govt Printing Office, Sydney)

**1897.** *Charity. T* **58***a and* **58***b. Wmk W* **40.** *P* 12×11 (1*d.*) *or* 11 (2½*d.*).
287*c* **58*a*** 1d. (1s.) green and brown (22.6) .. 40·00 40·00
287*d* **58*b*** 2½d. (2s. 6d.), gold, carmine & bl (28.6) £150 £150
287*c/d* Optd "Specimen" .. .. *Set of* 2 £200

These stamps, sold at 1s. and 2s. 6d. respectively, paid postage of 1d. and 2½d. only, the difference being given to a Consumptives' Home.

59

60

61

Dies of the 1d.

Die I

Die II

1d. Die I. The first pearl on the crown on the left side is merged into the arch, the shading under the fleur-de-lis is indistinct, the "S" of "WALES" is open.

Die II. The first pearl is circular, the vertical shading under the fleur-de-lis clear, the "S" of "WALES" not so open.

Dies of the 2½d.

Die I

Die II

2½d. Die I. There are 12 radiating lines in the star on the Queen's breast.

Die II. There are 16 radiating lines in the star and the eye is nearly full of colour.

**1897–99.** *W* **40** (*sideways on* 2½*d.*).
288 **59** 1d. carmine (Die I), *p* 11×12 .. .. 1·75 10
a. Perf 12×11½ .. .. 2·00 10
289 1d. scarlet (Die I), *p* 11×12 .. .. 1·75 10
a. Perf 12×11½ .. .. 4·50 40
b. Perf 12 .. .. .. 4·50 50
ba. Imperf horiz (vert pair) ..
290 1d. rose-carmine (Die II), *p* 11×12 1·75 10
a. Perf 12×11½ .. .. 1·50 10
b. Perf 12 .. .. .. 1·50 10
c. Imperf between (pair) .. £400
291 1d. salmon-red (Die II), *p* 12×11½ .. 1·75 10
a. Perf 12 .. .. .. 3·25 30
292 **60** 2d. deep dull blue, *p* 11×12 .. 1·75 10
a. Perf 12×11½ .. .. 1·75 10
b. Perf 12 .. .. .. 4·50 10
293 2d. cobalt-blue, *p* 11×12 .. .. 3·00 10
a. Perf 12×11½ .. .. 2·50 10
b. Perf 12 .. .. .. 3·00 10
294 2d. ultramarine, *p* 11×12 .. .. 2·50 10
a. Perf 12×11½ .. .. 1·75 10
b. Perf 12 .. .. .. 1·75 10
c. Imperf between (pair)
295 **61** 2½d. purple (Die I), *p* 12×11 .. 5·00 1·25
a. Perf 11½×12 .. .. 6·00 80
b. Perf 11 .. .. .. 6·00 1·75
296 2½d. deep violet (Die II), *p* 12×11 .. 3·50 80
a. Perf 11½×12 .. .. 6·00 1·25
b. Perf 12 .. .. .. 3·25 1·25
297 2½d. Prussian blue, *p* 12×11 .. 6·00
a. Perf 11½×12 .. .. 4·00 80
b. Perf 12 .. .. .. 3·25 80
288, 292, 294/5 Optd "Specimen" .. *Set of* 4 60·00

The perforations 11×12, 12×11½ and 12 are from comb machines, the perforation 11 is from a single-line machine.

**1897.** *Reissue of T* **24.** *W* **25.** *P* 11.
297*c* 5s. reddish purple (*shades*) .. .. 30·00 12·00
ca. Imperf between (pair) .. .. £2750
d. Perf 12 .. .. .. 38·00 20·00
e. Perf 11×12 or 12×11 .. .. 30·00 19·00

**1898–99.** *W* **40.** *P* 11×12.
297*f* **48** 6d. emerald-green (Optd S. £20) .. 30·00 5·00
fa. Perf 12×11½ .. .. 22·00 5·00
fb. Perf 12 .. .. .. 22·00 5·00
297*g* 6d. orange-yellow (1899) .. .. 14·00 3·00
ga. Perf 12×11½ .. .. 13·00 2·50
gb. Perf 12 .. .. .. 23·00 4·50
*gc. Yellow, p* 12×11½ .. .. 14·00 1·25

**1899**(Oct). *Chalk-surfaced paper. W* **40** (*sideways on* 2½*d.*). *P* 12×11½ *or* 11½×12 (2½*d.*), *comb.*
298 **58** ½d. blue-green (Die I) .. .. .. 90 10
a. Imperf (pair) .. .. 50·00 30·00
299 **59** 1d. carmine (Die II) .. .. .. 80 10
a. Imperf horiz (vert pair) .. £200
300 1d. scarlet (Die II) .. .. .. 80 10
301 1d. salmon-red (Die II) .. .. 80 10
a. Imperf (pair) .. .. 40·00 38·00
302 **60** 2d. cobalt-blue .. .. .. 1·75 10
a. Imperf (pair) .. .. 40·00
303 **61** 2½d. Prussian blue (Die II) .. .. 2·75 70
a. Imperf (pair) .. .. 45·00
303*b* **47** 4d. red-brown .. .. .. 9·00 3·00
c. Imperf (pair) .. .. £200
304 4d. orange-brown .. .. .. 9·00 3·00
305 **48** 6d. deep orange .. .. .. 11·00 90
a. Imperf (pair) .. .. £140
306 6d. orange-yellow .. .. .. 11·00 90
307 6d. emerald-green .. .. .. 38·00 2·00
a. Imperf (pair) .. .. £180
308 **49** 8d. magenta .. .. .. 11·00 2·50
309 **34** 9d. on 10d. dull brown .. .. 8·00 4·00
a. Surcharge double .. .. 90·00 70·00
b. Without surcharge .. .. 80·00
310 10d. violet .. .. .. 12·00 2·75
311 **50** 1s. maroon .. .. .. 12·00 80
312 1s. purple-brown .. .. .. 12·00 1·25
a. Imperf (pair) .. .. £150

62 Superb Lyrebird

63

**1902.** *Chalk-surfaced paper. W* **42** (*sideways on* 2½*d.*). *P* 12×11½ *or* 11½×12 (2½*d.*), *comb.*
313 **58** ½d. blue-green, (Die I) .. .. 2·75 10
a. Perf 12×11 .. .. 2·75
314 **59** 1d. carmine (Die II) .. .. .. 80 10
315 **60** 2d. cobalt-blue .. .. .. 1·50 10
316 **61** 2½d. dark blue (Die II) .. .. 2·75 10
317 **47** 4d. orange-brown .. .. .. 18·00 3·25
318 **48** 6d. yellow-orange .. .. .. 16·00 90
319 6d. orange .. .. .. 15·00 90
320 6d. orange-buff .. .. .. 15·00 90
321 **49** 8d. magenta .. .. .. 11·00 1·75
322 **34** 9d. on 10d. brownish orange .. 8·00 3·50
323 10d. violet .. .. .. 18·00 3·00
324 **50** 1s. maroon .. .. .. 12·00 80
325 1s. purple-brown .. .. .. 13·00 80
326 **62** 2s. 6d. green (Optd S. £35) .. 42·00 14·00

(Typo Victoria Govt Printer, Melbourne)

**1903** (18 July). *Wmk double-lined V over Crown. W w* **10.**
327 **63** 9d. brown & ultram, *p* 12¼×12½, *comb* (Optd S. £27) .. .. 7·50 1·75
328 9d. brown & dp blue, *p* 12¼×12½, *comb* .. .. .. 7·50 1·75
329 9d. brown and blue, *p* 11 .. .. £450 £275

Die II. Broad "H" in "HALF"

66

**1905–10.** *Chalk-surfaced paper. W* **66** *(sideways on 2½d.). P 12×11½ or 11½×12 (2½d.) comb, unless otherwise stated.*
330 **58** ½d. blue-green (Die I) .. 1·75 10
a. Perf 11½ × 11
331 ½d. blue-green (Die II) .. 90 10
a. Perf 11½ × 11 .. 1·75
332 **59** 1d. rose-carmine (Die II) .. 75 10
a. Perf. 11½ × 11 .. 1·75
333 **60** 2d. deep ultramarine .. 1·75 10
b. Perf 11½ × 11 .. 2·00
333*d* 2d. milky blue (1910) .. 1·75 10
da. Perf 11 .. 45·00
db. Perf 11½ × 11
334 **61** 2½d. Prussian blue (Die II) .. 2·75 80
335 **47** 4d. orange-brown .. 8·00 3·00
336 4d. red-brown .. 8·50 3·00
337 **48** 6d. dull yellow .. 13·00 1·00
a. Perf 11½ × 11 .. 21·00
338 6d. orange-yellow .. 13·00 90
a. Perf 11 × 11½ .. 27·00
339 6d. deep orange .. 11·00 90
a. Perf 11 .. £150
339*b* 6d. orange-buff .. 11·00 90
c. Perf 11½ × 11 .. 17·00 2·75
340 **49** 8d. magenta .. 11·00 2·00
341 8d. lilac-rose .. 11·00 2·25
342 **34** 10d. violet .. 14·00 2·75
a. Perf 11½ × 11 .. 13·00 2·50
b. Perf 11 .. 13·00 2·50
343 **50** 1s. maroon .. 11·00 85
344 1s. purple-brown (1908) .. 12·00 85
345 **62** 2s. 6d. blue-green .. 38·00 14·00
a. Perf 11½ × 11 .. 27·00 12·00
b. Perf 11 .. 30·00 15·00

67

**1905** (Dec). *Chalk-surfaced paper. W* **67**. *P* 11.
346 **52** 20s. cobalt-blue .. £160 60·00
a. Perf 12 .. £160 60·00
b. Perf 11 × 12 or 12 × 11 .. £160 60·00

(Typo Victoria Govt Printer, Melbourne)

**1906** (Sept). *Wmk double-lined "A" and Crown, W* **w 11**. *P 12×12½, comb.*
347 **63** 9d. brown and ultramarine .. 6·00 1·10
a. Perf 11 .. 42·00 35·00
348 9d. yellow-brown and ultramarine .. 6·00 90

**1907** (July). *W* **w 11**. *P 12×11½ or 11½×12 (2½d.), comb, unless otherwise stated.*
349 **58** ½d. blue-green (Die I) .. 2·00 10
351 **59** 1d. dull rose (Die II) .. 1·75 10
352 **60** 2d. cobalt-blue .. 1·75 10
353 **61** 2½d. Prussian blue (Die II) .. 42·00
354 **47** 4d. orange-brown .. 8·50 3·50
355 **48** 6d. orange-buff .. 20·00 4·00
356 6d. dull yellow .. 18·00 4·00
357 **49** 8d. magenta .. 11·00 3·50
358 **34** 10d. violet, *p* 11 .. 18·00
359 **50** 1s. purple-brown .. 16·00 3·00
a. Perf 11
360 **62** 2s. 6d. blue-green .. 45·00 25·00

OFFICIAL STAMPS

O S (O 1) O S (O 2) O S (O 3)

The space between the letters is normally 7 mm as illustrated, except on the 5d. and 8d. (11–11½ mm), 5s. (12 mm) and 20s. (14 mm). Later printings of the 3d., W **40**, are 5½ mm, and these are listed. Varieties in the settings are known on the 1d. (8 and 8½ mm), 2d. (8½ mm) and 3d. (9 mm).
Varieties of Type O 1 exist with "O" sideways.

*Nos. O1/35 overprinted with Type* O **1**

**1879.** *Wmk double-lined "6". P* 13.
O1 **14** 3d. dull green .. — £400

**1879** (Oct)–**85.** *W* **36**. *P* 13.
O 2 **26** 1d. salmon .. 8·50 2·00
a. Perf 10 (5.81) .. £180 30·00
b. Perf 13 × 10 (1881) .. 20·00 3·50
O 3 **28** 2d. blue .. 10·00 1·25
a. Perf 10 (7.81) .. £225 32·00
b. Perf 13 × 10 (1881) .. 20·00 2·50
c. Perf 10 × 13 (1881) .. 45·00 7·00
d. Perf 11 × 12 (11.84?) .. — £225
O 4 **14** 3d. dull green (R.) (12.79) .. £300 £200
O 5 **14** 3d. dull green (3.80) .. £250 45·00
a. Perf 10 (1881) .. £140 40·00
b. *Yellow-green*. Perf 10 (10.81) .. £140 25·00
c. Ditto. Perf 13 × 10 (1881) .. £140 25·00
d. Ditto. Perf 12 (4.85) .. £200 50·00
e. Ditto. Perf 12 × 10 (4.85) .. £200 50·00
O 6 **32** 4d. red-brown .. £160 7·50
a. Perf 10 (1881) .. — £190
b. Perf 13 × 10 (1881) .. £200 90·00
c. Perf 10 × 13 (1881) .. £200 11·00
O 7 **15** 5d. green, *p* 10 (8.84) .. 18·00 10·00
O 8 **37** 6d. pale lilac .. £225 4·50
a. Perf 10 (1881) .. — 40·00
b. Perf 13 × 10 (1881) .. £160 40·00
O 9 **19** 8d. yellow (R.) (12.79) .. — £140
O10 8d. yellow (1880) .. — 15·00
a. Perf 10 (1881) .. £275 75·00
O11 **34** 9d. on 10d. brown, *p* 10 (30.5.80) (Optd S. £60) .. £300 £160
O12 **38** 1s. black (R.) .. £225 7·50
a. Perf 10 (1881) .. — 16·00
b. Perf 13 × 10 (1881) .. — 9·00
c. Perf 10 × 13 (1881) .. — 45·00

Other stamps are known with red overprint but their status is in doubt.

**1880–88.** *Wmk "5/-", W* **25**. *(a) P* 13.
O13 **24** 5s. deep purple (15.2.80) .. £425 85·00
a. *Royal purple* .. — £300
b. *Deep rose-lilac* .. — £300

*(b) P* 10
O14 **24** 5s. deep purple (9.82) .. £425 £160
b. *Rose-lilac* (1883) .. £300 £100

*(c) P* 10 × 12
O15 **24** 5s. purple (10.86)

*(d) P* 12 × 10
O16 **24** 5s. reddish purple (1886) .. £325 £100

*(e) P* 12
O17 **24** 5s. purple .. — £150

*(f) P* 11
O18 **24** 5s. rose-lilac (1888) .. £170 65·00

**1880** (31 May). *Wmk "10", W* **35**. *P* 13.
O18*a* **34** 10d. lilac (Optd S. £60) .. £130 80·00
ab. Perf 10 and 11, compound .. £200 £180

**1882–85.** *W* **40**. *P* 10.
O19 **26** 1d. salmon .. 7·00 2·00
a. Perf 13 × 10 .. — £130
O20 1d. orange *to* scarlet .. 6·00 1·50
a. Perf 10 × 13 .. — £130
b. Perf 11 × 12, comb (1.84) .. 4·00 1·40
c. Perf 10 × 12 (4.85) .. — £110
d. Perf 12 × 11 (12.85)
O21 **28** 2d. blue .. 5·00 1·00
a. Perf 13 × 10
b. Perf 10 × 13 .. £190 75·00
c. Perf 11 × 12, comb (1.84) .. 5·00 1·00
d. Ditto. Opt double .. — £150
e. Perf 12 × 11 (12.85)
O22 **14** 3d. yellow-green (7 *mm*) .. 5·50 3·50
a. Perf 12 (4.85) .. £120 80·00
b. Perf 12 × 10 (4.85)
O23 3d. bluish green (7 *mm*) .. 5·50 3·50
a. Perf 12 (4.85) .. £120 80·00
b. Perf 12 × 10 (4.85)
c. Perf 10 × 11 (12.85)
O24 3d. yellow-green (5½ *mm*) .. 5·50 3·50
a. Perf 12 × 10 or 10 × 12 (4.85) .. 5·50 3·50
b. Perf 10 × 11 or 11 × 10 (12.85)
O25 3d. bluish green (5½ *mm*) (Optd S. £35) 5·50 3·50
a. Perf 12 × 10 or 10 × 12 (4.85) .. 6·00 3·50
c. Perf 10 × 11 or 11 × 10 (12.85) .. 5·00 3·50
O26 **32** 4d. red-brown .. 30·00 4·00
a. Perf 11 × 12, comb (1.84) .. 12·00 3·00
b. Perf 10 × 12 (4.85) .. — 70·00
O27 4d. dark brown .. 15·00 3·00
a. Perf 11 × 12, comb (1.84) .. 12·00 3·00
b. Perf 12 (4.85) .. £200 £150
c. Perf 10 × 12 (4.85) .. £200 90·00
O28 **15** 5d. dull green (Optd S. £35) .. 12·00 8·00
a. Perf 12 × 10 (4.85)
O29 5d. blue-green .. 13·00 9·00
a. Perf 12 (4.85) .. £100
b. Perf 10 × 11 .. 13·00 9·00
O30 **37** 6d. pale lilac .. 18·00 3·00
a. Perf 11 (12.85) .. 19·00 2·75
O31 6d. mauve .. 18·00 3·00
a. Perf 12 (4.85) .. — 45·00
b. Perf 12 × 10 (4.85) .. 18·00 2·75
c. Perf 10 × 12 (4.85) .. 80·00 38·00
d. Perf 11 × 10 (12.85) .. 18·00 2·75
e. Perf 12 × 11 (12.85) .. 55·00 15·00
O32 **19** 8d. yellow .. 20·00 10·00
a. Perf 12 (4.85) .. £130 38·00
b. Perf 12 × 10 or 10 × 12 (4.85) .. 20·00 9·00
d. Perf 11 (12.85) .. 22·00 10·00
da. Opt double
db. Opt treble .. † —
O33 **38** 1s. black (R.) .. 22·00 3·50
a. Perf 10 × 13 .. — 55·00
b. Perf 11 × 12, comb (1.84) .. 22·00 3·50
c. Ditto. Opt double .. — £200

**1886–87.** *W* **41**. *P* 10.
O34 **26** 1d. scarlet .. 20·00 3·00
O35 **28** 2d. deep blue
a. Perf 11 × 12

**1887–89.** *Nos. 247/8 overprinted in black. (a) With Type* O **1**.
O36 **43** 10s. claret and mauve, *p* 12 .. — £400

*(b) With Type* O **2** *(April 1889)*
O37 **43** 10s. claret and mauve, *p* 12 (Optd S. £75) .. £1200 £600
a. Perf 10 .. £2250 £1300

*(c) With Type* O **3** *(Jan 1887)*
O38 **43** £1 claret and rose-lilac, *p* 12 × 10 .. £3500 £2750

Only nine examples of No. O38 are recorded, three of which are mint. One of the used stamps, in the Royal Collection, shows overprint Type O **3** double.

**1888** (17 July)–**90.** *Optd as Type* O **1**. *(a) W* **40**. *P* 11 × 12.
O39 **45** 1d. lilac .. 1·75 10
a. Perf 12 .. 1·75 10
b. *Mauve* .. 1·75 10
ba. Perf 12 .. 1·75 10
O40 **46** 2d. Prussian blue (15.10.88) .. 2·00 10
a. Perf 12 .. 2·00 10
O41 **47** 4d. purple-brown (10.10.89) .. 7·50 2·00
a. Perf 12 .. 9·00 2·00
b. Perf 11
c. *Red-brown* .. 7·50 2·00
ca. Perf 12 .. 8·50 2·00
O42 **48** 6d. carmine (16.1.89) .. 8·00 2·50
a. Perf 12 .. 9·50 2·50
O43 **49** 8d. lilac-rose (1890) .. 14·00 6·50
a. Perf 12 .. — 9·00
O44 **50** 1s. maroon (9.1.90) .. 12·00 2·50
a. Perf 12 .. 13·00 2·50
b. *Purple-brown* .. 12·00 2·50
ba. Opt double
bb. Perf 12 .. 12·00 2·50

*(b) W* **41**. *P* 11 × 12 (1889)
O45 **45** 1d. mauve
O46 **46** 2d. blue

*(c) W* **25**. *P* 10
O47 **51** 5s. deep purple (9.1.90) .. £600 £500
O48 **52** 20s. cobalt-blue (10.3.90) .. £1100 £500
O39/44 Optd "Specimen" .. *Set of* 6 £200

**1890** (Feb)–**91.** *Optd as Type* O **1**. *W* **53** *(5s.) or* **54** *(20s.) P* 10.
O49 **51** 5s. lilac .. £140 65·00
a. *Mauve* .. £160 70·00
b. *Dull lilac*, *p* 12 .. £600
O50 **52** 20s. cobalt-blue (3.91) .. £1600 £600
O49/50 Optd "Specimen" .. *Set of* 2 £200

**1891** (Jan)–**92.** *Nos. 281/5 optd as Type* O **1**. *W* **40**. *P* 11 × 12.
O54 **55** 2½d. ultramarine .. 6·00 2·50
O55 **26** ½d. on 1d. grey .. 45·00 40·00
O56 **37** 7½d. on 6d. brown, *p* 10 .. 32·00 27·00
O57 **38** 12½d. on 1s. red .. 55·00 50·00
O58 **58** ½d. grey (5.92) .. 6·00 5·00
a. Perf 10 .. 7·00 9·00
b. Perf 12 .. 6·00 6·00
c. Perf 12 × 11½ .. 10·00
O54/8 Optd "Specimen" .. *Set of* 5 £160

Official stamps were withdrawn from the government departments on 31 December 1894.

POSTAGE DUE STAMPS

D 1

(Dies eng by A. Collingridge. Typo Govt Printing Office, Sydney)

**1891** (1 Jan)–**92.** *W* **40**. *P* 10.
D 1 **D 1** ½d. green (21.1.92) .. 2·50 2·00
D 2 1d. green .. 3·50 90
a. Perf 11 .. 3·75 90
b. Perf 12 .. 13·00 2·50
c. Perf 12 × 10 .. — 1·75
d. Perf 10 × 11 .. 6·50 90
e. Perf 11 × 12 or 12 × 11 .. 4·00 90
D 3 2d. green .. 5·50 80
a. Perf 11 .. 5·50 80
b. Perf 12 .. — 8·00
c. Perf 12 × 10 .. 15·00 3·00
d. Perf 10 × 11 .. 7·00 1·50
e. Perf 11 × 12 or 12 × 11 .. 5·50 80
D 4 3d. green .. 9·00 2·75
a. Perf 10 × 11 .. 9·00 2·75
D 5 4d. green .. 7·50 80
a. Perf 11 .. 8·50 80
b. Perf 10 × 11 .. 7·50 80
D 6 6d. green .. 14·00 2·00
D 7 8d. green .. 60·00 6·00
D 8 5s. green .. £120 30·00
a. Perf 11 .. £200 75·00
b. Perf 11 × 12 .. — £250
D 9 10s. green (early 1891) .. £180 45·00
a. Perf 12 × 10 .. £120 80·00
D10 20s. green (early 1891) .. £300 80·00
a. Perf 12 .. £300
b. Perf 12 × 10 .. £180 £100
D1/10 Optd "Specimen" .. *Set of* 10 £200

**1900.** *Chalk-surfaced paper. W* **40**. *P* 11.
D11 **D 1** ½d. emerald-green
D12 1d. emerald-green .. 3·50 1·75
a. Perf 12 .. 10·00 3·50
b. Perf 11 × 12 or 12 × 11 .. 3·50 1·00
D13 2d. emerald-green .. 6·50 2·75
a. Perf 12 .. — 12·00
b. Perf 11 × 12 or 12 × 11 .. 5·50 2·50
D14 3d. emerald-green, *p* 11 × 12 or 12 × 11 12·00 3·00
D15 4d. emerald-green .. 7·50 2·25

New South Wales became part of the Commonwealth of Australia on 1 January 1901.

## QUEENSLAND

The area which later became Queensland was previously part of New South Wales known as the Moreton Bay District. The first post office, at Brisbane, was opened in 1834 and the use of New South Wales stamps from the District became compulsory from 1 May 1854.

Queensland was proclaimed a separate colony on 10 December 1859, but continued to use New South Wales issues until 1 November 1860.

Post Offices opened in the Moreton Bay District before 10 December 1859, and using New South Wales stamps, were

| *Office* | *Opened* | *Numeral Cancellation* |
|---|---|---|
| Brisbane | 1834 | 95 |
| Burnett's Inn (*became* Goodes Inn) | 1850 | 108 |
| Callandoon | 1850 | 74 |
| Condamine | 1856 | 151 |
| Dalby | 1854 | 133 |
| Drayton | 1846 | 85 |
| Gayndah | 1850 | 86 |
| Gladstone | 1854 | 131 |
| Goodes Inn | 1858 | 108 |
| Ipswich | 1846 | 87 |
| Maryborough | 1849 | 96 |
| Rockhampton | 1858 | 201 |
| Surat | 1852 | 110 |
| Taroom | 1856 | 152 |
| Toowoomba | 1858 | 214 |
| Warwick | 1848 | 81 |

**PRICES FOR STAMPS ON COVER**

| | |
|---|---|
| Nos. 1/3 | *from* × 2 |
| Nos. 4/56 | *from* × 3 |
| Nos. 57/8 | — |
| Nos. 59/73 | *from* × 4 |
| Nos. 74/82 | *from* × 2 |
| Nos. 83/109 | *from* × 3 |
| Nos. 110/13 | *from* × 2 |
| Nos. 116/17 | *from* × 3 |
| Nos. 118/27 | — |
| Nos. 128/50 | *from* × 4 |
| Nos. 151/65 | — |
| Nos. 166/78 | *from* × 10 |
| Nos. 179/83 | *from* × 4 |
| Nos. 184/206 | *from* × 15 |
| No. 207 | — |
| Nos. 208/54 | *from* × 15 |
| Nos. 256/64 | *from* × 10 |
| Nos. 264*a*/*b* | *from* × 2 |
| Nos. 265/6 | *from* × 20 |
| Nos. 267/9 | *from* × 5 |
| Nos. 270/80*a* | — |
| Nos. 281/5 | *from* × 10 |
| Nos. 286/308 | *from* × 12 |
| No. 309 | — |
| Nos. F1/37 | — |

1

2 Large Star

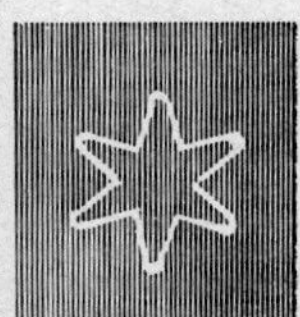

3 Small Star

(Dies eng W. Humphrys. Recess P.B.)

**1860** (1 Nov). *W* **2**. *Imperf.*

| | | | | |
|---|---|---|---|---|
| 1 | 1 | 1d. carmine-rose | £2250 | £800 |
| 2 | | 2d. blue | £5000 | £1500 |
| 3 | | 6d. green | £3500 | £800 |

**1860** (Nov). *W* **2**. *Clean-cut perf* 14–15½.

| | | | | |
|---|---|---|---|---|
| 4 | 1 | 1d. carmine-rose (1.11) | £1200 | £250 |
| 5 | | 2d. blue (1.11) | £450 | £100 |
| | | a. Imperf between (pair) | | |
| 6 | | 6d. green (15.11) | £500 | 60·00 |

**1860–61.** *W* **3**. *Clean-cut perf* 14–15½.

| | | | | |
|---|---|---|---|---|
| 7 | 1 | 2d. blue | £500 | £100 |
| | | a. Imperf between (horiz pair) | — | £900 |
| 8 | | 3d. brown (15.4.61) | £275 | 50·00 |
| | | a. Re-entry | — | £200 |
| | | b. Retouch (R. 2/8) | — | £200 |
| 9 | | 6d. green | £550 | 50·00 |
| 10 | | 1s. violet (15.11.60) | £500 | 70·00 |
| 11 | | "REGISTERED" (6d.) olive-yellow (1.61) | £350 | 70·00 |
| | | a. Imperf between (pair) | £2750 | |

The perforation of the 3d. is that known as "intermediate between clean-cut and rough".

The 3d. re-entry shows doubling of the left-hand arabesque and the retouch has redrawn spandrel dots under "EN" of "PENCE", a single dot in the centre of the circle under "E" and the bottom outer frame liner closer to the spandrel's frame line.

**1861** (July (?)). *W* **3**. *Clean-cut perf* 14.

| | | | | |
|---|---|---|---|---|
| 12 | 1 | 1d. carmine-rose | £100 | 35·00 |
| 13 | | 2d. blue | £275 | 50·00 |

**1861** (Sept). *W* **3**. *Rough perf* 14–15½.

| | | | | |
|---|---|---|---|---|
| 14 | 1 | 1d. carmine-rose | 75·00 | 28·00 |
| 15 | | 2d. blue | 90·00 | 28·00 |
| | | a. Imperf between (pair) | | |
| 16 | | 3d. brown | 50·00 | 30·00 |
| | | a. Imperf between (pair) | £1400 | |
| | | b. Re-entry | £200 | £110 |
| | | c. Retouch (R. 2/8) | — | £110 |
| 17 | | 6d. deep green | £100 | 27·00 |
| 18 | | 6d. yellow-green | £200 | 27·00 |
| 19 | | 1s. violet | £325 | 80·00 |
| 20 | | "REGISTERED" (6d.) orange-yellow | 45·00 | 35·00 |

(Printed and perforated in Brisbane)

**1862–67.** *Thick toned paper. No wmk.* (a) *P* 13 (1862–63).

| | | | | |
|---|---|---|---|---|
| 21 | 1 | 1d. Indian red (16.12.62) | £250 | 60·00 |
| 22 | | 1d. orange-vermilion (2.63) | 60·00 | 12·00 |
| | | a. Imperf (pair) | — | £500 |
| | | b. Imperf between (pair) | | |
| 23 | | 2d. blue (16.12.62) | 40·00 | 9·00 |
| 24 | | 2d. pale blue | 80·00 | 27·00 |
| | | a. Imperf (pair) | — | £500 |
| | | b. Imperf between (horiz pair) | — | £850 |
| | | c. Imperf between (vert pair) | £1100 | |
| 25 | | 3d. brown | 55·00 | 30·00 |
| | | a. Re-entry | — | £110 |
| | | b. Retouch (R. 2/8) | — | £110 |
| 26 | | 6d. apple-green (17.4.63) | 90·00 | 15·00 |
| 27 | | 6d. yellow-green | 80·00 | 12·00 |
| | | a. Imperf between (horiz pair) | — | £950 |
| 28 | | 6d. blue-green | £130 | 27·00 |
| | | a. Imperf (pair) | — | £500 |
| 29 | | 1s. grey (14.7.63) (H/S S. £40) | £130 | 22·00 |
| | | a. Imperf betwen (horiz pair) | — | £850 |
| | | b. Imperf between (vert pair) | | |

The top or bottom row of perforation was sometimes omitted from the sheet, resulting in stamps perforated on three sides only.

(b) *P* 12½ × 13 (1867)

| | | | | |
|---|---|---|---|---|
| 30 | 1 | 1d. orange-vermilion | 60·00 | 27·00 |
| 31 | | 2d. blue | 48·00 | 20·00 |
| 32 | | 3d. brown | 65·00 | 25·00 |
| | | a. Re-entry | — | 95·00 |
| | | b. Retouch (R. 2/8) | — | 95·00 |
| 33 | | 6d. apple-green | 85·00 | 27·00 |
| 34 | | 6d. yellow-green | 85·00 | 27·00 |
| 35 | | 1s. grey | £170 | 32·00 |
| | | a. Imperf between (horiz pair) | | |

The previously listed stamps perforated 13 round holes come from the same perforating machine as Nos. 21/9 after the pins had been replaced. The holes vary from rough to clean-cut.

**1864–65.** *W* **3**. (a) *P* 13.

| | | | | |
|---|---|---|---|---|
| 44 | 1 | 1d. orange-vermilion (1.65) | 55·00 | 20·00 |
| | | a. Imperf between (horiz pair) | £375 | |
| 45 | | 2d. pale blue (1.65) | 50·00 | 16·00 |
| 46 | | 2d. deep blue | 50·00 | 16·00 |
| | | a. Imperf between (vert pair) | £850 | |
| | | b. Bisected (1d.) (on cover) | | † £1800 |
| 47 | | 6d. yellow-green (1.65) | £120 | 22·00 |
| 48 | | 6d. deep green | £140 | 22·00 |
| 49 | | "REGISTERED" (6d.) orge-yell (21.6.64) | 65·00 | 30·00 |
| | | a. Double printed | £750 | |
| | | b. Imperf | | |

(b) *P* 12½ × 13

| | | | | |
|---|---|---|---|---|
| 50 | 1 | 1d. orange-vermilion | 95·00 | 40·00 |
| 50*a* | | 2d. deep blue | | |

**1866** (24 Jan). *Wmk* "QUEENSLAND/POSTAGE—POSTAGE/STAMPS—STAMPS" *in three lines in script capitals with double wavy lines above and below the wmk and single wavy lines with projecting sprays between each line of words. There are ornaments* ("*fleurons*") *between* "POSTAGE" "POSTAGE" *and between* "STAMPS" "STAMPS". *Single stamps only show a portion of one or two letters of this wmk.* (a) *P* 13.

| | | | | |
|---|---|---|---|---|
| 51 | 1 | 1d. orange-vermilion | £130 | 25·00 |
| 52 | | 2d. blue | 45·00 | 17·00 |

(b) *P* 12½ × 13

| | | | | |
|---|---|---|---|---|
| 52*a* | 1 | 1d. orange-vermilion | | |
| 52*b* | | 2d. blue | | |

**1866** (24 Sept). *Lithographed on thick paper. No wmk. P* 13.

| | | | | |
|---|---|---|---|---|
| 53 | 1 | 4d. slate (H/S S. £40) | £150 | 20·00 |
| | | a. Re-entry | — | 85·00 |
| | | b. Retouch (R. 2/8) | — | 85·00 |
| 55 | | 4d. lilac | 90·00 | 16·00 |
| | | a. Re-entry | — | 75·00 |
| | | b. Retouch (R. 2/8) | — | 75·00 |
| 56 | | 4d. reddish lilac | 90·00 | 16·00 |
| | | a. Re-entry | — | 75·00 |
| | | b. Retouch (R. 2/8) | — | 75·00 |
| 57 | | 5s. bright rose (H/S S. £40) | £275 | 80·00 |
| 58 | | 5s. pale rose | £200 | 55·00 |
| | | a. Imperf between (vert pair) | — | £600 |

The 4d. is from a transfer taken from the 3d. die, and the 5s. was taken from the 1s. die, the final "s" being added. The alteration in the values was made by hand on the stone, and there are many varieties, such as tall and short letters in "FOUR PENCE", some of the letters of "FOUR" smudged out, and differences in the position of the two words.

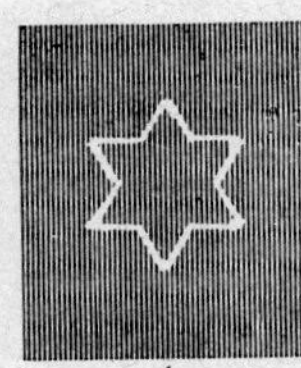

4

**1868–74.** *Wmk small truncated Star, W* **4** *on each stamp, and the word* "QUEENSLAND" *in single-lined Roman capitals four times in each sheet.* (a) *P* 13.

| | | | | |
|---|---|---|---|---|
| 59 | 1 | 1d. orange-vermilion (18.1.71) | 45·00 | 4·50 |
| 60 | | 2d. pale blue | 45·00 | 4·50 |
| 61 | | 2d. blue (3.4.68) | 40·00 | 2·75 |
| 62 | | 2d. bright blue | 50·00 | 2·75 |
| 63 | | 2d. greenish blue | 85·00 | 2·50 |
| 64 | | 2d. dark blue | 45·00 | 2·50 |
| | | a. Imperf | | |
| 65 | | 3d. olive-green (27.2.71) | 80·00 | 5·00 |
| | | a. Re-entry | — | 30·00 |
| | | b. Retouch (R. 2/8) | — | 30·00 |
| 66 | | 3d. greenish grey | 95·00 | 5·50 |
| | | a. Re-entry | — | 32·00 |
| | | b. Retouch (R. 2/8) | — | 32·00 |
| 67 | | 3d. brown | 80·00 | 5·50 |
| | | a. Re-entry | — | 32·00 |
| | | b. Retouch (R. 2/8) | — | 32·00 |
| 68 | | 6d. yellow-green (10.11.71) | £130 | 7·00 |
| 69 | 1 | 6d. green | £130 | 10·00 |
| 70 | | 6d. deep green | £170 | 17·00 |
| 71 | | 1s. greenish grey (13.11.72) | £325 | 32·00 |
| 72 | | 1s. brownish grey | £325 | 32·00 |
| 73 | | 1s. mauve (19.2.74) | £200 | 22·00 |
| 59/73 (*ex Nos.* 67, 71) H/S "Specimen" | | | £180 | |

(b) *P* 12 (about Feb 1874)

| | | | | |
|---|---|---|---|---|
| 74 | 1 | 1d. orange-vermilion | £250 | 24·00 |
| 75 | | 2d. blue | — | 35·00 |
| 76 | | 3d. greenish grey | — | £120 |
| | | a. Re-entry | | |
| | | b. Retouch (R. 2.8) | | |
| 77 | | 3d. brown | £250 | £120 |
| | | a. Re-entry | | |
| | | b. Retouch (R. 2/8) | | |
| 78 | | 6d. green | £850 | 40·00 |
| 79 | | 1s. mauve | — | 40·00 |

(c) *P* 13 × 12

| | | | | |
|---|---|---|---|---|
| 80 | 1 | 1d. orange-vermilion | — | £150 |
| 81 | | 2d. blue | £850 | 40·00 |
| 82 | | 3d. greenish grey | | |

Reprints were made in 1895 of all five values on the paper of the regular issue, and perforated 13; the colours are:—1d. orange and orange-brown, 2d. dull blue and bright blue, 3d. deep brown, 6d. yellow-green, 1s. red-violet and dull violet. The "Registered" was also reprinted with these on the same paper, but perforated 12. One sheet of the 2d. reprint is known to have had the perforations missing between the fourth and fifth vertical rows.

5

6

(4d., litho. Other values recess)

**1868–78.** *Wmk Crown and Q, W* **5**. (a) *P* 13 (1868–75).

| | | | | |
|---|---|---|---|---|
| 83 | 1 | 1d. orange-vermilion (10.11.68) | 50·00 | 4·50 |
| | | a. Imperf | £150 | |
| 84 | | 1d. pale rose-red (4.11.74) | 48·00 | 8·50 |
| 85 | | 1d. deep rose-red | 95·00 | 9·00 |
| 86 | | 2d. pale blue (4.11.74) | 48·00 | 1·75 |
| 87 | | 2d. deep blue (20.11.68) | 38·00 | 4·50 |
| | | a. Imperf (pair) | £275 | |
| | | b. Imperf between (vert pair) | | |
| 88 | | 3d. brown (11.6.75) | 70·00 | 12·00 |
| | | a. Re-entry | — | 55·00 |
| | | b. Retouch (R. 2/8) | — | 55·00 |
| 89 | | 4d. yellow (1.1.75) (H/S S. £60) | £750 | 40·00 |
| 90 | | 6d. deep green (9.4.69) | £120 | 9·00 |
| 91 | | 6d. yellow-green | 95·00 | 6·50 |
| 92 | | 6d. pale apple-green (1.1.75) | £130 | 9·00 |
| | | a. Imperf | £160 | |
| 93 | | 1s. mauve | £130 | 29·00 |

(b) *P* 12 (1876–78)

| | | | | |
|---|---|---|---|---|
| 94 | 1 | 1d. deep orange-vermilion | 38·00 | 5·00 |
| 95 | | 1d. pale orange-vermilion | 40·00 | 5·00 |
| | | a. Imperf between (vert pair) | | |
| 96 | | 1d. rose-red | 45·00 | 10·00 |
| 97 | | 1d. flesh | 60·00 | 10·00 |
| 98 | | 2d. pale blue | 80·00 | 15·00 |
| 99 | | 2d. bright blue | 22·00 | 1·00 |
| 100 | | 2d. deep blue | 25·00 | 1·50 |
| 101 | | 3d. brown | 60·00 | 9·00 |
| | | a. Re-entry | — | 45·00 |
| | | b. Retouch (R. 2/8) | — | 45·00 |
| 102 | | 4d. yellow | £600 | 25·00 |
| 103 | | 4d. buff | £600 | 20·00 |
| 104 | | 6d. deep green | £140 | 7·00 |
| 105 | | 6d. green | £130 | 4·25 |
| 106 | | 6d. yellow-green | £140 | 4·50 |
| 107 | | 6d. apple-green | £140 | 7·00 |
| 108 | | 1s. mauve | 40·00 | 9·00 |
| 109 | | 1s. purple | £140 | 5·00 |
| | | a. Imperf between (pair) | | |

(c) *P* 13 × 12 *or* 12 × 13

| | | | | |
|---|---|---|---|---|
| 110 | 1 | 1d. orange-vermilion | — | 85·00 |
| 110*a* | | 1d. rose-red | | |
| 111 | | 2d. deep blue | £1100 | £130 |
| 112 | | 4d. yellow | | |
| 113 | | 6d. deep green | — | £150 |

(d) *P* 12½ × 13

| | | | | |
|---|---|---|---|---|
| 114 | 1 | 1d. orange-vermilion | | |
| 115 | | 2d. deep blue | | |
| 115*a* | | 6d. yellow-green | | |

(e) *P* 12½

| | | | | |
|---|---|---|---|---|
| 115*b* | 1 | 2d. deep blue | | |

Reprints exist of the 1d., 2d., 3d., 6d. and 1s. on thicker paper, Wmk W **6**, and in different shades from the originals.

**1879.** *No wmk. P* 12.

| | | | | |
|---|---|---|---|---|
| 116 | 1 | 6d. pale emerald-green | £150 | 25·00 |
| | | a. Imperf between (horiz pair) | — | £550 |
| 117 | | 1s. mauve (*fiscal-cancel* £5) | 95·00 | 48·00 |

No. 117 has a very indistinct lilac *burelé* band at back.

Nos. 116/17 can be found showing portions of a papermaker's watermark, either T. H. Saunders & Co or A. Pirie & Sons.

**1881.** *Lithographed from transfers from the 1s. die. Wmk Crown and Q, W* **6**. *P* 12.

| | | | | |
|---|---|---|---|---|
| 118 | 1 | 2s. pale blue (6 Apr) | 60·00 | 22·00 |
| 119 | | 2s. blue (*fiscal-cancel* £3) | 60·00 | 22·00 |
| | | a. Imperf vert (horiz pair) | | |
| 120 | | 2s. deep blue (*fiscal-cancel* £3) | 75·00 | 22·00 |
| 121 | | 2s. 6d. dull scarlet (28 Aug) | £110 | 40·00 |
| 122 | | 2s. 6d. bright scarlet (*fiscal-cancel* £3) | £130 | 40·00 |
| 123 | | 5s. pale yellow-ochre (28 Aug) | £150 | 60·00 |
| 124 | | 5s. yellow-ochre (*fiscal-cancel* £4) | £150 | 60·00 |

125 1 10s. reddish brown (Mar) .. .. £350 £110
a. Imperf .. .. .. .. £375
126 10s. bistre-brown .. .. .. .. £350 £110
127 20s. rose (*fiscal-cancel £6*) .. .. £700 £130

Of the 2s. and 20s. stamps there are five types of each, and of the other values ten types of each.

Beware of fiscally used copies that have been cleaned and provided with forged postmarks.

7

Die I

Die II

Dies I and II often occur in the same sheet.

Die I. The white horizontal inner line of the triangle in the upper right-hand corner merges into the outer white line of the oval above the "L".

Die II. The same line is short and does not touch the inner oval.

**1879–80**. *Typo. P* 12. (*a*) *Wmk Crown and Q, W* **5**.
128 7 1d. reddish brown (Die I) .. .. 65·00 15·00
a. Die II .. .. .. £100 15·00
ab. "QOEENSLAND" .. .. £850 £150
129 1d. orange-brown (Die I) .. .. £100 15·00
130 2d. blue (Die I) .. .. .. 55·00 10·00
a. "PENGE" (R. 12/6) .. .. £650 £110
b. "QUEENSbAND" (R. 5/6) .. .. — £110
c. "QU" joined .. .. ..
131 4d. orange-yellow .. .. £300 35·00

(*b*) *No wmk, with lilac burelé band on back*
132 7 1d. reddish brown (Die I) .. .. £275 35·00
a. Die II .. .. .. £300 65·00
ab. "QOEENSLAND" .. .. — £1400
133 2d. blue (Die I) .. .. .. £350 17·00
a. "PENGE" (R. 12/6) .. .. £3250 £600
b. "QUEENSbAND" (R. 5/6) .. ..

(*c*) *Wmk Crown and Q, W* **6**
134 7 1d. reddish brown (Die I) .. .. 32·00 5·00
a. Imperf between (pair) .. .. — £200
b. Die II .. .. .. 40·00 5·00
ba. "QOEENSLAND" .. .. £200 40·00
bb. Imperf between (pair) .. .. — £200
135 1d. dull orange (Die I) .. .. 9·00 3·00
a. Die II .. .. .. 9·00 3·00
ab. "QOEENSLAND" .. .. 55·00 20·00
136 1d. scarlet (Die I) .. .. 12·00 1·75
a. Die II .. .. .. 14·00 2·25
ab. "QOEENSLAND" .. .. 80·00 24·00
137 2d. blue (Die I) .. .. .. 25·00 1·00
a. "PENGE" .. .. .. £120 40·00
b. "QUEENSbAND" .. .. £120 40·00
c. Die II .. .. .. 27·00 3·00
138 2d. grey-blue (Die I) .. .. 25·00 1·00
a. "PENGE" .. .. .. £120 40·00
b. "QUEENSbAND" .. .. £120 40·00
c. Die II .. .. ..
139 2d. bright blue (Die I) .. .. 28·00 1·00
a. "PENGE" .. .. .. £130 40·00
b. "QUEENSbAND" .. .. £130 40·00
c. Imperf between (pair) .. .. £375
d. Die II .. .. ..
140 2d. deep blue (Die I) .. .. 30·00 1·00
a. "PENGE" .. .. .. £140 40·00
b. "QUEENSbAND" .. .. £140 40·00
c. Die II .. .. .. 24·00 4·50
141 4d. orange-yellow .. .. £100 10·00
a. Imperf between (pair) .. ..
142 6d. deep green .. .. 55·00 4·50
a. Imperf between (pair) .. ..
143 6d. yellow-green .. .. 60·00 4·50
144 1s. deep violet .. .. 50·00 4·50
145 1s. pale lilac .. .. 45·00 5·50

The variety "QO" is No. 48 in the first arrangement, and No. 44 in a later arrangement on the sheets.

All these values have been seen imperf and unused, but we have no evidence that any of them were used in this condition.

The above were printed in sheets of 120, from plates made up of 30 groups of four electrotypes. There are four different types in each group, and two such groups of four are known of the 1d. and 2d., thus giving eight varieties of these two values. There was some resetting of the first plate of the 1d., and there are several plates of the 2d.; the value in the first plate of the latter value is in thinner letters, and in the last plate three types in each group of four have the "TW" of "TWO" joined, the letters of "PENCE" are larger and therefore much closer together, and in one type the "O" of "TWO" is oval, that letter being circular in the other types.

Half-penny
(8)

9

10

**1880** (21 Feb). *Surch with T* **8**.
151 7 ½d. on 1d. (No. 134) (Die I) .. .. £160 90·00
a. Die II .. .. .. £425 £350
ab. "QOEENSLAND" .. .. £850 £700

Examples with "Half-penny" reading downwards are forged surcharges.

**1882–86**. *Recess. P* 12. (*a*) *Thin paper. W* **5** *twice sideways*.
152 9 2s. bright blue .. .. .. 60·00 17·00
153 2s. 6d. vermilion .. .. .. 50·00 20·00
154 5s. rose .. .. .. .. 45·00 22·00
155 10s. brown .. .. .. 95·00 40·00
156 £1 deep green .. .. .. £225 £120
a. Re-entry (R. 1/2) .. .. — £180
b. Retouch (R. 6/4) .. .. — £180
152, 154/6 H/S "Specimen" .. .. *Set of* 4 £150

(*b*) *Thin paper. W* **6** *twice sideways*
157 9 2s. 6d. vermilion .. .. .. 40·00 30·00
158 5s. rose .. .. .. .. 45·00 20·00
159 10s. brown .. .. .. £180 50·00
160 £1 deep green .. .. .. £180 60·00
a. Re-entry (R. 1/2) .. .. — £100
b. Retouch (R. 6/4) .. .. — £100

(*c*) *Thick paper. W* **10**
161 9 2s. bright blue .. .. .. 70·00 20·00
162 2s. 6d. vermilion .. .. .. 38·00 20·00
163 5s. rose .. .. .. .. 35·00 28·00
164 10s. brown .. .. .. 95·00 40·00
165 £1 deep green .. .. .. £170 60·00
a. Re-entry (R. 1/2) .. .. — £100
b. Retouch (R. 6/4) .. .. — £100

The re-entry on the £1 shows as a double bottom frame line and the retouch occurs alongside the bottom left numeral.

See also Nos. 270/1.

11

12

In T **12** the shading lines do not extend entirely across, as in T **11**, thus leaving a white line down the front of the throat and point of the bust.

**1882–83**. *W* **6**. (*a*) *P* 12.
166 11 1d. pale vermilion-red .. .. 3·00 30
a. Double impression .. ..
167 1d. deep vermilion-red .. .. 3·00 30
168 2d. blue .. .. .. 4·25 30
a. Imperf between (horiz pair) ..
169 4d. pale yellow .. .. .. 12·00 1·40
a. "PENGE" for "PENCE" (R.8/1) £120 40·00
b. "EN" joined in "PENCE" (R.4/6) ..
c. Imperf .. .. ..
170 6d. green .. .. .. 9·00 70
171 1s. violet .. .. .. 16·00 1·90
172 1s. lilac .. .. .. 11·00 1·75
173 1s. deep mauve .. .. .. 11·00 1·40
174 1s. pale mauve .. .. .. 12·00 1·40
a. Imperf .. .. .. † —

(*b*) *P* 9½ × 12
176 11 1d. pale red .. .. .. 45·00 16·00
177 2d. blue .. .. .. £200 25·00
178 1s. mauve .. .. .. 90·00 19·00

The above were printed from plates made up of groups of four electrotypes as previously. In the 1d. the words of value are followed by a full stop. There are four types of the 4d., 6d., and 1s., eight types of the 1d., and twelve types of the 2d.

No. 169*c* is from a sheet used at Roma post office and comes cancelled with the "46" numeral postmark.

**1887–89**. *W* **6**. (*a*) *P* 12.
179 12 1d. vermilion-red .. .. 2·75 30
180 2d. blue .. .. .. 5·00 30
a. Oval white flaw on Queen's head behind diadem (R. 12/5) ..
181 2s. deep brown .. .. .. 55·00 23·00
182 2s. pale brown .. .. .. 50·00 20·00

(*b*) *P* 9½ × 12
183 12 2d. blue .. .. .. £150 22·00

These are from new plates; four types of each value grouped as before. The 1d. is without stop. In all values No. 2 in each group of four has the "L" and "A" of "QUEENSLAND" joined at the foot, and No. 3 of the 2d. has "P" of word "PENCE" with a long downstroke.

The 2d. is known bisected and used as a 1d. value.

13

14

**1890–94**. *W* **6** (*sideways on ½d.*). *P* 12½, 13 (*comb machine*).
184 13 ½d. pale green .. .. .. 2·75 50
185 ½d. deep green .. .. .. 2·75 50
186 ½d. deep blue-green .. .. 3·00 50
187 12 1d. vermilion-red .. .. 2·00 15
a. Imperf .. .. .. 23·00 23·00
b. Oval broken by tip of bust (R. 10/3)
188 2d. blue (old plate) .. .. 4·00 15
189 2d. pale blue (old plate) .. .. 3·75 15
190 2d. pale blue (retouched plate) .. 3·50 30
a. "FWO" for "TWO" (R. 8/7) .. — 20·00
191 14 2½d. carmine .. .. .. 10·00 55
192 12 3d. brown .. .. .. 8·50 1·40
193 11 4d. yellow .. .. .. 13·00 95
a. "PENGE" for "PENCE" (R. 8/1) .. 60·00
b. "EN" joined in "PENCE" (R. 4/6) ..
194 4d. orange .. .. .. 16·00 95
a. "PENGE" for "PENCE" (R. 8/1) 70·00 22·00
b. "EN" joined in "PENCE" (R. 4/6) ..
195 4d. lemon .. .. .. 20·00 1·25
a. "PENGE" for "PENCE" (R. 8/1) 80·00 28·00
b. "EN" joined in "PENCE" (R. 4/6) ..
196 6d. green .. .. .. 9·00 1·25
197 12 2s. red-brown .. .. .. 38·00 7·50
198 2s. pale brown .. .. .. 42·00 9·00

This issue is perforated by a new vertical comb machine, gauging about 12¾ × 12¾. The 3d. is from a plate similar to those of the last issue, No. 2 in each group of four types having "L" and "A" joined at the foot. The ½d. and 2½d. are likewise in groups of four types, but the differences are very minute. In the retouched plate of the 2d. the letters "L" and "A" no longer touch in No. 2 of each group and the "P" in No. 3 is normal.

**1894–95**. A. *Thick paper. W* **10**. (*a*) *P* 12½, 13.
202 12 1d. vermilion-red .. .. 2·50 15
a. Oval broken by tip of bust (R. 10/3)
203 1d. red-orange .. .. .. 2·50 15
a. Oval broken by tip of bust (R. 10/3)
204 2d. blue (retouched plate) .. .. 3·00 20
a. "FWO" for "TWO" (R. 8/7) .. .. — 20·00

(*b*) *P* 12
205 11 1s. mauve .. .. .. 12·00 2·75

B. *Unwmkd paper; with blue burelé band at back. P* 12½, 13
206 12 1d. vermilion-red .. .. 2·00 15
a. Oval broken by tip of bust (R. 10/3)
b. "PE" of "PENNY" omitted (R. 1/2) £100 75·00
206*c* 1d. red-orange .. .. ..

C. *Thin paper. Crown and Q faintly impressed. P* 12½, 13
207 12 2d. blue (retouched plate) .. .. 6·00
a. "FWO" for "TWO" (R. 8/7) .. ..

15

16

17

18

**1895–96**. A. *W* **6** (*sideways on ½d.*). (*a*) *P* 12½, 13.
208 15 ½d. green .. .. .. 1·00 45
a. Double impression .. ..
209 ½d. deep green .. .. .. 1·00 45
a. Printed both sides .. .. 60·00
210 16 1d. orange-red .. .. .. 2·25 20
211 1d. pale red .. .. .. 2·00 20
212 2d. blue .. .. .. 3·25 35
213 17 2½d. carmine .. .. .. 8·00 3·00
214 2½d. rose .. .. .. 9·00 3·00
215 18 5d. purple-brown .. .. 10·00 2·75

(*b*) *P* 12
217 16 1d. red .. .. .. 20·00
218 2d. blue .. .. .. — 12·00

B. *Thick paper. W* **10** (*sideways*) (*part only on each stamp*).

(*a*) *P* 12½, 13
219 15 ½d. green .. .. .. 1·00 45
220 ½d. deep green .. .. .. 1·00 45

(*b*) *P* 12
221 15 ½d. green .. .. .. 12·00
222 ½d. deep green .. .. .. 12·00

C. *No wmk; with blue burelé band at back*. (*a*) *P* 12½, 13
223 15 ½d. green .. .. .. 1·00 50
a. Without *burelé* band .. .. 40·00
224 ½d. deep green .. .. .. 1·00

(*b*) *P* 12
225 15 ½d. green .. .. .. 15·00
a. Without *burelé* band .. .. 50·00

Nos. 223a and 225a are from the margins of the sheet.

D. *Thin paper, with Crown and Q faintly impressed. P* 12½, 13
227 15 ½d. green .. .. .. 1·40 50
228 16 1d. orange-red .. .. .. 3·00 30

19

**1896**. *W* **6**. *P* 12½, 13.
229 19 1d. vermilion .. .. .. 7·50 40

Used examples of a 6d. green as Type **19** (figures in lower corners only) are known, mostly with readable 1902 postmark dates. It is believed that this 6d. was prepared, but not officially issued (*Price* £1000 *used*).

20

21

22

23

24

25

Die I

Die II

Two Dies of 4d.:

Die I. Serif of horizontal bar on lower right 4d. is clear of vertical frame line.
Die II. Serif joins vertical frame line.

**1897–1907.** *Figures in all corners.* W **6** (*sideways on* ½d). *P* 12½, 13.

| No. | Type | Description | Unused | Used |
|---|---|---|---|---|
| 231 | **20** | ½d. deep green | 3·50 | 2·00 |
| | | a. Perf 12 | — | 90·00 |
| 232 | **21** | 1d. orange-vermilion | 1·00 | 15 |
| 233 | | 1d. vermilion | 1·00 | 15 |
| 234 | | 2d. blue | 1·25 | 15 |
| | | a. Cracked plate | 50·00 | 20·00 |
| 235 | | 2d. deep blue | 1·25 | 15 |
| | | a. Cracked plate | 50·00 | 20·00 |
| 236 | **22** | 2½d. rose | 15·00 | 6·00 |
| 237 | | 2½d. purple/*blue* | 8·50 | 85 |
| 238 | | 2½d. brown-purple/*blue* | 8·50 | 85 |
| 239 | | 2½d. slate/*blue* | 11·00 | 2·75 |
| 240 | **21** | 3d. brown | 10·00 | 1·00 |
| 241 | | 3d. deep brown | 8·00 | 80 |
| 242 | | 3d. reddish brown (1906) | 8·00 | 80 |
| 243 | | 3d. grey-brown (1907) | 9·50 | 80 |
| 244 | | 4d. yellow (Die I) | 8·00 | 80 |
| | | a. Die II | 18·00 | 1·75 |
| 245 | | 4d. yellow-buff (Die I) | 8·00 | 80 |
| | | a. Die II | 18·00 | 1·75 |
| 246 | **23** | 5d. purple-brown | 7·00 | 80 |
| 247 | | 5d. dull brown (1906) | 8·00 | 1·50 |
| 248 | | 5d. black-brown (1907) | 9·00 | 1·75 |
| 249 | **21** | 6d. green | 7·00 | 1·25 |
| 250 | | 6d. yellow-green | 6·00 | 1·25 |
| 251 | **24** | 1s. pale mauve | 13·00 | 1·00 |
| 252 | | 1s. dull mauve | 13·00 | 1·00 |
| 253 | | 1s. bright mauve | 15·00 | 2·00 |
| 254 | **25** | 2s. turquoise-green | 30·00 | 7·00 |

The 1d. perf 12 × 9½ was not an authorised issue.

The cracked plate variety on the 2d. developed during 1901 and shows as a white break on the Queen's head and neck.

**1897–8.** W **6** (*a*) *Zigzag roulette in black.* (*b*) *The same but plain.* (*c*) *Roulette* (*a*) *and also* (*b*). (*d*) *Roulette* (*b*) *and perf* 12½, 13. (*e*) *Roulette* (*a*) *and perf* 12½, 13. (*f*) *Compound of* (*a*), (*b*), *and perf* 12½, 13.

| No. | Type | Description | Unused | Used |
|---|---|---|---|---|
| 256 | **21** | 1d. vermilion (*a*) | 5·00 | 4·00 |
| 257 | | 1d. vermilion (*b*) | 2·50 | 1·50 |
| 258 | | 1d. vermilion (*c*) | 4·75 | |
| 259 | | 1d. vermilion (*d*) | 3·00 | 2·50 |
| 260 | | 1d. vermilion (*e*) | 50·00 | |
| 261 | | 1d. vermilion (*f*) | 60·00 | |

26

27

**1899–1906.** W **6**. *P* 12½, 13.

| No. | Type | Description | Unused | Used |
|---|---|---|---|---|
| 262 | **26** | ½d. deep green | 1·00 | 20 |
| 263 | | ½d. grey-green | 1·00 | 20 |
| 264 | | ½d. pale green (1906) | 1·00 | 20 |

Stamps of T **26** without wmk, are proofs.

(Des F. Elliott)

**1900** (19 June). *Charity. T* **27** *and horiz design showing Queen Victoria in medallion inscr* "PATRIOTIC FUND 1900". W **6**. *P* 12.

| No. | Type | Description | Unused | Used |
|---|---|---|---|---|
| 264*a* | | 1d. (6d.) claret | £100 | £100 |
| 264*b* | | 2d. (1s.) violet | £225 | £225 |

These stamps, sold at 6d. and 1s. respectively, paid postage of 1d. and 2d. only, the difference being contributed to a Patriotic Fund.

28

QUEENSLAND
A

QUEENSLAND
B

**TWO TYPES OF "QUEENSLAND".** Three different duty plates, each 120 (12 × 10), were produced for Type **28**. The first contained country inscriptions as Type A and was only used for Nos. 265/6. The second duty plate used for Nos. 265/6 and 282/5 contained 117 examples as Type A and 3 as Type B occurring on R. 1/6, R. 2/6 and R. 3/6. The third plate, also used for Nos. 265/6 and 282/5, had all inscriptions as Type B.

(Typo Victoria Govt Printer, Melbourne)

**1903** (4 July). *W w* **10**. *P* 12½.

| No. | Type | Description | Unused | Used |
|---|---|---|---|---|
| 265 | **28** | 9d. brown and ultramarine (A) | 10·00 | 1·75 |
| 266 | | 9d. brown and ultramarine (B) | 10·00 | 1·75 |

**1903.** W **6**. *P* 12.

| No. | Type | Description | Unused | Used |
|---|---|---|---|---|
| 267 | **26** | ½d. green | 1·50 | 30 |
| 268 | **21** | 1d. vermilion | 2·25 | 70 |
| 269 | | 2d. blue | — | 5·00 |

Nos. 267/9 can be found with rough or clean cut holes from this comb machine. A perf 12½ line machine was also used, but stamps from it are difficult to distinguish.

**1905.** *Recess.* W **6**. *P* 12½, 13 (*irregular line*).

| No. | Type | Description | Unused | Used |
|---|---|---|---|---|
| 270 | **9** | 2s. 6d. vermilion | 60·00 | 32·00 |
| 271 | | £1 deep green | £450 | £300 |
| | | a. Re-entry (R. 1/2) | — | £400 |
| | | b. Retouch (R. 6/4) | — | £400 |

29

**1905–10.** *Litho.* A. W **6**, *twice sideways.* (*a*) *P* 12 (1905–6).

| No. | Type | Description | Unused | Used |
|---|---|---|---|---|
| 272 | **9** | 5s. rose (7.06) | 65·00 | 65·00 |
| 273 | | £1 deep green (7.11.05) | £250 | 90·00 |
| | | a. Re-entry (R. 1/2) | — | £150 |
| | | b. Retouch (R. 6/4) | — | £150 |

(*b*) *P* 12½, 13 (*irregular line*)

| No. | Type | Description | Unused | Used |
|---|---|---|---|---|
| 274 | **9** | £1 deep green (7.06) | £350 | £100 |
| | | a. Re-entry (R. 1/2) | — | £160 |
| | | b. Retouch (R. 6/4) | — | £160 |

B. W **29**, *twice sideways. P* 12½, 13 (*irregular line*) (1907–10)

| No. | Type | Description | Unused | Used |
|---|---|---|---|---|
| 275 | **9** | 2s. 6d. vermilion | 40·00 | 26·00 |
| 276 | | 2s. 6d. dull orange (1910) | 55·00 | 32·00 |
| 277 | | 5s. rose | 45·00 | 26·00 |
| 278 | | 5s. deep rose | 55·00 | 38·00 |
| 279 | | 10s. deep brown | £100 | 35·00 |
| 280 | | £1 bluish green | £170 | 80·00 |
| | | a. Re-entry (R. 1/2) | — | £130 |
| | | b. Retouch (R. 6/4) | — | £130 |
| 280*c* | | £1 deep green | £325 | £250 |
| | | ca. Re-entry (R. 1/2) | — | £350 |
| | | cb. Retouch (R. 6/4) | — | £350 |

The lithographic stone used for Nos. 272/80*c* took the full sheet of 30 so the varieties on the £1 recess-printed version also appear on the stamps printed by lithography.

30

32

Redrawn types of T **21**

T **30**. The head is redrawn, the top of the crown is higher and touches the frame, as do also the back of the chignon and the point of the bust. The forehead is filled in with lines of shading, and the figures in the corners appear to have been redrawn also.

T **32**. The forehead is plain (white instead of shaded), and though the top of the crown is made higher, it does not touch the frame; but the point of the bust and the chignon still touch The figure in the right lower corner does not touch the line below, and has not the battered appearance of that in the first redrawn type. The stamps are very clearly printed, the lines of shading being distinct.

**1906** (Sept). W **6**. *P* 12½, 13 (*comb*).

| No. | Type | Description | Unused | Used |
|---|---|---|---|---|
| 281 | **30** | 2d. dull blue (*shades*) | 5·00 | 1·50 |

(Typo Victoria Govt Printer, Melbourne)

**1906** (Sept)–**10**. *Wmk Crown and double-lined A, W w* **11**.

(*a*) *P* 12 × 12½.

| No. | Type | Description | Unused | Used |
|---|---|---|---|---|
| 282 | **28** | 9d. brown and ultramarine (A) | 22·00 | 2·50 |
| 283 | | 9d. brown and ultramarine (B) | 11·00 | 2·00 |
| 283*a* | | 9d. pale brown and blue (A) | | |
| 284 | | 9d. pale brown and blue (B) | 11·00 | 2·25 |

(*b*) *P* 11 (1910)

| No. | Type | Description | Unused | Used |
|---|---|---|---|---|
| 285 | **28** | 9d. brown and blue (B) | — | £200 |

**1907–09.** W **29**. (*a*) *P* 12½, 13 (*comb*).

| No. | Type | Description | Unused | Used |
|---|---|---|---|---|
| 286 | **26** | ½d. deep green | 1·00 | 20 |
| 287 | | ½d. deep blue-green | 1·00 | 20 |
| 288 | **21** | 1d. vermilion | 1·00 | 15 |
| | | a. Imperf (pair) | £150 | |
| 289 | **30** | 2d. dull blue | 1·40 | 15 |
| 289*a* | | 2d. bright blue (3.08) | 7·50 | 2·00 |
| 290 | **32** | 2d. bright blue (4.08) | 1·50 | 15 |
| 291 | **21** | 3d. pale brown (8.08) | 10·00 | 70 |
| 292 | | 3d. bistre-brown | 10·00 | 80 |
| 293 | | 4d. yellow (Die I) | 10·00 | 1·25 |
| | | a. Die II | 22·00 | 2·75 |
| 294 | | 4d. grey-black (Die I) (4.09) | 12·00 | 1·50 |
| | | a. Die II | 27·00 | 3·50 |
| 295 | **23** | 5d. dull brown | 7·50 | 1·25 |
| 295*a* | | 5d. sepia (12.09) | 11·00 | 2·00 |
| 296 | **21** | 6d. yellow-green | 8·50 | 1·25 |
| 297 | | 6d. bright green | 10·00 | 1·50 |
| 298 | **24** | 1s. violet (1908) | 11·00 | 1·60 |
| 299 | | 1s. bright mauve | 12·00 | 1·50 |
| 300 | **25** | 2s. turquoise-green (8.08) | 30·00 | 6·50 |

Stamps of this issue also exist with the irregular line perforation 12½, 13. This was used when the comb perforation was under repair.

(*b*) *P* 13 × 11 *to* 12½

| No. | Type | Description | Unused | Used |
|---|---|---|---|---|
| 301 | **26** | ½d. deep green | | |
| 302 | **21** | 1d. vermilion | 2·50 | 50 |
| 303 | **32** | 2d. blue | 4·00 | 1·00 |
| 304 | **21** | 3d. bistre-brown | 8·00 | 2·00 |
| 305 | | 4d. grey-black | 20·00 | |
| 306 | **23** | 5d. dull brown | 15·00 | |
| 307 | **21** | 6d. yellow-green | 16·00 | |
| 308 | **23** | 1s. violet | 25·00 | |

The perforation (*b*) is from a machine introduced to help cope with the demands caused by the introduction of penny postage. The three rows at top (or bottom) of the sheet show varieties gauging 13 × 11½, 13 × 11, and 13 × 12 respectively, these are obtainable in strips of three showing the three variations.

Many values of the 1907–09 issue were subsequently produced by lithography.

**1911.** W **29**. *Perf irregular compound,* 10½ *to* 12½.

| No. | Type | Description | Unused | Used |
|---|---|---|---|---|
| 309 | **21** | 1d. vermilion | — | £180 |

This was from another converted machine, formerly used for perforating Railway stamps. The perforation was very unsatisfactory and only one or two sheets were sold.

POSTAL FISCALS

Authorised for use from 1 January 1880 until 1 July 1892

**CANCELLATIONS**. Beware of stamps which have had pen-cancellations cleaned off and then had faked postmarks applied. Used prices quoted are for postally used examples between the above dates.

F 1

F 2

**1866–68.** A. *No wmk. P* 13.

| No. | Type | Description | Unused | Used |
|---|---|---|---|---|
| F 1 | **F 1** | 1d. blue | 25·00 | 5·00 |
| F 2 | | 6d. deep violet | 25·00 | 30·00 |
| F 3 | | 1s. blue-green | 30·00 | 9·00 |
| F 4 | | 2s. brown | 85·00 | 42·00 |
| F 5 | | 2s. 6d. dull red | 85·00 | 30·00 |
| F 6 | | 5s. yellow | £200 | 60·00 |
| F 7 | | 10s. green | £350 | £100 |
| F 8 | | 20s. rose | £425 | £150 |

B. *Wmk* F **2**. *P* 13

| No. | Type | Description | Unused | Used |
|---|---|---|---|---|
| F 9 | **F 1** | 1d. blue | 10·00 | 20·00 |
| F10 | | 6d. deep violet | 25·00 | 30·00 |
| F11 | | 6d. blue | 25·00 | 14·00 |
| F12 | | 1s. blue-green | 30·00 | 14·00 |
| F13 | | 2s. brown | 85·00 | 30·00 |
| F13*a* | | 5s. yellow | £200 | 65·00 |
| F14 | | 10s. green | £350 | £100 |
| F15 | | 20s. rose | £425 | £150 |

F 3

F 3*a*

**1871–2.** *P* 12 *or* 13. A. *Wmk Large Crown and Q, Wmk* F **3***a*.

| No. | Type | Description | Unused | Used |
|---|---|---|---|---|
| F16 | **F 3** | 1d. mauve | 10·00 | 5·00 |
| F17 | | 6d. red-brown | 20·00 | 10·00 |
| F18 | | 1s. green | 30·00 | 12·00 |
| F19 | | 2s. blue | 40·00 | 10·00 |
| F20 | | 2s. 6d. brick-red | 60·00 | 25·00 |
| F21 | | 5s. orange-brown | £100 | 25·00 |
| F22 | | 10s. brown | £200 | 75·00 |
| F23 | | 20s. rose | £350 | £120 |

B. *No wmk. Blue burelé band at back*

| No. | Type | Description | Unused | Used |
|---|---|---|---|---|
| F24 | **F 3** | 1d. mauve | 14·00 | 6·50 |
| F25 | | 6d. red-brown | 20·00 | 10·00 |
| F26 | | 6d. mauve | 22·00 | 12·00 |
| F27 | | 1s. green | 30·00 | 12·00 |
| F28 | | 2s. blue | 45·00 | 50·00 |
| F29 | | 2s. 6d. vermilion | 85·00 | 35·00 |
| F30 | | 5s. yellow-brown | £120 | 40·00 |
| F31 | | 10s. brown | £225 | 90·00 |
| F32 | | 20s. rose | £350 | £110 |

## *PRICES OF SETS*

Set prices are given for many issues, generally those containing three stamps or more. Definitive sets include one of each value or major colour change, but do not cover different perforations, die types or minor shades. Where a choice is possible the set prices are based on the cheapest versions of the stamps included in the listings.

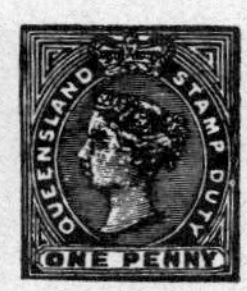
F 4

F 5

**1878–9.** A. *No wmk. Lilac burelé band at back. P* 12.
F33 F 4 1d. violet .. .. .. .. .. — 12·00

B. *Wmk Crown and Q, W* **5**. *P* 12
F34 F 4 1d. violet .. .. .. .. .. 15·00 8·00

Stamps as Type F **5** were not issued until 1 July 1892. The existence of postal cancellations on such issues was unauthorised.

Queensland became part of the Commonwealth of Australia on 1 January 1901.

## SOUTH AUSTRALIA

**PRICES FOR STAMPS ON COVER**

| | |
|---|---|
| Nos. 1/3 | *from* × 3 |
| No. 4 | † |
| Nos. 5/12 | *from* × 2 |
| Nos. 13/18 | *from* × 3 |
| Nos. 19/43 | *from* × 4 |
| Nos. 44/9*b* | — |
| Nos. 50/110 | *from* × 3 |
| No. 111 | — |
| Nos. 112/34 | *from* × 6 |
| Nos. 135/45 | *from* × 3 |
| Nos. 146/66 | *from* × 5 |
| Nos. 167/77 | *from* × 10 |
| Nos. 178/80 | — |
| Nos. 181/94 | *from* × 12 |
| Nos. 195/208 | — |
| Nos. 229/34 | *from* × 12 |
| No. 235 | — |
| Nos. 236/44 | *from* × 8 |
| Nos. 245/60 | *from* × 15 |
| Nos. 262/7 | *from* × 20 |
| Nos. 268/75 | *from* × 30 |
| Nos. 276/9 | — |
| Nos. 280/8 | *from* × 30 |
| Nos. 289/92 | — |
| Nos. 293/304 | *from* × 15 |
| No. 305 | — |
| Nos. O1/13 | — |
| Nos. O14/36 | *from* × 20 |
| Nos. O37/42 | *from* × 5 |
| Nos. O43/6 | *from* × 50 |
| Nos. O47/9 | — |
| Nos. O50/3 | *from* × 30 |
| No. O54 | *from* × 15 |
| Nos. O55/71 | *from* × 50 |
| Nos. O72/85 | *from* × 75 |
| Nos. O86/7 | — |

**SPECIMEN OVERPRINTS.** Those listed are from U.P.U. distributions between 1889 and 1895. Further "Specimen" overprints exist, but these were used for other purposes.

1

2 Large Star

(Eng Wm Humphrys. Recess P.B.)

**1855.** *Printed in London. W* **2**. *Imperf.*
1 1 1d. dark green (26.10.55) .. .. £2500 £350
2 2d. rose-carmine (*shades*) (1.1.55) .. £650 £110
3 6d. deep blue (26.10.55) .. .. £2000 £150

*Prepared and sent to the Colony, but not issued*
4 1 1s. violet .. .. .. .. £4750

A printing of 500,000 of these 1s. stamps was made and delivered, but as the colour was liable to be confused with that of the 6d. stamp, the stock was destroyed on 5 June 1857.

**NOTE.** Proofs of the 1d. and 6d. without wmk exist, and these are found with forged star watermarks added, and are sometimes offered as originals.

For reprints of the above and later issues, see note after No. 194.

**1856–58.** *Printed by Govt Ptr, Adelaide, from Perkins, Bacon plates. W* **2**. *Imperf.*
5 1 1d. deep yellow-green (15.6.58) .. £5000 £400
6 1d. yellow-green (11.10.58) .. .. — £475
7 2d. orange-red (23.4.56) .. .. — £110
8 2d. blood-red (14.11.56) .. .. £1200 90·00
a. Printed on both sides .. ..
9 2d. red (*shades*) (29.10.57) .. .. £650 55·00
a. Printed on both sides .. .. £600
10 6d. slate-blue (7.57) .. .. £2000 £200
11 1s. red-orange (8.7.57) .. .. — £400
12 1s. orange (11.6.58) .. .. £3750 £325

**1858–59.** *W* **2**. *Rouletted. (This first rouletted issue has the same colours as the local imperf issue).*
13 1 1d. yellow-green (8.1.59) .. .. £475 45·00
14 1d. light yellow-green (18.3.59) .. .. £475 50·00
a. Imperf between (pair) .. ..
15 2d. red (17.2.59) .. .. .. £110 18·00
a. Printed on both sides .. ..
17 6d. slate-blue (12.12.58) .. .. £375 25·00
18 1s. orange (18.3.59) .. .. £800 35·00
a. Printed on both sides .. .. — £1000

3

4

(5)

**1860–69.** *Second rouletted issue, printed in colours only found rouletted or perforated. Surch with T* **5** *(Nos. 35/7). W* **2**.
19 1 1d. bright yellow-green (22.4.61) .. 45·00 25·00
20 1d. dull blue-green (17.12.63) .. .. 40·00 23·00
21 1d. sage-green .. .. .. 50·00 27·00
22 1d. pale sage-green (27.5.65) .. .. 40·00
23 1d. deep green (1864) .. .. £225 65·00
24 1d. deep yellow-green (1869) .. .. 90·00
24*a* 2d. pale red .. .. .. 60·00 4·00
b. Printed on both sides .. .. — £375
25 2d. pale vermilion (3.2.63) .. .. 48·00 4·00
26 2d. bright vermilion (19.8.64) .. .. 38·00 2·75
a. Imperf between (horiz pair) .. .. £700 £300
27 3 4d. dull violet (24.1.67) .. .. 48·00 17·00
28 1 6d. violet-blue (19.3.60) .. .. £140 6·00
29 6d. greenish blue (11.2.63) .. .. 65·00 4·00
30 6d. dull ultramarine (25.4.64) .. .. 60·00 4·00
a. Imperf between (horiz pair) .. .. — £300
31 6d. violet-ultramarine (11.4.68) .. .. £150 6·00
32 6d. dull blue (26.8.65) .. .. £100 6·50
a. Imperf between (pair) .. .. — £600
33 6d. Prussian blue (7.9.69) .. .. £550 50·00
33*a* 6d. indigo .. .. .. — 55·00
34 4 9d. grey-lilac (24.12.60) .. .. 42·00 9·00
a. Imperf between (horiz pair) .. ..
35 10d. on 9d. orange-red (B.) (20.7.66) .. 90·00 24·00
36 10d. on 9d. yellow (B.) (29.7.67) .. £140 20·00
37 10d. on 9d. yellow (Blk.) (14.8.69) .. £1200 30·00
a. Surch inverted at the top .. .. — £2500
b. Printed on both sides .. .. — £800
c. Roul × perf 10 .. .. † —
38 1 1s. yellow (25.10.61) .. .. £450 28·00
a. Imperf between (vert pair) .. .. — £1200
39 1s. grey-brown (10.4.63) .. .. £150 16·00
40 1s. dark grey-brown (26.5.63) .. .. £130 16·00
41 1s. chestnut (25.8.63) .. .. £150 11·00
42 1s. lake-brown (27.3.65) .. .. £110 12·00
a. Imperf between (horiz pair) .. .. — £400
43 3 2s. rose-carmine (24.1.67) .. .. £160 25·00
a. Imperf between (vert pair) .. .. — £750

**1868–71.** *Remainders of old stock subsequently perforated by the 11½–12½ machine.*

(*a*) *Imperf stamps. P* 11½–12½
44 1 2d. pale vermilion (Feb 1868) .. .. — £900
45 2d. vermilion (18.3.68) .. .. — £1000

(*b*) *Rouletted stamps. P* 11½–12½
46 1 1d. bright green (9.11.69) .. .. — £450
47 2d. pale vermilion (15.8.68) .. .. — £400
48 6d. Prussian blue (8.11.69) .. .. — £200
aa. Horiz pair perf all round, roul between
48*a* 6d. indigo .. .. .. ..
49 4 9d. grey-lilac (29.3.71) .. .. £1500 £160
a. Perf × roulette .. .. .. — £150
49*b* 1 1s. lake-brown (23.5.70) .. .. ..

**1867–70.** *W* **2**. *P* 11½–12½ × *roulette.*
50 1 1d. pale bright green (2.11.67) .. .. £140 18·00
51 1d. bright green (1868) .. .. £100 18·00
52 1d. grey-green (26.1.70) .. .. £140 20·00
a. Imperf between (horiz pair) .. ..
53 1d. blue-green (29.11.67) .. .. £180 30·00
54 3 4d. dull violet (July 1868) .. .. £1400 £130
55 4d. dull purple (1869) .. .. — 90·00
56 1 6d. bright pale blue (29.5.67) .. .. £450 19·00
57 6d. Prussian blue (30.7.67) .. .. £400 19·00
a. Printed on both sides .. ..
58 6d. indigo (1.8.69) .. .. £500 24·00
59 4 10d. on 9d. yellow (B.) (2.2.69) .. £600 30·00
a. Printed on both sides .. .. — £550
60 1 1s. chestnut (April 1868) .. .. £250 15·00
61 1s. lake-brown (3.3.69) .. .. £250 15·00

**NOTE.** The stamps perf 11½, 12½, or compound of the two, are here combined in one list, as both perforations are on the one machine, and all the varieties *may* be found in each sheet of stamps. This method of classifying the perforations by the machines is by far the most simple and convenient.


(6)

7 (=Victoria *W* **20**)

**1868–79.** *Surch with T* **6** *(Nos. 66/8). W* **2**. *P* 11½–12½.
62 1 1d. pale bright green (8.2.68) .. .. £150 18·00
63 1d. grey-green (18.2.68) .. .. £120 40·00
64 1d. dark green (20.3.68) .. .. 50·00 17·00
a. Printed on both sides .. ..
65 1d. deep yellow-green (28.6.72) .. .. 45·00 18·00
66 3 3d. on 4d. Prussian blue (Blk.) (7.2.71) — £700
67 3d. on 4d. sky-blue (Blk.) (12.8.70) .. £275 10·00
a. Imperf .. .. ..
b. Rouletted .. .. .. — £500
68 3d. on 4d. deep ultramarine (Blk.) (9.72) 65·00 8·00
a. Surch double (10.9.74) .. .. — £3250
b. Additional surch on back .. .. — £2500
c. Surch omitted (26.4.74) .. .. £14000 £8000
70 4d. dull purple (1.2.68) .. .. 55·00 15·00
a. Imperf between (horiz pair) .. ..
71 4d. dull violet (1868) .. .. 50·00 8·00
72 1 6d. bright pale blue (23.2.68) .. .. £300 11·00
73 6d. Prussian blue (29.9.69) .. .. 90·00 6·00
a. Perf 11½ × imperf (horiz pair) .. ..
74 6d. indigo (1869) .. .. £120 17·00
75 4 9d. claret (7.72) .. .. 90·00 8·00
76 9d. bright mauve (1.11.72) .. .. 90·00 8·00
a. Printed on both sides .. .. — £300
77 9d. red-purple (15.1.74) .. .. 40·00 8·00
78 10d. on 9d. yellow (B.) (15.8.68) .. £1000 24·00
a. Error. Wmk Crown and S A (1868) — £900
79 10d. on 9d. yellow (Blk.) (13.9.69) .. £200 27·00
80 1 1s. lake-brown (9.68) .. .. £150 11·00
81 1s. chestnut (8.10.72) .. .. £110 16·00
82 1s. dark red-brown .. .. 90·00 11·00
83 1s. red-brown (6.1.69) .. .. £100 11·00
84 3 2s. pale rose-pink (10.10.69) .. .. £950 £150
85 2s. deep rose-pink (8.69) .. .. — £100
86 2s. crimson-carmine (16.10.69) .. .. 70·00 18·00
87 2s. carmine (1869) .. .. 60·00 10·00
a. Printed on both sides .. .. — £300

**1870–71.** *W* **2**. *P* 10.
88 1 1d. grey-green (6.70) .. .. £120 15·00
89 1d. pale bright green (9.8.70) .. .. £120 15·00
90 1d. bright green (1871) .. .. £100 15·00
91 3 3d. on 4d. dull ultramarine (R.) (6.8.70) £325 50·00
92 3d. on 4d. pale ultram (Blk.) (14.2.71) £250 14·00
93 3d. on 4d. ultramarine (Blk.) (14.8.71) £100 17·00
93*a* 3d. on 4d. Prussian blue (Blk.) (16.12.71)
94 4d. dull lilac (1870) .. .. £110 10·00
95 4d. dull purple (1871) .. .. £100 10·00
96 1 6d. bright blue (19.6.70) .. .. £180 17·00
97 6d. indigo (11.10.71) .. .. £225 16·00
98 1s. chestnut (4.1.71) .. .. £150 19·00

**1870–73.** *W* **2**. *P* 10 × 11½–12½, 11½–12½ × 10, *or compound.*
99 1 1d. pale bright green (11.10.70) .. £140 14·00
a. Printed on both sides .. ..
100 1d. grey-green .. .. .. £130 15·00
101 1d. deep green (19.6.71) .. .. 75·00 10·00
102 3 3d. on 4d. pale ultram (Blk.) (9.11.70) .. £180 30·00
103 4d. dull lilac (11.5.72) .. .. — 18·00
104 4d. slate-lilac (5.3.73) .. .. £120 18·00
105 1 6d. Prussian blue (2.3.70) .. .. £140 8·00
106 6d. bright Prussian blue (26.10.70) .. £150 10·00
107 4 10d. on 9d. yellow (Blk.) (1.70) .. £110 17·00
108 1 1s. chestnut (17.6.71) .. .. — 32·00
109 3 2s. rose-pink (24.4.71) .. .. — £170
110 2s. carmine (2.3.72) .. .. £120 25·00

**1871** (17 July). *W* **7**. *P* 10.
111 3 4d. dull lilac .. .. .. £1500 £250
a. Printed on both sides .. ..

8 Broad Star


(9)

**1876–1900.** *W* **8**. *Surch with T* **9** *(Nos. 118/21). (a) P* 11½–12½.
112 3 3d. on 4d. ultramarine (1.6.79) .. 50·00 15·00
a. Surch double .. .. — £1000
113 4d. violet-slate (15.3.79) .. .. 90·00 11·00
114 4d. plum (16.4.80) .. .. 40·00 6·00
115 4d. deep mauve (8.6.82) .. .. 40·00 5·00
116 1 6d. indigo (2.12.76) .. .. 90·00 4·50
a. Imperf between (horiz pair) ..
117 6d. Prussian blue (7.78) .. .. 55·00 4·00
118 4 8d. on 9d. brown-orange (7.76) .. 48·00 4·50
119 8d. on 9d. burnt umber (1880) .. 55·00 4·50
120 8d. on 9d. brown (9.3.80) .. .. 55·00 4·50
a. Imperf between (vert pair) .. £350
121 8d. on 9d. grey-brown (10.5.81) .. 48·00 6·00
a. Surch double .. .. — £350
122 9d. purple (9.3.80) .. .. 30·00 6·00
a. Printed on both sides .. .. — £200
123 9d. rose-lilac (21.8.80) .. .. 9·00 2·25
124 9d. rose-lilac (*large holes*) (26.5.00) 9·00 2·50
125 1 1s. red-brown (3.11.77) .. .. 42·00 2·75
a. Imperf between (horiz pair) .. — £250
126 1s. reddish lake-brown (1880) .. 40·00 3·00
127 1s. lake-brown (9.1.83) .. .. 45·00 2·75
128 1s. Vandyke brown (1891) .. .. 60·00 8·00
129 1s. dull brown (1891) .. .. 38·00 2·75
130 1s. chocolate (*large holes*) (6.5.97) 24·00 3·00
a. Imperf vert (horiz pair) .. £200
131 1s. sepia (*large holes*) (22.5.00) .. 24·00 3·00
a. Imperf between (vert pair) .. £150
132 3 2s. carmine (15.2.77) .. .. 25·00 4·00
a. Imperf between (horiz pair) .. — £400
b. Imperf (pair) .. ..
133 2s. rose-carmine (1885) .. .. 32·00 6·00
134 2s. rose-carmine (*large holes*) (6.12.98) 30·00 5·50

The perforation with larger, clean-cut holes resulted from the fitting of new pins to the machine.

*(b) P 10*

| No. | Type | Description | Unused | Used |
|---|---|---|---|---|
| 135 | 1 | 6d. Prussian blue (11.11.79) | 80·00 | 12·00 |
| 136 | | 6d. bright blue (1879) | £100 | 11·00 |
| 136a | | 1s. reddish lake-brown | £225 | |

*(c) P 10 × 11½–12½, 11½–12½ × 10, or compound*

| No. | Type | Description | Unused | Used |
|---|---|---|---|---|
| 137 | 3 | 4d. violet-slate (21.5.79) | £100 | 10·00 |
| 138 | | 4d. dull purple (4.10.79) | 25·00 | 2·00 |
| 139 | 1 | 6d. Prussian blue (29.12.77) | 48·00 | 2·50 |
| 140 | | 6d. bright blue | 70·00 | 5·50 |
| 141 | | 6d. bright ultramarine | 35·00 | 1·75 |
| 142 | | 1s. reddish lake-brown (9.2.85) | 75·00 | 9·00 |
| 143 | | 1s. dull brown (29.6.86) | 90·00 | 10·00 |
| 144 | 3 | 2s. carmine (27.12.77) | 40·00 | 5·00 |
| 145 | | 2s. rose-carmine (1887) | 35·00 | 4·50 |
| | | a. Imperf between (horiz pair) | — | £400 |

10

11

12

**1901–2.** *Wmk Crown SA (wide),* W **10.** *P* 11½–12½ *(large holes).*

| No. | Type | Description | Unused | Used |
|---|---|---|---|---|
| 146 | 4 | 9d. claret (1.2.02) | 10·00 | 10·00 |
| 147 | 1 | 1s. dark brown (12.6.01) | 20·00 | 9·00 |
| 148 | | 1s. dark reddish brown (1902) | 20·00 | 10·00 |
| | | a. Imperf between (vert pair) | | |
| 149 | | 1s. red-brown (aniline) (18.7.02) | 22·00 | 11·00 |
| 150 | 3 | 2s. crimson (29.8.01) | 25·00 | 12·00 |
| 151 | | 2s. carmine | 19·00 | 8·00 |

(Plates and electrotypes by D.L.R. Printed in Adelaide)

**1868–76.** W **10.** *(a) Rouletted.*

| No. | Type | Description | Unused | Used |
|---|---|---|---|---|
| 152 | 12 | 2d. deep brick-red (8.68) | 38·00 | 3·25 |
| 153 | | 2d. pale orange-red (5.10.68) | 35·00 | 2·75 |
| | | a. Printed on both sides | — | £200 |
| | | b. Imperf between (horiz pair) | — | £225 |
| | | *(b) P 11½–12½* | | |
| 154 | 11 | 1d. blue-green (10.1.75) | 65·00 | 11·00 |
| 155 | 12 | 2d. pale orange-red (5.5.69) | £850 | £190 |
| | | *(c) P 11½–12½ × roulette* | | |
| 156 | 12 | 2d. pale orange-red (20.8.69) | — | £120 |
| | | *(d) P 10 × roulette* | | |
| 157 | 12 | 2d. pale orange-red (7.5.70) | £200 | 20·00 |
| | | *(e) P 10* | | |
| 158 | 11 | 1d. blue-green (4.75) | 18·00 | 3·50 |
| 159 | 12 | 2d. brick-red (4.70) | 9·00 | 25 |
| 160 | | 2d. orange-red (1.7.70) | 8·00 | 20 |
| | | a. Printed on both sides | — | £160 |
| | | *(f) P 10 × 11½–12½, 11½–12½ × 10, or compound* | | |
| 161 | 11 | 1d. blue-green (27.8.75) | 38·00 | 10·00 |
| 162 | 12 | 2d. brick-red (19.1.71) | £400 | 6·00 |
| 163 | | 2d. orange-red (3.2.71) | £100 | 8·50 |
| | | a. Imperf (8.76) | £750 | |

**1869.** *Wmk Large Star,* W **2.** *(a) Rouletted.*

| No. | Type | Description | Unused | Used |
|---|---|---|---|---|
| 164 | 12 | 2d. orange-red (13.3.69) | 38·00 | 11·00 |
| | | *(b) P 11½–12½ × roulette* | | |
| 165 | 12 | 2d. orange-red (1.8.69) | — | 90·00 |
| | | *(c) P 11½–12½* | | |
| 165a | 12 | 2d. orange-red (7.69) | — | £800 |

**1871** (15 July). *Wmk V and Crown,* W **7.** *P* 10.

| No. | Type | Description | Unused | Used |
|---|---|---|---|---|
| 166 | 12 | 2d. brick-red | 40·00 | 12·00 |

13

HALF-

PENNY

(14)

**1876–85.** *Wmk Crown SA (close),* W **13.** *(a) P* 10.

| No. | Type | Description | Unused | Used |
|---|---|---|---|---|
| 167 | 11 | 1d. blue-green (9.2.76) | 4·50 | 1·25 |
| 168 | | 1d. yellowish green (11.78) | 4·75 | 1·25 |
| 169 | | 1d. deep green (11.79) | 5·00 | 1·25 |
| | | a. Imperf between (horiz pair) | | |
| 170 | 12 | 2d. orange-red (8.76) | 4·50 | 10 |
| 171 | | 2d. dull brick-red (21.5.77) | 4·50 | 10 |
| 172 | | 2d. blood-red (31.10.79) | £200 | 3·00 |
| 173 | | 2d. pale red (4.85) | 4·50 | 10 |
| | | *(b) P 10 × 11½–12½, or 11½–12½ × 10, or compound* | | |
| 174 | 11 | 1d. deep green (11.2.80) | 18·00 | 2·25 |
| 175 | | 1d. blue-green (2.3.80) | 8·00 | 1·90 |
| 176 | 12 | 2d. orange-red (4.9.77) | £120 | 3·00 |
| 177 | | 2d. brick-red (6.80) | £120 | 3·00 |
| | | *(c) P 11½–12½* | | |
| 178 | 11 | 1d. blue-green (2.84) | — | £110 |
| 179 | 12 | 2d. orange-red (14.9.77) | — | £110 |
| 180 | | 2d. blood-red (1.4.80) | — | £110 |

For stamps perf 15, see Nos. 238/40.

**1882** (1 Jan). *Surch with T* **14.** W **13.** *P* 10.

| No. | Type | Description | Unused | Used |
|---|---|---|---|---|
| 181 | 11 | ½d. on 1d. green | 8·50 | 3·00 |

15

16

17

18

**1883–95.** W **13** *(sideways on ½d.). (a) P* 10.

| No. | Type | Description | Unused | Used |
|---|---|---|---|---|
| 182 | 15 | ½d. chocolate (1.3.83) | 2·25 | 40 |
| | | a. Imperf between (horiz pair) | | |
| 183 | | ½d. Venetian red (4.4.89) | 2·00 | 35 |
| 184 | | ½d. brown (1895) | 2·25 | 35 |
| 185 | 16 | 3d. sage-green (12.86) (Optd S. £25) | 8·00 | 1·10 |
| 186 | | 3d. olive-green (6.6.90) | 8·00 | 1·50 |
| 187 | | 3d. deep green (12.4.93) | 5·50 | 60 |
| 188 | 17 | 4d. pale violet (3.90) (Optd S. £30) | 7·00 | 95 |
| 189 | | 4d. aniline violet (3.1.93) | 9·00 | 1·00 |
| 190 | 18 | 6d. pale blue (4.87) (Optd S. £25) | 7·00 | 1·40 |
| 191 | | 6d. blue (5.5.87) | 8·50 | 60 |
| | | *(b) P 10 × 11½–12½, 11½–12½ × 10, or compound* | | |
| 192 | 15 | ½d. pale brown (25.9.91) | 11·00 | 1·25 |
| 193 | | ½d. dark brown (9.9.92) | 4·00 | 95 |
| | | a. Imperf between (horiz pair) | 75·00 | |
| | | *(c) P 11½–12½* | | |
| 194 | 15 | ½d. Venetian red (12.10.90) | 5·50 | 75 |

For stamps perf 15, see Nos. 236/7 and 242/4 and for those perf 13 Nos. 247/8, 254/6 and 259/60.

**REPRINTS.** In 1884, and in later years, reprints on paper wmkd Crown SA, W **10**, were made of Nos. 1, 2, 3, 4, 12, 13, 14, 15, 19, 24, 27, 28, 32, 33, 34, 35, 36, 37, 38, 40, 43, 44, 49*a*, 53, 65, 67, 67 with surcharge in red, 70, 71, 72, 73, 78, 79, 81, 83, 86, 90, 118, 119, 120, 121, 122, 155, 158, 159, 164, 181, 182. They are overprinted "REPRINT".

In 1889 examples of the reprints for Nos. 1/3, 12, 15, 19, 27, 32/8, 44, 67, 67 surcharged in red, 70/1, 73, 83, 86, 118, 121/2, 158/9, 164 and 181/2, together with No. 141 overprinted "Specimen", were supplied to the U.P.U. for distribution.

19

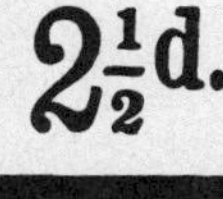

(20)

(21)

(Plates and electrotypes by D.L.R. Printed in Adelaide)

**1886–96.** *T* **19** *(inscr "POSTAGE & REVENUE").* W **13.** *Parts of two or more wmks, on each stamp, sometimes sideways. A. Perf 10. B. Perf 11½–12½ (small or large holes).*

| No. | Description | A | | B | |
|---|---|---|---|---|---|
| 195 | 2s. 6d. mauve | 25·00 | 8·00 | † | |
| | *a. Dull violet* | † | | 24·00 | 6·00 |
| | *b. Bright aniline violet* | † | | 25·00 | 7·00 |
| 196 | 5s. rose-pink | 40·00 | 12·00 | 32·00 | 12·00 |
| | *a. Rose-carmine* | † | | 35·00 | 14·00 |
| 197 | 10s. green | £110 | 35·00 | 80·00 | 35·00 |
| 198 | 15s. brownish yellow | £275 | — | £300 | £120 |
| 199 | £1 blue | £200 | 90·00 | £150 | 80·00 |
| 200 | £2 Venetian red | £475 | £200 | £475 | £200 |
| 201 | 50s. dull pink | £700 | £250 | £700 | — |
| 202 | £3 sage green | £750 | £200 | £750 | £200 |
| 203 | £4 lemon | £950 | — | £850 | — |
| 204 | £5 grey | £1600 | — | £1700 | — |
| 205 | £5 brown (1896) | † | | £1700 | £1000 |
| 206 | £10 bronze | £2500 | £700 | £1800 | £700 |
| 207 | £15 silver | £4500 | — | £4500 | — |
| 208 | £20 claret | £5000 | — | £5000 | — |
| 195/208 | *(all perf 10 ex No. 205)* Optd "Specimen" *Set of* 14 | £500 | | | |

Variations exist in the length of the words and shape of the letters of the value inscription.

The 2s. 6d. dull violet, 5s. rose-pink, 10s., £1 and £5 brown exist perf 11½–12½ with either large or small holes; the 2s. 6d. aniline, 5s. rose-carmine, 15s., £2 and 50s. with large holes only and the remainder only with small holes.

Stamps perforated 11½–12½ small holes, are, generally speaking, rather rarer than those with the 1895 (large holes) gauge.

Stamps perf 10 were issued on 20 Dec 1886. Stamps perf 11½–12½ (small holes) are known with earliest dates covering the period from June 1890 to Feb 1896. Earliest dates of stamps with large holes range from July 1896 to May 1902.

**1891** (1 Jan). *Colours changed and surch with T* **20/21.** W **13.**

*(a) P 10*

| No. | Type | Description | Unused | Used |
|---|---|---|---|---|
| 229 | 17 | 2½d. on 4d. pale grn (Br.) (Optd S. £25) | 5·50 | 2·50 |
| | | a. Fraction bar omitted | 90·00 | 75·00 |
| 230 | | 2½d. on 4d. deep green (Br.) | 6·00 | 1·75 |
| | | a. "2" and "½" closer together | 22·00 | 18·00 |
| | | b. Fraction bar omitted | | |
| | | c. Imperf between (horiz pair) | | |
| | | d. Imperf between (vert pair) | — | £325 |
| 231 | 18 | 5d. on 6d. pale brn (C.) (Optd S. £25) | 14·00 | 3·50 |
| 232 | | 5d. on 6d. dark brown (C.) | 14·00 | 3·25 |
| | | a. No stop after "5D" | £150 | |
| | | *(b) P 10 × 11½–12½ or 11½–12½ × 10* | | |
| 233 | 17 | 2½d. on 4d. pale green (Br.) | 7·00 | 3·00 |
| 234 | | 2½d. on 4d. deep green (Br.) | 7·00 | 3·00 |
| | | *(c) P 11½–12½* | | |
| 235 | 17 | 2½d. on 4d. green (Br.) | 25·00 | 40·00 |

**1893–4.** *Surch with T* **20** *(No. 241).* W **13** *(sideways on ½d.). P* 15.

| No. | Type | Description | Unused | Used |
|---|---|---|---|---|
| 236 | 15 | ½d. pale brown (1.93) | 2·50 | 30 |
| 237 | | ½d. dark brown | 2·50 | 30 |
| | | a. Perf 12½ between (pair) | £120 | 28·00 |
| | | b. Imperf between (horiz pair) | 80·00 | |
| 238 | 11 | 1d. green (8.5.93) | 3·00 | 1·25 |
| 239 | 12 | 2d. pale orange (9.2.93) | 5·50 | 10 |
| 240 | | 2d. orange-red | 6·00 | 10 |
| | | a. Imperf between (vert pair) | £150 | |
| 241 | 17 | 2½d. on 4d. green (14.10.93) | 8·00 | 2·50 |
| | | a. "2" and "½" closer | 32·00 | 22·00 |
| | | b. Fraction bar omitted | | |
| 242 | | 4d. purple (1.1.94) | 10·00 | 2·00 |
| 243 | | 4d. slate-violet | 10·00 | 1·75 |
| 244 | 18 | 6d. blue (20.11.93) | 19·00 | 3·50 |

22 Red Kangaroo

23

24 G.P.O., Adelaide

(Des Tannenberg, Melbourne; plates by D.L.R)

**1894** (1 Mar). W **13.** *P* 15.

| No. | Type | Description | Unused | Used |
|---|---|---|---|---|
| 245 | 22 | 2½d. violet-blue | 9·00 | 1·00 |
| 246 | 23 | 5d. brown-purple | 10·00 | 1·25 |
| 245/6 | | Optd "Specimen" *Set of* 2 | 50·00 | |

**1895–99.** W **13** *(sideways on ½d.). P* 13.

| No. | Type | Description | Unused | Used |
|---|---|---|---|---|
| 247 | 15 | ½d. pale brown (9.95) | 2·50 | 30 |
| 248 | | ½d. deep brown (19.3.97) | 2·50 | 30 |
| 249 | 11 | 1d. pale green (11.1.95) | 4·00 | 1·25 |
| 250 | | 1d. green | 4·00 | 1·25 |
| | | a. Imperf between (vert pair) | | |
| 251 | 12 | 2d. pale orange (19.1.95) | 3·50 | 10 |
| 252 | | 2d. orange-red (9.5.95) | 3·50 | 10 |
| 253 | 22 | 2½d. violet-blue (11.2.95) | 4·50 | 45 |
| 254 | 16 | 3d. pale olive-green (26.7.97) | 5·00 | 55 |
| 255 | | 3d. dark olive-green (27.11.99) | 5·00 | 50 |
| 256 | 17 | 4d. violet (21.1.96) | 6·00 | 40 |
| 257 | 23 | 5d. brown-purple (1.96) | 6·50 | 50 |
| 258 | | 5d. purple | 6·50 | 45 |
| 259 | 18 | 6d. pale blue (3.96) | 7·00 | 40 |
| 260 | | 6d. blue | 7·00 | 40 |

The 1d. in pale green, formerly listed under No. 261 as redrawn with slightly thicker lettering, is now accepted as resulting from a printing from a worn plate.

(½d. Typo D.L.R.)

**1898–1906.** W **13.**

A. *Perf* 13 (1898–1903). B. *Perf* 12 × 11½ (*comb*) (1904–6)

| No. | Type | Description | A | | B | |
|---|---|---|---|---|---|---|
| 262 | 24 | ½d. yellow-green | 1·25 | 20 | 1·50 | 15 |
| 263 | 11 | 1d. rosine | 2·00 | 10 | 5·00 | 10 |
| 264 | | 1d. scarlet | 2·75 | 10 | 3·00 | 10 |
| | | *a. Deep red* | 2·50 | 10 | † | |
| 265 | 12 | 2d. bright violet | 2·00 | 10 | 2·75 | 10 |
| 266 | 22 | 2½d. indigo | 4·50 | 30 | 5·50 | 30 |
| 267 | 23 | 5d. dull purple | † | | 7·00 | 85 |

*Earliest dates*: Perf 13. ½d., 27 Dec 1899; 1d. rosine, 8 August 1899; 1d. scarlet, 23 December 1903; 2d. 10 October 1899; 2½d. 25 March 1898.

Perf 12 × 11½. ½d. July 1905; 1d. rosine, 2 February 1904; 1d. scarlet, 25 July 1904; 2d. 11 October 1904; 2½d. 4 July 1906; 5d. January 1905.

25

The measurements given indicate the length of the value inscription in the bottom label. The dates are those of the earliest known postmarks.

**1902–4.** *As T* **19**, *but top tablet as T* **25** *(thin "POSTAGE").* W **13.**

*(a) P 11½–12½*

| No. | Description | Unused | Used |
|---|---|---|---|
| 268 | 3d. olive-green (18½ mm) (1.8.02) | 3·25 | 45 |
| 269 | 4d. red-orange (17 mm) (29.11.02) | 5·00 | 70 |
| 270 | 6d. blue-green (16–16½ mm) (29.11.02) | 6·00 | 70 |
| 271 | 8d. ultramarine (19 mm) (25.4.02) | 7·50 | 1·90 |
| 272 | 8d. ultramarine (16½ mm) (22.3.04) | 7·50 | 1·90 |
| | a. "EIGNT" | £800 | £1100 |
| 273 | 9d. rosy lake (19.9.02) | 7·00 | 1·00 |
| | a. Imperf between (vert pair) | £225 | |
| | b. Imperf between (horiz pair) | | |
| 274 | 10d. dull yellow (29.11.02) | 10·00 | 3·25 |
| 275 | 1s. brown (18.8.02) | 11·00 | 1·75 |
| | a. Imperf between (horiz pair) | | |
| | b. Imperf between (vert pair) | £450 | |
| | c. "POSTAGE" and value in red-brown | 45·00 | 20·00 |
| 276 | 2s. 6d. pale violet (19.9.02) | 27·00 | 9·00 |
| | *a. Bright violet* (2.2.03) | 20·00 | 7·00 |
| 277 | 5s. rose (17.10.02) | 55·00 | 40·00 |
| 278 | 10s. green (1.11.02) | £100 | 60·00 |
| 279 | £1 blue (1.11.02) | £225 | £120 |
| | *(b) P 12* | | |
| 280 | 3d. olive-green (20 mm) (15.4.04) | 3·75 | 70 |
| | a. "POSTAGE" omitted; value below "AUSTRALIA" | £350 | |
| 281 | 4d. orange-red (17½–18 mm) (18.2.03) | 5·50 | 70 |
| 282 | 6d. blue-green (15 mm) (14.11.03) | 15·00 | 2·25 |
| 283 | 9d. rosy lake (2.12.03) | 15·00 | 3·00 |

26

V

X

In Type X the letters in the bottom line are slightly larger than in Type V, especially the "A", "S" and "P".

Y

Z

In Type Z the letters "S" and "G" are more open than in Type Y.

Nos. 196/*a* and 277 are similar to Type Y with all letters thick and regular and the last "S" has the top curve rounded instead of being slightly flattened.

**1904–11.** *As T* **19**, *but top tablet as T* **26** (*thick* "POSTAGE"). *W* **13**. *P* 12.

| No. | Description | Unused | Used |
|---|---|---|---|
| 284 | 6d. blue-green (27.4.04) | 5·50 | 70 |
| | a. Imperf between (vert pair) | | |
| 285 | 8d. bright ultramarine (4.7.05) | 7·00 | 2·00 |
| | a. Value closer (15¼ mm) | 15·00 | |
| | *b. Dull ultramarine* (2.4.08) | 8·00 | 2·25 |
| | ba. Ditto. Value closer (15¼ mm) | 21·00 | |
| 286 | 9d. rosy lake (17–17¼ mm) (18.7.04) | 7·00 | 1·00 |
| | a. Value 16½–16¾ mm (2.06) | 15·00 | 3·50 |
| | *b. Brown-lake*. Perf 12½ small holes (6.6.11) | 10·00 | |
| 287 | 10d. dull yellow (8.07) | 14·00 | 4·25 |
| | a. Imperf between (horiz pair) | £275 | £200 |
| | b. Imperf between (vert pair) | £250 | |
| 288 | 1s. brown (12.4.04) | 11·00 | 1·75 |
| | a. Imperf between (vert pair) | £170 | |
| | b. Imperf between (horiz pair) | £225 | |
| 289 | 2s. 6d. bright violet (V.) (14.7.05) | 32·00 | 6·00 |
| | *a. Dull violet* (X) (8.06) | 32·00 | 6·00 |
| 290 | 5s. rose-scarlet (Y) (8.04) | 40·00 | 20·00 |
| | *a. Scarlet* (Z) (8.06) | 40·00 | 20·00 |
| | *b. Pale rose*. Perf 12½ (small holes) (Z) (7.10) | 55·00 | 22·00 |
| 291 | 10s. green (26.8.08) | £100 | £130 |
| 292 | £1 blue (29.12.04) | £150 | £100 |
| | a. Perf 12½ (small holes) (7.10) | £130 | 80·00 |

The "value closer" variety on the 8d. occurs six times in the sheet of 60. The value normally measures 16½ mm but in the variety it is 15¼ mm.

The 9d., 5s. and £1, perf 12½ (small holes), are late printings made in 1910–11 to use up the Crown SA paper.

No. 286*b* has the value as Type C of the 9d. on Crown over A paper.

27

**1905–11.** *W* **27**. *P* 12 × 11½ (*new comb machine*).

| No. | Type | Description | Unused | Used |
|---|---|---|---|---|
| 293 | **24** | ½d. pale green (4.07) | 1·00 | 20 |
| | | *a. Yellow-green* | 1·10 | 15 |
| 294 | **11** | 1d. rosine (2.12.05) | 1·90 | 10 |
| | | *a. Scarlet* (4.11) | 1·75 | 10 |
| 295 | **12** | 2d. bright violet (2.2.06) | 2·50 | 10 |
| | | aa. Imperf between (pair) | | |
| | | *a. Mauve* (4.08) | 1·60 | 10 |
| 296 | **22** | 2½d. indigo-blue (14.9.10) | 7·00 | 95 |
| 297 | **23** | 5d. brown-purple (11.3.08) | 7·50 | 1·40 |

Three types of the 9d., perf 12½, distinguishable by the distance between "NINE" and "PENCE".

A. Distance 1¾ mm. B. Distance 2¼ mm. C. Distance 2½ mm.

**1906–12.** *T* **19** ("POSTAGE" *thick as T* **26**). *W* **27**. *P* 12 *or* 12½ (*small holes*).

| No. | Description | Unused | Used |
|---|---|---|---|
| 298 | 3d. sage-green (19 mm) (26.6.06) | 4·25 | 70 |
| | a. Imperf between (horiz pair) | † | £500 |
| | b. Perf 12½. *Sage-green* (17 mm) (9.12.09) | 4·75 | 70 |
| | c. Perf 12½. *Deep olive* (20 mm) (7.10) | 18·00 | 3·25 |
| | d. Perf 12½. *Yellow-olive* (14 mm) (16.12.11) | 8·50 | 80 |
| | da. Perf 12½. *Bright olive-green* (19–19¾ mm) (5.12) | 8·00 | 70 |
| | e. Perf 11 (17 mm) (10.7.11) | £180 | £180 |
| 299 | 4d. orange-red (10.9.06) | 6·50 | 1·25 |
| | *a. Orange* | 8·00 | 1·10 |
| | b. Perf 12½. *Orange* (27.10.09) | 6·50 | 1·10 |
| 300 | 6d. blue-green (1.9.06) | 8·00 | 75 |
| | a. Perf 12½ (21.4.10) | 6·50 | 55 |
| | ab. Perf 12½. Imperf between (vert pair) | £275 | £250 |
| 301 | 8d. bright ultramarine (*p* 12½) (8.09) | 10·00 | 3·00 |
| | a. Value closer (8.09) | 28·00 | 24·00 |
| 302 | 9d. brown-lake (3.2.06) | 10·00 | 1·50 |
| | a. Imperf between (vert pair) | £225 | |
| | aa. Imperf between (horiz pair) | £225 | |
| | *b. Deep lake* (9.5.08) | 24·00 | 3·00 |
| | c. Perf 12½. *Lake* (A) (5.9.09) | 11·00 | 3·00 |
| | d. Perf 12½. *Lake* (B) (7.09) | 12·00 | 3·00 |
| | e. Perf 12½. *Brown-lake* (C) | 17·00 | 5·00 |
| | ea. Perf 12½. *Deep lake*. Thin paper (C) | 14·00 | 3·00 |
| | f. Perf 11 (1909) | — | £250 |
| 303 | 1s. brown (30.5.06) | 12·00 | 2·50 |
| | a. Imperf between (horiz pair) | £225 | |
| | b. Perf 12½ (10.3.10) | 10·00 | 1·00 |
| 304 | 2s. 6d. bright violet (X) (10.6.09) | 30·00 | 6·00 |
| | a. Perf 12½. *Pale violet* (X) (6.10) | 30·00 | 7·00 |
| | ab. Perf 12½. *Deep purple* (X) (5.11.12) | 35·00 | 5·50 |
| 305 | 5s. bright rose (*p* 12½) (Z) (24.4.11) | 55·00 | |

The "value closer" variety of the 8d. occurred 11 times in the sheet of 60 in the later printing only. On No. 301 the value measures 16½ mm while on No. 301a it is 15¼ mm.

The 1s. brown, perf compound of 11½ and 12½, formerly listed is now omitted, as it must have been perforated by the 12 machine, which in places varied from 11½ to 13. The 4d. has also been reported with a similar perforation.

## OFFICIAL STAMPS

### A. Departmentals

Following suspected abuses involving stamps supplied for official use it was decided by the South Australian authorities that such supplies were to be overprinted with a letter, or letters, indicating the department of the administration to which the stamps had been invoiced.

The system was introduced on 1 April 1868 using overprints struck in red. Later in the same year the colour of the overprints was amended to blue, and, during the latter months of 1869, to black.

In 1874 the Postmaster-General recommended that this somewhat cumbersome system be replaced by a general series of "O.S." overprints with the result that the separate accounting for the Departmentals ceased on 30 June of that year. Existing stocks continued to be used, however, and it is believed that much of the residue was passed to the Government Printer to pay postage on copies of the *Government Gazette*.

We are now able to provide a check list of these most interesting issues based on the definitive work, *The Departmental Stamps of South Australia* by A. R. Butler, FRPSL, RDP, published by the Royal Philatelic Society, London in 1978.

No attempt has been made to assign the various overprints to the catalogue numbers of the basic stamps, but each is clearly identified by both watermark and perforation. The colours are similar to those of the contemporary postage stamps, but there can be shade variations. Errors of overprint are recorded in footnotes, but not errors occurring on the basic stamps used.

Most departmental overprints are considered to be scarce to rare in used condition, with unused examples, used multiples and covers being regarded as considerable rarities.

Forgeries of a few items do exist, but most can be readily identified by comparison with genuine examples. A number of forged overprints on stamps not used for the genuine issues also occur.

#### A. (Architect)

Optd in red with stop. *W* **2**. 2d. (*roul*), 4d. (*p* 11½–12½), 6d. (*roul*), 1s. (*roul*)

Optd in red without stop. *W* **2**. *Roul*. 1d., 6d., 1s.

Optd in black. (*a*) *W* **2**. 4d. (*p* 11½–12½), 4d. (*p* 10), 4d. (*p* 10 × 11½–12½), 6d. (*p* 11½–12½), 2s. (*roul*)

(*b*) *W* **10**. 2d. D.L.R. (*roul*), 2d. D.L.R. (*p* 10)

#### A.G. (Attorney–General)

Optd in red. *W* **2**. *Roul*. 1d., 2d., 6d., 1s.

Optd in blue. (*a*) *W* **2**. *Roul*. 6d.

(*b*) *W* **10**. *Roul*. 2d. D.L.R.

Optd in black. (*a*) *W* **2**. 1d. (*p* 11½–12½ × *roul*), 4d. (*p* 11½–12½), 4d. (*p* 10), 6d. (*p* 11½–12½ × *roul*), 6d. (*p* 11½–12½), 1s. (*p* 11½–12½ × *roul*), 1s. (*p* 10)

(*b*) *W* **10**. 2d. D.L.R. (*roul*), 2d. D.L.R. (*p* 10)

#### A.O. (Audit Office)

Optd in red. *W* **2**. 2d. (*roul*), 4d. (*p* 11½–12½), 6d. (*roul*)

Optd in blue. (*a*) *W* **2**. *P* 11½–12½. 1d., 6d.

(*b*) *W* **10**. *Roul*. 2d. D.L.R.

Optd in black. (*a*) *W* **2**. 1d. (*p* 11½–12½), 1d. (*p* 10), 1d. (*p* 10 × 11½–12), 2d. D.L.R. (*roul*), 4d. (*p* 11½–12½), 4d. (*p* 10), 4d. (*p* 10 × 11½–12½), 6d. (*roul*), 6d. (*p* 11½–12½), 1s. (*p* 10), 1s. (*p* 11½–12½ × *roul*)

(*b*) *W* **7**. *P* 10. 4d.

(*c*) *W* **10**. 2d. D.L.R. (*roul*), 2d. D.L.R. (*p* 10)

#### B.D. (Barracks Department)

Optd in red. *W* **2**. *Roul*. 2d., 6d., 1s.

#### B.G. (Botanic Garden)

Optd in black. (*a*) *W* **2**. 1d. (*p* 11½–12½ × *roul*), 1d. (*p* 11½–12½), 1d. (*p* 10), 1d. (*p* 10 × 11½–12½), 2d. D.L.R. (*roul*), 6d. (*roul*), 6d. (*p* 11½–12½ × *roul*), 6d. (*p* 11½–12½), 6d. (*p* 10), 1s. (*p* 11½–12½ × *roul*), 1s. (*p* 11½–12½), 1s. (*p* 10 × 11½–12½)

(*b*) *W* **7**. *P* 10. 2d. D.L.R.

(*c*) *W* **10**. 2d. D.L.R. (*roul*), 2d. D.L.R. (*p* 10)

#### B.M. (Bench of Magistrates)

Optd in red. *W* **2**. *Roul*. 2d.

Optd in black. *W* **10**. *Roul*. 2d. D.L.R.

#### C. (Customs)

Optd in red. *W* **2**. 1d. (*roul*), 2d. (*roul*), 4d. (*p* 11½–12½), 6d. (*roul*), 1s. (*roul*)

Optd in blue. (*a*) *W* **2**. *Roul*. 1d., 4d., 6d., 1s., 2s.

(*b*) *W* **10**. *Roul*. 2d. D.L.R.

Optd in black. (*a*) *W* **2**. 1d. (*roul*), 1d. (*p* 10), 1d. (*p* 10 × 11½–12½), 2d. D.L.R. (*p* 10 × 11½–12½), 4d. (*p* 11½–12½), 4d. (*p* 10), 4d. (*p* 10 × 11½–12½), 6d. (*roul*), 6d. (*p* 11½–12½), 6d. (*p* 10), 1s. (*p* 11½–12½ × *roul*), 1s. (*p* 11½–12½), 2s. (*roul*)

(*b*) *W* **7**. *P* 10. 2d. D.L.R.

(*c*) *W* **10**. 2d. D.L.R. (*roul*), 2d. D.L.R. (*p* 10 × *roul*), 2d. D.L.R. (*p* 10), 2d. D.L.R. (*p* 10 × 11½–12½)

The 2d. (*W* **10**. *Roul*) with black overprint is known showing the error "G" for "C".

#### C.D. (Convict Department)

Optd in red. *W* **2**. 2d. (*roul*), 4d. (*p* 11½–12½), 6d. (*roul*), 1s. (*roul*)

Optd in black. (*a*) *W* **2**. 1d. (*p* 11½–12½ × *roul*), 2d. D.L.R. (*roul*), 2d. D.L.R. (*p* 11½–12½), 2d. D.L.R. (*p* 11½–12½ × *roul*), 4d. (*p* 11½–12½), 6d. (*p* 11½–12½ × *roul*), 1s. (*p* 11½–12½ × *roul*)

(*b*) *W* **10**. *Roul*. 2d. D.L.R.

#### C.L. (Crown Lands)

Optd in red. *W* **2**. 2d. (*roul*), 4d. (*p* 11½–12½), 6d. (*roul*), 1s. (*roul*)

Optd in blue. (*a*) *W* **2**. *Roul*. 4d., 6d.

(*b*) *W* **10**. *Roul*. 2d. D.L.R.

Optd in black. (*a*) *W* **2**. 2d. D.L.R. (*roul*), 4d. (*p* 11½–12½), 4d. (*p* 10), 4d. (*p* 10 × 11½–12½), 6d. (*roul*), 6d. (*p* 11½–12½), 1s. (*p* 11½–12½ × *roul*), 1s. (*p* 11½–12½), 2s. (*roul*), 2s. (*p* 11½–12½)

(*b*) *W* **7**. *P* 10. 2d. D.L.R., 4d.

(*c*) *W* **10**. 2d. D.L.R. (*roul*), 2d. D.L.R. (*p* 10), 2d. D.L.R. (*p* 10 × 11½–12½)

The 2s. (*W* **2**. *P* 11½–12½) with black overprint is known showing the stop omitted after "L".

#### C.O. (Commissariat Office)

Optd in red. *W* **2**. 2d. (*roul*), 4d. (*p* 11½–12½), 6d. (*roul*), 1s. (*roul*)

Optd in black. (*a*) *W* **2**. 4d. (*p* 11½–12½), 4d. (*p* 10), 4d. (*p* 10 × 11½–12½), 6d. (*p* 11½–12½), 1s. (*p* 11½–12½), 2s. (*p* 11½–12½)

(*b*) *W* **10**. 2d. D.L.R. (*roul*), 2d. D.L.R. (*p* 10)

The 2s. (*W* **2**. *P* 11½–12½) with black overprint is known showing the stop omitted after "O".

#### C.P. (Commissioner of Police)

Optd in red. *W* **2**. 2d. (*roul*), 4d. (*p* 11½–12½), 6d. (*roul*)

#### C.S. (Chief Secretary)

Optd in red. *W* **2**. 2d. (*roul*), 4d. (*p* 11½–12½), 6d. (*roul*), 1s. (*roul*)

Optd in blue. (*a*) *W* **2**. *Roul*. 4d., 6d.

(*b*) *W* **10**. *Roul*. 2d. D.L.R.

Optd in black. (*a*) *W* **2**. 2d. D.L.R. (*roul*), 4d. (*roul*), 4d. (*p* 11½–12½ × *roul*), 4d. (*p* 11½–12½), 4d. (*p* 10), 4d. (*p* 10 × 11½–12½), 6d. (*p* 11½–12½ × *roul*), 6d. (*p* 11½–12½), 6d. (*p* 10), 6d. (*p* 10 × 11½–12½), 1s. (*p* 11½–12½ × *roul*), 1s. (*p* 11½–12½), 1s. (*p* 10), 1s. (*p* 10 × 11½–12½), 2s. (*p* 10 × 11½–12½)

(*b*) *W* **7**. *P* 10. 4d.

(*c*) *W* **10**. 2d. D.L.R. (*roul*), 2d. D.L.R. (*p* 10)

#### C.Sgn. (Colonial Surgeon)

Optd in red. *W* **2**. 2d. (*roul*), 4d. (*p* 11½–12½), 6d. (*roul*)

Optd in black. (*a*) *W* **2**. 2d. D.L.R. (*roul*), 4d. (*p* 11½–12½), 4d. (*p* 10), 4d. (*p* 10 × 11½–12½), 6d. (*roul*), 6d. (*p* 11½–12½), 1s. (*p* 11½–12½ × *roul*)

(*b*) *W* **10**. 2d. D.L.R. (*roul*), 2d. D.L.R. (*p* 11½–12½ × *roul*), 2d. D.L.R. (*p* 10)

Two types of overprint exist on the 2d. D.L.R. (*W* **10**. *Roul*), the second type having block capitals instead of the serifed type used for the other values.

#### D.B. (Destitute Board)

Optd in red. *W* **2**. 1d. (*roul*), 2d. (*roul*), 4d. (*p* 11½–12½), 6d. (*roul*), 1s. (*roul*)

Optd in blue. (*a*) *W* **2**. *Roul*. 2d. D.L.R., 6d.

(*b*) *W* **10**. *Roul*. 2d. D.L.R.

Optd in black. (*a*) *W* **2**. 1d. (*p* 11½–12½), 4d. (*p* 11½–12½), 4d. (*p* 10), 6d. (*p* 10 × 11½–12½), 1s. (*p* 10)

(*b*) *W* **10**. 2d. D.L.R. (*roul*), 2d. D.L.R. (*p* 10), 2d. D.L.R. (*p* 10 × 11½–12½)

The 2d. D.L.R. (*W* **10**. *P* 10) with black overprint is known showing the stop omitted after "D".

#### D.R. (Deeds Registration)

Optd in red. *W* **2**. *Roul*, 2d., 6d.

#### E. (Engineer)

Optd in red. *W* **2**. 2d. (*roul*), 4d. (*p* 11½–12½), 6d. (*roul*), 1s. (*roul*)

Optd in blue. (*a*) *W* **2**. *Roul*. 1s.

(*b*) *W* **10**. *Roul*. 2d. D.L.R.

Optd in black. (*a*) *W* **2**. 4d. (*p* 11½–12½ × *roul*), 4d. (*p* 11½–12½), 4d. (*p* 10), 4d. (*p* 10 × 11½–12½), 6d. (*p* 11½–12½), 6d. (*p* 10 × 11½–12½), 1s. (*p* 11½–12½ × *roul*). 1s. (*p* 11½–12½), 1s. (*p* 10 × 11½–12½), 2s. (*p* 10 × 11½–12½)

(*b*) *W* **7**. *P* 10. 4d.

(*c*) *W* **10**. 2d. D.L.R. (*roul*), 2d. D.L.R. (*p* 10)

#### E.B. (Education Board)

Optd in red. *W* **2**. 2d. (*roul*), 4d. (*p* 11½–12½), 6d. (*roul*)

Optd in blue. (*a*) *W* **2**. *Roul*. 4d., 6d.

(*b*) *W* **10**. *Roul*. 2d. D.L.R.

Optd in black. (*a*) *W* **2**. 2d. D.L.R. (*roul*), 4d. (*roul*), 4d. (*p* 11½–12½), 4d. (*p* 10), 4d. (*p* 10 × 11½–12½), 6d. (*p* 11½–12½ × *roul*), 6d. (*p* 11½–12½)

(*b*) *W* **7**. *P* 10. 2d. D.L.R.

(*c*) *W* **10**. 2d. D.L.R. (*roul*), 2d. D.L.R. (*p* 10), 2d. D.L.R. (*p* 10 × 11½–12½)

#### G.F. (Gold Fields)

Optd in black. (*a*) *W* **2**. *Roul*. 6d.

(*b*) *W* **10**. 2d. D.L.R. (*p* 10 × *roul*), 2d. D.L.R. (*p* 10)

#### G.P. (Government Printer)

Optd in red. *W* **2**. *Roul*. 1d., 2d., 6d., 1s.

Optd in blue. (*a*) *W* **2**. *Roul*. 1d., 6d., 1s., 2s.

(*b*) *W* **10**. *Roul*. 2d. D.L.R.

Optd in black. (*a*) *W* **2**. 1d. (*roul*), 1d. (*p* 11½–12½ × *roul*), 1d. (*p* 11½–12½), 1d. (*p* 10), 1d. (*p* 10 × 11½–12½), 6d. (*p* 11½–12½ × *roul*), 1s. (*p* 10), 1s. (*p* 10 × 11½–12½), 2s. (*roul*), 2s. (*p* 11½–12½), 2s. (*p* 10 × 11½–12½)

(*b*) *W* **10**. 2d. D.L.R. (*roul*), 2d. D.L.R. (*p* 10)

The 1d. (*W* **2**. *Roul*) with red overprint is known showing "C.P." instead of "G.P.".

#### G.S. (Government Storekeeper)

Optd in red. *W* **2**. *Roul*. 2d., 6d., 1s.

#### G.T. (Goolwa Tramway)

Optd in red. *W* **2**. 1d. (*roul*), 2d. (*roul*), 4d. (*p* 11½–12½), 6d. (*roul*), 1s. (*roul*)

Optd in black. (*a*) *W* **2**. 2d. D.L.R. (*roul*), 4d. (*p* 11½–12½)

(*b*) *W* **10**. 2d. D.L.R. (*roul*), 2d. D.L.R. (*p* 10)

The 2d. and 6d. (both *W* **2**. *Roul*) with red overprint are known showing the stop omitted after "T". The 1s. (*W* **2**. *Roul*) with red overprint is known showing "C.T." instead of "G.T.".

**H. (Hospitals)**

Optd in black. (*a*) *W* **7.** *P* 10. 2d. D.L.R.
(*b*) *W* **10.** 2d. D.L.R. (*p* 10), 2d. D.L.R. (*p* 10 × 11½–12½)

**H.A. (House of Assembly)**

Optd in red. *W* **2.** 1d. (*roul*), 2d. (*roul*), 4d. (*p* 11½–12½), 6d. (*roul*), 1s. (*roul*)
Optd in black. (*a*) *W* **2.** 1d. (*p* 11½–12½), 1d. (*p* 10), 1d. (*p* 10 × 11½–12½), 4d. (*p* 11½–12½), 4d. (*p* 10), 6d. (*roul*), 6d. (*p* 11½–12½), 1s. (*p* 11½–12½ × *roul*), 1s. (*p* 11½–12½)
(*b*) *W* **10.** 2d. D.L.R. (*roul*), 2d. D.L.R. (*p* 10)

**I.A. (Immigration Agent)**

Optd in red. *W* **2.** 1d. (*roul*), 2d. (*roul*), 4d. (*p* 11½–12½), 6d. (*roul*)

**I.E. (Intestate Estates)**

Optd in black. W **10.** *P* 10. 2d. D.L.R.

**I.S. (Inspector of Sheep)**

Optd in red. *W* **2.** *Roul.* 2d., 6d.
Optd in blue. *W* **2.** *P* 11½–12½. 6d.
Optd in black. (*a*) *W* **2.** 2d. D.L.R. (*roul*), 6d. (*p* 11½–12½ × *roul*)
(*b*) *W* **10.** 2d. D.L.R. (*roul*), 2d. D.L.R. (*p* 10)

**L.A. (Lunatic Asylum)**

Optd in red. *W* **2.** 1d. (*roul*), 2d. (*roul*), 4d. (*p* 11½–12½), 6d. (*roul*), 1s. (*roul*)
Optd in black. (*a*) *W* **2.** 4d. (*p* 11½–12½), 4d. (*p* 10), 4d. (*p* 10 × 11½–12½), 6d. (*p* 11½–12½ × *roul*), 6d. (*p* 11½–12½), 1s. (*p* 11½–12½), 2s. (*roul*)
(*b*) *W* **10.** 2d. D.L.R. (*roul*), 2d. D.L.R. (*p* 10)

**L.C. (Legislative Council)**

Optd in red. *W* **2.** *Roul.* 2d., 6d.
Optd in black. (*a*) *W* **2.** *Roul.* 6d.
(*b*) *W* **10.** 2d. D.L.R. (*roul*), 2d. D.L.R. (*p* 10 × *roul*)
The 2d. and 6d. (both *W* **2.** *Roul*) with red overprint are known showing the stop omitted after "C".

**L.L. (Legislative Librarian)**

Optd in red. *W* **2.** 2d. (*roul*), 4d. (*p* 11½–12½), 6d. (*roul*)
Optd in black. (*a*) *W* **2.** *P* 11½–12½. 6d.
(*b*) *W* **10.** *P* 10. 2d. D.L.R.
The 2d. and 6d. (both *W* **2.** *Roul*) with red overprint are known showing the stop omitted from between the two letters.

**L.T. (Land Titles)**

Optd in red. *W* **2.** 2d. (*roul*), 4d. (*p* 11½–12½), 6d. (*roul*), 1s. (*roul*)
Optd in blue. *W* **10.** *Roul.* 2d. D.L.R.
Optd in black. (*a*) *W* **2.** 4d. (*p* 11½–12½), 4d. (*p* 10), 4d. (*p* 10 × 11½–12½), 6d. (*p* 11½–12½ × *roul*), 6d. (*p* 11½–12½), 6d. (*p* 10), 6d. (*p* 10 × 11½–12½)
(*b*) *W* **7.** *P* 10. 2d. D.L.R.
(*c*) *W* **10.** 2d. D.L.R. (*roul*), 2d. D.L.R. (*p* 10)
The 2d. and 6d. (both *W* **2.** *Roul*) with red overprint are known showing the stop omitted after "T".

**M. (Military)**

Optd in red. *W* **2.** *Roul.* 2d., 6d., 1s.
Optd in black. *W* **2.** 6d. (*p* 11½–12½ × *roul*), 1s. (*p* 11½–12½ × *roul*), 2s. (*roul*)

**M.B. (Marine Board)**

Optd in red. *W* **2.** 1d. (*roul*), 2d. (*roul*), 4d. (*roul*), 4d. (*p* 11½–12½), 6d. (*roul*), 1s. (*roul*)
Optd in black. (*a*) *W* **2.** 1d. (*roul*), 1d. (*p* 11½–12½), 2d. D.L.R. (*roul*), 4d. (*roul*), 4d. (*p* 11½–12½ × *roul*), 4d. (*p* 11½–12½), 4d. (*p* 10), 4d. (*p* 10 × 11½–12½), 6d. (*roul*), 6d. (*p* 11½–12½), 6d. (*p* 10), 6d. (*p* 10 × 11½–12½), 1s. (*p* 11½–12½ × *roul*), 1s. (*p* 11½–12½), 1s. (*p* 10), 1s. (*p* 10 × 11½–12½)
(*b*) *W* **7.** *P* 10. 2d. D.L.R., 4d.
(*c*) *W* **10.** 2d. D.L.R. (*roul*), 2d. D.L.R. (*p* 10)

**M.R. (Manager of Railways)**

Optd in red. *W* **2.** *Roul.* 2d., 6d.
Optd in black. (*a*) *W* **2.** 1d. (*p* 11½–12½), 1d. (*p* 10), 2d. D.L.R. (*roul*), 4d. (*roul*), 4d. (*p* 11½–12½), 6d. (*roul*), 6d. (*p* 11½–12½ × *roul*), 6d. (*p* 11½–12½), 10d. on 9d. (*roul*), 1s. (*roul*), 1s. (*p* 11½–12½ × *roul*), 2s. (*p* 11½–12½), 2s. (*p* 10 × 11½–12½)
(*b*) *W* **10.** 2d. D.L.R. (*roul*), 2d. D.L.R. (*p* 10), 2d. D.L.R. (*p* 10 × 11½–12½)

**M.R.G. (Main Roads Gambierton)**

Optd in red without stops. *W* **2.** *Roul.* 2d., 6d.
Optd in blue without stops. *W* **10.** *Roul.* 2d. D.L.R.
Optd in black without stops. *W* **10.** 2d. D.L.R. (*roul*), 2d. D.L.R. (*p* 10)
Optd in black with stops. *W* **10.** 2d. D.L.R. (*roul*), 2d. D.L.R. (*p* 10)
The 2d. D.L.R. (*W* **10.** *P* 10) with black overprint is known showing the stops omitted after "M" and "R".

**N.T. (Northern Territory)**

Optd in black. (*a*) *W* **2.** *P* 11½–12½. 1d., 3d. on 4d., 4d., 6d., 1s.
(*b*) *W* **10.** 2d. D.L.R. (*roul*), 2d. D.L.R. (*p* 10)

**O.A. (Official Assignee)**

Optd in red. *W* **2.** 2d. (*roul*), 4d. (*p* 11½–12½)
Optd in blue. *W* **10.** *Roul.* 2d. D.L.R.
Optd in black. (*a*) *W* **2.** 4d. (*p* 11½–12½), 4d. (*p* 10)
(*b*) *W* **7.** *P* 10. 2d. D.L.R.
(*c*) *W* **10.** 2d. D.L.R. (*roul*), 2d. D.L.R. (*p* 10 × *roul*), 2d. D.L.R. (*p* 10)

**P. (Police)**

Optd in blue. (*a*) *W* **2.** *Roul.* 6d.
(*b*) *W* **10.** *Roul.* 2d. D.L.R.
Optd in black. (*a*) *W* **2.** 6d. (*p* 11½–12½ × *roul*), 6d. (*p* 11½–12½), 6d. (*p* 10)
(*b*) *W* **7.** *P* 10. 2d. D.L.R.
(*c*) *W* **10.** 2d. D.L.R. (*roul*), 2d. D.L.R. (*p* 11½–12½), 2d. D.L.R. (*p* 11½–12½ × *roul*), 2d. D.L.R. (*p* 10 × *roul*), 2d. D.L.R. (*p* 10), 2d. D.L.R. (*p* 10 × 11½–12½)

**P.A. (Protector of Aborigines)**

Optd in red. *W* **2.** *Roul.* 2d., 6d.
Optd in black. (*a*) *W* **2.** *Roul.* 2d. D.L.R., 6d.
(*b*) *W* **10.** 2d. D.L.R. (*roul*), 2d. D.L.R. (*p* 10)

**P.O. (Post Office)**

Optd in red. *W* **2.** *Roul.* 1d., 2d., 6d., 1s.
Optd in blue. *W* **2.** *Roul.* 2d., 2d. D.L.R.
Optd in black. (*a*) *W* **2.** 1d. (*p* 10 × 11½–12½), 2d. D.L.R. (*roul*), 4d. (*p* 11½–12½), 6d. (*roul*), 6d. (*p* 11½–12½), 1s. (*p* 11½–12½ × *roul*), 1s. (*p* 11½–12½), 1s. (*p* 10), 1s. (*p* 10 × 11½–12½)
(*b*) *W* **10.** 2d. D.L.R. (*roul*), 2d. D.L.R. (*p* 10 × *roul*), 2d. D.L.R. (*p* 10)
The 6d. (*W* **2.** *Roul*) with red overprint is known showing the stop omitted after "O", but with two stops after "P".

**P.S. (Private Secretary)**

Optd in red. *W* **2.** 1d. (*roul*), 2d. (*roul*), 4d. (*p* 11½–12½), 6d. (*roul*), 1s. (*roul*)
Optd in black. (*a*) *W* **2.** 1d. (*p* 11½–12½ × *roul*), 1d. (*p* 11½–12½), 1d. (*p* 10), 3d. (*in black*) on 4d. (*p* 11½–12½), 3d. (*in red*) on 4d. (*p* 10), 3d. (*in black*) on 4d. (*p* 10), 4d. (*p* 11½–12½), 4d. (*p* 10), 4d. (*p* 10 × 11½–12½), 6d. (*roul*), 6d. (*p* 11½–12½ × *roul*), 6d. (*p* 11½–12½), 6d. (*p* 10), 9d. (*roul*), 9d. (*p* 11½–12½), 10d. on 9d. (*p* 10 × 11½–12½), 1s. (*p* 11½–12½ × *roul*), 2s. (*p* 11½–12½)
(*b*) *W* **7.** *P* 10. 2d. D.L.R.
(*c*) *W* **10.** 2d. D.L.R. (*roul*), 2d. D.L.R. (*p* 10)

**P.W. (Public Works)**

Optd in red without stop after "W". *W* **2.** *Roul.* 2d., 6d., 1s.
Optd in black. (*a*) *W* **2.** 2d. D.L.R. (*roul*), 4d. (*p* 10), 6d. (*roul*), 6d. (*p* 11½–12½), 1s. (*p* 11½–12½ × *roul*)
(*b*) *W* **10.** 2d. D.L.R. (*roul*), 2d. D.L.R. (*p* 10)

**R.B. (Road Board)**

Optd in red. *W* **2.** 1d. (*roul*), 2d. (*roul*), 4d. (*p* 11½–12½), 6d. (*roul*), 1s. (*roul*)
Optd in blue without stops. *W* **10.** *Roul.* 2d. D.L.R.
Optd in black. (*a*) *W* **2.** 1d. (*p* 11½–12½ × *roul*), 1d. (*p* 10), 4d. (*p* 10), 2s. (*roul*)
(*b*) *W* **7.** *P* 10. 2d. D.L.R.
(*c*) *W* **10.** 2d. D.L.R. (*roul*), 2d. D.L.R. (*p* 10)
The 6d. (*W* **2.** *Roul*) with red overprint is known showing the stop omitted after "B".

**R.G. (Registrar-General)**

Optd in red. *W* **2.** *Roul.* 2d., 6d., 1s.
Optd in blue. (*a*) *W* **2.** *P* 11½–12½ × *roul.* 6d.
(*b*) *W* **10.** 2d. D.L.R. (*roul*), 2d. D.L.R. (*p* 11½–12½ × *roul*)
Optd in black. (*a*) *W* **2.** 2d. D.L.R. (*roul*), 6d. (*p* 10), 6d. (*p* 10 × 11½–12½), 1s. (*p* 11½–12½ × *roul*), 1s. (*p* 10)
(*b*) *W* **7.** *P* 10. 2d. D.L.R.
(*c*) *W* **10.** 2d. D.L.R. (*roul*), 2d. D.L.R. (*p* 10 × *roul*), 2d. D.L.R. (*p* 10), 2d. D.L.R. (*p* 10 × 11½–12½)

**S. (Sheriff)**

Optd in red. *W* **2.** *Roul.* 2d., 6d.
Optd in blue. (*a*) *W* **2.** *P* 11½–12½ × *roul.* 6d.
(*b*) *W* **10.** *Roul.* 2d. D.L.R.
Optd in black. (*a*) *W* **2.** 4d. (*p* 11½–12½), 4d. (*p* 10), 6d. (*roul*), 6d. (*p* 11½–12½), 6d. (*p* 10)
(*b*) *W* **10.** 2d. D.L.R. (*roul*), 2d. D.L.R. (*p* 10 × *roul*), 2d. D.L.R. (*p* 10), 2d. D.L.R. (*p* 10 × 11½–12½)

**S.C. (Supreme Court)**

Optd in red. *W* **2.** *Roul.* 2d., 6d.
Optd in black. *W* **10.** *P* 10. 2d. D.L.R.

**S.G. (Surveyor-General)**

Optd in red. *W* **2.** 2d. (*roul*), 4d. (*p* 11½–12½), 6d. (*roul*)
Optd in blue. (*a*) *W* **2.** *Roul.* 4d.
(*b*) *W* **10.** *Roul.* 2d. D.L.R.
Optd in black. (*a*) *W* **2.** 2d. D.L.R. (*roul*), 4d. (*p* 11½–12½), 4d. (*p* 10), 4d. (*p* 10 × 11½–12½), 6d. (*p* 11½–12½ × *roul*), 6d. (*p* 11½–12½), 6d. (*p* 10), 6d. (*p* 10 × 11½–12½)
(*b*) *W* **7.** *P* 10. 2d. D.L.R.
(*c*) *W* **10.** 2d. D.L.R. (*roul*), 2d. D.L.R. (*p* 10 × *roul*), 2d. D.L.R. (*p* 10)

**S.M. (Stipendiary Magistrate)**

Optd in red. *W* **2.** 1d. (*roul*), 2d. (*roul*), 4d. (*roul*), 4d. (*p* 11½–12½), 6d. (*roul*), 1s. (*roul*)
Optd in blue. (*a*) *W* **2.** *Roul.* 2d., 4d., 6d.
(*b*) *W* **10.** *Roul.* 2d. D.L.R.
Optd in black. (*a*) *W* **2.** 1d. (*p* 11½–12½), 1d. (*p* 10), 2d. D.L.R. (*roul*), 4d. (*roul*), 4d. (*p* 11½–12½ × *roul*), 4d. (*p* 11½–12½), 4d. (*p* 10), 4d. (*p* 10 × 11½–12½), 6d. (*p* 11½–12½ × *roul*), 6d. (*p* 11½–12½), 6d. (*p* 10), 6d. (*p* 10 × 11½–12½), 1s. (*p* 11½–12½ × *roul*)
(*b*) *W* **7.** *P* 10. 2d. D.L.R.
(*c*) *W* **10.** 2d. D.L.R. (*roul*), 2d. D.L.R. (*p* 10 × *roul*), 2d. D.L.R. (*p* 10), 2d. D.L.R. (*p* 10 × 11½–12½)
The 2d. and 4d. (both *W* **2.** *Roul*) with red overprint are known showing the stop omitted after "M".

**S.T. (Superintendent of Telegraphs)**

Optd in red. *W* **2.** *Roul.* 2d., 6d.
Optd in blue. *W* **10.** 2d. D.L.R. (*roul*), 2d. D.L.R. (*p* 11½–12½)
Optd in black. (*a*) *W* **2.** *Roul.* 2d. D.L.R., 6d.
(*b*) *W* **7.** *P* 10. 2d. D.L.R.
(*c*) *W* **10.** 2d. D.L.R. (*roul*), 2d. D.L.R. (*p* 10 × *roul*), 2d. D.L.R. (*p* 10)
The 2d. and 6d. (both *W* **2.** *Roul*) with red overprint (2d., 6d.) or black overprint (6d.) are known showing the stop omitted after "T".

**T. (Treasury)**

Optd in red. *W* **2.** 1d. (*roul*), 2d. (*roul*), 4d. (*p* 11½–12½ × *roul*), 6d. (*roul*), 1s. (*roul*)
Optd in blue. (*a*) *W* **2.** *Roul.* 1d., 4d., 6d., 2s.
(*b*) *W* **10.** *Roul.* 2d. D.L.R.
Optd in black. (*a*) *W* **2.** 1d. (*p* 10), 2d. D.L.R. (*roul*), 4d. (*roul*), 4d. (*p* 11½–12½), 6d. (*roul*), 6d. (*p* 11½–12½), 1s. (*p* 11½–12½ × *roul*), 1s. (*p* 10 × 11½–12½), 2s. (*roul*), 2s. (*p* 11½–12½), 2s. (*p* 10 × 11½–12½)
(*b*) *W* **7.** *P* 10. 2d. D.L.R.
(*c*) *W* **10.** 2d. D.L.R. (*roul*), 2d. D.L.R. (*p* 10)

**T.R. (Titles Registration)**

Optd in black. (*a*) *W* **2.** 4d. (*p* 11½–12½), 4d. (*p* 10 × 11½–12½), 6d. (*p* 11½–12½), 6d. (*p* 10 × 11½–12½), 1s. (*p* 11½–12½)
(*b*) *W* **10.** *P* 10. 2d. D.L.R.

**V. (Volunteers)**

Optd in red. *W* **2.** *Roul.* 2d., 6d., 1s.
Optd in black. (*a*) *W* **2.** *Roul.* 6d.
(*b*) *W* **7.** *P* 10. 2d. D.L.R.
(*c*) *W* **10.** 2d. D.L.R. (*roul*), 2d. D.L.R. (*p* 10 × *roul*), 2d. D.L.R. (*p* 10)
The 2d. (*W* **10.** *P* 10 × *roul*) overprinted in black is only known showing the stop omitted after "V".

**VA. (Valuator of Runs)**

Optd in black without stop after "V". (*a*) *W* **2.** *P* 10. 4d.
(*b*) *W* **10.** *P* 10. 2d. D.L.R.

**VN. (Vaccination)**

Optd in black without stop after "V". *W* **2.** *P* 10. 4d.

**W. (Waterworks)**

Optd in red. *W* **2.** *Roul.* 2d.
Optd in black. (*a*) *W* **2.** *P* 11½–12½. 6d., 2s.
(*b*) *W* **10.** 2d. D.L.R. (*roul*), 2d. D.L.R. (*p* 10)
The 2d. (*W* **2.** *Roul*) with red overprint is known showing the stop omitted after "W".

B. General

**O.S.** (O 1) **O.S.** (O 2)

| | | | | |
|---|---|---|---|---|
| **1874–77.** | | *Optd with Type* O **1.** *W* **2.** (*a*) *P* 10. | | |
| O 1 | **3** | 4d. dull purple (18.2.74) | £1000 | £250 |
| | | (*b*) *P* 11½–12½ × 10. | | |
| O 2 | **1** | 1d. green (2.1.74) | — | 75·00 |
| O 3 | **3** | 4d. dull violet (12.2.75) | 45·00 | 5·00 |
| O 4 | **1** | 6d. Prussian blue (20.10.75) | — | 8·00 |
| O 4*a* | **3** | 2s. rose-pink | | |
| O 5 | | 2s. carmine (3.12.76) | — | 75·00 |
| | | (*c*) *P* 11½–12½ | | |
| O 6 | **1** | 1d. deep yellow-green (30.1.74) | — | 16·00 |
| | | a. Printed on both sides | — | £400 |
| O 7 | **3** | 3d. on 4d. ultramarine (26.6.77) | £1000 | £325 |
| | | a. No stop after "S" | — | £600 |
| O 8 | | 4d. dull violet (13.7.74) | 35·00 | 5·50 |
| | | a. No stop after "S" | — | 30·00 |
| O 9 | **1** | 6d. bright blue (31.8.75) | 60·00 | 11·00 |
| | | a. "O.S." double | — | 55·00 |
| O10 | | 6d. Prussian blue (27.3.74) | 50·00 | 6·00 |
| | | a. No stop after "S" | — | 35·00 |
| O11 | **4** | 9d. red-purple (22.3.76) | £350 | £110 |
| | | a. No stop after "S" | £600 | |
| O12 | **1** | 1s. red-brown (5.8.74) | 45·00 | 6·00 |
| | | a. "O.S." double | — | 65·00 |
| | | b. No stop after "S" | £100 | 35·00 |
| O13 | **3** | 2s. crimson-carmine (13.7.75) | 70·00 | 12·00 |
| | | a. No stop after "S" | — | 60·00 |
| | | b. No stops | — | 75·00 |
| | | c. Stops at top of letters | | |
| **1876–85.** | | *Optd with Type* O **1.** *W* **8.** (*a*) *P* 10. | | |
| O14 | **1** | 6d. bright blue (1879) | 65·00 | 8·00 |
| | | (*b*) *P* 10 × 11½–12½, 11½–12½ × 10, *or compound* | | |
| O15 | **3** | 4d. violet-slate (24.1.78) | 65·00 | 6·50 |
| O16 | | 4d. plum (29.11.81) | 38·00 | 2·75 |
| O17 | | 4d. deep mauve | 25·00 | 2·50 |
| | | a. No stop after "S" | £100 | 24·00 |
| | | b. No stop after "O" | | |
| | | c. "O.S." double | | |
| | | d. "O.S." inverted | — | £100 |
| O18 | **1** | 6d. bright blue (1877) | 38·00 | 4·25 |
| | | a. "O.S." inverted | | |
| | | b. No stop after "O" | | |
| O19 | | 6d. bright ultramarine (27.3.85) | 35·00 | 4·00 |
| | | a. "O.S." inverted | | |
| | | b. "O.S." double | | |
| | | c. "O.S." double, one inverted | — | £225 |
| | | d. No stop after "S" | — | 35·00 |
| | | e. No stops after "O" & "S" | | |
| O20 | | 1s. red-brown (27.3.83) | 35·00 | 5·00 |
| | | a. "O.S." inverted | | |
| | | b. No stop after "O" | | |
| | | c. No stop after "S" | — | 35·00 |
| O21 | **3** | 2s. carmine (16.3.81) | 48·00 | 7·50 |
| | | a. "O.S." inverted | — | £110 |
| | | b. No stop after "S" | — | 50·00 |
| | | (*c*) *P* 11½–12½ | | |
| O22 | **3** | 3d. on 4d. ultramarine | £750 | |
| O23 | | 4d. violet-slate (14.3.76) | £120 | 6·00 |
| O24 | | 4d. deep mauve (19.8.79) | 38·00 | 2·50 |
| | | a. "O.S." inverted | | |
| | | b. "O.S." double, one inverted | | |
| | | c. No stop after "S" | — | 25·00 |
| O25 | **1** | 6d. Prussian blue (6.77) | 42·00 | 4·50 |
| | | a. "O.S." double | — | 50·00 |
| | | b. "O.S." inverted | | |
| O26 | **4** | 8d. on 9d. brown (9.11.76) | £450 | £180 |
| | | a. "O.S." double | £750 | |
| | | b. "O" only | — | £350 |
| O26*c* | | 9d. purple | £1800 | |
| O27 | **1** | 1s. red-brown (12.2.78) | 28·00 | 3·50 |
| | | a. "O.S." inverted | £180 | 85·00 |
| | | b. No stop after "S" | £160 | 35·00 |
| O28 | | 1s. lake-brown (8.11.83) | 24·00 | 3·50 |

O29 3 2s. rose-carmine (12.8.85) 55·00 7·50
 a. "O.S." double — 75·00
 b. "O.S." inverted — 80·00
 c. No stop after "S" — 35·00

**1891–1903.** *Optd with Type* O **2.** (*a*) **W 8.** *P* 11½–12½.
O30 1 1s. lake-brown (18.4.91) 23·00 8·50
O31 1s. Vandyke brown 26·00 5·50
O32 1s. dull brown (2.7.96) 23·00 4·25
 a. No stop after "S" — 50·00
O33 1s. sepia (*large holes*) (4.1.02) 20·00 3·50
 a. "O.S." double
 b. No stop after "S"
O34 3 2s. carmine (26.6.00) 50·00 9·00
 a. No stop after "S"

(*b*) **W 8.** *P* 10 × 11½–12½
O35 3 2s. rose-carmine (9.11.95) 40·00 7·00
 a. No stop after "S" £100
 b. "O.S." double

(*c*) **W 10.** *P* 11½–12½
O36 1 1s. dull brown (7.3.03) 22·00 3·50

**1874–76.** *Optd with Type* O **1. W 10.** (*a*) *P* 10.
O37 11 1d. blue-green (30.9.75) 55·00 15·00
 a. "O.S." inverted
 b. No stop after "S"
O38 12 2d. orange-red (18.2.74) 10·00 30
 a. No stop after "S" — 20·00
 b. "O.S." double

(*b*) *P* 10 × 11½–12½, 11½–12½ × 10, *or compound*
O39 11 1d. blue-green (16.9.75)
 a. No stop after "S"
O40 12 2d. orange-red (27.9.76) — 3·75

(*c*) *P* 11½–12½
O41 11 1d. blue-green (13.8.75) — 12·00
 a. "O.S." inverted
 b. No stop after "S"
O42 12 2d. orange-red (20.5.74) — 80·00

**1876–80.** *Optd with Type* O **1. W 13.** (*a*) *P* 10.
O43 11 1d. blue-green (2.10.76) 5·50 25
 a. "O.S." inverted — 32·00
 b. "O.S." double 38·00 27·00
 c. "O.S." double, one inverted
 d. No stops — 18·00
 e. No stop after "S" — 10·00
 f. No stop after "O"
O44 1d. deep green 6·00 25
 a. "O.S." double — 30·00
O45 12 2d. orange-red (21.9.77) 6·00 25
 a. "O.S." double 45·00 25·00
 b. "O.S." inverted — 17·00
 c. "O.S." double, both inverted — 80·00
 d. "O.S." double, one inverted
 e. No stop after "O" — 14·00
 f. No stop after "S"
 g. No stops after "O" & "S" — 40·00
O46 2d. brick-red 23·00 65

(*b*) *P* 10 × 11½–12½, 11½–12½ × 10, *or compound*
O47 11 1d. deep green (14.8.80) — 18·00
 a. "O.S." double
O48 12 2d. orange-red (6.4.78) 35·00 6·00
 a. "O.S." inverted
 b. No stop after "S" — 40·00

(*c*) *P* 11½–12½
O49 12 2d. orange-red (15.7.80) — 60·00

**1882** (20 Feb). *No.* O43 *surch with T* **14. W 13.** *P* 10.
O50 11 ½d. on 1d. blue-green 35·00 14·00
 a. "O.S." inverted

**1888–91.** *Optd with Type* O **1. W 13.** *P* 10.
O51 17 4d. violet (24.1.91) 20·00 2·75
O52 18 6d. blue (15.11.88) 9·50 1·25
 a. "O.S." double
 b. No stop after "S"

**1891.** *As No.* O51 *surch with T* **20. W 13.** (*a*) *P* 10.
O53 17 2½d. on 4d. green (1.8.91) 32·00 6·00
 a. "2" and "½" closer — 40·00
 b. No stop after "S"
 c. "O.S." omitted (in pair with normal)
 d. "O.S." inverted
 e. "O.S." double

(*b*) *P* 10 × 11½–12½, 11½–12½ × 10, *or compound*
O54 17 2½d. on 4d. green (1.10.91) 38·00 8·50

(*c*) *P* 11½–12½
O54*a* 17 2½d. on 4d. green (1.6.91)

**1891–95.** *Optd with Type* O **2. W 13.** (*a*) *P* 10.
O55 15 ½d. brown (2.5.94) 6·00 3·00
 a. No stop after "S"
O56 11 1d. green (22.4.91) 6·00 25
 a. "O.S." double 40·00 25·00
 b. No stop after "S" 30·00 8·00
 c. "O.S." in blackish blue £200 2·75
 d. "O.S." double, one inverted
O57 12 2d. orange-red (22.4.91) 5·50 25
 a. No stop after "S" — 9·00
 b. "O.S." double
O58 17 2½d. on 4d. green (18.8.94) 28·00 4·00
 a. No stop after "S" — 30·00
 b. "O.S." inverted £120
 c. "2" and "½" closer 65·00 20·00
 d. Fraction bar omitted
O59 4d. pale violet (13.2.91) 18·00 2·75
 a. "O" only — 45·00
 b. "O.S." double
 c. No stop after "S"
O60 4d. aniline violet (31.8.93) 23·00 2·50
 a. No stop after "S"
 b. "O.S." double
O61 18 5d. on 6d. brown (2.12.91) 35·00 11·00
 a. No stop after "S" 85·00 30·00
 b. No stop after "5D" £170
O62 6d. blue (4.4.93) 8·50 1·25
 a. No stop after "S"
 b. "O.S." in blackish blue

(*b*) *P* 10 × 11½–12½
O63 15 ½d. pale brown (26.3.95) 6·50 3·00
O64 17 2½d. on 4d. green (17.9.95) — 35·00
 a. "O.S." double

(*c*) *P* 11½–12½
O65 15 ½d. Venetian red (13.6.91) 17·00 3·50

**1893–1901.** *Optd with Type* O **2. W 13.** *P* 15.
O66 15 ½d. pale brown (8.6.95) 5·50 2·75
O67 11 1d. green (8.9.94) 5·00 25
 a. No stop after "S"
 b. "O.S." double
O68 12 2d. orange-red (16.6.94) 5·50 25
 a. "O.S." double — 20·00
 b. "O.S." inverted — 14·00
O68*c* 22 2½d. violet-blue 20·00 2·75
O69 17 4d. slate-violet (4.4.95) 26·00 2·75
 a. "O.S." double — 24·00
O70 23 5d. purple (29.3.01) 45·00 4·00
O71 18 6d. blue (20.9.93) 9·50 1·25

**1895–1901.** *Optd with Type* O **2. W 13.** *P* 13.
O72 15 ½d. brown (17.5.98) 6·50 2·75
 a. Opt triple, twice sideways £150
O73 11 1d. green (20.5.95) 6·00 25
 a. No stop after "S" 30·00 8·00
O74 12 2d. orange (11.2.96) 5·00 25
 a. No stop after "S" — 8·00
 b. "O.S." double
O75 22 2½d. violet-blue (5.7.97) 20·00 2·25
 a. No stop after "S"
O76 17 4d. violet (12.96) 20·00 2·25
 a. No stop after "S" 60·00 20·00
 b. "O.S." double 60·00 25·00
O77 23 5d. purple (29.9.01) 40·00 4·25
 a. No stop after "S"
O78 18 6d. blue (13.9.99) 11·00 1·25
 a. No stop after "S" 40·00

**O. S.**

(O 3)

**1899–1901.** *Optd with Type* O **3. W 13.** *P* 13.
O80 24 ½d. yellow-green (12.2.00) 6·00 2·75
 a. No stop after "S"
 b. "O.S." inverted 40·00
O81 11 1d. rosine (22.9.99) 4·75 50
 a. "O.S." inverted — 28·00
 b. "O.S." double
 c. No stop after "S" — 14·00
O82 12 2d. bright violet (1.6.00) 7·00 50
 a. "O.S." inverted 30·00 30·00
 b. "O.S." double
 c. No stop after "S" 25·00
O83 22 2½d. indigo (2.10.01) 20·00 2·25
 a. "O.S." inverted — 35·00
 b. No stop after "S" 60·00
O84 17 4d. violet (18.11.00) 18·00 90
 a. "O.S." inverted 85·00
 b. No stop after "S" 65·00
O85 18 6d. blue (8.10.00) 9·50 1·00
 a. No stop after "S" 35·00

**1891** (May). *Optd as Type* O **3** *but wider.* **W 13.** *P* 10.
O86 19 2s. 6d. pale violet £2000 £1600
O87 5s. pale rose £2000 £1600

Only one sheet (60) of each of these stamps was printed.

Stamps overprinted for Official use were withdrawn on 30 September 1903.

South Australia became part of the Commonwealth of Australia on 1 January 1901.

## TASMANIA

| PRICES FOR STAMPS ON COVER | |
|---|---|
| Nos. 1/4 | *from* × 2 |
| Nos. 5/12 | *from* × 3 |
| Nos. 14/23 | *from* × 2 |
| No. 24 | — |
| Nos. 25/56 | *from* × 3 |
| Nos. 57/77 | *from* × 6 |
| Nos. 78/9 | — |
| Nos. 80/90 | *from* × 3 |
| No. 91 | — |
| Nos. 92/109 | *from* × 3 |
| No. 110 | — |
| Nos. 111/23 | *from* × 3 |
| Nos. 124/6 | — |
| Nos. 127/34 | *from* × 4 |
| Nos. 135/55 | *from* × 3 |
| Nos. 156/8 | *from* × 20 |
| Nos. 159/66 | *from* × 10 |
| Nos. 167/9 | *from* × 15 |
| Nos. 170/4 | *from* × 6 |
| Nos. 216/22 | *from* × 15 |
| Nos. 223/5 | — |
| Nos. 226/7 | *from* × 15 |
| Nos. 229/36 | *from* × 20 |
| Nos. 237/57 | *from* × 10 |
| No. 258 | — |
| Nos. 259/61 | *from* × 10 |
| Nos. F1/25 | — |
| Nos. F26/9 | *from* × 15 |
| Nos. F30/9 | — |

**SPECIMEN OVERPRINTS.** Those listed are from U.P.U. distributions between 1892 and 1904. Further "Specimen" overprints exist, but these were used for other purposes.

1

2

3

(Eng C. W. Coard. Recess H. and C. Best at the *Courier* newspaper, Hobart)

**1853** (1 Nov). *No wmk. Imperf. Twenty-four varieties in four rows of six each.*

(*a*) *Medium soft yellowish paper with all lines clear and distinct*
1 1 1d. pale blue £3250 £650
2 1d. blue £3250 £650

(*b*) *Thin hard white paper with lines of the engraving blurred and worn*
3 1 1d. pale blue £3000 £600
4 1d. blue £3000 £600

**1853–55.** *No wmk. Imperf. In each plate there are twenty-four varieties in four rows of six each.*

(*a*) *Plate I. Finely engraved. All lines in network and background thin, clear, and well defined.* (1853)

(i) *First state of the plate, brilliant colours*
5 2 4d. bright red-orange £2250 £500
 a. Double impression
6 4d. bright brownish orange — £650

(ii) *Second state of plate, with blurred lines and worn condition of the central background*
7 2 4d. red-orange £2000 £350
8 4d. orange £1800 £325
9 4d. pale orange — £325

(*b*) *Plate II. Coarse engraving, lines in network and background thicker and blurred* (1855)
10 2 4d. orange £2000 £300
 a. Double print, one albino
11 4d. dull orange £2000 £300
12 4d. yellowish orange £2000 £300

In the 4d. Plate I, the outer frame-line is thin all round. In Plate II it is, by comparison with other parts, thicker in the lower left angle.

The 4d. is known on vertically laid paper from proof sheets. Examples from Plate I have the lines close together and those from Plate II wide apart (*Price £5000 unused*).

In 1879 reprints were made of the 1d. in blue and the 4d., Plate I, in brownish yellow, on thin, tough, white wove paper, and perforated 11½. In 1887, a reprint from the other plate of the 4d. was made in reddish brown and in black, and in 1889 of the 1d. in blue and in black, and of the 4d. (both plates) in yellow and in black on white card, imperforate. As these three plates were defaced after the stamps had been superseded, all these reprints show two, or three thick strokes across the Queen's head.

All three plates were destroyed in July 1950.

(Eng. W. Humphrys, after water-colour sketch by E. Corbould. Recess P.B.)

**1855** (17 Aug–16 Sept). *Wmk Large Star,* **W w 1.** *Imperf.*
14 3 1d. carmine (16.9) £4000 £700
15 2d. deep green (16.9) £1500 £500
16 2d. green (16.9) £1500 £450
17 4d. deep blue £1200 85·00
18 4d. blue £1200 95·00

Proofs of the 1d. and 4d. on thick paper, *without watermark*, are sometimes offered as the issued stamps.

(Recess H. and C. Best, Hobart, from P.B. plates)

**1856** (Apr)–**57.** *No wmk. Imperf.* (*a*) *Thin white paper.*
19 3 1d. pale brick-red (4.56) £4000 £550
20 2d. dull emerald-green (1.57) £5000 £700
21 4d. deep blue (5.57) £600 85·00
22 4d. blue (5.57) £500 85·00
23 4d. pale blue (5.57) — £120

(*b*) *Pelure paper*
24 3 1d. deep red-brown (11.56) £3000 £600

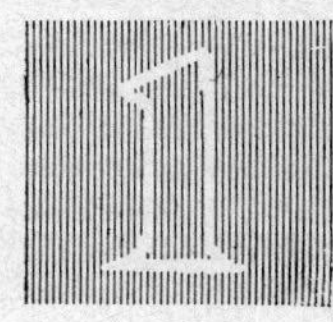
4

7

8

(Recess H. Best (August 1857–May 1859), J. Davies (August 1859–March 1862), J. Birchall (March 1863), M. Hood (October 1863–April 1864), Govt Printer (from July 1864), all from P.B. plates)

**1857** (Aug)–**69.** *Wmk double-lined numerals "1", "2" or "4" as* **W 4** *on appropriate value. Imperf.*
25 3 1d. deep red-brown £400 21·00
26 1d. pale red-brown £275 16·00
27 1d. brick-red (1863) £140 15·00
28 1d. dull vermilion (1865) 80·00 15·00
29 1d. carmine (1867) 80·00 15·00
 a. Double print — £120
 b. Error. Wmkd "2" (1869)
30 2d. dull emerald-green — 60·00
31 2d. green — 27·00
 a. Double print — £150
32 2d. yellow-green £200 55·00
33 2d. deep green (1858) £170 30·00
34 2d. slate-green (1860) £120 45·00
35 4d. deep blue — 70·00
 a. Double print — £150
36 4d. pale blue £100 11·00

| | | | | |
|---|---|---|---|---|
| 7 | 3 | 4d. blue | £100 | 15·00 |
| | | a. Double print | — | £150 |
| 8 | | 4d. bright blue | £100 | 15·00 |
| | | a. Printed on both sides | † | — |
| | | b. Double print | — | £120 |
| 9 | | 4d. cobalt-blue | — | 55·00 |

Printings before July 1864 were all carried out at the *Courier* printing works which changed hands several times during this period.

**CANCELLATIONS.** Beware of early Tasmanian stamps with pen-cancellations cleaned off and faked postmarks applied.

(Recess P.B.)

**1858** (Jan). *Wmk double-lined numerals "6" or "12" as W 4. Imperf.*

| | | | | |
|---|---|---|---|---|
| 40 | 7 | 6d. dull lilac | £600 | 65·00 |
| 41 | 8 | 1s. bright vermilion | £500 | 70·00 |
| 42 | | 1s. dull vermilion | — | 55·00 |

Examples of the 6d. lilac on paper watermarked Large Star exist from a proof sheet. These are always creased (*Price* £650 *unused*).

Recess J. Davies (March 1860), J. Birchall (April 1863), Govt Printer (from February 1865), all from P.B. plates)

**1860** (Mar)–**67**. *Wmk double-lined "6" as W 4. Imperf.*

| | | | | |
|---|---|---|---|---|
| 44 | 7 | 6d. dull slate-grey | £275 | 50·00 |
| 45 | | 6d. grey | — | 55·00 |
| 46 | | 6d. grey-violet (4.63) | £130 | 50·00 |
| | | a. Double print | — | £200 |
| 47 | | 6d. dull cobalt (2.65) | £130 | 40·00 |
| 48 | | 6d. slate-violet (2.65) | £250 | 45·00 |
| 49 | | 6d. reddish mauve (4.67) | £550 | £150 |

In 1871 reprints were made of the 6d. (in mauve) and the 1s. on white wove paper, and perforated 11½. They are found with or without "REPRINT". In 1889 they were again reprinted on white card, imperforate. These later impressions are also found overprinted "REPRINT" and perforated 11½.

**PERFORATED ISSUES.** From 1 October 1857 the Tasmania Post Office only supplied purchasers requiring five or more complete sheets of stamps. The public obtained their requirements, at face value, from licensed stamp vendors, who obtained their stocks at a discount from the Post Office.

From 1863 onwards a number of the stamp vendors applied their own roulettes or perforations. The Hobart firm of J. Walch & Sons achieved this so successfully that they were given an official contract in July 1869 to perforate sheets for the Post Office. The Government did not obtain a perforating machine until late in 1871.

**1863–71.** *Double-lined numeral watermarks. Various unofficial roulettes and perforations.*

*(a) By. J. Walch & Sons, Hobart*

(i) *Roulette about 8, often imperf × roul* (1863–68)

| | | | | |
|---|---|---|---|---|
| 50 | 3 | 1d. brick-red | — | £150 |
| 51 | | 1d. carmine | £300 | £100 |
| 52 | | 2d. yellow-green | — | £400 |
| 53 | | 2d. slate-green | | |
| 54 | | 4d. pale blue | — | £140 |
| 55 | 7 | 6d. dull lilac | — | £170 |
| 56 | 8 | 1s. vermilion | — | £500 |

(ii) *P* 10 (1864–69)

| | | | | |
|---|---|---|---|---|
| 57 | 3 | 1d. brick-red | 45·00 | 18·00 |
| 58 | | 1d. dull vermilion | 45·00 | 18·00 |
| 59 | | 1d. carmine | 42·00 | 18·00 |
| 60 | | 2d. yellow-green | £225 | 70·00 |
| 61 | | 2d. slate-green | £275 | £120 |
| 62 | | 4d. pale blue | 90·00 | 9·50 |
| 63 | | 4d. blue | 90·00 | 9·50 |
| | | a. Double print | — | £110 |
| 64 | 7 | 6d. grey-violet | £150 | 13·00 |
| 65 | | 6d. dull cobalt | 80·00 | 16·00 |
| 66 | | 6d. slate-violet | — | 18·00 |
| 67 | | 6d. reddish mauve | £300 | 60·00 |
| 68 | 8 | 1s. vermilion | 90·00 | 19·00 |
| | | a. Imperf vert (horiz pair) | | |

(iii) *P* 12 (1865–71—*from July 1869 under contract to the Post Office*)

| | | | | |
|---|---|---|---|---|
| 69 | 3 | 1d. dull vermilion | 45·00 | |
| 70 | | 1d. carmine | 35·00 | 6·50 |
| | | a. Error. Wmkd "2" (*pen cancel* £75) | — | £1000 |
| 71 | | 2d. yellow-green | £100 | 38·00 |
| 72 | | 4d. deep blue | 70·00 | 11·00 |
| 73 | | 4d. blue | 70·00 | 13·00 |
| 74 | | 4d. cobalt-blue | — | 28·00 |
| 75 | 7 | 6d. slate-violet | £120 | 18·00 |
| | | a. Imperf between (vert pair) | | |
| 76 | | 6d. reddish mauve | 70·00 | 32·00 |
| | | a. Imperf between (vert or horiz pair) | | |
| 77 | 8 | 1s. vermilion | 95·00 | 28·00 |
| | | a. Double print | — | £150 |
| | | b. Imperf between (horiz pair) | | |

(iv) *Perf compound* 10 × 12 (1865–69)

| | | | | |
|---|---|---|---|---|
| 78 | 3 | 1d. carmine | £1300 | |
| 79 | | 4d. blue | — | £900 |

*(b) P* 12½ *by R. Harris, Launceston* (1864–68)

| | | | | |
|---|---|---|---|---|
| 80 | 3 | 1d. brick-red | 45·00 | 23·00 |
| 81 | | 1d. dull vermilion | 42·00 | 17·00 |
| 82 | | 1d. carmine | 25·00 | 6·50 |
| 83 | | 2d. yellow-green | £225 | 80·00 |
| 84 | | 2d. sage-green | £200 | £100 |
| 85 | | 4d. blue | £130 | 35·00 |
| 86 | | 4d. bright blue | £130 | 35·00 |
| 87 | 7 | 6d. dull cobalt | £160 | 40·00 |
| 88 | | 6d. slate-violet | £170 | 40·00 |
| 89 | | 6d. reddish mauve | £350 | 90·00 |
| 90 | 8 | 1s. vermilion | £180 | 65·00 |

(c) *Imperf × oblique roulette* 11½ *at Oatlands* (1866)

| | | | | |
|---|---|---|---|---|
| 91 | 3 | 4d. blue | | |

(*d*) *Oblique roulette* 10–10½, *possibly at Deloraine* (1867)

| | | | | |
|---|---|---|---|---|
| 92 | 3 | 1d. brick-red | — | £325 |
| 93 | | 1d. carmine | £900 | £275 |
| 94 | | 2d. yellow-green | — | £425 |
| 95 | | 4d. bright blue | — | £375 |
| 96 | 7 | 6d. grey-violet | — | £600 |

(*e*) *Oblique roulette* 14–15, *probably at Cleveland* (1867–69)

| | | | | |
|---|---|---|---|---|
| 97 | 3 | 1d. brick-red | — | £375 |
| 98 | | 1d. dull vermilion | — | £375 |
| 99 | | 1d. carmine | — | £375 |
| 100 | | 2d. yellow-green | — | £425 |
| 101 | | 4d. pale blue | — | £325 |
| 102 | 7 | 6d. grey-violet | — | £600 |
| 103 | 8 | 1s. vermilion | — | £750 |

(*f*) *Pin-perf* 5½ *to* 9½ *at Longford* (1867)

| | | | | |
|---|---|---|---|---|
| 104 | 3 | 1d. carmine | £300 | 70·00 |
| 105 | | 2d. yellow-green | | |
| 106 | | 4d. bright blue | — | £160 |
| 107 | 7 | 6d. grey-violet | — | £150 |
| 108 | | 6d. reddish mauve | — | £425 |
| 109 | 8 | 1s. vermilion | | |

(*g*) *Pin-perf* 12 *at Oatlands* (1867)

| | | | | |
|---|---|---|---|---|
| 110 | 3 | 4d. blue | | |

(*h*) *Pin-perf* 13½ *to* 14½ (1867)

| | | | | |
|---|---|---|---|---|
| 111 | 3 | 1d. brick-red | — | £190 |
| 112 | | 1d. dull vermilion | — | £190 |
| 113 | | 1d. carmine | | |
| 114 | | 2d. yellow-green | — | £275 |
| 115 | | 4d. pale blue | — | £160 |
| 116 | 7 | 6d. grey-violet | — | £375 |
| 117 | 8 | 1s. vermilion | | |

(*j*) *Serrated perf* 19 *at Hobart* (1868–69)

| | | | | |
|---|---|---|---|---|
| 118 | 3 | 1d. carmine (*pen-cancel* £9) | £225 | £100 |
| 119 | | 2d. yellow-green | — | £200 |
| 120 | | 4d. deep blue | £550 | 95·00 |
| 121 | | 4d. cobalt-blue | — | 95·00 |
| 122 | 7 | 6d. slate-violet | — | £375 |
| 123 | 8 | 1s. vermilion | | |

(*k*) *Roul* 4½, *possibly at Macquarie River* (1868)

| | | | | |
|---|---|---|---|---|
| 124 | 3 | 4d. blue | | |
| 125 | 7 | 6d. reddish mauve | | |
| 126 | 8 | 1s. vermilion | | |

For stamps perforated 11½ or 12 by the Post Office see Nos. 135/43.

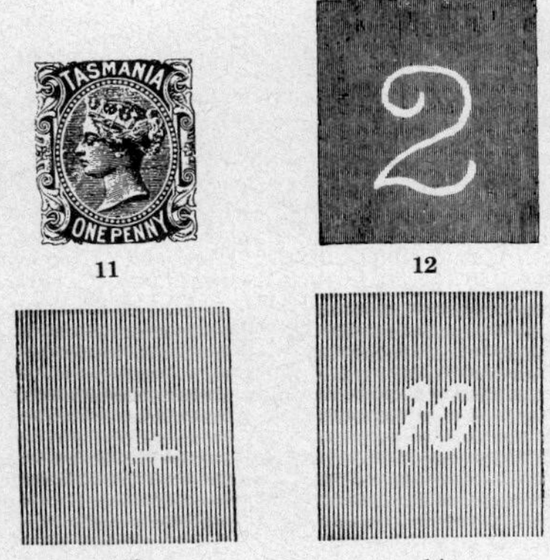

11 12 13 14

(Typo Govt Printer, Hobart, from plates made by D.L.R.)

**1870** (1 Nov)–**71**. *Wmk single-lined numerals* **W 12** (2d.), **13** (1d., 4d.) *or* **14** (1d., 10d.). (*a*) *P* 12 *by J. Walch & Sons.*

| | | | | |
|---|---|---|---|---|
| 127 | 11 | 1d. rose-red (*wmk* "10") | 27·00 | 8·50 |
| | | a. Imperf (pair) | £190 | £190 |
| | | *b. Deep rose-red* | 45·00 | 6·50 |
| 128 | | 1d. rose-red (*wmk* "4") (3.71) | 40·00 | 8·50 |
| | | a. Imperf (pair) | — | £160 |
| 129 | | 2d. yellow-green | 38·00 | 4·50 |
| | | a. Imperf (pair) | | |
| | | *b. Blue-green* | 42·00 | 4·50 |
| 130 | | 4d. blue | £700 | £400 |
| 131 | | 10d. black | 20·00 | 15·00 |
| | | a. Imperf (pair) | £110 | |

(*b*) *P* 11½ *by the Post Office* (1871)

| | | | | |
|---|---|---|---|---|
| 132 | 11 | 1d. rose-red (*wmk* "10") | £900 | |
| 133 | | 2d. yellow-green | 80·00 | 6·50 |
| | | *a. Blue-green* | 32·00 | 3·25 |
| | | ab. Double print | | |
| 134 | | 10d. black | 23·00 | 16·00 |

The above were printed on paper obtained from New South Wales.

See also Nos. 144/55, 156/8, 159/66, 170/4, 226/7, 242 and 255/6.

(Recess Govt Printer, Hobart)

**1871–91.** *Double-lined numeral watermarks as* **W 4**. *Perforated by the Post Office.* (*a*) *P* 11½.

| | | | | |
|---|---|---|---|---|
| 135 | 7 | 6d. dull mauve | 70·00 | 19·00 |
| 136 | | 6d. bright mauve | 65·00 | 19·00 |
| | | a. Imperf between (pair) | — | £425 |
| 137 | | 6d. dull purple (3.75) | 65·00 | 19·00 |
| | | a. Imperf (pair) | — | £400 |
| 138 | | 6d. bright purple (5.78) | 65·00 | 28·00 |
| | | a. Double print | — | £110 |
| | | b. Imperf between (horiz pair) | £750 | |
| 139 | | 6d. lilac-purple (10.79) | 70·00 | 38·00 |
| 140 | 8 | 1s. dull vermilion (1.73) | 80·00 | 38·00 |
| | | a. Imperf between (horiz pair) | | |
| 141 | | 1s. brownish vermilion (1.73) | 70·00 | 38·00 |

(*b*) *P* 12

| | | | | |
|---|---|---|---|---|
| 142 | 7 | 6d. bright purple (1884) | 80·00 | 16·00 |
| | | a. Imperf between (horiz pair) | £400 | |
| 143 | | 6d. dull claret (7.91) | 24·00 | 11·00 |

15

16

(Typo Govt Printer, Hobart, from plates made by D.L.R.)

**1871** (25 Mar)–**78**. **W 15**. (*a*) *P* 11½.

| | | | | |
|---|---|---|---|---|
| 144 | 11 | 1d. rose (5.71) | 3·25 | 50 |
| | | a. Imperf (pair) (*pen cancel* £25) | | |
| | | *b. Bright rose* | 3·25 | 50 |
| | | *c. Carmine* | 4·50 | 50 |
| | | *d. Pink* | 4·50 | 1·50 |
| | | *e. Vermilion* (4.75) | £200 | 65·00 |
| 145 | | 2d. deep green (11.72) | 12·00 | 50 |
| | | *a. Blue-green* | 20·00 | 50 |
| | | *b. Yellow-green* (12.75) | £110 | 1·50 |
| 146 | | 3d. pale red-brown | 30·00 | 3·25 |
| | | a. Imperf (pair) | £120 | |
| | | *b. Deep red-brown* | 30·00 | 3·75 |
| | | ba. Imperf between (pair) | | |
| | | *c. Purple-brown* (1.78) | 30·00 | 3·25 |
| | | ca. Imperf (pair) | — | £275 |
| | | *d. Brownish purple* | 30·00 | 3·25 |
| 147 | | 4d. pale yellow (8.8.76) | 35·00 | 9·50 |
| | | *a. Ochre* (7.78) | 42·00 | 5·50 |
| | | *b. Buff* | 35·00 | 6·50 |
| 148 | | 9d. blue (2.10.71) | 13·00 | 5·00 |
| | | a. Imperf (pair) | £120 | |
| | | b. Double print | | |
| 149 | | 5s. purple (*pen cancel* £3.75) | £130 | 30·00 |
| | | a. Imperf (pair) | | |
| | | *b. Mauve* | £110 | 30·00 |

(*b*) *P* 12

| | | | | |
|---|---|---|---|---|
| 150 | 11 | 1d. rose | 60·00 | 5·50 |
| | | *a. Carmine* | 65·00 | 7·00 |
| 151 | | 2d. green | £400 | 95·00 |
| | | a. Imperf (pair) | — | £150 |
| 152 | | 3d. red-brown | 60·00 | 14·00 |
| | | *a. Deep red-brown* | 60·00 | 14·00 |
| 153 | | 4d. buff | £225 | 15·00 |
| 154 | | 9d. pale blue | 28·00 | |
| 155 | | 5s. purple | £225 | |
| | | *a. Mauve* | £150 | |

(Typo D.L.R.)

**1878** (28 Oct). **W 16**. *P* 14.

| | | | | |
|---|---|---|---|---|
| 156 | 11 | 1d. carmine | 2·75 | 25 |
| | | *a. Rose-carmine* | 2·75 | 25 |
| | | *b. Scarlet* | 2·75 | 25 |
| 157 | | 2d. pale green | 3·00 | 25 |
| | | *a. Green* | 3·00 | 25 |
| 158 | | 8d. dull purple-brown | 14·00 | 3·25 |

(Typo Govt Printer, Hobart (some printings of 1d. in 1891 by *Mercury* Press) from plates made by Victoria Govt Printer, Melbourne (½d.) or D.L.R. (others))

**1880** (Apr)–**91**. **W 16** (*sideways on* 1d.). (*a*) *P* 11½.

| | | | | |
|---|---|---|---|---|
| 159 | 11 | ½d. orange (8.3.89) | 1·90 | 1·25 |
| | | *a. Deep orange* | 1·90 | 1·25 |
| 160 | | 1d. dull red (14.2.89) | 3·50 | 1·10 |
| | | *a. Vermilion-red* | 2·75 | 1·10 |
| 161 | | 3d. red-brown | 8·00 | 2·50 |
| | | a. Imperf (pair) | 80·00 | |
| 162 | | 4d. deep yellow (1.83) | 25·00 | 9·00 |
| | | *a. Chrome-yellow* | 25·00 | 10·00 |
| | | *b. Olive-yellow* | 90·00 | 20·00 |
| | | *c. Buff* | 26·00 | 6·50 |

(*b*) *P* 12

| | | | | |
|---|---|---|---|---|
| 163 | 11 | ½d. orange | 2·00 | 1·50 |
| | | *a. Deep orange* | 1·90 | 1·25 |
| 164 | | 1d. pink (1891) | 11·00 | 2·50 |
| | | a. Imperf (pair) | 90·00 | £100 |
| | | *b. Rosine* | 4·00 | 1·25 |
| | | *c. Dull rosine* | 6·50 | 2·75 |
| | | ca. Imperf (pair) | 65·00 | |
| 165 | | 3d. red-brown | 7·00 | 1·75 |
| | | a. Imperf between (pair) | £450 | |
| 166 | | 4d. deep yellow | 50·00 | 12·00 |
| | | *a. Chrome-yellow* | 70·00 | 12·00 |
| | | ab. Printed both sides | £180 | |

**SPECIMEN AND PRESENTATION REPRINTS OF TYPE 11.** In 1871 the 1d., 2d., 3d., 4d. blue, 9d., 10d. and 5s. were reprinted on soft white wove paper to be followed, in 1879, by the 4d. yellow and 8d. on rough white wove. Both these reprintings were perforated 11½. In 1886 it was decided to overprint remaining stocks with the word "REPRINT".

In 1889 Tasmania commenced sending sample stamps to the U.P.U. in Berne and a further printing of the 4d. blue was made, imperforate, on white card. This, together with the 5s. in mauve on white card, both perforated 11½ and overprinted "REPRINT", were included in presentation sets supplied to members of the states' legislatures in 1901.

**Halfpenny** (**17**)

d. 2½ (**18**) (2¼ mm between "d", and "2")

d. 2½ (**19**) (3½ mm between "d" and "2")

**1889** (1 Jan). *No.* 156*b surch locally with* **T 17**.

| | | | | |
|---|---|---|---|---|
| 167 | 11 | ½d. on 1d. scarlet | 8·00 | 6·00 |
| | | a. "al" in "Half" printed sideways (R. 1/2) | £700 | £475 |

No. 167a occurred in a second printing and was later corrected.

A reprint on white card, perforated 11½ or imperforate, overprinted "REPRINT" was produced in 1901.

**1891** (1 Jan–June). *Surch locally. W* **16**. *(a) With T* **18**. *P* 11½.
168 **11** 2½d. on 9d. pale blue .. .. .. 5·50 2·50
a. Surch double, one inverted .. .. £250 £275
*b. Deep blue* (May) .. .. .. .. 6·25 3·00
*(b) With T* **19**. *P* 12
169 **11** 2½d. on 9d. pale blue (June) .. .. .. 5·00 2·25
a. Blue surch.. .. .. .. ..
A reprint, using a third setting, perforated 11½ and overprinted "REPRINT" was produced in 1901.

(Typo Govt Printer, Hobart)

**1891** (Apr–Aug). *W* **15**. *(a) P* 11½.
170 **11** ½d. orange .. .. .. .. 12·00 4·00
*a. Brown-orange* .. .. .. .. 10·00 3·75
171 1d. rosine .. .. .. .. .. 10·00 4·00
*(b) P* 12
172 **11** ½d. orange .. .. .. .. 12·00 6·00
a. Imperf (pair) .. .. .. .. 60·00
173 1d. dull rosine .. .. .. .. 14·00 6·00
*a. Rosine* .. .. .. .. .. 25·00 10·00
174 4d. bistre (Aug).. .. .. .. 13·00 4·75

20

21

21*a*

**1892** (12 Feb)–**99**. *W* **16**. *P* 14.
216 **20** ½d. orange and mauve (11.92) .. 1·25 40
217 **21** 2½d. purple .. .. .. .. 2·50 1·00
218 **20** 5d. pale blue and brown .. .. 4·50 1·40
219 6d. violet and black (11.92) .. .. 5·50 1·75
220 **21a** 10d. purple-lake & deep green (30.1.99) 9·00 6·50
221 **20** 1s. rose and green (11.92) .. .. 6·00 1·75
222 2s. 6d. brown and blue (11.92) .. 20·00 9·00
223 5s. lilac and red (3.2.97) .. .. 38·00 18·00
224 10s. mauve and brown (11.92) .. 75·00 48·00
225 £1 green and yellow (2.97) .. .. £400 £150
216/25 .. .. .. *Set of* 10 £500 £200
216/25 Optd "Specimen" .. .. *Set of* 10 £250
See also Nos. 243 and 257/8.

(Typo Govt Printer, Hobart)

**1896**. *W* **16**. *P* 12.
226 **11** 4d. pale bistre .. .. .. .. 12·00 5·50
227 9d. pale blue .. .. .. .. 7·50 2·25
*a. Blue* .. .. .. .. .. 8·00 3·25

22 Lake Marion

23 Mount Wellington

24 Hobart

25 Tasman's Arch

26 Spring River, Port Davey

27 Russell Falls

28 Mount Gould, Lake St. Clair

29 Dilston Falls

30

(Eng. L. Phillips. Recess D.L.R.)

**1899** (Dec)–**1900**. *W* **30**. *P* 14.
229 **22** ½d. deep green (31.3.00) .. .. 3·50 1·00
230 **23** 1d. bright lake (13.12.99)* .. .. 3·50 40
231 **24** 2d. deep violet (15.12.99)* .. .. 3·50 25
232 **25** 2½d. indigo (1900) .. .. .. 10·00 4·50
233 **26** 3d. sepia (1900) .. .. .. 7·50 1·25
234 **27** 4d. deep orange-buff (1900) .. .. 13·00 1·75
235 **28** 5d. bright blue (31.3.00) .. .. 14·00 4·50
236 **29** 6d. lake (31.3.00) .. .. .. 18·00 4·50
229/36 .. .. .. *Set of* 8 65·00 16·00
229/36 Optd "Specimen" .. .. *Set of* 8 £225
* Earliest known postmark dates.
See also Nos. 237/9, 240/1, 245/8, 249/54 and 260/1.

**DIFFERENCES BETWEEN LITHOGRAPHED AND TYPOGRAPHED PRINTINGS OF TYPES 22/9**

| Lithographed | Typographed |
|---|---|
| *General appearance fine.* | *Comparatively crude and coarse appearance.* |
| **½d.** All "V over Crown" wmk. | All "Crown over A" wmk. |
| **1d.** The shading on the path on the right bank of the river consists of very fine dots. In printings from worn stones the dots hardly show. | The shading on the path is coarser, consisting of large dots and small patches of colour. |
| The shading on the white mountain is fine (or almost absent in many stamps). | The shading on the mountain is coarse, and clearly defined. |
| **2d.** Three rows of windows in large building on shore, at extreme left, against inner frame. | Two rows of windows. |
| **3d.** Clouds very white. | Clouds dark. |
| Stars in corner ornaments have long points. | Stars have short points. |
| Shading of corner ornaments is defined by a coloured outer line. | Shading of ornaments terminates against white background. |
| **4d.** Lithographed only. | — |
| **6d.** No coloured dots at base of waterfall. | Coloured dots at base of waterfall. |
| Outer frame of value tablets is formed by outer line of design. | Thick line of colour between value tablets and outer line. Small break in inner frame below second "A" of "TASMANIA". |

(Litho, using transfers from D.L.R. plates, Federal Government Printing Office, Melbourne)

**1902** (Jan)–**04**. *Wmk V over Crown, W* w **10** (*sideways on* ½d., 2d.). *P* 12½.
237 **22** ½d. green (2.03) .. .. .. 1·25 35
a. Wmk upright .. .. .. ..
b. Perf 11 .. .. .. .. 3·25 70
c. Perf comp of 12½ and 11 .. .. 50·00 35·00
d. Perf comp of 12½ and 12 .. ..
238 **23** 1d. carmine-red .. .. .. 4·00 30
239 **24** 2d. violet .. .. .. .. 2·50 10
a. Perf 11 .. .. .. .. 2·50 45
b. Perf comp of 12½ and 11 .. 55·00 35·00
c. Wmk upright (2.04) .. ..
*d. Purple* (4.05) .. .. .. 2·75 10
da. Perf 11 .. .. .. .. 3·75 30
237 and 239 Optd "Specimen" .. *Set of* 2 80·00
As the V and Crown paper was originally prepared for stamps of smaller size, portions of two or more watermarks appear on each stamp.
We only list the main groups of shades in this and the following issues. There are variations of shade in all values, particularly in the 2d. where there is a wide range, also in the 1d. in some issues.

(Typo, using electrotyped plates, Federal Govt Ptg Office, Melbourne)

**1902** (Oct)–**03**. *Wmk V over Crown, W* w **10**. *P* 12½.
240 **23** 1d. pale red (*wmk sideways*) .. .. 4·00 50
a. Perf 11 .. .. .. .. 17·00 50
b. Perf comp of 12½ and 11 .. £160 35·00
c. Wmk upright (1.03) .. ..
ca. Perf 11 .. .. .. ..
241 1d. rose-red (*wmk upright*) (4.03) (Optd S. £40) .. .. ..
a. Perf 11 .. .. .. .. 2·25 40
b. Perf comp of 12½ and 11 .. 15·00 50
*c. Deep carmine-red* .. .. £150 35·00
ca. Perf 11 .. .. .. .. 50·00 1·25
cb. Perf comp of 12½ and 11 .. — 15·00

(Typo Federal Govt Ptg Office, Melbourne)

**1903–05**. *Wmk V over Crown, W* w **10**. *P* 12½.
242 **11** 9d. blue (1905) .. .. .. 7·50 2·50
a. Perf 11 .. .. .. .. 8·00 3·25
b. Perf comp of 12½ and 11 .. — £375
c. Wmk sideways .. .. ..
*d. Pale blue* .. .. .. .. 9·50 3·25
*e. Bright blue* .. .. .. 9·50 3·50
*f. Ultramarine* .. .. .. £350
*g. Indigo* .. .. .. .. £130
243 **20** 1s. rose and green .. .. .. 9·00 3·00
a. Perf 11 .. .. .. .. 24·00
242/3 Optd "Specimen" .. .. *Set of* 2 £100

1½d. (31) ONE PENNY (32)

**1904** (29 Dec). *No.* 218 *surch with T* **31**.
244 **20** 1½d. on 5d. pale blue & brn (Optd S. £28) 1·25 9(
Stamps with inverted surcharge or without surcharge *se-tenan*[t] with stamps with normal surcharge were obtained irregularly and were not issued for postal use.

(Litho, using transfers from D.L.R. plates, Federal Govt Pt[g] Office, Melbourne)

**1905** (Sept)–**12**. *Wmk Crown over A, W* w **11** (*sideways on hori*[z.] *stamps*). *P* 12½.
245 **24** 2d. purple .. .. .. .. 3·50 15
a. Perf 11 .. .. .. .. 7·50 15
b. Perf comp of 12½ and 11 .. .. 17·00 3·00
c. Perf comp of 12½ and 12 .. .. — 42·00
d. Perf comp of 11 and 12 .. .. 90·00
*e. Dull purple* (1906) .. .. .. 2·75
ea. Perf 11 .. .. .. .. 15·00 25
246 **26** 3d. brown (5.06) .. .. .. 8·00 1·25
a. Perf 11 .. .. .. .. 12·00 2·25
b. Perf comp of 12½ and 11 .. .. 55·00
247 **27** 4d. orange-buff (3.07) .. .. 12·00 1·75
a. Perf 11 .. .. .. .. 13·00 2·00
b. Perf comp of 12½ and 11 (1909) .. £160
*c. Brown-ochre* (wmk sideways). Perf 11 (6.11) .. .. .. .. 24·00 14·00
*d. Orange-yellow* (3.12) .. .. 15·00 6·00
da. Perf 11 .. .. .. .. 20·00
db. Perf comp of 12½ and 11 .. ..
248 **29** 6d. lake (7.08) .. .. .. 26·00 3·50
a. Perf 11 .. .. .. .. 35·00 4·00
b. Perf comp of 12½ and 11 .. .. £130
Stamps with perf compound of 12½ and 12 or 11 and 12 are found on sheets which were sent from Melbourne incompletely perforated along the outside edge of the pane or sheet. The missing perforations were applied in Hobart using a line machine measuring 12 (11.8 is the exact gauge). This perforation can only occur on one side of a stamp.

(Typo, using electrotyped plates, Federal Govt Ptg Office Melbourne)

**1905** (Aug)–**11**. *Wmk Crown over A, W* w **11** (*sideways on horiz designs*). *P* 12½.
249 **22** ½d. yellow-green (10.12.08) .. .. 1·25 20
a. Perf 11 .. .. .. .. 1·25 20
b. Perf comp of 12½ and 11 .. .. 35·00
c. Perf comp of 11 and 12 .. .. 55·00
d. Wmk upright (1909) .. .. 4·00
da. Perf 11 .. .. .. ..
250 **23** 1d. rose-red .. .. .. .. 1·50 10
a. Perf 11 .. .. .. .. 1·75 10
b. Perf comp of 12½ and 11 .. .. 2·25 90
c. Perf comp of 12½ and 12 .. .. 40·00 5·50
d. Perf comp of 11 and 12 .. .. 45·00
e. Wmk sideways (1908) .. ..
*f. Bright rose* (3.10) .. .. .. — 15
fa. Perf 11 .. .. .. .. 4·00 15
fb. Perf comp of 12½ and 11 .. ..
fc. Perf comp of 12½ and 12 .. ..
fd. Perf comp of 11 and 12 .. ..
fe. Imperf (pair) .. .. ..
*g. Crimson* (3.10) .. .. ..
ga. Perf 11 .. .. .. .. — 40
gb. Perf comp of 12½ and 11 .. ..
gc. Perf comp of 12½ and 12 .. ..
gd. Perf comp of 11 and 12 .. ..
251 **24** 2d. purple (8.07) .. .. .. 3·00 10
a. Wmk upright .. .. ..
b. Perf 11 .. .. .. .. 2·50 10
ba. Wmk upright (12.07) .. ..
c. Perf comp of 12½ and 11 .. .. 20·00 6·00
d. Perf comp of 12½ and 12 .. ..
e. Perf comp of 11 and 12 .. .. 70·00 38·00
252 2d. bright violet (new plate)* (1.11) .. 3·00 40
a. Wmk upright .. .. ..
b. Perf 11 .. .. .. .. 3·25 30
c. Perf comp of 12½ and 11 .. .. 70·00
d. Perf comp of 12½ and 12 .. ..
253 **26** 3d. brown (3.09) .. .. .. 6·50 1·25
a. Perf 11 .. .. .. .. 9·50 1·50
b. Perf comp of 12½ and 11 .. .. £130
254 **29** 6d. dull lake (12.10) .. .. .. 15·00 7·00
a. Perf 11 .. .. .. .. 15·00 7·00
b. Perf comp of 12½ and 11 .. .. £180
c. Wmk upright (3.11) .. ..
*Stamps from this stereotyped plate differ from Nos. 251c and 251ca in the width of the design (33 to 33¾ mm, against just over 32 mm), in the taller, bolder letters of "TASMANIA", in the slope of the mountain in the left background, which is clearly outlined in white, and in the outer vertical frame-line at left, which appears "wavy". Compare Nos. 259, etc, which are always from this plate.
The note after No. 248 *re* perfs compound with perf 12 also applies here.

(Typo Federal Govt Printing Office, Melbourne)

**1906–13**. *Wmk Crown over A, W* w **11**. *P* 12½.
255 **11** 8d. purple-brown (1907) .. .. 17·00 4·00
a. Perf 11 .. .. .. .. 15·00 3·00
256 9d. blue (1907) .. .. .. .. 7·00 2·50
a. Perf 11 .. .. .. .. 7·00 2·50
b. Perf comp of 12½ and 11 (1909) .. 48·00
c. Perf comp of 12½ and 12 (1909) .. 90·00
d. Perf comp of 11 and 12 .. .. £180
257 **20** 1s. rose and green (1907) .. .. 11·00 2·00
a. Perf 11 (1907) .. .. .. 12·00 5·50
b. Perf comp of 12½ and 11 .. .. 15·00
c. Perf comp of 12½ and 12 .. .. 50·00
258 10s. mauve and brown (1906) .. .. £100 60·00
a. Perf 11 .. .. .. .. £150
b. Perf comp of 12½ and 12 .. .. £140
The note after No. 248 *re* perfs compound with perf 12, also applies here.

912 (Oct). *No. 252 surch with T* **32**. *P* 12½.
59 **24** 1d. on 2d. bright violet (R.) .. .. 90 30
a. Perf 11 .. .. 1·50 40
b. Perf comp of 12½ and 11 .. .. 85·00 85·00

Typo, using electrotyped plates, Federal Govt Ptg Office, Melbourne)

912 (Dec). *Thin paper, white gum (as Victoria,* 1912). *W w* **11** *(sideways on 3d.). P* 12½.
260 **23** 1d. crimson .. .. .. .. 9·00 1·25
a. Perf 11 .. .. .. .. 9·50 1·25
b. Perf comp of 12½ and 11 ..
261 **26** 3d. brown .. .. .. .. 30·00 35·00

POSTAL FISCAL STAMPS

**ALIDITY.** Nos. F1/29 were authorised for postal purposes on 1 November 1882.

**LEANED STAMPS.** Beware of postal fiscal stamps with pen-ancellations removed.

F 1

F 2

F 3

F 4

(Recess Alfred Bock, Hobart)

863–80. *Wmk double-lined* "1", *W* 4. (*a*) *Imperf.*
1 F 1 3d. green (1.65) .. .. .. 50·00 35·00
2 F 2 2s. 6d. carmine (11.63) .. .. .. 55·00 35·00
3 2s. 6d. lake (1880) .. ..
4 F 3 5s. brown (1.64) .. .. .. £140 £110
5 5s. sage-green (1880) .. .. 55·00 42·00
6 F 4 10s. orange (1.64) .. .. .. £180 £110
7 10s. salmon (1880) .. .. .. £130 £110

(*b*) *P* 10
F 8 F 1 3d. green .. .. .. 30·00 16·00
F 9 F 2 2s. 6d. carmine .. .. 32·00
F10 F 3 5s. brown .. .. .. 48·00
F11 F 4 10s. orange .. .. .. 32·00

(*c*) *P* 12
F12 F 1 3d. green .. .. .. 35·00 20·00
F13 F 2 2s. 6d. carmine .. .. 35·00 27·00
F14 F 3 5s. brown .. .. .. 60·00
F15 5s. sage-green .. .. 24·00 19·00
F16 F 4 10s. orange .. .. 32·00 27·00
F17 10s. salmon .. .. 25·00 20·00

(*d*) *P* 12½
F18 F 1 3d. green .. .. .. 60·00
F19 F 2 2s. 6d. carmine .. .. 60·00
F20 F 3 5s. brown .. .. .. 75·00
F21 F 4 10s. orange-brown .. .. 50·00

(*e*) *P* 11½
F22 F 1 3d. green .. .. ..
F23 F 2 2s. 6d. lake .. .. 30·00 25·00
F24 F 3 5s. sage-green .. .. 24·00 16·00
F25 F 4 10s. salmon .. .. 42·00 30·00

See also No. F30.

In 1879, the 3d., 2s. 6d., 5s. (brown), and 10s. (orange) were reprinted on thin, tough, white paper, and are found with or without "REPRINT". In 1889 another reprint was made on white card, imperforate and perforated 12. These are also found with or without "REPRINT".

F 5 Duck-billed Platypus

REVENUE

(F 6)

(Typo D.L.R.)

1880 (19 Apr). *W* **16** (*sideways*). *P* 14.
F26 F 5 1d. slate .. .. .. 9·00 3·25
F27 3d. chestnut .. .. .. 9·00 2·50
F28 6d. mauve .. .. .. 45·00 2·00
F29 1s. rose-pink .. .. .. 55·00 4·25

All values are known imperf, but not used.

Reprints are known of the 1d. in *deep blue* and the 6d. in lilac. The former is on yellowish white, the latter on white card. Both values also exist on wove paper, perf 12, with the word "REPRINT".

1888. *W* **16**. *P* 12
F30 F 2 2s. 6d. lake .. .. 15·00 11·00
a. Imperf between (horiz pair) .. £450

1900 (Nov). *Optd with Type* F 6. (*a*) *On Types* F 2 *and* F 4. *W* **16**. *P* 12.
F31 F 2 2s. 6d. carmine .. .. .. £160
a. "REVFNUE" .. .. .. £250
b. Opt inverted .. .. .. £350
c. Imperf .. .. .. £170
ca. "REVFNUE" .. .. .. £250
F32 F 4 10s. salmon .. .. ..
a. "REVFNUE" .. ..
b. On No. F 17 (wmk W 4) ..
ba. "REVFNUE" .. .. ..

(*b*) *On No.* F27
F33 F 5 3d. chestnut .. .. 15·00 15·00
a. Double opt, one vertical .. 75·00 £100

(*c*) *On stamps as Nos.* F26/9, *but litho locally. W* **15** (*No.* F34) *or W* **16** (*others*). *P* 12
F34 F 5 1d. blue .. .. .. 65·00
F35 1d. blue .. .. .. 18·00
a. Imperf between (horiz pair) .. £300
b. "REVENUE" inverted .. .. £100
c. "REVENUE" double .. .. £160
*d. Pale blue* .. .. .. 18·00
F36 2d. chestnut .. .. .. 20·00
a. Value omitted .. .. £180 £150
b. Value double .. .. £225 £150
c. Imperf between (horiz pair) .. £200
F37 6d. mauve .. .. .. 50·00
a. Double print .. .. £200
F38 1s. pink .. .. .. 75·00

(*d*) *On No.* 225
F39 **20** £1 green and yellow .. .. £150 £130
a. Opt double, one vertical .. .. £275

It was not intended that stamps overprinted with Type F 6 should be used for postal purposes, but an ambiguity in regulations permitted such usage until corrected on 1 December 1900. All postal fiscal stamps were invalidated for postal purposes after 30 June 1901.

Tasmania became part of the Commonwealth of Australia on 1 January 1901.

## VICTORIA

**PRICES FOR STAMPS ON COVER**

| | |
|---|---|
| Nos. 1/17 | *from* × 2 |
| Nos. 18/22 | *from* × 4 |
| Nos. 23/4 | *from* × 2 |
| No. 25 | *from* × 3 |
| Nos. 26/32 | *from* × 2 |
| No. 33 | *from* × 6 |
| No. 34 | *from* × 8 |
| Nos. 35/9 | *from* × 4 |
| No. 40 | *from* × 3 |
| No. 41/53 | *from* × 2 |
| No. 54 | *from* × 3 |
| No. 55 | — |
| No. 56 | *from* × 4 |
| Nos. 57/72 | *from* × 2 |
| No. 73 | *from* × 3 |
| No. 74/80 | *from* × 2 |
| No. 81 | *from* × 3 |
| Nos. 82/7 | *from* × 2 |
| Nos. 92/186 | *from* × 3 |
| Nos. 187/220 | *from* × 4 |
| Nos. 221/2 | *from* × 10 |
| Nos. 223/38 | *from* × 5 |
| Nos. 239/67 | *from* × 10 |
| Nos. 268/82 | — |
| Nos. 283/91 | *from* × 10 |
| Nos. 292/6 | — |
| Nos. 297/303 | *from* × 12 |
| Nos. 304/22 | *from* × 8 |
| Nos. 323/4 | — |
| Nos. 325/6 | *from* × 4 |
| Nos. 327/9 | *from* × 10 |
| Nos. 330/45 | *from* × 15 |
| Nos. 346/7 | *from* × 2 |
| Nos. 348/75 | *from* × 10 |
| Nos. 376/7 | — |
| Nos. 378/87 | *from* × 10 |
| Nos. 388/98 | — |
| Nos. 399/409 | *from* × 10 |
| Nos. 410/12 | — |
| Nos. 413/23 | *from* × 4 |
| Nos. 424/33 | — |
| Nos. 434/43 | *from* × 10 |
| No. 444 | — |
| No. 445 | *from* × 10 |
| Nos. 446/52 | *from* × 6 |
| No. 453 | — |
| No. 454 | *from* × 6 |
| Nos. F1/6 | — |
| Nos. F7/15 | *from* × 20 |
| Nos. F16/22 | — |
| Nos. F23/5 | *from* × 20 |
| Nos. F26/40 | — |
| Nos. F41/5 | *from* × 20 |
| Nos. F46/50 | — |
| Nos. F51/2 | *from* × 20 |
| Nos. F53/9 | — |
| Nos. D1/8 | *from* × 30 |
| Nos. D9/10 | — |
| Nos. D11/67 | *from* × 30 |

**SPECIMEN OVERPRINTS.** Those listed are from U.P.U. distributions in 1892 and 1897. Further "Specimen" overprints exist, but these were used for other purposes.

During the expansion of the Australian settlements in the fourth decade of the nineteenth century the growing population of the Port Phillip District in the south of New South Wales led to a movement for its creation as a separate colony. This aspiration received the approval of the British Government in 1849, but the colony of Victoria, as it was to be called, was not to be created until 1 July 1851.

In the meantime the New South Wales Legislative Council voted for the introduction of postal reforms, including the use of postage stamps, from 1 January 1850, and this act was also to apply to the Port Phillip District where stamps inscribed "VICTORIA" would predate the creation of that colony by eighteen months.

Until the end of 1859 the stamps of Victoria, with the exception of Nos. 40 and 73, were produced by local contractors working under the supervision of the colonial administration.

**HAM PRINTINGS.** The first contractor was Thomas Ham of Melbourne. He was responsible for the initial printings of the "Half-Length" 1d., 2d. and 3d., together with the replacement "Queen on Throne" 2d. The first printings were produced from small sheets of 30 (5×6) laid down directly from the engraved die which showed a single example of each value. Subsequent printings, of which No. 4*a* was the first, were in sheets of 120 (two panes of 60) laid down using intermediate stones of various sizes. Impressions from the first printings were fine and clear, but the quality deteriorated when intermediate stones were used.

1 Queen Victoria ("Half Length")

(Lithographed by Thomas Ham, Melbourne)

**1850** (3 Jan)–**53**. *Imperf.*

1d. Thin line at top

2d. Fine border and background

3d. White area to left of orb

(*a*) *Original state of dies*: 1d. (*tops of letters of* "VICTORIA" *reach to top of stamp*); 2d. (*fine border and background*); 3d. (*thicker white outline around left of orb, central band of orb does not protrude at left*). *No frame-lines on dies.*
1 **1** 1d. orange-vermilion .. .. .. — £1000
*a. Orange-brown* .. .. .. — £500
*b. Dull chocolate-brown (shades)* .. — £600
2 2d. lilac-mauve (*shades*) (Stone A) .. £2250 £400
3 2d. brown-lilac (*shades*) (Stone B) .. £2250 £250
*a. Grey-lilac* .. .. .. — £250
4 3d. bright blue (*shades*) .. .. £1800 £275
*a. Blue (shades)* .. .. .. — £170
ab. Retouched (between Queen's head and right border) (No. 11 in transfer-group) (8 varieties) .. .. .. — £275
ac. Retouched (under "V") (No. 10 in transfer group) .. .. ..

With the exception of No. 4*a* the above were printed from small stones of 30 (5×6) laid down directly from the engraved die which showed a single example of each value. There were two stones of the 2d. and one for each of the other values. No. 4*a* is the second printing of the 3d. for which the sheet size was increased to 120, the printing stone being constructed from an intermediate stone of 15 (5×3).

1d. Thick line at top

2d. Coarse background

3d. White area small and band protruding to left of orb

(*b*) *Second state of dies*: 1d. (*more colour over top of letters of* "VICTORIA"); 2d. (*fine border as* (*a*) *but with coarse background*); 3d. (*thinner white outline around left of orb, central band of orb protrudes at left*).
5 **1** 1d. red-brown (*shades*) (2.50) .. .. £2750 £275
*a. Pale dull red-brown* .. .. £2000 £275
6 2d. grey-lilac (*shades*) (1.50) .. .. £1100 80·00
*a. Dull grey* .. .. .. — 85·00
7 3d. blue (*shades*) (6.51) .. .. — £110
a. Retouched (22 varieties) .. *from* — £225

Printed in sheets of 120 (10×12) with the printing stones constructed from intermediate stones of 30 (5×6) for the 1d. and 2d. or 10 (5×2) for the 3d. It is believed that the use of the smaller intermediate stone for the latter resulted in the many retouches.

Frame-lines added

(*c*) *Third state of dies: As in* (*b*) *but with frame-lines added, very close up, on all four sides.*

8 **1** 1d. dull orange-vermilion (11.50) .. .. .. — £130
*a. Dull red (shades)* .. .. .. .. — £120
9 1d. deep red-brown (5.51) .. .. .. — £400
*a. Brownish red (shades)* .. .. .. — £110
*b. Dull rose (shades)* .. .. .. .. — £110
10 2d. grey (*shades*) (8.50) .. .. .. — £120
*a. Olive-grey (shades)* .. .. .. — £130
11 3d. blue (*shades*) (12.52) .. .. .. — 50·00
*a. Deep blue (shades)* .. .. .. .. — 50·00
*b. Pale greenish blue (shades)* .. .. .. — £100

Printed in sheets of 120 (12×10) produced from intermediate stones of 30 (6×5) for No. 8 and 12 (6×2) for the others.

White veil

(*d*) *As* (*c*) *but altered to give, for the 1d. and 3d., the so-called "white veils", and for the 2d., the effect of vertical drapes to the veil.*

12 **1** 1d. reddish brown (6.51) .. .. .. £600 £100
*a. Bright pinky red (shades)* .. .. £450 £100
13 2d. drab (1.51) .. .. .. .. — £110
*a. Grey-drab* .. .. .. .. — £110
*b. Lilac-drab* .. .. .. .. — £110
*c. Red-lilac* .. .. .. .. — £500
d. Void lower left corner .. .. — £1200
14 3d. blue (*shades*) (1.53) .. .. .. — 45·00
*a. Deep blue (shades)* .. .. .. — 45·00
*b. Greenish blue (shades)* .. .. .. — 50·00
c. Retouched (9 varieties) .. .. .. — £120

Printed in sheets of 120 (12×10) produced from intermediate stones of 12 (6×2) on which the details of the veil were amended as described above.

The "void corner" error occurred on the printing stone. It is believed that only four examples still exist.

2d. Coarse border and background

(*e*) *Fourth state of 2d. die only: Coarse border and background. Veil details as in original die.*

15 **1** 2d. red-lilac (*shades*) (5.50) .. .. — £180
*a. Lilac* .. .. .. .. .. — £180
*b. Grey* .. .. .. .. .. — £275
*c. Dull brownish lilac* .. .. .. — £100
d. Retouched lower label—value omitted *from* — £1800
e. Other retouches (17 varieties) *from* — £225

Printed in sheets of 120 (12×10) produced from an intermediate stone of 30 (6×5).

(*f*) *2d. as* (*e*), *but with veils altered to give effect of vertical drapes.*

16 **1** 2d. lilac-grey (1.51) .. .. .. — £110
*a. Deep grey* .. .. .. .. — £110
*b. Brown-lilac (shades)* .. .. .. — 60·00
17 2d. cinnamon (*shades*) (2.51) .. .. £500 95·00
*a. Drab (shades)* .. .. .. .. — 60·00
*b. Pale dull brown (shades)* .. .. — 70·00
*c. Greenish grey* .. .. .. .. — 60·00
*d. Olive-drab (shades)* .. .. .. — £110
*e. Buff* .. .. .. .. .. — £120

Printed in sheets of 120 (12×10) produced from two successive intermediate stones of 30 (6×5) on which the details of the veils were amended as described above.

This was the final printing of the 2d. "Half Length" as the die for this value had been damaged. A replacement 2d. design was ordered from Thomas Ham.

For the later printings of the 1d. and 3d. in this design see Nos. 23/4, 26/31, 48/9 and 78/9.

**2** Queen on Throne **3**

(Recess-printed by Thomas Ham)

**1852** (27 Dec). *Imperf.*

18 **2** 2d. reddish brown .. .. .. £130 22·00
*a. Chestnut* .. .. .. .. — £110
*b. Purple-brown* .. .. .. .. £130 22·00

Printed in sheets of 50 (10×5) from a hand-engraved plate of the same size. Each stamp in the sheet had individual corner letters made-up of various combinations, none of which contained the letter "J".

Reprints were made in 1891 using the original plate, on paper wmk V over Crown, both imperf and perf 12½.

For later printings of this design see Nos. 19/22 and 36/9.

**CAMPBELL & CO PRINTINGS.** In May 1853 the Victoria postal authorities placed an order for 1d. and 6d. stamps in the "Queen on Throne" design with Perkins, Bacon in London. These would not arrive for some time, however, and supplies of Ham's printings were rapidly becoming exhausted. Local tenders were, therefore, solicited for further supplies of the 1d. and 3d. "Half Lengths" and the 2d. "Queen on Throne". That received from J. S. Campbell & Co was accepted. The stamps were produced by lithography, using transfers from either the "Half Length" engraved die or the 2d. "Queen on Throne" engraved plate of 50. Stamps from the Campbell & Co printings can be distinguished from later printings in lithography by the good quality paper used.

(Lithographed by J. S. Campbell & Co, Melbourne, using transfers taken from Ham's engraved plate)

**1854** (Jan–July). *Good quality white or toned paper. Imperf.*

(*a*) *Clear impressions with details around back of throne generally complete*

19 **2** 2d. brownish purple .. .. .. £170 22·00
*a. Grey-brown* .. .. .. .. — 22·00
*b. Purple-black* .. .. .. .. — 22·00
*c. Dull lilac-brown (toned paper only)* .. — 40·00

(*b*) *Poor impressions with details around back of throne not fully defined*

20 **2** 2d. violet-black (2.54) .. .. .. — 22·00
*a. Grey-black* .. .. .. .. — 24·00
*b. Grey-lilac* .. .. .. .. — 24·00
*c. Dull brown (on toned)* .. .. .. — 24·00
ca. Substituted transfer (in pair) .. .. — £2000

(*c*) *Weak impressions with background generally white without details. Toned paper only*

21 **2** 2d. grey-purple (7.54) .. .. .. £130 20·00
*a. Purple-black* .. .. .. .. £130 20·00

(*d*) *Printings using an intermediate stone. Impression flat and blurred. Background details usually complete. Toned paper only*

22 **2** 2d. grey-drab (*shades*) (5.54) .. .. — 19·00
*a. Black* .. .. .. .. .. — £100

Nos. 19/21 were produced using transfers taken directly from the original Ham engraved plate. It is believed that the different strengths of the impressions were caused by the amount of pressure exerted when the tranfers were taken. The stamps were printed in sheets of 100 (2 panes 10×5). On one stone a block of four at bottom left, lettered "FL GM" over "QV RW", was damaged and the stone was repaired by using a block of four substituted transfers. These were lettered "VZ WA" over "FL GM". No. 20ca covers any one of these substituted transfers in pair with normal. As horizontal pairs these are lettered "WA HN" or "GM SX" and as vertical "VZ" over "VZ" or "WA" over "WA".

For No. 22 an intermediate stone was used to produce a printing stone of 300 (6 panes 10×5). The insertion of a further stage into the process caused the blurred appearance of stamps from this printing. No. 22*a* is believed to come from proof sheets issued to post offices for normal use. Examples are usually cancelled with Barred Oval 108 and Barred Numerals 1 and 2.

(Lithographed by J. S. Campbell & Co, Melbourne)

**1854** (Mar–June). *Good quality wove paper. Imperf.*

23 **1** 1d. orange-red (*shades*) .. .. .. £450 £110
*a. Rose* .. .. .. .. .. — £250
24 3d. blue (*shades*) (6.54) .. .. .. £475 32·00
a. Retouch under "C" of "VICTORIA" .. — £120

The 1d. was produced in sheets of 192 (two panes of 96 (12×8)) and the 3d. in sheets of 320 (two panes of 160 (18×9)). Both printing stones were constructed from transfers taken from intermediate stones of 24 (6×4). The spacing between stamps is far wider than on the Ham printings. The 3d. panes of 160 were constructed using six complete transfers of 24 and three of 6 with the final impression in the bottom two rows removed.

The 1d. Campbell printings have the frame lines almost completely absent due to lack of pressure when taking transfers.

The 3d. retouch, No. 24a, occurs on R.3/5 of the intermediate stone.

**CAMPBELL AND FERGUSSON PRINTINGS.** Increased postal rates in early 1854 led to a requirement for a 1s. value and in April a contract for this stamp was awarded to Campbell and Fergusson (the new corporate style of J. S. Campbell & Co). Further contracts to print the 1d. and 3d. "Half Lengths" and the 2d. "Queen on Throne" followed. All were produced by lithography with the two "Half Lengths" using transfers from the original engraved die and the 2d. "Queen on Throne" transfers from Ham's original engraved plate.

All Campbell and Fergusson printings were on paper of a poorer quality than that used for the earlier contract.

(Lithographed by Campbell & Fergusson)

**1854** (6 July). *Poorer quality paper. Imperf.*

25 **3** 1s. blue (*shades*) .. .. .. .. £650 22·00
*a. Greenish blue* .. .. .. .. £750 22·00
*b. Indigo-blue* .. .. .. .. — £110

No. 25 was produced in sheets of 100 (8×12 with an additional stamp appearing at the end of Rows 6 to 9). The printing stones used each contained four such sheets. They were constructed from an intermediate stone of 40 (8×5) taken from a single engraved die. Each pane of 100 showed two complete transfers of 40, one of 20 and one of a vertical strip of 4.

For this stamp rouletted or perforated see Nos. 54 and 81.

(Lithographed by Campbell & Fergusson)

**1854** (July)–**57**. *Poorer quality paper. Imperf.*

26 **1** 1d. brown (*shades*) .. .. .. £400 95·00
*a. Brick-red (shades)* .. .. .. — 75·00
*b. Dull red (shades)* .. .. .. £600 75·00
27 1d. orange-brown (*shades*) (8.55) .. .. — £100
*a. Dull rose-red (shades)* .. .. .. — 60·00
*b. Bright rose-pink* .. .. .. — £100
c. Retouched (6 varieties) .. .. .. — £400
28 **1** 1d. pink (*shades*) (2.55) .. .. .. £375 32·00
*a. Rose (shades)* .. .. .. .. £375 32·00
*b. Lilac-rose (shades)* .. .. .. — 32·00
*c. Dull brown-red (shades)* .. .. .. — £100
d. Retouched (8 varieties) .. .. .. £750 £325
29 3d. bright blue (*shades*) (7.57) .. .. £425 48·00
*a. Greenish blue (shades)* .. .. .. £375 40·00
b. Retouch under "C" of "VICTORIA" .. — 95·00
30 3d. Prussian blue (*shades*) (11.56) .. .. — 70·00
*a. Milky blue* .. .. .. .. — £110
b. Retouch under "C" of "VICTORIA" .. — £225
31 3d. steel-blue (*shades*) (*heavier impression*) (5.55) .. .. .. .. — 42·00
*a. Greenish blue (shades)* .. .. .. £350 30·00
*b. Blue (shades)* .. .. .. .. £350 30·00
*c. Deep blue (shades)* .. .. .. £350 30·00
*d. Indigo (shades)* .. .. .. .. — 38·00

The 1d. was produced in sheets of 400 (2 panes 20×10) constructed from transfers originating from the J. S. Campbell & Co intermediate stone. Each pane contained six complete tranfers of 24, three of 12, two of 8 and one of 4.

The 3d. was produced in sheets of 320 (2 panes of 160) (No. 29), 200 (No. 30) or 400 (2 panes of 200) (No. 31.) The stone for No. 29 was constructed from transfers taken from the J. S. Campbell intermediate stone with the retouch on R.3/5 still present. The panes of 160 contained six complete transfers of 24 and three of 6 with the last impression in both rows 8 and 9 removed. Quality of impression is generally poor. The stone for No. 30, once again taken from the Campbell intermediate stone, was laid down in the same combination of transfers as the 1d. value. Impressions from it were, however, so poor that transfers from a new intermediate stone were used for No. 31. Impressions from this stone, on which the panes of 200 were in a similar layout to the 1d., were much further apart than those on the stones used to produce Nos. 29/30.

The Campbell and Fergusson printings of the "Half Lengths" are listed in the order in which they were printed.

**CALVERT PRINTINGS.** Contracts for the provision of other values required by the postal rate changes in 1853 were placed with Samuel Calvert of Melbourne who used typography as the printing process. Calvert continued to print, and later roulette, stamps for the Victoria Post Office until March 1858 when it was discovered that he had placed some of the stock in pawn.

4 5 6

(Typographed from woodblocks by Samuel Calvert)

**1854** (1 Sept)–**55**. *Imperf.*

32 **4** 6d. reddish brown (13.9.54) .. .. .. £180 22·00
*a. Dull orange* .. .. .. .. £150 18·00
*b. Orange-yellow* .. .. .. .. £150 19·00
33 **5** 6d. ("TOO LATE") lilac and green (1.1.55) £600 £120
34 **6** 1s. ("REGISTERED") rose-pink and blue (1.12.54) .. .. .. .. £750 75·00
35 **4** 2s. dull bluish green/*pale yellow* .. .. £1000 £110

No. 33 was provided to pay the additional fee on letters posted after the normal closure of the mails. This service was only available in the larger towns; examples are usually postmarked Castlemaine, Geelong or Melbourne. The service was withdrawn on 1 July 1857 and remaining stocks of the "TOO LATE" stamps were used for normal postal purposes.

No. 34 was issued to pay the registration fee and was so used until 5 January 1858 after which remaining stocks were used for normal postage.

These four values were produced from individually-engraved boxwood woodblocks. The 6d. was in sheets of 100 printed by two impressions from two plates of 25. The 2s. was in sheets of 50 from a single plate of 25. The bicoloured "TOO LATE" and "REGISTERED" stamps are unusual in that Calvert used a common woodblock "key" plate of 25 for both values combined with "duty" plates made up from metal stereos. Both values were originally in sheets of 50, but the "REGISTERED" later appeared in sheets of 100 for which a second "key" plate of 25 was utilised.

For these stamps rouletted or perforated see Nos. 53, 55/8, 60/1 and 82.

(Lithographed by Campbell & Fergusson)

**1855** (Mar)–**56**. *Poorer quality paper. Imperf.*

(*a*) *Printings from stones which were not over-used; background around top of throne generally full and detail good*

36 **2** 2d. lilac (*shades*) (7.55) .. .. .. £140 19·00
*a. Purple (shades)* .. .. .. .. — 19·00
b. "TVO" for "TWO" .. .. .. .. — £600

(*b*) *Early printings from stones which were over-used. Similar characteristics to those above, though detail is not quite so full. Distinctive shades.*

37 **2** 2d. brown .. .. .. .. .. — 70·00
*a. Brown-purple* .. .. .. .. £170 22·00
*b. Warm purple* .. .. .. .. — 22·00
*c. Rose-lilac* .. .. .. .. — 22·00
d. Substituted transfer (pair) .. .. — £600

(*c*) *Later printings from the same stones used for No. 37 when in a worn condition. Impressions heavy, coarse and overcoloured; details blurred; generally white background around top of throne.*

38 **2** 2d. dull lilac-mauve (1856) .. .. .. £120 22·00
*a. Dull mauve* .. .. .. .. £120 22·00
*b. Grey-violet* .. .. .. .. — 22·00
*c. Red-lilac* .. .. .. .. — 24·00
d. Substituted transfer (pair) .. .. — £600

(*d*) *Printings from a stone giving blotchy and unpleasing results, with poor definition. Mainly shows in extra colour patches found on most stamps.*

39 **2** 2d. dull purple (7.55) .. .. .. — 40·00
*a. Dull grey-lilac* .. .. .. .. £170 40·00
b. On thick card paper .. .. .. — £500

The Campbell and Fergusson 2d. "Queen on Throne" printings were in sheets of 200 (4 panes 10 × 5) constructed from transfers taken from the original Ham engraved plate.

Four separate stones were used. On Stone A a creased ransfer running through R.4/8, 4/9 and 5/8 caused the "TVO" ariety on the stamp from the bottom row of one pane. On Stone the impression in the first vertical row of one pane were found o be so faulty that they were replaced by substituted transfers aken from elsewhere on the sheet causing abnormal horizontal airs lettered "UY BF", "TX MQ", "DI WA", "SW GM" and "CH W". The vertical pairs from the substituted transfers are ettered "UY" over "TX" and "DI" over "SW".

7 Queen on Throne

8 "Emblems"

(Recess Perkins, Bacon & Co, London)

**856** (23 Oct). *Wmk Large Star, W w 1. Imperf.*
0 **7** 1d. yellow-green .. .. .. .. £120 19·00

Supplies of this stamp, and the accompanying 6d. which was nly issued rouletted (see No. 73), arrived in the colony at the nd of 1854, but the 1d. was not placed on sale until almost two ears later.

No. 40 was reprinted from the original plate in 1891. xamples, in either dull yellow-green or bright blue-green, are nperforate and on V over Crown watermarked paper.

(Typographed from electrotypes by Calvert)

**857** (26 Jan–6 Sept). *Imperf. (a) Wmk Large Star, W w* **1**
1 **8** 1d. yellow-green (18 Feb) .. .. .. 95·00 13·00
*a. Deep green* .. .. .. .. £110 26·00
b. Printed on both sides .. .. .. † £700
2 4d. vermilion .. .. .. .. £250 10·00
*a. Brown-vermilion* .. .. .. .. £225 9·00
b. Printed on both sides .. .. .. † £700
3 4d. dull red (20 July) .. .. .. £160 7·50
4 4d. dull rose (6 Sept) .. .. .. £180 7·50

*(b) No wmk. Good quality medium wove paper*
5 **8** 2d. pale lilac (25 May) .. .. .. £160 10·00
*a. Grey-lilac* .. .. .. .. £160 10·00

Nos. 41/5 were produced in sheets of 120, arranged as four anes of 30 (6×5) (1d. and 4d.) or twelve panes of 10 (2×5) (2d.), sing electrotypes taken from a single engraved die of each alue. The setting of the 4d. was re-arranged before the printing Nos. 43/4.

Only two examples of No. 41b and No. 42b have been ecorded.

For this printing rouletted or perforated see Nos. 46/7, 50/2, 9, 74 and 77.

**OULETTES AND PERFORATIONS**. In August 1857 a ouletting machine was provided at the G.P.O., Melbourne, to nable the counter clerks to separate stamp stocks before sale to e public. This machine produced roulettes of 7½–9 in one rection across six rows at a time. There was also a single wheel evice which gauged 7–7½. Both were in use between the arliest known date of 12 August and the end of 1857.

Calvert was granted a separate contract in October 1857 to oulette the stamps he printed, but only Nos. 57/61 had been roduced when it was found, in April 1858, that he had pawned quantity of the sheets. His contracts were terminated and his ccessor, F. W. Robinson, used a roulette machine of a different uge before switching to a gauge 12 perforating machine in anuary 1859.

**857** (12 Aug–Sept). *Rouletted 7–9 by counter clerks at G.P.O., Melbourne.*
6 **8** 1d. yellow-green (No. 41) .. .. .. £275 65·00
7 2d. pale lilac (No. 45) .. .. .. — £225
*a. Grey-lilac* .. .. .. .. — £225
8 **1** 3d. blue (*shades*) (No. 24) .. .. .. — £150
a. Retouch under "C" of "VICTORIA" ..
9 3d. bright blue (*shades*) (No. 29) .. .. — £160
*a. Greenish blue (shades)* .. .. — £140
b. Retouch under "C" of "VICTORIA" ..
0 **8** 4d. vermilion (No. 42) .. .. .. — £100
1 4d. dull red (No. 43) .. .. .. — 38·00
2 4d. dull rose (No. 44) (Sept) .. .. — 26·00
3 **4** 6d. reddish brown (No. 32) .. .. — 42·00
*a. Dull orange* .. .. .. .. — 35·00
*b. Orange-yellow* .. .. .. — 42·00
4 **3** 1s. blue (*shades*) (No. 25) .. .. .. — 80·00
*a. Greenish blue* .. .. .. .. — 80·00
5 **6** 1s. ("REGISTERED") rose-pink and blue (No. 34) .. .. .. .. £3500 £180
6 **4** 2s. dull bluish green/*pale yellow* (No. 35) — £350

With the exception of the 1s., Nos. 54/*a*, these stamps are ormally found rouletted on one or two sides only.

**857** (Oct). *Rouletted by Calvert. (a) Rouletted 7–9 on all four sides and with finer points than No. 53b*
7 **4** 6d. orange-yellow (No. 32*b*)

*(b) Serpentine roulette* 10–10½
8 **4** 6d. orange-yellow (No. 32*b*) .. .. — 55·00

*(c) Serrated* 18–19
9 **8** 2d. grey-lilac (No. 45*a*) .. .. .. £500 £350
0 **4** 6d. orange-yellow (No. 32*b*) .. .. — 55·00

*(d) Compound of serrated* 18–19 *and serpentine* 10–10½
1 **4** 6d. orange-yellow (No. 32*b*) .. .. — 55·00

No. 59 was not covered by the contract given to Calvert, but it believed to be a test run for the rouletting machine. No. 61 ways shows serrated 18–19 on three sides and the serpentine ulette at the top or bottom of the stamp.

(Typo from electrotypes by Calvert)

**858** (14 Jan–Apr). *No wmk. Good quality white wove paper.*

*(a) Rouletted 7–9 on all four sides*
2 **8** 1d. pale emerald .. .. .. .. £300 14·00
*a. Emerald-green* .. .. .. £300 14·00
63 **8** 4d. rose-pink (18 Jan) .. .. .. £200 5·50
*a. Bright rose* .. .. .. .. £200 5·50
*b. Reddish pink* .. .. .. .. — 11·00
c. Imperf horiz (vert pair) .. .. .. † £400

*(b) Imperf* (Apr)
64 **8** 1d. pale emerald .. .. .. .. £190 10·00
*a. Emerald-green* .. .. .. .. — 13·00
65 4d. rose-pink .. .. .. .. £250 23·00
*a. Bright rose* .. .. .. .. — 23·00
*b. Reddish pink* .. .. .. .. — 30·00

Nos. 62/5 were produced in sheets of 120, arranged as four panes of 30 (6×5).

The Royal Collection contains a used horizontal pair of the 4d. showing the vertical roulettes omitted.

The majority of Nos. 64/5 were issued in April after Calvert's contracts had been terminated, although there is some evidence that imperforate sheets of the 4d., at least, were issued earlier.

For the 1d. of this issue perforated see No. 75.

**ROBINSON PRINTINGS**. Calvert's contracts were cancelled in April 1858 and the work was then placed with F. W. Robinson, who had unsuccessfully tendered in 1856. The same electrotypes were used, but a perforating machine was introduced from January 1859. Robinson continued to print and perforate stamps under contract until the end of 1859 when the Victoria Post Office purchased his equipment to set up a Stamp Printing Branch and appointed him Printer of Postage Stamps.

(Typo from electrotypes by Robinson)

**1858** (May–Dec). *(a) Imperf. (i) Coarse quality wove paper.*
66 **8** 4d. dull rose (*oily ink*) .. .. .. — 60·00

*(ii) Smooth vertically-laid paper*
67 **8** 4d. dull rose (*oily ink*) .. .. .. — 23·00
*a. Dull rose-red* .. .. .. .. — 23·00
68 4d. dull rose-red (*normal ink*) (20 May) .. £400 15·00

*(b) Rouletted* 5½–6½. *(i) Smooth laid paper*
69 **8** 2d. brown-lilac (*shades*) (*horiz laid*) (June) £120 5·50
a. Vert laid paper (21 Sept) .. .. £200 9·50
70 2d. violet (*horiz laid*) (27 Nov) .. .. £150 5·50
*a. Dull violet* .. .. .. .. — 18·00
71 4d. pale dull rose (*vert laid*) (1 June) .. £150 3·50
a. Horiz laid paper .. .. .. † £800
*b. Dull rose-red* .. .. .. .. £120 3·50
*c. Rose-red* .. .. .. .. £120 3·25
ca. Serrated 19 .. .. .. .. † £350

*(ii) Good quality wove paper*
72 **8** 1d. yellow-green (24 Dec) .. .. .. £275 23·00

Nos. 66/72 were produced in sheets of 120, arranged as four panes of 30 (6 × 5).

For stamps of this issue perforated see Nos. 76 and 80.

(Recess Perkins, Bacon & Co, London)

**1858** (1 Nov). *Wmk Large Star, W w* **1**. *Rouletted* 5½–6½.
73 **7** 6d. bright blue .. .. .. .. £100 12·00
*a. Light blue* .. .. .. .. £160 24·00

No. 73 was received from London at the same time as the 1d., No. 40, but was kept in store until November 1858 when the stock was rouletted by Robinson. When issued the gum was in a poor state.

Imperforate examples exist from Perkins, Bacon remainders. Imperforate reprints, in shades of indigo, were made from the original plate in 1891 on V over Crown watermarked paper.

**1859** (Jan–May). *P 12 by Robinson.*
74 **8** 1d. yellow-green (No. 41) .. .. .. — £275
75 1d. emerald-green (No. 64*a*) .. .. .. — £275
a. Imperf between (horiz pair) ..
76 1d. yellow-green (as No. 72) (11 Jan) £160 11·00
a. Imperf horiz (vert pair) .. .. — £300
b. Thin, glazed ("Bordeaux") paper .. † £150
77 2d. pale lilac (No. 45) .. .. .. — £225
*a. Grey-lilac* .. .. .. .. — £225
78 **1** 3d. blue (*shades*) (No. 24) (2 Feb) .. — £110
a. Retouch under "C" of "VICTORIA" .. — £250
79 3d. greenish blue (*shades*) (No. 29*a*) .. † £350
a. Retouch under "C" of "VICTORIA" ..
80 **8** 4d. dull rose-red (No. 68) .. .. — £300
81 **3** 1s. blue (*shades*) (No. 25) (10 Feb) .. £120 15·00
*a. Greenish blue* .. .. .. £110 12·00
*b. Indigo-blue* .. .. .. .. — 22·00
82 **4** 2s. dull bluish green/*pale yellow* (No. 35) (May) .. .. .. .. £200 25·00

The 1s. was reprinted in 1891 using transfers taken from the original die. These reprints were on V over Crown watermarked paper and perforated 12½.

(Typo from electrotypes by Robinson)

**1859** (17 Feb–23 Dec). *P 12. (a) Good quality wove paper*
83 **8** 4d. dull rose .. .. .. .. £150 2·75
a. Roul 5½–6½ .. .. .. .. † £800

*(b) Poorer quality wove paper*
84 **8** 1d. dull green (July) .. .. .. £120 7·50
*a. Green* (11 Nov) .. .. .. £120 7·50
85 4d. rose-carmine (16 July) .. .. £150 5·00
*a. Rose-pink* (*thick paper*) (30 Nov) .. — 9·00

*(c) Horizontally laid paper with the lines wide apart*
86 **8** 1d. dull green (18 July) .. .. .. — 15·00
a. Laid lines close together .. .. .. — 15·00
b. *Green* (*shades*) (Oct) .. .. .. £130 9·50
87 4d. rose-pink (*shades*) (23 Dec) .. .. £120 7·50
a. Laid lines close together .. .. — 10·00

B. GOVERNMENT STAMP PRINTING.
THE FIRST PERIOD, 1860–1884

Robinson was employed, in April 1858, to finish Calvert's uncompleted Contracts of 1857. Subsequently, under further Contracts, he printed more stamps. The work being satisfactory the Government (on 12.4.59) undertook to continue his employment and at the same time purchased the whole of his equipment, paper stocks, etc. As from 1.1.60 a Government Stamp Printing Branch was set up, Robinson was appointed its Chief Officer and there was no more Stamp Printing in terms of Private Contract. He was succeeded in 1867 by James Atkinson, and from 1883 to 1906 the same work was performed by William Bond. In December 1885 printing operations were transferred from the Post Office to the Government Printing Office and the Stamp Printer then joined the staff of the Government Printer. The Stamp Printers after Bond were J. Kemp and J. B. Cooke (1909–12), the latter being also appointed the first Commonwealth Stamp Printer.

*Note*: All issues of this period, 1860–84, were printed by typography from electrotypes.

9

10

12

11

(Dies for 3d., 4d. and 6d. (T **9**) designed and engraved by Frederick Grosse. The die for the 6d. T **11** consisted of a frame die engraved by Grosse into which was plugged a head portion, cut out of his die for the 6d. T **9**. The design, die and plate for the 1d. T **10** were all supplied by Messrs. De Gruchy and Leigh of Melbourne)

**1860–66.** *T* **4**, **8**, **9**, **10** *and* **11**. *P* 12.

(i) *No wmk. On horizontally laid paper (lines further apart, as* (vi) *(b) above)*
92 **9** 3d. deep blue (31.1.60) .. .. £300 23·00
*a. Light blue* .. .. .. .. £1200 £110

(ii) *No wmk. On thin glazed paper emanating from Bordeaux (see also under* (vii) *above)*
93 **8** 1d. bright green (25.5.60) .. .. — 22·00
94 **9** 4d. rose (21.4.60) .. .. .. £275 12·00
*a. Rose-pink* .. .. .. .. — 7·50

(iii) *No wmk. On a thicker coarser paper*
95 **9** 4d. rose-pink (7.60) .. .. .. £275 7·50

(iv) 1860–66: *Watermarked with the appropriate words of value as W* **12**. *The paper, which was hand-made, was supplied by T. H. Saunders of London*
96 **8** 1d. pale yellowish green (8.7.60) .. 65·00 4·50
*a. Yellow-green* .. .. .. 75·00 4·75
b. Wmk "FOUR PENCE" .. .. — £1200
97 **10** 1d. pale green (1.10.61) .. .. 75·00 5·50
*a. Olive-green* .. .. .. — 6·00
*b. Pale green* (*deep brown gum*) (2.63) 75·00 6·00
98 **8** 2d. brown-lilac (7.7.61) .. .. — 15·00
99 2d. bluish slate (8.61, 6.62) .. .. £100 4·75
*a. Greyish lilac* (9.61) .. .. £110 4·75
*b. Slate-grey* (1.62) .. .. .. — 4·75
100 **9** 3d. pale blue (1.61) .. .. .. £120 7·00
*a. Bright blue* (8.61) .. .. .. £120 8·00
*b. Blue* (*deep brown gum*) (2.63) .. £130 6·00
ba. "TRREE" for "THREE" in wmk ..
*c. Deep blue* (1864) .. .. .. £130 6·00
101 3d. maroon (13.2.66) .. .. .. £100 25·00
a. Perf 13 .. .. .. .. £120 28·00
102 4d. rose-pink (1.8.60) .. .. .. — 4·75
*a. Rose-red* (*shades*) (9.60) .. .. 80·00 3·00
*b. Rose-carmine* (12.60) .. .. — 7·50
*c. Dull rose* (*shades*) (1861) .. .. 80·00 3·00
103 6d. orange (18.10.60) .. .. .. £1600 £200
104 **4** 6d. black (22.6.61) .. .. .. £150 35·00
105 **9** 6d. black (20.8.61) .. .. .. 95·00 5·50
*a. Grey-black* .. .. .. .. 95·00 5·50
106 **11** 6d. grey (26.4.62) .. .. .. 80·00 5·00
*a. Grey-black* .. .. .. .. 80·00 6·50
*b. Jet black* (*deep brown gum*) (3.63) 85·00 7·50

Reprints on paper wmkd V over Crown (W **23**), perf 12½, were made in 1891 of the 1d. Type **10**, 3d. and 4d. Type **9** and 6d. Type **11**. In all cases new plates were used, and certain "die flaws" are found on the "Reprints" which are not met on the originals.

13

14

1862–63. *Emergency printings owing to supplies of the appropriate paper not being available.*

*(a) On paper wmkd* "FIVE SHILLINGS", *W* **13**
107 **9** 4d. dull rose-pink (11.9.62) .. .. £1500 20·00
*a. Dull rose* .. .. .. .. — 20·00

*(b) On paper wmkd* "THREE PENCE", *W* **12**
108 **8** 2d. pale slate (27.12.62) .. .. £110 10·00
*a. Bluish grey* (*deep brown gum*) (2.63) .. .. .. .. £120 12·00

*Note*: Certain stamps are to be met on the "words of value" papers with wmk *reversed* under Nos. 99, 100, 102, also 173 and 176. *Inverted* wmks may also be found in several cases. All these wmk varieties are scarce to rare.

(v) 1862–64: *Same types as before but wmkd with the appropriate single-lined numeral of value, as W* **14**, *the paper being supplied by De La Rue. P 12 unless otherwise described*
109 **10** 1d. olive-green (1.2.63) .. .. .. 55·00 4·50
*a. Pale green* (9.63) .. .. .. 55·00 4·50
*b. Apple-green* (4.64) .. .. .. 55·00 4·50

| | | | | |
|---|---|---|---|---|
| 110 | 8 | 2d. dull reddish lilac (21.4.63) | £160 | 5·50 |
| 111 | | 2d. grey-lilac (10.63) | £150 | 12·00 |
| | | a. Wmk "6" (10.63) | — | £4000 |
| | | *b. Grey-violet (shades)* (11.63) | £100 | 9·00 |
| | | *c. Slate* (12.63) | £150 | 18·00 |
| 112 | 9 | 4d. dull rose-pink (9.10.62) | 90·00 | 4·50 |
| | | *a. Dull rose (deep brown gum)* (2.63) | 95·00 | 4·75 |
| | | *b. Rose-red* | — | 4·50 |
| 113 | 11 | 6d. grey (18.6.63) | 70·00 | 4·50 |
| | | *a. Grey-black* (2.64) | 70·00 | 4·75 |
| | | *b. Intense black* | — | 5·50 |
| 114 | | 6d. jet-black (*p* 13) (12.64) | 80·00 | 5·00 |
| | | *a. Grey-black* | 80·00 | 5·50 |

July–Aug 1863: *Varieties due to a temporary break-down of the perforating machine.*

| | | | | |
|---|---|---|---|---|
| 115 | 9 | 4d. dull rose-pink (*imperf*) | — | 60·00 |
| 116 | | 4d. dull rose-pink (*roul*) | — | £250 |

*Notes on plate varieties found on stamps printed from plates made by Robinson.*

The electros prepared by Robinson over the period 1860–66 (many, e.g. the 4d., which lasted until 1881, remaining in use for a long time after) furnish perhaps the most interesting varieties found in typographed stamps. Since the lead moulds for these were struck by hand, on semifused metal, and without the aid of a "collar", the stamps present us with certain constant abnormalities, viz *partial strikes, double strikes* and *internal distortion* varieties of a nature and extent not found in any other issues, as well as also providing all the more usual types of flaw found in typographed stamps. The whole of the Robinson "Beaded Ovals" and "Laureates" are plateable since the process used made it *impossible* for any stamp to be a perfect reproduction of the die. The 6d. black (Type **11**) is the most interesting of all since the die here was in two parts. This meant the adherence of lead along the line of junction, etc, and gave rise to yet further classes of plate variety. For information on this stamp see various articles in the *London Philatelist*.

*Notes on the two single-line numeral watermark papers.*

Two different English firms supplied the single-line numeral wmk papers used from October 1862 onwards. The two classes of paper supplied are so distinct that they have now been given separate listing. Their characteristics are as follows:—

1. *De La Rue papers* (several consignments). Comprised *white* paper wmkd "1", "2", "4", "6" and "8" respectively, *blue* paper wmkd "1" and *green* paper wmkd "2". In certain printings particularly in the 1d., 2d. and 4d. Laureates and the 6d. black (1863–65) on this paper, a *pelure* type—thin, hard and semi-transparent—may be found. This variety has not been separately listed but is worthy of the specialist's attention. Generally the quality of these De La Rue papers varied considerably among the different consignments.

2. *T. H. Saunders papers* (one consignment only). Comprised *white* paper wmkd "1", "4" and "6" respectively, *blue* paper wmkd "1", *green* paper wmkd "2", and *pink* paper wmkd "10". It was first used in December 1865 and the white papers were exhausted by August 1867. The paper was (apart from the *blue* variety, which was rather thinner than the rest) of even quality throughout and was smoother, thicker, more brittle and (in the white variety) not so white as the De La Rue product. It will be noted that the "2" and "8" papers were supplied by De La Rue only, whereas the "10" paper (pink) was supplied by Saunders only. Comparison of these should assist collectors in accurate classification. The *coloured* papers lasted much longer than the white, as will be seen from the listings. The *blue* lasted until 1875, and the *green* and *pink* until 1879.

In both papers, in practically all cases, *reversed* and/or *inverted* wmks may be met. *Sideways* wmks have been found under Nos. 113, 124 and 200. Stamps showing little or no wmk are from the left or right sides of badly cut sheets.

15

16

17

18

19

(The *"Laureated"* series: Dies engraved by Frederick Grosse. Printing plates (see previous note) made by F. W. Robinson until late in 1867)

*Note.* Since various printings of the 2s. Calvert (Type **5**) were also made between 1864 and 1881 these have been included where appropriate.

**1863–80.**

(i) 1863–64. *Early printings. Wmkd with appropriate single-lined numeral as W* **14**, *on paper supplied by De La Rue. P* 12

| | | | | |
|---|---|---|---|---|
| 117 | 15 | 1d. pale green (8.9.64) | 75·00 | 7·00 |
| 118 | | 2d. violet (4.64) | 65·00 | 4·75 |
| | | *a. Dull violet* (10.64) | 70·00 | 5·00 |
| 119 | | 4d. deep rose (4.9.63) | — | 3·50 |
| | | a. Doubly printed | — | £500 |
| | | *b. Rose-pink* (9.63) | 85·00 | 2·50 |
| | | *c. Pink* (4.64) | 85·00 | 2·50 |

*Emergency printings on Perkins, Bacon paper wmkd double-lined numerals* "1" *and* "4" *respectively, supplied by Tasmania. P* 12.

| | | | | |
|---|---|---|---|---|
| 120 | 10 | 1d. yellow-green (10.12.63) | £110 | 7·00 |
| | | *a. Dull green* (4.64) | — | 7·00 |
| | | b. Imperf between (pair) | | |
| 121 | 15 | 4d. deep rose (7.1.64) | £110 | 3·75 |
| | | *a. Pale rose* | — | 3·75 |

Like the 1d. and 4d. Perkins, Bacon types of Van Diemen's Land most of the Victorian stamps printed on the above two papers may occasionally be found with wmk *inverted*. This applies both to the 1d. and 4d. above and also the various "Laureates" of the 1867–68 printings. Instances are also known where the wmk is *reversed* and one (in No. 132) where it is *sideways*. Most of these varieties are rare.

(ii) *Printings of* October 1864 *onwards. As* (i) *but P* 13

| | | | | |
|---|---|---|---|---|
| 122 | 15 | 1d. pale green (10.10.64) | 70·00 | 3·50 |
| | | *a. Bluish green* (12.64) | 65·00 | 2·75 |
| | | aa. Doubly printed | — | £550 |
| | | *b. Green (shades)* (8.65) | 65·00 | 3·50 |
| | | *c. Deep green* (12.65) | — | 3·00 |
| 123 | | 2d. dull violet (10.64) | 55·00 | 3·75 |
| | | *a. Dull lilac (shades)* (4.65) | 55·00 | 3·50 |
| | | *b. Reddish mauve* (11.65) | 60·00 | 3·50 |
| 124 | | 4d. dull rose (10.64) | 75·00 | 2·50 |
| | | *a. Dull rose-red* (2.65) | 75·00 | 2·50 |
| 125 | | 8d. orange (22.2.65) | £300 | 50·00 |
| 126 | 18 | 1s. blue/*blue* (10.4.65) | £100 | 3·50 |
| 127 | 4 | 2s. light blue/*green* (22.11.64) | £150 | 5·00 |
| | | *a. Deep blue/green* (1865) | £150 | 5·00 |

The above 1s. stamp can be immediately identified by the white patches (comprising an *albino* impression) due to the lack of a *make-ready* which are found on all stamps. The 8d. was withdrawn from issue on 11.6.69.

(iii) July–August 1865. *As before but P* 12 *or* 12 × 13 *from repaired state of* 12 *machine, with larger holes and sharper teeth than previously.* (a) *Perf* 12

| | | | | |
|---|---|---|---|---|
| 128 | 15 | 1d. green (*shades*) | 70·00 | 3·00 |
| | | *a. Deep green* | 70·00 | 3·00 |
| 129 | | 4d. dull rose-red (8.65) | £120 | 7·50 |
| 130 | 4 | 2s. dark blue/*green* | £170 | 8·50 |

(b) *Perf* 12 × 13

| | | | | |
|---|---|---|---|---|
| 131 | 15 | 1d. deep green | — | 6·00 |

August and December 1865. *Emergency printings* (2) *on Perkins, Bacon paper wmkd double-lined* "4" *supplied by Tasmania.*

| | | | | |
|---|---|---|---|---|
| 132 | 15 | 4d. dull reddish rose (*p* 13) (11.8.65) | £110 | 3·50 |
| | | a. Perf 12 | — | 3·75 |
| | | b. Perf 12 × 13 | — | 11·00 |
| 133 | | 4d. red (*p* 13) (16.12.65) | £120 | 3·50 |

October 1865. *Emergency printing on De La Rue paper wmkd single-lined* "8", *no* "10" *paper having arrived. P* 13.

| | | | | |
|---|---|---|---|---|
| 134 | 17 | 10d. grey (21.10.65) | £450 | £100 |
| | | *a. Grey-black* | £450 | £100 |

(iv) December 1865–66 *printings. These, in general, were of finer impression than the previous* 1865 *printings*

A. *On Saunders paper, wmkd with the appropriate single-line numerals as W* **14**.

| | | | | |
|---|---|---|---|---|
| 135 | 15 | 1d. deep yellow-green (*p* 13) (1.66) | 65·00 | 2·75 |
| | | a. Perf 12 | — | 6·50 |
| | | b. Perf 12 × 13 | — | 5·50 |
| 136 | | 4d. rose-red (*p* 13) (12.12.65) | 75·00 | 3·00 |
| | | a. Perf 12 | — | 4·75 |
| | | b. Perf 12 × 13 | — | 5·50 |
| 137 | 17 | 6d. blue (*p* 13) (28.5.66) | 21·00 | 1·50 |
| | | a. Perf 12 | 23·00 | 3·00 |
| | | b. Perf 12×13 | 21·00 | 1·75 |
| | | ba. Imperf between (pair) | — | £550 |
| 138 | | 10d. dull purple/*pink* (*p* 13) (22.3.66) | 65·00 | 5·00 |
| | | a. Perf 12 × 13 | 70·00 | 5·50 |
| | | *b. Blackish brown/pink* (*p* 13) (1869) | 75·00 | 5·50 |
| 139 | 18 | 1s. indigo-blue/*blue* (*p* 13) (1870) | 55·00 | 3·25 |
| | | a. Perf 12 (1873) | — | 5·00 |
| | | *b. Bright blue/blue* (*p* 13) (1.71) | 55·00 | 2·50 |
| | | ba. Perf 12 | — | 3·25 |
| | | *c. Pale dull blue/blue* (*p* 13) (1.75) | — | 7·00 |
| | | ca. Perf 12 | — | 3·25 |
| 140 | 4 | 2s. dark blue/*green* (12.67) | £160 | 5·50 |
| | | a. Perf 12 (1875) | £180 | 5·50 |
| | | *b. Blue/green* (1872, 1878) | £160 | 4·25 |
| | | *c. Greenish blue/green* (*p* 12) (1875) | £180 | 5·50 |
| | | *d. Deep greenish blue/green* (*p* 12½) (1880) | £160 | 7·50 |

The 1s. on Saunders paper was issued later than 1866 but it and the 2s. printing are included here for the sake of convenience. The Saunders green paper is distinctly *deeper* in shade and more apparently *green* than the De La Rue variety.

B. *On De La Rue paper wmkd with the appropriate single-line numerals as W* **14**. *P* 13.

| | | | | |
|---|---|---|---|---|
| 141 | 15 | 1d. bright yellow-green (1.67) | — | 15·00 |
| 142 | | 2d. rosy lilac (1.66) | 55·00 | 4·75 |
| | | a. Perf 12 × 13 | 55·00 | 4·75 |
| 143 | | 2d. dull lilac (6.66) | — | 4·75 |
| | | a. Perf 12 | — | 6·00 |
| | | b. Perf 12 × 13 | — | 7·50 |
| 144 | | 2d. grey (25.7.66) | 55·00 | 3·00 |
| | | a. Perf 12 | 85·00 | 6·00 |
| 145 | 17 | 6d. blue (13.2.66) | 23·00 | 2·50 |
| | | a. Perf 12 | 23·00 | 4·00 |
| | | b. Perf 12 × 13 | 21·00 | 1·75 |
| 146 | 18 | 1s. blue/*blue* (1866, 1869) | 55·00 | 3·00 |
| | | a. Perf 12 × 13 (1866) | 55·00 | 3·50 |
| | | *b. Bright blue/blue* (*p* 13) (1867, 1871) | — | 3·00 |
| | | ba. Perf 12 (1871) | — | 3·50 |
| | | *c. Indigo/blue* (*p* 13) | — | 2·75 |
| | | *d. Dull blue/blue* (*p* 12) (1874) | — | 3·50 |
| | | e. Imperf btwn (vert pair) (*p* 12×13) | — | £550 |
| 147 | 4 | 2s. blue/*green* (1868) | £140 | 4·25 |
| | | *a. Greenish blue/green* (1873) | £140 | 4·25 |
| | | aa. Perf 12 | £160 | 5·50 |
| | | *b. Dark blue/green* (*p* 12½) (1880) | £140 | 4·25 |

The 1d. of 1867 on De La Rue, distinguishable only by its shade, was presumably the result of the discovery of a small quantity of old stock. The 2d. and 4d. of 1866 may also be found 13 × 12 but are rare in *this* condition. The 10d. was withdrawn from issue on 21.6.71. There were, between 1864 and 1881, no less than 21 different printings of the 2s. blue on green. Only the main schools of colour have been listed.

**1866** (Sept)–**67**. *Various Emergency printings, all the results of the non-arrival of the first shipment of* "V over Crown" *paper.*

1. *Printings on De La Rue paper wmkd single-lined* "8". *P* 13.

| | | | | |
|---|---|---|---|---|
| 148 | 15 | 1d. bright yellow-green (27.12.66) | £120 | 9·50 |
| 149 | | 2d. grey (18.1.67) | £110 | 4·50 |
| 150 | 16 | 3d. lilac (29.9.66) | £160 | 20·00 |
| 151 | 15 | 4d. rose-red (?date) | † | £2000 |

2. *Printings on Saunders paper wmkd single-lined* "4". *P* 13.

| | | | | |
|---|---|---|---|---|
| 152 | 15 | 1d. bright yellow-green (6.3.67) | 85·00 | 6·50 |
| 153 | | 2d. grey (21.2.67) | 75·00 | 4·75 |

3. *Printings on paper wmkd single-lined* "6". *P* 13.

(a) *On De La Rue paper*

| | | | | |
|---|---|---|---|---|
| 154 | 15 | 1d. bright yellow-green (6.67) | — | 14·00 |

(b) *On Saunders paper*

| | | | | |
|---|---|---|---|---|
| 155 | 15 | 1d. bright yellow-green (6.67) | £120 | 11·00 |
| 156 | | 2d. grey (13.5.67) | £130 | 6·00 |

20 (*V*1)

9 9 NINEPENCE (21)

**WATERMARKS.** Many stamps watermarked V and Crown may be found with watermark inverted or sideways.

**1867–68**. *Printings on first consignment for paper wmkd* "V *over Crown*", *W* **20**, *received in April* 1867. *P* 13.

| | | | | |
|---|---|---|---|---|
| 157 | 15 | 1d. bright yellow-green (10.8.67) | 85·00 | 3·50 |
| 158 | | 2d. slate-grey (*shades*) (26.8.67) | 70·00 | 3·50 |
| | | *a. Grey-lilac* (1.68) | — | 4·75 |
| 159 | 16 | 3d. lilac (8.67) | £200 | 24·00 |
| | | *a. Grey-lilac* (8.68) | £225 | 26·00 |
| 160 | 15 | 4d. dull rose (11.67) | 75·00 | 5·00 |
| 161 | 17 | 6d. dark blue (12.67) | — | 3·00 |
| 162 | 19 | 5s. blue/*yellow* (26.12.67) | £1600 | £300 |
| | | a. Wmk reversed | — | £500 |

The above shades (there are also paper differences) are sufficiently distinctive to enable separation of the five lower values from *later* "V over Crown" printings. The 5s. was printed from the first electros prepared by Atkinson. There were two printings, both in sheets of 25 (5 × 5). The first (1200) was from a single vertical column of 5 electros clamped together. The second (2000) was from a plate of 25 impressions, comprising a different "5 vertical" repeated 5 times (i.e. giving 5 types). The reversed wmk variety belongs to the first printing and was created *deliberately* to avoid the appearance of the "page number" on the front of one stamp in every four sheets of 25.

**1867** (Sept)–**68** and **1870.** *Various Emergency printings due first to the* 1867 *shipment of white "V over Crown" paper being so small, later to its exhaustion and the non-arrival of the second shipment ordered, later still* (1870) *to a further shortage of this paper.*

1. *Printings on the Perkins, Bacon paper wmkd double-lined* "1" *received from Tasmania in* 1863. *P* 13.

| | | | | |
|---|---|---|---|---|
| 163 | 15 | 1d. pale yellowish green (24.9.67) | 65·00 | 3·5 |
| | | *a. Deep yellow-green* (6.68) | 65·00 | 3·5 |
| 164 | | 2d. slate (5.68) | £110 | 5·5 |
| | | *a. Mauve* (30.6.68) | £110 | 6·5 |
| 165 | 16 | 3d. grey-lilac (8.68) | £150 | 35·0 |
| 166 | 17 | 6d. blue (28.7.68) | 55·00 | 4·2 |

2. *Printings on the Perkins, Bacon paper wmkd double-lined* "4" *received from Tasmania in* 1863. *P* 13.

| | | | | |
|---|---|---|---|---|
| 167 | 15 | 1d. pale yellow-green (27.5.68) | £750 | 80·0 |
| 168 | | 2d. grey-lilac (3.2.68) | £110 | 4·2 |
| | | *a. Slate* (28.3.68) | £110 | 3·5 |
| | | *b. Mauve* (3.7.68) | — | 4·5 |
| 169 | | 4d. dull rose-red (5.68) | £110 | 5·0 |
| 170 | 17 | 6d. blue (5.68) | £150 | 13·0 |
| | | *a. Indigo-blue* | — | 15·0 |

3. *Printing on Saunders paper wmkd* "SIX PENCE" *as W* **12.** *P* 13

| | | | | |
|---|---|---|---|---|
| 171 | 15 | 1d. pale yellow-green (5.6.68) | £325 | 15·0 |
| 172 | | 2d. slate-grey | — | £110 |
| 173 | 17 | 6d. blue (23.5.68) | £150 | 11·0 |
| | | *a. Indigo-blue* | — | 15·0 |

Only one copy is apparently known of No. 172. From its shade it would appear to belong to an 1867–68 printing. No 171 is known with the wmk *sideways*.

4. *Printings on lilac paper wmkd V over Crown from* 1867 *consignment. P* 13.

| | | | | |
|---|---|---|---|---|
| 174 | 15 | 2d. mauve/*lilac* (12.8.68) | 55·00 | 6·5 |
| | | *a. Lilac/lilac* | 55·00 | 6·0 |

5. 1869–70: 6*d. value only. Printings on various wmkd papers as indicated. P* 13.

| | | | | |
|---|---|---|---|---|
| 175 | 17 | 6d. dull blue (THREE PENCE) (6.12.69) | £130 | 6·0 |
| | | *a. Deep blue* | — | 7·0 |
| 176 | | 6d. dull blue (FOUR PENCE) (18.6.70) | £250 | 22·0 |
| | | *a. Deep blue* | — | 23·0 |
| 177 | | 6d. dull blue ("4") (21.5.70) | — | £120 |
| 178 | | 6d. dull blue ("2") (1870) | — | £120 |

Of the six or seven copies known of No. 177 all but one have the watermark reversed.

**1868** (Aug)–**71.** *Printings on second and later consignments of* "V *over Crown paper. W* **20.** *P* 13 *only.* (i) *Printed from Robinson plates.*

| | | | | |
|---|---|---|---|---|
| 179 | 15 | 2d. lilac (26.8.68) | 50·00 | 3·2 |
| | | *a. Dull mauve (shades)* (10.68) | 50·00 | 3·2 |
| | | *b. Lilac-grey* (1.69) | — | 3·5 |
| | | *c. Lilac-rose* (2.69) | — | 3·0 |
| 180 | 16 | 3d. yellow-orange (12.6.69) | 15·00 | 3·0 |
| 181 | 15 | 4d. pale red (*aniline*) (21.4.69) | — | 6·5 |
| | | *a. Deep red (aniline)* (16.7.69) | — | 6·5 |
| | | *b. Rose-pink* (2.70) | — | 5·0 |
| 182 | 17 | 6d. blue (*shades*) (7.11.68) | 14·00 | 1·1 |
| | | *a. Indigo-blue* (1869) | 14·00 | 1·1 |
| 183 | 19 | 5s. indigo-blue and carmine (I) (8.10.68) | £200 | 15·0 |
| | | *a. Blue and carmine* (1869) | £170 | 11·0 |

Nos. 179*b*/*c* were printed from badly worn plates.

For the frame-plate of the 5s. (I) the electros of the 1867 plate with the Crown, "VICTORIA" and "FIVE SHILLINGS" cut out were employed. A new plate, also produced via cut-out portions of the 1867 plate, was bought into use for the red portion. The 1868 printing of the 5s. was produced, in April of that year using the residue of the first consignment.

(ii) *Printed from new plates made by Atkinson*

| | | | | |
|---|---|---|---|---|
| 184 | 15 | 1d. bright yellow-green (10.68) | 65·00 | 2·5 |
| | | *a. Bright olive-green* (1.69) | — | 14·0 |
| | | *b. Dull yellow-green* (4.69) | — | 2·1 |
| | | *c. Dull green* (3.70) | 65·00 | 2·1 |
| | | *d. Very pale green* (10.70) | — | 2·1 |

| | | | | |
|---|---|---|---|---|
| 185 | 15 | 2d. lilac-grey (15.1.69) | — | 3·75 |
| | | *a. Lilac-rose (shades)* (24.2.69) | 55·00 | 3·75 |
| | | *b. Mauve* (20.4.69) | — | 3·25 |
| | | *c. Red-lilac (shades)* (5.69) | 55·00 | 3·00 |
| | | *d. Dull lilac (shades)* (6.69) | 55·00 | 2·50 |
| | | *e. Silver-grey* (2.9.69) | £110 | 7·00 |

The Atkinson plates, produced by an improved technique; do not show the *double* and *partial strikes* and *internal distortion* varieties met on a large proportion of the stamps from the Robinson plates. Further, the later printings from the 2d. and 6d. Robinson plates show obvious signs of wear. These factors and the differing shades should make classification relatively easy. For the first two printings of the 2d. in 1869 the first of the new Atkinson plates was used in conjunction with the old Robinson plate, following which the latter was replaced by a second Atkinson plate. The dates of introduction of the Atkinson plates were 1d., October 1868; 2d., January 1869 and 6d., December 1875.

**1871.** *Provisional. Surch with* **T 21**, *in blue. On Saunders paper wmkd single-lined* "10". *P* 13.

| | | | | |
|---|---|---|---|---|
| 186 | 17 | 9d. on 10d. purple-brown/*pink* (22.4.71) | £180 | 10·00 |
| | | *a. Blackish brown/pink* | — | 12·00 |
| | | b. Surch double | — | £800 |

PERFORATIONS (TO 1883)

The perforations of Victoria, particularly those of the period October 1864–80, form a complex study for specialists. We have adopted in this listing a simplified classification based on *three* descriptions—Perf 12, Perf 13 and Perf 12½ respectively, the latter being substituted for Perf 13 for the period 1881 on. The position can be concisely put as follows:—

A. "*Perf* 12": Here the gauge is *never* quite 12 and nearer 11½. It is not found after 1883. There were two machines (both single-line), the first introduced by Robinson in January 1859 and the second purchased in 1871. No "perf 12" are found in the period mid 1866–mid 1871. At various periods, more particularly in 1865 and 1880, one or both of the machines was repaired, to give larger holes and sharper teeth over a succeeding period.

B. "*Perf* 13": Here the gauge is invariably *over* 12 and with a sole exception (covering a section of the pins on one machine over the period 1876–80) invariably *under* 13. Generally speaking up to the end of 1880, these machines gauged 12½ to 12¾. Two classes of machine are found:

(i) *Single-line* machines. These were three in number—purchased on October 1864, 1866 and 1873 respectively. Two of them were converted into combs in 1873. The other was repaired on several occasions, particularly in 1879–80, to give larger holes and sharper teeth.

(ii) *Comb* machines. First introduced in 1873 (see above). Over the period of use they gave various gauges, depending on the machine and its state of repair. They were all *vertical* combs adapted only for normal size stamps of either dimension as likewise (until 1913) were all other comb-machines used in Victoria for perforating stamps.

C. "*Perf* 12½": Found from late 1876 onwards, in both single-line (used mainly for the larger-size stamps) and vertical comb machines. Gradually superseded the A and B gauges. Certain stamps of the 1879–80 period are found in both B and C gauges but these are no longer differentiated as separate varieties, being only listed under the one or the other gauge. This applies also to the Postal Fiscal section.

"*Compound*" *perforations*: In previous editions certain 12 × 13 perforations were listed which were not true compounds of A and B but simply the product of one or other of the *comb* machines. Such varieties have now been eliminated. The "Compounds" now listed are all true compounds (or "mixeds") of A and B. They generally fall into two categories: (i) those of the 1865–66 period where the two machines were both used for the original perforating, one in the one direction (top to bottom) and the other in the other (sides); (ii) isolated examples, better termed "mixed" perfs, from 1873 on, where one gauge machine was used to correct off-centre perforating done by the other gauge machine. Such cases are almost invariably associated with "mends", viz the pasting of gummed strips down the back of the faulty line of perforations.

1871–84 PRINTINGS

These are listed separately from the 1868–71 printings because of the perforation changes made in the period, viz the reintroduction of the 12 gauge (1871), the introduction of comb machines (1873), the repairs of various 12 and 13 machines (1879), and the introduction of the 12½ gauge (1879–80). Many stamps issued in the latter period are found both perf 13 and 12½ but no distinction is made. The 13 gauge disappears in 1880–81.

*Papers*: All printings on white paper made after April 1878 and also the last 8d. printing were on the "*glazed*" variety of paper and this furnishes another means of identification. Some shades, e.g. 6d. blue of 1878–79 are found on *both* papers.

*Shades* are different from those found in the 1868–71 printings.

**1871–84.**

(i) *Printed from Robinson plates;* **W 20**; *P* 13, 12½ *unless otherwise described*

| | | | | |
|---|---|---|---|---|
| 187 | 16 | 3d. dull orange (1871) | 14·00 | 1·90 |
| | | a. Perf 12 (1872) | 14·00 | 20·00 |
| | | *b. Orange* (1874) | — | 2·25 |
| | | ba. Perf 12 | — | 2·10 |
| | | *c. Bright orange* | 20·00 | 2·50 |
| | | ca. Perf 12 | — | 2·50 |
| 188 | | 3d. orange-brown (1878) | 20·00 | 5·50 |
| 189 | | 3d. dull orange-yellow (1881) | 22·00 | 2·50 |
| | | a. Perf 12 | | |
| 190 | 15 | 4d. rose (*shades*) (1871–78) | 70·00 | 3·00 |
| | | a. Perf 12 | 70·00 | 3·00 |
| | | *b. Dull rose* (5.3.79) | 70·00 | 3·00 |
| | | ba. Perf 12 | — | 3·00 |
| | | *c. Dull rose-red* (23.12.79) | — | 3·00 |
| | | ca. Perf 12 | — | 3·00 |
| | | *d. Bright lilac-rose (aniline)* (3.3.80) | 75·00 | 3·75 |
| | | da. Perf 12 | — | 6·50 |
| 191 | | 4d. rosine (*aniline*) (22.9.80) | £200 | 5·00 |
| | | a. Perf 12 | 80·00 | 4·75 |
| | | b. Compound perf 12 with 12½ | — | £325 |
| 192 | 17 | 6d. Prussian blue (1872, 1874) | 12·00 | 90 |
| | | a. Perf 12 | 14·00 | 1·10 |
| | | *b. Indigo* (1873) | 14·00 | 1·40 |
| | | ba. Perf 12 | 18·00 | 1·75 |
| | | *c. Dull blue* (worn plate) | — | 90 |
| 193 | 15 | 8d. lilac-brown/*pink* (24.1.77) | 75·00 | 5·50 |
| | | *a. Purple-brown/pink* (21.3.78) | 75·00 | 5·50 |
| | | *b. Chocolate/pink* (6.8.78) | 80·00 | 5·00 |
| | | bb. Compound perf 13 × 12 | — | £325 |
| 194 | | 8d. red-brown/*pink* (20.5.78) | 75·00 | 5·00 |
| 195 | | 8d. dark red-brown/*pink* (*p* 12) (*glazed*) (30.11.80) | 75·00 | 5·50 |
| | | a. Perf 12½ | | |
| 196 | 18 | 1s. light blue/*blue* (5.75) | 75·00 | 6·50 |
| | | a. Perf 12 | — | 6·50 |
| 197 | 19 | 5s. pale bright blue and carmine (I) (7.77) | — | 15·00 |
| | | *a. Grey-blue and carmine* (8.78) | £160 | 13·00 |
| | | *b. Deep lavender-blue and carmine* (5.80) | £160 | 13·00 |
| 198 | | 5s. bright blue and red (II) (12.5.81) | £140 | 11·00 |
| | | a. Perf 12 | £130 | 12·00 |
| | | *b. Indigo-blue and red* | — | 15·00 |
| | | ba. Perf 12 | — | 16·00 |
| | | c. Second "I" in "SHILLINGS" short at foot | — | 90·00 |

The 4d. "pink" previously listed is a *faded* rosine. For the 5s. (Type II) new dies were made for *each* portion of the design. All Type I stamps have a blue line under the Crown, which is missing in Type II. The latter were printed in sheets of 100 (10 × 10), as compared with 25 (5 × 5) for Type I.

No. 197*b* has the watermark sideways.

1877–79. *Printings of the 8d. value on Saunders paper wmkd single-lined* "10". *P* 13, 12½ *unless otherwise stated.*

| | | | | |
|---|---|---|---|---|
| 199 | 15 | 8d. lilac-brown/*pink* (12.77) | — | £500 |
| | | *a. Purple-brown/pink* (20.2.78) | £100 | 6·00 |
| 200 | | 8d. red-brown/*pink* (8.8.79) | 85·00 | 5·00 |
| | | a. Perf 12 | — | 8·00 |

The 8d. printings (save that of 1880) were *mixed* and comprised stamps on *both* V over Crown and "10" papers.

½ ½

**HALF**

(22)

(ii) *Printed from plates made by Atkinson. The* ½d. *made by surch with* **T 22**, *in red*

| | | | | |
|---|---|---|---|---|
| 201 | 15 | ½d. on 1d. green (25.6.73) | 38·00 | 10·00 |
| | | a. Perf 12 | 45·00 | 12·00 |
| | | *b. Grass-green* | 40·00 | 10·00 |
| | | ba. Perf 12 | 45·00 | 12·00 |
| | | c. Short "1" at right | — | 70·00 |
| 202 | | 1d. pale green (1871) | 60·00 | 2·25 |
| | | a. Perf 12 (10.71) | 70·00 | 2·40 |
| | | *b. Green (shades)* | 60·00 | 2·25 |
| | | ba. Perf 12 | 60·00 | 2·25 |
| | | *c. Grass-green* | — | 2·40 |
| | | ca. Perf 12 | 60·00 | 2·40 |
| | | *d. Bluish green (shades)* | 60·00 | 2·40 |
| | | da. Perf 12 | — | 2·40 |
| 203 | 17 | 6d. dull ultramarine (2.12.75) | 19·00 | 1·25 |
| | | *a. Light Prussian-blue* (29.12.75) | — | 1·25 |
| | | *b. Dull violet-blue* (4.78) | — | 5·50 |
| | | c. Blue (13.5.78) | 20·00 | 90 |
| | | ca. Perf 12 | — | 90 |
| | | *d. Dull milky blue* (7.3.79) | 19·00 | 1·10 |
| | | da. Perf 12 | — | 1·10 |
| | | *e. Blue (light ink)* (8.80) | — | 90 |
| | | *f. Light blue* (10.5.81) | 20·00 | 1·10 |
| | | fa. Perf 12 | — | 2·40 |
| | | *g. Deep blue* (15.1.82) | 19·00 | 90 |

23 (V2)

24

The types of V over Crown watermark (1867–1912)

In all, *five* types were employed.

The first two types (V1 and V2) belong to the contracts made with De La Rue to supply postage stamp paper. That firm lost the contract in 1895 to Waterlow and Sons, who held it until 1912. The third and fourth types are therefore products of the Waterlow contracts. The fifth type (found only in 1912) was supplied by James Spicer & Sons. The change in the pattern from *V*1 to *V*2 is explained by the dandyroll (which was the property of De La Rue) requiring replacement. Since *all* the changes in pattern are also associated with changes in the nature and texture of the paper supplied, little difficulty should be encountered, with the new descriptions, in identifying the various types. Each pattern (save in a few cases of "left over" stock) succeeded the previous pattern.

Types *V*1 and *V*2 are mainly to be distinguished from one another by the four "points" around the top of the Crown which are found in *V*1 but not in *V*2. Also, as compared with *V*2, the shapes of the top ornaments in *V*1 resemble diamonds, and not ovals. It must be remembered that *V*1 *coloured* papers continued in use long after the exhaustion of the *V*1 white paper, the earliest date met for the *V*2 white paper being 15.8.82. The first *V*2 coloured papers (blue and green) were not used until February 1890. In general the papers supplied by De La Rue were whiter than their successors. The quality found with the *V*1 wmk varied greatly both with and without a pronounced mesh. The quality of the *V*2 papers on the other hand varied little. It is generally more "loaded" and opaque than any of the *V*1 papers and the wmk clearer when held to the light.

(iii) 1882–4. *As* (ii) *above but on paper wmkd V over Crown* (*V*2), **W 23.** *P* 12½

| | | | | |
|---|---|---|---|---|
| 204 | 16 | 3d. yellow-orange (13.4.83) | 18·00 | 4·50 |
| | | *a. Dull brownish orange* | 22·00 | 6·50 |
| 205 | 17 | 6d. dull violet-blue (10.11.82) | 12·00 | 1·00 |
| | | *a. Indigo-blue* (11.83) | 12·00 | 1·10 |
| | | *b. Light ultramarine* (9.84) | 12·00 | 1·25 |

The above 3d. was printed from two new plates made by Atkinson. For the 6d. the same Atkinson plates introduced in December 1875 were employed.

Reprints were made, in 1891, on V over Crown paper, Type **23**, perf 12½, of the 1d., 2d., 3d., 4d., 6d., 8d., 10d., 1s. and 5s. "Laureates". The shades are distinctive and a number of values show "die flaws" not found in the originals. The 3d. was printed in yellow, the 8d. in orange-yellow, the 10d. in greenish slate and the 5s. in blue and red.

(Printed in Melbourne from a double electrotyped plate of 240 subjects supplied by D.L.R.)

**1870** (28 Jan). *Wmk V over Crown* (V1), **W 20.** *P* 13.

| | | | | |
|---|---|---|---|---|
| 206 | 24 | 2d. brown-lilac | 48·00 | 1·50 |
| | | *a. Dull lilac-mauve* (9.70) | 38·00 | 1·00 |
| | | aa. Perf 12 (1871) | 48·00 | 1·50 |
| | | *b. Mauve* (worn plate, 3.73) | 38·00 | 1·25 |
| | | ba. Perf 12 | 48·00 | 1·00 |

25

26

27

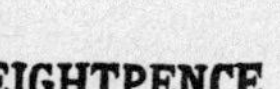

8d 8d EIGHTPENCE

(28)

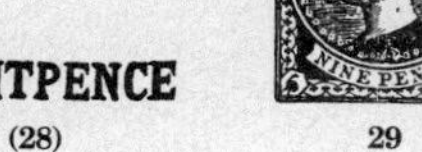

29

30

31 (Die I)

32 (Die II)

(Des and dies eng by William Bell and stamps printed from electrotyped plates)

**1873–84.** *Two dies of 2d.: I, single-lined outer oval; II, double-lined outer oval. The* 8d. *is made by surch with* **T 28** *in blue. P* 13 *unless otherwise described.*

(*a*) *On Saunders paper, wmkd single-lined* "10"

| | | | | |
|---|---|---|---|---|
| 207 | 29 | 9d. pale brown/*pink* (25.3.73) | 60·00 | 7·00 |
| | | a. Perf 12 | 65·00 | 10·00 |
| | | *b. Red-brown/pink* (8.74) | 55·00 | 7·50 |

(*b*) *Wmk V over Crown* (*V*1) (*sideways on* **T 25**), **W 20**

| | | | | |
|---|---|---|---|---|
| 208 | 25 | ½d. rose-red (10.2.74) | 4·50 | 50 |
| | | a. Perf 12 | 5·00 | 70 |
| | | *b. Lilac-rose* (1874) | 5·00 | 70 |
| | | ba. Perf 12 | 4·50 | 70 |
| | | *c. Rosine (shades)* (12.80) | 3·75 | 50 |
| | | ca. Perf 12 | 4·50 | 35 |
| | | *d. Pale red* (1882) | 4·50 | 35 |
| | | da. Perf 12 | 4·50 | 40 |
| | | e. Mixed perf 13 and 12 | — | £110 |
| 209 | 26 | 1d. dull bluish green (14.12.75) | 13·00 | 75 |
| | | a. Perf 12 | 15·00 | 75 |
| | | *b. Green (shades)* (1877) | 13·00 | 70 |
| | | ba. Perf 12 | 14·00 | 4·50 |
| | | *c. Yellow-green* (1878 and 1880) | 13·00 | 55 |
| | | ca. Perf 12 | — | 1·75 |
| 210 | 27 | 2d. deep lilac-mauve, Die I (1.10.73) | 13·00 | 35 |
| | | a. Perf 12 | — | 1·50 |
| | | *b. Dull violet-mauve* | 13·00 | 35 |
| | | ba. Perf 12 | — | 1·40 |
| | | *c. Dull mauve* | 13·00 | 35 |
| | | ca. Perf 12 | 15·00 | 50 |
| | | *d. Pale mauve (worn plate)* (1.79) | 14·00 | 50 |
| | | da. Perf 12 | — | 65 |
| | | e. Mixed perf 13 and 12 | £130 | £100 |
| 211 | | 2d. lilac-mauve, Die II (17.12.78) | 10·00 | 35 |
| | | a. Perf 12 | 14·00 | 35 |
| | | *b. Grey-mauve* (1.80) | — | 40 |
| | | ba. Perf 12 | — | 80 |
| | | *c. Pale mauve* (6.80) | 20·00 | 40 |
| | | ca. Perf 12 | — | 1·25 |
| | | e. Vert pair, lower stamp imperf horiz | | |
| 212 | 29 | 8d. on 9d. lilac-brn/*pink* (*p* 12) (1.7.76) | £120 | 15·00 |
| | | a. "F.IGHT" (broken "E") | — | £150 |
| 213 | | 9d. lilac-brown/*pink* (*p* 12) (1.12.75) | £100 | 11·00 |
| 214 | 30 | 1s. indigo-blue/*blue* (16.8.76) | 30·00 | 3·00 |
| | | *a. Deep blue/blue* (1877) | 32·00 | 3·00 |
| | | aa. Perf 12 (10.80) | — | 7·50 |
| | | *b. Blue/blue* (1878) | 35·00 | 3·00 |
| | | ba. Perf 12 | — | 7·50 |
| | | *c. Ultramarine/blue* (1879) | 45·00 | 7·50 |
| | | *d. Bright blue/blue* (11.83) | 45·00 | 5·00 |

(c) 18 February–April 1878. *Emergency printings on various coloured papers, due to the exhaustion of white V1 paper.* W **20** (*V1*) (*sideways on T* **25**). *P* 13 *only.*

| No. | Type | Description | Unused | Used |
|---|---|---|---|---|
| 215 | **25** | ½d. rose-red/*pink* (1.3.78) | 20·00 | 8·00 |
| 216 | **26** | 1d. yellow-green/*yellow* (25.2.78) | 50·00 | 11·00 |
| 217 | | 1d. yellow-green/*drab* (4.78) | £100 | 40·00 |
| 218 | **27** | 2d. violet-mauve/*green* (18.2.78) | £120 | 10·00 |
| 219 | | 2d. violet-mauve/*lilac* (21.2.78) | £1000 | £400 |
| 220 | | 2d. violet-mauve/*brown* (21.3.78) | £120 | 10·00 |

Two shades of yellow paper, termed *pale canary* and *deep canary* respectively, are found.

All supplies of *V*1 paper received in Victoria after 15.3.78 were, as compared with previous supplies, highly surfaced on the printing side. An experimental printing was made on the new paper in July 1877 (1d., 2d., 6d. and 5s.) and all printings on white *V*1 paper from April 1878 on were made on this glazed paper. The glazed *V*1 coloured papers, with few exceptions, made their appearance later.

(*d*) 1882–83. *On white paper wmkd V over Crown* (*V*2). *W* **23** (*sideways on T* **25**). *P* 13

| No. | Type | Description | Unused | Used |
|---|---|---|---|---|
| 221 | **25** | ½d. rosine (4.83) | 5·00 | 65 |
| | | a. Perf 12 | 50·00 | 15·00 |
| 222 | **26** | 1d. yellow-green (9.82) | 14·00 | 1·00 |
| | | a. Perf 12 | | |

*Reprints*: The ½d., 1d., 2d. (Die II), 9d. and 1s. values were reprinted in 1891, perf 12½. The first four from new plates, made from Dies containing *die flaws* not found in the originals. The 9d. was on *V*1 and the others on *V*2 paper.

33

34

35

(Des and eng by Charles Naish (T **33** & **34**) and William Bell (T **35**). Typo from electrotyped plates)

**1880–84.** *P* 12½ *unless otherwise described, this description including the P* 13 *varieties found in* 1880. (*a*) *W* **20** (*V*1).

| No. | Type | Description | Unused | Used |
|---|---|---|---|---|
| 223 | **33** | 2d. sepia (3.11.80) | 15·00 | 45 |
| | | a. Perf 12 | — | 38·00 |
| | | *b. Sepia-brown* (2.81) | 12·50 | 45 |
| | | ba. Perf 12 | £130 | 38·00 |
| | | *c. Brown* (*aniline*) (5.81) | 16·00 | 45 |
| | | ca. Perf 12 | — | 38·00 |
| | | *d. Dull black-brown* (10.81) | | 45 |
| | | *e. Dull grey-brown* (3.82) | 12·00 | 45 |
| | | f. Mixed perf 13 and 12 | — | £190 |
| 224 | | 2d. mauve (*worn plate*) (2.84) | — | 4·50 |
| 225 | **34** | 4d. rose-carmine (10.81) | 35·00 | 4·00 |
| | | *a. Rosine* (8.82) | 35·00 | 3·50 |
| 226 | **35** | 2s. dark blue (*shades*)/*green* (8.7.81) | £110 | 18·00 |
| | | *a. Light blue*/*green* (wmk sideways) (8.83) | £120 | 22·00 |
| | | *b. Ultramarine*/*green* (7.84) | — | 28·00 |
| | | ba. Wmk sideways | — | 48·00 |
| | | (*b*) *W* **23** (*V*2) | | |
| 227 | **33** | 2d. dull grey-brown (15.8.82) | 12·00 | 30 |
| 228 | | 2d. chocolate (3.83) | 12·00 | 30 |
| | | a. Perf 12 | — | 19·00 |
| 229 | | 2d. mauve (20.12.83) | 7·00 | 20 |
| | | a. Worn plate | 7·50 | 20 |
| | | b. Perf 12 | — | £180 |
| | | c. Mixed perfs 12½ and 12 | — | £180 |
| 230 | **34** | 4d. rose-red (3.83) | 40·00 | 4·50 |

For the scarce perf 12 stamps listed above the holes are large and the teeth sharp. See also the note about perf 12 stamps after No. 186b.

The first printings of the 2d. in mauve were from the two plates used for the browns. Later printings were from two new plates. Reprints were made in 1891 of the 2d. (brown), 4d. (in pale red) and 2s., all on *V*2 paper.

36

(Des and die eng Charles Naish. Typo)

**1883** (29 Oct)–**84.** *P* 12½. (*a*) *W* **20** (*V*1).

| No. | Type | Description | Unused | Used |
|---|---|---|---|---|
| 231 | **36** | 1d. green (2.84) | 90·00 | 6·00 |
| | | (*b*) *W* **23** (*V*2) | | |
| 232 | **36** | 1d. yellow-green (29.10.83) | 14·00 | 1·25 |
| | | *a. Green* | 12·00 | 1·25 |
| | | *b. Pale green* (5.84) | 12·00 | 1·25 |

Nos. 224 and 231 represent a printing on old stocks of paper.

C. THE "POSTAGE AND REVENUE" PERIOD, 1884–1901

Under the provisions of the Postage Act 1883 the stamps of the three series then in use (Postage, Duty, Fee) became, as from 1.1.84, mutually interchangeable. It was, at the same time, decided to issue (as soon as possible) the *one* stamp only, for any value, to serve *all* purposes. Since there were available many more dies (and plates) inscribed "Stamp Duty" than there were of either the "Postage" or "Fee" (Stamp Statute) series it was agreed that all values should be inscribed "Stamp Duty" by the beginning of 1885. All stamps *printed* after 1.1.84 are therefore true "Postage and Revenue" stamps whereas all Stamp Duty and Fee stamps printed before that date are Postal Fiscals, since they were originally printed solely for fiscal purposes. These principles have been strictly adhered to in our listing. Little difficulty should however be met in distinguishing between the printings of the one stamp found respectively in the main list and in the "Postal Fiscal" section since there are many major differences of printing, watermark, perforation and shade. On 1.1.84 there were no "Stamp Duty" designs for the ½d., 2d., 4d., 8d. and 2s. 6d. values. Also the existing "Stamp Duty" designs for the 1d., 6d., 1s. and 2s. were deemed to be too large to be convenient for general and extensive use. For all these values it was therefore necessary to produce new and smaller designs inscribed "Stamp Duty". Pending the preparation of new dies and plates, printings were made in 1884 (for the ½d., 1d., 2d., 4d., 6d., 1s. and 2s. values) from the existing "Postage" plates. These printings are also "Postage and Revenue" stamps but have naturally been included, for the sake of convenience, in the previous period. By the beginning of 1885 printings were available, in the new designs, of all values save the 1s. and 2s., and these latter appeared later.

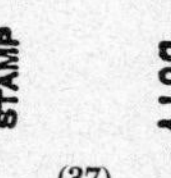

(37)

I. **1885.** *Postage Stamps optd with T* **37**. *The* 1s. *and* 2s. *appeared in February* 1885, 3*d. and* 4*d. in November* 1885. *P* 12½.

| No. | Type | Description | Unused | Used |
|---|---|---|---|---|
| | | (*a*) *W* **20** (*V*1) | | |
| 233 | **16** | 3d. dull orange-yellow (Pl 1) (B.) | — | £130 |
| 234 | **30** | 1s. ultramarine/*blue* | 95·00 | 20·00 |
| | | *a. Dull blue*/*blue* | — | 22·00 |
| 235 | | 1s. deep ultramarine/*blue* (**B.**) (F.C. £14) | — | £400 |
| 236 | **35** | 2s. ultramarine/*green* | 80·00 | 18·00 |
| | | a. Wmk sideways | 90·00 | 20·00 |
| | | (*b*) *W* **23** (*V*2) | | |
| 237 | **16** | 3d. yellow-orange (Pl 2) (B.) | 60·00 | 22·00 |
| | | *a. Dull brownish orange* (B.) | 65·00 | 24·00 |
| 238 | **34** | 4d. rose-carmine (B.) | 55·00 | 20·00 |

The overprinted 1s. was replaced by the 1s. Type **44** on lemon. Collectors should beware of faded black overprints purporting to be the "blue". In genuine examples the blue of the overprint is difficult to distinguish in the blue of the stamp.

*Reprints* of the 4d. and 1s. (with and without overprint) were made in 1895–6. The 1s. is wmkd *V*2 and the 4d. (from a new plate) is a pale red. Examples of the latter genuinely postally used are sometimes met.

38

39

40

41

42

43

(Typo. Dies for ½d., 2d., 3d., 4d., 8d. and 2s. 6d. eng by Charles Naish, the other values being derived from these)

II. **1884–95.** *New designs inscr* "STAMP DUTY". *P* 12½.

| No. | Type | Description | Unused | Used |
|---|---|---|---|---|
| | | (*a*) *W* **20** (*V*1) | | |
| 239 | **42** | 8d. rose/*pink* (*shades*) (1.1.85) | 19·00 | 5·50 |
| | | *a. Rose-red*/*pink* | 20·00 | 5·50 |
| 240 | **40** | 1s. deep dull blue/*lemon* (11.85) | 35·00 | 6·00 |
| | | *a. Dull blue*/*yellow* (6.86) | 35·00 | 6·50 |
| 241 | **42** | 2s. olive/*bluish green* (*shades*) (6.86) | 25·00 | 3·00 |
| | | (*b*) *W* **23** (*V*2) | | |
| 243 | **38** | ½d. pale rosine (1.1.85) | 4·50 | 65 |
| | | *a. Deep rosine* (7.85) | 5·00 | 1·00 |
| | | *b. Salmon* (9.85) | 5·50 | 1·25 |
| 244 | **39** | 1d. yellowish green (*shades*) (1.1.85) | 5·25 | 30 |
| | | *a. Dull pea-green* (2.85) | 8·00 | 1·75 |
| 245 | **40** | 2d. lilac (*shades*) (1.1.85) | 3·75 | 25 |
| | | *a. Mauve* (1.86) | 4·00 | 25 |
| | | *b. Rosy-mauve* (6.86) | 5·50 | 50 |
| 246 | **39** | 3d. yellowish brown (1.1.85) | 7·00 | 50 |
| | | *a. Pale ochre* (11.86) | 6·50 | 60 |
| | | *b. Bistre-yellow* (12.92) | 7·00 | 60 |
| 247 | **41** | 4d. magenta (1.1.85) | 27·00 | 3·00 |
| | | *a. Bright mauve-rose* (1.87) | 30·00 | 3·50 |
| 248 | | 4d. dull lilac (*error*) (12.86) | £2250 | £400 |
| 249 | **39** | 6d. chalky blue (1.1.85) | 30·00 | 2·50 |
| | | *a. Bright blue* (2.85) | 24·00 | 2·10 |
| | | *b. Cobalt* (9.85) | 24·00 | 2·10 |
| 250 | **42** | 8d. bright scarlet/*pink* (1892) | 22·00 | 7·50 |
| 251 | | 2s. olive-green/*pale green* (*shades*) (3.90) | 25·00 | 3·00 |
| 252 | | 2s. apple-green (12.8.95) | 25·00 | 15·00 |
| 253 | | 2s. blue-green (29.10.95) | 18·00 | 4·75 |
| 254 | **43** | 2s. 6d. brown-orange (23.4.84) | 80·00 | 11·00 |
| | | *a. Yellow* (1885) | 75·00 | 10·00 |
| | | *b. Lemon-yellow* (1.93) | 75·00 | 10·00 |

In each of the 1d., 6d., 1s. and 2s. values six types are to be found differing, *inter alia*, in the engraving of the words of value.

In the 2d. two die states are found: the *original* (1) which occurs on all but seven stamps in the Plate 1 sheet and the *damaged* (1a) which occurs on seven stamps in the Plate 1 sheet and on all 120 stamps in the Plate 2 sheet. The damage consists of a clear break in the top frame just in from the top right corner.

*4d. "error"*: This comprised a printing of 6000 stamps, 1886, in a *dull lilac* shade. It is true that only some seven unused specimens are known but it is not true (as previously stated) that it is unknown used, since a leading authority has himself seen upwards of 30 undoubted used copies, all of which have certain characteristics which distinguish them from certain colour changelings, accidental or deliberate. The records show that the whole printing of 6000 was issued which confirms the findings of so many used copies.

The 8d. value was withdrawn from sale on 24.8.95.

*Reprints* were made in 1891, using one of the original plates in each case, of the ½d., 1d., 2d., 4d., 6d. and 1s. values. In the three lower values the shades are fairly distinctive. The 1s. was wmkd *V*1. In all cases the wmk is equally common normal and inverted and this applies to *all* the Reprints made in 1891 or later.

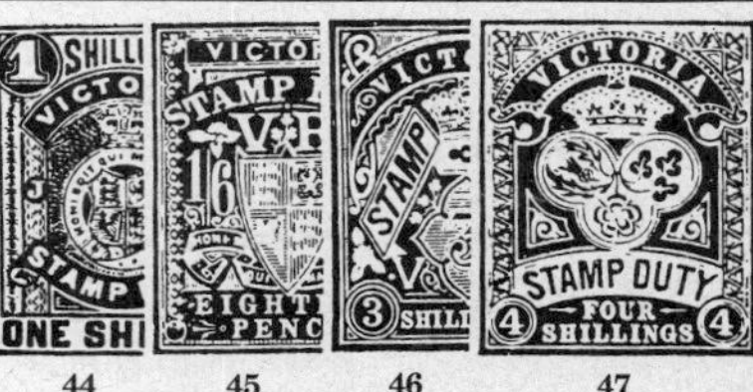
44 45 46 47

48 49 50 51

52 53 54 55

56 57 58

III. **1884–96.** *New printings, all typographed from electrotypes, of* "STAMP DUTY" *designs first issued in* 1879. (*Des Charles Jackson and Ludwig Lang. Dies eng by Charles Jackson, Arthur Williams, Charles Evans and possibly others, supplied* (1879) *by Messrs Sands and McDougall of Melbourne*). *P* 12½. *Wmk sideways save where shown as upright* (U). (*a*) *W* **20** (*V*1).

| No. | Type | Description | Unused | Used |
|---|---|---|---|---|
| 255 | **44** | 1s. ultramarine/*blue* (11.84) | 80·00 | 5·00 |
| 256 | | 1s. chalky blue/*lemon* (3.3.85) | 75·00 | 20·00 |
| 257 | **46** | 3s. maroon/*blue* (8.84) | 50·00 | 10·00 |
| 258 | **48** | 5s. reddish purple/*lemon* (6.87) | 30·00 | 10·00 |
| | | *a. Brown-red*/*yellow* (1.94) | 75·00 | 20·00 |
| 259 | **52** | £1 orange/*yellow* (9.84) | — | 45·00 |
| | | *a. Reddish orange*/*yellow* (12.90) | £325 | 45·00 |
| | | (*b*) *W* **23** (*V*2) | | |
| 260 | **45** | 1s. 6d. pink (2.85) | £100 | 19·00 |
| | | *a. Bright rose-carmine* (5.86) | £120 | 15·00 |
| 261 | **46** | 3s. drab (11.85) | 70·00 | 15·00 |
| | | *a. Olive-drab* (10.93) | 65·00 | 15·00 |
| 262 | **47** | 4s. red-orange (27.5.86) | 75·00 | 12·00 |
| | | *a. Yellow-orange* (S, U) | £100 | 8·50 |
| 263 | **48** | 5s. rosine (8.5.96) | 75·00 | 19·00 |
| 264 | **49** | 6s. pea-green (12.11.91) | £110 | 30·00 |
| | | *a. Apple-green* (U) (4.96) | £100 | 30·00 |
| 265 | **50** | 10s. dull bluish green (10.85) | £120 | 28·00 |
| | | *a. Grey-green* (9.87) | £100 | 25·00 |
| 266 | **51** | 15s. purple-brown (12.85) | £250 | 35·00 |
| 267 | | 15s. brown (U) (5.95) | £400 | 55·00 |
| 268 | **53** | £1 5s. pink† (U) (6.8.90) | £700 | 60·00 |
| 269 | **54** | £1 10s. pale olive† (10.88) | £500 | 50·00 |
| 270 | **55** | £2 blue† (8.88) | £700 | 60·00 |
| 271 | **56** | 45s. lilac† (15.8.90) | £2000 | 70·00 |
| 272 | **57** | £5 pink (10.85) | — | £190 |
| 273 | **58** | £10 lilac (7.85) | — | 80·00 |
| | | *a. Mauve*† (7.93) | — | 65·00 |

Stamps of the above designs printed by lithography or line-engraving, or similar designs not found in the above list should be looked for among the Postal Fiscals.

†Both here and later indicates that prices quoted are for stamps postmarked to order by the Victorian postal authorities for sale in sets.

59

IV. **1896–1900.** *T* **59** *and similar types. W* **23** *(V2) sideways (S) or upright (U). The line-engraved stamps were all printed singly direct from the dies and both the lithographed and typographed stamps were in sheets of* 10 (2 × 5). (i) *Lithographed. Printings of* 1886 *to* 1889.

| No. | | Description | Unused | Used |
|---|---|---|---|---|
| 274 | | £25 dull yellowish green (S, U) (1.86) | F.C. | 45·00 |
| | | *a. Dull blue-green* (U) (10.88) | F.C. | 45·00 |
| 275 | | £50 bright violet (U) (2.86) | F.C. | 55·00 |
| | | *a. Dull purple* (U) (10.87) | F.C. | 55·00 |
| 276 | | £100 rosine (S, U) (1.86) | F.C. | 85·00 |

(ii) *Recess-printed. Printings of November* 1890 *to April* 1897

| No. | | Description | Unused | Used |
|---|---|---|---|---|
| 277 | | £25 bright blue-green (S, U) (11.90) | F.C. | 45·00 |
| 278 | | £50 black-violet (S) (11.90) | F.C. | 55·00 |
| 279 | | £100 crimson (aniline) (S, U) (11.90) | F.C. | 85·00 |
| | | *a. Scarlet-red*† (1897) | — | £170 |

For earlier recess-printed printings, see under "POSTAL FISCALS".

(iii) *Typographed from electrotyped plates. Printings of November* 1897 *on*

| No. | | Description | Unused | Used |
|---|---|---|---|---|
| 280 | | £25 dull blue-green† (U) | — | 65·00 |
| 281 | | £50 bright mauve† (U) | — | 90·00 |
| 282 | | £100 pink-red† (U) (10.00) | — | £130 |

Collectors should beware of stamps with cleaned fiscal markings particularly in the higher values. Some of these bear forged cancellations but others, in fraud of the revenue, did genuine postal service.

60

61

62

63

64

VICTORIA 1S ONE SHILLING
65

66

67

(Typo. Previous 2d. and 4d. dies "lined" by Charles Naish; 1s. 6d. des and eng Charles Naish; rest des Philip Astley, probably eng Samuel Reading and supplied by Fergusson and Mitchell)

**1886–96.** *W* **23** *(V2) upright save in* ½d., 1s. *and high values (excepting the* £6) *where it is sideways. P* 12½.

| No. | Type | Description | Unused | Used |
|---|---|---|---|---|
| 283 | **60** | ½d. lilac-grey (20.8.86) | 15·00 | 3·00 |
| | | *a. Grey-black* | — | 35·00 |
| 284 | | ½d. pink (15.2.87) | 5·00 | 25 |
| | | *a. Rosine (aniline)* (12.89) | 4·75 | 25 |
| | | *b. Rose-red* (5.91) | 4·50 | 20 |
| | | *c. Vermilion* (3.96) | 4·75 | 35 |
| 285 | **61** | 1d. green (26.7.86) | 5·25 | 20 |
| | | *a. Yellow-green* (7.87) | 5·25 | 20 |
| 286 | **62** | 2d. pale lilac (17.12.86) | 2·75 | 20 |
| | | *a. Pale mauve* (1887) | 2·50 | 20 |
| | | *b. Deep lilac* (1888, 1892) | 2·50 | 20 |
| | | *c. Purple* (5.94) | 2·75 | 25 |
| | | *d. Violet* (5.95) | 2·50 | 20 |
| | | e. Imperforate (1890) | — | £700 |
| 287 | **63** | 4d. rose-red (1.4.87) | 6·50 | 1·00 |
| | | *a. Red* (1893) | 5·75 | 90 |
| 288 | **64** | 6d. bright ultramarine (27.8.86) | 7·50 | 65 |
| | | *a. Pale ultramarine* (10.87) | 7·00 | 50 |
| | | *b. Dull blue* (2.91) | 6·50 | 50 |
| 289 | **65** | 1s. dull purple-brown (14.3.87) | 20·00 | 2·00 |
| | | *a. Lake* (2.90) | 15·00 | 1·50 |
| | | *b. Carmine-lake* (5.92) | 14·00 | 1·00 |
| | | *c. Brownish red* (1.96) | 15·00 | 1·25 |
| 290 | **66** | 1s. 6d. pale blue (6.88) | £120 | 65·00 |
| 291 | | 1s. 6d. orange (18.9.89) | 15·00 | 4·50 |
| | | *a. Red-orange* | 15·00 | 5·00 |
| 292 | **67** | £5 pale blue and maroon† (7.2.88) | £1000 | 65·00 |
| 293 | | £6 yellow and pale blue† (1.10.87) | £1200 | 80·00 |
| 294 | | £7 rosine and black† (17.10.89) | £1400 | £110 |
| 295 | | £8 mauve and brown-orange† (U) (2.8.90) | £1500 | £140 |
| 296 | | £9 apple-green and rosine† (21.8.88) | £1800 | £150 |

Reprints of the ½d. grey and 1s. 6d. blue were made in 1894–5. They differ from the originals in shade. A £10 (T **67**) was prepared for use, but not issued.

An imperforate sheet of the 2d. was on sale at the Mortlake Post Office in 1890 and a pair was noted in 1902.

68

69

70

(1d. die supplied, des and eng by Samuel Reading; 2½d. and 5d. des by M. Tannenberg; 9d. first printed from the new Reprint plate of 1891. Typo)

**1890–96.** *New designs and values. P* 12½. (a) *W* **20** (V1).

| No. | Type | Description | Unused | Used |
|---|---|---|---|---|
| 297 | **68** | 1d. orange-brown/*pink* (16.6.91) | 3·50 | 1·25 |

This was an emergency printing, caused by a temporary shortage of white V2 paper.

(b) *W* **23** (V2)

| No. | Type | Description | Unused | Used |
|---|---|---|---|---|
| 298 | **68** | 1d. dull chestnut (1.1.90) | 2·10 | 15 |
| | | *a. Deep red-brown* (1.90) | 2·10 | 30 |
| | | *b. Orange-brown* (4.90) | 2·10 | 15 |
| | | *c. Yellow-brown* (4.91) | 1·90 | 15 |
| | | *d. Brown-red* (8.90) | 1·90 | 15 |
| | | *e. Bright yellow-orange* (9.93) | 50·00 | 12·00 |
| | | *f. Brownish orange* (6.94) | 1·75 | 15 |
| 299 | **69** | 2½d. red-brown/*lemon* (18.12.90) | 6·00 | 80 |
| 300 | | 2½d. brown-red/*yellow* (1892) | 5·50 | 80 |
| | | *a. Red/yellow* (1893) | 5·50 | 70 |
| 301 | **70** | 5d. purple-brown | 6·50 | 85 |
| | | *a. Pale reddish brown* (1892) | 6·00 | 80 |
| 302 | **29** | 9d. apple-green (18.10.92) | 20·00 | 9·00 |
| 303 | | 9d. carmine-rose (18.10.95) | 12·00 | 2·50 |
| | | *a. Rosine (aniline)* (1896) | 13·00 | 2·75 |

The yellow papers used for the 2½d. value differed considerably in tint.

71

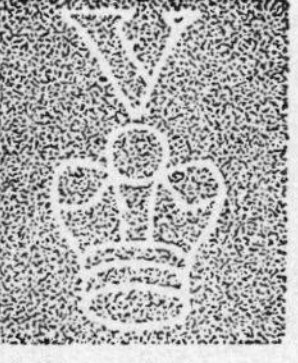
72 (V3)

(Eng A. Williams (1½d.))

**1896** (June)–**1899** (Aug). *W* **72** (V3). *Paper supplied by Waterlow and Sons. This paper differs noticeably from the previous De La Rue products. It is less white, softer and generally thicker, and has a coarser grain or mesh than any previous V over Crown paper. It will be noted that some coloured V2 papers of earlier manufacture were utilised during this period. T* **60, 65, 71** *and the larger size stamps have the wmk sideways unless marked* U *(upright). P* 12½.

| No. | Type | Description | Unused | Used |
|---|---|---|---|---|
| 304 | **60** | ½d. light scarlet (1.7.96) | 2·75 | 15 |
| | | *a. Carmine-rose* (11.97) | 3·25 | 15 |
| | | *b. Deep carmine-red (coarse impression)* (1899) | — | 75 |
| 305 | **68** | 1d. brown-red (13.6.96) | 2·00 | 10 |
| | | *a. Brownish orange* (11.97) | 1·90 | 10 |
| 306 | **71** | 1½d. apple-green (8.10.97) | 4·00 | 1·50 |
| 307 | **62** | 2d. violet (*shades*) (12.6.96) | 2·10 | 10 |
| 308 | **39** | 3d. ochre (11.96) | 7·00 | 55 |
| | | *a. Buff* (2.98) | 6·50 | 50 |
| 309 | **63** | 4d. red (6.97) | 5·00 | 90 |
| 310 | **70** | 5d. red-brown (7.97) | 8·00 | 95 |
| 311 | **64** | 6d. dull blue (9.96) | 6·50 | 55 |
| 312 | **29** | 9d. rosine (10.96) | 15·00 | 2·00 |
| | | *a. Rose-carmine* (4.98) | — | 2·00 |
| | | *b. Dull rose* (6.98) | 12·00 | 2·00 |
| 313 | **65** | 1s. brownish red (3.97) | 11·00 | 1·25 |
| 314 | **66** | 1s. 6d. brown-orange (8.98) | 23·00 | 7·50 |
| 315 | **42** | 2s. blue-green (4.97) | 21·00 | 5·00 |
| 316 | **43** | 2s. 6d. yellow (9.96) | 90·00 | 11·00 |
| | | *a. Yellow* (U) (9.98) | £100 | 11·00 |
| 317 | **46** | 3s. olive-drab (12.96) | 50·00 | 11·00 |
| | | *a. Olive-drab* (U) (10.98) | 50·00 | 10·00 |
| 318 | **47** | 4s. orange (9.97) | 75·00 | 4·50 |
| 319 | **48** | 5s. rosine (2.97) | 75·00 | 5·00 |
| | | *a. Rose-carmine* (11.97) | 75·00 | 5·00 |
| | | *b. Rosine* (U) (3.99) | 75·00 | 5·50 |
| 320 | **49** | 6s. pale yellow-green† (4.99) | 75·00 | 20·00 |
| 321 | **50** | 10s. grey-green (4.97) | 75·00 | 15·00 |
| | | *a. Blue-green* (7.98) | 75·00 | 15·00 |
| 322 | **51** | 15s. brown† (4.97) | £200 | 25·00 |
| 323 | **59** | £25 dull bluish green† (U) (1899) | — | 80·00 |
| 324 | | £50 dull purple† (U) (11.97) | — | 90·00 |

73

74

(Des M. Tannenberg. Eng A. Mitchelhill)

**1897** (7 Oct). *Charity. W* **72** (V3) *sideways. P* 12½.

| No. | Type | Description | Unused | Used |
|---|---|---|---|---|
| 325 | **73** | 1d. (1s.) blue | 18·00 | 18·00 |
| 326 | **74** | 2½d. (2s. 6d.) red-brown | 80·00 | 60·00 |
| 325/6 Optd "Specimen" | | *Set of* 2 | £140 | |

These stamps, sold at 1s. and 2s. 6d. respectively, paid postage of 1d. and 2½d. only, the difference being given to a Hospital Fund.

**1899** (1 Aug)–**1900.** *Colours changed for* ½d., 1d., 1½d. *and* 2½d. *P* 12½.

(a) *W* **23** (V2)

| No. | Type | Description | Unused | Used |
|---|---|---|---|---|
| 327 | **71** | 1½d. brown-red/*yellow* (1.8.99) | 3·00 | 1·75 |

(b) *W* **72** (V3)

| No. | Type | Description | Unused | Used |
|---|---|---|---|---|
| 328 | **60** | ½d. emerald (8.99) | 5·00 | 40 |
| 329 | **69** | 2½d. blue (1.8.99) | 5·00 | 1·75 |

75 (V4)

(c) *W* **75** (V4)

*This wmk and paper, like V3, was supplied by Waterlow and Sons and it continued in use until* 1905. *It was the result of an amended specification. Like the V3 paper it has a marked mesh but is whiter, smoother and harder. The* 1s. *and the four higher values have the wmk sideways, the* ½d. *being found with both positions.*

| No. | Type | Description | Unused | Used |
|---|---|---|---|---|
| 330 | **60** | ½d. emerald (1.8.99) | 4·75 | 40 |
| | | *a. Deep blue-green* | 5·00 | 40 |
| 331 | **68** | 1d. rosine (1.8.99) | 3·75 | 10 |
| | | *a. Rose-red* (6.00) | 3·75 | 15 |
| 332 | **62** | 2d. violet (*shades*)(1.8.99) | 2·50 | 10 |
| 333 | **69** | 2½d. blue (2.00) | 4·50 | 1·50 |
| 334 | **39** | 3d. bistre-yellow (9.99) | 5·25 | 55 |
| 335 | **63** | 4d. rose-red (12.99) | 4·75 | 95 |
| 336 | **70** | 5d. red-brown (10.99) | 5·50 | 95 |
| 337 | **64** | 6d. dull ultramarine (2.00) | 7·00 | 55 |
| 338 | **29** | 9d. rose-red (8.99) | 8·00 | 1·75 |
| 339 | **65** | 1s. brown-red (5.00) | 10·00 | 1·40 |
| 340 | **66** | 1s. 6d. orange (12.99) | 14·00 | 4·75 |
| 341 | **42** | 2s. blue-green (6.00) | 15·00 | 4·25 |
| 342 | **43** | 2s. 6d. yellow (1.00) | 90·00 | 10·00 |
| 343 | **46** | 3s. pale olive† (5.00) | £130 | 12·00 |
| 344 | **48** | 5s. rose-red (4.00) | £100 | 12·00 |
| 345 | **50** | 10s. green† (3.00) | £130 | 14·00 |

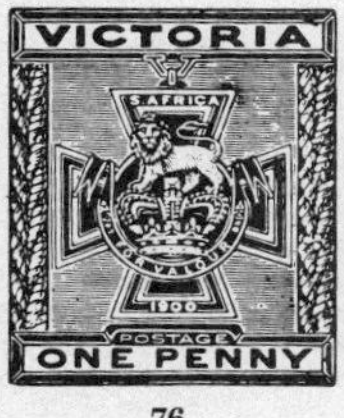

76

77

(Eng S. Reading)

**1900** (23 May). *Charity. W* **75** (V4) *sideways. P* 12½.

| No. | Type | Description | Unused | Used |
|---|---|---|---|---|
| 346 | **76** | 1d. (1s.) olive-brown | 35·00 | 25·00 |
| 347 | **77** | 2d. (2s.) emerald-green | £100 | 80·00 |

These stamps were sold for a Boer War Patriotic Fund, on a similar basis to the issue of 1897.

*V over Crown Wmks: A Note on "Abnormal" Watermark Positions*

It should always be remembered that the block of 120 wmks (12 × 10) in the sheet was designed to fit the normal size stamp in an upright position. *Other* sizes, larger and smaller, were printed, at various times, with the wmk *both* upright and sideways. The following note concerns only varieties as they are found on stamps of normal size.

*Inverted Wmks*: This description also embraces cases of wmks lying sideways with V at right found on stamps of Type **60** etc. which are of the same dimensions (but reversed) as the usual size stamps. In printings before 1882 all inverted wmks may be regarded as "abnormals". In this period all sheets of 240 wmks were, where necessary, cut into two before printing. From 1882 to mid-1896 the *only* inverted "abnormals" are found in certain of the common values where the area of the printing surface (i.e. 2 plates of 120) more or less equalled the area of the complete sheet of watermarked paper as it was supplied by De La Rue's. This was of 240 wmks, consisting of one pane of 120 wmks over another pane of 120. In this period the sheet of 240 wmks was not cut up before printing from single plates as had been done previously. Where only one plate was employed the sheet was fed in in one direction, removed, dried, and fed in the other direction, giving in the result of 120 normal and 120 inverted wmks. (This fact is of assistance when distinguishing certain Reprints.) From 1896 the same principle applied save that the complete sheets supplied were of 480 wmks so that the only "abnormal" inverteds found are in those cases, e.g. 1d. and 2d. where the stamps were printed from a block of similar size viz. of 4 plates of 120 impressions clamped together.

However, in 1901 to 1912, following a change in postal rates, resulting in a smaller demand for the 2d. value, this was again printed from two plates so that inverted watermarks in this period are always normal.

*Sideways Wmks*: This description includes upright wmks on stamps of the dimensions of Type **60** etc. They usually arose through the suppliers placing the paper in the wrong direction in the bound books (and later unbound reams) of paper supplied. *Three* periods concern us in this regard.

(i) 1867–1882: Before 1867 paper was supplied in single sheets of 120 wmks and from 1867 in double sheets of 240 wmks. From 1867 to 1882 wherever it was necessary (i.e. where only one plate was used) the double sheets were cut into half before printing. The variety may be found under the following numbers. All are extremely rare—viz. 174, 180, 190, 192, 193, 202, 214, 225.

(ii) 1882–1896. In this period no "abnormal" sideways wmks are met since the paper supplied was not cut up before printing and since the complete sheet supplied was rectangular and *not square* in shape.

(iii) 1896–1912: Here the wmkd paper supplied was of 480 (120 × 4) wmks and such sheets were practically square. One meets "abnormals" under the following numbers, many of these being extremely rare—viz. 304, 305, 307, 308, 312, 313, 328, 330, 331, 332, 334, 338, 356, 357, 359, 366, 367, 368, 371, 373, 386, 400, 405, 407, 414, 417, 445, 447, 451.

*Reversed Wmks*: These involved a printing on the wrong side of the paper. Since the side which should have been printed was usually "surfaced" to some degree these varieties almost invariably show the impression of the stamp coarser than normally and the back of the stamp smoother and glossier. From 1878 to 1896 the back of the paper supplied by De La Rue was treated with a special preparation to prevent the gum soaking through to the front. This preparation was susceptible to moisture and when printed upon and subsequently exposed to moisture occasionally shed portions of the design, so that in this period such varieties often bear the superficial appearance of having been printed on the gum, whereas in fact, up to July 1912, all gumming was done after printing. Reversed wmks, many of them very rare, have been found under the following Nos.—158, 162, 179, 181, 183, 184, 185, 187, 190, 192, 193, 197, 198, 206, 207 (inverted and reversed), 210, 211, 214, 228, 243, 244, 245, 263, 283, 284, 285, 286, 287, 288, 289, 298, 305, 307, 310, 331, 332, 356, 357, 366, 373, 400, 401, 403, 406, 407, 408, 447, 448—also in certain of the £25, £50 and £100 stamps (in both sections) and in various items in the Postal Fiscal list. In the reversed V over Crown cases—looking through the front of the stamp in a normal upright position—the double side of the "V" will appear on the *right* and not on the left as it should do.

### D. THE COMMONWEALTH PERIOD, 1901–12

All postage stamps issued by the States in this period were in reality COMMONWEALTH stamps. This viewpoint has now received official endorsement ("Commonwealth of Australia Philatelic Bulletin" No. 2, October 1953). Prior to the actual coming into being of the Commonwealth it had been agreed between the States that the Postal Services were to be the concern of the Commonwealth and that the postal revenue was to go to it. This decision meant, for Victoria, the separation of the Postal and the Fiscal systems. So long, however, as the Commonwealth lacked printing facilities and a Postal administration of its own the work had to be done by each State on its behalf. Separate series of Postage stamps (for which the State was obliged to account to the Commonwealth) and of Duty stamps (which were to continue as a State concern) therefore became necessary. The first Kangaroo stamps were not issued by the Commonwealth until January 1913, but in the intervening period a long chain of philatelic events had contributed to make this issue possible. From the beginning of 1902 all the stamps of Tasmania and Western Australia were printed in Melbourne, on Victorian paper. Later Papua (1907) and later again South Australia (1909) were added to these. In the same year (1902) the first Commonwealth Postage Dues, printed in Sydney on New South Wales paper, appeared. In 1903 a 9d. stamp of the same "Commonwealth" design was issued in New South Wales and Queensland. In 1905 all States commenced using one or other of four types of Crown over A paper, marginally wmkd "COMMONWEALTH OF AUSTRALIA". In 1909, printed in Melbourne, appeared new bi-coloured Postage Dues, the first stamps to be inscribed "AUSTRALIA". This followed the appointment of J. B. Cooke, the South Australian stamp printer, as Commonwealth Stamp Printer. As from 13.10.10 the stamps of any State could legally be used in any other State, and in April 1911 the first Commonwealth Postal Stationery was issued. In short, in the period 1901 to 1912, although certain States printed and issued postage stamps, this was a privilege, subject at all times to Commonwealth control and direction and conducted, in respect of the nett revenue received, solely for the Commonwealth's benefit.

The Commonwealth was proclaimed as from 1 January 1901. In only three cases in the first issue, viz. the 1d., 2½d. and 5d. values was there sufficient time to alter the dies and produce new plates. In all the other cases the same plates were used as had been employed to produce the 1891 Reprints.

**1901** (29 Jan)–**1905.** *P 12½ or 12 × 12½.*

(*a*) *Without the word* "POSTAGE" *in the design.* (i) *W* **72** (*V3*)

| | | | | |
|---|---|---|---|---|
| 348 | **35** | 2s. blue/*pink* | 35·00 | 10·00 |

(ii) *W* **75** (*V4*) (*sideways on T* **25**)

| | | | | |
|---|---|---|---|---|
| 349 | **25** | ½d. bluish green | 2·00 | 85 |
| | | a. "VICTCRIA" | 23·00 | 19·00 |
| 350 | **33** | 2d. reddish violet | 4·00 | 20 |
| 351 | **16** | 3d. dull orange | 10·00 | 1·25 |
| 352 | **34** | 4d. bistre-yellow | 25·00 | 6·50 |
| 353 | **17** | 6d. emerald | 9·00 | 5·00 |
| 354 | **30** | 1s. yellow | 30·00 | 15·00 |
| 355 | **19** | 5s. pale red and deep blue | 45·00 | 18·00 |

78

79

80

(*b*) *With the word "POSTAGE" in the design. W* **75** (*V4*)

| | | | | |
|---|---|---|---|---|
| 356 | **78** | 1d. rose (Die I) | 1·25 | 15 |
| | | *a. Dull red* (12.01) | 1·25 | 15 |
| 357 | | 1d. rose (Die II) (2.4.01) | 1·25 | 15 |
| | | *a. Dull red* (12.01) | 1·25 | 15 |
| 358 | | 1d. pale rose-red (Die III) (3.5.05) | 2·00 | 15 |
| 359 | **79** | 2½d. dull blue (1901) | 2·75 | 25 |
| | | *a. Deep blue* (1902) | 2·75 | 20 |
| 360 | **80** | 5d. reddish brown | 4·75 | 40 |
| | | *a. Purple-brown* (1903) | 4·00 | 40 |

I

II

III

I and II    III

Three dies of the 1d.: Principal differences are:

I. Horizontal lines over Queen's head fill oval surround under "VICTORIA". Found in two plates employed January 1901–February 1903.

II. Practically all the lines of shading to the left of and on top of the head have been "thinned", giving a lighter appearance. Some lines at the top have been cut away, leaving small white patches, particularly under the "OR". Found in ten plates in use between April 1901 and April 1905.

III. As II but with stop at lower left clearly separated from circle line at its right; spot of colour in shading between "O" and "R"; two lines of shading meet in lower left portion of "P" of "PENNY". Found in twelve plates in use between May 1905 and the end of 1912.

**1901** (June). *W* **75** (*V4*). *P* 12 × 12½.

| | | | | |
|---|---|---|---|---|
| 361 | **68** | 1d. olive (6.6.01) | 5·00 | 3·50 |
| 362 | **39** | 3d. slate-green (20.6.01) | 21·00 | 5·00 |

These stamps were available for postal purposes to 30 June 1901, afterwards for fiscal purposes only.

81 82 83 84 85 86 87 88 89

Type A "Postage" 6 mm — Type B "Postage" 7 mm

90

91

92

93

**1901** (June)–**10.** *Similar to former types but* "POSTAGE" *inserted in design. W* **75** (*V4*) (*sideways on* ½*d.*, 1½*d.*, £1, £2).

(*a*) *P* 12½ *or* 12 × 12½.

| | | | | |
|---|---|---|---|---|
| 363 | **81** | ½d. blue-green (*shades*) (Die I) (26.6.01) | 1·90 | 15 |
| | | *a. Blue-green* (U) | 1·90 | 15 |
| 364 | | ½d. pale blue-green (Die II) (6.04) | 2·50 | 15 |
| 365 | | ½d. pale bluish green (Die III) (6.05) | 5·00 | 50 |
| 366 | **82** | 1½d. maroon/*yellow* (9.7.01) | 3·00 | 85 |
| | | *a. Brown-red/yellow* (1901) | 2·10 | 55 |
| | | *b. Dull red/yellow* (1906) | 2·10 | 55 |
| 367 | **83** | 2d. lilac (16.7.01) | 1·90 | 30 |
| | | *a. Reddish violet* (1902) | 1·90 | 30 |
| | | *b. Violet* (1904) | 3·00 | 30 |
| | | *c. Bright purple* (1905) | 3·00 | 50 |
| 368 | **84** | 3d. dull orange-brown (2.7.01) | 4·75 | 55 |
| | | *a. Chestnut* (1901) | 4·75 | 55 |
| | | *b. Yellowish brown* (1903) | 4·75 | 55 |
| 369 | **85** | 4d. bistre-yellow (26.6.01) | 4·75 | 55 |
| | | *a. Brownish bistre* (1905) | 5·25 | 70 |
| 370 | **86** | 6d. emerald (5.7.01) | 7·50 | 80 |
| | | *a. Dull green* (1904) | 9·00 | 85 |
| 371 | **87** | 9d. dull rose-red (5.7.01) | 9·50 | 1·40 |
| | | *a. Pale red* (1901) | 10·00 | 1·25 |
| | | *b. Dull brownish red* (1905) | 10·00 | 1·75 |
| 372 | **88** | 1s. yellow-orange (Type A) (5.7.01) | 9·50 | 1·75 |
| | | *a. Yellow* (1902) | 12·00 | 1·75 |
| 373 | **89** | 1s. yellow (Type B) (4.03) | 12·00 | 3·00 |
| | | *a. Yellow-orange* (1903) | 10·00 | 2·50 |
| 374 | **90** | 2s. blue/*rose* (5.7.01) | 22·00 | 2·00 |
| 375 | **91** | 5s. rose-red and pale blue (5.7.01) | 70·00 | 11·00 |
| | | *a. Scarlet and deep blue* (1902) | 65·00 | 9·00 |
| | | *b. Rosine and blue* (1905) | 65·00 | 9·00 |
| 376 | **92** | £1 carmine-rose (18.11.01) | £275 | £100 |
| 377 | **93** | £2 deep blue (2.6.02) | £550 | £250 |

(*b*) *P* 11

| | | | | |
|---|---|---|---|---|
| 378 | **81** | ½d. blue-green (Die I) (9.02) | 4·00 | 75 |
| | | *a. Blue-green* (U) | 3·00 | 20 |
| 379 | | ½d. blue-green (Die II) | 3·00 | 25 |
| 380 | | ½d. bluish green (Die III) | 3·50 | 50 |
| 381 | **78** | 1d. dull red (Die I) | — | 22·00 |
| 382 | | 1d. dull red (Die II) | 40·00 | 18·00 |
| | | *a. Pale red* (*aniline*) (3.03) | 3·50 | 75 |
| | | *b. Pale rose* (*aniline*)(1904) | — | 3·00 |
| 383 | | 1d. pale rose-red (Die III) | 38·00 | 23·00 |
| 384 | **82** | 1½d. dull red/*yellow* (1910) | 28·00 | 28·00 |
| 385 | **83** | 2d. violet (1904) | — | £140 |
| | | *a. Bright purple* (1905) | — | £140 |
| 386 | **84** | 3d. orange-brown (1903) | 5·25 | 3·00 |
| 387 | **86** | 6d. emerald (1903) | 9·50 | 3·75 |
| | | *a. Dull green* (1905) | £250 | £160 |
| 388 | **92** | £1 carmine-red (1905) | £325 | £130 |
| 389 | **93** | £2 deep blue (1905) | £750 | £650 |

(*c*) *Compound or mixed perf* 12½ *and* 11

| | | | | |
|---|---|---|---|---|
| 390 | **81** | ½d. blue-green (Die I) | 15·00 | 4·00 |
| | | *a. Blue-green* (U) (1903) | — | 4·00 |
| 391 | | ½d. blue-green (Die II) (1904) | 14·00 | 11·00 |
| 392 | **78** | 1d. dull red (Die I) | — | £150 |
| 393 | | 1d. dull red (Die II) | — | £110 |
| 394 | **82** | 1½d. dull red/*yellow* | — | £200 |
| 395 | **83** | 2d. reddish violet | — | £250 |
| 396 | **84** | 3d. orange-brown | — | £200 |
| 397 | **86** | 6d. emerald | — | £200 |
| 398 | **91** | 5s. rose and blue | £800 | |

I    II    III

Three dies of the ½d.; Principal differences are:

I. Outer of two vertical lines of colour to left of "V" is continuous save for a marked break opposite top of "V". Found in two plates in use 1901–May 1904.

II. Outer vertical line to left of "V" is broken in three places; the triangular space S.W. of "V", has also been "opened up" and shows more white lines than in I. Found in two plates in use June 1904–June 1905.

III. As II but the vertical coloured line to right of the "A" of "VICTORIA" (previously broken in the middle) is now broken in four or five places. The triangular ornament to S.E. of the same "A" has also been "opened up", the white cross-hatching now being stronger than in I and II. Found in two plates introduced in June 1905 and in two subsequent plates introduced late in 1909.

The paper used for the 1½d. value for two printings in 1908–9 was yellow-buff in colour but in used copies the difference is not so marked as to warrant separate description.

There were two main states of the 2d. Die, the original showing the S.E. corner correctly squared and the later showing it damaged and blunter. There are other differences. The original state is found in all printings before April 1904 but not after, and the later state to a small extent (5 per cent) in the printings before April 1904 and *solely* in the printings from that date.

For the 1s. Type A the same plate was used as for the 1s. "No Postage" of 1901, the words "POSTAGE" being separately punched on. For Type B two new plates, prepared via an etched line-block, were introduced.

Certain *unlisted shades* (due to their being unsatisfactory) are found *only* punctured O.S. Marked instances of this are found in the 2d., 3d. and 4d. values.

**1905–13.** *Wmk Crown over A, W w* **11.** I. *Medium paper, supplied like the V4 paper, by Waterlow & Sons.*

(*a*) *P* 12½ *or* 12 × 12½

| | | | | |
|---|---|---|---|---|
| 399 | **81** | ½d. blue-green (21.10.05) | 1·60 | 15 |
| | | *a. Light bluish green* | 1·60 | 15 |
| 400 | **78** | 1d. rose-red (*shades*)(16.7.05) | 80 | 10 |
| | | *a. Pale rose* (1907) | 1·25 | 10 |
| | | *b. Rose-carmine* (9.11) | 2·50 | 15 |
| 401 | **83** | 2d. dull mauve (13.9.05) | 3·00 | 30 |
| | | *a. Bright mauve* (1906) | 3·00 | 25 |
| | | *b. Reddish violet* (1907) | 3·00 | 25 |
| | | *c. Lilac* (1910) | 2·40 | 40 |
| 402 | **79** | 2½d. blue (*shades*)(4.08) | 3·00 | 40 |
| | | *a. Indigo* (1909) | 3·00 | 40 |
| 403 | **84** | 3d. orange-brown (11.11.05) | 4·00 | 55 |
| | | *a. Yellow-orange* (1908) | 5·00 | 30 |
| | | *b. Dull orange-buff* (1909) | 4·75 | 30 |
| | | *c. Ochre* (1912) | 4·75 | 30 |
| 404 | **85** | 4d. yellow-bistre (15.1.06) | 6·00 | 65 |
| | | *a. Bistre* (1908) | 6·00 | 65 |
| | | *b. Yellow-olive* (1912) | 6·00 | 70 |
| 405 | **80** | 5d. chocolate (14.8.06) | 5·00 | 90 |
| | | *a. Dull reddish brown* (1908) | 5·00 | 65 |
| 406 | **86** | 6d. dull green (25.10.05) | 8·00 | 80 |
| | | *a. Dull yellow-green* (1907) | 7·50 | 80 |
| | | *b. Emerald* (1909) | 7·50 | 1·10 |
| | | *c. Yellowish green* (1911) | 7·50 | 1·00 |
| 407 | **87** | 9d. rose-red (11.12.05) | 9·50 | 1·25 |
| | | *a. Pale salmon-red* (1906) | 9·50 | 1·25 |
| | | *b. Brown-red* (1908) | 10·00 | 1·25 |
| | | *c. Pale dull rose* (worn plate) | 11·00 | 2·40 |
| | | *d. Rose-carmine* (new plate) (12.09) | 9·50 | 1·25 |

408 89 1s. yellow-orange (13.2.06) .. .. 8·00 2·00
 *a. Yellow* (1906) .. .. .. 10·00 2·00
 *b. Lemon* (1908) .. .. .. 12·00 2·00
409 91 5s. rose-red and ultramarine (U) (11.07) .. .. .. 70·00 13·00
 *a. Rose-red and blue* (U) (1912) 80·00 13·00
 *b. Rose-red and blue* (S) .. .. 80·00 16·00
410 92 £1 salmon (12.2.07) .. .. £275 £100
411 £1 dull rose (5.10) .. .. £275 £100
 *a. Deep dull rose* (U) (10.11) .. £275 £120
412 93 £2 dull blue (18.7.06) .. .. £600 £250

*Perforations of period 1901–12*

In general, up to 1910, five machines were available at any one time—three single-line (two "11" and one "12½") and two vertical combs (12 × 12½). Only single-line machines were used for the 5s., £1 and £2 values. The "12½" single line was used on many occasions for the ½d. and occasionally for other values. The "11" machines were primarily employed for larger size stamps, e.g. Victorian Duty Stamps, Tasmanian Pictorials and Papua, and their use for the normal size Victorian postage stamps was in the main restricted to emergencies. At certain periods, e.g. 1909–10 one encounters the true "compounds" i.e. the products of two single-line machines, 12½ and 11 respectively. For the ½d. the vertical comb 12 × 12½ was also used, particularly in the earlier period, on the sheet turned sideways. In the result the alternate vertical margins between stamps were left imperforate and a single-line machine (either 12½ or 11) was often used to complete the perforating, in the latter case (11) giving us a variety for separate listing. "Mixed" perforations in this period are, like their predecessors of the 70s, the result of the correction—with another machine—of faultily centred lines of perforation (either single-line or comb), the back of these faulty lines being usually pasted over with gummed strips to assist in tearing down the corrected lines.

The rotary-comb machines gauging 11½ × 12¼ were brought over from South Australia by J. B. Cooke when he moved to Melbourne in 1909.

The ½d. perf 11 and the 2½d. and 5s. first printings (all perforated with single line machines) may be met with *full imperforate base margins*. Likewise in the Crown over A issues the ½d. perf 12½ and the 5s. perf 12½ (1912) have been similarly found. Such varieties are, of course, rare.

(*b*) *P* 11

413 81 ½d. light bluish green .. .. .. 1·60 15
 *a. Blue-green* .. .. .. 1·60 15
414 78 1d. rose-red (1905) .. .. .. 1·60 75
 *a. Pale rose* (1907) .. .. .. 1·75 75
 *b. Rose-carmine* (1911) .. .. 5·00 2·75
415 83 2d. mauve (1906) .. .. .. — £150
 *a. Reddish violet* (1908) .. .. 65·00 15·00
 *b. Lilac* (1910) .. .. .. 19·00 7·50
416 79 2½d. blue (1909) .. .. .. 15·00 7·50
 *a. Indigo* (1909) .. .. .. 5·50 3·25
417 84 3d. brown (1908) .. .. .. 7·00 5·00
 *a. Orange-buff* (1909) .. .. 14·00 9·50
 *b. Dull orange-yellow* (1911) .. .. — £130
 *c. Ochre* (1912) .. .. .. 6·50 1·50
418 85 4d. yellow-bistre (1908) .. .. 7·00
 *a. Yellow-olive* (1912) .. .. 6·50 3·00
419 80 5d. reddish brown .. .. .. — £300
420 86 6d. emerald (1910) .. .. .. 8·50 2·40
 *a. Yellowish green* (1911) .. .. 11·00 2·40
421 87 9d. rose-carmine .. .. .. — £325
422 89 1s. yellow-orange .. .. .. £275
 *a. Yellow* .. .. .. — £225
423 91 5s. rose-red and ultramarine .. 70·00 9·50
424 92 £1 salmon (12.2.07) .. .. £325 £100
425 93 £2 dull blue (1.07) .. .. £650 £250

(*c*) *Compound or mixed perfs* 12½ *and* 11

426 81 ½d. light bluish green (6.09) .. .. 15·00 14·00
427 78 1d. rose-red .. .. .. 32·00 32·00
428 83 2d. mauve .. .. .. — £200
429 84 3d. brown (1908) .. .. .. £190 £225
 *a. Ochre* (1912) .. .. .. — £190
430 85 4d. bistre .. .. .. — £275
431 86 6d. yellowish green .. .. .. — £300
432 87 9d. dull rose-red .. .. .. — £375
433 89 1s. yellow-orange .. .. .. — £400

(*d*) *Rotary comb perf* 11½ × 12¼

434 78 1d. pale scarlet-red (2.10) .. .. 3·00 20
 *a. Rose-red* (3.10) .. .. .. 2·25 60
435 83 2d. lilac (*shades*) .. .. .. 3·50 75

II. *On thinner paper, ready gummed with white gum.* (July–Nov 1912).

(*a*) *P* 12½ *or* 12 × 12½

436 81 ½d. blue-green .. .. .. 3·00 25
437 78 1d. rose-red .. .. .. 4·50 25
438 83 2d. lilac .. .. .. 20·00 2·25
439 80 5d. brown .. .. .. 6·50 1·75
440 86 6d. emerald .. .. .. 9·50 2·25
441 89 1s. dull yellow (11.12) .. .. 15·00 6·00
 *a. Pale orange* (1.13) .. .. 15·00 6·00

(*b*) *P* 11

442 81 ½d. blue-green .. .. .. 12·00 7·50
443 78 1d. rose-red .. .. .. 5·00 2·25

(*c*) *P* 11 × 12½

444 81 ½d. blue-green .. .. .. £100 80·00

(*d*) *Rotary comb perf* 11½ × 12¼

445 78 1d. rose-carmine (2.7.12) .. .. 2·25 15
 *a. Rose-red* (10.12) .. .. .. 2·40 15

Two qualities of the "thin" paper were supplied, the first supply (earliest date 2.7.12) being thicker and with a less obvious mesh than the second (earliest date 2.10.12). The ½d. and 1d. are found on both classes of paper, the 2d. on the first only, and the 5d., 6d. and 1s. on the second only. There was a shortage pending the arrival of the second supply, and this gap was filled by the use of the "Stamp Duty" paper next described and the ONE PENNY overprint of 1.7.12. The 5d. perforated O.S. on the thin paper may be met in *dull red-brown.*



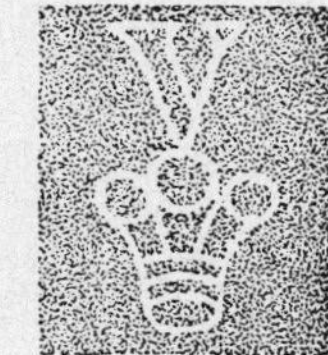

ONE PENNY

94 (V5) (95)

III. *Printed on "Stamp Duty" paper, W* **94** (V5). *This paper is rather softer and of a more pronounced mesh than the V4 paper.* (Aug–Oct 1912). (*a*) *P* 12½ *or* 12 × 12½.

446 81 ½d. bluish green .. .. .. 2·50 35
447 78 1d. rose-carmine (7.8.12) .. .. 2·25 20
448 83 2d. reddish violet .. .. .. 2·50 50
 *a. Lilac* .. .. .. 3·75 1·40
449 87 9d. carmine-red .. .. .. 9·50 2·10

(*b*) *P* 11

450 81 ½d. bluish green .. .. .. 12·00 9·00
451 78 1d. rose-carmine (8.12) .. .. 20·00 6·50
452 87 9d. carmine-red .. .. .. 13·00 3·50

(*c*) *Compound perf* 11 *with* 12½

453 87 9d. carmine-red .. .. .. — £350

This paper was supplied by Spicer Bros at the beginning of 1911 and continued to be used for many years in the production of Duty Stamps for this State.

**1912** (1 July). *Surch with T* **95** *in red. Wmk Crown over A. P* 11½ × 12¼.

454 83 1d. on 2d. lilac .. .. .. 70 45

Late in June 1912 the first consignment of "thin" paper was exhausted and the second had not arrived. A further supply of the 1d. value was urgently required, and the expedient of overprinting current 2d. stock was employed to fill the gap. The same reason also produced the 1d. and 2d. overprints of Tasmania and Western Australia, respectively.

POSTAL FISCALS

This section embraces those printings of Duty and Fee stamps made before 1.1.84. These were made available for postal purposes as from 1.1.84. The two series were in concurrent use between December 1879 and 1884.

A. The "STAMP STATUTE" series

This series was first issued on 26 April 1871 and it was in the main used to record the payment of various Court fees. The issue of the series ceased in April 1884.

F 1 F 2 F 3

F 4

**1870–83.** *Large rectangular stamps of various designs as Types* F 1 *to* F **4**. *All save the 3d. and 2s. 6d. (eng by James Turner) have the Queen's head included in the design (eng by William Bell). Typo at the Stamp Printing Office, Melbourne.*

(*a*) *Wmk single-lined numerals* (1, 2, *and* 10) *as used for Postage Stamps* (1863–67). *On Saunders paper unless otherwise noted. Both sideways and upright wmks are found in certain cases*

F 1 1s. blue/*blue* (*p* 13) .. .. .. 25·00 15·00
 a. Perf 12 .. .. .. 40·00 15·00
F 2 2s. blue/*green* (D.L.R.) (*p* 13) .. 50·00 45·00
 a. Perf 12 .. .. .. 50·00 45·00
F 3 2s. deep blue/*green* (S), (*p* 13) .. 50·00
 a. Perf 12 .. .. .. — 45·00
F 4 10s. brown-olive/*pink* (*p* 13) (6.71) ..
F 5 10s. red-brown/*pink* (*p* 13) (1879) .. £250 £100
 a. Perf 12 .. .. ..

(*b*) *Wmk V over Crown, W* **20** (V1)

The wmk is usually *sideways* but in certain cases the whole of a printing was *upright*. One also meets "abnormal" upright wmks.

F 7 ½d. on 1d. pale green (R.) (*p* 13) .. 12·50 25·00
F 8 1d. pale green (*p* 13) .. .. 12·50 15·00
 *a. Green* (*p* 12½) (U) (1880) .. 40·00 35·00
F 9 3d. mauve (*p* 13) (9.79) .. .. 45·00 75·00
F10 4d. rose (*p* 13) .. .. .. 40·00 55·00
F11 6d. blue (*p* 13) (1871) .. .. 30·00 15·00
 *a. Dull ultramarine* (*p* 13) (1876) .. 18·00 10·00
 aa. Perf 12 .. .. .. 35·00 12·50
F12 1s. blue/*blue* (*p* 13) (6.76) .. .. 25·00
 a. Perf 12 .. .. .. 40·00 18·00
 *b. Ultramarine/blue* (*p* 12½) (1882) .. — 25·00
 ba. Perf 12 .. .. .. — 20·00
 *c. Deep blue/blue* (*p* 12½) (1883) .. 25·00 15·00
 ca. Perf 12 .. .. .. — 15·00
F13 2s. blue/*green* (*p* 13) (7.76) .. .. 50·00 35·00
 a. Perf 12 .. .. .. 50·00
 *b. Deep blue/blue-green* (*p* 13) (1883) .. 50·00 40·00
 ba. Perf 12 .. .. .. 50·00 45·00
F15 2s. 6d. orange (*p* 13) (7.76) .. .. — 50·00
 a. Perf 12 .. .. ..
 *b. Yellow* (*p* 13) (11.78) .. .. £100
 ba. Perf 12 .. .. .. £100 55·00
 *c. Orange-yellow* (*p* 12½) (1882) .. — 60·00
 ca. Perf 12 .. .. ..
F16 5s. blue/*yellow* (*p* 13) .. .. £120 40·00
 a. Perf 12 .. .. .. £130
 *b. Ultramarine/lemon* (*p* 12½) (1881) .. £120 40·00
F17 10s. brown/*pink* (*p* 13) (8.76) .. .. £250 £100
 *a. Purple-brown/pink* (*p* 12½) (1882) .. £250 £100
 aa. Perf 12 .. .. ..
F18 £1 slate-violet/*yellow* (S, U) (*p* 13) (1871) .. £250
 a. Perf 12 (1880) .. .. .. £250
 *b. Mauve/yellow* (*p* 13) (1873) ..
 ba. Perf 12 (1881) .. .. .. £250
 bb. Perf 12½ (1882) .. .. .. £250 80·00
F19 £5 black and yellow-green (*p* 12) (11.71) ..
 a. Perf 13 .. .. ..
 b. Perf 12½ (U) .. .. ..

(*c*) 1882–3: *Wmk V over Crown, W* **23** (V2)

F20 1d. yellowish green (*p* 12½) .. .. 20·00 25·00
F21 2s. 6d. pale orange-yellow (*p* 12½) .. 75·00
F22 £5 black and yellow-green (*p* 12) .. .. — £400

*Reversed watermarks*, all rare, have been found under Nos. F12, F15, F18 and F19.

All the values of the "Stamp Statute" series were reprinted in 1891 on paper wmkd V1 (5s., 10s. and £1) and V2 (the rest). The colours used, in all cases, differed radically from the originals. Except for the £5, for which the old electrotypes were used, new plates were made for the Reprints, from dies which showed "die flaws" not to be found on the originals. In 1877 a 12s. 6d. value was prepared for use but although it was placed on sale at the Law Courts and was available there for some months not a single copy was sold, and it was withdrawn. Proofs are known.

B. The "STAMP DUTY" series

This series was used mainly to record the payment of duties on the sale of land, receipts and numerous other documents.

F 5 F 6 F 7 F 8

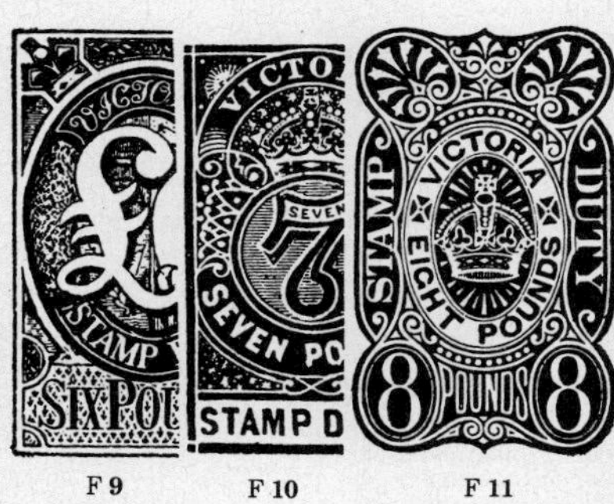


F 9 F 10 F 11

(Dies for these issues (except 1d. of 1880) supplied by Messrs. Sands and McDougall. Des Charles Jackson and Ludwig Lang. Eng Charles Jackson, Arthur Williams and others (See previously). The 1d. of 1880 was eng by Charles Naish)

**1879** (Dec)–**1883** (Dec). I. *December* 1879. *Litho Stamp Printing Office, Melbourne. Wmk V over Crown, W* **20** (V1). *Sideways unless otherwise indicated* (U). *P* 13.

F23 F 5 1d. blue-green .. .. .. 10·00 7·50
 a. Perf 12 .. .. .. 12·00 7·50
F24 45 1s. 6d. rosine .. .. .. 45·00 15·00
 a. Perf 12 .. .. .. — 20·00
F25 46 3s. purple/*blue* .. .. .. 40·00 15·00
 a. Perf 12 .. .. .. — 20·00
F26 47 4s. orange-red .. .. .. 50·00 15·00
 a. Perf 12 .. .. .. 50·00 15·00
F27 40 6s. apple-green (U) .. .. 60·00 20·00
 a. Perf 12 (U) .. .. ..
F28 50 10s. brown/*rose* (S, U) .. .. £250 50·00
 a. Perf 12 (S, U) .. .. ..
F29 51 15s. mauve .. .. .. — £100
F30 52 £1 red-orange .. .. .. — 25·00
F31 53 £1 5s. dull rose (U) .. .. — 60·00
F32 54 £1 10s. deep grey-olive (S, U) .. — 50·00
F33 35s. grey-violet (U) F.C. £150 £3000
F34 55 £2 blue .. .. .. — 50·00
F35 56 45s. dull brown-lilac (U) .. .. — 60·00
F36 57 £5 rose-red (U) .. .. — £120
F37 F 9 £6 blue/*pink* (U) .. .. — £350
F38 F 10 £7 violet/*blue* (U) .. .. — £350
F39 F 11 £8 brownish red/*yellow* (U) .. — £350
F40 — £9 yellow-green/*green* (U) F.C. £100 £1500

Apart from the "Half-Lengths", the 2d. Queen-on-Throne, the first 1s. Octagonal and the £25, £50 and £100 of 1886–89 these were the only stamps of Victoria to be printed by lithography and its adoption on this occasion was dictated by the necessity for speed of production. *All* the Lithographed stamps can be distinguished from the typographed stamps of the same design by their colours which are highly distinctive. Other differences, of wmk and perf, will be found. Some values, e.g. the 6s., 25s. and 30s. (1884–91) were available for postage over a considerable period.

No. F32 occurs with *reversed* watermark (rare).

II. Dec 1879–1882: *Typographed from electrotypes at Stamp Printing Office, Melbourne*

(i) *Wmk V over Crown, W* **20** (V1)

F41 F 5 1d. yellowish green (*p* 13) (12.79) .. 10·00 7·00
a. Perf 12 .. .. 12·00 7·50
F42 F 6 1d. pale bistre (*p* 12½) (6.80) .. 5·00 1·00
a. Perf 12 .. .. 5·00 2·00
F43 F 7 6d. dull blue (*p* 13) (12.79) .. 20·00 5·00
a. Perf 12 .. .. 25·00 12·00
F44 44 1s. deep blue/*blue* (*p* 13) (12.79) .. 20·00 2·00
a. Perf 12 .. .. 20·00 3·00
*b. Bright blue/blue* (*p* 12½) (1882) .. 20·00 2·50
ba. Perf 12 .. .. — 3·00
F45 F 8 2s. deep blue/*green* (*p* 13) (12.79) .. 40·00 10·00
a. Perf 12 .. .. — 12·00
*b. Indigo/green* .. .. 30·00 15·00
ba. Perf 12 .. .. 50·00 15·00
F46 48 5s. claret/*yellow* (*p* 13) (12.79) .. 30·00 3·00
a. Perf 12 .. .. 30·00 7·50
*b. Pale claret/yellow* (*p* 12½) (1880) .. 30·00 7·50
ba. Perf 12 .. .. 50·00 7·50
F47 50 10s. chocolate/*rose* (*p* 13) (S, U) (12.79) — 50·00
a. Perf 12 (S, U)
F48 52 £1 yellow-orange/*yellow* (*p* 12) (1882)
F49 55 £2 deep blue (*p* 12½) (1881) .. — 65·00
F50 58 £10 dull mauve (*p* 12) (1879) ..
*a. Deep red-lilac* (1882) .. — 55·00

(ii) 1882–3: *Wmk V over Crown, W* **23** (V2)

F51 F 6 1d. ochre (*shades*) (*p* 12½) .. 10·00 2·00
a. Perf 12 .. .. 10·00 2·00
F52 F 7 6d. ultramarine (*p* 12½) .. 20·00 3·00
a. Perf 12 .. .. 20·00 3·00
F53 55 £2 blue (*p* 12) .. .. — 60·00
F54 57 £5 rose-pink (*p* 12) .. .. — £120

III. 1879–80: *Recess-printed direct from the die*

(i) *Wmk V over Crown, W* **20** (V1). *P* 13

F55 59 £25 yellow-green (1879) .. F.C. 40·00
*a. Deep green* (1880) .. F.C. 40·00
F56 £50 bright mauve (1879) .. F.C. 65·00
F57 £100 crimson-lake (1879) .. F.C. 65·00

(ii) 1882–3: *Wmk V over Crown, W* **23** (V2). *P* 12½

F58 59 £50 dull lilac-mauve .. F.C. 80·00
F59 £100 crimson .. .. F.C. 95·00
a. Perf 12 .. .. F.C. 95·00

Nos. F44 and F45 occur with *reversed* watermark (both rare).

*Reprints of Stamp Duty Series*: The only stamps in this series to be reprinted in 1891 (on wmk *V2*) were the two types of 1d. which by then had become obsolete. Again the colours are distinctive from the originals.

In 1879 certain other values inscribed "STAMP DUTY" (of varying heraldic designs) viz; 7s., 8s., 9s., 11s., 12s., 13s., 14s., 16s., 17s., 18s. and 19s. were prepared for use but were not issued. Proofs are known.

POSTAGE DUE STAMPS

D 1

(Dies eng Arthur Williams (values) and John McWilliams (frame). Typo)

**1890–1908.** *Type* D **1**. A. *Wmk V over Crown, W* **23** (V2). *P* 12 × 12½. (i) 1 Nov 1890 (½*d*., 24.12.90).

D 1 ½d. dull blue and brown-lake .. 2·50 2·00
D 2 1d. dull blue and brown-lake .. 3·75 1·40
D 3 2d. dull blue and brown-lake .. 6·00 1·10
D 4 4d. dull blue and brown-lake .. 7·00 1·50
D 5 5d. dull blue and brown-lake .. 6·00 2·00
D 6 6d. dull blue and brown-lake .. 7·50 1·75
D 7 10d. dull blue and brown-lake .. 70·00 35·00
D 8 1s. dull blue and brown-lake .. 35·00 6·50
D 9 2s. dull blue and brown-lake .. £110 45·00
D10 5s. dull blue and brown-lake .. £160 90·00

The blue shades vary considerably.

(ii) 1890–94

D11 ½d. dull blue and deep claret (1890) .. 2·25 1·90
D12 1d. dull blue and brownish red (20.1.93) .. 4·00 1·10
D13 2d. dull blue and brownish red (28.3.93) .. 6·00 90
D14 4d. dull blue and pale claret (28.5.94) .. 6·00 6·00
D2/11 Optd "Specimen" .. *Set of* 10 £300

Nos. D1 and D11 were separate printings, both made in December 1890.

(iii) 17 Jan 1895. *Colours changed*

D15 ½d. rosine and bluish green .. 2·10 1·60
D16 1d. rosine and bluish green .. 1·60 40
D17 2d. rosine and bluish green .. 2·25 30
D18 4d. rosine and bluish green .. 4·50 1·50
D19 5d. rosine and bluish green .. 4·75 2·75
D20 6d. rosine and bluish green .. 4·50 2·75
D21 10d. rosine and bluish green .. 12·00 10·00
D22 1s. rosine and bluish green .. 7·50 3·25

(iv) 28 March 1895

D23 2s. pale red and yellowish green .. 60·00 20·00
D24 5s. pale red and yellowish green .. £100 40·00

(v) March 1896 onwards

D25 ½d. pale scarlet and yellow-green .. 2·25 1·50
D26 1d. pale scarlet and yellow-green .. 1·75 35
D27 2d. pale scarlet and yellow-green .. 2·50 30
D28 4d. pale scarlet and yellow-green .. 5·50 1·00
D29 5d. pale scarlet and yellow-green .. 5·00 2·50

B. *W* **72** (V3). *P* 12½ *or* 12 × 12½. (i) July 1897 onwards

D30 1d. pale scarlet and yellow-green .. 2·00 30
D31 2d. pale scarlet and yellow-green .. 3·00 30
D32 4d. pale scarlet and yellow-green .. 4·50 1·25
D33 5d. pale scarlet and yellow-green .. 5·00 2·50
D34 6d. pale scarlet and yellow-green .. 5·00 2·75

(ii) July–Sept 1899

D35 1d. dull red and bluish green .. 2·50 30
D36 2d. dull red and bluish green .. 3·00 35
D37 4d. dull red and bluish green .. 5·50 1·10

C. *W* **75** (V4). *P* 12½ *or* 12 × 12½. (i) 1900–1

D38 ½d. rose-red and pale green .. 2·50 1·50
D39 1d. rose-red and pale green .. 2·00 35
D40 2d. rose-red and pale green .. 2·50 30
D41 4d. rose-red and pale green .. 6·00 1·75

(ii) 1901–2

D42 ½d. pale red and deep green .. 1·50 1·50
D43 1d. pale red and deep green .. 1·50 35
D44 2d. pale red and deep green .. 2·75 35
D45 4d. pale red and deep green .. 5·00 1·40

(iii) 1902–3

D45*a* ½d. scarlet and deep green .. — 20·00
D46 1d. scarlet and deep green .. 2·50 30
D47 2d. scarlet and deep green .. 2·75 30
D48 4d. scarlet and deep green .. 5·50 1·00
D49 5d. scarlet and deep green .. 4·50 2·50
D50 1s. scarlet and deep green .. 8·00 2·75
D51 2s. scarlet and deep green .. £100 60·00
D52 5s. scarlet and deep green .. £120 60·00

The deep green of Nos. D45*a*–52 has more "yellow" than that of D42–45.

(iv) 1904

D53 ½d. rosine (*aniline*) and green .. 2·75 3·00
D54 1d. rosine (*aniline*) and green .. 2·00 40
D55 2d. rosine (*aniline*) and green .. 2·50 45
D56 4d. rosine (*aniline*) and green .. 6·00 1·50

D. *Wmk Crown over A* (*W w* **11**). *P* 12½ *or* 12 × 12½. (i) Jan 1906

D57 ½d. rosine (*aniline*) and pale green .. 3·25 3·00
D58 1d. rosine (*aniline*) and green .. 22·00 2·75

(ii) March 1906

D59 ½d. scarlet and pale yellow-green .. 2·00 1·50
D60 1d. scarlet and pale yellow-green .. 2·00 30

(iii) Dec 1906

D61 1d. scarlet (*aniline*) and deep yellow-green 2·25 30
D62 2d. scarlet (*aniline*) and deep yellow-green 3·00 45

(iv) 1907–8

D63 ½d. dull scarlet and pea-green .. 2·25 1·50
D64 1d. dull scarlet and pea-green .. 2·50 35
D65 2d. dull scarlet and pea-green .. 3·75 35
D66 4d. dull scarlet and pea-green .. 7·00 3·75

*Perf compound* 12 × 12½ *with* 11

D67 ½d. dull scarlet and pea-green .. £110 65·00

In D59 and D60 the centre is more clearly printed than in the later printings. A 5d. value was prepared and printed on Crown over A paper but was not issued. A few copies are known, some postmarked to order from presentation sets (*Price £1500 mint, £750 used c.t.o.*).

Victoria became part of the Commonwealth of Australia on 1 January 1901.

## WESTERN AUSTRALIA

**PRICES FOR STAMPS ON COVER**

| | |
|---|---|
| Nos. 1/6 | *from* × 4 |
| Nos. 15/32 | *from* × 3 |
| Nos. 33/46 | *from* × 4 |
| Nos. 49/51 | *from* × 5 |
| Nos. 52/62 | *from* × 8 |
| Nos. 63/*a* | *from* × 6 |
| No. 67 | *from* × 5 |
| Nos. 68/92*a* | *from* × 8 |
| Nos. 94/102 | *from* × 30 |
| Nos. 103/5 | *from* × 6 |
| Nos. 107/10*a* | *from* × 10 |
| Nos. 111*a*/*b* | — |
| Nos. 112/16 | *from* × 20 |
| Nos. 117/25 | *from* × 10 |
| Nos. 126/8 | — |
| Nos. 129/34 | *from* × 8 |
| Nos. 135/6 | — |
| Nos. 138/48 | *from* × 12 |
| Nos. 151/63 | *from* × 4 |
| Nos. 168/9 | *from* × 20 |
| Nos. 170/1 | *from* × 4 |
| Nos. 172/3 | *from* × 40 |
| Nos. F11/22 | *from* × 10 |
| Nos. T1/2 | — |

**SPECIMEN OVERPRINTS.** Those listed are from U.P.U. distributions between 1889 and 1892. Further "Specimen" overprints exist, but those were used for other purposes.

1

2

3

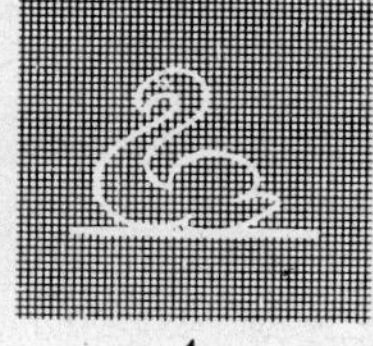

4

**GUM.** The 1854 issues are hardly ever seen with gum and so the unused prices quoted are for examples without gum.

(Eng W. Humphrys. Recess P.B.)

**1854** (1 Aug). *W* **4** (*sideways*). (*a*) *Imperf.*

1 1 1d. black .. .. £800 £180

(*b*) *Rouletted* 7½ *to* 14 *and compound*

2 1 1d. black .. .. £1100 £350

In addition to the supplies received from London a further printing, using the original plate and watermarked paper from Perkins, Bacon, was made in the colony before the date of issue.

The 1d. is also known pin-perforated.

(Litho H. Samson (later A. Hillman), Government Lithographer)

**1854** (1 Aug)–**55.** *W* **4** (*sideways*). (*a*) *Imperf.*

3 2 4d. pale blue .. .. £225 £150
*a. Blue* .. .. £225 £150
*b. Deep dull blue* .. .. £1200 £600
*c. Slate-blue* (1855) .. .. £1200 £650
4 3 1s. salmon .. .. — £1200
*a. Deep red-brown* .. .. £750 £375
*b. Grey-brown* (1.55) .. .. £450 £325
*c. Pale brown* (10.55) .. .. £325 £275

(*b*) *Rouletted* 7½ *to* 14 *and compound*

5 2 4d. pale blue .. .. £1100 £375
*a. Blue* .. .. — £375
*b. Slate-blue* (1855) .. .. — £1100
6 3 1s. grey-brown (1.55) .. .. £1400 £600
*a. Pale brown* (10.55) .. .. £1400 £600

The 1s. is also known pin-perforated.

The 4d. value was prepared from the Perkins, Bacon 1d. plate. A block of 60 (5 × 12) was taken as a transfer from this plate, the frames painted out and then individually replaced by transfers taken from a single impression master plate of the frame. Four transfers were then taken from this completed intermediate stone to construct the printing stone of 240 impressions. This first printing stone was used by H. Samson to print the initial supplies in July 1854.

The intermediate stone had carried several transfer errors, the most prominent of which was the "T" of "POSTAGE" sliced at foot, which appeared on four positions of the printing stone.

3d. "T" of "POSTAGE" shaved off to a point at foot (R.7/5, 7/10, 7/15, 7/20) .. .. £650 £475

The original printing stone also contained three scarce creased transfers, whose exact positions in the sheet have yet to be established. These were corrected during the first printing.

3e. Top of letters of "AUSTRALIA" cut off so that they are barely 1 mm high .. .. — £6000
f. "PEICE" instead of "PENCE" .. .. — £6000
g. "CE" of "Pence" close together .. .. — £8000

Further supplies were required in January 1855 and A. Hillman, Samson's successor, found, after printing three further sheets from the first printing stone, that two of the impressions on the intermediate stone were defective giving one inverted and one tilted frame. A second printing stone was then prepared on which the four positions of the inverted frame were individually corrected.

3h. Frame inverted (R.8/1, 8/6, 8/11, 8/16) .. — £60000
i. Tilted border (R.7/4, 7/9, 7/14, 7/19) .. .. £700 £500

None of the creased transfers from the first printing stone appear on the second, which exhibits its own range of similar varieties.

3j. "WEST" in squeezed-down letters and "F" of "FOUR" with pointed foot (R.2/17) .. .. £750 £550
k. "ESTERN" in squeezed-down letters and "U" of "FOUR" squeezed-up (R.3/17) .. .. £1200 £1000
l. Small "S" in "POSTAGE" (R.4/17) .. .. £750 £550
m. "EN" of "PENCE" shorter (R.6/4) .. .. £700 £500
n. "N" of "PENCE" tilted to right with thin first downstroke (R.6/16) .. .. £650 £475
o. Swan and water above "ENCE" damaged (R.6/20) .. .. £700 £500
p. "F" of "FOUR" slanting to left (R.7/17) .. £700 £500
q. "WESTERN" in squeezed-down letters only 1½ mm high (R.8/17) .. .. £800 £600
r. "P" of "PENCE" with small head (R.9/15) .. £700 £500
s. "RALIA" in squeezed-down letters only 1½ mm high (R.9/16) .. .. £750 £550
t. "PE" of "PENCE" close together (R.10/15) .. £700 £500
u. "N" of "PENCE" narrow (R.10/16) .. .. £700 £500
v. Part of right cross-stroke and down-stroke of "T" of "POSTAGE" cut off (R.11/15) .. £700 £500
w. "A" in "POSTAGE" with thin right limb (R.11/16) .. .. £650 £475

For the third printing in October 1855 the impressions showing the inverted frame were replaced on the printing stone with fresh individual transfers of the frame. On two of the positions traces of the original frame transfer remained visible.

3x. Coloured line above "AGE" of "POSTAGE" (R.8/6) .. .. £700 £500
y. No outer line above "GE" of "POSTAGE" and coloured line under "FOU" of "FOUR" (R.8/11) .. .. £750 £550

The same stone was used for a further printing in December 1855 and it is believed that the slate-blue shade occurred from one of the 1855 printings.

The above varieties, with the exception of Nos. 3e/g, also occur on the rouletted stamps.

The 1s. value was produced in much the same way, based on a transfer from the Perkins, Bacon 1d. plate.

5

(Litho A. Hillman, Government Lithographer)

**1857** (7 Aug)–**59.** *W* **4** (*sideways*). (*a*) *Imperf.*

15 5 2d. brown-black/*red* (26.2.58) .. £1700 £500
a. Printed both sides .. .. £1900 £800
16 2d. brown-black/*Indian red* (26.2.58) .. — £800
a. Printed both sides .. .. £1700 £850

17 5 6d. golden bronze .. .. .. £3000 £1300
18 6d. black-bronze .. .. .. £1800 £600
19 6d. grey-black (1859) .. .. .. £1900 £500
*(b) Rouletted 7½ to 14 and compound*
20 5 2d. brown-black/*red* .. .. .. £2500 £1000
a. Printed both sides .. .. ..
21 2d. brown-black/*Indian red* .. .. — £1200
22 6d. black-bronze .. .. .. £2250 £700
23 6d. grey-black .. .. .. .. — £750

The 2d. and 6d. are known pin-perforated.

Prices quoted for Nos. 15/23 are for "cut-square" examples. Collectors are warned against "cut-round" copies with corners added.

(Recess in the colony from P.B. plates)

**1860** (11 Aug)–**64**. *W* **4** *(sideways). (a) Imperf.*
24 1 2d. pale orange .. .. .. .. 65·00 50·00
25 2d. orange-vermilion .. .. .. 60·00 45·00
a. Wmk upright .. .. ..
25*b* 2d. deep vermilion .. .. .. £225 £300
26 4d. blue (21.6.64) .. .. .. £180 £1200
27 4d. deep blue .. .. .. .. £180 £1300
28 6d. sage-green (27.7.61) .. .. £1100 £400
28*a* 6d. deep sage-green .. .. .. — £475
*(b) Rouletted 7½ to 14*
29 1 2d. pale orange .. .. .. .. £300 £130
30 2d. orange-vermilion .. .. .. £375 £140
31 4d. deep blue .. .. .. .. £1600
32 6d. sage-green .. .. .. .. £1100 £375

(Recess P.B.)

**1861**. *W* **4** *(sideways). (a) Intermediate perf* 14–16.
33 1 1d. rose .. .. .. .. .. £225 75·00
34 2d. blue .. .. .. .. .. £110 38·00
35 4d. vermilion .. .. .. .. £300 £160
36 6d. purple-brown .. .. .. .. £250 50·00
37 1s. yellow-green .. .. .. .. £325 80·00
*(b) P 14 at Somerset House*
38 1 1d. rose .. .. .. .. .. £120 38·00
39 2d. blue .. .. .. .. .. 50·00 25·00
40 4d. vermilion .. .. .. .. £120 £100
*(c) Perf clean-cut 14–16*
41 1 2d. blue .. .. .. .. .. 60·00 24·00
a. Imperf between (pair) .. ..
42 6d. purple-brown .. .. .. .. £140 32·00
43 1s. yellow-green .. .. .. .. £250 45·00
*(d) P 14–16 very rough* (July)
44 1 1d. rose-carmine .. .. .. .. £150 24·00
45 6d. purple/*blue* .. .. .. .. £500 £100
46 1s. deep green .. .. .. .. £700 £170

Perkins, Bacon experienced considerable problems with their perforating machine during the production of these stamps.

The initial printing showed intermediate perforation 14–16. Further supplies were then sent, in late December 1860, to Somerset House to be perforated on their comb 14 machine. The Inland Revenue Board were only able to process the three lower values, although the 6d. purple-brown and 1s. yellow-green are known from this perforation overprinted "SPECIMEN".

The Perkins, Bacon machine was repaired the following month and the 6d., 1s. and a further supply of the 2d. were perforated on it to give a clean-cut 14–16 gauge.

A final printing was produced in July 1861, but by this time the machine had deteriorated so that it produced a very rough 14–16.

(Recess D.L.R. from P.B. plates)

**1863** (16 Dec)–**64**. *No wmk. P* 13.
49 1 1d. carmine-rose .. .. .. 40·00 5·50
50 1d. lake .. .. .. .. 40·00 5·00
51 6d. deep lilac (15.4.64) .. .. 75·00 30·00
51*a* 6d. dull violet (15.4.64) .. .. £100 35·00

Both values exist on thin and on thick papers, the former being the scarcer.

Both grades of paper show a marginal sheet watermark, "T H SAUNDERS 1860" in double-lined large and small capitals, but parts of this watermark rarely occur on the stamps.

(Recess D.L.R. from P.B. plates)

**1864** (27 Dec)–**79**. *Wmk Crown CC (sideways on* 1d.*). P* 12½.
52 1 1d. bistre .. .. .. .. 40·00 1·40
53 1d. yellow-ochre (16.10.74) .. .. 55·00 5·50
54 2d. chrome-yellow (18.1.65) .. .. 45·00 90
55 2d. yellow .. .. .. .. 42·00 90
a. Wmk sideways (5.79) .. .. — 15·00
b. Error. Mauve (1879) .. .. £5000 £2500
56 4d. carmine (18.1.65) .. .. .. 50·00 5·00
a. Doubly printed .. .. .. £5000
57 6d. violet (18.1.65) .. .. .. 60·00 6·00
a. Doubly printed .. .. .. † £7000
b. Wmk sideways .. .. .. — £150
58 6d. indigo-violet .. .. .. £225 28·00
59 6d. lilac (1872) .. .. .. £120 6·00
60 6d. mauve (12.5.75) .. .. .. £110 6·00
61 1s. bright green (18.1.65) (H/S S. £85) 80·00 12·00
62 1s. sage-green (10.68) .. .. £200 20·00

Beware of fakes of No. 55b made by altering the value tablet of No. 60.

7

ONE PENNY

(8)

(Typo D.L.R.)

**1871** (29 Oct)–**73**. *Wmk Crown CC (sideways). P* 14.
63 7 3d. pale brown (H/S S. £75) .. .. 24·00 4·00
*a. Cinnamon* (1873) .. .. .. 24·00 3·50

**1874** (10 Dec). *No.* 55 *surch with T* **8** *by Govt Printer.*
67 1 1d. on 2d. yellow (G.) .. .. .. £130 45·00
a. Pair, one without surch .. ..
b. Surch triple .. .. .. — £900
c. "O" of "ONE" omitted .. ..

Forged surcharges of T **8** are known on stamps wmk Crown CC perf 14, and on Crown CA, perf 12 and 14.

(Recess D.L.R. from P.B. plates)

**1876–81**. *Wmk Crown CC (sideways). P* 14.
68 1 1d. ochre .. .. .. .. 38·00 70
69 1d. bistre (1878) .. .. .. 45·00 2·75
70 1d. yellow-ochre (1879) .. .. 38·00 70
71 2d. chrome-yellow .. .. .. 38·00 50
a. Wmk upright (1877) .. .. 60·00 85
74 4d. carmine (1881) .. .. .. £225 75·00
75 6d. lilac (1877) .. .. .. 75·00 3·25
a. Wmk upright (1879) .. .. £450 15·00
75*b* 6d. reddish lilac (1879) .. .. 75·00 5·50

(Recess D.L.R. from P.B. plates)

**1882** (Mar)–**85**. *Wmk Crown CA (sideways). (a) P* 14.
76 1 1d. yellow-ochre .. .. .. 12·00 50
77 2d. chrome-yellow .. .. .. 16·00 50
a. Wmk upright .. .. .. † —
78 4d. carmine (8.82) .. .. .. 70·00 8·00
a. Wmk upright (1885) .. ..
79 6d. reddish lilac (1882) .. .. 70·00 3·00
80 6d. lilac (1884) (H/S S. £75) .. 70·00 4·00
*(b) P* 12 × 14
81 1 1d. yellow-ochre (2.83) .. .. £1000 £150
*(c) P* 12
82 1 1d. yellow-ochre (2.83) .. .. 60·00 1·25
83 2d. chrome-yellow (6.83) .. .. 75·00 1·25
a. Imperf between (pair) .. ..
84 4d. carmine (5.83) .. .. .. £110 25·00
85 6d. lilac (6.83) .. .. .. £180 19·00

(Typo D.L.R.)

**1882** (July)–**95**. *Wmk Crown CA (sideways). P* 14.
86 7 3d. pale brown .. .. .. 9·50 70
87 3d. red-brown (12.95) .. .. 8·50 70

The 3d. stamps in other colours, watermark Crown CA and perforated 12, are colour trials dating from 1883.

½ 1d. 1d.

(9) (10) (11)

**1884** (19 Feb). *Surch with T* **9**, *in red, by Govt Printer.*
89 1 ½ on 1d. yellow-ochre (No. 76) .. 13·00 14·00
a. Thin bar .. .. .. 70·00 48·00
90 ½ on 1d. yellow-ochre (No. 82) .. 9·00 10·00

Inverted or double surcharges are forgeries made in London about 1886.

The "Thin bar" varieties occur on R12/3, R12/8, R12/13 and R12/18, and show the bar only 0.2 mm thick.

**1885** (May). *Nos.* 63/*a surch, in green, by Govt Printer.*
*(a) Thick "1" with slanting top, T* **10** (Horizontal Rows 1/5)
91 1d. on 3d. pale brown .. .. .. 35·00 9·50
*a. Cinnamon* .. .. .. 26·00 7·50
b. Vert pair. Nos. 91/2 .. ..
*(b) Thin "1" with straight top, T* **11** (Horizontal Row 6)
92 1d. on 3d. pale brown .. .. .. 50·00 12·00
*a. Cinnamon* .. .. .. 38·00 13·00

12 13

14 15

(Typo D.L.R.)

**1885** (May)–**93**. *Wmk Crown CA (sideways). P* 14.
94 12 ½d. yellow-green .. .. .. 1·50 10
94*a* ½d. green .. .. .. 1·50 10
95 13 1d. carmine (2.90) .. .. .. 5·00 10
96 14 2d. bluish grey (6.90) .. .. 9·00 25
96*a* 2d. grey .. .. .. 8·00 25
97 15 2½d. deep blue (1.5.92) .. .. 5·50 35
97*a* 2½d. blue .. .. .. 6·00 35
98 4d. chestnut (7.90) .. .. 6·00 35
99 5d. bistre (1.5.92) .. .. 8·00 1·25
100 6d. bright violet (1.93) .. .. 14·00 1·00
101 1s. pale olive-green (4.90) .. .. 22·00 2·50
102 1s. olive-green .. .. .. 17·00 2·00
94, 96*a*, 97*a*/99, 101 Optd/H/S "Specimen" *Set of* 6 £200

(Recess D.L.R. from P.B. plates)

**1888** (Mar–Apr). *Wmk Crown CA (sideways). P* 14.
103 1 1d. carmine-pink .. .. .. 12·00 60
104 2d. grey .. .. .. .. 26·00 1·00
105 4d. red-brown (April) .. .. 80·00 18·00
103/5 H/S "Specimen" .. .. *Set of* 3 £150

ONE PENNY Half-penny

(16) (17)

**1893** (Feb). *Surch with T* **16**, *in green, by Govt Printer.*
107 7 1d. on 3d. pale brown (No. 63) .. .. 8·50 2·75
108 1d. on 3d. cinnamon (No. 63*a*) .. .. 8·50 3·00
a. Double surcharge .. .. £450
109 1d. on 3d. pale brown (No. 86) .. .. 30·00 4·25

**1895** (21 Nov). *Surch with T* **17** *by Govt Printer. (a) In green.*
110 7 ½d. on 3d. pale brown (No. 63) .. .. 7·50 14·00
110*a* ½d. on 3d. cinnamon (No. 63*a*) .. .. 5·50 10·00
b. Surcharge double .. .. £350
*(b) In red and in green*
111*a* 7 ½d. on 3d. cinnamon (No. 63*a*) .. .. 90·00
111*b* ½d. on 3d. red-brown (No. 87) .. .. 50·00

Green was the adopted surcharge colour but a trial had earlier been made in red on stamps watermarked Crown CC. As they proved unsatisfactory they were given another surcharge in green. The trial stamps were inadvertently issued and, to prevent speculation, a further printing of the duplicated surcharge was made, but on both papers, Crown CC (No. 111*a*) and Crown CA (No. 111*b*).

18 19

20 21

(Typo D.L.R.)

**1898** (Dec)–**1907**. *Wmk W Crown A, W* **18**. *P* 14.
112 13 1d. carmine .. .. .. 2·75 10
113 14 2d. bright yellow (1.99) .. .. 6·50 35
114 19 2½d. blue (1.01) .. .. .. 5·00 30
115 20 6d. bright violet (10.06) .. .. 14·00 50
116 21 1s. olive-green (4.07) .. .. 18·00 3·50

22 23 24

25 26 27

28 29 30

31 32 33

(Typo Victorian Govt Printer, Melbourne)

**1902** (Oct)–**12**. *Wmk V and Crown, W* **33** *(sideways on horiz designs).*
*(a) P* 12½ *or* 12½ × 12 *(horiz),* 12 × 12½ *(vert)*
117 22 1d. carmine-rose (1.03) .. .. 5·00 10
a. Wmk upright (10.02) .. .. 7·00 30
118 23 2d. yellow (4.1.03) .. .. .. 3·00 40
a. Wmk upright (12.7.04) .. .. — 90
119 24 4d. chestnut (4.03) .. .. .. 5·50 90
a. Wmk upright .. .. ..
120 15 5d. bistre (4.9.05) .. .. .. 65·00 42·00
121 25 8d. apple-green (3.03) .. .. 20·00 2·50
122 26 9d. yellow-orange (5.03) .. .. 26·00 4·75
a. Wmk upright (11.03) .. .. 35·00 14·00
123 27 10d. red (3.03) .. .. .. 28·00 4·50
124 28 2s. bright red/*yellow* .. .. 70·00 14·00
a. Wmk sideways .. .. .. — 16·00
*b. Orange/yellow* (7.06) .. .. 48·00 8·50
*c. Brown-red/yellow* (5.11) .. .. 48·00 8·50
125 29 2s. 6d. deep blue/*rose* .. .. 40·00 8·00
126 30 5s. emerald-green .. .. .. 80·00 18·00
127 31 10s. deep mauve .. .. .. £180 48·00
*a. Bright purple* (1910) .. .. £200 60·00
128 32 £1 orange-brown (1.11.02) .. .. £300 £150
*a. Orange* (10.7.09) .. .. £600 £300

(*b*) *P* 11

| | | | | |
|---|---|---|---|---|
| 129 | **22** | 1d. carmine-rose | 80·00 | 6·50 |
| | | a. Wmk upright | | |
| 130 | **23** | 2d. yellow | £100 | 8·00 |
| | | a. Wmk upright | | |
| 131 | **24** | 4d. chestnut | £325 | £100 |
| 132 | **15** | 5d. bistre | 42·00 | 23·00 |
| 133 | **26** | 9d. yellow-orange | 60·00 | 40·00 |
| 134 | **28** | 2s. bright red/*yellow* | £110 | 60·00 |
| | | *a. Orange/yellow* | £225 | £100 |

(*c*) *Perf compound of* 12½ *or* 12 *and* 11

| | | | | |
|---|---|---|---|---|
| 135 | **22** | 1d. carmine-rose | — | £160 |
| 136 | **23** | 2d. yellow | — | £200 |
| 137 | **24** | 4d. chestnut | | |

Type **22** is similar to Type **13** but larger.

**34**

**35**

**1905–12.** *Wmk Crown and A, W* **34** (*sideways*).

(*a*) *P* 12½ *or* 12½ × 12 (*horiz*), 12 × 12½ (*vert*)

| | | | | |
|---|---|---|---|---|
| 138 | **12** | ½d. green (6.10) | 1·50 | 70 |
| 139 | **22** | 1d. rose-pink (10.05) | 3·25 | 10 |
| | | a. Wmk upright (1.06) | 2·75 | 10 |
| | | *b. Carmine* (1909) | 3·75 | 15 |
| | | *c. Carmine-red* (1912) | 5·00 | 75 |
| 140 | **23** | 2d. yellow (15.11.05) | 1·75 | 40 |
| | | a. Wmk upright (4.10) | | |
| 141 | **7** | 3d. brown (2.06) | 4·50 | 50 |
| 142 | **24** | 4d. bistre-brown (12.06) | 5·50 | 1·25 |
| | | *a. Pale chestnut* (1908) | 8·50 | 85 |
| | | *b. Bright brown-red* (14.10.10) | 7·50 | 65 |
| 143 | **15** | 5d. pale olive-bistre (8.05) | 11·00 | 1·75 |
| | | *a. Olive-green* (1.09) | 11·00 | 1·75 |
| | | *b. Pale greenish yellow* (5.12) | 50·00 | 42·00 |
| 144 | **25** | 8d. apple-green (22.4.12) | 17·00 | 13·00 |
| 145 | **26** | 9d. orange (11.5.06) | 22·00 | 3·50 |
| | | *a. Red-orange* (6.10) | 32·00 | 3·50 |
| | | b. Wmk upright (7.12) | 38·00 | 22·00 |
| 146 | **27** | 10d. rose-orange (16.2.10) | 22·00 | 10·00 |
| 148 | **30** | 5s. emerald-grn (*wmk upright*) (9.07) | 60·00 | 42·00 |

(*b*) *P* 11

| | | | | |
|---|---|---|---|---|
| 150 | **12** | ½d. green | | |
| 151 | **22** | 1d. rose-pink | 12·00 | 2·50 |
| | | *a. Carmine-red* | 12·00 | 1·50 |
| | | b. Wmk upright | 12·00 | 4·50 |
| 152 | **23** | 2d. yellow | 12·00 | 4·00 |
| 153 | **7** | 3d. brown | 9·00 | 2·00 |
| 154 | **24** | 4d. yellow-brown | £375 | 85·00 |
| | | *a. Pale chestnut* | | |
| 155 | **15** | 5d. pale olive-bistre | 28·00 | 10·00 |
| | | *a. Olive-green* | 16·00 | 6·50 |
| 157 | **26** | 9d. orange | 70·00 | 75·00 |
| | | *a. Red-orange* | — | 65·00 |
| | | b. Wmk upright (inverted) | — | £250 |

(*c*) *Perf compound of* 12½ *or* 12 *and* 11

| | | | | |
|---|---|---|---|---|
| 161 | **22** | 1d. rose-pink | £150 | 75·00 |
| 162 | **23** | 2d. yellow | £170 | 80·00 |
| 163 | **7** | 3d. brown | £190 | 85·00 |
| 164 | **26** | 9d. red-orange | | |

Only six examples are known of No. 157b, all used in 1912 or 1913.

**1912** (Mar). *Wmk Crown and A* (*sideways*). *W* **35.** *P* 11½ × 12.

| | | | | |
|---|---|---|---|---|
| 168 | **20** | 6d. bright violet | 9·50 | 3·25 |
| 169 | **21** | 1s. sage-green | 23·00 | 4·75 |
| | | a. Perf 12½ (single line) | | |

**1912** (7 Aug). *W* **34** (*sideways*). *Thin paper and white gum* (*as Victoria*).

| | | | | |
|---|---|---|---|---|
| 170 | **7** | 3d. brown (*p* 12½) | 30·00 | 30·00 |
| | | a. Wmk upright | 30·00 | 30·00 |
| 171 | | 3d. brown (*p* 11) | | |
| | | a. Wmk upright | | |

**ONE PENNY**

**(36)**

**1912** (6 Nov). *Nos.* 140 *and* 162 *surch with T* **36** *in Melbourne.*

(*a*) *P* 12½ *or* 12 × 12½

| | | | | |
|---|---|---|---|---|
| 172 | **23** | 1d. on 2d. yellow | 80 | 30 |
| | | a. Wmk upright | 1·00 | 70 |

(*b*) *Perf compound of* 12½ *and* 11

| | | | | |
|---|---|---|---|---|
| 173 | **23** | 1d. on 2d. yellow | £275 | |

POSTAL FISCAL STAMPS

By the Post and Telegraph Act of 5 September 1893 the current issue of fiscal stamps up to and including the 1s. value, Nos. F11/15, was authorised for postal use.

These stamps had been initially supplied, for fiscal purposes, in February 1882 and had been preceded by a series of "I R" surcharges and overprints on postage stamps which were in use for a period of about six months. Examples of these 1881–82 provisionals can be found postally used under the terms of the 1893 Act but, as they had not been current for fiscal purposes for over eleven years, we no longer list them.

F 3

(Typo D.L.R.)

**1893** (5 Sept). *Definitive fiscal stamps of Feb* 1882. *Wmk CA over Crown. P* 14.

| | | | | |
|---|---|---|---|---|
| F11 | F 3 | 1d. dull purple | 5·00 | 55 |
| F12 | | 2d. dull purple | 65·00 | 32·00 |
| F13 | | 3d. dull purple | 19·00 | 1·75 |
| F14 | | 6d. dull purple | 22·00 | 2·75 |
| F15 | – | 1s. dull purple | 32·00 | 3·25 |

The 1s. value is as Type F **3** but with rectangular outer frame and circular frame surrounding swan.

Higher values in this series were not validated by the Act for postal use.

Two varieties of watermark exist on these stamps. Initial supplies showed an indistinct watermark with the base of the "A" 4 mm wide. From 1896 the paper used showed a clearer watermark on which the base of the "A" was 5 mm wide.

**1897.** *Wmk W Crown A, W* **18.** *P* 14.

| | | | | |
|---|---|---|---|---|
| F19 | F 3 | 1d. dull purple | 3·50 | 70 |
| F20 | | 3d. dull purple | 9·00 | 1·25 |
| F21 | | 6d. dull purple | 10·00 | 1·25 |
| F22 | – | 1s. dull purple | 24·00 | 3·00 |

TELEGRAPH STAMPS USED FOR POSTAGE

The 1d. Telegraph stamps were authorised for postal purposes from 25 October 1886.

T 1

**1886** (25 Oct). *Wmk Crown CC.*

| | | | | |
|---|---|---|---|---|
| T1 | T 1 | 1d. bistre (*p* 12½) | 18·00 | 2·50 |
| T2 | | 1d. bistre (*p* 14) | 20·00 | 4·00 |

Copies of a similar 6d. value are known postally used, but such use was unauthorised.

OFFICIAL STAMPS

Stamps of the various issues from 1854–85 are found with a circular hole punched out, the earlier size being about 3 mm. in diameter and the later 4 mm. These were used on official correspondence by the Commissariat and Convict Department, branches of the Imperial administration separate from the colonial government. This system of punching ceased by 1886. Subsequently many stamps between Nos. 94 and 148 may be found punctured, "PWD", "WA" or "OS".

Western Australia became part of the Commonwealth of Australia on 1 January 1901.

## COMMONWEALTH OF AUSTRALIA

On 1 March 1901 control of the postal service passed to the federal administration. The first national postage due stamps appeared in July 1902, but it was not until January 1913 that postage stamps inscribed "AUSTRALIA" were issued.

**PRICES FOR STAMPS ON COVER TO 1945**

| | |
|---|---|
| Nos. 1/27 | *from* × 4 |
| Nos. 29/34 | *from* × 2 |
| Nos. 35/50*d* | *from* × 3 |
| Nos. 51/3 | *from* × 4 |
| Nos. 56/75 | *from* × 3 |
| Nos. 76/84 | *from* × 4 |
| Nos. 85/104 | *from* × 3 |
| Nos. 105/6 | *from* × 4 |
| Nos. 107/15 | *from* × 3 |
| No. 116 | *from* × 5 |
| Nos. 117/20 | *from* × 4 |
| Nos. 121/39*a* | *from* × 2 |
| Nos. 140/*a* | *from* × 5 |
| Nos. 141/4 | *from* × 3 |
| No. 146 | *from* × 6 |
| Nos. 147/53 | *from* × 3 |
| Nos. 153*a*/*b* | *from* × 2 |
| Nos. 154/63 | *from* × 3 |
| Nos. 164/211 | *from* × 2 |
| Nos. D1/118 | *from* × 8 |
| Nos. O123/36 | *from* × 5 |

**PRINTERS.** Except where otherwise stated, all Commonwealth stamps to No. 581 were printed under Government authority at Melbourne. Until 1918 there were two establishments (both of the Treasury Dept)—the Note Printing Branch and the Stamp Printing Branch. The former printed T **3** and **4**.

In 1918 the Stamp Printing Branch was closed and all stamps were printed by the Note Printing Branch. In 1926 control was transferred from the Treasury to the Commonwealth Bank of Australia, and on 14 January 1960 the branch was attached to the newly established Reserve Bank of Australia.

Until 1942 stamps bore in the sheet margin the initials or names of successive managers and from 1942 to March 1952 the imprint "Printed by the Authority of the Government of the Commonwealth of Australia". After November 1952 (or Nos. D129/31 for Postage Dues) imprints were discontinued.

**SPECIMEN OVERPRINTS.** These come from Specimen sets, first produced in 1913. In these sets the lower values were cancelled-to-order, but stamps with a face value of 7s. 6d. or 75 c. were overprinted "Specimen" in different types. These overprints are listed as they could be purchased from the Australian Post Office.

It is, however, believed that examples of No. 112 overprinted "Specimen" were distributed by the U.P.U. in 1929. Supplies of the 1902 and 1902–04 postage due stamps overprinted "Specimen" were supplied to the U.P.U. by some of the states.

The sale of the cancelled-to-order sets ceased after 1966, but high value "Specimen" overprints were retained to support philatelic funds.

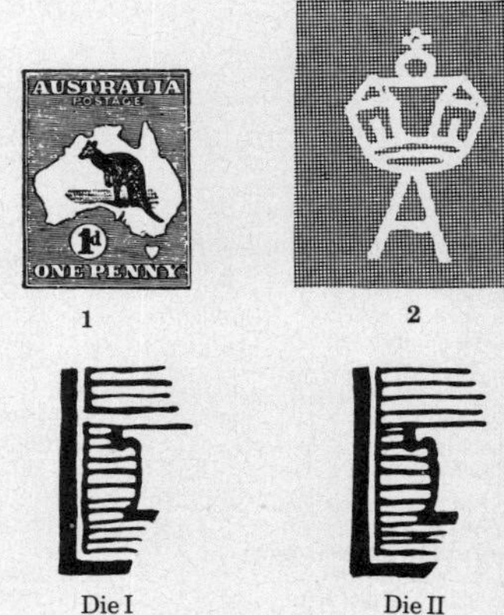

1 2

Die I Die II

Dies of Type 1 (mono-coloured values only):—

Die I. Break in inner frame line at lower left level with top of words of value.
Die II. Die repaired showing no break.

Die I was only used for the ½d., 1d., 2d. and 3d. Several plates were produced for each except the 3d. When the second plate of the 3d. was being prepared the damage became aggravated after making 105 out of the 120 units when the die was returned for repair. This gave rise to the *se-tenant* pairs showing the two states of the die.

Die II was used until 1945 and deteriorated progressively with damage to the frame lines and rounding of the corners.

Specialists recognise seven states of this die, but we only list the two most major of the later versions.

Die IIA. This state is as Die II, but, in addition, shows a break in the inner left-hand frame line, 9 mm from the top of the design.

Die IIB. As Die IIA, but now also showing break in outer frame line above "ST", and (not illustrated) an incomplete corner to the inner frame line at top right.

(Des B. Young. Eng S. Reading. Typo J. B. Cooke)

**1913** (Jan–Apr). *W* **2.** *P* 12.

| | | | | |
|---|---|---|---|---|
| 1 | **1** | ½d. green (Die I) (16 Jan) | 5·00 | 1·50 |
| | | a. Wmk sideways | † | — |
| 2 | | 1d. red (Die I) (2 Jan) | 6·50 | 50 |
| | | a. Wmk sideways | £700 | £100 |
| | | *b. Carmine* | 6·50 | 50 |
| | | c. Die II. *Red* | 6·50 | 50 |
| | | ca. Wmk sideways | £750 | £100 |
| | | *cb. Carmine* | 6·50 | 50 |
| | | d. Die IIA. *Red* | 8·00 | 50 |
| | | da. Wmk sideways | £700 | £100 |
| | | *db. Carmine* | 8·00 | 50 |
| 3 | | 2d. grey (Die I) (11 Jan) | 24·00 | 2·75 |
| 4 | | 2½d. indigo (Die II) (27 Jan) | 26·00 | 10·00 |
| 5 | | 3d. olive (Die I) (22 Jan) | 42·00 | 5·50 |
| | | a. Imperf three sides (pair) | £10000 | |
| | | b. In pair with Die II | £375 | £130 |
| | | *c. Yellow-olive* | 42·00 | 6·00 |
| | | ca. In pair with Die II | £375 | £130 |
| | | d. Die II. *Olive* | £140 | 45·00 |
| | | *da. Yellow-olive* | £140 | 45·00 |

6 1 4d. orange (Die II) (12 Feb) .. .. 48·00 22·00
*a. Orange-yellow* .. .. £170 48·00
8 5d. chestnut (Die II) (16 Jan) .. .. 40·00 28·00
9 6d. ultramarine (Die II) (11 Jan) .. .. 48·00 20·00
a. Retouched "E" .. .. .. £1500 £500
b. Die IIA .. .. .. .. £900 £225
10 9d. violet (Die II) (29 Jan) .. .. 45·00 20·00
11 1s. emerald (Die II) (21 Jan) .. .. 45·00 12·00
*a. Blue-green* .. .. .. 45·00 12·00
12 2s. brown (Die II) (25 Jan) .. .. £150 55·00
13 5s. grey and yellow (20 March) .. .. £250 £130
14 10s. grey and pink (20 March) .. .. £600 £400
15 £1 brown and blue (20 March) .. .. £1100 £1000
16 £2 black and rose (8 April) .. .. £2250 £1600
1/16 .. .. .. .. *Set of* 15 £4250 £3000
14/16 Optd "Specimen" .. .. *Set of* 3 £550

No. 9a shows a badly distorted second "E" in "PENCE", which is unmistakable. It occurs on the last stamp in the sheet and was replaced by a substitute cliché in Type IIA (No. 9b).

For the previous No. 12a see No. O11a.

See also Nos. 20/27 (*W* **5**), 35/45*b* (*W* **6**), 73/5 (*W* **6**, new colours), 107/14 (*W* **7**), 132/8 (*W* **15**), 212 (2s. re-engraved).

**INVERTED WATERMARKS** are met with in some values in this and subsequent issues.

3

4 Laughing Kookaburra

(Des R. A. Harrison. Eng and recess T. S. Harrison)

**1913** (8 Dec)–**14**. *No wmk. P* 11.
17 3 1d. red .. .. .. .. .. 2·00 4·00
*a. Pale rose-red* .. .. .. .. 6·50 10·00
b. Imperf horiz (vert pair) .. .. £1500
19 4 6d. claret (26.8.14) .. .. .. 70·00 38·00

All printing from Plate 1 of the 1d. were in the shade of No. 17*a*. This plate shows many retouches.

5

5*a*

(Typo J. B. Cooke)

**1915.** *W* **5**. *P* 12.
20 1 2d. grey (Die I) (2 Jan) .. .. .. 50·00 10·00
21 2½d. indigo (Die II) (July) .. .. 50·00 26·00
23 6d. ultramarine (Die II) (April) .. .. £130 22·00
*a. Bright blue* .. .. .. £170 48·00
b. Die IIA. *Ultramarine* .. .. £950 £200
*ba. Bright blue* .. .. .. £1200 £250
24 9d. violet (Die II) (9 July) .. .. £130 30·00
25 1s. blue-green (Die II) (Aug) .. .. £140 20·00
26 2s. brown (Die II) (April) .. .. £425 80·00
27 5s. grey and yellow (12 Feb) .. .. £600 £200
a. Yellow portion doubly printed .. £5500 £1100
20/27 .. .. .. .. *Set of* 7 £1400 £350

The watermark in this issue is often misplaced as the paper was made for the portrait stamps.

Die II

Die III

Die II. The flaw distinguishing the so-called Die II is now known to be due to a defective roller-die and occurs in 18 impressions on one of the plates. It appears as a white upward projection to right of the base of figure "1" in the shield containing value at left, as shown in the illustration.

Die III. In 1918 a printing (in sheets of 120) was made on paper prepared for printing War Savings Stamps, with wmk T **5**. A special plate was made for this printing, differing in detail from those previously used. The shading round the head is even; the solid background of the words "ONE PENNY" is bounded at each end by a *white* vertical line; and there is a horizontal white line cutting the vertical shading lines at left on the King's neck. *See* Nos. 55*b*/*c*.

(Dies eng P. B. Typo J. B. Cooke until 1918, then T. S. Harrison)

**1914–21.** *W* **5**. *P* 14.
29 5*a* ½d. bright green (22.2.15) .. .. 3·50 70
*a. Green* (13.5.16) .. .. .. 3·25 60
*b. Yellow-green* (8.16) .. .. 20·00 5·50
c. Thin "1" in fraction at right .. £1100 £500
30 1d. carmine-red (*shades*) (I) (17.7.14) .. 7·00 20
a. Rusted cliché (2 vars)* .. .. £4000 £400
b. Substituted cliché .. .. £1100 50·00
*c. Pale carmine* (*shades*) .. .. 14·00 20
*d. Carmine-pink* (1.18) .. .. 90·00 2·50
*e. Rose-red* (3.18) .. .. .. 10·00 1·50
*f. Carmine* (*aniline*) (1921) .. .. 15·00 1·75
31 5*a* 1d. carmine-red (*shades*) (II) (1914) .. £400 6·00
a. Substituted cliché .. .. .. £1100 50·00
*b. Pale red* (*shades*) .. .. .. £350 6·00
32 4d. orange (6.1.15) .. .. .. 38·00 2·25
*a. Yellow-orange* .. .. .. 38·00 3·25
*b. Pale orange-yellow* (10.15) .. .. 65·00 9·00
*c. Lemon-yellow* (1916) .. .. £120 14·00
*d. Dull orange* .. .. .. .. 45·00 3·25
e. Line through "FOUR PENCE" (*all shades*) .. .. .. *From* £500 £110
34 5d. brown (22.2.15) .. .. .. 16·00 1·40
*a. Yellow-brown* (1920) .. .. 25·00 2·00

The variety No. 29c was caused by the engraving of a new fraction in a defective electro.

*The two varieties listed under No. 30a were caused by rusting of the steel plate and show as white patches on the back of King's neck and on, and beside, the top of the right frame (upper left pane, No. 34); and on the left frame, wattles, head and ears of kangaroo (upper left pane, No. 35). These were noticed in late 1916 when the damaged impressions were removed and replaced by a pair of copper electros (Die II for No. 34 and Die I for No. 35), showing rounded corners and some frame damage, the former also showing a white spot under tail of emu. In time the tops of the crown quickly wore away. These substituted clichés (Nos. 30b and 31a) were formerly described as "Top of crown missing".

The 5d. is known printed on the gummed side of the paper.

Two machines were used for the 14 perforation, one an old single line, converted to that gauge, the other a new comb-machine. The former was used mainly for early printings of the 1d. and 5d. and very rarely for later printings of the ½d. and 1d.

See also Nos. 47/50*b* (*W* **5**, rough paper), 55*b*/*c* (1d. Die III), 51/5*a* (*W* **6**a), 56/66*b* and 76/84 (*W* **5**, new colours), 85/104 (*W* **7**), 124/31 (*W* **15**).

6

6*a*

Nos. 38ca and 73a
(R. 1/6, lower plate)

(Typo J. B. Cooke (to May 1918), T. S. Harrison (to February 1926), A. J. Mullett (to January 1927) and thereafter J. Ash)

**1915–28.** *W* **6** (*narrow Crown*). *P* 12.
35 1 2d. grey (Die I) (11.15) .. .. 28·00 4·00
a. In pair with Die IIA (1917)* .. .. £650 £300
*b. Silver-grey* (shiny paper) (2.18) .. 30·00 4·25
c. Die II. *Grey* (1918) .. .. .. 35·00 6·00
*ca. Silver-grey* (shiny paper) (2.18) .. 32·00 6·00
36 2½d. deep blue (Die II) (9.17) .. .. 22·00 7·00
*a. Deep indigo* (1920) .. .. .. 26·00 8·00
ab. "1" of fraction omitted .. .. £9000 £3000
37 3d. yellow-olive (Die I) (12.10.15) .. 27·00 3·00
a. In pair with Die II .. .. .. £225 80·00
*b. Olive-green* (1917) .. .. .. 30·00 3·00
ba. In pair with Die II .. .. .. £225 80·00
c. Die II. *Yellow-olive* .. .. .. 90·00 24·00
*ca. Olive-green* .. .. .. .. 90·00 24·00
d. Die IIB. *Light olive* (1923) .. .. 38·00 12·00
38 6d. ultramarine (Die II) (15.12.15) .. 55·00 6·00
a. Die IIA (substituted cliché) .. .. £700 £150
*b. Dull blue* .. .. .. .. 60·00 7·00
ba. Die IIA (substituted cliché) .. .. £800 £150
c. Die IIB. *Bright ultramarine* (23.7.21) .. .. .. .. 55·00 6·00
ca. Leg of kangaroo broken .. .. £2500 £500
39 9d. violet (Die II) (29.7.16) .. .. 38·00 4·75
a. Die IIB. *Violet* (16.4.19) .. .. 35·00 4·25
40 1s. blue-green (Die II) (6.16) .. .. 35·00 2·75
a. Die IIB (9.12.20) .. .. .. 35·00 2·50
b. Wmk sideways (1927) .. .. 70·00 £100
41 2s. brown (Die II) (6.16) .. .. £150 9·00
a. Imperf three sides (pair) .. .. £12000
*b. Red-brown* (*aniline*) .. .. .. £425 38·00
42 5s. grey and yellow (4.18) .. .. £180 65·00
*a. Grey and orange* (1920) .. .. £190 65·00
*b. Grey and deep yellow* .. .. £180 65·00
ba. Wmk sideways .. .. .. £2750 £1800
*c. Grey and pale yellow* (1928) .. .. £180 65·00
43 10s. grey and pink (5.2.17) .. .. £400 £150
*a. Grey and bright aniline pink* .. .. £350 £140
ab. Wmk sideways .. .. .. £3250 £1700
*b. Grey and pale aniline pink* (1928) .. £425 £150
44 £1 chocolate and dull blue (7.16) .. £1300 £700
*a. Chestnut and bright blue* (1917) .. £1400 £750
*b. Bistre-brown and bright blue* .. £1300 £700
ba. Wmk sideways .. .. .. £5500 £2250
45 £2 black and rose (12.19) .. .. £2250 £1300
*a. Grey and crimson* (1920) .. .. £2000 £1200
*b. Purple-black and pale rose* (1924) .. £1800 £1100
35/45*b* .. .. .. .. *Set of* 11 £3500 £1800
43/45 Optd "Specimen" .. .. *Set of* 3 £500

*The Die II of No. 35a is a substituted cliché introduced to replace a cracked plate which occurred on No. 55 of the upper left pane (Row 10, No. 1). The Die IIA characteristics are more pronounced in this cliché than on the sheet stamps from this die. The break at left, for instance, extends to the outer, in addition to the inner, frame line.

All values were printed by both Cooke and Harrison, and the 9d., 1s. and 5s. were also printed by Mullett and Ash.

**1916–18.** *W* **5**. *Rough paper, locally gummed. P* 14.
47 5*a* 1d. scarlet (I) (14.12.16) .. .. 22·00 1·25
48 1d. deep red (I) (1917) .. .. 22·00 1·00
49 1d. rose-red (I) (1918) .. .. 35·00 1·50
a. Substituted cliché .. .. .. £1100 75·00
49*b* 1d. rosine (I) (1918) .. .. .. 85·00 8·00
c. Substituted cliché .. .. .. £1400 £110
50 1d. rose-red (II) (1918) .. .. £275 20·00
aa. Substituted cliché .. .. .. £1100 75·00
50*a* 1d. rosine (II) (1918) .. .. .. £600 50·00
ab. Substituted cliché .. .. .. £1400 £110

For explanations of substituted cliché varieties, see 2nd paragraph of note below No. 34*a*.

For illustrations and descriptions of Dies II and III, see after T **5***a*.

For the previous No. 50*b* see No. O60.

(Typo J. B. Cooke or T. S. Harrison)

**1918–20.** *W* **6***a* (*Mult*). *P* 14.
51 5*a* ½d. green (*shades*) (8.1.18) .. .. 4·50 1·75
a. "1" in fraction at right thinner .. £100 40·00
b. Wmk sideways .. .. .. † £1800
52 1d. carmine-pink (I) (23.1.18) .. .. £120 40·00
*a. Deep red* (I) (1918) .. .. .. £750 £180
53 1d. carmine (I) (10.12.19) .. .. 32·00 5·00
*a. Deep red* (*aniline*) (I) (1920) .. .. £140 38·00
54 1½d. black-brown (30.1.19) .. .. 5·00 1·50
a. Very thin paper (3.19) .. .. 25·00 13·00
55 1½d. red-brown (4.19) .. .. .. 10·00 1·25
*a. Chocolate* .. .. .. .. 10·00 1·25

No. 51 was printed by Cooke and Harrison, Nos. 52/*a* by Cooke only and Nos. 53/55*a* by Harrison only. Nos. 52/*a* have rather yellowish gum, that of No. 53 being pure white.

**1918** (June). *Printed from a new plate* (Die III) *on white unsurfaced paper, locally gummed. W* **5**. *P* 14.
55*b* 5*a* 1d. rose-red (III) .. .. .. 65·00 26·00
55*c* 1d. rose-carmine (III) .. .. .. 65·00 26·00

(Typo T. S. Harrison and also A. J. Mullett for 1s. 4d. from March 1926)

**1918–23.** *W* **5**. *P* 14.
56 5*a* ½d. orange (9.11.23) .. .. .. 2·50 90
57 1d. violet (*shades*) (13.2.22) .. .. 4·50 60
a. Imperf three sides (pair) .. .. £7000
*b. Red-violet* .. .. .. .. 5·50 70
58 1½d. black-brown (9.11.18) .. .. 7·00 55
59 1½d. deep red-brown (4.19) .. .. 4·75 30
*a. Chocolate* .. .. .. .. 5·50 35
60 1½d. bright red-brown (20.1.22) .. .. 10·00 1·50
61 1½d. green (7.3.23) .. .. .. 2·00 25
a. Rough unsurfaced paper .. .. £110 50·00
62 2d. dull orange (5.10.20) .. .. 17·00 35
*a. Brown-orange* .. .. .. 15·00 35
63 2d. bright rose-scarlet (17.2.22) .. .. 6·50 40
*a. Dull rose-scarlet* .. .. .. 6·50 40
64 4d. violet (21.6.21) .. .. .. 9·00 10·00
a. Line through "FOUR PENCE" .. £7000 £3500
b. "FOUR PENCE" in thinner letters .. £500 £225
65 4d. ultramarine (*shades*) (23.3.22) .. 48·00 5·50
a. "FOUR PENCE" in thinner letters .. £600 £150
*b. Pale milky blue* .. .. .. 55·00 8·00
66 1s. 4d. pale blue (2.12.20) .. .. 65·00 18·00
*a. Dull greenish blue* (1923) .. .. 65·00 18·00
*b. Deep turquoise* .. .. .. £750 £110
56/66 .. .. .. .. *Set of* 11 £160 40·00

In addition to a number of mint pairs a single used example of No. 57 imperforate on three sides is known.

The 4d. ultramarine was originally printed by Cooke but the plates were worn in mid-1923 and Harrison prepared a new pair of plates. Stamps from these plates can only be distinguished by the minor flaws which are peculiar to them.

The variety of Nos. 64 and 65 with "FOUR PENCE" thinner, was caused by the correction of a defective cliché (No. 6, 2nd row, right-hand pane), which showed a line running through these words.

No. 61a was printed on a small residue of paper which had been employed for Nos. 47/50*d*.

(Typo T. S. Harrison (to February 1926), A. J. Mullett (to June 1927), thereafter J. Ash)

**1923–24.** *W* **6**. *P* 12.
73 1 6d. chestnut (Die IIB) (6.12.23) .. 20·00 1·00
a. Leg of kangaroo broken .. .. £100 60·00
74 2s. maroon (Die II) (1.5.24) .. .. 50·00 16·00
75 £1 grey (Die IIB) (1.5.24) (Optd S. £75) £425 £250

The 6d. and 2s. were printed by all three printers, but the £1 only by Harrison.

(Typo T. S. Harrison (to February 1926), thereafter A. J. Mullett)

**1924.** *P* 14. (*a*) *W* **5** (1 May).
76 5*a* 1d. sage-green .. .. .. 2·25 25
77 1½d. scarlet (*shades*) .. .. .. 2·00 20
a. Very thin paper .. .. .. 40·00 12·00
b. "HALEPENCE" .. .. .. 38·00 15·00
c. "RAL" of "AUSTRALIA" thin .. 38·00 15·00
d. Curved "1" and thin fraction at left 38·00 15·00
78 2d. red-brown .. .. .. .. 18·00 5·00
*a. Bright red-brown* .. .. .. 26·00 7·50
79 3d. dull ultramarine .. .. .. 24·00 1·25
a. Imperf three sides (horiz pair) .. £6500
80 4d. olive-yellow .. .. .. .. 26·00 2·00
*a. Olive-green* .. .. .. .. 28·00 2·00
81 4½d. violet .. .. .. .. 23·00 2·00

(*b*) *W* **6***a*
82 5*a* 1d. sage-green (20 May) .. .. 9·00 6·50

(*c*) *No wmk*
83 5*a* 1d. sage-green (18 August) .. .. 4·75 8·50
84 1½d. scarlet (14 August) .. .. .. 10·00 9·50
76/84 .. .. .. .. *Set of* 9 £100 32·00

Nos. 78/*a* and 82/4 were printed by Harrison only but the remainder were printed by both Harrison and Mullett.

In the semi-transparent paper of Nos. 54a and 77a the watermark is almost indistinguishable. Nos. 77b, 77c and 77d are typical examples of retouching of which there are many others in these issues. In No. 77c the letters "RAL" differ markedly from the normal. There is a white stroke cutting the oval frame-line above the "L", and the right-hand outer line of the Crown does not cut the white frame-line above the "A". No. 77b occurs on the row above No. 77c in the sheet, so that the varieties may be found *se-tenant*.

7

I

II

New Dies

1d. For differences see note after No. 27a.
1½d. From new steel plates made from a new die. Nos. 88 and 98 are the Ash printings, the ink of which is shiny.
2d. Die I. Height of frame 25.6 mm. Left-hand frame-line thick and uneven behind Kangaroo. Pearls in Crown vary in size.
Die II. Height of frame 25.6 mm. Left-hand frame-line thin and even. Pearls in Crown are all the same size.
Die III. Height 25.1 mm; lettering and figures of value bolder than Die I.
3d. Die II has bolder letters and figures than Die I, as illustrated above.
5d. Die II has a bolder figure "5" with flat top compared with Die I of the earlier issues.

(Typo by A. J. Mullett or J. Ash)

**1926–30.** *W* **7.** *(a) P* 14.
85 **5a** ½d. orange (10.3.27) .. .. .. 7·50 6·00
86 1d. sage-green (23.10.26) .. .. 3·75 75
87 1½d. scarlet (5.11.26) .. .. .. 6·00 70
88 1½d. golden scarlet (1927) .. .. 10·00 1·75
89 2d. red-brown (Die I) (17.8.27) .. 28·00 28·00
90 3d. dull ultramarine (12.26) .. .. 22·00 4·00
91 4d. yellow-olive (17.1.28) .. .. 48·00 28·00
92 4½d. violet (26.10.27) .. .. .. 15·00 3·00
93 1s. 4d. pale greenish blue (6.9.27) .. £150 75·00
85/93 .. .. .. .. .. *Set of* 8 £250 £130

*(b) P* 13½ × 12½
94 **5a** ½d. orange (21.11.28) .. .. .. 1·50 75
95 1d. sage-green (Die I) (23.12.26) .. 1·60 30
96 1d. sage-green (Die II).. .. .. 50·00 75·00
97 1½d. scarlet (14.1.27) .. .. .. 1·50 30
98 1½d. golden scarlet .. .. .. 2·00 35
98*a* 1½d. red-brown (16.9.30) .. .. 4·50 5·50
99 2d. red-brown (Die II) (28.4.28) .. 7·00 7·00
99*a* 2d. golden scarlet (Die II) (2.8.30) .. 8·50 90
99*b* 2d. golden scarlet (Die III) (9.9.30) .. 8·00 40
c. No wmk .. .. .. .. £750 £500
d. Tête-bêche (pair) .. .. .. £28000
100 3d. dull ultramarine (Die I) (23.2.28) 45·00 4·25
101 3d. deep ultramarine (Die II) (28.9.29) 23·00 1·25
102 4d. yellow-olive (4.29).. .. .. 23·00 2·00
103 4½d. violet (11.28) .. .. .. 48·00 20·00
103*a* 5d. orange-brown (Die II) (27.8.30) .. 17·00 2·25
104 1s. 4d. turquoise (30.9.28) .. .. 80·00 22·00
94/104 .. .. .. .. *Set of* 11 £190 55·00

Owing to defective manufacture, part of a sheet of the 2d. (Die III) escaped unwatermarked; while the watermark in other parts of the same sheet was faint or normal.

Only one example of No. 99d is known.

**8** Parliament House, Canberra

**9** "DH66" Biplane and Pastoral Scene

(Des R. A. Harrison. Die eng by Waterlow. Plates and printing by A. J. Mullett)

**1927** (9 May). *Opening of Parliament House, Canberra. No wmk. P* 11.
105 **8** 1½d. brownish lake .. .. .. 60 50
a. Imperf between (pair) .. .. £2750 £1900

(Eng T. S. Harrison. Recess J. Ash)

**1928** (29 Oct). *National Stamp Exhibition, Melbourne. As T* **4.** *No wmk. P* 11.
106 3d. blue .. .. .. .. 4·25 4·25
a. Pane of four with margins .. £170 £225
ab. Imperf (pane of four) .. .. £15000

No. 106a comes from special sheets of 60 stamps divided into 15 blocks of 4 (5 × 3) and separated by wide gutters perforated down the middle, printed and sold at the Exhibition.

(Typo J. Ash)

**1929–30.** *W* **7.** *P* 12.
107 **1** 6d. chestnut (Die IIB) (25.9.29) .. .. 22·00 4·00
108 9d. violet (Die IIB) (2.29).. .. 32·00 8·50
109 1s. blue-green (Die IIB) (12.6.29) .. 40·00 4·75
110 2s. maroon (Die II) (3.29) .. .. 50·00 14·00
111 5s. grey and yellow (30.11.29) .. £190 80·00
112 10s. grey and pink (2.29) .. .. £275 £400
114 **1** £2 black and rose (11.30) .. .. £1900 £425
107/114 .. .. .. .. *Set of* 7 £2250 £800
112/114 Optd "Specimen" .. .. *Set of* 2 £300

(Des R. A. Harrison and H. Herbert. Eng A. Taylor. Recess J. Ash)

**1929** (20 May). *Air. No wmk. P* 11.
115 **9** 3d. green (*shades*) .. .. .. 10·00 3·25

Variations of up to ¾ mm in the design size of No. 115 are due to paper shrinkage; the stamps having been printed by a "wet" process.

**10** Black Swan

**11** Capt. Charles Sturt

(Des Pitt Morison. Eng F. D. Manley. Recess J. Ash)

**1929** (28 Sept). *Centenary of Western Australia. No wmk. P* 11.
116 **10** 1½d. dull scarlet .. .. .. 1·00 1·25
a. Re-entry ("T" of "AUSTRALIA" clearly double) .. .. .. 55·00 42·00

(Des R. A. Harrison. Eng F. D. Manley. Recess J. Ash)

**1930** (2 June). *Centenary of Exploration of River Murray by Capt. Sturt. No wmk. P* 11.
117 **11** 1½d. scarlet .. .. .. .. 1·00 45
118 3d. blue .. .. .. .. 3·75 5·00

No. 117 with manuscript surcharge of "2d. paid P M L H I" was issued by the Postmaster of Lord Howe Island during a shortage of 2d. stamps between August and October 1930. A few copies of the 1½d. value No. 98 were also endorsed. These provisionals are not recognized by the Australian postal authorities. (*Price £550 un. or us., either stamp.*)

TWO

PENCE

(12)

**13** The *Southern Cross* above hemispheres

**1930** (1 Aug). *T* **5a** *surch as T* **12.** *W* **7.** *P* 13½ × 12½.
119 2d. on 1½d. golden scarlet .. .. 1·00 40
120 5d. on 4½d. violet .. .. .. 7·00 7·50

No. 120 is from a redrawn die in which the words "FOURPENCE HALFPENNY" are noticeably thicker than in the original die and the figure "4" has square instead of tapering serifs.

Stamps from the redrawn die without the surcharge were printed, but not issued thus. Some stamps, *cancelled to order*, were included in sets supplied by the post office. A few mint copies, which escaped the cancellation were found and some may have been used postally (*Price £2000 unused, £50 used c.t.o.*).

(Des and eng F. D. Manley. Recess John Ash)

**1931** (19 Mar). *Kingsford Smith's flights. No wmk. P* 11. *(a) Postage.*
121 **13** 2d. rose-red .. .. .. .. 75 45
122 3d. blue .. .. .. .. 5·00 4·00

*(b) Air. Inscr "AIR MAIL SERVICE"*
123 **13** 6d. violet .. .. .. .. 10·00 10·00
a. Re-entry ("FO" and "LD" double) .. 80·00 65·00
121/3 .. .. .. .. .. *Set of* 3 14·00 13·00

15

**17** Superb Lyrebird

(Typo John Ash)

**1931–36.** *W* **15.** *(a) P* 13½ × 12½.
124 **5a** ½d. orange (2.33) .. .. .. 3·25 5·00
125 1d. green (Die I) (10.31) .. .. 1·50 10
126 1½d. red-brown (10.36) .. .. .. 5·50 8·00
127 2d. golden scarlet (Die III) (18.12.31) 1·75 10
128 3d. ultramarine (Die II) (30.9.32) .. 16·00 55
129 4d. yellow-olive (2.33) .. .. .. 16·00 80
130 5d. orange-brown (Die II) (25.2.32) .. 14·00 15
131 1s. 4d. turquoise (18.8.32) .. .. 70·00 3·25
124/131 .. .. .. .. *Set of* 8 £110 16·00

*(b) P* 12
132 **1** 6d. chestnut (Die IIB) (20.4.32) .. .. 20·00 24·00
133 9d. violet (Die IIB) (20.4.32) .. .. 20·00 75
134 2s. maroon (Die II) (6.8.35) .. .. 5·00 45
135 5s. grey and yellow (12.32) .. .. £100 9·50
136 10s. grey and pink (31.7.32) .. .. £250 £100
137 £1 grey (Die IIB) (11.35).. .. .. £425 £150
138 £2 black and rose (6.34) .. .. £1600 £300
132/138 .. .. .. .. *Set of* 7 £2260 £500
136/138 Optd "Specimen" .. .. *Set of* 3 85·00

Stamps as No. 127, without wmk and perf 11 are forgeries made in 1932 to defraud the P.O.

For re-engraved type of No. 134, see No. 212.

(Recess John Ash)

**1931** (4 Nov). *Air Stamp. As T* **13** *but inscr "AIR MAIL SERVICE" in bottom tablet. No wmk. P* 11.
139 6d. sepia .. .. .. .. .. 16·00 12·00

**1931** (17 Nov). *Air. No. 139 optd with Type* O **4.**
139*a* 6d. sepia .. .. .. .. .. .. 35·00 42·00

This stamp was not restricted to official use but was on general sale to the public.

(Des F. D. Manley. Recess John Ash)

**1932** (15 Feb). *No wmk. P* 11.
140 **17** 1s. green .. .. .. .. 50·00 1·00
140*a* 1s. yellow-green .. .. .. 55·00 1·40

**18** Sydney Harbour Bridge

**19** Laughing Kookaburra

(Des R. A. Harrison. Eng F. D. Manley. Printed John Ash)

**1932** (14 Mar). *(a) Recess. No wmk. P* 11.
141 **18** 2d. scarlet .. .. .. .. 2·50 2·50
142 3d. blue .. .. .. .. .. 4·00 7·00
143 5s. blue-green .. .. .. .. £375 £180

*(b) Typo. W* **15.** *P* 10½.
144 **18** 2d. scarlet .. .. .. .. 2·75 85
141/4 .. .. .. .. .. *Set of* 4 £375 £180

Stamps as No. 144 without wmk and perf 11 are forgeries made in 1932 to defraud the P.O.

(Typo John Ash)

**1932** (1 June). *W* **15.** *P* 13½ × 12½.
146 **19** 6d. red-brown .. .. .. .. 25·00 45

**20** Melbourne and R. Yarra

**21** Merino Ram

(Des and eng F. D. Manley. Recess John Ash)

**1934** (2 July). *Centenary of Victoria. W* **15.**

| | | | I. *P* 10½. | | II. *P* 11½. | |
|---|---|---|---|---|---|---|
| 147 | **20** | 2d. orange-vermilion .. | 2·50 | 1·25 | 4·50 | 1·25 |
| 148 | | 3d. blue .. .. .. | 6·00 | 5·50 | 7·50 | 7·50 |
| 149 | | 1s. black .. .. | 45·00 | 12·00 | 45·00 | 12·00 |
| 147/9 | | .. .. .. *Set of* 3 | 48·00 | 17·00 | 50·00 | 18·00 |

(Des and eng F. D. Manley. Recess John Ash)

**1934** (1 Nov). *Death Centenary of Capt. John Macarthur. W* **15.** *P* 11½.
150 **21** 2d. carmine-red (A) .. .. .. 3·50 1·25
150*a* 2d. carmine-red (B) .. .. .. 32·00 3·00
151 3d. blue .. .. .. .. .. 9·00 8·00
152 9d. bright purple .. .. .. 35·00 32·00
150/2 .. .. .. .. .. *Set of* 3 42·00 38·00

Type A of the 2d. shows shading on the hill in the background varying from light to dark (as illustrated). Type B has the shading almost uniformly dark.

**22** Hermes

**23** Cenotaph, Whitehall

(Des F. D. Manley. Eng E. Broad and F. D. Manley. Recess John Ash until April 1940; W. C. G. McCracken thereafter)

**1934–48.** *(a) No wmk. P* 11.
153 **22** 1s. 6d. dull purple (1.12.34) .. .. 32·00 90

*(b) W* **15.** *P* 13½ × 14
153*a* **22** 1s. 6d. dull purple (22.10.37) .. .. 10·00 35
b. Thin rough paper (12.2.48).. .. 8·00 45

(Des B. Cottier; adapted and eng F. D. Manley. Recess John Ash)

**1935** (18 Mar). *20th Anniv of Gallipoli Landing. W* **15.** *P* 13½ × 12½ *or* 11 (1s.).
154 **23** 2d. scarlet .. .. .. .. 80 30
155 1s. black (*chalk-surfaced*) .. .. 48·00 38·00
a. Perf 13½ × 12½ .. .. .. £1500

**24** King George V on "Anzac"

**25** Amphitrite and Telephone Cable

(Des and eng F. D. Manley. Recess John Ash)

**1935** (2 May). *Silver Jubilee. Chalk-surfaced paper. W* **15** (*sideways*). *P* 11½.
156 **24** 2d. scarlet .. .. .. .. 1·00 30
157 3d. blue .. .. .. .. .. 6·00 6·00
158 2s. bright violet .. .. .. .. 45·00 38·00
156/8 .. .. .. .. .. *Set of* 3 48·00 40·00

(Des and eng F. D. Manley. Recess John Ash)

**1936** (1 Apr). *Opening of Submarine Telephone Link to Tasmania. W* **15**. *P* 11½.
159 **25** 2d. scarlet .. .. .. .. .. 60 35
160 3d. blue .. .. .. .. .. .. 2·50 3·25

**26** Site of Adelaide, 1836; Old Gum Tree, Glenelg; King William St., Adelaide

(Des and eng F. D. Manley. Recess John Ash)

**1936** (3 Aug). *Centenary of South Australia. W* **15**. *P* 11½.
161 **26** 2d. carmine .. .. .. .. .. 1·00 30
162 3d. blue .. .. .. .. .. .. 5·50 4·50
163 1s. green .. .. .. .. .. 10·00 8·00
161/3 .. .. .. .. .. *Set of* 3 15·00 11·50

**27** Wallaroo **28** Queen Elizabeth **29** King George VI

**30** King George VI **31** **32** Koala

Die I Die Ia Die II

**33** Merino Ram **34** Laughing Kookaburra **35** Platypus

**36** Superb Lyrebird **38** Queen Elizabeth **39** King George VI

**40** King George VI and Queen Elizabeth **40*a*** **40*b*** (Background evenly shaded, lettering strengthened)

Medal flaw
(Pl 2. Right pane R. 2/5)

(Des R. A. Harrison (T **28/30**), F. D. Manley (T **27**, **31/6**), H. Barr (T **38/9**), H. Barr and F. D. Manley (T **40**). Eng. F. D. Manley and T. C. Duffell (T **34**), T. C. Duffell (revised lettering for T **40*a/b***), F. D. Manley (others). All recess with John Ash, W. C. G. McCracken or "By Authority . . ." imprints)

**1937–49.** *W* **15** (*sideways on* 5*d*., 9*d*., 5*s*. *and* 10*s*.).

(*a*) *P* 13½ × 14 (*vert designs*) *or* 14 × 13½ (*horiz*)
164 **27** ½d. orange (3.10.38) .. .. .. 2·00 45
165 **28** 1d. emerald-green (10.5.37) .. .. 30 10
166 **29** 1½d. maroon (20.4.38) .. .. .. 9·00 2·75
167 **30** 2d. scarlet (10.5.37) .. .. .. 30 10
167*a* **31** 3d. blue (Die I, 1st ptg) (2.8.37) .. £110 70·00
168 3d. blue (Die I) (2.8.37) .. .. .. 55·00 8·00
168*a* 3d. blue (Die Ia) (1937) .. .. .. £130 6·50
168*b* 3d. blue (Die II) (1938) .. .. .. 55·00 3·00
169 3d. bright blue, *thin paper* (Die II) (21.12.38) .. .. .. .. 50·00 2·25
170 **32** 4d. green (1.2.38) .. .. .. 12·00 30
171 **33** 5d. purple (1.12.38) .. .. .. 4·00 40
172 **34** 6d. purple-brown (2.8.37) .. .. 26·00 90
173 **35** 9d. chocolate (1.9.38) .. .. .. 9·00 90
174 **36** 1s. grey-green (2.8.37) .. .. .. 55·00 1·90
175 **31** 1s. 4d. deep magenta (3.10.38) .. .. 2·75 1·75
*a. Pale magenta* .. .. .. 1·50 1·50

(*b*) *Chalk-surfaced paper. P* 13½
176 **38** 5s. claret (1.4.38) .. .. .. 10·00 75
a. Thin rough ordinary paper (4.2.48) .. .. .. 7·00 1·50
177 **39** 10s. dull purple (1.4.38) (Optd S. £30) 35·00 11·00
a. Thin rough ordinary paper (11.48) .. .. .. 55·00 23·00
178 **40** £1 bl-slate (1.11.38) (Optd S. £400) 60·00 28·00
a. Thin rough ordinary paper (4.4.49) .. .. .. £110 60·00
164/78 .. .. .. .. *Set of* 14 £250 45·00

(*c*) *P* 15 × 14 (*vert designs*) *or* 14 × 15 (*horiz*)
179 **27** ½d. orange (28.1.42) .. .. .. 55 10
a. Coil pair .. .. .. 12·00 14·00
180 **40*a*** 1d. emerald-green (1.8.38) .. .. 1·50 10
181 1d. maroon (10.12.41) .. .. .. 1·25 10
a. Coil pair .. .. .. 12·00 14·00
182 **29** 1½d. maroon (21.11.41) .. .. .. 4·50 7·50
183 1½d. emerald-green (10.12.41) .. .. 1·00 30
184 **40*b*** 2d. scarlet (11.7.38) .. .. .. 2·50 10
a. Coil pair .. .. .. £275 £325
b. Medal flaw .. .. .. 60·00
185 2d. bright purple (10.12 41) .. .. 50 50
a. Coil pair .. .. .. 27·00 32·00
b. Medal flaw .. .. .. 22·00
186 **31** 3d. bright blue (10.40) .. .. .. 42·00 2·25
187 3d. purple-brown (10.1.42) .. .. 30 10
188 **32** 4d. green (10.42) .. .. .. 1·50 10
188*a* **33** 5d. purple (5.46) .. .. .. 45 1·50
189 **34** 6d. red-brown (5.42) .. .. .. 2·00 10
*a. Purple-brown* (1944) .. .. .. 1·75 10
190 **35** 9d. chocolate (1943) .. .. .. 80 10
191 **36** 1s. grey-green (3.41) .. .. .. 1·00 10
179/91 .. .. .. .. *Set of* 14 55·00 11·00
For unwmkd issue, see Nos. 228/30*d*.

*Dies of the* 3*d*. In Die I the letters "TA" of "POSTAGE" at right are joined by a white flaw; the outline of the chin consists of separate strokes.

Die Ia is similar, but "T" and "A" have been clearly separated by retouches made on the plate.

In Die II "T" and "A" are separate and a continuous line has been added to the chin. The outline of the cheek extends to about 1 mm above the lobe of the King's right ear.

No. 167*a* is a preliminary printing made with unsuitable ink and may be detected by the absence of finer details; the King's face appears whitish and the wattles are blank. The greater part of this printing was distributed to the Press with advance notices of the issue.

No. 186 is re-engraved and differs from Nos. 167*a* to 169 in the King's left eyebrow which is shaded downwards from left to right instead of from right to left.

*Thin paper*. Nos. 176a, 177a, 178a. In these varieties the watermark is more clearly visible on the back and the design is much less sharp. Early printings of No. 176a have tinted paper.

**SPECIAL COIL PERFORATION**. This special perforation of large and small holes on the narrow sides of the stamps is intended for stamps issued in coils, to facilitate separation. When they exist we list them as "Coil pairs".

The following with "special coil" perforation were placed on sale in *sheets*: Nos. 204ba, 222*a* (1952), 228, 230, 237, 262 (1953), 309, 311, and 314. These are listed as "Coil blocks of four".

Coils with "normal" perforations also exist for some values.

**41** "Governor Phillip at Sydney Cove" (J. Allcot)

"Tail" flaw
(Left pane R. 7/1)

(Des and eng E. Broad and F. D. Manley. Recess J. Ash)

**1937** (1 Oct). *150th Anniv of Foundation of New South Wales. W* **15**. *P* 13½ × 14.
193 **41** 2d. scarlet .. .. .. .. .. 2·00 15
a. "Tail" flaw .. .. .. .. £190 50·00
194 3d. bright blue .. .. .. .. 10·00 2·25
195 9d. purple .. .. .. .. 22·00 8·00
193/5 .. .. .. .. *Set of* 3 30·00 9·25

**42** A.I.F. and Nurse

(Des and eng F. D. Manley from drawing by Virgil Reilly. Recess W. C. G. McCracken)

**1940** (15 July). *Australian Imperial Forces. W* **15** (*sideways*). *P* 14 × 13½.
196 **42** 1d. green .. .. .. .. .. 1·50 70
197 2d. scarlet .. .. .. .. .. 1·50 15
198 3d. blue .. .. .. .. .. 9·00 6·50
199 6d. brown-purple .. .. .. 20·00 10·00
196/9 .. .. .. .. *Set of* 4 29·00 16·00

(**43**) (**44**) (**45**)

(Opts designed by F. D. Manley)

**1941** (10 Dec). *Nos.* 184, 186 *and* 171 *surch with T* **43/5**.
200 **40*b*** 2½d. on 2d. scarlet (V.) .. .. 1·25 20
b. Medal flaw .. .. .. 60·00
201 **31** 3½d. on 3d. bright blue (Y. on Black) 1·50 1·50
202 **33** 5½d. on 5d. purple (V.) .. .. 7·50 3·25
200/2 .. .. .. .. *Set of* 3 9·00 4·50

**46** Queen Elizabeth **46*a*** **47** King George VI

**48** King George VI **49** King George VI **50** Emu

(Des and eng F. D. Manley)

**1942–44.** *Recess. W* **15**. *P* 15 × 14.
203 **46** 1d. brown-purple (1.1.43) .. .. 20 10
a. Coil pair .. .. .. 14·00 17·00
204 **46*a*** 1½d. green (1.12.42) .. .. .. 20 10
204*a* **47** 2d. bright purple (4.12.44) .. .. 40 30
b. Coil pair .. .. .. 55·00 55·00
ba. Coil block of four .. ..
205 **48** 2½d. scarlet (7.1.42) .. .. .. 20 10
a. Imperf (pair)* .. .. £1400
206 **49** 3½d. bright blue (3.42) .. .. .. 25 10
*a. Deep blue* .. .. .. 50 10
207 **50** 5½d. slate-blue (12.2.42) .. .. 65 10
203/207 .. .. .. .. *Set of* 6 1·75 40
*No. 205*a* is in pair with stamp which only has the right-hand side imperf.

For stamps as Nos. 204/*a* but without watermark see Nos. 229/30.

**52** Duke and Duchess of Gloucester

(Des and eng F. D. Manley. Recess)

**1945** (19 Feb). *Arrival of Duke and Duchess of Gloucester in Australia. W* **15**. *P* 14½.
209 **52** 2½d. lake .. .. .. .. .. 10 10
210 3½d. ultramarine .. .. .. .. 15 30
211 5½d. indigo .. .. .. .. 20 30
209/11 .. .. .. .. *Set of* 3 40 60

A B

**1946** (3 Jan). *Kangaroo type, as No. 134, but re-engraved as B. W* **15**. *P* 12.
212 **1** 2s. maroon .. .. .. .. .. 3·25 3·75
No. 134 has two background lines between the value circle and "TWO SHILLINGS"; No. 212 has only one line in this position. There are also differences in the shape of the letters.

53 Star and Wreath

56 Sir Thos. Mitchell and Queensland

(Des F. D. Manley (2½d.), F. D. Manley and G. Lissenden (3½d.), G. Lissenden (5½d.). Eng F. D. Manley. Recess)

**1946** (18 Feb). *Victory Commemoration. T* **53** *and similar designs. W* **15** (*sideways on* 5½*d.*). *P* 14½.

| | | | | |
|---|---|---|---|---|
| 213 | | 2½d. scarlet | 10 | 10 |
| 214 | | 3½d. blue | 25 | 75 |
| 215 | | 5½d. green | 30 | 50 |
| 213/15 | | *Set of* 3 | 60 | 1·25 |

Designs: *Horiz*—3½d. Flag and dove. *Vert*—5½d. Angel.

(Des and eng F. D. Manley. Recess)

**1946** (14 Oct). *Centenary of Mitchell's Exploration of Central Queensland. W* **15.** *P* 14½.

| | | | | |
|---|---|---|---|---|
| 216 | **56** | 2½d. scarlet | 10 | 10 |
| 217 | | 3½d. blue | 20 | 50 |
| 218 | | 1s. grey-olive | 25 | 20 |
| 216/18 | | *Set of* 3 | 50 | 65 |

57 Lt. John Shortland R.N.

58 Steel Foundry

59 Coal Carrier Cranes

(Des G. Lissenden, eng G. Lissenden and F. D. Manley (5½d.); des and eng F. D. Manley (others). Recess)

**1947** (8 Sept). *Sesquicentenary of City of Newcastle, New South Wales. W* **15** (*sideways on* 3½*d.*). *P* 14½ *or* 15 × 14 (2½*d.*).

| | | | | |
|---|---|---|---|---|
| 219 | **57** | 2½d. lake | 10 | 10 |
| | | a. Imperf three sides | £700 | |
| 220 | **58** | 3½d. blue | 20 | 40 |
| 221 | **59** | 5½d. green | 20 | 30 |
| 219/21 | | *Set of* 3 | 45 | 65 |

The following items are understood to have been the subject of unauthorised leakages from the Commonwealth Note and Stamp Printing Branch and are therefore not listed by us.

It is certain that none of this material was distributed to post offices for issue to the public.

*Imperforate all round.* 1d. Princess Elizabeth; 1½d. Queen; 2½d. King; 4d. Koala; 6d. Kookaburra; 9d. Platypus; 1s. Lyrebird (small); 1s. 6d. Air Mail (Type **22**); 2½d. Newcastle.

Also 2½d. Peace, unwatermarked; 2½d. King, *tête-bêche*; 3½d. Newcastle, in dull ultramarine; 2½d. King on "toned" paper.

60 Queen Elizabeth II when Princess

(Des R. A. Harrison. Eng F. D. Manley. Recess)

**1947** (20 Nov)–**48**. *Marriage of Princess Elizabeth. P* 14 × 15.

| | | | | |
|---|---|---|---|---|
| | | (*a*) *W* **15** (*sideways*) | | |
| 222 | **60** | 1d. purple | 15 | 10 |
| | | (*b*) *No wmk* | | |
| 222*a* | **60** | 1d. purple (8.48) | 10 | 10 |
| | | b. Coil pair | 2·00 | 4·50 |
| | | c. Coil block of four | 4·00 | |

61 Hereford Bull    61*a* Hermes and Globe

62 Aboriginal Art    62*a* Commonwealth Coat of Arms

(Des G. Sellheim (T **62**), F. D. Manley (others), Eng F. D. Manley and G. Lissenden (T **62**), F. D. Manley (others). Recess)

**1948** (16 Feb)–**56**. (*a*) *W* **15** (*sideways*). *P* 14½.

| | | | | |
|---|---|---|---|---|
| 223 | **61** | 1s. 3d. brown-purple | 1·75 | 85 |
| 223*a* | **61*a*** | 1s. 6d. blackish brown (1.9.49) | 1·75 | 10 |
| 224 | **62** | 2s. chocolate | 2·00 | 10 |
| | | (*b*) *W* **15.** *P* 14½ × 13½ | | |
| 224*a* | **62*a*** | 5s. claret (11.4.49) | 7·00 | 20 |
| | | ab. Thin paper | 20·00 | 65 |
| 224*b* | | 10s. purple (3.10.49) | 30·00 | 45 |
| 224*c* | | £1 blue (28.11.49) | 48·00 | 2·75 |
| 224*d* | | £2 green (16.1.50) | £100 | 14·00 |
| 224*b*/*d* | | Optd "Specimen" *Set of* 3 | £150 | |
| | | (*c*) *No wmk. P* 14½ | | |
| 224*e* | **61*a*** | 1s. 6d. blackish brown (6.12.56) | 20·00 | 70 |
| 224*f* | **62** | 2s. chocolate (21.7.56) | 20·00 | 45 |
| 223/224*f* | | *Set of* 9 | £200 | 18·00 |

No. 224ab is an emergency printing on white Harrison paper instead of the toned paper used for No. 224*a*.

63 William J. Farrer

64 F. von Mueller

65 Boy Scout

(Des and eng F. D. Manley. Recess)

**1948** (12 July). *William J. Farrer (wheat research). W* **15.** *P* 15 × 14.

| | | | | |
|---|---|---|---|---|
| 225 | **63** | 2½d. scarlet | 10 | 10 |

(Des and eng F. D. Manley. Recess)

**1948** (13 Sept). *Sir Ferdinand von Mueller (botanist). W* **15.** *P* 15 × 14.

| | | | | |
|---|---|---|---|---|
| 226 | **64** | 2½d. lake | 10 | 10 |

(Des and eng F. D. Manley. Recess)

**1948** (15 Nov). *Pan-Pacific Scout Jamboree, Wonga Park. W* **15** (*sideways*). *P* 14 × 15.

| | | | | |
|---|---|---|---|---|
| 227 | **65** | 2½d. lake | 10 | 10 |

See also No. 254.

Sky retouch (normally unshaded near hill)

"Green mist" retouch. A large area to the left of the bird's feathers is recut (upper plate left pane R. 9/3)

**1948–56.** *No wmk. P* 15 × 14 *or* 14 × 15 (9*d.*).

| | | | | |
|---|---|---|---|---|
| 228 | **27** | ½d. orange (9.49) | 20 | 10 |
| | | aa. Sky retouch (Rt. pane, R. 6/8) | 10·00 | |
| | | a. Coil pair | 75 | 2·25 |
| | | ab. Sky retouch (in pair) | 80·00 | |
| | | b. Coil block of four | 2·00 | |
| 229 | **46*a*** | 1½d. green (29.8.49) | 1·00 | 55 |
| 230 | **47** | 2d. bright purple (12.48) | 70 | 45 |
| | | aa. Coil pair | 3·00 | 5·00 |
| | | ab. Coil block of four | £300 | |
| 230*a* | **32** | 4d. green (18.8.56) | 2·00 | 45 |
| 230*b* | **34** | 6d. purple-brown (18.8.56) | 3·50 | 30 |
| 230*c* | **35** | 9d. chocolate (13.12.56) | 18·00 | 1·75 |
| 230*d* | **36** | 1s. grey-green (13.12.56) | 12·00 | 50 |
| | | da. "Green mist" retouch | £550 | |
| 228/230*d* | | *Set of* 7 | 35·00 | 3·75 |

66 "Henry Lawson" (Sir Lionel Lindsay)

67 Mounted Postman and Aeroplane

(Des F. D. Manley. Eng E. R. M. Jones. Recess)

**1949** (17 June). *Anniv of Birth of Henry Lawson (poet). P* 15 × 14.

| | | | | |
|---|---|---|---|---|
| 231 | **66** | 2½d. maroon | 15 | 10 |

(Des Sir Daryl Lindsay and F. D. Manley. Eng F. D. Manley. Recess)

**1949** (10 Oct). *75th Anniv of Founding of U.P.U. P* 15 × 14.

| | | | | |
|---|---|---|---|---|
| 232 | **67** | 3½d. ultramarine | 20 | 25 |

68 Lord Forrest of Bunbury

69 King George VI

70 Queen Elizabeth

(Des and eng F. D. Manley. Recess)

**1949** (28 Nov). *Lord Forrest of Bunbury (explorer and politician). W* **15.** *P* 15 × 14.

| | | | | |
|---|---|---|---|---|
| 233 | **68** | 2½d. lake | 15 | 10 |

(Des and eng F. D. Manley. Recess)

**1950–51.** *P* 15 × 14. (*a*) *W* **15.**

| | | | | |
|---|---|---|---|---|
| 234 | **69** | 2½d. scarlet (12.4.50) | 10 | 10 |
| 235 | | 3d. scarlet (28.2.51) | 15 | 10 |
| | | aa. Coil pair | 12·00 | 15·00 |
| | | (*b*) *No wmk* | | |
| 235*a* | **69** | 2½d. purple-brown (23.5.51) | 15 | 15 |
| 235*b* | | 3d. grey-green (14.11.51) | 15 | 10 |
| | | c. Coil pair | 17·00 | 26·00 |
| 234/5*b* | | *Set of* 4 | 50 | 30 |

On 14 October 1951 No. 235 was placed on sale in sheets of 144 originally intended for use in stamp booklets. These sheets contain 3 panes of 48 (16×3) with horizontal gutter margin between.

(Des and eng F. D. Manley. Recess)

**1950–51.** *P* 15 × 14.

| | | | | |
|---|---|---|---|---|
| 236 | **70** | 1½d. green (19.6.50) | 15 | 10 |
| 237 | | 2d. yellow-green (28.3.51) | 15 | 10 |
| | | a. Coil pair | 3·75 | 6·50 |
| | | b. Coil block of four | 8·00 | |

71 Aborigine

72

73

72 / 73 Reproductions of First Stamps of New South Wales and Victoria

(Des F. D. Manley. Eng E. R. M. Jones. Recess)

**1950** (14 Aug). *W* **15.** *P* 15 × 14.

| | | | | |
|---|---|---|---|---|
| 238 | **71** | 8½d. brown | 15 | 40 |

For T **71** in a larger size, see Nos. 253/*b*.

(Des and eng E. R. M. Jones (T **72**); des and eng G. Lissenden (T **73**). Recess)

**1950** (27 Sept). *Centenary of First Adhesive Postage Stamps in Australia. P* 15 × 14.

| | | | | |
|---|---|---|---|---|
| 239 | **72** | 2½d. maroon | 10 | 10 |
| | | a. Horiz pair. Nos. 239/40 | 20 | 55 |
| 240 | **73** | 2½d. maroon | 10 | 10 |

Nos. 239/40 were printed alternately in vertical columns throughout the sheet.

74 Sir Edmund Barton

75 Sir Henry Parkes

76 "Opening First Federal Parliament" (T. Roberts)

77 Federal Parliament House, Canberra

(Des and eng F. D. Manley. Recess)

**1951** (1 May). *Golden Jubilee of Commonwealth of Australia. P* 15 × 14.

| | | | | |
|---|---|---|---|---|
| 241 | **74** | 3d. lake | 30 | 10 |
| | | a. Horiz pair. Nos. 241/2 | 1·50 | 1·75 |
| 242 | **75** | 3d. lake | 30 | 10 |
| 243 | **76** | 5½d. blue | 20 | 1·50 |
| 244 | **77** | 1s. 6d. purple-brown | 35 | 50 |
| 241/4 | | *Set of* 4 | 1·75 | 2·00 |

Nos. 241/2 are printed alternately in vertical columns throughout the sheet.

78
E. H. Hargraves

79
C. J. Latrobe

80
King George VI

(Des and eng F. D. Manley. Recess)

**1951** (2 July). *Centenary of Discovery of Gold in Australia. P* 15 × 14.

| | | | | |
|---|---|---|---|---|
| 245 | **78** | 3d. maroon | 30 | 10 |
| | | a. Horiz pair. Nos. 245/6 | 70 | 95 |

(Des and eng F. D. Manley. Recess)

**1951** (2 July). *Centenary of Responsible Government in Victoria. P* 15 × 14.

| | | | | |
|---|---|---|---|---|
| 246 | **79** | 3d. maroon | 30 | 10 |

Nos. 245/6 were printed alternately in vertical columns throughout the sheet.

(Des and eng E. R. M. Jones. Recess)

**1951** (31 Oct). *W* **15**. *P* 15 × 14.

| | | | | |
|---|---|---|---|---|
| 247 | **80** | 7½d. blue | 15 | 45 |
| | | a. Imperf 3 sides (vert pr) | £1500 | |

81 King George VI

82 King George VI

(Des F. D. Manley. Eng G. Lissenden. Recess)

**1951–52.** *W* **15**. *P* 15 × 14.

| | | | | |
|---|---|---|---|---|
| 248 | **81** | 3½d. brown-purple (28.11.51) | 10 | 10 |
| 249 | | 4½d. scarlet (20.2.52) | 15 | 60 |
| 250 | | 6½d. brown (20.2.52) | 15 | 55 |
| 251 | | 6½d. emerald-green (9.4.52) | 10 | 15 |
| 248/51 | | *Set of* 4 | 45 | 1·25 |

(Des F. D. Manley. Eng D. Cameron (No. 252), E. R. M. Jones (Nos. 253/*b*). Recess)

**1952** (19 Mar)–**65**. *P* 14½. (*a*) *W* **15** (*sideways*).

| | | | | |
|---|---|---|---|---|
| 252 | **82** | 1s. 0½d. indigo | 35 | 30 |
| 253 | – | 2s. 6d. deep brown | 2·50 | 35 |
| | | (*b*) *No wmk* | | |
| 253*a* | – | 2s. 6d. deep brown (30.1.57) | 5·50 | 35 |
| | | *b. Sepia* (10.65) | 11·00 | 9·50 |

Design:—2s. 6d. As T **71** but larger (21 × 25½ *mm*).

No. 253*b* was an emergency printing and can easily be distinguished from No. 253*a* as it is on white Harrison paper, No. 253*a* being on toned paper.

(Des and eng F. D. Manley. Recess)

**1952** (19 Nov). *Pan-Pacific Scout Jamboree, Greystanes. As T* **65**, *but inscr* "1952–53". *W* **15** (*sideways*). *P* 14 × 15.

| | | | | |
|---|---|---|---|---|
| 254 | | 3½d. brown-lake | 10 | 10 |

83 Butter

84 Wheat

85 Beef

(Des P.O. artists; adapted G. Lissenden. Typo)

**1953** (11 Feb). *Food Production. P* 14½.

| | | | | |
|---|---|---|---|---|
| 255 | **83** | 3d. emerald | 30 | 10 |
| | | a. Strip of 3. Nos. 255/7 | 2·75 | |
| 256 | **84** | 3d. emerald | 30 | 10 |
| 257 | **85** | 3d. emerald | 30 | 10 |
| 258 | **83** | 3½d. scarlet | 30 | 10 |
| | | a. Strip of 3. Nos. 258/60 | 2·75 | |
| 259 | **84** | 3½d. scarlet | 30 | 10 |
| 260 | **85** | 3½d. scarlet | 30 | 10 |
| 255/60 | | *Set of* 6 | 5·00 | 40 |

The three designs in each denomination appear in rotation, both horizontally and vertically, throughout the sheet.

86 Queen Elizabeth II

87 Queen Elizabeth II

(Des F. D. Manley from photograph by Dorothy Wilding Ltd. Eng D. Cameron. Recess)

**1953–56.** *P* 15 × 14. (*a*) *No wmk.*

| | | | | |
|---|---|---|---|---|
| 261 | **86** | 1d. purple (19.8.53) | 15 | 10 |
| 261*a* | | 2½d. blue (23.6.54) | 20 | 10 |
| 262 | **86** | 3d. deep green (17.6.53) | 20 | 10 |
| | | aa. Coil pair | 5·00 | 7·00 |
| | | ab. Coil block of four | 12·00 | |
| 262*a* | | 3½d. brown-red (2.7.56) | 2·50 | 10 |
| 262*b* | | 6½d. orange (9.56) | 3·00 | 80 |
| | | (*b*) *W* **15** | | |
| 263 | **86** | 3½d. brown-red (21.4.53) | 20 | 10 |
| 263*a* | | 6½d. orange (23.6.54) | 1·50 | 10 |
| 261/3*a* | | *Set of* 7 | 7·00 | 1·00 |

(Des and eng F. D. Manley. Recess)

**1953** (25 May). *Coronation. P* 15 × 14.

| | | | | |
|---|---|---|---|---|
| 264 | **87** | 3½d. scarlet | 35 | 10 |
| 265 | | 7½d. violet | 1·50 | 55 |
| 266 | | 2s. dull bluish green | 5·50 | 30 |
| 264/6 | | *Set of* 3 | 6·50 | 75 |

88 Young Farmers and Calf

(Des P.O. artist; adapted P. E. Morriss. Eng E. R. M. Jones. Recess)

**1953** (3 Sept). *25th Anniv of Australian Young Farmers' Clubs. P* 14½.

| | | | | |
|---|---|---|---|---|
| 267 | **88** | 3½d. red-brown and deep green | 10 | 10 |

89 Lt.-Gov. D. Collins

90 Lt.-Gov. W. Paterson

91 Sullivan Cove, Hobart, 1804

(Des E. R. M. Jones, eng D. Cameron (T **89/90**); des and eng G. Lissenden (T **91**). Recess)

**1953** (23 Sept). *150th Anniv of Settlement in Tasmania. P* 15 × 14.

| | | | | |
|---|---|---|---|---|
| 268 | **89** | 3½d. brown-purple | 30 | 10 |
| | | a. Horiz pair. Nos. 268/9 | 80 | 1·25 |
| 269 | **90** | 3½d. brown-purple | 30 | 10 |
| 270 | **91** | 2s. green | 2·00 | 2·50 |
| 268/70 | | *Set of* 3 | 2·50 | 2·50 |

Nos. 268/9 were printed alternately in vertical columns throughout the sheet.

92 Stamp of 1853

(Des R. L. Beck; eng G. Lissenden. Recess)

**1953** (11 Nov). *Tasmanian Postage Stamp Centenary. P* 14½.

| | | | | |
|---|---|---|---|---|
| 271 | **92** | 3d. rose-red | 10 | 10 |

93 Queen Elizabeth II and Duke of Edinburgh

94 Queen Elizabeth II

Re-entry (R. 8/2)

(Des and eng F. D. Manley; border and lettering on 7½d. des by R. M. Warner. Recess)

**1954** (2 Feb). *Royal Visit. P* 14.

| | | | | |
|---|---|---|---|---|
| 272 | **93** | 3½d. scarlet | 20 | 10 |
| | | a. Re-entry | 28·00 | 8·00 |
| 273 | **94** | 7½d. purple | 35 | 60 |
| 274 | **93** | 2s. dull bluish green | 85 | 40 |
| 272/4 | | *Set of* 3 | 1·25 | 1·00 |

95 "Telegraphic Communications"

96 Red Cross and Globe

(Des R. M. Warner. Eng P. E. Morriss. Recess)

**1954** (7 Apr). *Australian Telegraph System Centenary. P* 14.

| | | | | |
|---|---|---|---|---|
| 275 | **95** | 3½d. brown-red | 10 | 10 |

(Des B. Stewart. Eng P. E. Morriss. Design recess; cross typo)

**1954** (9 June). *40th Anniv of Australian Red Cross Society. P* 14½.

| | | | | |
|---|---|---|---|---|
| 276 | **96** | 3½d. ultramarine and scarlet | 10 | 10 |

97 Black Swan

98 Locomotives of 1854 and 1954

(Des R. L. Beck. Eng G. Lissenden. Recess)

**1954** (2 Aug). *Western Australian Postage Stamp Centenary. P* 14½.

| | | | | |
|---|---|---|---|---|
| 277 | **97** | 3½d. black | 10 | 10 |

(Des R. M. Warner. Eng G. Lissenden. Recess)

**1954** (13 Sept). *Australian Railways Centenary. P* 14.

| | | | | |
|---|---|---|---|---|
| 278 | **98** | 3½d. purple-brown | 20 | 10 |

99 Territory Badge

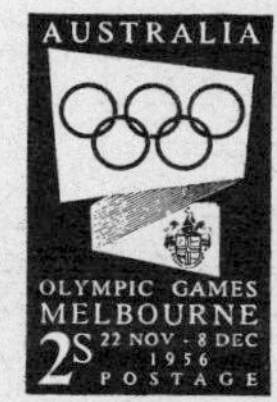


100 Olympic Games Symbol

(Des F. D. Manley. Eng G. Lissenden. Recess)

**1954** (17 Nov). *Australian Antarctic Research. P* 14½ × 13½.

| | | | | |
|---|---|---|---|---|
| 279 | **99** | 3½d. grey-black | 15 | 10 |

(Des R. L. Beck. Eng P. E. Morriss. Recess)

**1954–55.** *Olympic Games Propaganda. P* 14.

| | | | | |
|---|---|---|---|---|
| 280 | **100** | 2s. deep bright blue (1.12.54) | 70 | 40 |
| 280*a* | | 2s. deep bluish green (30.11.55) | 2·00 | 85 |

101 Rotary Symbol, Globe and Flags

102 Queen Elizabeth II

(Des and eng D. Cameron. Recess)

**1955** (23 Feb). *50th Anniv of Rotary International. P* 14 × 14½.

| | | | | |
|---|---|---|---|---|
| 281 | **101** | 3½d. carmine | 10 | 10 |

(Des F. D. Manley from bas-relief by W. L. Bowles. Eng G. Lissenden. Recess)

**1955** (9 Mar)–**57**. *P* 14½. (*a*) *W* **15** (*sideways*).

| | | | | |
|---|---|---|---|---|
| 282 | **102** | 1s. 0½d. deep blue | 3·00 | 40 |
| | | (*b*) *No wmk* | | |
| 282*a* | **102** | 1s. 7d. red-brown (13.3.57) | 3·50 | 15 |

103 American Memorial, Canberra

104 Cobb & Co. Coach (from dry-print by Sir Lionel Lindsay)

(Des R. L. Beck (head by F. D. Manley). Eng F. D. Manley. Recess)

**1955** (4 May). *Australian–American Friendship. P* 14 × 14½.

| | | | | |
|---|---|---|---|---|
| 283 | **103** | 3½d. violet-blue | 10 | 10 |

(Design adapted and eng by F. D. Manley. Recess)

**1955** (6 July). *Mail-coach Pioneers Commemoration. P* 14½ × 14.

| | | | | |
|---|---|---|---|---|
| 284 | **104** | 3½d. blackish brown | 25 | 10 |
| 285 | | 2s. reddish brown | 75 | 1·40 |

**105** Y.M.C.A. Emblem and Map of the World

**106** Florence Nightingale and Young Nurse

(Des E. Thake. Eng P. E. Morriss. Design recess; emblem typo)

**1955** (10 Aug). *World Centenary of Y.M.C.A. P* 14½ × 14.

| | | | | |
|---|---|---|---|---|
| 286 | **105** | 3½d. deep bluish green and red | 10 | 10 |
| | | a. Red (emblem) omitted | £4500 | |

(Des and eng F. D. Manley. Recess)

**1955** (21 Sept). *Nursing Profession Commemoration. P* 14 × 14½.

| | | | | |
|---|---|---|---|---|
| 287 | **106** | 3½d. reddish violet | 10 | 10 |

**107** Queen Victoria



**108** Badges of New South Wales, Victoria and Tasmania

(Des and eng D. Cameron. Recess)

**1955** (17 Oct). *Centenary of First South Australian Postage Stamps. P* 14½.

| | | | | |
|---|---|---|---|---|
| 288 | **107** | 3½d. green | 10 | 10 |

(Des and eng F. D. Manley. Recess)

**1956** (26 Sept). *Centenary of Responsible Government in New South Wales, Victoria and Tasmania. P* 14½ × 14.

| | | | | |
|---|---|---|---|---|
| 289 | **108** | 3½d. brown-lake | 10 | 10 |

**109** Arms of Melbourne

**110** Olympic Torch and Symbol

**111** Collins Street, Melbourne

**112** Melbourne across R. Yarra

(Des P. E. Morriss; eng F. D. Manley (4d.). Des and eng F. D. Manley (7½d.). Recess. Des and photo Harrison from photographs by M. Murphy and sketches by L. Coles (1s.). Des and photo Courvoisier from photographs by M. Murphy (2s.))

**1956** (31 Oct). *Olympic Games, Melbourne. P* 14½ (4d.), 14 × 14½ (7½d., 1s.) *or* 11½ (2s.).

| | | | | |
|---|---|---|---|---|
| 290 | **109** | 4d. carmine-red | 25 | 10 |
| 291 | **110** | 7½d. deep bright blue | 40 | 70 |
| 292 | **111** | 1s. multicoloured | 40 | 20 |
| 293 | **112** | 2s. multicoloured | 50 | 70 |
| 290/3 | | *Set of* 4 | 1·40 | 1·50 |

**113** Queen Elizabeth II

**114** Queen Elizabeth II

**115** South Australia Coat of Arms

(Des F. D. Manley from bas-relief by W. L. Bowles. Eng G. Lissenden. Recess)

**1957** (6 Mar–13 Nov). *P* 15 x 14.

| | | | | |
|---|---|---|---|---|
| 294 | **113** | 4d. lake (13 Mar) | 30 | 10 |
| 294*a* | **114** | 7½d. violet (13 Nov) | 1·25 | 1·25 |
| | | ab. Double print | £1000 | |
| 295 | **113** | 10d. deep grey-blue | 1·50 | 40 |

The 4d. exists in booklet panes of six stamps, with imperf outer edges, producing single stamps with one or two adjacent sides imperf.

(Des and eng P. E. Morriss. Recess)

**1957** (17 Apr). *Centenary of Responsible Government in South Australia. P* 14½.

| | | | | |
|---|---|---|---|---|
| 296 | **115** | 4d. red-brown | 10 | 10 |

**116** Map of Australia and Caduceus

(Des J. E. Lyle; adapted B. Stewart. Eng D. Cameron. Recess)

**1957** (21 Aug). *Flying Doctor Service. P* 14½ × 14.

| | | | | |
|---|---|---|---|---|
| 297 | **116** | 7d. ultramarine | 15 | 10 |

**117** "The Spirit of Christmas"

Re-entry (Row 10/1)

(Des and eng D. Cameron from a painting by Sir Joshua Reynolds. Recess)

**1957** (6 Nov). *Christmas. P* 14½ × 14.

| | | | | |
|---|---|---|---|---|
| 298 | **117** | 3½d. scarlet | 10 | 10 |
| | | a. Re-entry | 7·00 | 4·50 |
| 299 | | 4d. purple | 10 | 10 |

**118** Super-Constellation Airliner

(Des and eng P. E. Morriss. Recess)

**1958** (6 Jan). *Inauguration of Australian "Round the World" Air Service. P* 14½ × 14.

| | | | | |
|---|---|---|---|---|
| 301 | **118** | 2s. deep blue | 60 | 85 |

**119** Hall of Memory, Sailor and Airman

**120** Sir Charles Kingsford Smith and *Southern Cross*

(Des and eng G. Lissenden. Recess)

**1958** (10 Feb). *T* **119** *and similar horiz design. P* 14½ × 14.

| | | | | |
|---|---|---|---|---|
| 302 | **119** | 5½d. brown-red | 55 | 30 |
| | | a. Horiz pair. Nos. 302/3 | 1·25 | 5·50 |
| 303 | – | 5½d. brown-red | 55 | 30 |

No. 303 shows a soldier and service-woman respectively in place of the sailor and airman. Nos. 302/3 are printed alternately in vertical columns throughout the sheet.

(Des J. E. Lyle. Eng F. D. Manley. Recess)

**1958** (27 Aug). *30th Anniv of First Air Crossing of the Tasman Sea. P* 14 × 14½.

| | | | | |
|---|---|---|---|---|
| 304 | **120** | 8d. deep ultramarine | 60 | 85 |

**121** Silver Mine, Broken Hill

**122** The Nativity

(Des R. H. Evans; adapted and eng F. D. Manley. Recess)

**1958** (10 Sept). *75th Anniv of Founding of Broken Hill. P* 14½ × 14.

| | | | | |
|---|---|---|---|---|
| 305 | **121** | 4d. chocolate | 15 | 10 |

(Des D. Cameron. Eng P. E. Morriss. Recess)

**1958** (5 Nov). *Christmas. P* 14½ × 15.

| | | | | |
|---|---|---|---|---|
| 306 | **122** | 3½d. deep scarlet | 15 | 10 |
| 307 | | 4d. deep violet | 15 | 10 |

**PHOSPHOR STAMPS** ("**Helecon**"). "Helecon", a chemical substance of the zinc sulphide group, has been incorporated in stamps in two different ways, either in the ink with which the stamps are printed, or included in the surface coating of the stamp paper.

Owing to the difficulty of identification without the use of a U.V. lamp we do not list the helecon stamps separately but when in stock can supply them after testing under the lamp.

The first stamp to be issued was the 11d. Bandicoot from an experimental printing of four millions on helecon paper released to the public in December 1963. The next printing on ordinary paper was released in September 1964. The experimental printing was coarse, showing a lot of white dots and the colour is slate-blue, differing from both the ordinary and the later helecon paper.

The following helecon printings have been reported: 2d. and 3d. (sheets, coils and coil sheets) and 5d. (No. 354) Queen Elizabeth II; 8d. Tiger Cat; 11d. Bandicoot; 1s. Colombo Plan; 1s. 2d. Tasmanian Tiger; 2s. 3d. Wattle (No. 324*a*); and 6d. (No. 363*a*), 9d. and 1s. 6d. Birds (the 2s., 2s. 6d. and 3s. Birds were only issued on helecon paper). The 5d. Queen Elizabeth II in red (No. 354*b*) exists ordinary and with helecon ink. The coil pair was only issued with helecon ink; the booklet is normally with helecon ink but some were printed with ordinary ink by mistake. The Churchill stamp was printed on ordinary and helecon paper. The I.T.U. Centenary, Monash and later commemorative stamps were printed on helecon paper and all issues from No. 382 onwards were on helecon paper or paper coated with Derby Luminescence.

In 1982 a series of booklet stamps, Nos. 870/4, were printed by Enschedé on Harrison paper which gives a bluish white reaction under u.v. light.

**123**

**124**

**126**

**127**

**128**

**129**

Queen Elizabeth II

DIE I
Short break in outer line to bottom right of "4"

DIE II
Line unbroken

DIE A
Four short lines inside "5"

DIE B
Five short lines inside "5"

(Des G. Lissenden from photographs by Baron Studios. Eng F. D. Manley (2d.), D. Cameron (3d.). P. E. Morriss (others). Recess)

**1959–62.** *P* 14 × 15 (*horiz*), 15 × 14 (*vert*).

| | | | | |
|---|---|---|---|---|
| 308 | **123** | 1d. deep slate-purple (2.2.59) | 10 | 10 |
| | | *a. Deep slate-lilac* | 50 | 20 |
| 309 | **124** | 2d. brown (21.3.62) | 30 | 15 |
| | | a. Coil pair (1962) | 3·75 | 4·25 |
| | | b. Coil block of four | 7·50 | |
| 311 | **126** | 3d. blue-green (20.5.59) | 15 | 10 |
| | | a. Coil pair (8.60) | 3·50 | 4·25 |
| | | b. Coil block of four | 9·00 | |
| 312 | **127** | 3½d. deep green (18.3.59) | 15 | 15 |
| 313 | **128** | 4d. carmine-lake (Die I) (2.2.59) | 1·50 | 10 |
| | | *a. Carmine-red* | 1·50 | 10 |
| | | b. Die II | 1·50 | 10 |
| | | *ba. Carmine-red* | 1·50 | 10 |
| 314 | **129** | 5d. deep blue (Die A or B) (1.10.59) | 70 | 10 |
| | | a. Vert *se-tenant* pair (A and B) | 1·40 | 2·25 |
| | | b. Coil pair (early 1960) | 6·50 | 9·00 |
| | | c. Coil block of four | 22·00 | |
| 308/14 | | *Set of* 6 | 2·50 | 30 |

No. 313. Die I occurs in the upper pane and Die II in the lower pane of the sheet.

No. 314. Both dies occur in alternate horizontal rows in the sheet (Die A in Row 1, Die B in Row 2, and so on), and their value is identical.

Nos. 309a/b, 311a/b and 314b/c have horizontal coil perforations as described after No. 191.

The Note after No. 295 also applies to Nos. 313/14.

131 Numbat

137 Christmas Bells

142 Aboriginal Stockman

(Des Eileen Mayo (6d., 8d., 9d., 11d., 1s., 1s. 2d.), B. Stewart (5s.), Margaret Stones (others). Eng P. Morriss (11d.), F. D. Manley (1s.), B. Stewart (others). Recess)

**1959–64.** *T* **131, 137, 142** *and similar designs. W* **15** *(5s.), no wmk (others). P* 14 × 15 *(1s. 2d.),* 15 × 14 *(6d. to 1s.),* 14½ × 14 *(5s.) or* 14½ *(others).*

| | | | | |
|---|---|---|---|---|
| 316 | 6d. brown (30.9.60) | .. | 2·00 | 10 |
| 317 | 8d. red-brown (11.5.60) | .. | 75 | 10 |
| | *a. Pale red-brown* (1961) | .. | 75 | 10 |
| 318 | 9d. deep sepia (21.10.59) | .. | 2·75 | 35 |
| 319 | 11d. deep blue (3.5.61) | .. | 1·00 | 15 |
| 320 | 1s. deep green (9.9.59) | .. | 4·50 | 30 |
| 321 | 1s. 2d. deep purple (21.3.62) | .. | 1·00 | 15 |
| 322 | 1s. 6d. crimson/*yellow* (3.2.60) | .. | 2·50 | 80 |
| 323 | 2s. grey-blue (8.4.59) | .. | 1·25 | 10 |
| 324 | 2s. 3d. green/*maize* (9.9.59) | .. | 1·75 | 10 |
| 324*a* | 2s. 3d. yellow-green (28.10.64) | .. | 8·00 | 1·50 |
| 325 | 2s. 5d. brown/*yellow* (16.3.60) | .. | 7·00 | 45 |
| 326 | 3s. scarlet (15.7.59) | .. | 1·75 | 10 |
| 327 | 5s. red-brown (26.7.61) | .. | 25·00 | 75 |
| | a. White paper. *Brown-red* (17.6.64) | .. | £160 | 5·50 |
| 316/327 | .. | *Set of* 13 | 55·00 | 4·25 |

Designs: (*As T* 131) *Vert*—8d. Tiger Cat; 9d. Eastern Grey Kangaroos; 11d. Common Rabbit-Bandicoot; 1s. Platypus. *Horiz*—1s. 2d. Thylacine. (*As T* 137) *Vert*—2s. Flannel Flower; 2s. 3d. Wattle; 2s. 5d. Banksia; 3s. Waratah.

No. 327 is on toned paper. No. 327a was a late printing on the white paper referred to in the note below No. 360.

See notes after No. 307 *re* helecon ink.

143 Postmaster Isaac Nichols boarding the brig *Experiment*

144 Parliament House, Brisbane, and Arms of Queensland

(Des R. Shackel; adapted and eng F. D. Manley. Recess)

**1959** (22 Apr). *150th Anniv of the Australian Post Office. P* 14½ × 14.

| | | | | |
|---|---|---|---|---|
| 331 | **143** | 4d. slate | 15 | 10 |

(Des and eng G. Lissenden. Recess and typo)

**1959** (5 June). *Centenary of Self-Government in Queensland. P* 14 × 14½.

| | | | | |
|---|---|---|---|---|
| 332 | **144** | 4d. lilac and green | 10 | 10 |

145 "The Approach of the Magi"

146 Girl Guide and Lord Baden-Powell

(Des and eng F. D. Manley. Recess)

**1959** (4 Nov). *Christmas. P* 15 × 14.

| | | | | |
|---|---|---|---|---|
| 333 | **145** | 5d. deep reddish violet | 10 | 10 |

(Des and eng B. Stewart. Recess)

**1960** (18 Aug). *Golden Jubilee of Girl Guide Movement. P* 14½ × 14.

| | | | | |
|---|---|---|---|---|
| 334 | **146** | 5d. deep ultramarine | 30 | 15 |

147 "The Overlanders" (Sir Daryl Lindsay)

148 "Archer" and Melbourne Cup

Two types:

I Mane rough

II Mane smooth

Type II occurs on Pane A, Row 2 Nos. 8 and 9, Row 4 Nos. 1 to 12, Row 5 Nos. 10 to 12, and on Pane C, Row 4 Nos. 5 to 12, Row 5 Nos. 1 to 9, and Rows 6 to 10 inclusive; the stamps in Row 4 Nos. 5 to 12 and Row 5 Nos. 1 to 9 are considered to be of an intermediate type with the mane as in Type II but the ear and rein being as in Type I. All the rest are Type I.

(Adapted and eng P. E. Morriss. Recess)

**1960** (21 Sept). *Centenary of Northern Territory Exploration. P* 15 × 14½.

| | | | | |
|---|---|---|---|---|
| 335 | **147** | 5d. magenta (I) | 15 | 15 |
| | | a. Type II | 1·25 | 30 |

(Des F. D. Manley. Eng G. Lissenden. Recess)

**1960** (12 Oct). *100th Melbourne Cup Race Commemoration. P* 14½.

| | | | | |
|---|---|---|---|---|
| 336 | **148** | 5d. sepia | 15 | 10 |

149 Queen Victoria

150 Open Bible and Candle

(Des F. D. Manley. Eng B. Stewart. Recess)

**1960** (2 Nov). *Centenary of First Queensland Postage Stamp. P* 14½ × 15.

| | | | | |
|---|---|---|---|---|
| 337 | **149** | 5d. deep myrtle-green | 25 | 10 |

(Des K. McKay. Adapted and eng B. Stewart. Recess)

**1960** (9 Nov). *Christmas. P* 15 × 14½.

| | | | | |
|---|---|---|---|---|
| 338 | **150** | 5d. carmine-red | 10 | 10 |

151 Colombo Plan Bureau Emblem

152 Melba (after bust by Sir Bertram Mackennal)

(Des and eng G. Lissenden. Recess)

**1961** (30 June). *Colombo Plan. P* 14 × 14½.

| | | | | |
|---|---|---|---|---|
| 339 | **151** | 1s. red-brown | 10 | 10 |

See notes after No. 307 *re* helecon ink.

(Des and eng B. Stewart. Recess)

**1961** (20 Sept). *Centenary of Birth of Dame Nellie Melba (singer). P* 14½ × 15.

| | | | | |
|---|---|---|---|---|
| 340 | **152** | 5d. blue | 30 | 15 |

153 Open Prayer Book and Text

(Des G. Lissenden. Eng P. E. Morriss. Recess)

**1961** (8 Nov). *Christmas. P* 14½ × 14.

| | | | | |
|---|---|---|---|---|
| 341 | **153** | 5d. brown | 10 | 10 |

154 J. M. Stuart

155 Flynn's Grave and Nursing Sister

(Des W. Jardine. Eng P. E. Morriss. Recess)

**1962** (25 July). *Centenary of Stuart's Crossing of Australia from South to North. P* 14½ × 15.

| | | | | |
|---|---|---|---|---|
| 342 | **154** | 5d. brown-red | 15 | 10 |

(Des F. D. Manley. Photo)

**1962** (5 Sept). *50th Anniv of Australian Inland Mission. P* 13½.

| | | | | |
|---|---|---|---|---|
| 343 | **155** | 5d. multicoloured | 30 | 15 |
| | | a. Red omitted | £400 | £250 |

The note below No. 372b also applies to No. 343a.

156 "Woman"

157 "Madonna and Child"

(Des D. Dundas. Eng G. Lissenden. Recess)

**1962** (26 Sept). *"Associated Country Women of the World" Conference, Melbourne. P* 14 × 14½.

| | | | | |
|---|---|---|---|---|
| 344 | **156** | 5d. deep green | 10 | 10 |

(Des and eng G. Lissenden. Recess)

**1962** (17 Oct). *Christmas. P* 14½.

| | | | | |
|---|---|---|---|---|
| 345 | **157** | 5d. violet | 15 | 10 |

158 Perth and Kangaroo Paw (plant)

159 Arms of Perth and Running Track

(Des R. M. Warner (5d.), G. Hamori (2s. 3d.). Photo Harrison)

**1962** (1 Nov). *Seventh British Empire and Commonwealth Games, Perth. P* 14 *(5d.) or* 14½ × 14 *(2s. 3d.).*

| | | | | |
|---|---|---|---|---|
| 346 | **158** | 5d. multicoloured | 40 | 10 |
| | | a. Red omitted | £475 | |
| 347 | **159** | 2s. 3d. black, red, blue and green | 3·00 | 2·50 |

160 Queen Elizabeth II.

161 Queen Elizabeth II and Duke of Edinburgh

(Des and eng after portraits by Anthony Buckley, P. E. Morriss (5d.), B. Stewart (2s. 3d.). Recess)

**1963** (18 Feb). *Royal Visit. P* 14½.

| | | | | |
|---|---|---|---|---|
| 348 | **160** | 5d. deep green | 35 | 10 |
| 349 | **161** | 2s. 3d. brown-lake | 2·00 | 3·25 |

162 Arms of Canberra and W. B. Griffin (architect)

163 Centenary Emblem

(Des and eng B. Stewart. Recess)

**1963** (8 Mar). *50th Anniv of Canberra. P* 14½ × 14.

| | | | | |
|---|---|---|---|---|
| 350 | **162** | 5d. deep green | 15 | 10 |

(Des G. Hamori. Photo)

**1963** (8 May). *Red Cross Centenary. P* 13½ × 13.

| | | | | |
|---|---|---|---|---|
| 351 | **163** | 5d. red, grey-brown and blue | 25 | 10 |

164 Blaxland, Lawson and Wentworth on Mt. York

(Des T. Alban. Eng P. E. Morriss. Recess)

**1963** (28 May). *150th Anniv of First Crossing of Blue Mountains. P* 14½ × 14.
352 **164** 5d. ultramarine .. .. .. .. 15 10

**165** "Export" **166** Queen Elizabeth II

(Des and eng B. Stewart. Recess)

**1963** (28 Aug). *Export Campaign. P* 14½ × 14.
353 **165** 5d. red .. .. .. .. .. .. 10 10

(Des and eng P. E. Morriss from photograph by Anthony Buckley. Recess)

**1963** (9 Oct)–**65**. *P* 15 × 14.
354 **166** 5d. deep green .. .. .. .. .. 55 10
a. Imperf between (horiz pair) (31.7.64) 1·75 2·50
354*b* 5d. red (30.6.65) .. .. .. .. 45 10
c. Coil pair (30.6.65) .. .. .. .. 15·00 20·00

See notes after No. 307 *re* helecon ink.

The above exist in booklet panes of six stamps, with imperf outer edges, producing single stamps with one or two adjacent sides imperf.

No. 354a comes from sheets of uncut booklet panes containing 288 stamps (16 × 18) with wide margins intersecting the sheet horizontally below each third row, alternate rows of stamps imperforate between vertically and the outer left, right and bottom margins imperforate. This means that in each sheet there are 126 pairs of stamps imperf between vertically, plus a number with wide imperforate margins attached, as shown in the illustration.

**167** Tasman and *Heemskerk* **168** Dampier and *Roebuck*

(Des W. Jardine. Eng B. Stewart (4s., £1). E. R. M. Jones (10s.), P. E. Morriss (others). Recess)

**1963–65.** *T* **167/8** *and similar designs. No wmk* (4s.) *or W* **15** (*others*), (*sideways on* 5s., £1). *P* 14 *or* 14½ (5s., £1, £2).
355 4s. ultramarine (9.10.63) .. .. .. 4·50 40
356 5s. red-brown (25.11.64) .. .. .. 6·00 60
357 7s. 6d. olive (26.8.64) .. .. .. 17·00 16·00
358 10s. brown-purple (26.2.64) .. .. .. 42·00 4·25
a. White paper. *Deep brown-purple* (14.1.65) 55·00 6·50
359 £1 deep reddish violet (26.2.64) .. .. 48·00 12·00
a. White paper. *Deep bluish violet* (16.11.64) 70·00 22·00
360 £2 sepia (26.8.64) .. .. .. .. 85·00 70·00
355/360 .. .. .. *Set of* 6 £180 95·00
357/60 Optd "Specimen" .. .. *Set of* 4 £450

Designs: *As T* **167**—7s. 6d. Captain Cook; 10s. Flinders and *Investigator*. *As T* **168**—£1 Bass and whaleboat; £2 Admiral King and *Mermaid*.

Nos. 358 and 359 were printed on a toned paper but all the other values are on white paper, the 4s. being on rather thicker paper.

## NEW INFORMATION

The editor is always interested to correspond with people who have new information that will improve or correct the Catalogue.

**173** "Peace on Earth . . ." **174** "Commonwealth Cable"

(Des R. M. Warner. Eng B. Stewart. Recess)

**1963** (25 Oct). *Christmas. P* 14½.
361 **173** 5d. greenish blue .. .. .. 10 10

(Des P. E. Morriss. Photo)

**1963** (3 Dec). *Opening of COMPAC (Trans-Pacific Telephone Cable). Chalky paper. P* 13½.
362 **174** 2s. 3d. red, blue, black and pale blue 3·25 4·00

**175** Yellow-tailed Thornbill **176** Black-backed Magpie

(Des Mrs. H. Temple-Watts. Photo)

**1964** (11 Mar)–**65**. *T* **175/6** *and similar designs showing birds. Chalky paper* (*except No.* 367*a*). *P* 13½.
363 6d. brown, yellow, black and bluish green (19.8.64) .. .. .. .. 60 25
*a. Brown, yellow, black and emerald-green* (12.65) .. .. .. .. .. 2·50 1·75
364 9d. black, grey and pale green .. .. 1·50 3·25
365 1s. 6d. pink, grey, dull purple and black .. 1·00 1·25
366 2s. yellow, black and pink (21.4.65) .. 2·50 50
367 2s. 5d. deep royal blue, light violet-blue, yellow-orange, grey and black .. .. 7·00 3·25
367*a* 2s. 5d. deep blue, light blue, orange-brown, blue-grey and black (8.65) .. .. 24·00 12·00
368 2s. 6d. black, red, grey and green (21.4.65) .. 4·25 2·75
a. Red omitted (white breast) .. .. £800
369 3s. black, red, buff and yellow-green (21.4.65) 4·00 1·50
363/369 .. .. .. .. *Set of* 8 40·00 22·00

Designs: *Vert*—1s. 6d. Galah; 2s. Golden Whistler; 2s. 5d. Blue Wren; 3s. Straw-necked Ibis. *Horiz*—2s. 6d. Scarlet Robin.

No. 367*a* is from a printing on unsurfaced Wiggins Teape paper, the rest of the set being on chalk-surfaced Harrison paper. Apart from the differences in shade, the inscriptions, particularly "BLUE WREN", stand out very much more clearly on No. 367*a*. Although two colours are apparent in both stamps, the grey and black were printed from one plate.

See notes after No. 307 *re* helecon ink.

**182** "Bleriot" Aircraft (type flown by M. Guillaux, 1914) Re-entry (upper plate, R. 4/4)

(Des K. McKay. Adapted and eng P. E. Morriss. Recess)

**1964** (1 July). *50th Anniv of First Australian Airmail Flight. P* 14½ × 14.
370 **182** 5d. olive-green .. .. .. .. 40 10
a. Re-entry .. .. .. .. £100 40·00
371 2s. 3d. scarlet .. .. .. .. 2·50 2·00

**183** Child looking at Nativity Scene **184** "Simpson and his Donkey"

(Des P. E. Morriss and J. Mason. Photo)

**1964** (21 Oct). *Christmas. Chalky paper. P* 13½.
372 **183** 5d. red, blue, buff and black .. .. 10 10
a. Red omitted .. .. .. .. £250
b. Black omitted .. .. .. .. £350

The red ink is soluble and can be removed by bleaching and it is therefore advisable to obtain a certificate from a recognised expert committee before purchasing No. 372a.

(Des C. Andrew (after statue, Shrine of Remembrance, Melbourne). Eng E. R. M. Jones. Recess)

**1965** (14 Apr). *50th Anniv of Gallipoli Landing. P* 14 × 14½.
373 **184** 5d. drab .. .. .. .. .. 50 10
374 8d. blue .. .. .. .. .. 80 2·00
375 2s. 3d. reddish purple .. .. .. 1·40 2·00
373/5 .. .. .. .. .. *Set of* 3 2·40 3·75

**185** "Telecommunications" **186** Sir Winston Churchill

(Des J. McMahon and G. Hamori. Photo)

**1965** (10 May). *I.T.U. Centenary. P* 13½.
376 **185** 5d. black, brown, orange-brown & bl .. 30 10
a. Black (value and pylon) omitted .. £500

(Des P. E. Morriss from photo by Karsh. Photo)

**1965** (24 May). *Churchill Commemoration. Chalky paper. P* 13½.
377 **186** 5d. black, pale grey and light blue .. 15 10
a. Pale grey ("AUSTRALIA") omitted £500 £300

About half the printing was on helecon impregnated paper, differing slightly in the shade of the blue.

**187** General Monash **188** Hargrave and "Seaplane" (1902)

(Des O. Foulkes and W. Walters. Photo)

**1965** (23 June). *Birth Centenary of General Sir John Monash (engineer and soldier). Chalky paper. P* 13½.
378 **187** 5d. multicoloured .. .. .. 15 10

(Des G. Hamori. Photo)

**1965** (4 Aug). *50th Death Anniv of Lawrence Hargrave (aviation pioneer). Chalky paper. P* 13½.
379 **188** 5d. purple-brown, blk, yell-ochre & pur 15 10
a. Purple (value) omitted .. .. £160

**189** I.C.Y. Emblem **190** "Nativity Scene"

(Des H. Fallu from U.N. theme. Photo)

**1965** (1 Sept). *International Co-operation Year. Chalky paper. P* 13½.
380 **189** 2s. 3d. emerald and light blue .. .. 1·75 2·00

(Des J. Mason. Photo)

**1965** (20 Oct). *Christmas. P* 13½.
381 **190** 5d. multicoloured .. .. .. 15 10
a. Gold omitted .. .. .. £450
b. Blue omitted .. .. .. £275

No. 381a comes from the bottom row of a sheet in which the gold is completely omitted, the background appearing as black with "CHRISTMAS 1965" and "AUSTRALIA" omitted. The row above had the black missing from the lower two-fifths of the stamp.

**(New Currency. 100 cents = 1 dollar)**

**191** Queen Elizabeth II **192** Blue-faced Honeyeater **193** Humbug Fish

Nos. 401 (top), 401a (centre) and 401b (bottom). No. 401b shows the final form of the variety with a plate crack visible in sky and across sail (Lower sheet left pane. R. 10/1)

(Des Mrs. H. Temple-Watts (6 c. (No. 387), 13 c., 24 c.), Eileen Mayo (7 c. (No. 388) to 10 c.). Recess (T **191**, 40 c. to $4). Photo Chalky paper (others))

**1966** (14 Feb)–**73**. *Decimal currency. T* **191/3** *and similar designs, some reused from previous issues. No wmk. P* 15 × 14 (*T* **191**), 14 (40 *c.*, 75 *c.*, $1), 14½ (50 *c.*, $2, $4) *or* 13½ (*others*).

382 **191** 1 c. deep red-brown .. .. .. 25 10
383 2 c. olive-green .. .. .. 90 10
384 3 c. slate-green .. .. .. 90 10
385 4 c. red .. .. .. .. 20 10
a. Booklet pane. Five stamps plus one printed label .. .. 35·00
386 **175** 5 c. brown, yellow, black & emer-grn 25 10
a. Brown (plumage) omitted .. £600
*b. Brown, yellow, blk & bl-grn* (1.67) 25 15
386*c* **191** 5 c. deep blue (29.9.67) .. .. 2·50 10
ca. Booklet pane. Five stamps plus one printed label .. .. 10·00
cb. Imperf in horiz strip of 3* .. £850
387 **192** 6 c. olive-yellow, blk, blue & pale grey 70 45
aa. Blue (eye markings) omitted .. £130
387*a* **191** 6 c. orange (28.9.70) .. .. 45 10
388 **193** 7 c. black, grey, salmon and brown .. 1·50 10
388*a* **191** 7 c. purple (1.10.71) .. .. .. 1·50 10
389 – 8 c. red, yell, bl-grn & blackish green 1·50 25
390 – 9 c. brown-red, purple-brown, black and light yellow-olive .. .. 1·50 15
391 – 10 c. orange, blackish brown, pale turquoise-blue and olive-brown .. 1·50 10
392 – 13 c. red, black, grey & light turq-green 3·25 25
a. Red omitted .. .. .. £450
b. Grey (plumage and legs) omitted £400
393 – 15 c. rose-carmine, black, grey and light bluish green .. .. 2·50 50
a. Rose-carmine omitted .. .. £1600
394 – 20 c. yellow, black and pink .. .. 7·50 15
a. Yellow (plumage) omitted .. £450
395 – 24 c. ultramarine, yellow, blk & lt brn 90 55
396 – 25 c. black, red, grey and green .. 5·00 20
a. Red omitted .. .. .. £700
397 – 30 c. black, red, buff & lt yellow-green 24·00 45
a. Red omitted .. .. .. £600
398 **167** 40 c. ultramarine .. .. .. 12·00 10
399 **168** 50 c. red-brown .. .. .. 15·00 10
400 – 75 c. olive .. .. .. .. 1·00 1·50
401 – $1 brown-purple (*shades*) .. .. 3·75 15
a. Recut lines in sky .. .. 22·00
b. Recut lines and plate crack .. 30·00
c. Perf 15 × 14† (1973) .. .. £100 17·00
402 – $2 deep reddish violet .. .. 10·00 30
403 – $4 sepia .. .. .. .. 9·50 5·00
382/403 .. .. .. .. *Set of* 25 95·00 8·50
400/3 Optd "Specimen" .. .. *Set of* 4 90·00

Designs: *Vert* (*as T* **193**)—8 c. Coral Fish; 9 c. Hermit Crab; 10 c. Anemone Fish. (*as T* **192**)—13 c. Red-necked Avocet; 15 c. Galah; 20 c. Golden Whistler; 30 c. Straw-necked Ibis. *Horiz* (*as T* **192**)—24 c. Azure Kingfisher; 25 c. Scarlet Robin. *As T* **167**—75 c. Captain Cook; $1 Flinders and *Investigator*. *As T* **168**—$2 Bass and whaleboat; $4 Admiral King and *Mermaid*.

*This comprises two stamps imperforate all round and one imperforate at left only.

†The note below No. 553 also applies to No. 401c, its exact gauge being 14·9 × 14·1. No. 401 is 14·25 × 13·95.

No. 385 is normally printed with helecon ink, the rest being on helecon paper. Early in 1967 experimental printings of No. 385 on different kinds of paper coated with helecon or Derby Luminescents phosphor were put on sale. They cannot be distinguished by the naked eye.

**199** Queen Elizabeth II

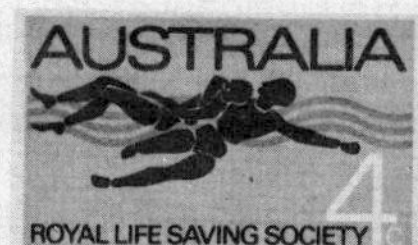


**200** "Saving Life"

**1966** (14 Feb)–**67**. *Coil stamps. Photo. P* 15 × *imperf.*
404 **199** 3 c. black, light brown and green .. 20 40
405 4 c. black, light brown & lt vermilion .. 45 20
405*a* 5 c. black, light brown and new blue (29.9.67) .. .. .. 60 10
404/5*a* .. .. .. .. *Set of* 3 1·10 60

(Des L. Mason. Photo)

**1966** (6 July). *75th Anniv of Royal Life Saving Society. P* 13½.
406 **200** 4 c. black, bright blue and blue .. 15 10

**201** "Adoration of the Shepherds"

**202** *Eendracht*

(Des L. Stirling, after medieval engraving. Photo)

**1966** (19 Oct). *Christmas. P* 13½.
407 **201** 4 c. black and yellow-olive .. 10 10
a. Value omitted .. .. .. £850

No. 407a was caused by a shift of the yellow-olive which covered the white face value.

(Des F. Eidlitz. Photo)

**1966** (24 Oct). *350th Anniv of Dirk Hartog's Landing in Australia. P* 13½.
408 **202** 4 c. multicoloured .. .. .. 10 10
a. Red (sphere) omitted .. .. £1100

**203** Open Bible

**204** Ancient Keys and Modern Lock

(Des L. Stirling. Photo)

**1967** (7 Mar). *150th Anniv of British and Foreign Bible Society in Australia. P* 13½.
409 **203** 4 c. multicoloured .. .. .. 10 10

(Des G. Andrews. Photo)

**1967** (5 Apr). *150th Anniv of Australian Banking. P* 13½.
410 **204** 4 c. black, light blue and emerald .. 10 10

**205** Lions Badge and 50 Stars

**206** Y.W.C.A. Emblem

(Des M. Ripper. Photo)

**1967** (7 June). *50th Anniv of Lions International. P* 13½.
411 **205** 4 c. black, gold and blue .. .. 10 10

(Des H. Williamson. Photo)

**1967** (21 Aug). *World Y.W.C.A. Council Meeting. Monash University, Victoria. P* 13½.
412 **206** 4 c. dp blue, ultramarine, lt pur & lt bl 10 10

**207** Anatomical Figures

5c

(**208**)

(Des R. Ingpen. Photo)

**1967** (20 Sept). *Fifth World Gynaecology and Obstetrics Congress, Sydney. P* 13½.
413 **207** 4 c. black, blue and light reddish violet 10 10

**1967** (29 Sept). *No. 385 surch with T* **208**.
414 **191** 5 c. on 4 c. red .. .. .. 70 10
a. Booklet pane. Five stamps plus one printed label .. .. .. 3·25

No. 414 was only issued in booklets and so only occurs with one or two adjacent sides imperforate. It only exists printed with helecon ink on normal paper.

**209** Christmas Bells and Gothic Arches

**210** Religious Symbols

(Des M. Ripper (5 c.), Erica McGilchrist (25 c.). Photo)

**1967**. *Christmas. P* 13½.
415 **209** 5 c. multicoloured (18.10.67) .. .. 20 10
a. Imperf three sides .. .. £1000
416 **210** 25 c. multicoloured (27.11.67) .. .. 1·25 1·75

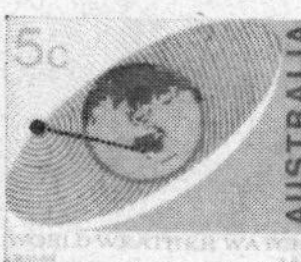


**211** Satellite in Orbit

**212** World Weather Map

(Des J. Mason. Photo)

**1968** (20 Mar). *World Weather Watch. P* 13½.
417 **211** 5 c. orange-brown, pl blue, blk & ochre 30 10
418 **212** 20 c. orange-brown, blue and black .. 1·75 3·75
a. White (radio waves) omitted .. £375
b. Orange-brown (triangle) omitted £1000

**213** Radar Antenna

**214** Kangaroo Paw (Western Australia)

(Des R. Ingpen. Photo)

**1968** (20 Mar). *World Telecommunications Intelsat II. P* 13½.
419 **213** 25 c. greenish blue, black & lt blue-green 3·00 5·50

(Des Nell Wilson (6c., 30 c.); R. and P. Warner (13 c., 25 c.); Dorothy Thornhill (15 c., 20 c.). Photo)

**1968** (10 July)–**71**. *State Floral Emblems. T* **214** *and similar vert designs. Multicoloured. P* 13½.
420 6 c. Type **214** .. .. .. 45 55
421 13 c. Pink Heath (Victoria) .. .. 55 30
422 15 c. Tasmanian Blue Gum (Tasmania) .. 2·00 20
423 20 c. Sturt's Desert Pea (South Australia) .. 9·00 30
424 25 c. Cooktown Orchid (Queensland) .. 4·50 50
425 30 c. Waratah (New South Wales) (Type I) 1·00 10
a. Green (leaves) omitted .. .. £425
b. Type II (29.6.71) .. .. 4·50 1·50
420/5 .. .. .. .. *Set of* 6 16·00 1·75

The 30 c. was reprinted in 1971 from new cylinders so that Type II shows greater areas of white in the pink tones of the petals.

**220** Soil Sample Analysis

(Des R. Ingpen. Photo)

**1968** (6 Aug). *International Soil Science Congress and World Medical Association Assembly. T* **220** *and similar horiz design. P* 13½.
426 **220** 5 c. orange-brn, stone, greenish bl & blk 10 10
a. Nos. 426/7 *se-tenant* with gutter margin between .. .. .. .. 14·00 15·00
427 – 5 c. greenish blue, dull ol-yell, rose & blk 10 10

Design:—No. 427, Rubber-gloved hands, syringe and head of Hippocrates.

The above were printed in sheets of 100 containing a pane of 50 of each design.

The major shades formerly listed have been deleted as there is a range of intermediate shades.

**222** Athlete carrying Torch, and Sunstone Symbol

**223** Sunstone Symbol and Mexican Flag

(Des H. Williamson. Photo)

**1968** (2 Oct). *Olympic Games, Mexico City. P* 13½.
428 **222** 5 c. multicoloured .. .. .. 30 10
429 **223** 25 c. multicoloured .. .. .. 45 1·50

**224** Houses and Dollar Signs

**225** Church Window and View of Bethlehem

(Des Erica McGilchrist. Photo)

**1968** (16 Oct). *Building and Savings Societies Congress. P* 13½.
430 **224** 5 c. multicoloured .. .. .. 10 30

(Des G. Hamori. Photo)

**1968** (23 Oct). *Christmas. P* 13½.
431 **225** 5 c. multicoloured .. .. .. 10 10
a. Green window (gold omitted) .. £325
b. Red (inscr) omitted .. .. £375

**226** Edgeworth David (geologist)

(Des Note Ptg Branch (Nos. 432, 434), A. Cook (others). Recess, background litho)

**1968** (6 Nov). *Famous Australians (1st series). T* **226** *and similar vert portraits. P* 15 × 14.

432 5 c. myrtle-green/*pale green* 75 15
a. Booklet pane. Five stamps plus one printed label 3·75
433 5 c. black/*pale blue* 75 15
a. Booklet pane. Five stamps plus one printed label 3·75
434 5 c. blackish brown/*pale buff* 75 15
a. Booklet pane. Five stamps plus one printed label 3·75
435 5 c. deep violet/*pale lilac* 75 15
a. Booklet pane. Five stamps plus one printed label 3·75
432/5 *Set of* 4 2·75 55

Designs:—No. 432, Type **226**; No. 433, A. B. Paterson (poet); No. 434, Albert Namatjira (artist); No. 435, Caroline Chisholm (social worker).

Nos. 432/5 were only issued in booklets and only exist with one or two adjacent sides imperf.

See also Nos. 446/9, 479/82, 505/8, 537/40, 590/5, 602/7 and 637/40.

**230** Macquarie Lighthouse

**231** Pioneers and Modern Building, Darwin

(Des and eng Note Ptg Branch. Recess; background litho)

**1968** (27 Nov). *150th Anniv of Macquarie Lighthouse. P* 14½ × 13½.

436 **230** 5 c. black/*pale yellow* 10 20

Used examples are known with the pale yellow background colour omitted.

(Des Mrs. M. Lyon. Photo)

**1969** (5 Feb). *Centenary of Northern Territory Settlement. P* 13½.

437 **231** 5 c. blackish brown, yellow-olive and yellow-ochre 10 10

**232** Melbourne Harbour

**233** Concentric Circles (symbolising Management, Labour and Government)

(Des J. Mason. Photo)

**1969** (26 Feb). *Sixth Biennial Conference of International Association of Ports and Harbours. P* 13½.

438 **232** 5 c. multicoloured 15 10

(Des G. Hamori. Photo.)

**1969** (4 June). *50th Anniv of International Labour Organisation. P* 13½.

439 **233** 5 c. multicoloured 15 10
a. Gold (middle circle) omitted £600

**234** Sugar Cane

**238** "The Nativity" (stained-glass window)

**240** Edmund Barton

(Des R. Ingpen. Photo)

**1969** (17 Sept). *Primary Industries. T* **234** *and similar vert designs. Multicoloured. P* 13½.

440 7 c. Type **234** 1·25 2·50
441 15 c. Timber 4·00 6·00
a. Black ("Australia" and value) omitted £650
442 20 c. Wheat 1·25 80
443 25 c. Wool 2·50 2·25
440/3 *Set of* 4 8·00 10·50

(Des G. Hamori (5 c.), J. Coburn (25 c.). Photo)

**1969** (15 Oct). *Christmas. T* **238** *and similar multicoloured designs. P* 13½.

444 5 c. Type **238** 25 10
a. Magenta (robe) omitted £350
b. Yellow omitted £300
445 25 c. "Tree of Life", Christ in Crib and Christmas Star (abstract) 1·25 1·75

(Des from drawings by J. Santry. Recess, background litho)

**1969** (22 Oct). *Famous Australians (2nd series). Prime Ministers. T* **240** *and similar vert designs each black on pale green. P* 15 × 14.

446 5 c. Type **240** 90 20
a. Booklet pane. Five stamps plus one printed label 4·00
447 5 c. Alfred Deakin 90 20
a. Booklet pane. Five stamps plus one printed label 4·00
448 5 c. J. C. Watson 90 20
a. Booklet pane. Five stamps plus one printed label 4·00
449 5 c. G. H. Reid 90 20
a. Booklet pane. Five stamps plus one printed label 4·00
446/9 *Set of* 4 3·25 70

Nos. 446/9 were only issued in booklets and only exist with one or two adjacent sides imperf.

**244** Capt. Ross Smith's Vickers "Vimy", 1919

**247** Symbolic Track and Diesel Locomotive

(Des E. Thake. Photo)

**1969** (12 Nov). *50th Anniv of First England–Australia Flight. T* **244** *and similar horiz designs. P* 13½.

450 5 c. olive-green, pale blue, black and red 15 10
a. Strip of 3. Nos. 450/2 1·50
451 5 c. black, red and olive-green 15 10
452 5 c. olive-green, black, pale blue and red 15 10
450/2 *Set of* 3 1·50 25

Designs:—No. 450, Type **244**; No. 451, Lt. H. Fysh and Lt. P. McGinness on 1919 survey with Ford car; No. 452, Capt. Wrigley and Sgt. Murphy in "BE 2E" taking off to meet the Smiths.

The three designs appear *se-tenant*, both horizontally and vertically, throughout the sheet.

(Des B. Sadgrove. Photo)

**1970** (11 Feb). *Sydney–Perth Standard Gauge Railway Link. P* 13½.

453 **247** 5 c. multicoloured 15 10

**248** Australian Pavilion, Osaka

**251** Australian Flag

(Des J. Copeland (5 c.), A. Leydin (20 c.). Photo)

**1970** (16 Mar). *World Fair, Osaka. T* **248** *and similar horiz design. P* 13½.

454 5 c. multicoloured 15 10
455 20 c. orange-red and black 35 65

Design:—20 c. "Southern Cross" and "from the Country of the South with warm feelings" (message).

(Des P.O. Artists (5 c.), J. Mason (30 c.). Photo)

**1970** (31 Mar). *Royal Visit. T* **251** *and similar horiz design. P* 13½.

456 5 c. black and deep ochre 35 15
457 30 c. multicoloured 90 2·25

Design:—5 c. Queen Elizabeth II and Prince Philip.

**252** Lucerne Plant, Bull and Sun

**253** Captain Cook and H.M.S. *Endeavour*

(Des R. Ingpen. Photo)

**1970** (13 Apr). *Eleventh International Grasslands Congress. P* 13½.

458 **252** 5 c. multicoloured 10 30

(Des R. Ingpen and "Team" (T. Keneally, A. Leydin, J. R. Smith). Photo)

**1970** (20 Apr). *Bicentenary of Captain Cook's Discovery of Australia's East Coast. T* **253** *and similar multicoloured designs. P* 13½.

459 5 c. Type **253** 35 10
a. Strip of 5. Nos. 459/63 2·25
460 5 c. Sextant and H.M.S. *Endeavour* 35 10
461 5 c. Landing at Botany Bay 35 10
462 5 c. Charting and exploring 35 10
463 5 c. Claiming possession 35 10
464 30 c. Captain Cook, H.M.S. *Endeavour*, sextant, aborigines and kangaroo (63 × 30 *mm*) 1·75 2·75
459/64 *Set of* 6 3·50 3·00
**MS**465 157 × 129 mm. Nos. 459/64. Imperf 15·00 15·00

The 5 c. stamps were issued horizontally *se-tenant* within the sheet, to form a composite design in the order listed.

50,000 miniature sheets were made available by the Post Office to the organisers of the Australian National Philatelic Exhibition which overprinted them in the white margin at each side of the 30 c. stamp with "Souvenir Sheet AUSTRALIAN NATIONAL PHILATELIC EXHIBITION" at left and "ANPEX 1970 SYDNEY 27 APRIL–1 MAY" at right in light red-brown and they were also serially numbered. These were put on sale at the exhibition on the basis of one sheet to each visitor paying 30 c. for admission. Although still valid for postage, since the stamps themselves had not been defaced, these sheets were not sold at post offices.

Subsequently further supplies were purchased and similarly overprinted and numbered by a private firm without the authority of the Post Office and ANPEX took successful legal action to stop their further sale to the public. This firm also had the unoverprinted sheets rouletted in colour between the stamps whilst further supplies of the normal sheets were overprinted with reproductions of old coins and others with an inscription commemorating the opening of Melbourne Airport on 1st July 1970, but all these are private productions. Further private productions have been reported.

**259** Sturt's Desert Rose

AUSTRALIA AUSTRALIA
I. II.

*Two types of* 2 c.

I. "AUSTRALIA" thin: "2c" thin; flower name lightly printed.

II. Redrawn. "AUSTRALIA" thicker; "2c" much more heavily printed; flower name thicker and bolder.

(Des Note Ptg Branch. Photo)

**1970–75.** *Coil Stamps. Vert designs as T* **259**. *Multicoloured. Perf* 15 × *imperf.*

465*a* 2 c. Type **259** (I) (1.10.71) 35 20
ab. Type II (1973) 40 20
466 4 c. Type **259** (27.4.70) 70 1·25
467 5 c. Golden Wattle (27.4.70) 20 10
468 6 c. Type **259** (28.9.70) 1·25 1·00
a. Green (leaves) omitted £200
468*b* 7 c. Sturt's Desert Pea (1.10.71) 40 30
c. Green (leaves) omitted 75·00
468*d* 10 c. As 7 c. (15.1.75) 30 25
465*a*/8*d* *Set of* 6 3·00 2·75

Nos. 465*a*/8*d* have horizontal coil perforations described after No. 191.

The 2 c. (No. 465*a*), 5 c. and 7 c. also exist on fluorescent paper; the 2 c. (No. 465ab) and 10 c. exist only on fluorescent paper (see note after No. 504).

**264** Snowy Mountains Scheme

**265** Rising Flames

(Des L. Mason (7 c.), R. Ingpen (8 c., 9 c.), B. Sadgrove (10 c.). Photo)

**1970** (31 Aug). *National Development (1st series). T* **264** *and similar horiz designs. Multicoloured. P* 13½.

469 7 c. Type **264** 30 65
470 8 c. Ord River Scheme 15 15
471 9 c. Bauxite to aluminium 15 15
472 10 c. Oil and Natural Gas 40 10
469/72 *Set of* 4 90 95

See also Nos. 541/4.

(Des G. Hamori. Photo)

**1970** (2 Oct). *16th Commonwealth Parliamentary Association Conference, Canberra. P* 13½.

473 **265** 6 c. multicoloured 10 10

## MINIMUM PRICE

The minimum price quote is 10p which represents a handling charge rather than a basis for valuing common stamps. For further notes about prices see introductory pages.

266 Milk Analysis and Dairy Herd

267 "The Nativity"

(Des R. Honisett. Photo)

**1970** (7 Oct). *18th International Dairy Congress, Sydney. P* 13½.
474 **266** 6 c. multicoloured . . . . . . 10 10

(Des W. Beasley. Photo)

**1970** (14 Oct). *Christmas. P* 13½.
475 **267** 6 c. multicoloured . . . . . . 10 10

268 U.N. "Plant" and Dove of Peace

269 Boeing "707" and Avro "504"

(Des Monad Ltd. Photo)

**1970** (19 Oct). *25th Anniv of United Nations. P* 13½.
476 **268** 6 c. multicoloured . . . . . . 15 10

(Des G. Hamori. Photo)

**1970** (2 Nov). *50th Anniv of QANTAS Airline. T* **269** *and similar horiz design. Multicoloured. P* 13½.
477 6 c. Type **269** . . . . . . . . 35 10
478 30 c. Avro "504" and Boeing "707" . . . . 90 1·50

270 The Duigan Brothers (Pioneer Aviators)

271 "Theatre"

(Des A. Cook (No. 480), T. Adams (No. 482), Note Ptg Branch (others). Recess (background litho))

**1970** (16 Nov). *Famous Australians* (3rd *series*). *T* **270** *and similar vert designs. P* 15 × 14.
479 6 c. blue . . . . . . . . . . 1·50 20
a. Booklet pane. Five stamps plus one printed label . . . . . . . . 6·50
480 6 c. black/*flesh* . . . . . . . . 1·50 20
a. Booklet pane. Five stamps plus one printed label . . . . . . . . 6·50
481 6 c. purple/*pink* . . . . . . . . 1·50 20
a. Booklet pane. Five stamps plus one printed label . . . . . . . . 6·50
482 6 c. brown-lake/*pink* . . . . . . . . 1·50 20
a. Booklet pane. Five stamps plus one printed label . . . . . . . . 6·50
479/82 . . . . . . . . *Set of* 4 5·50 75

Designs:—No. 479 Type **270**; No. 480 Lachlan Macquarie (Governor of N.S.W.); No. 481 Adam Lindsay Gordon (poet); No. 482 E. J. Eyre (explorer).

Nos. 479/82 were only issued in booklets and only exist with one or two adjacent sides imperf.

(Des D. Annand. Photo)

**1971** (6 Jan). *"Australia–Asia". T* **271** *and similar horiz designs. Multicoloured. P* 13½.
483 7 c. Type **271** . . . . . . . . 35 60
484 15 c. "Music" . . . . . . . . 60 1·00
485 20 c. "Sea Craft" . . . . . . . . 55 90
483/5 . . . . . . . . *Set of* 3 1·40 2·25

272 The Southern Cross

273 Market "Graph"

(Des R. Beck. Photo)

**1971** (21 Apr). *Centenary of Australian Natives' Association. P* 13½.
486 **272** 6 c. black, vermilion and bright blue . . 10 10

(Des Monad Ltd. Photo)

**1971** (5 May). *Centenary of Sydney Stock Exchange. P* 13½.
487 **273** 6 c. multicoloured . . . . . . 10 10

274 Rotary Emblem

275 "Mirage" Jets and "D.H.9a" Biplane

(Des H. Williamson. Photo)

**1971** (17 May). *50th Anniv of Rotary International in Australia. P* 13½.
488 **274** 6 c. multicoloured . . . . . . 15 10

(Des R. Honisett. Photo)

**1971** (9 June). *50th Anniv of R.A.A.F. P* 13½.
489 **275** 6 c. multicoloured . . . . . . 15 10
a. Black (face value and inscr) omitted £600

276 Draught-horse, Cat and Dog

277 Bark Painting

(Des R. Ingpen. Photo)

**1971** (5 July). *Animals. T* **276** *and similar vert designs. Multicoloured. P* 13½.
490 6 c. Type **276** . . . . . . . . 20 10
491 12 c. Vet and lamb ("Animal Science") . . 45 45
492 18 c. Red Kangaroo ("Fauna Conservation") . . 60 75
493 24 c. Guide-dog ("Animals Aid to Man") . . 1·50 2·25
490/3 . . . . . . . . *Set of* 4 2·50 3·25

The 6 c. commemorated the Centenary of the Australian R.S.P.C.A., and the others were short-term definitives.

(Des J. Mason. Photo)

**1971** (29 Sept). *Aboriginal Art. T* **277** *and similar multicoloured designs. P* 13½.
494 20 c. Type **277** . . . . . . . . 20 20
495 25 c. Body decoration . . . . . . 20 40
a. Black omitted* . . . . . . £350
496 30 c. Cave painting (*vert*) . . . . 30 20
497 35 c. Grave posts (*vert*) . . . . 30 15
494/7 . . . . . . . . *Set of* 4 90 85

*The omission of the black results in the stamp being without face-value and "AUSTRALIA".

Nos. 494/7 also exist on fluorescent paper and the 35 c. exists with both PVA gum and gum arabic.

278 The Three Kings and the Star

279 Andrew Fisher

(Des J. Lee. Photo)

**1971** (13 Oct). *Christmas. Colours of star and colour of "AUSTRALIA" given. P* 13½.
498 **278** 7 c. royal blue, pl mauve & pl lake-brn 1·00 15
a. Block of 7. Nos. 498/504 . . 38·00
499 7 c. pale mauve, pl lake-brown & white 1·00 15
500 7 c. pale mauve, white and black . . 7·00 80
501 7 c. black, green and black . . 1·00 15
502 7 c. lilac, green and lilac . . 1·00 15
503 7 c. black, pale lake-brown and white . . 1·00 15
504 7 c. royal blue, pale mauve and green . . 30·00 2·25
498/504 . . . . . . *Set of* 7 38·00 3·50

Nos. 498/504, which also exist on fluorescent paper, were issued in sheets having two panes of 50 stamps. Each half pane had its stamps arranged thus:—

| | | | | |
|---|---|---|---|---|
| 498 | 499 | 500 | 499 | 498 |
| 503 | 502 | 501 | 502 | 503 |
| 504 | 501 | 500 | 501 | 504 |
| 503 | 502 | 501 | 502 | 503 |
| 498 | 499 | 500 | 499 | 498 |

**FLUORESCENT VERY WHITE CHALKY PAPER.** As an experiment 10% of the above issue was printed on very white paper which fluoresces back and front under an ultraviolet lamp; it also has a strong coating of chalk on the surface. Late in 1972 this paper began to be introduced more generally and a number of stamps exist on both types of paper. The normal helecon paper does not fluoresce under the lamp but does react to the chalky test to a lesser degree.

Stamps reprinted on the white fluorescent paper are recorded below in footnotes and are listed in the *Australia Concise Catalogue*.

(Des J. Sandry. Recess)

**1972** (8 Mar). *Famous Australians* (4*th series*). *Prime Ministers. T* **279** *and similar vert designs. P* 15 × 14.
505 7 c. ultramarine (Type **279**) . . . . 70 20
a. Booklet pane. Five stamps plus one printed label . . . . . . . . 3·25
506 7 c. ultramarine. (W. M. Hughes) . . . . 70 20
a. Booklet pane. Five stamps plus one printed label . . . . . . . . 3·25
507 7 c. red (Joseph Cook) . . . . . . 70 20
a. Booklet pane. Five stamps plus one printed label . . . . . . . . 3·25
508 7 c. red (S. M. Bruce) . . . . . . 70 20
a. Booklet pane. Five stamps plus one printed label . . . . . . . . 3·25
505/8 . . . . . . . . *Set of* 4 2·50 70

Nos. 505/8 were issued only in booklets and exist with one or two adjacent sides imperf.

280 Cameo Brooch

281 Fruit

(Des Mrs. V. Mason. Photo)

**1972** (18 Apr). *50th Anniv of Country Women's Association. P* 13½.
509 **280** 7 c. multicoloured . . . . . . 20 10

(Des D. Annand. Photo)

**1972** (14 June). *Primary Industries. T* **281** *and similar horiz designs. Multicoloured. P* 13½.
510 20 c. Type **281** . . . . . . . . 3·50 4·50
511 25 c. Rice . . . . . . . . 3·50 5·50
512 30 c. Fish . . . . . . . . 3·50 3·50
513 35 c. Beef . . . . . . . . 8·00 2·00
510/13 . . . . . . . . *Set of* 4 17·00 14·00

282 Worker in Wheelchair

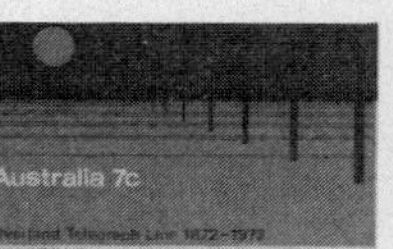


283 Telegraph Line

(Des from photographs by Barbara Ardizzone. Photo)

**1972** (2 Aug). *Rehabilitation of the Disabled. T* **282** *and similar designs. P* 13½.
514 12 c. yellow-brown and emerald . . . . 10 10
515 18 c. sage-green and yellow-orange . . . . 50 35
516 24 c. blue and yellow-brown . . . . 15 10
514/16 . . . . . . . . *Set of* 3 60 50

Designs: *Horiz*—18 c. Patient and teacher. *Vert*—24 c. Boy playing with ball.

The 12 c. and 24 c. also exist on fluorescent paper.

(Des J. Copeland. Photo)

**1972** (22 Aug). *Centenary of Overland Telegraph Line. P* 13½.
517 **283** 7 c. multicoloured . . . . . . 15 15

284 Athletics

285 Numerals and Computer Circuit

(Des B. Sadgrove. Photo)

**1972** (28 Aug). *Olympic Games, Munich. T* **284** *and similar vert designs. Multicoloured. P* 13½.
518 7 c. Type **284** . . . . . . . . 25 20
519 7 c. Rowing . . . . . . . . 25 20
520 7 c. Swimming . . . . . . . . 25 20
521 35 c. Equestrian . . . . . . . . 2·25 4·50
518/21 . . . . . . . . *Set of* 4 2·75 4·50

(Des G. Andrews. Photo)

**1972** (16 Oct). *Tenth International Congress of Accountants, Sydney. P* 13½.
522 **285** 7 c. multicoloured . . . . . . 15 15

**286** Australian-build Harvester

(Des R. Ingpen. Photo)

**1972** (15 Nov). *Pioneer Life. T* **286** *and similar multicoloured designs. P* 13½.

523 5 c. Pioneer family (*vert*) .. .. .. .. 15 10
524 10 c. Water-pump (*vert*) .. .. .. .. 40 10
525 15 c. Type **286** .. .. .. .. 15 10
a. Black (face value and inscr) omitted £275
526 40 c. House .. .. .. .. .. 30 50
527 50 c. Stage-coach .. .. .. .. 80 20
528 60 c. Morse key (*vert*) .. .. .. 50 85
529 80 c. *Gem* (paddle-steamer) .. .. .. 60 85
a. Black (face value and inscr) omitted £375
523/9 .. .. .. .. .. *Set of* 7 2·50 2·25

All values also exist on fluorescent paper and the 15 c. exists with both PVA gum and gum arabic.

**287** Jesus with Children **288** "Length"

(Des from drawing by Wendy Tamlyn (7 c.), L. Stirling (35 c.). Photo)

**1972** (29 Nov). *Christmas. T* **287** *and similar vert design. Multicoloured. P* 15×14 (7 *c.*) *or* 13½ (35 *c*).

530 7 c. Type **287** .. .. .. .. 30 10
a. Brown-red ("Australia 7c") omitted .. £275
b. Red-brown (inscr) omitted .. .. £275
531 35 c. Dove and spectrum motif .. .. 7·00 8·50

(Des Weatherhead & Stitt Pty. Ltd. Photo)

**1973** (7 Mar). *Metric Conversion. T* **288** *and similar multicoloured designs. P* 15×14. (*No.* 535) *or* 14×15 (*others*).

532 7 c. Type **288** .. .. .. .. 40 40
533 7 c. "Volume" .. .. .. .. 40 40
a. Yellow-olive omitted* .. .. £275
534 7 c. "Mass" .. .. .. .. 40 40
535 7 c. "Temperature" (*horiz*) .. .. 40 40
532/5 .. .. .. .. *Set of* 4 1·40 1·40

*This results in the man's drink and shorts appearing white, and the colour of the stool being the same as the background.

**289** Caduceus and Laurel Wreath **290** William Wentworth (statesman and explorer)

(Des H. Williamson. Photo)

**1973** (4 Apr). *25th Anniv of W.H.O. P* 15×14.

536 **289** 7 c. multicoloured .. .. .. 30 15

(Des J. Santry. Recess and litho)

**1973** (16 May). *Famous Australians* (5*th series*). *T* **290** *and similar vert designs. P* 15×14.

537 7 c. yellow-bistre and black .. .. .. 50 25
a. Block of 4. Nos. 537/40 .. .. 3·00
538 7 c. lilac and black .. .. .. 50 25
539 7 c. yellow-bistre and black .. .. .. 50 25
540 7 c. lilac and black .. .. .. 50 25
537/40 .. .. .. .. *Set of* 4 3·00 90

Designs:—No. 537, Type **290**; No. 538, Isaac Isaacs (first Australian-born Governor-General); No. 539, Mary Gilmore (writer); No. 540, Marcus Clarke (author).

Nos. 537/40 were printed in *se-tenant* blocks of four within the sheet. They also exist on fluorescent paper.

**291** Shipping **292** Banded Coral Shrimp

(Des J. Copeland. Photo)

**1973** (6 June). *National Development* (2*nd series*). *T* **291** *and similar vert designs. Multicoloured. P* 13½.

541 20 c. Type **291** .. .. .. .. 4·50 4·25
542 25 c. Iron ore and steel .. .. .. 4·50 4·50
543 30 c. Beef roads .. .. .. .. 4·75 4·50
544 35 c. Mapping .. .. .. .. 4·00 4·50
541/4 .. .. .. .. *Set of* 4 16·00 16·00

(Des Printing Bureau artists (1 to 4 c.), J. Mason (others). Photo)

**1973** (11 July)–**74**. *Marine Life and Gemstones. T* **292** *and similar multicoloured designs. P* 14×15 (1 *to* 4 *c.*) *or* 15×14 (*others*).

545 1 c. Type **292** .. .. .. .. 10 10
a. Black (inscr and face value) omitted .. 90·00
b. Yellow-brown omitted .. .. .. £225
546 2 c. Fiddler crab .. .. .. .. 10 10
547 3 c. Coral crab .. .. .. .. 10 10
a. Black (inscr and value) omitted .. £300
548 4 c. Mauve stinger .. .. .. .. 30 55
a. Black (face value and inscr) omitted .. £250
549 6 c. Chrysoprase (*vert*) .. .. .. 30 10
550 7 c. Agate (*vert*) .. .. .. .. 30 10
a. Black (value and "agate") omitted .. 90·00
551 8 c. Opal (*vert*) .. .. .. .. 30 10
a. Black (face value and inscr) omitted .. £100
552 9 c. Rhodonite (*vert*) .. .. .. 60 15
552*a* 10 c. Star sapphire (*vert*) (16.10.74) .. .. 30 10
ab. Black (value, inscr, etc.) omitted .. £100
ac. Turquoise-blue omitted* .. .. 10·00
545/52*a* .. .. .. .. *Set of* 9 2·00 1·25

*The turquoise-blue occurs on the gemstones, and is normally partly covered by the black.

The 1, 3, 7 and 10 c. exist with PVA gum as well as gum arabic.

**293** Children at Play **294** John Baptising Jesus

(Des G. Hamori. Photo)

**1973** (5 Sept). *50th Anniv of Legacy* (*Welfare Organisation*). *P* 13½.

553 **293** 7 c. cinnamon, deep claret and emerald 30 10

**PERFORATIONS.** From 1973 to 1975 two different perforating machines were used for some issues, giving gauges of 14½×14 or 15×14 (on horizontal stamps), the exact measurement being 14.4×14.1 or 14.9×14.1. The latter gauge was also used for a reprint of the $1 definitive (No. 401c).

(Des G. Hamori. Photo)

**1973** (3 Oct). *Christmas. T* **294** *and similar vert design. Multicoloured. P* 14×14½ (7 *c.*) *or* 13½ (30 *c.*).

554 7 c. Type **294** .. .. .. .. 35 10
a. Perf 14×15 .. .. .. .. 3·00 60
555 30 c. The Good Shepherd .. .. .. 1·40 1·50

**295** Sydney Opera House **296** Wireless Receiver and Speaker

(Des A. Leydin. Photo)

**1973** (17 Oct). *Architecture. T* **295** *and similar designs. P* 14½×14 (7, 10 *c.*) *or* 13½ (40, 50 *c.*).

556 7 c. pale turquoise-blue and new blue .. 30 15
a. Perf 15×14 .. .. .. .. 3·00 1·40
557 10 c. light ochre and sepia .. .. .. 80 70
558 40 c. black, drab and dull mauve .. .. 1·00 1·50
a. Dull mauve (background) omitted .. £750
559 50 c. multicoloured .. .. .. .. 1·25 2·50
556/9 .. .. .. .. *Set of* 4 3·00 4·25

Designs: *Horiz*—10 c. Buchanan's Hotel, Townsville; 40 c. Como House, Melbourne. *Vert*—50 c. St. James' Church, Sydney.

(Des E. Thake. Photo)

**1973** (21 Nov). *50th Anniv of Regular Radio Broadcasting. P* 13½.

560 **296** 7 c. lt turquoise-blue, brown-red & blk 15 10

**297** Common Wombat **298** "Sergeant of Light Horse" (G. Lambert)

(Des R. Bates. Photo)

**1974** (13 Feb). *Animals. T* **297** *and similar vert designs. Multicoloured. P* 14×15 (20, 30 *c.*) *or* 13½ (*others*).

561 20 c. Type **297** .. .. .. .. 35 10
562 25 c. Short-nosed Echidna .. .. .. 75 60
563 30 c. Brush-tailed Possum .. .. .. 40 15
a. Carmine-red (face-value, etc) omitted .. £375
564 75 c. Pygmy Glider .. .. .. .. 1·00 85
561/4 .. .. .. .. *Set of* 4 2·25 1·50

The 20 c. exists with gum arabic as well as PVA gum.

(Des P.O. artists. Litho Asher & Co, Melbourne ($5, $10). Photo R.B.A. (others))

**1974** (24 Apr)–**79**. *Paintings. Multicoloured designs as T* **298**. *P* 13½ ($1, $2, $4) *or* 14½ (*others*).

565 $1 Type **298** .. .. .. .. 1·00 10
a. Flesh omitted† .. .. .. ..
566 $2 "Red Gums of the Far North" (H. Heysen) (*horiz*) .. .. .. .. 1·50 25
566*a* $4 "Shearing the Rams" (Tom Roberts) (*horiz*) .. .. .. .. 3·00 2·25
567 $5 "McMahon's Point" (Sir Arthur Streeton) (14.3.79) .. .. .. .. 5·50 2·25
567*a* $10 "Coming South" (Tom Roberts) (19.10.77) 8·50 3·50
565/7*a* .. .. .. .. *Set of* 5 17·00 7·50
567/*a*, 778 Optd "Specimen" .. .. *Set of* 3 9·00

†The omission of the flesh colour results in much of the design appearing in different shades, most notably the shirt, which appears green (especially the folds), the hillside, which is green, and the man's skin, which has highlights in yellow.

The $1 and $2 exist with PVA gum as well as gum arabic.

Nos. 567/*a* and 778 optd "Specimen" come from a special "Ausipex 84" Presentation Pack issued on 9 February 1983.

**299** Supreme Court Judge **300** Rugby Football

(Des T. Thompson. Photo)

**1974** (15 May). *150th Anniv of Australia's Third Charter of Justice. P* 14×15.

568 **299** 7 c. multicoloured .. .. .. 20 10

(Des A. Leydin from drawings by D. O'Brien. Photo)

**1974** (24 July). *Non-Olympic Sports. T* **300** *and similar multicoloured designs. P* 15×14 (*Nos.* 569/70) *or* 14×15 (*others*).

569 7 c. Type **300** .. .. .. .. 55 35
570 7 c. Bowls .. .. .. .. 55 35
571 7 c. Australian football (*vert*) .. .. 55 35
572 7 c. Cricket (*vert*) .. .. .. .. 55 35
573 7 c. Golf (*vert*) .. .. .. .. 55 35
574 7 c. Surfing (*vert*) .. .. .. .. 55 35
575 7 c. Tennis (*vert*) .. .. .. .. 55 35
569/75 .. .. .. .. *Set of* 7 3·50 2·25

**301** "Transport of Mails" **302** Letter "A" and W. C. Wentworth (co-founder)

(Des J. Copeland. Photo)

**1974** (9 Oct). *Centenary of Universal Postal Union. T* **301** *and similar vert designs. Multicoloured. P* 15×14 (7 *c.*) *or* 13½ (30 *c.*).

576 7 c. Type **301** .. .. .. .. 40 20
a. Perf 14½×14 .. .. .. .. 60 30
577 30 c. Three-part version of Type **301** .. 1·25 1·90

(Des I. Dalton. Typo and litho)

**1974** (9 Oct). *150th Anniv of First Independent Newspaper, "The Australian". P* 14×15.

578 **302** 7 c. black/*light cinnamon* .. .. 30 30
a. Perf 14×14½ .. .. .. 80 35

= 9c

(**303**)

**304** "The Adoration of the Magi"

**1974** (16 Oct). *No.* 551 *surch with T* **303**, *in red.*

579 9 c. on 8 c. Opal .. .. .. .. 15 15

(Des and recess R.B.A.)

**1974** (13 Nov). *Christmas. Woodcuts by Dürer. T* **304** *and similar vert design. P* 14×15.

580 10 c. black/*cream* .. .. .. .. 25 10
581 35 c. black/*cream* .. .. .. .. 80 1·00

Design:—35 c. "The Flight into Egypt".

**PROCESS.** All the following issues to No. 772 were printed in photogravure, *except where otherwise stated.*

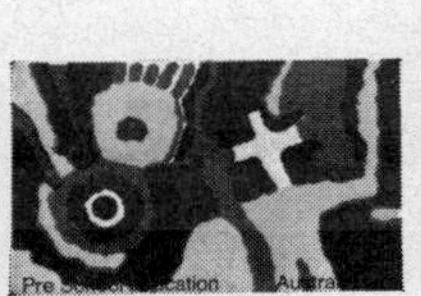

**305** "Pre-School Education"    **306** "Road Safety"

(Des Vivienne Binns (5 c.), Erica McGilchrist (11 c.), E. Tanner (15 c.), J. Meldrum (60 c.))

**1974** (20 Nov). *Education in Australia. T* **305** *and similar multi-coloured designs. P* 13½.
582 5 c. Type **305** . . . . 50 40
583 11 c. "Correspondence Schools" . . 50 25
584 15 c. "Science Education" . . 80 40
585 60 c. "Advanced Education" (*vert*) . . 2·00 2·75
582/5 . . *Set of* 4 3·50 3·50

(Des G. Andrews)

**1975** (29 Jan). *Environment Dangers. T* **306** *and similar horiz designs. Multicoloured. P* 14×14½ (*No.* 586) *or* 14½×14 (*others*).
586 10 c. Type **306** . . 40 40
587 10 c. "Pollution" . . 40 40
a. Perf 15×14 . . 9·00 3·00
588 10 c. "Bush Fires" . . 40 40
a. Perf 15×14 . . 1·00 85
586/8 . . *Set of* 3 1·10 1·10

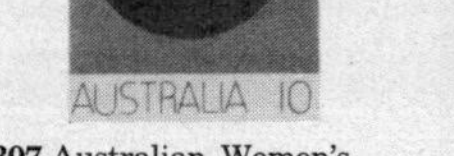

**307** Australian Women's Year Emblem    **308** J. H. Scullin

(Des Leonora Howlett)

**1975** (12 Mar). *International Women's Year. P* 14×15.
589 **307** 10 c. dp violet-blue, green & bluish vio . . 20 15
This stamp exists with PVA gum as well as gum arabic.

(Des B. Dunlop)

**1975** (26 Mar). *Famous Australians* (6*th series*). *Prime Ministers. T* **308** *and similar vert designs. Multicoloured. P* 14 × 15.
590 10 c. Type **308** . . 25 30
591 10 c. J. A. Lyons . . 25 30
592 10 c. Earle Page . . 25 30
593 10 c. Arthur Fadden . . 25 30
594 10 c. John Curtin . . 25 30
595 10 c. J. B. Chifley . . 25 30
590/5 . . *Set of* 6 1·40 1·60
Nos 591/2 and 594 exist with both PVA gum and gum arabic.

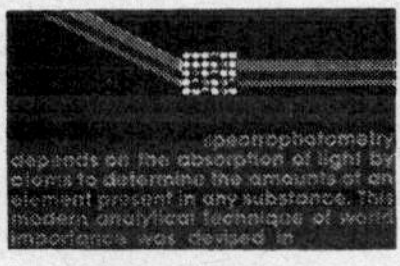

**309** Atomic Absorption Spectrophotometry    **310** Logo of Australian Postal Commission

(Des Weatherhead & Stitt)

**1975** (14 May). *Scientific Development. T* **309** *and similar horiz designs. Multicoloured. P* 13½.
596 11 c. Type **309** . . 60 40
597 24 c. Radio astronomy . . 1·40 1·90
598 33 c. Immunology . . 1·75 2·50
599 48 c. Oceanography . . 2·50 2·75
596/9 . . *Set of* 4 5·75 6·75

(Des P. Huveneers)

**1975** (1 July). *Inauguration of Australian Postal and Telecommunications Commissions. T* **310** *and similar horiz design. P* 14½×14.
600 10 c. black, rosine and pale grey . . 25 10
a. Pair. Nos. 600/1 . . 2·00 2·25
b. Perf 15×14 . . 25 10
ba. Pair. Nos. 600b/1b . . 1·75 2·00
601 10 c. black, orange-yellow and pale grey . . 25 10
b. Perf 15×14 . . 25 10
Design:—No. 601, Logo of Australian Telecommunications Commission.
Nos. 600/1 were printed together, *se-tenant* in horizontal and vertical pairs throughout the sheet.

## OMNIBUS ISSUES

Details, together with prices for complete sets, of the various Omnibus issues from the 1935 Silver Jubilee series to date are included in a special section following Zimbabwe at the end of Volume 2.

**311** Edith Cowan    **312** *Helichrysum thomsonii*    **313** "Tambaran" House and Sydney Opera House

(Des D. and J. O'Brien)

**1975** (6 Aug). *Famous Australians* (7*th series*). *Australian Women. T* **311** *and similar vert designs. Multicoloured.* A. *P* 14×14½. B. *P* 14×15.

| | | A. | | B. | |
|---|---|---|---|---|---|
| 602 | 10 c. Type **311** | 45 | 55 | 45 | 55 |
| 603 | 10 c. Louisa Lawson | 45 | 55 | 70 | 55 |
| 604 | 10 c. Ethel Richardson | 45 | 55 | 70 | 55 |
| 605 | 10 c. Catherine Spence | 45 | 55 | 55 | 55 |
| 606 | 10 c. Constance Stone | 60 | 55 | 45 | 55 |
| 607 | 10 c. Truganini | 45 | 55 | 50 | 55 |
| 602/7 | *Set of* 6 | 2·50 | 3·00 | 3·00 | 3·00 |

No. 604 is inscribed with the *nom de plume* "Henry Handel Richardson".

(Des F. Knight)

**1975** (27 Aug). *Wild Flowers. T* **312** *and similar multicoloured design. P* 15×14 (18 *c.*) *or* 14×15 (45 *c.*).
608 18 c. Type **312** . . 25 10
a. Black omitted . . 30·00
b. Grey (stem, etc) omitted . . 22·00
609 45 c. *Callistemon teretifolius* (*horiz*) . . 50 10
a. Black (face value and inscr) omitted . . £200
b. Yellow-green (twigs) omitted . . £100
The 18 c. exists with both PVA gum and gum arabic.

(Des D. Annand (18 c.) or G. Hamori (25 c.))

**1975** (16 Sept). *Papua New Guinea Independence. T* **313** *and similar horiz design. Multicoloured. P* 13½.
610 18 c. Type **313** . . 35 10
611 25 c. "Freedom" (bird in flight) . . 90 1·25

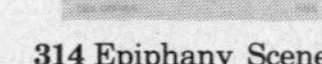

**314** Epiphany Scene    **315** Australian Coat of Arms

(Des D. O'Brien (15 c.) or J. Milne (45 c.))

**1975** (29 Oct). *Christmas. T* **314** *and similar horiz design. P* 14×15 (15 *c.*) *or* 13½ (45 *c.*).
612 15 c. multicoloured . . 25 10
613 45 c. reddish violet, greenish blue and silver 1·00 2·40
Design:—45 c. "Shining Star".

I    II

Two types of No. 614:
I. Emu's legs without toes.
II. Emu showing toes.
Other minor differences also occur.

(Des J. Spatchurst)

**1976** (5 Jan). *75th Anniv of Nationhood. P* 15 x 14.
614 **315** 18 c. multicoloured (I) . . 35 20
a. Buff (supporters) omitted . . £300
b. Type II . . 75 30
ba. Gold (shield and star) omitted . . £150

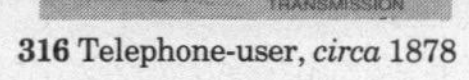

**316** Telephone-user, *circa* 1878    **317** John Oxley

(Des R. Ingpen)

**1976** (10 Mar). *Telephone Centenary. P* 13½.
615 **316** 18 c. multicoloured . . 20 15

(Des B. Dunlop)

**1976** (9 June). *19th Century Explorers. T* **317** *and similar horiz designs. Multicoloured. P* 13½.
616 18 c. Type **317** . . 40 40
617 18 c. Hume and Hovell . . 40 40
618 18 c. John Forrest . . 40 40
619 18 c. Ernest Giles . . 40 40
620 18 c. William Gosse . . 40 40
621 18 c. Peter Warburton . . 40 40
616/21 . . *Set of* 6 2·25 2·25

**318** Measuring Stick, Graph and Computer Tape    **319** Football

(Des R. Ingpen)

**1976** (15 June). *50th Anniv of Commonwealth Scientific and Industrial Research Organisation. P* 15×14.
622 **318** 18 c. multicoloured . . 20 15

(Des A. Leydin)

**1976** (14 July). *Olympic Games, Montreal. T* **319** *and similar multicoloured designs. P* 13½.
623 18 c. Type **319** . . 30 20
624 18 c. Gymnastics (*vert*) . . 30 20
625 25 c. Diving (*vert*) . . 50 50
626 40 c. Cycling . . 70 70
623/6 . . *Set of* 4 1·60 1·40
The 25 c. exists with gum arabic as well as PVA gum.

**320** Richmond Bridge, Tasmania    **321** Blamire Young (designer of first Australian stamp)

(Des O. Borchert)

**1976** (23 Aug). *Australian Scenes. T* **320** *and similar designs. Multicoloured. P* 14×15 (50 *c.*) *or* 15×14 (*others*).
627 5 c. Type **320** . . 15 10
628 25 c. Broken Bay, N.S.W. . . 40 20
629 35 c. Wittenoom Gorge, W.A. . . 35 20
630 50 c. Mt. Buffalo, Victoria (*vert*) . . 70 30
631 70 c. Barrier Reef . . 1·00 1·25
632 85 c. Ayers Rock, N.T. . . 1·00 1·75
627/32 . . *Set of* 6 3·25 3·50

(Des R. Honisett)

**1976** (27 Sept). *National Stamp Week. P* 13½.
633 **321** 18 c. multicoloured . . 15 15
**MS**634 101 × 112 mm. No. 633 × 4 . . 1·25 2·00
**MS**634 contains one stamp coloured as No. 633; the others, showing the different colour separations used in the printing, are each differently coloured.
The miniature sheet exists with "AUSTRALIAN STAMP PROMOTION COUNCIL" overprinted in red on the margin from a privately produced booklet.

**322** "Virgin and Child" (detail, Simone Cantarini)    **323** John Gould

(Des C. Medlycott (15 c.), Wendy Tamlyn (45 c.))

**1976** (1 Nov). *Christmas. T* **322** *and similar horiz design. P* 15×14 (15 *c.*) *or* 13½ (45 *c.*).
635 15 c. bright magenta and light azure . . 25 10
636 45 c. multicoloured . . 70 80
Design:—45 c. Toy koala bear and decorations.

(Des B. Weatherhead)

**1976** (10 Nov). *Famous Australians* (8*th series*). *T* **323** *and similar horiz designs. Multicoloured. P* 15×14.
637 18 c. Type **323** . . 50 45
638 18 c. Thomas Laby . . 50 45
a. Red-brown ("AUSTRALIA" etc.) omitted £160
639 18 c. Sir Baldwin Spencer . . 50 45
640 18 c. Griffith Taylor . . 50 45
637/40 . . *Set of* 4 1·75 1·60

**324** "Music"    **325** Queen Elizabeth II

**1977** (19 Jan). *Performing Arts. T* **324** *and similar vert designs. Multicoloured. P* 14×15.
641 20 c. Type **324** . . 25 25
642 30 c. Drama . . 40 35
643 40 c. Dance . . 55 40
644 60 c. Opera . . 1·00 1·75
641/4 . . *Set of* 4 2·00 2·50

(Des P.O. Artists. Litho Govt Printer, Sydney (2% of supplies) or by Norman J. Field, Melbourne)

**1977** (2 Feb). *Silver Jubilee. T* **325** *and similar vert design. Multicoloured. P* 14 × 15.
645 18 c. Type **325** .. .. .. .. .. 20 10
646 45 c. The Queen and Prince Philip .. .. 50 80

**326** Fielder and Wicket Keeper **327** Parliament House

(Des B. Weatherhead)

**1977** (9 Mar). *Australia–England Test Cricket Centenary. T* **326** *and similar vert designs. Multicoloured. P* 13½.
647 18 c. Type **326** .. .. .. .. .. 35 40
a. Horiz strip of 5. Nos. 647/51 .. .. 2·00
648 18 c. Umpire, batsman and scoreboard .. 35 40
649 18 c. Fielders .. .. .. .. .. 35 40
650 18 c. Batsman and umpire .. .. .. 35 40
651 18 c. Bowler and fielder .. .. .. 35 40
652 45 c. Batsman awaiting delivery .. .. 75 1·00
647/52 .. .. .. .. *Set of* 6 2·50 2·75

Nos. 647/51 were printed together, *se-tenant*, in horizontal strips of 5 throughout the sheet, forming a composite design.

(Des R.B.A.)

**1977** (13 Apr). *50th Anniv of Opening of Parliament House, Canberra. P* 15 × 14.
653 **327** 18 c. multicoloured .. .. .. .. 15 10

**328** Trade Unions Workers **329** Surfing Santa

(Des D. Lanyon; adapted B. Sadgrove)

**1977** (9 May). *50th Anniv of Australian Council of Trade Unions. P* 13½.
654 **328** 18 c. multicoloured .. .. .. .. 15 10

(Des R. Roberts (15 c.), J. O'Brien (45 c.))

**1977** (31 Oct). *Christmas. T* **329** *and similar vert design. Multicoloured. P* 14 × 15 (15 c.) *or* 13½ (45 c.).
655 15 c. Type **329** .. .. .. .. .. 25 10
656 45 c. Madonna and Child .. .. .. 1·00 90

**330** National Flag **331** Harry Hawker and Sopwith "Camel"

(Des Cato Hibberd Design)

**1978** (26 Jan). *Australia Day. P* 13½.
657 **330** 18 c. multicoloured .. .. .. .. 20 15

(Litho Asher and Co, Melbourne)

**1978** (19 Apr). *Early Australian Aviators. T* **331** *and similar horiz designs. Multicoloured. P* 15½.
658 18 c. Type **331** .. .. .. .. .. 35 45
a. Imperf (horiz pair) .. .. .. £500
659 18 c. Bert Hinkler and Avro "Avian" .. .. 35 45
a. Imperf (horiz pair) .. .. .. £550
660 18 c. Sir Charles Kingsford Smith and *Southern Cross* .. .. .. .. 35 45
a. Imperf (pair) .. .. .. .. £150
661 18 c. Charles Ulm and *Southern Cross* .. 35 45
658/61 .. .. .. .. *Set of* 4 1·25 1·60
**MS**662 100 × 112 mm. Nos. 660/1 × 2. Imperf .. 1·50 1·75

Forgeries of No. **MS**662 have been reported. These can be detected, under strong magnification, by the lack of magenta screen on the blue panel at right and by the presence of magenta dots in the yellow background to No. 661.

**332** Beechcraft "Baron" landing at Station Airstrip **333** Illawarra Flame Tree

**1978** (15 May). *50th Anniv of Royal Flying Doctor Service. P* 13½.
663 **332** 18 c. multicoloured .. .. .. .. 20 15

(Des D. Rose)

**1978** (1 June). *Trees. T* **333** *and similar vert designs. Multicoloured. P* 14 × 15 (18 c.) *or* 13½ (*others*).
664 18 c. Type **333** .. .. .. .. .. 35 15
665 25 c. Ghost Gum .. .. .. .. .. 65 1·50
666 40 c. Grass Tree .. .. .. .. .. 1·00 2·00
667 45 c. Cootamundra Wattle .. .. .. 1·00 1·25
664/7 .. .. .. .. .. *Set of* 4 2·75 4·50

**334** Sturt's Desert Rose and Map **335** Hooded Plover

(Des D. Pitt. Litho Asher and Co, Melbourne)

**1978** (19 June). *Establishment of State Government for the Northern Territory. P* 15½.
668 **334** 18 c. multicoloured .. .. .. .. 20 15

(Des Kay Breeden-Williams. Photo)

**1978** (3 July)–**80**. *Birds* (1*st series*). *Multicoloured designs as T* **335**. *P* 15 × 14 (20 c. (*both*)), 14 × 15 (22 c.) *or* 13½ (*others*).
669 1 c. Spotted-sided Finch (17.9.79) .. .. 10 15
670 2 c. Crimson Finch (17.9.79) .. .. .. 10 15
671 5 c. Type **335** (17.7.78) .. .. .. 15 10
a. Grey-brown (bird's back) omitted .. £100
672 15 c. Forest Kingfisher (*vert*) (17.9.79) .. 20 15
673 20 c. Australian Dabchick ("Little Grebe") .. 50 10
a. Yellow (beak and eye) omitted .. 50·00
674 20 c. Eastern Yellow Robin (17.9.79) .. .. 20 10
675 22 c. White-tailed Kingfisher (22 × 29 *mm*) (31.3.80) .. .. .. .. .. 30 10
676 25 c. Masked Plover (17.7.78) .. .. .. 70 35
677 30 c. Oystercatcher (17.7.78) .. .. .. 80 25
678 40 c. Variegated Wren (*vert*) (17.9.79) .. 30 45
679 50 c. Flame Robin (*vert*) (17.9.79) .. .. 40 50
680 55 c. Comb-crested Jacana ("Lotus-bird") .. 85 60
669/80 .. .. .. .. *Set of* 12 4·00 2·75

See also Nos. 734/40.

**336** 1928 3d. "National Stamp Exhibition" Commemorative **337** "The Madonna and Child" (after van Eyck)

(Des Cato Hibberd Design. Litho Asher and Co, Melbourne)

**1978** (25 Sept). *National Stamp Week. 50th Anniv of National Stamp Exhibition, Melbourne. P* 15½.
694 **336** 20 c. multicoloured .. .. .. .. 15 15
**MS**695 78 × 113 mm. No. 694 × 4 .. .. 1·40 1·75

(Litho Asher and Co, Melbourne)

**1978** (3 Oct–1 Nov). *Christmas. Paintings. T* **337** *and similar vert designs. Multicoloured. P* 14½.
696 15 c. Type **337** (1.11) .. .. .. .. 30 10
697 25 c. "The Virgin and Child" (Marmion) .. 45 55
698 55 c. "The Holy Family" (del Vaga) (1.11) .. 70 90
696/8 .. .. .. .. .. *Set of* 3 1·25 1·40

**338** "Tulloch" **339** Raising the Flag, Sydney Cove, 26 January 1788

(Des B. Clinton)

**1978** (18 Oct). *Race-horses. T* **338** *and similar multicoloured designs. P* 15 × 14 (20 c.) *or* 13½ (*others*).
699 20 c. Type **338** .. .. .. .. .. 35 10
700 35 c. "Bernborough" (*vert*) .. .. .. 60 70
701 50 c. "Phar Lap" (*vert*) .. .. .. .. 85 1·00
702 55 c. "Peter Pan" .. .. .. .. .. 90 1·00
699/702 .. .. .. .. *Set of* 4 2·40 2·50

(Des B. Clinton. Litho Asher and Co, Melbourne)

**1979** (26 Jan). *Australia Day. P* 15½.
703 **339** 20 c. multicoloured .. .. .. .. 15 15
a. Yellow omitted .. .. .. ..

**340** P.S. *Canberra* **341** Port Campbell, Victoria

(Des O. Borchert)

**1979** (14 Feb). *Ferries and Murray River Steamers. T* **340** *and similar horiz designs. Multicoloured. P* 15 × 14 (20 c.) *or* 13½ (*others*).
704 20 c. Type **340** .. .. .. .. .. 35 10
705 35 c. M.V. *Lady Denman* .. .. .. 60 85
706 50 c. P.S. *Murray River Queen* .. .. 80 1·25
707 55 c. H.V. *Curl Curl* .. .. .. .. 90 1·25
704/7 .. .. .. .. .. *Set of* 4 2·40 3·00

(Des M. Robinson. Litho Asher and Co. Melbourne)

**1979** (9 Apr). *National Parks. T* **341** *and similar multicoloured designs. P* 15½.
708 20 c. Type **341** .. .. .. .. .. 25 25
a. Horiz strip of 5. Nos. 708/12 .. .. 1·10
709 20 c. Uluru, Northern Territory .. .. 25 25
710 20 c. Royal, New South Wales .. .. .. 25 25
711 20 c. Flinders Ranges, South Australia .. 25 25
712 20 c. Nambung, Western Australia .. .. 25 25
713 20 c. Girraween, Queensland (*vert*) .. .. 25 25
a. Horiz pair. Nos. 713/14 .. .. .. 50 50
ab. Imperf (horiz pair)* .. .. .. £350
714 20 c. Mount Field, Tasmania (*vert*) .. .. 25 25
708/14 .. .. .. .. .. *Set of* 7 1·40 1·40

Nos. 708/14 were printed together, *se-tenant*; Nos. 708/12 in horizontal strips of 5 and Nos. 713/14 in horizontal pairs, throughout separate sheets.

*The imperforate error, No. 713ab, involves the two right-hand vertical columns of the sheet only, the left-hand stamp having vertical perforations at left.

**342** "Double Fairlie" Type Locomotive, Western Australia **343** Symbolic Swan

(Des R. Honisett)

**1979** (16 May). *Steam Railways. T* **342** *and similar horiz designs. Multicoloured. P* 14 × 15 (20 c.) *or* 13½ (*others*).
715 20 c. Type **342** .. .. .. .. .. 30 10
716 35 c. Locomotive, "Puffing Billy" Line, Victoria 55 70
717 50 c. Locomotive, Pichi Richi Line, South Australia .. .. .. .. .. 80 1·10
718 55 c. Locomotive, Zig Zag Railway, New South Wales .. .. .. .. .. 90 1·25
715/18 .. .. .. .. .. *Set of* 4 2·25 2·75

(Des B. Weatherhead)

**1979** (6 June). *150th Anniv of Western Australia. P* 13½.
719 **343** 20 c. multicoloured .. .. .. .. 15 15

**344** Children playing on Slide **345** Letters and Parcels

(Des Wendy Tamlyn. Litho Asher and Co, Melbourne)

**1979** (13 Aug). *International Year of the Child. P* 13½ × 13.
720 **344** 20 c. multicoloured .. .. .. .. 15 10

(Des A. Collins. Litho Asher and Co, Melbourne)

**1979** (24 Sept–1 Nov). *Christmas. T* **345** *and similar vert designs. Multicoloured. P* 13 × 13½.
721 15 c. Christ's Nativity (Eastern European icon) (1.11.79) .. .. .. .. .. 15 10
722 25 c. Type **345** .. .. .. .. .. 25 50
723 55 c. "Madonna and Child" (Buglioni) (1.11.79) 40 75
721/3 .. .. .. .. .. *Set of* 3 70 1·25

## MINIMUM PRICE

The minimum price quote is 10p which represents a handling charge rather than a basis for valuing common stamps. For further notes about prices see introductory pages.

346 Fly-fishing

347 Matthew Flinders

(Des B. Clinton)

**1979** (24 Oct). *Fishing. T* **346** *and similar vert designs. P* 14 × 15 (20 c.) *or* 13½ (*others*).
724 20 c. multicoloured . . . . . . . . . . 20 10
725 35 c. black, deep grey-blue and violet-blue . . 35 70
726 50 c. multicoloured . . . . . . . . . . 40 90
727 55 c. multicoloured . . . . . . . . . . 45 85
724/7 . . . . . . . . . . *Set of* 4 1·25 2·25
Designs:—35 c. Spinning; 50 c. Deep sea game-fishing; 55 c. Surf-fishing.

(Des B. Weatherhead. Litho Asher and Co, Melbourne)

**1980** (23 Jan). *Australia Day. P* 13½ × 13.
728 **347** 20 c. multicoloured . . . . . . 20 10

348 Dingo

349 Queen Elizabeth II

(Des Marg Towt. Litho Asher and Co, Melbourne)

**1980** (20 Feb). *Dogs. T* **348** *and similar horiz designs. Multi-coloured. P* 13½ × 13.
729 20 c. Type **348** . . . . . . . . . . 40 10
730 25 c. Border Collie . . . . . . . . . . 40 40
731 35 c. Australian Terrier . . . . . . . . 60 70
732 50 c. Australian Cattle Dog . . . . . . 1·40 1·75
733 55 c. Australian Kelpie . . . . . . . . 1·10 1·40
729/33 . . . . . . . . *Set of* 5 3·50 4·00

(Des Kay Breeden-Williams. Litho Asher and Co, Melbourne)

**1980** (31 Mar)–**83**. *Birds (2nd series). Multicoloured designs as T* **335**. *P* 12½.
734 10 c. Golden-shouldered Parrot (*vert*) (1.7.80) 30 10
a. Perf 14½ × 14 (5.83) . . . . . . 1·60 45
734*b* 18 c. Spotted Catbird (*vert*) (17.11.80) . . 60 95
735 28 c. Australian Bee Eater ("Rainbow Bird") (*vert*) . . . . . . . . . . 50 30
736 35 c. Regent Bowerbird (*vert*) (1.7.80) . . 35 10
737 45 c. Masked Wood Swallow (1.7.80) . . 40 10
a. Perf 14 × 14½ (5.83) . . . . . . 2·75 60
738 60 c. Australian King Parrot (*vert*) . . . . 50 15
739 80 c. Rainbow Pitta (1.7.80) . . . . . . 85 65
740 $1 Black-backed Magpie (*vert*) (1.7.80) . . 85 10
734/40 . . . . . . . . *Set of* 8 4·00 2·10
Designs of Nos. 734/40 measure 22 × 29 mm (vert) or 29 × 22 mm (horiz).

(Des B. Weatherhead. Litho Asher and Co, Melbourne)

**1980** (21 Apr). *Queen Elizabeth II's Birthday. P* 13 × 13½.
741 **349** 22 c. multicoloured . . . . . . 25 20

350 "Once a jolly Swagman camp'd by a Billabong"

351 High Court Buildings

(Des R. Roberts. Litho Asher and Co, Melbourne)

**1980** (7 May). *Folklore. Scenes and Verses from the Folksong "Waltzing Matilda". T* **350** *and similar vert designs. Multi-coloured. P* 13 × 13½.
742 22 c. Type **350** . . . . . . . . . . 40 10
a. Horiz strip of 5. Nos. 742/6 . . . . 1·75
743 22 c. "And he sang as he shoved that Jumbuck in his Tuckerbag" . . . . . . . . 40 10
744 22 c. "Up rode the Squatter, mounted on his Thoroughbred" . . . . . . . . 40 10
745 22 c. "Down came the Troopers one, two, three" 40 10
746 22 c. "And his Ghost may be heard as you pass by that Billabong" . . . . . . . . 40 10
742/6 . . . . . . . . *Set of* 5 1·75 45
Nos. 742/6 were printed together, *se-tenant*, in horizontal strips of 5 throughout the sheet, forming a composite design.

(Des Cato Hibberd Design. Litho Asher and Co, Melbourne)

**1980** (19 May). *Opening of High Court Building, Canberra. P* 13 × 13½.
747 **351** 22 c. multicoloured . . . . . . 20 20

352 Salvation Army


353 Postbox, *circa* 1900

(Des J. Spatchurst. Litho Asher and Co, Melbourne)

**1980** (11 Aug). *Community Welfare. T* **352** *and similar multi-coloured designs. P* 13½ × 13 (*Nos.* 748, 751) *or* 13 × 13½ (*others*).
748 22 c. Type **352** . . . . . . . . . . 40 40
749 22 c. St. Vincent de Paul Society (*vert*) . . 40 40
750 22 c. Meals on Wheels (*vert*) . . . . . . 40 40
751 22 c. "Life. Be in it" . . . . . . . . 40 40
748/51 . . . . . . . . *Set of* 4 1·40 1·40

(Des B. Weatherhead. Litho Asher and Co, Melbourne)

**1980** (29 Sept). *National Stamp Week. T* **353** *and similar vert designs showing postal history, circa* 1900. *Multicoloured. P* 13 × 13½.
752 22 c. Type **353** . . . . . . . . . . 30 10
a. Horiz strip of 5. Nos. 752/6 . . . . 1·40
753 22 c. Postman (facing left) . . . . . . 30 10
754 22 c. Mail van . . . . . . . . . . 30 10
755 22 c. Postman and postbox . . . . . . 30 10
756 22 c. Postman (facing right) . . . . . . 30 10
752/6 . . . . . . . . *Set of* 5 1·40 45
**MS**757 95 × 130 mm. Nos. 752, 754 and 756 . . 1·10 1·25
a. Error. Imperf
Nos. 752/6 were printed together, *se-tenant*, in horizontal strips of 5 throughout the sheet.
Stamps from No. **MS**757 have different backgrounds to the stamps from normal sheets.

354 "Holy Family" (painting, Prospero Fontana)

355 "Wackett", 1941

(Des B. Weatherhead. Litho Asher and Co, Melbourne)

**1980** (1 Oct–3 Nov). *Christmas. Works of Art. T* **354** *and similar vert designs. Multicoloured. P* 13 × 13½.
758 15 c. "The Virgin Enthroned" (detail of painting by Justin O'Brien) (3.11) . . 15 10
759 28 c. Type **354** . . . . . . . . . . 25 40
760 60 c. "Madonna and Child" (sculpture by School of M. Zuern) (3.11) . . . . 50 1·10
758/60 . . . . . . . . *Set of* 3 80 1·40

(Des O. Borchert. Litho Victorian Government Printer, Melbourne (22 c.), Asher and Co, Melbourne (others))

**1980** (19 Nov). *Aircraft. T* **355** *and similar horiz designs. Multi-coloured. P* 13½ × 14 (22 c.) *or* 13½ × 13 (*others*).
761 22 c. Type **355** . . . . . . . . . . 35 10
762 40 c. "Winjeel", 1955 . . . . . . . . 60 85
763 45 c. "Boomerang", 1944 . . . . . . . . 70 95
764 60 c. "Nomad", 1975 . . . . . . . . 90 1·25
761/4 . . . . . . . . *Set of* 4 2·25 2·75

356 Flag in shape of Australia

357 Caricature of Darby Munro (jockey)

(Des B. Weatherhead. Litho Asher and Co, Melbourne)

**1981** (21 Jan). *Australia Day. P* 13½ × 13.
765 **356** 22 c. multicoloured . . . . . . 20 20

(Des T. Rafty. Litho Cambec Press, Melbourne)

**1981** (18 Feb). *Sports Personalities. T* **357** *and similar vert designs showing caricatures. Multicoloured. P* 14 × 13½.
766 22 c. Type **357** . . . . . . . . . . 30 10
767 35 c. Victor Trumper (cricketer) . . . . 65 70
768 55 c. Sir Norman Brookes (tennis player) . . 85 90
769 60 c. Walter Lindrum (billiards player) . . 90 1·00
766/9 . . . . . . . . *Set of* 4 2·40 2·40

## ALTERED CATALOGUE NUMBERS

Any Catalogue numbers altered from the last edition are shown as a list in the introductory pages.

358 1931 Kingsford Smith's Flights 6d. Commemorative


359 Apex Emblem and Map of Australia

(Des Cato Hibberd Design. Litho Asher and Co, Melbourne)

**1981** (25 Mar). *50th Anniv of Official Australia–U.K. Airmail Service. T* **358** *and similar horiz design showing 1931 Kingsford Smith's Flights 6d. commemorative. P* 13 × 13½ (22 c.) *or* 13½ × 13 (60 c.).
770 22 c. blackish lilac, rosine and bright blue . . 20 10
771 60 c. blackish lilac, rosine and ultramarine . . 50 90

(Des P. Clark)

**1981** (6 Apr). *50th Anniv of Apex (young men's service club). P* 13½.
772 **359** 22 c. multicoloured . . . . . . 20 20

**ASHER AND CO.** From April 1981 this firm was known as Leigh-Mardon Ltd, Melbourne.

360 Queen's Personal Standard for Australia


361 "Licence Inspected"

(Litho Leigh-Mardon Ltd, Melbourne)

**1981** (21 Apr). *Queen Elizabeth II's Birthday. P* 13½ × 13.
773 **360** 22 c. multicoloured . . . . . . 20 20

(Des B. Weatherhead. Litho Leigh-Mardon Ltd, Melbourne)

**1981** (20 May). *Gold Rush Era. Sketches by S. T. Gill. T* **361** *and similar vert designs. Multicoloured. P* 13 × 13½.
774 22 c. Type **361** . . . . . . . . . . 20 25
775 22 c. "Puddling" . . . . . . . . . . 20 25
776 22 c. "Quality of washing stuff" . . . . 20 25
777 22 c. "On route to deposit gold" . . . . 20 25
774/7 . . . . . . . . *Set of* 4 70 90

362 "On the Wallaby Track" (Fred McCubbin)

(Litho Leigh-Mardon Ltd, Melbourne)

**1981** (17 June)–**84**. *Paintings. T* **362** *and similar horiz design. Multicoloured. P* 15 × 14½.
778 $2 Type **362** . . . . . . . . . . 1·75 30
779 $5 "A Holiday at Mentone, 1888" (Charles Conder) (4.4.84) (Optd S. £2·75) . . 4·75 1·25
For No. 778 overprinted "Specimen" see after No. 567*a*.

363 Thylacine

363*a* Blue Mountain Tree-Frog

363*b* *Papilio ulysses* (butterfly)

(Des C. McCubbin (4, 10, 20, 27 c. (No. 791), 30 c. (No. 792*a*), 35, 45, 60, 80 c., $1), F. Knight (5, 24, 25, 30 c. (No. 792), 50, 55 c.) or Beverley Bruen (others). Photo Note Ptg Branch, Reserve Bank of Australia and litho Leigh-Mardon (early ptgs of 24 c.), litho Leigh-Mardon (3, 5, 15, 24, 25, 27 c. (both), 30 c. (both), 40, 50, 55, 65, 75, 90 c.) or Cambec Press (others))

**1981** (19 July)–**84**. *Wildlife. Multicoloured designs as T* **363** (5, 24, 25, 30, 50, 55 *c.*), *T* **363***a* (1, 3, 5, 27 (No. 790), 40, 65, 70, 75, 85, 90, 95 *c.*) *or vert as T* **363***b* (*others*). *P* 13½ (1, 4, 10, 20, 24, 35, 45, 60, 70, 80, 85, 95 *c.*, $1), 14½ × 14 (27 *c.* (*No.* 791), 30 *c.* (*No.* 792*a*)) *or* 12½ (*others*).

781 1 c. Lace Monitor (2.2.83) .. .. 10 20
782 3 c. Corroboree Frog (19.4.82) .. .. 10 10
a. Perf 14 × 14½ (9.84) .. .. 70 15
783 4 c. *Euschemon rafflesia* (butterfly) (*vert*) (15.6.83) .. .. 70 35
784 5 c. Queensland Hairy-nosed Wombat (*vert*) (15.7.81) .. .. 10 10
a. Perf 14½ × 14 (3.84) .. .. 1·00 15
785 10 c. *Ornithoptera priamus* (butterfly) (*vert*) (15.6.83) .. .. 70 10
786 15 c. Eastern Snake-necked Tortoise (16.6.82) .. .. 20 30
a. Perf 14 × 14½ (3.84) .. .. 90 30
787 20 c. *Graphium macleayanus* (butterfly) (*vert*) (15.6.83) .. .. 1·00 35
788 24 c. Type **363** .. .. 35 10
a. Imperf (pair) .. .. £200
789 25 c. Common Rabbit-Bandicoot (*vert*) (15.7.81) .. .. 35 10
a. Perf 14×14½ (5.83) .. .. 1·10 35
790 27 c. Type **363***a* (19.4.82) .. .. 35 20
a. Perf 14×14½ (6.82) .. .. 90 15
791 27 c. Type **363***b* (15.6.83) .. .. 1·25 30
a. Imperf (pair) .. .. £300
792 30 c. Bridle Nail-tailed Wallaby (*vert*) (15.7.81) .. .. 40 15
792*a* 30 c. *Pseudalmenus chlorinda* (butterfly) (*vert*) (24.10.83) .. .. 1·25 20
793 35 c. *Danaus hamata* (butterfly) (*vert*) (15.6.83) .. .. 1·25 30
794 40 c. Smooth Knob-tailed Gecko (16.6.82) .. 45 50
a. Perf 14 × 14½ (3.84) .. .. 2·00 75
795 45 c. *Cressida cressida* (butterfly) (*vert*) (15.6.83) .. .. 1·00 30
796 50 c. Leadbeater's Possum (15.7.81) .. .. 50 10
a. Perf 14 × 14½ (1983) .. .. 1·25 30
797 55 c. Stick-nest Rat (*vert*) (15.7.81) .. .. 50 30
798 60 c. *Delias aganippe* (butterfly) (*vert*) (15.6.83) .. .. 1·25 30
799 65 c. Yellow-faced Whip Snake (19.4.82) .. 80 30
a. Perf 14 × 14½ (3.84) .. .. 1·50 55
800 70 c. Crucifix Toad (2.2.83) .. .. 65 90
801 75 c. Eastern Water Dragon (19.4.82) .. .. 80 40
a. Perf 14 × 14½ (3.84) .. .. 1·75 90
802 80 c. *Ogyris amaryllis* (butterfly) (*vert*) (15.6.83) .. .. 1·75 1·25
803 85 c. Centralian Blue-tongued Lizard (2.2.83) .. .. 1·10 1·10
804 90 c. Freshwater Crocodile (16.6.82) .. .. 1·10 1·10
805 95 c. Thorny Devil (2.2.83) .. .. 1·00 1·25
806 $1 *Tisiphone abeona* (butterfly) (*vert*) (15.6.83) .. .. 1·75 30
781/806 .. .. .. .. *Set of* 27 18·00 9·50

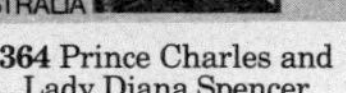

364 Prince Charles and Lady Diana Spencer

365 *Cortinarius cinnabarinus*

(Des B. Clinton. Litho Leigh-Mardon Ltd, Melbourne)

**1981** (29 July). *Royal Wedding. P* 13½ × 13.
821 **364** 24 c. multicoloured .. .. .. 25 10
822 60 c. multicoloured .. .. .. 75 1·00

(Des Celia Rosser. Litho Leigh-Mardon Ltd, Melbourne)

**1981** (19 Aug). *Australian Fungi. T* **365** *and similar vert designs. Multicoloured. P* 13 × 13½.
823 24 c. Type **365** .. .. .. .. 35 10
824 35 c. *Coprinus comatus* .. .. .. 50 50
825 55 c. *Armillaria luteobubalina* .. .. 70 70
826 60 c. *Cortinarius austrovenetus* .. .. 80 80
823/6 .. .. .. .. *Set of* 4 2·10 1·90

366 Disabled People playing Basketball

367 "Christmas Bush for His Adorning"

(Des J. Spatchurst. Litho Cambec Press, Melbourne)

**1981** (16 Sept). *International Year for Disabled Persons. P* 14 × 13½.
827 **366** 24 c. multicoloured .. .. .. 20 20

(Des F. Beck. Litho Leigh-Mardon Ltd, Melbourne)

**1981** (28 Sept–2 Nov). *Christmas. Scenes and Verses from Carols by W. James and J. Wheeler. T* **367** *and similar vert designs. Multicoloured. P* 13 × 13½.
828 18 c. Type **367** (2 Nov) .. .. .. .. 25 10
829 30 c. "The Silver Stars are in the Sky" .. 35 25
830 60 c. "Noeltime" (2 Nov) .. .. .. 60 70
828/30 .. .. .. .. *Set of* 3 1·10 90

368 Globe depicting Australia

369 Ocean Racing Yacht

(Des B. Weatherhead. Litho Leigh-Mardon Ltd, Melbourne)

**1981** (30 Sept). *Commonwealth Heads of Government Meeting, Melbourne. P* 13 × 13½.
831 **368** 24 c. black, pale blue and gold .. .. 20 10
832 60 c. black, pale blue and silver .. .. 50 75

(Des R. Fletcher. Litho Leigh-Mardon Ltd, Melbourne)

**1981** (14 Oct). *Yachts. T* **369** *and similar vert designs. Multicoloured. P* 13 × 13½.
833 24 c. Type **369** .. .. .. .. 35 10
834 35 c. "Sharpie" .. .. .. .. 50 50
835 55 c. "12 Metre" .. .. .. .. 75 85
836 60 c. "Sabot" .. .. .. .. 1·00 1·00
833/6 .. .. .. .. *Set of* 4 2·40 2·25

370 Aborigine, Governor Phillip (founder of N.S.W., 1788) and Post World War II Migrant

371 Humpback Whale

(Des B. Clinton. Litho Cambec Press, Melbourne)

**1982** (20 Jan). *Australia Day. "Three Great Waves of Migration". P* 13½ × 14.
837 **370** 24 c. multicoloured .. .. .. 35 25

(Des R. and Katrina Ingpen. Litho Cambec Press, Melbourne)

**1982** (17 Feb). *Whales. T* **371** *and similar multicoloured designs. P* 13½ × 14 (24, 60 *c.*) *or* 14 × 13½ (*others*).
838 24 c. Sperm Whale .. .. .. .. 40 10
839 35 c. Black Right Whale (*vert*) .. .. 60 60
840 55 c. Blue Whale (*vert*) .. .. .. 1·10 1·10
841 60 c. Type **371** (new blue background) .. 1·25 1·25
a. Solid greenish blue background .. £180
838/41 .. .. .. .. *Set of* 4 3·00 2·75

No. 841a comes from a small trial printing, some sheets of which were included amongst normal stock by mistake. The correct version of the 60 c. value shows the new blue background streaked with white at top left. On No. 841a the background is in greenish blue and is without the white streaks.

372 Queen Elizabeth II

373 "Marjorie Atherton"

(Des R. Honisett. Litho Cambec Press, Melbourne)

**1982** (21 Apr). *Queen Elizabeth II's Birthday. P* 14 × 13½.
842 **372** 27 c. multicoloured .. .. .. 35 15

(Des Betty Conabere. Litho Leigh-Mardon Ltd, Melbourne)

**1982** (19 May). *Roses. T* **373** *and similar vert designs. Multicoloured. P* 13 × 13½.
843 27 c. Type **373** .. .. .. .. 40 15
844 40 c. "Imp" .. .. .. .. 55 65
845 65 c. "Minnie Watson" .. .. .. 95 1·25
846 75 c. "Satellite" .. .. .. .. 1·10 1·40
843/6 .. .. .. .. *Set of* 4 2·75 3·00

374 Radio Announcer and 1930-style Microphone

375 Forbes Post Office

(Des Cato Hibberd Design. Litho Leigh-Mardon Ltd, Melbourne)

**1982** (16 June). *50th Anniv of ABC (Australian Broadcasting Commission). T* **374** *and similar horiz design. Multicoloured. P* 13½ × 13.
847 27 c. Type **374** .. .. .. .. 30 40
a. Pair. Nos. 847/8 .. .. .. 60 80
848 27 c. ABC logo .. .. .. .. 30 40

Nos. 847/8 were printed together, *se-tenant*, in horizontal and vertical pairs throughout the sheet.

(Des F. Beck. Litho Cambec Press, Melbourne)

**1982** (4 Aug). *Historic Australian Post Offices. T* **375** *and similar multicoloured designs. P* 14 × 13½ (*vert*) *or* 13½ × 14 (*horiz*).
849 27 c. Type **375** .. .. .. .. 40 35
850 27 c. Flemington Post Office .. .. 40 35
851 27 c. Rockhampton Post Office .. .. 40 35
852 27 c. Kingston S.E. Post Office (*horiz*) .. 40 35
853 27 c. York Post Office (*horiz*) .. .. 40 35
854 27 c. Launceston Post Office .. .. 40 35
855 27 c. Old Post and Telegraph Station, Alice Springs (*horiz*) .. .. .. 40 35
849/55 .. .. .. .. *Set of* 7 2·50 2·25

376 Early Australian Christmas Card

377 Boxing

(Des B. Weatherhead. Litho Leigh-Mardon Ltd, Melbourne)

**1982** (15 Sept–1 Nov). *Christmas. T* **376** *and similar multicoloured designs. P* 14½.
856 21 c. Bushman's Hotel, with Cobb's coach arriving (*horiz*) (1.11.82) .. .. 30 10
857 35 c. Type **376** .. .. .. .. 50 60
858 75 c. Little girl offering Christmas pudding to swagman (1.11.82) .. .. 75 1·40
856/8 .. .. .. .. *Set of* 3 1·40 1·90

(Des R. Carnielye. Litho Leigh-Mardon Ltd, Melbourne)

**1982** (22 Sept). *Commonwealth Games, Brisbane. T* **377** *and similar horiz designs. P* 14½.
859 27 c. stone, lemon and bright carmine .. 25 20
860 27 c. lemon, stone and emerald .. .. 25 20
861 27 c. stone, lemon and yellow-brown .. 25 20
862 75 c. multicoloured .. .. .. 75 90
859/62 .. .. .. .. *Set of* 4 1·40 1·40
**MS**863 130 × 95 mm. Nos. 859/61. P 13½ × 13 .. 1·10 1·25

Designs:—No. 859, Type **377**; No. 860, Archery; No. 861, Weightlifting; No. 862, Pole-vaulting.

378 Sydney Harbour Bridge 5s. Stamp of 1932

379 "Yirawala" Bark Painting

(Des Cato Hibberd Design. Litho Cambec Press, Melbourne)

**1982** (27 Sept). *National Stamp Week. P* 13½ × 14.
864 **378** 27 c. multicoloured .. .. .. 35 30

(Des Australia Post Graphic Design Section. Litho Leigh-Mardon Ltd, Melbourne)

**1982** (12 Oct). *Opening of Australian National Gallery. P* 14½.
865 **379** 27 c. multicoloured .. .. .. 30 25

380 Mimi Spirits Dancing

381 *Eucalyptus calophylla* "Rosea"

(Des D. Milaybuma (27 c.), L. Nabardayal (40 c.), J. Galareya (65 c.), D. Nguleingulei-Murrumurru (75 c.). Litho Cambec Press, Melbourne)

**1982** (17 Nov). *Aboriginal Culture. Music and Dance. T* **380** *and similar horiz designs depicting Aboriginal Bark Paintings of Mimi Spirits. P* 13½ × 14.
866 27 c. multicoloured .. .. .. .. .. 25 10
867 40 c. multicoloured .. .. .. .. .. 40 50
868 65 c. multicoloured .. .. .. .. .. 70 80
869 75 c. multicoloured .. .. .. .. .. 80 1·10
866/9 .. .. .. .. .. .. *Set of* 4 2·00 2·25

(Des Elizabeth Conabere. Photo Enschedé)

**1982** (17 Nov). *Booklet stamps. Eucalyptus Flowers. T* **381** *and similar horiz designs. Multicoloured. P* 12½ × 13½.
870 1 c. Type **381** .. .. .. .. .. 10 20
a. Booklet pane. Nos. 870/1 and 874 each × 2 90
b. Booklet pane. Nos. 870/1 each × 2, 872/3 and 874 × 3 .. .. .. .. .. 2·25
871 2 c. *Eucalyptus casia* .. .. .. .. .. 10 20
872 3 c. *Eucalyptus ficifolia* .. .. .. .. 35 55
873 10 c. *Eucalyptus globulus* .. .. .. .. 35 55
874 27 c. *Eucalyptus forrestiana* .. .. .. .. 35 40
870/4 .. .. .. .. .. .. *Set of* 5 1·10 1·75

Nos. 870/4 only exist from 60 c. (pane No. 870a) and $1 (pane No. 870b) stamp booklets and the stamps have one or two adjacent sides imperforate.

**382** Shand Mason Steam Fire Engine, 1891 **383** H.M.S. *Sirius*

(Des A. Puckett. Litho Cambec Press, Melbourne)

**1983** (12 Jan). *Historic Fire Engines. T* **382** *and similar horiz designs. Multicoloured. P* 13½ × 14.
875 27 c. Type **382** .. .. .. .. .. 35 10
876 40 c. Hotchkiss fire engine, 1914 .. .. .. 50 60
877 65 c. Ahrens-Fox PS2 fire engine, 1929 .. .. 90 1·25
878 75 c. Merryweather manual fire appliance, 1851 .. .. .. .. .. 1·00 1·40
875/8 .. .. .. .. .. .. *Set of* 4 2·50 3·00

(Des J. Spatchurst. Litho Leigh-Mardon Ltd, Melbourne)

**1983** (26 Jan). *Australia Day. T* **383** *and similar horiz design. Multicoloured. P* 14½.
879 27 c. Type **383** .. .. .. .. .. 40 50
a. Pair. Nos. 879/80 .. .. .. .. 80 1·00
880 27 c. H.M.S. *Supply* .. .. .. .. .. 40 50

Nos. 879/80 were printed together, *se-tenant*, in horizontal and vertical pairs throughout the sheet.

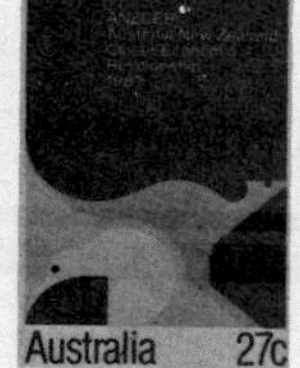

**384** Stylised Kangaroo and Kiwi **385** Equality and Dignity

(Des G. Emery. Litho Cambec Press, Melbourne)

**1983** (2 Feb). *Closer Economic Relationship Agreement with New Zealand. P* 14 × 13½.
881 **384** 27 c. multicoloured .. .. .. .. 30 30

(Des G. Emery. Litho Leigh-Mardon Ltd, Melbourne)

**1983** (9 Mar). *Commonwealth Day. T* **385** *and similar vert designs. Multicoloured. P* 14½.
882 27 c. Type **385** .. .. .. .. .. 25 25
883 27 c. Liberty and Freedom .. .. .. .. 25 25
884 27 c. Social Justice and Co-operation .. .. 25 25
885 75 c. Peace and Harmony .. .. .. .. 70 1·10
882/5 .. .. .. .. .. .. *Set of* 4 1·25 1·75

**386** R.Y. *Britannia* passing Sydney Opera House **387** "Postal and Telecommunications Services"

(Des J. Richards. Litho Leigh-Mardon Ltd, Melbourne)

**1983** (20 Apr). *Queen Elizabeth II's Birthday. P* 14½.
886 **386** 27 c. multicoloured .. .. .. .. 45 30

(Des B. Sadgrove. Litho Cambec Press, Melbourne)

**1983** (18 May). *World Communications Year. P* 13 × 13½.
887 **387** 27 c. multicoloured .. .. .. .. 30 30

**388** Badge of the Order of St. John **389** Jaycee Members and Badge

(Des T. McCauley. Litho Cambec Press, Melbourne)

**1983** (8 June). *Centenary of St. John Ambulance in Australia. P* 14 × 13½.
888 **388** 27 c. black and deep turquoise-blue .. 35 30

(Des B. Clinton. Litho Cambec Press, Melbourne)

**1983** (8 June). *50th Anniv of Australian Jaycees. P* 13½ × 14.
889 **389** 27 c. multicoloured .. .. .. .. 30 30

**390** "The Bloke" **391** Nativity Scene

(Des B. Clinton. Litho Leigh-Mardon Ltd, Melbourne)

**1983** (3 Aug). *Folklore. "The Sentimental Bloke" (humorous poem by C. J. Dennis). T* **390** *and similar vert designs. Multicoloured. P* 14½.
890 27 c. Type **390** .. .. .. .. .. 45 45
a. Horiz strip of 5. Nos. 890/4 .. .. 2·00
891 27 c. "Doreen—The Intro" .. .. .. .. 45 45
892 27 c. "The Stror' at Coot" .. .. .. .. 45 45
893 27 c. "Hitched" .. .. .. .. .. 45 45
894 27 c. "The Mooch o'Life" .. .. .. .. 45 45
890/4 .. .. .. .. .. .. *Set of* 5 2·00 2·00

Nos. 890/4 were printed together, *se-tenant*, in horizontal strips of 5 throughout the sheet.

(Des Holly Alvarez (24 c.), Deanne Head (35 c.), Justine Jacobi (85 c.). Litho Cambec Press, Melbourne)

**1983** (14 Sept–2 Nov). *Christmas. Children's Paintings. T* **391** *and similar horiz designs. Multicoloured. P* 13½ × 14.
895 24 c. Type **391** (2 November) .. .. .. 20 10
896 35 c. Kookaburra .. .. .. .. .. 35 45
897 85 c. Father Christmas in sleigh over beach (2 November) .. .. .. .. 90 1·10
895/7 .. .. .. .. .. .. *Set of* 3 1·25 1·50

**392** Sir Paul Edmund de Strzelecki **393** Cook Family Cottage, Melbourne

(Des Dianne Quinn. Litho Leigh-Mardon Ltd, Melbourne)

**1983** (26 Sept). *Explorers of Australia. T* **392** *and similar vert designs. Multicoloured. P* 14½.
898 30 c. Type **392** .. .. .. .. .. 35 40
899 30 c. Ludwig Leichardt .. .. .. .. 35 40
900 30 c. William John Wills and Robert O'Hara Burke .. .. .. .. .. 35 40
901 30 c. Alexander Forrest .. .. .. .. 35 40
898/901 .. .. .. .. .. *Set of* 4 1·25 1·40

(Des J. Quinn. Litho Cambec Press, Melbourne)

**1984** (26 Jan). *Australia Day. P* 13½ × 14.
902 **393** 30 c. black and stone .. .. .. .. 30 35

**MACHINE LABELS.** From 22 February 1984 gummed labels in the above design, ranging in value from 1 c. to $9.99, were available from seven automatic machines. The postcode at the top of the label indicates the location of the machine from which it was issued: 2000, Sydney; 2601, Canberra; 3000, Melbourne; 4000, Brisbane; 5000, Adelaide; 6000, Perth; 7000, Hobart.

These were replaced by a further series, with a background pattern of kangaroos, on 22 October 1985. This second series included 5790 (later 0800) Darwin and labels without code number.

On 25 August 1986 a further series, with a background pattern of platypuses, was issued. These exist either without code or with one of the eight numbers introduced for the earlier issues. The design was again changed on 2 September 1987 to show Echidnas to be followed by Ringtail Possums on 28 September 1988, Frill-necked Lizards on 1 September 1989 and Koalas on 3 September 1990.

A new square design showing an Emu was introduced on 2 January 1992.

As the number of machines increased rapidly only those situated at the State, or Capital Territory, General Post Offices showed a postcode. Later machines had a top label value of either $10 or $20.

**394** Charles Ulm, *Faith in Australia* and Trans-Tasman Cover

(Des G. Beck and J. Quinn. Litho Cambec Press, Melbourne)

**1984** (22 Feb). *50th Anniv of First Official Airmail Flights, New Zealand–Australia and Australia–Papua New Guinea. T* **394** *and similar horiz design. Multicoloured. P* 13½.
903 45 c. Type **394** .. .. .. .. .. 65 90
a. Horiz pair. Nos. 903/4 .. .. .. 1·50 2·00
904 45 c. As Type **394** but showing flown cover to Papua New Guinea .. .. .. .. 65 90

Nos. 903/4 were printed together, *se-tenant*, in horizontal pairs throughout the sheet.

**395** Thomson "Steamer", 1898 **396** Queen Elizabeth II

(Des A. Puckett. Litho Leigh-Mardon Ltd, Melbourne)

**1984** (14 Mar). *Veteran and Vintage Cars. T* **395** *and similar horiz designs. Multicoloured. P* 14½.
905 30 c. Type **395** .. .. .. .. .. 45 55
a. Vert strip of 5. Nos. 905/9 .. .. 2·00
906 30 c. Tarrant, 1906 .. .. .. .. .. 45 55
907 30 c. Gordon & Co "Australian Six", 1919 .. 45 55
908 30 c. Summit, 1923 .. .. .. .. .. 45 55
909 30 c. Chic, 1924 .. .. .. .. .. 45 55
905/9 .. .. .. .. .. .. *Set of* 5 2·00 2·50

Nos. 905/9 were printed together, *se-tenant*, in vertical strips of 5 throughout the sheet.

(Des B. Weatherhead. Litho Leigh-Mardon Ltd, Melbourne)

**1984** (18 Apr). *Queen Elizabeth II's Birthday. P* 14½.
910 **396** 30 c. multicoloured .. .. .. .. 30 35
a. Dull mauve (background) omitted £325

**397** *Cutty Sark* **398** Freestyle

(Des J. Earl and J. Quinn. Litho Cambec Press, Melbourne)

**1984** (23 May). *Clipper Ships. T* **397** *and similar multicoloured designs. P* 14 × 13½ (30 c., 85 c.) *or* 13½ × 14 (*others*).
911 30 c. Type **397** .. .. .. .. .. 40 25
912 45 c. *Orient* (*horiz*) .. .. .. .. 70 70
913 75 c. *Sobraon* (*horiz*) .. .. .. .. 1·25 1·25
914 85 c. *Thermopylae* .. .. .. .. 1·25 1·25
911/14 .. .. .. .. .. *Set of* 4 3·25 3·00

(Des B. Clinton. Litho Leigh-Mardon Ltd, Melbourne)

**1984** (6 June). *Skiing. T* **398** *and similar multicoloured designs. P* 14½.
915 30 c. Type **398** .. .. .. .. .. 40 45
916 30 c. Downhill racer .. .. .. .. 40 45
917 30 c. Slalom (*horiz*) .. .. .. .. 40 45
918 30 c. Nordic (*horiz*) .. .. .. .. 40 45
915/18 .. .. .. .. .. *Set of* 4 1·50 1·75

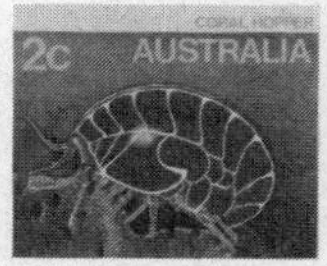

**399** Coral Hopper **400** Before the Event

(Des G. Ryan and R. Fletcher (2, 25, 30, 50, 55, 85 c.) or G. Ryan (others). Litho Leigh-Mardon Ltd, Melbourne (30, 33 c.) or Cambec Press, Melbourne (others))

**1984** (18 June)–**86**. *Marine Life. T* **399** *and similar horiz designs. Multicoloured. P* 14×14½ (30 c., 33 c.) *or* 13½ (*others*).

919 2 c. Type **399** .. .. .. .. 10 15
920 3 c. Jimble (11.6.86) .. .. .. 10 15
921 5 c. Tasselled Anglerfish (12.6.85) .. 10 10
922 10 c. Stonefish (11.6.86) .. .. .. 20 10
923 20 c. Red Handfish (12.6.85) .. .. 45 25
924 25 c. Orange-tipped Cowrie .. .. 45 25
925 30 c. Choat's Wrasse .. .. .. 45 30
926 33 c. Leafy Sea-dragon (20.3.85) .. 35 10
927 40 c. Red Velvet Fish (12.6.85) .. .. 65 40
928 45 c. Textile Cone (11.6.86) .. .. 80 35
929 50 c. Blue-lined Surgeonfish .. .. 80 40
930 55 c. Bennett's Nudibranch .. .. 80 50
a. New blue ("BENNETT'S NUDI-BRANCH") omitted .. .. † —
931 60 c. Lionfish (11.6.86) .. .. .. 90 60
932 65 c. Stingaree (11.6.86) .. .. .. 90 65
933 70 c. Blue-ringed Octopus (11.6.86) .. 90 65
934 80 c. Pineapple Fish (12.6.85) .. .. 1·25 70
935 85 c. Regal Angelfish .. .. .. 90 50
936 90 c. Crab-eyed Goby (12.6.85) .. .. 1·00 75
937 $1 Crown of Thorns Starfish (11.6.86) (Optd S. 50p.) .. .. .. 1·50 80
919/37 .. .. .. .. *Set of* 19 11·00 7·00

No. 930a only exists used on maximum card.

(Des O. Schmidinger and Christine Stead. Litho Cambec Press, Melbourne)

**1984** (25 July). *Olympic Games, Los Angeles. T* **400** *and similar multicoloured designs. P* 14 × 13½ (*No.* 943) *or* 13½ × 14 (*others*).

941 30 c. Type **400** .. .. .. .. 35 35
942 30 c. During the event.. .. .. .. 35 35
943 30 c. After the event (*vert*) .. .. 35 35
941/3 .. .. .. .. *Set of* 3 95 95

401 Australian 1913 1d. Kangaroo Stamp

402 "Angel" (stained-glass window, St. Francis' Church, Melbourne)

(Des Ken Cato Design Studio. Litho Cambec Press, Melbourne)

**1984** (22 Aug–21 Sept). *"Ausipex" International Stamp Exhibition, Melbourne. T* **401** *and similar vert designs. Multicoloured. P* 14½.

944 30 c. Type **401** .. .. .. .. 35 30
**MS**945 126 × 175 mm. 30 c. × 7, Victoria 1850 3d. "Half Length"; New South Wales 1850 1d. "Sydney View"; Tasmania 1853 1d.; South Australia 1855 1d.; Western Australia 1854 1d. "Black Swan"; Queensland 1860 6d.; Type **401** (21 Sept).. 3·25 4·00

On No. **MS**945 the emblem and inscription on the sheet margin are embossed.

(Des Ken Cato Design Studio. Litho Cambec Press, Melbourne)

**1984** (17 Sept–31 Oct). *Christmas. Stained-glass Windows. T* **402** *and similar vert designs. Multicoloured. P* 14 × 13½.

946 24 c. "Angel and Child" (Holy Trinity Church, Sydney) (31.10.84) .. .. 40 20
947 30 c. "Veiled Virgin and Child" (St. Mary's Catholic Church, Geelong) (31.10.84) .. 55 20
948 40 c. Type **402** .. .. .. .. 70 60
949 50 c. "Three Kings" (St. Mary's Cathedral, Sydney) (31.10.84) .. .. 90 80
950 85 c. "Madonna and Child" (St. Bartholomew's Church, Norwood) (31.10.84) .. 1·25 1·25
946/50 .. .. .. .. *Set of* 5 3·50 2·75

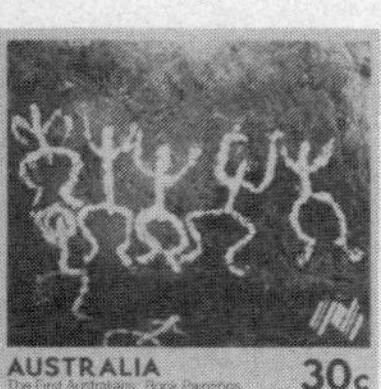


403 "Stick Figures" (Cobar Region)

404 Yellow-tufted Honeyeater

(Des Elizabeth Innes. Litho Leigh-Mardon Ltd, Melbourne)

**1984** (7 Nov). *Bicentenary of Australian Settlement* (1988) (1st *issue*). *The First Australians. T* **403** *and similar square designs showing aboriginal rock paintings. Multicoloured. P* 14½.

951 30 c. Type **403** .. .. .. .. 45 45
952 30 c. "Bunjil" (large figure), Grampians .. 45 45
953 30 c. "Quikans" (tall figures), Cape York .. 45 45
954 30 c. "Wandjina Spirit and Baby Snakes" (Gibb River) .. .. .. .. 45 45
955 30 c. "Rock Python" (Gibb River) .. .. 45 45
956 30 c. "Silver Barramundi" (fish) (Kakadu National Park) .. .. .. 45 45
957 30 c. Bicentenary emblem .. .. 45 45
958 85 c. "Rock Possum" (Kakadu National Park) 1·10 1·25
951/8 .. .. .. .. *Set of* 8 3·75 4·00

See also Nos. 972/6, 993/6, 1002/7, 1019/22, 1059/63, 1064/6, 1077/81, 1090/2, 1105/9, 1110, 1137/41, 1145/8 and 1149.

(Des. G. Emery. Litho Leigh-Mardon Ltd, Melbourne

**1984** (19 Nov). *150th Anniv of Victoria. T* **404** *and similar vert design. Multicoloured. P* 14½.

959 30 c. Type **404** .. .. .. .. 35 55
a. Pair. Nos. 959/60.. .. .. .. 70 1·10
960 30 c. Leadbeater's Possum .. .. 35 55

Nos. 959/60 were printed together, *se-tenant*, in horizontal and vertical pairs throughout the sheet.

405 "Musgrave Ranges" (Sidney Nolan)

406 Young People of Different Races, and Sun

(Des Sue Titcher. Litho Leigh-Mardon Ltd, Melbourne)

**1985** (25 Jan). *Australia Day. Birth Centenary of Dorothea Mackellar (author of poem "My Country"). T* **405** *and similar horiz design. Multicoloured. P* 14½.

961 30 c. Type **405** .. .. .. .. 45 55
a. *Tête-bêche* (vert pair) .. .. 1·25 1·75
b. Vert pair. Nos. 961/2 .. .. 90 1·10
962 30 c. "The Walls of China" (Russell Drysdale). 45 55
a. *Tête-bêche* (vert pair) .. .. 1·25 1·75

Nos. 961/2 were printed together, *se-tenant*, within the same sheet. In each pane of 25 No. 961 occurs in horizontal rows 1, 4, 5, 8 and 9, and No. 962 in rows 2, 3, 6, 7 and 10. Horizontal rows 3/4 and 7/8 are inverted forming *tête-bêche* pairs of the same design in addition to the vertical *se-tenant* pairs containing both designs.

(Des Derryn Vogelnest. Litho Cambec Press, Melbourne)

**1985** (13 Feb). *International Youth Year. P* 14 × 13½.

963 **406** 30 c. multicoloured .. .. .. 35 30

407 Royal Victorian Volunteer Artillery

408 District Nurse of early 1900's

(Des Pam Andrews. Litho Leigh-Mardon Ltd, Melbourne)

**1985** (25 Feb). *19th-Century Australian Military Uniforms. T* **407** *and similar vert designs. Multicoloured. P* 14½.

964 33 c. Type **407** .. .. .. .. 60 60
a. Horiz strip of 5. Nos. 964/8 .. .. 2·75
965 33 c. Western Australian Pinjarrah Cavalry .. 60 60
966 33 c. New South Wales Lancers .. .. 60 60
967 33 c. New South Wales Contingent to the Sudan .. .. .. .. 60 60
968 33 c. Victorian Mounted Rifles .. .. 60 60
964/8 .. .. .. .. *Set of* 5 2·75 2·75

Nos. 964/8 were printed together, *se-tenant*, in horizontal strips of 5 throughout the sheet.

(Des Wendy Tamlyn. Litho Leigh-Mardon Ltd, Melbourne)

**1985** (13 Mar). *Centenary of District Nursing Services. P* 14½.

969 **408** 33 c. multicoloured .. .. .. 40 35

409 Sulphur-crested Cockatoos

(Des R. Bevers. Litho Leigh-Mardon Ltd, Melbourne)

**1985** (13 Mar). *Booklet stamps. Multicoloured, background colour given. P* 14½×*imperf*.

970 **409** 1 c. flesh .. .. .. .. 1·25 1·75
a. Booklet pane. Nos. 970, and 971×3 2·40
971 33 c. pale turquoise-green .. .. 45 55

Nos. 970/1 only exist from $1 stamp booklets. As stamps from these booklets have their outer edges imperforate, the end example of No. 971 is only perforated along one side.

410 Abel Tasman and Journal Entry

411 Sovereign's Badge of Order of Australia

(Des G. Emery. Litho Cambec Press, Melbourne)

**1985** (10 Apr). *Bicentenary of Australian Settlement* (1988) (2*nd issue*). *Navigators. T* **410** *and similar square designs. Multicoloured. P* 13.

972 33 c. Type **410**.. .. .. .. .. 45 35
973 33 c. Dirk Hartog's *Eendracht* (detail, Aert Anthonisz) .. .. .. .. 45 35
974 33 c. "William Dampier" (detail, T. Murray) 45 35
975 90 c. Globe and hand with extract from Dampier's journal .. .. .. .. 1·10 1·50
972/5 .. .. .. .. *Set of* 4 2·25 2·25
**MS**976 150×115 mm. As Nos. 972/5, but with cream-coloured margins .. .. .. 3·00 3·00

(Des Elizabeth Innes. Litho Cambec Press, Melbourne)

**1985** (22 Apr). *Queen Elizabeth II's Birthday. P* 14×13½.

977 **411** 33 c. multicoloured .. .. .. 35 30

412 Tree, and Soil running through Hourglass ("Soil")

413 *Elves and Fairies* (Annie Rentoul and Ida Rentoul Outhwaite)

(Des L. Whaite and G. Jorgensen. Litho Cambec Press, Melbourne)

**1985** (15 May). *Conservation. T* **412** *and similar vert designs. Multicoloured. P* 14×13½.

978 33 c. Type **412**.. .. .. .. .. 45 20
979 50 c. Washing on line and smog ("air") .. 70 85
980 80 c. Tap and flower ("water") .. .. 1·10 1·40
981 90 c. Chain encircling flames ("energy") .. 1·25 1·75
978/81 .. .. .. .. *Set of* 4 3·25 3·75

(Des P. Leuver. Litho Leigh-Mardon Ltd, Melbourne)

**1985** (17 July). *Classic Australian Children's Books. T* **413** *and similar vert designs. Multicoloured. P* 14½.

982 33 c. Type **413**.. .. .. .. 50 60
a. Horiz strip of 5. Nos. 982/6 .. .. 2·25
983 33 c. *The Magic Pudding* (Norman Lindsay) 50 60
984 33 c. *Ginger Meggs* (James Charles Bancks) 50 60
985 33 c. *Blinky Bill* (Dorothy Wall) .. .. 50 60
986 33 c. *Snugglepot and Cuddlepie* (May Gibbs) 50 60
982/6 .. .. .. .. *Set of* 5 2·25 2·75

Nos. 982/6 were printed together, *se-tenant*, in horizontal strips of 5 throughout the sheet.

414 Dish Aerials

415 Angel in Sailing Ship

(Des J. Ostoja-Kotkowski. Litho Leigh-Mardon Ltd, Melbourne)

**1985** (18 Sept). *Electronic Mail Service. P* 14½.

987 **414** 33 c. multicoloured .. .. .. 35 30

(Des S. Hartshorne. Litho Leigh-Mardon Ltd, Melbourne)

**1985** (18 Sept–1 Nov). *Christmas. T* **415** *and similar horiz designs. Multicoloured. P* 14½.

988 27 c. Angel with holly wings (1.11) .. .. 30 15
989 33 c. Angel with bells (1.11).. .. .. 35 15
990 45 c. Type **415**.. .. .. .. 50 50
991 55 c. Angel with star (1.11) .. .. 65 70
992 90 c. Angel with Christmas tree bauble (1.11) .. .. .. .. 1·00 1·25
988/92 .. .. .. .. *Set of* 5 2·50 2·50

416 Astrolabe (*Batavia*, 1629)

417 Aboriginal Wandjina Spirit, Map of Australia and Egg

(Des G. Emery. Litho Cambec Press, Melbourne)

**1985** (2 Oct). *Bicentenary of Australian Settlement* (1988) (3*rd issue*). *Relics from Early Shipwrecks. T* **416** *and similar square designs. Multicoloured. P* 13.

993 33 c. Type **416**.. .. .. .. 40 15
994 50 c. German beardman jug (*Vergulde Draeck*, 1656) .. .. .. 70 70
995 90 c. Wooden bobbins (*Batavia*, 1629) and encrusted scissors (*Zeewijk*, 1727) .. 1·40 1·50
996 $1 Silver and brass buckle (*Zeewijk*, 1727) 1·60 1·50
993/6 .. .. .. .. *Set of* 4 3·75 3·50

(Des R. Meeks. Litho Leigh-Mardon Ltd, Melbourne)

**1986** (24 Jan). *Australia Day. P* 14½.
997 **417** 33 c. multicoloured .. .. .. 40 30

418 AUSSAT Satellite, Moon and Earth's Surface

419 H.M.S. *Buffalo*

(Des O. Schmidinger and Christine Stead. Litho Leigh-Mardon Ltd, Melbourne)

**1986** (24 Jan). *AUSSAT National Communications Satellite System. T* **418** *and similar vert design. Multicoloured. P* 14½.
998 33 c. Type **418**.. .. .. .. 50 15
999 80 c. AUSSAT satellite in orbit .. .. 1·50 1·60

(Des I. Kidd. Litho Cambec Press, Melbourne)

**1986** (12 Feb). *150th Anniv of South Australia. T* **419** *and similar horiz design. Multicoloured. P* 13½ × 14.
1000 33 c. Type **419** .. .. .. .. 60 70
a. Pair. Nos. 1000/1 .. .. .. 1·10 1·40
1001 33 c. "City Sign" sculpture (Otto Hajek), Adelaide .. .. .. .. 60 70

Nos. 1000/1 were printed together, *se-tenant*, in horizontal and vertical pairs throughout the sheet, the background of each horizontal pair showing an extract from the colony's Letters Patent of 1836.

420 *Banksia serrata*

421 Radio Telescope, Parkes, and Diagram of Comet's Orbit

(Des Sue Titcher. Litho Cambec Press, Melbourne)

**1986** (12 Mar). *Bicentenary of Australian Settlement* (1988) (*4th issue*). *Cook's Voyage to New Holland. T* **420** *and similar horiz designs. Multicoloured. P* 13.
1002 33 c. Type **420** .. .. .. .. 60 35
1003 33 c. *Hibiscus meraukensis* .. .. .. 60 35
1004 50 c. *Dillenia alata* .. .. .. .. 90 80
1005 80 c. *Correa reflexa* .. .. .. .. 1·60 1·50
1006 90 c. "Joseph Banks" (botanist) (Reynolds) and Banks with Dr. Solander .. .. 2·00 1·75
1007 90 c. "Sydney Parkinson" (self-portrait) and Parkinson drawing .. .. 2·00 1·75
1002/7 .. .. .. .. *Set of* 6 7·00 6·00

(Des J. Passmore. Litho Cambec Press, Melbourne)

**1986** (9 Apr). *Appearance of Halley's Comet. P* 14 × 13½.
1008 **421** 33 c. multicoloured .. .. .. 50 35

422 Queen Elizabeth II

423 Brumbies (wild horses)

(Des Fay Plamka. Litho Leigh-Mardon Ltd, Melbourne)

**1986** (21 Apr). *60th Birthday of Queen Elizabeth II. P* 14½.
1009 **422** 33 c. multicoloured .. .. .. 45 35

(Des R. Ingpen. Litho Leigh-Mardon Ltd, Melbourne)

**1986** (21 May). *Australian Horses. T* **423** *and similar horiz designs. Multicoloured. P* 14½.
1010 33 c. Type **423** .. .. .. .. 60 15
1011 80 c. Mustering .. .. .. .. 1·50 1·50
1012 90 c. Show-jumping .. .. .. .. 1·75 1·75
1013 $1 Child on pony .. .. .. .. 2·00 2·00
1010/13 .. .. .. .. *Set of* 4 5·25 5·00

## NEW INFORMATION

The editor is always interested to correspond with people who have new information that will improve or correct the Catalogue.

424 "The Old Shearer stands"

425 "King George III" (A. Ramsay) and Convicts

(Des R. Ingpen. Litho Leigh-Mardon Ltd, Melbourne)

**1986** (21 July). *Folklore. Scenes and Verses from the Folksong "Click go the Shears". T* **424** *and similar vert designs. Multicoloured. P* 14½.
1014 33 c. Type **424** .. .. .. .. 65 70
a. Horiz strip of 5. Nos. 1014/18 .. 3·00
1015 33 c. "The ringer looks around" .. .. 65 70
1016 33 c. "The boss of the board" .. .. 65 70
1017 33 c. "The tar-boy is there" .. .. 65 70
1018 33 c. "Shearing is all over" .. .. 65 70
1014/18 .. .. .. .. *Set of* 5 3·00 3·25

Nos. 1014/18 were printed together, *se-tenant*, in horizontal strips of 5 throughout the sheet, forming a composite design.

(Des D. Lancashire. Litho Cambec Press, Melbourne)

**1986** (6 Aug). *Bicentenary of Australian Settlement* (1988) (*5th issue*). *Convict Settlement in New South Wales. T* **425** *and similar horiz designs. Multicoloured. P* 13.
1019 33 c. Type **425** .. .. .. .. 70 40
1020 33 c. "Lord Sydney" (Gilbert Stuart) and convicts .. .. .. .. 70 40
1021 33 c. "Captain Arthur Phillip" (F. Wheatley) and ship .. .. .. .. 70 40
1022 $1 "Captain John Hunter" (W. B. Bennett) and aborigines .. .. 2·75 2·75
1019/22 .. .. .. .. *Set of* 4 4·25 3·50

426 Red Kangaroo

427 Royal Bluebell

428 Pink Enamel Orchid

(Des D. Higgins. Litho Leigh-Mardon Ltd, Melbourne)

**1986** (13 Aug). *Australian Wildlife* (*1st series*). *T* **426** *and similar vert designs. Multicoloured. P* 14½ × 14.
1023 36 c. Type **426** .. .. .. .. 55 55
a. Horiz strip of 5. Nos. 1023/7 .. 2·50
1024 36 c. Emu .. .. .. .. 55 55
1025 36 c. Koala .. .. .. .. 55 55
1026 36 c. Laughing Kookaburra .. .. 55 55
1027 36 c. Platypus .. .. .. .. 55 55
1023/7 .. .. .. .. *Set of* 5 2·50 2·50

Nos. 1023/7 were printed together, *se-tenant*, in horizontal strips of 5 throughout the sheet.

For 37 c. values see Nos. 1072/6.

(Des Betty Conabere. Litho Mercury-Walch Pty, Hobart)

**1986** (25 Aug). *Booklet stamps. Alpine Wildflowers. T* **427** *and similar vert designs. Multicoloured. Roul.*
1028 3 c. Type **427** .. .. .. .. 25 25
a. Booklet pane. Nos. 1028, 1029 and 1031 × 2 .. .. .. .. 1·90
b. Booklet pane. Nos. 1028, 1030 and 1031 × 2 .. .. .. .. 1·90
1029 5 c. Alpine Marsh Marigold .. .. 80 1·00
1030 25 c. Mount Buffalo Sunray .. .. 80 1·00
1031 36 c. Silver Snow Daisy .. .. .. 50 30
1028/31 .. .. .. .. *Set of* 4 2·10 2·25

Nos. 1028/31 only exist from 80 c. (pane No. 1028a) and $1 (pane No. 1028b) stamp booklets. The outer edges of the booklet panes are imperforate.

(Des O. Schmidinger and Christine Stead. Litho Leigh-Mardon Ltd, Melbourne)

**1986** (18 Sept). *Native Australian Orchids. T* **428** *and similar vert designs. Multicoloured. P* 14½.
1032 36 c. Type **428** .. .. .. .. 70 20
1033 55 c. *Dendrobium nindii* .. .. .. 1·25 1·00
1034 90 c. Duck Orchid .. .. .. .. 1·90 2·00
1035 $1 Queen of Sheba Orchid .. .. 2·00 2·00
1032/5 .. .. .. .. *Set of* 4 5·25 4·75

429 *Australia II* crossing Finishing Line

430 Dove with Olive Branch and Sun

(Des J. Passmore and G. Rowan. Litho Cambec Press, Melbourne)

**1986** (26 Sept). *Australian Victory in America's Cup*, 1983. *T* **429** *and similar vert designs. Multicoloured. P* 14 × 13½.
1036 36 c. Type **429** .. .. .. .. 65 55
1037 36 c. Boxing kangaroo flag of winning syndicate .. .. .. .. 65 55
a. Grey (inscr and face value) omitted .. £110
1038 36 c. America's Cup trophy .. .. .. 65 55
a. Grey (inscr and face value) omitted .. £120
1036/8 .. .. .. .. *Set of* 3 1·75 1·50

(Des K. Cato. Litho Cambec Press, Melbourne)

**1986** (22 Oct). *International Peace Year. P* 14 × 13½.
1039 **430** 36 c. multicoloured .. .. .. 65 35

Examples with the gutter margin overprinted to commemorate the Papal visit in November 1986 were not produced by the Australian Post Office.

431 Mary and Joseph

432 Australian Flag on Printed Circuit Board

(Des B. Clinton. Litho Leigh-Mardon Ltd, Melbourne)

**1986** (3 Nov–Dec). *Christmas. T* **431** *and similar multicoloured designs showing scenes from children's nativity play. P* 14½.
1040 30 c. Type **431** .. .. .. .. 40 30
a. Perf 14 × 13½ (12.86) .. .. .. 30 30
1041 36 c. Three Wise Men leaving gifts .. 50 45
1042 60 c. Angels (*horiz*) .. .. .. .. 90 1·50
1040/2 .. .. .. .. *Set of* 3 1·60 2·00
**MS**1043 147 × 70 mm. 30 c. Three angels and shepherd (*horiz*); 30 c. Kneeling shepherds (*horiz*); 30 c. Mary, Joseph and three angels; 30 c. Innkeeper and two angels; 30 c. Three Wise Men (*horiz*) .. .. .. .. .. 1·90 2·25

No. 1040a was printed by Cambec Press after stocks of the original printing by Leigh-Mardon Ltd ran short. It is believed that this Cambec Press printing was distributed in New South Wales, Tasmania, Victoria and Western Australia.

(Des J. Passmore. Litho CPE Australia Ltd, Melbourne)

**1987** (23 Jan). *Australia Day. T* **432** *and similar horiz design. Multicoloured. P* 13½ × 14.
1044 36 c. Type **432** .. .. .. .. 35 35
1045 36 c. "Australian Made" Campaign logos .. 35 35

433 Aerial View of Yacht

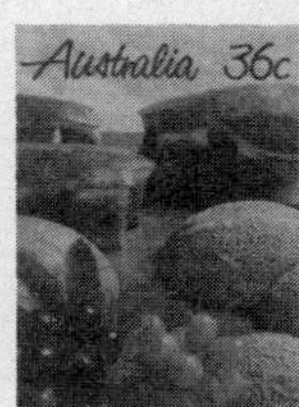

434 Grapes and Melons

(Des O. Schmidinger and Christine Stead. Litho Leigh-Mardon Ltd, Melbourne)

**1987** (28 Jan). *America's Cup Yachting Championship. T* **433** *and similar vert designs. Multicoloured. P* 14½.
1046 36 c. Type **433** .. .. .. .. 40 20
1047 55 c. Two yachts tacking .. .. .. 80 90
1048 90 c. Two yachts turning .. .. .. 1·25 1·40
1049 $1 Two yachts under full sail .. .. 1·40 1·50
1046/9 .. .. .. .. *Set of* 4 3·50 3·50

(Des Susan Tilley. Litho CPE Australia Ltd, Melbourne)

**1987** (11 Feb). *Australian Fruit. T* **434** *and similar vert designs. Multicoloured. P* 14 × 13½.
1050 36 c. Type **434** .. .. .. .. 40 20
1051 65 c. Tropical and sub-tropical fruits .. 85 1·00
1052 90 c. Citrus fruit, apples and pears .. 1·25 1·40
1053 $1 Stone and berry fruits .. .. 1·40 1·60
1050/3 .. .. .. .. *Set of* 4 3·50 3·75

435 Livestock

436 Queen Elizabeth in Australia, 1986

(Des D. Lancashire. Litho CPE Australia Ltd, Melbourne)

**1987** (10 Apr). *Agricultural Shows. T* **435** *and similar vert designs. Multicoloured. P* 14 × 13½.

1054 36 c. Type **435** .. .. .. .. .. 60 20
1055 65 c. Produce .. .. .. .. .. 1·25 1·40
1056 90 c. Sideshows .. .. .. .. .. 1·75 2·00
1057 $1 Competitions .. .. .. .. .. 1·90 2·00
1054/7 .. .. .. .. *Set of* 4 5·00 5·00

(Des Janet Boschen. Litho CPE Australia Ltd, Melbourne)

**1987** (21 Apr). *Queen Elizabeth II's Birthday. P* 13½ × 14.

1058 **436** 36 c. multicoloured .. .. .. 50 40

**437** Convicts on Quay

**438** "At the Station"

(Des Sue Passmore. Litho CPE Australia Ltd, Melbourne)

**1987** (13 May). *Bicentenary of Australian Settlement* (1988) (*6th issue*). *Departure of the First Fleet. T* **437** *and similar square designs. Multicoloured. P* 13.

1059 36 c. Type **437** .. .. .. .. 65 70
a. Horiz strip of 5. Nos. 1059/63 .. 3·00
1060 36 c. Royal Marines officer and wife .. 65 70
1061 36 c. Sailors loading supplies .. .. 65 70
1062 36 c. Officers being ferried to ships .. 65 70
1063 36 c. Fleet in English Channel .. .. 65 70
1059/63 .. .. .. .. *Set of* 5 3·00 3·25

Nos. 1059/63 were printed together, *se-tenant*, in horizontal strips of 5 throughout the sheet.

See also Nos. 1064/6, 1077/81, 1090/2 and 1105/9.

(Des Sue Passmore. Litho CPE Australia Ltd, Melbourne)

**1987** (3 June). *Bicentenary of Australian Settlement* (1988) (*7th issue*). *First Fleet at Tenerife. Square designs as T* **437**. *Multicoloured. P* 13.

1064 36 c. Ferrying supplies, Santa Cruz .. 50 65
a. Horiz pair. Nos. 1064/5 .. .. 1·00 1·25
1065 36 c. Canary Islands fishermen and departing fleet .. .. .. .. 50 65
1066 $1 Fleet arriving at Tenerife (Optd S. 50p) .. .. .. .. .. 1·25 1·40
1064/6 .. .. .. .. *Set of* 3 2·00 2·40

Nos. 1064/5 were printed together, *se-tenant*, in horizontal pairs throughout the sheet, forming a composite design.

(Des C. Lee. Litho CPE Australia Ltd, Melbourne)

**1987** (24 June). *Folklore. Scenes and Verses from Poem "The Man from Snowy River". T* **438** *and similar vert designs. Multicoloured. P* 14 × 13½.

1067 36 c. Type **438** .. .. .. .. 65 70
a. Horiz strip of 5. Nos. 1067/71 .. 3·00
1068 36 c. "Mountain bred" .. .. .. 65 70
1069 36 c. "That terrible descent" .. .. 65 70
1070 36 c. "At their heels" .. .. .. 65 70
1071 36 c. "Brought them back" .. .. .. 65 70
1067/71 .. .. .. .. *Set of* 5 3·00 3·25

Nos. 1067/71 were printed together, *se-tenant*, in horizontal strips of five throughout the sheet, forming a composite background design of mountain scenery.

(Des D. Higgins. Litho Leigh-Mardon Ltd, Melbourne)

**1987** (1 July). *Australian Wildlife* (*2nd series*). *Vert designs as T* **426**. *Multicoloured. P* 14½ × 14.

1072 37 c. Common Brushtail Possum .. .. 50 50
a. Horiz strip of 5. Nos. 1072/6 .. .. 2·25
1073 37 c. Sulphur-crested Cockatoo .. .. 50 50
1074 37 c. Common Wombat .. .. .. 50 50
1075 37 c. Crimson Rosella .. .. .. 50 50
1076 37 c. Echidna .. .. .. .. 50 50
1072/6 .. .. .. .. *Set of* 5 2·25 2·25

Nos. 1072/6 were printed together, *se-tenant*, in horizontal strips of 5 throughout the sheet.

(Des Sue Passmore. Litho CPE Australia Ltd, Melbourne)

**1987** (6 Aug). *Bicentenary of Australian Settlement* (1988) (*8th issue*). *First Fleet at Rio de Janeiro. Square designs as T* **437**. *Multicoloured. P* 13.

1077 37 c. Sperm Whale and fleet .. .. 60 70
a. Horiz strip of 5. Nos. 1077/81 .. 2·75
1078 37 c. Brazilian coast.. .. .. .. 60 70
1079 37 c. British officers in market .. .. 60 70
1080 37 c. Religious procession .. .. .. 60 70
1081 37 c. Fleet leaving Rio .. .. .. 60 70
1077/81 .. .. .. .. *Set of* 5 2·75 3·25

Nos. 1077/81 were printed together, *se-tenant*, in horizontal strips of 5, forming a composite design.

**439** Bionic Ear

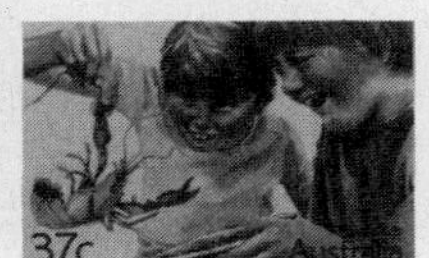

**440** Catching Crayfish

(Des. O. Schmidinger and Christine Stead. Litho Leigh-Mardon Ltd, Melbourne)

**1987** (19 Aug). *Australian Achievements in Technology. T* **439** *and similar vert designs. Multicoloured. P* 14½.

1082 37 c. Type **439** .. .. .. .. 40 35
1083 53 c. Microchips .. .. .. .. 65 60
1084 63 c. Robotics .. .. .. .. 75 70
1085 68 c. Ceramics .. .. .. .. 80 75
1082/5 .. .. .. .. *Set of* 4 2·40 2·25

(Des Elizabeth Honey. Litho Leigh-Mardon Ltd, Melbourne)

**1987** (16 Sept). *"Aussie Kids". T* **440** *and similar horiz designs. Multicoloured. P* 14½.

1086 37 c. Type **440** .. .. .. .. 35 35
1087 55 c. Playing cat's cradle .. .. .. 65 65
1088 90 c. Young football supporters .. .. 95 95
1089 $1 Children with kangaroo (Optd S. 50p) .. .. .. .. .. 1·10 1·10
1086/9 .. .. .. .. *Set of* 4 2·75 2·75

(Des Sue Passmore. Litho CPE Australia Ltd, Melbourne)

**1987** (13 Oct). *Bicentenary of Australian Settlement* (1988) (*9th issue*). *First Fleet at Cape of Good Hope. Square designs as T* **437**. *Multicoloured. P* 13.

1090 37 c. Marine checking list of livestock .. 50 50
a. Horiz pair. Nos. 1090/1 .. .. 1·00 1·00
1091 37 c. Loading livestock .. .. .. 50 50
1092 $1 First Fleet at Cape Town (Optd S. 50p) .. .. .. .. .. 1·25 1·25
1090/2 .. .. .. .. *Set of* 3 2·00 2·00

Nos. 1090/1 were printed together, *se-tenant*, in horizontal and vertical pairs throughout the sheet, the former showing a composite design.

**441** Detail of Spearthrower, Western Australia

**442** Grandmother and Granddaughters with Candles

(Des J. Passmore. Litho Leigh-Mardon Ltd, Melbourne)

**1987** (13 Oct). *Booklet stamps. Aboriginal Crafts. T* **441** *and similar horiz designs. Multicoloured. P* 15½ × *imperf.*

1093 3 c. Type **441** .. .. .. .. 80 1·00
a. Booklet pane. Nos. 1093 and 1095, each × 2 .. .. .. .. 3·00
1094 15 c. Shield pattern, New South Wales .. 1·00 1·40
a. Booklet pane. Nos. 1094, 1096 × 3 and 1097 × 2 .. .. .. .. 4·50
1095 37 c. Basket weave, Queensland .. .. 80 1·00
1096 37 c. Bowl design, Central Australia .. 80 1·00
1097 37 c. Belt pattern, Northern Territory .. 80 1·00
1093/7 .. .. .. .. *Set of* 5 3·75 5·00

Nos. 1093/7 only exist from 80 c. (pane No. 1093a) and $2 (pane No. 1094a) stamp booklets. The vertical edges of the booklet panes are imperforate.

(Des B. Clinton. Litho Leigh-Mardon Ltd, Melbourne (30 c.) or CPE Australia Ltd, Melbourne (37 c., 63 c.))

**1987** (2 Nov). *Christmas. T* **442** *and similar multicoloured designs showing carol singing by candlelight. P* 14½ (30 c.) *or* 13½ × 14 (37 c., 63 c.).

1098 30 c. Type **442** .. .. .. .. 40 40
a. Horiz strip of 5. Nos. 1098/102 .. 1·75
1099 30 c. Father and daughters.. .. .. 40 40
1100 30 c. Four children .. .. .. .. 40 40
1101 30 c. Family .. .. .. .. .. 40 40
1102 30 c. Six teenagers .. .. .. .. 40 40
1103 37 c. Choir (*horiz*) .. .. .. .. 45 45
1104 63 c. Father and two children (*horiz*) .. 75 75
1098/104 .. .. .. .. *Set of* 7 2·75 2·75

Nos. 1098/1102 were printed together, *se-tenant*, in horizontal strips of five throughout the sheet.

(Des Sue Passmore. Litho CPE Australia Ltd, Melbourne)

**1988** (26 Jan). *Bicentenary of Australian Settlement* (*10th issue*). *Arrival of First Fleet. Square designs as T* **437**. *Multicoloured. P* 13.

1105 37 c. Aborigines watching arrival of Fleet, Botany Bay .. .. .. .. 60 60
a. Horiz strip of 5. Nos. 1105/9 .. .. 2·75
1106 37 c. Aborigine family and anchored ships 60 60
1107 37 c. Fleet arriving at Sydney Cove .. 60 60
1108 37 c. Ship's boat .. .. .. .. 60 60
1109 37 c. Raising the flag, Sydney Cove, 26 January 1788 .. .. .. .. 60 60
1105/9 .. .. .. .. *Set of* 5 2·75 2·75

Nos. 1105/9 were printed together, *se-tenant*, in horizontal strips of five throughout the sheet, forming a composite design.

**443** Koala with Stockman's Hat and Eagle dressed as Uncle Sam

**444** "Religion" (A. Horner)

(Des R. Harvey. Litho CPE Australia Ltd, Melbourne)

**1988** (26 Jan). *Bicentenary of Australian Settlement* (*11th issue*). *Joint issue with U.S.A. P* 13.

1110 **443** 37 c. multicoloured .. .. .. 60 35

(Litho Leigh-Mardon Ltd, Melbourne (4, 5, 20, 25, 30, 37, 39, 40, 50, 53, 70, 80, 90 c., $1) or CPE Australia Ltd, Melbourne (others))

**1988** (17 Feb–28 Sept). *"Living Together". T* **444** *and similar square designs showing cartoons. Multicoloured* (*except* 30 c.). *P* 14.

1111 1 c. Type **444** (16.3) .. .. .. 10 10
1112 2 c. "Industry" (P. Nicholson) (16.3) .. 10 10
1113 3 c. "Local Government" (A. Collette) (16.3) .. .. .. .. .. 10 10
1114 4 c. "Trade Unions" (Liz Honey) .. .. 10 10
1115 5 c. "Parliament" (Bronwyn Halls) (16.3) 15 10
1116 10 c. "Transport" (Meg Williams) .. .. 15 10
1117 15 c. "Sport" (G. Cook) .. .. .. 15 20
1118 20 c. "Commerce" (M. Atcherson) .. .. 35 20
1119 25 c. "Housing" (C. Smith) .. .. .. 25 30
1120 30 c. "Welfare" (R. Tandberg) (black and pale rose-lilac) (16.3) .. .. .. 30 35
1121 37 c. "Postal Services" (P. Viska) .. .. 35 40
a. Booklet pane. No. 1121 × 10 (1.7.) .. 3·50
1121*b* 39 c. "Tourism" (J. Spooner) (28.9) .. 55 50
ba. Booklet pane. No. 1121*b* × 10 .. 5·50
1122 40 c. "Recreation" (R. Harvey) (16.3) .. 35 40
1123 45 c. "Health" (Jenny Coopes) .. .. 40 45
1124 50 c. "Mining" (G. Haddon) .. .. 45 50
1125 53 c. "Primary Industry" (S. Leahy) .. 75 70
1126 55 c. "Education" (Victoria Roberts) (16.3) 75 55
1127 60 c. "Armed Forces" (B. Green) (16.3) .. 55 60
1128 63 c. "Police" (J. Russell) (16.3) .. .. 1·25 75
1129 65 c. "Telecommunications" (B. Petty) (16.3) .. .. .. .. .. 85 75
1130 68 c. "The Media" (A. Langoulant) (16.3) 1·25 75
1131 70 c. "Science and Technology" (J. Hook).. 1·25 90
1132 75 c. "Visual Arts" (G. Dazeley) (16.3) .. 1·00 80
1133 80 c. "Performing Arts" (A. Stitt) .. .. 1·00 80
1134 90 c. "Banking" (S. Billington) .. .. 1·10 90
1135 95 c. "Law" (C. Aslanis) (16.3) .. .. 85 90
1136 $1 "Rescue and Emergency" (M. Leunig) (Optd S. 50p.) .. .. .. 1·10 90
1111/36 .. .. .. .. *Set of* 27 14·00 11·50

Although Leigh-Mardon printed the 37 c. and 39 c. sheet stamps, and some of the 37 c. booklets, Nos. 1121a and 1121ba were produced by CPE with the upper and lower edges of the panes imperforate, so that stamps from them exist imperforate at top or bottom. These panes also show margins at both right and left.

Early in 1989 Leigh-Mardon Ltd, whose works were situated at Moorabbin, took over C.P.E. Australia Ltd of Scoresby. Printings of the 15, 30, 40, 45, 60, 70, 75 and 80 c. were made at both printing works.

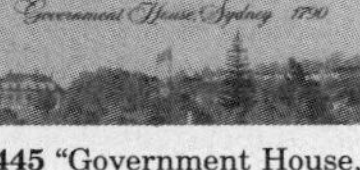

**445** "Government House, Sydney, 1790" (George Raper)

**446** Queen Elizabeth II (from photo by Tim Graham)

(Des J. Passmore. Litho CPE Australia Ltd, Melbourne)

**1988** (13 Apr). *Bicentenary of Australian Settlement* (*12th issue*). *"The Early Years, 1788–1809". T* **445** *and similar square designs showing paintings. Multicoloured. P* 13.

1137 37 c. Type **445** .. .. .. .. 50 50
a. Horiz strip of 5. Nos. 1137/41 .. 2·25
1138 37 c. "Government Farm, Parramatta, 1791" ("The Port Jackson Painter") .. 50 50
1139 37 c. "Parramatta Road, 1796" (attr Thomas Watling) .. .. .. 50 50
1140 37 c. "View of Sydney Cove, c. 1800" (detail) (Edward Dayes) .. .. .. 50 50
1141 37 c. "Sydney Hospital, 1803", (detail) (George William Evans) .. .. 50 50
1137/41 .. .. .. .. *Set of* 5 2·25 2·25

Nos. 1137/41 were printed together, *se-tenant*, in horizontal strips of 5 throughout the sheet, each strip forming a composite background design from the painting, "View of Sydney from the East Side of the Cove, *c.* 1808" by John Eyre.

(Des Sandra Baker. Litho Leigh-Mardon Ltd, Melbourne)

**1988** (21 Apr). *Queen Elizabeth II's Birthday. P* 14½.

1142 **446** 37 c. multicoloured .. .. .. 45 40

**447** Expo '88 Logo

**448** New Parliament House

(Des G. Emery. Litho CPE Australia Ltd, Melbourne)

**1988** (29 Apr). *"Expo '88" World Fair, Brisbane. P* 13.

1143 **447** 37 c. multicoloured .. .. .. 35 40

(Des B. Sadgrove. Litho Leigh-Mardon Ltd, Melbourne)

**1988** (9 May). *Opening of New Parliament House, Canberra. P* 14½.
1144 **448** 37 c. multicoloured .. .. .. .. 35 40

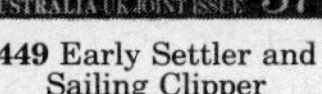

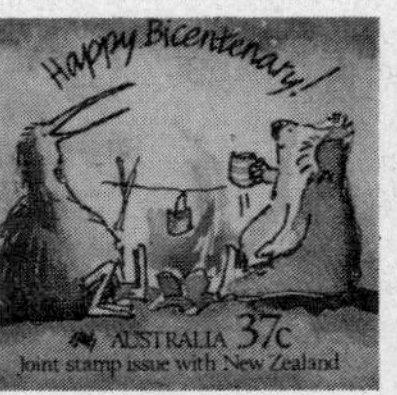


**449** Early Settler and Sailing Clipper
**450** Kiwi and Koala at Campfire

(Des G. Emery. Litho CPE Australia Ltd, Melbourne)

**1988** (21 June). *Bicentenary of Australian Settlement (13th issue). T* **449** *and similar square designs. Multicoloured. P* 13.
1145 37 c. Type **449** .. .. .. .. .. 65 70
a. Pair. Nos. 1145/6 .. .. .. .. 1·25 1·40
1146 37 c. Queen Elizabeth II with British and Australian Parliament Buildings .. 65 70
1147 $1 W. G. Grace (cricketer) and tennis racquet .. .. .. .. 1·75 1·90
a. Pair. Nos. 1147/8 .. .. .. .. 3·50 3·75
1148 $1 Shakespeare, John Lennon (entertainer) and Sydney Opera House .. 1·75 1·90
1145/8 .. .. .. .. .. *Set of* 4 4·25 4·50

Nos. 1145/6 and 1147/8 were printed together, *se-tenant*, in horizontal and vertical pairs throughout the sheets, each horizontal pair showing a background design of the Australian flag.

Stamps in similar designs were also issued by Great Britain.

(Des R. Harvey. Litho Leigh-Mardon Ltd, Melbourne)

**1988** (21 June). *Bicentenary of Australian Settlement (14th issue). P* 14½.
1149 **450** 37 c. multicoloured .. .. .. .. 65 40

A stamp in a similar design was also issued by New Zealand.

**451** "Bush Potato Country" (Turkey Tolsen Tjupurrula and David Corby Tjapaltjarri)
**452** Basketball

(Des Janet Boschen. Litho CPE Australia Ltd, Melbourne)

**1988** (1 Aug). *Art of the Desert. Aboriginal Paintings from Central Australia. T* **451** *and similar square designs. Multicoloured. P* 13.
1150 37 c. Type **451** .. .. .. .. 35 40
1151 55 c. "Courtship Rejected" (Limpi Puntungka Tjapangati) .. .. 55 60
1152 90 c. "Medicine Story" (artist unknown) .. 90 1·10
1153 $1 "Ancestor Dreaming" (Tim Leura Tjapaltjarri) .. .. .. .. 95 1·25
1150/3 .. .. .. .. .. *Set of* 4 2·50 3·00

(Des Sue Passmore. Litho Leigh-Mardon Ltd, Melbourne)

**1988** (14 Sept). *Olympic Games, Seoul. T* **452** *and similar horiz designs. Multicoloured. P* 14½.
1154 37 c. Type **452** .. .. .. .. 35 40
1155 65 c. Athlete crossing finish line .. .. 60 65
1156 $1 Gymnast with hoop .. .. .. 95 1·00
1154/6 .. .. .. .. .. *Set of* 3 1·75 1·90

**453** Rod and Mace

(Des K. Christos. Litho Leigh-Mardon Ltd, Melbourne)

**1988** (19 Sept). *34th Commonwealth Parliamentary Conference, Canberra. P* 14½.
1157 **453** 37 c. multicoloured .. .. .. 50 60

**454** Necklace by Peter Tully

(Des K. Christos. Litho Mercury-Walch Pty, Hobart)

**1988** (28 Sept). *Booklet stamps. Australian Crafts. T* **454** *and similar horiz designs. Multicoloured. Roul × imperf.*
1158 2 c. Type **454** .. .. .. .. 50 75
a. Booklet pane. Nos. 1158 and 1160 × 2 1·10
1159 5 c. Vase by Colin Levy .. .. .. 50 75
a. Booklet pane. Nos. 1159 and 1160 × 5 2·25
1160 39 c. Teapot by Frank Bauer .. .. 40 35
1158/60 .. .. .. .. *Set of* 3 1·10 1·60

Nos. 1158/60 only exist from 80 c. (pane No. 1158a) and $2 (pane No. 1159a) stamp booklets. The vertical edges of the booklet panes are imperforate.

**455** Pinnacles Desert
**456** "The Nativity" (Danielle Hush)

(Des K. Christos. Litho CPE Australia Ltd, Melbourne)

**1988** (17 Oct). *Panorama of Australia. T* **455** *and similar horiz designs. Multicoloured. P* 13.
1161 39 c. Type **455** .. .. .. .. 40 40
1162 55 c. Flooded landscape, Arnhem Land .. 55 55
1163 65 c. Twelve Apostles, Victoria .. .. 65 65
1164 70 c. Mountain Ash wood .. .. .. 70 70
1161/4 .. .. .. .. *Set of* 4 2·10 2·10

(Des Sandra Baker. Litho CPE Australia Ltd, Melbourne (32, 39 c.) or Leigh-Mardon Ltd, Melbourne (63 c.))

**1988** (31 Oct). *Christmas. T* **456** *and similar square designs. Multicoloured. P* 14½ *(63 c.) or* 13 *(others).*
1165 32 c. Type **456** .. .. .. .. 30 35
1166 39 c. "Koala as Father Christmas" (Kylie Courtney) .. .. .. .. 35 40
1167 63 c. "Christmas Cockatoo" (Benjamin Stevenson) .. .. .. .. 60 65
1165/7 .. .. .. .. *Set of* 3 1·10 1·25

**PRINTERS.** Early in 1989 Leigh-Mardon Ltd took over CPE Australia Ltd. Stamp printing continued at both the Moorabbin (original Leigh-Mardon) and Scoresby (ex-CPE) works with some stamps being printed at one and then perforated at the other.

**457** Sir Henry Parkes
**458** Bowls

(Des R. Bevers. Litho CPE Australia Ltd, Melbourne)

**1989** (25 Jan). *Australia Day. Centenary of Federation Speech by Sir Henry Parkes (N.S.W. Prime Minister). P* 14 × 13½.
1168 **457** 39 c. multicoloured .. .. .. 35 40

(Des Sue Passmore (5, 10, 20, 41, 43, 65 c., $1, $1.20), N. Stapleton (75, 80, 85, 90 c.), G. Cook (others). Litho Leigh-Mardon Ltd, Melbourne)

**1989** (13 Feb)–**91**. *Sports. T* **458** *and similar horiz designs. Multicoloured. P* 13½ *(5, 10, 20, 65 c., $1.20) or* 14 × 14½ *(others).*
1169 1 c. Type **458** .. .. .. .. .. 10 10
a. Perf 13½ (3.90) .. .. .. .. 10 10
1170 2 c. Tenpin-bowling .. .. .. .. 10 10
a. Perf 13½ (9.89) .. .. .. .. 10 10
1171 3 c. Australian football .. .. .. 10 10
1172 5 c. Kayaking and canoeing (17.1.90) .. 10 10
1174 10 c. Sailboarding (17.1.90) .. .. .. 10 15
1176 20 c. Tennis (17.1.90) .. .. .. .. 20 25
1179 39 c. Fishing .. .. .. .. .. 55 55
a. Booklet pane. No. 1179×10 .. .. 5·50
b. Perf 13½ (7.89) .. .. .. .. 1·00 1·00
1180 41 c. Cycling (23.8.89) .. .. .. 40 35
a. Booklet pane. No. 1180×10 .. .. 4·00
1181 43 c. Skateboarding (27.8.90) .. .. 40 45
a. Booklet pane. No. 1181×10 .. .. 4·00
1184 55 c. Kite-flying .. .. .. .. 50 55
1186 65 c. Rock-climbing (17.1.90) .. .. 60 65
1187 70 c. Cricket .. .. .. .. .. 65 70
1188 75 c. Netball (22.8.91) .. .. .. 70 75
1189 80 c. Squash (22.8.91) .. .. .. 75 80
1190 85 c. Diving (22.8.91) .. .. .. 80 85
1191 90 c. Soccer (22.8.91) .. .. .. 85 90
1192 $1 Fun-run (17.1.90) .. .. .. 90 1·00
a. Perf 13½ (6.91) .. .. .. .. 90 1·00
1193 $1.10, Golf .. .. .. .. .. 1·00 1·10
1194 $1.20, Hang-gliding (27.8.90) .. .. 1·10 1·25
1169/94 .. .. .. .. *Set of* 19 8·50 9·25
1192/4 Optd "Specimen" .. .. *Set of* 3 1·75

The booklet panes have the upper and lower edges imperforate, so that the stamps from them are imperforate at top or bottom, and have margins at both left and right. These were printed at the Moorabbin works and the sheet stamps at Scoresby.

Nos. 1169a, 1170a, 1179a and 1192a are Scoresby printings of values originally produced at Moorabbin.

For self-adhesive versions of Nos. 1180/1 see Nos. 1259/60*a*.

**WARNING.** The coating on a batch of paper used during 1989-90 was defective so that stamps lose parts of their design if immersed in water.

**459** Merino

(Des K. McEwan. Litho CPE Australia Ltd, Melbourne)

**1989** (27 Feb). *Sheep in Australia. T* **459** *and similar horiz designs. Multicoloured. P* 13½ × 14.
1195 39 c. Type **459** .. .. .. .. 45 40
1196 39 c. Poll Dorset .. .. .. .. 45 40
1197 85 c. Polwarth .. .. .. .. 80 85
1198 $1 Corriedale (Optd S. 70p.) .. .. 95 1·00
1195/8 .. .. .. .. *Set of* 4 2·40 2·40

**460** Adelaide Botanic Garden

(Des J. Passmore. Eng B. Stewart. Litho Leigh-Mardon Ltd and die-stamped Avon Graphics, both of Melbourne ($20), litho CPE Australia Ltd, Melbourne, and recess Note Ptg Branch, Reserve Bank of Australia (others))

**1989** (12 Apr)–**90**. *Botanic Gardens. T* **460** *and similar horiz designs. Multicoloured. P* 14 *($2 to $10) or* 14½×14 *($20).*
1199 $2 Nooroo, New South Wales (13.9.89) 1·90 2·00
a. Perf 13½ .. .. .. .. 2·25 2·00
1200 $5 Mawarra, Victoria (13.9.89) .. 4·50 4·75
a. Perf 13½ .. .. .. .. 6·00 4·75
1201 $10 Type **460** .. .. .. .. 9·25 9·50
1201*a* $20 "A View of the Artist's House and Garden in Mills Plains, Van Diemen's Land" (John Glover) (15.8.90) .. .. .. .. 18·00 19·00
1199/1201*a* .. .. .. *Set of* 4 29·00 30·00

**461** "Queen Elizabeth II" (sculpture, John Dowie)
**462** Arrival of Immigrant Ship, 1830's

(Des Sandra Baker. Litho Leigh-Mardon Ltd, Melbourne)

**1989** (21 Apr). *Queen Elizabeth II's Birthday. P* 14½.
1202 **461** 39 c. multicoloured .. .. .. 35 40

(Des D. Lancashire. Litho Leigh-Mardon Ltd, Melbourne)

**1989** (10 May). *Colonial Development (1st issue). Pastoral Era 1810–1850. T* **462** *and similar square designs. Multicoloured. P* 14½.
1203 39 c. Type **462** .. .. .. .. 40 40
a. Horiz strip of 5. Nos. 1203/7 .. .. 1·75
1204 39 c. Pioneer cottage and wool dray .. 40 40
1205 39 c. Squatter's homestead .. .. 40 40
1206 39 c. Shepherd with flock (from Joseph Lycett's "Views of Australia") .. 40 40
1207 39 c. Explorer in desert (after watercolour by Edward Frome) .. .. 40 40
1203/7 .. .. .. .. *Set of* 5 1·75 1·75

Nos. 1203/7 were printed together, *se-tenant*, in horizontal strips of five throughout the sheet.

See also Nos 1254/8 and 1264/8.

**463** Gladys Moncrieff and Roy Rene
**464** "Impression" (Tom Roberts)

(Des Sue Passmore. Litho Leigh-Mardon Ltd, Melbourne)

**1989** (12 July). *Australian Stage and Screen Personalities. T* **463** *and similar vert designs. Multicoloured. P* 14½.

1208 39 c. Type **463** . . . . . . . . 35 40
a. Perf 14 × 13½ . . . . . . . . 3·50 3·75
1209 85 c. Charles Chauvel and Chips Rafferty 80 85
1210 $1 Nellie Stewart and J. C. Williamson . . 95 1·00
1211 $1.10, Lottie Lyell and Raymond Longford . . . . . . . . 1·00 1·10
1208/11 . . . . . . . . *Set of* 4 2·75 3·00
1210/11 Optd "Specimen" . . . . *Set of* 2 1·40

No. 1208a was from a small first printing produced at the Scoresby (ex C.P.E.) plant and used in presentation packs or on first day covers. The rest of the 39 c. printing was perforated at the Moorabbin works.

(Des K. Christos. Litho Leigh-Mardon Ltd, Melbourne)

**1989** (23 Aug). *Australian Impressionist Paintings. T* **464** *and similar multicoloured designs. P* 14 × 13½ (*No.* 1214) *or* 13½ × 14 (*others*).

1212 41 c. Type **464** . . . . . . . . 40 45
1213 41 c. "Impression for Golden Summer" (Sir Arthur Streeton) . . . . . . 40 45
1214 41 c. "All on a Summer's Day" (Charles Conder) (*vert*) . . . . . . 40 45
1215 41 c. "Petit Déjeuner" (Frederick McCubbin) . . . . . . . . 40 45
1212/15 . . . . . . . . *Set of* 4 1·40 1·60

**465** Freeways

(Des Sally Newell and Carolyn Limonta. Litho Leigh-Mardon Ltd, Melbourne)

**1989** (1 Sept). *Booklet stamps. The Urban Environment. T* **465** *and similar horiz designs. P* 15½×*imperf*.

1216 41 c. black, maroon and blue-green . . 60 65
a. Booklet pane. Nos. 1216×2, 1217×3 and 1218×2 . . . . . . . . 3·75
1217 41 c. black, maroon and magenta . . 60 65
1218 41 c. black, maroon and bright blue . . 60 65
1216/18 . . . . . . . . *Set of* 3 1·60 1·75

Designs:—No. 1217, City buildings, Melbourne; No. 1218, Commuter train at platform.

Nos. 1216/18 only exist from $3 stamp booklets in which the vertical edges of the pane are imperforate.

**466** Hikers outside Youth Hostel

**467** Horse Tram, Adelaide, 1878

(Des Priscilla Cutter. Litho Leigh-Mardon Ltd, Melbourne)

**1989** (13 Sept). *50th Anniv of Australian Youth Hostels. P* 14½.

1219 **466** 41 c. multicoloured . . . . . . 45 45

(Des I. McKellar. Litho Leigh-Mardon Ltd, Melbourne)

**1989** (11 Oct). *Historic Trams. T* **467** *and similar horiz designs. Multicoloured. P* 13½×14.

1220 41 c. Type **467** . . . . . . . . 50 50
1221 41 c. Steam tram, Sydney, 1884 . . . . 50 50
1222 41 c. Cable tram, Melbourne, 1886 . . 50 50
a. Perf 14½ . . . . . . . . 1·00 1·00
ab. Booklet pane. No. 1222a×10 . . 10·00
1223 41 c. Double-deck electric tram, Hobart, 1893 . . . . . . . . 50 50
1224 41 c. Combination electric tram, Brisbane, 1901 . . . . . . . . 50 50
1220/4 . . . . . . . . *Set of* 5 2·25 2·25

The upper and lower edges of booklet pane No. 1222ab are imperforate. It was printed and perforated at the Moorabbin plant.

**468** "Annunciation" (15th-century Book of Hours)

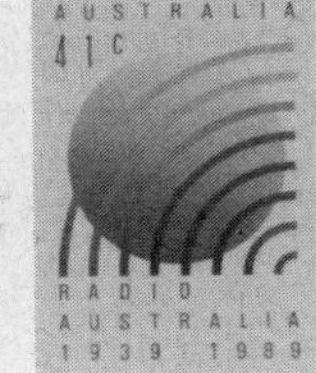


**469** Radio Waves and Globe

(Des Lynette Brown. Litho Leigh-Mardon Ltd, Melbourne)

**1989** (1 Nov). *Christmas. Illuminated Manuscripts. T* **468** *and similar vert designs. Multicoloured. P* 14×13½ (36 *c.*) *or* 14½ (*others*).

1225 36 c. Type **468** . . . . . . . . 35 40
a. Booklet pane. No. 1225×10 . . . . 3·50
1226 41 c. "Annunciation to the Shepherds" (Wharncliffe Book of Hours, c. 1475) 45 45
1227 80 c. "Adoration of the Magi" (15th-century Parisian Book of Hours) . . . . 95 95
1225/7 . . . . . . . . *Set of* 3 1·60 1·60

The vertical sides of booklet pane No. 1225a are imperforate.

(Des B. Sadgrove. Litho Leigh-Mardon Ltd, Melbourne)

**1989** (1 Nov). *50th Anniv of Radio Australia. P* 14×13½.

1228 **469** 41 c. multicoloured . . . . . . 45 45

**470** Golden Wattle

**471** Australian Wildflowers

(Des Celia Rosser. Litho Leigh-Mardon Ltd, Melbourne)

**1990** (17 Jan). *Australia Day. P* 14½.

1229 **470** 41 c. multicoloured . . . . . . 45 45

(Des Beverley Graham and G. Rogers. Litho Leigh-Mardon Ltd, Melbourne)

**1990** (7 Feb–3 Sept). *Greetings Stamps. P* 14×13½ (41 *c.*) *or* 14½ (43 *c.*).

1230 **471** 41 c. multicoloured . . . . . . 45 45
a. Booklet pane. No. 1230×10 . . 4·50
b. Perf 14½ (May) . . . . 80 80
ba. Booklet pane. No. 1230b×10 . . 8·00
1231 43 c. multicoloured (3 Sept) . . 35 40
a. Booklet pane. No. 1231×10 . . 3·50

The upper and lower edges of the booklet panes are imperforate.

**472** Dr. Constance Stone (first Australian woman doctor), Modern Doctor and Nurses

**473** Greater Glider

(Des Priscilla Cutter. Litho Leigh-Mardon Ltd, Melbourne)

**1990** (7 Feb). *Centenary of Women in Medical Practice. P* 14½.

1232 **472** 41 c. multicoloured . . . . . . 45 45

(Des D. Higgins. Litho Leigh-Mardon Ltd, Melbourne)

**1990** (21 Feb). *Animals of the High Country. T* **473** *and similar vert designs. Multicoloured. P* 14×13½.

1233 41 c. Type **473** . . . . . . . . 55 45
1234 65 c. Tiger Cat ("Spotted-tailed Quoll") 80 75
1235 70 c. Mountain Pygmy-possum . . 85 80
1236 80 c. Brush-tailed Rock-wallaby . . 95 90
1233/6 . . . . . . . . *Set of* 4 2·75 2·50

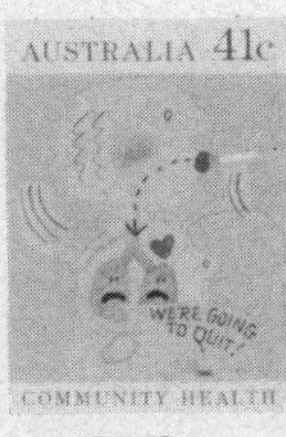


**474** "Stop Smoking"

**475** Soldiers from Two World Wars

(Des A. Stitt. Litho Leigh-Mardon Ltd, Melbourne)

**1990** (14 Mar). *Community Health. T* **474** *and similar vert designs. Multicoloured. P* 14×13½.

1237 41 c. Type **474** . . . . . . . . 55 55
1238 41 c. "Drinking and driving don't mix" . . 55 55
1239 41 c. "No junk food, please" . . . . 55 55
1240 41 c. "Guess who's just had a checkup?" . . 55 55
1237/40 . . . . . . . . *Set of* 4 2·00 2·00

(Des O. Schmidinger and Christine Stead. Litho Leigh-Mardon Ltd, Melbourne)

**1990** (12 Apr). *"The Anzac Tradition". T* **475** *and similar vert designs. Multicoloured. P* 14½.

1241 41 c. Type **475** . . . . . . . . 45 40
1242 41 c. Fighter pilots and munitions worker 45 40
1243 65 c. Veterans and Anzac Day parade . . 75 75
1244 $1 Casualty evacuation, Vietnam, and disabled veteran . . . . . . 1·10 1·10
1245 $1.10, Letters from home and returning troopships . . . . . . 1·25 1·25
1241/5 . . . . . . . . *Set of* 5 3·50 3·50
1244/5 Optd "Specimen" . . . . *Set of* 2 1·10

**476** Queen at Australian Ballet Performance, London, 1988

**477** New South Wales 1861 5s. Stamp

(Des Lynette Brown. Litho Leigh-Mardon Ltd, Melbourne)

**1990** (19 Apr). *Queen Elizabeth II's Birthday. P* 14½.

1246 **476** 41 c. multicoloured . . . . . . 40 40

(Des J. Passmore. Litho Leigh-Mardon Ltd, Melbourne)

**1990** (1 May). *150th Anniv of the Penny Black. T* **477** *and similar horiz designs showing stamps. Multicoloured. P* 13½×14.

1247 41 c. Type **477** . . . . . . . . 45 60
a. Block of 6. Nos. 1247/52 . . . . 2·40
1248 41 c. South Australia 1855 unissued 1s. . . 45 60
1249 41 c. Tasmania 1853 4d. . . . . . . 45 60
1250 41 c. Victoria 1867 5s. . . . . . . 45 60
1251 41 c. Queensland 1897 unissued 6d. . . 45 60
1252 41 c. Western Australia 1855 4d. with inverted frame . . . . . . 45 60
1247/52 . . . . . . . . *Set of* 6 2·40 3·25
**MS**1253 122×85 mm. Nos. 1247/52 . . 2·40 3·25

Nos. 1247/52 were printed together, *se-tenant*, throughout the sheet of 100 (two panes 5×10). The first and fifth vertical rows contained Nos. 1247 and 1250 alternately, the second and fourth rows Nos. 1248 and 1251, and the third row Nos. 1249 and 1252.

No. **MS**1253 also exists overprinted with the "Stamp World London 90" logo for sale at this international stamp exhibition

**478** Gold Miners on way to Diggings

**479** Glaciology Research

(Des B. Weatherhead. Litho Leigh-Mardon Ltd, Melbourne)

**1990** (16 May). *Colonial Development (2nd issue). Gold Fever. T* **478** *and similar square designs. Multicoloured. P* 13.

1254 41 c. Type **478** . . . . . . . . 45 45
a. Horiz strip of 5. Nos. 1254/8 . . 2·00
1255 41 c. Mining camp . . . . . . 45 45
1256 41 c. Panning and washing for gold . . 45 45
1257 41 c. Gold Commissioner's tent . . 45 45
1258 41 c. Moving gold under escort . . 45 45
1254/8 . . . . . . . . *Set of* 5 2·00 2·00

Nos. 1254/8 were printed together, *se-tenant*, in horizontal strips of 5 throughout the sheet.

**1990** (16 May)–**91**. *As Nos.* 1180/1, *but self-adhesive. P* 11½.

(*a*) *Typo Pemara Labels, Victoria*

1259 41 c. Cycling . . . . . . . . 50 60
1260 43 c. Skateboarding (27.8.90) . . . . 40 45

(*b*) *Litho Printset Pty Ltd*

1260*a* 43 c. Skateboarding (26.6.91) . . . . 40 45

Nos. 1259/60*a* were only available in rolls of 100, No. 1260*a* initially in rolls of 200, from major post offices or as strips of three from philatelic counters, each stamp, with die-cut perforations, being separate on the imperforate backing strip.

No. 1260*a* can be identified by its screened colours: on No. 1260 these are solid. The lithography printing also shows a kangaroo on the reverse and is on plain, rather than waxed, backing paper.

Due to the type of adhesive used examples should be retained on piece.

(Des Janet Boschen and Yu. Artsimenev. Litho Leigh-Mardon Ltd, Melbourne)

**1990** (13 June). *Australian-Soviet Scientific Co-operation in Antarctica. T* **479** *and similar horiz design. Multicoloured. P* 14½.

1261 41 c. Type **479** . . . . . . . . 45 40
1262 $1.10, Krill (marine biology research) (Optd S. 55p) . . . . . . 1·25 1·25
**MS**1263 85 × 65 mm. Nos. 1261/2 . . . . 1·60 1·75

Stamps in similar designs were also issued by Russia.

No. **MS**1263 also exists overprinted with the "New Zealand 1990" logo for sale at this international stamp exhibition in Auckland.

## PRICES OF SETS

Set prices are given for many issues, generally those containing three stamps or more. Definitive sets include one of each value or major colour change, but do not cover different perforations, die types or minor shades. Where a choice is possible the set prices are based on the cheapest versions of the stamps included in the listings.

480 Auctioning Building Plots

481 "Salmon Gums" (Robert Juniper)

(Des B. Clinton. Litho Leigh-Mardon Ltd, Melbourne)

**1990** (12 July). *Colonial Development* (3rd series). *Boomtime. T* **480** *and similar square designs. Multicoloured. P* 13.
1264 41 c. Type **480** . . . . 40 40
a. Horiz strip of 5. Nos. 1264/8 . . . . 1·75
1265 41 c. Colonial mansion . . . . 40 40
1266 41 c. Stock exchange . . . . 40 40
1267 41 c. Fashionable society . . . . 40 40
1268 41 c. Factories . . . . 40 40
1264/8 . . *Set of* 5 1·75 1·75
Nos. 1264/8 were printed together, *se-tenant*, in horizontal strips of 5 throughout the sheet.

(Des Sandra Baker. Litho Leigh-Mardon Ltd, Melbourne)

**1990** (3 Sept). *Booklet stamps. "Heidelberg and Heritage" Art Exhibition. T* **481** *and similar vert design. Multicoloured. Imperf* × *p* 14½.
1269 28 c. Type **481** . . . . 20 25
a. Booklet pane. Nos. 1269 and 1270 × 4 1·50
b. Imperf × p 15½ . . . . 40 45
ba. Booklet pane. Nos. 1269b and 1270a × 4 . . . . 3·00
1270 43 c. "The Blue Dress" (Brian Dunlop) . . 35 40
a. Imperf × p 15½ . . . . 70 80
Nos. 1269/70 only exist from $2 stamp booklets in which the horizontal edges of the pane are imperforate.

482 "Adelaide Town Hall" (Edmund Gouldsmith)

483 Laughing Kookaburras and Gifts

(Des Janet Boschen. Litho Leigh-Mardon Ltd, Melbourne)

**1990** (31 Oct). *150th Anniv of Local Government. P* 14½.
1271 **482** 43 c. multicoloured . . . . 35 40

(Des Marg Towt. Litho Leigh-Mardon Ltd, Melbourne)

**1990** (31 Oct). *Christmas. T* **483** *and similar multicoloured designs. P* 14½.
1272 38 c. Type **483** . . . . 40 40
a. Booklet pane. No. 1272 × 10 . . 4·00
1273 43 c. Baby Jesus with Koalas and Wallaby (*vert*) . . . . 40 40
1274 80 c. Possum on Christmas tree . . . . 80 1·00
1272/4 . . *Set of* 3 1·40 1·60
The upper and lower edges of booklet pane No. 1272a are imperforate, producing stamps imperforate top or bottom, and there are margins at left and right.

484 National Flag

485 Black-necked Stork

(Des Dianne Cook. Litho Leigh-Mardon Ltd, Melbourne)

**1991** (10 Jan). *Australia Day. 90th Anniv of Australian Flag. T* **484** *and similar horiz designs. P* 14½.
1275 43 c. deep ultramarine, brt scarlet & grey 40 40
1276 90 c. multicoloured . . . . 95 1·10
1277 $1 multicoloured . . . . 1·10 1·25
1278 $1.20, brt scarlet, dp ultramarine & grey 1·40 1·50
1275/8 . . *Set of* 4 3·50 3·75
Designs:—90 c. Royal Australian Navy ensign; $1 Royal Australian Air Force standard; $1.20, Australian merchant marine ensign.

(Des P. Margocsy. Litho Leigh-Mardon Ltd, Melbourne)

**1991** (14 Feb). *Waterbirds. T* **485** *and similar multicoloured designs. P* 14½.
1279 43 c. Type **485** . . . . 50 40
1280 43 c. Black Swan (*horiz*) . . . . 50 40
1281 85 c. Cape Barren Goose . . . . 1·00 1·25
1282 $1 Chestnut Teal (*horiz*) (Optd S. 55p) 1·25 1·40
1279/82 . . *Set of* 4 3·00 3·00

486 Recruitment Poster (Women's Services)

487 Queen Elizabeth at Royal Albert Hall, London

(Des Dianne Cook. Litho Leigh-Mardon Ltd, Melbourne)

**1991** (14 Mar). *Anzac Day. 50th Anniversaries. T* **486** *and similar horiz designs. P* 14½.
1283 43 c. multicoloured . . . . 50 40
1284 43 c. black, brown-olive & pale grey-brown 50 40
1285 $1.20, multicoloured (Optd S. 55p) . . 1·40 1·60
1283/5 . . *Set of* 3 2·25 2·25
Designs:—43 c. (No. 1284) Patrol (Defence of Tobruk); $1.20, "V-P Day Canberra" (Harold Abbot) (Australian War Memorial).

(Des R. Bulach. Litho Leigh-Mardon Ltd, Melbourne)

**1991** (11 Apr). *Queen Elizabeth II's Birthday. P* 14½.
1286 **487** 43 c. multicoloured . . . . 60 45

488 *Tectocoris diophthalmus* (bug)

489 "Bondi" (Max Dupain)

(Des D. Nelson. Litho Leigh-Mardon Ltd, Melbourne)

**1991** (11 Apr). *Insects. T* **488** *and similar horiz designs. Multicoloured. P* 14½.
1287 43 c. Type **488** . . . . 50 45
1288 43 c. *Cizara ardeniae* (hawk moth) . . 50 45
1289 80 c. *Petasida ephippigera* (grasshopper) 90 1·00
1290 $1 *Castiarina producta* (beetle) . . 1·10 1·25
1287/90 . . *Set of* 4 2·75 2·75

(Des Janet Boschen. Litho Leigh-Mardon Ltd, Melbourne)

**1991** (13 May). *150 Years of Photography in Australia. T* **489** *and similar vert designs. P* 14½.
1291 43 c. black, chestnut and deep ultramarine 50 50
a. Horiz pair. Nos. 1291/2 . . . . 1·00 1·00
1292 43 c. black, turquoise-green and chestnut 50 50
1293 70 c. black, yellow-green and chestnut . . 80 80
1294 $1.20, black, light brown and deep blue-green (Optd S. 55p) . . 1·25 1·25
1291/4 . . *Set of* 4 2·75 2·75
Designs:—No. 1292, "Gears for the Mining Industry, Vickers Ruwolt, Melbourne" (Wolfgang Sievers); No. 1293, "The Wheel of Youth" (Harold Cazneaux); No. 1294, "Teacup Ballet" (Olive Cotton).
Nos. 1291/2 were printed together, *se-tenant*, in horizontal pairs throughout the sheet.

490 Singing Group

491 Puppy

(Des O. Schmidinger and Christine Stead. Litho Leigh-Mardon Ltd, Melbourne)

**1991** (13 June). *Australian Radio Broadcasting. T* **490** *and similar vert designs showing listeners and scenes from radio programmes. Multicoloured. P* 14½.
1295 43 c. Type **490** . . . . 50 45
1296 43 c. "Blue Hills" serial . . . . 50 45
1297 85 c. "The Quiz Kids" . . . . 95 1·00
1298 $1 "The Argonauts' Club" children's programme (Optd S. 55p.) . . 1·00 1·00
1295/8 . . *Set of* 4 2·75 2·75

(Des Betina Ogden. Litho Leigh-Mardon Ltd, Melbourne)

**1991** (25 July). *Domestic Pets. T* **491** *and similar vert designs. Multicoloured. P* 14½.
1299 43 c. Type **491** . . . . 40 45
1300 43 c. Kitten . . . . 40 45
1301 70 c. Pony . . . . 65 70
1302 $1 Cockatoo . . . . 90 95
1299/1302 . . *Set of* 4 2·10 2·25

492 George Vancouver (1791) and Edward Eyre (1841)

493 *Seven Little Australians* (Ethel Turner)

(Des D. Lancashire. Litho Leigh-Mardon Ltd, Melbourne)

**1991** (25 Sept). *Exploration of Western Australia. P* 14½.
1303 **492** $1.05, multicoloured . . . . 95 1·00
**MS**1304 100 × 65 mm. No. 1303 . . . . 95 1·00
No. **MS**1304 also exists overprinted with the "Philanippon '91" logo for sale at this international stamp exhibition in Tokyo.

(Des Dianne Cook. Litho Leigh-Mardon Ltd, Melbourne)

**1991** (10 Oct). *Australian Writers of the* 1890*s. T* **493** *and similar multicoloured designs. P* 14½.
1305 43 c. Type **493** . . . . 40 45
1306 75 c. *On Our Selection* (Steele Rudd) . . 70 75
1307 $1 "Clancy of the Overflow" (poem, A. B. Paterson) (*vert*) . . . . 90 95
1308 $1.20, "The Drover's Wife" (short story, Henry Lawson) (*vert*) . . 1·10 1·25
1305/8 . . *Set of* 4 2·75 3·00

494 Shepherd

495 Parma Wallaby

(Des Sue Passmore. Litho Leigh-Mardon Ltd, Melbourne)

**1991** (1 Nov). *Christmas. T* **494** *and similar horiz designs. Multicoloured. P* 14½.
1309 38 c. Type **494** . . . . 35 40
a. Booklet pane. No. 1309 × 20 . . 7·00
1310 43 c. Infant Jesus . . . . 40 45
1311 90 c. Wise Man . . . . 85 90
1309/11 . . *Set of* 3 1·40 1·60
The vertical edges of booklet pane No. 1309a are imperforate, producing stamps imperforate at right or left, and there are margins at top and bottom.

(Des Betina Ogden. Litho Leigh-Mardon Ltd, Melbourne)

**1992** (2 Jan). *Threatened Species. T* **495** *and similar horiz designs. Multicoloured. P* 14 × 14½.
1312 45 c. Type **495** . . . . 40 45
a. Block of 6. Nos. 1312/17 . . . . 2·25
1313 45 c. Ghost Bat . . . . 40 45
1314 45 c. Long-tailed Dunnart . . . . 40 45
1315 45 c. Little Pygmy-possum . . . . 40 45
1316 45 c. Dusky Hopping-mouse . . . . 40 45
1317 45 c. Squirrel Glider . . . . 40 45
1312/17 . . *Set of* 6 2·25 2·50
Nos. 1312/17 were printed together, *se-tenant*, throughout the sheet of 100, giving fifteen blocks of 6 (3 × 2) and 10 single stamps.

496 Basket of Wild Flowers

(Des Priscilla Cutter. Litho Leigh-Mardon Ltd, Melbourne)

**1992** (2 Jan). *Greetings Stamp. P* 14½.
1318 **496** 45 c. multicoloured . . . . 40 45

## Index to Australian Stamp Designs from 1942

The following index is intended to facilitate the identification of all Australian stamps from 1942 onwards. Portrait stamps are usually listed under surnames only, views under the name of the town or city and other issues under the main subject or a prominent word and date chosen from the inscription. Simple abbreviations have occasionally been resorted to and when the same design or subject appears on more than one stamp, only the first of each series is indicated.


Aboriginal Art .224, 494, 865, 951, 997, 1093, 1150
Aborigine ... 238
Accountants ... 522
Adelaide ... 1201, 1271
Agricultural Shows ... 1054
Air Force ... 489
Aircraft .. 301, 304, 370, 450, 477, 489, 658, 761
Alice Springs ... 855
America's Cup ... 1036, 1046
Angel ... 988
Animal Science ... 491
Animals .. 316, 490, 561, 729, 781, 1232, 1312
Animals Aid to Man ... 493
Antarctic Research ... 279, 1259
Anteater ... 316, 562
Anzac ... 373, 1241, 1283
Apex ... 772
Arnhem Land ... 1162
"Ausipex" Int Stamp Exhib ... 944
AUSSAT Satellite ... 998
"Aussie Kids" ... 1086
*Australia II* (yacht) ... 1036
"Australia Asia" ... 483
Australia Day .. 657, 703, 728, 765, 837, 879, 902, 961, 997, 1044, 1168, 1229, 1275
Australian Broadcasting ... 847, 1295
Australian Natives Association ... 486
Australian Settlement Bicent ... 951, 972, 993, 1002, 1019, 1059, 1064, 1077, 1090, 1105, 1110, 1137, 1145, 1149
Australian-Soviet Scientific Co-operation ... 1261
Ayers Rock ... 632

Bandicoot ... 319
Banking ... 410
Banks ... 1006
Barrier Reef ... 631
Barton ... 241, 446
Bass ... 359, 402
Bat ... 1313
Beef ... 513
"Bernborough" (horse) ... 700
Bible Society ... 409
Bilby ... 789
Birds ... 363, 386, 392, 669, 734, 959, 1279
Black Swan ... 277
Blue Mountains ... 352
Boomtime ... 1264
Botanic Gardens ... 1199
*Britannia* ... 886
British Empire Games ... 346
Broadcasting ... 560, 847
Broken Bay ... 628
Broken Hill ... 305
Brookes ... 768
Bruce ... 508
*Buffalo* (ship) ... 1000
Buglioni ... 723
Building Societies ... 430
Bull ... 223
Butterflies ... 783

Cable ... 362
Canberra ... 244, 350, 653, 747
*Canberra* (ship) ... 704
Carols ... 828, 1098
Cars, Veteran and Vintage ... 905
Cartoons ... 1111
Cattle Industry ... 327
Cazneaux ... 1293
Charles, Prince ... 821
Charter of Justice ... 568
Chauvel ... 1209
Chic (car) ... 909
Chifley ... 595
Children's Books ... 982
Chisholm ... 435
Christmas ... 298, 306, 333, 338, 341, 345, 361, 372, 381, 407, 415, 431, 444, 475, 498, 530, 554, 580, 612, 635, 655, 696, 721, 758, 828, 856, 895, 946, 990, 1040, 1098, 1165, 1225, 1272, 1309
Churchill ... 377
Clarke ... 540
"Click go the Shears" (song) ... 1014
Clipper ships ... 911
Coat of Arms ... 224*a*
Cobb ... 284
Cockatoo ... 970, 1073
Collins ... 268
Colombo Plan ... 339
Colonial Development 1203, 1254, 1264
Commonwealth Day ... 882
Commonwealth Games ... 346, 859
Commonwealth Parliamentary Assn 473
Commonwealth Parliamentary Conference ... 1157
Community Health ... 1237
Community Welfare ... 748
Conder ... 779, 1214
Conservation ... 978

Cook, James ... 357, 400, 459, 1002
Cook, Joseph ... 507
Cook's Cottage ... 902
Coronation ... 264
Cotton ... 1294
Country Woman ... 344, 509
Cowan ... 602
Crafts ... 1158
Cricket ... 647
Crocodile ... 804
CSIRO ... 622
*Curl Curl* (ship) ... 707
Curtin ... 594
*Cutty Sark* (ship) ... 911

Dairy Congress ... 474
Dampier ... 356, 399, 974
David ... 432
Deakin ... 447
Del Vaga ... 698
Dennis ... 890
Disabled ... 827
Dish Aerials ... 987
District Nursing Services ... 969
Dogs ... 493, 729
Dowie ... 1202
Drysdale ... 962
Duigan ... 479
Dunlop ... 1270
Dunnart ... 1314
Dupain ... 1291
Dürer ... 550

Echidna ... 1076
Economic Agreement ... 881
Education ... 582
Electronic Mail Service ... 987
Elizabeth II ... 222, 261, 272, 282, 294, 300, 308, 348, 354, 382, 404, 414, 645, 741, 842, 886, 910, 977, 1009, 1058, 1142, 1202, 1246, 1286
Elizabeth II & Duke of Edinburgh .. 272, 349, 456, 646
Elizabeth, Queen Mother .. 203, 229, 236
Emu ... 207, 1024
"Encircling the Earth" ... 301
Environment Dangers ... 586
Eucalyptus ... 870
"Expo 70" ... 454
"Expo 88" ... 1143
Export ... 353
Eyre ... 482, 1303

Fadden ... 593
Farrer ... 225
Fauna Conservation ... 492, 1312
Fire Engines ... 875
First Air Mails ... 370, 903
First England–Australia Flight ... 450, 770
First Fleet ... 1059, 1064, 1077, 1090, 1105
Fish ... 388, 512, 545, 921
Fisher ... 505
Fishing ... 724
Flags ... 1275
Flemington ... 850
Flinders ... 358, 401, 728
Flowers . 322, 420, 465*a*, 608, 668, 843, 870, 1002, 1028, 1032
Flying Doctor ... 297, 663
Fontana ... 759
Forbes ... 849
Forrest, A. ... 901
Forrest, J. ... 233, 618
"Foundation of Commonwealth" .. 241
Frog ... 782
Frome ... 1207
Fruit ... 510, 1050
Fungi ... 823
Fysh ... 451

Gecko ... 794
Gemstones ... 549, 579
George III ... 1019
George VI ... 204*a*, 230, 234, 247
Giles ... 619
Gilmore ... 539
Girl Guides ... 334
Glider ... 564, 1233, 1317
Gloucester, Duke of ... 209
Glover ... 1201*a*
"Gold" ... 245, 1254
Golden Wattle ... 1229
Gordon ... 481
Gordon and Co "Australian Six" (car) ... 907
Gosse ... 620
Gould ... 637
Gouldsmith ... 1271
Grasslands Congress ... 458
Greetings stamps ... 1230, 1318
Griffin ... 350
Guide-dog ... 493
Gynaecology ... 413

Hajek ... 1001
Halley's Comet ... 1008
Hamori ... 554
Hargrave ... 379
Hargraves ... 245
Hartog ... 408, 973
Hawker ... 658
Heads of Government ... 831
Hermes and Globe ... 223*a*
Heysen ... 566
Hinkler ... 659
Hobart Town ... 270
Hopping-mouse ... 1316
Horse, Cat and Dog ... 490
Horses ... 1010

Hughes ... 506
Hume ... 617
Hunter ... 1022

Impressionist Paintings ... 1212, 1269
Inland Mission ... 343
Insects ... 1287
International Co-operation Year ... 380
International Labour Organization 439
International Peace Year ... 1039
International Women's Year ... 589
International Year of Child ... 720
International Youth Year ... 963
Isaacs ... 538

Jaycee ... 889
Juniper ... 1269

Kangaroo ... 228, 318, 492, 1023
Koala ... 230*a*, 1025
King ... 360, 403
Kingston ... 852
Kookaburra ... 230*b*, 694, 1026

Laby ... 638
*Lady Denman* (ship) ... 705
Lamb ... 491
Lambert ... 565
Latrobe ... 246
Launceston ... 854
Lawson, H. ... 231, 1308
Lawson, L. ... 603
Legacy ... 553
Leichardt ... 899
"Licence Inspected" ... 774
Life Saving ... 406
Lindrum ... 769
Lions ... 411
Lizard ... 803
Local Government ... 1271
Longford ... 1211
Lycett ... 1206
Lyell ... 1211
Lyons ... 591
Lyrebird ... 230*d*

McCubbin ... 778, 1215
Mackellar ... 961
Macquarie ... 436, 480
Marine Life ... 545, 919
Marmion ... 697
Mawarra ... 1200
Medical Association ... 427
Melba ... 340
Melbourne ... 558
Melbourne Cup ... 336
Mentone ... 779
Metric Conversion ... 532
Military Uniforms ... 964
Mills Plains ... 1201*a*
Mitchell ... 216
Monash ... 378
Moncrieff ... 1208
Monitor ... 781
Mountain Ash Wood ... 1164
Mt Buffalo ... 630
Mueller ... 226
Munro ... 766
*Murray River Queen* (ship) ... 706

Namatjira ... 434
National Development ... 469, 541
National Gallery ... 865
National Parks ... 708
Nationhood ... 614
Nativity play ... 1040
Necklace ... 1158
Newcastle ... 219
Newspaper ... 578
Nolan ... 961
Noroo ... 1199
Northern Territory ... 335, 437, 668

O'Brien ... 758
Olympic Games, Los Angeles ... 941
Olympic Games, Melbourne .. 280, 290
Olympic Games, Mexico ... 428
Olympic Games, Montreal ... 623
Olympic Games, Munich ... 518
Olympic Games, Seoul ... 1154
"On Route to deposit Gold" ... 777
"One Hundred Years" ... 239
Orchids ... 1032
Order of Australia ... 977
*Orient* (ship) ... 912
Osaka Fair ... 454
Oxley ... 616

Page ... 592
Panoramas ... 1161
Papua New Guinea ... 610, 904
Parkes ... 242, 1168
Parkinson ... 1007
Parliament House ... 1144
Pastoral Era ... 1203
Paterson, A. B. ... 433, 1307
Paterson, W. ... 269
Peace ... 213
Performing Arts ... 641
"Peter Pan" (horse) ... 702
Pets ... 1299
"Phar Lap" (horse) ... 701
Phillip ... 1021
Photography ... 1291
Pinnacles Desert ... 1161
Pioneer Life ... 523
Platypus ... 230*c*, 320, 1027
Ports and Harbours ... 438
Possum 563, 796, 960, 1072, 1235, 1315
Post Office ... 331
Postal Commission ... 600

Primary Industries ... 440, 510
"Produce Food" ... 255
Puddling ... 775

Qantas ... 477
"Quality of Washing Stuff" ... 776
Queensland ... 216, 332, 337

Radio Australia ... 1228, 1295
Rafferty ... 1209
Railway ... 278, 453, 715
Rat ... 797
Red Cross ... 276, 351
Rehabilitation ... 514
Reid ... 449
Rene ... 1208
Responsible Government ... 289, 296
Rice ... 511
Richardson ... 604
Richmond ... 627
Roberts ... 566*a*, 1212
Rockhampton ... 851
Rosella ... 1075
Roses ... 843
Rotary ... 281, 488
Royal Mail ... 284
R.S.P.C.A. ... 490
Royal Standard ... 773
Royal Visit ... 272, 456
Royal Wedding ... 821
Rudd ... 1306

*Sabraon* (ship) ... 913
St. John Ambulance ... 888
Scientific Development ... 596
Scout Jamboree ... 227, 254
Scullin ... 590
"Sentimental Bloke" ... 890
Sheep ... 1195
Shipwrecks ... 993
Sievers ... 1292
Silver Jubilee ... 645
*Sirius* (ship) ... 879
Skiing ... 915
Smith, Kingsford ... 660
Smith, Ross ... 450
Snake ... 799
Soil Science ... 426
South Australia ... 288, 1000
Spence ... 605
Spencer ... 639
Sports ... 569, 1169, 1259
Stage and Screen ... 1208
Stained-glass windows ... 946
Stamp Week ... 633, 694, 752
Stamps ... 239, 271, 277, 288, 337, 633, 694, 770, 864, 944, 1247
Standard Gauge ... 278
Stewart ... 1210
Stock Exchange ... 487
Stockman ... 327
Stone ... 606, 1232
Streeton ... 567, 1213
Strzelecki ... 898
Stuart ... 342
Sugar ... 440
Summit (car) ... 908
*Supply* (ship) ... 880
Sydney ... 556
Sydney, Lord ... 1020

Tarrant (car) ... 906
Tasman ... 355, 398, 977
Tasman Flight ... 304, 903
Tasmania ... 268
Tasmanian Tiger ... 321, 788
Taylor ... 640
Teapot ... 1160
Technology ... 1082
Telecommunication ... 376, 419
Telegraph ... 275, 517
Telephone ... 615
"The Man from Snowy River" (poem) 1067
*Thermopylae* (ship) ... 914
Thomson "steamer" (car) ... 905
Thorny Devil ... 805
Threatened Species ... 1312
Tiger Cat ... 317, 1234
Timber ... 441
Toad ... 800
Tobruk ... 1284
Tortoise ... 786
Townsville ... 557
Trade Unions ... 654
"Tradition of Service" ... 287
Trams ... 1220
Trees ... 664
Truganini ... 607
Trumper ... 767
"Tulloch" (horse) ... 699
Turner ... 1305
Twelve Apostles ... 1163

Ulm ... 661, 903
United Nations ... 476
U.P.U. ... 232, 576
Urban Environment ... 1216
U.S.A. Memorial ... 283

Vancouver ... 1303
Van Diemen's Land ... 271
Van Eyck ... 696
Vase ... 1159
Victoria ... 246, 959

Wallaby ... 792, 1236, 1312
"Waltzing Matilda" (song) ... 742
War Memorial ... 302, 1285
Warburton ... 621
Water Dragon ... 801

**Index to Australian Stamp Designs from 1942**—*Continued*


Watson .......... 448
Weather .......... 417
Wentworth .......... 537
Western Australia .......... 277, 719, 1303
Whales .......... 838
Wheat .......... 442
Wildflowers .......... 1230, 1318
Wildlife .......... 781, 1023, 1072, 1233
Williamson .......... 1210
Wills .......... 900
Wittenoom .......... 629
Wombat .......... 561, 784, 1074
Women in Medical Practice .......... 1232
Wool .......... 443
World Communications Year .......... 887
World Health Organization .......... 536
Wrigley .......... 452
Writers .......... 1305

Yachts .......... 833
Y.M.C.A. .......... 286
York .......... 853
Young .......... 633
Young Farmers .......... 267
Youth Hostels .......... 1219
Y.W.C.A. .......... 412

Zuern .......... 760

## POSTAGE DUE STAMPS

**POSTAGE DUE PRINTERS.** Nos. D1/62 were typographed at the New South Wales Government Printing Office, Sydney.

D1

D2

D3

Type D 1 adapted from plates of New South Wales Type D 1. No letters at foot.

**1902** (From July). *Chalk-surfaced paper. Wmk Type* D **2**.

*(a) P* 11½, 12

D 1 D 1 ½d. emerald-green .. .. .. .. 2·75 3·00
D 2 1d. emerald-green .. .. .. .. 8·00 4·00
D 3 2d. emerald-green .. .. .. .. 24·00 3·50
D 4 3d. emerald-green .. .. .. .. 38·00 17·00
D 5 4d. emerald-green .. .. .. .. 38·00 10·00
D 6 6d. emerald-green .. .. .. .. 55·00 9·00
D 7 8d. emerald-green .. .. .. .. 95·00 70·00
D 8 5s. emerald-green .. .. .. .. £180 70·00
D1/8 .. .. .. .. *Set of* 8 £400 £170
D1/7 Optd "Specimen" .. .. *Set of* 7 £200

*(b) P* 11½, 12, *compound with* 11

D 9 D 1 1d. emerald-green .. .. .. .. 95·00 45·00
D10 2d. emerald-green .. .. .. .. 95·00 45·00

*(c) P* 11

D12 D 1 1d. emerald-green .. .. .. .. £250 £110

The ½d., 6d. and 8d. exist in dull green.

Stamps may be found showing portions of the letters "N S W" at foot.

**1902–4.** *Type* D **3**, *space at foot filled in. Chalky paper. Wmk Type* D **2**.

*(a) P* 11½, 12

D13 1d. emerald-green .. .. .. .. 55·00 35·00
D14 2d. emerald-green .. .. .. .. 55·00 22·00
D15 3d. emerald-green .. .. .. .. 70·00 22·00
D17 5d. emerald-green .. .. .. .. 32·00 9·00
D18 10d. emerald-green .. .. .. .. 60·00 12·00
D19 1s. emerald-green .. .. .. .. 55·00 10·00
D20 2s. emerald-green .. .. .. .. 95·00 16·00
D21 5s. emerald-green .. .. .. .. £375 95·00

*(b) P* 11½, 12, *compound with* 11

D22 ½d. emerald-green .. .. .. .. 4·25 3·00
D23 1d. emerald-green .. .. .. .. 4·25 1·25
D24 2d. emerald-green .. .. .. .. 20·00 2·50
D25 3d. emerald-green .. .. .. .. 32·00 4·25
D26 4d. emerald-green .. .. .. .. 32·00 3·50
D27 5d. emerald-green .. .. .. .. 50·00 9·50
D28 6d. emerald-green .. .. .. .. 48·00 8·50
D29 8d. emerald-green .. .. .. .. 85·00 25·00
D30 10d. emerald-green .. .. .. .. 85·00 16·00
D31 1s. emerald-green .. .. .. .. 85·00 11·00
D32 2s. emerald-green .. .. .. .. £120 25·00
D33 5s. emerald-green .. .. .. .. £140 18·00

*(c) P* 11

D34 ½d. emerald-green .. .. .. .. 60·00 45·00
D35 1d. emerald-green .. .. .. .. 35·00 4·00
D36 2d. emerald-green .. .. .. .. 55·00 4·25
D37 3d. emerald-green .. .. .. .. 50·00 10·00
D38 4d. emerald-green .. .. .. .. 60·00 16·00
D39 5d. emerald-green .. .. .. .. 85·00 9·00
D40 6d. emerald-green .. .. .. .. 55·00 12·00
D41 1s. emerald-green .. .. .. .. £110 35·00
D42 5s. emerald-green .. .. .. .. £300 55·00
D43 10s. emerald-green .. .. .. .. £2000 £1000
D44 20s. emerald-green .. .. .. .. £3750 £2000
D13/44 .. .. .. .. *Set of* 14 £5500 £2750
D13/44 Optd "Specimen" .. .. *Set of* 14 £650

Most values exist in dull green.

D4

D6

**1906** (From Jan)–**08.** *Chalky paper. Wmk Type* D **4**.

*(a) P* 11½, 12, *compound with* 11

D45 D 3 ½d. green (1907) .. .. .. .. 6·50 4·25
D46 1d. green .. .. .. .. 8·00 2·25
D47 2d. green .. .. .. .. 20·00 3·25
D48 3d. green .. .. .. .. £225 £110
D49 4d. green (1907) .. .. .. .. 50·00 20·00
D50 6d. green (1908) .. .. .. .. 65·00 30·00
D45/50 .. .. .. .. *Set of* 6 £325 £150

*(b) P* 11

D51 D 3 1d. dull green .. .. .. .. £100 30·00
D52 4d. dull green .. .. .. .. £160 75·00

Shades exist.

**1907** (From July). *Chalky paper. Wmk Type* w **11** *(see Introduction). P* 11½ × 11.

D53 D 3 ½d. dull green .. .. .. .. 18·00 50·00
D54 1d. dull green .. .. .. .. 38·00 17·00
D55 2d. dull green .. .. .. .. 85·00 80·00
D56 4d. dull green .. .. .. .. £160 £100
D57 6d. dull green .. .. .. .. £190 £100
D53/7 .. .. .. .. *Set of* 5 £425 £300

**1908** (Sept)–**09.** *Stroke after figure of value. Chalky paper. Wmk Type* D **4**.

*(a) P* 11½ × 11

D58 D 6 1s. dull green (1909) .. .. .. 75·00 8·00
D59 5s. dull green .. .. .. .. £225 48·00

*(b) P* 11

D60 D 6 2s. dull green .. .. .. .. £900 £1000
D61 10s. dull green .. .. .. .. £2000 £1700
D62 20s. dull green .. .. .. .. £5000 £4250
D58/62 .. .. .. .. *Set of* 5 £7500 £6000

Nos. D1/62 were not for use in Victoria.

D7

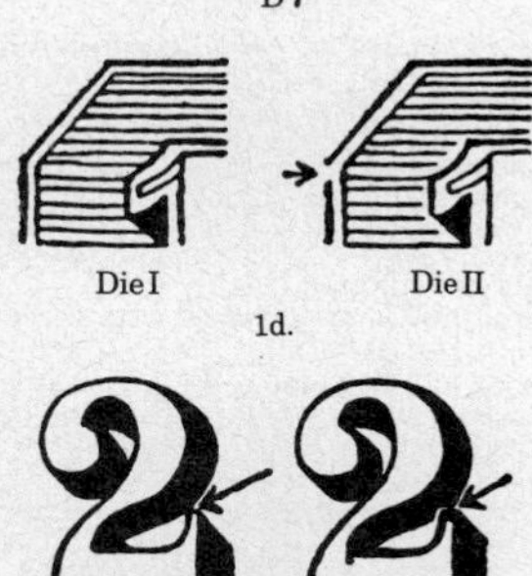


(Typo J. B. Cooke, Melbourne)

**1909** (July)–**1910.** *Type* D **7**. *Wmk Crown over A, Type* w **11**.

*(a) P* 12×12½ *(comb) or* 12½ *(line)*

D63 ½d. rosine and yellow-green .. .. 9·00 14·00
D64 1d. rosine and yellow-green (I) .. .. 13·00 3·50
a. Die II (7.10) .. .. .. 6·50 60
D65 2d. rosine and yellow-green (I) .. .. 24·00 3·50
a. Die II (7.10) .. .. .. 8·00 65
D66 3d. rosine and yellow-green (1910) .. 18·00 8·50
D67 4d. rosine and yellow-green .. .. 22·00 4·50
D68 6d. rosine and yellow-green .. .. 25·00 7·00
D69 1s. rosine and yellow-green .. .. 30·00 4·00
D70 2s. rosine and yellow-green .. .. 70·00 16·00
D71 5s. rosine and yellow-green .. .. 75·00 16·00
D72 10s. rosine and yellow-green .. .. £225 £140
D73 £1 rosine and yellow-green .. .. £425 £225

*(b) P* 11

D74 1d. rose and yellow-green (II) .. .. £400 £200
D74*a* 2d. rose and yellow-green (II) .. ..
D75 6d. rose and yellow-green .. .. £1700 £800
D63/75 .. .. .. .. *Set of* 11 £800 £400

Only one unused example, without gum, and another pen-cancelled are known of No. D74*a*.

The 1d. of this printing is distinguishable from No. D78 by the colours, the green being very yellow and the rose having less of a carmine tone. The paper is thicker and slightly toned, that of No. D78 being pure white; the gum is thick and yellowish, No. D78 having thin white gum.

All later issues of the 1d. and 2d. are Die II.

(Typo J. B. Cooke and T. S. Harrison (from May 1918))

**1912–23.** *Type* D **7**. *Thin paper. White gum. W* w **11**. *(a) P* 12½.

D76 ½d. scarlet and pale yellow-green (12.12) 18·00 22·00

*(b) P* 11

D77 ½d. rosine and bright apple-green (10.14) 4·00 6·00
a. Wmk sideways .. .. .. 3·75 6·00
D78 1d. rosine and bright apple-green (10.14) 2·50 55
a. Wmk sideways .. .. .. 6·00 90

*(c) P* 14

D79 ½d. rosine and bright apple-green (1914) 60·00 48·00
*a. Carmine and apple-green (Harrison)* (1920) .. .. .. .. 9·00 16·00
D80 1d. rosine and bright apple-green (10.14) 55·00 11·00
*a. Scarlet and pale yellow-green* (1918) 20·00 3·50
*b. Carmine and apple-green (Harrison)* (1919) .. .. .. .. 6·50 2·25
D81 2d. scarlet and pale yellow-green (1918) 17·00 6·00
*a. Carmine and apple-green (Harrison)* (1920) .. .. .. .. 12·00 3·25
D82 3d. rosine and apple-green (5.16) .. 70·00 27·00
a. Wmk sideways .. .. .. £400 £300
D83*b* 4d. carmine and apple-green (Harrison) (1918) .. .. .. .. 55·00 35·00
ba Wmk sideways .. .. .. £350 £250
*bb Carmine and pale yellow-green (Harrison)* (26.4.21) .. .. .. 45·00 35·00
D85 1s. scarlet and pale yellow-green (7.23) 25·00 12·00
D86 10 s. scarlet and pale yellow-green (5.21) £700 £800
D87 £1 scarlet and pale yellow-green (5.21) £600 £700
D76/87 .. .. .. .. *Set of* 8 £1300 £1400

Although printed by Cooke, the three higher values were not issued until some years later.

(Typo T. S. Harrison (to Feb. 1926), A. J. Mullet (to June 1927) and J. Ash (later))

**1919–30.** *Type* D **7**. *W* **6**. *(a) P* 14.

D91 ½d. carmine and yellow-green (5.23) . 3·75 4·75
D92 1d. carmine and yellow-green (1.3.22) . 3·75 65
D93 1½d. carmine and yellow-green (3.25) . 1·50 9·00
D94 2d. carmine and yellow-green (20.3.22) . 3·50 1·75
D95 3d. carmine and yellow-green (12.11.19) . 9·50 3·50
D96 4d. carmine and yellow-green (13.2.22) .. 32·00 11·00
D97 6d. carmine and yellow-green (13.2.22) .. 30·00 11·00

*(b) P* 11

D98 4d. carmine and yellow-green (9.30) .. 4·00 4·00
D91/8 .. .. .. .. *Set of* 8 75·00 40·00

All values perf 14 were printed by Harrison and all except the 4d. by Mullett and Ash. There is a wide variation of shades in this issue.

(Typo J. Ash)

**1931–37.** *Type* D **7**. *W* **15**. *(a) P* 14.

D100 1d. carmine and yellow-green (10.31) .. 8·50 11·00
D102 2d. carmine and yellow-green (19.10.31) .. 8·50 11·00

*(b) P* 11

D105 ½d. carmine and yellow-green (4.34) .. 7·50 14·00
D106 1d. carmine and yellow-green (11.32) .. 5·00 60
D107 2d. carmine and yellow-green (29.9.32) 5·00 60
D108 3d. carmine and yellow-green (3.37) .. 70·00 65·00
D109 4d. carmine and yellow-green (26.7.34) .. 3·75 2·00
D110 6d. carmine and yellow-green (4.36) .. £250 £250
D111 1s. carmine and yellow-green (8.34) .. 48·00 32·00
D105/11 .. .. .. .. *Set of* 7 £350 £325

D 8 D 9

A B C

The differences are found in the middle of the "D"

D

E

Type E. Larger "1" with only three background lines above; hyphen more upright.

(Frame recess. Value typo J. Ash)

**1938–39.** *W* **15**. *P* 14½×14.

D112 D 8 ½d. carmine and green (A) (1939) .. 2·25 2·00
D113 1d. carmine and green (A) .. .. 3·75 30
D114 2d. carmine and green (A) .. .. 5·00 1·00
D115 3d. carmine and green (B) .. .. 12·00 12·00
D116 4d. carmine and green (A) .. .. 6·00 30
D117 6d. carmine and green (A) .. .. 38·00 32·00
D118 1s. carmine and green (D) .. .. 60·00 12·00
D112/18 .. .. .. .. *Set of* 7 £110 55·00

Shades exist.

**1946–57.** *Redrawn as Type* C *and* E (1s.). *W* **15**. *P* 14½ × 14.

D119 D 9 ½d. carmine and green (9.56) .. 60 3·00
D120 1d. carmine and green (11.1.47) .. 60 60
D121 2d. carmine and green (9.46) .. 3·75 80
D122 3d. carmine and green (25.9.46) .. 4·75 75
D123 4d. carmine and green (11.52) .. 5·50 1·50
D124 5d. carmine and green (12.48) .. 6·00 2·50
D125 6d. carmine and green (9.47) .. 8·00 1·25
D126 7d. carmine and green (26.8.53) .. 4·00 8·50
D127 8d. carmine and green (24.4.57) .. 10·00 25·00
D128 1s. carmine and green (9.47) .. 16·00 1·25
D119/28 .. .. .. .. *Set of* 10 55·00 42·00

There are many shades in this issue.

D 10

**1953** (26 Aug)–**60.** *W* **15**. *P* 14½ × 14.

D129 D 10 1s. carmine & yellow-grn (17.2.54) 4·75 3·00
*a. Carmine and deep green* .. 9·00 8·00
D130 2s. carmine and yellow-green .. 18·00 12·00
*a. Carmine and deep green* .. £150 50·00
D131 5s. carmine and green .. .. 18·00 6·00
*a. Carmine and deep green* (1960) 12·00 70
D129/31 .. .. .. .. *Set of* 3 35·00 19·00
D129*a*/31*a* .. .. .. .. *Set of* 3 £160 55·00

A new die was introduced for No. D131*a*. This differs from the original in having a distinct gap between the two arms of the "5". On No. D131 these two features are joined.

I

II

Type I. Numeral, "D" and stop, generally unoutlined.

Type II. Clear white line separates numeral, etc. from background.

**1958–60.** *No wmk. P* 14½ × 14.
D132 **D 9** ½d. carmine and deep green (II) (27.2.58) .. .. .. 1·00 1·75
D133 1d. carmine and deep green (I) (25.2.58) .. .. .. 3·00 3·50
a. Type II (6.59) .. .. .. 1·00 65
D134 3d. carmine and deep green (II) (25.5.60) .. .. .. 1·75 2·50
D135 4d. carmine and deep green (I) (27.2.58) .. .. .. 3·75 9·00
a. Type II (6.59) .. .. .. 3·00 8·50
D136 5d. carmine and deep green (I) (27.2.58) .. .. .. 9·50 15·00
a. Type II (6.59) .. .. .. 60·00 75·00
D137 6d. carmine and deep green (II) (25.5.60) .. .. .. 2·75 2·75
D138 8d. carmine and deep green (II) (25.2.58) .. .. .. 10·00 35·00
D139 10d. carmine and deep green (II) (9.12.59) .. .. .. 5·50 3·25
D140 **D 10** 1s. carmine and deep green (8.9.58) 3·00 3·50
*a. Deep carmine & deep green* (6.59) .. .. .. 4·00 4·00
D141 2s. deep carmine and deep green (8.3.60) .. .. .. 20·00 22·00
D132/41 .. .. *Set of* 10 50·00 85·00
Nos. D140*a* and D141. Value tablets are re-engraved and have thicker and sharper printed lines than before.
The use of Postage Due stamps ceased on 13 January 1963.

OFFICIAL STAMPS

From 1902 the departments of the Commonwealth government were issued with stamps of the various Australian States perforated "OS" to denote official use. These were replaced in 1913 by Commonwealth of Australia issues with similar perforated initials as listed below.

During the same period the administrations of the Australian States used their own stamps and those of the Commonwealth perforated with other initials for the same purpose. These States issues are outside the scope of this catalogue.

Most shades listed under the postage issues also exist perforated "OS". Only those which are worth more than the basic colours are included below.

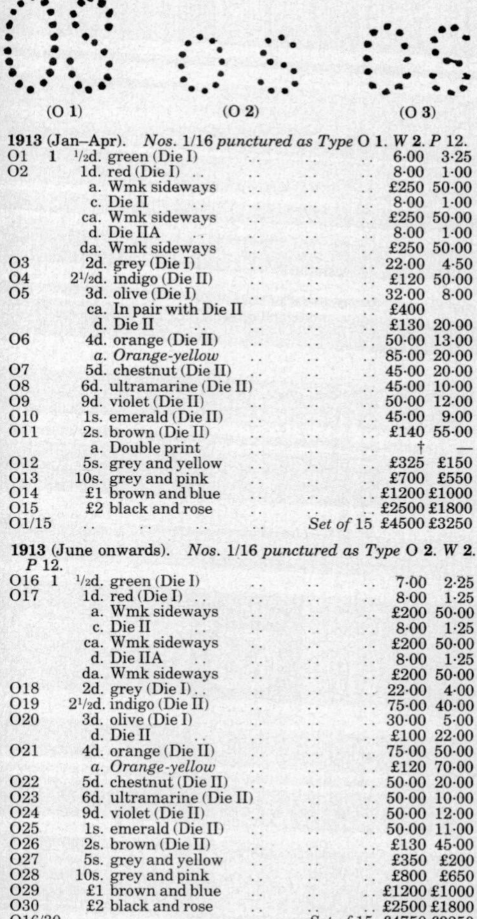

(O 1) (O 2) (O 3)

**1913** (Jan–Apr). *Nos.* 1/16 *punctured as Type* O **1**. **W 2**. *P* 12.
O1 **1** ½d. green (Die I) .. .. .. 6·00 3·25
O2 1d. red (Die I) .. .. .. .. 8·00 1·00
a. Wmk sideways .. .. .. £250 50·00
c. Die II .. .. .. 8·00 1·00
ca. Wmk sideways .. .. .. £250 50·00
d. Die IIA .. .. .. 8·00 1·00
da. Wmk sideways .. .. .. £250 50·00
O3 2d. grey (Die I) .. .. .. 22·00 4·50
O4 2½d. indigo (Die II) .. .. .. £120 50·00
O5 3d. olive (Die I) .. .. .. 32·00 8·00
ca. In pair with Die II .. .. £400
d. Die II .. .. .. £130 20·00
O6 4d. orange (Die II) .. .. .. 50·00 13·00
*a. Orange-yellow* .. .. .. 85·00 20·00
O7 5d. chestnut (Die II) .. .. .. 45·00 20·00
O8 6d. ultramarine (Die II) .. .. .. 45·00 10·00
O9 9d. violet (Die II) .. .. .. 50·00 12·00
O10 1s. emerald (Die II) .. .. .. 45·00 9·00
O11 2s. brown (Die II) .. .. .. £140 55·00
a. Double print .. .. .. † —
O12 5s. grey and yellow .. .. .. £325 £150
O13 10s. grey and pink .. .. .. £700 £550
O14 £1 brown and blue .. .. .. £1200 £1000
O15 £2 black and rose .. .. .. £2500 £1800
O1/15 .. .. .. *Set of* 15 £4500 £3250

**1913** (June onwards). *Nos.* 1/16 *punctured as Type* O **2**. **W 2**. *P* 12.
O16 **1** ½d. green (Die I) .. .. .. 7·00 2·25
O17 1d. red (Die I) .. .. .. 8·00 1·25
a. Wmk sideways .. .. .. £200 50·00
c. Die II .. .. .. 8·00 1·25
ca. Wmk sideways .. .. .. £200 50·00
d. Die IIA .. .. .. 8·00 1·25
da. Wmk sideways .. .. .. £200 50·00
O18 2d. grey (Die I) .. .. .. 22·00 4·00
O19 2½d. indigo (Die II) .. .. .. 75·00 40·00
O20 3d. olive (Die I) .. .. .. 30·00 5·00
d. Die II .. .. .. £100 22·00
O21 4d. orange (Die II) .. .. .. 75·00 50·00
*a. Orange-yellow* .. .. .. £120 70·00
O22 5d. chestnut (Die II) .. .. .. 50·00 20·00
O23 6d. ultramarine (Die II) .. .. .. 50·00 10·00
O24 9d. violet (Die II) .. .. .. 50·00 12·00
O25 1s. emerald (Die II) .. .. .. 50·00 11·00
O26 2s. brown (Die II) .. .. .. £130 45·00
O27 5s. grey and yellow .. .. .. £350 £200
O28 10s. grey and pink .. .. .. £800 £650
O29 £1 brown and blue .. .. .. £1200 £1000
O30 £2 black and rose .. .. .. £2500 £1800
O16/30 .. .. .. *Set of* 15 £4750 £3250

**1915**. *Nos.* 20 *and* 23/7 *punctured as Type* O **2**. **W 5**. *P* 12.
O31 **1** 2d. grey (Die I) .. .. .. 45·00 10·00
O33 6d. ultramarine (Die II) .. .. .. 85·00 12·00
b. Die IIA .. .. .. £700 £110
O34 9d. violet (Die II) .. .. .. £100 24·00
O35 1s. blue-green (Die II) .. .. .. £100 25·00
O36 2s. brown (Die II) .. .. .. £400 55·00
O37 5s. grey and yellow .. .. .. £350 80·00

**1914–21.** *Nos.* 29/34 *punctured as Type* O **2**. **W 5**. *P* 14.
O38 **5*a*** ½d. bright green .. .. .. 4·50 1·75
O39 1d. carmine-red (I) .. .. .. 5·00 25
O40 1d. carmine-red (II) .. .. .. £250 4·00
O41 4d. orange .. .. .. 27·00 2·75
*a. Yellow-orange* .. .. .. 27·00 5·00
*b. Pale orange-yellow* .. .. .. 40·00 12·00
*c. Lemon-yellow* .. .. .. £100 20·00
O42 5d. brown .. .. .. 27·00 2·00

**1915–28.** *Nos.* 35/45 *punctured as Type* O **2**. **W 6**. *P* 12.
O43 **1** 2d. grey (Die I) .. .. .. 15·00 2·00
c. Die II .. .. .. 15·00 2·00
O44 2½d. deep blue (Die II) .. .. .. 18·00 6·50
O45 3d. yellow-olive (Die I) .. .. .. 18·00 2·00
c. Die II .. .. .. 50·00 15·00
d. Die IIB .. .. .. 22·00 3·00
O46 6d. ultramarine (Die II) .. .. .. 30·00 3·00
a. Die IIA .. .. .. £400 £100
c. Die IIB .. .. .. 30·00 3·50
O47 9d. violet (Die II) .. .. .. 20·00 2·75
a. Die IIB .. .. .. 20·00 2·75
O48 1s. blue-green (Die II) .. .. .. 23·00 2·00
a. Die IIB .. .. .. 23·00 2·00
O49 2s. brown (Die II) .. .. .. 90·00 9·50
*a. Red-brown (aniline)* .. .. .. £225 35·00
O50 5s. grey and yellow .. .. .. £130 35·00
O51 10s. grey and pink .. .. .. £225 60·00
O52 £1 chocolate and dull blue .. .. £1200 £850
ba. Wmk sideways .. .. .. — £2000
O53 £2 black and rose .. .. .. £2000 £850
O43/53 .. .. .. *Set of* 11 £3250 £1600

**1916–18.** *Nos.* 47/50*a and* 5d. *as No.* 34 *punctured as Type* O **2**. **W 5**. *Rough paper. P* 14.
O54 **5*a*** 1d. scarlet .. .. .. 12·00 50
O55 1d. deep red (I) .. .. .. 12·00 50
O56 1d. rose-red (I) .. .. .. 14·00 50
O57 1d. rosine (I) .. .. .. 55·00 4·00
O58 1d. rose-red (II) .. .. .. £200 10·00
O59 1d. rosine (II) .. .. .. £400 25·00
O60 5d. bright chestnut (1918) .. .. £1100 £100
All examples of the 5d. on this paper were perforated "OS".

**1918–20.** *Nos.* 51 *and* 53/5 *punctured as Type* O **2**. **W 6*a***. *P* 14.
O61 **5*a*** ½d. green .. .. .. 7·00 1·00
O63 1d. carmine (I) .. .. .. 15·00 4·00
O64 1½d. black-brown .. .. .. 8·00 1·25
a. Very thin paper .. .. .. 12·00 4·00
O65 1½d. red-brown .. .. .. 8·50 1·00
O61/5 .. .. .. *Set of* 4 30·00 6·25

**1918–23.** *Nos.* 56/9 *and* 61/6 *punctured as Type* O **2**. **W 5**. *P* 14.
O66 **5*a*** ½d. orange .. .. .. 13·00 6·00
O67 1d. violet .. .. .. 17·00 1·50
O68 1½d. black-brown .. .. .. 13·00 1·00
O69 1½d. deep red-brown .. .. .. 10·00 80
O70 1½d. green .. .. .. 7·00 50
O71 2d. dull orange .. .. .. 12·00 75
O72 2d. bright rose-scarlet .. .. .. 7·50 75
O73 4d. violet .. .. .. 22·00 10·00
O74 4d. ultramarine .. .. .. 38·00 6·50
O75 1s. 4d. pale blue .. .. .. 50·00 15·00
*b. Deep turquoise* .. .. .. — £100
O66/75 .. .. .. *Set of* 10 £170 38·00

**1923–24.** *Nos.* 73/5 *punctured as Type* O **2**. **W 6**. *P* 12.
O76 **1** 6d. chestnut (Die IIB) .. .. .. 15·00 2·00
O77 2s. maroon (Die II) .. .. .. 50·00 10·00
O78 £1 grey (Die IIB) .. .. .. £450 £250
O76/8 .. .. .. *Set of* 3 £475 £250

**1924.** *Nos.* 76/84 *punctured as Type* O **2**. *P* 14. (*a*) **W 5**.
O79 **5*a*** 1d. sage-green .. .. .. 4·00 40
O80 1½d. scarlet .. .. .. 1·00 20
O81 2d. red-brown .. .. .. 20·00 5·00
*a. Bright red-brown* .. .. .. 25·00 7·50
O82 3d. dull ultramarine .. .. .. 25·00 3·25
O83 4d. olive-yellow .. .. .. 25·00 2·50
O84 4½d. violet .. .. .. 30·00 8·00

(*b*) **W 6*a***
O85 **5*a*** 1d. sage-green .. .. .. 9·00 4·50

(*c*) *No wmk*
O86 **5*a*** 1d. sage-green .. .. .. 40·00 40·00
O87 1½d. scarlet .. .. .. 60·00 45·00
O79/87 .. .. .. *Set of* 9 £180 95·00

**1926–30.** *Nos.* 85/104 *punctured as Type* O **2**. **W 7**. (*a*) *P* 14.
O88 **5*a*** ½d. orange .. .. .. £100 50·00
O89 1d. sage-green .. .. .. 3·75 50
O90 1½d. scarlet .. .. .. 4·75 70
O91 1½d. golden scarlet .. .. .. 7·00 1·25
O92 2d. red-brown (Die I) .. .. .. 55·00 30·00
O93 3d. dull ultramarine .. .. .. 20·00 6·00
O94 4d. yellow-olive .. .. .. 50·00 14·00
O95 4½d. violet .. .. .. 30·00 9·00
O96 1s. 4d. pale greenish blue .. .. £200 70·00
O88/96 .. .. .. *Set of* 8 £400 £160

(*b*) *P* 13½ × 12½
O97 **5*a*** ½d. orange .. .. .. 2·25 50
O98 1d. sage-green (Die I) .. .. .. 2·00 35
O99 1d. sage-green (Die II) .. .. .. 75·00 75·00
O100 1½d. scarlet .. .. .. 1·75 20
O101 1½d. golden scarlet .. .. .. 1·75 20
O102 1½d. red-brown .. .. .. 6·00 2·00
O103 2d. red-brown (Die II) .. .. .. 15·00 4·00
O104 2d. golden scarlet (Die II) .. .. 7·00 50
O105 2d. golden scarlet (Die III) .. .. 3·75 50
O106 3d. dull ultramarine (Die I) .. .. 22·00 4·00
O107 3d. dull ultramarine (Die II) .. .. 14·00 1·25
O108 4d. yellow-olive .. .. .. 17·00 3·00
O109 4½d. violet .. .. .. 65·00 30·00
O110 5d. orange-brown (Die II) .. .. 38·00 3·25
O111 1s. 4d. turquoise .. .. .. 85·00 14·00
O97/111 .. .. .. *Set of* 11 £225 50·00

**1927** (9 May). *Opening of Parliament House, Canberra. No.* 105 *punctured as Type* O **3**.
O112 **8** 1½d. brownish lake .. .. .. 12·00 9·00

**1928** (29 Oct). *National Stamp Exhibition, Melbourne. No.* 106 *punctured as Type* O **2**.
O113 3d. blue .. .. .. 13·00 9·00

**1929–30.** *Nos.* 107/14 *punctured as Type* O **2**. **W 7**. *P* 12.
O114 **1** 6d. chestnut (Die IIB) .. .. .. 15·00 2·00
O115 9d. violet (Die IIB) .. .. .. 18·00 4·50
O116 1s. blue-green (Die IIB) .. .. .. 22·00 2·00
O117 **1** 2s. maroon (Die II) .. .. .. 45·00 7·00
O118 5s. grey and yellow .. .. .. £150 40·00
O118*a* 10s. grey and pink .. .. .. £500 £375
O118*b* £2 black and rose .. .. .. £2000 £750

**1929** (20 May). *Air. No.* 115 *punctured as Type* O **3**.
O119 **9** 3d. green .. .. .. 20·00 12·00

**1929** (28 Sept). *Centenary of Western Australia. No.* 116 *punctured as Type* O **3**.
O120 **10** 1½d. dull scarlet .. .. .. 13·00 9·00

**1930** (2 June). *Centenary of Exploration of River Murray by Capt. Sturt. Nos.* 117/18 *punctured as Type* O **2**.
O121 **11** 1½d. scarlet .. .. .. 6·50 4·50
O122 3d. blue .. .. .. 13·00 9·50

**OS**

(O 4)

**1931** (4 May). Nos. 121/2 *optd with Type* O **4**.
O123 **13** 2d. rose-red .. .. .. 55·00 16·0
O124 3d. blue .. .. .. £200 38·0
For No. 139 overprinted with Type O **4**, see No. 139*a*.

**1932–33.** *Optd as Type* O **4**. (*a*) **W 7**. (i) *P* 13½ × 12½.
O125 **5*a*** 2d. golden-scarlet (Die III) .. .. 6·00 7
O126 4d. yellow-olive .. .. .. 40·00 3·7

(ii) *P* 12
O127 **1** 6d. chestnut .. .. .. 80·00 70·0

(*b*) **W 15**. (i) *P* 13½ × 12½
O128 **5*a*** ½d. orange .. .. .. 9·50 1·5
a. Opt inverted .. .. .. £2250 £120
O129 1d. green .. .. .. 4·00 4
O130 2d. golden scarlet (Die III) .. .. 6·00 5
a. Opt inverted .. .. .. — £160
O131 3d. ultramarine (Die II) (3.33) .. 7·50 5·0
O132 5d. orange-brown .. .. .. 65·00 38·0

(ii) *P* 12
O133 **1** 6d. chestnut .. .. .. 40·00 30·0

(*c*) *Recess. No wmk. P* 11
O134 **18** 2d. scarlet .. .. .. 8·00 2·0
O135 3d. blue .. .. .. 20·00 5·5
O136 **17** 1s. green .. .. .. 80·00 35·0
Issue of overprinted official stamps ceased in February 193 and thereafter mail from the federal administration was carried free.

## BRITISH COMMONWEALTH OCCUPATION FORCE (JAPAN)

Nos. J1/7 were used by the Australian forces occupying Japan after the Second World War. Initially their military post offices supplied unoverprinted Australian stamps, but it was decided to introduce the overprinted issue to prevent currency speculation

**B.C.O.F. JAPAN 1946**
(1)

B.C.O.F. JAPAN 1946
(2)

**1946** Wrong fount "6" (left pane R. 9/4)

**J.F. AN** Normal

**J.F. AN** Narrow "N" (right pane R. 1/8)

**1946** (11 Oct)–**48**. *Stamps of Australia optd as T* **1** (1*d*., 3*d*.) *or T* **2** (*others*) *at British Commonwealth Command Headquarters, Kure, Japan.*
J1 **27** ½d. orange (No. 179) .. .. .. 2·00 4·00
a. Wrong fount "6" .. .. .. 35·00 45·00
b. Narrow "N" .. .. .. 35·00 45·00
J2 **46** 1d. brown-purple (No. 203) .. .. 2·00 1·50
a. Error. Blue overprint .. .. 70·00 90·00
J3 **31** 3d. purple-brown (No. 187) .. .. 1·25 1·75
J4 **34** 6d. purple-brown (No. 189*a*) (8.5.47) .. 11·00 8·00
a. Wrong fount "6" .. .. .. £110 90·00
b. Stop after "JAPAN" (right pane R. 5/5) .. .. .. £110 90·00
c. Narrow "N" .. .. .. £110 90·00
J5 **36** 1s. grey-green (No. 191) (8.5.47) .. 11·00 9·00
a. Wrong fount "6" .. .. .. £140 £110
b. Stop after "JAPAN" (right pane R. 5/5) .. .. .. £140 £110
c. Narrow "N" .. .. .. £140 £110
J6 **1** 2s. maroon (No. 212) (8.5.47) .. .. 38·00 42·00
J7 **38** 5s. claret (No. 176) (8.5.47) .. .. £110 £130
a. Thin rough paper (No. 176a) (1948) .. £130 £150
J1/7 .. .. .. *Set of* 7 £150 £170
The ½d., 1d. and 3d. values were first issued on 11 October 1946 and withdrawn two days later, but were re-issued together with the other values on 8 May 1947.
The following values with T **2** in the colours given were from proof sheets which, however, were used for postage: ½d. (red), 1d. (red or black) and 3d. (gold, red or black). (*Prices for black opts £100, each, and for red or gold from £300 each, all un*)

The use of B.C.O.F. stamps ceased on 12 February 1949.

## AUSTRALIAN ANTARCTIC TERRITORY

For use at the Antarctic bases of Casey (opened early 1969: ɪsed Wilkes postmark until early 1970), Davis (closed from 1965 ɪntil early 1969), Heard Island (seasonal occupation only), Macquarie Island, Mawson and Wilkes (closed January 1969). Stamps of Australia were used from the bases before the ntroduction of Australian Antarctic Territory issues.

The following are also valid for use in Australia, where they are put on sale for a limited period when first issued.

**DATES OF ISSUE.** The dates given refer to release dates in Australia. Local release dates are usually later and where known they are given in footnotes.

1 1954 Expedition at Vestfold Hills and Map

(Des. T. Lawrence: adapted by artist of the Printing Branch. Recess)

**1957** (27 Mar). *P* 14½.
1 1 2s. ultramarine .. .. .. .. .. 1·75 70
Issued Macquarie Island 11.12.57, Davis 6.2.58, Mawson 18.2.58, Wilkes 1.2.59.

2 Members of Shackleton Expedition at South Magnetic Pole, 1909 — 3 Weazel and Team

**1959** (16 Dec). *T* 2 *and designs as T* 3. *Recess; new values surch typo* (5*d.*, 8*d.*). *P* 14½ (5*d.*), 14½ × 14 (8*d.*) *or* 14 × 14½ (*others*).
2 5d. on 4d. black and sepia .. .. .. .. 60 15
3 8d. on 7d. black and indigo .. .. .. .. 4·50 2·00
4 1s. deep green .. .. .. .. .. 4·50 1·75
5 2s. 3d. green .. .. .. .. .. 10·00 4·00
2/5 .. .. .. .. .. .. *Set of* 4 18·00 7·00
Designs: *Vert*—1s. Dog-team and iceberg; 2s. 3d. Map of Antarctica and Emperor Penguins. Issued Macquarie Island 26.12.59, Davis 30.1.60, Mawson 10.2.60, Wilkes 13.2.60.

6 — 7 Sir Douglas Mawson (Expedition leader)

**1961** (5 July). *Recess. P* 14½.
6 6 5d. deep blue .. .. .. .. .. 1·50 15
Issued Macquarie Island 6.12.61, Wilkes 10.1.62, Davis 20.1.62, Mawson 30.1.62.

**1961** (18 Oct). 50*th Anniv of* 1911–14 *Australasian Antarctic Expedition. Recess. P* 14½.
7 7 5d. myrtle-green .. .. .. .. .. 35 15
Issued Macquarie Island 6.12.61, Wilkes 10.1.62, Davis 20.1.62, Mawson 30.1.62.

**(New Currency. 100 cents = 1 Australian dollar)**

8 Aurora and Camera Dome — 9 Helicopter

(Des J. Mason. Photo)

**1966** (28 Sept)–**68**. *T* 8/10 *and similar multicoloured designs. P* 13½.
8 1 c. Type 8 (*shades*) .. .. .. .. 70 30
9 2 c. Banding penguins (*shades*) .. .. .. 2·25 70
10 4 c. Ship and iceberg .. .. .. .. 70 70
11 5 c. Banding Elephant-seals (25.9.68) .. 2·75 1·75
12 7 c. Measuring snow strata .. .. .. 80 60
13 10 c. Wind gauges .. .. .. .. 1·00 60
14 15 c. Weather balloon .. .. .. .. 4·00 2·00
15 20 c. Type 9 .. .. .. .. .. 4·25 2·25
16 25 c. Radio operator .. .. .. .. 5·00 3·75
17 50 c. Ice compression tests .. .. .. 17·00 9·00
18 $1 Parahelion ("mock sun") .. .. .. 42·00 15·00
8/18 .. .. .. .. .. .. *Set of* 11 70·00 32·00
The 1 c. to 15 c. are vert as Type 8; the 25 c., 50 c. and $1 are horiz as Type 9.

Nos. 8/10 and 12/18 placed on sale locally at Macquarie Island on 11.12.66, Wilkes 9.2.67 and Mawson 16.2.67.
No. 11 issued Macquarie Island 4.12.68, Mawson 13.1.69, Wilkes/Casey 9.2.69 and Davis 20.2.69.

11 Sastrugi (Snow Ridges) — 12 Capt. Cook, Sextant and Compass

(Des J. Mason. Photo)

**1971** (23 June). *Tenth Anniv of Antarctic Treaty. T* 11 *and similar horiz design. P* 13½.
19 6 c. blue and black .. .. .. .. 1·25 1·00
20 30 c. multicoloured (Pancake ice) .. .. 6·50 6·50
Issued Macquarie Island 23.11.71, Mawson 27.12.71, Davis 13.1.72 and Casey 17.1.72.

(Des J. Mason. Photo)

**1972** (13 Sept). *Bicentenary of Cook's Circumnavigation of Antarctica. T* 12 *and similar horiz design. Multicoloured. P* 13½.
21 7 c. Type 12 .. .. .. .. .. 2·50 75
22 35 c. Chart and H.M.S. *Resolution* .. .. 8·50 6·00
Issued Macquarie Island 19.11.72, Mawson 24.12.72, Davis 3.1.73 and Casey 22.1.73.

13 Plankton — 14 Admiral Byrd (expedition leader), Aircraft and Map of South Pole

(Des G. Browning (1, 7, 9, 10, 20 c., $1), R. Honisett (others). Photo)

**1973** (5 Aug). *T* 13 *and similar multicoloured designs. P* 13½.
23 1 c. Type 13 .. .. .. .. .. 20 15
24 5 c. Mawson's "Gipsy Moth", 1931 .. .. 30 30
25 7 c. Adélie Penguin .. .. .. .. 2·25 60
26 8 c. Rymill's "Fox Moth", 1934–7 .. .. 40 30
27 9 c. Leopard Seal (*horiz*) .. .. .. 40 30
28 10 c. Killer Whale (*horiz*) .. .. .. 5·50 1·25
a. Buff (overlay on seals) omitted .. .. £650
29 20 c. Wandering Albatross (*horiz*) .. .. 90 60
30 25 c. Wilkins' Lockheed "Vega", 1928 (*horiz*) 50 60
31 30 c. Ellsworth's Northrop "Gamma", 1935 .. 50 60
32 35 c. Christensen's Avro "Avian", 1934 (*horiz*) 50 60
33 50 c. Byrd's "Tri-Motor", 1929 .. .. 60 60
34 $1 Sperm Whale .. .. .. .. 1·00 1·40
23/34 .. .. .. .. .. *Set of* 12 11·50 6·50
Issued Macquarie Island 29.11.73, Mawson 30.12.73, Davis 10.1.74 and Casey 31.1.74.

(Des R. Honisett. Litho Asher and Co, Melbourne)

**1979** (20 June). 50*th Anniv of First Flight over South Pole. T* 14 *and similar horiz design. Multicoloured. P* 15½.
35 20 c. Type 14 .. .. .. .. .. 50 40
36 55 c. Admiral Byrd, aircraft and Antarctic terrain .. .. .. .. .. 1·25 1·60
Issued Macquarie Island 24.10.79, Davis 3.1.80, Mawson 13.1.80 and Casey 9.2.80.

15 M.V. *Thala Dan* — 16 Sir Douglas Mawson in Antarctic Terrain

(Des R. Honisett, Litho Asher and Co, Melbourne)

**1979** (29 Aug)–**81**. *Ships. Multicoloured designs as T* 15. *P* 13½ × 13 (*horiz*) *or* 13 × 13½ (*vert*).
37 1 c. S.Y. *Aurora* (*horiz*) (21.5.80) .. .. 10 10
38 2 c. R.Y. *Penola* (9.9.81) .. .. .. 20 10
39 5 c. Type 15 .. .. .. .. .. 20 30
40 10 c. H.M.S. *Challenger* (*horiz*) (9.9.81) .. 35 10
41 15 c. S.S. *Morning** (bow view) (*horiz*) (21.5.80) 1·60 2·50
42 15 c. S.Y. *Nimrod* (stern view) (*horiz*) (9.9.81) 75 30
43 20 c. R.R.S. *Discovery II* (*horiz*) .. .. 40 70
44 22 c. R.Y.S. *Terra Nova* (21.5.80) .. .. 70 90
45 25 c. S.S. *Endurance* .. .. .. .. 60 85
46 30 c. S.S. *Fram* (*horiz*) .. .. .. 60 85
47 35 c. M.S. *Nella Dan* (*horiz*) (21.5.80) .. 80 85
48 40 c. M.S. *Kista Dan* (9.9.81) .. .. 90 45
49 45 c. *L'Astrolabe* (*horiz*) (9.9.81) .. .. 70 50
50 50 c. S.S. *Norvegia* (*horiz*) (9.9.81) .. .. 70 55
51 55 c. S.Y. *Discovery* .. .. .. .. 85 1·60
52 $1 H.M.S. *Resolution* (21.5.80) .. .. 1·75 2·25
37/52 .. .. .. .. .. *Set of* 16 10·00 11·50
*No. 41 is incorrectly inscribed "S.Y. *Nimrod*".
On No. 46 the S.S. *Fram* is shown flying the Icelandic ensign, instead of the Norwegian.

Nos. 37, 41, 44, 47 and 52 issued Macquarie Island 27.10.80, Casey 1.12.80, Mawson 5.12.80 and Davis 11.12.80.
Nos. 38, 40, 42 and 48/50 issued Macquarie Island 21.10.81, Mawson 25.11.81, Davis 11.1.82 and Casey 25.1.82.
Nos. 39, 43, 45/6 and 51 issued Macquarie Island 24.10.79, Davis 3.1.80, Mawson 13.1.80 and Casey 9.2.80.

(Des R. Honisett. Litho Cambec Press, Melbourne)

**1982** (5 May). *Birth Centenary of Sir Douglas Mawson (Antarctic explorer). T* 16 *and similar vert design. Multicoloured. P* 14 × 13½.
53 27 c. Type 16 .. .. .. .. .. 50 30
54 75 c. Sir Douglas Mawson and map of Australian Antarctic Territory .. .. 1·50 2·25
Issued Macquarie Island 26.10.82, Casey 16.1.83, Davis 10.2.83 and Mawson 2.3.83.

17 Light-mantled Sooty Albatross — 18 Antarctic Scientist

(Des R. Honisett. Litho Leigh-Mardon Ltd, Melbourne)

**1983** (6 Apr). *Regional Wildlife. T* 17 *and similar vert designs. Multicoloured. P* 14½.
55 27 c. Type 17 .. .. .. .. .. 80 80
a. Horiz strip of 5. Nos. 55/9 .. .. 3·50
56 27 c. King Cormorant .. .. .. .. 80 80
57 27 c. Southern Elephant-Seal .. .. .. 80 80
58 27 c. Royal Penguin .. .. .. .. 80 80
59 27 c. Dove Prion .. .. .. .. .. 80 80
55/9 .. .. .. .. .. *Set of* 5 3·50 3·50
Nos. 55/9 were issued together, *se-tenant*, in horizontal strips of five, forming a composite design.
Issued Macquarie Island 21.10.83, Mawson 9.12.83, Casey 1.1.84 and Davis 2.1.84.

(Des R. Honisett. Litho Leigh-Mardon Ltd, Melbourne)

**1983** (17 Sept). 12*th Antarctic Treaty Consultative Meeting, Canberra. P* 14½.
60 18 27 c. multicoloured .. .. .. .. 75 50
Issued Macquarie Island 21.10.83, Mawson 9.12.83, Casey 1.1.84 and Davis 2.1.84.

19 Prismatic Compass and Lloyd-Creak Dip Circle — 20 Dog Team pulling Sledge

(Des R. Fletcher. Litho Leigh-Mardon Ltd, Melbourne)

**1984** (16 Jan). 75*th Anniv of Magnetic Pole Expedition. T* 19 *and similar horiz design. Multicoloured. P* 14½.
61 30 c. Type 19 .. .. .. .. .. 85 40
62 85 c. Aneroid barometer and theodolite .. 1·90 1·25
Issued Macquarie Island 23.10.84, Mawson 15.11.84, Casey 16.11.84 and Davis 1.2.85.

(Des G. Emery. Litho Cambec Press, Melbourne)

**1984** (18 July)–**87**. *Antarctic Scenes. T* 20 *and similar multicoloured designs. P* 14½ (2 *c.*, 10 *c.*, 20 *c.*, 36 *c.*, 60 *c.*), 14 × 13½ (45 *c.*, 90 *c.*) *or* 13½ × 14 (*others*).
63 2 c. Summer afternoon, Mawson Station (11.3.87) .. .. .. .. .. 10 10
64 5 c. Type 20 .. .. .. .. .. 10 10
65 10 c. Late summer evening, MacRobertson Land (11.3.87) .. .. .. .. 10 15
66 15 c. Prince Charles Mountains (7.8.85) .. 15 20
67 20 c. Summer morning, Wilkes Land (11.3.87) 20 25
68 25 c. Sea-ice and iceberg .. .. .. 25 30
69 30 c. Mount Coates .. .. .. .. 30 35
70 33 c. "Iceberg Alley", Mawson (7.8.85) .. 30 35
71 36 c. Early winter evening, Casey Station (11.3.87) .. .. .. .. .. 35 40
72 45 c. Brash ice (*vert*) (7.8.85) .. .. .. 40 45
73 60 c. Midwinter shadows, Casey Station (11.3.87) .. .. .. .. .. 55 60
74 75 c. Coastline .. .. .. .. .. 70 75
75 85 c. Landing strip .. .. .. .. 80 85
76 90 c. Pancake ice (*vert*) (7.8.85) .. .. 85 90
77 $1 Emperor Penguins (7.8.85) (Optd S. 50p) 90 95
64/77 .. .. .. .. .. *Set of* 15 5·25 6·00
Nos. 63, 65, 67, 71 and 73 issued Macquarie Island 6.10.87, Davis 25.11.87, Mawson 1.1.88 and Casey 13.1.88.
Nos. 64, 68/9 and 74/5 issued Macquarie Island 23.10.84, Mawson 15.11.84, Casey 16.11.84 and Davis 1.2.85.
Nos. 66, 70, 72 and 76/7 issued Heard Island 1.11.85, Casey 31.11.85, Mawson 6.12.85, Macquarie Island 6.12.85 and Davis 11.12.85.

**21** Prince Charles Mountains near Mawson Station

**22** Hourglass Dolphins and *Nella Dan*

(Des A. McGregor. Litho Cambec Press, Melbourne)

**1986** (17 Sept). *25th Anniv of Antarctic Treaty. P* 14 × 13½.

| | | | | |
|---|---|---|---|---|
| 78 | **21** | 36 c. multicoloured .. .. .. .. .. | 1·25 | 35 |

Issued Mawson 9.11.86, Davis 15.11.86, Casey 23.11.86 and Macquarie Island 7.12.86.

(Des Trish Hart. Litho CPE Australia Ltd, Melbourne)

**1988** (20 July). *Environment, Conservation and Technology. T* **22** *and similar square designs. Multicoloured. P* 13.

| | | | |
|---|---|---|---|
| 79 | 37 c. Type **22** .. .. .. .. | 65 | 60 |
| | a. Horiz strip of 5. Nos. 79/83 .. .. | 3·00 | |
| 80 | 37 c. Emperor Penguins and Davis Station .. | 65 | 60 |
| 81 | 37 c. Crabeater Seal and helicopter .. .. | 65 | 60 |
| 82 | 37 c. Adelie Penguins and tracked vehicle .. | 65 | 60 |
| 83 | 37 c. Grey-headed Albatross and photographer .. .. .. .. | 65 | 60 |
| 79/83 | .. .. .. .. *Set of* 5 | 3·00 | 2·75 |

Nos. 79/83 were printed together, *se-tenant*, in horizontal strips of five throughout the sheet.

Issued Macquarie Island 29.10.88, Casey 14.12.88, Mawson 21.12.88 and Davis 29.12.88.

**23** "Antarctica"

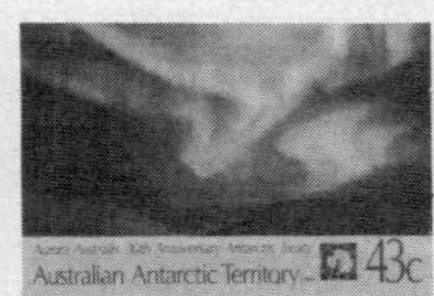

**24** Aurora Australis

(Des Janet Boschen. Litho CPE Australia Ltd, Melbourne)

**1989** (14 June). *Antarctic Landscape Paintings by Sir Sidney Nolan. T* **23** *and similar vert designs. Multicoloured. P* 14 × 13½.

| | | | |
|---|---|---|---|
| 84 | 39 c. Type **23** .. .. .. .. .. | 60 | 50 |
| 85 | 39 c. "Iceberg Alley" .. .. .. .. | 60 | 50 |
| 86 | 60 c. "Glacial Flow" .. .. .. .. | 85 | 75 |
| 87 | 80 c. "Frozen Sea" .. .. .. .. | 1·10 | 1·00 |
| 84/7 | .. .. .. .. *Set of* 4 | 2·75 | 2·50 |

Issued Casey 28.10.89, Davis 29.10.89, Mawson 17.11 89 and Macquarie Island 24.11.89.

Supplies of Australia Nos. 1261/3 were sent to the Antarctic and were issued at Macquarie Island on 24.11.90, Mawson 10.12.90, Davis 14.12.90 and Casey 19.12.90

(Des Lynette Brown. Litho Leigh-Mardon Ltd, Melbourne)

**1991** (20 June). *30th Anniv of Antarctic Treaty* (43 c.) *and Maiden Voyage of* Aurora Australis (*research ship*) ($1.20). *T* **24** *and similar horiz design. Multicoloured. P* 14½.

| | | | |
|---|---|---|---|
| 88 | 43 c. Type **24** .. .. .. .. .. | 50 | 50 |
| 89 | $1.20, *Aurora Australis* off Heard Island (optd S. 55p.) .. .. .. .. | 1·40 | 1·40 |

# Baghdad *see* Iraq

# Bahamas

The British Post Office at Nassau was established during the early days of the West Indies packet system, and was certainly operating by 1733. The first known local postmark dates from 1802.

The crowned-circle handstamps Nos. CC1/2 were issued in 1846 and were generally replaced, for the public mails, by various stamps of Great Britain in 1858.

Local mail deliveries were rudimentary until 1859 when Nos. 1/2 were issued by the colonial authorities for interisland mails. Examples used for this purpose are usually cancelled in manuscript or with a "27" postmark. The "local" 1d. stamp became valid for overseas mails in May, 1860, when the colonial authorities took over this service from the British G.P.O.

For illustrations of the handstamp and postmark types see BRITISH POST OFFICES ABROAD notes, following GREAT BRITAIN.

NASSAU

CROWNED-CIRCLE HANDSTAMPS

CC1 CC1 BAHAMAS (Nassau) (18.5.1846) (R.)
*Price on cover* £1500

No. CC1 was later struck in black and used as an Official Paid mark between July 1899 and September 1935. Handstamps as Types CC 2 and CC 3 (only three known) struck in black were used for the same purpose from 1933 until 1953; but it is believed that these were never employed during the pre-stamp period. *Price on cover from* £50.

*Stamps of* GREAT BRITAIN *cancelled* "A 05" *as Type* 2.

**1858 to 1860.**

Z1 1d. rose-red (1857), *perf* 14 .. .. .. .. £1600
Z2 2d. blue (1858) (Plate Nos. 7, 8) .. .. .. £1300
Z3 4d. rose (1857) .. .. .. .. .. £450
Z4 6d. lilac (1856) .. .. .. .. .. £350
Z5 1s. green (1856) .. .. .. .. .. £2000

| PRICES FOR STAMPS ON COVER TO 1945 | |
|---|---|
| Nos. 1/19a | *from* × 5 |
| Nos. 20/5 | *from* × 10 |
| Nos. 26/31 | *from* × 4 |
| No. 33 | *from* × 20 |
| Nos. 35/44a | *from* × 5 |
| Nos. 45/57 | *from* × 4 |
| Nos. 58/89 | *from* × 2 |
| Nos. 90/130 | *from* × 3 |
| Nos. 131/2 | *from* × 10 |
| Nos. 141/5 | *from* × 4 |
| Nos. 146/8 | *from* × 6 |
| Nos. 149/57 | *from* × 3 |
| Nos. 158/60 | *from* × 4 |
| No. 161 | *from* × 8 |
| Nos. 162/75 | *from* × 5 |
| No. S1 | *from* × 30 |
| Nos. S2/3 | *from* × 20 |

CROWN COLONY

1

2

3

(Eng and recess P.B.)

**1859** (10 June). *No wmk. Imperf. (a) Thick paper.*
1 1 1d. reddish lake .. .. .. .. .. £4500 £2250
*a. Brown-lake* .. .. .. .. £4500 £2250

*(b) Thin paper*
2 1 1d. dull lake .. .. .. .. .. 38·00 £1500

Collectors are warned against false postmarks upon the remainder stamps of 1d., imperf, on thin paper.

**1860** (Oct). *No wmk. Clean-cut perf* 14 *to* 16.
3 1 1d. lake .. .. .. .. .. .. £2250 £650

**1861** (June)–**62**. *No Wmk. (a) Rough perf* 14 *to* 16
4 1 1d. lake .. .. .. .. .. .. £750 £300
5 2 4d. dull rose (Dec, 1861).. .. .. .. £1400 £375
a. Imperf between (pair) .. .. .. £12000
6 6d. grey-lilac (Dec, 1861) .. .. .. £2500 £450
*a. Pale dull lilac* .. .. .. .. £2500 £450

*(b) P* 11 *to* 12½ (1862)
7 1 1d. lake .. .. .. .. .. .. £2000

No. 7 was a perforation trial on a new machine at Perkins, Bacon. It was not sent out to the Colony and is also known part perforated.

(Recess D.L.R.)

**1862.** *No wmk.* (a) P* 11½, 12.
8 1 1d. carmine-lake .. .. .. .. £750 £150
9 1d. lake .. .. .. .. .. £750 £160
10 2 4d. dull rose .. .. .. .. £3000 £375
11 6d. lavender-grey .. .. .. .. £3250 £400

*(b) P* 11½, 12, *compound with* 11
12 1 1d. carmine-lake .. .. .. .. £1800 £850
13 1d. lake .. .. .. .. .. £1800 £850
14 2 4d. dull rose .. .. .. .. £8500 £1800
15 6d. lavender-grey .. .. .. .. £9500 £1400

*(c) P* 13
16 1 1d. lake .. .. .. .. .. .. £650 £140
17 1d. brown-lake .. .. .. .. .. £650 £120
18 2 4d. dull rose .. .. .. .. .. £2500 £375
19 6d. lavender-grey .. .. .. .. £2750 £375
*a. Lilac* .. .. .. .. .. .. £2500 £500

*Stamps exist with part of papermaker's sheet wmk ("T. H. SAUNDERS" and date).

(T 3 Typo D.L.R.)

**1863–77.** *Wmk Crown CC. (a) P* 12½
20 1 1d. brown-lake .. .. .. .. .. 85·00 55·00
21 1d. carmine-lake .. .. .. .. .. 90·00 60·00
22 1d. carmine-lake (aniline) .. .. .. 95·00 60·00
23 1d. rose-red .. .. .. .. .. 55·00 40·00
24 1d. red .. .. .. .. .. .. 60·00 40·00
25 1d. vermilion .. .. .. .. .. 60·00 40·00
26 2 4d. dull rose .. .. .. .. .. £350 60·00
27 4d. bright rose .. .. .. .. .. £225 60·00
28 4d. brownish rose .. .. .. .. £350 80·00
28*a* 6d. rose-lilac .. .. .. .. .. £4250
29 6d. lilac (*shades*) .. .. .. .. £275 60·00
30 6d. deep violet .. .. .. .. .. £160 60·00
31 6d. violet (aniline) .. .. .. .. £250 90·00

No. 28*a*, believed to be the shade of the first printing only, is a very rare stamp, not to be confused with No. 29.

*(b) P* 14
33 1 1d. scarlet-vermilion (1877) .. .. .. 38·00 15·00
34 1d. scarlet (or scarlet-vermilion) (aniline) £1400 †
35 2 4d. bright rose (1876) .. .. .. .. £350 40·00
36 4d. dull rose .. .. .. .. .. £1500 40·00
37 4d. rose-lake .. .. .. .. .. £350 40·00

No. 34 is not known postally used, although manuscript fiscal cancellations are recorded on this shade.

(Typo D.L.R.)

**1863–80.** *Wmk Crown CC. (a) P* 12½.
38 3 1s. green (1865) .. .. .. .. .. £2500 £300

*(b) P* 14
39 3 1s. dark green .. .. .. .. .. £100 35·00
39*a* 1s. green (*thick paper*) (1880) .. .. .. 6·50 7·00

**1882** (March). *Wmk Crown CA. (a) P* 12.
40 1 1d. scarlet-vermilion .. .. .. .. 35·00 12·00
41 2 4d. rose .. .. .. .. .. .. £550 45·00

*(b) P* 14
42 1 1d. scarlet-vermilion .. .. .. .. £350 55·00
43 2 4d. rose .. .. .. .. .. .. £750 55·00

**1882** (Mar)–**98.** *Wmk Crown CA. P* 14.
44 3 1s. green .. .. .. .. .. .. 30·00 14·00
44*a* 1s. blue-green (1898) .. .. .. .. 35·00 20·00

FOURPENCE
(4)

5

Malformed "E"

**1883.** *No.* 30 *surch with T* 4.
45 2 4d. on 6d. deep violet .. .. .. .. £550 £400
a. Surch inverted .. .. .. .. .. £5000 £3500

Type 4 was applied by handstamp and occurs in various positions.

Caution is needed in buying Nos. 45 and 45a.

(Typo D.L.R.)

**1884–88.** *Wmk Crown CA. P* 14.
47 5 1d. pale rose .. .. .. .. .. 27·00 9·00
48 1d. carmine-rose .. .. .. .. .. 3·75 1·50
49 1d. bright carmine (aniline) .. .. .. 2·75 5·50
50 2½d. dull blue (1888) .. .. .. .. 32·00 15·00
51 2½d. blue .. .. .. .. .. .. 26·00 7·00
52 2½d. ultramarine .. .. .. .. .. 8·50 1·50
53 4d. deep yellow .. .. .. .. .. 8·50 3·75
54 6d. mauve (1890) .. .. .. .. .. 4·00 22·00
a. Malformed "E" (R.6/6) .. .. .. £140 £275
56 5s. sage-green .. .. .. .. .. 60·00 65·00
57 £1 Venetian red .. .. .. .. .. £300 £225
47/57 .. .. .. .. .. *Set of* 6 £350 £300
50 & 54 Optd "Specimen" .. .. .. *Set of* 2 £130

6 Queen's Staircase, Nassau

7

8

(Recess D.L.R.)

**1901** (23 Sept)–**03.** *Wmk Crown CC. P* 14.
58 6 1d. black and red .. .. .. .. .. 6·00 2·50
59 5d. black and orange (1.03) .. .. .. 8·00 35·00
60 2s. black and blue (1.03) .. .. .. .. 17·00 40·00
61 3s. black and green (1.03) .. .. .. .. 20·00 40·00
58/61 .. .. .. .. .. *Set of* 4 45·00 £110
58/61 Optd "Specimen" .. .. .. *Set of* 4 £120

For stamps in this design, but with Mult Crown CA or Mult Script CA watermarks see Nos 75/80 and 111/14.

(Typo D.L.R.)

**1902** (18 Dec)–**10.** *Wmk Crown CA. P* 14.
62 7 1d. carmine .. .. .. .. .. .. 1·50 90
63 2½d. ultramarine .. .. .. .. .. 6·50 1·25
64 4d. orange .. .. .. .. .. .. 11·00 30·00
65 4d. deep yellow (3.10) .. .. .. .. 13·00 32·00
66 6d. brown .. .. .. .. .. .. 5·50 12·00
a. Malformed "E" (R.6/6) .. .. .. £130 £180
67 1s. grey-black and carmine .. .. .. 12·00 28·00
68 1s. brownish grey and carmine (6.07) .. 13·00 28·00
69 5s. dull purple and blue .. .. .. .. 48·00 60·00
70 £1 green and black .. .. .. .. .. £250 £300
62/70 .. .. .. .. .. *Set of* 7 £300 £375
62/70 Optd "Specimen" .. .. .. *Set of* 7 £300

**1906** (Apr)–**11.** *Wmk Mult Crown CA. P* 14.
71 7 ½d. pale green (5.06) Optd S. £50) .. .. 3·25 1·25
72 1d. carmine-rose .. .. .. .. .. 9·50 90
73 2½d. ultramarine (4.07) .. .. .. .. 16·00 24·00
74 6d. bistre-brown (8.11) .. .. .. .. 16·00 48·00
a. Malformed "E" (R.6/6) .. .. .. £275 £475
71/4 .. .. .. .. .. *Set of* 4 40·00 65·00

**1911** (Feb)–**19.** *Wmk Mult Crown CA. P* 14.
75 6 1d. black and red .. .. .. .. .. 7·50 2·00
*a. Grey-black and scarlet* (1916) .. .. 2·00 2·50
*b. Grey-black & deep carmine-red* (1919) 3·00 4·00
76 3d. purple/*yellow* (*thin paper*) (18.5.17) .. 3·50 14·00
*a. Reddish purple/buff (thick paper)* (1.19) .. .. .. .. .. 3·25 4·50
77 3d. black and brown (21.3.19) .. .. .. 55 2·25
78 5d. black and mauve (18.5.17) .. .. .. 2·25 5·50
79 2s. black and blue (11.16) .. .. .. .. 18·00 35·00
80 3s. black and green (8.17) .. .. .. .. 38·00 42·00
75/80 .. .. .. .. .. *Set of* 6 55·00 80·00
76/8 Optd "Specimen" .. .. .. *Set of* 3 £100

(Typo D.L.R.)

**1912–19.** *Wmk Mult Crown CA. Chalk-surfaced paper* (1s. *to* £1). *P* 14.
81 8 ½d. green .. .. .. .. .. .. 80 5·50
*a. Yellow-green* .. .. .. .. .. 1·50 6·00
82 1d. carmine (aniline) .. .. .. .. .. 90 30
*a. Deep rose* .. .. .. .. .. 3·25 1·25
*b. Rose* .. .. .. .. .. .. 6·50 2·00
83 2d. grey (1919) .. .. .. .. .. 2·25 3·00
84 2½d. ultramarine .. .. .. .. .. 4·50 15·00
*a. Deep dull blue* .. .. .. .. .. 11·00 21·00
85 4d. orange-yellow .. .. .. .. .. 4·50 15·00
*a. Yellow* .. .. .. .. .. .. 2·25 9·00
86 6d. bistre-brown .. .. .. .. .. 1·75 4·00
a. Malformed "E" (R.6/6) .. .. .. 50·00 75·00
87 1s. grey-black and carmine .. .. .. 1·75 7·50
*a. Jet-black and carmine* .. .. .. 12·00 18·00
88 5s. dull purple and blue .. .. .. .. 26·00 55·00
*a. Pale dull purple and deep blue* .. .. 35·00 60·00
89 £1 dull green and black .. .. .. .. £150 £275
*a. Green and black* .. .. .. .. £180 £275
81/9 .. .. .. .. .. *Set of* 9 £170 £325
81/9 Optd "Specimen" .. .. .. *Set of* 9 £300

1.1.17.
(9)

WAR TAX
(10)

**1917** (18 May). *No.* 75*b optd with T* 9 *in red by D.L.R.*
90 6 1d. grey-black and deep carmine-red (Optd S. £60) .. .. .. .. .. 30 85
a. Long stroke to "7" (R.4/6) .. .. .. 45·00 65·00

It was originally intended to issue No. 90 on 1 January 1917, but the stamps were not received in the Bahamas until May. Half the proceeds from their sale were donated to the British Red Cross Society.

**1918** (21 Feb–10 July). *Nos.* 75/6, 81/2 *and* 87 *optd at Nassau with T* 10.
91 8 ½d. green .. .. .. .. .. .. 4·50 18·00
a. Opt double .. .. .. .. .. £800 £800
b. Opt inverted .. .. .. .. .. £800
92 1d. carmine (aniline) .. .. .. .. .. 30 50
a. Opt double .. .. .. .. .. £800 £800
b. Opt inverted .. .. .. .. .. £800
93 6 1d. black and red (10 July) .. .. .. 1·60 2·50
a. Opt double, one inverted .. .. .. £700
b. Opt double .. .. .. .. .. £1100
c. Opt inverted .. .. .. .. .. £900 £950
94 3d. purple/*yellow* (*thin paper*) .. .. .. 2·00 2·25
a. Opt double .. .. .. .. .. £950 £850
b. Opt inverted .. .. .. .. .. £850 £850
95 8 1s. grey-black and carmine .. .. .. 65·00 95·00
a. Opt double .. .. .. .. .. £1900
91/5 .. .. .. .. .. *Set of* 5 65·00 £100

No. 93 was only on sale for ten days.

WAR TAX
(11)

WAR TAX
(12)

WAR CHARITY 3.6.18.
(13)

**1918** (1 June–20 July). *Optd by D.L.R. in London with T* 11 *or* 12 (3*d*).
96 8 ½d. green .. .. .. .. .. .. 30 1·40
97 1d. carmine .. .. .. .. .. .. 30 35
a. Wmk sideways .. .. .. .. .. £500
98 6 3d. purple/*yellow* (20 July) .. .. .. 40 1·50
99 8 1s. grey-black and carmine (R.) .. .. 2·50 2·75
96/9 .. .. .. .. .. *Set of* 4 3·25 5·50
96/9 Optd "Specimen" .. .. .. *Set of* 4 £130

**1919** (21 Mar). *No. 77 optd with T* **12** *by D.L.R.*
100 **6** 3d. black and brown (Optd S. £45) .. 30 4·00
a. "C" and "A" missing from wmk ..

No. 100a shows the "C" omitted from one impression and the "A" missing from the next one to the right (as seen from the front of the stamp). The "C" is badly distorted in the second watermark.

**1919** (1 Jan). *No. 75b optd with T* **13** *by D.L.R.*
101 **6** 1d. grey-black and deep carmine-red (R.) (Optd S. £50) .. .. .. .. 30 2·25
a. Opt double .. .. .. .. £1300

The date is that originally fixed for the issue of the stamp. The year 1918 was also the bicentenary of the appointment of the first Royal governor.

WAR WAR

TAX TAX

(14) (15)

**1919** (14 July). *(a) Optd with T* **14** *by D.L.R.*
102 **8** ½d. green (R.) .. .. .. .. .. 20 1·25
103 1d. carmine .. .. .. .. 20 1·50
104 1s. grey-black and carmine (R.) .. .. 4·75 18·00
*(b) No. 77 optd with T* **15**
105 **6** 3d. black and brown .. .. .. .. 30 5·00
102/5 .. .. .. .. .. *Set of* 4 5·00 23·00
102/5 Optd "Specimen" .. .. *Set of* 4 £120

**16**

**17** Great Seal of the Bahamas.

(Recess D.L.R.)

**1920** (1 Mar). *Peace Celebration. Wmk Mult Crown CA* (sideways). *P* 14.
106 **16** ½d. green .. .. .. .. .. 55 3·50
107 1d. carmine .. .. .. .. .. 2·50 70
108 2d. slate-grey .. .. .. .. .. 2·50 6·50
109 3d. deep brown .. .. .. .. 2·50 8·50
110 1s. deep myrtle-green .. .. .. 10·00 27·00
106/10 .. .. .. .. *Set of* 5 16·00 42·00
106/10 Optd "Specimen" .. .. *Set of* 5 £150

**1921** (29 Mar)–**29**. *Wmk Script CA. P* 14.
111 **6** 1d. grey and rose-red .. .. .. 70 1·00
112 5d. black and purple (8.29) .. .. 3·00 23·00
113 2s. black and blue (11.22) .. .. 15·00 28·00
114 3s. black and green (9.24) .. .. 26·00 48·00
111/14 .. .. .. .. *Set of* 4 40·00 90·00
111/14 Optd/Perf "Specimen" .. *Set of* 4 £160

F PENN

Elongated "E" (left pane R. 9/6)

**1921** (8 Sept)–**37**. *Wmk Mult Script CA. Chalk-surfaced paper* (*3d., 1s., 5s., £1*). *P* 14.
115 **8** ½d. green (1924) .. .. .. 20 40
a. Elongated "E" .. .. ..
116 1d. carmine .. .. .. .. 60 15
117 1½d. brown-red (1934) .. .. .. 85 1·00
118 2d. grey (1927) .. .. .. .. 85 2·75
119 2½d. ultramarine (1922) .. .. .. 70 2·75
120 3d. purple/*pale yellow* (1931) .. .. 4·50 15·00
*a. Purple/orange-yellow* (1937) .. 4·50 15·00
121 4d. orange-yellow (1924) .. .. .. 70 5·00
122 6d. bistre-brown (1922) .. .. .. 60 1·25
a. Malformed "E" (R.6/6) .. .. 45·00 65·00
123 1s. black and carmine (1926) .. .. 2·50 5·50
124 5s dull purple and blue (1924) .. 27·00 42·00
125 £1 green and black (1926) .. .. £150 £250
115/25 .. .. .. .. *Set of* 11 £160 £275
115/25 Optd/Perf "Specimen" .. *Set of* 11 £350

(Recess B. W.)

**1930** (2 Jan). *Tercentenary of Colony. Wmk Mult Script CA. P* 12.
126 **17** 1d. black and scarlet .. .. .. 1·50 2·50
127 3d. black and deep brown .. .. 3·00 11·00
128 5d. black and deep purple .. .. 3·00 11·00
129 2s. black and deep blue .. .. 18·00 35·00
130 3s. black and green .. .. .. 32·00 55·00
126/30 .. .. .. *Set of* 5 50·00 £100
126/30 Perf "Specimen" .. .. *Set of* 5 £150

**18**

(Recess B.W.)

**1931.** *Wmk Mult Script CA. P* 12.
131 **18** 2s. black and deep blue .. .. 1·50 50
*a. Slate-purple and deep blue* .. 19·00 11·00
132 3s. black and green .. .. 1·50 85
*a. Slate-purple and green* .. 19·00 11·00
137/8 Perf "Specimen" .. .. *Set of* 2 70·00

**1935** (6 May). *Silver Jubilee. As Nos.* 91/4 *of Antigua. P* 13½ × 14.
141 1½d. deep blue and carmine.. .. .. 70 90
h. Dot by flagstaff.. .. .. .. 38·00
i. Dash by turret .. .. .. .. 45·00
142 2½d. brown and deep blue .. .. 2·25 3·00
f. Diagonal line by turret .. .. 60·00
g. Dot to left of chapel .. .. .. 50·00
143 6d. light blue and olive-green .. .. 5·00 6·50
g. Dot to left of chapel .. .. .. 75·00
144 1s. slate and purple .. .. .. 6·00 8·00
h. Dot by flagstaff.. .. .. .. 95·00
141/4 .. .. .. .. *Set of* 4 12·50 17·00
141/4 Perf "Specimen" .. .. *Set of* 4 90·00

For illustrations of plate varieties see Catalogue Introduction.

**19** Greater Flamingos in flight

**20** King George VI

(Recess Waterlow)

**1935** (22 May). *Wmk Mult Script CA. P* 12½.
145 **19** 8d. ultramarine and scarlet .. .. 4·50 2·75
145 Perf "Specimen" .. .. .. .. 40·00

**1937** (12 May). *Coronation. As Nos.* 95/7 *of Antigua, but printed by D.L.R. P* 14.
146 ½d. green .. .. .. .. .. 15 15
147 1½d. yellow-brown .. .. .. .. 30 40
148 2½d. bright blue .. .. .. .. 50 60
146/8 .. .. .. .. *Set of* 3 85 1·00
146/8 Perf "Specimen" .. .. *Set of* 3 60·00

Short "T" in "TWO" (right pane R. 3/6) (Retouched on No. 152c, although bottom of letter is still pointed)

(Typo D.L.R.)

**1938–52.** *Wmk Mult Script CA. Chalk-surfaced paper* (*1s. to £1*). *P* 14.
149 **20** ½d. bluish green (11.3.38) .. .. 15 60
a. Elongated "E" .. .. .. 15·00
*b. Myrtle-green* (11.12.46) .. .. 1·25 1·25
ba. Elongated "E" .. .. .. 38·00
149*c* ½d. brown-purple (18.2.52) .. .. 40 2·50
ca. Error. Crown missing .. .. £2000
cb. Error. St. Edward's Crown .. £1400
cc. Elongated "E" .. .. .. 22·00
150 1d. carmine (11.3.38) .. .. .. 8·50 4·75
150*a* 1d. grey (17.9.41) .. .. .. 20 30
151 1½d. red-brown (19.4.38) .. .. 40 55
*a. Pale red-brown* (19.4.48) .. .. 1·25 90
152 2d. grey (19.4.38) .. .. .. 13·00 9·00
a. Short T .. .. .. .. £140
152*b* 2d. scarlet (17.9.41) .. .. .. 30 55
ba. Short T .. .. .. .. 40·00
bb. "TWO PENCE" printed double .. † £2250
152*c* 2d. green (1.5.51) .. .. .. 30 80
153 2½d. blue (11.3.38) .. .. .. 3·00 2·00
153*a* 2½d. violet (1.7.43) .. .. .. 30 55
ab. "2½ PENNY" printed double .. £2000
154 3d. violet (19.4.38) .. .. .. 10·00 5·00
154*a* 3d. blue (4.43) .. .. .. .. 30 90
154*b* 3d. scarlet (1.2.52) .. .. .. 50 2·75
154*c* 10d. yellow-orange (18.11.46) .. .. 1·50 20
155 1s. black and carmine (15.9.38) .. 1·75 30
a. Ordinary paper (9.42) .. .. 1·75 30
156 5s. lilac and blue (19.4.38) .. .. £150 90·00
a. Ordinary paper. *Purple and blue* (9.42) .. .. .. .. 22·00 7·50
*b. Deep purple and bright blue* (19.4.48) .. .. .. .. 20·00 5·00
157 £1 green and black (15.9.38) .. .. £190 £120
a. Ordinary paper. *Blue-green and black* (5.43) .. .. .. .. 48·00 32·00
149/157*a* .. .. .. .. *Set of* 17 £100 60·00
149/157 Perf "Specimen" .. .. *Set of* 14 £400

Nos. 149/50*a* exist in coils, constructed from normal sheets.

No. 149cb occurs on a row in the watermark in which the crowns and letters "C A" alternate.

The ordinary paper of Nos. 155a, 156a and 157a is thick, smooth and opaque, and was used for printings between September 1942 and 1944 as a substitute for chalk-surfaced paper.

**21** Sea Garden, Nassau

**22** Fort Charlotte

**23** Greater Flamingos in Flight

(Recess Waterlow)

**1938** (1 July). *Wmk Mult Script CA. P* 12½.
158 **21** 4d. light blue and red-orange .. .. 80 30
159 **22** 6d. olive-green and light blue .. .. 60 25
160 **23** 8d. ultramarine and scarlet .. .. 2·50 90
158/60 .. .. .. .. *Set of* 3 3·50 1·25
158/60 Perf "Specimen" .. .. *Set of* 3 90·00

3d. (24)

1492 LANDFALL OF COLUMBUS 1942 (25)

**1940** (28 Nov). *No.* 153 *surcharged with T* **24** *by* The Nassau Guardian.
161 **20** 3d. on 2½d. blue .. .. .. .. 40 40

**1942** (12 Oct). *450th Anniv of Landing of Columbus in New World. Optd as T* **25** *by* The Nassau Guardian.
162 **20** ½d. bluish green .. .. .. .. 20 60
a. Elongated "E" .. .. .. 18·00
163 1d. grey .. .. .. .. .. 20 60
164 1½d. red-brown .. .. .. .. 30 50
165 2d. scarlet .. .. .. .. 30 65
a. Short T .. .. .. .. 35·00
166 2½d. blue .. .. .. .. .. 30 65
167 3d. blue .. .. .. .. .. 30 65
168 **21** 4d. light blue and red-orange .. .. 40 90
a. "COIUMBUS" .. .. .. £325 £350
169 **22** 6d. olive-green and light blue .. .. 40 1·75
a. "COIUMBUS" .. .. .. £350 £375
170 **23** 8d. ultramarine and scarlet .. .. 50 70
a. "COIUMBUS" .. .. .. £1800 £1400
171 **20** 1s. black and carmine .. .. .. 75 80
a. Ordinary paper .. .. .. 75 80
172 **18** 2s. black and deep blue .. .. .. 6·50 8·00
*a. Slate-purple and deep blue* .. 13·00 13·00
b. Stop after "COLUMBUS" (R. 2/12) £100
173 3s. black and green .. .. .. 22·00 18·00
*a. Slate-purple and green* .. .. 3·50 6·00
b. Stop after "COLUMBUS" (R. 2/12) 60·00
174 **20** 5s. purple and blue .. .. .. 10·00 8·00
a. Ordinary paper .. .. .. 8·50 8·00
175 £1 green and black .. .. .. 38·00 27·00
a. Ordinary paper. *Blue-green & black* 22·00 18·00
162/175 .. .. .. .. *Set of* 14 40·00 42·00
162/175 Perf "Specimen" .. .. *Set of* 14 £375

The "COIUMBUS" error (Nos. 168a, 169a, 170a) occurs on R.5/2.

**1946** (11 Nov). *Victory. As Nos.* 110/11 *of Antigua.*
176 1½d. brown .. .. .. .. .. 10 10
177 3d. blue .. .. .. .. .. 10 10
176/7 Perf "Specimen" .. .. *Set of* 2 50·00

**26** Infant Welfare Clinic

(Recess C.B.N.)

**1948** (11 Oct). *Tercentenary of Settlement of Island of Eleuthera. T* **26** *and similar horiz designs. P* 12.
178 ½d. orange .. .. .. .. .. 20 50
179 1d. sage-green .. .. .. .. 20 35
180 1½d. yellow .. .. .. .. .. 25 70
181 2d. scarlet .. .. .. .. .. 30 40
182 2½d. brown-lake .. .. .. .. 35 60
183 3d. ultramarine .. .. .. .. 40 75
184 4d. black .. .. .. .. .. 40 70
185 6d. emerald-green .. .. .. .. 1·00 70
186 8d. violet .. .. .. .. .. 35 70
187 10d. carmine .. .. .. .. .. 35 35
188 1s. sepia .. .. .. .. .. 60 30
189 2s. magenta .. .. .. .. .. 4·00 7·50
190 3s. blue .. .. .. .. .. 6·00 7·50
191 5s. mauve .. .. .. .. .. 3·75 4·00
192 10s. grey .. .. .. .. .. 6·00 8·00
193 £1 vermilion .. .. .. .. 9·00 9·50
178/93 .. .. .. .. *Set of* 16 30·00 38·00

Designs:—1d. Agriculture (combine harvester); 1½d. Sisal; 2d. Straw work; 2½d. Dairy farm; 3d. Fishing fleet; 4d. Island settlement; 6d. Tuna fishing; 8d. Paradise Beach; 10d. Modern hotels; 1s. Yacht racing; 2s. Water sports (skiing); 3s. Shipbuilding; 5s. Transportation; 10s. Salt production; £1, Parliament Buildings.

**1948** (1 Dec). *Royal Silver Wedding. As Nos.* 112/13 *of Antigua.*
194 1½d. red-brown .. .. .. .. 15 25
195 £1 slate-green .. .. .. .. 28·00 26·00

**1949** (10 Oct). *75th Anniv of Universal Postal Union. As Nos.* 114/17 *of Antigua.*
196 2½d. violet .. .. .. .. .. 35 40
197 3d. deep blue .. .. .. .. .. 80 1·00
198 6d. greenish blue .. .. .. .. 90 1·00
199 1s. carmine .. .. .. .. .. 90 75
196/9 .. .. .. .. .. *Set of* 4 2·75 2·75

**1953** (3 June). *Coronation. As No. 120 of Antigua.*

| | | | |
|---|---|---|---|
| 200 | 6d. black and pale blue | 15 | 35 |

42 Infant Welfare Clinic

43 Queen Elizabeth II

(Recess B.W.)

**1954** (1 Jan)–**63**. *Designs previously used for King George VI issue, but with portrait of Queen Elizabeth II as in T* **42**, *and commemorative inscr omitted. Wmk Mult Script CA. P* 11 × 11½.

| | | | |
|---|---|---|---|
| 201 | ½d. black and red-orange | 10 | 40 |
| 202 | 1d. olive-green and brown | 10 | 10 |
| 203 | 1½d. blue and black | 15 | 40 |
| 204 | 2d. yellow-brown and myrtle-green | 15 | 15 |
| | *a. Yellow-brn & dp myrtle-grn* (23.1.62) | 1·25 | 1·25 |
| 205 | 3d. black and carmine-red | 30 | 30 |
| 206 | 4d. turquoise-green & deep reddish purple | 30 | 25 |
| | *a. Turq-blue & dp reddish pur* (23.1.62) | 2·75 | 3·00 |
| 207 | 5d. red-brown and deep bright blue | 1·40 | 2·25 |
| 208 | 6d. light blue and black | 30 | 10 |
| 209 | 8d. black and reddish lilac | 30 | 25 |
| | *a. Black and deep reddish lilac* (21.11.56) | 50 | 70 |
| 210 | 10d. black and ultramarine | 30 | 10 |
| | *a. Black and deep ultramarine* (8.1.63) | 1·75 | 1·00 |
| 211 | 1s. ultramarine and olive-brown | 40 | 10 |
| | *a. Ultramarine & dp olive-sepia* (19.2.58) | 60 | 10 |
| 212 | 2s. orange-brown and black | 1·75 | 70 |
| | *a. Chestnut and black* (19.2.58) | 4·00 | 1·50 |
| 213 | 2s. 6d. black and deep blue | 3·25 | 1·50 |
| 214 | 5s. bright emerald and orange | 12·00 | 75 |
| | *a. Brt emerald & reddish orange* (14.1.59) | 18·00 | 3·50 |
| 215 | 10s. black and slate-black | 6·50 | 1·75 |
| 216 | £1 slate-black and violet | 12·00 | 5·00 |
| 201/216 | *Set of* 16 | 35·00 | 12·00 |

Designs:—1d. Agriculture (combine harvester); 1½d. Island settlement; 2d. Straw work; 3d. Fishing fleet; 4d. Water sports (skiing); 5d. Dairy farm; 6d. Transportation; 8d. Paradise Beach; 10d. Modern hotels; 1s. Yacht racing; 2s. Sisal; 2s. 6d. Shipbuilding; 5s. Tuna fishing; 10s. Salt production; £1 Parliament Buildings.

Nos. 201/2, 205, 208 and 211 exist in coils, constructed from normal sheets.

See also No. 246.

(Recess Waterlow)

**1959** (10 June). *Centenary of First Bahamas Postage Stamp.* W w **12**. *P* 13½.

| | | | | |
|---|---|---|---|---|
| 217 | **43** | 1d. black and scarlet | 20 | 10 |
| 218 | | 2d. black and blue-green | 25 | 40 |
| 219 | | 6d. black and blue | 25 | 25 |
| 220 | | 10d. black and chocolate | 25 | 45 |
| 217/20 | | *Set of* 4 | 85 | 1·10 |

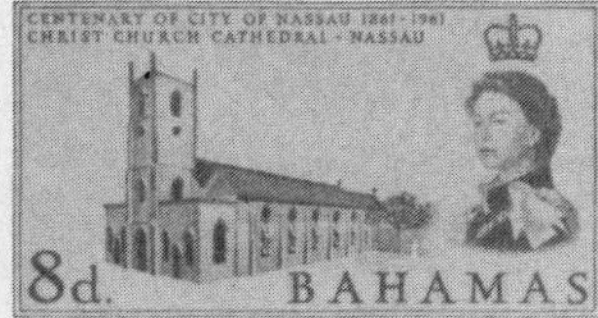


44 Christ Church Cathedral

(Photo Enschedé)

**1962** (30 Jan). *Nassau Centenary. T* **44** *and similar horiz design. P* 14 × 13.

| | | | |
|---|---|---|---|
| 221 | 8d. green | 25 | 20 |
| 222 | 10d. bluish violet | 25 | 15 |

Design:—10d. Nassau Public Library.

**1963** (4 June). *Freedom from Hunger. As No. 146 of Antigua.*

| | | | |
|---|---|---|---|
| 223 | 8d. sepia | 40 | 35 |
| | a. Name and value omitted | £800 | |

**BAHAMAS TALKS 1962**

(46)

**NEW CONSTITUTION 1964**

(47)

**1963** (15 July). *Bahamas Talks, 1962. Nos. 209/10 optd with T* **46**.

| | | | |
|---|---|---|---|
| 224 | 8d. black and reddish lilac | 40 | 45 |
| 225 | 10d. black and deep ultramarine | 50 | 55 |

**1963** (2 Sept). *Red Cross Centenary. As Nos. 147/8 of Antigua.*

| | | | |
|---|---|---|---|
| 226 | 1d. red and black | 25 | 30 |
| 227 | 10d. red and blue | 1·25 | 2·00 |

**SELF GOVERNMENT**

**1964** (7 Jan). *New Constitution. As Nos. 201/16 but* W w **12**, *optd with T* **47**, *by B.W.*

| | | | |
|---|---|---|---|
| 228 | ½d. black and red-orange | 10 | 30 |
| 229 | 1d. olive-green and brown | 10 | 15 |
| 230 | 1½d. blue and black | 40 | 30 |
| 231 | 2d. yellow-brown and deep myrtle-green | 10 | 20 |
| 232 | 3d. black and carmine-red | 40 | 30 |
| 233 | 4d. turquoise-blue and deep reddish purple | 40 | 45 |
| 234 | 5d. red-brown and deep bright blue | 30 | 65 |
| 235 | 6d. light blue and black | 30 | 30 |
| 236 | 8d. black and reddish lilac | 40 | 30 |
| 237 | 10d. black and deep ultramarine | 30 | 15 |
| 238 | 1s. ultramarine and olive-brown | 35 | 15 |
| 239 | 2s. chestnut and black | 1·50 | 1·75 |
| 240 | 2s. 6d. black and deep blue | 2·00 | 2·50 |
| 241 | 5s. bright emerald and orange | 4·25 | 3·25 |
| 242 | 10s. black and slate black | 4·00 | 5·50 |
| 243 | £1 slate-black and violet | 7·50 | 13·00 |
| 228/243 | *Set of* 16 | 20·00 | 26·00 |

**1964** (23 April). *400th Birth Anniv of William Shakespeare. As No. 164 of Antigua.*

| | | | |
|---|---|---|---|
| 244 | 6d. turquoise | 10 | 10 |

(48)

**1964** (1 Oct). *Olympic Games, Tokyo. As No. 211 but* W w **12**, *surch with T* **48**.

| | | | |
|---|---|---|---|
| 245 | 8d. on 1s. ultramarine and olive-brown | 10 | 10 |

**1964** (6 Oct). *As No. 204, but wmk* w **12**.

| | | | |
|---|---|---|---|
| 246 | 2d. yellow-brown and deep myrtle-green | 20 | 20 |

49 Colony's Badge

(64)

(Queen's portrait by Anthony Buckley. Litho and recess (portrait and "BAHAMAS") B.W.)

**1965** (7 Jan–14 Sept). *Horiz designs as T* **49**. W w **12**. *P* 13½.

| | | | |
|---|---|---|---|
| 247 | ½d. multicoloured | 15 | 60 |
| 248 | 1d. slate, light blue and orange | 25 | 20 |
| 249 | 1½d. rose-red, green and brown | 15 | 70 |
| 250 | 2d. slate, green and turquoise-blue | 15 | 10 |
| 251 | 3d. red, light blue and purple | 80 | 20 |
| 252 | 4d. green, blue and orange-brown | 55 | 1·00 |
| 253 | 6d. dull green, light blue and rose | 30 | 10 |
| 254 | 8d. reddish purple, light blue & bronze-green | 50 | 30 |
| 255 | 10d. orange-brown, green and violet | 25 | 10 |
| 256 | 1s. red, yellow, turquoise-blue & deep emer | 50 | 10 |
| | *a. Red, yellow, dull blue & emer* (14.9.65) | 30 | 10 |
| 257 | 2s. brown, light blue and emerald | 1·00 | 1·00 |
| 258 | 2s. 6d. yellow-olive, blue and carmine | 2·00 | 2·00 |
| 259 | 5s. orange-brown, ultramarine and green | 2·25 | 1·00 |
| 260 | 10s. rose, blue and chocolate | 8·00 | 2·25 |
| 261 | £1 chestnut, blue and rose-red | 9·00 | 5·00 |
| 247/261 | *Set of* 15 | 23·00 | 13·00 |

Designs:—1d. Out Island Regatta; 1½d. Hospital; 2d. High School; 3d. Greater Flamingo; 4d. R.M.S. *Queen Elizabeth*; 6d. "Development"; 8d. Yachting; 10d. Public Square; 1s. Sea Garden; 2s. Old Cannons at Fort Charlotte; 2s. 6d. Sikorsky "S–38" seaplane, 1929 and Boeing "707" airliner; 5s. Williamson film project, 1914 and Undersea Post Office, 1939; 10s. Conch shell; £1, Columbus' flagship.

Nos. 247/8, 251, 253 and 256 exist in coils, constructed from normal sheets.

**1965** (17 May). *I.T.U. Centenary. As Nos. 166/7 of Antigua.*

| | | | |
|---|---|---|---|
| 262 | 1d. light emerald and orange | 15 | 10 |
| 263 | 2s. purple and yellow-olive | 65 | 35 |

**1965** (12 July). *No. 254 surch with T* **64**.

| | | | |
|---|---|---|---|
| 264 | 9d. on 8d. reddish purple, light blue and bronze-green | 15 | 10 |

**1965** (25 Oct). *International Co-operation Year. As Nos. 168/9 of Antigua.*

| | | | |
|---|---|---|---|
| 265 | ½d. reddish purple and turquoise-green | 10 | 20 |
| 266 | 1s. deep bluish green and lavender | 30 | 40 |

**1966** (24 Jan). *Churchill Commemoration. As Nos. 170/3 of Antigua.*

| | | | |
|---|---|---|---|
| 267 | ½d. new blue | 10 | 25 |
| 268 | 2d. deep green | 30 | 30 |
| 269 | 10d. brown | 65 | 85 |
| 270 | 1s. bluish violet | 75 | 1·40 |
| 267/70 | *Set of* 4 | 1·60 | 2·50 |

**1966** (4 Feb). *Royal Visit. As Nos. 174/5 of Antigua, but inscr "to the Caribbean" omitted.*

| | | | |
|---|---|---|---|
| 271 | 6d. black and ultramarine | 90 | 50 |
| 272 | 1s. black and magenta | 1·60 | 1·25 |

**(New Currency. 100 cents = 1 dollar.)**

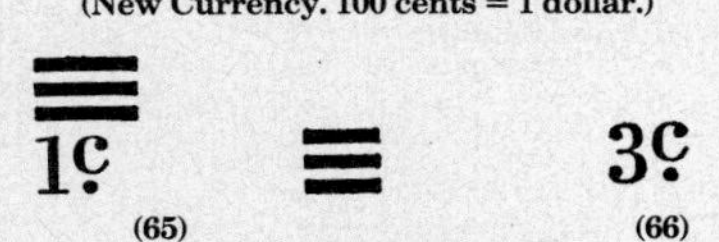


(65) (66)

**1966** (25 May). *Decimal Currency. Nos. 247/61 variously surch as T* **65/6**, *by B.W.*

| | | | |
|---|---|---|---|
| 273 | 1 c. on ½d. multicoloured | 10 | 10 |
| 274 | 2 c. on 1d. slate, light blue and orange | 10 | 10 |
| 275 | 3 c. on 2d. slate, green and turquoise-blue | 10 | 10 |
| 276 | 4 c. on 3d. red, light blue and purple | 20 | 10 |
| 277 | 5 c. on 4d. green, blue and orange-brown | 15 | 30 |
| | a. Surch omitted (vert strip of 10) | £2750 | |
| 278 | 8 c. on 6d. dull green, light blue and rose | 15 | 20 |
| 279 | 10 c. on 8d. reddish purple, light blue and bronze-green | 25 | 40 |
| 280 | 11 c. on 1½d. rose-red, green and brown | 15 | 20 |
| 281 | 12 c. on 10d. orange-brown, green and violet | 15 | 10 |
| 282 | 15 c. on 1s. multicoloured | 25 | 10 |
| 283 | 22 c. on 2s. brown, light blue and emerald | 60 | 80 |
| 284 | 50 c. on 2s. 6d. yellow-olive, blue and carmine | 90 | 1·10 |
| 285 | $1 on 5s. orange-brown, ultram & green | 1·25 | 1·50 |
| 286 | $2 on 10s. rose, blue and chocolate | 3·50 | 3·50 |
| 287 | $3 on £1 chestnut, blue and rose-red | 5·00 | 4·00 |
| 273/287 | *Set of* 15 | 11·50 | 11·00 |

The above were made on new printings some of which vary slightly in shade and in No. 273 the shield appears as vermilion and green instead of carmine and blue-green due to a different combination of the printing colours.

No. 277a. One sheet exists and the stamp can be distinguished from No. 252 when in a vertical strip of ten as these were printed in sheets of 100 whereas No. 252 was printed in sheets of 60 (six rows of ten across).

**1966** (1 July). *World Cup Football Championships. As Nos. 176/7 of Antigua.*

| | | | |
|---|---|---|---|
| 288 | 8 c. violet, yellow-green, lake & yell-brown | 15 | 15 |
| 289 | 15 c. chocolate, blue-green, lake & yell-brown | 25 | 25 |

**1966** (20 Sept). *Inauguration of W.H.O. Headquarters, Geneva. As Nos. 178/9 of Antigua.*

| | | | |
|---|---|---|---|
| 290 | 11 c. black, yellow-green and light blue | 25 | 20 |
| 291 | 15 c. black, light purple and yellow-brown | 30 | 25 |

**1966** (1 Dec). *20th Anniv of U.N.E.S.C.O. As Nos. 196/8 of Antigua.*

| | | | |
|---|---|---|---|
| 292 | 3 c. slate-violet, red, yellow and orange | 15 | 10 |
| 293 | 15 c. orange-yellow, violet and deep olive | 35 | 30 |
| 294 | $1 black, bright purple and orange | 1·50 | 2·25 |
| 292/4 | *Set of* 3 | 1·75 | 2·40 |

67 *Oceanic*

68 Conch Shell

(Portrait by Anthony Buckley. Litho and recess (portrait, "BAHAMAS" and value), B.W.)

**1967** (25 May)–**71**. *T* **67/8** *or designs as Nos. 247/51, 253/9 and 261 but values in decimal currency and colours changed. Toned paper.* W w **12**. *P* 13½.

| | | | |
|---|---|---|---|
| 295 | 1 c. multicoloured (as ½d.) | 10 | 60 |
| | a. Whiter paper (1970) | 20 | 60 |
| 296 | 2 c. slate, light blue & deep emerald (as 1d.) | 15 | 10 |
| | a. Whiter paper (1970) | 75 | 75 |
| 297 | 3 c. slate, green and violet (as 2d.) | 10 | 10 |
| | a. Whiter paper (1970) | 55·00 | 3·75 |
| 298 | 4 c. red, light blue and ultramarine (as 3d.) | 2·50 | 20 |
| | a. Whiter paper (9.70*) | 10·00 | 9·00 |
| 299 | 5 c. black, greenish blue and purple | 60 | 40 |
| | a. Whiter paper (1970) | 95 | 1·00 |
| 300 | 8 c. dull green, light blue and sepia (as 6d.) | 25 | 10 |
| | a. Whiter paper (1970) | £120 | 16·00 |
| 301 | 10 c. reddish pur, greenish bl & carm (as 8d.) | 30 | 40 |
| | a. Whiter paper (1970) | 80 | 1·00 |
| 302 | 11 c. rose-red, green and blue (as 1½d.) | 25 | 40 |
| | a. Whiter paper (1970) | 80 | 1·00 |
| 303 | 12 c. orange-brown, green and olive (as 10d.) | 25 | 10 |
| | a. Whiter paper (4.71) | 9·00 | 18·00 |
| 304 | 15 c. red, yellow, turquoise-bl & carm (as 1s.) | 55 | 10 |
| | a. Whiter paper (1970) | £150 | 20·00 |
| 305 | 22 c. brown, new blue and rose-red (as 2s.) | 70 | 65 |
| | a. Whiter paper (1970) | 1·75 | 2·25 |
| 306 | 50 c. yellow-olive, new bl & emer (as 2s. 6d.) | 2·00 | 75 |
| | a. Whiter paper (1970) | 2·25 | 2·50 |
| 307 | $1 orange-brown, ultram & slate-pur (as 5s.) | 2·00 | 60 |
| | a. Whiter paper (4.71) | 19·00 | 35·00 |
| 308 | $2 multicoloured | 7·00 | 2·00 |
| | a. Whiter paper (4.71) | 30·00 | 48·00 |
| 309 | $3 chestnut, new blue and purple (as £1) | 3·75 | 2·00 |
| | a. Whiter paper (4.71) | 30·00 | 48·00 |
| 295/309 | *Set of* 15 | 18·00 | 7·50 |
| 295a/309a | *Set of* 15 (whiter paper) | £375 | £190 |

*This is the earliest known date recorded in the Bahamas.

The 3 c. has the value at right instead of at left as on No. 250.

The 1970–71 printings on whiter paper were released as needed, the 12 c., $1, $2 and $3 only a week or two before the issue was withdrawn. Due to the marked difference in paper and the use of some new plates there are marked differences in shade in nearly all values.

69 Bahamas Crest

(Des R. Granger Barrett. Photo J. Enschedé)

**1967** (1 Sept). *Diamond Jubilee of World Scouting. T* **69** *and similar horiz design. Multicoloured.* W w **12** (*sideways*). *P* 14 × 13.

| | | | |
|---|---|---|---|
| 310 | 3 c. Type **69** | 20 | 15 |
| 311 | 15 c. Scout badge | 25 | 15 |

71 Globe and Emblem

74 Golf

(Des R. Granger Barrett, Litho D.L.R.)

**1968** (13 May). *Human Rights Year. T* **71** *and similar horiz designs. Multicoloured. W w* **12** *(sideways). P* 14 × 13½.

| | | | |
|---|---|---|---|
| 312 | 3 c. Type **71** | 10 | 10 |
| 313 | 12 c. Scales of Justice and emblem | 20 | 10 |
| 314 | $1 Bahamas Crest and emblem | 60 | 80 |
| 312/14 | *Set of* 3 | 80 | 85 |

(Litho B.W.)

**1968** (20 Aug). *Tourism. T* **74** *and similar vert designs. Multicoloured. P* 13.

| | | | |
|---|---|---|---|
| 315 | 5 c. Type **74** | 55 | 30 |
| 316 | 11 c. Yachting | 80 | 30 |
| 317 | 15 c. Horse-racing | 80 | 35 |
| 318 | 50 c. Water-skiing | 1·75 | 2·50 |
| 315/18 | *Set of* 4 | 3·50 | 3·00 |

78 Racing Yacht and Olympic Monument

(Photo Harrison)

**1968** (29 Sept). *Olympic Games, Mexico City. T* **78** *and similar horiz designs. No wmk. P* 14½ × 13½.

| | | | |
|---|---|---|---|
| 319 | 5 c. red-brown, orange-yellow & blue-green | 25 | 15 |
| 320 | 11 c. multicoloured | 35 | 25 |
| 321 | 50 c. multicoloured | 80 | 1·40 |
| 322 | $1 olive-grey, greenish blue and violet | 1·75 | 3·00 |
| 319/22 | *Set of* 4 | 2·75 | 4·25 |

Designs:—11 c. Long-jumping and Olympic Monument; 50 c. Running and Olympic Monument; $1, Type **78**.

It is understood that the above were released by the Philatelic Agency in the U.S.A. on 1st September.

81 Legislative Building

(Des J. Cooter, Litho Format)

**1968** (1 Nov). *14th Commonwealth Parliamentary Conference. T* **81** *and similar multicoloured designs. P* 14.

| | | | |
|---|---|---|---|
| 323 | 3 c. Type **81** | 10 | 10 |
| 324 | 10 c. Bahamas Mace and Westminster Clock-Tower *(vert)* | 15 | 15 |
| 325 | 12 c. Local straw market *(vert)* | 15 | 20 |
| 326 | 15 c. Horse-drawn Surrey | 20 | 25 |
| 323/6 | *Set of* 4 | 55 | 65 |

85 Obverse and reverse of $100 Gold Coin

(Recess D.L.R.)

**1968** (2 Dec). *Gold Coins commemorating the first General Election under the New Constitution. T* **85** *and similar "boomerang" shaped designs. P* 13½.

| | | | |
|---|---|---|---|
| 327 | 3 c. red/*gold* | 20 | 25 |
| 328 | 12 c. blue-green/*gold* | 35 | 50 |
| 329 | 15 c. dull purple/*gold* | 40 | 60 |
| 330 | $1 black/*gold* | 1·75 | 2·50 |
| 327/30 | *Set of* 4 | 2·40 | 3·50 |

Designs:—12 c. Obverse and reverse of $50 gold coin; 15 c. Obverse and reverse of $20 gold coin; $1, Obverse and reverse of $10 gold coin.

89 First Flight Postcard of 1919

90 Sikorsky "S–38" Seaplane of 1929

(Des V. Whiteley. Litho Format)

**1969** (30 Jan). *50th Anniv of Bahamas Airmail Service. P* 14.

| | | | | |
|---|---|---|---|---|
| 331 | **89** | 12 c. multicoloured | 50 | 40 |
| 332 | **90** | 15 c. multicoloured | 60 | 85 |

91 Game-fishing Boats

92 "The Adoration of the Shepherds" (Louis le Nain)

(Des J. Cooter. Litho Format)

**1969** (26 Aug). *Tourism. One Millionth Visitor to Bahamas. T* **91** *and similar horiz designs. Multicoloured. W w* **12** *(sideways). P* 14½.

| | | | |
|---|---|---|---|
| 333 | 3 c. Type **91** | 35 | 10 |
| 334 | 11 c. Paradise Beach | 50 | 15 |
| 335 | 12 c. "Sunfish" sailing boats | 50 | 15 |
| 336 | 15 c. Rawson Square and Parade | 60 | 25 |
| 333/6 | *Set of* 4 | 1·75 | 60 |
| **MS**337 | 130 × 96 mm. Nos. 333/6 | 2·50 | 3·00 |

(Des G. Drummond. Litho D.L.R.)

**1969** (15 Oct). *Christmas. T* **92** *and similar vert designs. W w* **12**. *P* 12.

| | | | |
|---|---|---|---|
| 338 | 3 c. Type **92** | 10 | 10 |
| 339 | 11 c. "The Adoration of the Shepherds" (Poussin) | 15 | 15 |
| 340 | 12 c. "The Adoration of the Kings" (Gerard David) | 15 | 15 |
| 341 | 15 c. "The Adoration of the Kings" (Vincenzo Foppa) | 20 | 25 |
| 338/41 | *Set of* 4 | 55 | 55 |

93 Badge of Girl Guides

(Des Mrs. R. Sands. Litho Harrison)

**1970** (23 Feb). *Girl Guides Diamond Jubilee. T* **93** *and similar designs. Multicoloured. W w* **12**. *P* 14½.

| | | | |
|---|---|---|---|
| 342 | 3 c. Type **93** | 20 | 10 |
| 343 | 12 c. Badge of Brownies | 35 | 20 |
| 344 | 15 c. Badge of Rangers | 40 | 35 |
| 342/4 | *Set of* 3 | 85 | 55 |

94 U.P.U. Headquarters and Emblem

(Des L. Curtis, Litho J.W.)

**1970** (20 May). *New U.P.U. Headquarters Building. W w* **12** *(sideways). P* 14.

| | | | | |
|---|---|---|---|---|
| 345 | **94** | 3 c. multicoloured | 10 | 10 |
| 346 | | 15 c. multicoloured | 20 | 30 |

95 Coach and Globe

(Des G. Drummond. Litho B.W.)

**1970** (14 July). *"Goodwill Caravan". T* **95** *and similar horiz designs. Multicoloured. W w* **12** *(sideways). P* 13½ × 13.

| | | | |
|---|---|---|---|
| 347 | 3 c. Type **95** | 30 | 10 |
| 348 | 11 c. Train and globe | 80 | 20 |
| 349 | 12 c. *Canberra* (liner), yacht and globe | 80 | 25 |
| 350 | 15 c. Airliner and globe | 80 | 55 |
| 347/50 | *Set of* 4 | 2·40 | 1·00 |
| **MS**351 | 165 × 125 mm Nos. 347/50 | 6·50 | 11·00 |

96 Nurse, Patients and Greater Flamingo

97 "The Nativity" (detail, Pittoni)

(Photo Harrison)

**1970** (1 Sept). *Centenary of British Red Cross. T* **96** *and similar horiz design. Multicoloured. W w* **12** *(sideways). P* 14½.

| | | | |
|---|---|---|---|
| 352 | 3 c. Type **96** | 25 | 10 |
| | a. Gold ("EIIR", etc.) omitted | £150 | |
| 353 | 15 c. Hospital and Dolphin | 30 | 40 |

(Des G. Drummond. Litho D.L.R.)

**1970** (3 Nov). *Christmas. T* **97** *and similar vert designs. Multicoloured. W w* **12**. *P* 13.

| | | | |
|---|---|---|---|
| 354 | 3 c. Type **97** | 10 | 10 |
| 355 | 11 c. "The Holy Family" (detail, Anton Raphael Mengs) | 15 | 15 |
| 356 | 12 c. "The Adoration of the Shepherds" (detail, Giorgione) | 15 | 15 |
| 357 | 15 c. "The Adoration of the Shepherds" (detail, School of Seville) | 25 | 30 |
| 354/7 | *Set of* 4 | 60 | 65 |
| **MS**358 | 114 × 140 mm. Nos. 354/7 plus two labels | 1·40 | 2·25 |

98 International Airport

(Des Mrs. W. Wasile. Litho Format)

**1971** (27 Apr–1 Sept). *Multicoloured designs as T* **98**. *W w* **12** *(sideways on $1 to $3). P* 14½ × 14 *(1 to 50 c.) or* 14 × 14½ *($1 to $3).*

| | | | |
|---|---|---|---|
| 359 | 1 c. Type **98** | 10 | 30 |
| 360 | 2 c. Breadfruit | 15 | 35 |
| 361 | 3 c. Straw market | 15 | 30 |
| 362 | 4 c. Hawksbill turtle | 1·25 | 3·25 |
| 363 | 5 c. Grouper | 35 | 40 |
| 364 | 6 c. As 4 c. (21.9.71) | 35 | 80 |
| 365 | 7 c. Hibiscus (21.9.71) | 1·50 | 1·50 |
| 366 | 8 c. Yellow Elder | 60 | 1·50 |
| 367 | 10 c. Bahamian sponge boat | 40 | 30 |
| 368 | 11 c. Greater Flamingos | 1·25 | 70 |
| 369 | 12 c. As 7 c | 2·00 | 3·00 |
| 370 | 15 c. Bonefish | 40 | 55 |
| 371 | 18 c. Royal Poinciana (21.9.71) | 55 | 65 |
| 372 | 22 c. As 18 c. | 2·75 | 6·50 |
| 373 | 50 c. Post Office, Nassau | 1·40 | 2·25 |
| 374 | $1 Pineapple *(vert)* | 4·75 | 3·00 |
| 375 | $2 Crawfish *(vert)* | 4·75 | 6·00 |
| 376 | $3 Junkanoo *(vert)* | 5·00 | 10·00 |
| 359/376 | *Set of* 18 | 25·00 | 38·00 |

See also Nos. 395/400, 460/73 and 518/25.

99 Snowflake

(Litho (15 c. additionally die-stamped in gold) Walsall)

**1971** (19 Oct). *Christmas. T* **99** *and similar horiz designs. W w* **12**. *P* 14 × 14½.

| | | | |
|---|---|---|---|
| 377 | 3 c. deep reddish purple, orange and gold | 10 | 10 |
| 378 | 11 c. light ultramarine and gold | 20 | 15 |
| 379 | 15 c. multicoloured | 20 | 20 |
| 380 | 18 c. bluish green, royal blue and gold | 25 | 25 |
| 377/80 | *Set of* 4 | 65 | 60 |
| **MS**381 | 126 × 95 mm. Nos. 377/80. P 15 | 1·00 | 1·50 |

Designs:—11 c. "Peace on Earth" (doves); 15 c. Arms of Bahamas and holly; 18 c. Starlit lagoon.

100 High jumping

(Des J. W. Litho B.W.)

**1972** (11 July). *Olympic Games, Munich. T* **100** *and similar horiz designs. Multicoloured. W w* **12**. *P* 13½.

382 10 c. Type **100** .. .. .. .. .. .. 20 25
383 11 c. Cycling .. .. .. .. .. .. 25 30
384 15 c. Running .. .. .. .. .. .. 30 45
385 18 c. Sailing .. .. .. .. .. .. 50 70
382/5 .. .. .. .. .. *Set of* 4 1·10 1·50
**MS**386 127 × 95 mm. Nos. 382/5 .. .. .. 1·40 2·00

101 Shepherd 102 Northerly Bahama Islands

(Des Jennifer Toombs. Litho (15 c. additionally embossed) J.W.)

**1972** (3 Oct). *Christmas. T* **101** *and similar vert designs. Multicoloured. W w* **12** *(sideways on 6 and 20 c.) P* 14.

387 3 c. Type **101** .. .. .. .. .. .. 10 10
388 6 c. Bells .. .. .. .. .. .. 10 10
389 15 c. Holly and Cross .. .. .. .. .. 15 20
390 20 c. Poinsettia .. .. .. .. .. 25 45
387/90 .. .. .. .. .. *Set of* 4 50 70
**MS**391 108 × 140 mm. Nos. 387/90 (wmk sideways) 80 1·25

(Des M. Shamir. Litho Format)

**1972** (1 Nov). *Tourism Year of the Americas. Sheet 133 × 105 mm, containing T* **102** *and similar vert designs. P* 15.

**MS**392 11, 15, 18 and 50 c. multicoloured .. 2·25 3·25

The four designs are printed horizontally *se-tenant* in **MS**392, forming a composite map design of the Bahamas.

103 Mace and Galleon

(Des (from photograph by D. Groves) and photo Harrison)

**1972** (13 Nov). *Royal Silver Wedding. Multicoloured; background colour given. W w* **12**. *P* 14 × 14½.

393 **103** 11 c. rose .. .. .. .. .. .. 15 15
394 18 c. bluish violet .. .. .. .. .. 15 20

**1972** (23 Nov)–**73**. *As Nos.* 363, 366 *and* 373/6 *but wmk sideways on 5 to 50 c.; upright on $1 to $3.*

395 5 c. Grouper .. .. .. .. .. .. 2·00 1·25
396 8 c. Yellow Elder (25.7.73) .. .. .. .. 2·00 1·75
397 50 c. Post Office, Nassau (25.7.73) .. .. .. 2·00 2·50
398 $1 Pineapple (25.7.73) .. .. .. .. 3·25 4·00
399 $2 Crawfish (25.7.73) .. .. .. .. 4·00 7·00
400 $3 Junkanoo (1973) .. .. .. .. .. 8·00 14·00
395/400 .. .. .. .. *Set of* 6 19·00 27·00

Nos. 401/9 vacant.

104 Weather Satellite

(Des C. Abbott. Litho Questa)

**1973** (3 Apr). *I.M.O./W.M.O. Centenary. T* **104** *and similar horiz design. Multicoloured. W w* **12**. *P* 14.

410 15 c. Type **104** .. .. .. .. .. .. 30 25
411 18 c. Weather radar .. .. .. .. .. 40 35

## NEW INFORMATION

The editor is always interested to correspond with people who have new information that will improve or correct the Catalogue.

INDEPENDENT

105 C. A. Bain (national hero) 106 "The Virgin in Prayer" (Sassoferrato)

(Des PAD Studio. Litho Questa)

**1973** (10 July–1 Aug). *Independence. T* **105** *and similar vert designs. Multicoloured. W w* **12** *(sideways). P* 14½ × 14.

412 3 c. Type **105** .. .. .. .. .. .. 10 10
413 11 c. Coat of arms .. .. .. .. .. 15 10
414 15 c. Bahamas flag .. .. .. .. .. 20 15
415 $1 Governor-General, M. B. Butler (1 Aug) 90 1·00
412/15 .. .. .. .. *Set of* 4 1·25 1·10
**MS**416 86 × 121 mm. Nos. 412/15 (1 Aug) .. 1·25 1·75

(Des C. Abbott. Litho Format)

**1973** (16 Oct). *Christmas. T* **106** *and similar vert designs. Multicoloured. W w* **12** *(sideways). P* 14.

417 3 c. Type **106** .. .. .. .. .. .. 10 10
418 11 c. "Virgin and Child with St. John" (Filippino Lippi) .. .. .. .. .. 15 15
419 15 c. "A Choir of Angels" (Simon Marmion) .. 15 15
420 18 c. "The Two Trinities" (Murillo) .. .. 25 25
417/20 .. .. .. .. *Set of* 4 60 55
**MS**421 120 × 99 mm. Nos. 417/20 .. .. .. 90 1·40

107 "Agriculture and Sciences"

(Des C. Abbott. Litho Questa)

**1974** (5 Feb). *25th Anniv of University of West Indies. T* **107** *and similar horiz design. Multicoloured. W w* **12**. *P* 13½.

422 15 c. Type **107** .. .. .. .. .. .. 20 25
423 18 c. "Arts, Engineering and General Studies" 25 30

108 U.P.U. Monument, Berne

(Des P. Powell. Litho Questa)

**1974** (23 Apr). *Centenary of Universal Postal Union. Designs as T* **108** *showing different arrangements of the U.P.U. Monument. W w* **12** *(upright on 3 c., 14 c. and* **MS**428*; sideways on others). P* 14.

424 **108** 3 c. multicoloured .. .. .. .. 10 10
425 – 13 c. multicoloured (*vert*) .. .. .. 20 25
426 – 14 c. multicoloured .. .. .. .. 20 30
427 – 18 c. multicoloured (*vert*) .. .. .. 25 35
424/7 .. .. .. .. *Set of* 4 65 90
**MS**428 128 × 95 mm. Nos. 424/7 .. .. .. 80 1·60

109 Roseate Spoonbills

(Des G. Drummond. Litho Questa)

**1974** (10 Sept). *15th Anniv of Bahamas National Trust. T* **109** *and similar horiz designs. Multicoloured. W w* **12** *(sideways). P* 13½.

429 13 c. Type **109** .. .. .. .. .. .. 85 65
430 14 c. White-crowned Pigeon .. .. .. .. 85 65
431 21 c. White-tailed Tropic Birds .. .. .. 1·25 1·00
432 36 c. Cuban Amazon .. .. .. .. .. 1·60 1·60
429/32 .. .. .. .. *Set of* 4 4·00 3·50
**MS**433 123 × 120 mm. Nos. 429/32 .. .. 5·00 5·50

110 "The Holy Family" (Jacques de Stella)

(Des J. W. Litho Enschedé)

**1974** (29 Oct). *Christmas. T* **110** *and similar horiz designs. Multicoloured. W w* **12** *(sideways). P* 13 × 13½.

434 8 c. Type **110** .. .. .. .. .. .. 10 10
435 10 c. "Madonna and Child" (16th-cent Brescian School) .. .. .. .. .. .. 15 15
436 12 c. "Virgin and Child with St. John the Baptist and St. Catherine" (Previtali) .. 15 15
437 21 c. "Virgin and Child with Angels" (Previtali) .. .. .. .. .. 25 30
434/7 .. .. .. .. *Set of* 4 60 60
**MS**438 126 × 105 mm. Nos. 434/7 .. .. .. 80 1·40

111 *Anteos maerula*

(Des PAD Studio. Litho D.L.R.)

**1975** (4 Feb). *Butterflies. T* **111** *and similar horiz designs. Multicoloured. W w* **12**. *P* 14 × 13½.

439 3 c. Type **111** .. .. .. .. .. .. 25 15
440 14 c. *Eurema nicippe* .. .. .. .. .. 80 50
441 18 c. *Papilio andraemon* .. .. .. .. 95 65
442 21 c. *Euptoieta hegesia* .. .. .. .. 1·10 85
439/42 .. .. .. .. *Set of* 4 2·75 2·00
**MS**443 119×94 mm. Nos. 439/42 .. .. .. 4·25 3·50

112 Sheep Husbandry 113 Rowena Rand (evangelist)

(Des Daphne Padden. Litho Questa)

**1975** (27 May). *Economic Diversification. T* **112** *and similar multicoloured designs. P* 14.

444 3 c. Type **112** .. .. .. .. .. .. 10 10
445 14 c. Electric-reel fishing (*vert*) .. .. .. 20 15
446 18 c. Farming .. .. .. .. .. .. 25 20
447 21 c. Oil Refinery (*vert*) .. .. .. .. 45 35
444/7 .. .. .. .. *Set of* 4 90 65
**MS**448 127 × 94 mm. Nos. 444/7 .. .. .. 90 1·50

(Des Jennifer Toombs. Litho Questa)

**1975** (22 July). *International Women's Year. T* **113** *and similar vert design. W w* **14** *(sideways). P* 14.

449 14 c. bistre-brown, lt turquoise-blue & ultram 20 25
450 18 c. lemon, bright yellow-green and sepia .. 25 30

Design:—18 c. I.W.Y. symbol and Harvest symbol.

114 "Adoration of the Shepherds" (Perugino)

(Des Jennifer Toombs. Litho J.W.)

**1975** (2 Dec). *Christmas. T* **114** *and similar horiz design. Multicoloured. W w* **14** *(sideways). P* 13.

451 3 c. Type **114** .. .. .. .. .. .. 10 10
452 8 c. "Adoration of the Magi" (Ghirlandaio) .. 20 10
453 18 c. As 8 c. .. .. .. .. .. .. 35 40
454 21 c. Type **114** .. .. .. .. .. .. 45 60
451/4 .. .. .. .. *Set of* 4 95 1·00
**MS**455 142 × 107 mm. Nos. 451/4. P 13½ .. 1·75 2·25

115 Telephones, 1876 and 1976

(Des G. Vasarhelyi. Litho D.L.R.)

**1976** (23 Mar). *Telephone Centenary. T* **115** *and similar horiz designs. Multicoloured. W w* **14** *(sideways). P* 14.

456 3 c. Type **115** . . . . 10 10
457 16 c. Radio-telephone link, Deleporte . . 25 30
458 21 c. Alexander Graham Bell . . . . 35 45
459 25 c. Satellite . . . . 40 55
456/9 . . *Set of* 4 1·00 1·25

**1976** (30 Mar)–**79**. *Designs as Nos.* 359/63, 365/7 *and* 373/6 *(some with new face values). W w* **14** *(sideways on $1 to $3). Ordinary paper.*

460 1 c. Type **98** (1.11.76) . . . . 1·50 1·75
a. Chalk-surfaced paper (1979) . . 7·50 8·00
461 2 c. Breadfruit . . . . 1·00 30
462 3 c. Straw market (1.11.76) . . 2·00 80
a. Chalk-surfaced paper (1979) . . 60 60
463 5 c. Grouper (1.11.76) . . 2·25 90
a. Chalk-surfaced paper (1979) . . 70 70
464 8 c. Yellow Elder . . 1·50 30
465 10 c. Bahamian sponge boat . . 80 30
466 16 c. As 7 c. (2.11.76) . . 70 35
a. Chalk-surfaced paper (1979) . . 70 80
467 21 c. As 2 c. (2.11.76) . . 1·00 80
a. Chalk-surfaced paper (1979) . . 80 1·25
468 25 c. As 4 c. (2.11.76) . . 75 40
a. Chalk-surfaced paper (1979) . . 90 2·00
469 40 c. As 10 c. (2.11.76) . . 1·25 75
470 50 c. Post Office, Nassau . . 1·75 1·75
471 $1 Pineapple . . 2·25 2·50
472 $2 Crawfish (2.5.76) . . 3·75 5·50
a. Chalk-surfaced paper (1979) . . 20·00 24·00
473 $3 Junkanoo (1.11.76) . . 5·00 9·00
460/73 . . *Set of* 14 23·00 23·00
460a72a . . *Set of* 7 28·00 35·00
No. 474 vacant.

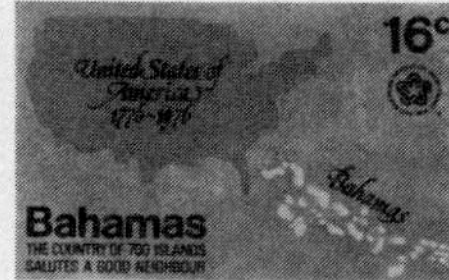

**116** Map of North America

(Des and litho Walsall)

**1976** (1 June). *Bicentenary of American Revolution. T* **116** *and similar horiz design. Multicoloured. W w* **14** *(sideways). P* 14.

475 16 c. Type **116** . . 30 30
476 $1 John Murray, Earl of Dunmore . . 1·50 1·75
**MS**477 127 × 100 mm. No. 476 × 4 . . 5·50 7·50

**117** Cycling

**118** "Virgin and Child" (detail, Lippi)

**1976** (13 July). *Olympic Games, Montreal. T* **117** *and similar vert designs. W w* **14**. *P* 14.

478 8 c. magenta, blue and pale cobalt . . 15 10
479 16 c. orange, brown and pale cobalt . . 20 15
480 25 c. blue, deep magenta and pale cobalt . . 25 35
481 40 c. brown, orange and pale cobalt . . 30 55
478/81 . . *Set of* 4 80 1·00
**MS**482 100 × 126 mm. Nos. 478/81 . . 1·00 1·75
Designs:—16 c. Jumping; 25 c. Sailing; 40 c. Boxing.

(Des G. Drummond. Litho Questa)

**1976** (5 Oct). *Christmas. T* **118** *and similar vert designs. Multicoloured. W w* **14**. *P* 14.

483 3 c. Type **118** . . 10 10
484 21 c. "Adoration of the Shepherds" (School of Seville) . . 15 15
485 25 c. "Adoration of the Kings" (detail, Foppa) 15 20
486 40 c. "Virgin and Child" (detail, Vivarini) . . 25 40
483/6 . . *Set of* 4 60 75
**MS**487 107 × 127 mm. Nos. 483/6 . . 1·00 1·50

**119** Queen beneath Cloth of Gold Canopy

(Des G. Vasarhelyi. Litho Cartor S.A., France)

**1977** (7 Feb). *Silver Jubilee. T* **119** *and similar horiz designs. Multicoloured. No wmk. P* 12.

488 8 c. Type **119** . . 10 10
489 16 c. The Crowning . . 15 15
490 21 c. Taking the Oath . . 15 15
491 40 c. Queen with sceptre and orb . . 25 30
488/91 . . *Set of* 4 60 60
**MS**492 122 × 90 mm. Nos. 488/91 . . 80 1·25

**120** Featherduster

(Des BG Studio. Litho J.W.)

**1977** (24 May). *Marine Life. T* **120** *and similar designs. Multicoloured. W w* **14** *(sideways). P* 13½.

493 3 c. Type **120** . . 15 15
494 8 c. Pork Fish and cave . . 30 20
495 16 c. Elkhorn Coral . . 55 40
496 21 c. Soft Coral and sponge . . 65 55
493/6 . . *Set of* 4 1·50 1·10
**MS**497 119 × 93 mm. Nos. 493/6. P 14½ . . 2·50 3·50

**121** Scouts around Campfire and Home-made Shower

Royal Visit
October 1977
(**122**)

(Des Harrison. Litho J.W.)

**1977** (27 Sept). *Sixth Caribbean Scout Jamboree. T* **121** *and similar horiz design. Multicoloured. W w* **14** *(sideways). P* 13½.

498 16 c. Type **121** . . 50 20
499 21 c. Boating scenes . . 60 25
One used example of No. 498 is known with the mauve (face value and inscription) omitted.

**1977** (19 Oct). *Royal Visit. As Nos.* 488/492, *but W w* **14** *(sideways), optd with T* **122**.

500 8 c. Type **119** . . 15 10
501 16 c. The Crowning . . 20 15
502 21 c. Taking the Oath . . 25 20
503 40 c. Queen with sceptre and orb . . 30 40
500/3 . . *Set of* 4 80 75
**MS**504 122 × 90 mm. Nos. 500/3 . . 1·00 1·40

**123** Virgin and Child

**124** Public Library, Nassau (Colonial)

(Des and litho J.W.)

**1977** (25 Oct). *Christmas. T* **123** *and similar vert designs. Multicoloured. W w* **14**. *P* 13½.

505 3 c. Type **123** . . 10 10
506 16 c. The Magi . . 20 25
507 21 c. Nativity scene . . 25 40
508 25 c. The Magi and star . . 30 45
505/8 . . *Set of* 4 75 1·10
**MS**509 136 × 74 mm. Nos. 505/8. P 14 . . 75 1·75

(Des G. Drummond. Litho Questa)

**1978** (28 Mar). *Architectural Heritage. T* **124** *and similar vert designs. W w* **14**. *P* 14½ × 14.

510 3 c. black and apple-green . . 10 10
511 8 c. black and pale greenish blue . . 15 10
512 16 c. black and mauve . . 20 20
513 18 c. black and salmon-pink . . 25 30
510/13 . . *Set of* 4 60 65
**MS**514 91 × 91 mm. Nos. 510/13 . . 70 1·40
Designs:—8 c. St. Matthew's Church (Gothic); 16 c. Government House (Colonial); 18 c. Hermitage, Cat Island (Spanish).

**125** Sceptre, St. Edward's Crown and Orb

**126** Coat of Arms within Wreath and Three Ships

(Des BG Studio. Litho Enschedé)

**1978** (27 June). *25th Anniv of Coronation. T* **125** *and similar vert design. Multicoloured. W w* **14**. *P* 14 × 13½.

515 16 c. Type **125** . . 15 10
516 $1 Queen in Coronation regalia . . 50 65
**MS**517 147 × 96 mm. Nos. 515/16 . . 1·25 1·50

**1978** (June). *As Nos.* 359/76, *but no wmk.*

518 1 c. Type **98** . . 35 90
519 5 c. Grouper . . 70 80
520 16 c. Hibiscus . . 1·25 1·50
521 25 c. Hawksbill Turtle . . 1·50 1·75
522 50 c. Post Office, Nassau . . 2·00 2·75
523 $1 Pineapple . . 2·50 3·00
524 $2 Crawfish . . 3·75 7·00
525 $3 Junkanoo . . 4·50 7·00
518/25 . . *Set of* 8 15·00 22·00
Nos. 526/31 vacant.

(Des Jennifer Toombs. Litho Questa)

**1978** (14 Nov). *Christmas. T* **126** *and similar horiz design. W w* **14** *(sideways). P* 14 × 14½.

532 5 c. gold, bright crimson and bright rose . . 15 10
533 21 c. gold, deep ultramarine and violet-blue . . 30 25
**MS**534 95 × 95 mm. Nos. 532/3 . . 2·25 3·00
Design:—21 c. Three angels with trumpets.

**127** Child reaching for Adult

**128** Sir Rowland Hill and Penny Black

(Litho J.W.)

**1979** (15 May). *International Year of the Child. T* **127** *and similar vert designs. Multicoloured. W w* **14**. *P* 13.

535 5 c. Type **127** . . 15 10
536 16 c. Boys playing leap-frog . . 30 35
537 21 c. Girls skipping . . 40 50
538 25 c. Bricks with I.Y.C. emblem . . 40 60
535/8 . . *Set of* 4 1·10 1·40
**MS**539 101 × 125 mm. Nos. 535/8. P 14 . . 1·10 1·50

(Des J. Cooter. Litho Walsall)

**1979** (14 Aug). *Death Centenary of Sir Rowland Hill. T* **128** *and similar horiz designs. Multicoloured. W w* **14** *(sideways). P* 13½ × 14.

540 10 c. Type **128** . . 25 10
541 21 c. Printing press, 1840 and 6d. stamp of 1862 35 30
542 25 c. Great Britain 6d. stamp of 1856 with "A 05" (Nassau) cancellation and Two-penny blue . . 40 45
543 40 c. Early mailboat and 1d. stamp of 1859 . . 50 55
540/3 . . *Set of* 4 1·40 1·25
**MS**544 115 × 80 mm. Nos. 540/3 . . 1·75 2·00

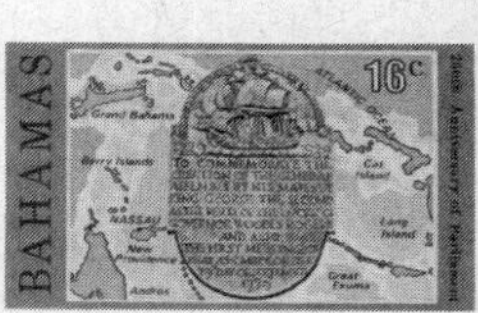

**129** Commemorative Plaque and Map of Bahamas

**130** Goombay Carnival Headdress

(Des G. Drummond. Litho Secura, Singapore)

**1979** (27 Sept). *250th Anniv of Parliament. T* **129** *and similar horiz designs. Multicoloured. W w* **14** *(sideways). P* 13½.

545 16 c. Type **129** . . 20 10
546 21 c. Parliament buildings . . 25 15
547 25 c. Legislative Chamber . . 25 15
548 $1 Senate Chamber . . 70 80
545/8 . . *Set of* 4 1·25 1·00
**MS**549 116 × 89 mm. Nos. 545/8 (wmk upright) 2·00 2·75

(Des BG Studio. Litho J.W.)

**1979** (6 Nov). *Christmas. T* **130** *and similar vert designs showing Goombay Carnival headdresses. W w* **14**. *P* 13.

550 5 c. multicoloured . . 10 10
551 10 c. multicoloured . . 10 10
552 16 c. multicoloured . . 15 10
553 21 c. multicoloured . . 20 20
554 25 c. multicoloured . . 20 20
555 40 c. multicoloured . . 30 35
550/5 . . *Set of* 6 90 85
**MS**556 50 × 88 mm. Nos. 550/5 (wmk sideways). P 13½ . . 1·50 2·00

**131** Landfall of Columbus, 1492

**132** Virgin and Child

(Des J. W. Litho Format)

**1980** (9 July). *Horiz designs as T* **131**. *Multicoloured. W w* **14**. *P* 14½.

557 1 c. Type **131** .. .. .. .. .. 20 40
558 3 c. Blackbeard the Pirate, 1718 .. .. .. 20 35
559 5 c. Eleutheran Adventurers (Articles and Orders, 1647) .. .. .. .. .. 30 20
560 10 c. Ceremonial Mace .. .. .. .. 20 30
561 12 c. The Loyalists, 1783–88 (Colonel Andrew Deveaux) .. .. .. .. .. 20 40
562 15 c. Slave Trading, Vendue House .. .. 2·25 40
563 16 c. Wrecking in the 1800's .. .. .. 30 40
564 18 c. Blockade running (American Civil War) 40 60
565 21 c. Bootlegging, 1919–29 .. .. .. 40 60
566 25 c. Pineapple cultivation .. .. .. 40 60
567 40 c. Sponge clipping .. .. .. .. 70 85
568 50 c. Tourist development .. .. .. 75 75
569 $1 Modern agriculture .. .. .. 1·40 2·25
570 $2 Modern air and sea transport .. .. 3·00 3·00
571 $3 Banking in the Bahamas (Central Bank) 3·50 4·00
572 $5 Independence, 10 July 1973 (Prince of Wales and Prime Minister L.O. Pindling) 5·50 6·00
557/72 .. .. .. .. .. *Set of* 16 18·00 19·00

See also Nos. 720/6 for stamps watermarked w **16**.

(Des B. Malone. Litho Walsall)

**1980** (28 Oct). *Christmas. Straw-work. T* **132** *and similar vert designs. Multicoloured. W w* **14**. *P* 14½ × 14.

573 5 c. Type **132** .. .. .. .. .. 10 10
574 21 c. Three Kings .. .. .. .. .. 25 10
575 25 c. Angel .. .. .. .. .. 25 15
576 $1 Christmas Tree .. .. .. .. .. 75 70
573/6 .. .. .. .. *Set of* 4 1·25 80
**MS**577 168 × 105 mm. Nos. 573/6 .. .. 1·25 2·00

**133** Disabled Person with Walking-stick

(Des and litho Walsall)

**1981** (10 Feb). *International Year for Disabled Persons. T* **133** *and similar horiz design. Multicoloured. W w* **14** *(sideways). P* 14½ × 14.

578 5 c. Type **133** .. .. .. .. .. 10 10
579 $1 Disabled person in wheelchair .. .. 1·25 1·25
**MS**580 120 × 60 mm. Nos. 578/9 .. .. .. 1·40 2·25

**134** Grand Bahama Tracking Site

**135** Prince Charles and Lady Diana Spencer

(Litho Enschedé)

**1981** (21 Apr). *Space Exploration. T* **134** *and similar multi-coloured designs. W w* **14** *(sideways on* 10 *and* 25 *c.). P* 13½.

581 10 c. Type **134** .. .. .. .. .. 15 15
582 20 c. Satellite view of Bahamas (*vert*) .. .. 35 40
583 25 c. Satellite view of Eleuthera .. .. 40 50
584 50 c. Satellite view of Andros and New Providence (*vert*) .. .. .. .. 65 80
581/4 .. .. .. .. *Set of* 4 1·40 1·75
**MS**585 115 × 99 mm. Nos. 581/4 (wmk sideways) 1·40 2·00

(Des C. Abbott. Litho Questa)

**1981** (22 July). *Royal Wedding. T* **135** *and similar horiz design. Multicoloured. W w* **14** *(sideways). P* 14 × 14½.

586 30 c. Type **135** .. .. .. .. .. 75 25
587 $2 Prince Charles and Prime Minister Pindling .. .. .. .. .. 3·75 1·75
**MS**588 142 × 120 mm. Nos. 586/7 .. .. 5·50 2·50
a. Upper stamp in miniature sheet imperf on 3 sides .. .. .. .. .. £600

No. **MS**588a shows the upper stamp in the miniature sheet perforated at foot only.

**136** Bahama Pintail

(Des Walsall. Litho Questa)

**1981** (25 Aug). *Wildlife (1st series). Birds. T* **136** *and similar horiz designs. Multicoloured. W w* **14** *(sideways). P* 14.

589 5 c. Type **136** .. .. .. .. .. 50 15
590 20 c. Reddish Egret .. .. .. .. 80 40
591 25 c. Brown Booby .. .. .. .. 90 45
592 $1 Black-billed Whistling Duck .. .. 2·00 3·25
589/92 .. .. .. .. *Set of* 4 3·75 3·75
**MS**593 100 × 74 mm. Nos. 589/92 .. .. 3·75 4·25

See also Nos. 626/30, 653/7 and 690/4.

COMMONWEALTH FINANCE MINISTERS' MEETING

(137)

**1981** (21 Sept). *Commonwealth Finance Ministers' Meeting. Nos.* 559/60, 566 *and* 568 *optd with T* **137**.

594 5 c. Eleutheran Adventurers (Articles and Orders, 1647) .. .. .. .. .. 10 15
a. Opt inverted .. .. .. .. .. 80·00
595 10 c. Ceremonial Mace .. .. .. .. 15 20
596 25 c. Pineapple cultivation .. .. .. 40 60
597 50 c. Tourist development .. .. .. 75 1·25
594/7 .. .. .. .. *Set of* 4 1·25 2·00

**138** Poultry

**139** Father Christmas

(Des L. McCombie. Litho J.W.)

**1981** (16 Oct). *World Food Day. T* **138** *and similar horiz designs. Multicoloured. W w* **14** *(sideways). P* 13.

598 5 c. Type **138** .. .. .. .. .. 10 10
599 20 c. Sheep .. .. .. .. .. 30 35
600 30 c. Lobsters .. .. .. .. .. 40 50
601 50 c. Pigs .. .. .. .. .. 75 1·25
598/601 .. .. .. .. *Set of* 4 1·40 2·00
**MS**602 115 × 63 mm. Nos. 598/601. P 14 .. 1·50 2·75

(Des local artists. Litho Format)

**1981** (24 Nov). *Christmas. T* **139** *and similar vert designs. Multicoloured. W w* **14**. *P* 13½ × 14.

603 5 c. Type **139** .. .. .. .. .. 25 25
a. Sheetlet of 9. Nos. 603/11 .. .. 3·75
604 5 c. Mother and child.. .. .. .. 25 25
605 5 c. St. Nicholas, Holland .. .. .. 25 25
606 25 c. Lussibruden, Sweden .. .. .. 50 50
607 25 c. Mother and child (*different*) .. .. 50 50
608 25 c. King Wenceslas, Czechoslovakia .. .. 50 50
609 30 c. Mother with child on knee .. .. 50 50
610 30 c. Mother carrying child .. .. .. 50 50
611 $1 Christkindl Angel, Germany .. .. 1·00 1·00
603/11 .. .. .. .. *Set of* 9 3·75 3·75

Nos. 603/11 were printed together, *se-tenant*, in a sheetlet of 9.

BAHAMAS 25c

Phoenicopterus ruber ♂

**140** Robert Koch

**141** Male Flamingo (*Phoenicopterus ruber*)

(Des A. Theobald. Litho Harrison)

**1982** (3 Feb). *Centenary of Discovery of Tubercle Bacillus by Robert Koch. T* **140** *and similar horiz designs. W w* **14** *(sideways). P* 14.

612 5 c. black, red-brown and rose-lilac .. .. 30 10
613 16 c. black, drab and dull orange .. .. 65 40
614 21 c. multicoloured .. .. .. .. 75 45
615 $1 multicoloured .. .. .. .. 2·50 3·50
612/15 .. .. .. .. *Set of* 4 3·75 4·00
**MS**616 94 × 97 mm. Nos. 612/15. P 14½.. .. 3·75 4·50

Designs:—16 c. Stylised infected person; 21 c. Early and modern microscopes; $1 Mantoux test.

(Des N. Arlott. Litho Questa)

**1982** (28 Apr). *Greater Flamingos. T* **141** *and similar vert designs. Multicoloured. W w* **14**. *P* 14 × 13½.

617 25 c. Type **141** .. .. .. .. .. 65 75
a. Horiz strip of 5. Nos. 617/21 .. .. 3·00
618 25 c. Female .. .. .. .. .. 65 75
619 25 c. Female with nestling .. .. .. 65 75
620 25 c. Juvenile .. .. .. .. .. 65 75
621 25 c. Immature bird .. .. .. .. 65 75
617/21 .. .. .. .. *Set of* 5 3·00 3·25

Nos. 617/21 were printed together, *se-tenant*, in horizontal strips of 5 throughout the sheet, forming a composite design.

## COVER PRICES

Cover factors are quoted at the beginning of each country for most issues to 1945. An explanation of the system can be found on page x. The factors quoted do not, however, apply to philatelic covers.

**142** Lady Diana Spencer at Ascot, June 1981

**143** House of Assembly Plaque

(Des C. Abbott. Litho Format)

**1982** (1 July). *21st Birthday of Princess of Wales. T* **142** *and similar vert designs. Multicoloured. W w* **14**. *P* 13½ × 14 (16 *c.*, $1) *or* 13½ *(others).*

622 16 c. Bahamas coat of arms .. .. .. 20 10
a. Perf 13½ .. .. .. .. .. 1·00 1·00
623 25 c. Type **142** .. .. .. .. .. 35 15
624 40 c. Bride and Earl Spencer arriving at St. Paul's .. .. .. .. .. 50 20
625 $1 Formal portrait .. .. .. .. 1·00 1·25
622/5 .. .. .. .. *Set of* 4 1·90 1·40

(Des Walsall. Litho Questa)

**1982** (18 Aug). *Wildlife (2nd series). Mammals. Horiz designs as T* **136**. *Multicoloured. W w* **14** *(sideways). P* 14.

626 10 c. Buffy Flower Bat .. .. .. 25 15
627 16 c. Bahaman Hutia.. .. .. .. 40 25
628 21 c. Common Racoon .. .. .. 55 35
629 $1 Common Dolphin .. .. .. 1·75 1·75
626/9 .. .. .. .. *Set of* 4 2·75 2·25
**MS**630 115×76 mm. Nos. 626/9 .. .. .. 2·75 3·25

(Des and litho Walsall)

**1982** (16 Oct). *28th Commonwealth Parliamentary Association Conference. T* **143** *and similar vert designs. Multicoloured. W w* **14**. *P* 14 × 13½.

631 5 c. Type **143** .. .. .. .. .. 15 10
632 25 c. Association coat of arms.. .. .. 45 35
633 40 c. Coat of arms .. .. .. .. 70 60
634 50 c. House of Assembly .. .. .. 85 75
631/4 .. .. .. .. *Set of* 4 1·90 1·60

**144** Wesley Methodist Church, Baillou Hill Road

(Des Jennifer Toombs. Litho Format)

**1982** (3 Nov). *Christmas. Churches. T* **144** *and similar horiz designs. Multicoloured. W w* **14** *(sideways). P* 14.

635 5 c. Type **144** .. .. .. .. .. 10 10
636 12 c. Centreville Seventh Day Adventist Church .. .. .. .. .. 20 20
637 15 c. The Church of God of Prophecy, East Street .. .. .. .. .. 25 25
638 21 c. Bethel Baptist Church, Meeting Street 30 30
639 25 c. St. Francis Xavier Catholic Church, Highbury Park .. .. .. .. 35 50
640 $1 Holy Cross Anglican Church, Highbury Park .. .. .. .. .. 1·50 2·50
635/40 .. .. .. .. *Set of* 6 2·50 3·50

**145** Prime Minister Lynden O. Pindling

(Des Walsall. Litho Questa)

**1983** (14 Mar). *Commonwealth Day T* **145** *and similar horiz designs. Multicoloured. W w* **14** *(sideways). P* 14.

641 5 c. Type **145** .. .. .. .. .. 10 10
642 25 c. Bahamian and Commonwealth flags .. 40 40
643 35 c. Map showing position of Bahamas .. 50 50
644 $1 Ocean liner .. .. .. .. 1·40 1·40
641/4 .. .. .. .. *Set of* 4 2·10 2·10

= 20c

(146)

**1983** (5 Apr). *Nos.* 562/5 *surch as T* **146**.

645 20 c. on 15 c. Slave Trading, Vendue House .. 50 35
646 31 c. on 21 c. Bootlegging, 1919–29 .. .. 60 55
647 35 c. on 16 c. Wrecking in the 1800's .. .. 70 60
648 80 c. on 18 c. Blockade running (American Civil War) .. .. .. .. .. 1·50 1·40
645/8 .. .. .. .. *Set of* 4 3·00 2·50

147 Customs Officers and Liner

148 Raising the National Flag

(Des Walsall. Litho Harrison)

**1983** (31 May). *30th Anniv of Customs Co-operation Council. T* **147** *and similar vert design. Multicoloured.* W w **14.** *P* 13½ × 13.
649 31 c. Type **147** .. .. .. .. .. 1·25 45
650 $1 Customs officers and airliner .. .. 2·50 2·00

(Des L. Curtis. Litho Questa)

**1983** (6 July). *10th Anniv of Independence.* W w **14.** *P* 14.
651 **148** $1 multicoloured .. .. .. 1·25 1·40
**MS**652 105 × 65 mm. No. 651. P 12 .. .. 1·25 1·40

(Des F. Solomon, adapted N. Arlott. Litho Harrison)

**1983** (24 Aug). *Wildlife (3rd series). Butterflies. Horiz designs as T* **136.** W w **14** *(sideways). P* 14½ × 14.
653 5 c. multicoloured .. .. .. .. 40 10
654 25 c. multicoloured .. .. .. .. 85 40
655 31 c. black, bistre-yellow and bright rose-red 95 45
656 50 c. multicoloured .. .. .. .. 1·25 70
653/6 .. .. .. .. .. *Set of* 4 3·00 1·50
**MS**657 120 × 80 mm. Nos. 653/6 .. .. 3·00 3·50
a. Perf 14 .. .. .. .. 3·00 4·00

Designs:—5 c. *Atalopedes carteri*; 25 c. *Ascia monuste*; 31 c. *Phoebis agarithe*; 50 c. *Dryas julia*.

No. **MS**657a was perforated by Questa, the remainder of the issue by Harrison.

149 "Loyalist Dreams"



150 Consolidated "Catalina"

(Des A. Lowe; adapted C. Abbott. Litho Questa)

**1983** (28 Sept). *Bicentenary of Arrival of American Loyalists in the Bahamas. T* **149** *and similar multicoloured designs.* W w **14** *(sideways on 31 c., 35 c.). P* 14.
658 5 c. Type **149** .. .. .. .. .. 10 10
659 31 c. New Plymouth, Abaco *(horiz)* .. .. 45 50
660 35 c. New Plymouth Hotel *(horiz)* .. .. 50 70
661 50 c. "Island Hope" .. .. .. .. 65 90
658/61 .. .. .. .. *Set of* 4 1·50 2·00
**MS**662 111 × 76 mm. Nos. 658/61. Wmk sideways 1·50 2·50

(Des and litho Harrison)

**1983** (13 Oct). *Air Bicentenary of Manned Flight. T* **150** *and similar horiz designs. Multicoloured.* W w **14** *(sideways). P* 14.
663 10 c. Type **150** .. .. .. .. .. 15 15
664 25 c. Avro "Tudor IV" .. .. .. .. 35 40
665 31 c. Avro "Lancastrian" .. .. .. 40 45
666 35 c. Consolidated "Commodore" .. .. 45 50
663/6 .. .. .. .. *Set of* 4 1·25 1·40

For these stamps without the Manned Flight logo see Nos. 699/702.

151 "Christmas Bells" (Monica Pinder)

152 1861 4d. Stamp

(Des local children, adapted G. Vasarhelyi. Litho Walsall)

**1983** (1 Nov). *Christmas. Children's Paintings. T* **151** *and similar multicoloured designs.* W w **14** *(sideways on 31 c. and 50 c.). P* 14.
667 5 c. Type **151** .. .. .. .. .. 10 10
668 20 c. "Flamingo" (Cory Bullard) .. .. 25 30
669 25 c. "Yellow Hibiscus with Christmas Candle" (Monique Bailey) .. .. .. .. 35 40
670 31 c. "Santa goes a Sailing" (Sabrina Seiler) *(horiz)* .. .. .. .. .. 40 45
671 35 c. "Silhouette scene with Palm Trees" (James Blake) .. .. .. .. 45 50
672 50 c. "Silhouette scene with Pelicans" (Erik Russell) *(horiz)* .. .. .. .. 65 70
667/72 .. .. .. .. *Set of* 6 1·90 2·25

(Des D. Miller. Litho Format)

**1984** (22 Feb). *125th Anniv of First Bahamas Postage Stamp. T* **152** *and similar vert design. Multicoloured.* W w **14.** *P* 14.
673 5 c. Type **152** .. .. .. .. .. 15 10
674 $1 1859 1d. stamp .. .. .. .. 1·60 1·50

153 R.M.S. *Trent*



154 Running

(Des L. Curtis. Litho Questa)

**1984** (25 Apr). *250th Anniv of "Lloyd's List" (newspaper). T* **153** *and similar vert designs. Multicoloured.* W w **14.** *P* 14½ × 14.
675 5 c. Type **153** .. .. .. .. .. 10 10
676 31 c. R.M.S. *Orinoco* .. .. .. .. 55 60
677 35 c. Nassau harbour .. .. .. .. 60 65
678 50 c. M.V. *Oropesa* (container ship) .. .. 90 95
675/8 .. .. .. .. *Set of* 4 1·90 2·10

(Des McCombie Skinner Studio. Litho Questa)

**1984** (20 June). *Olympic Games, Los Angeles. T* **154** *and similar horiz designs.* W w **14** *(sideways). P* 14 × 14½.
679 5 c. green, black and gold .. .. .. 10 10
680 25 c. new blue, black and gold .. .. .. 45 50
681 31 c. brown-lake, black and gold .. .. 55 60
682 $1 sepia, black and gold .. .. .. 1·75 2·00
679/82 .. .. .. .. *Set of* 4 2·50 2·75
**MS**683 115 × 80 mm. Nos. 679/82 .. .. 2·75 3·50

Designs:— 25 c. Shot-putting; 31 c. Boxing; $1 Basketball.

155 Bahamas and Caribbean Community Flags

156 Bahama Woodstar

(Des McCombie Skinner Studio. Litho Questa)

**1984** (4 July). *5th Conference of Caribbean Community Heads of Government.* W w **14.** *P* 14.
684 **155** 50 c. multicoloured .. .. .. 90 95

(Des N. Arlott. Litho Questa)

**1984** (15 Aug). *25th Anniv of National Trust. T* **156** *and similar vert designs. Multicoloured.* W w **14.** *P* 14.
685 31 c. Type **156**.. .. .. .. .. 90 1·00
a. Horiz strip of 5. Nos. 685/9 .. .. 4·00
686 31 c. Belted Kingfishers, Greater Flamingos and *Eleutherodactylus planirostris* (frog) .. .. .. .. .. 90 1·00
687 31 c. Black-necked Stilts, Greater Flamingos and *Phoebis sennae* (butterfly) .. 90 1·00
688 31 c. *Urbanus proteus* (butterfly) and *Chelonia mydas* (turtle) .. .. 90 1·00
689 31 c. Osprey and Greater Flamingos .. .. 90 1·00
685/9 .. .. .. .. *Set of* 5 4·00 4·50

Nos. 685/9 were printed together, *se-tenant*, in horizontal strips of 5 throughout the sheet, forming a composite design.

(Des N. Arlott. Litho Questa)

**1984** (18 Sept). *Wildlife (4th series). Reptiles and Amphibians. Horiz designs as T* **136.** W w **14** *(sideways). P* 14.
690 5 c. Allen's Cay Iguana .. .. .. 25 10
691 25 c. Curly-tailed Lizard .. .. .. 75 50
692 35 c. Greenhouse Frog .. .. .. .. 90 65
693 50 c. Atlantic Green Turtle .. .. .. 1·40 95
690/3 .. .. .. .. *Set of* 4 3·00 2·00
**MS**694 112 × 82 mm. Nos. 690/3 .. .. 3·00 4·00

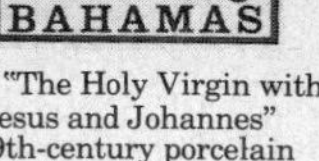


157 "The Holy Virgin with Jesus and Johannes" (19th-century porcelain plaque after Titian)

158 Brownie Emblem and Conch

(Des D. Slater. Litho J.W.)

**1984** (7 Nov). *Christmas. Religious Paintings. T* **157** *and similar vert designs. Multicoloured,* W w **14.** *P* 13½.
695 5 c. Type **157** .. .. .. .. .. 10 10
696 31 c. "Madonna with Child in Tropical Landscape" (aquarelle, Anais Colin) .. .. 55 60
697 35 c. "The Holy Virgin with the Child" (miniature on ivory, Elena Caula) .. .. 60 65
695/7 .. .. .. .. *Set of* 3 1·10 1·25
**MS**698 116 × 76 mm. Nos. 695/7. P 14. .. .. 1·25 2·00

**1985** (2 Jan). *Air. As Nos. 663/6, but without Manned Flight logo.* W w **14** *(sideways). P* 14.
699 10 c. Type **150** .. .. .. .. .. 20 20
700 25 c. Avro "Tudor IV" .. .. .. .. 40 40
701 31 c. Avro "Lancastrian" .. .. .. 45 45
702 35 c. Consolidated "Commodore" .. .. 45 45
699/702 .. .. .. .. *Set of* 4 1·40 1·40

See also Nos. 752/3 for stamps watermarked w **16** (sideways).

(Des Berta Dallen Sands. Litho Walsall)

**1985** (22 Feb). *International Youth Year. 75th Anniv of Girl Guide Movement. T* **158** *and similar horiz designs. Multicoloured.* W w **14** *(sideways). P* 14.
703 5 c. Type **158** .. .. .. .. .. 15 10
704 25 c. Tents and coconut palm .. .. .. 60 50
705 31 c. Guide salute and Greater Flamingos .. 80 60
706 35 c. Ranger emblem and marlin .. .. 85 65
703/6 .. .. .. .. *Set of* 4 2·00 1·75
**MS**707 95 × 74 mm. Nos. 703/6 .. .. .. 2·00 2·50

159 Killdeer

160 The Queen Mother at the Christening of Peter Phillips, 1977

(Des Josephine Martin. Litho Walsall)

**1985** (24 Apr). *Birth Bicentenary of John J. Audubon (ornithologist). T* **159** *and similar multicoloured designs.* W w **14** *(sideways on 5 c., $1). P* 14.
708 5 c. Type **159**.. .. .. .. .. 40 10
709 31 c. Mourning Dove *(vert)* .. .. .. 85 55
710 35 c. "Mourning Dove" (John J. Audubon) *(vert)* .. .. .. .. .. 95 60
711 $1 "Killdeer" (John J. Audubon) .. .. 1·75 1·60
708/11 .. .. .. .. *Set of* 4 3·50 2·50

(Des A. Theobald ($1.25), C. Abbott (others). Litho Questa)

**1985** (7 June). *Life and Times of Queen Elizabeth the Queen Mother. T* **160** *and similar vert designs. Multicoloured.* W w **16.** *P* 14½ × 14.
712 5 c. Visiting Auckland, New Zealand, 1927 .. .. .. .. .. 10 10
713 25 c. Type **160**.. .. .. .. .. 40 40
714 35 c. The Queen Mother attending church .. 55 55
715 50 c. With Prince Henry at his christening (from photo by Lord Snowdon).. .. 75 75
712/15 .. .. .. .. *Set of* 4 1·60 1·60
**MS**716 91 × 73 mm. $1.25, In horse-drawn carriage, Sark. Wmk sideways .. .. .. 1·75 1·90

161 Ears of Wheat and Emblems

162 Queen Elizabeth II

(Des A. Theobald. Litho Questa)

**1985** (26 Aug). *40th Annivs of United Nations and F.A.O. (Food and Agriculture Organization).* W w **16** *(sideways). P* 14.
717 **161** 25 c. multicoloured .. .. .. .. 40 40

(Des L. Curtis. Litho Walsall)

**1985** (16 Oct). *Commonwealth Heads of Government Meeting, Nassau. T* **162** *and similar vert design. Multicoloured.* W w **16.** *P* 14½.
718 31 c. Type **162**.. .. .. .. .. 1·25 1·10
719 35 c. Bahamas Prime Minister's flag and Commonwealth emblem .. .. 1·50 1·40

**1985** (6 Nov). *As Nos. 557/8, 560 and 566, but* W w **16.** *P* 14½.
720 1 c. Type **131**.. .. .. .. .. 80 1·25
721 3 c. Blackbeard the Pirate, 1718 .. .. 1·00 1·40
723 10 c. Ceremonial Mace .. .. .. 1·75 75
726 25 c. Pineapple cultivation .. .. .. 4·50 4·50
720/6 .. .. .. .. *Set of* 4 7·25 7·25

**163** "Grandma's Christmas Bouquet" (Alton Roland Lowe)

(Des D. Miller. Litho J.W.)

**1985** (12 Nov). *Christmas. Paintings by Alton Roland Lowe. T* **163** *and similar multicoloured designs. W* w **16** *(sideways on 5, 35 c.). P* 13×13½ (5, 35 c.) *or* 13½×13 *(others).*

736 5 c. Type **163** .. .. .. .. .. .. 20 10
737 25 c. "Junkanoo Romeo and Juliet" *(vert)* .. 75 65
738 31 c. "Bunce Gal" *(vert)* .. .. .. .. 95 90
739 35 c. "Home for Christmas" .. .. .. .. 1·25 1·10
736/9 .. .. .. .. .. .. *Set of* 4 2·75 2·50
**MS**740 110×68 mm. Nos. 736/9. Wmk sideways. P 14 .. .. .. .. .. .. .. 1·75 2·50

(Des A. Theobald. Litho Harrison)

**1986** (21 Apr). *60th Birthday of Queen Elizabeth II. Vert designs as T* **110** *of Ascension. Multicoloured. W* w **16**. *P* 14½×14.

741 10 c. Princess Elizabeth aged one, 1927 .. 15 20
742 25 c. The Coronation, 1953 .. .. .. .. 35 40
743 35 c. Queen making speech at Commonwealth Banquet, Bahamas, 1985 .. .. 50 55
744 40 c. In Djakova, Yugoslavia, 1972 .. .. 55 60
745 $1 At Crown Agents Head Office, London, 1983 .. .. .. .. .. .. 1·40 1·50
741/5 .. .. .. .. .. *Set of* 5 2·75 3·00

**164** 1980 1 c. and 18 c. Definitive Stamps

(Des G. Drummond. Litho Walsall)

**1986** (19 May). *"Ameripex '86" International Stamp Exhibition, Chicago. T* **164** *and similar designs. W* w **16** *(sideways on 5 to 50 c). P* 14.

746 5 c. multicoloured .. .. .. .. .. 10 10
747 25 c. multicoloured .. .. .. .. .. 35 40
748 31 c. multicoloured .. .. .. .. .. 40 45
749 50 c. multicoloured .. .. .. .. .. 70 75
750 $1 black, emerald and pale blue .. .. 1·40 2·00
746/50 .. .. .. .. .. *Set of* 5 2·50 3·25
**MS**751 80×80 mm. No. 750 .. .. .. 2·50 2·50

Designs: *Horiz* (showing Bahamas stamps)—25 c. 1969 50th Anniversary of Bahamas Airmail Service pair; 31 c. 1976 Bicentenary of American Revolution 16 c.; 50 c. 1981 Space Exploration miniature sheet. *Vert*—$1 Statue of Liberty.

Nos. 750/1 also commemorate the Centenary of the Statue of Liberty.

**1986** (17 June). *Air. As Nos.* 699/700, *but W* w **16** *(sideways). P* 14.

752 10 c. Type **150** .. .. .. .. .. 35 20
753 25 c. Avro "Tudor IV" .. .. .. .. .. 65 80

(Des D. Miller. Litho Walsall)

**1986** (23 July). *Royal Wedding. Square designs as T* **112** *of Ascension. Multicoloured. W* w **16**. *P* 14½×14.

756 10 c. Prince Andrew and Miss Sarah Ferguson .. .. .. .. .. .. 20 20
757 $1 Prince Andrew .. .. .. .. .. 1·60 1·60

**165** Rock Beauty (juvenile)

**166** Christ Church Cathedral, Nassau, 1861

(Des Harrison Studio. Litho Questa)

**1986** (5 Aug)–**90**. *Fishes. T* **165** *and similar horiz designs. Multicoloured. W* w **16**. *P* 14. A. *Without imprint date at foot.* B. *With imprint date.*

| No. | Description | A | | B | |
|---|---|---|---|---|---|
| 758 | 5 c. Type **165** | 40 | 40 | † | |
| 759 | 10 c. Stoplight Parrotfish | 20 | 15 | 20 | 25 |
| 760 | 15 c. Jackknife Fish | 80 | 60 | † | |
| 761 | 20 c. Flamefish | 55 | 50 | † | |
| 762 | 25 c. Swissguard Basslet | 70 | 50 | 45 | 55 |
| 763 | 30 c. Spotfin Butterflyfish | 45 | 45 | † | |
| 764 | 35 c. Queen Triggerfish | 50 | 50 | † | |
| 765 | 40 c. Four-eyed Butterflyfish | 55 | 55 | 60 | 70 |
| 766 | 45 c. Fairy Basslet | 60 | 60 | 75 | 80 |
| 767 | 50 c. Queen Angelfish | 70 | 70 | 85 | 95 |
| 768 | 60 c. Blue Chromis | 2·25 | 2·25 | † | |
| 769 | $1 Spanish Hogfish | 1·40 | 1·40 | 1·40 | 1·60 |
| 770 | $2 Harlequin Bass | 5·50 | 5·50 | 4·50 | 5·00 |
| 771 | $3 Blackbar Soldier Fish | 3·25 | 3·75 | 3·75 | 4·50 |
| 772 | $5 Pygmy Angelfish | 4·75 | 5·50 | 6·00 | 7·00 |
| 773 | $10 Red Hind | 11·00 | 13·00 | † | |
| 758A/73A | *Set of* 16 | 30·00 | 32·00 | | |
| 759B/72B | *Set of* 9 | | | 18·00 | 19·00 |

Dates of issue: 5.8.86, Nos. 758A/72A; 2.1.87 No. 773A; 15.8.88 Nos. 765B, 769B/70B; 8.90, Nos. 759B, 762B, 766B/7B, 771B/2B.

Nos. 765B and 769B exist with different imprint dates below the designs.

For these designs watermarked w **14** see Nos. 791/9.

(Des L. Curtis. Litho Walsall)

**1986** (16 Sept). *125th Annivs of City of Nassau, Diocese and Cathedral. T* **166** *and similar vert design. Multicoloured. W* w **16**. *P* 14½×14.

774 10 c. Type **166** .. .. .. .. .. .. 15 20
775 40 c. Christ Church Cathedral, 1986 .. .. 55 60
**MS**776 75×100 mm. Nos. 774/5 .. .. .. 1·50 2·00

**167** Man and Boy looking at Crib

**168** Great Isaac Lighthouse

(Des Jennifer Toombs. Litho Questa)

**1986** (4 Nov). *Christmas. International Peace Year. T* **167** *and similar horiz designs. Multicoloured. W* w **16** *(sideways). P* 14.

777 10 c. Type **167** .. .. .. .. .. .. 15 20
778 40 c. Mary and Joseph journeying to Bethlehem .. .. .. .. .. .. 55 60
779 45 c. Children praying and Star of Bethlehem .. .. .. .. .. .. 65 80
780 50 c. Children exchanging gifts .. .. .. 70 85
777/80 .. .. .. .. .. *Set of* 4 1·90 2·25
**MS**781 95×90 mm. Nos. 777/80 .. .. .. 4·50 5·00

(Des A. Lowe, adapted L. Curtis. Litho Walsall)

**1987** (31 Mar). *Lighthouses. T* **168** *and similar horiz designs. Multicoloured. W* w **16** *(sideways). P* 14×14½.

782 10 c. Type **168** .. .. .. .. .. .. 55 20
783 40 c. Bird Rock Lighthouse .. .. .. .. 1·75 1·00
784 45 c. Castle Island Lighthouse .. .. .. 1·75 1·10
785 $1 "Hole in the Wall" Lighthouse .. .. 2·75 3·50
782/5 .. .. .. .. .. *Set of* 4 6·25 5·25

**169** Anne Bonney

**170** Bahamasair Boeing "737"

(Des D. and Jane Hartley. Litho Questa)

**1987** (2 June). *Pirates and Privateers of the Caribbean. T* **169** *and similar vert designs. Multicoloured. W* w **16**. *P* 14½.

786 10 c. Type **169** .. .. .. .. .. .. 45 20
787 40 c. Edward Teach ("Blackbeard") .. .. 1·40 75
788 45 c. Captain Edward England .. .. .. 1·50 85
789 50 c. Captain Woodes Rogers .. .. .. 1·60 95
786/9 .. .. .. .. .. *Set of* 4 4·50 2·50
**MS**790 75×95 mm. $1.25, Map of Bahamas and colonial coat of arms .. .. .. .. .. 3·00 2·75

**1987** (25 June). *As Nos.* 758/60 *and* 765/70, *but W* w **14**. *With imprint date. P* 14.

791 5 c. Type **165** .. .. .. .. .. .. 15 15
792 10 c. Stoplight Parrotfish .. .. .. .. 30 20
793 15 c. Jackknife Fish .. .. .. .. .. 25 30
794 40 c. Four-eyed Butterflyfish .. .. .. 80 80
795 45 c. Fairy Basslet .. .. .. .. .. 90 90
796 50 c. Queen Angelfish .. .. .. .. .. 95 95
797 60 c. Blue Chromis .. .. .. .. .. 1·00 1·00
798 $1 Spanish Hogfish .. .. .. .. .. 1·75 2·00
799 $2 Harlequin Bass .. .. .. .. .. 2·50 3·25
791/9 .. .. .. .. .. *Set of* 9 7·75 8·50

The 5 c. and 10 c. exist with different imprint dates below the design.

(Des A. Theobald. Litho Questa)

**1987** (7 July). *Air. Aircraft. T* **170** *and similar horiz designs. Multicoloured. W* w **16**. *P* 14.

800 15 c. Type **170** .. .. .. .. .. .. 15 20
801 40 c. Eastern Airlines Boeing "757" .. .. 45 50
802 45 c. Pan Am Airbus "A300" .. .. .. .. 50 55
803 50 c. British Airways Boeing "747" .. .. 60 65
800/3 .. .. .. .. .. *Set of* 4 1·50 1·75

**171** Cruise Liner and Catamaran

**172** *Cattleyopsis lindenii*

(Des A. Theobald. Litho Questa)

**1987** (26 Aug). *Tourist Transport. T* **171** *and similar vert designs. Multicoloured. W* w **16**. *P* 14.

804 40 c. Type **171** .. .. .. .. .. .. 55 55
a. Horiz strip of 5. Nos. 804/8 .. .. 2·50
805 40 c. Liners and speedboat .. .. .. .. 55 55
806 40 c. Game fishing boat and cruising yacht .. 55 55
807 40 c. Game fishing boat and racing yachts .. 55 55
808 40 c. Fishing boat and schooner .. .. .. 55 55
809 40 c. Bahamasair airliner .. .. .. .. 55 55
a. Horiz strip of 5. Nos. 809/13 .. .. 2·50
810 40 c. Bahamasair and Pan Am Boeing airliners .. .. .. .. .. .. 55 55
811 40 c. Light aircraft and radio beacon .. .. 55 55
812 40 c. Aircraft and Nassau control tower .. 55 55
813 40 c. Helicopter and parked aircraft .. .. 55 55
804/13 .. .. .. .. .. *Set of* 10 5·00 5·00

Nos. 804/8 and 809/13 were each printed together, *se-tenant*, in horizontal strips of 5 throughout the sheets, each strip forming a composite design.

(Des. A. Lowe; adapted L. Curtis. Litho Questa)

**1987** (20 Oct). *Christmas. Orchids. T* **172** *and similar horiz designs. Multicoloured. W* w **16** *(sideways). P* 14×14½.

814 10 c. Type **172** .. .. .. .. .. .. 30 10
815 40 c. *Encyclia lucayana* .. .. .. .. .. 90 60
816 45 c. *Encyclia hodgeana* .. .. .. .. .. 95 70
817 50 c. *Encyclia lleidae* .. .. .. .. .. 1·25 80
814/17 .. .. .. .. .. *Set of* 4 3·00 2·00
**MS**818 120×92 mm. Nos. 814/17 .. .. .. 3·00 3·00

**173** King Ferdinand and Queen Isabella of Spain

**174** Whistling Ducks in Flight

(Des L. Curtis. Litho Format)

**1988** (24 Feb). *500th Anniv of Discovery of America by Columbus (1992) (1st issue). T* **173** *and similar vert designs. Multicoloured. W* w **14**. *P* 14×14½.

819 10 c. Type **173** .. .. .. .. .. .. 30 15
820 40 c. Columbus before Talavera Committee .. 85 55
821 45 c. Lucayan village .. .. .. .. .. 90 60
822 50 c. Lucayan potters .. .. .. .. .. 95 65
819/22 .. .. .. .. .. *Set of* 4 2·75 1·75
**MS**823 65×50 mm. $1.50, Map of Antilles, c. 1500. Wmk sideways .. .. .. .. 2·75 2·75

See also Nos. 844/8, 870/4 and 908/12.

(Des W. Oliver. Litho Walsall)

**1988** (29 Apr). *Black-billed Whistling Duck. T* **174** *and similar horiz designs. Multicoloured. W* w **14** *(sideways). P* 14×14½.

824 5 c. Type **174** .. .. .. .. .. .. 30 15
825 10 c. Whistling Duck in reeds .. .. .. 40 15
826 20 c. Pair with brood .. .. .. .. .. 65 40
827 45 c. Pair wading .. .. .. .. .. .. 1·00 1·00
824/7 .. .. .. .. .. *Set of* 4 2·10 1·50

**175** Grantstown Cabin, c. 1820

**176** Olympic Flame, High Jumping, Hammer throwing, Basketball and Gymnastics

(Des N. Shewring. Litho B.D.T.)

**1988** (9 Aug). *150th Anniv of Abolition of Slavery. T* **175** *and similar horiz design. Multicoloured. W* w **14** *(sideways). P* 13½.

828 10 c. Type **175** .. .. .. .. .. .. 15 15
829 40 c. Basket-making, Grantstown .. .. .. 50 55

(Des D. Miller. Litho Walsall)

**1988** (30 Aug). *Olympic Games, Seoul. T* **176** *and similar horiz designs taken from painting by James Martin. Multicoloured. W w* **16** *(sideways). P* 14.

| | | | |
|---|---|---|---|
| 830 | 10 c. Type **176** | 15 | 15 |
| 831 | 40 c. Athletics, archery, swimming, long jumping, weightlifting and boxing | 50 | 55 |
| 832 | 45 c. Javelin throwing, gymnastics, hurdling and shot put | 55 | 60 |
| 833 | $1 Athletics, hurdling, gymnastics and cycling | 1·25 | 1·40 |
| 830/3 | *Set of* 4 | 2·00 | 2·25 |
| **MS**834 | 113×85 mm. Nos. 830/3. W w **14** (sideways) | 2·25 | 2·40 |

(Des O. Bell and D. Miller (40 c.), E. Nisbet and D. Miller ($1), D. Miller (others). Litho Format)

**1988** (4 Oct). *300th Anniv of Lloyd's of London. Multicoloured designs as T* **123** *of Ascension. W w* **14** *(sideways on 40, 45 c.). P* 14.

| | | | |
|---|---|---|---|
| 835 | 10 c. Lloyd's List of 1740 | 20 | 15 |
| 836 | 40 c. Freeport Harbour *(horiz)* | 60 | 55 |
| 837 | 45 c. Space shuttle over Bahamas *(horiz)* | 65 | 60 |
| 838 | $1 *Yarmouth Castle* on fire | 1·40 | 1·40 |
| 835/8 | *Set of* 4 | 2·50 | 2·40 |

**177** "Oh Little Town of Bethlehem"

**178** Cuban Emerald

(Des Josephine Martin. Litho Questa)

**1988** (21 Nov). *Christmas. Carols. T* **177** *and similar vert designs. Multicoloured. W w* **16**. *P* 14½×14.

| | | | |
|---|---|---|---|
| 839 | 10 c. Type **177** | 15 | 15 |
| 840 | 40 c. "Little Donkey" | 50 | 55 |
| 841 | 45 c. "Silent Night" | 55 | 60 |
| 842 | 50 c. "Hark the Herald Angels Sing" | 60 | 65 |
| 839/42 | *Set of* 4 | 1·50 | 1·60 |
| **MS**843 | 88×108 mm. Nos. 839/42. W w **14** | 1·90 | 2·00 |

(Des A. Lowe (50 c.), L. Curtis (others). Litho Questa)

**1989** (25 Jan). *500th Anniv of Discovery of America by Columbus (1992) (2nd issue). Vert designs as T* **173**. *Multicoloured. W w* **16**. *P* 14½×14.

| | | | |
|---|---|---|---|
| 844 | 10 c. Columbus drawing chart | 20 | 15 |
| 845 | 40 c. Types of caravel | 70 | 70 |
| 846 | 45 c. Early navigational instruments | 75 | 75 |
| 847 | 50 c. Arawak artefacts | 80 | 85 |
| 844/7 | *Set of* 4 | 2·25 | 2·25 |
| **MS**848 | 64×64 mm. $1.50, Caravel under construction (from 15th-cent *Nuremburg Chronicles*) | 1·75 | 1·90 |

(Des N. Shewring. Litho Questa)

**1989** (29 Mar). *Hummingbirds. T* **178** *and similar vert designs. Multicoloured. W w* **16**. *P* 14½ × 14.

| | | | |
|---|---|---|---|
| 849 | 10 c. Type **178** | 35 | 15 |
| 850 | 40 c. Ruby-throated Hummingbird | 80 | 90 |
| 851 | 45 c. Bahama Woodstar | 85 | 95 |
| 852 | 50 c. Rufous Hummingbird | 95 | 1·10 |
| 849/52 | *Set of* 4 | 2·75 | 2·75 |

**179** Teaching Water Safety

**180** Church of the Nativity, Bethlehem

(Des S. Noon. Litho Questa)

**1989** (31 May). *125th Anniv of International Red Cross. T* **179** *and similar horiz design. Multicoloured. W w* **16** *(sideways). P* 14×14½.

| | | | |
|---|---|---|---|
| 853 | 10 c. Type **179** | 30 | 20 |
| 854 | $1 Henri Dunant (founder) and Battle of Solferino | 2·00 | 2·10 |

(Des A. Theobald ($2), D. Miller (others). Litho Questa)

**1989** (20 July). *20th Anniv of First Manned Landing on Moon. Multicoloured designs as T* **126** *of Ascension. W w* **16** *(sideways on 40, 45 c.). P* 14×13½ (10 c., $1) *or* 14 *(others).*

| | | | |
|---|---|---|---|
| 855 | 10 c. "Apollo 8" Communications Station, Grand Bahama | 15 | 20 |
| 856 | 40 c. Crew of "Apollo 8" (30×30 *mm*) | 50 | 55 |
| 857 | 45 c. "Apollo 8" emblem (30×30 *mm*) | 55 | 60 |
| 858 | $1 The Earth seen from "Apollo 8" | 1·25 | 1·40 |
| 855/8 | *Set of* 4 | 2·25 | 2·50 |
| **MS**859 | 100×83 mm. $2 "Apollo 11" astronauts in training, Manned Spacecraft Centre, Houston. P 14×13½ | 2·50 | 3·25 |

(Des E. Weishoff. Litho Questa)

**1989** (16 Oct). *Christmas. Churches of the Holy Land. T* **180** *and similar vert designs. Multicoloured. W w* **14**. *P* 14½×14.

| | | | |
|---|---|---|---|
| 860 | 10 c. Type **180** | 15 | 20 |
| 861 | 40 c. Basilica of the Annunciation, Nazareth | 50 | 55 |
| 862 | 45 c. Tabgha Church, Galilee | 55 | 60 |
| 863 | $1 Church of the Holy Sepulchre, Jerusalem | 1·25 | 1·40 |
| 860/3 | *Set of* 4 | 2·25 | 2·50 |
| **MS**864 | 92×109 mm. Nos. 860/3. Wmk sideways | 2·40 | 3·00 |

**181** 1974 U.P.U. Centenary 13 c. Stamp and Globe

(Des J. Sayer. Litho Questa)

**1989** (17 Nov). *"World Stamp Expo '89" International Stamp Exhibition, Washington. T* **181** *and similar multicoloured designs. W w* **16** *(sideways). P* 14.

| | | | |
|---|---|---|---|
| 865 | 10 c. Type **181** | 25 | 20 |
| 866 | 40 c. 1970 New U.P.U. Headquarters Building 3 c. and building | 70 | 60 |
| 867 | 45 c. 1986 "Ameripex '86" $1 and Capitol, Washington | 75 | 75 |
| 868 | $1 1949 75th anniversary of U.P.U. 2½d. and Bahamasair airliner | 1·90 | 2·25 |
| 865/8 | *Set of* 4 | 3·25 | 3·50 |
| **MS**869 | 107×80 mm. $2 Map showing route of Columbus, 1492 (30×38 mm). P 14½ | 3·75 | 4·25 |

(Des A. Lowe (50 c.), L. Curtis (others). Litho Questa)

**1990** (24 Jan). *500th Anniversary of Discovery of America by Columbus (1992) (3rd issue). Vert designs as T* **173**. *Multicoloured. W w* **14**. *P* 14½×14.

| | | | |
|---|---|---|---|
| 870 | 10 c. Launching caravel | 25 | 20 |
| 871 | 40 c. Provisioning ship | 75 | 75 |
| 872 | 45 c. Shortening sail | 85 | 85 |
| 873 | 50 c. Lucayan fishermen | 1·00 | 1·10 |
| 870/3 | *Set of* 4 | 2·50 | 2·50 |
| **MS**874 | 70×61 mm. $1.50, Departure of Columbus, 1492 | 2·75 | 3·50 |

**182** Bahamas Flag, O.A.S. Headquarters and Centenary Logo

(Des O. Bell. Litho Questa)

**1990** (14 Mar). *Centenary of Organization of American States. W w* **16** *(sideways). P* 14.

| | | | |
|---|---|---|---|
| 875 | **182** 40 c. multicoloured | 65 | 65 |

**183** Spitfire Mk I *Bahamas I*

(Des A. Theobald. Litho Questa)

**1990** (3 May). *"Stamp World London 90" International Stamp Exhibition, London. Presentation Fighter Aircraft. Sheet 107×78 mm. containing T* **183** *and similar horiz design. Multicoloured. W w* **16** *(sideways). P* 14.

| | | | |
|---|---|---|---|
| **MS**876 | $1 Type **183**; $1 Hurricane Mk IIc *Bahamas V* | 2·75 | 3·25 |

**184** Teacher with Boy

**185** Cuban Amazon preening

(Des G. Vasarhelyi. Litho Questa)

**1990** (27 June). *International Literacy Year. T* **184** *and similar horiz designs. Multicoloured. W w* **16** *(sideways). P* 14.

| | | | |
|---|---|---|---|
| 877 | 10 c. Type **184** | 20 | 15 |
| 878 | 40 c. Three boys in class | 60 | 70 |
| 879 | 50 c. Teacher and children with books | 75 | 85 |
| 877/9 | *Set of* 3 | 1·40 | 1·50 |

(Des D. Miller. Litho Questa)

**1990** (4 Aug). *90th Birthday of Queen Elizabeth the Queen Mother. Vert designs as T* **134** *(40 c.) or* **135** *($1.50) of Ascension. W w* **16**. *P* 14×15 *(40 c.) or* 14½ *($1.50).*

| | | | |
|---|---|---|---|
| 880 | 40 c. multicoloured | 50 | 50 |
| 881 | $1.50, brownish black and ochre | 2·00 | 2·00 |

Designs:—40 c. "Queen Elizabeth, 1938" (Sir Gerald Kelly); $1.50, Queen Elizabeth at garden party, France, 1938.

(Des N. Arlott. Litho Questa)

**1990** (26 Sept). *Cuban Amazon (Bahamian Parrot). T* **185** *and similar vert designs. Multicoloured. W w* **14**. *P* 14.

| | | | |
|---|---|---|---|
| 882 | 10 c. Type **185** | 25 | 20 |
| 883 | 40 c. Pair in flight | 70 | 65 |
| 884 | 45 c. Cuban Amazon's head | 80 | 75 |
| 885 | 50 c. Perched on branch | 1·00 | 1·00 |
| 882/5 | *Set of* 4 | 2·50 | 2·40 |
| **MS**886 | 73×63 mm. $1.50, Feeding on berries | 2·50 | 3·00 |

**186** The Annunciation

**187** Green Heron

(Des Jennifer Toombs. Litho B.D.T.)

**1990** (5 Nov). *Christmas. T* **186** *and similar vert designs. Multicoloured. W w* **14**. *P* 14×13½.

| | | | |
|---|---|---|---|
| 887 | 10 c. Type **186** | 20 | 15 |
| 888 | 40 c. The Nativity | 55 | 55 |
| 889 | 45 c. Angel appearing to Shepherds | 65 | 65 |
| 890 | $1 The three Kings | 1·60 | 1·75 |
| 887/90 | *Set of* 4 | 2·75 | 2·75 |
| **MS**891 | 94×110 mm. Nos. 887/90 | 2·75 | 3·25 |

(Des N. Arlott. Litho Questa)

**1991** (4 Feb–1 July). *Birds. T* **187** *and similar vert designs. Multicoloured. W w* **16** *(sideways). P* 14.

| | | | |
|---|---|---|---|
| 892 | 5 c. Type **187** | 10 | 10 |
| 893 | 10 c. Turkey Vulture | 10 | 15 |
| 894 | 15 c. Osprey | 15 | 20 |
| 895 | 20 c. Clapper Rail | 25 | 30 |
| 896 | 25 c. Royal Tern | 30 | 35 |
| 897 | 30 c. Key West Quail Dove | 35 | 40 |
| 898 | 40 c. Smooth-billed Ani | 45 | 50 |
| 899 | 45 c. Burrowing Owl | 50 | 55 |
| 900 | 50 c. Hairy Woodpecker | 60 | 65 |
| 901 | 55 c. Mangrove Cuckoo | 65 | 70 |
| 902 | 60 c. Bahama Mockingbird | 70 | 75 |
| 903 | 70 c. Red-winged Blackbird | 80 | 85 |
| 904 | $1 Thick-billed Vireo | 1·10 | 1·25 |
| 905 | $2 Bahama Yellowthroat | 2·25 | 2·40 |
| 906 | $5 Stripe-headed Tanager | 5·75 | 6·00 |
| 907 | $10 Greater Antillean Bullfinch (1 July) | 11·50 | 12·00 |
| 892/907 | *Set of* 16 | 22·00 | 23·00 |

(Des A. Lowe (55 c.), L. Curtis (others). Litho Questa)

**1991** (9 Apr). *500th Anniv of Discovery of America by Columbus (1992) (4th issue). Vert designs as T* **173**. *Multicoloured. W w* **16**. *P* 14½ × 14.

| | | | |
|---|---|---|---|
| 908 | 15 c. Columbus navigating by stars | 25 | 25 |
| 909 | 40 c. Fleet in mid-Atlantic | 65 | 65 |
| 910 | 55 c. Lucayan family worshipping at night | 85 | 85 |
| 911 | 60 c. Map of First Voyage | 95 | 95 |
| 908/11 | *Set of* 4 | 2·40 | 2·40 |
| **MS**912 | 56 × 61 mm. $1.50, *Pinta's* look-out sighting land | 2·40 | 3·00 |

(Des D. Miller. Litho Questa)

**1991** (17 June). *65th Birthday of Queen Elizabeth II and 70th Birthday of Prince Philip. Vert designs as T* **139** *of Ascension. Multicoloured. W w* **16** *(sideways). P* 14½ × 14.

| | | | |
|---|---|---|---|
| 913 | 15 c. Prince Philip | 50 | 50 |
| | a. Horiz pair. Nos. 913/14 separated by label | 1·75 | 1·75 |
| 914 | $1 Queen Elizabeth II | 1·25 | 1·25 |

Nos. 913/14 were printed in the same sheet format as Nos. 539/40 of Ascension.

**188** Radar Plot of Hurricane Hugo



**189** The Annunciation

(Des A. Theobald. Litho B.D.T)

**1991** (28 Aug). *International Decade for Natural Disaster Reduction. T* **188** *and similar horiz designs. Multicoloured. W w* **16** *(sideways). P* 14.

| | | | |
|---|---|---|---|
| 915 | 15 c. Type **188** | 15 | 20 |
| 916 | 40 c. Diagram of hurricane | 45 | 50 |
| 917 | 55 c. Flooding caused by Hurricane David, 1979 | 65 | 70 |
| 918 | 60 c. U.S. Dept of Commerce weather reconnaissance Lockheed WP-3D Orion | 70 | 75 |
| 915/18 | *Set of* 4 | 1·75 | 1·90 |

(Des Jennifer Toombs. Litho B.D.T.)

**1991** (28 Oct). *Christmas. T* **189** *and similar vert designs. Multicoloured. W w* **14**. *P* 14.

| | | | |
|---|---|---|---|
| 919 | 15 c. Type **189** | 15 | 20 |
| 920 | 55 c. Mary and Joseph travelling to Bethlehem | 65 | 70 |
| 921 | 60 c. Angel appearing to the shepherds | 70 | 75 |
| 922 | $1 Adoration of the Kings | 1·10 | 1·25 |
| 919/22 | *Set of* 4 | 2·40 | 2·50 |
| **MS**923 | 92 × 108 mm. Nos. 919/22 | 2·50 | 3·00 |

**190** First Progressive Liberal Party Cabinet

(Des G. Vasarhelyi. Litho B.D.T.)

**1992** (10 Jan). *25th Anniv of Majority Rule. T* **190** *and similar multicoloured designs. W w* **14** *(sideways on 15 c. and 40 c.). P* 14.

| | | | |
|---|---|---|---|
| 924 | 15 c. Type **190** | 15 | 20 |
| 925 | 40 c. Signing of Independence Constitution | 45 | 50 |
| 926 | 55 c. Prince of Wales handing over Constitutional Instrument *(vert)* | 65 | 70 |
| 927 | 60 c. First Bahamian Governor-General, Sir Milo Butler *(vert)* | 70 | 75 |
| 924/7 | *Set of* 4 | 1·75 | 1·90 |

(Des D. Miller. Litho Questa ($1), B.D.T. (others))

**1992** (6 Feb). *40th Anniv of Queen Elizabeth II's Accession. Horiz designs as T* **143** *of Ascension. Multicoloured. W w* **14** *(sideways). P* 14.

| | | | |
|---|---|---|---|
| 928 | 15 c. Queen Elizabeth with bouquet | 15 | 20 |
| 929 | 40 c. Queen Elizabeth with flags | 45 | 50 |
| 930 | 55 c. Queen Elizabeth at display | 65 | 70 |
| 931 | 60 c. Three portraits of Queen Elizabeth | 70 | 75 |
| 932 | $1 Queen Elizabeth II | 1·10 | 1·25 |
| 928/32 | *Set of* 5 | 2·75 | 3·00 |

## SPECIAL DELIVERY STAMPS

**SPECIAL DELIVERY**

(S 1)

**1916** (1 May). *No. 59 optd with Type* S **1** *by* The Nassau Guardian.

| | | | |
|---|---|---|---|
| S1 **6** | 5d. black and orange | 5·00 | 22·00 |
| | a. Opt double | £800 | £1200 |
| | b. Opt double, one inverted | £950 | £1300 |
| | c. Opt inverted | £1200 | £1200 |
| | d. Pair, one without opt | £12000 | £17000 |

There were three printings from similar settings of 30, and each sheet had to pass through the press twice. The first printing of 600 was on sale from 1 May 1916 in Canada at Ottawa, Toronto, Westmount (Montreal) and Winnipeg; and under an agreement with the Canadian P.O. were used in combination with Canadian stamps and were cancelled in Canada. The second printing (number unknown) was made about the beginning of December 1916, and the third of 6000, issued probably on 1 March 1917, were on sale only in the Bahamas. These printings caused the revocation, in mid-December 1916, of the agreement by Canada, which no longer accepted the stamps as payment of the special delivery fee and left them to be cancelled in the Bahamas.

It is not possible to identify the printings of the normal stamps without plating both the basic stamp and the overprint, though, in general, the word "SPECIAL" is further to the right in relation to "DELIVERY" in the third printing than in the first or second. Our prices for No. S1 are for the third printing and any stamps which can be positively identified as being from the first or second printings would be worth about eight times as much unused, and any on cover are very rare. All the errors appear to be from the third printing.

**SPECIAL DELIVERY** (S 2) | **SPECIAL DELIVERY** (S 3)

**1917** (2 July). *As No. 69, but Wmk Mult Crown CA. Optd with Type* S **2** *by D.L.R.*

| | | | |
|---|---|---|---|
| S2 **6** | 5d. black and orange (Optd S. £65) | 45 | 4·00 |

**1918**. *No. 78 optd with Type* S **3** *by D.L.R.*

| | | | |
|---|---|---|---|
| S3 **6** | 5d. black and mauve (R.) (Optd S. £65) | 30 | 1·25 |

Nos. S2/3 were only on sale in the Bahamas.

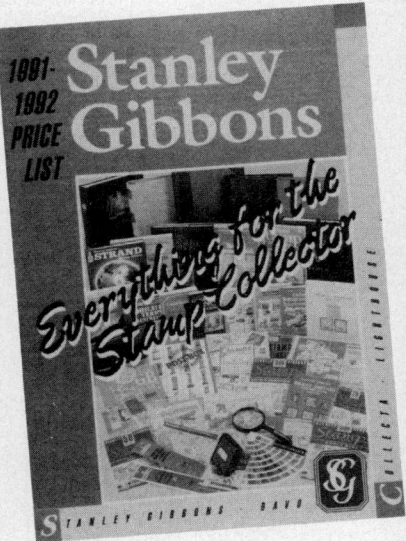

# Bahrain

An independent shaikhdom, with an Indian postal administration from 1884. A British postal administration operated from 1 April 1948 to 31 December 1965.

The first, and for 62 years the only, post office in Bahrain opened at the capital, Manama, on 1 August 1884 as a sub-office of the Indian Post Office at Bushire (Iran), both being part of the Bombay Postal Circle.

Unoverprinted postage stamps of India were supplied to the new office, continuing on sale there until 1933. Examples of the lower values can sometimes be found postmarked at Bahrain, but such cancellations on values over 4 a. are decidedly scarce. The occasional Official stamp can also be discovered, possibly used by the office of the Indian Political Agent.

The initial cancellation supplied showed a "B" against a circular background of horizontal lines, this being used in conjunction with a single ring date-stamp without any indication of the year of use.

1884 Cancellation and Date-stamp

This was followed by a squared-circle type, first seen in 1886, which was used into the early years of the 20th century. Its replacement was a single ring date-stamp, succeeded in turn by the first of a considerable number of Indian-style double-circle postmarks, all inscribed "BAHRAIN".

1886 Squared-circle

| PRICES FOR STAMPS ON COVER TO 1945 | |
|---|---|
| Nos. 1/14 | *from* × 5 |
| Nos. 15/19 | *from* × 6 |
| Nos. 20/37 | *from* × 2 |
| Nos. 38/50 | *from* × 6 |

BAHRAIN (1) BAHRAIN (2)

***Stamps of India overprinted with T 1 or T 2 (rupee values)***

**1933** (10 Aug–Dec). *King George V. Wmk Mult Star, T* **69**.

| No. | Type | Description | Unused | Used |
|---|---|---|---|---|
| 1 | **55** | 3 p. slate (12.33) | 1·50 | 45 |
| 2 | **56** | ½ a. green | 5·00 | 3·25 |
| 3 | **80** | 9 p. deep green | 3·25 | 80 |
| 4 | **57** | 1 a. chocolate | 5·00 | 2·50 |
| 5 | **82** | 1 a. 3 p. mauve | 2·75 | 45 |
| 6 | **70** | 2 a. vermilion | 7·00 | 4·50 |
| 7 | **62** | 3 a. blue | 19·00 | 30·00 |
| 8 | **83** | 3 a. 6 p. ultramarine | 2·75 | 30 |
| 9 | **71** | 4 a. sage-green | 18·00 | 30·00 |
| 10 | **65** | 8 a. reddish purple | 3·00 | 25 |
| 11 | **66** | 12 a. claret | 4·25 | 60 |
| 12 | **67** | 1 r. chocolate and green | 14·00 | 7·50 |
| 13 | | 2 r. carmine and orange | 27·00 | 35·00 |
| 14 | | 5 r. ultramarine and purple | 85·00 | £110 |
| 1/14 | | *Set of* 14 | £170 | £200 |

The 9 p. exists both offset-litho and typo.

**1934–37.** *King George V. Wmk Mult Star, T* **69**.

| No. | Type | Description | Unused | Used |
|---|---|---|---|---|
| 15 | **79** | ½ a. green (1935) | 2·75 | 55 |
| 16 | **81** | 1 a. chocolate (1935) | 4·50 | 40 |
| 17 | **59** | 2 a. vermilion (1935) | 16·00 | 7·50 |
| 17*a* | | 2 a. vermilion (*small die*) (1937) | 26·00 | 25 |
| 18 | **62** | 3 a. carmine | 4·75 | 30 |
| 19 | **63** | 4 a. sage-green (1935) | 3·00 | 30 |
| 15/19 | | *Set of* 6 | 50·00 | 8·50 |

**1938–41.** *King George VI.*

| No. | Type | Description | Unused | Used |
|---|---|---|---|---|
| 20 | **91** | 3 p. slate (5.38) | 3·00 | 85 |
| 21 | | ½ a. red-brown (5.38) | 50 | 10 |
| 22 | | 9 p. green (5.38) | 1·00 | 30 |
| 23 | | 1 a. carmine (5.38) | 70 | 10 |
| 24 | **92** | 2 a. vermilion (1939) | 3·00 | 40 |
| 26 | – | 3 a. yellow-green (1941) | 32·00 | 3·00 |
| 27 | – | 3½ a. bright blue (7.38) | 2·50 | 1·75 |
| 28 | – | 4 a. brown (1941) | £100 | 45·00 |
| 30 | – | 8 a. slate-violet (1940) | £120 | 35·00 |
| 31 | – | 12 a. lake (1940) | 90·00 | 48·00 |
| 32 | **93** | 1 r. grey and red-brown (1940) | 2·50 | 1·25 |
| 33 | | 2 r. purple and brown (1940) | 15·00 | 1·75 |
| 34 | | 5 r. green and blue (1940) | 30·00 | 13·00 |
| 35 | | 10 r. purple and claret (1941) | 65·00 | 17·00 |
| 36 | | 15 r. brown and green (1941) | 42·00 | 38·00 |
| 37 | | 25 r. slate-violet and purple (1941) | 95·00 | 65·00 |
| 20/37 | | *Set of* 16 | £550 | £225 |

**1942–45.** *King George VI on white background.*

| No. | Type | Description | Unused | Used |
|---|---|---|---|---|
| 38 | **100*a*** | 3 p. slate | 30 | 20 |
| 39 | | ½ a. purple | 1·25 | 45 |
| 40 | | 9 p. green | 3·25 | 3·50 |
| 41 | | 1 a. carmine | 1·50 | 20 |
| 42 | **101** | 1 a. 3 p. bistre | 3·00 | 5·00 |
| 43 | | 1½ a. dull violet | 3·25 | 1·00 |
| 44 | | 2 a. vermilion | 1·00 | 65 |
| 45 | | 3 a. bright violet | 4·75 | 2·50 |
| 46 | | 3½ a. bright blue | 2·50 | 5·50 |
| 47 | **102** | 4 a. brown | 1·25 | 50 |
| 48 | | 6 a. turquoise-green | 6·50 | 5·50 |
| 49 | | 8 a. slate-violet | 1·00 | 75 |
| 50 | | 12 a. lake | 2·00 | 1·50 |
| 38/50 | | *Set of* 13 | 28·00 | 25·00 |

***Stamps of Great Britain surcharged***

For similar surcharges without the name of the country, see BRITISH POSTAL AGENCIES IN EASTERN ARABIA.

BAHRAIN 1 ANNA (3) BAHRAIN 5 RUPEES (4)

**1948** (1 Apr)–**49**. *Surch as T* **3**, **4** *(2 r. and 5 r.) or similar surch with bars at foot (10 r.).*

| No. | Type | Description | Unused | Used |
|---|---|---|---|---|
| 51 | **128** | ½ a. on ½d. pale green | 30 | 20 |
| 52 | | 1 a. on 1d. pale scarlet | 30 | 30 |
| 53 | | 1½ a. on 1½d. pale red-brown | 30 | 40 |
| 54 | | 2 a. on 2d. pale orange | 30 | 20 |
| 55 | | 2½ a. on 2½d. light ultramarine | 50 | 80 |
| 56 | | 3 a. on 3d. pale violet | 30 | 10 |
| 57 | **129** | 6 a. on 6d. purple | 30 | 10 |
| 58 | **130** | 1 r. on 1s. bistre-brown | 90 | 10 |
| 59 | **131** | 2 r. on 2s. 6d. yellow-green | 3·00 | 3·75 |
| 60 | | 5 r. on 5s. red | 4·00 | 4·50 |
| 60*a* | **132** | 10 r. on 10s. ultramarine (4.7.49) | 55·00 | 40·00 |
| 51/60*a* | | *Set of* 11 | 60·00 | 45·00 |

BAHRAIN 2½ ANNAS (5) BAHRAIN 15 RUPEES (6)

**1948** (26 Apr). *Silver Wedding, surch as T* **5** *or* **6**.

| No. | Type | Description | Unused | Used |
|---|---|---|---|---|
| 61 | **137** | 2½ a. on 2½d. ultramarine | 30 | 30 |
| 62 | **138** | 15 r. on £1 blue | 35·00 | 40·00 |

**1948** (29 July). *Olympic Games, surch as T* **5**, *but in one line (6 a.) or two lines (others); the 1 r. also has a square of dots as T* **7**.

| No. | Type | Description | Unused | Used |
|---|---|---|---|---|
| 63 | **139** | 2½ a. on 2½d. ultramarine | 35 | 55 |
| | | a. Surch double | £650 | £1100 |
| 64 | **140** | 3 a. on 3d. violet | 35 | 75 |
| 65 | **141** | 6 a. on 6d. bright purple | 1·00 | 1·25 |
| 66 | **142** | 1 r. on 1s. brown | 1·10 | 2·00 |
| 63/6 | | *Set of* 4 | 2·50 | 4·00 |

Twelve used examples of No. 63a are known, postmarked at Experimental P.O. K-121 (Muharraq).

BAHRAIN 3 ANNAS

(7)

**1949** (10 Oct). *75th Anniv of U.P.U., surch as T* **7**, *in one line (2½ a.) or in two lines (others).*

| No. | Type | Description | Unused | Used |
|---|---|---|---|---|
| 67 | **143** | 2½ a. on 2½d. ultramarine | 35 | 90 |
| 68 | **144** | 3 a. on 3d. violet | 65 | 1·50 |
| 69 | **145** | 6 a. on 6d. bright purple | 65 | 1·75 |
| 70 | **146** | 1 r. on 1s. brown | 1·10 | 1·50 |
| 67/70 | | *Set of* 4 | 2·50 | 5·00 |

BAHRAIN 2 RUPEES (7*a*) "2" level with "RUPEES". "BAHRAIN" sharp

BAHRAIN 2 RUPEES (7*b*) "2" raised "BAHRAIN" worn

The third type (No. 77b) is as Type II but the vertical distance between "BAHRAIN" and "2 RUPEES" is 16 mm. instead of 15 mm. and the value is set more to the left of "BAHRAIN".

BAHRAIN

Extra bar (R. 6/1)

**1950** (2 Oct)–**55**. *Surch as T* **3** *or* **7*a*** *(rupee values).*

| No. | Type | Description | Unused | Used |
|---|---|---|---|---|
| 71 | **128** | ½ a. on ½d. pale orange (3.5.51) | 20 | 20 |
| 72 | | 1 a. on 1d. light ultramarine (3.5.51) | 30 | 10 |
| 73 | | 1½ a. on 1½d. pale green (3.5.51) | 30 | 4·75 |
| 74 | | 2 a. on 2d. pale red-brown (3.5.51) | 30 | 25 |
| 75 | | 2½ a. on 2½d. pale scarlet (3.5.51) | 30 | 4·75 |
| 76 | **129** | 4 a. on 4d. light ultramarine | 30 | 80 |
| 77 | **147** | 2 r. on 2s. 6d. yellow-green (3.5.51) | 13·00 | 3·75 |
| | | a. Surch with Type 7*b* (1953) | 50·00 | 25·00 |
| | | b. Third type (1955) | £600 | 60·00 |
| | | ba. "I" inverted and raised | £1500 | £400 |
| 78 | **148** | 5 r. on 5s. red (3.5.51) | 12·00 | 3·50 |
| | | a. Extra bar | £180 | |
| 79 | **149** | 10 r. on 10s. ultramarine (3.5.51) | 22·00 | 6·00 |
| 71/79 | | *Set of* 9 | 45·00 | 22·00 |

**1952** (5 Dec)–**54**. *Q.E. II (W* **153**), *surch as T* **3** *(in two lines on 2½ and 6 a.).*

| No. | Type | Description | Unused | Used |
|---|---|---|---|---|
| 80 | **154** | ½ a. on ½d. orange-red (31.8.53) | 10 | 10 |
| | | a. Fraction "½" omitted | 95·00 | £130 |
| 81 | | 1 a. on 1d. ultramarine (31.8.53) | 10 | 10 |
| 82 | | 1½ a. on 1½d. green | 10 | 10 |
| 83 | | 2 a. on 2d. red-brown (31.8.53) | 10 | 10 |
| 84 | **155** | 2½ a. on 2½d. carmine-red | 20 | 20 |
| 85 | | 3 a. on 3d. deep lilac (B.) (18.1.54) | 30 | 10 |
| 86 | **156** | 4 a. on 4d. ultramarine (2.11.53) | 5·00 | 20 |
| 87 | **157** | 6 a. on 6d. reddish purple (18.1.54) | 2·50 | 10 |
| 88 | **160** | 12 a. on 1s. 3d. green (2.11.53) | 3·00 | 20 |
| 89 | **159** | 1 r. on 1s. 6d. grey-blue (2.11.53) | 3·00 | 10 |
| 80/89 | | *Set of* 10 | 13·00 | 80 |

The word BAHRAIN is in taller letters on the 1½ a., 2½a., 3 a. and 6 a.

2½ ANNAS BAHRAIN (8)

**1953** (3 June). *Coronation. Surch as T* **8**, *or similarly.*

| No. | Type | Description | Unused | Used |
|---|---|---|---|---|
| 90 | **161** | 2½ a. on 2½d. carmine-red | 1·25 | 75 |
| 91 | **162** | 4 a. on 4d. ultramarine | 2·25 | 1·50 |
| 92 | **163** | 12 a. on 1s. 3d. deep yellow-green | 2·50 | 1·50 |
| 93 | **164** | 1 r. on 1s. 6d. deep grey-blue | 6·00 | 50 |
| 90/3 | | *Set of* 4 | 11·00 | 3·75 |

BAHRAIN 2 RUPEES I

BAHRAIN 2 RUPEES II

BAHRAIN 2 RUPEES III

(9)

BAHRAIN 5 RUPEES I

BAHRAIN 5 RUPEES II

(10)

BAHRAIN 10 RUPEES I

BAHRAIN 10 RUPEES II

(11)

TYPE I (T 9/11). Type-set opt. Bold thick letters with sharp corners and straight edges.

TYPE II (T 9/11). Plate-printed opt. Thinner letters, rounded corners and rough edges. Bars wider apart.

TYPE III (T 9). Plate-printed opt. Similar to Type II as regards the position of the bars on all 40 stamps of the sheet, but the letters are thinner and with more rounded corners than in II, while the ink of the surcharge is less black.

The general characteristics of Type II of the 2 r. are less pronounced than in the other values, but a distinguishing test is in the relative position of the bars and the "U" of "RUPEES". In Type II (except for the 1st stamp, 5th row) the bars start immediately beneath the left-hand edge of the "U". In Type I they start more to the right.

In the 10 r. the "1" and the "0" are spaced 0.9 mm in Type I and only 0.6 mm in Type II.

**1955** (23 Sept)–**60**. *T* **166/8** *(Waterlow ptgs) surch as T* **9/11**.

| No. | Type | Description | Unused | Used |
|---|---|---|---|---|
| 94 | **166** | 2 r. on 2s. 6d. black-brown (Type I) | 5·50 | 1·25 |
| | | a. Type II (13.5.58) | 9·00 | 7·50 |
| | | b. Type III (No. 536a, D.L.R.) (29.1.60) | 25·00 | 45·00 |
| 95 | **167** | 5 r. on 5s. rose-red (Type I) | 11·00 | 2·75 |
| | | a. Type II (19.8.57) | 11·00 | 7·50 |
| 96 | **168** | 10 r. on 10s. ultramarine (Type I) | 20·00 | 2·75 |
| | | a. Type II (13.5.58) | 48·00 | 90·00 |
| | | ab. Type II. Surch on No. 538a (D.L.R. ptg) | £160 | |
| 94I/6I | | *Set of* 3 | 32·00 | 6·00 |
| 94II/6II | | *Set of* 3 | 60·00 | 95·00 |

**1956–7.** *Q.E. II (W* **165**), *surch as T* **3** *(in two lines on 6 a.).*

| No. | Type | Description | Unused | Used |
|---|---|---|---|---|
| 97 | **154** | ½ a. on ½d. orange-red (1.57) | 10 | 15 |
| 98 | **156** | 4 a. on 4d. ultramarine (8.6.56) | 5·50 | 11·00 |
| 99 | **157** | 6 a. on 6d. reddish purple (5.12.56) | 50 | 40 |
| 100 | **160** | 12 a. on 1s. 3d. green (2.8.56) | 7·50 | 11·00 |
| 101 | **159** | 1 r. on 1s. 6d. grey-blue (4.3.57) | 4·00 | 10 |
| | | a. Surch double | | † £1400 |
| 97/101 | | *Set of* 5 | 16·00 | 20·00 |

**(New Currency. 100 naye paise = 1 rupee)**

BAHRAIN NP 1 NP (12) BAHRAIN NP 3 NP (13) BAHRAIN 75 NP (14)

**1957** (1 Apr)–**59.** *Q.E. II* (*W* **165**), *surch as T* **12** (1 *n.p.*, 15 *n.p.*, 25 *n.p.*, 40 *n.p.*, *and* 50 *n.p.*), *T* **14** (75 *n.p.*) *or T* **13** (*others*).

| | | | | |
|---|---|---|---|---|
| 102 | **157** | 1 n.p. on 5d. brown | 10 | 10 |
| 103 | **154** | 3 n.p. on ½d. orange-red | 30 | 30 |
| 104 | | 6 n.p. on 1d. ultramarine | 30 | 30 |
| 105 | | 9 n.p. on 1½d. green | 30 | 20 |
| 106 | | 12 n.p. on 2d. light red-brown | 30 | 20 |
| 107 | **155** | 15 n.p. on 2½d. carmine-red (Type I) | 25 | 15 |
| | | a. Type II (1959) | 55 | 20 |
| 108 | | 20 n.p. on 3d. deep lilac (B.) | 20 | 10 |
| 109 | **156** | 25 n.p. on 4d. ultramarine | 75 | 75 |
| 110 | **157** | 40 n.p. on 6d. reddish purple | 40 | 10 |
| | | *a. Deep claret* (1959) | 55 | 10 |
| 111 | **158** | 50 n.p. on 9d. bronze-green | 3·50 | 3·50 |
| 112 | **160** | 75 n.p. on 1s. 3d. green | 2·25 | 50 |
| 102/112 | | *Set of* 11 | 7·50 | 5·50 |

**BAHRAIN**
**15 NP**

(15)

**1957** (1 Aug). *World Scout Jubilee Jamboree. Surch in two lines as T* **15** (15 *n.p.*), *or in three lines* (*others*).

| | | | | |
|---|---|---|---|---|
| 113 | **170** | 15 n.p. on 2½d. carmine-red | 25 | 35 |
| 114 | **171** | 25 n.p. on 4d. ultramarine | 30 | 35 |
| 115 | **172** | 75 n.p. on 1s. 3d. green | 40 | 45 |
| 113/15 | | *Set of* 3 | 85 | 1·00 |

**1960** (24 May). *Q.E. II* (*W* **179**), *surch as T* **12**.

| | | | | |
|---|---|---|---|---|
| 116 | **155** | 15 n.p. on 2½d. carmine-red (Type II) | 2·75 | 11·00 |

16 17
Shaikh Sulman bin Hamed al-Khalifa

(Des M. Farrar Bell. Photo Harrison (T **16**). Des O. C. Meronti. Recess D.L.R. (T **17**))

**1960** (1 July). *P* 15 × 14 (*T* **16**) *or* 13½ × 13 (*T* **17**).

| | | | | |
|---|---|---|---|---|
| 117 | **16** | 5 n.p. bright blue | 10 | 10 |
| 118 | | 15 n.p. red-orange | 10 | 10 |
| 119 | | 20 n.p. reddish violet | 10 | 10 |
| 120 | | 30 n.p. bistre-brown | 10 | 10 |
| 121 | | 40 n.p. grey | 15 | 10 |
| 122 | | 50 n.p. emerald-green | 15 | 10 |
| 123 | | 75 n.p. chocolate | 25 | 15 |
| 124 | **17** | 1 r. black | 1·00 | 20 |
| 125 | | 2 r. rose-red | 2·75 | 50 |
| 126 | | 5 r. deep blue | 4·50 | 1·50 |
| 127 | | 10 r. bronze-green | 11·00 | 2·00 |
| 117/127 | | *Set of* 11 | 18·00 | 4·00 |

18 Shaikh Isa bin Sulman al-Khalifa

19 Air Terminal, Muharraq

20 Deep Water Harbour

(Des M. Farrar Bell. Photo Harrison (5 to 75 n.p.). Des D. C. Rivett. Recess B.W. (others))

**1964** (22 Feb). *P* 15 × 14 (*T* **18**) *or* 13½ × 13 (*T* **19/20**).

| | | | | |
|---|---|---|---|---|
| 128 | **18** | 5 n.p. bright blue | 10 | 10 |
| 129 | | 15 n.p. orange red | 10 | 10 |
| 130 | | 20 n.p. reddish violet | 10 | 10 |
| 131 | | 30 n.p. olive-brown | 10 | 10 |
| 132 | | 40 n.p. slate | 15 | 10 |
| 133 | | 50 n.p. emerald-green | 15 | 10 |
| 134 | | 75 n.p. brown | 25 | 10 |
| 135 | **19** | 1 r. black | 1·25 | 20 |
| 136 | | 2 r. carmine-red | 6·00 | 35 |
| 137 | **20** | 5 r. ultramarine | 8·00 | 4·75 |
| 138 | | 10 r. myrtle-green | 10·00 | 4·75 |
| 128/138 | | *Set of* 11 | 23·00 | 9·50 |

***MINIMUM PRICE***

The minimum price quote is 10p which represents a handling charge rather than a basis for valuing common stamps. For further notes about prices see introductory pages.

LOCAL STAMPS

The following stamps were issued primarily for postage within Bahrain, but apparently also had franking value when used on external mail.

L 1 Shaikh Sulman bin Hamed al-Khalifa L 2

(Types L 1/2. Recess D.L.R.)

**1953–56.** *P* 12 × 12½.

| | | | | |
|---|---|---|---|---|
| L1 | **L 1** | ½ a. deep green (1.10.56) | 2·00 | 45 |
| L2 | | 1 a. deep blue (1.10.56) | 2·00 | 45 |
| L3 | | 1½ a. carmine (15.2.53) | 50 | 1·25 |
| L1/3 | | *Set of* 3 | 4·00 | 2·00 |

**1957** (16 Oct). *As Nos.* L 1/3 *but values in new currency.*

| | | | | |
|---|---|---|---|---|
| L4 | | 3 p. deep green | 3·75 | 50 |
| L5 | | 6 p. carmine | 3·75 | 50 |
| L6 | | 9 p. deep blue | 3·75 | 50 |
| L4/6 | | *Set of* 3 | 10·00 | 1·40 |

**1961** (20 Mar). *P* 12 × 12½.

| | | | | |
|---|---|---|---|---|
| L 7 | **L 2** | 5 p. green | 65 | 20 |
| L 8 | | 10 p. carmine-red | 60 | 20 |
| L 9 | | 15 p. grey | 50 | 15 |
| L10 | | 20 p. blue | 60 | 15 |
| L11 | | 30 p. sepia | 50 | 15 |
| L12 | | 40 p. ultramarine | 60 | 20 |
| L7/12 | | *Set of* 6 | 3·00 | 95 |

The Bahrain Post Department took over the postal services on 1 January 1966. Later stamp issues will be found in Part 19 (*Middle East*) of the Stanley Gibbons catalogue.

## Bangkok

***see* British Post Office in Siam**

# Bangladesh

Prior to the issue of these stamps, various Pakistan issues were overprinted by local postmasters, mainly using handstamps. These are of philatelic interest, but are outside the scope of the catalogue.

1 Map of Bangladesh

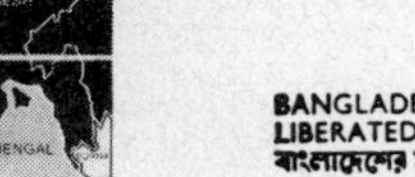


(2)

(Des B. Mullick. Litho Format)

**1971** (29 July). *Vert designs as T* **1**. *P* 14 × 14½.

| | | | |
|---|---|---|---|
| 1 | 10 p. indigo-blue, red-orange and pale blue | 10 | 10 |
| 2 | 20 p. multicoloured | 10 | 10 |
| 3 | 50 p. multicoloured | 10 | 10 |
| 4 | 1 r. multicoloured | 10 | 10 |
| 5 | 2 r. deep greenish blue, light new blue and rose-magenta | 25 | 35 |
| 6 | 3 r. apple-green, dull yellowish green and greenish blue | 30 | 45 |
| 7 | 5 r. multicoloured | 50 | 75 |
| 8 | 10 r. gold, rose-magenta & deep greenish blue | 1·00 | 1·75 |
| 1/8 | *Set of* 8 | 2·00 | 3·25 |

Designs:—20 p. "Dacca University Massacre"; 50 p. "75 Million People"; 1 r. Flag of Independence; 2 r. Ballot box; 3 r. Broken chain; 5 r. Shaikh Mujibur Rahman; 10 r. "Support Bangla Desh" and map.

Nos. 1/8 exist imperforate from stock dispersed by the liquidator of Format International Security Printers Ltd.

**1971** (20 Dec). *Liberation. Nos.* 1 *and* 7/8 *optd with T* **2**.

| | | | |
|---|---|---|---|
| 9 | 10 p. indigo-blue, red-orange and pale blue | 10 | 10 |
| 10 | 5 r. multicoloured (O.) | 1·50 | 1·50 |
| 11 | 10 r. gold, rose-magenta & deep greenish blue | 2·00 | 2·25 |
| 9/11 | *Set of* 3 | 3·25 | 3·50 |

The remaining values of the original issue were also overprinted and placed on sale in Great Britain but were not issued in Bangladesh. (*Price for the complete set £4 un.*)

On 1 February 1972 the Agency placed on sale a further issue in the flag, map and Shaikh Mujibur designs in new colours and new currency (100 paisas = 1 taka). This issue proved to be unacceptable to the Bangladesh authorities who declared them to be invalid for postal purposes, no supplies being sold within Bangladesh. The values comprise 1, 2, 3, 5, 7, 10, 15, 20, 25, 40, 50, 75 p., 1, 2 and 5 t. (*Price for set of 15 un., £1.*)

**(New Currency. 100 paisa = 1 taka)**

3 "Martyrdom"

4 Flames of Independence

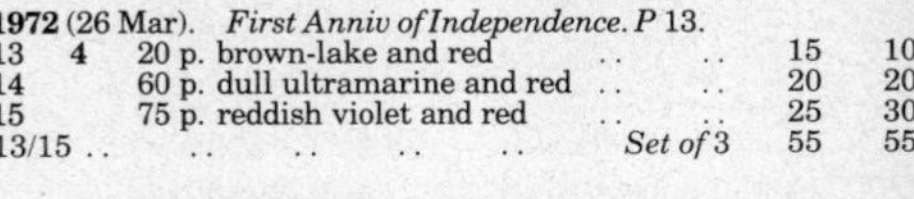

(Des and photo Indian Security Printing Press, Nasik)

**1972** (21 Feb). *In Memory of the Martyrs. P* 13.

| | | | | |
|---|---|---|---|---|
| 12 | **3** | 20 p. dull green and rose-red | 30 | 30 |

(Des N. Kundu. Photo Indian Security Printing Press, Nasik)

**1972** (26 Mar). *First Anniv of Independence. P* 13.

| | | | | |
|---|---|---|---|---|
| 13 | **4** | 20 p. brown-lake and red | 15 | 10 |
| 14 | | 60 p. dull ultramarine and red | 20 | 20 |
| 15 | | 75 p. reddish violet and red | 25 | 30 |
| 13/15 | | *Set of* 3 | 55 | 55 |

5 Doves of Peace

6 "Homage to Martyrs"

(Litho B.W.)

**1972** (16 Dec). *Victory Day. P* 13½.

| | | | | |
|---|---|---|---|---|
| 16 | **5** | 20 p. multicoloured | 15 | 10 |
| 17 | | 60 p. multicoloured | 20 | 20 |
| 18 | | 75 p. multicoloured | 20 | 20 |
| 16/18 | | *Set of* 3 | 50 | 45 |

(Des K. G. Mustafa. Litho B.W.)

**1973** (25 Mar). *In Memory of the Martyrs. P* 13½.

| | | | | |
|---|---|---|---|---|
| 19 | **6** | 20 p. multicoloured | 15 | 10 |
| 20 | | 60 p. multicoloured | 30 | 30 |
| 21 | | 1 t. 35, multicoloured | 65 | 70 |
| 19/21 | | *Set of* 3 | 1·10 | 1·00 |

7 Embroidered Quilt

8 Court of Justice

(Litho B.W.)

**1973** (30 Apr). *T* **7/8** *and similar designs. P* 14½ × 14 (50 *p.*, 1 *t.*, 5 *t.*, 10 *t.*) *or* 14 × 14½ (*others*).

| | | | |
|---|---|---|---|
| 22 | 2 p. black | 10 | 20 |
| 23 | 3 p. blue-green | 10 | 20 |
| | a. Imperf (pair) | | |
| 24 | 5 p. light brown | 10 | 10 |
| 25 | 10 p. slate-black | 10 | 10 |
| 26 | 20 p. yellow-green | 40 | 10 |
| 27 | 25 p. bright reddish mauve | 1·25 | 10 |
| 28 | 50 p. bright purple | 75 | 10 |
| 29 | 60 p. greenish slate | 60 | 15 |
| 30 | 75 p. yellow-orange | 65 | 15 |
| 31 | 90 p. orange-brown | 75 | 20 |
| 32 | 1 t. light violet | 2·75 | 10 |
| 33 | 2 t. olive-green | 3·50 | 40 |
| 34 | 5 t. grey-blue | 3·75 | 10 |
| 35 | 10 t. rose | 4·25 | 2·50 |
| 22/35 | *Set of* 14 | 17·00 | 4·75 |

Designs: *As T* **7**—3 p. Jute field; 5 p. Jack fruit; 10 p. Bullocks ploughing; 20 p. Rakta jaba (flower); 25 p. Tiger; 60 p. Bamboo grove; 75 p. Plucking tea; 90 p. Handicrafts. *Horiz* (28 × 22 *mm*)—50 p. Hilsa (fish). *Horiz as T* **8**—5 t. Fishing boat; 10 t. Sixty-dome mosque, Bagerhat. *Vert as T* **8**—2 t. Date tree.

See also Nos. 49/51*a* and 64/75.

9 Flame Emblem

10 Family, Map and Graph

(Des A. F. Karim. Litho B.W.)

**1973** (10 Dec). *5th Anniv of Declaration of Human Rights. P* 13½.
36 **9** 10 p. multicoloured .. .. .. .. 10 10
37 1 t. 25, multicoloured .. .. .. .. 20 20

(Des A. F. Karim. Litho B.W.)

**1974** (10 Feb). *First Population Census. P* 13½.
38 **10** 20 p. multicoloured .. .. .. .. 10 10
39 25 p. multicoloured .. .. .. .. 10 10
40 75 p. multicoloured .. .. .. .. 20 20
38/40 .. .. .. .. .. *Set of* 3 30 30

11 Copernicus and Heliocentric System

12 U.N. H.Q. and Bangladesh Flag

(Des K. G. Mustafa. Litho B.W.)

**1974** (22 July). *500th Birth Anniv of Copernicus. P* 13½.
41 **11** 25 p. yellow-orange, bluish violet & blk 10 10
a. Imperf (pair) .. .. .. .. 22·00
42 75 p. orange, yellow-green and black .. 25 40

(Des A. F. Karim. Litho B.W.)

**1974** (25 Sept). *Bangladesh's Admission to the U.N. Multi-coloured; frame colour given. P* 13½.
43 **12** 25 p. light lilac .. .. .. .. 10 10
44 1 t. light greenish blue .. .. .. .. 25 30

13 U.P.U. Emblem

14 Courts of Justice

(Des K. G. Mustafa. Litho B.W.)

**1974** (9 Oct). *Centenary of Universal Postal Union. T* **13** *and similar vert design. Multicoloured; country name on a yellow background (Nos. 45/6) or a blue background (Nos. 47/8). P* 13½.
45 25 p. Type **13** .. .. .. .. .. 10 10
46 1 t. 25, Mail runner .. .. .. .. .. 20 15
47 1 t. 75, Type **13** .. .. .. .. .. 25 25
48 5 t. As 1 t. 25 .. .. .. .. .. 80 1·40
45/8 .. .. .. .. .. *Set of* 4 1·25 1·60
The above exist imperforate in a miniature sheet from a restricted printing.

**1974–76.** *Nos. 32/5 redrawn with revised value inscriptions as T* **14**.
49 1 t. light violet .. .. .. .. 1·50 10
50 2 t. olive .. .. .. .. 1·75 70
51 5 t. grey-blue (1975) .. .. .. .. 2·25 70
51*a* 10 t. rose (1976) .. .. .. .. 6·00 3·25
49/51*a* .. .. .. .. *Set of* 4 10·50 4·25

15 Royal Bengal Tiger

16 Symbolic Family

(Des and litho B.W.)

**1974** (4 Nov). *Wildlife Preservation. T* **15** *and similar vert designs. Multicoloured. P* 13½.
52 25 p. Type **15** .. .. .. .. .. 70 10
53 50 p. Tiger whelp .. .. .. .. .. 1·25 60
54 2 t. Tiger in stream .. .. .. .. .. 2·75 3·25
52/4 .. .. .. .. *Set of* 3 4·25 3·50

(Des A. F. Karim. Litho B.W.)

**1974** (30 Dec). *World Population Year. "Family Planning for All". T* **16** *and similar multicoloured designs. P* 14.
55 25 p. Type **16** .. .. .. .. .. 15 10
56 70 p. Village family .. .. .. .. .. 25 40
57 1 t. 25, Heads of family (*horiz*) .. .. .. 40 85
55/7 .. .. .. .. .. *Set of* 3 70 1·25
The Bengali numerals on the 70 p. resemble "90".

17 Radar Antenna

18 Woman's Head

(Des and litho B.W.)

**1975** (14 June). *Inauguration of Betbunia Satellite Earth Station. P* 13½.
58 **17** 25 p. black, silver and dull red .. .. 10 10
59 1 t. black, silver and ultramarine .. 20 40

(Des A. F. Karim. Litho Asher & Co., Melbourne)

**1975** (31 Dec). *International Women's Year. P* 15.
60 **18** 50 p. multicoloured .. .. .. 10 10
61 2 t. multicoloured .. .. .. 25 55
a. Vert pair, bottom stamp imperf .. 75·00

(Litho Asher & Co., Melbourne)

**1976** (15 Jan)–**77**. *As Nos. 24/31 and 49/51a but redrawn in smaller size and colours changed (5, 75p.). P* 14½×15 *(50 p.),* 14½ *(1 to 10 t.) or* 15×14½ *(others). (a)* 23×18 *mm (50 p.) or* 18×23 *mm (others).*
64 5 p. deep yellow-green (11.2.76) .. .. 20 10
a. Imperf (pair) .. .. .. .. 10·00
65 10 p. slate-black (28.4.76) .. .. .. 20 10
66 20 p. yellow-green .. .. .. .. 60 10
a. Imperf (pair) .. .. .. .. 10·00
67 25 p. bright reddish mauve .. .. .. 1·00 10
a. Imperf (pair) .. .. .. .. 10·00
68 50 p. light purple (8.6.76) .. .. .. 1·50 10
69 60 p. greenish slate (10.11.76) .. .. 40 15
70 75 p. yellow-olive (10.11.76) .. .. 1·25 35
71 90 p. orange-brown (10.11.76) .. .. 40 15
*(b)* 20×32 *mm (2 t.) or* 32×20 *mm (others)*
72 1 t. light violet .. .. .. .. 2·00 10
73 2 t. olive-green (8.6.76) .. .. .. 2·50 10
a. Imperf (pair) .. .. .. ..
74 5 t. grey-blue (10.11.76) .. .. .. 2·75 80
75 10 t. rose (25.2.77) .. .. .. .. 3·50 1·25
64/75 .. .. .. .. *Set of* 12 14·50 2·75

19 Telephones, 1876 and 1976

20 Eye and Nutriments

(Des A. F. Karim. Litho Asher & Co., Melbourne)

**1976** (10 Mar). *Telephone Centenary. T* **19** *and similar vert design. P* 15.
76 2 t. 25, multicoloured .. .. .. .. 25 20
77 5 t. dull vermilion, apple-green and black .. 55 65
Design:— 5 t. Alexander Graham Bell.

(Des A. F. Karim. Litho Asher & Co., Melbourne)

**1976** (17 Apr). *Prevention of Blindness. P* 15.
78 **20** 30 p. multicoloured .. .. .. .. 15 10
79 2 t. 25, multicoloured .. .. .. .. 50 65

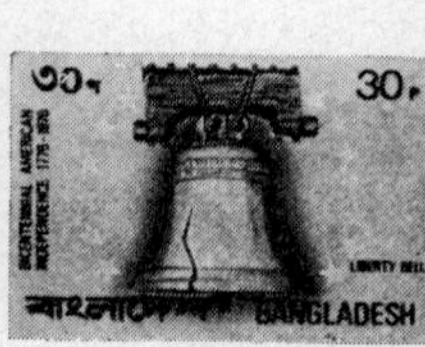


21 Liberty Bell

22 Industry, Science, Agriculture and Education

(Des E. W. Roberts. Photo Heraclio Fournier)

**1976** (29 May). *Bicentenary of American Revolution. T* **21** *and similar horiz designs. Multicoloured. P* 14.
80 30 p. Type **21** .. .. .. .. .. 10 10
81 2 t. 25, Statue of Liberty .. .. .. .. 30 25
82 5 t. *Mayflower* .. .. .. .. .. 80 50
83 10 t. Mount Rushmore .. .. .. .. 80 80
80/3 .. .. .. .. *Set of* 4 1·75 1·40
**MS**84 167 × 95 mm. Nos. 80/3 .. .. .. 2·50 3·00
No. **MS**84 also exists imperforate from a restricted printing.

(Des K. G. Mustafa. Litho Asher & Co., Melbourne)

**1976** (29 July). *25th Anniv of the Colombo Plan. P* 15.
85 **22** 30 p. multicoloured .. .. .. .. 15 10
86 2 t. 25, multicoloured .. .. .. .. 35 35

23 Hurdling

24 The Blessing

(Des K. G. Mustafa. Litho Asher & Co., Melbourne)

**1976** (29 Nov). *Olympic Games, Montreal. T* **23** *and similar multi-coloured designs. P* 14½.
87 25 p. Type **23** .. .. .. .. .. 10 10
88 30 p. Running (*horiz*) .. .. .. .. .. 10 10
a. Imperf (pair) .. .. .. .. ..
89 1 t. Pole vault .. .. .. .. .. 10 10
90 2 t. 25, Swimming (*horiz*) .. .. .. .. 30 30
91 3 t. 50, Gymnastics .. .. .. .. .. 55 55
92 5 t. Football .. .. .. .. .. 80 80
87/92 .. .. .. .. .. *Set of* 6 1·75 1·75

(Des and litho Harrison)

**1977** (7–17 Feb). *Silver Jubilee. T* **24** *and similar vert designs. Multicoloured. P* 14 × 14½.
93 30 p. Type **24** .. .. .. .. .. 10 10
94 2 t. 25, Queen Elizabeth II .. .. .. .. 35 35
95 10 t. Queen Elizabeth and Prince Philip .. 1·00 1·00
93/5 .. .. .. .. .. *Set of* 3 1·25 1·25
**MS**96 114 × 127 mm. Nos. 93/5. P 14½ (17 Feb) 1·50 2·00

25 Qazi Nazrul Islam (poet)

(Des K. G. Mustafa. Litho Harrison)

**1977** (29 Aug). *Qazi Nazrul Islam Commemoration. T* **25** *and similar design. P* 14.
97 40 p. blue-green and black .. .. .. 10 10
98 2 t. 25, sepia, stone and chestnut .. .. 30 30
Design: *Horiz*—2 t. 25, Head and shoulders portrait.

26 Bird with Letter

(Des A. F. Karim. Litho Harrison)

**1977** (29 Sept). *15th Anniv of Asian-Oceanic Postal Union. P* 14.
99 **26** 30 p. light rose, new blue and dull green 10 10
100 2 t. 25, light rose, new blue and light grey .. .. .. .. .. .. 20 25

27 Sloth Bear

28 Camp Fire and Tent

(Des K. G. Mustafa. Litho Harrison)

**1977** (9 Nov). *Animals. T* **27** *and similar multicoloured designs. P* 13.
101 40 p. Type **27** .. .. .. .. .. 20 10
102 1 t. Spotted Deer .. .. .. .. .. 30 10
103 2 t. 25, Leopard (*horiz*) .. .. .. .. 75 20
104 3 t. 50, Gaur (*horiz*) .. .. .. .. 80 35
105 4 t. Indian Elephant (*horiz*) .. .. .. 1·50 50
106 5 t. Tiger (*horiz*) .. .. .. .. .. 1·75 75
101/6 .. .. .. .. .. *Set of* 6 4·75 1·75
The Bengali numerals on the 40 p. resemble "80", and that on the 4 t. resembles "8".

(Des A. F. Karim. Litho Harrison)

**1978** (22 Jan). *First National Scout Jamboree. T* **28** *and similar designs. P* 13.

| | | | |
|---|---|---|---|
| 107 | 40 p. red, deep blue and light blue | 25 | 10 |
| 108 | 3 t. 50, carmine, deep blue and green | 85 | 30 |
| 109 | 5 t. reddish lilac, deep blue and bright green | 1·00 | 45 |
| 107/9 | *Set of* 3 | 1·90 | 70 |

Designs: *Horiz*—3 t. 50, Scout stretcher-team. *Vert*—5 t. Scout salute.

29 *Michelia champaca*

(Des and litho Harrison)

**1978** (29 Apr). *Flowers. T* **29** *and similar horiz designs. Multicoloured. P* 14.

| | | | |
|---|---|---|---|
| 110 | 40 p. Type **29** | 30 | 10 |
| 111 | 1 t. *Cassia fistula* | 45 | 10 |
| 112 | 2 t. 25, *Delonix regia* | 70 | 25 |
| 113 | 3 t. 50, *Nymphaea nouchali* | 90 | 50 |
| 114 | 4 t. *Butea monosperma* | 1·00 | 70 |
| 115 | 5 t. *Anthocephalus indicus* | 1·10 | 75 |
| 110/15 | *Set of* 6 | 4·00 | 2·10 |

30 St. Edward's Crown and Sceptres    31 Sir Alan Cobham's "DH50"

(Des and litho Harrison)

**1978** (20 May). *25th Anniv of Coronation. T* **30** *and similar vert designs. Multicoloured. P* 14.

| | | | |
|---|---|---|---|
| 116 | 40 p. Type **30** | 10 | 10 |
| 117 | 3 t. 50, Balcony scene | 25 | 35 |
| 118 | 5 t. Queen Elizabeth and Prince Philip | 40 | 55 |
| 119 | 10 t. Coronation portrait by Cecil Beaton | 80 | 1·00 |
| 116/19 | *Set of* 4 | 1·40 | 1·75 |
| **MS**120 | 89 × 121 mm. Nos. 116/19. P 14½ | 1·60 | 2·00 |

(Des and litho Harrison)

**1978** (15 June). *75th Anniv of Powered Flight. T* **31** *and similar horiz designs. P* 13.

| | | | |
|---|---|---|---|
| 121 | 40 p. multicoloured | 10 | 10 |
| 122 | 2 t. 25, blackish brown and light new blue | 40 | 35 |
| 123 | 3 t. 50, blackish brown and yellow | 55 | 55 |
| 124 | 5 t. multicoloured | 2·75 | 2·00 |
| 121/4 | *Set of* 4 | 3·50 | 2·75 |

Designs:—2 t. 25, Captain Hans Bertram's seaplane *Atlantis*; 3 t. 50, Wright brothers' *Flyer I*, 5 t. "Concorde".

32 Fenchuganj Fertilizer Factory    33 Tawaf-E-Ka'aba, Mecca

(Des P. Mandal (5 p.), A. F. Karim (10 p.), Harrison (30, 50 p., 1 t.). Photo Harrison)

**1978** (6 Nov)–**82**. *Designs as T* **32**. *P* 14½.

| | | | |
|---|---|---|---|
| 125 | 5 p. deep brown (25.3.79) | 10 | 10 |
| 126 | 10 p. turquoise-blue | 10 | 10 |
| 127 | 15 p. orange (1.8.80) | 10 | 10 |
| 128 | 20 p. brown-red (15.12.79) | 10 | 10 |
| 129 | 25 p. grey-blue (1982) | 15 | 10 |
| 130 | 30 p. deep green (10.12.80) | 40 | 10 |
| 131 | 40 p. maroon (15.12.79) | 20 | 10 |
| 132 | 50 p. black (1981) | 1·00 | 35 |
| 134 | 80 p. brown (1.8.80) | 15 | 10 |
| 136 | 1 t. reddish violet (6.81) | 1·00 | 10 |
| 137 | 2 t. dull ultramarine (21.10.81) | 40 | 50 |
| 125/37 | *Set of* 11 | 3·25 | 1·40 |

Designs: *Horiz*—5 p. Lalbag Fort; 25 p. Jute on a boat; 40 p., 50 p. Baital Mukarram Mosque; 1 t. Dotara (musical instrument); 2 t. Karnaphuli Dam. *Vert*—15 p. Pineapple; 20 p. Bangladesh gas; 30 p. Banana Tree; 80 p. Mohastan Garh.

(Des A. F. Karim. Litho J.W.)

**1978** (9 Nov). *Holy Pilgrimage to Mecca. T* **33** *and similar multicoloured design. P* 13.

| | | | |
|---|---|---|---|
| 140 | 40 p. Type **33** | 15 | 10 |
| 141 | 3 t. 50, Pilgrims in Wuquf, Arafat (*horiz*) | 40 | 30 |

34 Jasim Uddin

(Des P. Mandal. Litho J.W.)

**1979** (14 Mar). *3rd Death Anniv of Jasim Uddin (poet). P* 14.

| | | | | |
|---|---|---|---|---|
| 142 | **34** | 40 p. multicoloured | 20 | 20 |

35 Moulana Abdul Hamid Khan Bhashani    36 Sir Rowland Hill

(Des P. Mandal. Litho Harrison)

**1979** (17 Nov). *3rd Death Anniv of Moulana Abdul Hamid Khan Bhashani (national leader). P* 12½.

| | | | | |
|---|---|---|---|---|
| 143 | **35** | 40 p. multicoloured | 30 | 20 |

(Des A. F. Karim. Litho Harrison)

**1979** (26 Nov). *Death Centenary of Sir Rowland Hill. T* **36** *and similar designs. P* 14.

| | | | |
|---|---|---|---|
| 144 | 40 p. turquoise-blue, Venetian red and pale turquoise-blue | 10 | 10 |
| 145 | 3 t. 50, multicoloured | 35 | 30 |
| 146 | 10 t. multicoloured | 80 | 1·00 |
| 144/6 | *Set of* 3 | 1·10 | 1·25 |
| **MS**147 | 176 × 96 mm. Nos. 144/6 | 1·50 | 2·00 |

Designs: *Horiz*—3 t. 50, 1971 10 p. definitive stamp and Sir Rowland Hill; 10 t. 1974 1 t. 25, Centenary of U.P.U. commemorative stamp and Sir Rowland Hill.

37 Children with Hoops    38 Rotary International Emblem

(Des P. Mandal. Litho Harrison)

**1979** (17 Dec). *International Year of the Child. T* **37** *and similar vert designs. Multicoloured. P* 14 × 14½.

| | | | |
|---|---|---|---|
| 148 | 40 p. Type **37** | 10 | 10 |
| 149 | 3 t. 50, Child with kite | 35 | 35 |
| 150 | 5 t. Children playing | 50 | 50 |
| 148/50 | *Set of* 3 | 80 | 80 |
| **MS**151 | 170 × 120 mm. Nos. 148/50. P 14½ | 1·90 | 2·40 |

(Des P. Mandal. Litho Rosenbaum Bros, Vienna)

**1980** (23 Feb). *75th Anniv of Rotary International. T* **38** *and similar vert design showing club emblem. P* 13½×14.

| | | | |
|---|---|---|---|
| 152 | 40 p. black, vermilion and bistre-yellow | 15 | 10 |
| 153 | 5 t. gold and bright blue | 50 | 45 |

39 Canal Digging    40 A. K. Fazlul Huq

(Des A. F. Karim. Litho Rosenbaum Bros, Vienna)

**1980** (27 Mar). *Mass Participation in Canal Digging. P* 14×13½.

| | | | | |
|---|---|---|---|---|
| 154 | **39** | 40 p. multicoloured | 30 | 30 |

(Des P. Mandal. Litho Rosenbaum Bros, Vienna)

**1980** (27 Apr). *18th Death Anniv of A. K. Fazlul Huq (national leader). P* 13½×14.

| | | | | |
|---|---|---|---|---|
| 155 | **40** | 40 p. multicoloured | 20 | 20 |

On the face value the Bengali numerals resemble "80".

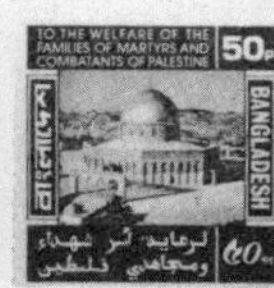


41 Early forms of Mail Transport    42 Dome of the Rock

(Des A. F. Karim. Litho Rosenbaum Bros, Vienna)

**1980** (5 May). *"London 1980" International Stamp Exhibition. T* **41** *and similar horiz design. Multicoloured. P* 14×13½.

| | | | |
|---|---|---|---|
| 156 | 1 t. Type **41** | 10 | 10 |
| 157 | 10 t. Modern forms of mail transport | 90 | 85 |
| **MS**158 | 140 × 95 mm. Nos. 156/7 | 1·00 | 1·50 |

(Des A. F. Karim. Litho Harrison)

**1980** (21 Aug). *Palestinian Welfare. P* 14½.

| | | | | |
|---|---|---|---|---|
| 159 | **42** | 50 p. deep mauve | 40 | 20 |

43 Outdoor Class

(Des P. Mandal. Litho Rosenbaum Bros, Vienna)

**1980** (23 Aug). *Education. P* 13½×14.

| | | | | |
|---|---|---|---|---|
| 160 | **43** | 50 p. multicoloured | 30 | 20 |

44 Beach Scene    45 Mecca

(Des A. F. Karim. Litho Rosenbaum Bros, Vienna)

**1980** (27 Sept). *World Tourism Conference, Manila. T* **44** *and similar horiz design showing different beach scene. P* 14.

| | | | |
|---|---|---|---|
| 161 | 50 p. multicoloured | 30 | 30 |
| | a. Horiz pair. Nos. 161/2 | 90 | 1·00 |
| 162 | 5 t. multicoloured | 60 | 70 |
| **MS**163 | 140 × 88 mm. Nos. 161/2 | 90 | 1·25 |

Nos. 161/2 were printed together, *se-tenant*, in horizontal pairs throughout the sheet.

(Des A. F. Karim. Litho Rosenbaum Bros, Vienna)

**1980** (11 Nov). *Moslem Year 1400 A.H. Commemoration. P* 14 × 13½.

| | | | | |
|---|---|---|---|---|
| 164 | **45** | 50 p. multicoloured | 20 | 20 |

46 Begum Roquiah    47 Spotted Deer and Scout Emblem

(Des A. F. Karim. Litho Rosenbaum Bros, Vienna)

**1980** (9 Dec). *Birth Centenary of Begum Roquiah (campaigner for women's rights). P* 14.

| | | | | |
|---|---|---|---|---|
| 165 | **46** | 50 p. multicoloured | 10 | 10 |
| 166 | | 2 t. multicoloured | 20 | 20 |

(Des A. F. Karim. Litho Rosenbaum Bros, Vienna)

**1981** (1 Jan). *5th Asia–Pacific/2nd Bangladesh Scout Jamboree. P* 13½×14.

| | | | | |
|---|---|---|---|---|
| 167 | **47** | 50 p. multicoloured | 15 | 10 |
| 168 | | 5 t. multicoloured | 60 | 70 |

2nd.
CENSUS
1981

(48)

**49** Queen Elizabeth the Queen Mother

**1981** (6 Mar). *Second Population Census. Nos. 38/40 optd with T* **48**.

169 **10** 20 p. multicoloured .. .. .. .. 10 10
170 25 p. multicoloured .. .. .. .. 10 10
171 75 p. multicoloured .. .. .. .. 20 20
169/71 .. .. .. .. *Set of* 3 30 30

(Des R. Granger Barrett. Litho Rosenbaum Bros, Vienna)

**1981** (16 Mar). *80th Birthday of Queen Elizabeth the Queen Mother. P* 13½×14.

172 **49** 1 t. multicoloured .. .. .. .. 15 15
173 15 t. multicoloured .. .. .. .. 3·00 2·50
**MS**174 95 × 73 mm. Nos. 172/3 .. .. .. .. 3·00 2·50

**50** Revolutionary with Flag and Sub-machine-gun

**51** Bangladesh Village and Farm Scenes

(Des P. Mandal. Litho Rosenbaum Bros, Vienna)

**1981** (26 Mar). *Tenth Anniv of Independence. T* **50** *and similar vert design. Multicolourd. P* 13½×14.

175 50 p. Type **50** .. .. .. .. .. .. 15 10
176 2 t. Figures on map symbolising Bangladesh life-style .. .. .. .. .. 25 35

(Des A. F. Karim. Litho Rosenbaum Bros, Vienna)

**1981** (1 Sept). *U.N. Conference on Least Developed Countries, Paris. P* 14 × 13½.

177 **51** 50 p. multicoloured .. .. .. .. 35 15

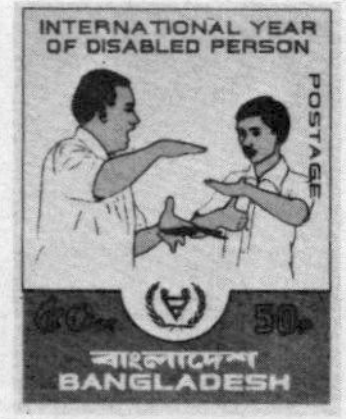


**52** Kemal Atatürk in Civilian Dress

**53** Deaf People using Sign Language

(Des F. Karim and P. Mandal. Litho Rosenbaum Bros, Vienna)

**1981** (10 Nov). *Birth Centenary of Kemal Atatürk (Turkish statesman). T* **52** *and similar vert design. Multicoloured. P* 13½×14.

178 50 p. Type **52** .. .. .. .. .. 20 15
179 1 t. Kemal Atatürk in uniform .. .. .. 30 25

(Des F. Karim. Litho Ueberreuter, Austria)

**1981** (26 Dec). *International Year for Disabled Persons. T* **53** *and similar multicoloured design. P* 13½ × 14 *(50 p.) or* 14 × 13½ *(2 t.).*

180 50 p. Type **53** .. .. .. .. .. 20 15
181 2 t. Disabled person writing (*horiz*) .. .. .. 60 50

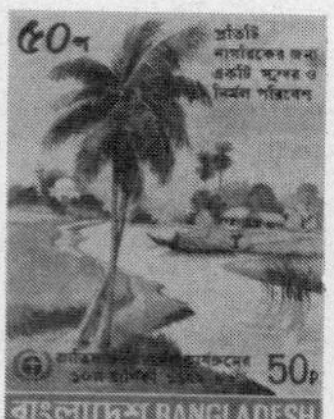


**54** Farm Scene and Wheat Ear

**55** River Scene

(Des F. Karim. Litho Ueberreuter, Austria)

**1981** (31 Dec). *World Food Day. P* 13½ × 14.

182 **54** 50 p. multicoloured .. .. .. .. 40 30

(Des P. Mandal. Litho Ueberreuter, Vienna)

**1982** (22 May). *10th Anniv of Human Environment Conference. P* 13½ × 14.

183 **55** 50 p. multicoloured .. .. .. .. 40 30

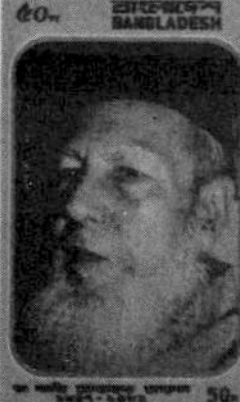

**56** Dr. M. Hussain

**57** Knotted Rope surrounding Bengali "75"

(Des F. Karim. Litho Ueberreuter, Vienna)

**1982** (9 Oct). *First Death Anniv of Dr. Motahar Hussain (educationist). P* 13½.

184 **56** 50 p. multicoloured .. .. .. .. 40 30

(Des F. Karim and P. Mandal. Litho Ueberreuter, Vienna)

**1982** (21 Oct). *75th Anniv of Boy Scout Movement and 125th Birth Anniv of Lord Baden-Powell. T* **57** *and similar multicoloured design. P* 14×13½ *(50 p.) or* 13½×14 *(2 t.).*

185 50 p. Type **57** .. .. .. .. .. 50 25
186 2 t. Lord Baden-Powell (*vert*) .. .. .. 1·50 1·50

সম্মিলিত
সশস্ত্র বাহিনী দিবস
২১ নভেম্বর,৮২

(58)

**59** Capt. Mohiuddin Jahangir

**1982** (21 Nov). *Armed Forces' Day. No. 175 optd with T* **58**.

187 50 p. Type **50** .. .. .. .. .. .. 70 50

(Litho Ueberreuter, Vienna)

**1982** (16 Dec). *Heroes and Martyrs of the Liberation. T* **59** *and similar horiz designs. Multicoloured: background colours of commemorative plaque given. P* 14×13½.

188 50 p. Type **59** (pale orange) .. .. .. 20 20
a. Horiz strip of 7. Nos. 188/94 .. .. 1·25
189 50 p. Sepoy Hamidur Rahman (apple-green) 20 20
190 50 p. Sepoy Mohammed Mustafa Kamal (dull claret) .. .. .. .. .. 20 20
191 50 p. Muhammed Ruhul Amin (bistre-yellow) 20 20
192 50 p. Flt. Lt. M. Matiur Rahman (olive-bistre) 20 20
193 50 p. Lance-Naik Munshi Abdur Rob (chestnut) .. .. .. .. .. 20 20
194 50 p. Lance-Naik Nur Mouhammad (bright green) .. .. .. .. .. 20 20
188/94 .. .. .. .. *Set of* 7 1·25 1·25

Nos. 188/94 were printed together, *se-tenant*, in horizontal strips of 7 throughout the sheet.

**60** Metric Scales

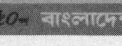

**61** Dr. Robert Koch

(Des F. Karim. Litho Ueberreuter, Vienna)

**1983** (10 Jan). *Introduction of Metric Weights and Measures. T* **60** *and similar multicoloured design. P* 13½×14 *(50 p.) or* 14×13½ *(2 t.).*

195 50 p. Type **60** .. .. .. .. .. 20 20
196 2 t. Weights, jug and tap measure (*horiz*) .. 70 90

(Des F. Karim. Litho Ueberreuter, Vienna)

**1983** (20 Feb). *Centenary (1982) of Robert Koch's Discovery of Tubercle Bacillus. T* **61** *and similar vert design. Multicoloured. P* 13½×14.

197 50 p. Type **61** .. .. .. .. .. 35 25
198 1 t. Microscope, slide and X-ray .. .. .. 90 1·00

**62** Open Stage Theatre

**63** Dr. Muhammed Shahidulla

(Des F. Karim and P. Mandal. Litho Ueberreuter, Vienna)

**1983** (14 Mar). *Commonwealth Day. T* **62** *and similar horiz designs. Multicoloured. P* 14.

199 1 t. Type **62** .. .. .. .. .. .. 10 15
200 3 t. Boat race .. .. .. .. .. .. 20 30
201 10 t. Snake dance .. .. .. .. .. 65 90
202 15 t. Picking tea .. .. .. .. .. 1·00 1·50
199/202 .. .. .. .. *Set of* 4 1·75 2·50

(Litho Ueberreuter, Vienna)

**1983** (10 July). *Dr. Muhammed Shahidulla (Bengali scholar) Commemoration. P* 13½×14.

203 **63** 50 p. multicoloured .. .. .. .. 45 30

**64** Magpie Robin

(Des F. Karim and P. Mandal. Litho Ueberreuter, Vienna)

**1983** (17 Aug). *Birds of Bangladesh. T* **64** *and similar multicoloured designs. P* 14×13½ *(50 p., 5 t.) or* 13½×14 *(2 t., 3 t. 75).*

204 50 p. Type **64** .. .. .. .. .. 85 30
205 2 t. White-brested Kingfisher (*vert*) .. 1·75 1·40
206 3 t. 75 Lesser Golden-backed Woodpecker (*vert*) .. .. .. .. .. 2·00 1·75
207 5 t. White-winged Wood Duck .. .. 2·50 2·50
204/7 .. .. .. .. *Set of* 4 6·50 5·50
**MS**208 165×110 mm. Nos. 204/7 (*sold at* 13 *t.*) .. 7·00 7·00

Visit of Queen
Nov. '83

**65** *Macrobrachium rosenbergii*

(66)

(Litho Ueberreuter, Vienna)

**1983** (31 Oct). *Fishes. T* **65** *and similar horiz designs. Multicoloured. P* 14×13½.

209 50 p. Type **65** .. .. .. .. .. 50 30
210 2 t. *Stromateus cinereus* .. .. .. .. 1·25 85
211 3 t. 75, *Labeo rohita*.. .. .. .. .. 1·75 1·25
212 5 t. *Anabas testudineus* .. .. .. .. 2·25 2·00
209/12 .. .. .. .. *Set of* 4 5·25 4·00
**MS**213 119×98 mm. Nos. 209/13. Imperf (*sold at* 13 *t.*) .. .. .. .. .. .. .. 3·50 4·00

**1983** (14 Nov). *Visit of Queen Elizabeth II. No. 95 optd with T* **66** *in red.*

214 10 t. Queen Elizabeth and Prince Philip .. 2·00 2·25
a. Optd "Nov '33" (R. 3/10) .. ..

**67** Conference Hall, Dhaka

**68** Early Mail Runner

(Des M. Begum and M. Shamim. Litho Ueberreuter, Vienna)

**1983** (5 Dec). *14th Islamic Foreign Ministers' Conference, Dhaka. T* **67** *and similar horiz design. Multicoloured. P* 14×13½.

215 50 p. Type **67** .. .. .. .. .. 25 25
216 5 t. Old Fort, Dhaka .. .. .. .. 75 1·00

(Litho Ueberreuter, Vienna)

**1983** (21 Dec). *World Communications Year. T* **68** *and similar multicoloured designs. P* 14×13½ *(10 t.) or* 13½×14 *(others).*

217 50 p. Type **68** .. .. .. .. .. 20 10
218 5 t. Sailing ship, steam train and jet air-liner .. .. .. .. .. 1·25 60
219 10 t. Mail runner and dish aerial (*horiz*) .. 1·90 1·40
217/19 .. .. .. .. *Set of* 3 3·00 1·90

প্রথম বাংলাদেশ জাতীয় ডাকটিকিট প্রদর্শনী - ১৯৮৪

**69** Carrying Mail by Boat

(70)

(Des M. Akond, P. Mandal and M. Shamim. Litho State Ptg Wks, Moscow)

**1983** (21 Dec)–**86.** *Postal Communications. T* **69** *and similar designs. P* 11½×12½ (5, 25 *p.*), 12×11½ (1, 2, 3, 5 *t.*) *or* 12½×11½ (*others*).
220 5 p. turquoise-blue .. .. .. .. 10 10
221 10 p. purple .. .. .. .. .. 10 10
222 15 p. new blue .. .. .. .. 10 10
223 20 p. grey-black .. .. .. .. 10 10
224 25 p. slate .. .. .. .. .. 10 10
225 30 p. brown .. .. .. .. .. 10 10
226 50 p. light brown .. .. .. .. 10 10
227 1 t. dull ultramarine .. .. .. 10 10
228 2 t. deep bluish green .. .. .. 10 10
228*a* 3 t. bistre (11.1.86) .. .. .. .. 50 20
229 5 t. bright purple .. .. .. .. 1·25 75
220/9 .. .. .. .. .. *Set of* 11 2·00 1·25
Designs: *Horiz* (22 × 17 *mm*)—10 p. Counter, Dhaka G.P.O.; 15 p. I.W.T.A. Terminal, Dhaka; 20 p. Inside railway travelling post office; 30 p. Emptying pillar box; 50 p. Mobile post office van. (30 × 19 *mm*)—1 t. Kamalapur Railway Station, Dhaka; 2 t. Zia International Airport; 3 t. Sorting mail by machine; 5 t. Khulna G.P.O. *Vert* (17×22 *mm*)—25 p. Delivering a letter.

**1984** (1 Feb). *1st National Stamp Exhibition* (*1st issue*). *Nos.* 161/2 *optd with T* **70** (5 *t.*) *or* "First Bangladesh National Philatelic Exhibition–1984" (50 *p.*), *both in red.*
230 **44** 50 p. multicoloured .. .. .. 30 40
a. Horiz pair. Nos. 230/1 .. .. 80 1·10
231 – 5 t. multicoloured .. .. .. 50 70

71 Girl with Stamp Album

(Des P. Mandal. Litho Harrison)

**1984** (12 May). *1st National Stamp Exhibition* (*2nd issue*). *T* **71** *and similar triangular design. Multicoloured. P* 14.
232 50 p. Type **71** .. .. .. .. .. 30 35
a. Pair. Nos. 232/3 .. .. .. .. 1·00 1·10
233 7 t. 50, Boy with stamp album .. .. 70 75
**MS**234 98×117 mm. Nos. 232/3 (*sold at* 10 *t.*) .. 1·40 1·60
Nos. 232/3 were printed together, *se-tenant*, in pairs throughout the sheet.

72 Sarus Crane and Gavial

73 Eagle attacking Hen with Chicks

(Des P. Mandal and M. Akond. Litho Ueberreuter, Vienna)

**1984** (17 July). *Dhaka Zoo. T* **72** *and similar vert design. Multicoloured. P* 13½×14.
235 1 t. Type **72** .. .. .. .. .. 75 50
236 2 t. Common Peafowl and Tiger .. .. 1·25 1·50

(Des K. Mostafa. Litho Harrison)

**1984** (3 Dec). *Centenary of Postal Life Insurance. T* **73** *and similar vert design. Multicoloured. P* 14.
237 1 t. Type **73** .. .. .. .. .. 25 20
238 5 t. Bangladesh family and postman's hand with insurance cheque .. .. .. 75 80

74 Abbasuddin Ahmad

খুলনাপেক্স—৮৪

(75)

(Des K. Mostafa. Litho Harrison)

**1984** (24 Dec). *Abbasuddin Ahmad* (*singer*) *Commemoration. P* 14.
239 **74** 3 t. multicoloured .. .. .. .. 40 30

**1984** (27 Dec). *"Khulnapex-84" Stamp Exhibition. No.* 86 *optd with T* **75**.
240 **22** 2 t. 25, multicoloured .. .. .. 40 30

76 Cycling

(Des M. Shamim. Litho Harrison)

**1984** (31 Dec). *Olympic Games, Los Angeles. T* **76** *and similar horiz designs. Multicoloured. P* 14.
241 1 t. Type **76** .. .. .. .. .. 20 15
242 5 t. Hockey .. .. .. .. .. 90 80
243 10 t. Volleyball .. .. .. .. .. 1·40 1·50
241/3 .. .. .. .. .. *Set of* 3 2·25 2·25

77 Farmer with Rice and Sickle

78 Mother and Baby

(Des M. Shamim. Litho Harrison)

**1985** (2 Feb). *9th Annual Meeting of Islamic Development Bank, Dhaka. T* **77** *and similar horiz design. Multicoloured. P* 14.
244 1 t. Type **77** .. .. .. .. .. 20 15
245 5 t. Citizens of four races .. .. .. 60 70

(Des M. Akond. Litho Harrison)

**1985** (14 Mar). *Child Survival Campaign. T* **78** *and similar vert design. Multicoloured. P* 14.
246 1 t. Type **78** .. .. .. .. .. 20 10
247 10 t. Young child and growth graph .. 1·10 90

উপজেলা নির্বাচন ১৯৮৫

(79)

**1985** (16 May). *Local Elections. Nos.* 110/15 *optd with T* **79**.
248 40 p. Type **29** .. .. .. .. .. 10 15
249 1 t. *Cassia fistula* .. .. .. .. 10 20
250 2 t. 25, *Delonix regia* .. .. .. 15 35
251 3 t. 50, *Nymphaea nouchali* .. .. .. 20 45
252 4 t. *Butea monosperma* .. .. .. 20 45
253 5 t. *Anthocephalus indicus* .. .. .. 30 55
248/53 .. .. .. .. .. *Set of* 6 85 1·90

80 Women working at Traditional Crafts

81 U.N. Building, New York, Peace Doves and Flags

(Des M. Akond. Litho Harrison)

**1985** (18 July). *United Nations Decade for Women. T* **80** *and similar vert design. Multicoloured. P* 14.
254 1 t. Type **80** .. .. .. .. .. 15 10
255 10 t. Women with microscope, computer terminal and in classroom .. .. .. 80 85

(Des M. Akond. Litho Harrison)

**1985** (14 Sept). *40th Anniv of United Nations Organization and 11th Anniv of Bangladesh Membership. T* **81** *and similar horiz design. Multicoloured. P* 14.
256 1 t. Type **81** .. .. .. .. .. 10 10
257 10 t. Map of world and Bangladesh flag .. 80 90

82 Head of Youth, Flowers and Symbols of Commerce and Agriculture

83 Emblem and Seven Doves

(Des M. Shamim. Litho Harrison)

**1985** (2 Nov). *International Youth Year. T* **82** *and similar vert design. Multicoloured. P* 14.
258 1 t. Type **82** .. .. .. .. .. 10 10
259 5 t. Head of youth, flowers and symbols of industry .. .. .. .. .. 40 60

(Des M. Akond. Litho Harrison)

**1985** (8 Dec). *1st Summit Meeting of South Asian Association for Regional Co-operation, Dhaka. T* **83** *and similar vert design. Multicoloured. P* 14.
260 1 t. Type **83** .. .. .. .. .. 10 10
261 5 t. Flags of member nations and lotus blossom .. .. .. .. .. .. 40 60

84 Zainul Abedin

তৃতীয় বাংলাদেশ জাতীয় জাম্বুরী ১৯৮৫-৮৬

(85)

(Des P. Mandal. Litho Harrison)

**1985** (28 Dec). *10th Death Anniv of Zainul Abedin* (*artist*). *P* 14.
262 **84** 3 t. multicoloured .. .. .. .. 40 30
a. Red-brown ("BANGLADESH" and face value) omitted .. ..

**1985** (29 Dec). *3rd National Scout Jamboree. No.* 109 *optd with T* **85**.
263 5 t. reddish lilac, deep blue and bright green 75 60

86 "Fishing Net" (Safiuddin Ahmed)

(Litho Harrison)

**1986** (6 Apr). *Bangladesh Paintings. T* **86** *and similar horiz designs. Multicoloured. P* 14.
264 1 t. Type **86** .. .. .. .. .. 15 10
265 5 t. "Happy Return" (Quamrul Hassan) .. 40 50
266 10 t. "Levelling the Ploughed Field" (Zainul Abedin) .. .. .. .. .. 70 80
264/6 .. .. .. .. .. *Set of* 3 1·10 1·25

87 Two Players competing for Ball

88 General M. A. G. Osmani

(Des K. Mostafa. Litho Harrison)

**1986** (29 June). *World Cup Football Championship, Mexico. T* **87** *and similar horiz design. Multicoloured. P* 15×14.
267 1 t. Type **87** .. .. .. .. .. 20 10
268 10 t. Goalkeeper and ball in net .. .. 1·10 80
**MS**269 105×75 mm. 20 t. Four players (60×44 *mm*). Imperf. .. .. .. .. 2·50 2·75

(Des P. Mandal. Litho Harrison)

**1986** (18 Sept). *General M. A. G. Osmani* (*army commander-in-chief*) *Commemoration. P* 14.
270 **88** 3 t. multicoloured .. .. .. .. 40 30

SAARC SEMINAR '86

(89)

90 Butterflies and Nuclear Explosion

**1986** (3 Dec). *South Asian Association for Regional Co-operation Seminar. No.* 183 *optd with T* **89**.
271 **55** 50 p. multicoloured .. .. .. .. 40 35

(Des M. Shamim. Litho State Ptg Wks, Moscow)

**1986** (29 Dec). *International Peace Year. T* **90** *and similar vert designs. Multicoloured. P* 12×12½.

| | | | |
|---|---|---|---|
| 272 | 1 t. Type **90** | 30 | 15 |
| 273 | 10 t. Flowers and ruined buildings | 1·40 | 1·10 |
| **MS**274 | 109×80 mm. 20 t. Peace dove and soldier | 1·50 | 1·75 |

TK. 1.00

CONFERENCE FOR
DEVELOPMENT '87

(91)

**1987** (12 Jan). *Conference for Development. Nos. 152/3 surch or optd as T* **91**.

| | | | | |
|---|---|---|---|---|
| 275 | **38** | 1 t. on 40 p. black, vermilion & bistre-yell | 10 | 15 |
| | | a. Surch double | | |
| | | b. Surch triple | | |
| | | c. Surch sideways | | |
| | | d. Surch inverted | | |
| 276 | – | 5 t. gold and bright blue | 30 | 60 |
| | | a. Opt double | | |
| | | b. Opt double, one inverted | | |
| | | c. Opt inverted | | |

92 Demonstrators with Placards

93 Nurse giving Injection

(Des B. Sardar. Litho State Ptg Wks, Moscow)

**1987** (21 Feb). *35th Anniv of Bangla Language Movement. T* **92** *and similar horiz design. Multicoloured. P* 12½×12.

| | | | |
|---|---|---|---|
| 277 | 3 t. Type **92** | 40 | 50 |
| | a. Horiz pair. Nos. 277/8 | 80 | 1·00 |
| 278 | 3 t. Martyrs' Memorial | 40 | 50 |

Nos. 277/8 were printed together, *se-tenant*, in horizontal pairs throughout the sheet, each pair forming a composite design.

(Litho State Ptg Wks, Moscow)

**1987** (7 Apr). *World Health Day. P* 11½×12.

| | | | |
|---|---|---|---|
| 279 **93** | 1 t. blue-black and deep blue | 50 | 40 |

See also No. 295.

94 Pattern and Bengali Script

95 Jute Shika

(Des M. Akond. Litho State Ptg Wks, Moscow)

**1987** (16 Apr). *Bengali New Year. T* **94** *and similar vert design. Multicoloured. P* 12×12½.

| | | | |
|---|---|---|---|
| 280 | 1 t. Type **94** | 10 | 10 |
| 281 | 10 t. Bengali woman | 40 | 60 |

(Des P. Mandal, K. Mustafa and M. Akond. Photo State Ptg Wks, Moscow)

**1987** (18 May). *Export Products. T* **95** *and similar multi-coloured designs. P* 12½×12 (5 *t.*) *or* 12×12½ (*others*).

| | | | |
|---|---|---|---|
| 282 | 1 t. Type **95** | 10 | 10 |
| 283 | 5 t. Jute carpet (*horiz*) | 20 | 30 |
| 284 | 10 t. Cane table lamp | 40 | 60 |
| 282/4 | *Set of* 3 | 60 | 85 |

96 Ustad Ayet Ali Khan and Surbahar

97 Palanquin

(Litho State Ptg Wks, Moscow)

**1987** (2 Sept). *20th Death Anniv of Ustad Ayet Ali Khan (musician and composer). P* 12×12½.

| | | | |
|---|---|---|---|
| 285 **96** | 5 t. multicoloured | 40 | 40 |

(Litho State Ptg Wks, Moscow)

**1987** (24 Oct). *Transport. T* **97** *and similar horiz designs. Multicoloured. P* 12½×12.

| | | | |
|---|---|---|---|
| 286 | 2 t. Type **97** | 15 | 15 |
| 287 | 3 t. Bicycle rickshaw | 20 | 20 |
| 288 | 5 t. River steamer | 30 | 35 |
| 289 | 7 t. Express diesel train | 40 | 50 |
| 290 | 10 t. Bullock cart | 45 | 75 |
| 286/90 | *Set of* 5 | 1·40 | 1·75 |

98 H. S. Suhrawardy

99 Villagers fleeing from Typhoon

(Des P. Mandal. Litho State Ptg Wks, Moscow)

**1987** (5 Dec). *Hossain Shahid Suhrawardy (politician) Commem. P* 12×12½.

| | | | |
|---|---|---|---|
| 291 **98** | 3 t. multicoloured | 20 | 30 |

(Des M. Akond. Litho State Ptg Wks, Moscow)

**1987** (15 Dec). *International Year of Shelter for the Homeless. T* **99** *and similar horiz design. Multicoloured. P* 12½×12.

| | | | |
|---|---|---|---|
| 292 | 5 t. Type **99** | 20 | 30 |
| | a. Horiz pair. Nos. 292/3 | 40 | 60 |
| 293 | 5 t. Villagers and modern houses | 20 | 30 |

Nos. 292/3 were printed together, *se-tenant*, in horizontal pairs throughout the sheet.

100 President Ershad addressing Parliament

(Des K. Mustafa. Litho State Ptg Wks, Moscow)

**1987** (31 Dec). *1st Anniv of Return to Democracy. P* 12½×12.

| | | | |
|---|---|---|---|
| 294 **100** | 10 t. multicoloured | 40 | 60 |

(Litho State Ptg Wks, Moscow)

**1988** (16 Jan). *World Health Day. Vert design as T* **93**. *P* 11½×12.

| | | | |
|---|---|---|---|
| 295 | 25 p. brown | 20 | 15 |

Design:—25 p. Oral rehydration.

101 Woman Planting Palm Saplings

(Des K. Mustafa. Litho State Ptg Wks, Moscow)

**1988** (26 Jan). *I.F.A.D. Seminar on Agricultural Loans for Rural Women. T* **101** *and similar horiz design. Multicoloured. P* 12½×12.

| | | | |
|---|---|---|---|
| 296 | 3 t. Type **101** | 15 | 20 |
| 297 | 5 t. Village woman milking cow | 20 | 40 |

102 Basketball

(Litho State Ptg Wks, Moscow)

**1988** (20 Sept). *Olympic Games, Seoul. T* **102** *and similar diamond-shaped designs. Multicoloured. P* 11½.

| | | | |
|---|---|---|---|
| 298 | 5 t. Type **102** | 20 | 25 |
| | a. Strip of 5. Nos. 298/302 | 90 | |
| 299 | 5 t. Weightlifting | 20 | 25 |
| 300 | 5 t. Tennis | 20 | 25 |
| 301 | 5 t. Rifle-shooting | 20 | 25 |
| 302 | 5 t. Boxing | 20 | 25 |
| 298/302 | *Set of* 5 | 90 | 1·10 |

Nos. 298/302 were printed together, *se-tenant*, in horizontal and vertical strips of five throughout the sheet.

103 Interior of Shait Gumbaz Mosque, Bagerhat

104 Henri Dunant (founder), Red Cross and Crescent

(Litho State Ptg Wks, Moscow)

**1988** (9 Oct). *Historical Buildings. T* **103** *and similar horiz designs. Multicoloured. P* 12½×12.

| | | | |
|---|---|---|---|
| 303 | 1 t. Type **103** | 10 | 10 |
| 304 | 4 t. Paharpur Monastery | 10 | 10 |
| 305 | 5 t. Kantanagar Temple, Dinajpur | 10 | 10 |
| 306 | 10 t. Lalbag Fort, Dhaka | 15 | 15 |
| 303/6 | *Set of* 4 | 30 | 30 |

(Litho State Ptg Wks, Moscow)

**1988** (26 Oct). *125th Anniv of International Red Cross and Red Crescent. T* **104** *and similar vert design. Multicoloured. P* 12 × 12½.

| | | | |
|---|---|---|---|
| 307 | 5 t. Type **104** | 20 | 25 |
| 308 | 10 t. Red Cross workers with patient | 40 | 45 |

105 Dr. Qudrat-i-Khuda in Laboratory

106 Wicket-keeper

(Litho State Ptg Wks, Moscow)

**1988** (3 Nov). *Dr. Qudrat-i-Khuda (scientist) Commemoration. P* 12 × 12½.

| | | | |
|---|---|---|---|
| 309 **105** | 5 t. multicoloured | 20 | 25 |

(Litho State Ptg Wks, Moscow)

**1988** (27 Nov). *Asia Cup Cricket. T* **106** *and similar vert designs. Multicoloured. P* 12 × 12½.

| | | | |
|---|---|---|---|
| 310 | 1 t. Type **106** | 40 | 50 |
| | a. Horiz strip of 3. Nos. 310/12 | 1·60 | |
| 311 | 5 t. Batsman | 60 | 75 |
| 312 | 10 t. Bowler | 75 | 90 |
| 310/12 | *Set of* 3 | 1·60 | 1·90 |

Nos. 310/12 were printed together, *se-tenant*, in horizontal strips of three throughout the sheet.

107 Labourers, Factory and Technician

(Litho State Ptg Wks, Moscow)

**1988** (29 Nov). *32nd Meeting of Colombo Plan Consultative Committee, Dhaka. P* 12×12½.

| | | | |
|---|---|---|---|
| 313 **107** | 3 t. multicoloured | 10 | 10 |
| 314 | 10 t. multicoloured | 40 | 45 |

***MINIMUM PRICE***

The minimum price quote is 10p which represents a handling charge rather than a basis for valuing common stamps. For further notes about prices see introductory pages.

**108** Dhaka G.P.O. Building

(Litho State Ptg Wks, Moscow)

**1988** (6 Dec). *25th Anniv of Dhaka G.P.O. Building. T* **108** *and similar horiz design. Multicoloured. P* 12.

315 1 t. Type **108** .. .. .. .. 10 10
316 5 t. Post Office counter .. .. .. 20 25

৫ম জাতীয় রোভার মুট
১৯৮৮-৮৯

(**109**)

**110** Bangladesh Airport

**1988** (29 Dec). *5th National Rover Scout Moot. No.* 168 *optd with T* **109**.

317 **47** 5 t. multicoloured .. .. .. 30 30
a. Opt inverted .. .. ..

(Des K. Mustafa (3, 10 t.), N. Islam (5 t.), M. Akond (20 t.). Litho State Ptg Wks, Moscow)

**1989** (1 Jan–1 July). *Bangladesh Landmarks. T* **110** *and similar designs. P* 12×11½ (3 *t.*), 12½×12 (5 *t.*), 11½×12 (10 *t.*) *or* 12×12½ (20 *t.*).

318 3 t. black and light blue .. .. .. 10 10
319 5 t. black and orange-brown (31 Mar) .. 15 20
320 10 t. rosine (1 July) .. .. .. 30 35
321 20 t. multicoloured (1 July) .. .. 60 65
318/21 .. .. .. *Set of* 4 1·00 1·25

Designs: *Vert* (22×33 *mm*)—5 t. Curzon Hall. (19½×31½ *mm*) 10 t. Fertiliser Factory, Chittagong. *Horiz* (33×23 *mm*)—20 t. Postal Academy, Rajshahi.

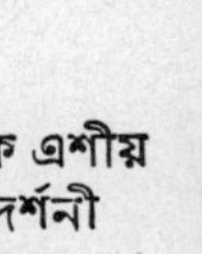

চতুর্থ দ্বিবার্ষিক এশীয়
চারুকলা প্রদর্শনী
বাংলাদেশ ১৯৮৯

(**111**)

**112** Irrigation Methods and Student with Telescope

**1989** (1 Mar). *4th Biennial Asian Art Exhibition. No.* 266 *optd with T* **111**.

322 10 t. "Levelling the Ploughed Field" (Zainul Abedin) .. .. .. .. .. 40 45

(Litho State Ptg Wks, Moscow)

**1989** (7 Mar). *12th National Science and Technology Week. P* 12×12½.

323 **112** 10 t. multicoloured .. .. .. 40 45

**113** Academy Logo

**114** Rejoicing Crowds, Paris, 1789

(Litho State Ptg Wks, Moscow)

**1989** (13 Mar). *75th Anniv of Police Academy, Sardah. P* 12×12½.

324 **113** 10 t. multicoloured .. .. .. 40 45

(Des K. Mostafa (Nos. **MS**327/8). Litho Harrison)

**1989** (12 July). *Bicentenary of French Revolution. T* **114** *and similar horiz design. Multicoloured. P* 14×14½.

325 17 t. Type **114** .. .. .. .. 70 75
a. Horiz pair. Nos. 325/6 plus label .. 1·40 1·50
326 17 t. Storming the Bastille, 1789 .. .. 70 75
**MS**327 125×125 mm. 5 t. Men with pickaxes; 10 t. "Liberty guiding the People" (detail) (Delacroix); 10 t. Crowd with cannon. P 14 .. 1·50 1·75
**MS**328 152×88 mm. 25 t. Storming the Bastille. Imperf .. .. .. .. .. .. 1·50 1·75

Nos. 325/6 were printed in sheets of 30 (6×5) with No. 325 in vertical columns one and four, labels showing the Bicentenary emblem in columns two and five, and No. 326 in columns three and six.

The design of No. **MS**328 incorporates the three scenes featured on No. **MS**327.

**115** Sowing and Harvesting

(Litho State Ptg Wks, Moscow)

**1989** (10 Aug). *10th Anniv of Asia-Pacific Integrated Rural Development Centre. T* **115** *and similar horiz design. Multicoloured. P* 12½×12.

329 5 t. Type **115** .. .. .. 45 45
a. Horiz pair. Nos. 329/30 .. .. 95 95
330 10 t. Rural activities .. .. .. 50 50

Nos. 329/30 were printed together, *se-tenant*, in horizontal pairs throughout the sheet, each pair forming a composite design.

**116** Helper and Child playing with Baby

**117** U.N. Soldier on Watch

(Litho State Ptg Wks, Moscow)

**1989** (22 Aug). *40th Anniv of S.O.S. International Children's Village. T* **116** *and similar horiz design. Multicoloured. P* 12½ × 12.

331 1 t. Type **116** .. .. .. .. 15 10
332 10 t. Foster mother with children .. .. 55 55

(Litho State Ptg Wks, Moscow)

**1989** (12 Sept). *1st Anniv of Bangladesh Participation in U.N. Peace-keeping Force. T* **117** *and similar vert design. Multicoloured. P* 12×12½.

333 4 t. Type **117** .. .. .. .. 25 20
334 10 t. Two soldiers checking positions .. 60 65

**118** Festival Emblem

**119** State Security Printing Press

(Litho State Ptg Wks, Moscow)

**1989** (17 Nov). *2nd Asian Poetry Festival, Dhaka. T* **118** *and similar vert design. P* 12×12½.

335 2 t. brt scarlet, dp carmine & myrtle-green 15 10
336 10 t. multicoloured .. .. .. 60 65

Design:—10 t. Festival emblem and hall.

(Litho State Security Ptg Press, Gazipur)

**1989** (7 Dec). *Inauguration of State Security Printing Press, Gazipur. P* 13½.

337 **119** 10 t. multicoloured .. .. .. 65 65



**120** Water Lilies and T.V. Emblem

(Litho State Ptg Wks, Moscow (5 t.), State Security Ptg Press, Gazipur (10 t.))

**1989** (25 Dec). *25th Anniv of Bangladesh Television. T* **120** *and similar horiz design. Multicoloured. P* 12½×12 (5 *t.*) *or* 13½ (10 *t.*).

338 5 t. Type **120** .. .. .. 30 30
339 10 t. Central emblem and water lilies .. 65 80

**121** Gharial in Shallow Water

**122** Symbolic Family

(Des K. Mostafa. Litho Harrison)

**1990** (31 Jan). *Endangered Wildlife. Gharial. T* **121** *and similar horiz designs. Multicoloured. P* 14.

340 50 p. Type **121** .. .. .. .. 20 20
a. Block of 4. Nos. 340/3 .. .. 1·75
341 2 t. Gharial feeding .. .. .. 30 30
342 4 t. Gharials basking on sand bank .. 45 45
343 10 t. Two gharials resting .. .. 90 90
340/3 .. .. .. *Set of* 4 1·75 1·75

Nos. 340/3 were printed together, *se-tenant*, in blocks of four throughout the sheet.

(Litho State Ptg Press, Gazipur)

**1990** (10 Feb). *Population Day. Litho. P* 13½.

344 **122** 6 t. multicoloured .. .. .. 35 35

**123** Justice S.M. Murshed

**124** Boy learning Alphabet

(Des P. Mondal. Litho State Ptg Wks, Moscow)

**1990** (3 Apr). *10th Death Anniv of Justice Syed Mahbub Murshed. P* 12½×12.

345 **123** 5 t. multicoloured .. .. .. 35 35

(Litho State Ptg Wks, Moscow)

**1990** (10 Apr). *International Literacy Year. T* **124** *and similar vert design. Multicoloured. P* 12×12½.

346 6 t. Type **124** .. .. .. 35 40
347 10 t. Boy teaching girl to write .. .. 75 60

**125** Penny Black with "Stamp World London 90" Exhibition Emblem

**126** Goalkeeper and Ball

(Des K. Mustafa. Litho State Security Ptg Press, Gazipur)

**1990** (6 May). *150th Anniv of the Penny Black. T* **125** *and similar vert design. Multicoloured. P* 13½.

348 7 t. Type **125** .. .. .. .. 50 45
349 10 t. Penny Black, 1983 World Communications Year stamp and Bengali mail runner .. .. .. .. .. 75 65

(Des M. Shamim. Litho State Security Ptg Press, Gazipur)

**1990** (12 June). *World Cup Football Championship, Italy. T* **126** *and similar horiz designs. Multicoloured. P* 13½.

350 8 t. Type **126** .. .. .. .. 60 60
351 10 t. Footballer with ball .. .. .. 80 80
**MS**352 104×79 mm. 25 t. Colosseum, Rome, with football. Imperf .. .. .. .. 2·25 2·25

**127** Mango

**128** Man gathering Wheat

(Des M. Shamim (1, 2 t.), N. Islam (3, 4 t.), P. Mondal (5, 10 t.). Litho State Ptg Wks, Moscow)

**1990** (16 July). *Fruit. T* **127** *and similar vert designs. Multicoloured. P* 12×12½.

353 1 t. Type **127** .. .. .. .. 10 10
354 2 t. Guava .. .. .. .. 10 10

355 3 t. Water-melon .. .. .. .. .. 15 15
356 4 t. Papaya .. .. .. .. .. 20 25
357 5 t. Bread fruit .. .. .. .. .. 30 35
358 10 t. Carambola .. .. .. .. .. 60 70
353/8 .. .. .. .. *Set of* 6 1·25 1·50

(Des M. Akond. Litho Security Printing Press, Gazipur)

**1990** (3 Sept). *U.N. Conference on Least Developed Countries, Paris. P* 14.
359 **128** 10 t. multicoloured .. .. .. .. 60 60
a. Blue (U.N. emblem and inscr) inverted .. .. ..

On the evidence of the sheet marginal markings it would appear that the blue on No. 359a may be printed correctly and the remainder of the colours inverted. Unequal margins at top and bottom of the sheet also cause the country name and face value, in green, to be displaced.

**129** Map of Asia with Stream of Letters

**130** Canoe Rowing

(Des K. Mustafa. Litho Security Printing Press, Gazipur)

**1990** (10 Sept). *20th Anniv of Asia–Pacific Postal Training Centre. T* **129** *and similar vert design. Multicoloured. P* 13½×14.
360 2 t. Type **129** .. .. .. .. .. 20 20
a. Horiz pair. Nos. 360/1 .. .. .. 50 50
361 6 t. Map of Pacific with stream of letters 30 30

Nos. 360/1 were printed together, *se-tenant*, in horizontal pairs throughout the sheet, forming a composite map design.

(Des K. Mustafa. Litho State Security Ptg Press, Gazipur)

**1990** (22 Sept). *Asian Games, Beijing. T* **130** *and similar horiz designs. Multicoloured. P* 14×13½.
362 2 t. Type **130** .. .. .. .. .. 15 10
363 4 t. Kabaddi .. .. .. .. .. 25 25
364 8 t. Wrestling .. .. .. .. .. 45 45
365 10 t. Badminton .. .. .. .. .. 70 70
362/5 .. .. .. .. *Set of* 4 1·40 1·40

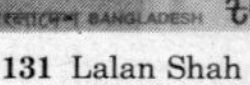

**131** Lalan Shah

**132** U.N. Logo and "40"

(Des K. Mustafa. Litho State Security Ptg Press, Gazipur)

**1990** (17 Oct). *1st Death Anniv of Lalan Shah (poet). P* 13½×14.
366 **131** 6 t. multicoloured .. .. .. .. 40 35

(Des M. Akond. Litho State Security Ptg Press, Gazipur)

**1990** (24 Oct). *40th Anniv of United Nations Development Programme. P* 14×13½.
367 **132** 6 t. multicoloured .. .. .. .. 40 35

**133** Immunization

**134** Salimullah Hall

(Des M. Akond (2 t.), P. Mondal (6 t.). Litho State Security Printing Press, Gazipur)

**1990** (29 Nov)–**91**. *P* 14½ × 14.
368 **133** 2 t. brown .. .. .. .. .. 10 10
369 **134** 6 t. slate-blue & greenish yell (30.1.91) 20 25

**135** *Danaus chrysippus*

**136** Drugs attacking Bangladesh

(Des M. Shamim. Litho State Security Ptg Press, Gazipur)

**1990** (3 Dec). *Butterflies. T* **135** *and similar square designs. Multicoloured. P* 13½ × 12.
376 6 t. Type **135** .. .. .. .. 35 35
a. Block of 4. Nos. 376/9 .. .. 1·50
377 6 t. *Precis almana* .. .. .. .. 35 35
378 10 t. *Ixias pyrene* .. .. .. .. 50 55
379 10 t. *Danaus plexippus* .. .. .. .. 50 55
376/9 .. .. .. .. *Set of* 4 1·50 1·60

Nos. 376/9 were printed together, *se-tenant*, in blocks of four throughout the sheet.

(Des F. Karim (2 t.), M. Akond (4 t.). Litho State Security Ptg Press, Gazipur)

**1991** (1 Jan). *United Nations Anti-Drugs Decade. T* **136** *and similar horiz design. Multicoloured. P* 14.
380 2 t. Type **136** .. .. .. .. .. 20 15
381 4 t. "Drug" snake around globe .. .. 25 25

**137** Silhouetted People on Map

**138** "Invincible Bangla" (statue)

(Des P. Mondal. Litho State Security Printing Press, Gazipur)

**1991** (12 Mar). *Third National Census. P* 14.
382 **137** 4 t. multicoloured .. .. .. .. 10 15

(Des M. Akond. Litho State Security Printing Press, Gazipur)

**1991** (26 Mar). *20th Anniv of Independence. T* **138** *and similar square designs. Multicoloured. P* 13½.
383 4 t. Type **138** .. .. .. .. .. 10 15
a. Horiz strip of 5. Nos. 383/7 .. .. 45
384 4 t. "Freedom Fighter" (statue) .. .. 10 15
385 4 t. Mujibnagar Memorial .. .. .. 10 15
386 4 t. Eternal Flame .. .. .. .. 10 15
387 4 t. National Martyrs' Memorial .. .. 10 15
383/7 .. .. .. .. *Set of* 5 45 70

Nos. 383/7 were printed together, *se-tenant*, in horizontal strips of five throughout the sheet, with the backgrounds forming a composite design.

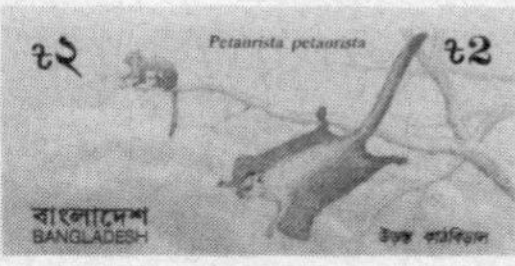

**139** Pres. Rahman Seated

**140** Red Giant Flying Squirrel

(Des P. Mondal. Litho Ueberreuter, Austria)

**1991** (30 May). *10th Death Anniv of President Ziaur Rahman. T* **139** *and similar vert design. Multicoloured. P* 13½ × 14.
388 50 p. Type **139** .. .. .. .. .. 10 10
389 2 t. President Rahman's head in circular decoration .. .. .. .. .. 10 10
**MS**390 146 × 75 mm. Nos. 388/9 (*sold at* 10 *t*.) 30 35

(Des K. Mustafa. Litho State Security Printing Press, Gazipur)

**1991** (16 June). *Endangered Species. T* **140** *and similar multicoloured designs. P* 12.
391 2 t. Type **140** .. .. .. .. .. 10 10
a. Vert pair. Nos. 391 and 394 .. .. 20 25
392 4 t. Black-faced Monkey (*vert*) .. .. 10 15
a. Horiz pair. Nos. 392/3 .. .. .. 30 40
393 6 t. Great Indian Hornbill (*vert*) .. .. 20 25
394 10 t. Armoured Pangolin .. .. .. 30 35
391/4 .. .. .. .. *Set of* 4 65 75

Nos. 391 and 394, and 392/3 were printed together, *se-tenant*, in vertical (Nos. 391 and 394) or horizontal (Nos. 392/3) pairs throughout separate sheets.

**141** Kaikobad

**142** Rabindranath Tagore and Temple

(Des K. Mustafa. Litho State Security Printing Press, Gazipur)

**1991** (21 July). *40th Death Anniv of Kaikobad (poet). P* 14.
395 **141** 6 t. multicoloured .. .. .. .. 20 25

(Des A. Karim. Litho State Security Printing Press, Gazipur)

**1991** (7 Aug). *50th Death Anniv of Rabindranath Tagore (poet). P* 14.
396 **142** 4 t. multicoloured .. .. .. .. 10 10

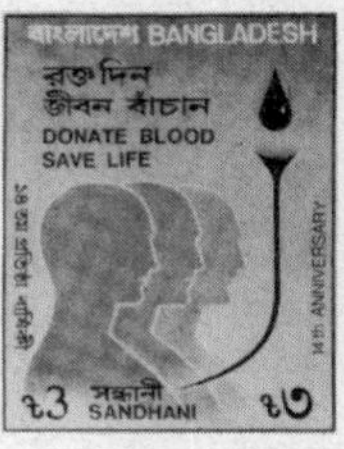

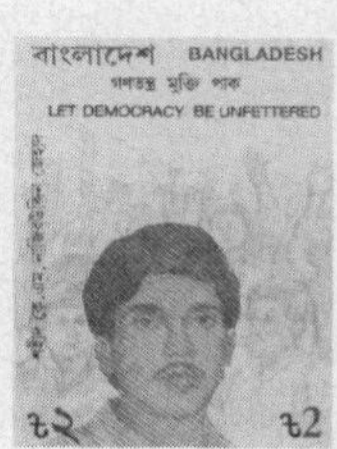


**143** Voluntary Blood Donation Programme

**144** Shahid Naziruddin and Crowd

(Des P. Mondal. Litho State Security Printing Press, Gazipur)

**1991** (19 Sept). *14th Anniv of "Sandhani" (medical students' association). T* **143** *and similar vert design. P* 14.
397 3 t. black and bright carmine .. .. .. 10 10
398 5 t. multicoloured .. .. .. .. 15 20
Design:—5 t. Blind man and eye

(Litho State Security Printing Press, Gazipur)

**1991** (10 Oct). *1st Death Anniv of Shahid Naziruddin Jahad (democrat). P* 14.
399 **144** 2 t. black, emerald and cinnamon .. .. 10 10

OFFICIAL STAMPS

**SERVICE** (O 1) **SERVICE** (O 2) **SERVICE** (O 3)

**1973** (30 Apr). *Nos.* 22/7, 29/30, 32 *and* 34 *optd with Type* O 1.
O 1 **7** 2 p. black (R.) .. .. .. .. 10 20
O 2 – 3 p. blue-green .. .. .. .. 10 20
O 3 – 5 p. light brown .. .. .. .. 15 10
O 4 – 10 p. slate-black (R.) .. .. .. 15 10
O 5 – 20 p. yellow-green .. .. .. .. 60 10
O 6 – 25 p. bright reddish mauve .. .. 1·50 10
O 7 – 60 p. greenish slate (R.) .. .. .. 1·75 40
O 8 – 75 p. yellow-orange .. .. .. .. 65 15
O 9 **8** 1 t. light violet .. .. .. .. 6·00 3·00
O10 – 5 t. grey-blue .. .. .. .. 3·75 4·00
O1/10 .. .. .. .. *Set of* 10 13·00 7·50

**1974–75.** *Nos.* 49/51 *optd with Type* O 1.
O11 **14** 1 t. light violet .. .. .. .. 2·00 25
O12 – 2 t. olive .. .. .. .. .. 3·00 90
O13 – 5 t. grey-blue (1975) .. .. .. 4·50 3·00
O11/13 .. .. .. .. *Set of* 3 8·50 3·75

**1976.** *Nos.* 64/70 *optd with Type* O 2 *and Nos.* 72/4 *optd with Type* O 3.
O14 5 p. deep yellow-green (11.2.76) .. .. 20 15
O15 10 p. slate-black (R.) (28.4.76) .. .. 40 15
O16 20 p. yellow-green (1.76) .. .. .. 60 15
O17 25 p. bright reddish mauve (1.76) .. .. 1·50 15
O18 50 p. light purple (8.6.76) .. .. .. 1·50 15
O19 60 p. greenish slate (R.) (10.11.76) .. .. 20 20
O20 75 p. yellow-olive (10.11.76) .. .. .. 20 25
O21 1 t. ultramarine (1.76) .. .. .. 1·50 20
O22 2 t. olive-green (8.6.76) .. .. .. 35 40
O23 5 t. grey-blue (10.11.76) .. .. .. 20 30
O14/23 .. .. .. .. *Set of* 10 6·00 1·90

**1979–82.** *Nos.* 125/37 *optd with Type* O 1.
O24 5 p. deep brown .. .. .. .. 20 15
O25 10 p. turquoise-blue .. .. .. .. 20 15
O26 15 p. orange (1980) .. .. .. .. 20 20
O27 20 p. brown-red .. .. .. .. 30 20
O28 25 p. grey-blue (1982) .. .. .. .. 80 50
O29 30 p. deep green .. .. .. .. 40 30
O30 40 p. maroon .. .. .. .. .. 50 15
O31 50 p. black (24.9.81) .. .. .. .. 30 10
O32 80 p. brown .. .. .. .. .. 60 15
O33 1 t. reddish violet (24.9.81) .. .. 30 10
O34 2 t. dull ultramarine (21.10.81) .. .. 35 60
O24/34 .. .. .. .. *Set of* 11 3·75 2·40

Service

(O 4)

**1983** (21 Dec). *Nos.* 220/8 *optd as Type* O 4 *in red, diagonally on* 1 *t. and* 2 *t.*
O35 5 p. turquoise-blue .. .. .. .. 10 10
O36 10 p. purple .. .. .. .. .. 10 10
O37 15 p. new blue .. .. .. .. .. 10 10
O38 20 p. grey-black .. .. .. .. .. 10 10
O39 25 p. slate .. .. .. .. .. 10 10
O40 30 p. brown .. .. .. .. .. 10 10
O41 50 p. light brown .. .. .. .. 10 10
O42 1 t. dull ultramarine .. .. .. .. 10 10
O43 2 t. deep bluish green .. .. .. .. 10 10
O35/43 .. .. .. .. *Set of* 9 50 50

# Barbados

Regular mails between Barbados and Great Britain were established at an early date in the island's development and it is believed that the British Mail Packet Agency at Bridgetown was opened in 1688 as part of the considerable expansion of the Packet Service in that year.

From 1 August 1851 the colonial authorities were responsible for the internal post system, but the British G.P.O. did not relinquish control of the overseas post until 1858.

For illustrations of the handstamp types see BRITISH POST OFFICES ABROAD notes, following GREAT BRITAIN.

CROWNED-CIRCLE HANDSTAMPS

CC1 CC 1 BARBADOES (3.10.1849) (R.) *Price on cover* £400

Combination covers exist with the local postage paid by a Barbados 1d. stamp and the overseas fee by an example of No. CC1.

During shortages of ½d. stamps in 1893 (17 February to 15 March) and of the ¼d. in 1896 (23 January to 4 May) No. CC1 was utilised, struck in black, on local mail. *Price on cover from* £95.

**PRICES FOR STAMPS ON COVER TO 1945**

| | |
|---|---|
| Nos. 1/35 | *from* × 5 |
| Nos. 43/63 | *from* × 4 |
| Nos. 64/6 | *from* × 10 |
| Nos. 67/83 | *from* × 5 |
| Nos. 86/8 | *from* × 3 |
| Nos. 89/103 | *from* × 4 |
| No. 104 | *from* × 20 |
| Nos. 105/15 | *from* × 4 |
| Nos. 116/24 | *from* × 8 |
| Nos. 125/33 | *from* × 5 |
| Nos. 135/44 | *from* × 4 |
| Nos. 145/52 | *from* × 6 |
| No. 153 | *from* × 8 |
| Nos. 158/62 | *from* × 5 |
| Nos. 163/9 | *from* × 3 |
| Nos. 170/96 | *from* × 4 |
| Nos. 197/8 | *from* × 10 |
| Nos. 199/212 | *from* × 6 |
| Nos. 213/39 | *from* × 3 |
| No. 240 | *from* × 10 |
| Nos. 241/4 | *from* × 5 |
| Nos. 245/7 | *from* × 6 |
| Nos. 248/56a | *from* × 4 |
| Nos. 257/61 | *from* × 5 |
| Nos. D1/3 | *from* × 25 |

**CROWN COLONY**

1 Britannia 2

(Recess Perkins, Bacon & Co)

**1852** (15 April)–**55**. *Paper blued. No wmk. Imperf.*
1 1 (½d.) yellow-green .. — £600
2 (½d.) deep green .. 80·00 £300
3 (1d.) blue .. 22·00 £190
4 (1d.) deep blue .. 12·00 65·00
4*a* (2d.) greyish slate .. £250 £1100
b. Bisected (1d.) (on cover) (1854) .. † £5000
5 (4d.) brownish red (1855) .. 45·00 £300

The bisect, No. 4b, was authorised for use between 4 August and 21 September 1854 during a shortage of 1d. stamps.

Nos. 5a/b were never sent to Barbados and come from the Perkins Bacon remainders sold in the 1880's.

Apart from the shade, which is distinctly paler, No. 4a can be distinguished from No. 5b by the smooth even gum, the gum of No. 5b being yellow and patchy, giving a mottled appearance to the back of the stamp. No. 5a also has the latter gum.

*Prepared for use but not issued*
5*a* 1 (No value), slate-blue (*shades*) .. 13·00
5*b* (No value), deep slate .. £300

**1855–58.** *White paper. No wmk. Imperf.*
7 1 (½d.) yellow-green (1857) .. £375 £110
8 (½d.) green (1858) .. 85·00 £200
9 (1d.) pale blue .. 60·00 60·00
10 (1d.) deep blue .. 19·00 50·00

**1858** (10 Nov). *No wmk. Imperf.*
11 2 6d. pale rose-red .. £850 £140
11*a* 6d. deep rose-red .. £700 £250
12 1s. brown-black .. £225 £110
12*a* 1s. black .. £140 70·00

**1860.** *No wmk. (a) Pin-perf 14.*
13 1 (½d.) yellow-green .. £1500 £375
14 (1d.) pale blue .. £1500 £150
15 (1d.) deep blue .. £1500 £150

*(b) Pin-perf 12½*
16 1 (½d.) yellow-green .. £3750 £700
16*a* (1d.) blue .. — £1200

*(c) Pin-perf 14 × 12½*
16*b* 1 (½d.) yellow-green .. — £3250

**1861.** *No wmk. Clean-cut perf 14 to 16.*
17 1 (½d.) deep green .. 50·00 7·50
18 (1d.) pale blue .. £500 29·00
19 (1d.) blue .. £650 29·00
a. Bisected (½d.) (on cover) .. † £2500

**1861–70.** *No wmk. (a) Rough perf 14 to 16.*
20 1 (½d.) deep green .. 12·00 11·00
21 (½d.) green .. 7·00 7·50
21*a* (½d.) blue-green .. 55·00 75·00
b. Imperf (pair) .. £475
22 (½d.) grass-green .. 20·00 10·00
a. Imperf (pair) .. £550
23 (1d.) blue (1861) .. 26·00 1·00
a. Imperf (pair) .. £450
24 (1d.) deep blue .. 19·00 3·00
a. Bisected diag (½d.) (on cover) (1863) † £1600
25 (4d.) dull rose-red (1861) .. 60·00 22·00
a. Imperf (pair) .. £600
26 (4d.) dull brown-red (1865) .. 80·00 35·00
a. Imperf (pair) .. £850
27 (4d.) lake-rose (1868) .. 60·00 45·00
a. Imperf (pair) .. £850
28 (4d.) dull vermilion (1869) .. £160 48·00
a. Imperf (pair) .. £850
29 2 6d. rose-red (1861) .. £170 11·00
30 6d. orange-red (1864) .. 65·00 15·00
31 6d. bright orange-vermilion (1868) .. 55·00 15·00
32 6d. dull orange-vermilion (1870) .. 55·00 11·00
a. Imperf (pair) .. £350
33 6d. orange (1870) .. 70·00 20·00
34 1s. brown-black (1863) .. 35·00 4·00
a. Error. Blue .. £12000
35 1s. black (1866) .. 28·00 6·00
a. Imperf between (horiz pair) .. £5000

*(b) Prepared for use, but not issued. P 11 to 12*
36 1 (½d.) grass-green .. £5500
37 (1d.) blue .. £2250

The bisect, No. 24a, was authorised for use in April 1863 and November 1866 during shortages of ½d. stamps.

No. 34a was an error on the part of the printer who supplied the first requisition of the 1s. value in the colour of the 1d. The 1s. blue stamps were never placed on sale, but the Barbados Colonial Secretary circulated some samples which were defaced by a manuscript corner-to-corner cross. A number of these samples subsequently had the cross removed.

Nos. 36/7 were never sent to Barbados and come from the Perkins Bacon remainders. It is believed that the imperforate pairs came from the same source.

**1870.** *Wmk Large Star, Type* w **1**. *Rough perf 14 to 16.*
43 1 (½d.) green .. 60·00 4·50
a. Imperf (pair) .. £500
43*b* (½d.) yellow-green .. 90·00 40·00
44 (1d.) blue .. £850 30·00
a. Blue paper .. — 65·00
45 (4d.) dull vermilion .. £650 55·00
46 2 6d. orange-vermilion .. £500 40·00
47 1s. black .. £190 16·00

**1871.** *Wmk Small Star, Type* w **2**. *Rough perf 14 to 16.*
48 1 (1d.) blue .. 70·00 1·25
49 (4d.) dull rose-red .. £600 24·00
50 2 6d. orange-vermilion .. £250 11·00
51 1s. black .. 95·00 7·50

**1872.** *Wmk Small Star, Type* w **2**. *(a) Clean-cut perf 14½ to 15½.*
52 1 (1d.) blue .. £160 90
a. Bisected diag (½d.) (on cover) .. † £1400
53 2 6d. orange-vermilion .. £450 38·00
54 1s. black .. 75·00 6·00

*(b) P 11 to 13 × 14½ to 15½*
56 1 (½d.) green .. £180 18·00
57 (4d.) dull vermilion .. £300 60·00

**1873.** *Wmk Large Star, Type* w **1**. *(a) Clean-cut perf 14½ to 15½.*
58 1 (½d.) green .. £160 10·00
59 (4d.) dull rose-red .. £600 85·00
60 2 6d. orange-vermilion .. £475 50·00
a. Imperf between (horiz pair) .. £3500
b. Imperf (pair) .. 85·00
61 1s. black .. 85·00 4·50
a. Imperf between (horiz pair) .. £4500

*(b) Prepared for use, but not issued. P 11 to 12*
62 2 6d. orange-vermilion

Only eight mint examples, in two strips of four, are known of No. 62.

Two used singles of No. 60b have been seen.

**1873** (June). *Wmk Small Star, Type* w **2** *(sideways = two points upwards). P 14.*
63 2 3d. brown-purple .. £325 £110

3

**1873** (June). *Wmk Small Star, Type* w **2** *(sideways). P 15½×15.*
64 3 5s. dull rose (H/S S. £300) .. £950 £300

**1874** (May). *Wmk Large Star, Type* w **1**. *(a) Perf 14.*
65 2 ½d. deep green .. 14·00 3·25
66 1d. deep blue .. 48·00 75

*(b) Clean-cut perf 14½ to 15½*
66*a* 2 1d. deep blue .. — £2250
b. Imperf (pair)

(Recess D.L.R.)

**1875–80.** *Wmk Crown CC (sideways on 6d., 1s.) (a) P 12½.*
67 2 ½d. bright green .. 20·00 1·50
68 4d. deep red .. £150 7·00
69 6d. bright yellow (aniline) .. £900 70·00
70 6d. chrome-yellow .. £550 65·00
a. Wmk upright .. † —
71 1s. violet (aniline) .. £500 6·00

*(b) P 14*
72 2 ½d. bright green (1876) .. 5·50 50
73 1d. dull blue .. 24·00 30
a. Bisected (½d.) (on cover) (1877) .. † £1100
74 1d. grey-blue .. 24·00 30
a. Wmk sideways .. — £850
75 3d. mauve-lilac (1878) .. 75·00 3·50
76 4d. red (1878) .. 70·00 7·00
77 4d. carmine .. £120 1·75
78 4d. crimson-lake .. £375 2·50
79 6d. chrome-yellow (1876) .. 90·00 1·00
80 6d. yellow .. £250 5·00
81 1s. purple (1876) .. £100 2·75
82 1s. violet (aniline) .. £1500 30·00
83 1s. dull mauve .. £250 1·50
a. Bisected (6d.) (on cover) (1.80) .. † £3250

*(c) P 14 × 12½*
84 2 4d. red .. £7000
72/3 (in red), 75/6, 79, 81 (in red) Handstamped "Specimen" .. *Set of 6* £500
72/3 (in black) H/S "Specimen" .. *Set of 2* £150

Very few examples of No. 84 have been found unused and only one used specimen is known.

1D. (A) 1D. (B) 1D. (C)

**1878** (March). *No. 64 with lower label removed, divided vertically by 11½ to 13 perforation, and each half surch sideways in black by West Indian Press.*

*(A) Large numeral "1", 7 mm high with curved serif, and large letter "D", 2¾ mm high.*
86 3 1d. on half 5s. dull rose .. £3250 £600
a. No stop after "D" .. £7000 £1200
b. Unsevered pair (both No. 86) .. £11000 £1800
c. Ditto, Nos. 86 and 87 .. — £3500
ca. Pair without dividing perf .. — £14000
d. Ditto, Nos. 86 and 88 .. £20000 £5500

*(B) As last, but numeral with straight serif.*
87 3 1d. on half 5s. dull rose .. £3750 £700
a. Unsevered pair .. — £2500

*(C) Smaller numeral "1", 6 mm high and smaller "D", 2½ mm high.*
88 3 1d. on half 5s dull rose .. £4500 £800
a. Unsevered pair .. £13000 £3500

All types of the surcharge are found reading upwards as well as downwards, and there are minor varieties of the type.

4 HALF-PENNY (5)

(Typo D.L.R.)

**1882** (28 Aug)–**86**. *Wmk Crown CA. P 14.*
89 4 ½d. dull green (1882) .. 4·25 80
90 ½d. green .. 3·75 80
91 1d. rose (1882) .. 21·00 1·25
a. Bisected (½d.) (on cover) .. † £800
92 1d. carmine .. 2·75 25
93 2½d. ultramarine (1882) .. 42·00 70
94 2½d. deep blue .. 48·00 50
95 3d. deep purple (1885) .. 80·00 25·00
96 3d. reddish purple .. 3·25 8·50
97 4d. grey (1882) .. £160 2·00
98 4d. pale brown (1885) .. 3·00 1·50
99 4d. deep brown .. 2·75 60
100 6d. olive-black (1886) .. 50·00 26·00
102 1s. chestnut (1886) .. 17·00 21·00
103 5s. bistre (1886) .. £140 £170
89/103 .. *Set of 9* £375 £200
95/103, except 97, Optd "Specimen" *Set of 5* £375

**1892** (July). *No. 99 surch with T* **5** *by West Indian Press.*
104 4 ½d. on 4d. deep brown .. 30 1·00
a. No hyphen .. 4·50 5·50
b. Surch double (R. + Bk.) .. £600 £900
ba. Surch double (R. + Bk.) both without hyphen .. £1300 £1300
c. Surch double, one albino
d. Surch "PENNY HALF" .. — £200

Nos. 104b/ba come from a sheet with a trial surcharge in red which was subsequently surcharged again in black and put back into stock.

No. 104c is known in a horizontal pair with the left hand stamp showing the first two letters of the second impression inked. The right hand stamp shows a complete albino surcharge.

6 Seal of Colony 7

(Typo D.L.R.)

**1892** (July)–**1903**. *Wmk Crown CA. P* 14.
105 **6** ¼d. slate-grey and carmine (5.5.96) .. 70 10
106 ½d. dull green .. .. .. .. 40 10
107 1d. carmine .. .. .. .. 1·50 10
108 2d. slate-black and orange (5.99) .. 6·00 65
109 2½d. ultramarine .. .. .. .. 5·50 20
110 5d. grey-olive .. .. .. .. 4·75 4·50
111 6d. mauve and carmine .. .. .. 5·00 2·00
112 8d. orange and ultramarine .. .. 2·50 15·00
113 10d. dull blue-green and carmine .. 4·50 6·50
114 2s. 6d. blue-black and orange .. 32·00 35·00
115 2s. 6d. violet and green (29.5.03) .. 48·00 60·00
105/15 .. .. .. .. *Set of* 11 £100 £110
105/15 Optd "Specimen" .. *Set of* 11 £160
See also Nos. 135/44 and 163/9.

(Typo D.L.R.)

**1897** (Dec)–**98**. *Diamond Jubilee. T* **7**. *Wmk Crown CC. P* 14.

(*a*) *White paper*
116 ¼d. grey and carmine .. .. .. 55 15
117 ½d. dull green .. .. .. .. 1·50 15
118 1d. rose .. .. .. .. .. 2·25 10
119 2½d. ultramarine .. .. .. .. 4·00 25
120 5d. olive-brown .. .. .. .. 8·50 10·00
121 6d. mauve and carmine .. .. .. 13·00 13·00
122 8d. orange and ultramarine .. .. 4·75 14·00
123 10d. blue-green and carmine .. .. 28·00 30·00
124 2s. 6d. blue-black and orange .. .. 30·00 40·00
116/124 .. .. .. *Set of* 9 85·00 95·00
116/124 Optd "Specimen" .. .. *Set of* 9 £150

(*b*) *Paper blued*
125 ¼d. grey and carmine .. .. .. 26·00 30·00
126 ½d. dull green .. .. .. .. 27·00 30·00
127 1d. carmine .. .. .. .. 35·00 40·00
128 2½d. ultramarine .. .. .. .. 38·00 45·00
129 5d. olive-brown .. .. .. .. £225 £250
130 6d. mauve and carmine .. .. .. £100 £110
131 8d. orange and ultramarine .. .. 85·00 £110
132 10d. dull green and carmine .. .. £130 £150
133 2s. 6d. blue-black and orange .. .. 85·00 90·00

**1905**. *Wmk Mult Crown CA. P* 14.
135 **6** ¼d. slate-grey and carmine .. .. 3·00 65
136 ½d. dull green.. .. .. .. 4·25 10
137 1d. carmine .. .. .. .. 3·00 10
139 2½d. blue .. .. .. .. 4·75 15
141 6d. mauve and carmine .. .. 10·00 12·00
142 8d. orange and ultramarine .. .. 22·00 45·00
144 2s. 6d. violet and green .. .. 23·00 48·00
135/144 .. .. .. .. *Set of* 7 65·00 95·00
See also Nos. 163/9.

8 Nelson Monument

(Des Mrs. G. Goodman. Recess D.L.R.)

**1906** (1 Mar). *Nelson Centenary. Wmk Crown CC. P* 14.
145 **8** ¼d. black and grey .. .. .. 2·00 30
146 ½d. black and pale green .. .. 4·00 15
147 1d. black and red .. .. .. 3·25 15
148 2d. black and yellow .. .. .. 1·75 3·50
149 2½d. black and bright blue .. .. 3·75 1·00
150 6d. black and mauve .. .. .. 15·00 18·00
151 1s. black and rose .. .. .. 16·00 30·00
145/151 .. .. .. *Set of* 7 42·00 48·00
145/51 Optd "Specimen" .. *Set of* 7 £130
Two sets may be made of the above: one on thick, opaque, creamy white paper; the other on thin, rather transparent, bluish white paper.
See also Nos. 158/62*a*.

9 *Olive Blossom*, 1605

**Kingston Relief Fund. 1d.**

(10)

(Des Lady Carter. Recess D.L.R.)

**1906** (15 Aug). *Tercentenary of Annexation. Wmk Multiple Crown CA (sideways). P* 14.
152 **9** 1d. black, blue and green .. .. 9·00 25
152 Optd "Specimen" .. .. .. .. 65·00

**1907** (25 Jan–25 Feb). *Kingston Relief Fund. No.* 108 *surch with T* **10** *by T. E. King & Co., Barbados.*
153 **6** 1d. on 2d. slate-black and orange (R.) .. 1·25 4·25
a. Surch inverted (25.2.07) .. .. 1·25 6·00
b. Surch double .. .. .. £550 £600
c. Surch double, both inverted .. .. £550
d. Surch *tête-bêche* (pair) .. .. £650
e. No stop after "1d." .. .. .. 20·00 35·00
ea. Do., surch inverted (25.2.07) .. 20·00 38·00
eb. Do., surch double .. .. .. — £900
f. Vert pair, one normal, one surch double .. .. .. .. — £700
The above stamp was sold for 2d. of which 1d. was retained for the postal revenue, and the other 1d. given to a fund for the relief of the sufferers by the earthquake in Jamaica.
An entire printing as No. 153a was created after a sheet of inverted surcharges was found in the initial supply.

**1907** (6 July). *Nelson Centenary. Wmk Mult Crown CA. P* 14.
158 **8** ¼d. black and grey .. .. .. 2·50 2·75
161 2d. black and yellow .. .. .. 12·00 19·00
162 2½d. black and bright blue .. .. 10·00 13·00
*a. Black and indigo* .. .. £1000 £1100
158/62 .. .. .. .. *Set of* 3 22·00 32·00

**1909** (July)–**10**. *Wmk Mult Crown CA. P* 14.
163 **6** ¼d. brown .. .. .. .. 50 30
164 ½d. blue-green .. .. .. .. 7·00 50
165 1d. red .. .. .. .. .. 1·50 10
166 2d. greyish slate (8.10) .. .. 3·75 8·50
167 2½d. bright blue (1910) .. .. 15·00 3·50
168 6d. dull and bright purple (1910) .. 4·00 14·00
169 1s. black/*green* (8.10) .. .. 7·50 14·00
163/9 .. .. .. .. *Set of* 7 35·00 35·00
163, 165/6, 168/9 Optd "Specimen" *Set of* 5 £100

11

12

13

(Typo D.L.R.)

**1912** (23 July)–**16**. *Wmk Mult Crown CA. P* 14.
170 **11** ¼d brown .. .. .. .. 30 15
*a. Pale brown* (1916) .. .. .. 55 30
171 ½d. green .. .. .. .. 85 10
172 1d. red (13.8.12) .. .. .. 1·25 10
*a. Scarlet* (1915) .. .. .. 7·00 90
173 2d. greyish slate (13.8.12) .. .. 2·00 7·50
174 2½d. bright blue (13.8.12) .. .. 1·25 30
175 **12** 3d. purple/*yellow* (13.8.12) .. .. 1·25 5·00
176 4d. red and black/*yellow* (13.8.12) .. 1·25 8·50
177 6d. purple and dull purple (13.8.12) .. 4·50 6·50
178 **13** 1s. black/*green* (13.8.12) .. .. 4·25 7·00
179 2s. blue and purple/*blue* (13.8.12) .. 26·00 38·00
180 3s. violet and green (13.8.12) .. 48·00 48·00
170/80 .. .. .. .. *Set of* 11 80·00 £110
170/80 Optd "Specimen" .. .. *Set of* 11 £140

14

**WAR TAX**

(15)

(Recess D.L.R.)

**1916** (16 June)–**19**. *Wmk Mult Crown CA. P* 14.
181 **14** ¼d. deep brown .. .. .. .. 45 15
*a. Chestnut-brown* (9.17) .. .. 65 35
*b. Sepia-brown* (4.18) .. .. 1·60 1·75
182 ½d. green .. .. .. .. 1·10 15
*a. Deep green* (9.17) .. .. 1·10 15
*b. Pale green* (4.18) .. .. 1·60 80
183 1d. deep red .. .. .. .. 8·50 4·50
*a. Bright carmine-red* (4.17) .. .. 2·00 15
*b. Pale carmine-red* (9.17) .. .. 3·50 65
184 2d. grey .. .. .. .. 3·50 8·00
*a. Grey-black* (9.19) .. ..
185 2½d. deep ultramarine .. .. .. 80 50
*a. Royal blue* (11.17) .. .. 80 50
186 3d. purple/*yellow* (thin paper) .. 1·50 2·50
*a. Deep purple/yellow* (thick paper) (9.19) .. .. .. .. 19·00 22·00
187 4d. red/*yellow* .. .. .. .. 70 7·00
188 6d. purple .. .. .. .. 2·00 3·25
189 1s. black/*green* .. .. .. 6·50 5·50
190 2s. purple/*blue* .. .. .. 14·00 7·50
191 3s. deep violet .. .. .. 28·00 65·00
181/91 .. .. .. .. *Set of* 11 55·00 90·00
181/91 Optd "Specimen" .. *Set of* 11 £180
Dates quoted for shades are those of despatch from Great Britain.
Examples of the ½d. and 1d. values can be found perforated either by line or by comb machines.
See also Nos. 199/200*a*.

**1917** (10 Oct)–**18**. *War Tax. Optd in London with T* **15**.
197 **11** 1d. bright red (Optd S. £55) .. .. 15 15
198 1d. pale red (*thicker bluish paper*) (4.18) 1·25 40

**1918** (18 Feb)–**20**. *Colours changed. Wmk Mult Crown CA. P* 14.
199 **14** 4d. black and red .. .. .. 60 2·75
200 3s. green and deep violet .. .. 16·00 35·00
*a. Green and bright violet* (1920) .. £140 £180
199/200 Optd "Specimen" .. *Set of* 2 £120
The centres of these are from a new die having no circular border line.

## OMNIBUS ISSUES

Details, together with prices for complete sets, of the various Omnibus issues from the 1935 Silver Jubilee series to date are included in a special section following Zimbabwe at the end of Volume 2.

16 Winged Victory from the Louvre.

17 Victory from Victoria Memorial, London

(Recess D.L.R.)

**1920** (9 Sept)–**21**. *Victory. P* 14.

(*a*) *Wmk Mult Crown CA (sideways on T* **17**)
201 **16** ¼d. black and bistre-brown .. .. 20 5
a. "C" missing from wmk ..
202 ½d. black and bright yellow-green .. 60 1
a. "C" missing from wmk ..
b. "A" missing from wmk ..
203 1d. black and vermilion .. .. 1·00 1
204 2d. black and grey .. .. 1·75 6·0
205 2½d. indigo and ultramarine .. .. 2·75 6·5
a. "C" missing from wmk ..
206 3d. black and purple .. .. 1·60 2·7
207 4d. black and blue-green .. .. 1·75 3·5
208 6d. black and brown-orange .. .. 2·50 5·5
209 **17** 1s. black and bright green .. .. 6·00 13·0
210 2s. black and brown .. .. 11·00 15·0
211 3s. black and dull orange .. .. 13·00 19·0
a. "C" missing from wmk ..

(*b*) *Wmk Mult Script CA*
212 **16** 1d. black and vermilion (22.8.21) .. 11·00 2
201/12 .. .. .. *Set of* 12 48·00 65·0
201/12 Optd "Specimen" .. .. *Set of* 12 £200

18

19

(Recess D.L.R.)

**1921** (14 Nov)–**24**. *P* 14. (*a*) *Wmk Mult Crown CA.*
213 **18** 3d. purple/*pale yellow* .. .. .. 1·25 4·2
214 4d. red/*pale yellow* .. .. .. 1·75 5·0
215 1s. black/*emerald* .. .. .. 4·50 11·0

(*b*) *Wmk Mult Script CA*
217 **18** ¼d. brown .. .. .. .. 15 1
219 ½d. green .. .. .. .. 70 1
220 1d. red .. .. .. .. 70 1
*a. Bright rose-carmine* .. .. 3·75 1·0
221 2d. grey .. .. .. .. 1·60 2
222 2½d. ultramarine .. .. .. 1·50 3·7
225 6d. reddish purple .. .. .. 2·25 4·5
226 1s. black/*emerald* (18.9.24) .. .. 35·00 45·0
227 2s. purple/*blue* .. .. .. 10·00 18·0
228 3s. deep violet .. .. .. 13·00 35·0
213/228 .. .. .. *Set of* 12 65·00 £12
213/28 Optd "Specimen" .. .. *Set of* 12 £160

**1925** (1 Apr)–**35**. *Wmk Mult Script CA. P* 14.
229 **19** ¼d. brown .. .. .. .. 10 1
230 ½d. green .. .. .. .. 10 1
a. Perf 13½×12½ (2.32) .. .. 60 1
231 1d. scarlet .. .. .. .. 25 1
a. Perf 13½×12½ (2.32) .. .. 70 3
231*b* 1½d. orange (1933) .. .. .. 3·50 8
ba. Perf 13½×12½ (15.8.32) .. .. 90 5
232 2d. grey .. .. .. .. 40 1·7
233 2½d. blue .. .. .. .. 50 5
*a. Bright ultramarine* (1933) .. .. 4·50 4
ab. Perf 13½×12½ (2.32) .. .. 4·50 9
234 3d. purple/*pale yellow* .. .. 50 3
*a. Reddish purple/yellow* (1935) .. 2·75 3·5
235 4d. red/*pale yellow* .. .. .. 50 7
236 6d. purple .. .. .. .. 50 5
237 1s. black/*emerald* .. .. .. 1·50 3·2
a. Perf 13½×12½ (8.32) .. .. 16·00 15·0
*b. Brownish black/bright yellow-green* (1934) .. .. .. 2·75 9·5
238 2s. purple/*blue* .. .. .. 6·00 6·5
238*a* 2s. 6d. carmine/*blue* (1.9.32) .. .. 15·00 20·0
239 3s. deep violet .. .. .. 9·00 13·0
229/39 .. .. .. *Set of* 13 32·00 45·0
229/39 Optd/Perf "Specimen" .. *Set of* 13 £170
Nos. 230/1 exist in coils constructed from normal sheets.

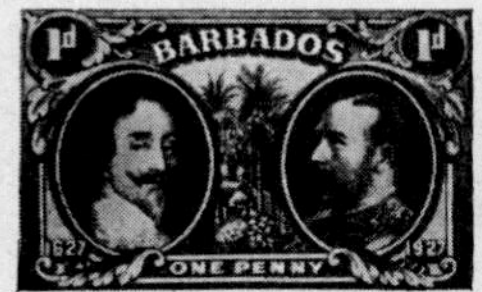


20 King Charles I and King George V

21 Badge of the Colony

(Recess B.W.)

**1927** (17 Feb). *Tercentenary of Settlement of Barbados. Wmk Mult Script CA. P* 12½.
240 **20** 1 d. carmine (Optd S. £40) .. .. 60 3(

**1935** (6 May). *Silver Jubilee. As Nos. 91/4 of Antigua, but ptd by Waterlow. P* 11 × 12.
241 1d. deep blue and scarlet .. .. .. 25 20
242 1½d. ultramarine and grey .. .. .. 1·75 2·25
243 2½d. brown and deep blue .. .. .. 2·00 85
244 1s. slate and purple .. .. .. 9·50 13·00
k. Kite and horizontal log .. .. 90·00
241/4 .. .. .. .. .. *Set of* 4 12·50 14·50
241/4 Perf "Specimen" .. .. *Set of* 4 65·00
For illustration of plate variety see Catalogue Introduction.

**1937** (14 May). *Coronation. As Nos.* 95/7 *of Antigua, but printed by D.L.R. P* 14.
245 1d. scarlet .. .. .. .. .. 30 15
246 1½d. yellow-brown .. .. .. .. 40 30
247 2½d. bright blue .. .. .. .. 70 45
245/7 .. .. .. .. *Set of* 3 1·25 80
245/7 Perf "Specimen" .. .. *Set of* 3 50·00

Vertical line over horse's head (R. 4/10) (corrected on Dec 1947 ptg)

"Flying mane" (R. 4/1) (corrected on Dec 1947 ptg)

Curved line at top right (R. 7/8)

(Recess D.L.R.)

**1938** (3 Jan)–**47**. *Wmk Mult Script CA. P* 13½×13.
248 **21** ½d. green .. .. .. .. 2·25 15
a. Perf 14 (8.42) .. .. .. 60·00 1·25
248*b* ½d. yellow-bistre (16.10.42) .. .. 10 15
249 1d. scarlet (1941) .. .. .. £140 2·00
a. Perf 14 (3.1.38) .. .. .. 11·00 10
249*b* 1d. blue-green (1943) .. .. .. 1·50 15
c. Perf 14 (16.10.42) .. .. .. 10 10
250 1½d. orange .. .. .. .. 10 10
a. Perf 14 (11.41) .. .. .. 2·50 15
250*b* 2d. claret (3.6.41) .. .. .. 35 80
250*c* 2d. carmine (20.9.43) .. .. .. 10 10
d. Perf 14 (11.9.44) .. .. .. 10 15
251 2½d. ultramarine .. .. .. 50 30
*a. Blue* (17.2.44) .. .. .. 40 3·50
ab. "A" missing from wmk .. ..
252 3d. brown .. .. .. .. 20 1·25
a. Vertical line over horse's head .. 55·00
b. Perf 14 (4.41) .. .. .. 15 20
ba. Vertical line over horse's head .. 55·00
252*c* 3d. blue (1.4.47) .. .. .. 10 40
ca. Vertical line over horse's head .. 55·00
253 4d. black .. .. .. .. 15 10
a. Flying mane .. .. .. 55·00
b. Curved line at top right .. .. 45·00
c. Perf 14 (11.9.44) .. .. .. 10 85
ca. Flying mane .. .. .. 55·00
cb. Curved line at top right .. .. 45·00
254 6d. violet .. .. .. .. 20 10
254*a* 8d. magenta (9.12.46) .. .. .. 45 90
255 1s. olive-green .. .. .. 11·00 1·25
*a. Deep brown-olive* (19.11.45) .. .. 20 10
256 2s. 6d. purple .. .. .. 2·50 85
256*a* 5s. indigo (3.6.41) .. .. .. 2·50 3·00
248/56*a* .. .. .. .. *Set of* 16 18·00 6·50
248/56*a* Perf "Specimen" .. .. *Set of* 16 £170
No. 249a was perforated by two machines, one gauging 13.8×14.1 (1938), the other 14.1 (1939).
Nos. 248/*b* and 249/*c* exist in coils constructed from normal sheets.

**22** Kings Charles I, George VI, Assembly Chamber and Mace

(Recess D.L.R.)

**1939** (27 June). *Tercentenary of General Assembly. Wmk Mult Script CA. P* 13½ × 14.
257 **22** ½d. green .. .. .. .. 1·25 25
258 1d. scarlet .. .. .. .. 1·25 25
259 1½d. orange .. .. .. .. 1·25 60
260 2½d. bright ultramarine .. .. .. 1·25 1·25
261 3d. brown .. .. .. .. 1·40 2·00
257/61 .. .. .. .. *Set of* 5 5·75 4·00
257/61 Perf "Specimen" .. .. *Set of* 5 £140

Two flags on tug (R. 5/2)

**1946** (18 Sept). *Victory. As Nos.* 110/11 *of Antigua.*
262 1½d. red-orange .. .. .. .. 10 10
a. Two flags on tug .. .. .. 12·00
263 3d. brown .. .. .. .. 10 10
262/3 Perf "Specimen" .. .. *Set of* 2 48·00

ONE PENNY
(23)

NY PEN

Short "Y" (R. 6/2) Broken "E" (R. 7/4 and 11/4)

(Surch by Barbados Advocate Co)

**1947** (21 Apr). *Surch with T* **23**. (*a*) *P* 14.
264 **21** 1d. on 2d. carmine (No. 250d) .. .. 15 40
a. Short "Y" .. .. .. .. 13·00
b. Broken "E" .. .. .. .. 9·00
(*b*) *P* 13½ × 13
264*c* **21** 1d. on 2d. carmine (No. 250c) .. .. 1·25 1·75
ca. Short "Y" .. .. .. .. 45·00
cb. Broken "E" .. .. .. .. 30·00
The relationship of the two words in the surcharge differs on each position of the sheet.

**1948** (24 Nov). *Royal Silver Wedding. As Nos.* 112/13 *of Antigua.*
265 1½d. orange .. .. .. .. .. 25 10
266 5s. indigo .. .. .. .. .. 9·00 4·50

**1949** (10 Oct). *75th Anniv of Universal Postal Union. As Nos.* 114/17 *of Antigua.*
267 1½d. red-orange .. .. .. .. 30 25
268 3d. deep blue .. .. .. .. 40 35
269 4d. grey .. .. .. .. .. 70 50
270 1s. olive .. .. .. .. .. 80 60
267/70 .. .. .. .. *Set of* 4 2·00 1·50

**(New Currency. 100 cents = 1 Barbados dollar)**

**24** Dover Fort

**27** Statue of Nelson

(Recess B.W.)

**1950** (1 May). *T* **24**, **27** *and similar designs. Wmk Mult Script CA. P* 11 × 11½ (*horiz*), 13½ (*vert*).
271 1 c. indigo .. .. .. .. 15 90
272 2 c. emerald-green .. .. .. 15 45
273 3 c. reddish brown and blue-green .. .. 15 60
274 4 c. carmine .. .. .. .. 15 20
275 6 c. light blue .. .. .. .. 15 60
276 8 c. bright blue and purple-brown .. .. 55 50
277 12 c. greenish blue and brown-olive .. .. 90 30
278 24 c. scarlet and black .. .. .. 70 30
279 48 c. violet .. .. .. .. 6·00 3·50
280 60 c. green and claret .. .. .. 6·00 4·00
281 $1.20, carmine and olive-green .. .. 6·50 2·50
282 $2.40, black .. .. .. .. 12·00 7·00
271/282 .. .. .. .. *Set of* 12 30·00 19·00
Designs: *Horiz*—2 c. Sugar cane breeding; 3 c. Public buildings; 6 c. Casting net; 8 c. *Frances W. Smith* (schooner); 12 c. Flying fish; 24 c. Old Main Guard Garrison; 60 c. Careenage; $2.40, Seal of Barbados. *Vert*—48 c. St. Michael's Cathedral; $1.20, Map of Barbados and wireless mast.

**1951** (16 Feb). *Inauguration of B.W.I. University College. As Nos.* 118/19 *of Antigua.*
283 3 c. brown and blue-green .. .. .. 15 15
284 12 c. blue-green and brown-olive .. .. 30 40

**36** King George VI and Stamp of 1852

(Recess Waterlow)

**1952** (15 Apr). *Barbados Stamp Centenary. Wmk Mult Script CA. P* 13½.
285 **36** 3 c. green and slate-green .. .. 15 20
286 4 c. blue and carmine .. .. .. 15 20
287 12 c. slate-green and bright green .. .. 15 20
288 24 c. red-brown and brownish black .. .. 15 20
285/8 .. .. .. .. *Set of* 4 55 70

**37** Harbour Police

(Recess B.W.)

**1953** (13 Apr)–**61**. *Designs previously used for King George VI issue, but with portrait or cypher* ($2.40) *of Queen Elizabeth II, as in T* **37**. *Wmk Mult Script CA. P* 11×11½ (*horiz*) *or* 13½ (*vert*).
289 1 c. indigo .. .. .. .. 10 30
290 2 c. orange and deep turquoise (15.4.54) .. 15 20
291 3 c. black and emerald (15.4.54) .. .. 15 20
292 4 c. black and orange (15.4.54) .. .. 20 15
*a. Black and reddish orange* (18.3.59) .. 70 55
293 5 c. blue and deep carmine-red (4.1.54) .. 20 20
294 6 c. red-brown (15.4.54) .. .. .. 15 20
295 8 c. black and blue (15.4.54) .. .. 70 20
296 12 c. turquoise-blue & brown-olive (15.4.54) 1·00 10
*a. Turquoise-grn & brown-olive* (18.3.59) 4·50 90
*b. Turquoise-blue & bronze-grn* (13.6.61) 3·00 70
297 24 c. rose-red and black (2.3.56) .. .. 45 10
298 48 c. deep violet (2.3.56) .. .. .. 2·00 80
299 60 c. blue-green and brown-purple (3.4.56) 6·00 1·50
*a. Blue-green and pale maroon* (17.5.60) 9·50 3·00
300 $1.20, carmine and bronze-green (3.4.56) 14·00 1·50
301 $2.40, black (1.2.57) .. .. .. 7·50 1·25
289/301 .. .. .. .. *Set of* 13 29·00 6·00
Designs: *Horiz*—1 c. Dover Fort; 2 c. Sugar cane breeding; 3 c. Public buildings; 6 c. Casting net; 8 c. *Frances W. Smith* (schooner); 12 c. Flying fish; 24 c. Old Main Guard Garrison; 60 c. Careenage; $2.40, Seal of Barbados. *Vert*—4 c. Statue of Nelson; 48 c. The Cathedral; $1.20, Map of Barbados and wireless mast.
See also Nos. 312/19.

**1953** (4 June). *Coronation. As No.* 120 *of Antigua.*
302 4 c. black and red-orange .. .. .. 10 10

**1958** (23 Apr). *Inauguration of British Caribbean Federation. As Nos.* 135/7 *of Antigua.*
303 3 c. deep green .. .. .. .. 20 15
304 6 c. blue .. .. .. .. .. 30 60
305 12 c. scarlet .. .. .. .. 35 15
303/5 .. .. .. .. *Set of* 3 75 80

**38** Deep Water Harbour, Bridgetown

(Recess B.W.)

**1961** (6 May). *Opening of Deep Water Harbour, Bridgetown. W* w **12**. *P* 11 × 12.
306 **38** 4 c. black and red-orange .. .. 10 15
307 8 c. black and blue .. .. .. 10 15
308 24 c. carmine-red and black .. .. 15 15
306/8 .. .. .. .. *Set of* 3 30 40

**SELF-GOVERNMENT**

**39** Scout Badge and Map of Barbados

**40** Deep Sea Coral

(Recess B.W.)

**1962** (9 Mar). *Golden Jubilee of Barbados Boy Scout Association. W* w **12**. *P* 11½ × 11.
309 **39** 4 c. black and orange .. .. .. 20 10
310 12 c. blue and olive-brown .. .. 40 15
311 $1.20, carmine and olive-green .. .. 1·10 1·50
309/11 .. .. .. .. *Set of* 3 1·50 1·60

**1964** (14 Jan)–**65**. *As Nos.* 289, *etc., but wmk* w **12**.
312 1 c. indigo (6.10.64) .. .. .. 50 75
313 4 c. black and orange .. .. .. 40 50
314 8 c. black and blue (29.6.65) .. .. 60 35
315 12 c. turquoise-blue and brown-olive (29.6.65) 60 50
316 24 c. rose-red and black (6.10.64) .. .. 50 35
317 48 c. deep violet .. .. .. 1·50 2·00
318 60 c. blue-green and brown-purple (6.10.64) .. 7·50 4·00
319 $2.40, black (29.6.65) .. .. .. 2·75 2·75
312/19 .. .. .. .. *Set of* 8 13·00 10·00
The above dates are for Crown Agents releases. The 14.1.64 printings were not released in Barbados until April 1964, the 6.10.64 printings until December 1964 and of the 29.6.65 printings the 8 c. and $2.40 were released from about 15 June 1965 but the 12 c. value was never put on sale in Barbados.

**1965** (17 May). *I.T.U. Centenary. As Nos.* 166/7 *of Antigua.*
320 2 c. lilac and red .. .. .. .. 25 15
321 48 c. yellow and grey-brown .. .. .. 1·00 1·00

(Des V. Whiteley, from drawings by Mrs. J. Walker. Photo Harrison)

**1965** (15 July). *Marine Life. Horiz designs as T* **40**. *W* w **12** (*upright*). *P* 14 × 13½.
322 1 c. black, pink and blue .. .. .. 10 25
323 2 c. olive-brown, yellow and magenta .. 10 15
324 3 c. olive-brown and orange .. .. .. 45 35
325 4 c. deep blue and olive-green .. .. 15 10
a. Imperf (pair) .. .. .. .. £225 £130
326 5 c. sepia, rose and lilac .. .. .. 20 10
327 6 c. multicoloured .. .. .. .. 45 10

328 8 c. multicoloured .. .. .. .. .. 25 10
329 12 c. multicoloured .. .. .. .. .. 35 10
a. Grey printing double .. .. .. .. 40·00
330 15 c. black, greenish yellow and red .. .. 60 55
331 25 c. ultramarine and yellow-ochre .. .. 95 60
332 35 c. brown-red and deep green .. .. 1·25 15
333 50 c. bright blue and apple-green .. .. 1·75 40
334 $1 multicoloured .. .. .. .. 2·50 1·25
335 $2.50, multicoloured .. .. .. 2·50 1·25
322/35 .. .. .. .. *Set of* 14 10·00 4·75

Designs:—2 c. Lobster; 3 c. Sea Horse; 4 c. Sea Urchin; 5 c. Staghorn Coral; 6 c. Butterfly Fish; 8 c. File Shell; 12 c. Balloon Fish; 15 c. Angel Fish; 25 c. Brain Coral; 35 c. Brittle Star; 50 c. Flying Fish; $1 Queen Conch Shell; $2.50, Fiddler Crab.

The 3 c. value is wrongly inscribed "Hippocanpus", the correct spelling being Hippocampus.

See also Nos. 342, etc.

**1966** (24 Jan). *Churchill Commemoration. As Nos.* 170/3 *of Antigua.*
336 1 c. new blue .. .. .. .. .. 10 10
337 4 c. deep green .. .. .. .. .. 30 10
338 25 c. brown .. .. .. .. .. 70 40
339 35 c. bluish violet .. .. .. .. 80 60
336/9 .. .. .. .. .. *Set of* 4 1·75 1·10

**1966** (4 Feb). *Royal Visit. As Nos.* 174/5 *of Antigua.*
340 3 c. black and ultramarine .. .. .. 40 25
341 35 c. black and magenta .. .. .. 1·60 80

**41** Dolphin

**54** Arms of Barbados

**1966** (15 Mar)–**69**. *As Nos.* 322/35 *but wmk* w **12** (*sideways*). *New value and design* (*as T* **41**).
342 1 c. black, pink and blue .. .. .. 10 15
343 2 c. olive-brown, yellow & magenta (16.5.67) .. .. .. .. 30 15
344 3 c. olive-brown and orange (4.12.67) .. 30 70
345 4 c. deep blue and olive-green .. .. 50 10
346 5 c. sepia, rose and lilac (23.8.66) .. .. 45 10
347 6 c. multicoloured (31.1.67) .. .. 70 10
348 8 c. multicoloured (19.9.67) .. .. 75 10
349 12 c. multicoloured (31.1.67) .. .. 45 10
350 15 c. black, greenish yellow and red .. 1·75 10
351 25 c. ultramarine and yellow-ochre .. 2·00 30
*a. Deep ultram & yellow-ochre* (26.9.66) 3·50 1·50
352 35 c. brown-red and deep green (23.8.66) 2·00 35
*a. Chestnut and deep green* (26.11.68) .. 3·50 2·00
353 50 c. bright blue and apple-green .. 1·50 80
354 $1 multicoloured (23.8.66) .. .. 3·25 80
355 $2.50, multicoloured (23.8.66) .. 5·00 3·00
355*a* $5 multicoloured (9.1.69) .. .. 8·50 7·00
342/55*a* .. .. .. *Set of* 15 25·00 12·00

The 3 c. value is correctly inscribed "Hippocampus".

All values except the 50 c. exist with PVA gum as well as gum arabic but the $5 exists with PVA gum only.

The $5 was released by the Crown Agents on 6 January but was not put on sale locally until 9 January.

## INDEPENDENT

(Des. V. Whiteley. Photo Harrison)

**1966** (2 Dec). *Independence. T* **54** *and similar multicoloured designs. P* 14.
356 4 c. Type **54** .. .. .. .. .. 10 10
357 25 c. Hilton Hotel (*horiz*) .. .. .. 10 10
358 35 c. G. Sobers (Test cricketer) .. .. 40 15
359 50 c. Pine Hill Dairy (*horiz*) .. .. 40 15
356/9 .. .. .. .. *Set of* 4 85 35

**1967** (6 Jan). *20th Anniv of U.N.E.S.CO. As Nos.* 196/8 *of Antigua.*
360 4 c. slate-violet, red, yellow and orange .. 30 10
361 12 c. orange-yellow, violet and deep olive .. 70 45
362 25 c. black, bright purple and orange .. .. 1·00 85
360/2 .. .. .. .. .. *Set of* 3 1·75 1·25

**58** Policeman and Anchor

**62** Governor-General Sir Winston Scott, G.C.M.G.

(Des V. Whiteley. Litho D.L.R.)

**1967** (16 Oct). *Centenary of Harbour Police. T* **58** *and similar multicoloured designs. P* 14.
363 4 c. Type **58** .. .. .. .. .. 10 10
364 25 c. Policeman with telescope .. .. 20 10
365 35 c. *BP1* (police launch) (*horiz*) .. .. 20 10
366 50 c. Policeman outside H.Q. .. .. .. 25 15
363/6 .. .. .. .. *Set of* 4 65 30

(Des V. Whiteley. Photo Harrison)

**1967** (4 Dec). *First Anniv of Independence. T* **62** *and similar multicoloured designs. P* 14½ × 14 (4 c.) *or* 14 × 14½ (*others*).
367 4 c. Type **62** .. .. .. .. .. 10 10
368 25 c. Independence Arch (*horiz*) .. .. 15 10
369 35 c. Treasury Building (*horiz*) .. .. 15 10
370 50 c. Parliament Building (*horiz*) .. .. 15 20
367/70 .. .. .. .. *Set of* 4 40 30

**66** U.N. Building, Santiago, Chile

**67** Radar Antenna

(Des G. Vasarhelyi. Photo Harrison)

**1968** (27 Feb). *20th Anniv of the Economic Commission for Latin America. P* 14½.
371 **66** 15 c. multicoloured .. .. .. .. 10 10

(Des G. Vasarhelyi. Photo Harrison)

**1968** (4 June). *World Meteorological Day. T* **67** *and similar multi-coloured designs. P* 14 × 14½ (25 c.) *or* 14½ × 14 (*others*).
372 3 c. Type **67** .. .. .. .. .. 10 10
373 25 c. Meteorological Institute (*horiz*) .. .. 20 10
374 50 c. Harp Gun and coat of arms .. .. 25 15
372/4 .. .. .. .. *Set of* 3 45 25

**70** Lady Baden-Powell, and Guide at Camp Fire

(Des V. Whiteley (from local designs). Photo Harrison)

**1968** (29 Aug). *50th Anniv of Girl Guiding in Barbados. T* **70** *and similar horiz designs. P* 14.
375 3 c. ultramarine, black and gold .. .. 15 10
376 25 c. turquoise-blue, black and gold .. .. 35 15
377 35 c. orange-yellow, black and gold .. .. 45 15
375/7 .. .. .. .. *Set of* 3 85 30

Designs:—25 c. Lady Baden-Powell and Pax Hill; 35 c. Lady Baden-Powell and Guide badge.

**73** Hands breaking Chain, and Human Rights Emblem

(Des V. Whiteley. Litho B.W.)

**1968** (10 Dec).* *Human Rights Year. T* **73** *and similar horiz designs. P* 11 × 12.
378 4 c. violet, brown and light green .. .. 10 10
379 25 c. black, blue and orange-yellow .. .. 10 10
380 35 c. multicoloured .. .. .. .. 10 10
378/80 .. .. .. .. *Set of* 3 15 15

Designs:—25 c. Human Rights emblem and family enchained; 35 c. Shadows of refugees beyond opening fence.

* This was the local release date but the Crown Agents issued the stamps on 29 October.

**76** Racehorses in the Paddock

(Des J. Cooter. Litho Format)

**1969** (20 Mar).* *Horse-Racing. T* **76** *and similar horiz designs. Multicoloured. P* 14.
381 4 c. Type **76** .. .. .. .. .. 15 10
382 25 c. Starting-gate .. .. .. .. 25 10
383 35 c. On the flat .. .. .. .. 25 10
384 50 c. Winning post .. .. .. .. 30 20
381/4 .. .. .. .. *Set of* 4 85 30
**MS**385 117 × 85 mm. Nos. 381/4 .. .. 2·25 2·75

*This was the local release date but the Crown Agents issued the stamps on 15 March.

## COVER PRICES

Cover factors are quoted at the beginning of each country for most issues to 1945. An explanation of the system can be found on page x. The factors quoted do not, however, apply to philatelic covers.

**80** Map showing "CARIFTA" Countries

**81** "Strength in Unity"

(Des J. Cooter. Photo Harrison)

**1969** (6 May). *First Anniv of CARIFTA (Caribbean Free Trade Area). W* w **12** (*sideways on T* **80**). *P* 14.
386 **80** 5 c. multicoloured .. .. .. 10 10
387 **81** 12 c. multicoloured .. .. .. 10 10
388 **80** 25 c. multicoloured .. .. .. 10 10
389 **81** 50 c. multicoloured .. .. .. 15 20
386/9 .. .. .. .. *Set of* 4 30 30

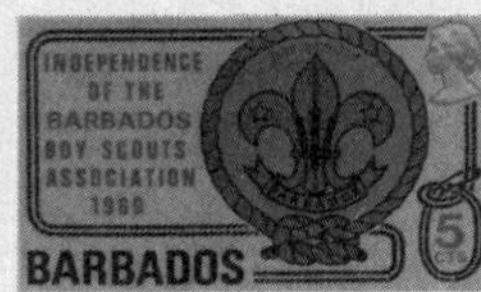


**82** I.L.O. Emblem and "1919-1969".

ONE
CENT
(**83**)

(Des Sylvia Goaman. Litho Enschedé)

**1969** (12 Aug). *50th Anniv of International Labour Organisation. P* 14 × 13.
390 **82** 4 c. black, emerald and turquoise-blue 10 10
391 25 c. black, cerise and brown-red .. 10 10

Although released by the Crown Agents on 5 August, the above were not put on sale in Barbados until 12 August.

**1969** (30 Aug). *No.* 363 *surch with T* **83**.
392 1 c. on 4 c. Type **58** .. .. .. .. 10 10
a. Surch double .. .. .. .. 65·00



**84** National Scout Badge

(Des J. Cooter. Litho Enschedé)

**1969** (16 Dec). *Independence of Barbados Boy Scouts Association and 50th Anniv of Barbados Sea Scouts. T* **84** *and similar horiz designs. Multicoloured. P* 13 × 13½.
393 5 c. Type **84** .. .. .. .. .. 10 10
394 25 c. Sea Scouts rowing .. .. .. 35 10
395 35 c. Scouts around camp fire .. .. .. 45 10
396 50 c. Scouts and National Scout Headquarters 60 40
393/6 .. .. .. .. *Set of* 4 1·40 55
**MS**397 155 × 115 mm. Nos. 393/6 .. .. 9·50 12·00

4 X
(**88**)

**89** Lion at Gun Hill

**1970** (11 Mar). *No.* 346 *surch locally with T* **88**.
398 4 c. on 5 c. sepia, rose and lilac .. .. 10 10
a. Vert pair, one without surch .. .. 35·00
b. Surch double .. .. .. .. 25·00
c. Vert pair, one normal, one surch double
d. Surch triple .. .. .. .. — £100
e. Surch normal on front, inverted on back 12·00
f. Surch omitted on front, inverted on back 16·00

(Des J. W. Photo D.L.R.)

**1970–71.** *Multicoloured designs as T* **89**. *W* w **12** (*sideways on 12 c. to $5*). *P* 12½. *A. Chalk-surfaced paper* (4.5.70) *B. Glazed, ordinary paper* (13.12.71, 12 c., 15 c. *and* $2.50; 15.3.71, *others*).

| | | A | | B | |
|---|---|---|---|---|---|
| 399 | 1 c. Type **89** .. .. | 10 | 20 | 10 | 30 |
| 400 | 2 c. Trafalgar Fountain .. | 20 | 30 | 10 | 40 |
| 401 | 3 c. Montefiore Drinking Fountain .. .. | 10 | 30 | 10 | 45 |
| 402 | 4 c. St. James' Monument .. | 30 | 15 | 10 | 10 |
| 403 | 5 c. St. Anne's Fort .. | 10 | 10 | 10 | 10 |
| 404 | 6 c. Old Sugar Mill, Morgan Lewis .. .. | 35 | 1·25 | † | |
| 405 | 8 c. Cenotaph .. .. | 10 | 10 | 10 | 10 |
| 406 | 10 c. South Point Lighthouse .. | 90 | 30 | 65 | 15 |
| 407 | 12 c. Barbados Museum .. | 30 | 10 | 70 | 20 |
| 408 | 15 c. Sharon Moravian Church | 30 | 15 | 60 | 30 |
| 409 | 25 c. George Washington House | 25 | 15 | 50 | 35 |
| 410 | 35 c. Nicholas Abbey .. | 30 | 65 | 45 | 65 |

411 50 c. Bowmanston Pumping Station .. .. .. 40 75 70 1·50
412 $1 Queen Elizabeth Hospital 70 2·25 3·25 4·50
413 $2.50, Modern sugar factory .. 2·00 4·00 15·00 15·00
414 $5 Seawell International Airport .. .. .. 5·00 10·00 10·00 15·00
399/414A .. .. *Set of* 16 9·50 18·00
399B/414B .. .. *Set of* 15 29·00 35·00
The 2 to 10 c. values are vertical; the 12 c. to $5 horizontal.
See also Nos. 455/67.

**105** Primary Schoolgirl

(Des V. Whiteley. Litho J.W.)

**1970** (26 June). *25th Anniv of United Nations. T* **105** *and similar horiz designs. Multicoloured. W w* **12**. *P* 14.
415 4 c. Type **106** .. .. .. .. .. 10 10
416 5 c. Secondary Schoolboy .. .. .. 10 10
417 25 c. Technical Student .. .. .. 35 10
418 50 c. University Buildings .. .. .. 55 45
415/18 .. .. .. .. *Set of* 4 90 55

**106** Minnie Root

**107** "Via Dolorosa" (Window, St. Margaret's Church, St. John)

(Des and litho J.W.)

**1970** (24 Aug). *Flowers of Barbados. T* **106** *and similar designs. Multicoloured. W w* **12** *(sideways on horiz designs). P* 14½.
419 1 c. Barbados Easter Lily (*vert*) .. .. 10 20
420 5 c. Type **106** .. .. .. .. .. 30 10
421 10 c. Eyelash Orchid .. .. .. .. 70 10
422 25 c. Pride of Barbados (*vert*) .. .. .. 85 55
423 35 c. Christmas Hope .. .. .. .. 90 70
419/23 .. .. .. .. *Set of* 5 2·50 1·50
**MS**424 162 × 101 mm. Nos. 419/23. Imperf .. 2·00 3·25

(Des Jennifer Toombs. Litho J.W.)

**1971** (7 Apr). *Easter. T* **107** *and similar vert design. Multicoloured. W w* **12**. *P* 14.
425 4 c. Type **107** .. .. .. .. .. 10 10
426 10 c. "The Resurrection" (Benjamin West) .. 10 10
427 35 c. Type **107** .. .. .. .. .. 15 10
428 50 c. As 10 c. .. .. .. .. .. 30 60
425/8 .. .. .. .. *Set of* 4 45 70

**108** Sail-fish Craft

(Des and litho Harrison)

**1971** (17 Aug). *Tourism. T* **108** *and similar horiz designs. Multicoloured. W w* **12** *(sideways on* 5 c. *and* 25 c.*). P* 14.
429 1 c. Type **108** .. .. .. .. .. 10 10
430 5 c. Tennis .. .. .. .. .. 15 10
431 12 c. Horse-riding .. .. .. .. 25 10
432 25 c. Water-skiing .. .. .. .. 30 20
433 50 c. Scuba-diving .. .. .. .. 50 65
429/33 .. .. .. .. *Set of* 5 1·10 90

**109** S. J. Prescod (politician) **110** Arms of Barbados

(Des J.W. litho Questa)

**1971** (28 Sept).* *Death Centenary of Samuel Jackman Prescod. W w* **12**. *P* 14.
434 **109** 3 c. multicoloured .. .. .. 10 10
435 35 c. multicoloured .. .. .. 15 10
*This is the local date but the Crown Agents released the stamps two days earlier.

(Des G. Drummond. Litho Questa)

**1971** (23 Nov). *Fifth Anniv of Independence. T* **110** *and similar horiz design. Multicoloured. W w* **12** *(sideways). P* 14.
436 4 c. Type **110** .. .. .. .. .. 10 10
437 15 c. National flag and map .. .. .. 20 10
438 25 c. Type **110** .. .. .. .. .. 30 10
439 50 c. As 15 c. .. .. .. .. .. 60 55
436/9 .. .. .. .. *Set of* 4 1·10 60

**111** Transmitting "Then and Now" **112** Map and Badge

(Des Cable & Wireless Ltd. Litho J.W.)

**1972** (28 Mar). *Cable Link Centenary. T* **111** *and similar horiz designs. Multicoloured. W w* **12** *(sideways). P* 14.
440 4 c. Type **111** .. .. .. .. .. 10 10
441 10 c. *Stanley Angwin* (cable ship) .. .. 15 10
442 35 c. Barbados Earth Station and "Intelsat 4" 35 15
443 50 c. Mt. Misery and Tropospheric Scatter Station .. .. .. .. .. 50 80
440/3 .. .. .. .. *Set of* 4 95 90

(Des Mrs. C. Barrow (50 c.), Major L. Quintyne (others) and adapted by G. Drummond. Litho Questa)

**1972** (1 Aug). *Diamond Jubilee of Scouts. T* **112** *and similar horiz designs. Multicoloured. W w* **12** *(sideways on* 5 c.*). P* 14.
444 5 c. Type **112** .. .. .. .. .. 10 10
445 15 c. Pioneers of scouting .. .. .. 15 10
446 25 c. Scouts .. .. .. .. .. 30 15
447 50 c. Flags .. .. .. .. .. 50 75
444/7 .. .. .. .. *Set of* 4 90 90

**113** Mobile Library

(Des PAD Studio. Litho Harrison)

**1972** (31 Oct). *International Book Year. T* **113** *and similar horiz designs. Multicoloured. W w* **12**. *P* 14.
448 4 c. Type **113** .. .. .. .. .. 10 10
449 15 c. Visual-aids van .. .. .. .. 15 10
450 25 c. Public library .. .. .. .. 20 10
451 $1 Codrington College .. .. .. 1·25 1·50
448/51 .. .. .. .. *Set of* 4 1·50 1·50

**1972** (17 Nov)–**74**. *As Nos.* 402B/14B, *but W w* **12** *(sideways on* 4 *to* 10 c.*; upright on* 12 c. *to* $5).
455 4 c. St. James' Monument .. .. .. 1·25 1·25
456 5 c. St. Anne's Fort .. .. .. .. 1·25 1·50
457 6 c. Old Sugar Mill, Morgan Lewis .. .. 3·75 6·50
458 8 c. Cenotaph .. .. .. .. .. 1·50 1·00
459 10 c. South Point Lighthouse (21.1.74) .. 3·50 5·50
460 12 c. Barbados Museum .. .. .. 2·25 2·50
461 15 c. Sharon Moravian Church .. .. 75 80
462 25 c. George Washington House .. .. 2·75 2·00
463 35 c. Nicholas Abbey .. .. .. .. 2·50 70
464 50 c. Bowmanston Pumping Station .. .. 4·25 1·25
465 $1 Queen Elizabeth Hospital .. .. 6·50 2·75
466 $2.50, Modern sugar factory (2.10.73) .. 3·50 5·50
467 $5 Seawell International Airport (2.10.73) 4·00 5·50
455/67 .. .. .. .. *Set of* 13 35·00 32·00

**114** Potter's Wheel

(Des PAD Studio. Litho Questa)

**1973** (1 Mar). *Pottery in Barbados. T* **114** *and similar horiz designs. Multicoloured. W w* **12**. *P* 14.
468 5 c. Type **114** .. .. .. .. .. 10 10
469 15 c. Kilns .. .. .. .. .. 20 10
470 25 c. Finished products .. .. .. .. 25 10
471 $1 Market scene .. .. .. .. 90 1·10
468/71 .. .. .. .. *Set of* 4 1·25 1·25

**115** First Flight, 1911

(Des C. Abbott. Litho Enschedé)

**1973** (25 July). *Aviation. T* **115** *and similar horiz designs. W w* **12** *(sideways). P* 12½ × 12.
472 5 c. multicoloured .. .. .. .. 15 10
473 15 c. multicoloured .. .. .. .. 60 10
474 25 c. grey-blue, black and cobalt .. .. 85 20
475 50 c. multicoloured .. .. .. .. 1·50 1·50
472/5 .. .. .. .. *Set of* 4 2·75 1·75
Designs:—15 c. First flight to Barbados, 1928; 25 c. Passenger aircraft, 1939; 50 c. "VC-10" airliner, 1973.

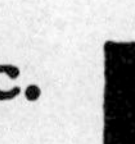
**116** University Chancellor (**117**)

(Des J. W. Litho Enschedé)

**1973** (11 Dec). *25th Anniv of University of West Indies. T* **116** *and similar horiz designs. Multicoloured. W w* **12**. *P* 13 × 14.
476 5 c. Type **116** .. .. .. .. .. 10 10
477 25 c. Sherlock Hall .. .. .. .. 20 15
478 35 c. Cave Hill Campus .. .. .. .. 25 25
476/8 .. .. .. .. *Set of* 3 45 40

**1974** (30 Apr). *No.* 462 *surch with T* **117**.
479 4 c. on 25 c. George Washington House .. 10 10
a. "4c." omitted .. .. .. .. 15·00
No. 479a occurs on R. 10/1, the overprint being applied to sheets consisting of two horizontal panes, 5 × 5. The variety occurs on plate 1A, and shows a clear albino impression of the "4c." on the reverse.

**118** Old Sail Boat

(Des J. Cooter. Litho Questa)

**1974** (11 June). *Fishing Boats of Barbados. T* **118** *and similar diamond-shaped designs. Multicoloured. W w* **12**. *P* 14.
480 15 c. Type **118** .. .. .. .. .. 20 15
481 35 c. Rowing-boat .. .. .. .. 45 25
482 50 c. Motor fishing-boat .. .. .. .. 60 60
483 $1 *Calamar* (fishing boat) .. .. .. 1·00 1·10
480/3 .. .. .. .. *Set of* 4 2·00 1·90
**MS**484 140 × 140 mm. Nos. 480/3 .. .. 2·50 3·00

**119** *Cattleya Gaskelliana Alba*

(Des PAD Studio. Photo Harrison)

**1974** (16 Sept)–**77**. *Orchids. T* **119** *and similar multicoloured designs. W w* **12** *(upright on* 1, 20, 25 c., $1 *and* $10; *sideways on others). P* 14½ × 14 ($1, $10) 14 × 14½ ($2.50, $5) *or* 14 *(others).*
485 1 c. Type **119** .. .. .. .. .. 15 50
486 2 c. *Renanthera storiei* .. .. .. 20 50
487 3 c. *Dendrobium* "Rose Marie" .. .. 20 45
488 4 c. *Epidendrum ibaguense* .. .. .. 1·40 70
489 5 c. *Schomburgkia humboldtii* .. .. 35 15
490 8 c. *Oncidium ampliatum* .. .. .. 65 45
491 10 c. *Arachnis maggie oei* .. .. .. 55 20
492 12 c. *Dendrobium aggregatum* .. .. 45 40
493 15 c. *Paphiopedilum puddle* .. .. .. 45 45
493a 20 c. *Spathoglottis* "The Gold" (3.5.77) .. 4·75 3·75
494 25 c. *Epidendrum ciliare* (Eyelash) .. .. 55 60
495 35 c. *Bletia patula* .. .. .. .. 1·75 90
495a 45 c. *Phalaenopsis schilleriana* "Sunset Glow" (3.5.77) .. .. .. .. 4·75 3·75
496 50 c. As 45 c. .. .. .. .. .. 2·75 1·75
497 $1 *Ascocenda* "Red Gem" .. .. .. 3·50 3·25
498 $2.50, *Brassolaeliocattleya* "Nugget" .. 3·50 3·25
499 $5 *Caularthron bicornutum* .. .. 3·50 6·00
500 $10 *Vanda* "Josephine Black" .. .. 4·00 11·00
485/500 .. .. .. .. *Set of* 18 30·00 35·00
The 1 c., 20 c., 25 c., $2.50 and $5 are horiz designs and the remainder are vert.
See also Nos. 510/24 and 543/51.

**120** 4d. Stamp of 1882, and U.P.U. Emblem

(Des Harrison. Litho Questa)

**1974** (9 Oct). *Centenary of Universal Postal Union. T* **120** *and similar horiz designs.* W w **12** (*sideways*). *P* 14.

501 8 c. magenta, light orange & lt grey-green .. 10 10
502 35 c. dp rose-red, dull orange & bistre-brown 20 10
503 50 c. ultramarine, cobalt and silver .. .. 25 30
504 $1 bright blue, dull brown and grey-black .. 55 80
501/4 .. .. .. .. .. *Set of* 4 1·00 1·10
**MS**505 126 × 101 mm. Nos. 501/4 .. .. 1·25 2·25

Designs:—35 c. Letters encircling the globe; 50 c. U.P.U. emblem and arms of Barbados; $1 Map of Barbados, sailing-ship and aeroplane.

**121** Royal Yacht *Britannia*

(Des Jennifer Toombs. Litho Harrison)

**1975** (18 Feb). *Royal Visit. T* **121** *and similar horiz design. Multicoloured.* W w **12** (*sideways on* 8 *and* 25 *c.*) *P* 14.

506 8 c. Type **121** .. .. .. .. .. 20 15
507 25 c. Type **121** .. .. .. .. .. 50 25
508 35 c. Sunset and palms .. .. .. 60 30
509 $1 As 35 c. .. .. .. .. .. 1·75 2·00
506/9 .. .. .. .. .. *Set of* 4 2·75 2·40

**1975** (30 Apr)–**79**. *As Nos.* 485/9, 491/3, 494 *and* 495*a*/500 *but* W w **14** (*sideways on* 1, 25 *c.*, $1 *and* $10).

510 1 c. Type **119** .. .. .. .. .. 15 45
511 2 c. *Renanthera storiei* .. .. .. 15 45
512 3 c. *Dendrobium* "Rose Marie" .. .. 15 45
513 4 c. *Epidendrum ibaguense* .. .. .. 50 1·50
514 5 c. *Schomburgkia humboldtii* (19.10.77) .. 35 10
515 10 c. *Arachnis maggie oei* (19.10.77) .. .. 35 10
516 12 c. *Dendrobium aggregatum* (19.10.77) .. 5·50 15
517 15 c. *Paphiopedilum puddle* .. .. .. 70 15
518 25 c. *Epidendrum ciliare* (Eyelash) (27.3.79) 70 10
519 45 c. *Phalaenopsis schilleriana* "Sunset Glow" (25.5.78) .. .. .. .. .. 60 15
520 50 c. As 45 c. (23.8.79) .. .. .. 4·00 3·25
521 $1 *Ascocenda* "Red Gem" .. .. .. 7·00 8·50
522 $2.50, *Brassolaeliocattleya* "Nugget" .. 7·00 3·75
523 $5 *Caularthron bicornutum* .. .. 8·50 6·00
524 $10 *Vanda* "Josephine Black" .. .. 11·00 11·00
a. Dull green (stems) omitted .. .. 95·00
510/24 .. .. .. .. *Set of* 15 42·00 32·00

No. 525 vacant.

**122** St. Michael's Cathedral **123** Pony Float

(Des R. Granger Barrett. Litho Questa)

**1975** (29 July). *150th Anniv of Anglican Diocese. T* **122** *and similar square designs. Multicoloured.* W w **12** (*sideways*). *P* 13½.

526 5 c. Type **122** .. .. .. .. .. 10 10
527 15 c. Bishop Coleridge .. .. .. .. 15 10
528 50 c. All Saints' Church .. .. .. 45 50
529 $1 "Archangel Michael and Satan" (stained-glass window, St. Michael's Cathedral, Bridgetown) .. .. .. .. 70 80
526/9 .. .. .. .. .. *Set of* 4 1·25 1·25
**MS**530 95 × 96 mm. Nos. 526/9 (wmk upright) .. 1·40 2·00

(Des R. Granger Barrett. Litho Questa)

**1975** (18 Nov). *Crop-over Festival. T* **123** *and similar horiz designs. Multicoloured.* W w **14** (*sideways*). *P* 14.

531 8 c. Type **123** .. .. .. .. .. 10 10
532 25 c. Man on stilts .. .. .. .. 10 10
533 35 c. Maypole dancing .. .. .. .. 15 10
534 50 c. Cuban dancers .. .. .. .. 30 45
531/4 .. .. .. .. .. *Set of* 4 55 60
**MS**535 127 × 85 mm. Nos. 531/4 .. .. .. 90 1·60

**124** Barbados Coat of Arms **125** 17th-Century Sailing Ship

(Des and litho Harrison)

**1975** (15 Dec). *Coil Definitives.* W w **12** *P* 15 × 14.

536 **124** 5 c. greenish blue .. .. .. 15 50
537 25 c. bluish violet .. .. .. .. 25 75

For 5 c. in this design, but watermarked W w **14**, see No. 743.

(Des PAD Studio. Litho J.W.)

**1975** (17 Dec). *350th Anniv of First Settlement. T* **125** *and similar vert designs. Multicoloured.* W w **14**. *P* 13½.

538 4 c. Type **125** .. .. .. .. .. 25 10
539 10 c. Bearded fig tree and fruit .. .. 30 15
540 25 c. Ogilvy's 17th-century map .. .. 50 30
541 $1 Captain John Powell .. .. .. 2·00 3·00
538/41 .. .. .. .. *Set of* 4 2·75 3·25
**MS**542 105 × 115 mm. Nos. 538/41. P 14 × 14½ 3·25 4·00

**1976** (20 Feb). *As Nos.* 485 *etc., but* W w **12** (*sideways on* 1 *c.*, 25 *c.*, $1) *or upright* (*others*).

543 1 c. Type **119** .. .. .. .. .. 35 1·00
544 2 c. *Renanthera storiei* .. .. .. 60 1·10
545 3 c. *Dendrobium* "Rose Marie" .. .. 65 1·25
546 4 c. *Epidendrum ibaguense* .. .. .. 45 1·50
547 10 c. *Arachnis maggie oei* .. .. .. 85 1·10
548 15 c. *Paphiopedilum puddle* .. .. .. 75 90
549 25 c. *Epidendrum ciliare* "Eyelash" .. .. 1·50 1·00
550 35 c. *Bletia patula* .. .. .. .. 1·75 1·50
551 $1 *Ascocenda* "Red Gem" .. .. .. 4·00 5·00
543/51 .. .. .. .. .. *Set of* 9 9·75 13·00

Nos. 552/8 vacant.

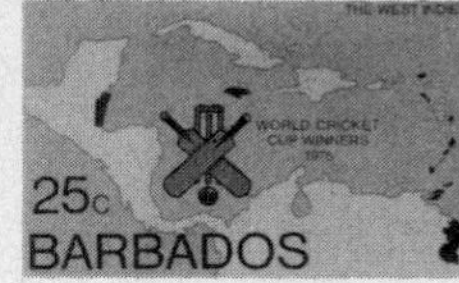


**126** Map of the Caribbean

(Des PAD Studio. Litho Questa)

**1976** (7 July). *West Indian Victory in World Cricket Cup. T* **126** *and similar design. No wmk. P* 14.

559 25 c. multicoloured .. .. .. .. 1·00 1·00
560 45 c. black and magenta .. .. .. 1·25 1·75

Design: *Vert*—45 c. The Prudential Cup.

**127** Flag and Map of S. Carolina

(Des G. Vasarhelyi. Litho Walsall)

**1976** (17 Aug). *Bicentenary of American Revolution. T* **127** *and similar horiz designs. Multicoloured.* W w **14** (*sideways*). *P* 13½.

561 15 c. Type **127** .. .. .. .. .. 25 15
562 25 c. George Washington and map of Bridgetown .. .. .. .. .. 30 15
563 50 c. Independence Declaration .. .. 40 60
564 $1 Prince Hall .. .. .. .. 60 1·50
561/4 .. .. .. .. .. *Set of* 4 1·40 2·25

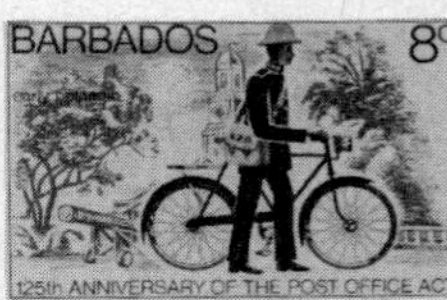


**128** Early Postman

(Des Jennifer Toombs. Litho Questa)

**1976** (19 Oct). *125th Anniv of Post Office Act. T* **128** *and similar horiz designs. Multicoloured.* W w **14** (*sideways*) *P* 14.

565 8 c. Type **128** .. .. .. .. .. 10 10
566 35 c. Modern postman .. .. .. .. 25 10
567 50 c. Early letter .. .. .. .. 30 25
568 $1 Delivery van .. .. .. .. 50 75
565/8 .. .. .. .. .. *Set of* 4 1·00 1·00

**129** Coast Guard Vessels

(Des PAD Studio. Litho J.W.)

**1976** (1 Dec).* *Tenth Anniv of Independence. T* **129** *and similar horiz designs. Multicoloured.* W w **14** (*sideways*). *P* 13 × 13½.

569 5 c. Type **129** .. .. .. .. .. 15 10
570 15 c. Reverse of currency note .. .. .. 15 10
571 25 c. National anthem .. .. .. .. 20 20
572 $1 Independence Day parade .. .. 55 1·25
569/72 .. .. .. .. .. *Set of* 4 95 1·40
**MS**573 90 × 125 mm. Nos. 569/72. P 14 .. .. 1·75 2·10

*This is the local date of issue; the Crown Agents released the stamps a day earlier.

## NEW INFORMATION

The editor is always interested to correspond with people who have new information that will improve or correct the Catalogue.

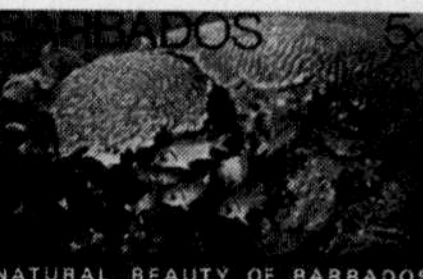


**130** Arrival of Coronation Coach at Westminster Abbey **131** Underwater Park

(Des C. Abbott. Litho Walsall)

**1977** (7 Feb). *Silver Jubilee. T* **130** *and similar vert designs. Multicoloured* W w **14**. *P* 13½.

574 15 c. Garfield Sobers being knighted, 1975 .. 60 25
575 50 c. Type **130** .. .. .. .. .. 75 40
576 $1 Queen entering abbey .. .. .. 1·10 70
574/6 .. .. .. .. .. *Set of* 3 2·25 1·25

For the above with different inscription, see Nos. 590/2.

(Des R. Granger Barrett. Litho Questa)

**1977** (3 May). *Natural Beauty of Barbados. T* **131** *and similar multicoloured designs.* W w **14** (*sideways on Nos.* 577 *and* 579). *P* 14.

577 5 c. Type **131** .. .. .. .. .. 15 10
578 35 c. Royal Palms (*vert*) .. .. .. 30 10
579 50 c. Underwater caves .. .. .. 40 35
580 $1 Stalagmite in Harrison's Cave (*vert*) .. 70 1·00
577/80 .. .. .. .. .. *Set of* 4 1·40 1·40
**MS**581 138 × 92 mm. Nos. 577/80 (wmk sideways) 2·00 2·75

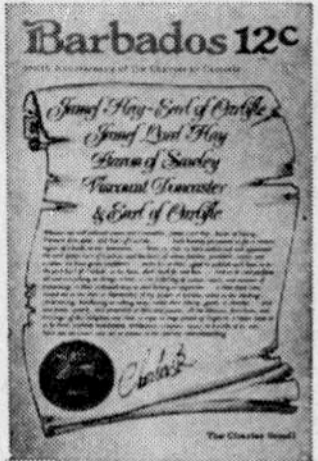


**132** Maces of the House of Commons **133** The Charter Scroll

(Des C. Abbott. Litho J. W.)

**1977** (2 Aug). *13th Regional Conference of the Commonwealth Parliamentary Association. T* **132** *and similar designs.* W w **14** (*sideways on* $1). *P* 13½.

582 10 c. pale orange, yellow and lake-brown .. 10 10
583 25 c. apple-green, orange and deep green .. 10 10
584 50 c. multicoloured .. .. .. .. 20 20
585 $1 pale blue, orange and deep violet-blue .. 55 75
582/5 .. .. .. .. .. *Set of* 4 80 95

Designs: *Vert.*—25 c. Speaker's Chair; 50 c. Senate Chamber. *Horiz*—$1 Sam Lord's Castle.

(Des Walsall. Litho J.W.)

**1977** (11 Oct). *350th Anniv of Granting of Charter to Earl of Carlisle. T* **133** *and similar multicoloured designs.* W w **14** (*sideways on* 45 *c. and* $1). *P* 13.

586 12 c. Type **133** .. .. .. .. .. 15 10
587 25 c. The earl receiving charter .. .. 15 10
588 45 c. The earl and Charles I (*horiz*) .. .. 30 35
589 $1 Ligon's map, 1657 (*horiz*) .. .. 50 1·00
586/9 .. .. .. .. .. *Set of* 4 1·00 1·40

(Des C. Abbott. Litho Walsall)

**1977** (31 Oct). *Royal Visit. As Nos.* 574/6 *but inscr at top* "SILVER JUBILEE ROYAL VISIT". W w **14**. *Roul* 5. *Self-adhesive.*

590 15 c. Garfield Sobers being knighted, 1975 .. 40 40
591 50 c. Type **130** .. .. .. .. .. 60 50
592 $1 Queen entering abbey .. .. .. 90 75
590/2 .. .. .. .. .. *Set of* 3 1·75 1·50

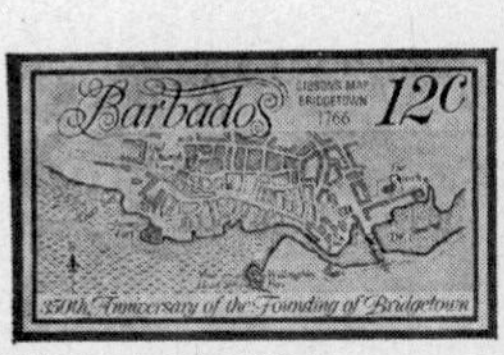

**134** Gibson's Map of Bridgetown, 1766 **135** Pelican

(Des J. W. Litho Questa)

**1978** (1 Mar). *350th Anniv of Founding of Bridgetown. T* **134** *and similar horiz designs.* W w **14** (*sideways*). *P* 14.

593 12 c. multicoloured .. .. .. .. 15 10
594 25 c. black, light green and gold .. .. 20 10
595 45 c. multicoloured .. .. .. .. 25 15
596 $1 multicoloured .. .. .. .. 40 60
593/6 .. .. .. .. .. *Set of* 4 90 80

Designs:—25 c. "A Prospect of Bridgetown in Barbados" (engraving by S. Copens, 1695); 45 c. "Trafalgar Square, Bridgetown" (drawing by J. M. Carter, 1835); $1 The Bridges, 1978.

(Des C. Abbott. Litho Questa)

**1978** (21 Apr). *25th Anniv of Coronation. T* **135** *and similar vert designs. P* 15.
597 50 c. yellow-olive, black and blue .. .. 25 50
a. Sheetlet. Nos. 597/9 × 2 .. .. .. 1·25
598 50 c. multicoloured .. .. .. 25 50
599 50 c. yellow-olive, black and blue .. .. 25 50
597/9 .. .. .. .. .. *Set of* 3 65 1·40

Designs:—No. 597, Griffin of Edward III; No. 598, Queen Elizabeth II; No. 599, Type **135**.

Nos. 597/9 were printed together in small sheets of 6 containing two *se-tenant* strips of 3, with horizontal gutter margin between.

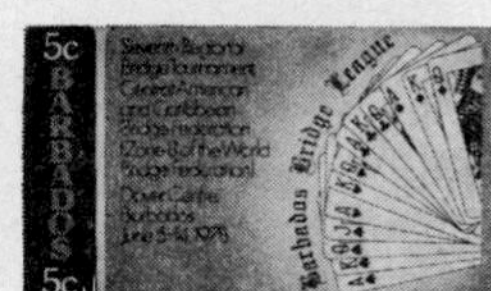

**136** Barbados Bridge League Logo

(Des J. W. Litho Questa)

**1978** (6 June). *7th Regional Bridge Tournament, Barbados. T* **136** *and similar horiz designs. Multicoloured. W w* 14 *(sideways). P* 14½.
600 5 c. Type **136** .. .. .. .. 10 10
601 10 c. Emblem of World Bridge Federation .. 15 10
602 45 c. Central American and Caribbean Bridge Federation emblem .. .. .. 25 10
603 $1 Playing cards on map of Caribbean .. 40 60
600/3 .. .. .. .. .. *Set of* 4 80 75
**MS**604 134 × 83 mm. Nos. 600/3 .. .. .. 1·25 2·50

**137** Camp Scene

(Des and litho Harrison)

**1978** (1 Aug). *Diamond Jubilee of Guiding. T* **137** *and similar diamond-shaped designs. Multicoloured. W w* 14 *(sideways on* 12, 28 *c.). P* 13½.
605 12 c. Type **137** .. .. .. .. 20 15
606 28 c. Community work .. .. .. 30 15
607 50 c. Badge and "60" *(vert)* .. .. .. 40 20
608 $1 Guide badge *(vert)* .. .. .. 60 60
605/8 .. .. .. .. .. *Set of* 4 1·40 1·00

**138** Garment Industry

(Des Walsall. Litho Harrison)

**1978** (14 Nov). *Industries. T* **138** *and similar multicoloured designs. W w* 14 *(sideways on* 12 *and* 50 *c.). P* 14.
609 12 c. Type **138** .. .. .. .. 10 10
610 28 c. Cooper *(vert)* .. .. .. .. 15 20
611 45 c. Blacksmith *(vert)* .. .. .. 20 40
612 50 c. Wrought iron working .. .. .. 25 40
609/12 .. .. .. .. *Set of* 4 60 1·00

**139** Early Mail Steamer

(Des J. Cooter. Litho J. W.)

**1979** (8 Feb). *Ships. T* **139** *and similar horiz designs. Multicoloured. W w* 14 *(sideways). P* 13.
613 12 c. Type **139** .. .. .. .. 30 10
614 25 c. *Queen Elizabeth 2* in Deep Water Harbour .. .. .. .. 45 15
615 50 c. *Ra II* nearing Barbados .. .. .. 65 65
616 $1 Early mail steamer *(different)* .. .. 90 1·50
613/16 .. .. .. .. *Set of* 4 2·10 2·25

**140** 1953 1 c. Definitive Stamp

(Des J.W. Litho Format)

**1979** (8 May). *Death Centenary of Sir Rowland Hill. T* **140** *and similar multicoloured designs showing stamps. W w* 14 *(sideways on* 12 *c.). P* 14.
617 12 c. Type **140** .. .. .. .. 15 15
618 28 c. 1975 350th anniv of first settlement 25 c. commemorative *(vert)* .. .. 20 25
a. Ultramarine (face value) omitted .. 85·00
619 45 c. Penny Black with Maltese Cross postmark *(vert)* .. .. .. 30 35
617/19 .. .. .. .. *Set of* 3 60 60
**MS**620 137 × 90 mm 50 c. Unissued "Britannia" blue (wmk sideways) .. .. .. 35 40

All examples of No. 618 show anniversary spelt as "anniverary".

28c +·4c

ST. VINCENT
RELIEF
FUND

(141)

**142** Grassland Yellow Finch

**1979** (29 May). *St Vincent Relief Fund. No. 495 surch with T* **141**.
621 28 c. + 4 c. on 35 c. *Bletia patula* .. .. 30 30

(Des J.W. Photo Harrison)

**1979** (7 Aug)–**82**. *Birds. Vert designs as T* **142**. *Multicoloured. W w* 14 *(sideways on* 1, 5, 10, 12, 15, 20, 25, 28, 40, 50, 55, 60, 70 *c. and* $1). *P* 14.
622 1 c. Type **142** .. .. .. .. 10 40
623 2 c. Grey Kingbird .. .. .. .. 10 40
624 5 c. Lesser Antillean Bullfinch .. .. 10 30
625 8 c. Magnificent Frigate Bird .. .. 10 30
626 10 c. Cattle Egret (deep slate inscr) .. .. 10 30
a. *Slate-blue inscr* .. .. .. 20 30
627 12 c. Green Heron .. .. .. .. 15 35
627*a* 15 c. Carib Grackle (1.3.82) .. .. .. 3·50 1·50
628 20 c. Antillean Crested Hummingbird .. 20 35
629 25 c. Scaly-breasted Ground Dove .. .. 20 40
630 28 c. As 15 c. .. .. .. .. 50 60
631 35 c. Green-throated Carib .. .. .. 30 60
a. Yellow omitted .. .. .. £180
631*b* 40 c. Red-necked Pigeon (1.3.82) .. .. 3·50 1·50
632 45 c. Zenaida Dove .. .. .. .. 35 60
633 50 c. As 40 c. .. .. .. .. 55 80
633*a* 55 c. American Golden Plover (1.9.81) .. 3·25 1·00
633*b* 60 c. Bananaquit (1.3.82) .. .. .. 3·75 2·00
634 70 c. As 60 c. .. .. .. .. 55 90
635 $1 Caribbean Elaenia .. .. .. 1·00 1·25
636 $2.50, American Redstart .. .. .. 2·00 3·50
637 $5 Belted Kingfisher .. .. .. 3·25 6·00
638 $10 Moorhen .. .. .. .. 6·50 12·00
622/38 .. .. .. .. *Set of* 21 27·00 32·00

No. 626*a* occurred in the initial supply sent to Barbados.

No. 631a shows the birds' plumage in blue instead of green and has the background flowers omitted.

**143** Gun aboard Landing Craft at Foul Bay

**144** Family

(Des G. Vasarhelyi. Litho Format)

**1979** (9 Oct). *Space Project Commemorations. T* **143** *and similar multicoloured designs. W w* 14 *(sideways on* 10, 28 *and* 45 *c.). P* 14.
639 10 c. Type **143** .. .. .. .. 10 10
640 12 c. Transporting launcher through Barbados *(vert)* .. .. .. .. 20 15
641 20 c. Firing of 16" launcher in daylight *(vert)* 15 15
642 28 c. Bath Earth Station and "Intelsat IV A" 25 25
643 45 c. "Intelsat V" over the Caribbean .. .. 35 35
644 50 c. "Intelsat IV A" over Atlantic *(vert)* 35 45
639/44 .. .. .. .. *Set of* 6 1·10 1·25
**MS**645 118 × 90 mm. $1 Lunar module descending on to Moon (wmk sideways) .. .. 65 80

Commemorations:—10 to 20 c. H.A.R.P. Gun experiment: 28 to 50 c. First use of "Intelsat" satellites; $1, 10th anniversary of Moon landing.

(Des R. Granger Barrett. Litho Questa)

**1979** (27 Nov). *International Year of the Child. T* **144** *and similar vert designs. Multicoloured. W w* 14. *P* 14.
646 12 c. Type **144** .. .. .. .. 10 10
647 28 c. Ring of children and map of Barbados .. 15 15
648 45 c. Child with teacher .. .. .. 20 20
649 50 c. Children playing .. .. .. 20 20
650 $1 Children and kite .. .. .. 35 45
646/50 .. .. .. .. *Set of* 5 80 90

**NEW INFORMATION**

The editor is always interested to correspond with people who have new information that will improve or correct the Catalogue.

**145** Map of Barbados

**146** Private, Artillery Company, Barbados Volunteer Force, *circa* 1909

(Des G. Hutchins. Litho Security Printers (M), Malaysia)

**1980** (19 Feb). *75th Anniv of Rotary International. T* **145** *and similar horiz designs. Multicoloured. W w* 14 *(sideways). P* 13.
651 12 c. Type **145** .. .. .. .. 10 10
652 28 c. Map of Caribbean .. .. .. 15 15
653 50 c. Rotary anniversary emblem .. .. 20 25
654 $1 Paul P. Harris (founder) .. .. .. 35 60
651/4 .. .. .. .. *Set of* 4 70 1·00

(Des J.W. Litho Questa)

**1980** (8 Apr). *Barbados Regiment. T* **146** *and similar vert designs. Multicoloured. W w* 14. *P* 14×14½.
655 12 c. Type **146** .. .. .. .. 20 10
656 35 c. Drum Major, Zouave Uniform .. .. 35 15
657 50 c. Sovereign's and Regimental colours .. 40 30
658 $1 Barbados Regiment Women's Corps .. 65 70
655/8 .. .. .. .. *Set of* 4 1·40 1·10

**147** Early Postman

**148** Underwater Scenery

(Des. V. Whiteley Studio. Litho Walsall)

**1980** (6 May). *"London 1980" International Stamp Exhibition. Two sheets each* 122 × 125 *mm containing T* **147** *or similar vert design. Multicoloured. W w* 14. *P* 14 × 13½.
**MS**659 (a) 28 c. × 6, Type **147**. (b) 50 c. × 6, Modern Postwoman and Inspector *Set of* 2 *sheets* 1·75 2·25

The two sheets each contain the stamp in full colour and in five different colour separations.

(Des G. Drummond. Litho Security Printers (M), Malaysia)

**1980** (30 Sept). *Underwater Scenery. T* **148** *and similar horiz designs. W w* 14 *(sideways). P* 13½.
660 12 c. multicoloured .. .. .. .. 15 10
661 28 c. multicoloured .. .. .. .. 25 15
662 50 c. multicoloured .. .. .. .. 40 25
663 $1 multicoloured .. .. .. .. 65 70
660/3 .. .. .. .. *Set of* 4 1·25 1·00
**MS**664 136 × 110 mm. Nos. 660/3 (wmk upright) 1·50 2·25

**149** Bathsheba Railway Station

(Des J. W. Litho Questa)

**1981** (13 Jan). *Early Transport. T* **149** *and similar horiz designs. Multicoloured. W w* 14 *(sideways). P* 14½ × 14.
665 12 c. Type **149** .. .. .. .. 10 10
666 28 c. Cab stand at The Green .. .. .. 20 15
667 45 c. Animal-drawn tram .. .. .. 30 25
668 70 c. Horse-drawn bus .. .. .. 45 50
669 $1 Railway station in Fairchild Street .. 60 85
665/9 .. .. .. .. *Set of* 5 1·50 1·75

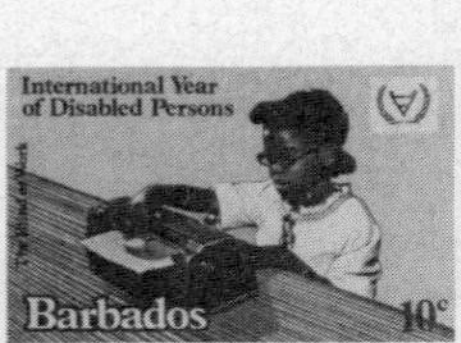

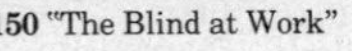

**150** "The Blind at Work"

**151** Prince Charles dressed for Polo

(Des BG Studio. Litho Walsall)

**1981** (19 May). *International Year for Disabled Persons. T* **150** *and similar multicoloured designs. W w* **14** *(sideways on* 10 c. *and* $2.50). *P* 14.

670 10 c. Type **150** .. .. .. .. .. .. 15 10
671 25 c. Sign language (*vert*) .. .. .. .. 30 20
672 45 c. "Be alert to the white cane" (*vert*) .. 55 35
673 $2.50, Children at play .. .. .. 2·00 2·75
670/3 .. .. .. .. .. *Set of* 4 2·75 3·00

(Des and litho J.W.)

**1981** (22 July). *Royal Wedding. T* **151** *and similar vert designs. Multicoloured. W w* **14**. *P* 13½ × 13.

674 28 c. Wedding bouquet from Barbados .. 20 10
675 50 c. Type **151** .. .. .. .. .. .. 25 15
676 $2.50, Prince Charles and Lady Diana Spencer .. .. .. .. .. .. 80 1·25
674/6 .. .. .. .. .. *Set of* 3 1·10 1·25

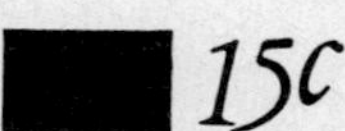


**152** Landship Manoeuvre (**153**)

(Des C. Abbott. Litho Harrison)

**1981** (11 Aug). *Carifesta (Caribbean Festival of Arts), Barbados. T* **152** *and similar vert designs. Multicoloured. W w* **14**. *P* 14½ × 14.

677 15 c. Type **152** .. .. .. .. .. .. 15 15
678 20 c. Yoruba dancers .. .. .. .. .. 15 15
679 40 c. Tuk band .. .. .. .. .. .. 25 25
680 55 c. Sculpture of Frank Collymore .. .. 35 35
681 $1 Harbour scene .. .. .. .. .. 60 75
677/81 .. .. .. .. .. *Set of* 5 1·40 1·50

**1981** (1 Sept). *Nos.* 630, 632 *and* 634 *surch as T* **153**.

682 15 c. on 28 c. Carib Grackle .. .. .. 15 15
683 40 c. on 45 c. Zenaida Dove .. .. .. 20 35
684 60 c. on 70 c. Bananaquit .. .. .. 30 45
682/4 .. .. .. .. .. *Set of* 3 60 85

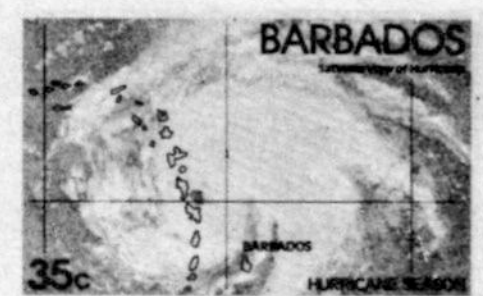


**154** Satellite view of Hurricane

(Des A. Theobald. Litho Walsall)

**1981** (29 Sept). *Hurricane Season. T* **154** *and similar horiz designs. W w* **14** *(sideways). P* 14.

685 35 c. black and blue .. .. .. .. .. 30 20
686 50 c. multicoloured .. .. .. .. .. 40 35
687 60 c. multicoloured .. .. .. .. .. 50 50
688 $1 multicoloured .. .. .. .. .. 75 90
685/8 .. .. .. .. .. *Set of* 4 1·75 1·75

Designs:—50 c. Hurricane "Gladys" from "Apollo 7"; 60 c. Police Department on hurricane watch; $1 Hurricane hunter (McDonnell "F2H-2P (Banshee)" jet aircraft).

**155** Twin Falls **156** Black Belly Ram

(Des. L. Curtis. Litho Format)

**1981** (1 Dec.) *Harrison's Cave. T* **155** *and similar vert designs. Multicoloured. W w* **14**. *P* 14 × 14½.

689 10 c. Type **155** .. .. .. .. .. .. 10 10
690 20 c. Stream in Rotunda Room .. .. .. 20 15
691 55 c. Formations in Rotunda Room .. .. 40 50
692 $2.50, Cascade Pool .. .. .. .. 1·25 2·25
689/92 .. .. .. .. .. *Set of* 4 1·75 2·75

(Des BG Studio. Litho Format)

**1982** (9 Feb). *Black Belly Sheep. T* **156** *and similar horiz designs. Multicoloured. W w* **14** *(sideways). P* 14.

693 40 c. Type **156** .. .. .. .. .. .. 30 30
694 50 c. Black Belly ewe .. .. .. .. .. 30 35
695 60 c. Ewe with lambs .. .. .. .. .. 40 60
696 $1 Ram and ewe, with map of Barbados .. 65 1·50
693/6 .. .. .. .. .. *Set of* 4 1·50 2·50

## COVER PRICES

Cover factors are quoted at the beginning of each country for most issues to 1945. An explanation of the system can be found on page x. The factors quoted do not, however, apply to philatelic covers.

**157** Barbados Coat of Arms and Flag

(Des Harrison. Litho Format)

**1982** (8 Apr). *President Reagan's Visit. T* **157** *and similar horiz design. Multicoloured. W w* **14** *(sideways). P* 14.

697 20 c. Type **157** .. .. .. .. .. .. 65 75
a. Pair. Nos. 697/8 .. .. .. .. .. 1·25 1·50
698 20 c. U.S.A. coat of arms and flag .. .. 65 75
699 55 c. Type **157** .. .. .. .. .. .. 1·00 1·25
a. Pair. Nos. 699/700 .. .. .. .. 2·00 2·50
700 55 c. As No. 698 .. .. .. .. .. 1·00 1·25
697/700 .. .. .. .. .. *Set of* 4 3·00 3·50

The two designs of each value were printed together, *se-tenant*, in horizontal and vertical pairs within small sheets of 8 stamps.

**158** Lighter **159** Bride and Earl Spencer proceeding up Aisle

(Des J.W. Litho Harrison)

**1982** (4 May). *Early Marine Transport. T* **158** *and similar horiz designs. Multicoloured. W w* **14** *(sideways). P* 14½.

701 20 c. Type **158** .. .. .. .. .. .. 20 15
702 35 c. Rowing boat .. .. .. .. .. 35 25
703 55 c. Speightstown schooner .. .. .. 50 40
704 $2.50, Inter-colonial schooner .. .. 2·00 2·25
701/4 .. .. .. .. .. *Set of* 4 2·75 2·75

(Des Jennifer Toombs. Litho Questa)

**1982** (1 July). *21st Birthday of Princess of Wales. T* **159** *and similar vert designs. Multicoloured W w* **14**. *P* 14½ × 14.

705 20 c. Barbados coat of arms .. .. .. 20 15
706 60 c. Princess at Llanelwedd, October 1981 .. 55 50
707 $1.20, Type **159** .. .. .. .. .. 90 1·10
708 $2.50, Formal portrait .. .. .. .. 1·50 1·90
705/8 .. .. .. .. .. *Set of* 4 2·75 3·25

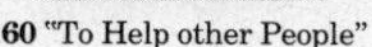

**160** "To Help other People" **161** Arms of George Washington

(Des G. Drummond. Litho Format)

**1982** (7 Sept). *75th Anniv of Boy Scout Movement. T* **160** *and similar multicoloured designs. W w* **14** *(sideways on Nos.* 710/11). *P* 14.

709 15 c. Type **160** .. .. .. .. .. .. 50 10
710 40 c. "I Promise to do my Best" (*horiz*) .. 80 25
711 55 c. "To do my Duty to God, the Queen and my Country" (*horiz*) .. .. .. .. 1·00 40
712 $1 National and Troop flags .. .. .. 1·50 1·25
709/12 .. .. .. .. .. *Set of* 4 3·50 1·75
**MS**713 119 × 93 mm. $1.50, The Scout Law .. 3·50 2·75

(Des and litho J.W.)

**1982** (2 Nov). *250th Birth Anniv of George Washington. T* **161** *and similar vert designs. Multicoloured. W w* **14**. *P* 13½ × 13.

714 10 c. Type **161** .. .. .. .. .. .. 10 10
715 55 c. Washington House, Barbados .. .. 45 45
716 60 c. Washington with troops .. .. .. 50 50
717 $2.50, Washington taking Oath .. .. 1·60 1·60
714/17 .. .. .. .. .. *Set of* 4 2·40 2·40

**162** *Agraulis vanillae*

(Des I. Loe. Litho J.W.)

**1983** (8 Feb). *Butterflies. T* **162** *and similar horiz designs. Multicoloured. W w* **14** *(sideways). P* 13 × 13½.

718 20 c. Type **162** .. .. .. .. .. .. 55 15
719 40 c. *Danaus plexippus* .. .. .. .. 75 40
720 55 c. *Hypolimnas misippus* .. .. .. 90 45
721 $2.50, *Hemiargus hanno* .. .. .. 2·25 2·00
718/21 .. .. .. .. .. *Set of* 4 4·00 2·75

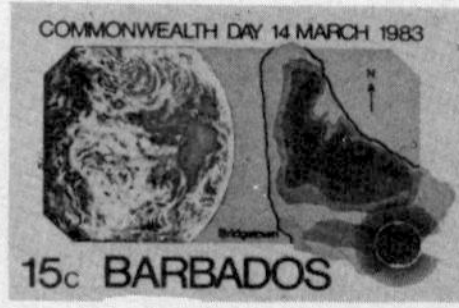


**163** Map of Barbados and Satellite View

(Des D. Bowen. Litho J.W.)

**1983** (14 Mar). *Commonwealth Day. T* **163** *and similar horiz designs. Multicoloured. W w* **14** *(sideways). P* 13.

722 15 c. Type **163** .. .. .. .. .. .. 25 10
723 40 c. Tourist beach .. .. .. .. .. 40 20
724 60 c. Sugar cane harvesting .. .. .. 60 40
725 $1 Cricket match .. .. .. .. .. 1·50 1·10
722/5 .. .. .. .. .. *Set of* 4 2·50 1·60

**164** U.S. Navy Dirigible

(Des L. Curtis. Litho Format)

**1983** (14 June). *Bicentenary of Manned Flight. T* **164** *and similar horiz designs. Multicoloured. W w* **14** *(sideways). P* 14.

726 20 c. Type **164** .. .. .. .. .. .. 45 10
727 40 c. Douglas "DC3" .. .. .. .. .. 60 30
728 55 c. Vickers "Viscount" .. .. .. .. 75 60
729 $1 Lockheed "Tristar" .. .. .. .. 1·25 1·75
726/9 .. .. .. .. .. *Set of* 4 2·75 2·50

**165** Nash "600", 1941 **166** Game in Progress

(Des and litho Harrison)

**1983** (9 Aug). *Classic Cars. T* **165** *and similar horiz designs. Multicoloured. W w* **14** *(sideways). P* 14.

730 25 c. Type **165** .. .. .. .. .. .. 30 20
731 45 c. Dodge, 1938 .. .. .. .. .. 40 30
732 75 c. Ford "Model AA", 1930 .. .. .. 60 70
733 $2.50, Dodge "Four", 1918 .. .. .. 1·75 2·25
730/3 .. .. .. .. .. *Set of* 4 2·75 3·00

(Des L. Curtis. Litho Questa)

**1983** (30 Aug). *Table Tennis World Cup Competition. T* **166** *and similar vert designs. Multicoloured. W w* **14**. *P* 14.

734 20 c. Type **166** .. .. .. .. .. .. 25 20
735 65 c. Map of Barbados .. .. .. .. 50 55
736 $1 World Table Tennis Cup .. .. .. 75 1·00
734/6 .. .. .. .. .. *Set of* 3 1·40 1·60

**167** Angel playing Lute (detail "The Virgin and Child") (Masaccio)) **168** Track and Field Events

(Des D. Miller. Litho Questa)

**1983** (1 Nov). *Christmas. 50th Anniv of Barbados Museum. T* **167** *and similar multicoloured designs. W w* **14** *(sideways on* 45 c., 75 c. *and* $2.50). *P* 14.

737 10 c. multicoloured .. .. .. .. .. 25 10
738 25 c. multicoloured .. .. .. .. .. 45 20
739 45 c. multicoloured .. .. .. .. .. 65 35
740 75 c. black and gold .. .. .. .. .. 1·00 1·00
741 $2.50, multicoloured .. .. .. .. 3·00 3·50
737/41 .. .. .. .. .. *Set of* 5 4·75 4·50
**MS**742 59 × 98 mm. $2 multicoloured .. .. 1·75 2·00

Designs: *Horiz*—45 c. "The Barbados Museum" (Richard Day); 75 c. "St. Ann's Garrison" (W. S. Hedges); $2.50, Needham's Point, Carlisle Bay. *Vert*—25 c., $2 Different details from "The Virgin and Child" (Masaccio).

**1983** (Dec). *Coil Definitive. As No. 536 but W w* **14.**
743 **124** 5 c. greenish blue .. .. .. .. 50 60
No. 743 was also available from sheets.

(Des McCombie Skinner Studio. Litho Walsall)

**1984** (28 Mar). *Olympic Games, Los Angeles. T* **168** *and similar horiz designs. W w* **14** *(sideways). P* 14.
745 50 c. bright green, black and olive-sepia .. 50 45
746 65 c. dull orange, black and drab .. .. 70 60
747 75 c. greenish blue, black and deep cobalt .. 80 70
748 $1 light brown, black and yellow-ochre .. 1·00 90
745/8 .. .. .. .. .. *Set of* 4 2·75 2·40
**MS**749 115 × 97 mm. Nos. 745/8 .. .. .. 4·00 4·75
Designs:—65 c. Shooting; 75 c. Sailing; $1 Cycling.

**169** Global Coverage **170** U.P.U. 1943 3d. Stamp and Logo

(Des C. Abbott. Litho Questa)

**1984** (25 Apr). *250th Anniv of Lloyd's List (newspaper). T* **169** *and similar vert designs. Multicoloured. W w* **14.** *P* 14½ × 14.
750 45 c. Type **169** .. .. .. .. .. 65 40
751 50 c. Bridgetown harbour .. .. .. 70 50
752 75 c. *Philosopher*, 1857 .. .. .. 95 70
753 $1 *Sea Princess*, 1984 .. .. .. 1·10 95
750/3 .. .. .. .. .. *Set of* 4 3·00 2·25

(Des McCombie Skinner Studio. Litho J.W.)

**1984** (6 June). *Universal Postal Union Congress, Hamburg. Sheet 90 × 75 mm. W w* **14** *(sideways). P* 13½.
**MS**754 **170** $2 multicoloured .. .. .. 2·75 2·75

**171** Local Junior Match **172** Poinsettia

(Des L. Curtis. Litho Walsall)

**1984** (8 Aug). *60th Anniv of World Chess Federation. T* **171** *and similar horiz designs. Multicoloured. W w* **14** *(sideways). P* 14½.
755 25 c. Type **171** .. .. .. .. .. 80 25
756 45 c. Staunton and 19th-century Knight .. 1·10 45
757 65 c. Staunton and 18th-century Queen .. 1·40 70
758 $2 Staunton and 17th-century Castle .. 2·75 3·00
755/8 .. .. .. .. .. *Set of* 4 5·50 4·00

(Des I. Loe. Litho Questa)

**1984** (24 Oct). *Christmas. Flowers. T* **172** *and similar vert designs. Multicoloured. W w* **14.** *P* 14.
759 50 c. Type **172** .. .. .. .. 1·25 60
760 65 c. Snow-on-the-Mountain .. .. .. 1·50 80
761 75 c. Christmas Candle .. .. .. 1·75 1·50
762 $1 Christmas Hope .. .. .. .. 2·00 2·25
759/62 .. .. .. .. *Set of* 4 6·00 4·50

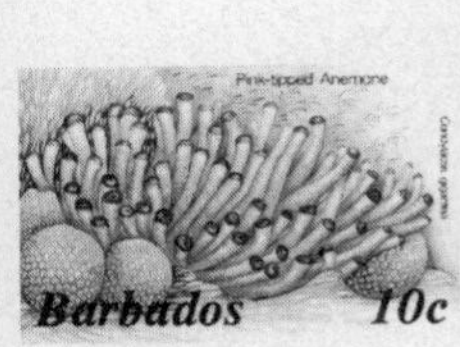

**173** Pink-tipped Anemone **174** The Queen Mother at the Docks

(Des I. Loe. Litho Questa)

**1985** (26 Feb)–**87**. *Marine Life. T* **173** *and similar horiz designs. Multicoloured. W w* **14** *(sideways). P* 14. *A. Without imprint date at foot. B. With imprint date* ("1987").

| | | | A | | B | |
|---|---|---|---|---|---|---|
| 763 | 1 c. Bristle Worm .. .. | 30 | 30 | 50 | 70 |
| 764 | 2 c. Spotted Trunkfish .. | 30 | 30 | 50 | 70 |
| 765 | 5 c. Coney .. .. .. | 30 | 15 | † | |
| 766 | 10 c. Type **173** .. .. | 40 | 15 | † | |
| 767 | 20 c. Christmas Tree Worm | 80 | 35 | 1·40 | 85 |
| 768 | 25 c. Hermit Crab .. .. | 90 | 30 | † | |
| 769 | 35 c. Animal Flower .. .. | 95 | 30 | † | |
| 770 | 40 c. Vase Sponge .. .. | 1·00 | 45 | † | |
| 771 | 45 c. Spotted Moray .. .. | 1·00 | 40 | † | |
| 772 | 50 c. Ghost Crab .. .. | 2·25 | 80 | 3·25 | 1·75 |
| 773 | 65 c. Flamingo Tongue Snail .. | 1·50 | 50 | † | |
| 774 | 75 c. Sergeant Major .. .. | 2·25 | 90 | 3·50 | 2·00 |
| 775 | $1 Caribbean Warty Anemone .. .. | 2·50 | 65 | † | |
| 776 | $2.50, Green Turtle .. .. | 5·00 | 3·50 | 7·00 | 7·00 |
| 777 | $5 Rock Beauty (fish) .. | 7·50 | 6·50 | 10·00 | 10·00 |
| 778 | $10 Elkhorn Coral .. .. | 8·50 | 8·50 | † | |
| 763/78A | .. .. *Set of* 16 | 32·00 | 21·00 | † | |
| 763/78B | .. .. *Set of* 7 | † | | 24·00 | 21·00 |

Dates of issue:—26.2.85, Nos. 766A/8A, 772A, 776A/7A; 9.4.85, Nos. 765A, 769A/70A, 773A, 778A; 7.5.85, Nos. 763A/4A, 771A, 774A/5A; 15.9.87, 763B/77B.
For these designs watermarked w **16** (sideways) see Nos. 794/809.

(Des A. Theobald ($2), C. Abbott (others). Litho Questa)

**1985** (7 June). *Life and Times of Queen Elizabeth the Queen Mother. T* **174** *and similar vert designs. Multicoloured. W w* **16.** *P* 14½ × 14.
779 25 c. In the White Drawing Room, Buckingham Palace, 1930s .. .. .. 15 20
780 65 c. With Lady Diana Spencer at Trooping the Colour, 1981 .. .. .. 45 50
781 75 c. Type **174** .. .. .. .. .. 55 60
782 $1 With Prince Henry at his christening (from photo by Lord Snowdon) .. 70 75
779/82 .. .. .. .. *Set of* 4 1·60 1·90
**MS**783 91 × 73 mm. $2 In Land Rover opening Syon House Garden Centre. Wmk sideways .. 1·40 1·50

**175** Peregrine Falcon

(Des D. Miller. Litho Walsall)

**1985** (6 Aug). *Birth Bicentenary of John J. Audubon (ornithologist). T* **175** *and similar multicoloured designs showing original paintings. W w* **14** *(sideways on 45 c.). P* 14.
784 45 c. Type **175** .. .. .. .. .. 1·10 45
785 65 c. Prairie Warbler (*vert*) .. .. .. 1·25 75
786 75 c. Great Blue Heron (*vert*) .. .. 1·50 1·00
787 $1 Yellow Warbler (*vert*) .. .. .. 1·75 1·75
784/7 .. .. .. .. .. *Set of* 4 5·00 3·50

**176** Intelsat Satellite orbitting Earth **177** Traffic Policeman

(Des L. Curtis. Litho Harrison)

**1985** (10 Sept). *20th Anniv of Intelsat Satellite System. W w* **14** *(sideways). P* 14.
788 **176** 75 c. multicoloured .. .. .. 75 60

(Des L. Curtis. Litho Format)

**1985** (19 Nov). *150th Anniv of Royal Barbados Police. T* **177** *and similar multicoloured designs. W w* **16.** *P* 14.
789 25 c. Type **177** .. .. .. .. .. 75 20
790 50 c. Police Band on bandstand .. .. 1·25 55
791 65 c. Dog handler .. .. .. .. 1·50 80
792 $1 Mounted policeman in ceremonial uniform .. .. .. .. .. 1·75 1·75
789/92 .. .. .. .. *Set of* 4 4·75 3·00
**MS**793 85 × 60 mm. $2 Police Band on parade (*horiz*). Wmk sideways .. .. .. 2·75 2·75

**1986** (6 Jan)–**87**. *As Nos. 763/78 but W w* **16** *(sideways). P* 14. *A. Without imprint date at foot. B. With imprint date.*

| | | A | | B | |
|---|---|---|---|---|---|
| 794 | 1 c. Bristle Worm .. .. | † | | 20 | 30 |
| 795 | 2 c. Spotted Trunkfish .. | † | | 20 | 30 |
| 796 | 5 c. Coney .. .. .. | 30 | 15 | 1·25 | 50 |
| 797 | 10 c. Type **173** .. .. | 30 | 15 | 30 | 20 |
| 798 | 20 c. Christmas Tree Worm .. | 60 | 25 | 30 | 30 |
| 799 | 25 c. Hermit Crab .. .. | 60 | 30 | 40 | 40 |
| 800 | 35 c. Animal Flower .. .. | 60 | 35 | 1·50 | 75 |
| 801 | 40 c. Vase Sponge .. .. | † | | 50 | 50 |
| 802 | 45 c. Spotted Moray .. .. | † | | 60 | 50 |
| 803 | 50 c. Ghost Crab .. .. | 1·25 | 75 | 60 | 60 |
| 804 | 65 c. Flamingo Tongue Snail .. | † | | 65 | 70 |
| 805 | 75 c. Sergeant Major .. .. | † | | 70 | 75 |
| 806 | $1 Caribbean Warty Anemone .. .. | † | | 85 | 85 |
| 807 | $2.50, Green Turtle .. .. | 3·50 | 3·50 | 2·00 | 1·75 |
| 808 | $5 Rock Beauty (fish) .. | 6·00 | 6·00 | 4·50 | 3·25 |
| 809 | $10 Elkhorn Coral .. .. | 10·00 | 10·00 | 9·00 | 8·00 |
| 794/809A | .. *Set of* 9 | 21·00 | 19·00 | † | |
| 794/809B | .. *Set of* 16 | † | | 21·00 | 17·00 |

Dates of issue:—6.1.86, Nos. 796A/800A, 803A, 807A/9A; 23.7.86, Nos. 794B/5B, 801B/2B; 18.8.86, Nos. 797B/9B, 803B/9B; 15.9.87, Nos. 796B, 800B.
Nos. 797B, 799B, 801B/2B, 804B, 806B and 809B exist with different imprint dates below the designs.

(Des A. Theobald. Litho Format)

**1986** (21 Apr). *60th Birthday of Queen Elizabeth II. Vert designs as T* **110** *of Ascension. Multicoloured. W w* **16.** *P* 14 × 14½.
810 25 c. Princess Elizabeth aged two, 1928 .. 15 20
811 50 c. At University College of West Indies, Jamaica, 1953 .. .. .. .. 35 40
812 65 c. With Duke of Edinburgh, Barbados, 1985 .. .. .. .. .. 45 50
a. Silver (logo) omitted .. .. .. £300
813 75 c. At banquet in Sao Paulo, Brazil, 1968 .. 55 60
814 $2 At Crown Agents Head Office, London, 1983 .. .. .. .. .. 1·40 1·50
810/14 .. .. .. .. *Set of* 5 2·50 3·00

**178** Trans-Canada "North Star DC-472" Airliner

(Des L. Curtis. Litho Format)

**1986** (2 May). *"Expo '86" World Fair, Vancouver. T* **178** *and similar horiz design. Multicoloured. W w* **16** *(sideways). P* 14.
815 50 c. Type **178** .. .. .. .. .. 35 40
816 $2.50, *Lady Nelson* (liner) .. .. 1·75 1·90

(Des D. Miller. Litho Walsall)

**1986** (22 May). *"Ameripex '86" International Stamp Exhibition, Chicago. Horiz designs as T* **164** *of Bahamas, showing Barbados stamps (Nos. 817/20). Multicoloured. W w* **16** *(sideways). P* 14.
817 45 c. 1976 Bicentenary of American Revolution 25 c. .. .. .. .. .. 60 35
818 50 c. 1976 Bicentenary of American Revolution 50 c. .. .. .. .. .. 65 40
819 65 c. 1981 Hurricane Season $1 .. .. 75 50
820 $1 1982 Visit of President Reagan 55 c. pair .. .. .. .. .. 95 75
817/20 .. .. .. .. *Set of* 4 2·75 1·75
**MS**821 90 × 80 mm. $2 Statue of Liberty and liner *Queen Elizabeth 2* .. .. .. 3·00 3·00
No. **MS**821 also commemorates the Centenary of the Statue of Liberty.

(Des D. Miller. Litho Walsall)

**1986** (23 July). *Royal Wedding. Square designs as T* **112** *of Ascension. Multicoloured. W w* **16.** *P* 14½ × 14.
822 45 c. Prince Andrew and Miss Sarah Ferguson .. .. .. .. .. 60 35
823 $1 Prince Andrew in Midshipman's uniform .. .. .. .. .. 1·00 75

**179** Transporting Electricity Poles, 1923 **180** *Alpinia purpurata* and Church Window

(Des A. Theobald. Litho B.D.T.)

**1986** (16 Sept). *75th Anniv of Electricity in Barbados. T* **179** *and similar multicoloured designs. W w* **16** *(sideways on 10, 65 c.). P* 13½.
824 10 c. Type **179** .. .. .. .. .. 15 10
825 25 c. Heathman Ladder, 1935 (*vert*) .. .. 25 20
826 65 c. Transport fleet, 1941 .. .. .. 60 50
827 $2 Bucket truck, 1986 (*vert*) .. .. 1·60 1·75
824/7 .. .. .. .. *Set of* 4 2·40 2·25

(Des A. Atkinson. Litho Questa)

**1986** (28 Oct). *Christmas. T* **180** *and similar vert designs showing flowers and church windows. Multicoloured. W w* **14.** *P* 14.
828 25 c. Type **180** .. .. .. .. .. 20 20
829 50 c. *Anthurium andraeanum* .. .. .. 45 45
830 75 c. *Heliconia rostrata* .. .. .. 70 70
831 $2 *Heliconia x psittacorum* .. .. .. 1·50 2·25
828/31 .. .. .. .. *Set of* 4 2·50 3·25

**181** Shot Putting **182** Barn Swallow

(Des G. Vasarhelyi. Litho Format)

**1987** (27 Mar). *10th Anniv of Special Olympics. T* **181** *and similar horiz designs. Multicoloured.* W w **14** *(sideways). P* 14.

832 15 c. Type **181** .. .. .. .. .. 25 15
833 45 c. Wheelchair racing .. .. .. .. 45 30
834 65 c. Long jumping .. .. .. .. .. 60 50
835 $2 Logo and slogan .. .. .. .. 1·75 2·00
832/5 .. .. .. .. .. *Set of* 4 2·75 2·75

(Des P. Broadbent. Litho Walsall)

**1987** (12 June). *"Capex '87" International Stamp Exhibition, Toronto. Birds. T* **182** *and similar vert designs. Multicoloured.* W w **16**. *P* 14.

836 25 c. Type **182** .. .. .. .. .. 75 30
837 50 c. Yellow Warbler .. .. .. .. 1·00 70
838 65 c. Audubon's Shearwater .. .. .. 1·25 1·00
839 75 c. Black-whiskered Vireo .. .. .. 1·40 1·25
840 $1 Scarlet Tanager .. .. .. .. 1·60 2·00
836/40 .. .. .. .. .. *Set of* 5 5·50 4·50

**183** Sea Scout saluting

**184** Bridgetown Synagogue

(Des L. Curtis. Litho Format)

**1987** (24 July). *75th Anniv of Scouting in Barbados. T* **183** *and similar vert designs. Multicoloured.* W w **16**. *P* 14.

841 10 c. Type **183** .. .. .. .. .. 20 10
842 25 c. Scout jamboree .. .. .. .. 30 20
843 65 c. Scout badges .. .. .. .. .. 65 45
844 $2 Scout band .. .. .. .. .. 1·60 1·75
841/4 .. .. .. .. .. *Set of* 4 2·50 2·25

(Des R. Edge. Litho Questa)

**1987** (6 Oct). *Restoration of Bridgetown Synagogue. T* **184** *and similar multicoloured designs.* W w **16** *(sideways on 50, 65 c.). P* 14×14½ *(horiz) or* 14½×14 *(vert).*

845 50 c. Type **184** .. .. .. .. .. 90 75
846 65 c. Interior of Synagogue .. .. .. 1·10 85
847 75 c. Ten Commandments *(vert)* .. .. 1·40 1·25
848 $1 Marble laver *(vert)* .. .. .. 1·75 2·00
845/8 .. .. .. .. .. *Set of* 4 4·50 4·25

**185** Arms and Colonial Seal

(Des D. Hartley. Litho Walsall)

**1987** (24 Nov). *21st Anniv of Independence. T* **185** *and similar multicoloured designs.* W w **16** *(sideways). P* 14×14½.

849 25 c. Type **185** .. .. .. .. .. 20 20
850 45 c. Flags of Barbados and Great Britain .. 30 30
851 65 c. Silver dollar and one penny coins .. 55 45
852 $2 Colours of Barbados Regiment .. .. 1·40 1·40
849/52 .. .. .. .. .. *Set of* 4 2·25 2·10
**MS**853 94×56 mm. $1.50, Prime Minister E. W. Barrow *(vert)*. Wmk upright. P 14½×14 .. 1·00 1·25

**186** Herman C. Griffith

**186*a***

(Des D. Hartley. Litho Walsall)

**1988** (6 June–11 July). *West Indian Cricket. T* **186** *and similar horiz designs, each showing portrait, cricket equipment and early belt buckle. Multicoloured.* W w **14** *(sideways). P* 14.

854 15 c. E. A. (Manny) Martindale .. .. .. 50 20
855 45 c. George Challenor .. .. .. .. 90 45
856 50 c. Type **186** (11.7) .. .. .. .. 1·00 70
a. Error. Portrait as Type **186*a***
857 75 c. Harold Austin .. .. .. .. 1·40 90
858 $2 Frank Worrell .. .. .. .. 2·50 2·75
854/8 .. .. .. .. .. *Set of* 5 5·75 4·50

As originally prepared the 50 c., inscribed "Herman C. Griffith", showed the portrait of another Barbadian cricketer, E. Lawson Bartlett, in error. The mistake was noticed two days prior to issue and the 50 c. was delayed until 11 July while supplies showing the correct portrait were printed. The instructions to withdraw the stamps with the Bartlett portrait, No. 856a, failed to reach the Parcel Post Department in time and, it is reported, 101 examples were sold in the normal course of business before the, belated, notification was received.

**187** *Kentropyx borckianus*

**188** Cycling

(Des Doreen McGuinness. Litho B.D.T.)

**1988** (13 June). *Lizards of Barbados. T* **187** *and similar vert designs. Multicoloured.* W w **14**. *P* 14.

859 10 c. Type **187** .. .. .. .. .. 30 10
860 50 c. *Hemidactylus mabouia* .. .. .. 80 35
861 65 c. *Anolis extremus* .. .. .. .. 90 55
862 $2 *Gymnophthalmus underwoodii* .. .. 2·25 2·00
859/62 .. .. .. .. .. *Set of* 4 3·75 2·75

(Des A. Edmonston. Litho Walsall)

**1988** (2 Aug). *Olympic Games, Seoul. T* **188** *and similar vert designs. Multicoloured.* W w **14**. *P* 14½×14.

863 25 c. Type **188** .. .. .. .. .. 15 20
864 45 c. Athletics .. .. .. .. .. 25 30
865 75 c. Relay swimming .. .. .. .. 45 50
866 $2 Yachting .. .. .. .. .. 1·25 1·40
863/6 .. .. .. .. .. *Set of* 4 1·90 2·10
**MS**867 144×63 mm. Nos. 863/6. W w **16** .. 2·10 2·40

(Des S. Noon and D. Miller (50, 65 c.), D. Miller (others). Litho Questa)

**1988** (18 Oct). *300th Anniv of Lloyd's of London. Designs as T* **123** *of Ascension.* W w **14** *(sideways on 50, 65 c.). P* 14.

868 40 c. multicoloured .. .. .. .. 45 30
869 50 c. multicoloured .. .. .. .. 55 35
870 65 c. multicoloured .. .. .. .. 70 45
871 $2 steel-blue and brown-lake .. .. 1·75 2·00
868/71 .. .. .. .. .. *Set of* 4 3·00 2·75

Designs: *Vert*—40 c. Royal Exchange, 1774; $2 Sinking of *Titanic*, 1912. *Horiz*—50 c. Early sugar mill; 65 c. *Author* (container ship).

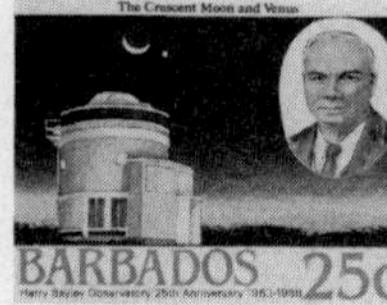


**189** Harry Bayley and Observatory

**190** LIAT BAe "748"

(Des Josephine Martin. Litho Walsall)

**1988** (28 Nov). *25th Anniv of Harry Bayley Observatory. T* **189** *and similar horiz designs. Multicoloured.* W w **16** *(sideways). P* 14×14½.

872 25 c. Type **189** .. .. .. .. .. 40 20
873 65 c. Observatory with North Star and Southern Cross constellations .. .. 70 45
874 75 c. Andromeda galaxy .. .. .. .. 85 50
875 $2 Orion constellation .. .. .. 2·00 2·25
872/5 .. .. .. .. .. *Set of* 4 3·50 3·00

(Des A. Theobald. Litho Walsall)

**1989** (20 Mar). *50th Anniv of Commercial Aviation in Barbados. T* **190** *and similar horiz designs. Multicoloured.* W w **16** *(sideways). P* 14.

876 25 c. Type **190** .. .. .. .. .. 40 20
877 65 c. Panam Douglas "DC-8" .. .. .. 70 50
878 75 c. British Airways "Concorde" at Grantley Adams Airport .. .. .. 85 60
879 $2 Caribbean Air Cargo Boeing "707-351c" .. .. .. .. .. 2·00 2·25
876/9 .. .. .. .. .. *Set of* 4 3·50 3·25

**191** Assembly Chamber

**192** Brown Hare

(Des A. Edmonston. Litho B.D.T.)

**1989** (19 July). *350th Anniv of Parliament. T* **191** *and similar square designs.* W w **16**. *P* 13½.

880 25 c. multicoloured .. .. .. .. 30 20
881 50 c. multicoloured .. .. .. .. 45 35
882 75 c. deep slate-blue and brownish black .. 70 50
883 $2.50, multicoloured .. .. .. .. 1·75 2·00
880/3 .. .. .. .. .. *Set of* 4 3·00 2·75

Designs:—50 c. The Speaker; 75 c. Parliament Buildings, c. 1882; $2.50, Queen Elizabeth II and Prince Philip in Parliament.

(Des R. Suffolk. Litho Questa)

**1989** (1 Aug). *Wildlife Preservation. T* **192** *and similar multicoloured designs.* W w **16** *(sideways on 50 c., $2). P* 14×13½ *(vert) or* 13½×14 *(horiz).*

884 10 c. Type **192** .. .. .. .. .. 20 10
885 50 c. Red-footed Tortoise *(horiz)* .. .. 50 35
886 65 c. Savanna ("Green") Monkey .. .. 60 45
887 $2 *Bufo marinus* (toad) *(horiz)* .. .. 1·75 1·60
884/7 .. .. .. .. .. *Set of* 4 2·75 2·25
**MS**888 87×97 mm. $1 Small Indian Mongoose 75 80

(Des A. Edmonston. Litho B.D.T.)

**1989** (9 Oct). *35th Commonwealth Parliamentary Conference. Square design as T* **191**. *Multicoloured.* W w **14**. *P* 13½.
**MS**889 108×69 mm. $1 Barbados Mace .. 75 1·00

**193** Bread 'n Cheese

**194** Water Skiing

(Des Rosanne Sanders. Litho Questa)

**1989** (1 Nov). *Wild Plants. T* **193** *and similar vert designs. Multicoloured.* W w **14**. *P* 14½.

890 2 c. Type **193** .. .. .. .. .. 20 30
891 5 c. Scarlet Cordia .. .. .. .. 30 30
892 10 c. Columnar Cactus .. .. .. .. 30 30
893 20 c. Spiderlily .. .. .. .. .. 35 30
894 25 c. Rock Balsam .. .. .. .. 40 35
895 30 c. Hollyhock .. .. .. .. .. 15 20
896 45 c. Yellow Shak-shak .. .. .. .. 55 55
897 50 c. Whitewood .. .. .. .. .. 55 55
898 55 c. Bluebell .. .. .. .. .. 30 35
899 65 c. Prickly Sage .. .. .. .. 75 75
900 70 c. Seaside Samphire .. .. .. .. 40 45
901 80 c. Flat-hand Dildo .. .. .. .. 45 50
902 $1.10, Lent Tree .. .. .. .. 65 70
903 $2.50, Rodwood .. .. .. .. 2·50 2·50
904 $5 Cowitch .. .. .. .. .. 5·00 5·50
905 $10 Maypole .. .. .. .. .. 9·50 11·00
890/905 .. .. .. .. *Set of* 16 20·00 22·00

For similar stamps but watermarked w **16**, see Nos. 921/36.

(Des C. Burke. Litho Harrison)

**1989** (17 Nov). *"World Stamp Expo '89" International Stamp Exhibition, Washington. Watersports. T* **194** *and similar vert designs. Multicoloured.* W w **16**. *P* 14.

906 25 c. Type **194** .. .. .. .. .. 35 25
907 50 c. Yachting .. .. .. .. .. 60 55
908 65 c. Scuba diving .. .. .. .. 80 75
909 $2.50, Surfing .. .. .. .. .. 2·75 3·00
906/9 .. .. .. .. .. *Set of* 4 4·00 4·00

**195** Barbados 1852 1d. Stamp

**196** Bugler and Jockeys

(Des D. Miller. Litho B.D.T.)

**1990** (3 May). *150th Anniv of the Penny Black and "Stamp World London 90" International Stamp Exhibition. T* **195** *and similar vert designs showing stamps.* W w **14**. *P* 14.

910 25 c. dp bluish green, blk & pale yell-ochre 30 20
911 50 c. multicoloured .. .. .. .. 45 35
912 65 c. multicoloured .. .. .. .. 55 50
913 $2.50, multicoloured .. .. .. .. 2·25 2·50
910/13 .. .. .. .. .. *Set of* 4 3·25 3·25
**MS**914 90×86 mm. 50 c. multicoloured; 50 c. multicoloured .. .. .. .. .. 95 1·25

Designs:—50 c. 1882 1d. Queen Victoria; 65 c. 1899 2d.; $2.50, 1912 3d.; miniature sheet, 50 c. Great Britain Penny Black, 50 c. Barbados 1906 Nelson Centenary 1s.

(Adapted G. Vasarhelyi. Litho B.D.T.)

**1990** (3 May). *Horse Racing. T* **196** *and similar multicoloured designs.* W w **14** *(sideways on 25, 45 and 75 c.). P* 14.

915 25 c. Type **196** .. .. .. .. .. 35 25
916 45 c. Horse and jockey in parade ring .. 50 45
917 75 c. At the finish .. .. .. .. 75 65
918 $2 Leading in the winner *(vert)* .. .. 2·00 2·25
915/18 .. .. .. .. .. *Set of* 4 3·25 3·25

(Des D. Miller. Litho Questa)

**1990** (8 Aug). *90th Birthday of Queen Elizabeth the Queen Mother. Vert designs as T* **134** *(75 c.) or* **135** *($2.50) of Ascension.* W w **16**. *P* 14×15 *(75 c.) or* 14½ *($2.50).*

919 75 c. multicoloured .. .. .. .. 60 45
920 $2.50, black and bronze-green .. .. 1·90 2·10

Designs:—75 c. Lady Elizabeth Bowes-Lyon, April 1923 (from painting by John Lander); $2.50, Lady Elizabeth Bowes-Lyon on her engagement, January 1923.

**1990** (Sept). *As Nos.* 890/4, 896/7, 899, 903/5, *but W* w **16**. *P* 14½.

| No. | Description | | |
|---|---|---|---|
| 921 | 2 c. Type **193** | 10 | 10 |
| 922 | 5 c. Scarlet Cordia | 10 | 10 |
| 923 | 10 c. Columnar Cactus | 10 | 10 |
| 924 | 20 c. Spiderlily | 10 | 15 |
| 925 | 25 c. Rock Balsam | 15 | 20 |
| 927 | 45 c. Yellow Shak-shak | 25 | 30 |
| 928 | 50 c. Whitewood | 30 | 35 |
| 930 | 65 c. Prickly Sage | 40 | 45 |
| 934 | $2.50, Rodwood | 1·40 | 1·50 |
| 935 | $5 Cowitch | 3·00 | 3·25 |
| 936 | $10 Maypole | 5·75 | 6·00 |
| 921/36 | *Set of* 11 | 10·50 | 11·00 |

**197** *Orthemis ferruginea* (dragonfly)

VISIT OF
HRH THE
PRINCESS ROYAL
OCTOBER 1990

(**198**)

(Des I. Loe. Litho Harrison)

**1990** (16 Oct). *Insects. T* **197** *and similar horiz designs. Multicoloured. P* 14.

| No. | Description | | |
|---|---|---|---|
| 937 | 50 c. Type **197** | 35 | 30 |
| 938 | 65 c. *Ligyrus tumulosus* (beetle) | 50 | 45 |
| 939 | 75 c. *Neoconocephalus* sp (grasshopper) | 60 | 50 |
| 940 | $2 *Bostra maxwelli* (stick-insect) | 1·10 | 1·25 |
| 937/40 | *Set of* 4 | 2·25 | 2·25 |

**1990** (21 Nov). *Visit of the Princess Royal. Nos.* 894, 901 *and* 903 *optd with T* **198**.

| No. | Description | | |
|---|---|---|---|
| 941 | 25 c. Rock Balsam | 20 | 15 |
| 942 | 80 c. Flat-hand Dildo | 60 | 60 |
| 943 | $2.50, Rodwood | 1·90 | 2·00 |
| 941/3 | *Set of* 3 | 2·40 | 2·50 |

**199** Star

**200** Adult Male Yellow Warbler

(Des D. Miller. Litho B.D.T.)

**1990** (4 Dec). *Christmas. T* **199** *and similar vert designs. Multicoloured. W* w **14**. *P* 14.

| No. | Description | | |
|---|---|---|---|
| 944 | 20 c. Type **199** | 20 | 15 |
| 945 | 50 c. Figures from crib | 40 | 35 |
| 946 | $1 Stained glass window | 70 | 65 |
| 947 | $2 Angel (statue) | 1·25 | 1·50 |
| 944/7 | *Set of* 4 | 2·25 | 2·40 |

(Des G. Drummond. Litho B.D.T.)

**1991** (4 Mar). *Endangered Species. Yellow Warbler. T* **200** *and similar horiz designs. Multicoloured. W* w **14** (*sideways*). *P* 14.

| No. | Description | | |
|---|---|---|---|
| 948 | 10 c. Type **200** | 20 | 15 |
| 949 | 20 c. Pair feeding chicks in nest | 25 | 20 |
| 950 | 45 c. Female feeding chicks in nest | 45 | 35 |
| 951 | $1 Male with fledgeling | 95 | 95 |
| 948/51 | *Set of* 4 | 1·75 | 1·50 |

**201** Sorting Daily Catch

**202** Masonic Building, Bridgetown

(Des M. Maynard, adapted G. Vasarhelyi. Litho Cartor, France)

**1991** (18 June). *Fishing in Barbados. T* **201** *and similar multicoloured designs. W* w **14** (*sideways on* 50, 75 *c.*). *P* 13½ × 14 (5 *c.*, $2.50) *or* 14 × 13½ (*others*).

| No. | Description | | |
|---|---|---|---|
| 952 | 5 c. Type **201** | 10 | 10 |
| 953 | 50 c. Line fishing (*horiz*) | 40 | 40 |
| 954 | 75 c. Fish cleaning (*horiz*) | 60 | 60 |
| 955 | $2.50, Game fishing | 1·75 | 2·00 |
| 952/5 | *Set of* 4 | 2·50 | 2·75 |

(Des N. Shewring. Litho B.D.T.)

**1991** (17 Sept). *250th Anniv of Freemasonry in Barbados* (1990). *T* **202** *and similar vert designs. W* w **14**. *P* 14.

| No. | Description | | |
|---|---|---|---|
| 956 | 25 c. multicoloured | 15 | 20 |
| 957 | 65 c. multicoloured | 40 | 45 |
| 958 | 75 c. black, greenish yellow & yellow-brown | 45 | 50 |
| 959 | $2.50, multicoloured | 1·40 | 1·50 |
| 956/9 | *Set of* 4 | 2·10 | 2·40 |

Designs:—65 c. Compass and Square (masonic symbols); 75 c. Royal Arch Jewel; $2.50, Ceremonial apron, columns and badge.

**203** *Battus polydamus*

(Des I. Loe. Litho B.D.T.)

**1991** (15 Nov). *"Philanippon '91" International Stamp Exhibition, Tokyo. Butterflies. T* **203** *and similar multicoloured designs. W* w **16** (*sideways on* 20 *c.*, 65 *c.*). *P* 14.

| No. | Description | | |
|---|---|---|---|
| 960 | 20 c. Type **203** | 10 | 15 |
| 961 | 50 c. *Urbanus proteus* (*vert*) | 30 | 35 |
| 962 | 65 c. *Phoebis sennae* | 40 | 45 |
| 963 | $2.50, *Junonia evarete* (*vert*) | 1·40 | 1·50 |
| 960/3 | *Set of* 4 | 2·00 | 2·25 |
| **MS**964 | 87×86 mm. $4 *Vanessa cardui*. Wmk sideways | 2·25 | 2·40 |

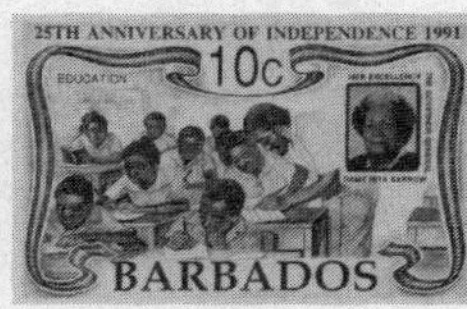


**204** School Class

(Des G. Vasarhelyi. Litho B.D.T.)

**1991** (20 Nov). *25th Anniv of Independence. T* **204** *and similar multicoloured designs. W* w **14** (*sideways*). *P* 14.

| No. | Description | | |
|---|---|---|---|
| 965 | 10 c. Type **204** | 10 | 10 |
| 966 | 25 c. Barbados Workers' Union Labour College | 15 | 20 |
| 967 | 65 c. Building a house | 40 | 45 |
| 968 | 75 c. Sugar cane harvesting | 45 | 50 |
| 969 | $1 Health clinic | 60 | 65 |
| 965/9 | *Set of* 5 | 1·50 | 1·60 |
| **MS**970 | 123 × 97 mm. $2.50, Gordon Greenidge and Desmond Haynes (cricketers) (*vert*). Wmk upright | 1·40 | 1·50 |

POSTAGE DUE STAMPS

D 1

D 2

(Typo D.L.R.)

**1934** (2 Jan)–**47**. *Wmk Mult Script CA. P* 14.

| No. | | Description | | |
|---|---|---|---|---|
| D1 | D 1 | ½d. green (10.2.35) | 50 | 2·00 |
| D2 | | 1d. black | 70 | 70 |
| | | a. Bisected (½d.) (on cover) | † | £500 |
| D3 | | 3d. carmine (13.3.47) | 15·00 | 16·00 |
| D1/3 | | *Set of* 3 | 15·00 | 17·00 |
| D1/3 Perf "Specimen" | | *Set of* 3 | 65·00 | |

The bisected 1d. was officially authorised for use between March 1934 and February 1935. Some specimens had the value "½d." written across the half stamp in red or black ink (*Price on cover* £600).

(Typo D.L.R.)

**1950** (8 Dec)–**53**. *Values in cents. Wmk Mult Script CA. Ordinary paper. P* 14.

| No. | | Description | | |
|---|---|---|---|---|
| D4 | D 1 | 1 c. green | 1·50 | 6·50 |
| | | a. Chalk-surfaced paper. *Deep green* (29.11.51) | 30 | 2·25 |
| | | ab. Error. Crown missing, W **9a** | £120 | |
| | | ac. Error. St. Edward's Crown, W **9b** | £100 | |
| D5 | | 2 c. black | 3·50 | 6·00 |
| | | a. Chalk-surfaced paper (20.1.53) | 40 | 2·00 |
| | | ac. Error. St. Edward's Crown, W **9b** | £120 | |
| D6 | | 6 c. carmine | 9·50 | 12·00 |
| | | a. Chalk-surfaced paper (20.1.53) | 1·50 | 7·00 |
| | | ab. Error. Crown missing, W **9a** | £110 | |
| | | ac. Error. St. Edward's Crown, W **9b** | 95·00 | |
| D4/6 | | *Set of* 3 | 13·00 | 22·00 |
| D4a/6a | | *Set of* 3 | 2·00 | 10·00 |

The 1 c. stamps have no dot below "c".

**1965** (3 Aug)–**68**. *As Nos.* D4/6 *but wmk* w **12** (*upright*). *Chalk-surfaced paper.*

| No. | | Description | | |
|---|---|---|---|---|
| D7 | D 1 | 1 c. deep green | 30 | 2·50 |
| | | *a. Green* | 90 | 3·50 |
| D8 | | 2 c. black | 30 | 2·75 |
| D9 | | 6 c. carmine | 50 | 3·00 |
| | | *a. Carmine-red* (14.5.68) | 1·40 | 6·00 |
| D7/9 | | *Set of* 3 | 1·00 | 7·50 |

The 1 c. has no dot below "c".

**1974** (4 Feb). *As No.* D9 *but W* w **12** (*sideways*). *Glazed, ordinary paper. P* 14 × 13½.

| No. | | Description | | |
|---|---|---|---|---|
| D10 | D 1 | 6 c. carmine | 5·50 | 12·00 |

**1974** (4 Dec). *W* w **12** (*sideways*). *P* 13.

| No. | | Description | | |
|---|---|---|---|---|
| D12 | D 1 | 2 c. black | 3·25 | 10·00 |
| D13 | | 6 c. carmine | 3·25 | 11·00 |

(Des Jennifer Toombs. Litho Questa)

**1976** (12 May)–**85**. *Different floral backgrounds as Type* D **2**. *W* w **14**. *P* 14.

| No. | Description | | |
|---|---|---|---|
| D14 | 1 c. deep mauve and light pink | 10 | 45 |
| | a. Perf 15 × 14 (7.85) | 10 | 10 |
| D15 | 2 c. ultramarine and light cobalt | 10 | 45 |
| | a. Perf 15 × 14 (7.85) | 10 | 10 |
| D16 | 5 c. reddish brown and yellow | 15 | 50 |
| | a. Perf 15 × 14 (7.85) | 10 | 10 |
| D17 | 10 c. royal blue and light lilac | 25 | 55 |
| | a. Perf 15 × 14 (7.85) | 10 | 10 |
| D18 | 25 c. deep green and bright yellow-green | 40 | 75 |
| | a. Perf 15 × 14 (7.85) | 15 | 20 |
| D19 | $1 rose-carmine and rose | 60 | 65 |
| D14/19 | *Set of* 6 | 1·40 | 3·00 |
| D14a/18a | *Set of* 5 | 30 | 35 |

# Barbuda
## (*see after* Antigua)

# Basutoland
## *see* Lesotho

# Batum

Batum, the outlet port on the Black Sea for the Russian Transcaucasian oilfields, was occupied by the Turks on 15 April 1918.

Under the terms of the armistice signed at Mudros on 30 October 1918 the Turks were to withdraw and be replaced by an Allied occupation of Batum, the Baku oilfields and the connecting Transcaucasia Railway. British forces arrived off Batum in early December and the oblast, or district, was declared a British military governorship on 25 December 1918. The Turkish withdrawal was completed five days later.

The provision of a civilian postal service was initially the responsibility of the Batum Town Council. Some form of mail service was in operation by February 1919 with the postage prepaid in cash. Letters are known showing a framed oblong handstamp, in Russian, to this effect. The Town Council was responsible for the production of the first issue, Nos. 1/6, but shortly after these stamps were placed on sale a strike by Council employees against the British military governor led to the postal service being placed under British Army control.

**SURCHARGES**. Types **2** and **4/8** were all applied by handstamp. Most values from No. 19 onwards are known showing the surcharge inverted.

### BRITISH OCCUPATION

**PRICES FOR STAMPS ON COVER**

| | |
|---|---|
| Nos. 1/6 | *from* × 60 |
| Nos. 7/10 | *from* × 15 |
| Nos. 11/18 | *from* × 60 |
| Nos. 19/20 | *from* × 15 |
| Nos. 21/44 | — |
| Nos. 45/53 | *from* × 200 |

1 Aloe Tree

БАТУМ. ОБ.

Руб 10 Руб

(2)

**1919** (4 Apr). *Litho. Imperf.*

| No. | Type | Description | Unused | Used |
|---|---|---|---|---|
| 1 | 1 | 5 k. green | 2·25 | 3·00 |
| 2 | | 10 k. ultramarine | 2·25 | 3·00 |
| 3 | | 50 k. yellow | 60 | 80 |
| 4 | | 1 r. chocolate | 85 | 1·10 |
| 5 | | 3 r. violet | 4·00 | 4·50 |
| 6 | | 5 r. brown | 5·00 | 5·50 |

Nos. 1/6 were printed in sheets of 198 (18×11).

**1919** (13 Apr). *Russian stamps (Arms types) handstamped with T* **2**.

| No. | Description | Unused | Used |
|---|---|---|---|
| 7 | 10 r. on 1 k. orange (*imperf*) | 15·00 | 17·00 |
| 8 | 10 r. on 3 k. carmine-red (*imperf*) | 8·00 | 9·50 |
| 9 | 10 r. on 5 k. brown-lilac (*perf*) | £140 | £140 |
| 10 | 10 r. on 10 on 7 k. deep blue (*perf*) | £140 | £140 |

A similar handstamped surcharge, showing the capital letters without serifs, is bogus.

BRITISH
OCCUPATION

(3)

**1919** (10 Nov.) *Colours changed and new values. Optd with T* **3**.

| No. | Type | Description | Unused | Used |
|---|---|---|---|---|
| 11 | 1 | 5 k. yellow-green | 4·00 | 4·50 |
| 12 | | 10 k. bright blue | 4·00 | 4·50 |
| 13 | | 25 k. orange-yellow | 3·50 | 4·00 |
| 14 | | 1 r. pale blue | 2·25 | 2·75 |
| 15 | | 2 r. pink | 60 | 80 |
| 16 | | 3 r. bright violet | 60 | 80 |
| 17 | | 5 r. brown | 85 | 1·10 |
| | | a. "CCUPATION" (R.5/1) | £120 | |
| 18 | | 7 r. brownish red | 2·00 | 2·50 |

Nos. 11/18 were printed in sheets of 432 (18×24).

(4)

БАТУМЪ
BRITISH
P. 15 P.
OCCUPATION
ОБЛ.

(5)

**1919** (27 Nov)–**20**. *Russian stamps (Arms types) handstamped with T* **4** *or* **5**. *Imperf.*

| No. | Description | Unused | Used |
|---|---|---|---|
| 19 | 10 r. on 3 k. carmine-red | 7·00 | 8·00 |
| 20 | 15 r. on 1 k. orange | 20·00 | 20·00 |
| | a. Red surch | 18·00 | 18·00 |
| | b. Violet surch (10.3.20) | 23·00 | 23·00 |

Nos. 20a/b have the handstamp in soluble ink. One example of No. 20a is recorded with double surcharge.

**1920** (12 Jan). *Russian stamps (Arms types) handstamped as T* **4**.

| No. | Description | Unused | Used |
|---|---|---|---|
| | *(a) Imperf* | | |
| 21 | 50 r. on 1 k. orange | £110 | £110 |
| 22 | 50 r. on 2 k. yellow-green (R.) | £160 | £160 |
| | *(b) Perf* | | |
| 23 | 50 r. on 2 k. yellow-green | £160 | £160 |
| 24 | 50 r. on 3 k. carmine-red | £350 | £350 |
| 25 | 50 r. on 4 k. red | £250 | £250 |
| 26 | 50 r. on 5 k. brown-lilac | £160 | £160 |
| 27 | 50 r. on 10 k. deep blue (R.) | £600 | £600 |
| 28 | 50 r. on 15 k. blue and red-brown | £160 | £160 |

(6)

**1920** (30 Jan–21 Feb). *Russian stamps (Arms types) handstamped as T* **6**. *(a) Perf*

| No. | Description | Unused | Used |
|---|---|---|---|
| 29 | 25 r. on 5 k. brown-lilac (21 Feb) | 16·00 | 17·00 |
| | a. Blue surch | 17·00 | 17·00 |
| 30 | 25 r. on 10 on 7 k. blue (21 Feb) | 48·00 | 48·00 |
| | a. Blue surch | 25·00 | 25·00 |
| 31 | 25 r. on 20 on 14 k. dp carmine & bl (21 Feb) | 26·00 | 26·00 |
| | a. Blue surch | 25·00 | 25·00 |
| 32 | 25 r. on 25 k. deep violet & lt green (21 Feb) | 48·00 | 48·00 |
| | a. Blue surch | 38·00 | 38·00 |
| 33 | 25 r. on 50 k. green and copper-red (21 Feb) | 25·00 | 25·00 |
| | a. Blue surch | 26·00 | 26·00 |
| 34 | 50 r. on 2 k. yellow-green | 38·00 | 38·00 |
| 35 | 50 r. on 3 k. carmine-red | 38·00 | 38·00 |
| 36 | 50 r. on 4 k. red | 35·00 | 35·00 |
| 37 | 50 r. on 5 k. brown-lilac | 26·00 | 26·00 |
| | *(b) Imperf* | | |
| 38 | 50 r. on 2 k. yellow-green | £110 | £110 |
| 39 | 50 r. on 3 k. carmine-red | £130 | £130 |
| 40 | 50 r. on 5 k. brown-lilac | £650 | £650 |

**1920** (10 Mar). *Romanov issue, as T* **25** *of Russia, handstamped with T* **6**.

| No. | Description | Unused | Used |
|---|---|---|---|
| 41 | 50 r. on 4 k. rose-carmine (B.) | 23·00 | 26·00 |

РУБ 25 ЛЕЙ

25 РУБ. 25

(7)

R.50R.
BRITISH
OCCUPATION
РУБ.

(8)

**1920** (1 Apr). *Nos.* 3, 11 *and* 13 *handstamped with T* **7** *(Nos. 42/3) or* **8** *(No. 44).*

| No. | Description | Unused | Used |
|---|---|---|---|
| 42 | 25 r. on 5 k. yellow-green | 11·00 | 11·00 |
| | a. Blue surch | 12·00 | 12·00 |
| 43 | 25 r. on 25 k. orange-yellow | 9·00 | 9·00 |
| | a. Blue surch | 32·00 | 32·00 |
| 44 | 50 r. on 50 k. yellow | 8·00 | 8·00 |
| | a. "50" cut | 6·00 | 6·00 |
| | b. Blue surch | 28·00 | 28·00 |
| | ba. "50" cut | 55·00 | 55·00 |

Nos. 44a and 44ba show the figures broken by intentional file cuts applied as a protection against forgery. The "5" is cut at the base and on the right side of the loop. The "0" is chipped at top and foot, and has both vertical lines severed.

**1920** (19 June). *Colours changed and new values. Optd with T* **3**. *Imperf.*

| No. | Type | Description | Unused | Used |
|---|---|---|---|---|
| 45 | 1 | 1 r. chestnut | 30 | 1·10 |
| | | a. "BPITISH" | 27·00 | |
| 46 | | 2 r. pale blue | 40 | 1·10 |
| | | a. "BPITISH" | 35·00 | |
| 47 | | 3 r. pink | 40 | 1·10 |
| | | a. "BPITISH" | 35·00 | |
| 48 | | 5 r. black-brown | 40 | 1·10 |
| | | a. "BPITISH" | 35·00 | |
| 49 | | 7 r. yellow | 40 | 1·10 |
| | | a. "BPITISH" | 35·00 | |
| 50 | | 10 r. myrtle-green | 40 | 1·10 |
| | | a. "BPITISH" | 35·00 | |
| 51 | | 15 r. violet | 70 | 2·00 |
| | | a. "BPITISH" | 75·00 | |
| 52 | 1 | 25 r. scarlet | 60 | 1·60 |
| | | a. "BPITISH" | 65·00 | |
| 53 | | 50 r. deep blue | 85 | 2·50 |
| | | a. "BPITISH" | £120 | |

Nos. 45/53 were printed in sheets of 308 (22×14). The "BPITISH" error occurs on R. 1/19 of the overprint.

Batum was handed over to the National Republic of Georgia on 7 July 1920.

# Bechuanaland
## *see* Botswana

# Belize
## (*formerly* British Honduras)

### BRITISH HONDURAS

It is recorded that the first local post office was established by the inhabitants in 1809, but Belize did not become a regular packet port of call until 1829. A branch office of the British G.P.O. was established in 1857 and the stamps of Great Britain were supplied for use on overseas mail from 1858.

The colonial authorities took over the postal service on 1 April, 1860, the Great Britain stamps being withdrawn the following month. There was no inland postal service until 1862.

For illustrations of the handstamp and postmark types see BRITISH POST OFFICES ABROAD notes, following GREAT BRITAIN.

### BELIZE

CROWNED-CIRCLE HANDSTAMPS

CC1 CC 1*b* BELIZE (R.)(13.11.1841) .. *Price on cover* £4000

*Stamps of* GREAT BRITAIN *cancelled* "A 06" *as Type* **2**.

**1858** *to* **1860**.

| No. | Description | Price |
|---|---|---|
| Z1 | 1d. rose-red (1857), *perf* 14 | £850 |
| Z2 | 4d. rose (1857) | £350 |
| Z3 | 6d. lilac (1856) | £350 |
| Z4 | 1s. green (1856) | £1300 |

**PRICES FOR STAMPS ON COVER TO 1945**

| | |
|---|---|
| Nos. 1/4 | *from* × 20 |
| Nos. 5/16 | *from* × 25 |
| Nos. 17/22 | *from* × 20 |
| Nos. 23/6 | *from* × 10 |
| Nos. 27/30 | *from* × 15 |
| Nos. 35/42 | *from* × 20 |
| Nos. 43/4 | *from* × 30 |
| Nos. 49/50 | *from* × 25 |
| Nos. 51/69 | *from* × 15 |
| Nos. 80/100 | *from* × 6 |
| Nos. 101/10 | *from* × 5 |
| Nos. 111/20 | *from* × 15 |
| Nos. 121/2 | *from* × 8 |
| No. 123 | *from* × 10 |
| Nos. 124/37 | *from* × 6 |
| Nos. 138/42 | *from* × 10 |
| Nos. 143/9 | *from* × 8 |
| Nos. 150/61 | *from* × 5 |
| Nos. D1/3 | *from* × 30 |

### CROWN COLONY

1

(Typo D.L.R.)

**1865** (1 Dec). *No wmk. P* 14.

| No. | Type | Description | Unused | Used |
|---|---|---|---|---|
| 1 | 1 | 1d. pale blue | 50·00 | 45·00 |
| | | a. Imperf between (pair) | | |
| 2 | | 1d. blue | 55·00 | 45·00 |
| 3 | | 6d. rose | £225 | £100 |
| 4 | | 1s. green | £250 | 95·00 |
| | | a. In horiz pair with 6d. | £15000 | |
| | | b. In vert pair with 1d. | £22000 | |

In the first printing all three values were printed in the same sheet separated by horizontal and vertical gutter margins. The sheet comprised two panes of 60 of the 1d. at the top with a pane of 60 of the 1s. at bottom left and another of 6d. at bottom right. Copies of 1d. *se-tenant* with the 6d. are not known. There were two later printings of the 1d. but they were in sheets without the 6d. and 1s.

**1872–79.** *Wmk Crown CC. (a) P 12½.*
5 1 1d. pale blue 60·00 16·00
6 1d. deep blue (1874) 60·00 16·00
7 3d. red-brown £100 65·00
8 3d. chocolate (1874) £120 80·00
9 6d. rose £160 27·00
9*a* 6d. bright rose-carmine (1874) £275 38·00
10 1s. green £275 28·00
10*a* 1s. deep green (1874) £225 20·00
b. Imperf between (horiz pair) — £13000

*(b) P 14 (1877–79)*
11 1 1d. pale blue (1878) 55·00 15·00
12 1d. blue 50·00 10·00
a. Imperf between (horiz pair) £3500
13 3d. chestnut 85·00 15·00
14 4d. mauve (1879) £120 7·50
15 6d. rose (1878) £275 £160
16 1s. green £160 11·00
a. Imperf between (pair)

**1882–87.** *Wmk Crown CA. P 14.*
17 1 1d. blue (4.84) 38·00 13·00
18 1d. rose (1884) 18·00 11·00
a. Bisected (½d.) (on cover)
19 1d. carmine (1887) 40·00 13·00
20 4d. mauve (7.82) 70·00 3·00
21 6d. yellow (1885) £250 £160
22 1s. grey (1.87) £250 £140
18,22 Optd "Specimen" *Set of* 2 £200

2 CENTS (2) TWO (3) 2 CENTS (4)

**1888** (1 Jan). *Stamps of 1872–79 (wmk Crown CC), surch locally as T* **2**. *(a) P 12½.*
23 1 2 c. on 6d. rose £120 90·00
24 3 c. on 3d. chocolate £9000 £4000

*(b) P 14*
25 1 2 c. on 6d. rose 70·00 65·00
a. Surch double £1100
b. Bisected (1 c.) (on cover) † £160
c. Slanting "2" with curved foot £750
26 3 c. on 3d. chestnut 55·00 55·00
There are very dangerous forgeries of these surcharges.

**1888.** *Stamps of 1882–87 (wmk Crown CA), surch locally as T* **2**, *P 14.*
27 1 2 c. on 1d. rose 7·00 15·00
a. Surch inverted £1100 £1000
b. Surch double £900 £900
c. Bisected (1 c.) (on cover) † £180
28 10 c. on 4d. mauve 30·00 15·00
29 20 c. on 6d. yellow 27·00 30·00
30 50 c. on 1s. grey £325 £450
a. Error. "5" for "50" £6000

Various settings were used for the surcharges on Nos. 23/30, the most common of which was of 36 (6 × 6) impressions. For No. 29 this setting was so applied that an albino surcharge occurs in the margin above each stamp in the first horizontal row.

The same setting was subsequently amended, by altering the "2" to "1", to surcharge the 4d. value. As this was in sheets of 30 it was only necessary to alter the values on the bottom five rows of the setting. Albino surcharges once again occur in the top margin of the sheet, but, as the type in the first horizontal row remained unaltered, these read "20 CENTS" rather than the "10 CENTS" on the actual stamps.

**1888** (Mar). *No. 30 further surch locally with T* **3**.
35 1 "TWO" on 50c. on 1s. grey (R.) 35·00 65·00
a. Bisected (1 c.) (on cover) † £200
b. Surch in black £8000 £7000
c. Surch double (R. + Blk.) £8000 £7000

**1888** (July)–**91**. *Surch in London as T* **4**. *Wmk Crown CA. P 14.*
36 1 1 c. on 1d. dull green (?12.91) 25 85
37 2 c. on 1d. carmine 20 1·25
a. Bisected (1 c.) (on cover) † 90·00
38 3 c. on 3d. red-brown 75 1·25
39 6 c. on 3d. ultramarine (?4.91) 1·10 7·50
40 10 c. on 4d. mauve 1·60 40
a. Surch double £1000
41 20 c. on 6d. yellow (2.89) 7·50 14·00
42 50 c. on 1s. grey (11.88) 17·00 48·00
36/42 *Set of* 7 25·00 65·00
36/42 Optd "Specimen" *Set of* 7 £350

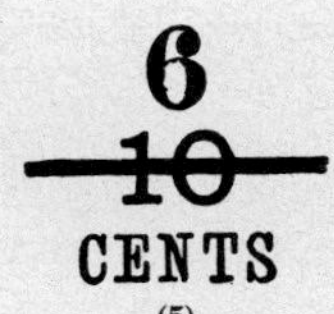

(5)

FIVE (6) 15 (7)

**1891.** *Stamps of 1888–9 surch locally. (a) With T* **5** (May).
43 1 6 c. on 10 c. on 4d. mauve (R.) 40 1·50
a. "6" and bar inverted £375 £375
b. "6" only inverted — £2250
44 6 c. on 10 c. on 4d. mauve (Blk.) 40 1·50
a. "6" and bar inverted £2250 £650
b. "6" only inverted — £2250

Of variety (b) only six copies of each can exist, as one of each of these errors came in the first six sheets, and the mistake was then corrected. Of variety (a) more copies exist.

Essays are known with "SIX" in place of "6", both with and without bars (*price £70 and £375 respectively*). Although not issued, we mention them, as two contemporary covers franked with them are known.

*(b) With T* **6/7** (23 Oct)
49 1 5 c. on 3 c. on 3d. red-brown 40 1·40
a. Wide space between "I" and "V" 45·00 65·00
b. "FIVE" and bar double £190
50 15 c. on 6 c. on 3d. ultramarine (R.) 6·00 17·00
a. Surch double

8

9

10

11

(Typo D.L.R.)

**1891** (July)–**1901**. *Wmk Crown CA. P 14.*
51 8 1 c. dull green (4.95) 80 30
52 2 c. carmine-rose 75 10
a. Repaired "S" at right
53 3 c. brown 3·00 1·25
54 5 c. ultramarine (4.95) 12·00 30
55 11 5 c. grey-black & ultram/*blue* (10.00) 5·50 85
56 8 6 c. ultramarine 3·00 55
57 9 10 c. mauve and green (4.95) 8·50 7·50
58 10 10 c. dull purple and green (1901) 4·00 7·00
59 9 12 c. pale mauve and green 23·00 5·50
*a. Violet and green* 2·50 2·00
60 24 c. yellow and blue 5·50 14·00
*a. Orange and blue* 26·00 48·00
61 25 c. red-brown and green (4.95) 30·00 55·00
62 10 50 c. green and carmine (3.98) 17·00 35·00
63 11 $1 green and carmine (12.99) 35·00 60·00
64 $2 green and ultramarine (12.99) 45·00 75·00
65 $5 green and black (12.99) £190 £250
51/65 *Set of* 15 £300 £450
51/65 Optd "Specimen" *Set of* 15 £300

For illustration of No. 52a see above Gambia No. 37.

**1899** (1 July). *Optd* "REVENUE" A. *Opt* 12 *mm long.* B. *Opt* 11 *mm long.*

| | | A | | B | |
|---|---|---|---|---|---|
| 66 | 5 c. (No. 54) | 3·25 | 2·00 | 8·00 | 6·50 |
| | a. "BEVENUE" | 65·00 | 75·00 | † | |
| 67 | 10 c. (No. 57) | 3·00 | 11·00 | 18·00 | 35·00 |
| | a. "BEVENUE" | £180 | — | † | |
| | b. "REVENU" | — | — | £350 | £375 |
| 68 | 25 c. (No. 61) | 2·75 | 20·00 | 4·00 | 28·00 |
| | a. "BEVENUE" | £120 | £190 | † | |
| | b. "REVE UE" | — | — | † | |
| 69 | 50 c. (No. 42) | £120 | £225 | £180 | £300 |
| | a. "BEVENUE" | £2500 | — | † | |

Two minor varieties, a small "U" and a tall, narrow "U" are found in the word "REVENUE".

The overprint setting of 60 (6 × 10) contained 43 examples of the 12 mm size and 17 of the 11 mm. The smaller size overprints occur on R.8/1, R8/3 to 6 and on all positions in Rows 9 and 10.

The "BEVENUE" error appears on R.6/4 and, it is believed, "REVE UE" comes from R.6/6. Both occur on parts of the printing only. The missing "E" developed during the overprinting and damage to this letter can be observed on at least eight positions in the setting. Examples of No. 67b are now known to exist on both sizes of the overprint.

14

15

(Typo D.L.R.)

**1902** (10 Oct)–**04**. *Wmk Crown CA. P 14.*
80 14 1 c. grey-green and green (28.4.04) 1·75 13·00
81 2 c. purple and black/*red* (18.3.03) 60 25
82 5 c. grey-black and blue/*blue* 2·25 30
83 15 20 c. dull and bright purple (28.4.04) 3·00 14·00
80/3 *Set of* 4 7·00 25·00
80/3 Optd "Specimen" *Set of* 4 70·00

**1904** (Dec)–**07**. *Wmk Mult Crown CA. Ordinary paper* (1, 2 c.) *or chalk-surfaced paper (others). P* 14.
84 14 1 c. grey-green and green (8.05) 90 1·50
a. Chalk-surfaced paper (1906) 50 90
85 2 c. purple and black/*red* 1·50 20
a. Chalk-surfaced paper (1906) 50 10
86 14 5 c. grey-black and blue/*blue* (5.2.06) 1·75 20
87 15 10 c. dull purple & emerald-green (20.9.07) 4·00 9·50
89 25 c. dull purple and orange (20.9.07) 6·00 29·00
90 50 c. grey-green and carmine (20.9.07) 10·00 45·00
91 14 $1 grey-green and carmine (20.9.07) 28·00 55·00
92 $2 grey-green and blue (20.9.07) 60·00 £100
93 $5 grey-green and black (20.9.07) £180 £250
84/93 *Set of* 9 £250 £425
87/93 Optd "Specimen" *Set of* 6 £225

**1908** (7 Dec)–**11**. *Colours changed. Wmk Mult Crown CA. Chalk-surfaced paper* (25 c.). *P* 14.
95 14 1 c. blue-green (1.7.10) 3·25 20
96 2 c. carmine 2·25 10
97 5 c. ultramarine (1.6.09) 1·75 10
100 15 25 c. black/*green* (14.10.11) 2·75 35·00
95/100 *Set of* 4 9·00 35·00
96/100 Optd "Specimen" *Set of* 3 70·00

16

17

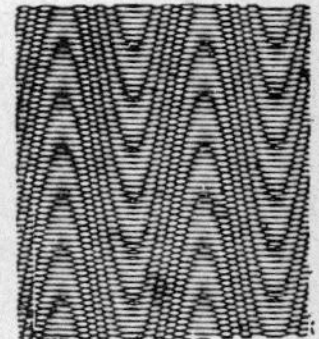

(18)

**1913–21.** *Wmk Mult Crown CA. Chalk-surfaced paper* (10 c. *to* $5). *P* 14.
101 16 1 c. blue-green 40 15
*a. Yellow-green* (13.3.17) 1·75 85
102 2 c. red 1·00 75
*a. Bright scarlet* (1915) 1·10 25
*b. Dull scarlet* (8.17) 2·50 1·25
*c. Red/bluish* 6·00 4·50
103 3 c. orange (16.4.17) 30 15
104 5 c. bright blue 2·00 30
105 17 10 c. dull purple and yellow-green 2·75 6·50
*a. Dull purple and bright green* (1917) 6·00 14·00
106 25 c. black/*green* 1·25 9·00
*a. On blue-green, olive back* (8.17) 2·00 7·00
*b. On emerald back* (1921) 1·75 20·00
107 50 c. purple and blue/*blue* 4·00 9·00
108 16 $1 black and carmine 6·50 19·00
109 $2 purple and green 48·00 55·00
110 $5 purple and black/*red* £170 £190
101/10 *Set of* 10 £200 £250
101/10 Optd "Specimen" *Set of* 10 £250

**1915–16.** *Optd with T* **18**, *in violet.*
111 16 1 c. green (30.12.15) 85 7·50
*a. Yellow-green* (6.6.16) 25 5·00
112 2 c. scarlet (3.11.15) 60 50
113 5 c. bright blue (29.7.15) 25 2·50
111/13 Optd "Specimen" *Set of* 3 £100

These stamps were shipped early in the 1914–18 war, and were thus overprinted, so that if seized by the enemy, they could be distinguished and rendered invalid.

WAR (19) WAR (20)

21

**1916** (23 Aug). *No. 111 optd locally with T* **19**.
114 16 1 c. green 10 30
a. Opt inverted £180 £200

**1917.** *Nos. 101 and 103 optd with T* **19**.
116 16 1 c. blue-green 20 1·25
*a. Yellow-green* 20 1·25
118 3 c. orange 20 1·60
a. Overprint double £300

**1918.** *Nos. 101 and 103 optd with T* **20**.
119 16 1 c. blue-green 10 25
*a. Yellow-green* 1·40 2·50
120 3 c. orange 10 75
119/20 Optd "Specimen" *Set of* 2 £100

(Recess D.L.R.)

**1921** (28 Apr). *Peace Commemoration. Wmk Mult Crown CA (sideways). P* 14.
121 21 2 c. rose-red (Optd S. £45) 1·00 25

**1921** (26 Nov). *Wmk Mult Script CA. P* 14.
122 16 1 c. green (Optd S. £40) 1·25 5·50

**1922** (4 Jan). *As T* **21** *but with words* "PEACE" *omitted. Wmk Mult Script CA (sideways). P* 14.
123 4 c. slate (Optd S. £45) 2·00 25

22

BELIZE RELIEF FUND PLUS 3 CENTS

(23)

(Typo D.L.R.)

**1922** (1 Aug)–**33**. *Ordinary paper* (1 c. *to* 5 c.) *or chalk-surfaced paper* (*others*). *P* 14 (*a*) *Wmk Mult Crown CA*.

124 **22** 25 c. black/*emerald* .. .. .. 3·50 22·00
125 $5 purple and black/*red* (1.10.24) .. £170 £190

(*b*) *Wmk Mult Script CA*

126 **22** 1 c. green (2.1.29) .. .. .. 75 2·00
127 2 c. brown (1.3.23) .. .. .. 30 15
128 2 c. rose-carmine (10.12.26) .. .. 45 10
129 3 c. orange (1933) .. .. .. 4·00 2·50
130 4 c. grey (1.10.29) .. .. .. 90 20
131 5 c. ultramarine .. .. .. 90 55
a. *Milky blue* (1923) .. .. .. 2·75 3·00
132 10 c. dull purple and sage-green (1.12.22) 60 25
133 25 c. black/*emerald* (1.10.24) .. .. 80 4·00
134 50 c. purple and blue/*blue* (1.11.23) .. 2·50 9·00
136 $1 black and scarlet (2.1.25) .. .. 4·00 14·00
137 $2 yellow-green and bright purple .. 27·00 60·00
124/37 .. .. .. .. *Set of* 13 £190 £275
124/37 Optd/Perf "Specimen" .. *Set of* 13 £250

**1932** (2 May). *Belize Relief Fund. Surch as T* **23**. *Wmk Mult Script CA. P* 14.

138 **22** 1 c. + 1 c. green .. .. .. 70 4·50
139 2 c. + 2 c. rose-carmine .. .. .. 75 4·50
140 3 c. + 3 c. orange .. .. .. 85 5·50
141 4 c. + 4 c. grey (R.) .. .. .. 1·50 9·50
142 5 c. + 5 c. ultramarine .. .. .. 4·00 13·00
138/42 .. .. .. .. *Set of* 5 7·00 32·00
138/42 Perf "Specimen" .. .. *Set of* 5 £110

**1935** (6 May). *Silver Jubilee. As Nos.* 91/4 *of Antigua, but ptd by B. W. & Co. P* 11 × 12.

143 3 c. ultramarine and grey-black .. .. 35 45
a. Extra flagstaff .. .. .. 50·00
b. Short extra flagstaff .. .. .. 38·00
c. Lightning conductor .. .. .. 38·00
d. Flagstaff on right-hand turret .. .. 45·00
144 4 c. green and indigo .. .. .. 70 50
a. Extra flagstaff .. .. .. £180
c. Lightning conductor .. .. .. £100
d. Flagstaff on right-hand turret .. .. £100
e. Double flagstaff .. .. .. £100
145 5 c. brown and deep blue .. .. 1·25 60
146 25 c. slate and purple .. .. .. 1·25 1·75
a. Extra flagstaff .. .. .. £250
b. Short extra flagstaff .. .. .. £150
c. Lightning conductor .. .. .. £150
d. Flagstaff on right-hand turret .. .. £150
e. Double flagstaff .. .. .. £150
143/6 .. .. .. .. *Set of* 4 3·25 3·00
143/6 Perf "Specimen" .. .. *Set of* 4 75·00

For illustrations of plate varieties see Catalogue Introduction.

**1937** (12 May). *Coronation. As Nos.* 95/7 *of Antigua, but printed by D.L.R. P* 14.

147 3 c. orange .. .. .. .. 30 25
148 4 c. grey-black .. .. .. .. 60 25
149 5 c. bright blue .. .. .. .. 70 40
147/9 .. .. .. .. *Set of* 3 1·40 80
147/9 Perf "Specimen" .. .. *Set of* 3 50·00

24 Maya Figures

25 Chicle Tapping

(Recess B.W.)

**1938** (10 Jan)–**47**. *T* **24/5** *and similar designs. Wmk Mult Script CA* (*sideways on horizontal stamps*). *P* 11½ × 11 (*horiz designs*) *or* 11 × 11½ (*vert designs*).

150 1 c. bright magenta and green (14.2.38) .. 10 35
151 2 c. black and scarlet (14.2.38) .. .. 10 30
a. Perf 12 (1947) .. .. .. 90 30
152 3 c. purple and brown .. .. .. 10 10
153 4 c. black and green .. .. .. 10 10
154 5 c. mauve and dull blue .. .. .. 10 10
155 10 c. green and reddish brown (14.2.38) .. 35 15
156 15 c. brown and light blue (14.2.38) .. 35 10
157 25 c. blue and green (14.2.38) .. .. 90 45
158 50 c. black and purple (14.2.38) .. .. 4·75 1·40
159 $1 scarlet and olive (28.2.38) .. .. 13·00 3·50
160 $2 deep blue and maroon (28.2.38) .. 14·00 12·00
161 $5 scarlet and brown (28.2.38) .. .. 16·00 19·00
150/61 .. .. .. .. *Set of* 12 45·00 35·00
150/61 Perf "Specimen" .. .. *Set of* 12 £160

Designs: *Vert*—3 c. Cohune palm; $1 Court House, Belize. $2 Mahogany felling; $5 Arms of Colony. *Horiz*—4 c. Local products; 5 c. Grapefruit; 10 c. Mahogany logs in river; 15 c. Sergeant's Cay; 25 c. Dorey; 50 c. Chicle industry.

**1946** (9 Sept). *Victory. As Nos.* 110/11 *of Antigua*.

162 3 c. brown .. .. .. .. 10 10
163 5 c. blue .. .. .. .. 10 10
162/3 Perf "Specimen" .. .. *Set of* 2 50·00

**1948** (1 Oct). *Royal Silver Wedding. As Nos.* 112/13 *of Antigua*.

164 4 c. green .. .. .. .. 15 35
165 $5 brown .. .. .. .. 13·00 28·00

36 Island of St George's Cay

37 H.M.S. *Merlin*

(Recess Waterlow)

**1949** (10 Jan). *150th Anniv of Battle of St. George's Cay. Wmk Mult Script CA. P* 12½.

166 **36** 1 c. ultramarine and green .. .. 10 10
167 3 c. blue and yellow-brown .. .. 10 15
168 4 c. olive and violet .. .. .. 10 20
169 **37** 5 c. brown and deep blue .. .. 20 10
170 10 c. green and red-brown .. .. 20 10
171 15 c. emerald and ultramarine .. .. 20 10
166/71 .. .. .. .. *Set of* 6 65 65

**1949** (10 Oct). *75th Anniv of U.P.U. As Nos.* 114/17 *of Antigua*.

172 4 c. blue-green .. .. .. .. 20 15
173 5 c. deep blue .. .. .. .. 35 15
174 10 c. red-brown .. .. .. .. 45 35
175 25 c. blue .. .. .. .. 50 40
172/5 .. .. .. .. *Set of* 4 1·40 95

**1951** (16 Feb). *Inauguration of B.W.I. University College. As Nos.* 118/19 *of Antigua*.

176 3 c. reddish violet and brown .. .. 35 20
177 10 c. green and brown .. .. .. 35 20

**1953** (2 June). *Coronation. As No.* 120 *of Antigua*.

178 4 c. black and green .. .. .. 15 30

38 Arms of British Honduras

46 Maya Indian

(Recess Waterlow (until 20.6.1961), then D.L.R.)

**1953** (2 Sept)–**62**. *T* **38**, **46** *and similar designs. Wmk Mult Script CA. P* 13½.

179 1 c. green and black .. .. .. 10 20
a. Perf 13½×13 (3.10.61) .. .. 10 20
180 2 c. yellow-brown and black .. .. 10 65
a. Perf 14 (18.9.57) .. .. .. 30 10
b. Perf 13½×13 (20.6.61) .. .. 10 20
181 3 c. reddish violet and bright purple .. 10 10
a. Perf 14 (18.9.57) .. .. .. 10 10
b. Perf 13½×13 (20.6.61) .. .. 1·75 2·75
*ba. Reddish lilac and pale magenta* (19.1.62) .. .. .. .. 45 70
182 4 c. brown and green .. .. .. 20 20
183 5 c. deep olive-green and scarlet .. .. 10 10
a. Perf 14 (15.5.57) .. .. .. 10 10
ab. D.L.R. ptg (3.10.61) .. .. .. 1·50 2·00
184 10 c. slate and bright blue .. .. .. 10 10
a. Perf 13½×13 (19.1.62) .. .. 10 10
185 15 c. green and violet .. .. .. 15 10
186 25 c. bright blue and yellow-brown .. 4·00 1·00
187 50 c. yellow-brown and reddish purple .. 1·75 1·25
*a. Pale yellow-brown & pale pur* (22.3.60) 3·50 1·50
188 $1 slate-blue and red-brown .. .. 4·00 3·25
189 $2 scarlet and grey .. .. .. 6·00 4·00
190 $5 purple and slate .. .. .. 25·00 14·00
179/90 .. .. .. .. *Set of* 12 38·00 22·00

Designs: *Horiz*—2 c. Baird's Tapir ("Mountain Cow"); 3 c. Mace and Legislative Council Chamber, 4 c. Pine industry; 5 c. Spiny Lobster; 10 c. Stanley Field Airport; 15 c. Maya frieze; 25 c. *Morpho peleides* (butterfly); $1 Nine-banded Armadillo; $2 Hawksworth Bridge. *Vert*—$5 Mountain Orchid.

Nos. 179/90 were released a day earlier by the Crown Agents in London.

Stamps from the Waterlow printings perforated 13½ × 13 or 14 have a very fine perforation tooth at the *top* of each vertical side. On the De La Rue printings this tooth is at the *bottom*.

50 "Belize from Fort George, 1842" (C. J. Hullmandel)

51 Public Seals, 1860 and 1960.

52 Tamarind Tree, Newtown Barracks.

(Recess B.W.)

**1960** (1 July). *Post Office Centenary. W w* **12**. *P* 11½ × 11.

191 **50** 2 c. green .. .. .. .. 10 10
192 **51** 10 c. deep carmine .. .. .. 10 10
193 **52** 15 c. blue .. .. .. .. 10 15
191/3 .. .. .. .. *Set of* 3 25 25

NEW CONSTITUTION 1960 (53)

HURRICANE HATTIE (54)

**1961** (1 Mar). *New Constitution. Nos.* 180a, 181a *and* 184/5 *optd with T* **53** *by Waterlow*.

194 2 c. yellow-brown and black .. .. 10 10
195 3 c. reddish violet and bright purple .. 15 10
196 10 c. slate and bright blue .. .. 15 10
197 15 c. green and violet .. .. .. 20 10
194/7 .. .. .. .. *Set of* 4 50 20

**1962** (15 Jan). *Hurricane Hattie Relief Fund. Nos.* 179a, 184a, 186 *and* 187 *optd with T* **54** *by D.L.R.*

198 1 c. green and black .. .. .. 10 10
199 10 c. slate and bright blue .. .. 10 10
200 25 c. bright blue and yellow-brown .. 60 30
201 50 c. yellow-brown and reddish purple .. 25 35
198/201 .. .. .. .. *Set of* 4 85 65

55 Great Curassow

(Des D. R. Eckelberry. Photo Harrison)

**1962** (2 Apr). *Horiz designs on T* **55**. *Multicoloured. W* w **12** (*upright*). *P* 14 × 14½.

202 1 c. Type **55** .. .. .. .. 60 40
a. Orange-yellow (knob) omitted .. ..
203 2 c. Red-legged Honey-creeper .. .. 90 10
a. Turquoise-blue (bird's head) omitted .. £130
204 3 c. Northern Jacana .. .. .. 90 40
a. Blue-green (legs) omitted .. .. £200
205 4 c. Great Kiskadee .. .. .. 1·40 40
206 5 c. Scarlet-rumped Tanager .. .. 1·40 10
207 10 c. Scarlet Macaw .. .. .. 1·40 10
a. Blue omitted .. .. .. £180
208 15 c. Slaty-tailed Trogon .. .. .. 90 10
209 25 c. Red-footed Booby .. .. .. 2·50 30
210 50 c. Keel-billed Toucan .. .. .. 2·50 35
a. Pale blue (claw and beak) omitted ..
211 $1 Magnificent Frigate Bird .. .. 6·00 75
212 $2 Rufous-tailed Jacamar .. .. 8·00 3·00
*a. Shade** .. .. .. .. 20·00 11·00
213 $5 Montezuma Oropendola .. .. 23·00 13·00
202/13 .. .. .. .. *Set of* 12 45·00 17·00

On No. 212*a*, the bird is myrtle-green and red-brown instead of yellow-green and orange-brown.

See also Nos. 239/45.

**1963** (4 June). *Freedom from Hunger. As No.* 146 *of Antigua*.

214 22 c. bluish green .. .. .. 30 15

**1963** (2 Sept). *Red Cross Centenary. As Nos.* 147/8 *of Antigua*.

215 4 c. red and black .. .. .. 10 10
216 22 c. red and blue .. .. .. 30 35

## SELF-GOVERNMENT

SELF GOVERNMENT 1964 (56)

DEDICATION OF SITE NEW CAPITAL 9th OCTOBER 1965 (57)

**1964.** *New Constitution. Nos.* 202, 204/5, 207 *and* 209 *optd with T* **56**.

217 1 c. Type **55** (20.4) .. .. .. 10 10
a. Opt inverted .. .. .. £130
b. Orange-yellow (knob) omitted .. 60·00
218 3 c. Northern Jacana (20.4) .. .. 20 10
219 4 c. Great Kiskadee (3.2) .. .. 20 10
220 10 c. Scarlet Macaw (20.4) .. .. 20 10
221 25 c. Red-footed Booby (3.2) .. .. 30 30
217/21 .. .. .. .. *Set of* 5 90 45

**1965** (17 May). *I.T.U. Centenary. As Nos.* 166/7 *of Antigua*.

222 2 c. orange-red and light green .. .. 10 10
223 50 c. yellow and light purple .. .. 35 25

**1965** (25 Oct). *International Co-operation Year. As Nos.* 168/9 *of Antigua*.

224 1 c. reddish purple and turquoise-green .. 10 10
225 22 c. deep bluish green and lavender .. 15 10

**1966** (24 Jan). *Churchill Commemoration. As Nos.* 170/3 *of Antigua*.

226 1 c. new blue .. .. .. .. 10 10
227 4 c. deep green .. .. .. .. 10 10
228 22 c. brown .. .. .. .. 25 10
229 25 c. bluish violet .. .. .. 30 25
226/9 .. .. .. .. *Set of* 4 60 35

**1966** (1 July). *Dedication of new Capital Site. As Nos.* 202, 204/5, 207 *and* 209 *but wmk sideways, optd with T* **57** *by Harrison*.

230 1 c. Type **55** .. .. .. .. 10 10
a. Orange-yellow (knob) omitted .. .. 60·00
231 3 c. Northern Jacana .. .. .. 20 10
232 4 c. Great Kiskadee .. .. .. 20 10
233 10 c. Scarlet Macaw .. .. .. 25 10
234 25 c. Red-footed Booby .. .. .. 35 30
230/4 .. .. .. .. *Set of* 5 1·00 45

58 Citrus Grove

(Des V. Whiteley. Photo Harrison)

**1966** (1 Oct). *Stamp Centenary. T* **58** *and similar horiz designs. Multicoloured. W* w **12**. *P* 14 × 14½.

235 5 c. Type **58** .. .. .. .. 10 10
236 10 c. Half Moon Cay .. .. .. 10 10
237 22 c. Hidden Valley Falls .. .. .. 10 10
238 25 c. Maya Ruins, Xunantunich .. .. 15 10
235/8 .. .. .. .. *Set of* 4 25 15

**1967.** *As Nos. 202, etc, but wmk sideways.*
239 1 c. Type **55** (16.2) .. .. 10 10
240 2 c. Red-legged Honey-creeper (28.11) .. 20 30
241 4 c. Great Kiskadee (16.2) .. .. 65 30
242 5 c. Scarlet-rumped Tanager (16.2) .. 40 10
243 10 c. Scarlet Macaw (28.11) .. .. 50 10
244 15 c. Slaty-tailed Trogon (28.11) .. .. 60 10
245 50 c. Keel-billed Toucan (16.2) .. .. 2·75 2·75
239/45 .. .. .. *Set of* 7 4·75 3·25
The 15 c. value exists with PVA gum as well as gum arabic.

59 Sailfish

60 *Schomburgkia tibicinis*

(Des R. Granger Barrett. Photo Harrison)

**1967** (1 Dec). *International Tourist Year. T* **59** *and similar horiz designs. W w* **12.** *P* 12½.
246 5 c. deep violet-blue, black and light yellow 10 10
247 10 c. brown, black and orange-red .. .. 10 10
248 22 c. yellow-orange, black and bright green .. 15 10
249 25 c. lt greenish blue, black & greenish yellow 15 15
246/9 .. .. .. *Set of* 4 30 20
Designs:—10 c. Red Brocket; 22 c. Jaguar; 25 c. Tarpon.

(Des Sylvia Goaman, Photo Harrison)

**1968** (16 Apr). *20th Anniv of Economic Commission for Latin America. T* **60** *and similar vert designs. Multicoloured. W w* **12** *(sideways). P* 14½ × 14.
250 5 c. Type **60** .. .. .. 20 10
251 10 c. *Maxillaria tenuifolia* .. .. 25 10
252 22 c. *Bletia purpurea* .. .. 30 10
253 25 c. *Sobralia macrantha* .. .. 40 20
250/3 .. .. .. *Set of* 4 1·10 25

61 Monument to Belizean Patriots

62 Monument at Site of New Capital

(Des G. Vasarhelyi. Litho B.W.)

**1968** (15 July). *Human Rights Year. W w* **12.** *P* 13½.
254 **61** 22 c. multicoloured .. .. 10 10
255 **62** 50 c. multicoloured .. .. 10 10

63 Jew Fish

(Des J. W. Litho D.L.R.)

**1968** (15 Oct). *Wildlife. Horiz designs as T* **63.** *Multicoloured. No wmk. P* 13 × 12½.
256 1 c. Type **63** .. .. .. 10 10
257 2 c. White-lipped Peccary ("Warree") .. 10 10
258 3 c. Grouper .. .. .. 10 10
259 4 c. Collared Anteater .. .. 10 20
260 5 c. Bonefish .. .. .. 10 20
261 10 c. Paca ("Gibnut") .. .. 15 10
262 15 c. Dolphin .. .. .. 30 20
263 25 c. Kinkajou ("Night Walker") .. 30 20
264 50 c. Mutton Snapper .. .. 70 80
265 $1 Tayra ("Bush Dog") .. .. 2·00 1·25
266 $2 Great Barracuda .. .. 2·50 2·00
267 $5 Puma .. .. .. 9·00 6·50
256/67 .. .. .. *Set of* 12 14·00 10·50
See also Nos. 276/8 and 338/40

64 *Rhyncholaelia digbyana*

65 Ziricote Tree

(Des Sylvia Goaman. Photo Harrison)

**1969** (9 Apr). *Orchids of Belize (1st series). T* **64** *and similar vert designs. Multicoloured. W w* **12** *(sideways). P* 14½ × 14.
268 5 c. Type **64** .. .. .. 35 10
269 10 c. *Cattleya bowringiana* .. .. 40 10
270 22 c. *Lycaste cochleatum* .. .. 65 10
271 25 c. *Coryanthes speciosum* .. .. 85 50
268/71 .. .. .. *Set of* 4 2·00 65
See also Nos. 287/90.

(Des V. Whiteley. Litho D.L.R.)

**1969** (1 Sept). *Indigenous Hardwoods (1st series). T* **65** *and similar vert designs. Multicoloured. W w* **12.** *P* 14.
272 5 c. Type **65** .. .. .. 10 10
273 10 c. Rosewood .. .. .. 10 10
274 22 c. Mayflower .. .. .. 15 10
275 25 c. Mahogany .. .. .. 15 20
272/5 .. .. .. *Set of* 4 35 30
See also Nos. 291/4, 315/18 and 333/7.

**1969–72.** *As Nos.* 257/8, 261, 267 *and new value and design* (½ c.), *but W w* **12** *(sideways).*
276 ½ c. Crana Fish (ultramarine background) (1.9.69) .. .. 10 10
277 ½ c. Crana Fish (yellow-olive background) (1.2.71) .. .. 30 35
a. Black (inscr and value) omitted .. £150
277*c* 2 c. White-lipped Peccary (5.5.72) .. 1·75 1·75
277*d* 3 c. Grouper (5.5.72) .. .. 1·75 1·75
277*e* 10 c. Paca (5.5.72) .. .. 2·25 2·25
278 $5 Puma (12.5.70) .. .. 8·00 12·00
276/8 .. .. .. *Set of* 6 13·00 16·00

66 "The Virgin and Child" (Bellini

POPULATION
CENSUS 1970
(68

(Des adapted by G. Drummond. Litho Format)

**1969** (1 Nov). *Christmas. Paintings. T* **66** *and similar vert design. Multicoloured. W w* **12.** *P* 14× 14½.
279 5 c. Type **66** .. .. .. 10 10
280 15 c. Type **66** .. .. .. 10 10
281 22 c. "The Adoration of the Kings" (Veronese) 10 10
282 25 c. As 22 c. .. .. .. 10 10
279/82 .. .. .. *Set of* 4 25 15
Although released by the Crown Agents on 1 October this issue was not put on sale locally until 1 November.

**1970** (2 Feb). *Population Census. As Nos.* 260 *and* 262/3 *but W w* 12 *(sideways) and No.* 277*e optd with T* **68.**
283 5 c. Bonefish .. .. .. 10 10
284 10 c. Paca .. .. .. 10 10
285 15 c. Dolphin .. .. .. 15 10
286 25 c. Kinkajou .. .. .. 15 10
283/6 .. .. .. *Set of* 4 30 20

(Des G. Drummond. Litho Format)

**1970** (2 Apr). *Orchids of Belize (2nd series). As T* **64.** *Multicoloured. W w* **12.** *P* 14.
287 5 c. Black Orchid .. .. .. 30 10
288 15 c. White Butterfly Orchid .. .. 45 10
289 22 c. Swan Orchid .. .. .. 60 10
290 25 c. Butterfly Orchid .. .. 60 30
287/90 .. .. .. *Set of* 4 1·75 50

69 Santa Maria

70 "The Nativity" (A. Hughes).

(Des Jennifer Toombs, Litho Questa)

**1970** (7 Sept). *Indigenous Hardwoods (2nd series). T* **69** *and similar vert designs. Multicoloured. W w* **12** *(sideways). P* 14 × 14½.
291 5 c. Type **69** .. .. .. 15 10
292 15 c. Nargusta .. .. .. 20 10
293 22 c. Cedar .. .. .. 25 10
294 25 c. Sapodilla .. .. .. 30 25
291/4 .. .. .. *Set of* 4 80 45

(Des J. Cooter Litho J.W.)

**1970** (7 Nov*). *Christmas. T* **70** *and similar vert design. Multicoloured. W w* **12.** *P* 14.
295 ½ c. Type **70** .. .. .. 10 10
296 5 c. "The Mystic Nativity" (Botticelli) .. 10 10
297 10 c. Type **70** .. .. .. 10 10
298 15 c. As 5 c .. .. .. 10 10
299 22 c. Type **70** .. .. .. 15 10
300 50 c. As 5 c. .. .. .. 25 30
295/300 .. .. .. *Set of* 6 45 40
*These stamps were released by the Crown Agents in London on 2 November.

71 Legislative Assembly House

(Des. G. Drummond. Litho Enschedé)

**1971** (30 Jan). *Establishment of New Capital, Belmopan. T* **71** *and similar horiz designs. Multicoloured. W w* **12** *upright* (5 c., 10 c.) *or sideways (others). P* 13 × 13½.
301 5 c. Old Capital, Belize .. .. 10 10
302 10 c. Government Plaza .. .. 10 10
303 15 c. Type **71** .. .. .. 10 10
304 22 c. Magistrates' Court .. .. 15 10
305 25 c. Police H.Q. .. .. .. 15 15
306 50 c. New G.P.O. .. .. .. 25 40
301/6 .. .. .. *Set of* 6 70 75
The 5 c. and 10 c. are larger, 60 × 22 mm.

72 *Tabebuia chrysantha*

(Des Sylvia Goaman. Litho Questa)

**1971** (27 Mar). *Easter. T* **72** *and similar horiz designs showing flowers. Multicoloured. W w* **12** *(sideways). P* 14.
307 ½ c. Type **72** .. .. .. 10 10
308 5 c. *Hymenocallis littoralis* .. .. 10 10
309 10 c. *Hippeastrum equestre* .. .. 10 10
310 15 c. Type **72** .. .. .. 10 10
311 22 c. As 5 c. .. .. .. 10 10
312 25 c. As 10 c. .. .. .. 15 20
307/12 .. .. .. *Set of* 6 35 40

RACIAL EQUALITY
YEAR-1971
(73)

74 Tubroos

**1971** (14 June). *Racial Equality Year. As No.* 264, *but W w* **12** *(sideways) and No.* 277*e optd with T* **73.**
313 10 c. Paca .. .. .. 15 10
314 50 c. Mutton Snapper .. .. 25 20

(Des Jennifer Toombs, Litho Questa)

**1971** (16 Aug). *Indigenous Hardwoods (3rd series). T* **74** *and similar vert designs. Multicoloured. W w* **12.** *P* 13½.
315 5 c. Type **74** .. .. .. 25 10
316 15 c. Yemeri .. .. .. 35 30
317 26 c. Billywebb .. .. .. 55 35
318 50 c. Logwood .. .. .. 1·10 1·25
315/18 .. .. .. *Set of* 4 2·00 1·75
**MS**319 96 × 171 mm. Nos. 315/18 .. 3·00 5·50
a. Silver (Queen's head) omitted .. £1200

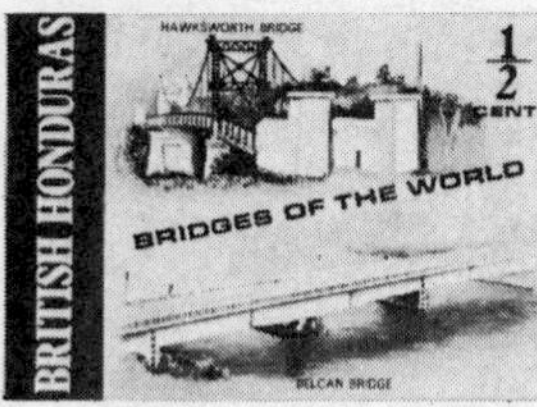

75 Hawksworth and Belcan Bridges

(Des and litho J.W.)

**1971** (23 Sept). *Bridges of the World. T* **75** *and similar horiz designs. Multicoloured. W w* **12** *(sideways). P* 13½.
320 ½ c. Type **75** .. .. .. 10 10
321 5 c. Narrows Bridge, N.Y. and Quebec Bridge 10 10
322 26 c. London Bridge (1871) and reconstructed, Arizona (1971) .. .. 20 10
323 50 c. Belize Mexican Bridge and Swing Bridge 30 35
320/3 .. .. .. *Set of* 4 50 40

76 *Petrae volubis*

77 Seated Figure

(Des G. Drummond. Litho Format)

**1972** (28 Feb). *Easter. T* **76** *and similar vert designs showing wild flowers. Multicoloured. W* w **12**. *P* 14½.

| | | | |
|---|---|---|---|
| 324 | 6 c. Type **76** | 15 | 10 |
| 325 | 15 c. Yemeri | 35 | 30 |
| 326 | 26 c. Mayflower | 50 | 45 |
| 327 | 50 c. Tiger's Claw | 80 | 70 |
| 324/7 | *Set of* 4 | 1·60 | 1·40 |

(Des Jennifer Toombs. Litho Questa)

**1972** (22 May). *Mayan Artefacts. T* **77** *and similar multicoloured designs. W* w **12** *(sideways except 16 c.). P* 13½ × 13 *(16 c.) or* 13 × 13½ *(others).*

| | | | |
|---|---|---|---|
| 328 | 3 c. Type **77** | 10 | 10 |
| 329 | 6 c. Priest in "dancing" pose | 15 | 10 |
| 330 | 16 c. Sun God's head *(horiz)* | 25 | 15 |
| 331 | 26 c. Priest and Sun God | 40 | 20 |
| 332 | 50 c. Full-front figure | 70 | 1·10 |
| 328/32 | *Set of* 5 | 1·40 | 1·40 |

Nos. 328/32 are inscribed on the reverse with information about the artefacts depicted.

78 Banak

79 Orchids of Belize

(Des Jennifer Toombs. Litho Questa)

**1972** (21 Aug). *Indigenous Hardwoods (4th series). T* **78** *and similar vert designs. Multicoloured. W* w **12** *(sideways). P* 14½.

| | | | |
|---|---|---|---|
| 333 | 3 c. Type **78** | 10 | 10 |
| 334 | 5 c. Quamwood | 10 | 10 |
| 335 | 16 c. Waika Chewstick | 25 | 15 |
| 336 | 26 c. Mamee-Apple | 45 | 20 |
| 337 | 50 c. My Lady | 80 | 1·10 |
| 333/7 | *Set of* 5 | 1·50 | 1·40 |

**1972** (17 Nov). *As Nos.* 258 *and* 260/1, *but W* w **12** *(upright).*

| | | | |
|---|---|---|---|
| 338 | 3 c. Grouper | 65 | 85 |
| 339 | 5 c. Bonefish | 75 | 1·00 |
| 340 | 10 c. Paca | 80 | 1·40 |
| 338/40 | *Set of* 3 | 2·00 | 3·00 |

(Des (from photograph by D. Groves) and photo Harrison)

**1972** (20 Nov). *Royal Silver Wedding. Multicoloured; background colour given. W* w **12**. *P* 14 × 14½.

| | | | |
|---|---|---|---|
| 341 **79** | 26 c. deep myrtle-green | 25 | 10 |
| 342 | 50 c. bright bluish violet | 40 | 40 |

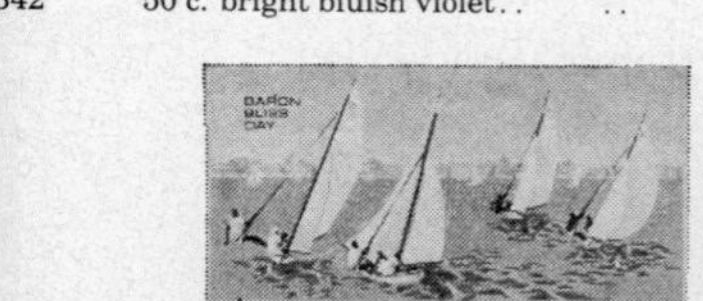


80 Baron Bliss Day

(Des J.W. Litho Questa)

**1973** (9 Mar). *Festivals of Belize. T* **80** *and similar horiz designs. Multicoloured. W* w **12**. *P* 14½ × 14.

| | | | |
|---|---|---|---|
| 343 | 3 c. Type **80** | 10 | 10 |
| 344 | 10 c. Labour Day | 15 | 10 |
| 345 | 26 c. Carib Settlement Day | 20 | 15 |
| 346 | 50 c. Pan American Day | 35 | 60 |
| 343/6 | *Set of* 4 | 65 | 75 |

## BELIZE

British Honduras was renamed Belize on 1 June 1973.

**✲BELIZE✲**

(81)

**1973** (11 June*). *As Nos.* 277/*b*, 278, 256, 259, 262/6 *and* 338/40 *optd with T* **81** *in black on silver by D.L.R. W* w **12** *(upright). P* 13×12½.

| | | | |
|---|---|---|---|
| 347 | ½ c. Crana | 10 | 10 |
| 348 | 1 c. Jew Fish | 10 | 10 |
| 349 | 2 c. White-lipped Peccary ("Waree") | 10 | 10 |
| 350 | 3 c. Grouper | 10 | 10 |
| | a. Silver background to opt omitted | † | — |
| 351 | 4 c. Collared Anteater | 10 | 10 |
| 352 | 5 c. Bone Fish | 10 | 10 |
| 353 | 10 c. Paca ("Gibnut") | 15 | 15 |
| | a. Black (value etc. omitted) | £200 | |
| 354 | 15 c. Dolphin | 20 | 20 |
| 355 | 25 c. Kinkajou ("Night Walker") | 35 | 35 |
| 356 | 50 c. Mutton Snapper | 55 | 55 |
| 357 | $1 Tayra ("Bush Dog") | 90 | 1·25 |
| 358 | $2 Great Barracuda | 1·75 | 2·00 |
| 359 | $5 Puma | 2·50 | 3·75 |
| 347/59 | *Set of* 13 | 6·00 | 8·00 |

*This is the local date of issue: the Crown Agents released the stamps on 1 June.

No. 350a shows the silver background to the overprint omitted. Traces of the adhesive used to apply the silver are visible.

**1973** (14 Nov). *Royal Wedding. As Nos.* 165/6 *of Anguilla. Centre multicoloured. W* w **12** *(sideways). P* 13½.

| | | | |
|---|---|---|---|
| 360 | 26 c. light turquoise-blue | 15 | 10 |
| 361 | 50 c. ochre | 15 | 20 |

82 Crana

**1974** (1 Jan). *Designs as Nos.* 256/67 *and* 277, *but inscr* "BELIZE" *as in T* **82**. *W* w **12**. *P* 13½.

| | | | |
|---|---|---|---|
| 362 | ½ c. Type **82** | 10 | 10 |
| 363 | 1 c. Jew Fish | 10 | 10 |
| 364 | 2 c. White-lipped Peccary ("Waree") | 10 | 10 |
| 365 | 3 c. Grouper | 10 | 10 |
| 366 | 4 c. Collared Anteater | 10 | 10 |
| 367 | 5 c. Bone Fish | 10 | 10 |
| 368 | 10 c. Paca ("Gibnut") | 15 | 15 |
| 369 | 15 c. Dolphin | 20 | 20 |
| 370 | 25 c. Kinkajou ("Night Walker") | 35 | 35 |
| 371 | 50 c. Mutton Snapper | 60 | 70 |
| 372 | $1 Tayra ("Bush Dog") | 1·00 | 1·50 |
| 373 | $2 Great Barracuda | 1·50 | 2·00 |
| 374 | $5 Puma | 3·50 | 5·00 |
| 362/74 | *Set of* 13 | 7·00 | 9·00 |

83 Deer

(Des Mrs. Hosek; adapted PAD Studio, Litho Questa)

**1974** (1 May). *Mayan Artefacts (1st series). T* **83** *and similar horiz designs showing pottery motifs. Multicoloured. W* w **12**. *P* 14½.

| | | | |
|---|---|---|---|
| 375 | 3 c. Type **83** | 10 | 10 |
| 376 | 6 c. Jaguar deity | 15 | 10 |
| 377 | 16 c. Sea monster | 20 | 10 |
| 378 | 26 c. Cormorant | 30 | 10 |
| 379 | 50 c. Scarlet macaw | 50 | 40 |
| 375/9 | *Set of* 5 | 1·10 | 65 |

See also Nos. 398/402.

84 *Parides arcas*

(Des J. Cooter from the collection of P. T. Hill. Litho Harrison)

**1974** (2 Sept)–**75**. *Butterflies. Horiz designs as T* **84**. *Multicoloured. W* w **12** *(sideways). P* 14 (½, 1, 2, 3, 4, 5, 10, 26 c.) *or* 14 × 14½ *(others).*

| | | | |
|---|---|---|---|
| 380 | ½ c. Type **84** | 40 | 50 |
| 381 | 1 c. *Evenus regalis* | 45 | 40 |
| 382 | 2 c. *Colobura dirce* | 40 | 45 |
| 383 | 3 c. *Catonephele numilia* | 40 | 45 |
| 384 | 4 c. *Battus belus* | 45 | 50 |
| 385 | 5 c. *Callicore patelina* | 85 | 45 |
| 386 | 10 c. *Diaethria astala* | 70 | 35 |
| 387 | 15 c. *Nessaea aglaura* | 1·75 | 1·50 |
| 388 | 16 c. *Prepona pseudojoiceyi* | 1·75 | 1·75 |
| 389 | 25 c. *Papilio thoas* | 1·75 | 35 |
| 390 | 26 c. *Hamadryas arethusa* | 2·50 | 4·25 |
| 391 | 50 c. *Panthiades bathildis* | 1·50 | 50 |
| 392 | $1 *Caligo uranus* | 3·50 | 1·50 |
| 393 | $2 *Heliconius sapho* | 3·00 | 1·25 |
| 394 | $5 *Eurytides philolaus* | 3·75 | 4·00 |
| 395 | $10 *Philaethria dido* (2.1.75) | 10·00 | 4·00 |
| 380/95 | *Set of* 16 | 30·00 | 20·00 |

See also Nos. 403/13 and 426/33.

**ALTERED CATALOGUE NUMBERS**

Any Catalogue numbers altered from the last edition are shown as a list in the introductory pages.

85 Churchill when Prime Minister, and Coronation Scene

86 The Actun Balam Vase

(Des J.W. Litho Questa)

**1974** (30 Nov). *Birth Centenary of Sir Winston Churchill. T* **85** *and similar horiz design. Multicoloured. W* w **14** *(sideways). P* 14.

| | | | |
|---|---|---|---|
| 396 | 50 c. Type **85** | 20 | 20 |
| 397 | $1 Churchill in stetson, and Williamsburg Liberty Bell | 30 | 30 |

(Des Mrs. Hosek; adapted P. Powell. Litho Questa)

**1975** (2 June). *Mayan Artefacts (2nd series). T* **86** *and similar vert designs showing decorated vessels. Multicoloured. W* w **14**. *P* 14.

| | | | |
|---|---|---|---|
| 398 | 3 c. Type **86** | 10 | 10 |
| 399 | 6 c. Seated figure | 10 | 10 |
| 400 | 16 c. Costumed priest | 20 | 10 |
| 401 | 26 c. Head with headdress | 25 | 20 |
| 402 | 50 c. Layman and priest | 35 | 40 |
| 398/402 | *Set of* 5 | 85 | 75 |

**1975–78**. *As Nos.* 380, 382/7 *and* 389 *and new value (35 c.), but W* w **14** *(sideways on* ½, 2, 3, 4, 5, 10 *and* 35 *c.). P* 14 × 14½ *(15, 25 c.) or* 14 *(others).*

| | | | |
|---|---|---|---|
| 403 | ½ c. Type **84** (11.6.75) | 1·25 | 1·75 |
| 405 | 2 c. *Colobura dirce* (17.5.77) | 35 | 45 |
| 406 | 3 c. *Catonephele numulia* (17.5.77) | 85 | 40 |
| 407 | 4 c. *Battus belus* (7.3.77) | 1·75 | 30 |
| 408 | 5 c. *Callicore patelina* (11.2.77) | 2·00 | 30 |
| 409 | 10 c. *Diaethria astala* (11.2.77) | 2·00 | 30 |
| 410 | 15 c. *Nessaea aglaura* (17.5.77) | 75 | 45 |
| 412 | 25 c. *Papilio thoas* (27.1.78) | 95 | 40 |
| 413 | 35 c. Type **84** (25.7.77) | 4·50 | 3·75 |
| 403/13 | *Set of* 9 | 13·00 | 7·25 |

**1975–77**. *As Nos.* 387, 389, 391 *and* 394 *but W* w **12** *upright.*

| | | | |
|---|---|---|---|
| 426 | 15 c. *Nessaea aglaura* (20.10.75) | 70 | 1·10 |
| 428 | 25 c. *Papilio thoas* (7.3.77) | 1·50 | 1·00 |
| 429 | 50 c. *Panthiades bathildis* (7.3.77) | 2·75 | 1·60 |
| 433 | $5 *Eurytides philolaus* (20.10.75) | 5·50 | 7·00 |
| 426/33 | *Set of* 4 | 9·50 | 9·50 |

87 Musicians

(Des PAD Studio. Litho Harrison)

**1975** (17 Nov). *Christmas. T* **87** *and similar multicoloured designs. W* w **12** *(upright on 6 c. 26 c.) or sideways (others). P* 14 × 14½ *(horiz) or* 14½ × 14 *(vert).*

| | | | |
|---|---|---|---|
| 435 | 6 c. Type **87** | 10 | 10 |
| 436 | 26 c. Children and "crib" | 15 | 10 |
| 437 | 50 c. Dancer and drummers *(vert)* | 25 | 20 |
| | a. Imperf (pair) | £100 | |
| 438 | $1 Family and map *(vert)* | 45 | 50 |
| 435/8 | *Set of* 4 | 85 | 75 |

88 William Wrigley Jr. and Chicle Tapping

(Des PAD Studio. Litho Questa)

**1976** (29 Mar). *Bicentenary of American Revolution. T* **88** *and similar horiz designs. Multicoloured. W* w **14** *(sideways). P* 14.

| | | | |
|---|---|---|---|
| 439 | 10 c. Type **88** | 10 | 10 |
| 440 | 35 c. Charles Lindbergh and *Spirit of St. Louis* | 25 | 40 |
| 441 | $1 J. L. Stephens (archaeologist) | 60 | 1·00 |
| 439/41 | *Set of* 3 | 85 | 1·40 |

89 Cycling

(Des J.W. Litho Walsall)

**1976** (17 July). *Olympic Games, Montreal. T* **89** *and similar horiz designs. Multicoloured. W* w **14** *(sideways). P* 14.

| | | | |
|---|---|---|---|
| 442 | 35 c. Type **89** | 15 | 10 |
| 443 | 45 c. Running | 20 | 15 |
| 444 | $1 Shooting | 35 | 50 |
| 442/4 | *Set of* 3 | 65 | 65 |

20c

5c

(90) (91)

**1976** (30 Aug). *No. 390 surch with T* **90** *by Harrison.*
445 20 c. on 26 c. *Hamadryas arethusa* .. .. 50 80

**1976** (18 Oct). *West Indian Victory in World Cricket Cup. As Nos. 559/60 of Barbados.*
446 35 c. Map of the Caribbean .. .. 50 50
447 $1 The Prudential Cup .. .. 1·10 1·75

**1976** (2 Dec). *No. 426 surch with T* **91** *by the Govt Printery, Belize.*
448 5 c. on 15 c. *Nessaea aglaura* .. .. 70 1·60

**92** Queen and Bishops

(Des R. Granger Barrett. Litho Enschedé)

**1977** (7 Feb). *Silver Jubilee. T* **92** *and similar horiz designs. Multicoloured. W w* **14** *(sideways). P* 13 × 13½.
449 10 c. Royal Visit, 1975 .. .. 10 10
450 35 c. Queen and Rose Window .. .. 30 20
451 $2 Type **92** .. .. 80 1·25
449/51 .. .. *Set of* 3 1·10 1·40

**93** Red-capped Manakin **94** Laboratory Workers

(Des and litho J.W.)

**1977** (3 Sept). *Birds (1st series). T* **93** *and similar vert designs. Multicoloured. W w* **14**. *P* 14.
452 8 c. Type **93** .. .. 75 20
453 10 c. Hooded Oriole .. .. 90 25
454 25 c. Blue-crowned Motmot .. .. 1·25 55
455 35 c. Slaty-breasted Tinamou .. .. 1·50 75
456 45 c. Ocellated Turkey .. .. 1·75 1·10
457 $1 White Hawk .. .. 3·00 3·25
452/7 .. .. *Set of* 6 8·25 5·50
**MS**458 110 × 133 mm. Nos. 452/7 .. .. 8·25 10·00
See also Nos. 467/73, 488/94 and 561/7.

(Des G. Hutchins. Litho J.W.)

**1977** (2 Dec). *75th Anniv of Pan-American Health Organisation. T* **94** *and similar horiz design. Multicoloured. W w* **14** *(sideways). P* 13½.
459 35 c. Type **94** .. .. 20 20
460 $1 Mobile medical unit .. .. 40 65
**MS**461 126 × 95 mm. Nos. 459/60. P 13 .. .. 85 1·25

**BELIZE DEFENCE FORCE**
**1ST JANUARY 1978**

(95)

**1978** (15 Feb). *Establishment of Belize Defence Force. Nos. 409 and 413 optd with T* **95** *in gold by Govt Printery, Belize.*
462 10 c. *Diaethria astala* .. .. 30 15
463 35 c. *Parides arcas* .. .. 70 40

**96** White Lion of Mortimer **97** *Russelia sarmentosa*

(Des. C. Abbott. Litho Questa)

**1978** (21 Apr). *25th Anniv of Coronation (1st issue). T* **96** *and similar vert designs. P* 15.
464 75 c. bistre, carmine and silver .. .. 25 30
a. Sheetlet. Nos. 464/6 × 2 .. .. 1·40
465 75 c. multicoloured .. .. 25 30
466 75 c. bistre, carmine and silver .. .. 25 30
464/6 .. .. *Set of* 3 65 80
Designs:—No. 464, Type **96**; No. 465, Queen Elizabeth II; No 466, Jaguar (Maya god of Day and Night).
Nos. 464/6 were printed together in small sheets of 6, containing two *se-tenant* strips of 3 with horizontal gutter margin between.
See also Nos. 495/503.

(Des. J.W. Litho Questa)

**1978** (31 July). *Birds (2nd series). Vert designs as T* **93**. *Multicoloured. W w* **14**. *P* 14½.
467 10 c. White-capped Parrot .. .. 35 30
468 25 c. Crimson-collared Tanager .. .. 80 45
469 35 c. Citreoline Trogon .. .. 1·00 55
470 45 c. American Finfoot .. .. 1·25 1·40
471 50 c. Muscovy Duck .. .. 1·40 1·60
472 $1 King Vulture .. .. 1·90 3·00
467/72 .. .. *Set of* 6 6·00 6·50
**MS**473 111 × 133 mm. Nos. 467/72 .. .. 6·00 8·50

(Des J. Cooter. Litho Questa)

**1978** (16 Oct). *Christmas. Wild Flowers and Ferns. T* **97** *and similar vert designs. Multicoloured. W w* **14**. *P* 14 × 13½.
474 10 c. Type **97** .. .. 15 10
475 15 c. *Lygodium polymorphum* .. .. 20 10
476 35 c. *Heliconia aurantiaca* .. .. 30 15
477 45 c. *Adiantum tetraphyllum* .. .. 35 30
478 50 c. *Angelonia ciliaris* .. .. 35 40
479 $1 *Thelypteris obliterata* .. .. 60 80
474/79 .. .. *Set of* 6 1·75 1·60

**98** Internal Airmail Service, 1937

(Des D. Bowen. Litho Questa)

**1979** (15 Jan). *Centenary of U.P.U. Membership. T* **98** *and similar horiz designs. Multicoloured. W w* **14** *(sideways). P* 13½ × 14.
480 5 c. Type **98** .. .. 10 10
481 10 c. M.V. *Heron H* on mail service, 1949 .. .. 15 10
482 35 c. Internal mail service, 1920 (canoe) .. .. 20 20
483 45 c. Stann Creek Railway mail, 1910 .. .. 55 55
484 50 c. Mounted mail courier, 1882 .. .. 40 40
485 $2 R.M.S. *Eagle*, 1856 .. .. 1·10 1·40
480/5 .. .. *Set of* 6 2·25 2·40

15¢

15c

(99) (100)

**1979**. *No. 413 surch. (a) By typography, locally, with T* **99**.
486 15 c. on 35 c. Type **84** (March) .. .. 28·00

*(b) By lithography, in Great Britain, with T* **100**
487 15 c. on 35 c. Type **84** (June) .. .. 30 1·00

(Des J.W. Litho Questa)

**1979** (16 Apr). *Birds (3rd series). Vert designs as T* **93**. *Multicoloured. P* 14.
488 10 c. Boat-billed Heron .. .. 40 10
489 25 c. Grey-necked Wood Rail .. .. 65 20
490 35 c. Lineated Woodpecker .. .. 75 30
491 45 c. Blue-grey Tanager .. .. 80 40
492 50 c. Laughing Falcon .. .. 80 70
493 $1 Long-tailed Hermit .. .. 1·25 1·40
488/93 .. .. *Set of* 6 4·25 2·75
**MS**494 113 × 136 mm. Nos. 488/93 .. .. 4·25 4·75

**PRINTER.** The following issues to No. 734 were printed in lithography by Lito Nacional, Porto, Portugal.

**AVAILABILITY.** Certain values of some issues to No. 734 were only available in restricted quantities in Belize.

**101** Paslow Building, Belize G.P.O.

(Des A. Medina)

**1979** (31 May). *25th Anniv of Coronation (2nd issue). T* **101** *and similar multicoloured designs. P* 14.
495 25 c. Type **101** .. .. 20 10
496 50 c. Houses of Parliament .. .. 35 10
497 75 c. Coronation State Coach .. .. 55 10
498 $1 Queen on horseback *(vert)* .. .. 70 10
499 $2 Prince of Wales *(vert)* .. .. 1·40 15
500 $3 Queen and Duke of Edinburgh *(vert)* .. .. 2·10 20
501 $4 Portrait of Queen *(vert)* .. .. 2·75 25
502 $5 St. Edward's Crown *(vert)* .. .. 3·50 30
495/502 .. .. *Set of* 8 10·00 1·00
**MS**503 Two sheets, both 126 × 95 mm: (a) $5 Princess Anne on horseback at Montreal Olympics *(vert)*, $10 Queen at Montreal Olympics *(vert)*; (b) $15 As Type **101** .. .. *Set of 2 sheets* 18·00
Nos. 495/502 also exist imperforate from a restricted printing *(price for set of* 8 *£40 mint).*

**102** Safety Aeroplane (1909)

(Des A. Medina)

**1979** (30 July). *Death Centenary of Sir Rowland Hill and 75th Anniv of I.C.A.O. (International Civil Aviation Organization). T* **102** *and similar horiz designs. Multicoloured. P* 14.
504 4 c. Type **102** .. .. 15 10
505 25 c. Boeing "707-720" .. .. 30 10
506 50 c. "Concorde" .. .. 60 10
507 75 c. Handley Page "W8b" (1922) .. .. 55 10
508 $1 Avro "F" (1912) .. .. 70 10
509 $1.50, Cody (1910) .. .. 1·25 15
510 $2 Triplane II (1909) .. .. 1·50 25
511 $3 Santos Dumont's aeroplane (1906) .. .. 2·25 35
512 $4 First motorized flight, Wright brothers (1903) .. .. 2·75 50
504/12 .. .. *Set of* 9 9·00 1·25
**MS**513 Two sheets: (a) 115 × 95 mm. $5 Dunne "D5" (1910), $5 G.B. 1969 "Concorde" stamp; (b) 130 × 95 mm. $10 Boeing "707–720" *(different)*. *Set of 2 sheets* 20·00
Nos. 504/12 also exist imperforate from a restricted printing *(price for set of* 9 *£55 mint).*

**103** Handball **104** Olympic torch

(Des A. Medina)

**1979** (10 Oct). *Olympic Games, Moscow (1980). T* **103** *and similar vert designs. Multicoloured. P* 14.
514 25 c. Type **103** .. .. 20 10
515 50 c. Weightlifting .. .. 35 10
516 75 c. Athletics .. .. 55 10
517 $1 Football .. .. 70 10
518 $2 Yachting .. .. 1·40 15
519 $3 Swimming .. .. 1·75 20
520 $4 Boxing .. .. 2·00 25
521 $5 Cycling .. .. 2·50 30
514/21 .. .. *Set of* 8 8·50 1·00
**MS**522 Two sheets: (a) 126 × 92 mm. $5 Athletics *(different)*, $10 Boxing *(different)*; (b) 92 × 126 mm. $15 As $5 .. .. *Set of 2 sheets* 16·00
Nos. 514/21 also exist imperforate from a restricted printing *(price for set of* 8 *£55 mint).*

(Des A. Medina)

**1979** (4 Dec). *Winter Olympic Games, Lake Placid (1980). T* **104** *and similar vert designs. Multicoloured. P* 14.
523 25 c. Type **104** .. .. 20 10
524 50 c. Giant slalom .. .. 35 10
525 75 c. Figure-skating .. .. 55 10
526 $1 Slalom skiing .. .. 70 10
527 $2 Speed-skating .. .. 1·40 15
528 $3 Cross-country skiing .. .. 2·10 20
529 $4 Shooting .. .. 2·75 25
530 $5 Gold, Silver and Bronze medals .. .. 3·50 30
523/30 .. .. *Set of* 8 10·00 1·00
**MS**531 Two sheets: (a) 127 × 90 mm. $5 Lighting the Olympic Flame, $10 Gold, Silver and Bronze medals *(different)*; (b) 90 × 127 mm. $15 Olympic Torch *(different)* .. .. *Set of 2 sheets* 20·00
Nos. 523/30 also exist imperforate from a restricted printing *(price for set of* 8 *£55 mint).*

105 *Cypraea zebra*

106 Girl and Flower Arrangement

(Des C. Abbott)

**1980** (7 Jan). *Shells. Multicoloured designs as T* **105**. *P* 14.

532 1 c. Type **105** 10 10
533 2 c. *Macrocallista maculata* 10 10
534 3 c. *Arca zebra (vert)* 15 10
535 4 c. *Chama macerophylla (vert)* 20 10
536 5 c. *Latirus cariniferus* 20 10
537 10 c. *Conus spurius (vert)* 30 10
538 15 c. *Murex cabritii (vert)* 40 10
539 20 c. *Atrina rigida* 45 10
540 25 c. *Chlamys imbricata (vert)* 45 10
541 35 c. *Conus granulatus* 60 10
542 45 c. *Tellina radiata (vert)* 75 10
543 50 c. *Leucozonia nassa leucozonalis* 85 10
544 85 c. *Tripterotyphis triangularis* 1·25 10
545 $1 *Strombus gigas (vert)* 1·50 10
546 $2 *Strombus gallus (vert)* 2·75 30
547 $5 *Fasciolaria tulipa* 5·00 75
548 $10 *Arene cruentata* 8·00 1·25
532/548 *Set of* 17 21·00 2·50
**MS**549 Two sheets, each 125 × 90 mm: (a) Nos. 544 and 547; (b) Nos. 546 and 548 16·00 15·00

Some of the above exist with a different date in the imprint at the foot of each stamp.

(Des A. Medina ($5), C. Mullin (others))

**1980** (15 Mar). *International Year of the Child. T* **106** *and similar vert designs. Multicoloured. P* 14.

550 25 c. Type **106** 20 10
551 50 c. Boy holding football 30 10
552 75 c. Boy with butterfly 45 10
553 $1 Girl holding doll 60 10
554 $1.50, Boy carrying basket of fruit 95 15
555 $2 Boy holding shell 1·25 20
556 $3 Girl holding posy 1·90 25
557 $4 Boy and girl wrapped in blanket 2·50 30
550/7 *Set of* 8 7·00 1·00
**MS**558 130 × 95 mm. $5 Three children of different races, $5 "Madonna with Cat" (A. Dürer) (*each 35 × 53 mm*). P 13. 6·00
MS559 111 × 151 mm. $10 Children and Christmas tree (*73 × 110 mm*). P 13 6·00

Nos. 550/7 also exist imperforate from a restricted printing (*price for set of* 8 £35 *mint*).

10¢

(107)

108 Jabiru

**1980** (March). *No.* 412 *surch with T* **107**.

560 10 c. on 25 c. *Papilio thoas* 40 70
a. Surch inverted 60·00

(Des J.W. Litho Questa)

**1980** (16 June). *Birds (4th series). T* **108** *and similar vert designs. Multicoloured. P* 13.

561 10 c. Type **108** 2·75 2·00
a. Sheetlet. Nos. 561/6 17·00
562 25 c. Barred Antshrike 3·00 2·00
563 35 c. Northern Royal Flycatcher 3·00 2·25
564 45 c. White-necked Puffbird 3·25 2·50
565 50 c. Ornate Hawk-eagle 3·25 2·75
566 $1 Golden-masked Tanager 4·00 3·25
561/6 *Set of* 6 17·00 13·50
**MS**567 85 × 90 mm. $2 Type **108**, $3 As $1 14·00 13·00

Nos. 561/6 were printed together, *se-tenant* in sheetlets of 6 or in "double" sheetlets of 12. Stamps from the "double" sheetlets have a red frame and red imprint at foot.

## *PRICES OF SETS*

Set prices are given for many issues, generally those containing three stamps or more. Definitive sets include one of each value or major colour change, but do not cover different perforations, die types or minor shades. Where a choice is possible the set prices are based on the cheapest versions of the stamps included in the listings.

109 Speed Skating

40c

(110)

**1980** (20 Aug). *Medal Winners, Winter Olympic Games, Lake Placid. T* **109** *and similar vert designs. Multicoloured. P* 14.

568 25 c. Type **109** 20 10
569 50 c. Ice hockey 30 10
570 75 c. Figure-skating 45 10
571 $1 Alpine skiing 60 10
572 $1.50, Giant slalom (women) 95 15
573 $2 Speed-skating (women) 1·25 20
574 $3 Cross-country skiing 1·90 25
575 $5 Giant slalom 3·00 30
568/75 *Set of* 8 7·50 1·00
**MS**576 Two sheets: (a) 126 × 91 mm. $5 Type **109**; $10 Type **109**; (b) 91 × 126 mm. $10 As 75 c. *Set of* 2 *sheets* 15·00

Nos. 568/75 also exist imperforate from a restricted printing (*price for set of* 8 £55 *mint*)

**1980** (3 Oct). "ESPAMER" *International Stamp Exhibition, Madrid. Nos.* 561/6 *optd (Nos.* 577/9) *or surch as T* **110**.

577 10 c. Type **107** 1·50 1·50
a. Sheetlet. Nos. 577/82 11·00
578 25 c. Barred Antshrike 1·75 1·75
579 35 c. Northern Royal Flycatcher 2·00 2·00
580 40 c. on 45 c. White-necked Puffbird 2·25 2·25
581 40 c. on 50 c. Ornate Hawk-eagle 2·25 2·25
582 40 c. on $1 Golden-masked Tanager 2·25 2·25
577/82 *Set of* 6 11·00 11·00

111 Witch in Sky

112 Queen Elizabeth The Queen Mother

(Des C. Mullin)

**1980** (24 Nov). *Fairy Tales. Sleeping Beauty. T* **111** *and similar vert designs illustrating the story. P* 14.

583 35 c. multicoloured 25 10
584 40 c. multicoloured 35 10
585 50 c. multicoloured 45 10
586 75 c. multicoloured 60 10
587 $1 multicoloured 70 15
588 $1.50, multicoloured 1·10 20
589 $3 multicoloured 2·10 25
590 $4 multicoloured 2·75 30
583/90 *Set of* 8 7·50 1·00
**MS**591 Two sheets: (a) 82 × 110 mm. $8 "Paumgartner Altar-piece" (Dürer); (b) 110 × 82 mm. $5 Marriage ceremony, $5 Sleeping Beauty and Prince on horseback *Set of* 2 *sheets* 12·50

Nos. 583/90 also exist imperforate from a restricted printing (*price for set of* 8 £55 *mint*).

(Des C. Mullen)

**1980** (12 Dec). *80th Birthday of Queen Elizabeth the Queen Mother. P* 13.

592 **112** $1 multicoloured 85 30
**MS**593 82 × 110 mm, $5 As Type **112** (*41 × 32 mm*) 4·00 4·00

No. 592 exists imperforate from a restricted printing (*price* £4.50 *mint*).

113 The Annunciation

$1

(114)

(Des C. Mullin)

**1980** (30 Dec). *Christmas. T* **113** *and similar vert designs. Multicoloured. P* 14.

594 25 c. Type **113** 20 10
595 50 c. Bethlehem 35 10
596 75 c. The Holy Family 55 10
597 $1 The Nativity 70 10
598 $1.50,The flight into Egypt 90 15
599 $2 Shepherds following the Star 1·10 20
600 $3 Virgin, Child and Angel 1·60 25
601 $4 Adoration of the Kings 1·90 30
594/601 *Set of* 8 6·50 1·00
**MS**602 Two sheets, each 82 × 111 mm: (a) $5 As $1; (b) $10 As $3 *Set of* 2 *sheets* 10·50

**1981** (22 May). *"WIPA" International Stamp Exhibition. Vienna. Nos.* 598 *and* 601/2b *surch with T* **114**.

603 $1 on $1.50, The flight into Egypt 60 65
604 $2 on $4 Adoration of the Kings 1·25 1·40
**MS**605 82 × 111 mm. $2 on $10 Virgin, Child and Angel 1·25 1·50

115 Paul Harris (founder)

116 Prince of Wales Coat of Arms

**1981** (26 May). *75th Anniv of Rotary International. T* **115** *and similar multicoloured designs. P* 14.

606 25 c. Type **115** 20 25
607 50 c. Emblems of Rotary activities 35 35
608 $1 75th Anniversary emblem 70 65
609 $1·50, Educational scholarship programme (*horiz*) 1·10 1·00
610 $2 "Project Hippocrates" 1·40 1·40
611 $3 Emblems (*horiz*) 2·10 2·00
612 $5 Emblem and handshake (*horiz*) 3·50 3·25
606/12 *Set of* 7 8·50 8·00
**MS**613 Two sheets: (a) 95 × 130 mm. $10 As 50 c.; (b) 130 × 95 mm, $5 As $1, $10 As $2 *Set of* 2 *sheets* 18·00

*Nos. 606/13, together with a 75 c. value showing a map, were originally issued on 30 March 1981, but were withdrawn from sale after two hours as there were objections to the colours used on the map. The stamps, without the offending 75 c., were reissued on 26 May. First Day covers carry the later date and there are no reports of examples used before 26 May.

(Des C. Mullin)

**1981** (16 July). *Royal Wedding. T* **116** *and similar vert designs. Multicoloured.* (a) *Size 22 × 38 mm (from sheets of 27). P* 13½ × 14.

614 50 c. Type **116** 35 40
a. Horiz pair. Nos. 614/15 1·10
615 $1 Prince Charles in military uniform 70 75
a. Horiz pair. Nos. 615/16 1·90
616 $1.50, Royal couple 1·10 1·25

(*b*) *Size 25 × 42 mm with gold borders (sheets of 6 stamps and 3 labels). P* 13.

617 50 c. Type **116** 35 15
618 $1 As No. 615 70 35
619 $1.50, As No. 616 1·10 45
614/19 *Set of* 6 3·75 3·00
**MS**620 145 × 85 mm. $3 × 3 As Nos 614/16, but 30 × 47 mm. P 14 3·00 4·25

Nos. 614/16 were each printed in blocks of 9 (3 × 3), the blocks *se-tenant* within the sheet.

Nos. 614/16 also exist imperforate from a restricted printing (*price for set of* 3 £7 *mint*).

10c

(117)

**1981** (22 Aug). *No.* 538 *surch with T* **117**.

621 10 c. on 15 c. *Murex cabritii* 1·00 1·40
a. Surch double † —

For a similar surcharge, but with rectangular obliterating panel see No. 728.

118 Athletics

(Des C. Mullin)

**1981** (14 Sept). *History of the Olympic Games. T* **118** *and similar vert designs. Multicoloured. P* 14.

622 85 c. Type **118** .. .. .. .. .. .. 60 10
623 $1 Cycling .. .. .. .. .. .. 70 10
624 $1.50, Boxing .. .. .. .. .. 1·10 10
625 $2 1984 Games–Los Angeles and Sarajevo 1·40 20
626 $3 Baron Pierre de Coubertin .. .. 2·10 30
627 $5 Olympic Flame .. .. .. .. 3·50 40
622/7 .. .. .. .. .. *Set of* 6 8·50 1·00
**MS**628 Two sheets, each 175 × 123 mm: (a) $5 As $3, $10 As $5 (*each* 35 × 53 *mm*). P 13½; (b) $15 As $2 (45 × 67 *mm*). P 14½. .. *Set of* 2 *sheets* 21·00

The two miniature sheets of No. **MS**628 also exist with the stamps and borders printed in gold from a restricted printing.

INDEPENDENCE

*Independence*
*21 Sept.,1981* $1

(119)

(120)

**1981** (21 Sept). *Independence Commemoration (1st issue). Optd as T* **119** *by Benex Press, Belize City. (a) On Nos.* 532/44 *and* 546/9.

629 1 c. Type **119** .. .. .. .. 10 10
630 2 c. *Macrocallista maculata* .. .. 10 10
631 3 c. *Arca zebra* (*vert*) .. .. .. 10 10
632 4 c. *Chama macerophylla* (*vert*) .. .. 10 10
a. Opt inverted .. .. .. ..
633 5 c. *Latirus cariniferus* .. .. .. 10 10
634 10 c. *Conus spurius* (*vert*) .. .. 10 10
a. Opt inverted .. .. .. ..
635 15 c. *Murex cabritii* (*vert*) .. .. 15 10
636 20 c. *Atrina rigida* .. .. .. .. 15 15
637 25 c. *Chlamys imbricata* (*vert*) .. .. 25 25
638 35 c. *Conus granulatus* .. .. .. 30 30
639 45 c. *Tellina radiata* (*vert*) .. .. 40 35
640 50 c. *Leucozonia nassa leucozonalis* .. 40 35
641 85 c. *Tripterotyphis triangularis* .. .. 65 60
a. Opt inverted .. .. .. ..
642 $2 *Strombus gallus* (*vert*) .. .. 1·50 1·40
643 $5 *Fasciolaria tulipa* .. .. .. 3·50 3·25
a. Opt inverted .. .. .. † —
644 $10 *Arene cruentata* .. .. .. 6·50 6·50
629/44 .. .. .. .. *Set of* 16 13·00 12·00
**MS**645 Two sheets, each 126 × 91 mm: (a) Nos. 641 and 643; (b) Nos. 642 and 644 .. *Set of* 2 *sheets* 13·00

On the vertical designs and the miniature sheets the overprint is in roman type.

The 10c. exists with different imprint dates.

Examples of the miniature sheets have been seen showing forged overprints apparently applied by rubber handstamp.

(*b*) *On Nos.* 606/13

646 25 c. Type **115** (Gold) .. .. .. 20 25
a. Opt double .. .. .. ..
647 50 c. Emblems of Rotary activities .. 35 35
648 $1 75th Anniversary emblem .. .. 70 65
649 $1.50, Educational scholarship programme 1·10 1·00
650 $2 "Project Hippocrates" (Gold) .. .. 1·40 1·40
651 $3 Emblems .. .. .. .. 2·10 2·00
652 $5 Emblems and handshake .. .. 3·50 3·25
646/52 .. .. .. .. *Set of* 7 10·50 8·00
**MS**653 Two sheets: (a) 95 × 130 mm. $10 As 50 c.; (b) 130 × 95 mm. $5 As $1, $10 As $2 (Gold) *Set of* 2 *sheets* 18·00

See also Nos. 657/63.

**1981** (13 Nov). *"ESPAMER" International Stamp Exhibition, Buenos Aires. Nos.* 609 *and* **MS**613b *surch with T* **120**.

654 $1 on $1.50, Educational scholarship programme .. .. .. .. 1·00 1·00
**MS**655 95 × 130 mm. $1 on $5 75th anniversary emblem, $1 on $10 "Project Hippocrates". .. 3·50 3·75

$1

(121)

**1981** (14 Nov). *"Philatelia 81" International Stamp Exhibition, Frankfurt. No.* **MS**549 *surch with T* **121** *in red.*

**MS**656 Two sheets, each 125 × 90 mm: (a) $1 on 85 c. *Tripterotyphis triangularis*, $1 on $5 *Fasciolaria tulipa*; (b) $1 on $2 *Strombus gallus*. $1 on $10 *Arene cruentata* .. .. *Set of* 2 *sheets* 18·00

122 Black Orchid

123 Uruguayan Footballer

(Des C. Mullin)

**1981** (18 Dec)–**82**. *Independence Commemoration (2nd issue) T* **122** *and similar multicoloured designs. P* 14.

657 10 c. Belize Coat of Arms (*horiz*) (10.2.82) .. 30 10
658 35 c. Map of Belize (10.2.82) .. .. 50 30
659 50 c. Type **122** .. .. .. .. 1·00 35
660 85 c. Baird's Tapir (*horiz*) .. .. 1·10 60
661 $1 Mahogany Tree .. .. .. 1·25 65
662 $2 Keel-billed Toucan (*horiz*) .. .. 2·50 1·40
657/62 .. .. .. .. *Set of* 6 6·00 3·00
**MS**663 130 × 98 mm. $5 As 10 c. P 14½ (10.2.82) 4·25 3·50

(Des C. Mullin)

**1981** (28 Dec). *World Cup Football Championship, Spain (1st issue). T* **123** *and similar vert designs. Multicoloured. P* 14.

664 10 c. Type **123** .. .. .. .. 30 10
665 25 c. Italian footballer .. .. .. 45 10
666 50 c. German footballer .. .. .. 55 15
667 $1 Brazilian footballer .. .. .. 90 20
668 $1.50, Argentinian footballer .. .. 1·50 35
669 $2 English footballer .. .. .. 2·00 45
664/9 .. .. .. .. *Set of* 6 5·25 1·25
**MS**670 Two sheets: (a) 145 × 115 mm. $2 "SPAIN '82" logo; (b) 155 × 115 mm. $3 Footballer (46 × 76 *mm*) .. .. .. *Set of* 2 *sheets* 5·00 4·25

124 British 19th-century Warship

(Des C. Mullin)

**1982** (15 Mar). *Sailing Ships. T* **124** *and similar horiz designs. Multicoloured. P* 14.

671 10 c. Type **124** .. .. .. .. 40 15
672 25 c. *Madagascar* (1837) .. .. .. 75 25
673 35 c. Brig *Whitby* (1838) .. .. .. 1·00 25
674 50 c. *China* (1838) .. .. .. 1·25 35
675 85 c. *Swiftsure* (1850) .. .. .. 1·75 50
676 $2 *Windsor Castle* (1857) .. .. 3·00 70
671/6 .. .. .. .. *Set of* 6 7·25 2·00
**MS**677 110 × 87 mm. $5 Ships in battle .. 7·50 5·00

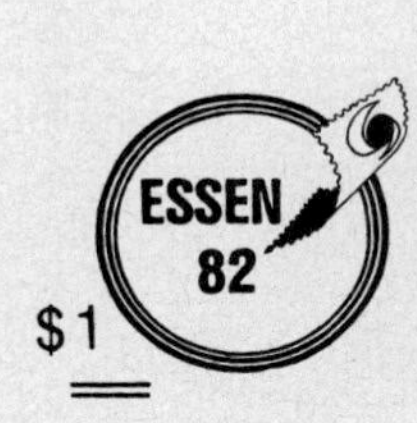


(125)

126 Princess Diana

**1982** (28 Apr). *"ESSEN '82" International Stamp Exhibition, West Germany. Nos.* 662 *and* 669 *surch with T* **125**.

678 $1 on $2 Keel-billed Toucan .. .. 1·25 75
679 $1 on $2 English footballer .. .. 1·25 75

(Des C. Mullin)

**1982** (20 May). *21st Birthday of Princess of Wales. T* **126** *and similar vert designs showing portrait of Princess of Wales with different backgrounds. (a) Size* 22 × 38 *mm (from sheets of* 25). *P* 13½ × 14.

680 50 c. multicoloured .. .. .. 35 35
a. *Tête-bêche* (pair) .. .. .. 70
681 $1 multicoloured .. .. .. 70 65
a. *Tête-bêche* (pair) .. .. .. 1·40
682 $1.50, multicoloured .. .. .. 1·10 1·00
a. *Tête-bêche* (pair) .. .. .. 2·25

(*b*) *Size* 25 × 43 *mm (from sheets of* 6 *stamps and* 3 *labels). P* 13

683 50 c. multicoloured .. .. .. 35 10
684 $1 multicoloured .. .. .. 70 20
685 $1.50, multicoloured .. .. .. 1·10 30
680/5 .. .. .. .. *Set of* 6 3·50 2·25
**MS**686 145 × 85 mm. $3 × 3 As Nos. 680/2, but 30 × 47 mm. P 14 .. .. .. 6·25 6·00

Stamps as Nos. 680/2, size 30×47 mm. and perforated 14, exist from a limited printing. These have gold backgrounds to the central ovals and gold frames. In addition the Queen's head and the centre oval are embossed (*Price per set of* 3 £10 *mint*).

127 Lighting Camp-fire

(Des C. Mullin)

**1982** (31 Aug). *125th Birth Anniv of Lord Baden-Powell. T* **127** *and similar horiz designs. Multicoloured. P* 14.

687 10 c. Type **127** .. .. .. .. 25 10
688 25 c. Bird watching .. .. .. 40 25
689 35 c. Three scouts, one playing guitar .. 50 30
690 50 c. Hiking .. .. .. .. 60 35
691 85 c. Scouts with flag .. .. .. 90 60
692 $2 Saluting .. .. .. .. 2·00 1·40
687/92 .. .. .. .. *Set of* 6 4·25 2·50
**MS**693 Two sheets: each 85 × 115 mm: (a) $2 Scout with flag; (b) $3 Portrait of Lord Baden-Powell .. *Set of* 2 *sheets* 6·00

128 *Gorgonia ventalina*

(Des C. Mullin)

**1982** (20 Sept). *First Anniv of Independence. Marine Life. T* **128** *and similar horiz designs. P* 14.

694 10 c. Type **128** .. .. .. .. 35 10
695 35 c. *Carpiuis corallinus* .. .. .. 75 10
696 50 c. *Plexaura flexuasa* .. .. .. 1·00 10
697 85 c. *Candylactis gigantea* .. .. 1·50 15
698 $1 *Stenopus hispidus* .. .. .. 1·75 30
699 $2 *Abudefduf saxatilis* .. .. .. 2·25 50
694/9 .. .. .. .. *Set of* 6 7·00 1·10
**MS**700 130 × 98 mm. $5 *Schyllarides aequinoctialis*. P 14½ .. .. .. .. 7·00 5·50

(129)

**1982** (1 Oct). *"BELGICA 82" International Stamp Exhibition, Brussels. Nos* 687/92 *optd as T* **129** *in gold.*

701 10 c. Type **127** .. .. .. .. 50 30
702 25 c. Bird watching .. .. .. 1·40 75
703 35 c. Three scouts, one playing guitar .. 1·75 1·00
704 50 c. Hiking .. .. .. .. 2·25 1·50
705 85 c. Scouts with flag .. .. .. 3·75 2·50
706 $2 Saluting .. .. .. .. 9·00 6·50
701/6 .. .. .. .. *Set of* 6 17·00 11·50

BIRTH OF H.R.H.

PRINCE
WILLIAM ARTHUR
PHILIP LOUIS
21ST JUNE 1982

(130)

131 Scotland v New Zealand

**1982** (21 Oct). *Birth of Prince William of Wales (1st issue). Nos.* 680/6 *optd as T* **130** *in silver. (a) Size* 22 × 38 *mm.*

707 50 c. multicoloured .. .. .. 35 35
a. *Tête-bêche* (pair) .. .. .. 70
b. Opt double .. .. .. 55·00
708 $1 multicoloured .. .. .. 70 65
a. *Tête-bêche* (pair) .. .. .. 1·40
709 $1.50, multicoloured .. .. .. 1·10 1·00
a. *Tête-beche* (pair) .. .. .. 2·25

(*b*) *Size* 25 × 43 *mm*

710 50 c. multicoloured .. .. .. 35 35
a. Opt double .. .. .. ..
711 $1 multicoloured .. .. .. 70 65
712 $1.50, multicoloured .. .. .. 1·10 1·00
707/12 .. .. .. .. *Set of* 6 3·50 3·50
**MS**713 145 × 85 mm. $3 × 3 As Nos. 707/9, but 30 × 47 mm. .. .. .. .. 6·25 6·00

A similar overprint exists on the stamps from the limited printing described beneath No. **MS**686 (*Price per set of* 3 £10 *mint*).

**1982** (25 Oct). *Birth of Prince William of Wales (2nd issue). Nos* 614/20 *optd as T* **130** *in gold (a) Size* 22 × 38 *mm.*

714 50 c. Type **116** .. .. .. .. 2·50 1·00
a. Horiz pair. Nos. 714/15 .. .. 7·50
715 $1 Prince Charles in military uniform .. 5·00 2·00
a. Horiz pair. Nos. 715/16 .. .. 12·50
716 $1.50, Royal couple .. .. .. 7·50 3·00

(*b*) *Size* 25 × 42 *mm*

717 50 c. Type **116** .. .. .. .. 35 35
718 $1 As No. 715 .. .. .. .. 70 70
719 $1.50, As No. 716 .. .. .. 1·10 1·10
714/9 .. .. .. .. *Set of* 6 16·00 7·25
**MS**720 145 × 85 mm. $3 × 3 As Nos. 714/16 but 30 × 47 mm .. .. .. .. 6·25 6·50

No. **MS**720 occurs with two different sizes of overprint. On the normal version the top line of the overprint, "BIRTH OF H.R.H." measures 19½ mm in length. On examples with the larger overprint this measures 22 mm. (*Price for miniature sheet with larger overprint* £35 *mint.*)

(Des Baumann)

**1982** (10 Dec). *World Cup Football Championship, Spain* (2nd *issue*). *T* **131** *and similar horiz designs. Multicoloured. P* 14.

721 20 c. + 10 c. Type **131** . . . . 40 35
722 30 c. + 15 c. Scotland v New Zealand (*different*) 50 35
723 40 c. + 20 c. Kuwait v France . . . . 60 35
724 60 c. + 30 c. Italy v Brazil . . . . 90 50
725 $1 + 50 c. France v Northern Ireland . . 1·50 65
726 $1.50 + 75 c. Austria v Chile . . . . 2·00 75
721/6 . . . . *Set of* 6 5·50 2·75
**MS**727 Two sheets: (a) 91 × 137 mm. $1 + 50 c. Germany v Italy (50 × 70 *mm*); (b) 122 × 116 mm. $2 + $1 England v France (50 × 70 *mm*) *Set of 2 sheets* 4·25 3·75

10c

(132)

133 Belize Cathedral

**1983** (28 Jan). *No.* 538 *surch with T* **132**.

728 10 c. on 15 c. *Murex cabritii* . . . .

No. 728 differs from the previous provisional, No. 621, in the size of the obliterating panel over the original face value. On No. 621 this measures 4½ × 4½ mm, but No. 728 shows it larger, 7 × 5½ mm.

**1983** (7 March). *Visit of Pope John Paul II. P* 13½.

729 **133** 50 c. multicoloured . . . . 1·50 70
**MS**730 135 × 110 mm. $2.50, Pope John Paul II (30 × 47 *mm*). P 14 . . . . 3·25 2·75

134 Map of Belize

10c

(135)

**1983** (14 Mar). *Commonwealth Day. T* **134** *and similar multicoloured designs. P* 13.

731 35 c. Type **134** . . . . 25 30
732 50 c. "Maya Stella" from Lamanai Indian church (*horiz*) . . . . 35 35
733 85 c. Supreme Court Building (*horiz*) . . 60 60
734 $2 University Centre, Belize (*horiz*) . . 1·40 1·40
731/4 . . . . *Set of* 4 2·40 2·40

**1983** (15 Apr). *No.* 658 *surch with T* **135**.

735 10 c. on 35 c. Map of Belize . . . .

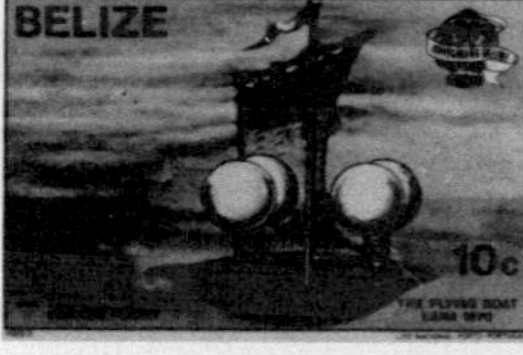

136 Lana's "Flying boat" 1670

(Des C. Mullin)

**1983** (16 May). *Bicentenary of Manned Flight. T* **136** *and similar horiz designs. Multicoloured. P* 14.

736 10 c. Type **136** . . . . 20 15
737 25 c. Barthelemy Lourenco's flying machine, 1709 . . . . 40 30
738 50 c. Guyton de Morveau's airship . . 50 40
739 85 c. Early dirigible . . . . 80 70
740 $1 The *Clement Bayard* . . . . 95 85
741 $1.50, *R-34* airship . . . . 1·40 1·25
736/41 . . . . *Set of* 6 3·75 3·25
**MS**742 Two sheets: (a) 125 × 84 mm. $3 Night scene from the *Nassau* balloon; (b) 115 × 128 mm. $3 Montgolfier balloon (*vert*) . . *Set of 2 sheets* 4·00 4·25

$1.25

$1.25

(137) (138)

**1983** (9 June). *Nos.* 662 *and* 699 *surch with T* **137/8**.

743 $1.25 on $2 Keel-billed Toucan (surch T 137) 3·50 4·00
a. Surch double . . . . † —
744 $1.25 on $2 *Abudefduf saxatilis* (surch T 138) 5·50 5·00

10C 10C

(139) (140)

**1983** (28 Sept). *No.* 541 *surch with T* **139/40**.

745 10 c. on 35 c. *Conus granulatus* (surch T **139**)
a. Surch inverted . . . . 38·00
b. Vert pair, lower stamp without "10 c"
c. Surch double . . . .
746 10 c. on 35 c. *Conus granulatus* (surch T **140**) 20·00
a. Surch triple . . . . 24·00

141 Altun Ha

(Des G. Vasarhelyi. Litho Format)

**1983** (14 Nov). *Maya Monuments. T* **141** *and similar horiz designs. Multicoloured. P* 13½ × 14.

747 10 c. Type **141** . . . . 10 10
748 15 c. Xunantunich . . . . 10 10
749 75 c. Cerros . . . . 55 60
750 $2 Lamanai . . . . 1·40 1·50
747/50 . . . . *Set of* 4 1·90 2·10
**MS**751 102 × 72 mm. $3 Xunantunich (*different*) 2·10 2·25

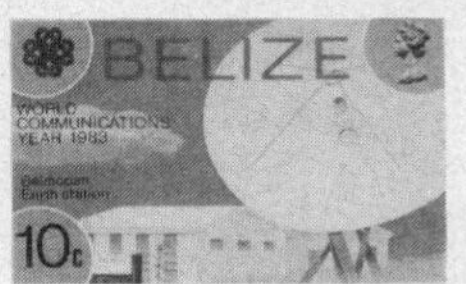

142 Belmopan Earth Station

(Des G. Vasarhelyi. Litho Format)

**1983** (28 Nov). *World Communications Year. T* **142** *and similar horiz designs. Multicoloured. P* 14.

752 10 c. Type **142** . . . . 20 10
753 15 c. *Telstar 2* . . . . 25 15
754 75 c. U.P.U. logo . . . . 80 90
755 $2 M.V. *Heron H* mail service . . 2·00 2·50
752/5 . . . . *Set of* 4 3·00 3·25

143 Jaguar Cub

(Des G. Vasarhelyi. Litho Format)

**1983** (9 Dec). *The Jaguar. T* **143** *and similar horiz designs. Multicoloured. P* 14.

756 5 c. Type **143** . . . . 20 10
757 10 c. Adult Jaguar . . . . 25 10
758 85 c. Jaguar in river . . . . 1·50 1·10
759 $1 Jaguar on rock . . . . 1·75 1·50
756/9 . . . . *Set of* 4 3·25 2·50
**MS**760 102 × 72 mm. $3 Jaguar in tree (44 × 28 *mm*). P 13½ × 14 . . . . 2·50 2·50

Nos. 757 and 759 exist imperforate from stock dispersed by the liquidator of Format International Security Printers Ltd.

144 Pope John Paul II

(Des G. Vasarhelyi. Litho Format)

**1983** (22 Dec). *Christmas. T* **144** *and similar designs showing Pope John Paul II at Papal Mass on 11 March 1983 in Belize. P* 13½ × 14.

761 10 c. multicoloured . . . . 25 10
762 15 c. multicoloured . . . . 30 10
763 75 c. multicoloured . . . . 1·00 75
764 $2 multicoloured . . . . 2·25 2·00
761/4 . . . . *Set of* 4 3·50 2·75
**MS**765 102 × 72 mm. $3 multicoloured . . 3·25 3·25

***NEW INFORMATION***

The editor is always interested to correspond with people who have new information that will improve or correct the Catalogue.

145 Foureye Butterflyfish

(Des G. Drummond. Litho Format)

**1984** (27 Feb)–**88**. *Marine Life from the Belize Coral Reef. T* **145** *and similar horiz designs. Multicoloured. A. P* 15. *B. P* 13½ (7.88).

| | | A | | B | |
|---|---|---|---|---|---|
| 766 | 1 c. Type **145** | 15 | 10 | † | |
| 767 | 2 c. Cushion Star | 15 | 10 | † | |
| 768 | 3 c. Flower Coral | 15 | 10 | † | |
| 769 | 4 c. Fairy Basslet | 15 | 10 | † | |
| 770 | 5 c. Spanish Hogfish | 20 | 10 | † | |
| 771 | 6 c. Star-eyed Hermit Crab | 20 | 10 | † | |
| 772 | 10 c. Sea Fans and Fire Sponge | 25 | 10 | 30 | 30 |
| 773 | 15 c. Blueheads | 30 | 20 | 40 | 40 |
| 774 | 25 c. Blue-striped Grunt | 35 | 25 | 55 | 55 |
| 775 | 50 c. Coral Crab | 60 | 40 | 1·00 | 1·00 |
| 776 | 60 c. Tube Sponge | 75 | 45 | 1·00 | 1·00 |
| 777 | 75 c. Brain Coral | 85 | 55 | † | |
| 778 | $1 Yellow-tail Snapper | 1·25 | 70 | 1·25 | 1·25 |
| 779 | $2 Common Lettuce Slug | 2·25 | 2·00 | † | |
| 780 | $5 Yellow Damselfish | 4·00 | 4·00 | † | |
| 781 | $10 Rock Beauty | 7·50 | 9·00 | † | |
| 766/81 | *Set of* 16 | 17·00 | 16·00 | | |

Nos. 776A and 778A exist overprinted for Hurricane Hattie in 1986. These stamps were not issued, but exist from stock dispersed by the liquidator of Format International Security Printers Ltd.

VISIT OF THE LORD
ARCHBISHOP OF CANTERBURY
8th-11th MARCH 1984

(146)

**1984** (8 Mar). *Visit of the Archbishop of Canterbury. Nos.* 772 *and* 775 *optd with T* **146**.

782 10 c. Sea Fans and Fire Sponge . . . . 30 20
783 50 c. Coral Crab . . . . 65 65

147 Shooting

(Des G. Vasarhelyi. Litho Format)

**1984** (30 Apr). *Olympic Games, Los Angeles,* (a) *Sheet stamps. T* **147** *and similar horiz designs. Multicoloured. P* 13½ × 14.

784 25 c. Type **147** . . . . 25 25
785 75 c. Boxing . . . . 60 60
786 $1 Marathon . . . . 80 80
787 $2 Cycling . . . . 1·40 1·60
784/7 . . . . *Set of* 4 2·75 3·00
**MS**788 101 × 72 mm. $3 Statue of Discus-thrower 2·10 2·50

(*b*) *Booklet stamps. Similar designs to T* **147** *but Royal cypher replaced by Queen's head. P* 14½.

789 5 c. 1896 Marathon . . . . 15 30
a. Booklet pane. No. 789 × 4 . . . . 60
790 20 c. Sprinting . . . . 25 40
a. Booklet pane. No. 790 × 4 . . . . 1·00
791 25 c. Shot-putting . . . . 30 50
a. Booklet pane. No. 791 × 4 . . . . 1·10
792 $2 Olympic torch . . . . 1·50 2·00
a. Booklet pane. No. 792 × 4 . . . . 6·00
789/92 . . . . *Set of* 4 2·00 3·00

148 British Honduras 1866 1s. Stamp

149 Prince Albert

(Des G. Vasarhelyi. Litho Format)

**1984** (26 Sept). *"Ausipex" International Stamp Exhibition, Melbourne. T* **148** *and similar horiz designs. Multicoloured. P* 14 × 13½ ($2) *or* 15 (*others*).

793 15 c. Type **148** . . . . 15 15
794 30 c. Bath mail coach, 1784 . . . . 25 25
795 65 c. Sir Rowland Hill and Penny Black . . 55 55
796 75 c. British Honduras railway locomotive, 1910 . . . . 65 65
797 $2 Royal Exhibition Buildings, Melbourne (46 × 28 *mm*) . . . . 1·50 1·75
793/7 . . . . *Set of* 5 2·75 3·00
**MS**798 103 × 73 mm. $3 Australia 1932 Sydney Harbour Bridge 5s. and British Honduras 1866 1s. stamps (44 × 28 *mm*). P 13½ × 14 . . 2·10 2·50

(Des G. Vasarhelyi. Litho Format)

**1984** (15 Oct). *500th Anniv of British Royal House of Tudor (1985). T* **149** *and similar vert designs showing members of the Royal Family. Multicoloured. P* 14.

799 50 c. Type **149** .. .. .. .. .. 45 55
a. Sheetlet. Nos. 799/800 × 2 .. .. 1·75
800 50 c. Queen Victoria .. .. .. .. 45 55
801 75 c. King George VI .. .. .. .. 70 90
a. Sheetlet. Nos. 801/2 × 2 .. .. 2·75
802 75 c. Queen Elizabeth the Queen Mother .. 70 90
803 $1 Princess of Wales .. .. .. .. 90 1·25
a. Sheetlet. Nos. 803/4 × 2 .. .. 3·50
804 $1 Prince of Wales .. .. .. .. 90 1·25
799/804 .. .. .. .. .. *Set of* 6 3·75 5·00
**MS**805 147 × 97 mm. $1.50, Prince Philip; $1.50, Queen Elizabeth II .. .. .. .. .. 2·25 2·75

Nos. 799/804 were only issued in sheetlets of four stamps of one value, two of each design, with an illustrated vertical gutter margin

**150** White-fronted Amazon

**151** Effigy Censer, 1450 (Santa Rita Site)

(Des. G. Vasarhelyi. Litho Format)

**1984** (1 Nov). *Parrots. T* **150** *and similar multicoloured designs. P* 11.

806 $1 Type **150** .. .. .. .. .. 1·50 1·25
a. Block of 4. Nos. 806/9 .. .. .. 5·50
807 $1 White-capped Parrot (*horiz*) .. .. 1·50 1·25
808 $1 Mealy Amazon (*horiz*) .. .. .. 1·50 1·25
809 $1 Red-lored Amazon .. .. .. 1·50 1·25
806/9 .. .. .. .. .. *Set of* 4 5·50 4·50
**MS**810 102 × 73 mm. $3 Scarlet Macaw. P 13½ × 14 3·25 3·25

Nos. 806/9 were issued together, *se-tenant*, in blocks of 4 throughout the sheet, each block forming a composite design.

(Des G. Vasarhelyi. Litho Format)

**1984** (30 Nov). *Maya Artefacts. T* **151** *and similar vert designs. Multicoloured. P* 15.

811 25 c. Type **151** .. .. .. .. .. 25 25
812 75 c. Vase, 675 (Actun Chapat) .. .. 60 60
813 $1 Tripod Vase, 500 (Santa Rita site) .. 80 80
814 $2 Sun god Kinich Ahau, 600 (Altun Ha site) 1·75 1·75
811/14 .. .. .. .. .. *Set of* 4 3·00 3·00

**152** Governor-General inspecting Girl Guides

**153** White-tailed Kite

(Des R. Granger Barrett. Litho Format)

**1985** (15 Mar). *International Youth Year and 75th Anniv of Girl Guide Movement. T* **152** *and similar horiz designs. Multicoloured. P* 15.

815 25 c. Type **152** .. .. .. .. .. 40 40
816 50 c. Girl Guides camping .. .. .. 60 60
817 90 c. Checking map on hike .. .. .. 95 95
818 $1.25, Students in laboratory .. .. 1·25 1·25
819 $2 Lady Baden-Powell (founder) .. .. 1·75 1·75
815/19 .. .. .. .. .. *Set of* 5 4·50 4·50

(Des G. Vasarhelyi. Litho Format ($1, $5) Questa (others))

**1985** (30 May)–**88**. *Birth Bicentenary of John J. Audubon (ornithologist). T* **153** *and similar multicoloured designs showing original paintings. P* 15 ($1) *or* 14 (*others*).

820 10 c. Type **153** .. .. .. .. .. 35 10
821 15 c. Ruby-crowned Kinglet (*horiz*) .. .. 45 15
822 25 c. Painted Bunting .. .. .. .. 60 30
822*a* 60 c. As 25 c. (1988) .. .. .. .. 80 60
823 75 c. Belted Kingfisher .. .. .. .. 1·00 85
824 $1 Common Cardinal .. .. .. .. 1·40 1·00
825 $3 Long-billed Curlew (*horiz*) .. .. 2·75 3·00
820/5 .. .. .. .. .. *Set of* 7 6·50 5·50
**MS**826 139 × 99 mm. $5 "John James Audubon" (John Syme). P 13½ × 14 .. .. .. .. 4·00 4·00

## MINIMUM PRICE

The minimum price quote is 10p which represents a handling charge rather than a basis for valuing common stamps. For further notes about prices see introductory pages.

**154** The Queen Mother with Princess Elizabeth, 1928

INAUGURATION OF
NEW GOVERNMENT –
21st. DECEMBER 1984

(**155**)

(Des G. Vasarhelyi. Litho Format)

**1985** (20 June). *Life and Times of Queen Elizabeth the Queen Mother. T* **154** *and similar multicoloured designs. P* 13½ × 14.

827 10 c. Type **154** .. .. .. .. .. 10 10
828 15 c. The Queen Mother, 1980 .. .. .. 10 10
829 75 c. Waving to the crowd, 1982 .. .. 55 60
830 $5 Four generations of Royal Family at Prince William's Christening .. .. 3·50 3·75
827/30 .. .. .. .. .. *Set of* 4 3·75 4·00
**MS**831 Two sheets, each 138 × 98 mm. (a) $2 The Queen Mother with Prince Henry (from photo by Lord Snowdon) (38 × 50 *mm*): (b) $5 The Queen Mother, 1984 (38 × 50 *mm*) .. *Set of 2 sheets* 5·00 5·50

**1985** (24 June). *Inauguration of New Government. Nos.* 772/3 *and* 775 *optd with T* **155**.

832 10 c. Sea Fans and Fire Sponge .. .. 20 10
833 15 c. Blueheads .. .. .. .. 25 15
834 50 c. Coral Crab .. .. .. .. 75 40
832/4 .. .. .. .. .. *Set of* 3 1·10 55

**156** British Honduras 1935 Silver Jubilee 25 c. stamp and King George V with Queen Mary in Carriage

(Des Harrison. Litho Format)

**1985** (25 July). *50th Anniv of First Commonwealth Omnibus Issue. T* **156** *and similar horiz designs showing British Honduras/Belize stamps. Multicoloured. P* 14.

835 50 c. Type **156** .. .. .. .. .. 35 40
a. Sheetlet. Nos. 835/44 .. .. .. 3·25
836 50 c. 1937 Coronation 3 c., and King George VI and Queen Elizabeth in Coronation robes .. .. .. .. .. 35 40
837 50 c. 1946 Victory 3 c., and Victory celebrations .. .. .. .. .. 35 40
838 50 c. 1948 Royal Silver Wedding 4 c., and King George VI and Queen Elizabeth at Westminster Abbey service .. .. 35 40
839 50 c. 1953 Coronation 4 c., and Queen Elizabeth II in Coronation robes .. 35 40
840 50 c. 1966 Churchill 25 c., Sir Winston Churchill and fighter aircraft .. .. 35 40
841 50 c. 1972 Royal Silver Wedding 50 c., and 1948 Wedding photograph .. .. 35 40
842 50 c. 1973 Royal Wedding 50 c., and Princess Anne and Capt. Mark Phillips at their Wedding .. .. .. .. .. 35 40
843 50 c. 1977 Silver Jubilee $2, and Queen Elizabeth II during tour .. .. 35 40
844 50 c. 1978 25th anniv of Coronation 75 c. and Imperial Crown .. .. .. .. 35 40
835/44 .. .. .. .. .. *Set of* 10 3·25 3·50
**MS**845 138 × 98 mm. $5 Queen Elizabeth II in Coronation robes (38 × 50 *mm*). P 13½ × 14 .. 4·50 4·00

Nos. 835/44 were printed together, *se-tenant*, in sheetlets of 10.

**157** Mounted Postboy and Early Letter to Belize

COMMONWEALTH SUMMIT
CONFERENCE, BAHAMAS
16th–22nd OCTOBER 1985

(**158**)

(Des G. Drummond. Litho Format)

**1985** (1 Aug). *350th Anniv of the British Post Office. T* **157** *and similar horiz designs. Multicoloured. P* 15.

846 10 c. Type **157** .. .. .. .. .. 30 10
847 15 c. Packet ship beating off privateer .. 45 15
848 25 c. P.O. packet *Duke of Marlborough* .. 50 25
849 75 c. P.O. packet *Diana* .. .. .. 1·00 60
850 $1 Falmouth P.O. packet ship .. .. 1·25 1·00
851 $3 S.S. *Conway* .. .. .. .. 3·00 3·00
846/51 .. .. .. .. .. *Set of* 6 6·00 4·50

A $5 miniature sheet was prepared, but not issued. Examples exist from stock dispersed by the liquidator of Format International Security Printers Ltd.

**1985** (5 Sept). *Commonwealth Heads of Government Meeting, Nassau, Bahamas. Nos.* 827/31 *optd with T* **158** *in silver.*

852 10 c. Type **154** .. .. .. .. .. 10 10
853 15 c. The Queen Mother, 1980 .. .. .. 10 15
854 75 c. Waving to the crowd, 1980 .. .. 55 60
855 $5 Four generations of Royal Family at Prince William's christening .. .. 3·50 3·75
852/5 .. .. .. .. .. *Set of* 4 3·75 4·00
**MS**856 Two sheets, each 138 × 98 mm. (a) $2 The Queen Mother with Prince Henry (from photo by Lord Snowdon) (38 × 50 *mm*): (b) $5 The Queen Mother, 1984 (38 × 50 *mm*) *Set of 2 sheets* 5·00 5·50

80TH ANNIVERSARY OF
ROTARY INTERNATIONAL

(**159**)

**160** Royal Standard and Belize Flag

**1985** (25 Sept). *80th Anniv of Rotary International. Nos.* 815/19 *optd with T* **159**.

857 25 c. Type **152** .. .. .. .. .. 35 25
858 50 c. Girl Guides camping .. .. .. 50 40
859 90 c. Checking map on hike .. .. .. 80 70
860 $1.25, Students in laboratory .. .. 1·25 95
861 $2 Lady Baden-Powell (founder) .. .. 1·75 1·50
857/61 .. .. .. .. .. *Set of* 5 4·25 3·50

(Des G. Vasarhelyi. Litho Format)

**1985** (9 Oct). *Royal Visit. T* **160** *and similar multicoloured designs. P* 15 × 14½.

862 25 c. Type **160** .. .. .. .. .. 35 50
a. Horiz strip of 3. Nos. 862/4 .. .. 3·50
863 75 c. Queen Elizabeth II .. .. .. 80 1·00
864 $4 Royal Yacht *Britannia* (81 × 39 *mm*) .. 2·75 3·00
862/4 .. .. .. .. .. *Set of* 3 3·50 4·00
**MS**865 138 × 98 mm. $5 Queen Elizabeth II (38 × 50 *mm*). P 13½ × 14 .. .. .. 4·75 4·25

Nos. 862/4 were printed together, *se-tenant*, in horizontal strips of 3 within small sheets of 9 stamps.

**161** Mountie in Canoe (Canada)

(Des Walt Disney Productions. Litho Format)

**1985** (1 Nov). *Christmas. 30th Anniv of Disneyland, U.S.A. T* **161** *and similar vert designs showing dolls from "It's a Small World" exhibition. Multicoloured. P* 11.

866 1 c. Type **161** .. .. .. .. .. 10 10
867 2 c. Indian chief and squaw (U.S.A.) .. 10 10
868 3 c. Incas climbing Andes (South America) 10 10
869 4 c. Africans beating drums (Africa) .. 10 10
870 5 c. Snake-charmer and dancer (India and Far East) .. .. .. .. .. 10 10
871 6 c. Boy and girl with donkey (Belize) .. 10 10
872 50 c. Musician and dancer (Balkans) .. 50 50
873 $1.50, Boys with camel (Egypt and Saudi Arabia) .. .. .. .. .. 1·40 1·40
874 $3 Woman and girls playing with kite (Japan) .. .. .. .. .. 2·50 2·50
866/74 .. .. .. .. .. *Set of* 9 4·25 4·25
**MS**875 127 × 102 mm. $4 Beefeater and castle (Great Britain). P 13½ × 14 .. .. .. 3·25 3·50

PRE "WORLD CUP FOOTBALL"
MEXICO 1986

(**162**)

**163** Indian Costume

**1985** (20 Dec). *World Cup Football Championship, Mexico (1986) (1st issue). Nos.* 835/45 *optd with T* **162**.

876 50 c. Type **156** .. .. .. .. .. 40 40
a. Sheetlet. Nos. 876/85 .. .. .. 3·50
877 50 c. 1937 Coronation 3 c., and King George VI and Queen Elizabeth in Coronation robes .. .. .. .. .. 40 40
878 50 c. 1946 Victory 3 c., and Victory celebrations .. .. .. .. .. 40 40
879 50 c. 1948 Royal Silver Wedding 4 c., and King George VI and Queen Elizabeth at Westminster Abbey service .. .. 40 40
880 50 c. 1953 Coronation 4 c., and Queen Elizabeth II in Coronation robes .. 40 40
881 50 c. 1966 Churchill 25 c., Sir Winston Churchill and fighter aircraft .. .. 40 40
882 50 c. 1972 Royal Silver Wedding 50 c., and 1948 Wedding photograph .. .. 40 40
883 50 c. 1973 Royal Wedding 50 c., and Princess Anne and Capt. Mark Phillips at their Wedding .. .. .. .. .. 40 40

884 50 c. 1977 Silver Jubilee $2, and Queen Elizabeth II during tour .. .. 40 40
885 50 c. 1978 25th anniv of Coronation 75 c., and Imperial Crown .. .. .. 40 40
876/85 .. .. .. .. *Set of* 10 3·50 3·50
**MS**886 138×98 mm. $5 Queen Elizabeth II in Coronation robes .. .. .. .. .. 3·75 3·75
See also Nos. 936/40.

(Des Jane Clark. Litho Format)

**1986** (15 Jan). *Costumes of Belize. T* **163** *and similar vert designs. Multicoloured. P* 15.
887 5 c. Type **163**.. .. .. .. .. .. 40 15
888 10 c. Maya .. .. .. .. .. .. 45 15
889 15 c. Garifuna.. .. .. .. .. .. 50 20
890 25 c. Creole .. .. .. .. .. .. 65 30
891 50 c. Chinese .. .. .. .. .. .. 1·10 70
892 75 c. Lebanese .. .. .. .. .. 1·50 1·10
893 $1 European *c* 1900 .. .. .. .. 1·75 1·50
894 $2 Latin .. .. .. .. .. .. 2·25 2·25
887/94 .. .. .. .. *Set of* 8 7·75 5·75
**MS**895 139×98 mm. $5 Amerindian (38×50 *mm*). P 13½×14. .. .. .. 6·00 7·00

164 Pope Pius X

165 Princess Elizabeth aged Three

(Des G. Vasarhelyi. Litho Format)

**1986** (15 Apr). *Easter. 20th-century Popes. T* **164** *and similar multicoloured designs. P* 11.
896 50 c. Type **164**.. .. .. .. .. .. 1·00 1·00
a. Sheetlet. Nos. 896/903 .. .. .. .. 7·25
897 50 c. Benedict XV .. .. .. .. .. 1·00 1·00
898 50 c. Pius XI .. .. .. .. .. .. 1·00 1·00
899 50 c. Pius XII .. .. .. .. .. .. 1·00 1·00
900 50 c. John XXIII .. .. .. .. .. 1·00 1·00
901 50 c. Paul VI .. .. .. .. .. .. 1·00 1·00
902 50 c. John Paul I .. .. .. .. .. 1·00 1·00
903 50 c. John Paul II .. .. .. .. .. 1·00 1·00
896/903 .. .. .. .. *Set of* 8 7·25 7·25
**MS**904 147×92 mm. $4 Pope John Paul II preaching (*vert*). P 13½×14 .. .. .. 7·50 7·50
Nos. 896/903 were printed together, *se-tenant*, in sheetlets of eight stamps and one stamp-size label.

(Des G. Vasarhelyi. Litho Format)

**1986** (21 Apr). *60th Birthday of Queen Elizabeth II. T* **165** *and similar vert designs. Multicoloured. P* 14×13½.
905 25 c. Type **165**.. .. .. .. .. .. 15 20
a. Sheetlet. Nos. 905/8, each×2 .. .. 6·25
906 50 c. Queen wearing Imperial State Crown .. 35 40
907 75 c. At Trooping the Colour .. .. .. 50 55
908 $3 Queen wearing diadem .. .. .. 2·10 2·25
905/8 .. .. .. .. *Set of* 4 2·75 3·00
**MS**909 147×93 mm. $4 Queen Elizabeth II (37×50 *mm*). P 13½×14 .. .. .. 2·75 3·25
Nos. 905/8 were printed together, *se-tenant*, in sheetlets of eight stamps, two of each value, and one stamp-size label.

166 Halley's Comet and Japanese *Planet A* Spacecraft

(Des G. Vasarhelyi. Litho Format)

**1986** (30 Apr). *Appearance of Halley's Comet. T* **166** *and similar multicoloured designs. P* 13½×14.
910 10 c. Type **166**.. .. .. .. .. .. 20 20
a. Sheetlet. Nos. 910/12, each×3 .. .. 2·40
911 15 c. Halley's Comet, 1910 .. .. .. 30 30
912 50 c. Comet and European *Giotto* spacecraft .. .. .. .. .. .. 40 40
913 75 c. Belize Weather Bureau .. .. .. 70 70
a. Sheetlet. Nos. 913/15, each×3 .. .. 8·50
914 $1 Comet and U.S.A. space telescope .. 95 95
915 $2 Edmond Halley .. .. .. .. 1·50 1·50
910/15 .. .. .. .. *Set of* 6 3·50 3·50
**MS**916 147×93 mm. $4 Computer enhanced photograph of Comet (37×50 *mm*) .. .. 4·00 4·00
Nos. 910/12 and 913/15 were each printed together, *se-tenant*, in horizontal and vertical strips of 3, within the two sheetlets of nine.

## COVER PRICES

Cover factors are quoted at the beginning of each country for most issues to 1945. An explanation of the system can be found on page x. The factors quoted do not, however, apply to philatelic covers.

167 George Washington

(Des G. Vasarhelyi. Litho Format)

**1986** (7 May). *United States Presidents. T* **167** *and similar vert designs. Multicoloured. P* 11.
917 10 c. Type **167**.. .. .. .. .. .. 35 35
a. Sheetlet. Nos. 917/22 .. .. .. .. 4·00
918 20 c. John Adams .. .. .. .. .. 40 40
919 30 c. Thomas Jefferson .. .. .. .. 45 45
920 50 c. James Madison .. .. .. .. .. 60 60
921 $1.50, James Monroe .. .. .. .. 1·25 1·25
922 $2 John Quincy Adams .. .. .. .. 1·50 1·50
917/22 .. .. .. .. *Set of* 6 4·00 4·00
**MS**923 147×93 mm. $4 George Washington (*different*). P 13½×14 .. .. .. .. 4·50 4·50
Nos. 917/19 and 920/2 were printed together, *se-tenant*, in horizontal strips of 3, separated by three stamp-size labels, within the sheetlet of six stamps.

168 Auguste Bartholdi (sculptor) and Statue's Head

(Des G. Vasarhelyi. Litho Format)

**1986** (15 May). *Centenary of Statue of Liberty. T* **168** *and similar multicoloured designs. P* 13½×14.
924 25 c. Type **168**.. .. .. .. .. .. 40 40
a. Sheetlet. Nos. 924/7, each×2 .. .. 7·50
925 50 c. Statue's head at U.S. Centennial Celebration, Philadelphia, 1876 .. .. 70 70
926 75 c. Unveiling Ceremony, 1886 .. .. 80 80
927 $3 Statue of Liberty and flags of Belize and U.S.A. .. .. .. .. .. .. 2·25 2·25
924/7 .. .. .. .. *Set of* 4 3·75 3·75
**MS**928 147×92 mm. $4 Statue of Liberty and New York skyline (37×50 *mm*) .. .. 3·50 3·75
Nos. 924/7 were printed together, *se-tenant*, in sheetlets of eight stamps, two of each value, and one stamp-size label.

169 British Honduras 1866 1s. Stamp

(Des G. Vasarhelyi. Litho Format)

**1986** (22 May). *"Ameripex" International Stamp Exhibition, Chicago. T* **169** *and similar multicoloured designs. P* 13½×14.
929 10 c. Type **169**.. .. .. .. .. .. 40 40
a. Sheetlet. Nos. 929/31, each×3 .. .. 4·50
930 15 c. 1981 Royal Wedding $1.50 stamp .. 55 55
931 50 c. U.S.A. 1918 24 c. airmail inverted centre error .. .. .. .. .. 75 75
932 75 c. U.S.S. *Constitution* (frigate) .. .. 1·00 1·00
a. Sheetlet. Nos. 932/4, each×3 .. .. 11·00
933 $1 Liberty Bell .. .. .. .. .. 1·25 1·25
934 $2 White House .. .. .. .. .. 1·60 1·60
929/34 .. .. .. .. *Set of* 6 5·00 5·00
**MS**935 147×93 mm. $4 Capitol, Washington (37×50 *mm*) .. .. .. .. .. 3·25 3·75
Nos. 929/31 and 932/4 were each printed together, *se-tenant*, in horizontal and vertical strips of 3, within the two sheetlets of nine.
Nos. 929/34 exist imperforate from stock dispersed by the liquidator of Format International Security Printers Ltd.

170 English and Brazilian Players

(Des G. Vasarhelyi. Litho Format)

**1986** (16 June) *World Cup Football Championship, Mexico (2nd issue). T* **170** *and similar multicoloured designs. P* 11.
936 25 c. Type **170**.. .. .. .. .. .. 75 75
a. Sheetlet. Nos. 936/9, each×2 .. .. 10·50
937 50 c. Mexican player and Maya statues .. 1·10 1·10
938 75 c. Two Belizean players .. .. .. 1·50 1·50
939 $3 Aztec stone calendar .. .. .. 2·50 2·50
936/9 .. .. .. .. *Set of* 4 5·25 5·25
**MS**940 147×92 mm. $4 Flags of competing nations on two footballs (37×50 *mm*). P 13½×14 .. .. .. .. .. 6·00 6·00
Nos. 936/9 were printed together, *se-tenant*, in sheetlets of eight stamps, two of each value, and one stamp-size label.

171 Miss Sarah Ferguson

ARGENTINA–
WINNERS 1986

(172)

(Des G. Vasarhelyi. Litho Format)

**1986** (23 July). *Royal Wedding. T* **171** *and similar multicoloured designs. P* 14½.
941 25 c. Type **171**.. .. .. .. .. .. 25 25
a. Horiz strip of 3. Nos. 941/3 .. .. 2·75
942 75 c. Prince Andrew .. .. .. .. 65 65
943 $3 Prince Andrew and Miss Sarah Ferguson (92×41 *mm*) .. .. .. .. 2·25 2·25
941/3 .. .. .. .. *Set of* 3 2·75 2·75
**MS**944 155×106 mm. $1 Miss Sarah Ferguson (*different*), $3 Prince Andrew (*different*) .. 3·75 4·00
Nos. 941/3 were printed together, *se-tenant*, in horizontal strips of 3 within small sheets of nine stamps.

**1986** (15 Aug). *World Cup Football Championship Winners, Mexico. Nos.* 936/40 *optd with T* **172**.
945 25 c. Type **170**.. .. .. .. .. .. 60 60
a. Sheetlet. Nos. 945/8, each×2 .. .. 10·00
946 50 c. Mexican player and Maya statues .. 1·00 1·00
947 75 c. Two Belizean players .. .. .. 1·40 1·40
948 $3 Aztec stone calendar .. .. .. 2·50 2·50
945/8 .. .. .. .. *Set of* 4 5·00 5·00
**MS**949 147×92 mm. $4 Flags of competing nations on two footballs (37×50 *mm*) .. .. 4·00 4·50

(173)

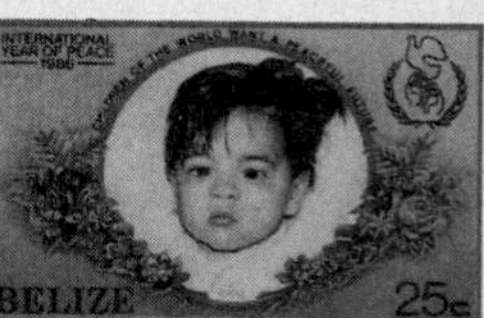


174 Amerindian Girl

**1986** (28 Aug). *"Stockholmia '86" International Stamp Exhibition, Sweden. Nos.* 929/35 *optd with T* **173**.
950 10 c. Type **169**.. .. .. .. .. .. 40 40
a. Sheetlet. Nos. 950/2, each×3 .. .. 4·75
951 15 c. 1981 Royal Wedding $1.50 stamp .. 50 50
952 50 c. U.S.A. 1918 24 c. airmail inverted centre error .. .. .. .. .. 70 70
953 75 c. U.S.S. *Constitution* .. .. .. .. 90 90
a. Sheetlet. Nos. 953/5, each×3 .. .. 10·50
954 $1 Liberty Bell .. .. .. .. .. 1·10 1·10
955 $2 White House .. .. .. .. .. 1·60 1·60
950/5 .. .. .. .. *Set of* 6 4·75 4·75
**MS**956 147×93 mm. $4 Capitol, Washington (37×50 *mm*) .. .. .. .. .. 4·25 4·75

(Des G. Vasarhelyi. Litho Format)

**1986** (3 Oct). *International Peace Year. T* **174** *and similar multicoloured designs. P* 13½×14.
957 25 c. Type **174**.. .. .. .. .. .. 45 45
a. Sheetlet. Nos. 957/60, each×2 .. .. 8·00
958 50 c. European boy and girl .. .. .. 70 70
959 75 c. Japanese girl .. .. .. .. .. 1·00 1·00
960 $3 Indian boy and European girl .. .. 2·25 2·25
957/60 .. .. .. .. *Set of* 4 4·00 4·00
**MS**961 132 × 106 mm. $4 As 25 c. but vert (35 × 47 *mm*) .. .. .. .. .. 4·00 4·50
Nos. 957/60 were printed together, *se-tenant*, in sheetlets of eight stamps, two of each value, and one stamp-size label.
No. **MS**961 exists imperforate from stock dispersed by the liquidator of Format International Security Printers Ltd.

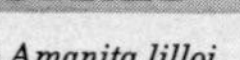

175 *Amanita lilloi*

176 Jose Carioca

(Des G. Drummond. Litho Format)

**1986** (30 Oct). *Fungi and Toucans. T* **175** *and similar vert designs. Multicoloured. P* 14×13½.

962 5 c. Type **175** .. .. .. .. 50 50
a. Sheetlet. Nos. 962, 964, 966 and 969, each × 2 .. .. 8·00
963 10 c. Keel-billed Toucan .. .. .. .. 60 60
a. Sheetlet. Nos. 963, 965 and 967/8, each × 2 .. .. 7·50
964 20 c. *Boletellus cubensis* .. .. .. .. 75 75
965 25 c. Collared Aracari .. .. .. .. 75 75
966 75 c. *Psilocybe caerulescens* .. .. .. 1·25 1·25
967 $1 Emerald Toucanet .. .. .. 1·25 1·25
968 $1.25, Crimson-rumped Toucanet .. 1·25 1·25
969 $2 *Russula puiggarii* .. .. .. 1·50 1·50
962/9 .. .. .. .. .. *Set of* 8 7·00 7·00

Nos. 962, 964, 966 and 969, and Nos. 963, 965 and 967/8, were each printed together, *se-tenant*, in sheetlets of eight stamps, two of each value, and one stamp-size label.

No. 962a exists imperforate from stock dispersed by the liquidator of Format International Security Printers Ltd.

(Des Walt Disney Productions. Litho Format)

**1986** (14 Nov). *Christmas. T* **176** *and similar vert designs showing Walt Disney cartoon characters in scenes from "Saludos Amigos". Multicoloured. P* 11.

970 2 c. Type **176** .. .. .. .. 10 10
a. Sheetlet. Nos. 970/8 .. .. 6·00
971 5 c. Jose Carioca, Panchito and Donald Duck .. .. .. .. 10 10
972 4 c. Daisy Duck as Rio Carnival dancer .. 10 10
973 5 c. Mickey and Minnie Mouse as musician and dancer .. .. .. .. 10 10
974 6 c. Jose Carioca using umbrella as flute .. 10 10
975 50 c. Donald Duck and Panchito .. .. 85 85
976 65 c. Jose Carioca and Donald Duck playing hide and seek .. .. .. .. 1·10 1·10
977 $1.35, Donald Duck playing maracas .. 1·75 1·75
978 $2 Goofy as matador .. .. .. 2·50 2·50
970/8 .. .. .. .. .. *Set of* 9 6·00 6·00
**MS**979 131 × 111 mm. $4 Donald Duck. P 13½×14 .. .. .. .. .. 5·00 5·50

Nos. 970/8 were printed together, *se-tenant*, in sheetlets of nine.

177 Princess Elizabeth in Wedding Dress, 1947

178 *America II*, 1983

(Des G. Vasarhelyi. Litho Format)

**1987** (7 Oct). *Royal Ruby Wedding. T* **177** *and similar vert designs. Multicoloured. P* 15.

980 25 c. Type **177** .. .. .. .. 25 20
981 75 c. Queen and Duke of Edinburgh, 1972 .. 55 50
982 $1 Queen on her 60th birthday .. .. 75 75
983 $4 In Garter robes .. .. .. 2·75 3·00
980/3 .. .. .. .. *Set of* 4 4·00 4·00
**MS**984 171×112 mm. $6 Queen and Duke of Edinburgh (44×50 *mm*). P 13½×14 .. .. 4·50 4·75

(Des G. Vasarhelyi. Litho Format)

**1987** (21 Oct). *America's Cup Yachting Championship. T* **178** *and similar multicoloured designs. P* 15.

985 25 c. Type **178** .. .. .. .. 30 25
986 75 c. *Stars and Stripes*, 1987 .. .. 60 50
987 $1 *Australia II*, 1983 .. .. .. 80 70
988 $4 *White Crusader* .. .. .. 3·00 3·25
985/8 .. .. .. .. *Set of* 4 4·25 4·25
**MS**989 171×112 mm. $6 Sails of *Australia II* (44×50 *mm*). P 13½×14 .. .. .. 4·75 5·50

179 "Mother and Child"

180 Black-handed Spider Monkey

(Des G. Vasarhelyi. Litho Format)

**1987** (4 Nov). *Wood Carvings by George Gabb. T* **179** *and similar vert designs. Multicoloured. P* 15.

990 25 c. Type **179** .. .. .. .. 15 20
991 75 c. "Standing Form" .. .. .. 45 50
992 $1 "Love-doves" .. .. .. .. 60 65
993 $4 "Depiction of Music" .. .. .. 2·40 2·50
990/3 .. .. .. .. *Set of* 4 3·25 3·50
**MS**994 173×114 mm. $6 "African Heritage" (44×50 *mm*). P 13½×14 .. .. .. 3·50 4·00

(Des G. Drummond. Litho Format)

**1987** (11 Nov). *Primates. T* **180** *and similar vert designs. Multicoloured. P* 15.

995 25 c. Type **180** .. .. .. .. 25 20
996 75 c. Black Howler Monkey .. .. .. 55 50
997 $1 Spider Monkeys with baby .. .. 75 70
998 $4 Two Black Howler Monkeys .. .. 3·00 3·25
995/8 .. .. .. .. *Set of* 4 4·00 4·25
**MS**999 171×112 mm. $6 Young Spider Monkey (41×48 *mm*). P 13½×14 .. .. .. 4·00 4·75

181 Guides on Parade

(Des G. Vasarhelyi. Litho Format)

**1987** (25 Nov). *50th Anniv of Girl Guide Movement in Belize. T* **181** *and similar multicoloured designs. P* 15.

1000 25 c. Type **181** .. .. .. .. 25 20
1001 75 c. Brownie camp .. .. .. .. 55 60
1002 $1 Guide camp .. .. .. .. 75 80
1003 $4 Olave, Lady Baden-Powell .. .. 2·75 3·00
1000/3 .. .. .. .. *Set of* 4 4·00 4·25
**MS**1004 173×114 mm. $6 As $4, but vert (44×50 *mm*). P 13½×14 .. .. .. 3·50 4·50

182 Indian Refugee Camp

183 *Laelia euspatha*

(Des G. Vasarhelyi. Litho Format)

**1987** (3 Dec). *International Year of Shelter for the Homeless. T* **182** *and similar horiz designs. Multicoloured. P* 15.

1005 25 c. Type **182** .. .. .. .. 25 20
1006 75 c. Filipino family and slum .. .. 55 50
1007 $1 Family in Middle East shanty town .. 75 70
1008 $4 Building modern house in Belize .. 2·75 3·00
1005/8 .. .. .. .. *Set of* 4 4·00 4·00

(Des G. Drummond. Litho Format)

**1987** (16 Dec). *Christmas. Orchids. T* **183** *and similar vert designs showing illustrations from Sanders'* Reichenbachia. *Multicoloured. P* 13½×14.

1009 1 c. Type **183** .. .. .. .. 30 30
a. Sheetlet. Nos. 1009/15, each × 2 .. 3·75
1010 2 c. *Cattleya citrina* .. .. .. 30 30
1011 3 c. *Masdevallia backhousiana* .. .. 30 30
1012 4 c. *Cypripedium tautzianum* .. .. 30 30
1013 5 c. *Trichopilia suavis alba* .. .. 30 30
1014 6 c. *Odontoglossum hebraicum* .. .. 30 30
1015 7 c. *Cattleya trianaei schroederiana* .. 30 30
1016 10 c. *Saccolabium giganteum* .. .. 45 45
a. Sheetlet. Nos. 1016/22, each × 2 .. 14·00
1017 30 c. *Cattleya warscewiczii* .. .. 60 60
1018 50 c. *Chysis bractescens* .. .. .. 80 80
1019 70 c. *Cattleya rochellensis* .. .. 90 90
1020 $1 *Laelia elegans schilleriana* .. .. 1·00 1·00
1021 $1.50, *Laelia anceps percivaliana* .. 1·40 1·40
1022 $3 *Laelia gouldiana* .. .. .. 1·90 1·90
1009/22 .. .. .. .. *Set of* 14 8·00 8·00
**MS**1023 Two sheets, each 171×112 mm. (a) $3 *Odontoglossum roezlii* (40×47 *mm*). (b) $5 *Cattleya dowiana aurea* (40×47 *mm*) *Set of* 2 *sheets* 6·00 6·50

Nos. 1009/1015 and 1016/22 were each printed together, *se-tenant*, in sheetlets of fourteen stamps, containing two of each value and one stamp-size label.

Examples of the $3 value from No. **MS**1023 with the orchid name incorrectly spelt are from stock dispersed by the liquidator of Format International Security Printers Ltd.

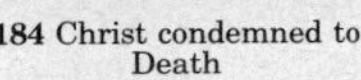


184 Christ condemned to Death

185 Basketball

(Des G. Vasarhelyi. Litho Format)

**1988** (21 Mar). *Easter. The Stations of the Cross. T* **184** *and similar vert designs. Multicoloured. P* 13½×14.

1024 40 c. Type **184** .. .. .. .. 30 30
a. Sheetlet. Nos. 1024/37 .. .. 3·75
1025 40 c. Christ carrying the Cross .. .. 30 30
1026 40 c. Falling for the first time .. .. 30 30
1027 40 c. Christ meets Mary .. .. .. 30 30
1028 40 c. Simon of Cyrene helping to carry the Cross .. .. .. .. .. 30 30
1029 40 c. Veronica wiping the face of Christ .. 30 30
1030 40 c. Christ falling a second time .. .. 30 30
1031 40 c. Consoling the women of Jerusalem 30 30
1032 40 c. Falling for the third time .. .. 30 30
1033 40 c. Christ being stripped .. .. 30 30
1034 40 c. Christ nailed to the Cross .. .. 30 30
1035 40 c. Dying on the Cross .. .. .. 30 30
1036 40 c. Christ taken down from the Cross .. 30 30
1037 40 c. Christ being laid in the sepulchre .. 30 30
1024/37 .. .. .. .. *Set of* 14 3·75 3·75

Nos. 1024/37 were printed together, *se-tenant*, in a sheetlet of 14 stamps and one stamp-size label which appears in the central position.

A $6 miniature sheet was prepared, but not issued. Examples exist from stock dispersed by the liquidator of Format International Security Printers Ltd.

(Des J. McDaniel. Litho Questa)

**1988** (15 Aug). *Olympic Games, Seoul. T* **185** *and similar vert designs. Multicoloured. P* 14.

1038 10 c. Type **185** .. .. .. .. 10 10
1039 25 c. Volleyball .. .. .. .. 15 20
1040 60 c. Table tennis .. .. .. .. 35 40
1041 75 c. Diving .. .. .. .. 45 50
1042 $1 Judo .. .. .. .. .. 60 65
1043 $2 Hockey .. .. .. .. 1·25 1·40
1038/43 .. .. .. .. *Set of* 6 2·50 3·00
**MS**1044 76×106 mm. $3 Gymnastics .. .. 1·75 2·25

186 Public Health Nurse, *c.* 1912

187 Collared Anteater ("Ants Bear")

(Des O. Fernandez. Litho Questa)

**1988** (18 Nov). *125th Anniv of International Red Cross. T* **186** *and similar horiz designs. Multicoloured. P* 14.

1045 60 c. Type **186** .. .. .. .. 50 40
1046 75 c. Hospital ship and ambulance launch, 1937 .. .. .. .. .. 65 55
1047 $1 Ambulance at hospital tent, 1956 .. 80 70
1048 $2 Ambulance plane, 1940 .. .. 1·40 1·60
1045/8 .. .. .. .. *Set of* 4 3·00 3·00

(Des J. Barberis. Litho Questa)

**1989** (24 Feb)–**90**. *Small Animals of Belize. T* **187** *and similar multicoloured designs. P* 14. (a) *W w* **16** (*sideways on* 25 c.).

1049 10 c. Paca ("Gibnut") (30.6.89) .. .. 25 25
1049*a* 25 c. Four-eyed Opossum (*vert*) (1.90) .. 35 35

(*b*) *No wmk*

1050 25 c. Four-eyed Opossum (*vert*) .. .. 35 35
1051 50 c. Type **187** .. .. .. .. 60 60
1052 60 c. As 10 c. .. .. .. .. 75 75
1053 75 c. Red Brocket .. .. .. .. 85 85
1054 $2 Collared Peccary .. .. .. 1·75 1·75
1049/54 .. .. .. .. *Set of* 7 4·50 4·50

(Des A. Theobald ($5), D. Miller (others). Litho Questa)

**1989** (20 July). *20th Anniv of First Manned Landing on Moon. Multicoloured designs as T* **126** *of Ascension. W w* **16** (*sideways on* 50, 75 *c.*). *P* 14×13½ (25 *c.*, $1) *or* 14 (*others*).

1055 25 c. Docking of "Apollo 9" modules .. 15 20
1056 50 c. "Apollo 9" command service module in space (30×30 *mm*) .. .. .. 30 35
1057 75 c. "Apollo 9" emblem (30×30 *mm*) .. 45 50
1058 $1 "Apollo 9" lunar module in space .. 60 65
1055/8 .. .. .. .. *Set of* 4 1·40 1·50
**MS**1059 83×100 mm. $5 "Apollo 11" command service module undergoing tests. P 14×13½. .. 3·00 3·50

5c

(188)

WORLD STAMP EXPO '89™
United States Postal Service
Nov. 17 — 20 and
Nov. 24 — Dec. 3, 1989
Washington Convention Center
Washington, DC

(189)

**1989** (15 Nov). *No.* 771 *surch with T* **188** *by Govt Printer, Belize.*

1060 5 c. on 6 c. Star-eyed Hermit Crab .. 3·00 70

**1989** (17 Nov). *"World Stamp Expo '89" International Stamp Exhibition, Washington. No.* **MS**1059 *optd with T* **189**.

**MS**1061 83×100 mm. $5 "Apollo 11" command service module undergoing tests .. .. 3·00 3·25

**190** Wesley Church

**191** White-winged Tanager and *Catonephele numilia*

(Des Jennifer Toombs. Litho B.D.T.)

**1989** (13 Dec). *Christmas. Belize Churches. T* **190** *and similar vert designs. W* w **16**. *P* 13½.

1062 10 c. black, rose-pink and cinnamon .. 10 10
1063 25 c. black, reddish lilac and rose-lilac .. 15 20
1064 60 c. black, pale turquoise-blue and cobalt 35 40
1065 75 c. black, pale blue-green and sage-green 45 50
1066 $1 blk, pale greenish yell & chrome-yell 60 65
1062/6 .. .. .. .. .. *Set of* 5 1·50 1·60

Designs:—25 c. Baptist Church; 60 c. St. John's Anglican Cathedral; 75 c. St. Andrew's Presbyterian Church; $1 Holy Redeemer Roman Catholic Cathedral.

(Des I. Loe. Litho Questa)

**1990** (1 Mar). *Birds and Butterflies. T* **191** *and similar vert designs. Multicoloured. W* w **14**. *P* 14.

1067 5 c. Type **191** .. .. .. .. 10 10
1068 10 c. Keel-billed Toucan and *Nessaea aglaura* .. .. .. .. 10 10
1069 15 c. Magnificent Frigate Bird and *Eurytides philolaus* .. .. 10 10
1070 25 c. Jabiru and *Heliconius sapho* .. 15 20
1071 30 c. Great Blue Heron and *Colobura dirce* 15 20
1072 50 c. Northern Oriole and *Hamadryas arethusia* .. .. .. .. 30 35
1073 60 c. Scarlet Macaw and *Evenus regalis* 35 40
1074 75 c. Red-legged Honeycreeper and *Callicore patelina* .. .. .. 45 50
1075 $1 Spectacled Owl and *Caligo uranus* .. 60 65
1076 $2 Green Jay and *Philaethria dido* .. 1·10 1·25
1077 $5 Turkey Vulture and *Battus belus* .. 3·00 3·25
1078 $10 Osprey and *Papilio thoas* .. 5·75 6·00
1067/78 .. .. .. .. *Set of* 12 11·00 11·50

**FIRST DOLLAR COIN 1990**

(**192**)

**193** Green Turtle

**1990** (1 Mar). *First Belize Dollar Coin. No.* 1075 *optd with T* **192** *in gold.*

1079 $1 Spectacled Owl and *Caligo uranus* .. 80 80

(Des G. Drummond. Litho B.D.T.)

**1990** (8 Aug). *Turtles. T* **193** *and similar horiz designs. Multicoloured. W* w **14** (*sideways*). *P* 14.

1080 10 c. Type **193** .. .. .. .. 15 10
1081 25 c. Hawksbill Turtle .. .. .. 20 20
1082 60 c. Saltwater Loggerhead Turtle .. 40 35
1083 75 c. Freshwater Loggerhead Turtle .. 55 55
1084 $1 Bocatora Turtle .. .. .. 70 70
1085 $2 Hicatee Turtle .. .. .. 1·25 1·40
1080/5 .. .. .. .. *Set of* 6 3·00 3·00

**194** Fairey Battle

**195** *Cattleya bowringiana*

(Des A. Theobald. Litho B.D.T)

**1990** (15 Sept). *50th Anniv of the Battle of Britain. T* **194** *and similar horiz designs. Multicoloured. W* w **16** (*sideways*). *P* 13½.

1086 10 c. Type **194** .. .. .. .. 15 10
1087 25 c. Bristol Beaufort .. .. .. 20 20
1088 60 c. Bristol Blenheim IV .. .. 40 35
1089 75 c. Armstrong-Whitworth Whitley .. 55 55
1090 $1 Vickers-Armstrong Wellington 1c .. 70 70
1091 $2 Handley-Page Hampden .. .. 1·25 1·40
1086/91 .. .. .. .. *Set of* 6 3·00 3·00

(Des Lynn Chadwick. Litho Questa)

**1990** (1 Nov). *Christmas. Orchids. T* **195** *and similar vert designs. Multicoloured. W* w **14**. *P* 14.

1092 25 c. Type **195** .. .. .. .. 25 20
1093 50 c. *Rhyncholaelia digbyana* .. .. 35 35
1094 60 c. *Sobralia macrantha* .. .. 45 40
1095 75 c. *Chysis bractescens* .. .. 60 55
1096 $1 *Vanilla planifolia* .. .. 70 70
1097 $2 *Epidendrum polyanthum* .. .. 1·25 1·40
1092/7 .. .. .. .. *Set of* 6 3·25 3·25

**196** Common Iguana

(Des G. Drummond. Litho B.D.T.)

**1991** (10 Apr). *Reptiles and Mammals. T* **196** *and similar horiz designs. Multicoloured. W* w **14** (*sideways*). *P* 14.

1098 25 c. Type **196** .. .. .. .. 25 25
1099 50 c. Morelet's Crocodile .. .. 40 40
1100 60 c. American Manatee .. .. 45 45
1101 75 c. Boa Constrictor .. .. .. 55 55
1102 $1 Baird's Tapir .. .. .. 70 70
1103 $2 Jaguar .. .. .. .. 1·25 1·25
1098/1103 .. .. .. *Set of* 6 3·25 3·25

(Des D. Miller. Litho Questa)

**1991** (17 June). *65th Birthday of Queen Elizabeth II and 70th Birthday of Prince Philip. Vert designs as T* **139** *of Ascension. Multicoloured. W* w **16** (*sideways*). *P* 14½×14.

1104 $1 Queen Elizabeth II wearing tiara 60 65
a. Horiz pair. Nos. 1104/5 separated by label .. .. .. .. 1·25 1·25
1105 $1 Prince Philip wearing panama .. 65 65

Nos. 1104/5 were printed in a similar sheet format to Nos. 539/40 of Ascension

**197** Weather Radar

(Des D. Miller. Litho Walsall)

**1991** (31 July). *International Decade for Natural Disaster Reduction. T* **197** *and similar horiz designs. W* w **14** (*sideways*). *P* 14.

1106 60 c. multicoloured .. .. .. 45 45
1107 75 c. multicoloured .. .. .. 55 55
1108 $1 greenish blue and grey-black .. 70 70
1109 $2 multicoloured .. .. .. 1·25 1·25
1106/9 .. .. .. .. *Set of* 4 2·75 2·75

Designs:—75 c. Weather station; $1 Floods in Belize after Hurricane Hattie, 1961; $2 Satellite image of Hurricane Gilbert.

**198** Thomas Ramos and Demonstration

(Des G. Vasarhelyi. Litho Questa)

**1991** (4 Sept). *10th Anniv of Independence. Famous Belizians. T* **198** *and similar horiz designs. Multicoloured. W* w **16** (*sideways*). *P* 14.

1110 25 c. Type **198** .. .. .. .. 15 20
1111 60 c. Sir Isaiah Morter and palm trees .. 35 40
1112 75 c. Antonio Soberanis and political meeting .. .. .. .. 45 50
1113 $1 Santiago Ricalde and cutting sugar-cane .. .. .. .. 60 65
1110/13 .. .. .. .. *Set of* 4 1·40 1·60

**199** "Anansi the Spider"

(Des G. Vasarhelyi. Litho B.D.T.)

**1991** (6 Nov). *Christmas. Folklore. T* **199** *and similar multicoloured designs. W* w **14** (*sideways on horiz designs*). *P* 14.

1114 25 c. Type **199** .. .. .. .. 15 20
1115 50 c. "Jack-o-Lantern" .. .. .. 30 35
1116 60 c. "Tata Duende" (*vert*) .. .. 35 40
1117 75 c. "Xtabai" .. .. .. .. 45 50
1118 $1 "Warrie Massa" (*vert*) .. .. 60 65
1119 $2 "Old Heg" .. .. .. .. 1·10 1·25
1114/19 .. .. .. .. *Set of* 6 2·75 3·00

**NEW INFORMATION**

The editor is always interested to correspond with people who have new information that will improve or correct the Catalogue.

POSTAGE DUE STAMPS

D 1

D 2

(Typo D.L.R.)

**1923–64.** *Wmk Mult Script CA. Ordinary paper. P* 14.

D1 D 1 1 c. black .. .. .. .. .. 50 5·50
a. Chalk-surfaced paper (25.9.56) .. 50 8·00
b. White uncoated paper (9.4.64) .. 14·00 23·00
D2 2 c. black .. .. .. .. .. 80 4·50
a. Chalk-surfaced paper (25.9.56) .. 50 8·00
D3 4 c. black .. .. .. .. .. 1·25 6·00
a. Chalk-surfaced paper (25.9.56) .. 90 8·50
D1/3 .. .. .. .. *Set of* 3 2·25 14·50
D1a/3a .. .. .. .. *Set of* 3 1·75 22·00
D1/3 Optd "Specimen" .. .. *Set of* 3 45·00

The early ordinary paper printings were yellowish and quite distinct from No. D1b.

**1965** (3 Aug)–**72.** *As Nos.* D2a *and* D3a, *but Wmk* w **12** (*sideways on* 2 c.). *P* 13½ × 13 (2 c.) *or* 13½ × 14 (4 c.).

D4 D 1 2 c. black (10.1.72) .. .. .. 1·25 3·00
D5 4 c. black .. .. .. .. 50 3·50

(Des P. Powell. Litho Questa)

**1976** (1 July). *Type* D **2** *and similar vert designs, but with different frames. W* w **14** (*sideways*). *P* 13½ x 14.

D 6 D 2 1 c. red and dull green .. .. 10 45
D 7 – 2 c. light magenta and bluish violet .. 10 45
D 8 – 5 c. dull green and orange-brown .. 15 55
D 9 – 15 c. apple-green and dull vermilion .. 20 80
D10 – 25 c. orange and olive-green .. .. 30 90
D6/10 .. .. .. .. *Set of* 5 70 2·75

## CAYES OF BELIZE

A chain of several hundred islands, coral atolls, reefs and sandbanks stretching along the eastern seaboard of Belize.

### Appendix

The following issues for the Cayes of Belize fall outside the criteria for full listing as detailed on page xi.

**1984**

*Marine Life, Map and Views.* 1, 2, 5, 10, 15, 25, 75 c., $3, $5
*250th Anniv of Lloyd's List* (*newspaper*). 25, 75 c., $1, $2.
*Olympic Games, Los Angeles.* 10, 15, 75 c., $2
*90th Anniv of "Caye Service" Local Stamps.* 10, 15, 75 c., $2

**1985**

*Birth Bicentenary of John J. Audubon* (*ornithologist*). 25, 75 c., $1, $3
*Shipwrecks.* $1 × 4

# Bermuda

The first internal postal system for Bermuda was organised by Joseph Stockdale, the proprietor of the *Bermuda Gazette*, in 1784. This service later competed with that of the colonial post office, set up in 1812.

Control of the overseas postal service passed to the British G.P.O. in 1818. The internal delivery system was discontinued between 1821 and 1830. The overseas posts became a colonial responsibility in 1859.

For illustrations of the handstamp types see BRITISH POST OFFICES ABROAD notes, following GREAT BRITAIN.

CROWNED-CIRCLE HANDSTAMPS

| | | | |
|---|---|---|---|
| CC1 | CC1 | ST. GEORGES BERMUDA (R.) (1.8.1845) *Price on cover* | £5500 |
| CC2 | | IRELAND ISLE BERMUDA (R.) (1.8.1845) *Price on cover* | £3750 |
| CC3 | | HAMILTON BERMUDA (R.) (13.11.1846) *Price on cover* | £3000 |

For Nos. CC1 and CC3 used as adhesive Postmasters' Stamps see Nos. O7 and O6.

**PRICES FOR STAMPS ON COVER TO 1945**

| | |
|---|---|
| Nos. 1/11 | *from* × 5 |
| Nos. 12/17 | *from* × 10 |
| Nos. 19/29*a* | *from* × 8 |
| Nos. 30/*a* | *from* × 10 |
| Nos. 31/4 | *from* × 4 |
| Nos. 34*a*/55 | *from* × 3 |
| Nos. 56/8 | *from* × 10 |
| Nos. 59/76 | *from* × 4 |
| Nos. 76*a*/93 | *from* × 3 |
| Nos. 94/7 | *from* × 4 |
| Nos. 98/106 | *from* × 3 |
| Nos. 107/15 | *from* × 4 |
| Nos. 116/21 | *from* × 5 |
| No. 122 | *from* × 20 |

**COLONY**

O 1

O 2

**1848–61.** *Postmasters' Stamps. Adhesives prepared and issued by the postmasters at Hamilton and St. Georges. Dated as given in brackets.*

*(a) By W. B. Perot at Hamilton*

| | | | | |
|---|---|---|---|---|
| O1 | O 1 | 1d. black/*bluish grey* (1848) | — | £75000 |
| O2 | | 1d. black/*bluish grey* (1849) | — | £100000 |
| O3 | | 1d. red/*thick white* (1853) | — | £75000 |
| O4 | | 1d. red/*bluish wove* (1854) | — | £225000 |
| O5 | | 1d. red/*bluish wove* (1856) | — | £150000 |
| O6 | O 2 | (1d.) carmine-red/*bluish laid* (1861) | — | £70000 |

*(b) By J. H. Thies at St. Georges*
*As Type O 2 but inscr "ST. GEORGES"*

| | | | | |
|---|---|---|---|---|
| O7 | – | (1d.) carmine-red/*buff* (1860) | — | £60000 |

Stamps of Type O 1 bear manuscript value and signature, the dates being those shown on the eleven known examples. The stamps are distributed between the dates as follows: 1848 three examples, 1849 two examples, 1853 three examples, 1854 two examples, 1856 one example.

It is believed that the franking value of Nos. O6/7 was 1d., although this is not shown on the actual stamps. Four examples are known of this type used from Hamilton from March 1861 (and one unused), and five used from St. Georges between July 1860 and January 1863.

Prices shown reflect our estimation of value based on known copies. For instance of the two copies known of No. O4, one is in the Royal collection and the other is on entire.

1

2

3

4

5

(Typo D.L.R.)

**1865–1903.** *Wmk Crown CC. (a) P 14.*

| | | | | |
|---|---|---|---|---|
| 1 | 1 | 1d. rose-red (25.9.65) | 70·00 | 1·25 |
| 2 | | 1d. pale rose | 85·00 | 5·00 |
| 3 | 2 | 2d. dull blue (14.3.66) | £110 | 15·00 |
| 4 | | 2d. bright blue | £120 | 9·00 |
| 5 | 3 | 3d. yellow-buff (10.3.73) | £450 | 60·00 |
| 5*a* | | 3d. orange | £550 | 55·00 |
| 6 | 4 | 6d. dull purple (25.9.65) | £750 | 75·00 |
| 7 | | 6d. dull mauve | 22·00 | 12·00 |
| 8 | 5 | 1s. green (25.9.65) | £180 | 35·00 |

*(b) Imperf*

| | | | | |
|---|---|---|---|---|
| 9 | 1 | 1d. rose-red | £12000 | £8500 |

*(c) P 14 × 12½*

| | | | | |
|---|---|---|---|---|
| 10 | 3 | 3d. yellow-buff (1882) | £150 | 60·00 |
| 10*a* | 4 | 6d. bright mauve (1903) | 13·00 | 22·00 |
| 11 | 5 | 1s. green (1894) | 11·00 | £100 |
| | | a. Vert strip of 3, two stamps imperf horiz | £9500 | |

Though manufactured early in 1880, stamps *P* 14 × 12½ were not issued until the dates given above.

THREE PENCE
(6)

THREE PENCE
(6*a*)

THREE PENCE
(7)

One Penny.
(8)

**1874** (12 Mar–19 May). *Nos. 1 and 8 surch diagonally.*

*(a) With T* **6** *("P" and "R" different type)*

| | | | | |
|---|---|---|---|---|
| 12 | 1 | 3d. on 1d. rose-red | £8000 | |
| 13 | 5 | 3d. on 1s. green | £2000 | £850 |

*(b) With T* **6***a* *("P" same type as "R")*

| | | | | |
|---|---|---|---|---|
| 13*b* | 5 | 3d. on 1s. green | £2000 | £800 |

*(c) With T* **7** *(19 May)*

| | | | | |
|---|---|---|---|---|
| 14 | 5 | 3d. on 1s. green | £1200 | £650 |

The 3d. on 1d. was a trial surcharge which was not regularly issued, though a few specimens were postally used before 1879. Nos. 13, 13*b* and 14, being handstamped, are found with double or partial double surcharges.

(Surch by Queen's Printer, Donald McPhee Lee)

**1875** (March–May). *Surch with T* **8**.

| | | | | |
|---|---|---|---|---|
| 15 | 2 | 1d. on 2d. (No. 4) (23 Apr) | £700 | £350 |
| | | a. No stop after "Penny" | £8000 | £5500 |
| 16 | 3 | 1d. on 3d. (No. 5) (8 May) | £450 | £350 |
| 17 | 5 | 1d. on 1s. (No. 8) (11 Mar) | £500 | £250 |
| | | a. Surch inverted | — | £10000 |
| | | b. No stop after "Penny" | — | £7000 |

It is emphasised that the prices quoted for Nos. 12/17 are for fine examples. The many stamps from these provisional issues which are in inferior condition are worth much less.

9

10

11

(Typo D.L.R.)

**1880** (23 Mar). *Wmk Crown CC. P* 14.

| No. | Type | Description | Unused | Used |
|---|---|---|---|---|
| 19 | 9 | ½d. stone | 1·50 | 3·50 |
| 20 | 10 | 4d. orange-red | 12·00 | 1·50 |

(Typo D.L.R.)

**1883–98.** *Wmk Crown CA. P* 14.

| No. | Type | Description | Unused | Used |
|---|---|---|---|---|
| 21 | 9 | ½d. dull green (Oct, 1892) | 1·90 | 1·90 |
| 21*a* | | ½d. deep grey-green (1893) | 1·90 | 70 |
| 22 | 1 | 1d. dull rose (Dec. 1883) | £100 | 3·00 |
| 23 | | 1d. rose-red | 60·00 | 2·25 |
| 24 | | 1d. carmine-rose (1886) | 32·00 | 70 |
| 24*a* | | 1d. aniline carmine (1889) | 3·50 | 20 |
| 25 | 2 | 2d. blue (Dec. 1886) | 35·00 | 3·25 |
| 26 | | 2d. aniline purple (July, 1893) | 8·50 | 3·75 |
| 26*a* | | 2d. brown-purple (1898) | 2·50 | 1·25 |
| 27 | 11 | 2½d. deep ultramarine (10.11.84) | 9·50 | 1·00 |
| 27*a* | | 2½d. pale ultramarine | 4·00 | 40 |
| 28 | 3 | 3d. grey (Jan, 1886) | 18·00 | 5·50 |
| 29 | 5 | 1s. yellow-brown (1893) | 15·00 | 13·00 |
| 29*a* | | 1s. olive-brown | 13·00 | 11·00 |
| 21/9*a* | | *Set of* 7 | 65·00 | 20·00 |
| 21, 26 & 29 Optd "Specimen" | | *Set of* 3 | £375 | |

**1893 PROVISIONAL POSTCARD.** During a shortage of 1d. stamps a limited supply of September 1880 postcard, franked with Nos. 19 and 22, was surcharged "One Penny" across the two stamps. This surcharge was applied by the *Royal Gazette* press. It is generally believed that an individual in the Post Office acquired all the examples, but provisional postcards are known used to Europe and, one example only, locally. *Price from* £550 *unused*, £1400 *used*.

(12)

13 Dry Dock

**1901.** *As Nos.* 29/*a but colour changed, surch with T* **12** *by D.L.R.*

| No. | Type | Description | Unused | Used |
|---|---|---|---|---|
| 30 | 5 | ¼d. on 1s. dull grey (11.1.01) (Optd S. £75) | 30 | 30 |
| 30*a* | | ¼d. on 1s. bluish grey (18.3.01) | 30 | 35 |
| | | ab. "F" in "FARTHING" inserted by handstamp | £4000 | |

Four examples of No. 30ab are known, one being in the Royal Collection and another used on postcard (*Price* £7000). It would appear that the "F" in position one of an unspecified horizontal row was either weak or missing and an additional impression of the letter was then inserted by a separate handstamp.

(Typo D.L.R.)

**1902** (Nov)–**04.** *Wmk Crown CA. P* 14.

| No. | Type | Description | Unused | Used |
|---|---|---|---|---|
| 31 | 13 | ½d. black and green (12.03) | 6·50 | 1·25 |
| 32 | | 1d. brown and carmine | 7·00 | 10 |
| 33 | | 3d. magenta and sage-green (9.03) | 1·75 | 1·75 |
| 34 | 10 | 4d. orange-brown (18.1.04) | 24·00 | 35·00 |
| 31/4 | | *Set of* 4 | 35·00 | 35·00 |
| 31/3 Optd "Specimen" | | *Set of* 3 | £130 | |

**1906–09.** *Wmk Mult Crown CA. P* 14.

| No. | Type | Description | Unused | Used |
|---|---|---|---|---|
| 34*a* | 13 | ¼d. brown and violet (9.08) | 50 | 2·00 |
| 35 | | ½d. black and green (12.06) | 8·50 | 65 |
| 36 | | 1d. brown and carmine (4.06) | 11·00 | 20 |
| 37 | | 2d. grey and orange (10.07) | 7·50 | 10·00 |
| 38 | | 2½d. brown and ultramarine (12.06) | 8·50 | 12·00 |
| 39 | | 4d. blue and chocolate (11.09) | 3·00 | 11·00 |
| 34*a*/39 | | *Set of* 6 | 35·00 | 32·00 |
| 34*a*, 37/39 Optd "Specimen" | | *Set of* 4 | £200 | |

**1908–10.** *Wmk Mult Crown CA. P* 14.

| No. | Type | Description | Unused | Used |
|---|---|---|---|---|
| 41 | 13 | ½d. green (3.09) | 3·75 | 2·50 |
| 42 | | 1d. red (5.08) | 13·00 | 10 |
| 43 | | 2½d. blue (14.2.10) | 12·00 | 5·75 |
| 41/3 | | *Set of* 3 | 26·00 | 7·50 |
| 41/3 Optd "Specimen" | | *Set of* 3 | £180 | |

14

15

**HIGH VALUE KEY TYPES.** The reign of King Edward VII saw the appearance of the first in a new series of "key type" designs, initially on the issues of Malaya — Straits Settlements and Nyasaland, to be used for high value denominations where a smaller design was felt to be inappropriate. The system was extended during the reign of King George V, using the portrait as Bermuda Type **15**, to cover Bermuda, Ceylon, Leeward Islands, Malaya — Straits Settlements, Malta and Nyasaland. A number of these territories continued to use the key type concept for high value King George VI stamps and one, Leeward Islands, for stamps of Queen Elizabeth II.

In each instance the King George V issues were printed in sheets of 60 (12 × 5) on various coloured papers. The system utilised a common "head" plate used with individual "duty" plates which printed the territory name and face value.

Two major plate flaws occur on the King George V head plate: the break in scroll on R.1/12 and the broken crown and scroll on R.2/12. Both of these occur in different states, having been repaired and then damaged once again, perhaps on several occasions. The prices quoted in the listings are for examples approximately as illustrated.

Break in scroll (R. 1/12)

Broken crown and scroll (R. 2/12)

(Recess (**14**), Typo (**15**) D.L.R.)

**1910–25.** *Wmk Mult Crown CA. Chalk-surfaced paper* (2*s. to* £1). *P* 14.

| No. | Type | Description | Unused | Used |
|---|---|---|---|---|
| 44 | 14 | ¼d. brown (26.3.12) | 1·50 | 2·25 |
| | | *a. Pale brown* | 40 | 1·50 |
| 45 | | ½d. green (4.6.10) | 1·25 | 25 |
| | | *a. Deep green* | 4·25 | 90 |
| 46 | | 1d. red (I) (15.10.10) | 10·00 | 25 |
| | | *a. Rose-red* | 13·00 | 25 |
| | | *b. Carmine* (12.19) | 35·00 | 5·50 |

47 14 2d. grey (1.13) .. .. .. 3·00 4·75
48 2½d. blue (27.3.12) .. .. .. 3·50 60
49 3d. purple/*yellow* (1.13) .. .. 1·75 5·00
49*a* 4d. red/*yellow* (1.9.19) .. .. 4·75 6·50
50 6d. purple (26.3.12) .. .. .. 13·00 17·00
*a. Pale claret* (2.6.24) .. .. 11·00 8·00
51 1s. black/*green* (26.3.12) .. .. 2·00 3·75
*a. Jet-black/olive* (1925) .. .. 3·50 9·00
51*b* 15 2s. purple and blue/*blue* (19.6.20) .. 11·00 32·00
ba. Break in scroll .. .. .. £110
bb. Broken crown and scroll .. .. £110
52 2s. 6d. black and red/*blue* (1.4.18) .. 18·00 50·00
a. Break in scroll .. .. .. £140
52*b* 4s. black and carmine (19.6.20) .. 60·00 75·00
ba. Break in scroll .. .. .. £225
bb. Broken crown and scroll .. .. £225
53 5s. deep green & dp red/*yellow* (1.4.18) 50·00 75·00
a. Break in scroll .. .. .. £190
b. Broken crown and scroll .. .. £190
*c. Green & carm-red/pale yell* (1920) 35·00 55·00
ca. Break in scroll .. .. .. £160
cb. Broken crown and scroll .. .. £160
54 10s. grn & carm/*pale bluish grn* (1.4.18) £150 £200
a. Break in scroll .. .. .. £400
b. Broken crown and scroll .. .. £400
*c. Green & red/pale bluish grn* (1922) £130 £170
ca. Break in scroll .. .. .. £350
cb. Broken crown and scroll .. .. £350
55 £1 purple and black/*red* (1.4.18) .. £400 £600
a. Break in scroll .. .. .. £800
b. Broken crown and scroll .. .. £900
44/55 .. .. .. *Set of* 15 £600 £900
44/55 Optd "Specimen" .. .. *Set of* 15 £1000

Nos. 44 to 51*a* are comb-perforated 13.8×14 or 14. No. 45 exists also line-perforated 14, probably from the printing dispatched to Bermuda on 13 March 1911.

Beware of cleaned copies of the 10s. with faked postmarks.

See also Nos. 76*b*/93

**WAR TAX** (16) **WAR TAX** (17)

**1918** (4 May). *Nos. 46 and 46a optd locally with T* **16**.
56 14 1d. red .. .. .. .. 35 40
*a. Rose-red* .. .. .. .. 30 90

**1920** (5 Feb). *No. 46b optd with T* **17**.
58 14 1d. carmine .. .. .. .. 20 80

The War Tax stamps represented a compulsory levy in addition to normal postal fees until 31 Dec 1920. Subsequently they were valid for ordinary postage.

18

19

(Des by the Governor (Gen. Sir James Willcocks). Typo D.L.R.)

**1920** (11 Nov)–**21**. *Tercentenary of Representative Institutions (1st issue). Chalk-surfaced paper (3d. to 1s.). P 14.*

(*a*) *Wmk Mult Crown CA (sideways)* (19.1.21)
59 18 ¼d. brown .. .. .. .. 60 6·50
a. "C" missing from wmk .. .. £110
b. "A" missing from wmk
60 ½d. green .. .. .. .. 1·25 7·00
61 2d. grey .. .. .. .. 8·50 23·00
a. "C" missing from wmk .. .. £200
62 3d. dull and deep purple/*pale yellow* .. 8·00 20·00
63 4d. black and red/*pale yellow* .. .. 8·50 18·00
64 1s. black/*blue-green* .. .. .. 16·00 38·00

(*b*) *Wmk Mult Script CA (sideways)*
65 18 1d. carmine .. .. .. .. 1·00 30
66 2½d. bright blue .. .. .. 6·50 8·00
67 6d. dull and bright purple (19.1.21) .. 15·00 38·00
59/67 .. .. .. *Set of* 9 60·00 £140
59/67 Optd "Specimen" .. .. *Set of* 9 £275

(Des. H. J. Dale. Recess D.L.R.)

**1921** (12 May). *Tercentenary of Representative Institutions (2nd issue). P 14.* (*a*) *Wmk Crown CA (sideways).*
68 19 2d. slate-grey .. .. .. 4·50 15·00
69 2½d. bright ultramarine .. .. .. 8·00 3·00
a. "C" missing from wmk .. .. £200
b. "A" missing from wmk .. .. £200
70 3d. purple/*pale yellow* .. .. .. 4·00 12·00
71 4d. red/*pale yellow* .. .. .. 14·00 17·00
72 6d. purple .. .. .. .. 8·00 29·00
a. "C" missing from wmk .. .. £250
73 1s. black/*green* .. .. .. .. 21·00 32·00

(*b*) *Wmk Mult Script CA (sideways)*
74 19 ¼d. brown .. .. .. .. 35 2·75
75 ½d. green .. .. .. .. 2·75 6·00
76 1d. deep carmine .. .. .. 2·00 35
a. "C" missing from wmk .. ..
68/76 .. .. .. *Set of* 9 60·00 £110
68/76 Optd "Specimen" .. .. *Set of* 9 £275

### *MINIMUM PRICE*

The minimum price quote is 10p which represents a handling charge rather than a basis for valuing common stamps. For further notes about prices see introductory pages.

I II III

*Three Types of the 1d.*
I. Scroll at top left very weak and figure "1" has pointed serifs.
II. Scroll weak. "1" has square serifs and "1d" is heavy.
III. Redrawn. Scroll is completed by a strong line and "1" is thinner with long square serifs.

I II

*Two Types of the 2½d.*
I. Short, thick figures, especially of the "1", small "d".
II. Figures taller and thinner, "d" larger.

**1922–34.** *Wmk Mult Script CA. Chalk-surfaced paper (2s. to 12s. 6d.). P 14.*
76*b* 14 ¼d. brown (7.28) .. .. .. 70 1·25
77 ½d. green (11.22) .. .. .. 50 15
78 1d. scarlet (I) (11.22) .. .. .. 7·50 60
*a. Carmine* (6.24) .. .. .. 13·00 60
78*b* 1d. carmine (II) (12.25) .. .. 16·00 2·25
*c. Scarlet* (8.27) .. .. .. 8·00 80
79 1d. scarlet (III) (10.28) .. .. 6·00 30
*a. Carmine-lake* (1934) .. .. 12·00 75
79*b* 1½d. red-brown (27.3.34) .. .. 3·50 35
80 2d. grey (12.23) .. .. .. 1·00 1·50
81 2½d. pale sage-green (12.22) .. .. 2·00 1·50
*a. Deep sage-green* (1924) .. .. 1·00 1·50
82 2½d. ultramarine (I) (1.12.26) .. .. 2·50 35
82*a* 2½d. ultramarine (II) (3.32) .. .. 1·75 35
83 3d. ultramarine (12.24) .. .. 15·00 25·00
84 3d. purple/*yellow* (10.26) .. .. 80 1·00
85 4d. red/*yellow* (8.24) .. .. .. 1·00 1·25
86 6d. purple (8.24) .. .. .. 80 80
87 1s. black/*emerald* (10.27) .. .. 4·75 6·00
*a. Brownish black/yellow-green* (1934) 30·00 45·00
88 15 2s. purple & brt blue/*pale blue* (1.9.27) 35·00 55·00
a. Break in scroll .. .. .. £130
b. Broken crown and scroll .. .. £130
*c. Purple and blue/grey-blue* (1931) .. 35·00 55·00
ca. Break in scroll .. .. .. £130
cb. Broken crown and scroll .. .. £130
89 2s. 6d. black & carmine/*pale blue* (4.27) 48·00 70·00
a. Break in scroll .. .. .. £160
b. Broken crown and scroll .. .. £160
*c. Black & red/blue to deep blue* (6.29) 48·00 70·00
ca. Break in scroll .. .. .. £160
cb. Broken crown and scroll .. .. £160
*d. Grey-black and pale orange-vermilion/grey-blue* (3.30) .. .. £2500 £2500
da. Break in scroll .. .. .. £3500
db. Broken crown and scroll .. .. £3500
*e. Black & vermilion/deep blue* (9.31) 48·00 70·00
ea. Break in scroll .. .. .. £160
eb. Broken crown and scroll .. .. £160
*f. Black & brt orge-verm/dp bl* (8.32) £2750 £2500
fb. Broken crown and scroll .. .. £3750
92 10s. green and red/*pale emerald* (12.24) £120 £180
b. Broken crown and scroll .. .. £350
*c. Green and red/deep emerald* (1931) £120 £170
cb. Broken crown and scroll .. .. £350
93 12s. 6d. grey and orange (8.32) .. £300 £350
a. Break in scroll .. .. .. £600
b. Broken crown and scroll .. .. £600
c. Error. Ordinary paper .. ..
76*b*/93 .. .. .. *Set of* 16 £475 £600
76*b*/93 Optd/Perf "Specimen" .. *Set of* 16 £850

Values to 1s. come perforated either comb (13.8×14) or line (13.75, 14, 13.75×14 or 14×13.75). Nos. 78/*a* and 83 only exist comb-perforated, Nos. 76*b*, 78*b*/9*b*, 81*a*, 82*a* and 87*a* line-perforated and the remainder come in both forms.

The true No. 89*d* is the only stamp on grey-blue paper; other deeper orange-vermilion shades exist on different papers.

Beware of fiscally used 2s. 6d. 10s. and 12s. 6d. stamps cleaned and bearing faked postmarks. Large quantities were used for a "head tax" levied on travellers leaving the country.

For 12s. 6d. design inscribed "Revenue" at both sides see No. F1 under POSTAL FISCAL.

(Recess Waterlow)

**1935** (6 May). *Silver Jubilee. As T* **13** *of Antigua. Wmk Mult Script CA. P 11 × 12.*
94 1d. deep blue and scarlet .. .. 45 55
95 1½d. ultramarine and grey .. .. 70 95
96 2½d. brown and deep blue .. .. 1·40 90
97 1s. slate and purple .. .. .. 9·00 14·00
j. Kite and vertical log .. .. 80·00
k. Kite and horizontal log .. .. 90·00
94/7 .. .. .. *Set of* 4 10·50 15·00
94/7 Perf "Specimen" .. .. *Set of* 4 £150

For illustrations of plate varieties see Catalogue Introduction.

**20** Hamilton Harbour

**21** South shore near Spanish Rock

**22** *Lucie* (yacht)

**23** Grape Bay, Paget Parish

**24** Point House, Warwick Parish

**25** House at Par-la-Ville, Hamilton

(Recess B.W.)

**1936** (14 Apr)–**47**. *Wmk Mult Script CA (sideways on horiz designs). P 12.*
98 20 ½d. bright green .. .. .. 10 10
99 21 1d. black and scarlet .. .. .. 15 15
100 1½d. black and chocolate .. .. .. 75 15
101 22 2d. black and pale blue .. .. .. 4·50 2·00
102 23 2½d. light and deep blue .. .. .. 80 25
103 24 3d. black and scarlet .. .. .. 2·25 90
104 25 6d. carmine-lake and violet .. .. 60 10
*a. Claret and dull violet* (6.47) .. 1·75 35
105 23 1s. green .. .. .. .. 3·25 4·75
106 20 1s. 6d. brown .. .. .. .. 30 10
98/106 .. .. .. *Set of* 9 11·50 7·50
98/106 Perf "Specimen" .. .. *Set of* 9 £225

All are line-perf 11.9, except printings of the 6d. from July 1951 onwards, which are comb-perf 11.9 × 11.75.

**1937** (14 May). *Coronation. As Nos. 95/7 of Antigua, but printed by D.L.R. P 14.*
107 1d. scarlet .. .. .. .. 50 50
108 1½d. yellow-brown .. .. .. 60 45
109 2½d. bright blue .. .. .. 1·10 1·50
107/9 .. .. .. *Set of* 3 2·00 2·25
107/9 Perf "Specimen" .. .. *Set of* 3 85·00

**26** Ships in Hamilton Harbour

**27** St. David's Lighthouse

**28** White-tailed Tropic Bird, Arms of Bermuda and Native Flower

(Des Miss Higginbotham (T **28**). Recess B.W.)

**1938** (20 Jan)–**1952**. *T* **22**, *T* **23** *(but with portrait of King George VI) and T* **26** *to* **28**. *Wmk Mult Script CA. P 12.*
110 26 1d. black and red (*a*) (*b*) .. .. 40 20
111 1½d. deep blue and purple-brown (*a*) (*b*) 2·50 1·00
*a. Blue and brown* (*a*) (3.43) .. 3·00 1·75
*b. Lt blue & purple-brn* (*a*) (*b*) (9.45) 1·25 35
112 22 2d. light blue and sepia (*a*) .. .. 38·00 5·00
112*a* 2d. ultramarine and scarlet (*a*) (*b*) (12.11.40) .. .. .. 1·50 80
113 23 2½d. light and deep blue (*a*) .. .. 11·00 90
113*a* 2½d. lt blue & sepia-black (*a*) (18.12.41) 2·00 80
*b. Pale blue & sepia-black* (*a*) (3.43) 2·25 1·25
*c. Bright blue and deep sepia-black* (*b*) (23.9.52) .. .. .. 1·50 80
114 27 3d. black and rose-red (*a*) .. .. 11·00 70
114*a* 3d. black & deep blue (*a*) (*b*) (16.7.41) 1·50 40
114*b* 28 7½d. black, blue & brt grn (*a*) (18.12.41) 4·75 1·50
*c. Black, blue & yellow-grn* (*a*) (3.43) 3·75 2·25
115 23 1s. green (*a*) (*b*) .. .. .. 1·75 50
*a. Bluish green* (*b*) (20.6.52) .. .. 5·00 3·50

*Perforations.* Two different perforating machines were used on the various printings of these stamps: (*a*) the original 11.9 line perforation; (*b*) 11.9 × 11.75 comb perforation, introduced in July 1950. These perforations occur as indicated above.

29 King George VI

Shading omitted from top right scroll (R. 1/1. March 1943 ptgs of 2s. and £1)

Lower right scroll with broken tail (R. 2/10. Line perforated printings only)

Broken top right scroll (R. 5/11. Line perforated ptgs only. A retouched state of the flaw is visible in later ptgs up to March 1943)

Broken lower right scroll (R. 5/12. Occurs on printings made between May 1941 and March 1943)

Gash in chin (R. 2/5. Occurs on ptgs made between May 1941 and March 1943)

(Typo D.L.R.)

**1938** (20 Jan)–**53.** *T* **29.** *Chalk-surfaced paper. P* 14 (*comb*).

(*a*) *Wmk Mult Script CA.*

116 2s. deep purple and ultramarine/*grey-blue* £100 10·00
a. Perf 14¹/₄ line. *Deep purple and ultram /grey-blue* (14.11.41)* £225 70·00
ac. Lower right scroll with broken tail £500 £180
ad. Broken top right scroll £600 £225
ae. Broken lower right scroll £600 £225
af. Gash in chin £500 £180
b. Ordinary paper. *Pur & bl/dp bl* (7.6.42) 7·00 1·50
be. Broken lower right scroll £140 50·00
bf. Gash in chin £120 40·00
c. Ordinary paper. *Purple and deep blue/ pale blue* (5.3.43) 9·00 1·50
cb. Shading omitted from top right scroll £400 £200
ce. Broken lower right scroll £350 £180
cf. Gash in chin £275 £140
d. Perf 13. Ordinary paper. *Dull purple and blue/pale blue* (15.2.50) 15·00 10·00
e. Perf 13. Ordinary paper. *Reddish purple and blue/pale blue* (10.10.50) 7·50 7·00
117 2s. 6d. black and red/*grey-blue* 60·00 6·50
a. Perf 14¹/₄ line. *Black and red/grey-blue* (21.2.42)* £325 £100
ac. Lower right scroll with broken tail £650 £250
ad. Broken top right scroll £800 £300
ae. Broken lower right scroll £800 £300
af. Gash in chin £650 £250
b. Ordinary paper. *Black and red/pale blue* (5.3.43) 16·00 6·50
be. Broken lower right scroll £300
bf. Gash in chin £225
c. Perf 13. Ordinary paper. *Black and orange-red/pale blue* (10.10.50) 18·00 9·00
d. Perf 13. Ordinary paper. *Black and red/ pale blue* (18.6.52) 13·00 9·00
118 5s. green and red/*yellow* £100 20·00
a. *Pale green and red/yellow* (14.3.39)* £170 42·00
b. Perf 14¹/₄ line. *Green and red/yellow* (5.1.43)* £170 28·00
bc. Lower right scroll with broken tail £325 £130
bd. Broken top right scroll £425 £170
be. Broken lower right scroll £425 £170
bf. Gash in chin £325 £130
c. Ordinary paper. *Dull yellow-green and carmine-red/pale yellow* (5.42) £180 75·00
ce. Broken lower right scroll £1500
cf. Gash in chin £1100
d. Ordinary paper. *Pale bluish green and carmine-red/pale yellow* (5.3.43) £100 50·00
de. Broken lower right scroll £400
df. Gash in chin £300
e. Ordinary paper. *Green and red/pale yellow* (11.45)* 38·00 15·00
f. Perf 13. Ordinary paper. *Yellow-green and red/pale yellow* (15.2.50) 13·00 11·00
g. Perf 13. *Green and scarlet/yellow (chalk-surfaced)* (10.10.50) 15·00 13·00
119 10s. green and deep lake/*pale emerald* £400 £250
a. *Bluish green and deep red/green* (8.39)* £200 £130
b. Perf 14¹/₄ line. Ordinary paper. *Yellowish green & dp red/green* (1942)* £300 £160
bc. Lower right scroll with broken tail £600 £375
bd. Broken top right scroll £750 £475
be. Broken lower right scroll £750 £475
bf. Gash in chin £600 £375
c. Ordinary paper. *Yellowish green and deep carmine-red/green* (5.3.43) 75·00 50·00
ce. Broken lower right scroll £1100
cf. Gash in chin £800
d. Ordinary paper. *Deep green and dull red/green (emerald back)* (11.12.46) 85·00 55·00
e. Perf 13. Ordinary paper. *Green and vermilion/green* (19.9.51) 27·00 28·00
f. Perf 13. Ordinary paper. *Green and dull red/green* (16.4.53) 22·00 32·00
120 12s. 6d. deep grey and brownish orange £475 £400
a. *Grey and brownish orange (shades)* £150 50·00
b. *Grey and pale orange* (9.11.40)* 70·00 40·00
c. Ordinary paper (2.3.44)* 70·00 40·00
ce. Broken lower right scroll £800
cf. Gash in chin £600
d. Ordinary paper. *Grey & yell*† (7.9.47)* £500 £475
e. Perf 13. *Grey and pale orange (chalk-surfaced)* (10.10.50) 85·00 60·00

(*b*) *Wmk Mult Crown CA*

121 £1 purple and black/*red* £250 £110
a. *Pale purple & black/pale red* (13.3.43)* 75·00 55·00
ab. Shading omitted from top right scroll £700
ae. Broken lower right scroll £600
af. Gash in chin £450
b. *Deep reddish purple and black/pale red* (29.3.45)* 60·00 45·00
be. Broken lower right scroll £750
bf. Gash in chin £600
c. Perf 13. *Violet & black/scarlet* (7.12.51) 45·00 60·00
d. Perf 13. *Brt violet & blk/scar* (10.12.52) £160 £130
110/21c *Set of* 16 £200 £130
110/21 Perf "Specimen" *Set of* 16 £1200

Following extensive damage to their printing works on 29 December 1940 much of De La Rue's work was transferred to other firms operating under their supervision. It is understood that Williams Lea & Co produced those new printings ordered for the Bermuda high value stamps during 1941. The first batch of these printings showed the emergency use, by Williams Lea, of a 14¹/₄ line perforating machine (exact gauge 14.15) instead of the comb perforation (exact gauge 13.9 × 13.8).

Dates marked * are those of earliest known use.

In No. 116*b* the coloured surfacing of the paper is mottled with white specks sometimes accompanied by very close horizontal lines. In Nos. 116*c*, 117*b* and 118*a* the surfacing is the same colour as the back, sometimes applied in widely spaced horizontal lines giving the appearance of laid paper.

†No. 120d is the so-called "lemon" shade.

HALF
PENNY

X X

(30)

31 Postmaster Perot's Stamp

**1940** (20 Dec). *No.* 110 *surch with T* **30**.
122 **26** ½d. on 1d. black and red (*shades*) 15 45

The spacing between "PENNY" and "X" varies from 12½ mm to 14 mm.

**1946** (6 Nov). *Victory. As Nos.* 110/11 *of Antigua.*
123 1½d. brown 15 15
124 3d. blue 15 15
123/4 Perf "Specimen" *Set of* 2 75·00

**1948** (1 Dec). *Royal Silver Wedding. As Nos.* 112/13 *of Antigua.*
125 1½d. red-brown 30 50
126 £1 carmine 48·00 48·00

(Recess B.W.)

**1949** (11 Apr). *Centenary of Postmaster Perot's Stamp. Wmk Mult Script CA. P* 13½.
127 **31** 2½d. blue and brown 15 15
128 3d. black and blue 15 15
129 6d. violet and green 15 15
127/9 *Set of* 3 40 40

**1949** (10 Oct). *75th Anniv of Universal Postal Union. As Nos.* 114/17 *of Antigua.*
130 2½d. blue-black 75 75
131 3d. deep blue 90 75
132 6d. purple 1·00 75
133 1s. blue-green 1·00 75
130/3 *Set of* 4 3·25 2·75

**1953** (4 June). *Coronation. As No.* 120 *of Antigua, but ptd by B.W.*
134 1½d. black and blue 35 15

32 Easter Lilies

34 Easter Lily

37 Map of Bermuda

Die I "Sandy's" Die II "Sandys"

(Des C. Deakins (½d., 3d., 1s. 3d., 5s.), J. Berry (1d., 1½d., 2½d., 4d., 1s.). B. Brown (2d., 6d., 8d.), D. Haig (4½d., 9d.), Pamela Braley-Smith (2s. 6d.) and E. C. Leslie (10s.) Recess (except £1, centre typo), B.W.)

**1953** (9 Nov)–**62.** *T* **32, 34, 37,** *and similar designs. Wmk Mult Script CA. P* 13½.
135 **32** ½d. olive-green 10 40
a. *Yellow-olive* (19.5.54) 10 35
136 – 1d. black and red 30 35
a. *Black and deep red* (19.5.54) 30 15
137 **34** 1½d. green 20 10
138 – 2d. ultramarine and brown-red 40 30
139 – 2½d. rose-red 1·25 50
140 **37** 3d. deep purple (I) 30 10
140*a* 3d. deep purple (II) (2.1.57) 80 10
141 – 4d. black and bright blue 30 30
142 – 4½d. emerald 45 80
143 – 6d. black and deep turquoise 4·00 40
143*a* – 8d. black and red (16.5.55) 1·75 20
143*b* – 9d. violet (6.1.58) 6·00 1·50
144 – 1s. orange 40 15
145 **37** 1s. 3d. blue (I) 1·50 30
a. *Greenish blue* (21.9.54) 2·00 60
145*b* 1s. 3d. blue (II) (2.1.57) 4·50 30
*bc. Bright blue* (14.8.62) 4·50 75
146 – 2s. brown 2·00 85
147 – 2s. 6d. scarlet 1·75 45
148 – 5s. carmine 10·00 85
149 – 10s. deep ultramarine 9·00 4·50
a. *Ultramarine* (13.2.57) 18·00 9·00
150 – £1 brown, blue, red, grn & bronze-grn 20·00 19·00
135/150 *Set of* 18 55·00 28·00

Designs: *Horiz*—1d., 4d. Postmaster Perot's stamps; 2d. *Victory II* (racing dinghy); 2½d. Sir George Somers and *Sea Venture*; 4½d., 9d. *Sea Venture*, inter-island boat, coin and Perot stamp; 6d., 8d. White-tailed Tropic Bird; 1s. Early Bermudian coinage; 2s. Arms of St. Georges; 5s. Hog coin; 10s. Obverse and reverse of hog coin; £1 Arms of Bermuda. *Vert.*—2s. 6d. Warwick Fort.

Nos. 136, 138 and 143 exist in coils, constructed from normal sheets.

**1953** (26 Nov). *Royal Visit. As No.* 143 *but inscr* "ROYAL VISIT 1953" *in top left corner.*
151 6d. black and deep turquoise 30 20

**Three Power Talks**
**December, 1953.**
(46)

**Three Power Talks**
**December, 1953.**
(46*a*)

First setting (Type **46**). First line 24¹/₂ mm long.
Second setting (Type **46***a*). First line 25¹/₄ mm long.

**1953** (8 Dec). *Three Power Talks. Nos.* 140 *and* 145 *optd with T* **46**.
152 **37** 3d. deep purple (Type **46**) (B.) 10 10
a. Optd with Type **46***a* 20 15
153 1s. 3d. blue (Type **46**) (R.) 10 10
a. Optd with Type **46***a* 90 1·00

**50TH ANNIVERSARY**
**U S – BERMUDA**
**OCEAN RACE 1956**
(47)

48 Perot's Post Office

**1956** (22 June). *50th Anniv of United States–Bermuda Yacht Race. Nos. 143a and 145a optd with T* **47** *by the Bermuda Press.*

154 8d. black and red (Bk.) .. .. .. 20 25
155 1s. 3d. greenish blue (R.) .. .. .. 20 30

(Des W. Harrington. Recess B.W.)

**1959** (1 Jan.) *Wmk Mult Script CA. P* 13½.

156 **48** 6d. black and deep mauve .. .. 30 15

**49** Arms of King James I and Queen Elizabeth II

(Des W. Harrington. Recess; arms litho D.L.R.)

**1959** (29 July). *350th Anniv of First Settlement. Arms, red, yellow and blue; frame colours below. W* w **12**. *P* 13.

157 **49** 1½d. grey-blue .. .. .. .. 20 10
158 3d. drab-grey .. .. .. .. 25 30
159 4d. reddish purple .. .. .. .. 30 35
160 8d. slate-violet .. .. .. .. 30 15
161 9d. olive-green .. .. .. .. 30 80
162 1s. 3d. brown .. .. .. .. 30 25
157/162 .. .. .. .. *Set of* 6 1·50 1·75

**50** The Old Rectory, St. George's, *circa* 1730 **67** *Tsotsi in the Bundu* (Finn class yacht)

(Des W. Harrington. Photo Harrison)

**1962** (26 Oct)–**68**. *Horiz designs as T* **50**. *W* w **12** *(upright). P* 12½.

163 1d. reddish purple, black and orange .. 10 35
164 2d. lilac, indigo, yellow and green .. 10 15
a. Lilac omitted .. .. .. £700 £350
b. Green omitted .. .. .. † —
c. Imperf (pair) .. .. .. £750
*d. Pale lilac, indigo, yellow and green* (22.10.68) .. .. .. 30 15
165 3d. yellow-brown and light blue .. 10 10
a. Yellow-brown omitted .. .. £2000
166 4d. red-brown and magenta .. .. 20 35
167 5d. grey-blue and rose .. .. 75 2·00
168 6d. grey-blue, emerald and light blue .. 20 20
169 8d. bright blue, bright green and orange 30 20
170 9d. light blue and brown .. .. 25 25
170*a* 10d. violet and ochre (8.2.65) .. 4·00 1·00
171 1s. black, emerald, bright blue & orange 20 10
172 1s. 3d. lake, grey and bistre .. .. 50 15
173 1s. 6d. violet and ochre .. .. 1·50 2·50
174 2s. red-brown and orange .. .. 2·00 1·25
175 2s. 3d. bistre-brown and yellow-green .. 2·00 5·50
176 2s. 6d. bistre-brn, bluish grn & olive-yell 55 35
177 5s. brown-purple and blue-green .. 1·25 1·50
178 10s. magenta, deep bluish green and buff 4·00 5·00
179 £1 black, yellow-olive and yellow-orange 14·00 13·00
163/79 .. .. .. *Set of* 18 29·00 30·00

Designs:—2d. Church of St. Peter, St. Georges; 3d. Government House, 1892; 4d. The Cathedral, Hamilton, 1894; 5d. H.M. Dockyard, 1811; 6d. Perot's Post Office, 1848; 8d. G.P.O. Hamilton, 1869; 9d. Library, Par-la-Ville; 10d., 1s. 6d. Bermuda cottage, *circa* 1705; 1s. Christ Church, Warwick, 1719; 1s. 3d. City Hall, Hamilton, 1960; 2s. Town of St. George; 2s. 3d. Bermuda house, *circa* 1710; 2s. 6d. Bermuda house, early 18th-century; 5s. Colonial Secretariat, 1833; 10s. Old Post Office, Somerset, 1890; £1 The House of Assembly, 1815.

A single copy of No. 164b is known, used on piece.

See also Nos. 195/200 and 246a.

**1963** (4 June). *Freedom from Hunger. As No.* 146 *of Antigua.*

180 1s. 3d. sepia .. .. .. .. 80 35

**1963** (2 Sept). *Red Cross Centenary. As Nos.* 147/8 *of Antigua.*

181 3d. red and black .. .. .. 75 25
182 1s. 3d. red and blue .. .. .. 2·00 1·75

(Des V. Whiteley. Photo D.L.R.)

**1964** (28 Sept). *Olympic Games, Tokyo. W* w **12**. *P* 14 × 13½.

183 **67** 3d. red, violet and blue .. .. .. 10 10

**1965** (17 May). *I.T.U. Centenary. As Nos.* 166/7 *of Antigua.*

184 3d. light blue and emerald .. .. 75 25
185 2s. yellow and ultramarine .. .. 1·50 1·25

(Des W. Harrington. Photo Harrison)

**1965** (24 July). *50th Anniv of Bermuda Boy Scouts Association. W* w **12**. *P* 12½.

186 **68** 2s. multicoloured .. .. .. 50 50

**1965** (25 Oct). *International Co-operation Year. As Nos.* 168/9 *of Antigua.*

187 4d. reddish purple and turquoise-green .. 50 20
188 2s. 6d. deep bluish green and lavender .. 1·50 80

**1966** (24 Jan). *Churchill Commemoration. As Nos.* 170/3 *of Antigua.*

189 3d. new blue .. .. .. .. 50 20
190 6d. deep green .. .. .. .. 1·00 45
191 10d. brown .. .. .. .. 1·25 75
192 1s. 3d. bluish violet .. .. .. 1·50 1·75
189/92 .. .. .. *Set of* 4 4·75 2·75

**1966** (1 July). *World Cup Football Championships. As Nos.* 176/7 *of Antigua.*

193 10d. violet, yellow-green, lake & yellow-brn .. 50 15
194 2s. 6d. chocolate, blue-grn, lake & yell-brn .. 75 65

**1966** (25 Oct)–**69**. *Designs as Nos.* 164, 167 (1s. 6d.), 169, 170*a*/1 *and* 174 *but W* w **12** *(sideways).*

195 2d. lilac, indigo, yellow and green (20.5.69) .. 1·75 2·00
196 8d. bright blue, bright green and orange (14.2.67) .. .. .. 50 70
197 10d. violet and ochre (1.11.66) .. 75 60
198 1s. black, emerald, bright blue and orange (14.2.67) .. .. .. 50 55
199 1s. 6d. grey-blue and rose (1.11.66) .. 3·25 1·75
200 2s. red-brown and orange .. .. 3·00 3·25
195/200 .. .. .. *Set of* 6 8·75 8·00

The 2d. value exists with PVA gum only, and the 8d. exists with PVA gum as well as gum arabic.

**1966** (1 Dec). *20th Anniv of U.N.E.S.C.O. As Nos.* 196/8 *of Antigua.*

201 4d. slate-violet, red, yellow and orange .. 60 15
202 1s. 3d. orange-yellow, violet and deep olive 1·25 65
203 2s. black, bright purple and orange .. 2·00 1·25
201/3 .. .. .. *Set of* 3 3·50 1·90

**69** G.P.O. Building

(Des G. Vasarhelyi. Photo Harrison)

**1967** (23 June). *Opening of New General Post Office. Hamilton. W* w **12**. *P* 14½.

204 **69** 3d. multicoloured .. .. .. 10 10
205 1s. multicoloured .. .. .. 10 10
206 1s. 6d. multicoloured .. .. .. 15 20
207 2s. 6d. multicoloured .. .. .. 15 30
204/7 .. .. .. *Set of* 4 45 55

**70** *Mercury* (cable ship) and Chain Links

(Des V. Whiteley. Photo Harrison)

**1967** (14 Sept). *Inauguration of Bermuda–Tortola Telephone Service. T* **70** *and similar horiz designs. Multicoloured. W* w **12**. *P* 14½ × 14.

208 3d. Type **70** .. .. .. .. 10 10
209 1s. Map, telephone and microphone .. .. 10 10
210 1s. 6d. Telecommunications media .. .. 20 20
211 2s. 6d. *Mercury* (cable ship) and marine fauna .. .. .. .. 25 30
208/11 .. .. .. *Set of* 4 50 55

**74** Human Rights Emblem and Doves

(Des M. Farrar Bell. Litho Harrison)

**1968** (1 Feb). *Human Rights Year. W* w **12**. *P* 14 × 14½.

212 **74** 3d. indigo, blue and dull green .. .. 10 10
213 1s. yellow-brown, blue and light blue .. 10 10
214 1s. 6d. black, blue and rose .. .. 10 10
215 2s. 6d. grey-green, blue and yellow .. 15 15
212/15 .. .. .. *Set of* 4 30 30

**REPRESENTATIVE GOVERNMENT**

**75** Mace and Queen's Profile

(Des R. Granger Barrett. Photo Harrison)

**1968** (1 July). *New Constitution. T* **75** *and similar horiz design. W* w **12**. *P* 14.

216 **75** 3d. multicoloured .. .. .. 10 10
217 1s. multicoloured .. .. .. 10 10
218 – 1s. 6d. greenish yellow, black & turq-bl 10 15
219 – 2s. 6d. lilac, black and orange-yellow .. 15 20
216/19 .. .. .. *Set of* 4 30 45

Design:—1s. 6d., 2s. 6d. Houses of Parliament and House of Assembly, Bermuda.

**77** Football, Athletics and Yachting

(Des V. Whiteley. Photo Harrison)

**1968** (24 Sept). *Olympic Games, Mexico. W* w **12**. *P* 12½.

220 **77** 3d. multicoloured .. .. .. 10 10
a. Red-brown ("BERMUDA" and value) omitted .. .. .. £2000
221 1s. multicoloured .. .. .. 10 10
222 1s. 6d. multicoloured .. .. .. 15 15
223 2s. 6d. multicoloured .. .. .. 20 30
220/3 .. .. .. *Set of* 4 45 50

**78** Brownie and Guide

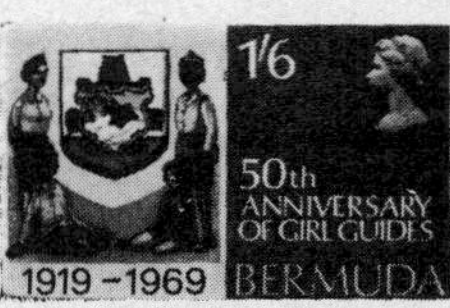


**79** Guides and Badge

(Des Harrison. Litho Format)

**1969** (17 Feb). *50th Anniv of Bermuda Girl Guides. P* 14.

224 **78** 3d. multicoloured .. .. .. 10 10
225 1s. multicoloured .. .. .. 20 10
226 **79** 1s. 6d. multicoloured .. .. .. 25 25
227 2s. 6d. multicoloured .. .. .. 35 50
224/7 .. .. .. *Set of* 4 80 80

1c

**80** Emerald-studded Gold Cross and Seaweed **(82)**

(Des K. Giles adapted by V. Whiteley. Photo Harrison)

**1969** (29 Sept). *Underwater Treasure. T* **80** *and similar vert design. Multicoloured. W* w **12** *(sideways). P* 14½ × 14.

228 4d. Type **80** .. .. .. .. 20 10
229 1s. 3d. Emerald-studded gold cross and seabed .. .. .. .. 35 15
230 2s. Type **80** .. .. .. .. 45 55
231 2s. 6d. As 1s. 3d. .. .. .. 45 80
228/31 .. .. .. *Set of* 4 1·25 1·40

**(New Currency. 100 cents = 1 dollar)**

**1970** (6 Feb). *Decimal Currency. As Nos.* 163, 165/6, 168, 170, 172, 175/9 *and* 195/200 *surch as T* **82**. *W* w **12** *(sideways on* 2, 5, 10, 12, 15, 18, 24, 30, 60 *c.,* $1.20 *and* $2.40*).*

232 1 c. on 1d. reddish purple, black and orange 10 40
233 2 c. on 2d. lilac, indigo, yellow and green .. 10 10
a. Lilac omitted .. .. .. £600
b. Pair, one without surch
c. Wmk upright (No. 164) .. .. 60 1·25
ca. Surch on No. 164*d* .. .. 70 1·40
234 3 c. on 3d. yellow-brown and light blue .. 10 10
235 4 c. on 4d. red-brown and magenta (Br.) .. 10 10
236 5 c. on 8d. bright blue, brt green & orange 15 35
237 6 c. on 6d. grey-blue, emerald & light blue 15 30
a. Horiz pair, one with albino surch, the other with albino bar .. ..
238 9 c. on 9d. light blue and brown (Br.) .. 30 55
239 10 c. on 10d. violet and ochre .. .. 30 25
240 12 c. on 1s. black, emerald, brt blue & orange 30 15
241 15 c. on 1s. 3d. lake, grey and bistre .. 1·50 1·00
242 18 c. on 1s. 6d. grey-blue and rose .. 80 65
243 24 c. on 2s. red-brown and orange .. .. 85 75

244 30 c. on 2s. 6d. bistre-brown, bluish green and olive-yellow .. 1·00 1·25
245 36 c. on 2s. 3d. bistre-brown and yellow-green 1·75 2·50
246 60 c. on 5s. brown-purple and blue-green .. 2·25 2·75
 a. Surch omitted† .. .. .. £600
247 $1.20, on 10s. mag., dp bluish grn & buff .. 4·00 8·50
248 $2.40, on £1 black, yellow-olive & yell-orge 7·00 14·00
232/48 .. .. .. .. *Set of* 17 18·00 30·00

†No. 246a differs from the normal No. 177 by its watermark, which is sideways, and its gum, which is PVA.

**83** Spathiphyllum

(Des W. Harrington. Photo D.L.R.)

**1970** (6 July)–**75**. *Flowers. Multicoloured designs as T* **83**. W w **12** (*sideways on horiz designs*). *P* 14.

249 1 c. Type **83** .. .. .. .. .. 10 20
250 2 c. Bottlebrush .. .. .. .. .. 20 25
251 3 c. Oleander (*vert*) .. .. .. .. 10 10
252 4 c. Bermudiana .. .. .. .. .. 10 10
253 5 c. Poinsettia .. .. .. .. .. 30 20
254 6 c. Hibiscus .. .. .. .. .. 30 30
255 9 c. Cereus .. .. .. .. .. 20 35
256 10 c. Bougainvillea (*vert*) .. .. .. 20 15
257 12 c. Jacaranda .. .. .. .. .. 80 60
258 15 c. Passion-Flower .. .. .. .. 90 1·40
258*a* 17 c. As 15 c. (2.6.75) .. .. .. 2·25 2·00
259 18 c. Coralita .. .. .. .. .. 1·75 2·25
259*a* 20 c. As 18 c. (2.6.75) .. .. .. 2·25 2·00
260 24 c. Morning Glory .. .. .. .. 1·50 3·25
260*a* 25 c. As 24 c. (2.6.75) .. .. .. 2·25 2·50
261 30 c. Tecoma .. .. .. .. .. 1·00 1·25
262 36 c. Angel's Trumpet .. .. .. 1·25 2·25
262*a* 40 c. As 36 c. (2.6.75) .. .. .. 2·25 2·75
263 60 c. Plumbago .. .. .. .. 1·75 2·75
263*a* $1 As 60 c. (2.6.75) .. .. .. 3·00 3·75
264 $1.20, Bird of Paradise flower .. .. 2·75 3·50
264*a* $2 As $1.20 (2.6.75) .. .. .. 5·00 7·00
265 $2.40, Chalice Cup.. .. .. .. 5·50 9·00
265*a* $3 As $2.40 (2.6.75) .. .. .. 9·00 10·00
249/65*a* .. .. .. .. *Set of* 24 40·00 50·00

See also Nos. 303/6 and 340/1.

**84** The State House, St. George's

(Des G. Drummond. Litho Questa)

**1970** (12 Oct). *350th Anniv of Bermuda Parliament. T* **84** *and similar horiz designs. Multicoloured.* W w **12** (*sideways*). *P* 14.

266 4 c. Type **84** .. .. .. .. .. 10 10
267 15 c. The Sessions House, Hamilton .. .. 25 15
268 18 c. St. Peter's Church, St George's .. 25 20
269 24 c. Town Hall, Hamilton .. .. .. 35 45
266/9 .. .. .. .. *Set of* 4 85 75
**MS**270 131 × 95 mm. Nos. 266/9 .. .. 1·75 4·00

**85** Street Scene, St. George's

(Des G. Drummond. Litho Questa)

**1971** (8 Feb). *"Keep Bermuda Beautiful". T* **85** *and similar horiz designs. Multicoloured.* W w **12** (*sideways*). *P* 14.

271 4 c. Type **85** .. .. .. .. .. 20 10
272 15 c. Horseshoe Bay .. .. .. .. 55 45
273 18 c. Gibb's Hill Lighthouse .. .. .. 1·00 1·10
274 24 c. Hamilton Harbour .. .. .. 1·25 1·75
271/4 .. .. .. .. *Set of* 4 2·75 3·00

**86** Building of the *Deliverance*

(Des E. Amos. Adapted C. Abbott. Litho Questa)

**1971** (10 May). *Voyage of the "Deliverance". T* **86** *and similar multicoloured designs.* W w **12** (*sideways on* 4 *c. and* 24 *c.*). *P* 14.

275 4 c. Type **86** .. .. .. .. .. 50 20
276 15 c. *Deliverance* and *Patience* at Jamestown 1·50 1·75
277 18 c. Wreck of the *Sea Venture* .. .. 1·75 2·25
278 24 c. *Deliverance* and *Patience* on the high seas 1·90 2·50
275/8 .. .. .. .. *Set of* 4 5·00 6·00

The 15 c. and 18 c. are vert designs.

**87** Green overlooking Ocean View

(Des G. Drummond. Litho D.L.R.)

**1971** (1 Nov). *Golfing in Bermuda. T* **87** *and similar horiz designs. Multicoloured.* W w **12** (*sideways*). *P* 13.

279 4 c. Type **87** .. .. .. .. .. 30 10
280 15 c. Golfers at Port Royal .. .. .. 60 60
281 18 c. Castle Harbour .. .. .. .. 70 60
282 24 c. Belmont .. .. .. .. .. 85 85
279/82 .. .. .. .. *Set of* 4 2·25 2·00

**HEATH - NIXON**
**DECEMBER 1971**

(**88**)

**1971** (20 Dec). *Anglo-American Talks. Nos.* 252, 258, 259 *and* 260 *optd with T* **88** *by Format.*

283 4 c. Bermudiana .. .. .. .. 10 10
284 15 c. Passion Glory .. .. .. .. 10 20
285 18 c. Coralita .. .. .. .. .. 15 55
286 24 c. Morning Glory .. .. .. .. 20 70
283/6 .. .. .. .. *Set of* 4 50 1·40

**89** Bonefish

(Des Maynard Reece. Litho B.W.)

**1972** (21 Aug). *World Fishing Records. T* **89** *and similar horiz designs. Multicoloured.* W w **12**. *P* 13½ × 14.

287 4 c. Type **89** .. .. .. .. .. 30 10
288 15 c. Wahoo .. .. .. .. .. 35 30
289 18 c. Yellowfin Tuna .. .. .. .. 40 45
290 24 c. Greater Amberjack .. .. .. 45 70
287/90 .. .. .. .. *Set of* 4 1·40 1·40

**90** "Admiralty Oar" and Mace

(Des (from photograph by D. Groves) and photo Harrison)

**1972** (20 Nov). *Royal Silver Wedding. Multicoloured; background colour given.* W w **12**. *P* 14 × 14½.

291 **90** 4 c. bright bluish violet .. .. .. 10 10
292 15 c. rose-carmine .. .. .. .. 15 30

**91** Palmetto **92** Bernard Park, Pembroke, 1973

(Des Jennifer Toombs. Litho J.W.)

**1973** (3 Sept). *Tree Planting Year. T* **91** *and similar vert designs. Multicoloured.* W w **12** (*sideways*). *P* 14.

293 4 c. Type **91** .. .. .. .. .. 30 10
294 15 c. Olivewood Bark .. .. .. .. 90 75
 a. Brown (Queen's head and value) omitted £700
295 18 c. Bermuda Cedar .. .. .. .. 1·00 1·00
296 24 c. Mahogany .. .. .. .. .. 1·10 1·40
293/6 .. .. .. .. *Set of* 4 3·00 3·00

**1973** (21 Nov*). *Royal Wedding. As Nos.* 165/6 *of Anguilla. Centre multicoloured.* W w **12** (*sideways*). *P* 13½.

297 15 c. bright mauve .. .. .. .. 10 15
298 18 c. steel blue .. .. .. .. .. 10 15

*This is the local date of issue. The Crown Agents released the stamps on the 14 November.

(Des J.W. Litho Questa)

**1973** (17 Dec). *Lawn Tennis Centenary. T* **92** *and similar horiz designs. Multicoloured.* W w **12**. *P* 14.

299 4 c. Type **92** .. .. .. .. .. 30 10
300 15 c. Clermont Court, 1873 .. .. .. 60 50
301 18 c. Leamington Spa Court, 1872 .. .. 70 1·00
302 24 c. Staten Island Courts, 1874 .. .. 85 1·25
299/302 .. .. .. .. *Set of* 4 2·25 2·50

**1974** (13 June)–**76**. *As Nos.* 253/4, 257 *and* 261, *but wmk upright.*

303 5 c. Poinsettia .. .. .. .. .. 90 2·50
304 6 c. Hibiscus .. .. .. .. .. 6·00 7·50
305 12 c. Jacaranda .. .. .. .. .. 1·75 2·75
306 30 c. Tecoma (11.6.76) .. .. .. .. 3·50 4·00
303/6 .. .. .. .. *Set of* 4 11·00 15·00

Nos. 307/19 vacant.

**93** Weather Vane, City Hall **94** Jack of Clubs and "good bridge hand"

(Des G. Drummond. Litho Questa)

**1974** (24 June). *50th Anniv of Rotary in Bermuda. T* **93** *and similar horiz designs. Multicoloured.* W w **12** (*sideways*). *P* 14.

320 5 c. Type **93** .. .. .. .. .. 15 10
321 17 c. St. Peter's Church, St George's .. .. 45 35
322 20 c. Somerset Bridge .. .. .. .. 50 1·00
323 25 c. Map of Bermuda, 1626 .. .. .. 60 1·60
320/3 .. .. .. .. *Set of* 4 1·50 2·75

(Des J.W. Litho Format)

**1975** (27 Jan). *World Bridge Championships, Bermuda. T* **94** *and similar vert designs. Multicoloured.* W w **12**. *P* 14.

324 5 c. Type **94** .. .. .. .. .. 25 10
325 17 c. Queen of Diamonds and Bermuda Bowl 65 50
326 20 c. King of Hearts and Bermuda Bowl .. 70 1·60
327 25 c. Ace of Spades and Bermuda Bowl .. 80 1·75
324/7 .. .. .. .. *Set of* 4 2·25 3·50

**95** Queen Elizabeth II and the Duke of Edinburgh

(Des and photo Harrison)

**1975** (17 Feb). *Royal Visit.* W w **14**. *P* 14 × 14½.

328 **95** 17 c. multicoloured .. .. .. .. 60 65
329 20 c. multicoloured .. .. .. .. 65 1·60

**96** "Cavalier" Flying-boat, 1937

(Des R. Granger Barrett. Litho Questa)

**1975** (28 Apr). *50th Anniv of Air-mail Service to Bermuda. T* **96** *and similar horiz designs. Multicoloured.* W w **14** (*sideways*). *P* 14.

330 5 c. Type **96** .. .. .. .. .. 40 10
331 17 c. Airship *Los Angeles*, 1925 .. .. 1·25 75
332 20 c. Lockheed "Constellation", 1946 .. .. 1·40 2·00
333 25 c. Boeing "747", 1970 .. .. .. 1·50 2·75
330/3 .. .. .. .. *Set of* 4 4·00 5·00
**MS**334 128 × 85 mm. Nos. 330/3 .. .. 8·50 10·00

**97** Supporters of American Army raiding Royal Magazine **98** Launching *Ready* (bathysphere)

(Des J. Cooter. Litho J.W.)

**1975** (27 Oct). *Bicentenary of Gunpowder Plot. St. George's. T* **97** *and similar horiz designs. Multicoloured.* W w **14** (*sideways*). *P* 13 × 13½.

335 5 c. Type **97** .. .. .. .. .. 20 10
336 17 c. Setting off for raid .. .. .. .. 40 30
337 20 c. Loading gunpowder aboard American ship .. .. .. .. .. 45 70
338 25 c. Gunpowder on beach .. .. .. 50 80
335/8 .. .. .. .. *Set of* 4 1·40 1·75
**MS**339 165 × 138 mm. Nos. 335/8. P 14 (*sold for* 75 *c.*) .. .. .. .. .. 2·75 5·50

**1975** (8 Dec)–**76**. *As Nos.* 250 *and* 254 *but W* w **14** (*sideways*).

| | | | | |
|---|---|---|---|---|
| 340 | 2 c. | Bottlebrush | 85 | 2·00 |
| 341 | 6 c. | Hibiscus (11.6.76) | 4·00 | 3·50 |

Nos. 342/56 vacant.

(Des G. Drummond. Litho Questa)

**1976** (29 Mar). *50th Anniv of Bermuda Biological Station. T* **98** *and similar multicoloured designs. W* w **14** (*sideways on* 17 *and* 20 c.). *P* 14.

| | | | | |
|---|---|---|---|---|
| 357 | 5 c. | Type **98** | 35 | 10 |
| 358 | 17 c. | View from the sea (*horiz*) | 70 | 60 |
| 359 | 20 c. | H.M.S. *Challenger*, 1873 (*horiz*) | 75 | 2·00 |
| 360 | 25 c. | Beebe's bathysphere descent, 1934 | 1·00 | 2·25 |
| 357/60 | | *Set of* 4 | 2·50 | 4·50 |

**99** *Christian Radich*

(Des R. Granger Barrett. Litho J.W.)

**1976** (15 June). *Tall Ships Race,* 1976. *T* **99** *and similar horiz designs. Multicoloured. W* w **12** (*sideways*). *P* 13.

| | | | | |
|---|---|---|---|---|
| 361 | 5 c. | Type **99** | 50 | 20 |
| 362 | 12 c. | *Juan Sebastian de Elcano* | 90 | 1·50 |
| 363 | 17 c. | U.S.C.G. *Eagle* | 1·10 | 1·50 |
| 364 | 20 c. | *Winston S. Churchill* | 1·25 | 2·25 |
| 365 | 40 c. | *Kruzenshtern* | 1·75 | 2·75 |
| 366 | $1 | *Cutty Sark* trophy | 2·75 | 6·00 |
| 361/6 | | *Set of* 6 | 7·50 | 13·00 |

**100** Silver Trophy and Club Flags

(Des C. Abbott. Litho Questa)

**1976** (16 Aug). *75th Anniv of the St. George's v. Somerset Cricket Cup Match. T* **100** *and similar horiz designs. Multicoloured. W* w **14** (*sideways*). *P* 14½ × 14.

| | | | | |
|---|---|---|---|---|
| 367 | 5 c. | Type **100** | 35 | 10 |
| 368 | 17 c. | Badge and Pavilion, St. George's Club | 75 | 55 |
| 369 | 20 c. | Badge and Pavilion Somerset Club | 1·00 | 2·50 |
| 370 | 25 c. | Somerset playing field | 1·50 | 3·50 |
| 367/70 | | *Set of* 4 | 3·25 | 6·00 |

**101** Royal Visit, 1975 **102** Stockdale House, St. George's 1784–1812

(Des Harrison. Litho Walsall)

**1977** (7 Feb). *Silver Jubilee. T* **101** *and similar vert designs. Multicoloured. W* w **14**. *P* 13½.

| | | | | |
|---|---|---|---|---|
| 371 | 5 c. | Type **101** | 15 | 10 |
| 372 | 20 c. | St. Edward's Crown | 25 | 20 |
| 373 | $1 | Queen in Chair of Estate | 80 | 1·25 |
| 371/3 | | *Set of* 3 | 1·10 | 1·40 |

(Des G. Drummond. Litho J.W.)

**1977** (20 June). *Centenary of U.P.U. Membership. T* **102** *and similar horiz designs. Multicoloured. W* w **14** (*sideways*). *P* 13.

| | | | | |
|---|---|---|---|---|
| 374 | 5 c. | Type **102** | 15 | 10 |
| 375 | 15 c. | Perot Post Office and stamp | 35 | 50 |
| 376 | 17 c. | St. George's P.O. *circa* 1860 | 35 | 50 |
| 377 | 20 c. | Old G.P.O., Hamilton, *circa* 1935 | 45 | 60 |
| 378 | 40 c. | New G.P.O., Hamilton, 1967 | 75 | 1·10 |
| 374/8 | | *Set of* 5 | 1·90 | 2·50 |

**103** 17th-Century Ship approaching Castle Island **104** Great Seal of Queen Elizabeth I

(Des R. Granger Barrett. Litho Questa)

**1977** (26 Sept). *Piloting. T* **103** *and similar horiz designs. Multicoloured. W* w **14** (*sideways*). *P* 13½.

| | | | | |
|---|---|---|---|---|
| 379 | 5 c. | Type **103** | 25 | 10 |
| 380 | 15 c. | Pilot leaving ship, 1795 | 50 | 45 |
| 381 | 17 c. | Pilots rowing out to paddle-steamer | 60 | 50 |
| 382 | 20 c. | Pilot gigs and brig *Harvest Queen* | 75 | 1·50 |
| 383 | 40 c. | Modern pilot cutter and R.M.S. *Queen Elizabeth 2* | 1·25 | 2·50 |
| 379/83 | | *Set of* 5 | 3·00 | 4·50 |

(Des BG Studio. Litho Questa)

**1978** (28 Aug). *25th Anniv of Coronation. T* **104** *and similar vert designs. Multicoloured. W* w **14**. *P* 14 × 13½.

| | | | | |
|---|---|---|---|---|
| 384 | 8 c. | Type **104** | 10 | 10 |
| 385 | 50 c. | Great Seal of Queen Elizabeth II | 30 | 30 |
| 386 | $1 | Queen Elizabeth II | 60 | 75 |
| 384/6 | | *Set of* 3 | 80 | 1·00 |

**105** White-tailed Tropic Bird

(Des G. Drummond. Photo Harrison)

**1978** (15 Nov)–**83**. *Wildlife. Horiz designs as T* **105**. *Multicoloured. W* w **14** (*sideways on* 8, 15, 20, 40 c. *and* $1). *P* 14 × 14½ (4, 5 c., $2, 3, 5) *or* 14 (*others*).

| | | | | |
|---|---|---|---|---|
| 387 | 3 c. | Type **105** | 60 | 40 |
| | | a. Perf 14×14½ (3.8.83)* | 1·25 | 65 |
| 388 | 4 c. | White-eyed Vireo | 75 | 40 |
| 389 | 5 c. | Eastern Bluebird | 75 | 35 |
| 390 | 7 c. | Whistling Frog (19.2.79) | 50 | 40 |
| 391 | 8 c. | Common Cardinal | 85 | 35 |
| 392 | 10 c. | Spiny Lobster (19.2.79) | 20 | 10 |
| 393 | 12 c. | Land Crab (19.2.79) | 30 | 40 |
| 394 | 15 c. | Lizard (Skink) (19.2.79) | 30 | 15 |
| 395 | 20 c. | Foureye Butterfly Fish (12.3.79) | 30 | 30 |
| 396 | 25 c. | Red Hind (12.3.79) | 30 | 20 |
| | | a. Greenish blue omitted | | |
| 397 | 30 c. | *Danaus plexippus* (butterfly) (19.2.79) | 1·75 | 1·50 |
| 398 | 40 c. | Rock Beauty (12.3.79) | 45 | 90 |
| 399 | 50 c. | Banded Butterfly Fish (12.3.79) | 55 | 60 |
| 400 | $1 | Blue Angelfish (12.3.79) | 95 | 1·75 |
| 401 | $2 | Humpback Whale (12.3.79) | 2·00 | 2·75 |
| 402 | $3 | Green Turtle (19.2.79) | 2·75 | 3·00 |
| 403 | $5 | Cahow | 6·50 | 6·00 |
| 387/403 | | *Set of* 17 | 18·00 | 17·00 |

*Earliest known postmark date.

**106** Map by Sir George Somers, 1609 **107** Policeman and Policewoman

(Des J. Cooter. Litho Questa)

**1979** (14 May). *Antique Maps. T* **106** *and similar multicoloured designs. W* w **14** (*sideways on* 8, 15, 25 *and* 50 c.) *P* 14 × 13½ (20 c.) *or* 13½ × 14 (*others*).

| | | | | |
|---|---|---|---|---|
| 404 | 8 c. | Type **106** | 15 | 10 |
| 405 | 15 c. | Map by John Seller, 1685 | 20 | 15 |
| 406 | 20 c. | Map by H. Moll, 1729–40 (*vert*) | 25 | 25 |
| 407 | 25 c. | Map by Desbruslins, 1740 | 30 | 30 |
| 408 | 50 c. | Map by Speed, 1626 | 45 | 70 |
| 404/8 | | *Set of* 5 | 1·25 | 1·25 |

(Des L. Curtis. Litho Questa)

**1979** (26 Nov). *Centenary of Police Force. T* **107** *and similar multicoloured designs. W* w **14** (*sideways on* 20 *and* 25 c.). *P* 14.

| | | | | |
|---|---|---|---|---|
| 409 | 8 c. | Type **107** | 20 | 10 |
| 410 | 20 c. | Policeman directing traffic (*horiz*) | 45 | 45 |
| 411 | 25 c. | Police patrol launch (*horiz*) | 50 | 50 |
| 412 | 50 c. | Police car and motorcycle | 90 | 1·00 |
| 409/12 | | *Set of* 4 | 1·90 | 1·90 |

BERMUDA

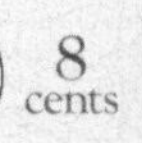

ROWLAND HILL AND THE PENNY POST

**108** 1848 1d. "Perot" and Penny Black Stamps

(Des J.W. Litho Enschedé)

**1980** (25 Feb). *Death Centenary of Sir Rowland Hill* (1979). *T* **108** *and similar horiz designs. Multicoloured. W* w **14** (*sideways*). *P* 13 × 13½.

| | | | | |
|---|---|---|---|---|
| 413 | 8 c. | Type **108** | 10 | 10 |
| 414 | 20 c. | 1848 1d. "Perot" stamp and Sir Rowland Hill | 15 | 25 |
| 415 | 25 c. | 1848 1d. "Perot" stamp and early letter | 15 | 30 |
| 416 | 50 c. | 1848 1d. "Perot" stamp and "Paid 1" cancellation | 25 | 70 |
| 413/16 | | *Set of* 4 | 60 | 1·25 |

**109** British Airways "Tristar 500" Airliner approaching Bermuda **110** Gina Swainson with Rose

(Des R. Granger Barrett. Litho Harrison)

**1980** (6 May). *"London 1980" International Stamp Exhibition. Mail-carrying Transport. T* **109** *and similar horiz designs. Multicoloured. W* w **14** (*sideways*). *P* 13 × 13½.

| | | | | |
|---|---|---|---|---|
| 417 | 25 c. | Type **109** | 30 | 15 |
| 418 | 50 c. | S.S. *Orduna* in Grassy Bay | 45 | 35 |
| 419 | $1 | *Delta* at St. George's Harbour | 85 | 1·00 |
| 420 | $2 | *Lord Sidmouth* in Old Ship Channel, St. George's | 1·40 | 1·75 |
| 417/20 | | *Set of* 4 | 2·75 | 3·00 |

(Des Walsall. Litho Questa)

**1980** (8 May). *"Miss World 1979–80" (Gina Swainson) Commemoration. T* **110** *and similar vert designs. Multicoloured. W* w **14**. *P* 14 × 13½.

| | | | | |
|---|---|---|---|---|
| 421 | 8 c. | Type **110** | 15 | 10 |
| 422 | 20 c. | After crowning ceremony | 20 | 20 |
| 423 | 50 c. | On Peacock Throne at "Welcome Home" party | 35 | 35 |
| 424 | $1 | In Bermuda carriage | 70 | 90 |
| 421/4 | | *Set of* 4 | 1·25 | 1·40 |

**111** Queen Elizabeth the Queen Mother

(Des and litho Harrison)

**1980** (4 Aug). *80th Birthday of Queen Elizabeth the Queen Mother. W* w **14** (*sideways*). *P* 14.

| | | | | |
|---|---|---|---|---|
| 425 | **111** | 25 c. multicoloured | 30 | 40 |

**112** Bermuda from Satellite **113** Kitchen, 18th-century

(Des. L. Curtis. Litho Questa)

**1980** (24 Sept). *Commonwealth Finance Ministers Meeting. T* **112** *and similar horiz designs. Multicoloured. W* w **14** (*sideways*). *P* 14.

| | | | | |
|---|---|---|---|---|
| 426 | 8 c. | Type **112** | 10 | 10 |
| 427 | 20 c. | "Camden" | 20 | 30 |
| 428 | 25 c. | Princess Hotel, Hamilton | 20 | 40 |
| 429 | 50 c. | Government House | 35 | 1·00 |
| 426/9 | | *Set of* 4 | 75 | 1·60 |

(Des J.W. Litho Questa)

**1981** (21 May). *Heritage Week. T* **113** *and similar horiz designs. Multicoloured. W* w **14** (*sideways*). *P* 14.

| | | | | |
|---|---|---|---|---|
| 430 | 8 c. | Type **113** | 15 | 10 |
| 431 | 25 c. | Gathering Easter lilies, 20th-century | 40 | 50 |
| 432 | 30 c. | Fishing, 20th-century | 50 | 65 |
| 433 | 40 c. | Stone cutting, 19th-century | 55 | 75 |
| 434 | 50 c. | Onion shipping, 19th-century | 65 | 90 |
| 435 | $1 | Privateering, 17th-century | 1·50 | 2·25 |
| 430/5 | | *Set of* 6 | 3·25 | 4·50 |

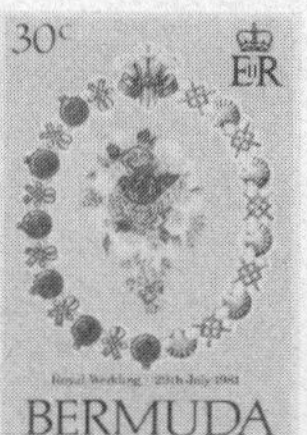

**114** Wedding Bouquet from Bermuda **115** "Service", Hamilton

(Des J.W. Litho Questa)

**1981** (22 July). *Royal Wedding. T* **114** *and similar vert designs. Multicoloured. W* w **14**. *P* 14.

| | | | | |
|---|---|---|---|---|
| 436 | 30 c. | Type **114** | 30 | 30 |
| 437 | 50 c. | Prince Charles as Royal Navy Commander | 50 | 55 |
| 438 | $1 | Prince Charles and Lady Diana Spencer | 90 | 1·25 |
| 436/8 | | *Set of* 3 | 1·50 | 1·90 |

(Des L. Curtis. Litho Questa)

**1981** (28 Sept). *25th Anniv of Duke of Edinburgh Award Scheme. T* **115** *and similar vert designs. Multicoloured. W* w **14**. *P* 14.

439 10 c. Type **115** .. .. .. .. .. .. 15 10
440 25 c. "Outward Bound", Paget Island .. .. 25 20
441 30 c. "Expedition", St. David's Island .. .. 25 30
442 $1 Duke of Edinburgh .. .. .. .. 80 1·25
439/42 .. .. .. .. .. *Set of* 4 1·25 1·75

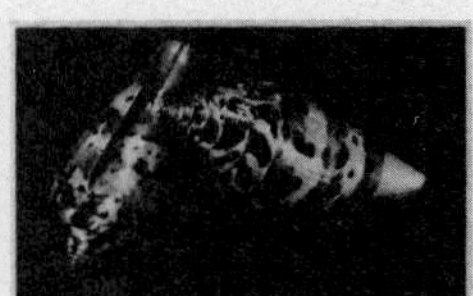

**116** *Conus species*

(Des Walsall. Litho Questa)

**1982** (22 Apr). *Sea-shells. T* **116** *and similar horiz designs. Multicoloured. W* w **14** (*sideways*). *P* 14.

443 10 c. Type **116** .. .. .. .. .. .. 25 10
444 25 c. *Bursa finlayi* .. .. .. .. .. 60 65
445 30 c. *Sconsia striata* .. .. .. .. .. 65 80
446 $1 *Murex pterynotus lightbourni* .. .. 1·75 2·75
443/6 .. .. .. .. .. *Set of* 4 3·00 3·75

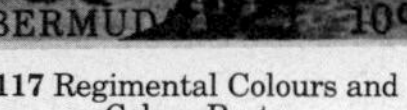

**117** Regimental Colours and Colour Party **118** Charles Fort

(Des G. Drummond. Litho Questa)

**1982** (17 June). *Bermuda Regiment. T* **117** *and similar horiz designs. Multicoloured. W* w **14** (*sideways*). *P* 14.

447 10 c. Type **117** .. .. .. .. .. .. 35 10
448 25 c. Queen's Birthday Parade .. .. .. 75 60
449 30 c. Governor inspecting Guard of Honour .. 85 85
450 40 c. Beating the Retreat .. .. .. .. 90 90
451 50 c. Ceremonial gunners .. .. .. .. 1·00 1·25
452 $1 Guard of Honour, Royal visit, 1975 .. 1·75 2·75
447/52 .. .. .. .. .. *Set of* 6 5·00 5·75

(Des L. Curtis. Litho Questa)

**1982** (18 Nov). *Historic Bermuda Forts. T* **118** *and similar multicoloured designs. W* w **14** (*sideways on* 30 c. *and* $1). *P* 14.

453 10 c. Type **118** .. .. .. .. .. .. 20 20
454 25 c. Pembroks Fort .. .. .. .. .. 50 75
455 30 c. Southampton Fort (*horiz*) .. .. .. 60 1·00
456 $1 Smiths Fort and Pagets Fort (*horiz*) .. 1·75 3·50
453/6 .. .. .. .. .. *Set of* 4 2·75 5·00

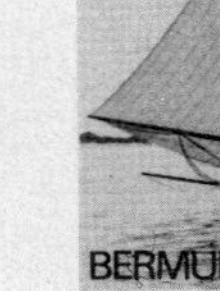


**119** Arms of Sir Edwin Sandys **120** Early Fitted Dinghy

(Des Harrison. Litho J.W.)

**1983** (14 Apr). *Coats of Arms* (1*st series*). *T* **119** *and similar vert designs. Multicoloured. W* w **14**. *P* 13.

457 10 c. Type **119** .. .. .. .. .. .. 45 15
458 25 c. Arms of the Bermuda Company .. .. 1·25 85
459 50 c. Arms of William Herbert, Earl of Pembroke .. .. .. .. .. 2·00 2·25
460 $1 Arms of Sir George Somers .. .. 2·75 3·75
457/60 .. .. .. .. .. *Set of* 4 5·75 6·25

See also Nos. 482/5 and 499/502.

(Des L. Curtis. Litho Harrison)

**1983** (23 June). *Fitted Dinghies. T* **120** *and similar vert designs. Multicoloured. W* w **14** (*sideways*). *P* 14.

461 12 c. Type **120** .. .. .. .. .. .. 20 15
462 30 c. Modern dinghy inshore .. .. .. .. 45 65
463 40 c. Early dinghy (*different*) .. .. .. 60 80
464 $1 Modern dinghy with red and white spinnaker .. .. .. .. .. 1·50 2·75
461/4 .. .. .. .. .. *Set of* 4 2·50 4·00

**121** Curtiss "Jenny" Seaplane (First Flight over Bermuda) **122** Joseph Stockdale

(Des A. Theobald. Litho Walsall)

**1983** (13 Oct). *Bicentenary of Manned Flight. T* **121** *and similar horiz designs. Multicoloured. W* w **14** (*sideways*). *P* 14.

465 12 c. Type **121** .. .. .. .. .. .. 30 15
466 30 c. *Pilot Radio*, Stinson seaplane (First completed flight between U.S.A. and Bermuda) .. .. .. .. .. 65 70
467 40 c. Short "Empire" flying boat *Cavalier* (First scheduled passenger flight) .. 80 1·00
468 $1 U.S.S. *Los Angeles* (airship) moored to U.S.S. *Patoka* .. .. .. .. 1·75 3·00
465/8 .. .. .. .. .. *Set of* 4 3·25 4·25

(Des L. Curtis. Litho Harrison)

**1984** (26 Jan). *Bicentenary of Bermuda's First Newspaper and Postal Service. T* **122** *and similar multicoloured designs. W* w **14** (*sideways on* 40 c. *and* $1). *P* 14.

469 12 c. Type **122** .. .. .. .. .. .. 20 15
470 30 c. *The Bermuda Gazette* .. .. .. .. 50 70
471 40 c. Stockdale's postal service (*horiz*) .. .. 70 1·00
472 $1 *Lady Hammond* (mail boat) (*horiz*) .. 2·00 3·25
469/72 .. .. .. .. .. *Set of* 4 3·00 4·50

**123** Sir Thomas Gates and Sir George Somers **124** Swimming

(Des R. Granger Barrett. Litho Walsall)

**1984** (3 May). *375th Anniv of First Settlement. T* **123** *and similar horiz designs. Multicoloured. W* w **14** (*sideways*). *P* 14.

473 12 c. Type **123** .. .. .. .. .. .. 20 15
474 30 c. Jamestown, Virginia .. .. .. .. 50 70
475 40 c. Wreck of *Sea Venture* .. .. .. .. 90 1·00
476 $1 Fleet leaving Plymouth, Devon .. .. 2·00 3·25
473/6 .. .. .. .. .. *Set of* 4 3·25 4·50
**MS**477 130 × 73 mm. Nos. 474 and 476 .. .. 2·75 4·50

(Des C. Collins. Litho J.W.)

**1984** (19 July). *Olympic Games, Los Angeles. T* **124** *and similar multicoloured designs. W* w **14** (*sideways on* 30 c., $1). *P* 14.

478 12 c. Type **124** .. .. .. .. .. .. 25 15
479 30 c. Track and field events (*horiz*) .. .. 60 60
480 40 c. Equestrian competition .. .. .. .. 80 85
481 $1 Sailing (*horiz*) .. .. .. .. .. 2·25 2·75
478/81 .. .. .. .. .. *Set of* 4 3·50 4·00

(Des Harrison. Litho J.W.)

**1984** (27 Sept). *Coats of Arms* (2*nd series*). *Vert designs as T* **119**. *Multicoloured. W* w **14**. *P* 13.

482 12 c. Arms of Henry Wriothesley, Earl of Southampton .. .. .. .. .. 40 15
483 30 c. Arms of Sir Thomas Smith .. .. .. 85 85
484 40 c. Arms of William Cavendish, Earl of Devonshire .. .. .. .. .. 1·10 1·25
485 $1 Town arms of St. George .. .. .. 2·50 3·00
482/5 .. .. .. .. .. *Set of* 4 4·25 4·75

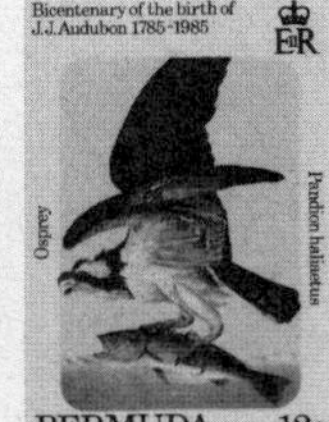


**125** Buttery **126** Osprey

(Des D. Miller. Litho Walsall)

**1985** (24 Jan). *Bermuda Architecture. T* **125** *and similar multicoloured designs. W* w **14** (*inverted on* 12 c., $1.50, *sideways on* 30 c., 40 c.). *P* 13½ × 13 (12 c., $1.50) *or* 13 × 13½ (30 c., 40 c.).

486 12 c. Type **125** .. .. .. .. .. .. 35 15
487 30 c. Limestone rooftops (*horiz*) .. .. .. 70 70
488 40 c. Chimneys (*horiz*) .. .. .. .. .. 85 85
489 $1.50, Entrance archway .. .. .. .. 2·75 3·25
486/9 .. .. .. .. .. *Set of* 4 4·25 4·50

(Des D. Miller. Litho Walsall)

**1985** (28 Mar). *Birth Bicentenary of John J. Audubon (ornithologist). T* **126** *and similar multicoloured designs showing original drawings. W* w **14** (*sideways on* 40 c.). *P* 14.

490 12 c. Type **126** .. .. .. .. .. .. 80 25
491 30 c. Yellow-crowned Night Heron .. .. 1·25 65
492 40 c. Great Egret (*horiz*) .. .. .. .. 1·50 85
493 $1.50, Eastern Bluebird .. .. .. .. 3·00 3·25
490/3 .. .. .. .. .. *Set of* 4 6·00 4·50

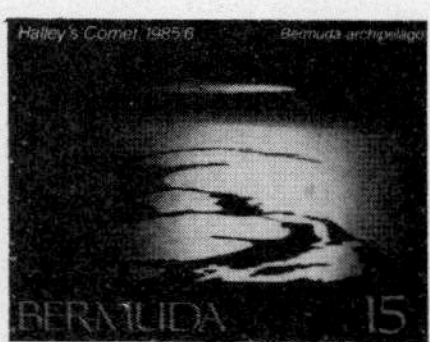


**127** The Queen Mother with Grandchildren, 1980 **128** Halley's Comet and Bermuda Archipelago

(Des A. Theobald ($1), C. Abbott (others). Litho Questa)

**1985** (7 June). *Life and Times of Queen Elizabeth the Queen Mother. T* **127** *and similar vert designs. Multicoloured. W* w **16**. *P* 14½ × 14.

494 12 c. Queen Consort, 1937 .. .. .. .. 25 15
495 30 c. Type **127** .. .. .. .. .. .. 50 50
496 40 c. At Clarence House on 83rd birthday .. 60 60
497 $1.50, With Prince Henry at his christening (from photo by Lord Snowdon) .. 2·25 2·75
494/7 .. .. .. .. .. *Set of* 4 3·25 3·50
**MS**498 91 × 73 mm. $1 With Prince Charles at 80th Birthday celebrations. Wmk sideways .. 1·50 2·00

(Des Harrison. Litho J.W.)

**1985** (19 Sept). *Coats of Arms* (3*rd series*). *Vert designs as T* **119**. *Multicoloured. W* w **14**. *P* 13 × 13½.

499 12 c. Hamilton .. .. .. .. .. .. 55 15
500 30 c. Paget .. .. .. .. .. .. 1·10 80
501 40 c. Warwick .. .. .. .. .. .. 1·25 1·25
502 $1.50, City of Hamilton .. .. .. .. 3·25 3·75
499/502 .. .. .. .. .. *Set of* 4 5·50 5·50

(Des Jennifer Toombs. Litho Walsall)

**1985** (21 Nov). *Appearance of Halley's Comet. T* **128** *and similar horiz designs. Multicoloured. W* w **16** (*sideways*). *P* 14 × 14½.

503 15 c. Type **128** .. .. .. .. .. .. 75 25
504 40 c. Halley's Comet, A.D. 684 (from Nuremberg Chronicles, 1493) .. .. .. .. 1·50 1·25
505 50 c. "Halley's Comet, 1531" (from Peter Apian woodcut, 1532) .. .. .. .. 1·75 1·50
506 $1.50, "Halley's Comet, 1759" (Samuel Scott) .. .. .. .. .. .. 3·25 3·50
503/6 .. .. .. .. .. *Set of* 4 6·50 6·00

**129** *Constellation* (1943)

(Des L. Curtis. Litho Questa)

**1986** (16 Jan)–**90**. *Ships Wrecked on Bermuda. T* **129** *and similar horiz designs. Multicoloured. W* w **16** (*sideways*). *P* 14. A. *Without imprint date at foot*. B. *With imprint date*.

| | | A | | B | |
|---|---|---|---|---|---|
| 507 | 3 c. Type **129** .. .. | 30 | 30 | 10 | 10 |
| 508 | 5 c. *Early Riser* (1876) .. | 10 | 10 | † | |
| 509 | 7 c. *Madiana* (1903) (20.3.86) | 10 | 10 | † | |
| 510 | 10 c. *Curlew* (1856) .. .. | 10 | 15 | † | |
| 511 | 12 c. *Warwick* (1619) .. | 15 | 20 | † | |
| 512 | 15 c. H.M.S. *Vixen* (1890) (18.9.86) .. .. | 15 | 20 | † | |
| 512*c* | 18 c. As 7 c. (22.9.88) .. | 20 | 25 | † | |
| 513 | 20 c. *San Pedro* (1594) (20.3.86) .. .. | 50 | 40 | 25 | 30 |
| 514 | 25 c. *Alert* (1877) (18.9.86) .. | 30 | 35 | † | |
| 515 | 40 c. *North Carolina* (1880) (18.9.86) .. .. | 45 | 50 | † | |
| 516 | 50 c. *Mark Antonie* (1777) (18.9.86) .. .. | 60 | 65 | † | |
| 517 | 60 c. *Mary Celestia* (1864) (20.3.86) .. .. | 70 | 75 | † | |
| 517*c* | 70 c. *Caesar* (1818) (27.10.88) | 80 | 85 | † | |
| 518 | $1 *L'Herminie* (1839) (18.9.86) .. .. | 2·75 | 2·00 | 1·10 | 1·25 |
| 519 | $1.50, As 70 c. (20.3.86) .. | 1·75 | 1·90 | † | |
| 520 | $2 *Lord Amherst* (1778) (20.3.86) .. .. | 4·00 | 4·25 | 2·25 | 2·40 |
| 521 | $3 *Minerva* (1849) (20.3.86) | 5·00 | 6·00 | 3·50 | 3·75 |
| 522 | $5 *Caraquet* (1923) (18.9.86) .. .. | 5·75 | 6·00 | † | |
| 523 | $8 H.M.S. *Pallas* (1788) .. | 9·25 | 9·50 | † | |
| 507A/23A | .. .. *Set of* 19 | 30·00 | 30·00 | | |
| 507B/21B | .. .. *Set of* 5 | | | 6·50 | 7·00 |

Dates of issue for stamps with imprint: 7.89, Nos. 518B, 520B/1B; 1.8.90, Nos. 507B, 513B.

## NEW INFORMATION

The editor is always interested to correspond with people who have new information that will improve or correct the Catalogue.

(Des A. Theobald. Litho Harrison)

**1986** (21 Apr). *60th Birthday of Queen Elizabeth II. Vert designs as T* **110** *of Ascension. Multicoloured.* W w **16**. P 14½×14.

| No. | Description | Unused | Used |
|---|---|---|---|
| 524 | 15 c. Princess Elizabeth aged three, 1929 | 30 | 30 |
| 525 | 40 c. With Earl of Rosebery at Oaks May Meeting, Epsom, 1954 | 60 | 60 |
| 526 | 50 c. With Duke of Edinburgh, Bermuda, 1975 | 75 | 75 |
| 527 | 60 c. At British Embassy, Paris, 1972 | 90 | 90 |
| 528 | $1.50, At Crown Agents Head Office, London, 1983 | 2·25 | 2·50 |
| 524/8 | *Set of* 5 | 4·25 | 4·50 |

(Des G. Drummond. Litho Walsall)

**1986** (22 May). *"Ameripex '86" International Stamp Exhibition, Chicago. Horiz designs as T* **164** *of Bahamas, showing Bermuda stamps (Nos. 529/32). Multicoloured.* W w **16** (*sideways*). P 14.

| No. | Description | Unused | Used |
|---|---|---|---|
| 529 | 15 c. 1984 375th Anniv of Settlement miniature sheet | 55 | 30 |
| 530 | 40 c. 1973 Lawn Tennis Centenary 24 c. | 85 | 70 |
| 531 | 50 c. 1983 Bicentenary of Manned Flight 12 c. | 1·00 | 1·00 |
| 532 | $1 1976 Tall Ships Race 17 c. | 2·00 | 2·50 |
| 529/32 | *Set of* 4 | 4·00 | 4·00 |
| **MS**533 | 80×80 mm. $1.50, Statue of Liberty and S.S. *Queen of Bermuda* | 4·00 | 4·00 |

No. **MS**533 also commemorates the Centenary of the Statue of Liberty.

(**130**)

**1986** (4 Dec). *25th Anniv of World Wildlife Fund. No. 402 surch with T* **130** *by J. W. Dunn Printers Ltd, Sutton, Surrey.*

| No. | Description | Unused | Used |
|---|---|---|---|
| 534 | 90 c. on $3 Green Turtle | 2·00 | 1·75 |
| | a. Surch double | £100 | |
| | b. Surch double, one inverted | £225 | |
| | c. "90 c" omitted | | |

**131** Train in Front Street, Hamilton, 1940

(Des A. Theobald. Litho Walsall)

**1987** (22 Jan). *Transport (1st series). Bermuda Railway. T* **131** *and similar horiz designs. Multicoloured.* W w **16** (*sideways*). P 14.

| No. | Description | Unused | Used |
|---|---|---|---|
| 535 | 15 c. Type **131** | 60 | 25 |
| 536 | 40 c. Train crossing Springfield Trestle | 1·10 | 90 |
| 537 | 50 c. "St. George Special" at Bailey's Bay Station | 1·40 | 1·50 |
| 538 | $1 50, Boat train at St. George | 2·50 | 3·50 |
| 535/8 | *Set of* 4 | 5·00 | 5·50 |

See also Nos. 535/8, 574/7 and 624/9.

**132** "Bermuda Settlers", 1901

(Des L. Curtis. Litho Walsall)

**1987** (30 Apr). *Paintings by Winslow Homer. T* **132** *and similar horiz designs. Multicoloured.* W w **16** (*sideways*). P 14×14½.

(*a*) *Sheet stamps* (*No. 541 with a buff frame*).

| No. | Description | Unused | Used |
|---|---|---|---|
| 539 | 15 c. Type **132** | 25 | 25 |
| 540 | 30 c. "Bermuda", 1900 | 45 | 45 |
| 541 | 40 c. "Bermuda Landscape", 1901 | 55 | 55 |
| 542 | 50 c. "Inland Water", 1901 | 70 | 70 |
| 543 | $1.50, "Salt Kettle", 1899 | 2·25 | 2·50 |
| 539/43 | *Set of* 5 | 3·75 | 4·00 |

(*b*) *Booklet stamps, each with grey frame*

| No. | Description | Unused | Used |
|---|---|---|---|
| 544 | 40 c. Type **132** | 70 | 80 |
| | a. Booklet pane. Nos. 544/8, each × 2 | 6·50 | |
| 545 | 40 c. As No. 540 | 70 | 80 |
| 546 | 40 c. As No. 541 | 70 | 80 |
| 547 | 40 c. As No. 542 | 70 | 80 |
| 548 | 40 c. As No. 543 | 70 | 80 |
| 544/8 | *Set of* 5 | 3·25 | 3·50 |

**133** PanAm Sikorsky "S-42B" *Bermuda Clipper* Flying Boat at Mooring

(Des A. Theobald. Litho Walsall)

**1987** (18 June). *50th Anniv of Inauguration of Bermuda – U.S.A. Air Service. T* **133** *and similar horiz designs. Multicoloured.* W w **16** (*sideways*). P 14.

| No. | Description | Unused | Used |
|---|---|---|---|
| 549 | 15 c. Type **133** | 60 | 15 |
| 550 | 40 c. Imperial Airways Short "S-23" *Cavalier* flying boat at mooring | 1·00 | 70 |
| 551 | 50 c. *Bermuda Clipper* in flight over signpost | 1·25 | 80 |
| 552 | $1.50, *Cavalier* on apron and *Bermuda Clipper* in flight | 3·00 | 3·00 |
| 549/52 | *Set of* 4 | 5·25 | 4·25 |

**134** 19th-century Wagon carrying Telephone Poles

**135** Mail Wagon, *c.* 1869

(Des L. Curtis. Litho B.D.T.)

**1987** (1 Oct). *Centenary of Bermuda Telephone Company. T* **134** *and similar horiz designs. Multicoloured.* W w **16** (*sideways*). P 14×13½.

| No. | Description | Unused | Used |
|---|---|---|---|
| 553 | 15 c. Type **134** | 35 | 15 |
| 554 | 40 c. Early telephone exchange | 80 | 60 |
| 555 | 50 c. Early and modern telephones | 90 | 70 |
| 556 | $1.50, Communications satellite orbiting Earth | 2·50 | 2·50 |
| 553/6 | *Set of* 4 | 4·00 | 3·50 |

(Des O. Bell. Litho Questa)

**1988** (3 Mar). *Transport (2nd series). Horse-drawn Carts and Wagons. T* **135** *and similar horiz designs. Multicoloured.* W w **16** (*sideways*). P 14.

| No. | Description | Unused | Used |
|---|---|---|---|
| 557 | 15 c. Type **135** | 25 | 15 |
| 558 | 40 c. Open cart, *c.* 1823 | 55 | 55 |
| 559 | 50 c. Closed cart, *c.* 1823 | 65 | 65 |
| 560 | $1.50, Two-wheeled wagon, *c.* 1930 | 2·00 | 2·50 |
| 557/60 | *Set of* 4 | 3·00 | 3·50 |

**136** "Old Blush"

**137** Devonshire Parish Militia, 1812

(Des R. Gorringe. Litho B.D.T.)

**1988** (21 Apr). *Old Garden Roses (1st series). T* **136** *and similar multicoloured designs.* W w **14** (*sideways on horiz designs*). P 14×13½ (*vert*) *or* 13½×14 (*horiz*).

| No. | Description | Unused | Used |
|---|---|---|---|
| 561 | 15 c. Type **136** | 25 | 25 |
| 562 | 30 c. "Anna Olivier" | 40 | 40 |
| 563 | 40 c. *Rosa chinensis semperflorens* (*vert*) | 55 | 55 |
| 564 | 50 c. "Archduke Charles" | 65 | 65 |
| 565 | $1.50, *Rosa chinensis viridiflora* (*vert*) | 1·75 | 1·90 |
| 561/5 | *Set of* 5 | 3·25 | 3·50 |

See also Nos. 584/8 and, for these designs with the royal cypher instead of the Queen's head, Nos. 589/98.

(Des D. Miller (18 c.), E. Nisbet and D. Miller (others). Litho Questa)

**1988** (13 Oct). *300th Anniv of Lloyd's of London. Multicoloured designs as T* **123** *of Ascension.* W w **16** (*sideways on 50, 60 c.*). P 14.

| No. | Description | Unused | Used |
|---|---|---|---|
| 566 | 18 c. Loss of H.M.S. *Lutine*, 1799 | 25 | 25 |
| 567 | 50 c. *Sentinel* (cable ship) (*horiz*) | 70 | 65 |
| 568 | 60 c. *Bermuda*, Hamilton, 1931 (*horiz*) | 80 | 75 |
| 569 | $2 Loss of H.M.S. *Valerian* in hurricane, 1926 | 2·75 | 3·00 |
| 566/9 | *Set of* 4 | 4·00 | 4·25 |

(Des A. Barbosa. Litho Harrison)

**1988** (10 Nov). *Military Uniforms. T* **137** *and similar vert designs. Multicoloured.* W w **14**. P 14½.

| No. | Description | Unused | Used |
|---|---|---|---|
| 570 | 18 c. Type **137** | 30 | 25 |
| 571 | 50 c. 71st (Highland) Regiment, 1831-34 | 70 | 65 |
| 572 | 60 c. Cameron Highlanders, 1942 | 80 | 75 |
| 573 | $2 Troop of horse, 1774 | 2·75 | 3·00 |
| 570/3 | *Set of* 4 | 4·00 | 4·25 |

**138** *Corona*

**139** Morgan's Island

(Des C. Abbott, adapted L. Curtis. Litho Questa)

**1989** (16 Feb). *Transport (3rd series). Ferry Services. T* **138** *and similar horiz designs. Multicoloured.* W w **16** (*sideways*). P 14.

| No. | Description | Unused | Used |
|---|---|---|---|
| 574 | 18 c. Type **138** | 25 | 25 |
| 575 | 50 c. Rowing boat ferry | 65 | 65 |
| 576 | 60 c. St. George's barge ferry | 75 | 75 |
| 577 | $2 *Laconia* | 2·50 | 2·75 |
| 574/7 | *Set of* 4 | 3·75 | 4·00 |

(Des A. Theobald. Litho Questa)

**1989** (11 May). *150 Years of Photography. T* **139** *and similar horiz designs. Multicoloured.* W w **14** (*sideways*). P 14×14½.

| No. | Description | Unused | Used |
|---|---|---|---|
| 578 | 18 c. Type **139** | 25 | 25 |
| 579 | 30 c. Front Street, Hamilton | 40 | 45 |
| 580 | 50 c. Waterfront, Front Street, Hamilton | 70 | 85 |
| 581 | 60 c. Crow Lane from Hamilton Harbour | 80 | 1·00 |
| 582 | 70 c. Shipbuilding, Hamilton Harbour | 95 | 1·25 |
| 583 | $1 Dockyard | 1·25 | 2·00 |
| 578/83 | *Set of* 6 | 4·00 | 5·25 |

(Des R. Gorringe. Litho B.D.T.)

**1989** (13 July). *Old Garden Roses (2nd series). Multicoloured designs as T* **136**. W w **14** (*sideways on 50, 60 c. and $1.50*). P 14×13½ (*18, 30 c.*) *or* 13½×14 (*others*).

| No. | Description | Unused | Used |
|---|---|---|---|
| 584 | 18 c. "Agrippina" (*vert*) | 30 | 25 |
| 585 | 30 c. "Smith's Parish" (*vert*) | 45 | 45 |
| 586 | 50 c. "Champney's Pink Cluster" | 80 | 85 |
| 587 | 60 c. "Rosette Delizy" | 90 | 1·10 |
| 588 | $1.50, *Rosa bracteata* | 2·00 | 2·75 |
| 584/8 | *Set of* 5 | 4·00 | 4·75 |

For these designs with the royal cypher instead of the Queen's head, see Nos. 589/98.

**1989** (13 July). *Booklet stamps. Old Garden Roses designs as Nos. 561/5 and 584/8, but with royal cypher at top left instead of Queen's head. Multicoloured.* W w **14** (*sideways on horiz, inverted on vert designs*). P 13½.

| No. | Description | Unused | Used |
|---|---|---|---|
| 589 | 50 c. As No. 565 (*vert*) | 70 | 75 |
| | a. Booklet pane. Nos. 589/98 | 6·25 | |
| 590 | 50 c. As No. 563 (*vert*) | 70 | 75 |
| 591 | 50 c. Type **136** | 70 | 75 |
| 592 | 50 c. As No. 562 | 70 | 75 |
| 593 | 50 c. As No. 564 | 70 | 75 |
| 594 | 50 c. As No. 585 (*vert*) | 70 | 75 |
| 595 | 50 c. As No. 584 (*vert*) | 70 | 75 |
| 596 | 50 c. As No. 586 | 70 | 75 |
| 597 | 50 c. As No. 587 | 70 | 75 |
| 598 | 50 c. As No. 588 | 70 | 75 |
| 589/98 | *Set of* 10 | 6·25 | 6·75 |

Booklet pane No. 589a has margins on three sides.

**140** Main Library, Hamilton

**141** 1865 1d. Rose

(Des O. Bell. Litho B.D.T.)

**1989** (5 Oct). *150th Anniv of Bermuda Library. T* **140** *and similar horiz designs. Multicoloured.* W w **14** (*sideways*). P 13½×14.

| No. | Description | Unused | Used |
|---|---|---|---|
| 599 | 18 c. Type **140** | 20 | 25 |
| 600 | 50 c. The Old Rectory, St. George's | 60 | 65 |
| 601 | 60 c. Somerset Library, Springfield | 70 | 75 |
| 602 | $2 Cabinet Building, Hamilton | 2·40 | 2·75 |
| 599/602 | *Set of* 4 | 3·50 | 4·00 |

(Des D. Miller. Litho Questa)

**1989** (3 Nov). *Commonwealth Postal Conference. T* **141** *and similar vert designs. Multicoloured.* W w **16**. P 14.

| No. | Description | Unused | Used |
|---|---|---|---|
| 603 | 18 c. brownish grey, brown-rose & brt scar | 20 | 25 |
| 604 | 50 c. brownish grey, slate-bl & pale grey-bl | 60 | 65 |
| 605 | 60 c. brownish grey, dull purple and purple | 70 | 75 |
| 606 | $2 brownish grey, dull green & brt emer | 2·40 | 2·75 |
| 603/6 | *Set of* 4 | 3·50 | 4·00 |

Designs:—50 c. 1866 2d. blue; 60 c. 1865 6d purple; $2 1865 1s. green.

**142** "Fairylands, c. 1890" (Ross Turner)

Stamp World London 90

(**143**)

(Des L. Curtis. Litho B.D.T.)

**1990** (19 Apr). *Bermuda Paintings (1st series). T* **142** *and similar horiz designs. Multicoloured.* W w **16** (*sideways*). P 13½.

| No. | Description | Unused | Used |
|---|---|---|---|
| 607 | 18 c. Type **142** | 30 | 25 |
| 608 | 50 c. "Shinebone Alley, *c.* 1953" (Ogden Pleissner) | 75 | 85 |
| 609 | 60 c. "Salt Kettle, 1916" (Prosper Senate) | 85 | 1·10 |
| 610 | $2 "St. George's, 1934" (Jack Bush) | 2·75 | 3·25 |
| 607/10 | *Set of* 4 | 4·25 | 5·00 |

See also Nos. 630/3.

**1990** (3 May). *"Stamp World London 90" International Stamp Exhibition, London. Nos.* 603/6 *optd with T* **143**.

611 18 c. brownish grey, brown-rose & brt scar .. 30 25
612 50 c. brownish grey, slate-bl & pale grey-bl .. 75 85
613 60 c. brownish grey, dull purple and purple .. 85 1·00
614 $2 brownish grey, dull green & brt emer .. 2·75 3·25
611/14 .. .. .. .. *Set of* 4 4·25 4·75

30c

———

(144)

**145** The Halifax and Bermudas Cable Company Office, Hamilton

**1990** (13 Aug). *Nos.* 511A, 516A *and* 519A *surch as T* **144**.

615 30 c. on 12 c. *Warwick* (1619) .. .. 35 40
616 55 c. on 50 c. *Mark Antonie* (1777) .. .. 65 70
617 80 c. on $1.50 *Caesar* (1818) .. .. 95 1·00
615/17 .. .. .. .. *Set of* 3 1·75 1·90

(Des C. Abbott. Litho Harrison)

**1990** (18 Oct). *Centenary of Cable and Wireless in Bermuda. T* **145** *and similar horiz designs. P* 14.

618 20 c. light brown and black .. .. 30 25
619 55 c. light brown and black .. .. 80 90
620 70 c. multicoloured .. .. .. 95 1·10
621 $2 multicoloured .. .. .. 2·50 2·75
618/21 .. .. .. .. *Set of* 4 4·00 4·50

Designs:—55 c. *Westmeath* (cable ship), 1890; 70 c. Wireless transmitter station, St. George's, 1928; $2 *Sir Eric Sharp* (cable ship).

(146)

**147** Two-seater Pony Cart, 1805

**1991** (16 Mar). *President Bush – Prime Minister Major Talks, Bermuda. Nos.* 618/19 *optd with T* **146** *by Island Press.*

622 **145** 20 c. light brown and black .. .. 35 35
623 – 55 c. light brown and black .. .. 1·10 1·25

(Des N. Shering. Litho Walsall)

**1991** (21 Mar). *Transport (4th series). Horse-drawn Carriages. T* **147** *and similar horiz designs. Multicoloured. W w* **14** *(sideways). P* 14½.

624 20 c. Type **147** .. .. .. .. 30 25
625 30 c. Varnished rockaway, 1830 .. .. 40 35
626 55 c. Vis-a-Vis victoria, 1895 .. .. 75 70
627 70 c. Semi-formal phaeton, 1900 .. .. 95 95
628 80 c. Pony runabout, 1905 .. .. 1·10 1·25
629 $1 Ladies phaeton, 1910 .. .. 1·40 1·60
624/9 .. .. *Set of* 6 4·50 4·50

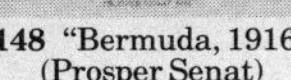

**148** "Bermuda, 1916" (Prosper Senat)

**149** Destroyer in Floating Dock

(Des L. Curtis. Litho Questa)

**1991** (16 May). *Bermuda Paintings (2nd series). T* **148** *and similar multicoloured designs. W w* **14** *(sideways on* 55 c., $2). *P* 13½×14 (20, 70 c.) *or* 14×13½ (55 c., $2).

630 20 c. Type **148** .. .. .. .. 35 30
631 55 c. "Bermuda Cottage", 1930 (Frank Allison) *(horiz)* .. .. .. 85 90
632 70 c. "Old Maid's Lane", 1934 (Jack Bush) 1·00 1·25
633 $2 "St. George's", 1953 (Ogden Pleissner) *(horiz)* .. .. .. .. 2·25 2·50
630/3 .. .. .. .. *Set of* 4 4·00 4·50

(Des D. Miller. Litho Questa)

**1991** (20 June). *65th Birthday of Queen Elizabeth II and 70th Birthday of Prince Philip. Vert designs as T* **139** *of Ascension. Multicoloured. W w* **16** *(sideways). P* 14½×14.

634 55 c. Prince Philip in tropical naval uniform 80 80
a. Horiz pair. Nos. 634/5 separated by label .. .. .. .. .. 1·75 1·75
635 70 c. Queen Elizabeth II in Bermuda .. 95 95

Nos. 634/5 were printed together in a similar sheet format to Nos. 539/40 of Ascension.

(Des N. Shewring. Litho Walsall)

**1991** (19 Sept). *50th Anniv of Second World War. T* **149** *and similar horiz designs. Multicoloured. W w* **14** *(sideways). P* 14.

636 20 c. Type **149** .. .. .. .. 25 30
637 55 c. Kindley airfield .. .. .. 65 70
638 70 c. Boeing "314" flying boat and map of Atlantic route .. .. .. 80 85
639 $2 Censored trans-Atlantic mail .. 2·25 2·40
636/9 .. .. .. .. *Set of* 4 3·50 3·75

(Des D. Miller. Litho Questa ($1), B.D.T. (others))

**1992** (6 Feb). *40th Anniv of Queen Elizabeth II's Accession. Horiz designs as T* **143** *of Ascension. Multicoloured. W w* **14** *(sideways). P* 14.

640 20 c. Old fort on beach .. .. .. 25 30
641 30 c. Public gardens .. .. .. 35 40
642 55 c. Cottage garden .. .. .. 65 70
643 70 c. Beach and hotels .. .. .. 80 85
644 $1 Queen Elizabeth II .. .. .. 1·10 1·25
640/4 .. .. .. .. *Set of* 5 2·75 3·25

POSTAL FISCAL

**1937** (1 Feb). *As T* **15**, *but inscr* "REVENUE" *at each side. Wmk Mult Script CA. Chalk-surfaced paper. P* 14.

F1 12s. 6d. grey and orange .. .. £1000 £1100
a. Break in scroll (R. 1/12) .. .. £2250
b. Broken crown and scroll (R. 2/12) .. £2250

No. F1 was issued for fiscal purposes during 1936. Its use as a postage stamp was authorised from 1 February to April 1937. The used price quoted above is for examples postmarked during this period. Later in the same year postmarks with other dates were obtained by favour.

For illustration of No. F1a/b see above No. 44.

# Botswana
## (*formerly* Bechuanaland)

Before the 1880s the only Europeans in the area which became Bechuanaland were scattered hunters and traders, together with the missionaries who were established at Kuruman as early as 1816.

Tribal conflicts in the early years of the decade led to the intervention of Boers from the Transvaal who established the independent republics of Goshen and Stellaland.

## STELLALAND

The Boer republic of Stellaland was proclaimed towards the end of 1882. A postal service was organised from the capital, Vryburg, and stamps were ordered from a firm in Cape Town. These were only valid within the republic. Until June 1885 mail to other parts of South Africa was sent through Christiana, in the Transvaal, and was franked with both Stellaland and Transvaal stamps.

No date stamps or obliterators were used by the Stellaland Post Office. Stamps were pen-cancelled with the initials of a postal official and the date.

**PRICES FOR STAMPS ON COVER**
The issues of Stellaland are very rare on cover.

1 Arms of the Republic

(Litho by Van der Sandt, de Villiers & Co, Cape Town)

**1884** (Feb). *P* 12.
1 1 1d. red .. .. .. .. .. .. £170 £275
a. Imperf between (pair) .. .. £1500
2 3d. orange .. .. .. .. 14·00 £275
a. Imperf between (pair) .. .. £400
3 4d. blue .. .. .. .. .. 14·00 £300
a. Imperf between (pair) .. .. £400
4 6d. lilac-mauve .. .. .. .. 14·00 £300
a. Imperf between (pair) .. .. £700
5 1s. green .. .. .. .. .. 32·00

In 1884 the British Government, following appeals from local chiefs for protection, decided to annex both Goshen and Stellaland. A force under Sir Charles Warren from the Cape reached Vryburg on 7 February 1885 and continued to Mafeking, the principal town of Goshen.

On 30 September Stellaland and other territory to the south of the Molopo River was constituted the Crown Colony of British Bechuanaland. A protectorate was also proclaimed over a vast tract of land to the north of the Molopo.

Stellaland stamps continued to be used until December 1885 with external mail routed via Barkly West and Kimberley in Griqualand West where Cape of Good Hope stamps were added and a date stamp applied.

**1885** (Oct). *Handstamped "Twee" sideways in violet-lake.*
6 1 2d. on 4d. blue .. .. .. .. .. £3500

## BRITISH BECHUANALAND

### CROWN COLONY

**PRICES FOR STAMPS ON COVER TO 1945**

| | |
|---|---|
| Nos. 1/8 | *from* × 12 |
| No. 9 | *from* × 80 |
| Nos. 10/21 | *from* × 8 |
| Nos. 22/8 | *from* × 10 |
| No. 29 | *from* × 10 |
| No. 30 | *from* × 10 |
| Nos. 31/2 | *from* × 12 |
| Nos. 33/7 | *from* × 20 |
| Nos. 38/9 | *from* × 25 |
| Nos. 40/51 | *from* × 10 |
| Nos. 52/8 | *from* × 6 |
| Nos. 59/71 | *from* × 6 |
| Nos. 72/82 | *from* × 5 |
| Nos. 83/98 | *from* × 4 |
| Nos. 99/110 | *from* × 6 |
| Nos. 111/17 | *from* × 10 |
| Nos. 118/28 | *from* × 4 |
| Nos. 129/31 | *from* × 10 |
| Nos. D1/3 | *from* × 50 |
| Nos. D4/6 | *from* × 60 |
| No. F1 | *from* × 5 |
| No. F2 | – |
| No. F3 | *from* × 5 |

BRITISH

British

Bechuanaland (1) BECHUANALAND (2)

**1885** (2 Dec)–**87**. *Stamps of Cape of Good Hope ("Hope" seated) optd with T* **1**, *by W. A. Richards & Sons, Cape Town.*

*(a) Wmk Crown CC (No. 3) or Crown CA (others)*
1 ½d. grey-black (No. 43*a*) (R.) .. .. 11·00 11·00
a. Opt in lake
b. Opt double (Lake+Black) .. .. £600
2 3d. pale claret (No. 40) .. .. .. 30·00 32·00
3 4d. dull blue (No. 30) (12.86?) .. .. 55·00 60·00

*(b) Wmk Anchor (Cape of Good Hope. Type* **13**)
4 ½d. grey-black (No. 48*a*) (3.87) .. .. 6·50 11·00
a. Error. "ritish" .. .. .. .. £1600
b. Opt double .. .. .. .. £1000
5 1d. rose-red (No. 49) .. .. .. 8·50 8·50
a. Error. "ritish" .. .. .. £1800 £1600
b. Opt double .. .. .. .. † £1800
6 2d. pale bistre (No. 50) .. .. .. 28·00 12·00
a. Error. "ritish" .. .. .. £3750 £3250
b. Opt double .. .. .. .. † £1300
7 6d. reddish purple (No. 52) .. .. 60·00 28·00
8 1s. yellow-green (No. 53) (11.86?) .. .. £200 £130
a. Error. "ritish" .. .. .. £9500 £7500

Nos. 1/8 were overprinted from settings of 120. The missing "B" errors are believed to have occurred on one position for one of these settings only.

Overprints with stop after "Bechuanaland" are forged.

**1887** (1 Nov). *No. 197 of Great Britain optd with T* **2**, *by D.L.R.*
9 ½d. vermilion (H/S S. £80) .. .. 60 90
a. Opt double .. .. .. .. £1800

3

4

5

(Typo D.L.R.)

**1887** (1 Nov). *(a) Wmk Orb (Great Britain Type* **48**). *P* 14.
10 3 1d. lilac and black .. .. .. 12·00 1·25
11 2d. lilac and black .. .. .. 40·00 80
*a. Pale dull lilac and black* .. .. 35·00 20·00
12 3d. lilac and black .. .. .. 3·25 4·75
*a. Pale reddish lilac and black* .. .. 45·00 13·00
13 4d. lilac and black .. .. .. 38·00 2·75
14 6d. lilac and black .. .. .. 42·00 3·25

*(b) Wmk Script "V R" (sideways, reading up). P* 13½
15 4 1s. green and black .. .. .. 28·00 4·50
16 2s. green and black .. .. .. 45·00 35·00
17 2s. 6d. green and black .. .. .. 60·00 40·00
18 5s. green and black .. .. .. 80·00 £100
19 10s. green and black .. .. .. £170 £275

*(c) Two Orbs (sideways). P* 14×13½
20 5 £1 lilac and black .. .. .. £900 £800
21 £5 lilac and black .. .. .. £2750 £1300
10/21 H/S "Specimen" .. .. *Set of* 12 £900

Nos. 10/21 were produced by overprinting a series of "Unappropriated Die" designs originally produced by the Board of Inland Revenue for use as Great Britain fiscal stamps.

Several values are known on blued paper. No. 11*a* is the first printing of the 2d. (on safety paper?) and has a faded appearance.

When purchasing Nos. 20/21 in used condition beware of copies with fiscal cancellations cleaned off and bearing forged postmarks.

For No. 15 surcharged "£5" see No. F2.

1d. (6) 1s. (7) One Half-Penny (8)

**1888** (7 Aug). *Nos. 10/11 and 13/15 surch as T* **6** *or* **7**, *by P. Townshend & Co, Vryburg.*
22 3 1d. on 1d. lilac and black .. .. 7·50 5·00
23 2d. on 2d. lilac and black (R.) .. .. 14·00 2·50
*a. Pale dull lilac and black* (No. 11*a*) .. 60·00 45·00
b. Curved foot to "2" .. .. .. £200 £150
c. Surch in green .. .. .. — £2250
25 4d. on 4d. lilac and black (R.) .. .. £150 £160
26 6d. on 6d. lilac and black .. .. 70·00 17·00
a. Surch in blue .. .. .. — £3000
28 4 1s. on 1s. green and black .. .. £100 55·00

Nos. 23*c* and 26*a* are from two sheets of surcharge trials subsequently put into stock and used at Vryburg (2d.) or Mafeking (6d.) during 1888–89.

**1888** (Dec.) *No. 12a surch with T* **8**, *by P. Townshend & Co, Vryburg.*
29 3 ½d. on 3d. pale reddish lilac and black £100 £120
a. Broken "f" in "Half" .. .. £4000

No. 29 was produced from a setting of 60 (12×5).

No. 29a shows the letter "f" almost completely missing and occurs on R. 5/11 of the setting. Four examples are known, one being in the Royal Collection.

Errors of spelling on this surcharge are bogus.

### *NEW INFORMATION*

The editor is always interested to correspond with people who have new information that will improve or correct the Catalogue.

British Bechuanaland. (9) British Bechuanaland. (10) BRITISH BECHUANALAND (11)

**1889** (Jan). *No. 48a of Cape of Good Hope (wmk Anchor) optd with T* **9**, *by P. Townshend & Co, Vryburg.*
30 ½d. grey-black (G.) .. .. .. 3·25 16·00
b. Opt double, one inverted .. .. £600
c. Opt double, one vertical .. .. £500
ca. *Se-tenant* with stamp without opt .. £2000
e. "British" omitted .. .. .. £2000

No. 30 was produced using a setting of 30 (6×5). No. 30e occurred on R. 5/1 of the setting on some sheets only.

**1891** (Nov). *Nos. 49/50 of Cape of Good Hope (wmk Anchor) optd with T* **10**, *reading upwards.*
31 1d. rose-red .. .. .. 9·50 8·00
a. Horiz pair, one without opt
b. "British" omitted .. .. .. — £500
c. "Bechuanaland" omitted .. .. £750
32 2d. pale bistre .. .. .. 3·25 2·25
a. No stop after "Bechuanaland" .. £180 £180
31/2 H/S "Specimen" .. .. *Set of* 2 £130

Nos. 31/2 were produced from separate settings of 120 (12×10). No. 32a occurs on R. 3/3.

See also Nos. 38 and 39.

**1891** (1 Dec)–**1904**. *Nos. 172, 200, 205, 208 and 211 of Great Britain optd with T* **11**, *by D.L.R.*
33 1d. lilac .. .. .. .. 4·50 60
34 2d. grey-green and carmine .. .. 3·50 2·25
35 4d. green and purple-brown .. .. 2·50 50
a. Bisected (2d.) (on cover) (11.99) .. † £2000
36 6d. purple/*rose-red* .. .. .. 3·00 1·75
37 1s. dull green (7.94) .. .. .. 13·00 16·00
a. Bisected (6d.) (on cover) (12.04) .. † —
33/7 .. .. .. *Set of* 5 24·00 19·00
33/6 H/S "Specimen" .. .. *Set of* 4 £170

No. 35a was used at Palapye station and No. 37a at Kanye.

**1893** (Dec)–**95**. *As Nos. 31/2, but T* **10** *reads downwards.*
38 1d. rose-red .. .. .. 1·60 2·00
a. Pair, one without opt
b. "British" omitted .. .. .. £475
c. Optd "Bechuanaland. British"
d. No dots to "i" of "British" (R.1/10) .. 80·00 80·00
e. Opt reading up, no dots to "i" of "British" £600
39 2d. pale bistre (15.3.95) .. .. 4·00 2·00
a. Opt double .. .. .. £750 £550
b. "British" omitted .. .. .. £325 £325
c. Optd "Bechuanaland. British" .. £300 £180
d. No dots to "i" of "British" (R.1/10) .. £100 £100

A common setting of 120 (12×10) was used for Nos. 38/9. Some sheets of the 1d. were overprinted the wrong way up, resulting in No. 38e.

On 16 November 1895 British Bechuanaland was annexed to the Cape of Good Hope and ceased to have its own stamps, but they remained in use in the Protectorate until superseded in 1897.

## BECHUANALAND PROTECTORATE

This large area north of the Molopo River was proclaimed a British Protectorate on 30 September 1885 at the request of the native chiefs.

A postal service using runners was inaugurated in August 1888 and Nos. 40 to 55 were issued as a temporary measure with the object of assessing the cost of this service.

Protectorate (12) 15½ mm Protectorate 1d (13)

**1888** (7 Aug). *No. 9 optd with T* **12** *and Nos. 10/19 surch or optd only as T* **13**.
40 – ½d. vermilion (H/S S. £60) .. .. 2·75 18·00
a. "Protectorate" double .. .. £300
41 3 1d. on 1d. lilac and black .. .. 5·50 11·00
a. Small figure "1" (R. 7/2) .. .. £250 £275
42 2d. on 2d. lilac and black .. .. 17·00 17·00
b. Curved foot to "2" .. .. £250 £250
43 3d. on 3d. pale reddish lilac and black 80·00 £110
44 4d. on 4d. lilac and black .. .. £160 £160
a. Small figure "4"
45 6d. on 6d. lilac and black .. .. 48·00 40·00
46 4 1s. green and black (H/S S. £80) .. 55·00 48·00
a. First "o" omitted .. .. .. £3000 £3000
47 2s. green and black .. .. .. £425 £550
a. First "o" omitted .. .. £5500
48 2s. 6d. green and black .. .. .. £500 £650
a. First "o" omitted .. .. £5500
49 5s. green and black .. .. .. £1100 £1500
a. First "o" omitted .. .. £6500
50 10s. green and black .. .. .. £3000 £4000
a. First "o" omitted .. .. £10000

Nos. 40/5 were produced from a basic setting of 120 (12×10) on which a faulty first "o" in "Protectorate" occurred on R.5/12. For Nos. 46/50 the setting was reduced to 84 (12×7) and on many sheets the first "o" on R.5/12 failed to print.

See also Nos. 54/5

**1888** (Dec). *No. 25 optd with T* **12**.
51 3 4d. on 4d. lilac and black .. .. 55·00 32·00

Bechuanaland

Protectorate.
(14)

Protectorate
Fourpence
(15)

**1889** (Jan). *No. 48a of Cape of Good Hope (wmk Anchor), optd with T* **14**.
52 ½d. grey-black (G.) .. 2·75 22·00
a. Opt double .. £375 £500
ab. Ditto, one reading "Protectorate Bechuanaland" .. £550
b. "Bechuanaland" omitted .. £550
c. Optd "Protectorate Bechuanaland" .. £225 £300

**1889** (Aug). *No. 9 surch with T* **15**.
53 4d. on ½d. vermilion (H/S S. £100) .. 13·00 2·75
a. Surch (T **15**) inverted .. — £3750

Protectorate
(16) 15 mm

Protectorate
(17)

**1890.** *No. 9 optd.*
54 **16** ½d. vermilion .. 80·00 90·00
a. Type **16** inverted .. 70·00 90·00
b. Type **16** double .. 75·00 90·00
c. Type **16** double and inverted .. £500 £500
d. Error. "Portectorate" and opt inverted
55 **17** ½d. vermilion .. £100 £120
a. Type **17** double .. £500
b. Error. "Protectorrte"

These were trial printings made in 1888 which were subsequently issued.

In June 1890 the Bechuanaland Protectorate and the Colony of British Bechuanaland came under one postal administration and the stamps of British Bechuanaland were used in the Protectorate until 1897.

BRITISH

BECHUANALAND
(18)

BECHUANALAND PROTECTORATE
(19)

**1897.** *No. 59 of Cape of Good Hope (wmk Anchor), optd as T* **18**.
*(a) Lines 13 mm apart, bottom line 16 mm long, by Taylor & Marshall, Cape Town*
56 ½d. yellow-green (July?) .. 2·25 6·00
*(b) Lines 13½ mm apart, bottom line 15 mm long, by P. Townshend & Co, Vryburg*
57 ½d. yellow-green (April) .. 14·00 55·00
*(c) Lines 10½ mm apart, bottom line 15 mm long, by W. A. Richards & Sons, Cape Govt Printers*
58 ½d. yellow-green (July?) .. 7·00 27·00

Although issued only in the Protectorate, the above were presumably overprinted "BRITISH BECHUANALAND" because stamps bearing this inscription were in use there at the time.

**1897** (Oct)–**1902**. *Nos. 172, 197, 200, 202, 205 and 208 of Great Britain (Queen Victoria) optd with T* **19** *by D.L.R.*
59 ½d. vermilion .. 60 1·50
60 ½d. blue-green (25.2.02) .. 1·25 2·00
61 1d. lilac .. 3·00 45
62 2d. grey-green and carmine .. 2·25 4·50
63 3d. purple/*yellow* (12.97) .. 5·50 8·50
64 4d. green and purple-brown .. 10·00 11·00
a. Bisected (2d.) (on cover) (1899) .. † £2000
65 6d. purple/*rose-red* .. 16·00 11·00
59/65 .. *Set of* 7 35·00 35·00
59/65 Optd "Specimen" .. *Set of* 7 £225

No. 64a was used at Palapye Station.

BECHUANALAND PROTECTORATE
(20)

BECHUANALAND PROTECTORATE
(21)

**1904** (29 Nov)–**13**. *Nos. 216, 218/19, 230 and 313/14 (Somerset House ptgs) of Great Britain (King Edward VII) optd with T* **20**, *by D.L.R.*
66 ½d. blue-green (3.06) .. 80 90
67 ½d. yellowish green (11.08) .. 2·00 3·50
68 1d. scarlet (4.05) (S. £50) .. 4·25 25
69 2½d. ultramarine .. 3·50 5·00
a. Stop after "P" in "PROTECTORATE" .. £800 £1200
70 1s. deep green and scarlet (10.12) .. 28·00 60·00
71 1s. green and carmine (1913) (S. £60) .. 29·00 65·00

No. 69a occurs on R.5/9 of the lower pane.

**1912** (Sept). *No. 342 of Great Britain (King George V, wmk Crown) optd with T* **20**.
72 1d. scarlet .. 55 60
a. No cross on crown .. — 75·00
*b. Aniline scarlet* (No. 343) .. £120 80·00

**1913** (July)–**24**. *Stamps of Great Britain (King George V) optd.*
*(a) Nos. 351, 357, 362, 367, 370/1, 376, 379, 385 and 395 (wmk Simple Cypher, T* **100**) *optd with T* **20**
73 ½d. green (*shades*) .. 1·10 1·75
74 1d. scarlet (*shades*) (4.15) .. 2·75 40
*a. Carmine-red* (1922) .. 3·75 70
75 1½d. red-brown (12.20) .. 1·75 3·00
76 2d. reddish orange (Die I) .. 2·50 3·50
*a. Orange* (Die I) (1921) .. 
77 2d. orange (Die II) (1924) .. 28·00 5·00
78 2½d. cobalt-blue .. 2·50 14·00
*a. Blue* (1915) .. 
79 3d. bluish violet .. 5·50 12·00
80 4d. grey-green .. 5·50 14·00
81 6d. reddish purple (*shades*) .. 6·50 14·00
82 1s. bistre (S. £60) .. 7·00 18·00
*a. Bistre-brown* (1923) .. 
73/82 .. *Set of* 9 32·00 75·00

*(b) With T* **21**
(i) *Waterlow printings* (*Nos. 399 and 401*) (1914–15)
83 2s. 6d. deep sepia-brown (1.15) .. £100 £180
a. Re-entry (R.2/1) .. £650 £850
b. Opt double, one albino .. £200
84 5s. rose-carmine (1914) .. £140 £300
a. Opt double, one albino .. £275
83/4 Optd "Specimen" .. *Set of* 2 £250
(ii) *D.L.R. printings* (*Nos. 407/8 and 409*) (1916–20)
85 2s. 6d. pale brown (7.16) .. £100 £170
a. Re-entry .. £750
86 2s. 6d. sepia (1920) .. £120 £190
a. Opt treble, two albino
87 5s. bright carmine (8.19) .. £225 £325
a. Opt double, one albino .. £325
(iii) *B.W. printings* (*Nos. 414 and 416*) (1920–23)
88 2s. 6d. chocolate-brown (7.23) .. 90·00 £160
a. Major re-entry .. £1500
b. Opt double, one albino
89 5s. rose-red (7.20) .. £120 £225
a. Opt treble, two albino .. £275
b. Opt double, one albino

**1925** (July)–**27**. *Nos. 418/19, 421, 423/4, 426/a and 429 of Great Britain (wmk Block Cypher, T* **111**) *optd with T* **20**.
91 ½d. green (1927) .. 70 1·75
92 1d. scarlet (8.25) .. 75 70
93 2d. orange (Die II) .. 1·50 1·00
94 3d. violet (10.26) .. 4·50 11·00
a. Opt double, one albino .. £200
95 4d. grey-green (10.26) .. 4·50 20·00
96 6d. reddish purple (*chalk-surfaced paper*) (12.25) .. 13·00 25·00
97 6d. purple (*ordinary paper*) (1926) .. 30·00 40·00
98 1s. bistre-brown (10.26) .. 8·50 24·00
91/8 .. *Set of* 8 55·00 £110

**22** King George V, Baobab Tree and Cattle drinking

**23** King George VI, Baobab Tree and Cattle drinking

(Des from photo by Resident Commissioner, Ngamiland, Recess Waterlow)

**1932** (12 Dec). *Wmk Mult Script CA. P* 12½.
99 **22** ½d. green .. 60 30
a. Imperf between (horiz pair) .. £9500
100 1d. scarlet .. 60 25
101 2d. brown .. 70 30
102 3d. ultramarine .. 90 50
103 4d. orange .. 1·00 3·25
104 6d. purple .. 2·50 1·50
105 1s. black and olive-green .. 5·00 7·00
106 2s. black and orange .. 22·00 35·00
107 2s.6d. black and scarlet .. 19·00 30·00
108 3s. black and purple .. 32·00 40·00
109 5s. black and ultramarine .. 42·00 45·00
110 10s. black and brown .. 90·00 £100
99/110 .. *Set of* 12 £180 £225
99/110 Perf "Specimen" .. *Set of* 12 £250

**1935** (4 May). *Silver Jubilee. As Nos. 91/4 of Antigua but ptd by B.W. P* 11 × 12.
111 1d. deep blue and scarlet .. 30 75
a. Extra flagstaff .. £110
b. Short extra flagstaff .. 70·00
c. Lightning conductor .. 70·00
d. Flagstaff on right-hand turret .. 70·00
e. Double flagstaff .. 70·00
112 2d. ultramarine and grey-black .. 75 75
a. Extra flagstaff .. 80·00
b. Short extra flagstaff .. 60·00
c. Lightning conductor .. 55·00
113 3d. brown and deep blue .. 75 1·00
a. Extra flagstaff .. £110
b. Short extra flagstaff .. 70·00
c. Lightning conductor .. 70·00
114 6d. slate and purple .. 1·75 1·00
a. Extra flagstaff .. 95·00
b. Short extra flagstaff .. 70·00
c. Lightning conductor .. 70·00
111/14 .. *Set of* 4 3·25 3·25
111/14 Perf "Specimen" .. *Set of* 4 75·00

For illustrations of plate varieties see Catalogue Introduction.

**1937** (12 May). *Coronation. As Nos. 95/7 of Antigua, but printed by D.L.R. P* 14.
115 1d. scarlet .. 35 40
116 2d. yellow-brown .. 60 55
117 3d. bright blue .. 60 70
115/17 .. *Set of* 3 1·40 1·50
115/17 Perf "Specimen" .. *Set of* 3 50·00

(Recess Waterlow)

**1938** (1 Apr)–**52**. *Wmk Mult Script CA. P* 12½.
118 **23** ½d. green .. 1·10 1·90
*a. Light yellowish green* (1941) .. 2·50 3·00
*b. Yellowish green* (4.43) .. 1·00 1·75
*c. Deep green* (4.49) .. 60 2·25
119 1d. scarlet .. 15 35
120 1½d. dull blue .. 4·50 1·50
*a. Light blue* (4.43) .. 30 55
121 2d. chocolate-brown .. 15 30
122 3d. deep ultramarine .. 20 80
123 4d. orange .. 30 1·40
124 6d. reddish purple .. 3·50 2·75
*a. Purple* (1944) .. 2·25 2·25
125 1s. black and brown-olive .. 1·25 1·75
*a. Grey-black and olive-green* (21.5.52) .. 5·50 7·50
126 2s.6d. black and scarlet .. 10·00 7·50
127 5s. black and deep ultramarine .. 23·00 7·50
*a. Grey-black & dp ultramarine* (10.46) .. 55·00 32·00
128 10s. black and red-brown .. 11·00 14·00
118/28 .. *Set of* 11 45·00 35·00
118/28 Perf "Specimen" .. *Set of* 11 £170

Bechuanaland
(24)

**24a** King George VI and Queen Elizabeth

**1945** (3 Dec). *Victory. Stamps of South Africa optd with T* **24**. *Inscr alternately in English and Afrikaans.*

| | | | *Un. pair* | *Used pair* |
|---|---|---|---|---|
| 129 | **55** | 1d. brown and carmine | 20 | 25 |
| 130 | **56** | 2d. slate-blue and violet | 20 | 35 |
| 131 | **57** | 3d. deep blue and blue | 20 | 35 |
| | | a. Opt omitted (in vert pair with normal) | £4000 | |
| 129/31 | | *Set of* 3 | 55 | 85 |

(Recess Waterlow)

**1947** (17 Feb). *Royal Visit. T* **24a** *and similar designs. Wmk Mult Script CA. P* 12½.
132 1d. scarlet .. 10 10
133 2d. green .. 10 10
134 3d. ultramarine .. 10 10
135 1s. mauve .. 10 10
132/5 .. *Set of* 4 35 20
132/5 Perf "Specimen" .. *Set of* 4 80·00

Designs: *Vert*—1d. King George VI. *Horiz*—3d. Princess Elizabeth and Princess Margaret; 1s. The Royal Family.

**1948** (1 Dec). *Royal Silver Wedding. As Nos. 112/13 of Antigua.*
136 1½d. ultramarine .. 30 10
137 10s. black .. 22·00 25·00

**1949** (10 Oct). *75th Anniv of Universal Postal Union. As Nos. 114/17 of Antigua.*
138 1½d. blue .. 25 15
139 3d. deep blue .. 55 50
140 6d. magenta .. 60 80
141 1s. olive .. 80 80
138/41 .. *Set of* 4 2·00 2·00

**1953** (3 June). *Coronation. As No. 120 of Antigua.*
142 2d. black and brown .. 10 30

**25** Queen Elizabeth II, Baobab Tree and Cattle drinking

**26** Queen Victoria, Queen Elizabeth II and Landscape

(Des from photo by Resident Commissioner, Ngamiland. Recess Waterlow)

**1955** (3 Jan)–**58**. *Wmk Mult Script CA. P* 13½ × 14.
143 **25** ½d. green .. 30 15
144 1d. rose-red .. 40 10
145 2d. red-brown .. 60 20
146 3d. ultramarine .. 1·40 30
*a. Bright ultramarine* (16.1.57) .. 1·75 40
146*b* 4d. red-orange (1.12.58) .. 4·50 5·00
147 4½d. blackish blue .. 1·00 35
148 6d. purple .. 60 50
149 1s. black and brown-olive .. 80 60
150 1s. 3d. black and lilac .. 7·00 7·50
151 2s. 6d. black and rose-red .. 7·50 7·50
152 5s. black and violet-blue .. 8·00 5·50
153 10s. black and red-brown .. 14·00 14·00
143/53 .. *Set of* 12 42·00 38·00

(Photo Harrison)

**1960** (21 Jan). *75th Anniv of Bechuanaland Protectorate. W* w **12**. *P* 14½ × 14.
154 **26** 1d. sepia and black .. 15 15
155 3d. magenta and black .. 20 10
156 6d. bright blue and black .. 20 20
154/6 .. *Set of* 3 50 40

**New Currency.** 100 cents = 1 rand

1c (27) 1c (I) 1c (II) 2½c (I) 2½c (II)

3 (I) 3 (II) 3 (III) (3½ c. on 4d.) 5c (I) 5c (II) R1 (I) R1 (II)

2½c Spaced "c" (R. 10/3)

**1961** (14 Feb–June). *Nos. 144/6a and 148/53 surch as T* **27** *by South African Govt Printer, Pretoria.*

157 **25** 1 c. on 1d. rose-red (Type I) .. .. 20 10
a. Type II (6 June) .. .. 10 10
158 2 c. on 2d. red-brown .. .. 10 10
159 2½ c. on 2d. red-brown (Type I) .. 15 10
a. Type II (26 July) .. .. 30 10
b. Vert pair, one without surch .. £1100
160 2½ c. on 3d. bright ultramarine .. 1·75 1·50
a. Spaced "c" (R.10/3) .. .. 28·00
161 3½ c. on 4d. red-orange (Type I) .. 40 20
a. Type II .. .. .. 1·25 1·00
b. Wide surch (I) .. .. 11·00 12·00
c. Wide surch (II) .. .. 35·00 38·00
d. Type III (6 June) .. .. 15 10
162 5 c. on 6d. purple (Type I) .. 85 30
a. Type II (12 May) .. .. 15 10
163 10 c. on 1s. black and brown-olive .. 15 10
a. Horiz pair, one without surch .. £900
164 12½ c. on 1s. 3d. black and lilac .. 25 15
165 25 c. on 2s. 6d. black and rose-red .. 1·25 40
166 50 c. on 5s. black and violet-blue .. 1·75 65
167 1 r. on 10s. black & red-brown (Type I) £225 90·00
a. Type II (surch at bottom left) (17 Mar) .. .. .. 5·00 3·00
b. Type II (surch at foot, either to right or central) (Apr) .. .. 3·25 2·00
157/67b .. .. .. *Set of* 11 9·00 4·25

Nos. 161/c occur from the same printing each sheet containing thirty-three examples of Type I, five of Type I with wide spacing, nineteen of Type II and three of Type II with wide spacing. The wide surcharge measures 9½ mm overall (with "C" spaced 1½ mm from "½") and comes on 8 of the 10 stamps in the last vertical row. The surcharge on the remainder of the sheet varies between 8½ and 9½ mm.

A later printing of the 12½ c. on 1s. 3d. was from a fresh setting of type, but is insufficiently different for separate listing. Later printings of the 10 c. and 25 c. were identical with the originals.

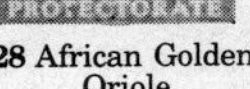

**28** African Golden Oriole **39** Bechuana Ox

(Des P. Jones. Photo Harrison)

**1961** (2 Oct). *T* **28, 39** *and similar designs. W w* **12**. *P* 14½ × 14 (25, 50 c.) *or* 14 × 14½ (*others*).

168 1 c. yellow, red, black and lilac .. .. 45 30
169 2 c. orange, black and yellow-olive .. 45 60
170 2½ c. carmine, green, black and bistre .. 45 10
171 3½ c. yellow, black, sepia and pink .. .. 50 50
172 5 c. yellow, blue, black and buff .. 1·25 50
173 7½ c. brown, red, black and apple-green .. 60 60
174 10 c. red, yellow, sepia & turquoise-green .. 75 50
175 12½ c. buff, blue, red and grey-black .. .. 11·00 3·25
176 20 c. yellow-brown and drab .. .. 50 70
177 25 c. deep brown and lemon .. .. 50 75
178 35 c. deep blue and orange .. .. 80 1·50
179 50 c. sepia and olive .. .. .. 1·00 2·25
180 1 r. black and cinnamon .. .. 3·00 2·50
181 2 r. brown and turquoise-blue .. .. 17·00 7·50
168/81 .. .. .. *Set of* 14 35·00 19·00

Designs: *Vert*—2 c. Hoopoe; 2½ c. Scarlet-chested Sunbird; 3½ c. Yellow-rumped Bishop; 5 c. Swallow-tailed Bee Eater; 7½ c. African Grey Hornbill; 10 c. Red-headed Weaver; 12½ c. Brown-hooded Kingfisher; 20 c. Woman musician; 35 c. Woman grinding maize; 1 r. Lion; 2 r. Police camel patrol. *Horiz*—25 c. Baobab Tree.

**1963** (4 June). *Freedom from Hunger. As No. 146 of Antigua.*
182 12½ c. bluish green .. .. .. .. 25 15

**1963** (2 Sept). *Red Cross Centenary. As Nos. 147/8 of Antigua.*
183 2½ c. red and black .. .. .. 20 10
184 12½ c. red and blue .. .. .. 40 35

**1964** (23 April). *400th Birth Anniv of William Shakespeare. As No. 164 of Antigua.*
185 12½c. light brown .. .. .. .. 15 15

## COVER PRICES

Cover factors are quoted at the beginning of each country for most issues to 1945. An explanation of the system can be found on page x. The factors quoted do not, however, apply to philatelic covers.

## BECHUANALAND

### INTERNAL SELF-GOVERNMENT

**42** Map and Gaberones Dam

(Des Mrs. M. Townsend, adapted V. Whiteley. Photo Harrison)

**1965** (1 Mar). *New Constitution. W w* **12**. *P* 14½ × 14.
186 **42** 2½ c. red and gold .. .. .. 10 10
187 5 c. ultramarine and gold .. .. 10 15
188 12½ c. brown and gold .. .. .. 10 15
189 25 c. green and gold .. .. .. 15 35
186/9 .. .. .. *Set of* 4 30 60

**1965** (17 May). *I.T.U. Centenary. As Nos. 166/7 of Antigua.*
190 2½ c. red and bistre-yellow .. .. .. 20 10
191 12½ c. mauve and brown .. .. .. 45 30

**1965** (25 Oct). *International Co-operation Year. As Nos. 168/9 of Antigua.*
192 1 c. reddish purple and turquoise-green 10 10
193 12½ c. deep bluish green and lavender .. 60 55

**1966** (24 Jan). *Churchill Commemoration. As Nos. 170/3 of Antigua.*
194 1 c. new blue .. .. .. .. 15 15
195 2½ c. deep green .. .. .. .. 25 10
196 12½ c. brown .. .. .. .. 65 20
197 20 c. bluish violet .. .. .. .. 70 25
194/7 .. .. .. *Set of* 4 1·50 65

**43** Haslar Smoke Generator

(Des V. Whiteley. Photo Harrison)

**1966** (1 June). *Bechuanaland Royal Pioneer Corps. T* **43** *and similar horiz designs. W w* **12**. *P* 14½.
198 2½ c. Prussian blue, red and light emerald .. 15 10
199 5 c. brown and light blue .. .. 15 10
200 15 c. Prussian blue, rosine and emerald .. 20 10
201 35 c. buff, blackish brown, red and green .. 30 60
198/201 .. .. .. *Set of* 4 70 70

Designs:—5 c. Bugler; 15 c. Gun-site; 35 c. Regimental cap badge.

## BOTSWANA

### INDEPENDENCE

Bechuanaland became the independent republic of Botswana, within the Commonwealth, on 30 September 1966.

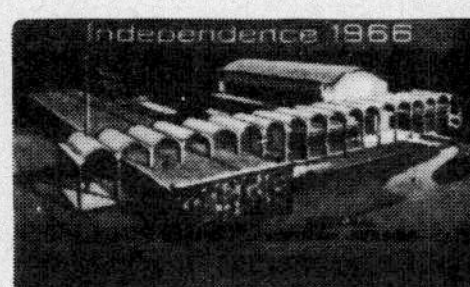


**47** National Assembly Building

(Des R. Granger Barrett. Photo Harrison)

**1966** (30 Sept). *Independence. T* **47** *and similar horiz designs. Multicoloured. P* 14½.
202 2½ c. Type **47** .. .. .. .. 15 10
a. Imperf (pair) .. .. .. £250
203 5 c. Abattoir, Lobatsi .. .. .. 15 10
204 15 c. National Airways "Dakota" .. .. 30 10
205 35 c. State House, Gaberones .. .. 30 20
202/5 .. .. .. *Set of* 4 80 30

REPUBLIC OF BOTSWANA

(51)

**52** Golden Oriole

**1966** (30 Sept). *Nos. 168/81 optd as T* **51**.
206 1 c. yellow, red, black and lilac .. .. 25 10
207 2 c. orange, black and yellow-olive .. 30 10
208 2½ c. carmine, green, black and bistre .. 30 10
209 3½ c. yellow, black, sepia and pink .. 40 15
*a. Yellow, black, sepia and flesh* .. 60 30
210 5 c. yellow, blue, black and buff .. 40 40
211 7½ c. brown, red, black and apple-green 40 50
a. Blue-green omitted
212 10 c. red, yellow, sepia & turquoise-green 60 20
213 12½ c. buff, blue, red and grey-black .. 3·50 1·25
214 20 c. yellow-brown and drab .. .. 60 45
215 25 c. deep brown and lemon .. .. 60 70
216 35 c. deep blue and orange .. .. 75 85
217 50 c. sepia and olive .. .. .. 50 70
218 1 r. black and cinnamon .. .. 75 1·25
219 2 r. brown and turquoise-blue .. 1·25 2·50
206/19 .. .. .. *Set of* 14 9·50 8·00

No. 209*a* was a special printing produced to make up quantities. It does not exist without the overprint.

No. 211a shows the background in yellow instead of apple-green, the blue-green overlay being omitted.

(Des D. M. Reid-Henry. Photo Harrison)

**1967** (3 Jan). *Birds. Vert designs as T* **52**. *Multicoloured. P* 14 × 14½.
220 1 c. Type **52** .. .. .. .. 30 15
a. Error. Wmk **105** of Malta .. .. † £700
221 2 c. Hoopoe .. .. .. .. 40 10
222 3 c. Groundscraper Thrush .. .. 55 10
223 4 c. Cordon-bleu .. .. .. 55 10
224 5 c. Secretary Bird .. .. .. 55 10
225 7 c. Yellow-billed Hornbill .. .. 60 70
226 10 c. Burchell's Gonolek .. .. 60 15
227 15 c. Malachite Kingfisher .. .. 5·00 75
228 20 c. African Fish Eagle .. .. 4·50 70
229 25 c. Go-away Bird .. .. .. 2·50 60
230 35 c. Scimitar-bill .. .. .. 4·75 90
231 50 c. Comb Duck .. .. .. 3·25 1·50
232 1 r. Levaillant's Barbet .. .. 6·00 3·25
233 2 r. Didric Cuckoo .. .. .. 9·50 11·00
220/33 .. .. .. *Set of* 14 35·00 18·00

A used copy of the 20 c. has been seen with the pale brown colour missing, resulting in the value (normally shown in white) being omitted.

The 1, 2, 4, 7 and 10 c. values exist with PVA gum as well as gum arabic.

**66** Students and University

(Des V. Whiteley. Photo Harrison)

**1967** (7 Apr). *First Conferment of University Degrees. P* 14 × 14½.
234 **66** 3 c. sepia, ultramarine & lt orange-yell 10 10
235 7 c. sepia, ultram & lt greenish bl .. 10 10
236 15 c. sepia, ultramarine and rose .. 10 10
237 35 c. sepia, ultramarine and light violet 20 20
234/7 .. .. .. *Set of* 4 30 30

**67** Bushbuck

(Des G. Vasarhelyi. Photo Harrison)

**1967** (2 Oct). *Chobe Game Reserve. T* **67** *and similar horiz designs. Multicoloured. P* 14.
238 3 c. Type **67** .. .. .. .. 10 10
239 7 c. Sable Antelope .. .. .. 15 15
240 35 c. Fishing on Chobe River .. .. 70 55
238/40 .. .. .. *Set of* 3 80 70

**70** Arms of Botswana and Human Rights Emblem

(Litho D.L.R.)

**1968** (8 Apr). *Human Rights Year. T* **70** *and similar horiz designs showing Arms of Botswana and Human Rights emblem arranged differently. P* 13½ × 13.
241 3 c. multicoloured .. .. .. 10 10
242 15 c. multicoloured .. .. .. 20 10
243 25 c. multicoloured .. .. .. 20 20
241/3 .. .. .. *Set of* 3 40 30

**73** Eland and Giraffe Rock Paintings, Tsodilo Hills **75** "Baobab Trees" (Thomas Baines)

**76** National Museum and Art Gallery

(Litho D.L.R.)

**1968** (30 Sept). *Opening of National Museum and Art Gallery. T* **73/6** *and similar multicoloured design. P* 12½ (7 *c.*), 12½ × 13½ (15 *c.*), *or* 13 × 13½ (*others*).

244 3 c. Type **73** .. .. .. .. .. .. 30 10
245 7 c. Girl wearing ceremonial beads (30 × 48 *mm*) .. .. .. .. .. .. 35 15
246 10 c. Type **75** .. .. .. .. .. .. 35 25
247 15 c. Type **76** .. .. .. .. .. .. 50 60
244/7 .. .. .. .. .. *Set of* 4 1·40 1·00
**MS**248 132 × 82 mm. Nos. 244/7. P 13 .. .. 1·40 2·00

**77** African Family, and Star over Village

(Des Mrs M. E. Townsend, adapted J. Cooter. Litho Enschedé)

**1968** (11 Nov). *Christmas. P* 13 × 14.

249 **77** 1 c. multicoloured .. .. .. .. 10 10
250 2 c. multicoloured .. .. .. .. 10 10
251 5 c. multicoloured .. .. .. .. 10 10
252 25 c. multicoloured .. .. .. .. 15 25
249/52 .. .. .. .. *Set of* 4 20 30

**78** Scout, Lion and Badge in Frame

(Des D.L.R. Litho Format)

**1969** (21 Aug). *22nd World Scout Conference, Helsinki. T* **78** *and similar multicoloured designs. P* 13½.

253 3 c. Type **78** .. .. .. .. .. .. 30 10
254 15 c. Scouts cooking over open fire (*vert*) .. 80 55
255 25 c. Scouts around camp fire .. .. .. .. 85 75
253/5 .. .. .. .. .. *Set of* 3 1·75 1·25

**81** Woman, Child and Christmas Star

**82** Diamond Treatment Plant, Orapa

(Des A. Vale, adapted V. Whiteley. Litho Harrison)

**1969** (6 Nov). *Christmas. P* 14½ × 14.

256 **81** 1 c. pale blue and chocolate .. .. 10 10
257 2 c. pale yellow-olive and chocolate .. 10 10
258 4 c. yellow and chocolate .. .. .. 10 10
259 35 c. chocolate and bluish violet .. .. 20 20
256/9 .. .. .. .. .. *Set of* 4 30 30
**MS**260 86 × 128 mm. Nos. 256/9. P 14½ (*shades*) 70 1·10

(Des J.W. Litho Harrison)

**1970** (23 Mar). *Developing Botswana. T* **82** *and similar designs. Multicoloured. P* 14½ × 14 (3 *c.*, 7 *c.*) *or* 14 × 14½ (*others*).

261 3 c. Type **82** .. .. .. .. .. .. 40 15
262 7 c. Copper-nickel mining .. .. .. .. 70 15
263 10 c. Copper-nickel mine, Selebi-Pikwe (*horiz*) 85 25
264 35 c. Orapa diamond mine, and diamonds (*horiz*) .. .. .. .. .. .. 2·00 85
261/4 .. .. .. .. .. *Set of* 4 3·50 1·25

**83** Mr. Micawber (*David Copperfield*)

(Des V. Whiteley. Litho Walsall)

**1970** (6 July). *Death Centenary of Charles Dickens. T* **83** *and similar horiz designs. Multicoloured. P* 11.

265 3 c. Type **83** .. .. .. .. .. .. 20 10
266 7 c. Scrooge (*A Christmas Carol*) .. .. 25 10
267 15 c. Fagin (*Oliver Twist*) .. .. .. 45 30
268 25 c. Bill Sykes (*Oliver Twist*) .. .. .. 75 55
265/8 .. .. .. .. .. *Set of* 4 1·50 80
**MS**269 114 × 81 mm. Nos. 265/8 .. .. .. 3·00 3·25

**84** U.N. Building and Emblem

(Des J. Cooter. Litho Walsall)

**1970** (24 Oct). *25th Anniv of United Nations. P* 11.

270 **84** 15 c. bright blue, chestnut and silver .. 30 30

**85** Crocodile

(Des A. Vale. Litho Questa)

**1970** (3 Nov). *Christmas. T* **85** *and similar horiz designs. Multicoloured. P* 14.

271 1 c. Type **85** .. .. .. .. .. .. 10 10
272 2 c. Giraffe .. .. .. .. .. .. 10 10
273 7 c. Elephant .. .. .. .. .. .. 10 10
274 25 c. Rhinoceros .. .. .. .. .. 30 45
271/4 .. .. .. .. .. *Set of* 4 45 55
**MS**275 128 × 90 mm. Nos. 271/4 .. .. .. 1·25 2·25

**86** Sorghum

(Des J.W. Litho Questa)

**1971** (6 April). *Important Crops. T* **86** *and similar horiz designs. Multicoloured. P* 14.

276 3 c. Type **86** .. .. .. .. .. .. 10 10
277 7 c. Millet .. .. .. .. .. .. 10 10
278 10 c. Maize .. .. .. .. .. .. 15 10
279 35 c. Groundnuts .. .. .. .. .. 45 40
276/9 .. .. .. .. .. *Set of* 4 60 50

**87** Map and Head of Cow

**88** King bringing Gift of Gold

(Des A. Vale, adapted L. Curtis. Litho Harrison)

**1971** (30 Sept). *Fifth Anniv of Independence. T* **87** *and similar vert designs inscr* "PULA" (*local greeting*). *P* 14½ × 14.

280 3 c. black, brown and apple-green .. .. 10 10
281 4 c. black, new blue and pale blue .. .. 10 10
282 7 c. black and red-orange .. .. .. 20 10
283 10 c. multicoloured .. .. .. .. 25 15
284 20 c. multicoloured .. .. .. .. 80 1·10
280/4 .. .. .. .. .. *Set of* 5 1·25 1·40

Designs:—4 c. Map and cogs; 7 c. Map and zebra; 10 c. Map and sorghum stalk crossed by tusk; 20 c. Arms and map of Botswana.

(Des A. Vale. Litho Questa)

**1971** (11 Nov). *Christmas. T* **88** *and similar vert designs. Multicoloured. P* 14.

285 2 c. Type **88** .. .. .. .. .. .. 10 10
286 3 c. King bearing frankincense .. .. .. 10 10
287 7 c. King bearing myrrh .. .. .. .. 10 10
288 20 c. Three Kings behold the star .. .. 35 50
285/8 .. .. .. .. .. *Set of* 4 40 55
**MS**289 85 × 128 mm. Nos. 285/8 .. .. .. 1·00 2·50

## ALTERED CATALOGUE NUMBERS

Any Catalogue numbers altered from the last edition are shown as a list in the introductory pages.

**89** Orion

**90** Postmark and Map

(Des R. Granger Barrett. Litho Questa)

**1972** (24 Apr). *"Night Sky". T* **89** *and similar vert designs. P* 14.

290 3 c. turquoise-blue, black and red .. .. 25 10
291 7 c. dull blue, black and yellow .. .. 50 60
292 10 c. dull green, black and orange .. .. 65 75
293 20 c. deep violet-blue, black and blue-green .. 1·10 1·25
290/3 .. .. .. .. .. *Set of* 4 2·25 2·40

Constellations:—7 c. The Scorpion; 10 c. The Centaur; 20 c. The Cross.

(Des M. Bryan. Litho A. & M.)

**1972** (21 Aug). *Mafeking-Gubulawayo Runner Post. T* **90** *and similar vert designs. Multicoloured. P* 13½ × 13.

294 3 c. Type **90** .. .. .. .. .. .. 30 10
a. Imperf (vert pair) .. .. .. .. £400
295 4 c. Bechuanaland stamp and map .. .. 30 35
296 7 c. Runners and map .. .. .. .. 45 50
297 20 c. Mafeking postmark and map .. .. 1·10 1·25
294/7 .. .. .. .. .. *Set of* 4 2·00 2·00
**MS**298 84 × 216 mm. Nos. 294/7 vertically *se-tenant*, forming a composite map design .. .. 7·50 9·50

For these designs redrawn smaller with changed inscriptions see Nos. 652/6.

**91** Cross, Map and Bells

**92** Thor

(Des M. Bryan. Litho Questa)

**1972** (6 Nov). *Christmas. Vert designs each with Cross and Map as T* **91**. *Multicoloured. P* 14.

299 2 c. Type **91** .. .. .. .. .. .. 10 10
300 3 c. Cross, map and candle .. .. .. 10 10
301 7 c. Cross, map and Christmas tree .. .. 15 20
302 20 c. Cross, map, star and holly .. .. 40 55
299/302 .. .. .. .. *Set of* 4 60 75
**MS**303 96 × 119 mm. Nos. 299/302 .. .. 1·25 2·50

(Des Edna Elphick. Litho Questa)

**1973** (23 Mar). *I.M.O./W.M.O. Centenary. T* **92** *and similar designs showing Norse myths. Multicoloured. P* 14.

304 3 c. Type **92** .. .. .. .. .. .. 15 10
305 4 c. Sun God's chariot (*horiz*) .. .. .. 20 15
306 7 c. Ymir, the frost giant .. .. .. .. 25 15
307 20 c. Odin and Sleipnir (*horiz*) .. .. .. 75 60
304/7 .. .. .. .. .. *Set of* 4 1·25 85

**93** Livingstone and River Scene

(Des G. Vasarhelyi. Litho Walsall Security Printers, Ltd)

**1973** (10 Sept). *Death Centenary of Dr. Livingstone. T* **93** *and similar horiz design. Multicoloured. P* 13½.

308 3 c. Type **93** .. .. .. .. .. .. 10 10
309 20 c. Livingstone meeting Stanley .. .. 50 60

**94** Donkey and Foal at Village Trough

**95** Gaborone Campus

(Des M. Bryan. Litho Questa)

**1973** (3 Dec). *Christmas. T* **94** *and similar multicoloured designs. P* 14.

| | | | |
|---|---|---|---|
| 310 | 3 c. Type **94** | 10 | 10 |
| 311 | 4 c. Shepherd and flock (*horiz*) | 10 | 10 |
| 312 | 7 c. Mother and child | 10 | 10 |
| 313 | 20 c. Kgotla meeting (*horiz*) | 40 | 60 |
| 310/13 | *Set of* 4 | 55 | 70 |

(Des. M. Bryan, adapted P. Powell. Litho Questa)

**1974** (8 May). *Tenth Anniv of University of Botswana, Lesotho and Swaziland. T* **95** *and similar horiz designs. Multicoloured. P* 14.

| | | | |
|---|---|---|---|
| 314 | 3 c. Type **95** | 10 | 10 |
| 315 | 7 c. Kwaluseni Campus | 10 | 10 |
| 316 | 20 c. Roma Campus | 15 | 20 |
| 317 | 35 c. Map and flags of the three countries | 20 | 35 |
| 314/17 | *Set of* 4 | 35 | 55 |

**96** Methods of Mail Transport

(Des. M. Bryan. Litho J.W.)

**1974** (29 May). *Centenary of Universal Postal Union. T* **96** *and similar horiz designs. Multicoloured. P* 14.

| | | | |
|---|---|---|---|
| 318 | 2 c. Type **96** | 45 | 35 |
| 319 | 3 c. Post Office, Palapye, *circa* 1889 | 45 | 35 |
| 320 | 7 c. Bechuanaland Police Camel Post, *circa* 1900 | 70 | 70 |
| 321 | 20 c. Mail-planes of 1920 and 1974 | 2·50 | 2·50 |
| 318/21 | *Set of* 4 | 3·50 | 3·50 |

**97** Amethyst

**98** *Stapelia variegata*

(Des M. Baylis, adapted PAD Studio. Photo Enschedé)

**1974** (1 July). *Botswana Minerals. T* **97** *and similar horiz designs. Multicoloured. P* 14 × 13.

| | | | |
|---|---|---|---|
| 322 | 1 c. Type **97** | 60 | 45 |
| 323 | 2 c. Agate—"Botswana Pink" | 60 | 45 |
| 324 | 3 c. Quartz | 65 | 45 |
| 325 | 4 c. Copper nickel | 70 | 50 |
| 326 | 5 c. Moss agate | 70 | 50 |
| 327 | 7 c. Agate | 80 | 50 |
| 328 | 10 c. Stilbite | 90 | 55 |
| 329 | 15 c. Moshaneng Banded Marble | 2·00 | 1·00 |
| 330 | 20 c. Gem diamonds | 3·25 | 1·25 |
| 331 | 25 c. Chrysotile | 3·50 | 90 |
| 332 | 35 c. Jasper | 4·25 | 1·75 |
| 333 | 50 c. Moss quartz | 4·50 | 3·25 |
| 334 | 1 r. Citrine | 7·50 | 7·50 |
| 335 | 2 r. Chalcopyrite | 17·00 | 15·00 |
| 322/35 | *Set of* 14 | 42·00 | 30·00 |

(Des M. Bryan. Litho Questa)

**1974** (4 Nov). *Christmas. T* **98** *and similar vert designs showing flowers. Multicoloured. P* 14.

| | | | |
|---|---|---|---|
| 336 | 2 c. Type **98** | 20 | 15 |
| 337 | 7 c. *Hibiscus lunarifolius* | 50 | 20 |
| 338 | 15 c. *Ceratotheca triloba* | 1·10 | 75 |
| 339 | 20 c. *Nerine laticoma* | 1·25 | 85 |
| 336/9 | *Set of* 4 | 2·75 | 1·75 |
| **MS**340 | 85 × 130 mm. Nos. 336/9 | 3·00 | 3·75 |

**99** President Sir Seretse Khama

**100** Ostrich

(Des M. Bryan, adapted G. Vasarhelyi. Photo Enschedé)

**1975** (24 Mar). *Tenth Anniv of Self-Government. P* 13½ × 13.

| | | | | |
|---|---|---|---|---|
| 341 | **99** | 4 c. multicoloured | 10 | 10 |
| 342 | | 10 c. multicoloured | 15 | 10 |
| 343 | | 20 c. multicoloured | 25 | 15 |
| 344 | | 35 c. multicoloured | 45 | 35 |
| 341/4 | | *Set of* 4 | 85 | 55 |
| **MS**345 | | 93 × 130 mm. Nos. 341/4 | 1·00 | 1·50 |

(Des M. Bryan. Litho Questa)

**1975** (23 June). *Rock Paintings, Tsodilo Hills. T* **100** *and similar horiz designs. Multicoloured. P* 14.

| | | | |
|---|---|---|---|
| 346 | 4 c. Type **100** | 25 | 10 |
| 347 | 10 c. White Rhinoceros | 70 | 10 |
| 348 | 25 c. Spotted Hyena | 1·75 | 45 |
| 349 | 35 c. Scorpion | 2·00 | 90 |
| 346/9 | *Set of* 4 | 4·25 | 1·40 |
| **MS**350 | 150 × 150 mm. Nos. 346/9 | 7·00 | 7·00 |

**101** Map of British Bechuanaland, 1885

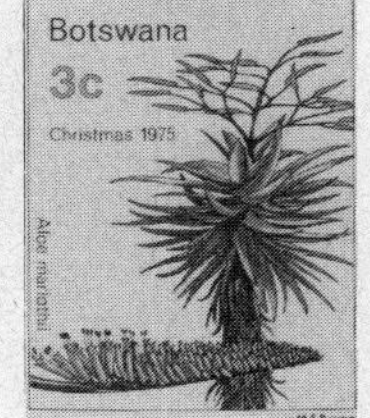


**102** *Aloe marlothii*

(Des M. Bryan, adapted G. Vasarhelyi. Litho Harrison)

**1975** (13 Oct). *Anniversaries. T* **101** *and similar multicoloured designs. P* 14 × 14½ (25 *c.*) *or* 14½ × 14 (*others*).

| | | | |
|---|---|---|---|
| 351 | 6 c. Type **101** | 30 | 15 |
| 352 | 10 c. Chief Khama, 1875 | 40 | 15 |
| 353 | 25 c. Chiefs Sebele, Bathoen and Khama, 1895 (*horiz*) | 80 | 65 |
| 351/3 | *Set of* 3 | 1·40 | 85 |

Events:—6 c. 90th Anniv of Protectorate; 10 c. Centenary of Khama's Accession; 25 c. 80th Anniv of Chiefs' visit to London.

(Des M. Bryan. Litho Questa)

**1975** (3 Nov). *Christmas. T* **102** *and similar vert designs showing aloes. Multicoloured. P* 14½.

| | | | |
|---|---|---|---|
| 354 | 3 c. Type **102** | 20 | 10 |
| 355 | 10 c. *Aloe lutescens* | 55 | 35 |
| 356 | 15 c. *Aloe zebrina* | 90 | 1·00 |
| 357 | 25 c. *Aloe littoralis* | 1·25 | 1·60 |
| 354/7 | *Set of* 4 | 2·50 | 2·75 |

**103** Drum

(Des M. Bryan. Litho Questa)

**1976** (1 Mar). *Traditional Musical Instruments. T* **103** *and similar horiz designs. Multicoloured. P* 14.

| | | | |
|---|---|---|---|
| 358 | 4 c. Type **103** | 15 | 10 |
| 359 | 10 c. Hand Piano | 25 | 10 |
| 360 | 15 c. Segankuru (violin) | 30 | 20 |
| 361 | 25 c. Kudu Signal Horn | 40 | 40 |
| 358/61 | *Set of* 4 | 1·00 | 65 |

**104** One Pula Note

(Des M. Bryan from banknotes by D.L.R. Litho Questa)

**1976** (28 June). *First National Currency. T* **104** *and similar horiz designs. Multicoloured. P* 14.

| | | | |
|---|---|---|---|
| 362 | 4 c. Type **104** | 15 | 10 |
| 363 | 10 c. Two pula note | 20 | 10 |
| 364 | 15 c. Five pula note | 35 | 20 |
| 365 | 25 c. Ten pula note | 45 | 35 |
| 362/5 | *Set of* 4 | 1·00 | 70 |
| **MS**366 | 163 × 107 mm. Nos. 362/5 | 1·50 | 2·50 |

**(New Currency. 100 thebe = 1 pula)**

| | | | |
|---|---|---|---|
| 1t (105) (Type I) | 1t (105) (Type II) | 2t (I) | 2t (II) |
| 4t (I) | 4t (II) | 5t (I) | 5t (II) |
| 15t (I) | 15t (II) | 20t (I) | 20t (II) |

(Surch in letterpress by Govt Printer, Pretoria (Type I), or in lithography by Enschedé (Type II) )

**1976** (23 Aug)–**77**. *Nos.* 322/35 *surch as T* **105**.

| | | | |
|---|---|---|---|
| 367 | 1 t. on 1 c. Type **97** (I) | 60 | 45 |
| | a. Type II Surch (15.7.77) | 1·00 | 50 |
| 368 | 2 t. on 2 c. Agate—"Botswana Pink" (I) | 60 | 40 |
| | a. Type II Surch (15.7.77) | 1·00 | 55 |
| 369 | 3 t. on 3 c. Quartz (surch at top right) (Gold) | 60 | 40 |
| | a. Surch at bottom right (17.10.77) | .. | |
| 370 | 4 t. on 4 c. Copper nickel (I) | 85 | 40 |
| | a. Type II Surch (15.7.77) | 1·40 | 60 |
| 371 | 5 t. on 5 c. Moss agate (I) | 85 | 30 |
| | a. Type II Surch (15.7.77) | 1·40 | 55 |
| 372 | 7 t. on 7 c. Agate (surch at top right) | 85 | 50 |
| | a. Surch at bottom right (17.10.77) | .. | |
| 373 | 10 t. on 10 c. Stilbite | 85 | 50 |
| 374 | 15 t. on 15 c. Moshaneng Banded Marble (I) (Gold) | 2·25 | 65 |
| | a. Type II Surch (15.7.77) | 3·25 | 1·50 |
| 375 | 20 t. on 20 c. Gem diamonds (I) | 4·50 | 65 |
| | a. Type II Surch (15.7.77) | 5·00 | 1·50 |
| 376 | 25 t. on 25 c. Chrysotile | 3·50 | 75 |
| 377 | 35 t. on 35 c. Jasper | 3·50 | 1·00 |
| 378 | 50 t. on 50 c. Moss quartz (surch at top right) | 4·50 | 1·50 |
| | a. Surch at bottom right (17.10.77) | .. | |
| 379 | 1 p. on 1 r. Citrine (surch at top right) | 6·00 | 3·50 |
| | a. Surch at bottom left (17.10.77) | .. | |
| 380 | 2 p. on 2 r. Chalcopyrite (Gold) | 9·00 | 8·00 |
| 367/80 | *Set of* 14 | 35·00 | 17·00 |
| 367a/75a | *Set of* 6 | 11·50 | 4·75 |

Nos. 369a, 372a, 378a and 379a come from a second Pretoria printing, using the same type, on a small stock returned from the Crown Agents.

**106** Botswanan Cattle

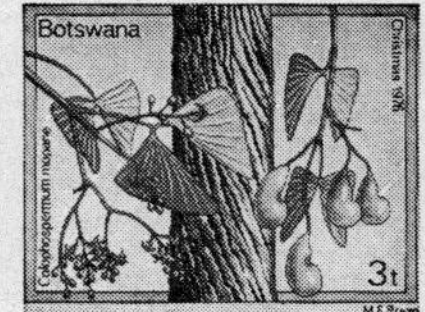


**107** *Colophospermum mopane*

(Des M. Bryan. Litho Questa)

**1976** (30 Sept). *Tenth Anniv of Independence. T* **106** *and similar multicoloured designs. P* 14.

| | | | |
|---|---|---|---|
| 381 | 4 t. Type **106** | 15 | 10 |
| 382 | 10 t. Deer, Okavango Delta (*vert*) | 30 | 10 |
| 383 | 15 t. Schools and pupils | 40 | 20 |
| 384 | 25 t. Rural weaving (*vert*) | 55 | 30 |
| 385 | 35 t. Miner (*vert*) | 90 | 50 |
| 381/5 | *Set of* 5 | 2·10 | 1·10 |

Nos. 381/5 were printed on sand-grained paper which has an uneven surface.

(Des M. Bryan. Litho J.W.)

**1976** (1 Nov). *Christmas. T* **107** *and similar horiz designs showing trees. Multicoloured. P* 13.

| | | | |
|---|---|---|---|
| 386 | 3 t. Type **107** | 15 | 10 |
| 387 | 4 t. *Baikiaea plurijuga* | 15 | 10 |
| 388 | 10 t. *Sterculia rogersii* | 40 | 15 |
| 389 | 25 t. *Acacia nilotica* | 80 | 50 |
| 390 | 40 t. *Kigelia africana* | 1·25 | 90 |
| 386/90 | *Set of* 5 | 2·50 | 1·50 |

**108** Coronation Coach

(Des M. Bryan, adapted G. Vasarhelyi. Litho Cartor S.A., France)

**1977** (7 Feb). *Silver Jubilee. T* **108** *and similar horiz designs. Multicoloured. P* 12.

| | | | |
|---|---|---|---|
| 391 | 4 t. Queen and Sir Seretse Khama | 10 | 10 |
| 392 | 25 t. Type **108** | 20 | 15 |
| 393 | 40 t. The Recognition | 35 | 45 |
| 391/3 | *Set of* 3 | 60 | 60 |

**109** African Clawless Otter

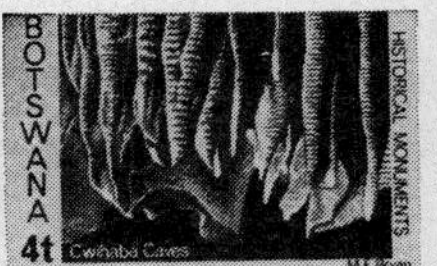


**110** Cwihaba Caves

(Des M. Bryan. Litho Questa)

**1977** (6 June). *Diminishing Species. T* **109** *and similar horiz designs. Multicoloured. P* 14.

| | | | |
|---|---|---|---|
| 394 | 3 t. Type **109** | 35 | 30 |
| 395 | 4 t. Serval | 35 | 30 |
| 396 | 10 t. Bat-eared Fox | 90 | 40 |
| 397 | 25 t. Temminck's Ground Pangolin | 2·00 | 1·25 |
| 398 | 40 t. Brown Hyena | 3·00 | 2·50 |
| 394/8 | *Set of* 5 | 6·00 | 4·25 |

(Des M. Bryan. Litho J.W.)

**1977** (12 Aug). *Historical Monuments. T* **110** *and similar horiz designs. Multicoloured. P* 14.

| | | | |
|---|---|---|---|
| 399 | 4 t. Type **110** | 20 | 10 |
| 400 | 5 t. Khama Memorial | 20 | 10 |
| 401 | 15 t. Green's Tree | 45 | 40 |
| 402 | 20 t. Mmajojo Ruins | 45 | 45 |
| 403 | 25 t. Ancient morabaraba board | 45 | 50 |
| 404 | 35 t. Matsieng's footprint | 55 | 60 |
| 399/404 | *Set of* 6 | 2·10 | 2·00 |
| **MS**405 | 154 × 105 mm. Nos. 399/404 | 2·50 | 3·00 |

111 *Hypoxis nitida*

112 Little Black Bustard

(Des M. Bryan. Litho Questa)

**1977** (7 Nov*). *Christmas. T* **111** *and similar vert designs showing lilies. Multicoloured. P* 14.

| No. | Value | Description | Unused | Used |
|---|---|---|---|---|
| 406 | 3 t. | Type **111** | 15 | 10 |
| 407 | 5 t. | *Haemanthus magnificus* | 15 | 10 |
| 408 | 10 t. | *Boophane disticha* | 35 | 10 |
| 409 | 25 t. | *Vellozia retinervis* | 75 | 35 |
| 410 | 40 t. | *Ammocharis coranica* | 1·00 | 75 |
| 406/10 | | *Set of* 5 | 2·25 | 1·10 |

*This is the local release date. The Crown Agents released the stamps on 31 October.

(Des M. Bryan. Photo Harrison)

**1978** (3 July). *Birds. Vert designs as T* **112**. *Multicoloured. P* 14 × 14½ (1 *to* 20 *t.*) *or* 14 (25*t to* 5 *p.*).

| No. | Value | Description | Unused | Used |
|---|---|---|---|---|
| 411 | 1 t. | Type **112** | 30 | 45 |
| 412 | 2 t. | Marabou Stork | 30 | 45 |
| 413 | 3 t. | Green Wood Hoopoe | 30 | 45 |
| 414 | 4 t. | Carmine Bee Eater | 30 | 40 |
| 415 | 5 t. | African Jacana | 30 | 30 |
| 416 | 7 t. | African Paradise Flycatcher | 40 | 40 |
| 417 | 10 t. | Bennett's Woodpecker | 75 | 40 |
| 418 | 15 t. | Red Bishop | 60 | 70 |
| 419 | 20 t. | Crowned Plover | 60 | 80 |
| 420 | 25 t. | Giant Kingfisher | 60 | 85 |
| 421 | 30 t. | White-faced Whistling Duck | 60 | 50 |
| 422 | 35 t. | Green Heron | 60 | 80 |
| 423 | 45 t. | Black-headed Heron | 65 | 90 |
| 424 | 50 t. | Spotted Eagle Owl | 2·00 | 85 |
| 425 | 1 p. | Gabar Goshawk | 1·25 | 1·25 |
| 426 | 2 p. | Martial Eagle | 2·00 | 4·50 |
| 427 | 5 p. | Saddle-bill Stork | 9·50 | 9·50 |
| 411/27 | | *Set of* 17 | 19·00 | 21·00 |

113 Tawana making Karos

(Des M. Bryan. Litho Questa)

**1978** (11 Sept). *Okavango Delta. T* **113** *and similar horiz designs. Multicoloured. P* 14.

| No. | Value | Description | Unused | Used |
|---|---|---|---|---|
| 428 | 4 t. | Type **113** | 10 | 10 |
| 429 | 5 t. | Tribe localities | 10 | 10 |
| 430 | 15 t. | Bushmen collecting roots | 30 | 30 |
| 431 | 20 t. | Herero woman milking | 35 | 35 |
| 432 | 25 t. | Yei poling "mokoro" (canoe) | 40 | 40 |
| 433 | 35 t. | Mbukushu fishing | 55 | 55 |
| 428/33 | | *Set of* 6 | 1·60 | 1·60 |
| **MS**434 | | 150 × 98 mm. Nos. 428/33 | 1·75 | 2·75 |

Nos. 428/34 were printed on sand-grained paper which has an uneven surface.

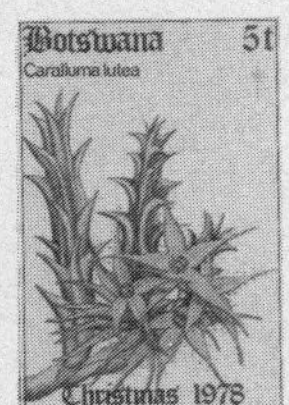

114 *Caralluma lutea*

115 Sip Well

(Des M. Bryan. Litho J.W.)

**1978** (6 Nov). *Christmas. Flowers. T* **114** *and similar vert designs. Multicoloured. P* 14.

| No. | Value | Description | Unused | Used |
|---|---|---|---|---|
| 435 | 5 t. | Type **114** | 25 | 10 |
| 436 | 10 t. | *Hoodia lugardii* | 35 | 15 |
| 437 | 15 t. | *Ipomoea transvaalensis* | 65 | 40 |
| 438 | 25 t. | *Ansellia gigantea* | 70 | 55 |
| 435/8 | | *Set of* 4 | 1·75 | 1·10 |

(Des M. Bryan. Litho Questa)

**1979** (12 Feb). *Water Development. T* **115** *and similar vert designs. Multicoloured. P* 14.

| No. | Value | Description | Unused | Used |
|---|---|---|---|---|
| 439 | 3 t. | Type **115** | 10 | 10 |
| 440 | 5 t. | Watering pit | 15 | 10 |
| 441 | 10 t. | Hand dug well | 15 | 10 |
| 442 | 25 t. | Windmill | 30 | 30 |
| 443 | 40 t. | Modern drilling rig | 55 | 55 |
| 439/43 | | *Set of* 5 | 1·10 | 1·00 |

## ALTERED CATALOGUE NUMBERS

Any Catalogue numbers altered from the last edition are shown as a list in the introductory pages.

116 Pottery

117 1885 British Bechuanaland 1d. Stamp and Sir Rowland Hill

(Des M. Bryan. Litho Questa)

**1979** (11 June). *Handicrafts. T* **116** *and similar vert designs. Multicoloured. P* 14½ × 14.

| No. | Value | Description | Unused | Used |
|---|---|---|---|---|
| 444 | 5 t. | Type **116** | 10 | 10 |
| 445 | 10 t. | Clay modelling | 15 | 10 |
| 446 | 25 t. | Basketry | 30 | 25 |
| 447 | 40 t. | Beadwork | 50 | 50 |
| 444/7 | | *Set of* 4 | 95 | 80 |
| **MS**448 | | 123 × 96 mm. Nos. 444/7 | 95 | 1·75 |

(Des M. Bryan. Litho Secura, Singapore)

**1979** (27 Aug). *Death Centenary of Sir Rowland Hill. T* **117** *and similar horiz designs showing stamps and Sir Rowland Hill. Multicoloured. P* 13½.

| No. | Value | Description | Unused | Used |
|---|---|---|---|---|
| 449 | 5 t. | Type **117** | 15 | 10 |
| 450 | 25 t. | 1932 Bechuanaland Protectorate 2d | 45 | 40 |
| 451 | 45 t. | 1967 2 c. definitive | 55 | 65 |
| 449/51 | | *Set of* 3 | 1·00 | 1·00 |

118 Children Playing

119 *Ximenia caffra*

(Des K. Mosinyi (5 t.), M. Bryan (10 t.). Litho Questa)

**1979** (24 Sept). *International Year of the Child. T* **118** *and similar multicoloured design. P* 14.

| No. | Value | Description | Unused | Used |
|---|---|---|---|---|
| 452 | 5 t. | Type **118** | 10 | 10 |
| 453 | 10 t. | Child playing with doll (*vert*) | 20 | 20 |

(Des M. Bryan. Litho Questa)

**1979** (12 Nov). *Christmas. Fruit. T* **119** *and similar vert designs. Multicoloured. P* 14.

| No. | Value | Description | Unused | Used |
|---|---|---|---|---|
| 454 | 5 t. | Type **119** | 10 | 10 |
| 455 | 10 t. | *Sclerocarya caffra* | 20 | 20 |
| 456 | 15 t. | *Hexalobus monopetalus* | 35 | 35 |
| 457 | 25 t. | *Ficus soldanella* | 45 | 45 |
| 454/7 | | *Set of* 4 | 1·00 | 1·00 |

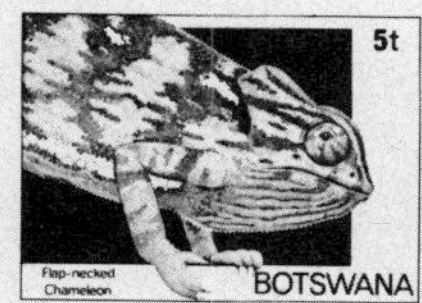

120 Flap-necked Chameleon

121 Rock Breaking

(Des M. Bryan. Litho Security Printers (M), Malaysia)

**1980** (3 Mar). *Reptiles. T* **120** *and similar horiz designs. Multicoloured. P* 13½.

| No. | Value | Description | Unused | Used |
|---|---|---|---|---|
| 458 | 5 t. | Type **120** | 15 | 10 |
| 459 | 10 t. | Leopard Tortoise | 20 | 15 |
| 460 | 25 t. | Puff Adder | 60 | 40 |
| 461 | 40 t. | White-throated Monitor | 80 | 60 |
| 458/61 | | *Set of* 4 | 1·60 | 1·10 |

(Des M. Bryan. Litho Secura, Singapore)

**1980** (7 July). *Early Mining. T* **121** *and similar horiz designs. Multicoloured. P* 13½.

| No. | Value | Description | Unused | Used |
|---|---|---|---|---|
| 462 | 5 t. | Type **121** | 15 | 10 |
| 463 | 10 t. | Ore hoisting | 20 | 15 |
| 464 | 15 t. | Ore transport | 40 | 30 |
| 465 | 20 t. | Ore crushing | 45 | 35 |
| 466 | 25 t. | Smelting | 50 | 45 |
| 467 | 35 t. | Tools and products | 65 | 60 |
| 462/7 | | *Set of* 6 | 2·10 | 1·75 |

122 "Chiwele and the Giant"

(Des W. Battiss. Litho Questa)

**1980** (8 Sept). *Folktales. T* **122** *and similar multicoloured designs. P* 14 (5 *t.*), 14 × 13½ (45 *t.*) *or* 14½ × 14 (*others*).

| No. | Value | Description | Unused | Used |
|---|---|---|---|---|
| 468 | 5 t. | Type **122** (35 × 22 *mm*) | 10 | 10 |
| 469 | 10 t. | "Kgori is not deceived" (28 × 37 *mm*) | 15 | 10 |
| 470 | 30 t. | "Nyambi's wife and Crocodile" (28 × 37 *mm*) | 45 | 45 |
| 471 | 45 t. | "Clever Hare" (44 × 27 *mm*) | 60 | 60 |
| 468/71 | | *Set of* 4 | 1·10 | 1·10 |

123 Game watching. Makgadikgadi Pans

(Des M. Bryan. Litho Govt Printer, Pretoria)

**1980** (6 Oct). *World Tourism Conference, Manila. P* 14.

| No. | Type | Description | Unused | Used |
|---|---|---|---|---|
| 472 | **123** | 5 t. multicoloured | 35 | 20 |

124 *Acacia gerrardii*

125 Heinrich von Stephan with Bechuanaland 1949 3d. and Botswana 1974 3 c. U.P.U. Anniversary Commemoratives

(Des M. Bryan. Litho Govt Printer, Pretoria)

**1980** (3 Nov). *Christmas. Flora. T* **124** *and similar vert designs. Multicoloured. P* 14 × 13½.

| No. | Value | Description | Unused | Used |
|---|---|---|---|---|
| 473 | 5 t. | Type **124** | 10 | 10 |
| 474 | 10 t. | *Acacia nilotica* | 20 | 10 |
| 475 | 25 t. | *Acacia erubescens* | 45 | 30 |
| 476 | 40 t. | *Dichrostachys cinerea* | 70 | 70 |
| 473/6 | | *Set of* 4 | 1·25 | 1·00 |

(Des M. Bryan. Litho Govt Printer, Pretoria)

**1981** (7 Jan). *150th Birth Anniv of Heinrich von Stephan (founder of U.P.U.). T* **125** *and similar horiz design showing Von Stephan and U.P.U. anniversary commemoratives. Multicoloured. P* 14.

| No. | Value | Description | Unused | Used |
|---|---|---|---|---|
| 477 | 6 t. | Type **125** | 20 | 15 |
| 478 | 20 t. | Bechuanaland 1949 6d. and Botswana 1974 7 c. | 55 | 55 |

126 *Anax imperator* (dragonfly)

127 Camphill Community Ramkoromane, Otse

(Des M. Bryan. Litho Govt Printer, Pretoria)

**1981** (23 Feb). *Insects. T* **126** *and similar vert designs. Multicoloured. P* 14.

| No. | Value | Description | Unused | Used |
|---|---|---|---|---|
| 479 | 6 t. | Type **126** | 15 | 10 |
| 480 | 7 t. | *Sphodromantis gastrica* (mantid) | 15 | 15 |
| 481 | 10 t. | *Zonocerus elegans* (grasshopper) | 20 | 15 |
| 482 | 20 t. | *Kheper nigroaeneus* (beetle) | 35 | 35 |
| 483 | 30 t. | *Papilio demodocus* (butterfly) | 70 | 50 |
| 484 | 45 t. | *Acanthocampa belina* (moth larva) | 80 | 65 |
| 479/84 | | *Set of* 6 | 2·10 | 1·75 |
| **MS**485 | | 180×89 mm. Nos. 479/84 | 3·00 | 3·50 |

(Des M. Bryan. Litho Govt Printer, Pretoria)

**1981** (6 Apr). *International Year for Disabled Persons. T* **127** *and similar horiz designs. Multicoloured. P* 14.

| No. | Value | Description | Unused | Used |
|---|---|---|---|---|
| 486 | 6 t. | Type **127** | 15 | 10 |
| 487 | 20 t. | Resource Centre for the Blind, Mochudi | 40 | 35 |
| 488 | 30 t. | Tlamelong Rehabilitation Centre, Tlokweng | 50 | 45 |
| 486/8 | | *Set of* 3 | 95 | 80 |

128 Woman reading Letter

129 Sir Seretse Khama and Building

(Des Petra Rouendaal. Litho Govt Printer, Pretoria)

**1981** (8 June). *Literacy Programme. T* **128** *and similar vert designs. Multicoloured. P* 14.

| No. | Value | Description | Unused | Used |
|---|---|---|---|---|
| 489 | 6 t. | Type **128** | 15 | 10 |
| 490 | 7 t. | Man filling in form | 15 | 15 |
| 491 | 20 t. | Boy reading newspaper | 40 | 35 |
| 492 | 30 t. | Child being taught to read | 55 | 45 |
| 489/92 | | *Set of* 4 | 1·10 | 90 |

(Des G. Vasarhelyi. Litho Format)

**1981** (13 July). *First Death Anniv of President Sir Seretse Khama. T* **129** *and similar horiz designs. Multicoloured. P* 14.

493 6 t. Type **129** .. .. .. .. .. 10 10
494 10 t. Seretse Khama and building (*different*) 15 15
495 30 t. Seretse Khama and Botswana flag .. 45 45
496 45 t. Seretse Khama and building (*different*) 70 70
493/6 .. .. .. .. .. *Set of* 4 1·25 1·25

25t

**(130)** **131** Traditional Ploughing

**1981** (1 Sept). *Nos.* 417 *and* 422 *surch as T* **130**.

497 25 t. on 35 t. Green Heron .. .. .. 1·25 1·25
498 30 t. on 10 t. Bennett's Woodpecker .. .. 1·25 1·25

(Des K. Mosinyi. Litho Format)

**1981** (21 Sept). *Cattle Industry. T* **131** *and similar horiz designs. Multicoloured. P* 14½.

499 6 t. Type **131** .. .. .. .. .. 10 10
500 20 t. Agricultural show .. .. .. 35 35
501 30 t. Botswana Meat Commission .. .. 45 45
502 45 t. Vaccine Institute, Botswana .. .. 70 70
499/502 .. .. .. .. .. *Set of* 4 1·40 1·40

**132** *Nymphaea caerulea* **133** "Cattle Post Scene" (Boitumelo Golaakwena)

(Des M. Bryan. Litho Govt Printer, Pretoria)

**1981** (11 Nov). *Christmas. Flowers. T* **132** *and similar vert designs. Multicoloured. P* 14.

503 6 t. Type **132** .. .. .. .. .. 20 10
504 10 t. *Nymphoides indica* .. .. .. 30 10
505 25 t. *Nymphaea lotus* .. .. .. .. 70 50
506 40 t. *Ottelia kunenensis* .. .. .. 1·00 90
503/6 .. .. .. .. .. *Set of* 4 2·00 1·40

(Litho Govt Printer, Pretoria)

**1982** (15 Feb). *Children's Art. T* **133** *and similar horiz designs. Multicoloured. P* 14.

507 6 t. Type **133** .. .. .. .. .. 40 10
508 10 t. "Kgotla Meeting" (Reginald Klinck) .. 50 15
509 30 t. "Village Water Supply" (Keromemang Matswiri) .. .. .. .. .. 1·25 45
510 45 t. "With the Crops" (Kennedy Balemoge) .. 1·75 70
507/10 .. .. .. .. .. *Set of* 4 3·50 1·25

**134** Common Type **135** African Masked Weaver

(Des K. Mosinyi and V. Moremi. Litho Govt Printer, Pretoria)

**1982** (3 May). *Traditional Houses. T* **134** *and similar horiz designs. Multicoloured. P* 14.

511 6 t. Type **134** .. .. .. .. .. 40 10
512 10 t. Kgatleng type .. .. .. .. 50 15
513 30 t. North Eastern type .. .. .. 1·25 80
514 45 t. Sarwa type .. .. .. .. 1·75 1·75
511/14 .. .. .. .. .. *Set of* 4 3·50 2·50

(Des M. Bryan. Photo Harrison)

**1982** (2 Aug). *Birds. T* **135** *and similar multicoloured designs. P* 14×14½ (1 *t. to* 10 *t.*) *or* 14½×14 (*others*).

515 1 t. Type **135** .. .. .. .. .. 35 40
516 2 t. Lesser Double-collared Sunbird .. .. 45 40
517 3 t. Red-throated Bee Eater .. .. .. 45 40
518 4 t. Ostrich .. .. .. .. .. 45 40
519 5 t. Grey-headed Gull .. .. .. .. 45 30
520 6 t. African Pygmy Goose .. .. .. 45 20
521 7 t. Cattle Egret .. .. .. .. 45 15
522 8 t. Lanner Falcon .. .. .. .. 65 45
523 10 t. Yellow-billed Stork .. .. .. 50 15
524 15 t. Red-billed Pintail (*horiz*) .. .. 60 15
525 20 t. Barn Owl (*horiz*) .. .. .. .. 2·00 95
526 25 t. Hammerkop (*horiz*) .. .. .. 1·25 55
527 30 t. South African Stilt (*horiz*) .. .. 1·50 55
528 35 t. Blacksmith Plover (*horiz*) .. .. 1·50 70
529 45 t. Senegal Wattled Plover (*horiz*) .. .. 1·75 85
530 50 t. Helmet Guineafowl (*horiz*) .. .. 2·00 1·40
531 1 p. Cape Vulture (*horiz*) .. .. .. 3·75 3·50
532 2 p. Augur Buzzard (*horiz*) .. .. .. 5·00 5·50
515/32 .. .. .. .. *Set of* 18 21·00 15·00

**136** *Coprinus comatus* **137** President Quett Masire

(Des G. Condy. Litho Mardon Printers Ltd, Zimbabwe)

**1982** (2 Nov). *Christmas. Fungi. T* **136** *and similar vert designs. Multicoloured. P* 14½.

533 7 t. Type **136** .. .. .. .. .. 65 10
534 15 t. *Lactarius deliciosus* .. .. .. 1·10 25
535 35 t. *Amanita pantherina* .. .. .. 2·00 65
536 50 t. *Boletus edulis* .. .. .. .. 2·75 1·25
533/6 .. .. .. .. .. *Set of* 4 6·00 2·00

(Des G. Vasarhelyi. Litho Questa)

**1983** (14 Mar). *Commonwealth Day. T* **137** *and similar horiz designs. Multicoloured. P* 14.

537 7 t. Type **137** .. .. .. .. .. 10 10
538 15 t. Native dancers .. .. .. .. 15 20
539 35 t. Melbourne conference centre .. .. 45 50
540 45 t. Meeting of Heads of State, Melbourne .. 55 60
537/40 .. .. .. .. .. *Set of* 4 1·00 1·25

**138** Wattled Crane **139** Wooden Spoons

(Des Petra Rouendaal (50 t.), G. Condy (others). Litho Mardon Printers Ltd, Zimbabwe)

**1983** (19 Apr). *Endangered Species. T* **138** *and similar vert designs. Multicoloured. P* 14×14½.

541 7 t. Type **138** .. .. .. .. .. 65 15
542 15 t. *Aloe lutescens* .. .. .. .. 80 45
543 35 t. Roan Antelope .. .. .. .. 1·25 1·25
544 50 t. Ivory Palm (*Hyphaene ventricosa*) .. 1·50 2·00
541/4 .. .. .. .. .. *Set of* 4 4·00 3·50

(Des M. Bryan. Litho Mardon Printers Ltd, Zimbabwe)

**1983** (20 July). *Traditional Artifacts. T* **139** *and similar vert designs. Multicoloured. P* 14½.

545 7 t. Type **139** .. .. .. .. .. 10 10
546 15 t. Personal ornaments .. .. .. 15 20
547 35 t. Ox-hide milk bag .. .. .. .. 45 50
548 50 t. Decorated knives .. .. .. .. 55 60
545/8 .. .. .. .. .. *Set of* 4 1·10 1·25
**MS**549 115 × 102 mm. Nos. 545/8 .. .. .. 2·00 2·50

**140** *Pantala flavescens* **141** Sorting Diamonds

(Des Beverley Boudreau. Litho Mardon Printers Ltd, Zimbabwe)

**1983** (7 Nov). *Christmas. Dragonflies. T* **140** *and similar horiz designs. Multicoloured. P* 14½×14.

550 6 t. Type **140** .. .. .. .. .. 20 10
551 15 t. *Anax imperator* .. .. .. .. 35 20
552 25 t. *Trithemis arteriosa* .. .. .. 50 40
553 45 t. *Chlorolestes elegans* .. .. .. 85 95
550/3 .. .. .. .. .. *Set of* 4 1·75 1·50

(Des M. Kahn. Litho Mardon Printers Ltd, Zimbabwe)

**1984** (19 Mar). *Mining Industry. T* **141** *and similar multicoloured designs. P* 14½.

554 7 t. Type **141** .. .. .. .. .. 45 15
555 15 t. Lime kiln .. .. .. .. .. 70 35
556 35 t. Copper-nickel smelter plant (*vert*) .. 1·25 65
557 50 t. Stockpiled coal (*vert*) .. .. .. 1·50 1·50
554/7 .. .. .. .. .. *Set of* 4 3·50 2·40

**142** Riding Cattle **143** Avro "504" Aircraft

(Des S. Mogotsi. Litho Mardon Printers Ltd, Zimbabwe)

**1984** (18 June). *Traditional Transport. T* **142** *and similar horiz designs. Multicoloured. P* 14½ × 14.

558 7 t. Type **142** .. .. .. .. .. 10 10
559 25 t. Sledge .. .. .. .. .. 25 35
560 35 t. Wagon .. .. .. .. .. 35 45
561 50 t. Two wheeled donkey cart .. .. 50 75
558/61 .. .. .. .. *Set of* 4 1·10 1·50

(Des V. Larsson. Litho Mardon Printers Ltd, Zimbabwe)

**1984** (8 Oct). *40th Anniv of International Civil Aviation Organization. T* **143** *and similar horiz designs, each with I.C.A.O. emblem. Multicoloured. P* 14½ × 14.

562 7 t. Type **143** .. .. .. .. .. 35 10
563 10 t. Westland "Wessex" .. .. .. 45 15
564 15 t. Junkers "Ju 52/3M" .. .. .. 70 35
565 25 t. De Havilland "Dragon Six" .. .. 80 50
566 35 t. Douglas "DC3 Dakota" .. .. .. 90 70
567 50 t. Fokker "F27 Friendship" .. .. 1·10 1·50
562/7 .. .. .. .. .. *Set of* 6 4·00 3·00

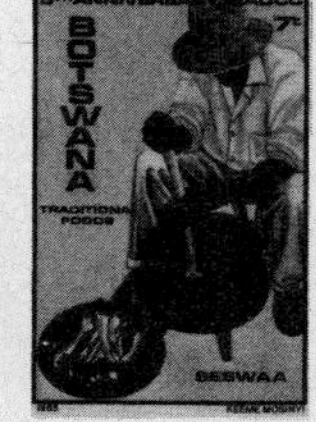


**144** *Papilio demodocus* **145** Seswaa (meat dish)

(Des M. Kahn. Litho Mardon Printers Ltd, Zimbabwe)

**1984** (5 Nov). *Christmas. Butterflies. T* **144** *and similar horiz designs. Multicoloured. P* 14½ × 14.

568 7 t. Type **144** .. .. .. .. .. 60 15
569 25 t. *Byblia anvatara* .. .. .. .. 1·00 60
570 35 t. *Danaus chrysippus* .. .. .. 1·25 85
571 50 t. *Graphium taboranus* .. .. .. 1·60 2·00
568/71 .. .. .. .. .. *Set of* 4 4·00 3·25

No. 570 is incorrectly inscribed "Hypolimnas misippus".

(Des K. Mosinyi. Litho Mardon Printers Ltd, Zimbabwe)

**1985** (18 Mar). *5th Anniv of Southern African Developmen[t] Co-ordination Conference. Traditional Foods. T* **145** *an[d] similar vert designs. Multicoloured. P* 14½.

572 7 t. Type **145** .. .. .. .. .. 10 1[0]
573 15 t. Bogobe (cereal porridge) .. .. 10 1[5]
574 25 t. Madila (soured coagulated cows milk) 15 2[0]
575 50 t. Phane (caterpillars) .. .. .. 35 4[0]
572/5 .. .. .. .. .. *Set of* 4 60 7[5]
**MS**576 117×103 mm. Nos. 572/5 .. .. 2·00 2·5[0]

BOTSWANA 7t

**146** 1885 British Bechuanaland Overprint on Cape of Good Hope ½d. **147** Bechuanaland Border Police, 1885–95

(Des D. Finlay and J. Hodgson. Litho Mardon Printers Lt[d], Zimbabwe)

**1985** (24 June). *Centenary of First Bechuanaland Stamps. T* **146** *and similar designs. P* 14½.

577 7 t. black, grey-black and orange-vermilion 35 1
578 15 t. black, deep brown and greenish yellow 45 1
579 25 t. black and bright scarlet .. .. 65 3
580 35 t. black, ultramarine and gold .. .. 75 4
581 50 t. multicoloured .. .. .. .. 85 8
577/81 .. .. .. .. *Set of* 5 2·75 1·6

Designs: *Vert*—15 t. 1897 Bechuanaland Protectorate overprint on G.B. 3d.; 25 t. Bechuanaland Protectorate 1932 1d definitive. *Horiz*—35 t. Bechuanaland 1965 Internal Self Government 5 c.; 50 t. Botswana 1966 Independence 2½ c.

(Des V. Larsson. Litho Mardon Printers Ltd, Zimbabwe)

**1985** (5 Aug). *Centenary of Botswana Police. T* **147** *and simila[r] horiz designs. Multicoloured. P* 14½×14.

582 7 t. Type **147** .. .. .. .. .. 70 1
583 10 t. Bechuanaland Mounted Police, 1895–1902 .. .. .. .. .. 90 2
584 25 t. Bechuanaland Protectorate Police, 1903–66 .. .. .. .. .. 1·50 8
585 50 t. Botswana Police, from 1966 .. .. 2·00 1·7
582/5 .. .. .. .. .. *Set of* 4 4·50 2·7

## MINIMUM PRICE

The minimum price quote is 10p which represents a handling charge rather than a basis for valuing common stamps. For further notes about prices see introductory pages.

148 *Cucumis metuliferus*

149 Mr. Shippard and Chief Gaseitsiwe of the Bangwaketse

(Des Audrey Renew. Litho Mardon Printers Ltd, Zimbabwe)

**1985** (4 Nov). *Christmas. Edible Wild Cucumbers. T* **148** *and similar horiz designs. Multicoloured. P* 14½×14.

586 7 t. Type **148** .. .. .. .. .. 25 10
587 15 t. *Acanthosicyos naudinianus* .. .. .. 35 30
588 25 t. *Coccinia sessifolia* .. .. .. 60 50
589 50 t. *Momordica balsamina* .. .. .. 1·00 1·40
586/9 .. .. .. .. .. *Set of* 4 2·00 2·10

(Des A. Campbell. Litho Mardon Printers Ltd, Zimbabwe)

**1985** (30 Dec). *Centenary of Declaration of Bechuanaland Protectorate. T* **149** *and similar vert designs. Multicoloured. P* 14×14½.

590 7 t. Type **149** .. .. .. .. .. 15 10
591 15 t. Sir Charles Warren and Chief Sechele of the Bakwena .. .. .. .. 25 20
592 25 t. Revd. Mackenzie and Chief Khama of the Bamangwato .. .. .. .. 40 30
593 50 t. Map showing Protectorate .. .. 70 70
590/3 .. .. .. .. .. *Set of* 4 1·40 1·10
**MS**594 130×133 mm. Nos. 590/3 .. .. 2·50 2·75

150 Halley's Comet over Serowe

151 Milk Bag

(Des L. Hutchings. Litho Mardon Printers Ltd, Zimbabwe)

**1986** (24 Mar). *Appearance of Halley's Comet. T* **150** *and similar horiz designs. Multicoloured. P* 14½×14.

595 7 t. Type **150** .. .. .. .. .. 30 10
596 15 t. Comet over Bobonong at sunset .. .. 50 15
597 35 t. Comet over Gomare at dawn .. .. 70 40
598 50 t. Comet over Thamaga and Letlhakeng 85 70
595/8 .. .. .. .. .. *Set of* 4 2·10 1·25

(Des B. Mazebedi. Litho Mardon Printers Ltd, Zimbabwe)

**1986** (23 June). *Traditional Milk Containers. T* **151** *and similar vert designs. Multicoloured. P* 14½.

599 8 t. Type **151** .. .. .. .. .. 10 10
600 15 t. Clay pot and calabashes .. .. .. 15 15
601 35 t. Wooden milk bucket .. .. .. 35 35
602 50 t. Milk churn .. .. .. .. 45 45
599/602 .. .. .. .. *Set of* 4 95 95

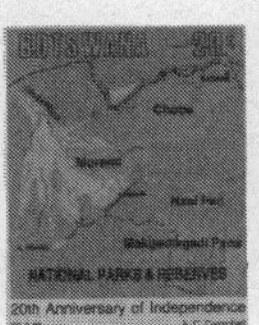

152 Map showing National Parks and Reserves

153 *Ludwigia stogonifera*

(Des K. Bogatsu, A. Campbell, I. Marshall and K. Mosinyi. Litho Govt Printer, Pretoria)

**1986** (30 Sept). *20th Anniv of Independence. Sheet* 100×120 *mm, containing T* **152** *and similar vert designs. Multicoloured. P* 14.

**MS**603 20 t. Type **152**; 20 t. Morupule Power Station; 20 t. Cattle breeding in Kgalagadi; 20 t. National Assembly Building .. .. .. 1·00 1·25

(Des Julia Cairns. Litho Mardon Printers Ltd, Zimbabwe)

**1986** (3 Nov). *Christmas. Flowers of Okavango. T* **153** *and similar vert designs. Multicoloured. P* 14×14½.

604 8 t. Type **153** .. .. .. .. .. 50 10
605 15 t. *Sopubia mannii* .. .. .. .. 90 40
606 35 t. *Commelina diffusa* .. .. .. 1·50 85
607 50 t. *Hibiscus diversifolius* .. .. .. 2·00 2·50
604/7 .. .. .. .. .. *Set of* 4 4·50 3·50

154 Divining

(155)

156 Oral Rehydration Therapy

(Des K. Mosinyi. Litho Mardon Printers Ltd, Zimbabwe)

**1987** (2 Mar). *Traditional Medicine. T* **154** *and similar horiz designs. Multicoloured. P* 14½×14.

608 8 t. Type **154** .. .. .. .. .. 25 10
609 15 t. Lightning prevention .. .. .. 45 25
610 35 t. Rain making .. .. .. .. 75 45
611 50 t. Blood letting .. .. .. .. 90 95
608/11 .. .. .. .. .. *Set of* 4 2·10 1·60

**1987** (1 Apr). *Nos.* 520, 523 *and* 530 *surch as T* **155**.

612 3 t. on 6 t. African Pygmy Goose .. .. 15 15
613 5 t. on 10 t. Yellow-billed Stork .. .. 15 15
614 20 t. on 50 t. Helmet Guineafowl (*horiz*) .. 30 25
612/14 .. .. .. .. .. *Set of* 3 55 50

(Des A. Nunoo. Litho Govt Printer, Pretoria)

**1987** (1 June). *U.N.I.C.E.F. Child Survival Campaign. T* **156** *and similar vert designs. Multicoloured. P* 14.

615 8 t. Type **156** .. .. .. .. .. 10 10
616 15 t. Growth monitoring .. .. .. 15 15
617 35 t. Immunization .. .. .. .. 35 50
618 50 t. Breast feeding .. .. .. .. 45 80
615/18 .. .. .. .. .. *Set of* 4 95 1·40

157 Cape Fox

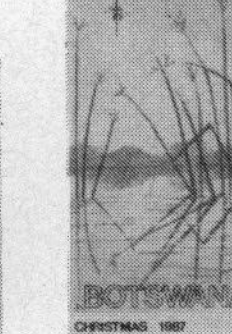

158 *Cyperus articulatus*

(Des P. Huebsch. Photo Harrison)

**1987** (3 Aug). *Animals of Botswana. T* **157** *and similar horiz designs. Multicoloured. P* 14.

619 1 t. Type **157** .. .. .. .. .. 10 10
620 2 t. Lechwe .. .. .. .. .. 10 10
621 3 t. Zebra .. .. .. .. .. 10 10
622 4 t. Duiker .. .. .. .. .. 10 10
623 5 t. Banded Mongoose .. .. .. 10 10
624 6 t. Rusty-spotted Genet .. .. .. 10 10
625 8 t. Hedgehog .. .. .. .. .. 10 10
626 10 t. Scrub Hare .. .. .. .. 10 10
627 12 t. Hippopotamus .. .. .. .. 10 10
628 15 t. Suricate .. .. .. .. .. 10 15
629 20 t. Caracal .. .. .. .. .. 10 15
630 25 t. Steenbok .. .. .. .. .. 15 20
631 30 t. Gemsbok .. .. .. .. .. 15 20
632 35 t. Square-lipped Rhinoceros .. .. 20 25
633 40 t. Mountain Reedbuck .. .. .. 20 25
634 50 t. Rock Dassie .. .. .. .. 25 30
635 1 p. Giraffe .. .. .. .. .. 55 60
636 2 p. Tsessebe .. .. .. .. .. 1·10 1·25
637 3 p. Side-striped Jackal .. .. .. 1·60 1·75
638 5 p. Hartebeest .. .. .. .. 2·75 3·00
619/38 .. .. .. .. *Set of* 20 6·75 7·75

(Des Julia Cairns. Litho National Printing & Packaging, Zimbabwe)

**1987** (26 Oct). *Christmas. Grasses and Sedges of Okavango. T* **158** *and similar vert designs. Multicoloured. P* 14×14½.

639 8 t. Type **158** .. .. .. .. .. 10 10
640 15 t. Broomgrass .. .. .. .. 15 15
641 30 t. *Cyperus alopurcides* .. .. .. 35 30
642 1 p. Bulrush Sedge .. .. .. .. 85 80
639/42 .. .. .. .. *Set of* 4 1·25 1·10
**MS**643 88×99 mm. Nos. 639/42 .. .. .. 1·25 1·50
a. 30 t. value imperf vert .. .. .. 40·00

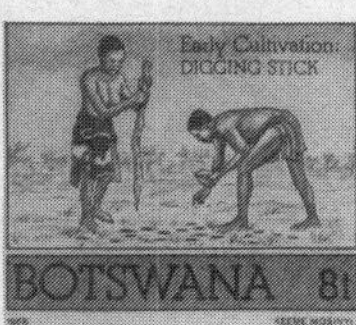

159 Planting Seeds with Digging Stick

160 Red Lechwe at Water-hole

(Des K. Mosinyi. Litho National Printing & Packaging, Zimbabwe)

**1988** (14 Mar). *Early Cultivation. T* **159** *and similar horiz designs. Multicoloured. P* 14½×14.

644 8 t. Type **159** .. .. .. .. .. 10 10
645 15 t. Using iron hoe .. .. .. .. 15 15
646 35 t. Wooden ox-drawn plough .. .. 30 30
647 50 t. Villagers using lesotlas .. .. 40 45
644/7 .. .. .. .. .. *Set of* 4 85 85

(Des P. Augustinus. Litho National Printing & Packaging, Zimbabwe)

**1988** (6 June). *Red Lechwe. T* **160** *and similar horiz designs. Multicoloured. P* 14½×14.

648 10 t. Type **160** .. .. .. .. .. 20 10
649 15 t. Red Lechwe and early morning sun 25 15
650 35 t. Female and calf .. .. .. .. 40 30
651 75 t. Herd on the move .. .. .. .. 80 60
648/51 .. .. .. .. .. *Set of* 4 1·50 1·00

## COVER PRICES

Cover factors are quoted at the beginning of each country for most issues to 1945. An explanation of the system can be found on page x. The factors quoted do not, however, apply to philatelic covers.

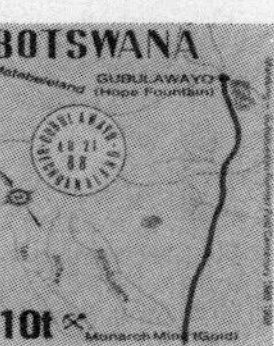

161 Gubulawayo Postmark and Route Southwards to Tati

162 Pope John Paul II and Outline Map of Botswana

(Des M. Bryan, adapted Lucy Phalayagae. Litho National Printing & Packaging, Zimbabwe)

**1988** (22 Aug). *Centenary of Mafeking-Gubalawayo Runner Post. Designs as Nos.* 294/8, *but redrawn smaller with changed inscription as in T* **161**. *Multicoloured. P* 14½.

652 10 t. Type **161** .. .. .. .. .. 20 10
653 15 t. Bechuanaland 1888 6d. on 6d. stamp and route from Tati southwards .. 30 20
654 30 t. Runners and twin routes south from Shoshong .. .. .. .. .. 50 40
655 60 t. Mafeking postmark and routes to Bechuanaland and Transvaal .. 75 65
652/5 .. .. .. .. *Set of* 4 1·60 1·10
**MS**656 81×151 mm. Nos. 652/5 vertically *se-tenant*, forming a composite map design .. 2·50 2·75

(Des P. Lodoen. Litho National Printing & Packaging, Zimbabwe)

**1988** (13 Sept). *Visit of Pope John Paul II. T* **162** *and similar vert designs. Multicoloured. P* 14×14½.

657 10 t. Type **162** .. .. .. .. .. 15 10
658 15 t. Pope John Paul II .. .. .. 20 15
659 30 t. Pope giving blessing and outline map 30 35
660 80 t. Pope John Paul II (*different*) .. .. 65 70
657/60 .. .. .. .. *Set of* 4 1·10 1·10

163 National Museum and Art Gallery

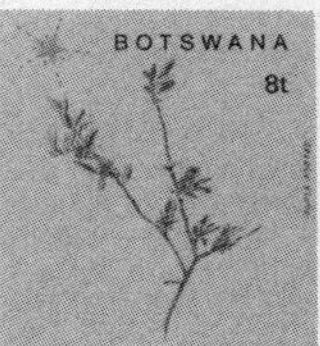

164 *Grewia flava*

(Des G. Mattsson and T. Sandberg (8 t.), A. Campbell (15 t.), K. Bogatsu (30 t.), T. Sandberg (60 t.). Litho National Printing & Packaging, Zimbabwe)

**1988** (30 Sept). *20th Anniv of National Museum and Art Gallery, Gaborone. T* **163** *and similar vert designs. Multicoloured. P* 14½.

661 8 t. Type **163** .. .. .. .. .. 10 10
662 15 t. Pottery .. .. .. .. .. 15 15
663 30 t. Blacksmith's buffalo bellows .. .. 25 25
664 60 t. Children and mobile museum van .. 45 50
661/4 .. .. .. .. *Set of* 4 85 90

(Des Verena Blomberg-Ermatinger. Litho National Printing & Packaging, Zimbabwe)

**1988** (31 Oct). *Flowering Plants of South-eastern Botswana. T* **164** *and similar vert designs. Multicoloured. P* 14×14½.

665 8 t. Type **164** .. .. .. .. .. 10 10
666 15 t. *Cienfuegosia digitata* .. .. .. 15 15
667 40 t. *Solanum seaforthianum* .. .. 35 35
668 75 t. *Carissa bispinosa* .. .. .. 60 60
665/8 .. .. .. .. *Set of* 4 1·10 1·10

165 Basket Granary

166 Female Slaty Egret with Eggs

(Des K. Mosinyi. Litho National Printing & Packaging, Zimbabwe)

**1989** (13 Mar). *Traditional Grain Storage. T* **165** *and similar vert designs. Multicoloured. P* 14 × 14½.

669 8 t. Type **165** .. .. .. .. .. 10 10
670 15 t. Large letlole granary .. .. .. 15 15
671 30 t. Pot granary .. .. .. .. 25 30
672 60 t. Two types of serala .. .. .. 40 50
669/72 .. .. .. .. *Set of* 4 80 95

The use of different paper stocks led to a wide range of shades in this issue.

(Des P. Augustinus. Litho Harrison)

**1989** (5 July). *Slaty Egret. T* **166** *and similar horiz designs. Multicoloured. P* 15×14.

673 8 t. Type **166** .. .. .. .. .. 20 10
674 15 t. Chicks in nest .. .. .. .. 30 10
675 30 t. Slaty Egret in flight .. .. .. 40 30
676 60 t. Pair building nest .. .. .. 65 60
673/6 .. .. .. .. *Set of* 4 1·40 1·00
**MS**677 119×89 mm. Nos. 673/6 .. .. 1·50 1·50

167 "My Work at Home" (Ephraim Seeletso)

168 *Eulophia angolensis*

(Litho Govt Printer, Pretoria)

**1989** (4 Sept). *Children's Paintings. T* **167** *and similar multicoloured designs. P* 14.

| | | | |
|---|---|---|---|
| 678 | 10 t. Type **167** | 20 | 10 |
| 679 | 15 t. "My Favourite Game" (hopscotch) (Neelma Bhatia) (*vert*) | 20 | 15 |
| 680 | 30 t. "My Favourite Toy" (clay animals) (Thabo Habana) | 35 | 40 |
| 681 | 1 p. "My School Day" (Thabo Olesitse) | 85 | 1·25 |
| 678/81 | *Set of* 4 | 1·40 | 1·60 |

(Des Julia Cairns. Litho Govt Printer, Pretoria)

**1989** (30 Oct). *Christmas. Orchids. T* **168** *and similar vert designs. Multicoloured. P* 14.

| | | | |
|---|---|---|---|
| 682 | 8 t. Type **168** | 25 | 10 |
| 683 | 15 t. *Eulophia hereroensis* | 40 | 15 |
| 684 | 30 t. *Eulophia speciosa* | 60 | 40 |
| 685 | 60 t. *Eulophia petersii* | 1·00 | 85 |
| 682/5 | *Set of* 4 | 2·00 | 1·40 |

169 Bechuanaland 1965 New Constitution 25 c. Stamp (25th anniv of Self Government)

(170)

(Des K. Mosinyi. Litho National Printing & Packaging, Zimbabwe)

**1990** (5 Mar). *Anniversaries. T* **169** *and similar horiz designs. P* 14½.

| | | | |
|---|---|---|---|
| 686 | 8 t. multicoloured | 20 | 10 |
| 687 | 15 t. multicoloured | 20 | 15 |
| 688 | 30 t. multicoloured | 30 | 35 |
| 689 | 60 t. black, new blue and yellow-ochre | 55 | 60 |
| 686/9 | *Set of* 4 | 1·10 | 1·10 |

Designs:—15 t. Casting vote in ballot box (25th anniv of First Elections); 30 t. Outline map and flags of Southern African Development Coordination Conference countries (10th anniv); 60 t. Penny Black (150th anniv of first postage stamp).

**1990** (27 Apr). *Nos.* 619, 624 *and* 627 *surch as T* **170**.

| | | | |
|---|---|---|---|
| 690 | 10 t. on 1 t. Type **157** | 15 | 10 |
| 691 | 20 t. on 6 t. Rusty-spotted Genet | 20 | 20 |
| 692 | 50 t. on 12 t. Hippopotamus | 45 | 50 |
| 690/2 | *Set of* 3 | 70 | 70 |

171 Telephone Engineer

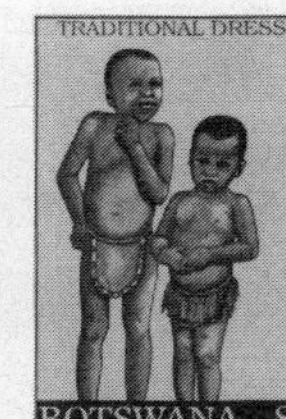

172 Young Children

(Des M. Kahn. Litho National Printing & Packaging, Zimbabwe)

**1990** (3 May). *"Stamp World London 90" International Stamp Exhibition. T* **171** *and similar vert designs. Multicoloured. P* 14½.

| | | | |
|---|---|---|---|
| 693 | 8 t. Type **171** | 10 | 10 |
| 694 | 15 t. Transmission pylon | 15 | 10 |
| 695 | 30 t. Public telephone | 25 | 25 |
| 696 | 2 p. Testing circuit board | 1·50 | 1·60 |
| 693/6 | *Set of* 4 | 1·75 | 1·90 |

(Des K. Mosinyi. Litho National Printing & Packaging, Zimbabwe)

**1990** (1 Aug). *Traditional Dress. T* **172** *and similar vert designs. Multicoloured. P* 14½.

| | | | |
|---|---|---|---|
| 697 | 8 t. Type **172** | 10 | 10 |
| 698 | 15 t. Young woman | 15 | 15 |
| 699 | 30 t. Adult man | 25 | 25 |
| 700 | 2 p. Adult woman | 1·25 | 1·40 |
| 697/700 | *Set of* 4 | 1·60 | 1·75 |
| **MS**701 | 104×150 mm. Nos. 697/700 | 2·00 | 2·25 |

173 *Acacia nigrescens*

174 Children running in front of Car

(Des Gill Condy. Litho National Printing & Packaging, Zimbabwe)

**1990** (30 Oct). *Christmas. Flowering Trees. T* **173** *and similar vert designs. Multicoloured. P* 14×14½.

| | | | |
|---|---|---|---|
| 702 | 8 t. Type **173** | 15 | 10 |
| 703 | 15 t. *Peltophorum africanum* | 20 | 10 |
| 704 | 30 t. *Burkea africana* | 25 | 30 |
| 705 | 2 p. *Pterocarpus angolensis* | 1·40 | 1·50 |
| 702/5 | *Set of* 4 | 1·75 | 1·75 |

(Des B. Heman-Ackah. Litho National Printing & Packaging, Zimbabwe)

**1990** (7 Dec). *First National Road Safety Day. T* **174** *and similar horiz designs. Multicoloured. P* 14½.

| | | | |
|---|---|---|---|
| 706 | 8 t. Type **174** | 15 | 10 |
| 707 | 15 t. Careless overtaking | 25 | 15 |
| 708 | 30 t. Cattle on road | 35 | 30 |
| 706/8 | *Set of* 3 | 65 | 50 |

175 Cattle

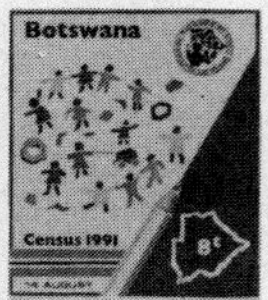

176 Children

(Des B. Mazebedi. Litho Questa)

**1991** (4 Mar). *Rock Paintings. T* **175** *and similar horiz designs. Multicoloured. P* 14.

| | | | |
|---|---|---|---|
| 709 | 8 t. Type **175** | 15 | 10 |
| 710 | 15 t. Cattle, drying frames and tree | 20 | 15 |
| 711 | 30 t. Animal hides | 30 | 30 |
| 712 | 2 p. Family herding cattle | 1·40 | 1·50 |
| 709/12 | *Set of* 4 | 1·90 | 1·75 |

Nos. 709/12 were printed on sand-grained paper which has an uneven surface.

(Des H. Methorst. Litho National Printing & Packaging, Zimbabwe)

**1991** (3 June). *National Census. T* **176** *and similar vert designs. Multicoloured.* A. *P* 14. B. *P* 14½.

| | | A | | B | |
|---|---|---|---|---|---|
| 713 | 8 t. Type **176** | 10 | 10 | 10 | 10 |
| 714 | 15 t. Village | 10 | 15 | 10 | 15 |
| 715 | 30 t. School | 15 | 20 | 15 | 20 |
| 716 | 2 p. Hospital | 1·10 | 1·25 | 1·10 | 1·25 |
| 713/16 | *Set of* 4 | 1·25 | 1·50 | 1·25 | 1·50 |

177 Tourists viewing Elephants

178 *Harpagophytum procumbens*

(Des P. Lodoen. Litho Govt Printer, Pretoria)

**1991** (30 Sept). *African Tourism Year. Okavango Delta. T* **177** *and similar multicoloured designs. P* 14 (2 *p.*) *or* 14×14½ (*others*).

| | | | |
|---|---|---|---|
| 717 | 8 t. Type **177** | 15 | 10 |
| 718 | 15 t. Crocodiles basking on river bank | 20 | 15 |
| 719 | 35 t. Fish Eagles and aircraft | 30 | 30 |
| 720 | 2 p. Okavango wildlife (26×44 *mm*) | 1·40 | 1·60 |
| 717/20 | *Set of* 4 | 1·90 | 2·00 |

(Des G. Condy. Litho Govt Printer, Pretoria)

**1991** (4 Nov). *Christmas. Seed Pods. T* **178** *and similar vert designs. Multicoloured. P* 14.

| | | | |
|---|---|---|---|
| 721 | 8 t. Type **178** | 10 | 10 |
| 722 | 15 t. *Tylosema esculentum* | 10 | 10 |
| 723 | 30 t. *Abrus precatorius* | 15 | 20 |
| 724 | 2 p. *Kigelia africana* | 1·10 | 1·25 |
| 721/4 | *Set of* 4 | 1·25 | 1·40 |

## ALTERED CATALOGUE NUMBERS

Any Catalogue numbers altered from the last edition are shown as a list in the introductory pages.

POSTAGE DUE STAMPS

BECHUANALAND PROTECTORATE

(D 1)

BECHUANALAND PROTECTORATE

(D 2)

**1926** (Jan). *Nos.* D9/10 *and* D13 *of Great Britain, optd with Types* D **1** *or* D **2** (2*d.*).

| | | | |
|---|---|---|---|
| D1 | ½d. emerald (No. D10) | 3·25 | 45·0 |
| D2 | 1d. carmine (No. D9) | 3·25 | 40·0 |
| D3 | 2d. agate (No. D13) | 6·00 | 70·0 |
| D1/3 | *Set of* 3 | 11·00 | £14 |

D 3

2d

Normal

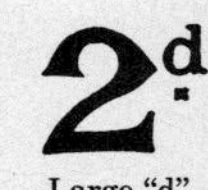

Large "d" (R. 9/6, 10/6)

(Typo D.L.R.)

**1932** (12 Dec)–**58**. *Wmk Mult Script CA. Ordinary paper. P* 14.

| | | | | |
|---|---|---|---|---|
| D4 | D **3** | ½d. sage-green | 4·50 | 18·0 |
| D5 | | 1d. carmine | 4·50 | 5·5 |
| | | a. Chalk-surfaced paper (27.11.58) | 30 | 5·0 |
| D6 | | 2d. violet | 6·00 | 18·0 |
| | | a. Large "d" | 35·00 | |
| | | b. Chalk-surfaced paper (27.11.58) | 60 | 8·0 |
| | | ba. Large "d" | 8·00 | |
| D4/6b | | *Set of* 3 | 4·75 | 28·0 |
| D4/6 Perf "Specimen" | | *Set of* 3 | 60·00 | |

No. D6a first occurred on the 1947 printing.

1c 1c

I (Small) II (Large)

**1961** (14 Feb). *Surch as T* **27**. *Chalk-surfaced paper* (*Nos* D7/8).

| | | | | |
|---|---|---|---|---|
| D7 | D **3** | 1 c. on 1d. (Type I) | 25 | 5 |
| | | a. Type II | 15 | 1·2 |
| | | ab. Double surch | £110 | |
| | | ac. Ordinary paper | 16·00 | |
| D8 | | 2 c. on 2d. (Type I) | 25 | 1·1 |
| | | a. Large "d" | 5·00 | |
| | | b. Type II | 15 | 1·5 |
| | | ba. Large "d" | 4·00 | |
| | | c. Ordinary paper. Type II | 65·00 | |
| | | ca. Large "d" | £200 | |
| D9 | | 5 c. on ½d. | 20 | 6 |
| D7/9 | | *Set of* 3 | 45 | 2·0 |

**1961** (15 Nov). *As Type* D **3** *but values in cents. Chalk-surfaced paper. Wmk Mult Script CA. P* 14.

| | | | |
|---|---|---|---|
| D10 | 1 c. carmine | 15 | 50 |
| D11 | 2 c. violet | 15 | 70 |
| D12 | 5 c. green | 30 | 1·00 |
| D10/12 | *Set of* 3 | 55 | 2·00 |

REPUBLIC OF BOTSWANA

(D 4)

D **5** African Elephant

D **6** Common Zebr

**1967** (1 Mar). *Nos.* D10/12 *optd with Type* D **4**.

| | | | |
|---|---|---|---|
| D13 | 1 c. carmine | 15 | 1·5 |
| D14 | 2 c. violet | 15 | 1·7 |
| D15 | 5 c. green | 20 | 1·7 |
| D13/15 | *Set of* 3 | 45 | 4·5 |

(Des and litho B.W.)

**1971** (9 June). *P* 13½.

| | | | | |
|---|---|---|---|---|
| D16 | D **5** | 1 c. carmine | 55 | 1·5 |
| D17 | | 2 c. bluish violet | 65 | 1·7 |
| D18 | | 6 c. sepia | 1·10 | 2·5 |
| D19 | | 14 c. blue-green | 1·75 | 3·0 |
| D16/19 | | *Set of* 4 | 3·75 | 8·0 |

(Des M. Bryan. Litho Govt Printer, Pretoria)

**1977** (18 Apr)–**84**. *P* 12½.

| | | | | |
|---|---|---|---|---|
| D20 | D **6** | 1 t. black and vermilion (1978) | 20 | 7 |
| | | *a. Black and bright orange* (1980) | 30 | 7 |
| | | b. Perf 14 (1982?) | 20 | 7 |
| D21 | | 2 t. black and emerald | 30 | 8 |
| | | a. Perf 14 (5.8.81*) | 20 | 8 |
| D22 | | 4 t. black and red | 30 | 8 |
| | | a. Perf 14 (28.9.81*) | 20 | 8 |
| D23 | | 10 t. black and deep ultramarine | 30 | 8 |
| | | a. Perf 14 (7.3.84) | 20 | 8 |
| D24 | | 16 t. black and chestnut | 50 | 1·5 |
| | | a. Perf 14 (7.3.84) | 30 | 1·5 |
| D20/24 | | *Set of* 5 | 1·40 | 4·2 |
| D20b/24a | | *Set of* 5 | 1·00 | 4·2 |

* First supplies of Nos. D20b, D21a and D22a were sent to Botswana in June 1981. The dates quoted for the 2 t. and 4 t. are earliest known dates of use. Early use of the 1 t. has yet to be identified.

Nos. D20b/4a are on white paper.

(Litho National Printing & Packaging, Zimbabwe)

**1989** (1 Apr). *P* 14½.

| | | | | | |
|---|---|---|---|---|---|
| D25 | **D 6** | 1 t. black and reddish orange .. | .. | 10 | 10 |
| D26 | | 2 t. black and emerald .. | .. | 10 | 10 |
| D27 | | 4 t. black and bright scarlet .. | .. | 10 | 10 |
| D28 | | 10 t. black and deep ultramarine | .. | 10 | 10 |
| D29 | | 16 t. black and reddish brown .. | .. | 10 | 10 |
| D25/9 | | .. .. .. .. *Set of* 5 | | 25 | 25 |

Details on the zebra and of the grass stems are less distinct on Nos. D25/9 than on previous versions of Type D **6**.

POSTAL FISCAL STAMPS

The following stamps issued for fiscal purposes were each allowed to be used for postal purposes for a short time. No. F2 was used by the public because the word "POSTAGE" had not been obliterated and No. F3 because the overprint did not include the words "Revenue only" as did the contemporary fiscal overprints for Basutoland and Swaziland.

| **Bechuanaland Protectorate** | **£5** | **Bechuanaland Protectorate.** |
|---|---|---|
| (F 1) | (F 2) | (F 3) |

**1910** (July). *No.* 266a *of Transvaal, optd with Type* **F 1** *by Transvaal Govt Ptg Wks, Pretoria.*

F1 6d. black and brown-orange (Bl-Blk) .. £120 £200

No. F1 was supplied to Assistant Commissioners in January 1907 for revenue purposes. The "POSTAGE" inscription was not obliterated, however, and the stamp is known postally used for a period of a year from July 1910.

**1918.** *No.* 15 *surch with Type* **F 2** *at top.*

F2 **4** £5 on 1s. green and black .. £5500

**1922.** *No.* 4b *of South Africa optd with Type* **F 3**, *in varying positions.*

F3 1d. scarlet .. .. .. .. .. 40·00 80·00

a. Opt double, one albino .. .. .. 90·00

# British Antarctic Territory

1 M.V. *Kista Dan*

(Des B.W. (No. 15*a*), M. Goaman (others). Recess B.W.)

**1963** (1 Feb)–**69**. *Horiz designs as T* 1, *W w* **12**. *P* 11 × 11½.

1 ½d. deep blue .. .. .. .. .. .. 45 85
2 1d. brown .. .. .. .. .. .. 70 50
3 1½d. orange-red and brown-purple .. .. 70 50
4 2d. purple .. .. .. .. .. .. 70 50
5 2½d. myrtle-green .. .. .. .. .. 80 50
6 3d. deep blue .. .. .. .. .. .. 1·75 50
7 4d. sepia .. .. .. .. .. .. 1·25 60
8 6d. olive and deep ultramarine .. .. 2·00 85
9 9d. olive-green .. .. .. .. .. 2·25 75
10 1s. deep turquoise-blue .. .. .. .. 1·50 50
11 2s. deep violet and orange-sepia .. .. 14·00 5·00
12 2s. 6d. blue .. .. .. .. .. .. 14·00 5·50
13 5s. red-orange and rose-red .. .. .. 20·00 8·50
14 10s. deep ultramarine and emerald .. .. 45·00 22·00
15 £1 black and light blue .. .. .. .. 85·00 48·00
15*a* £1 red and brownish black (1.12.69) .. £150 £120
1/15*a* .. .. .. .. .. *Set of* 16 £300 £190

Designs:—1d. Manhauling; 1½d. Muskeg (tractor); 2d. Skiing; 2½d. Beaver (aircraft); 3d. R.R.S. *John Biscoe II*, 4d. Camp scene; 6d. H.M.S. *Protector*; 9d. Sledging; 1s. Otter (aircraft); 2s. Huskies; 2s. 6d. Helicopter; 5s. Snocat (tractor); 10s. R.R.S. *Shackleton*; £1 (No. 15) Antarctic Map; £1 (No. 15*a*) H.M.S. *Endurance*.

**1966** (24 Jan). *Churchill Commemoration. As Nos.* 170/3 *of Antigua.*

16 ½d. new blue .. .. .. .. .. .. 80 70
17 1d. deep green .. .. .. .. .. 3·00 1·00
18 1s. brown .. .. .. .. .. .. 21·00 3·50
19 2s. bluish violet .. .. .. .. .. 24·00 4·50
16/19 .. .. .. .. .. *Set of* 4 45·00 8·75

17 Lemaire Channel and Icebergs

(Des R. Granger Barrett. Litho Format)

**1969** (6 Feb). *25th Anniv of Continuous Scientific Work. T* **17** *and similar horiz designs. W w* **12** (*sideways*). *P* 14.

20 3½d. black, pale blue and ultramarine .. 3·50 1·75
21 6d. multicoloured .. .. .. .. .. 3·50 1·75
22 1s. black, pale blue and vermilion .. .. 3·50 1·75
23 2s. black, orange and turquoise-blue .. 4·25 2·00
20/3 .. .. .. .. .. *Set of* 4 13·00 6·50

Designs:—6d. Radio Sonde balloon; 1s. Muskeg pulling tent equipment; 2s. Surveyors with theodolite.

½P

(18)

19 Setting up Camp

**1971** (15 Feb). *Decimal Currency. As Nos.* 1/14, *but glazed paper, colours changed and surch as T* **18**.

24 ½p. on ½d. blue .. .. .. .. .. 60 1·25
25 1p. on 1d pale brown .. .. .. .. 1·00 40
26 1½p. on 1½d. red and pale brown-purple .. 1·25 35
27 2p. on 2d. bright purple .. .. .. .. 1·25 30
28 2½p. on 2½d. green .. .. .. .. .. 1·75 40
29 3p. on 3d. blue .. .. .. .. .. 2·50 55
30 4p. on 4d. bistre-brown .. .. .. .. 2·25 55
31 5p. on 6d. olive and ultramarine .. .. 4·25 2·25
32 6p. on 9d. dull green .. .. .. .. 9·00 4·00
33 7½p. on 1s. turquoise-blue .. .. .. 9·00 4·25
34 10p. on 2s. violet and orange-sepia .. .. 16·00 10·00
35 15p. on 2s. 6d. pale blue .. .. .. 16·00 10·00
36 25p. on 5s. orange and pale rose-red .. .. 22·00 13·00
37 50p. on 10s. ultramarine and emerald .. .. 60·00 35·00
24/37 .. .. .. .. .. *Set of* 14 £130 75·00

(Des M. Goaman. Recess and litho Enschedé)

**1971** (23 June). *10th Anniv of Antarctic Treaty. Vert designs each including Antarctic Map and Queen Elizabeth, as T* **19**. *Multicoloured. W w* **12** (*sideways*). *P* 14 × 13.

38 1½p. Type **19** .. .. .. .. .. 5·50 2·50
39 4p. Snow Petrels .. .. .. .. .. 9·50 4·00
40 5p. Weddell Seals .. .. .. .. .. 9·50 4·00
41 10p. Adelie Penguins .. .. .. .. 14·00 6·00
38/41 .. .. .. .. .. *Set of* 4 35·00 15·00

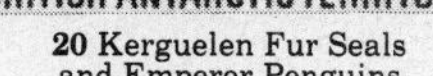

20 Kerguelen Fur Seals and Emperor Penguins

21 James Cook and H.M.S. *Resolution*

(Des (from photograph by D. Groves) and photo Harrison)

**1972** (13 Dec*). *Royal Silver Wedding. Multicoloured; background colour given. W w* **12**. *P* 14 × 14½.

42 **20** 5p. red-brown .. .. .. .. .. 3·75 1·50
43 10p. brown-olive .. .. .. .. .. 3·75 1·50

*This is the local release date; they were issued by the Crown Agents on 20 November.

(Des J.W. Litho Questa)

**1973** (14 Feb). *T* **21** *and similar vert designs. Multicoloured. W w* **12** (*sideways*). *P* 14 × 14½.

44 ½p. Type **21** (*shades*) .. .. .. .. 1·25 2·00
45 1p. Thaddeus Von Bellingshausen and *Vostok* 2·50 3·00
46 1½p. James Weddell and *Jane* .. .. .. 9·50 4·00
47 2p. John Biscoe and *Tula* .. .. .. .. 1·50 1·50
48 2½p. J. S. C. Dumont d'Urville and *L'Astrolabe* 1·50 1·50
49 3p. James Clark Ross and H.M.S. *Erebus* .. 95 1·50
50 4p. C. A. Larsen and *Jason* .. .. .. 95 1·50
51 5p. Adrien de Gerlache and *Belgica* .. .. 1·00 1·50
52 6p. Otto Nordenskjöld and *Antarctic* .. 1·25 1·50
53 7½p. W. S. Bruce and *Scotia* .. .. .. 1·75 2·00
54 10p. Jean-Baptiste Charcot and *Pourquoi Pas?* .. .. .. .. .. .. .. 2·75 2·50
55 15p. Ernest Shackleton and *Endurance* .. 4·00 4·00
56 25p. Hubert Wilkins and *San Francisco* .. 3·00 4·00
57 50p. Lincoln Ellsworth and *Polar Star* .. 3·00 6·00
58 £1 John Rymill and *Penola* .. .. .. 6·00 12·00
44/58 .. .. .. .. .. *Set of* 15 38·00 45·00

The 25 and 50p. show aircraft; the rest show ships.
See also Nos. 64/78.

**1973** (23 Dec*). *Royal Wedding. As Nos.* 165/6 *of Anguilla. Centre multicoloured. W w* **12** (*sideways*). *P* 13½.

59 5p. ochre .. .. .. .. .. .. 40 20
60 15p. light turquoise-blue .. .. .. .. 70 30

*This is the local date of issue: the Crown Agents released the stamps on 14 November.

22 Churchill and Churchill Peninsula, B.A.T.

(Des G. Vasarhelyi. Litho Format)

**1974** (10 Dec*). *Birth Centenary of Sir Winston Churchill. T* **22** *and similar horiz design. Multicoloured. W w* **12** (*sideways on* 5p). *P* 14.

61 5p. Type **22** .. .. .. .. .. 1·75 1·50
62 15p. Churchill and *Trepassey* ("Operation Tabarin", 1943) .. .. .. .. .. 2·25 2·00
**MS**63 114 × 88 mm. Nos. 61/2. Wmk upright .. 10·00 9·00

*This is the local date of issue: the Crown Agents released the stamps on 30 November.

**1975** (11 June)–**81**. *As Nos.* 44/58 *but W w* **14**. *Ordinary paper* (½, 2, 2½, 3, 5, 10, 15, 25, 50*p.*) *or chalk-surfaced paper* (1, 1½, 4, 6, 7½*p.*, £1). *P* 12 (4, 6, 7½*p.*) *or* 14 × 14½ (*others*).

64 ½p. Type **21** .. .. .. .. .. 1·50 1·75
a. Chalk-surfaced paper (14.3.78) .. .. 65 55
65 1p. Thaddeus von Bellingshausen and *Vostok* (14.3.78) .. .. .. .. 45 75
a. Ordinary paper (11.12.79) .. .. .. 55 1·00
66 1½p. James Weddell and *Jane* (14.3.78) .. 45 75
a. Ordinary paper (11.12.79) .. .. .. 55 1·00
67 2p. John Biscoe and *Tula* (11.12.79) .. .. 1·25 80
68 2½p. J. S. C. Dumont d'Urville and *L'Astrolabe* (11.12.79) .. .. .. .. .. 1·00 80
69 3p. James Clark Ross and H.M.S. *Erebus* (11.12.79) .. .. .. .. .. 1·75 85
70 4p. C. A. Larsen and *Jason* (5.12.80) .. 45 1·50
71 5p. Adrien de Gerlache and *Belgica* (11.12.79) .. .. .. .. .. 2·25 1·50
2·25 1·50
72 6p. Otto Nordenskjöld and *Antarctic* (5.12.80) .. .. .. .. .. .. 70 1·50
73 7½p. W. S. Bruce and *Scotia* (5.12.80) .. 1·50 1·75
74 10p. Jean-Baptiste Charcot and *Pourquoi Pas?* (11.12.79) .. .. .. .. 1·25 2·00
a. Perf 12. Chalk-surfaced paper (25.11.81) 1·00 2·25
75 15p. Ernest Shackleton and *Endurance* (11.12.79) .. .. .. .. .. 1·25 1·50
a. Perf 12. Chalk-surfaced paper (25.11.81) 1·00 2·25
76 25p. Hubert Wilkins and *San Francisco* (11.12.79) .. .. .. .. .. 1·25 1·50
a. Perf 12. Chalk-surfaced paper (25.11.81) 1·25 2·50
77 50p. Lincoln Ellsworth and *Polar Star* (11.12.79) .. .. .. .. .. 2·00 2·25
a. Perf 12. Chalk-surfaced paper (5.12.80) 1·25 1·75
78 £1 John Rymill and *Penola* (14.3.78) .. 4·00 2·00
a. Perf 12 (5.12.80) .. .. .. .. 2·00 3·50
64a/78a .. .. .. .. .. *Set of* 15 15·00 18·00

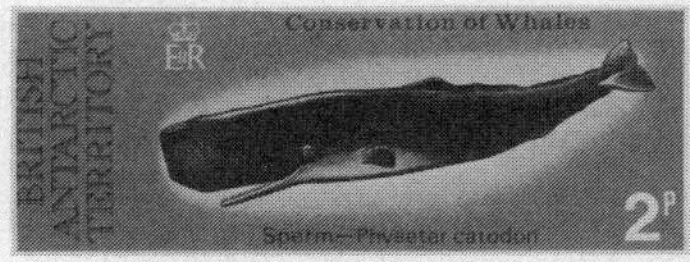


23 Sperm Whale

(Des J. Cooter. Litho Questa)

**1977** (4 Jan). *Whale Conservation. T* **23** *and similar horiz designs. W w* **14** (*sideways*). *P* 13½.

79 2p. brownish black, slate and bright blue .. 3·75 1·75
80 8p. grey, brownish black and rosine .. .. 4·75 2·25
81 11p. multicoloured .. .. .. .. .. 5·50 2·25
82 25p. grey-blue, brownish blk & lt blue-green 7·00 3·00
79/82 .. .. .. .. .. *Set of* 4 19·00 8·50

Designs:—8p. Fin Whale; 11p. Humpback Whale; 25p. Blue Whale.

24 The Queen before Taking the Oath

25 Emperor Penguin

(Des J.W. Litho Questa)

**1977** (7 Feb). *Silver Jubilee. T* **24** *and similar horiz designs Multicoloured. W w* **14** (*sideways*). *P* 13½.

83 6p. Prince Philip's visit, 1956/7 .. .. 95 20
84 11p. Coronation Oath .. .. .. .. 1·25 30
85 33p. Type **24** .. .. .. .. .. 1·50 45
83/5 .. .. .. .. .. *Set of* 3 3·25 85

(Des C. Abbott. Litho Questa)

**1978** (2 June). *25th Anniv of Coronation. T* **25** *and similar vert designs. P* 15.

86 25p. green, deep bluish green and silver .. 1·10 65
a. Sheetlet Nos. 86/8 × 2 .. .. .. 6·00
87 25p. multicoloured .. .. .. .. 1·10 65
88 25p. green, deep bluish green and silver .. 1·10 65
86/8 .. .. .. .. .. *Set of* 3 3·00 1·75

Designs:— No. 86. Black Bull of Clarence; No. 87, Queen Elizabeth II; No. 88, Type **25**.

Nos. 86/8 were printed together in small sheets of 6, containing two *se-tenant* strips of 3 with a horizontal gutter margin between.

26 Macaroni Penguins

(Des G. Drummond. Litho Walsall)

**1979** (14 Jan). *Penguins. T* **26** *and similar horiz designs. Multicoloured. W w* **14** (*sideways*). *P* 13½.

89 3p. Type **26** .. .. .. .. .. 7·00 4·75
90 8p. Gentoo penguins .. .. .. .. 2·75 1·75
91 11p. Adelie penguins .. .. .. .. 3·00 2·00
92 25p. Emperor penguins .. .. .. .. 4·00 2·50
89/92 .. .. .. .. .. *Set of* 4 15·00 10·00

27 Sir John Barrow and *Tula*

(Des A. Theobald. Litho Secura, Singapore)

**1980** (14 Dec†). *150th Anniv of Royal Geographical Society. Former Presidents. T* **27** *and similar horiz designs. Multicoloured. W w* **14** (*sideways*). *P* 13½.

93 3p. Type **27** .. .. .. .. .. 20 10
94 7p. Sir Clement Markham and *Discovery* .. 25 25
95 11p. Lord Curzon and launch *James Caird* 30 30
96 15p. Sir William Goodenough .. .. .. 35 35
97 22p. Sir James Wordie .. .. .. .. 50 55
98 30p. Sir Raymond Priestley .. .. .. 60 65
93/8 .. .. .. .. .. *Set of* 6 2·00 2·00

†This is the local date of issue; the Crown Agents released the stamps on 1 December.

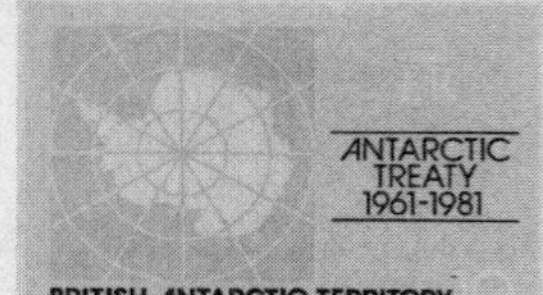


28 Map of Antarctic

(Des Walsall. Litho Questa)

**1981** (1 Dec). *20th Anniv of Antarctic Treaty. T* **28** *and similar horiz designs.* W w **14** (*sideways*). *P* 13½ × 14.

| | | | |
|---|---|---|---|
| 99 | 10p. black, new blue and azure | 30 | 60 |
| 100 | 13p. black, new blue and apple green | 35 | 70 |
| 101 | 25p. black, new blue and mauve | 50 | 85 |
| 102 | 26p. black, brown-ochre and rose-red | 50 | 90 |
| 99/102 | *Set of* 4 | 1·50 | 2·75 |

Designs:—13p. Conservation research ("scientific co-operation"); 25p. Satellite image mapping ("technical co-operation"); 26p. Global geophysics ("scientific co-operation").

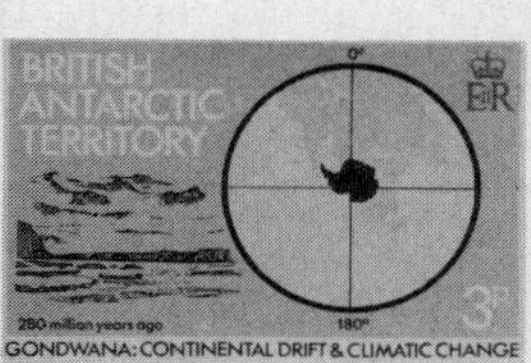

29 Map of Gondwana showing position of Continents 280 million years ago, and Contemporary Landscape Scene
30 British Antarctic Territory Coat of Arms

(Des C. Abbott. Litho Walsall)

**1982** (8 Mar). *Gondwana—Continental Drift and Climatic Change. T* **29** *and similar horiz designs depicting maps of Gondwana showing position of continents, and contemporary landscape scenes. Multicoloured.* W w **14** (*sideways*). *P* 13½ × 14.

| | | | |
|---|---|---|---|
| 103 | 3p. Type **29** | 20 | 35 |
| 104 | 6p. 260 million years ago | 25 | 45 |
| 105 | 10p. 230 million years ago | 30 | 55 |
| 106 | 13p. 175 million years ago | 35 | 60 |
| 107 | 25p. 50 million years ago | 55 | 70 |
| 108 | 26p. Present day | 55 | 70 |
| | a. Gold (royal cypher) omitted | | |
| 103/8 | *Set of* 6 | 2·00 | 3·00 |

(Des Jennifer Toombs. Litho Questa)

**1982** (1 July). *21st Birthday of Princess of Wales. T* **30** *and similar vert designs. Multicoloured.* W w **14**. *P* 14½ × 14.

| | | | |
|---|---|---|---|
| 109 | 5p. Type **30** | 20 | 20 |
| 110 | 17p. Princess of Wales (detail of painting by Bryan Organ) | 45 | 50 |
| 111 | 37p. Wedding ceremony | 85 | 1·00 |
| 112 | 50p. Formal portrait | 95 | 1·40 |
| 109/12 | *Set of* 4 | 2·25 | 2·75 |

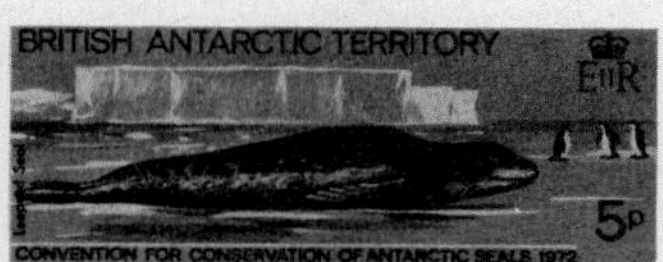


31 Leopard Seal

(Des R. Granger Barrett. Litho Walsall)

**1983** (3 Jan). *10th Anniv (1982) of Antarctic Seal Conservation Convention. T* **31** *and similar horiz designs. Multicoloured.* W w **14** (*sideways*). *P* 11.

| | | | |
|---|---|---|---|
| 113 | 5p. Type **31** | 35 | 35 |
| 114 | 10p. Weddell Seals | 40 | 40 |
| 115 | 13p. Southern Elephant Seals | 45 | 45 |
| 116 | 17p. Kerguelen Fur Seals | 55 | 55 |
| 117 | 25p. Ross Seal | 65 | 65 |
| 118 | 34p. Crabeater Seals | 85 | 85 |
| 113/18 | *Set of* 6 | 3·00 | 3·00 |

32 De Havilland "Twin Otter"

(Des Harrison. Litho Questa)

**1983** (20 Dec). *Bicentenary of Manned Flight. T* **32** *and similar horiz designs. Multicoloured.* W w **14** (*sideways*). *P* 14.

| | | | |
|---|---|---|---|
| 119 | 5p. Type **32** | 25 | 20 |
| 120 | 13p. De Havilland "Single Otter" | 40 | 35 |
| 121 | 17p. Consolidated "Canso" | 55 | 45 |
| 122 | 50p. Lockheed "Vega" | 1·10 | 1·10 |
| 119/22 | *Set of* 4 | 2·10 | 1·90 |

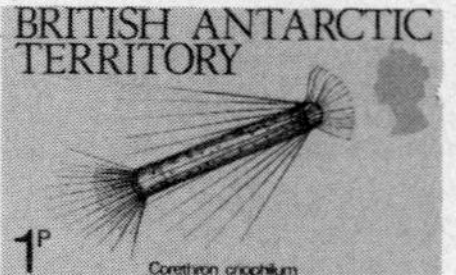


33 *Corethron criophilum*

(Des I. Loe. Litho Walsall)

**1984** (15 Mar). *Marine Life. T* **33** *and similar horiz designs. Multicoloured.* W w **14** (*sideways*). *P* 14.

| | | | |
|---|---|---|---|
| 123 | 1p. Type **33** | 25 | 40 |
| 124 | 2p. *Desmonena gaudichaudi* | 30 | 40 |
| 125 | 3p. *Tomopteris carpenteri* | 30 | 45 |
| 126 | 4p. *Pareuchaeta antarctica* | 35 | 50 |
| 127 | 5p. *Antarctomysis maxima* | 35 | 50 |
| 128 | 6p. *Antarcturus signiensis* | 40 | 60 |
| 129 | 7p. *Serolis cornuta* | 40 | 60 |
| 130 | 8p. *Parathemisto gaudichaudii* | 45 | 70 |
| 131 | 9p. *Bovallia gigantea* | 45 | 70 |
| 132 | 10p. *Euphausia superba* | 45 | 70 |
| 133 | 15p. *Colossendeis australis* | 60 | 80 |
| 134 | 20p. *Todarodes sagittatus* | 65 | 90 |
| 135 | 25p. *Notothenia neglecta* | 70 | 90 |
| 136 | 50p. *Chaenocephalus aceratus* | 1·25 | 1·60 |
| 137 | £1 Crabeater Seal | 1·75 | 2·00 |
| 138 | £3 Antarctic marine food chain | 5·00 | 5·50 |
| 123/38 | *Set of* 16 | 12·00 | 16·00 |

34 M.Y. *Penola* in Stella Creek
35 Robert McCormick and McCormick's Skua

(Des A. Theobald. Litho Questa)

**1985** (23 Mar). *50th Anniv of British Graham Land Expedition. T* **34** *and similar horiz designs. Multicoloured.* W w **14** (*sideways*). *P* 14½.

| | | | |
|---|---|---|---|
| 139 | 7p. Type **34** | 30 | 35 |
| 140 | 22p. Northern Base, Winter Island | 60 | 80 |
| 141 | 27p. D. H. Fox "Moth" at Southern Base, Barry Island | 70 | 90 |
| 142 | 54p. Dog team near Ablation Point, George VI Sound | 1·25 | 1·75 |
| 139/42 | *Set of* 4 | 2·50 | 3·50 |

(Des I. Strange. Litho Questa)

**1985** (4 Nov). *Early Naturalists. T* **35** *and similar vert designs. Multicoloured.* W w **14**. *P* 14½ × 14.

| | | | |
|---|---|---|---|
| 143 | 7p. Type **35** | 1·00 | 75 |
| 144 | 22p. Sir Joseph Dalton Hooker and *Deschampsia antarctica* | 1·40 | 1·10 |
| 145 | 27p. Jean René C. Quoy and Hourglass Dolphin | 1·60 | 1·40 |
| 146 | 54p. James Weddell and Weddell Seal | 2·50 | 2·00 |
| 143/6 | *Set of* 4 | 6·00 | 4·75 |

36 Dr. Edmond Halley
37 Snow Crystal

(Des A. Theobald. Litho Questa)

**1986** (6 Jan). *Appearance of Halley's Comet. T* **36** *and similar vert designs. Multicoloured.* W w **14**. *P* 14.

| | | | |
|---|---|---|---|
| 147 | 7p. Type **36** | 75 | 45 |
| 148 | 22p. Halley Station, Antarctica | 1·25 | 80 |
| 149 | 27p. "Halley's Comet, 1531" (from Peter Apian woodcut, 1532) | 1·40 | 90 |
| 150 | 54p. *Giotto* spacecraft | 2·25 | 1·50 |
| 147/50 | *Set of* 4 | 5·00 | 3·25 |

(Des C. Abbott. Litho Questa)

**1986** (6 Dec). *50th Anniv of International Glaciological Society. T* **37** *and similar vert designs showing snow crystals.* W w **16**. *P* 14½.

| | | | |
|---|---|---|---|
| 151 | 10p. cobalt and deep ultramarine | 50 | 50 |
| 152 | 24p. pale turquoise-green & dp bluish green | 80 | 80 |
| 153 | 29p. mauve and deep mauve | 90 | 90 |
| 154 | 58p. violet-blue and bright violet | 1·25 | 1·75 |
| 151/4 | *Set of* 4 | 3·00 | 3·50 |

***NEW INFORMATION***

The editor is always interested to correspond with people who have new information that will improve or correct the Catalogue.

38 Captain Scott, 1904
39 I.G.Y. Logo

(Des A. Theobald. Litho Questa)

**1987** (19 Mar). *75th Anniv of Captain Scott's Arrival at South Pole. T* **38** *and similar horiz designs. Multicoloured.* W w **16** (*sideways*). *P* 14 × 14½.

| | | | |
|---|---|---|---|
| 155 | 10p. Type **38** | 45 | 45 |
| 156 | 24p. Hut Point and *Discovery*, Ross Island, 1902–4 | 80 | 80 |
| 157 | 29p. Cape Evans Hut, 1911–13 | 95 | 1·00 |
| 158 | 58p. Scott's Expedition at South Pole, 1912 | 1·60 | 1·75 |
| 155/8 | *Set of* 4 | 3·50 | 3·50 |

(Des L. Curtis. Litho Questa)

**1987** (25 Dec). *30th Anniv of International Geophysical Year. T* **39** *and similar vert designs.* W w **16**. *P* 14½ × 14.

| | | | |
|---|---|---|---|
| 159 | 10p. black and pale green | 30 | 45 |
| 160 | 24p. multicoloured | 60 | 85 |
| 161 | 29p. multicoloured | 75 | 95 |
| 162 | 58p. multicoloured | 1·40 | 2·00 |
| 159/62 | *Set of* 4 | 2·75 | 3·75 |

Designs:—24p. Port Lockroy; 29p. Argentine Islands; 58p. Halley Bay.

40 Aurora over South Ice Plateau Station
41 *Xanthoria elegans*

(Des D. Hartley. Litho Questa)

**1988** (19 Mar). *30th Anniv of Commonwealth Trans-Antarctic Expedition. T* **40** *and similar vert designs. Multicoloured.* W w **16**. *P* 14.

| | | | |
|---|---|---|---|
| 163 | 10p. Type **40** | 30 | 30 |
| 164 | 24p. "Otter" aircraft at Theron Mountains | 60 | 60 |
| 165 | 29p. Seismic ice-depth sounding | 70 | 70 |
| 166 | 58p. "Sno-cat" over crevasse | 1·25 | 1·40 |
| 163/6 | *Set of* 4 | 2·50 | 2·75 |

(Des I. Loe. Litho Walsall)

**1989** (25 Mar). *Lichens. T* **41** *and similar horiz designs. Multicoloured.* W w **14** (*sideways*). *P* 14.

| | | | |
|---|---|---|---|
| 167 | 10p Type **41** | 40 | 50 |
| 168 | 24p *Usnea aurantiaco-atra* | 80 | 1·00 |
| 169 | 29p *Cladonia chlorophaea* | 85 | 1·10 |
| 170 | 58p *Umbilicaria antarctica* | 1·50 | 2·00 |
| 167/70 | *Set of* 4 | 3·25 | 4·25 |

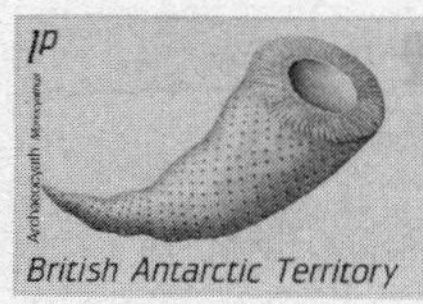

42 *Monocyathus* (archaeocyath)
43 Late Cretaceous Forest and Southern Beech Fossil

(Des I. Loe. Litho Questa)

**1990** (2 Apr). *Fossils. T* **42** *and similar horiz designs. Multicoloured.* W w **16** (*sideways*). *P* 14.

| | | | |
|---|---|---|---|
| 171 | 1p. Type **42** | 10 | 10 |
| 172 | 2p. *Lingulella* (brachiopod) | 10 | 10 |
| 173 | 3p. *Triplagnoslus* (trilobite) | 10 | 10 |
| 174 | 4p. *Lyriaspis* (trilobite) | 10 | 10 |
| 175 | 5p. *Glossopteris* leaf (gymnosperm) | 10 | 10 |
| 176 | 6p. *Gonatosorus* (fern) | 10 | 10 |
| 177 | 7p. *Belemnopsis* (belemnite) | 15 | 20 |
| 178 | 8p. *Sanmartinoceras* (ammonite) | 15 | 20 |
| 179 | 9p. *Pinna* (mussel) | 20 | 25 |
| 180 | 10p. *Aucellina* (mussel) | 20 | 25 |
| 181 | 20p. *Trigonia* (mussel) | 40 | 45 |
| 182 | 25p. *Perissoptera* (conch shell) | 50 | 55 |
| 183 | 50p. *Ainoceras* (ammonite) | 1·00 | 1·10 |
| 184 | £1 *Gunnarites* (ammonite) | 2·00 | 2·10 |
| 185 | £3 *Hoploparia* (crayfish) | 6·00 | 6·25 |
| 171/85 | *Set of* 15 | 10·00 | 10·50 |

(Des D. Miller. Litho Questa)

**1990** (25 Dec*). *90th Birthday of Queen Elizabeth the Queen Mother. Vert designs as T* **134** *(26p.) or* **135** *(£1) of Ascension. W w* **16**. *P* 14×15 *(26p.) or* 14½ *(£1).*

| | | | |
|---|---|---|---|
| 186 | 26p. multicoloured .. .. .. | 1·25 | 1·25 |
| 187 | £1 brownish black and olive-bistre .. | 3·25 | 3·25 |

Designs:—26p. Wedding of Prince Albert and Lady Elizabeth Bowes-Lyon, 1923; £1 The Royal Family, 1940.

*This is the local date of issue, the Crown Agents released the stamps on 4 August.

(Des N. Shewring. Litho Questa)

**1991** (27 Mar). *Age of the Dinosaurs. T* **43** *and similar horiz designs. Multicoloured. W w* **14** *(sideways). P* 14×13½.

| | | | |
|---|---|---|---|
| 188 | 12p. Type **43** .. .. .. .. .. | 40 | 40 |
| 189 | 26p. Hypsilophodont dinosaurs and skull .. | 80 | 80 |
| 190 | 31p. Frilled Sharks and tooth .. .. | 90 | 90 |
| 191 | 62p. Mosasaur, Plesiosaur, and Mosasaur vertebra .. .. .. .. | 1·75 | 1·75 |
| 188/91 | .. .. .. .. *Set of* 4 | 3·50 | 3·50 |

**44** Launching Meteorological Balloon, Halley IV Station

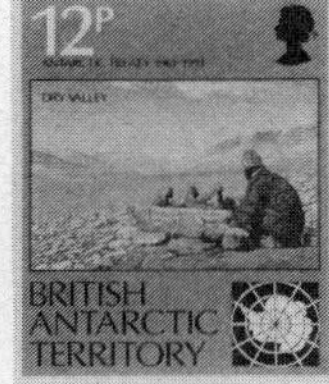


**45** Researching Dry Valley

(Des O. Bell. Litho Questa)

**1991** (30 Mar). *Discovery of Antarctic Ozone Hole. T* **44** *and similar horiz designs. Multicoloured. W w* **16** *(sideways). P* 14×13½.

| | | | |
|---|---|---|---|
| 192 | 12p. Type **44** .. .. .. .. .. | 35 | 35 |
| 193 | 26p. Measuring ozone with Dobson spectro-photometer .. .. .. .. | 75 | 75 |
| 194 | 31p. Satellite map showing ozone hole .. | 80 | 80 |
| 195 | 62p. ER-2 aircraft and graph of chlorine monoxide and ozone levels .. .. | 1·60 | 1·75 |
| 192/5 | .. .. .. .. *Set of* 4 | 3·25 | 3·25 |

(Des O. Bell. Litho Questa)

**1991** (2 Dec*). *30th Anniv of Antarctic Treaty. T* **45** *and similar vert designs. W w* **14**. *P* 13½×14 *(31p.) or* 14½×14 *(others).*

| | | | |
|---|---|---|---|
| 196 | 12p. multicoloured .. .. .. | 35 | 35 |
| 197 | 26p. multicoloured .. .. .. | 65 | 65 |
| 198 | 31p. black and blue-green .. .. | 75 | 75 |
| 199 | 62p. multicoloured .. .. .. | 1·50 | 1·60 |
| 196/9 | .. .. .. .. *Set of* 4 | 3·00 | 3·00 |

Designs:—26p. Relief map of ice sheet; 31p. BIOMASS logo; 62p. Ross Seal.

*This is the local date of issue, the Crown Agents released the stamps on 24 June.

**46** "H.M.S. *Erebus* and H.M.S. *Terror* in the Antarctic" (J. Carmichael)

(Des R. Watton. Litho Walsall)

**1991** (10 Dec). *Maiden Voyage of* James Clark Ross *(research ship). T* **46** *and similar horiz designs. Multicoloured. W w* **14** *(sideways). P* 14½.

| | | | |
|---|---|---|---|
| 200 | 12p. Type **46** .. .. .. .. .. | 25 | 30 |
| 201 | 26p. Launch of *James Clark Ross* .. | 50 | 55 |
| 202 | 31p. *James Clark Ross* in Antarctica .. | 60 | 65 |
| 203 | 62p. Scientific research .. .. .. | 1·25 | 1·40 |
| 200/3 | .. .. .. .. *Set of* 4 | 2·40 | 2·75 |

**1991** (24 Dec). *Birth Bicentenary of Michael Faraday (scientist). Nos. 200/3 additionally inscr* "200th Anniversary M. Faraday 1791–1867" *in blue.*

| | | | |
|---|---|---|---|
| 204 | 12p. Type **46** .. .. .. .. .. | 25 | 30 |
| 205 | 26p. Launch of *James Clark Ross* .. | 50 | 55 |
| 206 | 31p. *James Clark Ross* in Antarctica .. | 60 | 65 |
| 207 | 62p. Scientific research .. .. .. | 1·25 | 1·40 |
| 204/7 | .. .. .. .. *Set of* 4 | 2·40 | 2·75 |

## British Central Africa *see* Nyasaland Protectorate

## British Columbia and Vancouver Island *see* Canada

## British East Africa *see* Kenya

## British Forces in Egypt *see* Egypt

## British Guiana *see* Guyana

## British Honduras *see* Belize

# British Indian Ocean Territory

This Crown Colony was created on 8 November 1965 when it comprised the Chagos Archipelago, previously administered by Mauritius, together with the islands of Aldabra, Farquhar and Desroches, previously administered by Seychelles.

**(Currency. 100 cents=1 rupee)**

**B.I.O.T.**

(1)

**1968** (17 Jan). *As Nos.* 196/200, 202/4 *and* 206/12 *of Seychelles, optd with T* 1. W w 12 (*sideways on* 5, 10, 15, 20, 25, 50, 75 *c. and* 10 *r.*).

1 5 c. multicoloured . . 10 10
a. No stop after "I" . . 5·50 7·50
b. No stop after "O" . . 4·00 6·00
2 10 c. multicoloured . . 10 10
a. No stop after "I" . . 5·50 7·50
b. No stop after "O" . . 4·00 6·00
3 15 c. multicoloured . . 10 15
a. No stop after "I" . . 6·50 8·50
b. No stop after "O" . . 4·50 6·50
4 20 c. multicoloured . . 15 15
a. No stop after "I" . . 6·50 8·00
b. No stop after "O" . . 4·25 6·50
5 25 c. multicoloured . . 15 15
a. No stop after "I" . . 7·50 9·00
b. No stop after "O" . . 4·25 7·50
6 40 c. multicoloured . . 15 20
a. No stop after "I" . . 8·50 11·00
b. No stop after "O" . . 5·50 7·50
7 45 c. multicoloured . . 20 30
a. No stop after "I" . . 8·50 11·00
b. No stop after "B" . . 8·50 11·00
c. No stop after "O" . . 8·50 11·00
8 50 c. multicoloured . . 20 30
a. No stop after "I" . . 8·50 11·00
b. No stop after "O" . . 5·50 7·50
9 75 c. multicoloured . . 20 35
10 1 r. multicoloured . . 30 35
a. No stop after "I" . . 8·50 11·00
b. No stop after "O" . . 5·50 7·50
11 1 r. 50, multicoloured . . 1·75 1·50
a. No stop after "I" . . 14·00 16·00
b. No stop after "O" . . 9·50 12·00
12 2 r. 25, multicoloured . . 3·75 3·75
a. No stop after "I" . . 25·00 30·00
b. No stop after "O" . . 18·00 22·00
13 3 r. 50, multicoloured . . 4·00 4·50
a. No stop after "I" . . 30·00 35·00
b. No stop after "O" . . 20·00 24·00
14 5 r. multicoloured . . 5·50 7·50
a. No stop after "I" . . 42·00 48·00
b. No stop after "O" . . 27·00 35·00
15 10 r. multicoloured . . 13·00 15·00
a. No stop after "B" . . 65·00 75·00
b. No stop after "I" . . 65·00 75·00
c. No stop after "O" . . 55·00 60·00
1/15 . . *Set of* 15 27·00 30·00

These were issued by the Crown Agents on 15 January but owing to shipping delays they were not put on sale locally until 17 January.

The positions of the "no stop" varieties are as follows:

After "I": R. 2/4 on horiz stamps except 45 c. where it occurs on R. 3/3, and R. 8/5 on vert stamps except 10 r. where it occurs on R. 4/3.

After "O": R. 3/2 and 5/1 on vert stamps, R. 2/1 and 4/4 on horiz stamps (only occurs on R. 2/1 for 45 c.), and R. 2/7 and 5/9 on 10 r. value.

After "B": R. 10/4 (45 c.) or R. 1/8 (10 r.).

We have seen a sheet of the 5 c. and of the 10 c. with all stops in place so either the no stop varieties developed during printing or they were discovered and inserted during the printing.

2 Lascar

(Des G. Drummond, based on drawings by Mrs. W. Veevers-Carter. Litho D.L.R.)

**1968** (23 Oct)–**70**. *Marine Life. Multicoloured designs as T* **2**. *White paper (Nos.* 20*a*, 23*a*, 24*a*) *or cream paper (others).* W w **12** (*sideways on horiz, inverted on vert designs*). P 14.

16 5 c. Type **2** . . 30 60
17 10 c. Hammerhead Shark (*vert*) . . 30 50
18 15 c. Tiger Shark . . 30 50
19 20 c. Bat Ray . . 30 50
20 25 c. Butterfly Fish (*vert*) . . 80 1·00
20*a* 30 c. Robber Crab (7.12.70) . . 3·00 2·75
21 40 c. Caranx . . 40 40
22 45 c. Garfish (*vert*) . . 2·25 2·50
23 50 c. Barracuda . . 45 30
23*a* 60 c. Spotted Pebble Crab (7.12.70) . . 3·00 3·25
24 75 c. Parrot Fish . . 2·50 2·75
24*a* 85 c. Dorade (*Elegatis bipinnulatus*) (7.12.70) 4·50 3·50
25 1 r. Giant Hermit Crab . . 1·00 35
26 1 r. 50, Humphead . . 2·50 2·50
27 2 r. 25, Rock Cod . . 7·00 8·50
28 3 r. 50, Black Marlin . . 4·00 3·75
29 5 r. black, blue-green and greenish blue (Whale Shark) (*vert*) . . 7·50 6·50
30 10 r. Lion Fish . . 7·50 8·00
a. Imperf (pair) . . £275
16/30 . . *Set of* 18 42·00 42·00

See also No. 52.

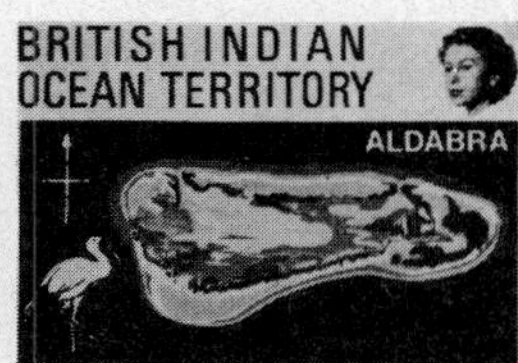


3 Sacred Ibis and Aldabra Coral Atoll

(Des and litho D.L.R.)

**1969** (10 July). *Coral Atolls.* W w **12** (*sideways*). P 13½ × 13.

31 **3** 2 r. 25, multicoloured . . 1·25 35

4 Outrigger Canoe

(Des Mrs. M. Hayward adapted by V. Whiteley. Litho D.L.R.)

**1969** (15 Dec.) *Ships of the Islands. T* **4** *and similar horiz designs. Multicoloured.* W w **12** (*sideways*). P 13½ × 14.

32 45 c. Type **4** . . 65 75
33 75 c. Pirogue . . 65 80
34 1 r. M. V. *Nordvaer* . . 70 90
35 1 r. 50, *Isle of Farquhar* . . 80 1·00
32/5 . . *Set of* 4 2·50 3·00

5 Giant Land Tortoise

(Des G. Drummond. Litho Format)

**1971** (1 Feb). *Aldabra Nature Reserve. T* **5** *and similar horiz designs. Multicoloured.* W w **12** (*sideways*). P 13½.

36 45 c. Type **5** . . 2·50 2·00
37 75 c. Aldabra Lily . . 3·00 2·50
38 1 r. Aldabra Snail . . 3·50 2·75
39 1 r. 50, Western Reef Herons . . 8·50 5·00
36/9 . . *Set of* 4 16·00 11·00

6 Arms of Royal Society and White-throated Rail

(Des V. Whiteley. Litho J.W.)

**1971** (30 June). *Opening of Royal Society Research Station on Aldabra.* W w **12** (*sideways*). P 13½.

40 **6** 3 r. 50, multicoloured . . 13·00 8·50

7 Staghorn Coral

(Des V. Whiteley. Litho A. & M.)

**1972** (1 Mar). *Coral. T* **7** *and similar horiz designs. Multicoloured.* W w **12** (*sideways*). P 13½.

41 40 c. Type **7** . . 3·00 2·00
42 60 c. Brain coral . . 3·50 2·50
43 1 r. Mushroom coral . . 3·50 3·00
44 1 r. 75, Organ Pipe coral . . 4·50 4·00
41/4 . . *Set of* 4 13·00 10·00

On some sheets of No. 43 the inks have been applied in a different order, resulting in an almost total absence of blue.

8 White-throated Rail and Sacred Ibis

9 "Christ on the Cross"

(Des (from photograph by D. Groves) and photo Harrison)

**1972** (20 Nov). *Royal Silver Wedding. Multicoloured; background colour given.* W w **12**. P 14 × 14½.

45 **8** 95 c. deep dull green . . 65 40
a. Silver (frame and inscr) ptd double . . £450
*b. Slate-green* . . 1·40 1·75
46 1 r. 50, bright bluish violet . . 65 40

(Des Jennifer Toombs. Litho Questa)

**1973** (9 Apr). *Easter. T* **9** *and similar vert design showing illustrations from 17th-century Ethiopian manuscript. Multicoloured.* W w **12** (*sideways*). P 14.

47 45 c. Type **9** . . 25 40
48 75 c. Joseph and Nicodemus burying Jesus . . 35 55
49 1 r. Type **9** . . 35 60
50 1 r. 50. As 75 c. . . 40 70
47/50 . . *Set of* 4 1·25 2·00
**MS**51 126 × 110 mm. Nos. 47/50 . . 1·75 4·00

**1973** (2 Oct). *As No.* 16 *but white paper and wmk upright.*

52 5 c. Type **2** . . 60 2·00

No. 52 differs in shade from No. 16 because of the change of paper.

10 Upsidedown Jellyfish

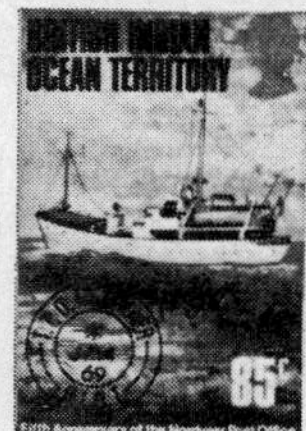


11 M.V. *Nordvaer*

(Des G. Drummond. Litho Walsall)

**1973** (12 Nov). *Wildlife* (1*st series*). *T* **10** *and similar vert designs. Multicoloured. W w* **12** (*sideways*). *P* 14.

| | | | |
|---|---|---|---|
| 53 | 50 c. Type **10** | 3·00 | 3·00 |
| 54 | 1 r. *Hypolimnas misippus* and *Belenois aldabrensis* (butterflies) | 3·00 | 3·00 |
| 55 | 1 r. 50, *Nephila madagascariensis* (spider) | 3·50 | 3·00 |
| 53/5 | *Set of* 3 | 8·50 | 8·00 |

See also Nos. 58/61, 77/80 and 86/9.

(Des C. Abbott. Litho Walsall)

**1974** (14 July). *Fifth Anniv of "Nordvaer" Travelling Post Office. T* **11** *and similar vert design. Multicoloured. W w* **12** (*sideways*). *P* 14.

| | | | |
|---|---|---|---|
| 56 | 85 c. Type **11** | 50 | 75 |
| 57 | 2 r. 50, *Nordvaer* off shore | 75 | 1·25 |

12 Auger Shells

(Des PAD Studio. Litho J.W.)

**1974** (12 Nov). *Wildlife* (2*nd series*). *T* **12** *and similar horiz designs showing shells. Multicoloured. W w* **12**. *P* 13½ × 14.

| | | | |
|---|---|---|---|
| 58 | 45 c. Type **12** | 1·50 | 1·00 |
| 59 | 75 c. Green Turban | 1·60 | 1·25 |
| 60 | 1 r. Drupe Snail | 2·00 | 1·50 |
| 61 | 1 r. 50, Helmet Shell | 2·25 | 1·75 |
| 58/61 | *Set of* 4 | 6·50 | 5·00 |

13 Aldabra Drongo

14 *Grewia salicifolia*

(Des R. Granger Barrett. Litho Questa)

**1975** (28 Feb). *Birds. Multicoloured designs as T* **13**. *W w* **12** (*sideways on horiz designs*). *P* 14.

| | | | |
|---|---|---|---|
| 62 | 5 c. Type **13** | 90 | 1·75 |
| 63 | 10 c. Black Coucal | 90 | 1·75 |
| 64 | 20 c. Mascarene Fody | 90 | 1·75 |
| 65 | 25 c. White Tern | 90 | 2·00 |
| 66 | 30 c. Crested Tern | 90 | 2·00 |
| 67 | 40 c. Brown Booby | 90 | 2·00 |
| 68 | 50 c. Common Noddy (*horiz*) | 90 | 2·25 |
| 69 | 60 c. Grey Heron | 90 | 2·50 |
| 70 | 65 c. Blue-faced Booby (*horiz*) | 90 | 2·50 |
| 71 | 95 c. Madagascar White Eye (*horiz*) | 1·00 | 2·50 |
| 72 | 1 r. Green Heron (*horiz*) | 1·25 | 2·50 |
| 73 | 1 r. 75, Lesser Frigate Bird (*horiz*) | 2·00 | 3·75 |
| 74 | 3 r. 50, White-tailed Tropic Bird (*horiz*) | 2·75 | 3·75 |
| 75 | 5 r. Souimanga Sunbird (*horiz*) | 4·00 | 5·00 |
| 76 | 10 r. Madagascar Turtle Dove (*horiz*) | 8·00 | 9·00 |
| 62/76 | *Set of* 15 | 24·00 | 40·00 |

(Des Sylvia Goaman. Litho Questa)

**1975** (10 July). *Wildlife* (3*rd series*). *T* **14** *and similar vert designs showing seashore plants. Multicoloured. W w* **12** (*sideways*). *P* 14.

| | | | |
|---|---|---|---|
| 77 | 50 c. Type **14** | 40 | 70 |
| 78 | 65 c. *Cassia aldabrensis* | 45 | 80 |
| 79 | 1 r. *Hypoestes aldabrensis* | 60 | 1·00 |
| 80 | 1 r. 60, *Euphorbia pyrifolia* | 75 | 1·10 |
| 77/80 | *Set of* 4 | 2·00 | 3·25 |

15 Map of Aldabra

(Des L. Curtis. Litho Questa)

**1975** (8 Nov). 10*th Anniv of Territory. Maps. T* **15** *and similar horiz designs. Multicoloured. W w* **12**. *P* 13½.

| | | | |
|---|---|---|---|
| 81 | 50 c. Type **15** | 60 | 65 |
| 82 | 1 r. Desroches | 75 | 85 |
| 83 | 1 r. 50, Farquhar | 85 | 1·00 |
| 84 | 2 r. Diego Garcia | 95 | 1·25 |
| 81/4 | *Set of* 4 | 2·75 | 3·25 |
| **MS**85 | 147 × 147 mm. Nos. 81/4 (wmk sideways) | 6·00 | 8·50 |

16 *Utetheisa pulchella* (moth)

(Des PAD Studio. Litho Questa)

**1976** (22 Mar). *Wildlife* (4*th series*). *T* **16** *and similar horiz designs. Multicoloured. W w* **12** (*sideways*). *P* 13½.

| | | | |
|---|---|---|---|
| 86 | 65 c. Type **16** | 60 | 1·10 |
| 87 | 1 r. 20, *Dysdercus fasciatus* (bug) | 75 | 1·25 |
| 88 | 1 r. 50, *Sphex torridus* (wasp) | 80 | 1·40 |
| 89 | 2 r. *Oryctes rhinoceros* (beetle) | 85 | 1·40 |
| 86/9 | *Set of* 4 | 2·75 | 4·50 |

When the Seychelles achieved independence on 29 June 1976 the islands of Aldabra, Farquhar and Desroches reverted to its administration so that British Indian Ocean Territory from that date consisted of the Chagos Archipelago, an island group, the largest of whose five main atolls is Diego Garcia. The indigenous population was resettled on Mauritius and Diego Garcia was developed as a U.S. Navy base while remaining under British administration.

Nos. 62/76 were withdrawn in August 1979 and, until May 1990, base personnel used British and American forces mail facilities routed via the Philippines and San Francisco. From 1987 British mails were routed via Singapore. The growing number of civilian workers eventually led to the re-introduction of a public postal service in May 1990 using stamps with face values in sterling.

**(New Currency. Sterling)**

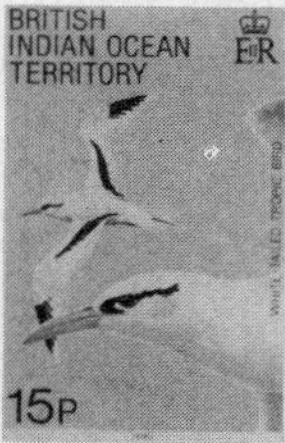


17 White-tailed Tropic Bird

18 1974 Wildlife 1 r. 50 Stamp

(Des N. Arlott. Litho Questa)

**1990** (3 May). *Birds. T* **17** *and similar vert designs. Multicoloured. W w* **16** (*sideways*). *P* 14.

| | | | |
|---|---|---|---|
| 90 | 15p. Type **17** | 30 | 35 |
| 91 | 20p. Turtle Dove | 40 | 45 |
| 92 | 24p. Greater Frigate Bird | 50 | 55 |
| 93 | 30p. Little Green Heron | 60 | 65 |
| 94 | 34p. Greater Sand Plover | 70 | 75 |
| 95 | 41p. Crab Plover | 80 | 85 |
| 96 | 45p. Crested Tern | 90 | 95 |
| 97 | 54p. Lesser Crested Tern | 1·10 | 1·25 |
| 98 | 62p. Fairy Tern | 1·25 | 1·40 |
| 99 | 71p. Red-footed Booby | 1·40 | 1·50 |
| 100 | 80p. Indian Mynah | 1·60 | 1·75 |
| 101 | £1 Madagascar Fody | 2·00 | 2·10 |
| 90/101 | *Set of* 12 | 10·50 | 11·50 |

(Des D. Miller. Litho Walsall)

**1990** (3 May). *"Stamp World London 90" International Stamp Exhibition. T* **18** *and similar horiz designs showing stamps. Multicoloured. W w* **14** (*sideways*). *P* 14.

| | | | |
|---|---|---|---|
| 102 | 15p. Type **18** | 50 | 50 |
| 103 | 20p. 1976 Wildlife 2 r. | 60 | 60 |
| 104 | 34p. 1975 Diego Garcia map 2 r. | 95 | 95 |
| 105 | 54p. 1969 *Nordvaer* 1 r. | 1·50 | 1·50 |
| 102/5 | *Set of* 4 | 3·25 | 3·25 |

(Des D. Miller. Litho Questa)

**1990** (4 Aug). 90*th Birthday of Queen Elizabeth the Queen Mother. Vert designs as T* **134** (24*p.*) *or* **135** (£1) *of Ascension. W w* **16**. *P* 14×15 (24*p.*) *or* 14½ (£1).

| | | | |
|---|---|---|---|
| 106 | 24p. multicoloured | 75 | 75 |
| 107 | £1 brownish black and purple-brown | 2·75 | 2·75 |

Designs:—24p. Lady Elizabeth Bowes-Lyon, 1923; £1 Queen Elizabeth and her daughters, 1940.

19 Territory Flag

20 Postman emptying Pillar Box

(Des D. Miller. Litho Questa)

**1990** (8 Nov). 25*th Anniv of British Indian Ocean Territory. T* **19** *and similar vert designs. Multicoloured. W w* **14**. *P* 14×13½.

| | | | |
|---|---|---|---|
| 108 | 20p. Type **19** | 70 | 70 |
| 109 | 24p. Coat of arms | 80 | 80 |
| **MS**110 | 63×99 mm. £1 Map of Chagos Archipelago | 3·00 | 3·25 |

(Des O. Bell. Litho Walsall)

**1991** (3 June). *British Indian Ocean Territory Administration. T* **20** *and similar horiz designs. Multicoloured. W w* **14** (*sideways*). *P* 14.

| | | | |
|---|---|---|---|
| 111 | 20p. Type **20** | 60 | 60 |
| 112 | 24p. Commissioner inspecting guard of Royal Marines | 70 | 70 |
| 113 | 34p. Policemen outside station | 1·10 | 1·10 |
| 114 | 54p. Customs officers boarding yacht | 1·75 | 1·75 |
| 111/14 | *Set of* 4 | 3·75 | 3·75 |

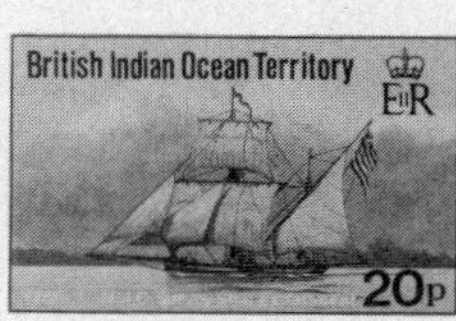


21 *Experiment* (E.I.C. survey brig), 1786

(Des E. Nisbet. Litho Walsall)

**1991** (8 Nov). *Visiting Ships. T* **21** *and similar horiz designs. Multicoloured. W w* **14** (*sideways*). *P* 14.

| | | | |
|---|---|---|---|
| 115 | 20p. Type **21** | 40 | 45 |
| 116 | 24p. *Pickering* (American brig), 1819 | 50 | 55 |
| 117 | 34p. *Emden* (German cruiser), 1914 | 70 | 75 |
| 118 | 54p. H.M.S. *Edinburgh* (destroyer), 1988 | 1·10 | 1·25 |
| 115/18 | *Set of* 4 | 2·40 | 2·75 |

(Des D. Miller. Litho Questa (54p.), Walsall (others))

**1992** (6 Feb). 40*th Anniv of Queen Elizabeth II's Accession. Horiz designs as T* **143** *of Ascension. Multicoloured. W w* **14** (*sideways*). *P* 14.

| | | | |
|---|---|---|---|
| 119 | 15p. Catholic chapel, Diego Garcia | 30 | 35 |
| 120 | 20p. Planter's house, Diego Garcia | 40 | 45 |
| 121 | 24p. Railway tracks on wharf, Diego Garcia | 50 | 55 |
| 122 | 34p. Three portraits of Queen Elizabeth | 70 | 75 |
| 123 | 54p. Queen Elizabeth II | 1·10 | 1·25 |
| 119/23 | *Set of* 5 | 2·75 | 3·00 |

# British Levant

The term "British Levant" is used by stamp collectors to describe the issues made by various British Post Offices within the former Turkish Empire.

Arrangements for the first such service were included amongst the terms of a commercial treaty between the two countries in 1832, but the system did not start operations until September 1857 when a post office for civilian use was opened in Constantinople, replacing the Army Post Office which had existed there since June 1854.

Eventually the number of British Post Offices grew to five:

Beyrout (Beirut, Lebanon). Opened 1873, closed 30 September 1914.

Constantinople (Istanbul). Opened 1 September 1857, closed 30 September 1914, re-opened 4 February 1919, finally closed 27 September 1923.

Salonica (Thessalonika, Greece). Opened 1 May 1900, closed October 1914. The city was captured by Greek troops on 7 November 1912 and incorporated into Greece by the Treaty of London (July 1913).

Smyrna (Izmir). Opened 1872, closed 30 September 1914, re-opened 1 March 1919, finally closed September 1922. Between 15 May 1919 and 8 September 1922 the city was under Greek occupation.

Stamboul (a sub-office of Constantinople). Opened 1 April 1884, closed 25 August 1896, re-opened 10 February 1908, finally closed 30 September 1914.

Stamps from the two British Post Offices in Egypt, still technically part of the Turkish Empire, are listed under EGYPT.

## A. BRITISH POST OFFICES IN TURKISH EMPIRE, 1857–1914

For illustrations of the postmark types see BRITISH POST OFFICES ABROAD notes, following GREAT BRITAIN.

After 15 August 1905 the post offices were supplied with Great Britain stamps overprinted "LEVANT". Subsequent examples of unoverprinted stamps with Levant postmarks did not originate from the post offices and are now omitted from the listing. The use of such stamps during 1919–22 at Constantinople and Smyrna is, however, covered by a later note.

### BEYROUT (BEIRUT)

*Stamps of* GREAT BRITAIN *cancelled "G 06" or circular postmark as in Types* **8**, **18** *or* **20**.

**1873.**

Z 1 ½d. rose-red (1870–90) .. *From* 25·00
Plate Nos. 12, 13, 14, 19, 20.
Z 2 1d. rose-red (1864–79) .. *From* 9·00
Plate Nos. 107, 118, 130, 140, 145, 148, 155, 157, 162, 167, 177, 179, 180, 184, 185, 186, 187, 195, 198, 200, 203, 204, 211, 213, 215, 218, 220, 222.
Z 3 1½d. lake-red (1870–74) (Plate 3) .. £200
Z 4 2d. blue (1858–69) .. *From* 14·00
Plate Nos. 13, 14, 15.
Z 5 2½d. rosy mauve (1875) (*blued paper*) .. 70·00
Plate No. 1.
Z 6 2½d. rosy mauve (1875–76) .. *From* 30·00
Plate Nos. 1, 2, 3.
Z 7 2½d. rosy mauve (1876–79) .. *From* 25·00
Plate Nos. 3, 4, 5, 6, 7, 8, 9, 10, 11, 12, 13, 14, 15, 16, 17.
Z 8 2½d. blue (1880) .. *From* 15·00
Plate Nos. 17, 18, 19, 20.
Z 9 2½d. blue (1881) .. *From* 9·00
Plate Nos. 21, 22, 23.
Z10 3d. rose (1867–73) (Plate No. 10) ..
Z11 3d. rose (1873–76) ..
Plate Nos. 12, 15, 16, 18, 19, 20.
Z12 3d. rose (1881) (Plate Nos. 20, 21) ..
Z13 4d. vermilion (1865–73) .. *From* 32·00
Plate Nos. 11, 12, 13, 14.
Z14 4d. vermilion (1876) (Plate No. 15) .. £180
Z15 4d. sage-green (1877) ..
Plate Nos. 15, 16.
Z16 4d. grey-brown (1880) *wmk* Large Garter (Plate No. 17) ..
Z17 4d. grey-brown (1880) *wmk* Crown ..
Plate Nos. 17, 18.
Z18 6d. mauve (1870) (Plate Nos. 8, 9) ..
Z19 6d. buff (1872–73) .. *From* 75·00
Plate Nos. 11, 12.
Z20 6d. chestnut (1872) (Plate No. 11) .. 32·00
Z21 6d. grey (1873) (Plate No. 12) ..
Z22 6d. grey (1874–80) .. *From* 25·00
Plate Nos. 13, 14, 15, 16, 17.
Z23 8d. orange (1876) ..
Z24 10d. red-brown (1867) .. £160
Z25 1s. green (1867–73) .. 18·00
Plate Nos. 6, 7.
Z26 1s. green (1873–77) .. *From* 32·00
Plate Nos. 8, 9, 10, 12, 13.
Z27 1s. orange-brown (1880) (Plate No. 13) ..
Z28 1s. orange-brown (1881) .. 45·00
Plate Nos. 13, 14.
Z29 2s. blue (1867) .. £130
Z30 5s. rose (1867) (Plate Nos. 1, 2) .. *From* £600

**1880.**

Z31 ½d. deep green .. 4·50
Z32 ½d. pale green .. 5·50
Z33 1d. Venetian red .. 7·00
Z34 1½d. Venetian red .. £130
Z35 2d. pale rose .. 32·00
Z36 2d. deep rose .. 32·00
Z37 5d. indigo .. 60·00

**1881.**

Z38 1d. lilac (14 *dots*) ..
Z39 1d. lilac (16 *dots*) ..

**1884.**

Z40 ½d. slate-blue ..
Z41 1½d. lilac ..
Z42 2d. lilac ..
Z43 2½d. lilac ..
Z44 4d. dull green ..
Z45 5d. dull green ..
Z46 1s. dull green ..

**1887–92.**

Z47 ½d. vermilion ..
Z48 1½d. dull purple and pale green ..
Z49 2d. green and scarlet ..
Z50 2½d. purple/*blue* ..
Z51 3d. purple/*yellow* ..
Z52 4½d. green and carmine ..
Z53 5d. dull purple and blue (Die II) ..
Z54 6d. purple/*rose-red* ..
Z55 1s. dull green ..

**1900.**

Z56 ½d. blue-green ..
Z57 1s. green and carmine ..

**1902–04.** *De La Rue ptgs.*

Z58 ½d. blue-green ..
Z59 ½d. yellowish green ..
Z60 1d. scarlet ..
Z61 2½d. ultramarine ..
Z62 5d. purple and ultramarine ..
Z63 10d. purple and carmine ..
Z64 1s. dull green and carmine ..

#### POSTAL FISCALS

Z65 1d. purple (*wmk* Anchor) ..
Z66 1d. purple (*wmk* Orb) ..

### CONSTANTINOPLE

*Stamps of* GREAT BRITAIN *cancelled "C" or circular postmark as in Types* **1**, **10**, **18** *or* **19**.

**1857.**

Z 68 ½d. rose-red (1870–79) .. *From* 20·00
Plate Nos. 5, 6, 10, 11, 12, 13, 14, 15, 20.
Z 69 1d. red-brown (1854), Die I, *wmk* Small Crown, *perf* 16 ..
Z 70 1d. red-brown (1855), Die II, *wmk* Small Crown, *perf* 14 ..
Z 71 1d. red-brown, (1855), Die II, *wmk* Large Crown, *perf* 14 .. 16·00
Z 72 1d. rose-red (1857) .. 6·00
Z 73 1d. rose-red (1861) Alphabet IV ..
Z 74 1d. rose-red (1864–79) .. *From* 5·00
Plate Nos. 71, 72, 73, 74, 76, 78, 79, 80, 81, 83, 85, 87, 89, 90, 92, 93, 94, 95, 96, 97, 99, 101, 102, 105, 106, 108, 109, 110, 113, 116, 118, 119, 120, 121, 122, 123, 124, 125, 127, 129, 130, 131, 134, 135, 136, 137, 138, 140, 141, 143, 144, 145, 146, 147, 148, 149, 150, 151, 152, 155, 156, 157, 158, 159, 160, 161, 162, 163, 164, 166, 167, 170, 171, 172, 173, 174, 175, 176, 177, 178, 179, 180, 181, 183, 184, 186, 187, 188, 189, 190, 191, 192, 193, 194, 195, 196, 197, 198, 200, 201, 203, 204, 205, 206, 207, 208, 210, 212, 214, 215, 216, 220, 222, 224.
Z 75 1½d. rose-red (1870) (Plate 1) .. £180
Z 76 2d. blue (1855), *wmk* Large Crown, *perf* 14. (Plate Nos. 5, 6) ..
Z 77 2d. blue (1858–69) .. *From* 9·00
Plate Nos. 8, 9, 12, 13, 14, 15.
Z 78 2½d. rosy mauve (1875–76) (*blued paper*) (Plate Nos. 1, 2) .. *From* 50·00
Z 79 2½d. rosy mauve (1875–76) .. *From* 27·00
Plate Nos. 1, 2, 3.
Z 80 2½d. rosy mauve (*Error of Lettering*) ..
Z 81 2½d. rosy mauve (1876–79) .. *From* 23·00
Plate Nos. 3 to 17.
Z 82 2½d. blue (1880–81) .. *From* 11·00
Plate Nos. 17, 18, 19, 20.
Z 83 2½d. blue (1881) (Plate Nos. 21, 22, 23) .. 7·00
Z 84 3d. carmine-rose (1862) (Plate No. 2) .. £110
Z 85 3d. rose (1865) (Plate No. 4) .. 65·00
Z 86 3d. rose (1867–73) (Plate Nos. 4 to 10) .. 65·00
Z 87 3d. rose (1873–76) .. 20·00
Plates, 11, 12, 15, 16, 17, 18, 19.
Z 88 3d. rose (1881) (Plate No. 21) ..
Z 89 3d. on 3d. lilac (1883) (Plate No. 21) ..
Z 90 4d. rose (1857) .. 40·00
*a. Rose-carmine* ..
Z 91 4d. red (1862) (Plate Nos. 3, 4) .. *From* 35·00
Z 92 4d. vermilion (1865–73) .. *From* 26·00
Plate Nos. 7 to 14.
Z 93 4d. vermilion (1876) (Plate No. 15) .. £150
Z 94 4d. sage-green (1877) .. 85·00
Plate Nos. 15, 16.
Z 95 4d. grey-brown (1880) *wmk* Large Garter (Plate No. 17) ..
Z 96 4d. grey-brown (1880) *wmk* Crown (Plate Nos. 17, 18) .. *From* 25·00
Z 97 6d. lilac (1856) .. 50·00
Z 98 6d. lilac (1862) (Plate Nos. 3, 4) .. *From* 35·00
Z 99 6d. lilac (1865–67) .. 32·00
Plate Nos. 5, 6.
Z100 6d. lilac (1867) (Plate No. 6) .. 40·00
Z101 6d. violet (1867–70) .. *From* 32·00
Plate Nos. 6, 8, 9.
Z102 6d. buff (1872–73) .. 48·00
Plate Nos. 11, 12.
Z103 6d. chestnut (1872) (Plate No. 11) .. 26·00
Z104 6d. grey (1873) (Plate No. 12) .. 70·00
Z105 6d. grey (1874–76) .. *From* 20·00
Plate Nos. 13, 14, 15, 16.
Z106 6d. grey (1881–82) (Plate Nos. 17, 18) .. 20·00
Z107 6d. on 6d. lilac (1883) .. 65·00
a. Dots slanting (Letters MI or SJ) .. £110
Z108 8d. orange (1876) .. £275
Z109 10d. red-brown (1867), *wmk* Emblems .. £12000
Z110 10d. red-brown (1867) .. £160
Z111 1s. green (1856) .. £100
Z112 1s. green (1862) .. 60·00
Z113 1s. green (1862) ("K" *variety*) ..
Z114 1s. green (1862) (*thick paper*) ..
Z115 1s. green (1865) (Plate No. 4) .. 60·00
Z116 1s. green (1867–73) .. *From* 10·00
Plate Nos. 4, 5, 6, 7.
Z117 1s. green (1873–77) .. *From* 26·00
Plate Nos. 8, 9, 10, 11, 12, 13.
Z118 1s. orange-brown (1880) (Plate No. 13) .. £180
Z119 1s. orange-brown (1881) .. *From* 40·00
Plate Nos. 13, 14.
Z120 2s. blue (1867) .. 85·00
Z121 5s. rose (1867–74) .. *From* £250
Plate Nos. 1, 2.
Z122 5s. rose (1882) (*white paper*) .. £850
Z123 5s. rose (1882) (*blued paper*) .. £1000

**1880.**

Z124 ½d. deep green .. 4·00
Z125 ½d. pale green .. 5·00
Z126 1d. Venetian red .. 3·50
Z127 2d. pale rose .. 32·00
Z128 2d. deep rose .. 32·00
Z129 5d. indigo ..

**1881.**

Z130 1d. lilac (14 *dots*) ..
Z131 1d. lilac (16 *dots*) .. 2·25

**1883–84.**

Z132 ½d. slate-blue .. 3·75
Z133 1½d. lilac ..
Z134 2d. lilac ..
Z135 2½d. lilac ..
Z136 3d. lilac ..
Z137 4d. dull green ..
Z138 5d. dull green ..
Z139 6d. dull green ..
Z140 9d. dull green ..
Z141 1s. dull green ..
Z142 2s. 6d. lilac (*blued paper*) .. £500
Z143 2s. 6d. lilac (*white paper*) .. 80·00
Z144 5s. rose (*blued paper*) ..
Z145 5s. rose (*white paper*) ..

**1887–92.**

Z146 ½d. vermilion ..
Z147 1½d. dull purple and pale green ..
Z148 2d. grey-green and carmine ..
Z149 2½d. purple/*blue* ..
Z150 3d. purple/*yellow* ..
Z151 4d. green and purple-brown ..
Z152 4½d. green and carmine ..
Z153 5d. dull purple and blue (Die II) ..
Z154 6d. purple/*rose-red* ..
Z155 9d. dull purple and blue ..
Z156 10d. dull purple and carmine ..
Z157 1s. dull green ..

**1900.**

Z158 ½d. blue-green ..
Z159 1s. green and carmine ..

**1902–04.** *De La Rue ptgs.*

Z160 ½d. blue-green ..
Z161 ½d. yellowish green ..
Z162 1d. scarlet ..
Z163 1½d. purple and green ..
Z164 2d. green and carmine-red ..
Z165 2½d. ultramarine ..
Z166 3d. purple/*orange-yellow* ..
Z167 4d. green and brown ..
Z168 5d. purple and ultramarine ..
Z169 6d. purple ..
Z170 9d. purple and ultramarine ..
Z171 10d. purple and carmine ..
Z172 1s. green and carmine ..
Z173 2s. 6d. lilac ..
Z174 5s. carmine ..

#### POSTAL FISCAL

Z175 1d. purple (No. F19) (1868) ..

### SALONICA

*Stamps of* GREAT BRITAIN *cancelled with circular postmark as in Type* **18** *or double-circle datestamp.*

**1900.**

Z202 ½d. vermilion (1887) .. 10·00
Z203 ½d. green (1900) .. 12·00
Z204 1d. lilac (1881) .. 12·00
Z205 6d. purple/*red* (1887) .. 16·00
Z206 1s. green and carmine (1900) .. 75·00
Z207 5s. rose (*white paper*) (1883) .. £600

**1902.**

Z208 ½d. blue-green .. 16·00
Z209 ½d. yellow-green .. 9·50
Z209*a* 1d. scarlet .. 9·50
Z209*b* 2½d. blue .. 13·00
Z209*c* 1s. green and carmine .. 27·00

### SMYRNA (IZMIR)

*Stamps of* GREAT BRITAIN *cancelled "F 87" or circular postmark as in Type* **8**, **16** *or* **18**.

**1872.**

Z210 ½d. rose-red (1870–79) .. *From* 20·00
Plates 11, 12, 13, 14, 15.
Z211 1d. rose-red (1864–79) .. *From* 7·00
Plate Nos. 120, 124, 134, 137, 138, 139, 140, 142, 143, 145, 146, 148, 149, 150, 151, 152, 153, 155, 156, 157, 158, 159, 160, 161, 162, 163, 164, 166, 167, 168, 169, 170, 171, 172, 173, 174, 175, 176, 177, 178, 183, 184, 185, 186, 187, 188, 191, 193, 195, 196, 198, 200, 201, 204, 210, 215, 217, 218.
Z212 1½d. lake-red (1870–74) (Plate Nos. 1, 3) *From* £200

Z213 2d. blue (1858) *wmk* Large Crown, *perf* 16
Z214 2d. blue (1858–69) .. .. .. *From* 12·00
Plate Nos. 13, 14, 15.
Z215 2½d. rosy mauve (1875) (*blued paper*) .. .. 55·00
Plate No. 1.
Z216 2½d. rosy mauve (1875–76) .. .. *From* 26·00
Plate Nos. 1, 2, 3.
Z217 2½d. rosy mauve (*Error of lettering*) .. ..
Z218 2½d. rosy mauve (1876–79) .. .. *From* 22·00
Plate Nos. 3, 4, 5, 6, 7, 8, 9, 10, 11, 12, 13, 14, 15, 16, 17.
Z219 2½d. blue (1880) .. .. .. .. *From* 9·00
Plate Nos. 17, 18, 19, 20.
Z220 2½d. blue (1881) .. .. .. .. .. 7·50
Plate Nos. 21, 22, 23.
Z221 3d. rose (1867–73) .. .. .. .. 25·00
Plate Nos. 5, 7, 9, 10.
Z222 3d. rose (1873–76) (Plate No. 14) .. ..
Z223 4d. vermilion (1865–73) .. .. .. 26·00
Plate Nos. 12, 13, 14.
Z224 4d. vermilion (1876) (Plate No. 15) .. .. £150
Z225 4d. sage-green (1877) .. .. .. .. 90·00
Plate Nos. 15, 16.
Z226 4d. grey-brown (1880) *wmk* Large Garter (Plate No. 17)
Z227 4d. grey-brown (1880) *wmk* Crown (Plate Nos. 17, 18) .. .. .. *From* 25·00
Z228 6d. buff (1872–73) .. .. .. *From* 70·00
Plate Nos. 11, 12.
Z229 6d. chestnut (1872) (Plate No. 11) .. ..
Z230 6d. grey (1873) (Plate No. 12) .. .. .. 75·00
Z231 6d. grey (1874–80) .. .. .. *From* 22·00
Plate Nos. 13, 14, 15, 16, 17.
Z232 6d. grey (1881–82) (Plate Nos. 17, 18) .. .. 50·00
Z233 6d. on 6d. lilac (1883) .. .. .. .. 70·00
Z234 8d. orange (1876) .. .. .. ..
Z235 9d. straw (1867) .. .. .. .. £180
Z236 10d. red-brown (1867) .. .. .. .. £130
Z237 1s. green (1867–73) (Plate Nos. 6, 7) .. ..
Z238 1s. green (1873–77) .. .. .. *From* 27·00
Plate Nos. 8, 9, 10, 11, 12, 13.
Z239 1s. orange-brown (1880) (Plate No. 13) .. £160
Z240 1s. orange-brown (1881) (Plate Nos. 13, 14) .. 40·00
Z241 5s. rose (1867–74) (Plate No. 2) .. ..

**1880.**
Z242 ½d. deep green .. .. .. .. .. 4·50
Z243 ½d. pale green .. .. .. .. .. 5·50
Z244 1d. Venetian red .. .. .. .. 7·00
Z245 1½d. Venetian red .. .. .. .. 70·00
Z246 2d. pale rose .. .. .. .. .. 32·00
Z247 2d. deep rose .. .. .. .. .. 32·00
Z248 5d. indigo .. .. .. .. .. 50·00

**1881.**
Z249 1d. lilac (16 *dots*) .. .. .. .. 3·75

**1884.**
Z250 ½d. slate-blue .. .. .. .. .. 6·00
Z251 2d. lilac .. .. .. .. ..
Z252 2½d. lilac .. .. .. .. ..
Z253 4d. dull green .. .. .. ..
Z254 5d. dull green .. .. .. ..
Z255 1s. dull green .. .. .. ..

**1887.**
Z256 ½d. vermilion .. .. .. .. ..
Z257 1½d. dull purple and pale green .. ..
Z258 2d. grey-green and carmine .. ..
Z259 2½d. purple/*blue* .. .. .. ..
Z260 3d. purple/*yellow* .. .. .. ..
Z261 4d. green and brown .. .. ..
Z262 5d. dull purple and blue (Die II) .. ..
Z263 6d. purple/*rose-red* .. .. .. ..
Z264 1s. dull green .. .. .. ..

**1900.**
Z265 ½d. blue-green .. .. .. ..
Z266 1s. green and carmine .. .. ..

**1902–04.** *De La Rue ptgs.*
Z267 ½d. blue-green .. .. .. ..
Z268 ½d. yellowish green .. .. ..
Z269 1d. scarlet .. .. .. ..
Z270 1½d. purple and green .. .. ..
Z271 2d. green and carmine-red .. ..
Z272 2½d. ultramarine .. .. .. ..
Z273 3d. purple/*orange-yellow* .. ..
Z274 4d. green and brown .. .. ..
Z275 5d. purple and ultramarine .. ..
Z276 6d. purple .. .. .. ..
Z277 9d. purple and ultramarine .. ..
Z278 10d. purple and carmine .. ..
Z279 1s. green and carmine .. ..
Z280 2s. 6d. purple .. .. ..
Z281 5s. carmine .. .. ..

### STAMBOUL (CONSTANTINOPLE)

*Stamps of* GREAT BRITAIN *cancelled* "S" *as Type* **10**, *or circular postmarks inscribed either* "BRITISH POST OFFICE CONSTANTINOPLE S" *or* "BRITISH POST OFFICE STAMBOUL" *as Type* **18**.

**1884.**
Z296 ½d. slate-blue .. .. .. .. 15·00
Z297 1d. lilac .. .. .. .. 7·00
Z298 2d. lilac .. .. .. ..
Z299 2½d. lilac .. .. .. .. 9·00
Z300 5d. dull green .. .. .. .. 80·00

**1887–92.**
Z306 ½d. vermilion .. .. .. ..
Z307 1½d. dull purple and pale green .. ..
Z308 2d. grey-green and carmine .. ..
Z309 2½d. purple/*blue* .. .. ..
Z310 3d. purple/*yellow* .. .. ..
Z311 4d. green and brown .. ..
Z312 4½d. green and carmine .. ..
Z313 5d. dull purple and blue (Die II) ..
Z314 6d. purple/*rose-red* .. .. ..
Z315 9d. dull purple and blue .. ..
Z316 10d. purple and carmine .. ..
Z317 1s. dull green .. .. ..

The "S" cancellation was in use from 1885 to 1891 and the "Stamboul" mark from 1892 to 1896, when the office was closed, and from its reopening in 1908 to 1914. The "CONSTANTINOPLE S" handstamp was normally used as a back stamp, but can be found cancelling stamps in the period 1885 to 1892.

| PRICES FOR STAMPS ON COVER | |
|---|---|
| Nos. 1/3*a* | *from* × 8 |
| Nos. 4/6*a* | *from* × 5 |
| Nos. 7/40 | *from* × 3 |
| Nos. L1/10 | *from* × 6 |
| Nos. L11/17 | *from* × 3 |

### I. TURKISH CURRENCY

Following the depreciation of the Turkish piastre against sterling in 1884 it was decided to issue stamps surcharged in Turkish currency to avoid speculation. During the early period unsurcharged stamps of Great Britain remained on sale from the British Post Offices at the current rate of exchange until replaced by "LEVANT" overprints.

**80 PARAS** (1) **4 PIASTRES** (2) **12 PIASTRES** (3)

***Stamps of Great Britain (Queen Victoria) surch as T 1 to 3***

**PRINTERS.** Nos. 1/24 were surcharged or overprinted by De La Rue, *unless otherwise stated.*

**1885** (1 Apr).
1 **64** 40 pa. on 2½d. lilac .. .. .. 65·00 75
2 **62** 80 pa. on 5d. green .. .. .. £180 9·50
3 **58** 12 pi. on 2s. 6d. lilac/*bluish* .. .. £250 £200
a. On white paper .. .. .. 38·00 £200

**1887** (June)–**96.**
4 **74** 40 pa. on 2½d. purple/*blue* .. .. 1·75 10
a. Surch double .. .. .. £1800 £2500
5 **78** 80 pa. on 5d. purple and blue (6.90) .. 9·00 25
a. Small "0" in "80" .. .. .. £130 75·00
6 **81** 4 pi. on 10d. dull purple and carmine (11.96) .. .. .. 28·00 10·00
*a. Dull purple and deep bright carmine* .. .. .. 28·00 11·00
b. Large, wide "4" .. .. .. 90·00 55·00

No. 5a occurs twice on each sheet in positions R.4/1 and R.4/7 of both the upper and the lower pane.

**1893** (25 Feb). *Roughly handstamped at Constantinople, as T* **1**.
7 **71** 40 pa. on ½d. vermilion .. .. .. £400 £100

This provisional was in use for five days only at the Constantinople and Stamboul offices. As fraudulent copies were made with the original handstamp, and can be found "used" on piece cancelled by fraudulent use of the usual canceller, this stamp should only be purchased from undoubted sources. It is also known with genuine handstamp inverted (*Price £650 unused. £250 used*).

**1902–5.** *Stamps of King Edward VII surch as T* **1** *to* **3**.
8 **86** 40 pa. on 2½d. ultramarine (3.02) .. 4·50 10
*a. Pale ultramarine* .. .. .. 4·50 10
ab. Surch double .. .. .. † £2000
9 **89** 80 pa. on 5d. purple & ultramarine (5.6.02) 3·00 85
a. Small "0" in "80" .. .. .. £180 £190
10 **92** 4 pi. on 10d. dull purple & carm (6.9.02) 8·50 4·00
a. No cross on crown .. .. .. 90·00 90·00
b. Chalk-surfaced paper .. .. 6·00 8·50
ba. Chalk-surfaced paper. No cross on crown .. .. .. 85·00 £100
11 **94** 12 pi. on 2s. 6d. lilac (29.8.03) .. .. 25·00 32·00
a. Chalk-surfaced paper. *Pale dull pur* 60·00 70·00
b. Chalk-surfaced paper. *Dull purple* 28·00 32·00
12 **95** 24 pi. on 5s. carmine (15.8.05) .. .. 30·00 48·00
8/12 .. .. .. .. *Set of* 5 60·00 80·00
9/11 Optd "Specimen" .. .. *Set of* 3 £150

No. 9a only occurs on the first printing of 80 pa. on 5d.

**1 PIASTRE** (4)

**1905–08.** *Surch in* "PIASTRES" *instead of* "PARAS" *as T* **4** *and* **2**.
13 **86** 1 pi. on 2½d. ultramarine (17.4.06) .. 3·25 10
14 **89** 2 pi. on 5d. dull purple & ultram (11.11.05) 11·00 2·00
a. Chalk-surfaced paper (1.08) .. 10·00 1·50
*ab. Slate-purple and ultramarine* .. 17·00 6·00

**1 Piastre** (5) **1 PIASTRE 10 PARAS** (6)

**1906** (2 July). *Issued at Beyrout. No. L4 surch with T* **5** *by American Press, Beyrout.*
15 **85** 1 pi. on 2d. grey-green and carmine .. £1300 £600

**1909** (16 Nov–Dec.) *Stamps of King Edward VII surch as T* **1** (*30 pa.*), **6**, *and* **2** (*5 pi*). *Ordinary paper (No. 19) or chalk-surfaced paper (others).*
16 **84** 30 pa. on 1½d. pale dull purple and green 4·00 1·25
a. Surch double, one albino ..
17 **87** 1 pi. 10 pa. on 3d. dull purple/*orange-yell* 7·00 18·00
18 **88** 1 pi. 30 pa. on 4d. green & chocolate-brn 6·00 14·00
19 1 pi. 30 pa. on 4d. pale orange (16.12.09) 8·50 20·00
20 **83** 2 pi. 20 pa. on 6d. dull purple .. 15·00 38·00
21 **93** 5 pi. on 1s. dull grn & carm (Optd S. £60) 3·75 6·00
16/21 .. .. .. .. *Set of* 6 40·00 85·00

**1¾ PIASTRE** (7) **4** Normal "4" **4** Pointed "4"

**1910** (24 Jan). *Stamps of King Edward VII surch as T* **7**. *Chalk-surfaced paper (Nos. 22 and 24).*
22 **87** 1¼ pi. on 3d. dull purple/*orange-yellow* .. 40 1·00
23 **88** 1¾ pi. on 4d. pale orange .. .. 40 60
*a. Orange-red* .. .. .. 2·25 3·50
b. Thin, pointed "4" in fraction .. 7·00 25·00
24 **83** 2½ pi. on 6d. dull purple .. .. 90 65
22/4 .. .. .. .. *Set of* 3 1·50 2·00

No. 23b occurs in the first and seventh vertical rows of the sheet. The variety also occurs on No. 38, but not on No. 38b.

**1 PIASTRE** (8) **1 PIASTRE** (9)

**TYPE DIFFERENCES.** In T **4** the letters are tall and narrow and the space enclosed by the upper part of the "A" is small.

In T **8** the opening of the "A" is similar but the letters are shorter and broader, the "P" and the "E" being particularly noticeable.

In T **9** the letters are short and broad, but the "A" is thin and open.

**1911–13.** *Stamps of King Edward VII, Harrison or Somerset House ptgs, surch at Somerset House.*

(*a*) *Surch with T* **4** (20 July)
25 **86** 1 pi. on 2½d. bright blue (*perf* 14) .. 4·25 3·00
a. Surch double, one albino .. £200
26 1 pi. on 2½d. bright blue (*perf* 15×14) (14.10.11) .. .. .. 6·00 1·75
*a. Dull blue* .. .. .. 6·00 1·25

(*b*) *Surch with T* **8**
27 **86** 1 pi. on 2½d. bright blue (*perf* 15×14) (3.12) .. .. .. 10·00 2·00
*a. Dull blue* .. .. .. 14·00 3·00

(*c*) *Surch with T* **9** (7.12)
28 **86** 1 pi. on 2½d. bright blue (*perf* 15×14) 30·00 45
*a. Dull blue* .. .. .. 30·00 45

(*d*) *Surch with T* **1** *to* **3** (1911–13)
29 **84** 30 pa. on 1½d. reddish purple and bright green (22.8.11) .. .. .. 4·25 55
*a. Slate-purple and green* .. .. 5·50 2·25
b. Surch double, one albino .. 50·00
30 **89** 2 pi. on 5d. dull reddish purple and bright blue (13.5.12) .. .. 3·25 1·50
*a. Deep dull reddish purple and bright blue* .. .. .. 4·00 2·00
31 **92** 4 pi. on 10d. dull purple & scar (26.6.12) 15·00 8·00
*a. Dull reddish purple & aniline pink* £180 70·00
*b. Dull reddish purple and carmine* 9·00 11·00
c. No cross on crown .. ..
32 **93** 5 pi. on 1s. green and carmine (1913) .. 11·00 5·00
a. Surch double, one albino .. £200
33 **94** 12 pi. on 2s. 6d. dull reddish pur (3.2.12) 90·00 £110
*a. Dull greyish purple* .. .. 35·00 30·00
*b. Pale dull reddish purple* .. 35·00 30·00
34 **95** 24 pi. on 5s. carmine (1913) .. .. 48·00 60·00
a. Surch double, one albino .. £200
29/34 .. .. .. .. *Set of* 6 £100 95·00

**1913** (Apr)–**14.** *Stamps of King George V, wmk Royal Cypher, surch as T* **1** (*30 pa.*), **9** (*1 pi.*), **7** *or* **2** (*4 and 5 pi.*).
35 **105** 30 pa. on 1½d. red-brown (4.13) .. 3·00 6·00
a. Surch double, one albino .. £100
36 **104** 1 pi. on 2½d. cobalt-blue (6.13) .. 1·50 10
*a. Bright blue* .. .. .. 1·00 15
37 **106** 1¼ pi. on 3d. dull reddish violet (9.13) .. 1·50 4·25
*a. Violet* .. .. .. .. 2·00 5·00
b. Surch double, one albino .. £300
38 1¾ pi. on 4d. deep grey-green (7.13) .. 3·00 5·50
a. Thin, pointed "4" in fraction .. 45·00 80·00
*b. Grey-green* .. .. .. 2·50 5·00
39 **108** 4 pi. on 10d. turquoise-blue (12.13) .. 5·00 12·00
40 5 pi. on 1s. bistre-brown (1.14) .. 19·00 45·00
35/40 .. .. .. .. *Set of* 6 29·00 65·00

### II. BRITISH CURRENCY

Stamps overprinted "LEVANT", were for use on parcels, newspapers and printed matter. The face values were left in sterling to simplify accounting with the steamship and railway companies involved in the transmission of these classes of mail. They replaced those unoverprinted Great Britain stamps which had remained on sale from the Levant Post Offices after the introduction of the Turkish currency surcharges.

**LEVANT** (L 1)

**1905** (15 Aug)–**12.** *Stamps of King Edward VII optd with Type* L **1**.

(*a*) *De La Rue ptgs*
L 1 **83** ½d. pale yellowish green .. .. 1·50 15
*a. Yellowish green* .. .. .. 1·50 15
L 2 1d. scarlet .. .. .. .. 1·25 15
*a. Bright scarlet* .. .. .. 2·00 90
L 3 **84** 1½d. dull purple and green .. .. 4·50 1·50
a. Chalk-surfaced paper .. .. 11·00 2·00
L 4 **85** 2d. grey-green and carmine .. .. 3·00 13·00
a. Chalk-surfaced paper .. .. 2·00 6·00
*ab. Pale blue-green and carmine* .. 3·00 7·00
L 5 **86** 2½d. ultramarine .. .. .. 7·50 17·00
L 6 **87** 3d. purple/*orange-yellow* .. .. 5·50 13·00
L 7 **88** 4d. grey-green and brown .. .. 7·00 16·00
*a. Green and chocolate-brown* .. 9·00 16·00
L 8 **89** 5d. dull purple and ultramarine .. 14·00 25·00
L 9 **83** 6d. pale dull purple .. .. 11·00 25·00
L10 **93** 1s. dull green and carmine .. .. 25·00 30·00
a. Chalk-surfaced paper .. .. 25·00 30·00
L1/10 .. .. .. .. *Set of* 10 70·00 £120

*(b) Harrison ptgs optd at Somerset House*

L11 **83** ½d. dull yellow-green (*p.* 14) (2.12) .. 7·00 10·00
*a. Dull green* .. .. .. 7·00 10·00
*b. Deep dull green* .. .. .. 7·00 10·00

On 28 December 1909 all values, except for the ½d., 1d. and 2d. stamps, were withdrawn from sale. Subsequent dated cancellations on the withdrawn values are philatelic, being worth only a fraction of the used prices quoted.

**ANT**

Distorted "N" (R. 2/10, 12/10)

**1911–13.** *Stamps of King George V optd with Type* L 1 *at Somerset House. (a) Die A. Wmk Crown.*

L12 **98** ½d. green (No. 322) (12.9.11) .. 40 90
a. Distorted "N" .. .. 15·00
L13 **99** 1d. carmine-red (No. 327) (1.1.12) 40 3·75
a. No cross on crown .. £150
b. Opt double, one albino .. £100
c. Distorted "N" .. .. 15·00

*(b) Redrawn types. Wmk Crown*

L14 **101** ½d. green (No. 339) (21.3.12) .. 25 10
*a. Yellow-green* .. .. 50 15
b. Distorted "N" .. .. 12·00
L15 **102** 1d. bright scarlet (No. 341) (24.2.12) 25 20
*a. Scarlet* (No. 342) .. .. 60 20
b. Opt triple, two albino .. .. 50·00
c. Distorted "N" .. .. 12·00

*(c) New types. Wmk Royal Cypher (7.13)*

L16 **105** ½d. green (No. 351) .. .. 15 25
*a. Yellow-green* .. .. 20 50
b. Distorted "N" .. .. 10·00
L17 **104** 1d. scarlet (No. 357) .. .. 15 1·75
*a. Vermilion* .. .. 1·50 2·75
b. Distorted "N" .. .. 10·00

Similar overprints were issued when the British Post Offices reopened in 1919, and are listed below.

## B. BRITISH POST OFFICES IN CONSTANTINOPLE AND SMYRNA, 1919–1923

### CONSTANTINOPLE

Following the occupation of Constantinople by Allied forces a British Military Post Office was opened for civilian use on 4 February 1919. During the period of its existence stamps of Great Britain with face values to 10s. were available and such use can be identified by the following cancellations:

"FIELD POST OFFICE H12" (4 February 1919 to 18 March 1919)
"ARMY POST OFFICE Y" (20 March 1919 to May 1920)
"ARMY POST OFFICE S.X.3" (April 1919 to August 1920)
"BRITISH A.P.O. CONSTANTINOPLE" (5 July 1919 to 1 Sept 1920).

Of these four marks the first two types were also used for military mail.

The office reverted to civilian control in July 1920, Nos. 41/50 and L18/24 being intended for its use.

Z 1 Z 2

Z 3 Z 4

**1919–20.** *Used at the Army Post Office. Stamps of* GREAT BRITAIN *cancelled with Types* Z 1, Z 2, Z 3, Z 4.

Z176 ½d. green
Z177 1d. scarlet
Z178 1½d. brown
Z179 2d. orange (Die I)
Z180 2½d. blue
Z181 4d. grey-green
Z182 6d. purple
Z183 9d. agate
Z184 1s. bistre
Z185 2s. 6d. brown
Z186 5s. rose-red
Z187 10s. dull grey-blue

**1920–21.** *Used at the Civilian Post Office. Stamps of* GREAT BRITAIN *cancelled with Type* 18 *or double-circle datestamp.*

Z188 ½d. green
Z189 1d. scarlet
Z190 1½d. brown
Z191 2d. orange (Die I)
Z192 2½d. blue
Z193 3d. violet
Z194 4d. grey-green
Z195 5d. brown
Z196 6d. purple
Z197 10d. turquoise-blue
Z198 1s. bistre
Z199 2s. 6d. brown
Z200 5s. rose-red
Z201 10s. dull grey-blue

### SMYRNA

When the office re-opened on 1 March 1919 existing stocks of surcharged or overprinted issues were utilised until they were exhausted in mid-1920. During this period examples of Nos. 24, 29*a*, 30*a*, 33*b*/7, 39/40, L4*b*, L14/17 are known with commercial postmarks. These stamps were supplemented and finally replaced in mid-1920 by ordinary stamps of Great Britain.

*Stamps of* GREAT BRITAIN *cancelled with circular postmark as Type* 18 *or with* "REGISTERED" *oval.*

Z282 ½d. green
Z283 1d. scarlet
Z284 1½d. brown
Z285 2d. orange (Die I)
Z286 2d. orange (Die II)
Z287 2½d. blue
Z288 2½d. dull Prussian blue
Z289 4d. grey-green
Z290 6d. purple
Z291 10d. turquoise-blue
Z292 1s. bistre
Z293 2s. 6d. brown
Z294 5s. rose-red
Z295 10s. dull grey-blue

**PRICES FOR STAMPS ON COVER**

| | |
|---|---|
| Nos. 41/50 | *from* × 2 |
| Nos. L18/24 | *from* × 5 |

***Stamps of Great Britain surch at Somerset House***

I. TURKISH CURRENCY

**1½ PIASTRES** (10) **15 PIASTRES** (11)

**18¾**

Short hyphen bar (R. 4/12, 14/12.)

**1921** (Aug). *Stamps of King George V, wmk Royal Cypher, surch as T* 1 *(30 pa.),* 10 *and* 11 *(15 and 18¾ pi.).*

41 **105** 30 pa. on ½d. green .. .. 30 4·00
*a. Yellow-green* .. .. 50 5·50
42 **104** 1½ pi. on 1d. bright scarlet .. 30 10
*a. Vermilion* .. .. 1·00 1·00
*b. Scarlet-vermilion* .. .. 70 90
43 3¾ pi. on 2½d. blue .. .. 60 25
*a. Dull Prussian blue* .. 10·00 2·00
44 **106** 4½ pi. on 3d. violet .. .. 1·25 2·75
*a. Bluish violet* .. .. 1·60 2·50
45 **107** 7½ pi. on 5d. brown .. .. 30 10
*a. Yellow-brown* .. .. 55 20
46 **108** 15 pi. on 10d. turquoise-blue .. 45 15
47 18¾ pi. on 1s. bistre-brown .. 3·75 3·75
a. Short hyphen bar .. 50·00
*b. Olive-bistre* .. .. 3·75 4·50
ba. Short hyphen bar .. 50·00

**45 PIASTRES** (12) **45** Joined figures (second stamp in each horiz row)

**1921.** *Stamps of King George V (Bradbury, Wilkinson printing) surch as T* 12.

48 **109** 45 pi. on 2s. 6d. chocolate-brown .. 20·00 40·00
a. Joined figures .. .. 27·00 50·00
*b. Olive-brown* .. .. 48·00 60·00
ba. Joined figures .. .. 60·00 75·00
49 90 pi. on 5s. rose-red .. .. 25·00 30·00
50 180 pi. on 10s. dull grey-blue .. 45·00 40·00
a. Opt double, one albino
41/50 .. .. .. *Set of* 10 85·00 £110
47/50 Optd "Specimen" .. *Set of* 4 £225

II. BRITISH CURRENCY

**1921.** *Stamps of King George V optd as Type* L 1.

L18 **106** 2d. reddish orange (Die I) .. 1·25 16·00
*a. Bright orange* .. .. 2·00 16·00
L19 3d. bluish violet .. .. 7·50 10·00
L20 4d. grey-green .. .. 4·50 13·00
L21 **107** 5d. yellow-brown .. .. 9·00 19·00
L22 6d. dull purple (*chalk-surfaced paper*) 17·00 24·00
*a. Reddish purple* .. .. 15·00 8·00
L23 **108** 1s. bistre-brown (Optd S. £65) .. 10·00 6·50
*a. Olive-bistre* .. .. 10·00 6·50
L24 **109** 2s. 6d. chocolate-brown (Optd S. £130) 35·00 65·00
*a. Olive-brown* .. .. 65·00 95·00
L18/24 .. .. .. *Set of* 7 70·00 £120

On No. L24 the letters of the overprint are shorter, being only 3 mm high.

Nos. 41/50 and L18/24 were used at the Constantinople office only.

## C. BRITISH FIELD OFFICE IN SALONICA

These overprints were originally prepared for use by a civilian post office to be set up on Mt Athos, Northern Greece. When the project was abandoned they were placed on sale at the Army Field Office in Salonica.

**PRICES FOR STAMPS ON COVER**

| | |
|---|---|
| Nos. S1/8 | *from* × 10 |

**Levant**

(S 1)

**1916** (end Feb–9 Mar). *Stamps of Gt. Britain, optd with Type* S 1 *by Army Printing Office, Salonica.*

S 1 **105** ½d. green .. .. 22·00 80·00
a. Opt double .. .. £1700 £2000
b. Vert pair, one without opt .. £800 £1000
S 2 **104** 1d. scarlet .. .. 22·00 80·00
a. Opt double .. .. £1000 £1300
S 3 **106** 2d. reddish orange (Die I) .. 85·00 £180
S 4 3d. bluish violet .. .. 75·00 £180
a. Opt double
S 5 4d. grey-green .. .. 85·00 £180
S 6 **107** 6d. reddish pur (*chalk-surfaced paper*) 55·00 £140
a. Vert pair, one without opt .. £900 £1200
S 7 **108** 9d. agate .. .. £250 £450
a. Opt double .. .. £6500 £6500
S 8 1s. bistre-brown .. .. £200 £400
S1/8 .. .. .. *Set of* 8 £700 £1500

There are numerous forgeries of this overprint.

All values can be found with an additional albino overprint, inverted on the gummed side.

# British New Guinea

*see* Papua New Guinea

# British Occupation of Iraq

*see* Iraq

# British Occupation of Italian Colonies

**PRICES FOR STAMPS ON COVER TO 1945**

| | |
|---|---|
| Nos. M1/21 | *from* × 4 |
| Nos. MD1/5 | *from* × 10 |
| Nos. S1/9 | *from* × 4 |

The above prices refer to covers from the territories concerned, not examples used in Great Britain.

## MIDDLE EAST FORCES

For use in territory occupied by British Forces in Eritrea (1942), Italian Somaliland (1942), Cyrenaica (1943), Tripolitania (1943), and some of the Dodecanese Islands (1945).

**PRICES.** Our prices for used stamps with "M.E.F." overprints are for specimens with identifiable postmarks of the territories in which they were issued. These stamps were also used in the United Kingdom with official sanction, from the summer of 1950 onwards, and with U.K. postmarks are worth about 25 per cent less.

**PRINTERS.** Considerable research has been undertaken to discover the origins of Nos. M1/10. It is now suggested that Nos. M1/5, previously assigned to Harrison and Sons, were produced by the Army Printing Services, Cairo, and that the smaller printing, Nos. M6/10, previously identified as the work of the Army Printing Services, Cairo, was from an unidentified printer within the Middle East Forces area.

M.E.F. (M 1) — Opt. 14 mm long. Regular lettering and upright oblong stops.

M.E.F. (M 2) — Opt. 13½ mm long. Regular lettering and square stops.

M.E.F. (M 2*a*) — Opt. 13½ mm long. Rough lettering and round stops.

(*Illustrations twice actual size*)

M.E.F. — Sliced "M" (R.6/10)

**1942** (2 Mar). *Stamps of Great Britain optd. W* **127**. *P* 15 × 14.

(*a*) *With Type* M 1

| No. | Type | Description | Unused | Used |
|---|---|---|---|---|
| M 1 | 128 | 1d. scarlet (No. 463) | 35 | 40 |
| | | a. Sliced "M" | | |
| M 2 | | 2d. orange (No. 465) | 15 | 90 |
| | | a. Sliced "M" | | |
| M 3 | | 2½d. ultramarine (No. 466) | 15 | 15 |
| | | a. Sliced "M" | | |
| M 4 | | 3d. violet (No. 467) | 15 | 10 |
| | | a. Opt double | — | £1500 |
| | | b. Sliced "M" | | |
| M 5 | 129 | 5d. brown | 15 | 15 |
| | | a. Sliced "M" | | |

(*b*) *With Type* M 2

| No. | Type | Description | Unused | Used |
|---|---|---|---|---|
| M 6 | 128 | 1d. scarlet (No. 463) | 25·00 | 6·50 |
| | | a. Optd. with Type M **2*a*** | 22·00 | 6·00 |
| | | b. Nos. M6/a *se-tenant* vert | 75·00 | 45·00 |
| M 7 | | 2d. orange (No. 465) | 35·00 | 35·00 |
| | | a. Optd with Type M **2*a*** | 28·00 | 28·00 |
| | | b. Nos. M7/a *se-tenant* vert | £120 | 90·00 |
| M 8 | | 2½d. ultramarine (No. 466) | 18·00 | 6·50 |
| | | a. Optd with Type M **2*a*** | 15·00 | 5·00 |
| | | b. Nos. M8/a *se-tenant* vert | 70·00 | 38·00 |
| M 9 | | 3d. violet (No. 467) | 50·00 | 17·00 |
| | | a. Optd with Type M **2*a*** | 40·00 | 14·00 |
| | | b. Nos. M9/a *se-tenant* vert | £160 | 70·00 |
| M10 | 129 | 5d. brown | £160 | 50·00 |
| | | a. Optd with Type M **2*a*** | £150 | 45·00 |
| | | b. Nos. M10/a *se-tenant* vert | £500 | £275 |

See note after No. M21.

Nos. M6/10 were issued in panes of 60 (6 × 10), rows 2, 3, and 7 being overprinted with Type M **2** and the other seven rows with Type M **2*a***.

M.E.F. (M 3) — Optd 13½ mm long. Regular lettering and upright oblong stops.

(*Illustration twice actual size*)

**1943** (1 Jan)–**1947**. *Stamps of Great Britain optd with Type* M **3** *by Harrison & Sons. W* **127**, *P* 15 × 14 (1d. to 1s.); *W* **133**, *P* 14 (*others*).

| No. | Type | Description | Unused | Used |
|---|---|---|---|---|
| M11 | 128 | 1d. pale scarlet (No. 486) | 60 | 10 |
| M12 | | 2d. pale orange (No. 488) | 60 | 10 |
| M13 | | 2½d. light ultramarine (No. 489) | 30 | 10 |
| M14 | | 3d. pale violet (No. 490) | 55 | 10 |
| M15 | 129 | 5d. brown | 75 | 10 |
| M16 | | 6d. purple | 30 | 10 |
| M17 | 130 | 9d. deep olive-green | 75 | 10 |
| M18 | | 1s. bistre-brown | 50 | 10 |
| M19 | 131 | 2s. 6d. yellow-green | 6·00 | 30 |
| M20 | | 5s. red (1947) | 11·00 | 17·00 |
| M21 | 132 | 10s. ultramarine (1947) | 14·00 | 8·00 |
| M11/21 | | *Set of* 11 | 32·00 | 23·00 |
| M18/21 Optd "Specimen" | | *Set of* 4 | £600 | |

The overprint on No. M15 should not be confused with the other overprints on the 5d. value. It can be distinguished from No. M5 by the ½ mm difference in length; and from No. M10 by the more intense colour, thicker lettering and larger stops.

POSTAGE DUE STAMPS

M.E.F. (MD 1)

**1942.** *Postage Due Stamps of Great Britain optd with Type* MD **1**, *in blue-black. W* **127** (*sideways*). *P* 14 × 15.

| No. | Type | Description | Unused | Used |
|---|---|---|---|---|
| MD1 | D 1 | ½d. emerald | 30 | 2·75 |
| MD2 | | 1d. carmine | 30 | 1·25 |
| MD3 | | 2d. agate | 1·25 | 1·00 |
| MD4 | | 3d. violet | 50 | 2·75 |
| MD5 | | 1s. deep blue (Optd S. £150) | 2·50 | 5·50 |
| MD1/5 | | *Set of* 5 | 4·25 | 12·00 |



## CYRENAICA

In June 1949 the British authorities recognised the leader of the Senussi, Amir Mohammed Idris Al-Senussi, as Amir of Cyrenaica with autonomy in internal affairs.

**(Currency. 1000 millièmes = 1 Egyptian pound)**

24 Mounted Warrior 25

(Recess Waterlow)

**1950** (16 Jan). *P* 12½.

| No. | Type | Description | Unused | Used |
|---|---|---|---|---|
| 136 | 24 | 1 m brown | 15 | 40 |
| 137 | | 2 m. carmine | 30 | 40 |
| 138 | | 3 m. orange-yellow | 30 | 40 |
| 139 | | 4 m. blue-green | 1·00 | 2·25 |
| 140 | | 5 m. grey-black | 40 | 55 |
| 141 | | 8 m. orange | 40 | 45 |
| 142 | | 10 m. violet | 45 | 45 |
| 143 | | 12 m. scarlet | 45 | 45 |
| 144 | | 20 m. blue | 50 | 50 |
| 145 | 25 | 50 m. ultramarine and purple-brown | 1·90 | 2·75 |
| 146 | | 100 m. carmine and black | 6·00 | 8·50 |
| 147 | | 200 m. violet and deep blue | 9·50 | 23·00 |
| 148 | | 500 m. orange-yellow and green | 32·00 | 55·00 |
| 136/148 | | *Set of* 13 | 48·00 | 85·00 |

POSTAGE DUE STAMPS

D 26

(Recess Waterlow)

**1950** (16 Jan). *P* 12½

| No. | Type | Description | Unused | Used |
|---|---|---|---|---|
| D149 | D 26 | 2 m. brown | 40·00 | 48·00 |
| D150 | | 4 m. blue-green | 40·00 | 48·00 |
| D151 | | 8 m. scarlet | 40·00 | 48·00 |
| D152 | | 10 m. orange | 40·00 | 48·00 |
| D153 | | 20 m. orange-yellow | 40·00 | 48·00 |
| D154 | | 40 m. blue | 40·00 | 48·00 |
| D155 | | 100 m. grey-brown | 40·00 | 48·00 |
| D149/155 | | *Set of* 7 | £250 | £300 |

On 24 December 1951 Cyrenaica united with Tripolitania, Fezzan and Ghadames to form the independent Kingdom of Libya, whose issues are listed in Part 13 (*Africa since Independence F—M*) of this catalogue.

## ERITREA

From early 1950 examples of Nos. E1/32 exist precancelled in manuscript by a black or blue horizontal line for use by British troops on concession rate mail.

BRITISH MILITARY ADMINISTRATION

B.M.A. ERITREA 10 CENTS (E 1)

B.M.A. ERITREA 5 SHILLINGS (E 2)

Normal Misplaced Stop

**1948–9.** *Stamps of Great Britain surch as Types* E **1** *or* E **2**.

| No. | Type | Description | Unused | Used |
|---|---|---|---|---|
| E 1 | 128 | 5 c. on ½d. pale green | 30 | 65 |
| E 2 | | 10 c. on 1d. pale scarlet | 40 | 1·75 |
| E 3 | | 20 c. on 2d. pale orange | 45 | 2·25 |
| E 4 | | 25 c. on 2½d. light ultramarine | 30 | 60 |
| E 5 | | 30 c. on 3d. pale violet | 85 | 3·00 |
| E 6 | 129 | 40 c. on 5d. brown | 30 | 2·50 |
| E 7 | | 50 c. on 6d. purple | 30 | 60 |
| E 7*a* | 130 | 65 c. on 8d. bright carmine (1.2.49) | 5·00 | 2·00 |
| E 8 | | 75 c. on 9d. deep olive-green | 50 | 75 |
| E 9 | | 1 s. on 1s. bistre-brown | 50 | 50 |
| E10 | 131 | 2 s. 50 c. on 2s. 6d. yellow-green | 5·00 | 10·00 |
| | | a. Misplaced stop (R. 4/7) | 55·00 | |
| E11 | | 5 s. on 5s. red | 5·00 | 13·00 |
| E12 | 132 | 10 s. on 10s. ultramarine | 10·00 | 17·00 |
| E1/12 | | *Set of* 13 | 26·00 | 48·00 |

BRITISH ADMINISTRATION

**1950** (6 Feb). *As Nos.* E1/12, *but surch* "B.A. ERITREA" *and new values instead of* "B.M.A." *etc.*

| No. | Type | Description | Unused | Used |
|---|---|---|---|---|
| E13 | 128 | 5 c. on ½d. pale green | 30 | 3·75 |
| E14 | | 10 c. on 1d. pale scarlet | 30 | 1·50 |
| E15 | | 20 c. on 2d. pale orange | 30 | 70 |
| E16 | | 25 c. on 2½d. light ultramarine | 30 | 60 |
| E17 | 128 | 30 c. on 3d. pale violet | 30 | 70 |
| E18 | 129 | 40 c. on 5d. brown | 40 | 80 |
| E19 | | 50 c. on 6d. purple | 30 | 20 |
| E20 | 130 | 65 c. on 8d. bright carmine | 40 | 1·00 |
| E21 | | 75 c. on 9d. deep olive-green | 30 | 25 |
| E22 | | 1 s. on 1s. bistre-brown | 30 | 15 |
| E23 | 131 | 2 s. 50 c. on 2s. 6d. yellow-green | 3·25 | 4·50 |
| E24 | | 5 s. on 5s. red | 5·50 | 9·00 |
| E25 | 132 | 10 s. on 10s. ultramarine | 30·00 | 35·00 |
| E13/25 | | *Set of* 13 | 38·00 | 50·00 |

**1951** (3 May). *Nos.* 503/4, 506/7 *and* 509/11 *of Great Britain surch* "B.A. ERITREA" *and new values.*

| No. | Type | Description | Unused | Used |
|---|---|---|---|---|
| E26 | 128 | 5 c. on ½d. pale orange | 30 | 50 |
| E27 | | 10 c. on 1d. light ultramarine | 30 | 35 |
| E28 | | 20 c. on 2d. pale red-brown | 30 | 25 |
| E29 | | 25 c. on 2½d. pale scarlet | 30 | 25 |
| E30 | 147 | 2 s. 50 c. on 2s. 6d. yellow-green | 5·00 | 8·00 |
| E31 | 148 | 5 s. on 5s. red | 14·00 | 16·00 |
| E32 | | 10 s. on 10s. ultramarine | 14·00 | 16·00 |
| E26/32 | | *Set of* 7 | 30·00 | 38·00 |

POSTAGE DUE STAMPS

B. M. A. ERITREA 10 CENTS (ED 1)

**1948.** *Postage Due stamps of Great Britain surch as Type* ED **1**.

| No. | Type | Description | Unused | Used |
|---|---|---|---|---|
| ED1 | D 1 | 5 c. on ½d. emerald | 9·00 | 18·00 |
| ED2 | | 10 c. on 1d. carmine | 7·50 | 17·00 |
| | | a. No stop after "B" | 55·00 | |
| ED3 | | 20 c. on 2d. agate | 7·00 | 12·00 |
| | | a. No stop after "A" | 40·00 | |
| | | b. No stop after "B" (R. 1/9) | 50·00 | |
| ED4 | | 30 c. on 3d. violet | 8·00 | 11·00 |
| ED5 | | 1 s. on 1s. deep blue | 15·00 | 20·00 |
| ED1/5 | | *Set of* 5 | 42·00 | 70·00 |

**1950** (6 Feb). *As Nos.* ED1/5, *but surch* "B.A. ERITREA" *and new values instead of* "B.M.A." *etc.*

| No. | Type | Description | Unused | Used |
|---|---|---|---|---|
| ED6 | D 1 | 5 c. on ½d. emerald | 10·00 | 24·00 |
| ED7 | | 10 c. on 1d. carmine | 8·00 | 14·00 |
| | | a. "C" of "CENTS" omitted | £950 | |
| | | ab. "C" omitted and vertical oblong for "E" of "CENTS" | | |
| ED8 | | 20 c. on 2d. agate | 9·00 | 12·00 |
| ED9 | | 30 c. on 3d. violet | 9·00 | 12·00 |
| ED10 | | 1 s. on 1s. deep blue | 14·00 | 20·00 |
| ED6/10 | | *Set of* 5 | 45·00 | 75·00 |

No. ED7a, and probably No. ED7ab, occurred on R.7/20, but the error was quickly corrected.

Stamps of Ethiopia were used in Eritrea after 15 September 1952 following federation with Ethiopia.

## SOMALIA

BRITISH OCCUPATION

E.A.F. (S 1. "East Africa Forces")

**1943** (15 Jan)–**46**. *Stamps of Great Britain optd with Type* S **1**, *in blue.*

| No. | Type | Description | Unused | Used |
|---|---|---|---|---|
| S1 | 128 | 1d. pale scarlet | 60 | 40 |
| S2 | | 2d. pale orange | 60 | 90 |
| S3 | | 2½d. light ultramarine | 30 | 1·75 |
| S4 | | 3d. pale violet | 40 | 15 |
| S5 | 129 | 5d. brown | 40 | 40 |
| S6 | | 6d. purple | 30 | 90 |
| S7 | 130 | 9d. deep olive-green | 60 | 2·00 |
| S8 | | 1s. bistre-brown | 80 | 15 |
| S9 | 131 | 2s. 6d. yellow-green (1946) | 5·00 | 4·25 |
| S1/9 | | *Set of* 9 | 8·00 | 9·75 |
| S8/9 Optd "Specimen" | | *Set of* 2 | £250 | |

The note *re* used prices above Type M 1 of Middle East Forces also applies to the above issue.

BRITISH MILITARY ADMINISTRATION

**1948** (27 May). *Stamps of Great Britain surch* "B.M.A./ SOMALIA" *and new values, as Types* E **1** *and* E **2** *of Eritrea.*

| No. | Type | Description | Unused | Used |
|---|---|---|---|---|
| S10 | 128 | 5 c. on ½d. pale green | 20 | 1·25 |
| S11 | | 15 c. on 1½d. pale red-brown | 55 | 7·00 |
| S12 | | 20 c. on 2d. pale orange | 20 | 2·25 |
| S13 | | 25 c. on 2½d. light ultramarine | 20 | 2·00 |
| S14 | | 30 c. on 3d. pale violet | 1·75 | 9·00 |
| S15 | 129 | 40 c. on 5d. brown | 30 | 20 |
| S16 | | 50 c. on 6d. purple | 30 | 2·00 |
| S17 | 130 | 75 c. on 9d. deep olive-green | 2·00 | 9·00 |
| S18 | | 1 s. on 1s. bistre-brown | 1·25 | 20 |
| S19 | 131 | 2 s. 50 c. on 2s. 6d. yellow-green | 3·00 | 13·00 |
| | | a. Misplaced stop (R. 4/7) | 75·00 | |
| S20 | | 5 s. on 5s. red | 6·00 | 20·00 |
| S10/20 | | *Set of* 11 | 14·00 | 60·00 |

For illustration of No. S19a, see previous column above No. E1 of Eritrea.

BRITISH ADMINISTRATION

**1950** (2 Jan). *As Nos.* S10/20, *but surch* "B.A./SOMALIA" *and new values, instead of* "B.M.A." *etc.*

| No. | Type | Description | Unused | Used |
|---|---|---|---|---|
| S21 | 128 | 5 c. on ½d. pale green | 20 | 85 |
| S22 | | 15 c. on 1½d. pale red-brown | 60 | 8·00 |
| S23 | | 20 c. on 2d. pale orange | 60 | 2·75 |
| S24 | | 25 c. on 2½d. light ultramarine | 40 | 2·75 |
| S25 | | 30 c. on 3d. pale violet | 1·00 | 3·00 |
| S26 | 129 | 40 c. on 5d. brown | 55 | 85 |
| S27 | | 50 c. on 6d. purple | 40 | 1·00 |
| S28 | 130 | 75 c. on 9d. deep olive-green | 1·00 | 4·50 |
| S29 | | 1 s. on 1s. bistre-brown | 60 | 1·50 |

S30 **131** 2 s. 50 c. on 2s. 6d. yellow-green .. 4·00 14·00
S31 5 s. on 5s. red .. .. .. .. 7·50 17·00
S21/31 .. .. .. .. *Set of* 11 15·00 50·00

Somalia reverted to Italian Administration on 1 April 1950 later becoming independent. Later issues will be found listed in Part 8 (*Italy and Switzerland*) of this catalogue.

### TRIPOLITANIA

#### BRITISH MILITARY ADMINISTRATION

**4 M.A.L.** **4 M.A.L.**

Normal Misaligned surcharge (R.8/8, 18/8)

**1948** (1 July). *Stamps of Great Britain surch* "B.M.A./TRIPOLITANIA" *and new values, as Types* **E 1** *and* **E 2** *of Eritrea, but expressed in M(ilitary) A(dministration) L(ire).*
T 1 **128** 1 l. on ½d. pale green .. .. 25 80
T 2 2 l. on 1d. pale scarlet .. .. 20 25
T 3 3 l. on 1½d. pale red-brown .. 20 50
a. Misaligned surch .. ..
T 4 4 l. on 2d. pale orange .. .. 25 50
a. Misaligned surch .. ..
T 5 5 l. on 2½d. light ultramarine .. 25 20
T 6 6 l. on 3d. pale violet .. .. 20 40
T 7 **129** 10 l. on 5d. brown .. .. .. 20 25
T 8 12 l. on 6d. purple .. .. .. 25 20
T 9 **130** 18 l. on 9d. deep olive-green .. .. 50 65
T10 24 l. on 1s. bistre-brown .. .. .. 50 65
T11 **131** 60 l. on 2s. 6d. yellow-green .. .. 1·75 4·50
T12 120 l. on 5s. red .. .. .. .. 5·50 14·00
T13 **132** 240 l. on 10s. ultramarine .. .. 11·00 55·00
T1/13 .. .. .. .. .. *Set of* 13 19·00 70·00

#### BRITISH ADMINISTRATION

**1950** (6 Feb). *As Nos.* T1/13, *but surch.* "B.A. TRIPOLITANIA" *and new values, instead of* "B.M.A." *etc.*
T14 **128** 1 l. on ½d. pale green .. .. 40 4·25
T15 2 l. on 1d. pale scarlet .. .. 50 40
T16 3 l. on 1½d. pale red-brown .. .. 35 3·75
a. Misaligned surch .. ..
T17 4 l. on 2d. pale orange .. .. 25 3·50
a. Misaligned surch .. ..
T18 5 l. on 2½d. light ultramarine .. 25 70
T19 6 l. on 3d. pale violet .. .. 40 1·25
T20 **129** 10 l. on 5d. brown .. .. .. 25 1·25
T21 12 l. on 6d. purple .. .. .. 25 50
T22 **130** 18 l. on 9d. deep olive-green .. .. 35 1·60
T23 24 l. on 1s. bistre-brown .. .. .. 45 3·00
T24 **131** 60 l. on 2s. 6d. yellow-green .. .. 3·75 9·50
T25 120 l. on 5s. red .. .. .. .. 11·00 19·00
T26 **132** 240 l. on 10s. ultramarine .. .. 13·00 27·00
T14/26 .. .. .. .. .. *Set of* 13 27·00 65·00

**1951** (3 May). *Nos.* 503/7 *and* 509/11 *of Great Britain surch* "B.A. TRIPOLITANIA" *and new values.*
T27 **128** 1 l. on ½d. pale orange .. .. .. 20 1·75
T28 2 l. on 1d. light ultramarine .. .. 20 90
T29 3 l. on 1½d. pale green .. .. .. 25 2·50
T30 4 l. on 2d. pale red-brown .. .. 20 1·25
T31 5 l. on 2½d. pale scarlet .. .. 20 2·50
T32 **147** 60 l. on 2s. 6d. yellow-green .. .. 3·50 12·00
T33 **148** 120 l. on 5s. red .. .. .. 7·50 16·00
T34 **149** 240 l. on 10s. ultramarine .. .. 17·00 27·00
T27/34 .. .. .. .. .. *Set of* 8 26·00 55·00

#### POSTAGE DUE STAMPS

**1948.** *Postage Due stamps of Great Britain surch.* "B.M.A./TRIPOLITANIA" *and new values, as Type* **ED 1** *of Eritrea, but expressed in M(ilitary) A(dministration) L(ire).*
TD1 **D 1** 1 l. on ½d. emerald .. .. .. 3·50 23·00
a. No stop after "A" .. .. .. 40·00
TD2 2 l. on 1d. carmine .. .. .. 2·50 23·00
a. No stop after "A" .. .. .. 30·00
TD3 4 l. on 2d. agate .. .. .. 5·50 15·00
a. No stop after "A" .. .. .. 50·00
TD4 6 l. on 3d. violet .. .. .. 7·50 20·00
TD5 24 l. on 1s. deep blue .. .. .. 26·00 65·00
TD1/5 .. .. .. .. .. *Set of* 5 40·00 £130

**1950** (6 Feb). *As Nos.* TD1/5, *but surch* "B.A. TRIPOLITANIA" *and new values, instead of* "B.M.A." *etc.*
TD 6 **D 1** 1 l. on ½d. emerald .. .. .. 6·00 30·00
a. No stop after "B" .. .. 70·00
TD 7 2 l. on 1d. carmine .. .. .. 2·50 17·00
a. No stop after "B" .. .. 50·00
TD 8 4 l. on 2d. agate .. .. .. 2·75 18·00
a. No stop after "B" .. .. 50·00
TD 9 6 l. on 3d. violet .. .. .. 13·00 48·00
a. No stop after "B" .. .. 90·00
TD10 24 l. on 1s. deep blue .. .. .. 29·00 70·00
a. No stop after "A" .. .. £160
b. No stop after "B" .. .. £160
TD7/10 .. .. .. .. *Set of* 5 48·00 £160

Tripolitania became part of the independent kingdom of Libya on 24 December 1951.

### *ALTERED CATALOGUE NUMBERS*

Any Catalogue numbers altered from the last edition are shown as a list in the introductory pages.

## British P.Os in Crete

#### BRITISH ADMINISTRATION OF CANDIA PROVINCE (HERAKLEION)

Crete, formerly part of the Turkish Empire, was made autonomous, under Turkish suzerainty, in November 1898 with British, French, Italian and Russian troops stationed in separate zones to keep the peace.

Overseas mail franked with Nos. 1/5 was forwarded through the Austrian post office at Canea, being additionally franked with stamps of the Austro-Hungarian Post Offices in the Turkish Empire.

**PRICES FOR STAMPS ON COVER**
No. 1 *from* × 10
Nos. 2/5 —

1

2

**1898** (25 Nov). *Handstruck locally. Imperf.*
1 **1** 20 pa. bright violet .. .. .. £350 £225

**1898** (3 Dec). *Litho by M. Grundmann, Athens. P* 11½.
2 **2** 10 pa. blue .. .. .. .. 8·00 12·00
a. Imperf (pair) .. .. .. £250
3 20 pa. green .. .. .. .. 9·00 12·00
a. Imperf (pair) .. .. .. £250

**1899.** *P* 11½.
4 **2** 10 pa. brown .. .. .. .. 8·00 15·00
a. Imperf (pair) .. .. .. £250
5 20 pa. rose .. .. .. .. 14·00 15·00
a. Imperf (pair) .. .. .. £250

The British postal service closed at the end of 1899.

## British P.O. in Siam
### (Bangkok)

An overseas postal service for foreign residents was operated by the British Consulate at Bangkok from 1858. Mail was despatched by steamer to Singapore and from 1867 onwards was increasingly franked with Straits Settlements stamps. These were initially cancelled on arrival at Singapore, but later postmarks inscribed "BRITISH CONSULATE BANGKOK" or "BANGKOK" were used. Such cancellations can also be found on Hong Kong stamps between 1881 and 1885.

**PRICES FOR STAMPS ON COVER**
The issues of the British Post Office in Siam are worth from × 40 the prices quoted for used stamps when on cover.

**B**

(1)

**1882** (May)–**85**. *Stamps of Straits Settlements optd with T* **1**.

(*a*) *On issue of* 1867
1 – 32 c. on 2 a. yellow (No. 9) .. .. £6500 £7500

(*b*) *On issues of* 1867–82. *Wmk Crown CC*
2 **5** 2 c. brown .. .. .. .. £650 £750
3 4 c. rose .. .. .. .. .. £650 £650
a. Opt double .. .. .. .. — £5000
4 **18** 5 c. purple-brown .. .. .. £110 £110
5 **5** 6 c. lilac .. .. .. .. .. 75·00 55·00
6 **6** 8 c. orange .. .. .. .. £1000 £100
7 **19** 10 c. slate .. .. .. .. £110 65·00
8 **6** 12 c. blue .. .. .. .. .. £500 £225
9 **7** 24 c. green .. .. .. .. £225 65·00
10 **8** 30 c. claret .. .. .. .. £7000 £4000
11 **9** 96 c. grey .. .. .. .. .. £1700 £1100

(*c*) *On issue of April* 1883
12 **9** 2 c. on 32 c. pale red (*Wide* "E" (No. 59)) £700 £900
13 2 c. on 32 c. pale red (*Wide* "S" (No. 60)) £1000 £1200

(*d*) *On issues of* 1882–84. *Wmk Crown CA*
14 **5** 2 c. brown .. .. .. .. £100 90·00
15 2 c. rose .. .. .. .. .. 30·00 25·00
a. Opt inverted .. .. .. £8000 £3000
b. Opt double .. .. .. .. £2750
16 4 c. rose .. .. .. .. .. £130 £100
17 4 c. brown .. .. .. .. 50·00 45·00
a. Opt double .. .. .. .. £3250
18 **18** 5 c. blue .. .. .. .. .. £110 70·00
19 **5** 6 c. lilac .. .. .. .. .. 75·00 50·00
20 **6** 8 c. orange .. .. .. .. 50·00 38·00
a. Opt inverted .. .. .. £6000 £3500
21 **19** 10 c. slate .. .. .. .. .. 60·00 45·00
22 **6** 12 c. dull purple .. .. .. .. £120 85·00
23 **7** 24 c. green .. .. .. .. .. £1500 £950

The use of these stamps ceased on 30 June 1885. Siam joined the Universal Postal Union on 1 July 1885.

## British Postal Agencies in Eastern Arabia

Certain Arab States in Eastern Arabia, whilst remaining independent, had British postal administrations.

Bahrain and Kuwait (from 1948) and Qatar (from 1957) used British stamps overprinted and surcharged in local currency. Abu Dhabi (from 1964) and Trucial States (from 1961 and used only in Dubai) had definitive issues made under the auspices of the British Agencies.

In addition, British stamps were surcharged with value only for use in Muscat and certain other states. They were formerly listed under Muscat as they were first put on sale there, but in view of their more extended use, the list has been transferred here, retaining the same numbering.

The stamps were used in Muscat from 1 April 1948 to 29 April 1966; in Dubai from 1 April 1948 to 6 January 1961; in Qatar: Doha from August 1950, Umm Said from February 1956, to 31 March 1957; and in Abu Dhabi from 30 March 1963 (Das Island from December 1960) to 29 March 1964.

Certain of them were placed on sale in Kuwait Post Offices in 1951 and in 1953 due to shortages of stamps with "KUWAIT" overprint; and they can all be found commercially used from that state and from Bahrain.

#### Stamps of Great Britain surcharged

(3) (4)

**1948** (1 Apr). *Surch with T* **3** (½ *a. to* 1 *r.*) *or* **4** (2 *r.*).
16 **128** ½ a. on ½d. pale green .. .. 75 90
17 1 a. on 1d. pale scarlet .. .. 75 20
18 1½ a. on 1½d. pale red-brown .. .. 75 20
19 2 a. on 2d. pale orange .. .. 60 45
20 2½ a. on 2½d. light ultramarine .. .. 80 1·40
21 3 a. on 3d. pale violet .. .. .. 80 10
22 **129** 6 a. on 6d. purple .. .. .. 80 10
23 **130** 1 r. on 1s. bistre-brown .. .. 2·75 50
24 **131** 2 r. on 2s. 6d. yellow-green .. .. 6·50 16·00
16/24 .. .. .. .. .. *Set of* 9 13·00 18·00

One example of No. 22 is known with the surcharge almost completely omitted from position R. 20/2 in the sheet.

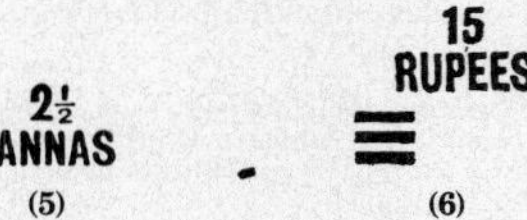

(5) (6)

**1948** (26 Apr). *Royal Silver Wedding. Nos.* 493/4 *surch with T* **5** *or* **6**.
25 **137** 2½ a. on 2½d. ultramarine .. .. 70 40
26 **138** 15 r. on £1 blue .. .. .. .. 28·00 35·00

**1948** (29 July). *Olympic Games. Nos.* 495/8 *surch with new values in* "ANNAS" *or* "1 RUPEE", *as T* **5/6**, *but in one line on* 2½ *a. (vert) or* 6 *a. and* 1 *r. (horiz) and grills obliterating former values of all except* 2½ *a.*
27 **139** 2½ a. on 2½d. ultramarine .. .. 35 70
28 **140** 3 a. on 3d. violet .. .. .. 45 90
29 **141** 6 a. on 6d. bright purple .. .. 45 90
30 **142** 1 r. on 1s. brown .. .. .. 75 1·50
a. Surch double .. .. .. £550
27/30 .. .. .. .. .. *Set of* 4 1·75 3·50

**1949** (10 Oct). *75th Anniv of Universal Postal Union. Nos.* 499/502 *surch with new values in* "ANNAS" *or* "1 RUPEE" *as T* **3/4**, *but all in one line, with grills obliterating former values.*
31 **143** 2½ a. on 2½d. ultramarine .. .. 60 1·25
32 **144** 3 a. on 3d. violet .. .. .. 60 1·25
33 **145** 6 a. on 6d. bright purple .. .. 60 1·10
34 **146** 1 r. on 1s. brown .. .. .. 1·75 1·40
31/4 .. .. .. .. .. *Set of* 4 3·25 4·50

**2 RUPEES** **2 RUPEES**

(6*a*) (6*b*)

Type **6a**. "2" and "RUPEES" level and in line with lower of the two bars.

Type **6b**. "2" raised in relation to "RUPEES" and whole surcharge below the lower bar.

**1950** (2 Oct)–**55**. *Nos.* 503/8 *surch as T* **3** *and No.* 509 *with T* **6a**.
35 **128** ½ a. on ½d. pale orange (3.5.51) .. 30 2·50
36 1 a. on 1d. light ultramarine (3.5.51) .. 30 1·25
37 1½ a. on 1½d. pale green (3.5.51) .. 1·50 7·50
38 2 a. on 2d. pale red-brown (3.5.51) .. 30 3·75
39 2½ a. on 2½d. pale scarlet (3.5.51) .. 30 7·50

| | | | | |
|---|---|---|---|---|
| 40 | 129 | 4 a. on 4d. light ultramarine | 30 | 1·75 |
| 41 | 147 | 2 r. on 2s. 6d. yellow-green (3.5.51) | 22·00 | 4·00 |
| | | a. Surch with Type 6*b* (1955) | 85·00 | 55·00 |
| 35/41 | | *Set of* 7 | 23·00 | 25·00 |

**1952** (5 Dec)–**54**. *Stamps of Queen Elizabeth II wmk Tudor Crown, surch as T* **3** *(in one line on 2½ and 6 a.).*

| | | | | |
|---|---|---|---|---|
| 42 | 154 | ½ a. on ½d. orange-red (31.8.53) | 10 | 10 |
| 43 | | 1 a. on 1d. ultramarine (31.8.53) | 10 | 10 |
| 44 | | 1½ a. on 1½d. green | 10 | 10 |
| 45 | | 2 a. on 2d. red-brown (31.8.53) | 10 | 10 |
| 46 | 155 | 2½ a. on 2½d. carmine-red | 10 | 10 |
| 47 | | 3 a. on 3d. deep lilac (B.) (18.1.54) | 20 | 10 |
| 48 | 156 | 4 a. on 4d. ultramarine (2.11.53) | 55 | 75 |
| 49 | 157 | 6 a. on 6d. reddish purple (18.1.54) | 35 | 10 |
| 50 | 160 | 12 a. on 1s. 3d. green (2.11.53) | 2·00 | 30 |
| 51 | 159 | 1 r. on 1s. 6d. grey-blue (2.11.53) | 2·00 | 10 |
| 42/51 | | *Set of* 10 | 5·00 | 1·40 |

**1953** (10 June). *Coronation. Nos. 532/5 surch with new values.*

| | | | | |
|---|---|---|---|---|
| 52 | 161 | 2½ a. on 2½d. carmine-red | 1·75 | 95 |
| 53 | 162 | 4 a. on 4d. ultramarine | 1·75 | 95 |
| 54 | 163 | 12 a. on 1s. 3d. deep yellow-green | 3·25 | 95 |
| 55 | 164 | 1 r. on 1s. 6d. deep grey-blue | 4·50 | 45 |
| 52/5 | | *Set of* 4 | 10·00 | 3·00 |

2 RUPEES I

2 RUPEES II

2 RUPEES III

(7)

5 RUPEES I

5 RUPEES II

(8)

Types of surcharges

2 rupees.

Type I. *On Waterlow ptg.* Top of "R" level with top of "2" and other letters of "RUPEES". Bars 7 mm long.

Type II. *On Waterlow ptg.* "R" dropped out of alignment with "2" and other letters of "RUPEES". Bars 6½ mm long.

Type III. *On De La Rue ptg.* Top of "R" below level of top of "2". Bars 7–7¼ mm long and with left sides aligned with "S".

5 rupees.

Type I. *On Waterlow ptg.* Ends of letters square and sharp. There were two printings made in March and May 1957.

Type II. *On De La Rue ptg.* Type is thicker and ends of letters are relatively rounded.

For differences between Waterlow and De La Rue printings of the basic stamps see notes in Great Britain after No. 539.

**1955–60.** *T* **166/7** *(Waterlow ptgs) (W* **165**, *St. Edward's Crown) surch with T* **7/8**.

| | | | | |
|---|---|---|---|---|
| 56 | 166 | 2 r. on 2s. 6d. black-brown (Type I) (23.9.55) | 3·25 | 70 |
| | | a. Type II (2.57) | 4·00 | 2·00 |
| | | b. Type III (No. 536a D.L.R.) (6.60) | 27·00 | 48·00 |
| 57 | 167 | 5 r. on 5s. rose-red (Type I) (1.3.57) | 9·00 | 2·00 |
| | | a. Wide surcharge | £200 | £180 |
| | | b. Type II (No. 537a D.L.R.) (27.1.60) | 25·00 | 48·00 |

No. 57a ("5" and "R" spaced 2¼ mm instead of 1¼ mm) occurred on R. 8/4 of the first surcharging of No. 57 only.

**1956–57.** *Stamps of Queen Elizabeth II, W* **165**, *St. Edward's Crown, surch as T* **3** *(in one line on 2½ and 6 a.).*

| | | | | |
|---|---|---|---|---|
| 58 | 154 | 1 a. on 1d. ultramarine (4.3.57) | 35 | 50 |
| 58*a* | | 1½ a. on 1½d. green (1956) | — | £450 |
| 59 | | 2 a. on 2d. red-brown (8.6.56) | 70 | 90 |
| 60 | 155 | 2½ a. on 2½d. carmine-red (8.6.56) | 80 | 1·25 |
| 61 | | 3 a. on 3d. deep lilac (B.) (3.2.57) | 1·00 | 2·50 |
| 62 | 156 | 4 a. on 4d. ultramarine (9.12.56) | 5·00 | 9·00 |
| 63 | 157 | 6 a. on 6d. red-purple (10.2.57) | 1·10 | 2·50 |
| 64 | 159 | 1 r. on 1s. 6d. grey-blue (2.8.56) | 3·25 | 15 |
| 58/64 (*ex* 58*a*) | | *Set of* 7 | 11·00 | 15·00 |

NP 1 NP (9)  NP 3 NP (10)  75 NP (11)

**1957** (1 Apr)–**59.** *Value in naye paise. Stamps of Queen Elizabeth II, W* **165**, *St. Edward's Crown, surch as T* **9** *(1, 15, 25, 40, 50 n.p.),* **11** *(75 n.p.) or* **10** *(others).*

| | | | | |
|---|---|---|---|---|
| 65 | 157 | 1 n.p. on 5d. brown | 10 | 20 |
| 66 | 154 | 3 n.p. on ½d. orange-red | 20 | 50 |
| 67 | | 6 n.p. on 1d. ultramarine | 20 | 50 |
| 68 | | 9 n.p. on 1½d. green | 20 | 30 |
| 69 | | 12 n.p. on 2d. light red-brown | 30 | 35 |
| 70 | 155 | 15 n.p. on 2½d. carmine-red (Type I) | 30 | 10 |
| | | a. Type II (4.59) | 30 | 90 |
| 71 | | 20 n.p. on 3d. deep lilac (B.) | 20 | 10 |
| 72 | 156 | 25 n.p. on 4d. ultramarine | 70 | 1·50 |
| 73 | 157 | 40 n.p. on 6d. reddish purple | 30 | 10 |
| | | *a. Deep claret* (3.59) | 35 | 10 |
| 74 | 158 | 50 n.p. on 9d. bronze-green | 1·25 | 40 |
| 75 | 160 | 75 n.p. on 1s. 3d. green | 2·00 | 35 |
| 65/75 | | *Set of* 11 | 5·00 | 3·75 |

15 NP

(12)

**1957** (1 Aug). *World Scout Jubilee Jamboree. Nos. 557/9 surch in one line as T* **12** *(15 n.p.), or in two lines (others).*

| | | | |
|---|---|---|---|
| 76 | 15 n.p. on 2½d. carmine-red | 25 | 60 |
| 77 | 25 n.p. on 4d. ultramarine | 30 | 60 |
| 78 | 75 n.p. on 1s. 3d. green | 35 | 65 |
| 76/8 | *Set of* 3 | 80 | 1·75 |

**1960** (26 Apr)–**61.** *Stamps of Queen Elizabeth II, W* **179**, *Mult Crown, surch as T* **9** *(1, 15, 30, 40, 50 n.p.),* **11** *(75 n.p.),* **3** *(1 r.),* **7** *(2 r., 5 r.) or* **10** *(others).*

| | | | | |
|---|---|---|---|---|
| 79 | 157 | 1 n.p. on 5d. brown (30.8.60) | 10 | 20 |
| 80 | 154 | 3 n.p. on ½d. orange-red (21.6.60) | 55 | 80 |
| 81 | | 5 n.p. on 1d. ultramarine (8.4.61) | 50 | 40 |
| 82 | | 6 n.p. on 1d. ultramarine (21.6.60) | 1·25 | 90 |
| 83 | | 10 n.p. on 1½d. green (8.4.61) | 50 | 40 |
| 84 | | 12 n.p. on 2d. light red-brown (21.6.60) | 2·50 | 2·50 |
| 85 | 155 | 15 n.p. on 2½d. carmine-red (Type II) | 25 | 10 |
| 86 | | 20 n.p. on 3d. deep lilac (B.) (28.9.60) | 25 | 10 |
| 87 | 156 | 30 n.p. on 4½d. chestnut (8.4.61) | 40 | 40 |
| 88 | 157 | 40 n.p. on 6d. deep claret (28.9.60) | 45 | 10 |
| 89 | 158 | 50 n.p. on 9d. bronze-green (8.4.61) | 80 | 80 |
| 90 | 160 | 75 n.p. on 1s. 3d. green (8.4.61) | 1·25 | 90 |
| 91 | 159 | 1 r. on 1s. 6d. grey-blue (8.4.61) | 6·50 | 1·75 |
| 92 | 166 | 2 r. on 2s. 6d. black-brown (No. 595) (8.4.61) | 7·00 | 18·00 |
| 93 | 167 | 5 r. on 5s. rose-red (No. 596) (8.4.61) | 16·00 | 32·00 |
| 79/93 | | *Set of* 15 | 35·00 | 55·00 |

## British Solomon Islands *see* Solomon Islands

## British Somaliland *see* Somaliland Protectorate

## British South Africa Company *see* Rhodesia

# British Virgin Islands

### CROWN COLONY

Apart from the 1951 Legislative Council issue, the word "BRITISH" did not appear regularly on the stamps until 1968 when it was introduced to avoid confusion with the nearby Virgin Islands of the United States (the former Danish West Indies).

Most mail from the early years of the islands' history was sent via the Danish island of St. Thomas.

It is not known exactly when the first post office, or agency, was established on Tortola, but an entry in a G.P.O. account book suggest that it was operating by 1787 and the earliest letter postmarked "TORTOLA" dates from June of that year. The stamps of Great Britain were used from 1858 to May 1860, when the colonial authorities assumed responsibility for the overseas mails from the British G.P.O.

For illustrations of the handstamp and postmark types see BRITISH POST OFFICES ABROAD notes, following GREAT BRITAIN.

### TORTOLA

CROWNED-CIRCLE HANDSTAMPS

| | | | |
|---|---|---|---|
| CC1 | CC 1 | TORTOLA (R.) (15.12.1842) *Price on cover* | £4000 |
| CC2 | CC 5 | TORTOLA (R.) (21.6.1854) *Price on cover* | — |

No. CC2 is known used as an Official Paid mark during the years 1900 to 1918. *Price on cover* £900.

*Stamps of* GREAT BRITAIN *cancelled* "A 13" *as Type* **2**.

**1858** *to* **1860.**

| | | |
|---|---|---|
| Z1 | 1d. rose-red (1857), *perf* 14 | £3000 |
| Z2 | 4d. rose (1857) | £2750 |
| Z3 | 6d. lilac (1856) | £1100 |
| Z4 | 1s. green (1856) | |

**PRICES FOR STAMPS ON COVER TO 1945**

| | |
|---|---|
| Nos. 1/7 | *from* × 12 |
| Nos. 8/22 | *from* × 8 |
| Nos. 24/31 | *from* × 6 |
| Nos. 32/41 | *from* × 5 |
| No. 42 | *from* × 10 |
| Nos. 43/50 | *from* × 4 |
| Nos. 54/77 | *from* × 3 |
| Nos. 78/81 | *from* × 6 |
| Nos. 82/101 | *from* × 3 |
| Nos. 103/6 | *from* × 4 |
| Nos. 107/9 | *from* × 6 |
| Nos. 110/21 | *from* × 2 |

1 St. Ursula 2

(Litho Nissen & Parker from original dies by Waterlow)

**1866** (Dec). *No wmk. P* 12 *(a) White wove paper.*

| | | | | |
|---|---|---|---|---|
| 1 | 1 | 1d. green | 45·00 | 60·00 |
| 2 | | 1d. deep green | 45·00 | 60·00 |
| 3 | 2 | 6d. rose | 90·00 | £110 |
| 4 | | 6d. deep rose | £130 | £140 |
| | | a. Large "V" in "VIRGIN" | £450 | £550 |
| | | *(b) Toned paper* | | |
| 5 | 1 | 1d. green | 45·00 | 60·00 |
| | | a. Perf 15 × 12 | £4250 | £5500 |
| 6 | | 1d. deep green | £100 | £120 |
| 7 | 2 | 6d. rose-red | 60·00 | 90·00 |
| | | a. Large "V" in "VIRGIN" (R. 2/1) | £350 | £425 |

The above were printed in sheets of 25.

6d. stamps showing part of the papermaker's watermark ("A. Cowan & Sons Extra Superfine A. C. & S.") are worth 50% more.

Beware of fakes of No. 5a made from perf 12 stamps.

3 4

Normal Variety

1s. Long-tailed "S" in "ISLANDS" (R. 3/1)

(Litho Nissen and Parker from original dies by Waterlow)

**1867–70.** *No wmk. P* 15. *1s. with double-lined frame.*

| | | | | |
|---|---|---|---|---|
| | | *(a) White wove paper* | | |
| 8 | 1 | 1d. yellow-green (1868) | 80·00 | 80·00 |
| 9 | | 1d. blue-green (1870) | 65·00 | 70·00 |
| 10 | 2 | 6d. pale rose | £475 | £475 |
| 11 | 4 | 1s. black and rose-carmine | £200 | £275 |
| | | a. Long-tailed "S" | £550 | £600 |
| | | *(b) Toned paper* | | |
| 12 | 1 | 1d. yellow-green (1868) | 85·00 | 80·00 |
| 13 | 2 | 6d. dull rose (1868) | £225 | £275 |
| 14 | 4 | 1s. black and rose-carmine (*blued*) | £225 | £300 |
| | | aa. Long-tailed "S" | £600 | £650 |
| 14*a* | | 1s. black and rose-carmine | £300 | £325 |
| | | b. Long-tailed "S" | £600 | £650 |
| | | *(c) Pale rose paper* | | |
| 15 | 3 | 4d. lake-red | 50·00 | 70·00 |
| | | *(d) Buff paper* | | |
| 16 | 3 | 4d. lake-red | 40·00 | 60·00 |
| 17 | | 4d. lake-brown | 40·00 | 60·00 |

The thin lines of the frame on the 1s. are close together and sometimes merge into one.

The 1d. from the 1868 printing was in sheets of 20 with narrow margins between the stamps. Later printings were in sheets of 12 with wider margins. The 4d. was in sheets of 25; and the remaining two values in sheets of 20.

In Type 4 the figure of the Virgin was printed by typography and the remainder of the design by lithography.

**1867.** *As T 4, but with crimson frames superimposed with bands extending through margins. P 15.*

18 4 1s. black and rose-carmine (*white paper*) 48·00 60·00
a. Long-tailed "S" £120 £140
b. Figure of Virgin omitted 55000
19 1s. black and rose-carmine (*toned paper*) 48·00 60·00
a. Long-tailed "S" £120 £140
20 1s. black and rose-carmine (*greyish paper*) £700 £850
a. Long-tailed "S" £1600 £1400

**1868.** *Nos. 11 and 14a with frame lines retouched so as to make them single lines. Margins remain white. P 15.*

21 4 1s. black and rose-carmine (*white paper*) £130 £160
aa. Long-tailed "S" £300 £375
21*a* 1s. black and rose-carmine (*toned paper*) £130 £160
b. Long-tailed "S" £300 £375

(Litho D.L.R.)

**1878.** *Wmk Crown CC (sideways). P 14.*

22 1 1d. green 70·00 85·00
*a. Yellow-green* £170 £130
ab. Wmk upright 90·00 £120

6 (Die I)

(7)

(Typo D.L.R.)

**1879–80.** *Wmk Crown CC. P 14.*

24 6 1d. emerald-green (1880) 50·00 80·00
25 2½d. red-brown 80·00 £110

**1883** (June)**–84.** *Wmk Crown CA. P 14.*

26 6 ½d. yellow-buff 65·00 80·00
27 ½d. yellow-green (11.83) 3·25 8·00
*a. Dull bluish green* (1884) 8·00 13·00
29 1d. pale rose (15.9.83) 18·00 23·00
*a. Deep rose* (1884) 50·00 55·00
31 2½d. ultramarine (9.84) 2·50 9·00

(Litho D.L.R.)

**1887–89.** *Wmk Crown CA. P 14.*

32 1 1d. red (5.89) 2·00 7·00
33 1d. rose-red 2·25 7·00
34 1d. rose 5·00 14·00
35 3 4d. chestnut 40·00 75·00
36 4d. pale chestnut 40·00 75·00
37 4d. brown-red 50·00 80·00
38 2 6d. dull violet 15·00 48·00
39 6d. deep violet 15·00 48·00
40 4 1s. sepia (2.89) 70·00 £110
41 1s. brown *to* deep brown 50·00 80·00
34/40 Optd "Specimen" *Set of* 4 £300

The De La Rue transfers of T **1** to **4** are new transfers and differ from those of Messrs. Nissen and Parker, particularly T **4**

**1888** (July). *Nos. 18/19 surch with T 7, in violet, in Antigua.*

42 4 4d. on 1s. black and rose-carmine (*toned paper*) £110 £150
a. Surch double £6000
b. Surch inverted (in pair with normal) £40000
c. Long-tailed "S" £325 £450
42*d* 4d. on 1s. black and rose-carmine (*white paper*) £130 £170

The special issues for Virgin Islands were superseded on 31 October 1890, by the general issue for Leeward Islands. In 1899, however, a new special issue (given below) appeared; it did not supersede the general issue for Leeward Islands, but was used concurrently, as were all subsequent issues, until 1 July 1956, when the general Leeward Islands stamps were withdrawn.

8 9 10

(Recess D.L.R.)

**1899** (Jan). *Wmk Crown CA. P 14.*

43 8 ½d. yellow-green 60 55
a. Error. "HALFPFNNY" (R. 10/1) 80·00 £110
b. Error. "HALFPENNY" (R. 8/2) 80·00 £110
c. Imperf between (horiz pair) £6500
44 1d. brick-red 2·25 2·25
45 2½d. ultramarine 12·00 4·00
46 4d. brown 5·00 12·00
a. Error "FOURPENCF" (R.10/3) £1100 £1300
47 6d. dull violet 4·50 4·50
48 7d. deep green 7·00 8·00
49 1s. brown-yellow 18·00 30·00
50 5s. indigo 65·00 80·00
43/50 *Set of* 8 £100 £130
43/50 Optd "Specimen" *Set of* 8 £180

Nos. 43a/b and 46a were corrected after the first printing.

(Typo D.L.R.)

**1904** (1 June). *Wmk Mult Crown CA. P 14.*

54 9 ½d. dull purple and green 50 40
55 1d. dull purple and scarlet 85 35
56 10 2d. dull purple and ochre 3·25 4·50
57 9 2½d. dull purple and ultramarine 1·75 2·00
58 10 3d. dull purple and black 2·75 3·00
59 9 6d. dull purple and brown 2·75 3·00
60 10 1s. green and scarlet 2·75 4·75
61 2s. 6d. green and black 18·00 40·00
62 9 5s. green and blue 38·00 60·00
54/62 *Set of* 9 60·00 £100
54/62 Optd "Specimen" *Set of* 9 £160

11 12

(Typo D.L.R.)

**1913** (Feb)**–19.** *Wmk Mult Crown CA. Chalk-surfaced paper (3d. to 5s.). P 14.*

63 11 ½d. green 75 1·60
64 ½d. yellow-green (8.16) 1·25 3·50
65 ½d. blue-green and deep green (3.19) 85 3·25
66 1d. deep red 7·50 9·00
67 1d. deep red and carmine 2·25 8·50
68 1d. scarlet (10.17) 1·75 8·50
69 1d. carmine-red (3.19) 28·00 22·00
70 12 2d. grey 3·75 10·00
71 2d. slate-grey (1919) 4·00 15·00
72 11 2½d. bright blue 4·00 6·50
73 12 3d. purple/*yellow* 1·40 4·75
74 11 6d. dull and bright purple 2·75 3·75
75 12 1s. black/*green* 3·25 4·00
76 2s. 6d. black and red/*blue* 35·00 38·00
77 11 5s. green and red/*yellow* 32·00 75·00
63/77 *Set of* 9 75·00 £140
63/77 Optd "Specimen" *Set of* 9 £200

WAR STAMP

(13) 14

**1916** (20 Oct)**–19.** *Optd with T 13.*

78 11 1d. carmine 90 12·00
a. Watermark sideways £900
*b. Pale red/bluish* 20 3·00
*c. Scarlet* 20 1·75
79 12 3d. purple/*yellow* 25 7·00
*a. Purple/lemon* 2·00 7·00
*b. Purple/pale yellow* (11.3.19) 85 13·00
78/9 Optd "Specimen" *Set of* 2 70·00

**1921** (18 Nov). *As 1913–19, but wmk Mult Script CA.*

80 11 ½d. green 85 15·00
81 1d. scarlet and deep carmine 1·25 10·00
80/1 Optd "Specimen" *Set of* 2 70·00

(Typo D.L.R.)

**1922** (15 June)**–29.** *P 14. (a) Wmk Mult Crown CA. Chalk-surfaced paper.*

82 14 3d. purple/*pale yellow* 40 6·00
83 1s. black/*emerald* 65 8·50
84 2s. 6d. black and red/*blue* 3·75 9·00
85 5s. green and red/*pale yellow* 32·00 65·00
82/5 *Set of* 4 32·00 80·00
82/5 Optd "Specimen" *Set of* 4 £100

*(b) Wmk Mult Script CA. Chalk-surfaced paper (5d. to 5s.)*

86 14 ½d. dull green 20 75
87 1d. rose-carmine 20 50
88 1d. bright violet (1927) 70 2·00
89 1d. scarlet (1929) 5·00 7·00
90 1½d. carmine-red (1927) 1·25 2·25
91 1½d. Venetian red (1928) 1·75 2·00
92 2d. grey 60 3·00
93 2½d. pale bright blue 1·50 7·00
94 2½d. dull orange (1.9.23) 1·25 1·25
95 2½d. bright blue (1927) 80 3·50
96 3d. purple/*pale yellow* (1928) 1·25 4·50
97 5d. dull purple and olive 5·00 26·00
98 6d. dull and bright purple 1·25 4·75
99 1s. black/*emerald* (1928) 1·25 7·00
100 2s. 6d. black and red/*blue* (1928) 17·00 26·00
101 5s. green and red/*yellow* (1.9.23) 19·00 45·00
86/101 *Set of* 16 50·00 £130
86/101 Optd/Perf "Specimen" *Set of* 16 £300

In the 1½d. stamps the value is in colour on a white ground.

**1935** (6 May). *Silver Jubilee. As Nos. 91/4 of Antigua but printed by Waterlow. P 11 × 12.*

103 1d. deep blue and scarlet 45 90
j. Kite and vertical log 35·00
k. Kite and horizontal log 35·00
104 1½d. ultramarine and grey 45 90
j. Kite and vertical log 38·00
k. Kite and horizontal log 38·00
105 2½d. brown and deep blue 55 95
j. Kite and vertical log 45·00
k. Kite and horizontal log 45·00
106 1s. slate and purple 3·50 7·00
j. Kite and vertical log 75·00
k. Kite and horizontal log 75·00
103/6 *Set of* 4 4·50 8·75
103/6 Perf "Specimen" *Set of* 4 85·00

For illustrations of plate varieties see Catalogue Introduction.

**1937** (12 May). *Coronation. As Nos. 95/7 of Antigua. P 11×11½.*

107 1d. carmine 20 30
108 1½d. yellow-brown 40 80
109 2½d. blue 45 70
107/9 *Set of* 3 95 1·60
107/9 Perf "Specimen" *Set of* 3 55·00

15 King George VI and Badge of Colony

16 Map

(Photo Harrison)

**1938** (1 Aug)**–47.** *Wmk Mult Script CA. Chalk-surfaced paper. P 14.*

110 15 ½d. green 45 50
a. Ordinary paper (10.43) 30 30
111 1d. scarlet 45 45
a. Ordinary paper (10.43) 30 30
112 1½d. red-brown 45 40
a. Ordinary paper (10.43) 65 40
113 2d. grey 80 30
a. Ordinary paper (10.43) 40 40
114 2½d. ultramarine 60 35
a. Ordinary paper (10.43) 50 35
115 3d. orange 70 30
a. Ordinary paper (10.43) 30 30
116 6d. mauve 1·50 35
a. Ordinary paper (10.43) 85 40
117 1s. olive-brown 1·75 40
a. Ordinary paper (8.42) 1·25 30
118 2s. 6d. sepia 6·50 3·00
a. Ordinary paper (8.42) 6·00 3·00
119 5s. carmine 13·00 4·00
a. Ordinary paper (8.42) 9·00 4·00
120 10s. blue (1.12.47) 7·00 8·00
121 £1 black (1.12.47) 11·00 20·00
110/21 *Set of* 12 35·00 35·00
110/21 Perf "Specimen" *Set of* 12 £250

The ordinary paper, used as a substitute for the chalk-surfaced for printings between 1942 and 1945, is thick, smooth and opaque.

**1946** (1 Nov). *Victory. As Nos. 110/11 of Antigua.*

122 1½d. lake-brown 10 10
123 3d. orange 10 10
122/3 Perf "Specimen" *Set of* 2 55·00

**1949** (3 Jan). *Royal Silver Wedding. As Nos. 112/13 of Antigua.*

124 2½d. ultramarine 10 10
125 £1 black 9·00 10·00

**1949** (10 Oct). *75th Anniv of U.P.U. As Nos. 114/17 of Antigua.*

126 2½d. ultramarine 20 15
127 3d. orange 40 20
128 6d. magenta 40 15
129 1s. olive 40 35
126/9 *Set of* 4 1·25 75

**(New Currency. 100 cents = 1 B.W.I. dollar)**

**1951.** *Inauguration of B.W.I. University College. As Nos. 118/19 of Antigua.*

130 3 c. black and brown-red (10.4) 30 15
131 12 c. black and redish violet (16.2) 35 25

(Recess Waterlow)

**1951** (2 Apr). *Restoration of Legislative Council. Wmk Mult Script CA. P 14½ x 14.*

132 16 6 c. orange 20 50
133 12 c. purple 20 50
134 24 c. olive 20 50
135 $1.20 carmine 45 75
132/5 *Set of* 4 95 2·00

17 Sombrero Lighthouse

18 Map of Jost Van Dyke

(Recess D.L.R.)

**1952** (15 Apr). *T 17/18 and similar designs. Wmk Mult Script CA. P 12½ × 13 (vert) or 13 × 12½ (horiz).*

136 1 c. black 30 40
137 2 c. deep green 35 30
138 3 c. black and brown 30 40
139 4 c. carmine-red 35 40
140 5 c. claret and black 45 50
141 8 c. bright blue 35 30
142 12 c. dull violet 35 30
143 24 c. deep brown 35 30
144 60 c. yellow-green and blue 2·25 8·00
145 $1.20, black and bright blue 3·75 6·50
146 $2.40, yellowish green and red-brown 8·00 6·00
147 $4.80, bright blue and carmine 8·00 8·00
136/47 *Set of* 12 22·00 28·00

Designs: *Horiz*—3 c. Sheep industry; 4 c. Map of Anegada; 5 c. Cattle industry; 8 c. Map of Virgin Gorda; 12 c. Map of Tortola; 60 c. Dead Man's Chest; $1.20, Sir Francis Drake Channel; $2.40, Road Town; $4.80, Map of Virgin Islands. *Vert*—24 c. Badge of the Presidency.

**1953** (2 June). *Coronation. As No.* 120 *of Antigua.*
148 2 c. black and green .. .. .. .. .. 15 45

29 Map of Tortola

30 Brown Pelican

(Recess D.L.R.)

**1956** (1 Nov)–**62**. *Designs as T* **29/30**. *Wmk Mult Script CA. P* 13×12½ (½ *c. to* $1.20) *or* 12×11½ ($2.40 *and* $4.80).
149 ½ c. black and reddish purple .. .. .. 20 10
a. *Black and deep reddish purple* (19.4.60) 20 40
150 1 c. turquoise-blue and slate .. .. .. 75 20
a. *Turquoise and slate-violet* (26.11.62) 2·50 1·25
151 2 c. vermilion and black .. .. .. .. 30 10
152 3 c. blue and deep olive .. .. .. .. 30 20
153 4 c. deep brown and turquoise-green .. .. 35 15
154 5 c. grey-black .. .. .. .. .. 45 10
155 8 c. yellow-orange and deep blue .. .. .. 35 40
156 12 c. ultramarine and rose-red .. .. .. 75 35
157 24 c. myrtle-green and brown-orange .. .. 55 30
158 60 c. indigo and yellow-orange .. .. .. 3·75 4·00
159 $1.20, deep yellow-green and carmine-red 1·25 3·50
160 $2.40, lemon and deep dull purple .. 19·00 10·00
161 $4.80, blackish brown and turquoise-blue 19·00 13·00
149/61 .. .. .. .. *Set of* 13 42·00 29·00

Designs: *Size as T* **29**—1 c. Virgin Islands Sloop; 2 c. Nelthrop Red Poll Bull; 3 c. Road Harbour; 4 c. Mountain travel; 5 c. Badge of the Presidency; 8 c. Beach scene; 12 c. Boat launching; 24 c. White Cedar tree; 60 c. Bonito; $1.20, Treasury Square. *Size as T* **30**—$4.80, Magnificent Frigate Bird.

**(New Currency. 100 cents = 1 U.S. dollar)**

≡ 1¢

(42)

**1962** (10 Dec). *Nos.* 149/53 *and* 155/61 *surch in U.S. currency as T* **42** *by D.L.R. W w* **12**.
162 1 c. on ½ c. black and deep reddish purple .. 30 10
163 2 c. on 1 c. turquoise and slate-violet .. 30 10
164 3 c. on 2 c. vermilion and black .. .. 30 10
165 4 c. on 3 c. black and deep olive .. .. 30 10
166 5 c. on 4 c. deep brown and turquoise-green 30 10
167 8 c. on 8 c. yellow-orange and deep blue .. 30 10
168 10 c. on 12 c. ultramarine and rose-red .. 30 10
169 12 c. on 24 c. myrtle-green and brown-orange 30 10
170 25 c. on 60 c. indigo and yellow-orange .. 80 45
171 70 c. on $1.20, dp yellow-green & carmine-red 35 45
a. Stop to right of C in surcharge instead of beneath it (in pair with normal).. .. 4·25 6·50
172 $1.40 on $2.40, lemon and deep dull purple 6·00 3·00
173 $2.80 on $4.80, blackish brown and turquoise-blue .. .. .. .. 6·50 3·00
162/73 .. .. .. .. *Set of* 12 14·50 6·50

No. 171a occurs on the first stamp on Rows 1 to 10.

**1963** (4 June). *Freedom from Hunger. As No.* 146 *of Antigua.*
174 25 c. reddish violet .. .. .. .. .. 20 10

**1963** (2 Sept). *Red Cross Centenary. As Nos.* 147/8 *of Antigua.*
175 2 c. red and black .. .. .. .. .. 10 10
176 25 c. red and blue .. .. .. .. .. 25 20

**1964** (23 Apr). *400th Birth Anniv of William Shakespeare. As No.* 164 *of Antigua.*
177 10 c. bright blue .. .. .. .. .. 10 10

43 Bonito

44 Map of Tortola

45 Badge of the Colony

(Des and recess D.L.R.)

**1964** (2 Nov)–**68**. *Designs as T* **43/5**. *W w* **12**. *P* 11½×12 ($2.80), 13×13½ (70 c., $1, $1.40), *or* 13×12½ (*others*).
178 1 c. blue and olive-green .. .. .. 30 30
179 2 c. yellow-olive and rose-red .. .. 15 10
180 3 c. sepia and turquoise-blue .. .. 1·75 50
181 4 c. black and carmine-red .. .. .. 40 40
182 5 c. black and deep bluish green .. .. 35 35
183 6 c. black and brown-orange .. .. .. 20 35
184 8 c. black and magenta .. .. .. .. 20 30
185 10 c. lake and deep lilac .. .. .. .. 40 10
a. *Bright lake and reddish lilac* (26.11.68) 2·00 65
186 12 c. deep bluish green and deep violet-blue 75 55
187 15 c. yellow-green and grey-black .. .. 35 70
188 25 c. green and purple .. .. .. .. 7·00 55
189 70 c. black and yellow-brown .. .. .. 2·25 1·50
190 $1 yellow-green and chestnut .. .. 2·75 1·50
191 $1.40, light blue and rose .. .. .. 11·00 5·50
192 $2.80, black and bright purple .. .. 11·00 8·00
178/92 .. .. .. .. .. *Set of* 15 35·00 19·00

Designs: *Horiz as T* **43**—2 c. Soper's Hole; 3 c. Brown Pelican; 4 c. Dead Man's Chest; 5 c. Road Harbour; 6 c. Fallen Jerusalem; 8 c. The Baths, Virgin Gorda; 10 c. Map of Virgin Islands; 12 c. *Youth of Tortola* (Tortola-St. Thomas ferry); 15 c. The Towers, Tortola; 25 c. Beef Island Airfield. *Vert as T* **44**—$1 Virgin Gorda; $1.40, Yachts at anchor.

**1965** (17 May). *I.T.U. Centenary. As Nos.* 166/7 *of Antigua.*
193 4 c. yellow and turquoise .. .. .. 10 10
194 25 c. light blue and orange-buff .. .. .. 20 15

**1965** (25 Oct). *International Co-operation Year. As Nos.* 168/9 *of Antigua.*
195 1 c. reddish purple and turquoise-green .. 10 10
196 25 c. deep bluish green and lavender .. .. 30 15

**1966** (24 Jan). *Churchill Commemoration. As Nos.* 170/3 *of Antigua.*
197 1 c. new blue .. .. .. .. .. .. 10 10
198 2 c. deep green .. .. .. .. .. 10 10
199 10 c. brown .. .. .. .. .. .. 30 10
200 25 c. bluish violet .. .. .. .. .. 60 25
197/200 .. .. .. .. .. *Set of* 4 90 40

**1966** (22 Feb). *Royal Visit. As Nos.* 174/5 *of Antigua.*
201 4 c. black and ultramarine .. .. .. 30 10
202 70 c. black and magenta .. .. .. .. 1·10 45

58 R.M.S. *Atrato*, 1866

(Des R. Granger Barrett. Litho B.W.)

**1966** (25 Apr). *Stamp Centenary. T* **58** *and similar horiz designs. W w* **12** (*sideways*). *P* 13.
203 5 c. black, red, yellow and emerald .. .. 15 10
204 10 c. black, green and rose-red/*cream*.. .. 25 10
205 25 c. black, rose-red and blue/*pale green* .. 40 10
206 60 c. black, red and green/*pale blue* .. .. 75 40
203/6 .. .. .. .. .. *Set of* 4 1·40 65

Design:—10 c. 1d. and 6d. stamps of 1866; 25 c. Air mail transport, Beef Island, and 6d. stamp of 1866; 60 c. Landing mail at Roadtown, 1866 and 1d. stamp of 1866.

50c.

(62)

**1966** (15 Sept). *As Nos.* 189 *and* 191/2 *but wmk sideways, surch as T* **62**.
207 50 c. on 70 c. black and yellow-brown.. .. 70 70
208 $1.50 on $1.40, light blue and rose .. .. 2·00 2·00
209 $3 on $2.80, black and bright purple .. 2·50 2·75
207/9 .. .. .. .. .. *Set of* 3 4·75 5·00

**1966** (1 Dec). *20th Anniv of U.N.E.S.C.O. As Nos.* 196/8 *of Antigua.*
210 2 c. slate-violet, red, yellow and orange .. 10 10
211 12 c. orange-yellow, violet and deep olive .. 20 10
212 60 c. black, bright purple and orange.. .. 50 20
210/12 .. .. .. .. .. *Set of* 3 65 30

63 Map of Virgin Islands

(Des G. Vasarhelyi. Photo Harrison)

**1967** (18 Apr). *New Constitution. W w* **12**. *P* 14½.
213 **63** 2 c. multicoloured .. .. .. .. 10 10
214 10 c. multicoloured .. .. .. .. 15 10
215 25 c. multicoloured .. .. .. .. 15 10
216 $1 multicoloured .. .. .. .. 55 25
213/16 .. .. .. .. .. *Set of* 4 75 30

## NEW INFORMATION

The editor is always interested to correspond with people who have new information that will improve or correct the Catalogue.

64 *Mercury* (cable ship) and Bermuda-Tortola Link

(Des G. Drummond, Photo Harrison)

**1967** (14 Sept). *Inauguration of Bermuda-Tortola Telephone Service. T* **64** *and similar horiz designs. Multicoloured. W w* **12**. *P* 14½.
217 4 c. Type **64** .. .. .. .. .. .. 10 10
218 10 c. Chalwell Telecommunications Station 10 10
219 50 c. *Mercury* (cable ship) .. .. .. 30 20
217/19 .. .. .. .. .. *Set of* 3 45 30

67 Blue Marlin

(Des V. Whiteley. Photo Enschedé)

**1968** (2 Jan). *Game Fishing. T* **67** *and similar horiz designs. W w* **12** (*sideways*). *P* 12½ × 12.
220 2 c. multicoloured .. .. .. .. .. 10 25
221 10 c. multicoloured .. .. .. .. .. 25 10
222 25 c. black, blue and bright violet .. .. 55 10
223 40 c. multicoloured .. .. .. .. .. 85 30
220/3 .. .. .. .. .. *Set of* 4 1·60 55

Designs—10 c. Cobia; 25 c. Wahoo; 40 c. Fishing launch and map.

1968
INTERNATIONAL
YEAR FOR
HUMAN RIGHTS

(71)

72 Dr. Martin Luther King, Bible, Sword and Armour Gauntlet

**1968** (29 July). *Human Rights Year. Nos.* 185 *and* 188 *optd with T* **71**.
224 10 c. lake and deep lilac .. .. .. .. 15 10
225 25 c. green and purple.. .. .. .. .. 25 20

29 July was the date of issue in the islands. The Crown Agents supplies went on sale in London on 1 July, the local consignment being delayed in transit.

(Des V. Whiteley. Litho Format)

**1968** (15 Oct). *Martin Luther King Commemoration. W w* **12** (*sideways*). *P* 14.
226 **72** 4 c. multicoloured .. .. .. .. 15 15
227 25 c. multicoloured .. .. .. .. 25 15

73 DHC-6 "Twin Otter"

(Des R. Granger Barrett. Litho Format)

**1968** (16 Dec). *Opening of Beef Island Airport Extension. T* **73** *and similar horiz designs. Multicoloured. P* 14.
228 2 c. Type **73** .. .. .. .. .. .. 10 20
229 10 c. HS "748" Airliner .. .. .. .. 10 10
230 25 c. HS "Heron" .. .. .. .. .. 20 10
231 $1 Royal Engineers cap badge .. .. .. 60 70
228/31 .. .. .. .. .. *Set of* 4 90 90

77 Long John Silver and Jim Hawkins

78 Jim Hawkins escaping from the Pirates

(Des Jennifer Toombs. Photo Enschedé)

**1969** (18 Mar). *75th Death Anniv of Robert Louis Stevenson. Scenes from "Treasure Island". T* **77/8** *and similar designs. W* w **12** *(sideways on* 10 c., $1). *P* 13½ × 13 (4 c., 40 c.) *or* 13 × 13½ *(others).*

232 4 c. indigo, pale yellow and carmine-red .. 25 10
233 10 c. multicoloured .. .. .. .. 30 10
234 40 c. brown, black and blue .. .. .. .. 50 20
235 $1 multicoloured .. .. .. .. 75 50
232/5 .. .. .. .. .. *Set of* 4 1·60 75

Designs: *Vert*—40 c. The fight with Israel Hands. *Horiz*—$1 Treasure trove.

**82** Yachts in Road Harbour, Tortola

(Des J. Cooter, Litho P.B.)

**1969** (20 Oct). *Tourism. T* **82** *and similar multicoloured designs. W* w **12** *(sideways on* 2 c., $1). *P* 12½.

236 2 c. Tourist and Rock Grouper (fish) *(vert)* .. 15 20
237 10 c. Type **82** .. .. .. .. .. 20 10
238 20 c. Sun-bathing at Virgin Gorda National Park .. .. .. .. .. 30 10
239 $1 Tourist and Pipe Organ Cactus, at Virgin Gorda *(vert)* .. .. .. .. 75 75
236/9 .. .. .. .. .. *Set of* 4 1·25 95

**85** Carib Canoe

(Des and litho J.W.)

**1970** (16 Feb)–**74**. *Horiz designs as T* **85**. *W* w **12** *(sideways). P* 14.

240 ½ c. buff, red-brown and sepia .. .. 10 35
241 1 c. new blue, apple-green and chalky blue .. 15 30
a. Perf 13½ (12.11.74) .. .. .. 75 1·00
242 2 c. yellow-orange, red-brown and slate .. 25 50
243 3 c. orange-red, cobalt and sepia .. .. 25 35
244 4 c. greenish blue, chalky blue & bistre-brn 25 35
245 5 c. emerald, pink and black .. .. .. 30 10
246 6 c. reddish violet, mauve and myrtle-green 40 55
247 8 c. apple-green, greenish yellow and sepia .. 50 1·00
248 10 c. greenish blue, yellow-brown & red-brown 50 15
a. Perf 13½ (12.11.74) .. .. .. 1·75 2·00
249 12 c. yellow, crimson and brown .. .. 65 50
a. Perf 13½ (12.11.74) .. .. .. 2·00 2·50
250 15 c. turquoise-green, orange & bistre-brown 3·00 75
a. Perf 13½ (12.11.74) .. .. .. 2·25 2·50
251 25 c. grey-green, steel-blue and plum .. .. 3·75 1·25
252 50 c. magenta, dull green and purple-brown .. 2·25 1·50
253 $1 salmon, olive-green and red-brown .. 3·00 3·50
254 $2 buff, slate and grey .. .. .. 5·00 6·00
255 $3 ochre, deep blue and sepia .. .. 5·00 6·50
256 $5 violet and grey .. .. .. .. 8·00 9·00
240/56 .. .. .. .. *Set of* 17 30·00 29·00

Designs:—1 c. *Santamariagallante* (Columbus' flagship). 2 c. *Elizabeth Bonaventure* (Drake's flagship); 3 c. Dutch Buccaneer, *circa* 1660; 4 c. *Thetis*, 1827 (after etching by E. W. Cooke); 5 c. Henry Morgan's ship (17th-century); 6 c. H.M.S. *Boreas* (Captain Nelson, 1784); 8 c. H.M.S. *Eclair*, 1804; 10 c. H.M.S. *Formidable*, 1782; 12 c. H.M.S. *Nymph*, 1778; 15 c. *Windsor Castle*, Post Office Packet, 1807; 25 c. H.M.S. *Astrea*, 1808; 50 c. Wreck of R.M.S. *Rhone*, 1860; $1 Tortola Sloop; $2 H.M.S. *Frobisher*; $3 Tanker *Booker Viking*, 1967; $5 Hydrofoil *Sun Arrow*.

See also Nos. 295/300.

**102** *A Tale of Two Cities*

(Des W. G. Brown. Litho D.L.R.)

**1970** (4 May). *Death Centenary of Charles Dickens. T* **102** *and similar horiz designs showing original book illustrations. W* w **12** *(sideways). P* 14.

257 5 c. black, light rose and grey .. .. 10 10
258 10 c. black, light blue and pale green .. .. 20 10
259 25 c. black, light green and pale yellow .. 30 20
257/9 .. .. .. .. .. *Set of* 3 55 30

Designs:—10 c. *Oliver Twist*; 25 c. *Great Expectations*.

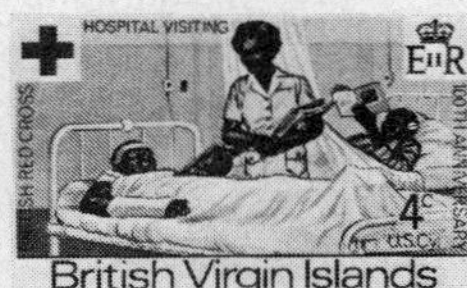


**103** Hospital Visit

(Des R. Granger Barrett. Litho Questa)

**1970** (10 Aug). *Centenary of British Red Cross. T* **103** *and similar horiz designs. Multicoloured. W* w **12** *(sideways). P* 14.

260 4 c. Type **103** .. .. .. .. .. 15 10
261 10 c. First Aid Class .. .. .. .. 25 10
262 25 c. Red Cross and Coat of Arms .. .. 45 20
260/2 .. .. .. .. .. *Set of* 3 75 30

**104** Mary Read

**105** Children and "UNICEF"

(Des and litho J.W.)

**1970** (16 Nov). *Pirates. T* **104** *and similar vert designs. Multicoloured. W* w **12**. *P* 14 × 14½.

263 ½ c. Type **104** .. .. .. .. .. 10 10
264 10 c. George Lowther .. .. .. .. 35 10
265 30 c. Edward Teach (Blackbeard) .. .. 85 20
266 60 c. Henry Morgan .. .. .. .. 1·25 60
263/6 .. .. .. .. .. *Set of* 4 2·25 85

(Des L. Curtis. Litho Format)

**1971** (13 Dec). *25th Anniv of UNICEF. W* w **12** *(sideways). P* 13½ × 14.

267 **106** 15 c. multicoloured .. .. .. 10 10
268 30 c. multicoloured .. .. .. 20 25

VISIT OF
H.R.H.
THE
PRINCESS MARGARET
1972 1972

**(106)**

**1972** (7 Mar). *Royal Visit of Princess Margaret. Nos.* 244 *and* 251 *optd with T* **106**.

269 4 c. greenish blue, chalky blue & bistre-brn 15 10
270 25 c. grey-green, steel-blue and plum .. .. 25 30

**107** Seaman of 1800

**108** Sailfish and the *Sir Winston Churchill* (cadet ship)

(Des J. W. Litho Questa)

**1972** (17 Mar). *"Interpex" Stamp Exhibition, New York. T* **107** *and similar vert designs showing Naval Uniforms. Multicoloured. W* w **12** *(sideways). P* 13½.

271 ½ c. Type **107** .. .. .. .. .. 10 10
272 10 c. Boatswain, 1787–1807 .. .. .. 35 10
273 30 c. Captain, 1795–1812 .. .. .. 85 45
274 60 c. Admiral, 1787–95. .. .. .. 1·50 1·25
271/4 .. .. .. .. .. *Set of* 4 2·50 1·75

(Des (from photograph by D. Groves) and photo Harrison)

**1972** (24 Nov). *Royal Silver Wedding. Multicoloured; background colour given. W* w **12**. *P* 14 × 14½.

275 **108** 15 c. bright blue .. .. .. .. 20 15
276 25 c. turquoise-blue .. .. .. 20 15
a. Blue omitted* .. .. .. £250

*The omission of the blue colour results in the Duke's suit appearing sepia instead of deep blue.

**109** Blue Marlin

(Des G. Drummond. Litho Questa)

**1972** (12 Dec). *Game Fish. T* **109** *and similar horiz designs. Multicoloured. W* w **12**. *P* 13½.

277 ½ c. Type **109** .. .. .. .. .. 10 15
a. Pair. Nos. 277/8 .. .. .. .. 15 30
278 ½ c. Wahoo .. .. .. .. .. 10 15
279 15 c. Allison Tuna .. .. .. .. 35 25
280 25 c. White Marlin .. .. .. .. 40 30
281 50 c. Sailfish .. .. .. .. .. 90 80
282 $1 Dolphin .. .. .. .. .. 1·75 1·75
277/82 .. .. .. .. *Set of* 6 3·25 3·00
**MS**283 194 × 158 mm. Nos. 277/82 .. .. 6·50 8·00

Nos. 277/8 were printed horizontally and vertically *se-tenant* within the sheet.

**110** J. C. Lettsom

**111** Green-throated Carib and Antillean Crested Hummingbird

(Des J. Cooter. Litho Questa)

**1973** (9 Mar). *"Interpex 1973" (Quakers). T* **110** *and similar multicoloured designs. W* w **12** *(sideways on* ½ c. *and* 15 c.). *P* 13½.

284 ½ c. Type **110** .. .. .. .. .. 10 10
285 10 c. Lettsom House *(horiz)* .. .. .. 15 10
286 15 c. Dr. W. Thornton .. .. .. .. 20 10
287 30 c. Dr. Thornton and Capitol, Washington *(horiz)* .. .. .. .. .. 25 20
288 $1 William Penn *(horiz)* .. .. .. 70 85
284/8 .. .. .. .. .. *Set of* 5 1·25 1·10

(Des G. Drummond. Litho Questa)

**1973** (30 June). *First Issue of Coinage. T* **111** *and similar horiz designs showing coins and local scenery. Multicoloured. W* w **12**. *P* 14.

289 1 c. Type **111** .. .. .. .. .. 10 10
290 5 c. Zenaida Dove .. .. .. .. 40 10
291 10 c. Ringed Kingfisher .. .. .. .. 55 10
292 25 c. Mangrove Cuckoo .. .. .. .. 75 15
293 50 c. Brown Pelican .. .. .. .. 85 1·00
294 $1 Magnificent Frigatebird .. .. .. 1·25 1·75
289/94 .. .. .. .. *Set of* 6 3·50 2·75

**1973** (17 Oct). *As Nos.* 240, 243/5 *and* 248/9, *but wmk upright.*

295 ½ c. buff, red-brown and sepia .. .. 40 1·00
296 3 c. orange-red, cobalt and sepia .. .. 1·00 1·50
297 4 c. greenish blue, chalky blue & bistre-brn 1·00 1·50
298 5 c. emerald, pink and black .. .. .. 1·00 1·50
299 10 c. greenish blue, yellow-brown & red-brown 1·25 2·00
300 12 c. yellow, dull crimson and light brown .. 2·00 3·00
295/300 .. .. .. .. *Set of* 6 6·00 9·50

**1973** (14 Nov). *Royal Wedding. As Nos.* 165/6 *of Anguilla. Centre multicoloured. W* w **12** *(sideways). P* 13½.

301 5 c. brown-ochre .. .. .. .. 10 10
302 50 c. light turquoise-blue .. .. .. 20 15

**112** "The Virgin and Child" (Pintoricchio)

**113** Crest of the *Canopus* (French)

(Des G. Drummond. Litho Questa)

**1973** (7 Dec). *Christmas. T* **112** *and similar vert designs Multicoloured. W* w **12**. *P* 14.

303 ½ c. Type **112** .. .. .. .. .. 10 10
304 3 c. "Virgin and Child" (Lorenzo di Credi) .. 10 10
305 25 c. "Virgin and Child" (Crivelli) .. .. 15 10
306 50 c. "Virgin and Child with St. John" (Luini) 30 40
303/6 .. .. .. .. .. *Set of* 4 50 50

(Des J. Cooter. Litho Questa)

**1974** (22 Mar). *"Interpex 1974" (Naval Crests). T* **113** *and similar vert designs. Multicoloured. W* w **12**. *P* 14.

307 5 c. Type **113** .. .. .. .. .. 15 10
308 18 c. U.S.S. *Saginaw* .. .. .. .. 30 25
309 25 c. H.M.S. *Rothesay* .. .. .. .. 35 30
310 50 c. H.M.C.S. *Ottawa* .. .. .. .. 60 60
307/10 .. .. .. .. *Set of* 4 1·25 1·10
**MS**311 196 × 128 mm. Nos. 307/10 .. .. 1·75 3·25

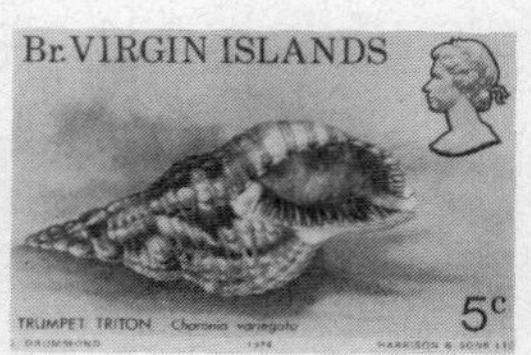


**114** Christopher Columbus **115** Trumpet Triton

(Des J. W. Litho Format)

**1974** (19 Aug). *Historical Figures. T* **114** *and similar vert designs. W w* **12**. *P* 14.
312 5 c. orange and black .. .. .. .. 20 10
313 10 c. greenish blue and black .. .. .. 35 10
314 25 c. reddish violet and black .. .. .. 50 25
315 40 c. yellow-brown and sepia .. .. .. 70 75
312/15 .. .. .. .. *Set of* 4 1·60 1·00
**MS**316 84 × 119 mm. Nos. 312/15 .. .. .. 1·60 2·00
Portraits:—10 c. Sir Walter Raleigh; 25 c. Sir Martin Frobisher; 40 c. Sir Francis Drake.

(Des G. Drummond. Litho Harrison)

**1974** (30 Sept). *Seashells. T* **115** *and similar horiz designs. Multicoloured. W w* **12**. *P* 13 × 13½.
317 5 c. Type **115** .. .. .. .. .. 30 15
a. Wmk T **53** of Lesotho (sideways) .. £140
318 18 c. West Indian Murex .. .. .. 60 30
319 25 c. Bleeding Tooth .. .. .. .. 75 35
320 75 c. Virgin Islands Latirus .. .. .. 1·75 1·75
317/20 .. .. .. .. *Set of* 4 3·00 2·25
**MS**321 146 × 95 mm. Nos. 317/20 .. .. .. 3·00 5·00

**116** Churchill and St. Mary, Aldermanbury, London **117** H.M.S. *Boreas*

(Des J. W. Litho Questa)

**1974** (30 Nov). *Birth Centenary of Sir Winston Churchill. T* **116** *and similar horiz design. Multicoloured. W w* **14** (*sideways*). *P* 14.
322 10 c. Type **116** .. .. .. .. 15 10
323 50 c. St. Mary, Fulton, Missouri .. .. 35 50
**MS**324 141 × 108 mm. Nos. 322/3 .. .. .. 80 1·40

(Des J. Cooter. Litho J. W.)

**1975** (14 Mar). *"Interpex 1975" Stamp Exhibition, New York. Ships' Figureheads. T* **117** *and similar vert designs. Multicoloured. W w* **12**. *P* 13.
325 5 c. Type **117** .. .. .. .. .. 15 10
326 18 c. *Golden Hind* .. .. .. .. 40 15
327 40 c. H.M.S. *Superb* .. .. .. .. 60 20
328 85 c. H.M.S. *Formidable* .. .. .. 1·25 1·00
325/8 .. .. .. .. *Set of* 4 2·25 1·25
**MS**329 192 × 127 mm. Nos. 325/8. (Wmk inverted). P 14 .. .. .. .. .. .. 3·00 5·50

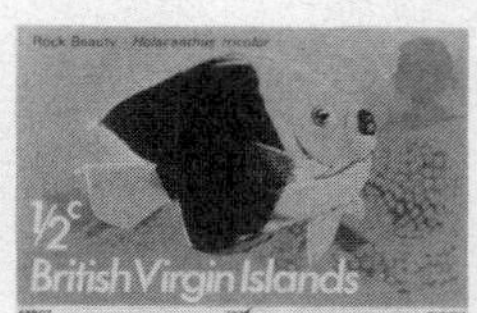


**118** Rock Beauty

(Des C. Abbott. Litho Questa)

**1975** (16 June–15 Aug). *Fishes. Horiz designs as T* **118**. *Multicoloured. W w* **14** (*sideways*). *P* 14.
330 ½ c. Type **118** .. .. .. .. 15 30
331 1 c. Squirrelfish .. .. .. .. 30 40
332 3 c. Queen Triggerfish .. .. .. 40 40
333 5 c. Blue Angelfish .. .. .. .. 30 20
334 8 c. Stoplight Parrotfish .. .. .. 30 25
335 10 c. Queen Angelfish .. .. .. .. 30 25
336 12 c. Nassau Grouper .. .. .. .. 40 30
337 13 c. Blue Tang .. .. .. .. 40 30
338 15 c. Sergeant Major .. .. .. .. 40 35
339 18 c. Jewfish .. .. .. .. .. 60 70
340 20 c. Bluehead Wrasse .. .. .. 60 70
341 25 c. Grey Angelfish .. .. .. .. 60 60
342 60 c. Glasseye Snapper .. .. .. 1·25 1·50
343 $1 Blue Chromis .. .. .. .. 1·75 1·75
344 $2.50, French Angelfish .. .. .. 3·50 4·00
345 $3 Queen Parrotfish .. .. .. 4·25 5·00
346 $5 Four-eye Butterfly Fish (15.8) .. .. 8·00 7·50
330/46 .. .. .. *Set of* 17 21·00 22·00
The original imprint at foot has the date "1975". Some values were later reprinted with the date altered to "1977".
The imprints on all the stamps show the designer's name as "Abbot".

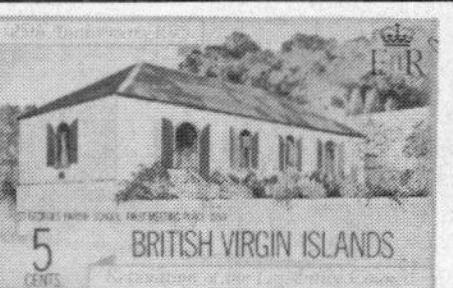


**119** St. George's Parish School (First meeting-place, 1950)

(Des R. Granger Barrett. Litho Questa)

**1975** (27 Nov). *25th Anniv of Restoration of Legislative Council. T* **119** *and similar horiz designs. Multicoloured. W w* **14** (*sideways*). *P* 14.
347 5 c. Type **119** .. .. .. .. .. 10 10
348 25 c. Legislative Council Building .. .. 25 10
349 40 c. Mace and gavel .. .. .. .. 35 15
350 75 c. Commemorative scroll .. .. .. 55 65
347/50 .. .. .. .. *Set of* 4 1·10 80

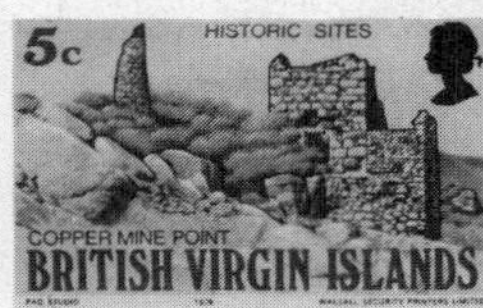


**120** Copper Mine Point

(Des PAD Studio. Litho Walsall)

**1976** (12 Mar). *Historic Sites. T* **120** *and similar horiz designs. Multicoloured. W w* **14** (*sideways*). *P* 14½.
351 5 c. Type **120** .. .. .. .. .. 10 10
352 18 c. Pleasant Valley .. .. .. .. 20 10
353 50 c. Callwood Distillery .. .. .. 40 30
354 75 c. The Dungeon .. .. .. .. 60 65
351/4 .. .. .. .. *Set of* 4 1·10 1·00

**121** Massachusetts Brig *Hazard*

(Des J. W. Litho Questa)

**1976** (29 May). *Bicentenary of American Revolution. T* **121** *and similar horiz designs. Multicoloured, W w* **14** (*sideways*). *P* 14.
355 8 c. Type **121** .. .. .. .. .. 50 15
356 22 c. American Privateer *Spy* .. .. .. 1·00 45
357 40 c. Continental Navy frigate *Raleigh* .. 1·50 1·00
358 75 c. Frigate *Alliance* and H.M.S. *Trepassy* .. 2·00 1·90
355/8 .. .. .. .. *Set of* 4 4·50 3·25
**MS**359 114×89 mm. Nos. 355/8 .. .. .. 6·50 9·50

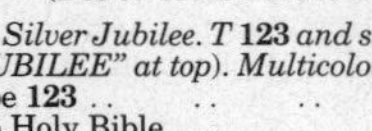

**122** Government House, Tortola **123** Royal Visit, 1966

(Des Walsall. Litho Questa)

**1976** (29 Oct). *Fifth Anniv of Friendship Day with U.S. Virgin Is. T* **122** *and similar multicoloured designs. W w* **14** (*sideways on* 8 *and* 75 *c.*). *P* 14.
360 8 c. Type **122** .. .. .. .. .. 10 10
361 15 c. Government House, St. Croix (*vert*) .. 10 10
362 30 c. Flags (*vert*) .. .. .. .. 15 10
363 75 c. Government seals .. .. .. 30 40
360/3 .. .. .. .. *Set of* 4 50 55

(Des J. Cooter. Litho Walsall)

**1977** (7 Feb). *Silver Jubilee. T* **123** *and similar vert designs* (*inscr "SILVER JUBILEE" at top*). *Multicoloured. W w* **14**. *P* 13½.
364 8 c. Type **123** .. .. .. .. .. 10 10
365 30 c. The Holy Bible .. .. .. .. 15 15
366 60 c. Presentation of Holy Bible .. .. 25 40
364/6 .. .. .. .. *Set of* 3 40 50
For stamps with different inscription, see Nos. 371/3.
The imprint at the stamp's foot gives the designer (wrongly) as "Waddington Studio".

**124** Chart of 1739

(Des J. Cooter. Litho Walsall)

**1977** (13 June). *18th-Century Maps. T* **124** *and similar horiz designs. Multicoloured. W w* **14**. *P* 13½.
367 8 c. Type **124** .. .. .. .. .. 30 10
368 22 c. French Map, 1758 .. .. .. 55 30
369 30 c. Map from English and Danish surveys, 1775 .. .. .. .. .. .. 75 65
370 75 c. Map of 1779 .. .. .. .. 1·25 1·50
367/70 .. .. .. .. *Set of* 4 2·50 2·25

**1977** (26 Oct). *Royal Visit. Designs as Nos.* 364/6 *but inscr.* "SILVER JUBILEE ROYAL VISIT" *at top, and face-values changed.*
371 5 c. Type **123** .. .. .. .. .. 10 10
372 25 c. The Holy Bible .. .. .. .. 15 10
373 50 c. Presentation of Holy Bible .. .. 30 25
371/3 .. .. .. .. *Set of* 3 45 35
The above also differ from Nos. 364/6 in having the silver frame removed and the silver lettering replaced by white. The imprint at foot now has the designer's name correctly given as "J. E. Cooter".

**125** Divers checking Equipment **126** Fire Coral

(Des J. W. Litho Rosenbaum Bros, Vienna)

**1978** (10 Feb). *Tourism. T* **125** *and similar vert designs. Multicoloured. W w* **14**. *P* 13½.
374 ½ c. Type **125** .. .. .. .. .. 10 10
375 5 c. Cup coral on wreck of *Rhone* .. .. 15 10
376 8 c. Sponge formation on wreck of *Rhone* .. 20 10
377 22 c. Cup coral and sponges .. .. .. 50 15
378 30 c. Sponges inside cave .. .. .. 60 20
379 75 c. Marine life .. .. .. .. 1·10 85
374/9 .. .. .. .. *Set of* 6 2·25 1·25

(Des G. Drummond. Litho Harrison)

**1978** (27 Feb). *Corals. T* **126** *and similar horiz designs. Multicoloured. W w* **14** (*sideways*). *P* 14.
380 8 c. Type **126** .. .. .. .. .. 25 15
381 15 c. Staghorn coral .. .. .. .. 40 30
382 40 c. Brain coral .. .. .. .. 75 85
383 75 c. Elkhorn coral .. .. .. .. 1·50 1·60
380/3 .. .. .. .. *Set of* 4 2·50 2·50

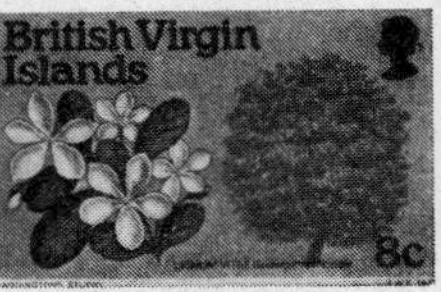


**127** Iguana **128** Lignum Vitae

(Des Jennifer Toombs. Litho Questa)

**1978** (2 June). *25th Anniv of Coronation. T* **127** *and similar vert designs. P* 15.
384 50 c. brown-ochre, green and silver .. .. 25 40
a. Sheetlet. Nos. 384/6 × 2 .. .. 1·25
385 50 c. multicoloured .. .. .. .. 25 40
386 50 c. brown-ochre, green and silver .. .. 25 40
384/6 .. .. .. .. *Set of* 3 65 1·10
Designs:—No. 384, Plantagenet Falcon; No. 385, Queen Elizabeth II; No. 386, Type **127**.

(Des and litho J.W.)

**1978** (4 Sept). *Flowering Trees. T* **128** *and similar horiz designs. Multicoloured. W w* **14** (*sideways*). *P* 13.
387 8 c. Type **128** .. .. .. .. .. 15 10
388 22 c. Ginger Thomas .. .. .. .. 25 15
389 40 c. Dog Almond .. .. .. .. 35 20
390 75 c. White Cedar .. .. .. .. 60 70
387/90 .. .. .. .. *Set of* 4 1·25 1·00
**MS**391 131 × 95 mm. Nos. 387/90. P 14 .. .. 1·75 2·75

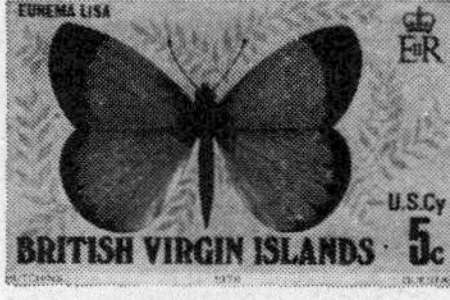


**129** *Eurema lisa*

(Des G. Hutchins. Litho Questa)

**1978** (4 Dec). *Butterflies. T* **129** *and similar horiz designs. Multicoloured. W w* **14** (*sideways*). *P* 14.
392 5 c. Type **129** .. .. .. .. .. 25 10
393 22 c. *Agraulis vanillae* .. .. .. .. 75 20
394 30 c. *Heliconius charithonia* .. .. .. 85 30
395 75 c. *Hemiargus hanno* .. .. .. .. 1·25 1·25
392/5 .. .. .. .. *Set of* 4 2·75 1·75
**MS**396 159×113 mm. No. 392×6 and 393×3 .. 2·50 4·00

**130** Spiny Lobster

(Des Picton Print. Litho Harrison)

**1979** (10 Feb). *Wildlife Conservation. T* **130** *and similar multi-coloured designs.* W w **14** (*sideways on* 5 *and* 22 *c.*). *P* 14.

397 5 c. Type **130** .. 15 10
398 15 c. Large Iguana (*vert*) .. 30 10
399 22 c. Hawksbill Turtle .. 50 15
400 75 c. Black Coral (*vert*) .. 1·10 90
397/400 .. *Set of* 4 1·90 1·10
**MS**401 130 × 153 mm. Nos. 397/400 (wmk sideways) .. 2·25 3·25

**131** Strawberry Cactus **132** West Indian Girl

(Des BG Studio. Litho Format)

**1979** (7 May). *Cacti. T* **131** *and similar vert designs. Multi-coloured.* W w **14**. *P* 14.

402 ½ c. Type **131** .. 10 10
403 5 c. Snowy Cactus .. 15 10
404 13 c. Barrel Cactus .. 25 20
405 22 c. Tree Cactus .. 40 35
406 30 c. Prickly Pear .. 45 40
407 75 c. Dildo Cactus .. 80 1·00
402/7 .. *Set of* 6 1·90 1·90

(Des R. Granger Barrett. Litho Questa)

**1979** (9 July). *International Year of the Child. T* **132** *and similar vert designs. Multicoloured.* W w **14** (*inverted*). *P* 14½ × 14.

408 5 c. Type **132** .. 10 10
409 10 c. African boy .. 10 10
410 13 c. Asian girl .. 10 10
411 $1 European boy .. 50 85
408/11 .. *Set of* 4 65 1·00
**MS**412 91 × 114 mm. Nos. 408/11 .. 70 1·50

**133** 1956 Road Harbour 3 c. Definitive Stamp **134** Pencil Urchin

(Des J. W. Photo Heraclio Fournier)

**1979** (1 Oct). *Death Centenary of Sir Rowland Hill. T* **133** *and similar designs showing stamps. P* 13½.

413 5 c. deep blue, new blue and brown-olive .. 10 10
414 13 c. deep blue and claret .. 10 10
415 75 c. deep blue and bright purple .. 45 50
413/15 .. *Set of* 3 55 55
**MS**416 37 × 91 mm. $1 deep blue & carm-red. P 13 70 1·25

Designs: (39 × 27 *mm*)—13 c. 1889 2½d.; 75 c. Great Britain unissued 1910 2d. Tyrian plum. (40 × 28 *mm*)—$1. 1867 1s. "Missing Virgin" error.

(Des BG Studio. Litho Questa)

**1979** (17 Dec)–**82**. *Marine Life. Vert designs as T* **134**. *Multi-coloured.* W w **14**. *Ordinary paper. P* 14.

417 ½ c. Calcified Algae (1.4.80) .. 20 40
418 1 c. Purple-tipped Sea Anemone (1.4.80) .. 25 45
419 3 c. Common Starfish (1.4.80) .. 30 45
420 5 c. Type **134** .. 35 30
a. Chalk-surfaced paper (27.8.82) .. 30 30
421 8 c. Triton's Trumpet (shell) .. 50 40
a. Chalk-surfaced paper (27.8.82) .. 55 40
422 10 c. Christmas Tree Worms .. 30 40
423 13 c. Flamingo Tongue Snail (1.4.80) .. 50 60
a. Chalk-surfaced paper (27.8.82) .. 55 40
424 15 c. Spider Crab .. 40 40
a. Chalk-surfaced paper (27.8.82) .. 55 40
425 18 c. Sea Squirts (1.4.80) .. 70 75
426 20 c. True Tulip (shell) .. 55 55
a. Chalk-surfaced paper (27.8.82) .. 60 50
427 25 c. Rooster Tail Conch (shell) .. 1·00 1·00
428 30 c. Fighting Conch (shell) (1.4.80) .. 85 80
a. Chalk-surfaced paper (27.8.82) .. 85 65
429 60 c. Mangrove Crab (1.4.80) .. 1·75 1·50
430 $1 Coral Polyps (1.4.80) .. 2·50 2·75
431 $2.50, Peppermint Shrimp .. 3·50 4·25
432 $3 West Indian Murex (shell) .. 4·00 4·75
433 $5 Carpet Anemone (1.4.80) .. 7·75 8·50
417/33 .. *Set of* 17 23·00 25·00

Nos. 420a/28a were printed with a changed imprint date, "1982".

**135** Rotary Athletics Meeting, Tortola **136** Brown Booby

(Des J. W. Litho Enschedé)

**1980** (23 Feb). *75th Anniv of Rotary International. T* **135** *and similar horiz designs. Multicoloured.* W w **14** (*sideways*). *P* 13½ × 14.

434 8 c. Type **135** .. 10 10
435 22 c. Paul P. Harris (founder) and Rotary emblem .. 15 10
436 60 c. "Creation of a National Park", Mount Sage, Tortola .. 40 40
437 $1 Rotary anniversary emblem .. 70 75
434/7 .. *Set of* 4 1·25 1·25
**MS**438 149 × 148 mm. Nos. 434/7 .. 1·75 2·75

(Des K. Penny. Litho Secura, Singapore)

**1980** (6 May). *"London 1980" International Stamp Exhibition. Birds. T* **136** *and similar horiz designs. Multicoloured.* W w **14** (*sideways*). *P* 13½.

439 20 c. Type **136** .. 20 20
a. Wmk upright .. 40 40
440 25 c. Magnificent Frigate Bird .. 25 25
a. Wmk upright .. 1·75 1·75
441 50 c. White-tailed Tropic Bird .. 40 40
a. Wmk upright .. 65 65
442 75 c. Brown Pelican .. 55 55
439/42 .. *Set of* 4 1·25 1·25
**MS**443 152 × 130 mm. Nos. 439/42 .. 1·25 1·75

CARIBBEAN
COMMONWEALTH
PARLIAMENTARY
ASSOCIATION
MEETING
TORTOLA 11-19 JULY 1980

(**137**)

**138** Sir Francis Drake

**1980** (7 July). *Caribbean Commonwealth Parliamentary Association Meeting, Tortola. Nos.* 414/15 *optd with T* **137**.

444 13 c. deep blue and claret .. 15 10
445 75 c. deep blue and bright blue .. 40 40

(Des Franklin Mint. Litho Questa)

**1980** (26 Sept). *Sir Francis Drake Commemoration. T* **138** *and similar vert designs. Multicoloured.* W w **14** (*inverted on* 75 *c.*). *P* 14 × 14½.

446 8 c. Type **138** .. 40 10
447 15 c. Queen Elizabeth I .. 60 15
448 30 c. Drake receiving knighthood .. 75 30
449 75 c. *Golden Hind* and coat of arms .. 1·50 80
446/9 .. *Set of* 4 3·00 1·25
**MS**450 171 × 121 mm. Nos. 446/9. Wmk inverted 3·00 3·75
a. 75 c. value in miniature sheet imperf .. £150
b. 30 c. value in miniature sheet imperf .. £150

**139** Jost van Dyke

(Des Jennifer Toombs. Litho Rosenbaum Bros, Vienna)

**1980** (1 Dec). *Island Profiles. T* **139** *and similar horiz designs. Multicoloured.* W w **14** (*sideways*). *P* 13½.

451 2 c. Type **139** .. 10 10
452 5 c. Peter Island .. 10 10
453 13 c. Virgin Gorda .. 15 10
454 22 c. Anegada .. 20 10
455 30 c. Norman Island .. 30 15
456 $1 Tortola .. 85 1·00
451/6 .. *Set of* 6 1·50 1·10
**MS**457 95 × 88 mm. No. 456 (wmk upright) .. 85 1·50
a. Error. Imperf .. £325
b. Gold and black omitted .. £325

## OMNIBUS ISSUES

Details, together with prices for complete sets, of the various Omnibus issues from the 1935 Silver Jubilee series to date are included in a special section following Zimbabwe at the end of Volume 2.

**140** Dancing Lady **141** Wedding Bouquet from British Virgin Islands

(Des C. Abbott. Litho Walsall)

**1981** (3 Mar). *Flowers. T* **140** *and similar vert designs. Multi-coloured.* W w **14** (*sideways*). *P* 11.

458 5 c. Type **140** .. 15 10
459 20 c. Love in the Mist .. 40 25
460 22 c. *Pitcairnia angustifolia* .. 40 25
461 75 c. Dutchman's Pipe .. 1·40 1·40
462 $1 Maiden Apple .. 1·60 1·60
458/62 .. *Set of* 5 3·50 3·25

(Des J. W. Litho Harrison)

**1981** (22 July). *Royal Wedding. T* **141** *and similar vert designs. Multicoloured.* W w **14**. *P* 14.

463 10 c. Type **141** .. 10 10
464 35 c. Prince Charles and Queen Elizabeth the Queen Mother in Garter robes .. 30 15
465 $1.25, Prince Charles and Lady Diana Spencer .. 80 80
463/5 .. *Set of* 3 1·10 90

**142** Stamp Collecting **143** "Development through Education"

(Des BG Studio. Litho Questa)

**1981** (10 Oct). *25th Anniv of Duke of Edinburgh Award Scheme. T* **142** *and similar vert designs. Multicoloured.* W w **14**. *P* 14.

466 10 c. Type **142** .. 10 10
467 15 c. Athletics .. 10 10
468 50 c. Camping .. 25 25
469 $1 Duke of Edinburgh .. 40 45
466/9 .. *Set of* 4 65 80

(Des G. Vasarhelyi. Litho Walsall)

**1981** (19 Oct). *International Year for Disabled Persons. T* **143** *and similar horiz designs. Multicoloured.* W w **14** (*sideways*). *P* 14.

470 15 c. Type **143** .. 20 20
471 20 c. Fort Charlotte Children's Centre .. 30 30
472 30 c. "Developing cultural awareness" .. 40 40
473 $1 Fort Charlotte Children's Centre (*different*) .. 1·25 1·25
470/3 .. *Set of* 4 2·00 2·00

**144** Detail from "The Adoration of the Shepherds" (Rubens) **145** Green-throated Caribs and Erythrina

(Des J. W. Litho Questa)

**1981** (30 Nov). *Christmas. T* **144** *and similar designs showing details from "The Adoration of the Shepherds" by Rubens.* W w **14**. *P* 14.

474 5 c. multicoloured .. 10 10
475 15 c. multicoloured .. 20 10
476 30 c. multicoloured .. 40 15
477 $1 multicoloured .. 1·00 1·10
474/7 .. *Set of* 4 1·50 1·25
**MS**478 117 × 90 mm. 50 c. multicoloured (*horiz*) (wmk sideways) .. 1·10 85

(Des Walsall. Litho Format)

**1982** (5 Apr). *Hummingbirds. T* **145** *and similar vert designs. Multicoloured.* W w **14**. *P* 14 × 14½.

479 15 c. Type **145** .. 40 15
480 30 c. Green-throated Carib and Bougainvillea 65 45
481 35 c. Antillean Crested Hummingbirds and *Granadilla passiflora* .. 75 55
482 $1.25, Antillean Crested Hummingbird and Hibiscus .. 2·50 2·75
479/82 .. *Set of* 4 4·00 3·50

**146** "People caring for People"

**147** Princess at Victoria and Albert Museum, November 1981

(Des Harrison. Litho Format)

**1982** (3 May). *Tenth Anniv of Lions Club of Tortola. T* **146** *and similar horiz designs. Multicoloured. W* w **14** *(sideways). P* 13½ × 14.

483 10 c. Type **146** .. .. .. .. .. 20 15
484 20 c. Tortola Headquarters .. .. .. .. 40 20
485 30 c. "We Serve" .. .. .. .. .. 50 30
486 $1.50, "Lions" symbol .. .. .. .. 1·90 1·75
483/6 .. .. .. .. .. .. *Set of* 4 2·75 2·25
**MS**487 124 × 102 mm. Nos. 483/6 .. .. .. 3·25 3·75

(Des C. Abbott. Litho Harrison)

**1982** (2 July*). *21st Birthday of Princess of Wales. T* **147** *and similar vert designs. Multicoloured. W* w **14**. *P* 14½ × 14.

488 10 c. British Virgin Islands coat of arms .. 15 10
489 35 c. Type **147** .. .. .. .. .. 30 30
490 50 c. Bride and groom proceeding into Vestry 50 50
491 $1.50, Formal portrait .. .. .. .. 1·25 1·60
488/91 .. .. .. .. .. *Set of* 4 2·00 2·25

*This is the local release date. The Crown Agents released the stamps on 1 July.

**148** Douglas "DC-3"

(Des A. Theobald. Litho Questa)

**1982** (10 Sept). *10th Anniv of Air BVI. T* **148** *and similar horiz designs. Multicoloured. W* w **14** *(sideways). P* 14.

492 10 c. Type **148** .. .. .. .. .. 20 15
493 15 c. Britten-Norman "Islander" .. .. .. 25 20
494 60 c. Hawker Siddeley "748" .. .. .. 90 75
495 75 c. Runway scene .. .. .. .. 1·10 90
492/5 .. .. .. .. .. *Set of* 4 2·25 1·75

**149** Scouts raising Flag

(Des R. Vigurs. Litho Questa)

**1982** (18 Nov). *75th Anniv of Boy Scout Movement* ($1) *and 50th Anniv of Scouting in B.V.I. (others). T* **149** *and similar horiz designs. Multicoloured. W* w **14** *(sideways). P* 14.

496 8 c. Type **149** .. .. .. .. .. 20 10
497 20 c. Cub Scout .. .. .. .. .. 45 25
498 50 c. Sea Scout .. .. .. .. .. 85 55
499 $1 First camp, Brownsea Island, and portrait of Lord Baden-Powell .. .. .. .. 1·50 1·50
496/9 .. .. .. .. .. *Set of* 4 2·75 2·25

**150** Legislature in Session

**151** Florence Nightingale

(Des G. Vasarhelyi. Litho Enschedé)

**1983** (10 Mar). *Commonwealth Day. T* **150** *and similar horiz designs. Multicoloured. W* w **14** *(sideways). P* 13 × 13½.

500 10 c. Type **150** .. .. .. .. .. 10 10
501 30 c. Tourism .. .. .. .. .. 25 20
502 35 c. Satellite view of Earth showing Virgin Islands .. .. .. .. .. 25 25
503 75 c. B.V.I. and Commonwealth flags .. .. 70 90
500/3 .. .. .. .. .. *Set of* 4 1·10 1·25

(Des L. Curtis. Litho Questa)

**1983** (9 May). *Nursing Week. T* **151** *and similar multicoloured designs. W* w **14** *(sideways on* 60 c. *and* 75 c.). *P* 14.

504 10 c. Type **151** .. .. .. .. .. 40 15
505 30 c. Staff nurse and assistant nurse .. .. 75 45
506 60 c. Public Health nurses testing blood pressure *(horiz)* .. .. .. .. 1·40 95
507 75 c. Peebles Hospital *(horiz)* .. .. .. 1·75 1·25
504/7 .. .. .. .. .. *Set of* 4 4·00 2·50

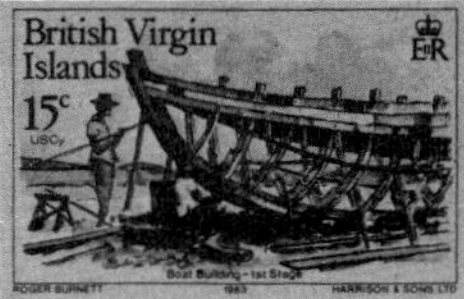


**152** Frame Construction

(Des R. Burnett. Litho Harrison)

**1983** (25 July). *Traditional Boat-building. T* **152** *and similar horiz designs. Multicoloured. W* w **14** *(sideways). P* 14.

508 15 c. Type **152** .. .. .. .. .. 30 25
509 25 c. Planking .. .. .. .. .. 45 40
510 50 c. Launching .. .. .. .. .. 80 70
511 $1 Maiden voyage .. .. .. .. 1·50 1·40
508/11 .. .. .. .. .. *Set of* 4 2·75 2·50
**MS**512 127 × 101 mm. Nos. 508/11 .. .. 3·00 3·75

**153** Grumman "Goose" Seaplane

**154** "Madonna and Child with the Infant Baptist"

(Des Walsall. Litho Questa)

**1983** (15 Sept). *Bicentenary of Manned Flight. T* **153** *and similar horiz designs. Multicoloured. W* w **14** *(sideways). P* 14.

513 10 c. Type **153** .. .. .. .. .. 20 15
514 30 c. De Havilland "Heron" .. .. .. 45 45
515 60 c. EMB "110P1 Bandeirante" .. .. .. 85 85
516 $1.25, British Aerospace "HS 748" .. .. 1·50 1·60
513/16 .. .. .. .. .. *Set of* 4 2·75 2·75

(Des M. Joyce. Litho Questa)

**1983** (7 Nov). *Christmas. 500th Birth Anniv of Raphael. T* **154** *and similar vert designs showing details of different paintings. Multicoloured. W* w **14**. *P* 14½ × 14.

517 8 c. Type **154** .. .. .. .. .. 10 10
518 15 c. "La Belle Jardiniére" .. .. .. 20 25
519 50 c. "Madonna Del Granduca" .. .. .. 65 70
520 $1 "The Terranuova Madonna" .. .. .. 1·25 1·40
517/20 .. .. .. .. .. *Set of* 4 2·00 2·25
**MS**521 108 × 101 mm. Nos. 517/20 .. .. 2·10 3·25

**155** Local Tournament

**156** Port Purcell

(Des L. Curtis. Litho Questa)

**1984** (20 Feb). *60th Anniv of World Chess Federation. T* **155** *and similar multicoloured designs. W* w **14** *(sideways on* 10 c. *and* $1, *inverted on* 35 c.). *P* 14.

522 10 c. Type **155** .. .. .. .. .. 75 30
523 35 c. "Staunton" chess pieces *(vert)* .. .. 1·40 80
524 75 c. Winning position, 1980 Chess Olympiad *(vert)* .. .. .. .. .. 2·75 2·50
525 $1 B.V.I. Gold Medal from 1980 Chess Olympiad .. .. .. .. .. 3·25 3·25
522/5 .. .. .. .. .. *Set of* 4 7·25 6·25

(Des L. Curtis. Litho Questa)

**1984** (16 Apr). *250th Anniv of "Lloyd's List" (newspaper). T* **156** *and similar vert designs. Multicoloured. W* w **14**. *P* 14½ × 14.

526 15 c. Type **156** .. .. .. .. .. 25 30
527 25 c. Boeing "747" .. .. .. .. 45 50
528 50 c. Loss of R.M.S. *Rhone* .. .. .. 90 95
529 $1 M.S. *Booker Viking* .. .. .. 1·50 1·60
526/9 .. .. .. .. .. *Set of* 4 2·75 3·00

**157** Mail Ship *Boyne*, Aeroplane and U.P.U. Logo

(Des L. Curtis. Litho Walsall)

**1984** (16 May). *Universal Postal Union Congress, Hamburg. Sheet* 90 × 69 *mm. W* w **14** *(sideways). P* 14.

**MS**530 **157** $1 pale blue and black .. .. 2·50 2·50

**158** Running

**159** Steel Band

(Des R. Granger Barrett. Litho Walsall)

**1984** (3 July). *Olympic Games, Los Angeles. T* **158** *and similar horiz designs. Multicoloured. W* w **14** *(sideways). P* 14.

531 15 c. Type **158** .. .. .. .. .. 30 30
a. Pair. Nos. 531/2 .. .. .. .. 60 60
532 15 c. Runner .. .. .. .. .. 30 30
533 20 c. Wind-surfing .. .. .. .. 35 35
a. Pair. Nos. 533/4 .. .. .. .. 70 70
534 20 c. Surfer .. .. .. .. .. 35 35
535 30 c. Sailing .. .. .. .. .. 50 50
a. Pair. Nos. 535/6 .. .. .. .. 1·00 1·00
536 30 c. Yacht .. .. .. .. .. 50 50
531/6 .. .. .. .. .. *Set of* 6 2·10 2·10
**MS**537 97 × 69 mm. $1 Torch bearer. Wmk upright 1·50 1·90

Nos. 531/2, 533/4 and 535/6 were printed together, *se-tenant*, in horizontal and vertical pairs throughout the sheets.

(Des D. Miller. Litho Format)

**1984** (14 Aug). *150th Anniv of Abolition of Slavery. T* **159** *and similar vert designs showing various aspects of Emancipation Festival. Multicoloured. W* w **14**. *P* 14.

538 10 c. Type **159** .. .. .. .. .. 20 25
a. Horiz strip of 5. Nos. 538/42 .. .. 90
539 10 c. Dancing girls .. .. .. .. 20 25
540 10 c. Men in traditional costumes .. .. 20 25
541 10 c. Girl in traditional costume .. .. 20 25
542 10 c. Festival Queen .. .. .. .. 20 25
543 30 c. Green and yellow dinghies .. .. 40 45
a. Horiz strip of 5. Nos. 543/7 .. .. 1·75
544 30 c. Blue and red dinghies .. .. .. 40 45
545 30 c. White and blue dinghies .. .. .. 40 45
546 30 c. Red and yellow dinghies .. .. .. 40 45
547 30 c. Blue and white dinghies .. .. .. 40 45
538/47 .. .. .. .. .. *Set of* 10 2·50 3·00

Nos. 538/42 and 543/7 were each printed together, *se-tenant*, in horizontal strips of 5 throughout the sheet, forming composite designs. On Nos. 543/7 the sail colours of the dinghies are described to assist identification.

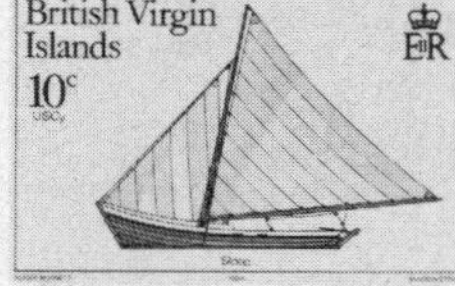


**160** Sloop

(Des R. Burnett. Litho J .W.)

**1984** (15 Nov). *Boats. T* **160** *and similar horiz designs. Multicoloured. W* w **14** *(sideways). P* 13 × 13½.

548 10 c. Type **160** .. .. .. .. .. 30 20
549 35 c. Fishing boat .. .. .. .. 85 65
550 60 c. Schooner .. .. .. .. .. 1·40 1·10
551 75 c. Cargo boat .. .. .. .. 1·60 1·40
548/51 .. .. .. .. .. *Set of* 4 3·75 3·00
**MS**552 125 × 90 mm. Nos. 548/51. P 14 .. .. 3·75 3·50

**161** One Cent Coin and Aerial View

**162** Red-billed Tropic Bird

(Litho Walsall)

**1985** (15 Jan). *New Coinage. T* **161** *and similar horiz designs showing coins and local scenery. Multicoloured. W* w **14** *(sideways). P* 14½.

553 1 c. Type **161** .. .. .. .. .. 10 10
554 5 c. Five cent coin and boulders on beach .. 10 10
555 10 c. Ten cent coin and scuba diving .. .. 20 20
556 25 c. Twenty-five cent coin and yachts .. .. 45 45
557 50 c. Fifty cent coin and jetty .. .. .. 90 1·00
558 $1 One dollar coin and beach at night .. 1·75 2·00
553/8 .. .. .. .. .. *Set of* 6 3·00 3·50
**MS**559 103 × 156 mm. Nos. 553/8 .. .. 3·00 5·00

A set of stamps, 55 c. and $1·50 each × 2, showing Michael Jackson the entertainer was prepared in 1985, but was never released for postal use. Samples of the $1.50 values were, however, distributed for publicity purposes and both values exist from stock dispersed by the liquidator of Format International Security Printers Ltd.

(Des N. Arlott. Litho Questa)

**1985** (3 July). *Birds of the British Virgin Islands. T* **162** *and similar vert designs. Multicoloured. W* w **14**. *P* 14.

| | | | |
|---|---|---|---|
| 560 | 1 c. Type **162** | 15 | 20 |
| 561 | 2 c. Yellow-crowned Night Heron | 15 | 20 |
| 562 | 5 c. Mangrove Cuckoo | 20 | 20 |
| 563 | 8 c. Northern Mockingbird | 20 | 20 |
| 564 | 10 c. Grey Kingbird | 65 | 30 |
| 565 | 12 c. Red-necked Pigeon | 20 | 20 |
| 566 | 15 c. Least Bittern | 80 | 50 |
| 567 | 18 c. Smooth-billed Ani | 30 | 30 |
| 568 | 20 c. Clapper Rail | 90 | 60 |
| 569 | 25 c. American Kestrel | 1·00 | 75 |
| 570 | 30 c. Pearly-eyed Thrasher | 50 | 55 |
| 571 | 35 c. Bridled Quail Dove | 1·25 | 85 |
| 572 | 40 c. Green Heron | 55 | 60 |
| 573 | 50 c. Scaly-breasted Ground Dove | 70 | 80 |
| 574 | 60 c. Little Blue Heron | 80 | 1·00 |
| 575 | $1 Audubon's Shearwater | 3·50 | 2·00 |
| 576 | $2 Blue-faced Booby | 2·75 | 2·25 |
| 577 | $3 Cattle Egret | 7·00 | 5·50 |
| 578 | $5 Zenaida Dove | 7·00 | 6·50 |
| 560/78 | *Set of* 19 | 26·00 | 21·00 |

For these stamps watermarked w **16** see Nos. 647/60.

**IMPERFORATES AND MISSING COLOURS.** Various issues between Nos. 579 and 609 exist either imperforate or with colours omitted. Such items are not listed as there is no evidence that they fulfil the criteria outlined on page xi of this catalogue.

**163** The Queen Mother at Festival of Remembrance

**164** Seaside Sparrow

(Des Maxine Marsh. Litho Format)

**1985** (26 Aug). *Life and Times of Queen Elizabeth the Queen Mother. Various vertical portraits as T* **163**. *Multicoloured. P* 12½. A. *W* w **15** (*sideways*). B. *No wmk.*

| | | A. | | B. | |
|---|---|---|---|---|---|
| 579 | 10 c. Type **163** | 15 | 20 | 2·50 | 2·50 |
| | a. Horiz pair. Nos. 579/80 | 30 | 40 | 5·00 | 5·00 |
| 580 | 10 c. At Victoria Palace Theatre, 1984 | 15 | 20 | 2·50 | 2·50 |
| 581 | 25 c. At the engagement of the Prince of Wales, 1981 | 35 | 40 | 2·50 | 2·50 |
| | a. Horiz pair. Nos. 581/2 | 70 | 80 | 5·00 | 5·00 |
| 582 | 25 c. Opening Celia Johnson Theatre, 1985 | 35 | 40 | 2·50 | 2·50 |
| 583 | 50 c. The Queen Mother on her 82nd birthday | 70 | 75 | 3·00 | 3·00 |
| | a. Horiz pair. Nos. 583/4 | 1·40 | 1·50 | 6·00 | 6·00 |
| 584 | 50 c. At the Tate Gallery, 1983 | 70 | 75 | 3·00 | 3·00 |
| 585 | 75 c. At the Royal Smithfield Show, 1983 | 1·10 | 1·25 | 3·00 | 3·00 |
| | a. Horiz pair. Nos. 585/6 | 2·25 | 2·50 | 6·00 | 6·00 |
| 586 | 75 c. Unveiling Mountbatten statue, 1983 | 1·10 | 1·25 | 3·00 | 3·00 |
| 579/86 | *Set of* 8 | 4·25 | 4·50 | 20·00 | 20·00 |
| **MS**587 | 85×114 mm. $1 At Columbia University; $1 At a Wedding, St. Margaret's Westminster, 1983 | 3·50 | 4·00 | † | |

The two designs of each value were issued, *se-tenant*, in horizontal pairs within the sheets.

Each *se-tenant* pair shows a floral pattern across the bottom of the portraits which stops short of the left-hand edge on the left-hand stamp and of the right-hand edge on the right-hand stamp.

Sets of four miniature sheets, containing the two designs of each value, were prepared, but not issued. Examples exist from stock dispersed by the liquidator of Format International Security Printers Ltd.

Designs as Nos. 583/4 and 585/6, but with face values of $1×2 and $2.50×2, also exist in additional miniature sheets from a restricted printing issued 18 December 1985.

(Des R. Vigurs. Litho Format)

**1985** (17 Dec). *Birth Bicentenary of John J. Audubon (ornithologist). T* **164** *and similar vert designs. showing original paintings. Multicoloured. P* 15.

| | | | |
|---|---|---|---|
| 588 | 5 c. Type **164** | 40 | 15 |
| 589 | 30 c. Passenger Pigeon | 1·00 | 60 |
| 590 | 50 c. Yellow-breasted Chat | 1·25 | 1·25 |
| 591 | $1 American Kestrel | 2·00 | 2·00 |
| 588/91 | *Set of* 4 | 4·25 | 3·50 |

**165** S.V. *Flying Cloud*

MIAMI

B.V.I.

INAUGURAL FLIGHT

(**166**)

(Des G. Drummond. Litho Format)

**1986** (27 Jan). *Visiting Cruise Ships. T* **165** *and similar horiz designs. Multicoloured. W* w **15**. *P* 15.

| | | | |
|---|---|---|---|
| 592 | 35 c. Type **165** | 1·50 | 85 |
| 593 | 50 c. M.V. *Newport Clipper* | 2·00 | 1·25 |
| 594 | 75 c. M.V. *Cunard Countess* | 2·50 | 2·00 |
| 595 | $1 M.V. *Sea Goddess* | 2·75 | 2·50 |
| 592/5 | *Set of* 4 | 8·00 | 6·00 |

**1986** (17 Apr). *Inaugural Flight of Miami–Beef Island Air Service. Nos.* 581/2 *and* 585/6 *optd with T* **166**. A. *W* w **15** (*sideways*). B. *No wmk.*

| | | A. | | B. | |
|---|---|---|---|---|---|
| 596 | 25 c. At the engagement of the Prince of Wales, 1981 | 35 | 40 | 2·25 | 2·25 |
| | a. Horiz pair. Nos. 596/7 | 70 | 80 | 4·50 | 4·50 |
| 597 | 25 c. Opening Celia Johnson theatre, 1985 | 35 | 40 | 2·25 | 2·25 |
| 598 | 75 c. At the Royal Smithfield Show, 1983 | 1·10 | 1·25 | 2·25 | 2·25 |
| | a. Horiz pair. Nos. 598/9 | 2·25 | 2·50 | 4·50 | 4·50 |
| 599 | 75 c. Unveiling Mountbatten statue, 1983 | 1·10 | 1·25 | 2·25 | 2·25 |
| 596/9 | *Set of* 4 | 2·50 | 3·00 | 8·00 | 8·00 |

**167** Queen Elizabeth II in 1958

(Des Court House Studio. Litho Format)

**1986** (21 Apr). *60th Birthday of Queen Elizabeth II. T* **167** *and similar multicoloured designs. P* 12½.

| | | | |
|---|---|---|---|
| 600 | 12 c. Type **167** | 15 | 20 |
| 601 | 35 c. At a Maundy Service | 40 | 45 |
| | a. Wmk w **15** (sideways) | 2·00 | |
| 602 | $1.50. Queen Elizabeth | 1·90 | 2·00 |
| | a. Wmk w **15** (sideways) | 3·00 | |
| 603 | $2 During a visit to Canberra, 1982 (*vert*) | 2·00 | 2·75 |
| 600/3 | *Set of* 4 | 4·00 | 4·75 |
| **MS**604 | 85×115 mm $3 Queen with bouquet | 4·50 | 5·00 |

Examples of the 12 c., 35 c. and $1.50 values with the blue (ribbons and frame) omitted are from stock dispersed by the liquidator of Format International Security Printers Ltd.

Unissued sets of five miniature sheets, each containing one value, come from the same source.

**168** Miss Sarah Ferguson

**169** Harvesting Sugar Cane

(Des Court House Studio. Litho Format)

**1986** (23 July–15 Oct). *Royal Wedding. T* **168** *and similar multicoloured designs. P* 12½.

| | | | |
|---|---|---|---|
| 605 | 35 c. Type **168** | 50 | 55 |
| | a. Pair. Nos. 605/6 | 1·00 | 1·10 |
| | b. Wmk w **15** | 3·50 | |
| | ba. Pair. Nos. 605b/6b | 7·00 | |
| 606 | 35 c. Prince Andrew and Miss Sarah Ferguson | 50 | 55 |
| | b. Wmk w **15** | 3·50 | |
| 607 | $1 Prince Andrew in morning dress (*horiz*) | 1·25 | 1·50 |
| | a. Pair. Nos. 607/8 | 2·50 | 3·00 |
| 608 | $1 Miss Sarah Ferguson (*different*) (*horiz*) | 1·25 | 1·50 |
| 605/8 | *Set of* 4 | 3·25 | 3·75 |
| **MS**609 | 115×85 mm. $4 Duke and Duchess of York in carriage after wedding (*horiz*) (15.10.86) | 5·00 | 5·25 |

Nos. 605/6 and 607/8 were each printed together, *se-tenant*, in horizontal and vertical pairs throughout the sheets.

Nos. 605/8 imperforate come from souvenir stamp booklets.

Nos. 605/8 overprinted "Congratulations to T.R.H. The Duke & Duchess of York" were not issued.

(Des Toni Lance. Litho Questa)

**1986** (30 July). *History of Rum Making. T* **169** *and similar horiz designs. Multicoloured. W* w **15**. *P* 14.

| | | | |
|---|---|---|---|
| 610 | 12 c. Type **169** | 65 | 35 |
| 611 | 40 c. Bringing sugar cane to mill | 1·25 | 1·00 |
| 612 | 60 c. Rum distillery | 1·75 | 1·75 |
| 613 | $1 Delivering barrels of rum to ship | 2·75 | 3·00 |
| 610/13 | *Set of* 4 | 5·75 | 5·50 |
| **MS**614 | 115×84 mm. $2 Royal Navy rum issue. Wmk sideways | 5·50 | 6·00 |

**170** C.S. *Sentinel*

**171** Statue of Liberty at Sunset

(Des Court House Studio. Litho Format)

**1986** (28 Oct). *20th Anniv of Cable and Wireless Caribbean Headquarters, Tortola. T* **170** *and similar horiz designs. Multicoloured. W* w **15**. *P* 12½.

| | | | |
|---|---|---|---|
| 615 | 35 c. Type **170** | 55 | 65 |
| | a. Vert pair. Nos. 615/16 | 1·10 | 1·25 |
| 616 | 35 c. C.S. *Retriever* (1961) | 55 | 65 |
| 617 | 60 c. C.S. *Cable Enterprise* (1964) | 1·00 | 1·25 |
| | a. Vert pair. Nos. 617/18 | 2·00 | 2·50 |
| 618 | 60 c. C.S. *Mercury* (1962) | 1·00 | 1·25 |
| 619 | 75 c. C.S. *Recorder* (1955) | 1·25 | 1·40 |
| | a. Vert pair. Nos. 619/20 | 2·50 | 2·75 |
| 620 | 75 c. C.S. *Pacific Guardian* (1984) | 1·25 | 1·40 |
| 621 | $1 S.S. *Great Eastern* (1860's) | 1·50 | 1·75 |
| | a. Vert pair. Nos. 621/2 | 3·00 | 3·50 |
| 622 | $1 C.S. *Cable Venture* (1977) | 1·50 | 1·75 |
| 615/22 | *Set of* 8 | 7·75 | 9·00 |
| **MS**623 | Four sheets, each 102×131 mm. (a) 40 c. × 2 As 35 c. (b) 50 c. × 2 As 60 c. (c) 80 c. × 2 As 75 c. (d) $1.50 × 2 As $1 — *Set of* 4 *sheets* | 9·50 | 10·00 |

The two designs of each value were printed, *se-tenant*, in vertical pairs throughout the sheets.

(Des Court House Studio. Litho Format)

**1986** (15 Dec). *Centenary of Statue of Liberty. T* **171** *and similar vert views of Statue in separate miniature sheets. Multicoloured. P* 14×13½.

| | | | |
|---|---|---|---|
| **MS**624 | Nine sheets, each 85×115 mm. 50 c.; 75 c.; 90 c.; $1; $1.25; $1.50; $1.75; $2; $2.50 — *Set of* 9 *sheets* | 18·00 | 18·00 |

**172** 18th-century Spanish Galleon

**173** Outline Map and Flag of Montserrrat

(Des J. Batchelor. Litho Questa)

**1987** (15 Apr). *Shipwrecks. T* **172** *and similar horiz designs. Multicoloured. W* w **15**. *P* 14.

| | | | |
|---|---|---|---|
| 625 | 12 c. Type **172** | 60 | 30 |
| 626 | 35 c. H.M.S. *Astrea*, 1808 | 1·25 | 85 |
| 627 | 75 c. R.M.S. *Rhone*, 1867 | 2·00 | 2·00 |
| 628 | $1.50, S.S. *Rocus*, 1929 | 3·50 | 3·75 |
| 625/8 | *Set of* 4 | 6·50 | 6·25 |
| **MS**629 | 86×65 mm. $2.50, *Volvart*, 1819 | 7·00 | 7·50 |

(Des R. Burnett. Litho Walsall)

**1987** (28 May). *11th Meeting of Organization of Eastern Caribbean States. T* **173** *and similar vert designs, each showing outline map and flag. Multicoloured. W* w **16**. *P* 14.

| | | | |
|---|---|---|---|
| 630 | 10 c. Type **173** | 35 | 35 |
| 631 | 15 c. Grenada | 40 | 40 |
| 632 | 20 c. Dominica | 45 | 45 |
| 633 | 25 c. St. Kitts–Nevis | 50 | 50 |
| 634 | 35 c. St. Vincent and Grenadines | 70 | 70 |
| 635 | 50 c. British Virgin Islands | 90 | 90 |
| 636 | 75 c. Antigua and Barbuda | 1·25 | 1·25 |
| 637 | $1 St. Lucia | 1·75 | 1·75 |
| 630/7 | *Set of* 8 | 5·75 | 5·75 |

**174** Spider Lily

**175** Early Mail Packet and 1867 1s. Stamp

(Des Jennifer Toombs. Litho Questa)

**1987** (20 Aug). *Opening of Botanical Gardens. T* **174** *and similar vert designs. Multicoloured. W* w **16**. *P* 14.

| | | | |
|---|---|---|---|
| 638 | 12 c. Type **174** | 60 | 30 |
| 639 | 35 c. Barrel Cactus | 1·25 | 80 |
| 640 | $1 Wild Plantain | 2·25 | 2·50 |
| 641 | $1.50, Little Butterfly Orchid | 5·00 | 5·00 |
| 638/41 | *Set of* 4 | 8·25 | 7·75 |
| **MS**642 | 139×104 mm. $2.50, White Cedar | 3·75 | 5·50 |

**1987** (28 Oct). *As Nos.* 564, 566, 568/9, 571, 575 *and* 577 *but* W w **16**. *P* 14.
647 10 c. Grey Kingbird .. .. .. .. .. 20 15
649 15 c. Least Bittern .. .. .. .. .. 30 30
651 20 c. Clapper Rail .. .. .. .. .. 35 35
652 25 c. American Kestrel .. .. .. .. 40 40
654 35 c. Bridled Quail Dove .. .. .. .. 50 50
658 $1 Audubon's Shearwater .. .. .. .. 1·50 1·60
660 $3 Cattle Egret .. .. .. .. .. 3·75 4·00
647/60 .. .. .. .. *Set of* 7 6·25 6·50

(Des and litho Walsall)

**1987** (17 Dec). *Bicentenary of Postal Services. T* **175** *and similar horiz designs, each including stamp and cancellation. Multicoloured.* W w **16** (*sideways*). *P* 14½.
662 10 c. Type **175** .. .. .. .. .. 40 30
663 20 c. Map and 1899 1d. .. .. .. .. 70 55
**664** 35 c. Road Town Post Office and Customs House, 1913, and 1867 4d. .. .. .. 1·25 80
665 $1.50, Mail plane and 1964 25 c. definitive 3·50 3·75
662/5 .. .. .. .. .. *Set of* 4 5·25 4·75
**MS**666 70 × 60 mm. $2.50, Mail ship, 1880's, and 1880 1d. .. .. .. .. .. .. 3·50 4·00

(Litho Questa)

**1988** (11 Aug). 500*th Birth Anniv of Titian (artist). Vert designs as T* **238** *of Antigua. Multicoloured. P* 13½×14.
667 10 c. "Salome" .. .. .. .. .. 25 25
668 12 c. "Man with the Glove" .. .. .. .. 30 30
669 20 c. "Fabrizio Salvaresio" .. .. .. .. 40 40
670 25 c. "Daughter of Roberto Strozzi" .. .. 50 50
671 40 c. "Pope Julius II" .. .. .. .. 70 70
672 50 c. "Bishop Ludovico Beccadelli" .. .. 75 75
673 60 c. "King Philip II" .. .. .. .. 85 85
674 $1 "Empress Isabella of Portugal" .. .. 1·50 1·50
667/74 .. .. .. .. *Set of* 8 4·75 4·75
**MS**675 Two sheets, each 110×95 mm. (a) $2 "Emperor Charles V at Muhlberg" (detail). (b) $2 "Pope Paul III and his Grandsons" (detail) *Set of 2 sheets* 5·00 6·00

**176** Aircraft over Sir Francis Drake Channel and Pawn

(Des B. Bundock. Litho Questa)

**1988** (25 Aug). *First British Virgin Islands Open Chess Tournament. T* **176** *and similar horiz designs. Multicoloured. P* 14.
676 35 c. Type **176** .. .. .. .. .. 1·50 1·00
677 $1 Jose Capablanca (former World Champion) and king .. .. .. 3·25 3·25
**MS**678 109 × 81 mm. $2 Chess match .. .. 5·00 6·00

**177** Hurdling

(Des L. Fried. Litho B.D.T.)

**1988** (8 Sept). *Olympic Games, Seoul. T* **177** *and similar horiz designs. Multicoloured. P* 14.
679 12 c. Type **177** .. .. .. .. .. 20 20
680 20 c. Windsurfing .. .. .. .. .. 30 30
681 75 c. Basketball .. .. .. .. .. 95 95
682 $1 Tennis .. .. .. .. .. 1·40 1·40
679/82 .. .. .. .. *Set of* 4 2·50 2·50
**MS**683 71 × 102 mm. $2 Athletics .. .. 2·40 3·00

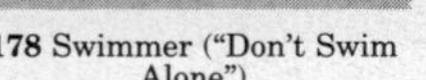

**178** Swimmer ("Don't Swim Alone")

**179** Princess Alexandra

(Des I. Arbell. Litho Questa)

**1988** (26 Sept). 125*th Anniv of International Red Cross. T* **178** *and similar designs. P* 14.
684 12 c. black, bright scarlet and cobalt .. 40 30
685 30 c. black, bright scarlet and cobalt .. 75 60
686 60 c. black, bright scarlet and cobalt .. 1·25 1·25
687 $1 black, bright scarlet and cobalt .. 2·00 2·00
684/7 .. .. .. .. *Set of* 4 4·00 3·75
**MS**688 68 × 96 mm. 50 c. × 4 black and bright scarlet .. .. .. .. .. .. 3·50 4·00
Designs: *Horiz*—30 c. Swimmers ("No swimming during electrical storms"); 60 c. Beach picnic ("Don't eat before swimming"); $1 Boat and equipment ("Proper equipment for boating"). *Vert*—50 c. × 4 Recovery position; clearing airway; mouth-to-mouth resuscitation; cardiac massage.

(Litho Questa)

**1988** (9 Nov). *Visit of Princess Alexandra. T* **179** *and similar vert designs showing different portraits. P* 14.
689 40 c. multicoloured .. .. .. .. 1·25 75
690 $1.50, multicoloured .. .. .. .. 3·00 3·25
**MS**691 102 × 98 mm. $2 multicoloured .. .. 3·50 3·75

**180** Brown Pelican in Flight

**181** Anegada Rock Iguana

(Des S. Barlowe. Litho Questa)

**1988** (30 Nov). *Wildlife (1st series). Aquatic Birds. T* **180** *and similar multicoloured designs. P* 14.
692 10 c. Type **180** .. .. .. .. .. 50 30
693 12 c. Brown Pelican perched on post .. .. 60 35
694 15 c. Brown Pelican .. .. .. .. 70 50
695 35 c. Brown Pelican swallowing fish .. .. 1·50 1·50
692/5 .. .. .. .. *Set of* 4 3·00 2·40
**MS**696 106 × 76 mm. $2 Northern Shoveler (*horiz*) .. .. .. .. .. .. 4·00 4·25
No. **MS**696 is without the WWF logo.

(Des S. Barlowe. Litho Questa)

**1988** (15 Dec). *Wildlife (2nd series). Endangered Species. T* **181** *and similar multicoloured designs. P* 14.
697 20 c. Type **181** .. .. .. .. .. 45 35
698 40 c. Virgin Gorda Dwarf Gecko .. .. 85 70
699 60 c. Hawksbill Turtle .. .. .. .. 1·25 95
700 $1 Humpback Whale .. .. .. .. 1·75 2·00
697/700 .. .. .. .. *Set of* 4 4·00 3·50
**MS**701 106 × 77 mm. $2 Trunk Turtle (*vert*) .. 3·00 3·50

**182** Yachts at Start

**183** "Apollo 11" Emblem

(Des D. Miller. Litho Questa)

**1989** (7 Apr). *Spring Regatta. T* **182** *and similar multicoloured designs. P* 14.
702 12 c. Type **182** .. .. .. .. .. 15 20
703 40 c. Yacht tacking (*horiz*) .. .. .. .. 45 50
704 75 c. Yachts at sunset .. .. .. .. 85 90
705 $1 Yachts rounding buoy (*horiz*) .. .. 1·10 1·25
702/5 .. .. .. .. *Set of* 4 2·25 2·50
**MS**706 83×69 mm. $2 Yacht under full sail .. 2·25 2·40

(Des D. Miller. Litho Questa)

**1989** (8 May). 500*th Anniv of Discovery of America by Columbus* (1992) (1*st issue*). *Pre-Columbian Arawak Society. Multicoloured designs as T* **247** *of Antigua, but horiz. P* 14.
707 10 c. Arawak in hammock .. .. .. 10 15
708 20 c. Making fire .. .. .. .. 25 30
709 25 c. Making implements .. .. .. 30 35
710 $1.50, Arawak family .. .. .. 1·75 1·90
707/10 .. .. .. .. *Set of* 4 2·10 2·40
**MS**711 85×70 mm. $2 Religious ceremony .. 2·25 2·40
See also Nos. 741/5 and 793/7.

(Des W. Hanson. Litho Questa)

**1989** (28 Sept). 20*th Anniv of First Manned Landing on Moon. T* **183** *and similar multicoloured designs. P* 14.
712 15 c. Type **183** .. .. .. .. .. 15 20
713 30 c. Edwin Aldrin deploying scientific experiments .. .. .. .. .. 35 40
714 65 c. Aldrin and U.S. flag on Moon .. .. 75 80
715 $1 "Apollo 11" capsule after splashdown .. 1·10 1·25
712/15 .. .. .. .. *Set of* 4 2·10 2·40
**MS**716 102×77 mm. $2 Neil Armstrong (38×50 *mm*). *P* 13½×14 .. .. .. 2·25 2·40

**184** Black Harry and Nathaniel Gilbert preaching to Slaves

**185** Player tackling

(Des R. Vigurs. Litho Questa)

**1989** (24 Oct). *Bicentenary of Methodist Church in British Virgin Islands. T* **184** *and similar multicoloured designs. P* 14.
717 12 c. Type **184** .. .. .. .. .. 15 20
718 25 c. Methodist school exercise book .. .. 30 35
719 35 c. East End Methodist Church, 1810 .. 40 45
720 $1.25, Revd. John Wesley (founder of Methodism) and church youth choir .. 1·40 1·50
717/20 .. .. .. .. *Set of* 4 2·00 2·25
**MS**721 100×69 mm. $2 Dr. Thomas Coke .. 2·25 2·40

(Des R. Vigurs. Litho Questa)

**1989** (6 Nov). *World Cup Football Championship, Italy,* 1990. *T* **185** *and similar vert designs. Multicoloured. P* 14.
722 5 c. Type **185** .. .. .. .. .. 10 10
723 10 c. Player dribbling ball .. .. .. 10 15
724 20 c. Two players chasing ball .. .. .. 25 30
725 $1.75, Goalkeeper diving for ball .. .. 2·00 2·10
722/5 .. .. .. .. *Set of* 4 2·10 2·40
**MS**726 100×70 mm. $2 British Virgin Islands team captain .. .. .. .. .. 2·25 2·40

**186** Princess Alexandra and Sunset House

(Litho Questa)

**1990** (3 May). *"Stamp World London 90" International Stamp Exhibition. Royal Visitors. T* **186** *and similar horiz designs. Multicoloured. P* 14.
727 50 c. Type **186** .. .. .. .. .. 60 65
a. Sheetlet. Nos. 727/30 .. .. .. 2·10
728 50 c. Princess Margaret and Government House .. .. .. .. .. .. 60 65
729 50 c. Hon. Angus Ogilvy and Little Dix Bay Hotel .. .. .. .. .. .. 60 65
730 50 c. Princess Diana with Princes William and Harry and Necker Island Resort .. 60 65
727/30 .. .. .. .. *Set of* 4 2·10 2·40
**MS**731 89×80 mm. $2 Royal Yacht *Britannia* 2·25 2·40
Nos. 727/30 were printed together, *se-tenant*, in sheetlets of four.

**187** Audubon's Shearwater

**188** Queen Elizabeth the Queen Mother

(Litho Questa)

**1990** (15 May). *Birds. T* **187** *and similar multicoloured designs showing birds and eggs. P* 14.
732 5 c. Type **187** .. .. .. .. .. 10 10
733 12 c. Red-necked Pigeon .. .. .. .. 15 20
734 20 c. Moorhen ("Common Gallinule") .. .. 25 30
735 25 c. Green Heron .. .. .. .. .. 30 35
736 40 c. Yellow Warbler .. .. .. .. 45 50
737 60 c. Smooth-billed Ani .. .. .. .. 70 75
738 $1 Antillean Crested Hummingbird .. 1·10 1·25
739 $1.25, Black-faced Grassquit .. .. 1·40 1·50
732/9 .. .. .. .. *Set of* 8 4·00 4·50
**MS**740 Two sheets, each 98×70 mm. (a) $2 Royal Tern egg (*vert*). (b) $2 Red-billed Tropicbird egg (*vert*) .. .. .. .. *Set of 2 sheets* 4·75 5·00

(Des Mary Walters. Litho Questa)

**1990** (18 June). 500*th Anniv of Discovery of America by Columbus* (1992) (2*nd issue*). *New World Natural History–Fishes. Multicoloured designs as T* **260** *of Antigua, but horiz. P* 14.
741 10 c. Blue Tang .. .. .. .. .. 10 15
742 35 c. Glasseye .. .. .. .. .. 40 45
743 50 c. Slippery Dick .. .. .. .. 60 65
744 $1 Porkfish .. .. .. .. .. 1·10 1·25
741/4 .. .. .. .. *Set of* 4 2·00 2·25
**MS**745 100×70 mm. $2 Yellowtail Snapper .. 2·25 2·40

(Litho Questa)

**1990** (30 Aug). 90*th Birthday of Queen Elizabeth the Queen Mother. T* **188** *and similar vert designs showing recent photographs. P* 14.
746 12 c. multicoloured .. .. .. .. 15 20
747 25 c. multicoloured .. .. .. .. 30 35
748 60 c. multicoloured .. .. .. .. 70 75
749 $1 multicoloured .. .. .. .. 1·10 1·25
746/9 .. .. .. .. *Set of* 4 2·00 2·25
**MS**750 75×75 mm. $2 multicoloured .. .. 2·25 2·40

189 Footballers

190 Judo

(Litho Questa)

**1990** (10 Dec). *World Cup Football Championship, Italy. T* **189** *and similar vert designs showing footballers. P* 14.

751 12 c. multicoloured .. .. .. .. 15 20
752 20 c. multicoloured .. .. .. .. 25 30
753 50 c. multicoloured .. .. .. .. 60 65
754 $1.25, multicoloured .. .. .. .. 1·40 1·50
751/4 .. .. .. .. *Set of* 4 2·10 2·40
**MS**755 91×76 mm. $2 multicoloured .. .. 2·25 2·40

(Litho Questa)

**1990** (20 Dec). *Olympic Games, Barcelona* (1992). *T* **190** *and similar horiz designs. Multicoloured. P* 14.

756 12 c. Type **190** .. .. .. .. 15 20
757 40 c. Yachting .. .. .. .. 45 50
758 60 c. Hurdling .. .. .. .. 70 75
759 $1 Show jumping .. .. .. .. 1·10 1·25
756/9 .. .. .. .. *Set of* 4 2·10 2·40
**MS**760 78×105 mm. $2 Windsurfing .. .. 2·25 2·40

191 Tree-fern, Sage Mountain National Park

192 Haiti Haiti

(Litho Questa)

**1991** (1 Mar). *30th Anniv of National Parks Trust. T* **191** *and similar multicoloured designs. P* 14.

761 10 c. Type **191** .. .. .. .. 10 15
762 25 c. Coppermine ruins, Virgin Gorda (*horiz*) 30 35
763 35 c. Ruined windmill, Mount Healthy .. 40 45
764 $2 The Baths (rock formation), Virgin Gorda (*horiz*) .. .. .. .. 2·25 2·40
761/4 .. .. .. .. *Set of* 4 2·75 3·00

(Des Wendy Smith-Griswold. Litho Questa)

**1991** (1 May). *Flowers. T* **192** *and similar vert designs. Multicoloured. P* 14.

765 1 c. Type **192** .. .. .. .. 10 10
766 2 c. Lobster Claw .. .. .. .. 10 10
767 5 c. Frangipani .. .. .. .. 10 10
768 10 c. Autograph Tree .. .. .. .. 10 15
769 12 c. Yellow Allamanda .. .. .. .. 15 20
770 15 c. Lantana .. .. .. .. 15 20
771 20 c. Jerusalem Thorn .. .. .. .. 25 30
772 25 c. Turk's Cap .. .. .. .. 30 35
773 30 c. Swamp Immortelle .. .. .. .. 35 40
774 35 c. White Cedar .. .. .. .. 40 45
775 40 c. Mahoe Tree .. .. .. .. 45 50
776 45 c. Pinguin .. .. .. .. 50 55
777 50 c. Christmas Orchid .. .. .. .. 60 65
778 70 c. Lignum Vitae .. .. .. .. 80 85
779 $1 African Tulip Tree .. .. .. .. 1·10 1·25
780 $2 Beach Morning Glory .. .. .. .. 2·25 2·40
781 $3 Organ Pipe Cactus .. .. .. .. 3·50 3·75
782 $5 Tall Ground Orchid .. .. .. .. 5·75 6·00
765/82 .. .. .. .. *Set of* 18 14·50 16·00

193 *Phoebis sennae*

194 *Victoria* in Pacific (Magellan, 1519–21)

(Litho Questa)

**1991** (28 June). *Butterflies. T* **193** *and similar multicoloured designs. P* 14.

784 5 c. Type **193** .. .. .. .. 10 10
785 10 c. *Dryas iulia* .. .. .. .. 10 10
786 15 c. *Junonia evarete* .. .. .. .. 15 20
787 20 c. *Dione vanillae* .. .. .. .. 25 30
788 25 c. *Battus polydamus* .. .. .. .. 30 35
789 30 c. *Eurema lisa* .. .. .. .. 35 40
790 35 c. *Heliconius charitonius* .. .. 40 45
791 $1.50, *Siproeta stelenes* .. .. .. 1·75 1·90
784/91 .. .. .. .. *Set of* 8 3·00 3·50
**MS**792 Two sheets. (a) 77×117 mm. $2 *Danaus plexippus* (*horiz*). (b) 117×77 mm. $2 *Biblis hyperia* (*horiz*) .. .. *Set of* 2 *sheets* 4·50 4·75

(Des T. Agans. Litho Questa)

**1991** (20 Sept). *500th Anniv of Discovery of America by Columbus* (1992) (3*rd issue*). *History of Exploration. T* **194** *and similar designs. P* 14.

793 12 c. multicoloured .. .. .. .. 10 10
794 50 c. multicoloured .. .. .. .. 60 65
795 75 c. multicoloured .. .. .. .. 85 90
796 $1 multicoloured .. .. .. .. 1·10 1·25
793/6 .. .. .. .. *Set of* 4 2·40 2·50
**MS**797 105×76 mm. $2 black and red-orange .. 2·25 2·50

Designs: *Horiz*—50 c. La Salle on the Mississippi, 1682; 75 c. John Cabot landing in Nova Scotia, 1497–98; $1 Cartier discovering the St. Lawrence, 1534. *Vert*—$2 *Santa Maria* (woodcut).

195 "Cottage with Decrepit Barn and Stooping Woman" (Van Gogh)

(Litho B.D.T.)

**1991** (1 Nov). *Death Centenary of Vincent van Gogh (artist)* (1990). *T* **195** *and similar multicoloured designs. P* 13.

798 15 c. Type **195** .. .. .. .. 15 20
799 30 c. "Paul Gauguin's Armchair" (*vert*) .. 35 40
800 75 c. "Breton Women" .. .. .. .. 85 90
801 $1 "Vase with Red Gladioli" (*vert*) .. 1·10 1·25
798/801 .. .. .. .. *Set of* 4 2·25 2·50
**MS**802 103×81 mm. $2 "Dance Hall in Arles" (detail) .. .. .. .. 2·25 2·50

196 "The Virgin and Child Enthroned" (detail, Q. Massys)

(Litho Walsall)

**1991** (12 Dec). *Christmas. Religious Paintings by Quinten Massys. T* **196** *and similar vert designs. Multicoloured. P* 12.

803 15 c. Type **196** .. .. .. .. 15 20
804 30 c. "The Virgin and Child Enthroned" (different detail) .. .. .. 35 40
805 60 c. "Adoration of the Magi" (detail) .. 70 75
806 $1 "Virgin in Adoration" .. .. .. 1·10 1·25
803/6 .. .. .. .. *Set of* 4 2·00 2·25
**MS**807 Two sheets, each 102×127 mm. (a) $2 "The Virgin standing with Angels"; (b) $2 "The Adoration of the Magi". P 14×14½. *Set of* 2 *sheets* 4·00 4·25

OFFICIAL STAMPS

OFFICIAL

(O 1)

Two varieties of overprint:

Type I. Foot of "OFFICIAL" 15–16 mm from top of design. Light impression with little or no black outline to letters.

Type II. Foot of "OFFICIAL" 20 mm from top of design. Heavy impression with thick black outline to letters.

**1985** (Feb). *Nos.* 418/19, 420*a*/1*a*, 423*a*/4*a*, 425, 426*a*, 427, 428*a and* 429/33 *optd as Type* O 1 *in silver by Questa*.

O 1 1 c. Purple-tipped Sea Anemone (I) .. .. 25 40
a. Opt Type II .. .. .. .. 15·00
O 2 3 c. Common Starfish (I) .. .. .. 35 40
a. Opt Type II .. .. .. .. 15·00
O 3 5 c. Type 134 (II) .. .. .. .. 35 20
O 4 8 c. Triton's Trumpet (shell) (I) .. .. 45 20
a. Opt Type II .. .. .. ..
O 5 13 c. Flamingo Tongue Snail (II) .. .. 60 40
O 6 15 c. Spider Crab (I) .. .. .. 65 55
O 7 18 c. Sea Squirts (I) .. .. .. 70 60
a. Opt Type II .. .. .. ..
O 8 20 c. True Tulip (shell) (I) .. .. .. 70 60
O 9 25 c. Rooster Tail Conch (shell) (I) .. .. 80 70
O10 30 c. Fighting Conch (shell) (I) .. .. 90 80
a. Optd on No. 428 .. .. .. 7·00
O11 60 c. Mangrove Crab (I) .. .. .. 2·00 2·00
O12 $1 Coral Polyps (I) .. .. .. 2·75 3·00
O13 $2.50, Peppermint Shrimp (I) .. .. 4·75 5·50
O14 $3 West Indian Murex (shell) (I) .. .. 6·50 7·50
a. Opt inverted .. .. .. ..
O15 $5 Carpet Anemone (I) .. .. .. 9·50 12·00
O1/15 .. .. .. .. *Set of* 15 28·00 32·00

Postally used examples of No. O14a are known.

**OFFICIAL** (O 2) OFFICIAL (O 3)

**1986** (10 Feb–Sept). *Nos.* 560/78 *optd with Type* O **2** *by Questa*.

O16 1 c. Type **162** (9.86) .. .. .. 20 30
O17 2 c. Yellow-crowned Night Heron .. .. 30 35
O18 5 c. Mangrove Cuckoo (9.86) .. .. 30 35
O19 8 c. Northern Mockingbird .. .. .. 40 40
O20 10 c. Grey Kingbird (9.86) .. .. .. 40 40
O21 12 c. Red-necked Pigeon .. .. .. 50 50
O22 15 c. Least Bittern (9.86) .. .. .. 50 50
O23 18 c. Smooth-billed Ani .. .. .. 60 60
O24 20 c. Clapper Rail (9.86) .. .. .. 60 60
O25 25 c. American Kestrel (9.86) .. .. 60 60
O26 30 c. Pearly-eyed Thrasher (9.86) .. .. 70 70
O27 35 c. Bridled Quail Dove (9.86) .. .. 70 70
O28 40 c. Green Heron .. .. .. .. 1·00 1·00
O29 50 c. Scaly-breasted Ground Dove .. .. 1·50 1·50
O30 60 c. Little Blue Heron .. .. .. 1·75 1·75
O31 $1 Audubon's Shearwater .. .. .. 2·75 2·75
O32 $2 Blue-faced Booby .. .. .. 4·75 5·00
O33 $3 Cattle Egret .. .. .. .. 6·50 7·50
O34 $5 Zenaida Dove (9.86) .. .. .. 8·50 9·50
O16/34 .. .. .. .. *Set of* 19 29·00 32·00

**1991** (Sept). *Nos.* 767/8, 771, 773/9 *and* 781 *optd with Type* O **3**.

O35 5 c. Frangipani .. .. .. ..
O36 10 c. Autograph Tree .. .. .. ..
O37 20 c. Jerusalem Thorn .. .. .. ..
O38 30 c. Swamp Immortelle .. .. .. ..
O39 35 c. White Cedar .. .. .. ..
O40 40 c. Mahoe Tree .. .. .. ..
O41 45 c. Pinguin .. .. .. ..
O42 50 c. Christmas Orchid .. .. .. ..
O43 70 c. Lignum Vitae .. .. .. ..
O44 $1 African Tulip Tree .. .. .. ..
O45 $3 Organ Pipe Cactus .. .. .. ..

Nos. O35/45 were used on mail from the Philatelic Bureau and were not sold unused.

# Brunei

**Sultan Hashim Jalil-ul-alam Akamudin, 1885–1906**

For many years the status of the 1895 issue remained uncertain to such an extent that the 1906 provisionals on Labuan were taken to be the first issue of Brunei.

The 1895 "Star and Crescent" design stamps were, from their first appearance, considered bogus or, at best, as an issue made purely for philatelic purposes. Research into the background of the events surrounding the set led to the publication, in 1933, of the original agreement between Sultan Hashim and J. C. Robertson dated 20 August 1894 which made clear that the stamps fulfilled a genuine postal purpose. Although Robertson and his partners intended to exploit the philatelic sales for their own benefit the agreement testifies, as does other evidence, to the use of the stamps by the Sultan for his postal service. As Brunei did not, at that time, belong to any local or international postal union the stamps were only valid within the state or on mail to Labuan or Sarawak. Items for further afield required franking with Labuan stamps in addition. Although most covers surviving are addressed to Robertson's associates enough commercial covers and cards exist to show that there was, indeed, a postal service.

**PRICES FOR STAMPS ON COVER TO 1945**

Nos. 1/10 are rare used on cover.
Nos. 11/22 *from* × 30
Nos. 23/33 *from* × 25
Nos. 34/50 *from* × 10
Nos. 51/9 *from* × 12
Nos. 60/78 *from* × 8

The Sarawak Government maintained a post office at the coal mining centre of Brooketon, and the stamps of SARAWAK were used there from 1893 until the office was handed over to Brunei in February 1907.

1 Star and Local Scene

(Litho in Glasgow)

**1895** (18 July). *P* 13–13½.

| | | | | |
|---|---|---|---|---|
| 1 | 1 | ½ c. brown | 1·00 | 10·00 |
| 2 | | 1 c. brown-lake | 1·00 | 9·00 |
| 3 | | 2 c. grey-black | 3·50 | 9·00 |
| 4 | | 3 c. deep blue | 3·00 | 8·50 |
| 5 | | 5 c. deep blue-green | 6·00 | 10·00 |
| 6 | | 8 c. plum | 8·50 | 13·00 |
| 7 | | 10 c. orange-red | 7·50 | 15·00 |
| | | a. Imperf (pair) | £550 | |
| 8 | | 25 c. turquoise-green | 18·00 | 28·00 |
| 9 | | 50 c. yellow-green | 18·00 | 50·00 |
| 10 | | $1 yellow-olive | 20·00 | 70·00 |
| 1/10 | | *Set of* 10 | 75·00 | £200 |

BRUNEI. (2) — BRUNEI. TWO CENTS. (3) — BRUNEI. 25 CENTS. (4)

(Optd by Govt Printer, Singapore)

**1906** (1 Oct). *Stamps of Labuan, T* **18** (*Nos.* 116*c, etc.*), *optd with T* **2**, *or surch as T* **3** *or* **4** (*25 c.*), *in red. P* 13½ *or* 14 (*1 c.*).

| | | | |
|---|---|---|---|
| 11 | 1 c. black and purple | 18·00 | 28·00 |
| | a. Error. Opt in black | £1700 | £2500 |
| 12 | 2 c. on 3 c. black and sepia | 1·50 | 4·50 |
| | a. "BRUNEI" double | £3500 | £2500 |
| | b. "TWO CENTS" in double | £7000 | |
| 13 | 2 c. on 8 c. black and vermilion | 20·00 | 55·00 |
| | a. "TWO CENTS" double | £5500 | |
| | b. "TWO CENTS" omitted in vert pair with normal | £7000 | |
| 14 | 3 c. black and sepia | 20·00 | 55·00 |
| 15 | 4 c. on 12 c. black and yellow | 1·25 | 4·25 |
| 16 | 5 c. on 16 c. green and brown | 27·00 | 40·00 |
| 17 | 8 c. black and vermilion | 8·50 | 17·00 |
| 18 | 10 c. on 16 c. green and brown | 6·00 | 16·00 |
| 19 | 25 c. on 16 c. green and brown | 90·00 | £120 |
| 20 | 30 c. on 16 c. green and brown | 80·00 | £110 |
| 21 | 50 c. on 16 c. green and brown | 80·00 | £110 |
| 22 | $1 on 8 c. black and vermilion | 80·00 | £110 |
| 11/22 | *Set of* 12 | £375 | £600 |

Only one sheet of the 1 c. received the black overprint.

The surcharges were applied in settings of 50. Nos. 13a/b occur from one sheet on which the surcharge from the second impression of the setting was misplaced to give two surcharges on row five and none on row ten.

**Sultan Mohamed Jemal-ul-Alam, 1906–1924**

**PRINTERS.** All Brunei stamps from Nos. 23 to 113 were recess-printed by De La Rue.

5 View on Brunei River

**1907** (26 Feb)–**10**. *Wmk Mult Crown CA. P* 14.

| | | | | |
|---|---|---|---|---|
| 23 | 5 | 1 c. grey-black and pale green | 2·25 | 7·00 |
| 24 | | 2 c. grey-black and scarlet | 2·50 | 4·50 |
| 25 | | 3 c. grey-black and chocolate | 9·00 | 18·00 |
| 26 | | 4 c. grey-black and mauve | 6·00 | 10·00 |
| | | *a. Grey-black and reddish purple* (1910) | 50·00 | 60·00 |
| 27 | | 5 c. grey-black and blue | 30·00 | 55·00 |
| 28 | | 8 c. grey-black and orange | 5·50 | 23·00 |
| 29 | | 10 c. grey-black and deep green | 4·50 | 7·00 |
| 30 | | 25 c. pale blue and ochre-brown | 20·00 | 30·00 |
| 31 | | 30 c. violet and black | 13·00 | 22·00 |
| 32 | | 50 c. green and deep brown | 13·00 | 22·00 |
| 33 | | $1 red and grey | 45·00 | 75·00 |
| 23/33 | | *Set of* 11 | £130 | £250 |
| 23/33 Optd "Specimen" | | *Set of* 11 | £275 | |

I

II

I Double plate. Lowest line of shading on water is dotted.
II Single plate. Dotted line of shading removed.

Stamps printed in two colours are as I.

**1908** (12 June)–**20.** *Colours changed. Double or single plates. Wmk Mult Crown CA. P* 14.

| | | | | |
|---|---|---|---|---|
| 34 | 5 | 1 c. green (I) | 50 | 2·00 |
| 35 | | 1 c. green (II) (1911) | 25 | 75 |
| | | a. "A" missing from wmk | | |
| | | b. "C" missing from wmk | £200 | |
| 36 | | 2 c. black and brown (5.4.11) | 80 | 1·25 |
| 37 | | 3 c. scarlet (I) | 1·40 | 75 |
| 38 | | 3 c. scarlet (II) (1916) | 28·00 | 27·00 |
| 39 | | 4 c. claret (II) | 75 | 75 |
| 40 | | 5 c. black and orange | 6·50 | 7·00 |
| 41 | | 8 c. blue and indigo-blue (10.08) | 6·00 | 11·00 |
| 42 | | 10 c. purple/*yellow* (II) (1912) | 1·25 | 85 |
| | | *a. On pale yellow* (Optd S. £30) | 1·00 | 2·75 |
| 43 | | 25 c. deep lilac (II) (30.5.12) | 2·25 | 3·00 |
| 44 | | 30 c. purple and orange-yellow (18.3.12) | 8·50 | 12·00 |
| 45 | | 50 c. black/*green* (II) (1912) | 19·00 | 45·00 |
| | | *a. On blue-green* (1920) | 8·00 | 19·00 |
| 46 | | $1 black and red/*blue* (18.3.12) | 20·00 | 48·00 |
| 47 | | $5 carmine/*green* (I) (1910) | 70·00 | £140 |
| 48 | | $25 black/*red* (I) (1910) | £450 | £850 |
| 34/47 | | *Set of* 12 | £110 | £225 |
| 34/48 Optd "Specimen" | | *Set of* 13 | £450 | |

The used price for No. 48 is for a cancelled-by-favour example, dated before December 1941; there being no actual postal rate for which this value could be used. Examples dated after 1945 are worth much less.

5c Retouch — 5c Normal — MALAYA-BORNEO EXHIBITION. 1922. (6)

**RETOUCHES.** We list the very distinctive 5 c. Retouch (top left value tablet, 1st row, 8th stamp) but there are others of interest, notably in the clouds.

**1916.** *Colours changed. Single plates. Wmk Mult Crown CA. P* 14.

| | | | | |
|---|---|---|---|---|
| 49 | 5 | 5 c. orange | 6·00 | 8·00 |
| | | a. "5 c." retouch | £160 | £190 |
| 50 | | 8 c. ultramarine | 4·50 | 14·00 |
| 49/50 Optd "Specimen" | | *Set of* 2 | £100 | |

**MALAYA-BORNEO EXHIBITION OVERPRINTS.** These were produced from a setting of 30 examples, applied twice to overprint the complete sheet of 60 stamps. Three prominent overprint flaws exist, each occurring on all the stamps in two vertical rows of the sheet.

HI — Short "I" (all stamps in 2nd and 8th vertical rows)
EX — Broken "E" (all stamps in 4th and 10th vertical rows)
NE — Broken "N" (all stamps in 6th and 12th vertical rows)

(Optd by Govt Printer, Singapore)

**1922** (31 Mar). *Optd with T* **6**, *in black.*

| | | | | |
|---|---|---|---|---|
| 51 | 5 | 1 c. green (II) | 1·75 | 17·00 |
| | | a. Short "I" | 5·50 | |
| | | b. Broken "E" | 5·50 | |
| | | c. Broken "N" | 5·50 | |
| 52 | | 2 c. black and brown | 3·75 | 20·00 |
| | | a. Short "I" | 10·00 | |
| | | b. Broken "E" | 10·00 | |
| | | c. Broken "N" | 10·00 | |
| 53 | 5 | 3 c. scarlet (II) | 5·00 | 32·00 |
| | | a. Short "I" | 12·00 | |
| | | b. Broken "E" | 12·00 | |
| | | c. Broken "N" | 12·00 | |
| 54 | | 4 c. claret (II) | 4·00 | 40·00 |
| | | a. Short "I" | 10·00 | |
| | | b. Broken "E" | 10·00 | |
| | | c. Broken "N" | 10·00 | |
| 55 | | 5 c. orange (II) | 7·50 | 55·00 |
| | | a. "5 c." retouch | £275 | £600 |
| | | b. Short "I" | 16·00 | |
| | | c. Broken "E" | 16·00 | |
| | | d. Broken "N" | 16·00 | |
| 56 | | 10 c. purple/*yellow* (II) | 6·50 | 55·00 |
| | | a. Short "I" | 14·00 | |
| | | b. Broken "E" | 14·00 | |
| | | c. Broken "N" | 14·00 | |
| 57 | | 25 c. purple (II) | 14·00 | 80·00 |
| | | a. Short "I" | 30·00 | |
| | | b. Broken "E" | 30·00 | |
| | | c. Broken "N" | 30·00 | |
| 58 | | 50 c. black/*blue-green* (II) | 45·00 | £150 |
| | | a. Short "I" | 80·00 | |
| | | b. Broken "E" | 80·00 | |
| | | c. Broken "N" | 80·00 | |
| 59 | | $1 black and red/*blue* | 70·00 | £190 |
| | | a. Short "I" | £120 | |
| | | b. Broken "E" | £120 | |
| | | c. Broken "N" | £120 | |
| 51/9 | | *Set of* 9 | £140 | £550 |

**Sultan Ahmed Tajudin Akhazul Khairi Wadin, 1924–1950**

7 Native houses, Water Village

**1924** (Feb)–**37.** *Printed from single plates as Type* II, *except* 30 *c. and* $1 *as Type* I. *Wmk Mult Script CA. P* 14.

| | | | | |
|---|---|---|---|---|
| 60 | 5 | 1 c. black (9.26) | 30 | 35 |
| 61 | | 2 c. brown (3.24) | 90 | 3·00 |
| 62 | | 2 c. green (3.33) | 30 | 30 |
| 63 | | 3 c. green (3.24) | 80 | 4·50 |
| 64 | | 4 c. maroon (3.24) | 1·25 | 75 |
| 65 | | 4 c. orange (1929) | 65 | 50 |
| 66 | | 5 c. orange-yellow* (3.24) | 1·50 | 90 |
| | | a. "5 c." retouch | £100 | £110 |
| 67 | | 5 c. grey (1931) | 6·50 | 3·75 |
| | | a. "5 c." retouch | £250 | £250 |
| 68 | | 5 c. chocolate (1933) | 1·25 | 15 |
| | | a. "5 c." retouch | 70·00 | 50·00 |
| 69 | 7 | 6 c. intense black** (3.24) | 8·00 | 9·00 |
| 70 | | 6 c. scarlet (1931) | 3·75 | 90·00 |
| 71 | 5 | 8 c. ultramarine (9.27) | 4·25 | 5·00 |
| 72 | | 8 c. grey-black (1933) | 2·25 | 55 |
| 73 | | 10 c. purple/*yellow* (3.37) | 6·50 | 14·00 |
| 74 | 7 | 12 c. blue | 4·50 | 8·00 |
| | | *a. Pale greenish blue* (1927) | £130 | £200 |
| 75 | 5 | 25 c. slate-purple (1931) | 5·00 | 8·00 |
| 76 | | 30 c. purple and orange-yellow (1931) | 4·50 | 12·00 |
| 77 | | 50 c. black/*emerald* (1931) | 7·00 | 13·00 |
| 78 | | $1 black and red/*blue* (1931) | 24·00 | 50·00 |
| 60/78 | | *Set of* 19 | 75·00 | £120 |
| 60/72, 74/8 Optd/Perf "Specimen" | | *Set of* 18 | £350 | |

*For 5 c. orange, see No. 82. No. 66 is a "Wet" printing and No. 82 a "Dry".

**For 6 c. black, see No. 83. Apart from the difference in shade there is a variation in size, No. 69 being 37¾ mm long and No. 83 39 mm.

The 2 c. orange and 3 c. blue-green in Type **5**, and the 6 c. greenish black, 8 c. red and 15 c. ultramarine in Type **7** were not issued without the Japanese Occupation overprint, although unoverprinted examples exist.

During the life of this issue De La Rue changed the method of production from a "Wet" to a "Dry" process. Initially the stamps were printed on ungummed paper which was dampened before being put on the press. Once the paper had dried, and contracted in the process, the gum was then applied. "Dry" printings, introduced around 1934, were on pre-gummed paper. The contraction of the "Wet" printings was considerable and usually involves a difference of between 0.5 mm and 1 mm when compared with the larger "Dry" printings. The following stamps occur from both "Wet" and "Dry" versions: 1 c., 2 c. green, 4 c. orange, 5 c. chocolate, 6 c. scarlet, 8 c. grey-black, 10 c. and 25 c.

Stamps of this issue can be found either line or comb perforated.

After the cessation of hostilities with the Japanese postal services were re-introduced by the British Military Administration. Post offices under B.M.A. control were opened at Brunei Town and Kuala Belait on 17 December 1945 where B.M.A. overprints on the stamps of NORTH BORNEO and SARAWAK were used until the reappearance of Brunei issues on 2 January 1947.

Redrawn clouds (R. 1/1 of No. 80*ab* only)

**1947** (2 Jan)–**51.** *Colours changed and new values. Wmk Mult Script CA. P* 14.

| No. | Type | Description | Unused | Used |
|---|---|---|---|---|
| 79 | 5 | 1 c. chocolate | 50 | 60 |
| | | a. "A" missing from wmk | £1100 | |
| 80 | | 2 c. grey | 40 | 75 |
| | | a. Perf 14½ × 13½ (25.9.50) | 1·50 | 1·40 |
| | | *ab. Black* (27.6.51) | 1·50 | 2·50 |
| | | ac. Redrawn clouds | 50·00 | |
| 81 | 7 | 3 c. green | 75 | 1·75 |
| 82 | 5 | 5 c. orange* | 60 | 80 |
| | | a. "5 c." retouch | 55·00 | 60·00 |
| | | b. Perf 14½ × 13½ (25.9.50) | 4·00 | 5·50 |
| | | c. Ditto. "5 c." retouch | 85·00 | 90·00 |
| 83 | 7 | 6 c. black* | 90 | 2·00 |
| 84 | 5 | 8 c. scarlet | 40 | 40 |
| | | a. Perf 13 (25.1.51) | 40 | 3·00 |
| 85 | | 10 c. violet | 30 | 10 |
| | | a. Perf 14½ × 13½ (25.9.50) | 1·75 | 2·25 |
| 86 | | 15 c. ultramarine | 30 | 30 |
| 87 | | 25 c. purple | 55 | 40 |
| | | a. Perf 14½ × 13½ (25.1.51) | 60 | 3·25 |
| 88 | | 30 c. black and orange | 45 | 50 |
| | | a. Perf 14½ × 13½ (25.1.51) | 60 | 4·25 |
| 89 | | 50 c. black | 50 | 30 |
| | | a. Perf 13 (25.9.50) | 1·50 | 8·00 |
| 90 | | $1 black and scarlet | 1·25 | 60 |
| 91 | | $5 green and red-orange (2.2.48) | 16·00 | 14·00 |
| 92 | | $10 black and purple (2.2.48) | 27·00 | 32·00 |
| 79/92 | | *Set of* 14 | 45·00 | 48·00 |
| 79/92 Perf "Specimen" | | *Set of* 14 | £190 | |

*See also Nos. 66 and 69.

The 1, 2, 3, 5, 6, 10 and 25 c. values utilised the plates of the pre-war issue and were line perforated until the introduction of the 14½×13½ comb machine for some values in 1950–51. The 8, 15, 50 c., $1, $2 and $5 were from new plates with the sheets comb perforated. The 30 c. was initially a pre-war plate, but it is believed that a new plate was introduced in 1951.

8 Sultan Ahmed Tajudin and Water Village

**1949** (22 Sept). *Sultan's Silver Jubilee. Wmk Mult Script CA. P* 13.

| No. | Type | Description | Unused | Used |
|---|---|---|---|---|
| 93 | 8 | 8 c. black and carmine | 55 | 60 |
| 94 | | 25 c. purple and red-orange | 55 | 50 |
| 95 | | 50 c. black and blue | 70 | 80 |
| 93/5 | | *Set of* 3 | 1·60 | 1·75 |

**1949** (10 Oct). *75th Anniv of Universal Postal Union. As Nos.* 114/17 *of Antigua.*

| No. | Description | Unused | Used |
|---|---|---|---|
| 96 | 8 c. carmine | 65 | 80 |
| 97 | 15 c. deep blue | 1·25 | 90 |
| 98 | 25 c. magenta | 1·25 | 90 |
| 99 | 50 c. blue-black | 1·50 | 90 |
| 96/9 | *Set of* 4 | 4·25 | 3·25 |

**Sultan Sir Omar Ali Saifuddin-Wasa'adul Khairi Wadin, 1950–1967**

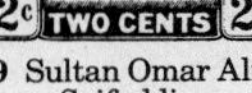


9 Sultan Omar Ali Saifuddin

10 Native houses, Water Village

**1952** (1 Mar)–**58.** *Wmk Mult Script CA. P* 13.

| No. | Type | Description | Unused | Used |
|---|---|---|---|---|
| 100 | 9 | 1 c. black | 10 | 30 |
| 101 | | 2 c. black and orange | 10 | 35 |
| 102 | | 3 c. black and lake-brown | 10 | 10 |
| 103 | | 4 c. black and green | 10 | 10 |
| 104 | | 6 c. black and grey | 10 | 10 |
| 105 | | 8 c. black and crimson | 20 | 10 |
| | | *a. Black and crimson-lake* (15.2.56) | 40 | 10 |
| 106 | | 10 c. black and sepia | 15 | 10 |
| 107 | | 12 c. black and violet | 80 | 10 |
| 108 | | 15 c. black and pale blue | 1·00 | 10 |
| 109 | | 25 c. black and purple | 90 | 10 |
| | | *a. Black and reddish purple* (8.10.53) | 2·25 | 30 |
| 110 | | 50 c. black and ultramarine | 50 | 10 |
| | | *a. Black and blue* (22.6.55) | 1·00 | 10 |
| 111 | 10 | $1 black and green | 1·25 | 60 |
| | | *a. Black and bronze-green* (23.7.58) | 2·25 | 1·25 |
| 112 | | $2 black and scarlet | 4·50 | 2·00 |
| 113 | | $5 black and maroon | 9·50 | 3·50 |
| | | *a. Black and brown-purple* (15.2.56) | 9·00 | 3·00 |
| 100/13 | | *Set of* 14 | 17·00 | 6·00 |

No. 106 exists in coils constructed from normal sheets.

See also Nos. 118/31 and 202/9.

11 Brunei Mosque and Sultan Omar

(Recess B.W.)

**1958** (24 Sept). *Opening of Brunei Mosque.* W w **12**. *P* 13½.

| No. | Type | Description | Unused | Used |
|---|---|---|---|---|
| 114 | 11 | 8 c. black and myrtle-green | 10 | 45 |
| 115 | | 15 c. black and carmine | 10 | 15 |
| 116 | | 35 c. black and deep lilac | 20 | 70 |
| 114/16 | | *Set of* 3 | 35 | 1·10 |

12 "Protein Foods"

(Des M. Goaman. Photo Harrison)

**1963** (4 June). *Freedom from Hunger.* W w **12**. *P* 14 × 14½.

| No. | Type | Description | Unused | Used |
|---|---|---|---|---|
| 117 | 12 | 12 c. sepia | 2·00 | 90 |

**1964–72.** *As Nos.* 100/13, *but* W w **12**. *Glazed paper* ($2, 5) *or ordinary paper* (*others*).

| No. | Type | Description | Unused | Used |
|---|---|---|---|---|
| 118 | 9 | 1 c. black (17.3.64) | 20 | 30 |
| | | a. Glazed paper. *Grey* (28.11.69) | 25 | 50 |
| | | *ab. Slate-grey* (30.6.72) | 10 | 20 |
| 119 | | 2 c. black and orange (17.3.64) | 60 | 10 |
| | | a. Glazed paper (27.5.70) | 20 | 10 |
| 120 | | 3 c. black and lake-brown (10.11.64) | 75 | 15 |
| | | a. Glazed paper (27.5.70) | 30 | 10 |
| 121 | | 4 c. black and green (12.5.64) | 20 | 10 |
| | | a. Glazed paper (22.4.70) | 20 | 10 |
| | | *ab. Black and emerald* (19.11.71) | 35 | 1·25 |
| 122 | | 6 c. black and grey (12.5.64) | 90 | 10 |
| | | *a. Black* (28.11.69) | 3·50 | 3·50 |
| | | b. Glazed paper (28.11.69) | 35 | 10 |
| | | *ba. Light grey* (19.11.71) | 50 | 95 |
| 123 | | 8 c. black and crimson-lake (12.5.64) | 40 | 10 |
| | | a. Glazed paper (27.5.70) | 50 | 15 |
| | | *ab. Black and brown-red* (19.11.71) | 45 | 90 |
| 124 | | 10 c. black and sepia (12.5.64) | 30 | 10 |
| | | a. Glazed paper (31.3.70) | 85 | 10 |
| | | *ab. Grey and pale brown* (coil) (11.10.71) | 85 | 90 |
| 125 | | 12 c. black and violet (12.5.64) | 75 | 10 |
| | | a. Glazed paper (5.11.70) | 2·00 | 55 |
| 126 | | 15 c. black and pale blue (12.5.64) | 40 | 10 |
| | | a. Glazed paper (28.11.69) | 50 | 10 |
| 127 | | 25 c. black and purple (12.5.64) | 1·00 | 10 |
| | | a. Glazed paper (18.5.70) | 4·00 | 2·00 |
| | | ab. Glazed paper. *Black and reddish violet* (30.4.71) | 4·25 | 70 |
| 128 | | 50 c. black and ultramarine (10.11.64) | 1·25 | 10 |
| | | *a. Black & brt ultramarine* (17.3.69) | 2·00 | 40 |
| | | b. Glazed paper (5.11.70) | 4·00 | 75 |
| | | *ba. Grey and indigo* (21.12.71) | 5·00 | 60 |
| 129 | 10 | $1 black and bronze-green (14.5.68) | 1·75 | 2·25 |
| | | a. Glazed paper (5.11.70) | 2·75 | 3·25 |
| 130 | | $2 black and scarlet (5.11.70) | 22·00 | 15·00 |
| 131 | | $5 black and maroon (5.11.70) | 25·00 | 20·00 |
| 118/29 | | *Set of* 12 | 7·75 | 3·00 |
| 118a/29a, 130/1 | | *Set of* 14 | 55·00 | 38·00 |

Printings of the 6 and 15 c. issued on 28 November 1969 were on both ordinary and glazed paper, the 6 c. on ordinary producing a distinct shade.

No. 124a exists in coils constructed from normal sheets.

13 I.T.U. Emblem

(Des M. Goaman. Litho Enschedé)

**1965** (17 May). *I.T.U. Centenary.* W w **12**. *P* 11 × 11½.

| No. | Type | Description | Unused | Used |
|---|---|---|---|---|
| 132 | 13 | 4 c. mauve and orange-brown | 35 | 10 |
| 133 | | 75 c. orange-yellow and light emerald | 1·00 | 75 |

14 I.C.Y. Emblem

(Des V. Whiteley. Litho Harrison)

**1965** (25 Oct). *International Co-operation Year.* W w **12**. *P* 14.

| No. | Type | Description | Unused | Used |
|---|---|---|---|---|
| 134 | 14 | 4 c. reddish purple and turquoise-green | 20 | 10 |
| 135 | | 15 c. deep bluish green and lavender | 55 | 35 |

15 Sir Winston Churchill and St. Paul's Cathedral in Wartime

(Des Jennifer Toombs. Photo Harrison)

**1966** (24 Jan). *Churchill Commemoration.* W w **12**. *P* 14.

| No. | Type | Description | Unused | Used |
|---|---|---|---|---|
| 136 | 15 | 3 c. black, cerise, gold and new blue | 30 | 15 |
| 137 | | 10 c. black, cerise, gold and deep green | 1·25 | 20 |
| 138 | | 15 c. black, cerise, gold and brown | 1·50 | 35 |
| 139 | | 75 c. black, cerise, gold and bluish violet | 3·00 | 2·00 |
| 136/9 | | *Set of* 4 | 5·50 | 2·50 |

16 Footballer's Legs, Ball and Jules Rimet Cup

(Des V. Whiteley. Litho Harrison)

**1966** (4 July). *World Cup Football Championships.* W w **12** (*sideways*). *P* 14.

| No. | Type | Description | Unused | Used |
|---|---|---|---|---|
| 140 | 16 | 4 c. violet, yellow-green, lake & yell-brn | 20 | 15 |
| 141 | | 75 c. chocolate, blue-grn, lake & yell-brn | 75 | 60 |

17 W.H.O. Building

(Des M. Goaman. Litho Harrison)

**1966** (20 Sept). *Inauguration of W.H.O. Headquarters, Geneva.* W w **12** (*sideways*). *P* 14.

| No. | Type | Description | Unused | Used |
|---|---|---|---|---|
| 142 | 17 | 12 c. black, yellow-green and light blue | 35 | 20 |
| 143 | | 25 c. black, light purple and yellow-brown | 55 | 35 |

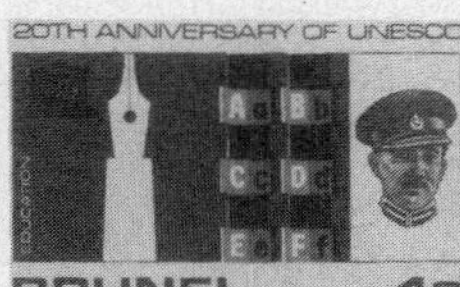


18 "Education"

19 "Science"

20 "Culture"

(Des Jennifer Toombs. Litho Harrison)

**1966** (1 Dec). *20th Anniv of U.N.E.S.C.O.* W w **12** (*sideways*). *P* 14.

| No. | Type | Description | Unused | Used |
|---|---|---|---|---|
| 144 | 18 | 4 c. slate-violet, red, yellow and orange | 35 | 10 |
| 145 | 19 | 15 c. orange-yellow, violet and deep olive | 75 | 45 |
| 146 | 20 | 75 c. black, bright purple and orange | 2·25 | 2·75 |
| 144/6 | | *Set of* 3 | 3·00 | 3·00 |

**Sultan Sir Hassanal Bolkiah Mu'izzadin Waddaulah, 1967**

21 Religious Headquarters Building

(Des and photo Harrison)

**1967** (19 Dec). *1400th Anniv of Revelation of the Koran.* W w **12** (*sideways*). *P* 12½.

| No. | Type | Description | Unused | Used |
|---|---|---|---|---|
| 147 | 21 | 4 c. multicoloured | 10 | 10 |
| 148 | | 10 c. multicoloured | 15 | 10 |
| 149 | – | 25 c. multicoloured | 20 | 20 |
| 150 | – | 50 c. multicoloured | 35 | 50 |
| 147/50 | | *Set of* 4 | 70 | 80 |

Nos. 149/50 are as T **21** but have sprigs of laurel flanking the main design (which has a smaller circle) in place of flagpoles.

## COVER PRICES

Cover factors are quoted at the beginning of each country for most issues to 1945. An explanation of the system can be found on page x. The factors quoted do not, however, apply to philatelic covers.

**22** Sultan of Brunei, Mosque and Flags

(Des V. Whiteley. Photo Enschedé)

**1968** (9 July). *Installation of Y.T.M. Seri Paduka Duli Pengiran Temenggong. T* **22** *and similar multicoloured design. P* 14 × 13 (12 c.) *or* 13 × 14 (*others*).

| No. | Description | Unused | Used |
|---|---|---|---|
| 151 | 4 c. Type **22** | 15 | 25 |
| 152 | 12 c. Sultan of Brunei, Mosque and Flags (*horiz*) | 40 | 65 |
| 153 | 25 c. Type **22** | 50 | 1·10 |
| 151/3 | *Set of* 3 | 95 | 1·75 |

**23** Sultan of Brunei **24** Sultan of Brunei

(Des V. Whiteley. Litho D.L.R.)

**1968** (15 July). *Sultan's Birthday.* W w **12** (*sideways*). *P* 12.

| No. | Type | Description | Unused | Used |
|---|---|---|---|---|
| 154 | **23** | 4 c. multicoloured | 10 | 15 |
| 155 | | 12 c. multicoloured | 20 | 25 |
| 156 | | 25 c. multicoloured | 30 | 50 |
| 154/6 | | *Set of* 3 | 55 | 80 |

(Des V. Whiteley. Photo Harrison)

**1968** (1 Aug). *Coronation of the Sultan of Brunei.* W w **12** (*sideways*). *P* 14½ × 14.

| No. | Type | Description | Unused | Used |
|---|---|---|---|---|
| 157 | **24** | 4 c. multicoloured | 15 | 15 |
| 158 | | 12 c. multicoloured | 25 | 30 |
| 159 | | 25 c. multicoloured | 40 | 45 |
| 157/9 | | *Set of* 3 | 70 | 80 |

**25** New Building and Sultan's Portrait

**26** New Building and Sultan's Portrait

(Photo Enschedé)

**1968** (29 Sept). *Opening of Language and Literature Bureau.* W w **12** (*sideways*). *P* 13½ (10 c.) *or* 12½ × 13½ (*others*).

| No. | Type | Description | Unused | Used |
|---|---|---|---|---|
| 160 | **25** | 10 c. multicoloured | 15 | 50 |
| | | a. Tête-bêche (pair) | 30 | 1·00 |
| 161 | **26** | 15 c. multicoloured | 20 | 30 |
| 162 | | 30 c. multicoloured | 40 | 60 |
| 160/2 | | *Set of* 3 | 65 | 1·25 |

The above were scheduled for release in 1967, and when finally issued had the year altered by overprinting.

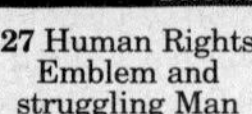

**27** Human Rights Emblem and struggling Man **28** Sultan of Brunei and W.H.O. Emblem

(Des V. Whiteley. Litho Harrison)

**1968** (16 Dec). *Human Rights Year.* W w **12**. *P* 14.

| No. | Type | Description | Unused | Used |
|---|---|---|---|---|
| 163 | **27** | 12 c. black, yellow and green | 10 | 15 |
| 164 | | 25 c. black, yellow and blue | 15 | 20 |
| 165 | | 75 c. black, yellow and dull purple | 45 | 1·00 |
| 163/5 | | *Set of* 3 | 65 | 1·25 |

(Des V. Whiteley. Litho Format)

**1968** (19 Dec). *20th Anniv of World Health Organization. P* 14.

| No. | Type | Description | Unused | Used |
|---|---|---|---|---|
| 166 | **28** | 4 c. yellow, black and cobalt | 15 | 25 |
| 167 | | 15 c. yellow, black and deep bluish violet | 30 | 35 |
| 168 | | 25 c. yellow, black and pale yellow-olive | 40 | 65 |
| 166/8 | | *Set of* 3 | 75 | 1·10 |

**29** Deep Sea Oil-Rig, Sultan of Brunei and inset portrait of Pengiran Di-Gadong

(Des adapted by V. Whiteley. Photo Enschedé)

**1969** (10 July). *Installation (9th May, 1968) of Pengiran Shahbandar as Y.T.M. Seri Paduka Duli Pengiran Di-Gadong Sahibol Mal.* W w **12**. *P* 14 × 13.

| No. | Type | Description | Unused | Used |
|---|---|---|---|---|
| 169 | **29** | 12 c. multicoloured | 35 | 25 |
| 170 | | 40 c. multicoloured | 70 | 70 |
| 171 | | 50 c. multicoloured | 80 | 80 |
| 169/71 | | *Set of* 3 | 1·75 | 1·60 |

**30** Aerial View of Parliament Buildings

(Des Harrison. Litho D.L.R.)

**1969** (23 Sept). *Opening of Royal Audience Hall and Legislative Council Chamber. P* 15.

| No. | Type | Description | Unused | Used |
|---|---|---|---|---|
| 172 | **30** | 12 c. multicoloured | 15 | 15 |
| 173 | | 25 c. multicoloured | 25 | 30 |
| 174 | – | 50 c. rose-red and bluish violet | 50 | 60 |
| 172/4 | | *Set of* 3 | 80 | 95 |

Design:—50 c. Elevation of new buildings.

**32** Youth Centre and Sultan's Portrait

(Des V. Whiteley. Litho D.L.R.)

**1969** (20 Dec). *Opening of the New Youth Centre.* W w **12**. *P* 15 × 14½.

| No. | Type | Description | Unused | Used |
|---|---|---|---|---|
| 175 | **32** | 6 c. flesh, slate-lilac and black | 15 | 20 |
| 176 | | 10 c. olive-yellow, grey-green and blackish brown | 20 | 10 |
| 177 | | 30 c. yellow-olive, yellow-brown & black | 55 | 45 |
| 175/7 | | *Set of* 3 | 80 | 65 |

**33** Soldier, Sultan and Badge **34** Badge, and Officer in Full-dress Uniform

(Des Maj. M. A. Bowman. Adapted V. Whiteley. Litho Questa)

**1971** (3 May). *Tenth Anniv of Royal Brunei Malay Regiment. Multicoloured designs, each with Badge and Sultan's portrait as T* **33**. W w **12** (*sideways on* 15 *and* 75 *c.*). *P* 14½.

| No. | Description | Unused | Used |
|---|---|---|---|
| 178 | 10 c. Type **33** | 45 | 30 |
| 179 | 15 c. Helicopter (*horiz*) | 55 | 55 |
| 180 | 75 c. *Pahlawan* (patrol boat) (*horiz*) | 2·50 | 4·25 |
| 178/80 | *Set of* 3 | 3·25 | 4·50 |

(Des Supt. T. Swan. Litho Format)

**1971** (14 Aug). *50th Anniv of Royal Brunei Police Force. T* **34** *and similar vert designs. Multicoloured.* W w **12** (*sideways*). *P* 14½.

| No. | Description | Unused | Used |
|---|---|---|---|
| 181 | 10 c. Type **34** | 50 | 30 |
| 182 | 15 c. Badge and Patrol Constable | 70 | 80 |
| 183 | 50 c. Badge and Traffic Constable | 2·25 | 4·25 |
| 181/3 | *Set of* 3 | 3·00 | 4·75 |

**35** Perdana Wazir, Sultan of Brunei and view of Water Village

(Des and litho Harrison)

**1971** (27 Aug). *Installation of the Yang Teramat Mulia as the Perdana Wazir* (1970). *T* **35** *and similar horiz designs showing different views of Brunei Town.* W w **12**. *P* 14.

| No. | Type | Description | Unused | Used |
|---|---|---|---|---|
| 184 | **35** | 15 c. multicoloured | 40 | 50 |
| 185 | – | 25 c. multicoloured | 70 | 1·00 |
| 186 | – | 50 c. multicoloured | 1·40 | 2·75 |
| 184/6 | | *Set of* 3 | 2·25 | 3·75 |

**36** Pottery

(Des C. Abbott. Litho Questa)

**1972** (29 Feb). *Opening of Brunei Museum. T* **36** *and similar horiz designs. Multicoloured.* W w **12** (*sideways*). *P* 13½.

| No. | Description | Unused | Used |
|---|---|---|---|
| 187 | 10 c. Type **36** | 25 | 10 |
| 188 | 12 c. Straw-work | 30 | 20 |
| 189 | 15 c. Leather-work | 35 | 20 |
| 190 | 25 c. Gold-work | 1·00 | 1·10 |
| 191 | 50 c. Museum Building (58 × 21 *mm*) | 2·00 | 2·50 |
| 187/91 | *Set of* 5 | 3·50 | 3·75 |

**37** Brunei Museum, Queen Elizabeth and Sultan of Brunei

(Des locally. Photo Enschedé)

**1972** (29 Feb). *Royal Visit. T* **37** *and similar horiz designs each with portraits of Queen and Sultan. Multicoloured.* W w **12** (*sideways*). *P* 13 × 13½.

| No. | Description | Unused | Used |
|---|---|---|---|
| 192 | 10 c. Type **37** | 20 | 20 |
| 193 | 15 c. Native houses | 30 | 30 |
| 194 | 25 c. Mosque | 75 | 1·00 |
| 195 | 50 c. Royal Assembly Hall | 2·00 | 3·00 |
| 192/5 | *Set of* 4 | 3·00 | 4·00 |

**38** Secretariat Building

(Des Harrison. Litho J.W.)

**1972** (4 Oct). *Renaming of Brunei Town as Bandar Seri Begawan. T* **38** *and similar horiz designs.* W w **12** (*sideways*). *P* 13½.

| No. | Description | Unused | Used |
|---|---|---|---|
| 196 | 10 c. multicoloured | 20 | 15 |
| 197 | 15 c. green, light yellow and black | 25 | 15 |
| 198 | 25 c. ultramarine, lemon and black | 40 | 45 |
| 199 | 50 c. rosine, pale turquoise-blue and black | 80 | 1·10 |
| 196/9 | *Set of* 4 | 1·50 | 1·75 |

Views:—15 c. Darul Hana Palace; 25 c. Old Brunei Town; 50 c. Town and Water Village.

**39** Blackburn "Beverley" parachuting Supplies

(Des Trident Artists. Litho Questa)

**1972** (15 Nov). *Opening of R.A.F. Museum, Hendon. T* **39** *and similar horiz design. Multicoloured.* W w **12** (*sideways on* 75 *c.*). *P* 14 × 13½ (25 c.) *or* 13½ × 14 (75 c.).

| No. | Description | Unused | Used |
|---|---|---|---|
| 200 | 25 c. Type **39** | 1·50 | 1·25 |
| 201 | 75 c. Blackburn "Beverley" landing | 3·00 | 3·25 |

**1972** (17 Nov)–**74**. *As Nos.* 119/26, *but W w* **12** (*sideways*). *Glazed paper.*

202 **9** 2 c. black and orange (9.5.73) 20 2·00
203 3 c. black and lake-brown 1·00 40
204 4 c. black and green 50 40
205 6 c. black and grey 1·60 30
206 8 c. black and brown-red (9.5.73) 50 1·50
207 10 c. black and sepia 70 30
*a. Black and bistre-brown* (24.7.74) 80 1·25
208 12 c. black and violet 1·50 2·25
209 15 c. black and pale blue 1·75 2·25
202/9 *Set of* 8 7·00 8·50

**40** Girl with Traditional Flower-pot, and Boy with Bowl and Pipe

(Des (from photograph by D. Groves) and photo Harrison)

**1972** (20 Nov). *Royal Silver Wedding. Multicoloured; background colour given. W* w **12**. *P* 14 × 14½.

210 **40** 12 c. carmine-red 10 10
211 75 c. deep myrtle-green 20 50

**41** Interpol H.Q., Paris

(Des Shamir Bros. Litho Harrison)

**1973** (7 Sept). *50th Anniv of Interpol. T* **41** *and similar horiz design. W* w **12** (*inverted on* 50 *c.*). *P* 14 × 14½.

212 25 c. bright green, purple and dull blue-black 1·25 1·25
213 50 c. pale greenish blue, ultramarine & carm 1·25 1·25

The 50 c. shows a different view of the H.Q.

**42** Sultan, Princess Anne and Capt. Phillips

(Des PAD Studio. Litho Format)

**1973** (14 Nov). *Royal Wedding. W* w **12**. *P* 14.

214 **42** 25 c. multicoloured 10 10
215 50 c. multicoloured 15 25

**43** Churchill Painting

**44** Sultan Sir Hassanal Bolkiah Mu'izzaddin Waddaulah

(Des C. Abbott. Litho Questa)

**1973** (31 Dec). *Opening of Churchill Memorial Building. T* **43** *and similar vert design. Multicoloured. W* w **12** (*sideways*). *P* 14 × 13½.

216 12 c. Type **43** 10 15
217 50 c. Churchill Statue 30 85

(Des Staff Artists, Dept of Language and Literature. Photo Harrison)

**1974** (15 July*). *Multicoloured; background colour given. W* w **12** (*sideways*). *P* 13½ × 14½.

218 **44** 4 c. turquoise-green 10 10
219 5 c. pale blue 10 10
220 6 c. olive 40 15
221 10 c. lavender 15 10
222 15 c. light brown 20 10
223 20 c. stone 20 15
224 25 c. sage-green 30 15
225 30 c. bright blue 30 15
226 **44** 35 c. grey 35 20
227 40 c. bright purple 35 20
228 50 c. cinnamon 40 20
229 75 c. light yellow-green 60 1·00
230 $1 pale salmon 1·25 2·00
231 $2 greenish yellow 2·25 4·25
232 $5 silver 4·50 10·00
233 $10 gold 8·00 18·00
218/33 *Set of* 16 17·00 32·00

*This was the London release date. The stamps were not put on sale locally until 29 August 1974, but First Day Covers were cancelled with the 15 July date.

See also Nos. 244/59 and 260/2.

**45** Aerial View of Airport

(Des Harrison. Litho B.W.)

**1974** (18 July). *Inauguration of Brunei International Airport. T* **45** *and similar horiz design. Multicoloured. W* w **12** (*sideways on* 75 *c.*). *P* 14 × 14½ (50 *c.*) *or* 12½ × 13 (75 *c.*).

234 50 c. Type **45** 75 1·00
235 75 c. Sultan in Army uniform, and airport (48 × 36 *mm*) 1·25 1·50

**46** U.P.U. Emblem and Sultan

(Des J.W. Litho Harrison)

**1974** (28 Oct). *Centenary of Universal Postal Union. W* w **12** (*sideways*). *P* 14½.

236 **46** 12 c. multicoloured 20 20
237 50 c. multicoloured 40 1·00
238 75 c. multicoloured 50 1·25
236/8 *Set of* 3 1·00 2·25

**47** Sir Winston Churchill

(Des C. Abbott. Litho Questa)

**1974** (30 Nov). *Birth Centenary of Sir Winston Churchill. T* **47** *and similar horiz design. Multicoloured. W* w **14** (*sideways*). *P* 14.

239 12 c. Type **47** 20 20
240 75 c. Churchill smoking cigar (profile) 35 70

**48** Boeing "737" and R.B.A. Crest

(Des PAD Studio. Litho Enschedé)

**1975** (14 May). *Inauguration of Royal Brunei Airlines. T* **48** *and similar horiz designs. Multicoloured. No wmk. P* 12½ × 12.

241 12 c. Type **48** 30 25
242 35 c. "737" over Bandar Seri Begawan Mosque 80 1·00
243 75 c. "737" in flight 1·75 2·00
241/3 *Set of* 3 2·50 3·00

**1975** (13 Aug)–**78**. *As Nos.* 218/33, *but W w* **14** (*sideways*).

244 **44** 4 c. turquoise-green 30 40
245 5 c. pale blue 30 40
246 6 c. olive 30 55
247 10 c. lavender 30 10
*a. Pale bluish violet* (19.4.77) 20 10
248 15 c. light brown 40 40
249 20 c. stone 50 40
250 25 c. sage-green 60 50
*a. Grey-olive* (25.5.78) 50 40
251 30 c. bright blue 35 50
252 35 c. grey 45 60
253 40 c. bright purple 55 60
254 50 c. cinnamon 90 40
a. Blue omitted† 40·00
255 75 c. light yellow-green 80 1·00
256 $1 pale salmon 90 1·25
257 **44** $2 greenish yellow 2·25 3·50
258 $5 silver 4·50 8·50
259 $10 gold 12·00 17·00
244/59 *Set of* 16 23·00 32·00

†The blue colour on the 50 c. value is only evident in the bluish green stripes of the sash and on several of the medal ribbons.

**1976** (12 Apr). *As Nos.* 221 *and* 223/4 *but W* w **12** (*upright*).

260 **44** 10 c. lavender 1·00 60
261 20 c. stone 1·25 1·75
262 25 c. sage-green 1·25 1·75
260/2 *Set of* 3 3·25 3·75

**10**
**sen**

(49)

**50** Royal Coat of Arms

(Surchd by Govt Printer, Brunei)

**1976** (16 Aug). *No.* 246 *surch with T* **49** *in silver.*

263 **44** 10 c. on 6 c. olive 85 50
a. Surch on No. 220

(Des C. Abbott. Litho D.L.R.)

**1977** (7 June). *Silver Jubilee. T* **50** *and similar vert designs. Multicoloured. W* w **14**. *P* 13½ × 14.

264 10 c. Type **50** 15 20
265 20 c. Imperial State Crown 20 35
a. Silver omitted £200
266 75 c. Queen Elizabeth (portrait by Annigoni) 45 75
264/6 *Set of* 3 70 1·10

**51** The Moment of Crowning

**52** Royal Crest

(Des J. Cooter. Litho Enschedé)

**1978** (2 June). *25th Anniv of Coronation. T* **51** *and similar vert designs. Multicoloured. W* w **14**. *P* 13½ × 13.

267 10 c. Type **51** 10 10
268 20 c. Queen in Coronation regalia 15 20
269 75 c. Queen's departure from Abbey 50 80
267/9 *Set of* 3 65 1·00

(Des local artist; adapted BG Studio. Litho Cartor S.A., France)

**1978** (1 Aug). *10th Anniv of Sultan's Coronation. T* **52** *and similar vert designs. W* w **14** (*inverted*). *P* 12.

270 10 c. black, scarlet and greenish yellow 10 10
271 20 c. multicoloured 15 20
272 75 c. multicoloured 50 75
270/2 *Set of* 3 65 95
**MS**273 182 × 77 mm. Nos. 270/2 6·00 8·00

Designs:—20 c. Coronation ceremony; 75 c. Royal Crown.

**53** Human Rights Emblem and struggling Man

**54** Smiling Children

(Des V. Whiteley; adapted L. McCombie. Litho Questa)

**1978** (10 Dec). *Human Rights Year. W* w **14**. *P* 14½.

274 **53** 10 c. black, yellow and scarlet 10 10
275 20 c. black, yellow and violet 20 20
276 75 c. black, yellow and bistre 50 75
274/6 *Set of* 3 70 90

Type **53** is similar to the design used for the 1968 Human Rights Year issue.

(Des L. Curtis. Litho Harrison)

**1979** (30 June). *International Year of the Child. T* **54** *and similar horiz design. W w* **14** *(sideways). P* 14.
277 10 c. multicoloured .. .. .. .. 10 10
278 $1 black and dull green .. .. .. 65 1·00
Design:—$1 I.Y.C. emblem.

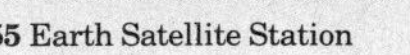
**55** Earth Satellite Station

**56** Hegira Symbol

(Des A. Theobald. Litho Questa)

**1979** (23 Sept). *Telisai Earth Satellite Station. T* **55** *and similar horiz designs. Multicoloured. W w* **14** *(sideways). P* 14.
279 10 c. Type **55** .. .. .. .. .. 10 10
280 20 c. Satellite and antenna .. .. .. 15 20
281 75 c. Television camera, telex machine and telephone .. .. .. .. .. 40 1·25
279/81 .. .. .. .. *Set of* 3 60 1·40

(Litho Secura, Singapore)

**1979** (21 Nov). *Moslem Year* 1400 *AH Commemoration. W w* **14**. *P* 13 × 13½.
282 **56** 10 c. black, yellow and emerald .. .. 10 15
283 20 c. black, yellow and light blue .. 15 25
284 75 c. black, yellow and violet .. .. 45 1·25
282/4 .. .. .. .. *Set of* 3 60 1·50
**MS**285 178 × 200 mm. Nos. 282/4 .. .. 1·75 2·25

**57** Installation Ceremony

**58** Royal Umbrella and Sash

(Des BG Studio. Litho Questa)

**1980** (8 Nov). *1st Anniv of Prince Sufri Bolkiah's Installation as First Wazir. T* **57** *and similar vert design. Multicoloured. W w* **14**. *P* 13½.
286 10 c. Type **57** .. .. .. .. 15 10
287 75 c. Prince Sufri .. .. .. .. 50 65
Nos. 286/7 have blue borders.

(Des BG Studio. Litho Secura, Singapore)

**1980** (6 Dec). *1st Anniv of Prince Jefri Bolkiah's Installation as Second Wazir. Vert designs as T* **57**. *Multicoloured. W w* **14**. *P* 13½.
288 10 c. Installation ceremony .. .. .. 15 10
289 75 c. Prince Jefri .. .. .. .. 45 70
Nos. 288/9 have green borders.

(Des BG Studio. Litho Security Printers (M), Malaysia)

**1981** (18 Jan*). *Royal Regalia (1st series). T* **58** *and similar multicoloured designs. P* 13½ × 13 *(50 c.) or* 12 × 11½ *(others).*
290 10 c. Type **58** .. .. .. .. 15 15
291 15 c. Sword and Shield .. .. .. 20 20
292 20 c. Lance and Sheath .. .. .. 25 35
293 30 c. Betel-leaf Container .. .. .. 35 55
294 50 c. Coronation Crown (23 × 40 *mm*) .. 60 1·75
290/4 .. .. .. .. *Set of* 5 1·40 2·75
**MS**295 98 × 142 mm. Nos. 290/4 .. .. 2·25 3·50
*This is the local release date. The Crown Agents released the stamps on 19 January.
See also Nos. 298/303, 314/19 and 320/5.

**59** I.T.U. and W.H.O. Emblems

**60** Shield and Broadsword

(Litho Security Printers (M), Malaysia)

**1981** (17 May). *World Telecommunications and Health Day. P* 13 × 13½.
296 **59** 10 c. black and bright crimson .. .. 30 20
297 75 c. black, chalky blue & pale violet-bl 1·25 2·10

(Des BG Studio. Litho Security Printers (M), Malaysia)

**1981** (15 July). *Royal Regalia (2nd series). T* **60** *and similar multicoloured designs. P* 12.
298 10 c. Type **60** .. .. .. .. 10 10
299 15 c. Blunderbuss and Pouch .. .. .. 15 15
300 20 c. Crossed Lances and Sash .. .. 20 20
301 30 c. Sword, Shield and Sash .. .. .. 30 45
302 50 c. Forked Lance .. .. .. .. 50 1·00
303 75 c. Royal Drum (29 × 45 *mm*) .. .. 70 1·75
298/303 .. .. .. .. *Set of* 6 1·60 3·25

**61** Prince Charles as Colonel of the Welsh Guards

**62** Fishing

(Des J.W. Litho Format)

**1981** (29 July). *Royal Wedding. T* **61** *and similar vert designs. Multicoloured. W w* **14**. *P* 14.
304 10 c. Wedding bouquet from Brunei .. .. 35 15
305 $1 Type **61** .. .. .. .. .. 1·10 1·25
306 $2 Prince Charles and Lady Diana Spencer 1·40 2·25
304/6 .. .. .. .. *Set of* 3 2·50 3·25

(Des local artist. Litho Secura, Singapore)

**1981** (16 Oct). *World Food Day. T* **62** *and similar vert design. Multicoloured. P* 12 × 11½.
307 10 c. Type **62** .. .. .. .. 30 15
308 $1 Farm produce and machinery .. .. 2·10 2·50

**63** Blind Man and Braille Alphabet

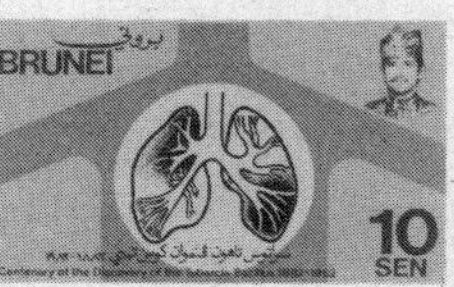
**64** Drawing of Infected Lungs

(Des local artist. Litho Security Printers (M), Malaysia)

**1981** (16 Dec). *International Year for Disabled Persons. T* **63** *and similar vert designs. Multicoloured. W w* **14**. *P* 12.
309 10 c. Type **63** .. .. .. .. 35 15
310 20 c. Deaf people and sign language .. .. 80 45
a. Wmk sideways .. .. .. 1·00 75
311 75 c. Disabled person and wheelchairs .. 2·00 2·75
309/11 .. .. .. .. *Set of* 3 2·75 3·00

(Des local artist. Litho Security Printers (M), Malaysia)

**1982** (24 May). *Centenary of Robert Koch's Discovery of Tubercle Bacillus. T* **64** *and similar horiz design. Multicoloured. W w* **14**. *P* 12 *(10 c.) or* 13½ *(75 c.).*
312 10 c. Type **64** .. .. .. .. 30 25
313 75 c. Magnified tubercle bacillus and microscope .. .. .. .. 1·10 2·00

(Des PAD Studio. Litho Security Printers (M), Malaysia)

**1982** (31 May). *Royal Regalia (3rd series). Multicoloured designs as T* **60**. *W w* **14** *(sideways). P* 13½ *(75 c.) or* 12 × 11½ *(others).*
314 10 c. Ceremonial Ornament .. .. .. 10 10
315 15 c. Silver Betel Caddy .. .. .. 15 15
316 20 c. Traditional Flower-pot .. .. .. 20 20
317 30 c. Solitary Candle .. .. .. .. 30 45
318 50 c. Golden Pipe .. .. .. .. 50 1·10
319 75 c. Royal Chin Support (28 × 45 *mm*) .. 70 2·00
314/19 .. .. .. .. *Set of* 6 1·75 3·50

(Des BG Studio. Litho Security Printers (M), Malaysia)

**1982** (15 July). *Royal Regalia (4th series). Multicoloured designs as T* **60**. *W w* **14** *(sideways). P* 12 *(75 c.) or* 12 × 11½ *(others).*
320 10 c. Royal Mace .. .. .. .. 20 10
321 15 c. Ceremonial Shield and Spears .. .. 30 15
322 20 c. Embroidered Ornament .. .. .. 40 20
323 30 c. Golden-tasselled Cushion .. .. 55 65
324 50 c. Ceremonial Dagger and Sheath .. .. 90 1·75
325 75 c. Religious Mace (28 × 45 *mm*) .. 1·25 2·25
320/5 .. .. .. .. *Set of* 6 3·25 4·50

**65** Brunei Flag

(Des Siti Zaleha Haji Kaprawi. Litho Secura, Singapore)

**1983** (14 Mar). *Commonwealth Day. T* **65** *and similar horiz designs. P* 13 × 13½.
326 10 c. multicoloured .. .. .. .. 15 15
a. Horiz strip of 4. Nos. 326/9 .. .. 1·75
327 20 c. bright blue, black and buff .. .. 20 20
328 75 c. bright blue, black and bright green .. 45 55
329 $2 bright blue, black and lemon .. .. 1·10 1·75
326/9 .. .. .. .. *Set of* 4 1·75 2·40
Designs:—20 c. Brunei Mosque; 75 c. Machinery; $2 Sultan of Brunei.
Nos. 326/9 were printed together, *se-tenant*, in horizontal strips of four throughout the sheet.

**66** "Postal Service"

**67** Football

(Litho Secura, Singapore)

**1983** (15 Aug). *World Communications Year. T* **66** *and similar horiz designs. P* 13½.
330 10 c. multicoloured .. .. .. .. 10 10
331 75 c. yellow, orange-brown and black .. 50 60
332 $2 multicoloured .. .. .. .. 1·40 2·00
330/2 .. .. .. .. *Set of* 3 1·75 2·40
Designs:—75 c. "Telephone Service"; $2 "Communications".

(Litho Security Printers (M), Malaysia)

**1983** (23 Sept). *Official Opening of the Negara Hassanal Bolkiah Stadium. T* **67** *and similar multicoloured designs. P* 12.
333 10 c. Type **67** .. .. .. .. 30 10
334 75 c. Athletics .. .. .. .. 1·10 1·10
335 $1 View of stadium (44 × 27 *mm*) .. 1·40 1·90
333/5 .. .. .. .. *Set of* 3 2·50 2·75

**68** Fishermen and Crustacea

(Litho Secura, Singapore)

**1983** (23 Sept). *Fishery Resources. T* **68** *and similar horiz designs. Multicoloured. P* 13½ × 14.
336 10 c. Type **68** .. .. .. .. 15 15
337 50 c. Fishermen with net .. .. .. 50 65
338 75 c. Fishing trawler .. .. .. 70 1·00
339 $1 Fishing with hook and tackle .. .. 90 1·40
336/9 .. .. .. .. *Set of* 4 2·00 2·75

## INDEPENDENCE

From No. 349 onwards issues are inscribed "BRUNEI DARUSSALAM".

**69** Royal Assembly Hall

(Des Haji Salleh Bin Haji Ibrahim (No. 346) Pengiran Haji Muhammed Bin Pengiran Duraman (No. **MS**348) or Siti Zaleha Haji Kaprawi (others). Litho Cartor, France)

**1984** (1 Jan). *Independence. T* **69** *and similar designs. P* 13.
340 10 c. pale stone and bright orange .. .. 10 10
341 20 c. flesh and brown-red .. .. .. 15 20
342 35 c. rose-pink and plum .. .. .. 30 35
343 50 c. pale blue and new blue .. .. .. 40 50
344 75 c. bright yellow-green and emerald .. 55 70
345 $1 light brownish grey and light brown .. 75 1·00
346 $3 multicoloured .. .. .. .. 2·25 3·75
340/6 .. .. .. .. *Set of* 7 4·00 6·00
**MS**347 150 × 120 mm. Nos. 340/6 .. .. 4·50 7·00
**MS**348 Two sheets each 150 × 120 mm. containing 4 stamps (34 × 69 *mm*.). (a) 25 c. × 4 grey-black and new blue (Signing of the Brunei Constitution). (b) 25 c. × 4 multicoloured (Signing of Brunei-U.K. Friendship Agreement) .. .. *Set of* 2 *sheets* 1·60 2·75
Designs:—34 × 25 *mm*. 20 c. Government Secretariat Building; 35 c. New Supreme Court; 50 c. Natural gas well; 75 c. Omar Ali Saifuddin Mosque; $1 Sultan's Palace; 68 × 29 *mm*. $3 Brunei flag and map of South-East Asia.

**70** Natural Forests and Enrichment Planting

(Des Awang Nor Ariffin bin Md. Yassin. Litho Secura, Singapore)

**1984** (21 Apr). *Forestry Resources. T* **70** *and similar horiz designs. Multicoloured. P* 13½ × 14.

| | | | | |
|---|---|---|---|---|
| 349 | | 10 c. Type **70** | 35 | 20 |
| 350 | | 50 c. Forests and water resources | 85 | 1·00 |
| 351 | | 75 c. Recreation forests | 1·25 | 1·75 |
| 352 | | $1 Forests and wildlife | 1·75 | 2·50 |
| 349/52 | | *Set of* 4 | 3·75 | 5·00 |

**71** Sultan Omar Saifuddin 50 c. Stamp of 1952

(Recess and litho D.L.R.)

**1984** (22 Oct). *"Philakorea" International Stamp Exhibition, Seoul. T* **71** *and similar vert designs. Multicoloured. P* 13.

| | | | | |
|---|---|---|---|---|
| 353 | | 10 c. Type **71** | 10 | 10 |
| 354 | | 75 c. Brunei River view 10 c. stamp of 1907 | 55 | 80 |
| 355 | | $2 Star and view ½ c. stamp of 1895 | 1·50 | 2·25 |
| 353/5 | | *Set of* 3 | 1·90 | 2·75 |
| **MS**356 | | Three sheets, 117 × 100 mm, each containing one stamp as Nos. 353/5 *Set of 3 sheets* | 2·25 | 3·50 |
| | | a. Line perf 14 at left *Set of 3 sheets* | 4·50 | 6·50 |

The stamps within the miniature sheets were perforated by means of a three-sided comb gauging 13 and completed by a line perforation at left. Normally this line perforation is also 13, but on **MS**356a it measures 14.

**72** United Nations Emblem

**73** Young People and Brunei Flag

(Des Awang Nor Ariffin bin Md. Yassin (Nos. 357, 359), Haji Salleh bin Haji Ibrahim (358) or Siti Zaleha Haji Kaprawi (360). Litho Cartor, France)

**1985** (23 Sept). *Admission of Brunei to World Organizations (1st issue). T* **72** *and similar horiz designs. W w* **17** *(sideways). P* 13.

| | | | | |
|---|---|---|---|---|
| 357 | | 50 c. black, gold and pale greenish blue | 40 | 50 |
| 358 | | 50 c. multicoloured | 40 | 50 |
| 359 | | 50 c. multicoloured | 40 | 50 |
| 360 | | 50 c. multicoloured | 40 | 50 |
| 357/60 | | *Set of* 4 | 1·40 | 1·75 |
| **MS**361 | | 110 × 151 mm. Nos. 357/60 | 2·00 | 2·50 |

Designs:—No. 357, Type **72**; No. 358, Islamic Conference Organization logo; 359, Commonwealth logo; 360, A.S.E.A.N. emblem.

See also Nos. 383/7.

(Des Siti Zaleha Haji Kaprawi. Litho Security Printers (M), Malaysia)

**1985** (17 Oct). *International Youth Year. T* **73** *and similar horiz designs. Multicoloured. P* 12.

| | | | | |
|---|---|---|---|---|
| 362 | | 10 c. Type **73** | 20 | 15 |
| 363 | | 75 c. Young people at work | 1·00 | 1·75 |
| 364 | | $1 Young people serving the community | 1·25 | 2·25 |
| 362/4 | | *Set of* 3 | 2·25 | 3·75 |

**74** Palestinian Emblem

**75** Early and Modern Scout Uniforms

(Des Haji Salleh bin Haji Ibrahim. Litho Secura, Singapore)

**1985** (29 Nov). *International Palestinian Solidarity Day. P* 12 × 12½.

| | | | | |
|---|---|---|---|---|
| 365 | **74** | 10 c. multicoloured | 20 | 15 |
| 366 | | 50 c. multicoloured | 65 | 85 |
| 367 | | $1 multicoloured | 1·10 | 1·75 |
| 365/7 | | *Set of* 3 | 1·75 | 2·50 |

(Des Awang Nor Ariffin bin Md. Yassin. Litho Secura, Singapore)

**1985** (14 Dec). *National Scout Jamboree. T* **75** *and similar vert designs. Multicoloured. P* 13½.

| | | | | |
|---|---|---|---|---|
| 368 | | 10 c. Type **75** | 20 | 10 |
| 369 | | 20 c. Scout on tower signalling with flag | 30 | 35 |
| 370 | | $2 Jamboree emblem | 1·75 | 3·00 |
| 368/70 | | *Set of* 3 | 2·00 | 3·00 |

**76** Sultan Sir Hassanal Bolkiah Mu'izzaddin Waddaulah

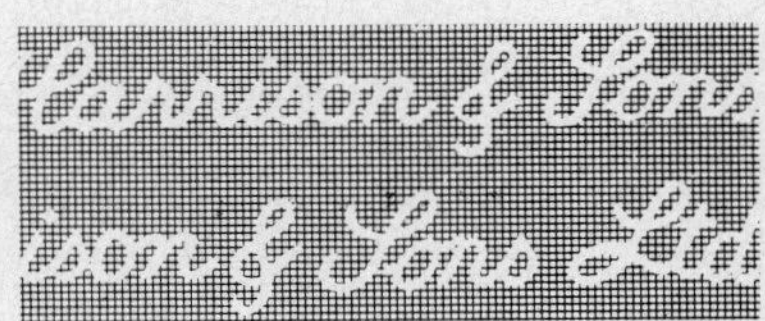

**77**

(Des Awang Nor Ariffin bin Md. Yassin. Photo Harrison)

**1985** (23 Dec)–**86**. *W* **77**. *P* 13½ × 14½ (10 *to* 75 *c.*) *or* 14 ($1 *to* $10).

| | | | | |
|---|---|---|---|---|
| 371 | **76** | 10 c. multicoloured | 10 | 15 |
| 372 | | 15 c. multicoloured | 10 | 15 |
| 373 | | 20 c. multicoloured | 15 | 20 |
| 374 | | 25 c. multicoloured | 15 | 20 |
| 375 | | 35 c. multicoloured (15.1.86) | 25 | 30 |
| 376 | | 40 c. multicoloured (15.1.86) | 25 | 30 |
| 377 | | 50 c. multicoloured (15.1.86) | 35 | 40 |
| 378 | | 75 c. multicoloured (15.1.86) | 50 | 55 |
| 379 | | $1 multicoloured (23.2.86) | 70 | 75 |
| 380 | | $2 multicoloured (23.2.86) | 1·40 | 1·50 |
| 381 | | $5 multicoloured (23.2.86) | 3·50 | 3·75 |
| 382 | | $10 multicoloured (29.3.86) | 6·75 | 7·00 |
| 371/82 | | *Set of* 12 | 13·00 | 13·50 |

Nos. 379/82 are larger, size 32 × 39 mm.

(Des Awang Nor Ariffin bin Md. Yassin. Litho Cartor, France)

**1986** (30 Apr). *Admission of Brunei to World Organizations (2nd issue). Horiz designs as T* **72**. *W w* **17** *(sideways). P* 13.

| | | | | |
|---|---|---|---|---|
| 383 | | 50 c. black, gold and bright yellow-green | 40 | 60 |
| 384 | | 50 c. black, gold and bright pinkish mauve | 40 | 60 |
| 385 | | 50 c. black, gold and orange-red | 40 | 60 |
| 386 | | 50 c. black, gold and dull ultramarine | 40 | 60 |
| 383/6 | | *Set of* 4 | 1·40 | 2·25 |
| **MS**387 | | 105 × 155 mm. Nos. 383/6. Wmk upright | 1·50 | 2·75 |

Designs:—No. 383, World Meteorological Organization emblem; 384, International Telecommunication Union emblem; 385, Universal Postal Union emblem; 386, International Civil Aviation Organization emblem.

**78** Soldiers on Assault Course and Helicopter

**79** Tunggul Charok Buritan, Alam Bernaga (Alam Besar), Pisang-Pisang and Sandaran

(Des Awang Nor Ariffin bin Md. Yassin. Litho Secura, Singapore)

**1986** (31 May). *25th Anniv of Brunei Armed Forces. T* **78** *and similar horiz designs. Multicoloured. P* 13½.

| | | | | |
|---|---|---|---|---|
| 388 | | 10 c. Type **78** | 60 | 75 |
| | | a. Horiz strip of 4. Nos. 388/91 | 3·00 | |
| 389 | | 20 c. Operating computer | 70 | 85 |
| 390 | | 50 c. Anti-aircraft missile, helicopter and missile boat | 90 | 1·25 |
| 391 | | 75 c. Army commanders and parade | 1·00 | 1·40 |
| 388/91 | | *Set of* 4 | 3·00 | 3·75 |

Nos. 388/91 were printed together, *se-tenant*, in horizontal strips of 4 throughout the sheet, forming a composite design.

(Des Awang Nor Ariffin bin Md. Yassin. Litho Secura, Singapore)

**1986** (15 July). *Royal Ensigns (1st series). T* **79** *and similar vert designs. P* **12**.

| | | | | |
|---|---|---|---|---|
| 392 | | 10 c. black, greenish yellow and red | 20 | 10 |
| 393 | | 75 c. multicoloured | 80 | 80 |
| 394 | | $2 black, greenish yellow and green | 1·75 | 2·25 |
| 392/4 | | *Set of* 3 | 2·50 | 2·75 |

Designs:—75 c. Ula-Ula Besar, Sumbu Layang and Payong Haram; $2 Panji-Panji, Chogan Istiadat (Chogan Di-Raja) and Chogan Ugama.

(Des Awang Nor Ariffin bin Md. Yassin. Litho Secura, Singapore)

**1986** (30 Sept). *Royal Ensigns (2nd series). Vert designs as T* **79**. *P* 12.

| | | | | |
|---|---|---|---|---|
| 395 | | 10 c. multicoloured | 20 | 10 |
| 396 | | 75 c. black, red and greenish yellow | 80 | 80 |
| 397 | | $2 multicoloured | 1·75 | 2·25 |
| 395/7 | | *Set of* 3 | 2·50 | 2·75 |

Designs:—10 c. Dadap, Tunggul Kawan, Ambal, Payong Ubor-Ubor, Sapu-Sapu Ayeng and Rawai Lidah; 75 c. Payong Tinggi and Payong Ubor-Ubor Tiga Ringkat; $2 Lambang Duli Yang Maha Mulia and Mahligai.

**80** Stylised Peace Doves

**81** Drug Addict in Cage and Syringe (poster by Othman bin Ramboh)

(Des Zainal Abidin Haji Ibrahim. Litho Security Printers (M), Malaysia)

**1986** (24 Oct). *International Peace Year. T* **80** *and similar horiz designs. Multicoloured. P* 12.

| | | | | |
|---|---|---|---|---|
| 398 | | 50 c. Type **80** | 65 | 65 |
| 399 | | 75 c. Stylised hands and "1986" | 80 | 80 |
| 400 | | $1 International Peace Year emblem and arms of Brunei | 1·00 | 1·00 |
| 398/400 | | *Set of* 3 | 2·25 | 2·25 |

(Litho Security Printers (M), Malaysia)

**1987** (15 Mar). *National Anti-drug Campaign. Children's Posters. T* **81** *and similar vert designs. Multicoloured. P* 12.

| | | | | |
|---|---|---|---|---|
| 401 | | 10 c. Type **81** | 25 | 15 |
| 402 | | 75 c. Drug addict and noose (Arman bin Mohd. Zaman) | 80 | 1·25 |
| 403 | | $1 Blindfolded drug addict and noose (Abidin bin Hj. Rashid) | 1·00 | 1·75 |
| 401/3 | | *Set of* 3 | 1·90 | 2·75 |

**82** Cannon ("badil")

**83** Map showing Member Countries

(Des Haji Salleh bin Haji Ibrahim. Litho Security Printers (M), Malaysia)

**1987** (15 July). *Brassware (1st series). T* **82** *and similar vert designs. Multicoloured. P* 12.

| | | | | |
|---|---|---|---|---|
| 404 | | 50 c. Type **82** | 40 | 40 |
| 405 | | 50 c. Lamp ("pelita") | 40 | 40 |
| 406 | | 50 c. Betel container ("langguai") | 40 | 40 |
| 407 | | 50 c. Water jug ("kiri") | 40 | 40 |
| 404/7 | | *Set of* 4 | 1·40 | 1·40 |

See also Nos. 434/7.

(Des Zainal Abidin bin Haji Ibrahim. Litho Security Printers (M), Malaysia)

**1987** (8 Aug). *20th Anniv of Association of South East Asian Nations. T* **83** *and similar horiz designs. Multicoloured. P* 14 × 13½.

| | | | | |
|---|---|---|---|---|
| 408 | | 20 c. Type **83** | 15 | 15 |
| 409 | | 50 c. Dates and figures "20" | 30 | 35 |
| 410 | | $1 Flags of member states | 60 | 65 |
| 408/10 | | *Set of* 3 | 95 | 1·00 |

**84** Brunei Citizens

(Des Pengiran Haji Muhammad bin Pengiran Duraman. Litho Secura, Singapore)

**1987** (29 Sept). *25th Anniv of Language and Literature Bureau (1986). T* **84** *and similar horiz designs. Multicoloured. P* 13×12½.

411 10 c. Type **84** .. .. .. .. .. .. 15 15
a. Horiz strip of 3. Nos. 411/13 .. .. 1·50
412 50 c. Flame emblem and hands holding open book .. .. .. .. .. .. 30 35
413 $2 Scenes of village life .. .. .. 1·25 1·40
411/13 .. .. .. .. *Set of* 3 1·50 1·75

Nos. 411/13 were printed together, *se-tenant*, in horizontal strips of three throughout the sheet, each strip forming a composite design taken from a mural.

**85** *Artocarpus odoratissima*

(Litho Security Printers (M), Malaysia)

**1987** (31 Oct). *Local Fruits* (1*st series*). *T* **85** *and similar horiz designs. Multicoloured. P* 12.

414 50 c. Type **85** .. .. .. .. .. 30 35
a. Horiz strip of 4. Nos. 414/17 .. .. 1·10
415 50 c. *Canarium odontophyllum mig*.. .. 30 35
416 50 c. *Litsea garciae* .. .. .. .. 30 35
417 50 c. *Mangifera foetida lour* .. .. .. 30 35
414/17 .. .. .. .. *Set of* 4 1·10 1·25

Nos. 414/17 were printed together, *se-tenant*, in horizontal strips of 4 throughout the sheet.

See also Nos. 421/4, 459/62 and 480/2.

**86** Modern House **87** Wooden Lathe

(Litho Security Printers (M), Malaysia)

**1987** (28 Nov). *International Year of Shelter for the Homeless. T* **86** *and similar horiz designs, each showing modern Brunei housing. P* 13×12½.

418 50 c. multicoloured .. .. .. .. 30 35
419 75 c. multicoloured .. .. .. .. 45 50
420 $1 multicoloured .. .. .. .. 60 65
418/20 .. .. .. .. *Set of* 3 1·25 1·40

(Des Awang Nor Ariffin bin Md. Yassin. Litho Security Printers (M), Malaysia)

**1988** (30 Jan). *Local Fruits* (2*nd series*). *Horiz designs as T* **85**. *Multicoloured. P* 12.

421 50 c. *Durio spp* .. .. .. .. .. 30 35
a. Horiz strip of 4. Nos. 421/4 .. .. 1·10
422 50 c. *Durio oxleyanus*.. .. .. .. 30 35
423 50 c. *Durio graveolens* (blue background) .. 30 35
424 50 c. *Durio graveolens* (white background) .. 30 35
421/4 .. .. .. .. *Set of* 4 1·10 1·25

Nos. 421/4 were printed together, *se-tenant*, in horizontal strips of four throughout the sheet.

(Des Awang Padzil bin Haji Ahmad. Litho Security Printers (M), Malaysia)

**1988** (29 Feb). *Opening of Malay Technology Museum. T* **87** *and similar vert designs. Multicoloured. P* 12.

425 10 c. Type **87** .. .. .. .. .. 10 10
426 75 c. Crushing sugar cane .. .. .. 45 50
427 $1 Bird scarer .. .. .. .. 60 65
425/7 .. .. .. .. *Set of* 3 1·00 1·10

**88** Beragi Bunga Sakah-Sakah dan Bunga Cengkih Cloth **89** Sultan reading Proclamation

(Des Awang Nor Ariffin bin Md. Yassin. Litho Security Printers (M), Malaysia)

**1988** (30 Apr). *Handwoven Material* (1*st series*). *T* **88** *and similar horiz designs showing different patterns. Multicoloured. P* 12.

428 10 c. Type **88** .. .. .. .. 10 10
429 20 c. Jong Sarat cloth .. .. .. 10 10
430 25 c. Si Pugut cloth .. .. .. 15 20
431 40 c. Si Pugut Bunga Berlapis cloth .. 25 30
432 75 c. Si Lobang Bangsi Bunga Belitang Kipas cloth .. .. .. .. 45 50
428/32 .. .. .. *Set of* 5 90 1·10
**MS**433 150×204 mm. Nos. 428/32 .. .. 1·00 1·50

See also Nos. 442/7.

(Des Haji Salleh bin Haji Ibrahim. Litho Security Printers (M), Malaysia)

**1988** (30 June). *Brassware* (2*nd series*). *Vert designs as T* **82**. *Multicoloured. P* 12.

434 50 c. Lidded two-handled pot ("periok") .. 30 35
435 50 c. Candlestick ("lampong") .. .. 30 35
436 50 c. Shallow circular dish with stand ("gangsa") .. .. .. .. 30 35
437 50 c. Repousse box with lid ("celapa") .. 30 35
434/7 .. .. .. .. *Set of* 4 1·10 1·25

(Des Awang Nor Ariffin bin Md. Yassin. Litho Security Printers (M), Malaysia)

**1988** (1 Aug). *20th Anniv of Sultan's Coronation. T* **89** *and similar vert designs. Multicoloured. P* 14 (20, 75 *c.*) *or* 12½×13 ($2).

438 20 c. Type **89** .. .. .. .. 10 10
439 75 c. Sultan reading from Koran .. .. 45 50
440 $2 In Coronation robes (26×63 *mm*) .. 1·25 1·40
438/40 .. .. .. .. *Set of* 3 1·60 1·75
**MS**441 164×125 mm. Nos. 438/40 .. .. 1·75 2·25

In No. **MS**441 the perforations of the stamps are as Nos. 438/40 except for the 75 c. which is perforated 13 at right.

(Des Awang Nor Ariffin bin Md. Yassin. Litho Security Printers (M), Malaysia)

**1988** (29 Sept). *Handwoven Material* (2*nd series*). *Horiz designs as T* **88**. *Multicoloured. P* 12.

442 10 c. Beragi cloth .. .. .. .. 10 10
443 20 c. Bertabur cloth .. .. .. .. 10 10
444 25 c. Sukma Indra cloth .. .. .. 15 20
445 40 c. Si Pugut Bunga cloth .. .. .. 25 30
446 75 c. Beragi Si Lobang Bangsi Bunga Cendera Kesuma cloth .. .. .. 45 50
442/6 .. .. .. .. *Set of* 5 90 1·10
**MS**447 150×204 mm. Nos. 442/6 .. .. 1·00 1·50

**90** Malaria-carrying Mosquito

(Litho Cartor, France)

**1988** (17 Dec). *40th Anniv of World Health Organization. T* **90** *and similar horiz designs. Multicoloured. P* 14×13½.

448 25 c. Type **90** .. .. .. .. 20 20
449 35 c. Man with insecticide spray and sample on slide .. .. .. .. .. 25 25
450 $2 Microscope and magnified malaria cells 1·40 1·40
448/50 .. .. .. .. *Set of* 3 1·60 1·60

**91** Sultan and Council of Ministers **92** Dove escaping from Cage

(Des Awang Nor Ariffin bin Md Yassin. Litho Security Printers (M), Malaysia)

**1989** (23 Feb). *5th Anniv of National Day. T* **91** *and similar multicoloured designs. P* 12.

451 20 c. Type **91** .. .. .. .. 15 15
452 30 c. Guard of honour .. .. .. 25 25
453 60 c. Firework display (27 × 55 *mm*) .. 40 40
454 $2 Congregation in mosque .. .. 1·40 1·40
451/4 .. .. .. .. *Set of* 4 2·00 2·00
**MS**455 164 × 124 mm. Nos. 451/4 .. .. 2·25 2·75

(Des Haji Salleh bin Haji Ibrahim. Litho Secura, Singapore)

**1989** (1 Apr). *"Freedom of Palestine". T* **92** *and similar horiz designs. Multicoloured. P* 13½.

456 20 c. Type **92** .. .. .. .. 15 15
457 75 c. Map and Palestinian flag .. .. 65 65
458 $1 Dome of the Rock, Jerusalem .. .. 80 80
456/8 .. .. .. .. *Set of* 3 1·40 1·40

(Des Awang Nor Ariffin bin Md. Yassin. Litho Secura, Singapore)

**1989** (31 Oct). *Local Fruits* (3*rd series*). *Horiz designs as T* **85**. *Multicoloured. P* 12.

459 60 c. *Daemonorops fissa* .. .. .. 55 75
a. Horiz strip of 4. Nos. 459/62 .. .. 2·00
460 60 c. *Eleiodoxa conferta* .. .. .. 55 75
461 60 c. *Salacca zalacca* .. .. .. 55 75
462 60 c. *Calamus ornatus* .. .. .. 55 75
459/62 .. .. .. .. *Set of* 4 2·00 2·75

Nos. 459/62 were printed together, *se-tenant*, in horizontal strips of four throughout the sheet.

**93** Oil Pump

(Des Brunei Shell Petroleum Co. Litho Secura, Singapore)

**1989** (28 Dec). *60th Anniv of Brunei Oil and Gas Industry. T* **93** *and similar horiz designs. Multicoloured. P* 13½.

463 20 c. Type **93** .. .. .. .. 15 15
464 60 c. Loading tanker .. .. .. 50 50
465 90 c. Oil well at sunset .. .. .. 70 80
466 $1 Pipe laying .. .. .. .. 75 90
467 $2 Oil terminal .. .. .. .. 1·40 1·75
463/7 .. .. .. .. *Set of* 5 3·25 3·75

**94** Museum Building and Exhibits

(Des Awang Padzil bin Haji Ahmad ($1), Mohd Yamin bin Haji Abd. Momin (others). Litho Security Printers (M), Malaysia)

**1990** (1 Jan). *25th Anniv of Brunei Museum. T* **94** *and similar horiz designs. Multicoloured. P* 12.

468 30 c. Type **94** .. .. .. .. 25 30
469 60 c. Official opening, 1965 .. .. 55 70
470 $1 Brunei Museum .. .. .. 85 1·10
468/70 .. .. .. .. *Set of* 3 1·50 1·90

**95** Letters from Malay Alphabet **96** Tarsier in Tree

(Des Pengiran Haji Muhammad bin Pengiran Duraman. Litho Security Printers (M), Malaysia)

**1990** (15 July). *International Literacy Year. T* **95** *and similar horiz designs. Multicoloured. P* 12.

471 15 c. Type **95** .. .. .. .. 15 10
472 90 c. English alphabet .. .. .. 85 90
473 $1 Literacy Year emblem and letters .. 95 1·00
471/3 .. .. .. .. *Set of* 3 1·75 1·75

(Des Haji Salleh bin Haji Ibrahim. Litho Security Printers (M), Malaysia)

**1990** (29 Sept). *Endangered Species. Western Tarsier. T* **96** *and similar vert designs. Multicoloured. P* 12 (20 *c.*) *or* 12½×13 (*others*).

474 20 c. Western Tarsier on branch .. .. 20 20
475 60 c. Western Tarsier feeding .. .. 55 60
476 90 c. Type **96** .. .. .. .. 90 1·00
474/6 .. .. .. .. *Set of* 3 1·50 1·60

**97** Symbolic Family **98** Proboscis Monkey on Ground

(Litho Security Printers (M), Malaysia)

**1990** (1 Dec). *Worldwide Campaign against AIDS. T* **97** *and similar vert designs. Multicoloured. P* 12½.

477 20 c. Type **97** .. .. .. .. 20 20
478 30 c. Sources of infection .. .. .. 40 45
479 90 c. "AIDS" headstone surrounded by skulls 90 95
477/9 .. .. .. .. *Set of* 3 1·40 1·40

(Litho Security Printers (M), Malaysia)

**1990** (31 Dec). *Local Fruits* (4*th series*). *Horiz designs as T* **85**. *Multicoloured. P* 12.

480 60 c. *Willoughbea* sp. (brown fruit) .. 55 65
a. Horiz strip of three. Nos. 480/2 .. 1·50
481 60 c. Ripe *Willoughbea* sp. (yellow fruit) .. 55 65
482 60 c. *Willoughbea angustifolia* .. .. 55 65
480/2 .. .. .. .. *Set of* 3 1·50 1·75

Nos. 480/2 were printed together, *se-tenant*, in horizontal strips of three throughout the sheet.

(Des Haji Salleh bin Haji Ibrahim. Litho Cartor, France)

**1991** (30 Mar). *Endangered Species. Proboscis Monkey. T* **98** *and similar vert designs. Multicoloured. P* 13½×14.

| | | | |
|---|---|---|---|
| 483 | 15 c. Type **98** | 15 | 15 |
| 484 | 20 c. Head of monkey | 20 | 20 |
| 485 | 50 c. Monkey sitting on branch | 50 | 55 |
| 486 | 60 c. Female monkey with baby climbing tree | 60 | 70 |
| 483/6 | *Set of* 4 | 1·25 | 1·40 |

**99** Junior School Classes

**100** Young Brunei Beauty

(Des Awang Nor Ariffin bin Md Yassin. Litho, Secura Singapore)

**1991** (23 Sept). *Teachers' Day. T* **99** *and similar horiz design. Multicoloured. P* 13½×14.

| | | | |
|---|---|---|---|
| 487 | 60 c. Type **99** | 55 | 60 |
| 488 | 90 c. Secondary school class | 85 | 90 |

(Des Padzil bin Haji Ahmad. Litho Security Printers (M), Malaysia)

**1991** (1 Oct). *Fishes. Brunei Beauty. T* **100** *and similar horiz designs. Multicoloured. P* 12½.

| | | | |
|---|---|---|---|
| 489 | 30 c. Type **100** | 30 | 30 |
| 490 | 60 c. Female fish | 55 | 60 |
| 491 | $1 Male fish | 95 | 1·00 |
| 489/91 | *Set of* 3 | 1·60 | 1·75 |

**101** Graduate with Family

(Des A. Mansur. Litho Cartor)

**1991** (30 Nov). *Happy Family Campaign. T* **101** *and similar vert designs. Multicoloured. P* 13.

| | | | |
|---|---|---|---|
| 492 | 20 c. Type **101** | 15 | 20 |
| 493 | 60 c. Mothers with children | 40 | 45 |
| 494 | 90 c. Family | 60 | 65 |
| 492/4 | *Set of* 3 | 1·00 | 1·10 |

## JAPANESE OCCUPATION OF BRUNEI

Japanese forces landed in Northern Borneo on 16 December 1941 and the whole of Brunei had been occupied by 6 January 1942.

Brunei, North Borneo, Sarawak and, after a short period, Labuan, were administered as a single territory by the Japanese. Until September–October 1942, previous stamp issues, without overprint, continued to be used in conjunction with existing postmarks. From the Autumn of 1942 onwards unoverprinted stamps of Japan were made available and examples can be found used from the area for much of the remainder of the War. Japanese Occupation issues for Brunei, North Borneo and Sarawak were equally valid throughout the combined territory but not, in practice, equally available.

**PRICES FOR STAMPS ON COVER**

| | |
|---|---|
| Nos. J1/16 | *from* × 5 |
| Nos. J17/20 | — |

本 日 大

便 郵 國 帝

(**1**)

("Imperial Japanese Government")

(**2**)

("Imperial Japanese Postal Service $3")

**1942** (Oct)–**44.** *Stamps of Brunei handstamped with T* **1** *in violet to blue. Wmk Mult Script CA (except Nos.* J18/19, *Mult Crown CA). P* 14.

| | | | | |
|---|---|---|---|---|
| J 1 | **5** | 1 c. black | 5·00 | 15·00 |
| J 2 | | 2 c. green | 28·00 | 85·00 |
| J 3 | | 2 c. orange (9.44) | 2·50 | 6·00 |
| J 4 | | 3 c. green | 23·00 | 65·00 |
| J 5 | | 4 c. orange | 3·00 | 10·00 |
| J 6 | | 5 c. chocolate | 3·00 | 10·00 |
| | | a. "5 c." retouch | £150 | £325 |
| J 7 | **7** | 6 c. greenish grey (*p* 14 × 11½) (9.44) | 50·00 | £120 |
| J 8 | | 6 c. scarlet | £550 | £550 |
| J 9 | **5** | 8 c. grey-black | £600 | £850 |
| J10 | **7** | 8 c. red | 3·00 | 10·00 |
| J11 | **5** | 10 c. purple/*yellow* (9.44) | 7·00 | 18·00 |
| J12 | **7** | 12 c. blue (9.44) | 8·00 | 18·00 |
| J13 | | 15 c. ultramarine (9.44) | 8·00 | 18·00 |
| J14 | **5** | 25 c. slate-purple (9.44) | 17·00 | 32·00 |
| J15 | | 30 c. purple and orange-yellow | 90·00 | £180 |
| J16 | | 50 c. black/*emerald* (9.44) | 32·00 | 42·00 |
| J17 | | $1 black and red/*blue* (9.44) | 48·00 | 60·00 |
| J18 | | $5 carmine/*green* (9.44) | £800 | |
| J19 | | $25 black/*red* (9.44) | £850 | |

The overprint varies in shade from violet to blue, and, being handstamped, exists double and treble.

Nos. J3, J7, J10 and J13 were not issued without the overprint.

**1944** (May). *No.* 60 *of Brunei surch with T* **2** *in orange-red.*

| | | | | |
|---|---|---|---|---|
| J20 | **5** | $3 on 1 c. black | £3000 | £2250 |

# Burma

Stamps of India were used in Burma from 1854 and, after 1856, individual examples can be identified by the use of the concentric octagonal postmarks of the Bengal Postal Circle of which the following were supplied to Burmese post offices:

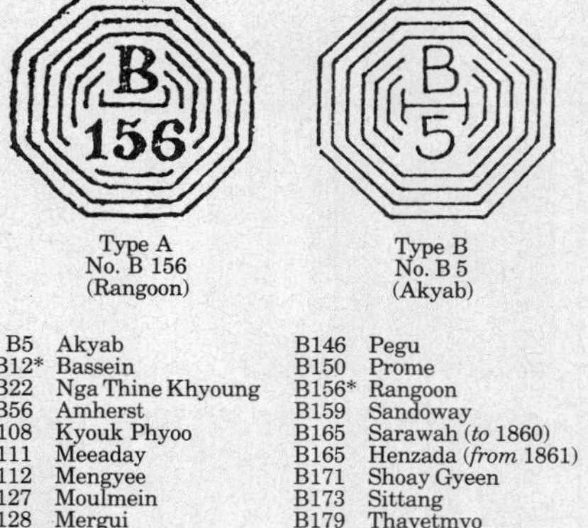


Type A
No. B 156
(Rangoon)

Type B
No. B 5
(Akyab)

| | | | |
|---|---|---|---|
| B5 | Akyab | B146 | Pegu |
| B12* | Bassein | B150 | Prome |
| B22 | Nga Thine Khyoung | B156* | Rangoon |
| B56 | Amherst | B159 | Sandoway |
| B108 | Kyouk Phyoo | B165 | Sarawah (*to* 1860) |
| B111 | Meeaday | B165 | Henzada (*from* 1861) |
| B112 | Mengyee | B171 | Shoay Gyeen |
| B127 | Moulmein | B173 | Sittang |
| B128 | Mergui | B179 | Thayetmyo |
| B129 | Tavoy | B181 | Toungoo |
| B133 | Myanoung | B227 | Port Blair |
| B136 | Namayan | | |

*Exists in black or blue. Remainder in black only.

Akyab, Moulmein and Rangoon used postmarks as both Type A and Type B, Port Blair as Type B only and the remainder as Type A only.

From 1860 various types of duplex cancellations were introduced and Burmese examples can be identified when sufficient of the left-hand portion is visible on the stamp. Such marks were issued for the following offices:

| | |
|---|---|
| Akyab | Rangoon |
| Bassein | Rangoon C.R.H. |
| Mandalay | (Cantonment Receiving House) |
| Moulmein | Thayetmyo |
| Port Blair | Toungoo |
| Prome | |

1862 Duplex from
Toungoo

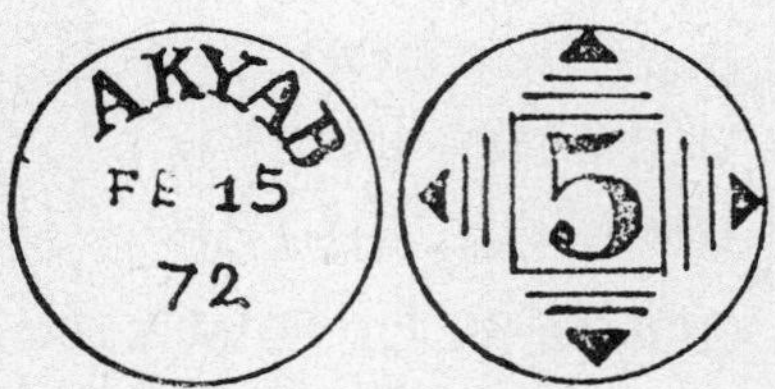


1865 Duplex from
Akyab

During 1875, a further series of duplex marks was introduced in which the right-hand portion of the cancellation included the office code number, prefixed by the letter "R" for Rangoon:

| | | | |
|---|---|---|---|
| R–1 | Rangoon | 1/R–8 | Amherst |
| R–1/1 | Rangoon Cantonment | R–9 | Myanoung |
| R–2 | Akyab | R–10 | Port Blair |
| R–3 | Bassein | R–11 | Prome |
| R–4 | Henzada | R–12 | Sandoway |
| R–5 | Kyouk Phyoo | R–13 | Shwegyeen |
| R–6 | Mandalay | R–14 | Tavoy |
| R–7 | Mergui | R–15 | Thayetmyo |
| R–8 | Moulmein | R–16 | Toungoo |

1875 type from
Rangoon

1875 type from Rangoon
Cantonment Receiving House

From 1886 the whole of Burma was united under the Crown and the post offices were supplied with circular date stamps giving the name of the town.

Most Indian stamps, both postage and official, issued during the period were supplied to post offices in Burma. None of the imperforates printed by De La Rue have been seen however, and from the later issues the following have not been recorded with Burma postmarks:

Nos. 39a, 66a, 68, 85a, 92a, 110a/b, 148a, 155a, 165, 192a/c, 195a/b, O15, O38, O40b, O50a/b, O76a, O101a, O102, O103/a, O104/5 and O142.

The value of most India stamps used in Burma coincides proportionately with the used prices quoted for India, but some, especially the provisional surcharges, are extremely rare with Burmese postmarks. Stamps of the face value of 2 r. and above from the reigns of Victoria and Edward VII are more common with telegraph cancellations than with those of the postal service.

**PRICES FOR STAMPS ON COVER TO 1945**

| | |
|---|---|
| Nos. 1/18 | *from* × 6 |
| Nos. 18a/33 | *from* × 4 |
| No. 34 | *from* × 5 |
| Nos. 35/50 | *from* × 8 |
| Nos. O1/27 | *from* × 15 |

**BRITISH ADMINISTRATION**

From 1 January 1886 Burma was a province of the Indian Empire but was separated from India and came under direct British administration on 1 April 1937.

BURMA (1)    BURMA (1a)

**1937** (1 April). *Stamps of India (King George V inscr* "INDIA POSTAGE") *optd with T* **1** *or* **1a** *(rupee values). W* **69**. *P* 14.

| | | | |
|---|---|---|---|
| 1 | 3 p. slate | 30 | 10 |
| 2 | ½ a. green | 30 | 10 |
| 3 | 9 p. deep green | 30 | 10 |
| 4 | 1 a. chocolate | 30 | 10 |
| 5 | 2 a. vermilion (*small die*) | 30 | 10 |
| 6 | 2½ a. orange | 30 | 10 |
| 7 | 3 a. carmine | 65 | 30 |
| 8 | 3½ a. deep blue | 65 | 10 |
| | *a. Dull blue* | 4·00 | 4·00 |
| 9 | 4 a. sage-green | 70 | 10 |
| 10 | 6 a. bistre | 60 | 35 |
| 11 | 8 a. reddish purple | 1·50 | 10 |
| 12 | 12 a. claret | 2·00 | 85 |
| 13 | 1 r. chocolate and green | 7·00 | 65 |
| 14 | 2 r. carmine and orange | 11·00 | 6·00 |
| 15 | 5 r. ultramarine and purple | 24·00 | 9·00 |
| 16 | 10 r. green and scarlet | 48·00 | 27·00 |
| 17 | 15 r. blue and olive | £130 | 80·00 |
| 18 | 25 r. orange and blue | £250 | £150 |
| 1/18 | *Set of* 18 | £425 | £250 |

The opt is at top on all values except the 3 a.

2 King George VI and "Chinthes"

3 King George VI and "Nagas"

4 Royal Barge

8 King George VI and Peacock

10 Elephants' Heads

Extra trees flaw (R. 11/8)

(Des Maung Kyi (2 a. 6 p.), Maung Hline (3 a.), Maung Ohn Pe (3 a. 6 p.) and N. K. D. Naigamwalla (8 a.). Litho Security Ptg Press, Nasik)

**1938** (15 Nov)–**40**. *T* **2/4**, **8** *and similar designs. W* **10**. *P* 14 (*vert*) *or* 13½ × 13 (*horiz*).

| | | | | |
|---|---|---|---|---|
| 18a | **2** | 1 p. red-orange (1.8.40) | 1·00 | 60 |
| 19 | | 3 p. bright violet | 10 | 20 |
| 20 | | 6 p. bright blue | 10 | 10 |
| 21 | | 9 p. yellow-green | 1·00 | 80 |
| 22 | **3** | 1 a. purple-brown | 10 | 10 |
| 23 | | 1½ a. turquoise-green | 20 | 55 |
| 24 | | 2 a. carmine | 45 | 10 |
| 25 | **4** | 2 a. 6 p. claret | 75 | 45 |
| 26 | – | 3 a. dull violet | 2·25 | 60 |
| 27 | – | 3 a. 6 p. light blue and blue | 1·25 | 3·25 |
| | | a. Extra trees flaw | 20·00 | |
| 28 | **3** | 4 a. greenish blue | 35 | 10 |
| 29 | – | 8 a. myrtle-green | 1·75 | 30 |
| 30 | **8** | 1 r. purple and blue | 5·00 | 20 |
| 31 | | 2 r. brown and purple | 6·00 | 85 |
| 32 | – | 5 r. violet and scarlet | 38·00 | 11·00 |
| 33 | – | 10 r. brown and myrtle | 48·00 | 35·00 |
| 18a/33 | | *Set of* 16 | 95·00 | 48·00 |

Designs: *Horiz (as T* **4**)—3 a. Burma teak; 3 a. 6 p. Burma rice; 8 a. River Irrawaddy. *Vert (as T* **8**)—5 r., 10 r. King George VI and "Nats".

The 1 a. exists lithographed and typographed, the latter having a "Jubilee" line in the sheet margin.

COMMEMORATION
POSTAGE STAMP
6th MAY 1840

(11)

**1940** (6 May). *Centenary of First Adhesive Postage Stamps. No.* 25 *surch with T* **11**.

| | | | | |
|---|---|---|---|---|
| 34 | **4** | 1 a. on 2 a. 6 p. claret | 1·50 | 35 |

For stamps issued in 1942–45 see under Japanese Occupation.

**CHIN HILLS DISTRICT.** This area, in the far north-west of the country, remained in British hands when the Japanese overran Burma in May 1942.

During the period July to December 1942 the local officials were authorised to produce provisional stamps and the letters "OHMS" are known overprinted by typewriter on Nos. 3, 20, 22, 23, 24, 28 and 31 of Burma or handstamped, in violet, on Nos. 25, 27 and 29. The two types can also occur together or in combination with a handstamped "Service".

From early in 1943 ordinary postage stamps of India were used from the Chin Hills post offices of Falam, Haka, Fort White and Tiddim, this expedient continuing until the fall of Falam to the Japanese on 7 November 1943.

The provisional stamps should only be collected on Official cover where dates and the sender's handwriting can be authenticated.

**BRITISH MILITARY ADMINISTRATION**

MILY ADMN (12)    MILY ADMN (13)

**1945** (from 16 June). *Nos.* 18*a to* 33, *optd with T* **12** (*small stamps*) *or* **13** (*others*).

| | | | | |
|---|---|---|---|---|
| 35 | **2** | 1 p. red-orange | 10 | 10 |
| | | a. Opt omitted (in pair with normal) | £850 | |
| 36 | | 3 p. bright violet | 10 | 30 |
| 37 | | 6 p. bright blue | 10 | 30 |
| 38 | | 9 p. yellow-green | 10 | 30 |
| 39 | **3** | 1 a. purple-brown (16.6) | 10 | 10 |
| 40 | | 1½ a. turquoise-green (16.6) | 10 | 15 |
| 41 | | 2 a. carmine | 10 | 15 |
| 42 | **4** | 2 a. 6 p. claret | 20 | 60 |
| 43 | – | 3 a. dull violet | 60 | 20 |
| 44 | – | 3 a. 6 p. light blue and blue | 10 | 70 |
| | | a. Extra trees flaw | 7·00 | |
| 45 | **3** | 4 a. greenish blue | 10 | 25 |
| 46 | – | 8 a. myrtle-green | 10 | 40 |
| 47 | **8** | 1 r. purple and blue | 15 | 50 |
| 48 | | 2 r. brown and purple | 20 | 80 |
| 49 | – | 5 r. violet and scarlet | 20 | 80 |
| 50 | – | 10 r. brown and myrtle | 50 | 80 |
| 35/50 | | *Set of* 16 | 2·25 | 5·50 |

**BRITISH CIVIL ADMINISTRATION**

**1946** (1 Jan). *As Nos.* 19/33, *but colours changed.*

| | | | | |
|---|---|---|---|---|
| 51 | **2** | 3 p. brown | 10 | 65 |
| 52 | | 6 p. deep violet | 10 | 10 |
| 53 | | 9 p. green | 10 | 60 |
| 54 | **3** | 1 a. blue | 10 | 10 |
| 55 | | 1½ a. orange | 10 | 10 |

| | | | | |
|---|---|---|---|---|
| 56 | 3 | 2 a. claret | 10 | 30 |
| 57 | 4 | 2 a. 6 p. greenish blue | 10 | 80 |
| 57a | – | 3 a. blue-violet | 1·75 | 85 |
| 57b | – | 3 a. 6 p. black and ultramarine | 10 | 60 |
| | | ba. Extra trees flaw | 7·00 | |
| 58 | 3 | 4 a. purple | 10 | 30 |
| 59 | – | 8 a. maroon | 1·50 | 65 |
| 60 | 8 | 1 r. violet and maroon | 50 | 15 |
| 61 | | 2 r. brown and orange | 2·50 | 1·25 |
| 62 | – | 5 r. green and brown | 2·50 | 4·25 |
| 63 | – | 10 r. claret and violet | 2·50 | 7·00 |
| 51/63 | | *Set of* 15 | 10·50 | 16·00 |

14 Burman

(Des A. G. I. McGeogh. Litho Nasik)

**1946** (2 May). *Victory. T* **14** *and similar vert designs. W* **10** *(sideways). P* 13.

| | | | | |
|---|---|---|---|---|
| 64 | | 9 p. turquoise-green | 10 | 10 |
| 65 | | 1½ a. violet | 10 | 10 |
| 66 | | 2 a. carmine | 15 | 10 |
| 67 | | 3 a. 6 p. ultramarine | 15 | 10 |
| 64/7 | | *Set of* 4 | 40 | 30 |

Designs:—1½ a. Burmese woman; 2 a. Chinthe; 3 a. 6 p. Elephant.

### INTERIM BURMESE GOVERNMENT

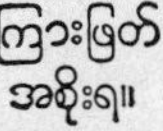

(**18** *Trans.* "Interim Government")

**1947** (1 Oct). *Stamps of* 1946 *optd with T* **18** *(small stamps) or larger opt (others).*

| | | | | |
|---|---|---|---|---|
| 68 | 2 | 3 p. brown | 50 | 20 |
| 69 | | 6 p. deep violet | 10 | 25 |
| 70 | | 9 p. green | 20 | 25 |
| | | a. Opt inverted | 16·00 | 16·00 |
| 71 | 3 | 1 a. blue | 10 | 25 |
| | | a. Vert pair, one with opt omitted | | |
| 72 | | 1½ a. orange | 55 | 10 |
| 73 | | 2 a. claret | 20 | 15 |
| | | a. Horiz pair, one with opt omitted | | |
| 74 | 4 | 2 a. 6 p. greenish blue | 70 | 40 |
| 75 | – | 3 a. blue-violet | 55 | 50 |
| 76 | – | 3 a. 6 p. black and ultramarine | 10 | 40 |
| | | a. Extra trees flaw | 7·00 | |
| 77 | 3 | 4 a. purple | 50 | 30 |
| 78 | – | 8 a. maroon | 90 | 50 |
| 79 | 8 | 1 r. violet and maroon | 1·00 | 30 |
| 80 | | 2 r. brown and orange | 1·00 | 1·25 |
| 81 | – | 5 r. green and brown | 1·50 | 2·50 |
| 82 | – | 10 r. claret and violet | 1·60 | 2·50 |
| 68/82 | | *Set of* 15 | 8·00 | 8·75 |

The 3 p., 6 p., 2 a., 2 a. 6 p., 3 a. 6 p. and 1 r. are also known with overprint inverted.

### OFFICIAL STAMPS

BURMA BURMA

SERVICE SERVICE

(O 1) (O 1*a*)

**1937** (Apr–June). *Stamps of India (King George V inscr "INDIA POSTAGE") optd with Type* O **1** *or* O **1a** *(rupee values). W* **69**. *P* 14.

| | | | | |
|---|---|---|---|---|
| O 1 | | 3 p. slate | 10 | 10 |
| O 2 | | ½ a. green | 35 | 10 |
| O 3 | | 9 p. deep green | 30 | 30 |
| O 4 | | 1 a. chocolate | 30 | 10 |
| O 5 | | 2 a. vermilion (*small die*) | 30 | 35 |
| O 6 | | 2½ a. orange | 85 | 65 |
| O 7 | | 4 a. sage-green | 60 | 10 |
| O 8 | | 6 a. bistre | 1·25 | 3·00 |
| O 9 | | 8 a. reddish purple (1.4.37) | 70 | 30 |
| O10 | | 12 a. claret (1.4.37) | 1·00 | 2·00 |
| O11 | | 1 r. chocolate and green (1.4.37) | 6·00 | 1·50 |
| O12 | | 2 r. carmine and orange | 15·00 | 13·00 |
| O13 | | 5 r. ultramarine and purple | 48·00 | 28·00 |
| O14 | | 10 r. green and scarlet | £110 | 70·00 |
| O1/14 | | *Set of* 14 | £170 | £110 |

For the above issue the stamps were either overprinted "BURMA" and "SERVICE" at one operation or had the two words applied separately. Research has yet to establish if all values exist with both forms of overprinting.

SERVICE SERVICE

(O 2) (O 3)

**1939.** *Nos.* 19/24 *and* 28 *optd with Type* O **2** *(typo) and Nos.* 25 *and* 29/33 *optd with Type* O **3** *(litho).*

| | | | | |
|---|---|---|---|---|
| O15 | 2 | 3 p. bright violet | 10 | 20 |
| O16 | | 6 p. bright blue | 10 | 20 |
| O17 | | 9 p. yellow-green | 4·50 | 40 |
| O18 | 3 | 1 a. purple-brown | 10 | 15 |
| O19 | | 1½ a. turquoise-green | 4·50 | 40 |
| O20 | 3 | 2 a. carmine | 70 | 20 |
| O21 | 4 | 2 a. 6 p. claret | 8·50 | 3·25 |
| O22 | 3 | 4 a. greenish blue | 5·50 | 45 |
| O23 | – | 8 a. myrtle-green | 16·00 | 3·00 |
| O24 | 8 | 1 r. purple and blue | 16·00 | 3·00 |
| O25 | | 2 r. brown and purple | 21·00 | 4·00 |
| O26 | – | 5 r. violet and scarlet | 48·00 | 23·00 |
| O27 | – | 10 r. brown and myrtle | 85·00 | 29·00 |
| O15/27 | | *Set of* 13 | £190 | 60·00 |

**1946.** *British Civil Administration. Nos.* 51/6 *and* 58 *optd with Type* O **2** *(typo) and Nos.* 57 *and* 59/63 *optd with Type* O **3** *(litho).*

| | | | | |
|---|---|---|---|---|
| O28 | 2 | 3 p. brown | 30 | 70 |
| O29 | | 6 p. deep violet | 35 | 65 |
| O30 | | 9 p. green | 10 | 1·25 |
| O31 | 3 | 1 a. blue | 10 | 90 |
| O32 | | 1½ a. orange | 10 | 15 |
| O33 | | 2 a. claret | 10 | 80 |
| O34 | 4 | 2 a. 6 p. greenish blue | 35 | 1·50 |
| O35 | 3 | 4 a. purple | 10 | 60 |
| O36 | – | 8 a. maroon | 15 | 90 |
| O37 | 8 | 1 r. violet and maroon | 50 | 1·75 |
| O38 | | 2 r. brown and orange | 3·50 | 8·00 |
| O39 | – | 5 r. green and brown | 7·00 | 16·00 |
| O40 | – | 10 r. claret and violet | 9·50 | 25·00 |
| O28/40 | | *Set of* 13 | 20·00 | 50·00 |

**1947.** *Interim Burmese Government. Nos.* O28/40 *optd with T* **18** *(small stamps) or larger opt (others).*

| | | | | |
|---|---|---|---|---|
| O41 | 2 | 3 p. brown | 10 | 40 |
| O42 | | 6 p. deep violet | 20 | 10 |
| O43 | | 9 p. green | 20 | 70 |
| O44 | 3 | 1 a. blue | 1·25 | 55 |
| O45 | | 1½ a. orange | 1·75 | 20 |
| O46 | | 2 a. claret | 1·25 | 15 |
| O47 | 4 | 2 a. 6 p. greenish blue | 3·25 | 1·75 |
| O48 | 3 | 4 a. purple | 1·50 | 35 |
| O49 | – | 8 a. maroon | 2·25 | 1·25 |
| O50 | 8 | 1 r. violet and maroon | 5·00 | 1·25 |
| O51 | | 2 r. brown and orange | 11·00 | 10·00 |
| O52 | – | 5 r. green and brown | 11·00 | 14·00 |
| O53 | – | 10 r. claret and violet | 13·00 | 23·00 |
| O41/53 | | *Set of* 13 | 45·00 | 48·00 |

Later stamp issues will be found listed in Part 21 (*South-East Asia*) of this catalogue.

## JAPANESE OCCUPATION OF BURMA

**PRICES FOR STAMPS ON COVER**

| | |
|---|---|
| Nos. J1/44 | — |
| Nos. J45/71 | *from* × 5 |
| No. J72 | *from* × 6 |
| Nos. J73/94 | *from* × 12 |
| Nos. J95/101 | — |
| Nos. J102/8 | *from* × 15 |

### BURMA INDEPENDENCE ARMY ADMINISTRATION

The Burma Independence Army, formed by Aung San in 1941, took control of the Delta area of the Irrawaddy in May 1942. They reopened a postal service in the area and were authorised by the Japanese to overprint local stocks of stamps with the Burmese emblem of a peacock.

Postage and Official stamps with the peacock overprints or handstamps were used for ordinary postal purposes with the probable exception of No. J44.

DISTINGUISHING FEATURES. Type **1**. Body and head of Peacock always clearly outlined by broad uncoloured band. There are four slightly different sub-types of overprint Type **1**.

Type **2**. Peacock with slender neck and more delicately detailed tail. Clear spur on leg at right. Heavy fist-shaped blob of ink below and parallel to beak and neck.

Type **4**. No basic curve. Each feather separately outlined. Straight, short legs.

Type **5**. Much fine detail in wings and tail in clearly printed overprints. Thin, long legs ending in claws which, with the basic arc, enclose clear white spaces in well-printed copies. Blob of colour below beak shows shaded detail and never has the heavy fist-like appearance of this portion in Type **2**.

Two sub-types may be distinguished in Type **5**, the basic arc of one having a chord of 14–15 mm and the other 12½–13 mm.

Type **6**. Similar to Type **5**, but with arc deeply curved and reaching nearly to the top of the wings. Single diagonal line parallel to neck below beak.

Collectors are warned against forgeries of these overprints, often in the wrong colours or on the wrong values.

(1)

(2)

(3)

**1942** (May). *Stamps of Burma overprinted with the national device of a Peacock.*

I. *Overprinted at Myaungmya*

A. *With Type* **1** *in black*

*On Postage Stamps of King George V*

| | | | | |
|---|---|---|---|---|
| J 1 | | 9 p. deep green (No. 3) | 60·00 | |
| J 2 | | 3½ a. deep blue (No. 8) | 32·00 | |

*On Official Stamp of King George V*

| | | | | |
|---|---|---|---|---|
| J 3 | | 6 a. bistre (No. O8) | 55·00 | |

*On Postage Stamps of King George VI*

| | | | | |
|---|---|---|---|---|
| J 4 | 2 | 9 p. yellow-green | £140 | |
| J 5 | 3 | 1 a. purple-brown | £325 | |
| J 6 | | 4 a. greenish blue (opt black on red) | £130 | |
| | | a. Triple opt, black on double red | £375 | |

*On Official Stamps of King George VI*

| | | | | |
|---|---|---|---|---|
| J 7 | 2 | 3 p. bright violet | 12·00 | 35·00 |
| J 8 | | 6 p. bright blue | 9·00 | 25·00 |
| J 9 | 3 | 1 a. purple-brown | 8·50 | 18·00 |
| J 9a | | 1½ a. turquoise-green | £600 | |
| J10 | | 2 a. carmine | 13·00 | 35·00 |
| J11 | | 4 a. greenish blue | 12·00 | 30·00 |

The overprint on No. J6 was apparently first done in red in error, and then corrected in black. Some stamps have the black overprint so accurately superimposed that the red hardly shows. These are rare.

Nos. J5 and J9 exist with the Peacock overprint on both the typographed and the litho printings of the original stamps.

B. *With Types* **2** *or* **3** *(rupee values), in black*

*On Postage Stamps of King George VI*

| | | | | |
|---|---|---|---|---|
| J12 | 2 | 3 p. bright violet | 10·00 | 32·00 |
| J13 | | 6 p. bright blue | 27·00 | 40·00 |
| J14 | | 9 p. yellow-green | 10·50 | 28·00 |
| J15 | 3 | 1 a. purple-brown | 9·00 | 24·00 |
| J16 | | 2 a. carmine | 9·50 | 26·00 |
| J17 | | 4 a. greenish blue | 22·00 | 38·00 |
| | | a. Opt double | | |
| | | b. Opt inverted | £475 | |
| | | c. Opt double, one inverted | £325 | |
| | | d. Opt double, both inverted | £475 | |
| J18 | | 1 r. purple and blue | £190 | |
| J19 | | 2 r. brown and purple | £120 | |

The Myaungmya overprints (including No. J44) are usually clearly printed.

(4)

(5)

(6)

Type **5** generally shows the details of the peacock much less clearly and, due to heavy inking, or careless impression, sometimes appears as almost solid colour.

Type **6** was officially applied only to postal stationery. However, the handstamp remained in the possession of a postal official who used it on postage stamps after the war. These stamps are no longer listed.

II. *Handstamped (at Pyapon?) with T* **4**, *in black (so-called experimental type)*

*On Postage Stamps of King George VI*

| | | | | |
|---|---|---|---|---|
| J19a | 3 | 1 a. purple-brown | 95·00 | |
| J20 | | 2 a. carmine | 60·00 | |
| J21 | | 4 a. greenish blue | £325 | |

Unused specimens of these stamps are usually in poor condition.

III. *Overprinted at Henzada with T* **5** *in blue, or blue-black*

*On Postage Stamps of King George V*

| | | | | |
|---|---|---|---|---|
| J22 | | 3 p. slate (No. 1) | 2·75 | 11·00 |
| | | a. Opt double | 9·50 | 30·00 |
| J23 | | 9 p. deep green (No. 3) | 17·00 | 40·00 |
| | | a. Opt double | 60·00 | |
| J24 | | 2 a. vermilion (No. 5) | 60·00 | £110 |

*On Postage Stamps of King George VI*

| | | | | |
|---|---|---|---|---|
| J25 | 2 | 1 p. red-orange | 90·00 | £130 |
| J26 | | 3 p. bright violet | 20·00 | 45·00 |
| J27 | | 6 p. bright blue | 18·00 | 38·00 |
| | | a. Opt double | 75·00 | |
| | | b. Clear opt, on back and front | £150 | |
| J28 | | 9 p. yellow-green | £325 | |
| J29 | 3 | 1 a. purple-brown | 7·50 | 18·00 |
| | | a. Opt inverted | £160 | |
| J30 | | 1½ a. turquoise-green | 13·00 | 30·00 |
| | | a. Opt omitted (in pair with normal) | | |
| J31 | | 2 a. carmine | 13·00 | 30·00 |
| J32 | | 4 a. greenish blue | 35·00 | 60·00 |
| | | a. Opt double | £110 | |
| | | b. Opt inverted | £550 | |

*On Official Stamps of King George VI*

| | | | | |
|---|---|---|---|---|
| J33 | 2 | 3 p. bright violet | 75·00 | £120 |
| J34 | | 6 p. bright blue | 75·00 | £110 |
| J35 | 3 | 1½ a. turquoise-green | 75·00 | £110 |
| J35a | | 2 a. carmine | £250 | £250 |
| J36 | | 4 a. greenish blue | £500 | |

**MINIMUM PRICE**

The minimum price quote is 10p which represents a handling charge rather than a basis for valuing common stamps. For further notes about prices see introductory pages.

(6*a*)

("Yon Thon" = "Office use")

V. *Official Stamp of King George VI optd at Myaungmya with Type* **6***a in black*

J44 **7** 8 a. myrtle-green .. .. .. 60·00

No. J44 was probably for official use.

There are two types of T **6***a*, one with base of peacock 8 mm long and the other with base about 5 mm long. The neck and other details also vary. The two types are found *se-tenant* in the sheet.

Stocks of the peacock types were withdrawn when the Japanese Directorate-General took control of the postal services in the Delta in August 1942.

### JAPANESE ARMY ADMINISTRATION

7

8 Farmer

**1942** (1 June). *Impressed by hand. Thick yellowish paper. P* 12 × 11. *No gum.*

J45 **7** (1 a.) red .. .. .. .. .. 35·00 50·00

This device was the personal seal of Yano Sitza, the Japanese official in charge of the Posts and Telegraphs department of the Japanese Army Administration. It was impressed on paper already perforated by a line machine. Some stamps show part of the papermaker's watermark, either "ABSORBO DUPLICATOR" or "ELEPHANT BRAND", each with an elephant.

Other impressions of this seal on different papers, and showing signs of wear, were not valid for postal purposes.

(Des T. Kato. Typo *Rangoon Gazette* Press)

**1942** (15 June). *Value in annas. P* 11 *or* 11 × 11½. *Laid bâtonné paper. No gum.*

J46 **8** 1 a. scarlet .. .. .. .. 14·00 14·00

Some stamps show part of the papermaker's watermark, either "ELEPHANT BRAND" or "TITAGHUR SUPERFINE", each with an elephant.

½A. (9)    1R. (10)

**1942** (22 Sept). (*a*) *Contemporary Japanese definitive stamps* (*Cat. Nos. in brackets*) *surch as T* **9**/**10**.

J47 **9** ¼ a. on 1 s. chestnut (317) .. .. 15·00 20·00
a. Surch inverted .. .. 70·00 70·00
b. Surch double, one inverted .. 85·00
J48 ½ a. on 2 s. scarlet (318) .. .. 15·00 20·00
a. Surch inverted .. .. 55·00
b. Surch double, one inverted .. 75·00
J49 ¾ a. on 3 s. green (319) .. .. 32·00 35·00
a. Surch inverted .. .. 75·00 75·00
b. Surch double, one inverted .. — £100
J50 1 a. on 5 s. claret (396) .. .. 24·00 28·00
a. Surch inverted .. .. 75·00 75·00
b. Surch double, one inverted .. 95·00 95·00
c. Surch omitted (in pair with normal) — £120
J51 3 a. on 7 s. green (323) .. .. 42·00 48·00
a. Surch inverted .. .. 85·00
J52 4 a. on 4 s. green (320) .. .. 28·00 32·00
a. Surch inverted .. .. 85·00
J53 8 a. on 8 s. violet (324) .. .. £130 £140
a. Surch inverted .. .. £150 £160
b. Surch double, one inverted .. £275
c. Surch in red .. .. £225 £250
d. Red surch inverted .. .. £325
e. Surch double (black and red) .. £325
J54 **10** 1 r. on 10 s. lake (325) .. .. 15·00 20·00
a. Surch inverted .. .. 80·00 80·00
b. Surch double .. .. 80·00
c. Surch double (black and red) .. £170
d. Surch omitted (in pair with normal) £110 £110
e. Surch omitted (in pair with inverted surch) .. .. .. .. £150
J55 2 r. on 20 s. ultramarine (328) .. .. 38·00 38·00
a. Surch inverted .. .. 95·00 £100
b. Surch double, one inverted .. 95·00
c. Surch omitted (in pair with normal black surch) .. .. .. £120 £120
d. Surch in red .. .. 38·00 38·00
e. Red surch inverted .. .. £100 £100
f. Red surch double .. .. £100 £100
g. Surch omitted (in pair with normal red surch) .. .. .. — £150
h. Surch double (black and red) .. £160
J56 **9** 5 r. on 30 s. blue-green (330) .. 12·00 17·00
a. Surch inverted .. .. £130
b. Surch double .. .. £100
c. Surch double, one inverted .. £150
d. Surch omitted (in pair with normal surch) .. .. .. £130 £130
e. Surch omitted (in pair with inverted black surch) .. .. .. £200
f. Surch in red .. .. 23·00 27·00
fa. Red surch inverted .. .. 75·00 75·00
fb. J56a and J56fa *se-tenant* .. £275 £275
fc. Surch omitted (in pair with normal red surch) .. .. .. £120 £120

(*b*) *Japanese stamp commemorating the fall of Singapore similarly surch*

J56*g* **9** 4 a. on 4 + 2 s. green and red (386) .. £110 £120
h. Surch omitted (in pair with normal) £450
ha. Surch omitted (in pair with inverted surch) .. .. .. .. £450
i. Surch inverted .. .. .. £300

**(New Currency. 100 cents = 1 rupee)**

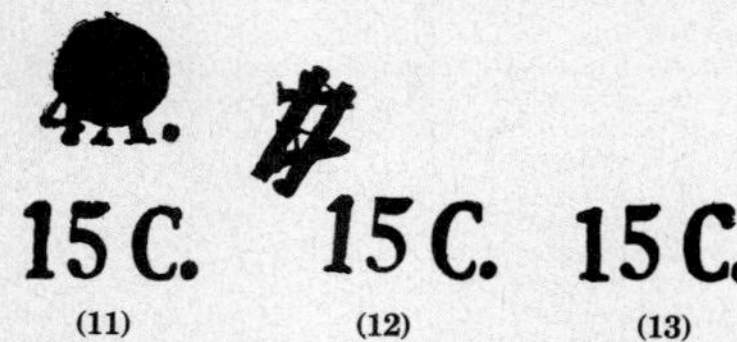

(11)  (12)  (13)

**1942** (15 Oct). *Previous issues, with "anna" surcharges obliterated, and handstamped with new value in cents, as T* **11** *and* **12** (*No. J57 handstamped with new value only*). (*a*) *T* **8** (*Farmer*).

J57 5 c. on 1 a. scarlet .. .. .. 8·50 12·00

(*b*) *Contemporary Japanese issues*

J58 1 c. on ¼ a. on 1 s. (J47) .. .. 29·00 29·00
a. "1 c." omitted in pair with normal .. £325
J59 2 c. on ½ a. on 2 s. (J48) .. .. 29·00 29·00
J60 3 c. on ¾ a. on 3 s. (J49) .. .. 32·00 32·00
a. Surch in blue .. .. 95·00
J61 5 c. on 1 a. on 5 s. (J50) .. .. 42·00 48·00
J62 10 c. on 3 a. on 7 s. (J51) .. .. 60·00 65·00
J63 15 c. on 4 a. on 4 s. (J52) .. .. 24·00 26·00
J64 20 c. on 8 a. on 8 s. (J53) .. .. £150 £140
a. 20 c. on 8 a. (R.) on 8 s. (J53c) .. £190 £130

The "anna" surcharges were obliterated by any means available, in some cases by a bar or bars, and in others by the butt of a pencil dipped in ink. In the case of the fractional surcharges, the letter "A" and one figure of the fraction, were sometimes barred out, leaving the remainder of the fraction to represent the new value, e.g. the "1" of "½" deleted to create the 2 c. surcharge or the "4" of "¾" to create the 3 c. surcharge.

**1942.** *Contemporary stamps of Japan* (*Cat. Nos. in brackets*) *surcharged in cents only, as T* **13**.

J65 1 c. on 1 s. chestnut (317) .. .. 12·00 15·00
a. Surch inverted .. .. 65·00 65·00
J66 2 c. on 2 s. scarlet (318) .. .. 26·00 26·00
J67 3 c. on 3 s. green (319) .. .. 24·00 26·00
a. Pair, with and without surch .. — £110
b. Surch inverted .. .. 80·00
c. Surch in blue .. .. 75·00 85·00
d. Surch in blue inverted .. .. £150 £160
J68 5 c. on 5 s. claret (396) .. .. 30·00 30·00
a. Surch in violet .. .. £110
b. Surch in violet inverted .. .. — £140
J69 10 c. on 7 s. green (323) .. .. 28·00 32·00
J70 15 c. on 4 s. green (320) .. .. 12·00 15·00
a. Surch inverted .. .. 75·00 80·00
b. Pair, with and without surch .. — £110
J71 20 c. on 8 s. violet (324) .. .. 80·00 70·00

Nos. J67c and J68a were issued for use in the Shan States.

### BURMESE GOVERNMENT

On 1 November 1942 the Japanese Army Administration handed over the control of the postal department to the Burmese Government. On 1 August 1943 Burma was declared by the Japanese to be independent.

14 Burma State Crest

15 Farmer

(Des U Tun Tin and Maung Tin from drawing by U Ba Than. Typo Rangoon)

**1943** (15 Feb). *P* 11. *No gum.*

J72 **14** 5 c. scarlet .. .. .. 10·00 12·00
a. Imperf .. .. .. 11·00 13·00
ab. Printed on both sides .. .. 80·00

No. J72 was usually sold affixed to envelopes, particularly those with the embossed 1 a. King George VI stamp, which it covered. Unused specimens off cover are not often seen and blocks are rare.

**1943.** *P* 11½. *Typo. No gum.*

J73 **15** 1 c. orange (22 March) .. .. 70 1·25
*a. Brown-orange* .. .. 70 1·50
J74 2 c. yellow-green (24 March) .. 60 90
*a. Blue-green* .. .. 3·50
J75 3 c. light blue (25 March) .. 60 75
a. On laid paper .. .. 10·00 12·00
J76 5 c. carmine (small "c") (17 March) 6·00 5·00
J77 5 c. carmine (large "C") .. .. 70 1·25
a. Imperf (pair) .. .. £200
b. "G" for "C" (R.2/6) .. .. £150
J78 10 c. grey-brown (25 March) .. 1·25 1·50
a. Imperf (pair) .. .. £200
J79 15 c. magenta (26 March) .. .. 30 70
a. On laid paper .. .. 6·00 11·00
b. Inverted "C" in value .. 85·00
J80 20 c. grey-lilac (29 March) .. 30 65
J81 30 c. deep blue-green (29 March) .. 30 70

The 1 c., 2 c. and 3 c. have large "C" in value as illustrated. The 10 c. and higher values have small "c". Nos. J73/81 had the face values inserted individually into the plate used for No. J46 with the original face value removed. There were a number of printings for each value, often showing differences such as missing stops, various founts of figures or "c", etc., in the value tablets.

There are marked varieties of shade in this issue.

16 Soldier carving word "Independence"

17 Rejoicing Peasant

18 Boy with National Flag

(Des Maung Ba Thit (**16**), Naung Ohn Maung (**17**), and Maung Soi Yi (**18**). Typo State Press, Rangoon)

**1943** (1 Aug). *Independence Day.* (*a*) *P* 11.

J82 **16** 1 c. orange .. .. .. 4·75 7·00
J83 **17** 3 c. light blue .. .. .. 5·50 7·50
J84 **18** 5 c. carmine .. .. .. 5·50 6·50

(*b*) *Rouletted*

J82*a* **16** 1 c. orange .. .. .. 90 1·50
b. Perf × roul .. .. 45·00
c. Imperf (pair) .. .. 42·00 50·00
J83*a* **17** 3 c. light blue .. .. .. 90 1·50
b. Perf × roul .. .. 45·00
c. Imperf (pair) .. .. 42·00 50·00
J84*a* **18** 5 c. carmine .. .. .. 90 1·50
aa. Horiz roulette omitted (vert pair)
b. Perf × roul .. .. 32·00 38·00
c. Imperf (pair) .. .. 42·00 50·00

The stamps perf × rouletted may have one, two, or three sides perforated.

The rouletted stamps often appear to be roughly perforated owing to failure to make clean cuts. These apparent perforations are very small and quite unlike the large, clean holes of the stamps perforated 11.

A few imperforate sets, mounted on a special card folder and cancelled with the commemorative postmark were presented to officials. These are rare.

19 Burmese Woman

20 Elephant carrying Log

21 Watch Tower, Mandalay

(Typo G. Kolff & Co, Batavia)

**1943** (1 Oct). *P* 12½.

J85 **19** 1 c. red-orange .. .. .. 5·50 8·00
J86 2 c. yellow-green .. .. 30 1·00
J87 3 c. deep violet .. .. 50 1·50
*a. Bright violet* .. .. 60 1·50
J88 **20** 5 c. carmine .. .. .. 45 50
J89 10 c. blue .. .. .. 55 75
J90 15 c. red-orange .. .. 45 80
J91 20 c. yellow-green .. .. 35 1·25
J92 30 c. olive-brown .. .. 35 1·25
J93 **21** 1 r. red-orange .. .. .. 30 1·00
J94 2 r. bright violet .. .. 30 2·00

22 Bullock Cart

23 Shan Woman

ဗမာနိုင်ငံတော်
၂၀ ဆင့်။

(24 "Burma State" and value)

(Typo G. Kolff & Co, Batavia)

**1943.** *Issue for Shan States. P* 12½.

J 95 **22** 1 c. olive-brown .. .. .. 11·00 16·00
J 96 2 c. yellow-green .. .. 11·00 16·00
J 97 3 c. bright violet .. .. 2·75 4·25
J 98 5 c. ultramarine .. .. 2·00 4·25
J 99 **23** 10 c. blue .. .. .. 8·00 13·00
J100 20 c. carmine .. .. 14·00 12·00
J101 30 c. olive-brown .. .. 10·00 16·00

The Shan States, except for the frontier area around Keng Tung which was ceded to Thailand, were placed under the administration of the Burmese Government on 24 December 1943, and these stamps were later overprinted as T **24** for use throughout Burma.

**1944** (1 Nov). *Optd as T* **24** (*the lower characters differ for each value*).

J102 **22** 1 c. olive-brown .. .. .. 1·25 2·75
J103 2 c. yellow-green .. .. 30 75
a. Opt inverted .. .. £200
J104 3 c. bright violet .. .. 1·00 2·75
J105 5 c. ultramarine .. .. 65 75
J106 **23** 10 c. blue .. .. .. 1·60 1·60
J107 20 c. carmine .. .. 30 1·25
J108 30 c. olive-brown .. .. 30 1·25

The British 14th Army recaptured Mandalay on 20 March 1945 and Rangoon on 6 May.

# Bushire

BRITISH OCCUPATION

**PRICES FOR STAMPS ON COVER**

| | |
|---|---|
| Nos. 1/14 | *from* × 10 |
| Nos. 15/29 | *from* × 5 |

**BUSHIRE**
**Under British**
**Occupation.**
(1)

*Stamps of Iran (Persia) overprinted with T* 1

**1915** (15 Aug). *Nos.* 361, *etc.* (*Ahmed Mirza*).

| No. | Description | Unused | Used |
|---|---|---|---|
| 1 | 1 ch. orange and green | 20·00 | 25·00 |
| | a. No stop | 60·00 | 65·00 |
| 2 | 2 ch. sepia and carmine | 22·00 | 21·00 |
| | a. No stop | 60·00 | 60·00 |
| 3 | 3 ch. green and grey | 23·00 | 30·00 |
| | a. No stop | 70·00 | 90·00 |
| 4 | 5 ch. carmine and brown | £225 | £225 |
| 5 | 6 ch. brown-lake and green | 19·00 | 18·00 |
| | a. No stop | 55·00 | 55·00 |
| 6 | 9 ch. indigo-lilac and brown | 22·00 | 25·00 |
| | a. No stop | 70·00 | 75·00 |
| | b. Opt double | | |
| 7 | 10 ch. brown and carmine | 24·00 | 24·00 |
| | a. No stop | 75·00 | 75·00 |
| 8 | 12 ch. blue and green | 30·00 | 35·00 |
| | a. No stop | 90·00 | £100 |
| 9 | 24 ch. green and purple | 45·00 | 35·00 |
| | a. No stop | £130 | £100 |
| 10 | 1 kr. carmine and blue | 45·00 | 25·00 |
| | a. Double overprint | £4500 | |
| | b. No stop | £130 | 80·00 |
| 11 | 2 kr. claret and green | £130 | £110 |
| | a. No stop | £350 | £300 |
| 12 | 3 kr. black and lilac | £140 | £150 |
| | a. No stop | £350 | £350 |
| 13 | 5 kr. blue and red | 70·00 | 65·00 |
| | a. No stop | £225 | £225 |
| 14 | 10 kr. rose and bistre-brown | 60·00 | 60·00 |
| | a. No stop | £200 | £200 |

Nos. 1/14 were overprinted in strips of 10, five different settings having been identified. The "No stop" variety occurs on the second setting stamp 10 (where the gap between "Under" and "British" measures 2 mm) and stamp 9 of the third, fourth and fifth settings (on which position the gap is 3 mm).

**1915** (Sept). *Nos.* 426, *etc.* (*Coronation of Shah Ahmed*) *optd in strips of* 5.

| No. | Description | Unused | Used |
|---|---|---|---|
| 15 | 1 ch. deep blue and carmine | £300 | £300 |
| 16 | 2 ch. carmine and deep blue | £5000 | £5500 |
| 17 | 3 ch. deep green | £375 | £400 |
| 18 | 5 ch. vermilion | £3750 | £4000 |
| 19 | 6 ch. carmine and green | £3000 | £3250 |
| 20 | 9 ch. deep violet and brown | £475 | £500 |
| 21 | 10 ch. brown and deep green | £800 | £850 |
| 22 | 12 ch. ultramarine | £900 | £1000 |
| 23 | 24 ch. sepia and brown | £375 | £400 |
| 24 | 1 kr. black, brown and silver | £350 | £375 |
| 25 | 2 kr. carmine, slate and silver | £300 | £325 |
| 26 | 3 kr. sepia, dull lilac and silver | £425 | £450 |
| 27 | 5 kr. slate, sepia and silver | £400 | £425 |
| | a. Opt inverted | — | £8500 |
| 28 | 1 t. black, violet and gold | £350 | £400 |
| 29 | 3 t. red, crimson and gold | £2250 | £2500 |

Examples of overprint Type 1 on Iran No. 414, 1 ch. on 5 ch. (previously No. 30), are now believed to be forged.

Bushire, a seaport town of Persia, was occupied by the British on 8 August 1915. The Persian postal authorities resumed control on 16 October 1915.

# Cameroons

BRITISH OCCUPATION

Allied operations against the German protectorate of Kamerun commenced in August 1914 and were completed by February 1916. The territory was divided, under an Anglo-French agreement, on 1 April 1916 with the British administering areas in the north and in the west along the Nigerian border.

Supplies of Kamerun stamps were found on the German steamer *Professor Woermann* captured at Freetown and these were surcharged, probably in Sierra Leone, and issued by the Cameroons Expeditionary Force at Duala in June 1915. It is believed that further stocks of German stamps found in the post office were used, unsurcharged, during 1916.

**PRICES FOR STAMPS ON COVER**

The stamps of British Occupation of Cameroons are rare used on cover.

A

B

C. E. F.
1d.
(1)

C. E. F.
1s.
(2)

**SETTINGS.** Nos. 1/3 were surcharged from a setting of 100 (10 × 10) with the face value changed for the 1d.

Nos. 4 and 6/9 were surcharged from a common setting of 50 (5 × 10) with the face value amended.

No. 5 was surcharged from a setting of 10 in a vertical strip repeated across the sheet. The figures of the surcharge on this value are in a different style from the remainder of the pence stamps.

Nos. 10/13 were surcharged from a common setting of 20 (4×5) with the face value amended.

| | |
|---|---|
| Different fount "d" (R. 1/10, 6/9, 10/10) | "1" with thin serifs (R. 5/1) |
| Large "3" (R. 3/5, 3/10) | Short "4" (R. 10/2, 10/7) |

"s" inverted
(R. 3/4)

**1915** (June). *Stamps of German Kamerun, Types* A *and* B, *surch as T* 1 (*Nos.* 1/9) *or* 2 (*Nos.* 10/13) *in black or blue.*

| No. | Type | Description | Unused | Used |
|---|---|---|---|---|
| 1 | A | ½d. on 3 pf. (No. K7) (B.) | 4·25 | 12·00 |
| | | a. Different fount "d" | 38·00 | 75·00 |
| 2 | | ½d. on 5 pf. (No. K21 *wmk lozenges*) (B.) | 1·25 | 5·50 |
| | | a. Different fount "d" | 9·50 | 32·00 |
| | | b. Surch double | — | £450 |
| | | ba. Surch double, one albino | £100 | |
| 3 | | 1d. on 10 pf. (No. K22 *wmk lozenges*) (B.) | 1·25 | 4·00 |
| | | a. "1" with thin serifs | 11·00 | 32·00 |
| | | b. Surch double | £140 | |
| | | ba. Surch double, one albino | 65·00 | |
| | | c. "1d." only double | £1300 | |
| | | d. Surch triple, two albino | £140 | |
| | | e. Surch in black | 12·00 | 28·00 |
| | | ea. "1" with thin serifs | £100 | |
| | | eb. "C.E.F." omitted | £1900 | |
| 4 | | 2d. on 20 pf. (No. K23 *wmk lozenges*) | 3·25 | 11·00 |
| | | a. Surch double, one albino | £150 | |
| 5 | | 2½d. on 25 pf. (No. K11) | 9·00 | 24·00 |
| | | a. Surch double | £4500 | |
| | | ab. Surch double, one albino | | |
| 6 | | 3d. on 30 pf. (No. K12) | 9·00 | 24·00 |
| | | a. Large "3" | £400 | |
| | | b. Surch triple, two albino | £150 | |
| 7 | | 4d. on 40 pf. (No. K13) | 9·00 | 24·00 |
| | | a. Short "4" | £375 | |
| | | b. Surch triple, two albino | £150 | |
| | | c. Surch quadruple, three albino | | |
| 8 | | 6d. on 50 pf. (No. K14) | 9·00 | 24·00 |
| | | a. Surch double, one albino | £140 | |
| 9 | | 8d. on 80 pf. (No. K15) | 9·00 | 24·00 |
| 10 | B | 1s. on 1 m. (No. K16) | £120 | £325 |
| | | a. "s" inverted | £450 | £1100 |
| 11 | | 2s. on 2 m. (No. K17) | £120 | £325 |
| | | a. "s" inverted | £450 | £1100 |
| | | b. Surch double, one albino | £700 | |
| 12 | | 3s. on 3 m. (No. K18) | £120 | £325 |
| | | a. "s" inverted | £450 | £1100 |
| | | b. Surch double | £4000 | |
| | | ba. Surch double, one albino | £700 | |
| 13 | | 5s. on 5 m. (No. K25a *wmk lozenges*) | £150 | £350 |
| | | a. "s" inverted | £500 | £1100 |
| 1/13 | | *Set of* 13 | £500 | £1300 |

The stamps of Nigeria were subsequently used in British Cameroons and the area was administered as part of Nigeria from February 1924.

For stamps optd "CAMEROONS U.K.T.T.", see under SOUTHERN CAMEROONS.

# Canada

Separate stamp issues appeared for British Columbia and Vancouver Island, Canada, New Brunswick, Newfoundland, Nova Scotia and Prince Edward Island before these colonies joined the Dominion of Canada.

## BRITISH COLUMBIA & VANCOUVER ISLAND

Vancouver Island was organised as a Crown Colony in 1849 and the mainland territory was proclaimed a separate colony, as British Columbia, in 1858. The two colonies combined, as British Columbia, in 1866.

**PRICES FOR STAMPS ON COVER**

| | |
|---|---|
| No. 1 | — |
| Nos. 2/3 | *from* × 6 |
| Nos. 11/12 | *from* × 2 |
| Nos. 13/14 | *from* × 6 |
| Nos. 21/2 | *from* × 10 |
| Nos. 23/7 | *from* × 6 |
| Nos. 28/33 | *from* × 10 |

1

(Typo D.L.R.)

**1860.** *No Wmk. Imperf.*

| No. | Type | Description | Unused | Used |
|---|---|---|---|---|
| 1 | 1 | 2½d. pale dull red | £2500 | |

**1860.** *No wmk. P* 14.

| No. | Type | Description | Unused | Used |
|---|---|---|---|---|
| 2 | 1 | 2½d. deep reddish rose | £275 | £180 |
| 3 | | 2½d. pale reddish rose | £275 | £180 |

From 20 June 1864 to 1 November 1865, the 2½d. was sold for 3d., and did duty as a 3d. provisional. No 1 was never actually issued.

Though bearing the names of both colonies the 2½d. of 1860 was mainly used for inland postage in British Columbia.

### VANCOUVER ISLAND

2

3

(Typo D.L.R.)

**1865** (19 Sept). *Wmk Crown CC.* (*a*) *Imperf.*

| No. | Type | Description | Unused | Used |
|---|---|---|---|---|
| 11 | 2 | 5c. rose | £20000 | £8000 |
| 12 | 3 | 10 c. blue | £1600 | £1100 |
| | | (*b*) *P* 14 | | |
| 13 | 2 | 5 c. rose | £200 | £130 |
| 14 | 3 | 10 c. blue | £200 | £140 |

Medium or poor copies of Nos. 11 and 12 can be supplied at much lower prices, when in stock.

### BRITISH COLUMBIA

4

(Typo D.L.R.)

**1865** (1 Nov)–**67**. *Wmk Crown CC. P* 14.

| No. | Type | Description | Unused | Used |
|---|---|---|---|---|
| 21 | 4 | 3d. deep blue | 70·00 | 60·00 |
| 22 | | 3d. pale blue (1867) | 70·00 | 60·00 |

TWO CENTS
(5)

5.CENTS.5
(6)

**1868–71.** *T* 4 *in various colours. Wmk Crown CC. Surch as T* 5 *or* 6.

| No. | Description | Unused | Used |
|---|---|---|---|
| | (*a*) *P* 12½ (3.69) | | |
| 23 | 5 c. red (Bk.) | £500 | £500 |
| 24 | 10 c. lake (B.) | £400 | £400 |
| 25 | 25 c. yellow (V.) | £350 | £350 |
| 26 | 50 c. mauve (R.) | £400 | £350 |
| 27 | $1 green (G.) | £600 | £700 |
| | (*b*) *P* 14 | | |
| 28 | 2 c. brown (Bk.) (1.68) | 70·00 | 70·00 |
| 29 | 5 c. pale red (Bk.) (5.69) | 85·00 | 85·00 |
| 30 | 10 c. lake (B.) | £600 | |
| 31 | 25 c. yellow (V.) (7.69) | £100 | £100 |
| 32 | 50 c. mauve (R.) (2.71) | £400 | £750 |
| 33 | $1 green (G.) | £600 | |

Nos. 30 and 33 were not issued.

British Columbia joined the Dominion of Canada on 20 July 1871.

## COLONY OF CANADA

The first British post offices in what was to become the colony of Canada were opened at Quebec, Montreal and Trois Rivières during 1763. These, and subsequent, offices remained part of the British G.P.O. system until 6 April 1851.

The two provinces of Upper Canada (Ontario) and Lower Canada (Quebec) were united in 1840.

For illustration of the handstamp types see BRITISH POST OFFICES ABROAD notes, following GREAT BRITAIN.

**NEW CARLISLE, GASPÉ**

POSTMASTER'S PROVISIONAL ENVELOPE

1

## Let us help you find that ELUSIVE CANADIAN RARITY!

**Choice Classics!**

**Modern Errors!**

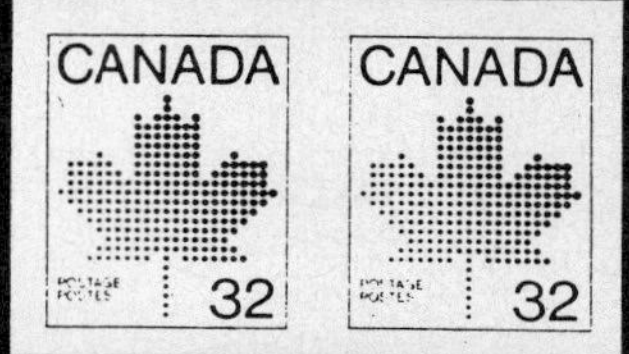

**Our Speciality ··· the Unusual!**

Our Current illustrated catalogue of CANADIAN & BNA Stamps featuring CHOICE CLASSICS through MODERN ERRORS & VARIETIES

**FREE ON REQUEST!**

# SASKATOON STAMP CENTRE

**Internationally Recognized as a Leading Buyer of Canadian Errors and Varieties.**

P.O. Box 1870, SASKATOON, SASK., CANADA S7K 3S2

Telephone: (306) 931–6633 TOLL FREE (North America only) 1–800–667–6900 Fax: (306) 975–3728

# MISSING OUT? PUT AN...

Each year at Eastern Auctions we offer over twenty-five thousand lots of USA, Commonwealth, foreign, and especially, CANADA and NEWFOUNDLAND.

## CONSIDER THE ADVANTAGES

★1. Building a collection? There's no better place to find those elusive items you've been looking for than pages of our monthly auction catalogues. British North American stamps are our speciality! We hold four public and eight mail auctions annually.

★2. Thinking of selling? We've helped hundreds of collectors over the years. Our terms are competitive and our catalogues expertly produced. Your choice of public auction or outright purchase can be arranged. Contact Gary Lyon for further details!

★3. Having trouble with that want list? Well send it along to us. We'll get to work right away. We maintain an excellent stock of Canada, Newfoundland and provinces.

★4. We get results! Whether buying or selling, our international contacts and mailing list can work for you.

So if you've been missing out, why not write, phone, or FAX us today for a FREE Mail Auction Catalogue. Public Auction Catalogues are also available on request. Auction catalogues are free for the asking! Or an annual subscription together with prices realized is just $15.00 (payable by Access, Visa, Mastercard).

# Eastern Auctions Ltd.

P.O. Box 250G, Bathurst, N.B., Canada E2A 3Z4 PH: (506) 548–8986. FAX (506) 546–6627

**1851** (7 April).
1 1 3d. black
Only one example is known, with the impression cancelled by the signature of the postmaster, R. W. Kelly.

## QUEBEC

CROWNED-CIRCLE HANDSTAMPS

CC1 CC 1*b* QUEBEC L.C. (R.) (13.1.1842) *Price on cover* £150

**PRICES FOR STAMPS ON COVER**
Nos. 1/23 *from* × 2
Nos. 25/8 *from* × 3
Nos. 29/43*a* *from* × 3
Nos. 44/5 *from* × 8

1 American Beaver (Designed by Sir Sandford Fleming)

2 Prince Albert

3

Major re-entry: Line though "EE PEN" (Upper pane R. 5/7)

(T **1/6**. Eng and recess Rawdon, Wright, Hatch and Edson, New York)

**1851.** *Imperf. Laid paper.*
1 1 3d. red (23 April) £7000 £600
1*a* 3d. orange-vermilion £7000 £600
b. Major re-entry — £1600
2 2 6d. slate-violet (15 May) £7500 £900
3 6d. brown-purple £8000 £1200
a. Bisected (3d.) on cover † £20000
4 3 12d. black (14 June) £60000 £40000

There are several re-entries on the plate of the 3d. in addition to the major re-entry listed. All re-entries occur in this stamp on all papers.

Forgeries of the 3d. are known without the full stop after "PENCE".

4

5

6 Jacques Cartier

**1852–57.** *Imperf.*

A. *Handmade wove paper, varying in thickness* (1852–56)
5 1 3d. red £950 £160
a. Bisected (1½d.) on cover † £22000
6 3d. deep red £1000 £160
7 3d. scarlet-vermilion £1400 £170
8 3d. brown-red £1000 £160
a. Bisected (1½d.) on cover † —
b. Major re-entry (*all shades*) *from* — £650
9 2 6d. slate-violet £7500 £950
a. Bisected (3d.) on cover † £12000
10 6d. greenish grey £7500 £950
11 6d. brownish grey £8000 £1000
12 5 7½d. yellow-green (*shades*) (2.6.57) £7000 £1500
13 6 10d. bright blue (1.55) £7000 £1200
14 10d. dull blue £6500 £1100
15 10d. blue *to* deep blue £7000 £1200
a. Major re-entry (*all shades*) *from* — £2000
16 3 12d. black — £45000

B. *Machine-made medium to thick wove paper of a more even hard texture with more visible mesh. Clearer impressions* (1857)
17 4 ½d. deep rose (1.8.57) £600 £375
18 1 3d. red £1400 £450
a. Bisected (1½d.) on cover † £15000
b. Major re-entry — £1200
19 2 6d. grey-lilac £12000 £2000
20 6 10d. blue *to* deep blue £6500 £1200
a. Major re-entry — £2500

C. *Thin soft horizontally ribbed paper* (1857)
21 4 ½d. deep rose £3250 £1600
a. Vertically ribbed paper £5000 £2250
22 1 3d. red £3000 £400
a. Major re-entry — £1100

D. *Very thick soft wove paper* (1857)
23 2 6d. reddish purple £11000 £2500
a. Bisected (3d.) on cover † £18000

Bisected examples of the 3d. value were used to make up the 7½d. Canadian Packet rate to England from May 1856 until the introduction of the 7½d. value on 2 June 1857.

The 7½d. and 10d. values can be found in wide and narrow versions. These differences are due to shrinkage of the paper, which was wetted before printing and then contracted unevenly during drying. The width of these stamps varies between 17 and 18 mm.

The listed major re-entry on the 10d. occurs on R.3/5 and shows strong doubling of the top frame line and the left-hand "8d. stg." with a line through the lower parts of "ANAD" and "ENCE". Smaller re-entries occur on all values.

Examples of the 12d. come from a proof sheet used for postal purposes by the postal authorities.

The 3d. is known perforated 14 and also *percé en scie* 13. Both are contemporary, but were unofficial.

**1858–59.** *P* 11¾. A. *Machine-made medium to thick wove paper with a more even hard texture.*
25 4 ½d. deep rose (12.58) £1300 £500
*a. Lilac-rose* £1600 £600
26 1 3d. red (1.59) £2250 £300
a. Major re-entry — £950
27 2 6d. brownish grey (1.59) £5500 £1900
*a. Slate-violet* £5500 £1700

B. *Thin soft horizontally ribbed paper*
27*b* 4 ½d. deep rose-red — £3250
28 1 3d. red — £1200
a. Major re-entry

**(New Currency. 100 cents = 1 dollar)**

7

8 American Beaver

9 Prince Albert

10

11 Jacques Cartier

(Recess A.B.N. Co)

(On 1 May 1858, Messrs. Rawdon, Wright, Hatch and Edson joined with eight other firms to form "The American Bank Note Co" and the "imprint" on sheets of the following stamps has the new title of the firm with "New York" added.)

**1859** (1 July). *P* 12.
29 7 1 c. pale rose (to rose-red) £160 22·00
30 1 c. deep rose (to carmine-rose) £180 40·00
a. Imperf (pair) £2750
b. Imperf × perf
31 8 5 c. pale red £160 10·00
32 5 c. deep red £160 10·00
a. Re-entry* (R.3/8) £2500 £500
b. Imperf (pair) £7000
c. Bisected (2½ c.) with 10 c. on cover † £3750
33 9 10 c. black-brown £5000 £1300
a. Bisected (5 c.), on cover † £5500
33*b* 10 c. deep red-purple £2250 £500
ba. Bisected (5 c.), on cover † £3750
34 10 c. purple (*shades*) £600 35·00
a. Bisected (5 c.), on cover † £3750
35 10 c. brownish purple £550 35·00
36 10 c. brown (to pale) £550 35·00
a. Bisected (5 c.), on cover † £4500
37 10 c. dull violet £500 35·00
38 10 c. bright red-purple £500 35·00
a. Imperf (pair) £5500
39 10 12½ c. deep yellow-green £475 38·00
40 12½ c. pale yellow-green £375 38·00
41 12½ c. blue-green £375 38·00
a. Imperf (pair) £2500
b. Imperf between (vert pair)
42 11 17 c. deep blue £600 60·00
a. Imperf (pair) £3000
43 17 c. slate-blue £750 90·00
43*a* 17 c. indigo £600 60·00
b. Imperf (pair) £3000

*The price of No. 32a is for the very marked re-entry showing oval frame line doubled above "CANADA". Slighter re-entries are worth from £30 upwards in used condition.

As there were numerous P.O. Dept. orders for the 10 c., 12½ c. and 17 c. and some of these were executed by more than one separate printing, with no special care to ensure uniformity of colour, there is a wide range of shade, especially in the 10 c., and some shades recur at intervals after periods during which other shades predominated. The colour-names given in the above list therefore represent groups only.

It has been proved by leading Canadian specialists that the perforations may be an aid to the approximate dating of a particular stamp, the gauge used measuring 11¾ × 11¾ from mid-July, 1859 to mid 1863, 12 × 11¾ from March 1863 to mid 1865 and 12 × 12 from April 1865 to 1868. Exceptionally in the 5 c. value many sheets were perforated 12 × 12 between May and October, 1862, whilst the last printings of the 12½ c. and 17 c. perf 11¾ × 11¾ were in July 1863, the perf 12 × 11¾ starting towards the end of 1863.

12

(Recess A.B.N. Co)

**1864** (1 Aug). *P* 12.
44 12 2 c. rose-red £375 £110
45 2 c. bright rose £375 £110
a. Imperf (pair) £1500

The Colony of Canada became part of the Dominion of Canada on 1 July 1867.

## NEW BRUNSWICK

New Brunswick, previously part of Nova Scotia, became a separate colony in June 1784.

**PRICES FOR STAMPS ON COVER**
Nos. 1/6 *from* × 2
Nos. 7/19 *from* × 3

1 Royal Crown and Heraldic Flowers of the United Kingdom

(Recess P.B.)

**1851** (5 Sept). *Blue paper. Imperf.*
1 1 3d. bright red £1800 £300
2 3d. dull red £2500 £300
a. Bisected (1½d.) (on cover) † £2750
2*b* 6d. mustard-yellow £6000 £2500
3 6d. yellow £5000 £800
4 6d. olive-yellow £4500 £700
a. Bisected (3d.) (on cover) † £3000
b. Quartered (1½d.) (on cover) † £20000
5 1s. reddish mauve £16000 £5500
6 1s. dull mauve £14000 £4500
a. Bisected (6d.) (on cover) † £20000
b. Quartered (3d.) (on cover) † £20000

Reprints of all three values were made in 1890 on thin, hard, white paper. The 3d. is bright orange, the 6d. and 1s. violet-black.

Nos. 2a and 4b were to make up the 7½d. rate to Great Britain, introduced on 1 August 1854.

2 Locomotive

3

3*a* Charles Connell

4

5

6 Paddle-steamer *Washington*

7 King Edward VII when Prince of Wales

(Recess A.B.N. Co)

**1860** (15 May)–**63**. *No wmk. P* 12.
7 2 1 c. brown-purple 32·00 27·00
8 1 c. purple 19·00 19·00
9 1 c. dull claret 19·00 19·00
a. Imperf vert (horiz pair) £500
10 3 2 c. orange (1863) 12·00 14·00
11 2 c. orange-yellow 13·00 14·00
12 2 c. deep orange 12·00 14·00
a. Imperf horiz (vert pair) £450
13 3*a* 5 c. brown £2750
14 4 5 c. yellow-green 12·00 12·00
15 5 c. deep green 12·00 12·00
16 5 c. sap-green (deep yellowish green) £300 40·00
17 5 10 c. red 35·00 24·00
a. Bisected (5 c.) (on cover) (1860) † £800
18 6 12½ c. indigo 50·00 40·00
19 7 17 c. black 32·00 27·00

Beware of forged cancellations.

New Brunswick joined the Dominion of Canada on 1 July 1867 and its stamps were withdrawn in March of the following year.

## *PRICES OF SETS*

Set prices are given for many issues, generally those containing three stamps or more. Definitive sets include one of each value or major colour change, but do not cover different perforations, die types or minor shades. Where a choice is possible the set prices are based on the cheapest versions of the stamps included in the listings.

## NEWFOUNDLAND

Newfoundland became a self-governing colony in 1855 and a Dominion in 1917. In 1934 the adverse financial situation led to the suspension of the constitution.

The first local postmaster, at St. John's, was appointed in 1805, the overseas mails being routed via Halifax, Nova Scotia. A regular packet service was established between these two ports in 1840, the British G.P.O. assuming control of the overseas mails at the same time.

The responsibility for the overseas postal service reverted to the colonial administration on 1 July 1851.

For illustrations of the handstamp types see BRITISH POST OFFICES ABROAD notes, following GREAT BRITAIN.

### ST. JOHN'S

CROWNED-CIRCLE HANDSTAMPS

CC1 CC 1a ST. JOHNS NEWFOUNDLAND (R.) (27.6.1846) .. .. *Price on cover* £900

**PRICES FOR STAMPS ON COVER TO 1945**

| | |
|---|---|
| Nos. 1/24*e* | *from* × 2 |
| Nos. 25/43 | *from* × 4 |
| Nos. 44/61 | *from* × 5 |
| Nos. 62/5*a* | *from* × 2 |
| Nos. 66/79 | *from* × 3 |
| Nos. 80/1 | *from* × 2 |
| No. 82 | — |
| Nos. 83/94 | *from* × 5 |
| Nos. 95/127 | *from* × 2 |
| Nos. 130/41 | *from* × 3 |
| Nos. 142/3 | — |
| Nos. 144/8*f* | *from* × 2 |
| Nos. 149/62 | *from* × 3 |
| No. 163 | — |
| Nos. 164/78 | *from* × 2 |
| Nos. 179/90 | *from* × 3 |
| No. 191 | — |
| Nos. 192/220 | *from* × 2 |
| No. 221 | — |
| Nos. 222/9 | *from* × 3 |
| Nos. 230/4 | *from* × 2 |
| No. 235 | — |
| Nos. 236/91 | *from* × 2 |
| Nos. D1/6 | *from* × 10 |

1

2

4

3

5

Royal Crown and Heraldic flowers of the United Kingdom

(Recess P.B.)

**1857** (1 Jan–15 Feb). *No wmk. Thick paper. Imperf.*

| No. | Type | Description | Unused | Used |
|---|---|---|---|---|
| 1 | 1 | 1d. brown-purple | 75·00 | £120 |
| | | a. Bisected (½d.) (on cover) | | † £6500 |
| 2 | 2 | 2d. scarlet-vermilion (15 Feb) | £11000 | £4500 |
| 3 | 3 | 3d. yellowish green | £300 | £375 |
| 4 | 4 | 4d. scarlet-vermilion | £6000 | £2500 |
| | | a. Bisected (2d.) (on cover) | | |
| 5 | 1 | 5d. brown-purple | £180 | £300 |
| 6 | 4 | 6d. scarlet-vermilion | £11000 | £2750 |
| 7 | 5 | 6½d. scarlet-vermilion | £2250 | £2750 |
| 8 | 4 | 8d. scarlet-vermilion | £200 | £250 |
| | | a. Bisected (4d.) (on cover) | | † £3000 |
| 9 | 2 | 1s. scarlet-vermilion | £14000 | £3750 |
| | | a. Bisected (6d.) (on cover) | | † £9500 |

The 6d. and 8d. differ from the 4d. in many details, as does also the 1s. from the 2d.

**1860** (Aug). *Medium paper. Imperf.*

| No. | Type | Description | Unused | Used |
|---|---|---|---|---|
| 10 | 2 | 2d. orange-vermilion | £250 | £300 |
| 11 | 3 | 3d. green *to* deep green* | 48·00 | £120 |
| 12 | 4 | 4d. orange-vermilion | £1400 | £500 |
| | | a. Bisected (2d.) (on cover) | | † £7500 |
| 13 | 1 | 5d. Venetian red | 60·00 | £190 |
| 14 | 4 | 6d. orange-vermilion | £2500 | £600 |
| 15 | 2 | 1s. orange-vermilion | £20000 | £7000 |
| | | a. Bisected (6d.) (on cover) | | |

*No. 11 includes stamps from the November 1861 printing which are very difficult to distinguish.

The 1s. on horizontally or vertically *laid* paper is now considered to be a proof.

**BISECTS.** Collectors are warned against buying bisected stamps of these issues without a reliable guarantee.

**1861.** *New colours. Imperf. (a) 1st printing. Soft paper* (July).

| No. | Type | Description | Unused | Used |
|---|---|---|---|---|
| 16 | 2 | 2d. deep rose-lake | £150 | £475 |
| 17 | 4 | 4d. deep rose-lake | 60·00 | £170 |
| | | a. Bisected (2d.) (on cover) | | |
| 18 | | 6d. deep rose-lake | 60·00 | £180 |
| | | a. Bisected (3d.) (on cover) | | |
| 19 | 5 | 6½d. deep rose-lake | £200 | £500 |
| 20 | 2 | 1s. deep rose-lake | £225 | £500 |
| | | a. Bisected (6d.) (on cover) | | † £13000 |

*(b) 2nd printing. Hard paper* (Nov)

| No. | Type | Description | Unused | Used |
|---|---|---|---|---|
| 21 | 1 | 1d. chocolate-brown | £100 | £180 |
| | | *a. Red-brown* | £3500 | |
| 22 | 2 | 2d. pale rose-lake | £110 | £350 |
| 23 | 4 | 4d. pale rose-lake | 16·00 | 80·00 |
| 24 | 1 | 5d. chocolate-brown | 32·00 | £250 |
| | | *a. Red-brown* | 28·00 | £150 |
| 24*b* | 4 | 6d. pale rose-lake | 15·00 | £100 |
| 24*c* | 5 | 6½d. pale rose-lake | 55·00 | £325 |
| 24*d* | 4 | 8d. pale rose-lake | 50·00 | £350 |
| 24*e* | 2 | 1s. pale rose-lake | 23·00 | £170 |

Stamps of the second printing of the pale rose-lake shades have a more transparent look due to the paper being generally thinner, but paper thickness alone is not a sure test for distinguishing the printings.

Stamps of this issue may be found with part of the paper-maker's watermark "STACEY WISE 1858".

Beware of buying used specimens of the stamps which are worth much less in unused condition, as many unused stamps have been provided with faked postmarks. A guarantee should be obtained.

**6** Codfish

**7** Common Seal on Ice-floe

**8** Prince Consort

**9** Queen Victoria

**10** Schooner

**11** Queen Victoria

(Recess A.B.N. Co)

**1865** (15 Nov)–**75**. *P* 12. *(a) Thin yellowish paper.*

| No. | Type | Description | Unused | Used |
|---|---|---|---|---|
| 25 | 6 | 2 c. yellowish green | £120 | 29·00 |
| | | a. Bisected (1 c.) (on cover) | | † £3750 |
| 26 | 7 | 5 c. brown | £500 | £150 |
| | | a. Bisected (2½ c.) (on cover) | | |
| 27 | 8 | 10 c. black | £250 | 48·00 |
| | | a. Bisected (5 c.) (on cover) | | † £2750 |
| 28 | 9 | 12 c. red-brown | £350 | £150 |
| | | a. Bisected (6 c.) (on cover) | | |
| 29 | 10 | 13 c. orange-yellow | 65·00 | 48·00 |
| 30 | 11 | 24 c. blue | 32·00 | 32·00 |

*(b) Medium white paper*

| No. | Type | Description | Unused | Used |
|---|---|---|---|---|
| 31 | 6 | 2 c. bluish green (*to* deep) (1870) | 60·00 | 27·00 |
| 32 | 8 | 10 c. black (1875) | £150 | 23·00 |
| 33 | 9 | 12 c. chestnut (1870) | 38·00 | 38·00 |
| 33*a* | 11 | 24 c. blue (1870?) | £500 | £180 |

**12** King Edward VII when Prince of Wales

**14** Queen Victoria

I

II

In Type II the white oval frame line is unbroken by the scroll containing the words "ONE CENT", the letters "N.F." are smaller and closer to the scroll, and there are other minor differences.

(Recess National Bank Note Co, New York)

**1868** (Nov). *P* 12.

| No. | Type | Description | Unused | Used |
|---|---|---|---|---|
| 34 | 12 | 1 c. dull purple (I) | 40·00 | 45·00 |

(Recess A.B.N. Co)

**1868** (Nov)–**73**. *P* 12.

| No. | Type | Description | Unused | Used |
|---|---|---|---|---|
| 35 | 12 | 1 c. brown-purple (II) (5.71) | 60·00 | 48·00 |
| 36 | 14 | 3 c. vermilion (7.70) | £300 | £100 |
| 37 | | 3 c. blue (1.4.73) | £350 | 15·00 |
| 38 | 7 | 5 c. black | £190 | £100 |
| 39 | 14 | 6 c. rose (7.70) | 5·50 | 16·00 |

**1876–79.** *Rouletted.*

| No. | Type | Description | Unused | Used |
|---|---|---|---|---|
| 40 | 12 | 1 c. lake-purple (II) (1877) | 75·00 | 38·00 |
| 41 | 6 | 2 c. bluish green (1879) | £120 | 45·00 |
| 42 | 14 | 3 c. blue (1877) | £250 | 3·00 |
| 43 | 7 | 5 c. blue | £170 | 2·75 |
| | | a. Imperf (pair) | | |

**15** King Edward VII when Prince of Wales

**16** Codfish

**17**

**18** Common Seal on Ice-floe

(Recess British American Bank Note Co, Montreal)

**1880–82.** *P* 12.

| No. | Type | Description | Unused | Used |
|---|---|---|---|---|
| 44 | 15 | 1 c. dull grey-brown | 15·00 | 7·00 |
| | | *a. Dull brown* | 12·00 | 7·00 |
| | | *b. Red-brown* | 19·00 | 12·00 |
| 46 | 16 | 2 c. yellow-green (1882) | 42·00 | 20·00 |
| 47 | 17 | 3 c. pale dull blue | 40·00 | 5·00 |
| | | *a. Bright blue* | 42·00 | 1·00 |
| 48 | 18 | 5 c. pale dull blue | £190 | 4·25 |

**19** Newfoundland Dog

**20** Atlantic Brigantine

**21** Queen Victoria

(Recess British American Bank Note Co, Montreal)

**1888** (Jan). *New colours and values. P* 12.

| No. | Type | Description | Unused | Used |
|---|---|---|---|---|
| 49 | 19 | ½ c. rose-red | 5·50 | 6·00 |
| 50 | 15 | 1 c. blue-green | 6·00 | 4·00 |
| | | *a. Green* | 5·00 | 1·25 |
| | | *b. Yellow-green* | 7·00 | 5·50 |
| 51 | 16 | 2 c. orange-vermilion | 9·50 | 3·00 |
| 52 | 17 | 3 c. deep brown | 30·00 | 70 |
| 53 | 18 | 5 c. deep blue | 60·00 | 3·50 |
| 54 | 20 | 10 c. black | 45·00 | 45·00 |
| 49/54 | | *Set of* 6 | £140 | 55·00 |

For reissues of 1880/87 stamps in similar colours, see Nos. 62/65*a*.

(Recess B.A.B.N.)

**1890** (Nov). *P* 12.

| No. | Type | Description | Unused | Used |
|---|---|---|---|---|
| 55 | 21 | 3 c. deep slate | 17·00 | 75 |
| | | a. Imperf (pair) | | |
| 56 | | 3 c. slate-grey (*to* grey) | 19·00 | 75 |
| | | a. Imperf horiz (vert pair) | £500 | |
| 57 | | 3 c. slate-violet | 19·00 | 2·50 |
| 58 | | 3 c. grey-lilac | 19·00 | 75 |
| 58*a* | | 3 c. brown-grey | 19·00 | 5·00 |
| 58*b* | | 3 c. purple-grey | 22·00 | 4·50 |

There is a very wide range of shades in this stamp, and those given only cover the main groups.

Stamps on pink paper are from a consignment recovered from the sea and which were affected by the salt water.

(Recess British American Bank Note Co, Montreal)

**1894** (Aug–Dec). *Changes of colour. P* 12.

| No. | Type | Description | Unused | Used |
|---|---|---|---|---|
| 59 | 19 | ½ c. black (11.94) | 3·75 | 3·50 |
| 59*a* | 18 | 5 c. bright blue (12.94) | 45·00 | 1·50 |
| 60 | 14 | 6 c. crimson-lake (12.94) | 7·50 | 14·00 |
| 61 | 9 | 12 c. deep brown | 32·00 | 42·00 |

The 6 c. is printed from the old American Bank Note Company's plates.

**1896–97.** *Reissues. P* 12.

| No. | Type | Description | Unused | Used |
|---|---|---|---|---|
| 62 | 19 | ½ c. orange-vermilion | 32·00 | 45·00 |
| 63 | 15 | 1 c. deep green | 12·00 | 6·50 |
| 63*a* | | 1 c. deep brown | 40·00 | 30·00 |
| 64 | 16 | 2 c. green | 45·00 | 27·00 |
| 65 | 17 | 3 c. deep blue | 35·00 | 7·50 |
| 65*a* | | 3 c. chocolate-brown | 42·00 | 28·00 |
| 62/65*a* | | *Set of* 6 | £190 | £130 |

The above were *reissued* for postal purposes. The colours were generally brighter than those of the original stamps.

**22** Queen Victoria

**23** Jean Cabot

**24** Cape Bonavista

**25** Reindeer-hunting

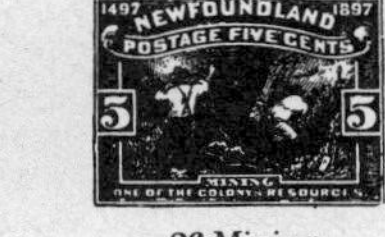

**26** Mining

**27** Logging

**28** Fishing

**29** *Matthew* (Cabot)

**30** Willow Grouse

**31** Group of Grey Seals

**32** Salmon-fishing

**33** Seal of the Colony

**34** Iceberg off St. John's

**35** Henry VII

(Recess A.B.N. Co)

**1897** (24 June). *400th Anniv of Discovery of Newfoundland and 60th year of Queen Victoria's reign. P* 12.

| No. | Type | Description | Unused | Used |
|---|---|---|---|---|
| 66 | **22** | 1 c. green | 80 | 2·25 |
| 67 | **23** | 2 c. bright rose | 80 | 1·50 |
| | | a. Bisected (1 c.) on cover | † | £400 |
| 68 | **24** | 3 c. bright blue | 1·00 | 30 |
| | | a. Bisected (1½ c.) on cover | † | £300 |
| 69 | **25** | 4 c. olive-green | 6·50 | 1·50 |
| 70 | **26** | 5 c. violet | 5·50 | 1·50 |
| 71 | **27** | 6 c. red-brown | 4·75 | 1·50 |
| | | a. Bisected (3 c.) on cover | † | £350 |
| 72 | **28** | 8 c. orange | 11·00 | 6·50 |
| 73 | **29** | 10 c. sepia | 18·00 | 1·75 |
| 74 | **30** | 12 c. deep blue | 25·00 | 1·75 |
| 75 | **31** | 15 c. bright scarlet | 10·00 | 10·00 |
| 76 | **32** | 24 c. dull violet-blue | 16·00 | 14·00 |
| 77 | **33** | 30 c. slate-blue | 28·00 | 38·00 |
| 78 | **34** | 35 c. red | 48·00 | 48·00 |
| 79 | **35** | 60 c. black | 9·50 | 7·00 |
| 66/79 | | *Set of* 14 | £170 | £120 |

The 60 c. surcharged "TWO—2—CENTS" in three lines is an essay made in December 1918.

**36** Prince Edward later Duke of Windsor

**37** Queen Victoria

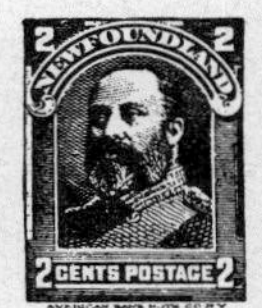

**38** King Edward VII when Prince of Wales

**39** Queen Alexandra when Princess of Wales

**40** Queen Mary when Duchess of York

**41** King George V when Duke of York

(Recess A.B.N. Co)

**1897–1918.** *P* 12.

| No. | Type | Description | Unused | Used |
|---|---|---|---|---|
| 83 | **36** | ½ c. olive (8.97) | 80 | 60 |
| | | a. Imperf (pair) | £225 | |
| 84 | **37** | 1 c. carmine (4.12.97) | 1·75 | 2·25 |
| 85 | | 1 c. blue-green (6.98) | 3·25 | 10 |
| | | *a. Yellow-green* | 4·25 | 10 |
| | | b. Imperf horiz (vert pair) | £170 | |
| 86 | **38** | 2 c. orange (4.12.97) | 80 | 1·40 |
| | | a. Imperf (pair) | | |
| 87 | | 2 c. scarlet (6.98) | 6·00 | 15 |
| | | a. Imperf (pair) | £225 | |
| | | b. Imperf between (pair) | | |
| 88 | **39** | 3 c. orange (6.98) | 5·00 | 10 |
| | | a. Imperf horiz (vert pair) | £250 | |
| | | b. Imperf (pair) | £225 | |
| | | *c. Red-orange/bluish* (6.18) | 18·00 | 2·75 |
| 89 | **40** | 4 c. violet (10.01) | 17·00 | 2·25 |
| | | a. Imperf (pair) | £200 | |
| 90 | **41** | 5 c. blue (6.99) | 23·00 | 2·75 |
| 83/90 | | *Set of* 8 | 50·00 | 9·00 |

No. 88c was an emergency war-time printing made by the American Bank Note Co from the old plate, pending receipt of the then current 3 c. from England.

The imperforate error of this issue are found used, but only as philatelic "by favour" items. It is possible that No. 86a only exists in this condition.

ONE CENT

(42)

ONE CENT

(43)

ONE CENT

(44)

**1897** (Oct). *T* **21** *surch with T* **42** *to T* **44** *by Royal Gazette, St. Johns, on stamps of various shades.*

| No. | Type | Description | Unused | Used |
|---|---|---|---|---|
| 91 | **42** | 1 c. on 3 c. grey-purple | 30·00 | 15·00 |
| | | a. Surch double, one diagonal | £1100 | |
| | | d. Vert pair, one without lower bar and "ONE CENT" | £3500 | |
| 92 | **43** | 1 c. on 3 c. grey-purple | 80·00 | 70·00 |
| 93 | **44** | 1 c. on 3 c. grey-purple | £450 | £325 |

Nos. 91/3 occur in the same setting of 50 (10×5) applied twice to each sheet. Type **42** appeared in the first four horizontal rows. Type **43** on R. 5/1–8 and Type **44** on R. 5/9 and 10.

Trial surcharges in red or red and black were not issued. (*Price*: Type **42** *in red* £1100, *in red and black* £1100: Type **43** *in red* £2750, *in red and black* £3000: Type **44** *in red* £5000, *in red and black* £6000).

These surcharges exist on stamps of various shades, but those on brown-grey are clandestine forgeries, having been produced by one of the printers at the *Royal Gazette*.

**45** Map of Newfoundland

(Recess A.B.N. Co)

**1908** (Sept). *P* 12.

| No. | Type | Description | Unused | Used |
|---|---|---|---|---|
| 94 | **45** | 2 c. lake | 16·00 | 20 |

**46** King James I

**47** Arms of Colonisation Co

**48** John Guy

**49** *Endeavour* (immigrant ship), 1610

**50** Cupids

**51** Sir Francis Bacon

**52** View of Mosquito

53 Logging Camp

54 Paper Mills

55 King Edward VII

56 King George V

(Litho Whitehead, Morris & Co, Ltd)

**1910** (15 Aug). (*a*) *P* 12.

95 **46** 1 c. green .. .. .. .. 2·00 30
a. "NFWFOUNDLAND" (Right pane R. 5/1) .. .. 27·00 45·00
b. "JANES" (Right pane R. 5/2) .. .. 27·00 45·00
c. Imperf between (horiz pair) .. £275 £300
96 **47** 2 c. rose-carmine .. .. .. 3·25 50
97 **48** 3 c. olive .. .. .. 2·00 11·00
98 **49** 4 c. violet .. .. .. 8·00 11·00
99 **50** 5 c. bright blue .. .. .. 5·50 4·00
100 **51** 6 c. claret (A) .. .. .. 38·00 £110
100*a* 6 c. claret (B) .. .. .. 18·00 45·00
101 **52** 8 c. bistre-brown .. .. .. 40·00 65·00
102 **53** 9 c. olive-green .. .. .. 35·00 55·00
103 **54** 10 c. purple-slate .. .. .. 40·00 70·00
104 **55** 12 c. pale red-brown .. .. .. 45·00 65·00
a. Imperf (pair) .. .. .. £400
105 **56** 15 c. black .. .. .. 50·00 75·00
95/105 .. .. .. *Set of* 11 £225 £350

6 c. (A) "Z" in "COLONIZATION" reversed. (B) "Z" correct.

(*b*) *P* 12 × 14

106 **46** 1 c. green .. .. .. 2·25 3·50
a. "NFWFOUNDLAND" .. .. 25·00 50·00
b. "JANES" .. .. 25·00 50·00
c. Imperf between (pair) .. .. £450 £500
107 **47** 2 c. rose-carmine .. .. 2·75 35
a. Imperf between (pair) .. .. £400
108 **50** 5 c. bright blue (*p* 14×12) .. .. 8·00 2·50

(*c*) *P* 12×11

109 **46** 1 c. green .. .. .. 1·25 20
a. Imperf between (horiz pair) .. .. £250
b. Imperf between (vert pair) .. .. £300
c. "NFWFOUNDLAND" .. .. 22·00 35·00
e. "JANES" .. .. .. 22·00 35·00

(*d*) *P* 12 × 11½

110 **47** 2 c. rose-carmine .. .. .. 85·00 85·00

(Dies eng Macdonald & Sons. Recess A. Alexander & Sons, Ltd)

**1911** (7 Feb). *As T* **51** *to* **56**, *but recess printed. P* 14.

111 6 c. claret (B) .. .. .. 13·00 25·00
112 8 c. yellow-brown .. .. .. 38·00 48·00
a. Imperf between (horiz pair) .. .. £400
b. Imperf (pair) .. .. .. £300
113 9 c. sage-green .. .. .. 28·00 55·00
a. Imperf between (horiz pair) .. .. £225
114 10 c. purple-black .. .. .. 60·00 80·00
a. Imperf between (horiz pair) .. .. £300
b. Imperf (pair) .. .. .. £250
115 12 c. red-brown .. .. .. 42·00 55·00
116 15 c. slate-green .. .. .. 50·00 90·00
111/16 .. .. .. *Set of* 6 £200 £325

The 9 c. and 15 c. exist with papermaker's watermark "E. TOWGOOD FINE".

57 Queen Mary

58 King George V

59 Duke of Windsor when Prince of Wales

60 King George VI when Prince Albert

61 Princess Mary, the Princess Royal

62 Prince Henry Duke of Gloucester

63 Prince George, Duke of Kent

64 Prince John

65 Queen Alexandra

66 Duke of Connaught

67 Seal of Newfoundland

(1 c. to 5 c., 10 c. eng and recess D.L.R.; others eng Macdonald & Co, recess A. Alexander & Sons)

**1911** (19 June)–**16.** *Coronation. P* 13½ × 14 (*comb*) (1 *c. to* 5 *c.*, 10 *c.*) *or* 14 (*line*) (*others*).

117 **57** 1 c. yellow-green .. .. .. 3·00 20
*a. Blue-green* (1915) .. .. .. 2·00 20
118 **58** 2 c. carmine .. .. .. 1·75 20
*a. Rose-red* (*blurred impression*). Perf 14 (1916) .. .. 3·00 55
119 **59** 3 c. red-brown .. .. .. 11·00 23·00
120 **60** 4 c. purple .. .. .. 14·00 22·00
121 **61** 5 c. ultramarine .. .. .. 3·75 80
122 **62** 6 c. slate-grey .. .. .. 10·00 22·00
123 **63** 8 c. aniline blue .. .. .. 45·00 75·00
*a. Greenish blue* .. .. .. 48·00 85·00
124 **64** 9 c. violet-blue .. .. .. 9·00 28·00
125 **65** 10 c. deep green .. .. .. 16·00 29·00
126 **66** 12 c. plum .. .. .. 12·00 29·00
127 **67** 15 c. lake .. .. .. 13·00 38·00
117/27 .. .. .. *Set of* 11 £120 £250

The 2 c. rose-red, No. 118*a* is a poor war-time printing by Alexander & Sons.

Although No. 123 has a typical aniline appearance it is believed that the shade results from the thinning of non-aniline ink.

68 Reindeer

**FIRST TRANS-ATLANTIC AIR POST April, 1919.**

(69)

(Des J. H. Noonan. Recess D.L.R.)

**1919** (2 Jan). *Newfoundland Contingent*, 1914–1918. *P* 14.

130 **68** 1 c. green (*a*) (*b*) .. .. .. 60 20
131 2 c. scarlet (*a*) (*b*) .. .. .. 70 40
*a. Carmine-red* (*b*) .. .. .. 1·75 45
132 3 c. brown (*a*) (*b*) .. .. .. 1·00 20
*a. Red-brown* (*b*) .. .. .. 2·00 30
133 4 c. mauve (*a*) .. .. .. 2·00 60
*a. Purple* (*b*) .. .. .. 2·25 30
134 5 c. ultramarine (*a*) (*b*) .. .. .. 1·50 60
135 6 c. slate-grey (*a*) .. .. .. 4·50 22·00
136 8 c. bright magenta (*a*) .. .. .. 4·25 29·00
137 10 c. deep grey-green (*a*) .. .. .. 3·50 1·75
138 12 c. orange (*a*) .. .. .. 15·00 32·00
139 15 c. indigo (*a*) .. .. .. 14·00 38·00
*a. Prussian blue* (*a*) .. .. .. 80·00 £140
140 24 c. bistre-brown (*a*) .. .. .. 18·00 24·00
141 36 c. sage-green (*a*) .. .. .. 7·50 16·00
130/41 .. .. .. *Set of* 12 65·00 £150

Each value bears with "Trail of the Caribou" the name of a different action: 1 c. Suvla Bay; 3 c. Gueudecourt; 4 c. Beaumont Hamel; 6 c. Monchy; 10 c. Steenbeck; 15 c. Langemarck; 24 c. Cambrai; 36 c. Combles; 2 c., 5 c., 8 c., and 12 c. inscribed "Royal Naval Reserve-Ubique".

*Perforations.* Two perforating heads were used: (*a*) comb 14 × 13.9; (*b*) line 14.1 × 14.1.

**1919** (12 Apr). *Air. No.* 132 *optd with T* **69**, *by Robinson & Co Ltd, at the offices of the "Daily News".*

142 **68** 3 c. brown .. .. .. £14000 £8000

These stamps franked correspondence carried by Lieut. H. Hawker on his Atlantic flight. 18 were damaged and destroyed, 95 used on letters, 11 given as presentation copies, and the remaining 76 were sold in aid of the Marine Disasters Fund.

**1919** (19 April). *Nos.* 132 *optd in MS.* "Aerial Atlantic Mail. J.A.R.".

142*a* **68** 3 c. brown .. .. .. — £20000

This provisional was made by W. C. Campbell, the Secretary of the Postal Department, and the initials are those of the Postmaster, J. A. Robinson, for use on correspondence intended to be carried on the abortive Morgan-Raynham Trans-Atlantic flight. The mail was eventually delivered by sea.

In addition to the 25 to 30 used examples, one unused, no gum, copy of No. 142*a* is known.

A single example of a similar overprint on the 2 c., No. 131, is known used on cover together with an unoverprinted example of the same value.

**Trans-Atlantic AIR POST, 1919. ONE DOLLAR.**

(70)

**THREE CENTS**

(71)

**1919** (9 June). *Air. No.* 75 *surch with T* **70** *by Royal Gazette, St. Johns.*

143 **31** $1 on 15 c. bright scarlet .. .. 90·00 90·00
a. No comma after "AIR POST" .. .. £200 £225
b. As Var a and no stop after "1919" .. £425 £425
c. As Var a and "A" of "AIR" under "a" of "Trans" .. .. £425 £425

These stamps were issued for use on the mail carried on the first successful flight across the Atlantic by Capt. J. Alcock and Lieut. A. Brown, and on other projected Trans-Atlantic flights (Alcock flown cover, *Price* £2500).

The surcharge was applied in a setting of 25 of which 16 were normal, 7 as No. 143a, 1 as No. 143b and 1 as No. 143c.

**1920** (Sept). *Nos.* 75 *and* 77/8 *surch as T* **71**, *by Royal Gazette* (2 *c. with only one bar, at top of stamp*).

A. Bars of surch 10½ mm apart. B. Bars 13½ mm apart.

144 **33** 2 c. on 30 c. slate-blue (23 Sept) .. 3·50 9·00
a. Surch inverted .. .. .. £500
145 **31** 3 c. on 15 c. bright scarlet (A) (13 Sept) 80·00 80·00
a. Surch inverted .. .. .. £700
146 3 c. on 15 c. bright scarlet (B) (13 Sept) 6·50 9·00
147 **34** 3 c. on 35 c. red (15 Sept) .. .. 4·00 7·50
a. Surch inverted .. .. ..
b. Lower bar omitted .. .. .. £110 £120
c. "THREE" omitted .. .. .. £1100

Our prices for Nos. 147b and 147c are for stamps with lower bar or "THREE" entirely missing. The bar may be found in all stages of incompleteness and stamps showing broken bar are not of much value.

On the other hand, stamps showing either only the top or bottom of the letters "THREE" are scarce, though not as rare as No. 147c.

The 6 c. T **27**, surcharged "THREE CENTS", in red or black, is an essay (*Price* £300). The 2 c. on 30 c. with red surcharge is a colour trial (*Price* £300).

**AIR MAIL to Halifax, N.S. 1921.**

(72)

**1921** (16 Nov). *Air. No.* 78 *optd with T* **72** *by Royal Gazette.*

I. 2¾ *mm between* "AIR" *and* "MAIL"

148 **34** 35 c. red .. .. .. 90·00 90·00
a. No stop after "1921" .. .. 80·00 80·00
b. No stop and first "1" of "1921" below "f" of "Halifax" .. .. £180 £180
c. As No. 148, inverted .. .. £3250
d. As No. 148a, inverted .. .. £3000
e. As No. 148b, inverted .. .. £6500

II. 1½ *mm between* "AIR" *and* "MAIL"

148*f* **34** 35 c. red .. .. .. £100 £100
g. No stop after "1921" .. .. £120 £120
h. No stop and first "1" of "1921" below "f" of "Halifax" .. .. £180 £180
i. As No. 148f, inverted .. .. £3750
k. As No. 148g, inverted .. .. £4500
l. As No. 148h, inverted .. .. £6500

Type **72** was applied as a setting of 25 which contained ten stamps as No. 148a, seven as No. 148, four as No. 148*f*, two as No. 148g, one as No. 148b and one as No. 148h.

73 Twin Hills, Tor's Cove

74 South-West Arm, Trinity

75 Statue of the Fighting Newfoundlander, St. John's

(Recess D.L.R.)

**1923** (9 July)–**26.** *T* **73/5** *and similar designs. P* 14 (*comb or line*).

149 1 c. green .. .. .. 60 10
a. Booklet pane of 8 (1926) .. .. £250
150 2 c. carmine .. .. .. 60 10
a. Imperf (pair) .. .. .. £160
b. Booklet pane of 8 (1926) .. .. £140
151 3 c. brown .. .. .. 55 10
152 4 c. deep purple .. .. .. 90 25
153 5 c. ultramarine .. .. .. 1·50 70
154 6 c. slate .. .. .. 1·50 5·50
155 8 c. purple .. .. .. 1·50 3·25
156 9 c. slate-green .. .. .. 13·00 25·00
157 10 c. violet .. .. .. 2·50 1·75
*a. Purple* .. .. .. 3·00 2·25
158 11 c. sage-green .. .. .. 1·50 10·00
159 12 c. lake .. .. .. 2·00 7·50
160 15 c. Prussian blue .. .. .. 2·00 11·00
161 20 c. chestnut (28.4.24) .. .. 3·00 10·00
162 24 c. sepia (22.4.24) .. .. 35·00 65·00
149/62 .. .. .. *Set of* 14 60·00 £130

Designs: *Horiz* (*as T* **73**)—6 c. Upper Steadies, Humber River; 11 c. Shell Bird Island; 20 c. Placentia. (*As T* **74**)—8 c. Quidi Vidi, near St. John's; 9 c. Reindeer crossing lake; 12 c. Mount Moriah, Bay of Islands. *Vert* (*as T* **75**)—4 c. Humber River; 5 c. Coast at Trinity; 10 c. Humber River Cañon; 15 c. Humber River near Little Rapids; 24 c. Topsail Falls.

*Perforations.* Three perforating heads were used: comb 13.8 × 14 (all values); line 13.7 and 14, and combinations of these two (for all except 6, 8, 9 and 11 c.).

Air Mail DE PINEDO 1927

(87)

**1927** (18 May). *Air. No.* 79 *optd with T* **87**, *by Robinson & Co, Ltd.*

163 **35** 60 c. black (R.) .. .. .. £18000 £5000

For the mail carried by De Pinedo to Europe 300 stamps were overprinted, 230 used on correspondence, 66 presented to De Pinedo, Government Officials, etc., and 4 damaged and destroyed. Stamps without overprint were also used.

**NEW INFORMATION**

The editor is always interested to correspond with people who have new information that will improve or correct the Catalogue.

**88** Newfoundland and Labrador

**89** S.S. *Caribou*

**90** King George V and Queen Mary

**91** Duke of Windsor when Prince of Wales

**92** Express Train

**93** Newfoundland Hotel, St. John's

**94** Heart's Content

**95** Cabot Tower, St. John's

**96** War Memorial, St. John's

**97** G.P.O., St. John's

**98** Vickers "Vimy" Aircraft

**99** Parliament House, St. John's

**100** Grand Falls, Labrador

(Recess D.L.R.)

**1928** (3 Jan)–**29**. *"Publicity" issue. P* 13 *to* 14.

164 **88** 1 c. deep green (*a*) .. .. .. 55 80
165 **89** 2 c. carmine (*b*) .. .. .. .. 1·00 40
166 **90** 3 c. brown (*b*) (*c*) .. .. .. .. 1·25 30
167 **91** 4 c. mauve (*b*) .. .. .. .. 1·50 1·00
a. *Rose-purple* (1929) .. .. .. 3·75 4·75
168 **92** 5 c. slate-grey (*b*) (*c*) .. .. .. 8·00 2·75
169 **93** 6 c. ultramarine (*b*) (*c*) .. .. .. 1·50 9·00
170 **94** 8 c. red-brown (*c*) .. .. .. 1·50 12·00
171 **95** 9 c. deep green (*c*) .. .. .. 1·50 7·00
172 **96** 10 c. deep violet (*b*) (*c*) .. .. .. 3·00 5·00
173 **97** 12 c. carmine-lake (*c*) .. .. .. 1·50 10·00
174 **95** 14 c. brown-purple (*b*) (*c*) .. .. .. 3·00 5·00
175 **98** 15 c. deep blue (*c*) .. .. .. .. 2·50 18·00
176 **99** 20 c. grey-black (*b*) (*c*) .. .. .. 1·75 6·50
177 **97** 28 c. deep green (*c*) .. .. .. 17·00 38·00
178 **100** 30 c. sepia (*c*) .. .. .. .. 4·50 10·00
164/78 .. .. .. .. *Set of* 15 45·00 £110

See also Nos. 179/87 and 198/208.

*Perforations*. Three perforating heads were used: (*a*) comb 14 × 13.9; (*b*) comb 13.5 × 12.75; (*c*) line 13.7 to 14 or compound.

D 1 c. P

D 2 c. P

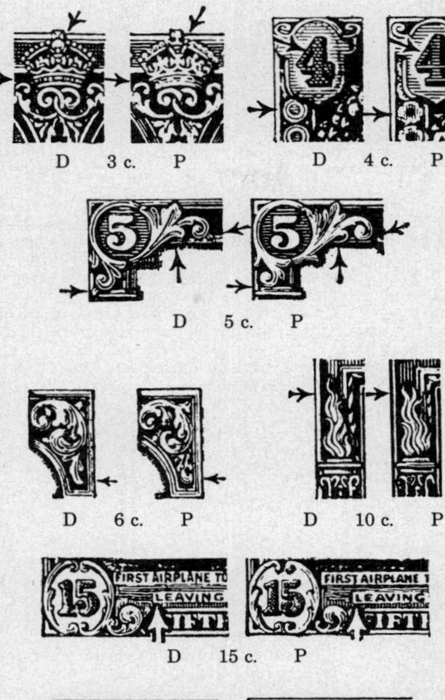

D 3 c. P D 4 c. P

D 5 c. P

D 6 c. P D 10 c. P

D 15 c. P

D 20 c. P

D. "De La Rue" printing

P. "Perkins, Bacon" printing

**1929** (10 Aug)–**31**. *"Perkins, Bacon" printing. Former types re-engraved. No wmk. P* 13½ to 14.

179 **88** 1 c. green (*a*) (*d*) (26.9.29) .. .. 2·75 20
a. Imperf between (vert pair) .. £120
b. Imperf (pair) .. .. .. £110
180 **89** 2 c. scarlet (*b*) (*d*) .. .. .. 1·25 10
a. Imperf (pair) .. .. .. 80·00
181 **90** 3 c. red-brown (*c*) .. .. .. 80 10
a. Imperf (pair) .. .. .. 90·00
182 **91** 4 c. reddish purple (*c*) (26.8.29) .. 1·50 20
a. Imperf (pair) .. .. .. 95·00
183 **92** 5 c. deep grey-green (*c*) (14.9.29) .. 4·00 90
184 **93** 6 c. ultramarine (*b*) (*d*) (8.11.29) .. 2·00 6·50
185 **96** 10 c. violet (*c*) (5.10.29) .. .. .. 2·00 1·50
186 **98** 15 c. blue (*c*) (1.30) .. .. .. 15·00 60·00
187 **99** 20 c. black (*d*) (1.1.31) .. .. .. 15·00 32·00
179/87 .. .. .. .. *Set of* 9 40·00 90·00

*Perforations*. Four perforating heads were used: (*a*) comb 14 × 13.9; (*b*) comb 13.6 × 13.5; (*c*) comb 13.6 × 13.8; (*d*) line 13.7 to 14 or compound.

**THREE CENTS**

(101)

**Trans-Atlantic AIR MAIL By B. M. "Columbia" September 1930 Fifty Cents**

(102)

(Surch by Messrs D. R. Thistle, St. John's)

**1929** (23 Aug). *No.* 154 *surch with T* **101**.

188 3 c. on 6 c. slate (R.) .. .. .. .. 55 2·40
a. Surch inverted .. .. .. .. £600 £900
b. Surch in black .. .. .. .. £700

**1930** (25 Sept). *Air. No.* 141 *surch with T* **102** *by Messrs D. R. Thistle*.

191 **68** 50 c. on 36 c. sage-green .. .. £4250 £4000

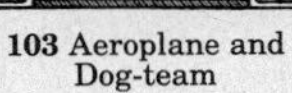

**103** Aeroplane and Dog-team

**104** Vickers-Vimy Biplane and early Sailing Packet

**105** Routes of historic Transatlantic Flights

**106**

(Des A. B. Perlin. Recess P.B.)

**1931**. *Air. P* 14. (*a*) *Without wmk* (2.1.31)

192 **103** 15 c. chocolate .. .. .. .. 3·00 7·00
a. Imperf between (horiz or vert pair) £400
b. Imperf (pair) .. .. .. £350
193 **104** 50 c. green .. .. .. .. 18·00 26·00
a. Imperf between (horiz or vert pair) £400 £350
b. Imperf (pair) .. .. .. £375
194 **105** $1 deep blue .. .. .. .. 32·00 70·00
a. Imperf between (horiz or vert pair) £400
b. Imperf (pair) .. .. .. £350
192/4 .. .. .. .. *Set of* 3 48·00 95·00

(*b*) *Wmk W* **106**, (*sideways*) (13.3.31)

195 **103** 15 c. chocolate .. .. .. .. 2·50 8·00
a. Pair, with and without wmk .. 29·00
b. Imperf between (horiz or vert pair) £375
ba. Ditto, one without wmk (vert pair) £800
c. Imperf (pair) .. .. .. £225
d. Wmk Cross (pair) .. .. 70·00
196 **104** 50 c. green .. .. .. .. 15·00 50·00
a. Imperf between (horiz or vert pair) £400
b. Imperf (pair) .. .. .. £250
c. Pair, with and without wmk ..
197 **105** $1 deep blue .. .. .. .. 48·00 95·00
a. Imperf between (horiz or vert pair) £450
b. Imperf horiz (vert pair) .. .. £450
c. Pair, with and without wmk ..
d. Imperf (pair) .. .. .. £300
195/7 .. .. .. .. *Set of* 3 60·00 £140

**"WITH AND WITHOUT WMK" PAIRS** listed in the issues from No. 195a onwards must have one stamp *completely* without any trace of watermark.

**1931** (25 March–July). *"Perkins, Bacon" printing (re-engraved types). W* **106** *(sideways on* 1 *c.,* 4 *c.,* 30 *c.). P* 13½ *to* 14.

198 **88** 1 c. green (7.31) .. .. .. 1·50 1·25
a. Imperf between (horiz pair) .. £600
199 **89** 2 c. scarlet (7.31) .. .. .. 2·25 1·25
200 **90** 3 c. red-brown (7.31) .. .. .. 1·50 80
201 **91** 4 c. reddish purple (7.31) .. .. 1·50 70
202 **92** 5 c. deep grey-green (7.31) .. .. 6·50 7·00
203 **93** 6 c. ultramarine .. .. .. 9·00 16·00
204 **94** 8 c. chestnut (1.4.31) .. .. .. 9·00 22·00
205 **96** 10 c. violet (1.4.31) .. .. .. 4·00 7·00
206 **98** 15 c. blue (1.7.31) .. .. .. 17·00 42·00
207 **99** 20 c. black (1.7.31) .. .. .. 20·00 10·00
208 **100** 30 c. sepia (1.7.31) .. .. .. 14·00 24·00
198/208 .. .. .. .. *Set of* 11 75·00 £120

*Perforations*. Two perforating heads were used: comb 13.4 × 13.4 for 1 c.; comb 13.6 × 13.8 for other values.

**107** Codfish

**108** King George V

**109** Queen Mary

**110** Duke of Windsor when Prince of Wales

**111** Reindeer

**112** Queen Elizabeth II when Princess

**113** Salmon

**114** Newfoundland Dog

**115** Harp Seal

**116** Cape Race

117 Sealing Fleet

118 Fishing Fleet

(Recess P.B.)

**1932** (1 Jan). **W 106** *(sideways on vert designs). P* 13½ *(comb).*

209 **107** 1 c. green 1·00 15
a. Imperf (pair) 75·00
b. Perf 13 (line) 22·00 28·00
ba. Imperf between (vert pair) £110
bb. Booklet pane of 4 £100
210 **108** 2 c. carmine 1·25 10
a. Imperf (pair) 75·00
b. Booklet pane of 4 27·00
c. Perf 13 (line) 15·00 22·00
ca. Booklet pane of 4 75·00
211 **109** 3 c. orange-brown 80 10
a. Imperf (pair) 75·00
b. Booklet pane of 4 80·00
c. Perf 13 (line) 24·00
ca. Booklet pane of 4 £110
d. Perf 14 (line). Small holes 18·00
da. Imperf between (vert pair) £110
db. Booklet pane of 4 80·00
212 **110** 4 c. bright violet 2·00 70
213 **111** 5 c. maroon 2·00 45
a. Imperf (pair) £150
214 **112** 6 c. light blue 4·00 9·00
215 **113** 10 c. black-brown 55 25
a. Imperf (pair) 65·00
216 **114** 14 c. black 80 1·50
a. Imperf (pair) £120
217 **115** 15 c. claret 1·25 1·75
a. Imperf (pair) £130
b. Perf 14 (line) 11·00 14·00
218 **116** 20 c. green 1·00 50
a. Imperf (pair) £110
b. Perf 14 (line) 35·00
219 **117** 25 c. slate 1·25 1·75
a. Imperf (pair) £120
b. Perf 14 (line) 8·50 17·00
ba. Imperf between (vert pair) £250
220 **118** 30 c. ultramarine 15·00 22·00
a. Imperf (pair) £250
b. Imperf between (vert pair) £450
c. Perf 14 (line) £160
209/20 *Set of* 12 28·00 35·00

For similar stamps in different perforations see Nos. 222/8c and 276/89.

**TRANS-ATLANTIC**
**WEST TO EAST**
**Per Dornier DO-X**
**May, 1932.**
**One Dollar and Fifty Cents**

(119)

**1932** (19 May). *Air. No.* 197 *surch as* **T 119**, *by Messrs. D. R. Thistle. P* 14.

221 **105** $1.50 on $1 deep blue (R.) £180 £225
a. Surch inverted £7500

120 Queen Mother, when Duchess of York

121 Paper Mills

122 Bell Island

(Recess P.B.)

**1932** (15 Aug)–**38**. *Wmk* **W 106** *(sideways on vert designs). P* 13½ *(comb).*

222 **107** 1 c. grey 30 10
a. Imperf (pair) 40·00
b. Booklet pane of 4 80·00
c. Perf 14 (line) 6·00
d. Perf 14 (line). Small holes 19·00
da. Booklet pane of 4 80·00
e. Pair, with and without wmk 30·00
223 **108** 2 c. green 40 10
a. Imperf (pair) 45·00
b. Booklet pane of 4 26·00
c. Perf 14 (line) 6·00
ca. Imperf between (horiz pair) £250
d. Perf 14 (line). Small holes 14·00
da. Booklet pane of 4 50·00
e. Pair, with and without wmk 24·00
224 **110** 4 c. carmine (21.7.34) 40 15
a. Imperf (pair) 50·00
b. Perf 14 (line) 3·25
ba. Imperf between (horiz or vert pair) £120
225 **111** 5 c. violet (Die I) 2·00 45
a. Imperf (pair) 50·00
b. Perf 14 (line). Small holes 23·00
c. Die II 60 20
ca. Imperf (pair) 60·00
cb. Perf 14 (line) 18·00
cc. Imperf between (horiz pair) £180
cd. Pair, with and without wmk
226 **120** 7 c. red-brown 85 2·50
b. Perf 14 (line) 90·00
ba. Imperf between (horiz pair) £425
c. Imperf (pair) £120
227 **121** 8 c. brownish red 2·50 1·50
a. Imperf (pair) 75·00
228 **122** 24 c. bright blue 60 1·75
a. Imperf (pair) £160
b. Doubly printed £750
228*c* **118** 48 c. red-brown (1.1.38) 4·50 9·00
ca. Imperf (pair) 75·00
222/8*c* *Set of* 8 9·00 14·00

No. 223. Two dies exist of the 2 c. Die I was used for No. 210 and both dies for No. 223. The differences, though numerous, are very slight.

No. 225. There are also two dies of the 5 c., Die I only being used for No. 213 and both dies for the violet stamp. In Die II the antler pointing to the "T" of "POSTAGE" is taller than the one pointing to the "S" and the individual hairs on the underside of the caribou's tail are distinct.

For similar stamps in a slightly larger size and perforated 12½ or 13½ (5 c.) see Nos. 276/89.

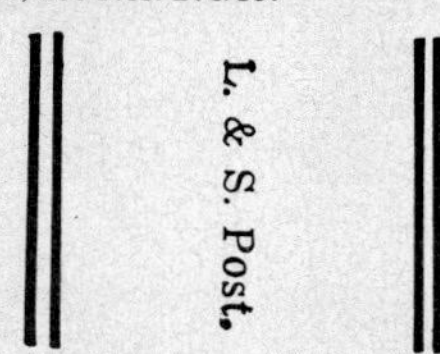

(123) "L.&S."—Land and Sea

**1933** (9 Feb). *No.* 195 *optd with* **T 123** *for ordinary postal use, by Messrs D. R. Thistle.* **W 106** *(sideways). P* 14.

229 **103** 15 c. chocolate 1·50 4·00
a. Pair, one without wmk 22·00
b. Opt reading up £1200
c. Vertical pair, one without surch £1800

124 Put to Flight

125 Land of Hearts Delight

(Des J. Scott. Recess P.B.)

**1933** (31 May). *Air.* **T 124/5** *and similar horiz designs.* **W 106** *(sideways). P* 14 *(5, 30, 75 c.) or* 11½ *(10, 60 c.).*

230 5 c. red-brown 7·50 13·00
a. Imperf (pair) £130
b. Imperf between (horiz or vert pair) £1500
231 10 c. orange-yellow 4·00 14·00
a. Imperf (pair) £110
232 30 c. light blue 20·00 32·00
a. Imperf (pair) £250
233 60 c. green 35·00 55·00
a. Imperf (pair) £250
234 75 c. yellow-brown 35·00 55·00
a. Imperf (pair) £140
b. Imperf between (horiz or vert pair) £2250
230/4 *Set of* 5 90·00 £150

Designs:—30 c. Spotting the herd; 60 c. News from home; 75 c. Labrador.

**1933**
**GEN. BALBO**
**FLIGHT.**
**$4.50**

(129)

(Surch by Robinson & Co, St. John's)

**1933** (24 July). *Air. Balbo Transatlantic Mass Formation Flight. No.* 234 *surch with* **T 129. W 106.** *P* 14.

235 $4.50 on 75 c. yellow-brown £275 £325
a. Surch inverted £20000
b. Surch on 10 c. (No. 231) £20000

No. 235a. When this error was discovered the stamps were ordered to be officially destroyed but four copies which had been torn were recovered and skilfully repaired. In addition four undamaged examples exist and the price quoted is for one of these.

130 Sir Humphrey Gilbert

131 Compton Castle, Devon

132 Gilbert Coat of Arms

(Recess P.B.)

**1933** (3 Aug). *350th Anniv of the Annexation by Sir Humphrey Gilbert.* **T 130/2** *and similar designs.* **W 106** *(sideways on vert designs). P* 13½ *(comb).**

236 1 c. slate 50 60
a. Imperf (pair) 45·00
237 2 c. green 65 35
a. Imperf (pair) 48·00
b. Doubly printed £300
238 3 c. chestnut 65 1·00
239 4 c. carmine 45 30
a. Imperf (pair) 45·00
240 5 c. violet 75 70
241 7 c. greenish blue 3·25 11·00
a. Perf 14 15·00 35·00
242 8 c. vermilion 5·00 7·50
*a. Brownish red* £250
b. Bisected (4 c.) (on cover) † £350
243 9 c. ultramarine 4·50 6·50
a. Imperf (pair) £150
b. Perf 14 18·00 35·00
244 10 c. brown-lake 3·75 4·00
a. Imperf (pair) £300
b. Perf 14 24·00 42·00
245 14 c. grey-black 7·00 26·00
a. Perf 14 16·00 45·00
246 15 c. claret 7·00 14·00
247 20 c. grey-green 7·00 12·00
a. Perf 14 13·00 27·00
248 24 c. maroon 7·00 20·00
a. Imperf (pair) £120
b. Perf 14 20·00 35·00
249 32 c. olive-black 6·00 35·00
a. Perf 14 22·00 55·00
236/49 *Set of* 14 45·00 £120

Designs: *Horiz*—4 c. Eton College; 7 c. Gilbert commissioned by Elizabeth; 8 c. Fleet leaving Plymouth, 1583; 9 c. Arrival at St. John's; 10 c. Annexation, 5 August 1583; 20 c. Map of Newfoundland. *Vert*—5 c. Anchor token; 14 c. Royal Arms; 15 c. Gilbert in the *Squirrel*; 24 c. Queen Elizabeth I. 32 c. Gilbert's statue at Truro.

**Perforations.* Two perforating heads were used: comb 13.4 × 13.4 for all values; line 13.8 (listed above as 14) for a second printing of some values.

**1935** (6 May). *Silver Jubilee. As Nos.* 91/4 *of Antigua, but ptd by B.W. P* 11 × 12.

250 4 c. rosine 50 50
251 5 c. bright violet 90 60
252 7 c. blue 1·00 4·50
253 24 c. olive-green 2·75 3·75
250/3 *Set of* 4 4·50 8·50
250/3 Perf "Specimen" *Set of* 4 £120

**1937** (12 May). *Coronation Issue. As Nos.* 95/7 *of Antigua, but name and value uncoloured on coloured background. P* 11×11½.

254 2 c. green 90 1·25
255 4 c. carmine 1·10 50
256 5 c. purple 1·60 2·00
254/6 *Set of* 3 3·25 3·25
254/6 Perf "Specimen" *Set of* 3 70·00

144 Codfish

Die I

Die II

No. 258. In Die II the shading of the King's face is heavier and dots have been added down the ridge of the nose. The top frame line is thicker and more uniform.

Re-entry to right of design (inscr oval, tree and value) (R.4/8)

(Recess P.B.)

**1937** (12 May). *Additional Coronation Issue.* **T 144** *and similar horiz designs.* **W 106.** A. *P* 14 *or* 13½ *(line).* B. *P* 13 *(comb).*

| | | A | | B | |
|---|---|---|---|---|---|
| 257 | 1 c. grey | 70 | 15 | 16·00 | 28·00 |
| | a. Pair, with and without wmk | 18·00 | — | — | — |
| 258 | 3 c. orange-brown (I) | 2·50 | 1·00 | 1·40 | 70 |
| | a. Pair, with and without wmk | 42·00 | — | † | |
| | b. Die I. Imperf between (horiz or vert pair) | £350 | — | † | |
| | c. Die II | 1·40 | 1·25 | 2·00 | 1·25 |
| | d. Die II. Imperf between (horiz or vert pair) | £450 | — | † | |
| | e. Die II. Pair, with and without wmk | — | — | 80·00 | — |
| 259 | 7 c. bright ultramarine | 1·00 | 60 | £200 | £300 |
| | a. Pair, with and without wmk | — | — | † | |
| | b. Re-entry at right | 40·00 | | | |

| | | | | | | |
|---|---|---|---|---|---|---|
| 260 | 8 c. scarlet .. .. .. | 1·00 | 1·00 | 3·00 | 3·00 |
| | a. Pair, with and without wmk | 30·00 | — | † | |
| | b. Imperf between (horiz or vert pair) .. .. | £500 | — | † | |
| | c. Imperf (pair) .. .. | £250 | — | † | |
| 261 | 10 c. deep olive .. .. .. | 2·75 | 3·25 | 3·25 | 5·00 |
| | a. Pair, with and without wmk | 45·00 | — | † | |
| 262 | 14 c. black .. .. .. | 1·40 | 2·00 | £2750 | £1400 |
| | a. Pair, with and without wmk | 35·00 | — | † | |
| 263 | 15 c. claret .. .. .. | 6·00 | 4·00 | 12·00 | 12·00 |
| | a. Pair, with and without wmk | 50·00 | – | 75·00 | — |
| | b. Imperf between (vert pair) | £325 | — | † | |
| 264 | 20 c. green .. .. .. | 2·25 | 3·50 | 2·50 | 6·00 |
| | a. Pair, with and without wmk | 85·00 | — | † | |
| | b. Imperf between (vert pair) | £475 | — | † | |
| 265 | 24 c. light blue .. .. | 2·25 | 2·50 | 12·00 | 12·00 |
| | a. Pair, with and without wmk | 85·00 | — | † | |
| | b. Imperf between (vert pair) | £550 | — | † | |
| 266 | 25 c. slate .. .. .. | 2·75 | 1·75 | 11·00 | 22·00 |
| | a. Pair, with and without wmk | 60·00 | — | † | |
| 267 | 48 c. slate-purple .. .. | 6·00 | 4·00 | 17·00 | 30·00 |
| | a. Pair, with and without wmk | 90·00 | — | † | |
| | b. Imperf between (vert pair) | £550 | — | † | |
| 257/67 | .. .. *Set of* 11 | 24·00 | 21·00 | | |

Designs:—3 c. Map of Newfoundland; 7 c. Reindeer; 8 c. Corner Brook paper mills; 10 c. Salmon; 14 c. Newfoundland dog; 15 c. Harp Seal; 20 c. Cape Race; 24 c. Bell Island; 25 c. Sealing fleet; 48 c. The Banks fishing fleet.

The line perforation "A" was produced by two machines measuring respectively 13.7 and 14.1. The comb perforation "B" measures 13.3 × 13.2.

Three used examples of No. 259B have now been identified on separate covers.

**155** King George VI

**156** Queen Mother

(Recess P.B.)

**1938** (12 May). *T* **155/6** *and similar vert designs. W* **106** *(sideways). P* 13½ *(comb).*

| | | | |
|---|---|---|---|
| 268 | 2 c. green .. .. .. .. | 1·00 | 15 |
| | a. Pair, with and without wmk .. | £130 | |
| | b. Imperf (pair) .. .. .. | 65·00 | |
| 269 | 3 c. carmine .. .. .. .. | 80 | 30 |
| | a. Perf 14 (line) .. .. .. | £275 | £130 |
| | b. Pair, with and without wmk .. | £180 | |
| | c. Imperf (pair) .. .. .. | 55·00 | |
| 270 | 4 c. light blue .. .. .. .. | 1·25 | 15 |
| | a. Pair, with and without wmk .. | 80·00 | |
| | b. Imperf (pair) .. .. .. | 65·00 | |
| 271 | 7 c. deep ultramarine .. .. | 65 | 2·50 |
| | a. Imperf (pair) .. .. .. | 65·00 | |
| 268/71 | .. .. .. *Set of* 4 | 3·25 | 2·75 |

Designs:—4 c. Queen Elizabeth II as princess; 7 c. Queen Mary.

For similar designs, perf 12½, see Nos. 277/281.

**159** King George VI and Queen Elizabeth

(Recess B.W.)

**1939** (17 June). *Royal Visit. No wmk. P* 13½.

| | | | | |
|---|---|---|---|---|
| 272 | **159** | 5 c. deep ultramarine .. .. .. | 75 | 30 |

2

CENTS

**(160)**

**1939** (20 Nov). *No. 272 surch as T* **160**, *at St. John's.*

| | | | | |
|---|---|---|---|---|
| 273 | **159** | 2 c. on 5 c. deep ultramarine (Br.) .. | 1·25 | 20 |
| 274 | | 4 c. on 5 c. deep ultramarine (C.) .. | 70 | 20 |

**161** Grenfell on the *Strathcona* (after painting by Gribble)

**162** Memorial University College

(Recess C.B.N.)

**1941** (1 Dec). *Sir Wilfred Grenfell's Labrador Mission. P* 12.

| | | | | |
|---|---|---|---|---|
| 275 | **161** | 5 c. blue .. .. .. .. .. | 15 | 20 |

(Recess Waterlow)

**1941–44.** *W* **106** *(sideways on vert designs). P* 12½ *(line).*

| | | | | |
|---|---|---|---|---|
| 276 | **107** | 1 c. grey .. .. .. .. | 20 | 30 |
| 277 | **155** | 2 c. green .. .. .. .. | 20 | 10 |
| 278 | **156** | 3 c. carmine .. .. .. .. | 30 | 10 |
| | | a. Pair, with and without wmk .. | 55·00 | |
| 279 | – | 4 c. blue (As No. 270) .. .. | 1·00 | 10 |
| | | a. Pair, with and without wmk .. | £100 | |
| 280 | **111** | 5 c. violet (Die I) *(p* 13½ *comb).* .. | 75·00 | |
| | | a. Perf 12½ (line) (6.42) .. .. | 1·25 | 30 |
| | | ab. Pair, with and without wmk .. | 95·00 | |
| | | ac. Printed double .. .. | | |
| | | ad. Imperf vert (horiz pair) .. .. | £300 | |
| | | b. Imperf (pair) .. .. | | |
| 281 | – | 7 c. deep ultramarine (As No. 271) .. | 3·50 | 4·50 |
| | | a. Pair, with and without wmk .. | £100 | |
| 282 | **121** | 8 c. rose-red .. .. .. | 1·00 | 1·75 |
| | | a. Pair, with and without wmk .. | £100 | |
| 283 | **113** | 10 c. black-brown .. .. .. | 1·50 | 75 |
| 284 | **114** | 14 c. black .. .. .. .. | 1·50 | 3·25 |
| 285 | **115** | 15 c. claret .. .. .. .. | 3·50 | 4·25 |
| 286 | **116** | 20 c. green .. .. .. .. | 3·75 | 4·00 |
| 287 | **122** | 24 c. blue .. .. .. .. | 3·00 | 4·75 |
| 288 | **117** | 25 c. slate .. .. .. .. | 4·50 | 5·00 |
| 289 | **118** | 48 c. red-brown (1944) .. .. | 2·50 | 5·00 |
| 276/89 | | .. .. *Set of* 14 | 25·00 | 30·00 |

Nos. 276/89 are redrawn versions of previous designs with slightly larger dimensions; the 5 c., for example, measures 21 mm in width as opposed to the 20.4 mm of the Perkins Bacon printings.

No. 280. For Die I see note relating to No. 225.

(Recess C.B.N.)

**1943** (2 Jan). *P* 12.

| | | | | |
|---|---|---|---|---|
| 290 | **162** | 30 c. carmine .. .. .. .. | 1·00 | 80 |

**163** St. John's

TWO

CENTS

**(164)**

(Recess C.B.N.)

**1943** (1 June). *Air. P* 12.

| | | | | |
|---|---|---|---|---|
| 291 | **163** | 7 c. ultramarine .. .. .. | 20 | 30 |

**1946** (21 Mar). *No. 290 surch locally with T* **164**.

| | | | | |
|---|---|---|---|---|
| 292 | **162** | 2 c. on 30 c. carmine .. .. .. | 20 | 20 |

**165** Queen Elizabeth II when Princess

**166** Cabot off Cape Bonavista

(Recess Waterlow)

**1947** (21 Apr). *Princess Elizabeth's 21st Birthday. W* **106** *(sideways). P* 12½.

| | | | | |
|---|---|---|---|---|
| 293 | **165** | 4 c. light blue .. .. .. | 15 | 20 |
| | | a. Imperf vert (horiz pair) .. .. | | |

(Recess Waterlow)

**1947** (23 June). *450th Anniv of Cabot's Discovery of Newfoundland. W* **106** *(sideways). P* 12½.

| | | | | |
|---|---|---|---|---|
| 294 | **166** | 5 c. mauve .. .. .. | 15 | 35 |
| | | a. Imperf between (horiz pair) .. | £1000 | |

POSTAGE DUE STAMPS

D 1

D 6ac

(Litho John Dickinson & Co, Ltd)

**1939** (1 May)–**49.** *P* 10.

| | | | | |
|---|---|---|---|---|
| D1 | D 1 | 1 c. green .. .. .. | 1·75 | 6·00 |
| | | a. Perf 11 (1949) .. .. | 3·00 | 8·50 |
| D2 | | 2 c. vermilion .. .. .. | 5·00 | 5·00 |
| | | a. Perf 11 × 9 (1946) .. .. | 7·00 | 15·00 |
| D3 | | 3 c. ultramarine .. .. .. | 4·00 | 17·00 |
| | | a. Perf 11 × 9 (1949) .. .. | 9·00 | 18·00 |
| | | b. Perf 9 .. .. .. | £300 | |
| D4 | | 4 c. orange .. .. .. | 5·50 | 11·00 |
| | | a. Perf 11 × 9 (May 1948) .. | 10·00 | 35·00 |
| D5 | | 5 c. brown .. .. .. | 5·50 | 22·00 |
| D6 | | 10 c. violet .. .. .. | 6·00 | 15·00 |
| | | a. Perf 11 (W **106**) (1949) .. | 17·00 | 65·00 |
| | | ab. Ditto. Imperf between (vert pair) .. | £600 | |
| | | ac. "POSTAGE LUE" (R 3/3 or 3/8) .. | 90·00 | £225 |
| D1/6 | | .. .. .. *Set of* 6 | 25·00 | 70·00 |

Newfoundland joined the Dominion of Canada on 31 March 1949.

## NOVA SCOTIA

Organised postal services in Nova Scotia date from April 1754 when the first of a series of Deputy Postmasters was appointed, under the authority of the British G.P.O. This arrangement continued until 6 July 1851 when the colony assumed responsibility for its postal affairs.

For illustrations of the handstamp types see BRITISH POST OFFICES ABROAD notes, following GREAT BRITAIN.

### AMHERST

CROWNED-CIRCLE HANDSTAMPS

CC1 CC 1 AMHERST. N.S.(R) (March 1845)
*Price on cover* £1000

### ST. MARGARETS BAY

CROWNED-CIRCLE HANDSTAMPS

CC2 CC 1 ST. MARGARETS BAY. N.S.(R) (5.6.1845)
*Price on cover* £3250

Nos. CC1/2 were later used during temporary shortages of stamps, struck in red or black.

**PRICES FOR STAMPS ON COVER**

| | |
|---|---|
| Nos. 1/8 | *from* × 2 |
| Nos. 9/29 | *from* × 5 |

1

2

Crown and Heraldic Flowers of United Kingdom and Mayflower of Nova Scotia.

(Recess P.B.)

**1851** (1 Sept)–**57.** *Bluish paper. Imperf.*

| | | | | |
|---|---|---|---|---|
| 1 | 1 | 1d. red-brown (12.5.53) .. .. | £2000 | £400 |
| | | a. Bisected (½d.) (on cover) .. | † | £50000 |
| 2 | 2 | 3d. deep blue .. .. .. | £1500 | £200 |
| | | a. Bisected (1½d.) (on cover) .. | † | £2750 |
| 3 | | 3d. bright blue .. .. .. | £900 | £110 |
| | | a. Bisected (1½d.) (on cover) .. | † | £2750 |
| 4 | | 3d. pale blue (1857) .. .. | £700 | £130 |
| | | a. Bisected (1½d.) (on cover) .. | † | £2750 |
| 5 | | 6d. yellow-green .. .. | £4750 | £400 |
| | | a. Bisected (3d.) (on cover) .. | † | £3500 |
| 6 | | 6d. deep green (1857) .. .. | £12000 | £750 |
| | | a. Bisected (3d.) (on cover) .. | † | £6000 |
| | | b. Quartered (1½d.) (on cover) .. | † | £38000 |
| 7 | | 1s. cold violet .. .. .. | £19000 | £6000 |
| | | a. Bisected (6d.) (on cover) .. | † | £42000 |
| | | b. Quartered (3d.) (on cover) .. | † | £55000 |
| 7*c* | | 1s. deep purple (1851) .. .. | £15000 | £4250 |
| | | d. Watermarked .. .. | £20000 | £6000 |
| 8 | | 1s. purple (1857) .. .. | £14000 | £2500 |
| | | a. Bisected (6d.) (on cover) .. | † | £32000 |

The watermark on No. 7d consists of the whole or part of a letter from the name "P. H. SAUNDERS" (the papermakers).

The stamps formerly catalogued on almost white paper are probably some from which the bluish paper has been discharged.

Reprints of all four values were made in 1890 on thin, hard, white paper. The 1d. is brown, the 3d. blue, the 6d. deep green, and the 1s. violet-black.

The 3d. bisects are only found used on cover to make up the 7½d. rate.

3

4

5

(Recess American Bank Note Co, New York)

**1860–63.** *P* 12. *(a) Yellowish paper.*

| | | | | |
|---|---|---|---|---|
| 9 | 3 | 1 c. jet black .. .. .. | 3·00 | 12·00 |
| | | a. Bisected (½ c.) (on cover) .. | † | £10000 |
| 10 | | 1 c. grey-black .. .. .. | 3·00 | 12·00 |
| 11 | | 2 c. grey-purple .. .. .. | 11·00 | 15·00 |
| 11*a* | | 2 c. purple .. .. .. | 17·00 | 14·00 |
| 12 | | 5 c. blue .. .. .. | £225 | 16·00 |
| 13 | | 5 c. deep blue .. .. .. | £225 | 16·00 |
| 14 | 4 | 8½ c. deep green .. .. .. | 2·50 | |
| 15 | | 8½ c. yellow-green .. .. .. | 2·50 | |
| 16 | | 10 c. scarlet .. .. .. | 12·00 | 23·00 |
| 17 | 5 | 12½ c. black .. .. .. | 24·00 | 16·00 |
| 17*a* | | 12½ c. greyish black .. .. | — | 16·00 |
| | | *(b) White paper* | | |
| 18 | 3 | 1 c. black .. .. .. | 3·00 | 12·00 |
| | | a. Imperf vert (horiz pair) .. | £150 | |
| 19 | | 1 c. grey .. .. .. | 3·00 | 12·00 |
| 20 | | 2 c. dull purple .. .. .. | 3·25 | 14·00 |
| 21 | | 2 c. purple .. .. .. | 3·25 | 14·00 |
| 22 | | 2 c. grey-purple .. .. .. | 3·25 | 14·00 |
| | | a. Bisected (1 c.) (on cover) .. | † | £4500 |
| 23 | | 2 c. slate-purple .. .. .. | 3·25 | 12·00 |
| 24 | | 5 c. blue .. .. .. | £225 | 16·00 |
| 25 | | 5 c. deep blue .. .. .. | £225 | 16·00 |
| 26 | 4 | 8½ c. deep green .. .. .. | 17·00 | 40·00 |
| 27 | | 10 c. scarlet .. .. .. | 3·50 | 20·00 |
| 28 | | 10 c. vermilion .. .. .. | 4·00 | 20·00 |
| | | a. Bisected (5 c.) (on cover) .. | † | £1200 |
| 29 | 5 | 12½ c. black .. .. .. | 19·00 | 22·00 |

Nova Scotia joined the Dominion of Canada on 1 July 1867.

## PRINCE EDWARD ISLAND

Prince Edward Island, previously administered as part of Nova Scotia, became a separate colony in 1769.

| PRICES FOR STAMPS ON COVER | |
|---|---|
| Nos. 1/4 | *from* × 2 |
| Nos. 5/6 | — |
| Nos. 7/8 | *from* × 3 |
| Nos. 9/20 | *from* × 4 |
| Nos. 21/6 | *from* × 2 |
| Nos. 27/31 | *from* × 4 |
| Nos. 32/3 | *from* × 40 |
| Nos. 34/45 | *from* × 4 |
| Nos. 46/7 | *from* × 3 |

1 2 3 4 5 6

(Typo Charles Whiting, London)

**1861** (1 Jan). *Yellowish toned paper. (a) P 9.*

1 1 2d. rose £170 £100
a. Imperf between (horiz pair) £3000
b. Imperf horiz (vert pair)
c. Bisected (1d.) (on cover)
2 2d. rose-carmine £170 £100
3 2 3d. blue £375 £180
a. Bisected (1½d.) (on cover)
b. Double print £1000
4 3 6d. yellow-green £500 £250

*(b) Rouletted*

5 1 2d. rose £1700 £1200

The 2d. and 3d., perf 9, were authorised to be bisected and used for half their normal value.

**1862.** *Yellowish toned paper. P 11.*

6 4 1d. brown-orange 23·00 50·00
7 6 9d. bluish lilac (29.3.62) 40·00 16·00
8 9d. dull mauve 40·00 16·00

**1863–68.** *Yellowish toned paper. (a) P 11½ × 12.*

9 4 1d. yellow-orange 8·50 13·00
a. Bisected (½d.) (on cover) † £1200
b. Imperf between (horiz pair) £225
10 1d. orange-buff 11·00 12·00
11 1d. yellow 12·00 13·00
12 1 2d. rose 6·00 8·50
a. Imperf vert (horiz pair)
b. Bisected (1d.) (on cover) † £1300
13 2d. deep rose 7·00 11·00
14 2 3d. blue 8·50 12·00
a. Imperf horiz (vert pair)
b. Bisected (1½d.) (on cover)
15 3d. deep blue 8·50 8·00
16 5 4d. black (1867) 12·00 15·00
a. Imperf vert (horiz pair)
b. Bisected (2d.) (on cover) † £1100
17 3 6d. yellow-green (15.12.66) 17·00 17·00
a. Bisected (3d.) (on cover)
18 6d. blue-green (1868) 17·00 17·00
19 6 9d. lilac 16·00 16·00
20 9d. reddish mauve 16·00 16·00
a. Imperf vert (horiz pair) £325
b. Bisected (4½d.) (on cover) † £1300

*(b) Perf compound of 11 and 11–12½*

21 4 1d. yellow-orange £150 60·00
22 1 2d. rose £150 60·00
23 2 3d. blue £170 60·00
24 5 4d. black £190 £180
25 3 6d. yellow-green £170 £180
26 6 9d. reddish mauve £180 £180

**1870.** *Coarse, wove bluish white paper. P 11½–12.*

27 1 2d. rose 7·00 8·50
28 2d. rose-pink 5·50 8·00
a. "TWC" 65·00
b. Imperf between (horiz pair) £110
29 2 3d. pale blue 6·00 8·50
30 3d. blue 6·00 8·50
a. Imperf between (horiz pair) £250
31 5 4d. black 3·00 26·00
a. Imperf between (horiz pair) £110
b. Bisected (2d.) (on cover) † £1400
c. Perf compound 11 and 11½–12

7

(Recess British-American Bank Note Co., Montreal and Ottawa)

**1870** (1 June). *P 12.*

32 7 4½d. (3d. stg), yellow-brown 13·00 26·00
33 4½d. (3d. stg), deep brown 13·00 26·00

8 9 10

11 12 13

(Typo Charles Whiting, London)

**1872** (1 Jan). *(a) P 11½–12.*

34 8 1 c. orange 1·60 8·50
35 1 c. yellow-orange 1·60 7·00
36 1 c. brown-orange 2·50 8·50
37 10 3 c. rose 3·25 7·00
a. Stop between "PRINCE. EDWARD" 18·00 20·00
b. Bisected (1½ c.) (on cover)
c. Imperf horiz (vert pair) £300

*(b) Perf 12 to 12¼, large holes*

38 9 2 c. blue 8·00 24·00
a. Bisected (1 c.) (on cover)
39 11 4 c. yellow-green 1·50 15·00
40 4 c. deep green 2·50 10·00
a. Bisected (2 c.) (on cover) † £2000
41 12 6 c. black 1·60 10·00
a. Bisected (3 c.) (on cover) † £750
b. Imperf between (horiz pair) £190
c. Imperf vert (horiz pair)
42 13 12 c. reddish mauve 1·60 20·00

*(c) P 12½–13, smaller holes*

43 8 1 c. orange 12·00
44 1 c. brown-orange 1·60 7·50
45 10 3 c. rose 8·50 8·50
a. Stop between "PRINCE. EDWARD" 50·00 55·00
45*b* 12 6 c. black — £250

*(d) Perf compound of (a) and (c) 11½–12 × 12½–13*

46 8 1 c. orange 30·00 32·00
47 10 3 c. rose 32·00 32·00
a. Stop between "PRINCE. EDWARD" £170 £180

Prince Edward Island joined the Dominion of Canada on 1 July 1873.

## DOMINION OF CANADA

On July 1867, Canada, Nova Scotia and New Brunswick were united to form the Dominion of Canada.

The provinces of Manitoba (1870), British Columbia (1871), Prince Edward Island (1873), Alberta (1905), Saskatchewan (1905), and Newfoundland (1949) were subsequently added, as were the Northwest Territories (1870) and Yukon Territory (1898).

| PRICES FOR STAMPS ON COVER TO 1945 | |
|---|---|
| Nos. 46/61 | *from* × 2 |
| Nos. 62/7*b* | *from* × 3 |
| Nos. 68/75*b* | *from* × 2 |
| Nos. 76/*c* | *from* × 10 |
| Nos. 77/*a* | *from* × 5 |
| Nos. 78/83 | *from* × 3 |
| Nos. 115/20 | *from* × 6 |
| Nos. 121/49 | *from* × 3 |
| Nos. 150/65 | *from* × 2 |
| Nos. 166/72 | *from* × 3 |
| Nos. 173/87 | *from* × 5 |
| Nos. 188/95 | *from* × 2 |
| Nos. 196/215 | *from* × 3 |
| Nos. 219/224*b* | *from* × 4 |
| Nos. 225/45 | *from* × 2 |
| Nos. 246/55 | *from* × 8 |
| Nos. 256/310 | *from* × 2 |
| No. 312 | *from* × 20 |
| No. 313 | *from* × 10 |
| Nos. 315/18 | *from* × 2 |
| Nos. 319/28 | *from* × 3 |
| Nos. 329/40 | *from* × 2 |
| Nos. 341/400 | *from* × 1 |
| Nos. R1/11 | *from* × 5 |
| Nos. S1/3 | *from* × 8 |
| No. S4 | *from* × 6 |
| No. S5 | *from* × 5 |
| Nos. S6/11 | *from* × 3 |
| Nos. S12/14 | *from* × 5 |
| Nos. D1/8 | *from* × 4 |
| Nos. D9/13 | *from* × 5 |
| Nos. D14/24 | *from* × 4 |

13 14

*Large types*

**PRINTERS.** Nos. 46/120 were recess-printed by the British American Bank Note Co at Ottawa or Montreal.

**1868** (Mar)–**71.** *As T 13 and 14 (various frames). Ottawa printings. P 12.*

*(a) Thin rather transparent crisp paper*

46 13 ½ c. black 55·00 40·00
47 14 1 c. red-brown £300 40·00
48 2 c. grass-green £250 30·00
49 3 c. red-brown £550 20·00
50 6 c. blackish brown £700 £250
51 12½ c. bright blue £500 £150
52 15 c. deep reddish purple £750 £190

In these first printings the impression is generally blurred and the lines of the background are less clearly defined than in later printings.

*(b) Medium to stout wove paper (1868–71)*

53 13 ½ c. black 38·00 30·00
54 ½ c. grey-black 38·00 30·00
a. Imperf between (pair)
b. Watermarked £9000 £5500
55 14 1 c. red-brown £300 35·00
a. Laid paper £6500 £1600
b. Watermarked (1868) £1800 £180
56 1 c. deep orange (Jan, 1869) £650 60·00
56*a* 1 c. orange-yellow (May (?), 1869) £650 60·00
56*b* 1 c. pale orange-yellow £750 70·00
ba. Imperf
57 2 c. deep green £275 22·00
57*a* 2 c. pale emerald-green (1871) £350 28·00
ab. Bisected (1 c. with 2 c. to make 3 c. rate) on cover † £4000
ac. Laid paper — £48000
57*d* 2 c. bluish green £275 22·00
da. Watermarked (1868) £1400 £200
58 3 c. brown-red £650 15·00
a. Laid paper £6000 £300
b. Watermarked (1868) £2250 £160
59 6 c. blackish brown (*to chocolate*) £600 28·00
a. Watermarked (1868) £2000 £550
59*b* 6 c. yellow-brown (1870) £550 32·00
ba. Bisected (3 c.), on cover † £2000
60 12½ c. bright blue £350 32·00
a. Imperf horiz (vert pair) † —
b. Watermarked (1868) £1600 £225
60*c* 12½ c. pale dull blue (milky) £350 32·00
61 15 c. deep reddish purple £450 60·00
61*a* 15 c. pale reddish purple £400 60·00
ab. Watermarked (1868) — £1200
61*b* 15 c. dull violet-grey £200 28·00
ba. Watermarked (1868) — £500
61*c* 15 c. dull grey-purple £300 28·00

The watermark on the stout paper stamps consists of the words "E & G BOTHWELL CLUTHA MILLS," in large double-lined capitals. Portions of one or two letters only may be found on these stamps, which occur in the early printings of 1868.

The papers may, in most cases, be easily divided if the stamps are laid face downwards and carefully compared. The thin hard paper is more or less transparent and shows the design through the stamp; the thicker paper is softer to the feel and more opaque.

The paper of this issue may be still further subdivided in several values into sets on—(a) *Medium to stout wove.* (b) *Thin, soft, very white:* and (c) *Thinner and poorer quality, sometimes greyish or yellowish (from 1878 to end of issue).*

Of the 2 c. laid paper No. 57ac two examples only are known.

21

*Small type*

**1870–89.** *As T 21 (various frames). Ottawa (1870–73) and Montreal printings. P 12 (or slightly under).*
*Papers (a) 1870–80. Medium to stout wove.*
*(b) 1870–72. Thin, soft, very white.*
*(c) 1878–97. Thinner and poorer quality.*

62 21 1 c. bright orange (*a, b*) (1870–73) £110 20·00
a. Thick soft paper (1871)
62*b* 1 c. orange-yellow (*a*) (1876–79) 35·00 85
62*c* 1 c. pale dull yellow (*a*) (1877–79) 22·00 30
62*d* 1 c. bright yellow (*a, c*) (1878–97) 15·00 15
da. Imperf (pair) (*c*) £300
db. Bisected (½ c.) (on *Railway News*) † £3000
dc. Printed both sides £1400
62*e* 1 c. lemon-yellow (*c*) (1880)
63 2 c. deep green (*a, b*) (1872–73 & 1876–78) 70·00 50
63*a* 2 c. grass-green (*c*) (1878–88) 40·00 20
ab. Imperf (pair) (1891–93?) £325
ac. Bisected (1 c.) on cover † £1300
64 3 c. Indian red (*a*) (1.70) £800 70·00
a. Perf 12½ (2.70) £3500 £500
64*b* 3 c. pale rose-red (*a*) (9.70) £275 8·00
64*c* 3 c. deep rose-red (*a, b*) (1870–73) £300 8·50
ca. Thick soft paper (Jan, 1871) — £300
64*d* 3 c. dull red (*a, c*) (1876–88) 55·00 70
64*e* 3 c. orange-red (*a, c*) (1876–88) (*shades*) 45·00 55
64*f* 3 c. rose-carmine (*c*) (Oct 1888–April 1889) £350 11·00
65 5 c. olive-grey (*a, c*) (February, 1876–88) £130 3·75
66 6 c. yellowish brown (*a, b, c*) (1872–73 and 1876–90) £130 9·00
a. Bisected (3 c.) on cover † £1600

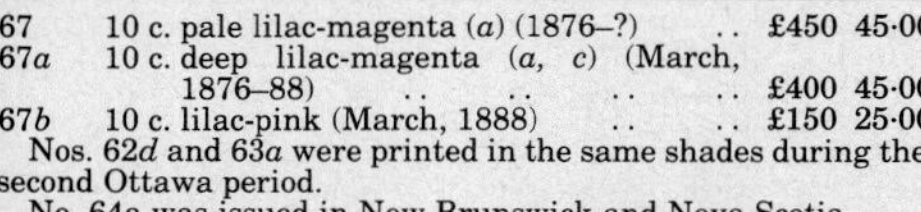

| No. | Type | Description | Unused | Used |
|---|---|---|---|---|
| 67 | | 10 c. pale lilac-magenta (*a*) (1876–?) | £450 | 45·00 |
| 67*a* | | 10 c. deep lilac-magenta (*a, c*) (March, 1876–88) | £400 | 45·00 |
| 67*b* | | 10 c. lilac-pink (March, 1888) | £150 | 25·00 |

Nos. 62*d* and 63*a* were printed in the same shades during the second Ottawa period.

No. 64a was issued in New Brunswick and Nova Scotia.

One used copy of the 10 c. perf 12½ has been reported.

22

**1873–79.** *As T* 13, 14, 21 *and* 22. *Montreal printings. Medium to stout wove paper. P* 11½ × 12 *or* 11¾ × 12.

| No. | Type | Description | Unused | Used |
|---|---|---|---|---|
| 68 | 13 | ½ c. black | 40·00 | 35·00 |
| 69 | 21 | 1 c. bright orange | £160 | 16·00 |
| 69a | | 1 c. orange-yellow (1873–79) | £140 | 8·00 |
| 69*b* | | 1 c. pale dull yellow (1877–79) | £130 | 13·00 |
| 69*c* | | 1 c. lemon-yellow (1879) | | |
| 70 | | 2 c. deep green (1873–78) | £170 | 11·00 |
| 71 | | 3 c. dull red (1875–79) | £190 | 9·00 |
| 71*a* | | 3 c. orange-red (1873–79) | £190 | 9·00 |
| 72 | 22 | 5 c. olive-green (1 Oct, 1875) | £700 | 65·00 |
| | | a. Perf 12 | £3500 | £800 |
| 72*b* | 21 | 5 c. olive-grey (1876–79) | £300 | 20·00 |
| 73 | | 6 c. yellowish brown (1873–79) | £300 | 20·00 |
| 74 | | 10 c. very pale lilac-magenta (1874) | £800 | £250 |
| 74*a* | | 10 c. deep lilac-magenta (1876–79) | £500 | £170 |
| 75 | 14 | 15 c. dull grey-purple (1874) | £600 | £225 |
| 75*a* | | 15 c. lilac-grey (Mar, 1877) | £800 | £225 |
| | | ab. Script Wmk* | £9000 | £2250 |
| | | ac. "BOTHWELL" watermark† | † | — |
| 75*b* | | 15 c. slate | £800 | £450 |

*The watermark on No. 75ab is part of the words "Alexr. Pirie & Sons" in script lettering, a very small quantity of paper thus watermarked having been used for printing this stamp.

†For description of this watermark see below No. 61c.

Several used examples of the 12½ c. have been reported in these perforations.

**1879–88.** *Montreal printings. Medium to stout wove paper. P* 12.

| No. | Type | Description | Unused | Used |
|---|---|---|---|---|
| 76 | 14 | 15 c. clear deep violet | £2250 | £500 |
| 76*a* | | 15 c. deep slate (1881) | £130 | 25·00 |
| 76*b* | | 15 c. slaty blue (1887) | £130 | 25·00 |
| 76*c* | | 15 c. slate-purple (*shades*) (July, 1888–92) | 60·00 | 16·00 |

The last printing of No. 76c took place at Ottawa.

27

**1882–97.** *Montreal* (*to March* 1889) *and Ottawa printings. Thinnish paper of poor quality. P* 12.

| No. | Type | Description | Unused | Used |
|---|---|---|---|---|
| 77 | 27 | ½ c. black (July, 1882–97) | 5·00 | 3·75 |
| 77*a* | | ½ c. grey-black | 5·00 | 3·75 |
| | | ab. Imperf (pair) (1891–93?) | £400 | |
| | | ac. Imperf between (pair) | £700 | |

**1889–97.** *As T* 14 *and* 21 (*various frames*). *Ottawa printings. Thinnish paper of poor quality, often toned grey or yellowish. P* 12.

| No. | Type | Description | Unused | Used |
|---|---|---|---|---|
| 78 | 21 | 2 c. dull sea-green | 35·00 | 20 |
| 78*a* | | 2 c. blue-green (July, 1889–91) | 28·00 | 30 |
| 79 | | 3 c. bright vermilion (April, 1889–97) | 20·00 | 10 |
| | | a. Imperf (pair) (1891–93?) | £350 | |
| 80 | | 5 c. brownish grey (May, 1889) | 42·00 | 30 |
| | | a. Imperf (pair) (1891–93) | £375 | |
| 81 | | 6 c. deep chestnut (Oct, 1890) | 28·00 | 7·00 |
| | | a. "5 c." re-entry* | £2000 | £1300 |
| 81*b* | | 6 c. pale chestnut | 28·00 | 7·00 |
| | | ba. Imperf (pair) (1891–93?) | £450 | |
| 82 | | 10 c. salmon-pink | £225 | £110 |
| 82*a* | | 10 c. carmine-pink (April, 1890) | £140 | 14·00 |
| | | ab. Imperf (pair) (1891–93?) | £325 | |
| 82*b* | | 10 c. brownish red (1894?) | £120 | 14·00 |
| | | ba. Imperf (pair) | £300 | |
| 83 | 14 | 15 c. slate-violet (*shades*) (May, 1890) | 60·00 | 16·00 |
| | | a. Imperf (brown-purple) (pair) | £800 | |

*No. 81a shows traces of the 5 c. value 2½ mm lower than the 6 c. design.

The 1 c. showed no change in the Ottawa printings, so is not included. The 2 c. reverted to its previous grass-green shade in 1891. The 15 c. stamps are generally found with yellowish streaky gum.

28

29

(Recess B.A.B.N.)

**1893** (17 Feb). *P* 12.

| No. | Type | Description | Unused | Used |
|---|---|---|---|---|
| 115 | 28 | 20 c. vermilion | £160 | 40·00 |
| | | a. Imperf (pair) | £1400 | |
| 116 | | 50 c. blue | £225 | 24·00 |
| | | a. Imperf (Prussian blue) (pair) | £1400 | |

**1893** (1 Aug). *P* 12.

| No. | Type | Description | Unused | Used |
|---|---|---|---|---|
| 117 | 29 | 8 c. pale bluish grey | 65·00 | 3·00 |
| | | a. Imperf (pair) | £450 | |
| 118 | | 8 c. bluish slate | 65·00 | 3·00 |
| 119 | | 8 c. slate-purple | 65·00 | 3·00 |
| 120 | | 8 c. blackish purple | 65·00 | 3·00 |

**PRINTERS.** The following stamps to No. 287 were recess-printed by the American Bank Note Co, Ottawa, which in 1923 became the Canadian Bank Note Co.

30

(Des L. Pereira and F. Brownell)

**1897** (19 June). *Jubilee issue. P* 12.

| No. | Type | Description | Unused | Used |
|---|---|---|---|---|
| 121 | 30 | ½ c. black | 42·00 | 45·00 |
| 122 | | 1 c. orange | 7·00 | 1·50 |
| 123 | | 1 c. orange-yellow | 7·00 | 1·50 |
| | | a. Bisected (½ c.) on cover | † | £2500 |
| 124 | | 2 c. green | 10·00 | 3·75 |
| 125 | | 2 c. deep green | 11·00 | 3·75 |
| 126 | | 3 c. carmine | 5·50 | 80 |
| 127 | | 5 c. slate-blue | 26·00 | 12·00 |
| 128 | | 5 c. deep blue | 24·00 | 9·00 |
| 129 | | 6 c. brown | 75·00 | 75·00 |
| 130 | | 8 c. slate-violet | 32·00 | 25·00 |
| 131 | | 10 c. purple | 50·00 | 35·00 |
| 132 | | 15 c. slate | 80·00 | 80·00 |
| 133 | | 20 c. vermilion | 80·00 | 80·00 |
| 134 | | 50 c. pale ultramarine | £120 | 95·00 |
| 135 | | 50 c. bright ultramarine | £120 | 95·00 |
| 136 | | $1 lake | £400 | £400 |
| 137 | | $2 deep violet | £700 | £275 |
| 138 | | $3 bistre | £800 | £600 |
| 139 | | $4 violet | £800 | £600 |
| 140 | | $5 olive-green | £800 | £600 |
| 121/40 | | *Set of* 16 | £3500 | £2500 |
| 133/40 Handstamped "Specimen" | | *Set of* 7 | £1800 | |

No 123a was used on issues of the *Railway News* of 5, 6 and 8 November 1897 and must be on a large part of the original newspaper with New Glasgow postmark.

31

32

(From photograph by W. & D. Downey, London)

**1897–98.** *P* 12.

| No. | Type | Description | Unused | Used |
|---|---|---|---|---|
| 141 | 31 | ½ c. grey-black (9.11.97) | 4·00 | 3·00 |
| 142 | | ½ c. black | 6·00 | 4·00 |
| | | a. Imperf (pair) | £375 | |
| 143 | | 1 c. blue-green (12.97) | 16·00 | 30 |
| | | a. Imperf (pair) | £375 | |
| 144 | | 2 c. violet (12.97) | 15·00 | 60 |
| | | a. Imperf (pair) | £375 | |
| 145 | | 3 c. carmine (1.98) | 20·00 | 35 |
| | | a. Imperf (pair) | £700 | |
| 146 | | 5 c. deep blue/*bluish* (12.97) | 55·00 | 70 |
| | | a. Imperf (pair) | £375 | |
| 147 | | 6 c. brown (12.97) | 55·00 | 16·00 |
| | | a. Imperf (pair) | £700 | |
| 148 | | 8 c. orange (12.97) | 70·00 | 5·00 |
| | | a. Imperf (pair) | £375 | |
| 149 | | 10 c. brownish purple (1.98) | £120 | 55·00 |
| | | a. Imperf (pair) | £375 | |
| 141/9 | | *Set of* 8 | £325 | 75·00 |

**IMPERF SIDES.** Stamps with one side, or two adjacent sides imperf come from booklet panes.

Two types of the 2 c.

Die Ia. Frame consists of four fine lines.

Die Ib. Frame has one thick line between two fine lines.

The die was retouched in 1900 for Plates 11 and 12 producing weak vertical frame lines and then retouched again in 1902 for Plates 15 to 20 resulting in much thicker frame lines. No. 155*b* covers both states of the retouching.

**1898–1902.** *P* 12.

| No. | Type | Description | Unused | Used |
|---|---|---|---|---|
| 150 | 32 | ½ c. black (9.98) | 1·50 | 85 |
| | | a. Imperf (pair) | £375 | |
| 151 | | 1 c. blue-green (6.98) | 20·00 | 15 |
| 152 | | 1 c. deep green/*toned paper* | 20·00 | 15 |
| | | a. Imperf (pair) | £700 | |
| 153 | | 2 c. dull purple (Die Ia) (9.98) | 22·00 | 30 |
| | | a. Thick paper (6.99) | 90·00 | 10·00 |
| 154 | | 2 c. violet (Die Ia) | 22·00 | 10 |
| 154*a* | | 2 c. reddish purple (Die Ia) | 55·00 | 1·50 |
| 155 | | 2 c. rose-carmine (Die Ia) (20.8.99) | 26·00 | 10 |
| | | a. Imperf (pair) | £300 | |
| 155*b* | | 2 c. rose-carmine (Die Ib) (1900) | 30·00 | 30 |
| | | c. Booklet pane of 6 (11.6.00) | £750 | |
| 156 | | 3 c. rose-carmine (6.98) | 30·00 | 20 |
| 157 | | 5 c. slate-blue/*bluish* | 75·00 | 70 |
| | | a. Imperf (pair) | £750 | |
| 158 | | 5 c. Prussian blue/*bluish* | 75·00 | 70 |
| 159 | | 6 c. brown (9.98) | 70·00 | 32·00 |
| | | a. Imperf (pair) | £650 | |
| 160 | | 7 c. greenish yellow (23.12.02) | 48·00 | 10·00 |
| 161 | | 8 c. orange-yellow (10.98) | 80·00 | 19·00 |
| 162 | | 8 c. brownish orange | 80·00 | 19·00 |
| | | a. Imperf (pair) | £650 | |
| 163 | | 10 c. pale brownish purple (11.98) | £160 | 11·00 |
| 164 | 32 | 10 c. deep brownish purple | £160 | 11·00 |
| | | a. Imperf (pair) | £650 | |
| 165 | | 20 c. olive-green (29.12.00) | £325 | 45·00 |
| 150/65 | | *Set of* 11 | £750 | £110 |

The 7 c. and 20 c. also exist imperf but unlike the values listed in this condition, they have no gum. (*Price*, 7 c. £275, 20 c. £1400 *pair, un.*)

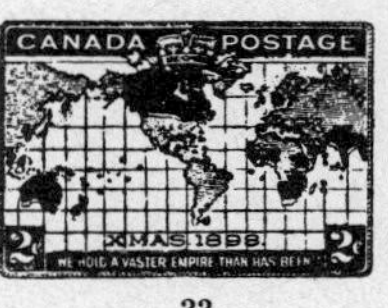


33

(Des Postmaster-General Mulock; frame, recess; colours, typo)

**1898** (7 Dec). *Imperial Penny Postage. Design in black. British possessions in red. Oceans in colours given. P* 12.

| No. | Type | Description | Unused | Used |
|---|---|---|---|---|
| 166 | 33 | 2 c. lavender | 27·00 | 3·75 |
| 167 | | 2 c. greenish blue | 20·00 | 3·50 |
| 168 | | 2 c. blue | 20·00 | 3·00 |
| | | a. Imperf (pair) | £350 | |

**1899** (5 Jan). *Provisionals used at Port Hood. No.* 156 *divided vertically and handstamped.*

| No. | Type | Description | Unused | Used |
|---|---|---|---|---|
| 169 | 32 | "1" in blue, on ⅓ of 3 c. | — | £3500 |
| 170 | | "2" in violet, on ⅔ of 3 c. | — | £3000 |

(34)

**35** King Edward VII

**1899.** *Surch with T* 34, *by Public Printing Office.*

| No. | Type | Description | Unused | Used |
|---|---|---|---|---|
| 171 | 31 | 2 c. on 3 c. carmine (8 Aug) | 11·00 | 4·50 |
| | | a. Surch inverted | £250 | |
| 172 | 32 | 2 c. on 3 c. rose-carmine (28 July) | 13·00 | 2·50 |
| | | a. Surch inverted | £250 | |

(Des King George V when Prince of Wales and J. A. Tilleard)

**1903** (1 July)–12. *P* 12.

| No. | Type | Description | Unused | Used |
|---|---|---|---|---|
| 173 | 35 | 1 c. pale green | 17·00 | 15 |
| 174 | | 1 c. deep green | 14·00 | 15 |
| 175 | | 1 c. green | 14·00 | 15 |
| 176 | | 2 c. rose-carmine | 12·00 | 10 |
| | | a. Booklet pane of 6 | £750 | |
| 177 | | 2 c. pale rose-carmine | 13·00 | 10 |
| | | a. Imperf (pair) (18.7.09) | 26·00 | 26·00 |
| 178 | | 5 c. blue/*bluish* | 55·00 | 90 |
| 179 | | 5 c. indigo/*bluish* | 55·00 | 1·25 |
| 180 | | 7 c. yellow-olive | 55·00 | 1·00 |
| 181 | | 7 c. greenish bistre | 65·00 | 1·50 |
| 181*a* | | 7 c. straw (1.12) | 90·00 | 35·00 |
| 182 | | 10 c. brown-lilac | 85·00 | 4·50 |
| 183 | | 10 c. pale dull purple | 85·00 | 4·50 |
| 184 | | 10 c. dull purple | 85·00 | 4·50 |
| 185 | | 20 c. pale olive-green (27.9.04) | £200 | 16·00 |
| 186 | | 20 c. deep olive-green (H/S S. £70) | £225 | 16·00 |
| 187 | | 50 c. deep violet (19.11.08) | £325 | 60·00 |
| 173/87 | | *Set of* 7 | £650 | 75·00 |

The 1 c., 5 c., 7 c. and 10 c. exist imperforate but are believed to be proofs.

**IMPERFORATE AND PART-PERFORATED SHEETS.** Prior to 1946 many Canadian issues exist imperforate, or with other perforation varieties, in the colours of the issued stamps and, usually, with gum. In the years before 1927 such examples are believed to come from imprimatur sheets, removed from the Canadian Post Office archives. From 1927 until 1946 it is known that the printers involved in the production of the various issues submitted several imperforate plate proof sheets of each stamp to the Post Office authorities for approval. Some of these sheets or part sheets were retained for record purposes, but the remainder found their way onto the philatelic market.

Part-perforated sheets also occur from 1927–29 issues.

From 1908 until 1946 we now only list and price such varieties of this type which are known to be genuine errors, sold from post offices. Where other imperforate or similar varieties are known they are recorded in footnotes.

It is possible, and in some cases probable, that some imperforate varieties listed before 1908 may have also been removed from the archives as mentioned above, but it is far harder to be explicit over the status of this earlier material.

**36** King George V and Queen Mary when Prince and Princess of Wales

**37** Jacques Cartier and Samuel Champlain

(Des Machado)

**1908** (16 July). *Quebec Tercentenary T* 36/7 *and similar horiz designs. P* 12.

| No. | Type | Description | Unused | Used |
|---|---|---|---|---|
| 188 | | ½ c. sepia | 3·25 | 2·00 |
| 189 | | 1 c. blue-green | 7·00 | 1·25 |
| 190 | | 2 c. carmine | 10·00 | 60 |
| 191 | | 5 c. indigo | 40·00 | 10·00 |
| 192 | | 7 c. olive-green | 45·00 | 30·00 |
| 193 | | 10 c. violet | 55·00 | 40·00 |

194 15 c. brown-orange .. .. .. .. 75·00 50·00
195 20 c. dull brown .. .. .. .. £100 60·00
188/95 .. .. .. .. *Set of* 8 £300 £170

Designs:—2 c. King Edward VII and Queen Alexandra; 5 c. Champlain's House in Quebec; 7 c. Generals Montcalm and Wolfe; 10 c. Quebec in 1700; 15 c. Champlain's departure for the West; 20 c. Cartier's arrival before Quebec.

Some values exist on both *toned* and *white* papers.

Nos. 188/95 exist imperforate.

**WET AND DRY PRINTINGS.** Until the end of December 1922 all Canadian stamps were produced by the "wet" method of recess-printing in which the paper was dampened before printing, dried and then gummed.

In late December 1922 the Canadian Bank Note Co. began to use the "dry" process in which the paper was gummed before printing. Late printings of the 3 c. brown were the first stamps to be produced by this method, but the changeover was not completed until January 1926.

"Dry" printings have a sharper appearance and can often be found with a degree of embossing showing on the reverse. Stamps from "wet" printings shrink during drying and are narrower than "dry" examples. In many cases the difference can be as great as 0.5 mm. On some early booklet panes the difference is in the vertical, rather than the horizontal, measurement.

On Nos. 196/215 all values only exist from "wet" printings except the 3 c., 20 c. and 50 c. which come from both types of printing.

44

**1911–22.** *P* 12.
196 44 1 c. yellow-green (22.12.11) .. .. 5·00 20
a. With fine horiz lines across stamp 32·00 8·50
197 1 c. bluish green .. .. .. 4·50 20
a. Booklet pane of 6 (1.5.13) .. .. 32·00
198 1 c. deep bluish green .. .. .. 5·50 20
199 1 c. deep yellow-green .. .. .. 4·50 20
a. Booklet pane of 6 .. .. .. 32·00
200 2 c. rose-red (22.12.11) .. .. .. 4·00 10
201 2 c. deep rose-red .. .. .. 4·25 10
a. Booklet pane of 6 (1.12) .. .. 32·00
202 2 c. pale rose-red .. .. .. 4·00 10
a. With fine horiz lines across stamp 20·00 6·00
203 2 c. carmine .. .. .. 5·00 10
204 3 c. brown (6.8.18) .. .. .. 6·00 10
205 3 c. deep brown .. .. .. 4·50 10
a. Booklet pane of 4 + 2 labels (2.22) 45·00
205*b* 5 c. deep blue (17.1.12) .. .. .. 55·00 50
206 5 c. indigo .. .. .. 55·00 70
206*a* 5 c. grey-blue .. .. .. 55·00 70
206*b* 7 c. straw (12.1.12) .. .. .. 65·00 12·00
207 7 c. pale sage-green (1914) .. .. £180 30·00
208 7 c. olive-yellow (1915) .. .. .. 20·00 1·50
209 7 c. yellow-ochre (1916) .. .. .. 18·00 1·50
210 10 c. brownish purple (12.1.12) .. .. 75·00 1·10
211 10 c. reddish purple .. .. .. 75·00 1·10
212 20 c. olive-green (23.1.12) .. .. 28·00 85
213 20 c. olive .. .. .. 28·00 85
214 50 c. grey-black (26.1.12) .. .. £100 6·00
215 50 c. sepia .. .. .. 40·00 2·25
196/215 .. .. .. *Set of* 8 £200 6·00

The 20 c. and 50 c. values exist imperforate.

**1912** (Nov)–**1921.** *For use in coil-machines.* (*a*) *P* 12 × *imperf.*
216 44 1 c. yellow-green (1914) .. .. 3·50 6·50
217 1 c. blue-green .. .. .. 11·00 18·00
a. Two large holes at top and bottom (pair) (7.18) .. .. .. 50·00 50·00
218 2 c. deep rose-red (1914) .. .. 22·00 13·00
218*a* 3 c. brown (1921) .. .. .. 3·00 4·00

No. 217a has two large holes about 3½ mm in diameter in the top and bottom margins. They were for experimental use in a vending machine at Toronto in July 1918 and were only in use for two days.

The 1 c. and 2 c. also exist with two small "V" shaped holes about 9.5 mm apart at top which are gripper marks due to modifications made in vending machines in 1917.

(*b*) *Imperf* × *perf* 8
219 44 1 c. yellow-green (9.12) .. .. 7·00 75
220 1 c. blue-green .. .. .. 9·00 75
a. With fine horiz lines across stamp 50·00
221 2 c. carmine (9.12) .. .. .. 11·00 30
222 2 c. rose-red .. .. .. 12·00 40
223 2 c. scarlet .. .. .. 27·00 3·50
224 3 c. brown (8.18) .. .. .. 3·50 20

(*c*) *P* 8 × *imperf*
224*a* 44 1 c. blue-green (15.2.13) .. .. 55·00 45·00
224*b* 2 c. carmine (15.2.13) .. .. 55·00 45·00

The stamps imperf × perf 8 were sold in coils over the counter; those perf 8 × imperf were on sale in automatic machines. Varieties showing perf 12 on 2 or 3 adjacent sides and 1 or 2 sides imperf are from booklets, or the margins of sheets.

(45)

46

47

**1915** (12 Feb). *Optd with T* 45.
225 44 5 c. blue .. .. .. £100 £160
226 20 c. olive-green .. .. .. 50·00 75·00
227 50 c. sepia (R.) .. .. .. 70·00 95·00
225/7 .. .. .. *Set of* 3 £190 £300

These stamps were intended for tax purposes, but owing to ambiguity in an official circular dated 16 April 1915, it was for a time believed that their use for postal purposes was authorised. The position was clarified by a further circular on 20 May 1916 which made clear that Nos. 225/7 were for fiscal use only.

**1915.** *P* 12.
228 46 1 c. green (15.4.15) .. .. .. 2·75 10
229 2 c. carmine-red (16.4.15) .. .. 3·00 20
230 2 c. rose-carmine .. .. .. 4·00 2·00

Die I

Die II

In Die I there is a long horizontal coloured line under the foot of the "T", and a solid bar of colour runs upwards from the "1" to the "T".

In Die II this solid bar of colour is absent, and there is a short horizontal line under the left side of the "T", with two short vertical dashes and a number of dots under the right-hand side.

**1916** (1 Jan). *P* 12.
231 47 2 c. + 1 c. rose-red (Die I) .. .. 9·50 55
232 2 c. + 1 c. bright carmine (Die I) .. 9·50 55
233 2 c. + 1 c. scarlet (Die I) .. .. 8·00 55

**1916** (Feb). *Imperf* × *perf* 8 (*coils*).
234 47 2 c. + 1 c. rose-red (Die I) .. .. 45·00 3·75

**1916** (July). *P* 12 × 8.
235 47 2 c. + 1 c. carmine-red (Die I) .. .. 12·00 30·00
236 2 c. + 1 c. bright rose-red (Die I) .. 12·00 30·00

**1916** (Aug). *P* 12.
237 47 2 c. + 1 c. carmine-red (Die II) .. .. 75·00 15·00

**1916** (Aug). *Colour changed.* (*a*) *P* 12.
238 47 2 c. + 1 c. brown (Die I) .. .. £110 13·00
239 2 c. + 1 c. yellow-brown (Die II) .. 2·25 10
a. Imperf (pair) .. .. .. £750
240 2 c. + 1 c. deep brown (Die II) .. .. 8·50 10

(*b*) *Imperf* × *perf* 8
241 47 2 c. + 1 c. brown (Die I) .. .. 60·00 3·25
a. Pair, 241 and 243 .. .. £350
243 2 c. + 1 c. deep brown (Die II) .. .. 26·00 80

No. 239a, which is a genuine error, should not be confused with ungummed proofs of the Die I stamp, No. 238.

This value also exists p 12 × imperf or imperf × p 12, but was not issued with these perforations.

48 Quebec Conference, 1864, from painting "The Fathers of Confederation", by Robert Harris

**1917** (15 Sept). *50th Anniv of Confederation. P* 12.
244 48 3 c. bistre-brown .. .. .. 16·00 55
245 3 c. deep brown .. .. .. 18·00 75

No. 244 exists imperforate.

I

II

Die I. Space between top of "N" and oval frame line and space between "CENT" and lower frame line.

Die II. "ONE CENT" appears larger so that "N" touches oval and "CENT" almost touches frame line. There are other differences but this is the most obvious one.

I

II

Die I. The lowest of the three horizontal lines of shading below the medals does not touch the three heavy diagonal lines; three complete white spaces over both "E's" of "THREE"; long centre bar to figures "3". Vertical spandrel lines fine.

Die II. The lowest horizontal line of shading touches the first of the three diagonal lines; two and a half spaces over first "E" and spaces over second "E" partly filled by stem of maple leaf; short centre bar to figures "3". Vertical spandrel lines thick. There are numerous other minor differences.

**WET AND DRY PRINTINGS.** See notes above No. 196.

On Nos. 246/63 all listed items occur from both "wet" and "dry" printings except Nos. 246aa/ab, 248aa, 256, 259, 260 and 262 which come "wet" only, and Nos. 246a, 248/a, 252/4*a*, 256b and 263 which are "dry" only.

**1922–31.** *As T* 44. (*a*) *P* 12.
246 44 1 c. chrome-yellow (Die I) (7.6.22) .. 2·50 15
aa. Booklet pane of 4 + 2 labels (7.22) 45·00
ab. Booklet pane of 6 (12.22) .. .. 22·00
a. Die II (1925) .. .. .. 4·75 10
247 2 c. deep green (6.6.22) .. .. 2·25 10
aa. Booklet pane of 4 + 2 labels (7.22) 27·00
ab. Booklet pane of 6 (12.22) .. .. £250
b. Thin paper (9.24) .. .. .. 2·75 3·50
248 3 c. carmine (Die I) (18.12.23) .. .. 2·25 10
aa. Booklet pane of 4 + 2 labels (12.23) 26·00
a. Die II (11.24) .. .. .. 14·00 10
249 4 c. olive-yellow (7.7.22) .. .. 7·00 1·25
*a. Yellow-ochre* .. .. .. 7·00 1·25
250 5 c. violet (2.2.22) .. .. .. 5·00 75
a. Thin paper (9.24) .. .. .. 5·00 8·00
*b. Reddish violet* (1925) .. .. 6·00 50
251 7 c. red-brown (12.12.24) .. .. 10·00 6·00
a. Thin paper .. .. .. £100 30·00
252 8 c. blue (1.9.25) .. .. .. 17·00 7·00
253 10 c. blue (20.2.22) .. .. .. 18·00 70
254 10 c. bistre-brown (1.8.25) .. .. 17·00 70
*a. Yellow-brown* .. .. .. 18·00 90
255 $1 brown-orange (22.7.23) .. .. 50·00 3·75
246/55 .. .. .. *Set of* 10 £110 18·00

The $1 differs from T 44 in that the value tablets are oval.

Nos. 249/55 exist imperforate.

(*b*) *Imperf* × *perf* 8
256 44 1 c. chrome-yellow (Die I) (1922) .. 3·75 3·00
a. Imperf horiz (vert pair) (1924) .. £300
b. Die II (1925) .. .. .. 4·50 5·00
c. Do. Imperf horiz (vert pair) (1927) 9·00
257 2 c. deep green (26.7.22) .. .. 6·50 50
b. Imperf horiz (vert pair) (1927) .. 10·00
258 3 c. carmine (Die I) (9.4.24) .. .. 38·00 4·50
a. Imperf horiz (vert pair) (1924) .. £350
b. Die II (1925) .. .. .. 75·00 18·00
256/8 .. .. .. *Set of* 3 42·00 7·25

Nos. 256a, 256c, 257b and 258a come from coil printings sold in sheet form. Those issued in 1924 were from "wet" printings and those in 1927 from "dry". A "wet" printing of No. 257b, issued in 1924, also exists (*Price* £300 *mint*), but cannot be identified from that issued in 1927 except by the differences between "wet" and "dry" stamps.

(*c*) *Imperf* (*pairs*)
259 44 1 c. chrome-yellow (Die I) (6.10.24) .. 65·00 65·00
260 2 c. deep green (6.10.24) .. .. 65·00 65·00
261 3 c. carmine (Die I) (31.12.23)† .. .. 35·00 40·00

(*d*) *P* 12 × *imperf*
262 44 2 c. deep green (9.24) .. .. .. 65·00 80·00

(*e*) *P* 12 × 8
263 44 3 c. carmine (Die II) (24.6.31) .. .. 2·00 1·75

Nos. 259 to 261 were on sale only at the Philatelic Branch P.O. Dept, Ottawa.

†Earliest known postmark.

**2 CENTS**

(49)

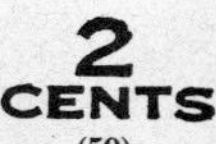


(50)

**1926.** *No.* 248 *surch.*

(*a*) *With T* 49, *by the Govt Printing Bureau*
264 44 2 c. on 3 c. carmine (12.10.26) .. .. 29·00 48·00
a. Pair, one without surch .. .. £275
b. On Die II .. .. .. £350

(*b*) *With T* 50, *by the Canadian Bank Note Co*
265 44 2 c. on 3 c. carmine (4.11.26) .. .. 10·00 15·00
a. Surch double (partly treble) .. £200

51 Sir J. A. Macdonald

52 "The Fathers of Confederation"

53 Parliament Buildings, Ottawa

54 Sir W. Laurier

55 Canada, Map 1867–1927

**1927** (29 June). *60th Anniv of Confederation. P* 12. *I. Commemorative Issue. Inscr* "1867–1927 CANADA CONFEDERATION".
266 51 1 c. orange .. .. .. .. 1·75 75
267 52 2 c. green .. .. .. .. 1·50 10
268 53 3 c. carmine .. .. .. .. 3·75 2·50
269 54 5 c. violet .. .. .. .. 2·75 2·25
270 55 12 c. blue .. .. .. .. 12·00 1·75
266/70 .. .. .. *Set of* 5 19·00 6·50

Nos. 266/70 exist imperforate, imperf × perf or perf × imperf.

**56** Darcy McGee

**57** Sir W. Laurier and Sir J. A. Macdonald

**58** R. Baldwin and L. H. Lafontaine

II. *Historical Issue*

| | | | | |
|---|---|---|---|---|
| 271 | **56** | 5 c. violet | 2·75 | 90 |
| 272 | **57** | 12 c. green | 9·50 | 3·75 |
| 273 | **58** | 20 c. carmine | 11·00 | 6·00 |
| 271/3 | | *Set of* 3 | 21·00 | 9·50 |

Nos. 271/3 exist imperforate, imperf × perf or perf × imperf.

**59**

(Des H. Schwartz)

**1928** (21 Sept). *Air. P* 12.

| | | | | |
|---|---|---|---|---|
| 274 | **59** | 5 c. olive-brown | 2·50 | 1·00 |

No. 274 exists imperforate, imperf × perf or perf × imperf.

**60** King George V

**61** Mt Hurd and Indian Totem Poles

**62** Quebec Bridge

**63** Harvesting with Horses

**64** *Bluenose* (fishing schooner)

**65** Parliament Buildings, Ottawa

**1928–29.** (*a*) *P* 12.

| | | | | |
|---|---|---|---|---|
| 275 | **60** | 1 c. orange (25.10.28) | 1·60 | 30 |
| | | a. Booklet pane of 6 | 17·00 | |
| 276 | | 2 c. green (16.10.28) | 65 | 10 |
| | | a. Booklet pane of 6 | 17·00 | |
| 277 | | 3 c. lake (12.12.28) | 13·00 | 8·00 |
| 278 | | 4 c. olive-bistre (16.8.29) | 13·00 | 3·50 |
| 279 | | 5 c. violet (12.12.28) | 3·75 | 1·50 |
| | | a. Booklet pane of 6 (6.1.29) | 80·00 | |
| 280 | | 8 c. blue (21.12.28) | 7·50 | 1·50 |
| 281 | **61** | 10 c. green (5.11.28) | 6·00 | 40 |
| 282 | **62** | 12 c. grey-black (6.1.29) | 13·00 | 3·50 |
| 283 | **63** | 20 c. lake (6.1.29) | 24·00 | 3·75 |
| 284 | **64** | 50 c. blue (6.1.29) | 90·00 | 25·00 |
| 285 | **65** | $1 olive-green (6.1.29) | £100 | 32·00 |
| | | *a. Brown-olive* | £250 | £110 |
| 275/85 | | *Set of* 11 | £225 | 70·00 |

(*b*) *Imperf × perf* 8 (5.11.28)

| | | | | |
|---|---|---|---|---|
| 286 | **60** | 1 c. orange | 7·00 | 14·00 |
| 287 | | 2 c. green | 7·00 | 1·25 |

Slight differences in the size of many Canadian stamps, due to paper shrinkage, are to be found.

Nos. 275/85 exist imperforate, imperf × perf or perf × imperf. *Tête-bêche* horizontal pairs of the 1 c., 2 c. and 5 c. are also known from uncut booklet sheets.

**PRINTERS.** The following stamps to No. 334 were recess-printed by the British American Bank Note Co, Ottawa.

**66**

**67** Parliamentary Library, Ottawa

**68** The Old Citadel, Quebec

**69** Harvesting with Tractor

**70** Acadian Memorial Church and Statue of "Evangeline", Grand Pre, Nova Scotia

**71** Mt Edith Cavell, Canadian Rockies

Die I 1 c. Die II

Die I 2 c. Die II

1 c. Die I. Three thick coloured lines and one thin between "P" and ornament, at right. Curved line in ball-ornament short.

Die II. Four thick lines. Curved line longer.

2 c. Die I. Three thick coloured lines between "P" and ornament, at left. Short line in ball.

Die II. Four thick lines. Curved line longer.

**1930–31.** (*a*) *P* 11.

| | | | | |
|---|---|---|---|---|
| 288 | **66** | 1 c. orange (I) (17.7.30) | 35 | 35 |
| 289 | | 2 c. green (I) (6.7.30) | 60 | 10 |
| | | a. Booklet pane of 6 (17.6.30) | 32·00 | |
| 290 | | 4 c. yellow-bistre (5.11.30) | 5·50 | 1·50 |
| 291 | | 5 c. violet (18.6.30) | 2·50 | 1·25 |
| 292 | | 8 c. blue (13.8.30) | 5·50 | 7·00 |
| 293 | **67** | 10 c. olive-green (15.9.30) | 7·00 | 30 |
| | | a. Imperf (pair) | £900 | |
| 294 | **68** | 12 c. grey-black (4.12.30) | 7·50 | 1·75 |
| 295 | **69** | 20 c. red (4.12.30) | 14·00 | 20 |
| 296 | **70** | 50 c. blue (4.12.30) | 80·00 | 9·50 |
| 297 | **71** | $1 olive-green (4.12.30) | 90·00 | 16·00 |
| 288/97 | | *Set of* 10 | £180 | 35·00 |

Nos. 294/7 exist imperforate.

(*b*) *Imperf × perf* 8½

| | | | | |
|---|---|---|---|---|
| 298 | **66** | 1 c. orange (I) | 8·00 | 7·00 |
| 299 | | 2 c. green (I) | 3·00 | 2·00 |

*Colours changed and new value.* (*a*) *P* 11

| | | | | |
|---|---|---|---|---|
| 300 | **66** | 1 c. green (I) (6.12.30) | 80 | 10 |
| | | a. Imperf (pair) | £600 | |
| | | b. Booklet pane of 6 (21.7.31) | 45·00 | |
| | | c. Booklet pane of 4 + 2 labels (13.11.31) | £110 | |
| | | d. Die II | 75 | 10 |
| 301 | | 2 c. scarlet (I) (17.11.30) | 70 | 30 |
| | | a. Booklet pane of 6 (17.11.30) | 21·00 | |
| | | b. Die II | 90 | 10 |
| 302 | | 2 c. deep brown (I) (4.7.31) | 1·00 | 2·50 |
| | | a. Booklet pane of 6 (23.7.31) | 35·00 | |
| | | b. Die II | 70 | 10 |
| | | ba. Booklet pane of 4 + 2 labels (13.11.31) | £120 | |
| 303 | | 3 c. scarlet (13.7.31) | 90 | 10 |
| | | a. Booklet pane of 4 + 2 labels | 30·00 | |
| 304 | | 5 c. deep slate-blue (13.11.30) | 5·00 | 10 |
| | | *a. Dull blue* | 11·00 | 10 |
| 305 | | 8 c. red-orange (5.11.30) | 5·00 | 1·50 |
| 300/5 | | *Set of* 6 | 12·00 | 1·50 |

(*b*) *Imperf × perf* 8½

| | | | | |
|---|---|---|---|---|
| 306 | **66** | 1 c. green (I) | 3·75 | 3·75 |
| 307 | | 2 c. scarlet (I) | 4·00 | 1·60 |
| 308 | | 2 c. deep brown (I) (4.7.31) | 7·00 | 55 |
| 309 | | 3 c. scarlet (13.7.31) | 12·00 | 30 |
| 306/9 | | *Set of* 4 | 24·00 | 5·50 |

Some low values in the above and subsequent issues have been printed by both Rotary and "Flat plate" processes. The former can be distinguished by the gum, which has a striped appearance.

For 13 c. bright violet, T **68**, see No. 325.

**72** Mercury and Western Hemisphere

**73** Sir Georges Etienne Cartier

(Des H. Schwartz)

**1930** (4 Dec). *Air. P* 11.

| | | | | |
|---|---|---|---|---|
| 310 | **72** | 5 c. deep brown | 12·00 | 9·00 |

**1931** (30 Sept). *P* 11.

| | | | | |
|---|---|---|---|---|
| 312 | **73** | 10 c. olive-green | 2·50 | 10 |

No. 312 exists imperforate.

(74)

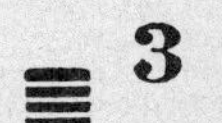


(75)

**1932** (22 Feb). *Air. No.* 274 *surch with T* 74.

| | | | | |
|---|---|---|---|---|
| 313 | **59** | 6 c. on 5 c. olive-brown | 1·50 | 1·25 |

Examples of this stamp with surcharge inverted, surcharge double, surcharge triple or surcharge omitted in pair with normal are not now believed to have been regularly issued. Such "errors" have also been forged and collectors are warned against forged examples, some of which bear unauthorized markings which purport to be the guarantee of Stanley Gibbons Ltd.

**1932** (21 June). *Nos.* 301/b *surch with T* 75.

| | | | | |
|---|---|---|---|---|
| 314 | **66** | 3 c. on 2 c. scarlet (I) | 1·50 | 1·40 |
| 314*a* | | 3 c. on 2 c. scarlet (II) | 75 | 10 |

**76** King George V

**77** Duke of Windsor when Prince of Wales

**78** Allegory of British Empire

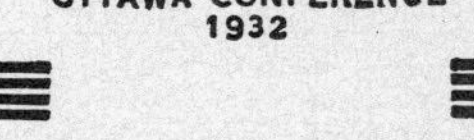


(79)

**1932** (12 July). *Ottawa Conference. P* 11. (*a*) *Postage stamps.*

| | | | | |
|---|---|---|---|---|
| 315 | **76** | 3 c. scarlet | 70 | 50 |
| 316 | **77** | 5 c. blue | 6·00 | 2·00 |
| 317 | **78** | 13 c. green | 7·00 | 4·50 |

(*b*) *Air. No.* 310 *surch with T* **79**

| | | | | |
|---|---|---|---|---|
| 318 | **72** | 6 c. on 5 c. deep brown (B.) | 10·00 | 8·50 |
| 315/18 | | *Set of* 4 | 21·00 | 14·00 |

**80** King George V

"3" level Die I

"3" raised Die II

**1932** (1 Dec)–**33**. (*a*) *P* 11.

| | | | | |
|---|---|---|---|---|
| 319 | **80** | 1 c. green | 60 | 10 |
| | | a. Booklet pane of 6 (28.12.33) | 15·00 | |
| | | b. Booklet pane of 4 + 2 labels (19.9.33) | 75·00 | |
| 320 | | 2 c. sepia | 70 | 10 |
| | | a. Booklet pane of 6 (7.9.33) | 15·00 | |
| | | b. Booklet pane of 4 + 2 labels (19.9.33) | 75·00 | |
| 321 | | 3 c. scarlet (Die I) | 1·00 | 10 |
| | | a. Booklet pane of 4 + 2 labels (22.8.33) | 35·00 | |
| | | b. Die II (29.11.32) | 85 | 10 |
| | | ba. Booklet pane of 4 + 2 labels (19.9.33) | 30·00 | |
| 322 | | 4 c. yellow-brown | 35·00 | 5·50 |
| 323 | | 5 c. blue | 9·00 | 10 |
| | | a. Imperf vert (horiz pair) | £700 | |
| 324 | | 8 c. red-orange | 18·00 | 1·50 |
| 325 | **68** | 13 c. bright violet | 32·00 | 1·00 |
| 319/25 | | *Set of* 7 | 85·00 | 7·50 |

Nos. 319/25 exist imperforate.

(*b*) *Imperf × perf* 8½ (1933)

| | | | | |
|---|---|---|---|---|
| 326 | **80** | 1 c. green | 12·00 | 1·50 |
| 327 | | 2 c. sepia | 14·00 | 45 |
| 328 | | 3 c. scarlet (Die II) | 8·50 | 25 |
| 326/8 | | *Set of* 3 | 30·00 | 2·00 |

**81** Parliament Buildings, Ottawa

**1933** (18 May). *U.P.U. Congress Preliminary Meeting. P* 11.

| | | | | |
|---|---|---|---|---|
| 329 | **81** | 5 c. blue | 3·75 | 1·50 |

No. 329 exists imperforate.

### *MINIMUM PRICE*

The minimum price quote is 10p which represents a handling charge rather than a basis for valuing common stamps. For further notes about prices see introductory pages.

WORLD'S
GRAIN EXHIBITION &
CONFERENCE

REGINA 1933

(82)

**1933** (24 July). *World's Grain Exhibition and Conference, Regina. Optd with T* **82**. *P* 11.

| | | | | |
|---|---|---|---|---|
| 330 | **69** | 20 c. red (B.) | 20·00 | 4·75 |

No. 330 exists imperforate.

83 S.S. *Royal William* (after S. Skillett)

1534 CANADA 1934 JACQUES CARTIER 3 CENTS 3

84 Jacques Cartier approaching Land

**1933** (17 Aug). *Centenary of First Trans-Atlantic Steamboat Crossing. P* 11.

| | | | | |
|---|---|---|---|---|
| 331 | **83** | 5 c. blue | 6·00 | 1·25 |

No. 331 exists imperforate.

**1934** (1 July). *Fourth Centenary of Discovery of Canada. P* 11.

| | | | | |
|---|---|---|---|---|
| 332 | **84** | 3 c. blue | 2·00 | 70 |

No. 332 exists imperforate.

85 U.E.L. Statue, Hamilton

86 Seal of New Brunswick

**1934** (1 July). *150th Anniv of Arrival of United Empire Loyalists. P* 11.

| | | | | |
|---|---|---|---|---|
| 333 | **85** | 10 c. olive-green | 9·50 | 3·00 |

No. 333 exists imperforate.

**1934** (16 Aug). *150th Anniv of Province of New Brunswick. P* 11.

| | | | | |
|---|---|---|---|---|
| 334 | **86** | 2 c. red-brown | 75 | 1·00 |

No. 334 exists imperforate.

**PRINTERS.** The following stamps were recess-printed (except where otherwise stated) by the Canadian Bank Note Co, Ottawa, until No. 616.

87 Queen Elizabeth II when Princess

89 King George V and Queen Mary

**1935** (4 May). *Silver Jubilee. T* **87, 89** *and similar designs. P* 12.

| | | | | |
|---|---|---|---|---|
| 335 | | 1 c. green | 55 | 40 |
| 336 | | 2 c. brown | 60 | 30 |
| 337 | | 3 c. carmine-red | 1·75 | 15 |
| 338 | | 5 c. blue | 3·00 | 2·00 |
| 339 | | 10 c. green | 2·50 | 1·50 |
| 340 | | 13 c. blue | 5·00 | 1·50 |
| 335/40 | | *Set of* 6 | 12·00 | 5·25 |

Designs: *Vert (as T* 87*)*—2 c. King George VI when Duke of York; 5 c. King Edward VIII when Prince of Wales. *Horiz (as T* 89*)*—10 c. Windsor Castle; 13 c. Royal Yacht *Britannia*.

Nos. 335/40 exist imperforate.

93 King George V

94 Royal Canadian Mounted Policeman

99 Daedalus

**1935** (1 June–5 Nov). *T* **93/4, 99** *and similar designs. (a) Postage. (i) P* 12.

| | | | | |
|---|---|---|---|---|
| 341 | **93** | 1 c. green | 30 | 10 |
| | | a. Booklet pane of 6 (19.8.35) | 22·00 | |
| | | b. Booklet pane of 4+2 labels (22.7.35) | 55·00 | |
| 342 | | 2 c. brown | 50 | 10 |
| | | a. Booklet pane of 6 (16.11.35) | 26·00 | |
| | | b. Booklet pane of 4+2 labels (22.7.35) | 55·00 | |
| 343 | | 3 c. scarlet | 60 | 10 |
| | | a. Booklet pane of 4 + 2 labels | 28·00 | |
| 344 | | 4 c. yellow | 1·50 | 60 |
| 345 | | 5 c. blue | 1·00 | 10 |
| | | a. Imperf vert (horiz pair) | £200 | |
| 346 | | 8 c. orange | 1·00 | 1·40 |
| 347 | **94** | 10 c. carmine | 3·50 | 15 |
| 348 | – | 13 c. purple | 3·75 | 20 |
| 349 | – | 20 c. olive-green | 10·00 | 35 |
| 350 | – | 50 c. deep violet | 25·00 | 3·00 |
| 351 | – | $1 bright blue | 38·00 | 3·25 |
| 341/51 | | *Set of* 11 | 75·00 | 8·00 |
| | | *(ii) Coil stamps. Imperf × perf* 8 | | |
| 352 | **93** | 1 c. green (5.11.35) | 10·00 | 2·00 |
| 353 | | 2 c. brown (14.10.35) | 6·00 | 1·75 |
| 354 | | 3 c. scarlet (20.7.35) | 5·50 | 40 |
| 352/4 | | *Set of* 3 | 19·00 | 3·75 |
| | | *(b) Air. P* 12 | | |
| 355 | **99** | 6 c. red-brown | 1·60 | 40 |
| | | a. Imperf vert (horiz pair) | £1800 | |

Designs: *Horiz (as T* 94*)*—13 c. Confederation Conference, Charlottetown, 1864; 20 c. Niagara Falls; 50 c. Parliament Buildings, Victoria, British Columbia; $1 Champlain Monument, Quebec.

Nos. 341/51 and 355 exist imperforate.

100 King George VI and Queen Elizabeth

**1937** (10 May). *Coronation. P* 12.

| | | | | |
|---|---|---|---|---|
| 356 | **100** | 3 c. carmine | 70 | 30 |

No. 356 exists imperforate.

101 King George VI

102 Memorial Chamber Parliament Buildings, Ottawa

107 Seaplane over S.S. *Distributor* on River Mackenzie

(T **101**. Photograph by Bertram Park)

**1937–38.** *T* **101/2, 107** *and similar designs. (a) Postage. (i) P* 12.

| | | | | |
|---|---|---|---|---|
| 357 | **101** | 1 c. green (1.4.37) | 80 | 10 |
| | | a. Booklet pane of 6 (18.5.37) | 3·50 | |
| | | b. Booklet pane of 4+2 labels (14.4.37) | 25·00 | |
| 358 | | 2 c. brown (1.4.37) | 1·00 | 10 |
| | | a. Booklet pane of 6 (3.5.38) | 10·00 | |
| | | b. Booklet pane of 4+2 labels (14.4.37) | 32·00 | |
| 359 | | 3 c. scarlet (1.4.37) | 1·25 | 10 |
| | | a. Booklet pane of 4+2 labels (14.4.37) | 4·25 | |
| 360 | | 4 c. yellow (10.5.37) | 3·00 | 85 |
| 361 | | 5 c. blue (10.5.37) | 3·00 | 10 |
| 362 | | 8 c. orange (10.5.37) | 3·00 | 90 |
| 363 | **102** | 10 c. rose-carmine (15.6.38) | 6·00 | 10 |
| | | *a. Red* | 6·00 | 10 |
| 364 | – | 13 c. blue (15.11.38) | 14·00 | 30 |
| 365 | – | 20 c. red-brown (15.6.38) | 22·00 | 20 |
| 366 | – | 50 c. green (15.6.38) | 50·00 | 5·00 |
| 367 | – | $1 violet (15.6.38) | 70·00 | 5·50 |
| | | a. Imperf horiz (vert pair) | £1800 | |
| 357/67 | | *Set of* 11 | £150 | 11·50 |

Nos. 357/67 exist imperforate.

| | | | | |
|---|---|---|---|---|
| | | *(ii) Coil stamps. Imperf × perf* 8 | | |
| 368 | **101** | 1 c. green (15.6.37) | 4·00 | 90 |
| 369 | | 2 c. brown (18.6.37) | 4·00 | 1·75 |
| 370 | | 3 c. scarlet (15.4.37) | 12·00 | 40 |
| 368/70 | | *Set of* 3 | 18·00 | 2·75 |
| | | *(b) Air. P* 12 | | |
| 371 | **107** | 6 c. blue (15.6.38) | 5·50 | 30 |

Designs: *Horiz (as T* 107*)*—13 c. Entrance to Halifax Harbour; 20 c. Fort Garry Gate, Winnipeg; 50 c. Entrance, Vancouver Harbour; $1 Chateau de Ramezay, Montreal.

***NEW INFORMATION***

The editor is always interested to correspond with people who have new information that will improve or correct the Catalogue.

108 Queen Elizabeth II when Princess and Princess Margaret

109 National War Memorial, Ottawa

110 King George VI and Queen Elizabeth

**1939** (15 May). *Royal Visit. P* 12.

| | | | | |
|---|---|---|---|---|
| 372 | **108** | 1 c. black and green | 90 | 10 |
| 373 | **109** | 2 c. black and brown | 50 | 30 |
| 374 | **110** | 3 c. black and carmine | 40 | 10 |
| 372/4 | | *Set of* 3 | 1·60 | 40 |

Nos. 372/4 exist imperforate.

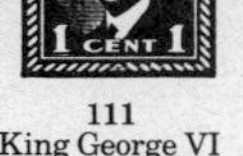

111 King George VI in Naval uniform

112 King George VI in Military uniform

113 King George VI in Air Force uniform

114 Grain Elevator

116 Parliament Buildings

117 Ram Tank

121 Air Training Camp

**1942** (1 July)–**1948.** *War Effort. T* **111/14, 116/17, 121** *and similar designs. (a) Postage. (i) P* 12.

| | | | | |
|---|---|---|---|---|
| 375 | **111** | 1 c. green | 75 | 10 |
| | | a. Booklet pane of 6 (24.11.42) | 2·50 | |
| | | b. Booklet pane of 4+2 labels (12.9.42) | 20·00 | |
| 376 | **112** | 2 c. brown | 1·50 | 10 |
| | | a. Booklet pane of 6 (6.10.42) | 18·00 | |
| | | b. Booklet pane of 4+2 labels (12.9.42) | 21·00 | |
| 377 | **113** | 3 c. carmine-lake | 1·00 | 30 |
| | | a. Booklet pane of 4+2 labels (20.8.42) | 4·25 | |
| 378 | | 3 c. purple (30.6.43) | 70 | 10 |
| | | a. Booklet pane of 6 (1.12.47) | 10·00 | |
| | | b. Booklet pane of 4+2 labels (28.8.43) | 5·00 | |
| 379 | **114** | 4 c. slate | 3·50 | 55 |
| 380 | **112** | 4 c. carmine-lake (9.4.43) | 45 | 10 |
| | | a. Booklet pane of 6 (3.5.43) | 3·50 | |
| 381 | **111** | 5 c. blue | 2·50 | 10 |
| 382 | – | 8 c. red-brown | 4·00 | 40 |
| 383 | **116** | 10 c. brown | 4·00 | 10 |
| 384 | **117** | 13 c. dull green | 3·75 | 4·25 |
| 385 | | 14 c. dull green (16.4.43) | 9·50 | 30 |
| 386 | – | 20 c. chocolate | 10·00 | 15 |
| 387 | – | 50 c. violet | 20·00 | 1·75 |
| 388 | – | $1 blue | 55·00 | 3·50 |
| 375/88 | | *Set of* 14 | £100 | 10·00 |

Nos. 375/88 exist imperforate.

| | | | | |
|---|---|---|---|---|
| | | *(ii) Coil stamps. Imperf × perf* 8 | | |
| 389 | **111** | 1 c. green (9.2.43) | 75 | 1·00 |
| 390 | **112** | 2 c. brown (24.11.42) | 1·75 | 1·00 |
| 391 | **113** | 3 c. carmine-lake (23.9.42) | 1·50 | 3·50 |
| 392 | | 3 c. purple (19.8.43) | 3·75 | 2·50 |
| 393 | **112** | 4 c. carmine-lake (13.5.43) | 3·50 | 1·25 |
| 389/93 | | *Set of* 5 | 10·00 | 8·25 |
| | | *(iii) Booklet stamps. Imperf × perf* 12 (1.9.43) | | |
| 394 | **111** | 1 c. green | 2·50 | 40 |
| | | a. Booklet pane of 3 | 7·50 | |
| 395 | **113** | 3 c. purple | 2·50 | 70 |
| | | a. Booklet pane of 3 | 7·50 | |
| 396 | **112** | 4 c. carmine-lake | 2·50 | 1·00 |
| | | a. Booklet pane of 3 | 7·50 | |
| 394/6 | | *Set of* 3 | 6·75 | 1·90 |

Nos. 394/6 are from booklets in which the stamps are in strips of three, imperforate at top and bottom and right-hand end.

(iv) *Coil stamps. Imperf × perf 9½*

| | | | | |
|---|---|---|---|---|
| 397 | 111 | 1 c. green (13.7.48) | 3·50 | 4·00 |
| 397*a* | 112 | 2 c. brown (1.10.48) | 7·50 | 17·00 |
| 398 | 113 | 3 c. purple (2.7.48) | 5·50 | 5·00 |
| 398*a* | 112 | 4 c. carmine-lake (22.7.48) | 6·50 | 3·50 |
| 397/8*a* | | *Set of* 4 | 21·00 | 27·00 |

(*b*) *Air. P* 12

| | | | | |
|---|---|---|---|---|
| 399 | 121 | 6 c. blue (1.7.42) | 6·50 | 2·50 |
| 400 | | 7 c. blue (16.4.43) | 1·25 | 10 |

Designs: *Horiz* (*as T* 114)—8 c. Farm scene. (*as T* 117)—20 c. Launching of Corvette H.M.C.S. *La Malbaie*, Sorel; 50 c. Munitions factory; $1 H.M.S. *Cossack* (destroyer).

122 Ontario Farm Scene

129 Alexander Graham Bell and "Fame"

**1946** (16 Sept—Dec). *Peace Re-conversion. T* **122** *and similar horiz designs. P* 12 (*a*). *Postage.*

| | | | |
|---|---|---|---|
| 401 | 8 c. brown | 1·00 | 90 |
| 402 | 10 c. olive-green | 1·25 | 10 |
| 403 | 14 c. sepia | 3·50 | 30 |
| 404 | 20 c. slate | 2·50 | 10 |
| 405 | 50 c. green | 14·00 | 1·25 |
| 406 | $1 purple | 29·00 | 1·25 |

(*b*) *Air*

| | | | |
|---|---|---|---|
| 407 | 7 c. blue | 2·50 | 10 |
| | a. Booklet pane of 4 (1.12.47) | 7·50 | |
| 401/7 | *Set of* 7 | 48·00 | 3·25 |

Designs:—7 c. Canada Geese in flight; 10 c. Great Bear Lake; 14 c. St. Maurice River Power Station; 20 c. Combine Harvester; 50 c. Lumbering in British Columbia; $1 *Abegweit* (train ferry), Prince Edward Is.

**1947** (3 Mar). *Birth Centenary of Bell* (*inventor of telephone*). *P* 12.

| | | | | |
|---|---|---|---|---|
| 408 | 129 | 4 c. blue | 10 | 10 |

130 "Canadian Citizenship".

131 Queen Elizabeth II when Princess

**1947** (1 July). *Advent of Canadian Citizenship and Eightieth Anniv of Confederation. P* 12.

| | | | | |
|---|---|---|---|---|
| 409 | 130 | 4 c. blue | 10 | 10 |

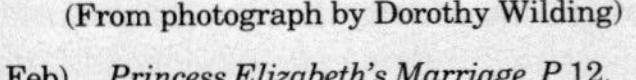

(From photograph by Dorothy Wilding)

**1948** (16 Feb). *Princess Elizabeth's Marriage. P* 12.

| | | | | |
|---|---|---|---|---|
| 410 | 131 | 4 c. blue | 10 | 10 |

132 Queen Victoria, Parliament Building, Ottawa, and King George VI

133 Cabot's Ship *Matthew*

**1948** (1 Oct). *One Hundred Years of Responsible Government. P* 12.

| | | | | |
|---|---|---|---|---|
| 411 | 132 | 4 c. grey | 10 | 10 |

**1949** (1 Apr). *Entry of Newfoundland into Canadian Confederation. P* 12.

| | | | | |
|---|---|---|---|---|
| 412 | 133 | 4 c. green | 10 | 10 |

134 "Founding of Halifax, 1749" (C. W. Jefferys)

**1949** (21 June). *Bicentenary of Halifax, Nova Scotia. P* 12.

| | | | | |
|---|---|---|---|---|
| 413 | 134 | 4 c. violet | 10 | 10 |

135

136

137

138 King George VI 139

(From photographs by Dorothy Wilding)

**1949** (15 Nov)–**51.** (i) *P* 12.

| | | | | |
|---|---|---|---|---|
| 414 | 135 | 1 c. green | 10 | 10 |
| 415 | 136 | 2 c. sepia | 15 | 20 |
| 415*a* | | 2 c. olive-green (25.7.51) | 30 | 10 |
| 416 | 137 | 3 c. purple | 20 | 10 |
| | | a. Booklet pane of 4+2 labels (12.4.50) | 1·75 | |
| 417 | 138 | 4 c. carmine-lake | 15 | 10 |
| | | a. Booklet pane of 6 (5.5.50) | 27·00 | |
| 417*b* | | 4 c. vermilion (2.6.51) | 40 | 10 |
| | | c. Booklet pane of 6 | 6·00 | |
| 418 | 139 | 5 c. blue | 80 | 10 |
| 414/18 | | *Set of* 7 | 1·90 | 35 |

(ii) *Imperf × perf* 9½ (*coil stamps*)

| | | | | |
|---|---|---|---|---|
| 419 | 135 | 1 c. green (18.5.50) | 70 | 1·00 |
| 420 | 136 | 2 c. sepia (18.5.50) | 3·50 | 3·75 |
| 420*a* | | 2 c. olive-green (9.10.51) | 1·50 | 1·00 |
| 421 | 137 | 3 c. purple (18.5.50) | 2·00 | 2·00 |
| 422 | 138 | 4 c. carmine-lake (20.4.50) | 10·00 | 7·50 |
| 422*a* | | 4 c. vermilion (27.11.51) | 1·25 | 1·25 |
| 419/22*a* | | *Set of* 6 | 17·00 | 15·00 |

(iii) *Imperf × perf* 12 (*booklets*)

| | | | | |
|---|---|---|---|---|
| 422*b* | 135 | 1 c. green (18.5.50) | 35 | 80 |
| | | ba. Booklet pane of 3 | 1·10 | |
| 423 | 137 | 3 c. purple (18.5.50) | 1·00 | 70 |
| | | a. Booklet pane of 3 | 3·00 | |
| 423*b* | 138 | 4 c. carmine-lake (18.5.50) | 13·00 | 6·50 |
| | | ba. Booklet pane of 3 | 38·00 | |
| 423*c* | | 4 c. vermilion (25.10.51) | 5·50 | 5·00 |
| | | ca. Booklet pane of 3 | 15·00 | |
| 422*b*/3*c* | | *Set of* 4 | 18·00 | 11·50 |

These booklet panes are imperforate at top, bottom and right-hand end.

140 King George VI

141 Oil Wells in Alberta

(From photograph by Dorothy Wilding

**1950** (19 Jan). *As T* **135/9** *but without* "POSTES POSTAGE", *as T* **140**. (i) *P* 12.

| | | | |
|---|---|---|---|
| 424 | 1 c. green | 10 | 15 |
| 425 | 2 c. sepia | 10 | 30 |
| 426 | 3 c. purple | 10 | 55 |
| 427 | 4 c. carmine-lake | 10 | 10 |
| 428 | 5 c. blue | 25 | 80 |
| 424/8 | *Set of* 5 | 50 | 1·60 |

(ii) *Imperf × perf* 9½ (*coil stamps*)

| | | | |
|---|---|---|---|
| 429 | 1 c. green | 15 | 50 |
| 430 | 3 c. purple | 55 | 1·00 |

**1950** (1 Mar). *P* 12.

| | | | | |
|---|---|---|---|---|
| 431 | 141 | 50 c. green | 7·00 | 50 |

142 Drying Furs

143 Fisherman

**1950** (2 Oct). *P* 12.

| | | | | |
|---|---|---|---|---|
| 432 | 142 | 10 c. brown-purple | 30 | 10 |

**1951** (1 Feb). *P* 12.

| | | | | |
|---|---|---|---|---|
| 433 | 143 | $1 ultramarine | 45·00 | 3·50 |

144 Sir R. L. Borden

145 W. L. Mackenzie King

**1951** (25 June). *Prime Ministers* (1*st issue*). *P* 12.

| | | | | |
|---|---|---|---|---|
| 434 | 144 | 3 c. blue-green | 10 | 30 |
| 435 | 145 | 4 c. rose-carmine | 10 | 10 |

See also Nos. 444/5, 475/6 and 483/4.

146 Mail Trains, 1851 and 1951

147 SS. *City of Toronto* and SS. *Prince George*

148 Mail Coach and Aeroplane

149 Reproduction of 3d., 1851

**1951** (24 Sept). *Canadian Stamp Centenary. P* 12.

| | | | | |
|---|---|---|---|---|
| 436 | 146 | 4 c. black | 35 | 10 |
| 437 | 147 | 5 c. violet | 65 | 1·50 |
| 438 | 148 | 7 c. blue | 35 | 45 |
| 439 | 149 | 15 c. scarlet | 35 | 10 |
| 436/9 | | *Set of* 4 | 1·50 | 1·90 |

150 Queen Elizabeth II when Princess and Duke of Edinburgh

151 Forestry Products

**1951** (26 Oct). *Royal Visit. P* 12.

| | | | | |
|---|---|---|---|---|
| 440 | 150 | 4 c. violet | 10 | 10 |

(Des A. L. Pollock)

**1952** (1 Apr). *P* 12.

| | | | | |
|---|---|---|---|---|
| 441 | 151 | 20 c. grey | 65 | 10 |

152 Red Cross Emblem

**1952** (26 July). *18th International Red Cross Conference, Toronto. Design recess; cross litho. P* 12.

| | | | | |
|---|---|---|---|---|
| 442 | 152 | 4 c. scarlet and blue | 15 | 10 |

153 Canada Goose

154 Pacific Coast Indian House and Totem Pole

(Des E. Hahn)

**1952** (3 Nov). *P* 12.

| | | | | |
|---|---|---|---|---|
| 443 | 153 | 7 c. blue | 30 | 10 |

**1952** (3 Nov). *Prime Ministers* (2*nd issue*). *Various portraits as T* **144**. *P* 12.

| | | | |
|---|---|---|---|
| 444 | 3 c. reddish purple | 15 | 10 |
| 445 | 4 c. orange-red | 15 | 10 |

Portraits:—3 c. Sir John J. C. Abbott; 4 c. A. Mackenzie.

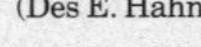

(Des E. Hahn)

**1953** (2 Feb). *P* 12.

| | | | | |
|---|---|---|---|---|
| 446 | 154 | $1 black | 7·50 | 20 |

155 Polar Bear

156 Elk

157 American Bighorn

(Des J. Crosby (2 c.), E. Hahn (others))

**1953** (1 Apr). *National Wild Life Week. P* 12.

| | | | | |
|---|---|---|---|---|
| 447 | 155 | 2 c. blue | 10 | 10 |
| 448 | 156 | 3 c. sepia | 10 | 10 |
| 449 | 157 | 4 c. slate | 15 | 10 |
| 447/9 | | *Set of* 3 | 30 | 15 |

158 Queen Elizabeth II 159

(From photograph by Karsh, Ottawa)

**1953** (1 May–3 Sept). *(a) Sheet stamps. P* 12.
450 **158** 1 c. purple-brown .. .. .. .. 10 10
451 2 c. green .. .. .. .. 15 10
452 3 c. carmine .. .. .. .. 15 15
a. Booklet pane of 4+2 labels (17.7) 1·25
453 4 c. violet .. .. .. .. 20 10
a. Booklet pane of 6 (6.7) .. .. 3·00
454 5 c. ultramarine .. .. .. .. 20 10
450/4 .. .. .. .. .. *Set of* 5 70 30

*(b) Coil stamps. Imperf × perf* 9½
455 **158** 2 c. green (30.7) .. .. .. .. 1·25 1·00
456 3 c. carmine (27.7) .. .. .. 1·50 1·00
457 4 c. violet (3.9) .. .. .. .. 1·50 1·00
455/7 .. .. .. .. .. *Set of* 3 3·75 2·75

*(c) Booklet stamps. Imperf × perf* 12 (12.8)
458 **158** 1 c. purple-brown .. .. .. .. 2·50 2·00
a. Booklet pane of 3 .. .. .. 7·50
459 3 c. carmine (17.7) .. .. .. 2·50 2·00
a. Booklet pane of 3 .. .. .. 7·50
460 4 c. violet (6.7) .. .. .. .. 2·50 2·00
a. Booklet pane of 3 .. .. .. 7·50
458/60 .. .. .. .. *Set of* 3 6·75 5·50

These booklet stamps have top and bottom or top, bottom and right-hand sides imperforate.

(Des E. Hahn)

**1953** (1 June). *Coronation. P* 12
461 **159** 4 c. violet .. .. .. .. 10 10

**160** Textile Industry **161** Queen Elizabeth II

(Des A. L. Pollock)

**1953** (2 Nov). *P* 12.
462 **160** 50 c. deep bluish green .. .. .. 1·00 10

(From photograph by Dorothy Wilding)

**1954–62.** (i) *P* 12.
463 **161** 1 c. purple-brown (10.6.54) .. .. 10 10
a. Booklet pane. Five stamps plus printed label (1.6.56) .. .. 1·00
p. Two phosphor bands (13.1.62) .. 80 2·00
464 2 c. green (10.6.54) .. .. .. 15 10
a. Pack. Two blocks of 25 (12.61) .. 5·00
p. Two phosphor bands (13.1.62) .. 80 2·00
465 3 c. carmine (10.6.54) .. .. .. 40 10
a. Imperf vert (horiz pair) .. .. £1200
p. Two phosphor bands (13.1.62) .. 1·00 2·50
466 4 c. violet (10.6.54) .. .. .. 30 10
a. Booklet pane. Five stamps plus printed label (1.6.56) .. .. 1·75
b. Booklet pane of 6 (7.7.55) .. .. 3·50
p. One phosphor band (13.1.62) .. 2·00 7·50
467 5 c. bright blue (1.4.54) .. .. .. 30 10
a. Booklet pane. Five stamps plus printed label (14.7.54) .. .. 1·50
b. Pack. One block of 20 (12.61) .. 4·50
p. Two phosphor bands (13.1.62) .. 2·00 7·00
468 6 c. red-orange (10.6.54) .. .. .. 1·00 30
463/8 .. .. .. .. .. *Set of* 6 2·00 45
463p/7p .. .. .. .. *Set of* 5 6·25 19·00

(ii) *Imperf × perf* 9½ *(coil stamps)*
469 **161** 2 c. green (9.9.54) .. .. .. 30 50
470 4 c. violet (23.8.54) .. .. .. 55 50
471 5 c. bright blue (6.7.54) .. .. .. 80 30
469/71 .. .. .. .. *Set of* 3 1·50 1·10

Nos. 464a and 467b are blocks with the outer edges imperf. These come from "One Dollar Plastic Packages" sold at post offices.

**WINNIPEG PHOSPHOR BANDS.** In 1962 facer-cancelling machines were introduced in Winnipeg which were activated by phosphor bands on the stamps. Under long or short wave ultra-violet light the phosphor glows and there is also a short after-glow when the lamp is turned off. This should not be confused with the fluorescent bands introduced in Ottawa in 1971.

**162** Walrus **163** American Beaver **164** Northern Gannet

(Des E. Hahn)

**1954** (1 Apr). *National Wild Life Week. P* 12.
472 **162** 4 c. slate-black .. .. .. .. 35 10
473 **163** 5 c. ultramarine .. .. .. .. 35 10
a. Booklet pane. Five stamps plus one printed label .. .. .. 1·40

(Des L. Hyde)

**1954** (1 Apr). *P* 12.
474 **164** 15 c. black .. .. .. .. 40 10

**1954** (1 Nov). *Prime Ministers (3rd issue). Various portraits as T* **144**. *P* 12.
475 4 c. violet .. .. .. .. .. 15 10
476 5 c. bright blue .. .. .. .. 15 10
Portraits:—4 c. Sir John Thompson; 5 c. Sir Mackenzie Bowell.

**165** Eskimo Hunter

(Des H. Beament)

**1955** (21 Feb). *P* 12.
477 **165** 10 c. purple-brown .. .. .. .. 15 10

**166** Musk Ox **167** Whooping Cranes

(Des E. Hahn (4 c.), Dr. W. Rowan (5 c.))

**1955** (4 Apr). *National Wild Life Week. P* 12.
478 **166** 4 c. violet .. .. .. .. .. 20 10
479 **167** 5 c. ultramarine .. .. .. .. 60 10

**168** Dove and Torch **169** Pioneer Settlers

(Des W. Lohse)

**1955** (1 June). *Tenth Anniv of International Civil Aviation Organisation. P* 12.
480 **168** 5 c. ultramarine .. .. .. .. 10 10

(Des L. Hyde)

**1955** (30 June). *50th Anniv of Alberta and Saskatchewan Provinces. P* 12.
481 **169** 5 c. ultramarine .. .. .. .. 15 15

**170** Scout Badge and Globe **173** Ice-hockey Players

(Des L. Hyde)

**1955** (20 Aug). *Eighth World Scout Jamboree, Niagara-on-the-Lake. P* 12.
482 **170** 5 c. orange-brown and green .. .. 20 10

**1955** (8 Nov). *Prime Ministers (4th issue). Various portraits as T* **144**. *P* 12.
483 4 c. violet .. .. .. .. .. 10 15
484 5 c. bright blue .. .. .. .. 10 10
Portraits:—4 c. R. B. Bennett; 5 c. Sir Charles Tupper.

(Des J. Simpkins)

**1956** (23 Jan). *Ice-hockey Commemoration. P* 12.
485 **173** 5 c. ultramarine .. .. .. .. 15 15

**174** Reindeer **175** Mountain Goat

(Des E. Hahn)

**1956** (12 Apr). *National Wild Life Week. P* 12.
486 **174** 4 c. violet .. .. .. .. 20 15
487 **175** 5 c. bright blue .. .. .. .. 20 10

**176** Pulp and Paper Industry **177** Chemical Industry

(Des A. J. Casson (20 c.), A. L. Pollock (25 c.))

**1956** (7 June). *P* 12.
488 **176** 20 c. green .. .. .. .. .. 30 10
489 **177** 25 c. red .. .. .. .. .. 35 10

**178**

(Des A. Price)

**1956** (9 Oct). *Fire Prevention Week. P* 12
490 **178** 5 c. red and black .. .. .. 30 10

**179** Fishing **180** Swimming

(Des L. Hyde)

**1957** (7 Mar). *Outdoor Recreation. T* **179/180** *and similar horiz designs. P* 12.
491 **179** 5 c. ultramarine .. .. .. .. 25 10
a. Block of 4. Nos. 491/4 .. .. 1·25
492 **180** 5 c. ultramarine .. .. .. .. 25 10
493 – 5 c. ultramarine .. .. .. .. 25 10
494 – 5 c. ultramarine .. .. .. .. 25 10
491/4 .. .. .. .. .. *Set of* 4 1·25 35

Designs:— No. 493, Hunting. No. 494, Skiing.

No. 491/4 are printed together in sheets of 50 (5 × 10). In the first, second, fourth and fifth vertical rows the four different designs are arranged in *se-tenant* blocks, whilst the central row is made up as follows (reading downwards):—Nos. 491/4, 491/2 (or 493/4), 491/4.

**183** White-billed Diver **184** Thompson with Sextant, and North American Map

(Des L. Hyde)

**1957** (10 Apr). *National Wild Life Week. P* 12.
495 **183** 5 c. black .. .. .. .. .. 20 10

(Des G. A. Gundersen)

**1957** (5 June). *Death Centenary of David Thompson (explorer). P* 12.
496 **184** 5 c. ultramarine .. .. .. .. 15 20

**185** Parliament Buildings, Ottawa **186** Globe within Posthorn

(Des Carl Mangold)

**1957** (14 Aug). *14th U.P.U. Congress, Ottawa. P* 12.
497 **185** 5 c. grey-blue .. .. .. .. 15 10
498 **186** 15 c. blackish blue .. .. .. .. 30 1·00

**187** Miner **188** Queen Elizabeth II and Duke of Edinburgh

(Des A. J. Casson)

**1957** (5 Sept). *Mining Industry. P* 12.
499 **187** 5 c. black .. .. .. .. .. 35 10

(From photographs by Karsh, Ottawa)

**1957** (10 Oct). *Royal Visit. P* 12.
500 **188** 5 c. black .. .. .. .. .. 30 10

**189** "A Free Press" **190** Microscope

(Des A. L. Pollock)

**1958** (22 Jan). *The Canadian Press. P* 12.
501 **189** 5 c. black .. .. .. .. 15 30

(Des A. L. Pollock)

**1958** (5 Mar). *International Geophysical Year. P* 12.
502 **190** 5 c. blue .. .. .. .. .. 20 10

**191** Miner panning for Gold

**192** La Verendrye (statue)

(Des J. Harman)

**1958** (8 May). *Centenary of British Columbia. P* 12.
503 **191** 5 c. deep turquoise-green .. .. 20 10

(Des G. Trottier)

**1958** (4 June). *La Verendrye (explorer) Commemoration. P* 12.
504 **192** 5 c. ultramarine .. .. .. 15 10

**193** Samuel de Champlain and the Heights of Quebec

**194** Nurse

(Des G. Trottier)

**1958** (26 June). *350th Anniv of Founding of Quebec. P* 12.
505 **193** 5 c. brown-ochre and deep green .. 30 10

(Des G. Trottier)

**1958** (30 July). *National Health. P* 12.
506 **194** 5 c. reddish purple .. .. .. 30 10

**195** "Petroleum 1858–1958"

**196** Speaker's Chair and Mace

(Des A. L. Pollock)

**1958** (10 Sept). *Centenary of Canadian Oil Industry. P* 12.
507 **195** 5 c. scarlet and olive .. .. .. 30 10

(Des G. Trottier and C. Dair)

**1958** (2 Oct). *Bicentenary of First Elected Assembly. P* 12.
508 **196** 5 c. deep slate .. .. .. .. 20 10

**197** The "Silver Dart"

**198** Globe showing N.A.T.O. Countries

**1959** (23 Feb). *50th Anniv of First Flight of the "Silver Dart" in Canada. P* 12.
509 **197** 5 c. black and ultramarine .. .. 20 10

(Des P. Weiss)

**1959** (2 Apr). *Tenth Anniv of North Atlantic Treaty Organisation. P* 12.
510 **198** 5 c. ultramarine .. .. .. 40 10

**199**

**200** Queen Elizabeth II

(Des Helen Fitzgerald)

**1959** (13 May). *"Associated Country Women of the World" Commemoration. P* 12.
511 **199** 5 c. black and yellow-olive .. .. 15 10

(Des after painting by Annigoni)

**1959** (18 June). *Royal Visit. P* 12.
512 **200** 5 c. lake-red .. .. .. .. 30 10

**201** Maple Leaf linked with American Eagle

**202** Maple Leaves

(Des A. L. Pollock, G. Trottier (of Canada); W. H. Buckley, A. J. Copeland, E. Metzl (of the United States))

**1959** (26 June). *Opening of St. Lawrence Seaway. P* 12.
513 **201** 5 c. ultramarine and red .. .. 20 10
a. Centre inverted .. .. .. £10000 £6000

It is believed that No. 513a occurred on two printer's sheets, each of 200 stamps. About 230 examples have been discovered.

(Des P. Weiss)

**1959** (10 Sept). *Bicentenary of Battle of Plains of Abraham (Quebec). P* 12.
514 **202** 5 c. deep green and red .. .. .. 30 10

**203**

**204** Dollard des Ormeaux

(Des Helen Fitzgerald)

**1960** (20 Apr). *Golden Jubilee of Canadian Girl Guides Movement. P* 12.
515 **203** 5 c. ultramarine and orange-brown .. 20 10

(Des P. Weiss)

**1960** (19 May). *Tercentenary of Battle of the Long Sault. P* 12.
516 **204** 5 c. ultramarine and light brown .. 20 10

**205** Surveyor, Bulldozer and Compass Rose

**206** E. Pauline Johnson

(Des B. J. Reddie)

**1961** (8 Feb). *Northern Development. P* 12.
517 **205** 5 c. emerald and red .. .. .. 15 10

(Des B. J. Reddie)

**1961** (10 Mar). *Birth Centenary of E. Pauline Johnson (Mohawk poetess). P* 12.
518 **206** 5 c. green and red .. .. .. 15 10

**207** Arthur Meighen (statesman)

**208** Engineers and Dam

**1961** (19 Apr). *Arthur Meighen Commemoration. P* 12.
519 **207** 5 c. ultramarine .. .. .. 15 10

(Des B. J. Reddie)

**1961** (28 June). *Tenth Anniv of Colombo Plan. P* 12.
520 **208** 5 c. blue and brown .. .. .. 30 10

**209** "Resources for Tomorrow"

**210** "Education"

(Des A. L. Pollock)

**1961** (12 Oct). *Natural Resources. P* 12.
521 **209** 5 c. blue-green and brown .. .. 15 10

(Des Helen Fitzgerald)

**1962** (28 Feb). *Education Year. P* 12.
522 **210** 5 c. black and orange-brown .. .. 15 10

**211** Lord Selkirk and Farmer

**212** Talon bestowing Gifts on Married Couple

(Des Phillips-Gutkin Ltd)

**1962** (3 May). *150th Anniv of Red River Settlement. P* 12.
523 **211** 5 c. chocolate and green .. .. 20 10

(Des P. Weiss)

**1962** (13 June). *Jean Talon Commemoration. P* 12.
524 **212** 5 c. blue .. .. .. .. .. 20 10

**213** Br Columbia & Vancouver Is 2½d. stamp of 1860, and Parliament Buildings, B.C.

**214** Highway (map version) and Provincial Arms

(Des Helen Bacon)

**1962** (22 Aug). *Centenary of Victoria, B.C. P* 12.
525 **213** 5 c. red and black .. .. .. 30 10

(Des A. L. Pollock)

**1962** (31 Aug). *Opening of Trans-Canada Highway. P* 12.
526 **214** 5 c. black and orange-brown .. .. 15 10

**215** Queen Elizabeth II and Wheat (agriculture) Symbol

**216** Sir Casimir Gzowski

(From drawing by Ernst Roch)

**1962–64.** *Horiz designs as T* **215** *showing Queen Elizabeth II and industry symbols.* (i) *P* 12.
527 1 c. chocolate (4.2.63) .. .. .. 10 10
a. Booklet pane. Five stamps plus one printed label (15.5.63) .. .. 3·25
p. Two phosphor bands (15.5.63) .. .. 15 40
528 2 c. green (2.5.63) .. .. .. 15 10
a. Pack. Two blocks of 25 .. .. 7·50
p. Two phosphor bands (15.5.63) .. .. 20 40
529 3 c. reddish violet† (2.5.63) .. .. 15 10
p. Two phosphor bands (15.5.63) .. .. 30 50
530 4 c. carmine-red (4.2.63) .. .. .. 15 10
a. Booklet pane. Five stamps plus one printed label (15.5.63) .. .. 3·25
b. Pack. One block of 25 .. .. 4·00
p. One centre phosphor band (*narrow*)* (2.63) .. .. .. .. 40 1·25
pa. One centre phosphor band (*wide*) (8.64) 2·25 3·25
pb. One side phosphor band (12.64) .. .. 40 75
531 5 c. ultramarine (3.10.62) .. .. .. 15 10
a. Booklet pane. Five stamps plus one printed label (5.63) .. .. 2·50
b. Pack. One block of 20 .. .. 4·75
c. Imperf horiz (vert pair) .. .. — £800
p. Two phosphor bands (31.1.63?) .. .. 35 30
pa. Pack. One block of 20 .. .. 14·00
527/31 .. .. .. .. *Set of* 5 65 15

(ii) *P* 9½ × *imperfl coil stamps*)
532 2 c. green (1963) .. .. .. 4·25 5·50
532*a* 3 c. reddish violet (1964) .. .. 4·25 2·75
533 4 c. carmine-red (15.5.63) .. .. 1·75 2·00
534 5 c. ultramarine (15.5.63) .. .. 1·75 40
532/4 .. .. .. .. *Set of* 4 11·00 9·50

Symbols:–1 c. Crystals (Mining); 2 c. Tree (Forestry); 3 c. Fish (Fisheries); 4 c. Electricity pylon (Industrial power).

Nos. 528a, 530b, 531b and 531pa are blocks with the outer edges imperf. These come from "One Dollar Plastic Packages" sold at post offices.

†This is a fugitive colour which tends to become reddish on drying. In successive printings the violet colour became more and more reddish as the printer tried to match the shade of each previous printing instead of referring back to the original shade. A deep reddish violet is also known from Plate 3. As there is such a range of shades it is not practical to list them.

*On No. 530p the band is 4 mm wide as against 8 mm on No. 530pa. No. 530pb exists with the band at either left or right side of the stamp, the bands being applied across alternate vertical perforations.

(Des P. Weiss)

**1963** (5 Mar). *150th Birth Anniv of Sir Casimir Gzowski (engineer). P* 12.
535 **216** 5 c. reddish purple .. .. .. 10 10

217 "Export Trade"

218 Frobisher and barque *Gabriel*

(Des A. L. Pollock)

**1963** (14 June). *P* 12.
536 **217** $1 carmine .. .. .. .. .. 8·00 1·75

(Des P. Weiss)

**1963** (21 Aug). *Sir Martin Frobisher Commemoration. P* 12.
537 **218** 5 c. ultramarine .. .. .. .. 20 10

219 Horseman and Map

220 Canada Geese

(Des B. J. Reddie)

**1963** (25 Sept). *Bicentenary of Quebec–Trois-Rivieres–Montreal Postal Service. P* 12.
538 **219** 5 c. red-brown and deep green .. .. 15 10

(Des A. Short and P. Arthur)

**1963** (30 Oct). *P* 12.
539 **220** 15 c. blue .. .. .. .. .. 1·25 10

221 Jet Airliner (composite) and Uplands Airport, Ottawa

222 "Peace on Earth"

**1964**. *P* 12.
540 **221** 7 c. blue (11 Mar) .. .. .. .. 35 65
540*a* 8 c. blue (18 Nov) .. .. .. .. 50 30

**1964** (8 Apr). *"Peace". Litho and recess. P* 12.
541 **222** 5 c. ochre, blue and turquoise-blue .. 15 10

223 Maple Leaves

**1964** (14 May). *"Canadian Unity". P* 12.
542 **223** 5 c. lake-red and light blue .. .. 10 10

224 White Trillium and Arms of Ontario

236 Maple Leaf and Arms of Canada

**1964–66**. *Provincial Emblems. T* **224**, **236** *and similar horiz designs. Recess (No. 555) or litho and recess (others). P* 12.
543 5 c. green, brown and orange (30.6.64) 40 20
544 5 c. green, orange-brown and yellow (30.6.64) 40 20
545 5 c. carmine-red, green and bluish violet (3.2.65) .. .. .. .. .. 30 20
546 5 c. blue, red and green (3.2.65) .. .. 30 20
547 5 c. purple, green and yellow-brown (28.4.65) 30 20
548 5 c. red-brown, deep bluish green and mauve (28.4.65) .. .. .. .. .. 30 20
549 5 c. slate-lilac, green and light reddish purple (21.7.65) .. .. .. .. .. 50 20
550 5 c. green, yellow and rose-red (19.1.66) .. 30 20
551 5 c. sepia, orange and green (19.1.66) .. 30 20
552 5 c. black, green and red (23.2.66) .. .. 30 20
553 5 c. drab, green and yellow (23.3.66).. .. 30 20
554 5 c. blue, green and rose-red (23.3.66) .. 30 20
555 5 c. red and blue (30.6.66) .. .. .. 30 20
543/55 .. .. .. .. *Set of* 13 4·00 2·40

Designs:—No. 543, Type **224**; No. 544, Madonna Lily and Arms of Quebec; No. 545, Purple Violet and Arms of New Brunswick; No. 546, Mayflower and Arms of Nova Scotia; No. 547, Dogwood and Arms of British Columbia; No. 548, Prairie Crocus and Arms of Manitoba; No. 549, Lady's Slipper and Arms of Prince Edward Island; No. 550, Wild Rose and Arms of Alberta; No. 551, Prairie Lily and Arms of Saskatchewan; No. 552, Pitcher Plant and Arms of Newfoundland; No. 553, Mountain Avens and Arms of Northwest Territories; No. 554, Fireweed and Arms of Yukon Territory; No. 555, Type **236**.

8
=

(237)

238 Fathers of the Confederation Memorial, Charlottetown

**1964** (15 July). *No.* 540 *surch with T* **237**.
556 **221** 8 c. on 7 c. blue .. .. .. .. 15 15
a. Surch omitted (left-hand stamp of horiz pair) .. .. .. .. .. £6000

(Des P. Weiss)

**1964** (29 July). *Centenary of Charlottetown Conference. P* 12.
557 **238** 5 c. black .. .. .. .. .. 10 10

239 Maple Leaf and Hand with Quill Pen

240 Queen Elizabeth II

(Des P. Weiss)

**1964** (9 Sept). *Centenary of Quebec Conference. P* 12.
558 **239** 5 c. light red and chocolate .. .. 15 10

(Portrait by Anthony Buckley)

**1964** (5 Oct). *Royal Visit. P* 12.
559 **240** 5 c. reddish purple .. .. .. .. 15 10

241 "Canadian Family"

242 "Co-operation"

**1964** (14 Oct). *Christmas. P* 12.
560 **241** 3 c. scarlet .. .. .. .. .. 10 10
a. Pack. Two blocks of 25 .. .. 5·50
p. Two phosphor bands .. .. 60 1·25
pa. Pack. Two blocks of 25 .. .. 11·00
561 5 c. ultramarine .. .. .. .. 10 10
p. Two phosphor bands .. .. 90 1·50

Nos. 560a and 560pa are blocks with the outer edges imperf. These come from "$1.50 Plastic Packages" sold at post offices.

**1965** (3 Mar). *International Co-operation Year. P* 12.
562 **242** 5 c. grey-green .. .. .. .. .. 35 10

243 Sir W. Grenfell

244 National Flag

**1965** (9 June). *Birth Centenary of Sir Wilfred Grenfell (missionary). P* 12.
563 **243** 5 c. deep bluish green .. .. .. .. 20 10

**1965** (30 June). *Inauguration of National Flag. P* 12.
564 **244** 5 c. red and blue .. .. .. .. 15 10

245 Sir Winston Churchill

246 Peace Tower, Parliament Buildings, Ottawa

(Des P. Weiss from photo by Karsh. Litho)

**1965** (12 Aug). *Churchill Commemoration. P* 12.
565 **245** 5 c. purple-brown .. .. .. .. 15 10

(Des Philips-Gutkin)

**1965** (8 Sept). *Inter-Parliamentary Union Conference, Ottawa. P* 12.
566 **246** 5 c. deep green .. .. .. .. .. 10 10

## COVER PRICES

Cover factors are quoted at the beginning of each country for most issues to 1945. An explanation of the system can be found on page x. The factors quoted do not, however, apply to philatelic covers.

247 Parliament Buildings, Ottawa, 1865

248 "Gold, Frankincense and Myrrh"

(Des G. Trottier)

**1965** (8 Sept). *Centenary of Proclamation of Ottawa as Capital. P* 12.
567 **247** 5 c. brown .. .. .. .. .. 10 10

(Des Helen Fitzgerald)

**1965** (13 Oct). *Christmas. P* 12.
568 **248** 3 c. olive-green .. .. .. .. .. 10 10
a. Pack. Two blocks of 25 .. .. 4·00
p. Two phosphor bands .. .. 10 25
pa. Pack. Two blocks of 25 .. .. 5·00
569 5 c. ultramarine .. .. .. .. 10 10
p. Two phosphor bands .. .. 10 25

Nos. 568a and 568pa are blocks with the outer edges imperf. These come from "$1.50 Plastic Packages" sold at post offices.

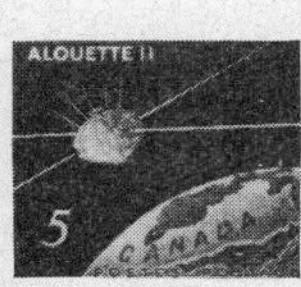

249 "Alouette 2" over Canada

250 La Salle

**1966** (5 Jan). *Launching of Canadian Satellite, "Alouette 2". P* 12.
570 **249** 5 c. ultramarine .. .. .. .. 15 10

(Des Brigdens Ltd., Toronto)

**1966** (13 Apr). *300th Anniv of La Salle's Arrival in Canada. P* 12.
571 **250** 5 c. deep bluish green .. .. .. .. 15 10

251 Road Signs

252 Canadian Delegation and Houses of Parliament

(Des Helen Fitzgerald)

**1966** (2 May). *Highway Safety. Invisible gum. P* 12.
572 **251** 5 c. yellow, blue and black .. .. 15 10

(Des P. Pederson (Brigdens Ltd))

**1966** (26 May). *London Conference Centenary. P* 12.
573 **252** 5 c. red-brown .. .. .. .. .. 10 10

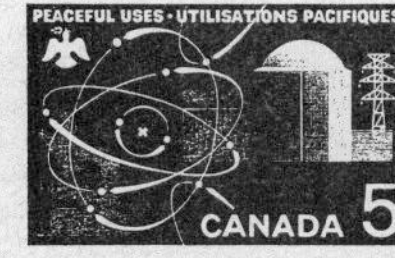

253 Douglas Point Nuclear Power Station

254 Parliamentary Library, Ottawa

(Des A. L. Pollock)

**1966** (27 July). *Peaceful Uses of Atomic Energy. P* 12.
574 **253** 5 c. ultramarine .. .. .. .. 10 10

(Des Brigdens Ltd)

**1966** (8 Sept). *Commonwealth Parliamentary Association Conference, Ottawa. P* 12.
575 **254** 5 c. purple .. .. .. .. .. 10 10

255 "Praying Hands", after Dürer

256 Flag and Canada on Globe

(Des G. Holloway)

**1966** (12 Oct). *Christmas. P* 12.

576 **255** 3 c. carmine . . . . 10 10
a. Pack. Two blocks of 25 . . . . 3·00
p. Two phosphor bands . . . . 15 45
pa. Pack. Two blocks of 25 . . . . 5·50
577 5 c. orange . . . . 10 10
p. Two phosphor bands . . . . 15 70

Nos. 576a and 576pa are blocks with the outer edges imperf. These come from "$1.50 Plastic Packages" sold at post offices.

(Des Brigdens Ltd)

**1967** (11 Jan). *Canadian Centennial. Invisible gum. P* 12.

578 **256** 5 c. scarlet and blue . . . . 10 10
p. Two phosphor bands . . . . 30 70

**257** Northern Lights and Dog-team

**263** "The Jack Pine" (T. Thomson)

**1967** (8 Feb)–**72**. *T* **257, 263** *and similar horiz designs.*

A. *Recess C.B.N.*

(i) *P* 12

579 1 c. brown . . . . 10 10
a. Booklet pane. Five stamps plus one printed label (2.67) . . . . 50
p. Two phosphor bands . . . . 30 50
pa. Centre phosphor band (12.68) . . . . 30 50
580 2 c. green . . . . 10 10
b. Booklet pane. No. 580 × 4 *se-tenant* with No. 581 × 4 with gutter margin between (26.10.70) . . . . 2·50
p. Two phosphor bands . . . . 30 50
pa. Centre phosphor band (12.68) . . . . 30 45
581 3 c. slate-purple . . . . 20 10
p. Two phosphor bands . . . . 30 60
582 4 c. red . . . . 20 10
a. Booklet pane. Five stamps plus one printed label (2.67) . . . . 1·75
b. Pack. One block of 25 (8.2.67) . . . . 10·00
p. One side phosphor band . . . . 1·00 1·25
pa. Centre phosphor band (3.69) . . . . 30 45
583 5 c. blue . . . . 20 10
a. Booklet pane. Five stamps plus one printed label (3.67) . . . . 6·00
b. Pack. One block of 20 (2.67) . . . . 17·00
p. Two phosphor bands . . . . 45 40
pa. Pack. One block of 20 (8.2.67) . . . . 35·00
pb. Centre phosphor band (12.68) . . . . 30 40
583*c* 6 c. black (2.72) . . . . 1·75 30
cp. Centre phosphor band (2.72) . . . . 1·50 1·00
584 8 c. purple-brown . . . . 35 30
585 10 c. olive-green . . . . 30 10
p. Two phosphor bands (9.12.69) . . . . 85 80
586 15 c. dull purple . . . . 30 10
p. Two phosphor bands (9.12.69) . . . . 1·50 1·75
587 20 c. deep blue . . . . 80 10
p. Two phosphor bands (9.12.69) . . . . 1·75 2·00
588 25 c. myrtle-green . . . . 1·25 10
p. Two phosphor bands (9.12.69) . . . . 3·25 3·50
589 50 c. cinnamon . . . . 1·50 10
590 $1 scarlet . . . . 3·50 40
579/90 . . *Set of* 13 9·25 1·25
579pa/588p . . *Set of* 10 9·25 10·50

(ii) *Perf* 9½ × *imperf* (*coil stamps*)

591 3 c. slate-purple (3.67) . . . . 1·50 1·75
592 4 c. red (3.67) . . . . 1·50 1·50
593 5 c. blue (2.67) . . . . 1·50 90

(iii) *Perf* 10 × *imperf* (*coil stamps*)

594 6 c. orange-red (1.69) . . . . 55 35
a. Imperf (vert pair) . . . . £250
595 6 c. black (8.70) . . . . 35 30
a. Imperf (vert pair) . . . . £350
596 7 c. green (30.6.71) . . . . 40 30
a. Imperf (vert pair) . . . . £450
597 8 c. black (30.12.71) . . . . 40 20
a. Imperf (vert pair) . . . . £180

B. *Recess B.A.B.N.*

(i) *P* 10 (*sheets* (601/p) *or booklets*)

598 1 c. brown (9.68) . . . . 30 40
a. Booklet pane. No. 598 × 5 *se-tenant* with No. 599 × 5 (9.68) . . . . 2·75
b. Booklet pane. No. 601 × 4 *se-tenant* with No. 598 plus one printed label (10.68) . . 2·50
599 4 c. red (9.68) . . . . 30 50
a. Booklet pane. 25 stamps plus two printed labels . . . . 9·00
600 5 c. blue (9.68) . . . . 30 50
a. Booklet pane of 20 . . . . 6·50
601 6 c. orange-red (10.68) . . . . 45 10
a. Booklet pane. 25 stamps plus two printed labels (1.69) . . . . 12·00
p. Two phosphor bands (1.11.68) . . . . 40 60
602 6 c. black (1.70) . . . . 85 60
a. Booklet pane. 25 stamps plus two printed labels . . . . 17·00
603 6 c. black (*re-engraved die*) (8.70) . . . . 3·75 2·25
a. Booklet pane of 4 . . . . 15·00

(ii) *P* 12½ × 12 (*sheets* (606/10) *or booklets*)

604 1 c. brown (30.6.71) . . . . 60 1·00
a. Booklet pane. Nos. 604 × 4,605 × 4 and 609 × 12 *se-tenant* . . . . 14·00
b. Booklet pane. No. 604 × 3, No. 608 and No. 610 × 2 *se-tenant* (30.12.71) . . . . 2·50
c. Booklet pane. No. 604 × 6, No. 608 and No. 610 × 11 *se-tenant* (30.12.71) . . . . 7·00
d. Booklet pane. No. 604, No. 605 and No. 609 × 3 *se-tenant* plus one printed label 5·00
e. Booklet pane. No. 604 × 4, No. 608 and No. 610 × 5 *se-tenant* (8.72) . . . . 3·75
605 3 c. slate-purple (30.6.71) . . . . 2·00 3·00
606 6 c. orange-red (3.69) . . . . 60 10
p. Two phosphor bands . . . . 75 45
607 6 c. black (7.1.70) . . . . 30 10
a. Booklet pane. 25 stamps plus two printed labels (8.70) . . . . 16·00
p. Two phosphor bands . . . . 60 1·00
608 6 c. black (*re-engraved die*) (9.70) . . . . 35 10
a. Booklet pane of 4 (11.70) . . . . 5·50
p. One centre phosphor band (9.71) . . 1·25 85
609 7 c. myrtle-green (30.6.71) . . . . 30 10
p. Two phosphor bands . . . . 60 80
610 8 c. slate-black (30.12.71) . . . . 30 10
p. Two phosphor bands . . . . 60 60

Designs: (*as T* **257**)—2 c. Totem pole; 3 c. Combine-harvester and oil derrick; 4 c. Ship in lock; 5 c. Harbour scene; 6 c., 7 c. "Transport"; 8 c. (Nos. 597, 610) Library of Parliament. (*as T* **263**)—8 c. (No. 584) "Alaska Highway" (A. Y. Jackson); 15 c. "Bylot Island" (L. Harris); 20 c. "Quebec Ferry" (J. W. Morrice); 25 c. "The Solemn Land" (J. E. H. MacDonald); 50 c. "Summer's Stores" (grain elevators) (J. Ensor); $1 "Oilfield" (near Edmonton) (H. G. Glyde).

Nos. 582b, 583b and 583pa are blocks with the outer edges imperf. These come from "One Dollar Plastic Packages" sold at post offices.

No. 582p comes with the band to the left or right of the stamp, the phosphor having been applied across alternate vertical perforations.

Normal

Re-engraved

When the basic postal rate was changed to 6 c. the C.B.N. lent their die to B.A.B.N. who made a duplicate die from it by transfer. Parts of this proved to be weak, but it was used for Nos. 601/2 and 606/7. B.A.B.N. later re-engraved their die to make fresh plates which were used for Nos. 603 and 608. No. 608 first appeared on sheets from Plate 4.

There are no records of dates of issue of the booklets, packs and coils, but supplies of these were distributed to depots in the months indicated.

**IMPERF BETWEEN PAIRS FROM COIL STAMPS.** Nos. 595/6 (and possibly others) are known in blocks or horizontal pairs imperf between vertically. Coils are supplied to post offices in batches of ten coils held together by roulettes between every fourth stamp so that they can easily be split apart. If two or more unsplit coils are purchased it is possible to obtain blocks or pairs imperf between vertically.

Vertical coil stamps are also known imperf between horizontally or with some stamps apparently completely imperf. These can result from blind perforations identifiable by slight indentations.

**WHITE FLUORESCENT PAPER.** Different papers with varying degrees of whiteness have been used for Canadian stamps, but during 1968–70 a distinctive very white and highly fluorescent paper was used known as "hybrite"; this fluoresces on the back and front. This paper has also been employed for commemorative issues, some of which exist on more than one type of paper. The white fluorescent papers are recorded in the Stanley Gibbons *Elizabethan Catalogue.*

**FLUORESCENT BANDS.** During the second half of 1971 new sorting machines were installed in the Ottawa area which were activated by stamps bearing fluorescent bands. These differ from the Winnipeg phosphor bands in that there is no after-glow and they are hardly visible to the naked eye and so can only be distinguished by using an ultra-violet lamp. For this reason they are outside the scope of this catalogue but instead are recorded in footnotes. They are, however, fully listed in the Stanley Gibbons *Elizabethan Catalogue.*

In the 1967–72 definitive issue fluorescent bands occur on some printings of Nos. 579, 580, 581, 582, 583*c*, 585, 586, 597, 604, 608 and 610.

The experiments were successful and what was at first called "Ottawa tagging" has since come into more general use and the Winnipeg phosphor was phased out. However, the substance at first used (known as OP–4) was found to migrate to envelopes, documents, album pages, etc. as well as to adjoining stamps. Late in 1972 this fault was cured by using another substance (called OP–2). The migrating bands were used on early printings of Nos. 604, 608 and 610 as well as certain stamps referred to in a footnote after No. 692. It is most advisable to use plastic mounts for housing stamps with migrating bands or else clear acetate should be affixed to the album leaves.

**269** Canadian Pavilion

**270** Allegory of "Womanhood" on Ballot-box

(Des C.B.N.)

**1967** (28 Apr). *World Fair, Montreal. P* 12.

611 **269** 5 c. blue and red . . . . 10 10

(Des Helen Fitzgerald. Litho)

**1967** (24 May). *50th Anniv of Women's Franchise. P* 12.

612 **270** 5 c. reddish purple and black . . . . 10 10

**271** Queen Elizabeth II and Centennial Emblem

**272** Athlete

(Portrait from photo by Anthony Buckley)

**1967** (30 June). *Royal Visit. P* 12.

613 **271** 5 c. plum and orange-brown . . . . 15 10

(Des Brigdens Ltd)

**1967** (19 July). *Fifth Pan-American Games, Winnipeg. P* 12.

614 **272** 5 c. rose-red . . . . 10 10

**273** "World News"

**274** Governor-General Vanier

(Des W. McLauchlan)

**1967** (31 Aug). *50th Anniv of the Canadian Press. P* 12.

615 **273** 5 c. blue . . . . 10 10

(Des from photo by Karsh)

**1967** (15 Sept). *Vanier Commemoration. P* 12.

616 **274** 5 c. black . . . . 10 10

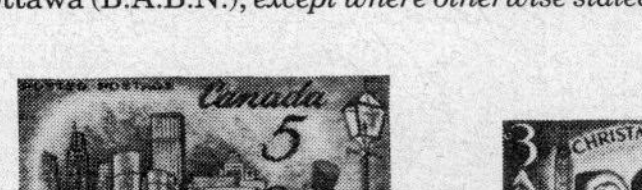

**PRINTERS.** The following were printed either by the Canadian Bank Note Co, Ottawa (C.B.N.) or the British American Bank Note Co, Ottawa (B.A.B.N.), *except where otherwise stated.*

**275** People of 1867 and Toronto, 1967

**276** Carol Singers

(Des and recess C.B.N.)

**1967** (28 Sept). *Centenary of Toronto as Capital City of Ontario P* 12.

617 **275** 5 c. myrtle-green and vermilion . . 10 10

(Des and recess B.A.B.N.)

**1967** (11 Oct). *Christmas. P* 12.

618 **276** 3 c. scarlet . . . . 10 10
a. Pack. Two blocks of 25 . . . . 3·00
p. Two phosphor bands . . . . 10 30
pa. Pack. Two blocks of 25 . . . . 3·25
619 5 c. emerald-green . . . . 10 10
p. Two phosphor bands . . . . 10 25

Nos. 618a and 618pa are blocks with the outer edges imperf These come from "$1.50 Plastic Packs" sold at post offices.

**277** Grey Jays

**278** Weather Map and Instruments

(Des M. G. Loates. Litho C.B.N.)

**1968** (15 Feb). *Wild Life. P* 12.

620 **277** 5 c. multicoloured . . . . 30 1

See also Nos. 638/40.

(Des and litho B.A.B.N.)

**1968** (13 Mar). *Bicentenary of First Meteorological Readings P* 11.

621 **278** 5 c. multicoloured . . . . 15 10

**279** Narwhal

**280** Globe, Maple Leaf and Rain Gauge

(Des J. A. Crosby. Litho B.A.B.N.)

**1968** (10 Apr). *Wildlife. P* 11.
622 **279** 5 c. multicoloured 15 10

No. 622 has a background of yellow-green and pale blue but copies are known with the yellow-green apparently missing. This "yellow-green" is produced by an overlay of yellow on the blue but we have not come across any copies where the yellow is completely missing and the wide range of colour variation is due to technical dificulties in maintaining an exact blend of the two colours.

(Des I. von Mosdossy. Litho B.A.B.N.)

**1968** (8 May). *International Hydrological Decade. P* 11.
623 **280** 5 c. multicoloured 15 10

**IMPERF EDGES.** On Nos. 624/54, 657 and 659 (stamps printed by the B.A.B.N. Co.) the outer edges of the sheets were guillotined to remove the imprints for P.O. stock so that single stamps may, therefore, be found with either one, or two adjacent sides imperforate.

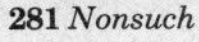

**281** *Nonsuch* **282** Lacrosse Players

(Recess and photo B.A.B.N.)

**1968** (5 June). 300*th Anniv of Voyage of the "Nonsuch". P* 10.
624 **281** 5 c. multicoloured 20 10

(Des J. E. Aldridge. Recess and photo B.A.B.N.)

**1968** (3 July). *Lacrosse. P* 10.
625 **282** 5 c. black, red and lemon 15 10

**283** Front Page of *The Globe*, George Brown and Legislative Building **284** H. Bourassa

(Des N. Sabolotny. Recess and photo B.A.B.N.)

**1968** (21 Aug). 150*th Birth Anniv of George Brown (politician and journalist). P* 10.
626 **283** 5 c. multicoloured 10 10

(Des, recess and litho C.B.N.)

**1968** (4 Sept). *Birth Centenary of Henri Bourassa (journalist and politician). P* 12.
627 **284** 5 c. black, red and pale cream 10 10

**285** John McCrae, Battlefield and First Lines of "In Flanders Fields" **286** Armistice Monument, Vimy

(Des I. von Mosdossy. Litho C.B.N.)

**1968** (15 Oct). 50*th Death Anniv of John McCrae (soldier and poet). P* 12.
628 **285** 5 c. multicoloured 10 10

(Des and recess C.B.N.)

**1968** (15 Oct). 50*th Anniversary of* 1918 *Armistice. P* 12.
629 **286** 15 c. slate-black 30 40

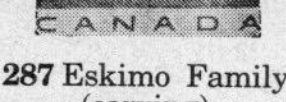

**287** Eskimo Family (carving) **288** "Mother and Child" (carving)

(Designs from Eskimo carvings by Munamee (6 c.) and unknown carver (5 c.). Photo C.B.N.)

**1968.** *Christmas. P* 12.
630 **287** 5 c. black and new blue (1.11.68) 10 10
a. Booklet pane of 10 (15.11.68) 2·25
p. One centre phosphor band 10 30
pa. Booklet pane of 10 (15.11.68) 2·50
631 **288** 6 c. black and ochre (15.11.68) 10 10
p. Two phosphor bands 15 30

**289** Curling **290** Vincent Massey

(Des D. Eales. Recess and photo B.A.B.N.)

**1969** (15 Jan). *Curling. P* 10.
632 **289** 6 c. black, new blue and scarlet 15 10

(Des I. von Mosdossy. Recess and litho C.B.N.)

**1969** (20 Feb). *Vincent Massey, First Canadian-born Governor-General. P* 12.
633 **290** 6 c. sepia and yellow-ochre 10 10

**291** "Return from the Harvest Field" (Suzor-Côté) **292** Globe and Tools

(Photo C.B.N.)

**1969** (14 Mar). *Birth Centenary of Marc Aurèle de Foy Suzor-Côté (painter). P* 12.
634 **291** 50 c. multicoloured 70 2·00

(Des J. Hébert. Recess B.A.B.N.)

**1969** (21 May). 50*th Anniv of International Labour Organisation. P* 12½ × 12.
635 **292** 6 c. bronze-green 10 10

**293** Vickers "Vimy" Aircraft over Atlantic Ocean **294** "Sir William Osler" (J. S. Sargent)

(Des R. W. Bradford. Recess and photo B.A.B.N.)

**1969** (13 June). 50*th Anniv of First Non-stop Transatlantic Flight. P* 12 × 12½.
636 **293** 15 c. chocolate, bright green & pale blue 40 55

(Des, recess and photo B.A.B.N.)

**1969** (23 June). 50*th Death Anniv of Sir William Osler (physician). P* 12½ × 12.
637 **294** 6 c. deep blue, light blue and chestnut 20 10

**295** White-throated Sparrows **298** Flags of Winter and Summer Games

(Des M. G. Loates. Litho C.B.N.)

**1969** (23 July). *Birds. T* **295** *and similar multicoloured designs. P* 12.
638 6 c. Type **295** 25 10
639 10 c. Savannah Sparrow (*horiz*) 65 80
640 25 c. Hermit Thrush (*horiz*) 1·90 2·50
638/40 *Set of* 3 2·50 3·00

(Des C. McDiarmid. Recess and litho C.B.N.)

**1969** (15 Aug). *Canadian Games. P* 12.
641 **298** 6 c. emerald, scarlet and blue 10 10

## ALTERED CATALOGUE NUMBERS

Any Catalogue numbers altered from the last edition are shown as a list in the introductory pages.

**299** Outline of Prince Edward Island showing Charlottetown **300** Sir Isaac Brock and Memorial Column

(Des L. Fitzgerald. Recess and photo B.A.B.N.)

**1969** (15 Aug). *Bicentenary of Charlottetown as Capital of Prince Edward Island. P* 12 × 12½.
642 **299** 6 c. yellow-brown, black and blue 20 10

(Des I. von Mosdossy. Recess and litho C.B.N.)

**1969** (12 Sept). *Birth Bicentenary of Sir Isaac Brock. P* 12.
643 **300** 6 c. orange, bistre and bistre-brown 10 10

**301** Children of the World in Prayer **302** Stephen Butler Leacock, Mask and "Mariposa"

(Des Rapid Grip and Batten Ltd. Litho C.B.N.)

**1969** (8 Oct). *Christmas. P* 12.
644 **301** 5 c. multicoloured 10 10
a. Booklet pane of 10 1·75
p. One centre phosphor band 10 30
pa. Booklet pane of 10 2·50
645 6 c. multicoloured 10 10
a. Black (inscr, value and frame omitted) £1100
p. Two phosphor bands 10 30

(Des, recess and photo B.A.B.N.)

**1969** (12 Nov). *Birth Centenary of Stephen Butler Leacock (humorist). P* 12 × 12½.
646 **302** 6 c. multicoloured 10 10

**303** Symbolic Cross-roads **304** "Enchanted Owl" (Kenojuak)

(Des K. C. Lochhead. Litho C.B.N.)

**1970** (27 Jan). *Centenary of Manitoba. P* 12.
647 **303** 6 c. ultramarine, lemon and vermilion 15 10
p. Two phosphor bands 15 40

(Des N. E. Hallendy and Miss S. Van Raalte. Recess C.B.N.)

**1970** (27 Jan). *Centenary of Northwest Territories. P* 12.
648 **304** 6 c. carmine-red and black 10 10

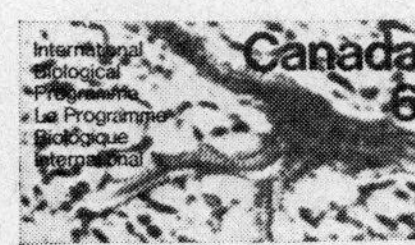

**305** Microscopic View of Inside of Leaf **306** Expo 67 Emblem and Stylized Cherry Blossom

(Des I. Charney. Recess and photo B.A.B.N.)

**1970** (18 Feb). *International Biological Programme. P* 12 × 12½.
649 **305** 6 c. emerald, orange-yellow & ultram 15 10

(Des E. R. C. Bethune. Litho C.B.N.)

**1970** (18 Mar). *World Fair, Osaka. T* **306** *and similar horiz designs. Multicoloured; colour of Cherry Blossom given. P* 12.
650 25 c. red 1·40 1·25
a. Block of 4. Nos. 650/3 5·00
p. Two phosphor bands 1·50 2·25
pa. Block of 4. Nos. 650p/3p 5·50
651 25 c. violet 1·40 1·25
p. Two phosphor bands 1·50 2·25
652 25 c. green 1·40 1·25
p. Two phosphor bands 1·50 2·25
653 25 c. blue 1·40 1·25
p. Two phosphor bands 1·50 2·25
650/3 *Set of* 4 5·00 4·50

Designs:—No. 650, Type **306**; No. 651, Dogwood and stylized cherry blossom; No. 652, White Trillium and stylized cherry blossom; No. 653, White Garden Lily and stylized cherry blossom.

Nos. 650/3 and 650p/3p are printed together in sheets of 50 (5 × 10). In the first, second, fourth and fifth vertical rows the four different designs are arranged in *se-tenant* blocks, whilst the centre row is composed as follows (reading downwards:—650(p)/3(p), 650(p) × 2, 653(p), 651(p), 652(p) and 650(p).

310 Henry Kelsey

311 "Towards Unification"

(Des D. Burton. Recess and photo B.A.B.N.)

**1970** (15 Apr). *300th Birth Anniv of Henry Kelsey (explorer). P 12 × 12½.*
654 **310** 6 c. multicoloured .. .. .. .. 10 10

(Des B. Fisher. Litho B.A.B.N.)

**1970** (13 May). *25th Anniv of United Nations. P 11.*
655 **311** 10 c. blue .. .. .. .. .. 30 30
p. Two phosphor bands .. .. 50 1·25
656 15 c. magenta and bluish lilac .. .. 40 35
p. Two phosphor bands .. .. 50 1·25

312 Louis Riel (Métis leader)

313 Mackenzie's Inscription, Dean Channel

(Des R. Derreth. Photo B.A.B.N.)

**1970** (19 June). *Louis Riel Commemoration. P 12½ × 12.*
657 **312** 6 c. greenish blue and vermilion .. 10 10

(Design from Government Archives photo. Recess C.B.N.)

**1970** (25 June). *Sir Alexander Mackenzie (explorer). P 12 × 11½.*
658 **313** 6 c. bistre-brown .. .. .. 15 10

314 Sir Oliver Mowat (statesman)

315 "Isles of Spruce" (A. Lismer)

(Des E. Roch. Recess and photo B.A.B.N.)

**1970** (12 Aug). *Sir Oliver Mowat Commemoration. P 12×12½.*
659 **314** 6 c. vermilion and black .. .. 10 10

(Litho Ashton-Potter)

**1970** (18 Sept). *50th Anniv of "Group of Seven" (artists). P 11.*
660 **315** 6 c. multicoloured .. .. .. 10 10

316 "Horse-drawn Sleigh" (D. Niskala)

317 "Christ in Manger" (C. Fortier)

(Des from children's drawings. Litho C.B.N.)

**1970** (7 Oct). *Christmas. Horiz designs as T* **316/17**, *showing children's drawings. Multicoloured. P 12.*
661 5 c. Type **316** .. .. .. .. 40 20
a. Strip of 5. Nos. 661/5 .. .. .. 1·75
p. One centre phosphor band .. .. 70 70
pa. Strip of 5. Nos. 661p/5p .. .. 3·25
662 5 c. "Stable" and Star of Bethlehem" (L. Wilson) (26 × 21 *mm*) .. .. 40 20
p. One centre phosphor band .. .. 70 70
663 5 c. "Snowmen" (M. Lecompte) (26 × 21 *mm*) 40 20
p. One centre phosphor band .. .. 70 70
664 5 c. "Skiing" (D. Durham) (26 × 21 *mm*) .. 40 20
p. One centre phosphor band .. .. 70 70
665 5 c. "Santa Claus" (A. Martin) (26 × 21 *mm*) 40 20
p. One centre phosphor band .. .. 70 70
666 6 c. "Santa Claus" (E. Bhattacharya) (26 × 21 *mm*) .. .. .. .. .. 40 20
a. Strip of 5. Nos. 666/70 .. .. 1·75
p. Two phosphor bands .. .. .. 70 70
pa. Strip of 5. Nos. 666p/70p.. .. 3·25
667 6 c. "Christ in Manger" (J. McKinney) (26 × 21 *mm*) .. .. .. .. .. 40 20
p. Two phosphor bands .. .. .. 70 70
668 6 c. "Toy Shop" (N. Whateley) (26 × 21 *mm*) 40 20
p. Two phosphor bands .. .. .. 70 70
669 6 c. "Christmas Tree" (J. Pomperleau) (26 × 21 *mm*) .. .. .. .. .. 40 20
p. Two phosphor bands .. .. .. 70 70
670 6 c. "Church" (J. McMillan) (26 × 21 *mm*) .. 40 20
p. Two phosphor bands .. .. .. 70 70
671 10 c. Type **317** .. .. .. .. 30 30
p. Two phosphor bands .. .. .. 55 70
672 15 c. "Trees and Sledge" (J. Dojcak) (35 × 21 mm) .. .. .. .. .. 45 60
p. Two phosphor bands .. .. 70 1·25
661/72 .. .. .. .. *Set of* 12 3·75 2·50
661p/672p .. .. .. *Set of* 12 7·00 8·00

The designs of the 5 c. and 6 c. were each issued with the various designs *se-tenant* in a diamond shaped arrangement within the sheet. This generally results in *se-tenant* pairs both vert and horiz, but due to the sheet arrangement vert and horiz pairs of the same design exist from the two centre vert and horiz rows.

328 Sir Donald A. Smith

329 "Big Raven" (E. Carr)

(Des Dora de Pédery-Hunt. Litho C.B.N.)

**1970** (4 Nov). *150th Birth Anniv of Sir Donald Alexander Smith. P 12.*
673 **328** 6 c. yellow, brown and bronze-green .. 10 10

(Litho C.B.N.)

**1971** (12 Feb). *Birth Centenary of Emily Carr (painter). P 12.*
674 **329** 6 c. multicoloured .. .. .. 20 20

330 Laboratory Equipment

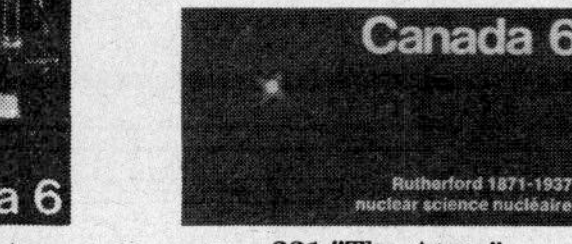


331 "The Atom"

(Des R. Webber. Litho B.A.B.N.)

**1971** (3 Mar). *50th Anniv of Discovery of Insulin. P 10½.*
675 **330** 6 c. multicoloured .. .. .. 30 20

(Des R. Webber. Litho B.A.B.N.)

**1971** (24 Mar). *Birth Centenary of Lord Rutherford (scientist). P 11.*
676 **331** 6 c. yellow, red and deep chocolate 20 10

332 Maple "Keys"

333 Louis Papineau

(Des Alma Duncan. Litho Ashton-Potter)

**1971.** *"The Maple Leaf in Four Seasons". T* **332** *and similar vert designs. Multicoloured. P 11.*
677 6 c. Type **332** (Spring) (14.4) .. .. .. 20 15
a. Imperf (pair) .. .. .. £650
678 6 c. Green leaves (Summer) (16.6) .. .. 20 15
679 7 c. Autumn leaves (3.9) .. .. .. 20 15
a. Grey (inscr and value) omitted .. .. £2000
680 7 c. Withered leaves and snow (Winter) (19.11) .. .. .. .. .. 20 15
677/80 .. .. .. .. *Set of* 4 70 55

(Des L. Marquart. Recess and photo B.A.B.N.)

**1971** (7 May). *Death Centenary of Louis-Joseph Papineau (politician). P 12½ × 12.*
681 **333** 6 c. multicoloured .. .. .. 15 15

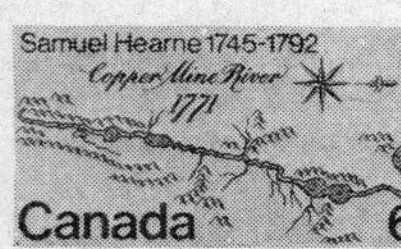


334 Chart of Coppermine River

335 "People" and Computer Tapes

(Des L. Marquart. Recess and photo B.A.B.N.)

**1971** (7 May). *Bicentenary of Samuel Hearne's Expedition to Coppermine River. P 12×12½.*
682 **334** 6 c. red, sepia and pale buff .. .. 30 30

(Des H. Kleefeld. Litho C.B.N.)

**1971** (1 June). *Centenary of First Canadian Census. P 11½.*
683 **335** 6 c. blue, red and black .. .. .. 20 10

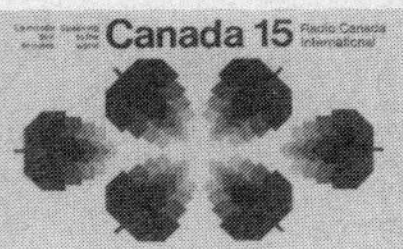


336 Maple Leaves

(Des B. Kramer. Litho C.B.N.)

**1971** (1 June). *Radio Canada International. P 12.*
684 **336** 15 c. red, yellow and black .. .. 50 1·00
p. Two phosphor bands .. .. 1·60 3·00

337 "BC"

(Des E. R. C. Bethune. Litho C.B.N.)

**1971** (20 July). *Centenary of British Columbia's Entry into the Confederation. P 12.*
685 **337** 7 c. multicoloured .. .. .. 15 10

338 "Indian Encampment on Lake Huron" (Kane)

339 "Snowflake"

(Des and litho B.A.B.N.)

**1971** (11 Aug). *Death Centenary of Paul Kane (painter). P 12½.*
686 **338** 7 c. multicoloured .. .. .. 20 10

(Des Lisl Levinsohn. Recess (6 c., 7 c.) or recess and litho (others) C.B.N.)

**1971** (6 Oct). *Christmas. T* **379** *and similar design. P 12.*
687 **339** 6 c. deep blue .. .. .. 10 10
p. One centre phosphor band .. .. 20 40
688 7 c. deep emerald .. .. .. 15 10
p. Two phosphor bands .. .. 30 45
689 – 10 c. silver and cerise .. .. 55 90
p. Two phosphor bands .. .. 70 1·75
690 – 15 c. silver, brown-purple and lavender 85 1·10
p. Two phosphor bands .. .. 85 2·25
687/90 .. .. .. .. *Set of* 4 1·50 2·00
687p/90p .. .. .. *Set of* 4 1·90 4·25

Design:—10 c., 15 c. "Snowflake" design similar to T **339** but square (26 × 26 mm).

340 Pierre Laporte (Quebec Cabinet Minister)

341 Skaters

(Des G. Gundersen. Recess and litho B.A.B.N.)

**1971** (20 Oct). *First Anniv of the Assassination of Pierre Laporte. P 12½ × 12.*
691 **340** 7 c. black/*pale buff* .. .. .. 15 10

(Des Design Workshop, Toronto. Litho C.B.N.)

**1972** (1 Mar). *World Figure Skating Championships, Calgary. P 12.*
692 **341** 8 c. purple .. .. .. .. 15 10

**MIGRATING FLUORESCENT BANDS.** These are referred to in the notes after No. 610. In the following issues they exist on Nos. 719/20 and 731/2 and on early printings only of Nos. 702/6.

342 J. A. MacDonald

343 Forest, Central Canada

**344** Vancouver

Type I

Type II

Two types of 10 c. (No. 702):
Type I. Light impression of green recess colour. Cross-hatching around "Canada" clearly visible (plate 1).
Type II. Green recess colour much more deeply etched. Cross-hatching around "Canada" entirely obscured (plates 2 and 3).

Type I

Type II

Two types of 15 c.:
Type I. Trees on hillside, shown in blue, clearly detailed (plate 1).
Type II. Trees shown in solid colour (plate 2).

Two types of 25 c.:
Type I. Bears' shadows evenly shaded.
Type II. Shadows have a solid central area.

(Des D. Annesley (1 to 10 c. (701)), R. Derreth (others))

**1972–77.** *Various designs as T* **342/4**.

(*a*) *T* **342** *and similar vert portraits. Recess C.B.N. (1 to 6 c. and last ptgs of 7 and 8 c. (No. 700), B.A.B.N. (7, 8, 10 c. and booklet panes). Two fluorescent bands. P 12 × 12½ (1 to 8 c.) or 13 (10 c.).* (17.10.73)

693 1 c. orange . . 10 10
a. Booklet pane. Nos. 693 × 3, 698 and 700 × 2 (10.4.74) . . 65
b. Booklet pane. Nos. 693 × 6, 698 and 700 × 11 (17.1.75) . . 2·25
c. Booklet pane Nos. 693 × 2, 694 × 4 and 701a × 4 (1.9.76) . . 2·00
694 2 c. deep green . . 10 10
695 3 c. agate . . 10 10
696 4 c. black . . 10 10
697 5 c. deep magenta . . 10 10
698 6 c. Indian red . . 10 10
699 7 c. reddish brown (8.4.74) . . 10 15
700 8 c. dull ultramarine . . 15 10
a. Perf 13 (12.76) . . 75 30
701 10 c. brown-lake (1.9.76) . . 30 10
a. Perf 12 × 12½ (*booklets*) . . 50 50

(*b*) *T* **343** *and similar vert designs. Recess and photo B.A.B.N. Two fluorescent bands. P 12½ × 12* (8.9.72)

702 10 c. dp green, blue-green & yellow-orge (I) 50 10
a. Type II (7.74) . . 40 15
b. Perf 13½ (2.76) . . 30 10
p. Two phosphor bands . . 90 1·50
703 15 c. dull ultramarine and orange-brown (I) 70 10
a. Type II (1975) . . 1·50 65
b. Perf 13½ (2.76) . . 30 10
p. Two phosphor bands . . 1·25 2·00
704 20 c. pale orange, reddish violet & ultram 55 10
a. Perf 13½ (2.76) . . 30 10
p. Two phosphor bands . . 1·50 2·50
705 25 c. deep ultramarine and pale blue (I) . . 65 10
a. Type II (1975) . . 4·50 1·25
b. Perf 13½ (2.76) . . 40 10
p. Two phosphor bands . . 2·40 3·50
706 50 c. blue-green, royal blue and buff . . 45 10
a. *Blue-green, ultramarine and buff* (8.74) 65 10
b. Perf 13½ (2.76) . . 40 10

(*c*) *T* **344** *and similar horiz design. Recess B.A.B.N. and litho Ashton-Potter. No fluorescent bands. P* 11 (17.3.72)

707 $1 multicoloured . . 5·00 4·00
708 $2 multicoloured . . 1·50 2·00

(*d*) *T* **344**. *Recess and photo B.A.B.N. Two fluorescent bands. P 12½ × 12* (24.10.73)

709 $1 multicoloured . . 1·25 80
a. Perf 13½ (4.77) . . 70 30

(*e*) *As Nos. 700/1. Recess C.B.N. Imperf × perf 10 (coil stamps)*

710 8 c. dull ultramarine (10.4.74) . . 55 20
a. Imperf (horiz pair) . . 70·00
711 10 c. brown-lake (1.9.76) . . 30 20
a. Imperf (horiz pair) . . £110

Designs (1 to 7c. show Canadian Prime Ministers):—2 c. W. Laurier; 3 c. R. Borden; 4 c. W. L. Mackenzie King; 5 c. R. B. Bennett; 6 c. L. B. Pearson; 7 c. Louis St. Laurent; 8 and 10 c. (Nos. 701/a, 711), Queen Elizabeth II; 15 c. American Bighorn sheep; 20 c. Prairie landscape from the air; 25 c. Polar Bears; 50 c. Seashore, Eastern Canada; $2 Quebec.

Stamps from booklets exist with one or two adjacent sides imperforate.

**345** Heart

(Des Joyce Wieland. Recess B.A.B.N.)

**1972** (7 Apr). *Heart Disease (World Health Day). P 12 × 12½.*

719 **345** 8 c. carmine . . 15 10

This stamp exists on two kinds of paper, with or without fluorescent bands.

**346** Frontenac and Fort Saint-Louis, Quebec

(Des L. Marquart. Recess and photo B.A.B.N.)

**1972** (17 May). *300th Anniv of Governor Frontenac's Appointment to New France. P 12 × 12½.*

720 **346** 8 c. brown-red, orange-brn & dp ultram 15 15

This exists with or without fluorescent bands.

**347** Plains Indians' Artefacts **347a** Buffalo Chase

(Des G. Beaupré. Litho Ashton-Potter (721/2, 725/6 and 729/30), B.A.B.N. (723/4), C.B.N. (727/8))

**1972–76.** *Canadian Indians. P 12 × 12½* (721/2, 725/6), 12 (723/4), 13 (727/30), 12½ × 12 (731/6) *or* 12½ (737/40).

(*a*) *Horiz designs issued in se-tenant pairs, the first showing Artefacts as T* **347**, *the second showing Scenes from Indian Life as T* **347a**

721 8 c. multicoloured (6.7.72) . . 40 10
a. Pair. Nos. 721/2 . . 85 1·00
722 8 c. deep brown, yellow & grey-black (6.7.72) 40 10
723 8 c. multicoloured (21.2.73) . . 40 10
a. Pair. Nos. 723/4 . . 85 1·00
724 8 c. multicoloured (21.2.73) . . 40 10
725 8 c. multicoloured (16.1.74) . . 40 10
a. Pair. Nos. 725/6 . . 85 1·00
726 8 c. dp brown, yellow & grey-black (16.1.74) 40 10
727 8 c. multicoloured (4.4.75) . . 40 10
a. Pair. Nos. 727/8 . . 85 1·00
ab. Imperf between (horiz pair) . . £450
728 8 c. multicoloured (4.4.75) . . 40 10
729 10 c. multicoloured (17.9.76) . . 40 20
a. Pair. Nos. 729/30 . . 85 1·00
730 10 c. light stone and black (17.9.76) . . 40 20

Designs show the following tribes: Nos. 721/2 (T **347**/*a*), Plains Indians; 723/4, Algonkians; 725/6, Pacific Coast Indians; 727/8, Subarctic Indians; 729/30, Iroquoians.

## MINIMUM PRICE

The minimum price quote is 10p which represents a handling charge rather than a basis for valuing common stamps. For further notes about prices see introductory pages.

**348** Thunderbird and Tribal Pattern **348a** Dancer in Ceremonial Costume

(Des G. Beaupré. Recess and photo B.A.B.N. (731/6). Litho and embossed Ashton-Potter (737, 739). Litho Ashton-Potter (738, 740))

(*b*) *Vert designs issued in se-tenant pairs, the first showing Thunderbird and pattern as T* **348**, *the second Costumes as T* **348a**

731 8 c. light yellow-orange, rose-red and black (4.10.72) . . 40 15
a. Pair. Nos. 731/2 . . 85 1·00
732 8 c. multicoloured (4.10.72) . . 40 15
733 8 c. light rose-red, violet and black (28.11.73) 40 10
a. Pair. Nos. 733/4 . . 85 1·00
734 8 c. turquoise-green, lake-brown and black (28.11.73) . . 40 10
735 8 c. rose-red and black (22.2.74) . . 40 10
a. Pair. Nos. 735/6 . . 85 1·00
736 8 c. multicoloured (22.2.74) . . 40 10
737 8 c. myrtle-green, grey-brown and black (4.4.75) . . 40 10
a. Pair. Nos. 737/8 . . 85 1·00
738 8 c. multicoloured (4.4.75) . . 40 10
739 10 c. olive-bistre, reddish orange and black (17.9.76) . . 40 20
a. Pair. Nos. 739/40 . . 85 1·00
740 10 c. multicoloured (17.9.76) . . 40 20
721/40 . . *Set of* 20 7·50 2·10

Designs show the following tribes: Nos. 731/2 (T **348**/*a*), Plains Indians; 733/4, Algonkians; 735/6, Pacific Coast Indians; 737/8, Subarctic Indians; 739/40, Iroquoians.

Nos. 721/2 and 731/2 exist with or without fluorescent bands and the remainder only with fluorescent bands.

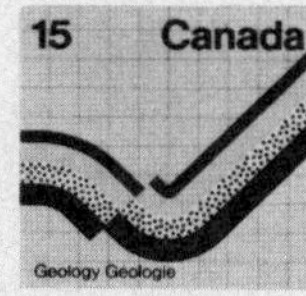

**349** Earth's Crust **350** Candles

(Des Gottschalk and Ash Ltd. Litho Ashton-Potter)

**1972** (2 Aug). *Earth Sciences. T* **349** *and similar square designs. P* 12.

741 15 c. multicoloured . . 1·00 1·40
a. Block of 4. Nos. 741/4 . . 3·50
742 15 c. pale grey, dull ultramarine and black . . 1·00 1·40
743 15 c. multicoloured . . 1·00 1·40
744 15 c. light emerald, red-orange and black . . 1·00 1·40
741/4 . . *Set of* 4 3·50 5·00

Designs and Events:—No. 741, Photogrammetric surveying (12th Congress of International Society of Photogrammetry); No. 742, "Siegfried" lines (6th Conference of International Cartographic Association); No. 743, Type **349** (24th International Geological Congress); No. 744, Diagram of village at road-intersection (22nd International Geographical Congress).

Nos. 741/4 were issued in sheets of 64, made up of 4 panes of 16, each pane having a marginal commemorative inscription. Within a pane are 4 copies of each design, arranged in *se-tenant* blocks of 4.

This issue exists with or without fluorescent bands.

(Des R. Webber. Litho Ashton-Potter)

**1972** (1 Nov). *Christmas. T* **350** *and similar designs. P 12½ × 12 (6 and 8 c.) or 11 × 10½ (others).*

745 **350** 6 c. multicoloured . . 15 10
p. One centre phosphor band . . 35 40
746 8 c. multicoloured . . 20 10
p. Two phosphor bands . . 40 50
747 – 10 c. multicoloured . . 60 35
p. Two phosphor bands . . 1·00 1·40
748 – 15 c. multicoloured . . 80 75
p. Two phosphor bands . . 1·25 2·00
745/8 . . *Set of* 4 1·60 1·10
745p/8p . . *Set of* 4 2·75 4·00

Designs: *Horiz* (36 × 20 *mm*)—10 c. Candles with fruits and pine boughs; 15 c. Candles with prayer-book, caskets and vase.

This issue also exists with fluorescent bands.

Canada 8

**351** "The Blacksmith's Shop" (Krieghoff) **352** François de Montmorency-Laval

(Des and litho B.A.B.N. and Saults & Pollard Ltd., Winnipeg)

**1972** (29 Nov). *Death Centenary of Cornelius Krieghoff (painter). P* 12½.

749 **351** 8 c. multicoloured . . 30 15

This stamp exists with or without fluorescent bands.

**FLUORESCENT BANDS.** Stamps from No. 750 onwards were issued only with two fluorescent bands, *unless otherwise stated.* Examples are known with the bands omitted in error, but such varieties are outside the scope of the catalogue.

(Des M. Fog and G. Lorange. Litho Ashton-Potter)

**1973** (31 Jan). *350th Birth Anniv of Monsignor de Laval (First Bishop of Quebec). P* 11.
750 **352** 8 c. ultramarine, gold and silver .. 20 30

**353** Commissioner French and Route of the March West

(Des Dallaire Morin DeVito Inc. Litho Ashton-Potter)

**1973** (9 Mar). *Centenary of Royal Canadian Mounted Police. T* **353** *and similar horiz designs. Multicoloured (except* 8 c.). *P* 11.
751 8 c. Type **353** (deep reddish brown, dull orange and orange-vermilion) .. .. 35 15
752 10 c. Spectrograph .. .. .. .. .. 1·25 1·75
753 15 c. Mounted policeman .. .. .. .. 1·75 2·00
751/3 .. .. .. .. .. *Set of* 3 3·00 3·50

**354** Jeanne Mance

(Des R. Bellemare. Litho Ashton-Potter)

**1973** (18 Apr). *300th Death Anniv of Jeanne Mance (nurse). P* 11.
754 **354** 8 c. multicoloured .. .. .. 20 30

**355** Joseph Howe

**356** "Mist Fantasy" (MacDonald)

(Des A. Fleming. Litho Ashton-Potter)

**1973** (16 May). *Death Centenary of Joseph Howe (Nova Scotian politician). P* 11.
755 **355** 8 c. gold and black .. .. .. 20 30

(Des and litho Ashton-Potter)

**1973** (8 June). *Birth Centenary of J. E. H. MacDonald (artist). P* 12½.
756 **356** 15 c. multicoloured .. .. .. 30 55

**357** Oaks and Harbour

(Des A. Mann. Recess and photo B.A.B.N.)

**1973** (22 June). *Centenary of Prince Edward Island's Entry into the Confederation. P* 12.
757 **357** 8 c. pale orange and brown-red .. 20 30

**358** Scottish Settlers

**359** Queen Elizabeth II

(Des P. Swan. Litho Ashton-Potter)

**1973** (20 July). *Bicentennial of Arrival of Scottish Settlers at Pictou, Nova Scotia. P* 12 × 12½.
758 **358** 8 c. multicoloured .. .. .. 25 20

(Des A. Fleming from photograph by Anthony Buckley. Eng G. A. Gundersen. Recess and photo B.A.B.N.)

**1973** (2 Aug). *Royal Visit and Commonwealth Heads of Government Meeting, Ottawa. P* 12 × 12½.
759 **359** 8 c. multicoloured .. .. .. 25 20
760 15 c. red, black and bright gold .. .. 1·00 1·90
*a. Red, black and pale dull gold* .. 1·10 1·90

**360** Nellie McClung

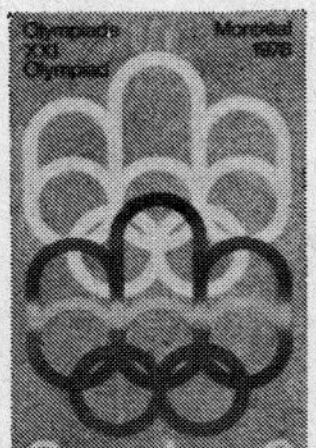


**361** Emblem of 1976 Olympics

(Des S. Mennie. Litho Ashton-Potter)

**1973** (29 Aug). *Birth Centenary of Nellie McClung (feminist). P* 10½ × 11.
761 **360** 8 c. multicoloured .. .. .. 20 30

(Des Wallis and Matanovic. Litho Ashton-Potter)

**1973** (20 Sept). *Olympic Games, Montreal* (1976) (*1st issue*). *P* 12 × 12½.
762 **361** 8 c. multicoloured .. .. .. 20 15
763 15 c. multicoloured .. .. .. 35 1·25
See also Nos. 768/71, 772/4, 786/9, 798/802, 809/11, 814/16, 829/31, 833/7 and 842/4.

**362** Ice-skate

**363** Diving

(Des A. Maggs. Litho Ashton-Potter)

**1973** (7 Nov). *Christmas. T* **362** *and similar vert designs. Multicoloured. P* 12½ × 12 (6, 8 c.) *or* 11 (*others*).
764 6 c. Type **362** .. .. .. .. .. 15 10
765 8 c. Bird decoration .. .. .. .. 20 10
766 10 c. Santa Claus (20 × 36 *mm*) .. .. 70 1·25
767 15 c. Shepherd (20 × 36 *mm*) .. .. 80 1·50
764/7 .. .. .. .. *Set of* 4 1·75 2·75

(Des Hunter, Straker, Templeton Ltd. Recess C.B.N.)

**1974** (22 Mar). *Olympic Games, Montreal* (1976) (*2nd issue*). *"Summer Activities". T* **363** *and similar vert designs. Each deep blue. P* 12.
768 8 c. Type **363** .. .. .. .. .. 20 25
a. Block of 4. Nos. 768/71 .. .. .. 70
769 8 c. "Jogging" .. .. .. .. .. 20 25
770 8 c. Cycling .. .. .. .. .. 20 25
771 8 c. Hiking .. .. .. .. .. 20 25
768/71 .. .. .. .. *Set of* 4 70 90
Nos. 768/71 were printed in *se-tenant* blocks of four throughout the sheet. Each design has a second (latent) image—the Canadian Olympic Games symbol—which appears when the stamp is viewed obliquely to the light.
See also Nos. 786/9.

(Des Wallis and Matanovic. Litho Ashton-Potter)

**1974** (17 Apr). *Olympic Games, Montreal* (1976) (*3rd issue*). *As T* **361** *but smaller* (20 × 36½ *mm*). *P* 12½.
772 **361** 8 c. + 2 c. multicoloured .. .. 15 35
773 10 c. + 5 c. multicoloured .. .. 25 70
774 15 c. + 5 c. multicoloured .. .. 30 1·00
772/4 .. .. .. .. *Set of* 3 65 1·90

**364** Winnipeg Signpost, 1872

**365** Postmaster and Customer

(Des J. R. MacDonald. Litho and embossed Ashton-Potter)

**1974** (3 May). *Winnipeg Centennial. P* 12½ × 12.
775 **364** 8 c. multicoloured .. .. .. 20 15

(Des S. Mennie. Litho Ashton-Potter)

**1974** (11 June). *Centenary of Canadian Letter Carrier Delivery Service. T* **365** *and similar horiz designs. Multicoloured. P* 13½.
776 8 c. Type **365** .. .. .. .. .. 55 45
a. Block of 6. Nos. 776/81 .. .. 3·00
777 8 c. Postman collecting mail .. .. .. 55 45
778 8 c. Mail handler .. .. .. .. 55 45
779 8 c. Mail sorters .. .. .. .. 55 45
780 8 c. Postman making delivery .. .. 55 45
781 8 c. Rural delivery by car .. .. .. 55 45
776/81 .. .. .. .. *Set of* 6 3·00 2·50
Nos. 776/81 were printed in *se-tenant* combinations throughout a sheet of 50, giving 6 blocks of 6 and 14 single stamps.

**366** "Canada's Contribution to Agriculture"

**367** Telephone Development

(Des M. Brett, P. Cowley-Brown, and A. McAllister. Litho Ashton-Potter)

**1974** (12 July). *"Agricultural Education". Centenary of Ontario Agricultural College. P* 12½ × 12.
782 **366** 8 c. multicoloured .. .. .. 20 20

(Des R. Webber. Litho Ashton-Potter)

**1974** (26 July). *Centenary of Invention of Telephone by Alexander Graham Bell. P* 12½.
783 **367** 8 c. multicoloured .. .. .. 20 20

**368** Bicycle Wheel

(Des Burns and Cooper. Recess and photo B.A.B.N.)

**1974** (7 Aug). *World Cycling Championships, Montreal. P* 12 × 12½.
784 **368** 8 c. black, rosine and silver .. .. 20 30

**369** Mennonite Settlers

(Des W. Davies. Litho Ashton-Potter)

**1974** (28 Aug). *Centenary of Arrival of Mennonites in Manitoba. P* 12½.
785 **369** 8 c. multicoloured .. .. .. 20 20

(Des Hunter, Straker, Templeton Ltd. Recess C.B.N.)

**1974** (23 Sept). *Olympic Games, Montreal* (1976) (*4th issue*). *"Winter Activities". Horiz designs as T* **363**, *each rosine. P* 13½ × 13.
786 8 c. Snow-shoeing .. .. .. .. 50 40
a. Block of 4. Nos. 786/9 .. .. .. 1·75
787 8 c. Skiing .. .. .. .. .. 50 40
788 8 c. Skating .. .. .. .. .. 50 40
789 8 c. Curling .. .. .. .. .. 50 40
786/9 .. .. .. .. *Set of* 4 1·75 1·40

**370** Mercury, Winged Horses and U.P.U. Emblem

(Des G. Gundersen. Recess and photo B.A.B.N.)

**1974** (9 Oct). *Centenary of Universal Postal Union. P* 12 × 12½.
790 **370** 8 c. violet, red-orange and cobalt .. 15 15
791 15 c. red-orange, violet and cobalt .. 50 1·50

**371** "The Nativity" (J. P. Lemieux)

**372** Marconi and St. John's Harbour, Newfoundland

(Des Wallis and Matanovic. Litho Ashton-Potter)

**1974** (1 Nov). *Christmas. T* **371** *and similar horiz designs showing paintings. Multicoloured. P* 13½.
792 6 c. Type **371** .. .. .. .. .. 10 10
793 8 c. "Skaters in Hull" (H. Masson) (34 × 31 *mm*) .. .. .. .. .. 10 10
794 10 c. "The Ice Cone, Montmorency Falls" (R. C. Todd) .. .. .. .. .. 20 60
795 15 c. "Village in the Laurentian Mountains" (C. A. Gagnon) .. .. .. .. 30 90
792/5 .. .. .. .. *Set of* 4 60 1·60

(Des J. Boyle. Litho Ashton-Potter)

**1974** (15 Nov). *Birth Centenary of Guglielmo Marconi (radio pioneer). P* 13.
796 **372** 8 c. multicoloured .. .. .. 20 20

**373** Merritt and Welland Canal **374** Swimming

(Des W. Rueter. Recess (B.A.B.N.) and litho (C.B.N.))

**1974** (29 Nov). *William Merritt Commemoration. P* 13 × 13½.

| | | | | |
|---|---|---|---|---|
| 797 | **373** | 8 c. multicoloured | 20 | 30 |

(Des Wallis and Matanovic. Litho C.B.N.)

**1975** (5 Feb). *Olympic Games, Montreal* (1976) (5*th issue*). *T* **374** *and similar horiz designs. Multicoloured.*

| | | | |
|---|---|---|---|
| 798 | 8 c. + 2 c. Type **374** | 25 | 40 |
| 799 | 10 c. + 5 c. Rowing | 30 | 80 |
| 800 | 15 c. + 5 c. Sailing | 35 | 1·00 |
| 798/800 | *Set of* 3 | 80 | 2·00 |

**375** "The Sprinter" **376** "Anne of Green Gables" (Lucy Maud Montgomery)

(Des A. R. Fleming. Litho and embossed Ashton-Potter)

**1975** (14 Mar). *Olympic Games, Montreal* (1976) (6*th issue*). *T* **375** *and similar multicoloured design showing sculpture by R. T. McKenzie. P* 12½ × 12 ($1) *or* 12 × 12½ ($2).

| | | | |
|---|---|---|---|
| 801 | $1 Type **375** | 2·25 | 3·25 |
| 802 | $2 "The Diver" (*vert*) | 2·75 | 4·75 |

(Des P. Swan (No. 803), C. Gagnon (No. 804). Litho Ashton-Potter)

**1975** (15 May). *Canadian Writers* (1*st series*). *T* **376** *and similar vert design. Multicoloured. P* 13½.

| | | | |
|---|---|---|---|
| 803 | 8 c. Type **376** | 20 | 10 |
| | a. Pair. Nos. 803/4 | 40 | 80 |
| 804 | 8 c. "Maria Chapdelaine" (Louis Hémon) | 20 | 10 |

Nos. 803/4 were printed horizontally and vertically *se-tenant* throughout the sheet.

See also Nos. 846/7, 940/1 and 1085/6.

**377** Marguerite Bourgeoys (founder of the Order of Notre Dame) **378** S. D. Chown (founder of United Church of Canada)

(Des Design and Communication, Montreal. Litho Ashton-Potter (Nos. 805/6). Des W. Southern. Eng G. Gundersen. Recess and photo B.A.B.N. (Nos. 807/8))

**1975** (30 May). *Canadian Celebrities. T* **377/8** *and similar vert designs.*

(*a*) *As T* **377.** *P* 12½ × 12

| | | | |
|---|---|---|---|
| 805 | 8 c. multicoloured | 50 | 30 |
| 806 | 8 c. multicoloured | 50 | 30 |

(*b*) *As T* **378.** *P* 12 × 12½

| | | | |
|---|---|---|---|
| 807 | 8 c. sepia, flesh and light yellow | 30 | 40 |
| | a. Pair. Nos. 807/8 | 60 | 1·25 |
| 808 | 8 c. sepia, flesh and light yellow | 30 | 40 |
| 805/8 | *Set of* 4 | 1·40 | 1·25 |

Designs:—No. 805, Type **377**; No. 806, Alphonse Desjardins (leader of Credit Union movement); No. 807, Type **378**; No. 808, Dr. J. Cook (first moderator of Presbyterian Church in Canada).

Nos. 807/8 were printed together in the sheet horizontally and vertically *se-tenant*.

**379** Pole-vaulting **380** "Untamed" (photo by Walt Petrigo)

(Des P. Swan. Litho Ashton-Potter)

**1975** (11 June). *Olympic Games, Montreal* (1976) (7*th issue*). *T* **379** *and similar vert designs. Multicoloured. P* 12 × 12½.

| | | | |
|---|---|---|---|
| 809 | 20 c. Type **379** | 35 | 50 |
| 810 | 25 c. Marathon-running | 50 | 80 |
| 811 | 50 c. Hurdling | 60 | 1·25 |
| 809/11 | *Set of* 3 | 1·25 | 2·25 |

(Des B. Reilander. Litho C.B.N.)

**1975** (3 July). *Centenary of Calgary. P* 12 × 12½.

| | | | | |
|---|---|---|---|---|
| 812 | **380** | 8 c. multicoloured | 20 | 30 |

**381** I.W.Y. Symbol **382** Fencing

(Des Susan McPhee. Recess and photo B.A.B.N.)

**1975** (14 July). *International Women's Year. P* 13.

| | | | | |
|---|---|---|---|---|
| 813 | **381** | 8 c. lt grey-brown, bistre-yellow & blk | 20 | 30 |

(Des J. Hill. Litho C.B.N.)

**1975** (6 Aug). *Olympic Games, Montreal* (1976) (8*th issue*). *T* **382** *and similar vert designs showing combat sports. Multicoloured. P* 13.

| | | | |
|---|---|---|---|
| 814 | 8 c. + 2 c. Type **382** | 30 | 45 |
| 815 | 10 c. + 5 c. Boxing | 35 | 1·00 |
| 816 | 15 c. + 5 c. Judo | 40 | 1·25 |
| 814/16 | *Set of* 3 | 95 | 2·40 |

**383** "Justice-Justitia" (statue by W. S. Allward) **384** *William D. Lawrence*

(Des A. Fleming. Litho Ashton-Potter)

**1975** (2 Sept). *Centenary of Canadian Supreme Court. P* 12½.

| | | | | |
|---|---|---|---|---|
| 817 | **383** | 8 c. multicoloured | 20 | 30 |

(Des T. Bjarnason. Recess and photo B.A.B.N.)

**1975** (24 Sept). *Canadian Ships* (1*st series*). *T* **384** *and similar horiz designs showing coastal ships. P* 13.

| | | | |
|---|---|---|---|
| 818 | 8 c. yellow-brown and black | 70 | 40 |
| | a. Block of 4. Nos. 818/21 | 2·50 | |
| 819 | 8 c. blue-green and black | 70 | 40 |
| 820 | 8 c. yellow-green and black | 70 | 40 |
| 821 | 8 c. yellow-brown and black | 70 | 40 |
| 818/21 | *Set of* 4 | 2·50 | 1·40 |

Designs:—No. 819, *Neptune*; No. 820, *Beaver*; No. 821, *Quadra*.

Nos. 818/21 were printed together, *se-tenant*, in different combinations throughout the sheet, giving ten blocks of 4 and ten single stamps.

See also Nos. 851/4, 902/5 and 931/4.

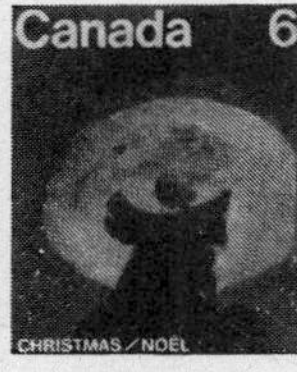

**385** "Santa Claus" (G. Kelly) **386** Text, Badge and Bugle

(Des B. Reilander from children's paintings. Litho Ashton-Potter)

**1975** (22 Oct). *Christmas. T* **385** *and similar multicoloured designs. P* 13.

| | | | |
|---|---|---|---|
| 822 | 6 c. Type **385** | 10 | 10 |
| | a. Pair. Nos. 822/3 | 20 | 40 |
| 823 | 6 c. "Skater" (Bill Cawsey) | 10 | 10 |
| 824 | 8 c. "Child" (D. Hébert) | 10 | 10 |
| | a. Pair. Nos. 824/5 | 25 | 45 |
| 825 | 8 c. "Family" (L. Caldwell) | 10 | 10 |
| 826 | 10 c. "Gift" (D. Lovely) | 20 | 50 |
| 827 | 15 c. "Trees" (R. Kowalski) (*horiz*) | 30 | 75 |
| 822/7 | *Set of* 6 | 85 | 1·90 |

Nos. 822/3 and 824/5 were respectively issued together *se-tenant* in an alternate arrangement within the sheet.

(Des R. Kavach. Recess and photo B.A.B.N.)

**1975** (10 Nov). 50*th Anniv of Royal Canadian Legion. P* 12½ × 13.

| | | | | |
|---|---|---|---|---|
| 828 | **386** | 8 c. multicoloured | 20 | 20 |

**387** Basketball

(Des J. Hill. Litho Ashton-Potter)

**1976** (7 Jan). *Olympic Games, Montreal* (9*th issue*). *T* **387** *and similar vert designs. Multicoloured. P* 13.

| | | | |
|---|---|---|---|
| 829 | 8 c. + 2 c. Type **387** | 30 | 40 |
| 830 | 10 c. + 5 c. Gymnastics | 35 | 1·00 |
| 831 | 20 c. + 5 c. Soccer | 45 | 1·25 |
| 829/31 | *Set of* 3 | 1·00 | 2·40 |

**388** Games Symbol and Snow Crystal **389** "Communications Arts"

(Des R. Harder. Litho Ashton-Potter)

**1976** (6 Feb). 12*th Winter Olympic Games. Innsbruck. P* 12½.

| | | | | |
|---|---|---|---|---|
| 832 | **388** | 20 c. multicoloured | 20 | 40 |

(Des R. Webber. Litho C.B.N.)

**1976** (6 Feb). *Olympic Games, Montreal* (10*th issue*). *T* **389** *and similar vert designs. Multicoloured. P* 12 × 12½.

| | | | |
|---|---|---|---|
| 833 | 20 c. Type **389** | 25 | 25 |
| 834 | 25 c. "Handicrafts" | 35 | 65 |
| 835 | 50 c. "Performing Arts" | 40 | 1·10 |
| 833/5 | *Set of* 3 | 90 | 1·75 |

**390** Place Ville Marie and Notre-Dame Church

(Des J. and P. Mercier. Recess and photo B.A.B.N.)

**1976** (12 Mar). *Olympic Games, Montreal* (11*th issue*). *T* **390** *and similar horiz design. Multicoloured. P* 13.

| | | | |
|---|---|---|---|
| 836 | $1 Type **390** | 2·50 | 5·50 |
| 837 | $2 Olympic Stadium and flags | 3·00 | 6·50 |

**391** Flower and Urban Sprawl **392** Benjamin Franklin and Map

(Des I. McLeod. Litho Ashton-Potter)

**1976** (12 May). *U.N. Conference on Human Settlements* (*HABITAT*), *Vancouver. P* 12 × 12½.

| | | | | |
|---|---|---|---|---|
| 838 | **391** | 20 c. multicoloured | 20 | 30 |

(Des B. Reilander. Recess and photo B.A.B.N.)

**1976** (1 June). *Bicentenary of American Revolution. P* 13.

| | | | | |
|---|---|---|---|---|
| 839 | **392** | 10 c. multicoloured | 20 | 35 |

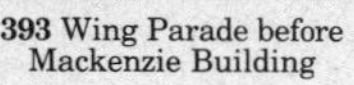

**393** Wing Parade before Mackenzie Building **394** Transfer of Olympic Flame by Satellite

(Des W. Davies. Litho C.B.N.)

**1976** (1 June). *Royal Military College Centenary. T* **393** *and similar vert design. Multicoloured. P* 12 × 12½.

840 8 c. Colour party and Memorial Arch .. 15 20
a. Pair. Nos. 840/1 .. 30 80
ab. Printed double (pair)
841 8 c. Type **393** .. 15 20

Nos. 840/1 were printed horizontally and vertically *se-tenant* throughout the sheet.

(Des P. Swan. Litho Ashton-Potter)

**1976** (18 June). *Olympic Games, Montreal* (12*th issue*). *T* **394** *and similar horiz designs. Multicoloured. P* 13½.

842 8 c. Type **394** .. 10 10
843 20 c. Carrying the Olympic flag .. 15 40
844 25 c. Athletes with medals .. 25 60
842/4 .. *Set of* 3 45 1·00

**395** Archer

(Des T. Bjarnason. Litho C.B.N.)

**1976** (3 Aug). *Olympiad for the Physically Disabled. P* 12 × 12½.

845 **395** 20 c. multicoloured .. 20 30

**396** "Sam McGee" (Robert W. Service) **397** "Nativity" (F. Mayer)

(Des D. Bierk (No. 846), A. Dumas (No. 847). Litho Ashton-Potter)

**1976** (17 Aug). *Canadian Writers* (2*nd series*). *T* **396** *and similar vert design. Multicoloured. P* 13.

846 8 c. Type **396** .. 15 20
a. Pair. Nos. 846/7 .. 30 75
847 8 c. "Le Survenant" (Germaine Guèvremont) 15 20

Nos. 846/7 were printed horizontally and vertically *se-tenant* throughout the sheet.

(Des B. Reilander. Litho Ashton-Potter)

**1976** (3 Nov). *Christmas. T* **397** *and similar vert designs showing stained-glass windows. Multicoloured. P* 13½.

848 8 c. Type **397** .. 10 10
849 10 c. "Nativity" (G. Maile & Son) .. 10 10
850 20 c. "Nativity" (Yvonne Williams) .. 20 50
848/50 .. *Set of* 3 30 50

**398** *Northcote* **399** Queen Elizabeth II

(Des T. Bjarnason. Recess and litho C.B.N.)

**1976** (19 Nov). *Canadian Ships* (2*nd series*). *T* **398** *and similar horiz designs showing inland vessels. P* 12 × 12½.

851 10 c. ochre, chestnut and black .. 30 30
a. Block of 4. Nos. 851/4 .. 1·10
852 10 c. violet-blue and black .. 30 30
853 10 c. bright blue and black .. 30 30
854 10 c. apple-green, olive-green and black .. 30 30
851/4 .. *Set of* 4 1·10 1·10

Designs:—No. 851, Type **398**; No. 852, *Passport*; No. 853, *Chicora*; No. 854, *Athabasca*.

Nos. 851/4 were printed together, *se-tenant*, in different combinations throughout the sheet, giving ten blocks of 4 and ten single stamps.

(Des K. Rodmell from photograph by P. Grugeon. Litho ("25" die-stamped) Ashton-Potter)

**1977** (4 Feb). *Silver Jubilee. P* 12½ × 12.

855 **399** 25 c. multicoloured .. 25 50

**400** Bottle Gentian **401** Queen Elizabeth II (bas-relief by J. Huta) **402** Houses of Parliament

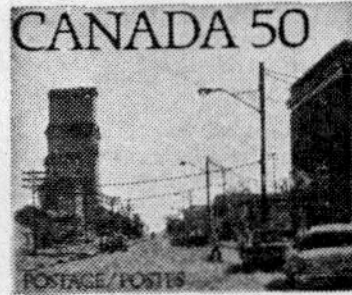


**403** Trembling Aspen **404** Prairie Town Main Street

**405** Fundy National Park

(Des R. Derreth (Nos. 870/4). T. Bjarnason (880/3*a*), R. Bolt (884), B. Laycock and W. Tibbles (884*b*), B. Laycock (884*c*), A. Collier (885), W. Tibbles and G. Weber (No. 885*a*), W. Terry and W. Tibbles (885*b*), L. Marois and W. Tibbles (885*c*), Heather Cooper (others). Eng Y. Baril (880/3*a*))

**1977** (1 Mar)–**86**. (*a*) *Vert designs as T* **400** *showing flowers. Multicoloured.* (i) *Recess and litho C.B.N. Sheet stamps. P* 12 × 12½.

856 1 c. Type **400** (22.4.77) .. 10 10
857 2 c. Red Columbine (22.4.77) .. 10 10
858 3 c. Canada Lily (22.4.77) .. 10 10
859 4 c. Hepatica (22.4.77) .. 10 10
860 5 c. Shooting Star (22.4.77) .. 10 10
861 10 c. Franklin's Lady's Slipper Orchid (22.4.77) .. 15 10
a. Perf 13×13½ (5.10.78) .. 40 30

(ii) *Recess and photo B.A.B.N. Booklet stamps* (1, 2 *c.*) *or sheet stamps* (*others*). *Chalk-surfaced paper. P* 12×12½ (1, 2 *c.*) *or* 13×13½ (*others*)

862 1 c. Type **400** (1.11.77) .. 45 1·75
a. Booklet pane. Nos. 862×2 and 867a×4 .. 2·75
b. Perf 13×13½ (from sheets) (16.6.79) 10 10
863 2 c. Red Columbine (1.4.78) .. 45 70
a. Booklet pane. Nos. 863×4 and 868a×3 plus one printed label .. 3·00
b. Perf 13×13½ (from sheets) (2.8.79) 10 10
864 3 c. Canada Lily (11.4.79) .. 10 10
864*a* 4 c. Hepatica (3.7.79) .. 10 10
865 5 c. Shooting Star (23.1.79) .. 10 10
865*a* 10 c. Franklin's Lady's Slipper Orchid (4.10.79) .. 40 10
866 12 c. Jewelweed (6.7.78) .. 15 30
866*a* 15 c. Canada Violet (16.8.79) .. 15 15

(*b*) *T* **401**. *Recess and photo B.A.B.N. Chalk-surfaced paper. P* 13×13½

867 12 c. black, grey and cobalt (1.3.77) .. 15 10
a. Perf 12×12½ (from booklets) (1.11.77) 50 60
868 14 c. black, grey and rose-red (7.3.78) 20 10
a. Perf 12×12½ (from booklets) (1.4.78) 55 70
ab. Booklet pane. No. 868a×25, plus two printed labels (13.11.78) .. 12·00
869 17 c. black, grey & yellowish green (8.3.79) 40 10
a. Perf 12×12½ (from booklets) (28.3.79) 40 20
ab. Booklet pane. No. 869a×25, plus two printed labels (3.7.79) .. 9·00
869*b* 30 c. maroon, grey & reddish pur (11.5.82) 50 50
ba. *Maroon, grey and bright mauve* (9.83) 90 70
869*c* 32 c. black, grey and light blue (24.5.83) .. 45 45

(*c*) *T* **402**. (i) *Recess C.B.N.* (*Nos.* 872*a*, 873/4) *or B.A.B.N.* (*others*). *Booklet stamps* (*Nos.* 870/1) *or sheet stamps* (*others*). *Chalk-surfaced paper* (1, 5, 12 *c.*). *P* 12×12½ (1, 5 *c.*) *or* 13×13½ (*others*)

870 1 c. indigo (28.3.79) .. 90 2·00
a. Booklet pane. Nos. 869a × 2, 870 and 871 × 3 .. 2·00
871 5 c. deep rose-lilac (28.3.79) .. 35 15
872 12 c. blue (chalk-surfaced paper) (3.5.77) .. 20 10
a. *New blue* (ordinary paper) (4.78) .. 30 10
873 14 c. scarlet (7.3.78) .. 15 10
874 17 c. deep green (8.3.79) .. 30 10

(ii) *Recess C.B.N. Coil stamps. Imperf* × *perf* 10

874*b* 12 c. new blue (3.5.77) .. 30 30
ba. Imperf (horiz pair) .. 90·00
874*c* 14 c. scarlet (7.3.78) .. 40 40
ca. Imperf (horiz pair) .. 90·00
874*d* 17 c. deep green (8.3.79) .. 40 20
da. Imperf (horiz pair) .. £100

(*d*) *Vert designs as T* **403** *showing leaves. Multicoloured. Recess and photo B.A.B.N. Chalk-surfaced paper. P* 13½

875 15 c. Type **403** (8.8.77) .. 15 10
876 20 c. Douglas Fir (8.8.77) .. 15 10
877 25 c. Sugar Maple (8.8.77) .. 15 10
878 30 c. Red Oak (7.3.78) .. 20 10
879 35 c. White Pine (8.3.79) .. 25 10

(*e*) *Horiz designs at T* **404** *showing city streets. Multicoloured. P* 13½

(i) *Recess and photo B.A.B.N. Chalk-surfaced paper. No fluorescent bands* (75, 80 *c.*) (6.7.78)

880 50 c. Type **404** .. 1·25 80
881 75 c. Eastern city street .. 85 90
882 80 c. Maritimes street .. 85 60

(ii) *Recess and litho C.B.N.*

883 50 c. Type **404** (13.12.78) .. 85 60
883*a* 60 c. Ontario city street (11.5.82) .. 65 45

(*f*) *Horiz designs as T* **405** *showing national parks. Multicoloured. Recess and litho C.B.N. or B.A.B.N.* (*ptgs of Nos.* 884*ba*, 885*b and* 885*d from* 26 *Sept* 1986). *No.* 884 *with or without fluorescent bands, others only exist without. P* 13½

884 $1 Type **405** (24.1.79) .. 90 50
ab. Black (inscr and value) ptd albino
884*b* $1 Glacier (*chalk-surfaced paper*) (15.8.84) .. 85 45
ba. Ordinary paper (12.7.85) .. 1·50 60
884*c* $1·50, Waterton Lakes (18.6.82) .. 2·50 2·25
885 $2 Kluane (27.4.79) .. 1·50 45
a. Chalk-surfaced paper (14.12.84) .. 3·00 1·50
885*b* $2 Banff (21.6.85) .. 3·25 90
885*c* $5 Point Pelee (10.1.83) .. 5·50 2·00
ca. Chalk-surfaced paper (14.12.84) .. 7·00 2·75
885*d* $5 La Mauricie (14.3.86) .. 5·50 3·00

The main differences between No. 861a and No. 865*a* are in the background. On No. 865*a* this is toned and has the blurred edges typical of photogravure. No. 861a has a background of solid appearance with the edges clean. The B.A.B.N. version also has stronger lines on the recess part of the design.

No. 883 can be identified from 880 in that the brown printing from the recess plate of the former is deeper and the detail more defined; the registration plate of the car in the foreground can clearly be seen under a glass as "1978". The "hidden date" (1977) occurs alongside the grain elevator door on No. 880. Also the colours from the lithographic plates of No. 883 are much bolder than those from the photogravure cylinders of 880. In addition the paper of No. 883 has a shiny appearance.

No. 884ab shows an uninked impression of the recess-printed part of the design.

Stamps with one or two adjacent sides imperforate come from booklets.

**406** Puma **407** "April in Algonquin Park"

(Des R. Bateman. Litho Ashton-Potter)

**1977** (30 Mar). *Endangered Wildlife* (1*st series*). *P* 12½.

886 **406** 12 c. multicoloured .. 20 20

See also Nos. 906, 936/7, 976/7 and 1006/7.

(Litho Ashton-Potter)

**1977** (26 May). *Birth Centenary of Tom Thomson* (*painter*). *T* **407** *and similar square design. Multicoloured. P* 12.

887 12 c. Type **407** .. 15 10
a. Pair. Nos. 887/8 .. 30 60
888 12 c. "Autumn Birches" .. 15 10

Nos. 887/8 were printed horizontally and vertically *se-tenant* throughout the sheet.

**408** Crown and Lion **409** Peace Bridge, Niagara River

(Des A. Hobbs. Litho (No. 890 also embossed) Ashton-Potter)

**1977** (30 June). *Anniversaries. T* **408** *and similar horiz design. Multicoloured. P* 12½.

889 12 c. Type **408** .. 15 15
890 12 c. Order of Canada .. 15 15

Events:—No. 889, 25th Anniv of first Canadian-born Governor-General; No. 890, Tenth Anniv of Order of Canada.

(Des R. Harder. Litho Ashton-Potter)

**1977** (4 Aug). *50th Anniv of Opening of Peace Bridge. P* 12½.

891 **409** 12 c. multicoloured .. 15 15

**410** Sir Sandford Fleming (engineer)

(Des W. Davies. Recess B.A.B.N.)

**1977** (16 Sept). *Famous Canadians. T* **410** *and similar horiz design. P* 13.

892 12 c. grey-blue .. 15 10
a. Pair. Nos. 892/3 .. 30 55
893 12 c. reddish brown .. 15 10

Design:—No. 892, Joseph E. Bernier (explorer) and C. G. S. *Arctic*.

The above were printed together, horizontally and vertically *se-tenant* throughout the sheet.

**411** Peace Tower, Parliament Buildings, Ottawa **412** Hunter Braves following Star

(Des S. Ash. Litho Ashton-Potter)

**1977** (19 Sept). *23rd Commonwealth Parliamentary Conference. P* 12½.

894 **411** 25 c. multicoloured .. 20 30

(Des R. G. White. Litho C.B.N.)

**1977** (26 Oct). *Christmas. T* **412** *and similar horiz designs depicting Canada's first Christmas carol "Jesous Ahatonhia". Multicoloured. P* 13½ × 13.

895 10 c. Type **412** .. .. .. .. .. .. 10 10
896 12 c. Angelic choir and the Northern Lights .. 10 10
 a. Imperf (vert pair) .. .. .. .. £500
897 25 c. Christ Child and chiefs .. .. .. 20 45
895/7 .. .. .. .. .. *Set of* 3 35 45

**413** Seal Hunter (soapstone sculpture)

**414** Pinky (fishing boat)

(Des R. Derreth. Litho Ashton-Potter)

**1977** (18 Nov). *Canadian Eskimos ("Inuits") (1st series). Hunting. T* **413** *and similar horiz designs. Multicoloured. P* 12 × 12½.

898 12 c. Type **413** .. .. .. .. .. 15 15
 a. Pair. Nos. 898/9 .. .. .. .. 30 50
899 12 c. Fishing with spear .. .. .. .. 15 15
900 12 c. Disguised archer .. .. .. .. 15 15
 a. Pair. Nos. 900/1 .. .. .. .. 30 50
901 12 c. Walrus hunting .. .. .. .. 15 15
898/901 .. .. .. .. *Set of* 4 60 55

Nos. 898/9 and 900/1 were each printed together, *se-tenant*, in horizontal and vertical pairs throughout the sheet.

See also Nos. 924/7, 958/61 and 989/92.

(Des T. Bjarnason. Recess and litho C.B.N.)

**1977** (18 Nov). *Canadian Ships (3rd series). T* **414** *and similar horiz designs, showing sailing craft. Multicoloured. P* 12 × 12½.

902 12 c. Type **414** .. .. .. .. .. 15 15
 a. Block of 4. Nos. 902/5 .. .. .. 55
903 12 c. Five-masted schooner .. .. .. 15 15
904 12 c. Tern schooner .. .. .. .. 15 15
905 12 c. Mackinaw boat .. .. .. .. 15 15
902/5 .. .. .. .. *Set of* 4 55 55

Nos. 902/5 were printed together, *se-tenant*, in different combinations throughout the sheet, giving ten blocks of 4 and ten single stamps.

**415** Peregrine Falcon

**416** Pair of 1851 12d. Black Stamps

(Des R. Bateman. Litho Ashton-Potter)

**1978** (18 Jan). *Endangered Wildlife (2nd series). P* 12½.

906 **415** 12 c. multicoloured .. .. .. 30 20

(Des C. Brett. Recess and photo B.A.B.N.)

**1978** (18 Jan). *"CAPEX 78" International Stamp Exhibition, Toronto (1st issue). P* 13.

907 **416** 12 c. black and brownish grey .. .. 10 10

See also Nos. 914/17.

**417** Games Emblem

**418** "Captain Cook" (Nathaniel Dance)

(Des S. Ash. Litho Ashton-Potter)

**1978** (31 Mar). *Commonwealth Games. Edmonton (1st issue). T* **417** *and similar horiz design. Multicoloured. P* 12½.

908 14 c. Type **417** .. .. .. .. .. 10 10
909 30 c. Badminton .. .. .. .. .. 20 40

See also Nos. 918/21.

(Des W. Rueter. Litho Ashton-Potter)

**1978** (26 Apr). *Bicentenary of Cook's Third Voyage. T* **418** *and similar vert design. Multicoloured. P* 13½.

910 14 c. Type **418** .. .. .. .. .. 20 15
 a. Pair. Nos. 910/11 .. .. .. .. 40 65
911 14 c. "Nootka Sound" (J. Webber) .. .. 20 15

Nos. 910/11 were printed together, *se-tenant*, in horizontal and vertical pairs throughout the sheet.

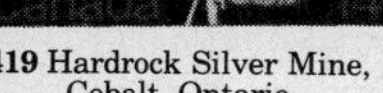


**419** Hardrock Silver Mine, Cobalt, Ontario

**420** Prince's Gate (Exhibition entrance)

(Des W. Davies. Litho Ashton-Potter)

**1978** (19 May). *Resource Development. T* **419** *and similar horiz design. Multicoloured. P* 12½.

912 14 c. Type **419** .. .. .. .. .. 15 15
 a. Pair. Nos. 912/13 .. .. .. .. 30 60
913 14 c. Giant excavators, Athabasca Tar Sands 15 15

Nos. 912/13 were printed together, *se-tenant*, in horizontal and vertical pairs throughout the sheet.

(Des C. Brett. Eng R. Couture. Recess and photo B.A.B.N.)

**1978** (10 June). *"CAPEX 78" International Stamp Exhibition, Toronto (2nd issue). Horiz designs as T* **416**. *Two fluorescent bands (none on $1.25 from miniature sheet). P* 13.

914 14 c. Prussian blue, pale grey and brownish grey .. .. .. .. .. 15 10
915 30 c. deep rose, pale grey and brownish grey 20 35
916 $1.25, slate-violet, pale grey & brnish grey 80 1·10
914/16 .. .. .. .. *Set of* 3 1·00 1·40
MS917 101 × 76 mm. Nos. 914/16 .. .. 1·50 2·25

Designs:—14 c. Pair of 1855 10d. Cartier stamps; 30 c. Pair of 1857 ½d. deep rose stamps; $1.25, Pair of 1851 6d. Prince Albert stamps.

(Des S. Ash. Litho Ashton-Potter)

**1978** (3 Aug). *Commonwealth Games, Edmonton (2nd issue). Horiz designs as T* **417**. *Multicoloured. P* 12½.

918 14 c. Games stadium .. .. .. .. 15 15
 a. Pair. Nos. 918/19 .. .. .. .. 30 55
919 14 c. Running .. .. .. .. .. 15 15
920 30 c. Alberta Legislature building .. .. 25 30
 a. Pair. Nos. 920/1 .. .. .. .. 50 1·25
921 30 c. Bowls .. .. .. .. .. 25 30
918/21 .. .. .. .. *Set of* 4 70 80

Nos. 918/19 and 920/1 were each printed together, *se-tenant*, in horizontal and vertical pairs throughout the sheet.

(Des T. Dimson, Litho Ashton-Potter)

**1978** (16 Aug). *Centenary of National Exhibition. P* 12½.

922 **420** 14 c. multicoloured .. .. .. 15 30

**421** Marguerite d'Youville

**422** "Madonna of the Flowering Pea" (Cologne School)

(Des A. Dumas. Litho C.B.N.)

**1978** (21 Sept). *Marguerite d'Youville (founder of Grey Nuns) Commemoration. P* 13.

923 **421** 14 c. multicoloured .. .. .. 15 20

(Des R. Derreth. Litho Ashton-Potter)

**1978** (27 Sept). *Canadian Eskimos ("Inuits") (2nd series). Travel. Horiz designs as T* **413**. *Multicoloured. P* 13½.

924 14 c. Woman on foot (painting by Pitseolak) .. 15 15
 a. Pair. Nos. 924/5 .. .. .. .. 30 65
925 14 c. "Migration" (soapstone sculpture of sailing umiak by Joe Talurinili) .. .. 15 15
926 14 c. Aeroplane (stonecut and stencil print by Pudlo) .. .. .. .. .. 15 15
 a. Pair. Nos. 926/7 .. .. .. .. 30 65
927 14 c. Dogteam and dogsled (ivory sculpture by Abraham Kingmeatook) .. .. .. 15 15
924/7 .. .. .. .. *Set of* 4 60 55

Nos. 924/5 and 926/7 were each printed together, *se-tenant*, in horizontal and vertical pairs throughout the sheet.

(Des J. Morin. Litho Ashton-Potter)

**1978** (20 Oct). *Christmas. Paintings. T* **422** *and similar vert designs. Multicoloured. P* 12½.

928 12 c. Type **422** .. .. .. .. .. 10 10
929 14 c. "The Virgin and Child with St. Anthony and Donor" (detail, Hans Memling) .. 10 10
930 30 c. "The Virgin and Child" (Jacopo di Cione) 25 50
928/30 .. .. .. .. *Set of* 3 35 55

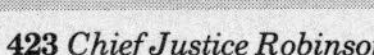


**423** *Chief Justice Robinson*

**424** Carnival Revellers

(Des T. Bjarnason. Recess and litho C.B.N.)

**1978** (15 Nov). *Canadian Ships (4th series). T* **423** *and similar horiz designs showing ice vessels. Multicoloured. P* 13.

931 14 c. Type **423** .. .. .. .. .. 35 35
 a. Block of 4. Nos. 931/4 .. .. .. 1·25
932 14 c. *St. Roch* .. .. .. .. .. 35 35
933 14 c. *Northern Light* .. .. .. .. 35 35
934 14 c. *Labrador* .. .. .. .. .. 35 35
931/4 .. .. .. .. *Set of* 4 1·25 1·25

Nos. 931/4 were printed together, *se-tenant*, in different combinations throughout the sheet, giving ten blocks of 4 and ten single stamps.

(Des A. Dumas. Litho Ashton-Potter)

**1979** (1 Feb). *Quebec Carnival. P* 13.

935 **424** 14 c. multicoloured .. .. .. 20 20

**425** Eastern Spiny Soft-shelled Turtle (*Trionyx spinifera*)

**426** Knotted Ribbon round Woman's Finger

(Des G. Lowe (17 c.), R. Bateman (35 c.). Litho Ashton-Potter)

**1979** (10 Apr). *Endangered Wildlife (3rd series). T* **425** *and similar horiz design. Multicoloured. P* 12½.

936 17 c. Type **425** .. .. .. .. .. 20 10
937 35 c. Bowhead Whale (*Balaena mysticetus*) .. 40 60

(Des D. Haws. Litho Ashton-Potter)

**1979** (27 Apr). *Postal Code Publicity. T* **426** *and similar vert design. Multicoloured. P* 13.

938 17 c. Type **426** .. .. .. .. .. 15 10
 a. Pair. Nos. 938/9 .. .. .. .. 30 50
939 17 c. Knotted string round man's finger .. 15 10

Nos. 938/9 were printed together, *se-tenant*, in horizontal and vertical pairs throughout the sheet.

**427** Scene from "Fruits of the Earth" by Frederick Philip Grove

**428** Charles-Michel de Salaberry (military hero)

(Des Rosemary Kilbourne (No. 940), Monique Charbonneau (941). Litho C.B.N.)

**1979** (3 May). *Canadian Writers (3rd series). T* **427** *and similar horiz design. Multicoloured. P* 13.

940 17 c. Type **427** .. .. .. .. .. 15 15
 a. Pair. Nos. 940/1 .. .. .. .. 30 85
941 17 c. Scene from "Le Vaisseau d'Or" by Émile Nelligan .. .. .. .. .. 15 15

Nos. 940/1 were printed together, *se-tenant*, in horizontal and vertical pairs throughout the sheet.

(Des T. Dimson. Litho and embossed Ashton-Potter)

**1979** (11 May). *Famous Canadians. T* **428** *and similar vert design. Multicoloured. P* 13.

942 17 c. Type **428** .. .. .. .. .. 25 15
 a. Pair. Nos. 942/3 .. .. .. .. 50 70
943 17 c. John By (engineer) .. .. .. .. 25 15

Nos. 942/3 were printed together, *se-tenant*, in horizontal and vertical pairs throughout the sheet.

**429** Ontario

**430** Paddling Kayak

(Des R. Bellemare. Litho Ashton-Potter)

**1979** (15 June). *Canada Day. Flags. Sheet* 128 × 140 *mm containing T* **429** *and similar horiz designs. Multicoloured. P* 13.

MS944 17 c. × 12; Type **429**; Quebec; Nova Scotia; New Brunswick; Manitoba; British Columbia; Prince Edward Island; Saskatchewan; Alberta; Newfoundland; Northwest Territories; Yukon Territory .. .. .. .. .. .. 2·75 3·50

(Des J. Eby. Litho Ashton-Potter)

**1979** (3 July). *Canoe-Kayak Championships. P* 12½.

956 **430** 17 c. multicoloured .. .. .. 15 30

**431** Hockey Players

**432** Toy Train

(Des J. Eby. Litho Ashton-Potter)

**1979** (16 Aug). *Women's Field Hockey Championships, Vancouver. P* 12½.

957 **431** 17 c. black, yellow and emerald .. .. 15 30

(Des R. Derreth. Litho Ashton-Potter)

**1979** (13 Sept). *Canadian Eskimos ("Inuits") (3rd series). "Shelter" (Nos. 958/9) and "Community" (Nos. 960/1). Horiz designs as T* **413**. *Multicoloured. P* 13.

| | | | |
|---|---|---|---|
| 958 | 17 c. "Summer Tent" (print by Kiakshuk) | 15 | 15 |
| | a. Pair. Nos. 958/9 | 30 | 80 |
| 959 | 17 c. "Five Eskimos building an Igloo" (soapstone sculpture by Abraham) | 15 | 15 |
| 960 | 17 c. "The Dance" (print by Kalvak) | 15 | 15 |
| | a. Pair. Nos. 960/1 | 30 | 80 |
| 961 | 17 c. "Inuit drum dance" (soapstone sculptures by Madeleine Isserkut and Jean Mapsalak) | 15 | 15 |
| 958/61 | *Set of* 4 | 60 | 55 |

Nos. 958/9 and 960/1 were each printed together, *se-tenant*, in horizontal and vertical pairs throughout the sheet.

(Des A. Maggs. Litho C.B.N.)

**1979** (17 Oct). *Christmas. T* **432** *and similar multicoloured designs showing toys. Fluorescent frame* (35 c.) *or two fluorescent bands (others). P* 13.

| | | | |
|---|---|---|---|
| 962 | 15 c. Type **432** | 10 | 10 |
| 963 | 17 c. Hobby-horse | 10 | 10 |
| 964 | 35 c. Rag-doll (*vert*) | 25 | 50 |
| 962/4 | *Set of* 3 | 35 | 50 |

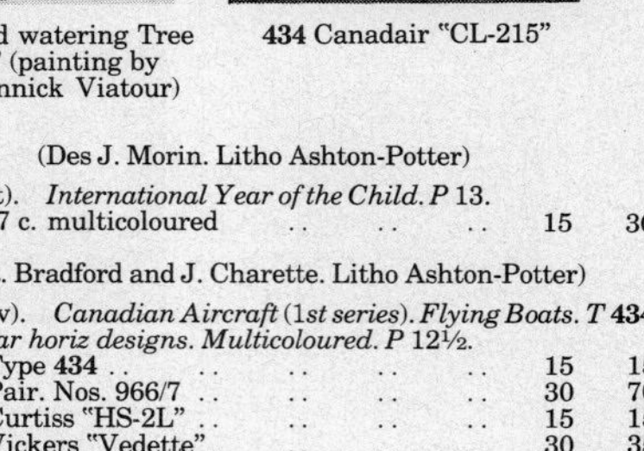


**433** "Child watering Tree of Life" (painting by Marie-Annick Viatour) **434** Canadair "CL-215"

(Des J. Morin. Litho Ashton-Potter)

**1979** (24 Oct). *International Year of the Child. P* 13.

| | | | |
|---|---|---|---|
| 965 **433** | 17 c. multicoloured | 15 | 30 |

(Des R. Bradford and J. Charette. Litho Ashton-Potter)

**1979** (15 Nov). *Canadian Aircraft (1st series). Flying Boats. T* **434** *and similar horiz designs. Multicoloured. P* 12½.

| | | | |
|---|---|---|---|
| 966 | 17 c. Type **434** | 15 | 15 |
| | a. Pair. Nos. 966/7 | 30 | 70 |
| 967 | 17 c. Curtiss "HS-2L" | 15 | 15 |
| 968 | 35 c. Vickers "Vedette" | 30 | 35 |
| | a. Pair. Nos. 968/9 | 60 | 1·10 |
| 969 | 35 c. Consolidated "Canso" | 30 | 35 |
| 966/9 | *Set of* 4 | 90 | 90 |

Nos. 966/7 and 968/9 were each printed together, *se-tenant*, in horizontal and vertical pairs throughout the sheet.

See also Nos. 996/9, 1026/9 and 1050/3.

**435** Map of Arctic Islands **436** Skiing

(Des Gottschalk and Ash Ltd. Litho Ashton-Potter)

**1980** (23 Jan). *Centenary of Arctic Islands Acquisition. P* 13.

| | | | |
|---|---|---|---|
| 970 **435** | 17 c. multicoloured | 15 | 30 |

(Des C. Malenfant. Litho C.B.N.)

**1980** (23 Jan). *Winter Olympic Games, Lake Placid, U.S.A. P* 13.

| | | | |
|---|---|---|---|
| 971 **436** | 35 c. multicoloured | 30 | 65 |

**437** "A Meeting of the School Trustees" (painting by Robert Harris) **438** Atlantic Whitefish (*Coregonus canadensis*)

(Des J. Morin. Litho Ashton-Potter)

**1980** (6 Mar). *Centenary of Royal Canadian Academy of Arts. T* **437** *and similar horiz designs. Multicoloured. P* 13.

| | | | |
|---|---|---|---|
| 972 | 17 c. Type **437** | 20 | 15 |
| | a. Pair. Nos. 972/3 | 40 | 50 |
| 973 | 17 c. "Inspiration" (sculpture by Philippe Hébert) | 20 | 15 |
| 974 | 35 c. "Sunrise on the Saguenay" (painting by Lucius O'Brien) | 30 | 35 |
| | a. Pair. Nos. 974/5 | 60 | 1·50 |
| 975 | 35 c. Sketch of design for original Parliament Buildings by Thomas Fuller | 30 | 35 |
| 972/5 | *Set of* 4 | 90 | 90 |

Nos. 972/3 and 974/5 were each printed together, *se-tenant*, in horizontal and vertical pairs throughout the sheet.

(Des M. Dumas (No. 976), R. Bateman (No. 977). Litho Ashton-Potter)

**1980** (6 May). *Endangered Wildlife (4th series). T* **438** *and similar horiz design. Multicoloured. P* 12½.

| | | | |
|---|---|---|---|
| 976 | 17 c. Type **438** | 15 | 15 |
| 977 | 17 c. Prairie Chicken (*Tympanuchus cupido pinnatus*) | 15 | 15 |

**439** Garden Flowers **440** "Helping Hand"

(Des Heather Cooper. Litho Ashton-Potter)

**1980** (29 May). *International Flower Show, Montreal. P* 13.

| | | | |
|---|---|---|---|
| 978 **439** | 17 c. multicoloured | 15 | 20 |

(Des R. Harder. Litho and embossed Ashton-Potter)

**1980** (29 May). *Rehabilitation. P* 12½.

| | | | |
|---|---|---|---|
| 979 **440** | 17 c. gold and ultramarine | 15 | 20 |

**441** Opening Bars of "O Canada" **442** John G. Diefenbaker

(Des F. Peter. Litho Ashton-Potter)

**1980** (6 June). *Centenary of "O Canada" (national song). T* **441** *and similar horiz design. Multicoloured. P* 12½.

| | | | |
|---|---|---|---|
| 980 | 17 c. Type **441** | 15 | 15 |
| | a. Pair. Nos. 980/1 | 30 | 40 |
| 981 | 17 c. Galixa Lavallee (composer), Adolphe-Basile Routhier (original writer) and Robert Stanley Wier (writer of English version) | 15 | 15 |

Nos. 980/1 were printed together, *se-tenant*, in horizontal and vertical pairs throughout.

(Des B. Reilander. Eng Y. Baril. Recess C.B.N.)

**1980** (20 June). *John G. Diefenbaker (former Prime Minister) Commemoration. P* 13½ × 13.

| | | | |
|---|---|---|---|
| 982 **442** | 17 c. deep ultramarine | 15 | 20 |

**443** Emma Albani (singer) **444** Alberta

(Des C. Webster (No. 985), H. Brown (others). Litho Ashton-Potter)

**1980** (4 July). *Famous Canadians. T* **443** *and similar multicoloured designs. P* 13.

| | | | |
|---|---|---|---|
| 983 | 17 c. Type **443** | 15 | 15 |
| | a. Pair. Nos. 983/4 | 30 | 45 |
| 984 | 17 c. Healey Willan (composer) | 15 | 15 |
| 985 | 17 c. Ned Hanlan (oarsman) (*horiz*) | 15 | 15 |
| 983/5 | *Set of* 3 | 40 | 40 |

Nos. 983/4 were printed together, *se-tenant*, in horizontal and vertical pairs throughout the sheet.

(Des G. Hunter and C. Yaneff. Litho Ashton-Potter)

**1980** (27 Aug). *75th Anniv of Alberta and Saskatchewan Provinces. T* **444** *and similar horiz design. Multicoloured. P* 13.

| | | | |
|---|---|---|---|
| 986 | 17 c. Type **444** | 15 | 15 |
| 987 | 17 c. Saskatchewan | 15 | 15 |

**445** Uraninite Molecular Structure **446** "Christmas Morning" (J. S. Hallam)

(Des J. Charette. Litho C.B.N.)

**1980** (3 Sept). *Uranium Resources. P* 13.

| | | | |
|---|---|---|---|
| 988 **445** | 35 c. multicoloured | 30 | 30 |

(Des R. Derreth. Litho C.B.N.)

**1980** (25 Sept). *Canadian Eskimos ("Inuits") (4th series). Spirits. Horiz designs as T* **413**. *Multicoloured. P* 13½.

| | | | |
|---|---|---|---|
| 989 | 17 c. "Return of the Sun" (print by Kenojouak) | 15 | 15 |
| | a. Pair. Nos. 989/90 | 30 | 45 |
| 990 | 17 c. "Sedna" (sculpture by Ashoona Kiawak) | 15 | 15 |
| 991 | 35 c. "Shaman" (print by Simon Tookoome) | 25 | 30 |
| | a. Pair. Nos. 991/2 | 50 | 80 |
| 992 | 35 c. "Bird Spirit" (sculpture by Doris Hagiolok) | 25 | 30 |
| 989/92 | *Set of* 4 | 70 | 80 |

Nos. 989/90 and 991/2 were each printed together, *se-tenant*, in horizontal and vertical pairs throughout the sheet.

(Des Yvon Laroche. Litho Ashton-Potter)

**1980** (22 Oct). *Christmas. Paintings. T* **446** *and similar vert designs. Multicoloured. P* 12½ × 12.

| | | | |
|---|---|---|---|
| 993 | 15 c. Type **446** | 10 | 10 |
| 994 | 17 c. "Sleigh Ride" (Frank Hennessy) | 15 | 10 |
| 995 | 35 c. "McGill Cab Stand" (Kathleen Morris) | 30 | 45 |
| 993/5 | *Set of* 3 | 50 | 45 |

**447** Avro Canada "CF-100"

(Des R. Bradford and J. Charette. Litho C.B.N.)

**1980** (10 Nov). *Canadian Aircraft (2nd series). T* **447** *and similar horiz designs. Multicoloured. P* 13.

| | | | |
|---|---|---|---|
| 996 | 17 c. Type **447** | 15 | 15 |
| | a. Pair. Nos. 996/7 | 30 | 50 |
| 997 | 17 c. Avro "Lancaster" | 15 | 15 |
| 998 | 35 c. Curtiss "JN-4 (Canuck)" | 30 | 35 |
| | a. Pair. Nos. 998/9 | 60 | 90 |
| 999 | 35 c. Hawker "Hurricane" | 30 | 35 |
| 996/9 | *Set of* 4 | 80 | 90 |

Nos. 996/7 and 998/9 were each printed together, *se-tenant*, in horizontal and vertical pairs throughout the sheet.

**448** Emmanuel-Persillier Lachapelle **449** Mandora Instrument (18th-century)

(Des J. Morin. Litho Ashton-Potter)

**1980** (5 Dec). *Dr. Emmanuel-Persillier Lachapelle (founder of Notre-Dame Hospital, Montreal) Commemoration. P* 13½.

| | | | |
|---|---|---|---|
| 1000 **448** | 17 c. cobalt, chocolate and brown | 15 | 15 |

(Des C. Webster. Litho Ashton-Potter)

**1981** (19 Jan). *"The Look of Music" Exhibition, Vancouver. P* 12½.

| | | | |
|---|---|---|---|
| 1001 **449** | 17 c. multicoloured | 15 | 15 |

**450** Henrietta Edwards **451** Vancouver Marmot (*Marmota vancouverensis*)

(Des Muriel Wood and D. Goddard. Litho C.B.N.)

**1981** (4 Mar). *Feminists. T* **450** *and similar horiz designs. Multicoloured. P* 13.

| | | | |
|---|---|---|---|
| 1002 | 17 c. Type **450** | 15 | 15 |
| | a. Block of 4. Nos. 1002/5 | 55 | |
| 1003 | 17 c. Louise McKinney | 15 | 15 |
| 1004 | 17 c. Idola Saint-Jean | 15 | 15 |
| 1005 | 17 c. Emily Stowe | 15 | 15 |
| 1002/5 | *Set of* 4 | 55 | 55 |

Nos. 1002/5 were printed together, *se-tenant*, in different combinations throughout the sheet, giving ten blocks of 4 and ten single stamps.

(Des M. Dumas (17 c.), R. Bateman (35 c.). Litho C.B.N.)

**1981** (6 Apr). *Endangered Wildlife (5th series). T* **451** *and similar horiz design. Multicoloured. P* 13.

| | | | |
|---|---|---|---|
| 1006 | 17 c. Type **451** | 15 | 10 |
| 1007 | 35 c. American Bison (*Bison bison athabascae*) | 35 | 30 |

**452** Kateri Tekakwitha **453** "Self Portrait" (Frederick H. Varley)

(Des L. Marquart. Litho Ashton-Potter)

**981** (24 Apr). *17th-century Canadian Catholic Women. Statues by Emile Brunet. T* **452** *and similar vert design. P* 12½.

008 17 c. red-brown and pale grey-olive .. .. 15 15
 a. Pair. Nos. 1008/9 .. .. .. 30 40
009 17 c. steel blue and new blue .. .. 15 15

Designs:—No. 1008, Type **452**; No. 1009, Marie de l'Incarnation.
Nos. 1008/9 were printed together, *se-tenant*, in horizontal and vertical pairs throughout the sheet.

Des P. Fontaine. Litho Ashton-Potter (17 c. (*both*)), B.A.B.N. (35 c.))

**981** (22 May). *Canadian Paintings. T* **453** *and similar multicoloured designs. P* 12½ (17 c. (*both*)) *or* 13 × 13½ (35 c.).

010 17 c. Type **453** .. .. .. .. .. 15 10
011 17 c. "At Baie Saint-Paul" (Marc-Aurele Fortin) (*horiz*) .. .. .. .. 15 10
012 35 c. "Untitled No. 6" (Paul-Emile Borduas) .. 30 30
010/12 .. .. .. .. *Set of* 3 55 45

**454** Canada in 1867 **455** Frère Marie-Victorin

(Des R. Bellemare. Litho B.A.B.N.)

**981** (30 June). *Canada Day. Maps showing evolution of Canada from Confederation to present day. T* **454** *and similar horiz designs. Multicoloured. P* 13½.

013 17 c. Type **454** .. .. .. .. .. 15 15
 a. Horiz strip of 4. Nos. 1013/16 .. .. 55
014 17 c. Canada in 1873 .. .. .. .. 15 15
015 17 c. Canada in 1905 .. .. .. .. 15 15
016 17 c. Canada since 1949 .. .. .. 15 15
013/16 .. .. .. .. *Set of* 4 55 55

Nos. 1013/16 were printed together, *se-tenant*, in horizontal strips of 4 throughout the sheet.

(Des R. Hill. Litho and embossed Ashton-Potter)

**981** (22 July). *Canadian Botanists. T* **455** *and similar vert design. Multicoloured. P* 12½ × 12.

017 17 c. Type **455** .. .. .. .. .. 15 15
 a. Pair. Nos. 1017/18 .. .. .. 30 40
018 17 c. John Macoun .. .. .. .. 15 15

Nos. 1017/18 were printed together, *se-tenant*, in horizontal and vertical pairs throughout the sheet.

**456** The Montreal Rose **457** Drawing of Niagara-on-the-Lake

(Des J.-P. Beaudin, J. Morin and T. Yakobina. Litho C.B.N.)

**1981** (22 July). *Montreal Flower Show. P* 13½.

1019 **456** 17 c. multicoloured .. .. .. 15 20

(Des J. Mardon. Recess and litho B.A.B.N.)

**981** (31 July). *Bicentenary of Niagara-on-the-Lake (town). P* 13 × 13½.

020 **457** 17 c. multicoloured .. .. .. 15 20

**458** Acadian Community **459** Aaron R. Mosher

(Des N. DeGrâce. Litho Ashton-Potter)

**1981** (14 Aug). *Centenary of first Acadia (community) Convention. P* 13½.

1021 **458** 17 c. multicoloured .. .. .. 15 20

(Des R. Hill. Litho Ashton-Potter)

**981** (8 Sept). *Birth Centenary of Aaron R. Mosher (founder of Canadian Labour Congress). P* 13½.

1022 **459** 17 c. multicoloured .. .. .. 15 20

## NEW INFORMATION

The editor is always interested to correspond with people who have new information that will improve or correct the Catalogue.

**460** Christmas Tree, 1781 **461** De Havilland "Tiger Moth"

(Des Anita Kunz and W. Tibbles. Litho Ashton-Potter)

**1981** (16 Nov). *Christmas. Bicentenary of First Illuminated Christmas Tree in Canada. T* **460** *and similar vert designs. Multicoloured. P* 13½.

1023 15 c. Type **460** .. .. .. .. .. 20 15
1024 15 c. Christmas Tree, 1881 .. .. .. 20 15
1025 15 c. Christmas Tree, 1981 .. .. .. 20 15
1023/5 .. .. .. .. *Set of* 3 55 40

(Des R. Bradford and J. Charette. Litho Ashton-Potter)

**1981** (24 Nov). *Canadian Aircraft (3rd series). T* **461** *and similar horiz designs. Multicoloured. P* 12½.

1026 17 c. Type **461** .. .. .. .. .. 20 15
 a. Pair. Nos. 1026/7 .. .. .. 40 40
1027 17 c. Canadair "CL-41 (Tutor)" .. .. 20 15
1028 35 c. Avro "Canada" jetliner .. .. .. 35 35
 a. Pair. Nos. 1028/9 .. .. .. 70 70
1029 35 c. De Havilland Canada "Dash 7" .. .. 35 35
1026/9 .. .. .. .. *Set of* 4 1·10 90

The two designs of each value were printed together, *se-tenant*, in horizontal and vertical pairs throughout the sheet.

**462** Canadian Maple Leaf Emblem **463** 1851 3d. Stamp

(Des R. Bellemare. Recess B.A.B.N. (No. 1030*a*), C.B.N. (others))

**1981** (29 Dec). *Ordinary paper.* (*a*) *Sheet stamp. P* 13 × 13½.

1030 **462** A (30 c.), bright scarlet .. .. 20 30
 *a. Carmine-red, chalk-surfaced paper* 20 25

(*b*) *Coil stamp. Imperf* × *perf* 10

1031 **462** A (30 c.), bright scarlet .. .. 30 50
 a. Imperf (pair) .. .. .. £300

Nos. 1030/1 were printed before a new first class domestic letter rate had been agreed, "A" representing the face value of the stamp later decided at 30 c. Because of U.P.U. regulations these stamps were only intended for use within Canada.

(Recess, or recess and photo (Nos. 1032/*b*), B.A.B.N. (Nos. 1032/5*b*) or C.B.N. (Nos. 1036/*a*))

**1982** (1 Mar)–**83**. *Designs as Nos.* 1030/1 *but including face values.*

(*a*) *Sheet stamps (Nos.* 1032, 1032*b*) *or from booklets (Nos.* 1032a, 1032ba). *Chalk-surfaced paper. P* 13×13½

1032 **462** 30 c. verm, slate-blue & azure (11.5.82) 30 30
 a. Perf 12 × 12½ (from booklets) (30.6.82) .. .. .. .. 50 70
 ab. Booklet pane. No. 1032a × 20 plus one printed label .. .. .. 9·00
1032*b* 32 c. verm, orge-brn & stone (10.2.83) 45 45
 ba. Perf 12 × 12½ (from booklets) (8.4.83) .. .. .. .. 45 70
 bb. Booklet pane. No. 1032ba × 25 plus two printed labels .. .. .. 11·00

(*b*) *Booklet stamps. Ordinary paper. P* 12 × 12½*

1033 **462** 5 c. maroon .. .. .. .. 10 10
 a. Booklet pane. Nos. 1033 × 2, 1034 and 1035 plus two printed labels in bottom row .. .. .. 1·75
 ab. Ditto. Printed labels in top row (10.82) .. .. .. .. 1·90
 b. Chalk-surfaced paper (8.82) .. 40 30
 ba. Booklet pane. Nos. 1033b × 2, 1034a and 1035a plus two printed labels in bottom row .. .. 5·50
 bb. Ditto. Printed labels in top row (10.82) .. .. .. .. 4·75
 c. Booklet pane. Nos. 1033 × 2, 1033*d* and 1035*b* plus two printed labels (15.2.83) .. .. .. .. 2·10
1033*d* 8 c. indigo (15.2.83) .. .. .. 80 75
1034 10 c. bottle green .. .. .. 75 55
 a. Chalk-surfaced paper .. .. 2·50 90
1035 30 c. carmine-red .. .. .. 1·00 80
 a. Chalk-surfaced paper .. .. 2·50 1·25
1035*b* 32 c. Indian red (15.2.83) .. .. 1·25 1·00

(*c*) *Coil stamps. Ordinary paper. Imperf*×*perf* 10

1036 **462** 30 c. bright scarlet (20.5.82)† .. .. 35 30
1036*a* 32 c. Indian red (10.2.83) .. .. 1·00 1·00
 ab. Imperf (pair) .. .. .. £140

*The 30 c. and 32 c. values are perforated on two sides, the other values on three.

†The 30 c. coil stamp was originally intended for release on 11 May, but, due to production difficulties, it was not placed on sale until 20 May; F.D.C.s, however, carry the 11 May postmark.

(Des Gottschalk and Ash Ltd. Litho C.B.N.)

**1982** (11 Mar–20 May). *"Canada 82" International Philatelic Youth Exhibition, Toronto. Stamps on Stamps. T* **463** *and similar horiz designs. Multicoloured. P* 13½.

1037 30 c. Type **463** .. .. .. .. .. 25 25
1038 30 c. 1908 Centenary of Quebec 15 c. commemorative (20.5.82) .. .. .. .. 25 25
1039 35 c. 1935 10 c. .. .. .. .. 25 30
1040 35 c. 1928 10 c. (20.5.82) .. .. .. 25 30
1041 60 c. 1929 50 c. (20.5.82) .. .. .. 50 75
1037/41 .. .. .. .. *Set of* 5 1·40 1·75
**MS**1042 159 × 108 mm. Nos. 1037/41 (20.5.82) .. 2·00 2·50

**464** Jules Léger **465** Stylised Drawing of Terry Fox

(Des P. Fontaine from photograph by M. Bedford. Litho Ashton-Potter)

**1982** (2 Apr). *Jules Léger (politician) Commemoration. P* 13½.

1043 **464** 30 c. multicoloured .. .. .. 20 20

(Des F. Peter. Litho Ashton-Potter)

**1982** (13 Apr). *Cancer-victim Terry Fox's "Marathon of Hope" (Trans-Canada fund-raising run) Commemoration. P* 12½.

1044 **465** 30 c. multicoloured .. .. .. 20 20

**466** Stylised Open Book

(Des F. Peter. Litho Ashton-Potter)

**1982** (16 Apr). *Patriation of Constitution. P* 12 × 12½.

1045 **466** 30 c. multicoloured .. .. .. 20 20

**467** 1880's Male and Female Salvationists with Street Scene **468** "The Highway near Kluane Lake" (Yukon Territory) (Jackson)

(Des T. Dimson. Litho C.B.N.)

**1982** (25 June). *Centenary of the Salvation Army in Canada. P* 13½.

1046 **467** 30 c. multicoloured .. .. .. 20 20

(Des J. Morin and P. Sasseville. Litho Ashton-Potter)

**1982** (30 June). *Canada Day. Paintings of Canadian Landscapes. Sheet, 139 × 139 mm, containing T* **468** *and similar horiz designs. Multicoloured. P* 12½ × 12.

**MS**1047 30 c. × 12, Type **468**; "Street Scene, Montreal" (Quebec) (Hébert); "Breakwater" (Newfoundland) (Pratt); "Along Great Slave Lake" (Northwest Territories) (Richard); "Till Hill" (Prince Edward Island) (Lamb); "Family and Rainstorm" (Nova Scotia) (Colville); "Brown Shadows" (Saskatchewan) (Knowles); "The Red Brick House" (Ontario) (Milne); "Campus Gates" (New Brunswick) (Bobak); "Prairie Town—Early Morning" (Alberta) (Kerr); "Totems at Ninstints" (British Columbia) (Plaskett); "Doc Snider's House" (Manitoba) (FitzGerald) .. .. .. .. 3·25 3·75

**469** Regina Legislature Building **470** Finish of Race

(Des Kim Martin and R. Russell. Litho Ashton-Potter)

**1982** (3 Aug). *Regina Centenary. P* 13½ × 13.

1048 **469** 30 c. multicoloured .. .. .. 20 20

(Des B. Reilander. Litho Ashton-Potter)

**1982** (4 Aug). *Centenary of Royal Canadian Henley Regatta. P* 12½.

1049 **470** 30 c. multicoloured .. .. .. 20 25

471 Fairchild "FC-2W1"

472 Decoy

(Des R. Bradford. Litho Ashton-Potter)

**1982** (5 Oct). *Canadian Aircraft (4th series). Bush Aircraft. T* **471** *and similar horiz designs. Multicoloured. P* 12½.

1050 30 c. Type **471** .. .. .. .. .. 35 20
  a. Pair. Nos. 1050/1 .. .. .. .. 70 90
1051 30 c. De Havilland Canada "Beaver" .. .. 35 20
1052 60 c. Fokker "Super Universal" .. .. 65 75
  a. Pair. Nos. 1052/3 .. .. .. .. 1·25 1·75
1053 60 c. Noorduyn "Norseman" .. .. .. 65 75
1050/3 .. .. .. .. *Set of* 4 1·90 1·75

Nos. 1050/1 and 1052/3 were each printed together, *se-tenant*, in horiz and vert pairs throughout the sheet.

(Des J. P. Beaudin and J. Morin. Litho C.B.N. (Nos. 1054a, 1055a, 1056a, 1057a, 1058a) or Ashton-Potter (others))

**1982** (19 Oct)–**87**. *Heritage Artifacts. T* **472** *and similar designs. No fluorescent bands (1 c. to 5 c.). Chalk-surfaced paper (2, 5, 10, 20, 25, 42, 48, 50, 72 c.). P* 12×12½ *(37 c. to 72 c.) or* 14×13½ *(others)*

1054 1 c. black, grey-brown and brown .. 10 10
  a. Chalk-surfaced paper (4.7.86) .. 10 10
  b. Perf 13×13½ (10.1.85) .. .. 30 30
1055 2 c. black, pale turquoise-blue & dp bl-grn 10 10
  a. Perf 13×13½ (10.2.84) .. .. 30 30
  ab. Imperf (horiz pair) .. .. £475
  ac. Ordinary paper (23.1.86) .. 10 10
1056 3 c. black, dull violet-blue and chalky blue 10 10
  a. Ordinary paper (4.7.86) .. .. 10 10
  b. Perf 13×13½ (10.1.85) .. .. 30 30
1057 5 c. black, flesh and chestnut .. 10 10
  a. Chalk-surfaced paper (15.8.86) .. 10 10
  b. Perf 13×13½ (*chalk-surfaced paper*) (6.7.84) .. .. .. 20 20
  ba. Ordinary paper (1.3.85) .. .. 10 10
1058 10 c. black, light blue & dp turquoise-blue 10 10
  a. Perf 13×13½ (*ordinary paper*) (15.3.85) .. .. .. 35 30
1059 20 c. black, brownish grey and sepia .. 20 10
1060 25 c. multicoloured (6.5.87) .. .. 35 10
1061 37 c. grey-black, deep yellow-green and sage-green (8.4.83) .. .. 50 40
  a. Chalk-surfaced paper (18.5.84) .. 50 40
1062 39 c. brownish black, violet-grey and slate-violet (1.8.85) .. .. 1·00 30
1063 42 c. multicoloured (6.5.87) .. .. 45 25
1064 48 c. blackish brown, red-brown and pale pink (8.4.83) .. .. .. 70 55
1065 50 c. blk, dull turq-bl & turq-bl (1.8.85) 1·10 20
1066 55 c. multicoloured (6.5.87) .. .. 55 40
1067 64 c. grey-black, black & pale grey (8.4.83) 80 65
  a. Chalk-surfaced paper (29.6.84) .. 90 75
1068 68 c. black, pale brn & reddish brn (1.8.85) 1·00 55
1069 72 c. multicoloured (6.5.87) .. .. 75 65
1054/69 .. .. .. *Set of* 16 7·00 4·00

Designs: *Vert (as T* **472***)*—2 c. Fishing spear; 3 c. Stable lantern; 5 c. Bucket; 10 c. Weathercock; 20 c. Skates; 25 c. Butter stamp. *Horiz (26×20 mm)*—37 c. Plough; 39 c. Settle-bed; 42 c. Linen chest; 48 c. Cradle; 50 c. Sleigh; 55 c. Iron kettle; 64 c. Kitchen stove; 68 c. Spinning wheel; 72 c. Hand-drawn cart.

No. 1058a has a fluorescent frame instead of bands.

475 Mary, Joseph and Baby Jesus

476 Globes forming Symbolic Designs

(Des J. Eby. Litho C.B.N.)

**1982** (3 Nov). *Christmas. Nativity Scenes. T* **475** *and similar vert designs. Multicoloured. P* 13.

1080 30 c. Type **475** .. .. .. .. .. 20 10
1081 35 c. The Shepherds .. .. .. .. 25 35
1082 60 c. The Three Wise Men .. .. .. 45 70
1080/2 .. .. .. .. *Set of* 3 80 1·00

(Des R. Bellemare. Litho Ashton-Potter)

**1983** (10 Mar). *World Communications Year. Fluorescent frame. P* 12 × 12½.

1083 **476** 32 c. multicoloured .. .. .. 30 25

477 Map of World showing Canada

(Des R. Harder. Litho Ashton-Potter)

**1983** (14 Mar). *Commonwealth Day. Without fluorescent bands. P* 12½.

1084 **477** $2 multicoloured .. .. .. 1·75 2·25

478 Scene from Novel "Angéline de Montbrun" by Laure Conan (Félicité Angers)

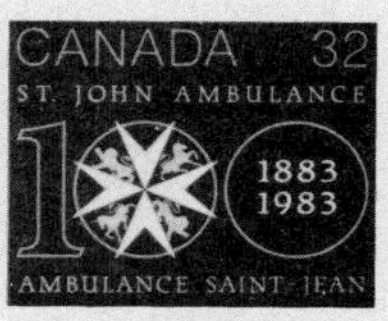

479 St. John Ambulance Badge and "100"

(Des R. Milot (No. 1085), Claire Pratt (No. 1086), adapted W. Tibbles. Litho C.B.N.)

**1983** (22 Apr). *Canadian Writers (4th series). T* **478** *and similar horiz design. Multicoloured. P* 13.

1085 32 c. Type **478** .. .. .. .. .. 25 20
  a. Pair. Nos. 1085/6 .. .. .. .. 50 70
1086 32 c. Woodcut illustrating "Sea-gulls" (poem by E. J. Pratt) .. .. .. .. 25 20

Nos. 1085/6 were printed together, *se-tenant*, in horizontal and vertical pairs throughout the sheet.

(Des L. Fishauf. Litho Ashton-Potter)

**1983** (3 June). *Centenary of St. John Ambulance in Canada. P* 13.

1087 **479** 32 c. brt rose-red, gold & dp chocolate 30 20

480 Victory Pictogram

481 Fort William, Ontario

(Des Krista Huebner, D. Kilvert and P.-Y. Pelletier. Litho C.B.N.)

**1983** (28 June). *"Universiade 83" World University Games, Edmonton. P* 13.

1088 **480** 32 c. multicoloured .. .. .. 25 15
1089 64 c. multicoloured .. .. .. 50 70

(Des R. Harder. Litho Ashton-Potter)

**1983** (30 June). *Canada Day. Forts (1st series). T* **481** *and similar horiz designs. Multicoloured. P* 12½ × 13.

1090 32 c. Fort Henry, Ontario (44 × 22 *mm*) 35 50
  a. Booklet pane. Nos. 1090/9 .. .. 3·25
1091 32 c. Type **481** .. .. .. .. 35 50
1092 32 c. Fort Rodd Hill, British Columbia .. 35 50
1093 32 c. Fort Wellington, Ontario (28 × 22 *mm*) .. 35 50
1094 32 c. Fort Prince of Wales, Manitoba (28 × 22 *mm*) .. .. .. .. 35 50
1095 32 c. Halifax Citadel, Nova Scotia (44 × 22 *mm*) 35 50
1096 32 c. Fort Chambly, Quebec .. .. 35 50
1097 32 c. Fort No. 1, Point Levis, Quebec .. 35 50
1098 32 c. Coteau-du-Lac Fort, Quebec (28 × 22 *mm*) 35 50
1099 32 c. Fort Beauséjour, New Brunswick (28 × 22 *mm*) .. .. .. .. 35 50
1090/9 .. .. .. *Set of* 10 3·25 4·50

Nos. 1090/9 were only available from $3.20 stamp booklets containing the *se-tenant* pane, No. 1090a.

See also Nos. 1163/72.

482 Scouting Poster by Marc Fournier (aged 12)

483 Cross Symbol

(Des F. Dallaire. Litho Ashton-Potter)

**1983** (6 July). *75th Anniv of Scouting in Canada and 15th World Scout Jamboree, Alberta. P* 13.

1100 **482** 32 c. multicoloured .. .. .. 30 30

(Des G. Tsetsekas. Recess and photo B.A.B.N.)

**1983** (22 July). *6th Assembly of the World Council of Churches, Vancouver. P* 13.

1101 **483** 32 c. blue-green and grey-lilac .. .. 30 20

484 Sir Humphrey Gilbert (founder)

485 "NICKEL" Deposits

(Des R. Hill. Litho C.B.N.)

**1983** (3 Aug). *400th Anniv of Newfoundland. P* 13.

1102 **484** 32 c. multicoloured .. .. .. 30 2

(Des J. Capon. Litho ("NICKEL" die-stamped) C.B.N.)

**1983** (12 Aug). *Centenary of Discovery of Sudbury Nick Deposits. P* 13.

1103 **485** 32 c. multicoloured .. .. .. 30 2

486 Josiah Henson and Escaping Slaves

487 Type 0-4-0, *Dorchester* Locomotive

(Des T. Kew and J. Hamel. Litho B.A.B.N.)

**1983** (16 Sept). *Nineteenth-century Social Reformers. T* **486** *an similar horiz design. Multicoloured. P* 13 × 13½ *(No. 1104) or* 1 *(No. 1105).*

1104 32 c. Type **486** .. .. .. .. .. 25 2
1105 32 c. Father Antoine Labelle and rural village (32 × 26 *mm*) .. .. .. .. 25 2

(Des E. Roch. Litho Ashton-Potter)

**1983** (3 Oct). *Railway Locomotives. (1st series). T* **487** *and simila horiz designs. Multicoloured. P* 12½ × 13.

1106 32 c. Type **487** .. .. .. .. 70 3
  a. Pair. Nos. 1106/7 .. .. .. .. 1·40 1·4
1107 32 c. Type 4-4-0, *Toronto* .. .. .. 70 3
1108 37 c. Type 0-6-0, *Samson* .. .. .. 70 7
1109 64 c. Type 4-4-0, *Adam Brown* .. .. .. 1·00 1·2
1106/9 .. .. .. .. *Set of* 4 2·75 2·4

Nos. 1106/7 were printed together, *se-tenant*, in horizontal an vertical pairs throughout the sheet.

See also Nos. 1132/6, 1185/8 and 1223/6.

488 School Coat of Arms


489 City Church

(Des Denise Saulnier. Litho C.B.N.)

**1983** (28 Oct). *Centenary of Dalhousie Law School. P* 13.

1110 **488** 32 c. multicoloured .. .. .. 30 3

(Des C. Simard. Litho Ashton-Potter)

**1983** (3 Nov). *Christmas. Churches. T* **489** *and similar hor designs. Multicoloured. P* 13.

1111 32 c. Type **489** .. .. .. .. .. 40 1
1112 37 c. Family walking to church .. .. 55 3
1113 64 c. Country chapel .. .. .. .. 90 1·5
1111/13 .. .. .. .. *Set of* 3 1·75 1·7

490 Royal Canadian Regiment and British Columbia Regiment

(Des W. Southern and R. Tibbles. Litho C.B.N.)

**1983** (10 Nov). *Canadian Army Regiments. T* **490** *and similar ve design. Multicoloured. P* 13.

1114 32 c. Type **490** .. .. .. .. .. 50 3
  a. Pair. Nos. 1114/15 .. .. .. .. 1·00 1·2
1115 32 c. Royal Winnipeg Rifles and Royal Canadian Dragoons .. .. .. .. 50 3

Nos. 1114/15 were printed together, *se-tenant*, in horizontal an vertical pairs throughout the sheet.

## PRICES OF SETS

Set prices are given for many issues, generall those containing three stamps or more. Definitiv sets include one of each value or major colou change, but do not cover different perforation die types or minor shades. Where a choice i possible the set prices are based on the cheapes versions of the stamps included in the listings.

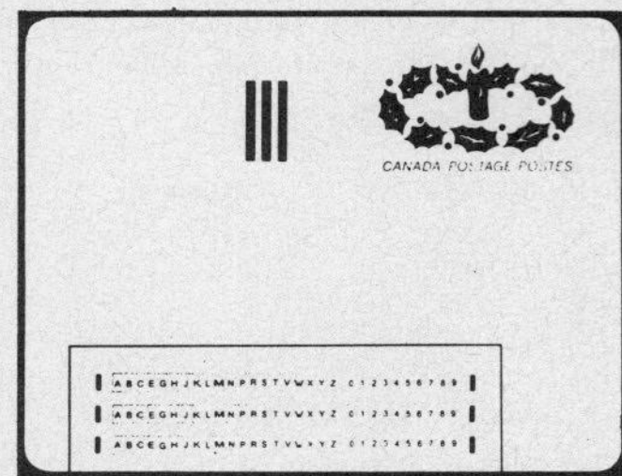

(*Illustration reduced: actual size* 112 × 88 mm)

**"STICK 'N TICK" POSTAGE LABELS.** Prepaid labels in the above design, printed in a combination of red, green and black, were tested by the Canadian Post Office in Winnipeg, Manitoba, between 21 November and 17 December 1983. These self-adhesive labels were sold to the public in kits of 12 or 25, at a saving of 35 c. or $1.11 on the normal postage. They were primarily intended for use on Christmas cards and were only valid on mail posted to Canadian addresses.

The label was affixed to normally addressed envelopes, but the user was then required to mark the postal code on the three lines at the foot. It was hoped that this incentive would increase the use of the postal codes and so speed automatic mail sorting.

The system was extended to seven other cities in 1984. The second version had separate postage paid and Postal Code labels, being available from 5 November until 17 December 1984.

**491** Gold Mine in Prospecting Pan — **492** Montreal Symphony Orchestra

(Des K. Hughes. Litho Ashton-Potter)

**1984** (15 Mar). *50th Anniv of Yellowknife. P* 13½.
1116 **491** 32 c. multicoloured .. .. .. 30 30

(Des J. Delisle and P. Kohler. Litho Ashton-Potter)

**1984** (24 Mar). *50th Anniv of Montreal Symphony Orchestra. P* 12½.
1117 **492** 32 c. multicoloured .. .. .. 35 30

**493** Jacques Cartier — **494** *Eagle* (U.S. Coastguard cadet ship)

(Des Y. Paquin, Engraved C. Haley. Recess French Govt Ptg Wks, Perigueux)

**1984** (20 Apr). *450th Anniv of Jacques Cartier's Voyage to Canada. P* 13.
1118 **493** 32 c. multicoloured .. .. .. 35 30

(Des O. Schenk. Litho Ashton-Potter)

**1984** (18 May). *Tall Ships Visit. P* 12 × 12½.
1119 **494** 32 c. multicoloured .. .. .. 35 30

**495** Service Medal — **496** Oared Galleys

(Des W. Tibbles and C. Webster. Litho Ashton-Potter)

**1984** (28 May). *75th Anniv of Canadian Red Cross Society. P* 13½.
1120 **495** 32 c. multicoloured .. .. .. 35 30

(Des P. Dorn. Photo and recess B.A.B.N.)

**1984** (18 June). *Bicentenary of New Brunswick. P* 13½.
1121 **496** 32 c. multicoloured .. .. .. 35 30

**497** St. Lawrence Seaway

(Des E. Barenscher. Litho C.B.N.)

**1984** (26 June). *25th Anniv of St. Lawrence Seaway. P* 13.
1122 **497** 32 c. multicoloured .. .. .. .. 45 30

**498** New Brunswick — **499** Loyalists of 1784

(Des J. Morin and T. Yakobina. Litho C.B.N.)

**1984** (29 June). *Canada Day. Paintings by Jean Paul Lemieux. Sheet,* 138 × 122 *mm, containing T* **498** *and similar multi-coloured designs. P* 13.
**MS**1123 32 c. × 12, Type **498**; British Columbia; Northwest Territories; Quebec; Manitoba; Alberta; Prince Edward Island; Saskatchewan; Nova Scotia (*vert*); Yukon Territory, Newfoundland; Ontario (*vert*) .. .. .. .. .. .. 5·00 5·50

The captions on the Northwest Territories and Yukon Territory paintings were transposed at the design stage.

(Des W. Davies. Litho B.A.B.N.)

**1984** (3 July). *Bicentenary of Arrival of United Empire Loyalists. P* 13 × 13½.
1124 **499** 32 c. multicoloured .. .. .. 30 30

**500** St. John's Basilica — **501** Coat of Arms of Pope John Paul II

(Des J. Morin and R. Ethier. Litho C.B.N.)

**1984** (17 Aug). *Bicentenary of Roman Catholic Church in Newfoundland. P* 13½.
1125 **500** 32 c. multicoloured .. .. .. 30 25

(Des L. Rivard. Litho Ashton-Potter)

**1984** (31 Aug). *Papal Visit. P* 12½.
1126 **501** 32 c. multicoloured .. .. .. 40 20
1127 64 c. multicoloured .. .. .. 85 1·10

**502** Louisbourg Lighthouse, 1734

(Des D. Noble and K. Rodmell. Litho Ashton-Potter)

**1984** (21 Sept). *Canadian Lighthouses* (*1st series*). *T* **502** *and similar horiz designs. Multicoloured. P* 12½.
1128 32 c. Type **502** .. .. .. .. 85 85
a. Block of 4. Nos. 1128/31 .. .. .. 3·00
1129 32 c. Fisgard Lighthouse, 1860 .. .. 85 85
1130 32 c. Ile Verte Lighthouse, 1809 .. .. 85 85
1131 32 c. Gibraltar Point Lighthouse, 1808 .. 85 85
1128/31 .. .. .. .. *Set of* 4 3·00 3·00

Nos. 1128/31 were printed together, *se-tenant*, in different combinations throughout the sheet, giving ten blocks of 4 and ten single stamps.

See also Nos. 1176/80.

**503** Type 0-6-0, *Scotia* Locomotive

(Des E. Roch. Litho Ashton-Potter)

**1984** (25 Oct). *Railway Locomotives* (*2nd series*). *T* **503** *and similar horiz designs. Multicoloured. P* 12½ × 13.
1132 32 c. Type **503** .. .. .. .. 75 30
a. Pair. Nos. 1132/3 .. .. .. 1·50 1·25
1133 32 c. Type 4-4-0, *Countess of Dufferin* .. 75 30
1134 37 c. Type 2-6-0, GT Class E3 .. .. 80 60
1135 64 c. Type 4-6-0, CP Class D10a .. .. 1·25 1·25
1132/5 .. .. .. .. *Set of* 4 3·25 2·25
**MS**1136 153 × 104 mm. As Nos. 1132/5, but with background colour changed from pale green to pale grey-blue .. .. .. .. .. 4·00 4·50

Nos. 1132/3 were issued together, *se-tenant*, in horizontal and vertical pairs throughout the sheet.

No. **MS**1136 commemorates "CANADA 84" National Stamp Exhibition, Montreal.

See also Nos. 1185/8 and 1223/6.

**504** "The Annunciation" (Jean Dallaire) — **505** Pilots of 1914–18, 1939–45 and 1984

(Des J. Morin and T. Yakobina. Litho Ashton-Potter)

**1984** (2 Nov). *Christmas. Religious Paintings. T* **504** *and similar horiz designs. Multicoloured. P* 13½.
1137 32 c. Type **504** .. .. .. .. 30 10
1138 37 c. "The Three Kings" (Simone Bouchard) .. 35 35
1139 64 c. "Snow in Bethlehem" (David Milne) .. 60 80
1137/9 .. .. .. .. *Set of* 3 1·10 1·10

(Des W. Southern and R. Tibbles. Litho Ashton-Potter)

**1984** (9 Nov). *60th Anniv of Royal Canadian Air Force. P* 12 × 12½.
1140 505 32 c. multicoloured .. .. .. 35 30

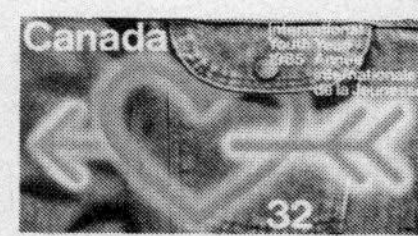

**506** Treffle Berthiaume (editor) — **507** Heart and Arrow

(Des P.-Y. Pelletier. Litho Ashton-Potter)

**1984** (16 Nov.) *Centenary of La Presse (newspaper). P* 13 × 13½.
1141 **506** 32 c. agate, vermilion and pale grey-brown .. .. .. .. .. 35 30

(Des F. Dallaire. Litho Ashton-Potter)

**1985** (8 Feb). *International Youth Year. P* 12½.
1142 **507** 32 c. multicoloured .. .. .. 30 30

**508** Astronaut in Space, and Planet Earth — **509** Emily Murphy

(Des L. Holloway. Litho Ashton-Potter)

**1985** (15 Mar). *Canadian Space Programme. P* 13½.
1143 **508** 32 c. multicoloured .. .. .. 40 30

(Des Muriel Wood and R. Tibbles. Litho Ashton-Potter)

**1985** (17 Apr). *Women's Rights Activists. T* **509** *and similar horiz design. Multicoloured. P* 13½.
1144 32 c. Type **509** .. .. .. .. 40 40
a. Horiz pair. Nos. 1144/5 .. .. 80 80
1145 32 c. Therese Casgrain .. .. .. 40 40

Nos. 1144/5 were printed together, *se-tenant*, in horizontal pairs throughout the sheet.

**510** Gabriel Dumont (Métis leader) and Battle of Batoche, 1885

(Des R. Derreth. Litho Ashton-Potter)

**1985** (6 May). *Centenary of the North-West Rebellion. P* 14 × 13½.
1146 **510** 32 c. blue, carmine and grey .. 30 30

**511** Rear View, Parliament Building, Ottawa — **512** Queen Elizabeth II — **512a** Queen Elizabeth II in 1984 (from photo by Karsh)

(Des R. Bellemare. Eng R. Couture (Nos. 1161/2). Des T. Yakobina and C. Candlish (Nos. 1162a/d), R. Harder (others))

**1985** (21 June)–**90**. *No fluorescent bands* (1 c. *to* 6 c.) *or fluorescent frame* (34 c., 36 c., 38 c., 39 c., 40 c.).

(a) *T* **511** *and similar horiz designs*

(i) *Booklet stamps. Recess B.A.B.N. Chalk-surfaced paper* (6 c. (*No.* 1150*b*), 37 c., 38 c.) *or ordinary paper* (*others*). *P* 12½×12.

1147 – 1 c. grey-olive (30.3.87) .. .. 40 70
a. Booklet pane. Nos. 1147×2, 1150×2, 1152 and label .. 2·75
b. Chalk-surfaced paper (1.10.87) 30 40
ba. Booklet pane. Nos. 1147b×2, 1150a×2, 1152a and label .. 2·25
bb. Booklet pane. Nos. 1147b, 1150a×2, 1153 and two labels (3.2.88) .. .. .. 1·50
1148 – 2 c. bottle green .. .. .. 10 10
a. Booklet pane. Nos. 1148×3, 1149×2 and 1151 .. .. 1·75
b. Chalk-surfaced paper (18.1.89) 10 10
ba. Booklet pane. Nos. 1148b×3, 1150*b*, 1154 and label .. 95
1149 – 5 c. sepia .. .. .. .. 20 20
1150 – 6 c. chestnut (30.3.87) .. .. 50 40
a. Chalk-surfaced paper (1.10.87) 30 10
1150*b* – 6 c. blackish purple (18.1.89) .. 30 35
1151 **511** 34 c. blue-black .. .. .. 85 80
1152 36 c. reddish purple (30.3.87) .. 1·10 1·00
a. Chalk-surfaced paper (1.10.87) 1·10 1·00
1153 37 c. dull ultramarine (3.2.88) .. 60 40
1154 38 c. deep blue (18.1.89) .. .. 50 60

(ii) *Litho C.B.N.* (*Nos.* 1155 (*from sheets*), 1156/7*c*), *B.A.B.N.* (*No.* 1155 (*from booklets*)) *or Ashton-Potter* (*Nos.* 1155b, 1156a, 1157a/ba, 1157ca/cb). *Chalk-surfaced paper* (*Nos.* 1155b/ba, 1156, 1156b/bb *and* 1157c/cb). *P* 13×13½ (*No.* 1157*c*) *or* 13½×13 (*others*).

1155 **511** 34 c. multicoloured .. .. 50 10
a. Booklet pane. No. 1155×25 (1.8.85) .. .. .. 11·50
b. Perf 13½×14 (4.7.86) .. 1·25 80
ba. Booklet pane. No. 1155b×25 .. 25·00
1156 36 c. multicoloured (30.3.87) .. 30 40
a. Ordinary paper .. .. 30 40
b. Perf 13½×14 .. .. .. 75 75
ba. Booklet pane. No. 1156a×10 .. 3·00
bb. Booklet pane. No. 1156a×25 (19.5.87) .. .. .. 7·25
1157 – 37 c. multicoloured (30.12.87) .. 75 35
a. Perf 13½×14 (5.1.88) .. 75 65
ab. Booklet pane. No. 1157a×10 .. 7·50
ac. Booklet pane. No. 1157a×25 (2.5.88) .. .. .. 17·00
ad. Chalk-surfaced paper (5.1.88) 1·25 90
ae. Booklet pane. No. 1157ad×25 .. 25·00
1157*c* – 38 c. multicoloured (29.12.88) .. 35 40
ca. Booklet pane. No. 1157c×10 and two labels .. .. 3·50
cb. Booklet pane. No. 1157c×25 and two labels .. .. 9·00

(iii) *Coil stamps. Recess C.B.N. P* 10×*imperf*

1158 **511** 34 c. purple-brown (1.8.85) .. 1·75 1·75
a. Imperf (pair) .. ..
1159 36 c. carmine-vermilion (19.5.87) .. 80 80
1160 37 c. deep ultramarine (22.2.88) .. 60 60
a. Imperf (pair) .. .. £160
1160*b* 38 c. bottle green (1.2.89) .. 40 40

(*b*) *Recess and photo B.A.B.N. P* 13×13½

1161 **512** 34 c. black and cobalt (12.7.85) .. 45 30
1162 36 c. reddish purple (1.10.87) .. 1·25 60

(*c*) *Litho B.A.B.N.* (*Nos.* 1162*a*/*c*) *or Ashton-Potter* (*Nos.* 1162ba, 1162ca, 1162*d*). *Chalk-surfaced paper* (40 c.). *P* 13½×13 (*No.* 1162*a*), 13×12½ (*No.* 1162*b*), *or* 13×13½ (*Nos.* 1162*c*, 1162*d*).

1162*a* **512*a*** 37 c. multicoloured (30.12.87) .. 1·25 30
1162*b* 38 c. multicoloured (29.12.88) .. 35 40
ba. Perf 13×13½. Chalk-surfaced paper .. .. 35 50
bb. Booklet pane. No. 1162ba×10 and two labels .. 3·50
1162*c* 39 c. multicoloured (12.1.90) .. 1·00 35
ca. Chalk-surfaced paper .. 1·00 55
cb. Booklet pane. No. 1162ca×10 10·00
cc. Perf 13×12½ (2.90) ..
1162*d* 40 c. multicoloured (28.12.90) .. 40 45
da. Booklet pane. No. 1162*d*×10 and two labels .. .. 4·00

Designs:—1 c., 5 c., 6 c. (No. 1150*b*) East Block, Parliament Building; 2 c., 6 c. (No. 1150) West Block, Parliament Building; 37 c. (No. 1157) Front view, Parliament Building; 38 c. (No. 1157*c*) Side view, Parliament Building.

Stamps from booklet panes Nos. 1147a, 1147ba/bb and 1148a/b have one or two adjacent sides imperforate. Stamps from the first and last vertical columns of booklet panes Nos. 1155a, 1155ba, 1156ba/bb, 1157ab/ac, 1157ae, 1157ca/cb, 1162bb, 1162cb and 1162da are imperforate at left or right. Those from the bottom row of No. 1157ac are also imperforate at foot.

Nos. 1157*c* and 1162*b*/*d* have a slightly larger design image, 21×17 mm.

(Des R. Harder. Litho Ashton-Potter)

**1985** (28 June). *Canada Day. Forts* (2*nd series*). *Horiz designs as T* **481**. *Multicoloured. P* 12½×13.

1163 34 c. Lower Fort Garry, Manitoba (44×22 *mm*) .. .. .. 50 55
a. Booklet pane. Nos. 1153/62 .. 4·50
1164 34 c. Fort Anne, Nova Scotia .. .. 50 55
1165 34 c. Fort York, Ontario .. .. 50 55
1166 34 c. Castle Hill, Newfoundland (28×22 *mm*) .. .. .. 50 55
1167 34 c. Fort Whoop Up, Alberta (28×22 *mm*) 50 55
1168 34 c. Fort Erie, Ontario (44×22 *mm*) .. 50 55
1169 34 c. Fort Walsh, Saskatchewan .. .. 50 55
1170 34 c. Fort Lennox, Quebec .. .. 50 55
1171 34 c. York Redoubt, Nova Scotia (28×22 *mm*) .. .. .. 50 55
1172 34 c. Fort Frederick, Ontario (28×22 *mm*) 50 55
1163/72 .. .. .. .. *Set of* 10 4·50 5·00

Nos. 1163/72 were only available from $3.40 stamp booklets containing the *se-tenant* pane, No. 1163a.

**513** Louis Hébert (apothecary)

**514** Parliament Buildings and Map of World

**515** Guide and Brownie Saluting

(Des C. Malenfant. Litho Ashton-Potter)

**1985** (30 Aug). *45th International Pharmaceutical Sciences Congress of Pharmaceutical Federation, Montreal. Fluorescent frame. P* 12½.

1173 **513** 34 c. multicoloured .. .. .. 45 35

(Des E. Barenscher. Litho Ashton-Potter)

**1985** (3 Sept). *74th Conference of Inter-Parliamentary Union, Ottawa. P* 13½.

1174 **514** 34 c. multicoloured .. .. .. 45 35

(Des Barbara Griffin. Recess and photo B.A.B.N.)

**1985** (12 Sept). *75th Anniv of Girl Guide Movement. Fluorescent frame. P* 13½×13.

1175 **515** 34 c. multicoloured .. .. .. 45 35

**516** Sisters Islets Lighthouse

**517** Santa Claus in Reindeer-drawn Sleigh

(Des B. Reilander (No. **MS**1180), L. Rivard (others). Litho Ashton-Potter)

**1985** (3 Oct). *Canadian Lighthouses* (2*nd series*). *T* **516** *and similar horiz designs. Multicoloured. P* 13½.

1176 34 c. Type **516** .. .. .. 1·00 1·10
a. Block of 4. Nos. 1176/9 .. .. 3·50
1177 34 c. Pelee Passage Lighthouse .. .. 1·00 1·10
1178 34 c. Haut-fond Prince Lighthouse .. .. 1·00 1·10
1179 34 c. Rose Blanche Lighthouse, Cains Island .. .. .. .. 1·00 1·10
1176/9 .. .. .. .. *Set of* 4 3·50 4·00
**MS**1180 109×90 mm. Nos. 1176/9 .. 4·00 4·25

Nos. 1176/9 were printed together, *se-tenant*, in different combinations throughout the sheet, giving ten blocks of 4 and ten single stamps.

No. **MS**1180 Publicises "Capex 87" International Stamp Exhibition, Toronto.

(Des Barbara Carroll and C. Yaneff. Litho Ashton-Potter)

**1985** (23 Oct). *Christmas. Santa Claus Parade. T* **517** *and similar horiz designs. Multicoloured. P* 13½.

1181 32 c. Canada Post's parade float .. .. 45 20
a. Booklet pane. No. 1181×10 .. 4·50
1182 34 c. Type **517** .. .. .. 60 10
1183 39 c. Acrobats and horse-drawn carriage .. 70 70
1184 68 c. Christmas tree, pudding and goose on float .. .. .. .. 1·25 1·25
1181/4 .. .. .. .. *Set of* 4 2·75 2·00

No. 1181 was only available from $3.20 stamp booklets, which had the upper and lower edges of the pane imperforate. This value was intended for use on greeting cards posted on or before 31 January 1986, and represented a 2 c. saving of postage. After this date these stamps could be used for any postal purpose in conjunction with other values.

(Des E. Roch. Litho Ashton-Potter)

**1985** (7 Nov). *Railway Locomotives* (3*rd series*). *Horiz designs as T* **503**. *Multicoloured. P* 12½×13.

1185 34 c. Class "K2" .. .. .. 65 40
a. Pair. Nos. 1185/6 .. .. 1·25 1·50
1186 34 c. Class "P2a" .. .. .. 65 40
1187 39 c. Class "O10a" .. .. .. 75 75
1188 68 c. Class "H4D" .. .. .. 1·10 1·10
1185/8 .. .. .. .. *Set of* 4 2·75 2·40

Nos. 1185/6 were printed together, *se-tenant*, in horizontal and vertical pairs throughout the sheet.

**518** Naval Personnel of 1910, 1939–45 and 1985

**519** "The Old Holton House, Montreal" (James Wilson Morrice)

(Des W. Southern and R. Tibbles. Litho C.B.N.)

**1985** (8 Nov). *75th Anniv of Royal Canadian Navy. Fluorescent frame. P* 13½×13.

1189 **518** 34 c. multicoloured .. .. .. 65 35

(Des L. Parent and J. Morin. Litho C.B.N.)

**1985** (15 Nov). *125th Anniv of Montreal Museum of Fine Art*
*P* 13½.

1190 **519** 34 c. multicoloured .. .. .. 40 3

**520** Map of Alberta showing Olympic Sites

(Des P.-Y. Pelletier. Litho Ashton-Potter)

**1986** (13 Feb). *Winter Olympic Games, Calgary* (1988) (1
*issue*). *Fluorescent frame. P* 12½×13.

1191 **520** 34 c. multicoloured .. .. .. 40

See also Nos. 1216/17, 1236/7, 1258/9 and 1281/4.

**521** Canada Pavilion

**522** Molly Brant

(Des Debbie Adams. Recess and photo B.A.B.N.)

**1986** (7 Mar). *"Expo '86" World Fair, Vancouver* (1*st issue*
*T* **521** *and similar horiz design. Multicoloured. Fluoresce*
*frame. P* 13×13½.

1192 34 c. Type **521** .. .. .. .. 60 4
1193 39 c. Early telephone, dish aerial and satellite .. .. .. .. .. 65 1·1

See also Nos. 1196/7.

(Des Sara Tyson. Litho Ashton-Potter)

**1986** (14 Apr). *250th Birth Anniv of Molly Brant* (*Iroquo*
*leader*). *P* 13½.

1194 **522** 34 c. multicoloured .. .. .. 40

**523** Philippe Aubert de Gaspé and Scene from *Les Anciens Canadiens*



**524** Canadian Field Post Office and Cancellation, 1944

(Des Y. Paquin and P. Fontaine. Litho Ashton-Potter)

**1986** (14 Apr). *Birth Bicentenary of Philippe Aubert de Gas*
(*author*). *Fluorescent frame. P* 12½.

1195 **523** 34 c. multicoloured .. .. .. 40

(Des Debbie Adams. Recess and photo B.A.B.N.)

**1986** (28 Apr). *"Expo '86" World Fair, Vancouver* (2*nd issu*
*Multicoloured designs as T* **521**. *Fluorescent fram*
*P* 13½×13 (34 c.) *or* 13×13½ (68 c.).

1196 34 c. Expo Centre, Vancouver (*vert*) .. 45
1197 68 c. Early and modern trains .. .. 1·00 1·

(Des J. DesRosiers. Litho Ashton-Potter)

**1986** (9 May). *75th Anniv of Canadian Forces Postal Servi*
*P* 13½.

1198 **524** 34 c. multicoloured .. .. .. 65

**525** Great Blue Heron

**526** Railway Rotary Snowplough

(Des J.-L. Grondin and P. Fontaine. Litho Ashton-Potter)

**1986** (22 May). *Birds of Canada. T* **525** *and similar hor*
*designs. Multicoloured. P* 13½.

1199 34 c. Type **525** .. .. .. 85
a. Block of 4. Nos. 1199/1202 .. 3·00
1200 34 c. Snow Goose .. .. .. 85
1201 34 c. Great Horned Owl .. .. 85
1202 34 c. Spruce Grouse .. .. .. 85
1199/1202 .. .. .. *Set of* 4 3·00 3·

Nos. 1199/1202 were printed together, *se-tenant*, in differe
combinations throughout the sheet, giving ten blocks of 4 ar
ten single stamps.

(Des R. Hill. Litho C.B.N.)

**86** (27 June). *Canada Day. Science and Technology. Canadian Inventions (1st series). T* **526** *and similar vert designs. Multicoloured. P* 13½.
03 34 c. Type **526** . . . . . . . . 75 85
a. Block of 4. Nos. 1203/6 . . . . 2·75
04 34 c. Space shuttle *Challenger* launching satellite with Canadarm . . . . 75 85
05 34 c. Pilot wearing anti-gravity flight suit and "Spitfire" . . . . . . . . 75 85
06 34 c. Variable-pitch propeller and Avro "504K" airplane . . . . . . 75 85
03/6 . . . . . . . . *Set of* 4 2·75 3·00
Nos. 1203/6 were printed together, *se-tenant*, in blocks of 4 roughout the sheet.
See also Nos. 1241/4 and 1292/5.

**527** C.B.C. Logos over Map of Canada **528** Ice Age Artefacts, Tools and Settlement

(Des R. Mah and G. Tsetsekas. Litho Ashton-Potter)

**86** (23 July). *50th Anniv of Canadian Broadcasting Corporation. P* 12½.
07 **527** 34 c. multicoloured . . . . . . 40 45

(Des F. Hagan. Litho Ashton-Potter)

**86** (29 Aug–1 Oct). *Exploration of Canada (1st series). Discoverers. T* **528** *and similar horiz designs. Multicoloured. P* 12½×13.
08 34 c. Type **528** . . . . . . . . 35 55
a. Block of 4. Nos. 1208/11 . . . . 1·25
09 34 c. Viking ships . . . . . . . . 35 55
10 34 c. John Cabot's *Matthew*, 1497, compass and fish . . . . . . . . 35 55
11 34 c. Henry Hudson cast adrift, 1611 . . 35 55
08/11 . . . . . . . . *Set of* 4 1·25 2·00
**IS**1212 119×84 mm. Nos. 1208/11 (1 Oct) . . 2·00 2·00
Nos. 1208/11 were printed together, *se-tenant*, in different mbinations throughout the sheet, giving ten blocks of 4 and n single stamps.
No. **MS**1212 publicises "Capex '87" International Stamp xhibition, Toronto.
See also Nos. 1232/5, 1285/8 and 1319/22.

**529** Crowfoot (Blackfoot Chief) and Indian Village **530** Peace Dove and Globe

(Des Wanda Lewicka and J. Morin. Litho C.B.N.)

**86** (5 Sept). *Founders of the Canadian West. T* **529** *and similar horiz design. Multicoloured. P* 13×13½.
13 34 c. Type **529** . . . . . . . . 35 55
a. Pair. Nos. 1213/14 . . . . . . 70 1·10
14 34 c. James Macleod of the North West Mounted Police and Fort Macleod . . 35 55
Nos. 1213/4 were printed together, *se-tenant*, in horizontal and rtical pairs throughout the sheet.

(Des Carole Jeghers. Litho and embossed Ashton-Potter)

**86** (16 Sept). *International Peace Year. P* 13½.
15 **530** 34 c. multicoloured . . . . . . 40 45

**531** Ice Hockey **532** Angel with Crown

(Des P.-Y. Pelletier. Litho C.B.N.)

**986** (15 Oct). *Winter Olympic Games, Calgary* (1988) (*2nd issue*). *T* **531** *and similar vert design. Multicoloured. P* 13½×13.
216 34 c. Type **531** . . . . . . . . 75 1·00
a. Pair. Nos. 1216/17 . . . . . . 1·50 2·00
217 34 c. Biathlon . . . . . . . . 75 1·00
Nos. 1216/17 were printed together, *se-tenant*, in horizontal nd vertical pairs throughout the sheet.
See also Nos. 1236/7, 1258/9 and 1281/4.

(Des T. Dimson. Litho Ashton-Potter)

**986** (29 Oct). *Christmas. T* **532** *and similar multicoloured designs. Fluorescent frame* (34 *to* 68 c.). *P* 13½×*imperf* (29 c.) *or* 12½ (*others*).
218 29 c. Angel singing carol (*36×22 mm*) . . 30 15
a. Booklet pane. No. 1218×10 . . 3·00
219 34 c. Type **532** . . . . . . . . 40 25
220 39 c. Angel playing lute . . . . . . 50 65
221 68 c. Angel with ribbon . . . . . . 75 1·40
218/21 . . . . . . . . *Set of* 4 1·75 2·25
No. 1218 was only available from $2.90 stamp booklets, which had the sides of the pane imperforate. In addition to the design each stamp in the pane included an integral horizontal label showing a bar code. This value was intended for use on greeting cards posted on or before 31 January 1987, and represented a 5 c. saving when used in conjunction with special postcoded envelopes. These stamps were valid for normal postal purposes after 31 January when used with other values.

**533** John Molson with Theatre Royal, Montreal, *Accommodation* (paddle-steamer) and Railway Train **534** Toronto's First Post Office

(Des C. Malenfant. Litho Ashton-Potter)

**1986** (4 Nov). *150th Death Anniv of John Molson (businessman). P* 12½.
1222 **533** 34 c. multicoloured . . . . . . 50 50

(Des E. Roch. Litho Ashton-Potter)

**1986** (21 Nov). *Railway Locomotives (4th series). Horiz designs as T* **503**, *but size* 60×22 *mm. Multicoloured. P* 12½×13.
1223 34 c. Class "V-1-a" . . . . . . . . 90 90
a. Pair. Nos. 1223/4 . . . . . . 1·75 1·75
1224 34 c. Class "T1a" . . . . . . . . 90 90
1225 39 c. Class "U-2-a" . . . . . . . . 1·00 90
1226 68 c. Class "H1c" . . . . . . . . 1·75 2·00
1223/6 . . . . . . . . *Set of* 4 4·00 4·25
Nos. 1223/6 were issued together, *se-tenant*, in horizontal and vertical pairs throughout the sheet.

(Des J. Mardon (stamps) and B. Reilander (sheet). Recess and litho B.A.B.N.)

**1987** (16 Feb–12 June). *"Capex '87" International Stamp Exhibition, Toronto. T* **534** *and similar horiz designs showing Post Offices. Fluorescent frame. P* 13×13½.
1227 34 c. Type **534** . . . . . . . . 40 20
1228 36 c. Nelson-Miramichi, New Brunswick (12.6) . . . . . . . . 50 35
1229 42 c. Saint-Ours, Quebec (12.6) . . . . 60 45
1230 72 c. Battleford, Saskatchewan (12.6) . . 90 85
1227/30 . . . . . . . . *Set of* 4 2·25 1·60
**MS**1231 155×92 mm. 36 c. As No. 1227 and Nos. 1228/30 (12.6) . . . . . . . . 2·00 2·25

**535** Étienne Brûlé exploring Lake Superior

(Des F. Hagan and J. Britton. Litho Ashton-Potter)

**1987** (13 Mar). *Exploration of Canada (2nd series). Pioneers of New France. T* **535** *and similar horiz designs. Multicoloured. P* 12½×13.
1232 34 c. Type **535** . . . . . . . . 65 45
a. Block of 4. Nos. 1232/5 . . . . 2·40
1233 34 c. Radisson and des Groseilliers with British and French flags . . . . 65 45
1234 34 c. Jolliet and Father Marquette on the Mississippi . . . . . . . . 65 45
1235 34 c. Jesuit missionary preaching to Indians . . . . . . . . . . 65 45
1232/5 . . . . . . . . *Set of* 4 2·40 1·60
Nos. 1232/5 were printed together, *se-tenant*, in different combinations throughout the sheet, giving ten blocks of 4 and ten single stamps.

(Des P.-Y. Pelletier. Litho C.B.N.)

**1987** (3 Apr). *Winter Olympic Games, Calgary* (1988) (*3rd issue*). *Vert designs as T* **531**. *Multicoloured. P* 13½×13.
1236 36 c. Speed skating . . . . . . . . 50 40
1237 42 c. Bobsleighing . . . . . . . . 75 60

**536** Volunteer Activities **537** Canadian Coat of Arms

(Des W. Davies. Litho Ashton-Potter)

**1987** (13 Apr). *National Volunteer Week. P* 12½×13.
1238 **536** 36 c. multicoloured . . . . . . 30 35

(Des R. Tibbles. Litho Ashton-Potter)

**1987** (15 Apr). *5th Anniv of Canadian Charter of Rights and Freedoms. Fluorescent frame. P* 14×13½.
1239 **537** 36 c. multicoloured . . . . . . 35 35

**538** Steel Girder, Gear Wheel and Microchip **539** R. A. Fessenden (AM Radio)

(Des L. Holloway, R. Kerr and Nita Wallace. Litho Ashton-Potter)

**1987** (19 May). *Centenary of Engineering Institute of Canada. P* 12½×13.
1240 **538** 36 c. multicoloured . . . . . . 35 40

(Des R. Hill. Litho C.B.N.)

**1987** (25 June). *Canada Day. Science and Technology. Canadian Inventors (2nd series). T* **539** *and similar vert designs. Multicoloured. P* 13½.
1241 36 c. Type **539** . . . . . . . . 35 35
a. Block of four. Nos. 1241/4 . . . . 1·25
1242 36 c. C. Fenerty (newsprint pulp) . . . . 35 35
1243 36 c. G.-E. Desbarats and W. Leggo (half-tone engraving) . . . . . . 35 35
1244 36 c. F. N. Gisborne (first North American undersea telegraph) . . . . 35 35
1241/4 . . . . . . . . *Set of* 4 1·25 1·25
Nos. 1241/4 were printed together, *se-tenant*, in blocks of four throughout the sheet.

**540** *Segwun* **541** Figurehead from *Hamilton*, 1813

(Des D. Champion. Litho C.B.N.)

**1987** (20 July). *Canadian Steamships. T* **540** *and similar multicoloured design. P* 13.
1245 36 c. Type **540** . . . . . . . . 1·00 1·25
a. Horiz pair. Nos. 1245/6 . . . . 2·00 2·50
1246 36 c. *Princess Marguerite* (52×22 *mm*) . . 1·00 1·25
Nos. 1245/6 were printed together horizontally, *se-tenant*, throughout the sheet of 25, with No. 1245 occurring in columns 1, 3 and 5 and No. 1246 in columns 2 and 4.

(Des L.-A. Rivard. Litho Ashton-Potter)

**1987** (7 Aug). *Historic Shipwrecks. T* **541** *and similar horiz designs. Multicoloured. P* 13½×13.
1247 36 c. Type **541** . . . . . . . . 45 45
a. Block of four. Nos. 1247/50 . . . . 1·60
1248 36 c. Hull of *San Juan*, 1565 . . . . 45 45
1249 36 c. Wheel from *Breadalbane*, 1853 . . 45 45
1250 36 c. Bell from *Ericsson*, 1892 . . . . 45 45
1247/50 . . . . . . . . *Set of* 4 1·60 1·60
Nos. 1247/50 were printed together, *se-tenant*, in different combinations throughout the sheet, giving ten blocks of 4 and ten single stamps.

**542** Air Canada Boeing "767 and Globe **543** Summit Symbol

(Des D. Carter and Debbie Adams. Litho C.B.N.)

**1987** (1 Sept). *50th Anniv of Air Canada. P* 13½.
1251 **542** 36 c. multicoloured . . . . . . 30 35

(Des C. Gaudreau. Litho Ashton-Potter)

**1987** (2 Sept). *2nd International Francophone Summit, Quebec. Fluorescent frame. P* 13×12½.
1252 **543** 36 c. multicoloured . . . . . . 30 35

**544** Commonwealth Symbol **545** Poinsettia

(Des G. Tsetsekas. Litho Ashton-Potter)

**1987** (13 Oct). *Commonwealth Heads of Government Meeting, Vancouver. Fluorescent frame. P* 13 × 12½.
1253 **544** 36 c. multicoloured 35 40

(Des C. Simard. Litho Ashton-Potter)

**1987** (2 Nov). *Christmas. Christmas Plants. T* **545** *and similar multicoloured designs. Fluorescent frame. P* 12½ × 13 (31 *c.*) *or* 13½ (*others*).
1254 31 c. Decorated Christmas tree and presents (36 × 20 *mm*) 30 35
a. Booklet pane. No. 1254 × 10 3·00
1255 36 c. Type **545** 35 40
1256 42 c. Holly wreath 40 45
1257 72 c. Mistletoe and decorated tree 65 70
1254/7 *Set of* 4 1·50 1·75

On No. 1254 the left-hand third of the design area is taken up by a bar code which has fluorescent bands between the bars. This value was only available from $3.10 stamp booklets which had the sides of the pane imperforate. This value was intended for use on greeting cards posted on or before 31 January 1988 and represented a 5 c. saving when used in conjunction with special postcoded envelopes.

(Des P.-Y. Pelletier. Litho C.B.N.)

**1987** (13 Nov). *Winter Olympic Games, Calgary* (1988) (*4th issue*). *Vert designs as T* **531**. *Multicoloured. Fluorescent frame. P* 13½ × 13.
1258 36 c. Cross-country skiing 35 40
a. Pair. Nos. 1258/9 70 80
1259 36 c. Ski-jumping 35 40

Nos. 1258/9 were printed together, *se-tenant*, in horizontal and vertical pairs throughout the sheet.

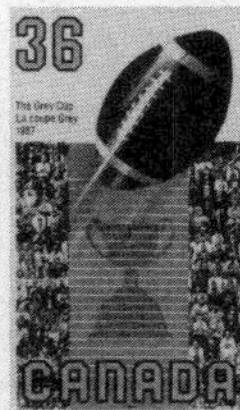

**546** Football, Grey Cup and Spectators

(Des L. Holloway. Litho Ashton-Potter)

**1987** (20 Nov). *75th Grey Cup Final* (*Canadian football championship*), *Vancouver. Fluorescent frame. P* 12½.
1260 **546** 36 c. multicoloured 35 40

**547** Flying Squirrel

**548** Lynx

**548***a* Runnymede Library, Toronto

(Des Gottschalk & Ash International (1 c. to 25 c.), B. Tsang (43 c. to 80 c.), R. Bellemare ($1, $2, $5). Litho Ashton-Potter (1 c. to 80 c.). Recess and litho B.A.B.N. ($1, $2, $5))

**1988** (18 Jan)–**90**. *Canadian Mammals and Architecture. Multicoloured. Fluorescent frame* (10 *c.* (*ptgs to Sept* 1991 *only*) *to* 80 *c.*) *or no fluorescent frame* (*others*).

(*a*) *Horiz designs as T* **547**. *Chalk-surfaced paper. P* 13 × 13½
1261 1 c. Type **547** (3.10.88) 10 10
1262 2 c. Porcupine (3.10.88) 10 10
1263 3 c. Muskrat (3.10.88) 10 10
1264 5 c. Varying Hare (3.10.88) 10 10
1265 6 c. Red Fox (3.10.88) 10 10
1266 10 c. Striped Skunk (3.10.88) 10 10
a. Perf 13 × 12½ 25 15
1267 25 c. American Beaver (3.10.88) 25 30

(*b*) *Horiz designs as T* **548**. *Chalk-surfaced paper* (45, 46, 57, 61, 63, 78, 80 *c.*) *or ordinary paper* (*others*). *P* 12 × 12½ (43, 57, 74 *c.*) *or* 14½ × 14 (*others*)
1268 43 c. Type **548** 90 50
1269 44 c. Walrus (18.1.89) 45 45
a. Perf 12½ × 13. Chalk-surfaced paper 80 60
ab. Booklet pane. No. 1269a × 5 and label with margins all round 4·00
b. Chalk-surfaced paper (9.6.89) 1·00 1·00
c. Perf 13½ × 13. Chalk-surfaced paper (1989) 9·00 1·25
1270 45 c. Pronghorn (12.1.90) 35 40
a. Perf 12½ × 13 35 40
ab. Booklet pane. No. 1270a × 5 and label with margins all round 1·75
b. Perf 13 (6.90) 1·00 1·00
1270*c* 46 c. Wolverine (28.12.90) 45 50
ca. Perf 13 60 60
cb. Perf 12½ × 13 45 50
cc. Booklet pane. No. 1270cb × 5 and label with margins all round 2·25
1271 57 c. Killer Whale 1·25 70
a. Ordinary paper (26.9.88) 1·75 1·40

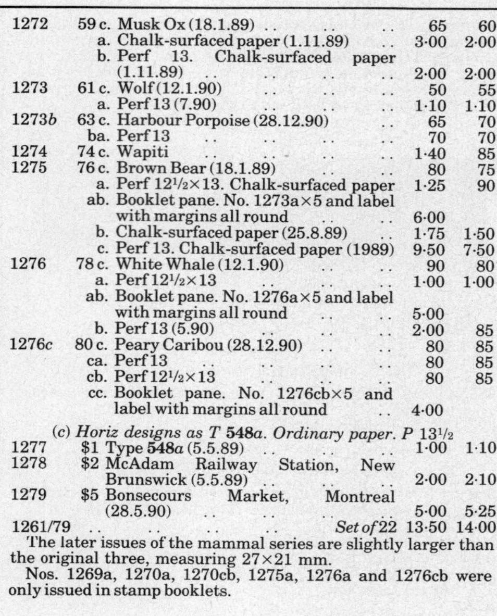

1272 59 c. Musk Ox (18.1.89) 65 60
a. Chalk-surfaced paper (1.11.89) 3·00 2·00
b. Perf 13. Chalk-surfaced paper (1.11.89) 2·00 2·00
1273 61 c. Wolf (12.1.90) 50 55
a. Perf 13 (7.90) 1·10 1·10
1273*b* 63 c. Harbour Porpoise (28.12.90) 65 70
ba. Perf 13 70 70
1274 74 c. Wapiti 1·40 85
1275 76 c. Brown Bear (18.1.89) 80 75
a. Perf 12½ × 13. Chalk-surfaced paper 1·25 90
ab. Booklet pane. No. 1273a × 5 and label with margins all round 6·00
b. Chalk-surfaced paper (25.8.89) 1·75 1·50
c. Perf 13. Chalk-surfaced paper (1989) 9·50 7·50
1276 78 c. White Whale (12.1.90) 90 80
a. Perf 12½ × 13 1·00 1·00
ab. Booklet pane. No. 1276a × 5 and label with margins all round 5·00
b. Perf 13 (5.90) 2·00 85
1276*c* 80 c. Peary Caribou (28.12.90) 80 85
ca. Perf 13 80 85
cb. Perf 12½ × 13 80 85
cc. Booklet pane. No. 1276cb × 5 and label with margins all round 4·00

(*c*) *Horiz designs as T* **548***a*. *Ordinary paper. P* 13½
1277 $1 Type **548***a* (5.5.89) 1·00 1·10
1278 $2 McAdam Railway Station, New Brunswick (5.5.89) 2·00 2·10
1279 $5 Bonsecours Market, Montreal (28.5.90) 5·00 5·25
1261/79 *Set of* 22 13·50 14·00

The later issues of the mammal series are slightly larger than the original three, measuring 27 × 21 mm.

Nos. 1269a, 1270a, 1270cb, 1275a, 1276a and 1276cb were only issued in stamp booklets.

(Des P.-Y. Pelletier. Litho Ashton-Potter)

**1988** (12 Feb). *Winter Olympic Games, Calgary* (*5th issue*). *Vert designs as T* **531**. *Multicoloured. Fluorescent frame. P* 12 × 12½ (37 *c.*) *or* 12½ (*others*).
1281 37 c. Slalom skiing 50 40
a. Pair. Nos. 1281/2 1·00 80
1282 37 c. Curling 50 40
1283 43 c. Figure skating 65 45
1284 74 c. Luge 1·00 70
1281/4 *Set of* 4 2·40 1·75

Nos. 1281/2 were printed together, *se-tenant*, in horizontal and vertical pairs throughout the sheet.

**549** Trade Goods, Blackfoot Encampment and Page from Anthony Henday's Journal

(Des F. Hagan. Litho Ashton-Potter)

**1988** (17 Mar). *Exploration of Canada* (*3rd series*). *Explorers of the West. T* **549** *and similar horiz designs. Multicoloured. Fluorescent frame. P* 12½ × 13.
1285 37 c. Type **549** 35 40
a. Block of 4. Nos. 1285/8 1·25
1286 37 c. *Discovery* and map of George Vancouver's voyage 35 40
1287 37 c. Simon Fraser's expedition portaging canoes 35 40
1288 37 c. John Palliser's surveying equipment and view of prairie 35 40
1285/8 *Set of* 4 1·25 1·40

Nos. 1285/8 were printed together, *se-tenant*, in different combinations throughout the sheet, giving ten blocks of 4 and ten single stamps.

**550** "The Young Reader" (Ozias Leduc)

**551** Duck landing on Marsh

(Des P.-Y. Pelletier. Eng G. Prosser. Recess and photo B.A.B.N.)

**1988** (20 May). *Canadian Art* (1*st series*). *No fluorescent bands. P* 13 × 13½.
1289 **550** 50 c. multicoloured 50 70

No. 1289 was issued in sheets of 16 with descriptive texts on the margins.

See also Nos. 1327, 1384 and 1421.

(Des T. Telmet and J. Gault. Litho C.B.N.)

**1988** (1 June). *Wildlife and Habitat Conservation. T* **551** *and similar horiz design. Multicoloured. Fluorescent frame. P* 13 × 13½.
1290 37 c. Type **551** 50 40
a. Pair. Nos. 1290/1 1·00 80
1291 37 c. Moose feeding in marsh 50 40

Nos. 1290/1 were printed together, *se-tenant*, in horizontal and vertical pairs throughout the sheet.

**552** Kerosene Lamp and Diagram of Distillation Plant

**553** *Papilio brevicauda*

(Des R. Hill. Litho Ashton-Potter)

**1988** (17 June). *Canada Day. Science and Technology. Cana- ian Inventions* (*3rd series*). *T* **552** *and similar vert design Multicoloured. Fluorescent frame. P* 12½ × 13.
1292 37 c. Type **552** 35 4
a. Block of 4. Nos. 1292/5 1·25
1293 37 c. Ears of Marquis wheat 35 4
1294 37 c. Electron microscope and magnified image 35 4
1295 37 c. Patient under "Cobalt 60" cancer therapy 35 4
1292/5 *Set of* 4 1·25 1·4

Nos. 1292/5 were printed together, *se-tenant*, in blocks of throughout the sheet.

(Des Heather Cooper. Litho Ashton-Potter)

**1988** (4 July). *Canadian Butterflies. T* **553** *and similar ve designs. Multicoloured. Fluorescent frame. P* 12 × 12½.
1296 37 c. Type **553** 40 4
a. Block of four. Nos. 1296/9 1·40
1297 37 c. *Lycaeides idas* 40 4
1298 37 c. *Oeneis macounii* 40 4
1299 37 c. *Papilio glaucus* 40 4
1296/9 *Set of* 4 1·40 1·4

Nos. 1296/9 were printed together, *se-tenant*, in differer combinations throughout the sheet, giving ten blocks of 4 an ten single stamps.

**554** St. John's Harbour Entrance and Skyline

**555** Club Members working on Forestry Project and Rural Scene

(Des L.-A. Rivard. Litho Ashton-Potter)

**1988** (22 July). *Centenary of Incorporation of St. John's Newfoundland. Fluorescent frame. P* 13½ × 13.
1300 **554** 37 c. multicoloured 35 4

(Des Debbie Adams. Litho Ashton-Potter)

**1988** (5 Aug). *75th Anniv of 4-H Clubs. Fluorescent frame P* 13½ × 13.
1301 **555** 37 c. multicoloured 35 4

**556** Saint-Maurice Ironworks

**557** Tahltan Bear Dog

(Des Hélène Racicot and Michèle Cayer. Eng Y. Baril. Reces and litho C.B.N.)

**1988** (19 Aug). *250th Anniv of Saint-Maurice Ironworks Québec. Fluorescent frame. P* 13½.
1302 **556** 37 c. black, pale orange and cinnamon 35 4

(Des Mia Lane and D. Nethercott. Litho Ashton-Potter)

**1988** (26 Aug). *Canadian Dogs. T* **557** *and similar hori designs. Multicoloured. Fluorescent frame. P* 12½ × 12.
1303 37 c. Type **557** 40 4
a. Block of 4. Nos. 1303/6 1·40
1304 37 c. Nova Scotia Duck Tolling Retriever 40 4
1305 37 c. Canadian Eskimo Dog 40 4
1306 37 c. Newfoundland 40 4
1303/6 *Set of* 4 1·40 1·4

Nos. 1303/6 were printed together, *se-tenant*, in differen combinations throughout the sheet, giving ten blocks of 4 and ten single stamps.

## COVER PRICES

Cover factors are quoted at the beginning of each country for most issues to 1945. An explanation of the system can be found on page x. The factors quoted do not, however, apply to philatelic covers.

**558** Baseball, Glove and Pitch

**559** Virgin with Inset of Holy Child

(Des L. Holloway. Litho C.B.N.)

988 (14 Sept). *150th Anniv of Baseball in Canada. Fluorescent frame. P* 13½ × 13.
307 **558** 37 c. multicoloured .. .. .. .. 35 40

(Des E. Roch and T. Yakobina. Litho Ashton-Potter)

988 (27 Oct). *Christmas. Icons. T* **559** *and similar multicoloured designs. Fluorescent frame. P* 12½×13 (32 *c.) or* 13½ (*others*).
308 32 c. Holy Family (36×21 *mm*) .. .. 30 35
a. Booklet pane. No. 1308×10 .. .. 3·00
309 37 c. Type **559** .. .. .. .. 35 40
310 43 c. Virgin and Child .. .. .. 40 45
311 74 c. Virgin and Child (*different*) .. .. 70 75
308/11 .. .. .. .. *Set of* 4 1·60 1·75

On No. 1308 the left-hand third of the design area is taken up y a bar code which has fluorescent bands between the bars. 'his value was only available from $3.20 stamp booklets which ad the sides and bottom of the pane imperforate. It was ntended for use on greeting cards posted on or before 31 anuary 1989.

No. 1309 also commemorates the Millenium of Ukrainian 'hristianity.

**560** Bishop Inglis and Nova Scotia Church

**561** Frances Ann Hopkins and "Canoe Manned by Voyageurs"

(Des S. Slipp and K. Sollows. Litho Ashton-Potter)

988 (1 Nov). *Bicentenary of Consecration of Charles Inglis (first Canadian Anglican bishop)* (1987). *Fluorescent frame. P* 12½ × 12.
312 **560** 37 c. multicoloured .. .. .. .. 35 40

(Des D. Nethercott. Litho Ashton-Potter)

988 (18 Nov). *150th Birth Anniv of Frances Ann Hopkins (artist). Fluorescent frame. P* 13½ × 13.
313 **561** 37 c. multicoloured .. .. .. .. 35 40

**562** Angus Walters and *Bluenose* (schooner)

**563** Chipewyan Canoe

(Des R. Hill. Litho Ashton-Potter)

988 (18 Nov). *20th Death Anniv of Angus Walters (yachtsman). Fluorescent frame. P* 13½.
314 **562** 37 c. multicoloured .. .. .. .. 35 40

(Des L.-A. Rivard and B. Leduc. Litho Ashton-Potter)

1989 (1 Feb). *Small Craft of Canada (1st series). Native Canoes. T* **563** *and similar horiz designs. Multicoloured. Fluorescent frame. P* 13½ × 13.
1315 38 c. Type **563** .. .. .. .. 50 50
a. Block of 4. Nos. 1315/18 .. .. 1·75
1316 38 c. Haida canoe .. .. .. .. 50 50
1317 38 c. Inuit kayak .. .. .. .. 50 50
1318 38 c. Micmac canoe .. .. .. .. 50 50
1315/18 .. .. .. .. *Set of* 4 1·75 1·75

Nos. 1315/18 were printed together, *se-tenant*, throughout the sheet, giving ten blocks of 4 and ten single stamps.

See also Nos. 1377/80 and 1428/31.

**564** Matonabbee and Hearne's Expedition

**565** Construction of Victoria Bridge, Montreal and William Notman

(Des F. Hagan. Litho Ashton-Potter)

**1989** (22 Mar). *Exploration of Canada (4th series). Explorers of the North. T* **564** *and similar horiz designs. Multicoloured. Fluorescent frame. P* 12½×13.
1319 38 c. Type **564** .. .. .. .. 55 55
a. Block of 4. Nos. 1319/22 .. .. 2·00
1320 38 c. Relics of Franklin's expedition and White Ensign .. .. .. .. 55 55
1321 38 c. Joseph Tyrrell's compass, hammer and fossil .. .. .. .. 55 55
1322 38 c. Vilhjalmur Stefansson, camera on tripod and sledge dog team .. .. 55 55
1319/22 .. .. .. .. *Set of* 4 2·00 2·00

Nos. 1319/22 were printed together, *se-tenant*, in different combinations throughout the sheet, giving ten blocks of 4 and ten single stamps.

(Des J. Morin and T. Yakobina. Litho Ashton-Potter)

**1989** (23 June). *Canada Day. "150 Years of Canadian Photography". T* **565** *and similar horiz designs, each showing early photograph and photographer. Multicoloured. P* 12½×12.
1323 38 c. Type **565** .. .. .. .. 50 50
a. Block of 4. Nos. 1323/6 .. .. 1·75
1324 38 c. Plains Indian village and W. Hanson Boorne .. .. .. .. 50 50
1325 38 c. Horse-drawn sleigh and Alexander Henderson .. .. .. .. 50 50
1326 38 c. Quebec street scene and Jules-Ernest Livernois .. .. .. .. 50 50
1323/6 .. .. .. .. *Set of* 4 1·75 1·75

Nos. 1323/6 were printed together, *se-tenant*, in blocks of 4 throughout the sheet.

**566** Tsimshian Ceremonial Frontlet, *c* 1900

**567** Canadian Flag and Forest

(Des P.-Y. Pelletier. Litho and die-stamped Ashton-Potter)

**1989** (29 June). *Canadian Art (2nd series). No fluorescent bands. P* 12½×13.
1327 **566** 50 c. multicoloured .. .. .. 55 60

No. 1327 was issued in a similar sheet format to No. 1289

(Des Gottschalk & Ash International. Litho Ashton-Potter)

**1989** (30 June)–**91**. *Self-adhesive booklet stamps. T* **567** *and similar horiz designs. Multicoloured. Fluorescent frame. Die-cut.*
1328 38 c. Type **567** .. .. .. .. 90 1·25
a. Booklet pane. No. 1328×12 .. 10·00
1328*b* 39 c. Canadian flag and prairie (8.2.90) .. 55 70
ba. Booklet pane. No. 1328*b*×12 .. 6·00
1328*c* 40 c. Canadian flag and sea (11.1.91) .. 40 45
ca. Booklet pane. No. 1328*c*×12 .. 4·75
1328/*c* .... .. .. .. *Set of* 3 1·10 1·40

Nos. 1328, 1328*b* and 1328*c* were only available from self-adhesive booklets in which the backing card forms the booklet cover.

**568** Archibald Lampman

**569** *Clavulinopsis fusiformis*

(Des R. Milot. Litho Ashton-Potter)

**1989** (7 July). *Canadian Poets. T* **568** *and similar horiz design. Multicoloured. Fluorescent frame. P* 13½.
1329 38 c. Type **568** .. .. .. .. 40 45
a. Pair. Nos. 1329/30 .. .. .. 80 90
1330 38 c. Louis-Honoré Fréchette .. .. .. 40 45

Nos. 1329/30 were printed together, *se-tenant*, in horizontal and vertical pairs throughout the sheet.

(Des E. Roch. Litho Ashton-Potter)

**1989** (4 Aug). *Mushrooms. T* **569** *and similar vert designs. Multicoloured. Fluorescent frame. P* 13½.
1331 38 c. Type **569** .. .. .. .. 50 45
a. Block of 4. Nos. 1331/4 .. .. 1·75
1332 38 c. *Boletus mirabilis* .. .. .. 50 45
1333 38 c. *Cantharellus cinnabarinus* .. .. 50 45
1334 38 c. *Morchella esculenta* .. .. .. 50 45
1331/4 .. .. .. .. *Set of* 4 1·75 1·60

Nos. 1331/4 were printed together, *se-tenant*, in different combinations throughout the sheet, giving ten blocks of 4 and ten single stamps.

**570** Night Patrol, Korea

**571** Globe in Box

(Des T. Telmet, N. Fontaine and J. Gault. Eng Y. Baril. Recess and litho C.B.N.)

**1989** (8 Sept). *75th Annivs of Canadian Regiments. T* **570** *and similar horiz design. Multicoloured. Fluorescent frame. P* 13.
1335 38 c. Type **570** (Princess Patricia's Canadian Light Infantry) .. .. 70 70
a. Vert pair. Nos. 1335/6 .. .. 1·40 1·40
1336 38 c. Trench raid, France, 1914-18 (Royal 22e Régiment) .. .. .. .. 70 70

Nos. 1335/6 were printed together, *se-tenant*, in vertical pairs throughout the sheet.

(Des L. Holloway and Nita Wallace. Litho Ashton-Potter)

**1989** (2 Oct). *Canada Export Trade Month. Fluorescent frame. P* 13½×13.
1337 **571** 38 c. multicoloured .. .. .. 40 45

**572** Film Director

**573** "Snow II" (Lawren S. Harris)

(Des W. Tibbles from paper sculptures by J. Milne. Litho Ashton-Potter)

**1989** (4 Oct). *Arts and Entertainment. T* **572** *and similar vert designs. Fluorescent frame. P* 13×13½.
1338 38 c. grey-brown, blackish brown and bright reddish violet .. .. .. 40 45
a. Block of 4. Nos. 1338/41 .. .. 1·50
1339 38 c. grey-brown, blackish brown & brt grn 40 45
1340 38 c. grey-brn, blackish brn & brt magenta 40 45
1341 38 c. grey-brown, blackish brown & new bl 40 45
1338/41 .. .. .. .. *Set of* 4 1·50 1·60

Designs:—No. 1339, Actors; No. 1340, Dancers; No. 1341, Musicians.

Nos. 1338/41 were printed together, *se-tenant*, in different combinations throughout the sheet, giving ten blocks of 4 and ten single stamps.

(Des D. Nethercott and Viviane Warburton. Litho Ashton-Potter)

**1989** (26 Oct). *Christmas. Paintings of Winter Landscapes. T* **573** *and similar multicoloured designs. Fluorescent frame. P* 12½×13 (33 *c.*), 13×13½ (38 *c.*) *or* 13½ (*others*).
1342 33 c. "Champ-de-Mars, Winter" (William Brymner) (35×21 *mm*) .. .. 35 40
a. Booklet pane. No. 1342×10 .. .. 3·50
1343 38 c. "Bend in the Gosselin River" (Marc-Aurèle Suzor-Coté) (21×35 *mm*) .. 40 45
a. Perf 13×12½ .. .. .. 40 45
ab. Booklet pane. No. 1343a×10 .. 4·00
1344 44 c. Type **573** .. .. .. .. 45 50
a. Booklet pane. No. 1344×5 plus one printed label .. .. .. 2·25
1345 76 c. "Ste. Agnès" (A. H. Robinson) .. 80 85
a. Booklet pane. No. 1345×5 plus one printed label .. .. .. 4·00
1342/5 .. .. .. .. *Set of* 4 1·75 2·00

On No. 1342 the left-hand third of the design area is taken up by a bar code which has fluorescent bands between the bars. This value was only available from $3.30 stamp booklets which had the sides and bottom of the pane imperforate. It was intended for use on greeting cards posted on or before 31 January 1990.

No. 1343a was only issued in $3.80 stamp booklets.

Booklet pane No. 1343ab has the outer edges of the pane imperforate while Nos. 1344a and 1345a have the vertical edges imperforate.

**574** Canadians listening to Declaration of War, 1939

(Des J.-P. Armanville and P.-Y. Pelletier. Litho C.B.N.)

**1989** (10 Nov). *50th Anniv of Second World War (1st issue). T* **574** *and similar horiz designs. Fluorescent frame. P* 13½.
1346 38 c. black, silver and slate-purple .. 40 45
a. Block of 4. Nos. 1346/9 .. .. 1·50
1347 38 c. black, silver and olive-grey .. .. 40 45
1348 38 c. black, silver and grey-green .. .. 40 45
1349 38 c. black, silver and azure .. .. 40 45
1346/9 .. .. .. .. *Set of* 4 1·50 1·60

Designs:—No. 1347, Army mobilization; No. 1348, British Commonwealth air crew training; No. 1349, North Atlantic convoy.

Nos. 1346/9 were printed together, *se-tenant*, in different combinations throughout the sheet, giving four blocks of 4.

See also Nos. 1409/12 and 1456/9.

575 Canadian Flag 576

**1989** (28 Dec)–**90**. *No fluorescent bands* (1, 5 c.) *or fluorescent frame* (39, 40 c.).

(*a*) *Booklet stamps. T* **575** *and similar horiz designs, each showing Canadian flag. Litho Ashton-Potter. Chalk-surfaced paper. P* 13½×14.

1350 **575** 1 c. multicoloured (12.1.90) .. .. 10 10
a. Booklet pane. Nos. 1350, 1351×2 and 1352 .. .. .. 55
b. Perf 12½×13 .. .. .. 30 20
ba. Booklet pane. Nos. 1350b, 1351a×2 and 1352a .. .. 1·75
c. Booklet pane. Nos. 1350×2, 1351 and 1353 (28.12.90) .. .. 50
1351 – 5 c. multicoloured (12.1.90) .. .. 10 10
a. Perf 12½×13 .. .. .. 15 15
1352 – 39 c. multicoloured (12.1.90) .. .. 50 35
a. Perf 12½×13 .. .. .. 1·50 1·00
1353 – 40 c. multicoloured (28.12.90) .. 40 45

(*b*) *Litho C.B.N.* (39 *c. from sheets until* 13 *February* 1990 *and* 40 *c. from sheets*) *or Ashton-Potter* (39 *c. from sheets after* 14 *February* 1990 *and from booklets,* 40 *c. from booklets*). *Chalk-surfaced paper. P* 13½×13.

1354 **576** 39 c. multicoloured .. .. 40 35
a. Booklet pane. No. 1354×10 and two labels .. .. .. 4·00
b. Booklet pane. No. 1354×25 and two labels .. .. .. 9·50
c. Perf 12½×13 .. .. .. 2·50 1·75
1355 – 40 c. multicoloured (28.12.90) .. 40 45
a. Booklet pane. No. 1355×10 and two labels .. .. .. 4·00
b. Booklet pane. No. 1355×25 and two labels .. .. .. 10·00

(*c*) *Coil stamps. Designs as T* **575**, *but different folds in flag. Recess C.B.N. P* 10×*imperf*

1356 – 39 c. deep purple (8.2.90) .. .. 60 75
1357 – 40 c. indigo (28.12.90) .. .. 40 45

Design:—40 c. (No. 1355) Canadian flag over forest.

Booklet panes Nos. 1350a/b have the vertical edges of the panes imperforate and each shows a margin at foot. Booklet panes Nos. 1354a/b and 1355a/b are imperforate at top and bottom.

**577** Norman Bethune in 1937, and performing Operation, Montreal

**578** Maple Leaf Mosaic

(Des J. Morin, Wanda Lewicka and Liu Xiang Ping. Eng Hu Zhenyuan and Yan Bingwu. Recess and litho C.B.N.)

**1990** (2 Mar). *Birth Centenary of Dr. Norman Bethune (surgeon). T* **577** *and similar horiz design. Multicoloured. Fluorescent frame. P* 13×13½.

1375 39 c. Type **577** .. .. .. .. 45 50
a. Pair. Nos. 1375/6 .. .. .. 90 1·00
1376 39 c. Bethune in 1939, and treating wounded Chinese soldiers .. .. 45 50

Nos. 1375/6 were printed together, *se-tenant*, in horizontal and vertical pairs throughout the sheet.

(Des L.-A. Rivard and B. Leduc. Litho Ashton-Potter)

**1990** (15 Mar). *Small Craft of Canada* (2*nd series*). *Early Work Boats. Horiz designs as T* **563**. *Multicoloured. Fluorescent frame. P* 13½×13.

1377 39 c. Fishing dory .. .. .. 50 55
a. Block of 4. Nos. 1377/80 .. .. 1·75
1378 39 c. Logging pointer .. .. .. 50 55
1379 39 c. York boat .. .. .. 50 55
1380 39 c. North canoe .. .. .. 50 55
1377/80 .. .. .. *Set of* 4 1·75 2·00

Nos. 1377/80 were printed together, *se-tenant*, throughout the sheet, giving ten blocks of 4 and ten single stamps.

(Des F. Peter. Recess and litho C.B.N.)

**1990** (5 Apr). *Multiculturalism. P* 13.

1381 **578** 39 c. multicoloured .. .. .. 35 40

**579** Mail Van (facing left)

**580** Amerindian and Inuit Dolls

(Des A. Rochon and J. Morin. Litho Ashton-Potter)

**1990** (3 May). *"Moving the Mail". T* **579** *and similar horiz design. Multicoloured. Fluorescent frame. P* 13½.

1382 39 c. Type **579** .. .. .. 45 55
a. Booklet pane. Nos. 1382/3, each × 4 3·25
b. Booklet pane. Nos. 1382×5, 1383×4 and 3 labels .. .. .. 3·50
1383 39 c. Mail van (facing right) .. .. 45 55

Nos. 1382/3 were only issued in $9.75 stamp booklets.

(Des P.-Y. Pelletier. Litho and die-stamped Ashton-Potter)

**1990** (3 May). *Canadian Art* (3*rd series*). *Vert design as T* **550**. *Multicoloured. No fluorescent bands. P* 12½×13.

1384 50 c. "The West Wind" (Tom Thomson) .. 55 65

No. 1384 was issued in a similar sheet format to No. 1289.

(Des Nita Wallace. Litho Ashton-Potter)

**1990** (8 June). *Dolls. T* **580** *and similar horiz designs. Multicoloured. Fluorescent frame. P* 12½×12.

1385 39 c. Type **580** .. .. .. 55 60
a. Block of 4. Nos. 1385/8 .. .. 2·00
1386 39 c. 19th-century settlers' dolls .. .. 55 60
1387 39 c. Commercial dolls, 1917–36 .. .. 55 60
1388 39 c. Commercial dolls, 1940–60 .. .. 55 60
1385/8 .. .. .. *Set of* 4 2·00 2·10

Nos. 1385/8 were printed together, *se-tenant*, in different combinations throughout the sheet, giving ten blocks of 4 and ten single stamps.

**581** Canadian Flag and Fireworks

**582** *Stromatolites* (fossil algae)

(Des C. Malenfont. Litho Ashton-Potter)

**1990** (1 July*). *Canada Day. Fluorescent frame. P* 13×12½

1389 **581** 39 c. multicoloured .. .. .. 45 50

No. 1389 was issued in sheets of 16 with descriptive texts on the coloured margins.

*First day covers of No. 1389 are postmarked 29 June 1990. The stamp was available from two temporary post offices in Ottawa on Sunday 1 July, but was not sold throughout Canada until 3 July.

(Des R. Harder. Eng Y. Baril. Recess and litho C.B.N.)

**1990** (12 July). *Prehistoric Canada* (1*st series*). *Primitive Life. T* **582** *and similar horiz designs. Multicoloured. Fluorescent frame. P* 13×13½.

1390 39 c. Type **582** .. .. .. 60 60
a. Block of 4. Nos. 1390/3 .. .. 2·25
1391 39 c. *Opabinia regalis* (soft invertebrate) 60 60
1392 39 c. *Paradoxides davidis* (trilobite) .. 60 60
1393 39 c. *Eurypterus remipes* (sea scorpion) .. 60 60
1390/3 .. .. .. *Set of* 4 2·25 2·25

Nos. 1390/3 were printed together, *se-tenant*, in different combinations throughout the sheet, giving four blocks of 4 and four single stamps.

See also Nos. 1417/20.

**583** Acadian Forest

**584** Clouds and Rainbow

(Des M.and J. Waddell. Litho Ashton-Potter)

**1990** (7 Aug). *Canadian Forests. T* **583** *and similar horiz designs. Multicoloured. Fluorescent frame. P* 12½×13.

1394 39 c. Type **583** .. .. .. 60 60
a. Block of 4. Nos. 1394/7 .. .. 2·25
1395 39 c. Great Lakes–St. Lawrence forest .. 60 60
1396 39 c. Pacific Coast forest .. .. 60 60
1397 39 c. Boreal forest .. .. .. 60 60
1394/7 .. .. .. *Set of* 4 2·25 2·25

Nos. 1394/7 were printed together, *se-tenant*, in different combinations throughout the sheet, giving four blocks of 4 and four single stamps.

Nos. 1394/7 also exist as blocks of four of the same design surrounded by margins. Such blocks were not available from post offices, but could be obtained for $1 each at Petro-Canada filling stations by using a previously-distributed voucher in conjunction with the purchase of 25 litres of petrol. They could also be obtained, at face value, from the Canadian Philatelic Service by post.

(Des D. L'Allier and Dominique Trudeau. Litho Ashton-Potter)

**1990** (5 Sept). 150*th Anniv of Weather Observing in Canada. Fluorescent frame. P* 12½×13½.

1398 **584** 39 c. multicoloured .. .. .. 40 50

No. 1398 has a break in the lower vertical sides of the fluorescent frame to allow the clouds to run on to the margins.

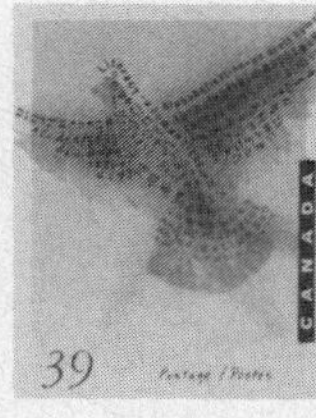

**585** "Alphabet" Bird

**586** Sasquatch

(Des Debbie Adams. Recess and litho C.B.N.)

**1990** (7 Sept). *International Literacy Year. Fluorescent frame. P* 13½×13.

1399 **585** 39 c. multicoloured .. .. .. 40 50

(Des A. Cormack, Deborah Drew-Brook and R. Tibbles. Litho Ashton-Potter)

**1990** (1 Oct). *Legendary Creatures. T* **586** *and similar horiz designs. Multicoloured. Fluorescent frame. P* 12½×13½.

1400 39 c. Type **586** .. .. .. 60 60
a. Block of 4. Nos. 1400/3 .. .. 2·25
1401 39 c. Kraken .. .. .. 60 60
1402 39 c. Werewolf .. .. .. 60 60
1403 39 c. Ogopogo .. .. .. 60 60
1400/3 .. .. .. *Set of* 4 2·25 2·25

Nos. 1400/3 were printed together, *se-tenant*, in different combinations throughout the sheet, giving ten blocks of four and ten single stamps.

**587** Agnes Macphail

**588** "Virgin Mary with Christ Child and St. John the Baptist" (Norval Morrisseau)

(Des E. Waddell. Litho Ashton-Potter)

**1990** (9 Oct). *Birth Centenary of Agnes Macphail (first woman elected to Parliament). Fluorescent frame. P* 13×13½.

1404 **587** 39 c. multicoloured .. .. .. 40 50

(Des C. Malenfant. Litho Ashton-Potter)

**1990** (25 Oct). *Christmas. Native Art. T* **588** *and similar designs. Fluorescent frame. P* 12½×13 (34 *c.*) *or* 13½ (*others*).

1405 34 c. multicoloured (35×21 *mm*) .. 30 35
a. Booklet pane. No. 1405×10 .. .. 3·00
1406 39 c. multicoloured .. .. 35 40
a. Booklet pane. No. 1406×10 .. .. 3·50
1407 45 c. multicoloured .. .. 40 45
a. Booklet pane. No. 1407×5 plus one printed label .. .. .. 2·00
1408 78 c. black, bright scarlet and violet-grey 70 75
a. Booklet pane. No. 1408×5 plus one printed label .. .. .. 3·50
1405/8 .. .. .. *Set of* 4 1·60 1·75

Designs:—34 c. "Rebirth" (Jackson Beardy); 45 c. "Mother and Child" (Inuit sculpture, Cape Dorset); 78 c. "Children of the Raven" (Bill Reid).

On No. 1405 the left-hand third of the design area is taken up by a bar code which has fluorescent bands between the bars. This value was only available from $3.40 stamp booklets which had the sides and bottom of the pane imperforate. It was intended for use on greeting cards posted on or before 31 January 1991.

Booklet panes Nos. 1406a, 1407a and 1408a also have the side and bottom edges imperforate.

(Des J.-P. Armanville and P.-Y. Pelletier. Litho Ashton-Potter)

**1990** (9 Nov). 50*th Anniv of Second World War* (2*nd issue*). *Horiz designs as T* **574**. *Fluorescent frame. P* 12½×12.

1409 39 c. black, silver and grey-olive .. .. 55 55
a. Block of 4. Nos. 1409/12 .. .. 2·00
1410 39 c. black, silver and red-brown .. .. 55 55
1411 39 c. black, silver and bistre-brown .. 55 55
1412 39 c. black, silver and dull mauve .. 55 55
1409/12 .. .. .. *Set of* 4 2·00 2·00

Designs:—No. 1409, Canadian family at home, 1940; No. 1410, Packing parcels for the troops; No. 1411, Harvesting; No. 1412, Testing anti-gravity flying suit.

Nos. 1409/12 were printed together, *se-tenant*, in different combinations throughout the sheet, giving four blocks of 4.

**589** Jennie Trout (first woman physician) and Women's Medical College, Kingston

**590** Blue Poppies and Butchart Gardens, Victoria

(Des R. Milot. Litho Ashton-Potter)

**1991** (15 Mar). *Medical Pioneers. T* **589** *and similar vert designs. Multicoloured. Fluorescent frame. P* 13½.

1413 40 c. Type **589** .. .. .. 50 50
a. Block of 4. Nos. 1413/16 .. .. 1·75
1414 40 c. Wilder Penfield (neurosurgeon) and Montreal Neurological Institute .. 50 50
1415 40 c. Frederick Banting (discoverer of insulin) and University of Toronto medical faculty .. .. .. 50 50
1416 40 c. Harold Griffith (anesthesiologist) and Queen Elizabeth Hospital, Montreal 50 50
1413/16 .. .. .. *Set of* 4 1·75 1·75

Nos. 1413/16 were printed together, *se-tenant*, in different combinations throughout the sheet, giving ten blocks of 4 and ten single stamps.

(Des R. Harder. Eng L. Bloss. Recess and litho Ashton-Potter)

**1991** (5 Apr). *Prehistoric Canada (2nd series). Primitive Vertebrates. Horiz designs as T* **582**. *Multicoloured. Fluorescent frame. P* 12½×13½.
1417 40 c. *Eusthenopteron foordi* (fish fossil) .. 50 50
a. Block of 4. Nos. 1417/20 .. .. 1·75
1418 40 c. *Hylonomus lyelli* (land reptile) .. 50 50
1419 40 c. Fossil Conodonts (fossil teeth) .. 50 50
1420 40 c. *Archaeopteris halliana* (early tree) .. 50 50
1417/20 .. .. .. .. *Set of* 4 1·75 1·75
Nos. 1417/20 were printed together, *se-tenant*, in different combinations throughout the sheet, giving four blocks of 4 and four single stamps.

(Des P.-Y. Pelletier. Litho and die-stamped Ashton-Potter)

**1991** (7 May). *Canadian Art (4th series). Vert design as T* **550**. *Multicoloured. No fluorescent bands. P* 12½×13.
1421 50 c. "Forest, British Columbia" (Emily Carr) .. .. .. .. 50 55

(Des G. Gauci and D. Wyman. Litho Ashton-Potter)

**1991** (22 May). *Public Gardens. T* **590** *and similar vert designs. Multicoloured. Fluorescent frame. P* 13×12½.
1422 40 c. Type **590** .. .. .. .. 40 45
a. Booklet pane. Nos. 1422/6, each × 2 4·00
1423 40 c. Marigolds and International Peace Garden, Boissevain .. .. .. 40 45
1424 40 c. Lilac and Royal Botanical Gardens, Hamilton .. .. .. .. 40 45
1425 40 c. Roses and Montreal Botanical Gardens .. .. .. .. 40 45
1426 40 c. Rhododendrons and Halifax Public Gardens .. .. .. .. 40 45
1422/6 .. .. .. .. *Set of* 5 1·75 2·00
Nos. 1422/6 were only available from $4 stamp booklets containing No. 1422a, which is imperforate at top and bottom.

591 Maple Leaf

592 South Nahanni River

(Des J.-P. Veilleux, Lisa Miller and R. Séguin. Litho C.B.N.)

**1991** (28 June). *Canada Day. Fluorescent frame. P* 13½×13.
1427 **591** 40 c. multicoloured .. .. .. 40 45
No. 1427 was issued in sheets of 20 with inscribed and decorated margins.

(Des L.-A. Rivard and B. Leduc. Litho Ashton-Potter)

**1991** (18 July). *Small Craft of Canada (3rd series). Horiz designs as T* **563**. *Multicoloured. Fluorescent frame. P* 13½×13.
1428 40 c. Verchère rowboat .. .. .. 40 45
a. Block of 4. Nos. 1428/31 .. .. 1·40
1429 40 c. Touring kayak .. .. .. 40 45
1430 40 c. Sailing dinghy .. .. .. 40 45
1431 40 c. Cedar strip canoe .. .. .. 40 45
1428/31 .. .. .. .. *Set of* 4 1·40 1·60
Nos. 1428/31 were printed together, *se-tenant*, throughout the sheet, giving ten blocks of 4 and ten single stamps.

(Des M. and Jan Waddell. Litho Ashton-Potter)

**1991** (20 Aug). *Canadian Rivers. T* **592** *and similar vert designs. Multicoloured. Fluorescent frame. P* 13×12½.
1432 40 c. Type **592** .. .. .. .. 40 45
a. Booklet pane. Nos. 1432/6, each × 2 with margins all round .. .. 4·00
1433 40 c. Athabasca River .. .. .. 40 45
1434 40 c. Boundary Waters, Voyageur Waterway .. .. .. .. 40 45
1435 40 c. Jacques-Cartier River .. .. .. 40 45
1436 40 c. Main River .. .. .. .. 40 45
1432/6 .. .. .. .. *Set of* 5 1·75 2·00
Nos. 1432/6 were only issued in $4 stamp booklets.

593 "Leaving Europe"

594 Ski Patrol rescuing Climber

(Des J. Gault and T. Telmet. Litho C.B.N.)

**1991** (29 Aug). *Centenary of Ukrainian Immigration. Panels from "The Ukrainian Pioneer" by William Kurelek. T* **593** *and similar vert designs. Multicoloured. Fluorescent frame. P* 13½×13.
1437 40 c. Type **593** .. .. .. .. 40 45
a. Block of 4. Nos. 1437/40 .. .. 1·40
1438 40 c. "Canadian Winter" .. .. .. 40 45
1439 40 c. "Clearing the Land" .. .. .. 40 45
1440 40 c. "Harvest" .. .. .. .. 40 45
1437/40 .. .. .. .. *Set of* 4 1·40 1·60
Nos. 1437/40 were printed together, *se-tenant*, in different combinations throughout the sheet, giving four blocks of 4 and four single stamps.

(Des Suzanne Duranceau. Litho C.B.N.)

**1991** (23 Sept). *Emergency Services. T* **594** *and similar vert designs. Multicoloured. Fluorescent frame. P* 13½.
1441 40 c. Type **594** .. .. .. .. 40 45
a. Block of 4. Nos 1441/4 .. .. 1·40
1442 40 c. Police at road traffic accident .. 40 45
1443 40 c. Firemen on extending ladder .. 40 45
1444 40 c. Rescue helicopter and lifeboat .. 40 45
1441/4 .. .. .. .. *Set of* 4 1·40 1·60
Nos. 1441/4 were printed together, *se-tenant*, in different combinations throughout the sheet, giving ten blocks of 4 and ten single stamps.

595 "The Witched Canoe"

596 Grant Hall Tower

(Des A. Cormack, Deborah Drew-Brook and R. Tibbles. Litho Ashton-Potter)

**1991** (1 Oct). *Canadian Folktales. T* **595** *and similar vert designs. Multicoloured. Fluorescent frame. P* 13½×12½.
1445 40 c. Type **595** .. .. .. .. 40 45
a. Block of 4. Nos. 1445/8 .. .. 1·40
1446 40 c. "The Orphan Boy" .. .. .. 40 45
1447 40 c. "Chinook" .. .. .. .. 40 45
1448 40 c. "Buried Treasure" .. .. .. 40 45
1445/8 .. .. .. .. *Set of* 4 1·40 1·60
Nos. 1445/8 were printed together, *se-tenant*, in different combinations throughout the sheet, giving ten blocks of 4 and ten single stamps.

(Des R. Kerr and L. Holloway. Litho Ashton-Potter)

**1991** (16 Oct). *150th Anniv of Queen's University, Kingston. Fluorescent frame. P* 13×12½.
1449 **596** 40 c. multicoloured .. .. .. 40 45
a. Booklet pane. No. 1449×10 plus two printed labels with margins all round .. .. .. 4·00
No. 1449 was only issued in $4 stamp booklets.

597 North American Santa Claus

598 Players jumping for Ball

(Des S. Slipp. Litho Ashton-Potter)

**1991** (23 Oct). *Christmas. T* **597** *and similar multicoloured designs. Fluorescent frame. P* 12½×13 (35 *c.*) *or* 13½ (*others*).
1450 35 c. British Father Christmas (35×21 *mm*) .. .. .. .. 35 40
a. Booklet pane. No. 1450×10 .. .. 3·50
1451 40 c. Type **597** .. .. .. .. 40 45
a. Booklet pane. No. 1451×10 .. .. 4·00
1452 46 c. French Bonhomme Noel .. .. 45 50
a. Booklet pane. No. 1452×5 plus one printed label .. .. .. .. 2·25
1453 80 c. Dutch Sinterklaas .. .. .. 80 85
a. Booklet pane. No. 1453×5 plus one printed label .. .. .. .. 4·00
1450/3 .. .. .. .. *Set of* 4 1·75 2·00
On No. 1450 the left-hand third of the design area is taken up by a bar code which has fluorescent bands between the bars. This value was only available from $3.50 stamp booklets which had the edges of the pane imperforate. It was intended for use on greeting cards posted on or before 31 January 1992.
Nos. 1451a, 1452a and 1453a also have the vertical edges of the panes imperforate.

(Des J. Gault, C. Reynolds and T. Telmet. Litho Ashton-Potter)

**1991** (25 Oct). *Basketball Centenary. T* **598** *and similar vert designs. Multicoloured. Fluorescent frame. P* 13×13½.
1454 40 c. Type **598** .. .. .. .. 40 45
**MS**1455 155×90 mm. 40 c. Type **598**; 46 c. Player taking shot; 80 c. Player challenging opponent 1·75 1·90

(Des J.-P. Armanville and P.-Y. Pelletier. Litho C.B.N)

**1991** (8 Nov). *50th Anniv of Second World War (3rd issue). Horiz designs as T* **574**. *Fluorescent frame. P* 13½.
1456 40 c. black, silver and greenish blue .. 40 45
a. Block of 4. Nos. 1456/9 .. .. 1·40
1457 40 c. black, silver and brown .. .. 40 45
1458 40 c. black, silver and lilac .. .. 40 45
1459 40 c. black, silver and ochre .. .. 40 45
1456/9 .. .. .. .. *Set of* 4 1·40 1·60
Designs:—No. 1456, Women's services, 1941; No. 1457, Armament factory; No. 1458, Cadets and veterans; No. 1459, Defence of Hong Kong.
Nos. 1456/9 were printed together, *se-tenant*, in different combinations throughout the sheet, giving four blocks of 4.

599 McIntosh Apple

(Des C. Malenfant. Litho Ashton-Potter)

**1991** (27 Dec). *Fruit and Nut Trees. T* **599** *and similar horiz designs. Multicoloured. Fluorescent frame. P* 13.
1467 48 c. Type **599** .. .. .. .. 50 55
a. Perf 14½×14 .. .. .. 50 55
b. Booklet pane. No. 1467a×5 and label 2·40
1468 65 c. Black Walnut .. .. .. 65 70
1469 84 c. Stanley Plum .. .. .. 90 95
a. Perf 14½×14 .. .. .. 90 95
b. Booklet pane. No. 1469a×5 and label 4·25
1467/9 .. .. .. .. *Set of* 3 1·90 2·00
Nos. 1467a and 1469a were only issued in stamp booklets.
Booklet panes Nos. 1467b and 1469b each have the vertical edges of the pane imperforate.

## Index to Canada Stamp Designs from 1942

The following index is intended to facilitate the identification of Canadian issues from 1942. Portrait stamps are usually listed under surnames only, views under the name of the town or city and other issues under the main subject or a prominent word and date chosen from the inscription. Simple abbreviations have occasionally been resorted to and when the same design or subject appears on more than one stamp, only the first of each series is indicated.


Abbott 444
Academy of Arts 972
Acadia 1021
*Adam Brown* (loco) 1109
"Agricultural Education" 782
Air Canada 1251
Air Force 1140
Air Training camp 399
Aircraft 399, 438, 509, 540, 556, 636, 966, 996, 1026, 1050, 1251
Albani 983
Alberta and Saskatchewan 481
Algonkians 723
"Alouette" 570
Angels 1218
Antique instruments 1001
Archer 845
Architecture 1275
Arctic Islands 970
Arms and flowers 543
Artifacts 1054
Athabasca River 1433
*Athabasca* (ship) 854
Autumn 679
Avro "504K" (aircraft) 1206
Avro-Canada (aircraft) 996, 1028
Avro "Lancaster" (aircraft) 997

Banff 885*a*
Banting 1415
Baseball 1307
Basketball 829, 1454
Batoche 1146
Battleford Post Office 1230
Beardy 1405
"Be Prepared" 515
Beaver 473, 1267
*Beaver* (ship) 820
Bed 1061
Bell 408
Bennett 483, 697
Bernier 893
Berthiaume 1141
Bethune 1375
Biological programme 649
Bird decoration 765
Birds 407, 443, 474, 479, 495, 539, 620, 638, 906, 1199
Bison 1007
Boats 1315, 1377, 1428
Bobak **MS**1047
Bonsecours Market, Montreal 1279
Borden 434, 695
Borduas 1012
Bouchard 1137
Bourassa 627
Bourgeoys 805
Bowell 476
Bowls 921
Boxing 815
Brant 1194
*Breadalbane* (ship) 1249
British Columbia 503, 685
Brock 643
Brown 626
Brown Bear 1275
Brûlé 1232
Brymner 1342
Buried Treasure 1448
Butchart Gardens 1422
Butterflies 1296
By 943

Cabot 412, 1210
Cains Island 1179
Calgary 812
Canada Day **MS**944, 1013, **MS**1047, 1090, **MS**1123, 1163, 1203, 1241, 1292, 1323, 1389, 1427
Canada Export Month 1337
Canada Games 641
Canada Geese 407, 443, 539
Canadair (aircraft) 966, 1027
Canadian Broadcasting Corporation 1207
Canadian Forces Postal Service 1198
Canadian Indians 721
Canadian Press 615
Candles 745
Canoe 1315, 1380
"Capex '78" 907, 914
"Capex '87" **MS**1212, 1227
Caribou 486, 1276*c*
Carr 674, 1421
Cartier 1118
Cartography 742
Casgrain 1145
Castle Hill 1166
Census 683
Chair and mace 508
*Challenger* (space shuttle) 1204
Charlottetown 642
Charlottetown Conference 557
Charter of Rights and Freedoms 1239
Chemical industry 489
Cherry blossom 9650
*Chicora* (ship) 853
*Chief Justice Robinson* (ship) 931
Child 824
Children's paintings 661, 822
Chinook 1447
Chown 807
Christ in manger 667
Christmas 560, 568, 570, 618, 630, 644, 661, 687, 745, 764, 792, 822, 848, 895, 928, 962, 993, 1023, 1080, 1111, 1137, 1181, 1218, 1254, 1308, 1342, 1405, 1450
Christmas plants 1254
Christmas tree 669, 1023
Church 670, 1111
Churchill 565
Citizenship 409
City streets 880
City view 708
Civil aviation 480
Coat of arms and flowers 543
"Cobalt 60" 1295
Colombo Plan 520
Colville **MS**1047
Combine harvester 404
Commonwealth Day 1084
Commonwealth Games 908, 918
Commonwealth Heads of Govt Meeting 1253
Commonwealth Parliamentary Assn 575
Commonwealth Parliamentary Conf 894
Conan 1085
Congresses 741
Consolidated "Canso" (aircraft) 969
Constitution 1045
Cook, Dr. J. 808
Cook, James 910
Coteau-du-Lac 1098
Cougar 886
*Countess of Dufferin* (loco) 1133
Country women 511
CP Class D10a (loco) 1135
Cradle 1062
Crate 536
Crowfoot 1213
Curling 632, 789
Curtiss (aircraft) 967, 998
Cycling 770

Dalhousie Law School 1110
Dallaire 1137
Dance 1340
De Gaspé 1195
De Havilland (aircraft) 1026, 1051
Desbarats 1243
Desjardins 806
Destroyer 388
Diefenbaker 982
Diving 768
Dogs 1303
Dollard des Ormeaux 516
Dolls 1385
*Dorchester* (loco) 1106
Dory 1377
Drying furs 432
Duck 495, 1290
Dumont 1146

Education 522
Edwards 1002
Electron microscope 1294
Elizabeth II 410, 450, 463, 512, 527, 559, 579, 613, 700, 759, 855, 867, 1161
Elizabeth II and Duke of Edinburgh 440, 500
Emergency Services 1441
Engineering Institute 1240
*Ericsson* (ship) 1250
Eskimo hunter 477
Excavators 913
Exploration 1208, 1232, 1285, 1319
Expo '67 611
Expo '86 1192, 1196

Fairchild (aircraft) 1050
Family group 785, 825
Farm scene 382, 401
Fencing 814
Fenerty 1242
Ferry 587
Fessenden 1241
Films 1338
Fire Service 1443
"First Land Route" 538
First Non-stop Flight 636
Fisgard 1129
Fish 976
Fisherman 433
Fishing 491
FitzGerald **MS**1047
Flag and Canada 578
Flag **MS**944, 1328, 1350, 1389
Fleming 892
Flower and buildings 838
Flowers 543, 650, 856, 978, 1019, 1422
Flying Squirrel 1261
Folktales 1445
Fokker (aircraft) 1052
Football 831
Forest 702, 1328, 1394
Forestry 441
Fort Anne 1164
Fort Beauséjour 1099
Fort Chambly 1096
Fort Erie 1168
Fort Frederick 1172
Fort Henry 1090
Fortin 1011
Fort Lennox 1170
Fort No. 1, Point Levis 1097
Fort Prince of Wales 1094
Fort Rodd Hill 1092
Fort Walsh 1169
Fort Wellington 1093
Fort Whoop Up 1167
Fort William 1091
Fort York 1175
Fossils 1390
Fox 1044, 1265, 1417
Franklin, Benjamin 839
Franklin, Sir John 1320
Fraser 1287
Fréchette 1330
Free Press 501
French 751
Frobisher 537
Frontenac 720
Fuller 975
Fundy 884

Gagnon 795
Games, flags 641
Gannet 474
Gardens 1422
Gateway 922
Geography 744
Geology 743
George VI 375, 389, 414
Gibraltar Point 1131
Gilbert 1102
Girl Guides 515, 1175
Gisborne 1244
Glacier 884*b*
Globe 510
Grain elevator 379, 589
Great Bear Lake 402
Great Blue Heron 1199
Great Horned Owl 1201
Grey Cup 1260
Grey Jay 620
Grenfell 563
Griffith 1416
Group of Seven 660
Grove 940
GT Class E3 (loco) 1134
Guevremont 847
Gymnastics 830
Gzowski 535

4-H Clubs 1301
Halifax 413, 1095
Halifax Public Gardens 1426
*Hamilton* (ship) 1247
Hanlan 985
Hanson Boorne 1324
Harris, Lawren 1344
Harris, Robert 972
Haut-fond Prince 1178
Hawker "Hurricane" (aircraft) 999
Hearne 682, 1319
Hébert, L. 1173
Hébert, P. 973, **MS**1047
Hémon 804
Henday 1285
Henderson 1325
Hens 977
Henson 1104
Heritage 1054
Highway 584
Highway safety 572
Hiking 771
Hockey 957
Hong Kong 1459
Hopkins 1313
Horse-drawn sleigh 661
Houses of Parliament 870
Howe 755
Hudson 1211
Hunting 898
Hurdling 811
Hydrological Decade 623

Ice Age artifacts 1208
Ice hockey 485
Iceberg and boatman 477
Ice-skate 764
Icons 1308
Ile Verte 1130
Indians of the Pacific Coast 725
Indians of the Plains 721
Inglis 1312
Insulin 675
International Co-operation Year 562
International Francophone Summit 1252
International Labour Organisation 635
International Literacy Year 1399
International Peace Year 1215
International Women's Year 813
International Youth Year 1142
Interparliamentary Union 566, 1174
Inuits 898, 924, 958, 989, 1407
"I remember" 650
Iroquoians 729, 739

Jackson **MS**1047
Jacques-Cartier River 1435
Jamboree 482
"Jesous Ahatonhia" 895
Jesuits 1235
Jet airliner 540, 556, 1028
Jogging 769
Johnson 518
Judo 816

Kane 686
Kayak 956, 1317, 1429
Kelsey 654
Kerosene 1292
Kerr **MS**1047
Killer Whale 1271
King 435, 696
Kluane 885
Knowles **MS**1047
Kraken 1401
Krieghoff 749
Kurelek 1437

Labelle 1105
*Labrador* (ship) 934
Lachapelle 1000
Lacrosse 625
Lake 402
Lake Placid 971
La Mauricie 885*a*
Lamb **MS**1047
Lampman 1329
Landscapes 584, 704, **MS**1047
Laporte 691
"La Presse" 1141
La Salle 571
Launching 386
Laurier 694
La Verendrye 504
Leacock 646
Leaves 875
Leduc 1289
Legendary Creatures 1400
Leger 1043
Leggo 1243
Lemieux 792, **MS**1123
Lighthouses 1128, 1176
Livernois 1326
London Conference 573
Louisbourg 1128
Lower Fort Garry 1163
Loyalists 1124
Lumbering 405
Lynx 1268

McAdam Railway Station 1278
McClung 761
McCrae 628
MacDonald, J. A. 693
MacDonald, J. E. H. 756
Mackenzie, A. 445, 658
McKenzie, R. T. 801
McKinney 1003
Macleod 1214
Macphail 1404
Macoun 1018
Mail coach 438
Mail trains 436
Mail van 1382
Main River 1436
Mammals 1261
Mance 754
Manitoba 647
Map 536, 970, 1013
Maple leaf 555, 1030, 1427
Maple leaf and hand 558
Maple leaves 542, 677, 684
"Marathon of Hope" 1044
Marconi 796
Marie 1009
Marie-Victorin 1017
Marmot 1006
Marquette 1234
Massey 633, 889
Masson 79
Matonabbee 131
*Matthew* (ship) 412
Medical Pioneers 141
Meighen 51
Merritt 797
"Merry Christmas" 993, 102
Meteorology 621
Microscope 50
Milne **MS**1047, 113
Miner 499, 91
Molson 122
Montgomery 803
Montmorency-Laval 75
Montreal Botanical Gardens 1425
Montreal Museum of Fine Arts 118
Montreal Symphony Orchestra 1117
Moose 448, 129
Morrice 118
Morrisseau 140
Mosher 102
Mountain Goat 48
Mounted Police 75
Mowat 65
Multiculturalism 138
Munitions factory 38
Murphy 114
Mushrooms 1331
Music 1341
Musical instrument 1001
Musk Ox 478, 127
Muskrat 126

Narwhal 62
National flag 564, 578, 132
Nativity 848, 108
N.A.T.O. 51
Nelligan 941
Nelson-Miramichi Post Office 1228
*Neptune* (ship) 81
New Brunswick 112
Newfoundland 1102, 1125
Niagara-on-the-Lake 1020
Nickel 1103
*Nonsuch* (ship) 624
Noorduyn "Norseman" (aircraft) 105
*Northcote* (ship) 851
Northern development 517
*Northern Light* (ship) 933
Northwest Territories 648
Notman 1323
Nova Scotia 508
Nurse 506

O'Brien 974
"O Canada" 980
Ogopogo 1403
Oil wells 431, 590
Olympic Games, Innsbruck 832
Olympic Games, Montreal 762, 768, 786, 798, 809, 814, 829, 833, 842
Order of Canada 890
Orphan Boy 1446

**Index to Canada Stamp Designs from 1942—*Continued***


"OSM 50 MSO" .... 1117
Osler .... 637

"Pacem in Terris" .... 541
Paintings .... **MS**1123, 1137, 1289, 1421
Palliser .... 1288
Pan American Games .... 614
Papal Visit .... 1126
Papineau .... 681
Parliament Buildings .. 383, 567, 870, 1147, 1174
*Passport* (ship) .... 852
Peace Bridge .... 891
"Peaceful Uses" .... 574
Peace Garden .... 1423
Pearson .... 698
Pelee Passage .... 1177
Penfield .... 1414
Peregrine Falcon .... 906
Petroleum .... 507
Pharmaceutical Sciences Congress 1173
Philatelic Exhibition .... 1037
Photogrammetry .... 741
Photography .... 1323
Pine tree .... 585
Pinky (boat) .... 902
Plains of Abraham .... 514
Plaskett .... **MS**1047
Plough .... 1060
Poets .... 1329
Pointer .... 1378
Point Pelée .... 885*a*
Polar Bear .... 447, 705
Pole-vaulting .... 809
Police .... 1442
Porcupine .... 1262
Porpoise .... 1273*b*
Postman .... 777
Post Office .... 776
Postal Code .... 938
Power station .... 403
Prairie .... 1328*b*
Pratt, C .... **MS**1047
Pratt, E .... 1086
Praying hands .... 576
Prehistoric Canada .... 1390, 1417
"Prevent Fires" .... 490
Prince Edward Island .... 757
*Princess Marguerite* (ship) .... 1246
Pronghorn .... 1270
Pulp and paper .... 488

*Quadra* (ship) .... 821
Quebec .... 505
Quebec Carnival .... 935
Queen's University, Kingston .... 1449

Radio Canada .... 684
Radisson .... 1233
Railway locomotive .. 1106, 1132, 1185, 1223
Red Cross .... 442, 1120
Red Fox .... 1265
Red River Settlement .... 523
Regatta .... 1049
Regiments .... 1114, 1335
Regina .... 1048
Rehabilitation .... 979
Reid .... 1408
Rescue Service .... 1444
Reservoir .... 403
"Resources for Tomorrow" .... 521
Responsible Government .... 411
Richard .... **MS**1047
Riel .... 657
Rivers .... 1432
River scene .... 588
Robinson .... 1345
Roman Catholic Church (Newfoundland) .... 1125
Rose .... 1019
Rowing .... 799
Royal Botanical Gardens .... 1424
Royal Canadian Academy .... 972
Royal Canadian Legion .... 828
Royal Canadian Navy .... 1189
Royal Military College .... 840
Royal Visit .... 440, 512
Running .... 810, 919
Runnymede Library, Toronto .... 1277
Rutherford .... 676

Sailing .... 800
Saint-Jean .... 1004
St. John Ambulance .... 1087
St. John's .... 1125, 1300
St. Laurent .... 699
St. Lawrence Seaway .... 513, 1122
Saint Maurice Ironworks .... 1302
Saint Ours Post Office .... 1229
*St. Roch* (ship) .... 932
Salaberry .... 942
Salvation Army .... 1046
*Samson* (loco) .... 1108
*San Juan* (ship) .... 1248
Santa Claus .... 665, 766, 822, 1450
Santa Claus Parade .... 1181
Saskatchewan .... 987
Sasquatch .... 1400
Satellite .... 570
*Scotia* (loco) .... 1132
Scottish settlers .... 758
Scouting .... 1100
Second World War .... 1346, 1409, 1456
*Segwun* (ship) .... 1245
"SERVICE" .... 1120
Service, R. .... 846
Sheep .... 449, 703
Shelter .... 958
Shepherd .... 767
Ships .. 386, 406, 412, 437, 818, 851, 902, 931, 1119, 1245
Shipwrecks .... 1247
Shooting .... 493
"Silver Dart" (aircraft) .... 509
Sisters Islets .... 1176
Skating .... 692, 788, 823
Skiing .... 494, 664, 787
Ski Patrol .... 1441
Skyscrapers .... 707
Sleigh .... 1063
Smith .... 673
Snowflake .... 687
Snow Goose .... 1200
Snowmen .... 663
Snowplough .... 1203
South Nahanni River .... 1432
Space Programme .... 1143
Spinning wheel .... 1065
Spirits .... 989
"Spitfire" (aircraft) .... 1205
Spring .... 677
Spruce Grouse .... 1202
Stable and star .... 662
Stadium .... 918
Stained glass windows .... 848
Stamps .... 439, 525, 907, 914, 1037
Steamships .... 437, 1245
Stefansson .... 1322
Stove .... 1064
Stowe .... 1005
Striped Skunk .... 1266
Sub-Arctic Indians .... 727
Summer .... 678
Supreme Court .... 817
Suzor Côté .... 634, 1343
Swimming .... 492, 798

Tall Ships' visit .... 1119
Talon .... 524
Tank .... 384
Tekakwitha .... 1008
Telephone .... 783, 1193
Textile industry .... 462
Theatre .... 1339
"The Globe" .... 626
Thompson, D. .... 496
Thompson, J. .... 475
Thomson .... 887, 1384
Todd .... 794
*Toronto* (loco) .... 1107
Toronto Centenary .... 617
Toronto Post Office .... 1227
Totem pole .... 446
Toys .... 962
Toyshop .... 668
Train ferry .... 406
Trains .... 436, 1197
Transatlantic Flight .... 636
Trans-Canada Highway .... 526
Travel .... 924
Trees .... 827, 1467
Trees and sledge .... 672
Trout, J. .... 1413
Tsimshian Frontlet .... 1327
Tupper .... 484
Turtle .... 936
Tyrrell .... 1321

Ukrainian Immigration .... 1437
United Empire Loyalists .... 1124
United Nations .... 655
"Universiade 83" .... 1088
U.P.U. .... 497, 790
Uranium .... 988

Vancouver, George .... 1286
Vanier .... 616
Varley .... 1010
Varying Hare .... 1264
Vickers "Vedette" (aircraft) .... 968
Victoria B.C. .... 525
Viking ships .... 1209
Vimy Monument .... 629
Virgin and Child .... 928
Volunteers .... 1238
"Votes for Women" .... 612
Voyageur Waterway .... 1434

Walrus .... 472, 1269
Walters .... 1314
Wapiti .... 1274
Waterton Lakes .... 884*b*
Weather observation .... 1398
Werewolf .... 1402
Whale .... 622, 937, 1276
Wheat .... 1293
Whooping Cranes .... 479
Wigwam and furs .... 432
Wildlife Conservation .... 1290
Willan .... 984
*William D. Lawrence* (ship) .... 818
Winnipeg .... 775
Winter .... 680
Winter landscape .... 586
Winter Olympic Games, Calgary .. 1191, 1216, 1236, 1258, 1281
Witched Canoe .... 1445
Wolf .... 1273
Wolverine .... 1270*c*
World Communications Year .... 1083
World Council of Churches .... 1101
World Cycling Championships .... 784
World Figure Skating Championships .... 692
World Health Day .... 719

Year of Child .... 695
Yellowknife .... 1116
York Boat .... 1379
York Redoubt .... 1171
Youville .... 923

## REGISTRATION STAMPS

R 1

(Eng and recess – printed British-American Bank Note Co, Montreal and Ottawa)

**1875** (15 Nov)–**92.** *White wove paper.* (*a*) *P* 12 (*or slightly under*).

| No. | Type | Description | Unused | Used |
|---|---|---|---|---|
| R 1 | R 1 | 2 c. orange | 55·00 | 1·00 |
| R 2 | | 2 c. orange-red (1889) | 65·00 | 6·00 |
| R 3 | | 2 c. vermilion | 75·00 | 7·00 |
| | | a. Imperf (pair) | | |
| R 4 | | 2 c. rose-carmine (1888) | £130 | 35·00 |
| R 5 | | 5 c. yellow-green (1878) | 75·00 | 1·00 |
| R 6 | | 5 c. deep green | 60·00 | 1·00 |
| | | a. Imperf (pair) | £600 | |
| R 7 | | 5 c. blue-green (1888) | 80·00 | 1·25 |
| R 7*a* | | 5 c. dull sea-green (1892) | 95·00 | 3·25 |
| R 8 | | 8 c. bright blue | £325 | £225 |
| R 9 | | 8 c. dull blue | £325 | £225 |

(*b*) *P* 12 × 11½ *or* 12 × 11¾

| No. | Type | Description | Unused | Used |
|---|---|---|---|---|
| R10 | R 1 | 2 c. orange | £200 | 55·00 |
| R11 | | 5 c. green (*shades*) | £350 | £140 |

## SPECIAL DELIVERY STAMPS

**PRINTERS.** The following Special Delivery and Postage Due Stamps were recess-printed by the American Bank Note Co (to 1928), the British American Bank Note Co (to 1934), and the Canadian Bank Note Co (1935 onwards).

S 1

**1898–1920.** *P* 12.

| No. | Type | Description | Unused | Used |
|---|---|---|---|---|
| S1 | S 1 | 10 c. blue-green (28.6.98) | 70·00 | 6·00 |
| S2 | | 10 c. deep green (12.13) | 40·00 | 4·50 |
| S3 | | 10 c. yellowish green (8.20) | 42·00 | 3·75 |

The differences between Types I and II (figures "10" with and without shading) formerly illustrated were due to wear of the plate. There was only one die.

S 2

S 3 Mail-carrying, 1867 and 1927

**1922** (21 Aug). *P* 12.

| No. | Type | Description | Unused | Used |
|---|---|---|---|---|
| S4 | S 2 | 20 c. carmine-red | 30·00 | 2·50 |

No. S4 exists in two slightly different sizes due to the use of "wet" or "dry" printing processes. See note below No. 195.

**1927** (29 June). *60th Anniversary of Confederation. P* 12.

| No. | Type | Description | Unused | Used |
|---|---|---|---|---|
| S5 | S 3 | 20 c. orange | 8·00 | 7·00 |

No. S5 exists imperforate, imperf × perf or perf × imperf.

S 4

**1930** (2 Sept). *P* 11.

| No. | Type | Description | Unused | Used |
|---|---|---|---|---|
| S6 | S 4 | 20 c. brown-red | 35·00 | 4·00 |

**1932** (24 Dec). *Type as* S 4, *but inscr* "CENTS" *in place of* "TWENTY CENTS". *P* 11.

| No. | Type | Description | Unused | Used |
|---|---|---|---|---|
| S7 | | 20 c. brown-red | 42·00 | 11·00 |

***ALTERED CATALOGUE NUMBERS***

Any Catalogue numbers altered from the last edition are shown as a list in the introductory pages.

S 5 Allegory of Progress

(Des A. Foringer)

**1935** (1 June). *P* 12.

| No. | Type | Description | Unused | Used |
|---|---|---|---|---|
| S8 | S 5 | 20 c. scarlet | 3·50 | 1·25 |

No. S8 exists imperforate.

S 6 Canadian Coat of Arms

**1938–39.** *P* 12.

| No. | Type | Description | Unused | Used |
|---|---|---|---|---|
| S 9 | S 6 | 10 c. green (1.4.39) | 10·00 | 55 |
| S10 | | 20 c. scarlet (15.6.38) | 35·00 | 23·00 |

Nos. S9/10 exist imperforate.

≡10 10≡

(S 7)

**1939** (1 Mar). *Surch with Type* **S 7.**

| No. | Type | Description | Unused | Used |
|---|---|---|---|---|
| S11 | S 6 | 10 c. on 20 c. scarlet | 5·50 | 7·50 |

S 8 Coat of Arms and Flags

S 9 Trans-Canada Plane

**1942** (1 July)–**1943.** *War Effort. P* 12. (*a*) *Postage.*

| No. | Type | Description | Unused | Used |
|---|---|---|---|---|
| S12 | S 8 | 10 c. green | 1·75 | 20 |

(*b*) *Air*

| No. | Type | Description | Unused | Used |
|---|---|---|---|---|
| S13 | S 9 | 16 c. ultramarine | 1·75 | 20 |
| S14 | | 17 c. ultramarine (1.4.43) | 1·75 | 30 |

Nos. S12/14 exist imperforate.

S 10 Arms of Canada and Peace Symbols

S 11 Transatlantic Plane over Quebec

**1946** (16 Sept)–**1947.** *P* 12. (*a*) *Postage.*

| No. | Type | Description | Unused | Used |
|---|---|---|---|---|
| S15 | S 10 | 10 c. green | 1·25 | 20 |

(*b*) *Air.* (i) *Circumflex accent in* "EXPRÊS"

| No. | Type | Description | Unused | Used |
|---|---|---|---|---|
| S16 | S 11 | 17 c. ultramarine | 3·00 | 2·50 |

(ii) *Grave accent in* "EXPRÈS"

| No. | Type | Description | Unused | Used |
|---|---|---|---|---|
| S17 | S 11 | 17 c. ultramarine (1947) | 3·00 | 2·50 |

## POSTAGE DUE STAMPS

**PRINTERS.** See note under "Special Delivery Stamps".

D 1

D 2

**1906** (1 July)–**28.** *P* 12.

| No. | Type | Description | Unused | Used |
|---|---|---|---|---|
| D1 | D 1 | 1 c. dull violet | 6·00 | 2·50 |
| D2 | | 1 c. red violet (1916) | 8·50 | 2·75 |
| | | a. Thin paper (10.24) | 14·00 | 16·00 |
| D3 | | 2 c. dull violet | 11·00 | 70 |
| D4 | | 2 c. red-violet (1917) | 8·50 | 90 |
| | | a. Thin paper (10.24) | 20·00 | 14·00 |
| D5 | | 4 c. violet (3.7.28) | 45·00 | 50·00 |
| D6 | | 5 c. dull violet | 12·00 | 1·75 |
| D7 | | 5 c. red-violet (1917) | 12·00 | 1·75 |
| | | a. Thin paper (10.24) | 15·00 | 15·00 |
| D8 | | 10 c. violet (3.7.28) | 28·00 | 13·00 |
| D1/8 | | *Set of* 5 | 90·00 | 60·00 |

The 1 c., 2 c. and 5 c. values exist imperforate.

Printings up to October 1924 used the "wet" method, those from mid 1925 onwards the "dry". For details of the differences between these two methods, see above No. 196.

**1930–2.** *P* 11.

| No. | Type | Description | Unused | Used |
|---|---|---|---|---|
| D 9 | D 2 | 1 c. bright violet (14.7.30) | 8·00 | 10·00 |
| D10 | | 2 c. bright violet (21.8.30) | 7·00 | 85 |
| D11 | | 4 c. bright violet (14.10.30) | 15·00 | 8·00 |
| D12 | | 5 c. bright violet (12.12.31) | 13·00 | 17·00 |
| D13 | | 10 c. bright violet (24.8.32) | 65·00 | 26·00 |
| D9/13 | | *Set of* 5 | 95·00 | 55·00 |

Nos. D9/11 and D13 exist imperforate.

D 3

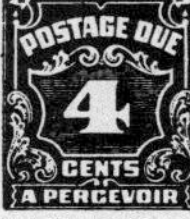

D 4

D 5

**1933–4.** *P* 11.

| No. | Type | Description | Unused | Used |
|---|---|---|---|---|
| D14 | D 3 | 1 c. violet (5.5.34) | 7·00 | 11·00 |
| D15 | | 2 c. violet (20.12.33) | 5·00 | 3·00 |
| D16 | | 4 c. violet (12.12.33) | 10·00 | 7·50 |
| D17 | | 10 c. violet (20.12.33) | 17·00 | 20·00 |
| D14/17 | | *Set of* 4 | 35·00 | 38·00 |

No. D14 exists imperforate.

**1935–65.** *P* 12.

| No. | Type | Description | Unused | Used |
|---|---|---|---|---|
| D18 | D 4 | 1 c. violet (14.10.35) | 40 | 10 |
| D19 | | 2 c. violet (9.9.35) | 40 | 10 |
| D20 | | 3 c. violet (4.65) | 2·50 | 7·00 |
| D21 | | 4 c. violet (2.7.35) | 80 | 10 |
| D22 | | 5 c. violet (12.48) | 1·00 | 35 |
| D23 | | 6 c. violet (1957) | 1·50 | 4·50 |
| D24 | | 10 c. violet (16.9.35) | 60 | 10 |
| D18/24 | | *Set of* 7 | 6·50 | 11·00 |

The 1 c., 2 c., 4 c. and 10 c., exist imperforate.

**1967–78.** *Litho. P* 12½ × 12 (20 c., 24 c., 50 c.) *or* 12 (*others*).

(*a*) *Size* 20 × 17½ *mm*

| No. | Type | Description | Unused | Used |
|---|---|---|---|---|
| D25 | D 5 | 1 c. scarlet (3.67) | 1·25 | 2·50 |
| D26 | | 2 c. scarlet (3.67) | 1·00 | 80 |
| D27 | | 3 c. scarlet (3.67) | 1·00 | 3·50 |
| D28 | | 4 c. scarlet (2.67) | 2·25 | 1·25 |
| D29 | | 5 c. scarlet (3.67) | 3·50 | 3·25 |
| D30 | | 6 c. scarlet (2.67) | 1·60 | 3·50 |
| D31 | | 10 c. scarlet (1.67) | 2·00 | 2·50 |
| D25/31 | | *Set of* 7 | 11·50 | 16·00 |

(*b*) *Size* 19½ × 16 *mm*

| No. | Type | Description | Unused | Used |
|---|---|---|---|---|
| D32 | D 5 | 1 c. scarlet (12.70) | 30 | 30 |
| | | a. Perf 12½ × 12 (11.77) | 15 | 80 |
| D33 | | 2 c. scarlet (1972) | 25 | 1·75 |
| D34 | | 3 c. scarlet (1.74) | 1·00 | 1·75 |
| D35 | | 4 c. scarlet (4.69) | 85 | 75 |
| | | a. Perf 12½ × 12 (11.77) | 45 | 1·50 |
| D36 | | 5 c. scarlet (2.69) | 20·00 | 35·00 |
| | | a. Perf 12½ × 12 (11.77) | 50 | 2·00 |
| D37 | | 6 c. scarlet (1972) | 1·75 | 3·00 |
| D38 | | 8 c. scarlet (1.69) | 75 | 60 |
| | | a. Perf 12½ × 12 (28.6.78) | 1·25 | 1·75 |
| D39 | | 10 c. scarlet (4.69) | 1·50 | 60 |
| | | a. Perf 12½ × 12 (9.77) | 60 | 80 |
| D40 | | 12 c. scarlet (1.69) | 1·25 | 65 |
| | | a. Perf 12½ × 12 (9.77) | 1·50 | 2·25 |
| D41 | | 16 c. scarlet (1.74) | 70 | 2·50 |
| D42 | | 20 c. scarlet (10.77) | 60 | 1·75 |
| D43 | | 24 c. scarlet (10.77) | 60 | 2·50 |
| D44 | | 50 c. scarlet (10.77) | 1·00 | 2·75 |
| D32a/44 | | *Set of* 13 | 8·50 | 19·00 |

There are no records of dates of issue of the above but supplies were distributed to depots in the months indicated.

Both white and ordinary papers have been used for Nos. D32/41. These are listed in Stanley Gibbons *Two Reigns Catalogue.*

### OFFICIAL STAMPS

We do not list stamps perforated "O.H.M.S.".

**O.H.M.S.**

(O 1)

**1949.** *Nos. 375/6, 378, 380 and 402/7 optd as Type O 1.*

*(a) Postage*

| | | | | |
|---|---|---|---|---|
| O1 | 111 | 1 c. green | 1·00 | 1·75 |
| | | a. Missing stop after "S" | £130 | 45·00 |
| O2 | 112 | 2 c. brown | 8·00 | 10·00 |
| | | a. Missing stop after "S" | £140 | 85·00 |
| O3 | 113 | 3 c. purple | 1·00 | 1·10 |
| O4 | 112 | 4 c. carmine-lake | 1·25 | 30 |
| O5 | – | 10 c. olive-green | 2·50 | 15 |
| | | a. Missing stop after "S" | 70·00 | 30·00 |
| O6 | – | 14 c. sepia | 4·00 | 80 |
| | | a. Missing stop after "S" | 90·00 | 45·00 |
| O7 | – | 20 c. slate | 8·50 | 60 |
| | | a. Missing stop after "S" | £130 | 45·00 |
| O8 | – | 50 c. green | £160 | £100 |
| | | a. Missing stop after "S" | £650 | £400 |
| O9 | – | $1 purple | 50·00 | 45·00 |
| | | a. Missing stop after "S" | £850 | £700 |

*(b) Air*

| | | | | |
|---|---|---|---|---|
| O10 | – | 7 c. blue | 18·00 | 5·00 |
| | | a. Missing stop after "S" | £120 | 60·00 |
| O1/10 | | *Set of* 10 | £225 | £140 |

**MISSING STOP VARIETIES.** These occur on R.6/2 of the lower left pane (Nos. O1a, O2a and O15a) or R.10/2 of the lower left pane (Nos. O5a, O6a, O7a, O8a, O9a and O10a).

**1949–50.** *Nos. 414/15, 416/17, 418 and 431 optd as Type O 1.*

| | | | | |
|---|---|---|---|---|
| O11 | 135 | 1 c. green | 30 | 40 |
| O12 | 136 | 2 c. sepia | 35 | 55 |
| O13 | 137 | 3 c. purple | 40 | 45 |
| O14 | 138 | 4 c. carmine-lake | 55 | 10 |
| O15 | 139 | 5 c. blue (1949) | 1·00 | 75 |
| | | a. Missing stop after "S" | 80·00 | 38·00 |
| O16 | 141 | 50 c. green (1950) | 26·00 | 24·00 |
| O11/16 | | *Set of* 6 | 26·00 | 24·00 |

**G** (O 2) **G** (O 3) **G** (O 4)

Type O 4 differs from Type O 3 in having a thinner appearance and an upward sloping left serif to the lower arm. It results from a new plate introduced in 1961/62. Variations in thickness are known in Type O 2 but these are due to wear and subsequent cleaning of the plate.

**1950** (2 Oct)–**52.** *Nos. 402/4, 406/7, 414/18 and 431 optd with Type* O **2** *(1 to 5 c.) or* O **3** *(7 c. to $1). (a) Postage.*

| | | | | |
|---|---|---|---|---|
| O17 | 135 | 1 c. green | 30 | 10 |
| O18 | 136 | 2 c. sepia | 60 | 40 |
| O19 | | 2 c. olive-green (11.51) | 75 | 10 |
| O20 | 137 | 3 c. purple | 50 | 10 |
| O21 | 138 | 4 c. carmine-lake | 1·00 | 20 |
| O22 | | 4 c. vermilion (1.5.52) | 1·00 | 10 |
| O23 | 139 | 5 c. blue | 2·00 | 30 |
| O24 | – | 10 c. olive-green | 1·50 | 10 |
| O25 | – | 14 c. sepia | 5·50 | 1·75 |
| O26 | – | 20 c. slate | 9·00 | 20 |
| O27 | 141 | 50 c. green | 7·00 | 6·50 |
| O28 | – | $1 purple | 50·00 | 42·00 |

*(b) Air*

| | | | | |
|---|---|---|---|---|
| O29 | – | 7 c. blue | 15·00 | 6·00 |
| O17/29 | | *Set of* 13 | 85·00 | 50·00 |

**1950–51.** *Nos. 432/3 optd with Type* O 3.

| | | | | |
|---|---|---|---|---|
| O30 | 142 | 10 c. brown-purple | 80 | 10 |
| | | a. Opt omitted in pair with normal | £375 | £400 |
| O31 | 143 | $1 ultramarine (1.2.51) | 55·00 | 55·00 |

**1952–53.** *Nos. 441, 443 and 446 optd with Type* O 3.

| | | | | |
|---|---|---|---|---|
| O32 | 153 | 7 c. blue (3.11.52) | 1·00 | 75 |
| O33 | 151 | 20 c. grey (1.4.52) | 80 | 10 |
| O34 | 154 | $1 black (2.2.53) | 7·00 | 7·00 |
| O32/4 | | *Set of* 3 | 8·00 | 7·00 |

**1953** (1 Sept)–**61.** *Nos. 450/4 and 462 optd with Type* O **2** *(1 to 5 c.) or* O **3** *(50 c.).*

| | | | | |
|---|---|---|---|---|
| O35 | 158 | 1 c. purple-brown | 15 | 10 |
| O36 | | 2 c. green | 20 | 10 |
| O37 | | 3 c. carmine | 20 | 10 |
| O38 | | 4 c. violet | 30 | 10 |
| O39 | | 5 c. ultramarine | 30 | 10 |
| O40 | 160 | 50 c. deep bluish green (2.11.53) | 2·25 | 50 |
| | | a. Opt Type O 4 (24.4.61*) | 2·00 | 2·25 |
| O35/40 | | *Set of* 6 | 2·75 | 60 |

* Earliest recorded date.

**1955–56.** *Nos. 463/4 and 466/7 optd with Type* O **2**.

| | | | | |
|---|---|---|---|---|
| O41 | 161 | 1 c. purple-brown (12.11.56) | 15 | 20 |
| O42 | | 2 c. green (19.1.56) | 15 | 10 |
| O43 | | 4 c. violet (23.7.56) | 30 | 10 |
| O44 | | 5 c. bright blue (11.1.55) | 15 | 10 |
| O41/4 | | *Set of* 4 | 65 | 30 |

**1955–62.** *Nos. 477 and 488 optd with Type* O 3.

| | | | | |
|---|---|---|---|---|
| O45 | 165 | 10 c. purple-brown (21.2.55) | 25 | 10 |
| | | a. Opt Type O 4 (28.3.62*) | 25 | 35 |
| O46 | 176 | 20 c. green (4.12.56) | 40 | 10 |
| | | a. Opt Type O 4 (10.4.62*) | 4·50 | 30 |

* Earliest recorded date.

**1963** (15 May). *Nos. 527/8 and 530/1 optd as Type* O **2**.

| | | | |
|---|---|---|---|
| O47 | 1 c. chocolate | 30 | 2·50 |
| O48 | 2 c. green | 30 | 2·25 |
| | a. Type O 2 omitted (vert pair with normal) | £550 | |
| O49 | 4 c. carmine-red | 30 | 1·75 |
| O50 | 5 c. ultramarine | 30 | 55 |
| O47/50 | *Set of* 4 | 1·10 | 6·50 |

No. O48a comes from the top row of an upper pane on which the overprint was misplaced downwards by one row. Owing to the margin between the panes the top row of the bottom pane had the overprint at the top of the stamp.

The use of official stamps was discontinued on 31 December 1963.

### OFFICIAL SPECIAL DELIVERY STAMPS

**1950.** *No. S15 optd as Type* O **1**, *but larger.*

| | | | | |
|---|---|---|---|---|
| OS1 | S 10 | 10 c. green | 14·00 | 14·00 |

**1950** (2 Oct). *No. S15 optd as Type* O **2**, *but larger.*

| | | | | |
|---|---|---|---|---|
| OS2 | S 10 | 10 c. green | 20·00 | 20·00 |

## Cape of Good Hope
## *see* South Africa

# Cayman Islands

The first post office was opened at Georgetown in April 1889. The stamps of Jamaica with the following cancellations were used until 19 February 1901. At some stage, probably around 1891, a supply of the Jamaica 1889 1d., No. 27, was overprinted "Cayman Islands", but these stamps were never issued. Two surviving examples are known, one unused and the other cancelled at Richmond in Jamaica.

**PRICES OF NOS. Z1/27.** These are for a single stamp showing a clear impression of the postmark. Nos. Z1, 2, 6/8, 11/13, 18, 22 and Z25 are known used on cover and these are worth considerably more.

### GEORGETOWN, GRAND CAYMAN

Z 1

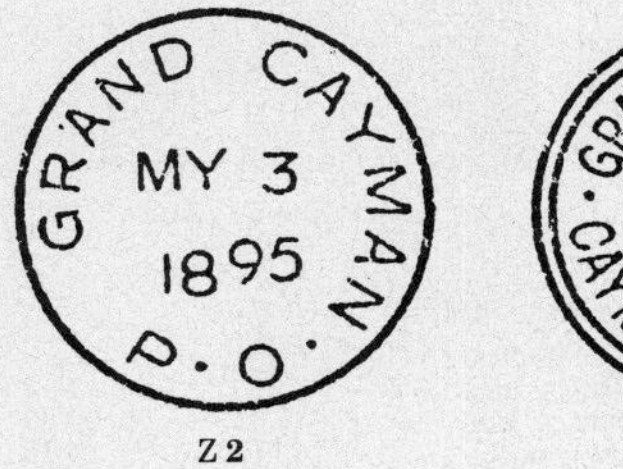


Z 2 Z 3

*Stamps of* JAMAICA *cancelled with Type* Z 1.

**1889** *to* **1894.**

| | | |
|---|---|---|
| Z1 | ½d. yellow-green (No. 16) | £400 |
| Z2 | 1d. purple and mauve (No. 27) | £400 |
| Z3 | 2d. green (No. 28) | £750 |
| Z4 | 2½d. dull purple and blue (No. 29) | £850 |
| Z5 | 4d. red-orange (No. 22) | £1800 |

*Stamps of* JAMAICA *cancelled with Type* Z 2.

**1895** *to* **1898.**

| | | |
|---|---|---|
| Z6 | ½d. yellow-green (No. 16) | £450 |
| Z7 | 1d. purple and mauve (No. 27) | £375 |
| Z8 | 2½d. dull purple and blue (No. 29) | £650 |
| Z9 | 3d. sage-green (No. 21) | £2250 |

*Stamps of* JAMAICA *cancelled with Type* Z 3.

**1898** *to* **1901.**

| | | |
|---|---|---|
| Z10 | ½d. yellow-green (No. 16) | £375 |
| | *a. Green (No. 16a)* | £375 |
| Z11 | 1d. purple and mauve (No. 27) | £375 |
| Z12 | 1d. red (No. 31) (1900) | £375 |
| Z13 | 2½d. dull purple and blue (No. 29) | £550 |

### OFFICIAL STAMPS

*Stamps of* JAMAICA *cancelled with Type* Z 1.

**1890** *to* **1894.**

| | | |
|---|---|---|
| Z14 | ½d. green (No. O1) | £750 |
| Z15 | ½d. green (No. O3) (1893) | £1200 |
| Z16 | 1d. rose (No. O4) | £1100 |
| Z17 | 2d. grey (No. O5) | £1800 |

*Stamps of* JAMAICA *cancelled with Type* Z 2.

**1895** *to* **1898.**

| | | |
|---|---|---|
| Z18 | ½d. green (No. O3) | £1300 |
| Z19 | 1d. rose (No. O4) | £2250 |
| Z20 | 2d. grey (No. O5) | £2250 |

### STAKE BAY, CAYMAN BRAC

Z 4 Z 5

*Stamps of* JAMAICA *cancelled with Type* Z 4.

**1898** *to* **1900.**

| | | |
|---|---|---|
| Z21 | ½d. yellow-green (No. 16) | £2250 |
| Z22 | 1d. purple and mauve (No. 27) | £2500 |
| Z23 | 2d. green (No. 28) | £3000 |
| Z24 | 2½d. dull purple and blue (No. 29) | £2250 |

*Stamps of* JAMAICA *cancelled with Type* Z 5.

**1900** *to* **1901.**

| | | |
|---|---|---|
| Z25 | ½d. yellow-green (No. 16) | £2500 |
| Z26 | 1d. purple and mauve (No. 27) | £1800 |
| Z27 | 1d. red (No. 31) | £2000 |
| Z28 | 2½d. dull purple and blue (No. 29) | £1800 |

**PRICES FOR STAMPS ON COVER TO 1945**

| | |
|---|---|
| Nos. 1/2 | *from* × 25 |
| Nos. 3/12 | *from* × 5 |
| Nos. 13/19 | *from* × 4 |
| Nos. 25/34 | *from* × 5 |
| Nos. 38/52*b* | *from* × 4 |
| Nos. 53/67 | *from* × 5 |
| Nos. 69/83 | *from* × 4 |
| Nos. 84/95 | *from* × 6 |
| Nos. 96/9 | *from* × 5 |
| Nos. 100/11 | *from* × 4 |
| Nos. 112/14 | *from* × 6 |
| Nos. 115/26 | *from* × 2 |

### DEPENDENCY OF JAMAICA

1

2

3

(T **1/9** and **12/13** typo D.L.R.)

**1900** (Nov). *Wmk Crown CA. P 14.*

| | | | | |
|---|---|---|---|---|
| 1 | 1 | ½d. deep green | 4·00 | 8·50 |
| | | *a. Pale green* | 1·50 | 7·00 |
| 2 | | 1d. rose-carmine | 2·25 | 75 |
| | | *a. Pale carmine* | 7·00 | 7·00 |
| 1/2 Optd "Specimen" | | *Set of* 2 | £100 | |

Dented frame under "A" (R. 1/6 of left pane)

**1902** (Jan)–**03.** *Wmk Crown CA. P 14.*

| | | | | |
|---|---|---|---|---|
| 3 | 2 | ½d. green (15.9.02) | 3·50 | 18·00 |
| | | a. Dented frame | 50·00 | |
| 4 | | 1d. carmine (6.3.03) | 5·50 | 6·50 |
| | | a. Dented frame | 70·00 | |
| 5 | | 2½d. bright blue | 6·00 | 10·00 |
| | | a. Dented frame | 80·00 | |
| 6 | | 6d. brown | 18·00 | 35·00 |
| | | a. Dented frame | £150 | |
| 7 | 3 | 1s. orange | 50·00 | 75·00 |
| | | a. Dented frame | £225 | |
| 3/7 | | *Set of* 5 | 75·00 | £130 |
| 3/7 Optd "Specimen" | | *Set of* 5 | £200 | |

**1905** (Mar–18 Oct). *Wmk Mult Crown CA. P 14.*

| | | | | |
|---|---|---|---|---|
| 8 | 2 | ½d. green | 1·50 | 3·50 |
| | | a. Dented frame | 35·00 | |
| 9 | | 1d. carmine (18 Oct) | 10·00 | 16·00 |
| | | a. Dented frame | £110 | |
| 10 | | 2½d. bright blue | 3·50 | 2·75 |
| | | a. Dented frame | 55·00 | |

11 2 6d. brown .. .. .. .. 16·00 35·00
a. Dented frame .. .. .. £160
12 3 1s. orange .. .. .. .. 30·00 48·00
a. Dented frame .. .. .. £190
8/12 .. .. .. .. Set of 5 55·00 95·00

**1907** (13 Mar). *Wmk Mult Crown CA. P 14.*
13 3 4d. brown and blue .. .. .. 18·00 27·00
a. Dented frame .. .. .. £160
14 2 6d. olive and rose .. .. .. 18·00 38·00
a. Dented frame .. .. .. £160
15 3 1s. violet and green .. .. .. 30·00 45·00
a. Dented frame .. .. .. £190
16 5s. salmon and green .. .. .. £170 £250
a. Dented frame .. .. .. £500
13/16 .. .. .. .. Set of 4 £200 £325
13/16 Optd "Specimen" .. .. Set of 4 £225

One Halfpenny. (4) ½D (5) 1D (6)

**1907** (30 Aug). *No. 9 surch at Govt Printing Office, Kingston, with T* 4.
17 2 ½d. on 1d. carmine .. .. .. 29·00 55·00
a. Dented frame .. .. .. £225

**1907** (Nov). *No. 16 handstamped at Georgetown P.O. with T* 5 *or* 6.
18 3 ½d. on 5s. salmon and green (26 Nov) .. £225 £300
a. Surch inverted .. .. .. £15000
b. Surch double .. .. .. £8000 £9000
c. Surch double, one inverted ..
d. Surch omitted (in pair with normal) £22000
e. Dented frame .. .. .. £850
19 1d. on 5s. salmon and green (23 Nov) .. £225 £300
a. Surch double .. .. .. £11000
b. Dented frame .. .. .. £850

The ½d. on 5s. may be found with the figures "1" or "2" omitted, owing to defective handstamping.

8 9 2½D (10)

**1907** (27 Dec)–**09**. *Chalk-surfaced paper* (3d. *to* 10s.). *P* 14.

(*a*) *Wmk Mult Crown CA*
25 8 ½d. green .. .. .. .. 70 1·75
26 1d. carmine .. .. .. .. 60 55
27 2½d. ultramarine (30.3.08) .. .. 2·75 3·50
28 9 3d. purple/*yellow* (30.3.08) .. .. 2·75 6·50
29 4d. black and red/*yellow* (30.3.08) .. 48·00 50·00
30 8 6d. dull and bright purple (2.10.08) .. 4·50 23·00
*a. Dull purple and violet-purple* .. 19·00 35·00
31 9 1s. black/*green* (5.4.09) .. .. 4·25 14·00
32 5s. green and red/*yellow* (30.3.08) .. 35·00 55·00

(*b*) *Wmk Crown CA* (30.3.08)
33 9 1s. black/*green* .. .. .. 32·00 65·00
34 8 10s. green and red/*green* .. .. £180 £275
25/34 .. .. .. Set of 10 £275 £425
25/34 (*except* 31) Optd "Specimen" .. Set of 9 £350

**1908** (12 Feb). *No. 13 handstamped locally with T* 10.
35 3 2½d. on 4d. brown and blue .. .. £1600 £2250
a. Surch double .. .. £21000 £16000
b. Dented frame .. .. £5000

No. 35 should only be purchased when accompanied by an expert committee's certificate or similar form of guarantee.

**MANUSCRIPT PROVISIONALS**. During May and June 1908 supplies of ½d. and 1d. stamps became exhausted, and the payment of postage was indicated by the Postmistress, Miss Gwendolyn Parsons, using a manuscript endorsement. Such endorsements were in use from 12 May to 1 June.

*Price on cover*
MP1 "(Postage Paid G.A.P.)" (12 May to 1 June) .. £1800
MP1*a* "½ (Postage Paid G.A.P.)" (23 May) .. £2500

In October of the same year there was a further shortage of ¼d. stamps and the manuscript endorsements were again applied by either the new Postmaster, William Graham McCausland, or by Miss Parsons who remained as his assistant.
MP2 "Pd ¼d. W. G. McC." (4 to 27 October) .. £250
MP3 "Paid" (7 October) .. .. £4000
MP4 "Pd ¼d" (8 October) .. .. £3000
MP5 "(Paid ¼GAP. asst.)" (15 October) .. £3000

No. MP2 exists in different inks and formats.

Manuscript endorsement for the 2½d. rate is also known, but this is thought to have been done by oversight.

A 1d. surcharge on 4d. (No. 29), issued in mid-May, was intended as a revenue stamp and was never authorised for postal use (*price* £225 *un.*). Used examples were either cancelled by favour or passed through the post in error. Exists with surcharge inverted (*price* £2000 *un.*), surcharge double (*price* £2500 *un.*) or surcharge double, both inverted (*price* £2500 *un.*).

11 12 13

**1908** (30 June)–**09**. *Wmk Mult Crown CA. Litho. P* 14.
38 11 ¼d. brown (Optd S. £65) .. .. 30 20
*a. Grey-brown* (2.09) .. .. 70 75

**1912** (24 Apr)–**20**. *Wmk Mult Crown CA. Chalk-surfaced paper* (3d. *to* 10s.). *P* 14.
40 13 ¼d. brown (10.2.13) .. .. 30 30
41 12 ½d. green .. .. .. 50 2·00
42 1d. red (25.2.13) .. .. .. 1·75 75
43 13 2d. pale grey .. .. .. 50 2·50
44 12 2½d. bright blue (26.8.14) .. .. 7·00 7·50
*a. Deep bright blue* (9.11.17) .. 9·50 15·00
45 13 3d. purple/*yellow* (26.11.14) .. 9·50 23·00
*a. White back* (19.11.13) .. .. 1·75 4·50
*b. On lemon* (12.3.18) (Optd S. £50) 1·50 11·00
*c. On orange-buff* (1920) .. 7·00 20·00
*d. On pale yellow* (1920) .. .. 3·25 20·00
46 4d. black and red/*yellow* (25.2.13) .. 75 3·50
47 12 6d. dull and bright purple (25.2.13) .. 2·25 5·00
48 13 1s. black/*green* (15.5.16) (Optd S. £50) .. 3·50 16·00
*a. White back* (19.11.13) .. .. 1·75 2·75
49 2s. purple and bright blue/*blue* .. 7·50 27·00
50 3s. green and violet .. .. 17·00 45·00
51 5s. green and red/*yellow* (26.8.14) .. 65·00 £100
52 12 10s. deep green and red/*green* (26.11.14) (Optd S. £80) .. .. 85·00 £140
*a. White back* (19.11.13) .. .. 80·00 £120
*b. On blue-green, olive back* (5.10.18) .. 70·00 £140
40/52*b* .. .. .. Set of 13 £160 £275
40/4, 45*a*, 46/7, 48*a*, 49/51, 52*a* Optd "Specimen" Set of 13 £375

WAR STAMP. 1½d (14) WAR STAMP. 1½d (15) 1½d Straight serif (Left-hand pane R. 10/2)

**1917** (26 Feb). *T* 12 *surch with T* 14 *or* 15 *at Kingston, Jamaica.*
53 14 1½d. on 2½d. deep blue .. .. 2·25 6·00
a. No fraction bar .. .. 50·00 90·00
b. Missing stop after "STAMP" (R.1/4) £200
54 15 1½d. on 2½d. deep blue .. .. 40 3·00
a. No fraction bar .. .. 29·00 65·00
b. Straight serif .. .. 35·00 75·00

On No. 53 "WAR STAMP" and "1½d." were applied separately.

WAR STAMP 1½d (16) WAR STAMP 1½d (17) WAR STAMP 1½d. (18)

**1917** (4 Sept). *T* 12 *surch with T* 16 *or* 17 *by D.L.R.*
55 16 1½d. on 2½d. deep blue .. .. £700 £1400
56 17 1½d. on 2½d. deep blue (Optd S.£100) 20 40

**1919–20**. *T* 12 *and* 13 (2½d. *special printing*), *optd only, or surch in addition at Kingston* (*No.* 58) *or by D.L.R.* (*others*).
57 16 ½d. green (4.2.19) .. .. 20 95
58 18 1½d. on 2d. grey (10.3.20) .. .. 90 3·75
59 17 1½d. on 2½d. orange (4.2.19) .. 25 80
57, 59 Optd "Specimen" .. Set of 2 90·00

In T 16 the "R" of "WAR" has a curved foot and the other letters vary slightly from T 17. "1½d." is in thin type. In T 17 the "R" has a straight foot, and the "1½d." differs.

The ½d. stamps on *buff* paper, and later consignments of the 2d. T 13 on *pinkish*, derived their colour from the paper in which they were packed for despatch from England.

19

20 King William IV and King George V

(Recess D.L.R.)

**1921** (4 Apr)–**26**. *P* 14. (*a*) *Wmk Mult Crown CA.*
60 19 3d. purple/*orange-buff* .. .. 1·50 7·00
*a. Purple/pale yellow* .. .. 45·00 60·00
62 4d. red/*yellow* (1.4.22) .. .. 80 3·75
63 1s. black/*green* .. .. .. 1·25 7·00
64 5s. yellow-green/*pale yellow* .. 16·00 48·00
*a. Deep green/pale yellow* .. 45·00 65·00
*b. Blue-green/pale yellow* .. 50·00 75·00
*c. Deep green/orange-buff* (19.11.21) 65·00 £100
67 10s. carmine/*green* (19.11.21) .. 55·00 90·00
60/7 .. .. .. Set of 5 70·00 £140
60/7 Optd "Specimen" .. .. Set of 5 £225

(*b*) *Wmk Mult Script CA*
69 19 ¼d. yellow-brown (1.4.22) .. .. 30 60
70 ½d. pale grey-green (1.4.22) .. .. 40 25
71 1d. deep carmine-red (1.4.22) .. .. 70 85
72 1½d. orange-brown .. .. .. 1·50 20
73 2d. slate-grey (1.4.22) .. .. 1·75 3·25
74 2½d. bright blue (1.4.22) .. .. 50 45
75 3d. purple/*yellow* (29.6.23) .. .. 50 85
76 4½d. sage-green (29.6.23) .. .. 1·25 3·00
77 6d. claret (1.4.22) .. .. 5·50 18·00
*a. Deep claret* .. .. .. 16·00 28·00
79 1s. black/*green* (15.5.25) .. .. 2·50 15·00
80 2s. violet/*blue* (1.4.22) .. .. 7·50 12·00
81 3s. violet (1.4.22) .. .. 17·00 15·00
82 5s. green/*yellow* (15.2.25) .. .. 22·00 35·00
83 10s. carmine/*green* (5.9.26) .. .. 48·00 65·00
69/83 .. .. .. Set of 14 95·00 £150
69/83 Optd "Specimen" .. .. Set of 14 £400

**"A.S.R." PROVISIONAL.** On the night of 9/10 November 1932 the Cayman Brac Post Office at Stake Bay, and its contents, was destroyed by a hurricane. Pending the arrival of replacement stamp stocks and cancellation the Postmaster, Mr. A. S. Rutty, initialled covers to indicate that postage had been paid. Those destined for overseas addresses additionally received a "Postage Paid" handstamp when they passed through Kingston, Jamaica.

*Price on cover*
MP6 Endorsed "A.S.R." in manuscript .. .. £3000
MP7 Endorsed "A.S.R." in manuscript and hand-stamped "Postage Paid" .. .. .. £3500

These emergency arrangements lasted until 19 December.

(Recess Waterlow)

**1932** (5 Dec). *Centenary of the "Assembly of Justices and Vestry". Wmk Mult Script CA. P* 12½.
84 20 ¼d. brown .. .. .. .. 50 90
85 ½d. green .. .. .. .. 1·50 4·50
a. "A" reversed in wmk .. ..
86 1d. scarlet .. .. .. .. 1·50 3·50
87 1½d. red-orange .. .. .. 1·50 1·00
88 2d. grey .. .. .. .. 1·50 1·75
89 2½d. ultramarine .. .. .. 1·50 1·00
90 3d. olive-green .. .. .. 1·75 2·75
91 6d. purple .. .. .. .. 6·00 12·00
92 1s. black and brown .. .. .. 13·00 20·00
93 2s. black and ultramarine .. .. 38·00 55·00
94 5s. black and green .. .. .. 80·00 £110
95 10s. black and scarlet .. .. £250 £350
84/95 .. .. .. Set of 12 £350 £500
84/95 Perf "Specimen" .. .. Set of 12 £500

No. 85a shows one "A" of the watermark reversed so that its head points to right *when seen from the back*. It is believed that this stamp also exists with the "A" omitted, but this has yet to be confirmed.

**1935** (6 May). *Silver Jubilee. As Nos.* 91/4 *of Antigua.*
96 ½d. black and green .. .. .. 15 20
f. Diagonal line by turret .. .. 20·00
h. Dot by flagstaff .. .. .. 22·00
97 2½d. brown and deep blue .. .. 60 1·00
98 6d. light blue and olive-green .. .. 1·00 1·25
h. Dot by flagstaff .. .. .. 60·00
99 1s. slate and purple .. .. .. 2·75 3·75
h. Dot by flagstaff .. .. .. 75·00
96/9 .. .. .. Set of 4 4·00 5·50
96/9 Perf "Specimen" .. .. Set of 4 85·00

For illustrations of plate varieties see Catalogue Introduction.

21 Cayman Islands

24 Conch Shells and Coconut Palms

(Recess Waterlow)

**1935** (1 May)–**36**. *T* 21, 24 *and similar designs. Wmk Mult Script CA. P* 12½.
100 21 ¼d. black and brown .. .. .. 15 50
101 – ½d. ultramarine & yellow-green (1.1.36) 60 30
102 – 1d. ultramarine and scarlet .. .. 2·25 50
103 24 1½d. black and orange .. .. .. 1·25 65
104 – 2d. ultramarine and purple .. .. 1·25 80
105 – 2½d. blue and black (1.1.36) .. .. 3·00 60
106 21 3d. black and olive-green .. .. 2·00 80
107 – 6d. bright purple and black (1.1.36) .. 8·50 3·00
108 – 1s. ultramarine and orange (1.1.36) .. 4·00 4·50
109 – 2s. ultramarine and black .. .. 40·00 30·00
110 – 5s. green and black .. .. .. 42·00 48·00
111 24 10s. black and scarlet .. .. 65·00 75·00
100/11 .. .. .. Set of 12 £150 £150
100/11 Perf "Specimen" .. .. Set of 12 £250

Designs: *Horiz*—½d., 2d., 1s. Cat boat; 1d., 2s. Red-footed Booby; 2½d., 6d. 5s. Hawksbill Turtles.

**1937** (13 May). *Coronation Issue. As Nos.* 95/7 *of Antigua. P* 11×11½.
112 ½d. green .. .. .. .. 30 15
113 1d. carmine .. .. .. .. 50 15
114 2½d. blue .. .. .. .. 95 35
112/14 .. .. .. Set of 3 1·60 60
112/14 Perf "Specimen" .. .. Set of 3 75·00

26 Beach View

27 Dolphin fish (*Coryphaena hippurus*)

(Recess D.L.R. (½d., 2d., 6d., 1s., 10s.), Waterlow (others))

**1938** (5 May)–**48**. *T* 26/7 *and similar designs. Wmk Mult Script CA* (*sideways on* ¼d., 1d., 1½d., 2½d., 3d., 2s., 5s.). *Various perfs.*
115 26 ¼d. red-orange (*p* 12½) .. .. 10 45
a. Perf 13½ × 12½ (16.7.43) .. .. 10 45
116 27 ½d. green (*p* 13 × 11½) .. .. 35 40
a. Perf 14 (16.7.43) .. .. .. 55 75
117 – 1d. scarlet (*p* 12½) .. .. .. 15 40
118 26 1½d. black (*p* 12½) .. .. .. 10 10
119 – 2d. violet (*p* 11½ × 13) .. .. 70 30
a. Perf 14 (16.7.43) .. .. .. 40 30

120 – 2½d. bright blue (p 12½) 15 20
120a – 2½d. orange (p 12½) (25.8.47) 1·50 30
121 – 3d. orange (p 12½) 15 15
121a – 3d. bright blue (p 12½) (25.8.47) 1·00 30
122 – 6d. olive-green (p 11½ × 13) 4·50 2·25
a. Perf 14 (16.7.43) 75 45
b. *Brownish olive* (p 11½ × 13) (8.7.47) 1·50 1·25
123 **27** 1s. red-brown (p 13 × 11½) 2·25 1·50
a. Perf 14 (16.7.43) 2·00 50
124 **26** 2s. yellow-green (*shades*) (p 12½) 38·00 14·00
a. *Deep green* (16.7.43) 18·00 7·00
125 – 5s. carmine-lake (p 12½) 23·00 12·00
a. *Crimson* (1948) 24·00 17·00
126 – 10s. chocolate (p 11½ × 13) 18·00 8·50
a. Perf 14 (16.7.43) 16·00 8·50
115/26a *Set of* 14 55·00 28·00
115/26 Perf "Specimen" *Set of* 14 £275

Designs: *Horiz* (*as T* **26**)—1d., 3d. Cayman Islands map; 2½d., 5s. *Rembro* (schooner). *Vert* (*as T* **27**)—2d., 6d., 10s. Hawksbill Turtles.

**1946** (26 Aug). *Victory. As Nos.* 110/11 *of Antigua.*
127 1½d. black 10 10
128 3d. orange-yellow 10 10
127/8 Perf "Specimen" *Set of* 2 65·00

**1948** (29 Nov). *Royal Silver Wedding. As Nos.* 112/13 *of Antigua.*
129 ½d. green 10 10
130 10s. violet-blue 10·00 6·50

**1949** (10 Oct). *75th Anniv of Universal Postal Union. As Nos.* 114/17 *of Antigua.*
131 2½d. orange 20 15
132 3d. deep blue 60 20
133 6d. olive 60 30
134 1s. red-brown 60 30
131/4 *Set of* 4 1·75 85

31 Cat Boat

32 Coconut Grove, Cayman Brac

(Recess B.W.)

**1950** (2 Oct). *T* **31/2** *and similar horiz designs. Wmk Mult Script CA. P* 11½ × 11.
135 ¼d. bright blue and pale scarlet 15 60
136 ½d. reddish violet and emerald-green 10 90
137 1d. olive-green and deep blue 60 75
138 1½d. green and brown 30 75
139 2d. reddish violet and rose-carmine 80 1·50
140 2½d. turquoise and black 50 60
141 3d. bright green and light blue 1·40 1·25
142 6d. red-brown and blue 1·00 1·25
143 9d. scarlet and grey-green 2·25 2·00
144 1s. brown and orange 3·00 2·75
145 2s. violet and reddish purple 7·00 5·50
146 5s. olive-green and violet 8·50 6·50
147 10s. black and scarlet 9·50 8·50
135/47 *Set of* 13 32·00 28·00

Designs:—1d. Green Turtle; 1½d. Thatch rope industry; 2d. Cayman seamen; 2½d. Map of Cayman Islands; 3d. Parrot Fish; 6d. Bluff, Cayman Brac; 9d. Georgetown harbour; 1s. Turtle in "crawl"; 2s. *Ziroma* (schooner); 5s. Boat-building; 10s. Government Offices, Grand Cayman.

44 South Sound Lighthouse, Grand Cayman

45 Queen Elizabeth II

**1953** (2 Mar)–**62**. *Designs previously used for King George VI issue but with portrait of Queen Elizabeth II as in T* **44/5**. *Wmk Mult Script CA. P* 11½×11 *or* 11×11½ (4d., £1).
148 ¼d. deep bright blue & rose-red (21.2.55) 45 30
a. *Bright blue and bright rose-red* (5.12.56) 45 30
149 ½d. purple and bluish green (7.7.54) 10 30
150 1d. brown-olive and indigo (7.7.54) 60 20
151 1½d. deep green and red-brown (7.7.54) 15 15
152 2d. reddish violet and cerise (2.6.54) 2·00 55
153 2½d. turquoise-blue and black (2.6.54) 3·00 40
154 3d. bright green and blue (21.2.55) 3·50 30
155 4d. black and deep blue 1·50 15
a. *Black and greenish blue* (13.10.54) 7·00 7·00
b. *Black and deep bright blue* (10.7.62) 4·50 4·00
156 6d. lake-brown and deep blue (7.7.54) 1·50 20
157 9d. scarlet and bluish green (2.6.54) 1·75 15
158 1s. brown and red-orange (21.2.55) 2·75 10
159 2s. slate-violet & reddish purple (21.2.55) 7·50 4·50
160 5s. olive-green and slate-violet (21.2.55) 8·50 3·50
161 10s. black and rose-red (21.2.55) 11·00 7·00
161a £1 blue (6.1.59) 24·00 9·50
148/61a *Set of* 15 60·00 24·00

Designs: *Horiz*—¼d. Cat boat; ½d. Coconut grove, Cayman Brac; 1d. Green Turtle; 1½d. Thatch rope industry; 2d. Cayman seamen; 2½d. Map of Cayman Islands; 3d. Parrot Fish; 6d. Bluff, Cayman Brac; 9d. Georgetown harbour; 1s. Turtle in "crawl"; 2s. *Ziroma* (schooner); 5s. Boat-building; 10s. Government Offices, Grand Cayman.

**1953** (2 June). *Coronation. As No.* 120 *of Antigua, but ptd by B.W.*
162 1d. black and emerald 10 50

46 Arms of the Cayman Islands

(Photo D.L.R.)

**1959** (4 July). *New Constitution. Wmk Mult Script CA. P* 12.
163 **46** 2½d. black and light blue 10 30
164 1s. black and orange 30 10

## CROWN COLONY

47 Cuban Amazon

48 Cat Boat

(Recess B.W.)

**1962** (28 Nov)–**64**. *T* **47/8** *and similar designs. W w* **12**. *P* 11×11½ (*vert*) *or* 11½×11 (*horiz*).
165 ¼d. emerald and red 15 35
a. *Emerald and rose* (18.2.64) 40 50
166 1d. black and yellow-olive 20 10
167 1½d. yellow and purple 1·50 45
168 2d. blue and deep brown 35 30
169 2½d. violet and bluish green 40 40
170 3d. bright blue and carmine 20 10
171 4d. deep green and purple 80 40
172 6d. bluish green and sepia 2·50 30
173 9d. ultramarine and purple 1·25 30
174 1s. sepia and rose-red 50 10
175 1s. 3d. bluish green and orange-brown 1·50 1·50
176 1s. 9d. deep turquoise and violet 6·00 70
177 5s. plum and deep green 4·50 2·00
178 10s. olive and blue 8·00 7·00
179 £1 carmine and black 14·00 13·00
165/79 *Set of* 15 38·00 24·00

Designs: *Horiz*—1½d. *Schomburgkia thomsoniana* (orchid); 2d. Map of Cayman Islands; 2½d. Fisherman casting net; 3d. West Bay Beach; 4d. Green Turtle; 6d. *Lydia E. Wilson* (schooner); 1s. Iguana; 1s. 3d. Swimming Pool, Cayman Brac; 1s. 9d. Water sports; 5s. Fort George. *Vert*—9d. Angler with Kingfish; 10s. Coat of Arms; £1 Queen Elizabeth II.

**1963** (4 June). *Freedom from Hunger. As No.* 146 *of Antigua.*
180 1s. 9d. carmine 30 10

**1963** (2 Sept). *Red Cross Centenary. As Nos.* 147/8 *of Antigua.*
181 1d. red and black 15 20
182 1s. 9d. red and blue 70 75

**1964** (23 April). *400th Birth Anniv of William Shakespeare. As No.* 164 *of Antigua.*
183 6d. magenta 10 10

**1965** (17 May). *I.T.U. Centenary. As Nos.* 166/7 *of Antigua.*
184 1d. blue and light purple 15 10
185 1s. 3d. bright purple and green 40 25

**1965** (25 Oct). *International Co-operation Year. As Nos.* 168/9 *of Antigua.*
186 1d. reddish purple and turquoise-green 10 10
187 1s. deep bluish green and lavender 40 25

**1966** (24 Jan). *Churchill Commemoration. As Nos.* 170/3 *of Antigua.*
188 ¼d. new blue 10 20
189 1d. deep green 15 10
190 1s. brown 35 10
191 1s. 9d. bluish violet 55 35
188/91 *Set of* 4 95 65

**1966** (4 Feb). *Royal Visit. As Nos.* 174/5 *of Antigua.*
192 1d. black and ultramarine 50 10
193 1s. 9d. black and magenta 1·50 45

**1966** (1 July). *World Cup Football Championships. As Nos.* 176/7 *of Antigua.*
194 1½d. violet, yellow-green, lake & yellow-brn 10 10
195 1s. 9d. chocolate, blue-grn, lake & yell-brn 40 25

**1966** (20 Sept). *Inauguration of W.H.O. Headquarters, Geneva. As Nos.* 178/9 *of Antigua.*
196 2d. black, yellow-green and light blue 25 10
197 1s. 3d. black, light purple and yellow-brown 55 45

62 Telephone and Map

(Des V. Whiteley. Litho Harrison)

**1966** (5 Dec). *International Telephone Links. W w* **12**. *P* 14½ × 14.
198 **62** 4d. red, black, greenish blue & ol-grn 15 10
199 9d. violet-blue, black, brown-red & lt grn 15 10

**1966** (12 Dec*). *20th Anniv of U.N.E.S.C.O. As Nos.* 196/8 *of Antigua.*
200 1d. slate-violet, red, yellow and orange 15 10
201 1s. 9d. orange-yellow, violet and deep olive 45 10
202 5s. black, bright purple and orange 1·25 55
200/2 *Set of* 3 1·75 65

*This is the local date of issue; the Crown Agents released the stamps on 1 December.

63 BAC 1-11 Airliner over Cayman Schooner

(Des V. Whiteley. Photo Harrison)

**1966** (17 Dec). *Opening of Cayman Jet Service. W w* **12**. *P* 14½.
203 **63** 1s. black, new blue and olive-green 20 15
204 1s. 9d. deep purple-brown, ultramarine and emerald 20 15

64 Water-skiing

(Des G. Vasarhelyi. Photo Harrison)

**1967** (1 Dec). *International Tourist Year. T* **64** *and similar horiz designs. Multicoloured. W w* **12**. *P* 14½ × 14.
205 4d. Type **64** 15 10
a. Gold omitted £140
206 6d. Skin diving 15 15
207 1s. Sport fishing 15 15
208 1s. 9d. Sailing 20 20
205/8 *Set of* 4 60 55

A used copy of No. 207 is known with yellow omitted.

68 Former Slaves and Emblem

(Des and photo Harrison)

**1968** (3 June). *Human Rights Year. W w* **12**. *P* 14½ × 14.
209 **68** 3d. deep bluish green, black and gold 10 10
210 9d. brown, gold and myrtle-green 10 10
211 5s. ultramarine, gold and myrtle-green 30 25
209/11 *Set of* 3 40 30

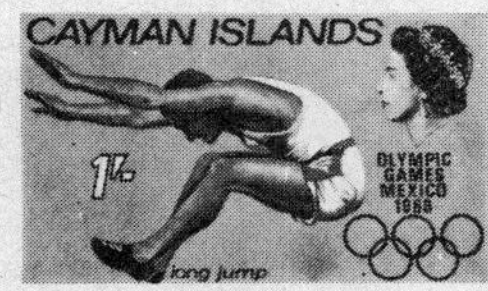

69 Long-jumping

(Des R. Granger Barrett. Litho P.B.)

**1968** (1 Oct). *Olympic Games, Mexico. T* **69** *and similar multi-coloured designs. W w* **12**. *P* 13½.
212 1s. Type **69** 10 10
213 1s. 3d. High jumping 15 15
214 2s. Pole vaulting (*vert*) 15 15
212/14 *Set of* 3 30 30

72 "The Adoration of the Shepherds" (Fabritius)

(Des and photo Harrison)

**1968–69**. *Christmas. T* **72** *and similar horiz design. Centres multicoloured; country name and frames in gold; value and background in colours given. P* 14 × 14½.

(*a*) *W w* **12**. (18.11.68)
215 **72** ¼d. brown 10 10
a. Gold omitted £180
216 – 1d. bluish violet 10 10
217 **72** 6d. bright blue 15 15
218 – 8d. cerise 15 15
219 **72** 1s. 3d. bright green 20 20
220 – 2s. grey 20 20

(*b*) *No wmk* (8.1.69)
221 **72** ¼d. bright purple 10 10
215/21 *Set of* 7 70 70

Design:—1d., 8d., 2s. "The Adoration of the Shepherds" (Rembrandt).

74 Grand Cayman Thrush

76 Arms of the Cayman Islands

(Des G. Vasarhelyi. Litho Format)

**1969** (5 June). *Designs as T* **74** *and T* **76** *in black, ochre and red (£1) or multicoloured (others). No wmk. P* 14.

| | | | |
|---|---|---|---|
| 222 | ¼d. Type **74** | 10 | 40 |
| 223 | 1d. Brahmin Cattle (*horiz*) | 10 | 10 |
| 224 | 2d. Blowholes on the coast (*horiz*) | 10 | 10 |
| 225 | 2½d. Map of Grand Cayman (*horiz*) | 15 | 10 |
| 226 | 3d. Georgetown scene (*horiz*) | 15 | 10 |
| 227 | 4d. Royal Poinciana (*horiz*) | 30 | 10 |
| 228 | 6d. Cayman Brac and Little Cayman on Chart (*horiz*) | 30 | 10 |
| 229 | 8d. Motor vessels at berth (*horiz*) | 30 | 10 |
| 230 | 1s. Basket-making (*horiz*) | 20 | 10 |
| 231 | 1s. 3d. Beach scene (*horiz*) | 35 | 1·00 |
| 232 | 1s. 6d. Straw-rope making (*horiz*) | 40 | 1·00 |
| 233 | 2s. Barracuda (*horiz*) | 1·00 | 80 |
| 234 | 4s. Government House (*horiz*) | 35 | 80 |
| 235 | 10s. Type **76** | 1·00 | 1·75 |
| 236 | £1 Queen Elizabeth II (*vert*) | 2·00 | 2·50 |
| 222/36 | *Set of* 15 | 6·00 | 7·75 |

**1969** (11 Aug). *As No.* 222, *but wmk w* **12** (*sideways*).

| | | | | |
|---|---|---|---|---|
| 237 | **74** | ¼d. multicoloured | 20 | 30 |

**(New Currency. 100 cents = 1 dollar.)**

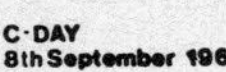

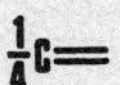


(89)

**1969** (8 Sept). *Decimal Currency. No.* 237, *and as Nos.* 223/36, *but wmk w* **12** (*sideways on horiz designs*), *surch as T* **89**.

| | | | |
|---|---|---|---|
| 238 | ¼ c. on ¼d. Type **74** | 10 | 40 |
| 239 | 1 c. on 1d. Brahmin Cattle | 10 | 10 |
| 240 | 2 c. on 2d. Blowholes on the coast | 10 | 10 |
| 241 | 3 c. on 4d. Royal Poinciana | 10 | 10 |
| 242 | 4 c. on 2½d. Map of Grand Cayman | 10 | 10 |
| 243 | 5 c. on 6d. Cayman Brac and Little Cayman on Chart | 10 | 10 |
| 244 | 7 c. on 8d. Motor vessels at berth | 10 | 10 |
| 245 | 8 c. on 3d. Georgetown scene | 15 | 10 |
| 246 | 10 c. on 1s. Basket-making | 25 | 10 |
| 247 | 12 c. on 1s. 3d. Beach scene | 35 | 50 |
| 248 | 15 c. on 1s. 6d. Straw-rope making | 45 | 50 |
| 249 | 20 c. on 2s. Barracuda | 1·25 | 1·50 |
| 250 | 40 c. on 4s. Government House | 45 | 80 |
| 251 | $1 on 10s. Type **76** | 1·50 | 1·60 |
| 252 | $2 on £1 Queen Elizabeth II | 2·00 | 3·25 |
| 238/52 | *Set of* 15 | 6·00 | 8·00 |

90 "Virgin and Child" (Vivarini)

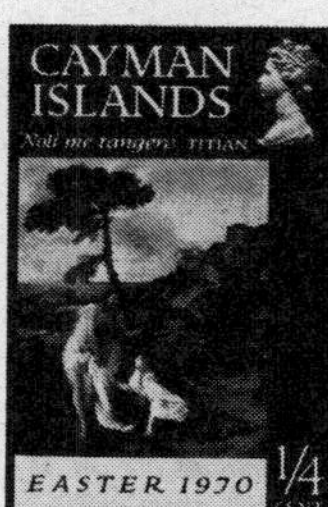

92 "Noli me tangere" (Titian)

(Des adapted by G. Drummond. Photo Harrison)

**1969** (14 Nov*). *Christmas. Multicoloured; background colours given. W w* **12** (*sideways on* 1, 7 *and* 20 *c.*). *P* 14½.

| | | | | |
|---|---|---|---|---|
| 253 | **90** | ¼ c. orange-red | 10 | 10 |
| 254 | | ¼ c. magenta | 10 | 10 |
| 255 | | ¼ c. emerald | 10 | 10 |
| | | a. Gold frame omitted | £140 | |
| 256 | | ¼ c. new blue | 10 | 10 |
| 257 | – | 1 c. ultramarine | 10 | 10 |
| 258 | **90** | 5 c. orange-red | 10 | 10 |
| 259 | – | 7 c. myrtle-green | 10 | 10 |
| 260 | **90** | 12 c. emerald | 15 | 10 |
| 261 | – | 20 c. brown-purple | 20 | 20 |
| 253/61 | | *Set of* 9 | 45 | 30 |

Design:—1, 7, 20 c. "The Adoration of the Kings" (Gossaert).

*This is the local release date. The Crown Agents released the stamps on 4 November.

(Des L. Curtis. Litho D.L.R.)

**1970** (23 Mar). *Easter. Paintings multicoloured; frame colours given. P* 14.

| | | | | |
|---|---|---|---|---|
| 262 | **92** | ¼ c. carmine-red | 10 | 10 |
| 263 | | ¼ c. deep green | 10 | 10 |
| 264 | | ¼ c. yellow-brown | 10 | 10 |
| 265 | | ¼ c. pale violet | 10 | 10 |
| 266 | | 10 c. chalky blue | 20 | 10 |
| 267 | | 12 c. chestnut | 20 | 10 |
| 268 | | 40 c. plum | 25 | 25 |
| 262/8 | | *Set of* 7 | 65 | 30 |

93 Barnaby (*Barnaby Rudge*)

97 Grand Cayman Thrush

(Des Jennifer Toombs. Photo Harrison)

**1970** (17 June). *Death Centenary of Charles Dickens. T* **93** *and similar vert designs. W w* **12** (*sideways*). *P* 14½ × 14.

| | | | |
|---|---|---|---|
| 269 | 1 c. black, olive-green and greenish yellow | 10 | 10 |
| 270 | 12 c. black, lake-brown and red | 10 | 10 |
| 271 | 20 c. black, ochre-brown and gold | 15 | 10 |
| 272 | 40 c. black, bright ultramarine and new blue | 20 | 25 |
| 269/72 | *Set of* 4 | 40 | 35 |

Designs:—12 c. Sairey Gamp (*Martin Chuzzlewit*); 20 c. Mr. Micawber and David (*David Copperfield*); 40 c. The "Marchioness" (*The Old Curiosity Shop*).

**1970** (8 Sept). *Decimal Currency. Designs as Nos.* 223/37, *but with values inscr in decimal currency as T* **97**. *W w* **12** (*sideways on cent values*).

| | | | |
|---|---|---|---|
| 273 | ¼ c. Type **97** | 10 | 10 |
| 274 | 1 c. Brahmin Cattle | 10 | 10 |
| 275 | 2 c. Blowholes on the coast | 10 | 10 |
| 276 | 3 c. Royal Poinciana | 20 | 10 |
| 277 | 4 c. Map of Grand Cayman | 20 | 10 |
| 278 | 5 c. Cayman Brac and Little Cayman on Chart | 35 | 10 |
| 279 | 7 c. Motor vessels at berth | 30 | 10 |
| 280 | 8 c. Georgetown scene | 30 | 10 |
| 281 | 10 c. Basket-making | 30 | 10 |
| 282 | 12 c. Beach scene | 90 | 45 |
| 283 | 15 c. Straw-rope making | 1·25 | 1·00 |
| 284 | 20 c. Barracuda | 2·50 | 1·25 |
| 285 | 40 c. Government House | 85 | 75 |
| 286 | $1 Type **76** | 1·75 | 2·50 |
| 287 | $2 Queen Elizabeth II | 2·75 | 4·00 |
| 273/87 | *Set of* 15 | 10·50 | 9·50 |

98 The Three Wise Men

(Des G. Drummond. Litho Format)

**1970** (8 Oct). *Christmas. T* **98** *and similar horiz design. W w* **12** (*sideways*). *P* 14.

| | | | | |
|---|---|---|---|---|
| 288 | **98** | ¼ c. apple-green, grey and emerald | 10 | 10 |
| 289 | – | 1 c. black, lemon and turquoise-green | 10 | 10 |
| 290 | **98** | 5 c. grey, red-orange and crimson | 10 | 10 |
| 291 | – | 10 c. black, lemon and orange-red | 10 | 10 |
| 292 | **98** | 12 c. grey, pale turquoise & ultram | 15 | 10 |
| 293 | – | 20 c. black, lemon and green | 20 | 15 |
| 288/93 | | *Set of* 6 | 55 | 30 |

Design:—1, 10, 20 c. Nativity scene and Globe.

100 Grand Cayman Terrapin

(Des V. Whiteley. Photo Harrison)

**1971** (28 Jan). *Turtles. T* **100** *and similar diamond-shaped designs. W w* **12** (*sideways, reading from inscr to* "ISLANDS"). *P* 14½ × 14.

| | | | |
|---|---|---|---|
| 294 | 5 c. Type **100** | 30 | 25 |
| 295 | 7 c. Green Turtle | 35 | 25 |
| 296 | 12 c. Hawksbill Turtle | 55 | 30 |
| 297 | 20 c. Turtle Farm | 1·00 | 1·40 |
| 294/7 | *Set of* 4 | 2·00 | 2·00 |

101 *Dendrophylax fawcettii*

102 "Adoration of the Kings" (French, 15th Cent)

(Des Sylvia Goaman. Litho Questa)

**1971** (7 Apr). *Orchids. T* **101** *and similar vert designs. Multicoloured. W w* **12**. *P* 14.

| | | | |
|---|---|---|---|
| 298 | ¼ c. Type **101** | 10 | 30 |
| 299 | 2 c. *Schomburgkia thomsoniana* | 40 | 40 |
| 300 | 10 c. *Vanilla claviculata* | 90 | 70 |
| 301 | 40 c. *Oncidium variegatum* | 2·75 | 3·50 |
| 298/301 | *Set of* 4 | 3·75 | 4·50 |

(Des Jennifer Toombs. Litho Questa)

**1971** (15 Oct*). *Christmas. T* **102** *and similar vert designs. Multicoloured. W w* **12**. *P* 14.

| | | | |
|---|---|---|---|
| 302 | ¼ c. Type **102** | 10 | 10 |
| 303 | 1 c. "The Nativity" (Parisian, 14th Cent.) | 10 | 10 |
| 304 | 5 c. "Adoration of the Magi" (Burgundian, 15th Cent.) | 10 | 10 |
| 305 | 12 c. Type **102** | 20 | 10 |
| 306 | 15 c. As 1 c. | 20 | 20 |
| 307 | 20 c. As 5 c. | 25 | 30 |
| 302/7 | *Set of* 6 | 70 | 65 |
| **MS**308 | 113 × 115 mm. Nos. 302/7 | 1·25 | 2·25 |

*This is the local date of issue. The Crown Agents released the stamps on 27 September.

103 Turtle and Telephone Cable

(Des Anglo Arts Associates. Litho Walsall)

**1972** (10 Jan). *Co-Axial Telephone Cable. W w* **12** (*sideways*). *P* 14.

| | | | | |
|---|---|---|---|---|
| 309 | **103** | 2 c. multicoloured | 10 | 10 |
| 310 | | 10 c. multicoloured | 10 | 10 |
| 311 | | 40 c. multicoloured | 25 | 40 |
| 309/11 | | *Set of* 3 | 30 | 45 |

104 Court House Building

(Des C. Abbott. Litho Questa)

**1972** (15 Aug). *New Government Buildings. T* **104** *and similar horiz design. Multicoloured. W w* **12**. *P* 13½.

| | | | |
|---|---|---|---|
| 312 | 5 c. Type **104** | 10 | 10 |
| 313 | 15 c. Legislative Assembly Building | 10 | 10 |
| 314 | 25 c. Type **104** | 15 | 15 |
| 315 | 40 c. As 15 c. | 20 | 30 |
| 312/15 | *Set of* 4 | 35 | 45 |
| **MS**316 | 121 × 108 mm. Nos. 312/15 | 70 | 2·00 |

105 Hawksbill Turtle and Conch Shell

(Des (from photograph by D. Groves) and photo Harrison)

**1972** (20 Nov). *Royal Silver Wedding. Multicoloured; background colour given. W w* **12**. *P* 14 × 14½.

| | | | | |
|---|---|---|---|---|
| 317 | **105** | 12 c. deep slate-violet | 15 | 10 |
| 318 | | 30 c. yellow-olive | 15 | 20 |
| | | a. Blue omitted* | £300 | |

*The omission of the blue colour results in the Duke's suit appearing sepia instead of deep blue.

106 $1 Coin and Note

107 "The Way of Sorrow"

(Des and photo D.L.R.)

**1973** (15 Jan). *First Issue of Currency. T* **106** *and similar horiz designs. Multicoloured. W w* **12** *(sideways). P* 13.

319 3 c. Type **106** .. .. .. .. .. 15 10
320 6 c. $5 Coin and note .. .. .. .. 15 10
321 15 c. $10 Coin and note .. .. .. .. 30 20
322 25 c. $25 Coin and note .. .. .. .. 40 35
319/22 .. .. .. .. .. *Set of* 4 90 60
**MS**323 128 × 107 mm. Nos. 319/22 .. .. 2·50 2·50

(Des G. Drummond. Litho Questa)

**1973** (11 Apr*). *Easter. T* **107** *and similar multicoloured designs showing stained-glass windows. W w* **12** *(sideways on 10 and 12 c.). P* 14½.

324 10 c. Type **107** .. .. .. .. .. 10 10
325 12 c. "Christ Resurrected" .. .. .. .. 15 10
326 20 c. "The Last Supper" *(horiz)* .. .. .. 20 15
327 30 c. "Christ on the Cross" *(horiz)* .. .. .. 25 25
324/7 .. .. .. .. .. *Set of* 4 60 45
**MS**328 122 × 105 mm. Nos. 324/7. Imperf .. 70 1·60

*This is the local date of issue; the Crown Agents released the stamps on 15 March.

108 "The Nativity" (Sforza Book of Hours)

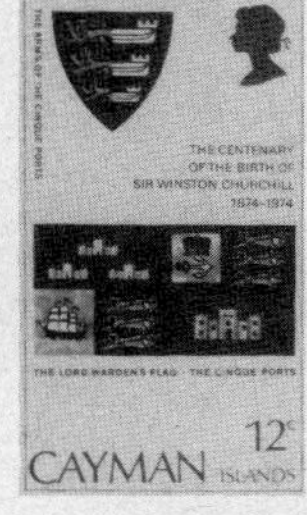


109 White-winged Dove

(Des J. Cooter. Litho Questa)

**1973** (2 Oct). *Christmas. T* **108** *and similar vert design. W w* **12** *(sideways). P* 14.

329 **108** 3 c. multicoloured .. .. .. .. 10 10
330 – 5 c. multicoloured .. .. .. .. 10 10
331 **108** 9 c. multicoloured .. .. .. .. 15 10
332 – 12 c. multicoloured .. .. .. .. 15 10
333 **108** 15 c. multicoloured .. .. .. .. 15 15
334 – 25 c. multicoloured .. .. .. .. 20 25
329/34 .. .. .. .. .. *Set of* 6 65 50

Design:—5, 12, 25 c. "The Adoration of the Magi" (Breviary of Queen Isabella).

**1973** (14 Nov). *Royal Wedding. As Nos.* 165/6 *of Anguilla. Centre multicoloured. W w* **12** *(sideways). P* 13½.

335 10 c. sage-green .. .. .. .. .. 10 10
336 30 c. bright mauve .. .. .. .. .. 15 10

(Des M. Goaman. Litho Walsall)

**1974** (2 Jan). *Birds (1st series). T* **109** *and similar vert designs. Multicoloured. W w* **12** *(sideways). P* 14.

337 3 c. Type **109** .. .. .. .. .. 1·40 20
338 10 c. Vitelline Warbler .. .. .. .. 2·00 20
339 12 c. Antillean Grackle .. .. .. .. 2·00 25
340 20 c. West Indian Red-bellied Woodpecker .. 3·25 65
341 30 c. Stripe-headed Tanager .. .. .. 5·00 1·50
342 50 c. Yucatan Vireo .. .. .. .. 7·00 2·75
337/42 .. .. .. .. *Set of* 6 19·00 5·00

See also Nos. 383/8.

110 Old School Building

(Des PAD Studio. Litho Questa)

**1974** (1 May). *25th Anniv of University of West Indies. T* **110** *and similar horiz designs. Multicoloured. W w* **12** *(sideways). P* 14.

343 12 c. Type **110** .. .. .. .. .. 10 10
344 20 c. New Comprehensive School .. .. .. 15 10
345 30 c. Creative Arts Centre, Mona .. .. .. 15 25
343/5 .. .. .. .. .. *Set of* 3 30 30

111 Hermit Crab and Staghorn Coral

(Des J.W. Litho Kynoch Press)

**1974** (1 Aug). *Multicoloured designs as T* **111** *(size* 41½ × 27 *mm). W w* **12** *(sideways on $1 and $2). P* 14.

346 1 c. Type **111** .. .. .. .. .. 2·25 65
347 3 c. Treasure-chest and Lion's Paw .. .. .. 2·25 60
348 4 c. Treasure and Spotted Scorpion-fish .. .. 50 60
349 5 c. Flintlock pistol and Brain Coral .. .. 2·00 60
350 6 c. Blackbeard and Green Turtle .. .. .. 35 80
351 9 c. Jewelled pomander and Pork-fish .. .. 3·00 4·00
352 10 c. Spiny Lobster and treasure .. .. .. 2·75 60
353 12 c. Jewelled sword and dagger, and Sea-fan .. 35 60
354 15 c. Cabrit's Murex and treasure .. .. .. 40 90
355 20 c. Queen Conch and treasure .. .. .. 6·50 1·75
356 25 c. Hogfish and treasure .. .. .. .. 45 70
357 40 c. Gold chalice and sea-whip .. .. .. 1·50 1·00
358 $1 Coat of arms *(vert)* .. .. .. .. 2·75 3·25
359 $2 Queen Elizabeth II *(vert)* .. .. .. 4·00 8·00
346/59 .. .. .. .. *Set of* 14 26·00 22·00

See also Nos. 364/6, 412/19 and 445/52.

112 Sea Captain and Ship (Shipbuilding)

(Des G. Vasarhelyi. Litho D.L.R.)

**1974** (7 Oct). *Local Industries. T* **112** *and similar horiz designs. Multicoloured. W w* **12** *(inverted on* 8 c. *and* 12 c.*). P* 14 × 13½.

360 8 c. Type **112** .. .. .. .. .. 10 10
361 12 c. Thatcher and cottages .. .. .. .. 10 10
362 20 c. Farmer and plantation .. .. .. .. 20 20
360/2 .. .. .. .. .. *Set of* 3 35 35
**MS**363 92 × 132 mm. Nos. 360/2 .. .. .. 1·25 2·00

**1974–75.** *As Nos.* 346/7 *and design of* 351, *but wmk sideways.*

364 1 c. Type **111** (29.9.75) .. .. .. .. 1·25 1·50
365 3 c. Treasure-chest and Lions-paw (12.11.74) 3·50 2·00
366 8 c. Jewelled pomander and Pork-fish (16.12.74) .. .. .. .. .. .. 2·50 8·00
364/6 .. .. .. .. .. *Set of* 3 6·50 10·00

Nos. 367/79 vacant.

113 Arms of Cinque Ports and Lord Warden's Flag

114 "The Crucifixion"

(Des P. Powell. Litho D.L.R.)

**1974** (30 Nov). *Birth Centenary of Sir Winston Churchill. T* **113** *and similar vert design. Multicoloured. W w* **12** *(sideways). P* 13½ × 14.

380 12 c. Type **113** .. .. .. .. .. 15 10
381 50 c. Churchill's coat of arms .. .. .. 45 70
**MS**382 98 × 86 mm. Nos. 380/1 .. .. .. 85 1·60

(Des M. Goaman. Litho Questa)

**1975** (1 Jan). *Birds (2nd series). Multicoloured designs as T* **109**. *W w* **12** *(sideways). P* 14.

383 3 c. Common Flicker .. .. .. .. 60 45
384 10 c. Black-billed Whistling Duck .. .. .. 90 45
385 12 c. Yellow Warbler .. .. .. .. 1·00 55
386 20 c. White-bellied Dove .. .. .. .. 1·75 1·60
387 30 c. Magnificent Frigate Bird .. .. .. 2·75 2·75
388 50 c. Cuban Amazon .. .. .. .. 3·25 4·00
a. Error. Wmk Lesotho T **53** (inverted) .. £500
383/8 .. .. .. .. .. *Set of* 6 9·00 9·00

(Des PAD Studio. Litho D.L.R.)

**1975** (24 Mar). *Easter. French Pastoral Staffs. T* **114** *and similar vert design showing "The Crucifixion" (different). Multicoloured. W w* **12** *(sideways). P* 13½ × 14.

389 **114** 15 c. multicoloured .. .. .. .. 10 15
390 – 35 c. multicoloured .. .. .. .. 20 30
**MS**391 128 × 98 mm. Nos. 389/90. W w **12** *(upright)* 65 1·75
a. Error. Imperf .. .. .. ..

See also Nos. 396/**MS**398.

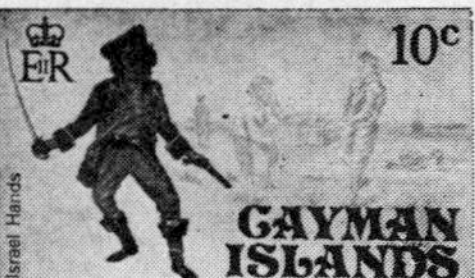


115 Israel Hands

(Des J.W. Litho Harrison)

**1975** (25 July). *Pirates. T* **115** *and similar horiz designs. Multicoloured. W w* **12** *(sideways). P* 14.

392 10 c. Type **115** .. .. .. .. .. 20 10
393 12 c. John Fenn .. .. .. .. .. 20 10
394 20 c. Thomas Anstis .. .. .. .. 40 35
395 30 c. Edward Low .. .. .. .. .. 55 55
392/5 .. .. .. .. .. *Set of* 4 1·25 1·00

(Des PAD Studio. Litho Questa)

**1975** (31 Oct). *Christmas. Vert designs as T* **114** *showing "Virgin and Child with Angels" (both different). W w* **14**. *P* 14.

396 12 c. multicoloured .. .. .. .. 10 10
397 50 c. multicoloured .. .. .. .. 30 30
**MS**398 113 × 85 mm. Nos. 396/7 .. .. .. 1·00 1·75

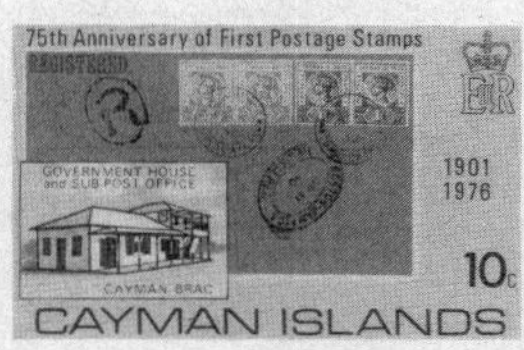


116 Registered Cover, Government House and Sub-Post Office

(Des J. Cooter. Litho Questa)

**1976** (12 Mar). *75th Anniv of First Cayman Is. Postage Stamp. T* **116** *and similar horiz designs. Multicoloured. W w* **14** *(sideways). P* 13½.

399 10 c. Type **116** .. .. .. .. .. 10 10
400 20 c. ½d. stamp and 1890–94 postmark .. .. 15 15
401 30 c. 1d. stamp and 1908 surcharge .. .. 25 25
402 50 c. ½d. and 1d. stamps .. .. .. .. 40 50
399/402 .. .. .. .. .. *Set of* 4 85 85
**MS**403 117 × 147 mm. Nos. 399/402 .. .. 1·75 3·00

117 Seals of Georgia, Delaware and New Hampshire

(Des P. Powell. Litho J.W.)

**1976** (29 May). *Bicentenary of American Revolution. T* **117** *and similar horiz designs showing seals of the States given. Multicoloured. W w* **14** *(sideways). P* 13½ × 14.

404 10 c. Type **117** .. .. .. .. .. 45 15
405 15 c. S. Carolina, New Jersey and Maryland .. 60 20
406 20 c. Virginia, Rhode Is. and Massachusetts .. 70 25
407 25 c. New York, Connecticut and N. Carolina 70 35
408 30 c. Pennsylvania seal, Liberty Bell and U.S. Great Seal .. .. .. .. .. .. 85 40
404/8 .. .. .. .. .. *Set of* 5 3·00 1·25
**MS**409 166 × 124 mm. Nos. 404/8. P 14 .. 5·00 7·00

118 Racing Dinghies

119 Queen Elizabeth II and Westminster Abbey

(Des C. Abbott. Litho D.L.R.)

**1976** (16 Aug). *Olympic Games, Montreal. T* **118** *and similar vert design. Multicoloured. W w* **14**. *P* 14.

410 20 c. Type **118** .. .. .. .. .. 15 10
411 50 c. Racing dinghy .. .. .. .. .. 45 50

**1976** (3 Sept)–**78.** *As Nos.* 347/9, 352, 355, 358/9 *and* 366, *but W w* **14** *(upright on $1, inverted on $2, sideways on others). Chalk-surfaced paper (4, 5 c. and $1) or ordinary paper (others).*

412 3 c. Treasure-chest and Lion's Paw .. .. 85 1·00
a. Chalk-surfaced paper (19.10.77) .. .. 2·50 2·75
413 4 c. Treasure and Spotted Scorpion-fish (19.10.77) .. .. .. .. .. .. 1·10 1·00

| | | | |
|---|---|---|---|
| 414 | 5 c. Flintlock pistol and Brain Coral (19.10.77) | 1·50 | 1·25 |
| 415 | 8 c. Jewelled pomander and Pork-fish | 2·25 | 1·25 |
| | a. Chalk-surfaced paper (19.10.77) | 3·25 | 3·50 |
| 416 | 10 c. Spiny Lobster and treasure | 1·25 | 1·75 |
| | a. Chalk-surfaced paper (27.1.78) | 1·75 | 2·75 |
| 417 | 20 c. Queen Conch and treasure | 3·25 | 3·00 |
| | a. Chalk-surfaced paper (27.1.78) | 3·50 | 4·00 |
| 418 | $1 Coat of arms (19.10.77) | 6·50 | 6·50 |
| 419 | $2 Queen Elizabeth II | 7·50 | 6·50 |
| | a. Chalk-surfaced paper (19.10.77) | 11·00 | 17·00 |
| 412/19 | *Set of* 8 | 22·00 | 20·00 |

Nos. 420/6 vacant.

(Des BG Studio. Litho Questa)

**1977** (7 Feb). *Silver Jubilee. T* **119** *and similar multicoloured designs. W w* **14** (*sideways on* 50 *c.*). *P* 13½.

| | | | |
|---|---|---|---|
| 427 | 8 c. Prince of Wales' visit, 1973 | 10 | 20 |
| 428 | 30 c. Type **119** | 15 | 40 |
| 429 | 50 c. Preparation for the Anointing (*horiz*) | 30 | 75 |
| 427/9 | *Set of* 3 | 50 | 1·25 |

**120** Scuba Diving

(Des Jennifer Toombs. Litho J.W.)

**1977** (25 July). *Tourism. T* **120** *and similar horiz designs. Multicoloured. W w* **14** (*sideways*). *P* 13½.

| | | | |
|---|---|---|---|
| 430 | 5 c. Type **120** | 10 | 10 |
| 431 | 10 c. Exploring a wreck | 15 | 10 |
| 432 | 20 c. Fairy Basslet (fish) | 45 | 20 |
| 433 | 25 c. Sergeant majors (fish) | 55 | 35 |
| 430/3 | *Set of* 4 | 1·10 | 60 |
| **MS**434 | 146 × 89 mm. Nos. 430/3. P 14½ | 2·00 | 2·75 |

**121** *Composia fidelissima* (moth)

(Des J. Cooter. Litho Enschedé)

**1977** (2 Dec). *Butterflies and Moth. T* **121** *and similar horiz designs. Multicoloured. W w* **14** (*sideways*). *P* 14×13.

| | | | |
|---|---|---|---|
| 435 | 5 c. Type **121** | 35 | 10 |
| 436 | 8 c. *Heliconius charithonia* | 40 | 15 |
| 437 | 10 c. *Danaus gilippus* | 40 | 15 |
| 438 | 15 c. *Agraulis vanillae* | 70 | 30 |
| 439 | 20 c. *Junonia evarete* | 85 | 35 |
| 440 | 30 c. *Anartia jatrophae* | 1·00 | 50 |
| 435/40 | *Set of* 6 | 3·25 | 1·40 |

**122** Cruise Liner *Southward*

**123** "The Crucifixion" (Dürer)

(Des G. Hutchins. Litho Questa)

**1978** (23 Jan). *New Harbour and Cruise Ships. T* **122** *and similar multicoloured designs. W w* **14** (*sideways on* 3, 5 *c.*). *P* 14 × 14½ (3, 5 *c.*) *or* 14½ × 14 (*others*).

| | | | |
|---|---|---|---|
| 441 | 3 c. Type **122** | 15 | 10 |
| 442 | 5 c. Cruise liner *Renaissance* | 20 | 10 |
| 443 | 30 c. New harbour (*vert*) | 70 | 25 |
| 444 | 50 c. Cruise liner *Daphne* (*vert*) | 90 | 55 |
| 441/4 | *Set of* 4 | 1·75 | 85 |

(Litho Walsall)

**1978** (16 Mar)–**80**. *Designs as Nos.* 346/7, 349, 352, 355 *and* 357/9 *but smaller,* 40 × 26 *or* 26 × 40 *mm. W w* **14** (*sideways on* 1 *to* 40 *c.*). *Chalk-surfaced paper.*

| | | | |
|---|---|---|---|
| 445 | 1 c. Type **111** | 80 | 90 |
| 446 | 3 c. Treasure-chest and Lion's Paw | 80 | 50 |
| 447 | 5 c. Flintlock pistol and Brain Coral (11.12.79) | 1·50 | 2·25 |
| 448 | 10 c. Spiny Lobster and treasure (25.5.78) | 1·60 | 60 |
| 449 | 20 c. Queen Conch and treasure (25.5.78) | 3·25 | 1·25 |
| 450 | 40 c. Gold chalice and sea-whip (1979*) | 11·00 | 14·00 |
| 451 | $1 Coat of arms (30.7.80) | 8·00 | 8·00 |
| 452 | $2 Queen Elizabeth II (3.4.80) | 7·00 | 15·00 |
| 445/52 | *Set of* 8 | 30·00 | 38·00 |

*Supplies of No. 450 were sent to Cayman Islands on 7 May 1979. It is not known when these stamps were first placed on sale.

Nos. 453/8 vacant.

(Des Jennifer Toombs. Litho Cartor S.A., France)

**1978** (20 Mar). *Easter and 450th Death Anniv of Dürer. T* **123** *and similar vert designs. W w* **14** (*inverted on* 20 *c.*). *P* 12.

| | | | |
|---|---|---|---|
| 459 | 10 c. magenta and black | 15 | 10 |
| 460 | 15 c. yellow and black | 25 | 15 |
| 461 | 20 c. turquoise-green and black | 30 | 20 |
| 462 | 30 c. lilac and black | 45 | 35 |
| 459/62 | *Set of* 4 | 1·00 | 70 |
| **MS**463 | 120 × 108 mm. Nos. 459/62 | 1·50 | 2·50 |

Designs:—15 c. "Christ at Emmaus"; 20 c. "The Entry into Jerusalem"; 30 c. "Christ washing Peter's Feet".

**124** "Explorers" Singing Game

**125** Yale of Beaufort

(Des Walsall. Litho Questa)

**1978** (25 Apr). *3rd International Council Meeting of Girls' Brigade. T* **124** *and similar vert designs. Multicoloured. W w* **14**. *P* 14.

| | | | |
|---|---|---|---|
| 464 | 3 c. Type **124** | 15 | 10 |
| 465 | 10 c. Colour party | 25 | 10 |
| 466 | 20 c. Girls and Duke of Edinburgh Award interests | 50 | 20 |
| 467 | 50 c. Girls using domestic skills | 1·00 | 80 |
| 464/7 | *Set of* 4 | 1·75 | 1·10 |

(Des C. Abbott. Litho Questa)

**1978** (2 June). *25th Anniv of Coronation. T* **125** *and similar vert designs. P* 15.

| | | | |
|---|---|---|---|
| 468 | 30 c. apple-green, deep magenta and silver | 15 | 25 |
| | a. Sheetlet. Nos. 468/70 × 2 | 90 | |
| 469 | 30 c. multicoloured | 15 | 25 |
| 470 | 30 c. apple-green, deep magenta and silver | 15 | 25 |
| 468/70 | *Set of* 3 | 40 | 65 |

Designs:—No. 468, Type **125**; No. 469, Queen Elizabeth II; No. 470, Screech Owl.

Nos. 468/70 were printed together in small sheets of 6, containing two *se-tenant* strips of 3, with horizontal gutter margin between.

**126** Four Eyed Butterfly Fish

(Des G. Hutchins. Litho Walsall)

**1978** (29 Aug). *Fish (1st series). T* **126** *and similar horiz designs. Multicoloured. W w* **14** (*sideways*). *P* 14.

| | | | |
|---|---|---|---|
| 471 | 3 c. Type **126** | 15 | 10 |
| 472 | 5 c. Grey Angel Fish | 20 | 10 |
| 473 | 10 c. Squirrel Fish | 35 | 10 |
| 474 | 15 c. Parrot Fish | 45 | 30 |
| 475 | 20 c. Spanish Hogfish | 50 | 35 |
| 476 | 30 c. Queen Angel Fish | 60 | 50 |
| 471/6 | *Set of* 6 | 2·00 | 1·25 |

Examples of the 15 c. value inscribed "SERGEANT MAJOR FISH" and 20 c. inscribed "PARROT FISH" were prepared, but not issued for postal purposes.

See also Nos. 483/8.

**127** Lockheed "Lodestar"

(Des A. Theobald. Litho Format)

**1979** (5 Feb). *25th Anniv of Owen Roberts Airfield. T* **127** *and similar horiz designs. Multicoloured. W w* **14** (*sideways*). *P* 14½ × 14.

| | | | |
|---|---|---|---|
| 477 | 3 c. Type **127** | 15 | 10 |
| 478 | 5 c. Consolidated "PBY" | 15 | 10 |
| 479 | 10 c. Vickers "Viking" | 20 | 10 |
| 480 | 15 c. B.A.C. "1-11" on tarmac | 30 | 20 |
| 481 | 20 c. Piper "Cheyenne", H.S. "125" and Bell "47" (helicopter) | 40 | 30 |
| 482 | 30 c. B.A.C. "1-11" over airfield | 60 | 45 |
| 477/82 | *Set of* 6 | 1·60 | 1·10 |

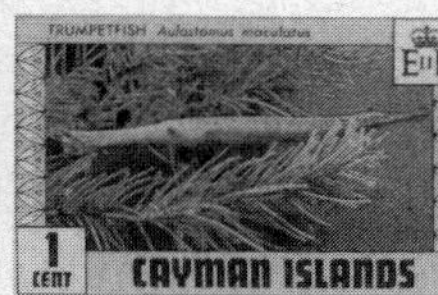

**128** Trumpetfish

(Des R. Granger Barrett. Litho Questa)

**1979** (20 Apr). *Fish (2nd series). T* **128** *and similar horiz designs. Multicoloured. W w* **14** (*sideways*). *P* 14.

| | | | |
|---|---|---|---|
| 483 | 1 c. Type **128** | 10 | 10 |
| 484 | 3 c. Nassau Grouper | 15 | 10 |
| 485 | 5 c. French Angelfish | 15 | 10 |
| 486 | 10 c. Schoolmaster Snappers | 20 | 10 |
| 487 | 20 c. Banded Butterflyfish | 35 | 25 |
| 488 | 50 c. Blackbar Soldierfish | 70 | 70 |
| 483/8 | *Set of* 6 | 1·40 | 1·25 |

**129** 1900 1d. Stamp

(Des J.W. Litho Walsall)

**1979** (15 Aug). *Death Centenary of Sir Rowland Hill. T* **129** *and similar horiz designs showing stamps and Sir Rowland Hill. W w* **14** (*sideways*). *P* 13½.

| | | | |
|---|---|---|---|
| 489 | 5 c. black, rose-carmine and grey-blue | 10 | 10 |
| 490 | 10 c. multicoloured | 10 | 10 |
| 491 | 20 c. multicoloured | 20 | 20 |
| 489/91 | *Set of* 3 | 25 | 25 |
| **MS**492 | 138 × 90 mm. 50 c. multicoloured | 45 | 65 |

Designs:—10 c. Great Britain 1902 3d.; 20 c. 1955 £1 definitive; 50 c. 1908 2½d.

**130** Holy Family and Angels

(Des G. Vasarhelyi. Litho Secura, Singapore)

**1979** (20 Nov). *Christmas. T* **130** *and similar horiz designs. Multicoloured. W w* **14** (*sideways*). *P* 13½ × 13.

| | | | |
|---|---|---|---|
| 493 | 10 c. Type **130** | 15 | 10 |
| 494 | 20 c. Angels appearing before shepherds | 20 | 10 |
| 495 | 30 c. Nativity scene | 30 | 20 |
| 496 | 40 c. Wise men following star | 40 | 30 |
| 493/6 | *Set of* 4 | 95 | 60 |

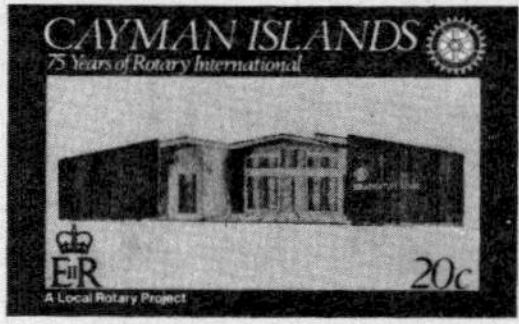

**131** Local Rotary Project

(Des Walsall. Litho Secura, Singapore)

**1980** (14 Feb). *75th Anniv of Rotary International. T* **131** *and similar designs in black, bistre-yellow and deep ultramarine. W w* **14** (*sideways on* 20 *c.*). *P* 13½ × 13 (20 *c.*) *or* 13 × 13½ (*others*).

| | | | |
|---|---|---|---|
| 497 | 20 c. Type **131** | 20 | 15 |
| 498 | 30 c. Paul P. Harris (founder) (*vert*) | 25 | 20 |
| 499 | 50 c. Rotary anniversary emblem (*vert*) | 35 | 30 |
| | a. Black (Royal cypher, and face value) omitted | | |
| 497/9 | *Set of* 3 | 70 | 60 |

**132** Walking Mail Carrier (late 19th-century)

(Des J.W. Litho Walsall)

**1980** (6 May). *"London 1980" International Stamp Exhibition. T* **132** *and similar horiz designs. Multicoloured. W w* **14** (*sideways*). *P* 14.

| | | | |
|---|---|---|---|
| 500 | 5 c. Type **132** | 10 | 10 |
| 501 | 10 c. Delivering mail by cat boat (late 19th-century) | 15 | 10 |
| 502 | 15 c. Mounted mail carrier (early 20th-century) | 20 | 10 |
| 503 | 30 c. Horse-drawn waggonette (early 20th-century) | 30 | 15 |
| 504 | 40 c. Postman on bicycle (mid 20th-century) | 30 | 15 |
| 505 | $1 Motor transport (late 20th-century) | 65 | 55 |
| 500/5 | *Set of* 6 | 1·50 | 1·00 |

**NEW INFORMATION**

The editor is always interested to correspond with people who have new information that will improve or correct the Catalogue.

**133** Queen Elizabeth the Queen Mother at the Derby, 1976 — **134** Atlantic Spiny Oyster

(Des and litho Harrison)

**1980** (4 Aug). *80th Birthday of Queen Elizabeth the Queen Mother.* W w **14** (*sideways*). *P* 14.
506 **133** 20 c. multicoloured . . . . . . 20 25

(Des J.W. Litho Walsall)

**1980** (12 Aug). *Shells* (*1st series*). *T* **134** *and similar horiz designs. Multicoloured.* W w **14** (*sideways*). *P* 14½ × 14.
507 5 c. Type **134** . . . . . . 20 10
508 10 c. West Indian Murex . . . . 20 10
509 30 c. Triton . . . . . . 50 35
510 50 c. Murex-line vase shell . . . . 65 65
507/10 . . . . . . *Set of* 4 1·40 1·10
See also Nos. 565/8 and 582/5.

**135** Lantana — **136** Juvenile Tarpon and Fire Sponge

(Des G. Hutchins. Litho Rosenbaum Bros, Vienna)

**1980** (21 Oct). *Flowers* (*1st series*). *T* **135** *and similar horiz designs. Multicoloured.* W w **14** (*sideways*). *P* 13½.
511 5 c. Type **135** . . . . . . 10 10
512 15 c. Bauhinia . . . . . . 25 10
513 30 c. Hibiscus Rosa . . . . . . 35 10
514 $1 Milk and Wine Lily . . . . 1·00 75
511/14 . . . . . . *Set of* 4 1·50 85
See also Nos. 541/4.

(Des G. Drummond. Litho J.W.)

**1980** (9 Dec)–**82**. *Flora and Fauna of the Mangrove Swamp. Vert designs as T* **136**. *Multicoloured.* W w **14**. *P* 13½ × 13.
A. *Without imprint date.*
B. *Printed with imprint date at foot of designs* (14.6.82).

| | | A | | B | |
|---|---|---|---|---|---|
| 515 | 3 c. Type **136** . . | 40 | 50 | 75 | 65 |
| 516 | 5 c. Mangrove Root Oyster . . | 50 | 50 | 60 | 50 |
| 517 | 10 c. Mangrove Crab . . | 40 | 40 | 65 | 55 |
| 518 | 15 c. Lizard and *Phyciodes phaon* (butterfly) . . | 50 | 60 | 1·00 | 95 |
| 519 | 20 c. Louisiana Heron . . | 1·50 | 1·25 | 2·25 | 1·50 |
| 520 | 30 c. Red Mangrove Flower . . | 70 | 80 | 90 | 1·00 |
| 521 | 40 c. Red Mangrove Seeds . . | 75 | 80 | 1·00 | 1·00 |
| 522 | 50 c. Waterhouse's Leaf-nosed Bat . . | 1·25 | 1·50 | 1·75 | 2·00 |
| 523 | $1 Black-crowned Night Heron | 4·00 | 4·25 | 4·00 | 4·25 |
| 524 | $2 Cayman Islands coat of arms . . | 3·00 | 3·75 | 3·75 | 5·00 |
| 525 | $4 Queen Elizabeth II . . | 5·00 | 6·50 | 8·00 | 10·00 |
| 515/25 | . . *Set of* 11 | 16·00 | 19·00 | 22·00 | 25·00 |

Nos. 516B/24B exist with different imprint dates.
For stamps in these designs, but watermark w **16**, see Nos. 626 and 631/2.

**137** Eucharist — **138** Wood Slave

(Des Jennifer Toombs. Litho Questa)

**1981** (17 Mar). *Easter. T* **137** *and similar vert designs. Multicoloured.* W w **14**. *P* 14.
526 3 c. Type **137** . . . . . . 10 10
527 10 c. Crown of thorns . . . . . . 10 10
528 20 c. Crucifix . . . . . . 20 10
529 $1 Lord Jesus Christ . . . . 70 80
526/9 . . . . . . *Set of* 4 90 90

(Des R. Granger Barrett. Litho Rosenbaum Bros, Vienna)

**1981** (16 June). *Reptiles and Amphibians. T* **138** *and similar horiz designs. Multicoloured.* W w **14** (*sideways*). *P* 13½.
530 20 c. Type **138** . . . . . . 30 20
531 30 c. Cayman Iguana . . . . . . 45 35
532 40 c. Lion Lizard . . . . . . 55 45
533 50 c. Terrapin ("Hickatee") . . . . 65 55
530/3 . . . . . . *Set of* 4 1·75 1·40

**139** Prince Charles — **140** Disabled Scuba Divers

(Des J.W. Litho Walsall)

**1981** (22 July). *Royal Wedding. T* **139** *and similar vert designs. Multicoloured.* W w **14**. *P* 14.
534 20 c. Wedding bouquet from Cayman Islands 25 10
535 30 c. Type **139** . . . . . . 40 10
536 $1 Prince Charles and Lady Diana Spencer 1·00 1·00
534/6 . . . . . . *Set of* 3 1·50 1·10

(Des J.W. Litho Walsall)

**1981** (29 Sept). *International Year for Disabled Persons. T* **140** *and similar horiz designs. Multicoloured.* W w **14** (*sideways*). *P* 14.
537 5 c. Type **140** . . . . . . 10 10
538 15 c. Old School for the Handicapped . . 30 20
539 20 c. New School for the Handicapped 35 25
540 $1 Disabled people in wheelchairs, by the sea 1·60 1·25
537/40 . . . . . . *Set of* 4 2·10 1·60

(Des G. Hutchins. Litho Questa)

**1981** (20 Oct). *Flowers* (*2nd series*). *Horiz designs as T* **135**. *Multicoloured.* W w **14**. *P* 13½.
541 3 c. Bougainvillea . . . . . . 10 10
542 10 c. Morning Glory . . . . . . 20 10
543 20 c. Wild Amaryllis . . . . . . 45 25
544 $1 Cordia . . . . . . 1·75 1·75
541/4 . . . . . . *Set of* 4 2·25 2·00

**141** Dr. Robert Koch and Microscope — **142** Bride and Groom walking down Aisle

(Des and litho Walsall)

**1982** (24 Mar). *Centenary of Robert Koch's Discovery of Tubercle Bacillus. T* **141** *and similar multicoloured designs.* W w **14** (*sideways on* 15 c., *inverted on* 30 c.). *P* 14½.
545 15 c. Type **141** . . . . . . 25 25
546 30 c. Koch looking through microscope (*vert*) 45 45
547 40 c. Microscope (*vert*) . . . . 70 70
548 50 c. Dr. Robert Koch (*vert*) . . . . 80 80
545/8 . . . . . . *Set of* 4 2·00 2·00

(Des Jennifer Toombs. Litho J.W.)

**1982** (1 July). *21st Birthday of Princess of Wales. T* **142** *and similar vert designs. Multicoloured.* W w **14**. *P* 13.
549 20 c. Cayman Islands coat of arms . . 35 35
550 30 c. Lady Diana Spencer in London, June 1981 . . . . . . 45 45
551 40 c. Type **142** . . . . . . 55 55
552 50 c. Formal portrait . . . . 65 70
549/52 . . . . . . *Set of* 4 1·75 1·90

**143** Pitching Tent — **144** "Madonna and Child with the Infant Baptist"

(Des L. Walker. Litho Questa)

**1982** (24 Aug). *75th Anniv of Boy Scout Movement. T* **143** *and similar horiz designs. Multicoloured.* W w **14** (*sideways*). *P* 14.
553 3 c. Type **143** . . . . . . 10 10
554 20 c. Scouts camping . . . . . . 40 40
555 30 c. Cub Scouts and Leaders . . . . 55 55
556 50 c. Boating skills . . . . . . 85 85
553/6 . . . . . . *Set of* 4 1·75 1·75

(Des PAD Studio. Litho Questa)

**1982** (26 Oct). *Christmas. Raphael Paintings. T* **144** *and similar vert designs. Multicoloured.* W w **14**. *P* 14½ × 14.
557 3 c. Type **144** . . . . . . 10 10
558 10 c. "Madonna of the Tower" . . . . 20 20
559 20 c. "Ansidei Madonna" . . . . 35 35
560 30 c. "Madonna and Child" . . . . 50 50
557/60 . . . . . . *Set of* 4 1·00 1·00

**145** Mace

(Des and litho Walsall)

**1982** (9 Nov). *150th Anniv of Representative Government. T* **145** *and similar horiz designs. Multicoloured.* W w **14** (*sideways*). *P* 14½ × 14.
561 3 c. Type **145** . . . . . . 10 10
562 10 c. Old Courthouse . . . . . . 20 20
563 20 c. Commonwealth Parliamentary Association coat of arms . . . . 35 35
564 30 c. Legislative Assembly building . . 50 60
561/4 . . . . . . *Set of* 4 1·00 1·10

(Des J.W. Litho Format)

**1983** (11 Jan). *Shells* (*2nd series*). *Horiz designs as T* **134**. *Multicoloured.* W w **14** (*sideways*). *P* 13½ × 13.
565 5 c. *Natica canrena* . . . . . . 15 10
566 10 c. *Cassis tuberosa* . . . . . . 25 20
567 20 c. *Strombus gallus* . . . . . . 45 40
568 $1 *Cypraecassis testiculus* . . . . 1·75 1·75
565/8 . . . . . . *Set of* 4 2·40 2·25

**146** Legislative Building, Cayman Brac

(Des C. Abbott. Litho Questa)

**1983** (15 Feb). *Royal Visit. T* **146** *and similar multicoloured designs.* W w **14** (*sideways on* 20 c., 30 c.). *P* 14.
569 20 c. Type **146** . . . . . . 45 35
570 30 c. Legislative Building, Grand Cayman . . 60 50
571 50 c. Duke of Edinburgh (*vert*) . . . . 1·25 90
572 $1 Queen Elizabeth II (*vert*) . . . . 2·00 2·00
569/72 . . . . . . *Set of* 4 4·00 3·25
**MS**573 113 × 94 mm. Nos. 569/72 (wmk sideways) 4·00 4·25

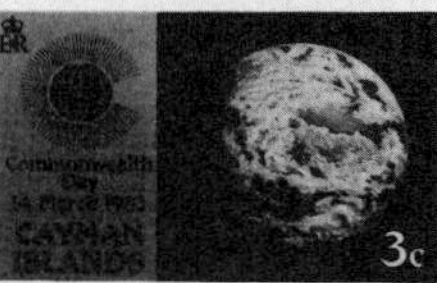


**147** Satellite View of Earth

(Des J.W. Litho Questa)

**1983** (14 Mar). *Commonwealth Day. T* **147** *and similar horiz designs. Multicoloured.* W w **14** (*sideways*). *P* 14.
574 3 c. Type **147** . . . . . . 10 10
575 15 c. Cayman Islands and Commonwealth flags . . . . . . 25 30
576 20 c. Fishing . . . . . . 30 35
577 40 c. Portrait of Queen Elizabeth II . . 60 65
574/7 . . . . . . *Set of* 4 1·10 1·25

**148** MRCU "Cessna" Aircraft — **149** *Song of Norway* (cruise liner)

(Des Harrison. Litho Questa)

**1983** (10 Oct). *Bicentenary of Manned Flight. T* **148** *and similar horiz designs. Multicoloured.* W w **14** (*sideways*). *P* 14.
578 3 c. Type **148** . . . . . . 15 10
579 10 c. Consolidated "PBY Catalina" . . 30 20
580 20 c. Boeing "727-200" . . . . 55 40
581 40 c. Hawker-Siddeley "HS 748" . . 80 1·10
578/81 . . . . . . *Set of* 4 1·60 1·60

(Des J.W. Litho Questa)

**1984** (18 Jan). *Shells* (*3rd series*). *Horiz designs as T* **134**. *Multicoloured.* W w **14** (*sideways*). *P* 14 × 14½.
582 3 c. *Natica floridana* . . . . . . 25 20
583 10 c. *Conus austini* . . . . . . 45 25
584 30 c. *Colubraria obscura* . . . . 90 80
585 50 c. *Turbo cailletii* . . . . . . 1·25 1·50
582/5 . . . . . . *Set of* 4 2·50 2·50

(Des G. Vasarhelyi and L. Curtis. Litho Questa)

**1984** (18 June). *250th Anniv of "Lloyd's List"* (*newspaper*). *T* **149** *and similar vert designs. Multicoloured.* W w **14**. *P* 14½ × 14.
586 5 c. Type **149** . . . . . . 15 10
587 10 c. View of old harbour . . . . 25 25
588 25 c. Wreck of R.M.S. *Ridgefield* . . 50 55
589 50 c. Schooner *Goldfield* . . . . 1·00 1·10
586/9 . . . . . . *Set of* 4 1·75 1·75
**MS**590 105 × 75 mm. $1 Schooner *Goldfield* (*different*) . . . . . . 2·10 2·25

**U.P.U. CONGRESS**
**HAMBURG 1984**

(150)

151 Snowy Egret

**1984** (18 June). *Universal Postal Union Congress, Hamburg. No. 589 optd with T* **150**.

| | | | |
|---|---|---|---|
| 591 | 50 c. Schooner *Goldfield* | 1·00 | 1·50 |

(Des Josephine Martin. Litho Questa)

**1984** (15 Aug). *Birds of the Cayman Islands (1st series). T* **151** *and similar horiz designs. Multicoloured. W* w **14** *(sideways). P* 14×14½.

| | | | | |
|---|---|---|---|---|
| 592 | 5 c. Type **151** | | 55 | 15 |
| 593 | 10 c. Bananaquit | | 65 | 25 |
| 594 | 35 c. Belted Kingfisher | | 2·00 | 1·25 |
| 595 | $1 Brown Booby | | 4·00 | 4·25 |
| 592/5 | | *Set of* 4 | 6·50 | 5·50 |

See also Nos. 627/30.

152 Couple on Beach at Sunset

153 *Schomburgkia thomsoniana (var. minor)*

(Des G. Wilby. Litho Questa)

**1984** (17 Oct). *Christmas. Local Festivities. T* **152** *and similar vert designs. Multicoloured. W* w **14** *(sideways). P* 14.

| | | | | |
|---|---|---|---|---|
| 596 | 5 c. Type **152** | | 15 | 20 |
| | a. Horiz strip of 4. Nos. 596/9 | | 55 | |
| 597 | 5 c. Family and schooner | | 15 | 20 |
| 598 | 5 c. Carol singers | | 15 | 20 |
| 599 | 5 c. East End bonfire | | 15 | 20 |
| 600 | 25 c. Yachts | | 55 | 55 |
| | a. Horiz strip of 4. Nos. 600/3 | | 2·00 | |
| 601 | 25 c. Father Christmas in power-boat | | 55 | 55 |
| 602 | 25 c. Children on beach | | 55 | 55 |
| 603 | 25 c. Beach party | | 55 | 55 |
| 596/603 | | *Set of* 8 | 2·40 | 2·75 |
| **MS**604 | 59×79 mm. $1 As No. 599, but larger, 27×41 mm | | 2·10 | 2·25 |

Nos. 597/600 and 601/4 were each printed together, *se-tenant*, in horizontal strips of 4 throughout the sheets, the four designs of each value forming a composite picture of a beach scene at night (5 c.) or in the daytime (25 c.).

(Des Liza Horstman. Litho J.W.)

**1985** (13 Mar). *Orchids. T* **153** *and similar vert designs. Multicoloured. W* w **14**. *P* 14×13½.

| | | | | |
|---|---|---|---|---|
| 605 | 5 c. Type **153** | | 40 | 10 |
| 606 | 10 c. *Schomburgkia thomsoniana* | | 65 | 20 |
| 607 | 25 c. *Encyclia plicata* | | 1·40 | 70 |
| 608 | 50 c. *Dendrophylax fawcettii* | | 1·60 | 2·00 |
| 605/8 | | *Set of* 4 | 3·50 | 2·75 |

154 Freighter Aground

155 Athletics

(Des Walsall. Litho J.W.)

**1985** (22 May). *Shipwrecks. T* **154** *and similar horiz designs. Multicoloured. W* w **14** *(sideways). P* 14.

| | | | | |
|---|---|---|---|---|
| 609 | 5 c. Type **154** | | 45 | 20 |
| 610 | 25 c. Submerged sailing ship | | 1·25 | 75 |
| 611 | 35 c. Wrecked trawler | | 1·50 | 1·50 |
| 612 | 40 c. Submerged wreck on its side | | 1·75 | 2·00 |
| 609/12 | | *Set of* 4 | 4·50 | 4·00 |

(Des Harrison. Litho Walsall)

**1985** (14 Aug). *International Youth Year. T* **155** *and similar multicoloured designs. W* w **14** *(sideways on 5 c., 15 c.). P* 14×14½ (5, 15 c.) *or* 14½×14 *(others).*

| | | | | |
|---|---|---|---|---|
| 613 | 5 c. Type **155** | | 10 | 10 |
| 614 | 15 c. Students in library | | 25 | 30 |
| 615 | 25 c. Football *(vert)* | | 45 | 50 |
| 616 | 50 c. Netball *(vert)* | | 85 | 90 |
| 613/16 | | *Set of* 4 | 1·50 | 1·60 |

156 Morse Key (1935)

157 Magnificent Frigate Bird

(Des G. Vasarhelyi. Litho Walsall)

**1985** (25 Oct). *50th Anniv of Telecommunications System. T* **156** *and similar vert designs. Multicoloured. W* w **16**. *P* 14.

| | | | | |
|---|---|---|---|---|
| 617 | 5 c. Type **156** | | 10 | 10 |
| 618 | 10 c. Hand cranked telephone | | 20 | 20 |
| 619 | 25 c. Tropospheric scatter dish (1966) | | 45 | 55 |
| 620 | 50 c. Earth station dish aerial (1979) | | 85 | 1·10 |
| 617/20 | | *Set of* 4 | 1·40 | 1·75 |

(Des A. Theobald. Litho Format)

**1986** (21 Apr). *60th Birthday of Queen Elizabeth II. Vert designs as T* **110** *of Ascension. Multicoloured. W* w **16**. *P* 14×14½.

| | | | | |
|---|---|---|---|---|
| 621 | 5 c. Princess Elizabeth at wedding of Lady May Cambridge, 1931 | | 10 | 10 |
| 622 | 10 c. In Norway, 1955 | | 15 | 20 |
| 623 | 25 c. Queen inspecting Royal Cayman Islands Police, 1983 | | 45 | 50 |
| 624 | 50 c. During Gulf tour, 1979 | | 85 | 90 |
| 625 | $1 At Crown Agents Head Office, London, 1983 | | 1·75 | 1·90 |
| 621/5 | | *Set of* 5 | 3·00 | 3·25 |

(Litho J.W.)

**1986** (Apr). *As No.* 516B, *but W* w **16**. *P* 13½×13.

| | | | |
|---|---|---|---|
| 626 | 5 c. Mangrove Root Oyster | 1·75 | 1·75 |

(Des Harrison. Litho Questa)

**1986** (21 May). *Birds of the Cayman Islands (2nd series). T* **157** *and similar multicoloured designs. W* w **16** *(sideways on* 10, 40 c.*). P* 14.

| | | | | |
|---|---|---|---|---|
| 627 | 10 c. Type **157** | | 45 | 20 |
| 628 | 25 c. Black-billed Whistling Duck *(vert)* | | 85 | 75 |
| 629 | 35 c. La Sagra's Flycatcher *(vert)* | | 95 | 1·10 |
| 630 | 40 c. Yellow-faced Grassquit | | 1·10 | 1·60 |
| 627/30 | | *Set of* 4 | 3·00 | 3·25 |

(Litho Questa)

**1986** (June). *As Nos.* 516B/17B, *but different printer and W* w **16**. *P* 14.

| | | | |
|---|---|---|---|
| 631 | 5 c. Mangrove Root Oyster | 1·75 | 1·75 |
| 632 | 10 c. Mangrove Crab | 2·25 | 2·25 |

(Des D. Miller. Litho Walsall)

**1986** (23 July) *Royal Wedding. Square designs as T* **112** *of Ascension. Multicoloured. W* w **16**. *P* 14½×14.

| | | | |
|---|---|---|---|
| 633 | 5 c. Prince Andrew and Miss Sarah Ferguson | 20 | 10 |
| 634 | 50 c. Prince Andrew aboard H.M.S. *Brazen* | 1·10 | 1·00 |

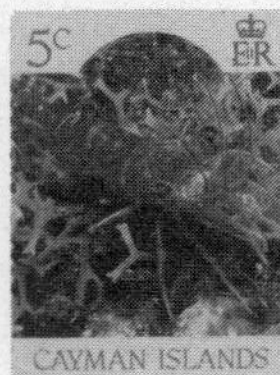


158 Red Coral Shrimp

159 Golf

(Des D. Miller. Litho Walsall)

**1986** (15 Sept). *Marine Life. T* **158** *and similar vert designs. Multicoloured. W* w **14**. *P* 13½×13.

| | | | | |
|---|---|---|---|---|
| 635 | 5 c. Type **158** | | 10 | 10 |
| 636 | 10 c. Yellow Crinoid | | 30 | 30 |
| 637 | 15 c. *Calcinus tibicen* (hermit crab) | | 20 | 25 |
| 638 | 20 c. Tube dwelling Anemone | | 30 | 35 |
| 639 | 25 c. Christmas Tree Worm | | 35 | 40 |
| 640 | 35 c. Spiny Puffer Fish | | 50 | 55 |
| 641 | 50 c. Orangeball Anemone | | 70 | 75 |
| 642 | 60 c. *Astrophyton muricatum* (basket starfish) | | 80 | 85 |
| 643 | 75 c. Flamingo Tongue Snail | | 1·00 | 1·10 |
| 644 | $1 *Condylactis gigantea* (sea anemone) | | 1·40 | 1·50 |
| 645 | $2 Diamond Blenny | | 2·75 | 3·00 |
| 646 | $4 Flaming Scallop | | 5·50 | 5·75 |
| 635/46 | | *Set of* 12 | 12·50 | 13·50 |

No. 644 is incorrectly inscribed "Conolylactis gigantea".

The 5, 10, 15, 20, 25, 35, 50 c., $1, $2 and $4 values exist with different imprint dates at foot.

For the 10 c. value with watermark w **16** see No. 696.

(Des L. Curtis. Litho Walsall)

**1987** (26 Jan). *Tourism. T* **159** *and similar horiz designs. Multicoloured. W* w **16** *(sideways). P* 13×13½.

| | | | | |
|---|---|---|---|---|
| 647 | 10 c. Type **159** | | 40 | 30 |
| 648 | 15 c. Sailing | | 60 | 40 |
| 649 | 25 c. Snorkelling | | 75 | 55 |
| 650 | 35 c. Paragliding | | 85 | 75 |
| 651 | $1 Game fishing | | 2·25 | 3·00 |
| 647/51 | | *Set of* 5 | 4·25 | 4·50 |

160 Ackee

161 Lion Lizard

(Des Jennifer Toombs. Litho Questa)

**1987** (20 May). *Cayman Islands Fruits. T* **160** *and similar vert designs. Multicoloured. W* w **16**. *P* 14½×14.

| | | | | |
|---|---|---|---|---|
| 652 | 5 c. Type **160** | | 10 | 10 |
| 653 | 25 c. Breadfruit | | 45 | 45 |
| 654 | 35 c. Pawpaw | | 60 | 60 |
| 655 | $1 Soursop | | 1·60 | 2·50 |
| 652/5 | | *Set of* 4 | 2·50 | 3·25 |

(Des I. Loe. Litho Questa)

**1987** (26 Aug). *Lizards. T* **161** *and similar horiz designs. Multicoloured. W* w **16** *(sideways). P* 13½×14.

| | | | | |
|---|---|---|---|---|
| 656 | 10 c. Type **161** | | 25 | 20 |
| 657 | 50 c. Iguana | | 90 | 90 |
| 658 | $1 Anole | | 1·75 | 1·75 |
| 656/8 | | *Set of* 3 | 2·75 | 2·50 |

162 Poinsettia

163 *Hemiargus ammon* and *Strymon martialis*

(Des Annette Robinson. Litho Walsall)

**1987** (18 Nov). *Flowers. T* **162** *and similar square designs. Multicoloured. W* w **16**. *P* 14½×14.

| | | | | |
|---|---|---|---|---|
| 659 | 5 c. Type **162** | | 25 | 10 |
| 660 | 25 c. Periwinkle | | 80 | 50 |
| 661 | 35 c. Yellow Allamanda | | 90 | 80 |
| 662 | 75 c. Blood Lily | | 1·75 | 2·25 |
| 659/62 | | *Set of* 4 | 3·25 | 3·25 |

(Des Jane Thatcher. Litho Questa)

**1988** (29 Mar). *Butterflies. T* **163** *and similar horiz designs. Multicoloured. W* w **16** *(sideways). P* 14.

| | | | | |
|---|---|---|---|---|
| 663 | 5 c. Type **163** | | 30 | 15 |
| 664 | 25 c. *Phocides pigmalion* | | 70 | 55 |
| 665 | 50 c. *Anaea troglodyta* | | 1·10 | 1·25 |
| 666 | $1 *Papilio andraemon* | | 1·75 | 2·25 |
| 663/6 | | *Set of* 4 | 3·50 | 3·75 |

164 Green Heron

165 Cycling

(Des Jane Thatcher. Litho Walsall)

**1988** (27 July). *Herons. T* **164** *and similar vert designs. Multicoloured. W* w **16**. *P* 14.

| | | | | |
|---|---|---|---|---|
| 667 | 5 c. Type **164** | | 40 | 15 |
| 668 | 25 c. Louisiana Heron | | 1·00 | 50 |
| 669 | 50 c. Yellow-crowned Night Heron | | 1·40 | 1·40 |
| 670 | $1 Little Blue Heron | | 1·75 | 2·25 |
| 667/70 | | *Set of* 4 | 4·00 | 3·75 |

(Des L. Curtis. Litho Walsall)

**1988** (21 Sept). *Olympic Games, Seoul. T* **165** *and similar horiz designs. Multicoloured. W* w **16** *(sideways). P* 14×14½.

| | | | | |
|---|---|---|---|---|
| 671 | 10 c. Type **165** | | 15 | 20 |
| 672 | 50 c. Cayman Airways airliner and national team | | 70 | 75 |
| 673 | $1 Sailing | | 1·40 | 1·50 |
| 671/3 | | *Set of* 3 | 2·00 | 2·25 |
| **MS**674 | 53×60 mm. $1 Tennis. W w **14** (sideways) | | 1·40 | 2·00 |

166 Princess Alexandra

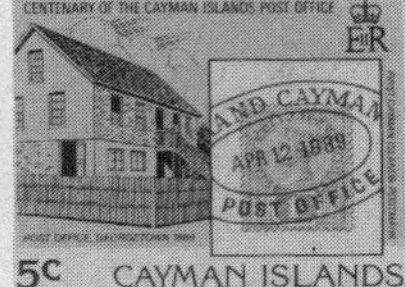


167 Georgetown Post Office and Cayman Postmark on Jamaica 1d., 1889

(Des N. Harvey. Litho B.D.T.)

**1988** (1 Nov). *Visit of Princess Alexandra. T* **166** *and similar vert design. Multicoloured. W* w **14**. *P* 15×14.

675 5 c. Type **166** .. .. .. .. .. 20 10
676 $1 Princess Alexandra in evening dress .. 1·75 1·50

(Des L. Curtis. Litho Questa)

**1989** (12 Apr). *Centenary of Cayman Islands Postal Service. T* **167** *and similar horiz designs. Multicoloured. W* w **16** (*sideways*). *P* 14×14½.

677 5 c. multicoloured .. .. .. .. 15 15
678 25 c. yellowish green, black and new blue 55 55
679 35 c. multicoloured .. .. .. .. 70 70
680 $1 multicoloured .. .. .. .. 1·75 1·75
677/80 .. .. .. .. *Set of* 4 2·75 2·75

Designs:—25 c. *Orinoco* (mail steamer) and 1900 ½d. stamp; 35 c. G.P.O., Grand Cayman and "London 1980" $1 stamp; $1 Cayman Airways plane and 1966 1s. Jet Service stamp.

168 Captain Bligh ashore in West Indies

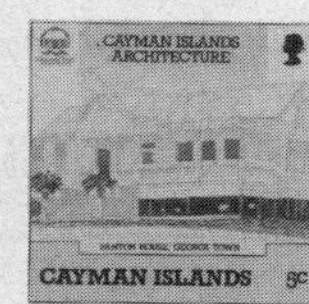


169 Panton House

(Des Jane Hartley. Litho B.D.T.)

**1989** (24 May). *Captain Bligh's Second Breadfruit Voyage, 1791-93. T* **168** *and similar vert designs. Multicoloured. W* w **16**. *P* 14.

681 50 c. Type **168** .. .. .. .. 1·50 1·50
a. Horiz strip of 5. Nos. 681/5 .. .. 6·75
682 50 c. H.M.S. *Providence* (sloop) at anchor .. 1·50 1·50
683 50 c. Breadfruit in tubs and H.M.S. *Assistant* (transport) .. .. .. 1·50 1·50
684 50 c. Sailors moving tubs of breadfruit .. 1·50 1·50
685 50 c. Midshipman and stores .. .. 1·50 1·50
681/5 .. .. .. .. *Set of* 5 6·75 6·75

Nos. 681/5 were printed together, *se-tenant* as a composite design, in horizontal strips of five throughout the sheet.

(Des S. Conlin. Litho Walsall)

**1989** (18 Oct). *Architecture. T* **169** *and similar square designs showing George Town buildings. Multicoloured. W* w **14**. *P* 14½×14.

686 5 c. Type **169** .. .. .. .. 10 15
687 10 c. Town Hall and Clock Tower .. .. 15 20
688 25 c. Old Court House .. .. .. 40 50
689 35 c. Elmslie Memorial Church .. .. 55 65
690 $1 Post Office .. .. .. .. 1·50 2·00
686/90 .. .. .. .. *Set of* 5 2·50 3·25

170 Map of Grand Cayman, 1773, and Surveying Instruments

171 French Angel Fish

(Des N. Shewring. Litho Walsall)

**1989** (15 Nov). *Island Maps and Survey Ships. T* **170** *and similar horiz designs. Multicoloured. W* w **16** (*sideways*). *P* 14×14½.

691 5 c. Type **170** .. .. .. .. 25 20
692 25 c. Map of Cayman Islands, 1956, and surveying instruments .. .. .. 80 70
693 50 c. H.M.S. *Mutine*, 1914 .. .. .. 1·40 1·40
694 $1 H.M.S. *Vidal*, 1956 .. .. .. 2·25 2·50
691/4 .. .. .. .. *Set of* 4 4·25 4·25

**1990** (Mar). *As No.* 636, *but W* w **16**. *P* 13½×13.

696 10 c. Yellow Crinoid .. .. .. .. 15 20

(Des D. Miller. Litho Questa)

**1990** (25 Apr). *Angel Fishes. T* **171** *and similar horiz designs. Multicoloured. W* w **16** (*sideways*). *P* 14.

707 10 c. Type **171** .. .. .. .. 35 30
708 25 c. Grey Angel Fish .. .. .. 70 60
709 50 c. Queen Angel Fish .. .. .. 1·40 1·40
710 $1 Rock Beauty .. .. .. .. 2·25 2·25
707/10 .. .. .. .. *Set of* 4 4·25 4·00

(Des D. Miller. Litho Questa)

**1990** (4 Aug). *90th Birthday of Queen Elizabeth the Queen Mother. Vert designs as T* **134** (50 c.) *or* **135** ($1) *of Ascension. W* w **16**. *P* 14×15 (50 c.) *or* 14½ ($1).

711 50 c. multicoloured .. .. .. .. 1·00 1·00
712 $1 black and blue .. .. .. .. 2·00 2·00

Designs:—50 c. Silver Wedding photograph, 1948; $1 King George VI and Queen Elizabeth with Winston Churchill, 1940.

172 *Danaus eresimus*

173 Goes Weather Satellite

(Des G. Drummond. Litho Questa)

**1990** (24 Oct). *"EXPO 90" International Garden and Greenery Exhibition, Osaka. Butterflies. T* **172** *and similar horiz designs. Multicoloured. W* w **16** (*sideways*). *P* 14.

713 5 c. Type **172** .. .. .. .. 20 20
714 25 c. *Brephidium exilis* .. .. .. 55 55
715 35 c. *Phyciodes phaon* .. .. .. 70 70
716 $1 *Agraulis vanillae* .. .. .. 1·90 1·90
713/16 .. .. .. .. *Set of* 4 3·00 3·00

(Des A. Theobald. Litho Questa)

**1991** (8 Aug). *International Decade for Natural Disaster Reduction. T* **173** *and similar horiz designs. Multicoloured. W* w **16** (*sideways*). *P* 14.

717 5 c. Type **173** .. .. .. .. 20 15
718 30 c. Meteorologist tracking hurricane .. 60 60
719 40 c. Damaged buildings .. .. .. 75 75
720 $1 U.S. Dept of Commerce weather reconnaisance Lockheed WP-3D Orion 2·25 2·25
717/20 .. .. .. .. *Set of* 4 3·50 3·25

174 Angels and *Datura candida*

175 Coconut Palm

(Des Jennifer Toombs. Litho Questa)

**1991** (6 Nov). *Christmas. T* **174** *and similar horiz designs. Multicoloured. W* w **16** (*sideways*). *P* 14.

721 5 c. Type **174** .. .. .. .. 10 10
722 30 c. Mary and Joseph going to Bethlehem and *Allamanda cathartica* .. .. 40 45
723 40 c. Adoration of the Kings and *Euphorbia pulcherrima* .. .. .. .. 55 60
724 60 c. Holy Family and *Guaiacum officinale* 80 85
721/4 .. .. .. .. *Set of* 4 1·60 1·75

(Des D. Miller. Litho Enschedé)

**1991** (11 Dec). *Island Scenes. T* **175** *and similar multicoloured designs. W* w **14** (*sideways on horiz designs*). *P* 12½×13 (*vert*) *or* 13×12½ (*horiz*).

725 5 c. Type **175** .. .. .. .. 10 10
726 15 c. Beach scene (*horiz*) .. .. .. 20 25
727 20 c. Poincianas in bloom (*horiz*) .. .. 30 35
728 30 c. Blowholes (*horiz*) .. .. .. 35 40
729 40 c. Police band (*horiz*) .. .. .. 50 55
730 50 c. Cruise liner at George Town .. .. 70 75
731 60 c. The Bluff, Cayman Brac (*horiz*) .. 80 85
732 80 c. Coat of arms .. .. .. .. 1·00 1·10
733 90 c. View of Hell (*horiz*) .. .. .. 1·00 1·10
734 $1 Game fishing (*horiz*) .. .. .. 1·40 1·50
735 $2 Cruise ships in harbour .. .. .. 2·75 3·00
736 $8 Queen Elizabeth II .. .. .. 11·00 11·50
725/36 .. .. .. .. *Set of* 12 18·00 19·00

(Des D. Miller. Litho Questa ($1), Leigh-Mardon Ltd, Melbourne (others))

**1992** (6 Feb). *40th Anniv of Queen Elizabeth II's Accession. Horiz designs as T* **143** *of Ascension. W* w **16** (*sideways*) (30, 40 c.) *or* w **14** (*sideways*) (*others*). *P* 14.

737 5 c. Caymans' house .. .. .. .. 10 10
738 20 c. Sunset over islands .. .. .. 30 35
739 30 c. Beach .. .. .. .. .. 40 45
740 40 c. Three portraits of Queen Elizabeth .. 60 65
741 $1 Queen Elizabeth II .. .. .. 1·40 1·50
737/41 .. .. .. .. *Set of* 5 2·50 2·75

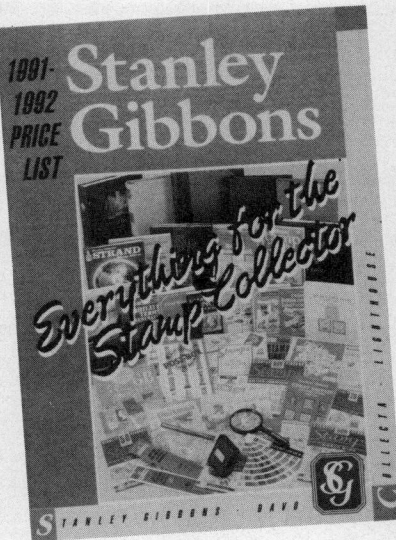

## Ceylon *see* Sri Lanka

Ceylon see Sri Lanka

## Channel Islands

These issues are now listed under GREAT BRITAIN after the Postal Fiscal Issues.

## China—British Post Offices *see after* Hong Kong

## Christmas Island

Formerly a part of the Straits Settlements and then of the Colony of Singapore, Christmas Island became an Australian territory on 15 October 1958.

Stamps of the STRAITS SETTLEMENTS and later SINGAPORE were used on Christmas Island from 1901 until 1942 and subsequently from 1946 to 1958.

**(Currency. 100 cents = 1 dollar (Malayan))**

1 Queen Elizabeth II

(Des G. Lissenden. Recess with name and value typo in black. Note Printing Branch, Commonwealth Bank, Melbourne)

**1958** (15 Oct). *No wmk. P* 14½.

| No. | Type | Description | Unused | Used |
|---|---|---|---|---|
| 1 | 1 | 2 c. yellow-orange | 55 | 30 |
| 2 | | 4 c. brown | 60 | 30 |
| 3 | | 5 c. deep mauve | 60 | 20 |
| 4 | | 6 c. grey-blue | 1·50 | 20 |
| 5 | | 8 c. black-brown | 3·00 | 50 |
| 6 | | 10 c. violet | 2·50 | 30 |
| 7 | | 12 c. carmine | 3·50 | 1·50 |
| 8 | | 20 c. blue | 3·00 | 1·50 |
| 9 | | 50 c. yellow-green | 4·50 | 1·50 |
| 10 | | $1 deep bluish green | 6·00 | 1·50 |
| 1/10 | | *Set of* 10 | 23·00 | 7·00 |

**PRINTERS.** Nos. 11/32 were printed by the Note Printing Branch, Reserve Bank of Australia, Melbourne. Nos. 33/82 were printed in photogravure by Harrison and Sons, Ltd, London.

2 Map

11 White-tailed Tropic Bird

(Des G. Lissenden (2, 8c.), P. Morriss (4, 5, 10, 20 c.), B. Stewart (others). Recess)

**1963** (28 Aug). *T* **2** *and similar designs and T* **11.** *P* 14½ × 14 ($1) *or* 14½ (*others*).

| No. | Description | Unused | Used |
|---|---|---|---|
| 11 | 2 c. orange | 55 | 30 |
| 12 | 4 c. red-brown | 50 | 20 |
| 13 | 5 c. purple | 50 | 20 |
| 14 | 6 c. indigo | 40 | 20 |
| 15 | 8 c. black | 2·50 | 40 |
| 16 | 10 c. violet | 40 | 20 |
| 17 | 12 c. brown-red | 40 | 30 |
| 18 | 20 c. blue | 1·00 | 35 |
| 19 | 50 c. green | 2·00 | 35 |
| 20 | $1 yellow | 5·50 | 60 |
| 11/20 | *Set of* 10 | 12·00 | 2·75 |

Designs: *Vert*—4 c. Moonflower; 5 c. Robber Crab; 8 c. Phosphate train; 10 c. Raising phosphate. *Horiz*—6 c. Island scene; 12 c. Flying Fish Cove; 20 c. Loading cantilever; 50 c. Christmas Island Frigate Bird.

I Thick lettering

II Thinner lettering

**1965.** 50*th Anniversary of Gallipoli Landing. As T* **184** *of Australia, but slightly larger* (22×34½ *mm*) *and colour changed. Photo. P* 13½.

| No. | Description | Unused | Used |
|---|---|---|---|
| 21 | 10 c. sepia, black and emerald (I) (14.4) | 30 | 35 |
| | *a. Black-brown, black and light emerald* (II) (24.4) | 1·75 | 1·50 |

**(New Currency. 100 cents = 1 dollar (Australian))**

12 Golden Striped Grouper

13 "Angel" (mosaic)

(Des G. Hamori. Photo)

**1968** (6 May)–**70.** *Fishes. T* **12** *and similar horiz designs. Multicoloured. P* 13½.

| No. | Description | Unused | Used |
|---|---|---|---|
| 22 | 1 c. Type **12** | 45 | 30 |
| 23 | 2 c. Moorish Idol | 60 | 20 |
| 24 | 3 c. Forceps Fish | 60 | 30 |
| 25 | 4 c. Queen Triggerfish | 60 | 20 |
| | a. Deep blue (face value) omitted | £550 | |
| 26 | 5 c. Regal Angelfish | 75 | 20 |
| 27 | 9 c. Surgeon Fish | 2·00 | 40 |
| 28 | 10 c. Scorpion Fish | 1·50 | 20 |
| 28*a* | 15 c. Saddleback Butterfly (fish) (14.12.70) | 12·00 | 7·00 |
| 29 | 20 c. Clown Butterfly (fish) | 4·00 | 55 |
| 29*a* | 30 c. Ghost Pipefish (14.12.70) | 12·00 | 7·00 |
| 30 | 50 c. Blue Lined Surgeon | 10·00 | 3·00 |
| 31 | $1 Meyers Butterfly (fish) | 15·00 | 5·00 |
| 22/31 | *Set of* 12 | 55·00 | 22·00 |

(Des G. Hamori. Photo)

**1969** (10 Nov). *Christmas. P* 13½.

| No. | Type | Description | Unused | Used |
|---|---|---|---|---|
| 32 | **13** | 5 c. red, deep blue and gold | 20 | 20 |

14 "The Ansidei Madonna" (Raphael)

15 "The Adoration of the Shepherds" (ascr to the School of Seville)

(Des Harrison)

**1970** (26 Oct). *Christmas. Paintings. T* **14** *and similar vert design. Multicoloured. P* 14 × 14½.

| No. | Description | Unused | Used |
|---|---|---|---|
| 33 | 3 c. Type **14** | 20 | 15 |
| 34 | 5 c. "The Virgin and Child, St. John the Baptist and an Angel" (Morando) | 20 | 15 |

(Des Harrison)

**1971** (4 Oct). *Christmas. T* **15** *and similar vert design. Multicoloured. W* w **12.** *P* 14.

| No. | Description | Unused | Used |
|---|---|---|---|
| 35 | 6 c. Type **15** | 50 | 50 |
| 36 | 20 c. "The Adoration of the Shepherds" (Reni) | 1·00 | 1·00 |

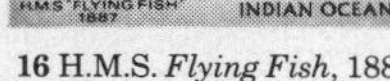


16 H.M.S. *Flying Fish*, 1887

17 Angel of Peace

(Des V. Whiteley)

**1972** (7 Feb)–**73.** *Ships. Horiz designs as T* **16.** *Multicoloured. P* 14 × 13½.

| No. | Description | Unused | Used |
|---|---|---|---|
| 37 | 1 c. *Eagle*, 1714 (5.6.72) | 25 | 35 |
| 38 | 2 c. H.M.S. *Redpole*, 1890 (5.6.72) | 30 | 40 |
| 39 | 3 c. M.V. *Hoi Houw*, 1959 (5.6.72) | 30 | 40 |
| 40 | 4 c. *Pigot*, 1771 (6.2.73) | 40 | 45 |
| 41 | 5 c. S.S. *Valetta*, 1968 (6.2.73) | 40 | 45 |
| 42 | 6 c. Type **16** | 40 | 45 |
| 43 | 7 c. *Asia*, 1805 | 40 | 45 |
| 44 | 8 c. T.S.S. *Islander*, 1929–60 | 45 | 50 |
| 45 | 9 c. H.M.S. *Imperieuse**, 1888 (6.2.73) | 65 | 50 |
| 46 | 10 c. H.M.S. *Egeria*, 1887 (4.6.73) | 55 | 50 |
| 47 | 20 c. *Thomas*, 1615 | 85 | 70 |
| 48 | 25 c. H.M.S. *Gordon*, 1864 (4.6.73) | 1·25 | 85 |
| 49 | 30 c. *Cygnet*, 1688 (4.6.73) | 1·50 | 85 |
| 50 | 35 c. S.S. *Triadic*, 1958 (4.6.73) | 1·75 | 90 |
| 51 | 50 c. H.M.S. *Amethyst*, 1857 (6.2.73) | 2·25 | 1·75 |
| 52 | $1 *Royal Mary*, 1643 (5.6.72) | 3·00 | 2·25 |
| 37/52 | *Set of* 16 | 13·00 | 10·50 |

*The design is wrongly inscribed "H.M.S. *Imperious*".

(Des Jennifer Toombs)

**1972** (2 Oct). *Christmas. T* **17** *and similar vert design. Multicoloured. P* 14.

| No. | Description | Unused | Used |
|---|---|---|---|
| 53 | 3 c. Type **17** | 65 | 65 |
| | a. Pair. Nos. 53/4 | 1·25 | 1·25 |
| 54 | 3 c. Angel of Joy | 65 | 65 |
| 55 | 7 c. Type **17** | 75 | 75 |
| | a. Pair. Nos. 55/6 | 1·50 | 1·50 |
| 56 | 7 c. As No. 54 | 75 | 75 |
| 53/6 | *Set of* 4 | 2·50 | 2·50 |

Nos. 53/4 and 55/6 have the two designs printed horizontally *se-tenant* within the sheet.

18 Virgin and Child, and Map

19 Mary and Holy Child within Christmas Star

(Des P. L. S. Cheong)

**1973** (2 Oct). *Christmas. P* 14 × 13.

| No. | Type | Description | Unused | Used |
|---|---|---|---|---|
| 57 | **18** | 7 c. multicoloured | 1·00 | 35 |
| 58 | | 25 c. multicoloured | 3·00 | 1·25 |

(Des Jennifer Toombs)

**1974** (2 Oct). *Christmas. P* 13 × 14½.

| No. | Type | Description | Unused | Used |
|---|---|---|---|---|
| 59 | **19** | 7 c. mauve and grey-black | 60 | 75 |
| 60 | | 30 c. light orange, bright yell & grey-blk | 1·75 | 2·50 |

20 "The Flight into Egypt"

21 Dove of Peace and Star of Bethlehem

(Des Jennifer Toombs)

**1975** (2 Oct). *Christmas. P* 14 × 13.

| No. | Type | Description | Unused | Used |
|---|---|---|---|---|
| 61 | **20** | 10 c. light greenish yellow, agate and gold | 50 | 35 |
| 62 | | 35 c. bright rose, deep blue and gold | 1·50 | 1·40 |

(Des R. Bates)

**1976** (2 Oct). *Christmas. P* 13½.

| No. | Type | Description | Unused | Used |
|---|---|---|---|---|
| 63 | **21** | 10 c. cerise, lemon and bright mauve | 40 | 65 |
| | | a. Pair. Nos. 63/4 | 80 | 1·25 |
| 64 | – | 10 c. cerise, lemon and bright mauve | 40 | 65 |
| 65 | **21** | 35 c. reddish violet, light greenish blue and light yellow-green | 70 | 70 |
| | | a. Pair. Nos. 65/6 | 1·40 | 1·40 |
| 66 | – | 35 c. reddish violet, light greenish blue and light yellow-green | 70 | 70 |
| 63/6 | | *Set of* 4 | 2·00 | 2·40 |

Nos. 64 and 66 are "mirror-images" of T **21**, the two designs of each value being printed horizontally *se-tenant* throughout the sheet.

22 William Dampier (explorer)

23 Australian Coat of Arms on Map of Christmas Island

(Des V. Whiteley Studio)

**1977** (30 Apr)–**78.** *Famous Visitors. Horiz designs as T* **22** *in black, vermilion and greenish yellow* (45 c.) *or multicoloured* (*others*). *P* 14 × 13.

| No. | Description | Unused | Used |
|---|---|---|---|
| 67 | 1 c. Type **22** | 15 | 30 |
| 68 | 2 c. Capt. de Vlamingh (explorer) (22.2.78) | 20 | 30 |
| 69 | 3 c. Vice-Admiral MacLear (22.2.78) | 30 | 30 |

70 4 c. Sir John Murray (oceanographer) (22.2.78) .. .. .. .. .. 30 40
71 5 c. Admiral Aldrich (31.5.78) .. .. .. 30 20
72 6 c. Andrew Clunies Ross (first settler) .. 30 40
73 7 c. J. J. Lister (naturalist) (31.5.78) .. 30 20
74 8 c. Admiral of the Fleet Sir William May (1.9.78) .. .. .. .. .. .. 35 40
75 9 c. Henry Ridley (botanist) .. .. .. 40 30
76 10 c. George Clunies Ross (phosphate miner) (1.9.78) .. .. .. .. .. .. 35 30
77 20 c. Capt. Joshua Slocum (yachtsman) (1.9.78) .. .. .. .. .. .. 50 40
78 45 c. Charles Andrews (naturalist) (31.5.78) .. 85 45
79 50 c. Richard Hanitsch (biologist) (31.5.78) .. 95 60
80 75 c. Victor Purcell (scholar) (1.9.78) .. .. 85 85
81 $1 Fam Choo Beng (educator) .. .. 1·25 1·25
82 $2 Sir Harold Spencer-Jones (astronomer) (22.2.78) .. .. .. .. .. .. 2·50 2·25
67/82 .. .. .. .. .. *Set of* 16 8·75 8·00

(Des Mrs S. Muir. Litho Harrison)

**1977** (2 June). *Silver Jubilee. P* 14½ × 13½.
83 **23** 45 c. multicoloured .. .. .. 60 70

24 "A Partridge in a Pear Tree"

25 Abbott's Booby

(Des Jennifer Toombs. Litho Questa)

**1977** (20 Oct)–**78**. *Christmas. T* **24** *and similar vert designs depicting the carol "The Twelve Days of Christmas". Multicoloured. P* 14.

A. *No wmk.* B. *W* w **14** (27.1.78)

| | | A. | | B. | |
|---|---|---|---|---|---|
| 84 | 10 c. Type **24** .. .. .. | 15 | 25 | 35 | 25 |
| | a. Sheetlet. Nos. 84/95 .. | 1·60 | — | 3·75 | — |
| 85 | 10 c. "Two turtle doves" .. | 15 | 25 | 35 | 25 |
| 86 | 10 c. "Three French hens" .. | 15 | 25 | 35 | 25 |
| 87 | 10 c. "Four calling birds" .. | 15 | 25 | 35 | 25 |
| 88 | 10 c. "Five gold rings" .. | 15 | 25 | 35 | 25 |
| 89 | 10 c. "Six geese a-laying" .. | 15 | 25 | 35 | 25 |
| 90 | 10 c. "Seven swans a-swimming" | 15 | 25 | 35 | 25 |
| 91 | 10 c. "Eight maids a-milking" .. | 15 | 25 | 35 | 25 |
| 92 | 10 c. "Nine ladies dancing" .. | 15 | 25 | 35 | 25 |
| 93 | 10 c. "Ten lords a-leaping" .. | 15 | 25 | 35 | 25 |
| 94 | 10 c. "Eleven pipers piping" .. | 15 | 25 | 35 | 25 |
| 95 | 10 c. "Twelve drummers drumming" .. | 15 | 25 | 35 | 25 |
| 84/95 | .. .. *Set of* 12 | 1·60 | 2·50 | 3·75 | 2·50 |

Nos. 84/95 were printed as a *se-tenant* block within a sheetlet 142 × 170 mm.

(Des Jennifer Toombs. Litho Questa)

**1978** (21 Apr). *25th Anniv of Coronation. T* **25** *and similar vert designs. P* 15.
96 45 c. black and bright ultramarine .. .. 60 95
a. Sheetlet. Nos. 96/8 × 2 .. .. .. 3·25
97 45 c. multicoloured .. .. .. 60 95
98 45 c. black and bright ultramarine .. .. 60 95
96/8 .. .. .. .. .. *Set of* 3 1·60 2·50

Designs:—No. 96, White Swan of Bohun; No. 97, Queen Elizabeth II; No. 98, Type **25**.

Nos. 96/8 were printed together in small sheets of 6, containing two *se-tenant* strips of 3 with horizontal gutter margin between.

26 "Christ Child"

27 Chinese Children

(Des Jennifer Toombs. Litho J.W.)

**1978** (2 Oct). *Christmas. Scenes from "The Song of Christmas". T* **26** *and similar horiz designs. Multicoloured. P* 14.
99 10 c. Type **26** .. .. .. .. .. 15 20
a. Sheetlet. Nos. 99/107 .. .. .. 1·25
100 10 c. "Herald Angels" .. .. .. .. 15 20
101 10 c. "Redeemer" .. .. .. .. 15 20
102 10 c. "Israel" .. .. .. .. .. 15 20
103 10 c. "Star" .. .. .. .. .. 15 20
104 10 c. "Three Wise Men" .. .. .. 15 20
105 10 c. "Manger" .. .. .. .. .. 15 20
106 10 c. "All He Stands For" .. .. .. 15 20
107 10 c. "Shepherds Came" .. .. .. 15 20
99/107 .. .. .. .. *Set of* 9 1·25 1·60

Nos. 99/107 were printed together, *se-tenant*, in a small sheet of 9.

(Des Jennifer Toombs. Litho Questa)

**1979** (20 Apr). *International Year of the Child. T* **27** *and similar vert designs showing children of different races. Multicoloured, colour of inscr given. P* 14.
108 20 c. apple-green (Type **27**) .. .. .. 45 45
a. Horiz strip of 5. Nos. 108/12 .. .. 2·00
109 20 c. turquoise-green (Malay children) .. 45 45
110 20 c. lilac (Indian children) .. .. .. 45 45
111 20 c. rose (European children) .. .. 45 45
112 20 c. orange-yellow ("Oranges and Lemons") .. 45 45
108/12 .. .. .. .. *Set of* 5 2·00 2·00

Nos. 108/12 were printed together, *se-tenant*, in horizontal strips of 5 throughout the sheet, forming a composite design.

28 1958 2 c. Definitive

29 Wise Men following Star

(Des J.W. Litho Questa)

**1979** (27 Aug). *Death Centenary of Sir Rowland Hill. T* **28** *and similar horiz designs showing stamps and Sir Rowland Hill. Multicoloured. P* 13½.
113 20 c. Type **28** .. .. .. .. .. 30 40
a. Horiz strip of 5. Nos. 113/17 .. .. 1·40
114 20 c. 1963 2 c. Map definitive .. .. .. 30 40
115 20 c. 1965 50th anniversary of Gallipoli Landing 10 c. commemorative .. .. 30 40
116 20 c. 1968 4 c. Queen Triggerfish definitive .. 30 40
117 20 c. 1969 5 c. Christmas issue .. .. 30 40
113/17 .. .. .. .. *Set of* 5 1·40 1·75

Nos. 113/17 were printed together, *se-tenant*, in horizontal strips of 5 throughout the sheet.

(Des L. Curtis. Litho Walsall)

**1979** (22 Oct). *Christmas. T* **29** *and similar horiz design. Multicoloured. P* 14 × 14½.
118 20 c. Type **29** .. .. .. .. .. 20 30
119 55 c. Virgin and Child .. .. .. .. 45 70

30 9th Green

31 Surveying

(Des R. Granger Barrett. Litho Format)

**1980** (12 Feb). *25th Anniv of Christmas Island Golf Club. T* **30** *and similar horiz design. Multicoloured. P* 14½ × 14.
120 20 c. Type **30** .. .. .. .. .. 60 45
121 55 c. Clubhouse .. .. .. .. .. 80 80

(Des L. Curtis. Litho Walsall)

**1980** (6 May). *Phosphate Industry* (1*st issue*). *T* **31** *and similar horiz designs. Multicoloured. P* 14.
122 15 c. Type **31** .. .. .. .. .. 15 20
123 22 c. Drilling for samples .. .. .. 20 25
124 40 c. Sample analysis .. .. .. .. 30 40
125 55 c. Mine planning .. .. .. .. 40 50
122/5 .. .. .. .. *Set of* 4 95 1·25

See also Nos. 126/9, 136/9 and 140/3.

(Des L. Curtis. Litho Walsall)

**1980** (14 July). *Phosphate Industry* (2*nd issue*). *Horiz designs as T* **31**. *Multicoloured. P* 14.
126 15 c. Jungle clearing .. .. .. .. 15 15
127 22 c. Overburden removal .. .. .. 20 20
128 40 c. Open cut mining .. .. .. .. 30 25
129 55 c. Restoration .. .. .. .. .. 35 30
126/9 .. .. .. .. *Set of* 4 90 80

32 Angel with Harp

33 *Cryptoblepharus egeriae*

(Des Jennifer Toombs. Litho Walsall)

**1980** (6 Oct). *Christmas. T* **32** *and similar vert designs. Multicoloured. P* 13½ × 13.
130 15 c. Type **32** .. .. .. .. .. 15 25
a. Sheetlet. Nos. 130/5 .. .. .. 1·40
131 15 c. Angel with wounded soldier .. .. 15 25
132 22 c. Virgin and Child .. .. .. .. 20 30
133 22 c. Kneeling couple .. .. .. .. 20 30
134 60 c. Angel with harp (*different*) .. .. 45 45
135 60 c. Angel with children .. .. .. 45 45
130/5 .. .. .. .. *Set of* 6 1·40 1·75

Nos. 130/5 were printed together in small sheets of 6, containing two *se-tenant* strips of 3 (Nos. 130, 132, 134 and 131, 133, 135) with horizontal gutter margin between.

(Des L. Curtis. Litho Walsall)

**1981** (9 Feb). *Phosphate Industry* (3*rd issue*). *Horiz designs as T* **31**. *Multicoloured. P* 14.
136 22 c. Screening and stockpiling .. .. 20 20
137 28 c. Train loading .. .. .. .. 25 25
138 40 c. Railing .. .. .. .. .. 40 40
139 60 c. Drying .. .. .. .. .. 55 55
136/9 .. .. .. .. *Set of* 4 1·25 1·25

(Des L. Curtis. Litho Walsall)

**1981** (4 May). *Phosphate Industry* (4*th issue*). *Horiz designs as T* **31**. *Multicoloured. P* 14.
140 22 c. Crushing .. .. .. .. .. 30 20
141 28 c. Conveying .. .. .. .. .. 40 25
142 40 c. Bulk storage .. .. .. .. 60 40
143 60 c. Ship loading .. .. .. .. 70 55
140/3 .. .. .. .. *Set of* 4 1·75 1·25

(Des L. Curtis. Litho Walsall)

**1981** (10 Aug). *Reptiles. T* **33** *and similar horiz designs. Multicoloured. P* 13.
144 24 c. Type **33** .. .. .. .. .. 25 25
145 30 c. *Emoia nativitata* .. .. .. .. 30 30
146 40 c. *Lepidodactylus listeri* .. .. .. 45 45
147 60 c. *Cyrtodactylus sp. nov.* .. .. .. 65 65
144/7 .. .. .. .. *Set of* 4 1·50 1·50

34 Scene from Carol "Away in a Manger"

35 Eastern Reef Heron

(Des Jennifer Toombs. Litho Questa)

**1981** (19 Oct). *Christmas. T* **34** *and similar horiz designs showing scenes from carol "Away in a Manger". P* 14½ × 14.
148 18 c. silver, deep blue and turquoise-blue .. 50 50
a. Sheetlet. Nos. 148/51 .. .. .. 2·25
149 24 c. multicoloured .. .. .. .. 55 55
150 40 c. multicoloured .. .. .. .. 65 65
151 60 c. multicoloured .. .. .. .. 75 75
148/51 .. .. .. .. *Set of* 4 2·25 2·25

Nos. 148/51 were printed together, *se-tenant*, in sheetlets of 4.

(Des N. Arlott. Litho Questa)

**1982** (8 Mar)–**83**. *Birds. Multicoloured designs as T* **35**. *P* 14.
152 1 c. Type **35** .. .. .. .. .. 35 20
153 2 c. Common Noddy .. .. .. .. 35 20
154 3 c. White-bellied Swiftlet (14.6.82) .. .. 35 45
155 4 c. Christmas Island Imperial Pigeon (14.6.82) .. .. .. .. .. 35 45
156 5 c. Christmas Island White Eye (21.2.83) .. 40 45
157 10 c. Island Thrush (14.6.82) .. .. .. 35 45
158 25 c. Red-tailed Tropic Bird .. .. .. 75 40
159 30 c. Emerald Dove (21.2.83) .. .. .. 50 50
160 40 c. Brown Booby (23.8.82) .. .. .. 60 45
161 50 c. Red-footed Booby (23.8.82) .. .. 55 45
162 65 c. Christmas Island Frigate Bird (23.8.82) .. 55 55
163 75 c. White-tailed Tropic Bird (23.8.82) .. 65 65
164 80 c. Australian Kestrel (*vert*) (21.2.83) .. 1·00 65
165 $1 Indonesian Hawk Owl (*vert*) (21.2.83) .. 1·50 90
166 $2 Australian Goshawk (*vert*) (14.6.82) .. 1·50 3·50
167 $4 Abbott's Booby (*vert*) .. .. .. 3·00 3·25
152/67 .. .. .. .. *Set of* 16 11·50 12·00

36 Joseph

37 "Mirror" Dinghy and Club House

(Des Jennifer Toombs. Litho and embossed Walsall)

**1982** (18 Oct). *Christmas. Origami Paper Sculptures. T* **36** *and similar vert designs. Multicoloured. P* 14½ × 14.
168 27 c. Type **36** .. .. .. .. .. 30 30
a. Horiz strip of 3. Nos. 168/70 .. .. 1·25
169 50 c. Angel .. .. .. .. .. 45 45
170 75 c. Mary and baby Jesus .. .. .. 65 65
168/70 .. .. .. .. *Set of* 3 1·25 1·25

Nos. 168/70 were printed together, *se-tenant*, in horiz strips of 3 throughout the sheet.

(Des L. McCombie. Litho Format)

**1983** (2 May). *25th Anniv of Christmas Island Boat Club. T* **37** *and similar multicoloured designs. P* 14 × 14½ (27, 35 c.) *or* 14½ × 14 (*others*).
171 27 c. Type **37** .. .. .. .. .. 35 35
172 35 c. Ocean-going yachts .. .. .. 40 40
173 50 c. Fishing launch and cargo ship (*horiz*) .. 50 50
174 75 c. Dinghy-racing and cantilever (*horiz*) .. 70 70
171/4 .. .. .. .. *Set of* 4 1·75 1·75

**NEW INFORMATION**

The editor is always interested to correspond with people who have new information that will improve or correct the Catalogue.

**38** Maps of Christmas Island and Australia, Eastern Grey Kangaroo and White-tailed Tropic Bird

**39** Candle and Holly

(Des A. Theobald. Litho Questa)

**1983** (1 Oct). *25th Anniv of Christmas Island as an Australian Territory. T* **38** *and similar horiz designs. Multicoloured. P* 14.

175 24 c. Type **38** .. 20 20
176 30 c. Christmas Island and Australian flag .. 30 30
177 85 c. Maps of Christmas Island and Australia, with Boeing "727" .. 70 70
175/7 .. *Set of* 3 1·10 1·10

(Des J.W. Litho Walsall)

**1983** (31 Oct). *Christmas. Candles. T* **39** *and similar vert designs. Multicoloured. P* 13.

178 24 c. Type **39** .. 20 20
179 30 c. Six gold candles .. 30 30
180 85 c. Candles .. 70 70
178/80 .. *Set of* 3 1·10 1·10

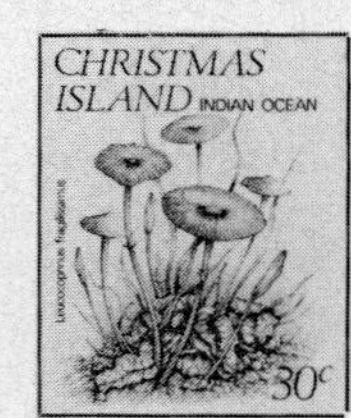


**40** Feeding on Leaf

**41** *Leucocoprinus fragilissimus*

(Des L. Curtis. Litho Questa)

**1984** (20 Feb). *Red Land Crab. T* **40** *and similar horiz designs showing various aspects of crab's life. Multicoloured. P* 14 × 14½.

181 30 c. Type **40** .. 30 30
182 40 c. Migration .. 40 40
183 55 c. Development stages .. 50 50
184 85 c. Adult female and young .. 70 70
181/4 .. *Set of* 4 1·75 1·75

(Des I. Loe. Litho Format)

**1984** (30 Apr). *Fungi. T* **41** *and similar vert designs. Multicoloured. P* 14 × 14½.

185 30 c. Type **41** .. 55 30
186 40 c. *Microporus xanthopus* .. 65 40
187 45 c. *Trogia anthidepas* .. 75 45
188 55 c. *Haddowia longipes* .. 85 60
189 85 c. *Phillipsia domingensis* .. 1·00 75
185/9 .. *Set of* 5 3·50 2·25

**42** Run-out

**43** Arrival of Father Christmas

(Des A. Theobald. Litho J.W.)

**1984** (23 July). *25th Anniversary of Cricket on Christmas Island. T* **42** *and similar horiz designs. Multicoloured. P* 14.

190 30 c. Type **42** .. 70 60
191 40 c. Bowled-out .. 80 70
192 55 c. Batsman in action .. 1·00 90
193 85 c. Fielder diving for catch .. 1·25 1·25
190/3 .. *Set of* 4 3·25 3·00

(Des D. Slater. Litho B.D.T.)

**1984** (21 Sept). *Christmas and "Ausipex" International Stamp Exhibition, Melbourne. Sheet* 100 × 100 *mm containing T* **43** *and similar horiz designs. Multicoloured. P* 13½.

**MS**194 30 c. Type **43**; 55 c. Distribution of presents; 85 c. Departure of Father Christmas .. 2·00 2·25

No. **MS**194 also contains three labels horizontally *se-tenant* with the stamps and forming composite designs with them.

**44** Robber Crab

**45** "Once in Royal David's City"

(Des L. Curtis. Litho Walsall)

**1985** (30 Jan). *Crabs* (*1st series*). *T* **44** *and similar horiz designs. Multicoloured. P* 13 × 13½.

195 30 c. Type **44** .. 65 50
196 40 c. Horn-eyed Ghost Crab .. 75 60
197 55 c. Purple Hermit Crab .. 90 75
198 85 c. Little Nipper .. 1·25 1·00
195/8 .. *Set of* 4 3·25 2·50

See also Nos. 199/202 and 203/6.

(Des L. Curtis. Litho Walsall)

**1985** (29 Apr). *Crabs* (*2nd series*). *Horiz designs as T* **44**. *Multicoloured. P* 13 × 13½.

199 33 c. Blue Crab .. 70 40
200 45 c. Tawny Hermit Crab .. 80 60
201 60 c. Red Nipper .. 95 75
202 90 c. Smooth-handed Ghost Crab .. 1·40 1·10
199/202 .. *Set of* 4 3·50 2·50

(Des L. Curtis. Litho Walsall)

**1985** (22 July). *Crabs* (*3rd series*). *Horiz designs as T* **44**. *Multicoloured. P* 13 × 13½.

203 33 c. Red Crab .. 70 55
204 45 c. Mottled Crab .. 85 85
205 60 c. Rock Hopper Crab .. 1·10 1·25
206 90 c. Yellow Nipper .. 1·50 1·75
203/6 .. *Set of* 4 3·75 4·00

(Des Jennifer Toombs. Litho Harrison)

**1985** (28 Oct). *Christmas. Carols. T* **45** *and similar vert designs. Multicoloured. P* 14 × 14½.

207 27 c. Type **45** .. 70 70
a. Horiz strip of 5. Nos. 207/11 .. 4·50
208 33 c. "While Shepherds Watched Their Flocks by Night" .. 80 80
209 45 c. "Away in a Manger" .. 95 95
210 60 c. "We Three Kings of Orient Are" .. 1·10 1·10
211 90 c. "Hark the Herald Angels Sing" .. 1·40 1·40
207/11 .. *Set of* 5 4·50 4·50

Nos. 207/11 were printed together, *se-tenant* in horizontal strips of 5 throughout the sheet.

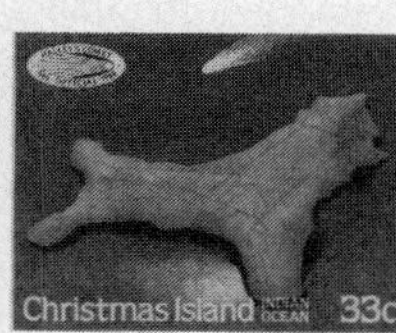


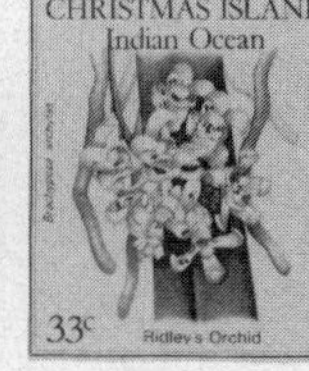


**46** Halley's Comet over Christmas Island

**47** Ridley's Orchid

(Des L. Curtis. Litho Format)

**1986** (30 Apr). *Appearance of Halley's Comet. T* **46** *and similar horiz designs. Multicoloured. P* 14.

212 33 c. Type **46** .. 55 55
213 45 c. Edmond Halley .. 70 80
214 60 c. Comet and ship loading phosphate .. 85 1·00
215 90 c. Comet over Flying Fish Cove .. 1·25 1·50
212/15 .. *Set of* 4 3·00 3·50

(Des I. Loe. Litho Format)

**1986** (30 June). *Native Flowers. T* **47** *and similar vert designs. Multicoloured. P* 14.

216 33 c. Type **47** .. 50 50
217 45 c. Hanging Flower .. 65 75
218 60 c. Hoya .. 75 90
219 90 c. Sea Hibiscus .. 1·10 1·40
216/19 .. *Set of* 4 2·75 3·25

(Des D. Miller. Litho Walsall)

**1986** (23 July). *Royal Wedding. Square designs as T* **112** *of Ascension. Multicoloured. P* 14½ × 14.

220 33 c. Prince Andrew and Miss Sarah Ferguson .. 45 35
221 90 c. Prince Andrew piloting helicopter, Digby, Canada, 1985 .. 95 1·40

**48** Father Christmas and Reindeer in Speed Boat

(Des G. Vasarhelyi. Litho Walsall)

**1986** (30 Sept). *Christmas. T* **48** *and similar horiz designs. Multicoloured. P* 13 × 13½.

222 30 c. Type **48** .. 55 40
223 36 c. Father Christmas and reindeer on beach .. 65 50
224 55 c. Father Christmas fishing .. 1·00 1·10
225 70 c. Playing golf .. 1·50 1·60
226 $1 Sleeping in hammock .. 1·75 2·00
222/6 .. *Set of* 5 5·00 5·00

**49** H.M.S. *Flying Fish* and Outline Map of Christmas Island

(Des L. Curtis. Litho Format)

**1987** (21 Jan). *Centenary of Visits by H.M.S. "Flying Fish" and H.M.S. "Egeria". T* **49** *and similar horiz design. Multicoloured. P* 14½.

227 36 c. Type **49** .. 80 60
228 90 c. H.M.S. *Egeria* and outline map .. 1·60 2·40

**50** Blind Snake

**51** Children watching Father Christmas in Sleigh

(Des G. Drummond. Litho Questa)

**1987** (25 Mar)–**89**. *Wildlife. T* **50** *and similar horiz designs. Multicoloured. P* 14.

229 1 c. Type **50** .. 30 30
a. Sheetlet of 16. Nos. 229/44 (1.3.88) .. 16·00
230 2 c. Blue-tailed Skink .. 30 30
231 3 c. Insectivorous Bat (24.6.87) .. 35 35
232 5 c. Grasshopper (1.3.88) .. 35 35
233 10 c. Christmas Island Fruit Bat (24.6.87) .. 35 35
234 25 c. Gecko .. 45 45
235 10 c. *Mantis religiosa* (mantid) (1.3.88) .. 55 55
236 36 c. Indonesian Hawk Owl (24.6.87) .. 90 90
237 40 c. Bull Mouth Helmet Shell (26.8.87) .. 55 55
237*a* 41 c. Nudibranch (*Phidiana* sp) (1.9.89) .. 55 60
238 50 c. Textile Cone Shell (26.8.87) .. 65 65
239 65 c. Brittle Stars (26.8.87) .. 65 70
240 75 c. Royal Angelfish (26.8.87) .. 65 75
241 90 c. *Appias paulina* (butterfly) (1.3.88) .. 1·75 1·75
242 $1 *Hypolimnas misippus* (butterfly) (1.3.88) .. 1·75 1·75
243 $2 Shrew (*Crocidura attenuata trichura*) (24.6.87) .. 2·50 2·50
244 $5 Green Turtle .. 4·50 5·00
229/44 .. *Set of* 17 15·00 16·00

No. 229a was originally only available from a presentation pack, but was, subsequently, sold separately by the Christmas Island Post Office. Stamps from it show "1988" imprint date. Examples from the ordinary sheets are without imprint date.

(Des D. Miller. Litho CPE Australia Ltd, Melbourne)

**1987** (7 Oct). *Christmas. Sheet*, 165 × 65 *mm, containing T* **51** *and similar multicoloured designs. P* 13½.

**MS**245 30 c. Type **51**; 37 c. Father Christmas distributing gifts (48 × 22 *mm*); 90 c. Children with presents (48 × 22 *mm*); $1 Singing carols .. 3·00 3·50

The stamps within No. **MS**245 form a composite design of a beach scene.

(Des Sue Passmore. Litho CPE Australia Ltd, Melbourne)

**1988** (26 Jan). *Bicentenary of Australian Settlement. Arrival of First Fleet. Square designs as Nos.* 1105/9 *of Australia, but each inscribed* "CHRISTMAS ISLAND Indian Ocean" *and* "AUSTRALIA BICENTENARY".

246 37 c. Aborigines watching arrival of Fleet, Botany Bay .. 90 90
a. Horiz strip of 5. Nos. 246/50 .. 4·00
247 37 c. Aboriginal family and anchored ships .. 90 90
248 37 c. Fleet arriving at Sydney Cove .. 90 90
249 37 c. Ship's boat .. 90 90
250 37 c. Raising the flag, Sydney Cove, 26 January 1788 .. 90 90
246/50 .. *Set of* 5 4·00 4·00

Nos. 246/50 were printed together, *se-tenant*, in horizontal strips of five throughout the sheet, forming a composite design.

**52** Captain William May

**53** Pony and Trap, 1910

(Des Josephine Martin. Litho Questa)

**1988** (8 June). *Centenary of British Annexation. T* **52** *and similar vert designs. Multicoloured. P* 14½ × 14.

251 37 c. Type **52** .. 35 40
252 53 c. Annexation ceremony .. 50 55
253 95 c. H.M.S. *Imperieuse* firing salute .. 90 95
254 $1.50, Building commemorative cairn .. 1·40 1·50
251/4 .. *Set of* 4 2·75 3·00

(Des L. Curtis. Litho Walsall)

**1988** (24 Aug). *Centenary of Permanent Settlement. T* **53** *and similar horiz designs. Multicoloured. P* 14×14½.

255 37 c. Type **53** 45 40
256 55 c. Phosphate mining, 1910 60 55
257 70 c. Steam locomotive, 1914 85 70
258 $1 Arrival of first aircraft, 1957 1·25 1·00
255/8 *Set of* 4 2·75 2·40

**54** Beach Toys

**55** Food on Table ("Good Harvesting")

(Des N. Shewring. Litho Format)

**1988** (15 Nov). *Christmas. Toys and Gifts. T* **54** *and similar vert designs. Multicoloured. P* 14.

259 32 c. Type **54** 40 35
260 39 c. Flippers, snorkel and mask 50 40
261 90 c. Model soldier, doll and soft toys 1·10 90
262 $1 Models of racing car, lorry and jet aircraft 1·25 1·00
259/62 *Set of* 4 3·00 2·40

(Des D. Miller. Litho Questa)

**1989** (31 Jan). *Chinese New Year. T* **55** *and similar horiz designs. Multicoloured. P* 14 × 14½.

263 39 c. Type **55** 45 40
264 70 c. Decorations ("Prosperity") 80 70
265 90 c. Chinese girls ("Good Fortune") 1·10 90
266 $1 Lion dance ("Progress Every Year") 1·25 1·00
263/6 *Set of* 4 3·25 2·75

**56** Sir John Murray

**57** Four Children

(Des S. Noon. Litho Walsall)

**1989** (16 Mar). *75th Death Anniv of Sir John Murray (oceanographer). T* **56** *and similar horiz designs. Multicoloured. P* 14 × 14½.

267 39 c. Type **56** 50 50
268 80 c. Map of Christmas Island showing Murray Hill 95 95
269 $1 Oceanographic equipment 1·25 1·25
270 $1.10, H.M.S. *Challenger* (survey ship) 1·50 1·50
267/70 *Set of* 4 3·75 3·75

(Des C. Burke. Litho Questa)

**1989** (31 May). *Malay Hari Raya Festival. T* **57** *and similar vert designs. Multicoloured. P* 14.

271 39 c. Type **57** 50 50
272 55 c. Man playing tambourine 70 70
273 80 c. Girl in festival costume 1·00 1·00
274 $1.10, Christmas Island Mosque 1·40 1·40
271/4 *Set of* 4 3·25 3·25

**58** *Huperzia phlegmaria*

**59** Virgin Mary and Star

(Des Kerrie Rockett. Litho Walsall)

**1989** (16 Aug). *Ferns. T* **58** *and similar vert designs. Multicoloured. P* 14.

275 41 c. Type **58** 60 60
276 65 c. *Asplenium polydon* 85 85
277 80 c. Common Bracken 1·00 1·00
278 $1.10, Birds-nest Fern 1·40 1·40
275/8 *Set of* 4 3·50 3·50

(Des G. Maynard. Litho Leigh-Mardon Ltd, Melbourne)

**1989** (4 Oct). *Christmas. T* **59** *and similar vert designs. Multicoloured. P* 14½.

279 36 c. Type **59** 35 40
280 41 c. Christ Child in manger 40 45
281 80 c. Shepherds and Star 75 80
282 $1.10, Three Wise Men following Star 1·00 1·10
279/82 *Set of* 4 2·25 2·50

**(60)**

**61** First Sighting, 1615

**1989** (18 Oct). *"Melbourne Stampshow '89". No. 237a and as No. 242, but with imprint date, optd with T* **60**.

283 41 c. Nudibranch (*Phidiana* sp) 40 45
284 $1 *Hypolimnas misippus* 1·00 1·00

(Des R. Honisett. Litho Note Ptg Branch, Reserve Bank of Australia)

**1990** (31 Jan). *375th Anniv of Discovery of Christmas Island. T* **61** *and similar vert design. Multicoloured. P* 14×15.

285 41 c. Type **61** 50 50
286 $1.10, Second sighting and naming, 1643 1·40 1·40

**62** Miniature Tractor pulling Phosphate

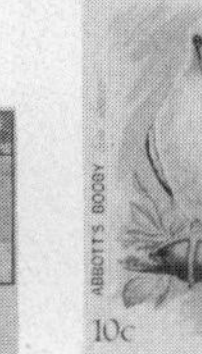

**63** Male Abbott's Booby

(Des C. Lee. Litho Leigh-Mardon Ltd, Melbourne)

**1990** (18 Apr–22 Aug). *Christmas Island Transport. T* **62** *and similar multicoloured designs. P* 13½×14 (*horiz*) *or* 14×13½ (*vert*).

287 1 c. Type **62** 10 10
288 2 c. Phosphate train (22 Aug) 10 10
289 3 c. Diesel railcar (*vert*) 10 10
290 5 c. Loading Road train (22 Aug) 10 10
291 10 c. Trishaw (*vert*) 10 15
292 15 c. Terex truck (22 Aug) 15 20
293 25 c. Articulated bus 25 30
294 30 c. Railway passenger rake (*vert*) 30 35
295 40 c. Passenger barge (*vert*) 35 40
296 50 c. Kolek (outrigger canoe) 45 50
297 65 c. Flying Doctor aircraft and ambulance (22 Aug) 60 65
298 75 c. Commercial van (22 Aug) 70 75
299 90 c. Vintage lorry (22 Aug) 85 90
300 $1 Water tanker (22 Aug) 90 95
301 $2 Traction engine (22 Aug) 1·90 2·00
302 $5 Steam locomotive and flat car 4·50 4·75
287/302 *Set of* 16 10·00 11·00

(Des N. Shewring. Litho Questa)

**1990** (6 June). *Abbott's Booby. T* **63** *and similar vert designs. Multicoloured. P* 13½×14.

303 10 c. Type **63** 30 30
304 20 c. Juvenile male 50 50
305 29 c. Female with egg 55 55
306 41 c. Pair with chick 70 70
303/6 *Set of* 4 1·90 1·90
**MS**307 122×68 mm. 41 c. Male with wings spread; 41 c. Male on branch; 41 c. Female with fledgling. P 14½ 1·90 2·25

The three stamps within No. **MS**307 form a composite design and are without the W.W.F. logo.

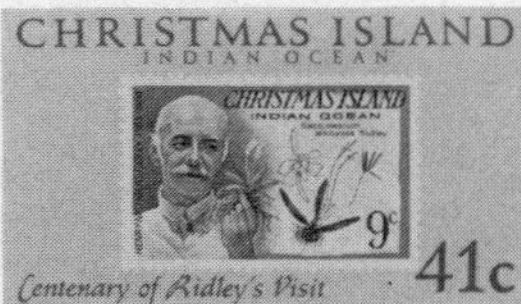

**64** 1977 Famous Visitors 9 c. Stamp

(Des Elizabeth Innes. Litho Leigh-Mardon Ltd, Melbourne)

**1990** (11 July). *Centenary of Henry Ridley's Visit. T* **64** *and similar multicoloured design. P* 15×14½ (41 c.) *or* 14½×15 (75 c.).

308 41 c. Type **64** 55 55
309 75 c. Ridley (botanist) in rainforest (*vert*) 85 95

**1990** (24 Aug). *"New Zealand 1990" International Stamp Exhibition, Auckland. No.* **MS**307 *optd* "NZ 1990 WORLD STAMP EXHIBITION AUCKLAND, NEW ZEALAND, 24 AUGUST – 2 SEPTEMBER 1990" *in purple on the sheet margins.*

**MS**310 122×68 mm. 41 c. Male with wings spread ; 41 c. Male on branch; 41 c. Female with fledgling 1·50 1·60

## NEW INFORMATION

The editor is always interested to correspond with people who have new information that will improve or correct the Catalogue.

**65** *Corymborkus veratrifolia*

**66** *Islander* (freighter), 1898

(Litho Leigh-Mardon Ltd, Melbourne)

**1990** (3 Oct). *Christmas. Flowers. T* **65** *and similar horiz designs. Multicoloured. P* 14½.

311 38 c. Type **65** 50 60
312 43 c. *Hoya aldrichii* 55 65
313 80 c. *Quisqualis indica* 95 1·10
314 $1.20, *Barringtonia racemosa* 1·50 1·60
311/14 *Set of* 4 3·25 3·50

**1990** (6 Dec). *"Birdpex '90" Stamp Exhibition, Christchurch. No.* **MS**307 *optd* "BIRDPEX '90 NATIONAL PHILATELIC EXHIBITION UNIVERSITY OF CANTERBURY CHRISTCHURCH NZ 6–9 DEC 1990 IN CONJUNCTION WITH THE 20th INTERNATIONAL ORNITHOLOGICAL CONGRESS" *in green on the sheet margins.*

**MS**315 122×68 mm. 41 c. Male with wings spread; 41 c. Male on branch; 41 c. Female with fledgling 1·10 1·25

(Des C. Lee. Litho Leigh-Mardon Ltd, Melbourne)

**1991** (13 Feb). *Centenary of First Phosphate Mining Lease. T* **66** *and similar vert designs. Multicoloured. P* 14½.

316 43 c. Type **66** 60 60
a. Horiz strip of 5. Nos. 316/20 5·00
317 43 c. Miners loading rail wagons, 1908 60 60
318 85 c. Shay steam locomotive No. 4, 1925 1·00 1·00
319 $1.20, Extracting phosphate, 1951 1·40 1·40
320 $1.70, Land reclamation, 1990 1·90 1·90
316/20 *Set of* 5 5·00 5·00

Nos. 316/20 were printed together, *se-tenant*, in horizontal strips of 5 throughout the sheet, the background forming a composite forest design.

**67** Teaching Children Road Safety

**68** Map of Christmas Island, 1991

(Des R. Honisett. Litho Leigh-Mardon Ltd, Melbourne)

**1991** (17 Apr). *Christmas Island Police Force. T* **67** *and similar horiz designs. Multicoloured. P* 14½.

321 43 c. Type **67** 60 60
322 43 c. Traffic control 60 60
323 90 c. Airport customs 1·40 1·40
324 $1.20, Police launch *Fregata Andrews* towing rescued boat 1·75 1·75
321/4 *Set of* 4 4·00 4·00
**MS**325 135×88 mm. Nos. 321/4 3·75 3·75

(Des D. Miller. Litho Questa)

**1991** (19 June). *Maps of Christmas Island. T* **68** *and similar vert designs. Multicoloured. P* 14×13½.

326 43 c. Type **68** 55 55
327 75 c. Goos Atlas, 1666 95 95
328 $1.10, De Manevillette, 1745 1·40 1·40
329 $1.20, Comberford, 1667 1·50 1·50
326/9 *Set of* 4 4·00 4·00

**69** *Bruguiera gymnorrhiza*

**70** "Family round Christmas Tree", (S'ng Yen Luiw)

(Des Jane Moore. Litho Leigh-Mardon Ltd, Melbourne)

**1991** (21 Aug). *Local Trees. T* **69** *and similar horiz designs. Multicoloured. P* 14.

330 43 c. Type **69** 55 55
331 70 c. *Syzygium operculatum* 90 90
332 85 c. *Ficus microcarpa* 1·10 1·10
333 $1.20, *Arenga listeri* 1·50 1·50
330/3 *Set of* 4 3·50 3·50

(Des Liz Innes. Litho Leigh-Mardon Ltd, Melbourne)

**1991** (2 Oct). *Christmas. Children's Paintings. T* **70** *and similar horiz designs. Multicoloured. P* 14½.

| | | | | |
|---|---|---|---|---|
| 334 | 38 c. Type **70** .. .. .. .. | 35 | 40 |
| | a. Horiz strip of 5. Nos 334/8 .. .. | 1·75 | |
| 335 | 38 c. "Opening Presents" (Liew Ann Nee) | 35 | 40 |
| 336 | 38 c. "Beach Party" (Foo Pang Chuan) .. | 35 | 40 |
| 337 | 38 c. "Christmas Walk" (Too Lai Peng) .. | 35 | 40 |
| 338 | 38 c. "Santa Claus and Christmas Tree" (Jesamine Wheeler) .. .. .. | 35 | 40 |
| 339 | 43 c. "Santa Claus fishing" (Ho Puay Ha) .. | 40 | 45 |
| 340 | $1 "Santa Claus in Boat" (Ng Hooi Hua) | 90 | 95 |
| 341 | $1.20, "Santa Claus surfing" (Yani Kawi) | 1·10 | 1·25 |
| 334/41 | .. .. .. .. *Set of* 8 | 3·75 | 4·25 |

Nos. 334/8 were printed together, *se-tenant*, in horizontal strips of 5 throughout the sheet.

**71** Discussing Evacuation, 1942

(Des C. Lee. Litho Leigh-Mardon Ltd, Melbourne)

**1992** (19 Feb). *50th Anniv of Partial Evacuation. T* **71** *and similar vert designs. Multicoloured. P* 14½.

| | | | |
|---|---|---|---|
| 342 | 45 c. Type **71** .. .. .. .. | 40 | 45 |
| 343 | 45 c. Families waiting to embark .. .. | 40 | 45 |
| 344 | $1.05, Ferrying evacuees to *Islander* .. | 95 | 1·00 |
| 345 | $1.20, Departure of *Islander* (freighter) .. | 1·10 | 1·25 |
| 342/5 | .. .. .. .. *Set of* 4 | 2·50 | 2·75 |

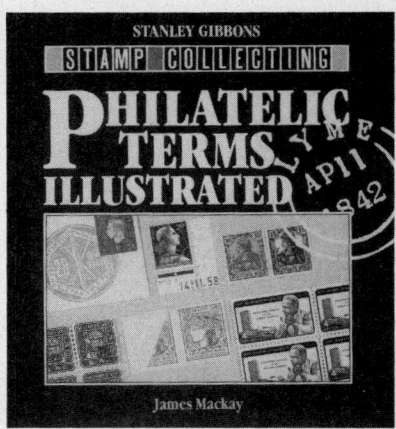

# Cocos (Keeling) Is.

The Cocos (Keeling) Islands, which had been settled by the Clunies Ross family in the 1820s, were annexed by Great Britain in 1857. In 1878 the group was attached to Ceylon, but was transferred to the Straits Settlements in 1886. During the Second World War the islands were under British military control exercised from Ceylon. At the end of hostilities administration from Singapore was continued until the islands were transferred to Australia on 23 November 1955.

The stamps of the STRAITS SETTLEMENTS were used by a postal agency operating on Cocos (Keeling) Islands from 1 April 1933 until 1 March 1937. The postal agency reopened on 2 September 1952 and used the stamps of SINGAPORE until the islands were transferred to Australia in 1955. From 1955 until 1963 stamps of AUSTRALIA were in use.

**PRINTERS.** All the following stamps to No. 31 were printed by the Note Printing Branch, Reserve Bank of Australia, Melbourne.

1 Copra Industry

2 "Super Constellation"

(Des K. McKay and E. Jones (5d.), E. Jones (others). Eng E. Jones. Recess)

**1963** (11 June). *T* **1/2** *and similar designs. P* 14½×14 (5*d.*, 2*s.* 3*d.*) *or* 14½ (*others*).

3d. chocolate .. 1·75 1·25
5d. ultramarine .. 1·50 65
8d. scarlet .. 4·50 1·75
1s. green .. 3·00 55
2s. deep purple .. 11·00 3·25
2s. 3d. deep green .. 42·00 3·25
/6 .. *Set of* 6 55·00 9·75

Designs: *Vert* (*as T* **1**)—8d. Map of islands; 2s. Jukong sailboat). *Horiz* (*as T* **1**)—1s. Palms. (*as T* **2**)—2s. 3d. White Tern.

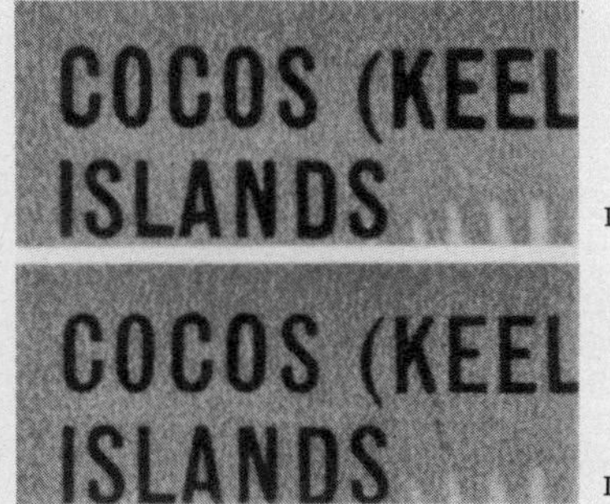


I

II

I Thick lettering

II Thinner lettering

**1965** (14 Apr). *50th Anniv of Gallipoli Landing. As T* **184** *of Australia, but slightly larger* (22×34½ *mm*) *and colour changed. Photo. P* 13½.

7 5d. sepia, black and emerald (I) .. 60 45
a. *Black-brown, black and light emerald* (II) 2·25 1·50

No. 7a comes from a second printing, using a new black cylinder, which was available from the end of April.

With the introduction of decimal currency on 14 February 1966, Australian stamps were used in Cocos Islands, until the appearance of the new definitives on 9 July 1969.

7 Reef Clam

8 Great Frigate Bird

(Des L. Annois (1 c. to 6 c.); P. Jones (10 c. to $1). Photo)

**1969** (9 July). *Decimal Currency. T* **8** *or designs as T* **7**. *Multicoloured. P* 13½.

8 1 c. Lajonkaines Turbo shell (*vert*) .. 30 30
9 2 c. Crocus Giant clam (*vert*) .. 1·00 45
10 3 c. Type **7** .. 30 15
11 4 c. *Petroscirtes mitratus* (fish) .. 30 15
a. Salmon-pink omitted .. £650
12 5 c. *Porites cocosensis* (coral) .. 35 15
13 6 c. Greater Spotted Flying Fish .. 75 20
14 10 c. Banded Rail .. 1·50 50
15 15 c. Java Sparrow .. 1·00 30
16 20 c. Red-tailed Tropic Bird .. 1·00 30
17 30 c. Sooty Tern .. 1·25 30
18 50 c. Eastern Reef Heron (*vert*) .. 2·00 30
19 $1 Type **8** .. 5·00 1·00
8/19 .. *Set of* 12 13·50 3·75

**9** *Dragon*, 1609

**10** Map of Cocos (Keeling) Islands Union Flag, Stars and Trees

(Des R. Honisett. Photo)

**1976** (29 Mar). *Ships. Multicoloured designs as T* **9**. *P* 13½.

20 1 c. Type **9** .. 30 40
21 2 c. H.M.S. *Juno*, 1857 .. 30 40
22 5 c. H.M.S. *Beagle*, 1836 .. 30 40
23 10 c. H.M.A.S. *Sydney*, 1914 .. 35 40
24 15 c. S.M.S. *Emden*, 1914 .. 80 55
25 20 c. *Ayesha*, 1907 .. 85 65
26 25 c. T.S.S. *Islander*, 1927 .. 90 1·00
27 30 c. M.V. *Cheshire*, 1951 .. 1·00 1·00
28 35 c. Jukong (sailboat) .. 1·00 1·00
29 40 c. C.S. *Scotia*, 1900 .. 1·00 1·00
30 50 c. R.M.S. *Orontes*, 1929 .. 1·40 1·10
31 $1 Royal Yacht *Gothic*, 1954 .. 1·75 1·40
20/31 .. *Set of* 12 9·00 8·50

The 2 c. to 20 c., 35 c. and 40 c. are horizontal designs.

(Des Marg Towt. Litho Asher and Co, Melbourne)

**1979** (3 Sept). *Inauguration of Independent Postal Service* (20 *c.*) *and Establishment of First Statutory Council* (50 *c.*). *T* **10** *and similar horiz design. Multicoloured. P* 15½ × 15.

32 20 c. Type **10** .. 25 30
33 50 c. Council seal and jukong (sailboat) .. 35 50

**11** Bright Yellow Long-nosed Butterfly Fish

**12** "Peace on Earth"

(Des Marg Towt. Litho Asher and Co, Melbourne)

**1979** (3 Sept)–**80**. *Fishes. Horiz designs as T* **11**. *Multicoloured. P* 13½ × 13 (22 *c.*, 28 *c.*, 60 *c.*) *or* 15½ × 15 (*others*).

34 1 c. Type **11** .. 30 50
35 2 c. Clown Butterfly Fish (19.11.79) .. 30 30
36 5 c. *Anthias sp.* .. 40 60
37 10 c. Meyer's Butterfly Fish (18.2.80) .. 30 30
38 15 c. Wrasse (19.11.79) .. 30 30
39 20 c. Charles' Clown Fish (19.11.79) .. 45 30
39*a* 22 c. Yellow-striped Emerald Triggerfish (1.7.80) .. 30 30
40 25 c. *Cheilinus fasciatus* (18.2.80) .. 45 35
40*a* 28 c. *Macropharyngodon meleagris* (1.7.80) .. 35 35
41 30 c. *Chaetodon madagascariensis* (19.11.79) 65 45
42 35 c. Angel Fish .. 65 1·25
43 40 c. Hog Fish (19.11.79) .. 70 60
44 50 c. Wrasse (*different*) (19.11.79) .. 85 75
45 55 c. *Anampses meleagrides* (18.2.80) .. 75 75
45*a* 60 c. Grouper (1.7.80) .. 75 75
46 $1 Surgeon Fish .. 1·75 2·75
47 $2 Three-banded Butterfly Fish (18.2.80) .. 2·00 2·75
34/47 .. *Set of* 17 10·00 12·00

(Des D. Pitt. Litho Asher & Co, Melbourne)

**1979** (22 Oct). *Christmas. T* **12** *and similar multicoloured design. P* 15 × 15½ (25 *c.*) *or* 15½ × 15 (55 *c.*).

48 25 c. Type **12** .. 25 35
49 55 c. "Goodwill Toward Men" (*horiz*) .. 40 55

**13** Star, Map of Cocos (Keeling) Islands and Island Landscape

**14** "Administered by the British Government, 1857"

(Des P. Arnold. Litho Asher and Co, Melbourne)

**1980** (22 Oct). *Christmas. T* **13** *and similar horiz designs. Multicoloured. P* 13.

50 15 c. Type **13** .. 10 10
51 28 c. Map and Wise Men following star .. 15 15
52 60 c. Map and Nativity scene .. 40 40
50/2 .. *Set of* 3 60 60

(Des Sue Wilson. Litho Asher and Co, Melbourne)

**1980** (24 Nov). *25th Anniv of Cocos (Keeling) Islands as an Australian Territory. T* **14** *and similar horiz designs. Multicoloured. P* 13½ × 13.

53 22 c. Type **14** .. 15 15
a. Horiz strip of 5. Nos. 53/7 .. 70
54 22 c. "Administered by the Government of Ceylon, 1878, 1942–6" .. 15 15
55 22 c. "Administered by the Straits Settlements, 1886" .. 15 15
56 22 c. "Administered by the Colony of Singapore, 1946" .. 15 15
57 22 c. "Administered by the Australian Government, 1955" .. 15 15
53/7 .. *Set of* 5 70 70

Nos. 53/7 were printed together, *se-tenant*, in horizontal strips of 5 throughout the sheet, forming a composite design.

**15** *Eye of the Wind* and Map of Cocos (Keeling) Islands

**16** Aerial View of Animal Quarantine Station

(Des Sue Wilson. Litho Asher and Co, Melbourne)

**1980** (18 Dec). *"Operation Drake" (round the world expedition) and 400th Anniv of Sir Francis Drake's Circumnavigation of the World. T* **15** *and similar multicoloured designs. P* 13.

58 22 c. Type **15** .. 20 15
59 28 c. Map of the World showing voyage routes (*horiz*) .. 20 15
60 35 c. Sir Francis Drake and *Golden Hind* .. 20 15
61 60 c. Prince Charles and *Eye of the Wind* .. 35 30
58/61 .. *Set of* 4 85 65

(Des Cato Hibberd Design. Litho Leigh-Mardon Ltd, Melbourne)

**1981** (12 May). *Opening of Animal Quarantine Station. T* **16** *and similar horiz designs. Multicoloured. P* 13½ × 13.

62 22 c. Type **16** .. 15 15
63 45 c. Unloading livestock .. 30 30
64 60 c. Livestock in pen .. 35 35
62/4 .. *Set of* 3 70 70

**17** Consolidated "Catalina" *Guba II* Flying Boat

**18** Prince Charles and Lady Diana Spencer

(Des R. Honisett. Litho Leigh-Mardon Ltd, Melbourne)

**1981** (23 June). *Aircraft. T* **17** *and similar horiz designs. Multicoloured. P* 13½ × 13.

65 22 c. Type **17** .. 25 25
a. Horiz strip of 5. Nos. 65/9 .. 1·10
66 22 c. Consolidated "Liberator" and Avro "Lancastrian" .. 25 25
67 22 c. Douglas "DC4 (Skymaster)" and Lockheed "Constellation" .. 25 25
68 22 c. Lockheed "Electra" .. 25 25
69 22 c. Boeing "727" airliners .. 25 25
65/9 .. *Set of* 5 1·10 1·10

Nos. 65/9 were printed together, *se-tenant*, in horizontal strips of 5 throughout the sheet.

(Des B. Clinton. Litho Leigh-Mardon Ltd, Melbourne)

**1981** (29 July). *Royal Wedding. P* 13½ × 13.

70 **18** 24 c. multicoloured .. 40 20
71 60 c. multicoloured .. 85 60

**19** "Angels we have heard on High"

**20** *Pachyseris speciosa* and *Heliofungia actiniformis* (corals)

(Des B. Weatherhead. Litho Leigh-Mardon Ltd, Melbourne)

**1981** (22 Oct). *Christmas. Scenes and Lines from Carol "Angels we have heard on High". T* **19** *and similar horiz designs. Multicoloured. P* 13½ × 13.

72 18 c. Type **19** .. 10 10
73 30 c. "Shepherds why this Jubilee?" .. 20 20
74 60 c. "Come to Bethlehem and see Him" .. 35 35
72/4 .. *Set of* 3 60 60

(Des B. Weatherhead. Litho Leigh-Mardon Ltd, Melbourne)

**1981** (28 Dec). *150th Anniv of Charles Darwin's Voyage. T* **20** *and similar horiz designs. Multicoloured. P* 13½ × 13.

75 24 c. Type **20** .. 35 15
76 45 c. Charles Darwin in 1853 and *Pavona cactus* (coral) .. 55 30
77 60 c. H.M.S. *Beagle*, 1832, and *Lobophyllia hemprichii* (coral) .. 70 35
75/7 .. *Set of* 3 1·40 70

**MS**78 130 × 95 mm. 24 c. Cross-section of West Island; 24 c. Cross-section of Home Island .. 75 85

21 Queen Victoria

22 Lord Baden-Powell

(Des B. Weatherhead. Litho Cambec Press, Melbourne)

**1982** (31 Mar). *125th Anniv of Annexation of Cocos (Keeling) Islands to British Empire. T* **21** *and similar horiz designs. Multicoloured. P* 13½ × 14.

79 24 c. Type **21** .. .. .. .. .. .. 20 15
80 45 c. Union flag .. .. .. .. .. .. 35 25
81 60 c. Capt. S. Fremantle (annexation visit, 1857) .. .. .. .. .. 40 35
79/81 .. .. .. .. .. *Set of* 3 85 65

(Des B. Clinton. Litho Cambec Press, Melbourne)

**1982** (21 July). *75th Anniv of Boy Scout Movement. T* **22** *and similar multicoloured design. P* 13½ × 14 (27 c.) *or* 14 × 13½ (75 c.).

82 27 c. Type **22** .. .. .. .. .. .. 30 15
83 75 c. "75" and map of Cocos (Keeling) Islands (*vert*) .. .. .. .. .. 1·10 60

23 *Precis villida*

24 "Call His Name Immanuel"

(Des B. Hargreaves. Litho Harrison)

**1982** (6 Sept)–**83**. *Butterflies and Moths. T* **23** *and similar multicoloured designs. P* 14.

84 1 c. Type **23** .. .. .. .. .. .. 55 45
85 2 c. *Cephonodes picus* (*horiz*) (6.1.83) .. .. 40 40
86 5 c. *Macroglossum corythus* (*horiz*) .. .. 75 50
87 10 c. *Chasmina candida* (6.1.83) .. .. 40 40
88 20 c. *Nagia linteola* (*horiz*) (6.4.83) .. .. 40 40
89 25 c. *Eublemma rivula* (1.7.83) .. .. 40 55
90 30 c. *Eurrhyparodes tricoloralis* (6.4.83) .. 40 40
91 35 c. *Hippotion boerhaviae* (*horiz*) .. .. 1·25 50
92 40 c. *Euploea core* (6.4.83) .. .. .. 40 50
93 45 c. *Psara hipponalis* (*horiz*) (6.4.83) .. 50 60
94 50 c. *Danaus chrysippus* (*horiz*) (1.7.83) .. 55 1·00
95 55 c. *Hypolimnas misippus* (6.1.83) .. .. 60 60
96 60 c. *Spodoptera litura* (1.7.83) .. .. 65 1·00
97 $1 *Achaea janata* .. .. .. .. 2·25 2·00
98 $2 *Panacra velox* (*horiz*) (1.7.83) .. .. 2·00 2·75
99 $3 *Utetheisa pulchelloides* (*horiz*) (6.1.83) 2·75 2·75
84/99 .. .. .. .. .. *Set of* 16 13·00 13·50

(Des G. Hamori. Litho Cambec Press, Melbourne)

**1982** (25 Oct). *Christmas. T* **24** *and similar horiz designs. Multicoloured. P* 13½ × 14.

100 21 c. Type **24** .. .. .. .. .. 20 20
101 35 c. "I bring you good tidings" .. .. .. 35 35
102 75 c. "Arise and flee into Egypt" .. .. .. 80 80
100/2 .. .. .. .. .. *Set of* 3 1·25 1·25

25 "God will look after us" (*Matt.* 1:20)

26 Hari Raya Celebrations

(Des R. Roberts. Litho Cambec Press, Melbourne)

**1983** (25 Oct). *Christmas. Extracts from the New Testament. T* **25** *and similar vert designs. Multicoloured. P* 14 × 13½.

103 24 c. Type **25** .. .. .. .. .. 30 30
a. Horiz strip of 5. Nos. 103/7 .. .. 1·40
104 24 c. "Our baby King, Jesus" (*Matthew* 2:2) .. 30 30
105 24 c. "Your Saviour is born" (*Luke* 2:11) .. 30 30
106 24 c. "Wise men followed the Star" (*Matthew* 2:9–10) .. .. .. .. .. 30 30
107 24 c. "And worship the Lord" (*Matthew* 2:11) 30 30
103/7 .. .. .. .. .. *Set of* 5 1·40 1·40

Nos. 103/7 were printed together, *se-tenant*, in horizontal strips of 5 throughout the sheet.

(Des Marg Towt. Litho Cambec Press, Melbourne)

**1984** (24 Jan). *Cocos-Malay Culture. (1st series). Festivals. T* **26** *and similar vert designs. Multicoloured. P* 13½ × 13.

108 45 c. Type **26** .. .. .. .. .. 45 35
109 75 c. Melenggok dancing .. .. .. 65 50
110 85 c. Cocos-Malay wedding .. .. .. 75 55
108/10 .. .. .. .. .. *Set of* 3 1·75 1·25

See also Nos. 126/8.

27 Unpacking Barrel

28 Captain William Keeling

(Des R. Honisett. Litho Cambec Press, Melbourne)

**1984** (20 Apr). *75th Anniv of Cocos Barrel Mail. T* **27** *and similar horiz designs. Multicoloured. P* 13½ × 14.

111 35 c. Type **27** .. .. .. .. .. 35 25
112 55 c. Jukong awaiting mail ship .. .. 60 50
113 70 c. P. & O. mail ship *Morea* .. .. 70 55
111/13 .. .. .. .. .. *Set of* 3 1·50 1·10
**MS**114 125 × 95 mm. $1 Retrieving barrel .. 90 1·25

(Des B. Clinton. Litho Cambec Press, Melbourne)

**1984** (10 July). *375th Anniv of Discovery of Cocos (Keeling) Islands. T* **28** *and similar vert designs. Multicoloured. P* 14.

115 30 c. Type **28** .. .. .. .. .. 70 40
116 65 c. Keeling's ship *Hector* .. .. .. 1·50 90
117 95 c. Mariner's astrolabe .. .. .. 1·75 1·25
118 $1. 10, Map *circa* 1666 .. .. .. 1·90 1·50
115/18 .. .. .. .. .. *Set of* 4 5·25 3·50

29 Malay Settlement, Home Island

30 "Rainbow" Fish

(Des E. Roberts. Litho Cambec Press, Melbourne)

**1984** (21 Sept). *"Ausipex" International Stamp Exhibition, Melbourne. T* **29** *and similar horiz designs. Multicoloured. P* 13½ × 14.

119 45 c. Type **29** .. .. .. .. .. 65 50
120 55 c. Airstrip, West Island .. .. .. 75 60
**MS**121 130 × 95 mm. $2 Jukongs (native craft) racing .. .. .. .. .. .. 2·75 2·50

(Des R. Roberts. Litho Cambec Press, Melbourne)

**1984** (31 Oct). *Christmas. T* **30** *and similar horiz designs. Multicoloured. P* 13½ × 14.

122 24 c. Type **30** .. .. .. .. .. 40 25
123 35 c. "Rainbow" butterfly .. .. .. 70 35
124 55 c. "Rainbow" bird .. .. .. .. 85 55
122/4 .. .. .. .. .. *Set of* 3 1·75 1·10

31 Cocos Islanders

32 Jukong building

(Des B. Weatherhead. Litho Cambec Press, Melbourne)

**1984** (30 Nov). *Integration of Cocos (Keeling) Islands with Australia. Sheet* 90 × 52 *mm. containing T* **31** *and similar horiz design. Multicoloured. P* 13½ × 14.

**MS**125 30 c. Type **31**: 30 c. Australian flag on island 1·00 1·00

(Des Marg Towt. Litho Cambec Press, Melbourne)

**1985** (30 Jan). *Cocos-Malay Culture (2nd series). Handicrafts. T* **32** *and similar vert designs. Multicoloured. P* 14 × 13½.

126 30 c. Type **32** .. .. .. .. .. 65 25
127 45 c. Blacksmithing .. .. .. .. 90 40
128 55 c. Woodcarving .. .. .. .. 1·10 50
126/8 .. .. .. .. .. *Set of* 3 2·40 1·10

33 C.S. *Scotia*

34 Red-footed Booby

(Des B. Clinton. Litho Cambec Press, Melbourne)

**1985** (24 Apr). *Cable-laying Ships. T* **33** *and similar hor designs. Multicoloured. P* 13½ × 14.

129 33 c. Type **33** .. .. .. .. .. 1·00 3
130 65 c. C.S. *Anglia* .. .. .. .. 1·60 7
131 80 c. C.S. *Patrol* .. .. .. .. 2·00 9
129/31 .. .. .. .. *Set of* 3 4·25 1·7

(Des Marg Towt. Litho Cambec Press, Melbourne)

**1985** (17 July). *Birds of Cocos (Keeling) Islands. T* **34** *an similar multicoloured designs. P* 13½.

132 33 c. Type **34** .. .. .. .. .. 1·50
a. Block of 3. Nos. 132/4 .. .. .. 5·00
ab. Imperf vert (block of 3) .. .. .. £500
133 60 c. Rufous Night Heron (juvenile) (*horiz*) .. 1·75 1·1
134 $1 Banded Rail (*horiz*) .. .. .. 2·25 1·5
132/4 .. .. .. .. .. *Set of* 3 5·00 3·0

Nos. 132/4 were printed together, *se-tenant*, in blocks of throughout the sheet, each block forming a composite design.

35 *Trochus maculatus*

36 Night Sky and Palm Trees

(Des G. Ryan. Litho Cambec Press, Melbourne)

**1985** (18 Sept)–**86**. *Shells and Molluscs. T* **35** *and similar hori designs. Multicoloured. P* 13½ × 14.

135 1 c. Type **35** .. .. .. .. .. 25 2
136 2 c. *Smaragdia rangiana* (29.1.86) .. .. 35 3
137 3 c. *Chama sp.* (29.1.86) .. .. .. 40 4
138 4 c. *Cypraea moneta* (30.7.86) .. .. 40 4
139 5 c. *Drupa morum* .. .. .. .. 40 4
140 10 c. *Conus miles* (29.1.86) .. .. .. 45 4
141 15 c. *Terebra maculata* (30.4.86) .. .. 55 5
142 20 c. *Fragum fragum* (30.4.86) .. .. 60 6
143 30 c. *Turbo lajonkaini* (30.4.86) .. .. 75 7
144 33 c. *Mitra fissurata* .. .. .. .. 75 7
145 40 c. *Lambis lambis* (30.4.86) .. .. 85 8
146 50 c. *Tridacna squamosa* (30.7.86) .. .. 95 9
147 60 c. *Cypraea histrio* (30.7.86) .. .. 1·25 1·2
148 $1 *Phillidia varicosa* .. .. .. 2·00 2·0
149 $2 *Halgerda tessellata* (30.7.86) .. .. 3·25 3·2
150 $3 *Harminoea cymbalum* (29.1.86) .. 4·25 4·2
135/50 .. .. .. .. *Set of* 16 16·00 16·0

(Des D. Goodwin. Litho Cambec Press, Melbourne)

**1985** (30 Oct). *Christmas. Sheet* 121 × 88 *mm, containing T* 3 *and similar horiz designs. P* 13½ × 14.

**MS**151 27 c. × 4 multicoloured .. .. .. 2·00 2·7

The stamps within **MS**151 show a composite design of the nigh sky seen through a grove of palm trees. The position of the fac value on the four stamps varies. Type **36** shows the top lef design. The top right stamp shows the face value at bottom right the bottom left at top left and the bottom right at top right.

37 Charles Darwin, *c* 1840

38 Coconut Palm and Holly Sprigs

(Des B. Clinton. Litho Cambec Press, Melbourne)

**1986** (1 Apr). *150th Anniv of Charles Darwin's Visit. T* **37** *and similar vert designs. Multicoloured. P* 14 × 13½.

152 33 c. Type **37** .. .. .. .. .. 70 5
153 60 c. Map of H.M.S. *Beagle*'s route Australia to Cocos Islands .. .. .. .. 1·25 1·2
154 $1 H.M.S. *Beagle* .. .. .. .. 1·75 2·0
152/4 .. .. .. .. .. *Set of* 3 3·25 3·2

(Des S. Hartshorne. Litho Cambec Press, Melbourne)

**1986** (29 Oct). *Christmas. T* **38** *and similar horiz designs Multicoloured. P* 13½ × 14.

155 30 c. Type **38** .. .. .. .. .. 45 4
156 90 c. Sea shell and Christmas tree bauble .. 1·25 1·5
157 $1 Tropical fish and bell .. .. .. 1·50 1·7
155/7 .. .. .. .. .. *Set of* 3 3·00 3·2

39 Jukong

40 Beach, Direction Island

(Des J. Earl. Litho Cambec Press, Melbourne)

**1987** (28 Jan). *Sailing Craft. T* **39** *and similar horiz designs. Multicoloured. P* 13½×14.
158 36 c. Type **39** .. .. .. .. .. 1·10 1·10
a. Horiz strip of 4. Nos. 158/61 .. .. 4·00
159 36 c. Ocean racing yachts .. .. .. 1·10 1·10
160 36 c. *Sarimanok* (replica outrigger).. .. 1·10 1·10
161 36 c. *Ayesha* (schooner) .. .. .. 1·10 1·10
158/61 .. .. .. .. *Set of* 4 4·00 4·00
Nos. 158/61 were printed together, *se-tenant*, in horizontal strips of 5 throughout the sheet, each strip forming a composite background design.

(Des H. Missingham and R. Fletcher. Litho CPE Australia Ltd, Melbourne)

**1987** (8 Apr). *Cocos Islands Scenes. T* **40** *and similar horiz designs. Multicoloured. P* 13½×14.
162 70 c. Type **40** .. .. .. .. .. 1·25 1·00
163 90 c. Palm forest, West Island .. .. 1·50 1·50
164 $1 Golf course .. .. .. .. 2·25 2·50
162/4 .. .. .. .. .. *Set of* 3 4·50 4·50

**41** Radio Transmitter and Palm Trees at Sunset

**42** Batik Printing

(Des R. Fletcher. Litho CPE Australia Ltd, Melbourne)

**1987** (29 July). *Communications. T* **41** *and similar horiz designs. Multicoloured. P* 13½×14.
165 70 c. Type **41** .. .. .. .. .. 1·25 1·25
166 75 c. Air liner at terminal .. .. .. 1·50 1·50
167 90 c. "Intelsat 5" satellite .. .. .. 1·75 1·75
168 $1 Airmail letter and globe .. .. 2·00 2·00
165/8 .. .. .. .. .. *Set of* 4 6·00 6·00

(Des B. Clinton. Litho CPE Australia Ltd, Melbourne)

**1987** (16 Sept). *Cocos (Keeling) Islands Malay Industries. T* **42** *and similar horiz designs. Multicoloured. P* 13½×14.
169 45 c. Type **42** .. .. .. .. .. 1·00 1·00
170 65 c. Jukong building .. .. .. .. 1·25 1·25
171 75 c. Copra production .. .. .. .. 1·50 1·50
169/71 .. .. .. .. *Set of* 3 3·25 3·25

**43** Hands releasing Peace Dove and Map of Islands

**44** Coconut Flower

(Des Marg Towt. Litho CPE Australia Ltd, Melbourne)

**1987** (28 Oct). *Christmas. T* **43** *and similar vert designs. Multicoloured. P* 14×13½.
172 30 c. Type **43** .. .. .. .. .. 40 30
173 90 c. Local children at Christmas party .. 1·25 85
174 $1 Island family and Christmas star .. 1·50 95
172/4 .. .. .. .. .. *Set of* 3 2·75 1·90

(Des Sue Passmore. Litho CPE Australia Ltd, Melbourne)

**1988** (26 Jan). *Bicentenary of Australian Settlement. Arrival of First Fleet. Square designs as Nos.* 1105/9 *of Australia but each inscribed* "COCOS (KEELING) ISLANDS" *and* "AUSTRALIA BICENTENARY".
175 37 c. Aborigines watching arrival of Fleet, Botany Bay .. .. .. .. .. 1·00 1·00
a. Horiz strip of 5. Nos. 175/9 .. .. 4·50
176 37 c. Aboriginal family and anchored ships .. .. .. .. .. 1·00 1·00
177 37 c. Fleet arriving at Sydney Cove.. .. 1·00 1·00
178 37 c. Ship's boat .. .. .. .. .. 1·00 1·00
179 37 c. Raising the flag, Sydney Cove, 26 January 1788.. .. .. .. .. 1·00 1·00
175/9.. .. .. .. .. *Set of* 5 4·50 4·50
Nos. 175/9 were printed together, *se-tenant*, in horizontal strips of five throughout the sheet, forming a composite design.

(Des Celia Rosser. Litho CPE Australia Ltd, Melbourne)

**1988** (13 Apr). *Life Cycle of the Coconut. T* **44** *and similar vert designs. Multicoloured. P* 14×13½.
180 37 c. Type **44** .. .. .. .. .. 50 40
181 65 c. Immature nuts .. .. .. .. 75 65
182 90 c. Coconut palm and mature nuts .. 1·10 90
183 $1 Seedlings .. .. .. .. .. 1·25 1·00
180/3 .. .. .. .. *Set of* 4 3·25 2·75
**MS**184 102×91 mm. Nos. 180/3 .. .. 3·50 3·50

## MINIMUM PRICE

The minimum price quote is 10p which represents a handling charge rather than a basis for valuing common stamps. For further notes about prices see introductory pages.

**45** Copra 3d. Stamp of 1963

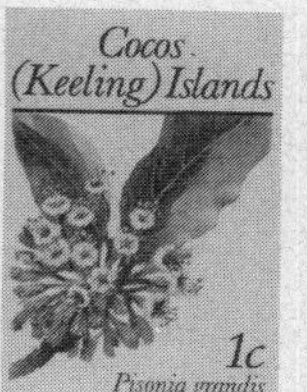


**46** *Pisonia grandis*

(Des R. Fletcher. Recess and litho Note Printing Branch, Reserve Bank of Australia, Melbourne)

**1988** (15 June). *25th Anniv of First Cocos (Keeling) Islands Stamps. T* **45** *and similar vert designs, each showing stamp from 1963 definitive set. P* 15×14.
185 37 c. chocolate, black and azure .. .. 70 70
186 55 c. green, black and pale drab .. .. 1·00 1·00
187 65 c. ultramarine, black and pale grey-lilac 1·10 1·10
188 70 c. scarlet, black and bluish grey .. 1·25 1·25
189 90 c. deep purple, black and greenish grey .. 1·50 1·50
190 $1 deep green, black and light brown .. 1·60 1·60
185/90 .. .. .. .. *Set of* 6 6·50 6·50
Designs:—55 c. Palms 1s.; 65 c. "Super Constellation" 5d.; 70 c. Map 8d.; 90 c. Jukong (sailboat) 2s.; $1 White Tern 2s. 3d.

(Des R. Fletcher. Litho CPE Australia Ltd, Melbourne)

**1988** (29 July)–**89**. *Flora. T* **46** *and similar vert designs. Multicoloured. P* 14×13½.
191 1 c. Type **46** .. .. .. .. .. 10 10
192 2 c. *Cocos nucifera* (18.1.89) .. .. 10 10
193 5 c. *Morinda citrifolia* .. .. .. 10 10
194 10 c. *Cordia subcordata* (18.1.89) .. .. 10 15
195 30 c. *Argusia argentea* (18.1.89) .. .. 25 30
196 37 c. *Calophyllum inophyllum* .. .. 35 40
197 40 c. *Barringtonia asiatica* (19.4.89) .. 35 40
198 50 c. *Caesalpinia bonduc* (19.4.89) .. .. 45 50
199 90 c. *Terminalia catappa* (19.4.89) .. .. 85 90
200 $1 *Pemphis acidula* (19.4.89) .. .. 90 95
201 $2 *Scaevola sericea* (18.1.89) .. .. 1·90 2·00
202 $3 *Hibiscus tiliaceus* .. .. .. 2·75 3·00
191/202 .. .. .. .. *Set of* 12 7·25 8·00

(Des R. Fletcher. Litho CPE Australia Ltd, Melbourne)

**1988** (30 July). *"Sydpex '88" National Stamp Exhibition, Sydney. Sheet* 70×85 *mm. Multicoloured. P* 14×13½.
**MS**203 $3 As No. 202 .. .. .. .. 3·50 3·00

**47** Beach at Sunset

**48** Capt. P. G. Taylor

(Des T. Bland. Litho CPE Australia Ltd, Melbourne)

**1988** (12 Oct). *Christmas. P* 13½×14.
204 **47** 32 c. multicoloured .. .. .. 70 35
205 90 c. multicoloured .. .. .. 1·50 1·25
206 $1 multicoloured .. .. .. 1·75 1·25
204/6 .. .. .. .. *Set of* 3 3·50 2·50

(Des B. Clinton. Litho CPE Australia Ltd, Melbourne)

**1989** (19 July). *50th Anniv of First Indian Ocean Aerial Survey. T* **48** *and similar vert designs. P* 14×13½.
207 40 c. multicoloured .. .. .. .. 60 60
208 70 c. multicoloured .. .. .. .. 85 85
209 $1 multicoloured .. .. .. .. 1·25 1·25
210 $1.10, deep ultramarine, pale lilac & black 1·40 1·40
207/10 .. .. .. .. *Set of* 4 3·75 3·75
Designs:—70 c. Consolidated Catalina "PBY2" *Guba II* and crew; $1 *Guba II* over Direction Island; $1.10, Unissued Australia 5s. stamp commemorating flight.

**49** Jukong and Star

**50** H.M.A.S. *Sydney* (cruiser)

(Des T. Bland. Litho Leigh-Mardon Ltd, Melbourne)

**1989** (18 Oct). *Christmas. P* 14×13½.
211 **49** 35 c. multicoloured .. .. .. 45 40
212 80 c. multicoloured .. .. .. 90 1·00
213 $1.10, multicoloured .. .. .. 1·10 1·25
211/13 .. .. .. .. *Set of* 3 2·25 2·40

(Des PCS Studios. Litho Leigh-Mardon Ltd, Melbourne)

**1989** (9 Nov). *75th Anniv of Destruction of German Cruiser* Emden. *T* **50** *and similar horiz designs. Multicoloured. P* 13½×14.
214 40 c. Type **50** .. .. .. .. .. 90 90
a. Horiz strip of 4, Nos. 214/17, with central label .. .. .. .. .. 3·75
215 70 c. *Emden* (German cruiser) .. .. 1·25 1·25
216 $1 *Emden's* steam launch .. .. 1·50 1·50
217 $1.10, H.M.A.S. *Sydney* and crest .. 1·50 1·50
214/17 .. .. .. .. *Set of* 4 4·75 4·75
**MS**218 145×90 mm. Nos. 214/17 .. .. 4·75 5·00
Nos. 214/17 were printed together, *se-tenant*, in horizontal strips of four stamps and one label throughout the sheet.

**51** Xanthid Crab

**52** Captain Keeling and *Hector*, 1609

(Des Jill Ruse. Litho Leigh-Mardon Ltd, Melbourne)

**1990** (31 May). *Cocos Islands Crabs. T* **51** *and similar multicoloured designs. P* 14½.
219 45 c. Type **51** .. .. .. .. .. 70 70
220 75 c. Ghost Crab .. .. .. .. .. 1·00 1·00
221 $1 Red-backed Mud Crab .. .. .. 1·25 1·25
222 $1.30, Coconut Crab (*vert*) .. .. 1·50 1·50
219/22 .. .. .. .. *Set of* 4 4·00 4·00

(Des Elizabeth and R. Innes. Litho Note Ptg Branch, Reserve Bank of Australia)

**1990** (24 Aug). *Navigators of the Pacific. T* **52** *and similar horiz designs. P* 14½.
223 45 c. dull mauve .. .. .. .. .. 75 75
224 75 c. dull mauve and pale azure .. .. 1·10 1·10
225 $1 dull mauve and pale stone .. .. 1·50 1·50
226 $1.30, dull mauve and pale buff .. 1·75 1·75
223/6 .. .. .. .. *Set of* 4 4·50 4·50
**MS**227 120×95 mm. As Nos. 223/6, but imperf 4·50 5·00
Designs:—75 c. Captain Fitzroy and *Beagle*, 1836; $1 Captain Belcher and *Samarang*, 1846; $1.30, Captain Fremantle and *Juno*, 1857.

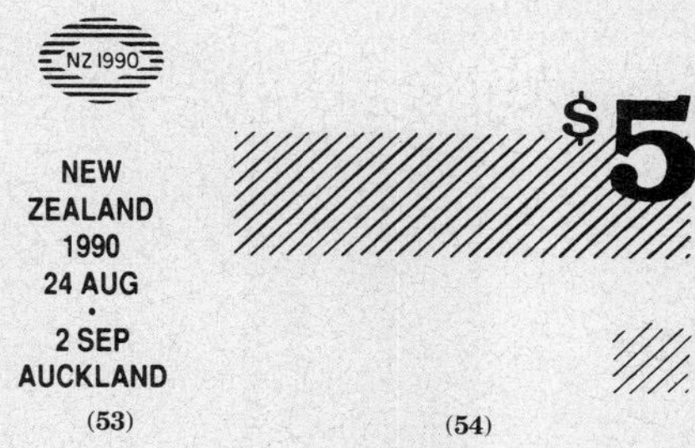


(**53**) (**54**)

(Des Elizabeth Innes (No. **MS**229). Litho Western Australian Govt Ptg Division, Perth)

**1990** (3 Sept). *"New Zealand 1990" International Stamp Exhibition, Auckland. No.* 188 *optd with T* **53** *in red and miniature sheet containing designs as Nos.* 194, 199 *and* 201.
228 70 c. scarlet, black and bluish grey .. 90 95
**MS**229 127×90 mm. As Nos. 194, 199 and 201, but self-adhesive. Roul 9 .. .. .. 3·00 3·25
Nos. 228/9 were available at the Exhibition from 24 August 1990, but were not sold locally until 3 September.

**1990** (11 Dec). *No.* 187 *surch with T* **54** *in deep ultramarine by Western Australian Govt Ptg Division, Perth.*
230 $5 on 65 c. ultram, black & pale grey-lilac 4·50 4·75

**55** Cocos Atoll from West and Star

(Des Stylegraphics, Perth. Litho Scott Four-Colour Print, Perth)

**1990** (12 Dec). *Christmas. T* **55** *and similar square designs. Multicoloured. Roul* 5.
231 40 c. Type **55** .. .. .. .. .. 45 45
a. Booklet pane. No. 231×4 and No. 232×2 plus 6 labels .. .. .. 3·25
b. Booklet pane. No. 231×10 plus 2 labels 4·25
232 70 c. Cocos atoll from south .. .. .. 80 85
233 $1.30, Cocos atoll from east .. .. 1·40 1·75
231/3 .. .. .. .. .. *Set of* 3 2·40 2·75
Booklet panes Nos. 231a/b have the upper and lower edges imperforate, producing stamps imperforate at top or bottom, and there are margins at left and right.

MAINLAND
POSTAGE PAID

(56)

LOCAL
POSTAGE PAID

(57)

**1990** (12 Dec)–**91**. *Nos. 140/1, 143 and 146/7 surch by Western Australian Govt Ptg Division.*

*(a) With T* **56** *in blue*

234 (43 c.) on 10 c. *Conus miles* .. .. 40 45

*(b) As T* **57** *with original face value obliterated*

235 (1 c.) on 30 c. *Turbo lajonkaini* (Type **57**) (B.) (21.1.91) .. .. .. 10 10
236 (43 c.) on 10 c. *Conus miles* ("MAINLAND") (B.) (7.3.91) .. .. .. .. 40 45
237 70 c. on 60 c. *Cypraea histrio* ("ZONE 1") (7.3.91) .. .. .. .. 65 70
238 80 c. on 50 c. *Tridacna squamosa* ("ZONE 2") (7.3.91) .. .. .. .. 75 80
239 $1.20 on 15 c. *Terebra maculata* ("ZONE 5") (7.3.91) .. .. .. .. 1·10 1·25
234/9 .. .. .. .. *Set of* 6 3·00 3·25

**58** Beaded Sea Star

**59** Cocos Islands

(Des Jill Ruse. Litho Leigh-Mardon Ltd, Melbourne)

**1991** (28 Feb). *Starfish and Sea Urchins. T* **58** *and similar horiz designs. Multicoloured. P* 14½.

240 45 c. Type **58** .. .. .. .. 55 55
241 75 c. Feather Star .. .. .. .. 95 95
242 $1 Slate Pencil Urchin .. .. .. 1·25 1·25
243 $1.30, Globose Sea Urchin .. .. 1·60 1·60
240/3 .. .. .. .. *Set of* 4 4·00 4·00

(Des P. Cunningham. Litho Leigh-Mardon Ltd, Melbourne)

**1991** (16 Apr). *Malay Hari Raya Festival. T* **59** *and similar horiz designs. Multicoloured. P* 14½.

244 45 c. Type **59** .. .. .. .. 55 55
245 75 c. Island house .. .. .. .. 95 95
246 $1.30, Islands scene .. .. .. 1·60 1·60
244/6 .. .. .. .. *Set of* 3 2·75 2·75

**60** Child praying

(Des R. Honisett. Litho Leigh-Mardon Ltd, Melbourne)

**1991** (6 Nov). *Christmas. T* **60** *and similar vert designs. Multicoloured. P* 15½.

247 38 c. Type **60** .. .. .. .. 35 40
248 43 c. Child dreaming of Christmas Day .. 40 45
249 $1 Child singing .. .. .. .. 90 95
250 $1.20, Child fascinated by decorations .. 1·10 1·25
247/50 .. .. .. .. *Set of* 4 2·50 2·75
**MS**251 118×74 mm. 38 c., 43 c., $1, $1.20, Local children's choir .. .. .. .. .. 2·75 3·00

The four values in No. MS251 form a composite design.

OFFICIAL STAMP

OFFICIAL PAID
MAINLAND

(O 1)

**1991** (25 Jan). *No. 182 surch with Type* O **1** *in deep violet-blue.*

O1 (43 c.) on 90 c. Coconut palm and mature nuts † 45

No. O1 was only sold to the public cancelled-to-order and not in unused condition.

# Cook Islands

## (Rarotonga)

These are also known as the Hervey Islands. The islands of Ianikiki, Rakahanga, and Pukapuka were annexed to the group ı October 1890, and use the same stamps.

**PRICES FOR STAMPS ON COVER TO 1945**

Nos. 1/4 *from* × 5
Nos. 5/74 *from* × 4
Nos. 75/145 *from* × 3

**BRITISH PROTECTORATE**

1

2 Queen Makea Takau

3 White Tern or Torea

(Des F. Moss. Typo Govt Printing Office, Wellington)

**892** (19 Apr). *No wmk. P* 12½.

A. *Toned paper*. B. *White paper*.

| | | | A. | | B. | |
|---|---|---|---|---|---|---|
| 1 | 1d. black | .. | 26·00 | 30·00 | 26·00 | 30·00 |
| | a. Imperf between (vert pair) | .. | £8500 | — | | † |
| | 1½d. mauve | .. | 38·00 | 38·00 | 38·00 | 38·00 |
| | a. Imperf (pair) | .. | £9000 | — | | † |
| | 2½d. blue | .. | 38·00 | 38·00 | 38·00 | 38·00 |
| | 10d. carmine | .. | £140 | £130 | £160 | £130 |
| /4 | | *Set of* 4 | £200 | £200 | £225 | £200 |

Nos. 1/4 were printed in sheets of 60 (6×10) from plates onstructed from a matrix of 6 slightly different types.

(Eng A. E. Cousins. Typo Govt Printing Office, Wellington)

**893** (28 July)–**1900.** *W* **12***b of New Zealand* (N Z *and Star wide apart*) (*sideways on T* **3**). (*a*) *P* 12 × 11½.

5 **2** 1d. brown .. .. 26·00 30·00
6 1d. blue (3.4.94) .. .. 6·00 1·50
a. Perf 12 × 11½ and 12½ mixed .. † £850
7 1½d. mauve .. .. 6·00 6·00
8 2½d. rose .. .. 26·00 23·00
*a. Rose-carmine* .. .. 60·00 55·00
ab. Perf 12 × 11½ and 12½ mixed .. £1500
9 5d. olive-black .. .. 13·00 13·00
0 10d. green .. .. 55·00 48·00
/10 .. *Set of* 6 £120 £110

(*b*) *P* 11 (July 1896–1900)

1 **3** ½d. steel blue (1st setting) (11.99) .. 20·00 26·00
a. Upper right "d" omitted .. £1200
b. Second setting .. .. 11·00 14·00
*ba. Deep blue* (1900) .. .. 3·50 4·75
2 **2** 1d. blue .. .. 3·00 4·50
3 1d. deep brown/*cream* (4.99) .. .. 8·00 12·00
a. Wmk sideways .. ..
*b. Bistre-brown* (1900) .. ..
4 1½d. deep lilac .. .. 5·50 6·00
*a. Deep mauve* (1900) .. .. 5·50 6·00
5 **3** 2d. brown/*thin toned* (7.98) .. .. 7·00 6·50
*a. Deep brown* (1900) .. .. 5·50 6·50
6 **2** 2½d. pale rose .. .. 38·00 38·00
*a. Deep rose* (1900) .. .. 9·00 9·00
7 5d. olive-black .. .. 18·00 17·00
8 **3** 6d. purple/*thin toned* (7.98) .. .. 22·00 28·00
*a. Bright purple* (1900) .. .. 16·00 19·00
9 **2** 10d. green .. .. 15·00 24·00
0 **3** 1s. red/*thin toned* (7.98) .. .. 60·00 70·00
*a. Deep carmine* (1900) .. .. 45·00 48·00
1/20*a* .. *Set of* 10 £120 £140

Examples of the 1d., 1½d., 2½d. and 5d. perforated 11 and on aid paper are perforation trials.

On the 1st setting of the ½d. the face values are misplaced in ach corner. As corrected in the second setting the face values re correctly positioned in each corner.

**ONE**
**HALF**
**PENNY**
(4)

(5)

**899** (24 Apr). *No.* 12 *surch with T* 4 *by Govt Printer, Rarotonga.*

21 **2** ½d. on 1d. blue .. .. 32·00 35·00
a. Surch inverted .. .. £800 £850
b. Surch double .. .. £900 £750

**NEW ZEALAND TERRITORY**

**1901** (8 Oct). *No.* 13 *optd with T* 5 *by Govt Printer, Rarotonga.*

22 **2** 1d. brown .. .. £140 £140
a. Crown inverted .. .. £1500 £1300
c. Optd with crown twice .. .. £1400 £1500

**1902.** *No wmk. P* 11.

(*a*) *Medium white Cowan paper* (Feb)

23 **3** ½d. blue-green .. .. 5·50 6·50
24 **2** 1d. dull rose .. .. 8·00 10·00

(*b*) *Thick white Pirie paper* (May)

25 **3** ½d. yellow-green .. .. 3·25 3·50
a. Imperf horiz (vert pair) .. £1100
26 **2** 1d. rose-red .. .. 9·00 10·00
*a. Rose-lake* .. .. 8·50 6·50
27 2½d. dull blue .. .. 7·00 20·00

**1902** (Sept). *W* **43** *of New Zealand (single-lined* NZ *and Star, close together; sideways on T* **2**). *P* 11.

28 **3** ½d. yellow-green .. .. 1·40 3·25
*a. Grey-green* .. .. 16·00 27·00
29 **2** 1d. rose-pink .. .. 2·00 3·00
30 1½d. deep mauve .. .. 2·50 7·00
31 **3** 2d. deep brown .. .. 3·75 10·00
a. No figures of value .. £1700 £2500
b. Perf 11 × 14 .. .. £750
32 **2** 2½d. deep blue .. .. 3·75 6·50
33 5d. olive-black .. .. 35·00 40·00
34 **3** 6d. purple .. .. 28·00 27·00
35 **2** 10d. green .. .. 48·00 80·00
36 **3** 1s. carmine .. .. 48·00 60·00
a. Perf 11 × 14 .. .. £750
28/36 .. *Set of* 9 £150 £200

**1909–11.** *W* **43** *of New Zealand.*

37 **3** ½d. green (*p* 14½×14) (1911) .. 4·50 6·00
38 **2** 1d. deep red (*p* 14) .. .. 19·00 22·00
a. Wmk sideways (24.12.09) .. 7·50 9·00

**1913–19.** *W* **43** *of New Zealand (sideways on T* **3**). *Chalk-surfaced paper.*

39 **3** ½d. deep green (*p* 14) (1915) .. 1·60 8·50
a. Wmk upright .. .. 2·25 8·50
40 **2** 1d. red (*p* 14) (7.13) .. .. 2·25 3·75
41 1d. red (*p* 14 × 14½) (1914) .. 4·50 4·75
42 1½d. deep mauve (*p* 14) (1915) .. 65·00 45·00
43 1½d. deep mauve (*p* 14 × 15) (1916) .. 4·75 3·25
44 **3** 2d. deep brown (*p* 15 × 14) (1919) .. 5·00 28·00
45 **2** 10d. green (*p* 14 × 15) (1918) .. 13·00 50·00
46 **3** 1s. carmine (*p* 15 × 14) (1919) .. 22·00 55·00
39/46 .. *Set of* 6 45·00 £130

**RAROTONGA**

**APA PENE**

(8)

**1919** (Apr–July). *Contemporary stamps of New Zealand surch as T* **8**.

(*a*) *Typographed. P* 14 × 15

50 **61** ½d. green (R.) (June) .. .. 20 50
51 **53** 1d. carmine (B.) (June) .. .. 20 60
52 **61** 1½d. orange-brown (R.) (June) .. 25 75
53 2d. yellow (R.) .. .. 30 70
54 3d. chocolate (B.) (July) .. .. 1·25 3·00

(*b*) *Recess.* (*a*) *P* 14 × 14½. (*b*) *P* 14 × 13½

55 **60** 2½d. blue (R.) (*a*) (June) .. .. 95 2·00
a. Vert pair. Nos. 55/6 .. .. 22·00 40·00
56 2½d. blue (R.) (*b*) .. .. 1·60 5·00
57 3d. chocolate (B.) (*a*) .. .. 70 1·50
a. Vert pair. Nos. 57/8 .. .. 22·00 45·00
58 3d. chocolate (B.) (*b*) .. .. 1·00 5·50
59 4d. violet (B.) (*a*) .. .. 1·00 4·00
a. Vert pair. Nos. 59/60 .. .. 23·00 50·00
60 4d. violet (B.) (*b*) .. .. 1·50 5·50
a. Re-entry (Pl 20 R.1/6) .. .. 60·00
b. Re-entry (Pl 20 R.4/10) .. .. 60·00
61 4½d. deep green (B.) (*a*) .. .. 1·10 5·50
a. Vert pair. Nos. 61/2 .. .. 25·00 60·00
62 4½d. deep green (B.) (*b*) .. .. 2·00 6·00
63 6d. carmine (B.) (*a*) (June) .. .. 1·50 5·00
a. Vert pair. Nos. 63/4 .. .. 45·00 75·00
64 6d. carmine (B.) (*b*) .. .. 2·75 7·50
65 7½d. red-brown (B.) (*b*) .. .. 1·25 5·50
66 9d. sage-green (R.) (*a*) .. .. 1·75 7·00
a. Vert pair. Nos. 66/7 .. .. 55·00 90·00
67 9d. sage-green (R.) (*b*) .. .. 3·25 7·00
68 1s. vermilion (B.) (*a*) (June) .. 2·75 11·00
a. Vert pair. Nos. 68/9 .. .. 70·00 £110
69 1s. vermilion (B.) (*b*) .. .. 9·00 22·00
50/68 (*cheapest*) .. *Set of* 12 11·00 40·00

9 Capt. Cook landing

10 Wharf at Avarua

11 "Capt. Cook" (Dance)

12 Palm Tree

13 Huts at Arorangi

14 Avarua Harbour

(Des, eng and recess Perkins, Bacon & Co)

**1920** (23 Aug). *No wmk. P* 14.

70 **9** ½d. black and green .. .. 3·75 6·50
71 **10** 1d. black and carmine-red .. .. 1·75 4·75
72 **11** 1½d. black and dull blue .. .. 7·00 8·50
73 **12** 3d. black and chocolate .. .. 2·00 5·50
74 **13** 6d. brown and yellow-orange .. .. 1·75 8·00
75 **14** 1s. black and violet .. .. 5·00 17·00
70/5 .. *Set of* 6 19·00 45·00

Examples of the 1d. and 1s. with centre inverted were not supplied to the Post Office.

**RAROTONGA**
(15)

**RAROTONGA**

Trimmed overprint (R. 1/6 and R. 3/7)

**1921** (Oct)–**23.** *Postal Fiscal stamps as Type* F 4 *of New Zealand optd with T* **15**. *W* **43** (*sideways*). *Chalk-surfaced "De La Rue" paper. P* 14½×14.

76 2s. deep blue (R.) .. .. 26·00 45·00
a. Trimmed opt .. .. 55·00
b. Carmine opt (1923) .. .. £140 £150
ba. Trimmed opt .. .. £300
77 2s. 6d. grey-brown (B.) .. .. 18·00 40·00
a. Trimmed opt .. .. 40·00
78 5s. yellow-green (R.) .. .. 26·00 48·00
a. Trimmed opt .. .. 55·00
79 10s. maroon (B.) .. .. 48·00 60·00
a. Trimmed opt .. .. 90·00
80 £1 rose-carmine (B.) .. .. 75·00 £100
a. Trimmed opt .. .. £130
76/80 .. *Set of* 5 £170 £250

See also Nos. 85/9.

16 Te Po, Rarotongan Chief

17 Harbour, Rarotonga and Mt Ikurangi

(2½d. from a print; 4d. des A. H. Messenger. Plates by P.B. Recess Govt Ptg Office, Wellington)

**1924–27.** *W* **43** *of New Zealand. P* 14.

81 **9** ½d. black and green (13.5.26) .. 3·50 3·50
82 **10** 1d. black and deep carmine (10.11.24) 4·00 1·50
83 **16** 2½d. red-brown and steel blue (15.10.27) 2·25 12·00
84 **17** 4d. green and violet (15.10.27) .. 3·00 12·00
81/4 .. *Set of* 4 11·50 26·00

**1926** (Feb–May). *As Nos.* 76/80, *but thick, opaque white chalk-surfaced "Cowan" paper.*

85 2s. blue (C.) .. .. £100 £120
a. Trimmed opt .. .. £190
86 2s. 6d. deep grey-brown (B.) .. .. 50·00 65·00
87 5s. yellow-green (R.) (May) .. .. 38·00 55·00
a. Trimmed opt .. .. 80·00
88 10s. brown-red (B.) (May) .. .. 55·00 70·00
89 £1 rose-pink (B.) (May) .. .. 80·00 95·00
85/9 .. *Set of* 5 £300 £350

**1926–28.** *T* **72** *("Admiral" Type) of New Zealand, overprinted with T* **15**. (*a*) *"Jones" chalk-surfaced paper.*

90 2s. deep blue (R.) (10.26) .. .. 10·00 38·00

(*b*) *"Cowan" thick chalk-surfaced paper*

91 2s. light blue (R.) (18.6.27) .. .. 15·00 38·00
92 3s. bright mauve (R.) (30.1.28) .. .. 16·00 40·00
90/2 .. *Set of* 3 38·00 £100

**TWO PENCE** (18)

**COOK ISLANDS.** (19)

**1931** (Mar). *Surch with T* **18**. *P* 14. (*a*) *No wmk.*

93 **11** 2d. on 1½d. black and blue (R.) .. 4·00 2·25

(*b*) *W* **43** *of New Zealand*

94 **11** 2d. on 1½d. black and blue (R.) .. 1·00 3·75

**1931** (12 Nov)–**32.** *Postal Fiscal stamps as Type* F **6** *of New Zealand. W* **43**. *Thick, opaque, white chalk-faced "Cowan" paper. P* 14.

(*a*) *Optd with T* **15**

95 2s. 6d. deep brown (B.) .. .. 7·50 18·00
96 5s. green (R.) .. .. 16·00 42·00
97 10s. carmine-lake (B.) .. .. 30·00 65·00
98 £1 pink (B.) .. .. 60·00 90·00

(*b*) *Optd with T* **19** (3.32)

98*a* £3 green (R.) .. .. 85·00 £170
98*b* £5 blue (R.) .. .. £170 £250

The £3 and £5 values were mainly used for fiscal purposes.

20 Capt. Cook landing

21 Capt. Cook

22 Double Maori Canoe

23 Natives working Cargo

24 Port of Avarua

25 R.M.S. *Monowai*

26 King George V

(Des L. C. Mitchell. Recess P.B.)

**1932** (15 Mar–2 May). *No wmk. P* 13.
99 **20** ½d. black and deep green 2·25 8·00
a. Perf 14 28·00 75·00
100 **21** 1d. black and lake 2·50 2·75
a. Centre inverted £2250 £2250
b. Perf 13 and 14 mixed £160 £180
c. Perf 14 15·00 17·00
101 **22** 2d. black and brown 2·00 3·75
a. Perf 14 8·00 14·00
102 **23** 2½d. black and deep blue 5·00 27·00
a. Perf 14 11·00 27·00
103 **24** 4d. black and bright blue 17·00 35·00
a. Perf 14 7·00 32·00
b. Perf 14×13 30·00 90·00
c. Perf comp of 14 and 13 60·00
104 **25** 6d. black and orange 24·00 45·00
a. Perf 14 2·75 10·00
105 **26** 1s. black and violet (*p* 14) (2 May) 5·00 16·00
99/105 *Set of* 7 24·00 90·00

No. 100b comes from the first vertical column of one sheet which was reperforated 14 at left.

Other major errors exist on this issue, but these are not listed as they originated from printer's waste which appeared on the market in 1935.

(Recess from P.B. plates at Govt Printing Office, Wellington)

**1933–36.** *W* **43** *of New Zealand (Single N Z and Star). P* 14.
106 **20** ½d. black and deep green 40 1·00
107 **21** 1d. black and scarlet (1935) 45 1·00
108 **22** 2d. black and brown (1936) 35 30
109 **23** 2½d. black and deep blue 30 1·25
110 **24** 4d. black and bright blue 30 35
111 **25** 6d. black and orange-yellow (1936) 65 2·25
112 **26** 1s. black and violet (1936) 16·00 18·00
106/12 *Set of* 7 17·00 22·00

SILVER JUBILEE
OF
KING GEORGE V.
1910-1935.
(27)

Normal letters
B K E N
B K E N
Narrow letters

**1935** (7 May). *Silver Jubilee. Optd with T* **27** *(wider vertical spacing on 6d.). Colours changed. W* **43** *of New Zealand. P* 14.
113 **21** 1d. red-brown and lake 60 70
a. Narrow "K" in "KING" 2·75
b. Narrow "B" in "JUBILEE" 3·75
114 **23** 2½d. dull and deep blue (R.) 75 1·00
a. Narrow first "E" in "GEORGE" 3·50 5·00
115 **25** 6d. green and orange 3·00 4·50
a. Narrow "N" in "KING" 16·00
113/15 *Set of* 3 4·00 5·50

**1936** (15 July)–**44.** *Stamps of New Zealand optd with T* **19**. *W* **43**.

*(a) Thick, white, opaque chalk-surfaced "Cowan" paper. P* 14

*(i) As T* **72** *("Admiral" type)*
116 2s. blue 12·00 35·00
117 3s. mauve 13·00 45·00

*(ii) As Type* **F 6** *("Arms" type)*
118 2s. 6d. deep brown 15·00 40·00
119 5s. green (R.) 18·00 50·00
120 10s. carmine-lake 32·00 75·00
121 £1 pink 50·00 £110
118/21 *Set of* 4 £100 £250

*(b) Thin, hard, chalk-surfaced "Wiggins, Teape" paper*
122 2s. 6d. dull brown (12.40) 75·00 70·00
123 5s. green (R.) (10.40) £250 £250
123*a* 10s. pale carmine-lake (11.44) £120 £130
123*b* £3 green (R.) (date?) £325 £475
122/3*b* *Set of* 4 £700 £850

COOK
IS'DS.
(28)

IS'DS.
Small second "S"
(R. 1/2)

**1937** (1 June). *Coronation. Nos.* 599/601 *of New Zealand optd with T* **28**.
124 **106** 1d. carmine 35 10
a. Small second "S" 6·00
125 2½d. Prussian blue 55 20
a. Small second "S" 8·00
126 6d. red-orange 55 20
a. Small second "S" 8·00
124/6 *Set of* 3 1·25 45

29 King George VI

30 Native Village

31 Native Canoe

32 Tropical Landscape

(Des J. Berry (2s., 3s., and frame of 1s.). Eng B.W. Recess Govt Ptg. Office, Wellington)

**1938** (2 May). *W* **43** *of New Zealand. P* 14.
127 **29** 1s. black and violet 2·75 2·75
128 **30** 2s. black and red-brown 7·50 6·00
129 **31** 3s. light blue and emerald-green 18·00 13·00
127/9 *Set of* 3 25·00 20·00

(Recess B.W.)

**1940** (2 Sept). *Surch as in T* **32**. *W* **98** *of New Zealand. P* 13½ × 14.
130 **32** 3d. on 1½d. black and purple 10 15

Type **32** was not issued without surcharge.

**1943–50.** *Postal Fiscal stamps as Type* **F 6** *of New Zealand optd with T* **19**. *W* **98**. *"Wiggins, Teape" chalk-surfaced paper. P* 14.
131 2s. 6d. dull brown (3.46) 6·50 9·00
132 5s. green (R.) (11.43) 5·50 12·00
133 10s. carmine-lake (10.48) 30·00 45·00
134 £1 pink (11.47) 32·00 45·00
135 £3 green (R.) (1946?) 50·00 £150
136 £5 blue (R.) (25.10.50) £200 £300
131/6 *Set of* 6 £275 £500

The £3 and £5 were mainly used for fiscal purposes.

For technical printing reasons all values also exist with watermark inverted. The prices quoted are for the cheapest form.

(Recess Govt Ptg Office, Wellington)

**1944–46.** *W* **98** *of New Zealand (sideways on* ½*d.* 1*d.,* 1*s., and* 2*s.). P* 14.
137 **20** ½d. black and deep green (11.44) 85 2·50
138 **21** 1d. black and scarlet (3.45) 2·00 35
139 **22** 2d. black and brown (2.46) 1·25 1·75
140 **23** 2½d. black and deep blue (5.45) 65 1·00
141 **24** 4d. black and blue (4.44) 1·75 2·75
142 **25** 6d. black and orange (6.44) 90 60
143 **29** 1s. black and violet (9.44) 90 1·00
144 **30** 2s. black and red-brown (8.45) 11·00 9·50
145 **31** 3s. light blue and emerald-green (6.45) 15·00 15·00
137/45 *Set of* 9 30·00 30·00

COOK
ISLANDS
(33)

**1946** (4 June). *Peace. Nos.* 668, 670, 674/5 *of New Zealand optd with T* **33** *(reading up and down at sides on 2d.).*
146 1d. green 10 10
147 2d. purple (B.) 10 15
148 6d. chocolate and vermilion 15 15
149 8d. black and carmine (B.) 15 15
146/9 *Set of* 4 45 45

34 Ngatangiia Channel, Rarotonga

41 Map and Statue of Capt. Cook

(Des J. Berry. Recess Waterlow)

**1949** (1 Aug)–**61.** *T* **34**, **41** *and similar designs. W* **98** *of New Zealand (sideways on shilling values). P* 13½ × 13 *(horiz) or* 13 × 13½ *(vert).*
150 ½d. violet and brown 10 55
151 1d. chestnut and green 1·75 1·25
152 2d. reddish brown and scarlet 60 1·25
153 3d. green and ultramarine 50 1·25
a. Wmk sideways (white opaque paper) (22.5.61) 2·50 2·50
154 5d. emerald-green and violet 70 1·00
155 6d. black and carmine 1·25 1·75
156 8d. olive-green and orange 40 3·00
157 1s. light blue and chocolate 4·25 3·00
158 2s. yellow-brown and carmine 3·00 6·50
159 3s. light blue and bluish green 4·75 8·50
150/9 *Set of* 10 16·00 25·00

Designs: *Horiz*—1d. Capt. Cook and map of Hervey Islands; 2d. Rarotonga and Revd. John Williams; 3d. Aitutaki and Palm trees; 5d. Rarotonga airfield; 6d. Penrhyn village; 8d. Native hut. *Vert*—2s. Native hut and palms; 3s. M.V. *Matua*.

See note on white opaque paper below No. 736 of New Zealand.

**1953** (25 May). *Coronation. As Nos.* 715 *and* 717 *of New Zealand, but inscr* "COOK ISLANDS".
160 3d. brown 1·00 55
161 6d. slate-grey 1·25 95

1/6

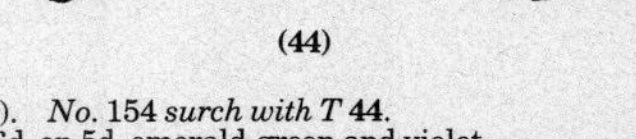
(44)

**1960** (1 Apr). *No.* 154 *surch with T* **44**.
162 1s. 6d. on 5d. emerald-green and violet 15 30

45 Tiare Maori

48 White Tern

52 Queen Elizabeth II

53 Island Scene

(Des J. Berry. Recess (1s. 6d.), litho (others) B.W.)

**1963** (4 June). *T* **45**, **48**, **52/3** *and similar designs. Wmk T* **98** *of New Zealand (sideways). P* 13½ × 13 *(1d., 2d., 8d.),* 13 × 13½ *(3d., 5d., 6d., 1s.) or* 13½ *(others).*
163 1d. emerald-green and yellow 35 10
164 2d. brown-red and yellow 10 10
165 3d. yellow, yellow-green & reddish violet 45 10
166 5d. blue and black 3·50 30
167 6d. red, yellow and green 1·00 20
168 8d. black and blue 1·25 45
169 1s. orange-yellow and yellow-green 40 20
170 1s. 6d. bluish violet 2·75 2·00
171 2s. bistre-brown and grey-blue 75 75
172 3s. black and yellow-green 1·25 1·00
173 5s. bistre-brown and blue 8·50 3·25
163/73 *Set of* 11 18·00 7·50

Designs: *Vert (as T* **45**)—2d. Fishing god; 8d. Skipjack Tuna. *Horiz (as T* **48**)—3d. Frangipani; 6d. Hibiscus; 1s. Oranges. *(As T* **53**)—3s. Administration Centre, Mangaia; 5s. Rarotonga.

56 Eclipse and Palm

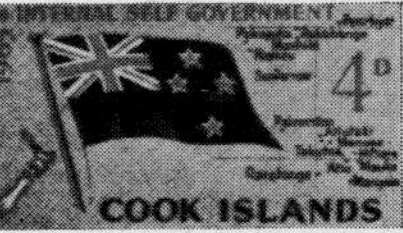
57 N.Z. Ensign and Map

(Des L. C. Mitchell. Litho B.W.)

**1965** (31 May). *Solar Eclipse Observation, Manuae Island. W* **98** *of New Zealand. P* 13½.
174 **56** 6d. black, yellow and light blue 10 10

SELF-GOVERNMENT

(Des R. M. Conly (4d.), L. C. Mitchell (10d., 1s.), J. Berry (1s. 9d.) Litho B.W.)

**1965** (16 Sept). *Internal Self-Government. T* **57** *and similar horiz designs. W* **98** *of New Zealand (sideways). P* 13½.
175 4d. red and blue 10 1
176 10d. multicoloured 10 1
177 1s. multicoloured 10 1
178 1s. 9d. multicoloured 30 4
175/8 *Set of* 4 55 6

Designs:—10d. London Missionary Society Church; 1s. Proclamation of Cession, 1900; 1s. 9d. Nikao School.

In Memoriam
SIR WINSTON CHURCHILL
1874 - 1965
(61)

Airmail
(62)

966 (24 Jan). *Churchill Commemoration. Nos.* 171/3 *and* 175/7 *optd with T* **61**, *in red.*

79 4d. red and blue . . 75 30
a. "l" for "1" in "1874" . . 3·00
80 10d. multicoloured . . 1·50 45
a. Opt inverted . . £160
b. "l" for "1" in "1874" . . 5·00
81 1s. multicoloured . . 1·50 65
a. Opt inverted . . £120
b. "l" for "1" in "1874" . . 5·00
82 2s. bistre-brown and grey-blue . . 1·50 1·25
a. "l" for "1" in "1874" . . 5·00
83 3s. black and yellow-green . . 1·50 1·25
a. "l" for "1" in "1874" . . 5·00
84 5s. bistre-brown and blue . . 2·00 1·75
a. "l" for "1" in "1874" . . 10·00
79/84 . . *Set of* 6 8·00 5·00

The lower case "l" for "1" in "1874" occurred on R. 6/5 for all alues and additionally on R. 12/5 for the 2s., 3s. and 5s.

966 (22 Apr). *Air. Various stamps optd with T* **62** *or surch also.*

85 6d. red, yellow and green (No. 167) . . 1·25 20
86 7d. on 8d. black and blue (No. 168) . . 1·25 25
87 10d. on 3d. yellow, yellow-green and reddish violet (No. 165) . . 1·00 15
88 1s. orange-yellow and yellow-green (No. 169) 1·00 15
89 1s. 6d. bluish violet (No. 170) . . 1·25 1·25
90 2s. 3d. on 3s. black and yellow-green (No. 172) 1·00 65
91 5s. bistre-brown and blue (No. 173) . . 1·50 1·50
92 10s. on 2s. bistre-brown and grey-blue (No. 171) . . 1·75 6·50
93 £1 pink (No. 134) . . 9·00 16·00
a. Aeroplane omitted . . 27·00 38·00
85/93 . . *Set of* 9 17·00 24·00

No. 193a occurred in all stamps of the last vertical row as nsufficient aeroplane symbols were available. There are also umerous other varieties on all values, notably aeroplanes of ifferent sizes and broken first "i" with dot missing owing to amaged type.

**PRINTERS.** The following stamps were printed in photogravure y Heraclio Fournier, Spain *except where otherwise stated.*

**63** "Adoration of the Magi" (Fra Angelico)

1966 (28 Nov). *Christmas. T* **63** *and similar multicoloured designs.*
A. *P* 13 × 12 (*horiz*) *or* 12 × 13 (*vert*).
B. *P* 13 × 14½ (*horiz*) *or* 14½ × 13 (*vert*).

| | | A | | B | |
|---|---|---|---|---|---|
| 194 | 1d. Type **63** | 35 | 30 | 10 | 10 |
| 195 | 2d. "The Nativity" (Memling) (*vert*) | 11·00 | 7·50 | 15 | 10 |
| 196 | 4d. "Adoration of the Magi" (Velazquez) (*horiz*) | 70 | 60 | 15 | 15 |
| 197 | 10d. "Adoration of the Magi" (Bosch) (*horiz*) | 2·00 | 2·50 | 15 | 15 |
| 198 | 1s. 6d. "Adoration of the Shepherds" (J. de Ribera) (*vert*) | 10·00 | 4·00 | 25 | 20 |
| 194/8 | *Set of* 5 | 22·00 | 13·50 | 70 | 50 |

**68** Tennis, and Queen Elizabeth II

(Des V. Whiteley)

1967 (12 Jan). *2nd South Pacific Games, Nouméa. T* **68** *and similar horiz designs in orange-brown, black and new blue* (1d.) *or multicoloured* (*others*). *P* 13½. (*a*) *Postage.*

199 ½d. Type **68** . . 10 10
200 1d. Netball and Games emblem . . 10 10
201 4d. Boxing and Cook Islands' team badge . . 10 10
202 7d. Football and Queen Elizabeth II . . 10 10

(*b*) *Air*

203 10d. Running and Games emblem . . 10 10
204 2s. 3d. Running and Cook Islands' team badge . . 15 10
199/204 . . *Set of* 6 40 30

**(New Currency, 100 cents = 1 dollar)**

1c (74) 2½c (I) 2½c (II)

1967 (3 Apr–6 June). *Decimal Currency. Nos.* 134/6, 163/70 *and* 172/5 *surch as T* **74** *by the Government Printer. Sterling values unobliterated except No.* 218.

205 1 c. on 1d. emerald-green and yellow (4.5) 45 1·10
206 2 c. on 2d. brown-red and yellow . . 10 10
207 2½ c. on 3d. yell, yellow-grn & reddish vio (I) 20 10
a. Horiz pair. Nos. 207/8 . . 40 20
208 2½ c. on 3d. yellow, yellow-green & reddish violet (II) . . 20 10
209 3 c. on 4d. red and blue . . 15 10
210 4 c. on 5d. blue and black (4.5) . . 1·00 20
211 5 c. on 6d. red, yellow and green . . 15 10
212 5 c. on 6d. black, yellow and light blue . . 2·50 40
213 7 c. on 8d. black and blue . . 15 10
214 10 c. on 1s. orange-yellow & yellow-green 15 10
215 15 c. on 1s. 6d. bluish violet (R.) (4.5.67) . . 2·00 1·00
216 30 c. on 3s. black & yellow-grn (R.) (4.5.67) 14·00 4·50
217 50 c. on 5s. bistre-brown & blue (R.) (4.5.67) 3·50 1·25
218 $1 and 10s. on 10d. mult (R.) (4.5.67) . . 14·00 6·50
219 $2 on £1 pink (R.) (6.6.67) . . 70·00 80·00
220 $6 on £3 green (R.) (6.6.67) . . £110 £120
221 $10 on £5 blue (R.) (6.6.67) . . £150 £160
205/18 . . *Set of* 14 32·00 13·00

The two types of the 2½ c. occur on alternate vertical rows within the sheet.

The surcharge on No. 218 is $1 and its equivalent of 10s. in the old currency. The "10d." is obliterated by three bars.

A large number of minor varieties exist in these surcharges, such as wrong fount letter "C" and figures.

**75** Village Scene. Cook Islands 1d. Stamp of 1892 and Queen Victoria (from "Penny Black")

(Des V. Whiteley)

1967 (3 July). *75th Anniv of First Cook Islands Stamps. T* **75** *and similar horiz designs. Multicoloured. P* 13½.

222 1 c. (1d.) Type **75** . . 10 10
223 3 c. (4d.) Post Office, Avarua, Rarotonga and Queen Elizabeth II . . 15 10
224 8 c. (10d.) Avarua, Rarotonga and Cook Islands 10d. stamp of 1892 . . 30 10
225 18 c. (1s. 9d.) S.S. *Moana Roa*, "DC-3" aircraft, map and Captain Cook . . 1·40 25
222/5 . . *Set of* 4 1·75 40
**MS**226 134 × 109 mm. Nos. 222/5 . . 2·25 2·75

The face values are expressed in decimal currency and in the sterling equivalent.

Each value was issued in sheets of 8 stamps and 1 label.

**79** Hibiscus **80** Queen Elizabeth II

**81** Queen Elizabeth and Flowers

Two types of $4

I. Value 32½ mm long. Coarse screen.
II. Value 33½ mm long. Finer screen.

(Floral designs from paintings by Mrs. Kay W. Billings)

1967–71. *Multicoloured designs as T* **79/81**. *P* 14 × 13½. A. *Without fluorescent security markings.* B. *With fluorescent security markings.*

| | | A | | B | |
|---|---|---|---|---|---|
| 227 | ½ c. Type **79** | 10 | 10 | 20 | 10 |
| 228 | 1 c. *Hibiscus syriacus* (27 × 37 *mm*) | 10 | 10 | 20 | 10 |
| 229 | 2 c. Frangipani (27 × 37 *mm*) | 10 | 10 | 20 | 10 |
| 230 | 2½ c. *Clitoria ternatea* (27 × 37 *mm*) | 20 | 10 | 20 | 10 |
| 231 | 3 c. "Suva Queen" (27 × 37 *mm*) | 45 | 10 | 40 | 10 |
| 232 | 4 c. Water Lily ("WALTER LILY") (27 × 37 *mm*) | 55 | 70 | † | |
| 233 | 4 c. Water Lily (27 × 37 *mm*) | 1·40 | 1·25 | 1·50 | 10 |
| 234 | 5 c. *Bauhinia bipinnata rosea* (27 × 37 *mm*) | 35 | 10 | 30 | 10 |
| 235 | 6 c. Hibiscus (27 × 37 *mm*) | 40 | 10 | 30 | 10 |
| 236 | 8 c. *Allamanda cathartica* (27 × 37 *mm*) | 40 | 10 | 30 | 10 |
| 237 | 9 c. Stephanotis (27 × 37 *mm*) | 40 | 10 | 30 | 10 |
| 238 | 10 c. *Poinciana regia flamboyant* (27 × 37 *mm*) | 40 | 10 | 30 | 10 |
| 239 | 15 c. Frangipani (27 × 37 *mm*) | 40 | 10 | 40 | 10 |
| 240 | 20 c. Thunbergia (27 × 37 *mm*) | 1·75 | 60 | 2·25 | 35 |
| 241 | 25 c. Canna Lily (27 × 37 *mm*) | 80 | 30 | 1·00 | 15 |
| 242 | 30 c. *Euphorbia pulcherrima poinsettia* (27 × 37 *mm*) | 65 | 50 | 2·00 | 40 |
| 243 | 50 c. *Gardinia taitensis* (27 × 37 *mm*) | 1·00 | 55 | 2·00 | 40 |
| 244 | $1 Type **80** | 2·25 | 80 | 1·75 | 80 |
| 245 | $2 Type **80** | 4·75 | 1·50 | 3·50 | 1·50 |
| 246 | $4 Type **81** (I) | 3·00 | 3·50 | 45·00 | 48·00 |
| 246*c* | $4 Type **81** (II) | | † | 11·00 | 8·50 |
| 247 | $6 Type **81** | 3·50 | 5·00 | 12·00 | 6·00 |
| 247*c* | $8 Type **81** | 8·00 | 12·00 | 17·00 | 10·00 |
| 248 | $10 Type **81** | 8·00 | 12·00 | 19·00 | 12·00 |
| 227/48 | *Set of* 22 | 35·00 | 35·00 | 65·00 | 35·00 |

Dates of issue:—Nos. 227/238A, 31.7.67; Nos. 239/243A, 11.8.67; Nos. 244/245A, 31.8.67; Nos. 246/247A, 30.4.68; No. 248A, 12.7.68; No. 247cA, 21.4.69; Nos. 227/243B, 9.2.70; Nos. 244/245B, 12.10.70; No. 246cB, 14.7.71; No. 246B, 11.11.70; No. 247B, 12.2.71; No. 247cB, 3.5.71; No. 248B, 14.6.71.

The "WALTER" spelling error occurred on all stamps in one of the four post office sheets which went to make up the printing sheet and this was corrected in later supplies.

**FLUORESCENT PAPER.** This is on paper treated with fluorescent security markings, in the form of faint multiple coats of arms. Stamps exist with these markings inverted. In addition an invisible synthetic gum has been used which prevents curling and is suitable for use in the tropics without interleaving the sheets.

Some of the above are known with these markings omitted and can be distinguished when in unused condition from the original printings without markings by their synthetic invisible gum.

**97** "Ia Orana Maria"

1967 (24 Oct). *Gauguin's Polynesian Paintings. T* **97** *and similar designs. Multicoloured. P* 13.

249 1 c. Type **97** . . 10 10
250 3 c. "Riders on the Beach" . . 10 10
251 5 c. "Still Life with Flowers" . . 15 10
252 8 c. "Whispered Words" . . 15 10
253 15 c. "Maternity" . . 35 10
254 22 c. "Why are you angry?" . . 40 15
249/54 . . *Set of* 6 1·00 35
**MS**255 156 × 132 mm. Nos. 249/54 . . 1·00 1·25

The 5 c. includes an inset portrait of Queen Elizabeth.

**98** "The Holy Family" (Rubens)

HURRICANE
RELIEF
PLUS 5c
(99)

1967 (4 Dec). *Christmas. Renaissance Paintings. T* **98** *and similar designs. Multicoloured. P* 12 × 13.

256 1 c. Type **98** . . 10 10
257 3 c. "Adoration of the Magi" (Dürer) . . 10 10
258 4 c. "The Lucca Madonna" (J. van Eyck) . . 10 10
259 8 c. "The Adoration of the Shepherds" (J. da Bassano) . . 15 10
260 15 c. "Adoration of the Shepherds" (El Greco) 30 10
261 25 c. "Madonna and Child" (Correggio) . . 35 10
256/61 . . *Set of* 6 90 30

1968 (12 Feb). *Hurricane Relief. Nos.* 231A, 233A, 251, 238A, 241A *and* 243/4A *surch as T* **99** *by Govt Printer, Rarotonga.*

262 3 c. + 1 c. "Suva Queen" . . 15 10
263 4 c. + 1 c. Water Lily . . 15 10
264 5 c. + 2 c. "Still Life with Flowers" . . 15 10
a. Black surch albino . .
265 10 c. + 2 c. *Poinciana regia flamboyant* . . 15 10
266 25 c. + 5 c. Canna Lily . . 25 10
267 50 c. + 10 c. *Gardinia taitensis* . . 35 15
268 $1 + 10 c. Type **80** . . 60 30
262/8 . . *Set of* 7 1·60 75

The surcharge on No. 268 is as T **99**, but with seriffed letters. On No. 264 silver blocking obliterates the design area around the lettering.

**100** "Matavai Bay, Tahiti" (J. Barralet)

**101** "*Resolution* and *Discovery*" (J. Webber)

(Des J. Berry)

**1968** (12 Sept). *Bicentenary of Captain Cook's First Voyage of Discovery. Multicoloured. Invisible gum. P* 13.

(*a*) *Postage. Vert designs as T* **100**

| | | | |
|---|---|---|---|
| 269 | ½ c. Type **100** .. | 10 | 10 |
| 270 | 1 c. "Island of Huaheine" (John Cleveley) .. | 15 | 10 |
| 271 | 2 c. "Town of St. Peter and St. Paul, Kamchatka" (J. Webber) | 40 | 35 |
| 272 | 4 c. "The Ice Islands" (Antarctica: W. Hodges) | 40 | 35 |

(*b*) *Air. Horiz designs as T* **101**

| | | | |
|---|---|---|---|
| 273 | 6 c. Type **101** .. | 90 | 65 |
| 274 | 10 c. "The Island of Tahiti" (W. Hodges) .. | 1·25 | 75 |
| 275 | 15 c. "Karakakooa, Hawaii" (J. Webber) .. | 1·50 | 90 |
| 276 | 25 c. "The Landing at Middleburg" (J. Sherwin) .. | 1·75 | 1·25 |
| 269/76 | *Set of* 8 | 6·00 | 4·00 |

Each value was issued in sheets of 10 stamps and 2 labels.

**FLUORESCENT PAPER.** From No. 277, *unless otherwise stated*, all issues are printed on paper treated with fluorescent security markings with invisible synthetic gum. These markings may be inverted or omitted in error.

**102** Sailing

**103** "Madonna and Child" (Titian)

**1968** (21 Oct). *Olympic Games, Mexico. T* **102** *and similar horiz designs. Multicoloured. P* 13.

| | | | |
|---|---|---|---|
| 277 | 1 c. Type **102** .. | 10 | 10 |
| 278 | 5 c. Gymnastics .. | 10 | 10 |
| 279 | 15 c. High-jumping .. | 15 | 10 |
| 280 | 20 c. High-diving .. | 15 | 10 |
| 281 | 30 c. Cycling .. | 15 | 10 |
| 282 | 50 c. Hurdling .. | 20 | 15 |
| 277/82 | *Set of* 6 | 70 | 30 |

Each value was issued in sheets of 10 stamps and 2 labels.

**1968** (2 Dec). *Christmas. Paintings. T* **103** *and similar vert designs. Multicoloured. P* 13½.

| | | | |
|---|---|---|---|
| 283 | 1 c. Type **103** .. | 10 | 10 |
| 284 | 4 c. "The Holy Family with Lamb" (Raphael) | 10 | 10 |
| 285 | 10 c. "The Virgin of the Rosary" (Murillo) .. | 25 | 10 |
| 286 | 20 c. "Adoration of the Kings" (Memling) .. | 30 | 10 |
| 287 | 30 c. "Adoration of the Magi" (Ghirlandaio) .. | 35 | 10 |
| 283/7 | *Set of* 5 | 95 | 30 |
| **MS**288 | 114 × 177 mm. Nos. 283/7 plus label .. | 1·60 | 1·60 |

**104** Camp-fire Cooking

**1969** (6 Feb). *Diamond Jubilee of New Zealand Scout Movement and Fifth National (New Zealand) Jamboree. T* **104** *and similar square designs. Multicoloured. P* 13½.

| | | | |
|---|---|---|---|
| 289 | ½ c. Type **104** .. | 10 | 10 |
| 290 | 1 c. Descent by rope .. | 10 | 10 |
| 291 | 5 c. Semaphore .. | 10 | 10 |
| 292 | 10 c. Tree-planting .. | 15 | 10 |
| 293 | 20 c. Constructing a shelter .. | 25 | 10 |
| 294 | 30 c. Lord Baden-Powell and island scene .. | 40 | 15 |
| 289/94 | *Set of* 6 | 90 | 35 |

Each value was issued in sheets of 10 stamps and 2 labels.

**105** High Jumping

**1969** (7 July). *Third South Pacific Games, Port Moresby. T* **105** *and similar triangular designs. Multicoloured. Without fluorescent security markings. P* 13 × 13½.

| | | | |
|---|---|---|---|
| 295 | ½ c. Type **105** .. | 10 | 10 |
| 296 | ½ c. Footballer .. | 10 | 10 |
| 297 | 1 c. Basketball .. | 15 | 10 |
| 298 | 1 c. Weightlifter .. | 15 | 10 |
| 299 | 4 c. Tennis-player .. | 20 | 15 |
| 300 | 4 c. Hurdler .. | 20 | 15 |
| 301 | 10 c. Javelin-thrower .. | 40 | 25 |
| 302 | 10 c. Runner .. | 40 | 25 |
| 303 | 15 c. Golfer .. | 60 | 35 |
| 304 | 15 c. Boxer .. | 60 | 35 |
| 295/304 | *Set of* 10 | 2·50 | 1·60 |
| **MS**305 | 174 × 129 mm. Nos. 295/304 plus two labels | 2·50 | 2·25 |

Each value was issued in sheets containing 5 *se-tenant* pairs of both designs and 2 labels.

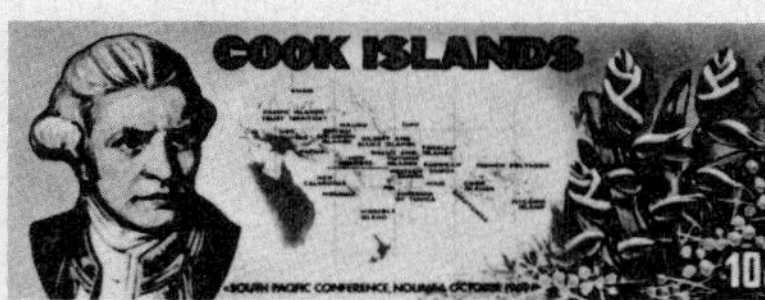


**106** Flowers, Map and Captain Cook

**1969** (8 Oct). *South Pacific Conference, Nouméa. T* **106** *and similar horiz designs. Multicoloured. Without fluorescent security markings. P* 13.

| | | | |
|---|---|---|---|
| 306 | 5 c. Flowers, map and Premier Albert Henry | 55 | 15 |
| 307 | 10 c. Type **106** .. | 1·00 | 55 |
| 308 | 25 c. Flowers, map and N.Z. arms .. | 1·10 | 75 |
| 309 | 30 c. Queen Elizabeth II, map and flowers .. | 1·10 | 85 |
| 306/9 | *Set of* 4 | 3·25 | 2·10 |

**107** "Virgin and Child with Saints Jerome and Dominic" (Lippi)

**108** "The Resurrection of Christ" (Raphael)

**1969** (21 Nov). *Christmas. Paintings. T* **107** *and similar designs. Multicoloured. Without fluorescent security markings. P* 13.

| | | | |
|---|---|---|---|
| 310 | 1 c. Type **107** .. | 10 | 10 |
| 311 | 4 c. "The Holy Family" (Fra Bartolomeo) .. | 10 | 10 |
| 312 | 10 c. "The Adoration of the Shepherds" (A. Mengs) .. | 15 | 10 |
| 313 | 20 c. "Madonna and Child with Saints" (R. Campin) .. | 25 | 10 |
| 314 | 30 c. "The Madonna of the Basket" (Correggio) | 25 | 15 |
| 310/14 | *Set of* 5 | 70 | 30 |
| **MS**315 | 132 × 97 mm. Nos. 310/14 .. | 85 | 1·40 |

Each value was issued in sheets of 9 stamps and 1 label.

**1970** (12 Mar). *Easter. Paintings. T* **108** *and similar vert designs showing "The Resurrection of Christ" by the artists named. Multicoloured. P* 13.

| | | | |
|---|---|---|---|
| 316 | 4 c. Type **108** .. | 10 | 10 |
| 317 | 8 c. Dirk Bouts .. | 10 | 10 |
| 318 | 20 c. Altdorfer .. | 15 | 10 |
| 319 | 25 c. Murillo .. | 20 | 10 |
| 316/19 | *Set of* 4 | 50 | 20 |
| **MS**320 | 132 × 162 mm. Nos. 316/19 .. | 80 | 1·25 |

Each value was issued in sheets of 8 stamps and 1 label.

KIA ORANA
APOLLO 13
ASTRONAUTS
Te Atua to
Tatou Irinakianga

**(109)**

**1970** (17–30 Apr). *Apollo* 13. *Nos.* 233, 236, 239/40, 242 *an[d]* 245/6 *optd with T* **109** (4 *c. to* $2) *or with first three lines only i[n] larger type* ($4), *by Govt Printer.* A. *Without fluorescent securit[y] markings.* B. *With fluorescent security markings.*

| | | A | | B | |
|---|---|---|---|---|---|
| 321 | 4 c. Water Lily .. | 10 | 10 | | † |
| | a. Opt albino .. | 42·00 | — | | † |
| 322 | 8 c. *Allamanda cathartica* .. | 10 | 10 | | † |
| 323 | 15 c. Frangipani .. | 10 | 10 | | † |
| 324 | 20 c. Thunbergia .. | 15 | 15 | | † |
| 325 | 30 c. *Euphorbia pulcherrima poinsettia* .. | 20 | 20 | | † |
| 326 | $2 Type **80** .. | 60 | 90 | | † |
| 327 | $4 Type **81** (30.4) .. | 55·00 | 65·00 | 1·25 | 2·7 |
| 321/6A, 327B | *Set of* 7 | 2·00 | 3·75 | | |

**110** The Royal Family

(Des V. Whiteley (5 c.), J. Berry ($1))

**1970** (12 June). *Royal Visit to New Zealand. T* **110** *and simila[r] horiz designs. Multicoloured. P* 13.

| | | | |
|---|---|---|---|
| 328 | 5 c. Type **110** .. | 65 | 3 |
| 329 | 30 c. Captain Cook and H.M.S. *Endeavour* .. | 2·75 | 1·7 |
| 330 | $1 Royal Visit commemorative coin .. | 4·00 | 3·0 |
| 328/30 | *Set of* 3 | 6·75 | 4·5 |
| **MS**331 | 145 × 97 mm. Nos. 328/30 .. | 9·00 | 9·5 |

Each value was issued in sheets of 8 stamps and 1 label.

FIFTH ANNIVERSARY
SELF-GOVERNMENT
AUGUST 1970

**(113)**

FOUR
DOLLARS
$4.00

**(114)**

**1970** (27 Aug). *5th Anniv of Self-Government Nos.* 328/30 *opt[d] with T* **113** (30 *c. and* $1), *or in single line in silver around fram[e] of stamp* (5 *c.*).

| | | | |
|---|---|---|---|
| 332 | 5 c. Type **110** .. | 40 | 1 |
| 333 | 30 c. Captain Cook and H.M.S. *Endeavour* .. | 1·25 | 3 |
| 334 | $1 Royal Visit commemorative coin .. | 2·00 | 9 |
| 332/4 | *Set of* 3 | 3·25 | 1·2 |

**1970** (11 Nov). *Nos.* 247*c and* 248 *surch with T* **114** *by Go[vt] Printer, Rarotonga.* A. *Without fluorescent security markings.* B. *With fluorescent security markings.*

| | | | A | | B | |
|---|---|---|---|---|---|---|
| 335 | **81** | $4 on $8 multicoloured | 35·00 | 30·00 | 4·00 | 3·0 |
| 336 | | $4 on $10 multicoloured | 48·00 | 48·00 | 1·50 | 1·7 |

There are variations in the setting of this surcharge and also i[n] the rule.

**115** Mary, Joseph and Christ in Manger

PLUS 20c
UNITED
KINGDOM
SPECIAL
MAIL SERVICE

**(116)**

(Des from De Lisle Psalter)

**1970** (30 Nov). *Christmas. T* **115** *and similar square designs. Multicoloured. P* 13.

| | | | |
|---|---|---|---|
| 337 | 1 c. Type **115** .. | 10 | 1 |
| 338 | 4 c. Shepherds and Apparition of the Angel | 10 | 1 |
| 339 | 10 c. Mary showing Child to Joseph .. | 15 | 1 |
| 340 | 20 c. The Wise Men bearing Gifts .. | 20 | 1 |
| 341 | 30 c. Parents wrapping Child in swaddling clothes .. | 25 | 1 |
| 337/41 | *Set of* 5 | 65 | 3 |
| **MS**342 | 100 × 139 mm. Nos. 337/41 plus label .. | 90 | 1·5 |

Each value was issued in sheets of 5 stamps and 1 label. Stamp[s] from the miniature sheet are smaller, since they do not have th[e] buff parchment border as on the stamps from the sheets.

**1971.** *Nos.* 242B *and* 243B *surch as T* **116**.

| | | | |
|---|---|---|---|
| 343 | 30 c. + 20 c. *Euphorbia pulcherrima poinsettia* (25.2) .. | 40 | 5 |
| 344 | 50 c. + 20 c. *Gardinia taitensis* (8.3) .. | 1·50 | 1·7 |

The premium of 20 c. was to prepay a private delivery service fe[e] in Great Britain during the postal strike. The mail was sent by ai[r] to a forwarding address in the Netherlands. No. 343 was intende[d] for ordinary airmail ½ oz letters, and No. 344 included registratio[n] fee.

The postal strike ended on 8 March and both stamps were with- drawn on 12 March.

117 Wedding of Princess Elizabeth and Prince Philip

(Des from photographs. Litho Format)

**1971** (11 Mar). *Royal Visit of H.R.H. The Duke of Edinburgh. T* **117** *and similar horiz designs. Multicoloured. P* 13½.

345 1 c. Type **117** .. .. .. .. .. 30 50
346 4 c. Queen Elizabeth, Prince Philip, Princess Anne and Prince Charles at Windsor .. 75 1·10
347 10 c. Prince Philip sailing .. .. .. 1·00 1·25
348 15 c. Prince Philip in polo gear .. .. 1·00 1·25
349 25 c. Prince Philip in naval uniform, and the Royal Yacht *Britannia* .. .. 1·50 2·00
345/9 .. .. .. .. .. *Set of* 5 4·00 5·50
**MS**350 168 × 122 mm. Nos 345/9 plus printed labels in positions 1, 3, 4, and 6 .. .. 4·50 7·00

Each value was issued in sheets of 7 stamps and 2 labels.

(118)

(119)

**1971** (8 Sept). *Fourth South Pacific Games, Tahiti. Nos.* 238B, 241B *and* 242B *optd with T* **118** *in black, or surch as T* **119** *in blue.*

351 10 c. *Poinciana regia flamboyant* .. .. 10 10
352 10 c. + 1 c. *Poinciana regia flamboyant* .. 10 10
353 10 c. + 3 c. *Poinciana regia flamboyant* .. 10 10
354 25 c. Canna Lily .. .. .. .. 15 10
355 25 c. + 1 c. Canna Lily .. .. .. 15 10
356 25 c. + 3 c. Canna Lily .. .. .. 15 10
357 30 c. *Euphorbia pulcherrima poinsettia* .. 15 10
358 30 c. + 1 c. *Euphorbia pulcherrima poinsettia* 15 10
359 30 c. + 3 c. *Euphorbia pulcherrima poinsettia* 15 10
351/9 .. .. .. .. .. *Set of* 9 1·10 50

The stamps additionally surcharged 1 c. or 3 c. helped to finance the Cook Islands' team at the games.

**10c ≡**

(120)

121 "Virgin and Child" (Bellini)

**1971** (20 Oct). *Nos.* 230B, 233B, 236B/7B *and* 239B *surch with T* **120**.

360 10 c. on 2½ c. *Clitoria ternatea* .. .. 15 25
361 10 c. on 4 c. Water Lily .. .. .. 15 25
362 10 c. on 8 c. *Allamanda cathartica* .. .. 15 25
a. Surch inverted .. .. .. .. £140
363 10 c. on 9 c. Stephanotis .. .. .. 15 25
364 10 c. on 15 c. Frangipani .. .. .. 15 25
a. Surch double .. .. .. .. 95·00
360/4 .. .. .. .. .. *Set of* 5 65 1·10

**1971** (30 Nov). *Christmas. T* **121** *and similar vert designs showing different paintings of the "Virgin and Child", by Bellini. P* 13.

365 1 c. multicoloured .. .. .. .. 10 10
366 4 c. multicoloured .. .. .. .. 10 10
367 10 c. multicoloured .. .. .. .. 25 10
368 20 c. multicoloured .. .. .. .. 50 10
369 30 c. multicoloured .. .. .. .. 50 20
365/9 .. .. .. .. .. *Set of* 5 1·25 35
**MS**370 135 × 147 mm. Nos. 365/9 .. .. 1·50 2·25
**MS**371 92 × 98 mm. 50 c. + 5 c. "The Holy Family in a Garland of Flowers (Jan Brueghel and Pieter van Avont) (41 × 41 *mm*) .. .. .. 60 1·40

Each value was issued in sheets of 8 stamps and 1 label.



**SOUTH PACIFIC COMMISSION FEB. 1947 - 1972**

(122)

123 St. John

**1972** (17 Feb). *25th Anniv of South Pacific Commission. No.* 244B *optd with T* **122**.

372 **80** $1 multicoloured .. .. .. 40 75

(Des from De Lisle Psalter)

**1972** (6 Mar). *Easter. T* **123** *and similar vert designs. Multicoloured. P* 13.

373 5 c. Type **123** .. .. .. .. .. 10 10
374 10 c. Christ on the Cross .. .. .. 10 10
375 30 c. Mary, Mother of Jesus .. .. .. 25 25
373/5 .. .. .. .. .. *Set of* 3 35 35
**MS**376 79 × 112 mm. Nos. 373/5 forming triptych of "The Crucifixion" .. .. .. .. 80 2·25

Stamps from the miniature sheet do not have a border around the perforations, and are therefore smaller than stamps from sheets.

**HURRICANE RELIEF PLUS 2c**

(124)

**Hurricane Relief Plus 5c**

(125)

**1972** (30 Mar). *Hurricane Relief. Nos.* 373/5 *surch as T* **124**, *and Nos.* 239B, 241B *and* 243B *surch as T* **125**, *by Govt Printer, Rarotonga.*

377 5 c. + 2 c. Type **123** (R.) .. .. .. 10 10
a. Albino surch .. .. .. .. 50·00
378 10 c. + 2 c. Christ on the Cross (R.) .. .. 15 15
379 15 c. + 5 c. Frangipani .. .. .. 20 20
380 25 c. + 5 c. Canna Lily .. .. .. 20 20
381 30 c. + 5 c. Mary, Mother of Jesus .. .. 20 20
a. Albino surch .. .. .. ..
382 50 c. + 10 c. *Gardinia taitensis* .. .. 25 25
377/82 .. .. .. .. *Set of* 6 90 90

126 Rocket heading for Moon 127

**1972** (17 Apr). *Apollo Moon Exploration Flights. T* **126/7** *and similar horiz designs. Multicoloured. P* 13.

383 5 c. Type **126** .. .. .. .. .. 15 10
384 5 c. Type **127** .. .. .. .. .. 15 10
385 10 c. } Astronauts on Moon .. .. .. 20 10
386 10 c. } .. 20 10
387 25 c. } Moon Rover and astronauts working .. 25 15
388 25 c. } .. 25 15
389 30 c. } Splashdown and helicopter .. .. 25 15
390 30 c. } .. 25 15
383/90 .. .. .. .. *Set of* 8 1·50 70
**MS**391 83 × 205 mm. Nos. 383/90 .. .. 3·00 4·50

These were issued in horizontal *se-tenant* pairs of each value, forming one composite design.

**HURRICANE RELIEF Plus 2c**

(128)

129 High-jumping

**1972** (24 May). *Hurricane Relief. Nos.* 383/91 *surch as T* **128**.

392 5 c. + 2 c. Type **126** .. .. .. .. 10 10
393 5 c. + 2 c. Type **127** .. .. .. .. 10 10
394 10 c. + 2 c. } Astronauts on Moon .. .. 10 10
395 10 c. + 2 c. } .. 10 10
396 25 c. + 2 c. } Moon Rover and astronauts .. 15 15
397 25 c. + 2 c. } .. 15 15
398 30 c. + 2 c. } Splashdown and astronauts .. 15 15
399 30 c. + 2 c. } .. 15 15
392/9 .. .. .. .. .. *Set of* 8 75 75
**MS**400 83 × 205 mm. **MS**391 surch 3 c. on each stamp .. .. .. .. .. .. 2·50 3·50

**1972** (26 June). *Olympic Games, Munich. T* **129** *and similar vert designs. Multicoloured. P* 13½.

401 10 c. Type **129** .. .. .. .. .. 15 10
402 25 c. Running .. .. .. .. .. 30 15
403 30 c. Boxing .. .. .. .. .. 30 20
401/3 .. .. .. .. .. *Set of* 3 70 40
**MS**404 88 × 78 mm. 50 c. + 5 c. Pierre de Coubertin 1·00 2·00
**MS**405 84 × 133 mm. Nos. 401/3 plus *se-tenant* label 1·25 2·00

Each value was issued in sheets of 8 stamps and 1 label.

130 "The Rest on the Flight into Egypt" (Caravaggio)

131 Marriage Ceremony

**1972** (11 Oct). *Christmas T* **130** *and similar vert designs. Multicoloured. P* 13.

406 1 c. Type **130** .. .. .. .. .. 10 10
407 5 c. "Madonna of the Swallow" (Guercino) 25 10
408 10 c. "Madonna of the Green Cushion" (Solario) .. .. .. .. .. 30 10
409 20 c. "Madonna and Child" (di Credi) .. 45 20
410 30 c. "Madonna and Child" (Bellini) .. .. 70 30
406/10 .. .. .. .. .. *Set of* 5 1·60 60
**MS**411 141 × 152 mm. Nos. 406/10 plus *se-tenant* label in position 1 .. .. .. .. 1·75 2·25
**MS**412 101 × 82 mm. 50 c + 5 c. "The Holy Night" (Correggio) (31 × 43 *mm*) .. .. .. 60 1·50

Each value was issued in sheets of 9 stamps and 1 label.

**1972** (20 Nov). *Royal Silver Wedding. T* **131** *and similar black and silver designs. P* 13.

413 5 c. Type **131** .. .. .. .. .. 25 15
414 10 c. Leaving Westminster Abbey .. .. 60 40
415 15 c. Bride and Bridegroom (40 × 41 *mm*) .. 75 50
416 30 c. Family Group (67 × 40 *mm*) .. .. 1·10 80
413/16 .. .. .. .. .. *Set of* 4 2·50 1·60

The 5, 10 and 15 c. values were each issued in sheets of 8 stamps and 1 label.

132 Taro Leaf

133 "Noli me Tangere" (Titian)

**1973** (15 Mar). *Silver Wedding Coinage. T* **132** *and similar designs showing coins. P* 13.

417 1 c. black, rosy carmine and gold .. .. 10 10
418 2 c. black, bright blue and gold .. .. 10 10
419 5 c. black, green and silver .. .. .. 10 10
420 10 c. black, royal blue and silver .. .. 25 10
421 20 c. black, deep blue-green and silver .. 35 10
422 50 c. black, carmine and silver .. .. 65 15
423 $1 black, bright blue and silver .. .. 1·10 30
417/23 .. .. .. .. .. *Set of* 7 2·25 50

Designs: *As T* **132**—2 c. Pineapple; 5 c. Hibiscus. 46 × 30 *mm*—10 c. Oranges; 20 c. White Tern; 50 c. Skipjack Tuna. 32 × 55 *mm*—$1 Tangaroa.

Each value was issued in sheets of 20 stamps and 1 label.

**1973** (9 Apr). *Easter. T* **133** *and similar vert designs. Multicoloured. P* 13.

424 5 c. Type **133** .. .. .. .. .. 15 10
425 10 c. "The Descent from the Cross" (Rubens) .. 20 10
426 30 c. "The Lamentation of Christ" (Dürer) .. 25 10
424/6 .. .. .. .. .. *Set of* 3 55 20
**MS**427 132 × 67 mm. Nos. 424/6 .. .. .. 55 1·25

Each value was issued in sheets of 15 stamps and 1 label.

**1973** (30 Apr). *Easter. Children's Charity. Designs as Nos.* 424/6 *in separate Miniature Sheets* 67 × 87 *mm, each with a face value of* 50 c. + 5 c. *P* 13 × 14.

**MS**428 As Nos. 424/6 .. .. *Set of 3 sheets* 1·60 2·75

**134** Queen Elizabeth II in Coronation Regalia

TENTH ANNIVERSARY CESSATION OF NUCLEAR TESTING TREATY

(135)

**1973** (1 June). *20th Anniv of Queen Elizabeth's Coronation. P* 14 × 13½.
429 **134** 10 c. multicoloured .. .. .. .. 65 1·25
**MS**430 64 × 89 mm. 50 c. as 10 c. P 13 × 14 .. 3·00 3·25
The perforated portion of **MS**430 is similar to No. 429, but has no borders.
No. 429 was issued in sheets of 5 stamps and 1 label.

**1973** (25 July). *Tenth Anniv of Treaty Banning Nuclear Testing. Nos.* 234B, 236B, 238B, *and* 240B/242B *optd with T* **135**.
431 5 c. *Bauhinia bi-pinnata rosea* .. .. .. 10 10
432 8 c. *Allamanda cathartica* .. .. .. 10 10
433 10 c. *Poinciana regia flamboyant* .. .. 10 10
434 20 c. Thunbergia .. .. .. .. 15 15
435 25 c. Canna Lily .. .. .. .. 20 15
436 30 c. *Euphorbia pulcherrima poinsettia* .. 20 15
431/6 .. .. .. .. .. *Set of* 6 70 65

**136** Tipairua

**1973** (17 Sept). *Maori Exploration of the Pacific. T* **136** *and similar horiz designs showing sailing craft. Multicoloured. P* 13.
437 ½ c. Type **136** .. .. .. .. 10 10
438 1 c. Wa'a Kaulua .. .. .. .. 10 10
439 1½ c. Tainui .. .. .. .. 15 10
440 5 c. War canoe .. .. .. .. 40 10
441 10 c. Pahi .. .. .. .. 60 15
442 15 c. Amastasi .. .. .. .. 1·00 30
443 25 c. Vaka .. .. .. .. 1·25 50
437/443 .. .. .. .. .. *Set of* 7 3·25 1·10

**137** The Annunciation

**138** Princess Anne

**1973** (30 Oct). *Christmas. T* **137** *and similar vert designs showing scenes from a 15th-century Flemish "Book of Hours". Multicoloured. P* 13.
444 1 c. Type **137** .. .. .. .. 10 10
445 5 c. The Visitation .. .. .. .. 10 10
446 10 c. Annunciation to the Shepherds .. .. 10 10
447 20 c. Epiphany .. .. .. .. 15 10
448 30 c. The Slaughter of the Innocents .. .. 20 15
444/8 .. .. .. .. .. *Set of* 5 40 30
**MS**449 121 × 128 mm. Nos. 444/8 plus *se-tenant* label .. .. .. .. .. .. 55 1·40
Each value was issued in sheets of 14 stamps and 1 label.
See also No. **MS**454.

**1973** (14 Nov). *Royal Wedding. T* **138** *and similar vert designs. Multicoloured. P* 14 × 13½.
450 25 c. Type **138** .. .. .. .. 20 10
451 30 c. Capt. Mark Phillips .. .. .. 25 10
452 50 c. Princess Anne and Capt. Phillips .. 30 15
450/2 .. .. .. .. .. *Set of* 3 65 30
**MS**453 119 × 100 mm. No. 450/2 plus *se-tenant* label. P 13 .. .. .. .. .. 75 45
Each value was issued in sheets of 8 stamps and 1 label.

**1973** (3 Dec). *Christmas. Children's Charity. Designs as Nos. 444/8 in separate Miniature Sheets* 50 × 70 *mm, each with a face value of* 50 c. + 5 c.
**MS**454 As Nos. 444/8 .. .. *Set of* 5 *sheets* 75 80

### NEW INFORMATION

The editor is always interested to correspond with people who have new information that will improve or correct the Catalogue.

**139** Running

**140** "Jesus carrying the Cross" (Raphael)

**1974** (24 Jan). *Commonwealth Games, Christchurch. T* **139** *and similar multicoloured designs. P* 14 × 13½ (1 *and* 3 *c.*) *or* 13½ × 14 (*others*).
455 1 c. Diving (*vert*) .. .. .. .. 10 10
456 3 c. Boxing (*vert*) .. .. .. .. 10 10
457 5 c. Type **139** .. .. .. .. .. 10 10
458 10 c. Weightlifting .. .. .. .. 10 10
459 30 c. Cycling .. .. .. .. .. 20 25
455/9 .. .. .. .. .. *Set of* 5 40 40
**MS**460 115 × 90 mm. 50 c. Discobolus .. .. 40 55
Each value was issued in sheets of 15 stamps and 1 label.

**1974** (25 Mar). *Easter. T* **140** *and similar vert designs. Multicoloured. P* 13½.
461 5 c. Type **140** .. .. .. .. .. 10 10
462 10 c. "The Holy Trinity" (El Greco) .. .. 15 10
463 30 c. "The Deposition of Christ" (Caravaggio) .. .. .. .. .. 25 20
461/3 .. .. .. .. .. *Set of* 3 40 30
**MS**464 130 × 70 mm. Nos. 461/3 .. .. .. 80 50
Each value was issued in sheets of 20 stamps and 1 label.

**1974** (22 Apr). *Easter. Children's Charity. Designs as Nos. 461/3 in separate Miniature Sheets* 59 × 87 *mm, each with a face value of* 50 c. + 5 c.
**MS**465 As Nos. 461/3 .. .. *Set of* 3 *sheets* 70 1·40

**141** Helmet Shell

**142** Queen Elizabeth II

**1974** (17 May)–**75**. *Horiz designs as T* **141** *showing sea-shells* (½ *to* 60 *c.*), *T* **142** *or larger horiz design* ($4 *to* $10). *Multicoloured. P* 14×13½ ($4 *to* $10) *or* 13½ (*others*).
466 ½ c. Type **141** .. .. .. .. 30 10
467 1 c. Vase shell .. .. .. .. 30 10
468 1½ c. Cockle shell .. .. .. .. 30 10
469 2 c. *Terebellum terebellum* .. .. .. 30 10
470 3 c. Bat volutes .. .. .. .. 45 10
471 4 c. Conch shell .. .. .. .. 50 10
472 5 c. Triton shell .. .. .. .. 50 10
473 6 c. Snake-head cowries .. .. .. 50 45
474 8 c. Helmet shell (*different*) .. .. .. 60 10
475 10 c. Auger shell .. .. .. .. 60 10
476 15 c. Metre shell .. .. .. .. 70 15
477 20 c. Naticacid shell .. .. .. .. 1·00 15
478 25 c. Scallop shell .. .. .. .. 1·00 30
479 30 c. Soldier Cone shell .. .. .. 1·00 20
480 50 c. Cloth of Gold Cone shell (26.8.74) .. 6·00 2·50
481 60 c. Olive shell (26.8.74) .. .. .. 6·00 2·50
482 $1 Type **142** (26.8.74) .. .. .. 2·50 3·00
483 $2 Type **142** (27.1.75) .. .. .. 2·50 2·25
484 $4 Queen Elizabeth II and seashells (17.3.75) .. .. .. .. 3·50 4·50
485 $6 As $4 (29.4.75) .. .. .. .. 11·00 7·00
486 $8 As $4 (30.5.75) .. .. .. .. 11·00 8·00
487 $10 As $4 (30.6.75) .. .. .. .. 12·00 9·00
466/87 .. .. .. .. .. *Set of* 22 55·00 35·00
Nos. 484/7 are larger, 60×39 mm.

**143** Footballer and Australasian Map

**144** Obverse and Reverse of Commemorative $2·50 Silver Coin

**1974** (5 July). *World Cup Football Championships, West Germany. T* **143** *and similar horiz designs. Multicoloured. P* 13.
488 25 c. Type **143** .. .. .. .. .. 15 10
489 50 c. Map and Munich Stadium .. .. 30 25
490 $1 Footballer, stadium and World Cup .. 50 45
488/90 .. .. .. .. *Set of* 3 85 70
**MS**491 89 × 100 mm. Nos. 488/90 .. .. .. 1·25 2·75
Each value was issued in sheets of 8 stamps and 1 label.

**1974** (22 July). *Bicentenary of Capt. Cook's Second Voyage of Discovery. T* **144** *and similar vert design. P* 14.
492 $2.50, silver, black and violet .. .. 13·00 7·00
493 $7.50, silver, black and deep turquoise-green 27·00 13·00
**MS**494 73 × 73 mm. Nos. 492/3 .. .. .. 48·00 48·00
Design:—$7.50. As T **144** but showing $7.50 coin.
Each value was issued in sheets of 5 stamps and 1 label.

**145** Early Stamps of Cook Islands

**146** "Madonna of the Goldfinch" (Raphael)

**1974** (16 Sept). *Centenary of Universal Postal Union. T* **145** *and similar horiz designs. Multicoloured. P* 13½ × 14.
495 10 c. Type **145** .. .. .. .. .. 15 15
496 25 c. Old landing strip, Rarotonga, and stamp of 1898 .. .. .. .. .. 30 40
497 30 c. Post Office, Rarotonga, and stamp of 1920 30 40
498 50 c. U.P.U. emblem and stamps .. .. 40 65
495/8 .. .. .. .. .. *Set of* 4 1·00 1·40
**MS**499 118 × 79 mm. Nos. 495/8. P 13 .. .. 1·00 1·75
Each value was issued in sheets of 8 stamps and 1 label.

**1974** (15 Oct). *Christmas. T* **146** *and similar vert designs. Multicoloured. P* 13.
500 1 c. Type **146** .. .. .. .. .. 10 10
501 5 c. "The Sacred Family" (Andrea del Sarto) 10 10
502 10 c. "The Virgin adoring the Child" (Correggio) .. .. .. .. 15 10
503 20 c. "The Holy Family" (Rembrandt) .. 25 20
504 30 c. "The Virgin and Child" (Rogier Van Der Weyden) .. .. .. .. .. 30 30
500/504 .. .. .. .. *Set of* 5 75 60
**MS**505 114 × 133 mm. Nos. 500/4 plus *se-tenant* label .. .. .. .. .. .. 75 1·25
Each value was issued in sheets of 15 stamps and 1 label.
See also No. **MS**512.

**147** Churchill and Blenheim Palace

**1974** (20 Nov). *Birth Centenary of Sir Winston Churchill. T* **147** *and similar horiz designs. Multicoloured. P* 13 × 14.
506 5 c. Type **147** .. .. .. .. .. 25 15
507 10 c. Churchill and Houses of Parliament .. 40 15
508 25 c. Churchill and Chartwell .. .. 80 30
509 30 c. Churchill and Buckingham Palace .. 90 35
510 50 c. Churchill and St. Paul's Cathedral .. 1·25 65
506/10 .. .. .. .. *Set of* 5 3·25 1·40
**MS**511 108 × 114 mm. Nos. 506/10 plus *se-tenant* label .. .. .. .. .. .. 4·00 2·25
Each value was issued in sheets of 5 stamps and 1 label.

**1974** (9 Dec). *Christmas. Children's Charity. Designs as Nos. 500/504 in separate miniature sheets* 53 × 69 *mm, each with a face value of* 50 c. + 5 c.
**MS**512 As Nos. 500/4 .. .. *Set of* 5 *sheets* 90 1·60

**148** Vasco Nuñez de Balboa and Discovery of Pacific Ocean (1513).

**1975** (3 Feb). *Pacific Explorers. T* **148** *and similar horiz designs. Multicoloured. P* 13.
513 1 c. Type **148** .. .. .. .. .. 10 10
514 5 c. Fernando de Magellanes and map (1520) 35 20
515 10 c. Juan Sebastian de Elcano and *Vitoria* (1520) .. .. .. .. .. 60 20
516 25 c. Friar de Urdaneta and ship (1564–67) .. 1·50 75
517 30 c. Miguel Lopez de Legazpi and ship (1564–67) .. .. .. .. .. 1·60 80
513/17 .. .. .. .. *Set of* 5 3·75 1·90

149 "Apollo" Capsule

**1975** (15 July). *"Apollo-Soyuz" Space Project. T* **149** *and similar horiz designs. Multicoloured. P* 13½.

| | | | |
|---|---|---|---|
| 518 | 25 c. Type **149** | 30 | 15 |
| 519 | 25 c. "Soyuz" capsule | 30 | 15 |
| 520 | 30 c. "Soyuz" crew | 35 | 15 |
| 521 | 30 c. "Apollo" crew | 35 | 15 |
| 522 | 50 c. Cosmonaut within "Soyuz" | 40 | 25 |
| 523 | 50 c. Astronauts within "Apollo" | 40 | 25 |
| 518/23 | *Set of* 6 | 1·90 | 1·00 |
| **MS**524 | 119 × 119 mm. Nos. 518/23. P 13 × 14 | 2·00 | 2·50 |

Each value was issued in sheets containing 9 horizontal *se-tenant* pairs of the two designs, together with 2 labels.

150 $100 Commemorative Gold Coin

**1975** (8 Aug). *Bicentenary of Captain Cook's Second Voyage. P* 13.

| | | | |
|---|---|---|---|
| 525 | **150** $2 brown, gold and bluish violet | 6·50 | 2·75 |

No. 525 was issued in sheets of 5 stamps and 1 label.

151 Cook Islands' Flag and Map

**1975** (8 Aug). *Tenth Anniv of Self-Government. T* **151** *and similar multicoloured designs. P* 13.

| | | | |
|---|---|---|---|
| 526 | 5 c. Type **151** | 20 | 10 |
| 527 | 10 c. Premier Sir Albert Henry and flag (*vert*) | 30 | 10 |
| 528 | 25 c. Rarotonga and flag | 70 | 30 |
| 526/8 | *Set of* 3 | 1·10 | 45 |

152 "Madonna by the Fireside" (R. Campin)

153 "Entombment of Christ" (Raphael)

**1975** (1 Dec). *Christmas. T* **152** *and similar vert designs. Multicoloured. P* 13½.

| | | | |
|---|---|---|---|
| 529 | 6 c. Type **152** | 10 | 10 |
| 530 | 10 c. "Madonna in the Meadow" (Raphael) | 15 | 10 |
| 531 | 15 c. "Madonna of the Oak" (attrib Raphael) | 20 | 10 |
| 532 | 20 c. "Adoration of the Shepherds" (J. B. Maino) | 25 | 15 |
| 533 | 35 c. "The Annunciation" (Murillo) | 30 | 20 |
| 529/33 | *Set of* 5 | 90 | 45 |
| **MS**534 | 110 × 124 mm. Nos. 529/33 | 90 | 90 |

**1975** (15 Dec). *Christmas. Children's Charity. Designs as Nos. 529/33 in separate miniature sheets* 53 × 71 *mm, each with a face value of* 75 *c.* + 5 *c.*

| | | | |
|---|---|---|---|
| **MS**535 | As Nos. 529/33 *Set of 5 sheets* | 1·50 | 1·75 |
| | a. Error. Miniature sheet as No. 531 imperf | £250 | |

**1976** (29 Mar). *Easter. T* **153** *and similar square designs. Multicoloured. P* 13.

| | | | |
|---|---|---|---|
| 536 | 7 c. Type **153** | 20 | 10 |
| 537 | 15 c. "Pietà" (Veronese) | 30 | 15 |
| 538 | 35 c. "Pietà" (El Greco) | 40 | 25 |
| 536/8 | *Set of* 3 | 80 | 40 |
| **MS**539 | 144 × 57 mm. Nos. 536/8 | 80 | 85 |

Each value was issued in sheets of 20 stamps and 1 label.

**1976** (3 May). *Easter. Children's Charity. Designs as Nos. 536/8 in separate miniature sheets* 69 × 69 *mm. each with a face value of* 60 *c.* + 5 *c.*

| | | | |
|---|---|---|---|
| **MS**540 | As Nos. 536/8 *Set of 3 sheets* | 1·40 | 1·60 |

## NEW INFORMATION

The editor is always interested to correspond with people who have new information that will improve or correct the Catalogue.

154 Benjamin Franklin and H.M.S. *Resolution*

**1976** (29 May). *Bicentenary of American Revolution. T* **154** *and similar horiz designs. Multicoloured. P* 13.

| | | | |
|---|---|---|---|
| 541 | $1 Type **154** | 6·00 | 1·50 |
| 542 | $2 Captain Cook and H.M.S. *Resolution* | 8·00 | 2·50 |
| **MS**543 | 118×58 mm. $3 Cook, Franklin and H.M.S. *Resolution* (74×31 *mm*) | 16·00 | 8·00 |

Each value was issued in sheets of 5 stamps and 1 label.

*Royal Visit July 1976*

(155)

**1976** (9 July). *Visit of Queen Elizabeth to the U.S.A. Nos. 541/3 optd with T* **155**.

| | | | |
|---|---|---|---|
| 544 | $1 Type **154** | 3·50 | 1·50 |
| 545 | $2 Captain Cook and H.M.S. *Resolution* | 5·50 | 2·50 |
| **MS**546 | $3 Cook, Franklin and H.M.S. *Resolution* | 10·00 | 7·50 |

156 Hurdling

157 "The Visitation"

**1976** (22 July). *Olympic Games, Montreal. T* **156** *and similar square designs. Multicoloured. P* 13.

| | | | |
|---|---|---|---|
| 547 | 7 c. } Type **156** | 10 | 10 |
| 548 | 7 c. } | 10 | 10 |
| 549 | 15 c. } Hockey | 15 | 15 |
| 550 | 15 c. } | 15 | 15 |
| 551 | 30 c. } Fencing | 25 | 15 |
| 552 | 30 c. } | 25 | 15 |
| 553 | 35 c. } Football | 30 | 20 |
| 554 | 35 c. } | 30 | 20 |
| 547/54 | *Set of* 8 | 1·40 | 1·10 |
| **MS**555 | 104 × 146 mm. Nos. 547/54 | 1·40 | 2·00 |

Each value was issued in sheets containing 5 horizontal *se-tenant* pairs and 2 labels. In each pair the first stamp has the face-value on the right, the second has it on the left. Illustrated is the left-hand stamp of the 7 c. design.

**1976** (12 Oct). *Christmas. T* **157** *and similar vert designs showing Renaissance sculptures. Multicoloured. P* 14 × 13½.

| | | | |
|---|---|---|---|
| 556 | 6 c. Type **157** | 10 | 10 |
| 557 | 10 c. "Adoration of the Shepherds" | 10 | 10 |
| 558 | 15 c. "Adoration of the Shepherds" (*different*) | 15 | 10 |
| 559 | 20 c. "The Epiphany" | 20 | 20 |
| 560 | 35 c. "The Holy Family" | 25 | 25 |
| 556/60 | *Set of* 5 | 70 | 60 |
| **MS**561 | 116 × 110 mm. Nos. 556/60. P 13 | 85 | 1·75 |

Each value was issued in sheets of 20 stamps and 1 label.

**1976** (2 Nov.) *Christmas. Children's Charity. Designs as Nos. 556/60 in separate miniature sheets* 66 × 80 *mm, each with a face value of* 75 *c.* + 5 *c.*

| | | | |
|---|---|---|---|
| **MS**562 | As Nos. 556/60 *Set of 5 sheets* | 2·00 | 2·00 |

158 Obverse and Reverse of $5 Mangaia Kingfisher Coin

**1976** (15 Nov). *National Wildlife and Conservation Day. P* 13.

| | | | |
|---|---|---|---|
| 563 | **158** $1 multicoloured | 3·50 | 1·25 |

No. 563 was issued in sheets of 5 stamps and 1 label.

159 Imperial State Crown

160 "Christ on the Cross"

**1977** (7 Feb). *Silver Jubilee. T* **159** *and similar vert designs. Multicoloured. P* 13.

| | | | |
|---|---|---|---|
| 564 | 25 c. Type **159** | 90 | 75 |
| 565 | 25 c. Queen with regalia | 90 | 75 |
| 566 | 50 c. Westminster Abbey | 1·50 | 1·50 |
| 567 | 50 c. Coronation Coach | 1·50 | 1·50 |
| 568 | $1 Queen and Prince Philip | 3·50 | 3·25 |
| 569 | $1 Royal Visit, 1974 | 3·50 | 3·25 |
| 564/9 | *Set of* 6 | 10·50 | 10·00 |
| **MS**570 | 130× 136 mm. As Nos. 564/9 (borders and "COOK ISLANDS" in a different colour) | 7·50 | 7·50 |

The two designs of each value are printed horizontally *se-tenant* throughout the sheet, and stamps from **MS**570 have borders and "COOK ISLANDS" in a different colour.

**1977** (28 Mar). *Easter and 400th Birth Anniv of Rubens. T* **160** *and similar vert designs. Multicoloured. P* 14 × 13½.

| | | | |
|---|---|---|---|
| 571 | 7 c. Type **160** | 30 | 10 |
| 572 | 15 c. "Christ on the Cross" | 45 | 15 |
| 573 | 35 c. "The Deposition of Christ" | 80 | 30 |
| 571/3 | *Set of* 3 | 1·40 | 50 |
| **MS**574 | 118 × 65 mm. Nos. 571/3. P 13 | 1·40 | 1·60 |

Each value was issued in sheets of 24 stamps and 1 label.

**1977** (18 Apr). *Easter. Children's Charity. Designs as Nos. 571/3 in separate miniature sheets* 60 × 79 *mm, each with a face value of* 60 *c.* + 5 *c. P* 13 × 14.

| | | | |
|---|---|---|---|
| **MS**575 | As Nos. 571/3 *Set of 3 sheets* | 1·00 | 1·00 |

161 "Virgin and Child" (Memling)

162 Obverse and Reverse of $5 Cook Islands Swiftlet Coin

**1977** (3 Oct). *Christmas. T* **161** *and similar vert designs. Multicoloured. P* 14.

| | | | |
|---|---|---|---|
| 576 | 6 c. Type **161** | 10 | 10 |
| 577 | 10 c. "Madonna and Child with Saints and Donors" (Memling) | 10 | 10 |
| 578 | 15 c. "Adoration of the Kings" (Geertgen) | 20 | 10 |
| 579 | 20 c. "Virgin and Child with Saints" (Crivelli) | 25 | 15 |
| 580 | 35 c. "Adoration of the Magi" (16th-cent Flemish School) | 30 | 20 |
| 576/80 | *Set of* 5 | 85 | 50 |
| **MS**581 | 118 × 111 mm. Nos. 576/80. P 13½ | 85 | 1·50 |

Each value was issued in sheets of 24 stamps and 1 label.

**1977** (31 Oct). *Christmas. Children's Charity. Designs as Nos. 576/80 in separate miniature sheets* 69 × 69 *mm, each with a face value of* 75 *c.* + 5 *c.*

| | | | |
|---|---|---|---|
| **MS**582 | As Nos. 576/80 *Set of 5 sheets* | 1·40 | 1·50 |

**1977** (15 Nov). *National Wildlife and Conservation Day. P* 13.

| | | | |
|---|---|---|---|
| 583 | **162** $1 multicoloured | 3·50 | 1·75 |

No. 583 was issued in sheets containing 10 stamps and 2 labels.

163 Captain Cook and H.M.S. *Resolution* (from paintings by N. Dance and H. Roberts)

**1978** (20 Jan). *Bicentenary of Discovery of Hawaii. T* **163** *and similar horiz designs. Multicoloured. P* 13½.

| | | | |
|---|---|---|---|
| 584 | 50 c. Type **163** | 1·50 | 60 |
| 585 | $1 Earl of Sandwich, and Cook landing at Owhyhee (from paintings by Thomas Gainsborough and J. Cleveley) | 2·00 | 1·00 |
| 586 | $2 Obverse and reverse of $200 coin and Cook monument, Hawaii | 3·25 | 1·75 |
| 584/6 | *Set of* 3 | 6·00 | 3·00 |
| **MS**587 | 118 × 95 mm. Nos. 584/86 | 7·00 | 8·00 |

Each value was issued in sheets of 5 stamps and 1 label.

164 "Pieta" (Van der Weyden)

165 Queen Elizabeth II

**1978** (20 Mar). *Easter. Paintings from National Gallery, London. T* **164** *and similar horiz designs. Multicoloured. P* 13.
588 15 c. Type **164** . . 30 15
589 35 c. "The Entombment" (Michelangelo) . . 40 30
590 75 c. "The Supper at Emmaus" (Caravaggio) 65 55
588/90 . . *Set of* 3 1·25 90
**MS**591 114 × 96 mm. Nos. 588/90 . . 1·25 2·00
Each value was issued in sheets of 5 stamps and 1 label.

**1978** (10 Apr). *Easter. Children's Charity. Designs as Nos.* 588/90 *in separate miniature sheets, 85 × 72 mm, each with a face value of* 60 *c. +* 5 *c. P* 13½.
**MS**592 As Nos. 588/90 . . *Set of 3 sheets* 1·10 1·10

**1978** (6 June). *25th Anniv of Coronation. T* **165** *and similar vert designs. Multicoloured. P* 13.
593 50 c. Type **165** . . 30 30
594 50 c. The Lion of England . . 30 30
595 50 c. Imperial State Crown . . 30 30
596 50 c. Statue of Tangaroa (god) . . 30 30
597 70 c. Type **165** . . 35 35
598 70 c. Sceptre with Cross . . 35 35
599 70 c. St. Edward's Crown . . 35 35
600 70 c. Rarotongan staff god . . 35 35
593/600 . . *Set of* 8 2·40 2·40
**MS**601 103 × 142 mm. Nos. 593/600*. . . 1·75 2·25
Each value was issued in sheets containing the 4 designs and 2 labels.
* In No **MS**601 the designs of Nos. 595 and 599 are transposed.

5c 

(166)

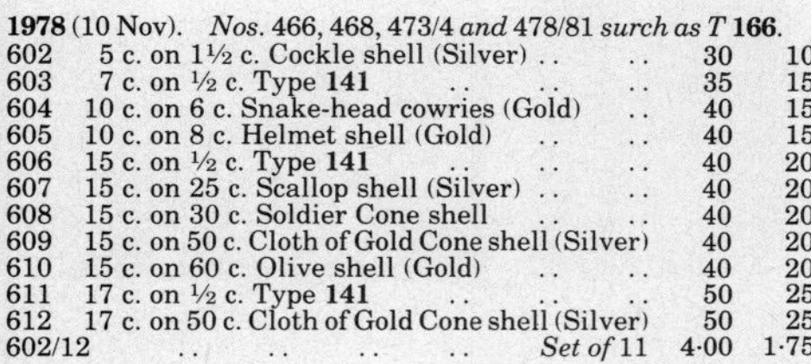

**1978** (10 Nov). *Nos.* 466, 468, 473/4 *and* 478/81 *surch as T* **166**.
602 5 c. on 1½ c. Cockle shell (Silver) . . 30 10
603 7 c. on ½ c. Type **141** . . 35 15
604 10 c. on 6 c. Snake-head cowries (Gold) . . 40 15
605 10 c. on 8 c. Helmet shell (Gold) . . 40 15
606 15 c. on ½ c. Type **141** . . 40 20
607 15 c. on 25 c. Scallop shell (Silver) . . 40 20
608 15 c. on 30 c. Soldier Cone shell . . 40 20
609 15 c. on 50 c. Cloth of Gold Cone shell (Silver) 40 20
610 15 c. on 60 c. Olive shell (Gold) . . 40 20
611 17 c. on ½ c. Type **141** . . 50 25
612 17 c. on 50 c. Cloth of Gold Cone shell (Silver) 50 25
602/12 . . *Set of* 11 4·00 1·75

1728 · 250th ANNIVERSARY OF COOK'S BIRTH · 1978

(167)

**1978** (13 Nov). *250th Birth Anniv of Captain Cook. Nos.* 584/7 *optd with T* **167** *on silver.*
613 50 c. Type **163** . . 1·50 75
614 $1 Earl of Sandwich, and Cook landing at Owhyhee (from paintings by Thomas Gainsborough and J. Cleveley) . . 2·00 1·00
615 $2 Obverse and reverse of $200 coin and Cook monument, Hawaii . . 3·00 2·00
613/15 . . *Set of* 3 6·00 3·25
**MS**616 Nos. 613/15 . . 15·00 15·00

168 Obverse and Reverse of $5 Pitcairn Warblers Coin

**1978** (15 Nov). *National Wildlife and Conservation Day. P* 13.
617 **168** $1 multicoloured . . 2·00 1·00

169 "The Virgin and Child" (Van der Weyden)

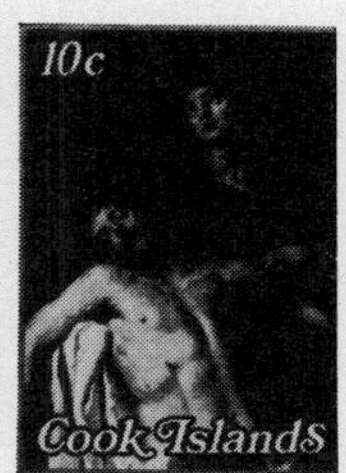

170 Virgin with Body of Christ

**1978** (8 Dec). *Christmas. Paintings. T* **169** *and similar vert designs. Multicoloured. P* 13.
618 15 c. Type **169** . . 30 10
619 17 c. "The Virgin and Child" (Crivelli) . . 30 15
620 35 c. "The Virgin and Child" (Murillo) . . 45 30
618/20 . . *Set of* 3 95 50
**MS**621 107 x 70 mm. Nos. 618/20. . . 95 1·50

### MINIMUM PRICE

The minimum price quote is 10p which represents a handling charge rather than a basis for valuing common stamps. For further notes about prices see introductory pages.

**1979** (12 Jan). *Christmas. Children's Charity. Designs as Nos.* 618/20 *in separate miniature sheets 57 x 87 mm. each with a face value of* 75 *c. +* 5 *c. P* 13½
**MS**622 As Nos. 618/20 . . *Set of 3 sheets* 1·00 1·00

**1979** (5 Apr). *Easter. Details of Painting "Descent" by Gaspar de Crayar. T* **170** *and similar vert designs. Multicoloured. P* 13.
623 10 c. Type **170** . . 15 10
624 12 c. St. John . . 20 15
625 15 c. Mary Magdalene . . 25 20
626 20 c. Weeping angels . . 25 20
623/6 . . *Set of* 4 75 60
**MS**627 83 × 100 mm. As Nos. 623/6, but each with charity premium of 2 c. . . 65 75
Stamps from No. **MS**627 are slightly smaller, 32 × 40 mm, and are without borders.

171 "Captain Cook" (James Weber)

172 Post-Rider

**1979** (23 July). *Death Bicentenary of Captain Cook. T* **171** *and similar vert designs. Multicoloured. P* 14 × 13.
628 20 c. Type **171** . . 45 20
629 30 c. H.M.S. *Resolution* . . 70 35
630 35 c. H.M.S. *Endeavour* . . 80 45
631 50 c. "Death of Captain Cook" (George Carter) 85 60
628/31 . . *Set of* 4 2·50 1·40
**MS**632 78 × 112 mm. Nos. 628/31 . . 2·25 2·00
Stamps from No. **MS**632 have black borders.

**1979** (10 Sept). *Death Centenary of Sir Rowland Hill. History of Mail Transport. T* **172** *and similar square designs. Multicoloured. P* 14.
633 30 c. Type **172** . . 35 25
634 30 c. Mail coach . . 35 25
635 30 c. Automobile . . 35 25
636 30 c. Railway train . . 35 25
637 35 c. *Cap-Horniers* (sailing ship) . . 40 25
638 35 c. River steamer . . 40 25
639 35 c. *Deutschland* (liner) . . 40 25
640 35 c. *United States* (liner) . . 40 25
641 50 c. Balloon *Neptune* . . 50 30
642 50 c. Junkers "F13" (aeroplane) . . 50 30
643 50 c. *Graf Zeppelin* . . 50 30
644 50 c. "Concorde" . . 50 30
633/44 . . *Set of* 12 4·50 3·00
**MS**645 132 × 104 mm. Nos. 633/44 . . 4·50 5·50
Nos. 633/6, 637/40 and 641/4 were each printed together, *se-tenant*, in blocks of 4 throughout the sheets.

6c 

(173)

**1979** (12 Sept). *Nos.* 466, 468 *and* 481 *surch as T* **173**.
646 6 c. on ½ c. Type 141 (Gold) . . 15 15
647 10 c. on 1½ c. Cockle shell (Silver) . . 20 20
648 15 c. on 60 c. Olive shell (Gold) . . 30 30
646/8 . . *Set of* 3 60 60

174 Brother and Sister

175 "Apollo 11" Emblem

**1979** (10 Oct). *International Year of the Child. T* **174** *and similar horiz designs. Multicoloured. P* 13.
649 30 c. Type **174** . . 25 25
650 50 c. Boy with tree drum . . 40 40
651 65 c. Children dancing . . 50 50
649/51 . . *Set of* 3 1·00 1·00
**MS**652 102 × 75 mm. As Nos. 649/51, but each with charity premium of 5 c. P 13½ × 13 . . 1·00 1·50
Designs for stamps from No. **MS**652 are as Nos. 649/51 but have I.Y.C. emblem in red.

**1979** (7 Nov). *10th Anniv of Moon Landing. T* **175** *and similar vert designs. Multicoloured. P* 14.
653 30 c. Type **175** . . 35 40
654 50 c. Crew of "Apollo 11" . . 45 60
655 60 c. Astronaut on Moon . . 55 70
656 65 c. Command module after splashdown . . 60 75
653/6 . . *Set of* 4 1·75 2·25
**MS**657 119 × 105 mm. Nos. 653/6. P 13½ . . 1·75 2·25

176 Obverse and Reverse of $5 Rarotongan Fruit Dove Coin

177 Glass Christmas Tree Ornaments

**1979** (15 Nov). *National Wildlife and Conservation Day. P* 13 × 14.
658 **176** $1 multicoloured . . 2·75 2·25

**1979** (14 Dec). *Christmas. T* **177** *and similar vert designs. Multicoloured. P* 13½. (a) *Postage.*
659 6 c. Type **177** . . 10 10
660 10 c. Hibiscus flower and star. . . 10 10
661 12 c. Poinsettia flower, bells and candle . . 10 10
662 15 c. Poinsettia leaves and Tiki (god). . . 15 15

(b) *Air*
663 20 c. Type **177** . . 15 15
664 25 c. As 10 c. . . 20 20
665 30 c. As 12 c. . . 25 25
666 35 c. As 15 c. . . 30 30
659/66 . . *Set of* 8 1·10 1·10

**1980** (15 Jan). *Christmas. Children's Charity. Designs as Nos.* 659/66 *with additional premiums. (a) Postage.*
667 6 c. + 2 c. Type **177** . . 10 10
668 10 c. + 2 c. Hibiscus flower and star . . 15 15
669 12 c. + 2 c. Poinsettia flower, bells and candle 15 20
670 15 c. + 2 c. Poinsettia leaves and Tiki (god) . . 15 20

(b) *Air*
671 20 c. + 4 c. Type **177** . . 15 25
672 25 c. + 4 c. As 10 c. . . 15 25
673 30 c. + 4 c. As 12 c. . . 20 30
674 35 c. + 4 c. As 15 c. . . 25 35
667/74 . . *Set of* 8 1·00 1·60

178 "Flagellation"

179 Dove with Olive Twig

**1980** (31 Mar). *Easter. Illustrations by Gustave Doré. T* **178** *and similar vert designs in sepia and gold. P* 13.
675 20 c. Type **178** . . 15 20
676 20 c. "Crown of Thorns" . . 15 20
677 30 c. "Jesus Insulted" . . 25 30
678 30 c. "Jesus Falls" . . 25 30
679 35 c. "The Crucifixion" . . 25 30
680 35 c. "The Descent from the Cross" . . 25 30
675/80 . . *Set of* 6 1·10 1·40
**MS**681 120 × 110 mm. As Nos. 675/80, but each with charity premium of 2 c. . . 1·10 1·50
Nos. 675/6, 677/8 and 679/80 were each printed together, *se-tenant*, in vertical pairs throughout the sheet.

**1980** (23 Apr). *Easter. Children's Charity. Designs as Nos.* 675/80 *in separate miniature sheets* 60 × 71 *mm, each with a face value of* 75 *c. +* 5 *c. P* 13.
**MS**682 As Nos. 675/80 . . *Set of 6 sheets* 90 1·50

**1980** (27 May). *75th Anniv of Rotary International. T* **179** *and similar horiz designs. Multicoloured. P* 14.
683 30 c. Type **179** . . 35 35
684 35 c. Hibiscus flower . . 40 40
685 50 c. Ribbons . . 50 50
683/5 . . *Set of* 3 1·10 1·10
**MS**686 72 × 113 mm. Nos. 683/5 but each with premium of 3 c. P 13½ . . 1·10 1·50

ZEAPEX STAMP EXHIBITION–AUCKLAND 1980

(180)

181 Queen Elizabeth the Queen Mother

**1980** (22 Aug). *"Zeapex 80" International Stamp Exhibition, Auckland. Nos.* 633/45 *optd with T* **180** *in black on silver background.*
687 30 c. Type **172** . . 30 30
688 30 c. Mail coach . . 30 30
689 30 c. Automobile . . 30 30
690 30 c. Railway train . . 30 30
691 35 c. *Cap-Horniers* (sailing ship) . . 35 35
692 35 c. River steamer . . 35 35

693 35 c. *Deutschland* (liner) . . . . . . 35 35
694 35 c. *United States* (liner) . . . . . . 35 35
695 50 c. Balloon *Neptune* . . . . . . 65 45
696 50 c. Junkers "F13" (aeroplane) . . . . 65 45
697 50 c. *Graf Zeppelin* . . . . . . 65 45
698 50 c. "Concorde" . . . . . . 65 45
687/98 . . . . *Set of* 12 4·75 4·00
MS699 132 × 104 mm. Nos. 687/98 . . . . 5·00 6·00

**1980** (22 Aug). *"Zeapex 80" International Stamp Exhibition, Auckland. As No.* **MS**681 *but containing stamps without charity premium of* 2 c. *optd "Zeapex '80 Auckland + 10 c" in black on gold background.*
MS700 120 × 110 mm. Nos. 675/80 (*sold at* $1.80) 80 1·75
Stamps from No. **MS**700 are unaffected by the overprint which appears on the sheet margin.

**1980** (23 Sept). *80th Birthday of Queen Elizabeth the Queen Mother. P* 13.
701 **181** 50 c. multicoloured . . . . 1·40 90
MS702 64 × 78 mm. **181** $2 multicoloured . . 2·00 2·25

**182** Satellites orbiting Moon

**183** Scene from novel *From the Earth to the Moon*

**1980** (7 Nov). *350th Death Anniv of Johannes Kepler (astronomer). T* **182** *and similar horiz designs. Multicoloured. P* 13.
703 12 c. Type **182** . . . . . . 50 35
704 12 c. Space-craft orbiting Moon . . . . 50 35
705 50 c. Space-craft orbiting Moon (*different*) . . 1·00 80
706 50 c. Astronaut and Moon vehicle . . . . 1·00 80
703/6 . . . . *Set of* 4 2·75 2·10
MS707 122 × 122 mm. Nos. 703/6 . . . . 2·75 2·75
Nos. 703/4 and 705/6 were each printed together, *se-tenant*, in horizontal pairs throughout the sheet.

**1980** (7 Nov). *75th Death Anniv of Jules Verne (author). T* **183** *and similar vert designs showing scenes from the novel "From the Earth to the Moon". P* 13.
708 20 c. multicoloured (green background) . . 45 35
709 20 c. multicoloured (brown background) . . 45 35
710 30 c. multicoloured (mauve background) . . 55 45
711 30 c. multicoloured (blue background) . . 55 45
708/11 . . . . *Set of* 4 1·75 1·40
MS712 121 × 122 mm. Nos. 708/11 . . . . 1·75 2·00
Nos. 708/9 and 710/11 were each printed together, *se-tenant*, in horizontal pairs throughout the sheet.

**184** *Siphonogorgia*

**185** Annunciation

**1980** (21 Nov)–**82**. *Corals (1st series). Multicoloured designs as T* **184**. *P* 13 (1 c. *to* $1) *or* 14 × 13½ ($2 *to* $10).
713 1 c. Type **184** . . . . . . 20 10
714 1 c. *Pavona praetorta* . . . . . . 20 10
715 1 c. *Stylaster echinatus* . . . . . . 20 10
716 1 c. *Tubastraea* . . . . . . 20 10
717 3 c. *Millepora alcicornis* . . . . 25 10
718 3 c. *Junceella gemmacea* . . . . 25 10
719 3 c. *Fungia fungites* . . . . 25 10
720 3 c. *Heliofungia actiniformis* . . . . 25 10
721 4 c. *Distichopora violacea* . . . . 25 10
722 4 c. *Stylaster* . . . . . . 25 10
723 4 c. *Gonipora* . . . . . . 25 10
724 4 c. *Caulastraea echinulata* . . . . 25 10
725 5 c. *Ptilosarcus gurneyi* . . . . 25 15
726 5 c. *Stylophora pistillata* . . . . 25 15
727 5 c. *Melithaea squamata* . . . . 25 15
728 5 c. *Porites andrewsi* . . . . 25 15
729 6 c. *Lobophyllia bemprichii* . . . . 25 15
730 6 c. *Palauastrea ramosa* . . . . 25 15
731 6 c. *Bellonella indica* . . . . 25 15
732 6 c. *Pectinia alcicornis* . . . . 25 15
733 8 c. *Sarcophyton digitatum* . . . . 25 15
734 8 c. *Melithaea albitincta* . . . . 25 15
735 8 c. *Plerogyra sinuosa* . . . . 25 15
736 8 c. *Dendrophyllia gracilis* . . . . 25 15
737 10 c. Type **184** (19.12.80) . . . . 30 15
738 10 c. As No. 714 (19.12.80) . . . . 30 15
739 10 c. As No. 715 (19.12.80) . . . . 30 15
740 10 c. As No. 716 (19.12.80) . . . . 30 15
741 12 c. As No. 717 (19.12.80) . . . . 30 15
742 12 c. As No. 718 (19.12.80) . . . . 30 15
743 12 c. As No. 719 (19.12.80) . . . . 30 15
744 12 c. As No. 720 (19.12.80) . . . . 30 15
745 15 c. As No. 721 (19.12.80) . . . . 30 20
746 15 c. As No. 722 (19.12.80) . . . . 30 20
747 15 c. As No. 723 (19.12.80) . . . . 30 20
748 15 c. As No. 724 (19.12.80) . . . . 30 20
749 20 c. As No. 725 (19.12.80) . . . . 35 30
750 20 c. As No. 726 (19.12.80) . . . . 35 30
751 20 c. As No. 727 (19.12.80) . . . . 35 30
752 20 c. As No. 728 (19.12.80) . . . . 35 30
753 25 c. As No. 729 (19.12.80) . . . . 35 30
754 25 c. As No. 730 (19.12.80) . . . . 35 30
755 25 c. As No. 731 (19.12.80) . . . . 35 30
756 25 c. As No. 732 (19.12.80) . . . . 35 30
757 30 c. As No. 733 (19.12.80) . . . . 40 30
758 30 c. As No. 734 (19.12.80) . . . . 40 30
759 30 c. As No. 735 (19.12.80) . . . . 40 30
760 30 c. As No. 736 (19.12.80) . . . . 40 30
761 35 c. Type **184** (16.3.81) . . . . 45 35
762 35 c. As No. 714 (16.3.81) . . . . 45 35
763 35 c. As No. 715 (16.3.81) . . . . 45 35
764 35 c. As No. 716 (16.3.81) . . . . 45 35
765 50 c. As No. 717 (16.3.81) . . . . 65 55
766 50 c. As No. 718 (16.3.81) . . . . 65 55
767 50 c. As No. 719 (16.3.81) . . . . 65 55
768 50 c. As No. 720 (16.3.81) . . . . 65 55
769 60 c. As No. 721 (16.3.81) . . . . 75 65
770 60 c. As No. 722 (16.3.81) . . . . 75 65
771 60 c. As No. 723 (16.3.81) . . . . 75 65
772 60 c. As No. 724 (16.3.81) . . . . 75 65
773 70 c. As No. 725 (13.4.81) . . . . 1·25 75
774 70 c. As No. 726 (13.4.81) . . . . 1·25 75
775 70 c. As No. 727 (13.4.81) . . . . 1·25 75
776 70 c. As No. 728 (13.4.81) . . . . 1·25 75
777 80 c. As No. 729 (13.4.81) . . . . 1·25 80
778 80 c. As No. 730 (13.4.81) . . . . 1·25 80
779 80 c. As No. 731 (13.4.81) . . . . 1·25 80
780 80 c. As No. 732 (13.4.81) . . . . 1·25 80
781 $1 As No. 733 (20.5.81) . . . . 2·00 1·00
782 $1 As No. 734 (20.5.81) . . . . 2·00 1·00
783 $1 As No. 735 (20.5.81) . . . . 2·00 1·00
784 $1 As No. 736 (20.5.81) . . . . 2·00 1·00
785 $2 As No. 723 (27.11.81) . . . . 7·50 3·50
786 $3 As No. 720 (27.11.81) . . . . 8·50 4·50
787 $4 As No. 726 (11.1.82) . . . . 4·50 6·50
788 $6 As No. 715 (11.1.82) . . . . 6·00 8·50
789 $10 As No. 734 (5.3.82) . . . . 18·00 20·00
713/89 . . . . *Set of* 77 75·00 60·00
Nos. 761/84 are 30 × 40 mm and Nos. 785/9, which include a portrait of Queen Elizabeth II in each design, are 55 × 35 mm in size.
The four designs of each value to the $1 were printed together, *se-tenant*, in horizontal strips of 4 (Nos. 713/60) or in blocks of 4 (Nos. 761/84) throughout the sheet.
For similar designs with redrawn frames and inscriptions see Nos. 966/92.

**1980** (1 Dec). *Christmas. Illustrations from 13th-century French Prayer Book. T* **185** *and similar vert designs. Multicoloured. P* 14 × 13½.
801 15 c. Type **185** . . . . . . 20 15
802 30 c. Visitation . . . . . . 30 25
803 40 c. Nativity . . . . . . 40 30
804 50 c. Epiphany . . . . . . 50 40
801/4 . . . . *Set of* 4 1·25 1·00
MS805 89 × 114 mm. Nos. 801/4. P 13½ . . . . 1·50 1·50

**1981** (9 Jan). *Christmas. Children's Charity. Designs as Nos. 801/4 in separate miniature sheets 55 × 68 mm, each with a face value of* 75 c. + 5 c. *Imperf.*
MS806 As Nos. 801/4 . . *Set of 4 sheets* 2·75 3·00

**186** "The Crucifixion" (from book of Saint-Amand)

**187** Prince Charles

**1981** (10 Apr). *Easter. Illustrations from 12th-century French Prayer Books. T* **186** *and similar horiz designs. Multicoloured. P* 13½ × 14.
807 15 c. Type **186** . . . . . . 20 20
808 25 c. "Placing in Tomb" (from book of Ingeburge) . . . . 30 30
809 40 c. "Mourning at the Sepulchre" (from book of Ingeburge) . . . . 40 40
807/9 . . . . *Set of* 3 80 80
MS810 72 × 116 mm. As Nos. 807/9 but each with charity premium of 2 c. P 13½ . . . . 90 90

**1981** (28 Apr). *Easter. Children's Charity. Designs as Nos. 807/9 in separate miniature sheets 64 × 53 mm, each with a face value of* 75 c. + 5 c. *Imperf.*
MS811 As Nos. 807/9 . . *Set of 3 sheets* 1·50 1·50

**1981** (29 July). *Royal Wedding. T* **187** *and similar vert design. Multicoloured. P* 14.
812 $1 Type **187** . . . . . . 1·50 1·50
813 $2 Prince Charles and Lady Diana Spencer 2·75 2·75
MS814 106 × 59 mm. Nos. 812/13. P 13½ . . 5·00 5·00
Nos. 812/13 were each printed in small sheets of 4.

**188** Footballers

+
5
c

**(189)**

**1981** (20 Oct). *World Cup Football Championship, Spain* (1982). *T* **188** *and similar horiz designs showing footballers. Multicoloured. P* 13½ × 14.
815 20 c. Type **188** . . . . . . 30 20
816 20 c. Figures to right of stamp . . . . 30 20
817 30 c. Figures to left . . . . . . 40 30
818 30 c. Figures to right . . . . . . 40 30
819 35 c. Figures to left . . . . . . 40 35
820 35 c. Figures to right . . . . . . 40 35
821 50 c. Figures to left . . . . . . 50 45
822 50 c. Figures to right . . . . . . 50 45
815/22 . . . . *Set of* 8 3·00 2·40
MS823 180 × 94 mm. As Nos. 815/22, but each stamp with a charity premium of 3 c. P 13½ . . 3·00 4·00
The two designs of each value were printed together, *se-tenant*, in horizontal pairs throughout the sheet, forming composite designs.

**1981** (10 Nov). *International Year for Disabled Persons. Nos. 812/14 surch as T* **189**.
824 $1 + 5 c. Type **187** . . . . 2·50 2·50
825 $2 + 5 c. Prince Charles and Lady Diana Spencer . . . . 4·50 5·00
MS826 106 × 59 mm. $1 + 10 c., $2 + 10 c. As Nos. 824/5 . . . . . . 7·00 9·00
Nos. 824/6 have commemorative inscriptions overprinted on the sheet margins.

**190** "Holy Virgin with Child"

**191** Princess of Wales (inscr "21st Birthday")

**1981** (14 Dec). *Christmas. Details from Paintings by Rubens. T* **190** *and similar vert designs. Multicoloured. P* 14 × 13½.
827 8 c. Type **190** . . . . . . 40 10
828 15 c. "Coronation of St. Catherine" . . . . 45 20
829 40 c. "Adoration of the Shepherds" . . . . 65 50
830 50 c. "Adoration of the Magi" . . . . 75 60
827/30 . . . . *Set of* 4 2·00 1·25
MS831 86 × 110 mm. As Nos. 827/30, but each with a charity premium of 3 c. P 13½ . . . . 2·00 2·50

**1982** (18 Jan). *Christmas. Children's Charity. Designs as Nos. 827/30 in separate miniature sheets 62 × 78 mm, each with a face value of* 75 c. + 5 c.
MS832 As Nos. 827/30 . . *Set of 4 sheets* 3·00 3·50

**1982** (21 June). *21st Birthday of Princess of Wales. T* **191** *and similar horiz designs. Multicoloured. P* 14.
833 $1.25, Type **191** . . . . . . 1·25 1·25
a. Pair. Nos. 833/4 . . . . . . 2·50 2·50
834 $1.25, As Type **191**, but inscr "1 July 1982" . . 1·25 1·25
835 $2.50, Princess (*different*) (inscr "21st Birthday") . . . . . . 1·75 1·75
a. Pair. Nos. 835/6 . . . . . . 3·50 3·50
836 $2.50, As No. 835, but inscr "1 July 1982" . . 1·75 1·75
833/6 . . . . *Set of* 4 5·50 5·50
MS837 92 × 72 mm. $1.25, Type **191**; $2.50, As No. 835. Both inscribed "21st Birthday 1 July 1982". P 13½ . . . . . . 2·75 2·75
The two designs for each value were printed together, *se-tenant*, in small sheets of 4.

ROYAL BIRTH · 21 JUNE 1982

**(192)**

**1982** (12 July). *Birth of Prince William of Wales (1st issue). Nos. 812/14 optd as T* **192**.
838 $1 Type **187** (optd with T **192**) . . . . 3·50 2·25
a. Pair. Nos. 838/9 . . . . . . 7·00 4·50
839 $1 Type **187** (optd "PRINCE WILLIAM OF WALES") . . . . 3·50 2·25
840 $2 Prince Charles and Lady Diana Spencer (optd with T **192**) . . . . 6·00 5·00
a. Pair. Nos. 840/1 . . . . . . 12·00 10·00
841 $2 Prince Charles and Lady Diana Spencer (optd. "PRINCE WILLIAM OF WALES") 6·00 5·00
838/41 . . . . *Set of* 4 17·00 13·00
MS842 106 × 59mm. Nos. 812/13 optd "21 JUNE 1982. ROYAL BIRTH" . . . . 9·00 7·00

**1982** (3 Aug). *Birth of Prince William of Wales (2nd issue). Designs as Nos. 833/7 but with changed inscriptions. Multicoloured. P* 14.
843 $1.25, As Type **191** (inscr "Royal Birth") . . 1·25 1·25
a. Pair. Nos. 843/4 . . . . . . 2·50 2·50
844 $1.25, As Type **191** (inscr "21 June 1982") . . 1·25 1·25
845 $2.50, As No. 835 (inscr "Royal Birth") . . 1·75 1·75
a. Pair. Nos. 845/6 . . . . . . 3·50 3·50
846 $2.50, As No. 835 (inscr "21 June 1982") . . 1·75 1·75
843/6 . . . . *Set of* 4 5·50 5·50
MS847 92 × 73 mm. $1.25, As Type **191**; $2.50, As No. 835. Both inscribed "Royal Birth 21 June 1982". P 13½ . . . . . . 2·75 2·75

**193** "Serenade" **194** Franklin D. Roosevelt

(Litho Format)

**1982** (10 Sept). *Norman Rockwell (painter) Commemoration. T* **193** *and similar vert designs. Multicoloured. P* 13½ × 14.

848 5 c. Type **193** .. .. .. .. .. 25 10
849 10 c. "The Hikers" .. .. .. .. 25 15
850 20 c. "The Doctor and the Doll" .. .. 40 25
851 30 c. "Home from Camp" .. .. .. 50 30
848/51 .. .. .. .. *Set of* 4 1·25 70

**1982** (30 Sept). *Air. American Anniversaries. T* **194** *and similar vert designs. Multicoloured. P* 14.

852 60 c. Type **194** .. .. .. .. .. 1·25 70
853 80 c. Benjamin Franklin .. .. .. 1·50 80
854 $1.40, George Washington.. .. .. 1·75 1·25
852/4 .. .. .. .. .. *Set of* 3 4·00 2·50
**MS**855 116 × 60 mm. Nos. 852/4. P 13½ .. .. 4·00 3·00

Anniversaries:—60 c. Roosevelt birth centenary; 80 c. "Articles of Peace" negotiations bicentenary; $1.40, Washington 250th birth anniv.

**195** "Virgin with Garlands" (detail) (Rubens) and Princess Diana with Prince William

**196** Princess Diana and Prince William

**1982** (30 Nov). *Christmas. T* **195** *and similar horiz designs depicting different details from Rubens' painting "Virgin with Garlands". P* 13½ × 14.

856 35 c. multicoloured .. .. .. .. 75 40
857 48 c. multicoloured .. .. .. .. 90 60
858 60 c. multicoloured .. .. .. .. 1·10 75
859 $1.70, multicoloured .. .. .. .. 1·75 1·60
856/9 .. .. .. .. .. *Set of* 4 4·00 3·00
**MS**860 104 × 83 mm. 60 c × 4. Designs, each 27 × 32 mm, forming complete painting "Virgin with Garlands". P 13 × 13½ .. .. .. .. 2·50 3·25

**1982** (30 Nov). *Christmas. Birth of Prince William of Wales. Children's Charity. Sheet* 73 × 59 *mm. P* 13.

**MS**861 **196** 75 c. + 5 c. multicoloured .. .. 1·40 2·00

No. **MS**861 comes with 4 different background designs showing details from painting "Virgin with Garlands" (Rubens).

**197** Statue of Tangaroa **198** Scouts using Map and Compass

**1983** (14 Mar). *Commonwealth Day. T* **197** *and similar vert designs. Multicoloured. P* 14 × 13½.

862 60 c. Type **197** .. .. .. .. .. 55 60
863 60 c. Rarotonga oranges .. .. .. 55 60
864 60 c. Rarotonga airport .. .. .. 55 60
865 60 c. Prime Minister Sir Thomas Davis .. 55 60
862/5 .. .. .. .. .. *Set of* 4 2·00 2·10

Nos. 862/5 were issued together, *se-tenant*, in blocks of four throughout the sheet.

**1983** (5 Apr). *75th Anniv of Boy Scout Movement and 125th Birth Anniv of Lord Baden-Powell. T* **198** *and similar vert designs. Multicoloured. P* 13.

866 12 c. Type **198** .. .. .. .. .. 50 20
867 12 c. Hiking .. .. .. .. .. 50 20
868 36 c. Campfire cooking .. .. .. 80 40
869 36 c. Erecting tent .. .. .. .. 80 40
870 48 c. Hauling on rope .. .. .. .. 95 55
871 48 c. Using bos'n's chair .. .. .. 95 55
872 60 c. Digging hole for sapling.. .. .. 1·00 70
873 60 c. Planting sapling .. .. .. .. 1·00 70
866/73 .. .. .. .. *Set of* 8 6·00 3·25
**MS**874 161 × 132 mm. As Nos. 866/73, but each with a premium of 2 c. .. .. .. .. 5·00 4·75

The two designs of each value were printed together, *se-tenant*, in horizontal pairs throughout the sheets.

XV WORLD JAMBOREE

**(199)**

**1983** (4 July). *15th World Scout Jamboree, Alberta, Canada. Nos. 866/74 optd with T* **199** *(Nos. 875, 877, 879, 881) or with "ALBERTA, CANADA 1983" (others).*

875 12 c. Type **198** .. .. .. .. .. 20 20
876 12 c. Hiking .. .. .. .. .. 20 20
877 36 c. Campfire cooking .. .. .. 40 40
878 36 c. Erecting tent .. .. .. .. 40 40
879 48 c. Hauling on rope .. .. .. .. 55 55
880 48 c. Using bos'n's chair .. .. .. 55 55
881 60 c. Digging hole for sapling.. .. .. 70 70
882 60 c. Planting sapling .. .. .. .. 70 70
875/82 .. .. .. .. *Set of* 8 3·25 3·25
**MS**883 161 × 132 mm. As Nos. 875/82, but each with a premium of 2 c. .. .. .. .. 3·25 3·75

The two designs of each value were printed together, *se-tenant*, in horizontal pairs throughout the sheet. In each such pair the left-hand design is overprinted with Type **199** and the right-hand with "ALBERTA, CANADA 1983".

**18c**
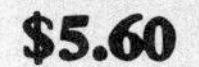
**$5.60**

**(200)** **(201)**

**1983** (12–30 Aug). *Various stamps surch. (a) Nos. 733/6, 745/8,753/ 64 and 773/6 as T* **200.**

884 18 c. on 8 c. multicoloured (No. 733) .. .. 40 40
885 18 c. on 8 c. multicoloured (No. 734) .. .. 40 40
886 18 c. on 8 c. multicoloured (No. 735) .. .. 40 40
887 18 c. on 8 c. multicoloured (No. 736) .. .. 40 40
888 36 c. on 15 c. multicoloured (No. 745) .. .. 70 70
889 36 c. on 15 c. multicoloured (No. 746) .. .. 70 70
890 36 c. on 15 c. multicoloured (No. 747) .. .. 70 70
891 36 c. on 15 c. multicoloured (No. 748) .. .. 70 70
892 36 c. on 30 c. multicoloured (No. 757) .. .. 70 70
893 36 c. on 30 c. multicoloured (No. 758) .. .. 70 70
894 36 c. on 30 c. multicoloured (No. 759) .. .. 70 70
895 36 c. on 30 c. multicoloured (No. 760) .. .. 70 70
896 36 c. on 35 c. multicoloured (No. 761) (30.8.83) .. 70 70
897 36 c. on 35 c. multicoloured (No. 762) (30.8.83) .. 70 70
898 36 c. on 35 c. multicoloured (No. 763) (30.8.83) .. 70 70
899 36 c. on 35 c. multicoloured (No. 764) (30.8.83) .. 70 70
900 48 c. on 25 c. multicoloured (No. 753) .. .. 90 90
901 48 c. on 25 c. multicoloured (No. 754) .. .. 90 90
902 48 c. on 25 c. multicoloured (No. 755) .. .. 90 90
903 48 c. on 25 c. multicoloured (No. 756) .. .. 90 90
904 72 c. on 70 c. multicoloured (No. 773) .. .. 1·25 1·25
905 72 c. on 70 c. multicoloured (No. 774) .. .. 1·25 1·25
906 72 c. on 70 c. multicoloured (No. 775) .. .. 1·25 1·25
907 72 c. on 70 c. multicoloured (No. 776) .. .. 1·25 1·25

(*b*) *Nos.* 788/9, 813, 835/6 *and* 854, *as T* **201** *in gold*

908 96 c. on $1.40, George Washington .. .. 1·50 1·50
909 96 c. on $2 Prince Charles and Lady Diana Spencer .. .. .. .. .. 8·50 5·50
a. Surch double .. .. .. .. £130
b. Error. Surch on No. 840 .. .. .. 16·00
ba. Pair, Nos. 909 b/c .. .. .. 32·00
c. Error. Surch on No. 841 .. .. .. 16·00
910 96 c. on $2.50 Princess Diana (inscr "21st Birthday") (30.8.83) .. .. .. 3·00 3·00
911 96 c. on $2.50. As No. 910 but inscr "1 July 1982" (30.8.83) .. .. .. .. 3·00 3·00
912 $5.60 on $6 *Stylaster echinatus* .. .. 15·00 13·00
913 $5.60 on $10 *Melithaea albitincta* (30.8.83) .. 15·00 13·00
884/913 .. .. .. .. *Set of* 30 60·00 50·00

The surcharge on No. 908 is printed in gold, on a black background, over the old value.

**202** Union Flag **203** Dish Aerial, Satellite Earth Station

**1983** (9 Sept). *Cook Islands Flags and Ensigns. T* **202** *and similar horiz designs. Multicoloured. P* 13½ × 14. (*a*) *Postage. Gold frames.*

914 6 c. Type **202** .. .. .. .. .. 15 10
915 6 c. Group Federal flag .. .. .. 15 10
916 12 c. Raratonga ensign .. .. .. 15 10
917 12 c. Flag of New Zealand .. .. .. 15 10
918 15 c. Cook Islands' flag (1973–79) .. .. 20 15
919 15 c. Cook Islands' National flag .. .. 20 15

(*b*) *Air. Silver frames and backgrounds changed*

920 20 c. Type **202** .. .. .. .. .. 30 25
921 20 c. Group Federal flag .. .. .. 30 25
922 30 c. Raratonga ensign .. .. .. 40 30
923 30 c. Flag of New Zealand .. .. .. 40 30
924 35 c. Cook Islands' flag (1973–79) .. .. 45 35
925 35 c. Cook Islands' National flag .. .. 45 35
914/25 .. .. .. .. *Set of* 12 3·00 2·00
**MS**926 Two sheets, each 132 × 120 mm. (a) Nos. 914/19; (b) Nos. 920/5. P 13 .. .. .. 1·90 3·00

The two designs of each value were issued as *se-tenant* horizontal pairs within the sheets.

**1983** (10 Oct). *World Communications Year. T* **203** *and similar vert designs showing satellites. P* 13.

927 36 c. multicoloured .. .. .. .. 30 35
928 48 c. multicoloured .. .. .. .. 45 45
929 60 c. multicoloured .. .. .. .. 55 60
930 96 c. multicoloured .. .. .. .. 85 90
927/30 .. .. .. .. *Set of* 4 1·90 2·10
**MS**931 90 × 65 mm. $2 multicoloured .. .. 1·75 2·00

**204** "La Belle Jardinière" **205** Montgolfier Balloon 1783

**1983** (14 Nov). *Christmas. 500th Birth Anniv of Raphael. T* **204** *and similar vert designs. Multicoloured. P* 14 × 13½.

932 12 c. Type **204** .. .. .. .. .. 20 20
933 18 c. "Madonna and Child with Five Saints" .. 40 40
934 36 c. "Madonna and Child with St. John" .. 65 65
935 48 c. "Madonna of the Fish" .. .. .. 75 75
936 60 c. "The Madonna of the Baldacchino" .. 95 95
932/6 .. .. .. .. .. *Set of* 5 2·75 2·75
**MS**937 139 × 113 mm. As Nos. 932/6 but each with a premium of 3 c. .. .. .. .. 2·00 2·25

Nos. 932/6 were each printed in small sheets of 5 stamps and 1 label.

**1983** (9 Dec). *Christmas. 500th Birth Anniv of Raphael. Children's Charity. Designs as Nos. 932/6 in separate miniature sheets 66 × 82 mm., each with a face value of 85 c. + 5 c. P* 13.

**MS**938 As Nos. 932/6 .. .. *Set of 5 sheets* 4·00 4·25

**1984** (16 Jan). *Bicentenary of Manned Flight* (1983). *T* **205** *and similar vert designs. Multicoloured. P* 13.

939 36 c. Type **205** .. .. .. .. .. 30 35
940 48 c. Adorne's ascent, Strasbourg, 1784 .. 40 45
941 60 c. Balloon driven by sails, 1785 .. .. 55 60
942 72 c. Ascent of man on horse, 1798 .. .. 70 75
943 96 c. Godard's aerial acrobatics, 1850 .. 85 90
939/43 .. .. .. .. *Set of* 5 2·50 2·75
**MS**944 104 × 85 mm. $2.50, Blanchard and Jeffries crossing Channel, 1785 .. .. .. .. 2·25 2·75
**MS**945 122 × 132 mm. As Nos. 939/43 but each with a premium of 5 c. .. .. .. .. 2·50 3·00

Nos. 939/43 were each printed in small sheets of 5 stamps and 1 label.

**206** Cuvier's Beaked Whale **207** Athens, 1896

**1984** (10 Feb). *Save the Whales. T* **206** *and similar horiz designs. Multicoloured. P* 13.

946 10 c. Type **206** .. .. .. .. .. 45 45
947 18 c. Risso's Dolphin .. .. .. .. 65 65
948 20 c. True's Beaked Whale .. .. .. 65 65
949 24 c. Long-finned Pilot Whale .. .. 70 70
950 30 c. Narwhal .. .. .. .. .. 80 80
951 36 c. White Whale (Beluga) .. .. .. 95 95
952 42 c. Common Dolphin .. .. .. 1·25 1·25
953 48 c. Commerson's Dolphin .. .. .. 1·40 1·40
954 60 c. Bottle-nosed Dolphin .. .. .. 1·60 1·60
955 72 c. Sowerby's Beaked Whale .. .. 1·75 1·75
956 96 c. Common Porpoise .. .. .. 2·00 2·00
957 $2 Boutu .. .. .. .. .. 2·75 2·75
946/57 .. .. .. .. *Set of* 12 13·50 13·50

**1984** (8 Mar). *Olympic Games, Los Angeles. T* **207** *and similar vert designs showing official posters of earlier Games. Multicoloured. P* 13½.

958 18 c. Type **207** .. .. .. .. .. 15 20
959 24 c. Paris, 1900 .. .. .. .. .. 20 25
960 36 c. St. Louis, 1904 .. .. .. .. 30 35
961 48 c. London, 1948 .. .. .. .. 40 45
962 60 c. Tokyo, 1964 .. .. .. .. 45 50
963 72 c. Berlin, 1936 .. .. .. .. 55 60
964 96 c. Rome, 1960 .. .. .. .. 75 80
965 $1.20 Los Angeles, 1930 .. .. .. 90 95
958/65 .. .. .. .. *Set of* 8 3·50 3·75

**208** *Siphonogorgia*

*$3.60*

(209)

**1984** (23 Mar–10 Aug). *Corals (2nd series). (a) Designs as No. 713 etc, but with redrawn frames and inscriptions as in T* **208**. *Multi-coloured. P* 13.

966 1 c. Type **208** .. .. .. .. 10 10
967 2 c. *Millepora alcicornis* .. .. .. 10 10
968 3 c. *Distichopora violacea* .. .. .. 10 10
969 5 c. *Ptilosarcus gurneyi* .. .. .. 10 10
970 10 c. *Lobophyllia bemprichii* .. .. .. 10 10
971 12 c. *Sarcophyton digitatum* .. .. .. 10 10
972 14 c. *Pavona praetorta* .. .. .. 10 10
973 18 c. *Junceella gemmacea* .. .. .. 10 15
974 20 c. *Stylaster* .. .. .. .. 10 15
975 24 c. *Stylophora pistillata* .. .. .. 15 20
976 30 c. *Palauastrea ramosa* .. .. .. 20 25
977 36 c. *Melithaea albitincta* .. .. .. 25 30
978 40 c. *Stylaster echinatus* .. .. .. 25 30
979 42 c. *Fungia fungites* .. .. .. 30 35
980 48 c. *Gonipora* .. .. .. .. 30 35
981 50 c. *Melithaea squamata* (15 May) .. .. 35 40
982 52 c. *Bellonella indica* (15 May) .. .. 35 40
983 55 c. *Plerogyra sinuosa* (15 May) .. .. 35 40
984 60 c. *Tubastraea* (15 May) .. .. .. 40 45
985 70 c. *Heliofungia actiniformis* (15 May) .. 45 50
986 85 c. *Caulastraea echinulata* (15 May) .. 55 60
987 96 c. *Porites andrewsi* (15 May) .. .. 65 70
988 $1.10, *Pectinia alcicornis* (15 May) .. 75 80
989 $1.20, *Dendrophyllia gracilis* (15 May) .. 80 85

(b) *Nos. 785/9 surch as T* **209** *in gold on black*

990 $3.60 on $2 *Gonipora* (28 June) .. 2·40 2·50
991 $4.20 on $3 *Heliofungia actiniformis* (28 June) .. .. .. .. .. 2·75 3·00
992 $5 on $4 *Stylophora pistillata* (28 June) .. 3·25 3·50
993 $7.20 on $6 *Stylaster echinatus* (20 July) 4·75 5·00
994 $9.60 on $10 *Melithaea albitincta* (10 Aug) 6·25 6·50
966/94 .. .. .. .. *Set of* 29 22·00 24·00

Equestrian
Team Dressage
Germany

(210)

**1984** (24 Aug). *Olympic Gold Medal Winners. Nos. 963/5 optd as T* **210**.

995 72 c. Berlin, 1936 (optd T **210**) .. .. 60 65
996 96 c. Rome, 1960 (optd "Decathlon Daley Thompson Great Britain") .. .. 80 85
997 $1.20 Los Angeles, 1930 (optd "Four Gold Medals Carl Lewis U.S.A." .. .. 1·00 1·10
995/7 .. .. .. .. .. *Set of* 3 2·25 2·40

**211** Capt. Cook's Cottage, Melbourne

**1984** (20 Sept). *"Ausipex" International Stamp Exhibition, Melbourne. T* **211** *and similar horiz designs. Multicoloured. P* 13.

998 36 c. Type **211** .. .. .. .. 90 90
999 48 c. "H.M.S. *Endeavour* careened for Repairs" (Sydney Parkinson) .. .. 1·40 1·40
1000 60 c. "Cook's landing at Botany Bay" (E. Phillips Fox) .. .. .. .. .. 2·00 2·00
1001 $2 "Capt. James Cook" (John Webber) .. 3·25 3·25
998/1001 .. .. .. .. *Set of* 4 6·75 6·75
**MS**1002 140 × 100 mm. As Nos. 998/1001, but each stamp with a face value of 90 c. .. .. .. 6·50 7·00

Commemorating-
15 Sept. 1984

(212)

**213** "Virgin on Throne with Child" (Giovanni Bellini)

**1984** (15 Oct). *Birth of Prince Henry. Nos. 812 and 833/6 optd or surch (No. 1007) as T* **212**.

1003 $1.25, Type **191** (optd with T **212**) (Gold) .. 1·75 1·10
a. Pair. Nos. 1003/4 .. .. .. 3·50 2·25
1004 $1.25, As Type **191**, but inscr "1 July 1982" (optd "Birth H.R.H. Prince Henry") (Gold) 1·75 1·10
1005 $2.50, Princess Diana (inscr "21st Birthday") (optd with T **212**) (Gold) .. .. .. 3·00 2·00
a. Pair. Nos. 1005/6 .. .. .. .. 6·00 4·00
1006 $2.50, As No. 835, but inscr "1 July 1982" (optd "Birth H.R.H. Prince Henry") (Gold) 3·00 2·00
1007 $3 on $1 Type **187** (surch "Royal Birth Prince Henry 15 Sept. 1984") (Sil.) .. .. 6·00 4·00
1003/7 .. .. .. .. *Set of* 5 13·50 9·25

**1984** (21 Nov). *Christmas. T* **213** *and similar vert designs. Multi-coloured. P* 14.

1008 36 c. Type **213** .. .. .. .. 35 35
1009 48 c. "Virgin and Child" (anonymous, 15th century) .. .. .. .. .. 45 45
1010 60 c. "Virgin and Child with Saints" (Alvise Vivarini) .. .. .. .. .. 50 50
1011 96 c. "Virgin and Child with Angels" (H. Memling) .. .. .. .. .. 80 80
1012 $1.20, "Adoration of Magi" (G. Tiepolo) .. 95 95
1008/12 .. .. .. .. *Set of* 5 2·75 2·75
**MS**1013 120 × 113 mm. As Nos. 1008/12, but each with a premium of 5 c. P 13½. .. .. .. 2·75 3·00

**1984** (10 Dec). *Christmas. Designs as Nos. 1008/12 in separate miniature sheets, 62 × 76 mm, each with a face value of* 95 c. + 5 c. *P* 13½.

**MS**1014 As Nos. 1008/12 .. .. *Set of* 5 *sheets* 3·75 4·00

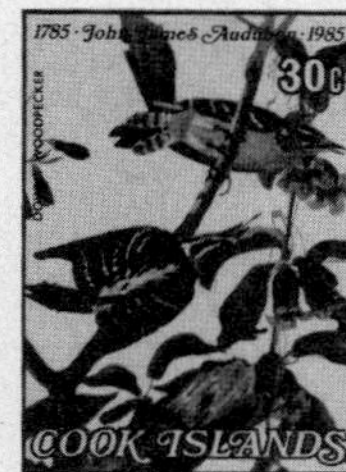


**214** Downy Woodpecker

**1985** (23 Apr). *Birth Bicentenary of John J. Audubon (ornithologist). T* **214** *and similar vert designs showing original paintings. Multicoloured. P* 13 × 13½.

1015 30 c. Type **214** .. .. .. .. 1·00 60
1016 55 c. Black-throated Blue Warbler .. .. 1·40 1·00
1017 65 c. Yellow-throated Warbler .. .. 1·50 1·25
1018 75 c. Chestnut-sided Warbler .. .. 1·60 1·50
1019 95 c. Dickcissel .. .. .. .. 1·75 1·60
1020 $1.15, White-crowned Sparrow .. .. 1·90 1·75
1015/20 .. .. .. .. *Set of* 6 8·25 7·00
**MS**1021 Three sheets, each 76×75 mm. (a) $1.30, Red-cockaded Woodpecker. (b) $2.80, Seaside Sparrow. (c) $5.30, Zenaida Dove .. .. .. .. *Set of* 3 *sheets* 8·50 8·50

**215** "The Kingston Flyer" (New Zealand)

(Des and litho Format)

**1985** (14 May). *Famous Trains. T* **215** *and similar horiz designs. Multicoloured. Ordinary paper. P* 14 × 13½.

1022 20 c. Type **215** .. .. .. .. 85 50
1023 55 c. Class "640" (Italy) .. .. .. 1·25 85
1024 65 c. "Gotthard" type (Switzerland) .. 1·50 90
1025 75 c. Union Pacific No. 6900 (U.S.A.) .. 1·75 1·10
1026 95 c. "Super Continental" type (Canada) .. 2·00 1·25
1027 $1.15, "TGV" type (France) .. .. 2·25 1·50
1028 $2.20, "The Flying Scotsman" (Great Britain) .. .. .. .. .. 3·25 2·50
1029 $3.40, "The Orient Express" .. .. 3·50 3·75
1022/9 .. .. .. .. *Set of* 8 14·50 11·00

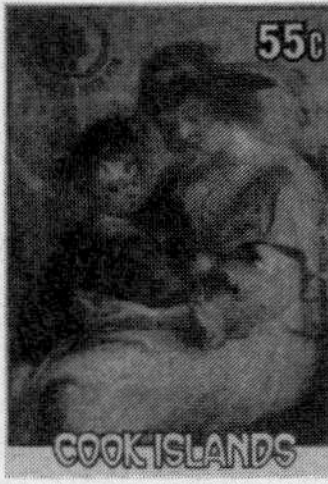

**216** "Helena Fourment" (Peter Paul Rubens) **217** "Lady Elizabeth, 1908" (Mabel Hankey)

**1985** (6 June). *International Youth Year. T* **216** *and similar vert designs. Multicoloured. P* 13.

1030 55 c. Type **216** .. .. .. .. 85 85
1031 65 c. "Vigee-Lebrun and Daughter" (E. Vigee-Lebrun) .. .. .. .. 1·10 1·10
1032 75 c. "On the Terrace" (P. Renoir) .. .. 1·25 1·25
1033 $1.30, "Young Mother Sewing" (M. Cassatt) .. .. .. .. .. 1·75 1·75
1030/3 .. .. .. .. *Set of* 4 4·50 4·50
**MS**1034 103×106 mm. As Nos. 1030/3, but each with a premium of 10 c. .. .. .. .. 3·75 4·25

**1985** (28 June). *Life and Times of Queen Elizabeth the Queen Mother. T* **217** *and similar vert designs showing paintings. Multicoloured. P* 13.

1035 65 c. Type **217** .. .. .. .. 50 55
1036 75 c. "Duchess of York, 1923" (Savely Sorine) .. .. .. .. .. 60 65
1037 $1.15, "Duchess of York, 1925" (Philip de Laszlo) .. .. .. .. .. 90 95
1038 $2.80, "Queen Elizabeth, 1938" (Sir Gerald Kelly) .. .. .. .. .. 2·10 2·25
1035/8 .. .. .. .. *Set of* 4 3·75 4·00
**MS**1039 69 × 81 mm. $5.30, As $2.80 .. .. 4·00 4·25

Nos. 1035/8 were each printed in small sheets of 4 stamps.

For these designs in a miniature sheet, each with a face value of 55 c., see No. **MS**1079.

**218** Albert Henry (Prime Minister, 1965–78) **219** Golf

**1985** (29 July). *20th Anniv of Self-Government. T* **218** *and similar vert designs. Multicoloured. P* 13.

1040 30 c. Type **218** .. .. .. .. 35 30
1041 50 c. Sir Thomas Davis (Prime Minister, 1978–Apr 1983 and from Nov 1983) .. 55 45
1042 65 c. Geoffrey Henry (Prime Minister, Apr–Nov 1983) .. .. .. .. 65 55
1040/2 .. .. .. .. *Set of* 3 1·40 1·10
**MS**1043 134×70 mm. As Nos. 1040/2, but each stamp with a face value of 55 c. .. .. .. 1·25 1·40

**1985** (29 July). *South Pacific Mini Games, Rarotonga. T* **219** *and similar vert designs. Multicoloured. P* 14.

1044 55 c. Type **219** .. .. .. .. 2·00 2·00
1045 65 c. Rugby .. .. .. .. 2·25 2·25
1046 75 c. Tennis .. .. .. .. 2·50 2·50
1044/6 .. .. .. .. *Set of* 3 6·00 6·00
**MS**1047 126×70 mm. Nos. 1044/6, but each with a premium of 10 c. P 13½. .. .. .. 5·50 5·50

**220** Sea Horse, Gearwheel and Leaves **221** "Madonna of the Magnificat"

**1985** (29 July). *Pacific Conferences, Rarotonga. P* 13.

1048 **220** 55 c. black, gold and rosine .. .. 45 50
1049 65 c. black, gold and violet .. .. 50 55
1050 75 c. black, gold and blue-green .. 60 65
1048/50 .. .. .. .. *Set of* 3 1·40 1·50
**MS**1051 126×81 mm. As Nos. 1048/50, but each stamp with a face value of 50 c. .. .. .. 1·25 1·40

No. 1048 shows the South Pacific Bureau for Economic Co-operation logo and is inscribed "S.P.E.C. Meeting, 30 July–1 Aug 1985, Rarotonga". No. 1049 also shows the S.P.E.C. logo, but is inscribed "South Pacific Forum, 4–6 Aug 1985, Rarotonga". No. 1050 shows the Pacific Islands Conference logo and the inscription "Pacific Islands Conference, 7–10 Aug 1985, Rarotonga".

**1985** (18 Nov). *Christmas. Virgin and Child Paintings by Botticelli. T* **221** *and similar vert designs. Multicoloured. P* 14.

1052 55 c. Type **221** .. .. .. .. 80 60
1053 65 c. "Madonna with Pomegranate" .. 85 65
1054 75 c. "Madonna and Child with Six Angels" .. .. .. .. .. 1·00 75
1055 95 c. "Madonna and Child with St. John" .. 1·40 95
1052/5 .. .. .. .. *Set of* 4 3·50 2·75
**MS**1056 90×104 mm. As Nos. 1052/5, but each stamp with a face value of 50 c. P 13½. .. 2·00 2·25

**1985** (9 Dec). *Christmas. Virgin and Child Paintings by Botticelli. Square designs* (46×46 *mm*) *as Nos. 1052/5 in separate miniature sheets,* 50×51 *mm, with face values of* $1.20, $1.45, $2.20 *and* $2.75. *Imperf.*

**MS**1057 As Nos. 1052/5 .. *Set of* 4 *sheets* 7·00 8·50

**222** "The Eve of the Deluge" (John Martin) **223** Queen Elizabeth II

**1986** (13 Mar). *Appearance of Halley's Comet. Paintings. T* **222** *and similar vert designs. Multicoloured. P* 14.

1058 55 c. Type **222** .. 1·00 1·00
1059 65 c. "Lot and his Daughters" (Lucas van Leyden) .. 1·10 1·10
1060 75 c. "Auspicious Comet" (from treatise c 1587) .. 1·25 1·25
1061 $1.25, "Events following Charles I" (Herman Saftleven) .. 2·00 2·00
1062 $2 "Ossian receiving Napoleonic Officers" (Anne Louis Girodet-Trioson) .. 2·75 2·75
1058/62 *Set of* 5 7·25 7·25
**MS**1063 130 × 100 mm. As Nos. 1058/62, but each with a face value of 70 c. P 13½ .. 3·00 4·00
**MS**1064 84 × 63 mm. $4 "Halley's Comet of 1759 over the Thames" (Samuel Scott). P 13½ .. 3·25 4·25

**1986** (21 Apr). *60th Birthday of Queen Elizabeth II. T* **223** *and similar vert designs showing formal portraits. P* 13 × 13½.

1065 95 c. multicoloured .. 1·25 1·25
1066 $1.25, multicoloured .. 1·50 1·50
1067 $1.50, multicoloured .. 1·75 1·75
1065/7 *Set of* 3 4·00 4·00
**MS**1068 Three sheets, each 44 × 75 mm. As Nos. 1065/7, but with face values of $1.10, $1.95 and $2.45 .. *Set of 3 sheets* 7·00 8·00

**224** U.S.A. 1847 Franklin 5 c. Stamp and H.M.S. *Resolution* at Rarotonga

**225** Head of Statue of Liberty

**1986** (21 May). *"Ameripex '86" International Stamp Exhibition, Chicago. T* **224** *and similar horiz designs. Multicoloured. P* 14.

1069 $1 Type **224** .. 2·25 2·25
1070 $1.50, Chicago .. 2·75 2·75
1071 $2 1975 definitive $2, Benjamin Franklin and H.M.S. *Resolution* .. 3·25 3·25
1069/71 *Set of* 3 7·50 7·50

**1986** (4 July). *Centenary of Statue of Liberty. T* **225** *and similar vert designs. Multicoloured. P* 14.

1072 $1 Type **225** .. 75 75
1073 $1.25, Hand and torch of Statue .. 90 90
1074 $2.75, Statue of Liberty .. 2·00 2·00
1072/4 *Set of* 3 3·25 3·25

**226** Miss Sarah Ferguson

Stampex 86

Adelaide

**(227)**

**1986** (23 July). *Royal Wedding. T* **226** *and similar multicoloured designs. P* 14 ($1, $2) *or* 13½ × 13 ($3).

1075 $1 Type **226** .. 1·00 1·00
1076 $2 Prince Andrew .. 1·75 1·75
1077 $3 Prince Andrew and Miss Sarah Ferguson (57 × 31 *mm*) .. 2·50 2·50
1075/7 *Set of* 3 4·75 4·75

Nos. 1075/7 were each printed in small sheets of 4 stamps.

**1986** (4 Aug). *"Stampex '86" Stamp Exhibition, Adelaide. No.* **MS**1002 *optd with T* **227** *in gold (circle) and black (inscr) only on design as No.* 1001.

**MS**1078 90 c. × 4 multicoloured .. 4·25 5·00

The "Stampex '86" exhibition emblem is also overprinted on the sheet margin.

**1986** (4 Aug). *86th Birthday of Queen Elizabeth the Queen Mother. Designs as Nos.* 1035/8 *in miniature sheet, 91 × 116 mm, each stamp with a face value of 55 c. Multicoloured. P* 13 × 13½.

**MS**1079 55 c. × 4. As Nos. 1035/8 .. 2·50 3·00

**228** "The Holy Family with St. John the Baptist and St. Elizabeth"

+10c

**(229)**

**1986** (17 Nov). *Christmas. Paintings by Rubens. T* **228** *and similar vert designs. Multicoloured. P* 13½.

1080 55 c. Type **228** .. 50 50
1081 $1.30, "Virgin with the Garland" .. 1·25 1·25
1082 $2.75, "The Adoration of the Magi" (detail) .. 2·50 2·50
1080/2 *Set of* 3 3·75 3·75
**MS**1083 140 × 100 mm. As Nos. 1080/2, but each size 36 × 46 mm with a face value of $2.40 .. 6·50 8·00
**MS**1084 80 × 70 mm. $6.40, As No. 1081 but size 32 × 50 mm .. 6·50 8·00

**1986** (21 Nov). *Visit of Pope John Paul II to South Pacific. Nos.* 1080/4 *surch as T* **229** *in silver.*

1085 55 c. + 10 c. Type **228** .. 1·25 1·25
1086 $1.30 + 10 c. "Virgin with the Garland" 1·75 1·75
1087 $2.75 + 10 c. "The Adoration of the Magi" (detail) .. 3·00 3·00
1085/7 *Set of* 3 5·50 5·50
**MS**1088 140 × 100 mm. As Nos. 1085/7, but each size 36 × 46 mm with a face value of $2.40 + 10 c. 8·50 10·00
**MS**1089 80 × 70 mm. $6.40 + 50 c. As No. 1086 but size 32 × 50 mm .. 8·50 10·00

**10c**

**(230)**

**HURRICANE RELIEF**
**+50c**

**(231)**

**1987** (10–12 Feb). *Various stamps surch as T* **230** *by N.Z. Govt Printer.*

(*a*) *On Nos.* 741/56, 761/76 *and* 787/8

1090 10 c. on 15 c. *Distichopora violacea* (11.2) .. 10 10
1091 10 c. on 15 c. *Stylaster* (11.2) .. 10 10
1092 10 c. on 15 c. *Gonipora* (11.2) .. 10 10
1093 10 c. on 15 c. *Caulastraea echinulata* (11.2) 10 10
1094 10 c. on 25 c. *Lobophyllia bemprichii* (11.2) 10 10
1095 10 c. on 25 c. *Palauastrea ramosa* (11.2) .. 10 10
1096 10 c. on 25 c. *Bellonella indica* (11.2) .. 10 10
1097 10 c. on 25 c. *Pectinia alcicornis* (11.2) .. 10 10
1098 18 c. on 12 c. *Millepora alcicornis* (11.2) .. 15 15
1099 18 c. on 12 c. *Junceella gemmacea* (11.2) .. 15 15
1100 18 c. on 12 c. *Fungia fungites* (11.2) .. 15 15
1101 18 c. on 12 c. *Heliofungia actiniformis* (11.2) .. 15 15
1102 18 c. on 20 c. *Ptilosarcus gurneyi* (11.2) .. 15 15
1103 18 c. on 20 c. *Stylophora pistillata* (11.2) .. 15 15
1104 18 c. on 20 c. *Melithaea squamata* (11.2) .. 15 15
1105 18 c. on 20 c. *Porites andrewsi* (11.2) .. 15 15
1106 55 c. on 35 c. Type **184** (11.2) .. 40 45
1107 55 c. on 35 c. *Pavona praetorta* (11.2) .. 40 45
1108 55 c. on 35 c. *Stylaster echinatus* (11.2) .. 40 45
1109 55 c. on 35 c. *Tubastraea* (11.2) .. 40 45
1110 65 c. on 50 c. As No. 1098 (11.2) .. 45 50
1111 65 c. on 50 c. As No. 1099 (11.2) .. 45 50
1112 65 c. on 50 c. As No. 1100 (11.2) .. 45 50
1113 65 c. on 50 c. As No. 1101 (11.2) .. 45 50
1114 65 c. on 60 c. As No. 1090 (11.2) .. 45 50
1115 65 c. on 60 c. As No. 1091 (11.2) .. 45 50
1116 65 c. on 60 c. As No. 1092 (11.2) .. 45 50
1117 65 c. on 60 c. As No. 1093 (11.2) .. 45 50
1118 75 c. on 70 c. As No. 1102 (11.2) .. 55 60
1119 75 c. on 70 c. As No. 1103 (11.2) .. 55 60
1120 75 c. on 70 c. As No. 1104 (11.2) .. 55 60
1121 75 c. on 70 c. As No. 1105 (11.2) .. 55 60
1122 $6.40 on $4 *Stylophora pistillata* .. 4·50 4·75
1123 $7.20 on $6 *Stylaster echinatus* .. 5·00 5·25

(*b*) *On Nos.* 812/13 *in gold* (12 Feb)

1124 $9.40 on $1 Type **187** .. 15·00 16·00
1125 $9.40 on $2 Prince Charles and Lady Diana Spencer .. 15·00 16·00

(*c*) *On Nos.* 835/6 *in gold* (12 Feb)

1126 $9.40 on $2.50 Princess of Wales (inscr "21st Birthday") .. 15·00 16·00
1127 $9.40 on $2.50 As No. 1126, but inscr "1 July 1982" .. 15·00 16·00

(*d*) *On Nos.* 966/8, 971/2, 975, 979/80, 982 *and* 987/9

1128 5 c. on 1 c. Type **208** .. 10 10
1129 5 c. on 2 c. *Millepora alcicornis* .. 10 10
1130 5 c. on 3 c. *Distichopora violacea* .. 10 10
1131 5 c. on 12 c. *Sarcophyton digitatum* .. 10 10
1132 5 c. on 14 c. *Pavona praetorta* .. 10 10
1133 18 c. on 24 c. *Stylophora pistillata* .. 15 15
1134 55 c. on 52 c. *Bellonella indica* .. 40 45
1135 65 c. on 42 c. *Fungia fungites* .. 45 50
1136 75 c. on 48 c. *Gonipora* .. 55 60
1137 95 c. on 96 c. *Porites andrewsi* .. 70 75
1138 95 c. on $1.10 *Pectinia alcicornis* .. 70 75
1139 95 c. on $1.20 *Dendrophyllia gracilis* .. 70 75

(*e*) *On Nos.* 998/1001 *in gold* (No. 1143) *or gold* (*value*) *and black* (*bars*) (*others*) (12 Feb)

1140 $1.30 on 36 c. Type **211** .. 1·40 1·50
1141 $1.30 on 48 c. "The *Endeavour* careened for Repairs" (Sydney Parkinson) .. 1·40 1·50
1142 $1.30 on 60 c. "Cook's landing at Botany Bay" (E. Phillips Fox) .. 1·40 1·50
1143 $1.30 on $2 "Capt. James Cook" (John Webber) .. 1·40 1·50

(*f*) *On Nos.* 1065/7 *in gold* (12 Feb)

1144 **223** $2.80 on 95 c. multicoloured .. 7·00 7·50
1145 – $2.80 on $1.25 multicoloured .. 7·00 7·50
1146 – $2.80 on $1.50 multicoloured .. 7·00 7·50

(*g*) *On Nos.* 1075/7 *in gold* (*value*) *and black* (*bars*) (12 Feb)

1147 $2.80 on $1 Type **226** .. 6·00 6·50
1148 $2.80 on $2 Prince Andrew .. 6·00 6·50
1149 $2.80 on $3 Prince Andrew and Miss Sarah Ferguson (57 × 31 *mm*) .. 6·00 6·50
1090/149 *Set of* 60 £100 £120

**1987** (17 June). *Various stamps surch as T* **230**.

(*a*) *On Nos.* 785/6 *and* 789

1150 $2.80 on $2 *Gonipora* .. 2·10 2·25
1151 $5 on $3 *Heliofungia actiniformis* .. 4·00 4·25
1152 $9.40 on $10 *Melithaea albitincta* .. 7·50 7·75

(*b*) *On Nos.* 838/42 (*in gold on Nos.* 1153/6)

1153 $9.40 on $1 Type **187** (No. 838) .. 7·50 7·75
a. Pair. Nos. 1153/4 .. 15·00 16·00
1154 $9.40 on $1 Type **187** (No. 839) .. 7·50 7·75
1155 $9.40 on $2 Prince Charles and Lady Diana Spencer (No. 840) .. 7·50 7·75
a. Pair. Nos. 1155/6 .. 15·00 16·00
1156 $9.40 on $2 Prince Charles and Lady Diana Spencer (No. 841) .. 7·50 7·75
1150/6 *Set of* 7 40·00 40·00
**MS**1157 106 × 59 mm. $9.20 on $1 Type **187**; $9.20 on $2 Prince Charles and Lady Diana Spencer .. 14·50 17·00

**1987** (30 June–31 July). *Hurricane Relief Fund. Various stamps surch as T* **231**.

(*a*) *On Nos.* 1035/9 *in silver*

1158 65 c. + 50 c. Type **217** .. 80 85
1159 75 c. + 50 c. "Duchess of York, 1923" (Savely Sorine) .. 85 90
1160 $1.15 + 50 c. "Duchess of York, 1925" (Philip de Laszlo) .. 1·10 1·25
1161 $2.80 + 50 c. "Queen Elizabeth, 1938" (Sir Gerald Kelly) .. 2·25 2·40
**MS**1162 69 × 81 mm. $5.30 + 50 c. As $2.80 + 50 c. .. 4·00 4·50

(*b*) *On Nos.* 1058/62 (*in silver on Nos.* 1164/6)

1163 55 c. + 50 c. Type **222** .. 75 80
1164 65 c. + 50 c. "Lot and his Daughters" (Lucas van Leyden) .. 80 85
1165 75 c. + 50 c. "Auspicious Comet" (from treatise c 1587) .. 85 90
1166 $1.25 + 50 c. "Events following Charles I" (Herman Saftleven) .. 1·25 1·40
1167 $2 + 50 c. "Ossian receiving Napoleonic Officers" (Anne Louis Girodet-Trioson) .. 1·75 2·00

(*c*) *On Nos.* 1065/8 (*in silver on No.* 1169) (31 July)

1168 **223** 95 c. + 50 c. multicoloured .. 1·00 1·10
1169 – $1.25 + 50 c. multicoloured .. 1·25 1·40
1170 – $1.50 + 50 c. multicoloured .. 1·40 1·50
**MS**1171 Three sheets, each 44 × 75 mm. As Nos. 1168/70, but with face values of $1.10 + 50 c., $1.95 + 50 c., $2.45 + 50 c. *Set of 3 sheets* 5·00 6·50

(*d*) *On Nos.* 1069/71 (*in silver on No.* 1172)

1172 $1 + 50 c. Type **224** .. 1·00 1·10
1173 $1.50 + 50 c. Chicago .. 1·40 1·50
1174 $2 + 50 c. 1975 definitive $2, Benjamin Franklin and H.M.S. *Resolution* .. 1·75 1·90

(*e*) *On Nos.* 1072/4 (*in silver on Nos.* 1175 *and* 1177)

1175 $1 + 50 c. Type **225** .. 1·00 1·10
1176 $1.25 + 50 c. Hand and torch of Statue .. 1·25 1·40
1177 $2.75 + 50 c. Statue of Liberty .. 2·25 2·40

(*f*) *On Nos.* 1075/7 *in silver* (31 July)

1178 $1 + 50 c. Type **226** .. 1·00 1·25
1179 $2 + 50 c. Prince Andrew .. 1·75 1·90
1180 $3 + 50 c. Prince Andrew and Miss Sarah Ferguson (57 × 31 *mm*) .. 2·40 2·50

(*g*) *On Nos.* 1080/4 *in silver*

1181 55 c. + 50 c. Type **228** .. 75 80
1182 $1.30 + 50 c. "Virgin with the Garland" .. 1·25 1·40
1183 $2.75 + 50 c. "The Adoration of the Magi" (detail) .. 2·25 2·40
**MS**1184 140 × 100 mm. As No. 1181/3, but each size 36 × 46 mm with a face value of $2.40 + 50 c. 6·00 7·50
**MS**1185 80 × 70 mm. $6.40 + 50 c. As No. 1182, but size 32 × 50 mm. .. 4·75 5·50

(*h*) *On Nos.* 1122, 1134/7 *and* 1150/1

1186 55 c. + 25 c. on 52 c. *Bellonella indica* .. 55 60
1187 65 c. + 25 c. on 42 c. *Fungia fungites* .. 65 70
1188 75 c. + 25 c. on 48 c. *Gonipora* .. 70 75
1189 95 c. + 25 c. on 96 c. *Porites andrewsi* .. 85 90
1190 $2.80 + 50 c. on $2 *Gonipora* .. 2·25 2·40
1191 $5 + 50 c. on $3 *Heliofungia actiniformis* 3·75 4·00
1192 $6.40 + 50 c. on $4 *Stylophora pistillata* .. 4·75 5·00
1158/92 *Set of* 31 40·00 45·00

**ROYAL WEDDING FORTIETH ANNIVERSARY**

**(232)**

**1987** (20 Nov). *Royal Ruby Wedding. Nos.* 484 *and* 787 *optd with T* **232** *in black on gold.*

1193 $4 Queen Elizabeth II and seashells .. 3·75 3·75
1194 $4 Queen Elizabeth II and *Stylophora pistillata* .. 3·75 3·75

**233** "The Holy Family" (Rembrandt)

**1987** (7 Dec). *Christmas. T* **233** *and similar horiz designs showing different paintings of the Holy Family by Rembrandt. P* 13½.
1195 $1.25, multicoloured .. .. .. .. 1·50 1·50
1196 $1.50, multicoloured .. .. .. .. 1·75 1·75
1197 $1.95, multicoloured .. .. .. .. 2·25 2·25
1195/7 .. .. .. .. *Set of* 3 5·00 5·00
**MS**1198 100×140 mm. As Nos. 1195/7, but each size 47×36 mm with a face value of $1.15 .. 2·75 3·25
**MS**1199 70×80 mm. $6 As No. 1196, but size 40×31 mm. P 13×13½ .. .. .. .. 4·50 5·50

**234** Olympic Commemorative $50 Coin

(Des G. Vasarhelyi)

**1988** (26 Apr). *Olympic Games, Seoul. T* **234** *and similar vert designs. Multicoloured. P* 13½×14.
1200 $1.50, Type **234** .. .. .. .. 1·40 1·50
a. Horiz strip of 3. Nos. 1200/2 .. .. 3·75
1201 $1.50, Olympic torch and Seoul Olympic Park .. .. .. .. .. 1·40 1·50
1202 $1.50, Steffi Graf playing tennis and Olympic medal .. .. .. .. 1·40 1·50
1200/2 .. .. .. .. *Set of* 3 3·75 4·00
**MS**1203 131×81 mm. $10 Combined design as Nos. 1200/2, but measuring 114×47 mm. P 13½ 8·50 9·50
Nos. 1200/2 were printed together, *se-tenant*, in horizontal strips of 3 throughout the sheet, each strip forming a composite design.

**MILOSLAV MECIR**
**CZECHOSLOVAKIA**
**GOLD MEDAL WINNER**
**MEN'S TENNIS**

(235)

**1988** (12 Oct). *Olympic Tennis Medal Winners, Seoul. Nos.* 1200/3 *optd as T* **235**.
1204 $1.50, Type **234** (optd with T **235**) .. 1·10 1·25
a. Horiz strip of 3. Nos. 1204/6 .. .. 3·00
1205 $1.50, Olympic torch and Seoul Olympic Park (optd "TIM MAYOTTE UNITED STATES GABRIELA SABATINI ARGENTINA SILVER MEDAL WINNERS") .. .. .. .. 1·10 1·25
1206 $1.50, Steffi Graf playing tennis and Olympic medal (optd "GOLD MEDAL WINNER STEFFI GRAF WEST GERMANY") .. .. .. 1·10 1·25
1204/6 .. .. .. .. *Set of* 3 3·00 3·50
**MS**1207 131×81 mm. $10 Combined design as Nos. 1200/2, but measuring 114×47 mm. (optd "GOLD MEDAL WINNER SEOUL OLYMPIC GAMES STEFFI GRAF-WEST GERMANY") .. 7·00 8·00

**236** "Virgin and Child" **237** "Apollo II" leaving Earth

**1988** (11 Nov). *Christmas. T* **236** *and similar vert designs showing paintings of "The Nativity"* ($6.40) *or different versions of "Virgin and Child" by Dürer. P* 13½.
1208 70 c. multicoloured .. .. .. .. 1·00 1·00
1209 85 c. multicoloured .. .. .. .. 1·25 1·25
1210 95 c. multicoloured .. .. .. .. 1·40 1·40
1211 $1.25, multicoloured .. .. .. .. 1·60 1·60
1208/11 .. .. .. .. *Set of* 4 4·75 4·75
**MS**1212 80 × 100 mm. $6.40, multicoloured (45 × 60 *mm*) .. .. .. .. .. 4·50 5·50

(Des G. Vasarhelyi)

**1989** (14 July). *20th Anniv of First Manned Landing on Moon. T* **237** *and similar horiz designs. Multicoloured. P* 13.
1213 40 c. Type **237** .. .. .. .. 40 40
a. Horiz pair. Nos. 1213/14 .. .. 80 80
1214 40 c. Lunar module over Moon .. .. 40 40
1215 55 c. Armstrong stepping onto Moon .. 55 55
a. Horiz pair. Nos. 1215/16 .. .. 1·10 1·10
1216 55 c. Astronaut on Moon .. .. .. 55 55
1217 65 c. Working on lunar surface .. .. 65 65
a. Horiz pair. Nos. 1217/18 .. .. 1·25 1·25
1218 65 c. Conducting experiment .. .. 65 65
1219 75 c. "Apollo 11" leaving Moon .. .. 70 70
a. Horiz pair. Nos. 1219/20 .. .. 1·40 1·40
1220 75 c. Splashdown in South Pacific .. 70 70
1213/20 .. .. .. .. *Set of* 8 4·00 4·00
**MS**1221 108×91 mm. $4.20, Astronauts on Moon .. .. .. .. .. .. 3·25 3·75
Nos. 1213/14, 1215/16, 1217/18 and 1219/20 were each printed together, horizontally *se-tenant*, in sheets of 12.

**238** Rarotonga Flycatcher

(Des G. Drummond)

**1989** (4 Oct). *Endangered Birds of the Cook Islands. T* **238** *and similar horiz designs. Multicoloured. (a) Postage. P* 13½×13
1222 15 c. Type **238** .. .. .. .. 45 45
1223 20 c. Pair of Rarotonga Flycatchers .. 45 45
1224 65 c. Pair of Rarotongan Fruit Doves .. 1·10 1·10
1225 70 c. Rarotongan Fruit Dove .. .. 1·10 1·10
1222/5 .. .. .. .. *Set of* 4 2·75 2·75
(*b*) *Air. P* 13½
**MS**1226 Four sheets, each 70×53 mm. As Nos. 1222/5, but with face values of $1, $1.25, $1.50, $1.75 and each size 50×32 mm. .. *Set of 4 sheets* 4·00 4·50

**239** Villagers

**1989** (24 Nov). *Christmas. T* **239** *and similar multicoloured designs showing details from "Adoration of the Magi" by Rubens. P* 13.
1227 70 c. Type **239** .. .. .. .. 65 65
1228 85 c. Virgin Mary .. .. .. .. 80 80
1229 95 c. Christ Child .. .. .. .. 85 85
1230 $1.50, Boy with gift .. .. .. 1·50 1·50
1227/30 .. .. .. .. *Set of* 4 3·50 3·50
**MS**1231 85×120 mm. $6.40, "Adoration of the Magi" (45×60 mm). P 13½ .. .. .. 4·75 5·50

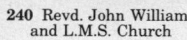

**240** Revd. John Williams and L.M.S. Church **241** "Woman writing Letter" (Terborch)

(Des Jennifer Toombs)

**1990** (19 Feb). *Christianity in the Cook Islands. T* **240** *and similar square designs. Multicoloured. P* 13.
1232 70 c. Type **240** .. .. .. .. 65 65
1233 85 c. Mgr. Bernardine Castanié and Roman Catholic Church .. .. .. 80 80
1234 95 c. Elder Osborne Widstoe and Mormon Church .. .. .. .. 85 85
1235 $1.60, Dr. J. E. Caldwell and Seventh Day Adventist Church .. .. 1·50 1·50
1232/5 .. .. .. .. *Set of* 4 3·50 3·50
**MS**1236 90×90 mm. As Nos. 1232/5, but each with a face value of 90 c. P 13½ .. .. 3·50 4·00

**1990** (2 May). *150th Anniv of the Penny Black. T* **241** *and similar vert designs showing paintings. Multicoloured. P* 13½.
1237 85 c. Type **241** .. .. .. .. 70 70
1238 $1.15, "George Gisze" (Holbein the Younger) .. .. .. .. 90 90
1239 $1.55, "Mrs. John Douglas" (Gainsborough) .. .. .. .. 1·25 1·25
1240 $1.85, "Portrait of a Gentleman" (Dürer) 1·60 1·60
1237/40 .. .. .. .. *Set of* 4 4·00 4·00
**MS**1241 82×150 mm. As Nos. 1237/40, but each with a face value of $1.05 .. .. .. 4·25 4·50

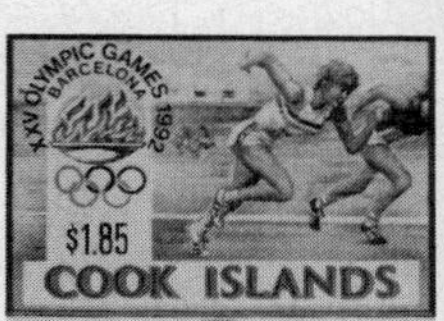


**242** Sprinting **243** Queen Elizabeth the Queen Mother

(Des G. Vasarhelyi)

**1990** (15 June). *Olympic Games, Barcelona, and Winter Olympic Games, Albertville* (1992). *T* **242** *and similar horiz designs. Multicoloured. P* 14.
1242 $1.85, Type **242** .. .. .. .. 1·90 1·90
a. Horiz strip of 3. Nos. 1242/4 .. .. 5·00
1243 $1.85, Cook Islands $50 commemorative coin .. .. .. .. .. 1·90 1·90
1244 $1.85, Skiing .. .. .. .. 1·90 1·90
1242/4 .. .. .. .. *Set of* 3 5·00 5·00
Nos. 1242/4 were printed together, *se-tenant*, in horizontal strips of 3 throughout the sheet of 18.

**1990** (20 July). *90th Birthday of Queen Elizabeth the Queen Mother. P* 13½.
1245 **243** $1.85, multicoloured .. .. .. 2·00 2·00
**MS**1246 66×101 mm. **243** $6.40, multicoloured 6·00 6·50

**244** "Adoration of the Magi" (Memling) (**245**)

(Litho Questa)

**1990** (29 Nov). *Christmas. Religious Paintings. T* **244** *and similar multicoloured designs. P* 14.
1247 70 c. Type **244** .. .. .. .. 65 65
1248 85 c. "Holy Family" (Lotto) .. .. 75 75
1249 95 c. "Madonna and Child with Saints John and Catherine" (Titian) .. .. 90 90
1250 $1.50, "Holy Family" (Titian) .. .. 1·40 1·40
1247/50 .. .. .. .. *Set of* 4 3·25 3·25
**MS**1251 98×110 mm. $6.40, "Madonna and Child enthroned, surrounded by Saints" (Vivarini) (*vert*) .. .. .. .. 5·00 5·50

**1990** (5 Dec). *"Birdpex '90" Stamp Exhibition, Christchurch, New Zealand. No.* **MS**1226 *optd with T* **245**.
**MS**1252 Four sheets, each 70×53 mm. As Nos. 1222/5, but with face values of $1, $1.25, $1.50, $1.75 and each size 50×32 mm .. *Set of 4 sheets* 4·75 5·50

**246** Athletes, Coin, Olympic Torch and Rings, and Skier

**1991** (12 Feb). *Olympic Games, Barcelona, and Winter Olympic Games, Albertville* (1992). *Sheet* 109×52 *mm. P* 13½.
**MS**1253 **246** $6.40, multicoloured .. .. 5·00 5·50

65th BIRTHDAY

**247** Columbus (engraving by Theodoro de Bry) (**248**)

**1991** (14 Feb). *500th Anniv of Discovery of America by Columbus* (1992). *P* 13½×13.
1254 **247** $1 multicoloured .. .. .. .. 85 85

**1991** (22 Apr). *65th Birthday of Queen Elizabeth II. No.* 789 *optd with T* **248** *in gold.*
1255 $10 *Melithaea albitincta* .. .. 8·50 8·75

**249** "Adoration of the Child" (G. delle Notti)

(Des G. Vasarhelyi. Litho Questa)

**1991** (12 Nov). *Christmas. Religious Paintings. T* **249** *and similar multicoloured designs. P* 14.

| | | | |
|---|---|---|---|
| 1256 | 70 c. Type **249** | 45 | 50 |
| 1257 | 85 c. "The Birth of the Virgin" (B. Murillo) | 55 | 60 |
| 1258 | $1.15, "Adoration of the Shepherds" (Rembrandt) | 75 | 80 |
| 1259 | $1.50, "Adoration of the Shepherds" (L. le Nain) | 1·00 | 1·10 |
| 1256/9 | *Set of* 4 | 2·50 | 2·75 |
| **MS**1260 | 79×103 mm. $6.40, "Madonna and Child" (Lippi) (*vert*) | 4·25 | 4·50 |

**250** Red-breasted Maori Wrasse

(Litho Questa)

**1992** (22 Jan). *Reef Life. T* **250** *and similar horiz designs. Multicoloured. P* 14.

| | | | |
|---|---|---|---|
| 1261 | 5 c. Type **250** | 10 | 10 |
| 1262 | 10 c. Blue Sea Star | 10 | 10 |
| 1263 | 15 c. Black and Gold Angelfish | 10 | 10 |
| 1264 | 20 c. Spotted Pebble Crab | 10 | 10 |
| 1265 | 25 c. Black-tipped Cod | 15 | 20 |
| 1266 | 30 c. Spanish Dancer | 20 | 25 |
| 1267 | 50 c. Royal Angelfish | 35 | 40 |
| 1268 | 80 c. Squirrel Fish | 55 | 60 |
| 1261/8 | *Set of* 8 | 1·25 | 1·50 |

OFFICIAL STAMPS

O.H.M.S. (O 1) O.H.M.S. (O 2)

**1975** (17 Mar–19 May). *Nos.* 228/31, 233, 235/7, 239/40, 243/5 *and* 246*c*/7 *optd with Type* O **1** (5, 10, 18, 25 *and* 30 *c. surch also*), *in black and silver*

| | | | |
|---|---|---|---|
| O 1 | 1 c. *Hibiscus syriacus* | | |
| O 2 | 2 c. Frangipani | | |
| O 3 | 3 c. "Suva Queen" | | |
| O 4 | 4 c. Water Lily | | |
| O 5 | 5 c. on 2½ c. *Clitoria ternatea* | | |
| O 6 | 8 c. *Allamanda cathartica* | | |
| O 7 | 10 c. on 6 c. Hibiscus | | |
| O 8 | 18 c. on 20 c. Thunbergia | | |
| O 9 | 25 c. on 9 c. Stephanotis | | |
| O10 | 30 c. on 15 c. Frangipani | | |
| O11 | 50 c. *Gardinia taitensis* | | |
| O12 | $1 Type **80** | | |
| O13 | $2 Type **80** | | |
| O14 | $4 Type **81** (19 May) | | |
| O15 | $6 Type **81** (19 May) | | |
| O1/15 | *Set of* 15 | † | 30·00 |

These stamps were only sold to the public cancelled-to-order and not in unused condition.

**1978** (19 Oct)–**79**. *Nos.* 466/7, 474, 478/81, 484/5, 542 *and* 568/9 *optd or surch* (2, 5, 10, 15, 18 *and* 35 *c.*) *as Type* O **2**.

| | | | |
|---|---|---|---|
| O16 | 1 c. Vase shell (Silver) | 30 | 10 |
| O17 | 2 c. on ½ c. Type **141** | 30 | 10 |
| O18 | 5 c. on ½ c. Type **141** | 30 | 10 |
| O19 | 10 c. on 8 c. Helmet shell (Silver) | 35 | 10 |
| O20 | 15 c. on 50 c. Cloth of Gold Cone shell (Silver) | 45 | 10 |
| O21 | 18 c. on 60 c. Olive shell (Silver) | 45 | 15 |
| O22 | 25 c. Scallop shell | 50 | 20 |
| O23 | 30 c. Soldier Cone shell (Silver) | 50 | 25 |
| O24 | 35 c. on 60 c. Olive shell (Silver) | 65 | 30 |
| O25 | 50 c. Cloth of Gold Cone shell (Silver) | 1·00 | 35 |
| O26 | 60 c. Olive shell (Silver) | 1·10 | 45 |
| O27 | $1 Queen and Prince Philip (Silver) | 3·75 | 1·25 |
| O28 | $1 Royal Visit, 1974 (Silver) | 3·75 | 1·25 |
| O29 | $2 Captain Cook and H.M.S. *Resolution* | 4·75 | 3·00 |
| O30 | $4 Queen Elizabeth II and seashells (15.2.79) | 7·50 | 3·25 |
| O31 | $6 As $4 (15.2.79) | 9·50 | 6·00 |
| O16/31 | *Set of* 16 | 32·00 | 15·00 |

These stamps were originally only sold to the public cancelled-to-order and not in unused condition. They were made available to overseas collectors in mint condition during 1980.

### *COVER PRICES*

Cover factors are quoted at the beginning of each country for most issues to 1945. An explanation of the system can be found on page x. The factors quoted do not, however, apply to philatelic covers.

O.H.M.S. (O 3) 75c O.H.M.S. (O 4)

O.H.M.S. (O 5)

**1985** (10 July)–**90**. (*a*) *Nos.* 969/74, 976, 978, 981, 984/6 *and* 988/9 *optd or surch as Type* O **3** *by silver foil embossing.*

| | | | |
|---|---|---|---|
| O32 | 5 c. *Ptilosarcus gurneyi* | 10 | 10 |
| O33 | 10 c. *Lobophyllia bemprichii* | 10 | 10 |
| | a. Opt double, one albino | 50·00 | |
| O34 | 12 c. *Sarcophyton digitatum* (5.5.86) | 10 | 10 |
| O35 | 14 c. *Pavona praetorta* (5.5.86) | 10 | 10 |
| O36 | 18 c. *Junceella gemmacea* (5.5.86) | 10 | 15 |
| O37 | 20 c. *Stylaster* | 10 | 15 |
| O38 | 30 c. *Palauastrea ramosa* | 20 | 25 |
| O39 | 40 c. *Stylaster echinatus* | 25 | 30 |
| O40 | 50 c. *Melithaea squamata* (5.5.86) | 35 | 40 |
| O41 | 55 c. on 85 c. *Caulastraea echinulata* | 35 | 40 |
| | a. "O.H.M.S." albino | † | — |
| O42 | 60 c. *Tubastraea* | 40 | 45 |
| O43 | 70 c. *Heliofungia actiniformis* (5.5.86) | 45 | 50 |
| O44 | $1.10, *Pectinia alcicornis* | 75 | 80 |
| O45 | $2 on $1.20, *Dendrophyllia gracilis* | 1·25 | 1·40 |

(*b*) *Nos.* 862/5 *surch with Type* O 4 *by gold foil embossing*

| | | | |
|---|---|---|---|
| O46 | 75 c. on 60 c. Type **197** (5.5.86) | 50 | 55 |
| O47 | 75 c. on 60 c. Rarotonga oranges (5.5.86) | 50 | 55 |
| O48 | 75 c. on 60 c. Rarotonga airport (5.5.86) | 50 | 55 |
| O49 | 75 c. on 60 c. Prime Minister Sir Thomas Davis (5.5.86) | 50 | 55 |

(*c*) *Nos.* 786/9 *surch as T* **209** *in silver and black further optd with Type* O **5** *by silver foil embossing.*

| | | | |
|---|---|---|---|
| O50 | $5 on $3 *Heliofungia actiniformis* (5.5.86) | 3·25 | 3·50 |
| O51 | $9 on $4 *Stylophora pistillata* (30.5.89) | 6·00 | 6·25 |
| O52 | $14 on $6 *Stylaster echinatus* (12.7.89) | 9·25 | 9·50 |
| O53 | $18 on $10 *Melithaea albitincta* (4.6.90) | 12·00 | 12·50 |
| O32/53 | *Set of* 12 | 30·00 | 32·00 |

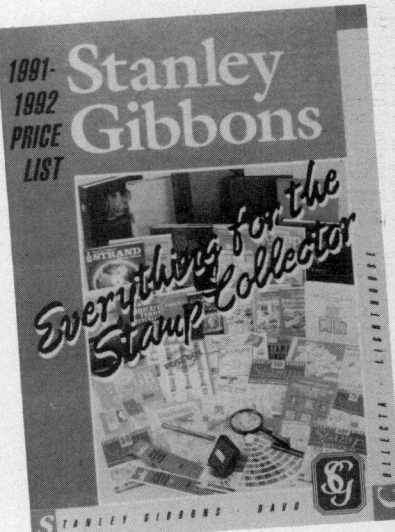

# AITUTAKI

Stamps of COOK ISLANDS were used in Aitutaki from 1892 until 1903.

**PRICES FOR STAMPS ON COVER TO 1945**

| | |
|---|---|
| Nos. 1/8 | *from* × 4 |
| Nos. 9/14 | *from* × 3 |
| Nos. 15/29 | *from* × 4 |
| Nos. 30/2 | *from* × 6 |

## A. NEW ZEALAND DEPENDENCY

The island of Aitutaki, previously under British protection, was annexed by New Zealand on 11 June 1901.

***Stamps of New Zealand overprinted or surcharged.***

**AITUTAKI.**
(1)

**Ava Pene.**
(2) ½d.

**Tai Pene.**
(3) 1d.

**Rua Pene Ma Te Ava.**
(4) 2½d.

**Toru Pene.**
(5) 3d.

**Ono Pene.**
(6) 6d.

**Tai Tiringi.**
(7) 1s.

**1903** (29 June)–**11**. *1902 issue surch with T* 1 *at top, and T* **2** *to* 7 *at foot. W* **43**. *(a) P* 14.

| | | | | |
|---|---|---|---|---|
| 1 | **23** | ½d. green (R.) | 3·25 | 6·50 |
| 2 | **42** | 1d. carmine (B.) | 4·50 | 5·50 |
| 3 | **27** | 2½d. deep blue (R.) (9.11) | 7·00 | 17·00 |
| | | a. "Ava" without stop | £130 | £170 |
| 1/3 | | *Set of* 3 | 13·50 | 26·00 |
| | | *(b) P* 11 | | |
| 4 | **27** | 2½d. blue (R.) | 8·00 | 11·00 |
| 5 | **28** | 3d. yellow-brown (B.) | 7·00 | 15·00 |
| 6 | **31** | 6d. rose-red (B.) | 20·00 | 25·00 |
| 7 | **34** | 1s. bright red (B.) | 55·00 | 85·00 |
| | | a. "Tiringi" without stop (R. 7/12) | £375 | £500 |
| 8 | | 1s. orange-red (B.) | 65·00 | 95·00 |
| | | a. "Tiringi" without stop (R. 7/12) | £500 | £650 |
| | | *b. Orange-brown* | £140 | £160 |
| | | c. Do. "Tiringi" without stop (R. 7/12) | £950 | £1100 |
| 4/7 | | *Set of* 4 | 80·00 | £120 |

Nos. 1/2 and 4/7 were placed on sale in Auckland on 12 June 1903.

There were four states of the overprint used for No. 3. On the first the "no stop" variety (No. 3a) occurs on R. 6/8, on the second it appears on R. 1/4, 2/4 and 6/8, on the third on R. 5/8 and 6/8, and on the fourth all stops are present.

**AITUTAKI.**

**Ono Pene.**
(8)

**1911–16.** ½d. *and* 1d. *surch as on Nos.* 1/2, 6d. *and* 1s. *as T* **8**.

| | | | | |
|---|---|---|---|---|
| 9 | **51** | ½d. green (R.) (9.11) | 75 | 2·50 |
| 10 | **53** | 1d. carmine (B.) (2.13) | 3·00 | 8·00 |
| 11 | **52** | 6d. carmine (B.) (*p* 14 × 14½)(23.5.16) | 35·00 | 70·00 |
| 12 | | 1s. vermilion (B.) (*p* 14 × 14½) (9.14) | 55·00 | £120 |
| 9/12 | | *Set of* 4 | 80·00 | £180 |

**1916–17.** *King George V stamps surch as T* **8**. *P* 14 × 14½.

| | | | | |
|---|---|---|---|---|
| 13 | **60** | 6d. carmine (B.) (6.6.16) | 7·50 | 22·00 |
| | | a. Perf 14 × 13½ | 14·00 | 42·00 |
| | | b. Vert pair. Nos. 13/13a | 48·00 | £110 |
| 14 | | 1s. vermilion (B.) (3.17) | 32·00 | 75·00 |
| | | a. Perf 14 × 13½ | 28·00 | 75·00 |
| | | b. Vert pair. Nos. 14/14a | £130 | £275 |
| | | c. "Tai" without dot | £200 | £350 |
| | | d. "Tiringi" no dot on second "i" | £250 | £400 |
| | | e. "Tiringi" no dot on third "i" | £300 | £450 |

**1917–18.** *King George V stamps optd* "AITUTAKI", *only, as in T* **8**. *W* **43**. *P* 14 × 14½.

| | | | | |
|---|---|---|---|---|
| 15 | **60** | 2½d. deep blue (R.) (12.18) | 1·40 | 10·00 |
| | | a. Perf 14 × 13½ | 2·00 | 10·00 |
| | | b. Vert pair. Nos. 15/15a | 60·00 | £120 |
| 16 | | 3d. chocolate (B.)(1.18) | 1·25 | 12·00 |
| | | a. Perf 14 × 13½ | 1·75 | 13·00 |
| | | b. Vert pair. Nos. 16/16a | 55·00 | £120 |
| 17 | | 6d. carmine (B.)(11.17) | 4·50 | 12·00 |
| | | a. Perf 14 × 13½ | 7·00 | 19·00 |
| | | b. Vert pair. Nos. 17/17a | 60·00 | £120 |
| 18 | | 1s. vermilion (B.)(11.17) | 12·00 | 22·00 |
| | | a. Perf 14 × 13½ | 15·00 | 29·00 |
| | | b. Vert pair. Nos. 18/18a | 85·00 | £160 |
| 15/18 | | *Set of* 4 | 17·00 | 50·00 |

**1917–20.** *Optd* "AITUTAKI", *as in T* **8**. *Typo. W* **43**. *P* 14 × 15.

| | | | | |
|---|---|---|---|---|
| 19 | **61** | ½d. green (R.) (2.20) | 1·00 | 4·00 |
| 20 | **53** | 1d. carmine (B.)(5.20) | 2·50 | 8·00 |
| 21 | **61** | 1½d. slate (R.)(11.17) | 3·50 | 20·00 |
| 22 | | 1½d. orange-brown (R.) (2.19) | 80 | 6·50 |
| 23 | | 3d. chocolate (B.)(6.19) | 3·50 | 12·00 |
| 19/23 | | *Set of* 5 | 10·00 | 45·00 |

(Des and recess Perkins, Bacon & Co)

**1920** (23 Aug). *As Types of Cook Islands, but inscr* "AITUTAKI". *No wmk. P* 14.

| | | | | |
|---|---|---|---|---|
| 24 | **9** | ½d. black and green | 3·00 | 15·00 |
| 25 | **10** | 1d. black and dull carmine | 3·00 | 6·00 |
| 26 | **11** | 1½d. black and sepia | 6·00 | 11·00 |
| 27 | **12** | 3d. black and deep blue | 1·75 | 12·00 |
| 28 | **13** | 6d. red-brown and slate | 5·00 | 14·00 |
| 29 | **14** | 1s. black and purple | 8·50 | 16·00 |
| 24/29 | | *Set of* 6 | 24·00 | 65·00 |

(Recess Govt Printing Office, Wellington)

**1924–27.** *As Types of Cook Islands, but inscr* "AITUTAKI". *W* **43** *of New Zealand. P* 14.

| | | | | |
|---|---|---|---|---|
| 30 | **9** | ½d. black and green (5.27) | 2·00 | 7·50 |
| 31 | **10** | 1d. black and deep carmine (10.24) | 2·75 | 6·50 |
| 32 | **16** | 2½d. black and dull blue (10.27) | 7·50 | 38·00 |
| 30/2 | | *Set of* 3 | 11·00 | 48·00 |

Cook Islands stamps superseded those of Aitutaki on 15 March 1932. Separate issues were resumed in 1972.

## B. PART OF COOK ISLANDS

On 9 August 1972, Aitutaki became a Port of Entry into the Cook Islands, and at the close of business on the previous day, Cook Islands stamps were withdrawn from sale there. Whilst remaining part of the Cook Islands, Aitutaki has a separate postal service.

**PRINTERS.** Stamps of Aitutaki were printed in photogravure by Heraclio Fournier, Spain, *unless otherwise stated.* All issues are on paper treated with fluorescent security markings, and with synthetic gum. The fluorescent markings can be found inverted or omitted.

(9)

**Aitutaki**
(10)

(Optd by Govt Printer, Wellington)

**1972** (9 Aug). *Nos.* 227B *etc. of Cook Is. optd with T* **9** *(applied horizontally on* $1), *by New Zealand Govt Printer.*

| | | | | |
|---|---|---|---|---|
| 33 | | ½ c. Type **79** | 30 | 80 |
| 34 | | 1 c. *Hibiscus syriacus* | 70 | 1·40 |
| 35 | | 2½ c. *Clitoria ternatea* | 3·50 | 8·00 |
| 36 | | 4 c. Water Lily (No. 233B) | 70 | 85 |
| 37 | | 5 c. *Bauhinia bi-pinnata rosea* | 4·50 | 8·50 |
| 38 | | 10 c. *Poinciana regia flamboyant* | 4·50 | 6·50 |
| 39 | | 20 c. Thunbergia | 70 | 1·00 |
| 40 | | 25 c. Canna Lily | 70 | 1·00 |
| 41 | | 50 c. *Gardinia taitensis* | 3·75 | 3·25 |
| 42 | | $1 Type **80** | 6·50 | 6·50 |
| | | *a. Shade** | | |
| 33/42 | | *Set of* 10 | 23·00 | 35·00 |

* No. 42a has the border flowers predominantly in a carmine colour instead of scarlet, and may be due to a missing yellow colour.

**1972** (27 Oct). *Christmas. Nos.* 406/8 *of Cook. Is. optd in silver with T* **10**.

| | | | | |
|---|---|---|---|---|
| 43 | **130** | 1 c. multicoloured | 10 | 10 |
| 44 | – | 5 c. multicoloured | 10 | 15 |
| 45 | – | 10 c. multicoloured | 10 | 25 |
| 43/5 | | *Set of* 3 | 20 | 40 |

**1972** (20 Nov). *Royal Silver Wedding. As Nos.* 413 *and* 415 *of Cook Is., but inscr* "COOK ISLANDS Aitutaki".

| | | | | |
|---|---|---|---|---|
| 46 | **131** | 5 c. black and silver | 4·75 | 2·75 |
| 47 | – | 15 c. black and silver | 2·75 | 1·50 |

**AITUTAKI**
(11)

(12)

**1972** (24 Nov). *No.* 245B *of Cook Is. optd with T* **11** *by Govt Printer, Rarotonga.*

| | | | | |
|---|---|---|---|---|
| 48 | **80** | $2 multicoloured | 60 | 1·00 |
| | | a. Optd "AJTUTAKI" for "AITUTAKI" (R. 2/4) | 25·00 | |
| | | b. On No. 245A (gum arabic printing) | 50·00 | |
| | | ba. Optd "AJTUTAKI" for "AITUTAKI" (R. 2/4) | | |

**1972** (11 Dec). *Nos.* 227B *etc of Cook Is. optd with T* **12**, *by Heraclio Fournier.*

| | | | | |
|---|---|---|---|---|
| 49 | | ½ c. Type **79** | 15 | 10 |
| 50 | | 1 c. *Hibiscus syriacus* | 15 | 10 |
| 51 | | 2½ c. *Clitoria ternatea* | 20 | 10 |
| 52 | | 4 c. Water Lily (No. 233B) | 25 | 15 |
| 53 | | 5 c. *Bauhinia bi-pinnata rosea* | 25 | 15 |
| 54 | | 10 c. *Poinciana regia flamboyant* | 35 | 25 |
| 55 | | 20 c. Thunbergia | 70 | 50 |
| 56 | | 25 c. Canna Lily | 70 | 55 |
| 57 | | 50 c. *Gardinia taitensis* | 1·25 | 90 |
| 58 | | $1 Type **80** | 1·75 | 1·75 |
| 49/58 | | *Set of* 10 | 5·25 | 4·00 |

***MINIMUM PRICE***

The minimum price quote is 10p which represents a handling charge rather than a basis for valuing common stamps. For further notes about prices see introductory pages.

13 "Christ Mocked" (Grünewald)

**AITUTAKI**
(14)

**1973** (6 Apr). *Easter. T* **13** *and similar vert designs. Multicoloured. P* 13.

| | | | |
|---|---|---|---|
| 59 | 1 c. Type **13** | 15 | 10 |
| 60 | 1 c. "St. Veronica" (Van der Weyden) | 15 | 10 |
| 61 | 1 c. "The Crucified Christ with Virgin Mary, Saints and Angels" (Raphael) | 15 | 10 |
| 62 | 1 c. "Resurrection" (Piero della Francesca) | 15 | 10 |
| 63 | 5 c. "The Last Supper" (Master of Amiens) | 20 | 15 |
| 64 | 5 c. "Condemnation" (Holbein) | 20 | 15 |
| 65 | 5 c. "Christ on the Cross" (Rubens) | 20 | 15 |
| 66 | 5 c. "Resurrection" (El Greco) | 20 | 15 |
| 67 | 10 c. "Disrobing of Christ" (El Greco) | 20 | 15 |
| 68 | 10 c. "St. Veronica" (Van Oostsanen) | 20 | 15 |
| 69 | 10 c. "Christ on the Cross" (Rubens) | 20 | 15 |
| 70 | 10 c. "Resurrection" (Bouts) | 20 | 15 |
| 59/70 | *Set of* 12 | 2·00 | 1·25 |

Nos. 59/62, 63/6 and 67/70 were each printed together, *se-tenant*, in blocks of 4 throughout the sheet.

**1973** (14 May). *Silver Wedding Coinage. Nos.* 417/23 *of Cook Is. optd in silver and black as T* **14**.

| | | | |
|---|---|---|---|
| 71 | 1 c. black, rosy carmine and gold | 10 | 10 |
| 72 | 2 c. black, bright blue and gold | 10 | 10 |
| 73 | 5 c. black, green and silver | 10 | 10 |
| 74 | 10 c. black, royal blue and silver | 15 | 10 |
| 75 | 20 c. black, deep blue-green and silver | 20 | 15 |
| 76 | 50 c. black, carmine and silver | 40 | 30 |
| 77 | $1 black, bright blue and silver | 65 | 45 |
| 71/7 | *Set of* 7 | 1·40 | 1·00 |

TENTH ANNIVERSARY
CESSATION
OF
NUCLEAR TESTING
TREATY
(15)

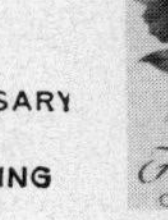

16 Red Hibiscus and Princess Anne

**1973** (13 Aug). *Tenth Anniv of Treaty Banning Nuclear Testing. Nos.* 236B, 238B, 240B *and* 243B *of Cook Is. optd with T* **15** *and T* **12** *together.*

| | | | |
|---|---|---|---|
| 78 | 8 c. *Allamanda cathartica* | 15 | 15 |
| 79 | 10 c. *Poinciana regia flamboyant* | 15 | 15 |
| 80 | 20 c. Thunbergia | 30 | 20 |
| 81 | 50 c. *Gardinia taitensis* | 70 | 50 |
| 78/81 | *Set of* 4 | 1·10 | 90 |

**1973** (14 Nov). *Royal Wedding. T* **16** *and similar horiz design. Multicoloured. P* 13½ × 14.

| | | | |
|---|---|---|---|
| 82 | 25 c. Type **16** | 25 | 10 |
| 83 | 30 c. Capt. Phillips and Blue Hibiscus | 25 | 10 |
| **MS**84 | 114 × 65 mm. Nos. 82/3. P 13 | 50 | 40 |

17 "Virgin and Child" (Montagna)

18 *Murex ramosus*

**1973** (10 Dec). *Christmas. T* **17** *and similar vert designs showing "The Virgin and Child" by the artists listed. Multicoloured. P* 13½.

| | | | |
|---|---|---|---|
| 85 | 1 c. Type **17** | 10 | 10 |
| 86 | 1 c. Crivelli | 10 | 10 |
| 87 | 1 c. Van Dyck | 10 | 10 |
| 88 | 1 c. Perugino | 10 | 10 |
| 89 | 5 c. Veronese (child at shoulder) | 15 | 10 |
| 90 | 5 c. Veronese (child on lap) | 15 | 10 |
| 91 | 5 c. Cima | 15 | 10 |
| 92 | 5 c. Memling | 15 | 10 |
| 93 | 10 c. Memling | 20 | 10 |
| 94 | 10 c. Del Colle | 20 | 10 |
| 95 | 10 c. Raphael | 20 | 10 |
| 96 | 10 c. Lotto | 20 | 10 |
| 85/96 | *Set of* 12 | 1·40 | 80 |

Nos. 85/8, 89/92 and 93/6 were each printed together, *se-tenant*, in blocks of 4 throughout the sheet.

**1974** (31 Jan)–**75**. *T* **18** *and similar horiz designs showing sea-shells. Multicoloured. P* 13.

| | | | |
|---|---|---|---|
| 97 | ½ c. Type **18** | 35 | 40 |
| 98 | 1 c. *Nautilus macromphallus* | 35 | 40 |

99 2 c. *Harpa major* .. 35 40
100 3 c. *Phalium strigatum* .. 40 40
101 4 c. *Cypraea talpa* .. 40 40
102 5 c. *Mitra stictica* .. 40 40
103 8 c. *Charonia tritonis* .. 45 40
104 10 c. *Murex triremis* .. 45 40
105 20 c. *Oliva sericea* .. 60 40
106 25 c. *Tritonalia rubeta* .. 70 40
107 60 c. *Strombus latissimus* .. 2·50 70
108 $1 *Biplex perca* .. 1·75 1·10
109 $2 Queen Elizabeth II and *Terebra maculata* (20.1.75) .. 6·00 7·00
110 $5 Queen Elizabeth II and *Cypraea hesitata* (28.2.75) .. 22·00 9·50
97/110 .. *Set of* 14 32·00 20·00
Nos. 109/110 are larger, 53 × 25 mm.

19 Bligh and H.M.S. *Bounty*

(Des G. Vasarhelyi)

**1974** (11 Apr). *William Bligh's Discovery of Aitutaki. T* **19** *and similar horiz designs. Multicoloured. P* 13½.
114 1 c. Type **19** .. 20 10
115 1 c. H.M.S. *Bounty* .. 20 10
116 5 c. Bligh, and H.M.S. *Bounty* at Aitutaki .. 40 15
117 5 c. Aitutaki chart of 1856 .. 40 15
118 8 c. Capt. Cook and H.M.S. *Resolution* .. 65 20
119 8 c. Map of Aitutaki and inset location map .. 65 20
114/119 .. *Set of* 6 2·25 80
Nos. 114/15, 116/17 and 118/19 were each printed together, *se-tenant*, in horizontal and vertical pairs throughout the sheet.
See also Nos. 123/8.

20 Aitutaki Stamps of 1903, and Map

21 "Virgin and Child" (Hugo van der Goes)

**1974** (15 July). *Centenary of Universal Postal Union. T* **20** *and similar horiz design. Multicoloured. P* 13½ × 14.
120 25 c. Type **20** .. 65 40
121 50 c. Stamps of 1903 and 1920, and map .. 85 60
**MS**122 66 × 75 mm. Nos. 120/1. P 13 .. 1·50 2·00
Each value was issued in sheets of 5 stamps and 1 label.

**1974** (9 Sept). *Air. As Nos.* 114/119, *but larger* (46 × 26 *mm*), *denominations changed, and inscr* "AIR MAIL".
123 10 c. Type **19** .. 50 15
124 10 c. H.M.S. *Bounty* .. 50 15
125 25 c. Bligh, and H.M.S. *Bounty* at Aitutaki 65 25
126 25 c. Aitutaki chart of 1856 .. 65 25
127 30 c. Capt. Cook and H.M.S. *Resolution* .. 65 25
128 30 c. Map of Aitutaki and inset location map 65 25
123/8 .. *Set of* 6 3·25 1·10
Nos. 123/4, 125/6 and 127/8 were each printed together, *se-tenant*, in horizontal and vertical pairs throughout the sheet.

**1974** (11 Oct). *Christmas. T* **21** *and similar vert designs showing "Virgin and Child" by the artists listed. Multicoloured. P* 13.
129 1 c. Type **21** .. 10 10
130 5 c. Bellini .. 10 10
131 8 c. Gerard David .. 10 10
132 10 c. Antonello da Messina .. 10 10
133 25 c. Joos van Cleve .. 20 20
134 30 c. Master of the Life of St. Catherine .. 20 20
129/34 .. *Set of* 6 65 65
**MS**135 127 × 134 mm. Nos. 129/34 .. 1·25 1·60
Each value was issued in sheets of 15 stamps and 1 label.

22 Churchill as Schoolboy

+1c
(23)

**1974** (29 Nov). *Birth Centenary of Sir Winston Churchill. T* **22** *and similar vert designs. Multicoloured. P* 13½.
136 10 c. Type **22** .. 30 25
137 25 c. Churchill as young man .. 60 50
138 30 c. Churchill with troops .. 75 60
139 50 c. Churchill painting .. 1·10 80
140 $1 Giving "V" sign .. 2·00 1·50
136/40 .. *Set of* 5 4·25 3·25
**MS**141 115 × 108 mm. Nos. 136/40 plus *se-tenant* label. P 13 .. 5·00 4·00
Each value was issued in sheets of 5 stamps and 1 label.

**1974** (2 Dec). *Children's Christmas Fund. Nos.* 129/34 *surch with T* **23**.
142 1 c. + 1 c. multicoloured .. 10 10
143 5 c. + 1 c. multicoloured .. 10 10
144 8 c. + 1 c. multicoloured .. 10 10
145 10 c. + 1 c. multicoloured .. 10 10
146 25 c. + 1 c. multicoloured .. 20 20
147 30 c. + 1 c. multicoloured .. 20 20
142/7 .. *Set of* 6 55 55

24 Soviet and U.S. Flags

25 "Madonna and Child with Saints Francis and John" (Lorenzetti)

**1975** (24 July). *"Apollo-Soyuz" Space Project. T* **24** *and similar horiz design. Multicoloured. P* 13 × 14.
148 25 c. Type **24** .. 30 20
149 50 c. Daedalus and space capsule .. 40 30
**MS**150 123 × 61 mm. Nos. 148/9 .. 1·00 1·10
Each value was issued in sheets of 8 stamps and 1 label.

**1975** (24 Nov). *Christmas. T* **25** *and similar vert designs. Multicoloured. P* 13½.
151 6 c. } Type **25** .. 10 10
152 6 c. } .. 10 10
153 6 c. } .. 10 10
154 7 c. } "Adoration of the Kings" (Van der Weyden) .. 10 10
155 7 c. } .. 10 10
156 7 c. } .. 10 10
157 15 c. } "Madonna and Child Enthroneth with Saints Onufrius and John the Baptist" (Montagna) .. 15 15
158 15 c. } .. 15 15
159 15 c. } .. 15 15
160 20 c. } "Adoration of the Shepherds" (Reni) .. 20 15
161 20 c. } .. 20 15
162 20 c. } .. 20 15
151/62 .. *Set of* 12 1·50 1·40
**MS**163 104 × 201 mm. Nos. 151/62. P 13 .. 2·25 2·50
Nos. 151/3, 154/6, 157/9 and 160/2 were each printed together, *se-tenant*, in horizontal strips of 3 throughout the sheet, forming composite designs. Type **25** shows the left-hand stamp of the 6 c. design.

**1975** (19 Dec). *Children's Christmas Fund. Nos.* 151/62 *surch as T* **23**, *in silver*.
164 6 c. + 1 c. } Type **25** .. 15 10
165 6 c. + 1 c. } .. 15 10
166 6 c. + 1 c. } .. 15 10
167 7 c. + 1 c. } "Adoration of the Kings" (Van der Weyden) .. 15 10
168 7 c. + 1 c. } .. 15 10
169 7 c. + 1 c. } .. 15 10
170 15 c. + 1 c. } "Madonna and Child" (Montagna) .. 20 15
171 15 c. + 1 c. } .. 20 15
172 15 c. + 1 c. } .. 20 15
173 20 c. + 1 c. } "Adoration of the Shepherds" (Reni) .. 25 20
174 20 c. + 1 c. } .. 25 20
175 20 c. + 1 c. } .. 25 20
164/75 .. *Set of* 12 2·00 1·50

26 "The Descent" (detail, 15th-cent Flemish School)

27 "The Declaration of Independence" (detail)

**1976** (5 Apr). *Easter. Various vert designs showing portions of "The Descent" as in T* **26**. *P* 13.
176 **26** 15 c. multicoloured .. 15 10
177 – 30 c. multicoloured .. 20 15
178 – 35 c. multicoloured .. 25 20
176/8 .. *Set of* 3 55 40
**MS**179 87 × 67 mm. Nos. 176/8 forming a complete picture of "The Descent". P 12½ × 13 .. 1·00 1·25
Stamps from No. **MS**179 have no borders and are therefore smaller than stamps from the sheets.
Each value was issued in sheets of 8 stamps and 1 label.

**1976** (1 June). *Bicentenary of American Revolution. T* **27** *and similar vert designs showing paintings by John Trumbull. Multicoloured. P* 13.
180 30 c. } Type **27** .. 60 30
181 30 c. } .. 60 30
182 30 c. } .. 60 30
183 35 c. } "The Surrender of Lord Cornwallis at Yorktown" .. 70 40
184 35 c. } .. 70 40
185 35 c. } .. 70 40
186 50 c. } "The Resignation of General Washington" .. 80 45
187 50 c. } .. 80 45
188 50 c. } .. 80 45
180/8 .. *Set of* 9 5·75 3·00
**MS**189 132 × 120 mm. Nos. 180/8. P 13 .. 5·00 4·25
Nos. 180/2, 183/5 and 186/8 were each printed together, *se-tenant*, in horizontal strips of 3 throughout the sheet, forming composite designs. Each sheet includes 3 stamp-size labels. Type **27** shows the left-hand stamp of the 30 c. design.
Stamps from No. **MS**189 have their borders in a different colour and come with a different inscription.

28 Cycling

**1976** (15 July). *Olympic Games, Montreal. T* **28** *and similar horiz designs. Multicoloured. P* 13 × 14.
190 15 c. Type **28** .. 20 15
191 35 c. Sailing .. 40 20
192 60 c. Hockey .. 55 25
193 70 c. Sprinting .. 60 30
190/3 .. *Set of* 4 1·60 80
**MS**194 107 × 97 mm. Nos. 190/3 .. 1·60 1·60
Stamps from No. **MS**194 have borders of a different colour.
Each value was issued in sheets of 5 stamps and 1 label.

ROYAL VISIT JULY 1976
(29)

30 "The Visitation"

**1976** (30 July). *Visit of Queen Elizabeth to the U.S.A. Nos.* 190/**MS**194 *optd with T* **29**.
195 15 c. Type **28** .. 25 15
196 35 c. Sailing .. 40 25
197 60 c. Hockey .. 60 40
198 70 c. Sprinting .. 70 45
195/8 .. *Set of* 4 1·75 1·10
**MS**199 107 × 97 mm. Nos. 195/8 .. 1·75 2·50

**1976** (18 Oct). *Christmas. T* **30** *and similar vert designs. Figures in gold; background colours given. P* 13.
200 6 c. } deep bluish green .. 10 10
201 6 c. } .. 10 10
202 7 c. } dull brown-purple .. 10 10
203 7 c. } .. 10 10
204 15 c. } deep blue .. 10 10
205 15 c. } .. 10 10
206 20 c. } reddish violet .. 15 15
207 20 c. } .. 15 15
200/207 .. *Set of* 8 60 60
**MS**208 128 × 96 mm. As Nos. 200/207 but with borders on three sides .. 1·00 1·40
Designs:—No. 201, Angel: No. 202, Angel; No. 203, Shepherds; No. 204, Joseph; No. 205, Mary and the Child; No. 206, Wise Man; No. 207, Two Wise Men.
Nos. 200/1, 202/3, 204/5 and 206/7 were each printed together, *se-tenant*, in horizontal pairs throughout the sheet, forming composite designs. Type **30** shows the left-hand stamp of the 6 c. design.

+1c
(31)

32 Alexander Graham Bell and First Telephone

**1976** (19 Nov). *Children's Christmas Fund. Nos.* 200/**MS**208 *surch in silver as T* **31**.
209 6 c. + 1 c. } "The Visitation" .. 10 10
210 6 c. + 1 c. } .. 10 10
211 7 c. + 1 c. } "Angel and Shepherds" .. 10 10
212 7 c. + 1 c. } .. 10 10
213 15 c. + 1 c. } "The Holy Family" .. 15 15
214 15 c. + 1 c. } .. 15 15
215 20 c. + 1 c. } "The Magi" .. 15 15
216 20 c. + 1 c. } .. 15 15
209/16 .. *Set of* 8 70 70
**MS**217 128 × 96 mm. As Nos. 209/216 but with a premium of "+ 2 c." and borders on three sides .. 80 1·40

**1977** (3 Mar). *Telephone Centenary* (1976). *T* **32** *and similar horiz design. P* 13.
218 25 c. black, gold and dull scarlet .. 20 15
219 70 c. black, gold and lilac .. 40 40
**MS**220 116 × 59 mm. As Nos. 218/19 but with different colours .. 70 1·00
Design:—70 c. Earth Station and satellite.

33 "Christ on the Cross" (detail)

977 (31 Mar). *Easter and 400th Birth Anniv of Rubens. T* **33** *and similar horiz designs. Multicoloured. P* 13½ × 14.
21 15 c. Type **33** .. .. .. .. .. .. 40 15
22 20 c. "Lamentation for Christ" .. .. 50 20
23 35 c. "Christ with Straw" .. .. .. 70 25
21/3 .. .. .. .. .. *Set of* 3 1·40 55
IS224 115 × 57 mm. Nos. 221/3. P 13 × 12½ .. 1·40 1·75
Each value was issued in sheets of 8 stamps and 1 label.

34 Capt. Bligh, George III and H.M.S. *Bounty*

977 (21 Apr). *Silver Jubilee. T* **34** *and similar horiz designs. Multicoloured. P* 13.
25 25 c. Type **34** .. .. .. .. .. .. 50 45
26 35 c. Rev. Williams, George IV and Aitutaki Church .. .. .. .. .. .. 60 50
27 50 c. Union Jack, Queen Victoria and island map .. .. .. .. .. .. 75 75
28 $1 Balcony scene, 1953 .. .. .. 1·25 1·25
25/8 .. .. .. .. .. *Set of* 4 2·75 2·75
IS229 130 × 87 mm. Nos. 225/8 but with gold borders. P 13½ × 13 .. .. .. 2·75 2·75
Each value was issued in sheets of 5 stamps and 1 label.

35 The Shepherds

+1c

(36)

977 (14 Oct). *Christmas. T* **35** *and similar vert designs. Multicoloured. P* 13½ × 14.
30 6 c. Type **35** .. .. .. .. .. .. 10 10
31 6 c. Angel .. .. .. .. .. .. 10 10
32 7 c. Mary, Jesus and ox .. .. .. .. 10 10
33 7 c. Joseph and donkey .. .. .. .. 10 10
34 15 c. Three Kings .. .. .. .. .. 10 10
35 15 c. Virgin and Child .. .. .. .. 10 10
36 20 c. Joseph .. .. .. .. .. .. 10 10
37 20 c. Mary and Jesus on donkey .. .. 10 10
30/7 .. .. .. .. .. *Set of* 8 55 55
IS238 130 × 95 mm. Nos. 230/7 .. .. 70 1·25
Each design covers two stamps; Type **35** shows the left-hand stamp of the 6 c. design.

977 (15 Nov). *Children's Christmas Fund. Nos. 230/7 surch with T* **36**.
39 6 c. + 1 c. } Type **35** .. .. .. .. 10 10
40 6 c. + 1 c. } .. 10 10
41 7 c. + 1 c. } The Holy Family .. .. 10 10
42 7 c. + 1 c. } .. 10 10
43 15 c. + 1 c. } The Three Kings with Virgin 15 10
44 15 c. + 1 c. } and Child .. .. .. .. 15 10
45 20 c. + 1 c. } Flight into Egypt .. 15 10
46 20 c. + 1 c. } .. 15 10
39/46 .. .. .. .. .. *Set of* 8 75 55
IS247 130 × 95 mm. As Nos. 239/46 but each with premium of "+ 2 c." .. .. .. .. 70 85

37 Hawaiian Goddess

38 "Christ on the Way to Calvary" (Martini)

978 (19 Jan). *Bicentenary of Discovery of Hawaii. T* **37** *and similar multicoloured designs. P* 13½.
48 35 c. Type **37** .. .. .. .. .. 45 25
49 50 c. Figurehead of H.M.S. *Resolution (horiz)* 75 40
50 $1 Hawaiian temple figure .. .. .. 1·00 70
48/50 .. .. .. .. .. *Set of* 3 2·00 1·25
IS251 168 × 75 mm. Nos. 248/50 .. .. 2·00 2·75

**1978** (17 Mar). *Easter. Details of Paintings from Louvre, Paris. T* **38** *and similar horiz designs. Multicoloured. P* 13½ × 14.
252 15 c. Type **38** .. .. .. .. .. 10 10
253 20 c. "Piéta of Avignon" (E. Quarton) .. 15 10
254 35 c. "Pilgrims at Emmaus" (Rembrandt) .. 20 15
252/4 .. .. .. .. .. *Set of* 3 40 30
**MS**255 108 × 83 mm. Nos. 252/4 .. .. 45 70
Each value was printed in two panes of 9 within the sheet, both panes including one *se-tenant* stamp-size label.

**1978** (17 Mar). *Easter. Children's Charity. Designs as Nos. 252/4, but smaller (34 × 26 mm) and without margins, in separate miniature sheets 75 × 58 mm, each with a face value of 50 c. + 5 c. P* 14.
**MS**256 As Nos. 252/4 .. .. *Set of* 3 *sheets* 1·00 1·00

39 Yale of Beaufort

40 "Adoration of the Infant Jesus"

**1978** (15 June). *25th Anniv of Coronation. T* **39** *and similar vert designs. Multicoloured. P* 13½ × 13.
257 $1 Type **39** .. .. .. .. .. 55 65
258 $1 Queen Elizabeth II .. .. .. 55 65
259 $1 Aitutaki ancestral statue .. .. 55 65
257/9 .. .. .. .. .. *Set of* 3 1·50 1·75
**MS**260 98 × 127 mm. Nos. 257/9 × 2 .. 1·75 1·75
Stamps from No. **MS**260 have coloured borders, the upper row in lavender and the lower in apple-green.
Nos. 257/9 were printed together, *se-tenant*, in small sheets of 6, containing two horizontal strips of 3.

**1978** (4 Dec). *Christmas. 450th Death Anniv of Dürer. T* **40** *and similar vert designs. Multicoloured. P* 13 × 14.
261 15 c. Type **40** .. .. .. .. .. 35 15
262 17 c. "The Madonna with Child" .. .. 40 15
263 30 c. "The Madonna with the Iris" .. .. 55 20
264 35 c. "The Madonna of the Siskin" .. .. 60 25
261/4 .. .. .. .. .. *Set of* 4 1·75 65
**MS**265 101 × 109 mm. As Nos. 261/4 but each with premium of "+ 2 c." .. .. .. .. 90 1·00
Nos. 261/4 were each printed in small sheets of 6, including 1 *se-tenant* stamp-size label.

41 "Captain Cook" (Nathaniel Dance)

42 Girl with Flowers

**1979** (20 July). *Death Bicentenary of Captain Cook. Paintings. T* **41** *and similar vert designs. Multicoloured. P* 14 × 13½.
266 50 c. Type **41** .. .. .. .. .. 1·00 80
267 75 c. "H.M.S. *Resolution* and *Adventure* at Matavai Bay" (William Hodges) .. 1·75 95
**MS**268 94 × 58 mm. Nos. 266/7. P 13½ .. 2·75 3·50

**1979** (1 Oct). *International Year of the Child. T* **42** *and similar vert designs. Multicoloured. P* 14 × 13½.
269 30 c. Type **42** .. .. .. .. .. 15 15
270 35 c. Boy playing guitar .. .. .. 20 20
271 65 c. Children in canoe .. .. .. 30 30
269/71 .. .. .. .. .. *Set of* 3 60 60
**MS**272 104 × 80 mm. As Nos. 269/71, but each with a premium of "+ 3 c." .. .. .. 70 1·00

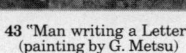

43 "Man writing a Letter" (painting by G. Metsu)

44 "The Burial of Christ" (detail, Quentin Metsys)

**1979** (14 Nov). *Death Centenary of Sir Rowland Hill. T* **43** *and similar horiz designs. Multicoloured. P* 13.
273 50 c. Type **43** .. .. .. .. .. 80 80
274 50 c. Sir Rowland Hill with Penny Black, 1903 ½d. and 1911 1d. stamps .. .. 80 80
275 50 c. "Girl in Blue reading a Letter" (painting by J. Vermeer) .. .. .. .. 80 80
276 65 c. "Woman writing a Letter" (painting by G. Terborch) .. .. .. .. .. 85 85
277 65 c. Sir Rowland Hill with Penny Black, 1903 3d. and 1920 ½d. stamps .. .. 85 85
278 65 c. "Lady reading a Letter" (painting by J. Vermeer) .. .. .. .. .. 85 85
273/8 .. .. .. .. .. *Set of* 6 4·50 4·50
**MS**279 151 × 85 mm. 30 c. × 6. As Nos. 273/8 .. 3·00 3·50
Nos. 273/5 and 276/8 were printed together, *se-tenant*, in horizontal strips of 3, the sheet having two panes separated by margin, one containing 273/5 × 3, the other containing 276/8 × 3.

**1980** (3 Apr). *Easter. T* **44** *and similar vert designs showing different details of painting "The Burial of Christ" by Quentin Metsys. P* 13.
280 20 c. multicoloured .. .. .. .. 25 15
281 30 c. multicoloured .. .. .. .. 35 25
282 35 c. multicoloured .. .. .. .. 40 30
280/2 .. .. .. .. .. *Set of* 3 90 60
**MS**283 93 × 71 mm. As Nos. 280/2, but each with premium of "+ 2 c." .. .. .. .. 75 75

45 Einstein as Young Man

46 Ancestor Figure, Aitutaki

**1980** (21 July). *25th Death Anniv of Albert Einstein (physicist). T* **45** *and similar vert designs. Multicoloured. P* 14 × 13½.
284 12 c. Type **45** .. .. .. .. .. 40 40
285 12 c. Atom and "E=mc²" equation .. .. 40 40
286 15 c. Einstein as middle-aged man .. .. 45 45
287 15 c. Cross over nuclear explosion (Nuclear Test Ban Treaty, 1963) .. .. .. 45 45
288 20 c. Einstein as old man .. .. .. 50 50
289 20 c. Hand over bomb explosion (Nuclear Test Ban Treaty, 1963) .. .. .. 50 50
284/9 .. .. .. .. .. *Set of* 6 2·40 2·40
**MS**290 113 × 118 mm. Nos. 284/9. P 13½ .. 2·40 2·40
Nos. 284/5, 286/7 and 288/9 were each printed together, *se-tenant*, in horizontal pairs throughout the sheet.

**1980** (26 Sept). *South Pacific Festival of Arts. T* **46** *and similar vert designs. Multicoloured. P* 13½.
291 6 c. Type **46** .. .. .. .. .. 10 10
292 6 c. Staff god image, Rarotonga .. .. 10 10
293 6 c. Trade adze, Mangaia .. .. .. 10 10
294 6 c. Carved image of Tangaroa, Rarotonga .. 10 10
295 12 c. Wooden image, Aitutaki .. .. .. 10 10
296 12 c. Hand club, Rarotonga .. .. .. 10 10
297 12 c. Carved mace "god", Mangaia .. .. 10 10
298 12 c. Fisherman's god, Rarotonga .. .. 10 10
299 15 c. Ti'i image, Aitutaki .. .. .. 15 15
300 15 c. Fisherman's god, Rarotonga (*different*) .. 15 15
301 15 c. Carved mace "god", Cook Islands .. 15 15
302 15 c. Carved image of Tangaroa, Rarotonga (*different*) .. .. .. .. .. 15 15
303 20 c. Chief's headdress, Aitutaki .. .. 15 15
304 20 c. Carved "mace" god, Cook Islands (*different*) .. .. .. .. .. 15 15
305 20 c. Staff god image, Rarotonga (*different*) .. 15 15
306 20 c. Carved image of Tangaroa, Rarotonga (*different*) .. .. .. .. .. 15 15
291/306 .. .. .. .. *Set of* 16 1·60 1·60
**MS**307 134 × 194 mm. Nos. 291/306 .. .. 1·60 1·75
The four designs of each value were printed together, *se-tenant*, in blocks of 4 throughout the sheet.

47 Virgin and Child (13th-century)

48 "Mourning Virgin"

**1980** (21 Nov). *Christmas. Sculptures. T* **47** *and similar vert designs showing various Virgin and Child works from the periods given. Multicoloured. P* 13.
308 15 c. Type **47** .. .. .. .. .. 15 15
309 20 c. 14th-century .. .. .. .. 15 15
310 25 c. 15th-century .. .. .. .. 15 15
311 35 c. 15th-century (*different*) .. .. .. 20 20
308/11 .. .. .. .. .. *Set of* 4 60 60
**MS**312 82 × 120 mm. As Nos. 306/11 but each with premium of 2 c. .. .. .. .. .. 70 80

**1981** (31 Mar). *Easter. Details of Sculpture "Burial of Christ" by Pedro Roldan. T* **48** *and similar vert designs. P* 14.
313 30 c. gold and myrtle-green .. .. .. 25 25
314 40 c. gold and deep reddish lilac .. .. 30 30
315 50 c. gold and Prussian blue .. .. .. 30 30
313/15 .. .. .. .. .. *Set of* 3 75 75
**MS**316 107 × 60 mm. As Nos. 313/15 but each with premium of 2 c. .. .. .. .. .. 75 85
Designs:—40 c. "Christ"; 50 c. "Saint John".

**49** Gouldian Finch (*Poephila gouldiae*)

**50** Prince Charles

**1981** (6 Apr)–**82**. *Birds* (1*st series*). *Multicoloured designs as T* **49**. *P* 14 × 13½ (1 *to* 10 c.), 13½ × 14 (15 *to* 70 c.) *or* 13 ($1 *to* $4).

317 1 c. Type **49** .. .. .. .. .. .. 35 30
318 1 c. Common Starling (*Sturnus vulgaris*) .. 35 30
319 2 c. Golden Whistler (*Pachycephala pectoralis*) .. .. .. .. 40 30
320 2 c. Scarlet Robin (*Petroica multicolor*) .. 40 30
321 3 c. Rufous Fantail (*Rhipidura rufifrous*) .. 40 30
322 3 c. Peregrine Falcon (*Falco peregrinus*) .. 40 30
323 4 c. Java Sparrow (*Padda oryzivora*) .. 50 30
324 4 c. Barn Owl (*Tyto alba*) .. .. .. 50 30
325 5 c. Tahitian Lory (*Vini peruviana*) .. .. 50 30
326 5 c. White-breasted Wood Swallow (*Artamus leucorhynchus*) .. .. .. .. 50 30
327 6 c. Purple Swamphen (*Porphyrio porphyrio*) 50 30
328 6 c. Rock Dove (*Columba livia*) .. .. 50 30
329 10 c. Chestnut-breasted Mannikin (*Lonchura castaneothorax*) .. .. .. .. 70 30
330 10 c. Zebra Dove (*Geopelia striata*) .. .. 70 30
331 12 c. Eastern Reef Heron (*Egretta sacra*) .. 70 40
332 12 c. Common Mynah (*Acridotheres tristis*) .. 70 40
333 15 c. Whimbrel (*Numenius phaeopus*) (*horiz*) (8.5.81) .. .. .. .. .. 80 40
334 15 c. Black-browed Albatross (*Diomeda melanophris*) (*horiz*) (8.5.81) .. .. 80 40
335 20 c. American Golden Plover (*Pluvialis dominica*) (*horiz*) (8.5.81) .. .. .. 1·00 55
336 20 c. White Tern (*Gygis alba*) (*horiz*) (8.5.81) 1·00 55
337 25 c. Spotbill Duck (*Anas superciliosa*) (*horiz*) (8.5.81) .. .. .. .. .. 1·25 70
338 25 c. Brown Booby (*Sula leucogaster*) (*horiz*) (8.5.81) .. .. .. .. .. 1·25 70
339 30 c. Great Frigate Bird (*Fregata minor*) (*horiz*) (8.5.81) .. .. .. .. 1·50 80
340 30 c. Pintail (*Anas acuta*) (*horiz*) (8.5.81) .. 1·50 80
341 35 c. Long-billed Reed Warbler (*Conopoderas caffra caffra*) (14.1.82) .. .. .. 1·75 90
342 35 c. Pomarine Skua (*Stercorarius pomarinus*) (14.1.82) .. .. .. .. .. 1·75 90
343 40 c. Banded Rail (*Gallirallus philippensis goodsoni*) (14.1.82) .. .. .. 2·00 1·00
344 40 c. Spotted Triller (*Lalage maculosa pumila*) (14.1.82) .. .. .. .. .. 2·00 1·00
345 50 c. Royal Albatross (*Diomedea epomophora*) (14.1.82) .. .. .. .. .. 2·25 1·25
346 50 c. Stephen's Lory (*Vini stepheni*) (14.1.82) 2·25 1·25
347 70 c. Red-headed Parrot Finch (*Erythrura cyaneovirens*) (14.1.82) .. .. .. 4·50 2·50
348 70 c. Orange Dove (*Ptilinopus victor victor*) (14.1.82) .. .. .. .. .. 4·50 2·50
349 $1 Blue-headed Flycatcher (*Myiagra azureocapilla whitneyi*) (15.2.82) .. .. 5·50 3·25
350 $2 Red-bellied Flycatcher (*Myiagra vanikorensis rufiventris*) (15.5.82) .. .. 9·00 7·00
351 $4 Red Munia (*Amandava amandava*) (19.3.82) .. .. .. .. .. .. 15·00 12·00
352 $5 Flat-billed Kingfisher (*Halcyon recurvirostris*) (19.3.82) .. .. .. .. 17·00 14·00
317/52 .. .. .. .. .. *Set of* 36 75·00 50·00

The two designs of each value (1 c. to 70 c.) were printed together, *se-tenant*, in horizontal and vertical pairs throughout the sheet.

Nos. 341/8 are 35 × 27 mm and Nos. 349/52, which include a portrait of Queen Elizabeth II, 35 × 48 mm in size.

See also Nos. 475/94 for redrawn designs as Type **65**.

Nos. 353/90 are vacant.

**1981** (10 June). *Royal Wedding. T* **50** *and similar multicoloured designs. P* 14 ($1.40) *or* 13 × 13½ (*others*).

391 60 c. Type **50** .. .. .. .. .. 50 60
392 80 c. Lady Diana Spencer .. .. .. .. 60 75
393 $1.40, Prince Charles and Lady Diana (87 × 70 *mm*) .. .. .. .. .. 1·00 1·10
391/3 .. .. .. .. .. *Set of* 3 1·90 2·25

(**51**) **52** Footballers

**53** "The Holy Family"

**1981** (23 Nov). *International Year for Disabled Persons. Nos.* 391/3 *surch with T* **51** *on gold background.*

394 60 c. + 5 c. Type **50** .. .. .. .. 1·25 1·25
395 80 c. + 5 c. Lady Diana Spencer .. .. .. 1·75 1·75
396 $1. 40 + 5 c.Prince Charles and Lady Diana.. .. .. .. .. .. 3·25 3·25
394/6 .. .. .. .. .. *Set of* 3 5·50 5·50

Nos. 394/6 have commemorative inscriptions overprinted on the sheet margins.

**1981** (30 Nov). *World Cup Football Championship, Spain* (1982). *T* **52** *and similar horiz designs showing footballers. Multicoloured. P* 14.

397 12 c. Ball to left of stamp .. .. .. .. 35 35
398 12 c. Ball to right .. .. .. .. .. 35 35
399 15 c. Ball to right .. .. .. .. .. 40 40
400 15 c. Ball to left .. .. .. .. .. 40 40
401 20 c. Ball to left .. .. .. .. .. 50 50
402 20 c. Ball to right .. .. .. .. .. 50 50
403 25 c. Type **52** .. .. .. .. .. 55 55
404 25 c. "ESPANA 82" inscr on printed background .. .. .. .. .. 55 55
397/404 .. .. .. .. .. *Set of* 8 3·25 3·25
**MS**405 100 × 137 mm. 12 c. + 2 c., 15 c. + 2 c., 20 c. + 2 c., 25 c. + 2 c., each × 2. As Nos. 397/404 3·50 3·00

The two designs of each value were printed together, *se-tenant*, in horizontal pairs throughout the sheet.

**1981** (10 Dec). *Christmas. Details from Etchings by Rembrandt. T* **53** *and similar designs in purple-brown and gold. P* 14.

406 15 c. Type **53** .. .. .. .. .. 40 40
407 30 c. "Virgin with Child" .. .. .. .. 60 60
408 40 c. "Adoration of the Shepherds" (*horiz*) .. 75 75
409 50 c. "The Holy Family" (*horiz*) .. .. .. 85 85
406/9 .. .. .. .. .. *Set of* 4 2·40 2·40
**MS**410 Designs as Nos. 406/9 in separate miniature sheets, 65 × 82 mm or 82 × 65 mm, each with a face value of 80 c. + 5 c. P 14 × 13½ .. *Set of* 4 *sheets* 3·00 3·00

**54** Princess of Wales

(**55**)

**1982** (24 June). *21st Birthday of Princess of Wales. T* **54** *and similar vert designs. Multicoloured. P* 14.

411 70 c. Type **54** .. .. .. .. .. 70 70
412 $1 Prince and Princess of Wales .. .. 85 85
413 $2 Princess Diana (*different*) .. .. 1·60 1·75
411/13 .. .. .. .. .. *Set of* 3 2·75 3·00
**MS**414 82 × 91 mm. Nos. 411/13 .. .. 3·00 2·75

Nos. 411/13 were each printed in small sheets of 6 including two *se-tenant* stamp-size labels. The silver markings in the margins of the individual stamps differ for each position in the sheetlet.

**1982** (13 July). *Birth of Prince William of Wales* (1*st issue*). *Nos.* 391/3 *optd as T* **55**.

415 60 c. Type **50** (optd with T **55**) .. .. .. 2·00 1·50
a. Pair. Nos. 415/16 .. .. .. .. 4·00 3·00
416 60 c. Type **50** (optd "COMMEMORATING THE ROYAL BIRTH") .. .. .. .. 2·00 1·50
417 80 c. Lady Diana Spencer (optd with T **55**) .. 2·50 1·75
a. Pair. Nos. 417/18 .. .. .. .. 5·00 3·50
418 80 c. Lady Diana Spencer (optd "COMMEMORATING THE ROYAL BIRTH") .. 2·50 1·75
419 $1.40, Prince Charles and Lady Diana (87 × 70 *mm*) (optd as T **55**) .. .. 4·50 3·00
a. Pair. Nos. 419/20 .. .. .. .. 9·00 6·00
420 $1.40, Prince Charles and Lady Diana (87 × 70 *mm*) (optd "COMMEMORATING THE ROYAL BIRTH") .. .. .. 4·50 3·00
415/20 .. .. .. .. .. *Set of* 6 16·00 11·00

Nos. 415/16, 417/18 and 419/20 were each printed together in *se-tenant* pairs, horiz and vert, throughout the sheets.

**1982** (5 Aug). *Birth of Prince William of Wales* (2*nd issue*). *As Nos.* 411/14, *but inscr* "ROYAL BIRTH 21 JUNE 1982 PRINCE WILLIAM OF WALES". *Multicoloured. P* 14.

421 70 c. Type **54** .. .. .. .. .. 70 70
422 $1 Prince and Princess of Wales .. .. 85 85
423 $2 Princess Diana (*different*) .. .. 1·60 1·60
421/3.. .. .. .. .. *Set of* 3 2·75 2·75
**MS**424 81 × 91 mm. Nos. 421/3 .. .. .. 2·75 3·00

**56** "Virgin and Child" (12th-century sculpture)

**57** Aitutaki Bananas

**1982** (10 Dec). *Christmas. Religious Sculptures. T* **56** *and similar vert designs. Multicoloured. P* 13.

425 18 c. Type **56** .. .. .. .. .. 50 50
426 36 c. "Virgin and Child" (12th-century) .. 65 65
427 48 c. "Virgin and Child" (13th-century) .. 75 75
428 60 c. "Virgin and Child" (15th-century) .. 90 90
425/8 .. .. .. .. .. *Set of* 4 2·50 2·50
**MS**429 99 × 115 mm. As Nos. 425/8 but each with 2 c. charity premium .. .. .. .. 2·00 2·75

Nos. 425/8 were each printed in small sheets of 6 including one *se-tenant*, stamp size, label, depicting the Prince and Princess of Wales with Prince William.

**1983** (14 Mar). *Commonwealth Day. T* **57** *and similar horiz designs. Multicoloured. P* 13.

430 48 c. Type **57** .. .. .. .. .. 90 5
431 48 c. Ancient Ti'i image .. .. .. .. 90 5
432 48 c. Tourist canoeing.. .. .. .. .. 90 5
433 48 c. Captain William Bligh and chart .. 90 5
430/3 .. .. .. .. .. *Set of* 4 3·25 1·7

Nos. 430/3 were issued together, *se-tenant*, in blocks of four throughout the sheet.

**58** Scouts around Campfire

15th WORLD SCOUT JAMBOREE

(**59**)

**1983** (18 Apr). *75th Anniv of Boy Scout Movement, T* **58** *and similar horiz designs. Multicoloured. P* 13½ × 14.

434 36 c. Type **58** .. .. .. .. .. 1·00 45
435 48 c. Scout saluting .. .. .. .. 1·25 55
436 60 c. Scouts hiking .. .. .. .. 1·50 75
434/6 .. .. .. .. .. *Set of* 3 3·25 1·60
**MS**437 78 × 107 mm. As Nos. 434/6 but each with premium of 3 c. P 13 .. .. .. .. 3·25 2·75

**1983** (11 July). *15th World Scout Jamboree, Alberta, Canada. Nos.* 434/7 *optd with T* **59**.

438 36 c. Type **58** .. .. .. .. .. 1·00 45
439 48 c. Scout saluting .. .. .. .. 1·25 55
440 60 c. Scouts hiking .. .. .. .. 1·50 75
438/40 .. .. .. .. .. *Set of* 3 3·25 1·60
**MS**441 78 × 107 mm. As Nos. 438/40 but each with a premium of 3 c. .. .. .. .. .. 2·50 2·75

**60** Modern Sport Balloon

18c (**61**) $1.20 (**62**)

**1983** (22 July). *Bicentenary of Manned Flight. T* **60** *and similar vert designs showing different modern sport balloons. P* 14 × 13.

442 18 c. multicoloured .. .. .. .. 30 15
443 36 c. multicoloured .. .. .. .. 50 30
444 48 c. multicoloured .. .. .. .. 65 35
445 60 c. multicoloured .. .. .. .. 80 45
442/5 .. .. .. .. .. *Set of* 4 2·00 1·10
**MS**446 64 × 80 mm. $2.50, multicoloured (48½ × 28½ *mm*) .. .. .. .. .. 1·90 2·50

Nos. 442/5 were each issued in small sheets of 4 stamps.

**1983** (22 Sept). *Various stamps surch.*

(*a*) *Nos.* 335/48 *and* 352 *as T* **61**

447 18 c. on 20 c. American Golden Plover (*Pluvialis dominica*) .. .. .. 70 50
448 18 c. on 20 c. White Tern (*Gygis alba*) .. 70 50
449 36 c. on 25 c. Spotbill Duck (*Anas superciliosa*) .. .. .. .. .. 1·00 75
450 36 c. on 25 c. Brown Booby (*Sula leucogaster*) 1·00 75
451 36 c. on 30 c. Great Frigate Bird (*Fregata minor*) .. .. .. .. .. 1·00 75
452 36 c. on 30 c. Pintail (*Anas acuta*) .. .. 1·00 75
453 36 c. on 35 c. Long-billed Reed Warbler (*Conopoderas caffra caffra*) .. .. 1·00 75
454 36 c. on 35 c. Pomarine Skua (*Stercorarius pomarinus*) .. .. .. .. 1·00 75
455 48 c. on 40 c. Banded Rail (*Gallirallus philippensis goodsoni*) .. .. .. 1·50 75
456 48 c. on 40 c. Spotted Triller (*Lalage maculosa pumila*) .. .. .. .. 1·50 75
457 48 c. on 50 c. Royal Albatross (*Diomedea epomophora*) .. .. .. .. 1·50 75
458 48 c. on 50 c. Stephen's Lory (*Vini stepheni*) 1·50 75
459 72 c. on 70 c. Red-headed Parrot Finch (*Erythrura cyaneovirens*) .. .. .. 2·50 1·25
460 72 c. on 70 c. Orange Dove (*Ptilinopus victor victor*) .. .. .. .. .. 2·50 1·25
461 $5.60 on $5 Flat-billed Kingfisher (*Halcyon recurvirostris*) .. .. .. 13·00 7·50

(*b*) *Nos.* 392/3 *and* 412/13 *as T* **62**

462 96 c. on 80 c. Lady Diana Spencer (Gold) .. 4·75 2·50
a. Error. Surch on No. 417 .. .. .. 12·00
ab. Pair. Nos. 462/a/b .. .. .. .. 25·00
b. Error. Surch on No. 418 .. .. .. 12·00
463 96 c. on $1 Prince and Princess of Wales .. 4·25 2·00
464 $1.20 on $1.40, Prince Charles and Lady Diana (Gold) .. .. .. .. 4·75 2·50
a. Error. Surch on No. 419 .. .. .. 12·00
ab. Pair. Nos. 464a/b .. .. .. .. 25·00
b. Error. Surch on No. 420 .. .. .. 12·00
465 $1.20 on $2, Princess Diana .. .. .. 4·25 2·00
447/65 .. .. .. .. .. *Set of* 19 45·00 25·00

On Nos. 462 and 464 the gold surcharge is printed on a black obliterating panel over the original face value.

**63** International Mail  **64** "Madonna of the Chair"

**1983** (29 Sept). *World Communications Year. T* **63** *and similar vert designs. Multicoloured. P* 14 × 13½.
466 48 c. Type **63** .. .. .. .. .. 65 45
467 60 c. Telecommunications .. .. .. 85 60
468 96 c. Space satellites .. .. .. 1·25 90
466/8 .. .. .. .. .. *Set of* 3 2·50 1·75
**MS**469 126 × 53 mm. Nos. 466/8. P 13 .. .. 2·50 2·50

**1983** (21 Nov). *Christmas. 500th Birth Anniv of Raphael. T* **64** *and similar horiz designs. Multicoloured. P* 13½ × 14.
470 36 c. Type **64** .. .. .. .. .. 25 30
471 48 c. "The Alba Madonna" .. .. .. 35 40
472 60 c. "Conestabile Madonna" .. .. .. 50 55
470/2 .. .. .. .. .. *Set of* 3 1·00 1·10
**MS**473 95 × 116 mm. As Nos. 470/2, but each with a premium of 3 c. P 13 .. .. .. .. 1·25 1·40

**1983** (15 Dec). *Christmas. 500th Birth Anniv of Raphael. Children's Charity. Designs as Nos.* 470/2 *in separate miniature sheets* 46 × 47 *mm, but each with different frames and a face value of* 85 *c.* + 5 *c. Imperf.*
**MS**474 As Nos. 470/2 .. .. *Set of 3 sheets* 3·00 2·75

**65** Gouldian Finch  **66** Javelin-throwing

**1984** (13 Feb–2 July). *Birds (2nd series). Designs as Nos.* 317 *etc. but with redrawn frames and inscriptions as in T* **65**. *Multicoloured. P* 13 × 13½ *($3 to $9.60) or* 14 *(others).*
475 2 c. Type **65** .. .. .. .. .. 10 10
476 3 c. Common Starling .. .. .. .. 10 10
477 5 c. Scarlet Robin .. .. .. .. 10 10
478 10 c. Golden Whistler .. .. .. .. 10 10
479 12 c. Rufous Fantail .. .. .. .. 10 10
480 18 c. Peregrine Falcon .. .. .. .. 10 10
481 24 c. Barn Owl .. .. .. .. 15 20
482 30 c. Java Sparrow .. .. .. .. 20 25
483 36 c. White-breasted Wood Swallow .. .. 25 30
484 48 c. Tahitian Lory .. .. .. .. 30 35
485 50 c. Rock Dove (26 Mar) .. .. .. 35 40
486 60 c. Purple Swamphen (26 Mar) .. .. 40 45
487 72 c. Zebra Dove (26 Mar) .. .. .. 50 55
488 96 c. Chestnut-breasted Mannikin (26 Mar) .. 65 70
489 $1.20, Common Mynah (26 Mar) .. .. 80 85
490 $2.10, Eastern Reef Heron (30 Apr) .. 1·40 1·50
491 $3 Blue-headed Flycatcher (30 × 42 *mm*) (30 Apr) .. .. .. .. .. 2·00 2·10
492 $4.20, Red-bellied Flycatcher (30 × 42 *mm*) (5 June) .. .. .. .. .. 2·75 3·00
493 $5.60, Red Munia (30 × 42 *mm*) (5 June) 3·75 4·00
494 $9.60, Flat-billed Kingfisher (30 × 42 *mm*) (2 July) .. .. .. .. .. 6·25 6·50
475/94 .. .. .. .. .. *Set of* 20 17·00 18·00

**1984** (24 July). *Olympic Games, Los Angeles. T* **66** *and similar vert designs showing Memorial Coliseum and various events. Multicoloured. P* 13 × 13½.
495 36 c. Type **66** .. .. .. .. .. 30 35
496 48 c. Shot-putting .. .. .. .. 40 45
497 60 c. Hurdling .. .. .. .. .. 45 55
498 $2 Basketball .. .. .. .. 1·10 1·50
495/8 .. .. .. .. .. *Set of* 4 2·00 2·50
**MS**499 88 × 117 mm. As Nos. 495/8, but each with a charity premium of 5 c. .. .. .. .. 2·00 3·00

**1984** (21 Aug). *Olympic Gold Medal Winners. Nos.* 495/8 *optd as T* **209** *of Cook Islands in gold on black background.*
500 36 c. Type **66** (optd "Javelin Throw Tessa Sanderson Great Britain") .. .. .. 30 35
501 48 c. Shot-putting (optd "Shot Put Claudia Losch Germany") .. .. .. .. 40 45
502 60 c. Hurdling (optd "Heptathlon Glynis Nunn Australia") .. .. .. .. 45 55
503 $2 Basketball (optd "Team Basketball United States") .. .. .. .. 1·10 1·50
500/3 .. .. .. .. .. *Set of* 4 2·00 2·50

## ALTERED CATALOGUE NUMBERS

Any Catalogue numbers altered from the last edition are shown as a list in the introductory pages.

15.9.84 Birth
Prince Henry
$3

**67** Capt. William Bligh and Chart  **(68)**

**1984** (14 Sept). *"Ausipex" International Stamp Exhibition, Melbourne. T* **67** *and similar horiz designs. Multicoloured. P* 14.
504 60 c. Type **67** .. .. .. .. .. 1·25 1·25
505 96 c. H.M.S. *Bounty* and map .. .. .. 1·50 1·50
506 $1.40, Aitutaki stamps of 1974, 1979 and 1981 with map .. .. .. .. 2·25 2·25
504/6 .. .. .. .. .. *Set of* 3 4·50 4·50
**MS**507 85 × 113 mm. As Nos. 504/6, but each with a premium of 5 c. P 13½ .. .. .. .. 3·50 3·75

**1984** (10 Oct). *Birth of Prince Henry (1st issue). No.* 391 *surch with T* **68** *in gold.*
508 $3 on 60 c. Type **50** .. .. .. .. 4·00 3·00
On No. 508 the gold surcharge is printed on a black obliterating panel over the original face value.

**69** The Annunciation  **70** Princess Diana with Prince Henry

**1984** (16 Nov). *Christmas. Details from Altarpiece, St. Paul's Church, Palencia, Spain. T* **69** *and similar vert designs. Multicoloured. P* 13½ × 13.
509 36 c. Type **69** .. .. .. .. .. 30 35
510 48 c. The Nativity .. .. .. .. 40 45
511 60 c. The Epiphany .. .. .. .. 45 50
512 96 c. The Flight into Egypt .. .. .. 75 80
509/12 .. .. .. .. .. *Set of* 4 1·75 1·90
**MS**513 Designs as Nos. 509/12 in separate miniature sheets, each 45 × 53 mm and with a face value of 90 c. + 7 c. Imperf. .. .. *Set of 4 sheets* 3·00 3·25

**1984** (10 Dec). *Birth of Prince Henry (2nd issue). T* **70** *and similar vert designs. Multicoloured. P* 14.
514 48 c. Type **70** .. .. .. .. .. 55 45
515 60 c. Prince William with Prince Henry .. 60 50
516 $2.10, Prince and Princess of Wales with children .. .. .. .. .. 1·75 1·60
514/16 .. .. .. .. .. *Set of* 3 2·75 2·25
**MS**517 113 × 65 mm. As Nos. 514/16, but each with a face value of 96 c. + 7 c. P 13½ .. .. .. 2·25 2·40

**71** Grey Kingbird  **72** The Queen Mother, aged Seven

**1985** (22 Mar). *Birth Bicentenary of John J. Audubon (ornithologist). T* **71** *and similar vert designs showing original paintings. Multicoloured. P* 13.
518 55 c. Type **71** .. .. .. .. .. 60 60
519 65 c. Bohemian Waxwing .. .. .. 65 65
520 75 c. Summer Tanager .. .. .. .. 75 75
521 95 c. Common Cardinal .. .. .. .. 90 90
522 $1.15, White-winged Crossbill .. .. 1·10 1·10
518/22 .. .. .. .. .. *Set of* 5 3·50 3·50

**1985** (14 June). *Life and Times of Queen Elizabeth the Queen Mother. T* **72** *and similar horiz designs. Multicoloured. P* 13.
523 55 c. Type **72** .. .. .. .. .. 45 50
524 65 c. Engagement photograph, 1922 .. 50 55
525 75 c. With young Princess Elizabeth .. 60 65
526 $1.30, With baby Prince Charles .. .. 1·00 1·10
523/6 .. .. .. .. .. *Set of* 4 2·25 2·50
**MS**527 75 × 49 mm. $3 Queen Mother on her 63rd birthday .. .. .. .. .. 2·25 2·40
Nos. 523/6 were each printed in sheetlets of 4.
For these stamps in a miniature sheet see No. **MS**550.

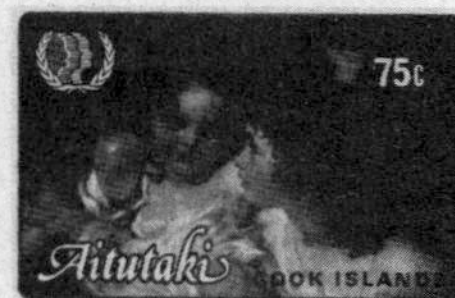


**73** "The Calmady Children" (T. Lawrence)

**1985** (16 Sept). *International Youth Year. T* **73** *and similar horiz designs. Multicoloured. P* 13.
528 75 c. Type **73** .. .. .. .. .. 75 55
529 90 c. "Madame Charpentier's Children" (Renoir) .. .. .. .. .. 85 65
530 $1.40, "Young Girls at Piano" (Renoir) .. 1·50 1·00
528/30 .. .. .. .. .. *Set of* 3 2·75 2·00
**MS**531 103 × 104 mm. As Nos. 528/30, but each with a premium of 10 c. .. .. .. .. 2·25 2·50

**74** "Adoration of the Magi" (Giotto) and *Giotto* Spacecraft

**1985** (15 Nov). *Christmas. Appearance of Halley's Comet* (1st *issue). T* **74** *and similar multicoloured designs. P* 13.
532 95 c. Type **74** .. .. .. .. .. 75 80
533 95 c. As Type **74** but showing *Planet A* spacecraft .. .. .. .. .. 75 80
534 $1.15, Type **74** .. .. .. .. .. 90 95
535 $1.15, As No. 533 .. .. .. .. 90 95
532/5 .. .. .. .. .. *Set of* 4 3·00 3·25
**MS**536 52 × 55 mm. $6.40, As Type **74** but without spacecraft (30 × 31 *mm*). Imperf .. .. 7·50 7·50
Nos. 532/3 and 534/5 were each printed together, *se-tenant*, in horizontal pairs throughout the sheets.

**75** Halley's Comet, A.D. 684 (from "Nuremberg Chronicle")  **76** Queen Elizabeth II on Coronation Day (from photo by Cecil Beaton)

**1986** (25 Feb). *Appearance of Halley's Comet (2nd issue). T* **75** *and similar multicoloured designs. P* 13½ × 13.
537 90 c. Type **75** .. .. .. .. .. 65 70
538 $1.25, Halley's Comet, 1066 (from Bayeux Tapestry) .. .. .. .. .. 85 90
539 $1.75, Halley's Comet, 1456 (from "Lucerne Chronicles") .. .. .. .. 1·25 1·40
537/9 .. .. .. .. .. *Set of* 3 2·50 2·75
**MS**540 107 × 82 mm. As Nos. 537/9, but each with a face value of 95 c. .. .. .. .. 1·90 2·50
**MS**541 65 × 80 mm. $4.20, "Melencolia I" (Albrecht Dürer woodcut) (61 × 76 *mm*). Imperf .. 2·75 3·50

**1986** (21 Apr). *60th Birthday of Queen Elizabeth II. T* **76** *and similar vert design. Multicoloured. P* 14.
542 95 c. Type **76** .. .. .. .. .. 85 85
**MS**543 58 × 68 mm. $4.20, As T **76**, but showing more of the portrait without oval frame. P 13½ 4·25 4·50
No. 542 was printed in sheetlets of five stamps and one stamp-size label at top left.

**77** Head of Statue of Liberty  **78** Prince Andrew and Miss Sarah Ferguson

**1986** (27 June). *Centenary of Statue of Liberty. T* **77** *and similar horiz design. Multicoloured. P* 14.
544 $1 Type **77** .. .. .. .. .. 70 75
545 $2.75, Statue of Liberty at sunset .. .. 1·90 2·00
**MS**546 91 × 79 mm. As Nos. 544/5, but each with a face value of $1.25. P 13½ .. .. .. 1·90 2·50

**1986** (23 July). *Royal Wedding. P* 14.
547 **78** $2 multicoloured .. .. .. .. 2·00 2·00
**MS**548 85×70 mm. **78** $5 mult. P 13½ .. .. 5·00 5·50
No. 547 was printed in sheetlets of 5 stamps and one stamp-size label at top left.

**1986** (4 Aug). *"Stampex '86" Stamp Exhibition, Adelaide. No.* **MS**507 *with "Ausipex" emblems obliterated in gold.*
**MS**549 As Nos. 504/6, but each with a premium of 5 c. .. .. .. .. .. .. 4·25 4·75
The "Stampex '86" exhibition emblem is overprinted on the sheet margin.

**1986** (4 Aug). *86th Birthday of Queen Elizabeth the Queen Mother. Nos. 523/6 in miniature sheet,* 132×82 *mm. P* 13½×13.
**MS**550 Nos. 523/6 .. .. .. .. .. 4·50 4·75

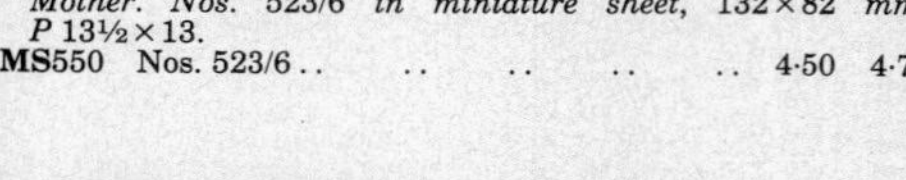

+10c

79 "St. Anne with Virgin and Child" (80)

**1986** (21 Nov). *Christmas. Paintings by Dürer. T* **79** *and similar vert designs. Multicoloured. P* 13½.
551 75 c. Type **79** .. .. .. .. .. 1·00 1·00
552 $1.35, "Virgin and Child" .. .. .. 1·50 1·50
553 $1.95, "The Adoration of the Magi" .. 2·00 2·00
554 $2.75, "Madonna of the Rosary" .. .. 2·50 2·50
551/4 .. .. .. .. .. *Set of* 4 6·25 6·25
**MS**555 88×125 mm. As Nos. 551/4, but each stamp with a face value of $1.65 .. .. 5·50 6·50

**1986** (25 Nov). *Visit of Pope John Paul II to South Pacific. Nos. 551/5 surch with T* **80** *in silver.*
556 75 c. + 10 c. Type **79** .. .. .. 1·50 1·50
557 $1.35 + 10 c. "Virgin and Child" .. .. 2·00 2·00
558 $1.95 + 10 c. "The Adoration of the Magi" 2·50 2·50
559 $2.75 + 10 c. "Madonna of the Rosary" .. 3·25 3·25
556/9 .. .. .. .. .. *Set of* 4 8·50 8·50
**MS**560 88 × 125 mm. As Nos. 556/9, but each stamp with a face value of $1.65 + 10 c. .. 9·00 9·50

2.50

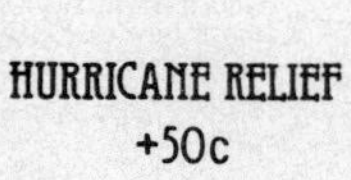


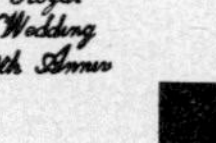


(81) (82)

**1987** (29 Apr). *Hurricane Relief Fund. Nos. 544/5, 547, 551/4 and 556/9 surch with T* **81** *in black (Nos. 563, 569) or silver (others).*
561 75 c. + 50 c. Type **79** .. .. .. .. 1·75 1·75
562 75 c. + 10 c. + 50 c. Type **79** .. .. 2·00 2·00
563 $1 + 50 c. Type **77** .. .. .. .. 2·25 2·25
564 $1.35 + 50 c. "Virgin and Child" (Dürer) .. 2·40 2·40
565 $1.35 + 10 c. + 50 c. "Virgin and Child" (Dürer) .. .. .. .. .. .. 2·50 2·50
566 $1.95 + 50 c. "The Adoration of the Magi" (Dürer) .. .. .. .. .. .. 3·00 3·00
567 $1.95 + 10 c. + 50 c. "The Adoration of the Magi" (Dürer) .. .. .. .. .. 3·00 3·00
568 $2 + 50 c. Type **78** .. .. .. .. 3·00 3·00
569 $2.75 + 50 c. Statue of Liberty at sunset .. 3·50 3·50
570 $2.75 + 50 c. "Madonna of the Rosary" (Dürer) .. .. .. .. .. .. 3·50 3·50
571 $2.75 + 10 c. + 50 c. "Madonna of the Rosary" (Dürer) .. .. .. .. .. 3·50 3·50
561/71 .. .. .. .. *Set of* 11 27·00 27·00

**1987** (20 Nov). *Royal Ruby Wedding. Nos. 391/3 surch as T* **82**.
572 $2.50 on 60 c. Type **50** .. .. .. 2·50 2·50
573 $2.50 on 80 c. Lady Diana Spencer .. .. 2·50 2·50
574 $2.50 on $1.40, Prince Charles and Lady Diana (87×70 *mm*) .. .. .. .. 2·50 2·50
572/4 .. .. .. .. .. *Set of* 3 6·75 6·75
On Nos. 572/4 the original values are obliterated in gold.



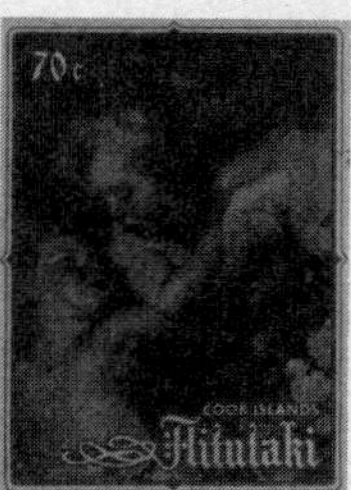

83 "Angels" (detail from "Virgin with Garland")

**1987** (10 Dec). *Christmas. T* **83** *and similar designs showing different details of angels from "Virgin with Garland" by Rubens. P* 13×13½.
575 70 c. multicoloured .. .. .. .. 85 85
576 85 c. multicoloured .. .. .. .. 1·00 1·00
577 $1.50, multicoloured .. .. .. .. 1·75 1·75
578 $1.85, multicoloured .. .. .. .. 2·00 2·00
575/8 .. .. .. .. .. *Set of* 4 5·00 5·00
**MS**579 92×120 mm. As Nos. 575/8, but each with a face value of 95 c. .. .. .. 6·00 6·50
**MS**580 96×85 mm. $6 "Virgin with Garland" (*diamond,* 56×56 *mm*). P 13 .. .. .. 8·00 8·50

84 Chariot Racing and Athletics

(Des G. Vasarhelyi. Litho Questa)

**1988** (22 Aug). *Olympic Games, Seoul. T* **84** *and similar horiz designs showing ancient and modern Olympic sports. Multicoloured. P* 14½.
581 70 c. Type **84** .. .. .. .. 60 70
582 85 c. Greek runners and football .. .. 70 80
583 95 c. Greek wrestling and handball .. .. 75 85
584 $1.40, Greek hoplites and tennis .. .. 1·25 1·40
581/4 .. .. .. .. .. *Set of* 4 3·00 3·25
**MS**585 103×101 mm. As Nos. 581 and 584, but each with face value of $2 .. .. .. 3·25 3·75

**1988** (10 Oct). *Olympic Medal Winners, Los Angeles. Nos. 581/4 optd as T* **235** *of Cook Islands.*
586 70 c. Type **84** (optd "FLORENCE GRIFFTH JOYNER UNITED STATES 100 M AND 200 M") .. .. .. .. 55 60
587 85 c. Greek runners and football (optd "GELINDO BORDIN ITALY MARATHON") .. .. .. .. 65 70
588 95 c. Greek wrestling and handball (optd "HITOSHI SAITO JAPAN JUDO") .. 70 75
589 $1.40, Greek hoplites and tennis (optd "STEFFI GRAF WEST GERMANY WOMEN'S TENNIS") .. .. .. 1·10 1·25
586/9 .. .. .. .. .. *Set of* 4 2·75 3·00

85 "Adoration of the Shepherds" (detail)

**1988** (2 Nov). *Christmas. T* **85** *and similar multicoloured designs showing paintings by Rembrandt. P* 13½.
590 55 c. Type **85** .. .. .. .. 70 70
591 70 c. "The Holy Family" .. .. .. 80 80
592 85 c. "Presentation in the Temple" .. .. 90 90
593 95 c. "The Holy Family" (*different*) .. .. 1·00 1·00
594 $1.15, "Presentation in the Temple" (*different*) .. .. .. .. .. 1·25 1·25
590/4 .. .. .. .. *Set of* 5 4·25 4·25
**MS**595 85 × 101 mm. $4.50, As Type **85** but 52 × 34 mm. P 14 .. .. .. .. 3·50 4·25

86 H.M.S. *Bounty* leaving Spithead and King George III

(Des Jennifer Toombs)

**1989** (3 July). *Bicentenary of Discovery of Aitutaki by Capt. Bligh. T* **86** *and similar horiz designs. Multicoloured. P* 13½×13.
596 55 c. Type **86** .. .. .. .. .. 80 80
597 65 c. Breadfruit plants .. .. .. 90 90
598 75 c. Old chart showing Aitutaki and Capt. Bligh .. .. .. .. .. .. 1·10 1·10
599 95 c. Native outrigger and H.M.S. *Bounty* off Aitutaki .. .. .. .. .. 1·50 1·50
600 $1.65, Fletcher Christian confronting Bligh .. .. .. .. .. .. 2·00 2·00
596/600 .. .. .. .. *Set of* 5 5·75 5·75
**MS**601 94×72 mm. $4.20, "Mutineers casting Bligh adrift" (Robert Dodd) (60×45 *mm*). P 13½ 5·00 6·00

87 "Apollo 11" Astronaut on Moon    88 Virgin Mary

**1989** (28 July). *20th Anniv of First Manned Landing on Moon. T* **87** *and similar horiz designs. Multicoloured. P* 13½×13.
602 75 c. Type **87** .. .. .. .. 55 60
603 $1.15, Conducting experiment on Moon .. 85 90
604 $1.80, Astronaut on Moon carrying equipment .. .. .. .. .. 1·40 1·50
602/4 .. .. .. .. *Set of* 3 2·50 2·75
**MS**605 105×86 mm. $6.40, Astronaut on Moon with U.S. flag (40×27 *mm*). P 13½ .. .. 4·75 5·50

**1989** (20 Nov). *Christmas. T* **88** *and similar vert designs showing details from "Virgin in the Glory" by Titian. Multicoloured. P* 13½×13.
606 70 c. Type **88** .. .. .. .. 70 70
607 85 c. Christ Child .. .. .. .. 85 85
608 95 c. Angel .. .. .. .. .. 95 95
609 $1.25, Cherubs .. .. .. .. 1·40 1·40
606/9 .. .. .. .. *Set of* 4 3·50 3·50
**MS**610 80×100 mm. $6 "Virgin in the Glory" (45×60 *mm*). P 13½ .. .. .. 5·00 6·00

Ninetieth Birthday

89 Human Comet striking Earth (90)

**1990** (16 Feb). *Protection of the Environment. T* **89** *and similar horiz design. Multicoloured. P* 13½×13.
611 $1.75, Type **89** .. .. .. .. 1·40 1·50
a. Horiz pair. Nos. 611/12 .. .. 2·75 3·00
612 $1.75, Comet's tail .. .. .. 1·40 1·50
**MS**613 108×43 mm. $3 As Nos. 611/12 .. 2·50 3·00
Nos. 611/12 were printed together, *se-tenant,* in horizontal pairs throughout the sheet, each pair forming a composite design.

**1990** (16 July). *90th Birthday of Queen Elizabeth the Queen Mother. No.* **MS**550 *optd with T* **90** *in black on gold on each stamp.*
**MS**614 132×82 mm. Nos. 523/6 .. .. 4·00 4·25

COMMEMORATING
65th BIRTHDAY
OF H.M. QUEEN
ELIZABETH II

91 "Madonna of the Basket" (Correggio)    (92)

(Litho Questa)

**1990** (28 Nov). *Christmas. Religious Paintings. T* **91** *and similar multicoloured designs. P* 14.
615 70 c. Type **91** .. .. .. .. 55 55
616 85 c. "Virgin and Child" (Morando) .. .. 70 70
617 95 c. "Adoration of the Child" (Tiepolo) .. 80 80
618 $1.75, "Mystic Marriage of St. Catherine" (Memling) .. .. .. .. .. 1·40 1·40
615/18 .. .. .. .. *Set of* 4 3·00 3·00
**MS**619 165×93 mm. $6 "Donne Triptych" (Memling) (*horiz*) .. .. .. .. 4·25 4·50

**1990** (5 Dec). *"Birdpex '90" Stamp Exhibition, Christchurch, New Zealand. Nos. 349/50 optd as T* **245** *of Cook Islands.*
620 $1 Blue-headed Flycatcher .. .. 1·00 1·00
621 $2 Red-bellied Flycatcher .. .. 1·50 1·50

**1991** (22 Apr). *65th Birthday of Queen Elizabeth II. No.* 352 *optd with T* **92**.

| | | | |
|---|---|---|---|
| 622 | $5 Flat-billed Kingfisher (*Halcyon recurvirostris*) .. .. .. | 4·00 | 4·00 |

**93** "The Holy Family" (A. Mengs)

(Des G. Vasarhelyi. Litho Questa)

**1991** (13 Nov). *Christmas. Religious Paintings. T* **93** *and similar vert designs. Multicoloured. P* 14.

| | | | |
|---|---|---|---|
| 623 | 80 c. Type **93** .. .. .. .. | 55 | 60 |
| 624 | 90 c. "Virgin and the Child" (Lippi) .. | 60 | 65 |
| 625 | $1.05, "Virgin and Child" (A. Dürer) .. | 70 | 75 |
| 626 | $1.75, "Adoration of the Shepherds" (G. de la Tour) .. .. .. .. | 1·10 | 1·25 |
| 623/6 | .. .. .. .. *Set of* 4 | 2·75 | 3·00 |
| **MS**627 | 79×103 mm. $6 "The Holy Family" (Michelangelo) .. .. .. .. .. | 4·00 | 4·25 |

OFFICIAL STAMPS

**O.H.M.S.**

(O 1)

**1978** (3 Nov)–**79**. *Nos.* 98/105, 107/10 *and* 227/8 *optd or surch (Nos.* O8/9 *and* O15) *as Type* O 1.

| | | | |
|---|---|---|---|
| O 1 | 1 c. *Nautilus macromphallus* .. .. | 55 | 10 |
| O 2 | 2 c. *Harpa major* .. .. .. | 65 | 10 |
| O 3 | 3 c. *Phalium strigatum* .. .. .. | 65 | 10 |
| O 4 | 4 c. *Cypraea talpa* (Gold) .. .. | 65 | 10 |
| O 5 | 5 c. *Mitra stictica* .. .. .. | 65 | 10 |
| O 6 | 8 c. *Charonia tritonis* .. .. .. | 75 | 10 |
| O 7 | 10 c. *Murex triremis* .. .. .. | 85 | 15 |
| O 8 | 15 c. on 60 c. *Strombus latissimus* .. | 1·50 | 20 |
| O 9 | 18 c. on 60 c. *Strombus latissimus* .. | 1·50 | 20 |
| O10 | 20 c. *Oliva sericea* (Gold) .. .. | 1·50 | 20 |
| O11 | 50 c. Union Jack, Queen Victoria and island map .. .. .. .. | 2·50 | 55 |
| O12 | 60 c. *Strombus latissimus* .. .. | 3·25 | 70 |
| O13 | $1 *Biplex perca* .. .. .. | 4·00 | 1·00 |
| O14 | $2 Queen Elizabeth II and *Terebra maculata* (20.2.79) .. .. .. .. | 6·50 | 1·50 |
| O15 | $4 on $1 Balcony scene, 1953 (Sil.) (20.2.79) | 9·00 | 2·50 |
| O16 | $5 Queen Elizabeth II and *Cypraea hesitata* (20.2.79) .. .. .. .. | 9·50 | 3·50 |
| O1/16 | .. .. .. .. .. *Set of* 16 | 40·00 | 9·50 |

These stamps were originally only sold to the public cancelled-to-order and not in unused condition.

They were made available to overseas collectors in mint condition during 1980.

75c

O.H.M.S. O.H.M.S.

(O 2) (O 3)

**1985** (9 Aug)–**90**. (*a*) *Nos.* 351/2, 475 *and* 477/94 *optd or surch as Type* O **2** *by foil embossing in blue* ($14, $18) *or emerald (others).*

| | | | |
|---|---|---|---|
| O17 | 2 c. Type **65** .. .. .. .. | 10 | 10 |
| O18 | 5 c. Scarlet Robin .. .. .. | 10 | 10 |
| O19 | 10 c. Golden Whistler .. .. .. | 10 | 10 |
| O20 | 12 c. Rufous Fantail .. .. .. | 10 | 10 |
| O21 | 18 c. Peregrine Falcon .. .. .. | 10 | 10 |
| O22 | 20 c. on 24 c. Barn Owl .. .. .. | 10 | 15 |
| O23 | 30 c. Java Sparrow .. .. .. | 20 | 25 |
| O24 | 40 c. on 36 c. White-breasted Wood Swallow | 25 | 30 |
| O25 | 50 c. Rock Dove .. .. .. .. | 35 | 40 |
| O26 | 55 c. on 48 c. Tahitian Lory .. .. | 35 | 40 |
| O27 | 60 c. Purple Swamphen .. .. .. | 40 | 45 |
| O28 | 65 c. on 72 c. Zebra Dove .. .. | 45 | 50 |
| O29 | 80 c. on 96 c. Chestnut-breasted Mannikin | 55 | 60 |
| O30 | $1.20, Common Mynah (15.6.88) .. | 80 | 85 |
| O31 | $2.10, Eastern Reef Heron (15.6.88) .. | 1·40 | 1·50 |
| O32 | $3 Blue-headed Flycatcher (30×42 *mm*) (1.10.86) .. .. .. .. | 2·00 | 2·10 |
| O33 | $4.20, Red-bellied Flycatcher (30×42 *mm*) (1.10.86) .. .. .. | 2·75 | 3·00 |
| O34 | $5.60, Red Munia (30×42 *mm*) (1.10.86) | 3·75 | 4·00 |
| O35 | $9.60, Flat-billed Kingfisher (30×42 *mm*) (1.10.86) .. .. .. | 6·25 | 6·50 |
| O36 | $14 on $4 Red Munia (35×48 *mm*) .. | 9·25 | 9·50 |
| O37 | $18 on $5 Flat-billed Kingfisher (35×48 *mm*) (2.7.90) .. .. .. | 12·00 | 12·50 |

(*b*) *Nos.* 430/3 *surch as Type* O **3** *by gold foil embossing*

| | | | |
|---|---|---|---|
| O38 | 75 c. on 48 c. Type **57** .. .. .. | 50 | 55 |
| O39 | 75 c. on 48 c. Ancient Ti'i image .. | 50 | 55 |
| O40 | 75 c. on 48 c. Tourist canoeing .. .. | 50 | 55 |
| O41 | 75 c. on 48 c. Captain William Bligh and chart .. .. .. .. | 50 | 55 |
| O17/41 | .. .. .. .. *Set of* 25 | 35·00 | 38·00 |

## PENRHYN ISLAND

Stamps of COOK ISLANDS were used on Penrhyn Island from late 1901 until the issue of the surcharged stamps in May 1902.

| PRICES FOR STAMPS ON COVER TO 1945 | |
|---|---|
| Nos. 1/8 | *from* × 4 |
| Nos. 9/10 | *from* × 50 |
| Nos. 11/13 | — |
| Nos. 14/18 | *from* × 3 |
| Nos. 19/23 | *from* × 2 |
| Nos. 24/37 | *from* × 3 |
| Nos. 38/40 | *from* × 5 |

### A. NEW ZEALAND DEPENDENCY

The island of Penrhyn, previously under British protection, was annexed by New Zealand on 11 June 1901.

***Stamps of New Zealand overprinted or surcharged***

PENRHYN ISLAND.
½ PENI.
(1)

PENRHYN ISLAND.
TAI PENI.
(2) 1d.

PENRHYN ISLAND.
2½ PENI.
(3)

**1902** (5 May). 1902 *issue surch with* **T 1, 2** *and* **3**.

(*a*) *Thick, white Pirie paper. No wmk. P* 11

1 **27** 2½d. blue (R.) .. .. .. .. .. 1·50 3·75
a. "½" and "P" spaced (all stamps in 8th vert row) .. .. .. 13·00 23·00

(*b*) *Thin, hard Basted Mills paper.* W **38** *of New Zealand.*

(i) *P* 11

3 **42** 1d. carmine (Br.) .. .. .. £700 £750

(ii) *P* 14

4 **23** ½d. green (R.) .. .. .. 80 3·50
a. No stop after "ISLAND" .. .. 90·00 £100
5 **42** 1d. carmine (Br.) .. .. .. 3·25 8·50
*a. Pale carmine* .. .. .. 3·25 8·50

(iii) *P* 11×14

7 **42** 1d. carmine (Br.) .. .. .. £650 £700

(iv) *Mixed perfs*

8 **42** 1d. carmine (Br.) .. .. .. £650

(*c*) *Thin, hard Cowan paper.* W **38** *of New Zealand.* (i) *P* 14

9 **23** ½d. green (R.) .. .. .. 90 3·50
a. No stop after "ISLAND" (R. 10/6) .. 90·00 £110
10 **42** 1d. carmine (B.) .. .. .. 90 2·75
a. No stop after "ISLAND" (R. 10/6) .. 40·00 55·00

(ii) *P* 11×14

11 **42** 1d. carmine (B.) .. .. .. £6000

(iii) *Mixed perfs*

12 **23** ½d. green (R.) .. .. .. £750 £800
13 **42** 1d. carmine (B.) .. .. .. £225 £275

PENRHYN ISLAND.
(4)

Toru Pene.
(5) 3d.

Ono Pene.
(6) 6d.

Tahi Silingi.
(7) 1s.

**1903** (28 Feb). 1902 *issue surch with name at top,* **T 4**, *and values at foot,* **T 5/7**. W **43** *of New Zealand. P* 11.

14 **28** 3d. yellow-brown (B.) .. .. .. 9·00 16·00
15 **31** 6d. rose-red (B.) .. .. .. 15·00 28·00
16 **34** 1s. brown-red (B.) .. .. .. 45·00 50·00
17 1s. bright red (B.) .. .. .. 45·00 48·00
18 1s. orange-red (B.) .. .. .. 50·00 50·00
14/16 .. .. .. .. *Set of* 3 60·00 85·00

**1914–15.** *Surch with* **T 1** (½d.) *or optd with* **T 4** *at top and surch with* **T 6/7** *at foot.*

19 **51** ½d. yellow-green (C.) (5.14) .. .. 90 4·00
a. No stop after "ISLAND" .. .. 35·00 70·00
b. No stop after "PENI" (R. 3/17) .. 75·00 £120
20 ½d. yellow-green (Verm.) (1.15) .. .. 70 4·00
a. No stop after "ISLAND" .. .. 16·00 38·00
b. No stop after "PENI" (R. 3/5, 3/17) .. 38·00 70·00
22 **52** 6d. carmine (B.) (8.14) .. .. 27·00 60·00
23 1s. vermilion (B.) (8.14) .. .. 45·00 80·00
19/23 .. .. .. .. *Set of* 4 65·00 £130

The "no stop after ISLAND" variety occurs on R. 1/4, 1/10, 1/16, 1/22, 6/4, 6/10, 6/16 and 6/22 of the carmine surcharge, No. 19, and on these positions plus R. 1/12, 1/24, 6/12 and 6/24 for the vermilion, No. 20.

**1917–20.** *King George V stamps optd with name only.* **T 4**. W **43** *of New Zealand. P* 14×14½.

24 **60** 2½d. blue (R.) (10.20) .. .. 1·50 4·00
a. No stop after "ISLAND" (R. 10/8) .. 95·00 £150
b. Perf 14×13½ .. .. 3·00 7·00
c. Vert pair. Nos. 24/4b .. .. 50·00 75·00
25 3d. chocolate (B.) (6.18) .. .. 9·50 35·00
a. Perf 14×13½ .. .. 9·50 35·00
b. Vert pair. Nos. 25/5a .. .. 70·00 £130
26 6d. carmine (B.) (1.18) .. .. 5·00 14·00
a. No stop after "ISLAND" (R. 10/8) .. £170 £275
b. Perf 14×13½ .. .. 7·00 19·00
c. Vert pair. Nos. 26/6b .. .. 55·00 £100
27 1s. vermilion (B.) (12.17) .. .. 12·00 27·00
a. No stop after "ISLAND" (R. 10/8) .. £250 £375
b. Perf 14×13½ .. .. 15·00 35·00
c. Vert pair. Nos. 27/7b .. .. £110 £180
24/7 .. .. .. .. *Set of* 4 25·00 70·00

**1917–20.** *Optd as* **T 4**. *Typo.* W **43** *of New Zealand. P* 14×15.

28 **61** ½d. green (R.) (2.20) .. .. 65 1·25
a. No stop after "ISLAND" (R. 2/24) .. 55·00 80·00
b. Narrow spacing .. .. 5·50 8·50
29 1½d. slate (R.) (11.17) .. .. 5·00 8·50
a. Narrow spacing .. .. 17·00 32·00
30 1½d. orange-brown (R.) (2.19) .. .. 60 7·50
a. Narrow spacing .. .. 5·00 24·00
31 3d. chocolate (B.) (6.19) .. .. 3·00 10·00
a. Narrow spacing .. .. 15·00 38·00
28/31 .. .. .. .. *Set of* 4 8·25 25·00

The narrow spacing variety occurs on R. 1/5–8, 4/21–4, 7/5–8 and 9/21–4.

(Recess P.B.)

**1920** (23 Aug). *As Types of Cook Islands but inscr* "PENRHYN". *No wmk. P* 14.

32 **9** ½d. black and emerald .. .. 1·00 5·50
a. Part imperf block of 4 .. .. £1200
33 **10** 1d. black and deep red .. .. 1·25 5·50
34 **11** 1½d. black and deep violet .. .. 6·50 11·00
35 **12** 3d. black and red .. .. 2·25 5·00
36 **13** 6d. red-brown and sepia .. .. 3·25 17·00
37 **14** 1s. black and slate-blue .. .. 9·00 17·00
32/7 .. .. .. .. *Set of* 6 21·00 55·00

No. 32a comes from sheets on which two rows were imperforate between horizontally and the second row additionally imperforate vertically.

Examples of the ½d. and 1d. with centre inverted were not supplied to the Post Office.

(Recess Govt Printing Office, Wellington)

**1927–29.** *As Types of Cook Islands, but inscr* "PENRHYN". W **43**. *P* 14.

38 **9** ½d. black and green (5.29) .. .. 2·50 10·00
39 **10** 1d. black and deep carmine (14.3.28) .. 2·50 7·50
40 **16** 2½d. red-brown and dull blue (10.27) .. 1·75 13·00
38/40 .. .. .. .. *Set of* 3 6·00 27·00

Cook Islands stamps superseded those of Penrhyn Islands on 15 March 1932. Separate issues were resumed in 1973.

### B. PART OF COOK ISLANDS

The following issues are for use in all the islands of the Northern Cook Islands group.

**PRINTERS.** The note above No. 33 of Aitutaki concerning printers and gum also applies here. All issues, except Nos. 41A/52A and **MS**412, are on paper treated with fluorescent security markings. The markings can be found inverted or omitted.

PENRHYN

NORTHERN
(8)

PENRHYN
NORTHERN
(9)

**1973** (24 Oct–14 Nov). *Nos.* 228/45 *of Cook Is optd with T* 8 (*without* "NORTHERN" *on* $1, $2).
A. *Without fluorescent security markings. Gum arabic*
B. *With fluorescent security markings. PVA gum*

| | | A. | | B. | |
|---|---|---|---|---|---|
| 41 | 1 c. multicoloured | 80 | — | 10 | 1 |
| 42 | 2 c. multicoloured | 1·25 | — | 10 | 1 |
| 43 | 3 c. multicoloured | 1·75 | — | 20 | 1 |
| 44 | 4 c. multicoloured (No. 233) | 2·00 | — | 10 | 1 |
| | a. Optd on Cook Is No. 232 | 60·00 | — | † | |
| 45 | 5 c. multicoloured | 2·50 | — | 10 | 1 |
| 46 | 6 c. multicoloured | 2·50 | — | 20 | 3 |
| 47 | 8 c. multicoloured | 2·75 | — | 30 | 4 |
| 48 | 15 c. multicoloured | 4·25 | — | 45 | 5 |
| 49 | 20 c. multicoloured | † | | 1·50 | 80 |
| 50 | 50 c. multicoloured | 16·00 | — | 1·75 | 1·75 |
| 51 | $1 multicoloured | 28·00 | — | 2·50 | 2·25 |
| 52 | $2 multicoloured (14.11) | 48·00 | — | 2·50 | 2·50 |
| 41A/52A | *Set of* 11 | £100 | — | † | |
| 41B/52B | *Set of* 12 | † | | 8·75 | 7·50 |

**1973** (14 Nov). *Royal Wedding. Nos.* 450/2 *of Cook Is optd as T* 9 *in silver.*

53 **138** 25 c. multicoloured .. .. .. 85 2
54 – 30 c. multicoloured .. .. .. 85 2
55 – 50 c. multicoloured .. .. .. 85 2
53/5 .. .. .. .. *Set of* 3 2·25 5

**10** *Ostracion sp*

**11** Penrhyn Stamps of 1902

**1974** (15 Aug)–**75**. *Multicoloured.* (*a*) *T* **10** *and similar horiz designs showing fishes. P* 13½

56 ½ c. Type **10** .. .. .. .. 50 4
57 1 c. *Monodactylus argenteus* .. .. .. 70 4
58 2 c. *Pomacanthus imperator* .. .. .. 80 4
59 3 c. *Chelmon rostratus* .. .. .. 80 4
60 4 c. *Chaetodon ornatissimus* .. .. .. 80 4
61 5 c. *Chaetodon melanotus* .. .. .. 80 4
62 8 c. *Chaetodon raffessi* .. .. .. 80 4
63 10 c. *Chaetodon ephippium* .. .. .. 85 4
64 20 c. *Pygoplites diacanthus* .. .. .. 1·75 4
65 25 c. *Heniochus acuminatus* .. .. .. 1·75 4
66 60 c. *Plectorhynchus chaetodonoides* .. .. 2·50 9
67 $1 *Balistipus undulatus* .. .. .. 2·75 1·2

(*b*) *Larger designs,* 63×25 *mm. P* 13×12½

68 $2 Birds-eye view of Penryhn (12.2.75) .. 6·00 8·5
69 $5 Satellite view of Australasia (12.3.75) 6·50 6·0
56/69 .. .. .. .. *Set of* 14 25·00 19·0

**1974** (27 Sept). *Centenary of Universal Postal Union. T* **11** *and similar vert design. Multicoloured. P* 13.

| | | | |
|---|---|---|---|
| 70 | 25 c. Type **11** .. .. .. .. .. | 20 | 20 |
| 71 | 50 c. Stamps of 1920 .. .. .. .. .. | 35 | 35 |

Each value was issued in sheets of 8 stamps and 1 label.

**12** "Adoration of the Kings" (Memling)

**1974** (30 Oct). *Christmas. T* **12** *and similar horiz designs. Multicoloured. P* 13.

| | | | |
|---|---|---|---|
| 72 | 5 c. Type **12** .. .. .. .. .. | 20 | 10 |
| 73 | 10 c. "Adoration of the Shepherds" (Hugo van der Goes) .. .. .. .. | 25 | 10 |
| 74 | 25 c. "Adoration of the Magi" (Rubens) .. | 40 | 15 |
| 75 | 30 c. "The Holy Family" (Borgianni) .. .. | 50 | 25 |
| 72/5 | .. .. .. .. .. *Set of* 4 | 1·25 | 50 |

**13** Churchill giving "V" Sign

**(14)**

**1974** (30 Nov.) *Birth Centenary of Sir Winston Churchill. T* **13** *and similar vert design. P* 13.

| | | | |
|---|---|---|---|
| 76 | 30 c. agate and gold .. .. .. .. | 90 | 70 |
| 77 | 50 c. myrtle-green and gold .. .. .. | 1·10 | 80 |

Design:—50 c. Full-face portrait.

**1975** (24 July). *"Apollo-Soyuz" Space Project. No. 69 optd with T* **14**.

| | | | |
|---|---|---|---|
| 78 | $5 Satellite view of Australasia .. .. | 3·50 | 4·50 |

**15** "Virgin and Child" (Bouts)

**16** "Pietà"

**1975** (21 Nov). *Christmas. T* **15** *and similar vert designs showing the "Virgin and Child". Multicoloured. P* 14 × 13.

| | | | |
|---|---|---|---|
| 79 | 7 c. Type **15** .. .. .. .. .. | 30 | 10 |
| 80 | 15 c. Leonardo da Vinci .. .. .. .. | 60 | 20 |
| 81 | 35 c. Raphael .. .. .. .. .. | 95 | 35 |
| 79/81 | .. .. .. .. *Set of* 3 | 1·75 | 60 |

**1976** (19 Mar). *Easter and 500th Birth Anniv of Michelangelo. T* **16** *and similar vert designs. P* 14 × 13.

| | | | |
|---|---|---|---|
| 82 | 15 c. sepia and gold .. .. .. .. | 25 | 15 |
| 83 | 20 c. blackish purple and gold .. .. .. | 30 | 15 |
| 84 | 35 c. myrtle-green and gold .. .. .. | 40 | 20 |
| 82/4 | .. .. .. .. *Set of* 3 | 85 | 45 |
| **MS**85 | 112 × 72 mm. Nos. 82/4 .. .. .. | 85 | 1·25 |

Each value was issued in sheets of 8 stamps and 1 label.

**17** "Washington crossing the Delaware" (E. Leutze)

**18** Running

**1976** (20 May). *Bicentenary of American Revolution. T* **17** *and similar vert designs. Multicoloured. P* 13.

| | | | |
|---|---|---|---|
| 86 | 30 c. } Type **17** .. .. .. .. .. | 50 | 15 |
| 87 | 30 c. } | 50 | 15 |
| 88 | 30 c. } | 50 | 15 |
| 89 | 50 c. } "The Spirit of '76" (A. M. Willard) .. | 60 | 20 |
| 90 | 50 c. } | 60 | 20 |
| 91 | 50 c. } | 60 | 20 |
| 86/91 | .. .. .. .. *Set of* 6 | 3·00 | 95 |
| **MS**92 | 103 × 103 mm. Nos. 86/91. P 13 .. .. | 3·00 | 3·50 |

Nos. 86/8 and 89/91 were each printed together, *se-tenant*, in horizontal strips of 3 throughout the sheet, forming composite designs. Each sheet includes 3 stamp-size labels. Type **17** shows the left-hand stamp of the 30 c. design.

**1976** (9 July). *Olympic Games, Montreal. T* **18** *and similar horiz designs. Multicoloured. P* 14.

| | | | |
|---|---|---|---|
| 93 | 25 c. Type **18** .. .. .. .. .. | 25 | 15 |
| 94 | 30 c. Long Jumping .. .. .. .. | 30 | 15 |
| 95 | 75 c. Throwing the Javelin .. .. .. | 55 | 25 |
| 93/5 | .. .. .. .. *Set of* 3 | 1·00 | 50 |
| **MS**96 | 86 × 128 mm. Nos. 93/5. P 14 × 13 .. | 1·00 | 1·75 |

**19** "The Flight into Egypt"

**20** The Queen in Coronation Robes

**1976** (20 Oct). *Christmas. Dürer Engravings. T* **19** *and similar horiz designs. P* 13.

| | | | |
|---|---|---|---|
| 97 | 7 c. black and silver .. .. .. .. | 10 | 10 |
| 98 | 15 c. steel blue and silver .. .. .. | 20 | 15 |
| 99 | 35 c. violet and silver .. .. .. .. | 30 | 25 |
| 97/9 | .. .. .. .. *Set of* 3 | 55 | 45 |

Designs:—15 c. "Adoration of the Magi"; 35 c. "The Nativity".

**1977** (24 Mar). *Silver Jubilee. T* **20** *and similar vert designs. Multicoloured. P* 13.

| | | | |
|---|---|---|---|
| 100 | 50 c. Type **20** .. .. .. .. | 60 | 70 |
| 101 | $1 Queen and Prince Philip .. .. .. | 70 | 75 |
| 102 | $2 Queen Elizabeth II .. .. .. | 1·00 | 1·00 |
| 100/2 | .. .. .. .. *Set of* 3 | 2·10 | 2·25 |
| **MS**103 | 128 × 87 mm. Nos. 100/2. P 13 .. .. | 2·75 | 2·75 |

Stamps from the miniature sheet have silver borders.

**21** "The Annunciation"

**22** Iiwi

**1977** (23 Sept). *Christmas. T* **21** *and similar designs showing illustrations by J. S. von Carolsfeld. P* 13.

| | | | |
|---|---|---|---|
| 104 | 7 c. light stone, purple-brown and gold .. | 30 | 15 |
| 105 | 15 c. pale rose, deep maroon and gold .. | 50 | 15 |
| 106 | 35 c. blackish green, pale green and gold .. | 90 | 30 |
| 104/6 | .. .. .. .. *Set of* 3 | 1·50 | 55 |

Designs:—15 c. "The Announcement to the Shepherds"; 35 c. "The Nativity".

**1978** (19 Jan). *Bicentenary of Discovery of Hawaii. T* **22** *and similar vert designs showing extinct Hawaiian birds or artefacts. Multicoloured. P* 13.

| | | | |
|---|---|---|---|
| 107 | 20 c. Type **22** .. .. .. .. .. | 70 | 30 |
| 108 | 20 c. Elgin cloak .. .. .. .. | 70 | 30 |
| 109 | 30 c. Apapane .. .. .. .. .. | 80 | 40 |
| 110 | 30 c. Feather image of a god .. .. .. | 80 | 40 |
| 111 | 35 c. Moorhen .. .. .. .. .. | 80 | 45 |
| 112 | 35 c. Feather cape, helmet and staff .. .. | 80 | 45 |
| 113 | 75 c. Hawaii O-o .. .. .. .. | 1·25 | 80 |
| 114 | 75 c. Feather image and cloak .. .. .. | 1·25 | 80 |
| 107/14 | .. .. .. .. *Set of* 8 | 6·50 | 3·50 |
| **MS**115 | Two sheets each 78 × 119 mm containing (a) Nos. 107, 109, 111, 113; (b) Nos. 108, 110, 112, 114 .. .. .. .. .. | 6·50 | 8·00 |

Nos. 107/8, 109/10, 111/12 and 113/14 were each printed together, *se-tenant*, in horizontal and vertical pairs throughout the sheet.

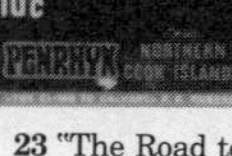


**23** "The Road to Calvary"

**24** Royal Coat of Arms

**1978** (10 Mar). *Easter and 400th Birth Anniv of Rubens. T* **23** *and similar vert designs. Multicoloured. P* 13.

| | | | |
|---|---|---|---|
| 116 | 10 c. Type **23** .. .. .. .. .. | 10 | 10 |
| 117 | 15 c. "Christ on the Cross" .. .. .. | 15 | 15 |
| 118 | 35 c. "Christ with Straw" .. .. .. | 25 | 25 |
| 116/18 | .. .. .. .. *Set of* 3 | 45 | 45 |
| **MS**119 | 87 × 138 mm. Nos. 116/18 .. .. .. | 60 | 1·25 |

Stamps from No. **MS**119 are slightly larger (28 × 36 mm.)

**1978** (17 Apr). *Easter. Children's Charity. Designs as Nos. 116/18 in separate miniature sheets. 49 × 68 mm, each with a face value of 60 c. + 5 c. P* 12½–13.

| | | | |
|---|---|---|---|
| **MS**120 | As Nos. 116/18 .. .. *Set of 3 sheets* | 1·25 | 2·25 |

**1978** (24 May). *25th Anniv of Coronation. T* **24** *and similar vert designs. P* 13.

| | | | |
|---|---|---|---|
| 121 | 90 c. black, gold and deep lilac .. .. | 55 | 75 |
| 122 | 90 c. multicoloured .. .. .. .. | 55 | 75 |
| 123 | 90 c. black, gold and deep bluish green .. | 55 | 75 |
| 121/3 | .. .. .. .. *Set of* 3 | 1·50 | 2·00 |
| **MS**124 | 75 × 122 mm. Nos. 121/3 .. .. .. | 1·50 | 2·25 |

Designs:—No. 122, Queen Elizabeth II; No. 123, New Zealand coat of arms.

Nos. 121/3 were printed together in small sheets of 6, containing two *se-tenant* strips of 3, with horizontal gutter margin between.

**25** "Madonna of the Pear"

**26** Sir Rowland Hill and G.B. Penny Black Stamp

**1978** (29 Nov). *Christmas. 450th Death Anniv of Dürer. T* **25** *and similar vert design. Multicoloured. P* 14.

| | | | |
|---|---|---|---|
| 125 | 30 c. Type **25** .. .. .. .. | 50 | 30 |
| 126 | 35 c. "The Virgin and Child with St. Anne" .. | 50 | 30 |
| **MS**127 | 101 × 60 mm. Nos. 125/6. P 13½ .. .. | 1·00 | 1·50 |

Nos. 125/6 were each printed in small sheets of 6.

**1979** (26 Sept). *Death Centenary of Sir Rowland Hill. T* **26** *and similar vert designs. Multicoloured. P* 13½ × 14.

| | | | |
|---|---|---|---|
| 128 | 75 c. Type **26** .. .. .. .. | 75 | 65 |
| 129 | 75 c. 1974 Centenary of Universal Postal Union 25 c. and 50 c. commemoratives .. | 75 | 65 |
| 130 | 90 c. Sir Rowland Hill .. .. .. .. | 90 | 80 |
| 131 | 90 c. 1978 25th anniv of Coronation 90 c. (Queen Elizabeth II) commemorative .. | 90 | 80 |
| 128/31 | .. .. .. .. *Set of* 4 | 3·00 | 2·75 |
| **MS**132 | 116 × 58 mm. Nos. 128/31 .. .. | 3·00 | 3·50 |

Stamps from No. **MS**132 have cream backgrounds.

Nos. 128/9 and 130/1 were each printed together, *se-tenant*, in horizontal and vertical pairs throughout small sheets of 8.

**27** Max and Moritz

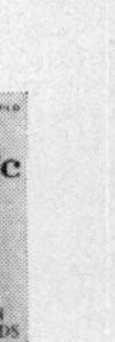


**28** "Christ carrying Cross" (Book of Ferdinand II)

**1979** (20 Nov). *International Year of the Child. Illustrations from Max and Moritz stories by Wilhelm Busch. T* **27** *and similar horiz designs. Multicoloured. P* 13.

| | | | |
|---|---|---|---|
| 133 | 12 c. Type **27** .. .. .. .. | 20 | 10 |
| 134 | 12 c. Max and Moritz looking down chimney .. | 20 | 10 |
| 135 | 12 c. Max and Moritz making off with food .. | 20 | 10 |
| 136 | 12 c. Cook about to beat dog .. .. .. | 20 | 10 |
| 137 | 15 c. Max sawing through bridge .. .. | 25 | 10 |
| 138 | 15 c. Pursuer approaching bridge .. .. | 25 | 10 |
| 139 | 15 c. Bridge collapsing under pursuer .. | 25 | 10 |
| 140 | 15 c. Pursuer in river .. .. .. .. | 25 | 10 |
| 141 | 20 c. Baker locking shop .. .. .. | 30 | 20 |
| 142 | 20 c. Max and Moritz coming out of hiding .. | 30 | 20 |
| 143 | 20 c. Max and Moritz falling in dough .. | 30 | 20 |
| 144 | 20 c. Max and Moritz after being rolled into buns by baker .. .. .. | 30 | 20 |
| 133/44 | .. .. .. .. *Set of* 12 | 2·75 | 1·50 |

Nos. 133/6, 137/40 and 141/4 were each printed together, *se-tenant*, in sheets of 4, either with or without labels containing extracts from the books on the top and bottom selvedge.

**1980** (28 Mar). *Easter. Scenes from 15th-century Prayer Books. T* **28** *and similar vert designs. Multicoloured. P* 13.

| | | | |
|---|---|---|---|
| 145 | 12 c. Type **28** .. .. .. .. | 10 | 10 |
| 146 | 20 c. "The Crucifixion" (William Vrelant, Book of Duke of Burgundy) .. .. .. | 15 | 15 |
| 147 | 35 c. "Descent from the Cross" (Book of Ferdinand II) .. .. .. .. .. | 25 | 25 |
| 145/7 | .. .. .. .. *Set of* 4 | 45 | 45 |
| **MS**148 | 111 × 65 mm. Nos. 145/7 .. .. | 45 | 1·00 |

Stamps from No. **MS**148 have cream borders.

**1980** (28 Mar). *Easter. Children's Charity. Designs as Nos. 145/7 in separate miniature sheets 54 × 85 mm, each with a face value of 70 c. + 5 c.*

| | | | |
|---|---|---|---|
| **MS**149 | As Nos. 145/7 .. .. *Set of 3 sheets* | 75 | 1·50 |

## PRICES OF SETS

Set prices are given for many issues, generally those containing three stamps or more. Definitive sets include one of each value or major colour change, but do not cover different perforations, die types or minor shades. Where a choice is possible the set prices are based on the cheapest versions of the stamps included in the listings.

29 "Queen Elizabeth, 1937" (Sir Gerald Kelly)  30 Falk Hoffman, D.D.R. (platform diving) (gold)

**1980** (17 Sept). *80th Birthday of Queen Elizabeth the Queen Mother. P* 13.
150 **29** $1 multicoloured .. .. .. .. 2·00 1·50
**MS**151 55 × 84 mm. **29** $2.50 multicoloured .. 3·00 2·75

**1980** (14 Nov). *Olympic Games, Moscow. Medal Winners. T* **30** *and similar vert designs. Multicoloured. P* 13½.
152 10 c. Type **30** .. .. .. .. .. 10 10
153 10 c. Martina Jaschke, D.D.R. (platform diving) (gold) .. .. .. .. 10 10
154 20 c. Tomi Polkolainen, Finland (archery) (gold) .. .. .. .. 15 15
155 20 c. Kete Losaberidse, U.S.S.R. (archery) (gold) .. .. .. .. 15 15
156 30 c. Czechoslovakia (football) (gold) .. .. 20 20
157 30 c. D.D.R. (football) (silver) .. .. .. 20 20
158 50 c. Barbel Wockel, D.D.R. (200-metre dash) (gold) .. .. .. .. 30 30
159 50 c. Pietro Mennea, Italy (200-metre dash) (gold) .. .. .. .. 30 30
152/9 .. .. .. .. .. *Set of* 8 1·40 1·40
**MS**160 150 × 106 mm. Nos. 152/9. P 13 .. .. 1·40 1·75
Stamps from No. **MS**160 have gold borders.
Nos. 152/3, 154/5, 156/7 and 158/9 were each printed together, *se-tenant*, in horizontal pairs throughout the sheet.

31 "The Virgin of Counsellors" (Luis Dalmau)  32 Amatasi

**1980** (5 Dec). *Christmas. Paintings. T* **31** *and similar vert designs. Multicoloured. P* 13.
161 20 c. Type **31** .. .. .. .. .. 15 15
162 35 c. "Virgin and Child" (Serra brothers) .. 20 20
163 50 c. "The Virgin of Albocacer" (Master of the Porciuncula) .. .. .. .. 30 30
161/3 .. .. .. .. .. *Set of* 3 60 60
**MS**164 135 × 75 mm. Nos. 161/3 .. .. .. 1·25 1·25

**1980** (5 Dec). *Christmas. Children's Charity. Designs as Nos.* 161/3 *in separate miniature sheets,* 54 × 77 *mm, each with a face value of* 70 c. + 5 c.
**MS**165 As Nos. 161/3 .. .. *Set of 3 sheets* 2·75 2·75

**1981** (16 Feb–21 Sept). *Sailing Craft and Ships (1st series). Multi-coloured designs as T* **32**. *P* 14 *(Nos.* 166/85*),* 13 × 14½ *(Nos.* 186/205*) or* 13½ *(Nos.* 206/8*).*
166 1 c. Type **32** .. .. .. .. .. 20 15
167 1 c. Ndrua .. .. .. .. .. 20 15
168 1 c. Waka .. .. .. .. .. 20 15
169 1 c. Tongiaki .. .. .. .. .. 20 15
170 3 c. Va'a Teu'ua .. .. .. .. 40 15
171 3 c. *Victoria*, 1500 .. .. .. .. 40 15
172 3 c. *Golden Hind*, 1560 .. .. .. 40 15
173 3 c. *Boudeuse*, 1760 .. .. .. .. 40 15
174 4 c. H.M.S. *Bounty*, 1787 .. .. .. 40 15
175 4 c. *L'Astrolabe*, 1811 .. .. .. 40 15
176 4 c. *Star of India*, 1861 .. .. .. 40 15
177 4 c. *Great Republic*, 1853 .. .. .. 40 15
178 6 c. *Balcutha*, 1886 .. .. .. .. 40 15
179 6 c. *Coonatto*, 1863 .. .. .. .. 40 15
180 6 c. *Antiope*, 1866 .. .. .. .. 40 15
181 6 c. *Teaping*, 1863 .. .. .. .. 40 15
182 10 c. *Preussen*, 1902 .. .. .. .. 45 35
183 10 c. *Pamir*, 1921 .. .. .. .. 45 35
184 10 c. *Cap Hornier*, 1910 .. .. .. 45 35
185 10 c. *Patriarch*, 1869 .. .. .. .. 45 35
186 15 c. As Type **32** (16 Mar) .. .. .. 45 50
187 15 c. As No. 167 (16 Mar) .. .. .. 45 50
188 15 c. As No. 168 (16 Mar) .. .. .. 45 50
189 15 c. As No. 169 (16 Mar) .. .. .. 45 50
190 20 c. As No. 170 (16 Mar) .. .. .. 45 50
191 20 c. As No. 171 (16 Mar) .. .. .. 45 50
192 20 c. As No. 172 (16 Mar) .. .. .. 45 50
193 20 c. As No. 173 (16 Mar) .. .. .. 45 50
194 30 c. As No. 174 (16 Mar) .. .. .. 45 60
195 30 c. As No. 175 (16 Mar) .. .. .. 45 60
196 30 c. As No. 176 (16 Mar) .. .. .. 45 60
197 30 c. As No. 177 (16 Mar) .. .. .. 45 60
198 50 c. As No. 178 (16 Mar) .. .. .. 85 1·25
199 50 c. As No. 179 (16 Mar) .. .. .. 85 1·25
200 50 c. As No. 180 (16 Mar) .. .. .. 85 1·25
201 50 c. As No. 181 (16 Mar) .. .. .. 85 1·25
202 $1 As No. 182 (15 May) .. .. .. 1·50 1·25
203 $1 As No. 183 (15 May) .. .. .. 1·50 1·25
204 $1 As No. 184 (15 May) .. .. .. 1·50 1·25
205 $1 As No. 185 (15 May) .. .. .. 1·50 1·25
206 $2 *Cutty Sark*, 1869 (26 June) .. .. 4·00 2·75

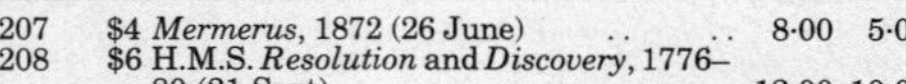
207 $4 *Mermerus*, 1872 (26 June) .. .. 8·00 5·00
208 $6 H.M.S. *Resolution* and *Discovery*, 1776–80 (21 Sept) .. .. .. .. 12·00 10·00
166/208 .. .. .. .. *Set of* 43 42·00 35·00
Nos. 186/205 are 41 × 25 mm and Nos. 206/8 47 × 33 mm in size.
On Nos. 166/205 the four designs of each value were printed together, *se-tenant*, in blocks of 4 throughout the sheet.
For redrawn versions of these designs in other face values see Nos. 337/55.

33 "Jesus at the Grove" (Veronese)  34 Prince Charles as Young Child

**1981** (5 Apr). *Easter. Paintings. T* **33** *and similar vert designs. Multicoloured. P* 14.
218 30 c. Type **33** .. .. .. .. .. 25 20
219 40 c. "Christ with Crown of Thorns" (Titian) .. 30 25
220 50 c. "Pietá" (Van Dyck) .. .. .. 40 30
218/20 .. .. .. .. *Set of* 3 85 65
**MS**221 110 × 68 mm. Nos. 218/20. P 13½ .. 2·00 2·25

**1981** (5 Apr). *Easter. Children's Charity. Designs as Nos.* 218/20 *in separate miniature sheets* 70 × 86 *mm., each with a face value of* 70 c. + 5 c. *P* 13½.
**MS**222 As Nos. 218/20 .. .. *Set of 3 sheets* 2·00 2·75

**1981** (10 July). *Royal Wedding. T* **34** *and similar vert designs. Multicoloured. P* 14.
223 40 c. Type **34** .. .. .. .. .. 35 40
224 50 c. Prince Charles as schoolboy .. .. 40 45
225 60 c. Prince Charles as young man .. .. 45 50
226 70 c. Prince Charles in ceremonial Naval uniform .. .. .. .. .. 50 55
227 80 c. Prince Charles as Colonel-in-Chief, Royal Regiment of Wales .. .. .. 55 60
223/7 .. .. .. .. *Set of* 5 2·00 2·25
**MS**228 99 × 89 mm. Nos. 223/7 .. .. 2·00 2·50
Nos. 223/7 were each printed in small sheets of 6 including one *se-tenant* stamp-size label.

**1981** (30 Nov). *International Year for Disabled Persons. Nos.* 223/8 *surch as T* **51** *of Aitutaki.*
229 40 c.+ 5 c. Type **34** .. .. .. .. 50 75
230 50 c.+ 5 c. Prince Charles as schoolboy .. 60 85
231 60 c.+ 5 c. Prince Charles as young man .. 70 95
232 70 c.+ 5 c. Prince Charles in ceremonial Naval uniform .. .. .. .. 75 85
233 80 c.+ 5 c. Prince Charles as Colonel-in-Chief, Royal Regiment of Wales.. .. .. 75 1·10
229/33 .. .. .. .. *Set of* 5 3·00 4·00
**MS**234 99 × 89 mm. As Nos. 229/33, but 10 c. premium on each stamp .. .. .. 3·50 5·00
Nos. 229/34 have commemorative inscriptions overprinted on the sheet margins.

35 Footballer  36 "The Virgin on a Crescent"

**1981** (7 Dec). *World Cup Football Championship, Spain* (1982). *T* **35** *and similar vert designs showing footballers. Multicoloured. P* 13.
235 15 c. Type **35** .. .. .. .. .. 15 15
236 15 c. Footballer wearing orange jersey with black and mauve stripes.. .. .. 15 15
237 15 c. Player in blue jersey .. .. .. 15 15
238 35 c. Player in blue jersey .. .. .. 25 25
239 35 c. Player in red jersey .. .. .. 25 25
240 35 c. Player in yellow jersey with green stripes 25 25
241 50 c. Player in orange jersey .. .. .. 35 35
242 50 c. Player in mauve jersey .. .. .. 35 35
243 50 c. Player in black jersey .. .. .. 35 35
235/43 .. .. .. .. *Set of* 9 2·00 2·00
**MS**244 113 × 151 mm. As Nos. 235/43, but each stamp with a premium of 3 c. .. .. .. 4·00 2·75
The three designs of each value were printed together, *se-tenant*, in horizontal strips of 3 throughout the sheet.

**1981** (15 Dec). *Christmas. Details from Engravings by Dürer. T* **36** *and similar vert designs in violet, deep reddish purple and stone. P* 13 × 13½.
245 30 c. Type **36** .. .. .. .. .. 65 65
246 40 c. "The Virgin at the Fence" .. .. 80 80
247 50 c. "The Holy Virgin and Child" .. .. 90 90
245/7 .. .. .. .. *Set of* 3 2·10 2·10
**MS**248 134 × 75 mm. As Nos. 245/7, but each stamp with a premium of 2 c. .. .. .. 2·00 2·25
**MS**249 Designs as Nos. 245/7 in separate miniature sheets, 58 × 85 mm, each with a face value of 70 c. + 5 c. P 14 × 13½ .. .. *Set of 3 sheets* 2·25 2·25

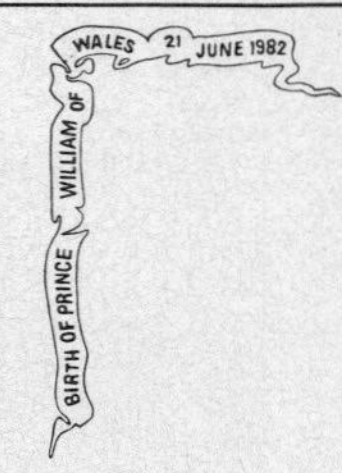


37 Lady Diana Spencer as Baby  (38)

**1982** (1 July). *21st Birthday of Princess of Wales. T* **37** *and similar vert designs. Multicoloured. P* 14.
250 30 c. Type **37** .. .. .. .. .. 30 30
251 50 c. As young child .. .. .. .. 45 45
252 70 c. As schoolgirl .. .. .. .. 60 60
253 80 c. As teenager .. .. .. .. 80 80
254 $1.40, As young lady.. .. .. .. 1·25 1·25
250/4 .. .. .. .. *Set of* 5 3·00 3·00
**MS**255 87 × 110 mm. Nos. 250/4 .. .. .. 3·00 3·50

**1982** (30 July). *Birth of Prince William of Wales. Nos.* 223/8 *optd with T* **38**.
256 40 c. Type **34** .. .. .. .. .. 90 80
257 50 c. Prince Charles as schoolboy .. .. 1·25 90
258 60 c. Prince Charles as young man .. .. 1·40 1·00
259 70 c. Prince Charles in ceremonial Naval uniform .. .. .. .. .. 1·60 1·25
260 80 c. Prince Charles as Colonel-in-Chief, Royal Regiment of Wales .. .. .. 2·00 1·60
256/60 .. .. .. .. *Set of* 5 6·50 5·00
**MS**261 99 × 89 mm. Nos. 256/60 .. .. 8·50 7·00

**1982** (6 Sept). *Birth of Prince William of Wales. As Nos.* 250/5 *but with changed inscriptions. Multicoloured. P* 13½ × 14.
262 30 c. As Type **37** (inscr "21 JUNE 1982. BIRTH OF PRINCE WILLIAM OF WALES") .. 25 30
263 30 c. As Type **37** (inscr "COMMEMORATING THE BIRTH OF PRINCE WILLIAM OF WALES") .. .. .. .. 25 30
264 50 c. As No. 251 (inscr. "21 JUNE 1982. BIRTH OF PRINCE WILLIAM OF WALES") .. 40 45
265 50 c. As No. 251 (inscr "COMMEMORATING THE BIRTH OF PRINCE WILLIAM OF WALES") .. .. .. .. 40 45
266 70 c. As No. 252 (inscr "21 JUNE 1982. BIRTH OF PRINCE WILLIAM OF WALES") .. 60 65
267 70 c. As No. 252 (inscr "COMMEMORATING THE BIRTH OF PRINCE WILLIAM OF WALES") .. .. .. .. 60 65
268 80 c. As No. 253 (inscr "21 JUNE 1982. BIRTH OF PRINCE WILLIAM OF WALES") .. 60 65
269 80 c. As No. 253 (inscr "COMMEMORATING THE BIRTH OF PRINCE WILLIAM OF WALES") .. .. .. .. 60 65
270 $1.40, As No. 254 (inscr "21 JUNE 1982. BIRTH OF PRINCE WILLIAM OF WALES") .. .. .. 1·10 1·25
271 $1.40, As No. 254 (inscr "COMMEMORATING THE BIRTH OF PRINCE WILLIAM OF WALES") .. .. 1·10 1·25
262/71 .. .. .. .. *Set of* 10 5·50 6·00
**MS**272 88 × 109 mm. As **MS**255 (stamps inscr "21 JUNE 1982. ROYAL BIRTH PRINCE WILLIAM OF WALES") .. .. .. .. 2·75 3·25
Nos. 262/3, 264/5, 266/7, 268/9 and 270/1 were printed together *se-tenant*, in sheets of 5 stamps and 1 label, there being three examples of the "21 JUNE 1982 . . ." and two of the "COMMEMORATING . . ." in each sheet.

39 "Virgin and Child" (detail, Joos Van Cleve)  40 Red Coral

**1982** (10 Dec). *Christmas. Details from Renaissance Paintings of "Virgin and Child". T* **39** *and similar vert designs. Multi-coloured. P* 14 × 13½.
273 35 c. Type **39** .. .. .. .. .. 30 40
274 48 c. "Virgin and Child" (Filippino Lippi) .. 45 55
275 60 c. "Virgin and Child" (Cima da Conegliano) 60 70
273/5 .. .. .. .. *Set of* 3 1·25 1·50
**MS**276 134 × 73 mm. As Nos. 273/5 but each with 2 c. charity premium. P 13 .. .. .. 1·60 2·00
Nos. 273/5 were each printed in small sheets of 6 including one *se-tenant*, stamp size, label, depicting the Prince and Princess of Wales with Prince William.

**1982** (10 Dec). *Christmas. Children's Charity. Designs as Nos.* 273/5, *but without frames, in separate miniature sheets,* 60 × 85 *mm, each with a face value of* 70 c. + 5 c. *P* 13.
**MS**277 As Nos. 273/5 .. .. *Set of 3 sheets* 1·75 1·90

**1983** (14 Mar). *Commonwealth Day. T* **40** *and similar vert designs. Multicoloured. P* 13.
278 60 c. Type **40** .. .. .. .. .. 50 60
279 60 c. Aerial view of Penrhyn atoll .. .. 50 60
280 60 c. Eleanor Roosevelt on Penrhyn during Second World War .. .. .. .. 50 60
281 60 c. Map of South Pacific .. .. .. 50 60
278/81 .. .. .. .. *Set of* 4 1·75 2·10
Nos. 278/81 were issued together, *se-tenant*, in blocks of four throughout the sheet.

XV WORLD JAMBOREE CANADA 1983

41 Scout Emblem and Blue Tropical Flower (42)

**1983** (5 Apr). *75th Anniv of Boy Scout Movement. T* **41** *and similar horiz designs. Multicoloured. P* 13 × 14.
282 36 c. Type **41** .. .. .. .. .. .. 1·00 45
283 48 c. Emblem and pink flower .. .. 1·25 55
284 60 c. Emblem and orange flower .. .. 1·40 75
282/4 .. .. .. .. *Set of* 3 3·25 1·60
**MS**285 86 × 46 mm. $2 As 48 c., but with elements of design reversed .. .. .. .. .. 2·40 2·75

**1983** (8 July). *15th World Scout Jamboree, Alberta, Canada. Nos.* 282/5 *optd with T* **42**.
286 36 c. Type **41** .. .. .. .. .. .. 1·00 40
287 48 c. Emblem and pink flower .. .. 1·25 55
288 60 c. Emblem and orange flower .. .. 1·40 75
286/8 .. .. .. .. *Set of* 3 3·25 1·60
**MS**289 86 × 46 mm. $2 As 48 c., but with elements of design reversed .. .. .. .. .. 2·40 2·75

43 School of Sperm Whales 44 *Mercury* (cable ship)

**1983** (29 July). *Whale Conservation. T* **43** *and similar vert designs. Multicoloured. P* 13.
290 8 c. Type **43** .. .. .. .. .. .. 65 30
291 15 c. Harpooner preparing to strike .. .. 90 45
292 35 c. Whale attacking boat .. .. .. 1·40 75
293 60 c. Dead whales marked with flags .. .. 2·25 1·00
294 $1 Dead whales on slipway .. .. .. 2·50 1·40
290/4 .. .. .. .. *Set of* 5 7·00 3·50

**1983** (23 Sept). *World Communications Year. T* **44** *and similar horiz designs. Multicoloured. P* 13.
295 36 c. Type **44** .. .. .. .. .. 40 35
296 48 c. Men watching cable being laid .. .. 50 45
297 60 c. *Mercury (different)* .. .. .. 70 60
295/7 .. .. .. .. *Set of* 3 1·40 1·25
**MS**298 115 × 90 mm. As Nos. 295/7 but each with charity premium of 3 c. .. .. .. .. 1·50 1·60
On No. **MS**298 the values are printed in black and have been transposed with the World Communications Year logo.

**1983** (26 Sept). *Various stamps surch as T* **200** *of Cook Islands.*

(a) *Nos.* 182/5, 190/7 *and* 206
299 18 c. on 10 c. *Preussen*, 1902 .. .. .. 20 20
300 18 c. on 10 c. *Pamir*, 1921 .. .. .. 20 20
301 18 c. on 10 c. *Cap Hornier*, 1910 .. .. 20 20
302 18 c. on 10 c. *Patriarch*, 1869 .. .. .. 20 20
303 36 c. on 20 c. Va'a Teu'ua .. .. .. 35 35
304 36 c. on 20 c. *Victoria*, 1500 .. .. .. 35 35
305 36 c. on 20 c. *Golden Hind*, 1560 .. .. 35 35
306 36 c. on 20 c. *Boudeuse*, 1760 .. .. .. 35 35
307 36 c. on 30 c. H.M.S. *Bounty*, 1787 .. .. 35 35
308 36 c. on 30 c. *L'Astrolabe*, 1811 .. .. 35 35
309 36 c. on 30 c. *Star of India*, 1861 .. .. 35 35
310 36 c. on 30 c. *Great Republic*, 1853 .. .. 35 35
311 $1.20 on $2 *Cutty Sark*, 1869 .. .. 1·40 1·40

(b) *Nos.* 252/3
312 72 c. on 70 c. Princess Diana as schoolgirl .. 2·00 1·50
313 96 c. on 80 c. Princess Diana as teenager .. 2·25 1·75
299/313 .. .. .. *Set of* 15 8·50 7·00

**1983** (28 Oct). *Nos.* 208, 225/6, 254 *and* 268/9 *surch as T* **200** *of Cook Islands.*
314 48 c. on 60 c. Prince Charles as young man (Gold) .. .. .. .. .. .. 3·50 1·50
a. Error. Surch on No. 258 .. .. .. 6·00 5·00
315 72 c. on 70 c. Prince Charles in ceremonial Naval uniform .. .. .. .. 4·00 1·75
a. Error. Surch on No. 259 .. .. .. 7·00 5·00
316 96 c. on 80 c. As No. 253 (inscr "21 JUNE 1982 . . .") .. .. .. .. .. 2·75 1·00
a. Error. Surch on No. 260 .. .. .. 8·00 5·50
317 96 c. on 80 c. As No. 253 (inscr "COMMEMORATING. . .") .. .. .. .. 1·75 1·00
318 $1.20 on $1.40, Princess Diana as young lady 3·25 1·50
319 $5.60 on $6, H.M.S. *Resolution* and *Discovery*, 1776–80 .. .. .. .. 12·00 6·50
314/19 .. .. .. .. *Set of* 6 25·00 12·00

45 George Cayley's Airship Design, 1837

**1983** (31 Oct). *Bicentenary of Manned Flight. T* **45** *and similar horiz designs. Multicoloured. P* 13. *A. Inscr* "NORTHERN COOK ISLANS". *B. Corrected spelling optd in black on silver over original inscription.*

| | | A | | B | |
|---|---|---|---|---|---|
| 320 | 36 c. Type **45** .. .. .. | 75 | 60 | 30 | 35 |
| 321 | 48 c. Dupuy De Lome's man-powered airship, 1872 .. | 1·00 | 70 | 40 | 45 |
| 322 | 60 c. Santos Dumont's sixth airship, 1901 .. .. | 1·25 | 1·00 | 45 | 50 |
| 323 | 96 c. Lebaudy's practical airship, 1902 .. .. .. | 2·00 | 1·50 | 75 | 80 |
| 324 | $1.32 LZ 127 *Graf Zeppelin*, 1929 .. .. .. | 3·00 | 2·00 | 1·00 | 1·10 |
| 320/4 | .. .. *Set of* 5 | 7·25 | 5·50 | 2·75 | 3·00 |
| **MS**325 | 113 × 138 mm. Nos. 320/4 | 8·00 | 11·00 | 2·75 | 4·25 |

46 "Madonna in the Meadow" 47 Waka

**1983** (30 Nov). *Christmas. 500th Birth Anniv of Raphael. T* **46** *and similar vert designs. Multicoloured. P* 13.
326 36 c. Type **46** .. .. .. .. .. 35 40
327 42 c. "Tempi Madonna" .. .. .. .. 35 40
328 48 c. "The Smaller Cowper Madonna" .. 45 50
329 60 c. "Madonna della Tenda" .. .. .. 55 60
326/9 .. .. .. .. *Set of* 4 1·60 1·75
**MS**330 87 × 115 mm. As Nos. 326/9 but each with a charity premium of 3 c. .. .. .. .. 1·75 2·00

**1983** (1 Dec). *Nos.* 266/7, 227 *and* 270/1 *surch as T* **200** *of Cook Islands.*
331 72 c. on 70 c. As No. 252 (inscr "21 JUNE 1982. . .") .. .. .. .. .. 2·00 1·25
332 72 c. on 70 c. As No. 252 (inscr "COMMEMORATING. . .") .. .. .. .. 1·25 90
333 96 c. on 80 c. Prince Charles as Colonel-in-Chief, Royal Regiment of Wales. .. 2·00 1·00
334 $1.20 on $1.40, As No. 254 (inscr "21 JUNE 1982. . .") .. .. .. .. .. 2·25 1·25
335 $1.20 on $1.40, As No. 254 (inscr "COMMEMORATING. . .") .. .. .. .. 1·75 1·00
331/5 .. .. .. .. *Set of* 5 8·50 5·00

**1983** (28 Dec). *Christmas. 500th Birth Anniv of Raphael. Children's Charity. Designs as Nos.* 326/9 *in separate miniature sheets,* 65 × 84 *mm, each with a face value of* 75 c. + 5 c. *P* 13.
**MS**336 As Nos. 326/9 .. .. *Set of* 4 *sheets* 3·00 3·50

**1984** (8 Feb–15 June). *Sailing Craft and Ships (2nd series). Designs as Nos.* 166, *etc. but with redrawn frames, inscriptions and compass rose at top right as in T* **47**. *Multicoloured. P* 13 × 13½ *($9.60),* 13 *($3, $5) or* 11 *(others).*
337 2 c. Type **47** .. .. .. .. .. .. 10 10
338 4 c. Amatasi .. .. .. .. .. .. 10 10
339 5 c. Ndrua .. .. .. .. .. .. 10 10
340 8 c. Tongiaki .. .. .. .. .. .. 10 10
341 10 c. *Victoria* .. .. .. .. .. 10 10
342 18 c. *Golden Hind* .. .. .. .. .. 10 10
343 20 c. *Boudeuse* .. .. .. .. .. 10 15
344 30 c. H.M.S. *Bounty* .. .. .. .. 20 25
345 36 c. *L'Astrolabe* .. .. .. .. .. 25 30
346 48 c. *Great Republic* .. .. .. .. 30 35
347 50 c. *Star of India* (21 Mar) .. .. .. 35 40
348 60 c. *Coonatto* (21 Mar) .. .. .. .. 40 45
349 72 c. *Antiope* (21 Mar) .. .. .. .. 50 55
350 80 c. *Balcutha* (21 Mar) .. .. .. .. 55 60
351 96 c. *Cap Hornier* (21 Mar) .. .. .. 65 70
352 $1.20, *Pamir* (21 Mar) .. .. .. .. 80 85
353 $3 *Mermerus* (41 × 31 *mm*) (4 May) .. 2·00 2·25
354 $5 *Cutty Sark* (41 × 31 *mm*) (4 May) .. 3·25 3·50
355 $9.60, H.M.S. *Resolution* and *Discovery* (41 × 31 *mm*) (15 June) .. .. .. 6·25 6·50
337/55 .. .. .. .. *Set of* 19 13·50 14·50

48 Olympic Flag

**1984** (20 July). *Olympic Games, Los Angeles. T* **48** *and similar horiz designs. Multicoloured. P* 13½ × 13.
356 35 c. Type **48** .. .. .. .. .. 30 35
357 60 c. Olympic torch and flags .. .. .. 50 55
358 $1.80, Ancient athletes and Coliseum .. 1·50 1·60
356/8 .. .. .. .. *Set of* 3 2·10 2·25
**MS**359 103 × 86 mm. As Nos. 356/8 but each with a charity premium of 5 c. .. .. .. .. 2·40 2·50

**NEW INFORMATION**

The editor is always interested to correspond with people who have new information that will improve or correct the Catalogue.

49 Penrhyn Stamps of 1978, 1979 and 1981

**1984** (20 Sept). *"Ausipex" International Stamp Exhibition, Melbourne. T* **49** *and similar horiz design. Multicoloured. P* 13½ × 13.

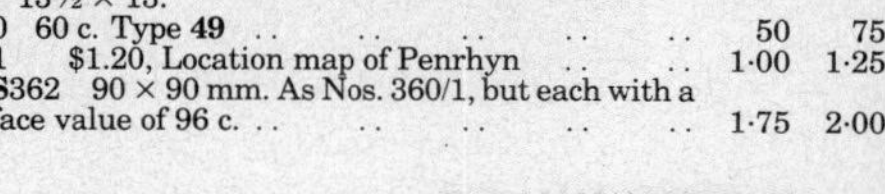

360 60 c. Type **49** .. .. .. .. .. .. 50 75
361 $1.20, Location map of Penrhyn .. .. 1·00 1·25
**MS**362 90 × 90 mm. As Nos. 360/1, but each with a face value of 96 c. .. .. .. .. .. 1·75 2·00

$2

Birth of
Prince Henry
15 Sept. 1984

(50) 51 "Virgin and Child" (Giovanni Bellini)

**1984** (18 Oct). *Birth of Prince Henry. Nos.* 223/4 *and* 250/1 *surch as T* **50**.
363 $2 on 30 c. Type **37** .. .. .. .. 2·25 1·50
364 $2 on 40 c. Type **34** .. .. .. .. 2·75 1·75
365 $2 on 50 c. Prince Charles as schoolboy .. 2·75 1·75
366 $2 on 50 c. Lady Diana as young child (Gold) 2·25 1·50
363/6 .. .. .. .. *Set of* 4 9·00 6·00

**1984** (15 Nov). *Christmas. Paintings of the Virgin and Child by different artists. T* **51** *and similar vert designs. Multicoloured. P* 13 × 13½.
367 36 c. Type **51** .. .. .. .. .. 30 35
368 48 c. Lorenzo di Credi .. .. .. .. 40 45
369 60 c. Palma the Older .. .. .. .. 45 50
370 96 c. Raphael .. .. .. .. .. 75 80
367/70 .. .. .. .. *Set of* 4 1·75 1·90
**MS**371 93 × 118 mm. As Nos. 367/70, but each with a charity premium of 5 c. .. .. .. .. 2·00 2·75

**1984** (10 Dec). *Christmas. Children's Charity. Designs as Nos.* 367/70, *but without frames, in separate miniature sheets* 67 × 81 *mm, each with a face value of* 96 c. + 10 c. *P* 13½.
**MS**372 As Nos. 367/70 .. .. *Set of* 4 *sheets* 3·00 3·25

52 Harlequin Duck

**1985** (9 Apr). *Birth Bicentenary of John J. Audubon (ornithologist). T* **52** *and similar horiz designs showing original paintings. Multicoloured. P* 13.
373 20 c. Type 52 .. .. .. .. .. .. 70 70
374 55 c. Sage Grouse .. .. .. .. .. 1·25 1·25
375 65 c. Solitary Sandpiper .. .. .. .. 1·40 1·40
376 75 c. Dunlin .. .. .. .. .. .. 1·75 1·75
373/6 .. .. .. .. *Set of* 4 4·50 4·50
**MS**377 Four sheets, each 70 × 53 mm. As Nos. 373/6, but each with a face value of 95 c. .. 3·50 4·50

53 Lady Elizabeth Bowes-Lyon, 1921 54 "The House in the Wood"

**1985** (24 June). *Life and Times of Queen Elizabeth the Queen Mother. T* **53** *and similar vert designs, each deep bluish violet, silver and yellow. P* 13.
378 75 c. Type **53** .. .. .. .. .. 60 65
379 95 c. With baby Princess Elizabeth, 1926 .. 75 80
380 $1.20, Coronation Day, 1937 .. .. .. 95 1·00
381 $2.80, On her 70th birthday .. .. .. 2·10 2·25
378/81 .. .. .. .. *Set of* 4 4·00 4·25
**MS**382 66 × 90 mm. $5 The Queen Mother .. 3·75 4·00
Nos. 378/81 were each printed in small sheets of 4 stamps.
For these stamps in a miniature sheet see No. **MS**403.

**1985** (10 Sept). *International Youth Year and Birth Centenary of Jacob Grimm (folklorist). T* **54** *and similar vert designs. Multicoloured. P* 13×13½.
383 75 c. Type **54** .. .. .. .. .. .. 80 70
384 95 c. "Snow-White and Rose-Red" .. .. .. 95 85
385 $1.15, "The Goose Girl" .. .. .. .. 1·25 1·10
383/5 .. .. .. .. .. *Set of* 3 2·75 2·40

**55** "The Annunciation"

**1985** (25 Nov). *Christmas. Paintings by Murillo. T* **55** *and similar horiz designs. Multicoloured. P* 14.
386 75 c. Type **55** .. .. .. .. .. .. 70 70
387 $1.15, "Adoration of the Shepherds" .. 1·00 1·00
388 $1.80, "The Holy Family" .. .. .. .. 1·75 1·75
386/8 .. .. .. .. .. *Set of* 3 3·00 3·00
**MS**389 66×131 mm. As Nos. 386/8, but each with a face value of 95 c. P 13½ .. .. .. 2·25 2·50
**MS**390 Three sheets, each 66×72 mm. As Nos. 386/8, but with face values of $1.20, $1.45 and $2.75. P 13½ .. .. .. *Set of 3 sheets* 4·00 4·25

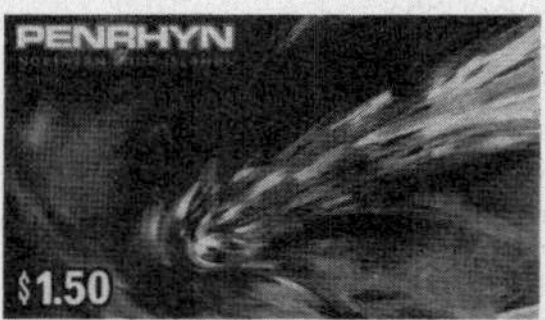


**56** Halley's Comet

**1986** (4 Feb). *Appearance of Halley's Comet. T* **56** *and similar horiz design showing details of the painting "Fire and Ice" by Camille Rendal. Multicoloured. P* 13½×13.
391 $1.50, Type **56** .. .. .. .. .. 1·10 1·25
392 $1.50, Stylised *Giotto* spacecraft .. .. 1·10 1·25
**MS**393 108×43 mm. $3 As Nos. 391/2 (104×39 *mm*). Imperf .. .. .. .. 2·25 2·50
Nos. 391/2 were printed together, *se-tenant*, in horizontal pairs throughout the sheet, forming a composite design of the complete painting.

**57** Princess Elizabeth aged Three, 1929, and Bouquet

**58** Statue of Liberty under Construction, Paris

**1986** (21 Apr). *60th Birthday of Queen Elizabeth II. T* **57** *and similar horiz designs. Multicoloured. P* 13½×13 ($2.50) *or* 14 *(others).*
394 95 c. Type **57** .. .. .. .. .. .. 80 80
395 $1.45, Profile of Queen Elizabeth and St. Edward's Crown .. .. .. .. .. 1·25 1·25
396 $2.50, Queen Elizabeth aged three and in profile with Imperial State Crown (56×30 *mm*) .. .. .. .. .. 2·00 2·00
394/6 .. .. .. .. .. *Set of* 3 3·50 3·50

**1986** (27 June). *Centenary of Statue of Liberty (1st issue). T* **58** *and similar vert designs, each black, gold and yellow-green. P* 13×13½.
397 95 c. Type **58** .. .. .. .. .. .. 65 70
398 $1.75, Erection of Statue, New York .. 1·10 1·25
399 $3 Artist's impression of Statue, 1876 .. 2·10 2·25
397/9 .. .. .. .. .. *Set of* 3 3·50 3·75
See also No. **MS**412.

**59** Prince Andrew and Miss Sarah Ferguson

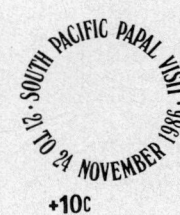

**$2.00**

**(60)**

**1986** (23 July). *Royal Wedding. T* **59** *and similar vert design. Multicoloured. P* 13.
400 $2.50, Type **59** .. .. .. .. .. 2·50 2·50
401 $3.50, Profiles of Prince Andrew and Miss Sarah Ferguson .. .. .. .. .. 3·25 3·25
Nos. 400/1 were each printed in sheetlets of 4 stamps and 2 stamp-size labels.

**1986** (4 Aug). *"Stampex '86" Stamp Exhibition, Adelaide. No.* **MS**362 *surch with T* **60** *in black on gold.*
**MS**402 $2 on 96 c.×2 .. .. .. .. 4·00 4·50
The "Stampex '86" exhibition emblem is overprinted on the sheet margin.

**1986** (4 Aug). *86th Birthday of Queen Elizabeth the Queen Mother. Nos. 378/81 in miniature sheet, 90×120 mm. P* 13×13½.
**MS**403 Nos. 378/81 .. .. .. .. .. 6·50 7·00

**61** "The Adoration of the Shepherds"

SOUTH PACIFIC PAPAL VISIT · 21 TO 24 NOVEMBER 1986 ·
+10c
**(62)**

**1986** (20 Nov). *Christmas. Engravings by Rembrandt. T* **61** *and similar vert designs, each red-brown, yellow-ochre and gold. P* 13.
404 65 c. Type **61** .. .. .. .. .. .. 80 80
405 $1.75 "Virgin and Child" .. .. .. .. 2·00 2·00
406 $2.50 "The Holy Family" .. .. .. .. 2·50 2·50
404/6 .. .. .. .. .. *Set of* 3 4·75 4·75
**MS**407 120×87 mm. As Nos. 404/6, but each size 31×39 mm with a face value of $1.50. P 13½×13 .. .. .. .. .. .. 5·00 6·00

**1986** (24 Nov). *Visit of Pope John Paul II to South Pacific. Nos. 404/7 surch as T* **62** *in greenish blue.*
408 65 c. + 10 c. Type **61** .. .. .. .. 1·50 1·50
409 $1.75 + 10 c. "Virgin and Child" .. .. 2·75 2·75
410 $2.50 + 10 c. "The Holy Family" .. .. 3·25 3·25
408/10 .. .. .. .. .. *Set of* 3 6·75 6·75
**MS**411 120×87 mm. As Nos. 408/10, but each size 31×39 mm with a face value of $1.50 + 10 c. .. 5·50 6·50

**63** Head and Torch of Statue of Liberty

**1987** (15 Apr). *Centenary of Statue of Liberty (1986) (2nd issue). Two sheets, each 122×122 mm, containing T* **63** *and similar multicoloured designs. Litho. P* 14×13½ *(vert) or* 13½×14 *(horiz).*
**MS**412 Two sheets (a) 65 c. Type **63**; 65 c. Torch at sunset; 65 c. Restoration workers with flag; 65 c. Statue and Manhattan skyline; 65 c. Workers and scaffolding. (b) 65 c. Workers on Statue crown *(horiz)*; 65 c. Aerial view of Ellis Island *(horiz)*; 65 c. Ellis Island Immigration Centre *(horiz)*; 65 c. View from Statue to Ellis Island and Manhattan *(horiz)*; 65 c. Restoration workers *(horiz)* .. .. .. *Set of 2 sheets* 8·50 9·00

*Fortieth Royal Wedding*
*Anniversary 1947–87*

**(64)**

**1987** (20 Nov). *Royal Ruby Wedding. Nos. 68/9 optd with T* **64** *in magenta.*
413 $2 Birds-eye view of Penrhyn .. .. 1·75 1·75
414 $5 Satellite view of Australasia .. .. 3·75 3·75

**65** "The Garvagh Madonna"

**66** Athletics

**1987** (11 Dec). *Christmas. Religious Paintings by Raphael. T* **65** *and similar vert designs. Multicoloured. P* 13½.
415 95 c. Type **65** .. .. .. .. .. .. 70 70
416 $1.60, "The Alba Madonna" .. .. .. 1·25 1·25
417 $2.25, "The Madonna of the Fish" .. .. 1·75 1·75
415/17 .. .. .. .. .. *Set of* 3 3·25 3·25
**MS**418 91×126 mm. As Nos. 415/17, but each with a face value of $1.15 .. .. .. 4·75 5·50
**MS**419 70×86 mm. $4.80, As No. 417, but size 36×39 mm .. .. .. .. .. .. 7·00 7·50

**1988** (29 July). *Olympic Games, Seoul. T* **66** *and similar horiz designs. Multicoloured. P* 13½×13 *(horiz) or* 13×13½ *(vert).*
420 55 c. Type **66** .. .. .. .. .. 45 45
421 95 c. Pole vaulting *(vert)* .. .. .. .. 70 70
422 $1.25, Shotputting .. .. .. .. 95 95
423 $1.50, Lawn Tennis *(vert)* .. .. .. 1·25 1·25
421/3 .. .. .. .. .. *Set of* 4 3·00 3·00
**MS**424 110×70 mm. As Nos. 421 and 423, but each with a face value of $2.50 .. .. .. 3·75 4·25

**1988** (14 Oct). *Olympic Gold Medal Winners, Seoul. Nos. 420/4 optd as T* **235** *of Cook Islands.*
425 55 c. Type **66** (optd "CARL LEWIS UNITED STATES 100 METERS") .. .. .. 40 45
426 95 c. Pole vaulting (optd "LOUISE RITTER UNITED STATES HIGH JUMP") .. .. 65 70
427 $1.25, Shot putting (optd "ULF TIMMERMANN EAST GERMANY SHOT-PUT") .. .. .. .. .. 90 95
428 $1.50, Lawn Tennis (optd "STEFFI GRAF WEST GERMANY WOMEN'S TENNIS") .. .. .. .. .. 1·10 1·25
425/8 .. .. .. .. .. *Set of* 4 2·75 3·00
**MS**429 110×70 mm. $2.50, As No. 421 (optd "JACKIE JOYNER-KERSEE United States Heptathlon"); $2.50, As No. 423 (optd "STEFFI GRAF West Germany Women's Tennis MILOSLAV MECIR Czechoslovakia Men's Tennis") .. .. .. .. .. .. 3·75 4·50

**67** "Virgin and Child"

**68** Neil Armstrong stepping onto Moon

**1988** (9 Nov). *Christmas. T* **67** *and similar designs showing different "Virgin and Child" paintings by Titian. P* 13 × 13½.
430 70 c. multicoloured .. .. .. .. 65 65
431 85 c. multicoloured .. .. .. .. 70 70
432 95 c. multicoloured .. .. .. .. 75 75
433 $1.25, multicoloured .. .. .. .. 90 95
430/3 .. .. .. .. .. *Set of* 4 2·75 2·75
**MS**434 100 × 80 mm. $6.40, As Type **67**, but diamond-shaped (57 × 57 *mm*). P 13 .. .. 4·50 5·00

(Des G. Vasarhelyi)

**1989** (24 July). *20th Anniv of First Manned Landing on Moon. T* **68** *and similar horiz designs. Multicoloured. P* 14.
435 55 c. Type **68** .. .. .. .. .. 40 45
436 75 c. Astronaut on Moon carrying equipment .. .. .. .. .. 55 60
437 95 c. Conducting experiment on Moon .. 70 75
438 $1.25, Crew of "Apollo 11" .. .. .. 95 1·00
439 $1.75, Crew inside "Apollo 11" .. .. 1·40 1·50
435/9 .. .. .. .. .. *Set of* 5 3·50 3·75

**69** Virgin Mary

**1989** (17 Nov). *Christmas. T* **69** *and similar multicoloured designs showing details from "The Nativity" by Dürer. P* 13.
440 55 c. Type **69** .. .. .. .. .. 60 60
441 70 c. Christ Child and cherubs .. .. 70 70
442 85 c. Joseph .. .. .. .. .. 85 85
443 $1.25, Three women .. .. .. .. 1·25 1·25
440/3 .. .. .. .. .. *Set of* 4 3·00 3·00
**MS**444 88×95 mm. $6.40, "The Nativity" (31×50 *mm*) .. .. .. .. .. 4·75 5·50

**70** Queen Elizabeth the Queen Mother

**1990** (24 July). *90th Birthday of Queen Elizabeth the Queen Mother. P* 13½.
445 **70** $2.25, multicoloured .. .. .. 1·50 1·60
**MS**446 85×73 mm. **70** $7.50, multicoloured .. 7·00 7·00

$1.50

71 "Adoration of the Magi" (Veronese)

(72)

(Litho Questa)

**1990** (26 Nov). *Christmas. Religious Paintings.* T **71** *and similar vert designs. Multicoloured. P* 14.

447 55 c. Type **71** .. .. .. .. 45 45
448 70 c. "Virgin and Child" (Quentin Metsys) .. 60 60
449 85 c. "Virgin and Child Jesus" (Hugo van der Goes) .. .. .. .. .. 70 70
450 $1.50, "Adoration of the Kings" (Jan Gossaert) .. .. .. .. 1·25 1·25
447/50 .. .. .. *Set of* 4 2·75 2·75
**MS**451 108×132 mm. $6.40, "Virgin and Child with Saints, Francis, John the Baptist, Zenobius and Lucy" (Domenico Veneziano) .. .. 4·25 4·50

**1990** (5 Dec). *"Birdpex '90" Stamp Exhibition, Christchurch, New Zealand. Nos.* 373/6 *surch as T* **72** *in red (Nos* 452, 455) *or black (others).*

452 $1.50 on 20 c. Type **52** .. .. .. 1·25 1·25
453 $1.50 on 55 c. Sage Grouse .. .. 1·25 1·25
454 $1.50 on 65 c. Solitary Sandpiper .. 1·25 1·25
455 $1.50 on 75 c. Dunlin .. .. .. 1·25 1·25
452/5 .. .. .. .. *Set of* 4 4·50 4·50

COMMEMORATING 65th
BIRTHDAY OF H.M.
QUEEN ELIZABETH II

(73)

**1991** (22 Apr). *65th Birthday of Queen Elizabeth II. No.* 208 *optd with T* **73**.

456 $6 H.M.S. *Resolution* and *Discovery*, 1776–80 .. .. .. .. 4·75 5·00

74 "The Virgin and Child with Saints" (G. David)

(Des G. Vasarhelyi. Litho Questa)

**1991** (11 Nov). *Christmas. Religious Paintings.* T **74** *and similar multicoloured designs. P* 14.

457 55 c. Type **74** .. .. .. 35 40
458 85 c. "Nativity" (Tintoretto) .. .. 55 60
459 $1.15, "Mystic Nativity" (Botticelli) .. 75 80
460 $1.85, "Adoration of the Shepherds" (B. Murillo) .. .. .. .. 1·25 1·40
457/60 .. .. .. *Set of* 4 2·50 3·00
**MS**461 79×103 mm. $6.40, "The Madonna of the Chair" (Raphael) (*vert*) .. .. .. 4·25 4·50

OFFICIAL STAMPS

**O.H.M.S.**

(O 1)

**1978** (14 Nov). *Nos.* 57/66, 89/91 *and* 101/2 *optd or surch (Nos.* O8/9 *and* O12) *as Type* O **1**.

O 1 1 c. *Mondactylus argenteus* .. .. .. 15 10
O 2 2 c. *Pomacanthus imperator* .. .. .. 15 10
O 3 3 c. *Chelmon rostratus* .. .. .. 25 10
O 4 4 c. *Chaetodon ornatissimus* .. .. 25 10
O 5 5 c. *Chaetodon melanotus* .. .. .. 30 10
O 6 8 c. *Chaetodon raffessi* .. .. .. 35 15
O 7 10 c. *Chaetodon ephippium* .. .. .. 40 15
O 8 15 c. on 60 c. *Plectorhynchus chaetodonoides* 45 25
O 9 18 c. on 60 c. *Plectorhynchus chaetodonoides* 50 25
O10 20 c. *Pygoplites diacanthus* .. .. .. 50 25
O11 25 c. *Heniochus acuminatus* (Silver) .. .. 55 30
O12 30 c. on 60 c. *Plectorhynchus chaetodonoides* 55 35
O13 50 c. } 70 55
O14 50 c. } "The Spirit of '76" (A. M. Willard) (Gold) 70 55
O15 50 c. } 70 55
O16 $1 Queen and Prince Philip (Silver) .. 2·25 1·40
O17 $2 Queen Elizabeth II (Gold) .. .. 4·50 2·75
O1/17 .. .. .. .. *Set of* 17 12·00 7·00

These stamps were originally only sold to the public cancelled-to-order and not in unused condition. They were made available to overseas collectors in mint condition during 1980.

***MINIMUM PRICE***

The minimum price quote is 10p which represents a handling charge rather than a basis for valuing common stamps. For further notes about prices see introductory pages.

65c

O.H.M.S.

O.H.M.S.

(O 2) (O 3)

**1985** (15 Aug)–**87**. (*a*) *Nos.* 206/8, 337/47 *and* 349/55 *optd or surch as Type* O **2** *by foil embossing in red* ($2, $4, $6) *or silver (others)*

O18 2 c. Type **47** .. .. .. .. .. 10 10
O19 4 c. Amatasi .. .. .. .. .. 10 10
O20 5 c. Ndrua .. .. .. .. .. 10 10
O21 8 c. Tongiaki .. .. .. .. .. 10 10
O22 10 c. *Victoria* .. .. .. .. .. 10 10
O23 18 c. *Golden Hind* .. .. .. .. 10 10
O24 20 c. *Boudeuse* .. .. .. .. .. 10 15
O25 30 c. H.M.S. *Bounty* .. .. .. .. 20 25
O26 40 c. on 36 c. *L'Astrolabe* .. .. .. 25 30
O27 50 c. *Star of India* .. .. .. .. 35 40
O28 55 c. on 48 c. *Great Republic* .. .. 35 40
O29 75 c. on 72 c. *Antiope* (29.4.86) .. .. 50 55
O30 75 c. on 96 c. *Cap Hornier* (29.4.86) .. 50 55
O31 80 c. *Balcutha* (29.4.86) .. .. .. 55 60
O32 $1.20, *Pamir* (29.4.86) .. .. .. 80 85
O33 $2 *Cutty Sark* (29.4.86) .. .. .. 1·25 1·40
O34 $3 *Mermerus* (29.4.86) .. .. .. 2·00 2·10
O35 $4 *Mermerus* (29.4.86) .. .. .. 2·75 3·00
O36 $5 *Cutty Sark* (2.11.87) .. .. .. 3·25 3·50
O37 $6 H.M.S. *Resolution* and *Discovery* (2.11.87) .. .. .. .. .. 4·00 4·25
O38 $9.60, H.M.S. *Resolution* and *Discovery* (2.11.87) .. .. .. .. .. 6·25 6·50

(*b*) *Nos.* 278/81 *surch as Type* O **3** *by silver foil embossing*

O39 65 c. on 60 c. Type **40** .. .. .. 45 50
O40 65 c. on 60 c. Aerial view of Penrhyn atoll .. 45 50
O41 65 c. on 60 c. Eleanor Roosevelt on Penrhyn during Second World War .. .. 45 50
O42 65 c. on 60 c. Map of South Pacific .. .. 45 50
O18/42 .. .. .. .. *Set of* 25 21·00 23·00

# Cyprus

Cyprus was part of the Turkish Ottoman Empire from 1571.

The first records of an organised postal service date from 1871 when a post office was opened at Nicosia (Lefkosa) under the jurisdiction of the Damascus Head Post Office. Various stamps of Turkey from the 1868 issue onwards are known used from this office, cancelled "KIBRIS", in Arabic, within a double-lined oblong. Manuscript cancellations have also been reported. The records report the opening of a further office at Larnaca (Tuzla) in 1873, but no cancellation for this office has been identified.

To provide an overseas postal service the Austrian Empire opened a post office in Larnaca during 1845. Stamps of the Austrian Post Offices in the Turkish Empire were placed on sale there from 1 June 1864 and were cancelled with an unframed straight-line mark or circular date stamp. This Austrian post office closed on 6 August 1878.

### BRITISH ADMINISTRATION

Following the convention with Turkey, Great Britain assumed the administration of Cyprus on 11 July 1878 and the first post office, as part of the British G.P.O. system, was opened at Larnaca on 27 July 1878. Further offices at Famagusta, Kyrenia, Limassol, Nicosia and Paphos followed in September 1878. In addition two Camp post offices, mainly for the use of the administration, were established at Nicosia (Headquarters Camp) and Polymedia (Polemidhia) (near Limassol). These were supplied with numeral postmarks in January 1881, which can be found cancelling Great Britain stamps for a short period after that date.

The stamps of Great Britain were supplied to the various offices as they opened and continued to be used until the Cyprus Administration assumed responsibility for the postal service on 1 April 1880, although scattered examples are known dating from 1881.

For illustrations of the postmark types see BRITISH POST OFFICES ABROAD notes, following GREAT BRITAIN.

### FAMAGUSTA

*Stamps of* GREAT BRITAIN *cancelled* "982" *as Type* **9**

**1878** *to* **1880–81.**
Z1 ½d. rose-red (1870–79) (Plate Nos. 11, 13) .. .. £475
Z2 1d. rose-red (1864–70) .. .. .. .. £300
Plate Nos. 145, 174, 181, 193, 202, 206, 215.
Z3 2d. blue (1858–69) (Plate Nos. 13, 14, 15) .. .. £900
Z4 2½d. rosy mauve (1876) (Plate Nos. 13, 16) .. .. £800
Z5 6d. grey (1874–80) (Plate No. 15) .. ..
Z6 1s. green (1873–77) (Plate No. 12) .. .. £1400
Z7 1s. orange-brown (1881) (Plate No. 14) .. .. £2000

### KYRENIA

*Stamps of* GREAT BRITAIN *cancelled* "974" *as Type* **9**

**1878** *to* **1880.**
Z 8 ½d. rose-red (1870–79) (Plate No. 1) .. ..
Z 9 1d. rose-red (1864–79) .. .. *From* £275
Plate Nos. 168, 171, 193, 196, 206, 207, 209, 220.
Z10 2d. blue (1858–69) (Plate Nos. 13, 15) .. *From* £600
Z11 2½d. rosy mauve (1876–79) .. .. *From* £200
Plate Nos. 12, 13, 14, 15.
Z12 4d. sage-green (1877) (Plate No. 16) .. ..
Z13 6d. grey (1874–80) (Plate No. 16) .. ..

### LARNACA

*Stamps of* GREAT BRITAIN *cancelled* "942" *as Type* **9**

**1878** *to* **1880–81.**
Z14 ½d. rose-red (1870–79) .. .. *From* £250
Plate Nos. 11, 12, 13, 14, 15, 19, 20.
Z15 1d. rose-red (1864–79) .. .. *From* £120
Plate Nos. 129, 131, 146, 154, 170, 171, 174, 175, 176, 177, 178, 179, 181, 182, 183, 184, 187, 188, 190, 191, 192, 193, 194, 195, 196, 197, 198, 199, 200, 201, 202, 203, 204, 205, 206, 207, 208, 209, 210, 212, 213, 214, 215, 216, 217, 218, 220, 221, 222, 225.
Z16 1½d. lake-red (1870) (Plate No. 3) .. .. £1400
Z17 2d. blue (1858–69 (Plate Nos. 9, 13, 14, 15) .. 85·00
Z18 2½d. rosy mauve (1876–79) .. .. *From* 35·00
Plate Nos. 4, 5, 6, 8, 10, 11, 12, 13, 14, 15, 16, 17.
Z19 2½d. blue (1880–81) (Plate Nos. 17, 18, 19, 20) .. £450
Z20 2½d. blue (1881) (Plate No. 21) .. .. £450
Z21 4d. sage-green (1877) (Plate Nos. 15, 16) .. .. £550
Z22 6d. grey (1874–76) (Plate Nos. 15, 16, 17) .. .. £375
Z23 6d. pale buff (1872–73) (Plate No. 11) .. .. £1300
Z24 8d. orange (1876) .. .. .. £3250
Z25 1s. green (1873–77) (Plate Nos. 12, 13) .. .. £500
Z26 1s. orange-brown (1881) (Plate No. 14) .. .. £1500
Z27 5s. rose (1874) (Plate No. 2) .. .. £3500

### LIMASSOL

*Stamps of* GREAT BRITAIN *cancelled* "975" *as Type* **9**

**1878** *to* **1880.**
Z28 ½d. rose-red (1870–79) (Plate Nos. 11, 13, 15, 19) £275
Z29 1d. rose-red (1864–79) .. .. *From* £100
Plate Nos. 160, 171, 173, 174, 177, 179, 184, 187, 190, 193, 195, 196, 197, 198, 200, 202, 206, 207, 208, 209, 210, 213, 215, 216, 218, 220, 221, 222, 225.
Z30 1½d. lake-red (1870–74) (Plate No. 3) .. .. £1600
Z31 2d. blue (1858–69) (Plate Nos. 14, 15) .. *From* £140
Z32 2½d. rosy-mauve (1876–80) .. .. *From* 85·00
Plate Nos. 11, 12, 13, 14, 15, 16.
Z33 2½d. blue (1880) (Plate Nos. 17, 19, 20) .. *From* £1200
Z34 4d. sage-green (Plate No. 16) .. .. £475

### NICOSIA

*Stamps of* GREAT BRITAIN *cancelled* "969" *as Type* **9**

**1878** *to* **1880–81.**
Z35 ½d. rose-red (1870–79) .. .. .. £300
Plate Nos. 12, 13, 14, 15, 20.
Z36 1d. rose-red (1864–79) .. .. *From* £100
Plate Nos. 170, 171, 174, 189, 190, 192, 193, 195, 196, 198, 200, 202, 203, 205, 206, 207, 210, 212, 214, 215, 218, 221, 222, 225.
Z37 2d. blue (1858–69) (Plate Nos. 14 and 15) ..
Z38 2½d. rosy mauve (1876–79) .. .. *From* £110
Plate Nos. 10, 11, 12, 13, 14, 15, 16.
Z39 2½d. blue (1880) (Plate No. 20) .. ..
Z40 2½d. blue (1881) (Plate No. 21) .. ..
Z41 4d. vermilion (1876) (Plate No. 15) .. ..
Z42 4d. sage-green (1877) (Plate No. 16) .. .. £600
Z43 6d. grey (1873) (Plate No. 16) .. .. £600

### PAPHOS

*Stamps of* GREAT BRITAIN *cancelled* "981" *as Type* **9**

**1878** *to* **1880.**
Z44 ½d. rose-red (1870–79) (Plate No. 13, 15) .. ..
Z45 1d. rose-red (1864–79) .. .. *From* £300
Plate Nos. 196, 201, 202, 204, 206, 213, 217.
Z46 2d. blue (1858–69) (Plate No. 15) .. .. £650
Z47 2½d. rosy mauve (1876–79) .. .. *From* £350
Plate Nos. 13, 14, 15.

### HEADQUARTER CAMP, NICOSIA

*Stamps of* GREAT BRITAIN *cancelled* "D 48" *as Type* **8**

**1881.**
Z48 ½d. rose-red (1870–79) (Plate Nos. 13, 20) .. .. £1200
Z49 1d. rose-red (1864–79) .. .. *From* £550
Plate Nos. 123, 171, 174, 177, 201, 204, 205, 214, 218.
Z50 2d. blue (1858–69) (Plate No. 15) .. .. £1200

### POLYMEDIA (POLEMIDHIA) CAMP, LIMASSOL

*Stamps of* GREAT BRITAIN *cancelled* "D 47" *as Type* **8**

**1881.**
Z51 ½d. rose-red (1870–79) (Plate No. 11) .. .. £1300
Z52 1d. rose-red (1864–79) .. .. *From* £550
Plate Nos. 78, 99, 110, 132, 175, 192, 197, 205, 206, 207, 208, 209.
Z53 2d. blue (1858–69) (Plate No. 15) .. .. £1100

"D 48" differs from Type **8** in that the "D" is taller and narrower and the "4" has pronounced serifs. Stamps with "D 47" and "D 48" having four bars instead of three were used in Great Britain before the altered postmarks were sent to Cyprus.

| PRICES FOR STAMPS ON COVER TO 1945 | |
|---|---|
| Nos. 1/10 | *from* × 7 |
| Nos. 11/49 | *from* × 4 |
| Nos. 50/122 | *from* × 3 |
| Nos. 123/43 | *from* × 4 |
| Nos. 144/50 | *from* × 3 |
| Nos. 151/63 | *from* × 5 |

**PERFORATION.** Nos. 1/122 are perf 14.

***Stamps of Great Britain overprinted***

CYPRUS (1) CYPRUS (2)

(Optd by D.L.R.)

**1880** (1 Apr).
1 1 ½d. rose .. .. .. 95·00 95·00
a. Opt double (Plate 15) .. .. —£7000

| Plate No. | Un. | Used. | Plate No. | Un. | Used |
|---|---|---|---|---|---|
| 12. .. | £150 | £225 | 19. .. | £3000 | £700 |
| 15. .. | 95·00 | 95·00 | | | |

2 2 1d. red .. .. .. 7·50 27·00
a. Opt double (Plate 208) .. .. £7500
aa. Opt double (Plate 218) .. .. £3250
b. Vert pair, top stamp without opt (Plate 208) .. .. £9000

| Plate No. | Un. | Used. | Plate No. | Un. | Used |
|---|---|---|---|---|---|
| 174. .. | £1000 | £1000 | 208. .. | 85·00 | 48·00 |
| 181. .. | £225 | £150 | 215. .. | 9·00 | 32·00 |
| 184. .. | £7000 | £2000 | 216. .. | 12·00 | 27·00 |
| 193. .. | £550 | † | 217. .. | 9·00 | 32·00 |
| 196. .. | £550 | † | 218. .. | 13·00 | 35·00 |
| 201. .. | 7·50 | 35·00 | 220. .. | £500 | £400 |
| 205. .. | 25·00 | 27·00 | | | |

3 2 2½d. rosy mauve .. .. .. 1·75 5·00
a. Large thin "C" (Plate 14) (BK, JK) .. 27·00 75·00
b. Large thin "C" (Plate 15) (BK, JK) .. 38·00 £150

| Plate No. | Un. | Used | Plate No. | Un. | Used |
|---|---|---|---|---|---|
| 14. .. | 1·75 | 5·00 | 15. .. | 2·50 | 16·00 |

4 2 4d. sage-green (Plate 16) .. .. £120 £170
5 6d. grey (Plate 16) .. .. £500 £650
6 1s. green (Plate 13) .. .. £600 £450
No. 3 has been reported from Plate 9.

HALF-PENNY (3) 18 mm HALF-PENNY (4) 16 or 16½ mm
HALF-PENNY (5) 13 mm 30 PARAS (6)

(Optd by Govt Ptg Office, Nicosia)

**1881** (Feb–June). *No. 2 surch.*
7 3 ½d. on 1d. red (Feb) .. .. 65·00 70·00
a. "HALFPENN" (BG, LG) (*all plates*) .. .. *From* £900 £900

| Plate No. | Un. | Used. | Plate No. | Un. | Used. |
|---|---|---|---|---|---|
| 174. .. | £110 | £225 | 215. .. | £450 | £500 |
| 181. .. | 90·00 | £110 | 216. .. | 65·00 | 70·00 |
| 201. .. | 65·00 | 75·00 | 217. .. | £550 | £450 |
| 205. .. | 70·00 | 80·00 | 218. .. | £350 | £400 |
| 208. .. | £150 | £225 | 220. .. | £180 | £200 |

8 4 ½d. on 1d. red (Apr) .. .. £120 £140
a. Surch double (Plates 201 and 216) £2250

| Plate No. | Un. | Used | Plate No. | Un. | Used |
|---|---|---|---|---|---|
| 201. .. | £120 | £140 | 218. .. | — | — |
| 216. .. | £325 | £375 | | | |

9 5 ½d. on 1d. red (June) .. .. 45·00 60·00
a. Surch double (Plate 201) ..
aa. Surch double (Plate 205) .. .. £600
ab. Surch double (Plate 215) .. .. £425 £475
b. Surch treble (Plate 205) .. .. £2000
ba. Surch treble (Plate 215) .. .. £600
bb. Surch treble (Plate 217) ..
bc. Surch treble (Plate 218) .. .. £900
c. Surch quadruple (Plate 205) .. .. £1800
ca. Surch quadruple (Plate 215) .. .. £1800
d. "CYPRUS" double (Plate 218) ..

| Plate No. | Un. | Used | Plate No. | Un. | Used |
|---|---|---|---|---|---|
| 201. .. | — | — | 217. .. | 75·00 | 60·00 |
| 205. .. | £140 | — | 218. .. | 65·00 | 75·00 |
| 215. .. | 45·00 | 65·00 | | | |

10 6 30 paras on 1d. red (June) .. .. 90·00 80·00
a. Surch double, one invtd (Plate 216) £2000
aa. Surch double, one invtd (Plate 220) £950 £950

| Plate No. | Un. | Used | Plate No. | Un. | Used |
|---|---|---|---|---|---|
| 201. .. | 95·00 | 80·00 | 217. .. | £130 | £130 |
| 216. .. | 90·00 | 80·00 | 220. .. | £130 | £130 |

The surcharge on No. 8 was handstamped; the others were applied by lithography.

**(New Currency: 40 paras = 1 piastre. 180 piastres = £1)**

7 ½ (8) ½ (9) 30 PARAS

(Typo D.L.R.)

**1881** (1 July). *Die I. Wmk Crown CC.*
11 7 ½ pi. emerald-green .. .. £180 40·00
12 1 pi. rose .. .. .. £350 30·00
13 2 pi. blue .. .. .. £450 30·00
14 4 pi. pale olive-green .. .. £850 £250
15 6 pi. olive-grey .. .. £1300 £400

Stamps of Queen Victoria initialled "J.A.B." or overprinted "POSTAL SURCHARGE" with or without the same initials were employed for accounting purposes between the Chief Post Office and sub-offices, the initials are those of the then Postmaster, Mr. J. A. Bulmer.

**1882** (Mar)–**86**. *Die I*. Wmk Crown CA.*
16 7 ½pi. emerald-green (5.82) .. .. £4000 £350
*a. Dull green* (4.83) .. .. 6·50 30
17 30 pa. pale mauve (7.6.82) .. .. 55·00 16·00
18 1 pi. rose (3.82) .. .. 65·00 70
19 2 pi. blue (4.83) .. .. 95·00 90
20 4 pi. deep olive-green (1883) .. .. £425 27·00
*a. Pale olive-green* .. .. £350 22·00
21 6 pi. olive-grey (1.83) .. .. 32·00 15·00
22 12 pi. orange-brown (1886) (Optd S. £500) £160 32·00
16*a*/22 .. .. *Set of* 7 £650 80·00

*For description and illustrations of Dies I and II see Introduction.

See also Nos. 31/7.

(Surch litho by Govt Ptg Office, Nicosia)

**1882.** *Surch with T* **8/9**. (*a*) *Wmk Crown CC.*
23 7 ½ on ½ pi. emerald-green (6.82) .. £400 65·00
24 30 pa. on 1 pi. rose (22.5.82) .. .. £1400 £100
(*b*) *Wmk Crown CA*
25 7 ½ on ½ pi. emerald-green (5.82) .. £110 6·50
a. Surch double .. .. —£2750

½ ½ (10) Two varieties of T **10**: (*a*) Fractions approx 6 mm apart (*b*) Fractions approx 8 mm apart

11

**1886** (Apr). *Surch with T* **10** (*a*) *by De La Rue in typography.*
(*a*) *Wmk Crown CC*
26 7 ½ on ½ pi. emerald-green .. .. £6000
(*b*) *Wmk Crown CA*
27 7 ½ on ½ pi. emerald-green .. .. £225 65·00
The status of No. 26 remains in doubt as it is not known used.

**1886** (May–June). *Surch with T* **10** (*b*) *by De La Rue in typography.*
(*a*) *Wmk Crown CC*
28 7 ½ on ½ pi. emerald-green .. .. £5500 £375
a. Large "1" at left .. .. —£1200
b. Small "1" at right .. .. £8500 £1900
(*b*) *Wmk Crown CA*
29 7 ½ on ½ pi. emerald-green (June) .. £180 7·00
a. Large "1" at left .. .. £1100 £180
b. Small "1" at right .. .. £1600 £250

A third type of this surcharge is known with the fraction spaced approximately 10 mm apart on CA paper with postmarks from August 1886. This may be due to the shifting of type.

**1892–94**. *Die II. Wmk Crown CA.*
31 7 ½ pi. dull green .. .. 2·50 30
32 30 pa. mauve .. .. 2·50 2·00
33 1 pi. carmine .. .. 7·00 80
34 2 pi. ultramarine .. .. 10·00 80
35 4 pi. olive-green .. .. 50·00 18·00
*a. Pale olive-green* .. .. 16·00 14·00
36 6 pi. olive-grey (1894) .. .. £120 £350
37 12 pi. orange-brown (1893) .. .. £120 £190
31/37 .. .. .. *Set of* 7 £250 £500

**894 (14 Aug)–96.** *Colours changed and new values. Die II. Wmk Crown CA.*

0 7 ½ pi. green and carmine (1896) .. .. 4·00 40
1 30 pa. bright mauve and green (1896) .. 2·00 55
2 1 pi. carmine and blue (1896) .. .. 4·00 45
3 2 pi. blue and purple (1896) .. .. 4·50 45
4 4 pi. sage-green and purple (1896) .. 9·50 3·00
5 6 pi. sepia and green (1896) .. .. 6·50 7·50
6 9 pi. brown and carmine.. .. .. 15·00 8·00
7 12 pi. orange-brown and black (1896) .. 12·00 45·00
8 18 pi. greyish slate and brown .. .. 48·00 38·00
9 45 pi. grey-purple and blue .. .. £110 £120
0/49 .. .. .. .. *Set of* 10 £180 £190
0/49 Optd "Specimen" .. .. *Set of* 10 £300

(Typo D.L.R.)

**902–04.** *Wmk Crown CA.*

0 11 ½ pi. green and carmine (12.02) .. 2·50 30
1 30 pa. violet and green (2.03) .. .. 3·25 80
*a. Mauve and green* .. .. .. 6·50 3·00
2 1 pi. carmine and blue (9.03) .. .. 9·00 1·75
3 2 pi. blue and purple (2.03) .. .. 22·00 6·50
4 4 pi. olive-green and purple (9.03) .. 22·00 10·00
5 6 pi. sepia and green (9.03) .. .. 35·00 55·00
6 9 pi. brown and carmine (5.04) .. 75·00 £140
7 12 pi. chestnut and black (4.03) .. 12·00 24·00
8 18 pi. black and brown (5.04) .. .. 55·00 85·00
9 45 pi. dull purple and ultramarine (10.03) .. .. .. .. £200 £350
0/59 .. .. .. .. *Set of* 10 £375 £600
0/59 Optd "Specimen" .. .. *Set of* 10 £450

**904–10.** *Wmk Mult Crown CA.*

60 11 5 pa. bistre and black (14.1.08) .. 30 20
61 10 pa. orange and green (12.06) .. 1·50 25
*a. Yellow and green* .. .. .. 27·00 5·50
62 ½ pi. green and carmine (1.7.04) .. 2·50 15
63 30 pa. purple and green (1.7.04) .. 6·00 75
*a. Violet and green* (1910) .. .. 8·00 1·50
64 1 pi. carmine and blue (11.04) .. 1·50 30
65 2 pi. blue and purple (11.04) .. .. 3·75 70
66 4 pi. olive-green and purple (2.05) .. 9·00 6·00
67 6 pi. sepia and green (17.7.04) .. 8·50 5·50
68 9 pi. brown and carmine (30.5.04) .. 15·00 6·50
*a. Yellow-brown and carmine* .. 14·00 14·00
69 12 pi. chestnut and black (4.06) .. 20·00 16·00
70 18 pi. black and brown (16.6.04) .. 25·00 8·00
71 45 pi. dull purple and ultram (15.6.04) 60·00 90·00
60/71 .. .. .. .. *Set of* 12 £130 £120
60/61 Optd "Specimen" .. .. *Set of* 2 £120

12 — 13

(Typo D.L.R.)

**1912 (July)–15.** *Wmk Mult Crown CA.*

74 12 10 pa. orange and green (11.12) .. 2·50 80
a. Wmk sideways .. .. .. — £1900
*b. Orange-yellow and bright green* (8.15) .. .. .. .. 2·25 40
75 ½ pi. green and carmine .. .. 1·50 20
*a. Yellow-green and carmine* .. .. 4·00 90
76 30 pa. violet and green (3.13) .. .. 1·50 20
77 1 pi. rose-red and blue (9.12) .. .. 3·75 1·25
*a. Carmine and blue* (8.15?) .. .. 12·00 4·00
78 2 pi. blue and purple (7.13) .. .. 4·75 90
79 4 pi. olive-green and purple .. .. 2·75 2·75
80 6 pi. sepia and green .. .. .. 2·75 5·00
81 9 pi. brown and carmine (3.15) .. 18·00 13·00
*a. Yellow-brown and carmine* .. 21·00 18·00
82 12 pi. chestnut and black (7.13) .. 8·00 14·00
83 18 pi. black and brown (3.15) .. .. 20·00 18·00
84 45 pi. dull purple and ultramarine (3.15) 55·00 90·00
74/84 .. .. .. .. *Set of* 11 £110 £130
74/84 Optd "Specimen" .. .. *Set of* 11 £325

**1921–23.** *(a) Wmk Mult Script CA.*

85 12 10 pa. orange and green .. .. 2·25 2·25
86 10 pa. grey and yellow (1923) .. .. 8·00 9·00
87 30 pa. violet and green .. .. .. 2·50 40
88 30 pa. green (1923) .. .. .. 4·25 40
89 1 pi. carmine and blue .. .. .. 6·00 16·00
90 1 pi. violet and red (1922) .. .. 3·00 2·75
91 1½ pi. yellow and black (1922) .. .. 3·25 3·75
92 2 pi. blue and purple .. .. .. 9·50 8·00
93 2 pi. carmine and blue (1922).. .. 9·00 22·00
94 2¾ pi. blue and purple (1922) .. .. 8·50 14·00
95 4 pi. olive-green and purple .. .. 5·50 12·00
96 6 pi. sepia and green (1923) .. .. 7·50 32·00
97 9 pi. brown and carmine (1922) .. 24·00 38·00
*a. Yellow-brown and carmine* .. 35·00 50·00
98 18 pi. black and brown (1923) .. .. 55·00 £100
99 45 pi. dull purple and ultramarine (1923) .. .. .. .. £140 £200
85/99 .. .. .. .. *Set of* 15 £250 £400
85/99 Optd "Specimen" .. .. *Set of* 15 £475

*(b) Wmk Mult Crown CA (1923)*

100 12 10s. green and red/*pale yellow* .. £350 £500
101 £1 purple and black/*red* .. .. £1000 £1200
100/101 Optd "Specimen" .. .. *Set of* 2 £500

**1924–28.** *Chalk-surfaced paper. (a) Wmk Mult Crown CA.*

102 13 £1 purple and black/*red* .. .. £325 £425

*(b) Wmk Mult Script CA*

103 13 ¼ pi. grey and chestnut .. .. 30 15
104 ½ pi. black .. .. .. .. 1·25 4·00
105 ¾ pi. green .. .. .. .. 1·00 50
106 1 pi. purple and chestnut .. .. 65 20
107 1½ pi. orange and black.. .. .. 90 3·50
108 2 pi. carmine and green .. .. 1·75 5·50
109 2¾ pi. bright blue and purple .. .. 1·75 1·75
110 4 pi. sage-green and purple .. .. 2·00 1·50
111 4½ pi. black and orange/*emerald* .. 2·25 3·00
112 6 pi. olive-brown and green .. .. 2·25 3·50
113 13 9 pi. brown and purple .. .. 2·75 3·00
114 12 pi. chestnut and black .. .. 5·00 28·00
115 18 pi. black and orange.. .. .. 16·00 4·50
116 45 pi. purple and blue .. .. .. 25·00 28·00
117 90 pi. green and red/*yellow* .. .. 60·00 90·00
117a £5 black/*yellow* (1928) (Optd S. £900) .. .. .. .. £3500 £5000

**CROWN COLONY**

**1925.** *Wmk Mult Script CA. Chalk-surfaced paper* (½, ¾ *and* 2 *pi.*)

118 13 ½ pi. green .. .. .. .. 1·75 1·25
119 ¾ pi. brownish black .. .. .. 1·75 10
120 1½ pi. scarlet .. .. .. .. 2·25 30
121 2 pi. yellow and black .. .. .. 4·00 3·25
122 2½ pi. bright blue .. .. .. 1·75 30
102/122 .. .. .. *Set of* 21 *to* £1 £400 £550
102/22 Optd "Specimen" .. .. *Set of* 21 £600

In the above set the fraction bar in the value is horizontal. In Nos. 91, 94, 107 and 109 it is diagonal.

14 Silver Coin of Amathus, 6th-cent B.C.

16 Map of Cyprus

(Recess B.W.)

**1928 (1 Feb).** *50th Anniv of British Rule. T* **14, 16** *and similar designs. Wmk Mult Script CA. P* 12.

123 ¾ pi. deep dull purple.. .. .. .. 1·25 40
124 1 pi. black and greenish blue .. .. 1·25 65
125 1½ pi. scarlet .. .. .. .. 2·75 2·00
126 2½ pi. light blue .. .. .. .. 1·75 2·00
127 4 pi. deep brown .. .. .. .. 5·00 7·00
128 6 pi. blue .. .. .. .. 5·00 15·00
129 9 pi. maroon .. .. .. .. 5·00 10·00
130 18 pi. black and brown .. .. .. 16·00 17·00
131 45 pi. violet and blue .. .. .. 32·00 45·00
132 £1 blue and bistre-brown .. .. £225 £300
123/132 .. .. .. .. *Set of* 10 £250 £350
123/32 Optd "Specimen" .. .. *Set of* 10 £500

Designs: *Vert*—1 pi. Zeno (philosopher); 2½ pi. Discovery of body of St Barnabas; 4 pi. Cloister, Abbey of Bella Paise; 9 pi. Tekke of Umm Haram; 18 pi. Statue of Richard I, Westminster; 45 pi. St. Nicholas Cathedral, Famagusta (now Lala Mustafa Pasha Mosque); £1 King George V. *Horiz*—6 pi. Badge of Cyprus.

24 Ruins of Vouni Palace

25 Small Marble Forum, Salamis

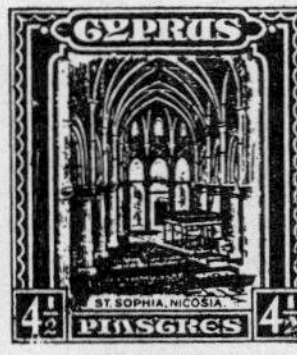

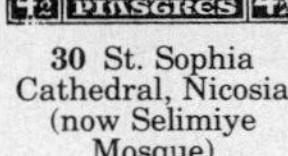

30 St. Sophia Cathedral, Nicosia (now Selimiye Mosque)

31 Bayraktar Mosque, Nicosia

(Recess Waterlow)

**1934 (1 Dec).** *T* **24/5, 30/31** *and similar designs. Wmk Mult Script CA (sideways on* ½ *pi.,* 1½ *pi,* 2½ *pi.,* 4½ *pi.,* 6 *pi.,* 9 *pi., and* 18 *pi.), P* 12½.

133 ¼ pi. ultramarine and orange-brown .. 25 50
a. Imperf between (vert pair) .. £12000 £12000
134 ½ pi. green .. .. .. .. 45 40
a. Imperf between (vert pair) .. £8500 £9000
135 ¾ pi. black and violet .. .. .. 70 10
a. Imperf between (vert pair) .. £12000
136 1 pi. black and red-brown .. .. 70 80
a. Imperf between (vert pair) .. £9000 £9000
b. Imperf between (horiz pair) .. £7500
137 1½ pi. carmine .. .. .. .. 70 45
138 2½ pi. ultramarine .. .. .. .. 1·25 80
139 4½ pi. black and crimson .. .. .. 3·00 2·25
140 6 pi. black and blue .. .. .. 6·00 11·00
141 9 pi. sepia and violet .. .. .. 3·00 3·25
142 18 pi. black and olive-green .. .. 35·00 26·00
143 45 pi. green and black .. .. .. 48·00 38·00
133/43 .. .. .. .. *Set of* 11 85·00 75·00
133/43 Perf "Specimen" .. .. *Set of* 11 £275

Designs: *Horiz.*—¾ pi. Church of St. Barnabas and St. Hilarion, Peristerona; 1 pi. Roman theatre, Soli; 1½ pi. Kyrenia Harbour; 2½ pi. Kolossi Castle; 45 pi. Forest scene, Troodos. *Vert*—9 pi. Queen's Window, St. Hilarion Castle; 18 pi. Buyuk Khan, Nicosia.

**1935 (6 May).** *Silver Jubilee. As Nos.* 91/4 *of Antigua, but ptd by Waterlow & Sons. P* 11 × 12.

144 ¾ pi. ultramarine and grey .. .. 55 15
145 1½ pi. deep blue and scarlet.. .. .. 2·25 2·50
k. Kite and horizontal log .. .. 65·00
146 2½ pi. brown and deep blue .. .. 3·75 1·50
147 9 pi. slate and purple .. .. .. 8·00 4·75
144/7 .. .. .. .. *Set of* 4 13·00 8·00
144/7 Perf "Specimen" .. .. *Set of* 4 95·00

For illustration of plate variety see Catalogue Introduction.

**1937 (12 May).** *Coronation. As Nos.* 95/7 *of Antigua. P* 11×11½

148 ¾ pi. grey .. .. .. .. .. 75 20
149 1½ pi. carmine .. .. .. .. 1·25 80
150 2½ pi. blue .. .. .. .. 3·50 1·75
148/50 .. .. .. .. *Set of* 3 5·00 2·50
148/50 Perf "Specimen" .. .. *Set of* 3 75·00

35 Vouni Palace

36 Map of Cyprus

37 Othello's Tower, Famagusta

38 King George VI

(Recess Waterlow)

**1938 (12 May)–1951.** *T* **35** *to* **38** *and other designs as* 1934, *but with portrait of King George VI. Wmk Mult Script CA. P* 12½.

151 35 ¼ pi. ultramarine and orange-brown .. 10 10
152 25 ½ pi. green .. .. .. .. 15 10
152a – ½ pi. violet (2.7.51) .. .. .. 1·50 20
153 – ¾ pi. black and violet .. .. .. 5·00 20
154 – 1 pi. orange .. .. .. .. 30 10
a. Perf 13½ × 12½ (1944) .. .. £300 25·00
155 – 1½ pi. carmine .. .. .. .. 4·50 1·50
155a – 1½ pi. violet (15.3.43) .. .. .. 20 30
155ab – 1½ pi. green (2.7.51) .. .. .. 1·75 30
155b – 2 pi. black and carmine (2.2.42) .. 20 10
c. Perf 12½ × 13½ (10.44) .. .. 1·75 3·25
156 – 2½ pi. ultramarine .. .. .. 10·00 4·00
156a – 3 pi. ultramarine (2.2.42) .. .. 35 15
156b – 4 pi. ultramarine (2.7.51) .. .. 3·00 30
157 36 4½ pi. grey .. .. .. .. 30 10
158 31 6 pi. black and blue .. .. .. 45 70
159 37 9 pi. black and purple .. .. .. 50 15
160 – 18 pi. black and olive-green .. .. 3·50 85
*a. Black and sage-green* (19.8.47) .. 5·00 1·50
161 – 45 pi. green and black .. .. .. 12·00 2·25
162 38 90 pi. mauve and black.. .. .. 23·00 3·50
163 £1 scarlet and indigo .. .. .. 40·00 17·00
151/63 .. .. .. .. *Set of* 19 95·00 28·00
151/63 Perf "Specimen" .. .. *Set of* 16 £375

Designs: *Horiz*—¾ pi., 2 pi. Peristerona Church; 1 pi. Soli Theatre; 1½ pi. Kyrenia Harbour; 2½ pi., 3 pi., 4 pi. Kolossi Castle; 45 pi. Forest scene. *Vert*—18 pi. Buyuk Khan, Nicosia.

**1946 (21 Oct).** *Victory. As Nos.* 110/11 *of Antigua.*

164 1½ pi. deep violet .. .. .. .. 15 10
165 3 pi. blue .. .. .. .. .. 15 15
164/5 Perf "Specimen" .. .. *Set of* 2 65·00

Extra decoration (R. 3/5)

**1948 (20 Dec).** *Royal Silver Wedding. As Nos.* 112/13 *of Antigua.*

166 1½ pi. violet .. .. .. .. 30 20
a. Extra decoration .. .. .. 25·00
167 £1 indigo .. .. .. .. 42·00 35·00

**1949 (10 Oct).** *75th Anniv of Universal Postal Union. As Nos.* 114/17 *of Antigua but inscr "CYPRUS" (recess).*

168 1½ pi. violet .. .. .. .. 60 55
169 2 pi. carmine-red .. .. .. .. 80 80
170 3 pi. deep blue .. .. .. .. 85 90
171 9 pi. purple .. .. .. .. 1·00 1·00
168/71 .. .. .. .. *Set of* 4 3·00 3·00

**1953 (2 June).** *Coronation. As No.* 120 *of Antigua, but ptd by B.W.*

172 1½ pi. black and emerald .. .. .. 35 10

**NEW INFORMATION**

The editor is always interested to correspond with people who have new information that will improve or correct the Catalogue.

**(New Currency. 1000 mils. = £1)**

**39** Carobs **42** Copper Pyrites Mine

**49** St. Hilarion Castle **52** Coins of Salamis, Paphos, Citium and Idalium

(Recess B.W.)

**1955** (1 Aug)–**60**. *T* **39, 42, 49, 52** *and similar designs. Wmk Mult Script CA. P* 13½ *(Nos.* 183/5*) or* 11½ *(others).*

173 2 m. blackish brown .. .. .. 10 40
174 3 m. blue-violet .. .. .. .. 10 15
175 5 m. brown-orange .. .. .. 10 10
*a. Orange-brown* (17.9.58) .. .. 40 10
176 10 m. deep brown and deep green .. 30 10
177 15 m. olive-green and indigo .. .. 1·40 35
*aa. Yellow-olive and indigo* (17.9.58) .. 5·50 1·50
*a. Bistre and indigo* (14.6.60) .. .. 8·00 2·50
178 20 m. brown and deep bright blue .. 25 15
179 25 m. deep turquoise-blue .. .. 50 35
*a. Greenish blue* (17.9.58) .. .. 3·25 1·50
180 30 m. black and carmine-lake .. .. 35 10
181 35 m. orange-brown & deep turquoise-blue 30 40
182 40 m. deep green and sepia .. .. 40 60
183 50 m. turquoise-blue and reddish brown .. 30 30
184 100 m. mauve and bluish green .. .. 6·50 40
185 250 m. deep grey-blue and brown .. .. 7·00 4·00
186 500 m. slate and purple .. .. 26·00 9·50
187 £1 brown-lake and slate .. .. 26·00 20·00
173/87 .. .. .. .. *Set of* 15 60·00 32·00

Designs: *Vert* (*as T* **40**)—3 m. Grapes; 5 m. Oranges. (*as T* **52**)—£1 Arms of Byzantium, Lusignan, Ottoman Empire and Venice. *Horiz* (as *T* **42**)—15 m. Troodos Forest; 20 m. Beach of Aphrodite; 25 m. Ancient coin of Paphos; 30 m. Kyrenia; 35 m. Harvest in Mesaoria; 40 m. Famagusta Harbour. (*as T* **50**)—100 m. Hala Sultan Tekke; 250 m. Kanakaria Church.

ΚΥΠΡΙΑΚΗ
ΔΗΜΟΚΡΑΤΙΑ
KIBRIS
CUMHURIYETI

(**54** "Cyprus Republic") **55** Map of Cyprus

**1960** (16 Aug)–**61**. *Nos.* 173/87 *optd as T* **54**, *in blue by B.W. Opt larger on Nos.* 191/7 *and in two lines on Nos.* 198/202.

188 2 m. blackish brown .. .. .. 20 20
189 3 m. blue-violet .. .. .. 20 15
190 5 m. brown-orange .. .. .. 35 10
*a. Orange-brown* (15.8.61) .. .. 40 10
191 10 m. deep brown and deep green .. 30 10
192 15 m. yellow-bistre and indigo .. .. 75 10
*a. Olive-green and indigo* .. .. 85·00 15·00
*b. Brownish bis & dp indigo* (10.10.61) 3·25 90
193 20 m. brown and deep bright blue .. 40 30
a. Opt double .. .. .. .. † £7000
194 25 m. deep turquoise-blue .. .. 80 45
*a. Greenish blue* .. .. .. 4·75 2·75
195 30 m. black and carmine-lake .. .. 1·25 10
a. Opt double .. .. .. .. † £11000
196 35 m. orange-brown & dp turquoise-blue 1·50 20
197 40 m. deep green and sepia .. .. 2·00 65
198 50 m. turquoise-blue and reddish brown .. 2·00 40
199 100 m. mauve and bluish green .. .. 9·00 40
200 250 m. deep grey-blue and brown .. .. 25·00 2·00
201 500 m. slate and purple .. .. 40·00 15·00
202 £1 brown-lake and slate .. .. 60·00 42·00
188/202 .. .. .. .. *Set of* 15 £130 55·00

Only a single used example of No. 195a is known.

(Recess B.W.)

**1960** (16 Aug). *Constitution of Republic. W w* **12.** *P* 11½.

203 **55** 10 m. sepia and deep green .. .. 30 10
204 30 m. ultramarine and deep brown .. 40 10
205 100 m. purple and deep slate .. .. 1·25 65
203/5 .. .. .. .. *Set of* 3 1·75 75

**PRINTERS.** All the following were lithographed by Aspioti-Elka, Athens, *unless otherwise stated.*

**56** Doves

(Des T. Kurpershoek)

**1962** (19 Mar). *Europa. P* 14 × 13.

206 **56** 10 m. purple and mauve .. .. 10 10
207 40 m. ultramarine and cobalt .. .. 20 10
208 100 m. emerald and pale green .. .. 20 15
206/8 .. .. .. .. *Set of* 3 40 30

**57** Campaign Emblem

**1962** (14 May). *Malaria Eradication. P* 14 × 13½.

209 **57** 10 m. black and olive-green .. .. 20 10
210 30 m. black and brown .. .. .. 25 10

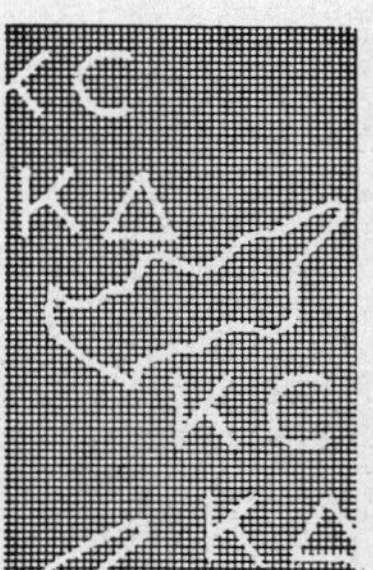

**58** Mult K C K Δ and Map

**WATERMARK VARIETIES.** The issues printed by Aspioti-Elka with W **58** are known with the vertical stamps having the watermark normal or inverted and the horizontal stamps with the watermark reading upwards or downwards.

**62** Selimiye Mosque, Nicosia **63** St. Barnabas's Church

**1962** (17 Sept). *T* **62/3** *and similar designs.* W **58** (*sideways on* 25, 30, 40, 50, 250 *m.*, £1). *P* 13½ × 14 (*vert*) *or* 14 × 13½ (*horiz*).

211 3 m. deep brown and orange-brown .. .. 10 30
212 5 m. purple and grey-green .. .. 10 10
213 10 m. black and yellow-green .. .. 15 10
214 15 m. black and reddish purple .. .. 20 15
215 25 m. deep brown and chestnut .. .. 30 20
216 30 m. deep blue and light blue .. .. 20 10
217 35 m. light green and blue .. .. 35 10
218 40 m. black and violet-blue .. .. 1·25 1·25
219 50 m. bronze-green and bistre .. .. 50 10
220 100 m. deep brown and yellow-brown .. 3·50 30
221 250 m. black and cinnamon .. .. 8·00 2·00
222 500 m. deep brown and light green .. 17·00 9·00
223 £1 bronze-green and grey .. .. 22·00 23·00
211/23 .. .. .. .. *Set of* 13 48·00 32·00

Designs: *Vert*—3 m. Iron Age jug; 5 m. Grapes; 10 m. Bronze head of Apollo; 35 m. Head of Aphrodite; 100 m. Hala Sultan Tekke; 500 m. Mouflon. *Horiz*—30 m. Temple of Apollo Hylates; 40 m. Skiing, Troodos; 50 m. Salamis Gymnasium; 250 m. Bella Paise Abbey; £1 St. Hilarion Castle.

**72** Europa "Tree"

(Des Lex Weyer)

**1963** (28 Jan). *Europa.* W **58** (*sideways*). *P* 14 × 13½.

224 **72** 10 m. bright blue and black .. .. 75 15
225 40 m. carmine-red and black .. .. 3·25 2·00
226 150 m. emerald-green and black .. .. 6·00 3·75
224/6 .. .. .. .. *Set of* 3 9·00 5·50

**73** Harvester **75** Wolf Cub in Camp

**1963** (21 Mar). *Freedom from Hunger. T* **73** *and similar vert design.* W **58.** *P* 13½ × 14.

227 25 m. ochre, sepia and bright blue .. .. 50 25
228 75 m. grey, black and lake .. .. 2·75 1·00

Design:— 75 m. Demeter, Goddess of Corn.

**1963** (21 Aug). *50th Anniv of Cyprus Scout Movement and Third Commonwealth Scout Conference, Platres. T* **75** *and similar vert designs. Multicoloured.* W **58.** *P* 13½ × 14.

229 3 m. Type **75** .. .. .. .. 10 15
230 20 m. Sea Scout .. .. .. .. 35 10
231 150 m. Scout with Mouflon .. .. 1·00 1·25
229/31 .. .. .. .. *Set of* 3 1·25 1·40
**MS**231*a* 110 × 90 mm. Nos. 229/31 (*sold at* 250 *m.*). Imperf .. .. .. .. £180 £225

**78** Nurse tending Child **79** Children's Centre, Kyrenia

**1963** (9 Sept). *Centenary of Red Cross.* W **58** (*sideways on* 100 *m.*). *P* 13½ × 14 (10 *m.*) *or* 14 × 13½ (100 *m.*).

232 **78** 10 m. red, blue, grey-bl, chestnut & blk 50 15
233 **79** 100 m. red, green, black and blue .. 3·50 3·50

**80** "Co-operation" (emblem) **(81)**

(Des A. Holm)

**1963** (4 Nov). *Europa.* W **58** (*sideways*). *P* 14 × 13½.

234 **80** 20 m. buff, blue and violet .. .. 1·25 40
235 30 m. grey, yellow and blue .. .. 1·50 40
236 150 m. buff, blue and orange-brown .. 6·00 7·50
234/6 .. .. .. .. *Set of* 3 8·00 7·50

**1964** (5 May). *U.N. Security Council's Cyprus Resolutions, March,* 1964, *Nos.* 213, 216, 218/20, *optd with T* **81** *in blue by Govt Printing Office, Nicosia.*

237 10 m. black and yellow-green .. .. 15 10
238 30 m. deep blue and light blue .. .. 15 10
239 40 m. black and violet-blue .. .. 15 15
240 50 m. bronze-green and bistre .. .. 15 10
241 100 m. deep brown and yellow-brown .. 20 40
237/41 .. .. .. .. *Set of* 5 70 70

**82** Soli Theatre

**1964** (15 June). *400th Birth Anniv of Shakespeare. T* **82** *and similar horiz designs. Multicoloured.* W **58.** *P* 13½ × 13.

242 15 m. Type **82** .. .. .. .. 35 15
243 35 m. Curium Theatre .. .. .. 35 15
244 50 m. Salamis Theatre .. .. .. 35 15
245 100 m. Othello Tower and scene from *Othello* .. 1·00 1·25
242/5 .. .. .. .. *Set of* 4 1·75 1·50

**86** Running **89** Europa "Flower"

**1964** (6 July). *Olympic Games, Tokyo. T* **86** *and similar designs.* W **58** (*sideways,* 25 *m.* 75 *m.*). *P* 13½ × 14 (10 *m.*) *or* 14 × 13½ (*others*)

246 10 m. brown, black and yellow .. .. 15 10
247 25 m. brown, blue and blue-grey .. .. 25 10
248 75 m. brown, black and orange-red .. .. 35 55
246/8 .. .. .. .. *Set of* 3 65 65
**MS**248*a* 110 × 90 mm. Nos. 246/8 (*sold at* 250 *m.*). Imperf .. .. .. .. 5·50 12·00

Designs: *Horiz*—25 m. Boxing; 75 m. Charioteers.

(Des G. Bétemps)

**1964** (14 Sept). *Europa.* W **58.** *P* 13½ × 14.

249 **89** 20 m. chestnut and light ochre .. .. 50 10
250 30 m. ultramarine and light blue .. .. 60 10
251 150 m. olive and light blue-green .. .. 3·25 3·50
249/51 .. .. .. .. *Set of* 3 4·00 3·50

90 Dionysus and Acme

91 Silenus (satyr)

**1964** (26 Oct). *Cyprus Wines. T* **90/1** *and similar multicoloured designs. W* **58** *(sideways, 10 m., or 100 m.). P* 14 × 13½ *(horiz)* 13½ × 14 *(vert).*

252 10 m. Type **90** .. .. .. .. .. 25 10
253 40 m. Type **91** .. .. .. .. .. 55 30
254 50 m. Commandaria Wine *(vert)* .. .. 65 10
255 100 m. Wine factory *(horiz)* .. .. .. 1·75 85
252/5 .. .. .. .. .. *Set of* 4 3·00 1·25

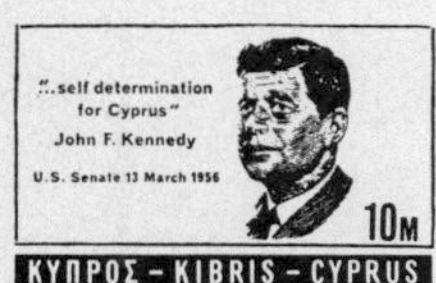

94 President Kennedy

**1965** (15 Feb). *President Kennedy Commemoration. W* **58** *(sideways). P* 14 × 13½.

256 **94** 10 m. ultramarine .. .. .. .. 10 10
257 40 m. green .. .. .. .. 15 15
258 100 m. carmine-lake .. .. .. .. 20 15
256/8 .. .. .. .. .. *Set of* 3 35 30
**MS**258*a* 110 × 90 mm. Nos. 256/8 *(sold at* 250 *m.).* Imperf .. .. .. .. .. .. .. 2·50 5·00

95 "Old Age"

96 "Maternity"

**1965** (12 Apr). *Social Insurance Law. T* **95/6** *and similar design. W* **58.** *P* 13½ × 12 *(75 m.) or* 13½ × 14 *(others).*

259 30 m. drab and dull green .. .. .. 20 10
260 45 m. light grey-green, blue & dp ultramarine 20 10
261 75 m. red-brown and flesh .. .. .. 80 1·25
259/61 .. .. .. .. *Set of* 3 1·10 1·25

Design: *Vert as T* **95**—45 m. "Accident".

98 I.T.U. Emblem and Symbols

**1965** (17 May). *I.T.U. Centenary, W* **58** *(sideways). P* 14 × 13½.

262 **98** 15 m. black, brown and yellow .. .. 50 20
263 60 m. black, green and light green .. 2·75 1·50
264 75 m. black, indigo and light blue .. 3·00 1·75
262/4 .. .. .. .. .. *Set of* 3 5·50 3·00

99 I.C.Y. Emblem

**1965** (17 May). *International Co-operation Year. W* **58** *(sideways). P* 14 × 13½.

265 **99** 50 m. brown, dp green & lt yellow-brown 1·00 10
266 100 m. purple, dp green & lt purple .. 1·50 30

100 Europa "Sprig"

**U. N.**
**Resolution**
**on Cyprus**
**18 Dec. 1965**
(101)

(Des. H. Karlsson)

**1965** (27 Sept). *Europa. W* **58** *(sideways). P* 14 × 13½.

267 **100** 5 m. black, orange-brown and orange .. 15 10
268 40 m. black, orange-brown & lt emerald 1·25 1·25
269 150 m. black, orange-brown & lt grey .. 2·25 2·75
267/9 .. .. .. .. .. *Set of* 3 3·25 3·75

**1966** (31 Jan). *U.N. General Assembly's Cyprus Resolution,* 18 *December* 1965. *Nos.* 211, 213, 216 *and* 221 *optd with T* **101**, *in blue by Govt Printing Office, Nicosia.*

270 3 m. deep brown and orange-brown .. 10 25
271 10 m. black and yellow-green .. .. 10 10
272 30 m. deep blue and light blue .. .. 20 15
273 250 m. black and cinnamon .. .. .. 45 1·75
270/3 .. .. .. .. .. *Set of* 4 75 2·00

102 Discovery of St. Barnabas's Body

104 St. Barnabas (icon)

103 St. Barnabas's Chapel

105 "Privileges of Cyprus Church"
*(Actual size 102 × 82 mm)*

**1966** (25 Apr). 1900*th Death Anniv of St. Barnabas. W* **58** *(sideways on* 15 *m.,* 100 *m.,* 250 *m.). P* 14 × 13 *(25 m). or* 13 × 14 *(others).*

274 **102** 15 m. multicoloured .. .. .. 15 10
275 **103** 25 m. drab, black and blue .. .. 15 10
276 **104** 100 m. multicoloured .. .. .. 35 1·25
274/6 .. .. .. .. .. *Set of* 3 60 1·25
**MS**277 110 × 91 mm. **105** 250 m. mult. Imperf .. 4·00 12·00

**5 M**

**Ξ**

(106)

107 General K. S. Thimayya and U. N. Emblem

**1966** (30 May). *No.* 211 *surch with T* **106** *by Govt Printing Office, Nicosia.*

278 5 m. on 3 m. deep brown & orange-brown 10 10

**1966** (6 June) *General Thimayya Commemoration. W* **58** *(sideways). P* 14 × 13.

279 **107** 50 m. black and light orange-brown .. 10 10

108 Europa "Ship"

(Des G. and J. Bender)

**1966** (26 Sept). *Europa. W* **58.** *P* 13½ × 14.

280 **108** 20 m. green and blue .. .. .. 30 10
281 30 m. bright purple and blue .. .. 30 10
282 150 m. bistre and blue .. .. .. 1·10 1·90
280/2 .. .. .. .. .. *Set of* 3 1·50 1·90

110 Church of St. James, Trikomo

119 Vase of 7th Century B.C.

120 Bronze Ingot-stand

**1966** (21 Nov)–**69**. *T* **110, 119/20** *and similar designs. W* **58** *(sideways on* 3, 15, 25, 50, 250, 500 *m.,* £1*). P* 12×13 *(3 m.),* 13×12 *(5, 10 m.),* 14×13½ *(15, 25, 50 m.),* 13½×14 *(20, 30, 35, 40, 100 m.) or* 13×14 *(others).*

283 3 m. grey-green, buff, black & light blue 30 30
284 5 m. bistre, black and steel-blue .. .. 10 10
*a. Brownish bistre, black and steel-blue* (18.4.69) .. .. .. .. .. .. 30 10
285 10 m. black and bistre .. .. .. 10 20
286 15 m. black, chestnut & light orange-brown 15 10
287 20 m. black, slate and brown .. .. 90 75
288 25 m. black, drab and lake-brown .. .. 30 10
289 30 m. black, yellow-ochre and turquoise .. 50 40
290 35 m. yellow, black and carmine-red .. 50 50
291 40 m. black, grey and new blue .. .. 70 40
a. Grey (background) omitted ..
292 50 m. black, slate and brown .. .. 90 10
293 100 m. black, red, pale buff and grey .. 2·75 15
294 250 m. olive-green, black & lt yellow-ochre 2·00 20
295 500 m. multicoloured .. .. .. 2·75 70
296 £1 black, drab and slate .. .. 6·50 5·50
283/96 .. .. .. .. *Set of* 14 16·00 8·25

Designs: *Horiz (as T* **110**)—3 m. Stavrovouni Monastery. *(As T* **119**)—15 m. Ancient ship (painting); 25 m. Sleeping Eros (marble statue); 50 m. Silver coin of Alexander the Great. *Vert (as T* **110**)—10 m. Zeno of Cibium (marble bust). *(As T* **119**)—20 m. Silver coin of Evagoras I; 30 m. St. Nicholas Cathedral, Famagusta; 35 m. Gold sceptre from Curium; 40 m. Silver dish from 7th century. *(As T* **120**)—500 m. "The Rape of Ganymede" (mosaic); £1 Aphrodite (marble statue).

123 Power Station, Limassol

124 Cogwheels

**1967** (10 Apr). *First Development Programme. T* **123** *and similar designs but horiz. Multicoloured. W* **58** *(sideways on 15 to 100 m.). P* 13½ × 14 *(10 m.) or* 14 × 13½ *(others).*

297 10 m. Type **123** .. .. .. .. 10 10
298 15 m. Arghaka-Maghounda Dam .. .. 15 10
299 35 m. Troodos Highway .. .. .. 20 10
300 50 m. Hilton Hotel, Nicosia .. .. .. 20 10
301 100 m. Famagusta Harbour .. .. .. 25 50
297/301 .. .. .. .. *Set of* 5 70 70

(Des O. Bonnevalle)

**1967** (2 May). *Europa. W* **58.** *P* 13½ × 14.

302 **124** 20 m. olive-green, green & pale yell-grn 35 10
303 30 m. reddish violet, lilac and pale lilac 35 10
304 150 m. brown, light reddish brown and pale yellow-brown .. .. .. 1·00 1·25
302/4 .. .. .. .. *Set of* 3 1·50 1·25

**125** Throwing the Javelin

**126** Running (amphora) and Map of Eastern Mediterranean
(*Actual size* 97 × 77 *mm*)

**1967** (4 Sept). *Athletic Games, Nicosia. T* **125** *and similar designs and T* **126**. *Multicoloured. W* **58**. *P* 13½ × 13.
305 15 m. Type **125** .. .. .. .. .. 20 10
306 35 m. Running .. .. .. .. .. 20 30
307 100 m. High-jumping .. .. .. .. 30 50
305/7 .. .. .. .. .. *Set of* 3 70 80
**MS**308 110 × 90 mm. 250 m. Type **126** (wmk sideways). Imperf .. .. .. .. .. .. 1·50 4·00

**127** Ancient Monuments **128** St. Andrew Mosaic

**1967** (16 Oct). *International Tourist Year. T* **127** *and similar horiz designs. Multicoloured. W* **58**. *P* 13 × 13½.
309 10 m. Type **127** .. .. .. .. .. 10 10
310 40 m. Famagusta Beach .. .. .. .. 15 60
311 50 m. "Comet" at Nicosia Airport .. .. .. 15 10
312 100 m. Skier and youth hostel .. .. .. .. 20 65
309/12 .. .. .. .. .. *Set of* 4 50 1·25

**1967** (8 Nov). *Centenary of St. Andrew's Monastery. W* **58** (*sideways*). *P* 13 × 13½.
313 **128** 25 m. multicoloured .. .. .. .. 10 10

**129** "The Crucifixion" (icon) **130** The Three Magi

(Photo French Govt Ptg Wks, Paris)

**1967** (8 Nov). *Cyprus Art Exhibition, Paris. P* 12½ × 13½.
314 **129** 50 m. multicoloured .. .. .. .. 10 10

**1967** (8 Nov). *20th Anniv of U.N.E.S.C.O. W* **58** (*sideways*). *P* 13 × 13½.
315 **130** 75 m. multicoloured .. .. .. .. 15 20

**131** Human Rights Emblem over Stars **132** Human Rights and U.N. Emblems

**133** Scroll of Declaration
(*Actual size* 95 × 75½ *mm*)

**1968** (18 Mar). *Human Rights Year. W* **58**. *P* 13 × 14.
316 **131** 50 m. multicoloured .. .. .. .. 10 10
317 **132** 90 m. multicoloured .. .. .. .. 30 50
**MS**318 95 × 75½ mm. **133** 250 m. multicoloured. W **58** (sideways). Imperf. .. .. .. .. .. 80 3·00

**134** Europa "Key"

(Des H. Schwarzenbach)

**1968** (29 Apr). *Europa. W* **58** (*sideways*). *P* 14 × 13.
319 **134** 20 m. multicoloured .. .. .. .. 20 10
320 30 m. multicoloured .. .. .. .. 20 10
321 150 m. multicoloured .. .. .. .. 45 1·25
319/21 .. .. .. .. *Set of* 3 75 1·25

**135** U.N. Children's Fund Symbol and Boy drinking Milk **136** Aesculapius

(Des A. Tassos)

**1968** (2 Sept). *21st Anniv of U.N.I.C.E.F. W* **58** (*sideways*). *P* 14 × 13.
322 **135** 35 m. yellow-brown, carmine-red & blk 10 10

(Des A. Tassos)

**1968** (2 Sept). *20th Anniv of W.H.O. W* **58**. *P* 13 × 14.
323 **136** 50 m. black, green and light olive .. 10 10

**137** Throwing the Discus **138** I.L.O. Emblem

**1968** (24 Oct). *Olympic Games, Mexico. T* **137** *and similar designs. Multicoloured. W* **58** (*sideways on* 100 *m.*). *P* 14 × 13 (100 *m.*) *or* 13 × 14 (*others*).
324 10 m. Type **137** .. .. .. .. .. 10 10
325 25 m. Sprint finish .. .. .. .. .. 10 10
326 100 m. Olympic Stadium (*horiz*) .. .. .. 20 75
324/6 .. .. .. .. .. *Set of* 3 30 80

(Des A. Tassos)

**1969** (3 Mar). *50th Anniv of International Labour Organization. W* **58**. *P* 12 × 13½.
327 **138** 50 m. yellow-brown, blue and light blue 10 10
328 90 m. yellow-brown, black and pale grey 10 25

**139** Mercator's Map of Cyprus, 1554

**140** Blaeu's Map of Cyprus, 1635

**1969** (7 Apr). *First International Congress of Cypriot Studies. W* **58** (*sideways*). *P* 14 × 14½.
329 **139** 35 m. multicoloured .. .. .. 15 3(
330 **140** 50 m. multicoloured .. .. .. 15 1(
a. Wmk upright .. .. .. — 2·5(
ab. Grey (shading on boats and cartouche) omitted .. .. .. £200

**141** Europa Emblem **142** Common Roller

(Des L. Gasbarra and G. Belli)

**1969** (28 Apr). *Europa. W* **58** (*sideways*). *P* 14 × 13½.
331 **141** 20 m. multicoloured .. .. .. 20 1
332 30 m. multicoloured .. .. .. 20 1
333 150 m. multicoloured .. .. .. 70 1·5
331/3 .. .. .. .. .. *Set of* 3 1·00 1·5

**1969** (7 July). *Birds of Cyprus. T* **142** *and similar designs. Multicoloured. W* **58** (*sideways on horiz designs*). *P* 13½ × 12 (*hori[z] designs*) *or* 12 × 13½ (*vert designs*).
334 5 m. Type **142** .. .. .. .. 50 1
335 15 m. Audouin's Gull .. .. .. .. 70 1
336 20 m. Cyprus Warbler .. .. .. .. 75 1
337 30 m. Jay (*vert*) .. .. .. .. 80 1
338 40 m. Hoopoe (*vert*) .. .. .. .. 1·00 3
339 90 m. Eleanora's Falcon (*vert*) .. .. .. 2·25 4·0
334/9 .. .. .. .. .. *Set of* 6 5·50 4·5

The above were printed on glazed Samuel Jones paper with very faint watermark.

**143** "The Nativity" (12th-century Wall Painting)

**145** "Virgin and Child between Archangels Michael and Gabriel" (6th–7th-century Mosaic)
(*Actual size* 102 × 81 *mm*)

**1969** (24 Nov). *Christmas. T* **143** *and similar horiz design, an[d] T* **145**. *Multicoloured. W* **58** (*sideways*). *P* 13½ × 13.
340 20 m. Type **143** .. .. .. .. 10 1
341 45 m. "The Nativity" (14th-century wall painting) .. .. .. .. 10 2
**MS**342 110 × 90 mm. 250 m. Type **145**. Imperf .. 4·25 8·0
a. Grey and light brown omitted .. £1500

**146** Mahatma Gandhi

**1970** (26 Jan). *Birth Centenary of Mahatma Gandhi. W* **58** (*side-ways*). *P* 14 × 13½.
343 **146** 25 m. ultramarine, drab and black .. 15 1
344 75 m. yellow-brown, drab and black .. 20 4

147 "Flaming Sun"

148 Gladioli

(Des L. le Brocquy)

**1970** (4 May). *Europa. W* **58** *(sideways). P* 14 × 13.

345 **147** 20 m. brown, greenish yellow & orange .. 20 10
346 30 m. new blue, greenish yellow & orge .. 20 10
347 150 m. bright purple, greenish yell & orge .. 70 1·50
345/7 .. .. .. .. .. *Set of* 3 1·00 1·50

**1970** (3 Aug). *European Conservation Year. T* **148** *and similar vert designs. Multicoloured. W* **58**. *P* 13 × 13½.

348 10 m. Type **148** .. .. .. .. 10 10
349 50 m. Poppies .. .. .. .. .. 15 10
350 90 m. Giant fennel .. .. .. .. 40 1·50
348/50 .. .. .. .. *Set of* 3 60 1·50

149 I.E.Y. Emblem

150 Mosaic

151 Globe, Dove and U.N. Emblem

(Des G. Simonis (75 m.))

**1970** (7 Sept). *International Events. W* **58** *(sideways on horiz designs). P* 13 × 14 *(5 m.), or* 14 × 13 *(others).*

351 **149** 5 m. black, red-brown & lt yellow-brn 10 10
352 **150** 15 m. multicoloured .. .. .. 10 10
353 **151** 75 m. multicoloured .. .. .. 15 35
351/3 .. .. .. .. .. *Set of* 3 25 45

Events:—5 m. International Education Year; 15 m. 50th General Assembly of International Vine and Wine Office; 75 m. 25th Anniv of United Nations.

152 Virgin and Child

153 Cotton Napkin

(Photo Harrison)

**1970** (23 Nov). *Christmas. Wall-painting from Church of Panayia Podhythou, Galata. T* **152** *and similar multicoloured designs. P* 14 × 14½.

354 25 m. Archangel (facing right) .. .. 15 15
a. Horiz strip of 3. Nos. 354/6 .. .. 40
355 25 m. Type **152** .. .. .. .. 15 15
356 25 m. Archangel (facing left) .. .. .. 15 15
357 75 m. Virgin and Child between Archangels 20 35
354/7 .. .. .. .. .. *Set of* 4 60 70

The 75 m. is horiz, size 42 × 30 mm, and the 25 m. values are vert, size as T **152**.

Nos. 354/6 were issued in *se-tenant* strips of three, throughout the sheet. The triptych thus formed is depicted in its entirety on the 75 m. value.

**1971** (22 Feb). *Multicoloured designs as T* **153**. *W* **58** *(sideways on horiz designs). (a) Vert designs* 23 × 33 *mm. P* 12 × 13½.

358 3 m. Type **153** .. .. .. .. 20 40
359 5 m. St. George and Dragon (19th-cent bas-relief) .. .. .. .. .. 10 10

*(b) Vert (10, 20, 25, 40, 50, 75 m.) or horiz (15, 30, 90 m.) designs, each* 24 × 37 *or* 37 × 24 *mm. P* 13 × 14 *(15, 30, 90 m) or* 14 × 13 *(others)*

360 10 m. Woman in festival costume .. .. 15 20
361 15 m. Archaic Bichrome Kylix (cup) .. 20 10
a. Vert laid paper .. .. .. .. 60
362 20 m. A pair of donors (St. Mamas Church) 35 30
363 25 m. "The Creation" (6th-cent mosaic) .. 30 10
364 30 m. Athena and horse-drawn chariot (4th-cent B.C. terracotta) .. .. 30 10
365 40 m. Shepherd playing pipe (14th-cent fresco) .. .. .. .. .. 1·00 80
366 50 m. Hellenistic head (3rd cent B.C.) .. 80 10
367 75 m. "Angel" (mosaic detail), Kanakaria Church .. .. .. .. .. 1·75 50
368 90 m. Mycenaean silver bowl .. .. 2·50 1·25

*(c) Horiz (250, 500 m.) or vert (£1) designs, each* 41 × 28 *or* 28 × 41 *mm. P* 13½ × 13 *(250, 500 m.) or* 13 × 13½ *(£1)*

369 250 m. Moufflon (detail of 3rd-cent mosaic) *(shades)* .. .. .. .. .. 2·75 40
370 500 m. Ladies and sacred tree (detail, 6th-cent amphora) .. .. .. .. 1·25 70
371 £1 Horned god from Enkomi (12th-cent bronze statue) .. .. .. .. 2·50 1·00
358/71 .. .. .. .. .. *Set of* 14 12·50 5·25

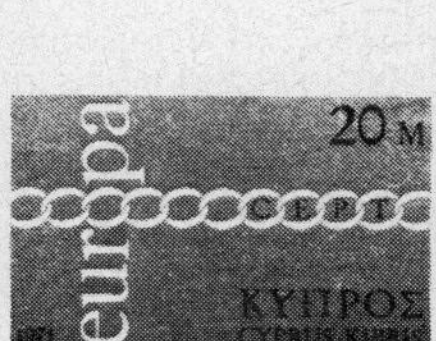


154 Europa Chain

155 Archbishop Kyprianos

(Des H. Haflidason)

**1971** (3 May). *Europa, W* **58** *(sideways). P* 14 × 13

372 **154** 20 m. pale blue, ultramarine and black 20 10
373 30 m. apple green, myrtle-green & blk 20 10
374 150 m. lemon, bright green and black .. 70 1·75
372/4 .. .. .. .. .. *Set of* 3 1·00 1·75

The above were printed on glazed paper with very faint watermark.

**1971** (9 July). *150th Anniv. of Greek War of Independence. T* **155** *and similar multicoloured designs. W* **58** *(sideways on 30 m.). P* 13½ × 12½ *(30 m.) or* 12½ × 13½ *(others).*

375 15 m. Type **155** .. .. .. .. 10 10
376 30 m. "Taking the Oath" *(horiz)* .. .. 10 10
377 100 m. Bishop Germanos, flag and freedom-fighters .. .. .. .. .. 20 50
375/7 .. .. .. .. *Set of* 3 30 55

156 Kyrenia Castle

157 Madonna and Child in Stable

**1971** (20 Sept). *Tourism. T* **156** *and similar multicoloured designs. W* **58** *(sideways on 15 and 100 m.). P* 13½ × 13 *(15 m., 100 m.) or* 13 × 13½ *(others).*

378 15 m. Type **156** .. .. .. .. 10 10
379 25 m. Gourd on sunny beach *(vert)* .. 10 10
380 60 m. Mountain scenery *(vert)* .. .. 20 60
381 100 m. Church of St. Evlalios, Lambousa .. 20 65
378/81 .. .. .. .. *Set of* 4 45 1·25

(Des A. Tassos)

**1971** (22 Nov). *Christmas. T* **157** *and similar vert designs. Multicoloured. W* **58**. *P* 13 × 14.

382 10 m. Type **157** .. .. .. .. 10 10
a. Horiz strip of 3. Nos. 382/4 .. .. 35
383 50 m. The Three Wise Men .. .. .. 15 35
384 100 m. The Shepherds .. .. .. 20 35
382/4 .. .. .. .. .. *Set of* 3 35 70

The 10 m. was issued in sheets of 100, and all three values were printed horizontally *se-tenant* in sheets of 36, the order being 50, 10 and 100 m.

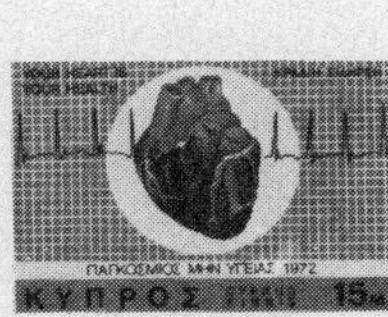


158 Heart

159 "Communications"

**1972** (11 Apr). *World Health Month. W* **58** *(sideways). P* 13½ × 12.

385 **158** 15 m. multicoloured .. .. .. 10 10
386 50 m. multicoloured .. .. .. 20 45

(Des P. Huovinen)

**1972** (22 May). *Europa. W* **58**. *P* 12½ × 13½.

387 **159** 20 m. yellow-orge, sepia & pale grey-brn 30 15
388 30 m. yell-orge, brt dp ultram & cobalt 30 15
389 150 m. yellow-orange, myrtle-green and pale-turquoise-green .. .. 1·75 2·75
387/9 .. .. .. .. .. *Set of* 3 2·10 2·75

160 Archery

**1972** (24 July). *Olympic Games. T* **160** *and similar horiz designs. Multicoloured. W* **58** *(sideways). P* 14 × 13.

390 10 m. Type **160** .. .. .. .. 10 10
391 40 m. Wrestling .. .. .. .. 15 10
392 100 m. Football .. .. .. .. 35 70
390/2 .. .. .. .. *Set of* 3 50 80

161 Stater of Marion

162 Bathing the Child Jesus

**1972** (25 Sept). *Ancient Coins of Cyprus* (1st series), *T* **161** *and similar horiz designs. W* **58** *(sideways), P* 14 × 13.

393 20 m. pale turquoise-blue, black and silver .. 20 10
394 30 m. pale violet-blue, black and silver .. 25 10
395 40 m. brownish stone, black and silver .. 30 20
396 100 m. light salmon-pink, black and silver .. 90 1·00
393/6 .. .. .. .. .. *Set of* 4 1·50 1·25

Coins:—30 m. Stater of Paphos; 40 m. Stater of Lapithos, 100 m. Stater of Idalion.

See also Nos. 486/9.

(Des A. Tassos)

**1972** (20 Nov). *Christmas. T* **162** *and similar vert designs showing portions of a mural in the Church of the Holy Cross of Agiasmati. Multicoloured. W* **58** *(sideways on* **MS**400*). P* 13 × 14.

397 10 m. Type **162** .. .. .. .. 10 10
398 20 m. The Magi .. .. .. .. 10 10
399 100 m. The Nativity .. .. .. .. 15 30
397/9 .. .. .. .. .. *Set of* 3 30 35
**MS**400 100 × 90 mm. 250 m. Showing the mural in full. Imperf .. .. .. .. .. .. 1·50 3·50

163 Mount Olympus, Troodos

**1973** (13 Mar). *29th Internation Ski Federation Congress. T* **163** *and similar horiz design. Multicoloured. W* **58** *(sideways). P* 14 × 13.

401 20 m. Type **163** .. .. .. .. 10 10
402 100 m. Congress emblem .. .. .. 25 35

164 Europa "Posthorn"

(Des I. F. Anisdahl)

**1973** (7 May). *Europa. W* **58** *(sideways). P* 14 × 13.

403 **164** 20 m. multicoloured .. .. .. 35 10
404 30 m. multicoloured .. .. .. 35 10
405 150 m. multicoloured .. .. .. 1·40 2·50
403/5 .. .. .. .. .. *Set of* 3 1·90 2·50

165 Archbishop's Palace, Nicosia

20M
(166)

**1973** (23 July). *Traditional Architecture. T* **165** *and similar multicoloured designs. W* **58** *(sideways on 20 and 100 m.). P* 14 × 13 *(20 and 100 m.) or* 13 × 14 *(others).*

406 20 m. Type **165** .. .. .. .. 10 10
407 30 m. House of Hajigeorgajis Cornessios, Nicosia *(vert)* .. .. .. .. 10 10
408 50 m. House at Gourri, 1850 *(vert)* .. 15 10
409 100 n. House at Rizokarpaso, 1772 .. 40 75
406/9 .. .. .. .. .. *Set of* 4 65 90

**1973** (24 Sept). *No. 361 surch with T* **166**.

410 20 m. on 15 m. Archaic Bichrome Kylix (cup) .. .. .. .. .. 15 15
a. Vert laid paper .. .. .. .. 60

167 Scout Emblem

168 Archangel Gabriel

**1973** (24 Sept). *Anniversaries. T* **167** *and similar designs. W* **58** *(sideways on 25 and 35 m.). P* 13 × 14 (10, 50 *and* 100 *m.*) *or* 14 × 13 (*others*).

411 10 m. yellow-olive and deep brown .. .. 20 10
412 25 m. deep blue, and slate-lilac .. .. 20 10
413 35 m. light brown-olive, stone and sage-green 25 25
414 50 m. dull blue and indigo .. .. .. 30 10
415 100 m. brown and sepia.. .. .. .. 70 65
411/15 .. .. .. .. *Set of* 5 1·50 90

Designs and Events: *Vert*—10 m. Type **167** (60th Anniv of Cyprus Boy Scouts); 50 m. Airline emblem (25th Anniv of Cyprus Airways); 100 m. Interpol emblem (50th Anniv of Interpol). *Horiz*—25 m. Outline of Cyprus and E.E.C. nations (Association of Cyprus with the E.E.C.); 35 m. F.A.O. emblem (Tenth Anniv of F.A.O.).

**1973** (26 Nov). *Christmas. Murals from Araka Church. T* **168** *and similar multicoloured designs. W* **58** *(sideways on 100 m.). P* 14 × 13 (100 *m.*) *or* 13 × 14 (*others*).

416 10 m. Type **168** .. .. .. .. 10 10
417 20 m. Madonna and Child .. .. .. 10 10
418 100 m. Araka Church (*horiz*) .. .. .. 40 75
416/18 .. .. .. .. *Set of* 3 45 75

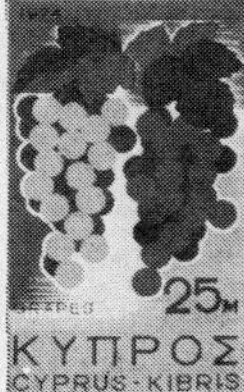


169 Grapes

170 "The Rape of Europa" (Silver Stater of Marion)

**1974** (18 Mar). *Products of Cyprus. T* **169** *and similar vert designs. Multicoloured. W* **58**. *P* 13 × 14.

419 25 m. Type **169** .. .. .. .. 10 15
420 50 m. Grapefruit .. .. .. .. 15 50
a. Horiz strip of 3, Nos. 420/2 .. .. 40
421 50 m. Oranges .. .. .. .. .. 15 50
422 50 m. Lemons .. .. .. .. .. 15 50
419/22 .. .. .. .. *Set of* 4 50 1·50

Nos. 420/2 were printed together, horizontally *se-tenant* throughout the sheet.

**1974** (29 Apr). *Europa. W* **58**. *P* 13½ × 14.

423 **170** 10 m. multicoloured .. .. .. 15 10
424 40 m. multicoloured .. .. .. 40 30
425 150 m. multicoloured .. .. .. 1·50 2·50
423/5 .. .. .. .. *Set of* 3 1·90 2·50

171 Title Page of A. Kyprianos' "History of Cyprus" (1788)

REFUGEE
FUND
ΤΑΜΕΙΟΝ
ΠΡΟΣΦΥΓΩΝ
GÖÇMENLER
FONU

10M

(172)

**1974** (22 July*). *Second International Congress of Cypriot Studies. T* **171** *and similar multicoloured designs. W* **58** *(sideways on 25 m. and* **MS**429). *P* 14 × 13½ (25 *m.*) *or* 13½ × 14 (*others*).

426 10 m. Type **171** .. .. .. .. 10 10
427 25 m. Solon (philosopher) in mosaic (*horiz*) .. 15 10
428 100 m. "St. Neophytos" (wall painting).. .. 60 75
426/8 .. .. .. .. *Set of* 3 70 80
**MS**429 111 × 90 mm. 250 m. Ortelius' map of Cyprus and Greek Islands, 1584. Imperf .. .. 1·75 4·25

*Although this is the date appearing on first day covers the stamps were not put on sale until the 24th.

**1974** (1 Oct). *Obligatory Tax. Refugee Fund No. 359 surch with T* **172**.

430 10 m. on 5 m. St. George and Dragon.. .. 10 10

## MINIMUM PRICE

The minimum price quote is 10p which represents a handling charge rather than a basis for valuing common stamps. For further notes about prices see introductory pages.

SECURITY
COUNCIL
RESOLUTION
353
20 JULY 1974

(173)

174 "Refugees"

**1974** (14 Oct). *U.N. Security Council Resolution* 353. *Nos.* 360, 365, 366 *and* 369 *optd as T* **173**.

431 10 m. Woman in festival costume .. .. 20 10
432 40 m. Shepherd playing pipe .. .. .. 40 50
433 50 m. Hellenistic head.. .. .. .. 40 10
434 250 m. Moufflon (*shades*) .. .. .. 70 2·50
431/4 .. .. .. .. *Set of* 4 1·50 2·75

**1974** (2 Dec). *Obligatory Tax. Refugee Fund. W* **58** *(sideways). P* 12 × 12½.

435 **174** 10 m. black and light grey .. .. 10 10

175 "Virgin and Child between Two Angels", Stavros Church

**1974** (2 Dec). *Christmas. T* **175** *and similar multicoloured designs showing wall-paintings. W* **58** *(sideways on 10 m. and 100 m.). P* 13 × 14 (50 *m.*) *or* 14 × 13 (*others*).

436 10 m. Type **175** .. .. .. .. 10 10
437 50 m. "Adoration of the Magi", Ayios Neophytos Monastery (*vert*) .. .. 20 10
438 100 m. "Flight into Egypt", Ayios Neophytos Monastery .. .. .. 25 45
436/8 .. .. .. .. *Set of* 3 45 50

176 Larnaca–Nicosia Mail-coach, 1878

177 "The Distaff" (M. Kashalos)

(Photo Harrison)

**1975** (17 Feb). *International Events. T* **176** *and similar designs. No wmk. P* 14.

439 **176** 20 m. multicoloured .. .. .. 35 10
440 – 30 m. ultramarine, slate-blk & dull orge 40 65
441 **176** 50 m. multicoloured .. .. .. 40 15
442 – 100 m. multicoloured .. .. .. 60 1·25
439/42 .. .. .. .. *Set of* 4 1·60 1·90

Designs and Events:—20 m., 50 m. Centenary of Universal Postal Union. *Vert*.—30 m. "Disabled Persons" (Eighth European Meeting of International Society for the Rehabilitation of Disabled Persons); 100 m. Council flag (25th Anniv of Council of Europe).

(Photo Harrison)

**1975** (28 Apr). *Europa. T* **177** *and similar vert designs. Multicoloured. P* 13½ × 14½.

443 20 m. Type **177** .. .. .. .. 35 50
a. Horiz strip of 3. Nos. 443/5 .. .. 1·10
444 30 m. "Nature Morte" (C. Savva) .. .. 35 60
445 150 m. "Virgin and Child of Liopetri" (G. P. Georghiou) .. .. .. 50 1·00
443/5 .. .. .. .. *Set of* 3 1·10 1·90

Nos. 443/5 were printed horizontally *se-tenant* throughout the sheet.

178 Red Cross Flag over Map

179 Submarine Cable Links

**1975** (4 Aug). *International Events. T* **178** *and similar horiz designs. P* 12½ × 13½ (25 *m.*) *or* 13½ × 12½ (*others*).

446 25 m. multicoloured .. .. .. .. 25 10
447 30 m. turquoise-green and greenish blue .. 25 10
448 75 m. red-brown, orge-brn & pale blue-grey .. 35 90
446/8 .. .. .. .. *Set of* 3 75 1·00

Designs and events: *Vert*—25 m. Type **178** (25th Anniversary of Cyprus Red Cross). *Horiz*—30 m. Nurse and lamp (International Nurses' Day); 75 m. Woman's Steatite Idol (International Women's Year).

**1975** (13 Oct). *Telecommunications Achievements. T* **179** *and similar design. W* **58** *(sideways on 100 m.). P* 12 × 13½ (50 *m.*) *or* 13½ × 12 (100 *m.*).

449 50 m. multicoloured .. .. .. .. 40 10
450 100 m. orange-yellow, dull violet and lilac .. 50 90

Design: *Horiz*—100 m. International subscriber dialling.

10M

(180)

181 Human-figured Vessel, 19th-Century

**1976** (5 Jan). *No. 358 surch with T* **180**.

451 10 m. on 3 m. Cotton napkin .. .. .. 15 10

**1976** (3 May). *Europa. T* **181** *and similar vert designs. Multicoloured. W* **58**. *P* 13 × 14.

452 20 m. Type **181** .. .. .. .. 25 10
453 60 m. Composite vessel, 2100–2000 B.C. .. 70 70
454 100 m. Byzantine goblet .. .. .. 1·25 1·60
452/4 .. .. .. .. *Set of* 3 2·00 2·10

182 Self-help Housing

183 Terracotta Statue of Youth

**1976** (3 May). *Economic Reactivation. T* **182** *and similar horiz designs. Multicoloured. W* **58** *(sideways). P* 14 × 13.

455 10 m. Type **182** .. .. .. .. 10 10
456 25 m. Handicrafts .. .. .. .. 20 20
457 30 m. Reafforestation .. .. .. .. 20 20
458 60 m. Air Communications .. .. .. 35 55
455/8 .. .. .. .. *Set of* 4 75 90

(Des A. Tassos)

**1976** (7 June). *Cypriot Treasures. T* **183** *and similar designs. W* **58** *(sideways on horiz designs, upright on vert designs). Ordinary cream paper. P* 12 × 13½ (5, 10 *m.*), 13 × 14 (20, 25, 30 *m.*), 14 × 13 (40, 50, 60 *m.*), 13½ × 12 (100 *m.*) *or* 13 × 13½ (250 *m. to* £1).

459 5 m. multicoloured .. .. .. .. 10 35
460 10 m. multicoloured .. .. .. .. 10 30
461 20 m. red, yellow and black .. .. .. 20 35
462 25 m. multicoloured .. .. .. .. 20 10
463 30 m. multicoloured .. .. .. .. 25 10
464 40 m. grey-green, light olive-bistre and black 35 35
465 50 m. buff, brown and black .. .. .. 35 10
466 60 m. multicoloured .. .. .. .. 45 10
467 100 m. multicoloured .. .. .. .. 50 20
468 250 m. deep dull blue, grey and black .. .. 70 1·00
469 500 m. black, stone and deep blue-green .. 80 1·75
470 £1 multicoloured .. .. .. .. 1·25 2·25
459/70 .. .. .. .. *Set of* 12 4·50 6·00

Sizes:—23 × 34 *mm*, 5 m., 10 m.; 34 × 23 *mm*, 100 m.; 24 × 37 *mm*, 20, 25, 30 m.; 37 × 24 *mm*, 40, 50, 60 m.; 28 × 41 *mm*, others.

Designs:—10 m. Limestone head; 20 m. Gold necklace from Lambousa; 25 m. Terracotta warrior; 30 m. Statue of a priest of Aphrodite; 40 m. Bronze tablet; 50 m. Mycenaean crater; 60 m. Limestone sarcophagus; 100 m. Gold bracelet from Lambousa; 250 m. Silver dish from Lambousa; 500 m. Bronze stand; £1 Statue of Artemis.

184 Olympic Symbol

185 "George Washington" (G. Stuart)

(Litho Harrison)

**1976** (5 July). *Olympic Games, Montreal. T* **184** *and similar designs. P* 14.

471 20 m. carmine-red, black and yellow .. .. 10 10
472 60 m. multicoloured .. .. .. .. 20 30
473 100 m. multicoloured .. .. .. .. 30 55
471/3 .. .. .. .. *Set of* 3 55 80

Designs: *Horiz*—60, 100 m. Olympic symbols (*different*).

**1976** (5 July). *Bicentenary of American Revolution. W* **58**. *P* 13 × 13½.

474 **185** 100 m. multicoloured .. .. .. 40 30

186 Children in Library 187 Archangel Michael

76 (27 Sept). *International Events. T* **186** *and similar vert designs. W* **58**. *P* 13½ × 12½ (50 *m.*) *or* 13½ (*others*).
5 40 m. multicoloured .. .. .. .. 20 15
6 50 m. yellow-brown and black .. .. .. 20 10
7 80 m. multicoloured .. .. .. .. 45 60
5/7 .. .. .. .. .. *Set of* 3 75 75

Designs and Events:—40 m. Type **186** (Promotion of Children's ooks); 50 m. Low-cost housing (HABITAT Conference, ancouver); 80 m. Eye protected by hands (World Health Day).

(Litho Harrison)

76 (15 Nov). *Christmas. T* **187** *and similar vert designs, showing icons from Ayios Neophytis Monastery. Multicoloured. P* 12½.
8 10 m. Type **187** .. .. .. .. 15 10
9 15 m. Archangel Gabriel .. .. .. 15 10
0 150 m. The Nativity .. .. .. .. 60 80
8/80 .. .. .. .. *Set of* 3 80 80

188 "Cyprus 74" (wood-engraving by A. Tassos) 189 "View of Prodhromos" (A. Diamantis)

977 (10 Jan)–82. *Obligatory Tax. Refugee Fund. W* **58**. *Ordinary cream paper. P* 13 × 12½.
1 **188** 10 m. grey-black .. .. .. .. .. 20 10
a. Chalk-surfaced cream paper (3.5.82)* .. .. .. ..

*Earliest known date of use.

For 1 c. value, see Nos. 634/b, 729 and 747.

77 (2 May). *Europa. T* **189** *and similar horiz designs. Multicoloured. No wmk. P* 13½ × 13.
2 20 m. Type **189** .. .. .. .. 20 10
3 60 m. "Springtime at Monagroulli" (T. Kanthos) .. .. .. .. 40 60
4 120 m. "Old Port, Limassol" (V. Ioannides) .. 70 1·25
2/4 .. .. .. .. .. *Set of* 3 1·10 1·75

190 Overprinted 500 m. Stamp of 1960 191 Bronze Coin of Emperor Trajan

977 (13 June). *Silver Jubilee. W* **58**. *P* 13 × 13½.
5 **190** 120 m. multicoloured .. .. .. 30 30

(Litho Harrison)

977 (13 June). *Ancient Coins of Cyprus* (2nd series). *T* **191** *and similar horiz designs. P* 14.
6 10 m. brownish black, gold and ultramarine .. 15 10
7 40 m. brownish black, silver and pale blue .. 30 30
8 60 m. brownish black, silver and dull orange .. 35 35
9 100 m. brownish black, gold and blue-green .. 50 95
6/9 .. .. .. .. .. *Set of* 4 1·10 1·50

Designs:—40 m. Silver tetradrachm of Demetrios Poliorcetes; m. Silver tetradrachm of Ptolemy VIII; 100 m. Gold Octadrachm Arsinoe II.

192 Archbishop Makarios in Ceremonial Robes 193 Embroidery, Pottery and Weaving

1977 (10 Sept). *Death of Archbishop Makarios. T* **192** *and similar vert designs. Multicoloured. P* 13 × 13½.
490 20 m. Type **192** .. .. .. .. 15 10
491 60 m. Archbishop and doorway .. .. .. 20 10
492 250 m. Head and shoulders portrait .. .. 50 1·10
490/2 .. .. .. .. .. *Set of* 3 75 1·10

1977 (17 Oct). *Anniversaries and Events. T* **193** *and similar horiz designs. W* **58** (*sideways*). *P* 13½ × 13.
493 20 m. Type **193** .. .. .. .. 10 10
494 40 m. Map of Mediterranean .. .. .. 15 20
495 60 m. Gold medals .. .. .. .. 20 20
496 80 m. "Sputnik" .. .. .. .. 20 85
493/6 .. .. .. .. *Set of* 4 60 1·25

Designs commemorate: 20 m. Revitalisation of handicrafts; 40 m. "Man and the Biosphere" Programme in the Mediterranean region; 60 m. Gold medals won by Cypriot students in the Orleans Gymnasiade; 80 m. 60th Anniv of Russian October Revolution.

194 "Nativity"

(Litho Harrison)

1977 (21 Nov). *Christmas. T* **194** *and similar horiz designs showing children's paintings. Multicoloured. P* 14 × 13½.
497 10 m. Type **194** .. .. .. .. 10 10
498 40 m. "The Three Kings" .. .. .. 10 10
499 150 m. "Flight into Egypt" .. .. .. 25 80
497/9 .. .. .. .. .. *Set of* 3 35 90

195 Demetrios Libertis 196 Chrysorrhogiatissa Monastery Courtyard

(Des A. Ioannides)

1978 (6 Mar). *Cypriot Poets. T* **195** *and similar horiz design. W* **58** (*sideways*). *P* 14 × 13.
500 40 m. dull brown and olive-bistre .. .. 10 10
501 150 m. grey, grey-black and light red .. .. 30 80

Design:—150 m. Vasilis Michaelides.

(Litho Harrison)

1978 (24 Apr). *Europa. Architecture. T* **196** *and similar horiz designs. Multicoloured. P* 14 × 13½.
502 25 m. Type **196** .. .. .. .. 15 10
503 75 m. Kolossi Castle .. .. .. .. 35 35
504 125 m. Municipal Library, Paphos .. .. 50 1·00
502/4 .. .. .. .. .. *Set of* 3 90 1·25

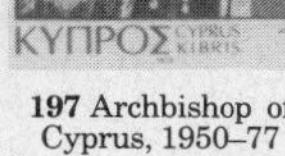


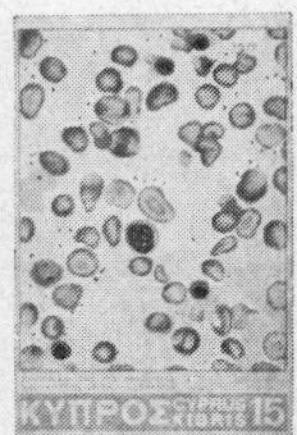


197 Archbishop of Cyprus, 1950–77 198 Affected Blood Corpuscles (Prevention of Thalassaemia)

(Des A. Ioannides (300 m.). Photo Harrison)

1978 (3 Aug). *Archbishop Makarios Commemoration. T* **197** *and similar vert designs. Multicoloured. P* 14 × 15.
505 15 m. Type **197** .. .. .. .. 15 20
a. Silver (inscr and emblem) omitted .. † —
b. Horiz strip of 5. Nos. 505/9 .. 85
ba. Imperf (horiz strip of 5) ..
bb. Silver omitted (horiz strip of 5) ..
506 25 m. Exiled in Seychelles, 9 March 1956–28 March 1957 .. .. .. 15 20
507 50 m. President of the Republic, 1960–77 .. 20 25
508 75 m. "Soldier of Christ" .. .. .. 20 30
509 100 m. "Fighter for Freedom" .. .. .. 25 35
a. Silver (inscr and emblem) omitted ..
505/9 .. .. .. .. .. *Set of* 5 85 1·10
**MS**510 110 × 80 mm. 300 m. "The Great Leader". Imperf .. .. .. .. 1·40 3·00

Nos. 505/9 were printed together, *se-tenant*, in horizontal strips of 5 throughout the sheet.

Sheets of this issue are known with the silver omitted completely or only from the first or last vertical rows.

1978 (23 Oct). *Anniversaries and Events. T* **198** *and similar designs. P* 13½ × 14 (15, 35 *m.*) *or* 14 × 13½ (*others*).
511 15 m. multicoloured .. .. .. .. 10 10
512 35 m. multicoloured .. .. .. .. 15 10
513 75 m. black and grey .. .. .. .. 20 30
514 125 m. multicoloured .. .. .. .. 35 80
511/14 .. .. .. .. .. *Set of* 4 70 1·10

Designs and commemorations: *Vert*—35 m. Aristotle (sculpture) (2300th death anniversary). *Horiz*—75 m. "Heads" (Human Rights); 125 m. Wright brothers and *Flyer* (75th anniversary of powered flight).

199 Icon Stand 200 Aphrodite (statue from Soli)

(Litho Harrison)

1978 (4 Dec). *Christmas. T* **199** *and similar vert designs showing icon stands. P* 14 × 14½.
515 15 m. multicoloured .. .. .. .. 10 10
516 35 m. multicoloured .. .. .. .. 15 10
517 150 m. multicoloured .. .. .. .. 40 60
515/17 .. .. .. .. .. *Set of* 3 60 65

(Litho Harrison)

1979 (12 Mar). *Aphrodite (Greek goddess of love and beauty) Commemoration* (1st issue). *T* **200** *and similar horiz design showing Aphrodite emerging from the sea at Paphos (legendary birthplace). Multicoloured. P* 14 × 13½.
518 75 m. Type **200** .. .. .. .. 25 10
519 125 m. Aphrodite on a shell (detail from "Birth of Venus" by Botticelli) .. 35 25

See also Nos. 584/5.

201 Van, Larnaca–Nicosia Mail-coach and Envelope 202 Peacock Wrasse (*thalassoma pavo*)

(Des G. Simonis)

1979 (30 Apr). *Europa. Communications. T* **201** *and similar horiz designs. Multicoloured. W* **58** (*sideways*). *P* 14 × 13.
520 25 m. Type **201** .. .. .. .. 15 10
521 75 m. Radar, satellite and early telephone .. 25 15
522 125 m. Aircraft, ship and envelopes .. .. 35 60
520/2 .. .. .. .. .. *Set of* 3 65 75

(Des A. Tassos)

1979 (25 June). *Flora and Fauna. T* **202** *and similar multicoloured designs. W* **58** (*sideways on* 25 *and* 125 *m.*). *P* 13½ × 12 (25, 125 *m.*) *or* 12 × 13½ (*others*).
523 25 m. Type **202** .. .. .. .. 15 10
524 50 m. Black Partridge (*Francolinus francolinus*) (*vert*) .. .. .. 45 20
525 75 m. Cedar (*Cedar brevifolia*) (*vert*) .. .. 45 20
526 125 m. Mule (*Equus mulus*) .. .. .. 50 60
523/6 .. .. .. .. .. *Set of* 4 1·40 1·00

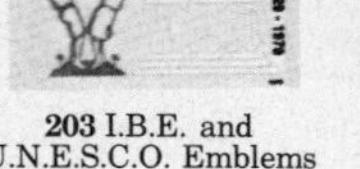

203 I.B.E. and U.N.E.S.C.O. Emblems 204 "Jesus" (from Church of the Virgin Mary of Arakas, Lagoudhera)

(Des Mrs. A. Kalathia (25 m.), A. Ioannides (others). Litho Harrison)

1979 (1 Oct). *Anniversaries and Events. T* **203** *and similar designs in black, yellow-brown and yellow-ochre* (50 *m.*) *or multicoloured* (*others*). *P* 12½.
527 15 m. Type **203** .. .. .. .. 10 10
528 25 m. Graphic design of dove and stamp album (*horiz*) .. .. .. .. 10 10
529 50 m. Lord Kitchener and map of Cyprus (*horiz*) .. .. .. .. 20 15
530 75 m. Child's face (*horiz*) .. .. .. 25 10
531 100 m. Graphic design of footballers (*horiz*) .. 30 20
532 125 m. Rotary International emblem and "75" 30 40
527/32 .. .. .. .. .. *Set of* 6 1·10 85

Commemorations:—15 m. 50th anniversary of International Bureau of Education; 25 m. 20th anniversary of Cyprus Philatelic Society; 50 m. Centenary of Cyprus Survey; 75 m. International Year of the Child; 100 m. 25th anniv of U.E.F.A. (European Football Association); 125 m. 75th anniv of Rotary International.

**1979** (5 Nov). *Christmas. Icons. T* **204** *and similar vert designs. Multicoloured.* W **58**. *P* 13 × 13½ (35 *m.*) *or* 13½ × 14 (*others*).
533 15 m. Type **204** .. .. .. .. .. 10 10
534 35 m. "Nativity" (from the Iconostasis of the Church of St. Nicholas, Famagusta District) (29 × 41 *mm*) .. .. .. .. 10 10
535 150 m. "Holy Mary" (from Church of the Virgin Mary of Arakas, Lagoudhera) .. .. 25 30
533/5 .. .. .. .. .. *Set of* 3 35 40

**205** 1880 ½d. Stamp with "969" (Nicosia) Postmark

**206** St. Barnabas (Patron Saint of Cyprus)

(Des A. Tassos)

**1980** (17 Mar). *Cyprus Stamp Centenary. T* **205** *and similar horiz designs. Multicoloured.* W **58** (*sideways*). *P* 13½ × 13.
536 40 m. Type **205** .. .. .. .. .. 10 10
537 125 m. 1880 2½d. stamp with "974" (Kyrenia) postmark .. .. .. .. .. 15 15
538 175 m. 1880 1s. stamp with "942" (Larnaca) postmark .. .. .. .. .. 15 20
536/8 .. .. .. .. .. *Set of* 3 30 35
**MS**539 105 × 85 mm. 500 m. 1880 1d., ½d., 2½d., 4d., 6d. and 1s. stamps (90 × 75 *mm*). Imperf .. 70 1·25

(Photo Harrison)

**1980** (28 Apr). *Europa. Personalities. T* **206** *and similar vert design. Multicoloured. P* 12½.
540 40 m. Type **206** .. .. .. .. .. 10 10
541 125 m. Zeno of Citium (founder of the Stoic philosophy) .. .. .. .. 20 20
a. Pale Venetian red omitted .. .. £100
The pale Venetian red colour on No. 541 appears as an overlay on the bust. On No. 541a the bust is pure grey.

**207** Sailing

**208** Gold Necklace, Arsos (7th-century BC)

(Des A. Ioannides)

**1980** (23 June). *Olympic Games, Moscow. T* **207** *and similar horiz designs. Multicoloured.* W **58** (*sideways*). *P* 13½ × 13.
542 40 m. Type **207** .. .. .. .. .. 10 10
543 125 m. Swimming .. .. .. .. .. 20 20
544 200 m. Gymnastics .. .. .. .. .. 25 25
542/4 .. .. .. .. .. *Set of* 3 50 50

**1980** (15 Sept). *Archaeological Treasures. Multicoloured designs as T* **208**. W **58** (*sideways on* 15, 40, 150 *and* 500 *m.*). *Chalk-surfaced cream paper. P* 14 × 13 (15, 40, 150 *and* 500 *m.*) *or* 13 × 14 (*others*).
545 10 m. Type **208** .. .. .. .. .. 30 35
546 15 m. Bronze cow, Vouni Palace (5th-century B.C.) (*horiz*) .. .. .. .. 30 35
547 25 m. Amphora, Salamis (6th-century B.C.) .. 30 10
548 40 m. Gold finger-ring, Enkomi (13th-century B.C.) (*horiz*) .. .. .. .. 40 30
549 50 m. Bronze cauldron, Salamis (8th-century B.C.) .. .. .. .. .. 40 10
550 75 m. Funerary stele, Marion (5th-century B.C.) .. .. .. .. .. 50 40
551 100 m. Jug (15–14th–century B.C.) .. .. 75 15
552 125 m. Warrior (Terracotta) (6–5th-century B.C.) .. .. .. .. .. 75 15
553 150 m. Lions attacking bull (bronze relief), Vouni Palace (5th-century B.C.) (*horiz*) 90 15
554 175 m. Faience rhyton, Kition (13th-century B.C.) .. .. .. .. .. 90 40
555 200 m. Bronze statue of Ingot God, Enkomi (12th-century B.C.) .. .. .. .. 90 30
556 500 m. Stone bowl, Khirokitia (6th-millennium B.C.) (*horiz*) .. .. .. .. 1·50 1·00
557 £1 Ivory plaque, Salamis (7th-century B.C.) 2·00 1·25
558 £2 "Leda and the Swan" (mosaic), Kouklia (3rd-century A.D.) .. .. .. .. 3·75 2·00
545/58 .. .. .. .. .. *Set of* 14 12·50 6·00

**209** Cyprus Flag

**210** Peace Dove and Head Silhouettes

**1980** (1 Oct). *20th Anniv of Republic. T* **209** *and similar multi-coloured designs. P* 13½ × 13 (125 *m.*) *or* 13 × 14 (*others*).
559 40 m. Type **209** .. .. .. .. .. 10 10
560 125 m. Signing Treaty of Establishment (41 × 29 *mm*) .. .. .. .. 20 15
561 175 m. Archbishop Makarios .. .. .. 35 25
559/61 .. .. .. .. .. *Set of* 3 60 45

**1980** (29 Nov). *International Palestinian Solidarity Day. T* **210** *and similar horiz design showing Peace Dove and head silhouettes.* W **58** (*sideways*). *P* 13½ × 13.
562 40 m. grey and black .. .. .. .. 20 20
a. Horiz pair. Nos. 562/3 .. .. .. 55 55
563 125 m. grey and black .. .. .. .. 35 35
Nos. 562/3 were printed together, *se-tenant*, in horizontal pairs throughout the sheet.

**211** Pulpit, Tripiotis Church, Nicosia

**212** Folk-dancing

**1980** (29 Nov). *Christmas. T* **211** *and similar vert designs. Multi-coloured.* W **58**. *P* 13 × 14.
564 25 m. Type **211** .. .. .. .. .. 10 10
565 100 m. Holy Doors, Panayia Church, Paralimni (24 × 37 *mm*) .. .. .. .. 15 15
566 125 m. Pulpit, Ayios Lazaros Church, Larnaca 15 15
564/6 .. .. .. .. .. *Set of* 3 30 30

(Litho Harrison)

**1981** (4 May). *Europa. Folklore. T* **212** *and similar vert design showing folk-dancing from paintings by T. Photiades. P* 14.
567 40 m. multicoloured .. .. .. .. 40 10
568 175 m. multicoloured .. .. .. .. 1·00 50

**213** Self-portrait

**214** *Ophrys kotschyi*

**1981** (15 June). *500th Anniv of Leonardo da Vinci's Visit. T* **213** *and similar multicoloured designs.* W **58** (*sideways on* 125 *m.*). *P* 12 × 14 (125 *m.*) *or* 13½ × 14 (*others*).
569 50 m. Type **213** .. .. .. .. .. 40 10
570 125 m. "The Last Supper" (50 × 25 *mm*) .. 70 40
571 175 m. Cyprus lace and Milan Cathedral .. 95 60
569/71 .. .. .. .. .. *Set of* 3 1·90 1·00

(Des A. Tassos)

**1981** (6 July). *Cypriot Wild Orchids. T* **214** *and similar vert designs. Multicoloured.* W **58**. *P* 13½ × 14.
572 25 m. Type **214** .. .. .. .. .. 60 60
a. Block of 4. Nos. 572/5 .. .. .. 2·75
573 50 m. *Orchis punctulata* .. .. .. 70 70
574 75 m. *Orphrys argolica elegans* .. .. 80 80
575 150 m. *Epipactis veratrifolia* .. .. .. 1·00 1·00
572/5 .. .. .. .. .. *Set of* 4 2·75 2·75
Nos. 572/5 were printed together, *se-tenant*, in blocks of 4 throughout the sheet.

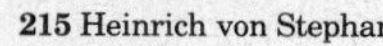
**215** Heinrich von Stephan

**216** "The Lady of the Angels" (from Church of the Transfiguration of Christ, Palekhori)

(Des A. Tassos (200 m.), A. Ioannides (others))

**1981** (28 Sept). *Commemorations. T* **215** *and similar horiz designs.* W **58** (*sideways*). *P* 13½ × 13.
576 25 m. brown-olive, dp yellow-green & brt bl .. 20 10
577 40 m. multicoloured .. .. .. .. 25 10
578 125 m. black, vermilion and deep yellow-green 50 25
579 150 m. multicoloured .. .. .. .. 60 30
580 200 m. multicoloured .. .. .. .. 60 35
576/80 .. .. .. .. .. *Set of* 5 1·90 95
Designs and commemorations:—25 m. Type **215** (150th birth anniversary of Henrich von Stephan (founder of U.P.U.)); 40 m. Stylised man holding dish of food (World Food Day); 125 m. Stylised hands (International Year for Disabled Persons); 150 m. Stylised building and flower (European Campaign for Urban Renaissance); 200 m. Prince Charles, Lady Diana Spencer and St. Paul's Cathedral (Royal Wedding).

(Des A. Tassos)

**1981** (16 Nov). *Christmas. Murals from Nicosia District Churches. T* **216** *and similar multicoloured designs.* W **58** (*sideways on* 25 *and* 125 *m.*). *P* 12½.
581 25 m. Type **216** .. .. .. .. .. 20 10
582 100 m. "Christ Pantokrator" (from Church of Madonna of Arakas, Lagoudera) (*vert*) 60 20
583 125 m. "Baptism of Christ" (from Church of Our Lady of Assinou, Nikitari) .. 70 30
581/3 .. .. .. .. .. *Set of* 3 1·25 50

**217** "Louomene" (statue of Aphrodite bathing, 250 B.C.)

**218** Naval Battle with Greek Fire

**1982** (12 Apr). *Aphrodite (Greek goddess of love and beauty) Commemoration (2nd issue). T* **217** *and similar vert design. Multicoloured.* W **58**. *P* 13½ × 14.
584 125 m. Type **217** .. .. .. .. .. 80 45
585 175 m. "Anadyomene" (Aphrodite emerging from the waters) (Titian) .. .. 95 65

(Photo Harrison)

**1982** (3 May). *Europa. Historic Events. T* **218** *and similar horiz design. Multicoloured. P* 12½.
586 40 m. Type **218** .. .. .. .. .. 60 10
587 175 m. Conversion of Roman Proconsul Sergius Paulus to Christianity, Paphos, 45 A.D. 1·50 1·75

**219** Monogram of Christ (mosaic)

100 =

**(220)**

**1982** (5 July). *World Cultural Heritage. T* **219** *and similar multi-coloured designs.* W **58** (*sideways on* 50 *and* 225 *m.*). *P* 13½ × 14 (125 *m.*) *or* 12½ (*others*).
588 50 m. Type **219** .. .. .. .. .. 30 10
589 125 m. Head of priest-king of Paphos (sculpture) (24 × 37 *mm*) .. .. .. .. 60 40
590 225 m. Theseus (Greek god) (mosaic) .. 1·00 70
588/90 .. .. .. .. .. *Set of* 3 1·75 1·10

**1982** (6 Sept). *No.* 550 *surch with T* **220** *by Govt Ptg Office, Nicosia.*
591 100 m. on 75 m. Funerary stele, Marion (5th-century B.C.) .. .. .. .. 50 40

**221** Cyprus and Stylised "75"

**222** Holy Communion—The Bread

(Des A. Tassos)

**1982** (8 Nov). *75th Anniv of Boy Scout Movement. T* **221** *and similar multicoloured designs.* W **58** (*sideways on* 100 *m. and* 175 *m.*). *P* 12½ × 13½ (125 *m.*) *or* 13½ × 12½ (*others*).
592 100 m. Type **221** .. .. .. .. .. 40 20
593 125 m. Lord Baden-Powell (*vert*) .. .. 45 30
594 175 m. Camp-site .. .. .. .. .. 55 55
592/4 .. .. .. .. .. *Set of* 3 1·25 95

**1982** (6 Dec). *Christmas. T* **222** *and similar designs.* W **58** (*sideways on* 25 *and* 250 *m.*). *P* 12½ × 12 (25 *and* 250 *m.*) *or* 13½ × 14 (100 *m.*).
595 25 m. multicoloured .. .. .. .. 10 10
596 100 m. gold and black .. .. .. .. 30 15
597 250 m. multicoloured .. .. .. .. 70 75
595/7 .. .. .. .. .. *Set of* 3 1·00 85
Designs: *Vert*—100 m. Holy Chalice. *Horiz*—250 m. Holy Communion—The Wine.

## PRICES OF SETS

Set prices are given for many issues, generally those containing three stamps or more. Definitive sets include one of each value or major colour change, but do not cover different perforations, die types or minor shades. Where a choice is possible the set prices are based on the cheapest versions of the stamps included in the listings.

**223** Cyprus Forest Industries' Sawmill

(Des A. Tassos)

**1983** (14 Mar). *Commonwealth Day.* *T* **223** *and similar horiz designs. Multicoloured. W* **58** *(sideways). P* 14 × 13½.

598 50 m. Type **223** .. .. .. .. .. 10 10
599 125 m. "Ikarios and the Discovery of Wine" (3rd-cent mosaic) .. .. .. .. 25 25
600 150 m. Folk-dancers, Commonwealth Film and Television Festival, 1980 .. .. 30 35
601 175 m. Royal Exhibition Building, Melbourne (Commonwealth Heads of Government Meeting, 1981) .. .. .. .. 35 40
598/601 .. .. .. .. *Set of* 4 90 1·00

**224** Cyprosyllabic Inscription (6th-cent B.C.)

**225** *Pararge aegeria*

(Des G. Simonis. Photo Harrison)

**1983** (3 May). *Europa.* *T* **224** *and similar horiz design. Multicoloured. P* 14½ × 14.

602 50 m. Type **224** .. .. .. .. .. 60 10
603 200 m. Copper ore, ingot (Enkomi 1400-1250 B.C.) and bronze jug (2nd-cent A.D.) .. 1·75 2·00

(Des A. Tassos)

**1983** (28 June). *Butterflies.* *T* **225** *and similar horiz designs. Multicoloured. W* w **58**. *P* 12½.

604 60 m. Type **225** .. .. .. .. .. 25 20
605 130 m. *Aricia agestis* .. .. .. .. 45 35
606 250 m. *Glaucopsyche melanops* .. .. .. 85 85
604/6 .. .. .. .. *Set of* 3 1·40 1·25

**(New Currency: 100 cents = £1 (Cyprus))**

1c

=

**(226)**

**227** View of Power Station

**1983** (3 Oct). *Nos.* 545/56 *surch as T* **226** *by Govt Printing Office, Nicosia.*

607 1 c. on 10 m. Type **208** .. .. .. 35 40
608 2 c. on 15 m. Bronze cow, Vouni Palace (5th-century B.C.) .. .. .. .. 35 40
609 3 c. on 25 m. Amphora, Salamis (6th-century B.C.) .. .. .. .. .. 35 20
610 4 c. on 40 m. Gold finger-ring, Enkomi (13th-century B.C.) .. .. .. .. 40 20
611 5 c. on 50 m. Bronze cauldron, Salamis (8th-century B.C.) .. .. .. .. 50 50
612 6 c. on 75 m. Funerary stele, Marion (5th-century B.C.) .. .. .. .. 50 20
613 10 c. on 100 m. Jug (15–14th-century B.C.) .. 60 40
614 13 c. on 125 m. Warrior (Terracotta) (6–5th-century B.C.) .. .. .. .. 70 50
615 15 c. on 150 m. Lions attacking bull (bronze relief), Vouni Palace (5th-century B.C.) 80 55
616 20 c. on 200 m. Bronze statue of Ingot God, Enkomi (12th-century B.C.) .. .. 85 65
617 25 c. on 175 m. Faience rhyton, Kition (13th-century B.C.) .. .. .. .. 95 1·10
618 50 c. on 500 m. Stone bowl, Khirokitia (6th-millennium B.C.) .. .. .. 1·50 2·00
607/18 .. .. .. .. *Set of* 12 7·00 6·50

(Des A. Tassos)

**1983** (27 Oct). *Anniversaries and Events.* *T* **227** *and similar vert designs. Multicoloured. W* **58**. *P* 13 × 14.

619 3 c. Type **227** .. .. .. .. .. 10 10
620 6 c. W.C.Y. logo .. .. .. .. .. 20 15
621 13 c. *Sol Olympia* (liner) and *Polys* (tanker) 40 30
622 15 c. Human Rights emblem and map of Europe .. .. .. .. .. 45 35
623 20 c. Nicos Kazantzakis (poet) .. .. .. 55 45
624 25 c. Archbishop Makarios in church .. .. 65 65
619/24 .. .. .. .. *Set of* 6 2·10 1·75

Commemorations:—3 c. 30th anniv of the Cyprus Electricity Authority; 6 c. World Communications Year; 13 c. 25th anniv of International Maritime Organization; 15 c. 35th anniv of Universal Declaration of Human Rights; 20 c. Birth centenary; 25 c. 70th birth anniv.

**228** St. Lazaros Church, Larnaca

**229** Waterside Cafe, Larnaca

(Des A. Tassos)

**1983** (12 Dec). *Christmas.* *T* **228** *and similar vert designs. Multicoloured. W* **58**. *P* 12 × 13½.

625 4 c. Type **228** .. .. .. .. .. 20 10
626 13 c. St. Varvara Church, Kaimakli, Nicosia 55 35
627 20 c. St. Ioannis Church, Larnaca .. .. 90 70
625/7 .. .. .. .. *Set of* 3 1·50 1·00

(Litho Harrison)

**1984** (6 Mar). *Old Engravings.* *T* **229** *and similar horiz designs. Each pale stone and black. P* 14½ × 14 (6 c.) *or* 14 *(others).*

628 6 c. Type **229** .. .. .. .. .. 15 10
629 20 c. Bazaar at Larnaca (30 × 25 *mm*) .. 50 65
630 30 c. Famagusta Gate, Nicosia (30 × 25 *mm*) 80 1·25
628/30 .. .. .. .. *Set of* 3 1·40 1·75
**MS**631 110 × 85 mm. 75 c. "The Confession" (St. Lazarus Church, Larnaca) .. .. .. 1·90 2·00

**230** C.E.P.T. 25th Anniversary Logo

(Des J. Larrivière. Litho Harrison)

**1984** (30 Apr). *Europa. W* **58**. *P* 12½.

632 **230** 6 c. apple-green, deep bl-green & blk .. 75 10
633 15 c. light blue, dull ultram & blk .. 1·50 1·75

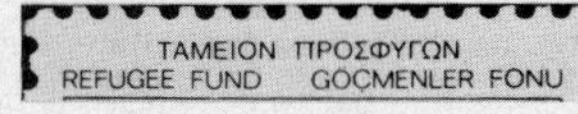


A. Waddington ptgs (Nos. 634/a)

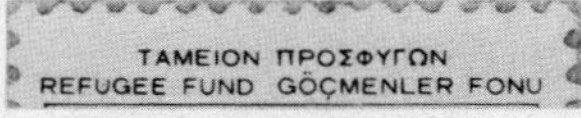


B. Aspioti-Elka ptg (No. 634*b*)

(Des A. Tassos)

**1984** (18 June)–**88**. *Obligatory Tax. Refugee Fund. Design as T* **188** *but new value and* "1984" *date. P* 13 × 12½.

(*a*) *Litho J.W. W* **58**. *Chalk-surfaced cream paper*

634 1 c. grey-black (A) .. .. .. .. 10 10
a. Wmk sideways. Ordinary paper (21.2.87)* .. .. .. .. 45 45

(*b*) *Litho Aspioti-Elka. W* **58**. *Chalk-surfaced cream paper*

634*b* 1 c. grey-black (B) (9.5.88)* .. .. 45 45

*Earliest known date of use.

In addition to the redrawn inscriptions there are other minor differences between the work of the two printers.

For a further version of this design, showing "1974" at top right, see Nos. 729 and 747.

**231** Running

(Des. K. Haine. Litho Harrison)

**1984** (18 June). *Olympic Games. Los Angeles.* *T* **231** *and similar horiz designs. Multicoloured. W* **58** *(sideways). P* 14.

635 3 c. Type **231** .. .. .. .. .. 20 10
636 4 c. Olympic column .. .. .. .. 20 10
637 13 c. Swimming .. .. .. .. .. 55 60
638 20 c. Gymnastics .. .. .. .. .. 80 1·00
635/8 .. .. .. .. *Set of* 4 1·60 1·60

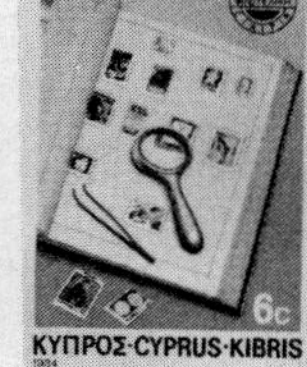


**232** Prisoners-of-War

**233** Open Stamp Album (25th Anniv of Cyprus Philatelic Society)

(Des A. Tassos)

**1984** (20 July). *10th Anniv of Turkish Landings in Cyprus.* *T* **232** *and similar horiz design. Multicoloured. P* 14 × 13½.

639 15 c. Type **232** .. .. .. .. .. 40 45
640 20 c. Map and burning buildings .. .. 50 55

(Litho Harrison)

**1984** (15 Oct). *Anniversaries and Events.* *T* **233** *and similar multicoloured designs. W* **58** *(sideways on horiz designs). P* 12½.

641 6 c. Type **233** .. .. .. .. .. 40 10
642 10 c. Football in motion (*horiz*) (50th anniv of Cyprus Football Association) .. .. 55 30
643 15 c. "Dr. George Papanicolaou" (medical scientist – birth cent) .. .. .. 75 70
644 25 c. Antique map of Cyprus and ikon (*horiz*) (International Symposia on Cartography and Medieval Paleography) .. .. 1·25 1·50
641/4 .. .. .. .. *Set of* 4 2·75 2·40

**234** St. Mark (miniature from 11th-century Gospel)

**235** Autumn at Platania, Troodos Mountains

(Litho Harrison)

**1984** (26 Nov). *Christmas. Illuminated Gospels.* *T* **234** *and similar vert designs. Multicoloured. W* **58**. *P* 12½.

645 4 c. Type **234** .. .. .. .. .. 35 10
646 13 c. Beginning of St. Mark's Gospel .. 1·00 75
647 20 c. St. Luke (miniature from 11th-century Gospel) .. .. .. .. .. 1·50 1·75
645/7 .. .. .. .. *Set of* 3 2·50 2·40

(Litho Harrison)

**1985** (18 Mar.) *Cyprus Scenes and Landscapes.* *T* **235** *and similar multicoloured designs. Ordinary white paper. P* 14 × 15 (6 c., 20 c., 25 c., £1, £5) *or* 15 × 14 *(others).*

648 1 c. Type **235** .. .. .. .. .. 20 40
649 2 c. Ayia Napa Monastery .. .. .. 20 40
650 3 c. Phini Village—panoramic view .. 20 30
651 4 c. Kykko Monastery .. .. .. .. 20 20
652 5 c. Beach at Makronissos, Ayia Napa .. 20 20
653 6 c. Village street, Omodhos (*vert*) .. .. 30 20
654 10 c. Panoramic sea view .. .. .. 40 35
655 13 c. Windsurfing .. .. .. .. 55 35
656 15 c. Beach at Protaras .. .. .. 65 40
657 20 c. Forestry for development (*vert*) .. 80 50
658 25 c. Sunrise at Protaras (*vert*) .. .. 1·00 1·00
659 30 c. Village house, Pera .. .. .. 1·25 1·25
660 50 c. Apollo Hylates Sanctuary, Curium .. 2·00 1·75
661 £1 Snow on Troodos Mountains (*vert*) .. 3·50 3·00
662 £5 Personification of Autumn, House of Dionyssos, Paphos (*vert*) .. .. 13·00 15·00
648/62 .. .. .. .. *Set of* 15 22·00 23·00

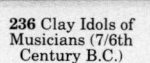

**236** Clay Idols of Musicians (7/6th Century B.C.)

**237** Cyprus Coat of Arms (25th Anniv of Republic)

(Litho Harrison)

**1985** (6 May). *Europa. European Music Year.* *T* **236** *and similar horiz design. Multicoloured. W* **58** *(sideways). P* 12½.

663 6 c. Type **236** .. .. .. .. .. 1·25 20
664 15 c. Violin, lute, flute and score from the "Cyprus Suite" .. .. .. .. 2·00 1·40

(Des G. Simonis (4 c., 13 c.), Harrison (others). Litho Harrison)

**1985** (23 Sept). *Anniversaries and Events.* *T* **237** *and similar designs. P* 14½ (4, 20 c.) *or* 14 × 13½ *(others).*

665 4 c. multicoloured .. .. .. .. 40 15
666 6 c. multicoloured .. .. .. .. 45 15
667 13 c. multicoloured .. .. .. .. 1·00 70
668 15 c. black, olive-black and yellow-orange .. 1·50 1·75
669 20 c. multicoloured .. .. .. .. 1·50 2·00
665/9 .. .. .. .. *Set of* 5 4·25 4·25

Designs: *Horiz* (43 × 30 *mm*)—6 c. "Barn of Liopetri" (detail) (Pol. Georghiou) (30th anniv of EOKA Campaign); 13 c. Three profiles (International Youth Year); 15 c. Solon Michaelides (composer and conductor) (European Music Year). *Vert* (*as T* **237**)—20 c. U.N. Building, New York, and flags (40th anniv of United Nations Organization).

**238** "The Visit of the Madonna to Elizabeth" (Lambadistis Monastery, Kalopanayiotis)

**239** Figure from Hellenistic Spoon Handle

(Litho Harrison)

**1985** (18 Nov). *Christmas. Frescoes from Cypriot Churches. T* **238** *and similar vert designs. Multicoloured. P* 12½.

| | | | |
|---|---|---|---|
| 670 | 4 c. Type **238** | 35 | 10 |
| 671 | 13 c. "The Nativity" (Lambadistis Monastery, Kalopanayiotis) | 1·25 | 65 |
| 672 | 20 c. "Candlemas-day" (Asinou Church) | 1·75 | 1·75 |
| 670/2 | *Set of* 3 | 3·00 | 2·25 |

(Des A. Ioannides. Litho Harrison)

**1986** (17 Feb). *New Archaeological Museum Fund. T* **239** *and similar horiz designs. Multicoloured. P* 15 × 14.

| | | | |
|---|---|---|---|
| 673 | 15 c. Type **239** | 1·00 | 45 |
| 674 | 20 c. Pattern from early Ionian helmet and foot from statue | 1·25 | 75 |
| 675 | 25 c. Roman statue of Eros and Psyche | 1·50 | 95 |
| 676 | 30 c. Head of statue | 1·75 | 1·10 |
| 673/6 | *Set of* 4 | 5·00 | 3·00 |
| **MS**677 | 111 × 90 mm. Nos. 673/6 (*sold at* £1) | 6·00 | 7·00 |

Two-thirds of the amount received from sales of Nos. 673/7 was devoted to the construction of a new Archaeological Museum, Nicosia.

No. 676 also commemorates the 50th anniversary of the Department of Antiquities.

**240** Cyprus Moufflon and Cedars

(Des G. Simonis)

**1986** (28 Apr). *Europa. Protection of Nature and the Environment. T* **240** *and similar horiz design. Multicoloured. W* **58** *(sideways). P* 14 × 13.

| | | | |
|---|---|---|---|
| 678 | 7 c. Type **240** | 1·00 | 15 |
| 679 | 17 c. Greater Flamingos at Larnaca Salt Lake | 2·50 | 2·50 |

**241** *Chlamys pesfelis*

7c

**(242)**

(Des T. Katsoulides)

**1986** (1 July). *Sea Shells. T* **241** *and similar horiz designs. Multicoloured. W* **58** *(sideways). P* 14 × 13½.

| | | | |
|---|---|---|---|
| 680 | 5 c. Type **241** | 40 | 15 |
| 681 | 7 c. *Charonia variegata* | 45 | 15 |
| 682 | 18 c. *Murex brandaris* | 1·00 | 1·00 |
| 683 | 25 c. *Cypraea spurca* | 1·50 | 1·75 |
| 680/3 | *Set of* 4 | 3·00 | 2·75 |

**1986** (13 Oct). *Nos.* 653 *and* 655 *surch as T* **242**.

| | | | |
|---|---|---|---|
| 684 | 7 c. on 6 c. Village street, Omodhos (*vert*) | 50 | 30 |
| 685 | 18 c. on 13 c. Windsurfing | 1·40 | 60 |

For 15 c. on 4 c. see No. 730.

**243** Globe, Outline Map of Cyprus and Swallows (Overseas Cypriots' Year)

(Des T. Katsoulides)

**1986** (13 Oct). *Anniversaries and Events. T* **243** *and similar horiz designs. Multicoloured. W* **58** *(sideways). P* 13½ × 13.

| | | | |
|---|---|---|---|
| 686 | 15 c. Type **243** | 1·25 | 45 |
| 687 | 18 c. Halley's Comet over Cyprus beach (40 × 23 *mm*) | 1·50 | 1·75 |
| | a. Horiz pair. Nos. 687/8 | 3·00 | 3·50 |
| 688 | 18 c. Comet's tail over sea and Edmond Halley (40 × 23 *mm*) | 1·50 | 1·75 |
| 686/8 | *Set of* 3 | 3·75 | 3·50 |

Nos. 687/8 were printed together, *se-tenant*, in horizontal pairs throughout the sheet, each pair forming a composite design.

**244** Pedestrian Crossing

**245** "The Nativity" (Church of Panayia tou Araka)

(Des A. Ioannides)

**1986** (10 Nov). *Road Safety Campaign. T* **244** *and similar horiz designs. Multicoloured. W* **58** *(sideways). P* 14 × 13.

| | | | |
|---|---|---|---|
| 689 | 5 c. Type **244** | 1·00 | 30 |
| 690 | 7 c. Motor cycle crash helmet | 1·10 | 30 |
| 691 | 18 c. Hands fastening car seat belt | 2·25 | 2·75 |
| 689/91 | *Set of* 3 | 4·00 | 3·00 |

(Des G. Simonis)

**1986** (24 Nov). *Christmas. International Peace Year. T* **245** *and similar vert designs showing details of Nativity frescoes from Cypriot churches. Multicoloured. W* **58** *(inverted). P* 13½ × 14.

| | | | |
|---|---|---|---|
| 692 | 5 c. Type **245** | 45 | 15 |
| 693 | 15 c. Church of Panayia tou Moutoulla | 1·50 | 90 |
| 694 | 17 c. Church of St. Nicholas tis Steyis | 1·75 | 1·10 |
| 692/4 | *Set of* 3 | 3·25 | 2·00 |

**246** Church of Virgin Mary, Asinou

(Photo Harrison)

**1987** (22 Apr). *Troodos Churches on the World Heritage List. T* **246** *and similar horiz designs. Multicoloured. P* 12½.

| | | | |
|---|---|---|---|
| 695 | 15 c. Type **246** | 1·00 | 1·00 |
| | a. Sheetlet. Nos. 695/703 | 8·00 | |
| 696 | 15 c. Fresco of Virgin Mary, Moutoulla's Church | 1·00 | 1·00 |
| 697 | 15 c. Church of Virgin Mary, Podithou | 1·00 | 1·00 |
| 698 | 15 c. Fresco of Three Apostles, St. Ioannis Lampadistis Monastery | 1·00 | 1·00 |
| 699 | 15 c. Annunciation fresco, Church of the Holy Cross, Pelentriou | 1·00 | 1·00 |
| 700 | 15 c. Fresco of Saints, Church of the Cross, Ayiasmati | 1·00 | 1·00 |
| 701 | 15 c. Fresco of Archangel Michael and Donor, Pedoula's Church of St. Michael | 1·00 | 1·00 |
| 702 | 15 c. Church of St. Nicolaos, Steyis | 1·00 | 1·00 |
| 703 | 15 c. Fresco of Prophets, Church of Virgin Mary, Araka | 1·00 | 1·00 |
| 695/703 | *Set of* 9 | 8·00 | 8·00 |

Nos. 695/703 were printed together, *se-tenant*, in sheetlets of nine.

**247** Proposed Central Bank of Cyprus Building

(Des G. Simonis)

**1987** (11 May). *Europa. Modern Architecture. T* **247** *and similar horiz design. W* **58** *(sideways). P* 14 × 13½.

| | | | |
|---|---|---|---|
| 704 | 7 c. multicoloured | 1·00 | 10 |
| 705 | 18 c. black, brownish grey and sage-green | 2·00 | 2·00 |

Design:—18 c. Headquarters complex, Cyprus Telecommunications Authority.

**248** Remains of Ancient Ship and Kyrenia Castle

(Des Y. Pantzopoulow)

**1987** (3 Oct). *Voyage of "Kyrenia II" (replica of ancient ship). T* **248** *and similar horiz designs. Multicoloured. W* **58** *(sideways). P* 14 × 13½.

| | | | |
|---|---|---|---|
| 706 | 2 c. Type **248** | 30 | 20 |
| 707 | 3 c. *Kyrenia II* under construction, 1982–5 | 30 | 20 |
| 708 | 5 c. *Kyrenia II* at Paphos, 1986 | 55 | 30 |
| 709 | 17 c. *Kyrenia II* at New York, 1986 | 1·40 | 1·10 |
| 706/9 | *Set of* 4 | 2·25 | 1·60 |

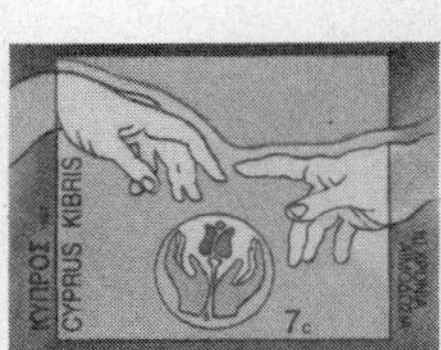

**249** Hands (from Michelangelo's *Creation*) and Emblem (10th anniv of Blood Donation Co-ordinating Committee)

**250** Nativity Crib

(Des A. Ioannides)

**1987** (2 Nov). *Anniversaries and Events. T* **249** *and similar horiz designs. Multicoloured. W* **58** *(sideways). P* 14 × 13½.

| | | | |
|---|---|---|---|
| 710 | 7 c. Type **249** | 60 | 2 |
| 711 | 15 c. Snail with flowered shell and countryside (European Countryside Campaign) | 1·40 | 1·2 |
| 712 | 20 c. Symbols of ocean bed and Earth's crust ("Troodos '87" Ophiolites and Oceanic Lithosphere Symposium) | 1·75 | 2·0 |
| 710/12 | *Set of* 3 | 3·25 | 3·2 |

(Des A. Ioannides)

**1987** (30 Nov). *Christmas. Traditional Customs. T* **250** *and similar square designs. Multicoloured. W* **58** *(sideways). P* 14

| | | | |
|---|---|---|---|
| 713 | 5 c. Type **250** | 35 | 1 |
| 714 | 15 c. Door knocker decorated with foliage | 1·10 | 8 |
| 715 | 17 c. Bowl of fruit and nuts | 1·25 | 1·1 |
| 713/15 | *Set of* 3 | 2·40 | 1·9 |

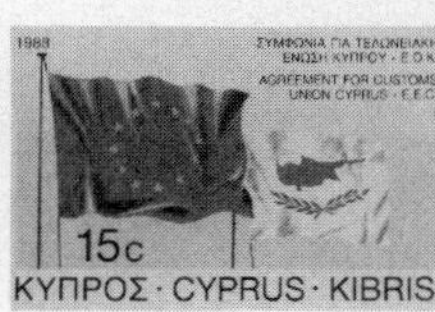

**251** Flags of Cyprus and E.E.C.

(Des G. Simonis. Litho Alexandros Matsoukis, Athens)

**1988** (11 Jan). *Cypriot–E.E.C. Customs Union. T* **251** *and similar horiz design. Multicoloured. W* **58**. *P* 13 × 13½.

| | | | |
|---|---|---|---|
| 716 | 15 c. Type **251** | 90 | 90 |
| 717 | 18 c. Outline maps of Cyprus and E.E.C. countries | 1·10 | 1·10 |

**252** Intelpost Telefax Terminal

(Des A. Ioannides. Litho Alexandros Matsoukis, Athens)

**1988** (9 May). *Europa. Transport and Communications. T* **252** *and similar horiz designs. Multicoloured. W* **58**. *P* 14 × 14½.

| | | | |
|---|---|---|---|
| 718 | 7 c. Type **252** | 65 | 6 |
| | a. Horiz pair. Nos. 718/19 | 1·25 | 1·2 |
| 719 | 7 c. Car driver using mobile telephone | 65 | 6 |
| 720 | 18 c. Nose of Cyprus Airways airliner and flamingos | 1·25 | 1·2 |
| | a. Horiz pair. Nos. 720/1 | 2·50 | 2·5 |
| 721 | 18 c. Airliner in flight and flamingos | 1·25 | 1·2 |
| 718/21 | *Set of* 4 | 3·25 | 3·2 |

The two designs of each value were printed together *se-tenant*, in horizontal pairs throughout the sheets of ten.

**253** Sailing

**254** Conference Emblem

(Des A. Ioannides. Photo Courvoisier)

**1988** (27 June). *Olympic Games, Seoul. T* **253** *and similar vert designs. Multicoloured. Granite paper. P* 12.

| | | | |
|---|---|---|---|
| 722 | 5 c. Type **253** | 30 | 2 |
| 723 | 7 c. Athletes at start | 35 | 4 |
| 724 | 10 c. Shooting | 40 | 5 |
| 725 | 20 c. Judo | 90 | 1·4 |
| 722/5 | *Set of* 4 | 1·75 | 2·2 |

(Des A. Ioannides. Litho M. A. Moatsos, Athens)

**988** (5 Sept). *Non-Aligned Foreign Ministers' Conference, Nicosia. T* **254** *and similar horiz designs. W* **58** *(sideways). P* 14×13½.

| | | | |
|---|---|---|---|
| 26 | 1 c. black, pale blue and emerald .. .. | 10 | 10 |
| 27 | 10 c. multicoloured .. .. .. .. | 45 | 30 |
| 28 | 50 c. multicoloured .. .. .. .. | 2·25 | 2·25 |
| 26/8 | .. .. .. .. *Set of* 3 | 2·50 | 2·40 |

Designs:— 10 c. Emblem of Republic of Cyprus; 50 c. Nehru, ito, Nasser and Makarios.

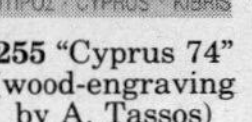


255 "Cyprus 74" (wood-engraving by A. Tassos)

256 "Presentation of Christ at the Temple" (Church of Holy Cross tou Agiasmati)

(Litho M. A. Moatsos, Athens)

**988** (12 Sept). *Obligatory Tax. Refugee Fund. Design as Nos.* 634/b, *but with upper and lower inscriptions redrawn and* "1974" *added as in T* **255**. *W* **58**. *Chalk-surfaced paper. P* 13×12½.

| | | | |
|---|---|---|---|
| 29 **255** | 1 c. brownish black and brownish grey .. | 20 | 20 |

For this design printed in photogravure and perforated 11½, ee No. 747, and in lithography, but perforated 13, see No. 807.

**988** (3 Oct). *No.* 651 *surch as T* **242**.

| | | | |
|---|---|---|---|
| '30 | 15 c. on 4 c. Kykko Monastery .. .. | 70 | 40 |

(Adapted G. Simonis. Litho M. A. Moatsos, Athens)

**988** (28 Nov). *Christmas. T* **256** *and similar vert designs showing frescoes from Cypriot churches. Multicoloured. W* **58**. *P* 13½ × 14.

| | | | |
|---|---|---|---|
| '31 | 5 c. Type **256** .. .. .. .. | 35 | 15 |
| '32 | 15 c. "Virgin and Child" (St. John Lampadistis Monastery) .. .. .. | 90 | 70 |
| '33 | 17 c. "Adoration of the Magi" (St. John Lampadistis Monastery) .. .. | 1·25 | 80 |
| '31/3 | .. .. .. .. *Set of* 3 | 2·25 | 1·50 |

257 Human Rights Logo

258 Basketball

(Des G. Simonis. Litho M. A. Moatsos, Athens)

**1988** (10 Dec). *40th Anniv of Universal Declaration of Human Rights. W* **58** *(inverted). P* 13½ × 14.

| | | | |
|---|---|---|---|
| 734 **257** | 25 c. azure, dull violet-blue and cobalt .. | 90 | 1·25 |

(Des A. Ioannides. Litho Alexandros Matsoukis, Athens)

**1989** (10 Apr). *Third Small European States' Games, Nicosia. T* **258** *and similar horiz designs. Multicoloured. P* 13½.

| | | | |
|---|---|---|---|
| 735 | 1 c. Type **258** .. .. .. .. | 10 | 15 |
| 736 | 5 c. Javelin .. .. .. .. | 20 | 20 |
| 737 | 15 c. Wrestling .. .. .. .. | 45 | 50 |
| 738 | 18 c. Athletics .. .. .. .. | 60 | 65 |
| 735/8 | .. .. .. .. *Set of* 4 | 1·25 | 1·40 |
| **MS**739 | 109×80 mm. £1 Angel and laurel wreath (99×73 *mm*). Imperf .. .. .. | 2·50 | 3·25 |

259 Lingri Stick Game

(Des S. Michael. Litho Alexandros Matsoukis, Athens)

**1989** (8 May). *Europa. Children's Games. T* **259** *and similar horiz designs. Multicoloured. P* 13×13½.

| | | | |
|---|---|---|---|
| 740 | 7 c. Type **259** .. .. .. .. | 25 | 35 |
| | a. Horiz pair. Nos. 740/1 .. .. | 50 | 70 |
| 741 | 7 c. Ziziros .. .. .. .. | 25 | 35 |
| 742 | 18 c. Sitsia .. .. .. .. | 50 | 70 |
| | a. Horiz pair. Nos. 742/3 .. .. | 1·00 | 1·40 |
| 743 | 18 c. Leapfrog .. .. .. .. | 50 | 70 |
| 740/3 | .. .. .. .. *Set of* 4 | 1·40 | 1·90 |

Nos. 740/1 and 742/3 were each printed together, *se-tenant*, in horizontal pairs throughout the sheets.

**MACHINE LABELS**. From 29 May 1989 gummed labels in the above design, ranging in value from 1 c. to £99.99, were available from machines at Eleftheria Square P.O., Nicosia ("001") and District P.O., Limassol ("002").

260 "Universal Man"

261 Stylized Human Figures

(Des A. Ioannides. Photo Courvoisier)

**1989** (7 July). *Bicentenary of the French Revolution. Granite paper. P* 11½.

| | | | |
|---|---|---|---|
| 744 **260** | 18 c. multicoloured .. .. .. | 60 | 60 |

(Des A. Ioannides. Litho Alexandros Matsoukis, Athens)

**1989** (4 Sept). *Centenary of Interparliamentary Union* (15 *c.*) *and 9th Non-Aligned Summit Conference, Belgrade* (30 *c.*). *T* **261** *and similar vert design. Multicoloured. P* 13½.

| | | | |
|---|---|---|---|
| 745 | 15 c. Type **261** .. .. .. .. | 50 | 40 |
| 746 | 30 c. Conference logo .. .. .. | 1·00 | 1·10 |

(Photo Courvoisier)

**1989** (4 Sept). *Obligatory Tax. Refugee Fund. As T* **255**, *but inscr* "1989" *or* "1990". *Granite paper. P* 11½.

| | | | |
|---|---|---|---|
| 747 **255** | 1 c. brownish black and brownish grey .. | 30 | 30 |

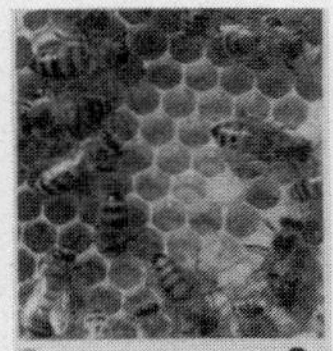


262 Worker Bees tending Larvae

263 Outstretched Hand and Profile (aid for Armenian earthquake victims)

(Litho Alexandros Matsoukis, Athens)

**1989** (16 Oct). *Bee-keeping. T* **262** *and similar vert designs. Multicoloured. P* 13½.

| | | | |
|---|---|---|---|
| 748 | 3 c. Type **262** .. .. .. .. | 15 | 10 |
| 749 | 10 c. Bee on Rock-rose flower .. .. | 40 | 30 |
| 750 | 15 c. Bee on Lemon flower .. .. .. | 60 | 40 |
| 751 | 18 c. Queen and worker bees .. .. | 65 | 50 |
| 748/51 | .. .. .. .. *Set of* 4 | 1·60 | 1·10 |

(Des A. Ioannides. Litho Alexandros Matsoukis, Athens)

**1989** (13 Nov). *Anniversaries and Events. T* **263** *and similar vert designs. Multicoloured. P* 13½.

| | | | |
|---|---|---|---|
| 752 | 3 c. Type **263** .. .. .. .. | 15 | 10 |
| 753 | 5 c. Airmail envelope (Cyprus Philatelic Society F.I.P. membership) .. .. | 20 | 20 |
| 754 | 7 c. Crab symbol and daisy (European Cancer Year) .. .. .. .. | 35 | 30 |
| 755 | 17 c. Vegetables and fish (World Food Day) | 65 | 65 |
| 752/5 | .. .. .. .. *Set of* 4 | 1·25 | 1·10 |

264 Winter (detail from "Four Seasons")

265 Hands and Open Book (International Literacy Year)

(Litho Alexandros Matsoukis, Athens)

**1989** (29 Dec). *Roman Mosaics from Paphos. T* **264** *and similar multicoloured designs showing details. P* 13 (1, 5, 7, 15 *c.*), 13×13½ (2, 4, 18, 40 *c.*), 13½×13 (3, 10, 20, 25 *c.*) *or* 14 (50 *c.*, $1, $3).

| | | | |
|---|---|---|---|
| 756 | 1 c. Type **264** .. .. .. .. | 10 | 10 |
| 757 | 2 c. Personification of Crete (32×24 *mm*) | 10 | 10 |
| 758 | 3 c. Centaur and Maenad (24×32 *mm*) | 10 | 10 |
| 759 | 4 c. Poseidon and Amymone (32×24 *mm*) | 10 | 15 |
| 760 | 5 c. Leda .. .. .. .. | 10 | 15 |
| 761 | 7 c. Apollon .. .. .. .. | 15 | 20 |
| 762 | 10 c. Hermes and Dionysos (24×32 *mm*) | 25 | 30 |
| 763 | 15 c. Cassiopeia .. .. .. .. | 35 | 40 |
| 764 | 18 c. Orpheus (32×24 *mm*) .. .. | 45 | 50 |
| 765 | 20 c. Nymphs (24×32 *mm*) .. .. | 50 | 55 |
| 766 | 25 c. Amazon (24×32 *mm*) .. .. | 60 | 65 |
| 767 | 40 c. Doris (32×24 *mm*) .. .. .. | 1·00 | 1·10 |
| 768 | 50 c. Heracles and the Lion (39×27 *mm*) | 1·25 | 1·40 |
| 769 | £1 Apollon and Daphne (39×27 *mm*) .. | 2·50 | 2·75 |
| 770 | £3 Cupid (39×27 *mm*) .. .. | 7·50 | 7·75 |
| 756/70 | .. .. .. .. *Set of* 15 | 13·50 | 14·50 |

(Des A. Ioannides. Litho Alexandros Matsoukis, Athens)

**1990** (3 Apr). *Anniversaries and Events. T* **265** *and similar horiz designs. Multicoloured. P* 13½.

| | | | |
|---|---|---|---|
| 771 | 15 c. Type **265** .. .. .. .. | 50 | 50 |
| 772 | 17 c. Dove and profiles (83rd Inter-Parliamentary Conference, Nicosia) .. | 60 | 60 |
| 773 | 18 c. Lions International emblem (Lions Europa Forum, Limassol) .. .. | 70 | 70 |
| 771/3 | .. .. .. .. *Set of* 3 | 1·60 | 1·60 |

266 District Post Office, Paphos

(Des A. Ioannides. Litho Alexandros Matsoukis, Athens)

**1990** (10 May). *Europa. Post Office Buildings. T* **266** *and similar horiz design. Multicoloured. P* 13×13½.

| | | | |
|---|---|---|---|
| 774 | 7 c. Type **266** .. .. .. .. | 35 | 25 |
| 775 | 18 c. City Centre Post Office, Limassol .. | 65 | 1·00 |

267 Symbolic Lips (25th anniv of Hotel and Catering Institute)

(Des A. Ioannides. Litho Alexandros Matsoukis, Athens)

**1990** (9 July). *European Tourism Year. T* **267** *and similar horiz designs. Multicoloured. P* 14.

| | | | |
|---|---|---|---|
| 776 | 5 c. Type **267** .. .. .. .. | 20 | 20 |
| 777 | 7 c. Bell tower, St. Lazarus Church (1100th anniv) .. .. .. .. | 25 | 25 |
| 778 | 15 c. Butterflies and woman .. .. | 40 | 40 |
| 779 | 18 c. Birds and man .. .. .. | 50 | 50 |
| 776/9 | .. .. .. .. *Set of* 4 | 1·25 | 1·25 |

268 Sun (wood carving)

269 *Chionodoxa lochiae*

(Des A. Ioannides. Photo Courvoisier)

**1990** (29 Sept). *30th Anniv of Republic. T* **268** *and similar square designs. Multicoloured. Granite paper. P* 11½.

| | | | |
|---|---|---|---|
| 780 | 15 c. Type **268** .. .. .. .. | 45 | 45 |
| 781 | 17 c. Bulls (pottery design) .. .. | 50 | 50 |
| 782 | 18 c. Fishes (pottery design) .. .. | 60 | 60 |
| 783 | 40 c. Tree and birds (wood carving) .. | 1·25 | 1·25 |
| 780/3 | .. .. .. .. *Set of* 4 | 2·50 | 2·50 |
| **MS**784 | 89×89 mm. £1 30th Anniversary emblem. Imperf .. .. .. .. | 2·75 | 3·00 |

(Litho Alexandros Matsoukis, Athens)

**1990** (5 Nov). *Endangered Wild Flowers. T* **269** *and similar vert designs taken from book illustrations by Elektra Megaw. Multicoloured. P* 13½×13.

| | | | |
|---|---|---|---|
| 785 | 2 c. Type **269** .. .. .. .. | 15 | 15 |
| 786 | 3 c. *Pancratium maritimum* .. .. | 15 | 15 |
| 787 | 5 c. *Paeonia mascula* .. .. .. | 20 | 20 |
| 788 | 7 c. *Cyclamen cyprium* .. .. | 25 | 25 |
| 789 | 15 c. *Tulipa cypria* .. .. .. | 45 | 45 |
| 790 | 18 c. *Crocus cyprius* .. .. .. | 65 | 75 |
| 785/90 | .. .. .. .. *Set of* 6 | 1·75 | 1·75 |

## OMNIBUS ISSUES

Details, together with prices for complete sets, of the various Omnibus issues from the 1935 Silver Jubilee series to date are included in a special section following Zimbabwe at the end of Volume 2.

270 "Nativity"

271 Archangel

(Litho Alexandros Matsoukis, Athens)

**1990** (3 Dec). *Christmas. 16th-Century Icons. T* **270** *and similar vert designs. Multicoloured. P* 13½.

| | | | |
|---|---|---|---|
| 791 | 5 c. Type **270** .. .. .. .. | 20 | 20 |
| 792 | 15 c. "Virgin Hodegetria" .. .. .. | 50 | 50 |
| 793 | 17 c. "Nativity" (*different*) .. .. .. | 70 | 70 |
| 791/3 | .. .. .. .. *Set of* 3 | 1·25 | 1·25 |

(Des A. Ioannides. Photo Courvoisier)

**1991** (28 Mar). *6th-century Mosaics from Kanakaria Church. T* **271** *and similar vert designs. Multicoloured. Granite paper. P* 12.

| | | | |
|---|---|---|---|
| 794 | 5 c. Type **271** .. .. .. .. | 15 | 15 |
| 795 | 15 c. Christ Child .. .. .. .. | 45 | 45 |
| 796 | 17 c. St. James .. .. .. .. | 55 | 55 |
| 797 | 18 c. St. Matthew .. .. .. .. | 60 | 60 |
| 794/7 | .. .. .. .. *Set of* 4 | 1·60 | 1·60 |

272 *Ulysses* Spacecraft

273 Young Cyprus Wheatear

(Des G. Simonis. Litho Alexandros Matsoukis, Athens)

**1991** (6 May). *Europa. Europe in Space. T* **272** *and similar horiz design. Multicoloured. P* 13×13½.

| | | | |
|---|---|---|---|
| 798 | 7 c. Type **272** .. .. .. .. | 25 | 20 |
| 799 | 18 c. *Giotto* and Halley's Comet .. .. | 70 | 80 |

(Des A. Ioannides. Litho Alexandros Matsoukis, Athens)

**1991** (4 July). *Cyprus Wheatear. T* **273** *and similar horiz designs. Multicoloured. P* 13½.

| | | | |
|---|---|---|---|
| 800 | 5 c. Type **273** .. .. .. .. | 15 | 15 |
| 801 | 7 c. Adult bird in autumn plumage .. | 20 | 20 |
| 802 | 15 c. Adult male in breeding plumage .. | 45 | 45 |
| 803 | 30 c. Adult female in breeding plumage .. | 90 | 90 |
| 800/3 | .. .. .. .. *Set of* 4 | 1·50 | 1·50 |

274 Mother and Child with Tents

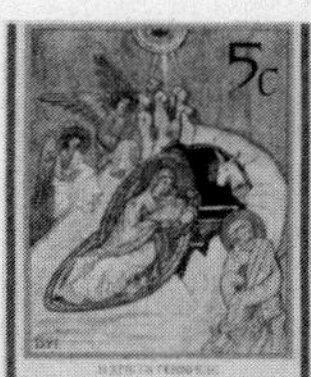


275 The Nativity

(Des A. Ioannides. Litho Alexandros Matsoukis, Athens)

**1991** (7 Oct). *40th Anniv of U.N. Commission for Refugees. T* **274** *and similar horiz designs, each brown, orange-brown and silver. P* 13½.

| | | | |
|---|---|---|---|
| 804 | 5 c. Type **274** .. .. .. .. | 10 | 15 |
| 805 | 15 c. Three pairs of legs .. .. .. | 35 | 40 |
| 806 | 18 c. Three children .. .. .. | 45 | 50 |
| 804/6 | .. .. .. .. *Set of* 3 | 80 | 95 |

(Litho Alexandros Matsoukis, Athens)

**1991** (7 Oct). *Obligatory Tax. Refugee Fund. As T* **255**, *but inscr* "1991". *Chalk-surfaced paper. P* 13.

| | | | |
|---|---|---|---|
| 807 | **255** 1 c. brownish black and brownish grey | 10 | 10 |

(Des Revd. D. Demosthenous. Litho Alexandros Matsoukis, Athens)

**1991** (25 Nov). *Christmas. T* **275** *and similar vert designs. Multicoloured. P* 13½.

| | | | |
|---|---|---|---|
| 808 | 5 c. Type **275** .. .. .. .. | 10 | 10 |
| | a. Sheetlet of 9. Nos. 808/10×3 .. | 2·25 | |
| 809 | 15 c. Saint Basil .. .. .. .. | 35 | 40 |
| 810 | 17 c. Baptism of Jesus .. .. .. | 40 | 45 |
| 808/10 | .. .. .. .. *Set of* 3 | 75 | 80 |

Nos. 808/10 were issued in separate sheets of 20 and in *se-tenant* sheetlets of 9.

***NEW INFORMATION***

The editor is always interested to correspond with people who have new information that will improve or correct the Catalogue.

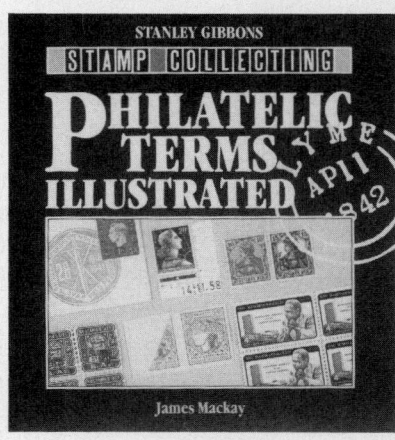

## TURKISH CYPRIOT POSTS

After the inter-communal clashes during December 1963, a parate postal service was established on 6 January 1964 between me of the Turkish Cypriot areas, using handstamps inscribed KIBRIS TURK POSTALARI". During 1964, however, an agree-ent was reached between representatives of the two communities r the restoration of postal services. This agreement, to which the nited Nations representatives were a party, was ratified in ovember 1966 by the Republic's Council of Ministers. Under the heme postal services were provided for the Turkish Cypriot mmunities in Famagusta, Larnaca, Limassol, Lefka, Nicosia and aphos staffed by Turkish Cypriot employees of the Cypriot epartment of Posts.

On 8 April 1970 5 m. and 15 m. locally-produced labels, orig-ally designated "Social Aid Stamps", were issued by the Turkish ypriot community and these can be found on commercial covers. hese local stamps are outside the scope of this catalogue.

On 29 October 1973 Nos. 1/7 were placed on sale, but were used ly on mail between the Turkish Cypriot areas.

Following the intervention by the Republic of Turkey on 20 July 974 these stamps replaced issues of the Republic of Cyprus in that art of the island, north and east of the Attila Line, controlled by e Autonomous Turkish Cypriot Administration.

1 50th Anniversary Emblem

KIBRIS
TÜRK
FEDERE
DEVLETI
13.2.1975

30M

(2)

Des F. Direkoglu Miss E. Ata and G. Pir. Litho Darbhane, Istanbul)

**974** (27 July*). *50th Anniv of Republic of Turkey. T* **1** *and similar designs in vermilion and black (15 m.) or multicoloured (others). P* 12 × 11½ *(vert) or* 11½ × 12 *(horiz).*

| | | | |
|---|---|---|---|
| | 3 m. Woman sentry *(vert)* | 30·00 | 30·00 |
| | 5 m. Military Parade, Nicosia | 60 | 40 |
| | 10 m. Man and woman with Turkish flags *(vert)* | 50 | 20 |
| | 15 m. Type **1** | 2·50 | 1·50 |
| | 20 m. Atatürk statue, Kyrenia Gate, Nicosia *(vert)* | 70 | 20 |
| | 50 m. "The Fallen" *(vert)* | 2·00 | 1·50 |
| | 70 m. Turkish flag and map of Cyprus | 16·00 | 16·00 |
| /7 | *Set of* 7 | 48·00 | 48·00 |

*This is the date on which Nos. 1/7 became valid for international nail.

On 13 February 1975 a Turkish Cypriot Federated State was roclaimed in that part of Cyprus under Turkish occupation and ater 9,000 Turkish Cypriots were transferred from the South to he North of the island.

**975** (3 Mar). *Proclamation of the Turkish Federated State of Cyprus. Nos.* 3 *and* 5 *surch as T* **2** *by Halkin Sesi, Nicosia.*

| | | | |
|---|---|---|---|
| | 30 m. on 20 m. Atatürk statue, Kyrenia Gate, Nicosia | 1·00 | 1·00 |
| | 100 m. on 10 m. Man and woman with Turkish flags | 1·50 | 2·25 |

On No. 9 the surcharge appears at the top of the stamp and the nscription at the bottom.

3 Namik Kemal's Bust, Famagusta

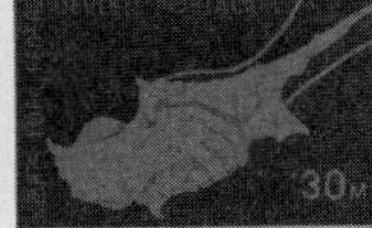

4 Map of Cyprus

(Des I. Özişik. Litho Güzel Sanatlar Matbaasi, Ankara)

**975** (21 Apr). *Multicoloured designs as T* **3**. *Imprint at foot with date* "1975". *P* 13.

| | | | |
|---|---|---|---|
| .0 | 3 m. Type **3** | 15 | 20 |
| .1 | 10 m. Atatürk Statue, Nicosia | 15 | 10 |
| .2 | 15 m. St. Hilarion Castle | 25 | 20 |
| .3 | 20 m. Atatürk Square, Nicosia | 35 | 20 |
| .4 | 25 m. Famagusta Beach | 35 | 25 |
| .5 | 30 m. Kyrenia Harbour | 45 | 10 |
| .6 | 50 m. Lala Mustafa Pasha Mosque, Famagusta *(vert)* | 60 | 10 |
| .7 | 100 m. Interior, Kyrenia Castle | 1·25 | 75 |
| .8 | 250 m. Castle walls, Kyrenia | 2·25 | 2·25 |
| .9 | 500 m. Othello Tower, Famagusta *(vert)* | 4·50 | 4·00 |
| .0/19 | *Set of* 10 | 9·50 | 7·00 |

See also Nos. 37/8.

Des B. Erkmen (30 m.), S. Tuga (50 m.), N. Cüneş (150 m). Litho Ajans-Türk Matbassi, Ankara)

**975** (20 July). *"Peace in Cyprus". T* **4** *and similar multicoloured designs. P* 13.

| | | | |
|---|---|---|---|
| 20 | 30 m. Type **4** | 70 | 15 |
| 21 | 50 m. Map, laurel and broken chain | 85 | 20 |
| 22 | 150 m. Map and laurel-sprig on globe *(vert)* | 2·25 | 1·00 |
| 20/2 | *Set of* 3 | 3·50 | 1·25 |

5 "Pomegranates" (I. V. Guney)

(Litho Güzel Sanatlar Matbaasi, Ankara)

**1975** (29 Dec). *Europa. Paintings. T* **5** *and similar horiz design. Multicoloured. P* 13.

| | | | |
|---|---|---|---|
| 23 | 90 m. Type **5** | 80 | 60 |
| 24 | 100 m. "Harvest Time" (F. Direkoglu) | 80 | 60 |

10 M ——

(6)

7 "Expectation"

**1976** (28 Apr). *Nos.* 16/17 *surch as T* **6** *at Govt Printing House, Nicosia in horizontal clichés of* 10.

| | | | |
|---|---|---|---|
| 25 | 10 m. on 50 m. Lala Mustafa Pasha Mosque, Famagusta | 50 | 70 |
| 26 | 30 m. on 100 m. Interior, Kyrenia Castle | 50 | 80 |

(Litho Ajans-Türk Matbassi, Ankara)

**1976** (3 May). *Europa. T* **7** *and similar vert design showing ceramic statuette. Multicoloured. P* 13.

| | | | |
|---|---|---|---|
| 27 | 60 m. Type **7** | 40 | 50 |
| 28 | 120 m. "Man in Meditation" | 50 | 75 |

8 Carob

9 Olympic Symbol "Flower"

(Des S. Atlihan. Litho Güzel Sanatlar Matbaasi, Ankara)

**1976** (28 June). *Export Products—Fruits. T* **8** *and similar horiz designs. Multicoloured. P* 13.

| | | | |
|---|---|---|---|
| 29 | 10 m. Type **8** | 25 | 10 |
| 30 | 25 m. Mandarin | 35 | 10 |
| 31 | 40 m. Strawberry | 40 | 15 |
| 32 | 60 m. Orange | 50 | 30 |
| 33 | 80 m. Lemon | 55 | 1·10 |
| 29/33 | *Set of* 5 | 1·90 | 1·60 |

(Des C. Mutver (60 m.), A. B. Kocamanoglu (100 m.). Litho Güzel Sanatlar Matbaasi, Ankara)

**1976** (17 July). *Olympic Games, Montreal. T* **9** *and similar horiz design. Multicoloured. P* 13.

| | | | |
|---|---|---|---|
| 34 | 60 m. Type **9** | 25 | 20 |
| 35 | 100 m. Olympic symbol and doves | 35 | 25 |

10 Kyrenia Harbour

11 Liberation Monument, Karaeglanoglu (Ay. Georghios)

(Des I. Özişik. Litho Ajans-Türk Matbassi, Ankara)

**1976** (2 Aug). *New design (5 m.) or as Nos.* 12/13 *but redrawn with lettering altered and new imprint at foot with date* "1976". *P* 13.

| | | | |
|---|---|---|---|
| 36 | 5 m. Type **10** | 30 | 10 |
| 37 | 15 m. St. Hilarion Castle | 40 | 10 |
| 38 | 20 m. Atatürk Square, Nicosia | 40 | 10 |
| 36/8 | *Set of* 3 | 1·00 | 25 |

Nos. 39/46 vacant.

(Des D. Erimez and C. Gizer. Litho Ajans-Türk Matbassi, Ankara)

**1976** (1 Nov). *Liberation Monument. T* **11** *and similar vert design. P* 13.

| | | | | |
|---|---|---|---|---|
| 47 | **11** | 30 m. lt turquoise-blue, lt flesh & black | 15 | 20 |
| 48 | – | 150 m. light verm, light flesh & blk | 35 | 45 |

No. 48 shows a different view of the Monument.

12 Hotel, Salamis Bay

(Litho Türk Tarih Kurumu Basimevi, Ankara)

**1977** (2 May). *Europa. T* **12** *and similar horiz design. Multicoloured. P* 13.

| | | | |
|---|---|---|---|
| 49 | 80 m. Type **12** | 30 | 65 |
| 50 | 100 m. Kyrenia Port | 35 | 65 |

13 Pottery

14 Arap Ahmet Pasha Mosque, Nicosia

(Litho Güzel Sanatlar Matbaasi, Ankara)

**1977** (27 June). *Handicrafts. T* **13** *and similar designs. Multicoloured. P* 13.

| | | | |
|---|---|---|---|
| 51 | 15 m. Type **13** | 10 | 10 |
| 52 | 30 m. Decorated gourds *(vert)* | 10 | 10 |
| 53 | 125 m. Basketware | 30 | 50 |
| 51/3 | *Set of* 3 | 40 | 65 |

(Litho APA Ofset Basimevi, Istanbul)

**1977** (2 Dec). *Turkish Buildings in Cyprus. T* **14** *and similar horiz designs. Multicoloured. P* 13.

| | | | |
|---|---|---|---|
| 54 | 20 m. Type **14** | 10 | 10 |
| 55 | 40 m. Paphos Castle | 10 | 10 |
| 56 | 70 m. Bekir Pasha aqueduct | 15 | 20 |
| 57 | 80 m. Sultan Mahmut library | 15 | 25 |
| 54/7 | *Set of* 4 | 45 | 60 |

15 Namik Kemal (bust) and House, Famagusta

16 Old Man and Woman

(Des B. Ozak. Litho Ticaret Matbaacilik TAS, Izmir)

**1977** (21 Dec). *Namik Kemal (patriotic poet). T* **15** *and similar multicoloured design. P* 12½ × 13 *(30 m.) or* 13 × 12½ *(140 m.)*

| | | | |
|---|---|---|---|
| 58 | 30 m. Type **15** | 15 | 15 |
| 59 | 140 m. Namik Kemal (portrait) *(vert)* | 35 | 50 |

**(New Currency. 100 kurus = 1 lira)**

(Des G. Pir. Litho Ajans-Türk Matbassi, Ankara)

**1978** (17 Apr). *Social Security. T* **16** *and similar vert designs. P* 13 × 13½.

| | | | |
|---|---|---|---|
| 60 | 150 k. black, yellow and blue | 10 | 10 |
| 61 | 275 k. black, red-orange and green | 15 | 15 |
| 62 | 375 k. black, blue and red-orange | 25 | 20 |
| 60/2 | *Set of* 3 | 45 | 40 |

Designs:—275 k. Injured man with crutch; 375 k. Woman with family.

17 Oratory in Büyük Han, Nicosia

18 Motorway Junction

(Des I. Özisik. Litho APA Ofset Basimevi, Istanbul)

**1978** (2 May). *Europa. T* **17** *and similar horiz design. Multicoloured. P* 13.

| | | | |
|---|---|---|---|
| 63 | 225 k. Type **17** | 30 | 20 |
| 64 | 450 k. Cistern in Selimiye Mosque, Nicosia | 45 | 35 |

(Litho APA Ofset Basimevi, Istanbul)

**1978** (10 July). *Communications. T* **18** *and similar horiz designs. Multicoloured. P* 13.

| | | | |
|---|---|---|---|
| 65 | 75 k. Type **18** | 10 | 10 |
| 66 | 100 k. Hydrofoil | 10 | 10 |
| 67 | 650 k. Boeing "720" at Ercan Airport | 25 | 25 |
| 65/7 | *Set of* 3 | 35 | 35 |

19 Dove with Laurel Branch

20 Kemal Atatürk

(Des E. Kaya (725 k.), C. Kirkbesoglu (others). Litho APA Ofset Basimevi, Istanbul)

**1978** (13 Sept). *National Oath. T* **19** *and similar designs. P* 13.
68 150 k. orange-yellow, violet and black .. .. 10 10
69 225 k. black, Indian red and orange-yellow .. 10 10
70 725 k. black, cobalt and orange-yellow .. 20 20
68/70 .. .. .. .. .. *Set of* 3 35 35
Designs: *Vert*—225 k. "Taking the Oath". *Horiz*—725 k. Symbolic dove.

(Des C. Mutver. Litho Türk Tarih Kurumu Basimevi, Ankara)

**1978** (10 Nov). *Kemal Atatürk Commemoration. P* 13.
71 **20** 75 k. pale turquoise-grn & turq-grn .. 10 10
72 450 k. pale flesh and light brown .. 15 15
73 650 k. pale blue and light blue .. .. 20 25
71/3 .. .. .. .. .. *Set of* 3 40 40

**50 Krs.**
(21)

**22** Gun Barrel with Olive Branch and Map of Cyprus

**1979** (4 June). *Nos.* 30/3 *surch as T* **21**, *by Govt Printing Office, Lefkosa*
74 50 k. on 25 m. Mandarin .. .. .. .. 10 10
75 1 l. on 40 m. Strawberry .. .. .. .. 15 10
76 3 l. on 60 m. Orange .. .. .. .. 15 10
77 5 l. on 80 m. Lemon .. .. .. .. 35 15
74/7 .. .. .. .. .. *Set of* 4 65 30

(Des N. Dündar. Litho Ajans-Türk Matbassi, Ankara)

**1979** (20 July). *5th Anniv of Turkish Peace Operation in Cyprus. Sheet* 72 × 52 *mm. Imperf.*
**MS**78 **22** 15 l. black, deep turquoise-blue and pale green .. .. .. .. .. 1·00 1·25

**23** Postage Stamp and Map of Cyprus

**24** Symbolised Microwave Antenna

(Des S. Mumcu. Litho Ajans-Türk Matbassi, Ankara)

**1979** (20 Aug). *Europa. Communications. T* **23** *and similar horiz designs. Multicoloured. P* 13.
79 2 l. Type **23** .. .. .. .. .. 10 10
80 3 l. Postage stamps, building and map .. 10 10
81 8 l. Telephones, Earth and satellite .. .. 20 30
79/81 .. .. .. .. .. *Set of* 3 35 45

(Litho Ticaret Matbaacilik TAS, Izmir)

**1979** (24 Sept). *50th Anniv of International Consultative Radio Committee. P* 13 × 12½.
82 **24** 2 l. multicoloured .. .. .. .. 20 10
83 5 l. multicoloured .. .. .. .. 20 10
84 6 l. multicoloured .. .. .. .. 25 15
82/4 .. .. .. .. .. *Set of* 3 60 30

**25** School Children

**26** Lala Mustafa Pasha Mosque, Magusa

(Des H. Hastürk (1½ l.), G. Akansel (4½ l.), P. Yalyali (6 l.). Litho APA Ofset Basimevi, Istanbul)

**1979** (29 Oct). *International Year of the Child. Children's Drawings. T* **25** *and similar multicoloured designs. P* 13.
85 1½ l. Type **25** .. .. .. .. .. 20 15
86 4½ l. Children and globe (*horiz*) .. .. 30 20
87 6 l. College children .. .. .. .. 40 20
85/7 .. .. .. .. .. *Set of* 3 80 50

(Des S. Mumcu (20 l.), I. Ozisik (others). Litho Ajans-Türk Matbassi, Ankara)

**1980** (23 Mar). *Islamic Commemorations. T* **26** *and similar vert designs. Multicoloured. P* 13.
88 2½ l. Type **26** .. .. .. .. .. 10 10
89 10 l. Arap Ahmet Pasha Mosque, Lefkosa .. 30 15
90 20 l. Mecca and Medina .. .. .. 50 20
88/90 .. .. .. .. .. *Set of* 3 80 40
Commemorations:—2½ l. 1st Islamic Conference in Turkish Cyprus; 10 l. General Assembly of World Islam Congress; 20 l. Moslem Year 1400AH.

**27** Ebu-Su'ud Efendi (philosopher)

**28** Omer's Shrine, Kyrenia

(Litho Ajans-Türk Matbassi, Ankara)

**1980** (23 May). *Europa. Personalities. T* **27** *and similar vert. design. Multicoloured. P* 13.
91 5 l. Type **27** .. .. .. .. .. 20 10
92 30 l. Sultan Selim II .. .. .. .. 90 40

(Litho Guzel Sanatlar Matbaasi, Ankara)

**1980** (25 June). *Ancient Monuments, T* **28** *and similar horiz designs. P* 13.
93 2½ l. new blue and stone .. .. .. 10 10
94 3½ l. grey-green and pale rose-pink .. .. 10 10
95 5 l. lake and pale blue-green .. .. 10 10
96 10 l. deep mauve and pale green .. .. 20 10
97 20 l. dull ultramarine & pale greenish yellow 35 25
93/7 .. .. .. .. .. *Set of* 5 65 45
Designs:—3½ l. Entrance gate, Famagusta; 5 l. Funerary monuments (16th-century), Famagusta; 10 l. Bella Paise Abbey, Kyrenia; 20 l. Selimiye Mosque, Nicosia.

**29** Cyprus 1880 6d.

**30** Dome of the Rock


**31** Extract from World Muslim Congress Statement in Turkish

(Des S. Mumcu. Litho Ajans-Türk Matbassi, Ankara)

**1980** (16 Aug). *Cyprus Stamp Centenary. T* **29** *and similar designs showing stamps. P* 14.
98 7½ l. black, drab and grey-olive .. .. 10 10
99 15 l. brown, grey-blue and blue .. .. 15 15
100 50 l. black, rose and grey .. .. .. 50 55
98/100 .. .. .. .. *Set of* 3 65 70
Designs: *Horiz*:—15 l. Cyprus 1960 Constitution of the Republic 30 m. commemorative. *Vert*—50 l. Social Aid local, 1970.

(Litho Guzel Sanatlar Matbaasi, Ankara)

**1980** (16 Oct). *Palestinian Solidarity. T* **30** *and similar multicoloured design. P* 13.
101 15 l. Type **30** .. .. .. .. .. 25 15
102 35 l. Dome of the Rock (*horiz*) .. .. 65 30

(Des S. Mumcu. Litho Turk Tarih Kurumu Basimevi, Ankara)

**1981** (24 Mar). *Solidarity with Islamic Countries Day. T* **31** *and similar vert design showing extract from World Muslim Congress statement. P* 13.
103 1 l. rosine, stone and olive-sepia .. .. 15 15
104 35 l. black, pale blue-green and myrtle-green 55 60
Design:—35 l. Extract in English

**32** "Atatürk" (F. Duran)

**33** Folk-dancing

(Litho Ajans-Türk Matbassi, Ankara)

**1981** (19 May). *Atatürk Stamp Exhibition, Lefkosa. P* 13.
105 **32** 20 l. multicoloured .. .. .. 25 35
No. 105 was printed in sheets of 100, including 50 *se-tenant* stamp-size labels.

(Litho Ticaret Matbaacilik TAS, Izmir)

**1981** (29 June). *Europa, Folklore. T* **33** *and similar horiz design showing folk-dancing. P* 12½ × 13.
106 10 l. multicoloured .. .. .. .. 35 15
107 30 l. multicoloured .. .. .. .. 60 35

**MINIMUM PRICE**

The minimum price quote is 10p which represents a handling charge rather than a basis for valuing common stamps. For further notes about prices see introductory pages.

**34** "Kemal Atatürk" (I. Calli)

**35** Wild Convolvulus

(Litho Basim Ofset, Ankara)

**1981** (23 July). *Birth Centenary of Kemal Atatürk. Sheet* 70 × 9[…] *mm. Imperf.*
**MS**108 **34** 150 l. multicoloured .. .. .. 1·10 1·2[…]

(Litho Turk Tarih Kurumu Basimevi, Ankara)

**1981** (28 Sept)–**82**. *Flowers, Multicoloured designs as T* **35**. *P* 13.
109 1 l. Type **35** .. .. .. .. .. 10 1[…]
110 5 l. Persian Cyclamen (*horiz*) (22.1.82) .. 10 1[…]
111 10 l. Spring Mandrake (*horiz*) .. .. 10 1[…]
112 25 l. Corn Poppy .. .. .. .. 10 1[…]
113 30 l. Wild Arum (22.1.82) .. .. .. 15 1[…]
114 50 l. Sage-leaved Rock Rose (*horiz*) (22.1.82) .. .. .. .. 30 1[…]
115 100 l. *Cistus salviaefolius L.* (22.1.82) .. 60 2[…]
116 150 l. Giant Fennel (*horiz*) .. .. .. 1·10 7[…]
109/16 .. .. .. .. .. *Set of* 8 2·25 1·2[…]

**36** Stylized Disabled Person in Wheelchair

**37** Turkish and Palestinian Flags

(Des H. Ulucam (7½ l.), N. Kozal (others). Litho Türk Tarih Kurumu Basimevi, Ankara)

**1981** (16 Oct). *Commemorations. T* **36** *and similar multicoloured designs. P* 13.
117 7½ l. Type **36** .. .. .. .. .. 25 20
118 10 l. Heads of people of different races, peace dove and barbed wire (*vert*) .. 40 35
119 20 l. People of different races reaching out from globe, with dishes (*vert*) .. 55 50
117/19 .. .. .. .. *Set of* 3 1·10 95
Commemorations:—7½ l. International Year for Disabled Persons; 10 l. Anti-apartheid Publicity; 20 l. World Food Day.

(Des H. Ulucam. Litho Türk Tarih Kurumu Basimevi, Ankara)

**1981** (29 Nov). *Palestinian Solidarity. P* 13.
120 **37** 10 l. multicoloured .. .. .. 25 20

**38** Prince Charles and Lady Diana Spencer

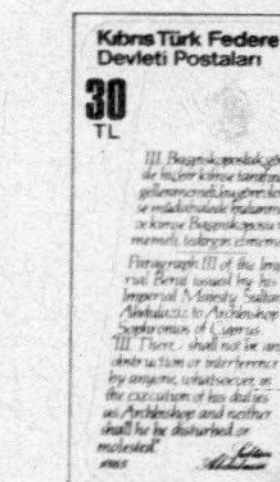

**39** Charter issued by Sultan Abdul Aziz to Archbishop Sophronios

(Des H. Ulucam. Litho Türk Tarih Kurumu Basimevi, Ankara)

**1981** (30 Nov). *Royal Wedding. P* 13
121 **38** 50 l. multicoloured .. .. .. 1·00 65

(Des H. Ulucam, Litho Tezel Ofset, Lefkosa)

**1982** (30 July). *Europa (CEPT). Sheet* 83 × 124 *mm containing T* **39** *and similar vert design. Multicoloured. P* 12½ × 13.
**MS**122 30 l. × 2. Type **39**; 70 l. × 2, Turkish forces landing at Tuzla, 1571 .. .. .. .. 4·00 4·00

**40** Buffavento Castle

**41** "Wedding" (A. Örek)

(Des H. Ulucam (Nos. 123/5). Litho Tezel Ofset, Lefkosa)

**1982** (20 Aug). *Tourism. T* **40** *and similar multicoloured designs. P* 12.
123 5 l. Type **40** .. .. .. .. .. .. 10 10
124 10 l. Windsurfing (*horiz*) .. .. .. .. 15 10
125 15 l. Kantara Castle (*horiz*) .. .. .. .. 20 10
126 30 l. Shipwreck (300 B.C.) (*horiz*) .. .. .. 45 30
123/6 .. .. .. .. .. .. *Set of* 4 80 50

(Litho Ajans-Türk Matbassi, Ankara)

**1982** (3 Dec). *Paintings (1st series). T* **41** *and similar multi-coloured design. P* 13.
127 30 l. Type **41** .. .. .. .. .. .. 15 30
128 50 l. "Carob Pickers" (O. Naxim Selenge) (*vert*) .. .. .. .. .. .. 30 70
See also Nos. 132/3, 157/8, 176/7, 185/6, 208/9, 225/7, 248/50, 284/5 and 315/16.

**42** Cross of Lorraine, Koch and Bacillus (Cent of Koch's Discovery of Tubercle Bacillus)

**43** "Calloused Hands" (Salih Oral)

(Des H. Ulucam. Litho Tezel Ofset, Lefkosa)

**1982** (15 Dec.) *Anniversaries and Events. T* **42** *and similar multi-coloured designs. P* 12.
129 10 l. Type **42** .. .. .. .. .. .. 30 20
130 30 l. Spectrum on football pitch (World Cup Football Championships, Spain) .. 55 45
131 70 l. "75" and Lord Baden-Powell (75th anniv of Boy Scout movement and 125th birth anniv) (*vert*) .. .. .. .. 1·10 1·40
129/31 .. .. .. .. .. *Set of* 3 1·75 1·90

(Litho Ajans-Türk Matbassi, Ankara)

**1983** (16 May). *Paintings (2nd series). T* **43** *and similar vert design. Multicoloured. P* 13.
132 30 l. Type **43** .. .. .. .. .. .. 70 70
133 35 l. "Malya—Limassol Bus" (Emin Cizenel) 70 70

**44** Old Map of Cyprus by Piri Reis

**45** First Turkish Cypriot 10 m. Stamp

(Litho Türk Tarih Kurumu Basimevi, Ankara)

**1983** (30 June). *Europa. Sheet* 82 × 78 *mm, containing T* **44** *and similar horiz design. Multicoloured. P* 13.
**MS**134 100 l. Type **44**; 100 l. Cyprus as seen from "Skylab" .. .. .. .. .. .. .. 1·40 2·00

(Des E. Ata (15 l.), A. Hasan (20 l.), G. Pir (25 l.), H. Ulucam (others). Litho Ajans-Türk Matbassi, Ankara)

**1983** (1 Aug). *Anniversaries and Events. T* **45** *and similar multi-coloured designs commemorating World Communications Year* (30, 50 *l.*) *or* 25*th Anniv. of T.M.T. (Turkish Cypriot Resistance Organization). P* 13.
135 15 l. Type **45** .. .. .. .. .. .. 30 30
136 20 l. "Turkish Achievements in Cyprus" (*horiz*)) .. .. .. .. .. .. 30 30
137 25 l. "Liberation Fighters" .. .. .. .. 35 35
138 30 l. Dish aerial and telegraph pole (*horiz*) .. 45 45
139 50 l. Dove and envelopes (*horiz*) .. .. .. 85 85
135/9 .. .. .. .. .. *Set of* 5 2·00 2·00

**46** European Bee Eater

Kuzey Kıbrıs
Türk Cumhuriyeti
15.11.1983

15

**(47)**

(Des E. Cizenel. Litho Ajans-Türks Matbassi, Ankara)

**1983** (10 Oct). *Birds of Cyprus. T* **46** *and similar horiz designs. Multicoloured. P* 13.
140 10 l. Type **46** .. .. .. .. .. .. 50 65
a. Block of 4. Nos. 140/3 .. .. .. .. 2·40
141 15 l. Goldfinch .. .. .. .. .. .. 55 70
142 50 l. European Robin .. .. .. .. .. 75 95
143 65 l. Golden Oriole .. .. .. .. .. 85 1·10
140/3 .. .. .. .. .. *Set of* 4 2·40 3·00
Nos. 140/3 were printed together, *se-tenant*, in blocks of 4 throughout the sheet.

**1983** (7 Dec). *Establishment of the Republic. Nos.* 109, 111/12 *and* 116 *surch as T* **47** *(No. 145) or optd only.*
144 10 l. *Mandragara officinarum* .. .. 15 15
145 15 l. on 1 l. Type **35** .. .. .. .. 15 15
a. Surch inverted .. .. .. .. 75·00
146 25 l. *Papaver rhoeas L* .. .. .. .. 20 20
147 150 l. *Ferula communis L* .. .. .. 1·00 1·75
144/7 .. .. .. .. .. *Set of* 4 1·40 2·00

**48** C.E.P.T. 25th Anniversary Logo.

**49** Olympic Flame

(Des J. Larrivière. Litho Tezel Ofset, Lefkosa)

**1984** (30 May). *Europa. P* 12 × 12½.
148 **48** 50 l. lemon, chestnut and black .. 1·50 1·50
a. Pair. Nos. 148/9 .. .. .. 3·00 3·00
149 100 l. pale blue, bright blue and black .. .. .. .. .. 1·50 1·50
Nos. 148/9 were printed together, *se-tenant*, in horizontal and vertical pairs throughout the sheet.

(Des H. Ulucam. Litho Tezel Ofset, Lefkosa)

**1984** (19 June). *Olympic Games, Los Angeles. T* **49** *and similar multicoloured designs. P* 12½ × 12 (10 *l.*) *or* 12 × 12½ *(others).*
150 10 l. Type **49** .. .. .. .. .. 10 10
151 20 l. Olympic events within rings (*horiz*) .. 15 15
152 70 l. Martial arts event (*horiz*) .. .. .. 30 65
150/2 .. .. .. .. .. *Set of* 3 45 80

**50** Atatürk Cultural Centre

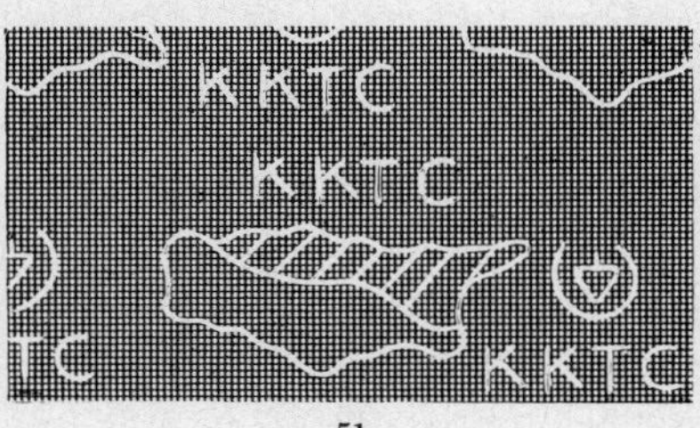

**51**

(Des H. Ulucam. Litho Tezel Ofset, Lefkosa)

**1984** (20 July). *Opening of Atatürk Cultural Centre, Lefkosa. W* **51**. *P* 12 × 12½.
153 **50** 120 l. stone, black and chestnut .. 90 1·00

**52** Turkish Cypriot Flag and Map

(Des C. Guzeloglu (20 l.), M. Gozbebek (70 l.). Litho Tezel Ofset Lefkosa)

**1984** (20 July). 10*th Anniv of Turkish Landings in Cyprus. T* **52** *and similar horiz design. W* **51**. *Multicoloured. P* 12 × 12½.
154 20 l. Type **52** .. .. .. .. .. 40 20
155 70 l. Turkish Cypriot flag within book .. 85 1·25

**53** Burnt and Replanted Forests

(Des H. Ulucam. Litho Tezel Ofset, Lefkosa)

**1984** (20 Aug). *World Forestry Resources. W* **51**. *P* 12 × 12½.
156 **53** 90 l. multicoloured .. .. .. 1·00 1·25

## ALTERED CATALOGUE NUMBERS

Any Catalogue numbers altered from the last edition are shown as a list in the introductory pages.

**54** "Old Turkish Houses, Nicosia" (Cevdet Cagdas)

**55** Kemal Atatürk, Flag and Crown

(Litho Tezel Ofset, Lefkosa)

**1984** (21 Sept). *Paintings (3rd series). T* **54** *and similar horiz design. Multicoloured. W* **51**. *P* 13 × 12½.
157 20 l. Type **54** .. .. .. .. .. 35 30
158 70 l. "Scenery" (Olga Rauf) .. .. .. 75 1·10
See also Nos. 176/7, 185/6, 208/9, 225/7, 248/50, 284/5 and 315/16.

(Des H. Ulucam (20 l.), F. Isiman (70 l.). Litho Tezel Ofset, Lefkosa)

**1984** (15 Nov). 1*st Anniv of Turkish Republic of Northern Cyprus. T* **55** *and similar multicoloured design. W* **51** *(sideways on* 20 *l., inverted on* 70 *l.). P* 12½.
159 20 l. Type **55** .. .. .. .. .. 20 15
160 70 l. Legislative Assembly voting for Republic (*horiz*) .. .. .. .. .. 50 70

**56** Taekwondo Bout

**57** "Le Regard" (Saulo Mercader)

(Des H. Ulucam. Litho Tezel Ofset, Lefkosa)

**1984** (10 Dec). *International Taekwondo Championship, Girne. T* **56** *and similar horiz design. W* **51** *(sideways on* 10 *l.). P* 12½.
161 10 l. black, pale cinnamon and grey-black .. 35 15
162 70 l. multicoloured .. .. .. .. 1·10 1·40
Design:—70 l. Emblem and flags of competing nations.

(Litho Tezel Ofset, Lefkosa)

**1984** (10 Dec). *Exhibition by Saulo Mercader (artist). T* **57** *and similar multicoloured design. W* **51** *(sideways on* 20 *l.). P* 12½ × 13 (20 *l.*) *or* 13 × 12½ (70 *l.*).
163 20 l. Type **57** .. .. .. .. .. 30 20
164 70 l. "L'equilibre de L'esprit (*horiz*) .. .. 1·10 1·40

**58** Musical Instruments and Music

**59** Dr. Fazil Kucuk (politician)

(Des H. Ulucam. Litho Tezel Ofset, Lefkosa)

**1984** (10 Dec). *Visit of Nurnberg Chamber Orchestra. W* **51** *(side-ways). P* 12½.
165 **58** 70 l. multicoloured .. .. .. 1·25 1·25

(Des Y. Calli (20 l.), E. Cizenel (70 l.). Litho Tezel Ofset, Lefkosa)

**1985** (15 Jan). 1*st Death Anniv of Dr. Fazil Kucuk (politician). T* **59** *and similar vert design. Multicoloured. W* **51** *(inverted on* 70 *l.).P* 12½ × 12.
166 20 l. Type **59** .. .. .. .. .. 30 20
167 70 l. Dr. Fazil Kucuk reading newspaper .. 95 1·10

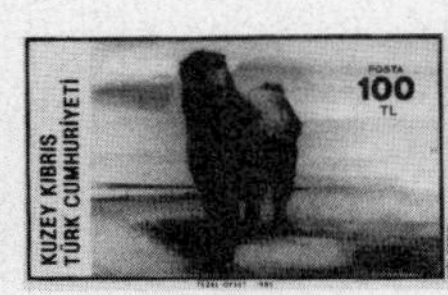

**60** Goat

**61** George Frederick Handel

(Des E. Cizenel. Litho Tezel Ofset, Lefkosa)

**1985** (29 May). *Domestic Animals. T* **60** *and similar horiz designs. Multicoloured. W* **51**. *P* 12×12½.
168 100 l. Type **60** .. .. .. .. .. 55 30
169 200 l. Cow and calf .. .. .. .. 90 70
170 300 l. Ram .. .. .. .. .. 1·25 1·25
171 500 l. Donkey .. .. .. .. .. 2·00 2·50
168/71 .. .. .. .. *Set of* 4 4·25 4·25

(Litho Tezel Ofset, Lefkosa)

**1985** (26 June). *Europa. Composers. T* **61** *and similar vert designs. W* **51** *(sideways). P* 12½×12.
172 20 l. brown-purple, myrtle-green & pale grn 1·25 1·25
a. Block of 4. Nos. 172/5 .. .. .. 5·50
173 20 l. brown-purple, lake-brown & pale pink 1·25 1·25
174 100 l. brown-purple, steel blue & pale grey-bl 1·75 1·75
175 100 l. brown-purple, bistre-brown & pale cinn 1·75 1·75
172/5 .. .. .. .. .. *Set of* 4 5·50 5·50

Designs:—No. 172, Type **61**; 173, Guiseppe Domenico Scarlatti; 174, Johann Sebastian Bach; 175, Buhurizade Mustafa Itri Efendi.

Nos. 172/5 were printed together, *se-tenant*, in blocks of four throughout the sheet.

(Litho Tezel Ofset, Lefkosa)

**1985** (15 Aug). *Paintings (4th series). Vert designs as T* **54**. *Multicoloured. W* **51**. *P* 12½×13.
176 20 l. "Village Life" (Ali Atakan) .. .. 45 30
177 50 l. "Woman carrying Water" (Ismet V. Güney) .. .. .. .. .. 1·25 1·50

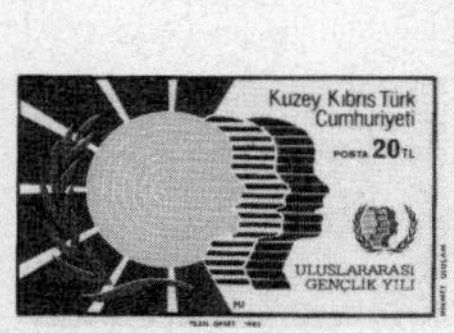


**62** Heads of Three Youths

**63** Parachutist (Aviation League)

(Des H. Uluçam. Litho Tezel Ofset, Lefkosa)

**1985** (29 Oct). *International Youth Year. T* **62** *and similar horiz design. Multicoloured. W* **51** *(sideways). P* 12×12½.
178 20 l. Type **62** .. .. .. .. .. 40 20
179 100 l. Dove and globe .. .. .. .. 1·40 1·60

(Des H. Uluçam. Litho Tezel Ofset, Lefkosa)

**1985** (29 Nov). *Anniversaries and Events. T* **63** *and similar designs. W* **51** *(inverted on Nos. 181/2, sideways on Nos. 183/4). P* 12×12½ *(Nos. 183/4) or* 12½×12 *(others).*
180 20 l. multicoloured .. .. .. .. 30 15
181 50 l. grey-black, light brown and dull ultramarine .. .. .. .. .. 65 50
182 100 l. light brown .. .. .. .. 1·00 1·00
183 100 l. multicoloured .. .. .. .. 1·00 1·00
184 100 l. multicoloured .. .. .. .. 1·00 1·00
180/4 .. .. .. .. .. *Set of* 5 3·50 3·25

Designs: *Vert*—No. 181, Louis Pasteur (Centenary of Discovery of Rabies vaccine); 182, İsmet İnönü (Turkish statesman) (birth centenary (1984)). *Horiz*—183, "40" in figures and symbolic flower (40th anniv of United Nations Organization); 184, Patient receiving blood transfusion (Prevention of Thalassaemia).

(Litho Tezel Ofset, Lefkosa)

**1986** (20 June). *Paintings (5th series). Horiz designs as T* **54**. *Multicoloured. W* **51** *(sideways). P* 13×12½.
185 20 l. "House with Arches" (Gönen Atakol) .. 45 20
186 100 l. "Atatürk Square" (Yalkin Muhtaroğlu) .. .. .. .. .. 1·60 90

**64** Griffon Vulture

**65** Karagöz Show Puppets

(Des E. Çizenel (100 l.), H. Uluçam (200 l.). Litho Tezel Ofset, Lefkosa)

**1986** (20 June). *Europa. Protection of Nature and the Environment. Sheet* 82×76 *mm. containing T* **64** *and similar horiz design. Multicoloured. W* **51** *(sideways). P* 12×12½.
**MS**187 100 l. Type **64**: 200 l. Litter on Cyprus landscape .. .. .. .. .. .. 2·50 2·25

(Des Y. Yazgin. Litho Tezel Ofset, Lefkosa)

**1986** (25 July). *Karagöz Folk Puppets. W* **51** *(inverted). P* 12½×13.
188 **65** 100 l. multicoloured .. .. .. 1·50 65

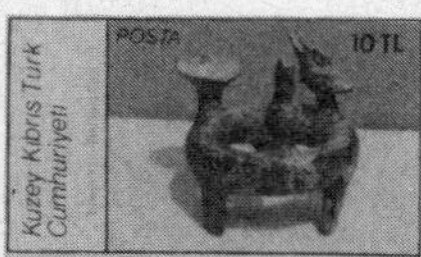
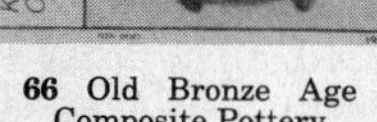


**66** Old Bronze Age Composite Pottery

**67** Soldiers, Defence Force Badge and Atatürk (10th anniv of Defence Forces)

(Litho Tezel Ofset, Lefkosa)

**1986** (15 Sept). *Archaeological Artifacts. Cultural Links with Anatolia. T* **66** *and similar multicoloured designs. W* **51** *(sideways on 10, 50 l., inverted on 20, 100 l.). P* 12×12½ *(10, 50 l.) or* 12½×12 *(20, 100 l.).*
189 10 l. Type **66** .. .. .. .. .. 30 10
190 20 l. Late Bronze Age bird jug (*vert*) .. 50 10
191 50 l. Neolithic earthenware pot .. .. 75 30
192 100 l. Roman statue of Artemis (*vert*) .. 1·25 75
189/92 .. .. .. .. *Set of* 4 2·50 1·10

(Des. H. Uluçam (No. 196). Litho Tezel Ofset, Lefkosa)

**1986** (13 Oct). *Anniversaries and Events. T* **67** *and similar multicoloured designs. W* **51** *(inverted on 20, 50 l., sideways on others). P* 12½×12 *(vert) or* 12×12½ *(horiz).*
193 20 l. Type **67** .. .. .. .. .. 40 10
194 50 l. Woman and two children (40th anniv of Food and Agriculture Organization) .. 55 30
195 100 l. Football and world map (World Cup Football Championship, Mexico) (*horiz*) .. .. .. .. .. 1·25 60
196 100 l. Orbit of Halley's Comet and *Giotto* spacecraft (*horiz*) .. .. .. 1·25 60
193/6 .. .. .. .. .. *Set of* 4 3·00 1·40

**68** Güzelyurt Dam and Power Station

**69** Prince Andrew and Miss Sarah Ferguson

(Litho Tezel Ofset, Lefkosa)

**1986** (17 Nov). *Modern Development (1st series). T* **68** *and similar horiz designs. Multicoloured. W* **51** *(sideways). P* 12×12½.
197 20 l. Type **68** .. .. .. .. .. 60 20
198 50 l. Low cost housing project, Lefkosa .. 75 40
199 100 l. Kyrenia Airport .. .. .. 1·40 1·00
197/9 .. .. .. .. .. *Set of* 3 2·50 1·40

See also Nos. 223/4 and 258/63.

(Litho Tezel Ofset, Lefkosa)

**1986** (20 Nov). *60th Birthday of Queen Elizabeth II and Royal Wedding. T* **69** *and similar vert design. Multicoloured. W* **51** *(inverted). P* 12½×13.
200 100 l. Type **69** .. .. .. .. .. 90 40
a. Pair. Nos. 200/1 .. .. .. 1·75 80
201 100 l. Queen Elizabeth II .. .. .. 90 40

Nos. 200/1 were printed together, *se-tenant*, in horizontal and vertical pairs throughout the sheet.

**70** Locomotive No. 11 and Trakhoni Station

(Des H. Uluçam (50 l.). Litho Tezel Ofset, Lefkosa)

**1986** (31 Dec). *Cyprus Railway. T* **70** *and similar horiz design. Multicoloured. W* **51** *(sideways). P* 12×12½.
202 50 l. Type **70** .. .. .. .. .. 1·25 75
203 100 l. Locomotive No. 1 .. .. .. 1·75 1·50

*Kuzey Kıbrıs Türk Cumhuriyeti*

(71)

**1987** (18 May). *Nos.* 94, 96/7 *and* 113 *optd as T* **71** *or surch also.*
204 10 l. deep mauve and pale green .. .. 25 25
205 15 l. on 3½ l. grey-green and pale rose-pink 25 25
206 20 l. dull ultramarine & pale greenish yellow 25 25
207 30 l. multicoloured .. .. .. .. 30 30
204/7 .. .. .. .. .. *Set of* 4 95 95

(Litho Tezel Ofset, Lefkosa)

**1987** (27 May). *Paintings (6th series). Vert designs as T* **54**. *Multicoloured. W* **51** *(inverted). P* 12½×13.
208 50 l. "Shepherd" (Feridun Işiman) .. .. 60 60
209 125 l. "Pear Woman" (Mehmet Uluhan) .. 1·00 1·25

**72** Modern House (architect A. Vural Behaeddin)

**73** Kneeling Folk Dancer

(Des H. Uluçam (50 l.). Litho Tezel Ofset, Lefkosa)

**1987** (30 June). *Europa. Modern Architecture. T* **72** *and similar horiz design. Multicoloured. W* **51** *(sideways). P* 12×12½.
210 50 l. Type **72** .. .. .. .. .. 40 20
a. Perf 12×imperf .. .. .. .. 75 75
ab. Booklet pane. Nos. 210a/11a, each × 2 3·75
211 200 l. Modern house (architect Necdet Turgay) .. .. .. .. .. .. 1·25 1·50
a. Perf 12 × imperf .. .. .. .. 1·25 1·50

Nos. 210a and 211a come from 500 l. stamp booklets containing *se-tenant* pane No. 210ab.

(Des B. Ruhi. Litho Tezel Ofset, Lefkosa)

**1987** (20 Aug). *Folk Dancers. T* **73** *and similar vert designs. Multicoloured. W* **51** *(inverted). P* 12½×12.
212 20 l. Type **73** .. .. .. .. .. 15 10
213 50 l. Standing male dancer .. .. .. 20 10
214 200 l. Standing female dancer .. .. .. 70 45
215 1000 l. Woman's headdress .. .. .. 2·75 2·40
212/15 .. .. .. .. .. *Set of* 4 3·50 2·75

**74** Regimental Colour (1st Anniv of Infantry Regiment)

**75** Ahmet Beliğ Pasha (Egyptian judge)

(Des H. Uluçam. Litho Tezel Ofset, Lefkosa)

**1987** (30 Sept–2 Nov). *Anniversaries and Events. T* **74** *and similar multicoloured designs. W* **51** *(inverted on vert designs, sideways on horiz). P* 12½×12 *(vert) or* 12×12½ *(horiz).*
216 50 l. Type **74** .. .. .. .. .. 35 30
217 50 l. Pres. Denktash and Turgut Özal (1st anniv. of Turkish Prime Minister's visit) (*horiz*) (2.11) .. .. .. 35 30
218 200 l. Emblem and Crescent (5th Islamic Summit Conference, Kuwait) .. .. 1·10 1·10
219 200 l. Emblem and laurel leaves (Membership of Pharmaceutical Federation) (*horiz*) .. .. .. .. .. 1·10 1·10
216/19 .. .. .. .. .. *Set of* 4 2·50 2·50

(Des H. Uluçam. Litho Tezel Ofset, Lefkosa)

**1987** (22 Oct). *Turkish Cypriot Personalities. T* **75** *and similar vert designs. W* **51** *(inverted). P* 12½×12.
220 **75** 50 l. brown and greenish yellow .. 20 15
221 – 50 l. multicoloured .. .. .. 20 15
222 – 125 l. multicoloured .. .. .. 50 35
220/2 .. .. .. .. .. *Set of* 3 80 60

Designs:—50 l. (No. 221) Mehmet Emin Pasha (Ottoman Grand Vizier); 125 l. Mehmet Kâmil Pasha (Ottoman Grand Vizier).

**76** Tourist Hotel, Girne

**77** *Piyale Pasha* (tug)

(Des A. Erduran. Litho Tezel Ofset, Lefkosa)

**1987** (20 Nov). *Modern Development (2nd series). T* **76** *and similar horiz design. Multicoloured. W* **51** *(sideways). P* 12×12½.
223 150 l. Type **76** .. .. .. .. .. 75 40
224 200 l. Dogu Akdeniz University .. .. 1·00 55

(Litho Tezel Ofset, Lefkosa)

**1988** (2 May). *Paintings (7th series). Multicoloured designs as T* **54**. *W* **51** *(inverted on 20, 150 l, sideways on 50 l.). P 12½×13 (20, 150 l.) or 13×12½ (50 l.).*

225 20 l. "Woman making Pastry" (Ayhan Mentes) (*vert*) .. .. .. .. 25 15
226 50 l. "Chair Weaver" (Osman Güvenir) .. 35 20
227 150 l. "Woman weaving a Rug" (Zekâi Yesiladali) (*vert*) .. .. .. 85 85
225/7 .. .. .. .. *Set of* 3 1·25 1·10

(Des H. Uluçam. Litho Tezel Ofset, Lefkosa)

**1988** (31 May). *Europa. Transport and Communications. T* **77** *and similar multicoloured design. W* **51** *(sideways on 200 l., inverted on 500 l.). P 12×12½ (200 l.) or 12½×12 (500 l.).*

228 200 l. Type **77** .. .. .. .. .. 75 30
229 500 l. Dish aerial and antenna tower, Selvilitepe (*vert*) .. .. .. .. 1·50 95

No. 229 also commemorates the 25th anniversary of Bayrak Radio and Television Corporation.

78 Lefkosa

79 Bülent Ecevit

(Litho Tezel Ofset, Lefkosa)

**1988** (17 June). *Tourism. T* **78** *and similar horiz designs. Multicoloured. W* **51** *(sideways). P 12×12½.*

230 150 l. Type **78** .. .. .. .. .. 35 30
231 200 l. Gazi-Magusa .. .. .. .. 45 40
232 300 l. Girne .. .. .. .. .. 65 55
230/2 .. .. .. .. *Set of* 3 1·25 1·10

(Litho. Tezel Ofset, Lefkosa)

**1988** (20 July). *Turkish Prime Ministers. T* **79** *and similar vert designs. Multicoloured. W* **51**. *P 12½×12.*

233 50 l. Type **79** .. .. .. .. .. 15 15
234 50 l. Bülent Ulusu .. .. .. .. 15 15
235 50 l. Turgut Ozal .. .. .. .. .. 15 15
233/5 .. .. .. .. *Set of* 3 40 40

80 Red Crescent Members on Exercise

81 Hodori the Tiger (Games mascot) and Fireworks

(Des N. Kozal. Litho Tezel Ofset, Lefkosa)

**1988** (8 Aug). *Civil Defence. W* **51** *(sideways). P 12×12½.*

236 **80** 150 l. multicoloured .. .. .. .. 30 30

(Des E. Cizenel (200 l.), N. Kozal (250 l.), H. Uluçam (400 l.). Litho Tezel Ofset, Lefkosa)

**1988** (17 Sept). *Olympic Games, Seoul. T* **81** *and similar horiz designs. Multicoloured. W* **51** *(sideways). P 12×12½.*

237 200 l. Type **81** .. .. .. .. .. 40 35
a. Imperf (pair) .. .. .. .. 70·00
238 250 l. Athletics .. .. .. .. .. 50 50
239 400 l. Shot and running track with letters spelling "SEOUL" .. .. .. .. 70 85
237/9 .. .. .. .. *Set of* 3 1·40 1·50

82 Sedat Simavi (journalist)

83 "Kemal Atatürk" (I. Calli)

(Des H. Uluçam (Nos. 241/3). Litho Tezel Ofset, Lefkosa)

**1988** (17 Oct). *Anniversaries and Events. T* **82** *and similar designs. W* **51** *(inverted on Nos. 240, 243 and 245, sideways on Nos. 241 and 244). P 12½×12 (vert) or 12×12½ (horiz).*

240 50 l. olive-green .. .. .. .. .. 15 15
241 100 l. multicoloured .. .. .. .. 20 20
242 300 l. multicoloured .. .. .. .. 50 50
243 400 l. multicoloured .. .. .. .. 70 70
244 400 l. multicoloured .. .. .. .. 70 70
245 600 l. multicoloured .. .. .. .. 90 90
240/5 .. .. .. .. *Set of* 6 2·75 2·75

Designs: *Horiz*—No. 241, Stylised figures around table and flags of participating countries (International Girne Conferences); 244, Presidents Gorbachev and Reagan signing treaty (Summit Meeting). *Vert*—No. 242, Cogwheels as flowers (North Cyprus Industrial Fair); 243, Globe (125th anniv of International Red Cross); 245, "Medical Services" (40th anniv of W.H.O.).

(Litho Tezel Ofset, Lefkosa)

**1988** (10 Nov). *50th Death Anniv of Kemal Atatürk. Sheet 72 × 102 mm containing T* **83** *and similar vert designs. Multicoloured. W* **51** *(inverted). P 12½ × 12.*

**MS**246 250 l. Type **83**; 250 l. "Kemal Atatürk" (N. Ismail); 250 l. In army uniform; 250 l. In profile .. .. .. .. .. .. 1·25 1·25

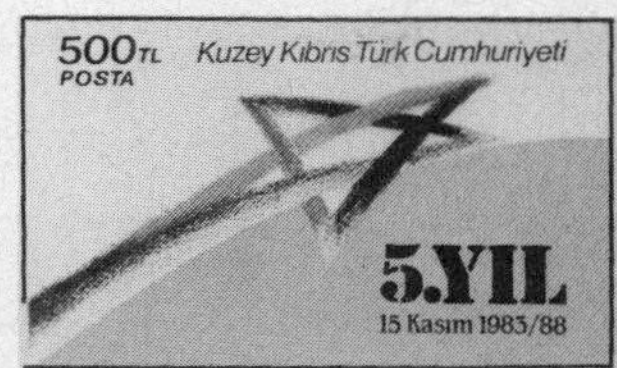


84 Abstract Design

(Des E. Cizenel. Litho Tezel Ofset, Lefkosa)

**1988** (15 Nov). *5th Anniv of Turkish Republic of Northern Cyprus. Sheet 98 × 76 mm. W* **51** *(sideways). Imperf.*

**MS**247 **84** 500 l. multicoloured .. .. .. 1·00 1·00

(Litho Tezel Ofset, Lefkosa)

**1989** (28 Apr). *Paintings (8th series). Multicoloured designs as T* **54**. *W* **51** *(sideways on 150, 400 l., inverted on 600 l.). P 12½×13 (600 l.) or 13×12½ (others).*

248 150 l. "Dervis Pasa Mansion, Lefkosa" (Inci Kansu) .. .. .. .. .. 35 20
249 400 l. "Gamblers' Inn, Lefkosa" (Osman Güvenir) .. .. .. .. .. 75 45
250 600 l. "Mosque, Paphos" (Hikmet Ulucam) (*vert*) .. .. .. .. 1·10 70
248/50 .. .. .. .. *Set of* 3 2·00 1·25

85 Girl with Doll

86 Meeting of Presidents Vassiliou and Denktash

(Des N. Kozal. Litho Tezel Ofset, Lefkosa)

**1989** (31 May). *Europa. Children's Games. T* **85** *and similar vert design. Multicoloured. W* **51**. *P 12½×12.*

251 600 l. Type **85** .. .. .. .. .. 90 70
a. Imperf × p 12 .. .. .. .. 90 90
ab. Booklet pane. Nos. 251a/2a, each ×2 4·50
252 1000 l. Boy with kite .. .. .. .. 1·50 1·50
a. Imperf × p 12 .. .. .. .. 1·50 1·75

Nos. 251a and 252a come from 3200 l. stamp booklets containing *se-tenant* pane No. 251ab.

(Litho Tezel Ofset, Lefkosa)

**1989** (30 June). *Cyprus Peace Summit, Geneva, 1988. W* **51** *(sideways). P 12×12½.*

253 **86** 500 l. deep rose-red and black .. .. 55 60

87 Chukar Partridge

88 Road Construction

(Des E. Cizenel. Litho Tezel Ofset, Lefkosa)

**1989** (31 July). *Wildlife. T* **87** *and similar horiz designs. Multicoloured. W* **51** *(sideways). P 12×12½.*

254 100 l. Type **87** .. .. .. .. .. 10 10
255 200 l. Cyprus Hare .. .. .. .. 20 25
256 700 l. Black Partridge .. .. .. .. 75 80
257 2000 l. Red Fox .. .. .. .. .. 2·10 2·25
254/7 .. .. .. .. *Set of* 4 2·75 3·00

(Litho Tezel Ofset, Lefkosa)

**1989** (29 Sept). *Modern Development (3rd series). T* **88** *and similar multicoloured designs. W* **51** *(sideways on 100, 700 l.). P 12×12½ (100, 700 l.) or 12½×12 (others).*

258 100 l. Type **88** .. .. .. .. .. 10 10
259 150 l. Laying water pipeline (*vert*) .. .. 15 20
260 200 l. Seedling trees (*vert*) .. .. .. 20 25
261 450 l. Modern telephone exchange (*vert*) .. 50 75
262 650 l. Steam turbine power station (*vert*) .. 70 1·00
263 700 l. Irrigation reservoir .. .. .. 75 1·25
258/63 .. .. .. .. *Set of* 6 2·25 3·25

## MINIMUM PRICE

The minimum price quote is 10p which represents a handling charge rather than a basis for valuing common stamps. For further notes about prices see introductory pages.

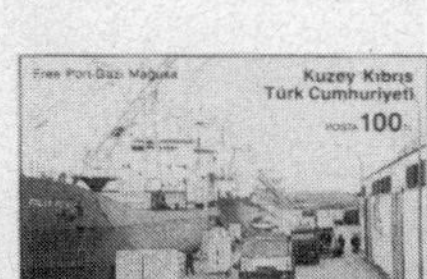


89 Unloading Freighter at Quayside (15th anniv of Gazi Magusa Free Port)

90 Erdal Inonu

(Des E. Çizenel (450, 600 l.), Ö. Özünalp (500 l.), S. Oral (1000 l.). Litho Tezel Ofset, Lefkosa)

**1989** (17 Nov). *Anniversaries. T* **89** *and similar designs. W* **51** *(inverted on 450 l., sideways on others). P 12½×13 (450 l.) or 12×12½ (others).*

264 100 l. multicoloured .. .. .. .. 10 15
265 450 l. black, dull ultramarine & scar- verm 50 55
266 500 l. black, yellow-ochre and olive-grey .. 55 60
267 600 l. black, vermilion and new blue .. 65 70
268 1000 l. multicoloured .. .. .. .. 1·10 1·25
264/8 .. .. .. .. *Set of* 5 2·50 3·00

Designs: *Vert* (26×47 *mm*)—450 l. Airmail letter and stylized bird (25th anniv of Turkish Cypriot postal service). *Horiz* (*as T* **89**)—500 l. Newspaper and printing press (centenary of *Saded* newspaper); 600 l. Statue of Aphrodite, lifebelt and seabird (30th anniv of International Maritime Organization); 1000 l. Soldiers (25th anniv of Turkish Cypriot resistance).

(Litho Tezel Ofset, Lefkosa)

**1989** (15 Dec). *Visit of Professor Erdal Inonu (Turkish politician). W* **51** *(inverted). P 12½×12.*

269 **90** 700 l. multicoloured .. .. .. .. 75 80

91 Mule-drawn Plough

92 Smoking Ashtray and Drinks

(Des N. Kozal. Litho Tezel Ofset, Lefkosa)

**1989** (25 Dec). *Traditional Agricultural Implements. T* **91** *and similar multicoloured designs. W* **51** *(sideways on 150, 450 l.). P 12½×12 (550 l.) or 12×12½ (others).*

270 150 l. Type **91** .. .. .. .. .. 15 20
271 450 l. Ox-drawn threshing sledge .. .. 50 55
272 550 l. Olive press (*vert*) .. .. .. 60 65
270/2 .. .. .. .. *Set of* 3 1·10 1·25

(Des O. Ozünalp (200 l.), H. Ulucam (700 l). Litho Tezel Ofset, Lefkosa)

**1990** (19 Apr). *World Health Day. T* **92** *and similar horiz design. Multicoloured. W* **51** *(sideways). P 12×12½.*

273 200 l. Type **92** .. .. .. .. .. 10 10
274 700 l. Smoking cigarette and heart .. .. 25 30

93 Yenierenköy Post Office

94 Song Thrush

(Des H. Billur. Litho Tezel Ofset, Lefkosa)

**1990** (31 May). *Europa. Post Office Buildings. T* **93** *and similar horiz design. Multicoloured. W* **51** *(sideways). P 12×12½.*

275 1000 t. Type **93** .. .. .. .. .. 40 45
276 1500 t. Atatürk Meydani Post Office .. .. 55 60
**MS**277 105×72 mm. Nos. 275/6, each × 2 .. 3·25 3·50

(Des H. Billur. Litho Tezel Ofset, Lefkosa)

**1990** (5 June). *World Environment Day. T* **94** *and similar vert designs showing birds. Multicoloured. W* **51** *(inverted). P 12½×12.*

278 150 l. Type **94** .. .. .. .. .. 10 10
279 300 l. Blackcap .. .. .. .. .. 10 15
280 900 l. Black Redstart .. .. .. .. 30 35
281 1000 l. Chiff-chaff .. .. .. .. 40 45
278/81 .. .. .. .. *Set of* 4 75 90

**95** Two Football Teams

**96** Amphitheatre, Soli

(Des H. Billur (1000 l.). Litho Tezel Ofset, Lefkosa)

**1990** (8 June). *World Cup Football Championship, Italy. T* **95** *and similar horiz design. Multicoloured.* W **51** (*sideways*). *P* 12×12½.
282 300 l. Type **95** .. .. .. .. .. 15 15
283 1000 l. Championship symbol, globe and ball 60 65

(Litho Tezel Ofset, Lefkosa)

**1990** (31 July). *Paintings* (*9th series*). *Multicoloured designs as T* **54**. W **51** (*sideways on* 300 *l.*). *P* 13×12½ (300 *l.*) *or* 12½×13 (1000 *l.*).
284 300 l. "Abstract" (Filiz Ankaçc) .. .. 15 15
285 1000 l. Wooden sculpture (S. Tekman) (*vert*) 60 65

(Litho Tezel Ofset, Lefkosa)

**1990** (24 Aug). *Tourism. T* **96** *and similar vert design. Multicoloured.* W **51**. *P* 12½.
286 150 l. Type **96** .. .. .. .. 10 10
287 1000 l. Swan mosaic, Soli .. .. .. .. 60 65

**97** Kenan Evren and Rauf Denktas

**98** Road Signs and Heart wearing Seat Belt

(Litho Tezel Ofset, Lefkosa)

**1990** (19 Sept). *Visit of President Kenan Evren of Turkey.* W **51** (*sideways*). *P* 12½.
288 **97** 500 l. multicoloured .. .. .. .. 40 45

(Des H. Billur. Litho Tezel Ofset, Lefkosa)

**1990** (21 Sept). *Traffic Safety Campaign. T* **98** *and similar horiz designs. Multicoloured.* W **51** (*sideways*). *P* 12½.
289 150 l. Type **98** .. .. .. .. 20 15
290 300 l. Road signs, speeding car and spots of blood .. .. .. .. .. 30 20
291 1000 l. Traffic lights and road signs .. 90 65
289/91 .. .. .. .. *Set of* 3 1·25 90

**99** Yildirim Akbulut

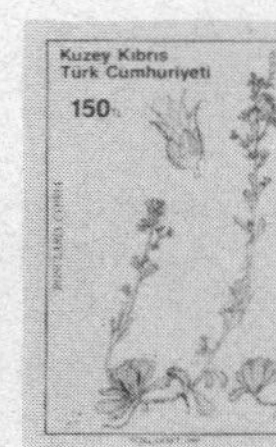


**100** *Rosularia cypria*

(Litho Tezel Ofset, Lefkosa)

**1990** (1 Oct). *Visit of Turkish Prime Minister Yildrim Akbulut.* W **51** (*inverted*). *P* 12½.
292 **99** 1000 l. multicoloured .. .. .. 60 65

(Des D. Viney and P. Jacobs (200, 1500 l.), D. Viney and C. Hessenberg (others). Litho Tezel Ofset, Lefkosa)

**1990** (31 Oct). *Plants. T* **100** *and similar vert designs. Multicoloured.* W **51**. *P* 12½.
293 150 l. Type **100** .. .. .. .. 10 10
294 200 l. *Silene fraudratrix* .. .. .. 10 10
295 300 l. *Scutellaria sibthorpii* .. .. 10 15
296 600 l. *Sedum lampusae* .. .. .. 20 25
297 1000 l. *Onosma caespitosum* .. .. 40 45
298 1500 l. *Arabis cypria* .. .. .. 55 60
293/8 .. .. .. .. *Set of* 6 1·10 1·40

**101** Kemal Atatürk at Easel (wood carving)

250 TL

(**102**)

(Des M. Uzel (300 l.), H. Billur (750 l.). Litho Tezel Ofset, Lefkosa)

**1990** (24 Nov). *International Literacy Year. T* **101** *and similar horiz design. Multicoloured.* W **51** (*sideways*). *P* 12½.
299 300 l. Type **101** .. .. .. .. 10 15
300 750 l. Globe, letters and books .. .. 30 35

**1991** (3 June). *Nos.* 189, 212 *and* 293 *surch as T* **102**.
301 250 l. on 10 l. Type **66** .. .. .. 10 10
302 250 l. on 20 l. Type **73** .. .. .. 10 10
303 500 l. on 150 l. Type **100** .. .. .. 10 15
301/3 .. .. .. .. *Set of* 3 20 25

**103** *Ophrys lapethica*

**104** *Hermes* (projected shuttle)

(Litho State Ptg Works, Lefkosa)

**1991** (8 July). *Orchids* (*1st series*). *T* **103** *and similar vert design. Multicoloured.* W **51** (*inverted*). *P* 14.
304 250 l. Type **103** .. .. .. .. 10 10
305 500 l. *Ophrys kotschyi* .. .. .. 10 15
See also Nos. 311/14

(Litho State Ptg Works, Lefkosa)

**1991** (29 July). *Europa. Europe in Space. Sheet* 78×82 *mm containing T* **104** *and similar vert design. Multicoloured.* W **51**. *P* 12½.
**MS**306 2000 l. Type **104**; 2000 l. *Ulysses* (satellite) .. .. .. .. .. 1·25 1·40

**105** Kucuk Medrese Fountain, Lefkosa

**106** Symbolic Roots (Year of Love to Yunus Emre)

(Des H. Billur. Litho State Ptg Works, Lefkosa)

**1991** (9 Sept). *Fountains. T* **105** *and similar horiz designs. Multicoloured.* W **51** (*sideways*). *P* 12½.
307 250 l. Type **105** .. .. .. .. 10 10
308 500 l. Cafer Pasa Fountain, Magusa .. 10 15
309 1500 l. Sarayönü Square Fountain, Lefkosa 30 35
310 5000 l. Arabahmet Mosque Fountain, Lefkosa .. .. .. .. 1·00 1·10
307/10 .. .. .. .. *Set of* 4 1·25 1·50

(Litho State Ptg Works, Lefkosa)

**1991** (10 Oct). *Orchids* (*2nd series*). *Vert designs as T* **103**. *Multicoloured.* W **51**. *P* 14.
311 100 l. *Serapias levantina* .. .. .. 10 10
312 500 l. *Dactylorhiza romana* .. .. 10 15
313 2000 l. *Orchis simia* .. .. .. 40 45
314 3000 l. *Orchis sancta* .. .. .. 60 65
311/14 .. .. .. .. *Set of* 4 1·00 1·10

(Litho State Ptg Works, Lefkosa)

**1991** (5 Nov). *Paintings* (*10th series*). *Multicoloured designs as T* **54**. W **51**. *P* 12½×13.
315 250 l. "Hindiler" (S. Çizel) (*vert*) .. 10 10
316 500 l. "Düsme" (A. Mene) (*vert*) .. 10 15

(Des K. Sarikavak (250 l.), H. Billur (500, 1500 l.). Litho State Ptg Works, Lefkosa)

**1991** (20 Nov). *Anniversaries and Events. T* **106** *and similar designs.* W **51** (*sideways on* 1500 *l., inverted on others*). *P* 12×12½ (1500 *l.*) *or* 12½×12 (*others*).
317 250 l. greenish yellow, black & brt mag .. 10 10
318 500 l. multicoloured .. .. .. 10 15
319 500 l. multicoloured .. .. .. 10 15

320 1500 l. multicoloured .. .. .. 30 35
317/20 .. .. .. .. *Set of* 4 50 60
Designs: *Vert*—No. 318, Mustafa Cagatay commemoration; No. 319, University building (5th anniv of Eastern Mediterranean University). *Horiz*—No. 320, Mozart (death bicent).

**107** Four Sources of Infection

**108** Lighthouse, Gazimagusa

(Litho State Ptg Works, Lefkosa)

**1991** (13 Dec). *AIDS Day.* W **51** (*sideways*). *P* 12×12½.
321 **107** 1000 l. multicoloured .. .. .. 20 25

(Des H. Billur. Litho State Ptg Works, Lefkosa)

**1991** (16 Dec). *Lighthouses. T* **108** *and similar horiz designs. Multicoloured.* W **51** (*sideways*). *P* 12×12½.
322 250 l. Type **108** .. .. .. .. 10 10
323 500 l. Ancient lighthouses, Girne harbour 10 15
324 1500 l. Modern lighthouse, Girne harbour .. 30 35
322/4 .. .. .. .. *Set of* 3 40 50

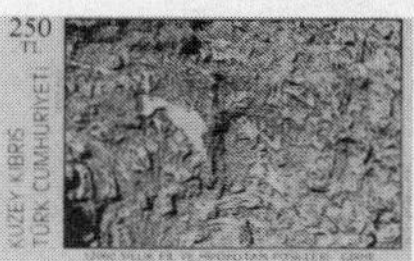


**109** Elephant and Hippopotamus Fossils, Karaoglanoglu

(Litho State Ptg Works, Lefkosa)

**1991** (27 Dec). *Tourism. T* **109** *and similar horiz designs. Multicoloured.* W **51** (*sideways*). *P* 12.
325 250 l. Type **109** .. .. .. .. 10 10
326 500 l. Roman fish ponds, Lambusa .. 10 15
327 1500 l. Roman remains, Lambusa .. .. 30 35
325/7 .. .. .. .. *Set of* 3 40 50

# Cyrenaica
# *see* British Occupation of Italian Colonies

# Dominica

### CROWN COLONY

A branch office of the British G.P.O. was opened at Roseau by 845, using the crowned-circle handstamp supplied in that year. The stamps of Great Britain were used between 8 May 1858 and May 1860, after which the colonial authorities assumed responsibility for the postal service. Until the introduction of Nos. 1/3 in 1874 No. CC1 and later handstamps were utilized.

For illustrations of handstamp and postmark types see BRITISH POST OFFICES ABROAD notes, following GREAT BRITAIN.

#### ROSEAU

CROWNED/CIRCLE HANDSTAMPS

CC1 CC 1 DOMINICA (R.) (17.5.1845) *Price on cover* £500

No. CC1 is also known struck in black on various adhesive stamps as late as 1883.

*Stamps of* GREAT BRITAIN *cancelled* "A 07" *as Type* **2**.

**1858 *to* 1860**

Z1 1d. rose-red (1857), *perf* 14 .. £190
Z2 2d. blue (1858) (Plate No. 7) .. £650
Z3 4d. rose (1857) .. £275
Z4 6d. lilac (1856) .. £275
Z5 1s. green .. £1100

| PRICES FOR STAMPS ON COVER TO 1945 | |
|---|---|
| Nos. 1/3 | *from* × 10 |
| Nos. 4/26 | *from* × 8 |
| Nos. 27/95 | *from* × 5 |
| Nos. 96/8 | *from* × 4 |
| Nos. 99/109 | *from* × 3 |
| Nos. R1/6 | *from* × 5 |

ONE PENNY
1

½
(2)

1/2
(3)

HALF PENNY
(4)

(Typo D.L.R.)

**1874** (4 May). *Wmk Crown CC. P* 12½.

1 1 1d. lilac .. £150 38·00
2 6d. green .. £475 85·00
3 1s. dull magenta .. £300 65·00

NCE
Normal

NCE
Malformed "CE"

**1877–79.** *Wmk Crown CC. P* 14.

4 1 ½d. olive-yellow (1879) .. 7·50 30·00
5 1d. lilac .. 4·50 1·50
a. Bisected vert or diag (½d.) (on cover or card) .. † £1600
6 2½d. red-brown (1879) .. £225 25·00
7 4d. blue (1879) .. 95·00 2·50
a. Malformed "CE" in "PENCE" .. £2000 £300
8 6d. green .. £140 20·00
9 1s. magenta .. £120 38·00

**1882** (25 Nov)–**83.** *No.* 5 *bisected and surch.*

10 2 ½ (d.), in *black*, on half 1d. .. £140 30·00
a. Surch inverted .. £800 £800
b. Surcharges *tête-bêche* (pair) .. £1400
11 3 ½ (d.), in *red*, on half 1d. (12.82) .. 28·00 12·00
a. Surch inverted .. £800 £300
c. Surch double .. £1600
14 4 ½d. in *black*, on half 1d. (3.83) .. 38·00 20·00
a. Unsevered pair .. £130 £140
b. Surch double .. £800

Type 4 is found reading up or down.

**1883–84.** *Wmk Crown CA. P* 14.

15 1 ½d. olive-yellow .. 1·00 4·00
16 2½d. red-brown (1884) .. £130 2·00

Half Penny
(5)

One Penny
(6)

**1886** (Mar). *Nos.* 8 *and* 9 *surch.*

17 5 ½d. on 6d. green .. 4·00 3·50
18 6 1d. on 6d. green .. £16000 £11000
a. Thick bar (approx 1 mm) .. † £15000
19 1d. on 1s. magenta .. 13·00 13·00
a. Surch double .. £4750 £2750

There are variations in the spacing of the letters of "One Penny" in the surcharge of No. 19

**1886–88.** *Wmk Crown CA. P* 14.

20 1 ½d. dull green .. 50 3·00
21 1d. lilac .. 15·00 5·00
a. Bisected (½d.) (on cover) .. † £1800
22 1d. rose (1887) .. 6·50 7·00
a. *Deep carmine* (1888) .. 2·50 2·75
b. Bisected (½d.) (on cover) .. † £1800
23 2½d. ultramarine (1888) .. 3·75 3·00
24 4d. grey .. 2·00 2·75
a. Malformed "CE" in "PENCE" .. £150 £180
25 6d. orange (1888) .. 5·50 17·00
26 1s. dull magenta (1888) .. £170 £225
20/6 .. *Set of* 7 £180 £225
20, 22/5 Optd "Specimen" .. *Set of* 5 £250

The stamps of Dominica were superseded by the general issue for Leeward Islands on 31 October 1890, but the sets following were in concurrent use with the stamps inscribed "LEEWARD ISLANDS" until 31 December 1939, when the island came under the administration of the Windward Islands.

9 View of Roseau from the Sea

10

(T 9 to 11 typo D.L.R.)

**1903** (1 Sept)–**07.** *Wmk Crown CC* (*sideways on T* 9). *Ordinary paper. P* 14.

27 9 ½d. green and grey-green .. 2·25 2·25
a. Chalk-surfaced paper (1906) .. 5·50 7·50
28 1d. grey and red .. 5·00 40
a. Chalk-surfaced paper (1906) .. 7·50 1·50
29 2d. green and brown .. 2·50 4·00
a. Chalk-surfaced paper (1906) .. 9·50 14·00
30 2½d. grey and bright blue .. 4·00 3·50
a. Chalk-surfaced paper (3.9.07) .. 9·00 12·00
31 3d. dull purple and grey-black .. 8·00 2·75
a. Chalk-surfaced paper (1906) .. 15·00 12·00
32 6d. grey and chestnut .. 4·25 13·00
33 1s. magenta and grey-green .. 16·00 22·00
a. Chalk-surfaced paper (1906) .. 50·00 70·00
34 2s. grey-black and purple .. 17·00 25·00
35 2s. 6d. grey-green and maize .. 17·00 48·00
36 10 5s. black and brown .. 85·00 £140
27/36 .. *Set of* 10 £140 £225
27/36 Optd "Specimen" .. *Set of* 10 £130

**1907–08.** *Wmk Mult Crown CA* (*sideways on T* 9). *Chalk-surfaced paper. P* 14.

37 9 ½d. green .. 1·25 2·00
a. Ordinary paper .. 2·25 3·50
38 1d. grey and red .. 2·00 25
39 2d. green and brown .. 5·00 12·00
40 2½d. grey and bright blue .. 4·50 18·00
41 3d. dull purple and grey-black .. 5·00 13·00
42 6d. black and chestnut (1908) .. 48·00 60·00
43 1s. magenta and grey-green .. 3·75 27·00
44 2s. grey-black and purple (1908) .. 20·00 32·00
45 2s. 6d. grey-green and maize (1908) .. 20·00 45·00
46 10 5s. black and brown (1908) .. 55·00 75·00
37/46 .. *Set of* 10 £150 £250

11

WAR TAX

ONE HALFPENNY
(12)

**1908–21.** *Wmk Mult Crown CA* (*sideways on T* 9). *Chalk-surfaced paper* (6*d. and* 5*s.*). *P* 14.

47 9 ½d. blue-green .. 2·25 1·40
a. *Deep green* (1918) .. 2·25 1·75
48 1d. carmine-red .. 2·50 25
a. *Scarlet* (1916) .. 1·00 40
49 2d. grey (1909) .. 3·00 11·00
a. *Slate* (1918) .. 3·50 11·00
50 2½d. blue .. 7·50 6·00
a. *Bright blue* (1918) .. 4·75 8·50
51 3d. purple/*yellow* (1909) .. 1·75 3·50
a. Chalk-surfaced paper (1912) .. 2·25 4·00
b. Ordinary paper. *On pale yell* (1920) 8·50 10·00
52 6d. dull and bright purple (1909) .. 10·00 15·00
a. Ordinary paper. *Dull purple* (1915) 3·50 14·00
53 1s. black/*green* (1910) .. 2·25 3·75
a. Chalk-surfaced paper (1912) .. 1·40 2·75
53*b* 2s. purple and deep blue/*blue* (1919) .. 20·00 45·00
53*c* 2s. 6d. black and red/*blue* (1921) .. 25·00 55·00
54 11 5s. red and green/*yellow* (1914) .. 45·00 65·00
47/54 .. *Set of* 10 95·00 £180
48/54 Optd "Specimen" (1s. optd in black) *Set of* 9 £180
53a Optd "Specimen" in red instead of black .. 45·00

**1916** (Sept). *No.* 47 *surch with T* 12.

55 9 ½d. on ½d. blue-green (R.) .. 10 75
a. Small "O" in "ONE" .. 6·50 16·00

No. 55a occurs on ten stamps within each sheet of 60.

**1918** (18 Mar). *No.* 47 *optd locally with T* 12 *but with* "ONE HALF-PENNY" *blanked out.*

56 9 ½d. blue-green (Blk.) .. 50 4·00

The blanking out of the surcharge was not completely successful so that it almost always appears as an albino to a greater or lesser extent.

WAR TAX
(14)

**1918** (June). *Nos.* 47 *and* 51 *optd in London with T* 14.

57 9 ½d. blue-green .. 10 30
58 3d. purple/*yellow* (R.) .. 20 2·00

WAR TAX
═1½D.═
(15)

1 ½D.
Short Fraction Bar (R.6/4)

**1919** (Dec). *As No.* 50, *but colour changed, surch with T* 15.

59 9 1½d. on 2½d. orange (R.) .. 10 55
a. Short fraction bar .. 7·00 22·00
b. "C" and "A" missing from wmk ..

No. 59b shows the "C" omitted from one impression with the "A" missing from the next one to the right (as seen from the front of the stamp). The "C" is badly distorted in the second watermark.

**1920.** *As No.* 59, *but without* "WAR TAX".

60 9 1½d. on 2½d. orange (Blk.) .. 1·25 3·75
a. Short fraction bar .. 50·00 65·00
55/60 Optd "Specimen" .. *Set of* 6 £180

**1921.** *Wmk Mult Script CA. Chalk-surfaced paper* (6*d.*). *P* 14.

62 9 ½d. blue-green .. 1·25 5·50
63 1d. carmine-red .. 1·10 2·50
64 1½d. orange .. 3·50 8·50
65 2d. grey .. 2·75 3·25
66 2½d. bright blue .. 1·25 8·00
67 6d. purple .. 2·50 26·00
69 2s. purple and blue/*blue* .. 24·00 48·00
70 2s. 6d. black and red/*blue* .. 24·00 55·00
62/70 .. *Set of* 8 55·00 £140
62/70 Optd "Specimen" .. *Set of* 8 £140

The 1½d. has figures of value, in the lower corner and no ornamentation below words of value.

16

(Typo D.L.R.)

**1923** (Feb)–**33.** *Chalk-surfaced paper. P* 14.

(*a*) *Wmk Mult Script CA*

71 16 ½d. black and green .. 65 30
72 1d. black and bright violet .. 1·25 40
73 1d. black and scarlet (1933) .. 5·50 80
74 1½d. black and scarlet .. 90 30
75 1½d. black and red-brown (1933) .. 5·50 50
76 2d. black and grey .. 85 40
77 2½d. black and orange-yellow .. 70 5·50
78 2½d. black and ultramarine (1927) .. 2·25 1·00
79 3d. black and ultramarine .. 70 8·00
80 3d. black and red/*yellow* (1927) .. 1·00 1·00
81 4d. black and brown .. 75 4·00
82 6d. black and bright magenta .. 1·75 3·50
83 1s. black/*emerald* .. 1·40 2·25
84 2s. black and blue/*blue* .. 3·50 11·00
85 2s. 6d. black and red/*blue* .. 9·50 13·00
86 3s. black and purple/*yellow* (1927) .. 2·50 8·00
87 4s. black and red/*emerald* .. 5·50 11·00
88 5s. black and green/*yellow* (1927) .. 15·00 28·00

(*b*) *Wmk Mult Crown CA*

89 16 3s. black and purple/*yellow* .. 4·00 40·00
90 5s. black and green/*yellow* .. 7·50 35·00
91 £1 black and purple/*red* .. £250 £300
71/91 .. *Set of* 21 £275 £400
71/91 Optd/Perf "Specimen" .. *Set of* 21 £350

**1935** (6 May). *Silver Jubilee. As Nos.* 91/4 *of Antigua.*

92 1d. deep blue and carmine .. 75 20
f. Diagonal line by turret .. 26·00
h. Dot by flagstaff .. 26·00
93 1½d. ultramarine and grey .. 1·00 40
f. Diagonal line by turret .. 35·00
h. Dot by flagstaff .. 35·00
94 2½d. brown and deep blue .. 1·40 75
95 1s. slate and purple .. 1·50 3·25
h. Dot by flagstaff .. 65·00
92/5 .. *Set of* 4 4·25 4·25
92/5 Perf "Specimen" .. *Set of* 4 70·00

For illustrations of plate varieties see Catalogue Introduction.

**1937** (12 May). *Coronation. As Nos.* 95/7 *of Antigua. P* 11×11½.

96 1d. carmine .. 40 10
97 1½d. yellow-brown .. 40 10
98 2½d. blue .. 60 75
96/8 .. *Set of* 3 1·25 85
96/8 Perf "Specimen" .. *Set of* 3 55·00

17 Fresh Water Lake

18 Layou River

(Recess Waterlow)

**1938** (15 Aug)–**47**. *T* **17**/**18** *and similar horiz designs. Wmk Mult Script CA. P* 12½.

99 **17** ½d. brown and green .. .. .. 10 15
100 **18** 1d. grey and scarlet .. .. .. 20 20
101 – 1½d. green and purple .. .. .. 20 45
102 – 2d. carmine and grey-black .. .. 40 35
103 – 2½d. purple and bright blue .. .. 4·00 1·50
a. *Purple & brt ultram* (8.42) .. 20 50
104 **18** 3d. olive-green and brown .. .. 30 40
104*a* – 3½d. ultramarine and purple (15.10.47) 1·25 45
105 **17** 6d. emerald-green and violet .. .. 50 50
105*a* 7d. green and yellow-brown (15.10.47) 1·25 50
106 – 1s. violet and olive-green .. .. 1·00 50
106*a* **18** 2s. slate and purple (15.10.47) .. 3·00 4·25
107 **17** 2s. 6d. black and vermilion .. .. 5·50 4·00
108 **18** 5s. light blue and sepia .. .. 5·00 3·50
108*a* – 10s. black and brown-orange (15.10.47) 8·50 12·00
99/108*a* .. .. .. .. *Set of* 14 25·00 25·00

Designs:—1½d., 2½d., 3½d. Picking limes; 2d., 1s., 10s. Boiling Lake.

**21** King George VI

(Photo Harrison)

**1940** (15 Apr)–**42**. *Wmk Mult Script CA. Chalk-surfaced paper. P* 15×14.

109 **21** ¼d. chocolate .. .. .. .. 30 15
a. Ordinary paper (1942) .. .. 10 10
99/109 Perf "Specimen" .. .. *Set of* 15 £225

**1946** (14 Oct). *Victory. As Nos.* 110/11 *of Antigua.*

110 1d. carmine .. .. .. .. .. 10 10
111 3½d. blue .. .. .. .. .. 10 10
110/11 Perf "Specimen" .. .. *Set of* 2 48·00

**1948** (1 Dec). *Royal Silver Wedding. As Nos.* 112/13 *of Antigua.*

112 1d. scarlet .. .. .. .. .. 15 10
113 10s. red-brown .. .. .. .. 6·00 12·00

**(New Currency. 100 cents = 1 dollar)**

**1949** (10 Oct). *75th Anniv of Universal Postal Union. As Nos.* 114/17 *of Antigua.*

114 5 c. blue .. .. .. .. .. 15 15
115 6 c. brown .. .. .. .. .. 30 20
116 12 c. purple .. .. .. .. .. 30 30
117 24 c. olive .. .. .. .. .. 30 30
114/17 .. .. .. .. *Set of* 4 95 85

**1951** (16 Feb). *Inauguration of B.W.I. University College. As Nos.* 118/19 *of Antigua.*

118 3 c. yellow-green and reddish violet .. .. 40 20
119 12 c. deep green and carmine .. .. 45 15

**22** King George VI

**23** Drying Cocoa

(Photo Harrison (½ c.). Recess B.W. (others) )

**1951** (1 July). *T* **22** *and designs as T* **23**. *Wmk Mult Script CA. Chalk-surfaced paper* (½ c.). *P* 15×14 (½ c.), 13½×13 ($2.40), 13×13½ (*others*).

120 ½ c. chocolate .. .. .. .. 10 15
121 1 c. black and vermilion .. .. .. 10 10
122 2 c. red-brown and deep green .. .. 10 10
123 3 c. green and reddish violet .. .. 10 30
124 4 c. brown-orange and sepia .. .. 20 15
125 5 c. black and carmine .. .. .. 50 15
a. "C" of "CA" missing from wmk .. £800
126 6 c. olive and chestnut .. .. .. 60 15
127 8 c. blue-green and blue .. .. .. 35 30
128 12 c. black and bright green .. .. 30 60
a. "C" of "CA" missing from wmk ..
129 14 c. blue and violet .. .. .. 55 60
130 24 c. reddish violet and rose-carmine .. 30 30
131 48 c. bright green and red-orange .. 1·00 3·25
132 60 c. carmine and black .. .. 1·00 2·00
133 $1.20, emerald and black .. .. 4·00 2·25
134 $2.40, orange and black .. .. 20·00 18·00
120/134 .. .. .. .. *Set of* 15 26·00 25·00

Designs: *Horiz*—2 c., 60 c. Making Carib baskets; 3 c., 48 c. Lime plantation; 4 c. Picking oranges; 5 c. Bananas; 6 c. Botanical Gardens; 8 c. Drying vanilla beans; 12 c., $1.20, Fresh Water Lake; 14 c. Layou River; 24 c. Boiling Lake. *Vert*—$2.40, Picking oranges.

**NEW CONSTITUTION 1951**

(34)

**1951** (15 Oct). *New Constitution. Nos.* 123, 125, 127 *and* 129 *optd with T* **34** *by B.W.*

135 3 c. green and reddish violet .. .. 15 30
136 5 c. black and carmine .. .. .. 15 20
137 8 c. blue-green and blue (R.) .. .. 15 15
138 14 c. blue and violet (R.) .. .. 15 15
135/8 .. .. .. .. *Set of* 4 55 70

**1953** (2 June). *Coronation. As No.* 120 *of Antigua.*

139 2 c. black and deep green .. .. .. 10 10

**35** Queen Elizabeth II

**36** Mat Making

**37** Picking Oranges

**38** Canoe Making

(Photo Harrison (½ c.). Recess B.W. (others) )

**1954** (1 Oct)–**62**. *Designs previously used for King George VI issue, but with portrait of Queen Elizabeth II as in T* **35**/**8**. *Wmk Mult Script CA. P* 15×14 (½ c.), 13½×13 ($2.40), 13×13½ (*others*).

140 **35** ½ c. brown .. .. .. .. 10 10
141 – 1 c. black and vermilion .. .. 10 10
142 – 2 c. chocolate and myrtle-green .. 10 10
a. *Chocolate and grey-green* (13.3.62) 1·40 1·40
143 – 3 c. green and purple .. .. .. 60 20
144 **36** 3 c. black and carmine (15.10.57) .. 1·50 55
145 **37** 4 c. brown-orange and sepia .. .. 15 10
146 – 5 c. black and carmine-red .. .. 60 20
147 **38** 5 c. light blue & sepia-brown (15.10.57) 8·00 50
a. *Blue and sepia* (13.3.62) .. 10·00 1·25
148 – 6 c. bronze-green and red-brown .. 15 10
149 – 8 c. deep green and deep blue .. .. 15 10
150 – 10 c. green and brown (15.10.57) .. 1·00 50
a. *Green and deep brown* (17.7.62) .. 1·25 40
151 – 12 c. black and emerald .. .. .. 50 10
152 – 14 c. blue and purple .. .. .. 30 10
153 – 24 c. purple and carmine .. .. 30 10
154 – 48 c. green and red-orange .. .. 1·25 5·00
155 **36** 48 c. deep brown and violet (15.10.57) 1·25 80
156 – 60 c. rose-red and black .. .. 50 75
157 – $1.20, emerald and black .. .. 9·50 5·50
158 – $2.40, yellow-orange and black .. 11·00 11·00
140/58 .. .. .. *Set of* 19 32·00 23·00

Designs: *Horiz*—1 c. Drying cocoa; 2 c., 60 c. Making Carib baskets; 3 c. (No. 143), 48 c. (No. 154) Lime plantation; 5 c. (No. 146) Bananas; 6 c. Botanical Gardens; 8 c. Drying vanilla beans; 10 c. Bananas (*different*); 12 c., $1.20, Fresh Water Lake; 14 c. Layou River; 24 c. Boiling Lake. *Vert*—$2.40, Picking oranges.

**1958** (22 Apr). *Inauguration of British Caribbean Federation. As Nos.* 135/7 *of Antigua.*

159 3 c. deep green .. .. .. .. 15 10
160 6 c. blue .. .. .. .. .. 20 20
161 12 c. scarlet .. .. .. .. 20 10
159/61 .. .. .. .. *Set of* 3 50 30

**40** Seashore at Rosalie

**48** Traditional Costume

Two types of 14 c.

I. Eyes of model looking straight ahead.
II. Eyes looking to her right.

(Des S. Scott. Photo Harrison)

**1963** (16 May)–**65**. *T* **40**, **48** *and similar designs. W* w **12** (*upright*). *P* 14 × 14½ (*vert*) *or* 14½ × 14 (*horiz*).

162 1 c. green, blue and sepia .. .. 10 10
163 2 c. bright blue .. .. .. .. 30 10
164 3 c. blackish brown and blue .. .. 30 20
165 4 c. green, sepia and slate-violet .. .. 10 10
166 5 c. magenta .. .. .. .. 30 10
167 6 c. green, bistre and violet .. .. 10 10
168 8 c. green, sepia and black .. .. 10 10
169 10 c. sepia and pink .. .. .. 10 10
170 12 c. green, blue and blackish brown .. 10 10
171 14 c. multicoloured (I) .. .. .. 30 10
171*a* 14 c. multicoloured (II) (1.4.65) .. 80 55
172 15 c. yellow, green and brown .. .. 40 10
173 24 c. multicoloured .. .. .. 3·50 10
174 48 c. green, blue and black .. .. 60 25
175 60 c. orange, green and black .. .. 75 50
176 $1.20, multicoloured .. .. .. 5·00 70
177 $2.40, blue, turquoise and brown .. 3·25 2·00
178 $4.80, green, blue and brown .. .. 8·00 13·00
162/78 .. .. .. *Set of* 17 22·00 16·00

Designs: *Vert*—2 c., 5 c. Queen Elizabeth II; 24 c. Imperial Amazon; $2.40, Trafalgar Falls; $4.80, Coconut Palm. *Horiz*—3 c. Sailing canoe; 4 c. Sulphur springs; 6 c. Road making; 8 c. Dug-out canoe; 10 c. Crapaud (toad); 12 c. Scott's Head; 15 c. Bananas; 48 c. Goodwill; 60 c. Cocoa tree; $1.20, Coat of Arms.

See also Nos. 200/4.

**1963** (4 June). *Freedom from Hunger. As No.* 146 *of Antigua.*

179 15 c. reddish violet .. .. .. 15 10

**1963** (2 Sept). *Red Cross Centenary. As Nos.* 147/8 *of Antigua.*

180 5 c. red and black .. .. .. .. 15 20
181 15 c. red and blue .. .. .. .. 30 45

**1964** (23 April). *400th Birth Anniv of William Shakespeare. As No.* 164 *of Antigua.*

182 15 c. bright purple .. .. .. .. 10 1

**1965** (17 May). *I.T.U. Centenary. As Nos.* 166/7 *of Antigua.*

183 2 c. light emerald and blue .. .. .. 10 1
184 48 c. turquoise-blue and grey .. .. .. 30 2

**1965** (25 Oct). *International Co-operation Year. As Nos.* 168/9 *of Antigua.*

185 1 c. reddish purple and turquoise-green .. 10 2
186 15 c. deep bluish green and lavender .. .. 20 1

**1966** (24 Jan). *Churchill Commemoration. As Nos.* 170/3 *of Antigua.*

187 1 c. new blue .. .. .. .. .. 10 1
a. Gold omitted .. .. .. .. £400
188 5 c. deep green .. .. .. .. 10 1
189 15 c. brown .. .. .. .. .. 20 1
190 24 c. bluish violet .. .. .. .. 30 2
187/90 .. .. .. .. *Set of* 4 55 3

**1966** (4 Feb). *Royal Visit. As Nos.* 174/5 *of Antigua.*

191 5 c. black and ultramarine .. .. .. 75 1
192 15 c. black and magenta .. .. .. 1·25 2

**1966** (1 July). *World Cup Football Championships. As Nos.* 176/7 *of Antigua.*

193 5 c. violet, yellow-green, lake & yellow-brown 10 1
194 24 c. chocolate, blue-green, lake & yell-brown 30 1

**1966** (20 Sept). *Inauguration of W.H.O. Headquarters, Geneva. As Nos.* 178/9 *of Antigua.*

195 5 c. black, yellow-green and light blue .. 10 15
196 24 c. black, light purple and yellow-brown .. 20 15

**1966** (1 Dec). *20th Anniv of U.N.E.S.C.O. As Nos.* 196/8 *of Antigua.*

197 5 c. slate-violet, red, yellow and orange .. 10 15
198 15 c. orange-yellow, violet and deep olive .. 25 10
199 24 c. black, bright purple and orange .. .. 25 15
197/9 .. .. .. .. .. *Set of* 3 55 30

**1966** (30 Dec)–**67**. *As Nos.* 165, 167/9 *and* 172 *but wmk* w **12** *sideways.*

200 4 c. green, sepia and slate-violet (16.5.67) .. 60 3
201 6 c. green, bistre and violet .. .. .. 15 1
202 8 c. green, sepia and black .. .. .. 30 1
203 10 c. sepia and pink (16.5.67) .. .. .. 40 1
204 15 c. yellow, green and brown (16.5.67) .. 40 1
200/4 .. .. .. .. .. *Set of* 5 1·75 60

**ASSOCIATED STATEHOOD**

**56** Children of Three Races

(Des and photo Harrison)

**1967** (2 Nov). *National Day. T* **56** *and similar horiz designs. Multicoloured. W* w **12**. *P* 14½.

205 5 c. Type **56** .. .. .. .. 10 10
206 10 c. The *Santa Maria* and motto .. .. 10 10
207 15 c. Hands holding motto ribbon .. .. 10 15
208 24 c. Belaire dancing .. .. .. 10 15
205/8 .. .. .. .. *Set of* 4 30 30

**57** John F. Kennedy

(Des G. Vasarhelyi. Litho D.L.R.)

**1968** (20 Apr). *Human Rights Year. T* **57** *and similar horiz designs. Multicoloured. W* w **12** (*sideways*). *P* 14 × 13½.

209 1 c. Type **57** .. .. .. .. 10 10
210 10 c. Cecil A. E. Rawle .. .. .. 10 10
a. Imperf (pair) .. .. .. £180
211 12 c. Pope John XXIII .. .. .. 25 10
212 48 c. Florence Nightingale .. .. 25 15
213 60 c. Albert Schweitzer .. .. .. 25 15
209/13 .. .. .. .. *Set of* 5 75 30

**ASSOCIATED STATEHOOD**
(58)

**NATIONAL DAY 3 NOVEMBER 1968**
(59)

**1968** (8 July). *Associated Statehood. As Nos.* 162, 170 *and* 174, *but wmk sideways, or Nos.* 163/4, 166, 170, 171*a*, 173, 175/8 *and* 200/4 *optd with T* **58**.

214 1 c. green, blue and sepia (Sil.) .. .. 10 10
215 2 c. bright blue (Sil.) .. .. .. 10 10
216 3 c. blackish brown and blue (Sil.) .. .. 10 10
217 4 c. green, sepia and slate-violet (Sil.) .. 10 10
218 5 c. magenta (Sil.) .. .. .. .. 10 10
219 6 c. green, bistre and violet .. .. .. 10 10
220 8 c. green, sepia and black .. .. .. 10 10
221 10 c. sepia and pink (Sil.) .. .. .. 35 10
222 12 c. green, blue and blackish brown (Sil.) (wmk sideways) .. .. .. 10 10
a. Wmk upright .. .. .. .. 10 10
224 14 c. multicoloured (II) (Sil.) .. .. 10 10
225 15 c. yellow, green and brown (Sil.) .. .. 10 10

26 24 c. multicoloured (Sil.) .. .. .. 1·50 10
27 48 c. green, bl & blk (Sil.) (wmk sideways) .. 55 90
a. Wmk upright .. .. .. .. 40 75
28 60 c. orange, green and black .. .. 90 70
29 $1.20, multicoloured .. .. .. 1·00 1·75
30 $2.40, blue, turquoise and brown (Sil.) .. 2·00 2·25
31 $4.80, green, blue and brown (Sil.) .. 2·00 3·75
14/31 .. .. .. .. .. *Set of* 17 8·00 9·00

The 2, 5, 6, 8 and 10 c. values exist with PVA gum as well as gum rabic.

968 (3 Nov). *National Day. Nos.* 162/4, 171 *and* 176 *optd with T* **59**.
32 1 c. green, blue and sepia .. .. .. 10 10
a. Opt inverted .. .. .. .. 45·00
33 2 c. bright blue .. .. .. .. 10 10
a. Opt double .. .. .. .. 30·00
34 3 c. blackish brown and blue .. .. 10 10
a. Opt inverted .. .. .. .. 30·00
35 14 c. multicoloured (I) .. .. .. 10 10
a. Opt double .. .. .. .. 70·00
36 $1.20, multicoloured .. .. .. 30 40
a. Opt double .. .. .. .. 30·00
b. Vert pair, one opt omitted, other opt double .. .. .. .. £150
32/6 .. .. .. .. .. *Set of* 5 30 40

The above set was put on sale by the New York Agency on 1 November but not sold locally until the 3 November.

**60** Forward shooting at Goal

(Des M. Shamir (1 c., 60 c.), K. Plowitz (5 c., 48 c.). Litho B.W.)

968 (25 Nov). *Olympic Games, Mexico. T* **60** *and similar horiz designs. Multicoloured. P* 11½ × 11.
37 1 c. Type **60** .. .. .. .. 10 10
a. Horiz pair. Nos. 237/8 .. .. .. 10 10
38 1 c. Goalkeeper trying to save goal .. .. 10 10
39 5 c. Swimmers about to dive .. .. .. 10 10
a. Horiz pair. Nos. 239/40 .. .. .. 10 10
40 5 c. Swimmers diving .. .. .. 10 10
41 48 c. Javelin-throwing .. .. .. 15 15
a. Horiz pair. Nos. 241/2 .. .. .. 30 30
42 48 c. Hurdling .. .. .. .. 15 15
43 60 c. Basketball .. .. .. .. 15 15
a. Horiz pair. Nos. 243/4 .. .. .. 30 30
44 60 c. Basketball players .. .. .. 15 15
37/44 .. .. .. .. *Set of* 8 70 70

Nos. 237/44 were issued in sheets of 40 containing two panes of *se-tenant* pairs.

**61** "The Small Cowper Madonna" (Raphael)

**62** "Venus and Adonis" (Rubens)

(Photo Delrieu, Paris)

1968 (23 Dec). *Christmas. P* 12½ × 12.
245 **61** 5 c. multicoloured .. .. .. 10 10

Three other values were issued: 12 c. "Madonna of the Chair" (Raphael); 24 c. "Madonna and Child" (Italo-Byzantine, XVI century); $1.20 "Madonna and Child" (Byzantine, XIII century). Sizes as T **61**.

These only come from miniature sheets, containing two *se-tenant* strips of each value.

(Litho D.L.R.)

1969 (30 Jan). *20th Anniv of World Health Organisation. Paintings. T* **62** *and similar vert designs. Multicoloured. W* w **12**. *P* 15.
246 5 c. Type **62** .. .. .. .. 10 10
247 15 c. "The Death of Socrates" (J.-L. David) .. 20 10
248 24 c. "Christ and the Pilgrims of Emmaus" (Velasquez) .. .. .. 20 10
249 50 c. "Pilate washing his Hands" (Rembrandt) 30 30
246/9 .. .. .. .. *Set of* 4 70 40

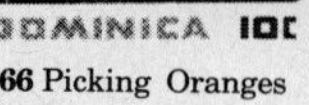


**66** Picking Oranges

**67** "Strength in Unity" Emblem and Fruit Trees

(Des K. Plowitz. Litho Harrison)

**1969** (10 Mar). *Tourism. T* **66** *and similar horiz designs. Multicoloured. W* w **12**. *P* 14½.
250 10 c. Type **66** .. .. .. .. 10 10
a. Horiz pair. Nos. 250/1 .. .. .. 15 15
251 10 c. Woman, child and ocean scene .. .. 10 10
252 12 c. Fort Yeoung Hotel .. .. .. 15 10
a. Horiz pair. Nos. 252/3 .. .. .. 30 20
253 12 c. Red-necked Amazons .. .. .. 15 10
254 24 c. Calypso band .. .. .. 15 15
a. Horiz pair. Nos. 254/5 .. .. .. 30 30
255 24 c. Women dancing .. .. .. 15 15
256 48 c. Underwater life .. .. .. 20 25
a. Horiz pair. Nos. 256/7 .. .. .. 40 50
257 48 c. Skin-diver and turtle .. .. .. 20 25
250/7 .. .. .. .. *Set of* 8 1·00 1·00

Each denomination was printed *se-tenant* throughout the sheet. The 12 c. values are on cream coloured paper.

(Litho B.W.)

**1969** (July). *First Anniv of CARIFTA (Caribbean Free Trade Area). T* **67** *and similar horiz designs. Multicoloured. P* 13½ × 13.
258 5 c. Type **67** .. .. .. .. 10 10
259 8 c. "HS 748" aircraft, emblem and island .. 10 10
260 12 c. Chart of Caribbean Sea and emblem .. 10 10
261 24 c. Steamship unloading, tug and emblem .. 15 10
258/61 .. .. .. .. *Set of* 4 30 20

**71** "Spinning"

**72** Mahatma Gandhi Weaving and Clock Tower, Westminster

(Litho B.W.)

**1969** (10 July). *50th Anniv of International Labour Organisation. T* **71** *and similar vert designs showing paintings of people at work by J. Millet, bordered by flags of member-nations of the I.L.O. Multicoloured. No wmk. P* 13 × 13½.
262 15 c. Type **71** .. .. .. .. 10 10
263 30 c. "Threshing" .. .. .. .. 15 15
264 38 c. "Flax-pulling" .. .. .. .. 15 15
262/4 .. .. .. .. *Set of* 3 30 30

(Des G. Vasarhelyi. Litho Format)

**1969** (20 Oct). *Birth Centenary of Mahatma Gandhi. T* **72** *and similar horiz designs. Multicoloured. P* 14½.
265 6 c. Type **72** .. .. .. .. 30 10
266 38 c. Gandhi, Nehru and Mausoleum .. .. 50 15
267 $1.20, Gandhi and Taj Mahal .. .. 1·40 40
265/7 .. .. .. .. *Set of* 3 2·00 50

Nos. 265/7 are incorrectly inscribed "Ghandi".

**75** "Saint Joseph"

(Des G. Vasarhelyi. Litho Govt Printer, Jerusalem)

**1969** (3 Nov). *National Day. Stained Glass Windows. T* **75** *and similar vert designs. Multicoloured. P* 14.
268 6 c. Type **75** .. .. .. .. 10 10
269 8 c. "Saint John" .. .. .. .. 10 10
270 12 c. "Saint Peter" .. .. .. .. 10 10
271 60 c. "Saint Paul" .. .. .. .. 30 50
268/71 .. .. .. .. *Set of* 4 40 60

Nos. 268/71 were printed in sheets of 16 (4 × 4) containing 12 stamps and four printed labels in the top row: The labels each contain two lines of a patriotic poem by W. O. M. Pond, the first letter from each line spelling "DOMINICA".

**79** Queen Elizabeth II

**80** Purple-throated Carib and Flower

**81** Government Headquarters

**82** Coat of Arms

(Photo D.L.R.)

**1969–72.** *T* **79/82** *and similar horiz designs. Multicoloured. W* **41** *of Singapore* (60 *c. to* $4.80) *or no wmk* (*others*). *P* 13½ × 14 (½ *c.*), 14 × 13½ (1 *to* 50 *c.*) *or* 14 (60 *c. to* $4.80).

A. *Chalk-surfaced paper* (26.11.69)
B. *Glazed paper* (1972)

| | | A | | B | |
|---|---|---|---|---|---|
| 272 | ½ c. Type **79** .. .. | 10 | 40 | 30 | 30 |
| 273 | 1 c. Type **80** .. .. | 30 | 40 | 1·25 | 30 |
| 274 | 2 c. Poinsettia .. .. | 15 | 10 | 50 | 15 |
| 275 | 3 c. Red-necked Pigeon .. | 75 | 60 | 1·50 | 30 |
| 276 | 4 c. Imperial Amazon .. | 75 | 60 | 1·50 | 30 |
| 277 | 5 c. *Battus polydamas* (butter-fly) .. .. | 1·00 | 30 | 1·50 | 40 |
| 278 | 6 c. *Dryas julia* (butterfly) .. | 1·00 | 75 | 1·50 | 70 |
| 279 | 8 c. Shipping Bananas .. | 20 | 10 | 40 | 20 |
| 280 | 10 c. Portsmouth Harbour .. | 20 | 10 | 35 | 20 |
| 281 | 12 c. Copra Processing Plant .. | 20 | 10 | 35 | 20 |
| 282 | 15 c. Straw Workers .. | 20 | 10 | 35 | 25 |
| 283 | 25 c. Timber Plant .. .. | 30 | 10 | 40 | 25 |
| 284 | 30 c. Pumice Mine .. .. | 1·50 | 80 | 1·50 | 70 |
| 285 | 38 c. Grammar School and Playing Field .. .. | 5·00 | 1·75 | 6·00 | 7·50 |
| 286 | 50 c. Roseau Cathedral .. .. | 50 | 45 | 80 | 90 |
| 287 | 60 c. Type **81** .. .. | 55 | 80 | † | |
| 288 | $1.20, Melville Hall Airport (40 × 27 *mm*) .. .. | 1·00 | 1·75 | † | |
| 289 | $2.40, Type **82** .. .. | 1·75 | 3·00 | † | |
| 290 | $4.80, Type **79** (26 × 39 *mm*) | 3·00 | 6·00 | † | |
| 272A/90A | .. .. *Set of* 19 | 16·00 | 16·00 | | |
| 272B/90B | .. .. *Set of* 15 | | | 16·00 | 11·50 |

**99** "Virgin and Child with St. John" (Perugino)

**101** Astronaut's First Step onto the Moon

(Des G. Vasarhelyi. Litho B.W.)

**1969** (19 Dec). *Christmas. Paintings. T* **99** *and similar vert designs. Multicoloured. P* 14 × 14½.
291 6 c. "Virgin and Child with St. John" (Lippi) 10 10
292 10 c. "Holy Family with the Lamb" (Raphael) 10 10
293 15 c. Type **99** .. .. .. .. 10 10
294 $1.20, "Madonna of the Rose Hedge" (Botticelli) .. .. .. 35 40
291/4 .. .. .. .. *Set of* 4 35 40
**MS**295 89 × 76 mm. Nos. 293/4. Imperf .. .. 55 90

(Des G. Vasarhelyi. Photo Banknote Printing Office, Helsinki)

**1970** (6 Feb*). *Moon Landing. T* **101** *and similar horiz designs. Multicoloured. P* 12½.
296 ½ c. Type **101** .. .. .. .. 10 10
297 5 c. Scientific Experiment on the Moon, and Flag .. .. .. .. 10 10
298 8 c. Astronauts collecting Rocks .. .. 10 10
299 30 c. Module over the Moon .. .. 20 15
300 50 c. Moon Plaque .. .. .. 30 25
301 60 c. Astronauts .. .. .. 30 30
296/301 .. .. .. .. *Set of* 6 90 80
**MS**302 116 × 112 mm. Nos. 298/301. Imperf .. 1·25 1·75

*This is the date of release in Dominica, but the above were released by the Philatelic Agency in the U.S.A. on 2 February.

**107** Giant Green Turtle

(Des G. Drummond. Litho Kyodo Printing Co, Tokyo)

**1970** (7 Sept). *Flora and Fauna. T* **107** *and similar horiz designs. Multicoloured. P* 13.
303 6 c. Type **107** . . 30 15
304 24 c. Flying fish . . 50 40
305 38 c. Anthurium lily . . 60 65
306 60 c. Imperial and Red-necked Amazons . . 2·25 1·75
303/6 . . *Set of* 4 3·25 2·75
**MS**307 160 × 111 mm. Nos. 303/6 . . 3·75 5·50

**108** 18th-Century National Costume
**109** Scrooge and Marley's Ghost

(Des G. Drummond from local designs. Litho Questa)

**1970** (30 Oct). *National Day. T* **108** *and similar horiz designs. Multicoloured. P* 14.
308 5 c. Type **108** . . 10 10
309 8 c. Carib Basketry . . 10 10
310 $1 Flag and Chart of Dominica . . 30 40
308/10 . . *Set of* 3 30 40
**MS**311 150 × 85 mm. Nos. 308/10 plus three labels 50 90

(Des R. Granger Barrett. Litho Questa)

**1970** (23 Nov). *Christmas and Charles Dickens' Death Centenary. T* **109** *and similar vert designs showing scenes from "A Christmas Carol". Multicoloured. P* 14 × 14½.
312 2 c. Type **109** . . 10 10
313 15 c. Fezziwig's Ball . . 10 10
314 24 c. Scrooge and his Nephew's Party . . 10 10
315 $1.20, Scrooge and the Ghost of Christmas Present . . 55 60
312/15 . . *Set of* 4 70 70
**MS**316 142 × 87 mm. Nos. 312/15 . . 1·50 3·00

**110** "The Doctor" (Sir Luke Fildes)

(Des G. Vasarhelyi. Litho Questa)

**1970** (28 Dec). *Centenary of British Red Cross. T* **110** *and similar horiz designs. Multicoloured. P* 14½ × 14.
317 8 c. Type **110** . . 10 10
318 10 c. Hands and Red Cross . . 10 10
319 15 c. Flag of Dominica and Red Cross Emblem 15 10
320 50 c. "The Sick Child" (E. Munch) . . 40 35
317/20 . . *Set of* 4 60 40
**MS**321 108 × 76 mm. Nos. 317/20 . . 1·25 2·00

**111** Marigot School

(Des G. Vasarhelyi. Litho Questa)

**1971** (1 Mar). *International Education Year* (1970). *T* **111** *and similar horiz designs. Multicoloured. P* 13½.
322 5 c. Type **111** . . 10 10
323 8 c. Goodwill Junior High School . . 10 10
324 14 c. University of West Indies (Jamaica) . . 10 10
325 $1 Trinity College, Cambridge . . 25 30
322/5 . . *Set of* 4 30 30
**MS**326 85 × 85 mm. Nos. 324/5 . . 50 75

**112** Waterfall

(Des O. Bonnevalle. Litho Questa)

**1971** (22 Mar). *Tourism. T* **112** *and similar horiz designs. Multicoloured. P* 13½.
327 5 c. Type **112** . . 10 10
328 10 c. Boat-building . . 10 10
329 30 c. Sailing . . 20 10
330 50 c. Yacht and motor launch . . 35 30
327/30 . . *Set of* 4 65 45
**MS**331 130 × 86 mm. Nos. 327/30 . . 65 75

**113** UNICEF Symbol in "D"
**114** German Boy Scout

(Des G. Drummond. Litho Questa)

**1971** (14 June). *25th Anniv of UNICEF. P* 14.
332 **113** 5 c. bluish violet, black and gold . . 10 10
333 10 c. yellow, black and gold . . 10 10
334 38 c. green, black and gold . . 10 10
335 $1.20 orange, black and gold . . 30 45
332/5 . . *Set of* 4 40 55
**MS**336 84 × 79 mm. Nos. 333 and 335 . . 50 85

(Litho Format)

**1971** (18 Oct). *World Scout Jamboree, Asagiri, Japan. T* **114** *and similar vert designs showing Boy Scouts from the nations listed. Multicoloured. W* w **12**. *P* 11.
337 20 c. Type **114** . . 15 10
338 24 c. Great Britain . . 20 10
339 30 c. Japan . . 25 10
340 $1 Dominica . . 50 40
337/40 . . *Set of* 4 1·00 55
**MS**341 114 × 102 mm. Nos. 339/40 . . 1·50 2·00
The above were printed on thick paper and the watermark is very faint.
Both No. 340 and the $1 value from the miniature sheet show the national flag of the Dominican Republic in error.
"Dominica" on the scout's shirt pocket is omitted on the $1 value from the miniature sheet.

**115** Groine at Portsmouth

(Des V. Whiteley. Litho Format)

**1971** (15 Nov). *National Day. T* **115** *and similar multicoloured designs. P* 13½.
342 8 c. Type **115** . . 10 10
343 15 c. Carnival scene . . 10 10
344 20 c. Carifta Queen (*vert*) . . 10 10
345 50 c. Rock of Atkinson (*vert*) . . 20 25
342/5 . . *Set of* 4 30 30
**MS**346 63 × 89 mm. $1.20, As 20 c. P 15 . . 45 70

**116** Eight Reals Piece, 1761

(Des G. Drummond. Litho Questa)

**1972** (7 Feb). *Coins. T* **116** *and similar designs. P* 14.
347 10 c. black, silver and violet . . 10 10
348 30 c. black, silver and yellowish green . . 15 15
349 35 c. black, silver and bright blue . . 20 20
350 50 c. black, silver and vermilion . . 40 60
347/50 . . *Set of* 4 75 90
**MS**351 86 × 90 mm. Nos. 349/50 . . 1·00 1·25
Designs: *Horiz*—30 c. Eleven and three bitt pieces, 1798. *Vert*—35 c. Two reals and two bitt pieces, 1770; 50 c. Mocos, Pieces-of-eight and eight reals-eleven bitts piece, 1798.

**117** Common Opossum

(Des R. Granger Barrett. Litho Questa)

**1972** (3 June). *U.N. Conference on the Human Environment, Stockholm. T* **117** *and similar horiz designs. Multicoloured. W* w **12** (*sideways*). *P* 14.
352 ½ c. Type **117** . . 10 10
353 35 c. Brazilian Agouti (rodent) . . 40 50
354 60 c. Orchid . . 2·00 50
355 $1.20, Hibiscus . . 2·25 1·60
352/5 . . *Set of* 4 4·25 2·00
**MS**356 139 × 94 mm. Nos. 352/5 . . 4·75 6·50

**118** Sprinter

(Des R. Granger Barrett. Litho Format)

**1972** (16 Oct*). *Olympic Games, Munich. T* **118** *and simil[...] multicoloured designs. P* 14.
357 30 c. Type **118** . . 10 [...]
358 35 c. Hurdler . . 15 [...]
359 58 c. Hammer-thrower (*vert*) . . 15 2[...]
360 72 c. Long-jumper (*vert*) . . 25 4[...]
357/60 . . *Set of* 4 60 7[...]
**MS**361 98 × 96 mm. Nos. 359/60. P 15 . . 60 9[...]
*This is the local release date; the American philatelic agenc[...] released the stamps on 9 October.

**119** General Post Office

(Des G. Vasarhelyi. Litho Format)

**1972** (1 Nov). *National Day. T* **119** *and similar horiz designs. Multicoloured. P* 13½.
362 10 c. Type **119** . . 10 1[...]
363 20 c. Morne Diablotin . . 10 1[...]
364 30 c. Rodney's Rock . . 15 1[...]
362/4 . . *Set of* 3 25 2[...]
**MS**365 83 × 96 mm. Nos. 363/4. P 15 . . 50 7[...]

**120** Bananas and Imperial Amazon

(Des (from photograph by D. Groves) and photo Harrison)

**1972** (20 Nov). *Royal Silver Wedding. Multicoloured; backgroun[...] colour given. W* w **12**. *P* 14 × 14½.
366 **120** 5 c. yellow-olive . . 10 1[...]
*a. Deep yellow-olive* . . 25 2[...]
367 $1 myrtle-green . . 40 4[...]

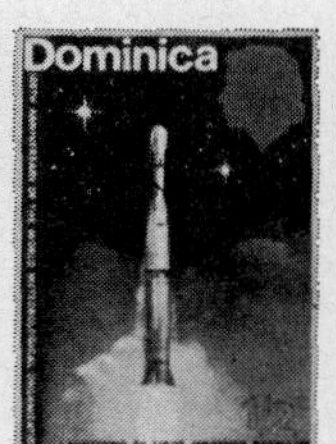


**121** "The Adoration of the Shepherds" (Caravaggio)
**122** Launching of Weather Satellite

(Des G. Vasarhelyi. Litho Format)

**1972** (4 Dec*). *Christmas. T* **121** *and similar vert designs. Mult[...] coloured. P* 13½.
368 8 c. Type **121** . . 10 1[...]
369 14 c. "The Myosotis Virgin" (Rubens) . . 10 1[...]
370 30 c. "Madonna and Child with St. Francesca Romana" (Gentileschi) . . 15 1[...]
371 $1 "Adoration of the Kings" (Mostaert) . . 40 7[...]
368/71 . . *Set of* 4 60 8[...]
**MS**372 102 × 79 mm. Nos. 370/1. Imperf. . . 65 8[...]
* This is the date of release in Dominica; the stamps were put o[...] sale by the Philatelic agency in the U.S.A. on 27 November.
No. 368 is wrongly attributed to Boccaccino in the design.

(Des G. Vasarhelyi. Litho Format)

**1973** (16 July). *I.M.O./W.M.O. Centenary. T* **122** *and simila[...] multicoloured designs. P* 14½.
373 ½ c. Type **122** . . 10 1[...]
374 1 c. Nimbus satellite . . 10 1[...]
375 2 c. Radiosonde balloon . . 10 1[...]
376 30 c. Radarscope (*horiz*) . . 15 1[...]
377 35 c. Diagram of pressure zones (*horiz*) . . 20 2[...]
378 50 c. Hurricane shown by satellite (*horiz*) . . 30 3[...]
379 $1 Computer weather-map (*horiz*) . . 60 6[...]
373/9 . . *Set of* 7 1·25 1·4[...]
**MS**380 90 × 105 mm. Nos. 378/9 . . 90 1·2[...]

**123** Going to Hospital **124** Cyrique Crab

(Des G. Vasarhelyi. Litho Format)

**1973** (20 Aug). *25th Anniv of W.H.O. T* **123** *and similar horiz designs. Multicoloured. P* 14½.

381 ½ c. Type **123** .. .. 10 10
382 1 c. Maternity care .. .. 10 10
383 2 c. Smallpox inoculation .. .. 10 10
384 30 c. Emergency service .. .. 20 15
385 35 c. Waiting for the doctor .. .. 25 15
386 50 c. Medical examination .. .. 30 25
387 $1 Travelling doctor .. .. 45 60
381/7 .. *Set of* 7 1·10 1·10
**MS**388 112 × 110 mm. Nos. 386/7. P 14 × 14½ .. 75 1·25
a. Perf 14½ .. .. 45·00 45·00

(Des G. Drummond. Litho Format)

**1973** (15 Oct). *Flora and Fauna. T* **124** *and similar vert designs. Multicoloured. P* 14½.

389 ½ c. Type **124** .. .. 10 10
390 22 c. Blue Land-crab .. .. 35 10
391 25 c. Bread Fruit .. .. 35 15
392 $1.20, Sunflower .. .. 1·50 2·00
389/92 .. *Set of* 4 2·00 2·00
**MS**393 91 × 127 mm. Nos. 389/92 .. .. 3·25 4·50

**125** Princess Anne and Captain Mark Phillips

(Des G. Drummond. Litho Format)

**1973** (14 Nov). *Royal Wedding. P* 13½.

394 **125** 25 c. multicoloured .. .. 10 10
395 – $2 multicoloured .. .. 30 30
**MS**396 79 × 100 mm. 75 c. as 25 c. and $1.20 as $2 40 30

No. 395 is as T **125**, but the portrait has a different frame.

Nos. 394/5 were each issued in small sheets of five stamps and one stamp-size label.

**126** "Adoration of the Kings" (Brueghel)

(Des M. Shamir. Litho Format)

**1973** (26 Nov). *Christmas. T* **126** *and similar horiz designs. Multicoloured. P* 14½.

397 ½ c. Type **126** .. .. 10 10
398 1 c. "Adoration of the Magi" (Botticelli) .. 10 10
399 2 c. "Adoration of the Magi" (Dürer) .. 10 10
400 12 c. "Mystic Nativity" (Botticelli) .. 15 10
401 22 c. "Adoration of the Magi" (Rubens) .. 20 10
402 35 c. "The Nativity" (Dürer) .. .. 20 10
403 $1 "Adoration of the Shepherds" (Giorgione) 55 55
397/403 .. *Set of* 7 1·00 80
**MS**404 122 × 98 mm. Nos. 402/3 .. .. 80 1·10

**127** Carib Basket-weaving

(Des G. Drummond. Litho Format)

**1973** (17 Dec). *National Day. T* **127** *and similar multicoloured designs. P* 13½.

405 5 c. Type **127** .. .. 10 10
406 10 c. Staircase of the Snake .. .. 10 10
407 50 c. Miss Caribbean Queen (*vert*) .. .. 15 15
408 50 c. Miss Carifta Queen (*vert*) .. .. 15 15
409 $1 Dance group .. .. 25 30
405/9 .. *Set of* 5 50 60
**MS**410 95×127 mm. Nos. 405/6 and 409 .. 40 65

**128** University Centre, Dominica

(Des G. Drummond. Litho Format)

**1974** (21 Jan). *25th Anniv of West Indies University. T* **128** *and similar horiz designs. Multicoloured. P* 14½.

411 12 c. Type **128** .. .. 10 10
412 30 c. Graduation ceremony .. .. 10 10
413 $1 University coat of arms .. .. 25 35
411/13 .. *Set of* 3 30 35
**MS**414 97 × 131 mm. Nos. 411/13 .. .. 30 55

**129** Dominicia 1d. Stamp of 1874 and Map **130** Footballer and Flag of Brazil

(Des G. Drummond. Litho Format)

**1974** (27 May). *Stamp Centenary. T* **129** *and similar horiz designs. Multicoloured. P* 14½.

415 ½ c. Type **129** .. .. 10 10
416 1 c. 6d. stamp of 1874 and posthorn .. 10 10
417 2 c. 1s. stamp of 1874 and arms .. 10 10
418 10 c. Type **129** .. .. 15 10
419 50 c. As 1 c. .. .. 55 30
420 $1.20, As 2 c. .. .. 85 70
415/20 .. *Set of* 6 1·50 1·00
**MS**421 105 × 121 mm. Nos. 418/20 .. .. 1·50 1·50

(Des V. Whiteley. Litho Format)

**1974** (12 Aug). *World Cup Football Championship, West Germany. T* **130** *and similar vert designs, showing footballers and flags of the countries given. Multicoloured. P* 14½.

422 ½ c. Type **130** .. .. 10 10
423 1 c. West Germany .. .. 10 10
424 2 c. Italy .. .. 10 10
425 30 c. Scotland .. .. 30 10
426 40 c. Sweden .. .. 30 10
427 50 c. Netherlands .. .. 35 15
428 $1 Yugoslavia .. .. 65 40
422/8 .. *Set of* 7 1·50 75
**MS**429 89 × 87 mm. Nos. 427/8 .. .. 70 80

**131** Indian Hole

(Des G. Vasarhelyi. Litho Format)

**1974** (1 Nov). *National Day. T* **131** *and similar horiz designs. Multicoloured. P* 13½.

430 10 c. Type **131** .. .. 10 10
431 40 c. Teachers' Training College .. .. 10 10
432 $1 Bay Oil distillery plant, Petite Savanne 30 45
430/2 .. *Set of* 3 40 45
**MS**433 96 × 143 mm. Nos. 430/2 .. .. 50 65

**132** Churchill with "Colonist"

(Des G. Drummond. Litho Format)

**1974** (25 Nov). *Birth Centenary of Sir Winston Churchill. T* **132** *and similar horiz designs. Multicoloured. P* 14½.

434 ½ c. Type **132** .. .. 10 10
435 1 c. Churchill and Eisenhower .. .. 10 10
436 2 c. Churchill and Roosevelt .. .. 10 10
437 20 c. Churchill and troops on assault-course .. 15 10
438 45 c. Painting at Marrakesh .. .. 25 10
439 $2 Giving the "V" sign .. .. 80 1·00
434/9 .. *Set of* 6 1·10 1·10
**MS**440 126 × 100 mm. Nos. 438/9. P 13 .. 1·10 1·75

**133** Mailboats *Orinoco* (1851) and *Geesthaven* (1974) **134** "The Virgin and Child" (Tiso)

(Des G. Drummond. Litho Format)

**1974** (4 Dec). *Centenary of Universal Postal Union. T* **133** *and similar horiz designs. Multicoloured. P* 13.

441 10 c. Type **133** .. .. 15 10
442 $2 De Havilland "4" (1918) and Boeing "747" (1974) .. .. 65 1·00
**MS**443 107 × 93 mm. $1.20 as 10 c. and $2.40 as $2 1·25 1·90

Nos. 442 and **MS**443 are inscr "De Haviland".

(Des M. Shamir. Litho Questa)

**1974** (16 Dec). *Christmas. T* **134** *and similar vert designs. Multicoloured. P* 14.

444 ½ c. Type **134** .. .. 10 10
445 1 c. "Madonna and Child with Saints" (Costa) 10 10
446 2 c. "The Nativity" (School of Rimini, 14th-cent) .. .. 10 10
447 10 c. "The Rest on the Flight into Egypt" (Romanelli) .. .. 15 10
448 25 c. "Adoration of the Shepherds" (da Sermoneta) .. .. 20 10
449 45 c. "The Nativity" (Guido Reni) .. 25 10
450 $1 "The Adoration of the Magi" (Caselli) .. 45 40
444/50 .. *Set of* 7 1·00 60
**MS**451 114 × 78 mm. Nos. 449/50 .. .. 60 75

**135** Trigger Fish

(Des G. Vasarhelyi. Litho Format)

**1975** (2 June). *Fishes. T* **135** *and similar horiz designs. Multicoloured. P* 14.

452 ½ c. Type **135** .. .. 10 10
453 1 c. Cola .. .. 10 10
454 2 c. Sailfish .. .. 10 10
455 3 c. Vayway .. .. 10 10
456 20 c. Bechine .. .. 1·00 50
457 $2 Grouper .. .. 4·25 2·75
452/7 .. *Set of* 6 5·00 3·25
**MS**458 104 × 80 mm. No. 457. P 13 .. .. 4·00 4·50

**136** *Myscelia antholia*

(Des J. W. Litho Format)

**1975** (28 July). *Dominican Butterflies. T* **136** *and similar horiz designs. Multicoloured. P* 14½.

459 ½ c. Type **136** .. .. 10 15
460 1 c. *Lycorea ceres* .. .. 10 15
461 2 c. *Anaea marthesia* ("*Siderone nemesis*") 15 15
462 6 c. *Battus polydamas* .. .. 50 15
463 30 c. *Anartia lytrea* .. .. 1·50 60
464 40 c. *Morpho peleides* .. .. 1·75 65
465 $2 *Dryas julia* .. .. 3·50 3·00
459/65 .. *Set of* 7 6·75 4·25
**MS**466 108 × 80 mm. No. 465. P 13 .. .. 3·00 3·25

**137** R.M.S. *Yare*

(Des J. W. Litho Questa)

**1975** (1 Sept). *"Ships Tied to Dominica's History". T* **137** *and similar horiz designs. Multicoloured. P* 14.

467 ½ c. Type **137** .. .. 10 10
468 1 c. R.M.S. *Thames* .. .. 10 10
469 2 c. S.S. *Lady Nelson* .. .. 10 10
470 20 c. S.S. *Lady Rodney* .. .. 45 35
471 45 c. M.V. *Statesman* .. .. 70 55
472 50 c. M.V. *Geestecape* .. .. 80 65
473 $2 M.V. *Geestestar* .. .. 4·50 3·25
467/73 .. *Set of* 7 6·00 4·50
**MS**474 78 × 103 mm. Nos. 472/3 .. .. 4·00 4·50

138 "Women in Agriculture"

139 Miss Caribbean Queen, 1975

(Litho Questa)

**1975** (20 Oct). *International Women's Year. T* **138** *and similar horiz design. Multicoloured. P* 14.

475 10 c. Type **138** . . . . . . . . 10 10
476 $2 "Women in Industry and Commerce" . . 40 60

(Litho Format)

**1975** (6 Nov). *National Day. T* **139** *and similar multicoloured designs. P* 14 × 13½ *(vert) or* 13½ × 14 *(horiz).*

477 5 c. Type **139** . . . . . . . . 10 10
478 10 c. Public Library *(horiz)* . . . . 10 10
479 30 c. Citrus Factory *(horiz)* . . . . 10 10
480 $1 National Day Trophy . . . . 25 50
477/80 . . . . . . *Set of* 4 35 60
**MS**481 130 × 98 mm. Nos. 478/80. Imperf . . 50 1·40

140 "Virgin and Child" (Mantegna)

141 Hibiscus

(Des M. Shamir. Litho Questa)

**1975** (24 Nov). *Christmas. T* **140** *and similar vert designs showing "Virgin and Child". Multicoloured. P* 14.

482 ½ c. Type **140** . . . . . . . . 10 10
483 1 c. Fra Filippo Lippi . . . . . . 10 10
484 2 c. Bellini . . . . . . . . 10 10
485 10 c. Botticelli . . . . . . . . 10 10
486 25 c. Bellini . . . . . . . . 10 10
487 45 c. Correggio . . . . . . . . 15 10
488 $1 Dürer . . . . . . . . 30 50
482/88 . . . . . . *Set of* 7 65 70
**MS**489 139 × 85 mm. Nos. 487/88 . . . . 80 1·50

(Des J.W. Litho Format)

**1975** (8 Dec)–**78**. *T* **141** *and similar multicoloured designs.*

*(a) Size as T* **141**. *P* 14½

490 ½ c. Type **141** . . . . . . . . 10 20
491 1 c. African Tulip . . . . . . 15 20
492 2 c. Castor Oil Tree . . . . . . 15 20
493 3 c. White Cedar Flower . . . . 15 20
494 4 c. Egg Plant . . . . . . . . 15 20
495 5 c. Gare . . . . . . . . 20 20
496 6 c. Ochro . . . . . . . . 20 30
497 8 c. Zenaida Dove . . . . . . 1·00 30
498 10 c. Screw Pine . . . . . . . . 20 10
a. Perf 13½ (1978) . . . . . . 25·00
499 20 c. Mango Longue . . . . . . 30 15
500 25 c. Crayfish . . . . . . . . 35 15
501 30 c. Common Opossum ("Manicou") . . 70 45

*(b) Size 28 × 44 mm ($10) or 44 × 28 mm (others). P* 13½

502 40 c. Bay Leaf Groves . . . . . . 75 45
503 50 c. Tomatoes . . . . . . . . 55 40
504 $1 Lime Factory . . . . . . . . 75 55
505 $2 Rum Distillery . . . . . . 2·50 2·75
506 $5 Bay Oil Distillery . . . . . . 4·25 4·50
507 $10 Queen Elizabeth II . . . . 10·00 15·00
490/507 . . . . . . *Set of* 18 20·00 24·00

142 American Infantry

143 Rowing

(Des J.W. Litho Format)

**1976** (12 Apr). *Bicentenary of American Revolution. T* **142** *and similar vert designs. Multicoloured. P* 14½.

508 ½ c. Type **142** . . . . . . . . 10 10
509 1 c. British three-decker, 1782 . . . . 10 10
510 2 c. George Washington . . . . . . 10 10
511 45 c. British sailors . . . . . . 75 30
512 75 c. British ensign . . . . . . 1·25 65
513 $2 Admiral Hood . . . . . . 3·00 2·00
508/13 . . . . . . *Set of* 6 4·50 2·75
**MS**514 105 × 92 mm. Nos. 512/13. P 13 . . . . 5·00 5·50

(Des J.W. Litho Format)

**1976** (24 May). *Olympic Games, Montreal. T* **143** *and similar vert designs. Multicoloured. P* 14½.

515 ½ c. Type **143** . . . . . . . . 10 10
516 1 c. Shot putting . . . . . . . . 10 10
517 2 c. Swimming . . . . . . . . 10 10
518 40 c. Relay . . . . . . . . 15 10
519 45 c. Gymnastics . . . . . . . . 15 10
520 60 c. Sailing . . . . . . . . 20 20
521 $2 Archery . . . . . . . . 55 80
515/21 . . . . . . *Set of* 7 1·10 1·10
**MS**522 90 × 104 mm. Nos. 520/1. P 13 . . . . 1·25 1·75

144 Ringed Kingfisher

145 Viking Spacecraft System

(Des G. Drummond. Litho Format)

**1976** (28 June). *Wild Birds. T* **144** *and similar multicoloured designs. P* 14½.

523 ½ c. Type **144** . . . . . . . . 10 15
524 1 c. Mourning Dove . . . . . . 15 15
525 2 c. Green Heron . . . . . . . . 15 15
526 15 c. Broad-winged Hawk . . . . . . 1·00 45
527 30 c. Blue-headed Hummingbird . . . . 1·50 70
528 45 c. Bananaquit . . . . . . . . 2·25 1·00
529 $2 Imperial Amazon . . . . . . 8·50 8·50
523/9 . . . . . . *Set of* 7 12·50 10·00
**MS**530 133 × 101 mm. Nos. 527/9. P 13 . . . . 11·00 12·00

**1976** (26 July). *West Indian Victory in World Cricket Cup. As Nos.* 559/60 *of Barbados.*

531 15 c. Map of the Caribbean . . . . 1·00 1·25
532 25 c. Prudential Cup . . . . . . 1·00 1·50

(Des PAD Studio. Litho Format)

**1976** (20 Sept). *Viking Space Mission. T* **145** *and similar multi-coloured designs. P* 14½.

533 ½ c. Type **145** . . . . . . . . 10 10
534 1 c. Launching pad *(horiz)* . . . . 10 10
535 2 c. Titan IIID and Centaur DII . . . . 10 10
536 3 c. Orbiter and lander capsule . . . . 10 10
537 45 c. Capsule, parachute unopened . . . . 30 15
538 75 c. Capsule, parachute opened . . . . 40 25
539 $1 Lander descending *(horiz)* . . . . 50 35
540 $2 Space vehicle on Mars *(horiz)* . . . . 80 60
533/40 . . . . . . *Set of* 8 2·00 1·40
**MS**541 104 × 78 mm. Nos. 539/40. P 13 . . . . 1·50 2·25

146 "Virgin and Child with Saints Anthony of Padua and Roch" (Giorgione)

147 Island Craft Co-operative

(Des M. Shamir. Litho Questa)

**1976** (1 Nov). *Christmas. T* **146** *and similar vert designs showing "Virgin and Child" by the artists named. Multicoloured. P* 14.

542 ½ c. Type **146** . . . . . . . . 10 10
543 1 c. Bellini . . . . . . . . 10 10
544 2 c. Mantegna . . . . . . . . 10 10
545 6 c. Mantegna *(different)* . . . . 10 10
546 25 c. Memling . . . . . . . . 10 10
547 45 c. Correggio . . . . . . . . 15 10
548 $3 Raphael . . . . . . . . 70 1·00
542/8 . . . . . . *Set of* 7 85 1·10
**MS**549 140 × 85 mm. 50 c. as No. 547 and $1 as No. 548 . . . . . . . . . . 65 1·10

(Des G. Drummond. Litho Questa)

**1976** (22 Nov). *National Day. T* **147** *and similar horiz designs. Multicoloured. P* 13½.

550 10 c. Type **147** . . . . . . . . 10 10
551 50 c. Harvesting bananas . . . . . . 15 10
552 $1 Boxing plant . . . . . . . . 30 35
550/2 . . . . . . *Set of* 3 45 45
**MS**553 96 × 122 mm. Nos. 550/2 . . . . 50 90

148 Common Sundial

149 The Queen Crowned and Enthroned

(Des J.W. Litho Questa)

**1976** (20 Dec). *Shells. T* **148** *and similar vert designs. Multi-coloured. P* 14.

554 ½ c. Type **148** . . . . . . . . 10 10
555 1 c. Flame Helmet . . . . . . . . 10 10
556 2 c. Mouse Cone . . . . . . . . 10 10
557 20 c. Caribbean vase . . . . . . 45 10
558 40 c. West Indian Fighting Conch . . . . 70 25
559 50 c. Short Coral Shell . . . . . . 70 25
560 $3 Apple Murex . . . . . . . . 3·50 2·75
554/60 . . . . . . *Set of* 7 5·00 3·00
**MS**561 101 × 55 mm. $2 Long-spined Star Shell 2·50 3·00

(Des J.W. Litho Questa)

**1977** (7 Feb). *Silver Jubilee. T* **149** *and similar horiz designs. Multicoloured. P* 14 × 13½.

562 ½ c. Type **149** . . . . . . . . 10 10
563 1 c. Imperial State Crown . . . . 10 10
564 45 c. Queen Elizabeth and Princess Anne . . 15 10
565 $2 Coronation Ring . . . . . . 25 30
566 $2.50, Ampulla and Spoon . . . . 30 40
562/6 . . . . . . *Set of* 5 60 70
**MS**567 104 × 79 mm. $5 Queen Elizabeth and Prince Philip . . . . . . . . 1·00 1·75

Nos. 562/6 also exist perf 12 × 11½ *(Price for set of* 5 £1 *mint or used)* from additional sheetlets of 5 stamps and one label. Stamps perforated 14 × 13½ are from normal sheets of 40. Stamps from the sheets of 5 have the arch at left in a different colour.

150 Joseph Haydn

151 Hiking

(Des J.W. Litho Questa)

**1977** (25 Apr). *150th Death Anniv of Ludwig van Beethoven. T* **150** *and similar vert designs. Multicoloured. P* 14.

568 ½ c. Type **150** . . . . . . . . 10 10
569 1 c. Scene from "Fidelio" . . . . . . 10 10
570 2 c. Maria Casentini (dancer) . . . . 10 10
571 15 c. Beethoven and pastoral scene . . . . 15 10
572 30 c. "Wellington's Victory" . . . . 25 10
573 40 c. Henriette Sontag (singer) . . . . 35 10
574 $2 The young Beethoven . . . . . . 1·50 1·25
568/74 . . . . . . *Set of* 7 2·00 1·50
**MS**575 138 × 93 mm. Nos. 572/4 . . . . 2·75 3·00

(Des J.W. Litho Questa)

**1977** (8 Aug). *Caribbean Scout Jamboree, Jamaica. T* **151** *and similar horiz designs. Multicoloured. P* 14.

576 ½ c. Type **151** . . . . . . . . 10 10
577 1 c. First-aid . . . . . . . . 10 10
578 2 c. Camping . . . . . . . . 10 10
579 45 c. Rock climbing . . . . . . 35 15
580 50 c. Canoeing . . . . . . . . 40 20
581 $3 Sailing . . . . . . . . 2·00 1·75
576/81 . . . . . . *Set of* 6 2·50 2·00
**MS**582 111 × 113 mm. 75 c. Map reading and $2 Campfire singsong . . . . . . . . 1·60 1·75

152 Holy Family

**ROYAL VISIT**
**W.I. 1977**

(153)

(Des G. Vasarhelyi. Litho Questa)

**1977** (17 Nov). *Christmas. T* **152** *and similar horiz designs showing book miniatures from Foix Book of Hours* ($3) *or De Lisle Psalter (others). Multicoloured. P* 14.

583 ½ c. Type **152** . . . . . . . . 10 10
584 1 c. Angel and Shepherds . . . . . . 10 10
585 2 c. Holy Baptism . . . . . . . . 10 10
586 6 c. Flight into Egypt . . . . . . 10 10
587 15 c. Three Kings with gifts . . . . 15 10
588 45 c. Holy Family in the Temple . . . . 30 10
589 $3 Flight into Egypt *(different)* . . . . 1·00 70
583/9 . . . . . . *Set of* 7 1·50 80
**MS**590 113 × 85 mm. 50 c. Virgin and Child; $2 Flight into Egypt *(different)* . . . . . . 60 75

977 (28 Nov). *Royal Visit. Nos.* 562/7 *optd with T* **153**. *A. In top left-hand corner**. *P* 14 × 13½. B. *Above "JUBILEE" P* 12 × 11½.

| | A. | | B. | |
|---|---|---|---|---|
| 91 ½ c. Type **149** | † | | 10 | 10 |
| 92 1 c. Imperial State Crown | † | | 10 | 10 |
| 93 45 c. Queen Elizabeth and Princess Anne | 15 | 10 | 20 | 10 |
| 94 $2 Coronation Ring | 30 | 30 | 55 | 55 |
| 95 $2.50, Ampulla and Spoon | 35 | 35 | 70 | 70 |
| 91/5 *Set of* 5 | † | | 1·50 | 1·40 |
| IS596 104 × 79 mm. $5 Queen Elizabeth and Prince Philip | 1·00 | 1·50 | † | |
| a. Optd "W.I. 1977" only on stamp | 11·00 | 14·00 | † | |

*Stamp from No. **MS**596 has the overprint to left of face-value.
No. **MS**596a is overprinted "W.I. 1977" beneath "ROYAL VISIT" ıscription to left of stamp design. Overprint as T **153**, but in one ne, appears at top left of *miniature sheet.*

**154** "Sousouelle Souris"

(Des L. Honychurch and J.W. Litho Questa)

978 (9 Jan). *"History of Carnival". T* **154** *and similar horiz designs. Multicoloured. P* 14.

97 ½ c. Type **154** . . 10 10
98 1 c. Sensay costume . . 10 10
99 2 c. Street musicians . . 10 10
00 45 c. Douiette band . . 15 10
01 50 c. Pappy Show wedding . . 15 10
02 $2 Masquerade band . . 45 60
97/602 *Set of* 6 75 75
IS603 104 × 88 mm. $2.50 as No. 602 . . 60 85

**155** Col. Charles Lindbergh and *Spirit of St. Louis*

**156** Queen receiving Homage

(Des G. Drummond. Litho Format)

1978 (13 Mar). *Aviation Anniversaries. T* **155** *and similar horiz designs. Multicoloured. P* 14½.

504 6 c. Type **155** . . 15 10
505 10 c. *Spirit of St. Louis*, New York, 20 May 1927 . . 20 10
506 15 c. Lindbergh and map of Atlantic . . 25 10
507 20 c. Lindbergh reaches Paris, 21 May 1927 . . 30 10
508 40 c. *LZ*1, Lake Constance, 1900 . . 35 20
509 60 c. Count F. von Zeppelin and *LZ*2, 1906 . . 45 30
510 $3 *LZ*127 (*Graf Zeppelin*), 1928 . . 95 1·10
504/10 *Set of* 7 2·40 1·75
MS611 139 × 108 mm. 50 c. *Spirit of St. Louis* in mid-Atlantic; $2 *Graf Zeppelin*, 1928 . . 80 1·10

The 6, 10, 15, 20 and 50 c. values commemorate the 50th anniversary of first solo transatlantic flight by Col. Charles Lindbergh; the other values commemorate anniversaries of various Zeppelin airships.

No. **MS**611 exists imperforate from stock dispersed by the liquidator of Format International Security Printers Ltd.

(Des J.W. Litho Questa)

1978 (2 June). *25th Anniv of Coronation. T* **156** *and similar vert designs. Multicoloured. P* 14.

612 45 c. Type **156** . . 15 10
613 $2 Balcony scene . . 30 30
614 $2.50, Queen and Prince Philip . . 40 40
612/14 *Set of* 3 75 65
MS615 76 × 107 mm. $5 Queen Elizabeth II . . 1·10 1·10

Nos. 612/14 also exist perf 12 (*Price for set of* 3 £1 *mint or used*) from additional sheetlets of 3 stamps and 1 label. Stamps perforated 14 come from sheets of 50. The stamps from sheetlets have changed background or inscription colours.

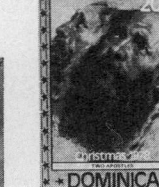

**157** Wilbur Wright's Aeroplane

**158** "Two Apostles" (Rubens)

(Des G. Vasarhelyi. Litho Format)

1978 (10 July). *75th Anniv of Powered Flight. T* **157** *and similar horiz designs. Multicoloured. P* 14½.

616 30 c. Type **157** . . 15 15
617 40 c. *Flyer*, 1908 . . 20 20
618 60 c. *Flyer* 1 . . 25 25
619 $2 *Flyer* 1 (*different*) . . 85 85
616/19 *Set of* 4 1·25 1·25
MS620 116 × 89 mm. $3 Wilbur and Orville Wright . . 90 1·00

Nos. 616/20 exist imperforate from stock dispersed by the liquidator of Format International Security Printers Ltd.

(Des BG Studio. Litho Questa)

1978 (16 Oct). *Christmas. Paintings. T* **158** *and similar vert designs. Multicoloured. P* 14.

621 20 c. Type **158** . . 10 10
622 45 c. "The Descent from the Cross" (Rubens) 15 10
623 50 c. "St Ildefonso receiving the Chasuble" (Rubens) . . 15 10
624 $3 "The Assumption of the Virgin" (Rubens) 55 80
621/4 *Set of* 4 75 90
MS625 113 × 83 mm. $2 "The Holy Family" (Sebastiano del Piombo*) . . 65 75

*This painting was incorrectly attributed to Rubens on the stamp.

## INDEPENDENT

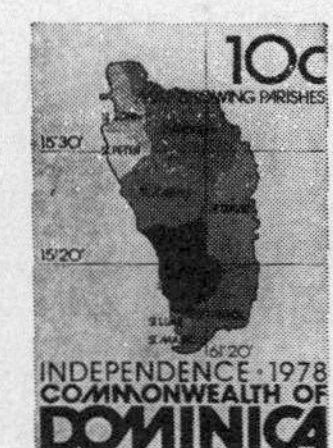


**159** Map showing Parishes

INDEPENDENCE
3rd NOVEMBER
1978

**(160)**

(Des J.W. Litho Questa)

1978 (3 Nov). *Independence. T* **159** *and similar vert designs. Multicoloured. P* 14.

626 10 c. Type **159** . . 10 10
627 25 c. *Sabinea carinalis* (National flower) . . 15 10
628 45 c. New National flag . . 25 15
629 50 c. Coat of arms . . 25 15
630 $2 Patrick John (Prime Minister) . . 70 70
626/30 *Set of* 5 1·25 90
MS631 113 × 90 mm. $2.50, Type **159** . . 2·00 2·25

1978 (3 Nov)–**79**. *Independence. Nos.* 490/507 (10 *c. now perf* 13½) *optd as T* **160** *by typography.*

632 ½ c. Type **141** . . 30 10
633 1 c. African Tulip . . 35 10
634 2 c. Castor Oil Tree . . 35 10
635 3 c. White Cedar Flower . . 40 15
636 4 c. Egg Plant . . 40 15
637 5 c. Gare . . 40 15
638 6 c. Ochro . . 40 15
639 8 c. Zenaida Dove . . 1·00 20
640 10 c. Screw Pine . . 50 15
a. Perf 14½. Litho opt (7.79) . . 85 30
641 20 c. Mango Longue . . 60 15
642 25 c. Crayfish . . 70 20
643 30 c. Common Opossum . . 70 20
644 40 c. Bay Leaf Groves . . 70 25
a. Litho opt (7.79) . . 70 40
645 50 c. Tomatoes . . 80 30
646 $1 Lime Factory . . 80 65
647 $2 Rum Distillery . . 1·25 1·00
648 $5 Bay Oil Distillery . . 2·50 2·25
649 $10 Queen Elizabeth II . . 5·50 4·50
a. Litho opt (7.79) . . 5·50 5·50
632/49 *Set of* 18 16·00 10·00

For History of Aviation gold foil stamps see Appendix at the end of the Dominica listing.

**161** Sir Rowland Hill

**162** Children and Canoe

(Des BG Studio. Litho Questa)

1979 (19 Mar). *Death Centenary of Sir Rowland Hill. T* **161** *and similar vert designs. P* 14.

650 25 c. multicoloured . . 20 10
651 45 c. multicoloured . . 25 10
652 50 c. black, reddish violet and magenta . . 25 10
653 $2 black, magenta and yellow . . 65 65
650/3 *Set of* 4 1·25 80
MS654 186 × 96 mm. $5 black and vermilion . . 1·25 1·75

Designs:—45 c. Great Britain 1840 2d. blue; 50 c. 1874 1d. stamp; $2 Maltese Cross cancellations; $5 Penny Black.

Nos. 650/3 also exist perf 12 (*Price for set of* 4 80*p mint or used*) from additional sheetlets of 5 stamps and 1 label. Shades of these stamps differ from those perforated 14 which come from sheets of 40.

(Des BG Studio. Litho Questa)

1979 (23 Apr). *International Year of the Child. T* **162** *and similar horiz designs. Multicoloured. P* 14.

655 30 c. Type **162** . . 30 15
656 40 c. Children with bananas . . 40 25
657 50 c. Children playing cricket . . 85 40
658 $3 Child feeding rabbits . . 1·75 1·50
655/8 *Set of* 4 3·00 2·10
MS659 117 × 85 mm. $5 Child with catch of fish . . 1·50 1·75

**163** Grouper

(Des G. Drummond. Litho Questa)

1979 (21 May). *Marine Wildlife. T* **163** *and similar horiz designs. Multicoloured. P* 14.

660 10 c. Type **163** . . 25 10
661 30 c. Striped Dolphin . . 50 15
662 50 c. White-tailed Tropic Bird . . 1·25 25
663 60 c. Brown Pelican . . 1·25 30
664 $1 Long-finned Pilot Whale . . 1·50 45
665 $2 Brown Booby . . 2·25 80
660/5 *Set of* 6 6·25 1·75
MS666 120 × 94 mm. $3 Elkhorn Coral . . 1·60 1·75

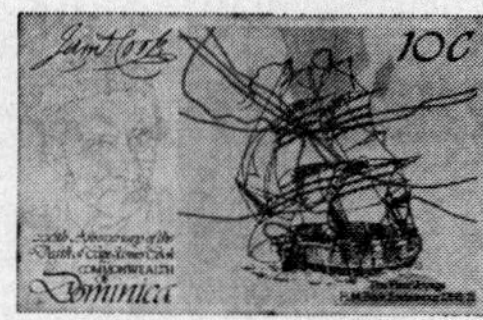


**164** H.M.S. *Endeavour*

(Des J.W. Litho Questa)

1979 (16 July). *Death Bicentenary of Captain Cook. T* **164** *and similar horiz designs. Multicoloured. P* 14.

667 10 c. Type **164** . . 35 10
668 50 c. H.M.S. *Resolution* . . 80 45
669 60 c. H.M.S. *Discovery* . . 90 55
670 $2 Detail of Cook's chart of New Zealand, 1770 . . 1·40 1·10
667/70 *Set of* 4 3·00 2·00
MS671 97 × 90 mm. $5 Captain Cook and signature . . 2·00 2·50

**165** Cooking at Camp-fire

**166** Colvillea

(Des M. Diamond. Litho Questa)

1979 (30 July). *50th Anniv of Girl Guide Movement in Dominica. T* **165** *and similar horiz designs. Multicoloured. P* 14.

672 10 c. Type **165** . . 20 10
673 20 c. Pitching emergency rain tent . . 25 10
674 50 c. Raising Dominican flag . . 35 10
675 $2.50, Singing and dancing to accordion . . 1·00 80
672/5 *Set of* 4 1·60 85
MS676 110 × 86 mm. $3 Guides of different age-groups . . 75 1·25

(Des J.W. Litho Questa)

1979 (3 Sept). *Flowering Trees. T* **166** *and similar vert designs. Multicoloured. P* 14.

677 20 c. Type **166** . . 20 10
678 40 c. Lignum Vitae . . 30 15
679 60 c. Dwarf Poinciana . . 45 25
680 $2 Fern Tree . . 1·00 90
677/80 *Set of* 4 1·75 1·25
MS681 114 × 89 mm. $3 Perfume Tree . . 75 1·10

**167** Cathedral of the Assumption, Roseau

(Des W. Grout. Litho Questa)

1979 (11 Oct). *Christmas. Cathedrals. T* **167** *and similar multicoloured designs. P* 14.

682 6 c. Type **167** . . 10 10
683 45 c. St. Paul's, London (*vert*) . . 15 10
684 60 c. St. Peter's, Rome . . 15 10
685 $3 Notre Dame, Paris (*vert*) . . 55 60
682/5 *Set of* 4 75 70
MS686 113 × 85 mm. 40 c. St. Patrick's, New York; $2 Cologne Cathedral (*both vert*) . . 50 80

**HURRICANE RELIEF**

(168)

169 Mickey Mouse and Octopus playing Xylophone

**1979** (29 Oct). *Hurricane Relief. Nos. 495, 502 and 506/7 optd as T* **168**.
687 5 c. Gare .. .. .. .. .. 10 10
688 40 c. Bay Leaf Groves .. .. .. .. 10 10
689 $5 Bay Oil Distillery .. .. .. 1·25 1·50
690 $10 Queen Elizabeth II .. .. .. 2·00 2·25
687/90 .. .. .. .. *Set of* 4 3·00 3·75

(Litho Format)

**1979** (2 Nov). *International Year of the Child. Walt Disney Cartoon Characters. T* **169** *and similar vert designs showing characters playing musical instruments. Multicoloured. P* 11.
691 ½ c. Type **169** .. .. .. .. .. 10 10
692 1 c. Goofy playing guitar on rocking-horse .. 10 10
693 2 c. Mickey Mouse playing violin and Goofy playing bagpipes .. .. .. .. 10 10
694 3 c. Donald Duck playing drum with pneumatic drill .. .. .. .. 10 10
695 4 c. Minnie Mouse playing saxophone on roller-skates .. .. .. .. 10 10
696 5 c. Goofy as one-man-band .. .. .. 10 10
697 10 c. Dale being blown from French horn by Horace Horsecollar .. .. .. 10 10
698 $2 Huey, Dewey and Louie playing bass .. 2·75 1·25
699 $2.50, Donald Duck playing piano and Huey playing trumpet .. .. .. 3·00 1·50
691/9 .. .. .. .. *Set of* 9 5·50 2·75
**MS**700 127 × 102 mm. $3 Mickey Mouse playing piano. P 13½ .. .. .. .. 2·50 2·50

170 Hospital Ward

(Des BG Studio. Litho Questa)

**1980** (31 Mar). *75th Anniv of Rotary International. T* **170** *and similar horiz designs. Multicoloured. P* 14.
701 10 c. Type **170** .. .. .. .. 10 10
702 20 c. Electric-cardiogram .. .. .. 15 10
703 40 c. Site for mental hospital .. .. .. 20 15
704 $2.50, Paul P. Harris (founder) .. .. 55 70
701/4 .. .. .. .. *Set of* 4 80 85
**MS**705 128 × 113 mm. $3 Interlocking cogs of Rotary emblem and globe .. .. .. 60 80

**1980** (6 May). *"London 1980" International Stamp Exhibition. As Nos. 650/3 optd with T* **262** *of Grenada. P* 12.
706 25 c. multicoloured .. .. .. .. 25 10
707 45 c. multicoloured .. .. .. .. 30 15
708 50 c. olive-brown, blue and rose-red .. .. 30 15
709 $2 olive-brown, vermilion and yellow .. 80 60
706/9 .. .. .. .. *Set of* 4 1·50 80

171 Shot Putting

(Des J.W. Litho Questa)

**1980** (27 May). *Olympic Games, Moscow. T* **171** *and similar horiz designs. Multicoloured. P* 14.
710 30 c. Type **171** .. .. .. .. 20 10
711 40 c. Basketball .. .. .. .. 35 15
712 60 c. Swimming .. .. .. .. 35 20
713 $2 Gymnastics .. .. .. .. 70 65
710/13 .. .. .. .. *Set of* 4 1·40 90
**MS**714 114 × 86 mm. $3 The Marathon .. .. 70 90

172 "Supper at Emmaus" (Caravaggio)

(Des J.W. Litho Questa)

**1980** (22 July). *Famous Paintings. T* **172** *and similar multicoloured designs. P* 13½.
715 20 c. Type **172** .. .. .. .. .. 10 10
716 25 c. "Portrait of Charles I Hunting" (Van Dyck) (*vert*) .. .. .. .. 10 10
717 30 c. "The Maids of Honour" (Velasquez) (*vert*) 15 10
718 45 c. "The Rape of the Sabine Women" (Poussin) .. .. .. .. 15 10
719 $1 "Embarkation for Cythera" (Watteau) .. 35 35
720 $5 "Girl before a Mirror" (Picasso) (*vert*) .. 1·50 1·50
715/20 .. .. .. .. *Set of* 6 2·00 2·00
**MS**721 114 × 111 mm. $3 "The Holy Family" (Rembrandt) (*vert*) .. .. .. .. 60 80

173 Scene from "Peter Pan"

(Litho Walsall)

**1980** (1 Oct). *Christmas. Scenes from Walt Disney's Cartoon Film "Peter Pan". T* **173** *and similar horiz designs. P* 11.
722 ½ c. multicoloured .. .. .. .. 10 10
723 1 c. multicoloured .. .. .. .. 10 10
724 2 c. multicoloured .. .. .. .. 10 10
725 3 c. multicoloured .. .. .. .. 10 10
726 4 c. multicoloured .. .. .. .. 10 10
727 5 c. multicoloured .. .. .. .. 10 10
728 10 c. multicoloured .. .. .. .. 10 10
729 $2 multicoloured .. .. .. .. 1·25 80
730 $2.50, multicoloured .. .. .. 1·50 95
722/30 .. .. .. .. *Set of* 9 2·75 1·90
**MS**731 124 × 98 mm. $4 multicoloured (*vert*) .. 2·50 2·75

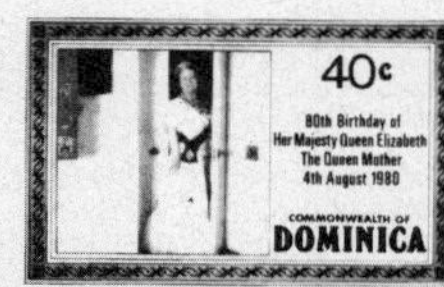

174 Queen Elizabeth the Queen Mother in Doorway

(Litho Questa)

**1980** (20 Oct). *80th Birthday of Queen Elizabeth the Queen Mother. P* 12.
732 **174** 40 c. multicoloured .. .. .. 50 40
733 $2.50, multicoloured .. .. .. 1·60 1·50
**MS**734 85 × 66 mm. **174** $3 multicoloured .. 2·00 2·00
Nos. 732/3 also exist perforated 14 (*price for pair* £1.90 *mint or used*) from additional sheetlets of 9. Stamps perforated 12 are from normal sheets of 50.

175 Douglas Bay

(Des G. Drummond. Litho Questa)

**1981** (12 Feb). *Dominica Safari. T* **175** *and similar multicoloured designs. P* 14.
735 20 c. Type **175** .. .. .. .. 10 10
736 30 c. Valley of Desolation .. .. .. 15 15
737 40 c. Emerald Pool (*vert*) .. .. .. 20 20
738 $3 Indian River (*vert*) .. .. .. 1·40 1·60
735/8 .. .. .. .. *Set of* 4 1·75 1·90
**MS**739 84 × 104 mm. $4 Trafalgar Falls (*vert*) .. 1·75 2·25

(Litho Format)

**1981** (30 Apr). *50th Anniv of Walt Disney's Cartoon Character, Pluto. Vert designs as T* **169**. *Multicoloured. P* 13½ × 14.
740 $2 Pluto and Fifi .. .. .. .. 1·25 1·25
**MS**741 128 × 102 mm. $4 Pluto in scene from film *Pluto's Blue Note* .. .. .. .. 2·40 2·50

176 Forest Thrush

177 Windsor Castle

(Des P. Barrett. Litho Questa)

**1981** (30 Apr). *Birds. T* **176** *and similar horiz designs. Multicoloured. P* 14.
742 20 c. Type **176** .. .. .. .. 55 20
743 30 c. Wied's Crested Flycatcher .. .. 65 25
744 40 c. Blue-hooded Euphonia .. .. 75 35
745 $5 Lesser Antillean Pewee .. .. .. 3·50 4·25
742/5 .. .. .. .. *Set of* 4 5·00 4·50
**MS**746 121 × 95 mm. $3 Imperial Amazon .. 2·50 1·75

(Des J.W. Litho Questa)

**1981** (23 June). *Royal Wedding. T* **177** *and similar vert designs. Multicoloured. A. P* 14. *B. P* 12.

| | | A | | B | |
|---|---|---|---|---|---|
| 747 | 45 c. Prince Charles and Lady Diana Spencer .. .. | 20 | 10 | 2·25 | 2·25 |
| 748 | 60 c. Type **177** .. .. | 25 | 15 | 2·25 | 2·25 |
| 749 | $4 Prince Charles as helicopter pilot .. .. | 1·00 | 1·00 | 2·25 | 2·25 |
| 747/9 | .. .. *Set of* 3 | 1·25 | 1·10 | 6·00 | 6·00 |
| **MS**750 | 96 × 82 mm. $5 Helicopter of Queen's Flight .. .. | 1·25 | 1·25 | † | |

Nos. 747B/9B also exist from additional sheetlets of five stamps and one label with changed background colours.

178 Lady Diana Spencer

179 Ixora

(Manufactured by Walsall)

**1981** (23 June). *Royal Wedding. Booklet stamps. T* **178** *and similar vert designs. Multicoloured. Roul* 5 × *imperf**. *Self-adhesive.*
751 25 c. Type **178** .. .. .. .. 20 35
a. Booklet pane. Nos. 751/2, each × 3 .. 2·50
752 $2 Prince Charles .. .. .. .. 70 1·00
753 $5 Prince Charles and Lady Diana Spencer 1·75 2·50
a. Booklet pane of 1.. .. .. 1·75
751/3 .. .. .. .. *Set of* 3 2·40 3·50
*The 25 c. and $2 values were separated by various combinations of rotary knife (giving a straight edge) and roulette. The $5 value exists only with straight edges.

(Litho Questa)

**1981** (2 Nov). *Christmas. Horiz designs as T* **169** *showing scenes from Walt Disney's cartoon film "Santa's Workshop". P* 13½.
754 ½ c. multicoloured .. .. .. .. 10 10
755 1 c. multicoloured .. .. .. .. 10 10
756 2 c. multicoloured .. .. .. .. 10 10
757 3 c. multicoloured .. .. .. .. 10 10
758 4 c. multicoloured .. .. .. .. 10 10
759 5 c. multicoloured .. .. .. .. 10 10
760 10 c. multicoloured .. .. .. .. 10 10
761 45 c. multicoloured .. .. .. .. 75 30
762 $5 multicoloured .. .. .. .. 3·50 2·50
754/62 .. .. .. .. *Set of* 9 4·00 2·75
**MS**763 129 × 103 mm. $4 multicoloured .. .. 2·50 2·50

(Des P. Barrett. Litho Questa)

**1981** (1 Dec)–**85**. *Plant Life. Horiz designs as T* **179**. *Multicoloured. A. Without imprint date. P* 14
764A 1 c. Type **179** .. .. .. .. 10 30
765A 2 c. Flamboyant .. .. .. .. 10 30
766A 4 c. Poinsettia .. .. .. .. 15 10
767A 5 c. Bois Caribe (national flower of Dominica) .. .. .. .. 15 10
768A 8 c. Annatto or Roucou .. .. .. 20 10
769A 10 c. Passion Fruit .. .. .. .. 30 10
770A 15 c. Breadfruit or Yampain .. .. .. 55 15
771A 20 c. Allamanda or Buttercup .. .. .. 40 15
772A 25 c. Cashew Nut .. .. .. .. 40 15
773A 35 c. Soursop or Couassol .. .. .. 45 30
774A 40 c. Bougainvillea .. .. .. .. 45 30
775A 45 c. Anthurium .. .. .. .. 50 35
776A 60 c. Cacao or Cocoa .. .. .. .. 1·25 55
777A 90 c. Pawpaw Tree or Papay .. .. .. 70 60
778A $1 Coconut Palm .. .. .. .. 1·50 70
779A $2 Coffee Tree or Café .. .. .. 1·00 2·00
780A $5 Heliconia or Lobster Claw .. .. 4·75 8·00
781A $10 Banana/Fig .. .. .. .. 7·00 12·00
764A/81A .. .. .. *Set of* 18 18·00 23·00

B. *With imprint date at foot of design. P* 14 (15, 60 *c.*) *or* 12 (*others*)
769B 10 c. Passion Fruit (1984) .. .. .. 45 15
a. Perf 14 (7.85) .. .. .. .. 55 30
770B 15 c. Breadfruit or Yampain (7.85) .. .. 55 20
776B 60 c. Cacao or Cocoa (7.85).. .. .. 1·00 35
778B $1 Coconut Palm (1984) .. .. .. 1·00 80
780B $5 Heliconia or Lobster Claw (1984) .. 3·25 4·00
781B $10 Banana Fig (1984) .. .. .. 5·00 8·00
769B/81B .. .. .. *Set of* 6 10·00 12·00

180 Curb slope for Wheelchairs

181 "Olga Picasso in an Armchair"

(Des BG Studio. Litho Format)

**1981** (22 Dec). *International Year for Disabled Persons. T* **180** *and similar vert designs. Multicoloured. P* 14½.

782 45 c. Type **180** .. .. .. .. .. .. 70 25
783 60 c. Bus with invalid step .. .. .. 80 35
784 75 c. Motor car controls adapted for handicapped .. .. .. .. .. 90 40
785 $4 Bus with wheelchair ramp .. .. 2·50 2·50
782/5 .. .. .. .. .. *Set of* 4 4·50 3·25
**MS**786 82 × 96 mm. $5 Specially designed elevator control panel .. .. .. .. .. 3·75 3·00

(Des J.W. Litho Format)

**1981** (30 Dec). *Birth Centenary of Picasso. T* **181** *and similar vert designs. Multicoloured. P* 14½.

787 45 c. Type **181** .. .. .. .. .. 65 25
788 60 c. "Bathers" .. .. .. .. .. 75 35
789 75 c. "Woman in Spanish Costume" .. .. 90 40
790 $4 "Detail of Dog and Cock" .. .. 2·50 2·50
787/90 .. .. .. .. *Set of* 4 4·25 3·25
**MS**791 140 × 115 mm. $5 "Sleeping Peasants" (detail) .. .. .. .. .. .. 3·75 2·75

(Litho Questa)

**1982** (29 Jan). *World Cup Football Championship, Spain. Walt Disney Cartoon Characters. Horiz designs as T* **169**. *Multicoloured. P* 14 × 13½.

792 ½ c. Goofy chasing ball with butterfly net .. 10 10
793 1 c. Donald Duck with ball in beak .. .. 10 10
794 2 c. Goofy as goalkeeper .. .. .. 10 10
795 3 c. Goofy looking for ball .. .. .. 10 10
796 4 c. Goofy as park attendant puncturing ball with litter spike .. .. .. .. .. 10 10
797 5 c. Pete and Donald Duck playing .. .. 10 10
798 10 c. Donald Duck after kicking rock instead of ball .. .. .. .. .. .. 10 10
799 60 c. Donald Duck feeling effects of a hard game and Daisy Duck dusting ball .. 75 55
800 $5 Goofy hiding ball under his jersey from Mickey Mouse .. .. .. .. 3·25 2·75
792/800 .. .. .. .. *Set of* 9 4·00 3·25
**MS**801 132 × 105 mm. $4 Dale making off with ball 2·25 2·25

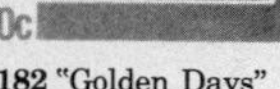


182 "Golden Days"

183 Elma Napier (first woman elected to B.W.I. Legislative Council)

(Des M.B.I. Studios. Litho Questa)

**1982** (10 Mar). *Norman Rockwell (painter) Commemoration. T* **182** *and similar vert designs. Multicoloured. P* 14 × 13½.

802 10 c. Type **182** .. .. .. .. .. 10 10
803 25 c. "The Morning News" .. .. .. 15 10
804 45 c. "The Marbles Champ" .. .. .. 30 30
805 $1 "Speeding Along" .. .. .. .. 55 55
802/5 .. .. .. .. .. *Set of* 4 95 95

(Des BG Studio. Litho Questa)

**1982** (15 Apr). *Decade for Women. T* **183** *and similar horiz designs. Multicoloured. P* 14.

806 10 c. Type **183** .. .. .. .. .. 10 10
807 45 c. Margaret Mead (anthropologist) .. 30 30
808 $1 Mabel ("Cissy") Caudeiron (folk song composer and historian) .. .. .. 55 55
809 $4 Eleanor Roosevelt .. .. .. .. 2·25 2·25
806/9 .. .. .. .. .. *Set of* 4 2·75 2·75
**MS**810 92 × 63 mm. $3 Florence Nightingale .. 1·75 2·25

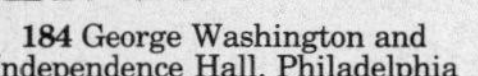


184 George Washington and Independence Hall, Philadelphia

185 *Anaea dominicana*

(Des J.W. Litho Format)

**1982** (1 May). *250th Birth Anniv of George Washington* (45, 90 c.) *and Birth Centenary of Franklin D. Roosevelt* (60 c., $2). *T* **184** *and similar horiz designs. Multicoloured. P* 14½.

811 45 c. Type **184** .. .. .. .. .. 40 25
812 60 c. Franklin D. Roosevelt and Capitol, Washington D.C. .. .. .. .. .. 50 35
813 90 c. Washington at Yorktown (detail, "The Surrender of Cornwallis" by Trumbull) 70 55
814 $2 Construction of dam (from W. Gropper's mural commemorating Roosevelt's "New Deal") .. .. .. .. .. .. 1·50 1·60
811/14 .. .. .. .. .. *Set of* 4 2·75 2·50
**MS**815 115 × 90 mm. $5 Washington and Roosevelt with U.S.A. flags of 1777 and 1933 .. .. 2·75 3·00

(Des P. Barrett. Litho Questa)

**1982** (1 June). *Butterflies. T* **185** *and similar vert designs. Multicoloured. P* 14.

816 15 c. Type **185** .. .. .. .. .. 1·00 35
817 45 c. *Heliconius charithonia* .. .. .. 1·75 65
818 60 c. *Hypolimnas misippus* .. .. .. 2·00 1·25
819 $3 *Biblis hyperia* .. .. .. .. 4·50 5·00
816/19 .. .. .. .. .. *Set of* 4 8·50 6·50
**MS**820 77×105 mm. $5 *Marpesia petreus* .. 5·00 5·00

186 Prince and Princess of Wales

187 Scouts around Campfire

(Des PAD Studio. Litho Questa)

**1982** (1 July). *21st Birthday of Princess of Wales. T* **186** *and similar vert designs. Multicoloured. P* 14½ × 14.

821 45 c. Buckingham Palace .. .. .. .. 30 30
822 $2 Type **186** .. .. .. .. .. 90 90
823 $4 Princess of Wales .. .. .. .. 1·60 1·60
821/3 .. .. .. .. .. *Set of* 3 2·50 2·50
**MS**824 103 × 75 mm. $5 Princess Diana (*different*) 2·00 2·25

Nos. 821/3 also exist in sheetlets of 5 stamps and 1 label.

(Des R. Sauber. Litho Questa)

**1982** (3 Aug). *75th Anniv of Boy Scout Movement. T* **187** *and similar multicoloured designs. P* 14.

825 45 c. Type **187** .. .. .. .. .. 1·25 50
826 60 c. Temperature study, Valley of Desolation 1·75 1·00
827 75 c. Learning about native birds .. .. 2·00 1·10
828 $3 Canoe trip along Indian River .. .. 3·75 4·50
825/8 .. .. .. .. .. *Set of* 4 8·00 6·50
**MS**829 99 × 70 mm. $5 Dominican scouts saluting the flag (*vert*) .. .. .. .. .. 2·75 3·25

**1982** (30 Aug). *Birth of Prince William of Wales. Nos. 821/4 optd with T* **171** *of Antigua.*

830 45 c. Buckingham Palace .. .. .. .. 30 30
831 $2 Type **186** .. .. .. .. .. 1·10 1·10
832 $4 Princess of Wales .. .. .. .. 1·90 1·90
830/2 .. .. .. .. .. *Set of* 3 3·00 3·00
**MS**833 103 × 75 mm. $5 Princess Diana (*different*) 2·25 2·75

Nos. 830/2 also exist in sheetlets of 5 stamps and 1 label.

188 "Holy Family of Francis I"

189 Cuvier's Beaked Whale

(Des Design Images. Litho Questa)

**1982** (3 Nov). *Christmas. Raphael Paintings. T* **188** *and similar vert designs. Multicoloured. P* 13½ × 14.

834 25 c. Type **188** .. .. .. .. .. 15 10
835 30 c. "Holy Family of the Pearl" .. .. 20 15
836 90 c. "Canigiani Holy Family" .. .. .. 55 55
837 $4 "Holy Family of the Oak Tree" .. .. 1·90 1·90
834/7 .. .. .. .. .. *Set of* 4 2·50 2·40
**MS**838 95 × 125 mm. $5 "Holy Family of the Lamb" .. .. .. .. .. .. 2·40 2·50

(Des J. Cooter. Litho Questa)

**1983** (15 Feb). *Save the Whales. T* **189** *and similar horiz designs. Multicoloured. P* 14.

839 45 c. Type **189** .. .. .. .. .. 1·00 65
840 60 c. Humpback Whale .. .. .. .. 1·25 1·00
841 75 c. Black Right Whale .. .. .. .. 1·40 1·25
842 $3 Melon-headed Whale .. .. .. 3·25 4·00
839/42 .. .. .. .. .. *Set of* 4 6·25 6·25
**MS**843 99×72 mm. $5 Pygmy Sperm Whale .. 3·50 3·75

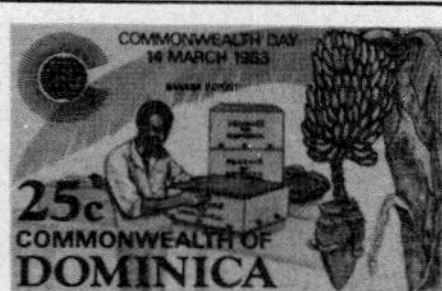


190 Banana Export

(Des R. Vigurs. Litho Questa)

**1983** (14 Mar). *Commonwealth Day. T* **190** *and similar horiz designs. Multicoloured. P* 14.

844 25 c. Type **190** .. .. .. .. .. 15 15
845 30 c. Road building .. .. .. .. 15 20
846 90 c. Community nursing .. .. .. 40 45
847 $3 Tourism—handicrafts .. .. .. 1·25 1·50
844/7 .. .. .. .. .. *Set of* 4 1·75 2·10

191 Map and Satellite Picture of Hurricane

(Des G. Vasarhelyi. Litho Questa)

**1983** (18 Apr). *World Communications Year. T* **191** *and similar horiz designs. Multicoloured. P* 14.

848 45 c. Type **191** .. .. .. .. .. 20 25
849 60 c. Aircraft-to-ship transmission .. .. 30 35
850 90 c. Satellite communications .. .. .. 40 45
851 $2 Shortwave radio .. .. .. .. 95 1·00
848/51 .. .. .. .. .. *Set of* 4 1·75 1·90
**MS**852 110 × 85 mm. $5 Communications satellite 2·50 2·75

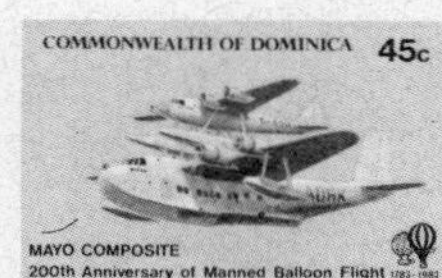


192 *Mayo-Mercury* Composite

(Des W. Wright. Litho Format)

**1983** (19 July). *Bicentenary of Manned Flight. T* **192** *and similar horiz designs. Multicoloured. P* 14½.

853 45 c. Type **192** .. .. .. .. .. 40 30
854 60 c. Macchi "M.39" seaplane .. .. .. 60 60
855 90 c. Fairey "Swordfish" biplane .. .. 85 85
856 $4 Zeppelin "LZ3" .. .. .. .. 2·75 3·00
853/6 .. .. .. .. .. *Set of* 4 4·25 4·25
**MS**857 105 × 79 mm. $5 *Double Eagle II* (balloon) 2·50 2·75

193 Duesenberg "SJ", 1935

(Des R. Sauber. Litho Questa)

**1983** (1 Sept). *Classic Motor Cars. T* **193** *and similar horiz designs. Multicoloured. P* 14.

858 10 c. Type **193** .. .. .. .. .. 10 10
859 45 c. Studebaker "Avanti", 1962 .. .. 25 25
860 60 c. Cord "812", 1936 .. .. .. .. 35 35
861 75 c. MG "TC", 1945 .. .. .. .. 40 40
862 90 c. Camaro "350 SS", 1967 .. .. .. 45 45
863 $3 Porsch "356", 1948 .. .. .. 1·40 1·50
858/63 .. .. .. .. .. *Set of* 6 2·50 2·50
**MS**864 110 × 75 mm. $5 Ferrari "312 T", 1975 .. 2·50 2·75

194 "Charity"

(Des Design Images. Litho Format)

**1983** (4 Oct). *Christmas. 500th Birth Anniv of Raphael. T* **194** *and similar horiz designs. Multicoloured. P* 13½.

865 45 c. Type **194** .. .. .. .. .. 55 30
866 60 c. "Hope" .. .. .. .. .. .. 70 50
867 90 c. "Faith" .. .. .. .. .. .. 80 60
868 $4 "The Cardinal Virtues" .. .. .. 2·50 3·00
865/8 .. .. .. .. .. *Set of* 4 4·00 4·00
**MS**869 101 × 127 mm. $5 "Justice" .. .. 2·50 2·75

195 Plumbeous Warbler

196 Donald Duck

(Des Jennifer Toombs. Litho Questa)

**1984** (24 Apr). *Birds. T* **195** *and similar horiz designs. Multicoloured. P* 14.

870 5 c. Type **195** . . . . 50 20
871 45 c. Imperial Amazon . . 1·25 45
872 60 c. Blue-headed Hummingbird . . 1·50 90
873 90 c. Red-necked Amazon . . 2·00 2·00
870/3 . . *Set of* 4 4·75 3·25
**MS**874 72×72 mm. $5 Greater Flamingos . . 3·75 4·25

(Litho Format)

**1984** (1 May). *Easter. T* **196** *and similar vert designs showing Disney cartoon characters and eggs. Multicoloured. P* 11.

875 ½ c. Type **196** . . 10 10
876 1 c. Mickey Mouse . . 10 10
877 2 c. Tortoise and Hare . . 10 10
878 3 c. Brer Rabbit and Brer Bear . . 10 10
879 4 c. Donald Duck (*different*) . . 10 10
880 5 c. White Rabbit . . 10 10
881 10 c. Thumper . . 10 10
882 $2 Pluto . . 2·75 2·25
883 $4 Pluto (*different*) . . 3·75 3·50
875/83 . . *Set of* 9 6·50 5·75
**MS**884 126 × 100 mm. $5 Chip and Dale. P 13½ × 14 . . 3·25 3·50

197 Gymnastics

198 *Atlantic Star*

(Des R. Sauber. Litho Questa)

**1984** (14 May). *Olympic Games, Los Angeles. T* **197** *and similar vert designs. Multicoloured. P* 14.

885 30 c. Type **197** . . 20 25
886 45 c. Javelin-throwing . . 30 35
887 60 c. High diving . . 40 45
888 $4 Fencing . . 2·00 2·50
885/8 . . *Set of* 4 2·50 3·25
**MS**889 104 × 85 mm. $5 Equestrian event . . 2·75 3·25

(Des W. Wright. Litho Questa)

**1984** (14 June). *Shipping. T* **198** *and similar horiz designs. Multicoloured. P* 14.

890 45 c. Type **198** . . 1·25 60
891 60 c. *Atlantic* (liner) . . 1·50 1·00
892 90 c. Carib fishing boat . . 2·00 1·25
893 $4 *Norway* (liner) . . 4·25 5·50
890/3 . . *Set of* 4 8·00 7·50
**MS**894 106×79 mm. $5 *Santa Maria*, 1492 . . 4·50 5·00

19th UPU
CONGRESS HAMBURG

(199)

200 *Guzmania lingulata*

**1984** (19 June). *Universal Postal Union Congress, Hamburg. Nos.* 769A *and* 780A *optd with T* **199**.

895 10 c. Passion Fruit . . 10 10
896 $5 Heliconia or Lobster Claw . . 3·25 3·50

(Des P. Barrett. Litho Questa)

**1984** (13 Aug). *"Ausipex" International Stamp Exhibition, Melbourne. Bromilaids. T* **200** *and similar vert designs. Multicoloured. P* 14.

897 45 c. Type **200** . . 30 35
898 60 c. *Pitcairnia angustifolia* . . 40 55
899 75 c. *Tillandsia fasciculata* . . 50 75
900 $3 *Aechmea smithiorum* . . 2·00 3·25
897/900 . . *Set of* 4 2·75 4·50
**MS**901 75 × 105 mm. $5 *Tillandsia utriculata* . . 3·25 3·75

201 "The Virgin and Child with Young St John" (Correggio)

202 "Before the Start" (Edgar Degas)

(Litho Format)

**1984** (30 Oct). *450th Death Anniv of Correggio (painter). T* **201** *and similar vert designs. Multicoloured. P* 15.

902 25 c. Type **201** . . 40 20
903 60 c. "Christ bids Farewell to the Virgin Mary" 70 40
904 90 c. "Do not Touch Me" . . 1·00 60
905 $4 "The Mystical Marriage of St Catherine" 2·75 2·75
902/5 . . *Set of* 4 4·25 3·50
**MS**906 89 × 60 mm. $5 "The Adoration of the Magi" . . 3·00 3·50

(Litho Format)

**1984** (30 Oct). *150th Birth Anniv of Edgar Degas (painter). T* **202** *and similar multicoloured designs. P* 15.

907 30 c. Type **202** . . 40 25
908 45 c. "Race on the Racecourse" . . 60 35
909 $1 "Jockeys at the Flagpole" . . 1·00 65
910 $3 "Racehorses at Longchamp" . . 2·25 2·25
907/10 . . *Set of* 4 3·75 3·25
**MS**911 89 × 60 mm. $5 "Self-portrait" (*vert*) . . 3·00 3·50

203 Tabby

204 Avro "748"

(Des. I. MacLaury. Litho Format)

**1984** (12 Nov). *Cats. T* **203** *and similar horiz designs. Multicoloured. P* 15.

912 10 c. Type **203** . . 20 10
913 15 c. Calico Shorthair . . 20 10
914 20 c. Siamese . . 30 15
915 25 c. Manx . . 30 20
916 45 c. Abyssinian . . 55 30
917 60 c. Tortoise-shell Longhair . . 70 40
918 $1 Cornish Rex . . 1·25 75
919 $2 Persian . . 1·75 2·00
920 $3 Himalayan . . 2·50 3·25
921 $5 Burmese . . 3·75 5·50
912/21 . . *Set of* 10 10·50 11·50
**MS**922 105 × 75 mm. $5 Grey Burmese, Persian and American Shorthair . . 3·00 4·50

(Des Bonny Redecker. Litho Questa)

**1984** (26 Nov). *40th Anniv of International Civil Aviation Organisation. T* **204** *and similar vert designs. Multicoloured. P* 14.

923 30 c. Type **204** . . 55 20
924 60 c. Twin "Otter" . . 1·00 40
925 $1 "Islander" . . 1·50 80
926 $3 "Casa" . . 3·00 3·00
923/6 . . *Set of* 4 5·50 4·00
**MS**927 102 × 75 mm. $5 Boeing "747" . . 3·00 3·50

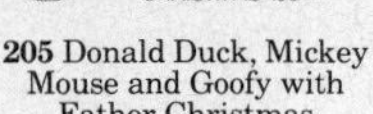


205 Donald Duck, Mickey Mouse and Goofy with Father Christmas

206 Mrs. M. Bascom presenting Trefoil to Chief Guide Lady Baden-Powell

(Litho Questa)

**1984** (30 Nov). *Christmas. Walt Disney Cartoon Characters. T* **205** *and similar vert designs. Multicoloured. P* 12 ($2) *or* 13½ × 14 (*others*).

928 45 c. Type **205** . . 90 30
929 60 c. Donald Duck as Father Christmas with toy train . . 1·10 50
930 90 c. Donald Duck as Father Christmas in sleigh . . 1·60 75
931 $2 Donald Duck and nephews in sledge . . 2·25 1·75
932 $4 Donald Duck in snow with Christmas tree 3·00 2·75
928/32 . . *Set of* 5 8·00 5·50
**MS**933 127 × 102 mm. $5 Donald Duck and nephews opening present . . 3·25 3·50

No. 931 was printed in sheetlets of 8 stamps.

(Des Marlise Najaka. Litho Questa)

**1985** (28 Feb). *75th Anniv of Girl Guide Movement. T* **206** *and similar multicoloured designs. P* 14.

934 35 c. Type **206** . . 50 30
935 45 c. Lady Baden-Powell inspecting Dominican Brownies . . 70 35
936 60 c. Lady Baden-Powell with Mrs. M. Bascom and Mrs. A. Robinson (Guide leaders) . . 85 55
937 $3 Lord and Lady Baden-Powell (*vert*) . . 2·25 2·75
934/7 . . *Set of* 4 4·00 3·50
**MS**938 77 × 105 mm. $5 Flags of Dominica and Girl Guide Movement . . 3·25 3·75

(Litho Questa)

**1985** (4 Apr). *Birth Bicentenary of John J. Audubon (ornithologist) (1st issue). Multicoloured designs as T* **198** *of Antigua showing original paintings. P* 14.

939 45 c. Clapper Rail . . 65 30
940 $1 Black and White Warbler (*vert*) . . 1·25 80
941 $2 Broad-winged Hawk (*vert*) . . 1·75 2·00
942 $3 Ring-necked Duck . . 2·25 2·50
939/42 . . *Set of* 4 5·50 5·00
**MS**943 101×73 mm. $5 Reddish Egret . . 3·25 3·50

Nos. 939/42 were each printed in sheetlets of five stamps and one stamp-size label which appears in the centre of the bottom row.

See also Nos. 1013/17.

207 Student with Computer

208 The Queen Mother visiting Sadlers Wells Opera

(Des BG Studio. Litho Questa)

**1985** (30 Apr). *Duke of Edinburgh's Award Scheme. T* **207** *and similar vert designs. Multicoloured. P* 14.

944 45 c. Type **207** . . 35 30
945 60 c. Assisting doctor in hospital . . 55 40
946 90 c. Two youths hiking . . 75 65
947 $4 Family jogging . . 2·75 3·25
944/7 . . *Set of* 4 4·00 4·25
**MS**948 100×98 mm. $5 Duke of Edinburgh . . 2·75 3·00

(Des J.W. Litho Questa)

**1985** (15 July). *Life and Times of Queen Elizabeth the Queen Mother. T* **208** *and similar vert designs. Multicoloured. P* 14.

949 60 c. Type **208** . . 50 40
950 $1 Fishing in Scotland . . 70 60
951 $3 On her 84th birthday . . 1·90 2·00
949/51 . . *Set of* 3 2·75 2·75
**MS**952 56×85 mm. $5 Attending Garter ceremony, Windsor Castle . . 3·00 3·00

209 Cricket Match ("Sports")

210 Two Players competing for Ball

(Des S. Heinmann. Litho Questa)

**1985** (22 July). *International Youth Year. T* **209** *and similar horiz designs. Multicoloured. P* 14.

953 45 c. Type **209** . . 2·00 80
954 60 c. Bird-watching ("Environmental Study") 2·25 1·00
955 $1 Stamp collecting ("Education") . . 2·50 1·75
956 $3 Boating ("Leisure") . . 3·25 4·50
953/6 . . *Set of* 4 9·00 7·25
**MS**957 96×65 mm. $5 Young people linking hands . . 3·75 4·50

(Des Susan David. Litho Questa)

**1985** (2 Sept). *300th Birth Anniv of Johann Sebastian Bach (composer). Vert designs as T* **206** *of Antigua showing antique musical instruments. P* 14.

958 45 c. multicoloured . . 1·25 40
959 60 c. multicoloured . . 1·50 60
960 $1 multicoloured . . 2·00 1·00
961 $3 multicoloured . . 3·75 3·50
958/61 . . *Set of* 4 7·75 5·00
**MS**962 109×75 mm. $5 black . . 4·00 4·50

Designs:—45 c. Cornett; 60 c. Coiled trumpet; $1 Piccolo; $3 Violoncello piccolo; $5 Johann Sebastian Bach.

(Litho Format)

**1985** (25 Oct). *Royal Visit. Multicoloured designs as T* **207** *of Antigua. P* 14½.

963 60 c. Flags of Great Britain and Dominica . . 1·00 55
964 $1 Queen Elizabeth II (*vert*) . . 1·75 1·50
965 $4 Royal Yacht *Britannia* . . 4·50 5·00
963/5 . . *Set of* 3 6·50 6·25
**MS**966 111×83 mm. $5 Map of Dominica . . 4·00 4·00

(Litho Questa)

**1985** (11 Nov). *150th Birth Anniv of Mark Twain (author). Horiz designs as T* **118** *of Anguilla showing Walt Disney cartoon characters in scenes from "Tom Sawyer". Multicoloured. P* 14×13½.

967 20 c. "The glorious whitewasher" .. .. 25 15
968 60 c. "Aunt Polly's home dentistry" .. .. 60 40
969 $1 "Aunt Polly's pain killer" .. .. 80 60
970 $1.50, Mickey Mouse balancing on fence .. 1·25 85
971 $2 "Lost in the cave with Becky" .. .. 1·50 1·25
967/71 .. .. .. .. *Set of* 5 4·00 3·00
**MS**972 126×101 mm. $5 Mickey Mouse as pirate .. .. .. .. .. .. 3·25 3·50

(Des Walt Disney Productions. Litho Questa)

**1985** (11 Nov). *Birth Bicentenaries of Grimm Brothers (folklorists). Horiz designs as T* **119** *of Anguilla showing Walt Disney cartoon characters in scenes from "Little Red Cap". Multicoloured. P* 14×13½.

973 10 c. Little Red Cap (Daisy Duck) meeting the Wolf .. .. .. .. .. 15 10
974 45 c. The Wolf at the door .. .. .. 40 30
975 90 c. The Wolf in Grandmother's bed .. 80 75
976 $1 The Wolf lunging at Little Red Cap .. 1·00 85
977 $3 The Woodsman (Donald Duck) chasing the Wolf .. .. .. .. .. 2·50 3·25
973/7 .. .. .. .. *Set of* 5 4·25 4·75
**MS**978 126×101 mm. $5 The Wolf falling into cooking pot .. .. .. .. .. 3·25 3·75

(Litho Format)

**1985** (27 Nov). *40th Anniv of United Nations Organization. Horiz designs as T* **208** *of Antigua showing United Nations (New York) stamps. Multicoloured. P* 14½.

979 45 c. Lord Baden-Powell and 1984 International Youth Year 35 c. .. .. 1·00 40
980 $2 Maimonides (physician) and 1966 W.H.O Building 11 c. .. .. .. 3·75 2·25
981 $3 Sir Rowland Hill (postal reformer) and 1976 25th anniv of U.N. Postal Administration 13 c. .. .. .. 3·75 2·50
979/81 .. .. .. .. *Set of* 3 7·75 4·75
**MS**982 110×85 mm. $5 "Apollo" spacecraft .. 3·50 3·75

(Des J. Iskowitz. Litho Questa)

**1986** (26 Mar). *World Cup Football Championship, Mexico. T* **210** *and similar vert designs. Multicoloured. P* 14.

983 45 c. Type **210** .. .. .. .. 1·00 35
984 60 c. Player heading ball .. .. .. 1·10 55
985 $1 Two players competing for ball (*different*) .. .. .. .. .. 1·40 80
986 $3 Player with ball .. .. .. 3·25 3·00
983/6 .. .. .. .. *Set of* 4 6·00 4·25
**MS**987 114×84 mm. $5 Three players .. .. 6·00 7·00

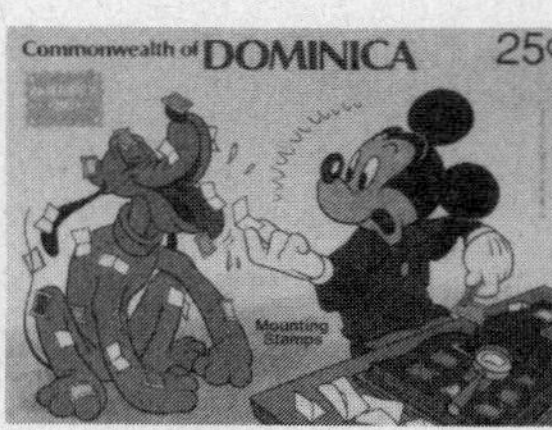

212 Mickey Mouse and Pluto mounting Stamps in Album

213 William I

(Des Walt Disney Productions. Litho Format)

**1986** (22 May). *"Ameripex" International Stamp Exhibition, Chicago. T* **212** *and similar horiz designs showing Walt Disney cartoon characters. Multicoloured. P* 11.

1002 25 c. Type **212** .. .. .. .. 60 40
1003 45 c. Donald Duck examining stamp under magnifying glass .. .. .. 80 65
1004 60 c. Chip n'Dale soaking and drying stamps .. .. .. .. .. 1·10 85
1005 $4 Donald Duck as scoutmaster awarding merit badges to Nephews .. .. 3·50 4·00
1002/5 .. .. .. .. *Set of* 4 5·50 5·50
**MS**1006 127×101 mm. $5 Uncle Scrooge conducting stamp auction. P 14×13½ .. .. 5·50 6·00

(Des Mary Walters. Litho Questa)

**1986** (9 June). *500th Anniv of Succession of House of Tudor to English Throne (1985). T* **213** *and similar vert designs. Multicoloured. P* 14.

1007 10 c. Type **213** .. .. .. .. 30 15
1008 40 c. Richard II .. .. .. .. 70 40
1009 50 c. Henry VIII .. .. .. .. 80 50
1010 $1 Charles II .. .. .. .. 1·40 1·00
1011 $2 Queen Anne .. .. .. .. 2·25 2·50
1012 $4 Queen Victoria .. .. .. 3·25 3·50
1007/12 .. .. .. .. *Set of* 6 8·00 7·25

Nos. 1007/12 were each issued in sheetlets of five stamps and one stamp-size label showing the monarch's consort.

(Litho Questa)

**1986** (18 June). *Birth Bicentenary of John J. Audubon (ornithologist) (1985) (2nd issue). Multicoloured designs as T* **198** *of Antigua showing original paintings. P* 12½×12 (25 c., $4) *or* 12×12½ (*others*).

1013 25 c. Black-throated Diver .. .. .. 1·00 45
1014 60 c. Great Blue Heron (*vert*) .. .. 1·50 95
1015 90 c. Yellow-crowned Night Heron (*vert*) 1·75 1·25
1016 $4 Common Shoveler .. .. .. 4·00 5·00
1013/16 .. .. .. .. *Set of* 4 7·50 7·00
**MS**1017 73×103 mm. $5 Canada Goose. P 14 .. 7·00 7·00

Nos. 1013/16 were each issued in sheetlets of five stamps and one stamp-size label, which appears in the centre of the bottom row.

(Litho Questa)

**1986** (1 July). *Royal Wedding. Vert designs as T* **213** *of Antigua. Multicoloured. P* 14.

1018 45 c. Prince Andrew and Miss Sarah Ferguson .. .. .. .. .. 35 30
1019 60 c. Prince Andrew .. .. .. .. 45 35
1020 $4 Prince Andrew climbing aboard aircraft .. .. .. .. .. 2·25 2·50
1018/20 .. .. .. .. *Set of* 3 2·75 2·75
**MS**1021 88×88 mm. $5 Prince Andrew and Miss Sarah Ferguson (*different*) .. .. .. 3·00 3·50

**1986** (15 Sept). *World Cup Football Championship Winners, Mexico. Nos. 983/7 optd with T* **216** *of Antigua in gold.*

1022 45 c. Type **210** .. .. .. .. 1·00 45
1023 60 c. Player heading ball .. .. .. 1·25 85
1024 $1 Two players competing for ball .. 1·75 1·50
1025 $3 Player with ball .. .. .. 4·25 4·75
1022/5 .. .. .. .. *Set of* 4 7·50 6·75
**MS**1026 114×84 mm. $5 Three players .. .. 6·50 7·00

214 "The Virgin at Prayer"

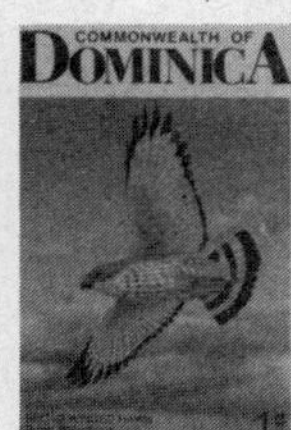

215 Broad-winged Hawk

(Litho Questa)

**1986** (2 Dec). *Christmas. Paintings by Dürer. T* **214** *and similar vert designs. Multicoloured. P* 14.

1027 45 c. Type **214** .. .. .. .. 60 35
1028 60 c. "Madonna and Child" .. .. .. 90 55
1029 $1 "The Madonna with the Pear" .. 1·25 1·00
1030 $3 "Madonna and Child with St. Anne" .. 3·25 4·25
1027/30 .. .. .. .. *Set of* 4 5·50 5·50
**MS**1031 76×102 mm. $5 "The Nativity" .. 6·00 6·50

**1986** (16 Dec). *Appearance of Halley's Comet (2nd issue). Nos. 993/7 optd as T* **218** *of Antigua (in silver on* $5).

1032 5 c. Nasir al Din al Tusi (Persian astronomer) and Jantal Mantar Observatory, Delhi .. .. .. .. .. 10 10
1033 10 c. Bell "X-1" Rocket Plane breaking sound barrier for first time, 1947 .. 10 10
1034 45 c. Halley's Comet of 1531 (from "Astronomicum Caesareum", 1540) .. .. 20 30
1035 $4 Mark Twain and quotation, 1910 .. 1·75 2·25
1032/5 .. .. .. .. *Set of* 4 1·90 2·50
**MS**1036 104×71 mm. $5 Halley's Comet over Dominica .. .. .. .. .. 2·25 3·00

(Des S. Heinmann. Litho Format)

**1987** (20 Jan). *Birds of Dominica. T* **215** *and similar vert designs. Multicoloured. Without imprint date. P* 15.

1037 1 c. Type **215** .. .. .. .. 15 20
1038 2 c. Ruddy Quail Dove .. .. .. 20 30
1039 5 c. Red-necked Pigeon .. .. .. 35 20
1040 10 c. Green Heron .. .. .. .. 35 20
1041 15 c. Moorhen .. .. .. .. 45 25
1042 20 c. Ringed Kingfisher .. .. .. 50 30
1043 25 c. Brown Pelican .. .. .. .. 50 30
1044 35 c. White-tailed Tropic Bird .. .. 55 35
1045 45 c. Red-legged Thrush .. .. .. 60 45
1046 60 c. Purple-throated Carib .. .. 85 55
1047 90 c. Magnificent Frigate Bird .. .. 75 60
1048 $1 Brown Trembler .. .. .. 1·25 85
1049 $2 Black-capped Petrel .. .. .. 2·25 1·75
1050 $5 Barn Owl .. .. .. .. 6·00 5·50
1051 $10 Imperial Parrot .. .. .. 9·00 10·00
1037/51 .. .. .. .. *Set of* 15 21·00 19·00

For similar stamps, with imprint date and perforated 14, see Nos. 1241/54.

(Des J. Iskowitz. Litho Format)

**1987** (16 Feb). *America's Cup Yachting Championship. Multicoloured designs as T* **222** *of Antigua. P* 15.

1052 45 c. *Reliance*, 1903 .. .. .. .. 30 25
1053 60 c. *Freedom*, 1980 .. .. .. .. 35 30
1054 $1 *Mischief*, 1881 .. .. .. .. 55 55
1055 $3 *Australia*, 1977 .. .. .. 1·50 1·75
1052/5 .. .. .. .. *Set of* 4 2·40 2·50
**MS**1056 113×83 mm. $5 *Courageous*, 1977 (*horiz*) .. .. .. .. .. .. 6·00 6·50

(Litho Questa)

**1987** (24 Mar). *Birth Centenary of Marc Chagall (artist). Multicoloured designs as T* **225** *of Antigua. P* 13½×14.

1057 25 c. "Artist and His Model" .. .. 15 15
1058 35 c. "Midsummer Night's Dream" .. 15 20
1059 45 c. "Joseph the Shepherd" .. .. 20 25
1060 60 c. "The Cellist" .. .. .. .. 25 30
1061 90 c. "Woman with Pigs" .. .. .. 40 45
1062 $1 "The Blue Circus" .. .. .. 45 50
1063 $3 "For Vava" .. .. .. .. 1·40 1·50
1064 $4 "The Rider" .. .. .. .. 1·75 1·90
1057/64 .. .. .. .. *Set of* 8 4·25 4·75
**MS**1065 Two sheets, each 110×95 mm. (a) $5 "Purim" (104×89 *mm*). (b) $5 "Firebird" (stage design) (104×89 *mm*) .. *Set of* 2 *sheets* 4·50 5·50

216 Morch Poulsen's Triton

217 *Cantharellus cinnabarinus*

(Des L. Birmingham. Litho Format)

**1987** (11 May). *Sea Shells. T* **216** *and similar designs. P* 15.

1066 35 c. multicoloured .. .. .. .. 20 20
1067 45 c. bluish violet, black and bright rose .. 25 25
1068 60 c. multicoloured .. .. .. .. 30 30
1069 $5 multicoloured .. .. .. .. 2·40 2·40
1066/9 .. .. .. .. *Set of* 4 2·75 2·75
**MS**1070 109×75 mm. $5 multicoloured .. .. 3·25 3·75

Designs: *Vert*—45 c. Swainson Globe Purple Sea Snail; 60 c. Banded Tulip; $5 (No. 1069) Lamarck Deltoid Rock Shell. *Horiz*—$5 (No. **MS**1070) *Junonia volute*.

No. 1066 is inscribed "TIRITON" in error.

(Des BG Studio. Litho Questa)

**1987** (15 June). *"Capex '87" International Stamp Exhibition, Toronto. Mushrooms of Dominica. T* **217** *and similar horiz designs. Multicoloured. P* 14.

1071 45 c. Type **217** .. .. .. .. 55 40
1072 60 c. *Boletellus cubensis* .. .. .. 75 70
1073 $2 *Eccilia cystiophorus* .. .. .. 2·25 2·00
1074 $3 *Xerocomus guadelupae* .. .. .. 2·75 2·75
1071/4 .. .. .. .. *Set of* 4 5·75 5·25
**MS**1075 85×85 mm. $5 *Gymnopilus chrysopellus* 3·75 4·50

218 Discovery of Dominica, 1493

219 "Virgin and Child with St. Anne" (Dürer)

(Des I. MacLaury. Litho Format)

**1987** (27 July). *500th Anniv of Discovery of America (1992) (1st issue). T* **218** *and similar horiz designs. Multicoloured. P* 15.

1076 10 c. Type **218** .. .. .. .. 35 20
1077 15 c. Caribs greeting Columbus's fleet .. 40 20
1078 45 c. Claiming the New World for Spain .. 55 35
1079 60 c. Wreck of *Santa Maria* .. .. .. 70 40
1080 90 c. Fleet leaving Spain .. .. .. 85 70
1081 $1 Sighting the New World .. .. 95 80

211 Police in Rowing Boat pursuing River Pirates, 1890

(Des J. Iskowitz. Litho Questa)

**1986** (27 Mar). *Centenary of Statue of Liberty. T* **211** *and similar multicoloured designs. P* 14.

988 15 c. Type **211** .. .. .. .. 65 30
989 25 c. Police patrol launch, 1986 .. .. 95 35
990 45 c. Hoboken Ferry Terminal, *c* 1890 .. 1·10 45
991 $4 Holland Tunnel entrance and staff, 1986 .. .. .. .. .. 3·50 4·00
988/91 .. .. .. .. *Set of* 4 5·75 4·50
**MS**992 104×76 mm. $5 Statue of Liberty (*vert*) .. 6·00 7·00

(Des W. Hanson. Litho Questa)

**1986** (17 Apr). *Appearance of Halley's Comet. Horiz designs as T* **123** *of Anguilla. Multicoloured. P* 14.

993 5 c. Nasir al Din al Tusi (Persian astronomer) and Jantal Mantar Observatory, Delhi .. .. .. .. .. 10 10
994 10 c. Bell "X-1" Rocket Plane breaking sound barrier for first time, 1947 .. 10 10
995 45 c. Halley's Comet of 1531 (from "Astronomicum Caesareum", 1540) .. .. 35 30
996 $4 Mark Twain and quotation, 1910 .. 2·25 2·50
993/6 .. .. .. .. *Set of* 4 2·50 2·50
**MS**997 104×71 mm. $5 Halley's Comet over Dominica .. .. .. .. .. 2·75 3·50

(Des and litho Questa)

**1986** (5 May). *60th Birthday of Queen Elizabeth II. Vert designs as T* **125** *of Anguilla. P* 14.

998 2 c. multicoloured .. .. .. .. 10 15
999 $1 multicoloured .. .. .. .. 70 70
1000 $4 multicoloured .. .. .. .. 2·25 2·40
998/1000 .. .. .. .. *Set of* 3 2·75 3·00
**MS**1001 120×85mm. $5 black and grey-brown .. 2·75 3·25

Designs:—2 c. Wedding photograph, 1947; $1 Queen meeting Pope John Paul II, 1982; $4 Queen on royal visit, 1971; $5 Princess Elizabeth with corgis, 1936.

1082 $3 Trading with Indians .. .. .. 2·00 2·50
1083 $5 Building settlement .. .. .. 3·00 3·75
1076/83 .. .. .. .. .. *Set of* 8 8·00 8·00
**MS**1084 Two sheets, each 109×79 mm. (a) $5 Fleet off Dominica, 1493. (b) $5 Map showing Columbus's route, 1493 .. *Set of* 2 *sheets* 5·00 6·00
See also Nos. 1221/5 and 1355/63.

(Des G. Welker. Litho Questa)

**1987** (28 Sept). *Milestones of Transportation. Multicoloured designs as T* **226** *of Antigua. P* 14.
1085 10 c. H.M.S. *Warrior* (first ironclad warship), 1860 .. .. .. .. 30 30
1086 15 c. MAGLEV-MLU 001 (fastest passenger train), 1979 .. .. .. 40 40
1087 25 c. *Flying Cloud* (fastest clipper passage New York–San Francisco) (*vert*) .. 50 50
1088 35 c. First elevated railway, New York, 1868 (*vert*) .. .. .. .. 60 60
1089 45 c. *Tom Thumb* (first U.S. passenger locomotive), 1830 .. .. .. .. 60 60
1090 60 c. *Spray* (Slocum's solo circumnavigation), 1895–8 (*vert*) .. .. .. 65 65
1091 90 c. *Sea-Land Commerce* (fastest Pacific passage), 1973 (*vert*) .. .. .. 80 80
1092 $1 First cable cars, San Francisco, 1873 .. 90 90
1093 $3 "Orient Express", 1883 .. .. .. 2·25 2·25
1094 $4 *Clermont* (first commercial steamboat), 1807 .. .. .. .. 2·50 2·50
1085/94 .. .. .. .. *Set of* 10 8·50 8·50

(Litho Questa)

**1987** (16 Nov). *Christmas. Religious Paintings. T* **219** *and similar vert designs. Multicoloured. P* 14.
1095 20 c. Type **219** .. .. .. .. 30 15
1096 25 c. "Virgin and Child" (Murillo) .. .. 30 15
1097 $2 "Madonna and Child" (Foppa) .. .. 1·50 1·50
1098 $4 "Madonna and Child" (Da Verona) .. 2·75 3·25
1095/8 .. .. .. .. .. *Set of* 4 4·25 4·50
**MS**1099 100×78 mm. $5 "Angel of the Annunciation" (anon, Renaissance period) .. .. 2·50 3·00

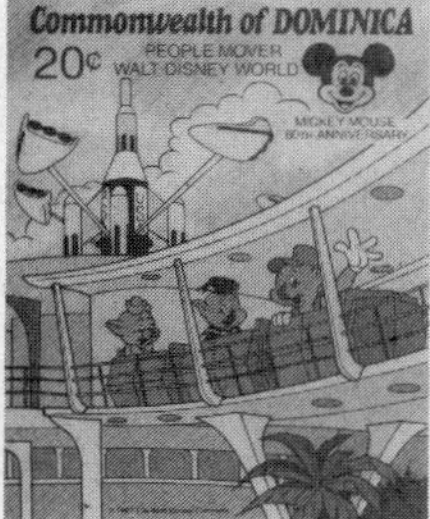

220 Three Little Pigs in People Mover, Walt Disney World

221 Kayak Canoeing

(Des Walt Disney Company. Litho Questa)

**1987** (22 Dec). *60th Anniv of Mickey Mouse (Walt Disney cartoon character). T* **220** *and similar multicoloured designs showing cartoon characters in trains. P* 13½×14.
1100 20 c. Type **220** .. .. .. .. 20 20
1101 25 c. Goofy driving horse tram, Disneyland 20 20
1102 45 c. Donald Duck in *Roger E. Broggie*, Walt Disney World .. .. .. 35 35
1103 60 c. Goofy, Mickey Mouse, Donald Duck and Chip n'Dale aboard Big Thunder Mountain train, Disneyland .. .. 45 45
1104 90 c. Mickey Mouse in *Walter E. Disney*, Disneyland .. .. .. .. 70 70
1105 $1 Mickey and Minnie Mouse, Goofy, Donald and Daisy Duck in monorail, Walt Disney World .. .. .. 80 80
1106 $3 Dumbo flying over *Casey Jr* .. .. 2·00 2·00
1107 $4 Daisy Duck and Minnie Mouse in *Lilly Belle*, Walt Disney World .. .. 2·50 2·50
1100/7 .. .. .. .. *Set of* 8 6·50 6·50
**MS**1108 Two sheets, each 127×101 mm. (a) $5 Seven Dwarfs in Rainbow Caverns Mine train, Disneyland (*horiz*). (b) $5 Donald Duck and Chip n'Dale on toy train (from film *Out of Scale*) (*horiz*). P 14×13½ .. *Set of* 2 *sheets* 4·50 5·50

(Des and litho Questa)

**1988** (15 Feb). *Royal Ruby Wedding. Vert designs as T* **234** *of Antigua. P* 14.
1109 45 c. multicoloured .. .. .. .. 55 25
1110 60 c. deep brown, black and light green .. 70 45
1111 $1 multicoloured .. .. .. .. 90 80
1112 $3 multicoloured .. .. .. .. 2·00 2·50
1109/12 .. .. .. .. *Set of* 4 3·75 3·50
**MS**1113 102×76 mm. $5 multicoloured .. 2·50 3·00
Designs:— 45 c. Wedding portrait with attendants, 1947; 60 c. Princess Elizabeth with Prince Charles, *c.* 1950; $1 Princess Elizabeth and Prince Philip with Prince Charles and Princess Anne, 1950; $3 Queen Elizabeth; $5 Princess Elizabeth in wedding dress, 1947.

(Des D. Miller. Litho Questa)

**1988** (14 Mar). *Olympic Games, Seoul. T* **221** *and similar vert designs. Multicoloured. P* 14.
1114 45 c. Type **221** .. .. .. .. 55 35
1115 60 c. Taekwon-do .. .. .. .. 65 50
1116 $1 High diving .. .. .. .. 90 85
1117 $3 Gymnastics on bars .. .. .. 2·00 2·50
1114/17 .. .. .. .. *Set of* 4 3·75 3·75
**MS**1118 81×110 mm. $5 Football .. .. 2·25 2·75

222 Carib Indian

223 White-tailed Tropic Bird

(Des K. Gromell. Litho Format)

**1988** (13 Apr). *"Reunion '88" Tourism Programme. T* **222** *and similar multicoloured designs. P* 15.
1119 10 c. Type **222** .. .. .. .. 10 10
1120 25 c. Mountainous interior (*horiz*) .. 15 15
1121 35 c. Indian River .. .. .. .. 15 20
1122 60 c. Belaire dancer and tourists .. .. 25 35
1123 90 c. Boiling Lake .. .. .. .. 40 55
1124 $3 Coral reef (*horiz*) .. .. .. 1·40 2·00
1119/24 .. .. .. .. *Set of* 6 2·10 3·00
**MS**1125 112×82 mm. $5 Belaire dancer .. 2·25 3·00

**1988** (1 June). *Stamp Exhibitions. Nos.* **MS**1084 *and* 1092/3 *optd as T* **241** *of Antigua showing various emblems.*
1126 $1 First cable cars, San Francisco, 1873 (optd "FINLANDIA 88", Helsinki) .. 45 50
1127 $3 "Orient Express", 1883 (optd "INDEPENDENCE 40", Israel) .. 1·25 1·40
a. Opt albino .. .. ..
**MS**1128 Two sheets, each 109 × 79 mm. (a) $5 Fleet off Dominica, 1493 (optd "OLYMPHILEX '88", Seoul). (b) $5 Map showing Columbus's route, 1493 (optd "Praga '88", Prague) *Set of* 2 *sheets* 4·25 4·75

(Des S. Barlow. Litho Questa)

**1988** (25 July). *Dominica Rain Forest Flora and Fauna. T* **223** *and similar vert designs. Multicoloured. P* 14½×14.
1129 45 c. Type **223** .. .. .. .. 40 40
a. Sheetlet. Nos. 1129/48 .. .. 7·25
1130 45 c. Blue-throated Euphonia .. .. 40 40
1131 45 c. Smooth-billed Ani .. .. .. 40 40
1132 45 c. Scaly-breasted Thrasher .. .. 40 40
1133 45 c. Purple-throated Carib .. .. 40 40
1134 45 c. *Marpesia petreus* and *Strymon maesites* (butterflies) .. .. 40 40
1135 45 c. Trembler .. .. .. .. 40 40
1136 45 c. Imperial Parrot .. .. .. 40 40
1137 45 c. Mangrove Cuckoo .. .. .. 40 40
1138 45 c. *Dynastes hercules* (beetle) .. .. 40 40
1139 45 c. *Historis odius* (butterfly) .. .. 40 40
1140 45 c. Red-necked Parrot .. .. .. 40 40
1141 45 c. Tillandsia (plant) .. .. .. 40 40
1142 45 c. Bananaquit and *Polystacha luteola* (plant) .. .. .. .. 40 40
1143 45 c. False Chameleon .. .. .. 40 40
1144 45 c. Iguana .. .. .. .. 40 40
1145 45 c. *Hypolimnas misippus* (butterfly) .. 40 40
1146 45 c. Green-throated Carib .. .. 40 40
1147 45 c. Heliconia (plant) .. .. .. 40 40
1148 45 c. Agouti .. .. .. .. 40 40
1129/48 .. .. .. .. *Set of* 20 7·25 7·25
Nos. 1129/48 were printed together, *se-tenant*, in a sheetlet of 20 forming a composite design.

224 Battery Hens

225 Gary Cooper

(Des J. Martin. Litho Questa)

**1988** (5 Sept). *10th Anniv of International Fund for Agricultural Development. T* **224** *and similar multicoloured designs. P* 14.
1149 45 c. Type **224** .. .. .. .. 40 30
1150 60 c. Pig .. .. .. .. .. 55 45
1151 90 c. Cattle .. .. .. .. .. 75 75
1152 $3 Black Belly Sheep .. .. .. 1·75 2·00
1149/52 .. .. .. .. *Set of* 4 3·00 3·25
**MS**1153 95×68 mm. $5 Tropical fruits (*vert*) .. 2·25 2·75

(Des Lynda Bruscheni. Litho Questa)

**1988** (8 Sept). *Entertainers. T* **225** *and similar vert designs. Multicoloured. P* 14.
1154 10 c. Type **225** .. .. .. .. 30 20
1155 35 c. Josephine Baker .. .. .. 40 35
1156 45 c. Maurice Chevalier .. .. .. 45 35
1157 60 c. James Cagney .. .. .. .. 50 40
1158 $1 Clark Gable .. .. .. .. 70 60
1159 $2 Louis Armstrong .. .. .. 1·10 1·10
1160 $3 Liberace .. .. .. .. 1·60 1·75
1161 $4 Spencer Tracy .. .. .. .. 2·00 2·50
1154/61 .. .. .. .. *Set of* 8 6·25 6·50
**MS**1162 Two sheets, each 105×75 mm. (a) $5 Humphrey Bogart. (b) $5 Elvis Presley. *Set of* 2 *sheets* 4·25 4·75

(Des Mary Walters. Litho Questa)

**1988** (29 Sept). *Flowering Trees. Horiz designs as T* **242** *of Antigua. Multicoloured. P* 14.
1163 15 c. Sapodilla .. .. .. .. 10 10
1164 20 c. Tangerine .. .. .. .. 10 10
1165 25 c. Avocado Pear .. .. .. .. 10 10
1166 45 c. Amherstia .. .. .. .. 20 25
1167 90 c. Lipstick Tree .. .. .. .. 40 45
1168 $1 Cannonball Tree .. .. .. 45 50
1169 $3 Saman .. .. .. .. .. 1·25 1·40
1170 $4 Pineapple .. .. .. .. 1·60 1·75
1163/70 .. .. .. .. *Set of* 8 3·75 4·25
**MS**1171 Two sheets, each 96 × 66 mm. (a) $5 Lignum Vitae. (b) $5 Sea Grape *Set of* 2 *sheets* 4·50 5·50

(Litho Questa)

**1988** (10 Oct). *500th Birth Anniv of Titian (artist). Vert designs as T* **238** *of Antigua. Multicoloured. P* 13½ × 14.
1172 25 c. "Jacopo Strada" .. .. .. 10 15
1173 35 c. "Titian's Daughter Lavinia" .. .. 15 20
1174 45 c. "Andrea Navagero" .. .. .. 20 25
1175 60 c. "Judith with Head of Holoferenes" .. 25 30
1176 $1 "Emilia di Spilimbergo" .. .. 45 50
1177 $2 "Martyrdom of St. Lawrence" .. .. 80 85
1178 $3 "Salome" .. .. .. .. 1·25 1·40
1179 $4 "St. John the Baptist" .. .. .. 1·60 1·75
1172/9 .. .. .. .. *Set of* 8 4·25 4·75
**MS**1180 Two sheets, each 110 × 95 mm. (a) $5 "Self Portrait". (b) $5 "Sisyphus" *Set of* 2 *sheets* 4·25 4·75

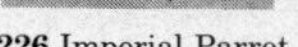
226 Imperial Parrot

227 President and Mrs. Kennedy

(Des K. Gromell. Litho Questa)

**1988** (31 Oct). *10th Anniv of Independence. T* **226** *and similar multicoloured designs. P* 14.
1181 20 c. Type **226** .. .. .. .. 35 15
1182 45 c. Dominica 1874 1d. stamp and landscape (*horiz*) .. .. .. .. 40 25
1183 $2 1978 Independence 10 c. stamp and landscape (*horiz*) .. .. .. 1·00 1·25
1184 $3 Carib Wood (national flower) .. .. 1·60 2·00
1181/4 .. .. .. .. *Set of* 4 2·40 2·75
**MS**1185 116 × 85 mm. $5 Government Band (*horiz*) .. .. .. .. .. 2·10 2·50

(Des J. Martin. Litho Questa)

**1988** (22 Nov). *25th Death Anniv of John F. Kennedy (American statesman). T* **227** *and similar multicoloured designs. P* 14.
1186 20 c. Type **227** .. .. .. .. 10 10
1187 25 c. Kennedy sailing .. .. .. 10 10
1188 $2 Outside Hyannis Port house .. .. 80 1·00
1189 $4 Speaking in Berlin (*vert*) .. .. 1·60 2·00
1186/9 .. .. .. .. *Set of* 4 2·40 2·75
**MS**1190 100 × 71 mm. $5 President Kennedy (*vert*) .. .. .. .. .. 2·10 2·50

228 Donald Duck's Nephews decorating Christmas Tree

229 Raoul Wallenberg (diplomat) and Swedish Flag

(Des Walt Disney Co. Litho Questa)

**1988** (1 Dec). *Christmas. "Mickey's Christmas Mall". T* **228** *and similar vert designs showing Walt Disney cartoon characters. Multicoloured. P* 13½ × 14.
1191 60 c. Type **228** .. .. .. .. 35 35
a. Sheetlet. Nos. 1191/8 .. .. 2·50
1192 60 c. Daisy Duck outside clothes shop .. 35 35
1193 60 c. Winnie the Pooh in shop window .. 35 35
1194 60 c. Goofy with parcels .. .. .. 35 35
1195 60 c. Donald Duck as Father Christmas .. 35 35
1196 60 c. Mickey Mouse contributing to collection .. .. .. .. 35 35
1197 60 c. Minnie Mouse .. .. .. .. 35 35
1198 60 c. Chip n' Dale with peanut .. .. 35 35
1191/8 .. .. .. .. *Set of* 8 2·50 2·50
**MS**1199 Two sheets, each 127 × 102 mm. (a) $6 Mordie Mouse with Father Christmas. (b) $6 Mickey Mouse at West Indian market *Set of* 2 *sheets* 5·00 6·50
Nos. 1191/8 were printed together, *se-tenant* as a composite design, in sheetlets of eight.

(Des J. Genzo. Litho B.D.T.)

988 (9 Dec). *40th Anniv of Universal Declaration of Human Rights. T* **229** *and similar multicoloured design. P* 14.
200 $3 Type **229** .. .. 1·25 1·40
IS1201 92 × 62 mm. $5 Human Rights Day logo (*vert*) .. .. 2·50 3·00

**230** Greater Amberjack

(Des J. Iskowitz. Litho Questa)

988 (22 Dec). *Game Fishes. T* **230** *and similar horiz designs. Multicoloured. P* 14.
202 10 c. Type **230** .. 15 10
203 15 c. Blue Marlin .. 15 10
204 35 c. Cobia .. 25 20
205 45 c. Dolphin Fish .. 35 25
206 60 c. Cero .. 45 40
207 90 c. Mahogany Snapper .. 65 55
208 $3 Yellowfin Tuna .. 2·00 2·50
209 $4 Rainbow Parrotfish .. 2·50 3·00
202/9 .. *Set of* 8 6·00 6·50
IS1210 Two sheets, each 104×74 mm. (a) $5 Manta Ray. (b) $5 Tarpon .. *Set of* 2 *sheets* 6·00 7·00

**231** Leatherback Turtle

Men's c-1, 500m
O. Heukrodt DDR

(**232**)

(Des W. Wright. Litho Questa)

988 (29 Dec). *Insects and Reptiles. T* **231** *and similar horiz designs. Multicoloured. P* 14.
211 10 c. Type **231** .. 30 15
212 25 c. *Danaus plexippus* (butterfly) .. 70 25
213 60 c. Green Anole (lizard) .. 80 55
214 $3 *Mantis religiosa* (mantid) .. 2·50 3·00
211/14 .. *Set of* 4 4·00 3·50
IS1215 119×90 mm. $5 *Dynastes hercules* (beetle) .. 3·00 3·50

989 (20 Mar). *Olympic Medal Winners, Seoul. Nos.* 1114/18 *optd as T* **232** *(horizontally on No.* **MS**1220*).*
216 45 c. Type **221** (optd with T **232**) .. 20 25
217 60 c. Taekwon-do (optd "Women's Fly-weight N. Y. Choo S. Korea") .. 25 30
218 $1 High diving (optd "Women's Platform Y. Xu China") .. 40 45
219 $3 Gymnastics on bars (optd "V. Artemov USSR") .. 1·25 1·40
216/19 .. *Set of* 4 1·90 2·10
IS1220 81×110 mm. $5 Football (optd "USSR defeated Brazil 3-2 on penalty kicks after a 1-1 tie") .. 2·10 2·25

(Des D. Miller. Litho Questa)

989 (8 May). *500th Anniv of Discovery of America by Columbus (1992) (2nd issue). Pre-Columbian Carib Society. Designs as T* **247** *of Antigua, but horiz. Multicoloured. P* 14.
221 20 c. Carib canoe .. 10 10
222 35 c. Hunting with bows and arrows .. 15 20
223 $1 Dugout canoe making .. 40 45
224 $3 Shield contest .. 1·25 1·40
221/4 .. *Set of* 4 1·75 1·90
IS1225 87×71 mm. $6 Ceremonial dance .. 2·50 2·75

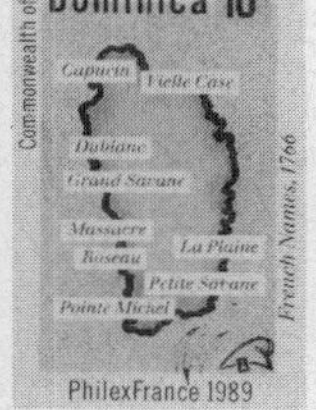

**233** Map of Dominica, 1766
**234** *Papilio homerus*

(Des U. Purins. Litho B.D.T.)

989 (17 July). *"Philexfrance 89" International Stamp Exhibition, Paris. T* **233** *and similar multicoloured designs. P* 14.
226 10 c. Type **233** .. 10 10
227 35 c. French coin of 1653 (*horiz*) .. 15 20
228 $1 French warship, 1720 (*horiz*) .. 40 45
229 $4 Coffee plant (*horiz*) .. 1·75 1·90
226/9 .. *Set of* 4 2·10 2·40
MS1230 98×98 mm. $5 Exhibition inscription (*horiz*) (black, grey and greenish yellow) .. 2·10 2·25

(Litho Questa)

**1989** (31 Aug). *Japanese Art. Paintings by Taikan. Designs as T* **250** *of Antigua, but vert. Multicoloured. P* 13½×14.
1231 10 c. "Lao-tzu" (detail) .. 10 10
1232 20 c. "Red Maple Leaves" (panels 1 and 2) 10 10
1233 45 c. "King Wen Hui learns a Lesson from his Cook" (detail) .. 20 25
1234 60 c. "Red Maple Leaves" (panels 3 and 4) 25 30
1235 $1 "Wild Flowers" (detail) .. 40 45
1236 $2 "Red Maple Leaves" (panels 5 and 6) 85 90
1237 $3 "Red Maple Leaves" (panels 7 and 8) 1·25 1·40
1238 $4 "Indian Ceremony of Floating Lamps on the River" (detail) .. 1·75 1·90
1231/8 .. *Set of* 8 4·25 4·75
**MS**1239 Two sheets (a) 78×102 mm. $5 "Innocence" (detail). (b) 101×77 mm. $5 "Red Maple Leaves" (detail) .. *Set of* 2 *sheets* 4·25 4·50

Nos. 1231/8 were each printed in sheetlets of 10 containing two vertical strips of 5 stamps separated by printed labels commemorating Emperor Hirohito.

(Litho Questa)

**1989** (31 Aug). *As Nos.* 1038/46 *and* 1048/51 *but with imprint date ("1989"). P* 14.
1241 2 c. Ruddy Quail Dove .. 15 20
1242 5 c. Red-necked Pigeon .. 20 15
1243 10 c. Green Heron .. 20 15
1244 15 c. Moorhen .. 20 15
1245 20 c. Ringed Kingfisher .. 20 20
1246 25 c. Brown Pelican .. 20 20
1247 35 c. White-tailed Tropic Bird .. 30 25
1248 45 c. Red-legged Thrush .. 35 30
1249 60 c. Purple-throated Carib .. 50 40
1251 $1 Brown Trembler .. 60 50
1252 $2 Black-capped Petrel .. 1·25 1·25
1253 $5 Barn Owl .. 4·25 4·25
1254 $10 Imperial Parrot .. 7·50 8·50
a. Perf 12 .. 7·50 8·50
1241/54 .. *Set of* 13 14·00 14·00

(Des W. Wright. Litho Questa)

**1989** (11 Sept). *Butterflies. T* **234** *and similar horiz designs. Multicoloured. P* 14.
1255 10 c. Type **234** .. 10 10
1256 15 c. *Morpho peleides* .. 10 10
1257 25 c. *Dryas julia* .. 10 15
1258 35 c. *Parides gundlachianus* .. 15 20
1259 60 c. *Danaus plexippus* .. 25 30
1260 $1 *Agraulis vanillae* .. 40 45
1261 $3 *Phoebis avellaneda* .. 1·25 1·40
1262 $5 *Papilio andraemon* .. 2·10 2·25
1255/62 .. *Set of* 8 4·00 4·25
**MS**1263 Two sheets. (a) 105×74 mm. $6 *Adelpha cytherea*. (b) 105×79 mm. $6 *Adelpha iphicla* *Set of* 2 *sheets* 5·00 5·25

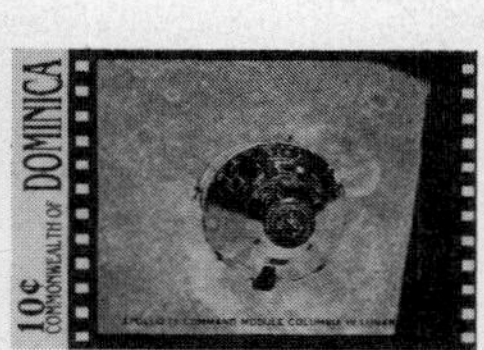


**235** *Oncidium pusillum*
**236** "Apollo 11" Command Module in Lunar Orbit

(Des W. Hanson Studio. Litho Questa)

**1989** (28 Sept). *Orchids. T* **235** *and similar vert designs. Multicoloured. P* 14.
1264 10 c. Type **235** .. 10 10
1265 35 c. *Epidendrum cochleata* .. 15 20
1266 45 c. *Epidendrum ciliare* .. 20 25
1267 60 c. *Cyrtopodium andersonii* .. 25 30
1268 $1 *Habenaria pauciflora* .. 40 45
1269 $2 *Maxillaria alba* .. 85 90
1270 $3 *Selenipedium palmifolium* .. 1·25 1·40
1271 $4 *Brassavola cucullata* .. 1·75 1·90
1264/71 .. *Set of* 8 4·50 5·00
**MS**1272 Two sheets, each 108×77 mm. (a) $5 *Oncidium lanceanum*. (b) $5 *Comparettia falcata* *Set of* 2 *sheets* 4·25 4·50

(Litho Questa)

**1989** (31 Oct). *20th Anniv of First Manned Landing on Moon. T* **236** *and similar multicoloured designs. P* 14.
1273 10 c. Type **236** .. 10 10
1274 60 c. Neil Armstrong leaving lunar module 25 30
1275 $2 Edwin Aldrin at Sea of Tranquility .. 85 90
1276 $3 Astronauts Armstrong and Aldrin with U.S. flag .. 1·25 1·40
1273/6 .. *Set of* 4 2·10 2·40
**MS**1277 62×77 mm. $6 Launch of "Apollo 11" (*vert*) .. 2·50 2·75

**237** Brazil v Italy Final, 1970

(Des G. Vasarhelyi. Litho Questa)

**1989** (8 Nov). *World Cup Football Championship, Italy. T* **237** *and similar horiz designs. Multicoloured. P* 14.
1278 $1 Type **237** .. 40 45
a. Sheetlet. Nos. 1278/81 .. 1·40
1279 $1 England v. West Germany, 1966 .. 40 45
1280 $1 West Germany v. Holland, 1974 .. 40 45
1281 $1 Italy v. West Germany, 1982 .. 40 45
1278/81 .. *Set of* 4 1·40 1·60
**MS**1282 106×86 mm. $6 Two players competing for ball .. 2·50 2·75

Nos. 1278/81 were printed together, *se-tenant*, in a sheetlet of 4 stamps, forming a composite central design of a football surrounded by flags of competing nations.

**238** George Washington and Inauguration, 1789

(Des W. Hanson Studio. Litho Questa)

**1989** (17 Nov). *"World Stamp Expo '89" International Stamp Exhibition, Washington (1st issue). Bicentenary of the U.S. Presidency. T* **238** *and similar horiz designs. Multicoloured. P* 14.
1283 60 c. Type **238** .. 25 30
a. Sheetlet. Nos. 1283/8 .. 1·50
1284 60 c. John Adams and Presidential Mansion, 1800 .. 25 30
1285 60 c. Thomas Jefferson, Graff House, Philadelphia and Declaration of Independence .. 25 30
1286 60 c. James Madison and U.S.S. *Constitution* defeating H.M.S. *Guerriere*, 1812 .. 25 30
1287 60 c. James Monroe and freed slaves landing in Liberia .. 25 30
1288 60 c. John Quincy Adams and barge on Erie Canal .. 25 30
1289 60 c. Millard Fillmore and Perry's fleet off Japan .. 25 30
a. Sheetlet. Nos. 1289/94 .. 1·50
1290 60 c. Franklin Pierce, Jefferson Davis and San Xavier Mission, Tucson .. 25 30
1291 60 c. James Buchanan, "Buffalo Bill" Cody carrying mail and Wells Fargo Pony Express stamp .. 25 30
1292 60 c. Abraham Lincoln and U.P.U. Monument, Berne .. 25 30
1293 60 c. Andrew Johnson, polar bear and Mt. McKinley, Alaska .. 25 30
1294 60 c. Ulysses S. Grant and Golden Spike Ceremony, 1869 .. 25 30
1295 60 c. Theodore Roosevelt and steam shovel excavating Panama Canal .. 25 30
a. Sheetlet. Nos. 1295/1300 .. 1·50
1296 60 c. William H. Taft and Admiral Peary at North Pole .. 25 30
1297 60 c. Woodrow Wilson and Curtis "Jenny" on first scheduled airmail flight, 1918 25 30
1298 60 c. Warren G. Harding and airship U.S.S. *Shenandoah* at Lakehurst .. 25 30
1299 60 c. Calvin Coolidge and Lindbergh's *Spirit of St. Louis* on trans-Atlantic flight .. 25 30
1300 60 c. Mt. Rushmore National Monument 25 30
1301 60 c. Lyndon B. Johnson and Earth from Moon as seen by "Apollo 8" crew .. 25 30
a. Sheetlet. Nos. 1301/6 .. 1·50
1302 60 c. Richard Nixon and visit to Great Wall of China .. 25 30
1303 60 c. Gerald Ford and *Gorch Fock* at Bicentenary of Revolution celebrations .. 25 30
1304 60 c. Jimmy Carter and Pres. Sadat of Egypt with Prime Minister Begin of Israel .. 25 30
1305 60 c. Ronald Reagan and space shuttle *Columbia* .. 25 30
1306 60 c. George Bush and Grumman "Avenger" (fighter-bomber) .. 25 30
1283/1306 .. *Set of* 24 5·50 6·50

Nos. 1283/8, 1289/94, 1295/1300 and 1301/6 were each printed together, *se-tenant*, in sheetlets of six stamps.

(Des Design Element. Litho Questa)

**1989** (17 Nov). *"Expo '89" International Stamp Exhibition, Washington (2nd issue). Landmarks of Washington. Sheet* 77×62 *mm. containing horiz design as T* **257** *of Antigua. Multicoloured. P* 14.
**MS**1307 $4 The Capitol .. 1·75 1·90

(Des Walt Disney Co. Litho Questa)

**1989** (30 Nov). *Mickey Mouse in Hollywood. Horiz designs as T* **267** *of Antigua showing Walt Disney cartoon characters. Multicoloured. P* 14×13½.
1308 20 c. Mickey Mouse reading script .. 10 10
1309 35 c. Mickey Mouse giving interview .. 15 20
1310 45 c. Mickey and Minnie Mouse with newspaper and magazines .. 20 25
1311 60 c. Mickey Mouse signing autographs 25 30
1312 $1 Trapped in dressing room .. 40 45
1313 $2 Mickey and Minnie Mouse with Pluto in limousine .. 85 90
1314 $3 Arriving at Awards ceremony .. 1·25 1·40
1315 $4 Mickey Mouse accepting award .. 1·75 1·90
1308/15 .. *Set of* 8 4·50 5·00
**MS**1316 Two sheets, each 127×102 mm. (a) $5 Mickey Mouse leaving footprints at cinema. (b) $5 Goofy interviewing .. *Set of* 2 *sheets* 4·25 4·50

(Litho Questa)

**1989** (4 Dec). *Christmas. Paintings by Botticelli. Vert designs as T* **259** *of Antigua. Multicoloured. P* 14.
1317 20 c. "Madonna in Glory with Seraphim" .. 10 10
1318 25 c. "The Annunciation" .. .. 10 15
1319 35 c. "Madonna of the Pomegranate" .. 15 20
1320 45 c. "Madonna of the Rosegarden" .. 20 25
1321 60 c. "Madonna of the Book" .. .. 25 30
1322 $1 "Madonna under a Baldachin" .. 40 45
1323 $4 "Madonna and Child with Angels" 1·75 1·90
1324 $5 "Bardi Madonna" .. .. 2·10 2·25
1317/24 .. .. .. .. *Set of* 8 4·50 5·00
**MS**1325 Two sheets, each 71×96 mm. (a) $5 "The Mystic Nativity". (b) $5 "The Adoration of the Magi" .. .. .. *Set of* 2 *sheets* 4·25 4·50

**240** Lady Olave Baden-Powell and Agatha Robinson

**241** Jawaharlal Nehru

(Des A. Fagbohun. Litho Questa)

**1989** (27 Dec). *60th Anniv of Girl Guides in Dominica. T* **240** *and similar multicoloured design showing Guide leaders. P* 14.
1326 60 c. Type **240** .. .. .. .. .. 25 30
**MS**1327 70×99 mm. $5 Dorris Stockmann and Judith Pestaina (*horiz*) .. .. .. .. 2·10 2·25

(Des A. Fagbohun. Litho Questa)

**1989** (29 Dec). *Birth Centenary of Jawaharlal Nehru (Indian statesman). T* **241** *and similar multicoloured design. P* 14.
1328 60 c. Type **241** .. .. .. .. .. 25 30
**MS**1329 101×72 mm. $5 Parliament House, New Delhi (*horiz*) .. .. .. .. 2·10 2·25

**242** Cocoa Damselfish

(Des P. Chinelli. Litho Questa)

**1990** (21 May). *Tropical Fishes. T* **242** *and similar horiz designs. Multicoloured. P* 14.
1330 45 c. Type **242** .. .. .. .. 20 25
a. Sheetlet. Nos. 1330/47 .. .. 3·25
1331 45 c. Stinging Jellyfish .. .. .. 20 25
1332 45 c. Dolphin Fish .. .. .. 20 25
1333 45 c. Queen Angelfish .. .. .. 20 25
1334 45 c. French Angelfish .. .. .. 20 25
1335 45 c. Blue-striped Grunt .. .. .. 20 25
1336 45 c. Pork Fish .. .. .. 20 25
1337 45 c. Hammerhead Shark .. .. 20 25
1338 45 c. Spadefish .. .. .. 20 25
1339 45 c. Great Barracuda .. .. .. 20 25
1340 45 c. Stingray .. .. .. 20 25
1341 45 c. Black Grunt .. .. .. 20 25
1342 45 c. Two-spotted Butterflyfish .. .. 20 25
1343 45 c. Dog Snapper .. .. .. 20 25
1344 45 c. Southern Puffer .. .. .. 20 25
1345 45 c. Four-eyed Butterflyfish .. .. 20 25
1346 45 c. Lane Snapper .. .. .. 20 25
1347 45 c. Green Moray .. .. .. 20 25
1330/47 .. .. .. .. *Set of* 18 3·25 4·00
Nos. 1330/47 were printed together, *se-tenant*, in sheetlets of 18, forming a composite design.

**243** St. Paul's Cathedral, London, *c.* 1840

**244** Blue-headed Hummingbird

(Des M. Pollard. Litho B.D.T.)

**1990** (18 June). *150th Anniv of the Penny Black and "Stamp World London 90" International Stamp Exhibition. T* **243** *and similar square designs. P* $13^1/_2$.
1348 45 c. deep blue-green and black .. .. 20 25
1349 50 c. greenish blue and black .. .. 20 25
1350 60 c. greenish blue and black .. .. 25 30
1351 90 c. deep blue-green and black .. .. 40 45
1352 $3 deep ultramarine and black .. .. 1·25 1·40
1353 $4 deep ultramarine and black .. .. 1·75 1·90
1348/53 .. .. .. .. *Set of* 6 3·75 4·25
**MS**1354 Two sheets. (a) 103×79 mm. $5 brown-ochre and black. (b) 85×86 mm. $5 dull vermilion and blackish brown .. *Set of* 2 *sheets* 4·25 4·50
Designs:—50 c. British Post Office "accelerator" carriage, 1830; 60 c. St. Paul's and City of London; 90 c. Travelling post office, 1838; $3 "Hen and chickens" delivery cycle, 1883; $4 London skyline; $5 (a) As Type **243**; (b) Motor mail van, 1899.

(Des Mary Walters. Litho B.D.T.)

**1990** (19 July). *500th Anniv of Discovery of America by Columbus (1992) (3rd issue). New World Natural History–Seashells. Vert designs as T* **260** *of Antigua. Multicoloured. P* 14.
1355 10 c. Reticulated Cowrie-helmet .. .. 10 10
1356 20 c. West Indian Chank .. .. .. 10 10
1357 35 c. West Indian Fighting Conch .. 15 20
1358 60 c. True Tulip .. .. .. .. 25 30
1359 $1 Sunrise Tellin .. .. .. 40 45
1360 $2 Crown Cone .. .. .. .. 85 90
1361 $3 Common Dove Shell .. .. 1·25 1·40
1362 $4 Atlantic Fig Shell .. .. .. 1·75 1·90
1355/62 .. .. .. .. *Set of* 8 4·25 4·75
**MS**1363 Two sheets, each 102×70 mm. (a) $5 King Helmet. (b) $5 Giant Tun *Set of* 2 *sheets* 4·25 4·50

(Des Mary Walters. Litho B.D.T.)

**1990** (26 July). *Birds. T* **244** *and similar vert designs. Multicoloured. P* 14.
1364 10 c. Type **244** .. .. .. .. 10 10
1365 20 c. Black-capped Petrel .. .. .. 10 10
1366 45 c. Red-necked Amazon .. .. .. 20 25
1367 60 c. Black Swift .. .. .. .. 25 30
1368 $1 Troupial .. .. .. .. 40 45
1369 $2 Common Noddy .. .. .. 85 90
1370 $4 Lesser Antillean Pewee .. .. 1·75 1·90
1371 $5 Little Blue Heron .. .. .. 2·10 2·25
1364/71 .. .. .. .. *Set of* 8 5·25 5·50
**MS**1372 Two sheets, each 103×70 mm. (a) $6 Imperial Amazon. (b) $6 House Wren *Set of* 2 *sheets* 5·00 5·25

(Litho Questa)

**1990** (10 Sept). *90th Birthday of Queen Elizabeth the Queen Mother. Vert designs as T* **266** *of Antigua showing recent photographs of The Queen Mother. P* 14.
1373 20 c. multicoloured .. .. .. .. 10 10
1374 45 c. multicoloured .. .. .. .. 20 25
1375 60 c. multicoloured .. .. .. .. 25 30
1376 $3 multicoloured .. .. .. .. 1·25 1·40
1373/6 .. .. .. .. *Set of* 4 1·60 1·90
**MS**1377 80×90 mm. $5 multicoloured .. .. 2·10 2·25

(Des B. Grout. Litho Questa)

**1990** (6 Nov). *Olympic Games, Barcelona (1992). Vert designs as T* **268** *of Antigua. Multicoloured. P* 14.
1378 45 c. Tennis .. .. .. .. 20 25
1379 60 c. Fencing .. .. .. .. 25 30
1380 $2 Swimming .. .. .. .. 85 90
1381 $3 Yachting .. .. .. .. 1·25 1·40
1378/81 .. .. .. .. *Set of* 4 2·25 2·50
**MS**1382 100×70 mm. $5 Rowing .. .. 2·10 2·25

**245** Barnes, England

(Des Young Phillips Studio. Litho Questa)

**1990** (6 Nov). *World Cup Football Championship, Italy. T* **245** *and similar multicoloured designs. P* 14.
1383 15 c. Type **245** .. .. .. .. 10 10
1384 45 c. Romario, Brazil .. .. .. 20 25
1385 60 c. Franz Beckenbauer, West Germany manager .. .. .. .. 25 30
1386 $4 Lindenberger, Austria .. .. 1·75 1·90
1383/6 .. .. .. .. *Set of* 4 2·00 2·25
**MS**1387 Two sheets, each 105×90 mm. (a) $6 McGrath, Ireland (*vert*). (b) $6 Litovchenko, Soviet Union (*vert*) .. .. *Set of* 2 *sheets* 5·00 5·25

**246** Mickey Mouse riding Herschell-Spillman Frog

(Des Walt Disney Co. Litho Questa)

**1990** (13 Dec). *Christmas. T* **246** *and similar multicoloured designs showing Walt Disney cartoon characters and American carousel animals. P* $13^1/_2$×14.
1388 10 c. Type **246** .. .. .. .. 10 10
1389 15 c. Huey, Duey and Louie on Allan Herschell elephant .. .. .. 10 10
1390 25 c. Donald Duck on Allan Herschell polar bear .. .. .. .. 10 15
1391 45 c. Goofy on Dentzel goat .. .. 20 25
1392 $1 Donald Duck on Zalar giraffe .. 40 45
1393 $2 Daisy Duck on Herschell-Spillman stork .. .. .. .. 85 90
1394 $4 Goofy on Dentzel lion .. .. 1·75 1·90
1395 $5 Daisy Duck on Stein and Goldstein palomino stander .. .. .. 2·10 2·25
1388/95 .. .. .. .. *Set of* 8 5·00 5·50
**MS**1396 Two sheets, each 127×101mm. (a) $6 Mickey, Morty and Ferdie Mouse on Philadelphia Toboggan Company swan chariot (*horiz*). P 14×$13^1/_2$. (b) $6 Mickey and Minnie Mouse with Goofy on Philadelphia Toboggan Company winged griffin chariot. P $13^1/_2$×14 *Set of* 2 *sheets* 5·00 5·25

**247** Glion-Roches De Naye Locomotive, 1890

(Des W. Hanson Studio. Litho Walsall)

**1991** (26 Mar). *Cog Railways. T* **247** *and similar multicoloured designs. P* 14.
1397 10 c. Type **247** .. .. .. .. 10 10
1398 35 c. Electric railcar on Mt Pilatus .. 15 20
1399 45 c. Cog railway line to Schynige Platte 20 25
1400 60 c. Bugnli Viaduct, Furka-Oberalp line (*vert*) .. .. .. .. 25 30
1401 $1 Jungfrau train, 1910 .. .. 40 45
1402 $2 Testing Pike's Peak railcar, Switzerland, 1983 .. .. .. .. 85 90
1403 $4 Brienz-Rothorn steam train, 1991 .. 1·75 1·90
1404 $5 Arth-rigi steam locomotive, 1890 .. 2·10 2·25
1397/1404 .. .. .. .. *Set of* 8 5·25 5·75
**MS**1405 Two sheets. (a) 100×70 mm. $6 Swiss Europa stamp of 1983 showing Riggenbach's locomotive of 1871 (50×37 *mm*). (b) 90×68 mm. $6 Brunig line train and Sherlock Holmes. (50×37 *mm*). P $13^1/_2$ .. .. *Set of* 2 *sheets* 5·00 5·25

(Des T. Agans. Litho Questa)

**1991** (8 Apr). *500th Anniv of Discovery of America by Columbus (1992) (4th issue). History of Exploration. Horiz designs as T* **194** *of British Virgin Islands. Multicoloured. P* 14.
1406 10 c. Gil Eannes sailing south of Cape Bojador, 1433–34 .. .. .. 10 10
1407 25 c. Alfonso Baldaya sailing south to Cape Blanc, 1436 .. .. .. .. 10 10
1408 45 c. Bartolomeu Dias in Table Bay, 1487 20 25
1409 60 c. Vasco da Gama on voyage to India, 1497–99 .. .. .. .. 25 30
1410 $1 Vallarte the Dane off African coast 40 45
1411 $2 Aloisio Cadamosto in Cape Verde Islands, 1456–58 .. .. .. 85 90
1412 $4 Diogo Gomes on River Gambia, 1457 1·75 1·90
1413 $5 Diogo Cao off African coast, 1482–85 2·10 2·25
1406/13 .. .. .. .. *Set of* 8 5·25 5·75
**MS**1414 Two sheets, each 105×71 mm. (a) $6 Red and Yellow Macaw and bow of *Santa Maria*. (b) $6 Blue and Yellow Macaw and caravel *Set of* 2 *sheets* 5·00 5·25

**248** Donald Duck as Shogun's Guard

(Des Walt Disney Co. Litho Questa)

**1991** (22 May). *"Philanippon '91" International Stamp Exhibition, Tokyo. T* **248** *and similar multicoloured designs showing Walt Disney cartoon characters in Japanese costumes. P* 14×$13^1/_2$ (*horiz*) *or* $13^1/_2$×14 (*vert*).
1415 10 c. Type **248** .. .. .. .. 10 10
1416 15 c. Mickey Mouse as Kabuki actor .. 10 10
1417 25 c. Minnie and Mickey Mouse as bride and groom .. .. .. .. 10 10
1418 45 c. Daisy Duck as geisha (*vert*) .. 20 25
1419 $1 Mickey Mouse in Sokutai court dress (*vert*) .. .. .. .. 40 45
1420 $2 Goofy as Mino farmer (*vert*) .. 85 90
1421 $4 Pete as Shogun (*vert*) .. .. 1·75 1·90
1422 $5 Donald Duck as Samurai .. .. 2·10 2·25
1415/22 .. .. .. .. *Set of* 8 5·00 5·50
**MS**1423 Two sheets, each 127×112 mm. (a) $6 Mickey Mouse as Noh actor (*vert*). (b) $6 Goofy as Kabubei-jishi dancer (*vert*) .. *Set of* 2 *sheets* 5·00 5·25

POSTAL FISCALS

**REVENUE** (R 1)    **Revenue** (R 2)

**1879–86.** *Optd with Type* R **1**. (*a*) *Wmk Crown CC.*

| | | | | |
|---|---|---|---|---|
| R1 | **1** | 1d. lilac | 55·00 | 7·50 |
| | | a. Bisected vert (½d.) on cover | | |
| R2 | | 6d. green | 3·00 | 13·00 |
| R3 | | 1s. magenta | 9·00 | 16·00 |
| R1/3 | | *Set of* 3 | 60·00 | 32·00 |

(*b*) *Wmk Crown CA*

| | | | | |
|---|---|---|---|---|
| R4 | **1** | 1d. lilac (1886) | 1·75 | 2·00 |

**1888.** *Optd with Type* R **2**. *Wmk Crown CA.*

| | | | | |
|---|---|---|---|---|
| R6 | **1** | 1d. carmine | 70·00 | 55·00 |

## Appendix

The following stamps have either been issued in excess of postal needs, or have not been made available to the public in reasonable quantities at face value. Miniature sheets, imperforate stamps etc., are excluded from this section.

**1978–79**

*History of Aviation.* $16 × 30, each embossed on gold foil.



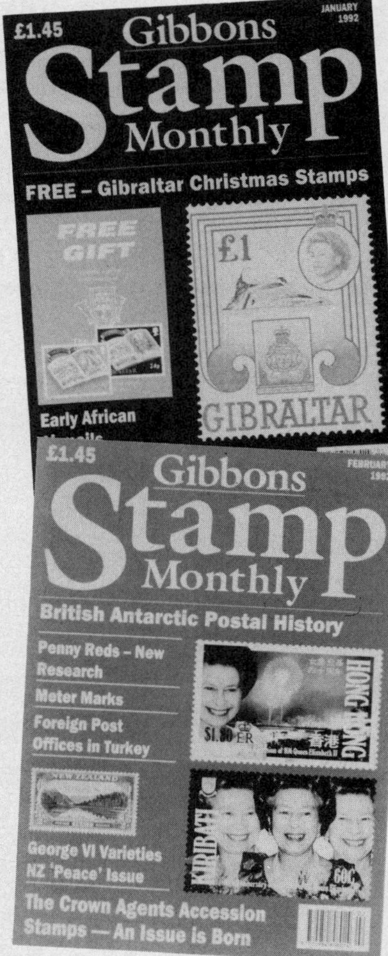

## East Africa (G.E.A.) *see* Tanzania

## East Africa and Uganda Protectorates *see* Kenya, Uganda and Tanzania

# Egypt

### TURKISH SUZERAINTY

In 1517 Sultan Selim I added Egypt to the Ottoman Empire, and it stayed more or less under Turkish rule until 1805, when Mohammed Ali became governor. He established a dynasty of governors owing nominal allegiance to the Sultan of Turkey until 1914.

**Khedive Ismail**

**18 January 1863–26 June 1879**

He obtained the honorific title of Khedive (viceroy) from the Sultan in 1867.

The operations of British Consular Post Offices in Egypt date from 1839 when the first office, at Alexandria, was opened. Further offices at Suez (1847) and Cairo (1859) followed.

Great Britain stamps were issued to Alexandria and Suez offices in 1860 and continued to be used there until the three offices closed in 1882, following the British Military Occupation.

Stamps issued after 1877 can be found with the Egyptian cancellation "Port Said", but these are on letters posted from British ships.

For cancellations used during the 1882 campaign see ARMY FIELD OFFICES at the end of the BRITISH POST OFFICES ABROAD section, following GREAT BRITAIN.

For illustrations of the handstamp and postmark types see BRITISH POST OFFICES ABROAD NOTES, following GREAT BRITAIN.

### ALEXANDRIA

CROWNED-CIRCLE HANDSTAMPS

CC1 CC**1b** ALEXANDRIA (R. *or* Black) (5.1843) *Price on cover* £1300

*Stamps of* **GREAT BRITAIN** *cancelled* "B 01" *as in Types* **2**, **8**, **12** *or* **15**.

**1860** *to* **1879.**

Z 1 ½d. rose-red (1870–79) *From* 16·00
Plate Nos. 5, 6, 8, 10, 13, 14, 15, 19, 20.
Z 2 1d. rose-red (1857) 6·00
Z 3 1d. rose-red (1861) (Alph IV)
Z 4 1d. rose-red (1864–79) *From* 7·00
Plate Nos. 71, 72, 73, 74, 76, 78, 79, 80, 81, 82, 83, 84, 85, 86, 87, 88, 89, 90, 91, 92, 93, 94, 95, 96, 97, 98, 99, 101, 102, 103, 104, 106, 107, 108, 109, 110, 111, 112, 113, 114, 115, 117, 118, 119, 120, 121, 122, 123, 124, 125, 127, 129, 130, 131, 133, 134, 136, 137, 138, 139, 140, 142, 143, 144, 145, 146, 147, 148, 149, 150, 152, 154, 156, 157, 158, 159, 160, 162, 163, 165, 168, 169, 170, 171, 172, 174, 175, 177, 179, 180, 181, 182, 183, 185, 188, 190, 198, 200, 203, 206, 210, 220.
Z 5 2d. blue (1858–69) *From* 7·00
Plate Nos. 7, 8, 9, 13, 14, 15.
Z 6 2½d. rosy mauve (1875) (blued *paper*) *From* 60·00
Plate Nos. 1, 2.
Z 7 2½d. rosy mauve (1875–6) (Plate Nos. 1, 2, 3) 27·00
Z 8 2½d. rosy mauve (*Error of Lettering*) £1300
Z 9 2½d. rosy mauve (1876–79) *From* 21·00
Plate Nos. 3, 4, 5, 6, 7, 8, 9.
Z10 3d. carmine-rose (1862) £110
Z11 3d. rose (1865) (Plate No. 4) 55·00
Z12 3d. rose (1867–73) (Plate Nos. 4, 5, 6, 7, 8, 9) *From* 21·00
Z13 3d. rose (1873–76) *From* 21·00
Plate Nos. 11, 12, 14, 15, 16, 18, 19.
Z14 3d. rose (1881) (Plate No. 20)
Z15 4d. rose (1857) 40·00
Z16 4d. red (1862) (Plate Nos. 3, 4) *From* 40·00
Z17 4d. vermilion (1865–73) 23·00
Plate Nos. 7, 8, 9, 10, 11, 12, 13, 14.
Z18 4d. vermilion (1876) (Plate No. 15) £140
Z19 4d. sage-green (1877) (Plate No. 15) 90·00
Z20 6d. lilac (1856) 45·00
Z21 6d. lilac (1862) (Plate Nos. 3, 4) *From* 40·00
Z22 6d. lilac (1865–67) (Plate Nos. 5, 6) *From* 32·00
Z23 6d. lilac (1867) (Plate No. 6) 42·00
Z24 6d. violet (1867–70) (Plate Nos. 6, 8, 9) *From* 30·00
a. Imperf (Plate No. 8) £1200
Z25 6d. buff (1872–73) (Plate Nos. 11, 12) *From* 55·00
Z26 6d. chestnut (1872) (Plate No. 11) 27·00
Z27 6d. grey (1873) (Plate No. 12) 70·00
Z28 6d. grey (1874–76) (Plate Nos. 13, 14, 15) *From* 21·00
Z29 9d. straw (1862) £140
Z30 9d. bistre (1862)
Z31 9d. straw (1865)
Z32 9d. straw (1867)
Z33 10d. red-brown (1867) £120
Z34 1s. green (1856) £100
Z35 1s. green (1862) 60·00
Z36 1s. green (1862) ("K" *variety*)
Z37 1s. green (1865) (Plate No. 4) 30·00
Z38 1s. green (1867–73) (Plate Nos. 4, 5, 6, 7) *From* 12·00
Z39 1s. green (1873–77) *From* 27·00
Plate Nos. 8, 9, 10, 11, 12, 13.
Z40 2s. blue (1867) 95·00
Z41 5s. rose (1867–74) (Plate Nos. 1, 2) *From* £250

### CAIRO

CROWNED-CIRCLE HANDSTAMPS

CC2 CC**6** CAIRO (R.) (23.3.1859) *Price on cover* £1800

### SUEZ

CROWNED-CIRCLE HANDSTAMPS

CC3 CC**1** SUEZ (R., B. *or* Black) (16.7.1847) *Price on cover* £2000

*Stamps of* GREAT BRITAIN *cancelled* "B 02" *as in Types* **2** *and* **8**, *or with circular date stamp as Type* **5**.

**1860** *to* **1879.**

Z42 ½d. rose-red (1870–79) 25·00
Plate Nos. 6, 10, 11, 12, 13, 14.
Z43 1d. rose-red (1857) 8·00
Z44 1d. rose-red (1864–79) *From* 8·50
Plate Nos. 73, 74, 78, 79, 80, 81, 83, 84, 86, 87, 90, 91, 93, 94, 96, 97, 100, 101, 106, 107, 108, 110, 113, 118, 119, 120, 121, 122, 123, 124, 125, 129, 130, 131, 134, 137, 138, 140, 142, 143, 144, 145, 147, 148, 149, 150, 151, 152, 153, 154, 156, 158, 159, 160, 161, 162, 163, 164, 165, 166, 167, 168, 170, 174, 176, 177, 178, 179, 180, 181, 182, 184, 185, 186, 187, 189, 190, 205.
Z45 2d. blue (1858–69) *From* 12·00
Plate Nos. 8, 9, 13, 14, 15.
Z46 2½d. rosy mauve (1875) (blued *paper*) *From* 55·00
Plate Nos. 1, 2, 3.
Z47 2½d. rosy mauve (1875–76) (Plate Nos. 1, 2, 3) *From* 30·00
Z48 2½d. rosy mauve (*Error of Lettering*) £1300
Z49 2½d. rosy mauve (1876–79) *From* 24·00
Plate Nos. 3, 4, 5, 6, 7, 8, 9, 10.
Z50 3d. carmine-rose (1862) £120
Z51 3d. rose (1865) (Plate No. 4) 60·00
Z52 3d. rose (1867–73) (Plate Nos. 5, 6, 7, 8, 10)
Z53 3d. rose (1873–76) (Plate Nos. 12, 16) *From* 24·00
Z54 4d. rose (1857) 50·00
Z55 4d. red (1862) (Plate Nos. 3, 4) *From* 42·00
Z56 4d. vermilion (1865–73) *From* 27·00
Plate Nos. 7, 8, 9, 10, 11, 12, 13, 14.
Z57 4d. vermilion (1876) (Plate No. 15)
Z58 4d. sage-green (1877) (Plate No. 15) 95·00
Z59 6d. lilac (1856) 45·00
Z60 6d. lilac (1862) (Plate Nos. 3, 4) *From* 40·00
Z61 6d. lilac (1865–67) (Plate Nos. 5, 6) *From* 32·00
Z62 6d. lilac (1867) (Plate No. 6) 42·00
Z63 6d. violet (1867–70) (Plate Nos. 6, 8, 9) *From* 32·00
Z64 6d. buff (1872–73) (Plate Nos. 11, 12) *From* 60·00
Z65 6d. pale chestnut (Plate No. 12) (1872) £2250
Z66 6d. chestnut (1872) (Plate No. 11) 27·00
Z67 6d. grey (1873) (Plate No. 12) 75·00
Z68 6d. grey (1874–76) (Plate Nos. 13, 14, 15, 16) *From* 23·00
Z69 8d. orange (1876)
Z70 9d. straw (1862) £150
a. Thick paper
Z71 9d. bistre (1862)
Z72 9d. straw (1867)
Z73 10d. red-brown (1867) £150
Z74 1s. green (1856) £100
Z75 1s. green (1862) 65·00
Z76 1s. green (1862) ("K" *variety*)
Z77 1s. green (1865) (Plate No. 4) 40·00
Z78 1s. green (1867–73) (Plate Nos. 4, 5, 6, 7) *From* 12·00
Z79 1s. green (1873–77) *From* 27·00
Plate Nos. 8, 9, 10, 11, 12.
Z80 2s. blue (1867) £150
Z81 5s. rose (1867–74) (Plate Nos. 1, 2) *From* £275

**PRICES FOR STAMPS ON COVER**

| | |
|---|---|
| Nos. 1/41 | *from* × 8 |
| Nos. 42/3 | *from* × 30 |
| Nos. 44/83 | *from* × 5 |
| Nos. 84/97 | *from* × 2 |
| Nos. D57/70 | *from* × 12 |
| Nos. D71/86 | *from* × 5 |
| Nos. D84/103 | *from* × 2 |
| Nos. O64/87 | *from* × 5 |
| Nos. O88/101 | *from* × 2 |

**(Currency: 40 paras = 1 piastre)**

1

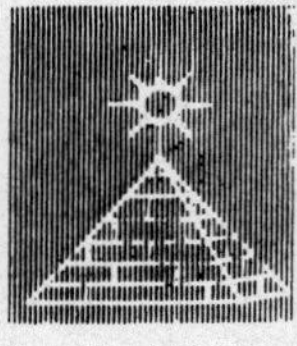
2

(3)

(Printed by Pellas Bros, Genoa. Litho, except for 1 pi. (typo). Black inscription (T **3**) litho, except on 1 pi. and 2 pi. (typo))

**1866** (1 Jan). *Various designs as T* **1** *with black inscription as T* **3**. *The lowest group of characters indicates the value.* 1 *pi. no wmk, others W* **2** (*usually inverted*). *P* 12½.

1 5 pa. grey 27·00 22·00
a. *Greenish grey* 27·00 22·00
b. Imperf (pair) £150
c. Imperf between (pair) £250
d. Perf 12½×13 and compound 38·00 38·00
e. Perf 13 £200 £250
2 10 pa. brown 45·00 24·00
a. Imperf (pair) £110
b. Imperf between (pair) £300
c. Perf 12½×13 and compound 65·00 38·00
d. Perf 12½×15 £225 £250
e. Perf 13 £150 £170
3 20 pa. pale blue 65·00 24·00
a. *Greenish blue* 65·00 24·00
b. Imperf (pair) £200
c. Imperf between (pair) £350
d. Perf 12½×13 and compound 90·00 75·00
e. Perf 13 £350 £200
4 1 pi. claret 50·00 4·00
a. Imperf (pair) £100
b. Imperf between (pair) £300
c. Perf 12½×13 and compound 90·00 20·00
d. Perf 13 £250 £180
5 2 pi. yellow 80·00 35·00
a. *Orange-yellow* 80·00 35·00
b. Imperf (pair)
c. Imperf between (pair) £300 £300
d. Bisected diag (1 pi.) (on cover) † £2250
e. Perf 12½×13 and compound £110 45·00
f. Perf 12½×15 £120
6 5 pi. rose £200 £150
a. Imperf (pair)
b. Imperf between (pair) £800
c. Perf 12½×13 and compound £225
d. Error. Inscr 10 pi., perf 12½×15 £750 £650
e. Do. but imperf £450
7 10 pi. slate £225 £225
a. Imperf (pair)
b. Imperf between (pair) £1500
c. Perf 12½×13 and compound £350 £350
d. Perf 13 £1200

The 2 pi. bisected was authorised for use between 16 and 31 July 1867.

Stamps perforated 13 all round occurred only in the corner of a sheet and so are very rare; of the 10 pi. only 1 copy has been recorded unused. Compound perforations occur in many combinations.

The two halves of each background differ in minor details of the ornamentation. All values can be found with either half at the top.

Proofs of all values exist in smooth paper, without watermark. Beware of forgeries.

4

5

6

(Des F. Hoff, Hirschberg, Silesia. Litho V. Penasson, Alexandria)

**1867** (1 Aug)–**69.** *W* **6**. *P* 15 × 12½.

11 **4** 5 pa. orange-yellow 17·00 7·00
a. Imperf (pair)
b. Imperf between (horiz pair) £150
12 10 pa. dull lilac 55·00 8·00
b. *Bright mauve* (7.69) 38·00 8·00
ba. Bisected diag (5 pa.) (on piece) (12.71) † £750
13 20 pa. deep blue-green 80·00 12·00
a. *Pale blue-green* 80·00 12·00
b. *Yellowish green* (7.69) 90·00 12·00
14 **5** 1 pi. dull rose-red *to* rose 9·00 90
a. *Lake* 75·00 23·00
b. Imperf (pair)
c. Imperf between (horiz pair) £150
d. Bisected diag (20 pa.) (on piece) † £750
e. Rouletted 50·00
15 2 pi. bright blue 90·00 12·00
a. *Pale blue* 90·00 12·00
b. Imperf (pair)
c. Imperf between (pair) £350
d. Bisected diag (1 pi.) (on cover) † —
e. Perf 12½ £200
16 5 pi. brown £300 £180

Each value was engraved four times, the resulting blocks eing used to form sheets of 200. There are therefore four types howing minor variations for each value.

No. 12ba was used on newspapers.

Stamps printed both sides, both imperf and perf, come from prin-ers' waste. The 1 pi. rose without watermark is a proof.

7

8 (Side panels transposed and inverted)

8*a* (I)

8*a* (II)

**ATERMARK 8*a*.** There are two types of this watermark hich, as they are not always easy to distinguish, we do not list eparately. Type II is slightly wider and less deep and the rescent is flatter than in Type I. The width measurement for ype I is generally about 14 mm and for Type II about 15 mm, ut there is some variation within the sheets for both types.

Nos. 26/43, 45/7*a*, 49/*a*, 50/1 and 57 come with Type I only. os. 44*a*, 48/*a*, 52, 54*b*, 73/7 and 78 exist with both types of atermark (but No. 83 and official overprints on these stamps ill require research); our prices are generally for Type II. Other atermarked issues between 1888 and 1907 have Type II atermarks only.

**872** (1 Jan)–**75**. *T* **7** (*the so-called "Penasson" printing**). *Thick opaque paper*. *W* **8*a***. I. *P* 12½×13½. II. *P* 13½.

A. LITHOGRAPHED

| No. | Type | | I | | II | |
|---|---|---|---|---|---|---|
| 6 | 7 | 20 pa. blue (*shades*) | £100 | 32·00 | £170 | 50·00 |
| | | a. Imperf (pair) | — | — | † | |
| | | b. Imperf between (pair) | — | £1500 | † | |
| 7 | | 1 pi. red (*shades*) | £200 | 4·50 | £400 | 10·00 |

B. TYPOGRAPHED

| No. | Type | | I | | II | |
|---|---|---|---|---|---|---|
| 8 | 7 | 5 pa. brown (*shades*) | 7·00 | 4·00 | 17·00 | 7·00 |
| 9 | | 10 pa. mauve | 6·00 | 3·00 | 6·00 | 2·50 |
| 0 | | 20 pa. blue (*shades*) | 32·00 | 3·50 | 50·00 | 14·00 |
| 1 | | 1 pi. rose-red | 27·00 | 75 | 50·00 | 3·00 |
| | | a. Bisected (20 pa.) (on piece with No. 31) (7.75) | † | £600 | † | |
| 2 | | 2 pi. chrome-yellow | 55·00 | 3·50 | 15·00 | 3·50 |
| | | a. Bisected (1 pi.) (on piece) | † | £650 | † | |
| 3 | | 2½ pi. violet | 55·00 | 8·50 | £600 | £170 |
| 4 | | 5 pi. yellow-green | £180 | 35·00 | £250 | 50·00 |
| | | a. Tête-bêche (pair) | † | | † | |

*The lithographed stamps are now believed to have been printed y Penasson, but the typographed by the Government Printing Vorks at Bûlâq, Cairo.

The lithographed and typographed stamps each show the charac-eristic differences between these two processes:—

The typographed stamps show the coloured lines of the design mpressed into the paper and an accumulation of ink along the nargins of the lines.

The lithographed stamps are essentially flat in appearance, vithout the heaping of the ink. Many of the 20 pa. show evidence f retouching, particularly of the outer frame lines.

The 2 pi. vertically bisected was used at Gallipoli.

See also the footnote below No. 41.

**874** (Oct)–**75**. *Typo from new stereos at Bûlâq, on thinner paper*. *W* **8*a***. I. *P* 12½. II. *P* 13½ × 12½.

| No. | Type | | I | | II | |
|---|---|---|---|---|---|---|
| 5 | 8 | 5 pa. brown (4.75) | 5·50 | 2·50 | 3·50 | 2·50 |
| | | a. Tête-bêche (vert pair) | 35·00 | 35·00 | 60·00 | 60·00 |
| | | ab. Tête-bêche (horiz pair) | £250 | £250 | £300 | £300 |
| | | b. Imperf (pair) | — | — | † | |
| | | c. Imperf between) (pair) | £100 | £120 | † | |
| 6 | 7 | 10 pa. grey-lilac (*shades*) | 6·50 | 3·00 | 8·00 | 2·25 |
| | | a. Tête-bêche (pair) | £120 | £120 | £120 | £120 |
| | | b. Imperf (pair) | — | — | † | |
| 7 | | 20 pa. grey-blue (*shades*) | 60·00 | 3·00 | 4·75 | 2·50 |
| | | a. Imperf between (pair) | | † | £250 | — |
| | | b. Bisected diag (10 pa.) (on cover) | | † | — | † |
| 8 | | 1 pi. red (*shades*) | 3·50 | 65 | 32·00 | 1·25 |
| | | a. Tête-bêche (vert pair) | 75·00 | 75·00 | £300 | £300 |
| | | ab. Tête-bêche (horiz pair) | £250 | £250 | — | — |
| | | b. Imperf (pair) | — | — | † | |
| | | c. Imperf between (pair) | — | 60·00 | † | |
| 9 | | 2 pi. yellow | 55·00 | 3·00 | 5·50 | 4·25 |
| | | a. Tête-bêche (pair) | £350 | £350 | £350 | £350 |
| | | aa. Bisected diag (1 pi.) (on cover) | | † | | † £2500 |
| | | b. Perf 12½×13½ | | † | 42·00 | 7·00 |
| | | ba. Tête-bêche (pair) | | † | £750 | — |
| 0 | | 2½ pi. violet | 8·50 | 5·00 | † | |
| | | a. Tête-bêche (pair) | £275 | — | † | |
| | | b. Perf 12½×13½ | | † | 35·00 | 15·00 |
| | | ba. Tête-bêche (pair) | | † | £850 | £750 |
| 1 | | 5 pi. green | 55·00 | 17·00 | † | |
| | | a. Perf 12½×13½ | | † | £300 | £275 |
| | | b. Imperf (pair) | — | — | † | |

The 1872 printings have a thick line of colour in the top margin f the sheet and the other margins are all plain, an exception being the 5 pa., which on the majority of the sheets has the line at the righthand side of the sheet. The 1874–75 printings have a wide fancy border all round every sheet.

The 1872 printings are on thick opaque paper, with the impressions sharp and clear. The 1874–75 printings are on thinner paper, often semi-transparent and oily in appearance, and having the impressions very blurred and badly printed. These are only general distinctions and there are a number of exceptions.

The majority of the 1874–75 stamps have blind or defective perforations, while the 1872 stamps have clean-cut perfs.

There seem to be many different compositions of the sheets, containing the *tête-bêche* varieties, settings being known with 1, 3, 9 and 10 inverted stamps in various sheets. Sheets of the 5 pa. are known with 9 of the 20 horizontal rows inverted, giving vertical *tête-bêche* pairs; four stamps were inverted within their row giving four horizontal *tête-bêche* pairs.

(9)

**1879** (1 Jan). *Stamps of* 1874 *surch as T* **9**, *at Bûlâq*.
I. *P* 12½. II. *P* 12½ × 13½

| No. | Type | | I | | II | |
|---|---|---|---|---|---|---|
| 42 | 7 | 5 pa. on 2½ pi. violet | 6·00 | 6·00 | 6·50 | 6·50 |
| | | a. Surch inverted | 70·00 | 70·00 | £140 | £140 |
| | | b. Tête-bêche (pair) | £3000 | | — | — |
| | | c. Imperf (pair) | — | — | † | |
| 43 | | 10 pa. on 2½ pi. violet | 10·00 | 10·00 | 15·00 | 15·00 |
| | | a. Surch inverted | 75·00 | 75·00 | £110 | £110 |
| | | b. Tête-bêche (pair) | £1300 | — | £1300 | — |
| | | c. Imperf (pair) | — | — | † | |

10

11

12

13

14

15

(Typo De La Rue)

**1879** (1 Apr). *Ordinary paper*. *W* **8*a***. *P* 14.

| No. | Type | | | |
|---|---|---|---|---|
| 44 | 10 | 5 pa. deep brown | 40 | 15 |
| | | *a. Pale brown* | 40 | 15 |
| 45 | 11 | 10 pa. reddish lilac | 42·00 | 3·00 |
| 46 | 12 | 20 pa. pale blue | 60·00 | 1·50 |
| 47 | 13 | 1 pi. rose | 18·00 | 10 |
| | | *a. Pale rose* | 18·00 | 10 |
| 48 | 14 | 2 pi. orange | 19·00 | 40 |
| | | *a. Orange-yellow* | 18·00 | 50 |
| 49 | 15 | 5 pi. green | 55·00 | 6·00 |
| | | *a. Blue-green* | 55·00 | 5·00 |

See also Nos. 50/6.

### Khedive Tewfik

**26 June 1879–7 January 1892**

British troops were landed in Egypt in 1882 to secure the Suez Canal against a nationalist movement led by Arabi Pasha. Arabi was defeated at Tel-el-Kebir and British troops remained in Egypt until 1954. A British resident and consul-general advised the Khedive. Holders of this post were Sir Evelyn Baring (Lord Cromer), 1883–1907; Sir Eldon Gorst, 1907–11; and Lord Kitchener, 1911–14.

**1881–1902**. *Colours changed*. *Ordinary paper*. *W* **8*a***. *P* 14.

| No. | Type | | | |
|---|---|---|---|---|
| 50 | 11 | 10 pa. claret (1.81) | 48·00 | 4·00 |
| 51 | | 10 pa. bluish grey (25.1.82) | 5·50 | 1·00 |
| 52 | | 10 pa. green (15.12.84) | 40 | 20 |
| 53 | 12 | 20 pa. rose-carmine (15.12.84) | 5·00 | 50 |
| | | *a. Bright rose* | 5·00 | 40 |
| 54 | 13 | 1 pi. blue (15.12.84) | 2·00 | 10 |
| | | *a. Deep ultramarine* | 4·50 | 20 |
| | | *b. Pale ultramarine* | 1·50 | 10 |
| | | c. Chalk-surfaced paper. *Ultramarine* (1902) | 2·00 | 10 |
| | | ca. Do. *Blue* | 1·75 | 10 |
| 55 | 14 | 2 pi. orange-brown (1.8.93) | 12·00 | 30 |
| | | a. Chalk-surfaced paper (1902) | 12·00 | 10 |
| | | ab. Do. *Orange* | 17·00 | 60 |
| 56 | 15 | 5 pi. pale grey (15.12.84) | 12·00 | 50 |
| | | *a. Slate* | 11·00 | 40 |
| | | b. Chalk-surfaced paper. *Slate-grey* (1902) | 15·00 | 15 |

PARAS 20

(17)

**1884** (1 Feb). *Surch with T* **17** *at Bûlâq*.

| No. | Type | | | |
|---|---|---|---|---|
| 57 | 15 | 20 pa. on 5 pi. green | 6·50 | 1·25 |
| | | a. Surch inverted | 65·00 | 60·00 |

**(New Currency: 1000 milliemes = 100 piastres = £1 Egyptian)**

18

19

20

21

22

**1888** (1 Jan)–**1906**. *Ordinary paper*. *W* **8*a***. *P* 14.

| No. | Type | | | |
|---|---|---|---|---|
| 58 | 18 | 1 m. pale brown | 40 | 10 |
| | | *a. Deep brown* | 55 | 10 |
| | | b. Chalk-surfaced paper. *Pale brown* (1902) | 30 | 10 |
| | | ba. Do. *Deep brown* | 30 | 10 |
| 59 | 19 | 2 m. blue-green | 50 | 10 |
| | | *a. Green* | 50 | 10 |
| | | ab. Chalk-surfaced paper (1902) | 50 | 10 |
| 60 | 20 | 3 m. maroon (1.1.92) | 2·00 | 1·00 |
| 61 | | 3 m. yellow (1.8.93) | 1·25 | 15 |
| | | *a. Orange-yellow* | 1·25 | 15 |
| | | ab. Chalk-surfaced paper (1902) | 1·25 | 10 |
| 62 | 21 | 4 m. vermilion (*chalk-surfaced paper*) (1906) | 60 | 10 |
| 63 | | 5 m. rose-carmine | 1·00 | 10 |
| | | *a. Bright rose* | 1·10 | 10 |
| | | *b. Aniline rose* | 1·25 | 10 |
| | | c. Chalk-surfaced paper. *Rose* (1902) | 1·00 | 10 |
| | | ca. Do. *Deep aniline rose* | 1·50 | 10 |
| 64 | 22 | 10 p. mauve | 15·00 | 80 |
| | | *a. Aniline mauve* | 17·00 | 80 |
| | | b. Chalk-surfaced paper. *Mauve* (1902) | 20·00 | 50 |

### Khedive Abbas Hilmi

**7 January 1892–19 December 1914**

29 Nile Felucca

30 Cleopatra with Head-dress of Isis

31 Ras-el-Tin Palace, Alexandria

35 Pylon of Karnak Temple, Luxor

37 Rock Temples of Abu Simbel

(Typo De La Rue)

**1914** (8 Jan). *W* **8*a***. *P* 14.

| No. | Type | | | |
|---|---|---|---|---|
| 73 | 29 | 1 m. sepia | 15 | 30 |
| 74 | 30 | 2 m. green | 35 | 15 |
| 75 | 31 | 3 m. yellow-orange | 40 | 30 |
| | | a. Double impression | | |
| 76 | – | 4 m. vermilion | 80 | 75 |
| 77 | – | 5 m. lake | 60 | 10 |
| | | a. Wmk sideways (booklets) | 10·00 | 18·00 |
| 78 | – | 10 m. dull blue | 1·50 | 10 |
| 79 | 35 | 20 m. olive | 4·75 | 10 |
| 80 | – | 50 m. purple | 7·00 | 40 |
| 81 | 37 | 100 m. slate | 10·00 | 60 |
| 82 | – | 200 m. maroon | 24·00 | 1·75 |
| 73/82 | | *Set of* 10 | 45·00 | 4·00 |

Designs: *As T* **29**—4 m. Pyramids at Giza; 5 m. Sphinx; 10 m. Colossi of Thebes. *As T* **35**—50 m. Cairo Citadel; 200 m. Aswân Dam.

All the above exist imperforate, but imperforate stamps without watermark are proofs.

See also Nos. 84/95.

### BRITISH PROTECTORATE

On 18 December 1914, after war with Turkey had begun, Egypt was declared to be a British protectorate. Abbas Hilmi was deposed, and his uncle, Hussein Kamil, was proclaimed Sultan of Egypt.

### Sultan Hussein Kamil

**19 December 1914–9 October 1917**

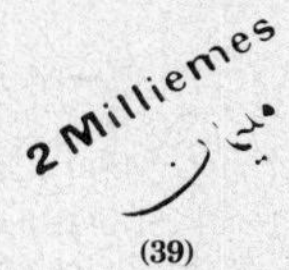

(39)

**1915** (15 Oct). *Surch with T* **39**, *at Bûlâq.*
83 **31** 2 m. on 3 m. yellow-orange .. .. 55 80
a. Surch inverted .. .. £200 £200
b. Surch double, one albino .. .. £120

### Sultan Ahmed Fuad

**9 October 1917–15 March 1922**

**40**

(A)

(B)

(Typo Harrison & Sons)

**1921–22.** W **40**. (*a*) *As Nos.* 73/82. (i) *P* 13½ × 14.
84 **29** 1 m. sepia (A) .. .. 30 50
a. Two dots omitted (B) .. .. 35·00 40·00
85 **30** 2 m. green .. .. 1·75 90
a. Imperf between (pair) .. ..
86 2 m. vermilion (1922) .. .. 35 35
87 **31** 3 m. yellow-orange (12.21) .. .. 1·00 35
88 – 4 m. green (1922) .. .. 1·50 2·25
89 – 5 m. lake (1.21) .. .. 1·00 10
a. Imperf between (pair) .. ..
90 – 5 m. pink (11.21) .. .. 1·25 10
91 – 10 m. dull blue .. .. 2·00 20
92 – 10 m. lake (9.22) .. .. 1·50 15

(ii) *P* 14
93 **35** 20 m. olive .. .. 5·00 10
94 – 50 m. purple .. .. 10·00 30
95 **37** 100 m. slate (1922) .. .. 40·00 4·00
84/95 .. .. *Set of* 12 60·00 8·25

**41** Statue of Rameses II **42**

(*b*) *New design. P* 13½ × 14
96 **41** 15 m. indigo (3.22) .. .. 1·50 15
97 **42** 15 m. indigo .. .. 11·00 2·25

Type **42** was printed first; but because the inscription at right was erroneous the stamps were withheld and the corrected Type **41** printed and issued. Type **42** was released later.

## POSTAGE DUE STAMPS

D 1

D 2

D 3

(Des L. Barkhausen. Litho V. Penasson, Alexandria)

**1884** (1 Jan). *Impressed W* **6**. *P* 10½.
D57 **D 1** 10 pa. red .. .. 25·00 7·00
a. Imperf (pair) .. ..
b. Imperf between (pair) .. .. £100
D58 20 pa. red .. .. 70·00 12·00
D59 1 pi. red .. .. £100 25·00
D60 2 pi. red .. .. £130 10·00
D61 5 pi. red .. .. 13·00 22·00

**1886** (1 Aug). *No wmk. P* 10½.
D62 **D 1** 10 pa. rose-red .. .. 26·00 3·50
a. Imperf between (pair) .. .. 75·00
D63 20 pa. rose-red .. .. £140 25·00
a. Imperf between (pair) .. ..
D64 1 pi. rose-red .. .. 17·00 3·00
a. Imperf between (pair) .. .. £100 £100
D65 2 pi. rose-red .. .. 17·00 3·00
a. Imperf between (pair) .. .. £100

Specialists distinguish four types of each value in both these issues.

(Litho V. Penasson, Alexandria)

**1888** (1 Jan). *No wmk. P* 11½.
D66 **D 2** 2 m. green .. .. 7·00 8·50
a. Imperf between (pair) .. .. £150 £150
D67 5 m. rose-carmine .. .. 16·00 7·50
D68 1 p. blue .. .. 75·00 35·00
a. Imperf between (pair) .. .. £150
D69 2 p. orange .. .. 95·00 10·00
D70 5 p. grey .. .. £150 £140
a. With stop after left-hand "PIASTRES" .. .. £200 £170

Specialists distinguish four types of each value.
Beware of forgeries of the 5 p.

(Typo De La Rue)

**1889** (Apr). *Ordinary or chalk-surfaced paper. W* **8a** (*upright*). *P* 14.
D71 **D 3** 2 m. green .. .. 6·00 50
a. Bisected (1 m.) (on cover with unbisected 2 m.) .. .. † £250
D72 4 m. maroon .. .. 1·75 50
D73 1 p. ultramarine .. .. 5·00 70
D74 2 p. orange .. .. 5·00 85
a. Bisected diagonally (1 p.) (on cover)

See also Nos. D84/6 for stamps with watermark sideways.

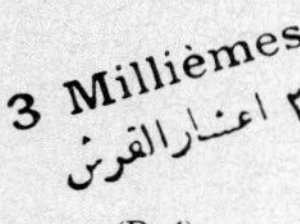

(D 4)

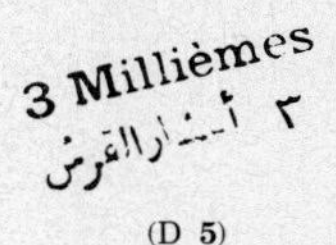

(D 5)

Type D **4**

The Arabic figure at right is less than 2 mm from the next character, which consists of a straight stroke only.

Type D **5**

The distance is 3 mm and the straight character has a comma-like character above it. There are other minor differences.

**1898** (Apr)–**1905**. *No.* D74 *surch, At Bûlâq.*

(*a*) *With Type* D **4**. *Ordinary paper*
D75 **D 3** 3 m. on 2 p. orange .. .. 45 1·75
a. Surch inverted .. .. 50·00 50·00
b. Pair, one without surch .. ..
c. Arabic "2" for "3" .. ..
d. Arabic "3" over "2" .. ..

No. D75c occurred in the first printing on positions 10, 20, 30, 40, 50 and 60 of the pane of 60 (the Arabic figure is the right-hand character of the second line—see illustration on page xvii). In the second printing the correct figure was printed on top to form No. D75d. The error was corrected in subsequent printings.

(*b*) *With Type* D **5**. *Ordinary or chalk-surfaced paper* (1905)
D76 **D 3** 3 m. on 2 p. orange .. .. 2·75 5·00
a. Surch inverted .. .. 50·00 50·00
b. Surch double .. .. £150

**1918.** *As Nos.* D71/3 *but wmk sideways.*
D84 **D 3** 2 m. bright green .. .. 7·00 3·00
D85 4 m. maroon .. .. 7·00 4·50
D86 1 p. dull ultramarine .. .. 14·00 8·00

D 6

D 7

(Typo Harrison)

**1921** (Oct)–**22.** *Chalk-surfaced paper. W* **40**. *P* 14 × 13½.
D 98 **D 6** 2 m. green .. .. 1·25 2·00
D 99 2 m. scarlet (1922) .. .. 70 60
D100 4 m. scarlet .. .. 5·00 5·50
D101 4 m. green .. .. 1·75 60
D102 **D 7** 10 m. deep slate-blue (11.21) .. .. 3·50 7·50
D103 10 m. lake (1922) .. .. 3·00 60
D98/103 .. .. *Set of* 6 13·50 15·00

## OFFICIAL STAMPS

O 1

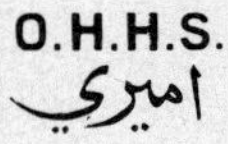

(O 2)

"O.H.H.S."

(O 3)

(Typo De La Rue)

**1893** (1 Jan). *Ordinary or chalk-surfaced paper. W* **8a**. *P* 14.
O64 **O 1** (–) chestnut .. .. 50 10
a. Wmk sideways .. .. 8·00 4·50

This stamp, with overprint 3 P.T. and Arabic equivalent, is a fiscal.

**1907.** *Nos.* 54ca, 55b, 58b, 59ab, 61ab *and* 63c *optd with Type* O **2**, *by De La Rue.*
O73 **18** 1 m. pale brown .. .. 55 10
O74 **19** 2 m. green .. .. 1·00 10
a. Opt double .. ..
O75 **20** 3 m. orange-yellow .. .. 2·00 55
O76 **21** 5 m. rose .. .. 1·75 10
O77 **13** 1 p. blue .. .. 1·25 10
O78 **15** 5 p. slate-grey .. .. 9·00 30
O73/8 .. .. *Set of* 6 14·00 1·00

**1913** (Nov). *No.* 63c *optd at Bûlâq.*

(*a*) *With Type* O **3**
O79 **21** 5 m. rose .. .. — £200
a. Opt inverted .. ..

(*b*) *As Type* O **3** *but without inverted commas*
O80 **21** 5 m. rose .. .. 1·75 10
a. No stop after "S" (pos. 130) .. .. 22·00 15·00
b. Opt inverted .. .. £180 75·00

O.H.H.S. اميرى
(O 4)

O.H.H.S. أميرى
(O 5)

O.H.H.S أميرى
(O 6)

**1914** (Dec)–**15.** *Stamps of* 1902–6 *and* 1914 *optd with Type* O *at Bûlâq.*
O83 **29** 1 m. sepia (1.15) .. .. 1·00 2·0
a. No stop after "S" .. .. 12·00 18·0
O84 **19** 2 m. green (3.15) .. .. 1·50 2·0
a. No stop after "S" .. .. 12·00 18·0
b. Opt inverted .. .. 35·00 35·0
c. Opt double .. .. £300
O85 **31** 3 m. yellow-orange (3.15) .. .. 1·25 2·0
a. No stop after "S" .. .. 12·00 18·0
O86 **21** 4 m. vermilion (12.14) .. .. 2·00 1·2
a. Opt inverted .. .. £180 £13
b. Pair, one without opt .. ..
O87 – 5 m. lake (1.15) .. .. 2·25 5
a. No stop after "S" .. .. 12·00 17·0
O83/7 .. .. *Set of* 5 7·25 7·0

**1915** (Oct). *Nos.* 59ab, 62 *and* 77 *optd lithographically wit Type* O **5**, *at Bûlâq.*
O88 **19** 2 m. green .. .. 70 1·0
a. Opt inverted .. .. 15·00 15·0
b. Opt double .. .. 20·00
O89 **21** 4 m. vermilion .. .. 1·00 2·0
O90 – 5 m. lake .. .. 1·25 9
a. Pair, one without opt .. .. £225

**1922.** *Nos.* 84, *etc. optd lithographically with Type* O **6**, *Bûlâq.*
O 98 **29** 1 m. sepia (A) (28.6) .. .. 2·25 4·5
a. Two dots omitted (B) .. .. £200
O 99 **30** 2 m. vermilion (16.6) .. .. 4·75 5·5
O100 **31** 3 m. yellow-orange (28.6) .. .. 65·00 85·0
O101 – 5 m. pink (13.3) .. .. 8·50 2·2

Egypt was declared to be an independent kingdom on 15 Marc 1922, and Sultan Ahmed Fuad became king.

Later stamp issues will be found listed in Part 19 (*Middle Eas* of this catalogue.

## EGYPTIAN POST OFFICES ABROAD

From 1865 Egypt operated various post offices in foreig countries. No special stamps were issued for these offices ar use in them of unoverprinted Egyptian stamps can only b identified by the cancellation. Stamps with such cancellation are worth more than the used prices quoted in the Egyp listings.

Such offices operated in the following countries. An * indicate that details will be found under that heading elsewhere in th catalogue.

### ETHIOPIA

A B

C

D

MASSAWA. *Open Nov* 1867 *to Dec* 1885. *Postmark types* (*also without* REGIE), B, C, D. *An Arabic seal type is a known on stampless covers.*

SENHIT (near Keren). *Open* 1878 *to* April 1885. *Only o cover, cancelled* "Mouderie Senhit" *in* 1879, *is know together with one showing a possible hand-dra cancellation.*

A post office is also recorded at Harar, but no postal markir has so far been reported.

### SOMALILAND*

Unoverprinted stamps of Egypt used from 1876 until 1884.

### SUDAN*

Unoverprinted stamps of Egypt used from 1867 until 1897.

### MINIMUM PRICE

The minimum price quote is 10p which represen a handling charge rather than a basis for valuin common stamps. For further notes about price see introductory pages.

### TURKISH EMPIRE

E F

G H

I J

K L

M N

O

The offices are listed according to the spelling on the ancellation. The present-day name (if different) and country re given in brackets.

ALESSANDRETTA (Iskenderun, Turkey). *Open* 14 July 1870 *to* Feb 1872. *Postmark types* E, I.
BAIROUT (Beirut, Lebanon). *Open* 14 July 1870 *to* Feb 1872. *Postmark types* E, J.
CAVALA (Kavala, Greece). *Open* 14 July 1870 *to* Feb 1872. *Postmark type* E.
COSTANTINOPOLI (Istanbul, Turkey). *Open* 13 June 1865 *to* 30 June 1881. *Postmark types* E, F, O.
DARDANELLI (Canakkale, Turkey). *Open* 10 June 1868 *to* 30 June 1881. *Postmark types* H, K.
DJEDDAH, *see* GEDDA.
GALIPOLI (Gelibolu, Turkey). *Open* 10 June 1868 *to* 30 June 1881. *Postmark types* E, L.
GEDDA, DJEDDAH (Jeddah, Saudi Arabia). *Open* 8 June 1865 *to* 30 June 1881. *Postmark types* F, G (*also with year replacing solid half-circle*), O (*all spelt* GEDDA), D (*spelt* DJEDDAH).
IAFFA (Jaffa, Israel). *Open* 14 July 1870 *to* Feb 1872. *Postmark type* E.
LAGOS (Port Lago, Greece). *Open* 14 July 1870 *to* Feb 1872. *Postmark type* E.
LATAKIA (Syria). *Open* 14 July 1870 *to* Feb 1872. *Postmark type* E.
LEROS (Aegean Is.). *Open* July 1873 *to* Jan 1874 *and* May *to* Oct 1874. *Postmark type* E.
MERSINA (Mersin, Turkey). *Open* 14 July 1870 *to* Feb 1872. *Postmark type* E.
METELINO (Lesbos, Greece). *Open* 14 July 1870 *to* 30 June 1881. *Postmark types* E, M.
RODI (Rhodes, Greece). *Open* 13 Aug 1872 *to* 30 June 1881. *Postmark type* E.
SALONNICCHI (Thessaloniki, Greece). *Open* 14 July 1870 *to* Feb 1872. *Postmark type* E.
SCIO (Chios, Aegean Is.). *Open* 14 July 1870 *to* 30 June 1881. *Postmark types* E, N.
SMIRNE (Izmir, Turkey). *Open* 14 Nov 1865 *to* 30 June 1881. *Postmark types* E (*also without* "V. R."), F.
TENEDOS (Bozcaada, Turkey). *Open* 14 July 1870 *to* Mar 1871. *Postmark type* E.
TRIPOLI (Lebanon). *Open* 14 July 1870 *to* Feb 1872. *Postmark type* E.
VOLO (Volos, Greece). *Open* 14 July 1870 *to* Feb 1872. *Postmark type* E.

## BRITISH FORCES IN EGYPT

From 1 November 1932, to 29 February 1936 members of the British Forces in Egypt and their families were allowed to send letters to the British Isles at reduced rates. Special seals which were on sale in booklets at N.A.A.F.I. Institutes and Canteens were used instead of Egyptian stamps, and were stuck on the back of the envelopes, letters bearing the seals being franked on the front with a hand-stamp inscribed "EGYPT POSTAGE PREPAID" in a double circle surmounted by a crown.

**PRICES FOR STAMPS ON COVER**

| | |
|---|---|
| Nos. A1/9 | *from* × 5 |
| No. A10 | *from* × 2 |
| No. A11 | *from* × 5 |
| No. A12 | *from* × 100 |
| No. A13 | *from* × 20 |
| No. A14 | *from* × 200 |
| No. A15 | *from* × 20 |

A 1

A 2

(Des Lt.-Col. C. Fraser. Typo Hanbury, Tomsett & Co, London)

**1932** (1 Nov)–**33.** *P* 11. (*a*) *Inscr* "POSTAL SEAL".

| | | | | |
|---|---|---|---|---|
| A1 | A 1 | 1 p. deep blue and red .. .. .. | 40·00 | 2·50 |

(*b*) *Inscr* "LETTER SEAL"

| | | | | |
|---|---|---|---|---|
| A2 | A 1 | 1 p. deep blue and red (8.33) .. .. | 14·00 | 55 |

(Des Sgt. W. F. Lait. Litho Walker & Co, Amalgamated Press, Cairo)

**1932** (26 Nov)–**35.** *Christmas Seals. P* 11½.

| | | | | |
|---|---|---|---|---|
| A3 | A 2 | 3 m. black/*azure* .. .. .. | 32·00 | 50·00 |
| A4 | | 3 m. brown-lake (13.11.33) .. .. | 6·00 | 27·00 |
| A5 | | 3 m. deep blue (17.11.34) .. .. | 7·00 | 15·00 |
| A6 | | 3 m. vermilion (23.11.35) .. .. | 1·25 | 12·00 |
| | | *a. Pale vermilion* (19.12.35) .. .. | 5·00 | 11·00 |

A 3

(Des Miss Waugh. Photo Harrison)

**1934** (1 June)–**35.** (*a*) *P* 14½ × 14.

| | | | | |
|---|---|---|---|---|
| A7 | A 3 | 1 p. carmine .. .. .. .. | 27·00 | 50 |
| A8 | | 1 p. green (5.12.34) .. .. .. | 3·00 | 2·75 |

(*b*) *P* 13½ × 14

| | | | | |
|---|---|---|---|---|
| A9 | A 3 | 1 p. carmine (24.4.35) .. .. .. | 90 | 85 |

JUBILEE
COMMEMORATION
1935

(A 4)

**1935** (6 May). *Silver Jubilee. As No.* A9, *but colour changed and optd with Type* A **4**, *in red.*

| | | | | |
|---|---|---|---|---|
| A10 | A 3 | 1 p. ultramarine .. .. .. | £200 | £180 |

Xmas 1935
3 Milliemes

(A 5)

**1935** (16 Dec). *Provisional Christmas Seal. No.* A9 *surch with Type* A **5**.

| | | | | |
|---|---|---|---|---|
| A11 | A 3 | 3 m. on 1 p. carmine .. .. .. | 15·00 | 50·00 |

The seals and letter stamps were replaced by the following Army Post stamps issued by the Egyptian Postal Administration. No. A9 was accepted for postage until 15 March 1936.

A **6** King Fuad I

A **7** King Farouk

W 48 of Egypt

(Types A **6**/A **7**. Photo Survey Dept, Cairo)

**1936.** *W* **48** *of Egypt. P* 13½ × 14.

| | | | | |
|---|---|---|---|---|
| A12 | A **6** | 3 m. green (9.11.36) .. .. .. | 75 | 60 |
| A13 | | 10 m. carmine (1.3.36) .. .. .. | 1·00 | 10 |

**1939** (12 Dec). *W* **48** *of Egypt. P* 13 × 13½.

| | | | | |
|---|---|---|---|---|
| A14 | A **7** | 3 m. green .. .. .. .. | 60 | 2·00 |
| A15 | | 10 m. carmine .. .. .. .. | 60 | 10 |

These stamps were withdrawn in April 1941 but the concession, without the use of special stamps, continued until October 1951 when the postal agreement was abrogated.

# Falkland Islands

**PRICES FOR STAMPS ON COVER TO 1945**

| | |
|---|---|
| Nos. 1/4 | *from* × 10 |
| Nos. 5/12 | *from* × 12 |
| Nos. 13/38 | *from* × 10 |
| Nos. 41/2 | *from* × 5 |
| Nos. 43/59 | *from* × 6 |
| Nos. 60/80 | *from* × 4 |
| No. 115 | *from* × 2 |
| Nos. 116/26 | *from* × 5 |
| Nos. 127/38 | *from* × 4 |
| Nos. 139/42 | *from* × 5 |
| Nos. 143/5 | *from* × 8 |
| Nos. 146/63 | *from* × 3 |

**CROWN COLONY**

(1) (2)

**1869–76.** *The Franks.*

| | | | |
|---|---|---|---|
| FR1 | 1 | In black, *on cover* .. .. .. | £6500 |
| FR2 | 2 | In red, *on cover* (1876) .. .. | £10000 |

On *piece*, No. FR1 on white or coloured papers £75; No. FR2 on white £110. The use of these franks ceased when the first stamps were issued.

3

½d.

(4)

In the ½d., 2d., 2½d. and 9d. the figures of value in the lower corners are replaced by small rosettes and the words of value are in colour.

**NOTE.** Nos. 1, 2, 3, 4, 8, 10, 11 and 12 exist with one or two sides imperf from the margin of the sheets.

(Recess B.W.)

**1878–79.** *No wmk. P* 14, 14½.
1 3 1d. claret (19.6.78) .. .. .. £550 £375
2 4d. grey-black (Sept 1879) .. .. £1000 £130
a. On wmkd paper .. .. .. £1800 £400
3 6d. blue-green (19.6.78) .. .. 45·00 45·00
4 1s. bistre-brown (1878) .. .. 45·00 45·00

No. 2a shows portions of the papermaker's watermark—"R. TURNER, CHAFFORD MILLS"—in ornate double-lined capitals.

**1882** (22 Nov). *Wmk Crown CA (upright). P* 14, 14½.
5 3 1d. dull claret .. .. .. .. £300 85·00
a. Imperf between (horiz pair) .. £35000
6 4d. grey-black .. .. .. 80·00 55·00

**1885** (23 Mar)–**87.** *Wmk Crown CA (sideways to left or right). P* 14, 14½.
7 3 1d. pale claret .. .. .. .. 50·00 32·00
8 1d. brownish claret (3.10.87) .. .. 60·00 30·00
a. Bisected (on cover) (1891)* .. .. † £2000
9 4d. pale grey-black .. .. .. £250 30·00
10 4d. grey-black (3.10.87) .. .. £250 30·00
*See note below No. 14.

**1889** (26 Sept)–**91.** *Wmk Crown CA (upright). P* 14, 14½.
11 3 1d. red-brown (21.5.91) .. .. .. 85·00 50·00
a. Bisected (on cover)* .. .. † £2000
12 4d. olive grey-black .. .. 65·00 42·00
*See note below No. 14.

**1891** (Jan). *Nos. 8 and 11 bisected diagonally and each half handstamped with T* 4.
13 3 ½d. on half of 1d. brownish claret (No. 8) £425 £300
a. Unsevered pair .. .. .. £1600 £1000
b. Unsevered pair *se-tenant* with unsurcharged whole stamp .. £7000
14 ½d. on half 1d. red-brown (No. 11) .. £425 £225
a. Unsevered pair .. .. .. £1600 £850
b. Unsevered pair *se-tenant* with unsurcharged whole stamp ..

**1891 PROVISIONALS.** In 1891 the postage to the United Kingdom and Colonies was reduced from 4d. to 2½d. per half ounce. As no ½d. or 2½d. stamps were available the bisection of the 1d. was authorised from 1 January 1891. This authorisation was withdrawn on 11 January 1892, although bisects were accepted for postage until July of that year. The ½d. and 2½d. stamps were placed on sale from 10 September 1891.

Cork Cancel used in 1891

The Type 4 surcharge was not used regularly; unsurcharged bisects being employed far more frequently. Genuine bisects should be cancelled with the cork cancel illustrated above. The use of any other postmark, including a different cork cancel, requires date evidence linked to known mail ship sailings to prove authenticity.

Posthumous strikes of the surcharge on "souvenir" bisects usually show a broken "2" and/or a large full stop. These are known on bisected examples of No. 18 and on varieties such as surcharge inverted, double or sideways. Forgeries exist of all these provisionals.

**1891** (May)–**1902.** *Wmk Crown CA (upright). P* 14, 14½.
15 3 ½d. blue-green (May–Nov 1891) .. 14·00 20·00
16 ½d. green (20.5.92) .. .. .. 14·00 16·00
*a. Deep dull green* (15.4.96) .. .. 27·00 27·00
17 ½d. deep yellow-green (1894–95) .. 14·00 20·00
*a. Yellow-green* (19.6.99) .. .. 2·00 1·25
*b. Dull yellowish green* (13.1.1902) .. 3·75 1·25
18 1d. orange red-brown (14.10.91) .. 50·00 42·00
*a. Brown* (1891?) .. .. .. 38·00 40·00
19 1d. reddish chestnut (20.4.92) .. .. 35·00 40·00
20 1d. orange-brn (*Wmk reversed*) (18.1.94) 25·00 27·00
21 1d. claret (23.7.94) .. .. .. 35·00 35·00
22 1d. Venetian red (pale to deep) (1895–96) .. .. .. 8·50 7·00
*a. Venetian claret* (1898?) .. .. 17·00 10·00
23 1d. pale red (19.6.99) .. .. 5·00 1·00
24 1d. orange-red (13.1.1902) .. .. 6·00 2·00
25 2d. purple (pale to deep) (1895–98) .. 6·50 12·00
26 2d. reddish purple (15.4.96) .. .. 5·00 11·00
27 2½d. pale chalky ultram (May–Aug 1891) 75·00 35·00
28 2½d. dull blue (19.11.91) .. .. 45·00 14·00
29 2½d. Prussian blue (18.1.94) .. .. £200 £180
30 2½d. ultramarine (1894–96) .. .. 16·00 6·50
*a. Pale ultramarine* (10.6.98) .. .. 18·00 10·00
*b. Deep ultramarine* (18.9.1901) .. 18·00 22·00
31 4d. brownish black (wmk reversed) (18.1.94) .. .. .. £375 £190
32 4d. olive-black (11.5.95) .. .. 14·00 20·00
33 6d. orange-yellow (19.11.91) .. .. 32·00 32·00
34 6d. yellow (15.4.96) .. .. .. 27·00 32·00
35 9d. pale reddish orange (15.11.95) .. 22·00 48·00
36 9d. salmon (15.4.96) .. .. .. 27·00 48·00
37 1s. grey-brown (15.11.95) .. .. 30·00 38·00
38 1s. yellow-brown (15.4.96) .. .. 27·00 35·00
15/38 .. .. .. .. *Set of* 8 £100 £140
15, 26, 28, 33, 35 Optd "Specimen" .. *Set of* 5 £650

**NOTES.** The dates shown above are those on which the printer delivered the various printings to the Crown Agents. Several months could elapse before the stamps went on sale in the Colony, depending on the availability of shipping.

The plates used for these stamps did not fit the paper so that the watermark appears in all sorts of positions on the stamp. Well centred examples are scarce. Examples can also be found showing parts of the marginal watermarks, either CROWN AGENTS horizontally in letters 12 mm high or "CROWN AGENTS FOR THE COLONIES" vertically in 7 mm letters. Both are in double-lined capitals.

Many stamps between Nos. 5 and 38 can be found with the watermark reversed, inverted or both, in addition to those noted above where such variations are a constant feature.

The 2½d. ultramarine printing can sometimes be found in a violet shade, but the reason for this is unknown.

5

6

(Recess B.W.)

**1898** (June). *Wmk Crown CC. P* 14, 14½.
41 5 2s. 6d. deep blue .. .. .. £200 £250
42 6 5s. red .. .. .. .. £180 £200
41/2 Optd "Specimen" .. .. *Set of* 2 £450

7

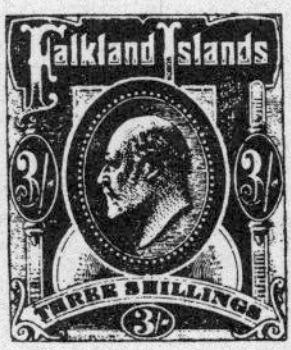


8

(Recess D.L.R.)

**1904–12.** *Wmk Mult Crown CA. P* 14.
43 7 ½d. yellow-green .. .. .. 2·00 85
44 ½d. pale yellow-green on thick paper (1908) 5·50 8·00
45 ½d. deep yellow-green (1911) .. .. 4·00 3·00
46 1d. vermilion .. .. .. .. 4·00 1·25
47 1d. vermilion on thick paper (1908) .. 5·00 1·00
48 1d. dull coppery red on thick paper (1908) £160 35·00
49 1d. orange-vermilion (1911) .. .. 3·75 2·00
50 2d. purple .. .. .. .. 9·50 24·00
51 2d. reddish purple (1912) .. .. £225 £250
52 2½d. ultramarine (*shades*) .. .. 26·00 7·00
53 2½d. deep blue (1912) .. .. .. £225 £180
54 6d. orange .. .. .. .. 32·00 48·00
55 1s. brown .. .. .. .. 38·00 30·00
56 8 3s. green .. .. .. .. £130 £120
57 3s. deep green (1906) .. .. .. £120 £130
58 5s. red .. .. .. .. £140 £140
43/58 .. .. .. .. *Set of* 8 £325 £350
43/58 Optd "Specimen" .. .. *Set of* 8 £450

**1906.** *Wmk Mult Crown CA (sideways). P* 14.
59 7 1d. vermilion .. .. .. .. 75 1·75

**SOUTH GEORGIA UNDERPRINT.** The Post Office on South Georgia opened on 3 December 1909, a stock of Falkland Islands stamps with values from ½d. to 5s. being supplied, together with a straight-line handstamp inscribed "South Georgia". It was intended that this mark should be struck on covers, below the stamps, as an indication of the origin of the mail, the stamps themselves being cancelled with a Falkland Islands postmark. Examples are known on the Edward VII stamps and on some values of the Victorian issue. This underprint can, on occasion, be found struck across the stamps, rather than below them.

Its use continues after the introduction of the South Georgia cancellation in July 1910, but no example has been reported after June 1912. (*Price for example of underprint on cover* (a) *In conjunction with* "FALKLAND ISLANDS" *postmark* (December 1909 *to* June 1910) *from* £1800 (b) *In conjunction with* "SOUTH GEORGIA" *postmark* (July 1910 *to* June 1912) *from* £900).

**SOUTH GEORGIA PROVISIONAL HANDSTAMPS.** During October 1911 the arrival of the German South Polar Expedition at Grytviken, South Georgia, resulted in the local supply of stamps becoming exhausted. The Acting Magistrate, Mr. E. B. Binnie, who was also responsible for the postal facilities, produced a handstamp reading "Paid At SOUTH GEORGIA" which, together with a manuscript indication of the postage paid and his signature, was used on mail from 18 October 1911 to January 1912.
PH1 "Paid 1 At SOUTH GEORGIA EBB" *Price on cover* £4000
PH2 "Paid 2½ At SOUTH GEORGIA EBB" *Price on cover* £4750

9

10

(Recess D.L.R.)

**1912–20.** *Wmk Mult Crown CA. P* 13¾ × 14 *(comb)* (½d. *to* 1s.) *or* 14 *(line)* (3s. *to* £1).
60 9 ½d. yellow-green .. .. .. 1·75 2·50
a. Perf 14 (line). *Dp yellow-green* (1914) 27·00 35·00
b. Perf 14 (line). *Deep olive* (1918) .. 23·00 17·00
*c. Deep olive* (1919) .. .. .. 2·75 6·00
ca. Printed both sides .. .. .. † £5500
*d. Dull yellowish green* (on thick greyish paper) (1920) .. .. .. 4·50 18·00
61 9 1d. orange-red .. .. .. .. 3·75 2·50
a. Perf 14 (line). *Orge-vermilion* (1914) 6·00 1·75
b. Perf 14 (line). *Vermilion* (1918) .. † £550
*c. Orange-vermilion* (1919) .. .. 3·25 2·75
*d. Orange-vermilion* (on thick greyish paper) (1920) .. .. .. 5·50 1·60
62 2d. maroon .. .. .. .. 9·00 17·00
a. Perf 14 (line). *Deep reddish purple* (1914) .. .. .. .. 45·00 50·00
b. Perf 14 (line). *Maroon* (1918) .. 50·00 55·00
*c. Deep reddish purple* (1919) .. .. 5·00 13·00
63 2½d. deep bright blue .. .. .. 11·00 16·00
a. Perf 14 (line). *Deep bright blue* (1914) 12·00 15·00
b. Perf 14 (line). *Deep blue* (1916, 1918) 12·00 15·00
*c. Deep blue* (1919) .. .. .. 5·50 14·00
64 6d. yellow-orange .. .. .. 11·00 17·00
*a. Brown-orange* (1919) .. .. 9·00 23·00
65 1s. light bistre-brown .. .. .. 26·00 27·00
*a. Pale bistre-brown* (1919) .. .. 35·00 42·00
*b. Deep brown* (on thick greyish paper) (1920) .. .. .. .. 32·00 75·00
66 10 3s. slate-green .. .. .. 55·00 70·00
67 5s. deep rose-red .. .. .. 60·00 85·00
*a. Reddish maroon* (1914) .. .. £130 £140
*b. Maroon* (1916) .. .. .. 65·00 85·00
68 10s. red/*green* (1914) .. .. .. £140 £200
69 £1 black/*red* (1914) .. .. .. £350 £400
60/9 (*incl* 67*b*) .. .. *Set of* 11 £650 £800
60/9 (*incl* 67*a*) Optd "Specimen" *Set of* 11 £1200

The exact measurement of the comb perforation used for Type **9** is 13.7 × 13.9. The line perforation, used for the 1914, 1916 and 1918 printings and for all the high values in Type **10**, measured 14.1 × 14.1.

It was previously believed that all examples of the 1d. in vermilion with the line perforation were overprinted to form No. 90, but it has now been established that some unoverprinted sheets of No. 61b were used during 1919.

Many of the sheets showed stamps from the left-hand side in a lighter shade than those from the right. It is believed that this was due to the weight of the impression. Such differences are particularly noticeable on the 2½d. 1916 and 1918 printings where the lighter shades, approaching milky blue in appearance, are scarce.

All 1919 printings show weak impressions of the background either side of the head caused by the poor paper quality.

**SOUTH GEORGIA BISECTS.** The 2½d. No. 63*c* and 6d. No. 64*a* were bisected and used as 1d. and 2½d. respectively in S. Georgia in March 1923. This procedure was not authorised from Port Stanley. (*Prices on cover*: 2½d. £4000, 6d. £10000.)

**PORT FOSTER HANDSTAMP.** Postal facilities at Port Foster, Deception Island, South Shetlands were first provided during the 1912–13 whaling season. Permission was given for stamps on cover to be cancelled with a straight-line "PORT FOSTER" handstamp as an indication of origin. The handstamp is known to have been applied to Edward VII 1d. and George V ½d. and 1d. Falkland Islands issues. It is sometimes used in conjunction with a "FALKLAND ISLANDS" circular postmark.

Unused stamps and higher values with this handstamp were, it is believed, subsequently "made to order".

WAR STAMP
(11)

2½D
(12)

**1918** (7 Oct)–**20.** *Optd by Govt Printing Press, Stanley, with T* **11**.
70 9 ½d. deep olive (line perf) (No. 60b) .. 1·00 6·50
*a. Yellow-green* (No. 60) (4.19) .. 7·50
ab. Albino opt .. .. .. £1000
*b. Deep olive* (comb perf) (No. 60*c*) (4.19) 50 6·50
*c. Dull yellowish green* (on thick greyish paper) (No. 60*d*) (5.20) .. 17·00 60·00
71 1d. vermilion (line perf) (No. 61b) .. 3·00 12·00
a. Opt double, one albino .. .. £400
*b. Orange-vermilion* (line perf) (No. 61a) (4.19) .. .. .. .. 7·00
*c. Orange-vermilion* (comb perf) (No. 61c) (4.19) .. .. .. .. 50 3·50
ca. Opt double .. .. .. £1500
*d. Orange-vermilion* (on thick greyish paper) (No. 61*d*) (5.20) .. 55·00 £120
72 1s. light bistre-brown (No. 65) .. 30·00 48·00
*a. Pale bistre-brown* (No. 65*a*) (4.19) 6·00 32·00
ab. Opt double, one albino .. .. £1100
ac. Opt omitted (in pair with normal) .. £5500
*b. Deep brown* (on thick greyish paper) (No. 65*b*) (5.20) .. .. 15·00 38·00
ba. Opt double, one albino .. .. £1100

There were five printings of the "WAR STAMP" overprint, but all, except that in May 1920, used the same setting. Composition of the five printings was as follows:
October 1918. Nos. 70, 71 and 72
January 1919. Nos. 70, 71 and 72
April 1919. Nos. 70*a*/*b*, 71*b*/*c* and 72*a*
October1919. Nos. 70*b*, 71*c* and 72*a*
May 1920. Nos. 70*c*, 71*c*/*d* and 72*b*.

**1921–28.** *Wmk Mult Script CA. P* 14.
73 9 ½d. yellowish green .. .. .. 2·50 2·75
*a. Green* (1925) .. .. .. 2·25 2·75
74 1d. dull vermilion (1924) .. .. 3·00 80
*a. Orange-vermilion* (*shades*) (1925) .. 4·25 80
75 2d. deep brown-purple (1923) .. .. 5·00 4·00
*a. Purple-brown* (1927) .. .. 5·00 4·25
*b. Reddish maroon* (1.28) .. .. 5·50 3·00
76 2½d. deep blue .. .. .. 22·00 15·00
*a. Indigo* (1927) .. .. .. 13·00 20·00
*b. Deep steel-blue* (1.28) .. .. 5·00 16·00
*c. Prussian blue* (10.28) .. .. £375 £550
77 2½d. deep purple/*pale yellow* (1923) .. 3·75 26·00
*a. Pale purple/pale yellow* (1925) .. 4·00 28·00
78 6d. yellow-orange (1925) .. .. 6·50 27·00
79 1s. deep ochre .. .. .. 18·00 42·00
80 10 3s. slate-green (1923) .. .. 80·00 £120
73/80 .. .. .. .. *Set of* 8 £110 £200
73/80 (*incl* 76*a*) Optd "Specimen" .. *Set of* 9 £550

Dates quoted above are those of despatch from Great Britain. No. 76c only occurred in part of the October 1928 printing. The remainder were in the deep steel-blue shade of the January 1928 despatch, No. 76*b*.

**1928** (7 Feb). *No. 75a surch with T* **12**.
115 **9** 2½d. on 2d. purple-brown .. .. £650 £700
a. Surch double .. .. £30000

No. 115 was produced on South Georgia during a shortage of 2½d. stamps. The provisional was withdrawn on 22 February 1928.

**13** Fin Whale and Gentoo Penguins **14**

(Recess P.B.)

**1929** (2 Sept)–**36.** *P* 14. (*a*) *Wmk Mult Script CA.*
116 **13** ½d. green .. .. .. .. .. 60 1·00
117 1d. scarlet .. .. .. .. .. 70 35
*a. Deep red* .. .. .. .. 6·00 12·00
118 2d. grey .. .. .. .. .. 70 70
119 2½d. blue .. .. .. .. .. 70 1·00
120 **14** 4d. orange (1931) .. .. .. 5·50 12·00
*a. Deep orange* .. .. .. .. 20·00 42·00
121 **13** 6d. purple .. .. .. .. 6·00 6·50
*a. Reddish purple* (1936) .. .. 24·00 25·00
122 1s. black/*emerald* .. .. .. 11·00 17·00
*a. On bright emerald* (1936) .. .. 20·00 25·00
123 2s. 6d. carmine/*blue* .. .. .. 22·00 25·00
124 5s. green/*yellow* .. .. .. 40·00 55·00
125 10s. carmine/*emerald* .. .. .. 70·00 95·00

(*b*) *Wmk Mult Crown CA*
126 **13** £1 black/*red* .. .. .. .. £350 £450
116/126 .. .. .. *Set of* 11 £450 £600
116/26 Perf "Specimen" .. *Set of* 11 £1000

Two kinds of perforation exist:
A. Comb perf 13.9:—original values of 1929.
B. Line perf 13.9, 14.2 or compound:—4d. and 1936 printings of ½d., 1d., 6d. and 1s.

**15** Romney Marsh Ram **26** King George V

(Des (except 6d.) by G. Roberts. Eng and recess B.W.)

**1933** (2 Jan). *Centenary of British Administration. T* **15**, **26** *and similar designs. Wmk Mult Script CA. P* 12.
127 ½d. black and green .. .. .. .. 1·50 3·75
128 1d. black and scarlet .. .. .. .. 3·25 1·25
129 1½d. black and blue .. .. .. .. 5·50 7·50
130 2d. black and brown .. .. .. .. 7·00 14·00
131 3d. black and violet .. .. .. .. 9·00 7·50
132 4d. black and orange .. .. .. .. 10·00 12·00
133 6d. black and slate .. .. .. .. 40·00 45·00
134 1s. black and olive-green .. .. .. 30·00 45·00
135 2s. 6d. black and violet .. .. .. £100 £130
136 5s. black and yellow .. .. .. .. £500 £650
*a. Black and yellow-orange* .. .. £1000 £1200
137 10s. black and chestnut .. .. .. £550 £650
138 £1 black and carmine .. .. .. £1300 £1800
127/138 .. .. .. *Set of* 12 £2250 £3000
127/38 Perf "Specimen" .. *Set of* 12 £2250

Designs: *Horiz*—1d. Iceberg; 1½d. Whale-catcher *Bransfield*; 2d. Port Louis; 3d. Map of Falkland Islands; 4d. South Georgia; 6d. Fin Whale; 1s. Government House, Stanley. *Vert*—2s. 6d. Battle Memorial; 5s. King Penguin; 10s. Coat of Arms.

Examples of all values are known with forged Port Stanley postmarks, dated 6 January 1933.

**1935** (7 May). *Silver Jubilee. As Nos. 91/4 of Antigua, but printed by B.W. P* 11 × 12.
139 1d. deep blue and scarlet .. .. .. 1·75 40
b. Short extra flagstaff .. .. .. £130
d. Flagstaff on right-hand turret .. .. 85·00
e. Double flagstaff .. .. .. 85·00
140 2½d. brown and deep blue .. .. .. 3·75 1·25
b. Short extra flagstaff .. .. .. £225
d. Flagstaff on right-hand turret .. .. £150
e. Double flagstaff .. .. .. £150
l. Re-entry on value tablet (R. 8/1) .. £200 £100
141 4d. green and indigo .. .. .. 3·75 1·25
b. Short extra flagstaff .. .. .. £225
d. Flagstaff on right-hand turret .. .. £150
e. Double flagstaff .. .. .. £150
142 1s. slate and purple .. .. .. 4·00 1·25
a. Extra flagstaff .. .. .. £2500 £2500
b. Short extra flagstaff .. .. .. £275
c. Lightning conductor .. .. .. £325
d. Flagstaff on right-hand turret .. .. £200
e. Double flagstaff .. .. .. £200
139/42 .. .. .. *Set of* 4 12·00 3·75
139/42 Perf "Specimen" .. *Set of* 4 £200

For illustrations of plate varieties see Catalogue Introduction.

**1937** (12 May). *Coronation. As Nos. 95/7 of Antigua. P* 11×11½.
143 ½d. green .. .. .. .. .. 30 10
144 1d. carmine .. .. .. .. .. 40 20
145 2½d. blue .. .. .. .. .. 80 35
143/5 .. .. .. .. *Set of* 3 1·40 60
143/5 Perf "Specimen" .. *Set of* 3 £120

**27** Whales' Jaw Bones

(Des G. Roberts (Nos. 146, 148/9, 158 and 160/3). Recess B.W.)

**1938** (3 Jan)–**50.** *Horiz designs as T* **27**. *Wmk Mult Script CA. P* 12.
146 ½d. black and green (*shades*) .. .. 15 30
147 1d. black and carmine .. .. .. 15·00 1·50
*a. Black and scarlet* .. .. .. 3·00 30
148 1d. black and violet (14.7.41) .. .. 90 75
*a. Black and purple-violet* (1.43) .. 2·25 95
149 2d. black and deep violet .. .. .. 1·00 40
150 2d. black and carmine-red (14.7.41) .. 75 2·25
*a. Black and red* (1.43) .. .. .. 75 30
151 2½d. black and bright blue .. .. .. 45 30
152 2½d. black and blue (15.6.49) .. .. 2·25 3·50
153 3d. black and blue (14.7.41) .. .. 2·25 1·25
*a. Black and deep blue* (1.43) .. .. 2·50 1·25
154 4d. black and purple .. .. .. 1·75 50
155 6d. black and brown .. .. .. 4·50 3·50
156 6d. black (15.6.49) .. .. .. 2·75 4·50
157 9d. black and grey-blue .. .. .. 4·00 50
158 1s. pale blue .. .. .. .. 55·00 18·00
*a. Deep blue* (1941) .. .. .. 8·00 2·50
159 1s. 3d. black and carmine-red (10.12.46) .. 1·50 1·10
160 2s. 6d. slate .. .. .. .. 45·00 6·50
161 5s. bright blue and pale brown .. .. 80·00 35·00
*b. Indigo and yellow-brown* (1942) .. £375 £160
*c. Blue and buff-brown* (9.2.50) .. 85·00 42·00
162 10s. black and orange .. .. .. 50·00 27·00
163 £1 black and violet .. .. .. 90·00 45·00
146/63 .. .. .. *Set of* 18 £250 £120
146/63 (*ex* 152, 156) Perf "Specimen" *Set of* 16 £800

Designs:—Nos. 147 and 150, Black-necked Swan; Nos. 148/9, Battle Memorial; Nos. 151 and 153, Flock of sheep; Nos. 152 and 154, Magellan Goose; No. 155/6, R.R.S. *Discovery II*; No. 157, R.R.S. *William Scoresby*; No. 158, Mount Sugar Top; No. 159; Turkey Vultures; No. 160, Gentoo Penguins; No. 161, Southern Sealion; No. 162, Deception Island; No. 163, Arms of Falkland Islands.

**1946** (7 Oct). *Victory. As Nos. 110/11 of Antigua.*
164 1d. dull violet .. .. .. .. 30 15
165 3d. blue .. .. .. .. .. 30 15
164/5 Perf "Specimen" .. .. *Set of* 2 £120

**1948** (1 Nov). *Royal Silver Wedding. As Nos. 112/13 of Antigua.*
166 2½d. ultramarine .. .. .. .. 2·00 70
167 £1 mauve .. .. .. .. .. 90·00 55·00

**1949** (10 Oct). *75th Anniv of Universal Postal Union. As Nos. 114/17 of Antigua.*
168 1d. violet .. .. .. .. .. 1·50 75
169 3d. deep blue .. .. .. .. 4·50 1·50
170 1s. 3d. deep blue-green .. .. .. 5·50 2·25
171 2s. blue .. .. .. .. .. 5·50 5·00
168/71 .. .. .. .. *Set of* 4 15·00 8·50

**39** Sheep **43** Arms of the Colony

(Recess Waterlow)

**1952** (2 Jan). *T* **39**, **43** *and similar designs. Wmk Mult Script CA. P* 13 × 13½ (*vert*) *or* 13½ × 13 (*horiz*).
172 ½d. green .. .. .. .. .. 70 70
173 1d. scarlet .. .. .. .. .. 80 40
174 2d. violet .. .. .. .. .. 3·25 1·50
175 2½d. black and light ultramarine .. .. 95 50
176 3d. deep ultramarine .. .. .. 1·00 75
177 4d. reddish purple .. .. .. 6·50 2·50
178 6d. bistre-brown .. .. .. .. 12·00 1·00
179 9d. orange-yellow .. .. .. .. 7·50 4·50
180 1s. black .. .. .. .. .. 12·00 80
181 1s. 3d. orange .. .. .. .. 4·00 11·00
182 2s. 6d. olive-green .. .. .. 12·00 10·00
183 5s. purple .. .. .. .. .. 6·00 6·50
184 10s. grey .. .. .. .. .. 14·00 30·00
185 £1 black .. .. .. .. .. 22·00 30·00
172/185 .. .. .. *Set of* 14 90·00 90·00

Designs: *Horiz*—1d. R.M.S. *Fitzroy*; 2d. Magellan Goose; 2½d. Map of Falkland Islands; 4d. Auster aircraft; 6d. M.S.S. *John Biscoe*; 9d. View of the Two Sisters; 1s. 3d. Kelp goose and gander; 10s. Southern Sealion and South American Fur Seal; £1 Hulk of *Great Britain*. *Vert*—1s. Gentoo Penguins; 2s. 6d. Sheep-shearing; 5s. Battle Memorial.

**1953** (4 June). *Coronation. As No. 120 of Antigua.*
186 1d. black and scarlet .. .. .. .. 1·00 1·25

**53** M.S.S. *John Biscoe* **54** Austral Thrush

(Recess Waterlow)

**1955–57.** *Designs previously used for King George VI issue bi with portrait of Queen Elizabeth II as in T* **53**. *Wmk Mult Scrij CA. P* 13 × 13½ (*vert*) *or* 13½ × 13 (*horiz*).
187 ½d. green (2.9.57) .. .. .. .. 70 1·2
188 1d. scarlet (2.9.57) .. .. .. .. 1·25 6
189 2d. violet (3.9.56) .. .. .. .. 2·75 4·5
190 6d. deep yellow-brown (1.6.55) .. .. 5·50 6
191 9d. orange-yellow (2.9.57) .. .. .. 23·00 17·(
192 1s. black (15.7.55) .. .. .. .. 3·50 1·2
187/92 .. .. .. .. *Set of* 6 32·00 23·(

Designs: *Horiz*—½d. Sheep; 1d. R.M.S. *Fitzroy*; 2d. Magella Goose; 9d. View of Two Sisters. *Vert*—1s. Gentoo Penguins.

(Recess Waterlow, then D.L.R. (from 9.1.62 onwards))

**1960** (10 Feb)–**66**. *T* **54** *and similar horiz designs. W* w 1: (*upright*). *P* 13½.
193 ½d. black and myrtle-green .. .. 1·75 4
*a. Black and green* (DLR) (9.1.62) .. 5·00 2·0
194 1d. black and scarlet .. .. .. 1·25 3
*a. Black and carmine-red* (DLR) (15.7.63) 4·50 1·5
195 2d. black and blue .. .. .. 2·25 6
*a. Black and deep blue* (DLR) (25.10.66) 8·50 5·0
196 2½d. black and yellow-brown .. .. 1·50 2
197 3d. black and olive .. .. .. 80 1
198 4d. black and carmine .. .. .. 1·25 5
199 5½d. black and violet .. .. .. 1·50 1·0
200 6d. black and sepia .. .. .. 1·50 1
201 9d. black and orange-red .. .. .. 1·50 8
202 1s. black and maroon .. .. .. 80 1
203 1s. 3d. black and ultramarine .. .. 9·00 8·5
204 2s. black and brown-red .. .. .. 27·00 1·5
*a. Black and lake-brown* (DLR) (25.10.66) 55·00 17·0
205 5s. black and turquoise .. .. .. 24·00 8·5
206 10s. black and purple .. .. .. 45·00 11·0
207 £1 black and orange-yellow .. .. 48·00 25·0
193/207 .. .. .. *Set of* 15 £150 50·0

Designs:—1d. Southern Black-backed Gull; 2d. Gento Penguins; 2½d. Long-tailed Meadowlark; 3d. Magellan Geese; 4d Falkland Islands Flightless Steamer Ducks; 5½d. Rockhoppe Penguin; 6d. Black-browed Albatross; 9d. Silvery Grebe; 1s. Magel lanic Oyster-catchers; 1s. 3d. Chilean Teal: 2s. Kelp Geese; 5s. Kin Cormorants; 10s. Common Caracara; £1 Black-necked Swan.

Waterlow

De La Rue

The De La Rue printings of the ½d., 1d., 2d. and 2s. are al from Plate 2 and can be distinguished by the finer lines o shading on the Queen's face, neck and shoulders (appearing as a white face) and also the very faint cross hatching left of the face Apart from this the shades differ in varying degrees. The existing Waterlow plate was used by De La Rue to print initia supplies of the 6d. and these stamps have little to distinguish them from the original printing. A De La Rue Plate 2 wa subsequently used for this value which, although it shows the usual plate characteristics, does not differ in shade from the Waterlow printing.


See also No. 227.

**69** Morse Key **70** One-valve Receiver

(Des M. Goaman. Photo Enschedé)

**1962** (5 Oct). *50th Anniv of Establishment of Radio Communi cations. T* **69/70** *and similar vert design. W* w **12**. *P* 11½ × 11.
208 **69** 6d. carmine-lake and orange .. .. 1·00 3
209 **70** 1s. deep bluish green and yellow-olive 1·25 3
210 – 2s. deep violet and ultramarine .. 1·25 4
208/10 .. .. .. .. *Set of* 3 3·25 9

Design:—2s. Rotary Spark Transmitter.

**1963** (4 June). *Freedom from Hunger. As No. 146 of Antigua.*
211 1s. ultramarine .. .. .. .. 13·00 8

**1963** (2 Sept). *Red Cross Centenary. As Nos. 147/8 of Antigua.*
212 1d. red and black .. .. .. .. 4·00 5
213 1s. red and blue .. .. .. .. 17·00 4·5

**1964** (23 April). *400th Birth Anniv of William Shakespeare. A No. 164 of Antigua.*
214 6d. black .. .. .. .. .. 1·00 3

72 H.M.S. *Glasgow*

(Recess D.L.R.)

**964** (8 Dec) *50th Anniv of the Battle of the Falkland Islands. T* **72** *and similar designs.* W w **12**. *P* 13 × 14 (2s.) *or* 13 (*others*).
15 2½d. black and red .. .. .. .. 6·00 2·25
16 6d. black and light blue .. .. .. 1·00 25
a. Centre Type **72** .. .. .. £16000
17 1s. black and carmine-red .. .. 1·75 60
18 2s. black and blue .. .. .. 2·50 75
15/18 .. .. .. *Set of* 4 10·00 3·50
Designs: *Horiz*—6d. H.M.S. *Kent*; 1s. H.M.S. *Invincible*. *'ert*—2s. Battle Memorial.
It is believed that No. 216a came from a sheet which was first rinted with the centre of the 2½d. and then accidently included mong the supply of the 6d. value and thus received the wrong rame. There have been seventeen reports of stamps showing he error, although it is believed that some of these *may* refer to he same example.

**965** (26 May). *I.T.U. Centenary. As Nos.* 166/7 *of Antigua.*
19 1d. light blue and deep blue .. .. .. 85 20
20 2s. lilac and bistre-yellow .. .. .. 12·00 1·50

**965** (25 Oct). *International Co-operation Year. As Nos.* 168/9 *of Antigua.*
21 1d. reddish purple and turquoise-green .. 1·50 20
22 1s. deep bluish green and lavender .. .. 7·50 1·10

**966** (24 Jan). *Churchill Commemoration. As Nos.* 170/3 *of Antigua.*
23 ½d. new blue .. .. .. .. .. 65 30
24 1d. deep green .. .. .. .. .. 2·25 15
25 1s. brown .. .. .. .. .. 6·50 80
26 2s. bluish violet .. .. .. .. 8·00 1·25
23/6 .. .. .. .. *Set of* 4 15·00 2·25

**966** (25 Oct). *As No.* 193*a*, *but wmk* w **12** *sideways*.
27 **54** ½d. black and green .. .. .. 30 30

**76** Globe and Human Rights Emblem

**77** Dusty Miller

(Des M. Farrar Bell. Photo Harrison)

**968** (4 July). *Human Rights Year.* W w **12**. *P* 14 × 14½.
28 **76** 2d. multicoloured .. .. .. 50 15
a. Yellow omitted ("1968" white) .. £800
29 6d. muticoloured .. .. .. .. 55 15
30 1s. multicoloured .. .. .. .. 60 15
31 2s. multicoloured .. .. .. .. 70 30
28/31 .. .. .. .. *Set of* 4 2·10 65

(Des Sylvia Goaman. Photo Harrison)

**968** (9 Oct). *Flowers. Designs as T* **77**. *Chalk-surfaced paper.* W w **12** (*sideways on vert designs*). *P* 14.
232 ½d. multicoloured .. .. .. .. 15 40
233 1½d. multicoloured .. .. .. .. 20 15
234 2d. multicoloured .. .. .. .. 30 15
235 3d. multicoloured .. .. .. .. 1·25 15
236 3½d. multicoloured .. .. .. .. 30 15
237 4½d. multicoloured .. .. .. .. 50 50
238 5½d. olive-yellow, brown and yellow-green .. 50 80
239 6d. carmine, black and yellow-green .. 50 20
240 1s. multicoloured .. .. .. .. 60 50
241 1s. 6d. multicoloured .. .. .. 4·50 8·50
242 2s. multicoloured .. .. .. .. 5·50 6·50
243 3s. multicoloured .. .. .. .. 9·00 5·50
244 5s. multicoloured .. .. .. .. 24·00 13·00
245 £1 multicoloured .. .. .. .. 13·00 2·00
232/245 .. .. .. *Set of* 14 55·00 35·00
Designs: *Horiz*—1½d. Pig Vine; 3½d. Sea Cabbage; 5½d. Arrowleaf Marigold; 6d. Diddle Dee; 1s. Scurvy Grass; 5s. Felton's Flower. *Vert*—2d. Pale Maiden; 3d. Dog Orchid; 4½d. Vanilla Daisy; 1s. 6d. Prickly Burr; 2s. Fachine; 3s. Lavender; £1 Yellow Orchid.
For stamps inscribed in decimal currency see Nos. 276/88, 293/5 and 315.

**91** DHC-2 Beaver Floatplane

(Des V. Whiteley. Litho Format)

**1969** (8 Apr). *21st Anniv of Government Air Services. T* **91** *and similar horiz designs. Multicoloured.* W w **12** (*sideways*). *P* 14.
246 2d. Type **91** .. .. .. .. .. 35 30
247 6d. "Norseman" .. .. .. .. 40 35
248 1s. "Auster" .. .. .. .. .. 50 35
249 2s. Falkland Islands Arms .. .. .. 1·75 70
246/9 .. .. .. .. *Set of* 4 2·75 1·50

**92** Holy Trinity Church, 1869

(Des G. Drummond. Litho Format)

**1969** (30 Oct). *Centenary of Bishop Stirling's Consecration. T* **92** *and similar horiz designs.* W w **12** (*sideways*). *P* 14.
250 2d. black, grey and apple-green .. .. 40 30
251 6d. black, grey and orange-red .. .. 50 30
252 1s. black, grey and lilac .. .. .. 55 30
253 2s. multicoloured .. .. .. .. 80 55
250/3 .. .. .. .. *Set of* 4 2·00 1·25
Designs:—6d. Christ Church Cathedral, 1969; 1s. Bishop Stirling; 2s. Bishop's Mitre.

**96** Mounted Volunteer

**97** S.S. *Great Britain* (1843)

(Des R. Granger Barrett. Litho B.W.)

**1970** (30 Apr). *Golden Jubilee of Defence Force. T* **96** *and similar designs. Multicoloured.* W w **12** (*sideways on* 2d. *and* 1s.). *P* 13.
254 2d. Type **96** .. .. .. .. .. 1·90 50
255 6d. Defence Post (*horiz*) .. .. .. 2·00 50
256 1s. Corporal in Number One Dress Uniform 2·25 50
257 2s. Defence Force Badge (*horiz*) .. .. 4·00 75
254/7 .. .. .. .. *Set of* 4 9·00 2·00

(Des V. Whiteley. Litho J.W.)

**1970** (30 Oct). *Restoration of S.S. "Great Britain". T* **97** *and views of the ship at different dates. Multicoloured.* W w **12** (*sideways*). *P* 14½ × 14.
258 2d. Type **97** .. .. .. .. .. 1·75 40
259 4d. In 1845 .. .. .. .. .. 2·00 80
260 9d. In 1876 .. .. .. .. .. 2·00 80
261 1s. In 1886 .. .. .. .. .. 2·00 80
262 2s. In 1970 .. .. .. .. .. 2·25 90
258/62 .. .. .. .. *Set of* 5 9·00 3·25

½p

**(98)**

**99** Dusty Miller

**1971** (15 Feb). *Decimal Currency. Nos.* 232/44 *surch as T* **98**. W w **12** (*sideways on vert designs*). *P* 14.
263 ½p. on ½d. multicoloured .. .. .. 25 20
264 1p. on 1½d. multicoloured .. .. .. 30 15
a. Error. Surch 5p. .. .. .. £325
b. Do. but surch at right .. .. .. £750
c. Surch albino .. .. .. .. £150
d. Surch albino in pair with normal .. £1600
265 1½p. on 2d. multicoloured .. .. .. 30 15
266 2p. on 3d. multicoloured .. .. .. 50 20
267 2½p. on 3½d. multicoloured .. .. .. 30 20
268 3p. on 4½d. multicoloured .. .. .. 30 20
269 4p. on 5½d. olive-yellow, brown & yell-grn 30 20
270 5p. on 6d. carmine, black and yellow-green 30 20
271 6p. on 1s. multicoloured .. .. .. 5·50 2·50
272 7½p. on 1s. 6d. multicoloured .. .. 8·00 3·25
273 10p. on 2s. multicoloured .. .. .. 8·50 3·00
274 15p. on 3s. multicoloured .. .. .. 6·50 2·75
275 25p. on 5s. multicoloured .. .. .. 7·00 3·25
263/75 .. .. .. .. *Set of* 13 35·00 15·00

**1972** (1 June). *As Nos.* 232/44, *but Glazed, ordinary paper and with values inscr in decimal currency as T* **99**. W w **12** (*sideways on* ½, 1½, 2, 3, 7½, 10 *and* 15*p.*). *P* 14.
276 ½p. multicoloured .. .. .. .. 35 1·75
277 1p. multicoloured (as 1½d.) .. .. .. 30 40
278 1½p. multicoloured (as 2d.) .. .. .. 30 1·00
279 2p. multicoloured (as 3d.) .. .. .. 8·50 1·25
280 2½p. multicoloured (as 3½d.) .. .. .. 35 1·00
281 3p. multicoloured (as 4½d.) .. .. .. 35 1·00
282 4p. olive-yellow, brown & yell-grn (as 5½d.) 40 50
283 5p. carmine, black and yellow-green (as 6d.) 40 55
284 6p. multicoloured (as 1s.) .. .. .. 17·00 9·50
285 7½p. multicoloured (as 1s. 6d.) .. .. 1·50 4·00
286 10p. multicoloured (as 2s.) .. .. .. 7·50 4·50
287 15p. multicoloured (as 3s.) .. .. .. 4·50 5·00
288 25p. multicoloured (as 5s.) .. .. .. 4·50 6·00
276/88 .. .. .. .. *Set of* 13 42·00 32·00
See also Nos. 293/5 and 315.

**100** Romney Marsh Sheep and Southern Sealions

(Des (from photograph by D. Groves) and photo Harrison)

**1972** (20 Nov). *Royal Silver Wedding. Multicoloured; background colour given.* W w **12**. *P* 14 × 14½.
289 **100** 1p. grey-green .. .. .. .. 30 25
290 10p. bright blue .. .. .. .. 70 85

**1973** (14 Nov). *Royal Wedding. As Nos.* 165/6 *of Anguilla. Centre multicoloured.* W w **12** (*sideways*). *P* 13½.
291 5p. bright mauve .. .. .. .. 25 10
292 15p. brown-ochre .. .. .. .. 40 20

**1974** (25 Feb–18 Oct). *As Nos.* 276, 279 *and* 284, *but wmk upright on* ½*p. and* 2*p. and sideways on* 6*p.* *P* 14.
293 ½p. multicoloured (18.10.74) .. .. .. 11·00 20·00
294 2p. multicoloured .. .. .. .. 13·00 2·75
295 6p. multicoloured (28.3.74) .. .. .. 2·00 2·25
293/5 .. .. .. .. *Set of* 3 23·00 23·00

**101** South American Fur Seal

**102** 19th-Century Mail-coach

(Des J. Cooter. Litho Walsall)

**1974** (6 Mar). *Tourism. T* **101** *and similar horiz designs. Multicoloured.* W w **12**. *P* 14.
296 2p. Type **101** .. .. .. .. .. 2·25 1·00
297 4p. Trout-fishing .. .. .. .. 3·00 1·25
298 5p. Rockhopper penguins .. .. .. 7·00 2·25
299 15p. Long-tailed Meadowlark .. .. .. 10·00 3·25
296/9 .. .. .. .. *Set of* 4 20·00 7·00

(Des PAD Studio. Litho Questa)

**1974** (31 July). *Centenary of Universal Postal Union. T* **102** *and similar vert designs. Multicoloured.* W w **12** (*sideways*). *P* 14.
300 2p. Type **102** .. .. .. .. .. 25 25
301 5p. Packet ship, 1841 .. .. .. .. 35 45
302 8p. First U.K. aerial post, 1911 .. .. 40 55
303 16p. Ship's catapult mail, 1920's .. .. 60 75
300/3 .. .. .. .. *Set of* 4 1·40 1·75

**103** Churchill and Houses of Parliament

(Des G. Vasarhelyi. Litho Enschedé)

**1974** (30 Nov). *Birth Centenary of Sir Winston Churchill. T* **103** *and similar horiz design. Multicoloured.* W w **12**. *P* 13½.
304 16p. Type **103** .. .. .. .. .. 1·40 1·40
305 20p. Churchill and warships .. .. .. 1·90 1·60
**MS**306 108 × 83 mm. Nos. 304/5 .. .. .. 8·00 7·00

**104** H.M.S. *Exeter*

**105** Seal and Flag Badge

(Des J.W. Litho Harrison)

**1974** (13 Dec). *35th Anniv of the Battle of the River Plate. T* **104** *and similar horiz designs. Multicoloured.* W w **12** (*sideways*). *P* 14.
307 2p. Type **104** .. .. .. .. .. 2·50 1·60
308 6p. H.M.N.Z. *Achilles* .. .. .. .. 4·00 3·00
309 8p. *Admiral Graf Spee* .. .. .. .. 4·50 4·25
310 16p. H.M.S. *Ajax* .. .. .. .. 7·50 10·00
307/10 .. .. .. .. *Set of* 4 17·00 17·00

(Des PAD Studio. Litho Walsall)

**1975** (28 Oct). *50th Anniv of Heraldic Arms. T* **105** *and similar vert designs. Multicoloured.* W w 14 (*inverted*). P 14.

| | | | |
|---|---|---|---|
| 311 | 2p. Type **105** | 50 | 35 |
| 312 | 7½p. Coat of arms, 1925 | 1·00 | 1·00 |
| 313 | 10p. Coat of arms, 1948 | 1·10 | 1·25 |
| 314 | 16p. Arms of the Dependencies, 1952 | 1·75 | 1·60 |
| 311/14 | *Set of* 4 | 4·00 | 3·75 |

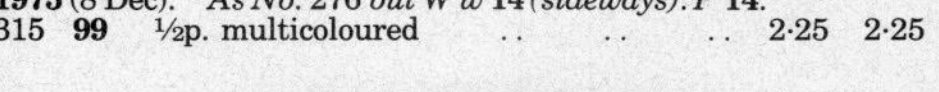

**1975** (8 Dec). *As No. 276 but* W w 14 (*sideways*). P 14.

| | | | | |
|---|---|---|---|---|
| 315 | **99** | ½p. multicoloured | 2·25 | 2·25 |

**106** ½p. Coin and Trout

(Des G. Drummond. Litho Questa)

**1975** (31 Dec). *New Coinage. T* **106** *and similar horiz designs each showing coin as T* **106**. *Multicoloured.* W w 12 (*sideways*). P 14.

| | | | |
|---|---|---|---|
| 316 | 2p. Type **106** | 85 | 45 |
| 317 | 5½p. Gentoo Penguin and 1p. coin | 1·00 | 90 |
| 318 | 8p. Magellan Goose and 2p. coin | 1·10 | 1·25 |
| 319 | 10p. Black-browed Albatross and 5p. coin | 1·40 | 1·40 |
| 320 | 16p. Southern Sealion and 10p. coin | 1·75 | 1·75 |
| 316/20 | *Set of* 5 | 5·50 | 5·25 |

**107** Gathering Sheep

(Des PAD Studio. Litho J.W.)

**1976** (28 Apr). *Sheep Farming Industry. T* **107** *and similar horiz designs. Multicoloured.* W w 14 (*sideways*). P 13½.

| | | | |
|---|---|---|---|
| 321 | 2p. Type **107** | 45 | 30 |
| 322 | 7½p. Shearing | 1·10 | 75 |
| 323 | 10p. Dipping | 1·40 | 95 |
| 324 | 20p. Shipping | 2·00 | 1·60 |
| 321/4 | *Set of* 4 | 4·50 | 3·25 |

**108** The Queen awaiting Anointment

(Des M. and G. Shamir; adapted J.W. Litho Questa)

**1977** (7 Feb–1 Nov). *Silver Jubilee. T* **108** *and similar horiz designs. Multicoloured.* P 13½. (*a*) W w 14 (*sideways*).

| | | | |
|---|---|---|---|
| 325 | 6p. Visit of Prince Philip, 1957 | 1·50 | 95 |
| 326 | 11p. Queen Elizabeth, ampulla and anointing spoon | 80 | 75 |
| | a. Booklet pane of 4 with blank margins (1.11.77) | 3·25 | |
| 327 | 33p. Type **108** | 1·00 | 1·25 |
| | a. Booklet pane of 4 with blank margins (1.11.77) | 4·00 | |
| | (*b*) W w 12 (*sideways*) (*from booklets only*) (1.11.77) | | |
| 327*b* | 6p. Visit of Prince Philip,1957 | 3·50 | 3·25 |
| | ba. Booklet pane of 4 with blank margins | 14·00 | |
| 325/7*b* | *Set of* 4 | 6·50 | 5·50 |

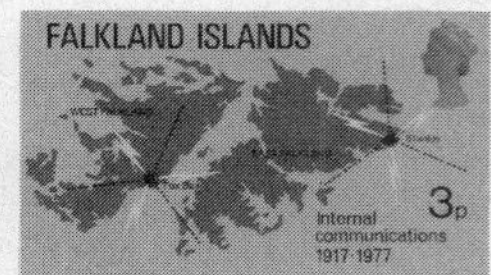

**109** Map of Falkland Islands

(Des K. Penny. Litho Questa)

**1977** (24 Oct). *Telecommunications. T* **109** *and similar horiz designs. Multicoloured.* W w 14 (*sideways*). P 14½.

| | | | |
|---|---|---|---|
| 328 | 3p. Type **109** | 35 | 15 |
| 329 | 11p. Ship to shore communications | 75 | 40 |
| 330 | 40p. Telex and telephone service | 2·50 | 1·40 |
| 328/30 | *Set of* 3 | 3·25 | 1·75 |

**110** *A.E.S.*, 1957–74

(Des J. Smith; adapted R. Granger Barrett. Litho Questa)

**1978** (25 Jan)–**82**. *Mail Ships. Horiz designs as T* **110**. *Multicoloured.* W w 14 (*sideways*). P 14. *A. Printed without imprint date. B. With imprint date ("1982") at foot of designs* (13.7.82*).

| | | A | | B | |
|---|---|---|---|---|---|
| 331 | 1p. Type **110** | 20 | 20 | 45 | 70 |
| 332 | 2p. *Darwin*, 1957–73 | 30 | 20 | 50 | 70 |
| 333 | 3p. *Merak-N.*, 1951–2 | 25 | 30 | 65 | 70 |
| 334 | 4p. *Fitzroy*, 1936–57 | 30 | 30 | 65 | 75 |
| 335 | 5p. *Lafonia*, 1936–41 | 30 | 30 | 65 | 75 |
| 336 | 6p. *Fleurus*, 1924–33 | 30 | 30 | 65 | 75 |
| 337 | 7p. *Falkland*, 1914–34 | 30 | 50 | 70 | 85 |
| 338 | 8p. *Oravia*, 1900–12 | 35 | 40 | 70 | 1·00 |
| 339 | 9p. *Memphis*, 1890–97 | 35 | 40 | 70 | 1·00 |
| 340 | 10p. *Black Hawk*, 1873–80 | 35 | 35 | 70 | 1·00 |
| 341 | 20p. *Foam*, 1863–72 | 1·75 | 1·50 | 1·25 | 1·60 |
| 342 | 25p. *Fairy*, 1857–61 | 1·75 | 2·00 | 1·25 | 2·00 |
| 343 | 50p. *Amelia*, 1852–54 | 2·25 | 3·00 | 2·25 | 2·75 |
| 344 | £1 *Nautilus*, 1846–48 | 4·00 | 6·00 | 2·50 | 4·50 |
| 345 | £3 *Hebe*, 1842–46 | 11·00 | 16·00 | 5·50 | 9·50 |
| 331/45 | *Set of* 15 | 21·00 | 28·00 | 17·00 | 26·00 |

*Nos. 331B/45B were not available locally until 1 December 1982.

**111** Short "Hythe" at Stanley

(Des L. McCombie. Litho Walsall)

**1978** (28 Apr). *26th Anniv of First Direct Flight, Southampton–Port Stanley. T* **111** *and similar horiz design. Multicoloured.* W w 14 (*sideways*). P 14.

| | | | |
|---|---|---|---|
| 346 | 11p. Type **111** | 2·00 | 1·25 |
| 347 | 33p. Route map and Short "Hythe" | 2·50 | 1·75 |

**112** Red Dragon of Wales

**113** First Fox Bay P.O. and 1d. Stamp of 1878

(Des C. Abbott. Litho Questa)

**1978** (2 June). *25th Anniv of Coronation. T* **112** *and similar vert designs.* P 15.

| | | | |
|---|---|---|---|
| 348 | 25p. bistre, bright blue and silver | 1·00 | 1·00 |
| | a. Sheetlet. Nos. 348/50 × 2 | 6·00 | |
| 349 | 25p. multicoloured | 1·00 | 1·00 |
| 350 | 25p. bistre, bright blue and silver | 1·00 | 1·00 |
| 348/50 | *Set of* 3 | 2·75 | 2·75 |

Designs:—No. 348, Type **112**; No. 349, Queen Elizabeth II; No. 350, Hornless Ram.

Nos. 348/50 were printed together in small sheets of 6, containing two *se-tenant* strips of 3, with horizontal gutter margin between.

(Des J. Cooter. Litho B.W.)

**1978** (8 Aug). *Centenary of First Falkland Is Postage Stamps. T* **113** *and similar vert designs. Multicoloured.* W w 14. P 13½ × 13.

| | | | |
|---|---|---|---|
| 351 | 3p. Type **113** | 20 | 20 |
| 352 | 11p. Second Stanley P.O. and 4d. stamp of 1879 | 35 | 40 |
| 353 | 15p. New Island P.O. and 6d. stamp of 1878 | 40 | 50 |
| 354 | 22p. First Stanley P.O. and 1s. stamp of 1878 | 70 | 65 |
| 351/4 | *Set of* 4 | 1·50 | 1·60 |

**114** *Macrocystis pyrifera*

**115** Britten-Norman "Islander" over Falkland Islands

(Des I. Strange. Litho Questa)

**1979** (19 Feb). *Kelp and Seaweed. T* **114** *and similar multicoloured designs.* W w 14 (*sideways on* 11 *and* 15p.). P 14.

| | | | |
|---|---|---|---|
| 355 | 3p. Type **114** | 20 | 15 |
| 356 | 7p. *Durvillea* sp | 40 | 25 |
| 357 | 11p. *Lessonia* sp (*horiz*) | 50 | 30 |
| 358 | 15p. *Callophyllis* sp (*horiz*) | 70 | 35 |
| 359 | 25p. *Iradaea* sp | 90 | 55 |
| 355/9 | *Set of* 5 | 2·50 | 1·40 |

(Des G. Hutchins. Litho Rosenbaum Bros, Vienna)

**1979** (1 May). *Opening of Stanley Airport. T* **115** *and similar horiz designs showing diagrammatic drawings. Multicoloured.* W w 14 (*sideways*). P 13½.

| | | | |
|---|---|---|---|
| 360 | 3p. Type **115** | 30 | 20 |
| 361 | 11p. Fokker "F27" over South Atlantic | 70 | 60 |
| 362 | 15p. Fokker "F28" over Airport | 80 | 60 |
| 363 | 25p. Cessna "172 (Skyhawk)", Britten-Norman "Islander", Fokker "F27" and "F28" over runway | 1·50 | 80 |
| 360/3 | *Set of* 4 | 3·00 | 2·00 |

**116** Sir Rowland Hill and 1953 Coronation 1d. Commemorative

(Des J.W. Litho Questa)

**1979** (27 Aug). *Death Centenary of Sir Rowland Hill. T* **116** *and similar multicoloured designs showing stamps and portrait.* W w 14 (*sideways on* 3 *and* 25p.). P 14.

| | | | |
|---|---|---|---|
| 364 | 3p. Type **116** | 25 | 25 |
| 365 | 11p. 1878 1d. stamp (*vert*) | 50 | 70 |
| 366 | 25p. Penny Black | 75 | 85 |
| 364/6 | *Set of* 3 | 1·40 | 1·60 |
| **MS**367 | 137 × 98 mm. 33p. 1916 5s. stamp (*vert*) | 85 | 1·50 |

**117** Mail Drop by "Beaver" Aircraft

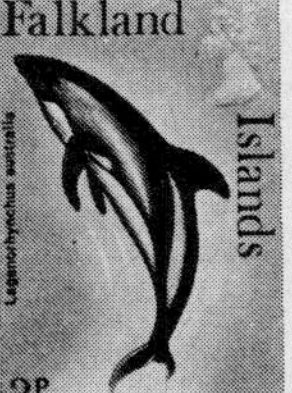

**118** Peale's Dolphin

(Des A. Peake; adapted J.W. Litho Questa)

**1979** (26 Nov). *Centenary of U.P.U. Membership. T* **117** *and similar horiz designs. Multicoloured.* W w 14 (*sideways*). P 14.

| | | | |
|---|---|---|---|
| 368 | 3p. Type **117** | 20 | 20 |
| 369 | 11p. Mail by horseback | 45 | 55 |
| 370 | 25p. Mail by schooner *Gwendolin* | 75 | 1·00 |
| 368/70 | *Set of* 3 | 1·25 | 1·60 |

(Des I. Strange. Litho Harrison)

**1980** (25 Feb). *Dolphins and Porpoises. T* **118** *and similar designs.* W w 14 (*sideways on* 6, 7, 15 *and* 25p.). P 14.

| | | | |
|---|---|---|---|
| 371 | 3p. black, chestnut and blue | 30 | 25 |
| 372 | 6p. multicoloured | 40 | 40 |
| 373 | 7p. multicoloured | 40 | 40 |
| 374 | 11p. black, new blue and rose-red | 70 | 65 |
| 375 | 15p. black, chestnut and greyish blue | 80 | 75 |
| 376 | 25p. multicoloured | 1·25 | 1·25 |
| 371/6 | *Set of* 6 | 3·50 | 3·25 |

Designs: *Horiz*—6p. Commerson's Dolphin; 7p. Hourglass Dolphin; 15p. Dusky Dolphin; 25p. Killer Whale. *Vert*—11p. Spectacled Porpoise.

**119** 1878 Falkland Islands Postmark

(Des G. Hutchins. Litho Walsall)

**1980** (6 May). *"London 1980" International Stamp Exhibition. T* **119** *and similar horiz designs showing postmarks.* W w 14 (*sideways*). P 14.

| | | | |
|---|---|---|---|
| 377 | 11p. black, gold and light blue | 30 | 35 |
| | a. Block of 6. Nos. 377/82 | 1·60 | |
| 378 | 11p. black, gold and greenish yellow | 30 | 35 |
| 379 | 11p. black, gold and blue-green | 30 | 35 |
| 380 | 11p. black, gold and pale violet | 30 | 35 |
| 381 | 11p. black, gold and claret | 30 | 35 |
| 382 | 11p. black, gold and flesh | 30 | 35 |
| 377/82 | *Set of* 6 | 1·60 | 1·90 |

Designs:—No. 377, Type **119**; No. 378, 1915 New Island; No. 379, 1901 Falkland Islands; No. 380, 1935 Port Stanley; No. 381, 1952 Port Stanley first overseas airmail; No. 382, 1934 Fox Bay.

Nos. 377/82 were printed together, *se-tenant*, as a sheetlet, containing one of each design.

**120** Queen Elizabeth the Queen Mother at Ascot, 1971

(Des Harrison. Litho Questa)

980 (4 Aug). *80th Birthday of Queen Elizabeth the Queen Mother. W w* **14** *(sideways). P* 14.
83 **120** 11p. multicoloured .. .. .. 40 30

**121** Forster's Caracara

(Des I. Strange. Litho Secura, Singapore)

980 (11 Aug). *Birds of Prey. T* **121** *and similar horiz designs. Multicoloured. W w* **14** *(sideways). P* 13 × 13½.
384 3p. Type **121** .. .. .. 30 25
385 11p. Red-backed Buzzard .. .. .. 70 60
386 15p. Common Caracara .. .. .. 85 75
387 25p. Peregrine Falcon .. .. .. 1·25 1·00
384/7 .. .. .. .. *Set of* 4 2·75 2·40

**122** Stanley

(Des C. Abbott. Litho Rosenbaum Bros, Vienna)

1981 (7 Jan). *Early Settlements. T* **122** *and similar horiz designs. Multicoloured. W w* **14** *(sideways). P* 14.
388 3p. Type **122** .. .. .. 20 15
389 11p. Port Egmont .. .. .. 40 35
390 25p. Port Louis .. .. .. 80 65
391 33p. Mission House, Keppel Island .. .. 1·10 80
388/91 .. .. .. *Set of* 4 2·25 1·75

**123** Sheep

(Des P. Oxenham. Litho Questa)

1981 (9 Jan). *Farm Animals. T* **123** *and similar horiz designs. Multicoloured. W w* **14** *(sideways). P* 14.
392 3p. Type **123** .. .. .. 20 25
393 11p. Cattle .. .. .. 35 55
394 25p. Horse .. .. .. 70 95
395 33p. Dogs .. .. .. 1·00 1·25
392/5 .. .. .. *Set of* 4 2·00 2·75

**124** Bowles and Carver, 1779

**125** Wedding Bouquet from Falkland Islands

(Des I. Strange. Litho Walsall)

1981 (22 May). *Early Maps. T* **124** *and similar horiz designs in black, dull rose and stone* (26p.) *or multicoloured* (*others*). *W w* **14** *(sideways). P* 14.
396 3p. Type **124** .. .. .. 20 20
397 10p. J. Hawkesworth, 1773 .. .. 40 45
398 13p. Eman, Bowen, 1747 .. .. 55 60
399 15p. T. Boutflower, 1768 .. .. 55 65
400 25p. Philippe de Pretot, 1771 .. .. 70 75
401 26p. Bellin *Petite Atlas Maritime*, Paris, 1764 70 75
396/401 .. .. .. *Set of* 6 2·75 3·00

(Des and litho J.W.)

1981 (22 July). *Royal Wedding. T* **125** *and similar vert designs. Multicoloured. W w* **14**. *P* 13½ × 13.
402 10p. Type **125** .. .. .. 45 40
403 13p. Prince Charles riding .. .. 55 50
404 52p. Prince Charles and Lady Diana Spencer 1·00 1·00
402/4 .. .. .. *Set of* 3 1·75 1·75

## COVER PRICES

Cover factors are quoted at the beginning of each country for most issues to 1945. An explanation of the system can be found on page x. The factors quoted do not, however, apply to philatelic covers.

**126** "Handicrafts"

**127** "The Adoration of the Holy Child" (16th-century Dutch artist)

(Des BG Studio. Litho Questa)

1981 (14 Sept). *25th Anniv of Duke of Edinburgh Award Scheme. T* **126** *and similar vert designs. Multicoloured. W w* **14**. *P* 14.
405 10p. Type **126** .. .. .. 30 20
406 13p. "Camping" .. .. .. 50 30
407 15p. "Canoeing" .. .. .. 55 40
408 26p. Duke of Edinburgh .. .. .. 75 60
405/8 .. .. .. *Set of* 4 1·90 1·40

(Des BG Studio. Litho Walsall)

1981 (2 Nov). *Christmas. Paintings. T* **127** *and similar vert designs. Multicoloured. W w* **14**. *P* 14.
409 3p. Type **127** .. .. .. 20 20
410 13p. "The Holy Family in an Italian Landscape" (17th-century Genoan artist) .. 35 45
411 26p. "The Holy Virgin" (Reni) .. .. 55 75
409/11 .. .. .. *Set of* 3 1·00 1·25

**128** Falkland Herring

(Des I. Strange. Litho Questa)

1981 (7 Dec). *Shelf Fishes. T* **128** *and similar multicoloured designs. W w* **14** *(sideways on* 5, 15 *and* 25p.). *P* 14 × 13½ (13, 26p.) *or* 13½ × 14 (*others*).
412 5p. Type **128** .. .. .. 15 15
413 13p. Rock Cod (*vert*) .. .. .. 30 30
414 15p. Patagonian Hake .. .. .. 35 35
415 25p. Southern Blue Whiting .. .. 60 65
416 26p. Grey-tailed Skate (*vert*) .. .. 60 65
412/16 .. .. .. *Set of* 5 1·75 1·90

**129** *Lady Elizabeth*, 1913

(Des J. Smith. Litho Questa)

1982 (15 Feb). *Shipwrecks. T* **129** *and similar horiz designs. Multicoloured. W w* **14** *(sideways). P* 14½.
417 5p. Type **129** .. .. .. 30 50
418 13p. *Capricorn*, 1882 .. .. .. 40 70
419 15p. *Jhelum*, 1870 .. .. .. 45 85
420 25p. *Snowsquall*, 1864 .. .. .. 75 1·10
421 26p. *St. Mary*, 1890 .. .. .. 75 1·10
417/21 .. .. .. *Set of* 5 2·40 3·75

### ARGENTINE OCCUPATION
**2 April to 15 June 1982**

Following incidents, involving the illegal presence of Argentine scrap-metal workers on the dependency of South Georgia during March 1982, Argentine forces attacked Port Stanley, the capital of the Falkland Islands early in the morning of 2 April. The small garrison of Royal Marines was overwhelmed and the Governor forced to agree to a cease-fire, before being deported.

South Georgia was occupied by the Argentines on the following day.

British forces, dispatched from the United Kingdom, recaptured South Georgia on 25 April, and, after landing at various points on East Falkland, forced the surrender of the Argentine troops throughout the islands on 15 June.

The last mail to be dispatched from the Falkland Islands prior to the invasion left on 31 March. The Port Stanley Post Office was closed on 2 April, when all current issues were withdrawn. From 5 April an Argentine post office operated in the town, initially accepting mail without stamps, which was then cancelled by a postmark inscribed "ISLAS MALVINAS". Any letters tendered franked with Falkland Islands issues had these cancelled by ball-point pen. A limited range of Argentine stamps was placed on sale from 8 April. The Argentine definitive overprinted "LAS MALVINAS SON ARGENTINAS" for use throughout the country, was also available.

Following the Argentine surrender a rudimentary mail service was operating by 17 June, but the Port Stanley Post Office did not re-open until 24 June.

The last mail from South Georgia before the invasion was sent out on 16 March, although items remaining in the post office there were evacuated by the Deputy Postmaster when he was deported to the United Kingdom by the Argentines. The first mail left after recapture by the British on 2 May.

### BRITISH ADMINISTRATION RESTORED

**130** Charles Darwin

**131** Falkland Islands Coat of Arms

(Des L. Curtis. Litho Questa)

1982 (5 July*). *150th Anniv of Charles Darwin's Voyage. T* **130** *and similar horiz designs. Multicoloured. W w* **14** *(sideways). P* 14.
422 5p. Type **130** .. .. .. 20 20
423 17p. Darwin's microscope .. .. 50 55
424 25p. Falkland Islands Wolf ("Warrah") .. 65 75
425 34p. H.M.S. *Beagle* .. .. .. 85 95
a. Pale brown (background to side panels) omitted .. .. .. £650
422/5 .. .. .. *Set of* 4 2·00 2·25

*It was initially intended that these stamps were to be issued on 19 April. First Day covers were prepared, postmarked with this date, but, because of the Argentine invasion, the stamps were not actually released until 5 July. A postmark showing the actual date of issue was struck alongside the stamps on the First Day covers.

(Des C. Abbott. Litho J.W.)

1982 (16 Aug). *21st Birthday of Princess of Wales. T* **131** *and similar vert designs. Multicoloured. W w* **14**. *P* 13.
426 5p. Type **131** .. .. .. 15 20
427 17p. Princess at Royal Opera House, Covent Garden, November 1981 .. .. 40 50
428 37p. Bride and groom in doorway of St Paul's 75 90
429 50p. Formal portrait .. .. .. 1·00 1·25
426/9 .. .. .. *Set of* 4 2·10 2·50

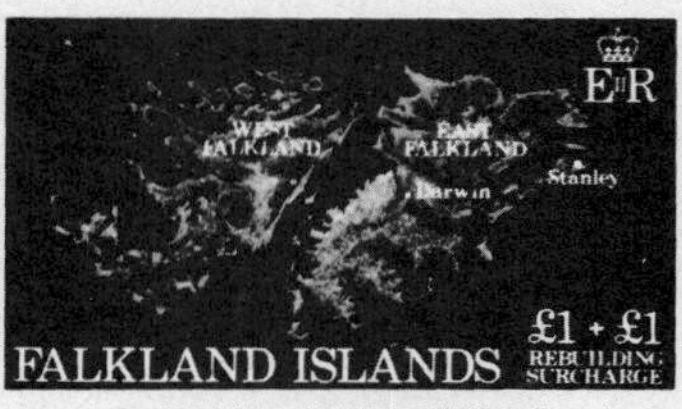


**132** Map of Falkland Islands

(Des PAD Studio. Litho Format)

1982 (13 Sept). *Rebuilding Fund. W w* **14** *(sideways). P* 11.
430 **132** £1 + £1 multicoloured .. .. .. 3·50 4·75

1st PARTICIPATION
COMMONWEALTH GAMES 1982

(**133**)

**134** Blackish Cinclodes

1982 (7 Oct). *Commonwealth Games, Brisbane. Nos.* 335B *and* 342B *optd with T* **133**.
431 5p. *Lafonia*, 1936–41 .. .. .. 15 30
432 25p. *Fairy*, 1857–61 .. .. .. 60 1·10

(Des I. Strange. Litho W. S. Cowells Ltd)

1982 (6 Dec). *Birds of the Passerine Family. T* **134** *and similar vert designs. Multicoloured. W w* **14** *(inverted on* 10p.). *P* 15 × 14½.
433 5p. Type **134** .. .. .. 15 15
434 10p. Black-chinned Siskin .. .. 25 25
435 13p. Short-billed Marsh Wren .. .. 30 30
436 17p. Black-throated Finch .. .. 35 35
437 25p. Correndera Pipit .. .. .. 50 50
438 34p. Dark-faced Ground Tyrant .. .. 65 65
433/8 .. .. .. *Set of* 6 2·00 2·00

**135** Raising Flag, Port Louis, 1833

**136** 1933 British Administration Centenary 3d. Commemorative

(Des I. Strange and J. Sheridan. Litho Questa)

**1983** (3 Jan). *150th Anniv of British Administration. T* **135** *and similar multicoloured designs. W* w **14** *(sideways on 2, 10, 15, 25 and 50p.). P* 14 × 13½ *(1, 5, 20, 40p., £1, £2) or* 13½ × 14 *(others).*

439 1p. Type **135** .. .. .. .. .. .. 20 20
440 2p. Chelsea pensioners and barracks, 1849 *(horiz)* .. .. .. .. .. .. 30 30
441 5p. Development of wool trade, 1874 .. 30 30
442 10p. Ship-repairing trade, 1850–1890 *(horiz)* 60 60
443 15p. Government House, early 20th century *(horiz)* .. .. .. .. .. .. 70 70
444 20p. Battle of Falkland Islands, 1914 .. 90 90
445 25p. Whalebone Arch, 1933 *(horiz)* .. .. 90 90
446 40p. Contribution to War effort, 1939–45 .. 1·40 1·40
447 50p. Duke of Edinburgh's visit, 1957 *(horiz)* .. 1·75 1·75
448 £1 Royal Marine uniforms .. .. .. 2·50 2·50
449 £2 Queen Elizabeth II .. .. .. 3·75 4·50
439/49 .. .. .. .. *Set of* 11 12·00 12·50

(Des L. Curtis. Litho Questa)

**1983** (28 Mar*). *Commonwealth Day. T* **136** *and similar multicoloured designs. W* w **14** *(sideways on 5p., 17p.). P* 14.

450 5p. Type **136** .. .. .. .. .. 15 15
451 17p. 1933 British Administration Centenary ½d. commemorative .. .. .. 35 45
452 34p. 1933 British Administration Centenary 10s. commemorative *(vert)* .. .. 70 80
453 50p. 1983 British Administration 150th anniversary £2 commemorative *(vert)* .. 1·00 1·25
450/3 .. .. .. .. .. *Set of* 4 2·00 2·40

*This is the local date of issue: the Crown Agents released the stamps on 14 March.

**137** British Army advancing across East Falkland

(Des A. Theobald. Litho Questa)

**1983** (14 June). *First Anniv of Liberation. T* **137** *and similar horiz designs. Multicoloured. W* w **14** *(sideways). P* 14.

454 5p. Type **137** .. .. .. .. .. 15 25
455 13p. S.S. *Canberra* and M.V. *Norland* at San Carlos .. .. .. .. .. 30 45
456 17p. R.A.F. Hawker "Harrier" fighter .. 35 55
457 50p. H.M.S. *Hermes* (aircraft carrier) .. 1·00 1·25
454/7 .. .. .. .. .. *Set of* 4 1·60 2·25
**MS**458 169 × 130 mm. Nos. 454/7. P 12 .. .. 2·25 2·25

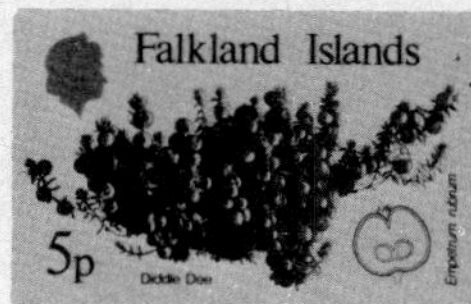


**138** Diddle Dee

(Des A. Chater. Litho Questa)

**1983** (10 Oct). *Native Fruits. T* **138** *and similar horiz designs. Multicoloured. W* w **14** *(sideways). P* 14.

459 5p. Type **138** .. .. .. .. .. 20 20
460 17p. Tea Berry .. .. .. .. .. 45 50
461 25p. Mountain Berry .. .. .. .. 70 65
462 34p. Native Strawberry .. .. .. .. 85 80
459/62 .. .. .. .. *Set of* 4 2·00 1·90

**139** Britten-Norman "Islander"

(Des Harrison. Litho Questa)

**1983** (14 Nov). *Bicentenary of Manned Flight. T* **139** *and similar horiz designs. Multicoloured. W* w **14** *(sideways). P* 14.

463 5p. Type **139** .. .. .. .. .. 15 20
464 13p. "DHC-2 Beaver" .. .. .. .. 35 45
465 17p. Noorduyn "Norseman" .. .. .. 40 50
466 50p. Auster .. .. .. .. .. 1·00 1·25
463/6 .. .. .. .. *Set of* 4 1·75 2·25

17 p

(140)

**1984** (3 Jan). *Nos. 443 and 445 surch as T* **140** *by Govt Printer, Port Stanley.*

467 17p. on 15p. Government House, early 20th century .. .. .. .. .. 60 45
468 22p. on 25p. Whalebone Arch, 1933 .. .. 65 55

**141** *Araneus cinnabarinus* (juvenile spider)

**142** *Wavertree*

(Des I. Strange. Litho Questa)

**1984** (3 Jan)–**86**. *Insects and Spiders. T* **141** *and similar horiz designs. Multicoloured. W* w **14** *(sideways). P* 14×14½.

*A. Without imprint date*

469A 1p. Type **141** .. .. .. .. 20 30
470A 2p. *Alopophion occidentalis* (fly) .. 50 70
471A 3p. *Pareuxoina falkandica* (moth) .. 30 30
472A 4p. *Lissopterus quadrinotatus* (beetle) .. 20 30
473A 5p. *Issoria cytheris* (butterfly) .. .. 20 30
474A 6p. *Araneus cinnabarinus* (adult spider) 20 30
475A 7p. *Trachysphyrus penai* (fly) .. .. 20 30
476A 8p. *Caphornia ochricraspia* (moth) .. 20 30
477A 9p. *Caneorhinus biangulatus* (weevil) .. 20 30
478A 10p. *Syrphus octomaculatus* (fly) .. .. 20 30
479A 20p. *Malvinius compressiventris* (weevil) 1·50 75
480A 25p. *Metius blandus* (beetle) .. .. 75 90
481A 50p. *Parudenus falkandicus* (cricket) .. 1·00 1·50
482A £1 *Emmenomma beauchenieus* (spider) 1·75 2·25
483A £3 *Cynthia carye* (butterfly) .. .. 5·00 6·00
469A/83A .. .. .. *Set of* 15 11·00 13·50

*B. With imprint date at foot of design*

470B 2p. *Alopophion occidentalis* (fly) (19.5.86) 60 60

(Des A. Theobald. Litho Questa)

**1984** (7 May). *250th Anniv of "Lloyd's List" (newspaper). T* **142** *and similar vert designs. Multicoloured. W* w **14**. *P* 14½ × 14.

484 6p. Type **142** .. .. .. .. .. 40 25
485 17p. Port Stanley .. .. .. .. .. 80 50
486 22p. R.M.S. *Oravia* stranded .. .. .. 85 55
487 52p. *Cunard Countess*.. .. .. .. 1·50 1·25
484/7 .. .. .. .. .. *Set of* 4 3·25 2·25

**143** Ship, Aircraft and U.P.U. Logo

**144** Great Grebe

(Des E. Nisbet, adapted L. Curtis. Litho Questa)

**1984** (25 June). *Universal Postal Union Congress, Hamburg. W* w **14** *(sideways). P* 14.

488 **143** 22p. multicoloured .. .. .. .. 55 65

(Des I. Strange. Litho Questa)

**1984** (6 Aug). *Grebes. T* **144** *and similar vert designs. Multicoloured. W* w **14**. *P* 14½.

489 17p. Type **144**.. .. .. .. .. 85 70
490 22p. Silvery Grebe .. .. .. .. 1·00 90
491 52p. White-tufted Grebe .. .. .. 2·25 2·25
489/91 .. .. .. .. *Set of* 3 3·75 3·50

**145** Black-browed Albatross

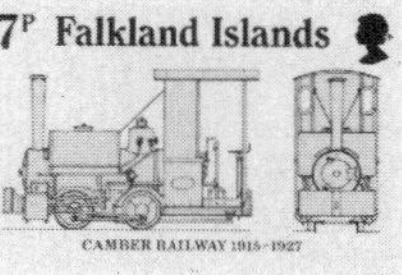


**146** Technical Drawing of "Wren" Class Locomotive

(Des I. Strange. Litho Questa)

**1984** (5 Nov). *Nature Conservation. T* **145** *and similar vert designs. Multicoloured. W* w **14**. *P* 14½ × 14.

492 6p. Type **145**.. .. .. .. .. 90 55
493 17p. Tussock grass .. .. .. .. 1·10 80
494 22p. Dusky Dolphin and Southern Sealion .. 1·40 1·00
495 52p. *Notothenia* (fish) and krill .. .. 2·00 2·00
492/5 .. .. .. .. .. *Set of* 4 5·00 4·00
**MS**496 130×90 mm. Nos. 492/5 .. .. .. 5·00 4·00

(Des C. Abbott. Litho Questa)

**1985** (18 Feb). *70th Anniv of Camber Railway. T* **146** *and similar horiz designs, each black, deep brown and pale cinnamon. W* w **14** *(sideways). P* 14.

497 7p. Type **146** .. .. .. .. .. 35 30
498 22p. Sail-propelled trolley .. .. .. 70 65
499 27p. Locomotive at work .. .. .. 85 75
500 54p. "Falkland Islands Express" passenger train (75 × 25 *mm*). .. .. .. 1·50 1·50
497/500 .. .. .. .. *Set of* 4 3·00 3·00

**147** Construction Workers' Camp

**148** The Queen Mother on 84th Birthday

(Des N. Shewring. Litho Questa)

**1985** (12 May). *Opening of Mount Pleasant Airport. T* **14** *and similar horiz designs. Multicoloured. W* w **16** *(sideways P* 14½×14.

501 7p. Type **147**.. .. .. .. .. 50 3
502 22p. Building construction .. .. .. 1·00 8
503 27p. Completed airport .. .. .. 1·25 9
504 54p. Airliner over runway .. .. .. 1·60 1·7
501/4 .. .. .. .. .. *Set of* 4 4·00 3·5

(Des A. Theobald (£1), C. Abbott (others). Litho Questa)

**1985** (7 June). *Life and Times of Queen Elizabeth the Quee Mother. T* **148** *and similar vert designs. Multicoloured. W* w **16** *P* 14½×14.

505 7p. Attending reception at Lancaster House .. .. .. .. .. .. 25 2
506 22p. With Prince Charles, Mark Phillips and Princess Anne at Falklands Memorial Service .. .. .. .. .. .. 60 5
507 27p. Type **148**.. .. .. .. .. 70 6
508 54p. With Prince Henry at his christening (from photo by Lord Snowdon).. .. 1·25 1·2
505/8 .. .. .. .. .. *Set of* 4 2·50 2·2
**MS**509 91×73 mm. £1 With Princess Diana at Trooping the Colour. Wmk sideways .. .. 2·00 2·2

**149** Captain J. McBride and H.M.S. *Jason*, 1765

**150** Painted Keyhole Limpet

(Des O. Bell. Litho Questa)

**1985** (30 Sept). *Early Cartographers. T* **149** *and similar hori designs. Multicoloured. W* w **14** *(sideways). P* 14×14½.

510 7p. Type **149**.. .. .. .. .. 60 3
511 22p. Commodore J. Byron and H.M.S. *Dolphin* and *Tamar*, 1765 .. .. .. 90 7
512 27p. Vice-Admiral R. FitzRoy and H.M.S. *Beagle*, 1831 .. .. .. .. 95 7
513 54p. Admiral Sir B. J. Sullivan and H.M.S. *Philomel*, 1842 .. .. .. .. 1·60 1·5
510/13 .. .. .. .. *Set of* 4 3·50 3·0

(Des I. Strange. Litho Questa)

**1985** (4 Nov). *Early Naturalists. Vert designs as T* **35** *of Britis Antarctic Territory. Multicoloured. W* w **14**. *P* 14½×14.

514 7p. Philibert Commerson and Commerson's Dolphin .. .. .. .. .. 75 3
515 22p. René Primevère Lesson and *Lessonia sp.* (kelp).. .. .. .. .. 1·25 8
516 27p. Joseph Paul Gaimard and Common Diving Petrel .. .. .. .. 1·60 1·2
517 54p. Charles Darwin and *Calceolaria darwinii* .. .. .. .. .. 1·90 2·0
514/17 .. .. .. .. *Set of* 4 5·00 4·0

(Des I. Strange. Litho Questa)

**1986** (10 Feb). *Seashells. T* **150** *and similar horiz designs Multicoloured. W* w **16** *(sideways). P* 14×14½.

518 7p. Type **150**.. .. .. .. .. 65 3
519 22p. Magellanic Volute .. .. .. 1·25 8
520 27p. Patagonian Scallop .. .. .. 1·40 9
521 54p. Rough Thorn Drupe .. .. .. 2·25 1·6
518/21 .. .. .. .. *Set of* 4 5·00 3·2

(Des A. Theobald. Litho Format)

**1986** (21 Apr). *60th Birthday of Queen Elizabeth II. Vert designs as T* **110** *of Ascension. Multicoloured. W* w **16**. *P* 14×14½.

522 10p. With Princess Margaret at St Paul's, Walden Bury, Welwyn, 1932.. .. 35 25
523 24p. Queen making Christmas television broadcast, 1958 .. .. .. .. 65 55
524 29p. In robes of Order of the Thistle, St. Giles Cathedral, Edinburgh, 1962 .. .. 75 60
525 45p. Aboard Royal Yacht *Britannia*, U.S.A., 1976 .. .. .. .. .. 1·25 95
526 58p. At Crown Agents Head Office, London, 1983 .. .. .. .. .. 1·40 1·25
522/6 .. .. .. .. *Set of* 5 4·00 3·25

## MINIMUM PRICE

The minimum price quote is 10p which represents a handling charge rather than a basis for valuing common stamps. For further notes about prices see introductory pages.

**151** S.S. *Great Britain* crossing Atlantic, 1845

**152** Head of Rockhopper Penguin

(Des O. Bell. Litho Format)

**986** (22 May). *"Ameripex '86" International Stamp Exhibition, Chicago. Centenary of Arrival of S.S. "Great Britain" in Falkland Islands. T* **151** *and similar horiz designs. Multicoloured. W w* **16** *(sideways). P* 14.

27 10p. Type **151** . . . . . . . . 40 30
28 24p. Beached at Sparrow Cove, 1937 . . . . 75 65
29 29p. Refloated on pontoon, 1970 . . . . 85 70
30 58p. Undergoing restoration, Bristol, 1986 . . 1·40 1·25
27/30 . . . . . . *Set of* 4 3·00 2·50
**MS**531 109×109 mm. Nos. 527/30. Wmk upright 3·00 3·25

(Des I. Strange. Litho Questa)

**986** (25 Aug). *Rockhopper Penguins. T* **152** *and similar vert designs. Multicoloured. W w* **16**. *P* 14½×14.

32 10p. Type **152** . . . . . . 60 30
33 24p. Rockhopper Penguins at sea . . . . 1·00 60
34 29p. Courtship display . . . . . . 1·10 65
35 58p. Adult with chick . . . . . . 1·75 1·25
32/5 . . . . . . *Set of* 4 4·00 2·50

**153** Prince Andrew and Miss Sarah Ferguson presenting Polo Trophy, Windsor

**154** Survey Party, Sapper Hill

(Des D. Miller. Litho Questa)

**986** (10 Nov). *Royal Wedding. T* **153** *and similar vert designs. Multicoloured. W w* **16**. *P* 14½×14.

536 17p. Type **153** . . . . . . . . 65 40
537 22p. Prince Andrew and Duchess of York on wedding day . . . . . . 75 50
538 29p. Prince Andrew in battledress at opening of Fox Bay Mill . . . . 90 60
536/8 . . . . . . *Set of* 3 2·10 1·40

(Des L. Curtis. Litho Questa)

**1987** (9 Feb). *Bicentenary of Royal Engineers' Royal Warrant. T* **154** *and similar horiz designs. Multicoloured. W w* **16** *(sideways). P* 14×14½.

539 10p. Type **154** . . . . . . . . 80 35
540 24p. Mine clearance by robot . . . . 1·40 75
541 29p. Boxer Bridge, Stanley . . . . . . 1·60 90
542 58p. Unloading mail, Mount Pleasant Airport . . . . . . 2·25 1·40
539/42 . . . . . . *Set of* 4 5·50 3·00

**155** Southern Sea Lion

**156** *Suillus luteus*

(Des I. Strange. Litho Questa)

**1987** (27 Apr). *Seals. T* **155** *and similar horiz designs. Multicoloured. W w* **16** *(sideways). P* 14½.

543 10p. Type **155** . . . . . . . . 40 25
544 24p. Falkland Fur Seal . . . . . . 1·00 55
545 29p. Southern Elephant Seal . . . . 1·10 65
546 58p. Leopard Seal . . . . . . 1·90 1·25
543/6 . . . . . . *Set of* 4 4·00 2·40

(Des I. Strange. Litho Questa)

**1987** (14 Sept). *Fungi. T* **156** *and similar vert designs. Multicoloured. W w* **16**. *P* 14½×14.

547 10p. Type **156** . . . . . . . . 1·00 75
548 24p. *Mycena* sp. . . . . . . 1·75 1·25
549 29p. *Camarophyllus adonis* . . . . 2·00 1·75
550 58p. *Gerronema schusteri* . . . . 2·75 2·75
547/50 . . . . . . *Set of* 4 6·75 6·00

**157** Victoria Cottage Home, *c* 1912

**158** Morris Truck, Fitzroy, 1940

(Des D. Hartley. Litho Questa)

**1987** (8 Dec). *Local Hospitals. T* **157** *and similar horiz designs. Multicoloured. W w* **16** *(sideways). P* 14.

551 10p. Type **157** . . . . . . . . 30 25
552 24p. King Edward VII Memorial Hospital, *c* 1914 . . . . . . 65 55
553 29p. Churchill Wing, King Edward VII Memorial Hospital, *c* 1953 . . . . 75 60
554 58p. Prince Andrew Wing, New Hospital, 1987 . . . . . . 1·25 1·25
551/4 . . . . . . *Set of* 4 2·75 2·40

(Des D. Hartley. Litho Questa)

**1988** (11 Apr). *Early Vehicles. T* **158** *and similar horiz designs. Multicoloured. W w* **16** *(sideways). P* 14.

555 10p. Type **158** . . . . . . . . 30 25
556 24p. Citroen "Kegresse" half-track, San Carlos, 1929 . . . . . . 65 55
557 29p. Ford one ton truck, Port Stanley, 1933 75 60
558 58p. Ford "Model T" car, Darwin, 1935 . . 1·25 1·25
555/8 . . . . . . *Set of* 4 2·75 2·40

**159** Kelp Goose

(Des I. Strange. Litho Walsall)

**1988** (25 July). *Falkland Islands Geese. T* **159** *and similar horiz designs. Multicoloured. W w* **16** *(sideways). P* 13½×14.

559 10p. Type **159** . . . . . . . . 60 35
560 24p. Magellan ("Upland") Goose . . . . 1·00 60
561 29p. Ruddy-headed Goose . . . . . . 1·10 70
562 58p. Ashy-headed Goose . . . . . . 1·75 1·40
559/62 . . . . . . *Set of* 4 4·00 2·75

(Des D. Miller (10, 24p.), E. Nesbit and D. Miller (29, 58p.). Litho Format)

**1988** (14 Nov). *300th Anniv of Lloyd's of London. Multicoloured designs as T* **123** *of Ascension. W w* **14** *(sideways on 24, 29p.). P* 14.

563 10p. Silver from Lloyd's Nelson Collection . . 25 25
564 24p. Falkland Islands hydroponic market garden (*horiz*) . . . . . . 55 55
565 29p. *A.E.S.* (freighter) (*horiz*) . . . . 60 60
566 58p. *Charles Cooper* (full-rigged sailing ship), 1866 . . . . . . 1·25 1·25
563/6 . . . . . . *Set of* 4 2·40 2·40

**160** *Padua* (barque)

(Des A. Theobald. Litho Questa)

**1989** (28 Feb)–**90**. *Cape Horn Sailing Ships. T* **160** *and similar multicoloured designs. W w* **14** *(sideways on horiz designs). P* 14.

567 1p. Type **160** . . . . . . . . 10 10
568 2p. *Priwall* (barque) (*vert*) . . . . 15 15
569 3p. *Passat* (barque) . . . . . . 15 15
570 4p. *Archibald Russell* (barque) (*vert*) . . 10 10
571 5p. *Pamir* (barque) (*vert*) . . . . 10 15
572 6p. *Mozart* (barquentine) . . . . . . 20 20
573 7p. *Pommern* (barque) . . . . . . 15 20
574 8p. *Preussen* (full-rigged ship) . . . . 15 20
575 9p. *Fennia* (barque) . . . . . . 30 30
576 10p. *Cassard* (barque) . . . . . . 20 25
577 20p. *Lawhill* (barque) . . . . . . 40 45
578 25p. *Garthpool* (barque) . . . . . . 50 55
579 50p. *Grace Harwar* (full-rigged ship) . . 1·00 1·10
580 £1 *Criccieth Castle* (full-rigged ship) . . 2·50 2·75
581 £3 *Cutty Sark* (full-rigged ship) (*vert*) . . 6·00 6·25
582 £5 *Flying Cloud* (full-rigged ship) (2.1.90) 10·00 10·50
567/82 . . . . . . *Set of* 16 20·00 21·00

For 2, 3, 6, 9p. and £1 values watermarked w **16** and with imprint dates see Nos. 613/25.

**161** Southern Right Whale

(Des I. Strange. Litho Questa)

**1989** (15 May). *Baleen Whales. T* **161** *and similar horiz designs. Multicoloured. W w* **16** *(sideways). P* 13½×14.

583 10p. Type **161** . . . . . . . . 45 30
584 24p. Minke Whale . . . . . . . . 90 70
585 29p. Humpback Whale . . . . . . 1·10 75
586 58p. Blue Whale . . . . . . . . 1·90 1·50
583/6 . . . . . . *Set of* 4 4·00 3·00

**162** "Gymkhana" (Sarah Gilding)

**163** Vice-Admiral Sturdee and H.M.S. *Invincible* (battle cruiser)

(Adapted G. Vasarhelyi. Litho Walsall)

**1989** (16 Sept). *Sports Associations' Activities. T* **162** *and similar horiz designs showing children's drawings. Multicoloured. W w* **16** *(sideways). P* 14.

587 5p. Type **162** . . . . . . . . 20 20
588 10p. "Steer Riding" (Karen Steen) . . . . 30 30
589 17p. "Sheep Shearing" (Colin Shepherd) . . 45 45
590 24p. "Sheepdog Trials" (Rebecca Edwards) 60 70
591 29p. "Horse Racing" (Dilys Blackley) . . 70 80
592 45p. "Sack Race" (Donna Newell) . . . . 1·00 1·10
587/92 . . . . . . *Set of* 6 3·00 3·25

(Des C. Collins. Litho B.D.T.)

**1989** (8 Dec). *75th Anniv of Battle of the Falkland Islands and 50th Anniv of Battle of the River Plate. T* **163** *and similar vert designs. Multicoloured. W w* **16**. *P* 13½.

593 10p. Type **163** . . . . . . . . 30 30
594 24p. Vice-Admiral Graf von Spee and *Scharnhorst* (German cruiser) . . 70 75
595 29p. Commodore Harwood and H.M.S. *Ajax* (cruiser) . . . . . . 80 85
596 58p. Captain Langsdorff and *Admiral Graf Spee* (German pocket battleship) . . 1·50 1·60
593/6 . . . . . . *Set of* 4 3·00 3·25

**164** Southern Sea Lions on Kidney Island

**165** Spitfire Mk 1 *Falkland Islands I*

(Des I. Strange. Litho Questa)

**1990** (9 Apr). *Nature Reserves and Sanctuaries. T* **164** *and similar vert designs. Multicoloured. W w* **16**. *P* 14½.

597 12p. Type **164** . . . . . . . . 35 35
598 26p. Black-browed Albatrosses on Beauchene Island . . . . . . 70 70
599 31p. Penguin colony on Bird Island . . 80 80
600 62p. Tussock grass on Elephant Jason Island . . . . . . . . 1·40 1·40
597/600 . . . . . . *Set of* 4 3·00 3·00

(Des A. Theobald. Litho B.D.T.)

**1990** (3 May). *"Stamp World London 90" International Stamp Exhibition, London. Presentation Spitfires. T* **165** *and similar horiz designs. Multicoloured. W w* **14** *(sideways). P* 14.

601 12p. Type **165** . . . . . . . . 40 35
602 26p. Spitfire Mk I *Falkland Islands VII* . . 80 70
603 31p. Cockpit and wing of *Falkland Islands I* 90 80
604 62p. Squadron scramble, 1940 . . . . 1·40 1·40
601/4 . . . . . . *Set of* 4 3·25 3·00
**MS**605 114×100 mm. £1 Spitfire Mk I in action, 1940 . . . . . . . . 2·50 2·50

For No. **MS**605 with additional inscription see No. **MS**628.

(Des D. Miller. Litho Questa)

**1990** (4 Aug). *90th Birthday of Queen Elizabeth the Queen Mother. Vert designs as T* **134** *(26p.) or* **135** *(£1) of Ascension. W w* **16**. *P* 14×15 *(26p.) or* 14½ *(£1).*

606 26p. multicoloured . . . . . . 75 65
607 £1 brownish black and deep carmine-red 2·50 2·75

Designs:—26p. Queen Mother in Dover; £1 On bridge of liner *Queen Elizabeth*, 1946.

## PRICES OF SETS

Set prices are given for many issues, generally those containing three stamps or more. Definitive sets include one of each value or major colour change, but do not cover different perforations, die types or minor shades. Where a choice is possible the set prices are based on the cheapest versions of the stamps included in the listings.

**166** Black-browed Albatrosses

**167** *Gavilea australis*

(Des I. Strange. Litho Questa)

**1990** (3 Oct). *Black-browed Albatross. T* **166** *and similar vert designs. Multicoloured. W w* **16**. *P* 13½×14.

608 12p. Type **166** .. .. .. .. 35 35
609 26p. Female with egg .. .. .. 70 70
610 31p. Adult and chick .. .. .. 85 85
611 62p. Black-browed Albatross in flight .. 1·60 1·75
608/11 .. .. .. .. *Set of* 4 3·25 3·25

**1991** (7 Jan). *As Nos.* 568/9, 572, 575 *and* 580, *but W w* **16** (*sideways on horiz designs*) *and with imprint date added at foot. P* 14.

613 2p. *Priwall* (barque) (*vert*) .. .. 10 10
614 3p. *Passat* (barque) .. .. .. 10 10
617 6p. *Mozart* (barquentine) .. .. .. 10 15
620 9p. *Fennia* (barque) .. .. .. 20 25
625 £1 *Criccieth Castle* (full-rigged ship) .. 2·00 2·10
613/25 .. .. .. .. *Set of* 5 2·10 2·40

(Des A. Theobald. Litho B.D.T.)

**1991** (18 Mar). *Second Visit of H.R.H. The Duke of Edinburgh. As No.* **MS**605, *but with Exhibition emblem replaced by* "SECOND VISIT OF HRH THE DUKE OF EDINBURGH". *W w* **16** (*sideways*). *P* 14.

**MS**628 114×100 mm. £1 Spitfire Mk. I in action, 1940 .. .. .. .. .. .. 3·00 3·50

The margin of No. **MS**628 also shows the Exhibition emblem omitted and has the same commemorative inscription added.

(Des I. Strange. Litho Questa)

**1991** (18 Mar). *Orchids. T* **167** *and similar vert designs. Multicoloured. W w* **14**. *P* 14×13½.

629 12p. Type **167** .. .. .. .. 40 40
630 26p. Dog Orchid .. .. .. .. 75 75
631 31p. *Chlorea gaudichaudii* .. .. .. 90 90
632 62p. Yellow Orchid .. .. .. .. 1·75 2·00
629/32 .. .. .. .. *Set of* 4 3·50 3·50

**168** Heads of Two King Penguins

**169** ½d and 2½d Stamps of September 1891

(Des I. Strange. Litho Questa)

**1991** (26 Aug). *Endangered Species. King Penguin. T* **168** *and similar vert designs. Multicoloured. W w* **16**. *P* 14.

633 2p. Type **168** .. .. .. .. 15 15
634 6p. Female incubating egg .. .. .. 20 25
635 12p. Female with two chicks .. .. .. 35 35
636 20p. Penguin underwater .. .. .. .. 60 65
637 31p. Parents feeding their chick .. .. 80 85
638 62p. Courtship dance .. .. .. .. 1·50 1·60
633/8 .. .. .. .. *Set of* 6 3·25 3·50

(Des D. Miller. Litho Questa)

**1991** (10 Sept). *Centenary of Bisected Surcharges. T* **169** *and similar horiz designs. Multicoloured. W w* **16** (*sideways*). *P* 14½.

639 12p. Type **169** .. .. .. .. 35 35
640 26p. Cover of March 1891 franked with strip of five ½d bisects .. .. .. .. 70 70
641 31p. Unsevered pair of ½d. surcharge .. 85 85
642 62p. *Isis* (mail ship) .. .. .. .. 1·50 1·60
639/42 .. .. .. .. *Set of* 4 3·00 3·25

**170** Map of Re-enactment Voyages and *Eye of the Wind* (cadet ship)

**171** Laying Foundation Stone, 1890

(Des R. Watton. Litho Walsall)

**1991** (12 Dec). *500th Anniv of Discovery of America by Columbus and Re-enactment Voyages. T* **170** *and similar horiz designs. Multicoloured. W w* **14** (*sideways*). *P* 13½×14.

643 14p. Type **170** .. .. .. .. 25 30
644 29p. Compass rose and *Soren Larsen* (cadet ship) .. .. .. .. .. 50 55
645 34p. *Santa Maria, Pinta* and *Nina* .. .. 60 65
646 68p. Columbus and *Santa Maria* .. .. 1·25 1·30
643/6 .. .. .. .. *Set of* 4 2·40 2·50

(Des D. Miller. Litho Questa (68p.), Walsall (others))

**1992** (6 Feb). *40th Anniv of Queen Elizabeth II's Accession. Horiz designs as T* **143** *of Ascension. Multicoloured. W w* **14** (*sideways*). *P* 14.

647 7p. "Stanley through the Narrows" (A. Asprey) .. .. .. .. .. 15 20
648 14p. "Hill Cove" (A. Asprey) .. .. .. 30 35
649 29p. "San Carlos Water" (A. Asprey) .. 60 65
650 34p. Three portraits of Queen Elizabeth .. 70 75
651 68p. Queen Elizabeth II .. .. .. .. 1·40 1·50
647/51 .. .. .. .. *Set of* 5 2·75 3·00

(Des N. Shewring. Litho Questa)

**1992** (21 Feb). *Centenary of Christ Church Cathedral, Stanley. T* **171** *and similar multicoloured designs. W w* **16** (*sideways on 68p*). *P* 14½.

652 14p. Type **171** .. .. .. .. 30 35
653 29p. Interior of Cathedral, 1920 .. .. 60 65
654 34p. Bishop's chair .. .. .. .. 70 75
655 68p. Cathedral in 1900 (*horiz*) .. .. 1·40 1·50
652/5 .. .. .. .. *Set of* 4 2·75 3·00

POSTAGE DUE STAMPS

D 1 Penguin

(Des O. Bell. Litho Questa)

**1991** (7 Jan). *W w* **14** (*sideways*). *P* 15×14.

D1 D 1 1p. brown-lake and cerise .. .. 10 10
D2 2p. red-orange and pale orange .. 10 10
D3 3p. brown-ochre and chrome-yellow .. 10 10
D4 4p. deep blue-green & light blue-green 10 10
D5 5p. greenish blue & light greenish blue 10 15
D6 10p. deep violet-blue and cobalt .. 20 25
D7 20p. deep reddish violet and lilac .. 40 45
D8 50p. yellowish green and apple-green .. 1·00 1·10
D1/8 .. .. .. .. *Set of* 8 1·75 2·00

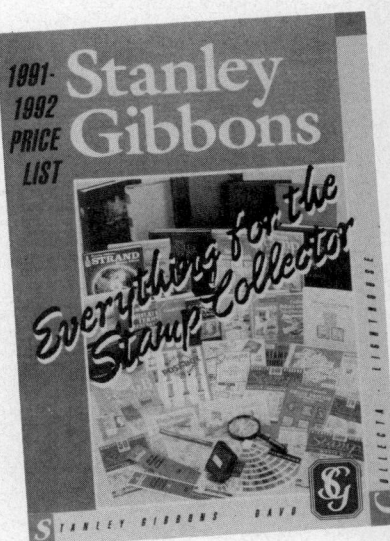

## FALKLAND ISLANDS DEPENDENCIES

The stamps of FALKLAND ISLANDS were used on South Georgia (Grytviken) from 3 December 1909 until 1944 and at Port Foster, Deception Island in the South Shetlands group from 1912 to 1931, both offices operating during the whaling season only.

**PRICES FOR STAMPS ON COVER TO 1945**
Nos. A1/D8 *from* × 10

### A. GRAHAM LAND

For use at Port Lockroy (established February 1944) and Hope Bay (established 12 February 1945) bases.

**GRAHAM LAND**

**DEPENDENCY OF**

(A 1)

**1944** (12 Feb)–**45**. *Falkland Islands Nos.* 146, 148, 150, 153/5, 157 *and* 158*a optd with Type* A 1, *in red, by* B.W.

A1 ½d. black and green .. .. .. 30 1·00
*a. Blue-black and green* .. .. .. £300 £300
A2 1d. black and violet .. .. .. 30 1·00
A3 2d. black and carmine-red .. .. .. 40 1·00
A4 3d. black and blue .. .. .. 30 1·00
A5 4d. black and purple .. .. .. 1·75 1·25
A6 6d. black and brown .. .. .. 8·50 2·25
*a. Blue-black and brown* (24.9.45) .. 20·00
A7 9d. black and grey-blue .. .. .. 1·50 1·00
A8 1s. deep blue .. .. .. 1·50 1·00
A1/8 Perf "Specimen" .. .. *Set of* 8 £300

### B. SOUTH GEORGIA

The stamps of Falkland Islands were used at Grytviken from 1909 until replaced by Nos. B1/8.

**1944** (3 Apr)–**45**. *Falkland Islands Nos.* 146, 148, 150, 153/5, 157 *and* 158*a optd* "SOUTH GEORGIA/DEPENDENCY OF", *in red, as Type* A 1, *of Graham Land.*

B1 ½d. black and green .. .. .. 30 1·00
B2 1d. black and violet .. .. .. 30 1·00
B3 2d. black and carmine-red .. .. .. 40 1·00
B4 3d. black and blue .. .. .. 30 1·00
B5 4d. black and purple .. .. .. 1·75 1·25
B6 6d. black and brown .. .. .. 8·50 2·25
*a. Blue-black and brown* (24.9.45) .. 20·00
B7 9d. black and grey-blue .. .. .. 1·50 1·00
B8 1s. deep blue .. .. .. 1·50 1·00
B1/8 Perf "Specimen" .. .. *Set of* 8 £300

For later issues, see after No. G44.

### C. SOUTH ORKNEYS

Used from the *Fitzroy* in February 1944 and at Laurie Island (established January 1946).

**1944** (21 Feb)–**45**. *Falkland Islands Nos.* 146, 148, 150, 153/5, 157 *and* 158*a optd* "SOUTH ORKNEYS/DEPENDENCY OF", *in red as Type* A 1 *of Graham Land.*

C1 ½d. black and green .. .. .. 30 1·00
C2 1d. black and violet .. .. .. 30 1·00
C3 2d. black and carmine-red .. .. .. 40 1·00
C4 3d. black and blue .. .. .. 30 1·00
C5 4d. black and purple .. .. .. 1·75 1·25
C6 6d. black and brown .. .. .. 8·50 2·25
*a. Blue-black and brown* (24.9.45) .. 20·00
C7 9d. black and grey-blue .. .. .. 1·50 1·00
C8 1s. deep blue .. .. .. 1·50 1·00
C1/8 Perf "Specimen" .. .. *Set of* 8 £300

### D. SOUTH SHETLANDS

For use at Deception Island base (established 3 February 1944).

**1944** (5 Feb)–**45**. *Falkland Islands Nos.* 146, 148, 150, 153/5, 157 *and* 158*a optd* "SOUTH SHETLANDS/DEPENDENCY OF", *in red, as Type* A 1 *of Graham Land.*

D1 ½d. black and green .. .. .. 30 1·00
D2 1d. black and violet .. .. .. 30 1·00
D3 2d. black and carmine-red .. .. .. 40 1·00
D4 3d. black and blue .. .. .. 30 1·00
D5 4d. black and purple .. .. .. 1·75 1·25
D6 6d. black and brown .. .. .. 8·50 2·25
*a. Blue-black and brown* (24.9.45) .. 20·00
D7 9d. black and grey-blue .. .. .. 1·50 1·00
D8 1s. deep blue .. .. .. 1·50 1·00
D1/8 Perf "Specimen" .. .. *Set of* 8 £300
A1/D8 .. .. .. .. *Set of* 32 50·00 35·00

From 12 July 1946 to 16 July 1963, Graham Land, South Georgia, South Orkneys and South Shetlands used FALKLAND ISLANDS DEPENDENCIES stamps.

## *PRICES OF SETS*

Set prices are given for many issues, generally those containing three stamps or more. Definitive sets include one of each value or major colour change, but do not cover different perforations, die types or minor shades. Where a choice is possible the set prices are based on the cheapest versions of the stamps included in the listings.

### E. FALKLAND ISLANDS DEPENDENCIES

For use in all four dependencies.

G 1

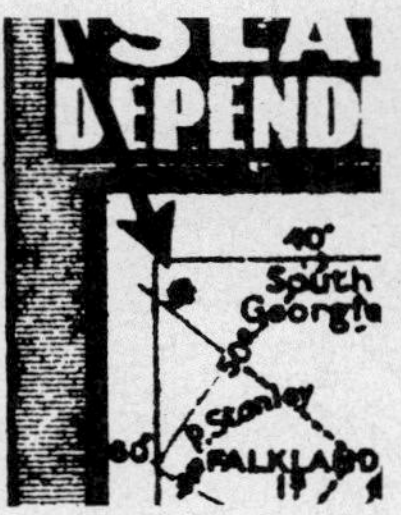

Extra island (Plate 1 R. 3/9)

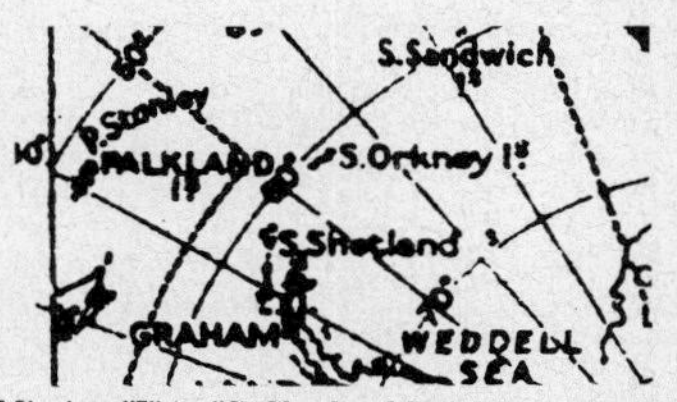

Missing "I" in "S. Shetland Is." (Plate 1 R. 1/2)

(Map litho, frame recess D.L.R.)

**1946** (11 Feb)–**49**. *Wmk Mult Script CA* (*sideways*). *P* 12.

*(a) Map thick and coarse*

G 1 G 1 ½d. black and green .. .. .. 1·00 2·00
a. Extra island .. .. .. 15·00
b. Missing "I" .. .. .. 15·00
G 2 1d. black and violet .. .. .. 1·00 1·75
a. Extra island .. .. .. 15·00
b. Missing "I" .. .. .. 15·00
G 3 2d. black and carmine .. .. .. 1·00 2·50
a. Extra island .. .. .. 18·00
b. Missing "I" .. .. .. 18·00
G 4 3d. black and blue .. .. .. 1·00 3·50
a. Extra island .. .. .. 20·00
b. Missing "I" .. .. .. 20·00
G 5 4d. black and claret .. .. .. 2·25 4·25
G 6 6d. black and orange .. .. .. 4·25 4·50
a. Extra island .. .. .. 45·00
b. Missing "I" .. .. .. 45·00
*c. Black and ochre* .. .. .. 45·00 90·00
ca. Extra island .. .. .. £150
cb. Missing "I" .. .. .. £150
G 7 9d. black and brown .. .. .. 1·75 2·75
G 8 1s. black and purple .. .. .. 2·00 4·00
G1/8 .. .. .. *Set of* 8 13·00 23·00
G1/8 Perf "Specimen" .. .. *Set of* 8 £400

*(b) Map thin and clear* (16.2.48)

G 9 G 1 ½d. black and green .. .. 2·25 7·50
a. Recess frame printed double, one albino and inverted ..
G10 1d. black and violet .. .. 1·50 11·00
G11 2d. black and carmine .. .. 6·50 14·00
G11*a* 2½d. black and deep blue (6.3.49) .. 9·50 7·00
G12 3d. black and blue .. .. 2·75 4·50
G13 4d. black and claret .. .. 11·00 15·00
G14 6d. black and orange .. .. 12·00 11·00
G15 9d. black and brown .. .. 12·00 10·00
G16 1s. black and purple .. .. 13·00 10·00
G9/16 .. .. *Set of* 9 65·00 80·00

In Nos. G1/8 a variety with a gap in the 80th parallel occurs six times in each sheet of all values in positions R. 1/4. 1/9, 3/4, 3/9, 5/4 and 5/9 (*Price for set of 8 £60 mint*).

In Nos. G9 to G16 the map is redrawn; the "o°" meridian does not touch the "S" of "COATS", the "n" of "Alexander" is not joined to the "L" of "Land" below, and the loops of letters "s" and "t" are generally more open.

A constant variety, dot on "T" of "SOUTH", occurs on R. 5/2, 5/4, 5/6, 5/8 and 5/10.

**1946** (4 Oct). *Victory. As Nos.* 110/11 *of Antigua.*

G17 1d. deep violet .. .. .. 50 15
G18 3d. blue .. .. .. 50 15
G17/18 Perf "Specimen" .. *Set of* 2 £110

**1948** (6 Dec). *Royal Silver Wedding. As Nos.* 112/13 *of Antigua, but* 1s. *in recess.*

G19 2½d. ultramarine .. .. .. 1·00 75
G20 1s. violet-blue .. .. .. 5·50 1·75

**1949** (10 Oct). *75th Anniv of U.P.U. As Nos.* 114/17 *of Antigua.*

G21 1d. violet .. .. .. 2·00 1·25
G22 2d. carmine-red .. .. .. 6·50 2·50
G23 3d. deep blue .. .. .. 8·00 1·25
G24 6d. red-orange .. .. .. 12·00 3·00
G21/4 .. .. *Set of* 4 26·00 7·00

**1953** (4 June). *Coronation. As No.* 120 *of Antigua.*

G25 1d. black and violet .. .. .. 1·50 1·25

G 2 *John Biscoe I*, 1947–52

G 3 *Trepassey*, 1945–47

(Recess Waterlow, then D.L.R. (from 27.3.62))

**1954** (1 Feb)–**62**. *Types* G 2/3 *and similar designs showing ships. Wmk Mult Script CA. P* 12½.

G26 ½d. black and bluish green .. .. 30 65
*a. Black and deep green* (DLR) (17.4.62) 3·25 4·50
G27 1d. black and sepia-brown .. .. 75 65
*a. Black and sepia* (DLR) (27.3.62) .. 12·00 6·00
G28 1½d. black and olive .. .. 75 65
*a. Black and yellow-olive* (DLR) (21.9.62) 8·50 3·00
G29 2d. black and rose-red .. .. 90 20
G30 2½d. black and yellow-ochre .. .. 90 15
G31 3d. black and deep bright blue .. .. 90 15
G32 4d. black and bright reddish purple .. 2·50 30
G33 6d. black and deep lilac .. .. 2·50 35
G34 9d. black .. .. 2·50 40
G35 1s. black and brown .. .. 2·50 40
G36 2s. black and carmine .. .. 15·00 9·00
G37 2s. 6d. black and pale turquoise .. 15·00 6·00
G38 5s. black and violet .. .. 32·00 6·50
G39 10s. black and blue .. .. 48·00 18·00
G40 £1 black .. .. £110 48·00
G26/40 .. .. *Set of* 15 £200 80·00

Designs: *Horiz*—1½d. *Wyatt Earp*, 1934–36; 2d. *Eagle*, 1944–45; 2½d. *Penola*, 1934–37; 3d. *Discovery II*, 1929–37; 4d. *William Scoresby*, 1926–46; 1s. *Deutschland*, 1910–12; 2s. *Pourquoi-pas?*, 1908–10; 10s. *Antarctic*, 1901–03. *Vert*—6d. *Discovery*, 1925–27; 9d. *Endurance*, 1914–16; 2s. 6d. *Français*, 1903–05; 5s. *Scotia*, 1902–04; £1 *Belgica*, 1897–99.

**TRANS-ANTARCTIC EXPEDITION 1955-1958**

(G 4)

**1956** (30 Jan). *Trans-Antarctic Expedition. Nos.* G27, G30/1 *and* G33 *optd with Type* G 4.

G41 1d. black and sepia-brown .. .. 10 30
G42 2½d. black and yellow-ochre .. .. 40 30
G43 3d. black and deep bright blue .. .. 40 30
G44 6d. black and deep lilac .. .. 40 30
G41/4 .. .. *Set of* 4 1·25 1·10

The stamps of Falkland Islands Dependencies were withdrawn on 16 July 1963 after Graham Land, South Orkneys and South Shetlands had become a separate colony, BRITISH ANTARCTIC TERRITORY. From 17 July 1963 to 4 May 1980 South Georgia and South Sandwich Islands used SOUTH GEORGIA stamps.

### F. SOUTH GEORGIA

1 Reindeer

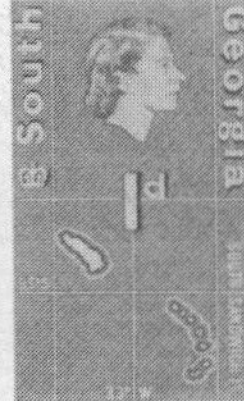

2 South Sandwich Islands

(Des D.L.R. (No. 16), M. Goaman (others). Recess D.L.R.)

**1963** (17 July)–**69**. *T* 1/2 *and similar designs. Ordinary or glazed paper* (*No.* 16). *W w* 12. *P* 15.

1 ½d. brown-red .. .. 50 30
a. Perf 14 × 15 (13.2.67) .. .. 1·00 1·50
2 1d. violet-blue .. .. 70 15
3 2d. turquoise-blue .. .. 70 15
4 2½d. black .. .. 2·75 80
5 3d. bistre .. .. 1·25 15
6 4d. bronze-green .. .. 2·25 30
7 5½d. deep violet .. .. 1·25 15
8 6d. orange .. .. 75 15
9 9d. blue .. .. 2·75 30
10 1s. purple .. .. 75 15
11 2s. yellow-olive and light blue .. .. 11·00 4·00
12 2s. 6d. blue .. .. 12·00 4·00
13 5s. orange-brown .. .. 16·00 4·00
14 10s. magenta .. .. 38·00 10·00
15 £1 ultramarine .. .. 95·00 48·00
16 £1 grey-black (1.12.69) .. .. 10·00 16·00
1/16 .. .. *Set of* 16 £180 80·00

Designs: *Vert*—2d. Sperm Whale; 3d. South American Fur Seal; 6d. Light-mantled Sooty Albatross; 10s. Plankton and krill; £1 (No. 16) King Penguins. *Horiz*—2½d. Bearded and King Penguin; 4d. Fin Whale; 5½d. Southern Elephant-Seal; 9d. Whale-catcher; 1s. Leopard Seal; 2s. Shackleton's Cross; 2s. 6d. Wandering Albatross; 5s. Southern Elephant-Seal and South American Fur Seal; £1 (No. 15) Blue Whale.

**1970** (22 Jan). *As No.* 1, *but wmk w* 12 *sideways and on glazed paper.*

17 ½d. brown-red .. .. .. 2·50 2·00

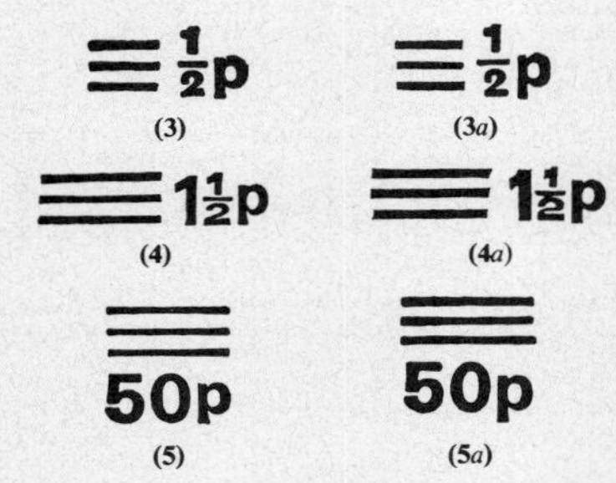

(3) (3*a*) (4) (4*a*) (5) (5*a*)

**1971** (15 Feb)–**76.** *Decimal Currency. Nos.* 17 *and* 2/14 *surch as T* **3/4**. *Nos.* 18/*a wmk sideways, glazed paper. Others wmk upright, ordinary paper.*

18 ½p. on ½d. brown-red (T **3**) .. .. .. 1·50 1·60
 a. Surch with T **3a** (16.6.72) .. .. 1·00 90
 b. Do. Wmk upright (24.8.73) .. .. 2·50 4·25
19 1p. on 1d. violet-blue .. .. .. .. 1·50 55
 a. Glazed paper (1.12.72) .. .. .. 3·50 1·75
 b. Do. but wmk sideways (9.3.76) .. .. 1·50 4·00
20 1½p. on 5½d. deep violet (T **4**) .. .. 3·00 2·00
 b. Surch with T **4a**. Glazed paper (24.8.73) 5·00 4·00
21 2p. on 2d. turquoise-blue .. .. .. 70 40
22 2½p. on 2½d. black .. .. .. .. 1·50 40
23 3p. on 3d. bistre .. .. .. .. 1·00 50
24 4p. on 4d. bronze-green .. .. .. 90 50
25 5p. on 6d. orange .. .. .. .. 90 30
26 6p. on 9d. blue .. .. .. .. 1·50 70
27 7½p. on 1s. purple .. .. .. .. 2·00 70
28 10p. on 2s. yellow-olive and light blue .. 18·00 12·00
29 15p. on 2s. 6d. blue .. .. .. .. 15·00 11·00
30 25p. on 5s. orange-brown .. .. .. 13·00 9·00
31 50p. on 10s. magenta (Type **5**) .. .. 35·00 16·00
 a. Surch with Type **5a**. Glazed paper (1.12.72) .. .. .. 22·00 23·00
 b. Do. but wmk sideways (9.3.76) .. .. 25·00 38·00
18/31a .. .. .. .. *Set of* 14 70·00 48·00

The surcharge on No. 19b shows a larger "p".

See also Nos. 53/66.

**6** *Endurance* beset in Weddell Sea

(Des R. Granger Barrett. Litho A. & M.)

**1972** (5 Jan). *50th Death Anniv of Sir Ernest Shackleton. T* **6** *and similar horiz designs. Multicoloured. W w* **12** (*sideways*). *P* 13½.

32 1½p. Type **6** .. .. .. .. .. 1·00 60
33 5p. Launching the longboat *James Caird* .. 1·25 85
34 10p. Route of the *James Caird* .. .. 1·75 1·00
35 20p. Sir Ernest Shackleton and the *Quest* .. 2·00 1·25
32/5 .. .. .. .. .. *Set of* 4 5·50 3·25

**7** Southern Elephant-Seal and King Penguins

(Des (from photograph by D. Groves) and photo Harrison)

**1972** (20 Nov). *Royal Silver Wedding. Multicoloured; background colour given. W w* **12**. *P* 14 × 14½.

36 **7** 5p. slate-green .. .. .. .. 1·00 35
37 10p. bluish violet .. .. .. .. 1·00 35

**1973** (1 Dec*). *Royal Wedding. As Nos.* 165/6 *of Anguilla. Centre multicoloured. W w* **12** (*sideways*). *P* 13½.

38 5p. brown-ochre .. .. .. .. 25 10
39 15p. bright lilac .. .. .. .. 35 20

*This is the local date of issue: the Crown Agents released the stamps on 14 November.

**8** Churchill and Westminster Skyline

**9** Captain Cook

(Des L. Curtis. Litho Questa)

**1974** (14 Dec*). *Birth Centenary of Sir Winston Churchill. T* **8** *and similar horiz design. Multicoloured. W w* **12** (*sideways*). *P* 14½.

40 15p. Type **8** .. .. .. .. .. 1·75 1·00
41 25p. Churchill and warship .. .. .. 2·00 1·00
**MS**42 122 × 98 mm. Nos. 40/1 .. .. .. 6·00 6·00

*This is the local date of issue: the Crown Agents released the stamps on 30 November.

(Des J. Cooter. Litho Questa)

**1975** (26 Apr). *Bicentenary of Possession by Captain Cook. T* **9** *and similar horiz designs. Multicoloured. W w* **12** (*sideways on* 8 *and* 16*p.*). *P* 13.

43 2p. Type **9** .. .. .. .. .. 1·60 1·00
44 8p. H.M.S. *Resolution* .. .. .. 2·75 1·50
45 16p. Possession Bay .. .. .. .. 3·25 1·75
43/5 .. .. .. .. .. *Set of* 3 7·00 3·75

**10** *Discovery* and Biological Laboratory

**11** Queen and Retinue after Coronation

(Des J. W. Litho Format)

**1976** (21 Dec). *50th Anniv of "Discovery" Investigations. T* **10** *and similar vert designs. Multicoloured. W w* **14**. *P* 14.

46 2p. Type **10** .. .. .. .. 1·00 35
47 8p. *William Scoresby* and water-sampling bottles .. .. .. .. 1·40 50
48 11p. *Discovery II* and plankton net .. .. 1·75 55
49 25p. Biological Station and krill .. .. 2·50 85
46/9 .. .. .. .. .. *Set of* 4 6·00 2·00

(Des G. Drummond. Litho Questa)

**1977** (7 Feb). *Silver Jubilee. T* **11** *and similar horiz designs. Multicoloured. W w* **14** (*sideways*). *P* 13½.

50 6p. Visit by Prince Philip, 1957 .. .. 80 30
51 11p. Queen Elizabeth and Westminster Abbey 90 35
52 33p. Type **11** .. .. .. .. 1·25 50
50/2 .. .. .. .. .. *Set of* 3 2·75 1·00

**1977** (17 May)–**78.** *As Nos.* 18*a etc., but W w* **14** (*inverted on* 1*p.; upright on* 3*p.,* 5*p. and* 50*p.; sideways on others*). *Glazed paper.*

53 ½p. on ½d. brown-red .. .. .. 1·00 1·75
54 1p. on 1d. violet-blue (16.8.77) .. .. 80 1·75
55 1½p. on 5½d. deep violet (16.8.77) .. .. 90 1·75
57 2½p. on 2½d. black (16.8.77) .. .. 8·00 3·50
58 3p. on 3d. bistre (16.8.77) .. .. 7·00 3·50
59 4p. on 4d. bronze-green (16.8.77) .. .. 18·00 14·00
60 5p. on 6d. orange .. .. .. .. 3·50 2·75
62 7½p. on 1s. purple (16.8.77) .. .. 4·00 8·00
63 10p. on 2s. yellow-olive and light blue (16.8.77) 4·00 8·00
64 15p. on 2s. 6d. blue (16.8.77) .. .. 4·00 8·00
65 25p. on 5s. orange-brown (16.8.77) .. .. 4·50 8·00
66 50p. on 10s. pale magenta (12.78) .. .. 3·00 8·50
53/66 .. .. .. .. *Set of* 12 50·00 60·00

Surcharges on the above differ from those on Nos. 18a/30 by having straight outlines and being slightly more slender. The change in paper also results in the colours appearing brighter.

**12** Fur Seal

**13** H.M.S. *Resolution*

(Des C. Abbott. Litho Questa)

**1978** (2 June). *25th Anniv of Coronation. T* **12** *and similar vert designs. P* 15.

67 25p. indigo, ultramarine and silver .. .. 75 1·00
 a. Sheetlet. Nos. 67/9 × 2 .. .. .. 4·00
68 25p. multicoloured .. .. .. .. 75 1·00
69 25p. indigo, ultramarine and silver .. .. 75 1·00
67/9 .. .. .. .. .. *Set of* 3 2·00 2·75

Designs:—No. 67, Panther of Henry VI; No. 68, Queen Elizabeth II; No. 69, Type **12**.

Nos. 67/9 were printed together in small sheets of 6, containing two *se-tenant* strips of 3, with horizontal gutter margin between.

(Des and litho (25p. also embossed) Walsall)

**1979** (14 Feb). *Bicentenary of Captain Cook's Voyages,* 1768–79. *T* **13** *and similar vert designs. Multicoloured. P* 11.

70 3p. Type **13** .. .. .. .. .. 1·50 80
71 6p. *Resolution* and map of South Georgia and S. Sandwich Isles showing route .. .. 1·50 70
72 11p. King Penguin (based on drawing by George Forster) .. .. .. .. 2·50 2·00
73 25p. Flaxman/Wedgwood medallion of Captain Cook .. .. .. .. .. 2·75 2·25
70/3 .. .. .. .. .. *Set of* 4 7·50 5·25

From 5 May 1980 South Georgia and South Sandwich Islands used stamps inscribed FALKLAND ISLANDS DEPENDENCIES.



## G. FALKLAND ISLANDS DEPENDENCIES

For use in South Georgia and South Sandwich Islands.

**14** Map of Falkland Islands Dependencies

**15** Magellanic Clubmoss

(Des and litho J.W.)

**1980** (5 May)–**84.** *Horiz designs as T* **14**. *Multicoloured. W w* **14** (*sideways*). *P* 13½. A. *Without imprint date.* B. *With imprint date* ("1984") *at foot of design* (3.5.84).

| | | A | | B | |
|---|---|---|---|---|---|
| 74 | 1p. Type **14** .. .. .. | 30 | 30 | 25 | 30 |
| 75 | 2p. Shag Rocks .. .. | 30 | 30 | 25 | 30 |
| 76 | 3p. Bird and Willis Islands .. | 30 | 30 | 25 | 30 |
| 77 | 4p. Gulbrandsen Lake .. | 30 | 30 | 25 | 30 |
| 78 | 5p. King Edward Point .. | 30 | 30 | 35 | 30 |
| 79 | 6p. Sir Ernest Shackleton's Memorial Cross, Hope Point | 60 | 30 | 30 | 30 |
| 80 | 7p. Sir Ernest Shackleton's Grave, Grytviken .. .. | 60 | 40 | 30 | 30 |
| 81 | 8p. Grytviken Church .. | 50 | 40 | 30 | 30 |
| 82 | 9p. Coaling Hulk *Louise* at Grytviken .. .. .. | 50 | 45 | 30 | 35 |
| 83 | 10p. Clerke Rocks .. .. | 50 | 45 | 50 | 35 |
| 84 | 20p. Candlemas Island .. .. | 2·25 | 1·50 | 2·00 | 1·25 |
| 85 | 25p. Twitcher Rock and Cook Island, Southern Thule .. | 2·25 | 1·75 | 2·00 | 1·50 |
| 86 | 50p. R.R.S. *John Biscoe II* in Cumberland Bay .. .. | 1·50 | 2·00 | 2·00 | 1·75 |
| 87 | £1 R.R.S. *Bransfield* in Cumberland Bay .. .. | 2·00 | 2·75 | † | |
| 88 | £3 H.M.S. *Endurance* in Cumberland Bay .. .. | 5·00 | 6·50 | † | |
| 74/88 | .. .. .. *Set of* 15 | 15·00 | 16·00 | | |
| 74B/86B | .. .. *Set of* 13 | | | 8·00 | 7·00 |

For some of these designs watermarked W **16** (sideways) see Nos. 148/52.

(Des L. McCombie. Litho Rosenbaum Bros, Vienna)

**1981** (5 Feb). *Plants. T* **15** *and similar vert designs. Multicoloured. W w* **14** (*inverted on* 25*p.*). *P* 14.

89 3p. Type **15** .. .. .. .. .. 25 25
90 6p. Alpine Cat's-tail .. .. .. .. 30 30
91 7p. Greater Burnet .. .. .. .. 30 30
92 11p. Antarctic Bedstraw .. .. .. 50 40
93 15p. Brown Rush .. .. .. .. 70 55
 a. Light brown (Queen's head and territory inscr) omitted .. .. .. .. £1800
94 25p. Antarctic Hair Grass .. .. .. 1·00 80
89/94 .. .. .. .. .. *Set of* 6 2·75 2·40

**16** Wedding Bouquet from Falkland Islands Dependencies

**17** Introduced Reindeer during Calving, Spring

(Des J.W. Litho Format)

**1981** (22 July). *Royal Wedding. T* **16** *and similar vert designs. Multicoloured. W w* **14**. *P* 14.

95 10p. Type **16** .. .. .. .. .. 30 40
96 13p. Prince Charles dressed for skiing .. 40 50
97 52p. Prince Charles and Lady Diana Spencer 1·00 1·00
95/7 .. .. .. .. .. *Set of* 3 1·50 1·75

(Des A. Theobald. Litho Format)

**1982** (29 Jan). *Reindeer. T* **17** *and similar horiz designs. Multicoloured. W w* **14** (*sideways*). *P* 14.

98 5p. Type **17** .. .. .. .. .. 45 60
99 13p. Bull at rut, Autumn .. .. .. 65 80
100 25p. Reindeer and mountains, Winter .. 1·10 1·25
101 26p. Reindeer feeding on tussock grass, late Winter .. .. .. .. .. 1·10 1·25
98/101 .. .. .. .. .. *Set of* 4 3·00 3·50

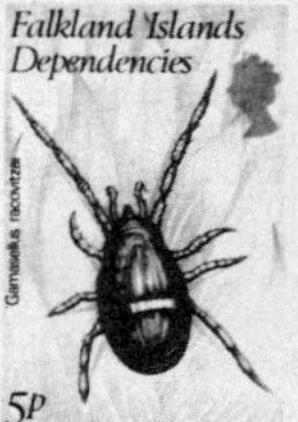

**18** *Gamasellus racovitzai* (tick)

**19** Lady Diana Spencer at Tidworth, Hampshire, July 1981

(Des I. Loe. Litho Questa)

**982** (16 Mar). *Insects. T* **18** *and similar vert designs. Multicoloured. W* w **14**. *P* 14.
)2 5p. Type **18** .. .. .. .. 20 25
)3 10p. *Alaskozetes antarcticus* (mite) .. 30 35
)4 13p. *Cryptopygus antarcticus* (spring-tail) .. 35 40
)5 15p. *Nottomaso australis* (spider) .. .. 40 45
)6 25p. *Hydromedion sparsutum* (beetle) .. 65 70
)7 26p. *Parochlus steinenii* (midge) .. .. 65 70
)2/7 .. .. .. .. *Set of* 6 2·25 2·50

(Des C. Abbott. Litho Format)

**982** (7 Sept). *21st Birthday of Princess of Wales. T* **19** *and similar vert designs. Multicoloured. W* w **14**. *P* 13½ × 14.
08 5p. Falklands Islands Dependencies coat of arms .. .. .. .. .. 10 15
09 17p. Type **19** .. .. .. .. .. 30 35
a. Perf 13½ .. .. .. .. .. 8·50 8·50
10 37p. Bride and groom on steps of St Paul's .. 75 80
11 50p. Formal portrait .. .. .. .. 1·00 1·10
08/11 .. .. .. .. *Set of* 4 1·90 2·25

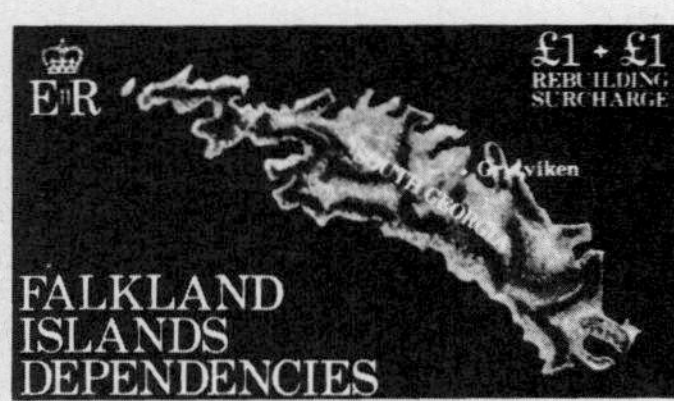


**20** Map of South Georgia

(Des PAD Studio. Litho Format)

**982** (13 Sept). *Rebuilding Fund. W* w **14** (*sideways*). *P* 11.
12 **20** £1 + £1 multicoloured .. .. .. .. 3·50 4·50

**21** Westland "Whirlwind" **22** *Euphausia superba*

(Des Harrison. Litho Questa)

.**983** (23 Dec). *Bicentenary of Manned Flight. T* **21** *and similar horiz designs. Multicoloured. W* w **14** (*sideways*). *P* 14.
.13 5p. Type **21** .. .. .. .. .. 30 20
.14 13p. Westland "Wasp" .. .. .. 55 45
.15 17p. Saunders-Roe "Walrus" .. .. .. 60 50
.16 50p. Auster .. .. .. .. .. 1·40 1·25
.13/16 .. .. .. .. *Set of* 4 2·50 2·25

(Des N. Weaver. Litho Questa)

.**984** (23 Mar). *Crustacea. T* **22** *and similar vert designs. Multicoloured. W* w **14**. *P* 14½ × 14.
.17 5p. Type **22** .. .. .. .. .. 20 20
.18 17p. *Glyptonotus antarcticus* .. .. .. 50 50
.19 25p. *Epimeria monodon* .. .. .. 60 60
.20 34p. *Serolis pagenstecheri* .. .. .. 90 80
.17/20 .. .. .. .. *Set of* 4 2·00 1·90

**23** Zavodovski Island

(Des. J.W. Litho Questa)

**1984** (8 Nov). *Volcanoes of South Sandwich Islands. T* **23** *and similar horiz designs. Multicoloured. W* w **14** (*sideways*). *P* 14 × 14½.
121 6p. Type **23** .. .. .. .. .. 70 50
122 17p. Mt Michael, Saunders Island .. .. 1·50 75
123 22p. Bellingshausen Island .. .. .. 1·60 85
124 52p. Bristol Island .. .. .. .. 2·25 1·60
121/4 .. .. .. .. *Set of* 4 5·50 3·25

**24** Grey-headed Albatross **25** The Queen Mother

(Des I. Loe. Litho Questa)

**1985** (5 May). *Albatrosses. T* **24** *and similar horiz designs. Multicoloured. W* w **14** (*sideways*). *P* 14½.
125 7p. Type **24** .. .. .. .. .. 85 45
126 22p. Black-browed Albatross .. .. 1·50 75
127 27p. Wandering Albatross .. .. .. 1·60 85
128 54p. Light-mantled Sooty Albatross .. 2·00 1·50
125/8 .. .. .. .. *Set of* 4 5·50 3·25

(Des A. Theobald (£1), C. Abbott (others). Litho Questa)

**1985** (23 June). *Life and Times of Queen Elizabeth the Queen Mother. T* **25** *and similar vert designs. Multicoloured. W* w **16**. *P* 14½ × 14.
129 7p. At Windsor Castle on Princess Elizabeth's 14th Birthday, 1940 .. .. 20 25
130 22p. With Princess Anne, Lady Sarah Armstrong-Jones and Prince Edward at Trooping the Colour .. .. .. 50 60
131 27p. Type **25** .. .. .. .. .. 60 70
132 54p. With Prince Henry at his christening (from photo by Lord Snowdon) .. 1·25 1·25
129/32 .. .. .. .. *Set of* 4 2·25 2·50
**MS**133 91 × 73 mm. £1 Disembarking from Royal Yacht *Britannia*. Wmk sideways .. .. 2·25 2·75

(Des I. Strange. Litho Questa)

**1985** (4 Nov). *Early Naturalists. Vert designs as T* **35** *of British Antarctic Territory. Multicoloured. W* w **14**. *P* 14½ × 14.
134 7p. Dumont d'Urville and *Durvillea antarctica* (kelp) .. .. .. .. 75 50
135 22p. Johann Reinhold Forster and King Penguin .. .. .. .. .. 1·50 1·00
136 27p. Johann Georg Adam Forster and Tussock Grass .. .. .. .. 1·60 1·25
137 54p. Sir Joseph Banks and Dove Prion .. 2·25 2·25
134/7 .. .. .. .. *Set of* 4 5·50 4·50

**1985** (18 Nov). *As Nos. 84/8 but W* w **16** (*sideways*). *With imprint date* ("1985"). *P* 13½.
148 20p. Candlemas Island .. .. .. 2·25 2·50
149 25p. Twitcher Rock and Cook Island, Southern Thule .. .. .. .. .. 2·25 2·50
150 50p. R.R.S. *John Biscoe* in Cumberland Bay .. .. .. .. .. 2·25 2·75
151 £1 R.R.S. *Bransfield* in Cumberland Bay .. 3·00 3·25
152 £3 H.M.S. *Endurance* in Cumberland Bay .. .. .. .. .. 7·00 7·50
148/52 .. .. .. .. *Set of* 5 15·00 17·00

Under the new constitution, effective 3 October 1985, South Georgia and South Sandwich Islands ceased to be dependencies of the Falkland Islands. Issues inscribed for the separate territory are listed under SOUTH GEORGIA AND SOUTH SANDWICH ISLANDS.

# Fiji

**PRICES FOR STAMPS ON COVER TO 1945**

| | |
|---|---|
| Nos. 1/9 | *from* × 6 |
| Nos. 10/34 | *from* × 5 |
| Nos. 35/59 | *from* × 8 |
| Nos. 60/3 | — |
| Nos. 64/9 | *from* × 20 |
| Nos. 70/5 | *from* × 5 |
| Nos. 76/103 | *from* × 8 |
| Nos. 104/14 | *from* × 5 |
| Nos. 115/24 | *from* × 4 |
| Nos. 125/37 | *from* × 3 |
| Nos. 138/241 | *from* × 4 |
| Nos. 242/5 | *from* × 3 |
| Nos. 246/8 | *from* × 8 |
| Nos. 249/66*b* | *from* × 2 |
| No. 267 | *from* × 8 |
| Nos. D1/5c | *from* × 4 |
| Nos. D6/10 | *from* × 15 |
| Nos. D11/18 | *from* × 20 |

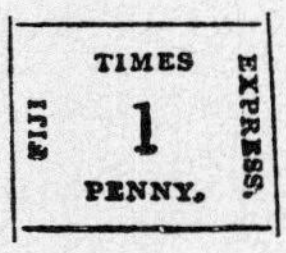


1

(Type-set and printed at the office of *The Fiji Times*, Levuka, Ovalau, Fiji)

**1870** (1 Nov)–**71**. *Rouletted in the printing.* (*a*) *Quadrillé paper.*
1 1 1d. black/*rose* .. .. .. .. £2500 £2500
2 3d. black/*rose* .. .. .. .. £2250 £2500
3 6d. black/*rose* .. .. .. .. £2000 £2000
4 1s. black/*rose* .. .. .. .. £1500 £1800

(*b*) *Laid bâtonné paper* (1871)
5 1 1d. black/*rose* .. .. .. .. £750 £1400
6 3d. black/*rose* .. .. .. .. £1200 £1800
7 6d. black/*rose* .. .. .. .. £800 £1500
8 9d. black/*rose* .. .. .. .. £1300 £2000
9 1s. black/*rose* .. .. .. .. £800 £1000

Nos. 1/4 were printed *se-tenant* as a sheet of 24 (6 × 4) with the 6d. stamps in the first horizontal row, the 1s. in the second, the 1d. in the third and the 3d. in the fourth. Nos. 5/9 were produced from the same plate on which three of the 3d. impressions had been replaced with three 9d. values.

The issued stamps showed the vertical frame lines continuous from top to bottom of the sheet with the horizontal rules broken and not touching the verticals.

There are no reprints of these stamps, but the 1d., 3d., 6d. and 1s. are known in the correct type on *yellow wove* paper and are believed to be proofs.

There are also three different sets of imitations made by the proprietors of *The Fiji Times* to meet the demands of collectors:—

The first was produced in 1876 on *white wove* or *vertically laid* paper, rouletted on dotted lines and arranged in sheets of 40 (5 rows of 8) comprising 1d., 3d., 6d., 9d. and 1s.; the horizontal frame lines are continuous and the vertical ones broken.

The second was produced before 1888 on *thick rosy mauve wove* paper, rouletted on dotted lines and arranged in sheets of 30 (5 rows of 6) comprising 1s., 9d., 6d., 3d. and 1d.; the vertical frame lines are continuous and the horizontal ones broken.

The third only came to light in the 1960s and is rare, only one complete sheet being known. The sheet arrangement is the same as Nos. 1/4, which suggests that this was the first imitation to be produced. It is on *off-white wove* paper, rouletted on closely dotted or solid lines, with vertical frame lines continuous and the horizontal ones broken, as in the originals. These differ from the proofs mentioned above in that the lettering is slightly larger and the figures also differ.

The *Fiji Times* Express service ceased on 17 January 1872.

**King Cakobau, June 1871–Oct 1874**

Two Cents

2 3 (4)

(Eng and electrotyped by A. L. Jackson. Typo Govt Printing Office, Sydney)

**1871** (Oct). *Wove paper. Wmk* "FIJI POSTAGE" *in small sans-serif capitals across the middle row of stamps in the sheet. P* 12½.
10 **2** 1d. blue .. .. .. .. .. .. 70·00 £120
11 3d. pale yellow-green .. .. .. .. £150 £250
12 **3** 6d. rose .. .. .. .. .. .. £160 £275

The 3d. differs from T **2** in having a white circle containing square dots surrounding the centre.

All three values are known *imperf*, but were not issued in that condition.

See notes after No. 33b.

**1872** (13 Jan). *Surch as T* **4**, *at Govt Ptg Office, Sydney.*
13 **2** 2 c. on 1d. pale blue .. .. .. 38·00 48·00
*a. Deep blue* .. .. .. .. 25·00 40·00
14 6 c. on 3d. yellow-green .. .. .. 55·00 55·00
15 **3** 12 c. on 6d. carmine-rose .. .. .. 75·00 75·00

**CROWN COLONY**

Ceded to Great Britain, 10 October 1874

V.R. V.R. 2d.
(5) (6) (7)

Varieties:—

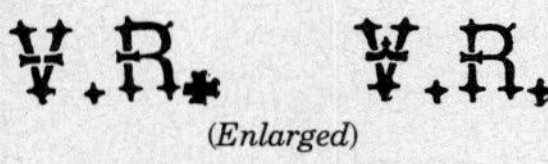


(*Enlarged*)

Cross pattée stop Inverted "A"

Cross pattée stop after "R" (R. 3/6).
Round raised stop after "V" (R. 3/8).
Round raised stops after "V" and "R" (R. 3/9).
Inverted "A" for "V" (R. 3/10).
No stop after "R" (R. 2/3 on T **5**, R. 5/3 on T **6**).

(Optd at *Polynesian Gazette* Office, Levuka)

**1874** (10 Oct). *Nos.* 13/15 *optd.* (*a*) *With T* **5**.
16 **2** 2 c. on 1d. blue .. .. .. .. £650 £180
a. No stop after "R" .. .. .. — £1000
b. Cross pattée stop after "R" .. .. — £1000
c. Round raised stop after "V" .. .. — £1000
d. Round raised stops after "V" and "R" — £1000
e. Inverted "A" for "V" .. .. .. — £1000
17 6 c. on 3d. green .. .. .. .. £950 £450
a. No stop after "R" .. .. ..
b. Cross pattée stop after "R" .. ..
c. Round raised stop after "V" ..
d. Round raised stops after "V" and "R"
e. Inverted "A" for "V" .. .. £2250
18 **3** 12 c. on 6d. rose .. .. .. .. £475 £170
a. No stop after "R" .. .. .. — £1000
b. Cross pattée stop after "R" .. .. — £1000
c. Round raised stop after "V" .. .. — £1000
d. Round raised stops after "V" and "R" — £1000
e. Inverted "A" for "V" .. .. .. — £1000
f. Opt inverted .. .. .. — £3500

(*b*) *With T* **6**
19 **2** 2 c. on 1d. blue .. .. .. .. £750 £190
a. No stop after "R" .. .. .. £1900 £1000
20 6 c. on 3d. green .. .. .. .. £1400 £700
a. No stop after "R" .. .. .. £3000
21 **3** 12 c. on 6d. rose .. .. .. .. £600 £180
a. No stop after "R" .. .. .. — £1000
b. Opt inverted .. .. .. £4000

Nos. 16/21 were produced in sheets of 50 (10 × 5) of which the top three rows were overprinted with Type **5** and the lower two with Type **6**.

**1875.** *Stamps of* 1874 *surch at* Polynesian Gazette *Office, Levuka, with T* **7**.

(*a*) *In red* (May)

22 **2** 2d. on 6 c. on 3d. green (No. 17) .. £375 £130
a. No stop after "R" .. .. .. £1500 £650
b. Cross pattée stop after "R" .. .. £1500 £650
c. Round raised stop after "V" .. £1500 £650
d. Round raised stops after "V" and "R" £1500 £650
e. Inverted "A" for "V" .. .. £1500 £650
f. No stop after "2d" (R. 1/2) .. .. £1500 £650
23 2d. on 6 c. on 3d. green (No. 20) .. £475 £190
a. No stop after "R" .. .. .. £1500 £650
b. Stop between "2" and "d" (R. 5/7) £1500 £650

(*b*) *In black* (30 Sept)

24 **2** 2d. on 6 c. on 3d. green (No. 17) .. £900 £350
a. No stop after "R" .. .. .. £2500 £1200
b. Cross pattée stop after "R" .. .. £2500 £1200
c. Round raised stop after "V" .. .. £2500 £1200
d. Round raised stops after "V" and "R" £2500 £1200
e. Inverted "A" for "V" .. .. £2500 £1200
f. No stop after "2d" (R. 1/2) .. .. £2500 £1200
g. "V.R." double .. ..
25 2d. on 6 c. on 3d. green (No. 20) .. £1300 £475
a. No stop after "R" .. .. .. £2500 £1200
b. Stop between "2" and "d" (R. 5/7) .. £2500 £1200
c. "V.R." double .. .. .. — £3250

**1875** (20 Nov). *No.* 15 *surch at* Polynesian Gazette *Office, Levuka, with T* **7** *and* "V.R." *at one operation.* (*a*) "V.R." *T* **5**.

26 **3** 2d. on 12 c. on 6d. rose .. .. £900 £475
aa. Round raised stop after "R"
a. Inverted "A" for "V" (R. 1/3, 2/8, 4/4) £1100 £650
b. Do. and round raised stop after "V" (R. 3/3, 3/6, 3/8, 3/10) .. .. £1000 £600
c. As "a" and round raised stops after "R" and "V" (R. 3/2, 3/9) .. .. £1200 £700
d. Surch double .. .. .. — £2750

(*b*) "V.R." *T* **6**

27 **3** 2d. on 12 c. on 6d. rose .. .. .. £900 £475
a. Surch double .. .. .. — £3000

The setting used for Nos. 26/7 was similar to that of Nos. 16/21, but the fourth stamp in the fourth row had a Type **5** "V.R." instead of a Type **6**.

The position of No. 26aa is not known.

(8)

Two Pence

(9)

(Typo Govt Printing Office, Sydney, from plates of 1871)

**1876–77.** *On paper previously lithographed* "VR" *as T* **8**, *the* 3d. *surch with T* **9**. *P* 12½. (*a*) *Wove paper* (31.1.76).

28 **2** 1d. grey-blue .. .. .. 45·00 45·00
*a. Dull blue* .. .. .. 45·00 45·00
b. Doubly printed .. ..
c. Void corner .. .. ..
d. Imperf vert (horiz pair) .. ..
29 2d. on 3d. pale green .. .. 35·00 48·00
*a. Deep green* .. .. .. 35·00 48·00
30 **3** 6d. pale rose .. .. .. 60·00 60·00
*a. Dull rose* .. .. .. 48·00 50·00
*b. Carmine-rose* .. .. .. 55·00 50·00
c. Doubly printed .. ..

(*b*) *Laid paper* (5.1.77)

31 **2** 1d. blue .. .. .. .. 13·00 22·00
*a. Deep blue* .. .. .. 14·00 22·00
b. Void corner .. .. .. £250 £190
c. Imperf vert (horiz pair) .. .. £850
32 2d. on 3d. yellow-green .. .. 55·00 55·00
*a. Deep yellow-green* .. .. 55·00 55·00
b. Imperf between (pair) .. .. £850
c. Perf 10 .. .. .. £250
ca. Imperf vert (horiz pair) .. ..
d. Perf 11 .. .. .. £300
33 **3** 6d. rose .. .. .. .. 42·00 27·00
*a. Carmine-rose* .. .. .. 42·00 32·00
b. Imperf vert (horiz pair) .. .. £850

The 3d. *green* is known without the surcharge T **9** on wove paper and also without the surcharge and the monogram. In this latter condition it can only be distinguished from No. 11 by its colour, which is a fuller, deeper yellow-green.

Stamps on both wove and laid paper *imperf* are from printer's trial or waste sheets and were not issued.

All values are known on laid paper without the monogram "VR" and the 3d. stamp also without the surcharge but these are also believed to be from printer's trial sheets and were never issued. Being on laid paper they are easily distinguishable from Nos. 10/12.

**1877** (12 Oct). *Optd with T* **8** *and surch as T* **9**. *Laid paper. P* 12½.

34 **2** 4d. on 3d. mauve .. .. .. 65·00 30·00
a. Imperf vert (horiz pair) .. .. £850

10

11

A Four Pence

B Four Pence

Type A: Length 12½ mm
Type B: Length 14 mm
Note also the different shape of the two "e"s.

(Typo from new plates made from original dies of 1871 with "CR" altered to "VR" at Govt Printing Office, Sydney. 2d. and 4d. made from old 3d. die.)

**1878–99.** *Surcharges as T* **9** *or as Types* A *or* B *for* 4d. *value. Wove paper with paper-maker's name* "T. H. SAUNDERS" *or* "SANDERSON" *in double-lined capitals extending over seven stamps in each full sheet.* (*a*) *P* 12½ (1878–80).

35 **10** 1d. pale ultramarine (19.2.79) .. 3·50 4·00
*a. Ultramarine* .. .. .. 7·00 6·50
36 2d. on 3d. green (17.10.78) .. 4·00 7·00
37 2d. yellow-green (1.9.79) .. 9·50 8·00
*a. Blue-green* .. .. .. 15·00 13·00
b. Error. Ultramarine .. .. £18000
38 **11** 6d. rose (30.7.80) .. .. 80·00 12·00

(*b*) *P* 10 (1881–90)

39 **10** 1d. dull blue (11.5.82) .. .. 24·00 2·25
*a. Ultramarine* .. .. .. 6·50 2·00
*b. Cambridge blue* (12.7.83) .. 24·00 2·75
40 2d. yellow-green (20.10.81) .. 7·00 90
*a. Blue-green* .. .. .. 9·50 3·00
41 4d. on 1d. mauve (29.1.90) .. 18·00 11·00
42 4d. on 2d. pale mauve (A) (23.5.83) .. 55·00 9·00
*a. Dull purple* .. .. .. 55·00 9·00
43 4d. on 2d. dull purple (B) (7.11.88) .. — £110
44 4d. mauve (13.9.90) .. .. 42·00
*a. Deep purple* .. .. .. 42·00 50·00
45 **11** 6d. pale rose (11.3.85) .. .. 60·00 11·00
*a. Bright rose* .. .. .. 14·00 14·00

(*c*) *P* 10 × 12½ (1881–82)

46 **10** 1d. ultramarine (11.5.82) .. .. 60·00 25·00
47 2d. green (20.10.81) .. .. £160 40·00
48 **11** 6d. rose (20.10.81) .. .. £325 38·00

(*d*) *P* 12½ × 10 (1888–90)

49 **10** 1d. ultramarine (1890) .. ..
49*a* 2d. green (1888) .. ..

(*e*) *P* 10 × *nearly* 12 (3.9.86)

50 **10** 1d. ultramarine .. .. .. 48·00 6·50
51 2d. yellow-green .. .. .. 48·00 6·50

(*f*) *P nearly* 12 × 10 (1886–88)

51*a* **10** 1d. dull blue (7.11.88) .. ..
51*b* 2d. yellow-green (3.9.86) .. ..
52 **11** 6d. rose (1887) .. .. ..

(*g*) *P* 11 × 10 (1892–93)

53 **10** 1d. ultramarine (18.8.92) .. .. 5·50 6·00
54 4d. pale mauve (18.8.92) .. .. 6·00 7·00
55 **11** 6d. pale rose (14.2.93) .. .. 6·50 11·00
*a. Rose* .. .. .. .. 10·00 13·00

(*h*) *P* 11 (1897–99)

56 **10** 4d. mauve (14.7.96) .. .. 7·00 6·00
57 **11** 6d. dull rose (14.7.96) .. .. 25·00 32·00
a. Printed both sides (12.99) .. £550 £500
*b. Bright rose* .. .. .. 35·00 18·00

(*i*) *P* 11 × *nearly* 12 (1896)*

58 **10** 4d. deep purple (14.7.96) .. .. 20·00
*a. Bright purple* .. .. .. 6·50 6·50
59 **11** 6d. rose (23.7.96) .. .. 28·00
*a. Bright rose* .. .. .. 6·00 4·50

(*j*) *Imperf* (1882–90)

60 **10** 1d. ultramarine .. .. ..
61 2d. yellow-green .. .. ..
62 4d. on 2d. pale mauve .. .. ..
63 **11** 6d. rose .. .. .. ..

*Under this heading are included stamps from several perforating machines with a gauge varying between 11·6 and 12.

Only four examples of No. 37b have been reported, one of which was subsequently destroyed.

In the absence of detailed information on dates of issue printing dates are quoted for Nos. 35/63 and 76/103.

12

13

(Typo Govt Printing Office, Sydney)

**1881–99.** *Paper-maker's name wmkd as previous issue.*

(*a*) *P* 10 (19.10.81)

64 **12** 1s. pale brown .. .. .. 45·00 11·00
*a. Deep brown* .. .. .. 45·00 13·00

(*b*) *P* 11 × 10 (1894)

65 **12** 1s. pale brown .. .. .. 35·00 32·00

(*c*) *P* 11 (1897)

66 **12** 1s. pale brown .. .. .. 27·00 14·00

(*d*) *P* 11 × *nearly* 12 (5.99)

67 **12** 1s. pale brown .. .. .. 23·00 8·50
*a. Brown* .. .. .. .. 23·00 8·50
*b. Deep brown* .. .. .. 35·00 40·00

(*e*) *P nearly* 12 × 11 (3.97)

68 **12** 1s. brown .. .. .. 35·00 38·00

Dates given of earliest known use.
Forgeries exist.

(Centre typo, frame litho Govt Printing Office, Sydney)

**1882** (23 May). *Toned paper wmkd with paper-maker's name* "Cowan" *in old English outline type once in each sheet. P* 10.

69 **13** 5s. dull red and black .. .. 50·00 35·00

In July 1900, an electrotyped plate of a 5s. stamp was made and stamps were printed from it with pale orange-red centre and grey-black frame; these are known *perf* 10, *perf nearly* 12, and *imperf*. These stamps were sold as remainders with a special obliteration dated "15 Dec., 00," but were not issued for postal use. The design differs in many particulars from the issued stamp.

**2½d.** (14) **2 ½d.** (15)

T **14**. Fraction bar 1 mm from "2".
T **15**. Fraction bar 2 mm from "2".

(Stamps typo in Sydney and surch at Govt Printing Office, Suva)

**1891** (1 Jan). *T* **10** *surch. P* 10.

70 **14** 2½d. on 2d. green .. .. .. 48·00 48·0
71 **15** 2½d. on 2d. green .. .. .. £130 £13

**½d.** (16) **5d** (17)

**FIVE PENCE** (18) 2 mm spacing

**FIVE PENCE** (19) 3 mm spacing

**1892** (1 Mar)–**93.** *P* 10. (*a*) *Surch on T* **10**.

72 **16** ½d. on 1d. dull blue .. .. .. 45·00 65·00
*a. Ultramarine* .. .. .. 35·00 60·00
73 **17** 5d. on 4d. deep purple (25.7.92) .. 45·00 65·00
*a. Dull purple* .. .. .. 45·00 65·00

(*b*) *Surch on T* **11**

74 **18** 5d. on 6d. brownish rose (30.11.92) .. 55·00 65·00
*a. Bright rose* .. .. .. 55·00 60·00
b. Perf 10 × 12½ .. ..
75 **19** 5d. on 6d. rose (4.1.93) .. .. 70·00
*a. Deep rose* .. .. .. 60·00
*b. Brownish rose* .. .. .. 60·00

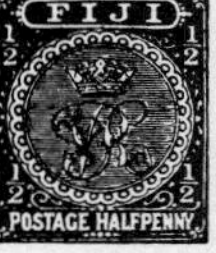


20

21 Native Canoe

22

(Typo in Sydney)

**1891–1902.** *Wmk in sheet, either* "SANDERSON" *or* "NEW SOUTH WALES GOVERNMENT" *in outline capitals.*

(*a*) *P* 10 (1891–94)

76 **20** ½d. slate-grey (26.4.92) .. .. 3·50 3·0
77 **21** 1d. black (19.9.94) .. .. 5·50 3·5
78 2d. pale green (19.9.94) .. .. 85·00 9·5
79 **22** 2½d. chocolate (8.6.91) .. .. 26·00 11·0
80 **21** 5d. ultramarine (14.2.93) .. .. 55·00 30·0

(*b*) *P* 11 × 10 (1892–93)

81 **20** ½d. slate-grey (20.10.93) .. .. 4·00 11·0
82 **21** 1d. black (14.2.93) .. .. 4·75 2·5
83 2d. green (14.2.93) .. .. 6·00 3·2
84 **22** 2½d. chocolate (17.8.92) .. .. 19·00 15·0
*a. Brown* .. .. .. 7·00 6·5
*b. Yellowish brown* .. ..
85 **21** 5d. ultramarine (14.2.93) .. .. 7·00 7·5

(*c*) *P* 11 (1893–96)

86 **20** ½d. slate-grey (2.6.96) .. .. 3·00 5·0
*a. Greenish slate* .. .. .. 2·50 6·0
87 **21** 1d. black (31.10.95) .. .. 2·50 3·0
88 1d. pale mauve (2.6.96) .. .. 3·00 1·0
*a. Rosy mauve* .. .. .. 3·00 1·0
89 2d. dull green (17.3.94) .. .. 4·75 8
*a. Emerald-green* .. .. .. 5·00 2·0
90 **22** 2½d. brown (31.10.95) .. .. 10·00 6·0
*a. Yellowish brown* .. .. 18·00 12·0
91 **21** 5d. ultramarine (14.2.93) .. .. £400

(*d*) *P* 10 × *nearly* 12 (1893–94)

93 **21** 1d. black (20.7.93) .. .. 10·00 5·0
94 2d. dull green (19.9.94) .. .. £425 £22

(*e*) *P nearly* 12 × 10 (19.9.94)

94*a* **20** ½d. pale grey .. .. ..

(*f*) *Perf nearly* 12 (1894–98)

95 **20** ½d. greenish slate (19.9.94) .. .. 2·75 7·5
*a. Grey* .. .. .. .. 18·00
96 **21** 1d. black (19.9.94) .. .. £140 15·0
97 1d. rosy mauve (4.5.98) .. .. 4·50 4·5
98 2d. dull green (19.9.94) .. .. 70·00 29·0

(*g*) *P* 11 × *nearly* 12 (1895–97)

99 **20** ½d. greenish slate (8.10.97) .. .. 1·00 2·5
100 **21** 1d. black (31.10.95) .. .. £225
101 1d. rosy mauve (14.7.96) .. .. 3·25 5
*a. Pale rosy mauve* .. .. 3·50 2·0
102 2d. dull green (26.7.97) .. .. 27·00 4·0
103 **22** 2½d. brown (26.7.97) .. .. 11·00 16·0
*a. Yellow-brown* .. .. .. 5·00 5·0

(*h*) *P nearly* 12 × 11 (1897–98)

103*b* **20** ½d. greenish slate (8.10.97) .. ..
103*c* **21** 1d. rosy mauve (10.2.97) .. ..
103*d* 2d. dull green (4.5.98) .. ..

The 2½d. brown is known *doubly printed*, but only occurs in the remainders and with the special obliteration. It was never issued for postal use.

23

24

(Typo D.L.R.)

**1903** (1 Feb). *Wmk Crown CA. P* 14.

| No. | Type | Description | Unused | Used |
|---|---|---|---|---|
| 104 | **23** | ½d. green and pale green | 1·75 | 1·50 |
| 105 | | 1d. dull purple and black/*red* | 6·00 | 55 |
| 106 | **24** | 2d. dull purple and orange | 1·50 | 1·25 |
| 107 | **23** | 2½d. dull purple and blue/*blue* | 14·00 | 15·00 |
| 108 | | 3d. dull purple and purple | 1·25 | 4·00 |
| 109 | **24** | 4d. dull purple and black | 1·25 | 2·50 |
| 110 | **23** | 5d. dull purple and green | 1·25 | 5·00 |
| 111 | **24** | 6d. dull purple and carmine | 1·50 | 2·50 |
| 112 | **23** | 1s. green and carmine | 10·00 | 22·00 |
| 113 | **24** | 5s. green and black | 25·00 | 60·00 |
| 114 | **23** | £1 grey-black and ultramarine | £325 | £350 |
| 104/14 | | *Set of* 11 | £350 | £375 |
| 104/14 Optd "Specimen" | | *Set of* 11 | £325 | |

**1904–9.** *Wmk Mult Crown CA. Chalk-surfaced paper* (1s.). *P* 14.

| No. | Type | Description | Unused | Used |
|---|---|---|---|---|
| 115 | **23** | ½d. green and pale green | 5·00 | 1·50 |
| 116 | | 1d. purple and black/*red* | 9·00 | 10 |
| 117 | | 1s. green and carmine (1909) | 25·00 | 40·00 |
| 115/17 | | *Set of* 3 | 35·00 | 40·00 |

**1906–12.** *Colours changed. Wmk Mult Crown CA. Chalk-surfaced paper* (6d. *to* £1). *P* 14.

| No. | Type | Description | Unused | Used |
|---|---|---|---|---|
| 118 | **23** | ½d. green (1908) | 6·50 | 2·00 |
| 119 | | 1d. red (1906) | 2·00 | 10 |
| 120 | | 2½d. bright blue (1910) | 3·50 | 5·50 |
| 121 | **24** | 6d. dull purple (1910) | 5·50 | 12·00 |
| 122 | **23** | 1s. black/*green* (1911) | 4·00 | 10·00 |
| 123 | **24** | 5s. green and red/*yellow* (1911) | 38·00 | 48·00 |
| 124 | **23** | £1 purple and black/*red* (1912) | £325 | £375 |
| 118/24 | | *Set of* 7 | £350 | £400 |
| 119/24 Optd "Specimen" | | *Set of* 6 | £350 | |

25     26     WAR STAMP (27)

(Typo D.L.R.)

**1912** (Oct)–**23.** *Wmk Mult Crown CA. Chalk-surfaced paper* (5d. *to* £1). *P* 14.

| No. | Type | Description | Unused | Used |
|---|---|---|---|---|
| 125 | **26** | ¼d. brown (1.4.16) | 20 | 30 |
| | | *a. Deep brown* | 60 | 40 |
| 126 | **25** | ½d. green | 40 | 55 |
| | | *a. Yellow-green* (1915) | 5·00 | 5·00 |
| | | *b. Blue-green* (1917) | 1·00 | 50 |
| 127 | | 1d. carmine | 1·90 | 10 |
| | | *a. Bright scarlet* (1.16) | 1·75 | 45 |
| | | *b. Deep rose* (1919) | 4·50 | 50 |
| 128 | **26** | 2d. greyish slate (5.14) | 80 | 10 |
| | | a. Wmk sideways | | |
| 129 | **25** | 2½d. bright blue (5.14) | 3·50 | 3·50 |
| 130 | | 3d. purple/*yellow* (5.14) | 2·75 | 3·50 |
| | | a. Wmk sideways | £500 | |
| | | *b. On lemon* (1915) | 2·00 | 8·00 |
| | | *c. On pale yellow* (Die I) | 1·50 | 10·00 |
| | | *d. On pale yellow* (Die II) (1923) | 2·50 | 15·00 |
| 131 | **26** | 4d. black and red/*yellow* (5.14) | 8·50 | 15·00 |
| | | *a. On lemon* | 5·00 | 14·00 |
| | | *b. On orange-buff* (1.21) | 42·00 | 65·00 |
| | | *c. On pale yellow* (Die I) (1921) | 7·50 | 14·00 |
| | | *d. On pale yellow* (Die II) (1923) (Optd S. £35) | 3·75 | 15·00 |
| 132 | **25** | 5d. dull purple and olive-green (5.14) | 7·00 | 9·00 |
| 133 | **26** | 6d. dull and bright purple (5.14) | 2·00 | 5·00 |
| 134 | **25** | 1s. black/*green* (10.13) | 1·25 | 12·00 |
| | | *a. White back* (4.14) | 1·00 | 8·00 |
| | | *b. On blue-green, olive back* (1917) | 4·75 | 10·00 |
| | | *c. On emerald back* (Die I) (1921) (Optd S. £35) | 4·00 | 22·00 |
| | | *d. On emerald back* (Die II) (1923) | 3·50 | 17·00 |
| 135 | **26** | 2s. 6d. black and red/*blue* (19.1.16) | 29·00 | 28·00 |
| 136 | | 5s. green and red/*yellow* | 29·00 | 40·00 |
| 137 | **25** | £1 purple and black/*red* (Die I) (5.14) | £250 | £275 |
| | | a. Die II | £250 | £275 |
| 125/37a | | *Set of* 13 | £275 | £325 |
| 125/37 Optd "Specimen" | | *Set of* 13 | £425 | |

**1915** (1 Dec)–**19.** *Optd with T* **27** *by Govt Printer, Suva.*

| No. | Type | Description | Unused | Used |
|---|---|---|---|---|
| 138 | **25** | ½d. blue-green | 30 | 1·50 |
| | | *a. Yellow-green* | 35 | 2·25 |
| | | b. Opt inverted | £500 | |
| | | c. Opt double | | |
| 139 | | 1d. carmine | 17·00 | 22·00 |
| | | *a. Bright scarlet* | 60 | 75 |
| | | ab. Horiz pair, one without opt | £6500 | |
| | | c. Opt inverted | £650 | |
| | | *d. Deep rose* (1919) | 1·40 | 1·40 |
| 138/9 H/S "Specimen" | | *Set of* 2 | £100 | |

No. 139ab occurred on one pane of 120 only, the overprint being so misplaced that all the stamps of the last vertical row escaped it entirely.

Nos. 140/227 no longer used.

**1922–27.** *Wmk Mult Script CA. Chalk-surfaced paper* (1s. *to* 5s.). *P* 14.

| No. | Type | Description | Unused | Used |
|---|---|---|---|---|
| 228 | **26** | ¼d. deep brown (1923) | 1·75 | 12·00 |
| 229 | **25** | ½d. green (1923) | 40 | 1·25 |
| 230 | | 1d. carmine-red | 2·50 | 2·00 |
| 231 | | 1d. violet (6.1.27) | 1·00 | 10 |
| 232 | **26** | 1½d. scarlet (6.1.27) | 4·00 | 3·25 |
| 233 | | 2d. grey | 80 | 10 |
| | | a. Face value omitted | | |
| 234 | **25** | 3d. bright blue (1924) | 90 | 1·25 |
| 235 | **26** | 4d. black and red/*lemon* (1924) | 5·00 | 7·00 |
| | | *a. On orange-buff* (1927) | 17·00 | 22·00 |
| 236 | **25** | 5d. dull purple and sage-green | 1·50 | 2·00 |
| 237 | **26** | 6d. dull and bright purple | 1·75 | 1·25 |
| 238 | **25** | 1s. black/*emerald* (1924) | 2·50 | 6·00 |
| 239 | **26** | 2s. purple and blue/*blue* (6.1.27) | 25·00 | 48·00 |
| 240 | | 2s. 6d. black and red/*blue* (1925) | 10·00 | 32·00 |
| 241 | | 5s. green and red/*yellow* (1926) | 25·00 | 50·00 |
| 228/241 | | *Set of* 14 | 75·00 | £150 |
| 228/41 Optd "Specimen" | | *Set of* 14 | £300 | |

The 2d. imperforate with watermark Type **10** of Ireland came from a trial printing and was not issued.

Only one example of No. 233a is known. It was caused by an obstruction during the printing of the duty plate.

**1935** (6 May). *Silver Jubilee. As Nos.* 91/4 *of Antigua.*

| No. | Description | Unused | Used |
|---|---|---|---|
| 242 | 1½d. deep blue and carmine | 45 | 2·50 |
| | *a. Deep blue and aniline red* | 2·75 | 8·00 |
| | b. Frame printed double, one albino | £1000 | |
| | f. Diagonal line by turret | 35·00 | |
| | h. Dot by flagstaff | 38·00 | |
| 243 | 2d. ultramarine and grey | 1·00 | 35 |
| | f. Diagonal line by turret | 45·00 | |
| | g. Dot to left of chapel | 50·00 | |
| 244 | 3d. brown and deep blue | 2·50 | 2·50 |
| 245 | 1s. slate and purple | 4·50 | 3·50 |
| 242/5 | *Set of* 4 | 7·50 | 8·00 |
| 242/5 Perf "Specimen" | *Set of* 4 | 85·00 | |

For illustrations of plate varieties see Catalogue Introduction.

**1937** (12 May). *Coronation. As Nos.* 95/7 *of Antigua. P* 11×11½.

| No. | Description | Unused | Used |
|---|---|---|---|
| 246 | 1d. purple | 70 | 45 |
| 247 | 2d. grey-black | 80 | 45 |
| 248 | 3d. Prussian blue | 80 | 45 |
| 246/8 | *Set of* 3 | 2·10 | 1·25 |
| 246/8 Perf "Specimen" | *Set of* 3 | 55·00 | |

**28** Native sailing Canoe

**29** Native Village

**30** Camakua (canoe)

**31** Map of Fiji Islands

Two Dies of Type **30**:

Die I Empty Canoe     Die II Native in Canoe

Two Dies of Type **31**:

Die I Without "180°"     Die II With "180°"

Extra palm frond (R. 5/8)

Spur on arms medallion (Pl 2 R. 4/2) (ptg of 26 Nov 1945)

(Des V. E. Ousey (½d., 1s., 2s. 6d.), Miss C. D. Lovejoy (1d., 1½d., 5d.), Miss I. Stinson (3d., 5s.) and A. V. Guy (2d. (Nos. 253/4), 2½d., 6d., 2s.). Recess De La Rue (½d., 1½d., 2d., (Nos. 253/5a), 2½d., 6d., 8d., 1s. 5d., 1s. 6d.), Waterlow (others))

**1938** (5 Apr)–**1955.** *T* **28/31** *and similar designs. Wmk Mult Script CA. Various perfs.*

| No. | Type | Description | Unused | Used |
|---|---|---|---|---|
| 249 | **28** | ½d. green (*p* 13½) | 10 | 20 |
| | | a. Perf 14 (10.41) | 18·00 | 3·50 |
| | | b. Perf 12 (8.48) | 30 | 60 |
| | | ba. Extra palm frond | 10·00 | |
| 250 | **29** | 1d. brown and blue (*p* 12½) | 15 | 10 |
| 251 | **30** | 1½d. carmine (Die I) (*p* 13½) | 13·00 | 35 |
| 252 | | 1½d. carmine (Die II) (*p* 13½) (1.10.40) | 50 | 90 |
| | | *a. Deep carmine* (10.42) | 4·00 | 3·25 |
| | | b. Perf 14 (6.42) | 13·00 | 16·00 |
| | | c. Perf 12 (21.7.49) | 90 | 1·25 |
| 253 | **31** | 2d. brown and green (Die I) (*p* 13½) | 38·00 | 30 |
| 254 | | 2d. brn & grn (Die II) (*p* 13½) (1.10.40) | 16·00 | 16·00 |
| 255 | – | 2d. green & magenta (*p* 13½) (19.5.42) | 40 | 30 |
| | | a. Perf 12 (27.5.46) | 55 | 30 |
| 256 | **31** | 2½d. brown & grn (Die II) (*p* 14) (6.1.42) | 50 | 20 |
| | | a. Perf 13½ (1.44) | 40 | 30 |
| | | b. Perf 12 (19.1.48) | 70 | 50 |
| 257 | – | 3d. blue (*p* 12½) | 60 | 15 |
| | | a. Spur on arms medallion | 65·00 | |
| 258 | – | 5d. blue and scarlet (*p* 12½) | 42·00 | 9·00 |
| 259 | – | 5d. yellow-grn & scar (*p* 12½) (1.10.40) | 15 | 15 |
| 260 | **31** | 6d. black (Die I) (*p* 13×12) | 65·00 | 10·00 |
| 261 | | 6d. black (Die II) (*p* 13½) (1.10.40) | 3·00 | 80 |
| | | *a. Violet-black* (1.44) | 25·00 | 20·00 |
| | | b. Perf 12. *Black* (5.6.47) | 1·25 | 40 |
| 261*c* | – | 8d. carmine (*p* 14) (15.11.48) | 40 | 25 |
| | | d. Perf 13 (7.6.50) | 70 | 1·75 |
| 262 | – | 1s. black and yellow (*p* 12½) | 35 | 20 |
| 263 | – | 1s. 5d. black & carmine (*p* 14) (13.6.40) | 15 | 10 |
| 263*a* | – | 1s. 6d. ultramarine (*p* 14) (1.8.50) | 3·00 | 1·00 |
| | | b. Perf 13 (16.2.55) | 1·25 | 15·00 |
| 264 | – | 2s. violet and orange (*p* 12½) | 1·25 | 30 |
| 265 | – | 2s. 6d. green and brown (*p* 12½) | 1·25 | 70 |
| 266 | – | 5s. green and purple (*p* 12½) | 2·00 | 70 |
| 266*a* | – | 10s. orange & emer (*p* 12½) (13.3.50) | 30·00 | 40·00 |
| 266*b* | – | £1 ultram & carm (*p* 12½) (13.3.50) | 45·00 | 48·00 |
| 249/66*b* | | *Set of* 22 | £225 | £120 |
| 249/66 excl 261c and 263a Perf "Specimen" | | *Set of* 18 | £450 | |

Designs: *Horiz* (*as T* **30**)—2d. (Nos. 255/a) Government Offices. (*As T* **29**)—3d. Canoe and arms of Fiji; 8d., 1s. 5d., 1s. 6d. Arms of Fiji; 2s. Suva Harbour; 2s. 6d. River scene; 5s. Chief's hut. *Vert* (*as T* **29**)—5d. Sugar cane; 1s. Spearing fish by torchlight; 10s. Pawpaw Tree; £1 Police bugler.

**2½d.**

(42)

**1941** (10 Feb). *No.* 254 *surch with T* **42** *by Govt Printer, Suva.*

| No. | Type | Description | Unused | Used |
|---|---|---|---|---|
| 267 | **31** | 2½d. on 2d. brown and green | 30 | 10 |

**1946** (17 Aug). *Victory. As Nos.* 110/11 *of Antigua.*

| No. | Description | Unused | Used |
|---|---|---|---|
| 268 | 2½d. green | 10 | 15 |
| | a. Printed double, one albino | £200 | |
| 269 | 3d. blue | 10 | 10 |
| 268/9 Perf "Specimen" | *Set of* 2 | 60·00 | |

**1948** (17 Dec). *Royal Silver Wedding. As Nos.* 112/13 *of Antigua.*

| No. | Description | Unused | Used |
|---|---|---|---|
| 270 | 2½d. green | 40 | 30 |
| 271 | 5s. violet-blue | 14·00 | 5·00 |

**1949** (10 Oct). *75th Anniv of U.P.U. As Nos.* 114/17 *of Antigua.*

| No. | Description | Unused | Used |
|---|---|---|---|
| 272 | 2d. bright reddish purple | 55 | 30 |
| 273 | 3d. deep blue | 90 | 1·00 |
| 274 | 8d. carmine-red | 90 | 1·00 |
| 275 | 1s. 6d. blue | 1·10 | 1·00 |
| 272/5 | *Set of* 4 | 3·00 | 3·00 |

**43** Children Bathing

**44** Rugby Football

(Recess B.W.)

**1951** (17 Sept). *Health Stamps. Wmk Mult Script CA. P* 13½.

| No. | Type | Description | Unused | Used |
|---|---|---|---|---|
| 276 | **43** | 1d. + 1d. brown | 10 | 30 |
| 277 | **44** | 2d. + 1d. green | 20 | 30 |

**1953** (2 June). *Coronation. As No.* 120 *of Antigua.*

| No. | Description | Unused | Used |
|---|---|---|---|
| 278 | 2½d. black and green | 50 | 30 |

**45** Arms of Fiji

(Recess D.L.R.)

**1953** (16 Dec). *Royal Visit. Wmk Mult Script CA. P* 13.

| No. | Type | Description | Unused | Used |
|---|---|---|---|---|
| 279 | **45** | 8d. deep carmine-red | 15 | 10 |

46 Queen Elizabeth II (after Annigoni)

47 Government Offices

48 Loading Copra

49 Sugar Cane Train

50 Preparing Bananas for Export

51 Gold Industry

(Des V. E. Ousey (½d., 1s., 2s. 6d.), A. V. Guy (6d.). Recess D.L.R. (½d., 2d., 6d., 8d.), Waterlow (1s., 2s. 6d., 10s., £1) B.W. (others))

**1954** (1 Feb)–**59**. *T* **46/51** *and similar designs previously used for King George VI issue (but with portrait of Queen Elizabeth II as in T* **47**). *Wmk Mult Script CA. P* 12 (2*d*.), 13 (8*d*.), 12½ (6*d*., 1*s*., 2*s*. 6*d*., 10*s*., £1), 11½×11 (3*d*., 1*s*. 6*d*., 2*s*., 5*s*.) *or* 11½ (½*d*., 1*d*., 1½*d*., 2½*d*.).

280 – ½d. myrtle-green (1.7.54) .. .. 15 30
281 **46** 1d. turquoise-blue (1.6.56) .. .. 40 10
282 1½d. sepia (1.10.56) .. .. .. 40 10
283 **47** 2d. green and magenta .. .. 1·00 30
284 **46** 2½d. blue-violet (1.10.56) .. .. 70 10
285 **48** 3d. brown and reddish violet (1.10.56) 1·00 15
a. *Brown & dp reddish vio* (10.11.59) 2·75 30
287 – 6d. black (1.7.54) .. .. .. 75 30
288 – 8d. deep carmine-red (1.7.54) .. .. 1·00 75
a. *Carmine-lake* (6.3.58) .. .. 2·25 90
289 – 1s. black and yellow .. .. .. 70 10
290 **49** 1s. 6d. blue and myrtle-green (1.10.56) 15·00 90
291 **50** 2s. black and carmine (1.10.56) .. 5·50 20
292 – 2s. 6d. bluish green and brown .. 70 10
a. *Bluish green & red-brown* (14.9.54) 50 10
293 **51** 5s. ochre and blue (1.10.56) .. 22·00 1·00
294 – 10s. orange and emerald (1.7.54) .. 11·00 20·00
295 – £1 ultramarine and carmine (1.7.54) 42·00 18·00
280/95 .. .. .. .. *Set of* 15 90·00 38·00

Designs: *Vert* (22½ × 36 *mm*)—½d. Fijians sailing canoe. (25 × 31 *mm*)—1s. Spearing fish by torchlight; 10s. Paw-paw tree; £1 Police bugler. *Horiz* (36 × 22½ *mm*)—6d. Map of Fiji. (31 × 25 *mm*)—8d. Arms of Fiji; 2s. 6d. River scene.

52 River Scene

53 Cross of Lorraine

(Recess B.W.)

**1954** (1 Apr). *Health Stamps. Wmk Mult Script CA. P* 11 × 11½.
296 **52** 1½d. + ½d. bistre-brown and green .. 10 20
297 **53** 2½d. + ½d. orange and black .. .. 10 10

54 Queen Elizabeth II (after Annigoni)

55 Fijian beating Lali

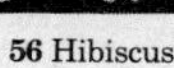

56 Hibiscus

60 Red Shining Parrot

(Des M. Goaman: Photo Harrison (8d., 4s.). Recess. B.W. (others))

**1959–63**. *T* **54/6**, **60** *and similar designs. Wmk Mult Script CA. P* 11½ (*T* **46** *and* **54**), 11½ × 11 (6*d*., 10*d*., 1*s*., 2*s*. 6*d*., 10*s*., £1), 14½ × 14 (8*d*.) *or* 14 × 14½ (4*s*).

298 **46** ½d. emerald-green (14.11.61) .. .. 15 30
299 **54** 1d. deep ultramarine (3.12.62) .. .. 1·00 60
300 1½d. sepia (3.12.62) .. .. .. 1·00 30
301 **46** 2d. rose-red (14.11.61) .. .. 50 25
302 2½d. orange-brown (3.12.62) .. .. 1·25 2·00
303 **55** 6d. carmine and black (14.11.61) .. 1·00 10
304 **56** 8d. scarlet, yellow, green & blk (1.8.61) 50 25
305 – 10d. brown and carmine (1.4.63) .. 2·25 50
306 – 1s. light blue and blue (14.11.61) .. 1·50 10
307 – 2s. 6d. black and purple (14.11.61) .. 11·00 10
308 **60** 4s. red, green, blue & slate-grn (13.7.59) 1·75 1·75
309 – 10s. emerald and deep sepia (14.11.61) .. 8·00 3·50
310 – £1 black and orange (14.11.61) .. 25·00 7·00
298/310 .. .. .. .. *Set of* 13 50·00 15·00

Designs: *Horiz* (*as T* **55**)—10d. Yaqona ceremony; 1s. Location map; 2s. 6d. Nadi Airport; 10s. Cutting sugar-cane; £1 Arms of Fiji.
Nos. 299 and 311 have turtles either side of "Fiji" instead of shells.

63 Queen Elizabeth II

64 International Dateline

65 White Orchid

66 Orange Dove

(Des M. Goaman. Photo Harrison (3d., 9d. 1s. 6d., 2s., 4s., 5s.). Recess B.W. (others))

**1962** (3 Dec)–**67**. *W w* **12** (*upright*). *P* 11½ (1*d*., 2*d*.), 12½ (3*d*.), 11½×11 (6*d*., 10*d*., 1*s*., 2*s*. 6*d*., 10*s*., £1), 14½×14 (9*d*., 2*s*.) *or* 14×14½ (1*s*. 6*d*., 4*s*., 5*s*.).

311 **54** 1d. deep ultramarine (14.1.64) .. .. 70 1·25
312 **46** 2d. rose-red (3.8.65) .. .. .. 45 15
313 **63** 3d. multicoloured .. .. .. 25 10
314 **55** 6d. carmine and black (9.6.64) .. .. 2·00 10
315 **56** 9d. scarlet, yellow, grn & ultram (1.4.63) 90 65
316 – 10d. brown and carmine (14.1.64) .. 60 40
317 – 1s. light blue and blue (24.1.66*) .. 2·00 30
318 **64** 1s. 6d. red, yellow, gold, black & blue .. 3·50 90
a. Error. Wmk sideways .. .. £550
319 **65** 2s. yellow-green, green & copper .. 14·00 1·75
a. *Apple-green, grn & copper* (16.5.67) 18·00 3·00
320 – 2s. 6d. black and purple (3.8.65) .. 75 25
a. *Black and deep purple* (8.67) .. 1·00 30
321 **60** 4s. red, yellow-green, bl & grn (1.4.64) 4·00 3·50
322 4s. red, green, blue & slate-grn (1.3.66) 2·25 4·00
323 **66** 5s. red, yellow and grey .. .. 13·00 35
324 – 10s. emerald and deep sepia (14.1.64) .. 7·00 6·00
325 – £1 black and orange (9.6.64) .. 16·00 11·00
311/25 .. .. .. .. *Set of* 15 60·00 27·00

Designs: *Horiz* (*as T* **55**)—10d. Yaqona Ceremony; 1s. Location map; 2s. 6d. Nadi Airport; 10s. Cutting sugar-cane; £1 Arms of Fiji.
*This is the earliest known used date in Fiji and it was not released by the Crown Agents until 1 November.
The 3d. value exists with PVA gum as well as gum arabic.
For 4s. with watermark sideways see No. 359.

ROYAL VISIT
1963
(67)

ROYAL VISIT 1963
(68)

**1963** (1 Feb). *Royal Visit. Nos.* 313 *and* 306 *optd with T* **67/8**.
326 **67** 3d. multicoloured .. .. .. 10 10
327 **68** 1s. light blue and blue .. .. .. 10 10

**1963** (4 June). *Freedom from Hunger. As No.* 146 *of Antigua*.
328 2s. ultramarine .. .. .. .. 4·75 70

69 Running

(73 C.S. *Retriever*.)

(Des M. Goaman. Photo Harrison)

**1963** (6 Aug). *First South Pacific Games, Suva. T* **69** *and similar designs. W w* **12**. *P* 14½.
329 3d. red-brown, yellow and black .. .. 25 10
330 9d. red-brown, violet and black .. .. 35 30
331 1s. red-brown, green and black .. .. 35 10
332 2s. 6d. red-brown, light blue and black .. 90 40
329/32 .. .. .. .. *Set of* 4 1·75 70

Designs: *Vert*—9d. Throwing the discus; 1s. Hockey. *Horiz*—2s. 6d. High-jumping.

**1963** (2 Sept). *Red Cross Centenary. As Nos.* 147/8 *of Antigua*.
333 2d. red and black .. .. .. .. 50 10
334 2s. red and blue .. .. .. .. 2·50 90

**1963** (3 Dec). *Opening of COMPAC (Trans-Pacific Telephone Cable). No.* 317 *optd with T* **73** *by B.W.*
335 1s. light blue and blue .. .. .. 25 10

74 Jamborette Emblem

75 Scouts of Three Races

(Des V. Whiteley assisted by Norman L. Joe, Asst. D.C., Fiji Scouts for Jamboree emblem. Photo Harrison)

**1964** (4 Aug). *50th Anniv of Fijian Scout Movement. W w* **12**. *P* 12½.
336 **74** 3d. multicoloured .. .. .. 10 15
337 **75** 1s. violet and yellow-brown .. .. 10 15

76 Flying-boat *Aotearoa*

78 *Aotearoa* and Map

(Des V. Whiteley. Photo Harrison)

**1964** (24 Oct). *25th Anniv of First Fiji-Tonga Airmail Service. T* **76**, **78** *and similar design. W w* **12**. *P* 14½ × 14 (1*s*.) *or* 12½ (*others*).
338 3d. black and vermilion .. .. .. 20 10
339 6d. vermilion and bright blue .. .. 30 20
340 1s. black and turquoise-blue .. .. 35 20
338/40 .. .. .. .. *Set of* 3 75 45

Design: *Vert* (*as T* **76**)—6d. Fiji Airways "Heron".

**1965** (17 May). *I.T.U. Centenary. As Nos.* 166/7 *of Antigua*.
341 3d. blue and rose-carmine .. .. .. 50 10
342 2s. orange-yellow and bistre .. .. 1·25 25

**1965** (25 Oct). *International Co-operation Year. As Nos.* 168/9 *of Antigua*.
343 2d. reddish purple and turquoise-green .. 30 10
344 2s. 6d. deep bluish green and lavender .. 70 25

**1966** (24 Jan). *Churchill Commemoration. As Nos.* 170/3 *of Antigua*.
345 3d. new blue .. .. .. .. 70 10
346 9d. deep green .. .. .. .. 90 40
347 1s. brown .. .. .. .. 90 10
348 2s. 6d. bluish violet .. .. .. 1·00 50
345/8 .. .. .. .. *Set of* 4 3·25 1·00

**1966** (1 July). *World Cup Football Championships. As Nos.* 176/7 *of Antigua*.
349 2d. violet, yellow-green, lake & yellow-brn .. 20 10
350 2s. chocolate, blue-green, lake & yellow-brn 50 20

79 H.M.S. *Pandora* approaching Split Island, Rotuma

(Des V. Whiteley. Photo Enschedé)

**1966** (29 Aug). *175th Anniv of Discovery of Rotuma. T* **79** *and similar horiz designs. Multicoloured. W w* **12** (*sideways*). *P* 14 × 13.
351 3d. Type **79** .. .. .. .. 15 10
352 10d. Rotuma Chiefs .. .. .. 15 10
353 1s. 6d. Rotumans welcoming H.M.S. *Pandora* 25 15
351/3 .. .. .. .. *Set of* 3 50 20

**1966** (20 Sept). *Inauguration of W.H.O. Headquarters, Geneva. As Nos.* 178/9 *of Antigua*.
354 6d. black, yellow-green and light blue .. 1·00 20
355 2s. 6d. black, light purple and yellow-brown 2·50 55

LEGISLATIVE ASSEMBLY

82 Running

(Des V. Whiteley. Photo Harrison)

**1966** (5 Dec*). *2nd South Pacific Games, Nouméa. T* **82** *and similar designs.* W w **12** (*sideways on 9d.*). *P* 14½ × 14 (*9d.*) *or* 14 × 14½ (*others*).
356 3d. black, chestnut and yellow-olive .. 10 10
357 9d. black, chestnut and greenish blue .. 15 15
358 1s. multicoloured .. .. .. .. .. 15 15
356/8 .. .. .. .. .. *Set of* 3 30 30
Designs: *Vert*—9d. Putting the shot. *Horiz*—1s. Diving.
*These were not released in London until 8.12.66.

**1967** (16 Feb). *As No.* 321 *but wmk* w **12** *sideways.*
359 **60** 4s. red, yellow-green, blue and green .. 3·25 1·25

**85** Military Forces Band

(Des G. Vasarhelyi. Photo Enschedé)

**1967** (20 Oct). *International Tourist Year. T* **85** *and similar horiz designs. Multicoloured.* W w **12** (*sideways*). *P* 14 × 13.
360 3d. Type **85** .. .. .. .. .. 10 10
361 9d. Reef diving .. .. .. .. 10 10
362 1s. Beqa fire walkers .. .. .. 10 10
363 2s. *Oriana* (cruise liner) at Suva .. .. 40 15
360/3 .. .. .. .. .. *Set of* 4 60 30

**89** Bligh (bust), H.M.S. *Providence* and Chart

**91** Bligh's Tomb

**90** "*Bounty*'s longboat being chased in Fiji waters"

(Des V. Whiteley. Photo Harrison)

**1967** (11 Dec). *150th Death Anniv of Admiral Bligh.* W w **12** (*sideways on* 1s.). *P* 12½ × 13 (1s.) *or* 15 × 14 (*others*).
364 **89** 4d. multicoloured .. .. .. 10 10
365 **90** 1s. multicoloured .. .. .. 10 10
366 **91** 2s. 6d. multicoloured .. .. .. 15 15
364/6 .. .. .. .. .. *Set of* 3 30 30

**92** Simmonds "Spartan" Seaplane

(Des V. Whiteley. Photo Harrison)

**1968** (5 June). *40th Anniv of Kingsford Smith's Pacific Flight via Fiji. T* **92** *and similar horiz designs.* W w **12**. *P* 14 × 14½.
367 2d. black and green .. .. .. .. 10 10
368 6d. greenish blue, black and lake .. .. 10 10
369 1s. deep violet and turquoise-green .. .. 15 10
370 2s. orange-brown and blue .. .. .. 20 15
367/70 .. .. .. .. .. *Set of* 4 50 30
Designs—6d. H.S. "748" and airline insignias; 1s. *Southern Cross* and crew; 2s. Lockheed "Altair" monoplane.

**96** Bure Huts

**97** Eastern Reef Heron (after Belcher)

**98** Sea Snake

**99** Queen Elizabeth and Arms of Fiji

(Des G. Hamori (½d., 1d., 9d.), W. O. Cernohorsky (2d., 4s.) H. S. Robinson (4d., 10d.), D. W. Blair (6d., 5s.), P. D. Clarke (1s.), G. Vasarhelyi (2s. 6d.), W. O. Cernohorsky and E. Jones (3s.), E. Jones and G. Hamori (10s.), E. Jones (£1). Adapted V. Whiteley. Photo D.L.R.)

**1968** (15 July). *T* **96/9** *and similar designs.* W w **12** (*sideways on all vert designs*). *P* 14 × 13½ (*2s., 2s. 6d., 5s., £1*), 13½ × 14 (*3d., 1s., 1s. 6d., 4s., 10s.*) *or* 13½ × 13 (*others*).
371 ½d. multicoloured .. .. .. .. 10 10
372 1d. deep greenish blue, red and yellow .. 10 10
373 2d. new blue, brown and ochre .. .. 10 10
374 3d. blackish green, blue and ochre .. .. 35 10
375 4d. multicoloured .. .. .. .. 80 15
376 6d. multicoloured .. .. .. .. 25 10
377 9d. multicoloured .. .. .. .. 15 15
378 10d. royal blue, orange and blackish brown .. 1·25 20
379 1s. Prussian blue and brown-red .. .. 20 10
380 1s. 6d. multicoloured .. .. .. 4·25 3·50
381 2s. turquoise, black and rosine .. .. 1·00 2·00
382 2s. 6d. multicoloured .. .. .. 1·00 75
383 3s. multicoloured .. .. .. .. 4·50 5·50
384 4s. yellow-ochre, black and olive .. .. 5·00 2·75
385 5s. multicoloured .. .. .. .. 4·00 2·50
386 10s. lake-brown, black and ochre .. .. 3·50 3·50
387 £1 multicoloured .. .. .. .. 3·50 7·50
371/87 .. .. .. .. *Set of* 17 24·00 26·00
Designs: *Horiz* (*as T* **96**)—1d. Passion Flowers; 2d. Pearly Nautilus; 4d. *Psilogramma jordana* (moth); 6d. Angel Fish; 9d. Bamboo raft; 10d. *Asota woodfordi* (moth); 3s. Golden Cowrie Shell. *Vert* (*as T* **97**)—1s. Black Marlin; 1s. 6d. Orange-breasted Honeyeaters (after Belcher); 4s. Mining industry; 10s. Ceremonial Whale's Tooth. *Horiz as T* **98**—2s. 6d. Outrigger canoes; 5s. Bamboo Orchids.

**113** Map of Fiji, W.H.O. Emblem and Nurses

(Des V. Whiteley. Litho D.L.R.)

**1968** (9 Dec). *20th Anniv of World Health Organization. T* **113** *and similar horiz designs. Multicoloured.* W w **12** (*sideways*). *P* 14.
388 3d. Type **113** .. .. .. .. .. 10 10
389 9d. Transferring patient to Medical Ship *Vuniwai* .. .. .. .. .. 15 10
390 3s. Recreation .. .. .. .. 20 20
388/90 .. .. .. .. *Set of* 3 40 30

**(New Currency. 100 cents = 1 dollar.)**

**116** Passion Flowers

**117** Fijian Soldiers overlooking the Solomon Islands

**1969** (13 Jan)–**70**. *Decimal Currency. Designs as Nos.* 371/87, *but with values inscr in decimal currency as T* **116**. W w **12** (*sideways on vert designs*) *Chalk-surfaced paper. P* 14 × 13½ (*20, 25, 50 c. $2*) 13½ × 14 (*3, 10, 15, 40 c., $1*) *or* 13½ × 13 (*others*).
391 **116** 1 c. deep greenish blue, red and yellow .. 10 10
392 – 2 c. new blue, brown and ochre (as 2d.) .. 10 10
393 **97** 3 c. blackish green, blue and ochre .. 30 10
394 – 4 c. multicoloured (as 4d.) .. .. 1·25 10
395 – 5 c. multicoloured (as 6d.) .. .. 20 10
396 **96** 6 c. multicoloured .. .. .. 10 10
397 – 8 c. multicoloured (as 9d.) .. .. 10 10
398 – 9 c. royal blue, orange and blackish brown (as 10d.) .. .. .. 1·25 70
399 – 10 c. Prussian blue and brown-red (as 1s.) 20 10
400 – 15 c. multicoloured (as 1s. 6d.) .. .. 6·50 3·00
401 **98** 20 c. turquoise, black and rosine .. 75 80
402 – 25 c. multicoloured (as 2s. 6d.) .. .. 75 30
403 – 30 c. multicoloured (as 3s.) .. .. 6·50 2·25
404 – 40 c. yellow-ochre, black and olive (as 4s.) 5·00 3·25
405 – 50 c. multicoloured (as 5s.) .. .. 4·50 30
a. Glazed, ordinary paper (3.9.70) .. 6·00 1·50
406 – $1 lake-brown, black and ochre (as 10s.) 4·00 60
a. Glazed, ordinary paper (3.9.70) .. 6·00 3·50
407 **99** $2 multicoloured .. .. .. 4·00 5·00
391/407 .. .. .. *Set of* 17 28·00 14·00

(Des G. Drummond. Photo Harrison)

**1969** (23 June). *25th Anniv of Fijian Military Forces' Solomons Campaign. T* **117** *and similar horiz designs.* W w **12**. *P* 14.
408 3 c. yellow-brown, black and bright emerald 15 10
409 10 c. multicoloured .. .. .. .. 20 10
410 25 c. multicoloured .. .. .. .. 30 20
408/10 .. .. .. .. *Set of* 3 60 30
Designs:—10 c. Regimental Flags and Soldiers in full dress and battledress; 25 c. Cpl. Sefanaia Sukanaivalu and Victoria Cross.

**120** Javelin Thrower

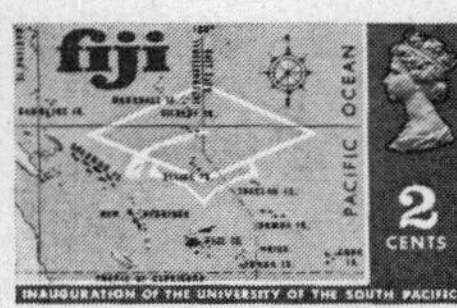

**123** Map of South Pacific and "Mortar-board"

(Des L. Curtis. Photo Harrison)

**1969** (18 Aug). *3rd South Pacific Games, Port Moresby. T* **120** *and similar vert designs.* W w **12** (*sideways*). *P* 14½ × 14.
411 4 c. black, brown and vermilion .. .. 10 10
412 8 c. black, grey and new blue .. .. 10 10
413 20 c. multicoloured .. .. .. 20 20
411/13 .. .. .. .. *Set of* 3 30 30
Designs:—8 c. Yachting; 20 c. Games medal and winners' rostrum.

(Des G. Drummond. Photo Harrison)

**1969** (10 Nov). *Inauguration of University of the South Pacific. T* **123** *and similar horiz designs. Multicoloured.* W w **12**. *P* 14 × 15.
414 2 c. Type **123** .. .. .. .. .. 10 15
415 8 c. R.N.Z.A.F. badge and "Sunderland" flying-boat over Laucala Bay (site of University) .. .. .. .. 15 10
416 25 c. Science students at work .. .. 25 15
414/16 .. .. .. .. *Set of* 3 45 30

ROYAL VISIT
1970

(**126**)

**127** Chaulmugra Tree, Makogai

**1970** (4 Mar). *Royal Visit. Nos.* 392, 399 *and* 402 *optd with T* **126**.
417 2 c. new blue, brown and ochre .. 10 20
418 10 c. Prussian blue and brown-red .. .. 10 10
419 25 c. multicoloured .. .. .. 20 10
417/19 .. .. .. .. *Set of* 3 35 30

(Des G. Drummond. Photo Harrison)

**1970** (25 May). *Closing of Leprosy Hospital, Makogai, T* **127** *and similar designs.* W w **12** (*sideways on* 10 *c.*). *P* 14 × 14½.
420 2 c. multicoloured .. .. .. 10 10
421 10 c. pale turquoise-green and black .. .. 10 10
a. Pair. Nos. 421/2 .. .. .. 15 20
422 10 c. turquoise-blue, black and magenta .. 10 10
423 30 c. multicoloured .. .. .. 20 40
420/3 .. .. .. .. *Set of* 4 35 60
Designs: *Vert*—No. 421, "Cascade" (Semisi Maya); No. 422, "Sea Urchins" (Semisi Maya). *Horiz*—No. 423, Makogai Hospital.
Nos. 421/2 were printed together *se-tenant* throughout the sheet.

**131** Abel Tasman and Log, 1643

(Des V. Whiteley. Litho D.L.R.)

**1970** (18 Aug). *Explorers and Discoverers. T* **131** *and similar horiz designs.* W w **12** (*sideways*). *P* 13 × 12½.
424 2 c. black, brown and turquoise .. .. 40 25
425 3 c. multicoloured .. .. .. 1·00 25
426 8 c. multicoloured .. .. .. 1·00 15
427 25 c. multicoloured .. .. .. 1·00 15
424/7 .. .. .. .. *Set of* 4 3·00 70
Designs:—3 c. Captain Cook and H.M.S. *Endeavour*, 1774; 8 c. Captain Bligh and longboat, 1789; 25 c. Fijian and ocean-going canoe.

INDEPENDENT

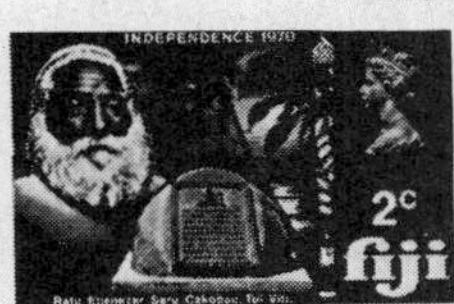

**135** King Cakobau and Cession Stone

**139** 1d. and 6d. Stamps of 1870

(Des J.W. Litho Format)

**1970** (10 Oct). *Independence. T* **135** *and similar horiz designs. Multicoloured.* W w **12** (*sideways*). *P* 14.
428 2 c. Type **135** .. .. .. .. 10 10
429 3 c. Children of the World .. .. 10 10
430 10 c. Prime Minister and Fijian flag .. .. 10 10
431 25 c. Dancers in costume .. .. .. 20 20
428/31 .. .. .. .. *Set of* 4 30 30
The design for the 10 c. value does not incorporate the Queen's head profile.

(Des V. Whiteley. Photo Harrison)

**1970** (2 Nov). *Stamp Centenary. T* **139** *and similar horiz designs. Multicoloured.* W w **12** *(sideways on 15 c.). P* 14½ × 14.

432 4 c. Type **139** .. .. .. .. .. 10 10
433 15 c. Fijian Stamps of all Reigns .. .. 15 15
434 20 c. *Fiji Times* Office and modern G.P.O. .. 15 15
432/4 .. .. .. .. .. *Set of* 3 35 35

The 15 c. is larger, 61 × 21 mm.

**140** Grey-backed White Eye

**141** Masked Shining Parrot

(Des G. Drummond. Litho Questa)

**1971** (6 Aug)–**72**. *Birds and Flowers. Vert designs as T* **140/1**. *Multicoloured.* W w **12** *(upright).*

*(a) Size as T* **140**. *P* 13½ × 14

435 1 c. *Cirrhopetalum umbellatum* (4.1.72) .. 15 20
436 2 c. Cardinal Honeyeater (22.11.71) .. .. 10 10
437 3 c. *Calanthe furcata* (23.6.72) .. .. 35 20
438 4 c. *Bulbophyllum sp nov* (23.6.72) .. .. 35 20
439 5 c. Type **140** .. .. .. .. .. 35 10
440 6 c. *Phaius tancarvilliae* (23.6.72) .. .. 3·00 80
441 8 c. Blue-headed Flycatcher (22.11.71) .. 35 10
442 10 c. *Acanthephippium vitiense* (4.1.72) .. 40 10
443 15 c. *Dendrobium tokai* (23.6.72) .. .. 3·50 90
444 20 c. Slaty Flycatcher .. .. .. .. 90 30

*(b) Size as T* **141**. *P* 14

445 25 c. Yellow-faced Honeyeater (22.11.71) .. 1·50 20
446 30 c. *Dendrobium gordonii* (4.1.72) .. .. 6·00 90
447 40 c. Type **141** .. .. .. .. .. 3·75 50
448 50 c. White-throated Pigeon .. .. .. 3·25 50
449 $1 Collared Lory (22.11.71) .. .. 4·00 1·25
450 $2 *Dendrobium platygastrium* (4.1.72) .. 6·50 11·00
435/50 .. .. .. .. *Set of* 16 30·00 15·00

See also Nos. 459/73 and 505/20.

**142** Women's Basketball

**143** Community Education

(Des R. Granger Barrett. Litho Questa)

**1971** (6 Sept). *Fourth South Pacific Games, Tahiti. T* **142** *and similar vert designs.* W w **12**. *P* 14.

451 8 c. multicoloured .. .. .. .. 10 10
452 10 c. cobalt, black and brown .. .. .. 10 10
453 25 c. pale turquoise-green, black and brown .. 30 25
451/3 .. .. .. .. .. *Set of* 3 45 30

Designs:—10c. Running; 25 c. Weightlifting.

(Des V. Whiteley. Litho Questa)

**1972** (7 Feb). *25th Anniv of South Pacific Commission. T* **143** *and similar vert designs. Multicoloured.* W w **12**. *P* 14.

454 2 c. Type **143** .. .. .. .. .. 10 10
455 4 c. Public Health .. .. .. .. 10 10
456 50 c. Economic Growth .. .. .. .. 35 65
454/6 .. .. .. .. .. *Set of* 3 40 70

**144** "Native Canoe"

**145** Flowers, Conch and Ceremonial Whale's Tooth

(Des locally and adapted by A. B. New. Litho Questa)

**1972** (10 Apr). *South Pacific Festival of Arts, Suva.* W w **12**. *P* 14.

457 **144** 10 c. black, orange and new blue .. 10 10

**1972** (17 Nov)–**74**. *As Nos.* 436/41, 443/5 *and* 447/50 *but* W w **12** *sideways.*

459 2 c. Cardinal Honey-eater (12.12.73) .. 30 3·50
460 3 c. *Calanthe furcata* (8.3.73) .. .. 90 45
461 4 c. *Bulbophyllum sp nov* (11.4.73) .. 4·00 45
462 5 c. Type **140** (8.3.73).. .. .. 2·25 80
463 6 c. *Phaius tancarvilliae* (11.4.73) .. 4·00 1·25
464 8 c. Blue-crested Broadbill (11.4.73).. .. 2·75 75
466 15 c. *Dendrobium tokai* (11.4.73) .. .. 3·25 2·25
467 20 c. Slaty Flycatcher .. .. .. .. 5·50 2·00
468 25 c. Kandavu Honey-eater (11.4.73).. .. 1·75 1·40
470 40 c. Type **141** (15.3.74) .. .. .. 3·00 3·50
471 50 c. White-throated Pigeon (15.3.74) .. 3·00 3·50
472 $1 Collared Lory .. .. .. .. 4·50 6·50
473 $2 *Dendrobium platygastrium* .. .. 9·00 11·00
459/73 .. .. .. .. *Set of* 13 40·00 35·00

(Des (from photograph by D. Groves) and photo Harrison)

**1972** (20 Nov). *Royal Silver Wedding. Multicoloured; background colour given.* W w **12**. *P* 14 × 14½.

474 10 c. slate-green .. .. .. .. 20 15
475 25 c. bright purple .. .. .. .. 30 15
a. Blue printing omitted* .. .. .. £160

*The omission of the blue colour results in the Duke's suit appearing brown instead of deep blue.

HURRICANE
RELIEF
+10c

**(146)**

**147** Line Out

**1972** (4 Dec). *Hurricane Relief. Nos.* 400 *and* 403 *surch as T* **146**, *by the Reserve Bank of Australia.*

476 15 c. + 5 c. multicoloured .. .. .. 15 15
477 30 c. + 10 c. multicoloured .. .. .. 15 15

(Des J.W. Litho Questa)

**1973** (9 Mar). *Diamond Jubilee of Fiji Rugby Union. T* **147** *and similar vert designs. Multicoloured.* W w **12** *(sideways). P* 14.

478 2 c. Type **147** .. .. .. .. .. 15 10
479 8 c. Body tackle .. .. .. .. 25 10
480 25 c. Conversion .. .. .. .. 65 30
478/80 .. .. .. .. .. *Set of* 3 95 40

**148** Forestry Development

**149** Christmas

(Des J.W. from local ideas. Litho Questa)

**1973** (23 July). *Development Projects. T* **148** *and similar horiz designs. Multicoloured.* W w **12**. *P* 14.

481 5 c. Type **148** .. .. .. .. .. 10 10
482 8 c. Rice irrigation scheme .. .. .. 10 10
483 10 c. Low income housing .. .. .. 10 10
484 25 c. Highway construction .. .. .. 15 20
481/4 .. .. .. .. .. *Set of* 4 35 30

(Des L. Curtis. Litho Questa)

**1973** (26 Oct). *Festivals of Joy. T* **149** *and similar vert designs. Multicoloured.* W w **12** *(sideways). P* 14.

485 3 c. Type **149** .. .. .. .. .. 10 10
486 10 c. Diwali .. .. .. .. .. 10 10
487 20 c. Id-ul-Fitar .. .. .. .. 15 10
488 25 c. Chinese New Year .. .. .. .. 15 10
485/8 .. .. .. .. .. *Set of* 4 35 30

**150** Athletics

**151** Bowler

(Des G. Drummond. Litho Questa)

**1974** (7 Jan). *Commonwealth Games, Christchurch. T* **150** *and similar vert designs. Multicoloured.* W w **12** *(sideways). P* 14.

489 3 c. Type **150** .. .. .. .. .. 15 10
490 8 c. Boxing .. .. .. .. .. 15 10
491 50 c. Bowling .. .. .. .. .. 50 65
489/91 .. .. .. .. .. *Set of* 3 70 70

(Des Hon. P. Snow. Adapted J.W. Litho Questa)

**1974** (21 Feb). *Cricket Centenary. T* **151** *and similar multi-coloured designs.* W w **12** *(sideways on* 3 *and* 25 *c.). P* 14.

492 3 c. Type **151** .. .. .. .. .. 50 25
493 25 c. Batsman and wicketkeeper .. .. 1·75 35
494 40 c. Fielder *(horiz)* .. .. .. .. 2·50 90
492/4 .. .. .. .. .. *Set of* 3 4·25 1·40

**152** Fijian Postman

(Des L. Curtis. Litho Format)

**1974** (22 May). *Centenary of the Universal Postal Union. T* **152** *and similar horiz designs. Multicoloured.* W w **12**. *P* 14.

495 3 c. Type **152** .. .. .. .. .. 10 10
496 8 c. Loading mail onto *Fijian Princess* .. 10 10
497 30 c. Fijian post office and mail bus .. .. 20 20
498 50 c. Modern aircraft .. .. .. .. 35 60
495/8 .. .. .. .. .. *Set of* 4 60 80

**153** Cubs lighting Fire

**154** Cakobau Club and Flag

(Des E. W. Roberts. Litho Questa)

**1974** (30 Aug). *First National Scout Jamboree, Lautoka. T* **153** *and similar multicoloured designs.* W w **12** *(sideways on* 40 *c.). P* 14.

499 3 c. Type **153** .. .. .. .. .. 15 10
500 10 c. Scouts reading map .. .. .. .. 20 10
501 40 c. Scouts and Fijian flag *(vert)* .. .. 65 1·00
499/501 .. .. .. .. .. *Set of* 3 90 1·10

(Des J.W. Litho Enschedé)

**1974** (9 Oct). *Centenary of Deed of Cession and Fourth Anniv of Independence. T* **154** *and similar horiz designs. Multicoloured.* W w **12** *(sideways on* 8 *and* 50 *c.). P* 13½ × 13 *(3 c.) or* 13 × 13½ *(others).*

502 3 c. Type **154** .. .. .. .. .. 10 10
503 8 c. King Cakobau and Queen Victoria .. 10 10
504 50 c. Raising the Royal Standard at Nasova Ovalau .. .. .. .. .. 30 55
502/4 .. .. .. .. .. *Set of* 3 40 60

**1975** (9 Apr)–**77**. *As Nos.* 435/44 *and* 446/50, *but* W w **14** *(sideways on* 1 *and* 10 *c).*

505 1 c. *Cirrhopetalum umbellatum* .. .. 20 75
506 2 c. Cardinal Honey-eater .. .. .. 20 75
507 3 c. *Calanthe furcata* .. .. .. .. 30 80
508 4 c. *Bulbophyllum sp nov* (3.9.76) .. .. 1·50 10
509 5 c. Type **140** .. .. .. .. .. 30 55
510 6 c. *Phaius tancarvilliae* (3.9.76) .. .. 1·25 10
511 8 c. Blue-crested Broadbill (3.9.76) .. .. 35 10
512 10 c. *Acanthephippium vitiense* .. .. 40 35
513 15 c. *Dendrobium tokai* (3.9.76) .. .. 1·50 60
514 20 c. Slaty Flycatcher (15.7.77) .. .. 3·00 55
516 30 c. *Dendrobium gordonii* (3.9.76) .. .. 5·50 95
517 40 c. Type **141** (3.9.76).. .. .. 3·00 60
518 50 c. White-throated pigeon (3.9.76) .. 3·25 65
519 $1 Collared Lory (3.9.76) .. .. 3·50 3·00
520 $2 *Dendrobium platygastrium* (3.9.76) .. 5·50 3·50
505/20 .. .. .. .. *Set of* 15 27·00 12·00

**155** "Diwali" (Hindu Festival)

**156** Steam Locomotive No. 21

(Des Jennifer Toombs. Litho Walsall)

**1975** (31 Oct). *Festivals of Joy. T* **155** *and similar vert designs. Multicoloured.* W w **14** *(inverted). P* 14.

521 3 c. Type **155** .. .. .. .. .. 10 10
522 15 c. "Id-Ul-Fitar" (Muslim Festival) .. .. 10 10
523 25 c. Chinese New Year .. .. .. .. 15 15
524 30 c. Christmas .. .. .. .. .. 20 30
521/4 .. .. .. .. .. *Set of* 4 40 50
**MS**525 121 × 101 mm. Nos. 521/4. W w **14** (sideways) .. .. .. .. .. 1·75 5·50
a. Imperf between (vert) .. .. .. £1000

(Des R. Granger Barrett. Litho Questa)

**1976** (26 Jan). *Sugar Trains. T* **156** *and similar horiz designs. Multicoloured.* W w **14** *(sideways). P* 14.

526 4 c. Type **156** .. .. .. .. .. 25 10
527 15 c. Diesel locomotive No. 8 .. .. .. 70 30
528 20 c. Diesel locomotive No. 1 .. .. .. 80 40
529 30 c. Free passenger train .. .. .. .. 95 70
526/9 .. .. .. .. .. *Set of* 4 2·50 1·25

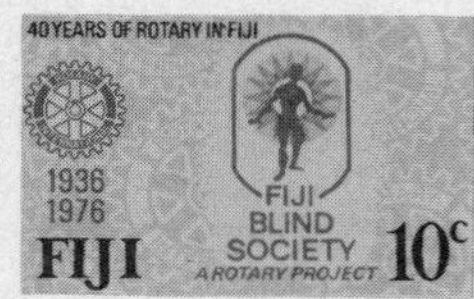


**157** Fiji Blind Society and Rotary Symbols

(Des V. Whiteley Studio. Litho J.W.)

**1976** (26 Mar). *40th Anniv of Rotary in Fiji. T* **157** *and similar horiz design. W* w **14** (*sideways*). *P* 13.

530 10 c. ultramarine, pale sage-green and black .. 15 10
531 25 c. multicoloured .. .. .. .. .. 40 50

Design:—25 c. Ambulance and Rotary symbol.

**158** D. H. "Drover"

(Des P. Powell. Litho Questa)

**1976** (1 Sept). *25th Anniv of Air Services. T* **158** *and similar horiz designs. Multicoloured. W* w **14**. *P* 13½ × 14.

532 4 c. Type **158** .. .. .. .. .. 40 20
533 15 c. B.A.C. "1–11" .. .. .. .. .. 1·00 1·00
534 25 c. H.S. "748" .. .. .. .. .. 2·00 1·25
535 30 c. Britten-Norman "Trislander" .. .. 2·25 2·75
532/5 .. .. .. .. .. *Set of* 4 5·00 4·75

**159** The Queen's Visit to Fiji, 1970 **160** Map of the World

(Des L. Curtis. Litho Questa)

**1977** (7 Feb). *Silver Jubilee. T* **159** *and similar vert designs. Multicoloured. W* w **14**. *P* 13½.

536 10 c. Type **159** .. .. .. .. .. 10 10
537 25 c. King Edward's Chair .. .. .. .. 15 10
538 30 c. Queen wearing cloth-of-gold supertunica 25 15
536/8 .. .. .. .. .. *Set of* 3 40 30

(Des J.W. Litho Walsall)

**1977** (12 Apr). *E.E.C./A.C.P.* Council of Ministers Conference, Fiji. T* **160** *and similar horiz design. Multicoloured. W* w **14** (*sideways*). *P* 14.

539 4 c. Type **160** .. .. .. .. .. 10 10
540 30 c. Map of Fiji group.. .. .. .. .. 30 65

*A.C.P. = African, Caribbean, Pacific Group.

**161** *Hibiscus rosa-sinensis*

(Des V. Whiteley Studio. Litho Walsall)

**1977** (27 Aug). *21st Anniv of Fiji Hibiscus Festival. T* **161** *and similar horiz designs. W* w **14** (*sideways*). *P* 14.

541 **161** 4 c. multicoloured .. .. .. .. 10 10
542 – 15 c. multicoloured .. .. .. .. 15 10
543 – 30 c. multicoloured .. .. .. .. 25 15
544 – 35 c. multicoloured .. .. .. .. 40 35
541/4 .. .. .. .. .. *Set of* 4 80 60

Nos. 542/44 show different varieties of *H rosa-sinensis*.

**162** Drua **163** White Hart of Richard II

(Des P. Powell. Litho Questa)

**1977** (7 Nov). *Canoes. T* **162** *and similar horiz designs. Multicoloured. W* w **14** (*sideways*). *P* 14.

545 4 c. Type **162** .. .. .. .. .. 10 5
546 15 c. Tabilai .. .. .. .. .. 20 20
547 25 c. Takai .. .. .. .. .. 25 25
548 40 c. Camakua.. .. .. .. .. 35 70
545/8 .. .. .. .. .. *Set of* 4 80 1·10

(Des C. Abbott. Litho Questa)

**1978** (21 Apr). *25th Anniv of Coronation. T* **163** *and similar vert designs. P* 15.

549 25 c. bistre, blue-green and silver .. .. 20 25
a. Sheetlet. Nos. 549/51 × 2 .. .. 1·10
550 25 c. multicoloured .. .. .. .. 20 25
551 25 c. bistre, blue-green and silver .. .. 20 25
549/51 .. .. .. .. .. *Set of* 3 55 65

Designs:—No. 549, Type **163**; No. 550, Queen Elizabeth II; No. 551, Banded Iguana.

Nos. 549/51 were printed together in small sheets of 6, containing two *se-tenant* strips of 3, with horizontal gutter margin between.

**164** Defence Force surrounding Plane, Suva

(Des A. Theobald. Litho Harrison)

**1978** (26 June). *Aviation Anniversaries. T* **164** *and similar horiz designs. Multicoloured. W* w **14** (*sideways*). *P* 14.

552 4 c. Type **164** .. .. .. .. .. 15 10
553 15 c. *Southern Cross* prior to leaving Naselai Beach .. .. .. .. .. 25 30
554 25 c. Wright *Flyer* .. .. .. .. .. 50 55
555 30 c. Bristol "F2B" .. .. .. .. .. 50 70
552/5 .. .. .. .. .. *Set of* 4 1·25 1·40

Anniversaries:—25 c. 75th of powered flight; 30 c. 60th of R.A.F.; others. 50th of first trans-Pacific flight by Kingsford-Smith.

**165** Shallow Wooden Oil Dish in shape of Human Figure **166** Advent Crown with Candles (Christmas)

(Des J. Cooter. Litho Questa)

**1978** (14 Aug). *Fijian Artifacts. T* **165** *and similar multicoloured designs. W* w **14** (*sideways on* 15 *and* 25 c.). *P* 14.

556 4 c. Type **165** .. .. .. .. .. 10 10
557 15 c. Necklace of cachalot teeth (*horiz*) .. 10 10
558 25 c. Double water bottle (*horiz*) .. .. 15 10
559 30 c. Finely carved Ula or throwing club .. 15 15
556/9 .. .. .. .. .. *Set of* 4 35 35

(Des Jennifer Toombs. Litho Harrison)

**1978** (30 Oct). *Festivals. T* **166** *and similar horiz designs. Multicoloured. W* w **14** (*sideways*). *P* 14.

560 4 c. Type **166** .. .. .. .. .. 10 10
561 15 c. Lamps (Diwali) .. .. .. .. 10 10
562 25 c. Coffee pot, cups and fruit (Id-Ul-Fitr) .. 10 10
563 40 c. Lion (Chinese New Year) .. .. .. 25 40
560/3 .. .. .. .. .. *Set of* 4 35 60

**167** Banded Iguana

(Des L. Curtis and G. Drummond. Litho Questa)

**1979** (19 Mar). *Endangered Wildlife. T* **167** *and similar horiz designs. Multicoloured. W* w **14** (*sideways*). *P* 14.

564 4 c. Type **167** .. .. .. .. .. 10 10
565 15 c. Tree Frog.. .. .. .. .. 30 10
566 25 c. Long-legged Warbler .. .. .. 50 20
567 30 c. Pink-billed Parrot Finch.. .. .. 65 55
564/7 .. .. .. .. .. *Set of* 4 1·40 80

**168** Women with Dholak

(Des J.W. Litho Questa)

**1979** (11 May). *Centenary of Arrival of Indians. T* **168** *and similar horiz designs. Multicoloured. W* w **14** (*sideways*). *P* 14.

568 4 c. Type **168** .. .. .. .. .. 10 10
569 15 c. Men sitting round tanoa.. .. .. .. 10 10
570 30 c. Farmer and sugar cane plantation .. 15 10
571 40 c. Sailing ship *Leonidas* .. .. .. 40 25
568/71 .. .. .. .. .. *Set of* 4 60 45

**169** Soccer

(Des BG Studio. Litho Questa)

**1979** (2 July). *6th South Pacific Games. T* **169** *and similar horiz designs. Multicoloured. W* w **14** (*sideways*). *P* 14.

572 4 c. Type **169** .. .. .. .. .. 10 10
573 15 c. Rugby Union .. .. .. .. .. 25 10
574 30 c. Lawn tennis .. .. .. .. .. 55 35
575 40 c. Weightlifting .. .. .. .. 60 45
572/5 .. .. .. .. .. *Set of* 4 1·40 80

**170** Indian Child and Map of Fiji

(Des D. Bowen. Litho Walsall)

**1979** (17 Sept). *International Year of the Child. T* **170** *and similar horiz designs showing children and map of Fiji. Multicoloured. W* w **14** (*sideways*). *P* 14½ × 14.

576 4 c. + 1 c. Type **170** .. .. .. .. 10 10
577 15 c. + 2 c. European child .. .. .. 15 15
578 30 c. + 3 c. Chinese child .. .. .. 15 15
579 40 c. + 4 c. Fijian child .. .. .. 15 20
576/9 .. .. .. .. .. *Set of* 4 45 50

**171** Old Town Hall, Suva

(Des J. W. Litho Questa (1, 2, 3, 4, 10, 15, 20, 30 c., $5) or Harrison (others))

**1979** (11 Nov)–**91**. *Architecture. Multicoloured designs as T* **171**. *W* w **14** (*sideways on horiz designs*). *P* 13½×13 ($1), 13×13½ ($2), 13½×14 ($5) *or* 14 (*others*).

A. *Without imprint date at foot. Chalk-surfaced paper* (1, 2, 3, 10, 15, 20, 30 *c*., $5). B. *With imprint date.*

| No. | Value | Description | A | | B | |
|---|---|---|---|---|---|---|
| 580 | 1 c. | Type **171** .. .. | 15 | 35 | † | |
| | | a. Ordinary paper .. | 30 | 30 | † | |
| 581 | 2 c. | Dudley Church, Suva .. | 35 | 40 | 50 | 60 |
| | | a. Ordinary paper .. | 35 | 40 | 50 | 60 |
| 582 | 3 c. | Fiji International Telecommunications Building, Suva .. .. | 35 | 40 | † | |
| | | a. Ordinary paper .. | 35 | 40 | † | |
| 582*c* | 4 c. | Lautoka Mosque .. | † | | 10 | 10 |
| 583 | 5 c. | As 4 c. .. .. .. | 10 | 10 | 10 | 10 |
| 584 | 6 c. | General Post Office, Suva .. .. .. | 10 | 10 | 10 | 10 |
| 585 | 10 c. | Fiji Visitors Bureau, Suva .. .. .. | 30 | 15 | † | |
| | | a. Ordinary paper .. | 30 | 30 | 10 | 10 |
| 586 | 12 c. | Public School, Levuka | 10 | 10 | † | |
| 587 | 15 c. | Colonial War Memorial Hospital, Suva .. | 40 | 30 | † | |
| | | a. Ordinary paper .. | 35 | 35 | 10 | 15 |
| 588 | 18 c. | Labasa Sugar Mill .. | 15 | 20 | † | |
| 589 | 20 c. | Rewa Bridge, Nausori | 55 | 30 | † | |
| | | a. Ordinary paper .. | 55 | 35 | † | |
| 590 | 30 c. | Sacred Heart Cathedral, Suva (*vert*) .. .. | 65 | 40 | † | |
| | | a. Ordinary paper .. | 25 | 30 | † | |
| 591 | 35 c. | Grand Pacific Hotel, Suva .. .. .. | 30 | 40 | † | |
| 592 | 45 c. | Shiva Temple, Suva .. | 35 | 40 | † | |
| 593 | 50 c. | Serua Island Village .. | 40 | 40 | † | |
| 594 | $1 | Solo Rock Lighthouse (30×46 *mm*) .. .. | 1·00 | 80 | † | |
| 595 | $2 | Baker Memorial Hall, Nausori (46×30 *mm*) .. | 1·60 | 1·75 | † | |
| 595*a* | $5 | Government House, Suva (46×30 *mm*) .. | 4·00 | 4·25 | † | |
| 580/95*a* | | .. .. *Set of* 17 | 9·00 | 9·25 | † | |

Dates of issue:—11.11.79 Nos. 580A/82A, 585A, 587A, 589A/90A, 595*a*A; 13.6.80 Nos. 580aA, 581aA, 582aA, 585aA, 587aA, 589aA, 590aA; 22.12.80 Nos. 583A/84A, 586A, 588A, 591A/5A; 15.6.83 No. 584B; 1.84 No. 583B; 2.84 581aB; 19.11.86 No. 581B. 11.91 Nos. 582*c*B, 585aB, 587aB.

No. 581aB exists with different imprint dates beneath the design.

For these designs and similar 8 c. watermarked w **16** see Nos. 719/35.

**172** *Southern Cross*, 1873

(Des L. Dunn. Litho Secura, Singapore)

**1980** (28 Apr). *"London 1980" International Stamp Exhibition. Mail-carrying Ships. T* **172** *and similar horiz designs. Multicoloured.* W w **14** (*sideways*). *P* 13½.

596 6 c. Type **172** .. .. 15 10
597 20 c. *Levuka*, 1910 .. .. 15 10
598 45 c. *Matua*, 1936 .. .. 30 35
599 50 c. *Oronsay*, 1951 .. .. 30 40
596/9 .. .. *Set of* 4 80 80

**173** Sovi Bay

(Des BG Studio. Litho Questa)

**1980** (18 Aug). *Tourism. T* **173** *and similar horiz designs. Multicoloured.* W w **14** (*sideways*). *P* 13½ × 14.

600 6 c. Type **173** .. .. 10 10
601 20 c. Evening scene, Yanuca Island .. .. 15 15
602 45 c. Dravuni Beach .. .. 20 40
603 50 c. Wakaya Island .. .. 20 45
600/3 .. .. *Set of* 4 50 95

**174** Official Opening of Parliament, 1979

(Des J. Cooter. Litho J.W.)

**1980** (6 Oct). *10th Anniv of Independence. T* **174** *and similar multicoloured designs.* W w **14** (*sideways on* 6 *and* 45 c.). *P* 13.

604 6 c. Type **174** .. .. 10 10
605 20 c. Fiji coat of arms (*vert*) .. .. 15 10
606 45 c. Fiji flag .. .. 20 20
607 50 c. Queen Elizabeth II (*vert*) .. .. 25 35
604/7 .. .. *Set of* 4 55 60

**175** "Coastal Scene" (painting, Semisi Maya)  **176** Prince Charles Sailing

(Des J.W. Litho Questa)

**1981** (21 Apr). *International Year for Disabled Persons. T* **175** *and similar multicoloured designs.* W w **14** (*sideways on* 6 *and* 35 c.). *P* 14.

608 6 c. Type **175** .. .. 10 10
609 35 c. "Underwater Scene" (painting, Semisi Maya) .. .. 45 30
610 50 c. Semisi Maya (disabled artist) at work (*vert*) .. .. 55 40
611 60 c. "Peacock" (painting, Semisi Maya) (*vert*) 60 45
608/11 .. .. *Set of* 4 1·50 1·10

(Des J.W. Litho Questa)

**1981** (22 July). *Royal Wedding. T* **176** *and similar vert designs. Multicoloured.* W w **14**. *P* 14.

612 6 c. Wedding bouquet from Fiji .. .. 10 10
613 45 c. Type **176** .. .. 45 15
614 $1 Prince Charles and Lady Diana Spencer 75 60
612/14 .. .. *Set of* 3 1·10 75

**177** Operator Assistance Centre  **178** "Eat Fiji Foods"

(Des A. Theobald. Litho Format)

**1981** (17 Aug). *Telecommunications. T* **177** *and similar horiz designs. Multicoloured.* W w **14** (*sideways*). *P* 14.

615 6 c. Type **177** .. .. 10 10
616 35 c. Microwave station .. .. 55 50
617 50 c. Satellite earth station .. .. 75 75
618 60 c. Cable ship *Retriever* .. .. 90 90
615/18 .. .. *Set of* 4 2·10 2·00

(Des J.W. Litho Format)

**1981** (21 Sept). *World Food Day.* W w **14**. *P* 14½ × 14.

619 **178** 20 c. multicoloured .. .. 30 10

**179** Ratu Sir Lala Sukuna (first Speaker, Legislative Council)

(Des A. Theobald. Litho Format)

**1981** (19 Oct). *Commonwealth Parliamentary Association Conference, Suva. T* **179** *and similar horiz designs.* W w **14** (*sideways*). *P* 14.

620 6 c. black, buff and orange-brown .. .. 10 10
621 35 c. multicoloured .. .. 30 30
622 50 c. multicoloured .. .. 45 45
620/2 .. .. *Set of* 3 75 75
**MS**623 73 × 53 mm. 60 c. multicoloured .. .. 70 1·00

Designs:—35 c. Mace of the House of Representatives; 50 c. Suva Civic Centre; 60 c. Flags of C.P.A. countries.

**180** Bell "P-39 Airacobra"

(Des A. Theobald. Litho Walsall)

**1981** (7 Dec). *World War II Aircraft. T* **180** *and similar horiz designs. Multicoloured.* W w **14** (*sideways*). *P* 14.

624 6 c. Type **180** .. .. 35 10
625 18 c. Consolidated "PBY-5 Catalina" .. .. 70 25
626 35 c. Curtiss "P-40 Warhawk" .. .. 80 40
627 60 c. Short "Singapore" .. .. 1·10 85
624/7 .. .. *Set of* 4 2·75 1·40

**181** Scouts constructing Shelter

(Des B. Melton. Litho Questa)

**1982** (22 Feb). *75th Anniv of Boy Scout Movement. T* **181** *and similar multicoloured designs.* W w **14** (*sideways on* 6 *and* 45 c.). *P* 14½.

628 6 c. Type **181** .. .. 15 10
629 20 c. Scouts sailing (*vert*) .. .. 50 30
630 45 c. Scouts by campfire .. .. 85 50
631 60 c. Lord Baden-Powell (*vert*) .. .. 1·00 1·00
628/31 .. .. *Set of* 4 2·25 1·75

**182** Fiji Soldiers at U.N. Checkpoint

(Des J.W. Litho Format)

**1982** (3 May). *Disciplined Forces. T* **182** *and similar horiz designs. Multicoloured.* W w **14** (*sideways*). *P* 14.

632 12 c. Type **182** .. .. 25 10
633 30 c. Soldiers engaged in rural development 50 45
634 40 c. Police patrol .. .. 70 60
635 70 c. *Kiro* (minesweeper) .. .. 1·00 1·10
632/5 .. .. *Set of* 4 2·25 2·00

**183** Footballers and Fiji Football Association Logo  **184** Bride and Groom leaving St. Paul's

(Des A. Theobald. Litho Walsall)

**1982** (15 June). *World Cup Football Championship, Spain. T* **183** *and similar horiz designs.* W w **14** (*sideways*). *P* 14.

636 6 c. rosine, black and lemon .. .. 10 10
637 18 c. multicoloured .. .. 25 20
638 50 c. multicoloured .. .. 70 60
639 90 c. multicoloured .. .. 1·10 1·25
636/9 .. .. *Set of* 4 1·90 1·90

Designs:—18 c. Footballers and World Cup emblem; 50 c. Footballer and Bernabeu Stadium; 90 c. Footballers and Naranjito (mascot).

(Des C. Abbott. Litho Harrison)

**1982** (1 July). *21st Birthday of Princess of Wales. T* **184** *and similar vert designs. Multicoloured.* W w **14**. *P* 14½ × 14.

640 20 c. Fiji coat of arms .. .. 25 25
641 35 c. Lady Diana Spencer at Broadlands, May 1981 .. .. 35 35
642 45 c. Type **184** .. .. 50 50
643 $1 Formal portrait .. .. 1·25 1·25
640/3 .. .. *Set of* 4 2·10 2·10

**185** Prince Philip  **186** Baby Jesus with Mary and Joseph

(Des C. Abbott. Litho Format)

**1982** (1 Nov). *Royal Visit. T* **185** *and similar multicoloured designs.* W w **14**. *P* 14.

644 6 c. Type **185** .. .. 10 10
645 45 c. Queen Elizabeth II .. .. 65 1·40
**MS**646 128 × 88 mm. Nos. 644/5 and $1 Royal Yacht *Britannia* (*horiz*). Wmk sideways .. .. 2·25 2·75

(Des G. Wilby. Litho Questa)

**1982** (22 Nov). *Christmas. T* **186** *and similar horiz designs. Multicoloured.* W w **14** (*sideways*). *P* 14 × 14½.

647 6 c. Type **186** .. .. 10 10
648 20 c. Three Wise Men presenting gifts .. 30 20
649 35 c. Carol-singing .. .. 45 35
647/9 .. .. *Set of* 3 75 55
**MS**650 94 × 42 mm. $1 "Faith" (from the "Three Virtues" by Raphael) .. .. 1·25 1·50

**187** Red-throated Lorikeet  **188** Bure in Traditional Village

(Des N. Arlott. Litho Questa)

**1983** (14 Feb). *Parrots. T* **187** *and similar vert designs. Multicoloured.* W w **14**. *P* 14.

651 20 c. Type **187** .. .. 90 15
652 40 c. Blue-crowned Lory .. .. 1·25 40
653 55 c. Masked Shining Parrot .. .. 1·40 70
654 70 c. Red Shining Parrot .. .. 1·50 1·25
651/4 .. .. *Set of* 4 4·50 2·25

(Des B. Melton. Litho Questa)

**1983** (14 Mar). *Commonwealth Day. T* **188** *and similar horiz designs. Multicoloured.* W w **14** (*sideways*). *P* 14.

655 8 c. Type **188** .. .. 10 10
656 25 c. Barefoot firewalkers .. .. 20 15
657 50 c. Sugar industry .. .. 30 35
658 80 c. Kava "Yagona" ceremony .. .. 55 70
655/8 .. .. *Set of* 4 1·00 1·10

**189** First Manned Balloon Flight, 1783  **190** Nawanawa

(Des Harrison. Litho Questa)

**1983** (18 July). *Bicentenary of Manned Flight. T* **189** *and similar horiz designs. Multicoloured. W w* **14** *(sideways). P* 14.

659 8 c. Type **189** .. .. .. .. .. 10 10
660 20 c. Wright brothers' *Flyer* .. .. .. .. 25 30
661 25 c. Douglas "Super DC3" .. .. .. .. 35 40
662 40 c. De Havilland "Comet" .. .. .. .. 55 60
663 50 c. Boeing "747" .. .. .. .. 65 70
664 58 c. Space Shuttle .. .. .. .. 75 80
659/64 .. .. .. .. *Set of* 6 2·40 2·50

(Des Harrison. Litho Format)

**1983** (26 Sept). *Flowers (1st series). T* **190** *and similar vert designs. Multicoloured. W w* **14**. *P* 14 × 14½.

665 8 c. Type **190** .. .. .. .. .. 10 10
666 25 c. Rosawa .. .. .. .. .. 35 30
667 40 c. Warerega .. .. .. .. .. 55 50
668 $1 Saburo .. .. .. .. .. 1·25 1·40
665/8 .. .. .. .. *Set of* 4 2·00 2·00

See also Nos. 680/3.

**191** Fijian beating Lali and Earth Satellite Station

**192** *Dacryopinax spathularia*

(Des Garden Studio. Litho Questa)

**1983** (7 Nov). *World Communications Year. W w* **14**. *P* 13½.

669 **191** 50 c. multicoloured .. .. .. .. 50 70

(Des Jennifer Toombs. Litho Enschedé)

**1984** (9 Jan). *Fungi. T* **192** *and similar multicoloured designs. W w* **14** *(sideways on* 50 *c. and* $1). *P* 13½ × 13 (8 *c. to* 40 *c.) or* 13 × 13½ *(others).*

670 8 c. Type **192** .. .. .. .. .. 40 10
671 15 c. *Podoscypha involuta* .. .. .. .. 60 25
672 40 c. *Lentinus squarrosulus* .. .. .. .. 1·00 70
673 50 c. *Scleroderma flavidum (horiz)* .. .. .. 1·25 80
674 $1 *Phillipsia domingensis (horiz)* .. .. 1·60 1·75
670/4 .. .. .. .. *Set of* 5 4·25 3·25

**193** *Tui Lau* on Reef

(Des L. Curtis. Litho Questa)

**1984** (7 May). *250th Anniv of "Lloyd's List" (newspaper). T* **193** *and similar vert designs. Multicoloured. W w* **14**. *P* 14½ × 14.

675 8 c. Type **193** .. .. .. .. .. 30 10
676 40 c. S.S. *Tofua* .. .. .. .. .. 85 65
677 55 c. S.S. *Canberra* .. .. .. .. 1·00 85
678 60 c. Suva wharf .. .. .. .. .. 1·10 95
675/8 .. .. .. .. *Set of* 4 3·00 2·25

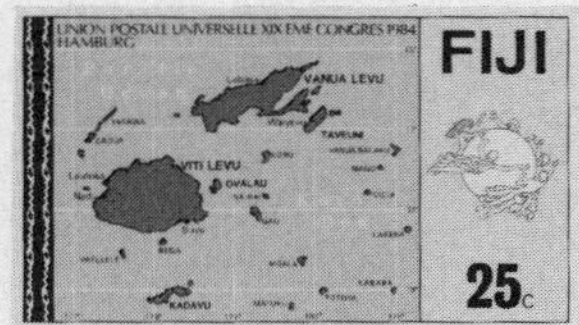


**194** Map of Fijian Islands

(Des J. Cooter. Litho Questa)

**1984** (14 June). *Universal Postal Union Congress, Hamburg. Sheet* 77 × 66 *mm. W w* **14** *(sideways). P* 14½.

**MS**679 **194** 25 c. multicoloured .. .. .. .. 75 75

(Des Harrison. Litho Format)

**1984** (9 July). *Flowers (2nd series). Horiz designs as T* **190**. *W w* **14**. *P* 14 × 14½.

680 15 c. Drividrivi .. .. .. .. .. 25 25
681 20 c. Vesida .. .. .. .. .. 35 35
682 50 c. Vuga .. .. .. .. .. 80 80
683 70 c. Qaiqi .. .. .. .. .. 1·10 1·10
680/3 .. .. .. .. *Set of* 4 2·25 2·25

## NEW INFORMATION

The editor is always interested to correspond with people who have new information that will improve or correct the Catalogue.

**195** Prize Bull, Yalavou Cattle Scheme

(Des D. Hartley-Marjoram. Litho Walsall)

**1984** (17 Sept). *"Ausipex" International Stamp Exhibition, Melbourne. T* **195** *and similar multicoloured designs. W w* **14** *(sideways on* 8, 40 *c. and* $1). *P* 14½ × 14 (25 *c.) or* 14 × 14½ *(others).*

684 8 c. Type **195** .. .. .. .. .. 15 10
685 25 c. Wailoa Power Station *(vert)* .. .. .. 40 40
686 40 c. Air Pacific Boeing "737" airliner .. .. 65 65
687 $1 Container ship *Fua Kavenga* .. .. 1·60 1·60
684/7 .. .. .. .. *Set of* 4 2·50 2·40

**196** The Stable at Bethlehem

(Des G. Vasarhelyi. Litho Format)

**1984** (5 Nov). *Christmas. Children's Paintings. T* **196** *and similar multicoloured designs. W w* **14** *(sideways on horiz designs). P* 14.

688 8 c. Type **196** .. .. .. .. .. 10 10
689 20 c. Outrigger canoe .. .. .. .. 30 20
690 25 c. Father Christmas and Christmas tree .. 35 25
691 40 c. Going to church .. .. .. .. 60 60
692 $1 Decorating Christmas tree *(vert)* .. 1·50 1·60
688/92 .. .. .. .. *Set of* 5 2·50 2·50

**197** *Danaus plexippus*

**198** Outrigger Canoe off Toberua Island

(Des Annette Robinson. Litho Questa)

**1985** (4 Feb). *Butterflies. T* **197** *and similar multicoloured designs. W w* **14** *(sideways on* 8 *c. and* 25 *c.). P* 14.

693 8 c. Type **197** .. .. .. .. .. 60 10
694 25 c. *Hypolimnas bolina* .. .. .. .. 1·10 50
695 40 c. *Lampides boeticus (vert)* .. .. .. 1·50 80
696 $1 *Precis villida (vert)* .. .. .. 2·00 2·75
693/6 .. .. .. .. *Set of* 4 4·75 3·75

(Des D. Miller. Litho B.D.T.)

**1985** (1 Apr). *"Expo '85" World Fair, Japan. T* **198** *and similar vert designs. Multicoloured. W w* **14**. *P* 14.

697 20 c. Type **198**. .. .. .. .. .. 50 30
698 25 c. Wainivula Falls.. .. .. .. .. 85 40
699 50 c. Mana Island .. .. .. .. .. 95 70
700 $1 Sawa-I-Lau Caves .. .. .. .. 1·25 1·40
697/700 .. .. .. .. *Set of* 4 3·25 2·50

**199** With Prince Charles at Garter Ceremony

**200** Horned Squirrel Fish

(Des A. Theobald ($1), C. Abbott (others). Litho Questa)

**1985** (7 June). *Life and Times of Queen Elizabeth the Queen Mother. T* **199** *and similar vert designs. Multicoloured. W w* **16**. *P* 14½ × 14.

701 8 c. With Prince Andrew on her 60th Birthday .. .. .. .. .. 10 10
702 25 c. Type **199**.. .. .. .. .. 35 40
703 40 c. The Queen Mother at Epsom Races .. 50 65
704 50 c. With Prince Henry at his christening (from photo by Lord Snowdon).. .. 65 90
701/4 .. .. .. .. *Set of* 4 1·40 1·90
**MS**705 91 × 73 mm. $1 With Prince Andrew at Royal Wedding, 1981. Wmk sideways .. .. 1·25 1·75

(Des M. Raj. Litho Questa)

**1985** (23 Sept). *Shallow Water Marine Fishes. T* **200** *and similar horiz designs. Multicoloured. W w* **14** *(sideways). P* 14½.

706 40 c. Type **200**.. .. .. .. .. 85 55
707 50 c. Yellow-banded Goatfish .. .. .. 1·00 70
708 55 c. Fairy Cod .. .. .. .. .. 1·00 75
709 $1 Peacock Rock Cod .. .. .. 1·75 2·25
706/9 .. .. .. .. *Set of* 4 4·25 3·75

**201** Collared Petrel

**202** Children and "Peace for Fiji and the World" Slogan

(Des Doreen McGuinness. Litho Walsall)

**1985** (4 Nov). *Seabirds. T* **201** *and similar vert designs. Multicoloured. W w* **14**. *P* 14 × 13½.

710 15 c. Type **201**.. .. .. .. .. 75 30
711 20 c. Lesser Frigate Bird .. .. .. .. 85 35
712 50 c. Brown Booby .. .. .. .. 1·60 1·60
713 $1 Crested Tern .. .. .. .. 2·75 3·25
710/13 .. .. .. .. *Set of* 4 5·50 5·00

(Des A. Theobald. Litho Format)

**1986** (21 Apr). *60th Birthday of Queen Elizabeth II. Vert designs as T* **110** *of Ascension. Multicoloured. W w* **16**. *P* 14 × 14½.

714 20 c. With Duke of York at Royal Tournament, 1936 .. .. .. .. 30 30
715 25 c. Royal Family on Palace balcony after Princess Margaret's wedding, 1960 .. 35 35
716 40 c. Queen inspecting guard of honour, Suva, 1982 .. .. .. .. 55 55
717 50 c. In Luxembourg, 1976 .. .. .. 65 85
718 $1 At Crown Agents Head Office, London, 1983 .. .. .. .. .. 1·10 1·60
714/18 .. .. .. .. *Set of* 5 2·75 3·25

(Litho Harrison (4 c. (1988 ptg), 8 c.) or Questa (others))

**1986** (Apr)–**91**. *As Nos.* 580/2, 582*c*, 585, 587, 589, 591, 593/4 *and new value. W w* **16** *(sideways on* 1, 2, 3, 4, 8, 10, 15, 20, 35, 50 *c.). Chalk-surfaced paper* (2 *c.). With imprint date. P* 14 × 13½ ($1) *or* 14 *(others).*

719 1 c. Type **171** (11.3.91) .. .. .. 10 10
720 2 c. Dudley Church, Suva .. .. .. 10 10
a. Ordinary paper (11.3.91) .. .. .. 10 10
721 3 c. Fiji International Telecommunications Building, Suva (1.6.88) .. .. .. 10 10
722 4 c. Lautoka Mosque (1.6.88) .. .. .. 10 10
724 8 c. Public School, Levuka (as No. 586) (1.12.86) .. .. .. .. 10 10
725 10 c. Fiji Visitors Bureau, Suva (1.3.90) .. 10 10
726 15 c. Colonial War Memorial Hospital, Suva (11.3.91) .. .. .. .. 10 15
730 20 c. Rewa Bridge, Nausori (1.6.88) .. .. 15 20
732 35 c. Grand Pacific Hotel, Suva (11.3.91) .. 30 35
734 50 c. Serua Island Village (11.3.91) .. .. 40 45
735 $1 Solo Rock Lighthouse (30×46 *mm*) (11.3.91) .. .. .. .. 80 85
719/35 .. .. .. .. *Set of* 11 1·90 2·10

From the 11 March 1991 printing all values were produced by Questa. The 4 c. (No. 722) was the only stamp in this issue to be printed by both Harrison and Questa.

Nos. 720/2, 725 and 730 exist with different imprint dates below the design.

(Des G. Vasarhelyi. Litho Format)

**1986** (23 June). *International Peace Year. T* **202** *and similar vert design. Multicoloured. W w* **16**. *P* 14½.

736 8 c. Type **202**.. .. .. .. .. 15 10
737 40 c. Peace dove and houses .. .. .. 60 75

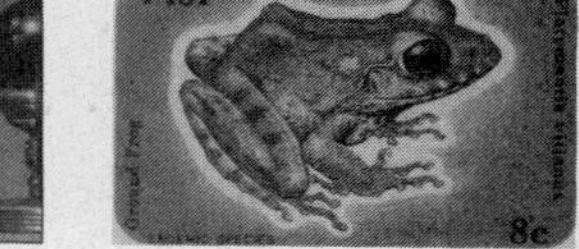


**203** Halley's Comet in Centaurus Constellation and Newton's Reflector

**204** Ground Frog

(Des D. Hartley. Litho B.D.T.)

**1986** (7 July). *Appearance of Halley's Comet. T* **203** *and similar vert designs. Multicoloured. W w* **16**. *P* 13½.

738 25 c. Type **203**.. .. .. .. .. 75 40
739 40 c. Halley's Comet over Lomaiviti .. .. 95 65
740 $1 *Giotto* spacecraft photographing Comet nucleus .. .. .. .. .. 1·75 2·50
738/40 .. .. .. .. *Set of* 3 3·00 3·25

(Litho Format)

**1986** (1 Aug). *Reptiles and Amphibians. T* **204** *and similar horiz designs. Multicoloured.* W w **16** *(sideways). P* 14½.

| | | | |
|---|---|---|---|
| 741 | 8 c. Type **204** | 45 | 10 |
| 742 | 20 c. Burrowing Snake | 70 | 30 |
| 743 | 25 c. Spotted Gecko | 80 | 35 |
| 744 | 40 c. Crested Iguana | 1·00 | 80 |
| 745 | 50 c. Blotched Skink | 1·25 | 1·50 |
| 746 | $1 Speckled Skink | 1·75 | 2·50 |
| 741/6 | *Set of* 6 | 5·50 | 5·00 |

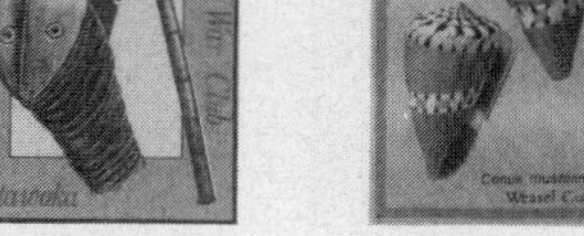


**205** Gatawaka　　**206** Weasel Cone

(Des M. Raj. Litho Walsall)

**1986** (10 Nov). *Ancient War Clubs. T* **205** *and similar vert designs. Multicoloured.* W w **16**. *P* 14.

| | | | |
|---|---|---|---|
| 747 | 25 c. Type **205** | 70 | 35 |
| 748 | 40 c. Siriti | 90 | 60 |
| 749 | 50 c. Bulibuli | 1·10 | 1·25 |
| 750 | $1 Culacula | 1·90 | 2·50 |
| 747/50 | *Set of* 4 | 4·25 | 4·25 |

(Des A. Riley. Litho Format)

**1987** (26 Feb). *Cone Shells of Fiji. T* **206** *and similar vert designs. Multicoloured.* W w **16**. *P* 14×14½.

| | | | |
|---|---|---|---|
| 751 | 15 c. Type **206** | 70 | 25 |
| 752 | 20 c. Pertusus Cone | 80 | 30 |
| 753 | 25 c. Admiral Cone | 85 | 35 |
| 754 | 40 c. Leaden Cone | 1·25 | 70 |
| 755 | 50 c. Imperial Cone | 1·40 | 1·25 |
| 756 | $1 Geography Cone | 1·90 | 2·25 |
| 751/6 | *Set of* 6 | 6·25 | 4·50 |

**207** Tagimoucia Flower　　(**208**)

(Des M. Raj. Litho Format)

**1987** (23 Apr). *Tagimoucia Flower. Sheet* 72×55 *mm.* W w **14** *(sideways). P* 14½.

**MS**757 **207** $1 multicoloured .. 2·25 2·00

**1987** (13 June). *"Capex '87" International Stamp Exhibition, Toronto. No.* **MS**757 *optd with T* **208**.

**MS**758 72×55 mm. $1 Type **207** .. 1·50 1·25

Stamps from Nos. **MS**757 and **MS**758 are identical as the overprint on **MS**758 appears on the margin of the sheet.

**209** Traditional Fijian House

(Des National Focal Point, adapted L. Curtis. Litho Format)

**1987** (20 July). *International Year of Shelter for the Homeless. T* **209** *and similar horiz design. Multicoloured.* W w **16** *(sideways). P* 14.

| | | | |
|---|---|---|---|
| 759 | 55 c. Type **209** | 45 | 50 |
| 760 | 70 c. Modern bungalows | 55 | 60 |

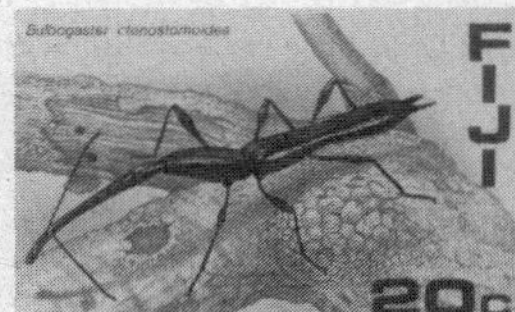


**210** *Bulbogaster ctenostomoides* (stick insect)

(Des R. Lewington. Litho Walsall)

**1987** (7 Sept). *Fijian Insects. T* **210** *and similar horiz designs. Multicoloured.* W w **16** *(sideways). P* 13½×14.

| | | | |
|---|---|---|---|
| 761 | 20 c. Type **210** | 35 | 30 |
| 762 | 25 c. *Paracupta flaviventris* (beetle) | 40 | 35 |
| 763 | 40 c. *Cerambyrhynchus schoenherri* (beetle) | 55 | 45 |
| 764 | 50 c. *Rhinoscapha lagopyga* (weevil) | 65 | 60 |
| 765 | $1 *Xixuthrus heros* (beetle) | 1·00 | 1·10 |
| 761/5 | *Set of* 5 | 2·75 | 2·50 |

**REPUBLIC**

Following a military coup on 25 September 1987 Fiji was declared a republic on 7 October. The Governor-General resigned on 15 October 1987 and Fiji's Commonwealth membership lapsed.

For the convenience of collectors we continue to list later issues in this volume.

**211** The Nativity　　**212** Windsurfer and Beach

(Des G. Vasarhelyi. Litho Walsall)

**1987** (19 Nov). *Christmas. T* **211** *and similar multicoloured designs.* W w **16** *(sideways on 40 c., 50 c.). P* 14×13½ *(vert) or* 13½×14 *(horiz).*

| | | | |
|---|---|---|---|
| 766 | 8 c. Type **211** | 20 | 10 |
| 767 | 40 c. The Shepherds *(horiz)* | 70 | 35 |
| 768 | 50 c. The Three Kings *(horiz)* | 80 | 65 |
| 769 | $1 The Three Kings presenting gifts | 1·25 | 1·00 |
| 766/9 | *Set of* 4 | 2·75 | 1·90 |

(Des Ahgrafik. Litho Questa)

**1988** (27 Apr). *"Expo '88" World Fair, Brisbane.* W w **16** *(sideways). P* 14.

770 **212** 30 c. multicoloured .. 60 50

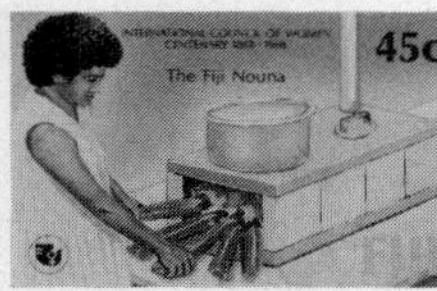

**213** Woman using Fiji "Nouna" (stove)　　**214** Pottery Bowl

(Litho Questa)

**1988** (14 June). *Centenary of International Council of Women.* W w **16** *(sideways). P* 14.

771 **213** 45 c. multicoloured .. 65 60

(Des N. Ahmed. Litho Questa)

**1988** (29 Aug). *Ancient Fijian Pottery. T* **214** *and similar multicoloured designs.* W w **14** *(sideways)* (69 c.) *or* w **16** *(others, sideways on 75 c.). P* 14.

| | | | |
|---|---|---|---|
| 772 | 9 c. Type **214** | 15 | 10 |
| 773 | 23 c. Cooking pot | 25 | 25 |
| 774 | 58 c. Priest's drinking vessel | 50 | 60 |
| 775 | 63 c. Drinking vessel | 55 | 70 |
| 776 | 69 c. Earthenware oil lamp | 60 | 75 |
| 777 | 75 c. Cooking pot with relief pattern *(vert)* | 70 | 80 |
| 772/7 | *Set of* 6 | 2·50 | 2·75 |

**215** Fiji Tree Frog　　**216** *Dendrobium mohlianum*

(Des Doreen McGuinness. Litho Walsall)

**1988** (3 Oct). *Fiji Tree Frog. T* **215** *and similar vert designs. Multicoloured.* W w **16**. *P* 14×13½.

| | | | |
|---|---|---|---|
| 778 | 18 c. Type **215** | 50 | 30 |
| 779 | 23 c. Frog climbing grass stalks | 65 | 45 |
| 780 | 30 c. On leaf | 80 | 75 |
| 781 | 45 c. Moving from one leaf to another | 1·10 | 1·25 |
| 778/81 | *Set of* 4 | 2·75 | 2·50 |

(Des M. Raj. Litho Walsall)

**1988** (21 Nov). *Native Flowers. T* **216** *and similar vert designs. Multicoloured.* W w **14**. *P* 14.

| | | | |
|---|---|---|---|
| 782 | 9 c. Type **216** | 35 | 15 |
| 783 | 30 c. *Dendrobium cattilare* | 60 | 45 |
| 784 | 45 c. *Degeneria vitiensis* | 70 | 55 |
| 785 | $1 *Degeneria roseiflora* | 1·25 | 1·50 |
| 782/5 | *Set of* 4 | 2·50 | 2·40 |

**217** Battle of Solferino, 1859

(Des L. Curtis. Litho Questa)

**1989** (6 Feb). *125th Anniv of International Red Cross. T* **217** *and similar designs.* W w **16** *(sideways on 58, 69 c.). P* 13½ × 14 *(horiz) or* 14 × 13½ *(vert).*

| | | | |
|---|---|---|---|
| 786 | 58 c. multicoloured | 70 | 60 |
| 787 | 63 c. multicoloured | 80 | 80 |
| 788 | 69 c. multicoloured | 85 | 85 |
| 789 | $1 black and bright scarlet | 1·10 | 1·25 |
| 786/9 | *Set of* 4 | 3·00 | 3·25 |

Designs: *Vert*—63 c. Henri Dunant (founder); $1 Anniversary logo. *Horiz*—69 c. Fijian Red Cross worker with blood donor.

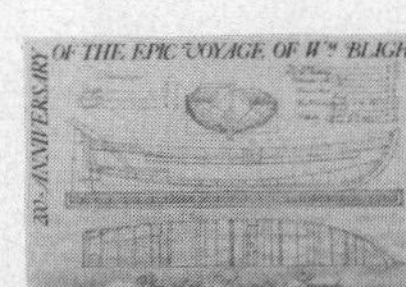


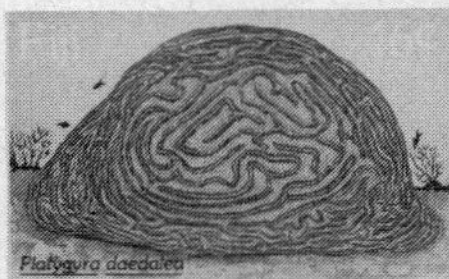


**218** Plan of *Bounty's* Launch　　**219** *Platygyra daedalea*

(Des Jennifer Toombs. Litho Questa)

**1989** (28 Apr). *Bicentenary of Captain Bligh's Boat Voyage. T* **218** *and similar horiz designs. Multicoloured.* W w **16** *(sideways). P* 14×14½.

| | | | |
|---|---|---|---|
| 790 | 45 c. Type **218** | 70 | 50 |
| 791 | 58 c. Cup, bowl and Bligh's journal | 80 | 65 |
| 792 | 80 c. Bligh and extract from journal | 1·25 | 1·25 |
| 793 | $1 *Bounty's* launch and map of Fiji | 1·40 | 1·50 |
| 790/3 | *Set of* 4 | 3·75 | 3·50 |

(Des M. Raj. Litho Harrison)

**1989** (21 Aug). *Corals. T* **219** *and similar multicoloured designs.* W w **14** *(sideways on 46, 60 c.). P* 14.

| | | | |
|---|---|---|---|
| 794 | 46 c. Type **219** | 65 | 65 |
| 795 | 60 c. *Caulastrea furcata* | 85 | 85 |
| 796 | 75 c. *Acropora echinata* (*vert*) | 1·00 | 1·00 |
| 797 | 90 c. *Acropora humilis* (*vert*) | 1·25 | 1·50 |
| 794/7 | *Set of* 4 | 3·25 | 3·50 |

**220** Goalkeeper　　**221** Congregation in Church

(Des S. Noon. Litho Questa)

**1989** (25 Sept). *World Cup Football Championship, Italy (1990). T* **220** *and similar horiz designs. Multicoloured.* W w **16** *(sideways). P* 14×14½.

| | | | |
|---|---|---|---|
| 798 | 35 c. Type **220** | 50 | 40 |
| 799 | 63 c. Goalkeeper catching ball | 80 | 80 |
| 800 | 70 c. Player with ball | 90 | 90 |
| 801 | 85 c. Tackling | 1·25 | 1·50 |
| 798/801 | *Set of* 4 | 3·00 | 3·25 |

(Des L. Curtis. Litho Questa)

**1989** (1 Nov). *Christmas. T* **221** *and similar vert designs. Multicoloured.* W w **14**. *P* 14½×14.

| | | | |
|---|---|---|---|
| 802 | 9 c. Type **221** | 20 | 10 |
| 803 | 45 c. *Delonix regia* (Christmas tree) | 65 | 50 |
| 804 | $1 The Nativity | 1·25 | 1·25 |
| 805 | $1.40, Fijian children under *Delonix regia* (tree) | 1·60 | 1·75 |
| 802/5 | *Set of* 4 | 3·25 | 3·25 |

**222** Mangrove Jack　　**223** 1968 3d. Heron Definitive

(Des M. Raj. Litho Questa)

**1990** (23 Apr). *Freshwater Fishes. T* **222** *and similar horiz designs. Multicoloured. W* w **16** (*sideways*). *P* 14½.
806 50 c. Type **222** .. .. .. .. .. 75 60
807 70 c. Orange-spotted Therapon Perch .. 1·00 90
808 85 c. Spotted Scat .. .. .. .. .. 1·25 1·25
809 $1 Flagtail .. .. .. .. .. 2·00 2·25
806/9 .. .. .. .. .. *Set of* 4 4·50 4·50

(Des D. Miller. Litho Questa)

**1990** (1 May). *"Stamp World London 90" International Stamp Exhibition, London. Sheet,* 120×70 *mm, containing T* **223** *and similar vert design. Multicoloured. W* w **16** (*sideways*). *P* 14.

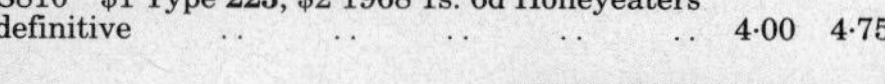

**MS**810 $1 Type **223**; $2 1968 1s. 6d Honeyeaters definitive .. .. .. .. .. 4·00 4·75

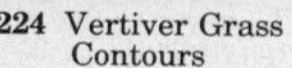

**224** Vertiver Grass Contours  **225** *Dacrydium nidulum*

(Des Ahgrafik. Litho Questa)

**1990** (23 July). *Soil Conservation. T* **224** *and similar multicoloured designs. W* w **14** (*sideways on* 50, 70, 90 *c.*). *P* 14.
811 50 c. Type **224** .. .. .. .. .. 60 50
812 70 c. Mulching .. .. .. .. .. 80 80
813 90 c. Hillside contour cultivation .. .. 1·00 1·00
814 $1 Land use rotation (*vert*) .. .. 1·25 1·40
811/14 .. .. .. .. *Set of* 4 3·25 3·25

(Des M. Raj. Litho Questa)

**1990** (2 Oct). *Timber Trees. T* **225** *and similar vert designs. Multicoloured. W* w **14**. *P* 14.
815 25 c. Type **225** .. .. .. .. .. 30 20
816 35 c. *Decussocarpus vitiensis* .. .. .. 40 30
817 $1 *Agathis vitiensis* .. .. .. .. 1·25 1·25
818 $1.55, *Santalum yasi* .. .. .. .. 1·75 2·00
815/18 .. .. .. .. *Set of* 4 3·25 3·25

**226** "Hark the Herald Angels sing"  **227** Sigatoka Sand Dunes

(Des Jennifer Toombs. Litho Walsall)

**1990** (26 Nov). *Christmas. Carols. T* **226** *and similar horiz designs. Multicoloured. W* w **14** (*sideways*). *P* 14.
819 10 c. Type **226** .. .. .. .. .. 15 10
820 35 c. "Still the Night, Holy the Night" .. 40 30
821 65 c. "Joy to the World!" .. .. .. 75 75
822 $1 "The Race that long in Darkness pined" 1·25 1·25
819/22 .. .. .. .. *Set of* 4 2·25 2·25

(Des L. Curtis. Litho Leigh-Mardon Ltd, Melbourne)

**1991** (25 Feb). *Environmental Protection. T* **227** *and similar square designs. Multicoloured. P* 14.
823 35 c. Type **227** .. .. .. .. .. 40 30
824 50 c. Monu and Monuriki Islands .. .. 50 45
825 65 c. Ravilevu Nature Reserve, Taveuni .. 75 70
826 $1 Colo-I-Suva Forest Park .. .. .. 1·25 1·40
823/6 .. .. .. .. *Set of* 4 2·50 2·50

**228** H.M.S. *Pandora*  **229** *Scylla serrata*

(Des D. Miller. Litho Questa)

**1991** (8 Aug). *Bicentenary of Discovery of Rotuma Island. T* **228** *and similar horiz designs. Multicoloured. W* w **14** (*sideways*). *P* 14.
827 54 c. Type **228** .. .. .. .. .. 60 60
828 70 c. Map of Rotuma .. .. .. .. 75 75
829 75 c. Natives welcoming H.M.S. *Pandora* .. 80 80
830 $1 Mount Soloroa and Uea Island .. 1·25 1·25
827/30 .. .. .. .. *Set of* 4 3·00 3·00

(Des Katrina Hindle. Litho Questa)

**1991** (26 Sept). *Mangrove Crabs. T* **229** *and similar horiz designs. Multicoloured. W* w **14** (*sideways*). *P* 14×14½.
831 38 c. Type **229** .. .. .. .. .. 40 35
832 54 c. *Metopograpsus messor* .. .. .. 65 60
833 96 c. *Parasesarma erythrodactyla* .. .. 1·00 1·10
834 $1.65, *Cardisoma carnifex* .. .. .. 1·75 1·90
831/4 .. .. .. .. *Set of* 4 3·50 3·50

**230** Mary and Joseph travelling to Bethlehem  **231** De Havilland "Dragon Rapide" of Fiji Airways

(Des A. Wheatcroft. Litho Leigh-Mardon Ltd, Melbourne)

**1991** (31 Oct). *Christmas. T* **230** *and similar horiz designs. Multicoloured. W* w **16**. *P* 14.
835 11 c. Type **230** .. .. .. .. .. 15 10
836 75 c. Manger scene .. .. .. .. 80 80
837 96 c. Presentation in the Temple .. .. 95 95
838 $1 Infant Jesus with symbols .. .. 1·00 1·00
835/8 .. .. .. .. *Set of* 4 2·50 2·50

(Des D. Wood. Litho Questa)

**1991** (18 Nov). *40th Anniv of Air Pacific. T* **231** *and similar horiz designs. Multicoloured. W* w **16** (*sideways*). *P* 14½.
839 54 c. Type **231** .. .. .. .. .. 60 60
840 75 c. Douglas "DC3" .. .. .. .. 80 80
841 96 c. ATR "42" .. .. .. .. .. 1·00 1·00
842 $1.40, Boeing "767" .. .. .. .. 1·40 1·60
839/42 .. .. .. .. *Set of* 4 3·50 3·50

## POSTAGE DUE STAMPS

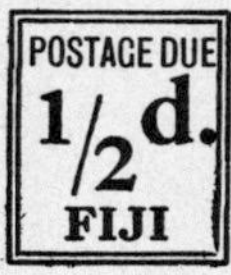

D 1  D 2

(Typo Govt Printer, Suva)

**1917** (1 Jan). *Thick yellowish white laid paper. No gum. P* 11.
D1 D 1 ½d. black .. .. .. .. .. £600 £325
a. *Se-tenant* strip of 8: 1d. (×3) + ½d. + 4d. + 3d. (×3) .. .. .. .. £9000
D2 1d. black .. .. .. .. .. £250 65·00
D3 2d. black .. .. .. .. .. £200 55·00
D4 3d. black .. .. .. .. .. £250 70·00
D5 4d. black .. .. .. .. .. £600 £325

Nos. D1/2 and D4/5 were printed, *se-tenant*, in sheets of 96 (8×12) with each horizontal row containing three 1d., one ½d., one 4d. and three 3d. in that order. Only thirty-one such sheets were issued. The 2d. was printed separately in sheets of 84 (7×12). On all these sheets marginal copies were imperforate on the outer edge.

**1917** (21 April)–**18**. *Narrower setting, value in* ½*d. as Type* D **2**.
D5*a* ½d. black .. .. .. .. .. £550 £225
D5*b* 1d. black .. .. .. .. .. £225 £100
D5*c* 2d. black (5.4.18) .. .. .. .. £750 £500

1d. and 2d. stamps must have wide margins (3½ to 4 mm) on the vertical sides to be Nos. D2 or D3. Stamps with narrow margins of approximately the same width on all four sides are Nos. D5*b* or D5*c*.

Nos. D5*a/c* were printed in separate sheets of 84 (7 × 12). The marginal copies are perforated on all sides.

D 3  D 4

(Typo D.L.R.)

**1918** (1 June). *Wmk Mult Crown CA. P* 14.
D 6 D **3** ½d. black .. .. .. .. .. 2·25 13·00
D 7 1d. black .. .. .. .. .. 2·50 4·50
D 8 2d. black .. .. .. .. .. 2·50 7·50
D 9 3d. black .. .. .. .. .. 3·00 23·00
D10 4d. black .. .. .. .. .. 5·50 17·00
D6/10 .. .. .. .. *Set of* 5 14·00 60·00
D6/10 Optd "Specimen" .. .. *Set of* 5 £150

No postage due stamps were in use between 31 August 1931 and 3 July 1940.

(Typo Waterlow)

**1940** (3 July). *Wmk Mult Script CA. P* 12½.
D11 D **4** 1d. emerald-green .. .. .. .. 4·50 40·00
D12 2d. emerald-green .. .. .. .. 6·00 40·00
D13 3d. emerald-green .. .. .. .. 8·50 50·00
D14 4d. emerald-green .. .. .. .. 11·00 50·00
D15 5d. emerald-green .. .. .. .. 12·00 50·00
D16 6d. emerald-green .. .. .. .. 14·00 60·00
D17 1s. carmine-lake .. .. .. .. 19·00 80·00
D18 1s. 6d. carmine-lake .. .. .. .. 20·00 £120
D11/18 .. .. .. .. *Set of* 8 85·00 £450
D11/18 Perf "Specimen" .. .. *Set of* 8 £180

The use of postage due stamps was discontinued on 30 April 1946.

# Gambia

**PRICES FOR STAMPS ON COVER TO 1945**

| | |
|---|---|
| Nos. 1/4 | *from* × 20 |
| Nos. 5/8 | *from* × 15 |
| Nos. 10/20 | *from* × 20 |
| Nos. 21/31 | *from* × 30 |
| Nos. 32/36 | *from* × 15 |
| Nos. 37/44 | *from* × 8 |
| Nos. 45/142 | *from* × 5 |
| Nos. 143/6 | *from* × 4 |
| Nos. 147/9 | *from* × 8 |
| Nos. 150/61 | *from* × 3 |

## WEST AFRICAN SETTLEMENT

**PRICES.** The prices of Nos. 1 to 8 are for fine copies, with good margins and embossing. Brilliant or poor copies can be supplied at prices consistent with their condition.

**DOUBLE EMBOSSING.** The majority of the stamps of T 1 with so-called "double embossing" are merely specimens in which the printing and embossing do not register accurately and have no special value. We no longer list "twice embossed" or "twice embossed, once inverted" varieties as they are considered to be outside the scope of this catalogue.

1

(Typo and embossed by D.L.R.)

**1869** (18 Mar)–**72**. *No wmk. Imperf.*

| No. | Type | Description | Unused | Used |
|---|---|---|---|---|
| 1 | 1 | 4d. brown | £475 | £150 |
| 2 | | 4d. pale brown (1871) | £400 | £200 |
| 3 | | 6d. deep blue (19.4.69) | £400 | £180 |
| 3*a* | | 6d. blue (30.4.69) | £500 | £150 |
| 4 | | 6d. pale blue (17.2.72) | £2250 | £1000 |

Our prices for the 6d., pale blue, No. 4, are for stamps which are pale by comparison with specimens of the "deep blue" and "blue" colour groups listed under Nos. 3 and 3*a*. An exceptionally pale shade is recognized by specialists and this is rare. The dates given are those of the earliest known postmarks.

**1874** (Aug). *Wmk Crown CC. Imperf.*

| No. | Type | Description | Unused | Used |
|---|---|---|---|---|
| 5 | 1 | 4d. brown | £350 | £180 |
| 6 | | 4d. pale brown | £350 | £180 |
| 7 | | 6d. deep blue | £300 | £200 |
| 8 | | 6d. blue | £300 | £180 |
| | | a. Sloping label | £450 | £275 |
| | | b. Wmk sideways | | |

**SLOPING LABEL VARIETY.** Traces of this flaw first occur in the 6d. imperforate on R.1/1 and R.1/5. In the perforated printings the variety on R.1/5 is much more pronounced and appears as illustrated above. Our listings are these examples from R.1/5, less noticeable varieties of this type from R.1/1, which slope from right to left, being worth less. These varieties continued to appear until the introduction of a new 6d. plate in 1893, used for No. 34.

**1880–81.** *Wmk Crown CC. P 14**. A. *Wmk sideways*. B. *Wmk upright*.

| No. | Type | Description | A | | B | |
|---|---|---|---|---|---|---|
| 10 | 1 | ½d. orange | £130 | £110 | 3·75 | 8·50 |
| 11 | | ½d. dull orange | | † | 3·75 | 8·50 |
| 12 | | 1d. maroon | £225 | £180 | 2·50 | 4·50 |
| 13 | | 2d. rose | 70·00 | 35·00 | 18·00 | 9·50 |
| 14 | | 3d. bright ultramarine | £275 | £200 | 45·00 | 25·00 |
| 14*b* | | 3d. pale dull ultramarine | | † | 42·00 | 25·00 |
| 15 | | 4d. brown | £250 | 35·00 | £140 | 14·00 |
| 16 | | 4d. pale brown | £225 | 30·00 | £130 | 15·00 |
| 17 | | 6d. deep blue | £110 | 70·00 | 70·00 | 45·00 |
| | | a. Sloping label | £325 | £225 | £225 | £150 |
| 18 | | 6d. blue | £110 | 70·00 | 70·00 | 45·00 |
| | | a. Sloping label | £325 | £225 | £225 | £150 |
| 19 | | 1s. green | £350 | £200 | £180 | £100 |
| 20 | | 1s. deep green | £350 | £200 | £180 | £100 |
| 10/20 | | *Set of* 7 | £1200 | £750 | £400 | £180 |

*There were three different printings of these stamps. The original supply, sent in June 1880 and covering all seven values, had watermark sideways and was perforated by a line machine. In October of the same year a further printing of the lowest five values had the watermark changed to upright, but was still with line perforation. The final printing, sent May 1881 and containing all values, also had watermark upright, but was perforated on a comb machine.

**1886–93.** *Wmk Crown CA, sideways. P* 14.

| No. | Type | Description | Unused | Used |
|---|---|---|---|---|
| 21 | 1 | ½d. myrtle-green (1887) | 70 | 80 |
| 22 | | ½d. grey-green | 1·25 | 1·60 |
| 22*b* | | 1d. maroon | † | £15000 |
| 23 | | 1d. crimson (1887) | 3·25 | 3·75 |
| 23*a* | | 1d. aniline crimson | 6·00 | 8·50 |
| 23*b* | | 1d. pale carmine | 6·00 | 8·00 |
| 24 | | 2d. orange (1887) | 5·50 | 5·50 |
| 25 | | 2d. deep orange | 1·40 | 5·00 |
| 26 | | 2½d. ultramarine (1887) | 2·00 | 2·75 |
| 27 | | 2½d. deep bright blue | 1·75 | 1·50 |
| 28 | | 3d. slate-grey (1886) | 2·00 | 9·50 |
| 29 | | 3d. grey | 2·00 | 9·00 |
| 30 | | 4d. brown (1887) | 2·25 | 2·00 |
| 31 | | 4d. deep brown | 2·25 | 2·00 |
| | | a. Wmk upright | — | £450 |
| 32 | | 6d. yellowish olive-green (1886) | 50·00 | 30·00 |
| | | a. Sloping label | £120 | 75·00 |
| 32*b* | | 6d. olive-green (1887) | 50·00 | 45·00 |
| | | ba. Sloping label | £150 | £130 |
| 33 | | 6d. bronze-green (1889) | 19·00 | 35·00 |
| | | a. Sloping label | 55·00 | 75·00 |
| 33*b* | | 6d. deep bronze-green (1889) | 19·00 | 38·00 |
| | | ba. Sloping label | 55·00 | 75·00 |
| 34 | | 6d. slate-green (1893) | 10·00 | 26·00 |
| 35 | | 1s. violet (1887) | 2·75 | 14·00 |
| 36 | | 1s. deep violet | 2·75 | 16·00 |
| 36*b* | | 1s. aniline violet | £1100 | |
| 21/36 | | *Set of* 8 | 22·00 | 55·00 |
| 21/24, 32 Optd "Specimen" | | *Set of* 4 | £400 | |

The above were printed in panes of 15 on paper intended for larger panes. Hence the watermark is sometimes misplaced or omitted and letters from "CROWN AGENTS FOR THE COLONIES" from the margin may appear on the stamps.

The ½d., 2d., 3d., 4d., 6d. (No. 32) and 1s. with watermark Crown CA are known imperf (*price from* £1500).

The previously listed 3d. "pearl-grey" shade has been deleted as it is impossible to distinguish from other 3d. shades when it occurs on a single stamp. Sheets from this late printing can be identified by three coloured dots in the left sheet margin and one in the right, this being the reverse of the normal arrangement.

## CROWN COLONY

2

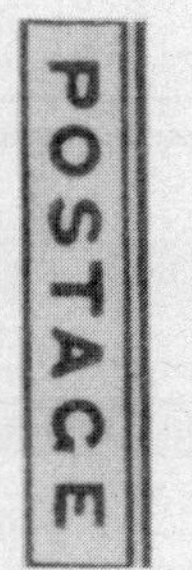


Normal

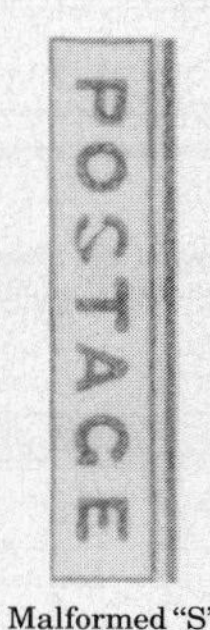


Malformed "S"

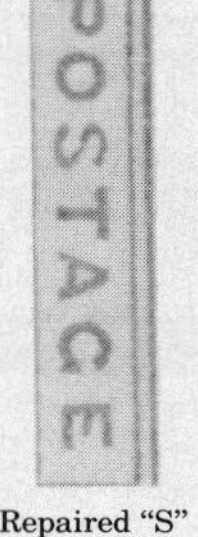


Repaired "S"

The Malformed "S" occurs on R. 7/3 of the left pane from Key Plate 2. This was used to print the initial supply of all values. Printings of the ½d., 1d. and 2½d. despatched in September 1898 had the "S" repaired as shown above. Subsequent printings of the ½d., 1d. and 3d. were from Key Plate 3.

(Typo D.L.R.)

**1898** (2 May)–**1902**. *Wmk Crown CA. P* 14.

| No. | Type | Description | Unused | Used |
|---|---|---|---|---|
| 37 | 2 | ½d. dull green (*shades*) | 1·75 | 1·75 |
| | | a. Malformed "S" | £100 | |
| | | b. Repaired "S" | £110 | |
| 38 | | 1d. carmine (*shades*) | 1·25 | 75 |
| | | a. Malformed "S" | £100 | |
| | | b. Repaired "S" | £120 | |
| 39 | | 2d. orange and mauve | 2·75 | 3·50 |
| | | a. Malformed "S" | £110 | |
| 40 | | 2½d. ultramarine | 1·40 | 1·50 |
| | | a. Malformed "S" | £100 | |
| | | b. Repaired "S" | £120 | |
| 41 | | 3d. reddish purple and blue | 6·00 | 12·00 |
| | | a. Malformed "S" | £120 | |
| | | *b. Deep purple and ultramarine* (1902) | 85·00 | £100 |
| 42 | | 4d. brown and blue | 4·75 | 16·00 |
| | | a. Malformed "S" | £120 | |
| 43 | | 6d. olive-green and carmine | 8·00 | 15·00 |
| | | a. Malformed "S" | £130 | |
| 44 | | 1s. violet and green | 15·00 | 32·00 |
| | | a. Malformed "S" | £160 | |
| 37/44 | | *Set of* 8 | 38·00 | 75·00 |
| 37/44 Optd "Specimen" | | *Set of* 8 | £150 | |

3

4

Dented frame (R. 1/6 of left pane)

**1902** (13 Mar)–**05**. *Wmk Crown CA. P* 14.

| No. | Type | Description | Unused | Used |
|---|---|---|---|---|
| 45 | 3 | ½d. green (19.4.02) | 60 | 2·00 |
| | | a. Dented frame | 20·00 | |
| 46 | | 1d. carmine | 1·00 | 55 |
| | | a. Dented frame | 24·00 | |
| 47 | | 2d. orange and mauve (14.6.02) | 3·25 | 2·00 |
| | | a. Dented frame | 45·00 | |
| 48 | | 2½d. ultramarine (14.6.02) | 15·00 | 15·00 |
| | | a. Dented frame | 85·00 | |
| 49 | | 3d. purple and ultramarine (19.4.02) | 9·50 | 3·25 |
| | | a. Dented frame | 85·00 | |
| 50 | | 4d. brown and ultramarine (14.6.02) | 3·00 | 14·00 |
| | | a. Dented frame | 70·00 | |
| 51 | | 6d. pale sage-green & carmine (14.6.02) | 3·25 | 9·50 |
| | | a. Dented frame | 70·00 | |
| 52 | | 1s. violet and green (14.6.02) | 48·00 | 65·00 |
| | | a. Dented frame | £150 | |
| 53 | 4 | 1s. 6d. green and carmine/*yellow* (6.4.05) | 5·50 | 15·00 |
| | | a. Dented frame | 90·00 | |
| 54 | | 2s. deep slate and orange (14.6.02) | 27·00 | 45·00 |
| | | a. Dented frame | £110 | |
| 55 | | 2s. 6d. purple and brown/*yellow* (6.4.05) | 15·00 | 45·00 |
| | | a. Dented frame | £110 | |
| 56 | | 3s. carmine and green/*yellow* (6.4.05) | 16·00 | 45·00 |
| | | a. Dented frame | £110 | |
| 45/56 | | *Set of* 12 | £120 | £225 |
| 45/56 Optd "Specimen" | | *Set of* 12 | £180 | |

**1904** (Aug)–**06**. *Wmk Mult Crown CA. P* 14.

| No. | Type | Description | Unused | Used |
|---|---|---|---|---|
| 57 | 3 | ½d. green (9.05) | 1·25 | 25 |
| | | a. Dented frame | 27·00 | |
| 58 | | 1d. carmine | 3·25 | 15 |
| | | a. Dented frame | 35·00 | |
| 59 | | 2d. orange and mauve (23.2.06) | 9·00 | 2·25 |
| | | a. Dented frame | 85·00 | |
| 60 | | 2½d. bright blue (8.05) | 2·00 | 3·00 |
| | | *a. Bright blue and ultramarine* | 9·00 | 17·00 |
| | | b. Dented frame | 45·00 | |
| 61 | | 3d. purple and ultramarine (9.05) | 4·50 | 2·00 |
| | | a. Dented frame | 60·00 | |
| 62 | | 4d. brown and ultramarine (23.2.06) | 6·50 | 23·00 |
| | | a. Dented frame | 90·00 | |
| 63 | 4 | 5d. grey and black (6.4.05) | 8·00 | 12·00 |
| | | a. Dented frame | 75·00 | |
| 64 | 3 | 6d. olive-green and carmine (23.2.06) | 8·00 | 23·00 |
| | | a. Dented frame | 90·00 | |
| 65 | 4 | 7½d. green and carmine (6.4.05) | 5·00 | 18·00 |
| | | a. Dented frame | 70·00 | |
| 66 | | 10d. olive and carmine (6.4.05) | 8·50 | 18·00 |
| | | a. Dented frame | 85·00 | |
| 67 | 3 | 1s. violet and green (9.05) | 15·00 | 38·00 |
| | | a. Dented frame | £110 | |
| 68 | 4 | 2s. deep slate and orange (7.05) | 42·00 | 48·00 |
| | | a. Dented frame | £110 | |
| 57/68 | | *Set of* 12 | £100 | £170 |
| 63, 65/6 Optd "Specimen" | | *Set of* 3 | 70·00 | |

See also Nos. 72/85.

HALF PENNY

(5)

ONE PENNY

(6)

**1906** (10 Apr). *Nos. 55 and 56 surch with T* **5** *or* **6** *by Govt Printer.*

| No. | Description | Unused | Used |
|---|---|---|---|
| 69 | ½d. on 2s. 6d. purple and brown/*yellow* | 40·00 | 60·00 |
| | a. Dented frame | £150 | |
| 70 | 1d. on 3s. carmine and green/*yellow* | 55·00 | 35·00 |
| | a. Surch double | £1800 | £5000 |
| | b. Dented frame | £160 | |

No. 69 was surcharged in a setting of 30 (6 × 5), the spacing between the words and the bars being 5 mm on rows 1, 2 and 5; and 4 mm on rows 3 and 4. Constant varieties occur on R.2/1 (broken "E") and R.5/1 (dropped "Y") of the setting.

No. 70 was surcharged in a setting of 60 (6 × 10) and a similar dropped "Y" variety occurs on R.6/3 and R.8/5.

Both values were withdrawn on 24 April when fresh supplies of ½d. and 1d. definitives were received from London.

**1909** (1 Oct). *Colours changed. Wmk Mult Crown CA. P* 14.

| No. | Type | Description | Unused | Used |
|---|---|---|---|---|
| 72 | 3 | ½d. blue-green | 2·50 | 2·0 |
| | | a. Dented frame | 30·00 | |
| 73 | | 1d. red | 2·50 | 15 |
| | | a. Dented frame | 35·00 | |
| 74 | | 2d. greyish slate | 1·40 | 4·0 |
| | | a. Dented frame | 45·00 | |
| 75 | | 3d. purple/*yellow* | 2·75 | 1·5 |
| | | *a. Purple/lemon-yellow* | 5·50 | 2·0 |
| | | b. Dented frame | 55·00 | |
| 76 | | 4d. black and red/*yellow* | 80 | 65 |
| | | a. Dented frame | 60·00 | |
| 77 | 4 | 5d. orange and purple | 1·00 | 1·25 |
| | | a. Dented frame | 60·00 | |
| 78 | 3 | 6d. dull and bright purple | 1·50 | 2·25 |
| | | a. Dented frame | 60·00 | |
| 79 | 4 | 7½d. brown and blue | 1·25 | 2·5 |
| | | a. Dented frame | 60·00 | |
| 80 | | 10d. pale sage-green and carmine | 1·75 | 6·5 |
| | | a. Dented frame | 60·00 | |
| 81 | 3 | 1s. black/*green* | 1·50 | 7·5 |
| | | a. Dented frame | 60·00 | |
| 82 | 4 | 1s. 6d. violet and green | 7·00 | 24·0 |
| | | a. Dented frame | 80·00 | |
| 83 | | 2s. purple and bright blue/*blue* | 4·25 | 15·0 |
| | | a. Dented frame | 70·00 | |

84 4 2s. 6d. black and red/*blue* .. .. .. 20·00 18·00
a. Dented frame .. .. .. .. £110
85 3s. yellow and green .. .. .. 20·00 38·00
a. Dented frame .. .. .. .. £110
72/85 .. .. .. *Set of* 14 60·00 £110
73/85 Optd "Specimen" .. .. *Set of* 13 £225

7

8

Split "A" (R. 8/3 of left pane) (ptgs to 1918)

(Typo D.L.R.)

**1912** (1 Sept)–**22**. *Wmk Mult Crown CA. Chalk-surfaced paper (5s.). P* 14.
86 7 ½d. deep green .. .. .. .. .. 45 70
*a. Green* .. .. .. .. .. 50 70
*b. Pale green* (1916) .. .. .. .. 80 95
c. Split "A" .. .. .. .. .. 15·00
87 1d. red .. .. .. .. .. .. 55 35
*a. Rose-red* .. .. .. .. .. 75 30
*b. Scarlet* (1916) .. .. .. .. 1·00 65
c. Split "A" .. .. .. .. .. 15·00
88 8 1½d. olive-green and blue-green .. .. 30 30
a. Split "A" .. .. .. .. .. 20·00
89 7 2d. greyish slate .. .. .. .. 45 85
a. Split "A" .. .. .. .. .. 20·00
90 2½d. deep bright blue .. .. .. .. 4·00 2·50
*a. Bright blue* .. .. .. .. 4·50 2·50
b. Split "A" .. .. .. .. .. 35·00
91 3d. purple/*yellow* .. .. .. .. 30 30
*a. On lemon* (1917) .. .. .. 12·00 18·00
*b. On orange-buff* (1920) .. .. .. 10·00 8·00
*c. On pale yellow* .. .. .. .. 40 75
d. Split "A" .. .. .. .. .. 25·00
92 4d. black and red/*yellow* .. .. .. 75 7·00
*a. On lemon* (1917) .. .. .. .. 90 6·50
*b. On orange-buff* (1920) .. .. .. 4·25 10·00
*c. On pale yellow* .. .. .. .. 1·50 5·00
d. Split "A" .. .. .. .. .. 30·00
93 8 5d. orange and purple .. .. .. .. 50 1·25
a. Split "A" .. .. .. .. .. 30·00
94 7 6d. dull and bright purple .. .. .. 50 90
a. Split "A" .. .. .. .. .. 30·00
95 8 7½d. brown and blue .. .. .. .. 80 3·75
a. Split "A" .. .. .. .. .. 65·00
96 10d. pale sage-green and carmine .. .. 2·00 15·00
*a. Deep sage-green and carmine* .. .. 1·50 13·00
b. Split "A" .. .. .. .. .. 65·00
97 7 1s. black/*green* .. .. .. .. 45 1·00
*a. On emerald back* (1921) .. .. .. 50 8·00
b. Split "A" .. .. .. .. .. 30·00
98 8 1s. 6d. violet and green .. .. .. 4·00 8·50
a. Split "A" .. .. .. .. .. 90·00
99 2s. purple and blue/*blue* .. .. .. 2·25 6·00
a. Split "A" .. .. .. .. .. 90·00
100 2s. 6d. black and red/*blue* .. .. .. 2·50 11·00
a. Split "A" .. .. .. .. .. £100
101 3s. yellow and green .. .. .. .. 7·00 16·00
a. Split "A" .. .. .. .. .. £100
102 5s. green and red/*pale yellow* (1922) .. 40·00 60·00
86/102 .. .. .. .. *Set of* 17 60·00 £120
86/102 Optd "Specimen" .. .. *Set of* 17 £325

**1921–22**. *Wmk Mult Script CA. Chalk-surfaced paper (4s.). P* 14.
108 7 ½d. dull green .. .. .. .. .. 30 6·00
109 1d. carmine-red .. .. .. .. .. 1·00 2·00
110 8 1½d. olive-green and blue-green .. .. 1·25 8·50
111 7 2d. grey .. .. .. .. .. .. 1·00 70
112 2½d. bright blue .. .. .. .. .. 50 3·50
113 8 5d. orange and purple .. .. .. .. 1·75 9·00
114 7 6d. dull and bright purple .. .. .. 1·75 8·00
115 8 7½d. brown and blue .. .. .. .. 2·00 17·00
116 10d. pale sage-green and carmine .. .. 6·00 14·00
117 4s. black and red (1922) .. .. .. 40·00 60·00
108/17 .. .. .. .. *Set of* 10 50·00 £120
108/17 Optd "Specimen" .. .. *Set of* 10 £200

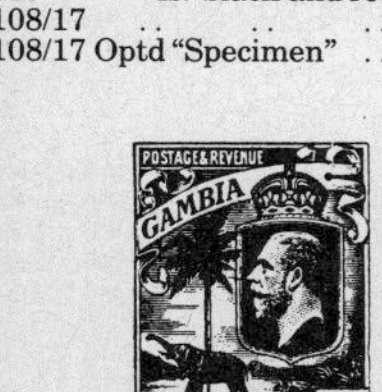
9

10

(Recess D.L.R.)

**1922** (1 Sept)–**29**. *Portrait and shield in black. P* 14*.

(*a*) *Wmk Mult Crown CA*
118 9 4d. red/*yellow* (*a*) .. .. .. .. 1·25 1·50
119 7½d. purple/*yellow* (*a*) .. .. .. .. 1·50 6·50
120 10 1s. purple/*yellow* (*a*) .. .. .. .. 4·00 18·00
121 5s. green/*yellow* (*c*) .. .. .. .. 25·00 60·00
118/21 .. .. .. .. *Set of* 4 29·00 75·00
118/21 Optd/H/S "Specimen" .. .. *Set of* 4 £180

(*b*) *Wmk Mult Script CA*
122 9 ½d. green (*abd*) .. .. .. .. 45 40
123 ½d. deep green (*bd*) (1925) .. .. .. 1·25 65
124 1d. brown (*abd*) .. .. .. .. .. 60 10
125 1½d. bright rose-scarlet (*abd*) .. .. .. 70 10
126 2d. grey (*ab*) .. .. .. .. .. 70 80
127 2½d. orange-yellow (*b*) .. .. .. .. 80 5·50
128 3d. bright blue (*abd*) .. .. .. .. 75 10
129 9 4d. red/*yellow* (*bd*) (1.3.27) .. .. .. 2·75 7·00
130 5d. sage-green (*a*) .. .. .. .. 2·00 10·00
131 6d. claret (*ad*) .. .. .. .. .. 90 15
132 7½d. purple/*yellow* (*ab*) (1927) .. .. 6·00 21·00
133 10d. blue (*a*) .. .. .. .. .. 4·00 16·00
134 10 1s. purple/*yellow* (*aef*) (9.24) .. .. 2·25 25
*a. Blackish purple/yellow-buff* (*c*) (1929) 30·00 40·00
135 1s. 6d. blue (*af*) .. .. .. .. 7·00 12·00
136 2s. purple/*blue* (*ac*) .. .. .. .. 3·00 3·00
137 2s. 6d. deep green (*a*) .. .. .. .. 3·75 9·50
138 3s. bright aniline violet (*a*) .. .. .. 10·00 32·00
139 3s. slate-purple (*c*) (1928) .. .. .. £180 £350
140 4s. brown (*cce*) .. .. .. .. .. 3·75 16·00
141 5s. green/*yellow* (*acf*) (9.26) .. .. .. 8·00 26·00
142 10s. sage-green (*ce*) .. .. .. .. 55·00 75·00
122/42 .. .. .. .. *Set of* 19 £100 £200
122/42 Optd "Specimen" .. .. *Set of* 19 £475

*Perforations.* A number of different perforating machines were used for the various printings of these stamps and the following varieties are known: (*a*) the original 14 line perforation; (*b*) 14 × 13.8 comb perforation used for Type **9**; (*c*) 13.8 × 13.7 comb perforation used for Type **10**; (*d*) 13.7 line perforation used for Type **9**; (*e*) 14 × 13.8 compound line perforation used for Type **10**; (*f*) 13.8 × 14 compound line perforation used for Type **10**. The occurrence of these perforations on the individual values is indicated by the letters shown after the colour descriptions above.

No. 139 has been faked, but note that this stamp is comb perf 13.8 × 13.7 whereas No. 138 is line perf 14 exactly. There are also shades of the slate-purple.

**1935** (6 May). *Silver Jubilee. As T* **13** *of Antigua. Recess B.W. Wmk Mult Script CA. P* 11 × 12.
143 1½d. deep blue and scarlet .. .. .. .. 50 30
a. Extra flagstaff .. .. .. .. £100
b. Short extra flagstaff .. .. .. 60·00
c. Lightning conductor .. .. .. 70·00
d. Flagstaff on right-hand turret .. .. 60·00
e. Double flagstaff .. .. .. .. 50·00
144 3d. brown and deep blue .. .. .. .. 55 70
a. Extra flagstaff .. .. .. .. £150
b. Short extra flagstaff .. .. .. £100
c. Lightning conductor .. .. .. 90·00
145 6d. light blue and olive-green .. .. .. 90 90
a. Extra flagstaff .. .. .. .. £140
b. Short extra flagstaff .. .. .. £100
c. Lightning conductor .. .. .. 90·00
d. Flagstaff on right-hand turret .. .. 95·00
146 1s. slate and purple .. .. .. .. 1·75 90
a. Extra flagstaff .. .. .. .. £200
b. Short extra flagstaff .. .. .. £150
c. Lightning conductor .. .. .. £140
d. Flagstaff on right-hand turret .. .. £160
143/6 .. .. .. .. *Set of* 4 3·25 2·50
143/6 Perf "Specimen" .. .. *Set of* 4 90·00

For illustrations of plate varieties see Catalogue Introduction.

Examples of Nos 145a and 146a are known with the extra flagstaff erased from the stamp with a sharp point.

**1937** (12 May). *Coronation. As Nos.* 95/7 *of Antigua. P* 11×11½.
147 1d. yellow-brown .. .. .. .. .. 20 10
148 1½d. carmine .. .. .. .. .. 20 15
149 3d. blue .. .. .. .. .. 55 35
147/9 .. .. .. .. *Set of* 3 85 50
147/9 Perf "Specimen" .. .. *Set of* 3 60·00

11 Elephant (from Colony Badge)

(Recess B.W.)

**1938** (1 Apr)–**46**. *Wmk Mult Script CA. P* 12.
150 11 ½d. black and emerald-green .. .. .. 15 20
151 1d. purple and brown .. .. .. .. 20 20
152 1½d. lake and carmine .. .. .. .. 35·00 7·00
*a. Lake and scarlet* (1942) .. .. .. 30 40
152*b* 1½d. blue and black (2.1.45) .. .. .. 30 50
153 2d. blue and black .. .. .. .. 80 1·40
153*a* 2d. lake and scarlet (1.10.43) .. .. .. 30 40
154 3d. light blue and grey-blue .. .. .. 20 10
154*a* 5d. sage-green & purple-brn (13.3.41) .. 35 30
155 6d. olive-green and claret .. .. .. 30 20
156 1s. slate-blue and violet .. .. .. 65 10
156*a* 1s. 3d. chocolate & lt blue (28.11.46) .. 1·00 60
157 2s. carmine and blue .. .. .. .. 3·25 2·75
158 2s. 6d. sepia and dull green .. .. .. 7·00 1·75
159 4s. vermilion and purple .. .. .. 12·00 2·00
160 5s. blue and vermilion .. .. .. .. 12·00 3·50
161 10s. orange and black .. .. .. .. 12·00 6·00
150/161 .. .. .. .. *Set of* 16 45·00 18·00
150/61 Perf "Specimen" .. .. *Set of* 16 £225

**1946** (6 Aug). *Victory. As Nos.* 110/11 *of Antigua.*
162 1½d. black .. .. .. .. .. 10 10
163 3d. blue .. .. .. .. .. 10 10
162/3 Perf "Specimen" .. .. *Set of* 2 55·00

**1948** (24 Dec). *Royal Silver Wedding. As Nos.* 112/13 *of Antigua.*
164 1½d. black .. .. .. .. .. 25 10
165 £1 mauve .. .. .. .. .. 12·00 11·00

**1949** (10 Oct). *75th Anniv of Universal Postal Union. As Nos.* 114/17 *of Antigua.*
166 1½d. blue-black .. .. .. .. .. 20 30
167 3d. deep blue .. .. .. .. .. 60 30
168 6d. magenta .. .. .. .. .. 60 30
169 1s. violet .. .. .. .. .. 65 20
166/9 .. .. .. .. *Set of* 4 1·90 1·00

**1953** (2 June). *Coronation. As No.* 120 *of Antigua, but ptd by B.W.*
170 1½d. black and deep bright blue .. .. 10 30

12 Tapping for Palm Wine

13 Cutter

(Des Mrs O. W. Meronti. Recess D.L.R.)

**1953** (2 Nov)–**59**. *T* **12/13** *and similar horiz designs. Wmk Mult Script CA. P* 13½.
171 12 ½d. carmine-red and bluish green .. 30 20
*a. Carmine and bluish green* (7.1.59) 30 45
172 13 1d. deep ultramarine and deep brown .. 40 15
*a. Deep ultramarine & choc* (22.8.56) 1·50 60
173 – 1½d. deep brown and grey-black .. 20 30
174 – 2½d. black and carmine-red .. .. 45 60
175 – 3d. deep blue and slate-lilac .. .. 35 10
176 – 4d. black and deep blue .. .. 60 1·25
177 12 6d. brown and reddish purple .. .. 35 10
178 – 1s. yellow-brown and yellow-green .. 60 10
179 13 1s. 3d. ultramarine and pale blue .. 6·00 20
*a. Ultramarine and light blue* (22.2.56) 6·50 35
180 – 2s. indigo and carmine .. .. 2·75 2·25
181 13 2s. 6d. deep bluish green and sepia .. 3·00 1·00
182 – 4s. grey-blue and Indian red .. .. 3·00 1·25
183 – 5s. chocolate and bright blue .. .. 2·00 1·50
184 – 10s. deep blue and myrtle-green .. 8·00 6·50
185 – £1 green and black .. .. .. 8·50 9·00
171/85 .. .. .. *Set of* 15 32·00 22·00

Designs:—1½d., 5s. Wollof woman; 2½d., 2s. Barra canoe; 3d., 10s. S.S. *Lady Wright*; 4d., 4s. James Island; 1s., 2s. 6d. Woman hoeing; £1 Elephant and palm (from Colony Badge).

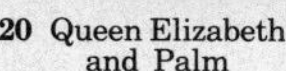
20 Queen Elizabeth II and Palm

21 Queen Elizabeth II and West African Map

(Des J. R. F. Ithier (T **20**), A. W. Morley (T **21**). Recess B.W.)

**1961** (2 Dec). *Royal Visit. W w* **12**. *P* 11½.
186 20 2d. green and purple .. .. .. 10 10
187 21 3d. turquoise-blue and sepia .. .. 15 10
188 6d. blue and cerise .. .. .. 15 15
189 20 1s. 3d. violet and myrtle-green .. .. 20 50
186/9 .. .. .. .. *Set of* 4 55 70

**1963** (4 June). *Freedom from Hunger. As No.* 146 *of Antigua.*
190 1s. 3d. carmine .. .. .. .. 40 15

**1963** (2 Sept). *Red Cross Centenary. As Nos.* 147/8 *of Antigua.*
191 2d. red and black .. .. .. .. 15 10
192 1s. 3d. red and blue .. .. .. .. 40 35

## SELF-GOVERNMENT

22 Beautiful Sunbird

SELF GOVERNMENT
1963
(35)

(Des V. Whiteley. Photo Harrison)

**1963** (4 Nov). *Birds. Horiz designs as T* **22**. *Multicoloured. W w* **12**. *P* 12½ × 13.
193 ½d. Type **22** .. .. .. .. 15 30
194 1d. Yellow-mantled Whydah .. .. 20 20
195 1½d. Cattle Egret .. .. .. .. 80 60
196 2d. Senegal Parrot .. .. .. .. 80 40
197 3d. Rose-ringed Parakeet .. .. .. 1·25 20
198 4d. Violet Starling .. .. .. .. 60 50
199 6d. Village Weaver .. .. .. .. 1·25 10
200 1s. Rufous-crowned Roller .. .. .. 60 10
201 1s. 3d. Red-eyed Dove .. .. .. 8·50 1·40
202 2s. 6d. Double-spurred Francolin .. .. 7·00 2·25
203 5s. Palm-nut Vulture .. .. .. 5·50 2·75
204 10s. Orange-cheeked Waxbill .. .. 12·00 7·00
205 £1 African Emerald Cuckoo .. .. 22·00 14·00
193/205 .. .. .. *Set of* 13 55·00 27·00

**1963** (7 Nov). *New Constitution. Nos.* 194, 197, 200/1 *optd with T* **35**.
206 1d. Yellow-mantled Whydah .. .. 10 15
207 3d. Rose-ringed Parakeet .. .. .. 15 10
208 1s. Rufous-crowned Roller .. .. .. 15 10
a. Opt double .. .. .. .. † £4000
209 1s. 3d. Red-eyed Dove .. .. .. 20 25
206/9 .. .. .. .. *Set of* 4 50 50

**1964** (23 Apr). *400th Birth Anniv of William Shakespeare. As No.* 164 *of Antigua.*
210 6d. greenish blue .. .. .. .. 10 10

## INDEPENDENT

36 Gambia Flag and River

37 Arms

(Des V. Whiteley. Photo Harrison)

**1965** (18 Feb). *Independence. P* 14½.

| | | | | |
|---|---|---|---|---|
| 211 | **36** | ½d. multicoloured | 10 | 10 |
| 212 | **37** | 2d. multicoloured | 10 | 10 |
| 213 | **36** | 7½d. multicoloured | 10 | 10 |
| 214 | **37** | 1s. 6d. multicoloured | 10 | 10 |
| 211/14 | | *Set of* 4 | 30 | 15 |

**INDEPENDENCE 1965**

(38)

39 I.T.U. Emblem and Symbols

**1965** (18 Feb). *Nos.* 193/205 *optd with T* **38** *or with date centred* (1d., 2d., 3d., 4d., 1s., 5s.).

| | | | |
|---|---|---|---|
| 215 | ½d. Type **22** | 30 | 30 |
| 216 | 1d. Yellow-mantled Whydah | 30 | 10 |
| 217 | 1½d. Cattle Egret | 40 | 30 |
| 218 | 2d. Senegal Parrot | 40 | 15 |
| 219 | 3d. Rose-ringed Parakeet | 50 | 15 |
| 220 | 4d. Violet Starling | 50 | 30 |
| 221 | 6d. Village Weaver | 50 | 10 |
| 222 | 1s. Rufous-crowned Roller | 60 | 10 |
| 223 | 1s. 3d. Red-eyed Dove | 60 | 10 |
| 224 | 2s. 6d. Double-spurred Francolin | 60 | 15 |
| 225 | 5s. Palm-nut Vulture | 60 | 40 |
| 226 | 10s. Orange-cheeked Waxbill | 1·25 | 1·50 |
| 227 | £1 African Emerald Cuckoo | 3·25 | 6·00 |
| 215/27 | *Set of* 13 | 9·00 | 8·50 |

(Des V. Whiteley. Photo Harrison)

**1965** (17 May). *I.T.U. Centenary. P* 14½.

| | | | | |
|---|---|---|---|---|
| 228 | **39** | 1d. silver and Prussian blue | 15 | 10 |
| 229 | | 1s. 6d. gold and bluish violet | 45 | 15 |

**THE GAMBIA.** From this point onwards stamps are inscribed "The Gambia".

40 Sir Winston Churchill and Houses of Parliament

(Des Jennifer Toombs. Photo Harrison)

**1966** (24 Jan). *Churchill Commemoration. P* 14 × 14½.

| | | | | |
|---|---|---|---|---|
| 230 | **40** | 1d. multicoloured | 10 | 10 |
| 231 | | 6d. multicoloured | 20 | 10 |
| 232 | | 1s. 6d. multicoloured | 40 | 30 |
| 230/2 | | *Set of* 3 | 65 | 35 |

41 Red-cheeked Cordon Bleu

42 Pin-tailed Whydah

(Des V. Whiteley. Photo Harrison)

**1966** (18 Feb). *Birds. Horiz designs as T* **41**, *and T* **42**. *Multicoloured. P* 14 × 14½ (£1) *or* 12 × 13 (*others*).

| | | | |
|---|---|---|---|
| 233 | ½d. Type **41** | 40 | 20 |
| 234 | 1d. White-faced Whistling Duck | 30 | 15 |
| 235 | 1½d. Red-throated Bee Eater | 30 | 20 |
| 236 | 2d. Lesser Pied Kingfisher | 2·75 | 30 |
| 237 | 3d. Golden Bishop | 30 | 10 |
| 238 | 4d. African Fish Eagle | 50 | 30 |
| 239 | 6d. Yellow-bellied Green Pigeon | 40 | 10 |
| 240 | 1s. Blue-bellied Roller | 40 | 10 |
| 241 | 1s. 6d. African Pygmy Kingfisher | 85 | 30 |
| 242 | 2s. 6d. Spur-winged Goose | 95 | 70 |
| 243 | 5s. Cardinal Woodpecker | 1·00 | 75 |
| 244 | 10s. Violet Turaco | 1·25 | 2·75 |
| 245 | £1 Type **42** | 1·25 | 5·50 |
| 233/45 | *Set of* 13 | 9·50 | 10·00 |

The ½d., 1d. and 2d. to 1s. values exist with PVA gum as well as gum arabic.

54 Arms, Early Settlement and Modern Buildings

(Photo, arms die-stamped Harrison)

**1966** (24 June). *150th Anniv of Bathurst. P* 14½ × 14.

| | | | | |
|---|---|---|---|---|
| 246 | **54** | 1d. silver, brown and yellow-orange | 10 | 10 |
| 247 | | 2d. silver, brown and light blue | 10 | 10 |
| 248 | | 6d. silver, brown and light emerald | 10 | 10 |
| 249 | | 1s. 6d. silver, brown and light magenta | 15 | 15 |
| 246/9 | | *Set of* 4 | 30 | 30 |

55 I.T.Y. Emblem and Hotels

(Des and photo (emblem die-stamped) Harrison)

**1967** (20 Dec). *International Tourist Year. P* 14½ × 14.

| | | | | |
|---|---|---|---|---|
| 250 | **55** | 2d. silver, brown and apple-green | 10 | 10 |
| 251 | | 1s. silver, brown and orange | 10 | 10 |
| 252 | | 1s. 6d. silver, brown and magenta | 15 | 15 |
| 250/2 | | *Set of* 3 | 30 | 30 |

56 Handcuffs

(Des V. Whiteley. Photo Enschedé)

**1968** (15 July). *Human Rights Year. T* **56** *and similar horiz designs. Multicoloured. P* 14 × 13.

| | | | |
|---|---|---|---|
| 253 | 1d. Type **56** | 10 | 10 |
| 254 | 1s. Fort Bullen | 10 | 10 |
| 255 | 5s. Methodist Church | 30 | 30 |
| 253/5 | *Set of* 3 | 35 | 35 |

59 Queen Victoria, Queen Elizabeth II and 4d. Stamp of 1869

(Des G. Drummond. Photo and embossing (cameo head) Harrison)

**1969** (20 Jan). *Gambia Stamp Centenary. P* 14½ × 13½.

| | | | | |
|---|---|---|---|---|
| 256 | **59** | 4d. sepia and yellow-ochre | 15 | 10 |
| 257 | | 6d. Prussian blue and deep yellow-green | 15 | 10 |
| 258 | – | 2s. 6d. multicoloured | 35 | 55 |
| 256/8 | | *Set of* 3 | 60 | 60 |

Design:—2s. 6d. Queen Elizabeth II with 4d. and 6d. stamps of 1869.

In the 6d. value the stamp illustrated is the 6d. of 1869.

61 Catapult-Ship *Westfalen* launching Dornier "Wal"

(Des L. Curtis. Litho Format International)

**1969** (15 Dec). *35th Anniv of Pioneer Air Services. T* **61** *and similar horiz designs showing various forms of transport, map of South Atlantic and Lufthansa emblem. Multicoloured. P* 13½ × 14.

| | | | |
|---|---|---|---|
| 259 | 2d. Type **61** | 30 | 15 |
| 260 | 1s. Dornier "Wal" flying-boat | 35 | 15 |
| 261 | 1s. 6d. *Graf Zeppelin* airship | 45 | 80 |
| 259/61 | *Set of* 3 | 1·00 | 1·00 |

## REPUBLIC

63 Athlete and Gambian Flag

(Des Jennifer Toombs. Litho Format)

**1970** (16 July). *Ninth British Commonwealth Games, Edinburgh. P* 14.

| | | | | |
|---|---|---|---|---|
| 262 | **63** | 1d. multicoloured | 10 | 10 |
| 263 | | 1s. multicoloured | 10 | 10 |
| 264 | | 5s. multicoloured | 30 | 30 |
| 262/4 | | *Set of* 3 | 35 | 30 |

64 President Sir Dawda Kairaba Jawara and State House

(Des G. Vasarhelyi. Litho Questa)

**1970** (2 Nov). *Republic Day. T* **64** *and similar multicoloured designs. P* 14.

| | | | |
|---|---|---|---|
| 265 | 2d. Type **64** | 10 | 10 |
| 266 | 1s. President Sir Dawda Jawara | 15 | 10 |
| 267 | 1s. 6d. President and flag of Gambia | 20 | 15 |
| 265/7 | *Set of* 3 | 35 | 20 |

The 1s. and 1s. 6d. are both vertical designs.

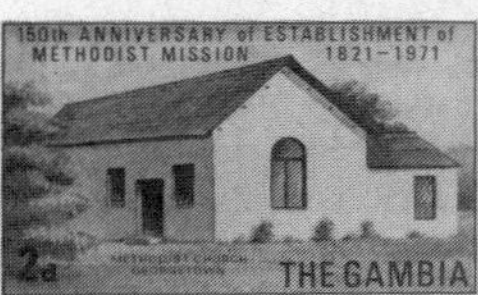


65 Methodist Church, Georgetown

(Des J. Cooter. Litho Questa)

**1971** (16 Apr). *150th Anniv of Establishment of Methodist Mission. T* **65** *and similar multicoloured designs. P* 14.

| | | | |
|---|---|---|---|
| 268 | 2d. Type **65** | 10 | 10 |
| 269 | 1s. Map of Africa and Gambian flag (*vert*) | 15 | 10 |
| 270 | 1s. 6d. John Wesley and scroll (*horiz*) | 15 | 15 |
| 268/70 | *Set of* 3 | 30 | 20 |

**(New Currency. 100 bututs = 1 dalasy)**

66 Yellowfin Tunny

(Des J.W. Litho Format)

**1971** (1 July). *New Currency. Fishes. Horiz designs as T* **66**. *Multicoloured. P* 14.

| | | | |
|---|---|---|---|
| 271 | 2 b. Type **66** | 10 | 30 |
| 272 | 4 b. Peters' Mormyrid | 10 | 15 |
| 273 | 6 b. Tropical Flying Fish | 15 | 30 |
| 274 | 8 b. African Sleeper Goby | 15 | 30 |
| 275 | 10 b. Yellowtail Snapper | 20 | 15 |
| 276 | 13 b. Rock Hind | 20 | 30 |
| 277 | 25 b. Gymnallabes | 35 | 30 |
| 278 | 38 b. Tiger Shark | 55 | 45 |
| 279 | 50 b. Electric Catfish | 70 | 55 |
| 280 | 63 b. Black Synbranchus | 80 | 1·00 |
| 281 | 1 d. 25, Smalltooth Sawfish | 1·75 | 2·00 |
| 282 | 2 d. 50, Barracuda | 4·00 | 4·25 |
| 283 | 5 d. Brown Bullhead | 5·50 | 6·50 |
| 271/83 | *Set of* 13 | 13·00 | 15·00 |

67 Mungo Park in Scotland

(Des J.W. from ideas by P. J. Westwood. Litho Questa)

**1971** (10 Sept). *Birth Bicentenary of Mungo Park (explorer). T* **67** *and similar horiz designs. Multicoloured. W w* **12** (*sideways*). *P* 13½ × 13.

| | | | |
|---|---|---|---|
| 284 | 4 b. Type **67** | 10 | 10 |
| 285 | 25 b. Dug-out canoe | 20 | 10 |
| 286 | 37 b. Death of Mungo Park, Busa Rapids | 30 | 35 |
| 284/6 | *Set of* 3 | 55 | 40 |

**68** Radio Gambia

(Des G. Drummond. Litho Questa)

**1972** (1 July). *Tenth Anniv of Radio Gambia. T* **68** *and similar horiz design. P* 14.

| No. | Type | Description | Unused | Used |
|---|---|---|---|---|
| 287 | **68** | 4 b. orange-ochre and black | 10 | 10 |
| 288 | – | 25 b. light new blue, red-orange and black | 10 | 20 |
| 289 | **68** | 37 b. bright green and black | 20 | 35 |
| 287/9 | | *Set of* 3 | 30 | 55 |

Design:—25 b. Broadcast-area map.

**69** High-jumping **70** Manding Woman

(Des and litho D.L.R.)

**1972** (31 Aug). *Olympic Games, Munich. P* 13.

| No. | Type | Description | Unused | Used |
|---|---|---|---|---|
| 290 | **69** | 4 b. multicoloured | 10 | 10 |
| 291 | | 25 b. multicoloured | 15 | 15 |
| 292 | | 37 b. multicoloured | 15 | 20 |
| 290/2 | | *Set of* 3 | 30 | 30 |

(Des C. Abbott. Litho Questa)

**1972** (16 Oct). *International Conference on Manding Studies, London. T* **70** *and similar vert designs. Multicoloured. P* 14 × 14½.

| No. | Description | Unused | Used |
|---|---|---|---|
| 293 | 2 b. Type **70** | 10 | 10 |
| 294 | 25 b. Musician playing the Kora | 15 | 15 |
| 295 | 37 b. Map of Mali Empire | 25 | 25 |
| 293/5 | *Set of* 3 | 40 | 40 |

**71** Children carrying Fanal **72** Groundnuts

(Des L. Curtis. Litho Enschedé)

**1972** (1 Dec). *Fanals (Model Boats). T* **71** *and similar horiz design. Multicoloured. P* 13 × 13½.

| No. | Description | Unused | Used |
|---|---|---|---|
| 296 | 2 b. Type **71** | 10 | 10 |
| 297 | 1 d. 25, Fanal with lanterns | 30 | 45 |

(Des locally; adapted G. Drummond. Litho Harrison)

**1973** (31 Mar). *Freedom from Hunger Campaign. P* 14½ × 14.

| No. | Type | Description | Unused | Used |
|---|---|---|---|---|
| 298 | **72** | 2 b. multicoloured | 10 | 10 |
| 299 | | 25 b. multicoloured | 15 | 10 |
| 300 | | 37 b. multicoloured | 25 | 20 |
| 298/300 | | *Set of* 3 | 40 | 30 |

**73** Planting and Drying Rice **74** Oil Palm

(Des PAD Studio. Litho J.W.)

**1973** (30 Apr). *Agriculture (1st series). T* **73** *and similar vert designs. Multicoloured. P* 14.

| No. | Description | Unused | Used |
|---|---|---|---|
| 301 | 2 b. Type **73** | 10 | 10 |
| 302 | 25 b. Guinea Corn | 20 | 15 |
| 303 | 37 b. Rice | 25 | 25 |
| 301/3 | *Set of* 3 | 45 | 40 |

(Des PAD Studio. Litho Format)

**1973** (16 July). *Agriculture (2nd series). T* **74** *and similar vert designs. Multicoloured. P* 12.

| No. | Description | Unused | Used |
|---|---|---|---|
| 304 | 2 b. Type **74** | 10 | 10 |
| 305 | 25 b. Limes | 30 | 30 |
| 306 | 37 b. Oil palm (fruits) | 40 | 40 |
| 304/6 | *Set of* 3 | 65 | 65 |

**75** Cassava

(Des PAD Studio. Litho Questa)

**1973** (15 Oct). *Agriculture (3rd series). T* **75** *and similar horiz design. Multicoloured. P* 14.

| No. | Description | Unused | Used |
|---|---|---|---|
| 307 | 2 b. Type **75** | 10 | 10 |
| 308 | 50 b. Cotton | 40 | 25 |

**76** O.A.U. Emblem

(Des and litho D.L.R.)

**1973** (1 Nov). *Tenth Anniv of O.A.U. P* 13½ × 13.

| No. | Type | Description | Unused | Used |
|---|---|---|---|---|
| 309 | **76** | 4 b. multicoloured | 10 | 10 |
| 310 | | 25 b. multicoloured | 15 | 10 |
| 311 | | 37 b. multicoloured | 15 | 15 |
| 309/11 | | *Set of* 3 | 30 | 20 |

**77** Red Cross **78** Arms of Banjul

(Des J. Cooter. Litho Questa)

**1973** (30 Nov). *25th Anniv of Gambian Red Cross. P* 14 × 14½.

| No. | Type | Description | Unused | Used |
|---|---|---|---|---|
| 312 | **77** | 4 b. dull orange-red, and black | 10 | 10 |
| 313 | | 25 b. dull orange-red, black and new blue | 15 | 15 |
| 314 | | 37 b. dull orange-red, black & lt yell-grn | 20 | 20 |
| 312/14 | | *Set of* 3 | 35 | 35 |

(Des and litho D.L.R.)

**1973** (17 Dec). *Change of Bathurst's Name to Banjul. P* 13½ × 13.

| No. | Type | Description | Unused | Used |
|---|---|---|---|---|
| 315 | **78** | 4 b. multicoloured | 10 | 10 |
| 316 | | 25 b. multicoloured | 15 | 15 |
| 317 | | 37 b. multicoloured | 15 | 20 |
| 315/17 | | *Set of* 3 | 30 | 30 |

**79** U.P.U. Emblem

(Des and litho D.L.R.)

**1974** (24 Aug). *Centenary of Universal Postal Union. P* 13½.

| No. | Type | Description | Unused | Used |
|---|---|---|---|---|
| 318 | **79** | 4 b. multicoloured | 10 | 10 |
| 319 | | 37 b. multicoloured | 20 | 30 |

**80** Churchill as Harrow Schoolboy **81** "Different Races"

(Des and litho J.W.)

**1974** (30 Nov). *Birth Centenary of Sir Winston Churchill. T* **80** *and similar vert designs. Multicoloured. P* 13½.

| No. | Description | Unused | Used |
|---|---|---|---|
| 320 | 4 b. Type **80** | 10 | 10 |
| 321 | 37 b. Churchill as 4th Hussars officer | 25 | 10 |
| 322 | 50 b. Churchill as Prime Minister | 40 | 35 |
| 320/2 | *Set of* 3 | 65 | 45 |

(Des G. Vasarhelyi. Litho Questa)

**1974** (16 Dec). *World Population Year. T* **81** *and similar horiz designs. Multicoloured. P* 14.

| No. | Description | Unused | Used |
|---|---|---|---|
| 323 | 4 b. Type **81** | 10 | 10 |
| 324 | 37 b. "Multiplication and Division of Races" | 15 | 15 |
| 325 | 50 b. "World Population" | 20 | 25 |
| 323/5 | *Set of* 3 | 35 | 40 |

**82** Dr. Schweitzer and River Scene

(Des G. Vasarhelyi. Litho Walsall)

**1975** (14 Jan). *Birth Centenary of Dr. Albert Schweitzer. T* **82** *and similar horiz designs. Multicoloured. P* 14.

| No. | Description | Unused | Used |
|---|---|---|---|
| 326 | 10 b. Type **82** | 15 | 10 |
| 327 | 50 b. Surgery scene | 35 | 25 |
| 328 | 1 d. 25, River journey | 75 | 55 |
| 326/8 | *Set of* 3 | 1·10 | 75 |

**83** Dove of Peace **84** Development Graph

(Des and litho D.L.R.)

**1975** (18 Feb). *Tenth Anniv of Independence. T* **83** *and similar horiz designs. Multicoloured. P* 13.

| No. | Description | Unused | Used |
|---|---|---|---|
| 329 | 4 b. Type **83** | 10 | 10 |
| 330 | 10 b. Gambian flag | 10 | 10 |
| 331 | 50 b. Gambian arms | 15 | 10 |
| 332 | 1 d. 25, Map of The Gambia | 35 | 40 |
| 329/32 | *Set of* 4 | 50 | 55 |

(Des PAD Studio. Litho Questa)

**1975** (31 Mar). *Tenth Anniv of African Development Bank. T* **84** *and similar vert designs. Multicoloured. P* 14½.

| No. | Description | Unused | Used |
|---|---|---|---|
| 333 | 10 b. Type **84** | 10 | 10 |
| 334 | 50 b. Symbolic plant | 20 | 15 |
| 335 | 1 d. 25, Bank emblem and symbols | 55 | 60 |
| 333/5 | *Set of* 3 | 70 | 75 |

**85** "Statue of David" (Michelangelo) **86** School Building

(Des C. Abbott. Litho Walsall)

**1975** (14 Nov). *500th Birth Anniv of Michelangelo. T* **85** *and similar multicoloured designs. P* 14½ × 14 (1 d. 25) *or* 14 × 14½ *(others).*

| No. | Description | Unused | Used |
|---|---|---|---|
| 336 | 10 b. Type **85** | 10 | 10 |
| 337 | 50 b. "Madonna of the Steps" | 25 | 10 |
| 338 | 1 d. 25, "Battle of the Centaurs" (*horiz*) | 50 | 60 |
| 336/8 | *Set of* 3 | 75 | 65 |

(Des G. Vasarhelyi. Litho Format)

**1975** (17 Nov). *Centenary of Gambia High School. T* **86** *and similar horiz designs. Multicoloured. P* 14½.

| No. | Description | Unused | Used |
|---|---|---|---|
| 339 | 10 b. Type **86** | 10 | 10 |
| 340 | 50 b. Pupil with scientific apparatus | 15 | 10 |
| 341 | 1 d. 50, School crest | 35 | 35 |
| 339/41 | *Set of* 3 | 50 | 40 |

## *NEW INFORMATION*

The editor is always interested to correspond with people who have new information that will improve or correct the Catalogue.

**87** "Teaching"

(Des A. B. Oliver; adapted by Jennifer Toombs. Litho Questa)

**1975** (15 Dec). *International Women's Year. T* **87** *and similar horiz designs. Multicoloured. P* 14½.

342 4 b. Type **87** .. .. .. .. .. .. 10 10
343 10 b. "Planting rice" .. .. .. .. .. 10 10
344 50 b. "Nursing" .. .. .. .. .. .. 35 15
345 1 d. 50, "Directing traffic" .. .. .. .. 85 35
342/5 .. .. .. .. .. .. *Set of* 4 1·25 55

**88** Woman playing Golf

**89** American Militiaman

(Des R. Granger Barrett. Litho J.W.)

**1976** (18 Feb). 11*th Anniv of Independence. T* **88** *and similar horiz designs. Multicoloured. P* 14½ × 14.

346 10 b. Type **88** .. .. .. .. .. .. 25 10
347 50 b. Man playing golf.. .. .. .. .. 90 20
348 1 d. 50, President playing golf .. .. .. 2·00 70
346/8 .. .. .. .. .. .. *Set of* 3 2·75 90

(Des C. Abbott. Litho Questa)

**1976** (15 May). *Bicentenary of American Revolution. T* **89** *and similar vert designs. Multicoloured. P* 14 × 13½.

349 25 b. Type **89** .. .. .. .. .. .. 30 10
350 50 b. Soldier of the Continental Army .. .. 50 20
351 1 d. 25, Independence Declaration .. .. .. 80 60
349/51 .. .. .. .. .. *Set of* 3 1·40 80
**MS**352 110 × 80 mm. Nos. 349/51 .. .. .. 2·50 3·75

**90** Mother and Child

**91** Serval

(Des G. Vasarhelyi. Litho Questa)

**1976** (28 Oct). *Christmas. P* 14.

353 **90** 10 b. multicoloured .. .. .. .. .. 10 10
354 50 b. multicoloured .. .. .. .. .. 15 10
355 1 d. 25, multicoloured .. .. .. .. 50 45
353/5 .. .. .. .. .. .. *Set of* 3 60 50

(Des G. Drummond. Litho Questa)

**1976** (29 Nov). *Abuko Nature Reserve (1st series). T* **91** *and similar horiz designs. Multicoloured. P* 13½.

356 10 b. Type **91** .. .. .. .. .. .. 35 10
357 25 b. Bushbuck .. .. .. .. .. .. 80 20
358 50 b. Sitatunga .. .. .. .. .. .. 1·25 40
359 1 d. 25, Leopard .. .. .. .. .. 2·75 1·25
356/9 .. .. .. .. .. *Set of* 4 4·75 1·75
**MS**360 137 × 110 mm. Nos. 356/9 .. .. .. 6·00 7·00

See also Nos. 400/3, 431/5 and 460/3.

**92** Festival Emblem and Gambian Weaver

(Des E. N. Sillah; adapted C. Abbott. Litho Walsall)

**1977** (12 Jan). *Second World Black and African Festival of Arts and Culture, Nigeria. P* 14.

361 **92** 25 b. multicoloured .. .. .. .. .. 15 10
362 50 b. multicoloured .. .. .. .. .. 20 15
363 1 d. 25, multicoloured .. .. .. .. 50 70
361/3 .. .. .. .. .. .. *Set of* 3 75 85
**MS**364 118 × 114 mm. Nos. 361/3 .. .. .. 2·25 3·25

**93** The Spurs and Jewelled Sword

(Des PAD Studio. Litho Questa)

**1977** (7 Feb). *Silver Jubilee. T* **93** *and similar horiz designs. Multicoloured. P* 13½.

365 25 b. Queen's visit, 1961 .. .. .. .. 70 60
366 50 b. Type **93** .. .. .. .. .. .. 40 40
367 1 d. 25, Oblation of the sword .. .. .. 75 75
365/7 .. .. .. .. .. .. *Set of* 3 1·60 1·60

**94** Stone Circles, Kuntaur

(Des J.W. Litho Questa)

**1977** (18 Feb). *Tourism. T* **94** *and similar horiz designs. Multicoloured. P* 14.

368 25 b. Type **94** .. .. .. .. .. .. 10 10
369 50 b. Ruined fort, James Island .. .. .. 20 20
370 1 d. 25, Mungo Park Monument .. .. .. 70 70
368/70 .. .. .. .. .. *Set of* 3 90 90

**95** Widow of Last Year

**96** Endangered Animals

(Des PAD Studio. Litho Questa)

**1977** (1 July)–**79**. *Flowers and Shrubs. Multicoloured designs as T* **95**. *Chalk-surfaced paper (No. 376a) or ordinary paper (others). P* 14.

371 2 b. Type **95** .. .. .. .. .. .. 10 15
a. Chalk-surfaced paper (23.11.79).. .. .. 40 25
372 4 b. White Water-lily.. .. .. .. .. 10 30
a. Chalk-surfaced paper (23.11.79).. .. .. 40 30
373 6 b. Fireball Lily .. .. .. .. .. 10 30
a. Chalk-surfaced paper (22.6.79) .. .. .. 40 30
374 8 b. Cocks-comb .. .. .. .. .. .. 10 15
a. Chalk-surfaced paper (23.11.79).. .. .. 30 15
375 10 b. Broad Leaved Ground Orchid .. .. .. 1·00 30
a. Chalk-surfaced paper (23.11.79).. .. .. 1·40 30
376 13 b. Fibre Plant (pale yellow background) .. 15 40
376*a* 13 b. Fibre Plant (pale olive-grey background) (*chalk-surfaced paper*) (25.7.79) .. .. 3·00 3·00
377 25 b. False Kapok .. .. .. .. .. 15 15
a. Chalk-surfaced paper (16.3.78) .. .. .. 55 35
378 38 b. Baobab .. .. .. .. .. .. 25 55
a. Chalk-surfaced paper (23.11.79).. .. .. 60 35
379 50 b. Coral Tree .. .. .. .. .. .. 35 35
a. Chalk-surfaced paper (16.3.78) .. .. .. 75 50
380 63 b. Gloriosa Lily .. .. .. .. .. 40 70
a. Chalk-surfaced paper (23.11.79).. .. .. 85 65
381 1 d. 25, Bell-flowered Mimosa .. .. .. 70 1·25
a. Chalk-surfaced paper (23.11.79).. .. .. 1·00 1·00
382 2 d. 50, Kindin Dolo .. .. .. .. .. 75 1·25
383 5 d. African Tulip Tree .. .. .. .. 1·25 2·00
371/83 .. .. .. .. .. *Set of* 14 7·50 9·00

The 6 to 38 b., 1 d. 25 and 2 d. 50 are vertical designs.

(Des N. Fortey (10, 50 b.), D. J. Thorp (25 b.), M. Langley (1 d. 25). Litho Questa)

**1977** (15 Oct). *Banjul Declaration. T* **96** *and similar vert designs. P* 14.

384 10 b. black and light new blue .. .. .. 15 10
385 25 b. multicoloured .. .. .. .. .. 40 10
386 50 b. multicoloured .. .. .. .. .. 65 20
387 1 d. 25, black and light vermilion .. .. 1·40 75
384/7 .. .. .. .. .. .. *Set of* 4 2·40 1·00

Designs:—25 b. Extract from Declaration; 50 b. Declaration in full; 1 d. 25, Endangered insects and flowers.

## ALTERED CATALOGUE NUMBERS

Any Catalogue numbers altered from the last edition are shown as a list in the introductory pages.

**97** "Flight into Egypt"

**98** Dome of the Rock, Jerusalem

(Des BG Studio and Enschedé. Litho Enschedé)

**1977** (15 Dec). 400*th Birth Anniv of Rubens. T* **97** *and similar vert designs. Multicoloured. P* 13½ × 14.

388 10 b. Type **97** .. .. .. .. .. 10 10
389 25 b. "The Education of the Virgin" .. .. 15 10
390 50 b. "Clara Serena Rubens" .. .. .. 35 20
391 1 d. "Madonna with Saints" .. .. .. 60 70
388/91 .. .. .. .. *Set of* 4 1·10 1·00

Nos. 388/91 were each printed in small sheets of 6 including 1 *se-tenant* stamp-size label.

(Des J. Cooter. Litho Questa)

**1978** (3 Jan). *Palestinian Welfare. P* 14½ × 14.

392 **98** 8 b. multicoloured .. .. .. 50 15
393 25 b. multicoloured .. .. .. 2·00 85

**99** Walking on a Greasy Pole

**100** Lion

(Des J.W. Litho Harrison)

**1978** (18 Feb). 13*th Anniv of Independence. T* **99** *and similar vert designs showing scenes from the Independence Regatta. Multicoloured. P* 14.

394 10 b. Type **99** .. .. .. .. .. 10 1
395 50 b. Pillow fighting .. .. .. .. 15 1
396 1 d. 25, Long rowing boat .. .. .. 35 4
394/6 .. .. .. .. .. *Set of* 3 50 5

(Des Jennifer Toombs. Litho Questa)

**1978** (15 Apr). 25*th Anniv of Coronation. T* **100** *and similar vert designs. P* 15.

397 1 d. black, agate and orange-yellow .. .. 35 6
a. Sheetlet. Nos. 397/9 × 2 .. .. .. 1·90
398 1 d. multicoloured .. .. .. .. 35 6
399 1 d. black, agate and orange-yellow .. .. 35 6
397/9 .. .. .. .. .. *Set of* 3 95 1·6

Designs:—No. 397, White Greyhound of Richmond; No. 398 Queen Elizabeth II; No. 399, Type **100**.

Nos. 397/9 were printed together in small sheets of 6, containing two *se-tenant* strips of 3, with horizontal gutter margin between.

**101** Verreaux's Eagle Owl

**102** M.V. *Lady Wright* (previous vessel)

(Des M. Bryan. Litho Questa)

**1978** (28 Oct). *Abuko Nature Reserve (2nd series). T* **101** *and similar vert designs. Multicoloured. P* 14 × 13½.

400 20 b. Type **101** .. .. .. .. .. 1·50 3
401 25 b. Lizard Buzzard .. .. .. .. 1·50 3
402 50 b. African Harrier Hawk .. .. .. 2·50 1·2
403 1 d. 25, Long-crested Eagle .. .. .. 3·50 3·5
400/3 .. .. .. .. .. *Set of* 4 8·00 4·7

(Des A. Theobald. Litho Questa)

**1978** (1 Dec). *New River Vessel "Lady Chilel Jawara" Commemoration. T* **102** *and similar horiz designs. Multicoloured. P* 14.

404 8 b. Type **102** .. .. .. .. .. 15 1
405 25 b. *Lady Chilel Jawara* (sectional view) .. 40 2
406 1 d. *Lady Chilel Jawara* .. .. .. 1·25 1·1
404/6 .. .. .. .. .. *Set of* 3 1·60 1·2

25b

103 Police Service (104)

(Des G. Vasarhelyi. Litho Questa)

**1979** (18 Feb). *14th Anniv of Independence. T* **103** *and similar horiz designs. Multicoloured. P* 14.

407 10 b. Type **103** .. .. .. .. .. 45 10
408 50 b. Fire service .. .. .. .. .. 75 25
409 1 d. 25, Ambulance service .. .. .. 1·25 80
407/9 .. .. .. .. .. *Set of* 3 2·25 1·00

**1979** (5–26 Mar). *Nos.* 376 *and* 380/1 *surch as T* **104**.

410 25 b. on 13 b. Fibre Plant .. .. .. 20 35
411 25 b. on 63 b. Gloriosa Lily (26.3.79) .. .. 15 20
412 25 b. on 1 d. 25, Bell-flowered Mimosa (26.3.79) 15 20
410/12 .. .. .. .. *Set of* 3 45 65

105 "Ramsgate Sands" (detail showing Children playing on Beach)

(Des C. Abbott. Litho Questa)

**1979** (25 May). *International Year of the Child. T* **105** *and similar multicoloured designs showing the painting "Ramsgate Sands" by William Powell Frith. P* 14 × 13½ (25 *b.*) *or* 13½ × 14 (*others*).

413 10 b. Type **105** .. .. .. .. .. 10 10
414 25 b. Detail showing child paddling (*vert*) .. 20 10
415 1 d. Complete painting (60 × 23 *mm*) .. 60 60
413/15 .. .. .. .. *Set of* 3 80 65

106 1883 2½d. Stamp

(Des J.W. Litho Questa)

**1979** (16 Aug). *Death Centenary of Sir Rowland Hill. T* **106** *and similar horiz designs showing stamps. Multicoloured. P* 14.

416 10 b. Type **106** .. .. .. .. .. 10 10
417 25 b. 1869 4d. .. .. .. .. .. 15 10
418 50 b. 1965 7½d. Independence commemorative .. .. .. .. .. 20 20
419 1 d. 25, 1935 1½d. Silver Jubilee commemorative .. .. .. .. .. 40 50
416/19 .. .. .. .. *Set of* 4 75 80
**MS**420 109 × 83 mm. No. 419 .. .. .. 65 1·00

107 Satellite Earth Station under Construction — 108 "Apollo 11" leaving Launch Pad

(Des A. Theobald. Litho Questa)

**1979** (20 Sept). *Abuko Satellite Earth Station. T* **107** *and similar horiz designs. Multicoloured. P* 14.

421 25 b. Type **107** .. .. .. .. .. 20 10
422 50 b. Satellite Earth Station (completed) .. 30 20
423 1 d. "Intelsat" satellites .. .. .. 65 60
421/3 .. .. .. .. *Set of* 3 1·00 80

(Des and litho Walsall)

**1979** (17 Oct). *10th Anniv of Moon Landing. T* **108** *and similar vert designs. Multicoloured.* (a) *Sheet stamps. P* 14.

424 25 b. Type **108** .. .. .. .. .. 20 10
425 38 b. "Apollo 11" in Moon orbit .. .. 25 20
426 50 b. Splashdown .. .. .. .. 30 40
424/6 .. .. .. .. *Set of* 3 65 60

(*b*) *Booklet stamps. Roul* 5 × *imperf.* Self-adhesive*

427 25 b. Type **108** .. .. .. .. .. 25 30
a. Booklet pane. Nos. 427/9, each × 2 .. 1·60
428 38 b. As No. 425 .. .. .. .. 30 35
429 50 b. As No. 426 .. .. .. .. 30 40
430 2 d. Lunar module on Moon .. .. 1·50 1·75
a. Booklet pane of 1 .. .. .. .. 1·50

*Nos. 427/9 are separated by various combinations of rotary-knife (giving a straight edge) and roulette. No. 430 exists only with straight edges.

109 *Acraea zetes*

(Des J. Cooter. Litho Questa)

**1980** (3 Jan). *Abuko Nature Reserve (3rd series). Butterflies. T* **109** *and similar horiz designs. Multicoloured. P* 13½.

431 25 b. Type **109** .. .. .. .. .. 35 20
432 50 b. *Precis hierta* .. .. .. .. 55 40
433 1 d. *Graphium leonidas* .. .. .. 85 80
434 1 d. 25, *Charaxes jasius* .. .. .. 90 85
431/4 .. .. .. .. *Set of* 4 2·40 2·00
**MS**435 145×122 mm. Nos. 431/4 .. .. 2·75 3·25

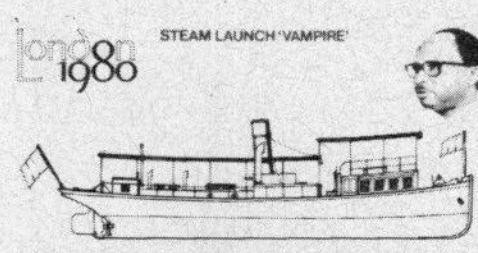


110 Steam Launch *Vampire*

(Des C. Abbott. Litho Harrison)

**1980** (6 May). *"London 1980" International Stamp Exhibition. Mail Boats. T* **110** *and similar multicoloured designs. P* 14 (10, 25 *b.*) *or* 13 × 14 (*others*).

436 10 b. Type **110** .. .. .. .. .. 15 10
437 25 b. T.S.S. *Lady Denham* .. .. .. 20 10
438 50 b. T.S.C.M.Y. *Mansa Kila Ba* (49 × 26 *mm*) 30 20
439 1 d. 25, T.S.S. *Prince of Wales* (49 × 26 *mm*) .. 50 60
436/9 .. .. .. .. *Set of* 4 1·00 85

111 Queen Elizabeth the Queen Mother

(Des and litho Harrison)

**1980** (4 Aug). *80th Birthday of Queen Elizabeth the Queen Mother. P* 14.

440 **111** 67 b. multicoloured .. .. .. 30 35

112 Phoenician Trading Vessel — 113 "Madonna and Child" (Francesco de Mura)

(Des A. Theobald. Litho Walsall)

**1980** (2 Oct). *Early Sailing Vessels. T* **112** *and similar horiz designs. Multicoloured. P* 14½ × 14.

441 8 b. Type **112** .. .. .. .. .. 10 10
442 67 b. Egyptian sea-going vessel .. .. 25 20
443 75 b. Portuguese caravel .. .. .. 30 30
444 1 d. Spanish galleon .. .. .. 50 50
441/4 .. .. .. .. *Set of* 4 1·00 1·00

(Des BG Studio. Litho Questa)

**1980** (23 Dec). *Christmas. Paintings. T* **113** *and similar vert designs. Multicoloured. P* 14.

445 8 b. Type **113** .. .. .. .. .. 10 10
446 67 b. "Praying Madonna with Crown of Stars" (workshop of Correggio) .. .. .. 25 25
447 75 b. "La Zingarella" (workshop replica of Correggio painting) .. .. .. 25 30
445/7 .. .. .. .. *Set of* 3 50 60

114 New Atlantic Hotel

(Des BG Studio. Litho Format)

**1981** (18 Feb). *World Tourism Conference, Manila. T* **114** *and similar horiz designs. Multicoloured. P* 14.

448 25 b. Type **114** .. .. .. .. .. 15 10
449 75 b. Ancient stone circle .. .. .. 40 40
450 85 b. Conference emblem .. .. .. 50 50
448/50 .. .. .. .. *Set of* 3 95 90

115 1979 Abuko Satellite Earth Station 50 b. Commemorative — 116 Prince Charles in Naval Uniform

(Des BG Studio. Litho Questa)

**1981** (17 May). *World Telecommunications Day. T* **115** *and similar horiz designs. P* 14.

451 50 b. multicoloured .. .. .. .. 55 30
452 50 b. multicoloured .. .. .. .. 55 30
453 85 b. black and brown-ochre .. .. .. 80 55
451/3 .. .. .. .. *Set of* 3 1·75 1·00

Designs:—No. 452, 1975 Birth Centenary of Dr. Albert Schweitzer 50 b. commemorative; No. 453, I.T.U. and W.H.O. emblems.

(Des and litho J.W.)

**1981** (22 July). *Royal Wedding. T* **116** *and similar vert designs. Multicoloured. P* 13½ × 13.

454 75 b. Wedding bouquet from Gambia .. .. 30 20
455 1 d. Type **116** .. .. .. .. .. 35 30
456 1 d. 25, Prince Charles and Lady Diana Spencer .. .. .. .. .. 40 35
454/6 .. .. .. .. *Set of* 3 95 75

117 Planting-out Seedlings

(Des Jennifer Toombs. Litho Format)

**1981** (4 Sept). *10th Anniv of West African Rice Development Association. T* **117** *and similar horiz designs. Multicoloured. P* 14.

457 10 b. Type **117** .. .. .. .. .. 10 10
458 50 b. Care of the crops .. .. .. .. 35 35
459 85 b. Winnowing and drying .. .. .. 55 55
457/9 .. .. .. .. *Set of* 3 85 85

118 Bosc's Monitor

(Des J. Cooter. Litho Format)

**1981** (17 Nov). *Abuko Nature Reserve (4th series). Reptiles. T* **118** *and similar horiz designs. Multicoloured. P* 14.

460 40 b. Type **118** .. .. .. .. .. 45 20
461 60 b. Dwarf Crocodile .. .. .. .. 70 35
462 80 b. Royal Python .. .. .. .. 90 60
463 85 b. Chameleon .. .. .. .. 95 65
460/3 .. .. .. .. *Set of* 4 2·75 1·60

60B

119 Examination Room (120)

(Des PAD Studio. Litho Walsall)

**1982** (16 Mar). *30th Anniv of West African Examinations Council. T* **119** *and similar horiz designs. Multicoloured. P* 14.

464 60 b. Type **119** .. .. .. .. .. 50 30
465 85 b. First High School .. .. .. .. 65 45
466 1 d. 10, Council's office .. .. .. 85 55
464/6 .. .. .. .. *Set of* 3 1·75 1·10

**1982** (19 Apr). *No.* 454 *surch with T* **120**.

467 60 b. on 75 b. Wedding bouquet from Gambia 2·50 2·50

**121** Tree-planting ("Conservation")

(Des L. Curtis. Litho Harrison)

**1982** (16 May). *75th Anniv of Boy Scout Movement. T* **121** *and similar horiz designs. Multicoloured. P* 14.

468 85 b. Type **121** .. 1·50 1·00
469 1 d. 25, Woodworking .. 1·75 1·75
470 1 d. 27, Lord Baden-Powell .. 1·75 2·00
468/70 .. *Set of* 3 4·50 4·25

**122** Gambia Football Team **123** Gambia Coat of Arms

(Des A. Theobald. Litho Questa)

**1982** (13 June). *World Cup Football Championship, Spain. T* **122** *and similar horiz designs. Multicoloured. P* 14.

471 10 b. Type **122** .. 15 10
472 1 d. 10, Gambian team practice .. 85 70
473 1 d. 25, Bernabéu Stadium, Madrid .. 90 75
474 1 d. 55, FIFA World Cup .. 95 80
471/4 .. *Set of* 4 2·50 2·10
**MS**475 114 × 85 mm. Nos. 471/4 .. 3·25 3·75

(Des C. Abbott. Litho Walsall)

**1982** (1 July). *21st Birthday of Princess of Wales. T* **123** *and similar vert designs. Multicoloured. P* 14½ × 14.

476 10 b. Type **123** .. 10 10
477 85 b. Princess at Cardiff City Hall, October 1981 .. 40 30
478 1 d. 10, Bride and groom returning to Buckingham Palace .. 50 45
479 2 d. 50, Formal portrait .. 1·25 1·25
476/9 .. *Set of* 4 2·00 1·90

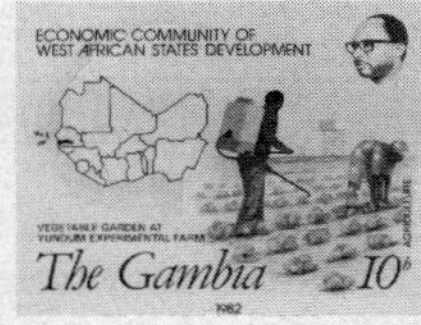


**124** Vegetable Garden at Yundum Experimental Farm

(Des Harrison. Litho Questa)

**1982** (5 Nov). *Economic Community of West African States Development. T* **124** *and similar horiz designs. Multicoloured. P* 14 × 14½.

480 10 b. Type **124** .. 25 15
481 60 b. Banjul/Kaolack microwave tower .. 1·25 90
482 90 b. Soap factory, Denton Bridge, Banjul .. 1·40 1·40
483 1 d. 25, Control tower, Yundum Airport .. 1·60 2·00
480/3 .. *Set of* 4 4·00 4·00

**125** *Kassina cassinoides*

(Des PAD Studio. Litho Questa)

**1982** (2 Dec). *Frogs. T* **125** *and similar horiz designs. Multicoloured. P* 14.

484 10 b. Type **125** .. 40 15
485 20 b. *Hylarana galamensis* .. 55 20
486 85 b. *Euphlyctis occipitalis* .. 1·00 80
487 2 d. *Kassina senegalensis* .. 2·00 2·50
484/7 .. *Set of* 4 3·50 3·25

**126** Satellite View of Gambia **127** Blessed Anne Marie Javouhey (foundress of the Order)

(Des Walsall. Litho Questa)

**1983** (14 Mar). *Commonwealth Day. T* **126** *and similar horiz designs. Multicoloured. P* 14.

488 10 b. Type **126** .. 10 10
489 60 b. Batik cloth .. 30 45
490 1 d. 10, Bagging groundnuts .. 50 65
491 2 d. 10, Gambia flag .. 90 1·25
488/91 .. *Set of* 4 1·60 2·25

(Des G. Vasarhelyi. Litho Format)

**1983** (8 Apr). *Centenary of Sisters of St. Joseph of Cluny's Work in Gambia. T* **127** *and similar multicoloured design. P* 13½.

492 10 b. Type **127** .. 10 10
493 85 b. Bathurst Hospital, nun and schoolchildren (*horiz*) .. 45 50

**128** Canoes

(Des A. Theobald. Litho Walsall)

**1983** (11 July). *River Craft. T* **128** *and similar horiz designs. Multicoloured. P* 14.

494 1 b. Type **128** .. 10 20
495 2 b. Upstream ferry .. 15 20
496 3 b. Dredger .. 15 20
497 4 b. *Sir Dawda* (harbour launch) .. 20 20
498 5 b. Cargo liner .. 20 20
499 10 b. *Lady Dale* (60 ft launch) .. 20 10
500 20 b. Container ship .. 30 20
501 30 b. Large sailing canoe .. 30 20
502 40 b. *Lady Wright* (passenger and cargo ferry) .. 30 25
503 50 b. Container ship (*different*) .. 35 25
504 75 b. Fishing boats .. 40 25
505 1 d. Tug with groundnut barges .. 45 35
506 1 d. 25, Groundnut canoe .. 55 40
507 2 d. 50, *Banjul* (car ferry) .. 1·00 1·25
508 5 d. *Bintang Bolong* (ferry) .. 1·60 2·00
509 10 d. *Lady Chilel Jawara* (passenger and cargo ferry) .. 2·75 3·25
494/509 .. *Set of* 16 8·00 8·50

Nos. 494/509 come with a pattern of blue fluorescent security markings, resembling rosettes, printed on the reverse beneath the gum.

**129** Osprey in Tree

(Des N. Arlott. Litho Questa)

**1983** (12 Sept). *The Osprey. T* **129** *and similar horiz designs. Multicoloured. P* 14.

510 10 b. Type **129** .. 75 20
511 60 b. Osprey .. 1·50 85
512 85 b. Osprey with catch .. 1·75 1·50
513 1 d. 10, In flight .. 2·00 2·00
510/13 .. *Set of* 4 5·50 4·00

**130** Local Ferry

(Des L. Curtis. Litho Questa)

**1983** (10 Oct). *World Communications Year. T* **130** *and similar horiz designs. Multicoloured. P* 14.

514 10 b. Type **130** .. 10 10
515 85 b. Telex operator .. 45 50
516 90 b. Radio Gambia .. 45 50
517 1 d. 10, Loading mail onto aircraft .. 60 65
514/17 .. *Set of* 4 1·40 1·60

**131** "St. Paul preaching at Athens" (detail) (Raphael)

(Des C. Abbott. Litho Questa)

**1983** (1 Nov). *500th Birth Anniv of Raphael. T* **131** *and similar designs. P* 14.

518 60 b. multicoloured .. 35 40
519 85 b. multicoloured .. 45 50
520 1 d. multicoloured .. 50 55
518/20 .. *Set of* 3 1·10 1·25
**MS**521 105 × 83 mm. 2 d. multicoloured .. 1·00 1·25

Nos. 519/21 show different details of "St. Paul preaching at Athens", the 85 b. and 1 d. being horizontal and the 2 d. vertical.

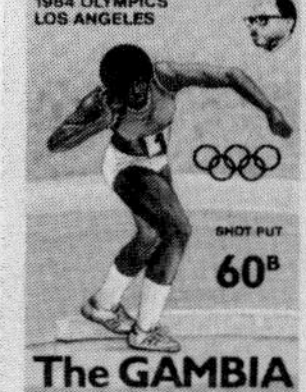


**132** Early Balloon and Siege of Paris Cover **133** Shot-putting

(Des Harrison. Litho Questa)

**1983** (12 Dec). *Bicentenary of Manned Flight. T* **132** *and similar horiz designs. Multicoloured. P* 14.

522 60 b. Type **132** .. 35 40
a. Booklet pane. Nos. 522/3, each × 2 .. 1·60
523 85 b. Lufthansa aircraft and flown cover .. 45 50
524 90 b. Junkers aircraft and Hans Bertram cover .. 45 50
a. Booklet pane. Nos. 524/5, each × 2 .. 2·25
525 1 d. 25, Lunar module and H. E. Sieger's space cover .. 65 70
526 4 d. *Graf Zeppelin* (airship) .. 2·00 2·50
a. Booklet pane of 1 .. 2·00
522/6 .. *Set of* 5 3·50 4·25

Nos. 522/6 come with a pattern of blue fluorescent security markings, resembling rosettes, printed on the reverse beneath the gum.

No. 526 only exists from booklets.

On 14 December 1983 four provisional surcharges, 1 d. 50 on 1 d. 25 (No. 439), 1 d. 50 on 1 d. 25 (No. 473), 2d. on 1 d. 25 (No. 456) and 2 d. on 1 d. 10 (No. 478), were issued in very limited quantities, there being, it is believed, no more than 600 complete sets (*Price for set of* 4 *£110 mint*).

(Des G. Vasarhelyi. Litho Questa)

**1984** (30 Mar). *Olympic Games, Los Angeles (1st issue). T* **133** *and similar multicoloured designs. P* 11.

527 60 b. Type **133** .. 25 30
528 85 b. High jumping (*horiz*) .. 35 40
529 90 b. Wrestling .. 35 40
530 1 d. Gymnastics .. 40 45
531 1 d. 25, Swimming (*horiz*) .. 50 55
532 2 d. Diving .. 80 85
527/32 .. *Set of* 6 2·40 2·75
**MS**533 100 × 80 mm. 5 d. Yachting. P 13½ × 14 2·00 2·25

See also Nos. 555/8.

**134** Goofy

(Litho Format)

**1984** (27 Apr). *Easter. T* **134** *and similar vert designs showing Walt Disney cartoon characters painting eggs. P* 11.

534 1 b. Type **134** .. 10 10
535 2 b. Mickey Mouse .. 10 10
536 3 b. Huey, Dewey and Louie .. 10 10
537 4 b. Goofy (*different*) .. 10 10
538 5 b. Donald Duck .. 10 10
539 10 b. Chip 'n Dale .. 10 10
540 60 b. Pluto .. 35 35
541 90 b. Scrooge McDuck .. 50 50
542 5 d. Morty and Ferdie .. 2·25 2·40
534/42 .. *Set of* 9 3·00 3·25
**MS**543 125 × 100 mm. 5 d. Donald Duck (*different*). P 13½ × 14 .. 2·25 2·50

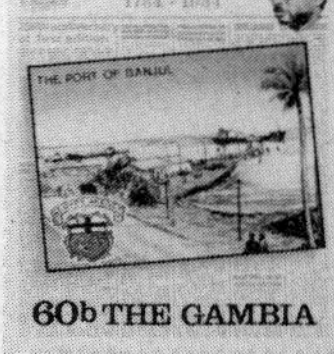


**135** Young Crocodiles Hatching **136** Port Banjul

(Des Doreen McGuinness. Litho Format)

**1984** (23 May). *The Nile Crocodile. T* **135** *and similar horiz designs. Multicoloured. P* 14.

544 4 b. Type **135** .. .. .. .. .. 10 10
545 6 b. Adult carrying young .. .. .. 10 10
546 90 b. Adult .. .. .. .. .. 1·00 1·25
547 1 d. 50, Crocodile at riverbank .. .. 1·90 2·50
544/7 .. .. .. .. .. *Set of* 4 2·75 3·75
**MS**548 126 × 94 mm. Nos. 544/7 .. .. .. 2·75 3·75

Nos. 544/8 come with a pattern of blue fluorescent security markings, resembling rosettes, printed on the reverse beneath the gum.

(Des C. Collins. Litho Questa)

**1984** (1 June). 250*th Anniv of "Lloyd's List"* (*newspaper*). *T* **136** *and similar vert designs. Multicoloured. P* 14½ × 14.

549 60 b. Type **136** .. .. .. .. .. 50 30
550 85 b. Bulk carrier .. .. .. .. 60 40
551 90 b. Sinking of the *Dagomba* .. .. .. 60 55
552 1 d. 25, 19th century frigate .. .. .. 1·10 85
549/52 .. .. .. .. *Set of* 4 2·50 1·90

Nos. 549/52 come with a pattern of blue fluorescent security markings, resembling rosettes, printed on the reverse beneath the gum.

**19th UPU CONGRESS HAMBURG**
(137)

138 Sprinting

**1984** (19 June). *Universal Postal Union Congress, Hamburg. Nos.* 507/8 *optd with T* **137**.

553 2 d. 50, *Banjul* (car ferry) .. .. .. 1·00 1·10
554 5 d. *Bintang Bolong* (ferry) .. .. .. 2·00 2·25

(Des G. Vasarhelyi. Litho Walsall)

**1984** (27 July). *Olympic Games, Los Angeles* (2*nd issue*). *T* **138** *and similar horiz designs. Multicoloured. P* 14.

555 60 b. Type **138** .. .. .. .. .. 25 30
556 85 b. Long jumping .. .. .. .. 35 40
557 90 b. Long-distance running .. .. .. 35 40
558 1 d. 25, Triple jumping .. .. .. 50 55
555/8 .. .. .. .. *Set of* 4 1·25 1·50

Nos. 555/8 come with a pattern of blue fluorescent security markings, resembling rosettes, printed on the reverse beneath the gum.

139 *Graf Zeppelin*

(Des D. Hartley-Marjoram. Litho Questa)

**1984** (1 Nov). 50*th Anniv of Gambia–South America Trans-atlantic Flights. T* **139** *and similar horiz designs. Multi-coloured. P* 14.

559 60 b. Type **139** .. .. .. .. .. 80 60
560 85 b. Dornier "Wal" on S.S. *Westfalen* .. 1·10 90
561 90 b. Dornier "DO.18" .. .. .. .. 1·10 1·00
562 1 d. 25, Dornier "Wal" .. .. .. 1·40 1·50
559/62 .. .. .. .. *Set of* 4 4·00 3·50

Nos. 559/62 come with a pattern of blue fluorescent security markings, resembling rosettes, printed on the reverse beneath the gum.

140 Pink Shrimp

(Des Pam Johnson. Litho Questa)

**1984** (27 Nov). *Marine Life. T* **140** *and similar horiz designs. Multicoloured. P* 14.

563 55 b. Type **140** .. .. .. .. .. 25 25
564 75 b. Atlantic Loggerhead Turtle .. .. 40 35
565 1 d. 50, Portuguese Man-of-War .. .. 70 70
566 2 d. 35, Fiddler Crab .. .. .. 95 1·25
563/6 .. .. .. .. *Set of* 4 2·10 2·25
**MS**567 105 × 70 mm. 5 d. Cowrie Snail .. .. 2·50 3·50

141 *Antanartia hippomene*

(Des Pam Johnson. Litho Questa)

**1984** (27 Nov). *Butterflies. T* **141** *and similar horiz designs. Multicoloured. P* 14.

568 10 b. Type **141** .. .. .. .. .. 20 20
569 85 b. *Pseudacraea eurytus* .. .. .. 70 70
570 90 b. *Charaxes lactitinctus* .. .. .. 70 70
571 3 d. *Graphium pylades* .. .. .. 1·75 2·75
568/71 .. .. .. .. *Set of* 4 3·00 4·00
**MS**572 105 × 75 mm. 5 d. *Eurema hapale* .. 5·50 6·00

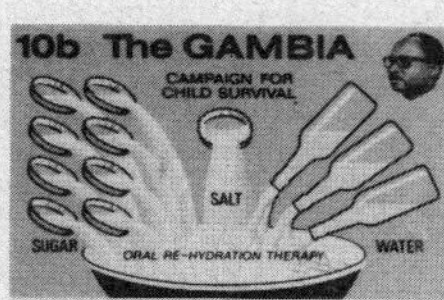
142 Oral Re-hydration Therapy

(Des L. Curtis. Litho Harrison)

**1985** (27 Feb). *Campaign for Child Survival. T* **142** *and similar horiz designs. P* 14.

573 10 b. black, cobalt and deep cinnamon .. 10 10
574 85 b. multicoloured .. .. .. .. 35 40
575 1 d. 10, multicoloured .. .. .. 45 50
576 1 d. 50, multicoloured .. .. .. 60 65
573/6 .. .. .. .. *Set of* 4 1·25 1·40

Designs:—85 b. Growth monitoring; 1 d. 10, Health care worker with women and babies ("Promotion of breast feeding"); 1 d. 50, Universal immunisation.

Nos. 573/6 come with a pattern of blue fluorescent security markings, resembling rosettes, printed on the reverse beneath the gum.

143 Women at Market

144 Turkey Vulture

(Des G. Vasarhelyi. Litho Format)

**1985** (11 Mar). *Women and Development. T* **143** *and similar horiz design. Multicoloured. P* 14.

577 60 b. Type **143** .. .. .. .. .. 25 30
578 85 b. Type **143** .. .. .. .. .. 35 40
579 1 d. Woman office worker .. .. .. 40 45
580 1 d. 25, As 1 d. .. .. .. .. 50 55
577/80 .. .. .. .. *Set of* 4 1·40 1·50

Nos. 577/80 come with a pattern of blue fluorescent security markings, resembling rosettes, printed on the reverse beneath the gum.

(Des and litho Questa)

**1985** (15 July). *Birth Bicentenary of John J. Audubon (ornithologist). T* **144** *and similar multicoloured designs showing original paintings. P* 14.

581 60 b. Type **144** .. .. .. .. .. 1·00 45
582 85 b. American Anhinga .. .. .. 1·25 95
583 1 d. 50, Green Heron .. .. .. 1·50 1·75
584 5 d. Wood Duck .. .. .. .. 2·75 3·25
581/4 .. .. .. .. *Set of* 4 6·00 5·75
**MS**585 100 × 70 mm. 10 d. Great Northern Diver (inscr "Common Loon") (*horiz*) .. .. .. 3·50 4·00

145 The Queen Mother

**GOLD MEDALLIST**
**CLAUDIA LOCH**
**WEST GERMANY**
(146)

(Des J.W. Litho Questa)

**1985** (29 July). *Life and Times of Queen Elizabeth the Queen Mother. T* **145** *and similar vert designs. Multicoloured. P* 14.

586 85 b. The Queen Mother and King George VI reviewing Home Guard .. .. .. 25 30
587 3 d. Type **145** .. .. .. .. .. 80 85
588 5 d. The Queen Mother with posy .. .. 1·40 1·50
586/8 .. .. .. .. *Set of* 3 2·25 2·40
**MS**589 56 × 85 mm. 10 d. The Queen Mother in Garter robes .. .. .. .. .. 2·75 3·00

(Des Walt Disney Studios. Litho Questa)

**1985** (30 Oct). 150*th Birth Anniv of Mark Twain* (*author*). *Horiz designs as T* **118** *of Anguilla showing Walt Disney cartoon characters in scenes from "Life on the Mississippi". Multicoloured. P* 14 × 13½.

590 1 d. 50, Mickey Mouse steering the *Calamity Jane* .. .. .. .. .. .. 40 45
591 2 d. Mickey and Minnie Mouse at antebellum mansion .. .. .. .. .. 55 60
592 2 d. 50, Donald Duck and Goofy heaving the lead .. .. .. .. .. .. 65 70
593 3 d. Poker game aboard the *Gold Dust* .. 80 85
590/3 .. .. .. .. *Set of* 4 2·25 2·40
**MS**594 126 × 101 mm. 10 d. Mickey Mouse and riverboat .. .. .. .. .. .. 2·75 3·25

(Des Walt Disney Productions. Litho Questa)

**1985** (30 Oct). *Birth Bicentenaries of Grimm Brothers (folklorists). Designs as T* **119** *of Anguilla, but vert, showing Walt Disney cartoon characters in scenes from "Faithful John". Multicoloured. P* 13½ × 14.

595 60 b. The King (Mickey Mouse) and portrait of the Princess (Minnie Mouse) .. 30 25
596 85 b. The King showing the Princess his treasures .. .. .. .. .. 35 30
597 2 d. 35, Faithful John (Goofy) playing trumpet .. .. .. .. .. .. 75 75
598 5 d. Faithful John turned to stone .. .. 1·75 1·75
595/8 .. .. .. .. *Set of* 4 2·75 2·75
**MS**599 126 × 101 mm. 10 d. Faithful John after recovery .. .. .. .. .. .. 3·50 4·00

**1985** (11 Nov). *Olympic Gold Medal Winners, Los Angeles. Nos.* 527/33 *optd as T* **146**.

600 60 b. Type **133** (optd with T **146**) .. .. 25 25
601 85 b. High jumping (optd "GOLD MEDALLIST ULRIKE MEYFARTH WEST GERMANY") .. .. .. .. .. 30 30
602 90 b. Wrestling (optd "GOLD MEDALLIST PASQUALE PASSARELLI WEST GERMANY") .. .. .. .. .. 30 30
603 1 d. Gymnastics (optd "GOLD MEDALLIST LI NING CHINA") .. .. .. 35 35
604 1 d. 25, Swimming (optd "GOLD MEDALLIST MICHAEL GROSS WEST GERMANY") .. .. .. .. .. 45 45
605 2 d. Diving (optd "GOLD MEDALLIST SYLVIE BERNIER CANADA") .. .. 65 65
600/5 .. .. .. .. *Set of* 6 2·10 2·10
**MS**606 100 × 80 mm. 5 d. Yachting (opt "GOLD MEDAL STAR CLASS U.S.A.") .. .. .. 1·75 1·90

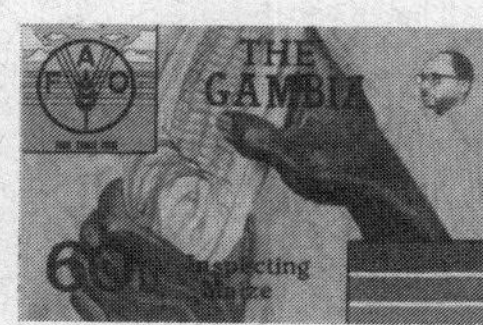
147 Inspecting Maize

(Des J. Farleo. Litho Questa)

**1985** (15 Nov). *United Nations Anniversaries. T* **147** *and similar horiz designs. Multicoloured. P* 14.

607 60 b. Type **147** .. .. .. .. .. 40 35
608 85 b. Football match, Independence Stadium, Banjul .. .. .. .. .. 50 40
609 1 d. 10, Rice fields .. .. .. .. 60 50
610 2 d. Central Bank of The Gambia .. .. 85 75
611 3 d. Cow and calf .. .. .. .. 1·50 1·40
612 4 d. Banjul harbour .. .. .. .. 2·00 2·00
613 5 d. Gambian fruits .. .. .. .. 2·25 2·25
614 6 d. Oyster Creek Bridge .. .. .. 2·50 2·75
607/14 .. .. .. .. *Set of* 8 9·50 9·25

Nos. 607, 609, 611 and 613 commemorate the 40th anniversary of the Food and Agriculture Organization and Nos. 608, 610, 612 and 614 the 40th anniversary of the United Nations Organization.

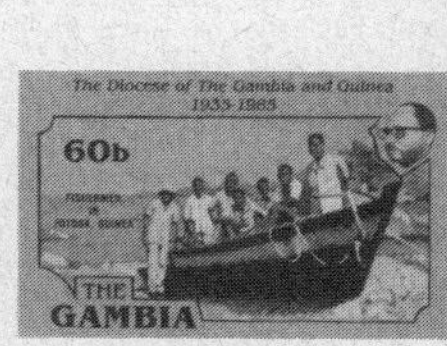
148 Fishermen in Fotoba, Guinea

149 "Virgin and Child" (Dieric Bouts)

(Des B. Bundock. Litho Questa)

**1985** (24 Dec). 50*th Anniv of Diocese of The Gambia and Guinea. T* **148** *and similar horiz designs. Multicoloured. P* 14.

615 60 b. Type **148** .. .. .. .. .. 30 30
616 85 b. St. Mary's Primary School, Banjul .. 30 40
617 1 d. 10, St. Mary's Cathedral, Banjul .. 35 65
618 1 d. 50, Mobile dispensary at Christy Kunda .. .. .. .. .. .. 50 85
615/18 .. .. .. .. *Set of* 4 1·25 2·00

(Des Mary Walters. Litho Format)

**1985** (24 Dec). *Christmas. Religious Paintings. T* **149** *and similar vert designs. Multicoloured. P* 15.

619 60 b. Type **149** .. .. .. .. .. 20 25
620 85 b. "The Annunciation" (Robert Campin) .. 25 30
621 1 d. 50, "Adoration of the Shepherds" (Gerard David) .. .. .. .. .. 45 50
622 5 d. "The Nativity" (Gerard David) .. .. 1·60 1·75
619/22 .. .. .. .. *Set of* 4 2·25 2·50
**MS**623 106 × 84 mm. 10 d. "Adoration of the Magi" (Hieronymus Bosch) .. .. .. 3·50 4·00

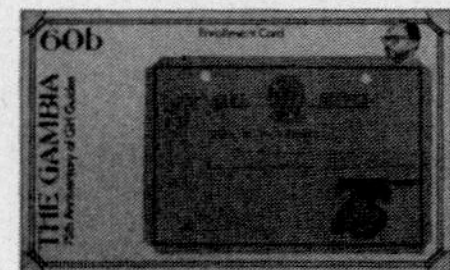

150 Enrolment Card

(Des N. Waldman. Litho Questa)

**1985** (27 Dec). *75th Anniv of Girl Guide Movement. T* **150** *and similar multicoloured designs. P* 14.
624 60 b. Type **150** .. .. .. .. .. 40 30
625 85 b. 2nd Bathurst Company centre .. 50 35
626 1 d. 50, Lady Baden-Powell (*vert*) .. .. 70 80
627 5 d. Miss Rosamond Fowlis (Gambian Guide Association leader) (*vert*) .. 2·00 3·00
624/7 .. .. .. .. .. *Set of* 4 3·25 4·00
**MS**628 97×67 mm. 10 d. Gambian Girl Guides (*vert*) .. .. .. .. .. .. 4·50 5·50

151 Girl and Village Scene

152 Two Players competing for Ball

(Des B. Bundock. Litho Questa)

**1985** (31 Dec). *International Youth Year. T* **151** *and similar horiz designs. Multicoloured. P* 14.
629 60 b. Type **151** .. .. .. .. 25 30
630 85 b. Youth and wrestling bout .. .. 30 35
631 1 d. 10, Girl and Griot storyteller .. .. 40 65
632 1 d. 50, Youth and crocodile pool .. .. 50 80
629/32 .. .. .. .. *Set of* 4 1·25 1·90
**MS**633 106×76 mm. 5 d. Herdsman with cattle .. 2·00 3·00

(Des W. Hanson. Litho Questa)

**1986** (18 Apr). *Appearance of Halley's Comet (1st issue). Horiz designs as T* **123** *of Anguilla. Multicoloured. P* 14.
634 10 b. Maria Mitchell (astronomer) and Kitt Peak National Observatory, Arizona .. 20 15
635 20 b. Neil Armstrong, first man on Moon, 1969 .. .. .. .. .. .. 30 20
636 75 b. "Skylab 4" and Comet Kohoutek, 1973 60 50
637 1 d. N.A.S.A.'s infra-red astronomical satellite and Halley's Comet .. .. 70 60
638 2 d. Comet of 1577 from Turkish painting .. 1·10 1·10
639 10 d. N.A.S.A.'s International Cometary Explorer .. .. .. .. .. 3·50 4·25
634/9 .. .. .. .. .. *Set of* 6 5·75 6·00
**MS**640 102×70 mm. 10 d. Halley's Comet .. 4·50 5·00
See also Nos. 679/84.

(Des and litho Questa)

**1986** (21 Apr). *60th Birthday of Queen Elizabeth II. Vert designs as T* **125** *of Anguilla. P* 14.
641 1 d. black and yellow .. .. .. .. 25 30
642 2 d. 50, multicoloured .. .. .. .. 65 80
643 10 d. multicoloured .. .. .. .. 2·50 3·25
641/3 .. .. .. .. .. *Set of* 3 3·00 4·00
**MS**644 120×85 mm. 10 d. black and grey-brown 2·50 3·00
Designs:—No. 641, Duke of York and family, Royal Tournament, 1936; 642, Queen attending christening, 1983; 643, In West Germany, 1978; **MS**644, Duchess of York with her daughters, Balmoral, 1935.

(Des J. Birdsong. Litho Questa)

**1986** (2 May). *World Cup Football Championship, Mexico. T* **152** *and similar vert designs. Multicoloured. P* 14.
645 75 b. Type **152** .. .. .. .. 50 50
646 1 d. Player kicking ball .. .. .. 70 70
647 2 d. 50, Player kicking ball (*different*) .. 1·50 1·50
648 10 d. Player heading ball .. .. .. 3·75 4·25
645/8 .. .. .. .. .. *Set of* 4 5·75 6·25
**MS**649 100×70 mm. 10 d. Goalkeeper saving goal .. .. .. .. .. .. 5·50 5·50

153 Mercedes "500" (1986)

(Des P. Rhymer. Litho Format)

**1986** (31 May). *"Ameripex" International Stamp Exhibition, Chicago. Centenary of First Benz Motor Car* (1985). *T* **153** *and similar horiz designs. Multicoloured. P* 15.
650 25 b. Type **153** .. .. .. .. 15 15
651 75 b. Cord "810" (1935) .. .. .. .. 40 40
652 1 d. Borgward "Isabella Coupe" (1957) .. 60 60
653 1 d. 25, Lamborghini "Countach" (1985/6) 70 70
654 2 d. Ford "Thunderbird" (1955) .. .. 1·25 1·25
655 2 d. 25, Citroen "DS19" (1956) .. .. 1·40 1·40
656 5 d. Bugatti "Atlante" (1936) .. .. 2·50 2·50
657 10 d. Horch "853" (1936) .. .. .. 4·50 4·50
650/7 .. .. .. .. .. *Set of* 8 10·50 10·50
**MS**658 Two sheets, each 100×70 mm. (a) 12 d. Benz "8/20" (1913). (b) 12 d. Steiger "10/50" (1924) .. .. .. *Set of* 2 *sheets* 9·50 12·00
The 25 b. value is inscribed "MECEDES" and the 10 d. "LARL BENZ".

(Des J. Iskowitz. Litho Questa)

**1986** (10 June). *Centenary of Statue of Liberty (1st issue). Multicoloured designs as T* **211** *of Dominica showing the Statue of Liberty and immigrants to the U.S.A. P* 14.
659 20 b. John Jacob Astor (financier) .. .. 10 10
660 1 d. Jacob Riis (journalist) .. .. .. 40 50
661 1 d. 25, Igor Sikorsky (aeronautics engineer) 50 65
662 5 d. Charles Boyer (actor) .. .. .. 2·00 2·50
659/62 .. .. .. .. *Set of* 4 2·75 3·25
**MS**663 114×80 mm. 10 d. Statue of Liberty (*vert*) .. .. .. .. .. .. 4·00 4·50
See also Nos. 705/9.

(Litho Questa)

**1986** (1 July). *Royal Wedding. Vert designs as T* **213** *of Antigua. Multicoloured. P* 14.
664 1 d. Prince Andrew and Miss Sarah Ferguson .. .. .. .. .. .. 40 45
665 2 d. 50, Prince Andrew .. .. .. 1·00 1·40
666 4 d. Prince Andrew as helicopter pilot .. 1·60 2·00
664/6 .. .. .. .. .. *Set of* 3 2·75 3·50
**MS**667 88×88 mm. 7 d. Prince Andrew and Miss Sarah Ferguson (*different*) .. .. 4·00 3·50

**1986** (16 Sept). *World Cup Football Championship Winners, Mexico. Nos. 645/9 optd with T* **216** *of Antigua in gold.*
668 75 b. Type **152** .. .. .. .. 30 40
669 1 d. Player kicking ball .. .. .. 40 55
670 2 d. 50, Player kicking ball (*different*) .. 1·00 1·25
671 10 d. Player heading ball .. .. .. 4·25 4·75
668/71 .. .. .. .. *Set of* 4 5·25 6·25
**MS**672 100×70 mm. 10 d. Goalkeeper saving goal .. .. .. .. .. .. 4·25 4·25

154 Minnie Mouse (Great Britain)

(Des Walt Disney Co. Litho Format)

**1986** (4 Nov). *Christmas. T* **154** *and similar vert designs showing Walt Disney cartoon characters posting letters in various countries. Multicoloured. P* 11.
673 1 d. Type **154** .. .. .. .. 75 50
674 1 d. 25, Huey (U.S.A.) .. .. .. 80 60
675 2 d. Huey, Dewey and Louie (France) .. 1·25 85
676 2 d. 35, Kanga and Roo (Australia) .. 1·40 90
677 5 d. Goofy (Germany) .. .. .. 2·25 2·00
673/7 .. .. .. .. .. *Set of* 5 5·75 4·25
**MS**678 127×101 mm. 10 d. Goofy (Sweden). P 13½×14 .. .. .. .. .. 3·50 3·50
Nos. 673/8 also show the emblem of "Stockholmia '86" International Stamp Exhibition.

**1986** (21 Dec). *Appearance of Halley's Comet (2nd issue). Nos. 634/40 optd with T* **218** *of Antigua in silver.*
679 10 b. Maria Mitchell (astronomer) and Kitt Peak National Observatory, Arizona .. 20 10
680 20 b. Neil Armstrong, first man on Moon, 1969 .. .. .. .. .. .. 30 10
681 75 b. "Skylab 4" and Comet Kohoutek, 1973 50 20
682 1 d. N.A.S.A.'s infra-red astronomical satellite and Halley's Comet .. .. 55 25
683 2 d. Comet of 1577 from Turkish painting 90 50
684 10 d. N.A.S.A.'s International Cometary Explorer .. .. .. .. .. 3·00 2·50
679/84 .. .. .. .. *Set of* 6 5·00 3·25
**MS**685 102×70 mm. 10 d. Halley's Comet .. 3·00 4·00

155 Bugarab and Tabala

156 "Snowing"

(Des B. Bundock. Litho Format)

**1987** (21 Jan). *Manding Musical Instruments. T* **155** *and similar multicoloured designs. P* 15.
686 75 b. Type **155** .. .. .. .. 15 20
687 1 d. Balaphong and fiddle .. .. .. 15 25
688 1 d. 25, Bolongbato and konting (*vert*) .. 20 30
689 10 d. Antique and modern koras (*vert*) .. 1·60 2·00
686/9 .. .. .. .. .. *Set of* 4 1·90 2·50
**MS**690 100×70 mm. 12 d. Sabarr .. .. 1·90 2·25

(Litho Questa)

**1987** (6 Feb). *Birth Centenary of Marc Chagall (artist). T* **156** *and similar multicoloured designs. P* 13½×14.
691 75 b. Type **156** .. .. .. .. 15 15
692 85 b. "The Boat" .. .. .. .. 20 20
693 1 d. "Maternity" .. .. .. .. 20 20
694 1 d. 25, "The Flute Player" .. .. .. 25 25
695 2 d. 35, "Lovers and the Beast" .. .. 45 45
696 4 d. "Fishers at Saint Jean" .. .. 70 70
697 5 d. "Entering the Ring" .. .. .. 85 85
698 10 d. "Three Acrobats" .. .. .. 1·75 1·75
691/8 .. .. .. .. .. *Set of* 8 4·00 4·00
**MS**699 Two sheets. (a) 110×68 mm. 12 d. "The Cattle Driver" (104×61 *mm*). (b) 109×95 mm. 12 d. "The Sabbath" (104×89 *mm*). Imperf. *Set of* 2 *sheets* 4·50 5·00

157 *America*, 1851

158 Arm of Statue of Liberty

(Des S. Heinmann. Litho Questa)

**1987** (3 Apr). *America's Cup Yachting Championship. T* **157** *and similar horiz designs. Multicoloured. P* 14.
700 20 b. Type **157** .. .. .. .. 10 10
701 1 d. *Courageous*, 1974 .. .. .. 25 25
702 2 d. 50, *Volunteer*, 1887 .. .. .. 55 55
703 10 d. *Intrepid*, 1967 .. .. .. 1·90 1·90
700/3 .. .. .. .. .. *Set of* 4 2·50 2·50
**MS**704 114×89 mm. 12 d. *Australia II*, 1983 .. 2·25 2·40

(Des P. Kaplan. Litho Questa)

**1987** (9 Apr). *Centenary of Statue of Liberty* (1986) (*2nd issue*). *T* **158** *and similar multicoloured designs. P* 14.
705 1 b. Type **158** .. .. .. .. 10 10
706 2 b. Launch passing Statue (*horiz*) .. 10 10
707 3 b. Schooner passing Statue (*horiz*) .. 10 10
708 5 b. Aircraft carrier and *Queen Elizabeth 2* (*horiz*) .. .. .. .. .. 10 10
709 50 b. Checking Statue for damage .. .. 10 10
710 75 b. Cleaning in progress .. .. .. 15 15
711 1 d. Working on Statue .. .. .. 15 20
712 1 d. 25, Statue and fireworks .. .. 20 25
713 10 d. Statue illuminated .. .. .. 1·60 1·75
714 12 d. Statue and fireworks (*different*) .. 1·90 2·00
705/14 .. .. .. .. *Set of* 10 3·75 4·00

159 *Lantana camara*

160 Front of Mail Bus

(Des Dot Barlowe. Litho Questa)

**1987** (25 May). *Flowers of Abuko Nature Reserve. T* **159** *and similar vert designs. Multicoloured. P* 14.
715 75 b. Type **159** .. .. .. .. 15 15
716 1 d. *Clerodendrum thomsoniae* .. .. 15 20
717 1 d. 50, *Haemanthus multiflorus* .. .. 25 30
718 1 d. 70, *Gloriosa simplex* .. .. .. 25 30
719 1 d. 75, *Combretum microphyllum* .. .. 30 35
720 2 d. 25, *Eulophia quineensis* .. .. 35 40
721 5 d. *Erythrina senegalensis* .. .. .. 80 85
722 15 d. *Dichrostachys glomerata* .. .. 2·40 2·50
715/22 .. .. .. .. *Set of* 8 4·25 4·50
**MS**723 Two sheets, each 100×70 mm. (a) 15 d. *Costus spectabilis*. (b) 15 d. *Strophanthus preussii* *Set of* 2 *sheets* 4·75 5·50

(Des BG Studio. Litho Questa)

**1987** (15 June). *"Capex '87" International Stamp Exhibition, Toronto and 10th Anniv of Gambia Public Transport Corporation. Mail Buses. T* **160** *and similar multicoloured designs. P* 14.
724 20 b. Type **160** .. .. .. .. 10 10
725 75 b. Bus in Banjul (*horiz*) .. .. .. 15 20
726 1 d. Passengers queuing for bus (*horiz*) .. 15 20
727 10 d. Two buses on rural road .. .. 1·60 2·50
724/7 .. .. .. .. .. *Set of* 4 1·75 2·75
**MS**728 77×70 mm. 12 d. Parked bus fleet (*horiz*) 2·25 3·00

161 Basketball

162 "A Partridge in a Pear Tree"

(Litho Questa)

**1987** (3 July). *Olympic Games, Seoul* (1988) (*1st issue*). *T* **161** *and similar vert designs. Multicoloured. P* 14.

729 50 b. Type **161** .. .. .. .. 25 20
730 1 d. Volleyball .. .. .. .. 40 35
731 3 d. Hockey (*horiz*) .. .. .. .. 95 85
732 10 d. Handball (*horiz*) .. .. .. 2·25 2·25
724/32 .. .. .. .. *Set of* 4 3·50 3·25
**MS**733 101×85 mm. 15 d. Football (*horiz*) .. 2·40 2·50
See also Nos. 779/83.

(Des Dot Barlowe. Litho Questa)

**1987** (2 Nov). *Christmas. T* **162** *and similar multicoloured designs showing a Victorian couple in scenes from carol "The Twelve Days of Christmas". P* 14.

734 20 b. Type **162** .. .. .. .. 10 10
a. Sheetlet. Nos. 734/45 .. .. .. 5·25
735 40 b. "Two turtle doves" .. .. .. 10 10
736 60 b. "Three French hens" .. .. .. 10 10
737 75 b. "Four calling birds" .. .. .. 15 15
738 1 d. "Five golden rings" .. .. .. 15 20
739 1 d. 25, "Six geese a-laying" .. .. .. 20 25
740 1 d. 50, "Seven swans a-swimming" .. .. 25 30
741 2 d. "Eight maids a-milking" .. .. .. 30 35
742 3 d. "Nine ladies dancing" .. .. .. 50 55
743 5 d. "Ten lords a-leaping" .. .. .. 80 85
744 10 d. "Eleven pipers piping" .. .. .. 1·60 1·75
745 12 d. "Twelve drummers drumming" .. .. 1·90 2·00
734/45 .. .. .. .. *Set of* 12 5·25 5·75
**MS**746 100×70 mm. 15 d. Exchanging presents (*horiz*) .. .. .. .. .. 2·40 3·00
Nos. 734/45 were printed together, *se-tenant*, in sheetlets of twelve.

163 Campfire Singsong

(Litho Questa)

**1987** (9 Nov). *World Scout Jamboree, Australia. T* **163** *and similar horiz designs. Multicoloured. P* 14.

747 75 b. Type **163** .. .. .. .. 25 15
748 1 d. Scouts examining African Katydid .. 30 25
749 1 d. 25, Scouts watching Red-tailed Tropic Bird .. .. .. .. .. 45 30
750 2 d. Scouts helping bus passenger .. .. 2·50 3·00
747/50 .. .. .. .. *Set of* 4 3·25 3·25
**MS**751 72×98 mm. 15 d. Scouts on field trip .. 3·00 3·50

(Des Walt Disney Company. Litho Questa)

**1987** (9 Dec). *60th Anniv of Mickey Mouse* (*Walt Disney cartoon character*). *Multicoloured designs as T* **220** *of Dominica, but horiz. P* 14×13½.

752 60 b. Morty and Ferdie examining Trevithick's locomotive, 1804 .. .. .. 10 10
753 75 b. Clarabelle Cow in "Empire State Express", 1893 .. .. .. .. 15 15
754 1 d. Donald Duck inspecting Stephenson's *Rocket*, 1829 .. .. .. .. 15 20
755 1 d. 25, Piglet and Winnie the Pooh with Santa Fe Railway locomotive, 1920 .. 20 25
756 2 d. Donald and Daisy Duck with Class "GG-1", Pennsylvania Railway, 1933.. 30 35
757 5 d. Mickey Mouse in *Stourbridge Lion*, 1829 80 85
758 10 d. Goofy in *Best Friend of Charleston*, 1830 1·60 1·75
759 12 d. Brer Bear and Brer Rabbit with Union Pacific No. M10001, 1934 .. .. 1·90 2·00
752/9 .. .. .. .. *Set of* 8 5·50 6·00
**MS**760 Two sheets, each 127×101 mm. (a) 15 d. Chip n'Dale in *The General*, 1855. (b) 15 d. Donald Duck and Mickey Mouse in modern French "TGV" train .. .. .. *Set of* 2 *sheets* 4·75 6·00

164 Common Duiker and Acacia

165 Wedding Portrait, 1947

(Des Mary Walters. Litho Format)

**1988** (9 Feb). *Flora and Fauna. T* **164** *and similar multi-coloured designs. P* 15.

761 50 b. Type **164** .. .. .. .. 15 10
762 75 b. Red-billed Hornbill and casuarina (*vert*) .. .. .. .. .. 20 15
763 90 b. West African Dwarf Crocodile and rice 20 20
764 1 d. Leopard and papyrus (*vert*) .. .. 20 20
765 1 d. 25, Crested Crane and millet .. .. 30 25
766 2 d. Waterbuck and baobab tree (*vert*) .. 35 35
767 3 d. Oribi and Senegal palm .. .. 50 55
768 5 d. Hippopotamus and papaya (*vert*) .. 80 85
761/8 .. .. .. .. *Set of* 8 2·40 2·40
**MS**769 98×69 mm. (a) 12 d. Red-throated Bee-eater and acacia (*vert*). (b) 12 d. Great White Pelican .. .. .. .. *Set of* 2 *sheets* 3·75 4·50
No. **MS**769 exists imperforate from stock dispersed by the liquidator of Format International Security Printers Ltd.

(Des and litho Questa)

**1988** (15 Mar). *Royal Ruby Wedding. T* **165** *and similar vert designs. P* 14.

770 75 b. deep brown, black and brown-orange 25 15
771 1 d. deep brown, black and bright new blue 30 20
772 3 d. multicoloured .. .. .. .. 70 80
773 10 d. multicoloured .. .. .. .. 2·00 2·50
770/3 .. .. .. .. *Set of* 4 3·00 3·25
**MS**774 100×75 mm. 15 d. multicoloured .. 2·50 3·25
Designs:— 1 d. Engagement photograph; 3 d. Wedding portrait, 1947 (*different*); 10 d. Queen Elizabeth II and Prince Philip (photo by Karsh), 1986; 15 d. Wedding portrait with page, 1947.

**1988** (19 Apr). *Stamp Exhibitions. Nos.* 689, 703, 722 *and* 726 *optd as T* **241** *of Antigua with various emblems.*

775 1 d. Passengers queuing for bus (optd "Independence 40", Israel) .. .. 15 20
776 10 d. Antique and modern koras (optd "FINLANDIA 88", Helsinki) .. .. .. 1·60 1·75
777 10 d. *Intrepid* (yacht), 1967 (optd "Praga '88", Prague) .. .. .. .. 1·60 1·75
778 15 d. *Dichrostachys glomerata* (optd "OLYMPHILEX '88", Seoul) .. .. 2·40 2·50
775/8 .. .. .. .. *Set of* 4 5·25 5·50

(Des A. DiLorenzo. Litho Questa)

**1988** (3 May). *Olympic Games, Seoul* (*2nd issue*). *Multicoloured designs as T* **161**. *P* 14.

779 1 d. Archery .. .. .. .. 15 20
780 1 d. 25, Boxing .. .. .. .. 20 25
781 5 d. Gymnastics .. .. .. .. 80 85
782 10 d. Start of 100 metre race (*horiz*) .. 1·60 1·75
779/82 .. .. .. .. *Set of* 4 2·50 2·75
**MS**783 74×102 mm. 15 d. Medal winners on rostrum .. .. .. .. .. 2·40 2·75

166 Red Cross Flag (125th anniv)

(Des W. Wright. Litho Questa)

**1988** (15 May). *Anniversaries and Events. T* **166** *and similar multicoloured designs. P* 14.

784 50 b. Type **166** .. .. .. .. 25 25
785 75 b. "Friendship" 7 spacecraft (25th anniv of first American manned Earth orbit) 30 30
786 1 d. British Airways "Concorde" (10th anniv of "Concorde" London–New York service) .. .. .. .. .. 50 50
787 1 d. 25, *Spirit of St. Louis* (60th anniv of first solo transatlantic flight) .. .. 50 50
788 2 d. "X-15" (20th anniv of fastest aircraft flight) .. .. .. .. .. 60 60
789 3 d. Bell "X-1" rocket plane (40th anniv of first supersonic flight) .. .. .. 75 75
790 10 d. English and Spanish galleons (400th anniv of Spanish Armada) .. .. 2·25 2·25
791 12 d. *Titanic* (75th anniv of sinking) .. 2·75 2·75
784/91 .. .. .. .. *Set of* 8 7·00 7·00
**MS**792 Two sheets. (a) 113×85 mm. 15 d. Kaiser Wilhelm Memorial Church, Berlin (*vert*) (750th anniv of Berlin). (b) 121×90 mm. 15 d. Kangaroo (Bicentenary of Australian Settlement) *Set of* 2 *sheets* 4·75 6·00

(Litho Questa)

**1988** (7 July). *500th Birth Anniv of Titian* (*artist*). *Vert designs as T* **238** *of Antigua. Multicoloured. P* 13½×14.

793 25 b. "Emperor Charles V" .. .. .. 10 10
794 50 b. "St. Margaret and the Dragon" .. .. 10 10
795 60 b. "Ranuccio Farnese" .. .. .. 10 15
796 75 b. "Tarquin and Lucretia" .. .. .. 15 15
797 1 d. "The Knight of Malta" .. .. .. 15 20
798 5 d. "Spain succouring Faith" .. .. .. 80 85
799 10 d. "Doge Francesco Venier" .. .. 1·60 1·75
800 12 d. "Doge Grimani before the Faith" (detail) .. .. .. .. .. 1·90 2·00
793/800 .. .. .. .. *Set of* 8 4·25 4·75
**MS**801 110×95 mm. (a) 15 d. "Jealous Husband" (detail). (b) 15 d. "Venus blindfolding Cupid" *Set of* 2 *sheets* 4·75 5·50

## NEW INFORMATION

The editor is always interested to correspond with people who have new information that will improve or correct the Catalogue.

167 John Kennedy sailing

(Des G. Hinlecky. Litho Questa)

**1988** (1 Sept). *25th Death Anniv of President John F. Kennedy. T* **167** *and similar multicoloured designs. P* 14.

802 75 b. Type **167** .. .. .. .. 15 15
803 1 d. Kennedy signing Peace Corps legislation, 1962 .. .. .. .. 15 20
804 1 d. 25, Speaking at U.N., New York (*vert*) 20 25
805 12 d. Grave and eternal flame, Arlington National Cemetery (*vert*) .. .. 1·90 2·00
802/5 .. .. .. .. *Set of* 4 2·10 2·40
**MS**806 99×72 mm. 15 d. John F. Kennedy (*vert*) 2·40 2·75

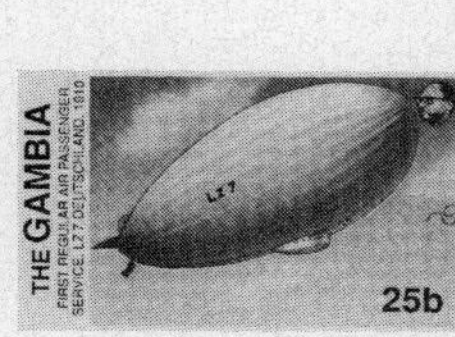


168 "LZ 7" *Deutschland* (first regular air passenger service), 1910

169 Emmett Kelley

(Des A. Fagbohun. Litho Questa)

**1988** (1 Nov). *Milestones of Transportation. T* **168** *and similar multicoloured designs. P* 14.

807 25 b. Type **168** .. .. .. .. 10 10
808 50 b. Stephenson's *Locomotion* (first permanent public railway), 1825 .. .. 10 10
809 75 b. G.M. *Sun Racer* (first world solar challenge), 1987 .. .. .. .. 15 15
810 1 d. Sprague's *Premiere* (first operational electric tramway), 1888 .. .. 15 20
811 1 d. 25, *Gold Rush* Bicycle (holder of man-powered land speed record), 1986 .. 20 25
812 2 d. 50 Robert Goddard and rocket launcher (first liquid fuel rocket), 1925 40 45
813 10 d. *Orukter Amphibolos* (first steam traction engine), 1805 .. .. 1·60 1·75
814 12 d. *Sovereign of the Seas* (largest cruise liner), 1988 .. .. .. .. 1·90 2·00
807/14 .. .. .. .. *Set of* 8 4·00 4·50
**MS**815 Two sheets, each 71 × 92 mm. (a) 15 d. U.S.S. *Nautilus* (first nuclear-powered submarine), 1954 (*vert*). (b) 15 d. Fulton's *Nautilus* (first fish-shaped submarine), 1800's (*vert*) .. .. .. .. *Set of* 2 *sheets* 4·75 5·50

(Des J. Iskowitz. Litho Questa)

**1988** (9 Nov). *Entertainers. T* **169** *and similar multicoloured designs. P* 14.

816 20 b. Type **169** .. .. .. .. 10 10
817 1 d. Gambia National Ensemble .. .. 25 25
818 1 d. 25, Jackie Gleason .. .. .. 30 30
819 1 d. 50, Laurel and Hardy .. .. .. 40 40
820 2 d. 50, Yul Brynner .. .. .. 65 65
821 3 d. Cary Grant .. .. .. .. 80 80
822 10 d. Danny Kaye .. .. .. .. 2·25 2·50
823 20 d. Charlie Chaplin .. .. .. 4·00 4·50
816/23 .. .. .. .. *Set of* 8 8·00 8·50
**MS**824 Two sheets. (a) 110 × 77 mm. 15 d. Marx Brothers (*horiz*). (b) 70 × 99 mm. 15 d. Fred Astaire and Rita Hayworth (*horiz*) *Set of* 2 *sheets* 8·50 8·50

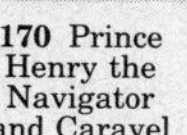


170 Prince Henry the Navigator and Caravel

171 Projected Space Plane and Ernst Mach (physicist)

(Des A. Fagbohun. Litho Questa)

**1988** (1 Dec). *Exploration of West Africa. T* **170** *and similar multicoloured designs. P* 14.

825 50 b. Type **170** .. .. .. .. 30 30
826 75 b. Jesse Ramsden's sextant, 1785 .. .. 35 35
827 1 d. 15th-century hourglass .. .. .. 45 45
828 1 d. 25, Prince Henry the Navigator and Vasco da Gama .. .. .. .. 60 60
829 2 d. 50, Vasco da Gama and ship .. .. 90 90
830 5 d. Mungo Park and map of Gambia River (*horiz*) .. .. .. .. .. 1·75 1·75

831 10 d. Map of West Africa, 1563 (*horiz*) .. 2·50 2·50
832 12 d. Portuguese caravel (*horiz*) .. 3·00 3·00
825/32 .. .. .. .. .. *Set of 8* 9·00 9·00
**MS**833 Two sheets, each 65 × 100 mm. (a) 15 d. Ship from Columbus's fleet off Gambia. (b) 15 d. 15th-century ship moored off Gambia *Set of 2 sheets* 4·75 6·00

(Des G. Welker. Litho Questa)

**1988** (12 Dec). *350th Anniv of Publication of Galileo's "Discourses". Space Achievements. T* **171** *and similar multicoloured designs. P* 14.
834 50 b. Type **171** .. .. .. .. .. 15 10
835 75 b. OAO III astronomical satellite and Niels Bohr (physicist) .. .. 20 15
836 1 d. Space shuttle, projected space station and Robert Goddard (physicist) (*horiz*) 25 20
837 1 d. 25, Jupiter probe, 1979, and Edward Barnard (astronomer) (*horiz*) .. 30 25
838 2 d. Hubble Space Telescope and George Hale (astronomer) .. .. .. 45 35
839 3 d. Earth-to-Moon laser measurement and Albert Michaelson (physicist) (*horiz*) .. 65 55
840 10 d. HEAO-2 *Einstein* orbital satellite and Albert Einstein (physicist) .. .. 1·75 2·00
841 20 d. *Voyager* (first non-stop round-the-world flight), 1987, and Wright Brothers (aviation pioneers) (*horiz*) .. 3·50 3·75
834/41 .. .. .. .. .. *Set of 8* 6·50 6·50
**MS**842 Two sheets. (a) 99 × 75 mm. 15 d. Great Red Spot on Jupiter (*horiz*). (b) 88 × 71 mm. 15 d. Neil Armstrong (first man on Moon), 1969 *Set of 2 sheets* 5·50 6·50

**172** Passing Out Parade

(Des J. Genzo. Litho Questa)

**1989** (10 Feb). *Army Day. T* **172** *and similar multicoloured designs. P* 14.
843 75 b. Type **172** .. .. .. .. .. 10 10
844 1 d. Standards of The Gambia Regiment .. 10 15
845 1 d. 25, Side drummer in ceremonial uniform (*vert*) .. .. .. 15 20
846 10 d. Marksman with Atlantic Shooting Cup (*vert*) .. .. .. .. .. 1·25 1·40
847 15 d. Soldiers on assault course (*vert*) .. 1·75 1·90
848 20 d. Gunner with 105 mm field gun .. 2·40 2·50
843/8 .. .. .. .. .. *Set of 6* 5·25 5·75

**173** Mickey Mouse, 1928

**174** "Le Coup de Lance" (detail)

(Des Walt Disney Company. Litho B.D.T.)

**1989** (6 Apr). *60th Birthday of Mickey Mouse. T* **173** *and similar multicoloured designs. P* 13.
849 2 d. Type **173** .. .. .. .. 25 30
a. Sheetlet of 9. Nos. 849/57 .. .. 2·00
850 2 d. Mickey Mouse, 1931 .. .. .. 25 30
851 2 d. Mickey Mouse, 1936 .. .. .. 25 30
852 2 d. Mickey Mouse, 1955 .. .. .. 25 30
853 2 d. Mickey Mouse, 1947 .. .. .. 25 30
854 2 d. Mickey Mouse as magician, 1940 .. 25 30
855 2 d. Mickey Mouse with palette, 1960 .. 25 30
856 2 d. Mickey Mouse as Uncle Sam, 1976 .. 25 30
857 2 d. Mickey Mouse, 1988 .. .. .. 25 30
849/57 .. .. .. .. .. *Set of 9* 2·00 2·40
**MS**858 138×109 mm. 15 d. Mickey Mouse at 60th birthday party (132×103 *mm*). Imperf .. 1·75 1·90
Nos. 849/57 were printed together, *se-tenant* as a composite design, in sheetlets of nine.

(Litho Questa)

**1989** (14 Apr). *Easter. Religious Paintings by Rubens. T* **174** *and similar vert designs showing details. Multicoloured. P* 13½×14.
859 50 b. Type **174** .. .. .. .. 10 10
860 75 b. "Flagellation of Christ" .. .. 10 10
861 1 d. "Lamentation for Christ" .. .. 10 15
862 1 d. 25, "Descent from the Cross" .. 15 20
863 2 d. "Holy Trinity" .. .. .. .. 25 30
864 5 d. "Doubting Thomas" .. .. .. 60 65
865 10 d. "Lamentation over Christ" .. .. 1·25 1·40
866 12 d. "Lamentation with Virgin and St. John" .. .. .. .. .. 1·40 1·50
859/66 .. .. .. .. .. *Set of 8* 3·50 4·00
**MS**867 Two sheets each 96×110 mm. (a) 15 d. "The Last Supper". (b) 15 d. "Raising of the Cross" .. .. .. .. *Set of 2 sheets* 3·50 3·75

**175** African Emerald Cuckoo

**176** *Druryia antimachus*

(Des W. Wright. Litho Questa)

**1989** (24 Apr). *West African Birds. T* **175** *and similar horiz designs. Multicoloured. P* 14.
868 20 b. Type **175** .. .. .. .. 10 10
869 60 b. Grey-headed Bush Shrike .. .. 10 10
870 75 b. Crowned Crane .. .. .. .. 10 10
871 1 d. Secretary Bird .. .. .. .. 10 15
872 2 d. Red-billed Hornbill .. .. .. 25 30
873 5 d. Superb Sunbird .. .. .. .. 60 65
874 10 d. Little Owl .. .. .. .. 1·25 1·40
875 12 d. Bateleur .. .. .. .. .. 1·40 1·50
868/75 .. .. .. .. .. *Set of 8* 3·50 3·75
**MS**876 Two sheets, each 115×86 mm. (a) 15 d. Ostrich. (b) 15 d. Red-billed Fire Finch *Set of 2 sheets* 3·50 3·75

(Des Mary Walters. Litho Questa)

**1989** (15 May). *Butterflies of Gambia. T* **176** *and similar vert designs. Multicoloured. P* 14.
877 50 b. Type **176** .. .. .. .. 10 10
878 75 b. *Euphaedra neophron* .. .. .. 10 10
879 1 d. *Aterica rabena* .. .. .. .. 10 15
880 1 d. 25, *Salamis parhassus* .. .. .. 15 20
881 5 d. *Precis rhadama* .. .. .. .. 60 65
882 10 d. *Papilio demodocus* .. .. .. 1·25 1·40
883 12 d. *Charaxes etesipe* .. .. .. 1·40 1·50
884 15 d. *Danaus formosa* .. .. .. 1·75 1·90
877/84 .. .. .. .. .. *Set of 8* 4·75 5·25
**MS**885 Two sheets, each 99×68 mm. (a) 15 d. *Euptera pluto*. (b) 15 d. *Euphaedra ceres* *Set of 2 sheets* 3·50 3·75

**177** Nigerian Steam Locomotive, 1959

**PHILEXFRANCE '89**
(**178**)

(Des A. Fagbohun. Litho Walsall)

**1989** (15 June). *African Steam Locomotives. T* **177** *and similar multicoloured designs. P* 14.
886 50 b. Type **177** .. .. .. .. 10 10
887 75 b. Garratt Class "14A" .. .. .. 10 10
888 1 d. British-built locomotive, Sudan .. 10 15
889 1 d. 25, American-built locomotive, 1925 15 20
890 5 d. Scottish-built locomotive, 1955 .. 60 65
891 7 d. Scottish-built locomotive, 1926 .. 85 90
892 10 d. East African Railways British-built tank locomotive .. .. .. 1·25 1·40
893 12 d. American-built locomotive, Ghana .. 1·40 1·50
886/93 .. .. .. .. .. *Set of 8* 4·00 4·50
**MS**894 82×58 mm. (a) 15 d. British-built Class "25" from front (*vert*). (b) 15 d. British-built Class "25" from side (*vert*) .. .. *Set of 2 sheets* 3·50 3·75

**1989** (23 June). *"Philexfrance '89" International Stamp Exhibition, Paris. Nos. 686/90 optd with T* **178**.
895 75 b. Type **155** .. .. .. .. 10 10
896 1 d. Balaphong and fiddle .. .. .. 10 15
897 1 d. 25, Bolongbato and konting (*vert*) .. 15 20
898 10 d. Antique and modern koras (*vert*) .. 1·25 1·40
895/8 .. .. .. .. .. *Set of 4* 1·40 1·60
**MS**899 100×70 mm. 12 d. Sabarr .. .. 1·40 1·50

(Litho Questa)

**1989** (7 July). *Japanese Art. Multicoloured designs as T* **250** *of Antigua. P* 13½×14.
900 50 b. "Sparrow and Bamboo" (Hiroshige) (*vert*) .. .. .. .. .. 10 10
901 75 b. "Peonies and a Canary" (Hokusai) (*vert*) .. .. .. .. .. 10 10
902 1 d. "Crane and Marsh Grasses" (Hiroshige) (*vert*) .. .. .. 10 15
903 1 d. 25, "Crossbill and Thistle" (Hokusai) (*vert*) .. .. .. .. .. 15 20
904 2 d. "Cuckoo and Azalea" (Hokusai) (*vert*) 25 30
905 5 d. "Parrot on a Pine Branch" (Hiroshige) (*vert*) .. .. .. .. .. 60 65
906 10 d. "Mandarin Ducks in a Stream" (Hiroshige) (*vert*) .. .. .. 1·25 1·40
907 12 d. "Bullfinch and Drooping Cherry" (Hokusai) (*vert*) .. .. .. 1·40 1·50
900/7 .. .. .. .. .. *Set of 8* 3·50 4·00
**MS**908 Two sheets, each 102×77 mm. (a) 15 d. "Tit and Peony" (Hiroshige). (b) 15 d. "Peony and Butterfly" (Shigenobou). P 14×13½ *Set of 2 sheets* 3·50 3·75
Nos. 900/7 were each printed in sheets of 10 containing two vertical strips of 5 stamps separated by printed labels commemorating Emperor Hirohito.

**179** Rialto Bridge, Venice

**180** *Vitex doniana*

(Des L. Fried. Litho B.D.T.)

**1989** (25 Aug). *World Cup Football Championship, Italy* (1990). *T* **179** *and similar horiz designs, each showing landmarks and players. Multicoloured. P* 14.
909 75 b. Type **179** .. .. .. .. 10 10
910 1 d. 25, The Baptistery, Pisa .. .. 15 20
911 7 d. Casino, San Remo .. .. .. 85 90
912 12 d. Colosseum, Rome .. .. .. 1·40 1·50
909/12 .. .. .. .. .. *Set of 4* 2·25 2·40
**MS**913 Two sheets, each 104×78 mm. (a) 15 d. St. Mark's Cathedral, Venice. (b) 15 d. Piazza Colonna, Rome .. .. .. *Set of 2 sheets* 3·50 3·75

(Des Jennifer Toombs. Litho Questa)

**1989** (18 Sept). *Medicinal Plants. T* **180** *and similar vert designs. Multicoloured. P* 14.
914 20 b. Type **180** .. .. .. .. 10 10
915 50 b. *Ricinus communis* .. .. .. 10 10
916 75 b. *Palisota hirsuta* .. .. .. 10 10
917 1 d. *Smilax kraussiana* .. .. .. 10 15
918 1 d. 25, *Aspilia africana* .. .. .. 15 20
919 5 d. *Newbouldia laevis* .. .. .. 60 65
920 8 d. *Monodora tenuifolia* .. .. .. 95 1·00
921 10 d. *Gossypium arboreum* .. .. .. 1·25 1·40
914/21 .. .. .. .. .. *Set of 8* 3·00 3·25
**MS**922 Two sheets, each 87×72 mm. (a) 15 d. *Kigelia africana*. (b) 15 d. *Spathodea campanulata* .. .. .. .. *Set of 2 sheets* 3·50 3·75

**181** Lookdown Fish

(Des Mary Walters. Litho B.D.T.)

**1989** (19 Oct). *Fishes. T* **181** *and similar horiz designs. Multicoloured. P* 14.
923 20 b. Type **181** .. .. .. .. 10 10
924 75 b. Boarfish .. .. .. .. .. 10 10
925 1 d. Grey Triggerfish .. .. .. 10 15
926 1 d. 25, Skipjack Tuna .. .. .. 15 20
927 2 d. Bermuda Chub .. .. .. .. 25 30
928 4 d. Atlantic Manta .. .. .. .. 50 55
929 5 d. Striped Mullet .. .. .. .. 60 65
930 10 d. Ladyfish .. .. .. .. 1·25 1·40
923/30 .. .. .. .. .. *Set of 8* 2·75 3·00
**MS**931 Two sheets, each 104×72 mm. (a) 15 d. Porcupinefish. (b) 15 d. Shortfin Mako Shark *Set of 2 sheets* 3·50 3·75

(Des Walt Disney Co. Litho Questa)

**1989** (29 Nov). *"World Stamp Expo '89" International Stamp Exhibition, Washington* (1*st issue*). *Horiz designs as T* **256** *of Antigua, each showing Walt Disney cartoon characters and American carousel horses. Multicoloured. P* 14×13½.
932 20 b. Little Hiawatha on Daniel Muller Indian Pony .. .. .. .. 10 10
933 50 b. Morty on Herschell-Spillman stander 10 10
934 75 b. Goofy on Gustav Dentzel stander .. 10 10
935 1 d. Mickey Mouse on Daniel Muller armoured stander .. .. .. 10 15
936 1 d. 25, Minnie Mouse on jumper from Smithsonian Collection .. .. 15 20
937 2 d. Webby on Illion "American Beauty" 25 30
938 8 d. Donald Duck on Zalar jumper .. 95 1·00
939 10 d. Mickey Mouse on Parker bucking horse .. .. .. .. .. 1·25 1·40
932/9 .. .. .. .. .. *Set of 8* 2·50 3·00
**MS**940 Two sheets, each 127×102 mm. (a) 12 d. Donald, Mickey and Goofy in carousel car. (b) 12 d. Donald's nephews on Roman chariot horses *Set of 2 sheets* 3·00 3·25

(Des Design Element. Litho Questa)

**1989** (29 Nov). *"World Stamp Expo '89" International Stamp Exhibition, Washington* (2*nd issue*). *Landmarks of Washington. Sheet 78×61 mm containing horiz design as T* **257** *of Antigua. Multicoloured. P* 14.
**MS**941 10 d. White House .. .. .. 1·25 1·40

**183** Mickey and Minnie Mouse in Pierce-Arrow, 1922

(Des Walt Disney Co. Litho Questa)

**1989** (29 Nov). *Christmas. T* **183** *and similar horiz designs showing Walt Disney cartoon characters with cars. Multicoloured. P* 14×13½.
942 20 b. Type **183** 10 10
943 50 b. Goofy in Spyker, 1919 10 10
944 75 b. Donald and Grandma Duck with Packard, 1929 10 10
945 1 d. Mickey Mouse driving Daimler, 1920 10 15
946 1 d. 25, Mickey Mouse in Hispano "Suiza", 1924 15 20
947 2 d. Mickey and Minnie Mouse in Opel "Laubfrosch", 1924 25 30
948 10 d. Donald Duck driving Vauxhall "30/98", 1927 1·25 1·40
949 12 d. Goofy with Peerless, 1923 1·40 1·50
942/9 *Set of* 8 3·00 3·50
**MS**950 Two sheets, each 127×102 mm. (a) 15 d. Mickey and Minnie Mouse picnicking by Stutz "Blackhawk Speedster", 1928. (b) 15 d. Donald Duck, Mickey and Minnie Mouse in Bentley "Supercharged", 1930 *Set of 2 sheets* 3·50 3·75

**184** Charles Nicolle (typhus transmission) and Vaccination

**185** *Bulbophyllum lepidum*

(Des J. Iskowitz. Litho Walsall)

**1989** (12 Dec). *Great Medical Discoveries. T* **184** *and similar horiz designs. Multicoloured. P* 14.
951 20 b. Type **184** 10 10
952 50 b. Paul Ehrlich (immunization pioneer) and medical examination 10 10
953 75 b. Selman Waksman (discoverer of streptomycin) and T.B. clinic 10 10
954 1 d. Edward Jenner (smallpox vaccination), and Jenner conducting experiment, 1796 10 15
955 1 d. 25, Robert Koch (developer of tuberculin test) and Gambian using vaccination gun 15 20
956 5 d. Sir Alexander Fleming (discoverer of penicillin) and doctor giving injection 60 65
957 8 d. Max Theiler (developer of yellow fever vaccine) and child clinic 95 1·00
958 10 d. Louis Pasteur (bacteriologist) and health survey 1·25 1·40
951/8 *Set of* 8 3·00 3·25
**MS**959 Two sheets, each 121×86 mm. (a) 15 d. Hughes Vicking medical helicopter. (b) 15 d. C-9 *Nightingale* medical relief plane *Set of 2 sheets* 3·50 3·75

(Des Mary Walters. Litho Walsall)

**1989** (18 Dec). *Orchids. T* **185** *and similar vert designs. Multicoloured. P* 14.
960 20 b. Type **185** 10 10
961 75 b. *Tridactyle tridactylites* 10 10
962 1 d. *Vanilla imperialis* 10 15
963 1 d. 25, *Oeceoclades maculata* 15 20
964 2 d. *Polystachya affinis* 25 30
965 4 d. *Ancistrochilus rothschildianus* 50 55
966 5 d. *Angraecum distichum* 60 65
967 10 d. *Liparis guineensis* 1·25 1·40
960/7 *Set of* 8 2·75 3·00
**MS**968 Two sheets, each 99×67 mm. (a) 15 d. *Plectrelminthus caudatus*. (b) 15 d. *Eulophia guineensis* *Set of 2 sheets* 3·50 3·75

**186** John Newcombe

**187** Lunar Module *Eagle*

(Des D. Miller. Litho Questa)

**1990** (2 Jan). *Wimbledon Tennis Champions. T* **186** *and similar vert designs. Multicoloured. P* 14½.
969 20 b. Type **186** 10 10
a. Vert pair. Nos. 969/70 10 10
970 20 b. Mrs. G. W. Hillyard 10 10
971 50 b. Roy Emerson 10 10
a. Vert pair. Nos. 971/2 10 10
972 50 b. Dorothy Chambers 10 10
973 75 b. Donald Budge 10 10
a. Vert pair. Nos. 973/4 20 20
974 75 b. Suzanne Lenglen 10 10
975 1 d. Laurence Doherty 10 10
a. Vert pair. Nos. 975/6 20 20
976 1 d. Helen Wills Moody 10 10
977 1 d. 25, Bjorn Borg 15 20
a. Vert pair. Nos. 977/8 30 40
978 1 d. 25, Maureen Connolly 15 20
979 4 d. Jean Borotra 50 55
a. Vert pair. Nos. 979/80 1·00 1·10
980 4 d. Maria Bueno 50 55
981 5 d. Anthony Wilding 60 65
a. Vert pair. Nos. 981/2 1·25 1·25
982 5 d. Louise Brough 60 65
983 7 d. Fred Perry 85 90
a. Vert pair. Nos. 983/4 1·75 1·75
984 7 d. Margaret Court 85 90
985 10 d. Bill Tilden 1·25 1·40
a. Vert pair. Nos. 985/6 2·50 2·75
986 10 d. Billie Jean King 1·25 1·40
987 12 d. Rod Laver 1·40 1·50
a. Vert pair. Nos. 987/8 2·75 3·00
988 12 d. Martina Navratilova 1·40 1·50
969/88 *Set of* 20 9·00 10·00
**MS**989 Two sheets, each 101×76 mm. (a) 15 d. Rod Laver (*different*). (b) 15 d. Martina Navratilova (*different*) *Set of 2 sheets* 3·50 3·75
The two designs for each value were printed together, *se-tenant*, in vertical pairs throughout the sheets of 20.

(Des K. Gromell. Litho B.D.T.)

**1990** (16 Feb). *20th Anniv of First Manned Landing on Moon* (1989). *T* **187** *and similar multicoloured designs. P* 14.
990 20 b. Type **187** 10 10
991 50 b. Lift-off of "Apollo 11" (*vert*) 10 10
992 75 b. Neil Armstrong stepping on to Moon 10 10
993 1 d. Buzz Aldrin and American flag 10 15
994 1 d. 25, "Apollo 11" emblem (*vert*) 15 20
995 1 d. 75, Crew of "Apollo 11" 20 25
996 8 d. Lunar Module *Eagle* on Moon 95 1·00
997 12 d. Recovery of "Apollo 11" after splash-down 1·40 1·50
990/7 *Set of* 8 2·75 3·00
**MS**998 Two sheets, each 110×89 mm. (a) 15 d. Neil Armstrong (*vert*). (b) 15 d. View of Earth from Moon (*vert*) *Set of 2 sheets* 3·50 3·75

**188** Bristol Blenheim Mk I

**189** White-faced Scops Owl

(Des J. Batchelor. Litho B.D.T.)

**1990** (8 May). *R.A.F. Aircraft of Second World War. T* **188** *and similar horiz designs. Multicoloured. P* 14.
999 10 b. Type **188** 10 10
1000 20 b. Fairey Battle 10 10
1001 50 b. Bristol Blenheim Mk IV 10 10
1002 60 b. Vickers-Armstrong Wellington Mk 1C 10 10
1003 75 b. Armstrong-Whitworth Whitley Mk V 10 10
1004 1 d. Handley-Page Hampden Mk 1 10 15
1005 1 d. 25, Supermarine Spitfire Mk 1A and Hawker Hurricane Mk I 15 20
1006 2 d. Avro Manchester 25 30
1007 3 d. Short Stirling Mk I 35 40
1008 5 d. Handley-Page Halifax Mk I 60 65
1009 10 d. Avro Lancaster Mk III 1·25 1·40
1010 12 d. De Havilland Mosquito Mk IV 1·40 1·50
999/1010 *Set of* 12 4·00 4·50
**MS**1011 Two sheets, each 107×77 mm. (a) 15 d. Supermarine Spitfire Mk 1A. (b) 15 d. Avro Lancaster Mk III (*different*) *Set of 2 sheets* 3·50 3·75

(Des Jennifer Toombs. Litho B.D.T.)

**1990** (14 May). *African Birds. T* **189** *and similar horiz designs. Multicoloured. P* 14.
1012 1 d. 25, Type **189** 15 20
a. Sheetlet. Nos. 1012/31 2·75
1013 1 d. 25, Village Weaver 15 20
1014 1 d. 25, Red-throated Bee-eater 15 20
1015 1 d. 25, Brown Harrier Eagle 15 20
1016 1 d. 25, Red Bishop 15 20
1017 1 d. 25, Scarlet-chested Sunbird 15 20
1018 1 d. 25, Red-billed Hornbill 15 20
1019 1 d. 25, Mosque Swallow 15 20
1020 1 d. 25, White-faced Whistling Duck 15 20
1021 1 d. 25, African Fish-eagle 15 20
1022 1 d. 25, Eastern White Pelican 15 20
1023 1 d. 25, Carmine Bee-eater 15 20
1024 1 d. 25, Hadada Ibis 15 20
1025 1 d. 25, Blackhead Plover 15 20
1026 1 d. 25, Yellow-bellied Sunbird 15 20
1027 1 d. 25, African Skimmer 15 20
1028 1 d. 25, Woodland Kingfisher 15 20
1029 1 d. 25, Jacana 15 20
1030 1 d. 25, African Pygmy Goose 15 20
1031 1 d. 25, Hammerkop 15 20
1012/31 *Set of* 20 2·75 3·50
Nos. 1012/31 were printed together, *se-tenant*, in sheetlets of twenty, forming a composite design of birds at a lake.

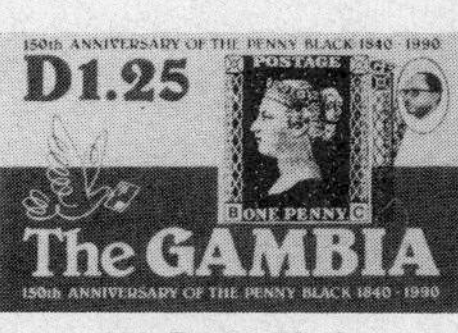

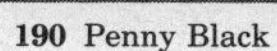

**190** Penny Black

**191** Flag and National Assembly Building

(Des S. Pollard. Litho Questa)

**1990** (4 June). *150th Anniv of the Penny Black. P* 14.
1032 **190** 1 d. 25, black and bright ultramarine 15 20
1033 12 d. black and scarlet 1·40 1·50
**MS**1034 79×73 mm. **190** 15 d. black, silver and dull orange 1·75 1·90
The design of No. **MS**1034 is without the additional stamps behind the Penny Black as shown on Type **190**.

(Des and litho Questa)

**1990** (5 June). *25th Anniv of Independence. T* **191** *and similar vert designs. Multicoloured. P* 14.
1035 1 d. Type **191** 10 15
1036 3 d. Pres. Sir Dawda Jawara 35 40
1037 12 d. Map of Yundum airport and Air Gambia airliner 1·40 1·50
1035/7 *Set of* 3 1·60 1·90
**MS**1038 100×69 mm. 18 d. State arms 2·10 2·25

**192** Baobab Tree

(Des W. Hanson Studio. Litho Questa)

**1990** (14 June). *Gambian Life. T* **192** *and similar multicoloured designs. P* 14.
1039 5 b. Type **192** 10 10
1040 10 b. Woodcarving, Albert Market, Banjul 10 10
1041 20 b. President Jawara planting seedling (*vert*) 10 10
1042 50 b. Sailing canoe and map 10 10
1043 75 b. Batik fabric 10 10
1044 1 d. Hibiscus and Bakau beach 10 15
1045 1 d. 25, Bougainvilla and Tendaba Camp 15 20
1046 2 d. Shrimp fishing and sorting 25 30
1047 5 d. Groundnut oil mill, Denton Bridge 60 65
1048 10 d. Handicraft pot and kora (musical instrument) 1·25 1·40
1049 15 d. *Ansellia africana* (orchid) (*vert*) 1·75 1·90
1050 30 d. *Euriphene gambiae* (butterfly) and ancient stone ring near Georgetown 3·50 3·75
1039/50 *Set of* 12 7·00 7·75

**193** Daisy Duck at 10 Downing Street

**194** Lady Elizabeth Bowes-Lyon in High Chair

(Des Walt Disney Co. Litho Questa)

**1990** (19 June). *"Stamp World London 90" International Stamp Exhibition. T* **193** *and similar multicoloured designs each showing Walt Disney cartoon characters in England. P* 14.
1051 20 b. Type **193** 10 10
1052 50 b. Goofy in Trafalgar Square 10 10
1053 75 b. Mickey Mouse on White Cliffs of Dover (*horiz*) 10 10
1054 1 d. Mickey Mouse at Tower of London 10 15
1055 5 d. Mickey Mouse and Goofy at Hampton Court Palace (*horiz*) 60 65
1056 8 d. Mickey Mouse by Magdalen Tower, Oxford 95 1·00
1057 10 d. Mickey Mouse on Old London Bridge (*horiz*) 1·25 1·40
1058 12 d. Scrooge McDuck and Rosetta Stone, British Museum (*horiz*) 1·40 1·50
1051/8 *Set of* 8 4·00 4·50
**MS**1059 Two sheets, each 125×100 mm. (a) 18 d. Mickey Mouse and Donald Duck at Piccadilly Circus (*horiz*). (b) 18 d. Mickey Mouse steering tug on River Thames (*horiz*) *Set of 2 sheets* 4·25 4·50

(Des Young Phillips Studio. Litho Questa)

**1990** (19 July). *90th Birthday of Queen Elizabeth the Queen Mother. T* **194** *and similar vert portraits*, 1900–09. *P* 14.
1060 6 d. black, dp magenta & greenish yellow 70 75
a. Strip of 3. Nos. 1060/2 1·90
1061 6 d. black, dp magenta & greenish yellow 70 75
1062 6 d. black, dp magenta & greenish yellow 70 75
1060/2 *Set of* 3 1·90 2·00
**MS**1063 90×75 mm. 18 d. multicoloured 2·10 2·25
Designs:—Nos. 1061, **MS**1063, Lady Elizabeth Bowes-Lyon as a young girl; No. 1062, Lady Elizabeth Bowes-Lyon with wild flowers.
Nos. 1060/2 were printed together, horizontally and vertically *se-tenant*, in sheetlets of 9 (3×3).

195 Vialli, Italy

196 Summit Logo

(Des Young Phillips Studio. Litho Questa)

**1990** (24 Sept). *World Cup Football Championship, Italy. T* **195** *and similar vert designs. Multicoloured. P* 14.

| | | | |
|---|---|---|---|
| 1064 | 1 d. Type **195** | 10 | 15 |
| 1065 | 1 d. 25, Cannegia, Argentina | 15 | 20 |
| 1066 | 3 d. Marchena, Costa Rica | 35 | 40 |
| 1067 | 5 d. Shaiba, United Arab Emirates | 60 | 65 |
| 1064/7 | *Set of* 4 | 1·10 | 1·25 |
| **MS**1068 | Two sheets, each 75×92 mm. (a) 18 d. Hagi, Rumania. (b) 18 d. Van Basten, Netherlands *Set of* 2 *sheets* | 4·25 | 4·50 |

(Des B. Grout. Litho Questa)

**1990** (1 Nov). *Olympic Games, Barcelona. Multicoloured designs as T* **268** *of Antigua. P* 14.

| | | | |
|---|---|---|---|
| 1069 | 1 d. Men's 200 metres | 10 | 15 |
| 1070 | 1 d. 25, Women's rhythmic gymnastics | 15 | 20 |
| 1071 | 3 d. Football | 35 | 40 |
| 1072 | 10 d. Men's marathon | 1·25 | 1·40 |
| 1069/72 | *Set of* 4 | 1·60 | 1·90 |
| **MS**1073 | 101×71 mm. 15 d. Parade of national flags (*horiz*) | 1·75 | 1·90 |

(Litho Questa)

**1990** (24 Dec). *Christmas. Paintings by Renaissance Masters. Multicoloured designs as T* **272** *of Antigua, but vert. P* 13½×14.

| | | | |
|---|---|---|---|
| 1074 | 20 b. "The Annunciation, with St. Emidius" (detail) (Crivelli) | 10 | 10 |
| 1075 | 50 b. "The Annunciation" (detail) (Campin) | 10 | 10 |
| 1076 | 75 b. "The Solly Madonna" (detail) (Raphael) | 10 | 15 |
| 1077 | 1 d. 25, "The Tempi Madonna" (Raphael) | 15 | 20 |
| 1078 | 2 d. "Madonna of the Linen Window" (detail) (Raphael) | 25 | 30 |
| 1079 | 7 d. "The Annunciation, with St. Emidius" (different detail) (Crivelli) | 85 | 90 |
| 1080 | 10 d. "The Orleans Madonna" (Raphael) | 1·25 | 1·40 |
| 1081 | 15 d. "Madonna and Child" (detail) (Crivelli) | 1·75 | 1·90 |
| 1074/81 | *Set of* 8 | 4·00 | 4·50 |
| **MS**1082 | 72×101 mm. 15 d. "Niccolini-Cowper Madonna" (Raphael) | 1·75 | 1·90 |

(Litho Questa)

**1990** (24 Dec). *350th Death Anniv of Rubens. Multicoloured designs as T* **273** *of Antigua. P* 14×13½.

| | | | |
|---|---|---|---|
| 1083 | 20 b. "The Lion Hunt" (sketch) | 10 | 10 |
| 1084 | 75 b. "The Lion Hunt" (detail) | 10 | 15 |
| 1085 | 1 d. "The Tiger Hunt" (detail) | 10 | 15 |
| 1086 | 1 d. 25, "The Tiger Hunt" (different detail) | 15 | 20 |
| 1087 | 3 d. "The Tiger Hunt" (different detail) | 35 | 40 |
| 1088 | 5 d. "The Boar Hunt" (detail) | 60 | 65 |
| 1089 | 10 d. "The Lion Hunt" (different detail) | 1·25 | 1·40 |
| 1090 | 15 d. "The Tiger Hunt" (different detail) | 1·75 | 1·90 |
| 1083/90 | *Set of* 8 | 4·00 | 4·50 |
| **MS**1091 | Four sheets. (a) 100×71 mm. 15 d. "The Boar Hunt". P 14×13½. (b) 100×71 mm. 15 d. "The Lion Hunt". P 14×13½. (c) 100×71 mm. 15 d. "The Crocodile and Hippopotamus Hunt". P 14×13½. (d) 71×100 mm. 15 d. "St. George slays the Dragon" (*vert*). P 13½×14 *Set of* 4 *sheets* | 7·25 | 7·50 |

(Litho Questa)

**1991** (2 Jan). *World Summit for Children, New York. P* 14.

| | | | |
|---|---|---|---|
| 1092 | **196** 1 d. multicoloured | 10 | 15 |

(Des Walt Disney Co. Litho Questa)

**1991** (14 Feb). *International Literacy Year. Multicoloured designs as T* **269** *of Antigua showing scenes from Disney cartoon film* The Sword in the Stone. *P* 14×13½.

| | | | |
|---|---|---|---|
| 1093 | 3 d. Sir Kay and Wart searching for lost arrow (*horiz*) | 35 | 40 |
| | a. Sheetlet. Nos. 1093/101 | 2·75 | |
| 1094 | 3 d. Merlin the Magician (*horiz*) | 35 | 40 |
| 1095 | 3 d. Merlin teaching Wart (*horiz*) | 35 | 40 |
| 1096 | 3 d. Wart writing on blackboard (*horiz*) | 35 | 40 |
| 1097 | 3 d. Wart transformed into bird and Madame Mim (*horiz*) | 35 | 40 |
| 1098 | 3 d. Merlin and Madame Mim (*horiz*) | 35 | 40 |
| 1099 | 3 d. Madame Mim transformed into dragon (*horiz*) | 35 | 40 |
| 1100 | 3 d. Wart pulling sword from stone (*horiz*) | 35 | 40 |
| 1101 | 3 d. King Arthur on throne (*horiz*) | 35 | 40 |
| 1093/101 | *Set of* 9 | 2·75 | 3·25 |
| **MS**1102 | Two sheets, each 131×106 mm. (a) 20 d. Sword in stone. (b) 20 d. Merlin. P 13½×14 *Set of* 2 *sheets* | 4·75 | 5·00 |

Nos. 1093/101 were printed together, *se-tenant*, in sheetlets of 9.

**197** *Bebearia senegalensis*

(Des Mary Walters. Litho Questa)

**1991** (13 May). *Wildlife. T* **197** *and similar multicoloured designs. P* 14.

| | | | |
|---|---|---|---|
| 1103 | 1 d. Type **197** | 10 | 15 |
| | a. Sheetlet. Nos. 1103/18 | 1·40 | |
| 1104 | 1 d. *Graphium ridleyanus* (butterfly) | 10 | 15 |
| 1105 | 1 d. *Precis antilope* (butterfly) | 10 | 15 |
| 1106 | 1 d. *Charaxes ameliae* (butterfly) | 10 | 15 |
| 1107 | 1 d. Addax | 10 | 15 |
| 1108 | 1 d. Sassaby | 10 | 15 |
| 1109 | 1 d. Civet | 10 | 15 |
| 1110 | 1 d. Green Monkey | 10 | 15 |
| 1111 | 1 d. Spur-winged Goose | 10 | 15 |
| 1112 | 1 d. Red-billed Hornbill | 10 | 15 |
| 1113 | 1 d. Osprey | 10 | 15 |
| 1114 | 1 d. Glossy Ibis | 10 | 15 |
| 1115 | 1 d. Egyptian Plover | 10 | 15 |
| 1116 | 1 d. Golden-tailed Woodpecker | 10 | 15 |
| 1117 | 1 d. Green Woodhoopoe | 10 | 15 |
| 1118 | 1 d. Gaboon Viper | 10 | 15 |
| 1103/18 | *Set of* 16 | 1·40 | 2·10 |
| **MS**1119 | 101×69 mm. 18 d. African Spoonbill (*vert*) | 2·10 | 2·25 |

Nos. 1103/18 were printed together, *se-tenant*, in sheetlets of sixteen, forming a composite design.

# Ghana

**(*formerly* Gold Coast)**

## GOLD COAST

Gold Coast originally consisted of coastal forts, owned by the Royal African Company, trading with the interior. In 1821, due to raids by the Ashanti king, the British Government took over the forts, together with some of the hinterland, and the Governor of Sierra Leone was appointed to the Gold Coast also.

The colony was reconstituted by Royal Charter on 24 July, 1874, and at that time also included the settlement at Lagos which became a separate colony in January, 1886.

Following the end of the final Ashanti War in 1900 the whole of the territory was annexed.

There is no record of British stamps being officially issued in the Colony before 1875, apart from those used on board the ships of the West African Squadron, but examples do, however, exist cancelled by Gold Coast postmarks.

### CROWN COLONY

| PRICES FOR STAMPS ON COVER TO 1945 | |
|---|---|
| Nos. 1/3 | *from* × 12 |
| Nos. 4/10 | *from* × 10 |
| Nos. 11/20 | *from* × 12 |
| Nos. 22/5 | — |
| Nos. 26/34 | *from* × 7 |
| Nos. 35/6 | *from* × 12 |
| Nos. 38/69 | *from* × 4 |
| Nos. 70/98 | *from* × 3 |
| Nos. 100/2 | — |
| Nos. 103/12 | *from* × 5 |
| Nos. 113/16 | *from* × 3 |
| Nos. 117/19 | *from* × 4 |
| Nos. 120/32 | *from* × 3 |
| Nos. D1/4 | *from* × 8 |

1

ONE
PENNY.

(2)

(Typo D.L.R.)

**1875** (1 July). *Wmk Crown CC. P* 12½.

1 1 1d. blue . . . . £425 75·00
2 4d. magenta . . . . £400 85·00
3 6d. orange . . . . £600 65·00

**1876–84.** *Wmk Crown CC. P* 14.

4 1 ½d. olive-yellow (1879) . . 28·00 22·00
5 1d. blue . . 13·00 6·50
a. Bisected (½d.) (on cover) (1884) . . † £2250
6 2d. green (1879) . . 48·00 11·00
a. Bisected (1d.) (on cover) (1884) . . † £2000
b. Quartered (½d.) (on cover) (1884) . . † £2750
7 4d. magenta . . £150 6·00
a. Bisected (2d.) (on cover) (1884) . . † £3500
b. Quartered (1d.) (on cover) (1884) . . † £4500
8 6d. orange . . 90·00 18·00
a. Bisected (3d.) (on cover) (1884) . . † £4000
b. Sixth (1d.) (on cover) (1884) . . † £5000

During 1884 some values were in short supply and the use of bisects and other divided stamps is known as follows:

No. 5a. Used as part of 2½d. rate from Quittah
No. 6a. Used as 1d. rate from Cape Coast Castle, Quittah, Salt Pond, Secondee and Winnebah
No. 6b. Used as part of 2½d. rate from Cape Coast Castle
No. 7a. Used as 2d or as part of 2½d. rate from Quittah
No. 7b. Used as 1d. rate from Appam, Axim, Cape Coast Castle and Winnebah
No. 8a. Used as 3d. rate from Secondee
No. 8b. Used as 1d. rate from Winnebah

**1883** (May)? *No. 7 surch locally.*

8c 1 "1d." on 4d. magenta

**1883.** *Wmk Crown CA. P* 14.

9 1 ½d. olive-yellow (January) . . £130 55·00
10 1d. blue (May) . . £850 60·00

**1884** (Aug)–**91.** *Wmk Crown CA. P* 14.

11 1 ½d. green . . 75 35
*a. Dull green* . . 65 30
12 1d. rose-carmine . . 90 40
*a. Carmine* . . 90 30
b. Bisected (½d.) on cover . . † £2750
13 2d. grey . . 2·50 2·50
*b. Slate* . . 1·40 50
c. Bisected (1d.) (on cover)
d. Quartered (½d.) (on cover)
14 2½d. ultramarine and orange (13.3.91) . . 1·25 35
15 3d. olive-yellow (9.89) . . 5·50 4·50
*a. Olive* . . 3·75 4·00
16 4d. deep mauve (3.85) . . 2·00 80
*a. Rosy mauve* . . 3·50 2·50
17 6d. orange (1.89) . . 3·00 2·75
*a. Orange-brown* . . 4·50 2·75
b. Bisected (3d.) (on cover)
18 1s. violet (1888) . . 20·00 12·00
*a. Bright mauve* . . 3·50 1·00
19 2s. yellow-brown (1888) . . 70·00 26·00
*a. Deep brown* . . 22·00 15·00
11/19a . . *Set of* 9 35·00 25·00
14/15, 18/19 Optd "Specimen" . . *Set of* 4 £150

During 1886 and 1889 some values were in short supply and the use of bisects and other divided stamps is known as follows:

No. 12b. Used as part of 2½d. rate from Cape Coast Castle
No. 13c. Used as 1d. or as part of 2d. rate from Cape Coast Castle, Chamah, Dixcove and Elmina
No. 13d. Used as part of 2½d. rate from Cape Coast Castle
No. 17b. Used as 3d. from Appam

**1889** (Mar). *No. 17 surch with T* **2**.

20 1 1d. on 6d. orange . . £100 48·00

In some sheets examples may be found with the bar and "PENNY" spaced 8 mm, the normal spacing being 7 mm.

**USED HIGH VALUES.** Until the introduction of airmail in 1929 there was no postal use for values over 10s. Post Offices did, however, apply postal cancellations to high value stamps required for telegram fees.

3

4

**1889** (Sept)–**94.** *Wmk Crown CA. P* 14.

22 3 5s. dull mauve and blue . . 45·00 12·00
23 10s. dull mauve and red . . 65·00 15·00
*a. Dull mauve and carmine* . . £325 £100
24 20s. green and red . . £3250
25 20s. dull mauve and black/*red* (4.94) . . £150 35·00
22/5 Optd "Specimen" . . *Set of* 4 £450

No. 24 was withdrawn from sale in April 1893 when a large part of the stock was stolen. No 20s. stamps were available until the arrival of the replacement printing a year later.

**1898** (May)–**1902.** *Wmk Crown CA. P* 14.

26 3 ½d. dull mauve and green . . 75 25
27 1d. dull mauve and rose . . 40 25
27a 4 2d. dull mauve and orange-red (1902) 24·00 48·00
28 3 2½d. dull mauve and ultramarine . . 4·00 3·00
29 4 3d. dull mauve and orange . . 4·50 1·00
30 6d. dull mauve and violet . . 5·50 1·00
31 3 1s. green and black (1899) . . 5·50 5·50
32 2s. green and carmine . . 9·00 14·00
33 5s. green and mauve (1900) . . 38·00 17·00
34 10s. green and brown (1900) . . 95·00 35·00
26/34 . . *Set of* 10 £160 £110
26/34 Optd "Specimen" . . *Set of* 10 £180

**1901** (6 Oct). *Nos. 28 and 30 surch with T* **2**.

35 1d. on 2½d. dull mauve and ultramarine . . 1·25 3·00
36 1d. on 6d. dull mauve and violet . . 1·25 3·00
a. "ONE" omitted . . £300 £550

6

7

8

**1902.** *Wmk Crown CA. P* 14.

38 6 ½d. dull purple and green . . 40 40
39 1d. dull purple and carmine . . 75 15
40 7 2d. dull purple and orange-red . . 3·75 2·75
41 6 2½d. dull purple and ultramarine . . 4·00 6·50
42 7 3d. dull purple and orange . . 1·50 1·00
43 6d. dull purple and violet . . 1·50 1·00
44 6 1s. green and black . . 2·75 2·50
45 2s. green and carmine . . 10·00 9·50
46 5s. green and mauve . . 17·00 35·00
47 10s. green and brown . . 38·00 75·00
48 20s. purple and black/*red* . . £110 £120
38/48 . . *Set of* 11 £170 £225
38/48 Optd "Specimen" . . *Set of* 11 £200

**1904–7.** *Wmk Mult Crown CA. Ordinary paper* (½d. *to* 3d.) *or chalk-surfaced paper* (6d., 2s. 6d.).

49 6 ½d. dull purple and green (3.06) . . 2·50 2·75
50 1d. dull purple and carmine (10.04) . . 1·00 10
a. Chalk-surfaced paper (5.06) . . 2·50 30
51 7 2d. dull purple and orange-red (11.04) . . 3·50 50
a. Chalk-surfaced paper (8.06) . . 7·00 50
52 6 2½d. dull purple and ultramarine (6.06) . . 25·00 16·00
53 7 3d. dull purple and orange (8.05) . . 14·00 2·00
a. Chalk-surfaced paper (4.06) . . 7·00 30
54 6d. dull purple and violet (9.06) . . 23·00 1·25
a. Ordinary paper (5.07) . . 23·00 1·25
57 2s. 6d. green & yell (3.06) (Optd S. £50) 26·00 60·00
49/57 . . *Set of* 7 80·00 70·00

**1907–13.** *Wmk Mult Crown CA. Ordinary paper* (½d. *to* 2½d. *and* 2s.) *or chalk-surfaced paper* (3d. *to* 1s., 2s. 6d., 5s.). *P* 14.

59 6 ½d. dull green (5.07) . . 1·50 30
a. *Blue-green* (1909) . . 2·25 90
60 1d. red (2.07) . . 80 10
61 7 2d. greyish slate (4.09) . . 2·00 30
62 6 2½d. blue (4.07) . . 3·50 1·75
63 7 3d. purple/*yellow* (16.4.09) . . 4·50 45
64 6d. dull and deep purple (12.08) . . 9·00 55
a. *Dull and bright purple* (1911) . . 3·50 2·50
65 6 1s. black/*green* (10.09) . . 4·50 40
66 2s. purple and blue/*blue* (1910) . . 3·50 12·00
a. Chalk-surfaced paper . . 6·50 12·00
67 7 2s. 6d. blue and red/*blue* (1911) . . 18·00 35·00
68 6 5s. green and red/*yellow* (1913) . . 40·00 75·00
59/68 . . *Set of* 10 70·00 £110
59/68 Optd "Specimen" . . *Set of* 10 £200

A 10s. green and red on green, and a 20s. purple and black on red, both Type **6**, were prepared for use but not issued. Both exist overprinted "Specimen" (*Price for 10s. in this condition* £325).

(Typo D.L.R.)

**1908** (Nov). *Wmk Mult Crown CA. P* 14.

69 8 1d. red (Optd S. £45) . . 30 10

9

10

11

(Typo D.L.R.)

**1913–21.** *Wmk Mult Crown CA. Chalk-surfaced paper* (3d. *to* 20s.). *P* 14.

70 9 ½d. green . . 65 50
*a. Yellow-green* (1916) . . 90 90
72 10 1d. red . . 20 10
*a. Scarlet* (1919) . . 65 30
74 11 2d. grey . . 1·50 2·25
*a. Slate-grey* (11.16) . . 7·50 4·00
76 9 2½d. bright blue . . 75 35
77 11 3d. purple/*yellow* (8.15) (Optd S. £30) . . 80 40
*a. White back* (9.13) . . 30 40
*b. On orange-buff* (1919) . . 3·25 6·50
*c. On pale yellow* (Die II) (1921) . . 6·00 5·00
78 6d. dull and bright purple . . 2·00 1·75
79 9 1s. black/*green* . . 60 1·00
a. Wmk sideways
*b. On blue-green, olive back* (1921) (Optd S. £30) . . 50 35
*c. On emerald back* (Die I) (1921) (Optd S. £30) . . 2·00 1·50
*d. On emerald back* (Die II) (1921) (Optd S. £35) . . 1·50 50
80 2s. purple and blue/*blue* (Die I) . . 5·00 1·10
a. Die II (1921) . . £130 65·00
81 11 2s. 6d. black and red/*blue* (Die I) . . 5·00 10·00
a. Die II (1921) . . 22·00 28·00
82 9 5s. green & red/*yell* (1916) (Optd S. £40) 5·50 27·00
*a. White back* (10.13) . . 7·50 38·00
*b. On orange-buff* . . 35·00 55·00
*c. On pale yellow* (Die I) (1921) . . 60·00 85·00
d. Die II (1921) . . 28·00 £110
83 10s. green and red/*green* . . 32·00 70·00
*a. On blue-green, olive back* (1919) . . 17·00 55·00
*b. On emerald back* (1921) . . 28·00 80·00
84 20s. purple and black/*red* (1916) . . £100 80·00
70/84 . . *Set of* 12 £120 £150
70/6, 77a, 78/81, 82a/4 Optd "Specimen" *Set of* 12 £250

WAR TAX

ONE PENNY

(12)

13 King George V and Christiansborg Castle

**1918** (May). *Surch with T* **12**.

85 10 1d. on 1d. red (Optd S. £50) . . 15 30

**1921–24.** *Wmk Mult Script CA. Chalk-surfaced paper* (6d. *to* £2). *P* 14.

86 9 ½d. green . . 30 30
87 10 1d. chocolate-brown (1922) . . 30 10
88 11 1½d. red (1922) . . 30 10
89 2d. grey . . 30 20
90 9 2½d. yellow-orange (1922) . . 30 5·50
91 11 3d. bright blue (1922) . . 30 30
94 6d. dull and bright purple . . 45 2·00
95 9 1s. black/*emerald* (1924) . . 95 2·25
96 2s. purple and blue/*blue* (1923) . . 2·00 3·25
97 11 2s. 6d. black and red/*blue* (1924) . . 4·00 9·00
98 9 5s. green and red/*pale yellow* (1924) . . 7·00 24·00
100 11 15s. dull purple and green (Die I) . . £110 £200
a. Die II (1924) (Optd S. £100) . . £100 £200
102 £2 green and orange (Die I) . . £400 £700
86/100a . . *Set of* 12 £110 £200
86/102 Optd "Specimen" . . *Set of* 13 £350

In Nos. 88, 100 and 102 the words "GOLD COAST" are in distinctly larger letters.

(Photo Harrison)

**1928** (1 Aug). *Wmk Mult Script CA. P* 13½ × 15.

103 13 ½d. green . . 20 30
104 1d. red-brown . . 20 10
105 1½d. scarlet . . 35 1·50
106 2d. slate . . 20 10
107 2½d. orange-yellow . . 90 3·50
108 3d. blue . . 55 40
109 6d. black and purple . . 55 30
110 1s. black and vermilion . . 75 75
111 2s. black and violet . . 8·50 2·50
112 5s. carmine and olive-green . . 22·00 30·00
103/12 . . *Set of* 10 30·00 35·00
103/12 Optd "Specimen" . . *Set of* 10 £180

**1935** (6 May). *Silver Jubilee. As Nos. 91/4 of Antigua, but printed by B.W. P* 11 × 12.

113 1d. ultramarine and grey-black . . 50 30
a. Extra flagstaff . . £120
b. Short extra flagstaff . . 85·00
c. Lightning conductor . . 75·00
d. Flagstaff on right-hand turret . . 80·00
114 3d. brown and deep blue . . 2·25 4·25
a. Extra flagstaff . . £120
c. Lightning conductor . . 85·00
115 6d. green and indigo . . 2·25 5·50
a. Extra flagstaff . . £120
b. Short extra flagstaff . . £100
c. Lightning conductor . . 85·00
d. Flagstaff on right-hand turret . . £120

| No. | Description | Unused | Used |
|---|---|---|---|
| 116 | 1s. slate and purple | 2·25 | 6·50 |
| | a. Extra flagstaff | £130 | |
| | b. Short extra flagstaff | £110 | |
| | c. Lightning conductor | £100 | |
| 113/16 | *Set of* 4 | 6·50 | 15·00 |
| 113/16 Perf "Specimen" | *Set of* 4 | 85·00 | |

For illustrations of plate varieties see Catalogue Introduction.

**1937** (12 May). *Coronation. As Nos.* 95/7 *of Antigua. P* 11×11½.

| No. | Description | Unused | Used |
|---|---|---|---|
| 117 | 1d. buff | 70 | 40 |
| 118 | 2d. slate | 80 | 1·00 |
| 119 | 3d. blue | 80 | 95 |
| 117/19 | *Set of* 3 | 2·10 | 2·10 |
| 117/19 Perf "Specimen" | *Set of* 3 | 50·00 | |

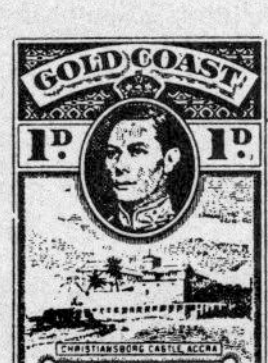


14

**15** King George VI and Christiansborg Castle, Accra

(Recess B.W.)

**1938** (1 Apr)–**41**. *Wmk Mult Script CA. P* 12×11½ (*T* **14**) *or* 11½×12 (*T* **15**)*.

| No. | Type | Description | Unused | Used |
|---|---|---|---|---|
| 120 | **14** | ½d. green | 30 | 30 |
| 121 | | 1d. red-brown | 30 | 10 |
| 122 | | 1½d. scarlet | 35 | 20 |
| 123 | | 2d. slate | 35 | 10 |
| 124 | | 3d. blue | 35 | 10 |
| 125 | | 4d. magenta | 50 | 50 |
| 126 | | 6d. purple | 50 | 10 |
| 127 | | 9d. orange | 50 | 40 |
| 128 | **15** | 1s. black and olive-green | 55 | 10 |
| 129 | | 1s. 3d. brown & turquoise-bl (12.4.41) | 80 | 10 |
| 130 | | 2s. blue and violet | 2·50 | 3·25 |
| 131 | | 5s. olive-green and carmine | 3·25 | 5·00 |
| 132 | | 10s. black and violet (7.40) | 5·00 | 13·00 |
| 120/32 | | *Set of* 13 | 13·50 | 20·00 |
| 120/32 Perf "Specimen" | | *Set of* 13 | £160 | |

*Nos. 120 to 132, except 1s. 3d. and 10s., exist in two perforations: (*a*) Line-perf 12, from early printings; (*b*) Comb-perf 12×11.8 (vertical design) or 11.8×12 (horiz design) from later printings. The 1s. 3d. and 10s. exist only comb-perf 11.8×12.

**1946** (14 Oct). *Victory. As Nos.* 110/11 *of Antigua. P* 13½×14.

| No. | Description | Unused | Used |
|---|---|---|---|
| 133 | 2d. slate-violet | 5·00 | 2·00 |
| | a. Perf 13½ | 10 | 10 |
| 134 | 4d. claret | 2·00 | 2·50 |
| | a. Perf 13½ | 30 | 80 |
| 133/4 Perf "Specimen" | *Set of* 2 | 50·00 | |

**16** Northern Territories Mounted Constabulary

**17** Christiansborg Castle

(Des B. A. Johnston (1½d.), M. Ziorkley and B. A. Abban (2d.), P.O. draughtsman (2½d.), C. Gomez (1s.), M. Ziorkley (10s.); others from photographs. Recess B.W.)

**1948** (1 July). *T* **16/17** *and similar designs. Wmk Mult Script CA. P* 12 × 11½ (*vert*) *or* 11½ × 12 (*horiz*).

| No. | Description | Unused | Used |
|---|---|---|---|
| 135 | ½d. emerald-green | 20 | 25 |
| 136 | 1d. blue | 15 | 10 |
| 137 | 1½d. scarlet | 1·25 | 70 |
| 138 | 2d. purple-brown | 55 | 10 |
| 139 | 2½d. yellow-brown and scarlet | 2·00 | 1·25 |
| 140 | 3d. light blue | 3·00 | 20 |
| 141 | 4d. magenta | 1·75 | 1·25 |
| 142 | 6d. black and orange | 30 | 10 |
| 143 | 1s. black and vermilion | 30 | 10 |
| 144 | 2s. sage-green and magenta | 2·25 | 1·25 |
| 145 | 5s. purple and black | 12·00 | 1·75 |
| 146 | 10s. black and sage-green | 8·00 | 4·00 |
| 135/46 | *Set of* 12 | 28·00 | 10·00 |
| 135/46 Perf "Specimen" | *Set of* 12 | £225 | |

Designs: *Horiz*—1½d. Emblem of Joint Provincial Council; 2½d. Map showing position of Gold Coast; 3d. Manganese mine; 4d. Lake Bosumtwi; 1s. Breaking cocoa pods; 2s. Trooping the Colour; 5s. Surfboats. *Vert*—2d. Talking drums; 6d. Cocoa farmer; 10s. Forest.

**1948** (20 Dec). *Royal Silver Wedding. As Nos.* 112/13 *of Antigua.*

| No. | Description | Unused | Used |
|---|---|---|---|
| 147 | 1½d. scarlet | 20 | 15 |
| 148 | 10s. grey-olive | 8·00 | 7·00 |

**1949** (10 Oct). *75th Anniv of U.P.U. As Nos.* 114/17 *of Antigua.*

| No. | Description | Unused | Used |
|---|---|---|---|
| 149 | 2d. red-brown | 30 | 30 |
| 150 | 2½d. orange | 1·00 | 1·50 |
| 151 | 3d. deep blue | 75 | 70 |
| 152 | 1s. blue-green | 75 | 50 |
| 149/52 | *Set of* 4 | 2·50 | 2·75 |

**28** Northern Territories Mounted Constabulary

(Recess B.W.)

**1952** (19 Dec)–**54**. *Designs previously used for King George VI issue, but with portrait of Queen Elizabeth II, as in T* **28**. *Portrait faces left on* ½*d.,* 4*d.,* 6*d.,* 1*s. and* 5*s. Wmk Mult Script CA. P* 12 × 11½ (*vert*) *or* 11½ × 12 (*horiz*).

| No. | Description | Unused | Used |
|---|---|---|---|
| 153 | ½d. yellow-brown and scarlet (1.4.53) | 10 | 10 |
| | *a. Bistre-brown and scarlet* (7.4.54) | 10 | 10 |
| 154 | 1d. deep blue (1.3.54) | 30 | 10 |
| 155 | 1½d. emerald-green (1.4.53) | 30 | 90 |
| 156 | 2d. chocolate (1.3.54) | 30 | 10 |
| 157 | 2½d. scarlet | 35 | 35 |
| 158 | 3d. magenta (1.4.53) | 50 | 10 |
| 159 | 4d. blue (1.4.53) | 30 | 20 |
| 160 | 6d. black and orange (1.3.54) | 30 | 10 |
| 161 | 1s. black and orange-red (1.3.54) | 30 | 10 |
| 162 | 2s. brown-olive and carmine (1.3.54) | 7·50 | 55 |
| 163 | 5s. purple and black (1.3.54) | 13·00 | 2·25 |
| 164 | 10s. black and olive-green (1.3.54) | 8·00 | 11·00 |
| 153/64 | *Set of* 12 | 28·00 | 14·00 |

Designs: *Horiz*—½d. Map showing position of Gold Coast; 1d. Christiansborg Castle; 1½d. Emblem of Joint Provincial Council; 3d. Manganese mine; 4d. Lake Bosumtwi; 1s. Breaking cocoa pods; 2s. Trooping the colour; 5s. Surfboats. *Vert*—2d. Talking drums; 6d. Cocoa farmer; 10s. Forest.

Nos. 153/4 exist in coils constructed from normal sheets.

**1953** (2 June). *Coronation. As No.* 120 *of Antigua, but ptd by B.W.*

| No. | Description | Unused | Used |
|---|---|---|---|
| 165 | 2d. black and sepia | 30 | 10 |

Gold Coast became the Dominion of Ghana on 6 March 1957.

## GHANA

### DOMINION

***CANCELLED REMAINDERS.** In 1961 remainders of some issues of 1957 to 1960 were put on the market cancelled-to-order in such a way as to be indistinguishable from genuine postally used copies for all practical purposes. Our used quotations which are indicated by an asterisk are the same for cancelled-to-order or postally used copies.

**29** Dr. Kwame Nkrumah, Palm-nut Vulture and Map of Africa

GHANA
INDEPENDENCE
6TH MARCH,
1957.

(**30**)

(Photo Harrison)

**1957** (6 Mar). *Independence. Wmk Mult Script CA. P* 14 × 14½.

| No. | Type | Description | Unused | Used |
|---|---|---|---|---|
| 166 | **29** | 2d. scarlet | 10 | 10* |
| 167 | | 2½d. green | 10 | 10* |
| 168 | | 4d. brown | 10 | 10* |
| 169 | | 1s. 3d. deep blue | 15 | 10* |
| 166/9 | | *Set of* 4 | 40 | 20* |

**1957** (6 Mar)–**58**. *Nos.* 153/64 *of Gold Coast optd as T* **30**.

| No. | Description | Unused | Used |
|---|---|---|---|
| 170 | ½d. bistre-brown and scarlet | 10 | 10* |
| | *a. Olive-brown and scarlet* | 10 | 10* |
| 171 | 1d. deep blue (R.) | 10 | 10* |
| 172 | 1½d. emerald-green | 10 | 10* |
| 173 | 2d. chocolate (26.5.58) | 30 | 30 |
| 174 | 2½d. scarlet (26.5.58) | 1·00 | 1·25 |
| 175 | 3d. magenta | 10 | 10* |
| 176 | 4d. blue (26.5.58) | 3·00 | 3·25 |
| 177 | 6d. black and orange (R.) | 10 | 10* |
| | a. Opt double | † | £200 |
| 178 | 1s. black and orange-red | 10 | 10* |
| 179 | 2s. brown-olive and carmine | 45 | 10* |
| 180 | 5s. purple and black | 50 | 10* |
| 181 | 10s. black and olive-green | 60 | 30* |
| 170/81 | *Set of* 12 | 5·50 | 4·75* |

Nos. 173/4 and 176 were officially issued on 26 May 1958 although, in error, small quantities were sold at certain post offices when the rest of the set appeared.

Nos. 170 and 171 exist in coils constructed from normal sheets.

**31** Viking Ship

(Des W. Wind. Recess E. A. Wright Bank Note Co., Philadelphia)

**1957** (27 Dec). *Inauguration of Black Star Shipping Line. T* **31** *and similar horiz designs. No wmk. P* 12.

| No. | Description | Unused | Used |
|---|---|---|---|
| 182 | 2½d. emerald-green | 35 | 20 |
| | a. Imperf between (vert pair) | £300 | |
| | b. Imperf between (horiz pair) | £300 | |
| 183 | 1s. 3d. deep blue | 65 | 90 |
| | a. Imperf horiz (vert pair) | £300 | |
| 184 | 5s. bright purple | 1·00 | 2·50 |
| | a. Imperf vert (horiz pair) | £375 | |
| 182/4 | *Set of* 3 | 1·75 | 3·25 |

Designs:—1s. 3d. Galleon; 5s. M.V. *Volta River.*

**PRINTERS.** Nos. 185/**MS**568 were printed in photogravure by Harrison & Sons *except where otherwise stated.*

**34** Ambassador Hotel, Accra

**35** Ghana Coat of Arms

**1958** (6 Mar). *First Anniv of Independence. T* **34/5** *and similar designs. Wmk Mult Script CA. P* 14½ × 14 (2*s.*) *or* 14 × 14½ (*others*).

| No. | Description | Unused | Used |
|---|---|---|---|
| 185 | ½d. black, red, yellow, green and carmine | 10 | 1 |
| 186 | 2½d. black, red, green and yellow | 10 | 1 |
| 187 | 1s. 3d. black, red, yellow, green and blue | 20 | 1 |
| 188 | 2s. red, yellow, blue, green, brown and black | 25 | 2 |
| 185/8 | *Set of* 4 | 55 | 3 |

Designs: *Horiz as T* **34**—2½d. State Opening of Parliament; 1s. 3d. National Monument.

**38** Map showing the Independent African States

**39** Map of Africa and Flaming Torch

(Des R. Milton)

**1958** (15 Apr). *First Conference of Independent African States, Accra. Wmk Mult Script CA. P* 13½ × 14½ (2½*d.,* 3*d*) *or* 14½ × 13½ (*others*).

| No. | Type | Description | Unused | Used |
|---|---|---|---|---|
| 189 | **38** | 2½d. black, bistre and bright carmine-red | 10 | 1 |
| 190 | | 3d. black, bistre, brown and bright green | 10 | 1 |
| 191 | **39** | 1s. black, yellow, red and dull blue | 10 | 1 |
| 192 | | 2s. 6d. black, yellow, red and dull violet | 20 | 2 |
| 189/92 | | *Set of* 4 | 30 | 3 |

**40** Palm-nut Vulture over Globe



**41** "Britannia" Airliner

(Des M. Goaman (2½d., 2s. 6d.), R. Milton (1s. 3d.), W. Wind (2s.))

**1958** (15 July). *Inauguration of Ghana Airways. T* **40/1** *and similar designs. Wmk Mult Script CA. P* 15 × 14 (2*s.* 6*d.*) *or* 14 × 15 (*others*).

| No. | Description | Unused | Used |
|---|---|---|---|
| 193 | 2½d. black, yellow-bistre & rose-carmine | 30 | 1 |
| 194 | 1s. 3d. multicoloured | 55 | 1 |
| 195 | 2s. multicoloured | 60 | 3 |
| 196 | 2s. 6d. black and bistre | 80 | 6 |
| 193/6 | *Set of* 4 | 2·00 | 1·0 |

Designs: *Horiz* (*as T* **41**)—2s. "Stratocruiser" and Yellow-nosed Albatross. (*As T* **40**)—2s. 6d. Palm-nut Vulture and je[t] aircraft.

PRIME
MINISTER'S
VISIT,
U.S.A. AND
CANADA

(**44**)

**45**

**1958** (18 July). *Prime Minister's Visit to the United States and Canada. Nos.* 166/9 *optd with T* **44**.

| No. | Type | Description | Unused | Used |
|---|---|---|---|---|
| 197 | **29** | 2d. scarlet | 10 | 1 |
| 198 | | 2½d. green | 10 | 1 |
| 199 | | 4d. brown | 10 | 1 |
| 200 | | 1s. 3d. deep blue | 15 | 2 |
| 197/200 | | *Set of* 4 | 30 | 3 |

(Des W. Wind)

**1958** (24 Oct). *United Nations Day. Wmk Mult Script CA P* 14 × 14½.

| No. | Type | Description | Unused | Used |
|---|---|---|---|---|
| 201 | **45** | 2½d. purple-brown, green and black | 10 | 1 |
| 202 | | 1s. 3d. purple-brown, blue and black | 15 | 1 |
| 203 | | 2s. 6d. purple-brown, violet and black | 20 | 2 |
| 201/3 | | *Set of* 3 | 30 | 3 |

46 Dr. Nkrumah and Lincoln Statue, Washington

47

(Des M. Goaman)

959 (12 Feb). *150th Birth Anniv of Abraham Lincoln. W* **47**. *P* 14 × 14½.

| | | | | |
|---|---|---|---|---|
| 04 **46** | 2½d. pink and deep purple .. .. .. | | 10 | 10 |
| 05 | 1s. 3d. light blue and blue .. .. | | 15 | 10 |
| 06 | 2s. 6d. orange-yellow & dp olive-green | | 20 | 20 |
| 04/6 .. | .. .. .. .. | *Set of* 3 | 30 | 30 |
| MS206*a* | 102 × 77 mm. Nos. 204/6. Imperf . .. | | 55 | 1·75 |

48 Kente Cloth and Traditional Symbols

Des Mrs. T. Sutherland (½d.), M. Karoly (2½d.), K. Antubam (1s. 3d.), A. M. Medina (2s.))

959 (6 Mar). *Second Anniv of Independence. T* **48** *and similar multicoloured designs. W* **47**. *P* 14½ × 14 (2s.) *or* 14 × 14½ (*others*).

| | | | | |
|---|---|---|---|---|
| 207 | ½d. Type **48** .. .. .. .. .. | | 10 | 10 |
| 208 | 2½d. Talking drums and elephant-horn blower .. .. .. .. | | 10 | 10 |
| 209 | 1s. 3d."Symbol of Greeting" (*vert*) .. | | 10 | 10 |
| 210 | 2s. Map of Africa, Ghana flag and palms .. | | 25 | 50 |
| 207/10 | .. .. .. .. .. | *Set of* 4 | 40 | 60 |

52 Globe and Flags

(Des Mrs. H. Potter)

959 (15 Apr). *Africa Freedom Day. W* **47** (*sideways*). *P* 14½ × 14.

| | | | |
|---|---|---|---|
| 211 **52** | 2½d. multicoloured .. .. .. | 15 | 10 |
| 212 | 8½d. multicoloured .. .. .. | 15 | 20 |

53 "God's Omnipotence"

54 Nkrumah Statue, Accra

55 Ghana Timber

56 Volta River

65*a* Red-fronted Gazelle

Two Types of ½d. and 3d:

I. Inscr "GOD'S OMNIPOTENCE"
II. Inscr "GYE NYAME"

(Des Mrs. T. Sutherland (½d., 3d.), Ghana Information Bureau (source of 1d. and 2d.), O. Haulkland (1½d.), A. Medina (2½d., 4d.), M. Goaman (6d., 1s 3d., 2s. 6d.), W. Wind (11d., 1s., 2s., 5s.), W. H. Brown (10s.), M. Shamir (£1)).

**1959** (5 Oct)–**61**. *T* **53/6**, **65*a***, *and similar multicoloured designs. W* **47** (*sideways on horiz designs*). *P* 11½ × 12 (½d.), 12 × 11½ (1d.), 14 × 14½ (1½d., 11d., 1s., 2s. *and* 5s.), 14 × 15 (10s.) *or* 14½ × 14 (*others*). (*a*) *Postage*.

| | | | | |
|---|---|---|---|---|
| 213 | ½d. Type **53** (I) .. .. .. .. | | 10 | 10 |
| | a. Type II (29.4.61) .. .. .. .. | | 30 | 10 |
| 214 | 1d. Type **54** .. .. .. .. | | 10 | 10 |
| 215 | 1½d. Type **55** .. .. .. .. | | 10 | 10 |
| 216 | 2d. Type **56** .. .. .. .. | | 10 | 10 |
| 217 | 2½d. Cocoa bean .. .. .. .. | | 10 | 10 |
| 218 | 3d. "God's Omnipotence" (I) .. .. .. | | 10 | 10 |
| | a. Type II (29.4.61) .. .. .. .. | | 30 | 10 |
| 219 | 4d. Diamond and Mine .. .. .. | | 1·40 | 30 |
| 220 | 6d. Red-crowned Bishop .. .. .. | | 50 | 10 |
| | a. Green (flag) omitted .. .. .. | | 45·00 | |
| 221 | 11d. Golden Spider Lily .. .. .. | | 25 | 10 |
| 222 | 1s. Shell Ginger .. .. .. | | 25 | 10 |
| 223 | 2s. 6d. Great Blue Turaco .. .. .. | | 2·00 | 15 |
| 224 | 5s. Tiger Orchid .. .. .. | | 5·00 | 50 |
| 225 | 10s. Tropical African Cichlid .. .. .. | | 2·75 | 70 |
| 225*a* | £1 Type **65*a*** (29.4.61) .. .. .. | | 11·00 | 4·75 |
| | (*b*) *Air* | | | |
| 226 | 1s. 3d. Pennant-winged Nightjar .. .. | | 1·75 | 10 |
| 227 | 2s. Crowned Cranes .. .. .. | | 1·50 | 10 |
| 213/27 | .. .. .. .. | *Set of* 16 | 24·00 | 6·00 |

Nos. 217/224 and 226/7 are as Types **55/6**, the 11d., 1s., 5s. and 2s. (air) being vertical and the remainder horizontal. No. 225 is as Type **65*a***.

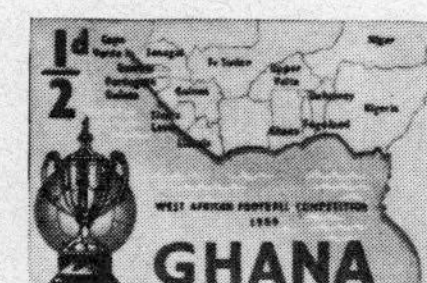


68 Gold Cup and West African Map

(Des K. Lehmann (½d., 3d.), M. & G. Shamir (1d.), W. Wind (8d.), and K. Antubam (2s. 6d.))

**1959** (15 Oct). *West African Football Competition*, 1959. *T* **68** *and similar multicoloured designs. W* **47** (*sideways on horiz designs*). *P* 14 × 14½ (1d., 2s. 6d) *or* 14½ × 14 (*others*).

| | | | | |
|---|---|---|---|---|
| 228 | ½d. Type **68** .. .. .. .. | | 10 | 10* |
| 229 | 1d. Footballers (*vert*) .. .. .. | | 10 | 10* |
| 230 | 3d. Goalkeeper saving ball .. .. .. | | 15 | 10* |
| 231 | 8d. Forward attacking goal .. .. .. | | 40 | 10* |
| 232 | 2s. 6d. "Kwame Nkrumah" Gold Cup (*vert*) | | 60 | 10* |
| 228/32 | .. .. .. .. | *Set of* 5 | 1·25 | 30* |

73 The Duke of Edinburgh and Arms of Ghana

(Des A. S. B. New)

**1959** (24 Nov). *Visit of the Duke of Edinburgh to Ghana. W* **47** (*sideways*). *P* 15 × 14.

| | | | |
|---|---|---|---|
| 233 **73** | 3d. black and magenta .. .. .. | 20 | 10* |

74 Ghana Flag and Talking Drums

75 Ghana Flag and U.N. Emblem

(Des K. Antubam (2s. 6d.), A. Medina (others))

**1959** (10 Dec). *United Nations Trusteeship Council. T* **74/5** *and similar multicoloured designs. W* **47** (*sideways on* 3d.). *P* 14½ × 14 (3d.) *or* 14 × 14½ (*others*).

| | | | | |
|---|---|---|---|---|
| 234 | 3d. Type **74** .. .. .. .. | | 10 | 10* |
| 235 | 6d. Type **75** .. .. .. .. | | 10 | 10* |
| 236 | 1s. 3d. Ghana flag and U.N. emblem (*vert*) | | 25 | 15* |
| 237 | 2s. 6d. "Totem Pole" (*vert*) .. .. | | 30 | 15* |
| 234/7 .. | .. .. .. .. | *Set of* 4 | 60 | 45* |

**ALTERED CATALOGUE NUMBERS**

Any Catalogue numbers altered from the last edition are shown as a list in the introductory pages.

78 Eagles in Flight

79 Fireworks

(Des A. Medina (½d.), M. Goaman (3d.), W. Wind (1s. 3d., 2s.))

**1960** (6 Mar). *Third Anniv of Independence. T* **78/9** *and similar vert designs. Multicoloured. W* **47**. *P* 14 × 14½.

| | | | | |
|---|---|---|---|---|
| 238 | ½d. Type **78** .. .. .. .. | | 10 | 10* |
| 239 | 3d. Type **79** .. .. .. .. | | 10 | 10* |
| 240 | 1s. 3d. "Third Anniversary" .. .. | | 25 | 10* |
| 241 | 2s. "Ship of State" .. .. .. | | 25 | 15* |
| 238/41 | .. .. .. .. | *Set of* 4 | 60 | 30* |

82

(Des W. Wind)

**1960** (15 Apr). *Africa Freedom Day. T* **82** *and similar horiz designs. Multicoloured. W* **47** (*sideways*). *P* 14½ × 14.

| | | | | |
|---|---|---|---|---|
| 242 | 3d. Type **82** .. .. .. .. | | 10 | 10* |
| 243 | 6d. Letter "f" .. .. .. .. | | 15 | 10* |
| 244 | 1s. Letter "d" .. .. .. .. | | 15 | 10* |
| 242/4 .. | .. .. .. .. | *Set of* 3 | 30 | 20* |

**REPUBLIC**

85 President Nkrumah

(Des A. Medina (3d., 10s.), W. Wind (1s. 3d., 2s.))

**1960** (1 July). *Republic Day. T* **85** *and similar multicoloured designs. W* **47**. *P* 14½ × 14 (10s.) *or* 14 × 14½ (*others*).

| | | | | |
|---|---|---|---|---|
| 245 | 3d. Type **85** .. .. .. .. | | 10 | 10 |
| 246 | 1s. 3d. Ghana flag .. .. .. | | 15 | 10 |
| 247 | 2s. Torch of Freedom .. .. .. | | 20 | 10 |
| 248 | 10s. Arms of Ghana (*horiz*) .. .. | | 70 | 70 |
| 245/8 .. | .. .. .. .. | *Set of* 4 | 1·00 | 80 |
| **MS**248*a* | 102 × 77 mm. Nos. 245/8. Imperf .. | | 40 | 1·25 |

89 Olympic Torch

90 Athlete

(Des A. Medina (T **89**), W. Wind (T **90**))

**1960** (15 Aug). *Olympic Games. W* **47** (*sideways on T* **90**). *P* 14 × 14½ (*T* **89**) *or* 14½ × 14 (*T* **90**).

| | | | | |
|---|---|---|---|---|
| 249 **89** | 3d. multicoloured .. .. .. | | 10 | 10 |
| 250 | 6d. multicoloured .. .. .. | | 10 | 10 |
| 251 **90** | 1s. 3d. multicoloured .. .. .. | | 15 | 10 |
| 252 | 2s. 6d. multicoloured .. .. .. | | 20 | 20 |
| 249/52 | .. .. .. .. | *Set of* 4 | 40 | 30 |

91 President Nkrumah

94 U.N. Emblem and Ghana Flag

(Des M. Goaman (3d., 6d.), W. Wind (1s. 3d.))

**1960** (21 Sept). *Founder's Day. T* **91** *and similar multicoloured designs. W* **47** *(sideways on 3d.). P* 14½ × 14 *(3d.) or* 14 × 14½ *(others).*

253 3d. Type **91** .. .. .. .. .. .. 10 10
254 6d. President Nkrumah (*vert*) .. .. 10 10
255 1s. 3d. Flag-draped column over map of African (*vert*) .. .. .. .. 15 15
253/5 .. .. .. .. .. *Set of* 3 25 25

(Des M. Goaman (3d., 1s. 3d.), W. Wind (6d.))

**1960** (10 Dec). *Human Rights Day. T* **94** *and similar vert designs. W* **47**. *P* 14 × 14½.

256 3d. multicoloured .. .. .. .. .. 10 10
257 6d. yellow, black and blue .. .. .. .. 15 10
258 1s. 3d. multicoloured .. .. .. .. .. 25 15
256/8 .. .. .. .. .. *Set of* 3 40 25

Designs:—6d. U.N. emblem and Torch; 1s. 3d. U.N. emblem.

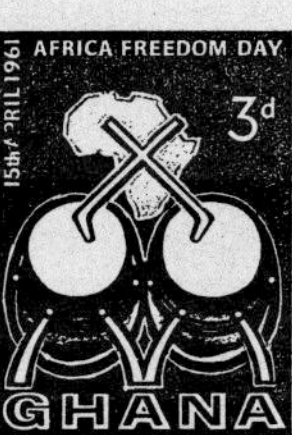


**97** Talking Drums

**100** Eagle on Column

(Des M. Goaman (3d.), A. S. B. New (6d.), W. Wind (2s.))

**1961** (15 Apr). *Africa Freedom Day. T* **97** *and similar designs. W* **47** *(sideways on 2s.). P* 14½ × 14 *(2s.) or* 14 × 14½ *(others).*

259 3d. multicoloured .. .. .. .. .. 10 10
260 6d. red, black and green .. .. .. .. 15 10
261 2s. multicoloured .. .. .. .. .. 30 25
259/61 .. .. .. .. .. *Set of* 3 50 30

Designs: *Vert.*—6d. Map of Africa. *Horiz*—2s. Flags and map.

(Des A. S. B. New (3d.), M. Shamir (1s. 3d.), W. Wind (2s.))

**1961** (1 July). *First Anniv of Republic. T* **100** *and similar vert designs. Multicoloured. W* **47**. *P* 14 × 14½.

262 3d. Type **100** .. .. .. .. .. 10 10
263 1s. 3d. "Flower" .. .. .. .. .. 10 10
264 2s. Ghana flags .. .. .. .. .. 20 30
262/4 .. .. .. .. .. *Set of* 3 30 40

**103** Dove with Olive Branch

**106** Pres. Nkrumah and Globe

(Des V. Whiteley)

**1961** (1 Sept). *Belgrade Conference. T* **103** *and similar designs. W* **47** *(sideways on 1s. 3d., 5s.). P* 14 × 14½ *(3d.) or* 14½ × 14 *(others).*

265 3d. yellow-green .. .. .. .. .. 10 10
266 1s. 3d. deep blue .. .. .. .. .. 20 10
267 5s. bright reddish purple .. .. .. .. 65 50
265/7 .. .. .. .. .. *Set of* 3 85 55

Designs: *Horiz.*—1s. 3d. World map, chain and olive branch; 5s. Rostrum, conference room.

(Des A. Medina (3d.), M. Goaman (1s. 3d.), Miriam Karoly (5s.))

**1961** (21 Sept). *Founder's Day. T* **106** *and similar multicoloured designs. W* **47** *(sideways on 3d.). P* 14½ × 14 *(3d.) or* 14 × 14½ *(others).*

268 3d. Type **106** .. .. .. .. .. 10 10
269 1s. 3d. President and Kente Cloth (*vert*) .. 20 10
270 5s. President in national costume (*vert*) .. 80 1·25
268/70 .. .. .. .. .. *Set of* 3 1·00 1·25
**MS**270*a* Three sheets 106 × 86 mm (3d.) or 86 × 106 mm (others) each with Nos. 268/70 in block of four. Imperf .. *Three sheets* 5·50 14·00

The 1s. 3d. Miniature Sheet is known with the brown colour omitted.

**109** Queen Elizabeth II and African Map

(Des M. Goaman)

**1961** (9 Nov). *Royal Visit. W* **47**. *P* 14½ × 14.

271 **109** 3d. multicoloured .. .. .. .. 15 10
272 1s. 3d. multicoloured .. .. .. .. 60 15
273 5s. multicoloured .. .. .. .. 1·75 1·75
271/3 .. .. .. .. .. *Set of* 3 2·25 1·75
**MS**273*a* 106 × 84 mm. No. 273 in block of four. Imperf .. .. .. .. .. 4·50 8·50

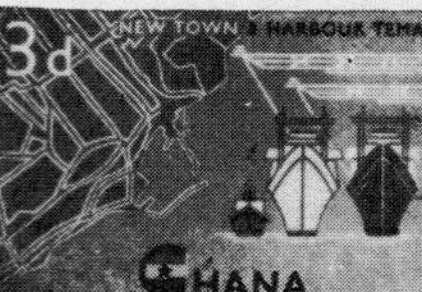


**110** Ships in Tema Harbour

(Des C. Bottiau. Litho Enschedé & Sons)

**1962** (10 Feb). *Opening of Tema Harbour. T* **110** *and similar horiz designs. Multicoloured. No wmk. P* 14 × 13. (*a*) *Postage.*

274 3d. Type **110** .. .. .. .. .. 15 10

(*b*) *Air*

275 1s. 3d. Aircraft and ships at Tema .. .. 40 10
276 2s. 6d. As 1s. 3d. .. .. .. .. 55 30
274/6 .. .. .. .. .. *Set of* 3 1·00 35

**112** Africa and Peace Dove

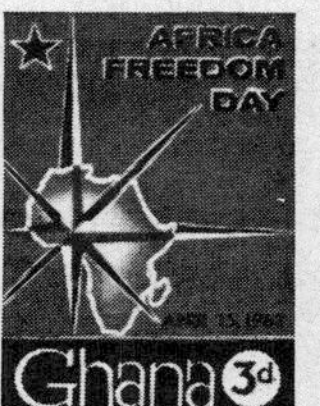


**113** Compass over Africa

(Des R. Hegeman. Litho Enschedé)

**1962** (6 Mar). *First Anniv of Casablanca Conference. No wmk. P* 13 × 14. (*a*) *Postage.*

277 **112** 3d. multicoloured .. .. .. .. 10 10

(*b*) *Air*

278 **112** 1s. 3d. multicoloured .. .. .. .. 20 10
279 2s. 6d. multicoloured .. .. .. .. 30 30
277/9 .. .. .. .. .. *Set of* 3 50 35

(Des R. Hegeman)

**1962** (24 Apr). *Africa Freedom Day. W* **47**. *P* 14 × 14½.

280 **113** 3d. sepia, blue-green and reddish purple 10 10
281 6d. sepia, blue-green and orange-brown 10 10
282 1s. 3d. sepia, blue-green and red .. 10 10
280/2 .. .. .. .. .. *Set of* 3 20 15

**114** Ghana Star and "Five Continents"

**115** Atomic Bomb-burst "Skull"

(Des M. Goaman (3d.), M. Shamir (6d.), W. Wind (1s. 3d.))

**1962** (21 June). *Accra Assembly, T* **114/15** *and similar vert design. W* **47**. *P* 14 × 14½.

283 3d. black and lake-red .. .. .. .. 10 10
284 6d. black and scarlet .. .. .. .. 15 15
285 1s. 3d. turquoise .. .. .. .. 20 15
283/5 .. .. .. .. .. *Set of* 3 35 30

Design:—1s. 3d. Dove of Peace.

**117** Patrice Lumumba

**118** Star over Two Columns

(Des A. S. B. New)

**1962** (30 June). *1st Death Anniv of Lumumba. W* **47**. *P* 14½ × 14.

286 **117** 3d. black and orange-yellow .. .. 10 10
287 6d. black, green and lake .. .. 10 10
288 1s. 3d. black, pink and black-green .. 15 15
286/8 .. .. .. .. .. *Set of* 3 20 20

(Des A. S. B. New (3d.), A. Medina (6d.), M. Goaman (1s. 3d.) Litho Enschedé)

**1962** (1 July). *2nd Anniv of Republic. T* **118** *and similar multicoloured designs. P* 14 × 13½ *(1s. 3d.) or* 13½ × 14 *(others).*

289 3d. Type **118** .. .. .. .. .. 10 10
290 6d. Flaming torch .. .. .. .. .. 15 15
291 1s. 3d. Eagle trailing flag (*horiz*) .. .. 25 25
289/91 .. .. .. .. .. *Set of* 3 40 40

**121** President Nkrumah

**125** Campaign Emblem

(Litho Enschedé)

**1962** (21 Sept). *Founder's Day. T* **121** *and similar vert designs P* 13 × 14½.

292 1d. multicoloured .. .. .. .. .. 10 10
293 3d. multicoloured .. .. .. .. .. 10 10
294 1s. 3d. black and bright blue .. .. 25 10
295 2s. multicoloured .. .. .. .. .. 25 20
292/5 .. .. .. .. .. *Set of* 4 60 30

Designs:—3d. Nkrumah medallion; 1s. 3d. President Nkrumah and Ghana Star; 2s. Laying "Ghana" Brick.

**1962** (3 Dec). *Malaria Eradication. W* **47**. *P* 14 × 14½.

296 **125** 1d. cerise .. .. .. .. .. 10 10
297 4d. yellow-green .. .. .. .. 20 15
298 6d. bistre .. .. .. .. .. 20 10
299 1s. 3d. bluish violet .. .. .. .. 25 20
296/9 .. .. .. .. .. *Set of* 4 60 40
**MS**299*a* 90 × 115 mm. Nos. 296/9. Imperf .. 65 1·25

**126** Campaign Emblem

**129** Map of Africa

**1963** (21 Mar). *Freedom from Hunger. T* **126** *and similar designs. W* **47** *(sideways on 4d., 1s. 3d.). P* 14 × 14½ *(1d.) or* 14½ × 14 *(others).*

300 1d. multicoloured .. .. .. .. .. 15 10
301 4d. sepia, yellow and orange .. .. .. 75 20
302 1s. 3d. ochre, black and green .. .. 1·60 65
300/2 .. .. .. .. .. *Set of* 3 2·25 85

Designs: *Horiz*—4d. Emblem in hands; 1s. 3d. World map and emblem.

**1963** (15 Apr). *Africa Freedom Day. T* **129** *and similar designs. W* **47** *(sideways on 4d.). P* 14½ × 14 *(4d.) or* 14 × 14½ *(others).*

303 1d. gold and red .. .. .. .. .. 10 10
304 4d. red, black and yellow .. .. .. 10 10
305 1s. 3d. multicoloured .. .. .. .. 15 10
306 2s. 6d. multicoloured .. .. .. .. 25 55
303/6 .. .. .. .. .. *Set of* 4 45 65

Designs: *Horiz*—4d. Carved stool. *Vert*—1s. 3d. Map and bowl of fire; 2s. 6d. Topi (antelope) and flag.

**133** Red Cross

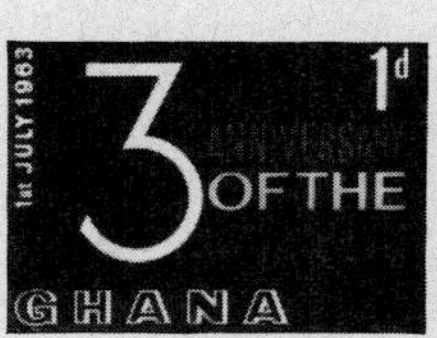


**137** "3rd Anniversary"

(Des R. Hegeman (4d.), M. Shamir (others))

**1963** (28 May). *Red Cross Centenary. T* **133** *and similar multicoloured designs. W* **47** *(sideways on 1½d., 4d.). P* 14½ × 14 *(1d., 1s. 3d.) or* 14 × 14½ *(others).*

307 1d. Type **133** .. .. .. .. .. 35 15
308 1½d. Centenary emblem (*horiz*) .. .. 45 60
309 4d. Nurses and child (*horiz*) .. .. 1·50 15
310 1s. 3d. Emblem, globe and laurel .. .. 2·75 1·60
307/10 .. .. .. .. .. *Set of* 4 4·50 2·25
**MS**310*a* 102 × 127 mm. Nos. 307/10. Imperf .. 3·00 7·50

(Des M. Goaman (1d., 4d.), R. Hegeman (others))

**1963** (1 July). *3rd Anniv of Republic. T* **137** *and similar multicoloured designs. W* **47** *(sideways on 1d., 4d.). P* 14½ × 14 *(horiz) or* 14 × 14½ *(vert).*

311 1d. Type **137** .. .. .. .. .. 10 10
312 4d. Three Ghanaian flags .. .. .. 10 10
a. Black (stars on flag) omitted .. .. † —
313 1s. 3d. Map, flag and star (*vert*) .. .. 20 10
314 2s. 6d. Flag and torch (*vert*) .. .. .. 30 50
311/14 .. .. .. .. .. *Set of* 4 60 60

141 President Nkrumah and Ghana Flag

145 Rameses II, Abu Simbel

(Des R. Hegeman (1d., 4d.), M. Shamir (1s. 3d.), G. Rose (5s.))

**1963** (21 Sept). *Founder's Day. T* **141** *and similar designs.* W **47** *(sideways on 1s. 3d., 5s.). P* 14 × 14½ *(vert) or* 14½ × 14 *(horiz).*
315 1d. multicoloured .. 10 10
316 4d. multicoloured .. 10 10
317 1s. 3d. multicoloured .. 15 10
a. Green omitted .. 55·00
318 5s. yellow and bright reddish purple .. 50 65
315/18 .. *Set of* 4 70 70
Designs: *Vert*—4d. Nkrumah and flag. *Horiz*—1s. 3d. Nkrumah and fireworks; 5s. Symbol of Wisdom.

(Des M. Farrar Bell and R. Hegeman. Litho (1½d., 2d.) or photo (others) Enschedé)

**1963** (1 Nov). *Nubian Monuments Preservation. T* **145** *and similar multicoloured designs. No wmk. P* 11½ × 11 *(vert) or* 11 × 11½ *(horiz).*
319 1d. Type **145** .. 10 10
320 1½d. Rock paintings *(horiz)* .. 15 50
321 2d. Queen Nefertari *(horiz)* .. 15 10
322 4d. Sphinx, Sebua .. 25 15
323 1s. 3d. Rock Temple, Abu Simbel *(horiz)* .. 70 85
319/23 .. *Set of* 5 1·25 1·50

**150** Steam and Diesel Locomotives

**151** Eleanor Roosevelt and "Flame of Freedom"

(Des H. L. W. Stevens)

**1963** (1 Dec). *60th Anniv of Ghana Railway.* W **47** *(sideways). P* 14½ × 14.
324 **150** 1d. multicoloured .. 10 10
325 6d. multicoloured .. 50 10
326 1s. 3d. multicoloured .. 1·00 60
327 2s. 6d. multicoloured .. 2·25 2·25
324/7 .. *Set of* 4 3·50 2·75

(Des R. Hegeman and F. H. Savage. Photo Enschedé)

**1963** (10 Dec). *15th Anniv of Declaration of Human Rights. T* **151** *and similar multicoloured designs. No wmk. P* 11 × 11½ *(1s. 3d.) or* 11½ × 11 *(others).*
328 1d. Type **151** .. 10 10
329 4d. Type **151** .. 10 10
330 6d. Eleanor Roosevelt .. 10 10
331 1s. 3d. Eleanor Roosevelt and emblems *(horiz)* .. 10 10
328/31 .. *Set of* 4 20 20
No. 329 differs from No. 328 in the arrangement of the trailing "flame" and of the background within the circular emblem.

**154** Sun and Globe Emblem

**155** Harvesting Corn on State Farm

**1964** (15 June). *International Quiet Sun Years.* W **47** *(sideways). Each blue, yellow, red and green; background colours given. P* 14½.
332 **154** 3d. pale brown .. 10 10
333 6d. pale grey .. 15 10
334 1s. 3d. mauve .. 15 10
332/4 .. *Set of* 3 30 20
**MS**334*a* 90 × 90 mm. No. 334 in block of four. Imperf .. 70 2·25
Nos. 332/4 each exist in a miniature sheet of 12 in different colours (i.e. 3d. in colours of 6d.; 6d. in colours of 1s. 3d.; 1s. 3d. in colours of 3d.) but these were not generally available to the public.

(Des M. Shamir. Photo Govt Printer, Israel)

**1964** (1 July). *4th Anniv of Republic. T* **155** *and similar horiz designs. P* 13 × 14.
335 3d. olive, brown and yellow-olive .. 10 10
336 6d. bluish green, brown and turquoise-green 10 10
337 1s. 3d. brown-red, brown and salmon-red .. 10 10
338 5s. multicoloured .. 40 60
335/8 .. *Set of* 4 55 65
**MS**338*a* 126 × 100 mm. Nos. 335/8. Imperf .. 55 2·00
ab. Olive (central design and face value of 3d.) omitted ..
Designs:—6d. Oil refinery, Tema; 1s. 3d. "Communal Labour"; 5s. Procession headed by flag.

**159** Globe and Dove

**163** Pres. Nkrumah and Hibiscus Flowers

(Des M. Shamir. Litho Lewin-Epstein Ltd, Bat Yam, Israel)

**1964** (15 July). *1st Anniv of African Unity Charter. T* **159** *and similar designs. P* 14.
339 3d. multicoloured .. 10 10
340 6d. deep bronze-green and red .. 10 10
341 1s. 3d. multicoloured .. 15 10
342 5s. multicoloured .. 45 60
339/42 .. *Set of* 4 65 65
Designs: *Vert*—6d. Map of Africa and quill pen; 5s. Planting flower. *Horiz*—1s. 3d. Hitched rope on map of Africa.

**1964** (21 Sept). *Founder's Day.* W **47** *(sideways). P* 14 × 14½.
343 **163** 3d. sepia, red, deep green and light blue 10 10
344 6d. sepia, red, deep green and yellow .. 10 10
345 1s. 3d. sepia, red, deep green and grey .. 25 10
346 2s. 6d. sepia, red, dp grn & light emerald 30 25
343/6 .. *Set of* 4 65 30
**MS**346*a* 90 × 122 mm. No. 346 in block of four. Imperf .. 70 2·50

**IMPERFORATE STAMPS.** Many issues, including miniature sheets, from here onwards exist imperforate, but these were not sold at post offices.

**164** Hurdling

(Des A. S. B. New (No. 352))

**1964** (25 Oct). *Olympic Games, Tokyo. T* **164** *and similar multicoloured designs.* W **47** *(sideways on 1d., 2½d., 6d., 5s.). P* 14½ × 14 *(horiz) or* 14 × 14½ *(vert).*
347 1d. Type **164** .. 10 10
348 2½d. Running .. 10 30
349 3d. Boxing *(vert)* .. 10 10
350 4d. Long-jumping *(vert)* .. 10 10
351 6d. Football *(vert)* .. 10 10
352 1s. 3d. Athlete holding Olympic Torch *(vert)* 15 10
353 5s. Olympic Rings and flags .. 65 2·00
347/53 .. *Set of* 7 1·10 2·25
**MS**353*a* 128 × 102 mm. Nos. 351/3. Imperf .. 75 2·25

**171** G. Washington Carver (botanist) and Plant

**173** African Elephant

(Des M. Shamir)

**1964** (7 Dec). *U.N.E.S.C.O. Week.* W **47**. *P* 14½.
354 **171** 6d. deep blue and green .. 15 10
355 – 1s. 3d. reddish purple and greenish blue 35 10
356 **171** 5s. sepia and orange-red .. 1·40 2·00
354/6 .. *Set of* 3 1·75 2·00
**MS**356*a* 127 × 77 mm. Nos. 354/6. Imperf .. 1·00 2·50
Design:—1s. 3d. Albert Einstein (scientist) and atomic symbol.

(Des A. S. B. New (No. 360). Photo Enschedé)

**1964** (14 Dec). *Multicoloured designs as T* **173**. *P* 11½ × 11 *(vert) or* 11 × 11½ *(horiz).*
357 1d. Type **173** .. 30 15
358 1½d. Secretary Bird *(horiz)* .. 45 1·00
359 2½d. Purple Wreath (flower) .. 45 1·00
360 3d. Grey Parrot .. 55 30
361 4d. Blue-naped Mousebird *(horiz)* .. 75 50
362 6d. African Tulip Tree *(horiz)* .. 45 20
363 1s. 3d. Violet Starling *(horiz)* .. 1·50 1·25
364 2s. 6d. Hippopotamus *(horiz)* .. 1·50 4·00
357/64 .. *Set of* 8 5·50 7·50
**MS**364*a* (a) 150×86 mm. Nos. 357/9. (b) 150×110 mm. Nos. 360/4. Imperf *Set of* 2 *sheets* 5·50 14·00

**NEW INFORMATION**

The editor is always interested to correspond with people who have new information that will improve or correct the Catalogue.

**181** I.C.Y. Emblem

**182** I.T.U. Emblem and Symbols

(Litho Enschedé)

**1965** (22 Feb). *International Co-operation Year. P* 14 × 12½.
365 **181** 1d. multicoloured .. 30 20
366 4d. multicoloured .. 85 45
367 6d. multicoloured .. 1·00 20
368 1s. 3d. multicoloured .. 1·60 1·90
365/8 .. *Set of* 4 3·25 2·50
**MS**368*a* 100 × 100 mm. No. 368 in block of four. Imperf .. 2·50 5·00

(Litho Enschedé)

**1965** (12 Apr). *I.T.U. Centenary. P* 13½.
369 **182** 1d. multicoloured .. 15 15
370 6d. multicoloured .. 45 15
371 1s. 3d. multicoloured .. 85 25
372 5s. multicoloured .. 2·25 2·75
369/72 .. *Set of* 4 3·25 3·00
**MS**372*a* 132 × 115 mm. Nos. 369/72. Imperf .. 4·50 8·00

**183** Lincoln's Home

(Des M. Farrar Bell (6d.), A. S. B. New (1s. 3d., 5s.), R. Hegeman (2s.))

**1965** (17 May). *Death Centenary of Abraham Lincoln. T* **183** *and similar square-shaped designs.* W **47** *(sideways). P* 12½.
373 6d. multicoloured .. 15 10
374 1s. 3d. black, red and blue .. 30 15
375 2s. black, orange-brown and greenish yellow 40 30
376 5s. black and red .. 85 1·50
373/6 .. *Set of* 4 1·50 1·75
**MS**376*a* 115 × 115 mm. Nos. 373/6. Imperf .. 1·50 3·50
ab. Green (part of flag on 6d.) omitted ..
Designs:—1s. 3d. Lincoln's Inaugural Address; 2s. Abraham Lincoln; 5s. Adaptation of U.S. 90 c. Lincoln Stamp of 1869.

**(New Currency. 100 pesewas = 1 cedi)**

**187** Obverse (Pres. Nkrumah) and Reverse of 5 p. Coin

(Photo Enschedé)

**1965** (19 July). *Introduction of Decimal Currency. T* **187** *and similar horiz designs. Multicoloured. P* 11 × 13 *(5 p., 10 p.),* 13 × 12½ *(25 p.) or* 13½ × 14 *(50 p.).*
377 5 p. Type **187** .. 20 10
378 10 p. As Type **187** .. 25 10
379 25 p. Size 63 × 39 mm .. 85 1·00
380 50 p. Size 71 × 43½ mm .. 1·75 2·25
377/80 .. *Set of* 4 2·75 3·00
The coins in Nos. 378/80 are all circular and express the same denominations as on the stamps.

₵2·40
Ghana New Currency
19th July. 1965.

**(188)**

**1965** (19 July). *Nos. 214, 216 and 218a/27 surch as T* **188** *diagonally upwards, (D) or horizontally, (H), by Govt Printer, Accra.*

*(a) Postage*
381 1 p. on 1d. multicoloured (R.) (D) .. 10 10
a. Surch inverted .. 15·00
b. Surch double ..
382 2 p. on 2d. multicoloured (Ultram.) (H) .. 10 10
a. Surch inverted ..
b. Surch double .. 10·00
c. Surch on back only ..
d. Surch on front and back ..
e. Red surch .. 26·00
f. Orange surch .. 26·00
g. Indigo surch ..

383 3 p. on 3d. multicoloured (II) (Br.) (H) .. 95 2·50
a. Surch inverted .. .. .. .. .. 18·00
b. Indigo surch .. .. .. .. ..
384 4 p. on 4d. multicoloured (B.) (H) .. .. 1·25 30
a. Surch inverted .. .. .. .. .. 14·00
b. Surch double .. .. .. .. ..
c. Red surch .. .. .. .. ..
385 6 p. on 6d. multicoloured (Blk.) (H) .. .. 30 10
a. Surch inverted .. .. .. .. .. 8·50
b. Surch double .. .. .. .. .. 15·00
c. Horiz pair, one without surch .. .. 50·00
d. Green (flag) omitted .. .. .. 55·00
386 11 p. on 11d. multicoloured (W.) (D) .. .. 25 10
a. Surch inverted .. .. .. .. .. 11·00
387 12 p. on 1s. multicoloured (B.) (D) .. .. 25 10
a. Surch double .. .. .. .. ..
b. Surch double, one albino inverted
c. Black surch .. .. .. .. .. 9·00
ca. Surch inverted .. .. .. .. 9·00
388 30 p. on 2s. 6d. multicoloured (B.) (H) .. .. 2·25 1·00
389 60 p. on 5s. multicoloured (B.) (D) .. .. 4·00 70
a. Surch double (G. + B.) .. .. .. 23·00
390 1 c. 20 on 10s. multicoloured (B.) (D) .. 1·75 2·25
a. Surch double (G. + B.) .. .. .. 80·00
391 2 c. 40 on £1 multicoloured (B.) (D) .. 2·00 6·00

*(b) Air*

392 15 p. on 1s. 3d. multicoloured (W.) (H) .. 2·00 35
a. Surch inverted .. .. .. .. ..
393 24 p. on 2s. multicoloured (G.) (D) .. .. 2·50 30
a. Surch on front and back .. .. .. 25·00
381/93 .. .. .. .. *Set of* 13 16·00 12·50

On the diagonal surcharges the values are horizontal.

The 30 p. was not released in Ghana until 30 July and the 3 p. sometime later.

Numerous minor varieties exist.

**189** "OAU" and Flag

**190** "OAU", Heads and Flag

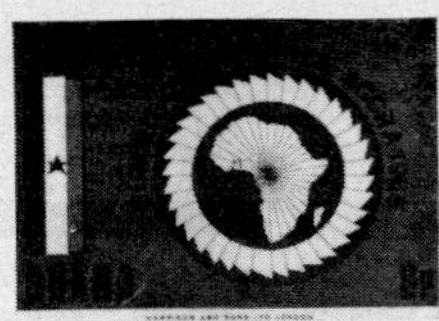


**191** "OAU" Emblem and Flag

**192** African Map and Flag

**1965** (21 Oct). *O.A.U. Summit Conference, Accra. T* **189/92** *and similar horiz designs. Multicoloured. W* **47** *(sideways, except on 6 p.). P 14 (T* **189/91***) or 14½ × 14 (others).*

394 1 p. Type **189** .. .. .. .. .. 10 10
395 2 p. Type **190** .. .. .. .. .. 10 10
396 5 p. Type **191** .. .. .. .. .. 10 10
397 6 p. Type **192** .. .. .. .. .. 10 10
398 15 p. "Sunburst", map and flag .. .. 20 25
399 24 p. "O.A.U." on map, and flag .. .. 35 50
394/9 .. .. .. .. .. *Set of* 6 75 90

**195** Goalkeeper saving Ball

**198** Pres. Kennedy and Grave Memorial

(Photo Enschedé)

**1965** (15 Nov). *African Soccer Cup Competition. T* **195** *and similar multicoloured designs. P 13 × 14 (15 p.) or 14 × 13 (others).*

400 6 p. Type **195** .. .. .. .. .. 10 10
401 15 p. Player with ball (*vert*) .. .. .. 20 20
402 24 p. Players, ball and soccer cup .. .. 35 40
400/2 .. .. .. .. .. *Set of* 3 60 60

(Des A. S. B. New (No. 405))

**1965** (15 Dec)–**66**. *2nd Anniv of President Kennedy's Death. T* **198** *and similar square-shaped designs. W* **47** *(sideways). P 12½.*

403 6 p. multicoloured .. .. .. .. 15 10
404 15 p. violet, red and green .. .. .. 40 35
405 24 p. black and reddish violet .. .. .. 50 60
406 30 p. dull purple and black .. .. .. 60 75
403/6 .. .. .. .. *Set of* 4 1·50 1·60
**MS**407 114½ × 114 mm. Nos. 403/6. Imperf (21.3.66) .. .. .. .. .. 3·75 6·50

Designs:—15 p. Pres. Kennedy and Eternal Flame; 24 p. Pres. Kennedy and memorial inscription; 30 p. President Kennedy.

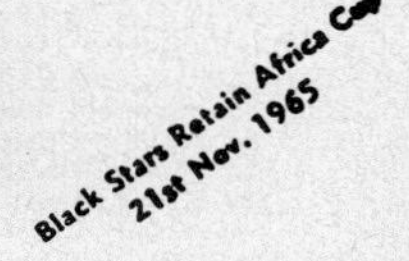

Black Stars Retain Africa Cup
21st Nov. 1965


**202** Section of Dam and Generators

**(206)**

(Des A. S. B. New (No. 411). Photo Enschedé)

**1966** (22 Jan). *Volta River Project. T* **202** *and similar horiz designs. P 11 × 11½.*

408 6 p. multicoloured .. .. .. .. 15 10
409 15 p. multicoloured .. .. .. .. 20 15
410 24 p. multicoloured .. .. .. .. 25 20
411 30 p. black and new blue .. .. .. 35 50
408/11 .. .. .. .. *Set of* 4 85 85

Designs:—15 p. Dam and Lake Volta; 24 p. Word "GHANA" as dam; 30 p. "Fertility".

**1966** (7 Feb). *"Black Stars" Victory in African Soccer Cup Competition. Nos. 400/2 optd with T* **206**, *in black.*

412 6 p. Type **195** .. .. .. .. .. 10 10
a. Green opt .. .. .. .. .. 20·00
b. Green opt double, one inverted ..
c. Stop after "Nov" omitted (R. 5/1) ..
413 15 p. Player with ball .. .. .. 20 20
414 24 p. Players, ball and cup .. .. 35 35
a. Opt inverted* .. .. .. .. 26·00
ab. Vert pair, one without opt, the other with opt inverted .. ..
b. Error. Opt for 15 p. on 24 p. inverted* ..
c. Stop after "Nov" omitted (R. 5/1) ..
412/14 .. .. .. .. *Set of* 3 60 60

*In No. 414a the overprint reads downwards (top right to bottom left), but in No. 414b it reads upwards (bottom right to top left).

**DATES OF ISSUE** of miniature sheets are approximate as they are generally released some time after the related ordinary stamps, but it known that the G.P.O. sometimes apply first-day cancellations months after the dates shown on the cancellations.

**207** W.H.O. Building and Ghana Flag

**1966** (1 July). *Inauguration of W.H.O. Headquarters, Geneva. T* **207** *and similar horiz design. Multicoloured. W* **47**. *P 14½ × 14.*

415 6 p. Type **207** .. .. .. .. .. 40 10
416 15 p. Type **207** .. .. .. .. .. 75 50
417 24 p. W.H.O. Building and emblem .. .. 1·00 1·00
418 30 p. As 24 p. .. .. .. .. .. 1·25 1·75
415/18 .. .. .. .. *Set of* 4 3·00 3·00
**MS**419 120 × 101 mm. Nos. 415/18. Imperf (11.66) 14·00 17·00

**209** Herring

**214** African "Links" and Ghana Flag

(Des O. Hamann. Photo Enschedé)

**1966** (10 Aug). *Freedom from Hunger. T* **209** *and similar horiz designs. Multicoloured. P 14 × 13.*

420 6 p. Type **209** .. .. .. .. .. 15 1
421 15 p. Flat Fish .. .. .. .. .. 35 1
422 24 p. Spade Fish .. .. .. .. 65 3
423 30 p. Red Snapper .. .. .. .. 80 7
424 60 p. Tuna .. .. .. .. .. 2·00 2·5
420/4 .. .. .. .. *Set of* 5 3·50 3·5
**MS**425 126 × 109 mm. No. 423 in block of four. Imperf (Nov) .. .. .. .. .. 7·50 12·0

(Photo Enschedé)

**1966** (11 Oct). *Third Anniv of African Charter. T* **214** *and similar multicoloured designs. P 13½.*

426 6 p. Type **214** .. .. .. .. .. 10 10
427 15 p. Flags as "Quill", and diamond (*horiz*) .. 25 20
428 24 p. Ship's wheel, map and cocoa bean (*horiz*) 30 25
426/8 .. .. .. .. *Set of* 3 60 45

**217** Player heading Ball, and Jules Rimet Cup

**1966** (14 Nov). *World Cup Football Championships, England. T* **217** *and similar horiz designs. Multicoloured. W* **47**. *P 14½ × 14.*

429 5 p. Type **217** .. .. .. .. .. 15 10
430 15 p. Goalkeeper clearing ball .. .. .. 40 20
431 24 p. Player and Jules Rimet Cup (replica) .. 55 35
432 30 p. Players and Jules Rimet Cup (replica) .. 75 90
433 60 p. Players with ball .. .. .. .. 1·50 2·50
429/33 .. .. .. .. *Set of* 5 3·00 3·50
**MS**434 120 × 102 mm. 60 p. (block of four). Imperf 14·00 16·00

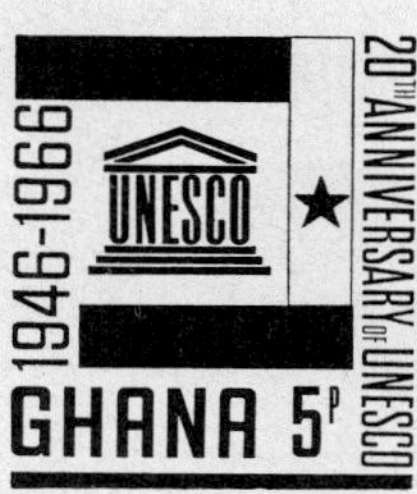


**222** U.N.E.S.C.O. Emblem

**1966** (23 Dec). *20th Anniv of U.N.E.S.C.O. W* **47** *(sideways). P 14½.*

435 **222** 5 p. multicoloured .. .. .. 25 15
436 15 p. multicoloured .. .. .. 50 35
437 24 p. multicoloured .. .. .. 80 80
438 30 p. multicoloured .. .. .. 1·25 1·75
439 60 p. multicoloured .. .. .. 2·25 3·50
435/9 .. .. .. .. *Set of* 5 4·50 6·00
**MS**440 140 × 115 mm. Nos. 435/9. Imperf .. 16·00 20·00

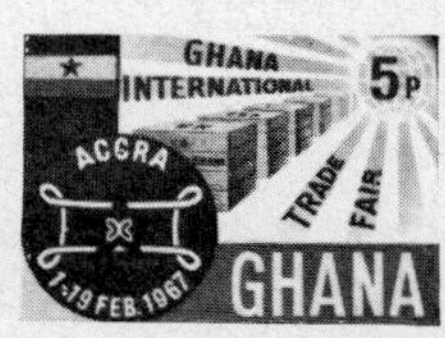


**223** Fair Emblem and Crates

**1967** (1 Feb). *Ghana Trade Fair, Accra. T* **223** *and similar multicoloured designs. W* **47** *(sideways on 24 p.). P 14 × 14½ (24 p.) or 14½ × 14 (others).*

441 5 p. Type **223** .. .. .. .. .. 10 10
442 15 p. Fair emblem and world map .. .. 15 15
443 24 p. Shipping and flags (*vert*) .. .. .. 25 30
444 36 p. Fair emblem and hand-held hoist .. 40 80
441/4 .. .. .. .. *Set of* 4 70 1·25

**(New Currency. 100 new pesewas = 1 new cedi (1·2 old cedi))**

1½Np (227)

N¢2.00 (228)

**229** Ghana Eagle and Flag

**1967** (23 Feb). *Nos. 216, 219/23, 225/6 and 393 surch as T* **227/8**.

*(a) Postage*

445 1½ n.p. on 2d. multicoloured (Blk.) .. 5·50 3·25
446 3½ n.p. on 4d. multicoloured (R.) .. 1·00 30
a. Surch double, one sideways ..
447 5 n.p. on 6d. multicoloured (R.) .. 35 15

448 9 n.p. on 11d. multicoloured (W.) .. 30 15
449 10 n.p. on 1s. multicoloured (W.) .. 30 15
450 25 n.p. on 2s. 6d. multicoloured (R.) .. 3·25 2·00
451 1 n.c. on 10s. multicoloured (R.) .. 6·50 11·00
452 2 n.c. on £1 multicoloured (R.) .. .. 12·00 22·00

*(b) Air*

453 12½ n.p. on 1s. 3d. multicoloured (W.) .. 3·00 90
454 20 n.p. on 24 p. on 2s. multicoloured (R.) .. 3·00 1·75
445/54 .. .. .. .. .. *Set of* 10 32·00 38·00

Inverted surcharges in a different type face on the 3½, 5 and 25 n.p. are fakes.

(Des M. Shamir)

**1967** (24 Feb). *First Anniv of February 24 Revolution. W* **47** *(sideways). P* 14 × 14½.

455 **229** 1 n.p. multicoloured .. .. .. 10 15
456 4 n.p. multicoloured .. .. .. 10 10
457 12½ n.p. multicoloured .. .. .. 40 55
458 25 n.p. multicoloured .. .. .. 85 2·00
455/8 .. .. .. .. .. *Set of* 4 1·25 2·50
**MS**459 89 × 108 mm. Nos. 455/8. Perf or imperf .. 8·00 12·00

**230** Maize

**231** Forest Kingfisher

**235** Rufous-crowned Roller

**236** Akosombo Dam

**1967** (1 June–4 Sept). *T* **230/1, 235/6** *and similar designs. W* **47** *(1½, 2, 4, 50 n.p. and 1 n.c.) or sideways (others). P* 11½ × 12 *(1, 8 n.p.),* 12 × 11½ *(4 n.p.),* 14 × 14½ *(1½, 2, 2½, 20 n.p., 2 n.c. 50) or* 14½ × 14 *(others).*

460 1 n.p. multicoloured .. .. .. 10 10
a. Salmon omitted** .. .. ..
461 1½ n.p. multicoloured .. .. .. 90 30
a. Blue omitted* .. .. .. 70·00
b. Green printed double, once inverted†
c. Green omitted† .. .. ..
462 2 n.p. multicoloured (4.9) .. .. 10 10
a. Green (part of flag) omitted ..
b. Gold (frame) omitted .. ..
463 2½ n.p. multicoloured (4.9) .. .. 35 10
a. Wmk upright .. .. .. 30·00
ab. Face value omitted .. .. £160
464 3 n.p. multicoloured .. .. .. 20 30
a. Green (part of flag) omitted ..
465 4 n.p. multicoloured .. .. .. 1·50 10
a. Green (part of flag) omitted ..
b. Red (part of flag) omitted .. ..
c. Black (star, bird markings and shadow) omitted .. .. .. 55·00
466 6 n.p. multicoloured .. .. .. 15 10
467 8 n.p. multicoloured .. .. .. 15 10
468 9 n.p. multicoloured (4.9) .. .. 45 10
469 10 n.p. multicoloured .. .. .. 15 10
470 20 n.p. deep blue and new blue (4.9) .. 20 10
471 50 n.p. multicoloured .. .. .. 3·50 35
472 1 n.c. multicoloured (4.9) .. .. 2·25 75
473 2 n.c. multicoloured (4.9) .. .. 2·00 3·00
474 2 n.c. 50, multicoloured .. .. 3·25 4·00
460/74 .. .. .. .. *Set of* 15 13·50 8·25

Designs: *Vert (as T* **231**)—2 n.p. The Ghana Mace; 2½ n.p. Commelina; 20 n.p. Bush Hare; 2 n.c. Frangipani; 2 n.c. 50, Seat of State. *Horiz (as T* **236**)—3 n.p. Mud-fish; 9 n.p. Chameleon; 10 n.p. Tema Harbour; 50 n.p. Black-winged Stilt; 1 n.c. Wooden Stool. *(As T* **230**)—8 n.p. Adomi Bridge.

*In this stamp the blue not only affects the bird but is printed over the yellow background to give the value in green, so that its omission results in the value also being omitted.

**This affects the maize flowers, corn and foreground.

†This affects the feather-tips and the flag.

The 2 n.p. and 20 n.p. were officially issued on 4 September but small quanties of both were released in error on 1 June. The 2½ n.p. is also known to have been released in error in June.

**245** Kumasi Fort

**249** "Luna 10"

(Des O. Hamann)

**1967** (1 July). *Castles and Forts. T* **245** *and similar designs. Multicoloured. W* **47** *(diagonal). P* 14½.

475 4 n.p. Type **245** .. .. .. .. 25 10
476 12½ n.p. Christiansborg Castle and British galleon .. .. .. .. 1·00 1·00
477 20 n.p. Elmina Castle and Portuguese galleon .. .. .. .. 1·40 2·00
478 25 n.p. Cape Coast Castle and Spanish galleon .. .. .. .. 1·75 2·50
475/8 .. .. .. .. .. *Set of* 4 4·00 5·00

(Des M. Shamir. Photo Enschedé)

**1967** (16 Aug). *"Peaceful Use of Outer Space". T* **249** *and similar square designs. Multicoloured. P* 13½ × 14.

479 4 n.p. Type **249** .. .. .. .. 10 10
480 10 n.p. "Orbiter 1" .. .. .. .. 10 15
481 12½ n.p. Man in Space .. .. .. 20 30
479/81 .. .. .. .. .. *Set of* 3 35 45
**MS**482 140 × 90 mm. Nos. 479/81. Imperf .. 95 2·50

**252** Scouts and Camp-fire

(Photo Enschedé)

**1967** (18 Sept). *50th Anniv of Ghanaian Scout Movement. T* **252** *and similar horiz designs. Multicoloured. P* 14½ × 13.

483 4 n.p. Type **252** .. .. .. .. 20 10
484 10 n.p. Scout on march .. .. .. 50 20
485 12½ n.p. Lord Baden-Powell .. .. .. 70 70
483/5 .. .. .. .. .. *Set of* 3 1·25 90
**MS**486 167 × 95 mm. Nos. 483/5. Imperf .. .. 6·00 9·50

**255** U.N. Headquarters Building

**256** General View of U.N. H.Q., Manhattan

(Litho D.L.R.)

**1967** (20 Nov). *United Nations Day (24 October). P* 13½.

487 **255** 4 n.p. multicoloured .. .. .. 15 10
488 10 n.p. multicoloured .. .. .. 20 15
489 **256** 50 n.p. multicoloured .. .. .. 40 70
490 2 n.c. 50, multicoloured .. .. 1·50 4·00
487/90 .. .. .. .. *Set of* 4 2·00 4·50
**MS**491 76 × 75 mm. No. 490. Imperf (4.12.67) .. 4·50 9·50

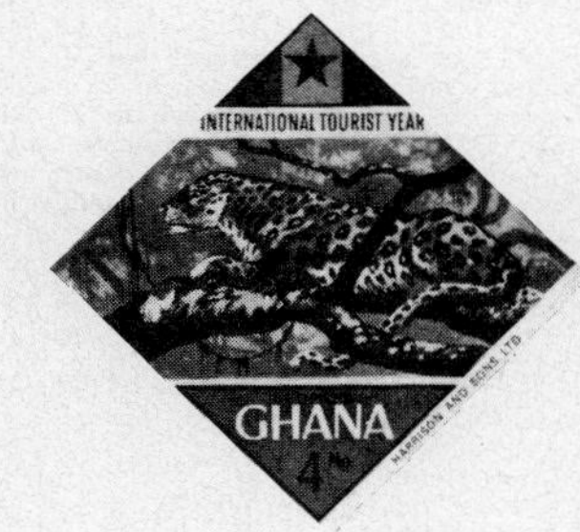


**257** Leopard

**1967** (28 Dec). *International Tourist Year. T* **257** *and similar diamond-shaped designs. Multicoloured. W* **47** *(diagonal). P* 12½.

492 4 n.p. Type **257** .. .. .. .. 50 10
493 12½ n.p. *Papilio demodocus* (butterfly) .. 1·00 1·25
494 20 n.p. Carmine Bee Eater .. .. .. 2·00 2·75
495 50 n.p. Waterbuck .. .. .. .. 3·00 4·75
492/5 .. .. .. .. .. *Set of* 4 6·00 8·00
**MS**496 126 × 126 mm. Nos. 493/5. Imperf .. 12·00 13·00

**261** Revolutionaries entering Accra

(Litho D.L.R.)

**1968** (24 Feb). *2nd Anniv of February Revolution. T* **261** *and similar horiz designs. Multicoloured. P* 14.

497 4 n.p. Type **261** .. .. .. .. 10 10
498 12½ n.p. Marching troops .. .. .. 20 20
499 20 n.p. Cheering people .. .. .. 30 40
500 40 n.p. Victory celebrations .. .. 50 1·25
497/500 .. .. .. .. *Set of* 4 1·00 1·75

**265** Microscope and Cocoa Beans

**1968** (18 Mar). *Cocoa Research. T* **265** *and similar horiz design. Multicoloured. W* **47** *(sideways). P* 14½ × 14.

501 2½ n.p. Type **265** .. .. .. .. 10 10
502 4 n.p. Microscope and cocoa tree, beans and pods .. .. .. .. .. 10 10
503 10 n.p. Type **265** .. .. .. .. 15 15
504 25 n.p. As 4 n.p. .. .. .. .. 60 80
501/4 .. .. .. .. .. *Set of* 4 80 90
**MS**505 102 × 102 mm. Nos. 501/4. Imperf .. 2·25 3·50

**267** Kotoka and Flowers

**271** Tobacco

(Des A. S. B. New (No. 508) and F. Mate (others) Litho D.L.R.)

**1968** (17 Apr). *1st Death Anniv of Lt.-Gen. E. K. Kotoka. T* **267** *and similar multicoloured designs. P* 14.

506 4 n.p. Type **267** .. .. .. .. 10 10
507 12½ n.p. Kotoka and wreath .. .. .. 20 20
508 20 n.p. Kotoka in civilian clothes .. .. 35 65
509 40 n.p. Lt.-Gen. Kotoka *(vert)* .. .. 50 1·00
506/9 .. .. .. .. .. *Set of* 4 1·00 1·75

(Des A. S. B. New (5 n.p.))

**1968** (19 Aug). *T* **271** *and similar vert designs. Multicoloured. W* **47** *(sideways). P* 14 × 14½.

510 4 n.p. Type **271** .. .. .. .. 15 10
511 5 n.p. North African Crested Porcupine .. 15 15
512 12½ n.p. Rubber .. .. .. .. 50 65
513 20 n.p. *Cymothoe sangaris* (butterfly) .. 1·00 1·75
514 40 n.p. *Charaxes ameliae* (butterfly) .. 1·75 3·50
510/14 .. .. .. .. .. *Set of* 5 3·25 5·50
**MS**515 88 × 114 mm. Nos. 410, 512/14. Imperf .. 3·50 8·00

**276** Surgeons, Flag and W.H.O. Emblem

**277** Hurdling

(Photo Enschedé)

**1968** (11 Nov). *20th Anniv of World Health Organization. P* 14 × 13.

516 **276** 4 n.p. multicoloured .. .. .. 20 10
517 12½ n.p. multicoloured .. .. .. 40 35
518 20 n.p. multicoloured .. .. .. 70 70
519 40 n.p. multicoloured .. .. .. 1·25 1·50
516/19 .. .. .. .. *Set of* 4 2·25 2·40
**MS**520 132 × 110 mm. Nos. 516/19. Imperf .. 3·50 6·00

**1969** (10 Jan). *Olympic Games, Mexico (1968). T* **277** *and similar vert designs. Multicoloured. W* **47** *(sideways). P* 14 × 14½.

521 4 n.p. Type **277** .. .. .. .. 10 10
522 12½ n.p. Boxing .. .. .. .. 20 30
523 20 n.p. Torch, Olympic Rings and flags .. 40 70
524 40 n.p. Football .. .. .. .. 70 1·50
521/4 .. .. .. .. .. *Set of* 4 1·25 2·25
**MS**525 89 × 114 mm. Nos. 521/4. Imperf (17.1.69) 3·50 5·00

**281** U.N. Building

**285** Dr. J. B. Danquah

(Litho D.L.R.)

**1969** (1 Feb). *United Nations Day (1968). T* **281** *and similar square-shaped designs. Multicoloured. P* 13½.

526 4 n.p. Type **281** .. .. .. .. 10 10
527 12½ n.p. Native stool, staff and U.N. emblem 15 20
528 20 n.p. U.N. building and emblem over Ghanaian flag .. .. .. .. 25 35
529 40 n.p. U.N. emblem encircled by flags .. 50 90
526/9 .. .. .. .. .. *Set of* 4 90 1·40
**MS**530 127 × 117 mm. No. 526/9. Imperf .. .. 1·10 3·25

**1969** (7 Mar). *Human Rights Year. T* **285** *and similar horiz design. Multicoloured.* W **47** (*sideways on* **MS**535). *P* 14½ × 14.

531 4 n.p. Type **285** .. .. .. .. 10 10
532 12½ n.p. Dr. Martin Luther King .. .. 20 30
533 20 n.p. As 12½ n.p. .. .. .. 35 60
534 40 n.p. Type **285** .. .. .. .. 55 1·10
531/4 .. .. .. .. *Set of* 4 1·10 1·75
**MS**535 116 × 50 mm. Nos. 531/4. Imperf (17.4.69) 80 3·00

**287** Constituent Assembly Building

**1969** (10 Sept). *Third Anniv of the Revolution. T* **287** *and similar horiz design.* W **47** (*sideways on* **MS**540). *P* 14½ × 14.

536 4 n.p. Type **287** .. .. .. .. 10 10
537 12½ n.p. Arms of Ghana .. .. .. 10 10
538 20 n.p. Type **287** .. .. .. .. 15 15
539 40 n.p. As 12½ n.p. .. .. .. 20 35
536/9 .. .. .. .. *Set of* 4 40 60
**MS**540 114 × 89 mm. Nos. 536/9. Imperf .. .. 70 2·25

**NEW CONSTITUTION**
**1969**

(289)

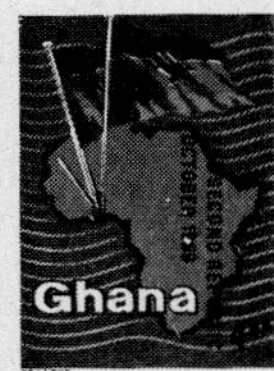


**290** Map of Africa and Flags

**1969** (1 Oct). *New Constitution. Nos. 460/74 optd with T* **289** *in various positions by Government Press, Accra.*

541 1 n.p. multicoloured (Horiz) .. .. .. 10 40
542 1½ n.p. multicoloured (Vert down) .. .. 60 60
 a. Opt vert up .. .. .. .. 6·00
 b. Horiz opt .. .. .. .. 25·00
 ba. Opt omitted (in vert pair with normal) .. .. .. .. £180
543 2 n.p. multicoloured (Vert up) .. .. 10 45
 a. Opt vert down .. .. .. .. 5·00
 b. Opt double .. .. .. .. 12·00
544 2½ n.p. multicoloured (Vert up) .. .. 10 45
 a. Opt vert down .. .. .. .. 18·00
545 3 n.p. multicoloured (Horiz) .. .. .. 45 60
 a. Opt inverted .. .. .. .. 15·00
546 4 n.p. multicoloured (Y.) (Vert down) .. .. 1·25 30
 a. Black opt (vert down) .. .. .. 6·00 1·00
 b. Black opt (vert up) .. .. .. 10·00
 c. Red opt (vert down) .. .. .. 18·00
 d. Opt double (White vert down + yellow vert up) .. .. .. .. 27·00
547 6 n.p. multicoloured (Horiz) .. .. .. 15 50
548 8 n.p. multicoloured (Horiz) .. .. .. 15 40
549 9 n.p. multicoloured (Horiz) .. .. .. 15 50
550 10 n.p. multicoloured (Horiz) .. .. .. 20 40
551 20 n.p. deep blue and new blue (Vert up) .. 35 70
 a. Opt vert down .. .. .. .. 20·00
552 50 n.p. multicoloured (Horiz) .. .. .. 4·00 4·25
 a. Opt double .. .. .. ..
553 1 n.c. multicoloured (Horiz) .. .. .. 2·25 4·50
554 2 n.c. multicoloured (R.) (Vert up) .. .. 3·50 7·00
 a. Opt double (vert up and down)
555 2 n.c. 50, multicoloured (Vert down) .. .. 3·50 8·00
541/55 .. .. .. .. *Set of* 15 15·00 26·00

The 1 n.p. is known with the overprint inverted, "NEW CONSTITUTION" appearing between the stamps across the perforations.

(Litho D.L.R.)

**1969** (4 Dec). *Inauguration of Second Republic. T* **290** *and similar vert designs. Multicoloured. P* 14.

556 4 n.p. Type **290** .. .. .. .. 10 10
557 12½ n.p. Figure "2", branch and Ghanaian colours .. .. .. .. 20 10
558 20 n.p. Hands receiving egg .. .. .. 30 30
559 40 n.p. Type **290** .. .. .. .. 60 70
556/9 .. .. .. .. *Set of* 4 1·10 1·00

**293** I.L.O. Emblem and Cog-wheels

**1970** (5 Jan). *50th Anniv of International Labour Organisation.* W **47** (*sideways*). *P* 14½ × 14.

560 **293** 4 n.p. multicoloured .. .. .. 10 10
561 12½ n.p. multicoloured .. .. .. 20 25
562 20 n.p. multicoloured .. .. .. 30 45
560/2 .. .. .. .. *Set of* 3 55 70
**MS**563 117 × 89 mm. Nos. 560/2. Imperf .. .. 70 2·25

***NEW INFORMATION***

The editor is always interested to correspond with people who have new information that will improve or correct the Catalogue.

**294** Red Cross and Globe

**298** General Kotoka, "VC-10" and Airport

**1970** (2 Feb). *50th Anniv of League of Red Cross Societies. T* **294** *and similar multicoloured designs.* W **47** (*sideways on 4 n.p.*). *P* 14 × 14½ (*4 n.p.*) *or* 14½ × 14 (*others*).

564 4 n.p. Type **294** .. .. .. .. 25 10
565 12½ n.p. Henri Dunant and Red Cross emblem (*horiz*) .. .. .. .. 45 20
566 20 n.p. Patient receiving medicine (*horiz*) .. 55 55
567 40 n.p. Patient having arm bandaged (*horiz*) 80 1·40
564/7 .. .. .. .. *Set of* 4 1·90 2·00
**MS**568 114 × 89 mm. Nos. 564/7. Imperf .. .. 2·50 6·00

(Des G. Vasarhelyi. Litho D.L.R.)

**1970** (17 Apr). *Inauguration of Kotoka Airport. T* **298** *and similar horiz designs. Multicoloured. P* 13 × 13½.

569 4 n.p. Type **298** .. .. .. .. 10 10
570 12½ n.p. Control tower and tail of "VC-10" .. 20 15
571 20 n.p. Aerial view of airport .. .. 30 30
572 40 n.p. Airport and flags .. .. .. 60 80
569/72 .. .. .. .. *Set of* 4 1·10 1·25

**302** Lunar Module landing on Moon

**306** Adult Education

(Des A. Medina (4 n.p., 12½ n.p.), G. Vasarhelyi (others). Litho D.L.R.)

**1970** (15 June). *Moon Landing. T* **302** *and similar multicoloured designs. P* 12½.

573 4 n.p. Type **302** .. .. .. .. 30 10
574 12½ n.p. Astronaut's first step onto the Moon .. 85 60
575 20 n.p. Astronaut with equipment on Moon (*horiz*) .. .. .. .. 1·40 1·40
576 40 n.p. Astronauts (*horiz*) .. .. .. 3·00 3·00
573/6 .. .. .. .. *Set of* 4 5·00 4·50
**MS**577 142 × 142 mm. Nos. 573/6. Imperf (with or without simulated perfs) .. .. .. 7·00 10·00

On 18 September 1970 Nos. 573/6 were issued overprinted "PHILYMPIA LONDON 1970" but it is understood that only 900 sets were made available for sale in Ghana and we do not consider that this is sufficient to constitute normal postal use. The miniature sheet was also overprinted but not issued in Ghana.

(Litho D.L.R.)

**1970** (10 Aug). *International Education Year. T* **306** *and similar horiz designs. Multicoloured. P* 13.

578 4 n.p. Type **306** .. .. .. .. 10 10
579 12½ n.p. International education .. .. 20 20
580 20 n.p. "Ntesie" and I.E.Y. symbols .. .. 35 30
581 40 n.p. Nursery schools .. .. .. 60 85
578/81 .. .. .. .. *Set of* 4 1·10 1·25

**310** Saluting March-Past

**314** *Crinum ornatum*

(Litho D.L.R.)

**1970** (1 Oct). *First Anniv of the Second Republic. T* **310** *and similar horiz designs. Multicoloured. P* 13 × 13½.

582 4 n.p. Type **310** .. .. .. .. 10 10
583 12½ n.p. Busia declaration .. .. .. 15 15
584 20 n.p. Doves symbol .. .. .. 25 30
585 40 n.p. Opening of Parliament .. .. 50 65
582/5 .. .. .. .. *Set of* 4 90 1·00

(Des G. Vasarhelyi. Photo Harrison)

**1970** (2 Nov). *Flora and Fauna. T* **314** *and similar horiz designs. Multicoloured.* W **47** (*sideways*). *P* 14½ × 14.

586 4 n.p. Type **314** .. .. .. .. 1·00 10
587 12½ n.p. Lioness .. .. .. .. 1·10 35
588 20 n.p. *Anselia africana* (flower) .. .. 1·25 80
589 40 n.p. African Elephant .. .. .. 3·50 2·50
586/9 .. .. .. .. *Set of* 4 6·25 3·25

**315** Kuduo Brass Casket

(Des G. Vasarhelyi. Photo Harrison)

**1970** (7 Dec). *Monuments and Archaeological Sites in Ghana. T* **315** *and similar horiz designs. Multicoloured.* W **47**. *P* 14½ × 14.

590 4 n.p. Type **315** .. .. .. .. 15 10
591 12½ n.p. Akan Traditional House .. .. 35 20
592 20 n.p. Larabanga Mosque .. .. .. 60 50
593 40 n.p. Funerary Clay Head .. .. .. 90 1·10
590/3 .. .. .. .. *Set of* 4 1·75 1·75
**MS**594 89 × 71 mm. Nos. 590, 592 and 12½ n.p. Basilica of Pompeii; 40 n.p. Pistrinum of Pompeii. (wmk sideways). Imperf (2.71) .. .. 4·25 7·50

**316** Trade Fair Building

(Des G. Drummond (4 n.p., 50 n.p.), A. Larkins (others). Photo Harrison)

**1971** (5 Feb). *International Trade Fair, Accra. T* **316** *and similar multicoloured designs.* W **47** (*sideways, except 50 n.p.*). *P* 14 × 14½ (*50 n.p.*) *or* 14½ × 14 (*others*).

595 4 n.p. Type **316** .. .. .. .. 10 10
596 12½ n.p. Cosmetics and Pharmaceutical Goods 40 20
597 20 n.p. Vehicles .. .. .. .. 45 25
598 40 n.p. Construction Equipment .. .. 80 95
599 50 n.p. Transport and Packing Case (*vert*) .. 90 1·10
595/9 .. .. .. .. *Set of* 5 2·40 2·25

**317** Christ on the Cross

**318** Corn Cob

(Des from stained-glass windows. Litho D.L.R.)

**1971** (19 May). *Easter. T* **317** *and similar square designs. Multicoloured. P* 13.

600 4 n.p. Type **317** .. .. .. .. 15 10
601 12½ n.p. Christ and Disciples .. .. .. 25 35
602 20 n.p. Christ blessing Disciples .. .. 40 75
600/2 .. .. .. .. *Set of* 3 70 1·00

(Photo Harrison)

**1971** (15 June). *Freedom from Hunger Campaign.* W **47**. *P* 14 × 14½.

603 **318** 4 n.p. multicoloured .. .. .. 10 10
604 12½ n.p. multicoloured .. .. .. 35 60
605 20 n.p. multicoloured .. .. .. 65 1·10
603/5 .. .. .. .. *Set of* 3 1·00 1·60

Remainder stocks of the above were overprinted on the occasion of the death of Lord Boyd Orr and the 4 n.p. surcharged 60 n.p.

It is understood that 8,070 sets from the New York Agency were overprinted locally and returned to the Agency. Limited remainders of these stamps (only 330 of the 60 n.p.) were sold at the G.P.O. We do not list these as they were not freely on sale in Ghana.

**319** Guides Emblem and Ghana Flag

**320** Child-care Centre

(Des and litho Questa)

**1971** (22 July). *Ghana Girl Guides Golden Jubilee. T* **319** *and similar horiz designs each with Guides Emblem. Multicoloured. P* 14.

606 4 n.p. Type **319** .. .. .. .. 20 10
607 12½ n.p. Mrs. E. Ofuatey-Kodjoe (founder) and guides with flags .. .. .. 60 50
608 20 n.p. Guides laying stones .. .. .. 90 90
609 40 n.p. Camp-fire and tent .. .. .. 1·50 1·75
610 50 n.p. Signallers .. .. .. .. 1·75 2·00
606/10 .. .. .. .. *Set of* 5 4·50 4·75
**MS**611 133 × 105 mm. Nos. 606/10. Imperf .. 10·00 13·00

(Des and litho D.L.R.)

**1971** (7 Aug). *Y.W.C.A. World Council Meeting, Accra. T* **320** *and similar horiz designs. Multicoloured. P* 13.

| | | | |
|---|---|---|---|
| 612 | 4 n.p. Type **320** | 10 | 10 |
| 613 | 12½ n.p. Council meeting | 10 | 15 |
| 614 | 20 n.p. School typing-class | 15 | 30 |
| 615 | 40 n.p. Building Fund Day | 30 | 60 |
| 612/15 | *Set of* 4 | 55 | 1·00 |
| **MS**616 | 84 × 83 mm. Nos. 612/15. Imperf | 70 | 2·00 |

**321** Firework Display

**322** Weighing Baby

(Photo Harrison)

**1971** (22 Nov). *Christmas. T* **321** *and similar horiz designs. Multicoloured. W* **47** *(sideways on* 3 *and* 6 *n.p.). P* 14 × 14½ (1 *n.p.*) *or* 14½ × 14 (*others*).

| | | | |
|---|---|---|---|
| 617 | 1 n.p. Type **321** | 10 | 20 |
| 618 | 3 n.p. African Nativity | 15 | 30 |
| 619 | 6 n.p. The flight into Egypt | 15 | 30 |
| 617/19 | *Set of* 3 | 30 | 70 |

(Litho D.L.R.)

**1971** (20 Dec). *25th Anniv of U.N.I.C.E.F. T* **322** *and similar multicoloured designs, each showing the U.N.I.C.E.F. symbol. No wmk* (**MS**624) *or W* **47** *(sideways on* 5 *and* 30 *n.p.). P* 13.

| | | | |
|---|---|---|---|
| 620 | 5 n.p. Type **322** | 10 | 10 |
| 621 | 15 n.p. Mother and child (*horiz*) | 30 | 30 |
| 622 | 30 n.p. Nurse | 40 | 70 |
| 623 | 50 n.p. Young boy (*horiz*) | 60 | 1·75 |
| 620/3 | *Set of* 4 | 1·25 | 2·50 |
| **MS**624 | 111 × 120 mm. Nos. 620/3. Imperf | 4·25 | 7·00 |

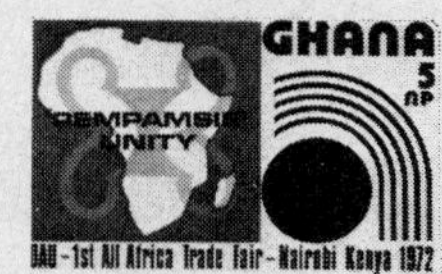


**323** Unity Symbol and Trade Fair Emblem

(Litho Questa)

**1972** (23 Feb). *All-Africa Trade Fair. T* **323** *and similar horiz designs. Multicoloured. W* **47**. *P* 14.

| | | | |
|---|---|---|---|
| 625 | 5 n.p. Type **323** | 10 | 10 |
| 626 | 15 n.p. Horn of Plenty | 20 | 30 |
| 627 | 30 n.p. Fireworks on map of Africa | 35 | 70 |
| 628 | 60 n.p. "Participating Nations" | 50 | 1·50 |
| 629 | 1 n.c. As No. 628 | 80 | 2·25 |
| 625/9 | *Set of* 5 | 1·75 | 4·25 |

All designs include the Trade Fair Emblem as in T **323**.

On 24 June 1972, on the occasion of the Belgian International Philatelic Exhibition, Nos. 625/9 were issued overprinted "BELGICA 72" in red. Only very limited supplies were sent to Ghana (we understand not more than 900 sets), and for this reason we do not list them.

**(New Currency. 100 pesewas = 1 cedi = 0.8 (1967) new cedi)**

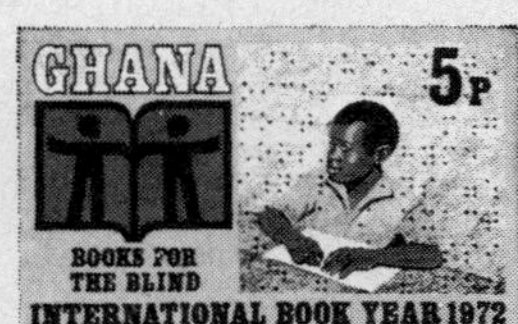


**324** Books for the Blind

(Des and litho D.L.R.)

**1972** (21 Apr). *International Book Year. T* **324** *and similar multicoloured designs. P* 13.

| | | | |
|---|---|---|---|
| 630 | 5 p. Type **324** | 15 | 10 |
| 631 | 15 p. Children's books | 40 | 50 |
| 632 | 30 p. Books for recreation | 70 | 85 |
| 633 | 50 p. Books for students | 1·25 | 2·00 |
| 634 | 1 c. Book and flame of knowledge (*vert*) | 2·00 | 2·75 |
| 630/4 | *Set of* 5 | 4·00 | 5·50 |
| **MS**635 | 99 × 106 mm. Nos. 630/4. Imperf | 7·50 | 11·00 |

**325** *Hypoxis urceolata*

(Litho D.L.R.)

**1972** (3 July). *Flora and Fauna. T* **325** *and similar horiz designs. Multicoloured. P* 13½.

| | | | |
|---|---|---|---|
| 636 | 5 p. Type **325** | 30 | 10 |
| 637 | 15 p. Mona Monkey | 65 | 65 |
| 638 | 30 p. *Crinum ornatum* | 3·50 | 2·50 |
| 639 | 1 c. De Winton's Tree Squirrel | 4·50 | 6·00 |
| 636/9 | *Set of* 4 | 8·00 | 8·50 |

**326** Football

(Litho D.L.R.)

**1972** (5 Sept). *Olympic Games, Munich. T* **326** *and similar horiz designs. Multicoloured. P* 13.

| | | | |
|---|---|---|---|
| 640 | 5 p. Type **326** | 10 | 10 |
| 641 | 15 p. Running | 20 | 20 |
| 642 | 30 p. Boxing | 40 | 60 |
| 643 | 50 p. Long-jumping | 70 | 1·40 |
| 644 | 1 c. High-jumping | 1·25 | 2·25 |
| 640/4 | *Set of* 5 | 2·40 | 4·00 |
| **MS**645 | 86 × 43 mm. 40 p. as No. 642 *se-tenant* with 60 p. as No. 640 | 2·00 | 6·00 |

**327** Senior Scout and Cub

(Litho Questa)

**1972** (2 Oct). *65th Anniv of Boy Scouts. T* **327** *and similar diamond-shaped designs. Multicoloured. P* 13½.

| | | | |
|---|---|---|---|
| 646 | 5 p. Type **327** | 30 | 10 |
| 647 | 15 p. Scout and tent | 65 | 45 |
| 648 | 30 p. Sea scouts | 1·25 | 1·00 |
| 649 | 50 p. Leader with cubs | 1·60 | 1·75 |
| 650 | 1 c. Training school | 3·00 | 3·25 |
| 646/50 | *Set of* 5 | 6·00 | 6·00 |
| **MS**651 | 110 × 110 mm. 40 p. as 30 p.; 60 p. as 1 c. | 2·75 | 5·00 |

**328** "The Holy Night" (Correggio)

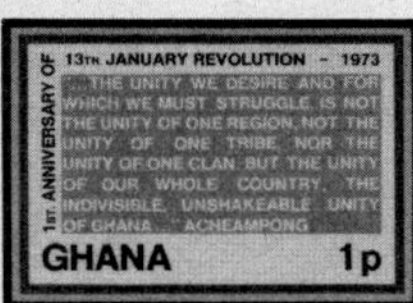


**329** Extract from Speech

(Des G. Vasarhelyi and L. Apelt. Litho Questa)

**1972** (1 Dec). *Christmas. T* **328** *and similar vert designs. Multicoloured. P* 13½.

| | | | |
|---|---|---|---|
| 652 | 1 p. Type **328** | 10 | 10 |
| 653 | 3 p. "Adoration of the Kings" (Holbein) | 10 | 10 |
| 654 | 15 p. "Madonna of the Passion" (School of Ricco) | 30 | 30 |
| 655 | 30 p. "King Melchior" | 55 | 55 |
| 656 | 60 p. "King Gaspar, Mary and Jesus" | 90 | 1·25 |
| 657 | 1 c. "King Balthasar" | 1·50 | 2·25 |
| 652/7 | *Set of* 6 | 3·00 | 4·00 |
| **MS**658 | 139 × 90 mm. Nos. 655/7. Imperf | 8·00 | 10·00 |

Nos. 655/7 are from a 16th-cent. Norman stained-glass window.

(Des and litho D.L.R.)

**1973** (10 Apr). *First Anniv of January 13 Revolution. T* **329** *and similar multicoloured designs. P* 13 × 14 (5, 15 *p.*) *or* 14 × 13 (*others*).

| | | | |
|---|---|---|---|
| 659 | 1 p. Type **329** | 10 | 10 |
| 660 | 3 p. Market scene | 10 | 10 |
| 661 | 5 p. Selling bananas (*vert*) | 10 | 10 |
| 662 | 15 p. Farmer with hoe and produce (*vert*) | 20 | 25 |
| 663 | 30 p. Market traders | 30 | 40 |
| 664 | 1 c. Farmer cutting palm-nuts | 70 | 1·40 |
| 659/64 | *Set of* 6 | 1·25 | 1·90 |
| **MS**665 | 90 × 55 mm. 40 p. as 1 c. and 60 p. Miners | 70 | 2·25 |

**330** Under 5's Clinic

(Litho D.L.R.)

**1973** (24 July). *25th Anniv of W.H.O. T* **330** *and similar square designs. Multicoloured. P* 13½.

| | | | |
|---|---|---|---|
| 666 | 5 p. Type **330** | 10 | 10 |
| 667 | 15 p. Radiography | 25 | 30 |
| 668 | 30 p. Immunisation | 35 | 50 |
| 669 | 50 p. Starving child | 50 | 1·25 |
| 670 | 1 c. W.H.O. H.Q., Geneva | 1·00 | 2·25 |
| 666/70 | *Set of* 5 | 2·00 | 4·00 |

1st WORLD SCOUTING CONFERENCE IN AFRICA

(**331**)

**1973** (14 Aug). *First World Scouting Conference, Nairobi/Addis Ababa. Nos. 646/51 optd with T* **331**.

| | | | |
|---|---|---|---|
| 671 | 5 p. Type **327** | 10 | 15 |
| 672 | 15 p. Scout and tent | 35 | 60 |
| 673 | 30 p. Sea scouts | 60 | 1·25 |
| 674 | 50 p. Leader with cubs | 80 | 1·75 |
| 675 | 1 c. Training school | 1·50 | 2·75 |
| 671/5 | *Set of* 5 | 3·00 | 6·00 |
| **MS**676 | 110 × 110 mm. 40 p. as 30 p.; 60 p. as 1 c. | 2·00 | 6·50 |

**332** Poultry Farming

(Litho Questa)

**1973** (11 Sept). *Tenth Anniv of World Food Programme. T* **332** *and similar horiz designs. Multicoloured. P* 14.

| | | | |
|---|---|---|---|
| 677 | 5 p. Type **332** | 10 | 10 |
| 678 | 15 p. Mechanisation | 15 | 15 |
| 679 | 50 p. Cocoa harvest | 40 | 90 |
| 680 | 1 c. F.A.O. H.Q., Rome | 60 | 1·90 |
| 677/80 | *Set of* 4 | 1·00 | 2·75 |
| **MS**681 | 92 × 104 mm. 40 p. as 15 p.; 60 p. as 1 c. | 60 | 2·25 |

**333** "Green Alert"

(Litho D.L.R.)

**1973** (1 Oct). *50th Anniv of Interpol. T* **333** *and similar horiz designs. Multicoloured. P* 13.

| | | | |
|---|---|---|---|
| 682 | 5 p. Type **333** | 15 | 10 |
| 683 | 30 p. "Red Alert" | 75 | 80 |
| 684 | 50 p. "Blue Alert" | 1·50 | 1·75 |
| 685 | 1 c. "Black Alert" | 3·00 | 4·00 |
| 682/5 | *Set of* 4 | 4·75 | 6·00 |

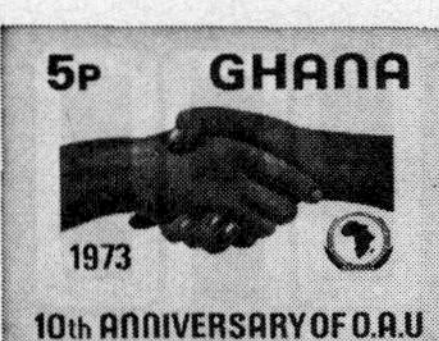


**334** Handshake

(Litho Format)

**1973** (22 Oct). *Tenth Anniv of O.A.U. T* **334** *and similar horiz designs. Multicoloured. P* 14 × 14½.

| | | | |
|---|---|---|---|
| 686 | 5 p. Type **334** | 10 | 10 |
| 687 | 30 p. Africa Hall, Addis Ababa | 15 | 30 |
| 688 | 50 p. O.A.U. emblem | 30 | 80 |
| 689 | 1 c. "X" in colours of Ghana flag | 45 | 1·25 |
| 686/9 | *Set of* 4 | 90 | 2·25 |

***MINIMUM PRICE***

The minimum price quote is 10p which represents a handling charge rather than a basis for valuing common stamps. For further notes about prices see introductory pages.

335 Weather Balloon

336 Epiphany Scene

(Des G. Vasarhelyi. Litho Format)

**1973** (16 Nov). *I.M.O./W.M.O. Centenary. T* **335** *and similar horiz designs. Multicoloured. P* 14 × 14½.
690 5 p. Type **335** .. .. .. .. .. 10 10
691 15 p. Satellite "Tiros" .. .. .. .. .. 20 20
692 30 p. Computer weather map .. .. .. .. 40 65
693 1 c. Radar .. .. .. .. .. 80 2·25
690/3 .. .. .. .. .. .. *Set of* 4 1·25 2·75
**MS**694 120 × 95 mm. 40 p. as 15 p.; 60 p. as 30 p. 1·00 2·75

(Litho D.L.R.)

**1973** (10 Dec). *Christmas. T* **336** *and similar vert designs. Multicoloured. P* 14.
695 1 p. Type **336** .. .. .. .. .. 10 10
696 3 p. Madonna and Child .. .. .. .. 10 10
697 30 p. "Madonna and Child" (Murillo) .. .. 30 75
698 50 p. "Adoration of the Magi" (Tiepolo) .. 45 1·00
695/8 .. .. .. .. .. *Set of* 4 1·25 2·75
**MS**699 77 × 103 mm. Nos. 695/8. Imperf. .. .. 1·25 3·00

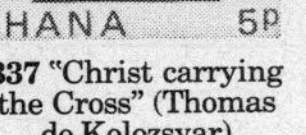


GHANA 5p

**337** "Christ carrying the Cross" (Thomas de Kolozsvar)

**338** Letters

(Des M. Shamir and A. Larkins. Litho D.L.R.)

**1974** (17 Apr). *Easter. T* **337** *and similar vert designs. P* 14.
700 5 p. multicoloured .. .. .. .. .. 10 10
701 30 p. bright blue, silver and sepia .. .. 20 35
702 50 p. light orange-vermilion, silver and sepia 30 60
703 1 c. dull yellow-green, silver and sepia .. 50 1·25
700/3 .. .. .. .. .. *Set of* 4 90 2·00
**MS**704 111 × 106 mm. 15 p. as No. 700, 20 p. as No. 701, 25 p. as No. 702. Imperf .. .. .. 80 1·75
Designs (from 15th-century English carved alabaster):—30 p. "The Betrayal"; 50 p. "The Deposition"; 1 c. "The Risen Christ and Mary Magdalene".

(Des A. Larkins. Litho Questa)

**1974** (21 May). *Centenary of Universal Postal Union. T* **338** *and similar horiz designs. Multicoloured. P* 14½.
705 5 p. Type **338** .. .. .. .. .. 10 10
706 9 p. U.P.U. Monument and H.Q. .. .. 15 15
707 50 p. Airmail letter .. .. .. .. 50 1·00
708 1 c. U.P.U. Monument and Ghana stamp .. 80 1·75
705/8 .. .. .. .. .. *Set of* 4 1·40 2·75
**MS**709 108 × 90 mm. 20 p. as No. 705, 30 p. as No. 706, 40 p. as No. 707, 60 p. as No. 708 .. .. 75 1·60

**1974** (7 June). *"Internaba 1974" Stamp Exhibition, Basle. Nos. 705/9 additionally inscribed* "INTERNABA 1974".
710 5 p. Type **338** .. .. .. .. .. 10 10
711 9 p. U.P.U. Monument and H.Q. .. .. 15 15
712 50 p. Airmail letter .. .. .. .. 40 1·00
713 1 c. U.P.U. Monument and Ghana stamp .. 60 1·75
710/13 .. .. .. .. .. *Set of* 4 1·10 2·75
**MS**714 108 × 90 mm. 20 p. as No. 710; 30 p. as No. 711; 40 p. as No. 712; 60 p. as No. 713 .. .. 1·50 3·50

**339** Footballers

(Des G. Vasarhelyi. Litho Format)

**1974** (17 June). *World Cup Football Championships, West Germany. T* **339** *and similar horiz designs showing footballers. P* 14½.
715 **339** 5 p. multicoloured .. .. .. .. 10 10
716 – 30 p. multicoloured .. .. .. .. 25 50
717 – 50 p. multicoloured .. .. .. .. 35 75
718 – 1 c. multicoloured .. .. .. .. 50 1·50
715/18 .. .. .. .. *Set of* 4 1·00 2·50
**MS**719 148 × 94 mm. 25, 40, 55 and 60 p. as Nos. 715/18 .. .. .. .. .. .. 1·00 3·00
Nos. 715/18 also exist perf 13 (*price for set of* 4 £2·25 *mint*, £3·00 *used*) from additional sheetlets of 5 stamps and 1 label. Stamps perforated 14½ are from normal sheets of 25.
The sheetlets, together with No. **MS**719, exist imperforate from stock dispersed by the liquidator of Format International Security Printers Ltd.

**340** Roundabout

WEST GERMANY WINNERS

**(341)**

(Des and litho B.W.)

**1974** (16 July). *Change to Driving on the Right. T* **340** *and similar designs. P* 13½ (5 *and* 15 *p.*) *or* 14½ × 14 (*others*).
720 5 p. bright yellow-grn, rose-vermilion & blk 10 10
721 15 p. lavender, dull red and black .. .. 25 35
722 30 p. multicoloured .. .. .. .. 45 60
723 50 p. multicoloured .. .. .. .. 70 1·10
724 1 c. multicoloured .. .. .. .. 1·40 2·00
720/4 .. .. .. .. .. *Set of* 5 2·75 3·75
Designs: *Horiz*—15 p. Warning triangle sign. *Vert* (29 × 42 *mm*)—30 p. Highway arrow and slogan; 50 p. Warning hands; 1 c. Car on symbolic hands.

**1974** (30 Aug). *West Germany's Victory in World Cup. Nos. 715/19 optd with T* **341**. *P* 14½.
725 **339** 5 p. multicoloured .. .. .. .. 10 10
726 – 30 p. multicoloured .. .. .. .. 35 40
727 – 50 p. multicoloured .. .. .. .. 50 55
728 – 1 c. multicoloured .. .. .. .. 90 1·25
725/8 .. .. .. .. .. *Set of* 4 1·75 2·10
**MS**729 148 × 94 mm. 25, 40, 55, 60 p. as Nos. 725/8 .. .. .. .. .. .. .. 1·25 2·50
This overprint also exists on the stamps perforated 13 mentioned below No. **MS**719 (*Price for set of* 4 £2 *mint or used*).

**342** "Planned Family"

(Des and litho D.L.R.)

**1974** (12 Sept). *World Population Year. T* **342** *and similar horiz designs. Multicoloured. P* 12½.
730 5 p. Type **342** .. .. .. .. .. 10 10
731 30 p. Family planning clinic .. .. .. 25 35
732 50 p. Immunization .. .. .. .. 35 60
733 1 c. Population census enumeration .. .. 60 1·40
730/3 .. .. .. .. .. *Set of* 4 1·10 2·25

**343** Angel

APOLLO
SOYUZ
JULY 15, 1975

**(344)**

(Des A. Medina (5 and 7 p.), A. Larkins (others). Litho D.L.R.)

**1974** (19 Dec). *Christmas. T* **343** *and similar multicoloured designs. P* 13½.
734 5 p. Type **343** .. .. .. .. .. 10 10
735 7 p. The Magi (*diamond* 47 × 47 *mm*) .. .. 10 10
736 9 p. The Nativity .. .. .. .. 10 10
737 1 c. The Annunciation .. .. .. .. 60 1·40
734/7 .. .. .. .. .. *Set of* 4 80 1·50
**MS**738 128 × 128 mm. 15 p. Type **343**; 30 p. as 7 p.; 45 p. as 9 p.; 60 p. as 1 c. Imperf .. .. .. 80 2·50

**1975** (15 Aug). *"Apollo–Soyuz" Space Link. Nos. 715/19 optd with T* **344**. *P* 14½.
739 5 p. multicoloured .. .. .. .. .. 10 10
740 30 p. multicoloured .. .. .. .. .. 25 25
741 50 p. multicoloured .. .. .. .. .. 45 55
742 1 c. multicoloured .. .. .. .. .. 70 80
739/42 .. .. .. .. .. *Set of* 4 1·25 1·50
**MS**743 148 × 94 mm. 25, 40, 55, 60 p. as Nos. 739/42 .. .. .. .. .. .. .. 1·50 2·00
This overprint also exists on the stamps perforated 13 mentioned below No. **MS**719 (*Price for set of* 4 £5·50 *mint or used*).

**345** Tractor Driver

(Des and litho D.L.R.)

**1975** (3 Sept). *International Women's Year. T* **345** *and similar horiz designs each showing I.W.Y. emblem. Multicoloured. P* 14 × 13½.
744 7 p. Type **345** .. .. .. .. .. 15 10
745 30 p. Motor mechanic .. .. .. .. 35 35
746 60 p. Factory workers .. .. .. .. 60 80
747 1 c. Cocoa research .. .. .. .. 90 1·40
744/7 .. .. .. .. .. *Set of* 4 1·75 2·40
**MS**748 136 × 110 mm. 15, 40, 65 and 80 p. as Nos. 744/7. Imperf .. .. .. .. .. .. 2·50 6·00

**346** Angel

(Litho D.L.R.)

**1975** (31 Dec). *Christmas. T* **346** *and similar horiz designs. P* 14 × 13½.
749 2 p. multicoloured .. .. .. .. .. 10 10
750 5 p. greenish yellow and light green .. .. 10 10
751 7 p. greenish yellow and light green .. .. 10 10
752 30 p. greenish yellow and light green .. .. 20 20
753 1 c. greenish yellow and light green .. .. 50 1·00
749/53 .. .. .. .. .. *Set of* 5 80 1·25
**MS**754 98 × 87 mm. 15, 40, 65 and 80 p. as Nos. 750/3. Imperf .. .. .. .. .. .. 90 3·00
Designs:—5 p. Angel with harp; 7 p. Angel with lute; 30 p. Angel with viol; 1 c. Angel with trumpet.

**347** Map Reading

(Litho Format)

**1976** (5 Jan). *14th World Scout Jamboree, Norway. T* **347** *and similar horiz designs. Multicoloured. P* 13½ × 14.
755 7 p. Type **347** .. .. .. .. .. 30 10
756 30 p. Sailing .. .. .. .. .. 85 75
757 60 p. Hiking .. .. .. .. .. 1·50 1·75
758 1 c. Life-saving .. .. .. .. .. 2·00 2·50
755/8 .. .. .. .. .. *Set of* 4 4·25 4·50
**MS**759 133 × 99 mm. 15, 40, 65 and 80 p. as Nos. 755/8 .. .. .. .. .. .. .. 3·50 5·50
Nos. 755, 757 and **MS**759 exist imperforate from stock dispersed by the liquidator of Format International Security Printers Ltd.

**348** Bottles (litre)

(Litho D.L.R.)

**1976** (5 Jan). *Metrication Publicity. T* **348** *and similar horiz designs. Multicoloured. P* 14.
760 7 p. Type **348** .. .. .. .. .. 15 10
761 30 p. Scales (kilogramme) .. .. .. .. 40 40
762 60 p. Tape measure and bale of cloth (metre) 80 1·00
763 1 c. Ice, thermometer and kettle (temperature) .. .. .. .. .. .. 1·25 1·75
760/3 .. .. .. .. .. *Set of* 4 2·40 2·75

**349** Fair Site

(Litho Format)

**1976** (6 Apr). *International Trade Fair, Accra. T* **349** *and similar horiz designs. P* 13½.
764 **349** 7 p. multicoloured .. .. .. .. 10 10
765 – 30 p. multicoloured .. .. .. .. 20 20
766 – 60 p. multicoloured .. .. .. .. 50 60
767 – 1 c. multicoloured .. .. .. .. 70 1·00
764/7 .. .. .. .. .. *Set of* 4 1·40 1·60
Nos. 765/7 are as T **349** but show different views of the Fair.
Nos. 764/7 exist imperforate from stock dispersed by the liquidator of Format International Security Printers Ltd.

'INTERPHIL' 76
BICENTENNIAL
EXHIBITION
(350)

351 Shot-put

976 (28 May). *Interphil Stamp Exhibition, Philadelphia. Nos. 755/9 optd with T* **350** *in blue.*
68 7 p. Type **347** .. 15 15
69 30 p. Sailing .. 35 50
70 60 p. Hiking .. 55 75
71 1 c. Life-saving .. 80 1·25
68/71 .. *Set of* 4 1·75 2·40
IS772 133 × 99 mm. 15, 40, 65 and 80 p. as Nos. 768/71 .. 1·50 2·50
Nos. 768/71 exist imperforate from stock dispersed by the quidator of Format International Security Printers Ltd.

(Des PAD Studio. Litho Format)

976 (9 Aug). *Olympic Games, Montreal. T* **351** *and similar vert designs. Multicoloured. P* 13½.
73 7 p. Type **351** .. 10 10
74 30 p. Football .. 20 25
75 60 p. Women's 1500 metres .. 35 50
76 1 c. Boxing .. 60 80
73/6 .. *Set of* 4 1·10 1·50
IS777 103 × 135 mm. 15, 40, 65 and 80 p. as Nos. 773/6 .. 2·00 2·00
Nos. 773/6 also exist perf 15 (*Price for set of* 4 £2·25 *mint or sed*) from additional sheetlets of 5 stamps and 1 label. Stamps erforated 13½ are from normal sheets of 30. The sheetlets also xist imperforate from stock dispersed by the liquidator of ormat International Security Printers Ltd.

352 Supreme Court

(Litho D.L.R.)

1976 (7 Sept). *Centenary of Supreme Court. T* **352** *and similar horiz designs. P* 14.
778 **352** 8 p. multicoloured .. 10 10
779 – 30 p. multicoloured .. 20 25
780 – 60 p. multicoloured .. 35 50
781 – 1 c. multicoloured .. 60 1·00
778/81 .. *Set of* 4 1·10 1·75
Nos. 779/81 show different views of the Court Building.

353 Examination for River Blindness

(Des and litho D.L.R.)

1976 (28 Oct). *Prevention of Blindness. T* **353** *and similar horiz designs. Multicoloured. P* 14 × 13½.
782 7 p. Type **353** .. 45 10
783 30 p. Entomologist .. 1·25 80
784 60 p. Normal vision .. 2·25 1·75
785 1 c. Blackfly eradication .. 3·25 3·25
782/5 .. *Set of* 4 6·50 5·50

354 Fireworks Party, Christmas Eve

(Des A. Adom & A. Larkins. Litho D.L.R.)

1976 (15 Dec). *Christmas. T* **354** *and similar horiz designs. Multicoloured. P* 13.
786 6 p. Type **354** .. 15 10
787 8 p. Children and gifts .. 20 15
788 30 p. Christmas feast .. 60 50
789 1 c. As 8 p. .. 1·50 2·00
786/9 .. *Set of* 4 2·25 2·50
**MS**790 122 × 98 mm. 15, 40, 65 and 80 p. as Nos. 786/9. Imperf .. 2·50 4·00

355 "Gallows Frame" Telephone and Alexander Graham Bell

EAST GERMANY
WINNERS
(356)

(Des A. Larkins. Litho Format)

1976 (17 Dec). *Telephone Centenary. T* **355** *and similar horiz designs showing telephones and Alexander Graham Bell. Multicoloured. P* 13.
791 8 p. Type **355** .. 20 15
792 30 p. 1895 telephone .. 45 45
793 60 p. 1929 telephone .. 90 90
794 1 c. 1976 telephone .. 1·40 1·40
791/4 .. *Set of* 4 2·75 2·75
**MS**795 125 × 92 mm. 15, 40, 65 and 80 p. as Nos. 791/4 .. 2·50 2·75

1977 (22 Feb). *Olympic Winners. Nos. 773/7 optd with the name of the country given, as T* **356**. *P* 13½.
796 7 p. East Germany .. 15 15
797 30 p. East Germany .. 40 40
798 60 p. U.S.S.R. .. 60 85
799 1 c. U.S.A. .. 80 1·50
796/9 .. *Set of* 4 1·75 2·50
**MS**800 103 × 135 mm. 15, 40, 65 and 80 p. as Nos. 796/9 .. 2·25 2·50

357 Dipo Dancers and Drum Ensemble

(Des A. Larkins. Litho Format)

1977 (24 Mar). *Second World Black and African Festival of Arts and Culture, Nigeria. T* **357** *and similar horiz designs. Multicoloured. P* 13½.
801 8 p. Type **357** .. 25 15
802 30 p. Arts and Crafts .. 70 70
803 60 p. Acon music and dancing priests .. 1·40 1·40
804 1 c. African huts .. 2·00 2·25
801/4 .. *Set of* 4 4·00 4·00
**MS**805 164 × 120 mm. 15, 40, 65 and 80 p. as Nos. 801/4 .. 4·00 4·25

PRINCE CHARLES
VISITS GHANA
17th TO 25th
MARCH, 1977
(358)

1977 (2 June). *Prince Charles's Visit to Ghana. Nos. 791/5 optd with T* **358**.
806 8 p. Type **355** .. 50 55
807 30 p. 1895 telephone .. 1·60 1·25
808 60 p. 1929 telephone .. 2·50 2·25
809 1 c. 1976 telephone .. 3·25 2·75
806/9 .. *Set of* 4 7·00 6·00
**MS**810 125 × 92 mm. 15, 40, 65 and 80 p. as Nos. 806/9 .. 7·00 7·00

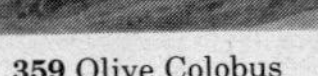
359 Olive Colobus

360 "Le Chapeau de Paille" (Rubens—400th Birth Anniv)

(Des PAD Studio. Litho Format)

1977 (22 June). *Wildlife. T* **359** *and similar horiz designs. Multicoloured. P* 13½.
811 8 p. Type **359** .. 45 15
812 20 p. Temminck's Giant Squirrel .. 1·25 80
813 30 p. Hunting Dog .. 1·75 1·25
814 60 p. African Manatee .. 3·00 2·25
811/14 .. *Set of* 4 5·75 4·00
**MS**815 140 × 101 mm. 15, 40, 65 and 80 p. as Nos. 811/14 .. 5·50 5·50
No. **MS**815 exists imperforate from stock dispersed by the liquidator of Format International Security Printers Ltd.

(Des PAD Studio. Litho Format)

1977 (Sept). *Painters' Anniversaries. T* **360** *and similar vert designs. Multicoloured. P* 14 × 13½.
816 8 p. Type **360** .. 15 10
817 30 p. "Isabella of Portugal" (Titian—500th Birth Anniv) .. 40 40
818 60 p. "Duke and Duchess of Cumberland" (Gainsborough—250th Birth Anniv) .. 50 65
819 1 c. "Rubens and Isabella Brandt" .. 85 1·25
816/19 .. *Set of* 4 1·75 2·25
**MS**820 99 × 149 mm. 15, 40, 65 and 80 p. as Nos. 816/19 .. 1·75 2·25
No. **MS**820 exists imperforate from stock dispersed by the liquidator of Format International Security Printers Ltd.

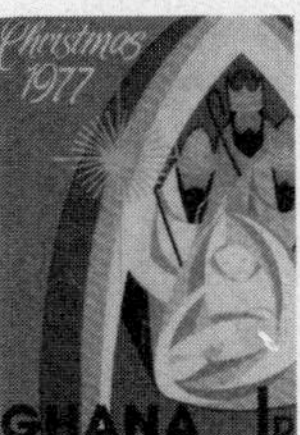

361 The Magi, Madonna and Child

REFERENDUM 1978
VOTE EARLY
(362)

(Litho De La Rue, Colombia)

1977 (30 Dec). *Christmas. T* **361** *and similar multicoloured designs. P* 14 (1 *p.*, 8 *p.*) *or* 14 × 13½ (*others*).
821 1 p. Type **361** .. 10 10
822 2 p. Choir from Abossey Okai (45 × 27 *mm*) .. 10 10
823 6 p. Methodist Church, Wesley, Accra (45 × 27 *mm*) .. 10 10
824 8 p. Madonna and Child .. 15 10
825 30 p. Holy Spirit Cathedral, Accra (45 × 27 *mm*) .. 50 50
826 1 c. Ebeneezer Presbyterian Church, Accra (45 × 27 *mm*) .. 1·60 1·60
821/6 .. *Set of* 6 2·25 2·25
**MS**827 122 × 97 mm. 15, 40, 65 and 80 p. as Nos. 822/3 and 825/6. Imperf .. 2·00 3·75
Nos. 822/3 and 825/6 all have as a background the score to the carol "Hark the Herald Angels Sing".

1978 (Mar). 1978 *Referendum. Nos. 821/7 optd with T* **362** *by De La Rue, Colombia.*
828 1 p. Type **361** .. 10 10
829 2 p. Choir from Abossey Okai .. 10 10
830 6 p. Methodist Church, Wesley, Accra .. 10 10
831 8 p. Madonna and Child .. 15 10
832 30 p. Holy Spirit Cathedral, Accra .. 50 50
833 1 c. Ebeneezer Presbyterian Church, Accra .. 1·50 1·50
828/33 .. *Set of* 6 2·10 2·10
**MS**834 122 × 97 mm. 15, 40, 65, 80 p. as Nos. 829/30 and 832/3 .. 24·00 15·00

363 Cutting Bananas

(Litho De La Rue, Colombia)

1978 (15 May). *Operation "Feed Yourself". T* **363** *and similar horiz designs. Multicoloured. P* 14.
835 2 p. Type **363** .. 10 10
836 8 p. Home produce .. 10 10
837 30 p. Market .. 35 35
838 60 p. Fishing .. 65 60
839 1 c. Mechanisation .. 1·00 1·25
835/9 .. *Set of* 5 2·00 2·10

364 Wright Biplane

"CAPEX 78
JUNE 9-18 1978"
(365)

(Des J.W. Litho Format)

1978 (6 June). *75th Anniv of Powered Flight. T* **364** *and similar vert designs. P* 14 × 13½.
840 8 p. black, deep brown and brown-ochre .. 20 10
841 30 p. black, deep brown and blue-green .. 40 30
842 60 p. black, deep brown and rosine .. 60 60
843 1 c. black, deep brown and ultramarine .. 1·40 1·10
840/3 .. *Set of* 4 2·40 1·90
**MS**844 167 × 100 mm. 15, 40, 65, 80 p. as Nos. 840/3 .. 2·50 2·10
Designs:—30 p. "Heracles"; 60 p. D.H. "Comet"; 1 c. "Concorde".
No. 841 exists imperforate from stock dispersed by the liquidator of Format International Security Printers Ltd.

**1978** (9 June). *"CAPEX 1978" International Stamp Exhibition, Toronto. Nos.* 840/4 *optd with T* **365**.

| | | | |
|---|---|---|---|
| 845 | 8 p. black, deep brown and brown-ochre | 15 | 15 |
| 846 | 30 p. black, deep brown and blue-green | 25 | 25 |
| 847 | 60 p. black, deep brown and rosine | 50 | 50 |
| 848 | 1 c. black, deep brown and ultramarine | 1·10 | 80 |
| 845/8 | *Set of* 4 | 1·75 | 1·50 |
| **MS**849 | 167 × 100 mm. 15, 40, 65, 80 p. as Nos. 845/8 | 1·75 | 2·25 |

**366** Players and African Cup Emblem

(Litho Format)

**1978** (1 July). *Football Championships. T* **366** *and similar horiz designs. Multicoloured. P* 13½ × 14.

| | | | |
|---|---|---|---|
| 850 | 8 p. Type **366** | 20 | 15 |
| 851 | 30 p. Players and African Cup emblem (*different*) | 30 | 30 |
| 852 | 60 p. Players and World Cup emblem | 60 | 60 |
| 853 | 1 c. Goalkeeper and World Cup emblem | 1·00 | 1·00 |
| 850/3 | *Set of* 4 | 1·90 | 1·90 |
| **MS**854 | 111 × 105 mm. 15, 40, 65, 80 p. as Nos. 850/3 | 1·40 | 1·75 |

The 8 and 30 p. values commemorate the African Nations Cup; the other values the World Cup Football Championship, Argentina.

Nos. 850/3 exist imperforate from stock dispersed by the liquidator of Format International Security Printers Ltd.

**367** "The Betrayal"

**"GHANA WINNERS"**

**(368)**

(Litho Format)

**1978** (15 July). *Easter. Details from drawings by Dürer. T* **367** *and similar vert designs. P* 14 × 13½.

| | | | |
|---|---|---|---|
| 855 | 11 p. black and bright reddish violet | 10 | 10 |
| 856 | 39 p. black and flesh | 25 | 30 |
| 857 | 60 p. black and orange-yellow | 40 | 45 |
| 858 | 1 c. black and pale yellow-green | 60 | 65 |
| 855/8 | *Set of* 4 | 1·25 | 1·40 |

Designs:—39 p. "The Crucifixion"; 60 p. "The Deposition"; 1 c. "The Resurrection".

**1978** (21 Aug). *Ghana—Winners of African Nations Football Cup and Argentina—Winners of World Cup Football Championship. Nos.* 850/1 *and* **MS**854 *optd with T* **368** *and Nos.* 852/3 *optd* "ARGENTINA WINS".

| | | | |
|---|---|---|---|
| 859 | 8 p. Type **366** | 15 | 15 |
| 860 | 30 p. Players and African Cup emblem (*different*) | 30 | 30 |
| 861 | 60 p. Players and World Cup emblem | 45 | 45 |
| 862 | 1 c. Goalkeeper and World Cup emblem | 75 | 75 |
| 859/62 | *Set of* 4 | 1·50 | 1·50 |
| **MS**863 | 111 × 105 mm. 15, 40, 65, 80 p. as Nos. 859/62 but all opt with T **368** | 1·40 | 1·60 |

Nos. 859/62 exist imperforate from stock dispersed by the liquidator of Format International Security Printers Ltd.

**369** *Bauhinia purpurea*

(Litho Format)

**1978** (20 Nov). *Flowers. T* **369** *and similar vert designs. Multicoloured. P* 14 × 13½.

| | | | |
|---|---|---|---|
| 864 | 11 p. Type **369** | 20 | 10 |
| 865 | 39 p. *Cassia fistula* | 65 | 55 |
| 866 | 60 p. *Plumeria acutifolia* | 85 | 70 |
| 867 | 1 c. *Jacaranda mimosifolia* | 1·25 | 1·00 |
| 864/7 | *Set of* 4 | 2·50 | 2·10 |

No. 864 exists imperforate from stock dispersed by the liquidator of Format International Security Printers Ltd.

**370** Mail Van

(Litho Format)

**1978** (4 Dec). *75th Anniv of Ghana Railways. T* **370** *and similar horiz designs. Multicoloured. P* 13½ × 14.

| | | | |
|---|---|---|---|
| 868 | 11 p. Type **370** | 50 | 10 |
| 869 | 39 p. Pay and bank car | 1·25 | 65 |
| 870 | 60 p. Steam locomotive, 1922 | 1·75 | 1·00 |
| 871 | 1 c. Diesel locomotive 1960 | 2·00 | 1·40 |
| 868/71 | *Set of* 4 | 5·00 | 2·75 |

No. 869 exists imperforate from stock dispersed by the liquidator of Format International Security Printers Ltd.

**371** "Orbiter" Spacecraft

(Litho Format)

**1979** (5 July). *"Pioneer" Venus Space Project. T* **371** *and similar horiz designs. Multicoloured. P* 14 × 13½.

| | | | |
|---|---|---|---|
| 872 | 11 p. Type **371** | 15 | 10 |
| 873 | 39 p. "Multiprobe" spacecraft | 35 | 30 |
| 874 | 60 p. "Orbiter" and "Multiprobe" spacecraft in Venus orbit | 45 | 45 |
| 875 | 3 c. Radar chart of Venus | 1·40 | 1·60 |
| 872/5 | *Set of* 4 | 2·10 | 2·25 |
| **MS**876 | 135 × 94 mm. 15, 40, 65 p., 2 c. as Nos. 872/5. Imperf | 1·10 | 1·25 |

**372** "O Come All Ye Faithful"

**373** Dr. J. B. Danquah (lawyer and nationalist)

(Litho D.L.R.)

**1979** (20 Dec). *Christmas. Opening Lines and Scenes from well known Carols. T* **372** *and similar horiz designs. Multicoloured. P* 14 × 14½.

| | | | |
|---|---|---|---|
| 877 | 8 p. Type **372** | 10 | 10 |
| 878 | 10 p. "O Little Town of Bethlehem" | 10 | 10 |
| 879 | 15 p. "We Three Kings of Orient Are" | 10 | 10 |
| 880 | 20 p. "I Saw Three Ships come Sailing By" | 10 | 15 |
| 881 | 2 c. "Away in a Manger" | 65 | 80 |
| 882 | 4 c. "Ding Dong Merrily on High" | 1·00 | 1·40 |
| 877/82 | *Set of* 6 | 1·90 | 2·40 |
| **MS**883 | 110 × 95 mm. 25, 65 p., 1, 2 c. as Nos. 877, 879 and 881/2 | 75 | 1·00 |

(Litho D.L.R.)

**1980** (21 Jan). *Great Ghanaians. T* **373** *and similar vert designs. Multicoloured. P* 14 × 13½.

| | | | |
|---|---|---|---|
| 884 | 20 p. Type **373** | 15 | 10 |
| 885 | 65 p. John Mensah Sarbah (nationalist) | 30 | 30 |
| 886 | 80 p. Dr. J. E. K. Aggrey (educationalist) | 40 | 40 |
| 887 | 2 c. Dr. Kwame Nkrumah (nationalist) | 65 | 65 |
| 888 | 4 c. G. E. (Paa) Grant (lawyer) | 1·40 | 1·60 |
| 884/8 | *Set of* 5 | 2·50 | 2·75 |

**374** Tribesman ringing Clack Bells

**375** Children in Classroom

(Des G. Vasarhelyi. Litho Format)

**1980** (12 Mar). *Death Centenary of Sir Rowland Hill* (1979). *T* **374** *and similar horiz designs. Multicoloured.* (*a*) *P* 14½.

| | | | |
|---|---|---|---|
| 889 | 20 p. Type **374** | 15 | 15 |
| 890 | 65 p. Chieftain with Golden Elephant staff | 45 | 50 |
| 891 | 2 c. Tribesman banging drums | 1·25 | 1·40 |
| 892 | 4 c. Chieftain with ivory and gold staff | 2·50 | 2·75 |
| 889/92 | *Set of* 4 | 3·75 | 4·25 |

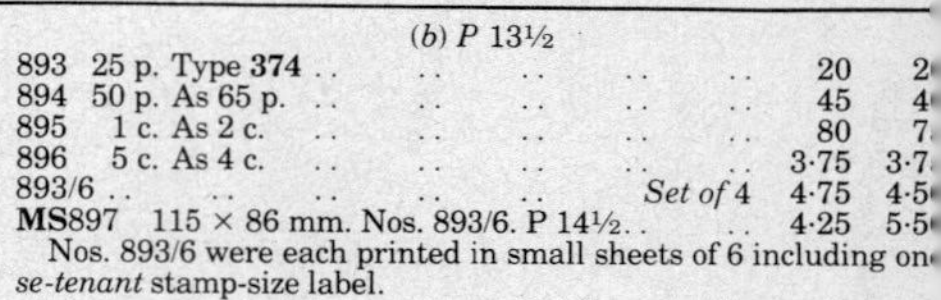

(*b*) *P* 13½

| | | | |
|---|---|---|---|
| 893 | 25 p. Type **374** | 20 | 2 |
| 894 | 50 p. As 65 p. | 45 | 4 |
| 895 | 1 c. As 2 c. | 80 | 7 |
| 896 | 5 c. As 4 c. | 3·75 | 3·7 |
| 893/6 | *Set of* 4 | 4·75 | 4·5 |
| **MS**897 | 115 × 86 mm. Nos. 893/6. P 14½ | 4·25 | 5·5 |

Nos. 893/6 were each printed in small sheets of 6 including on *se-tenant* stamp-size label.

(Des J.W. Litho Questa)

**1980** (2 Apr). *International Year of the Child* (1979). *T* **375** *an similar vert designs. Multicoloured. P* 14½.

| | | | |
|---|---|---|---|
| 898 | 20 p. Type **375** | 15 | 1 |
| 899 | 65 p. Children playing football | 35 | 4 |
| 900 | 2 c. Children playing in boat | 75 | 1·0 |
| 901 | 4 c. Mother and child | 1·40 | 1·7 |
| 898/901 | *Set of* 4 | 2·40 | 3·0 |
| **MS**902 | 156 × 94 mm. 25, 50 p., 1, 3 c. as Nos. 898/901 | 1·50 | 2·2 |

**"LONDON 1980"**
**6th - 14th May 1980**

**(376)**

**"PAPAL VISIT"**
**8th - 9th May**
**1980**

**(377)**

**1980** (6 May). *"London 1980" International Stamp Exhibition Nos.* 889/97 *optd with T* **376**. (*a*) *P* 14½.

| | | | |
|---|---|---|---|
| 903 | 20 p. Type **374** | 15 | 1 |
| 904 | 65 p. Chieftain with Golden Elephant staff | 45 | 6 |
| 905 | 2 c. Tribesman banging drums | 1·10 | 1·6 |
| 906 | 4 c. Chieftain with ivory and gold staff | 2·00 | 3·0 |
| 903/6 | *Set of* 4 | 3·25 | 4·7 |

(*b*) *P* 13½

| | | | |
|---|---|---|---|
| 907 | 25 p. Type **374** | 30 | 35 |
| 908 | 50 p. As 65 p. | 55 | 65 |
| 909 | 1 c. As 2 c. | 95 | 1·40 |
| 910 | 5 c. As 4 c. | 3·00 | 3·75 |
| 907/10 | *Set of* 4 | 4·25 | 5·50 |
| **MS**911 | 115 × 86 mm. Nos. 907/10. P 14½ | 3·75 | 5·50 |

**1980** (8 May). *Papal Visit. Nos.* 898/902 *optd with T* **377**.

| | | | |
|---|---|---|---|
| 912 | 20 p. Type **375** | 30 | 25 |
| 913 | 65 p. Children playing football | 70 | 60 |
| 914 | 2 c. Children playing in boat | 1·25 | 1·40 |
| 915 | 4 c. Mother and child | 2·25 | 2·50 |
| 912/15 | *Set of* 4 | 4·00 | 4·25 |
| **MS**916 | 156 × 94 mm. 25, 50 p., 1, 3 c. as Nos. 912/15 | 8·50 | 9·00 |

**378** Parliament House

**379** Airliner and Map of West Africa

(Litho Questa)

**1980** (4 Aug). *Third Republic Commemoration. T* **378** *and similar horiz designs. Multicoloured. P* 14.

| | | | |
|---|---|---|---|
| 917 | 20 p. Type **378** | 10 | 10 |
| 918 | 65 p. Supreme Court | 20 | 25 |
| 919 | 2 c. The Castle | 40 | 70 |
| 917/19 | *Set of* 3 | 60 | 95 |
| **MS**920 | 72 × 113 mm. 25 p., 1, 3 c. As Nos. 917/19 | 60 | 1·10 |

(Litho Questa)

**1980** (5 Nov). *Fifth Anniv of E.C.O.W.A.S. (Economic Community of West African States). T* **379** *and similar horiz designs showing symbols named and map of West Africa. Multicoloured. P* 14.

| | | | |
|---|---|---|---|
| 921 | 20 p. Type **379** | 10 | 10 |
| 922 | 65 p. Radio antenna | 15 | 20 |
| 923 | 80 p. Cog-wheels | 20 | 25 |
| 924 | 2 c. Corn ear | 35 | 50 |
| 921/4 | *Set of* 4 | 70 | 90 |

**380** "O.A.U."

**381** "The Adoration of the Magi"

(Litho Questa)

**1980** (26 Nov). *Organisation of African Unity First Economic Summit, Nigeria. T* **380** *and similar vert designs. Multicoloured. P* 14½ × 14.

| | | | |
|---|---|---|---|
| 925 | 20 p. Type **380** | 10 | 10 |
| 926 | 65 p. Banner with maps of Africa and Ghana | 15 | 20 |
| 927 | 80 p. Map of Africa | 20 | 25 |
| 928 | 2 c. Ghana flag, banner and map of Africa | 35 | 65 |
| 925/8 | *Set of* 4 | 70 | 1·00 |

(Litho Format)

980 (10 Dec). *Christmas. Paintings by Fra Angelico. T* **381** *and similar vert designs. Multicoloured. P* 14.
29 15 p. Type **381** .. 10 10
30 20 p. "The Virgin and Child enthroned with four Angels" .. 10 10
31 2 c. "The Virgin and Child enthroned with eight Angels" .. 35 80
32 4 c. "The Annunciation" .. 60 1·60
29/32 .. *Set of 4* 1·00 2·25
IS933 77 × 112 mm. 25, 50 p., 1, 3 c. As Nos. 929/32 .. 75 1·25

**382** "Health" **383** Narina Trogon

(Litho Format)

1980 (18 Dec). *75th Anniv of Rotary International. T* **382** *and similar horiz designs. Multicoloured. P* 14.
34 20 p. Type **382** .. 10 10
35 65 p. Rotary emblem and motto with maps of World and Ghana .. 15 30
936 2 c. Rotary emblem, globe and outstretched hands .. 35 85
937 4 c. "Eradication of Hunger" .. 60 1·50
934/7 .. *Set of 4* 1·10 2·50
MS938 121 × 93 mm. 25, 50 p., 1, 3 c. As Nos. 934/7 .. 1·10 2·00

(Des G. Drummond. Litho Harrison)

1981 (12 Jan). *Birds. T* **383** *and similar vert designs. Multicoloured. P* 14.
39 20 p. Type **383** .. 80 15
40 65 p. White-crowned Robin .. 1·75 50
41 2 c. Swallow-tailed Bee Eater .. 2·50 1·75
42 4 c. Rose-ringed Parakeet .. 4·00 3·25
939/42 .. *Set of 4* 8·00 5·00
MS943 89 × 121 mm. 25, 50 p., 1, 3 c. As Nos. 939/42. P 14½ .. 4·50 4·00

**384** Pope John Paul II and Archbishop of Canterbury with President Limann during Papal Visit
**385** Royal Yacht *Britannia*

(Litho Format)

**1981** (3 Mar). *First Anniv of Papal Visit. P* 14 × 13½.
944 **384** 20 p. multicoloured .. 35 15
945 65 p. multicoloured .. 75 55
946 80 p. multicoloured .. 95 70
947 2 c. multicoloured .. 2·00 2·00
944/7 .. *Set of 4* 3·50 3·00

(Des J.W. Litho Questa)

**1981** (8 July–16 Sept). *Royal Wedding. T* **385** *and similar vert designs. Multicoloured.* (i) *Sheet stamps* (8 July). (a) *P* 14.
948 20 p. Prince Charles and Lady Diana Spencer 15 10
949 80 p. Prince Charles on visit to Ghana .. 20 20
950 4 c. Type **385** .. 80 1·10
948/50 .. *Set of 3* 1·00 1·25
**MS**951 95 × 85 mm. 7 c. St. Paul's Cathedral .. 1·50 2·00

(*b*) *P* 12
952 65 p. As 20 p. .. 25 25
953 1 c. As 80 p. .. 45 45
954 3 c. Type **385** .. 1·00 1·40
952/4 .. *Set of 3* 1·50 1·90

(ii) *Booklet stamps. P* 14 (16 Sept)
955 2 c. Type **385** .. 1·25 1·25
a. Booklet pane. Nos. 955/6 each × 2 .. 7·50
956 5 c. As 20 p. .. 2·50 2·50

The 65 p., 1 and 3 c. values were each printed in small sheets of 6 including one *se-tenant* stamp-size label.

The above exist imperforate from a restricted printing (*Price for Nos.* 948/50 *set of* 3 £7, **MS**951 £9, *Nos.* 952/4 *set of* 3 £7·50 *and booklet pane No.* 955a £18, *all mint*).

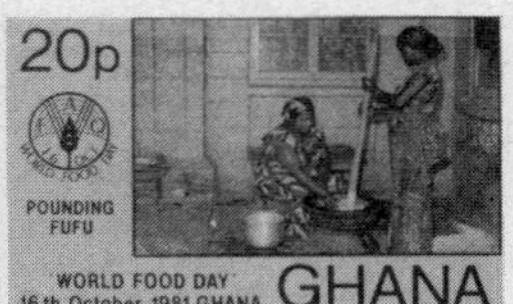


**386** Earth Satellite Station **387** Pounding Fufu

(Litho Questa)

**1981** (28 Sept). *Commissioning of Earth Satellite Station. T* **386** *and similar vert designs. Multicoloured. P* 14.
957 20 p. Type **386** .. 10 10
958 65 p. Satellites beaming signals to Earth .. 25 25
959 80 p. Satellite .. 30 30
960 4 c. Satellite orbiting Earth .. 1·75 1·75
957/60 .. *Set of 4* 2·10 2·10
**MS**961 112 × 100 mm. 25 p., 50 p., 1 c., 3 c. As Nos. 957/60 .. 1·50 2·00

(Des BG Studio. Litho Format)

**1981** (16 Oct). *World Food Day. T* **387** *and similar horiz designs. Multicoloured. P* 13½ × 14.
962 20 p. Type **387** .. 10 10
963 65 p. Plucking Cocoa .. 25 35
964 80 p. Preparing Banku .. 35 45
965 2 c. Garri processing .. 1·00 2·00
962/5 .. *Set of 4* 1·50 2·50
**MS**966 131 × 99 mm. 25 p., 50 p., 1 c., 3 c. As Nos. 962/5 .. 1·50 2·25

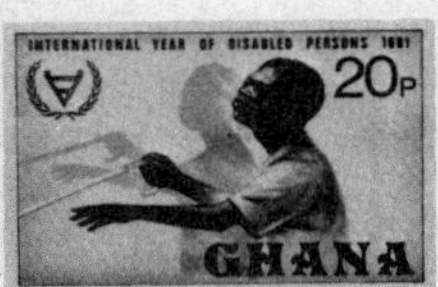


**388** "The Betrothal of St. Catherine of Alexandria" (Lucas Cranach)
**389** Blind Person

(Des Clover Mill. Litho Format)

**1981** (26 Nov). *Christmas. Details from Paintings. T* **388** *and similar vert designs. Multicoloured. P* 15.
967 15 p. Type **388** .. 20 10
968 20 p. "Angelic Musicians play for Mary and Child" (Aachener Altares) .. 20 10
969 65 p. "Child Jesus embracing his Mother" (Gabriel Metsu) .. 45 25
970 80 p. "Madonna and Child" (Fra Filippo Lippi) 55 30
971 2 c. "The Madonna with Infant Jesus" (Barnaba da Modena) .. 1·25 80
972 4 c. "The Immaculate Conception" (Murillo) 1·75 1·40
967/72 .. *Set of 6* 4·00 2·50
**MS**973 82 × 102 mm. 6 c. "Madonna and Child with Angels" (Hans Memling) .. 2·00 2·75

(Des G. Vasarhelyi. Litho Questa)

**1982** (8 Feb). *International Year for Disabled Persons. T* **389** *and similar horiz designs. Multicoloured. P* 14.
974 20 p. Type **389** .. 10 10
975 65 p. Disabled person with crutches .. 35 35
976 80 p. Blind child reading braille .. 45 45
977 4 c. Disabled people helping one another .. 2·25 2·25
974/7 .. *Set of 4* 2·75 2·75
**MS**978 109 × 85 mm. 6 c. Group of disabled people 2·75 3·00

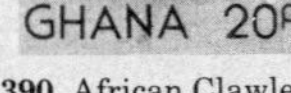


**390** African Clawless Otter **391** *Precis westermanni*

(Des G. Drummond. Litho Harrison)

**1982** (22 Feb). *Flora and Fauna. T* **390** *and similar vert designs. Multicoloured. P* 14.
979 20 p. Type **390** .. 15 15
980 65 p. Bushbuck .. 40 40
981 80 p. Aardvark .. 50 50
982 1 c. Scarlet Bell Tree .. 60 60
983 2 c. Glory-Lilies .. 1·25 1·25
984 4 c. Blue-Pea .. 2·25 2·25
979/84 .. *Set of 6* 4·75 4·75
**MS**985 76 × 100 mm. 5 c. Chimpanzee .. 2·50 4·00

(Litho Harrison)

**1982** (3 May). *Butterflies. T* **391** *and similar vert designs. Multicoloured. P* 14.
986 20 p. Type **391** .. 40 15
987 65 p. *Papilio menestheus* .. 80 45
988 2 c. *Antanartia delius* .. 1·75 2·25
989 4 c. *Charaxes castor* .. 2·50 3·25
986/9 .. *Set of 4* 5·00 5·50
**MS**990 98 × 123 mm. 25 p., 50 p., 1 c., 3 c. As Nos. 986/9. P 14½ .. 7·50 8·50

**392** Scouts planting Tree

(Des M. Diamond. Litho Format)

**1982** (1 June). *75th Anniv of Boy Scout Movement. T* **392** *and similar multicoloured designs. P* 14½ × 15.
991 20 p. Type **392** .. 35 15
992 65 p. Scouts cooking on camp-fire .. 90 55
993 80 p. Sea Scouts sailing .. 1·25 70
994 3 c. Scouts observing elephant .. 2·50 2·75
991/4 .. *Set of 4* 4·50 3·75
**MS**995 101 × 71 mm. 5 c. Lord Baden-Powell (*vert*). P 15 × 14½ .. 4·00 6·00

**393** Initial Stages of Construction

(Des C. Tetteh. Litho Questa)

**1982** (28 June). *Kpong Hydro-Electric Project. T* **393** *and similar horiz designs. Multicoloured. P* 14.
996 20 p. Type **393** .. 35 10
997 65 p. Truck removing rubble .. 75 45
998 80 p. Hydro-electric turbines .. 1·00 65
999 2 c. Aerial view of completed plant .. 2·00 1·60
996/9 .. *Set of 4* 3·75 2·50

**394** Footballers

(Des M. and S. Gerber Studio. Litho Format)

**1982** (19 July). *World Cup Football Championship, Spain. T* **394** *and similar horiz designs showing footballers.* (*a*) *P* 14½.
1000 **394** 20 p. multicoloured .. 10 10
1001 – 65 p. multicoloured .. 35 35
1002 – 80 p. multicoloured .. 45 45
1003 – 4 c. multicoloured .. 2·00 2·00
1000/3 .. *Set of 4* 2·50 2·50
**MS**1004 110 × 90 mm. 6 c. multicoloured .. 3·75 2·75

(*b*) *P* 14 × 14½
1005 **394** 30 p. multicoloured .. 20 20
1006 – 80 p. multicoloured (as No. 1001) .. 45 45
1007 – 1 c. multicoloured (as No. 1002) .. 55 55
1008 – 3 c. multicoloured (as No. 1003) .. 1·60 1·60
1005/8 .. *Set of 4* 2·50 2·50

Nos. 1005/8 were each printed in small sheets including one *se-tenant*, stamp-size, label.

**395** The Fight against Tuberculosis **396** The Shepherds worship Jesus

(Des M. Diamond. Litho Harrison)

**1982** (9 Aug). *Centenary of Robert Koch's Discovery of Tubercle Bacillus. T* **395** *and similar horiz designs. Multicoloured. P* 14.
1009 20 p. Type **395** .. 50 15
1010 65 p. Robert Koch .. 1·25 65
1011 80 p. Robert Koch in Africa .. 1·50 1·00
1012 1 c. Centenary of discovery of Tuberculosis .. 1·75 2·00
1013 2 c. Robert Koch and Nobel Prize, 1905 .. 2·50 3·00
1009/13 .. *Set of 5* 6·75 6·00

(Des E. Mensah. Litho Format)

**1982** (22 Dec). *Christmas. T* **396** *and similar vert designs. Multicoloured. P* 14½.
1014 15 p. Type **396** .. .. .. .. .. .. 10 10
1015 20 p. Mary, Joseph and baby Jesus .. .. 10 10
1016 65 p. The Three Kings sight star .. .. 30 30
1017 4 c. Winged Angel .. .. .. .. .. 1·40 1·75
1014/17 .. .. .. .. .. *Set of* 4 1·75 2·00
**MS**1018 90 × 110 mm. 6 c. The Three Kings with Jesus .. .. .. .. .. .. .. 1·60 2·40

**397** Ghana and Commonwealth Flags with Coat of Arms

WINNER ITALY
3-1
**(398)**

(Des J.W. Litho Format)

**1983** (14 Mar). *Commonwealth Day. T* **397** *and similar vert designs. Multicoloured. P* 14½.
1019 20 p. Type **397** .. .. .. .. .. .. 25 15
1020 55 p. Satellite view of Ghana .. .. .. 45 40
1021 80 p. Minerals of Ghana .. .. .. .. 85 85
1022 3 c. African Fish Eagle .. .. .. .. 2·50 3·00
1019/22 .. .. .. .. .. *Set of* 4 3·50 4·00

**1983** (30 May). *Italy's Victory in World Cup Football Championship* (1982). *Nos.* 1000/8 *optd with T* **398**, *in gold.* (a) *P* 14½.
1023 **394** 20 p. multicoloured .. .. .. .. 10 10
1024 – 65 p. multicoloured .. .. .. .. 30 30
1025 – 80 p. multicoloured .. .. .. .. 40 40
1026 – 4 c. multicoloured .. .. .. .. 1·90 1·90
1023/6 .. .. .. .. .. *Set of* 4 2·50 2·50
**MS**1027 110 × 90 mm. 6 c. multicoloured .. .. 1·75 2·00

(*b*) *P* 14 × 14½
1028 **394** 30 p. multicoloured .. .. .. .. 15 15
1029 – 80 p. multicoloured .. .. .. .. 50 50
1030 – 1 c. multicoloured .. .. .. .. 60 60
1031 – 3 c. multicoloured .. .. .. .. 1·50 1·75
1028/31 .. .. .. .. .. *Set of* 4 2·50 2·75

No. **MS**1027 has an additional overprint, "FINAL: ITALY V. W. GERMANY", on the sheet margin.

**INFLATION HANDSTAMPS.** During 1983 the value of the Ghanaian currency fell drastically and as a result, there was a considerable rise in postal rates.

To cope with this situation supplies of past commemorative issues were made available from the post offices, many being handstamped "NOT FOR PHILATELIC USE" in one line within a frame. These handstamps were usually applied in blue, haphazardly across the sheet with examples so far reported on Nos. 656/7, 664, 670, 680, 689, 703, 708, 718, 746/7, 753, 757, 762/3, 766, 775, 780/1, 791, 793, 799, 814, 817, 846, 850/1, 853, 856/7, 860, 865, 867, 869, 875 and 882.

**(398*a*)**

**399** Short-finned Pilot Whale

**1983** (Oct). *No.* 470 *surch with T* **398***a*.
1031*a* 1 c. on 20 n.p. deep blue and new blue .. 30 20
ab. Surch triple .. .. ..
ac. Surch double .. .. ..

(Des J. Iskowitz. Litho Format)

**1983** (15 Nov). *Coastal Marine Mammals. T* **399** *and similar horiz designs. Multicoloured. P* 14½.
1032 1 c. Type **399** .. .. .. .. .. 65 65
1033 1 c. 40, Risso's Dolphin .. .. .. .. 65 65
1034 2 c. 30, False Killer Whale .. .. .. .. 80 80
1035 3 c. Spinner Dolphin .. .. .. .. 1·00 1·00
1036 5 c. Atlantic Hump-backed Dolphin .. .. 1·40 1·40
1032/6 .. .. .. .. .. *Set of* 5 4·00 4·00
**MS**1037 117×76 mm. 6 c. As 5 c. .. .. .. 85 1·00

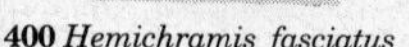
**400** *Hemichramis fasciatus*

**401** Communication Devices

(Des and litho De La Rue)

**1983** (12 Dec). *T* **400** *and similar designs. P* 14.
1038 5 p. multicoloured .. .. .. .. .. 10 10
1039 10 p. multicoloured .. .. .. .. .. 10 10
1040 20 p. multicoloured .. .. .. .. .. 20 10
1041 50 p. deep grey-green, yellow-orange and black 20 10
1042 1 c. yellow-orange, violet-blue and black .. 30 10
1043 2 c. multicoloured .. .. .. .. .. 20 10
1044 3 c. multicoloured .. .. .. .. .. 20 10
1045 4 c. multicoloured .. .. .. .. .. 20 10
1046 5 c. multicoloured .. .. .. .. .. 20 10
1047 10 c. multicoloured .. .. .. .. .. 20 10
1038/47 .. .. .. .. .. *Set of* 10 1·60 70

Designs: *Horiz*—10 p. *Hemichramis fasciatus (different)*; 2 c. Jet airliner. *Vert*—20 p. *Haemanthus rupestris*; 50 p. Mounted warrior; 1 c. Scorpion; 3 c. White-collared Mangabey; 4 c. Demidoff's Galago; 5 c. *Kaemferia nigerica*; 10 c. Grey-backed Camaroptera.

(Des PAD Studio. Litho Questa)

**1983** (13 Dec). *World Communications Year. T* **401** *and similar vert designs. Multicoloured. P* 14.
1048 1 c. Type **401** .. .. .. .. .. 15 15
1049 1 c. 40, Satellite dish aerial .. .. .. 20 20
1050 2 c. 30, Cable and cable-laying ship .. .. 35 35
1051 3 c. Switchboard operators .. .. .. 40 40
1052 5 c. Aircraft cockpit and air traffic controllers 50 50
1048/52 .. .. .. .. .. *Set of* 5 1·40 1·40
**MS**1053 95 × 70 mm. 6 c. Space satellite .. .. 30 50

**402** Children receiving Presents

**403** Soldiers with Rifles

(Des Designs Images. Litho Questa)

**1983** (28 Dec). *Christmas. T* **402** *and similar multicoloured designs. P* 14 × 13½ (70 *p. and* 3 *c.*) *or* 14½ × 14 (*others*).
1054 70 p. Type **402** .. .. .. .. .. 15 10
1055 1 c. Nativity and Star of Bethlehem (28 × 36 *mm*) .. .. .. .. .. .. 15 10
1056 1 c. 40, Children celebrating (28 × 36 *mm*) .. 25 20
1057 2 c. 30, Family praying (28 × 36 *mm*) .. 30 35
1058 3 c. Dancing to bongo drum .. .. .. 40 45
1054/8 .. .. .. .. .. *Set of* 5 1·10 1·10
**MS**1059 70 × 90 mm. 6 c. As 2 c. 30 .. .. 30 65

(Des and litho B.D.T.)

**1984** (26 Jan). *Namibia Day. T* **403** *and similar vert designs. P* 14.
1060 50 p. blue-green and black .. .. .. 10 10
1061 1 c. multicoloured .. .. .. .. 10 10
1062 1 c. 40, new blue, bright blue and black .. 15 15
1063 2 c. 30, multicoloured .. .. .. .. 20 25
1064 3 c. multicoloured .. .. .. .. 25 30
1060/4 .. .. .. .. .. *Set of* 5 65 75

Designs:—1 c. Soldiers supported by tank; 1 c. 40, Machete cutting chains; 2 c. 30, Peasant woman; 3 c. Soldiers and artillery support.

**(404)**

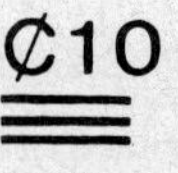
**(405)**

**1984** (8 Feb)–**85**. (*a*) *Nos.* 948/52 *and* 954 *surch as T* **404**
1065 1 c. on 20 p. Prince Charles and Lady Diana Spencer .. .. .. .. .. 4·00 3·00
1066 9 c. on 65 p. Prince Charles and Lady Diana Spencer (1985) .. .. .. 5·00 4·00
1067 9 c. on 80 p. Prince Charles on visit to Ghana .. .. .. .. .. .. 5·00 4·00
a. Imperf (pair) with surch inverted .. £275
1068 20 c. on 3 c. Type **385** (1985) .. .. 6·00 6·00
1069 20 c. on 4 c. Type **385** .. .. .. 6·00 6·00
**MS**1070 95×85 mm. 60 c. on 7 c. St. Paul's Cathedral .. .. .. .. .. .. 4·00 6·50

The above exist imperforate from a restricted printing (*Price for Nos.* 1065, 1067, 1069 *set of* 3 £10, *Nos.* 1066 *and* 1068 *set of* 2 £10 *and No.* **MS**1070 £20, *all mint*).

(*b*) *Nos.* 991/2 *and* 994/5 *surch as T* **405**
1071 10 c. on 20 p. Type **392** .. .. .. 40 45
1072 19 c. on 65 p. Scouts cooking on camp-fire .. 80 85
1073 30 c. on 3 c. Scouts observing elephant .. 1·25 1·40
**MS**1074 101×71 mm. 60 c. on 5 c. Lord Baden-Powell .. .. .. .. .. .. 2·00 3·50

(*c*) *Nos.* 1000/6 *and* 1008 *surch as T* **405**
1075 **394** 1 c. on 20 p. multicoloured .. .. 10 10
1076 – 9 c. on 65 p. multicoloured .. .. 40 45
1077 – 9 c. on 3 c. multicoloured .. .. 40 45
1078 **394** 10 c. on 30 p. multicoloured .. .. 40 45
1079 – 10 c. on 80 p. mult (No. 1002) .. .. 40 45
1080 – 20 c. on 4 c. mult (No. 1006) .. .. 85 90
1081 – 20 c. on 4 c. multicoloured .. .. 85 90
**MS**1082 110×90 mm. 60 c. on 6 c. multicoloured 2·00 2·25

(*d*) *Nos.* 1019/22 *surch as T* **405**
1083 1 c. on 20 p. Type **397** .. .. .. 10 10
1084 9 c. on 55 p. Satellite view of Ghana .. .. 40 45
1085 30 c. on 80 p. Minerals of Ghana .. .. 1·25 1·40
1086 50 c. on 3 c. African Fish Eagle .. .. 2·10 2·25

(*e*) *Nos.* 1023/9 *and* 1031 *surch as T* **405**
1087 **394** 1 c. on 20 p. multicoloured .. .. 10 10
1088 – 9 c. on 65 p. multicoloured .. .. 40 45
1089 – 9 c. on 3 c. multicoloured .. .. 40 45
1090 **394** 10 c. on 30 p. multicoloured .. .. 40 45
1091 – 10 c. on 80 p. mult (No. 1025) .. .. 40 45
1092 – 20 c. on 80 p. mult (No. 1029) .. .. 80 85
1093 – 20 c. on 4 c. multicoloured .. .. 80 85
**MS**1094 110×90 mm. 60 c. on 6 c. multicoloured 2·00 2·25
1065/9, 1071/3, 1075/81, 1083/93 .. *Set of* 26 35·00 32·00

c10
19TH U.P.U CONGRESS - HAMBURG
**(406)**

**1984** (19 June). *Universal Postal Union Congress, Hamburg. Nos.* 1035/7 *surch as T* **406**.
1095 10 c. on 3 c. Spinner Dolphin .. .. .. 40 45
1096 50 c. on 5 c. Atlantic Hump-backed Dolphin .. .. .. .. .. .. 2·10 2·25
**MS**1097 117×76 mm. 60 c. on 6 c. As No. 1096 .. 2·50 3·50

**407** Cross and Crown of Thorns

**408** Women's 400 Metre Race

(Litho Format)

**1984** (26 June). *Easter. T* **407** *and similar vert designs. Multicoloured. P* 15.
1098 1 c. Type **407** .. .. .. .. .. 10 10
1099 1 c. 40, Christ praying .. .. .. .. 10 10
1100 2 c. 30, The Resurrection .. .. .. .. 10 10
1101 3 c. Palm Sunday .. .. .. .. .. 10 15
1102 50 c. Christ on the road to Emmaus .. .. 1·90 2·25
1098/102 .. .. .. .. .. *Set of* 5 2·00 2·40
**MS**1103 102×86 mm. 60 c. Type **407** .. .. 2·00 3·00

(Des P. Cox and J. Iskowitz. Litho Format)

**1984** (13 Aug). *Olympic Games, Los Angeles. T* **408** *and similar vert designs. Multicoloured. P* 15.
1104 1 c. Type **408** .. .. .. .. .. 10 10
1105 1 c. 40, Boxing .. .. .. .. .. 15 10
1106 2 c. 30, Hockey .. .. .. .. .. 20 15
1107 3 c. Men's 400 metre hurdles race .. .. 20 15
1108 50 c. Rhythmic gymnastics .. .. .. .. 2·40 3·25
1104/8 .. .. .. .. .. *Set of* 5 2·75 3·25
**MS**1109 103×78 mm. 70 c. Football .. .. 2·50 3·50

**409** *Amorphophallus johnsonii*

**410** Young Bongo

(Litho Harrison)

**1984** (24 Aug). *Flowers. T* **409** *and similar vert designs. Multicoloured. P* 14.
1110 1 c. Type **409** .. .. .. .. .. 10 10
1111 1 c. 40, *Pancratium trianthum* .. .. .. 10 10
1112 2 c. 30, *Eulophia cucullata* .. .. .. 15 15
1113 3 c. *Amorphophallus abyssinicus* .. .. 15 15
1114 50 c. *Chlorophytum togoense* .. .. .. 3·25 4·50
1110/14 .. .. .. .. .. *Set of* 5 3·25 4·50
**MS**1115 70×96 mm. 60 c. Type **409** .. .. 3·00 4·00

(Des Susan David. Litho B.D.T.)

**1984** (7 Sept). *Endangered Antelopes. T* **410** *and similar horiz designs. Multicoloured. P* 14.
1116 1 c. Type **410** .. .. .. .. .. 20 20
1117 2 c. 30, Bongo bucks fighting .. .. .. 40 40
1118 3 c. Bongo family .. .. .. .. .. 50 50
1119 20 c. Bongo herd in high grass .. .. .. 2·25 2·75
1116/19 .. .. .. .. .. *Set of* 4 3·00 3·50
**MS**1120 Two sheets, each 100×71 mm. (a) 70 c. Head of Kob; (b) 70 c. Head of Bush buck *Set of* 2 *sheets* 7·00 8·50

## COVER PRICES

Cover factors are quoted at the beginning of each country for most issues to 1945. An explanation of the system can be found on page x. The factors quoted do not, however, apply to philatelic covers.

411 Dipo Girl

412 The Three Wise Men Bringing Gifts

(Des and litho B.D.T.)

**1984** (3 Oct). *Ghanaian Culture. T* **411** *and similar vert designs. Multicoloured. P* 14.

1121 1 c. Type **411** .. .. .. .. .. 10 10
1122 1 c. 40, Adowa dancer .. .. .. .. 10 10
1123 2 c. 30, Agbadza dancer .. .. .. .. 10 15
1124 3 c. Damba dancer .. .. .. .. 10 15
1125 50 c. Dipo dancer .. .. .. .. 1·75 3·00
1121/5 .. .. .. .. *Set of* 5 1·90 3·25
**MS**1126 70×84 mm. 70 c. Mandolin player. P 14×15 .. .. .. .. .. .. 2·00 3·00

(Litho D.L.R.)

**1984** (19 Nov). *Christmas. T* **412** *and similar vert designs. Multicoloured. P* 12×12½.

1127 70 p. Type **412** .. .. .. .. 10 10
1128 1 c. Choir of angels .. .. .. .. 10 10
1129 1 c. 40, Mary and shepherds at manger .. 10 10
1130 2 c. 30, The flight into Egypt .. .. 10 15
1131 3 c. Simeon blessing Jesus .. .. 10 15
1132 50 c. Holy Family and angels .. .. 1·75 3·00
1127/32 .. .. .. .. *Set of* 6 1·90 3·25
**MS**1133 70×90 mm. 70 c. Type **412** .. .. 2·50 2·75

**VALERIE BRISCO-HOOKS U.S.A.**
(413)

414 The Queen Mother attending Church Service

**1984** (3 Dec). *Olympic Medal Winners, Los Angeles. Nos.* 1104/9 *optd as T* **413** *in gold.*

1134 1 c. Type **408** (optd with T **413**) .. .. 10 10
1135 1 c. 40, Boxing (optd "U.S. WINNERS") .. 10 10
1136 2 c. 30, Field hockey (optd "PAKISTAN (FIELD HOCKEY)") .. .. .. 10 10
1137 3 c. Men's 400 metre hurdles race (optd "EDWIN MOSES U.S.A.") .. .. 10 10
1138 50 c. Rhythmic gymnastics (optd "LAURI FUNG CANADA") .. .. .. 1·50 1·60
1134/8 .. .. .. .. *Set of* 5 1·60 1·75
**MS**1139 103×78 mm. 70 c. Football (optd "FRANCE") .. .. .. .. .. 1·75 2·50

Nos. 1135 and **MS**1139 have the overprint in one line and Nos. 1136/8 in two.

(Des J.W. Litho Questa)

**1985** (24 July). *Life and Times of Queen Elizabeth the Queen Mother. T* **414** *and similar vert designs. Multicoloured. P* 14.

1140 5 c. Type **414** .. .. .. .. 15 20
1141 12 c. At Ascot Races .. .. .. .. 40 45
1142 100 c. At Clarence House on her 84th birthday .. .. .. .. .. 3·00 3·25
1140/2 .. .. .. .. *Set of* 3 3·25 3·50
**MS**1143 56×84 mm. 110 c. With Prince Charles at Garter ceremony .. .. .. .. 3·50 4·00

Stamps as Nos. 1140/2, but with face values of 8 c., 20 c. and 70 c., exist from additional sheetlets of 5 plus a label issued December 1985. These also have changed background colours and are perforated 12×12½ (*Price for set of 3 stamps £2.25 mint*).

415 Moslems going to Mosque

416 Youths clearing Refuse ("Make Ghana Clean")

(Des E. Mensah. Litho B.D.T.)

**1985** (1 Aug.) *Islamic Festival of Id-el-Fitr. T* **415** *and similar vert designs. Multicoloured. P* 14.

1144 5 c. Type **415** .. .. .. .. 15 20
1145 8 c. Moslems at prayer .. .. .. .. 25 30
1146 12 c. Pilgrims visiting the Dome of the Rock 40 45
1147 18 c. Preaching the Koran .. .. .. 55 60
1148 50 c. Banda Nkwanta Mosque, Accra, and map of Ghana .. .. .. .. 1·50 1·60
1144/8 .. .. .. .. *Set of* 5 2·50 2·75

(Des E. Mensah. Litho Questa)

**1985** (9 Aug). *International Youth Year. T* **416** *and similar vert designs. Multicoloured. P* 14×13½.

1149 5 c. Type **416** .. .. .. .. 10 10
1150 8 c. Planting sapling ("Make Ghana Green") .. .. .. .. .. 15 15
1151 12 c. Youth carrying bananas ("Feed Ghana") .. .. .. .. .. 20 25
1152 100 c. Open-air class ("Educate Ghana") .. 1·60 2·25
1149/52 .. .. .. .. *Set of* 4 1·75 2·50
**MS**1153 103×78 mm. 110 c. As 8 c. .. .. 1·75 3·00

417 Honda "Interceptor", 1984

418 Fork-tailed Flycatcher

(Litho Questa)

**1985** (9 Sept). *Centenary of the Motorcycle. T* **417** *and similar multicoloured designs. P* 14.

1154 5 c. Type **417** .. .. .. .. 45 45
1155 8 c. DKW, 1938 .. .. .. .. 55 55
1156 12 c. BMW "R 32", 1923 .. .. .. 85 85
1157 100 c. NSU, 1900 .. .. .. .. 4·25 4·75
1154/7 .. .. .. .. *Set of* 4 5·50 6·00
**MS**1158 78×108 mm. 110 c. Zündapp, 1973 (*vert*) .. .. .. .. .. 3·50 4·25

(Litho Questa)

**1985** (16 Oct). *Birth Bicentenary of John J. Audubon (ornithologist). T* **418** *and similar vert designs showing original paintings. Multicoloured. P* 14.

1159 5 c. Type **418** .. .. .. .. 60 30
1160 8 c. Barred Owl .. .. .. .. 1·50 1·00
1161 12 c. Black-throated Mango .. .. 1·50 1·25
1162 100 c. White-crowned Pigeon .. .. 3·75 4·50
1159/62 .. .. .. .. *Set of* 4 6·50 6·50
**MS**1163 85×115 mm. 110 c. Downy Woodpecker 3·00 3·00

No. 1159 is inscribed "York-tailed Fly Catcher" in error.

Nos. 1159/63 also exist imperforate from a limited printing.

419 United Nations Building, New York

(Des Mary Walters. Litho D.L.R.)

**1985** (24 Oct). *40th Anniv of United Nations Organization. T* **419** *and similar horiz designs. Multicoloured. P* 14½ (18 c.) *or* 14½×14 (*others*).

1164 5 c. Type **419** .. .. .. .. 10 10
1165 8 c. Flags of member nations and U.N. Building .. .. .. .. 15 15
1166 12 c. Dove with olive branch .. .. 20 25
1167 18 c. General Assembly .. .. .. 30 35
1168 100 c. Flags of Ghana and United Nations .. .. .. .. 1·60 1·75
1164/8 .. .. .. .. *Set of* 5 2·10 2·40
**MS**1169 90×70 mm. 110 c. United Nations (New York) 1955 4 cent 10th anniv stamp .. .. 1·50 2·00

Nos. 1164/9 also exist imperforate from a limited printing.

420 Coffee

(Des J. Iskowitz. Litho B.D.T.)

**1985** (4 Nov). *20th Anniv of United Nations Conference on Trade and Development. T* **420** *and similar horiz designs showing export products. Multicoloured. P* 14.

1170 5 c. Type **420** .. .. .. .. 10 10
1171 8 c. Cocoa .. .. .. .. .. 15 15
1172 12 c. Timber .. .. .. .. 25 25
1173 18 c. Bauxite .. .. .. .. 1·00 80
1174 100 c. Gold .. .. .. .. 4·50 5·00
1170/4 .. .. .. .. *Set of* 5 5·50 5·75
**MS**1175 104×74 mm. 110 c. Agricultural produce and plate of food. P 15×14 .. .. 2·00 2·50

## NEW INFORMATION

The editor is always interested to correspond with people who have new information that will improve or correct the Catalogue.

421 Growth Monitoring

(Des E. Mensah. Litho B.D.T.)

**1985** (16 Dec). *U.N.I.C.E.F. Child Survival Campaign. T* **421** *and similar horiz designs. Multicoloured. P* 14.

1176 5 c. Type **421** .. .. .. .. 20 10
1177 8 c. Oral rehydration therapy .. .. 30 20
1178 12 c. Breast feeding .. .. .. 45 30
1179 100 c. Immunization .. .. .. 2·25 3·25
1176/9 .. .. .. .. *Set of* 4 3·00 3·50
**MS**1180 99×69 mm. 110 c. Campaign logo. P 15×14 .. .. .. .. .. .. 1·75 2·25

422 Airline Stewardess and Boys with Stamp Album

(Litho Questa)

**1986** (27 Oct). *"Ameripex" International Stamp Exhibition, Chicago. T* **422** *and similar multicoloured designs. P* 14.

1181 5 c. Type **422** .. .. .. .. 10 10
1182 25 c. Globe and Ghana Airways aircraft .. 45 45
1183 100 c. Ghana Airways stewardess (*vert*) .. 1·75 2·75
1181/3 .. .. .. .. *Set of* 3 2·10 3·00
**MS**1184 90×70 mm. 150 c. Stamp collecting class .. .. .. .. .. .. 2·25 2·50

Nos. 1181/4 also exist imperforate from a limited printing.

423 Kejetia Roundabout, Kumasi

424 Tackling

(Litho B.D.T.)

**1986** (10 Nov). *"Inter-Tourism '86" Conference. T* **423** *and similar horiz designs. Multicoloured. P* 14.

1185 5 c. Type **423** .. .. .. .. 10 10
1186 15 c. Fort St. Jago, Elmina .. .. 30 30
1187 25 c. Tribal warriors .. .. .. 45 45
1188 100 c. Chief holding audience .. .. 1·75 3·00
1185/8 .. .. .. .. *Set of* 4 2·40 3·50
**MS**1189 110×70 mm. 150 c. African Elephants. P 15 × 14 .. .. .. .. .. 3·75 5·00

(Litho D.L.R.)

**1987** (16 Jan). *World Cup Football Championship, Mexico (1986). T* **424** *and similar vert designs. Multicoloured. P* 14×14½.

1190 5 c. Type **424** .. .. .. .. 15 10
1191 15 c. Player taking control of ball .. 20 15
1192 25 c. Player kicking ball .. .. .. 35 25
1193 100 c. Player with ball .. .. .. 1·10 1·25
1190/3 .. .. .. .. *Set of* 4 1·60 1·50
**MS**1194 90×70 mm. 150 c. Player kicking ball (*different*) .. .. .. .. .. 1·50 2·00

Nos. 1190/4 also exist imperforate from a limited printing.

425 Fertility Doll

426 Children of Different Races, Peace Doves and Sun

(Litho D.L.R.)

**1987** (22 Jan). *Ghanaian Fertility Dolls. T* **425** *and similar vert designs showing different dolls. P* 14×14½.

1195 **425** 5 c. multicoloured .. .. .. 10 10
1196 – 15 c. multicoloured .. .. .. 15 15
1197 – 25 c. multicoloured .. .. .. 30 25
1198 – 100 c. multicoloured .. .. .. 1·00 1·25
1195/8 .. .. .. .. *Set of* 4 1·40 1·50
**MS**1199 90×70 mm. **425** 150 c. multicoloured .. 1·50 2·00

(Litho D.L.R.)

**1987** (2 Mar). *International Peace Year* (1986). *T* **426** *and similar multicoloured designs. P* 14 × 14½ (100 *c.*) *or* 14½ × 14 (*others*).
1200 5 c. Type **426** .. .. .. .. .. 10 10
1201 25 c. Plough, peace dove and rising sun .. 40 25
1202 100 c. Peace dove, olive branch and globe (*vert*) .. .. .. .. .. 1·25 1·50
1200/2 .. .. .. .. *Set of* 3 1·50 1·75
**MS**1203 90 × 70 mm. 150 c. Dove perched on plough (*vert*). P 14 × 14½ .. .. .. .. 1·50 2·00

**427** Lumber and House under Construction

**428** Demonstrator and Arms breaking Shackles

(Des and litho B.D.T.)

**1987** (10 Mar). *"Gifex '87" International Forestry Exposition, Accra. T* **427** *and similar horiz designs. Multicoloured. P* 14.
1204 5 c. Type **427** .. .. .. .. 10 10
1205 15 c. Planks and furniture .. .. 15 15
1206 25 c. Felled trees .. .. .. .. 30 25
1207 200 c. Logs and wood carvings .. .. 1·90 2·25
1204/7 .. .. .. .. *Set of* 4 2·25 2·50

(Des W. Hanson. Litho D.L.R.)

**1987** (8 Apr). *Appearance of Halley's Comet* (1986). *Horiz designs as T* **123** *of Anguilla. Multicoloured. P* 14½ × 14.
1208 5 c. Mikhail Lomonosov (scientist) and Chamber of Curiosities, St. Petersburg .. .. .. .. .. 10 10
1209 25 c. Lunar probe "Surveyor 3", 1966 .. 50 25
1210 200 c. Wedgwood plaques for Isaac Newton, 1790, and "Apollo 11" Moon landing, 1968 .. .. .. .. .. 2·75 2·10
1208/10 .. .. .. .. *Set of* 3 3·00 2·25
**MS**1211 100 × 70 mm. 250 c. Halley's Comet .. 2·50 2·75
Nos. 1208/11 also exist imperforate from a limited printing.

(Litho D.L.R.)

**1987** (18 May). *Solidarity with the People of Southern Africa. T* **428** *and similar vert designs. Multicoloured. P* 14 × 14½.
1212 5 c. Type **428** .. .. .. .. 10 10
1213 15 c. Miner and gold bars .. .. .. 15 15
1214 25 c. Xhosa warriors .. .. .. 30 25
1215 100 c. Nelson Mandela and shackles .. 1·00 1·50
1212/15 .. .. .. .. *Set of* 4 1·40 1·75
**MS**1216 70 × 90 mm. 150 c. Nelson Mandela .. 1·50 2·00

**429** Aerophones

(Litho D.L.R.)

**1987** (13 July). *Musical Instruments. T* **429** *and similar horiz designs. Multicoloured. P* 14½ × 14.
1217 5 c. Type **429** .. .. .. .. 10 10
1218 15 c. Xylophone .. .. .. .. 15 15
1219 25 c. Chordophones .. .. .. .. 30 25
1220 100 c. Membranophones .. .. .. 1·00 1·25
1217/20 .. .. .. .. *Set of* 4 1·40 1·50
**MS**1221 90 × 70 mm. 200 c. Idiophones .. .. 1·90 2·25

**430** Woman filling Water Pot at Pump

**431** Ga Women preparing Kpokpoi for Homowo Festival

(Litho B.D.T.)

**1987** (21 Sept). *International Year of Shelter for the Homeless. T* **430** *and similar horiz designs. Multicoloured. P* 14.
1222 5 c. Type **430** .. .. .. .. 10 10
1223 15 c. Building house from breeze-blocks .. 10 15
1224 25 c. Modern village with stream .. 20 25
1225 100 c. Modern houses with verandahs .. 70 75
1222/5 .. .. .. .. *Set of* 4 95 1·00

(Litho Format)

**1988** (6 Jan). *Ghana Festivals. T* **431** *and similar vert designs. Multicoloured. P* 15.
1226 5 c. Type **431** .. .. .. .. 10 10
1227 15 c. Efute hunters with deer, Aboakyir festival .. .. .. .. .. 10 15
1228 25 c. Fanti chief dancing at Odwira festival 20 25
1229 100 c. Chief in palanquin, Yam festival .. 70 75
1226/9 .. .. .. .. *Set of* 4 95 1·00

**432** Port Installation

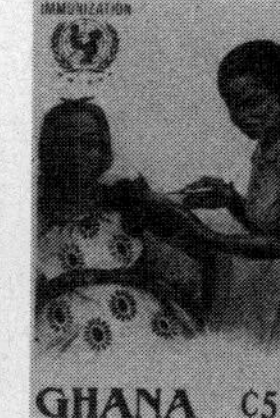


**433** Nurse giving Injection

(Litho National Ptg Wks, Havana)

**1988** (26 Jan). *5th Anniversary of 31 December Revolution* (1987). *T* **432** *and similar horiz designs. Multicoloured. P* 13.
1230 5 c. Type **432** .. .. .. .. 20 15
1231 15 c. Repairing railway line .. .. 35 30
1232 25 c. Planting cocoa .. .. .. 35 30
1233 100 c. Miners with ore truck .. .. 1·50 1·50
1230/3 .. .. .. .. *Set of* 4 2·25 2·00

(Litho Format)

**1988** (1 Feb). *U.N.I.C.E.F. Global Immunization Campaign. T* **433** *and similar vert designs. Multicoloured. P* 15.
1234 5 c. Type **433** .. .. .. .. 10 10
1235 15 c. Girl receiving injection .. .. 15 15
1236 25 c. Schoolgirl crippled by polio .. .. 30 30
1237 100 c. Nurse giving oral vaccine to baby .. 90 1·00
1234/7 .. .. .. .. *Set of* 4 1·25 1·25

**434** Fishing

**435** Akwadjan Men

(Des E. Mensah. Litho National Ptg Wks, Havana)

**1988** (14 Apr). *10th Anniv of International Fund for Agricultural Development. T* **434** *and similar horiz designs. Multicoloured. P* 13.
1238 5 c. Type **434** .. .. .. .. 10 10
1239 15 c. Women harvesting crops .. .. 15 15
1240 25 c. Cattle .. .. .. .. 30 30
1241 100 c. Village granaries .. .. .. 1·00 1·40
1238/41 .. .. .. .. *Set of* 4 1·40 1·75

(Litho Questa)

**1988** (9 May). *Tribal Costumes. T* **435** *and similar vert designs. Multicoloured. P* 14.
1242 5 c. Type **435** .. .. .. .. 10 10
1243 25 c. Banaa man .. .. .. .. 20 20
1244 250 c. Agwasen woman .. .. .. 1·50 1·50
1242/4 .. .. .. .. *Set of* 3 1·60 1·60

¢50 (436)

¢50.00 (437)

¢100.00 (438)

**1988** (19 July)–**90**. *Nos.* 460, 464/6, 469/70, 1031*a*, 1038/42, 1044 *and* 1046 *surch with T* **436/7** (*Nos.* 1248/9 *and* 1251/3) *or as T* **438** (*others*).
1245 – 20 c. on 50 p. dp grey-green, yellow-orange and black (No. 1041) .. 10 10
a. Horiz pair, one without surch
1246 – 20 c. on 1 c. yellow-orange, violet-blue and black (No. 1042) (9.88) .. 10 10
a. Surch double .. .. ..
b. Surch double, one albino ..
c. Surch double, one inverted ..
d. Surch double, one albino and one inverted .. .. .. ..
e. Surch inverted .. .. ..
f. Pair, one without surch ..
g. "2" omitted (R. 4/3) ..
h. Surch sideways .. .. ..
i. Albino surch .. .. ..
1247 – 50 c. on 10 n.p. mult (No. 469) .. 10 15
a. Vert pair, one without surch ..

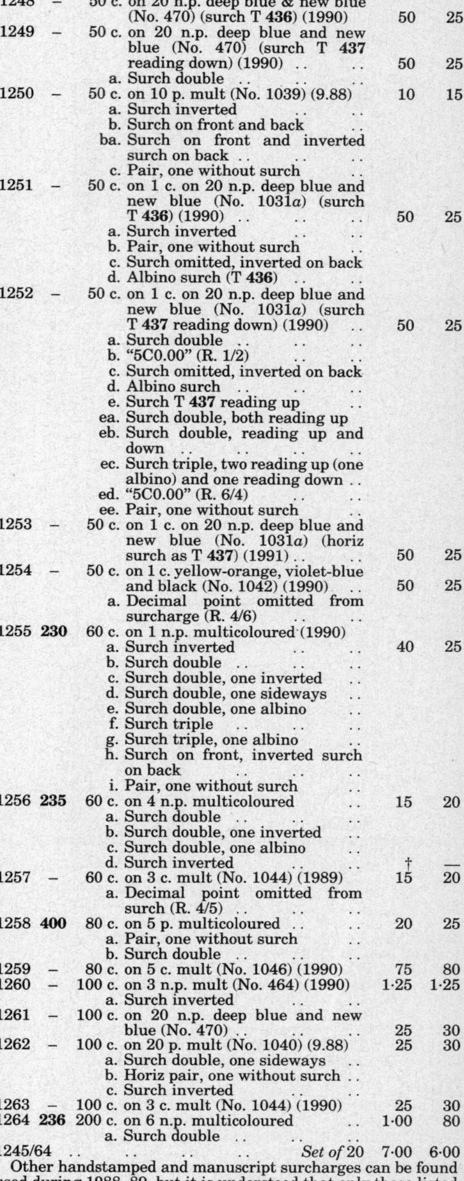

1248 – 50 c. on 20 n.p. deep blue & new blue (No. 470) (surch T **436**) (1990) 50 25
1249 – 50 c. on 20 n.p. deep blue and new blue (No. 470) (surch T **437** reading down) (1990) .. .. 50 25
a. Surch double .. ..
1250 – 50 c. on 10 p. mult (No. 1039) (9.88) 10 15
a. Surch inverted .. ..
b. Surch on front and back ..
ba. Surch on front and inverted surch on back .. .. ..
c. Pair, one without surch ..
1251 – 50 c. on 1 c. on 20 n.p. deep blue and new blue (No. 1031*a*) (surch T **436**) (1990) .. .. 50 25
a. Surch inverted .. ..
b. Pair, one without surch ..
c. Surch omitted, inverted on back
d. Albino surch (T **436**) ..
1252 – 50 c. on 1 c. on 20 n.p. deep blue and new blue (No. 1031*a*) (surch T **437** reading down) (1990) .. 50 25
a. Surch double .. ..
b. "5C0.00" (R. 1/2) ..
c. Surch omitted, inverted on back
d. Albino surch .. ..
e. Surch T **437** reading up ..
ea. Surch double, both reading up
eb. Surch double, reading up and down .. .. ..
ec. Surch triple, two reading up (one albino) and one reading down ..
ed. "5C0.00" (R. 6/4) ..
ee. Pair, one without surch ..
1253 – 50 c. on 1 c. on 20 n.p. deep blue and new blue (No. 1031*a*) (horiz surch as T **437**) (1991) .. 50 25
1254 – 50 c. on 1 c. yellow-orange, violet-blue and black (No. 1042) (1990) .. 50 25
a. Decimal point omitted from surcharge (R. 4/6) ..
1255 **230** 60 c. on 1 n.p. multicoloured (1990)
a. Surch inverted .. .. 40 25
b. Surch double .. ..
c. Surch double, one inverted ..
d. Surch double, one sideways ..
e. Surch double, one albino ..
f. Surch triple .. ..
g. Surch triple, one albino ..
h. Surch on front, inverted surch on back .. .. ..
i. Pair, one without surch ..
1256 **235** 60 c. on 4 n.p. multicoloured .. 15 20
a. Surch double .. ..
b. Surch double, one inverted ..
c. Surch double, one albino ..
d. Surch inverted .. .. † —
1257 – 60 c. on 3 c. mult (No. 1044) (1989) 15 20
a. Decimal point omitted from surch (R. 4/5) ..
1258 **400** 80 c. on 5 p. multicoloured .. 20 25
a. Pair, one without surch ..
b. Surch double .. ..
1259 – 80 c. on 5 c. mult (No. 1046) (1990) 75 80
1260 – 100 c. on 3 n.p. mult (No. 464) (1990) 1·25 1·25
a. Surch inverted .. ..
1261 – 100 c. on 20 n.p. deep blue and new blue (No. 470) .. .. 25 30
1262 – 100 c. on 20 p. mult (No. 1040) (9.88) 25 30
a. Surch double, one sideways ..
b. Horiz pair, one without surch ..
c. Surch inverted .. ..
1263 – 100 c. on 3 c. mult (No. 1044) (1990) 25 30
1264 **236** 200 c. on 6 n.p. multicoloured .. 1·00 80
a. Surch double .. ..
1245/64 .. .. .. *Set of* 20 7·00 6·00
Other handstamped and manuscript surcharges can be found used during 1988–89, but it is understood that only those listed above were issued by the postal authorities.

**440** Boxing

**441** Nutrition Lecture

(Litho Questa)

**1988** (10 Oct). *Olympic Games, Seoul. T* **440** *and similar horiz designs. Multicoloured. P* 14.
1265 20 c. Type **440** .. .. .. .. 15 15
1266 60 c. Athletics .. .. .. .. 45 45
1267 80 c. Discus-throwing .. .. .. 60 60
1268 100 c. Javelin-throwing .. .. .. 80 80
1269 350 c. Weightlifting .. .. .. 2·00 2·00
1265/9 .. .. .. .. *Set of* 5 3·50 3·50
**MS**1270 75 × 105 mm. 500 c. As 80 c. .. .. 3·50 3·00
Nos. 1265/70 also exist imperforate from a limited printing.

(Litho B.D.T.)

**1988** (14 Dec). *125th Anniv of International Red Cross. T* **441** *and similar vert designs. Multicoloured. P* 14.
1271 20 c. Type **441** .. .. .. .. 20 15
1272 50 c. Red Cross volunteer with blind woman .. .. .. .. .. 60 60
1273 60 c. Distributing flood relief supplies .. 70 70
1274 200 c. Giving first aid .. .. .. 1·75 1·75
1271/4 .. .. .. .. *Set of* 4 3·00 3·00

442 Tropical Forest

443 "African Solidarity"

(Litho B.D.T.)

**1988** (19 Dec). *Christmas. T* **442** *and similar multicoloured designs. P* 14.

1275 20 c. Type **442** .. .. .. .. .. 15 10
1276 60 c. Christ Child (*vert*) .. .. .. 35 35
1277 80 c. Virgin and Child with Star (*vert*) .. 50 60
1278 100 c. Three Wise Men following Star .. 60 70
1279 350 c. Symbolic Crucifixion (*vert*) .. 2·00 2·50
1275/9 .. .. .. .. .. *Set of* 5 3·25 3·75
**MS**1280 100×70 mm. 500 c. Virgin and Child (*vert*) .. .. .. .. .. .. 2·50 2·75

Nos. 1275/80 also exist imperforate from a limited printing.

(Litho B.D.T.)

**1989** (3 Jan). *25th Anniv of Organization of African Unity* (1988). *T* **443** *and similar multicoloured designs. P* 14.

1281 20 c. Type **443** .. .. .. .. .. 10 10
1282 50 c. O.A.U. Headquarters, Addis Ababa 15 20
1283 60 c. Emperor Haile Selassie and Ethiopian flag (*horiz*) .. .. 20 25
1284 200 c. Kwame Nkrumah (former Ghanaian President) and flag (*horiz*) .. 60 65
1281/4 .. .. .. .. .. *Set of* 4 90 1·00

444 "Amor"

A. ZUELOW
DDR
60 KG

(445)

(Litho B.D.T.)

**1989** (16 Jan). *500th Birth Anniversary of Titian (artist). T* **444** *and similar vert designs. Multicoloured. P* 14.

1285 20 c. Type **444** .. .. .. .. .. 10 10
1286 60 c. "The Appeal" .. .. .. .. 20 25
1287 80 c. "Bacchus and Ariadne" (detail) .. 25 30
1288 100 c. "Portrait of Musician" .. .. 30 35
1289 350 c. "Philip II seated" .. .. .. 1·00 1·10
1285/9 .. .. .. .. .. *Set of* 5 1·60 1·90
**MS**1290 77×115 mm. 500 c. "Portrait of a Gentleman" .. .. .. .. .. 1·50 1·60

**1989** (23 Jan). *Olympic Medal Winners, Seoul. Nos.* 1265/70 *optd as T* **445**.

1291 20 c. Type **440** (optd with T **445**) .. 10 10
1292 60 c. Athletics (optd "G. BORDIN ITALY MARATHON") .. .. .. 20 25
1293 80 c. Discus-throwing (optd "J. SCHULT DDR") .. .. .. .. 25 30
1294 100 c. Javelin-throwing (optd "T. KORJUS FINLAND") .. .. .. .. 30 35
1295 350 c. Weightlifting (optd "B. GUIDIKOV BULGARIA 75 KG") .. .. .. 1·00 1·10
1291/5 .. .. .. .. .. *Set of* 5 1·60 1·90
**MS**1296 75×105 mm. 500 c. As 80 c. (optd "GOLD J. SCHULT DDR SILVER R. OUBARTAS USSR BRONZE R. DANNEBERG W. GERMANY" on sheet margin) .. .. 1·50 1·60

(446)

C60 ==

(447)

**1989** (3 July–20 Nov). *Various stamps surch as T* **446/7**.

(*a*) *On Nos.* 949/50 *and* 952/4 (20 Nov)

1297 80 c. on 65 p. Prince Charles and Lady Diana Spencer .. .. .. .. 35 40
1298 100 c. on 80 p. Prince Charles on visit to Ghana .. .. .. .. .. 45 50
1299 100 c. on 1 c. Prince Charles on visit to Ghana .. .. .. .. .. 45 50
1300 300 c. on 3 c. Type **385** .. .. .. 1·25 1·40
1301 500 c. on 4 c. Type **385** .. .. .. 2·25 2·50
1297/1301 .. .. .. .. *Set of* 5 4·25 4·75

(*b*) *On Nos.* 1048/51 *and* **MS**1053 (18 Sept)

1302 60 c. on 1 c. Type **401** .. .. .. 25 30
1303 80 c. on 1 c. 40, Satellite dish aerial .. 35 40
1304 200 c. on 2 c. 30, Cable and cable-laying ship .. .. .. .. .. 90 95
1305 300 c. on 3 c. Switchboard operators .. 1·25 1·40
1302/5 .. .. .. .. .. *Set of* 4 2·50 2·75
**MS**1306 95×70 mm. 500 c. on 6 c. Space satellite .. .. .. .. .. 2·25 2·75

(*c*) *On Nos.* 1104/7 *and* **MS**1109

1307 60 c. on 1 c. Type **408** .. .. .. 25 30
1308 80 c. on 1 c. 40, Boxing .. .. .. 35 40
1309 200 c. on 2 c. 30, Hockey .. .. .. 90 95
1310 300 c. on 3 c. Men's 400 metre hurdles race 1·25 1·40
1307/10 .. .. .. .. .. *Set of* 4 2·50 2·75
**MS**1311 103×78 mm. 600 c. on 70 c. Football 2·50 3·00

(*d*) *On Nos.* 1134/7 *and* **MS**1139

1312 60 c. on 1 c. Type **408** (optd with T **413**) 25 30
1313 80 c. on 1 c. 40, Boxing (optd "U.S. WINNERS") .. .. .. .. .. 35 40
1314 200 c. on 2 c. 30, Field hockey (optd "PAKISTAN (FIELD HOCKEY)") .. 90 95
1315 300 c. on 3 c. Men's 400 metre hurdles race (optd "EDWIN MOSES U.S.A.") .. 1·25 1·40
1312/15 .. .. .. .. .. *Set of* 4 2·50 2·75
**MS**1316 103×78 mm. 600 c. on 70 c. Football (optd "FRANCE") .. .. .. .. 2·50 3·00

(*e*) *On Nos.* 1140/3 (20 Nov)

1317 80 c. on 5 c. Type **414** .. .. .. 35 40
1318 250 c. on 12 c. At Ascot Races .. .. 1·10 1·25
1319 300 c. on 100 c. At Clarence House on her 84th birthday .. .. .. .. 1·25 1·40
1317/19 .. .. .. .. .. *Set of* 3 2·50 2·75
**MS**1320 56×84 mm. 500 c. on 110 c. With Prince Charles at Garter Ceremony .. .. 2·50 2·75

(*f*) *On Nos.* 1159/61 *and* **MS**1163 (20 Nov)

1321 80 c. on 5 c. Type **418** .. .. .. 35 40
1322 100 c. on 8 c. Barred Owl .. .. .. 45 50
1323 300 c. on 12 c. Black-throated Mango .. 1·25 1·40
1321/3 .. .. .. .. .. *Set of* 3 1·90 2·10
**MS**1324 500 c. on 110 c. Downy Woodpecker .. 2·25 2·50

(*g*) *On Nos.* 1190/2 *and* **MS**1194

1325 60 c. on 5 c. Type **424** .. .. .. 25 30
1326 200 c. on 15 c. Player taking control of ball 90 95
1327 300 c. on 25 c. Player kicking ball .. 1·25 1·40
1325/7 .. .. .. .. .. *Set of* 3 2·10 2·40
**MS**1328 90×70 mm. 600 c. on 150 c. Player kicking ball (*different*) .. .. .. .. 2·50 3·00

(*h*) *As Nos.* 1190/2 *and* **MS**1194, *but with unissued "WINNERS" opt as T* **216** *of Antigua* (18 Sept)

1329 60 c. on 5 c. Type **424** .. .. .. 25 30
1330 200 c. on 15 c. Player taking control of ball 90 95
1331 300 c. on 25 c. Player kicking ball .. 1·25 1·40
1329/31 .. .. .. .. .. *Set of* 3 2·10 2·40
**MS**1332 90×70 mm. 600 c. on 150 c. Player kicking ball (*different*) .. .. .. .. 3·25 3·50

(*i*) *On Nos.* 1208/11

1333 60 c. on 5 c. Mikhail Lomonosov (scientist) and Chamber of Curiosities, St. Petersburg .. .. .. .. .. 25 30
1334 80 c. on 25 c. Lunar probe "Surveyor 3", 1966 .. .. .. .. .. 35 40
1335 500 c. on 200 c. Wedgwood plaques for Isaac Newton, 1790, and "Apollo 11" Moon landing, 1968 .. .. .. .. 2·25 2·50
1333/5 .. .. .. .. .. *Set of* 3 2·50 3·00
**MS**1336 100×70 mm. 750 c. on 250 c. Halley's Comet .. .. .. .. .. .. 3·50 4·00
a. Surch double, one inverted ..

(*j*) *As Nos.* 1208/11, *but with unissued logo opt as T* **218** *of Antigua* (18 Sept)

1337 60 c. on 5 c. Mikhail Lomonosov (scientist) and Chamber of Curiosities, St. Petersburg .. .. .. .. .. 25 30
1338 80 c. on 25 c. Lunar probe "Surveyor 3", 1966 .. .. .. .. .. 35 40
1339 500 c. on 200 c. Wedgwood plaques for Isaac Newton, 1790, and "Apollo 11" Moon landing, 1968 .. .. .. .. 2·25 2·50
1337/9 .. .. .. .. .. *Set of* 3 2·50 3·00
**MS**1340 100×70 mm. 750 c. on 250 c. Halley's Comet .. .. .. .. .. .. 3·50 4·00

On No. **MS**1336a the inverted surcharge occurs towards the bottom left of the miniature sheet.

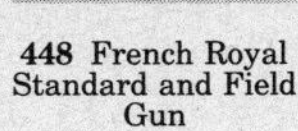


448 French Royal Standard and Field Gun

449 Storming the Bastille

(Litho B.D.T.)

**1989** (7 July). *"Philexfrance 89" International Stamp Exhibition, Paris. T* **448** *and similar multicoloured designs. P* 14.

1341 20 c. Type **448** .. .. .. .. .. 20 15
1342 60 c. Regimental standard, 1789, and French infantryman .. .. .. 40 35
1343 80 c. Revolutionary standard, 1789, and pistol .. .. .. .. .. 50 50
1344 350 c. Tricolour, 1794, and musket .. 2·00 2·25
1341/4 .. .. .. .. .. *Set of* 4 2·75 3·00
**MS**1345 77×106 mm. 600 c. Street plan of Paris, 1789 (*horiz*) .. .. .. .. .. 2·50 3·00

(Litho Questa)

**1989** (21 Aug). *Japanese Art. Portraits. Multicoloured designs as T* **250** *of Antigua. P* $13^1/_2$×14.

1346 20 c. "Minamoto-no-Yoritomo" (Fujiwara-no-Takanobu) (*vert*) .. .. .. 10 10
1347 50 c. "Takami Senseki" (Watanabe Kazan) (*vert*) .. .. .. .. .. 15 20
1348 60 c. "Ikkyu Sojun" (study) (Bokusai) (*vert*) .. .. .. .. .. 20 25
1349 75 c. "Nakamura Kuranosuka" (Ogata Korin) (*vert*) .. .. .. .. 20 25
1350 125 c. "Portrait of a Lady" (Kyoto branch, Kano School) (*vert*) .. .. 35 40
1351 150 c. "Portrait of Zemmui" (anon, 12th-century) (*vert*) .. .. 45 50
1352 200 c. "Ono no Komachi the Poetess" (Hokusai) (*vert*) .. .. .. .. 60 65
1353 500 c. "Kobo Daisi as a Child" (anon) (*vert*) 1·50 1·60
1346/53 .. .. .. .. .. *Set of* 8 3·25 3·50
**MS**1354 Two sheets, each 102×77 mm. (a) 500 c. "Kodai-no-Kimi" (attr Fujiwara-no-Nobuzane) (*vert*). P $13^1/_2$×14. (b) 500 c. "Emperor Hanazono" (Fujiwara-no-Goshin). P 14×$13^1/_2$ *Set of* 2 *sheets* 3·00 3·25

Nos. 1346/53 were each printed in sheetlets of 10 containing two vertical strips of 5 stamps separated by printed labels commemorating Emperor Hirohito.

(Litho B.D.T.)

**1989** (22 Sept). *Bicentenary of the French Revolution. T* **449** *and similar multicoloured designs. P* 14×$13^1/_2$ (*vert*) *or* $13^1/_2$×14 (*horiz*).

1355 20 c. Type **449** .. .. .. .. .. 10 10
1356 60 c. Declaration of Human Rights .. 20 25
1357 80 c. Storming the Bastille (*horiz*) .. 25 30
1358 200 c. Revolution monument (*horiz*) .. 60 65
1359 350 c. Tree of Liberty (*horiz*) .. .. 1·00 1·10
1355/9 .. .. .. .. .. *Set of* 5 1·90 2·10

450 Spindle Shank

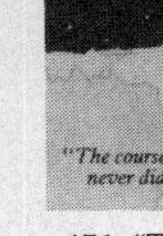

451 "The Course of True Love . ."

(Des L. Nelson. Litho B.D.T.)

**1989** (2 Oct). *Fungi (1st series). T* **450** *and similar vert designs. Multicoloured. P* 14.

1360 20 c. Type **450** .. .. .. .. .. 10 10
1361 50 c. Shaggy Ink Cap .. .. .. .. 15 20
1362 60 c. *Xerocomus subtomentosus* .. .. 20 25
1363 80 c. Purple Blewit .. .. .. .. 25 30
1364 150 c. *Suillus placidus* .. .. .. 45 50
1365 200 c. *Lepista nuda* .. .. .. .. 60 65
1366 300 c. Fairy Ring Champignon .. .. 90 95
1367 500 c. Field Mushroom .. .. .. 1·50 1·60
1360/7 .. .. .. .. .. *Set of* 8 3·75 4·00
**MS**1368 Two sheets, each 110×80 mm. (a) 600 c. *Boletus rhodoxanthus*. (b) 600 c. *Amanita rubescens* .. .. .. *Set of* 2 *sheets* 3·50 3·75

Nos. 1360/8 also exist imperforate from a limited printing.

See also Nos. 1489/97.

(Des N. Waldman. Litho Walsall)

**1989** (9 Oct). *425th Birth Anniv of Shakespeare. T* **451** *and similar vert designs showing lines and scenes from* A Midsummer Night's Dream. *Multicoloured. P* $13^1/_2$×13.

1369 40 c. Type **451** .. .. .. .. .. 10 15
a. Sheetlet. Nos. 1369/89 .. .. .. 1·90
1370 40 c. "Love looks not with the eye, but with the mind" .. .. .. .. .. 10 15
1371 40 c. "Nature here shows art" .. .. 10 15
1372 40 c. "Things growing are not ripe till their season" .. .. .. .. .. 10 15
1373 40 c. "He is defiled that draws a sword on thee" .. .. .. .. .. .. 10 15
1374 40 c. "It is not enough to speak, but to speak true" .. .. .. .. .. 10 15
1375 40 c. "Thou art as wise as thou art beautiful" .. .. .. .. .. 10 15
1376 40 c. Wildcat in wood (face value at left) .. 10 15
1377 40 c. Man .. .. .. .. .. .. 10 15
1378 40 c. Woman with flower .. .. .. 10 15
1379 40 c. King and queen .. .. .. .. 10 15
1380 40 c. Bottom .. .. .. .. .. 10 15
1381 40 c. Wildcat in wood (face value at right) 10 15
1382 40 c. Woman .. .. .. .. .. 10 15
1383 40 c. Leopard .. .. .. .. .. 10 15
1384 40 c. Tree trunk and man .. .. .. 10 15
1385 40 c. Meadow flowers .. .. .. .. 10 15
1386 40 c. Mauve flowers .. .. .. .. 10 15
1387 40 c. Plants .. .. .. .. .. 10 15
1388 40 c. Lion .. .. .. .. .. .. 10 15
1389 40 c. Fern and flowers .. .. .. .. 10 15
1369/89 .. .. .. .. .. *Set of* 21 1·90 2·75

Nos. 1369/89 were printed together, *se-tenant*, as a sheetlet of 21, forming a composite design.

(Des Mary Walters. Litho B.D.T.)

**1989** (16 Oct)–**90**. *Birds. Multicoloured designs as T* **244** *of Dominica. P* 14.

1390 20 c. Village Weaver (*horiz*) .. .. 10 10
1391 50 c. African Pied Wagtail (*horiz*) .. 15 20
1392 60 c. African Pygmy Kingfisher (inscr "*Halcyon malimbicus*") (*horiz*) .. 50 50
1392*a* 60 c. African Pygmy Kingfisher (inscr "*Ispidina picta*") (6.90) (*horiz*) .. 20 25
1393 80 c. Blue-breasted Kingfisher (inscr "*Ispidina picta*") (*horiz*) .. .. 70 70
1393*a* 80 c. Blue-breasted Kingfisher (inscr "*Halcyon malimbicus*") (*horiz*) (6.90) .. .. .. .. .. 25 30
1394 150 c. Striped Kingfisher .. .. .. 45 50
1395 200 c. Shikra .. .. .. .. .. 60 65
1396 300 c. Grey Parrot .. .. .. .. 90 95
1397 500 c. Black Kite .. .. .. .. 1·50 1·60
1390/7 .. .. .. .. .. *Set of* 10 4·50 4·75
**MS**1398 (a) 128×83 mm. 600 c. Finch and swallow (*horiz*). (b) 83×128 mm. 600 c. Birds on branch .. .. .. *Set of* 2 *sheets* 3·50 3·75

The original printings of Nos. 1392/3 had the Latin names of the birds transposed. Corrected versions of the two designs were supplied during 1990.

Nos. 1390/8 also exist imperforate from a limited printing.

**452** Command Module *Columbia* orbiting Moon

(Des K. Gromell. Litho B.D.T.)

**1989** (6 Nov). *20th Anniv of First Manned Landing on Moon. T* **452** *and similar horiz designs. Multicoloured. P* 14.

1399 20 c. Type **452** .. .. .. .. 10 10
1400 80 c. Neil Armstrong's footprint on Moon 25 30
1401 200 c. Edwin Aldrin on Moon .. .. 60 65
1402 300 c. "Apollo 11" capsule on parachutes 90 95
1399/1402 .. .. .. .. *Set of* 4 1·60 1·75
**MS**1403 Two sheets, each 100×72 mm. (a) 500 c. Launch of "Apollo 11". (b) 500 c. Earth seen from Moon .. .. .. .. *Set of 2 sheets* 3·00 3·25

**453** Desertification of Pasture

(Litho B.D.T.)

**1989** (15 Nov). *World Environment Day. T* **453** *and similar horiz designs. Multicoloured. P* 14.

1404 20 c. Type **453** .. .. .. .. 10 10
1405 60 c. Wildlife fleeing bush fire .. .. 20 25
1406 400 c. Industrial pollution .. .. 1·25 1·40
1407 500 c. Erosion .. .. .. .. 1·50 1·60
1404/7 .. .. .. .. *Set of* 4 2·75 3·00

**454** *Bebearia arcadius* **455** *Cardium costatum* Linne

(Des Mary Walters. Litho B.D.T.)

**1990** (20 Feb). *Butterflies. T* **454** *and similar horiz designs. Multicoloured. P* 14.

1408 20 c. Type **454** .. .. .. .. 10 10
1409 60 c. *Charaxes laodice* .. .. .. 20 25
1410 80 c. *Euryphura porphyrion* .. .. 25 30
1411 100 c. *Neptis nicomedes* .. .. .. 30 35
1412 150 c. *Citrinophila erastus* .. .. 45 50
1413 200 c. *Aethiopana honorius* .. .. 60 65
1414 300 c. *Precis westermanni* .. .. 90 95
1415 500 c. *Cymothoe hypatha* .. .. 1·50 1·60
1408/15 .. .. .. .. *Set of* 8 3·75 4·25
**MS**1416 Two sheets, each 104×72 mm. (a) 600 c. *Telipna acraea*. (b) 600 c. *Pentila abraxas* *Set of 2 sheets* 3·50 3·75
Nos. 1408/16 also exist imperforate from a limited printing.

(Des E. Mensah. Litho D.L.R.)

**1990** (23 Feb). *Seashells. T* **455** *and similar vert designs. Multicoloured. P* 14×14½.

1417 20 c. Type **455** .. .. .. .. 10 10
1418 60 c. *Cymbium glans* Gmelin .. .. 20 25
1419 80 c. *Conus genuanus* Linne .. .. 25 30
1420 200 c. *Ancilla tankervillei* Swainson .. 60 65
1421 350 c. *Tectarius coronatus* Valenciennes 1·00 1·10
1417/21 .. .. .. .. *Set of* 5 1·90 2·10
Nos. 1417/18 show the shell descriptions transposed in error.

**456** Nehru welcoming President Nkrumah of Ghana

(Des E. Mensah. Litho D.L.R.)

**1990** (27 Mar). *Birth Centenary of Jawaharlal Nehru (Indian statesman). T* **456** *and similar multicoloured designs. P* 14½×14 *(horiz) or* 14×14½ *(others)*.

1422 20 c. Type **456** .. .. .. .. 10 10
1423 60 c. Nehru addressing Bandung Conference, 1955 .. .. .. .. 20 25
1424 80 c. Nehru with garland and flowers (*vert*) .. .. .. .. 25 30
1425 200 c. Nehru releasing pigeon (*vert*) .. 60 65
1426 350 c. Nehru (*vert*) .. .. .. 1·00 1·10
1422/6 .. .. .. .. *Set of* 5 1·90 2·10

**457** Wyon Medal, 1838 **458** Anniversary Emblem

(Des S. Pollard. Litho B.D.T.)

**1990** (23 May). *150th Anniv of Penny Black. T* **457** *and similar horiz designs. P* 13½.

1427 20 c. black and reddish violet .. .. 10 10
1428 60 c. black and deep grey-green .. .. 20 25
1429 80 c. black and reddish violet .. .. 25 30
1430 200 c. black and deep grey-green .. .. 60 65
1431 350 c. black and deep grey-green .. .. 1·00 1·10
1432 400 c. black and rosine .. .. 1·25 1·40
1427/32 .. .. .. .. *Set of* 6 3·00 3·50
**MS**1433 Two sheets, each 112×83 mm. (a) 600 c. red-brown and black; (b) 600 c. deep brown, buff and black .. .. .. *Set of 2 sheets* 5·00 5·50
Designs:—60, 600 c. (No. **MS**1433b) Bath mail coach, 1840; 80 c. Leeds mail coach, 1840; 200 c. Proof of Queen's head engraved by Heath, 1840; 350 c. Master die, 1840; 400 c. London mail coach, 1840; 600 c. (No. MS1433a) Printing the Penny Black.
Nos. 1427/33 also exist imperforate from a limited printing.

(Litho D.L.R.)

**1990** (5 June). *Tenth Anniv (1989) of 4 June Revolution. T* **458** *and similar vert designs. Multicoloured. P* 14½×14.

1434 20 c. Type **458** .. .. .. .. 10 10
1435 60 c. Foodstuffs .. .. .. .. 20 25
1436 80 c. Cocoa .. .. .. .. 25 30
1437 200 c. Mining .. .. .. .. 60 65
1438 350 c. Scales of Justice and sword .. 1·00 1·10
1434/8 .. .. .. .. *Set of* 5 1·90 2·10

**459** Map of Africa and Satellite Network

(Litho D.L.R.)

**1990** (12 July). *25th Anniv of Intelsat Satellite System. T* **459** *and similar horiz designs. Multicoloured. P* 14×14½.

1439 20 c. Type **459** .. .. .. .. 10 10
1440 60 c. Map of Americas .. .. .. 20 25
1441 80 c. Map of Asia and Pacific .. .. 25 30
1442 200 c. Map of South America and Africa .. 60 65
1443 350 c. Map of Indian Ocean and Pacific .. 1·00 1·10
1439/43 .. .. .. .. *Set of* 5 1·90 2·10

**460** Housewife using Telephone **461** Blue Flycatcher

(Litho D.L.R.)

**1990** (16 July). *Second Anniversary of Introduction of International Direct Dialling Service. T* **460** *and similar horiz designs. Multicoloured. P* 14×14½.

1444 20 c. Type **460** .. .. .. .. 10 10
1445 60 c. Businessman using telephone .. 20 25
1446 80 c. Man using phonecard telephone .. 25 30
1447 200 c. Public telephones for internal and IDD services .. .. .. 60 65
1448 350 c. Satellite station .. .. .. 1·00 1·10
1444/8 .. .. .. .. *Set of* 5 1·90 2·10

(Des W. Wright. Litho Questa)

**1990** (25 Oct). *African Tropical Rain Forest. T* **461** *and similar multicoloured designs. P* 14×14½.

1449 40 c. Type **461** .. .. .. .. 10 15
a. Sheetlet. Nos. 1449/68 .. .. 1·75
1450 40 c. Boomslang (snake) .. .. 10 15
1451 40 c. Superb Sunbird .. .. .. 10 15
1452 40 c. Bateleur .. .. .. .. 10 15
1453 40 c. Yellow-casqued Hornbill .. .. 10 15
1454 40 c. *Salamis temora* (butterfly) .. .. 10 15
1455 40 c. Potto .. .. .. .. 10 15
1456 40 c. Leopard .. .. .. .. 10 15
1457 40 c. Bongo .. .. .. .. 10 15
1458 40 c. Grey Parrot .. .. .. .. 10 15
1459 40 c. Okapi .. .. .. .. 10 15
1460 40 c. Gorilla .. .. .. .. 10 15
1461 40 c. Flap-necked Chameleon .. .. 10 15
1462 40 c. West African Dwarf Crocodile .. 10 15
1463 40 c. Python .. .. .. .. 10 15
1464 40 c. Giant Ground Pangolin .. .. 10 15
1465 40 c. *Pseudacraea boisduvali* (butterfly) .. 10 15
1466 40 c. North African Crested Porcupine .. 10 15
1467 40 c. Rosy-columned Aerangis (orchid) .. 10 15
1468 40 c. *Cymothoe sangaris* (butterfly) .. 10 15
1449/68 .. .. .. .. *Set of* 20 1·75 2·50
**MS**1469 100×75 mm. 600 c. Head of Leopard (*vert*). P 14½×14 .. .. .. 1·75 1·90
Nos. 1449/68 were printed together, *se-tenant*, as a sheetlet of 20, forming a composite design.

**462** Jupiter **463** *Eulophia guineensis*

(Des K. Gromell. Litho Questa)

**1990** (13 Dec). *Space Flight of* "Voyager 2". *T* **462** *and similar multicoloured designs. P* 14.

1470 100 c. Type **462** .. .. .. .. 30 35
a. Sheetlet. Nos. 1470/8 .. .. 2·40
1471 100 c. Neptune and Triton .. .. 30 35
1472 100 c. Ariel, moon of Uranus .. .. 30 35
1473 100 c. Saturn from Mimas .. .. 30 35
1474 100 c. Saturn .. .. .. .. 30 35
1475 100 c. Rings of Saturn .. .. .. 30 35
1476 100 c. Neptune .. .. .. .. 30 35
1477 100 c. Uranus from Miranda .. .. 30 35
1478 100 c. Volcano on Io .. .. .. 30 35
1470/8 .. .. .. .. *Set of* 9 2·40 2·75
**MS**1479 Two sheets. (a) 111×81 mm. 600 c. "Voyager 2" spacecraft (*vert*). (b) 80×111 mm. 600 c. Lift off of "Voyager 2" (*vert*) *Set of 2 sheets* 3·50 3·75
Nos. 1470/8 were printed together, *se-tenant*, as a sheetlet of 9.

(Litho B.D.T.)

**1990** (17 Dec). *Orchids. T* **463** *and similar vert designs. Multicoloured. P* 14.

1480 20 c. Type **463** .. .. .. .. 10 10
1481 40 c. *Eurychone rothschildiana* .. .. 10 15
1482 60 c. *Bulbophyllum barbigerum* .. .. 20 25
1483 80 c. *Polystachya galeata* .. .. 25 30
1484 200 c. *Diaphananthe kamerunensis* .. 60 65
1485 300 c. *Podangis dactyloceras* .. .. 90 95
1486 400 c. *Ancistrochilus rothschildianus* .. 1·25 1·40
1487 500 c. *Rangaeris muscicola* .. .. 1·50 1·60
1480/7 .. .. .. .. *Set of* 8 4·25 4·75
**MS**1488 Two sheets, each 101×70 mm. (a) 600 c. *Bolusiella imbricata*. (b) 600 c. *Diaphananthe rutila* .. .. .. .. *Set of 2 sheets* 3·50 3·75

**464** *Coprinus atramentarius*

(Litho B.D.T.)

**1990** (18 Dec). *Fungi (2nd series). T* **464** *and similar horiz designs. Multicoloured. P* 14.

1489 20 c. Type **464** .. .. .. .. 10 10
1490 50 c. *Marasmius oreades* .. .. 15 20
1491 60 c. *Oudemansiella radicata* .. .. 20 25
1492 80 c. *Boletus edulis* ("Cep") .. .. 25 30
1493 150 c. *Hebeloma crustuliniforme* .. .. 45 50
1494 200 c. *Coprinus micaceus* .. .. 60 65
1495 300 c. *Lepiota procera* .. .. .. 90 95
1496 500 c. *Amanita phalloides* .. .. 1·50 1·60
1489/96 .. .. .. .. *Set of* 8 3·75 4·00
**MS**1497 Two sheets, each 104×82 mm. (a) Nos. 1489, 1491/2 and 1496. (b) Nos. 1490 and 1493/5 *Set of 2 sheets* 4·00 4·50

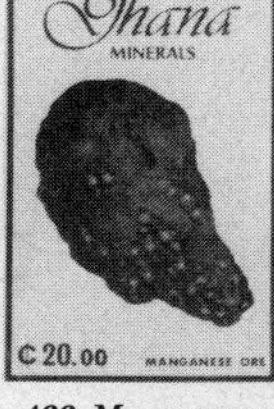


**465** Italian and Swedish Players chasing Ball **466** Manganese Ore

(Des Young Phillips Studio. Litho Questa)

**1990** (18 Dec). *World Cup Football Championship, Italy. T* **465** *and similar multicoloured designs. P* 14.

1498 20 c. Type **465** .. .. .. .. 10 10
1499 50 c. Egyptian player penetrating Irish defence .. .. .. .. 15 20
1500 60 c. Cameroon players celebrating .. 20 25
1501 80 c. Rumanian player beating challenge 25 30

1502 100 c. Russian goalkeeper Dassayev 30 35
1503 150 c. Roger Milla of Cameroon (*vert*) 45 50
1504 400 c. South Korean player challenging opponent 1·25 1·40
1505 600 c. West German player celebrating 1·75 1·90
1498/505 *Set of* 8 4·00 4·50
**MS**1506 Two sheets, each 88×98 mm. (a) 800 c. United Arab Emirates player watching ball. (b) 800 c. Colombian player *Set of* 2 *sheets* 4·75 5·00

(Litho Questa)

**1990** (24 Dec). *350th Death Anniv of Rubens. Multicoloured designs as T* **273** *of Antigua, but vert. P* 13½×14.
1507 20 c. "Duke of Mantua" 10 10
1508 50 c. "Jan Brant" 15 20
1509 60 c. "Portrait of a Young Man" 20 25
1510 80 c. "Michel Ophovius" 25 30
1511 100 c. "Caspar Gevaerts" 30 35
1512 200 c. "Head of Warrior" (detail) 60 65
1513 300 c. "Study of a Bearded Man" 90 95
1514 400 c. "Paracelsus" 1·25 1·40
1507/14 *Set of* 8 3·25 3·75
**MS**1515 Two sheets, each 71×100 mm. (a) 600 c. "Warrior with two Pages" (detail). (b) 600 c. "Archduke Ferdinand" (detail) *Set of* 2 *sheets* 3·50 3·75

(Des E. Mensah. Litho D.L.R.)

**1991** (2 May). *Minerals. T* **466** *and similar vert designs. Multicoloured. P* 14½×14.
1516 20 c. Type **466** 10 10
1517 60 c. Iron ore 20 25
1518 80 c. Bauxite ore 25 30
1519 200 c. Gold ore 60 65
1520 350 c. Diamond 1·00 1·10
1516/20 *Set of* 5 1·90 2·10
**MS**1521 70×90 mm. 600 c. Uncut and cut diamonds 1·75 2·00

**467** Dance Drums

**468** *Amorphophallus dracontioides*

(Des E. Mensah. Litho D.L.R.)

**1991** (9 May). *Tribal Drums. T* **467** *and similar vert designs. Multicoloured. P* 14½×14.
1522 20 c. Type **467** 10 10
1523 60 c. Message drums 20 25
1524 80 c. War drums 25 30
1525 200 c. Dance drums (different) 60 65
1526 350 c. Ceremonial drums 1·00 1·10
1522/6 *Set of* 5 1·90 2·10
**MS**1527 70×90 mm. 600 c. Drum with carrying strap 1·75 1·90

(Des E. Mensah. Litho D.L.R.)

**1991** (15 May). *Flowers (1st series). T* **468** *and similar vert designs. Multicoloured. P* 14½×14.
1528 20 c. Type **468** 10 10
1529 60 c. *Anchomanes difformis* 20 25
1530 80 c. *Kaemferia nigerica* 25 30
1531 200 c. *Aframomum sceptrum* 60 65
1532 350 c. *Amorphophallus flavovirens* 1·00 1·10
1528/32 *Set of* 5 1·90 2·10
**MS**1533 70×90 mm. 600 c. *Amorphophallus flavovirens* (different) 1·75 1·90

(Des E. Mensah. Litho D.L.R.)

**1991** (17 May). *Flowers (2nd series). Vert designs as T* **468**, *but inscr* "GHANA" *in block capitals. Multicoloured. P* 14½×14.
1534 20 c. *Urginea indica* 10 10
1535 60 c. *Hymenocallis littoralis* 20 25
1536 80 c. *Crinum jagus* 25 30
1537 200 c. *Dipcadi tacazzeanum* 60 65
1538 350 c. *Haemanthus rupestris* 1·00 1·10
1534/8 *Set of* 5 1·90 2·10
**MS**1539 70×90 mm. 600 c. *Urginea indica* (different) 1·75 1·90

**469** Transport and Telecommunication Symbols

**470** Drawing of Scout from First Handbook

(Des E. Mensah. Litho Francoise-Charles Oberthur)

**1991** (21 June). *40th Anniv of United Nations Development Programme. T* **469** *and similar vert designs. Multicoloured. P* 13½×14.
1540 20 c. Type **469** 10 10
1541 60 c. Agricultural research 20 25
1542 80 c. Literacy 25 30
1543 200 c. Advances in agricultural crop growth 60 65
1544 350 c. Industrial symbols 1·00 1·10
1540/4 *Set of* 5 1·90 2·10

(Des W. Hanson Studio. Litho B.D.T.)

**1991** (18 July). *50th Death Anniv of Lord Baden-Powell. T* **470** *and similar designs. P* 14.
1545 20 c. black and pale buff 10 10
1546 50 c. grey, pale blue and black 15 20
1547 60 c. multicoloured 20 25
1548 80 c. black and pale buff 25 30
1549 100 c. multicoloured 30 35
1550 200 c. multicoloured 60 65
1551 500 c. multicoloured 1·50 1·60
1552 600 c. multicoloured 1·75 1·90
1545/52 *Set of* 8 4·50 5·00
**MS**1553 Two sheets. (a) 104×75 mm. 800 c. multicoloured; (b) 74×105 mm. 800 c. mult *Set of* 2 *sheets* 4·50 4·75

Designs: *Vert*—50 c. Lord Baden-Powell; 80 c. Handbook illustration by Norman Rockwell; 500 c. Scout at prayer. *Horiz*—60 c. Hands holding Boy Scout emblem; 100 c. Mafeking Siege 1d. Goodyear stamp and African runner; 200 c. Scouts with blitz victim, London, 1944; 600 c. Mafeking Siege 1d. Goodyear stamp; 800 c. (**MS**1553a) Scout camp; 800 c. (**MS**1553b) Envelope from Mafeking Siege.

**471** Women sorting Fish

(Litho D.L.R.)

**1991** (22 July). *Chorkor Smoker (fish smoking process). T* **471** *and similar horiz designs. Multicoloured. P* 14×14½.
1554 20 c. Type **471** 10 10
1555 60 c. Cleaning the ovens 20 25
1556 80 c. Washing fish 25 30
1557 200 c. Laying fish on pallets 60 65
1558 350 c. Stacking pallets over ovens 1·00 1·10
1554/8 *Set of* 5 1·90 2·10

## POSTAGE DUE STAMPS

D 1

(Typo D.L.R.)

**1923.** *Yellowish toned paper. Wmk Mult Script CA. P* 14.
D1 D 1 ½d. black 14·00 75·00
D2 1d. black 75 1·00
D3 2d. black 12·00 14·00
D4 3d. black 18·00 9·50
D1/4 *Set of* 4 40·00 90·00
D1/4 Optd "Specimen" *Set of* 4 70·00

Normal — Lower serif at left of "3" missing (R. 9/1)

**1951–52.** *Chalk-surfaced paper. Wmk Mult Script CA. P* 14.
D5 D 1 2d. black (13.12.51) 2·00 9·00
a. Error. Crown missing, W **9a** £250
b. Error. St Edward's Crown, W **9b** £160
D6 3d. black (13.12.51) 1·50 8·00
a. Error. Crown missing, W **9a** £250
b. Error. St. Edward's Crown, W **9b** £160
c. Missing serif 12·00
D7 6d. black (1.10.52) 2·00 10·00
a. Error. Crown missing, W **9a** £350
b. Error. St. Edward's Crown, W **9b** £225
D8 1s. black (1.10.52) 2·25 32·00
b. Error. St. Edward's Crown, W **9b** £325
D5/8 *Set of* 4 7·00 55·00

GHANA
(D 2)

D 3

**1958** (25 June). *Nos.* D5/8 *and similar* 1d. *value optd with Type* D **2** *in red.*
D 9 D 1 1d. black 10 20
D10 2d. black 10 25
D11 3d. black 10 30
a. Missing serif 2·00
D12 6d. black 15 45
D13 1s. black 20 80
D9/13 *Set of* 5 50 1·75

(Typo De La Rue)

**1958** (1 Dec). *Chalk-surfaced paper. Wmk Mult Script CA. P* 14.
D14 D 3 1d. carmine 10 20
D15 2d. green 10 20
D16 3d. orange 10 30
a. Missing serif 2·50
D17 6d. bright ultramarine 10 50
D18 1s. reddish violet 15 1·75
D14/18 *Set of* 5 45 2·75

3p.
Ghana New Currency
19th July, 1965.
(D 4)

1½Np
(D 5)

**1965** (19 July). *Nos.* D14/18 *surch as Type* D **4** *diagonally upwards* (D) *or horiz* (H), *by Govt Printer, Accra.*
D19 D 3 1 p. on 1d. (D) 10 40
a. Surch inverted 6·00
b. Surch double
D20 2 p. on 2d. (B.) (H) 10 40
a. Surch inverted 4·50
D21 3 p. on 3d. (Indigo) (H) 10 40
a. Surch inverted
b. Ultramarine surch
ba. Ditto. Surch inverted 7·50
bb. Ditto. Surch on back and face
c. Black surch
d. Missing serif 1·50
D22 6 p. on 6d. (R.) (H) 10 70
a. Surch inverted
b. Purple-brown surch
ba. Ditto. Surch double 19·00
c. Green surch 13·00
D23 12 p. on 1s. (B.) (D) 15 1·10
D19/23 *Set of* 5 45 2·75

On the diagonal surcharges the figures of value are horizontal.

**1968** (Feb)–**70**. *Nos.* D20/2 *additionally surch as Type* D **5**, *in red* (1½ *n.p.*, 5 *n.p.*) *or black* (2½ *n.p.*).
D24 D 3 1½ n.p. on 2 p. on 2d. 5·50 4·25
a. Type D **5** double, one albino
b. Albino surch (Type D **4**)
D25 2½ n.p. on 3 p. on 3d. (4.70?) 1·00 4·00
a. Type D **5** double, one albino 5·00
b. Missing serif 3·00
D26 5 n.p. on 6 p. on 6d. (1970) 1·00
D24/6 *Set of* 3 6·00

The above were three in a series of surcharges, the others being 1 n.p. on 1 p. and 10 n.p. on 12 p., which were prepared, but owing to confusion due to the two surcharges in similar currency it was decided by the authorities not to issue the stamps, however, Nos. D24/6 were issued in error.

(Litho D.L.R.)

**1970.** *Inscr in new currency. P* 14¼ × 14.
D27 D 3 1 n.p. carmine-red 30 1·25
D28 1½ n.p. green 30 1·50
D29 2½ n.p. yellow-orange 40 1·75
D30 5 n.p. ultramarine 55 2·00
D31 10 n.p. reddish violet 75 2·50
D27/31 *Set of* 5 2·10 8·00

(Litho D.L.R.)

**1980–81.** *Currency described as "p". P* 14½ × 14.
D32 D 3 2 p. reddish orange 40 1·00
D33 3 p. brown 40 1·00

# Gibraltar

## CROWN COLONY

Early details of postal arrangements in Gibraltar are hard to establish, although it is known that postal facilities were provided by the Civil Secretary's Office from the early 1750s. Gibraltar became a packet port in 1806, although the Civil Secretary's Office continued to be responsible for other mail. The two services were amalgamated on 1 January 1857 as a Branch Office of the British G.P.O., the control of the postal services not reverting to Gibraltar until 1 January 1886.

Spanish stamps could be used at Gibraltar from their introduction in 1850 and, indeed, such franking was required on letters weighing over ½ oz. sent to Spain after 1 July 1854. From 1 July 1856 until 31 December 1875 all mail to Spain required postage to be prepaid by Spanish stamps and these issues were supplied by the Gibraltar postal authorities, acting as a Spanish Postal Agent. The mail, forwarded under this system was cancelled at San Roque with a horizontal barred oval, later replaced by a cartwheel type mark showing numeral 63.

Stamps of Great Britain were issued for use in Gibraltar from 3 September 1857 to the end of 1885.

For illustrations of the postmark types see BRITISH POST OFFICES ABROAD notes, following GREAT BRITAIN.

*Stamps of* GREAT BRITAIN *cancelled* "G" *as Type* **1** (3 Sept 1857 *to* 19 Feb 1859).

Z 1 1d. red-brown (1854) Die I .. .. .. .. £300
Z 2 1d. red-brown (1855), Die II, *wmk* Small Crown, *perf* 16 .. .. .. .. £550
Z 3 1d. red-brown (1855), Die II, *wmk* Small Crown, *perf* 14 .. .. .. .. £250
Z 4 1d. red-brown (1855), Die II, *wmk* Large Crown, *perf* 14 .. .. .. .. 65·00
Z 5 1d. rose-red (1857), Die II, *wmk* Large Crown, *perf* 14 .. .. .. .. 20·00
Z 6 2d. blue (1855), *wmk* Small Crown, *perf* 14 .. £300
Z 7 2d. blue (1855–58), *wmk* Large Crown, *perf* 16 .. £275
Z 8 2d. blue (1855), *wmk* Large Crown, *perf* 14 *From* 55·00
Plate Nos. 5, 6.
Z 9 2d. blue (1858) (Plate No. 7) .. .. .. £200
Z10 4d. rose (1857) .. .. .. .. 42·00
a. Thick glazed paper .. .. .. ..
Z11 6d. lilac (1856) .. .. .. .. 40·00
Z12 6d. lilac (1856) (blued *paper*) .. .. .. £750
Z13 1s. green (1856) .. .. .. .. £100
a. Thick paper .. .. .. ..
Z14 1s. green (1856) (blued *paper*) .. .. .. £1300

*Stamps of* GREAT BRITAIN *cancelled* "A 26" *as in Types* **2, 5, 11** *or* **14** (20 Feb 1859 *to* 31 Dec 1885).

Z15 ½d. rose-red (1870–79) .. .. .. *From* 15·00
Plate Nos. 4, 5, 6, 8, 10, 11, 12, 13, 14, 15, 19, 20.
Z16 1d. red-brown (1841), *imperf* .. .. .. £850
Z17 1d. red-brown (1855), *wmk* Large Crown, *perf* 14 .. £150
Z18 1d. rose-red (1857), *wmk* Large Crown, *perf* 14 .. 12·00
Z19 1d. rose-red (1864–79) .. .. .. *From* 17·00
Plate Nos. 71, 72, 73, 74, 76, 78, 79, 80, 81, 82, 83, 84, 85, 86, 87, 88, 89, 90, 91, 92, 93, 94, 95, 96, 97, 98, 99, 100, 101, 102, 103, 104, 105, 106, 107, 108, 109, 110, 111, 112, 113, 114, 115, 116, 117, 118, 119, 120, 121, 122, 123, 124, 125, 127, 129, 130, 131, 132, 133, 134, 135, 136, 137, 138, 139, 140, 141, 142, 143, 144, 145, 146, 147, 148, 149, 150, 151, 152, 153, 154, 155, 156, 157, 158, 159, 160, 161, 162, 163, 164, 165, 166, 167, 168, 169, 170, 171, 172, 173, 174, 175, 176, 177, 178, 179, 180, 181, 182, 183, 184, 185, 186, 187, 188, 189, 190, 191, 192, 193, 194, 195, 196, 197, 198, 199, 200, 201, 202, 203, 204, 205, 206, 207, 208, 209, 210, 211, 212, 213, 214, 215, 216, 217, 218, 219, 220, 221, 222, 223, 224, 225.
Z20 1½d. lake-red (1870) (Plate No. 3) .. .. .. £275
Z21 2d. blue (1855), *wmk* Large Crown, *perf* 14 .. £100
Plate No. 6.
Z22 2d. blue (1858–69) .. .. .. .. *From* 17·00
Plate Nos. 7, 8, 9, 12, 13, 14, 15.
Z23 2½d. rosy mauve (1875) (blued *paper*) .. *From* £100
Plate Nos. 1, 2, 3.
Z24 2½d. rosy mauve (1875–76) (Plate Nos. 1, 2, 3) *From* 27·00
Z25 2½d. rosy mauve (*Error of Lettering*) .. .. .. £1600
Z26 2½d. rosy mauve (1876–79) .. .. .. *From* 20·00
Plate Nos. 3, 4, 5, 6, 7, 8, 9, 10, 11, 12, 13, 14, 15, 16, 17.
Z27 2½d. blue (1880–81) (Plate Nos. 17, 18, 19, 20) *From* 12·00
Z28 2½d. blue (1881) (Plate Nos. 21, 22, 23) .. *From* 10·00
Z29 3d. carmine-rose (1862) .. .. .. .. £150
Z30 3d. rose (1865) (Plate No. 4) .. .. .. 45·00
Z31 3d. rose (1867–73) .. .. .. .. *From* 18·00
Plate Nos. 4, 5, 6, 7, 8, 9, 10.
Z32 3d. rose (1873–76) .. .. .. .. *From* 22·00
Plate Nos. 11, 12, 14, 15, 16, 17, 18, 19, 20.
Z33 3d. rose (1881) (Plate Nos. 20, 21) .. .. ..
Z34 3d. lilac (1883) (3d. *on* 3d) .. .. .. 70·00
Z35 4d. rose (1857) .. .. .. .. 42·00
Z36 4d. red (1862) (Plate Nos. 3, 4) .. .. *From* 45·00
Z37 4d. vermilion (1865–73) .. .. .. *From* 30·00
Plate Nos. 7, 8, 9, 10, 11, 12, 13, 14.
Z38 4d. vermilion (1876) (Plate No. 15) .. .. .. £225
Z39 4d. sage-green (1877) (Plate Nos. 15, 16) .. .. 90·00
Z40 4d. grey-brown (1880) *wmk* Large Garter .. .. £140
Plate No. 17.
Z41 4d. grey-brown (1880) *wmk* Crown .. .. *From* 28·00
Plate Nos. 17, 18.
Z42 6d. lilac (1856) .. .. .. .. 42·00
Z43 6d. lilac (1862) (Plate Nos. 3, 4) .. .. *From* 38·00
Z44 6d. lilac (1865–67) (Plate Nos. 5, 6) .. .. *From* 32·00
Z45 6d. lilac (1867) (Plate No. 6) .. .. .. 42·00
Z46 6d. violet (1867–70) (Plate Nos. 6, 8, 9) .. *From* 32·00
Z47 6d. buff (1872–73) (Plate Nos. 11, 12) .. *From* £180
Z48 6d. chestnut (1872) (Plate No. 11) .. .. .. 28·00
Z49 6d. grey (1873) (Plate No. 12) .. .. .. 75·00
Z50 6d. grey (1874–80) .. .. .. .. *From* 24·00
Plate Nos. 13, 14, 15, 16, 17.
Z51 6d. grey (1881) (Plate Nos. 17, 18) .. .. .. £150
Z52 6d. lilac (1883) (6d. *on* 6d.) .. .. .. 80·00
Z53 8d. orange (1876) .. .. .. .. £180
Z54 9d. bistre (1862) .. .. .. .. £160
Z55 9d. straw (1862) .. .. .. .. £600
Z56 9d. straw (1865) .. .. .. .. £550
Z57 9d. straw (1867) .. .. .. .. £120
Z58 10d. red-brown (1867) .. .. .. .. £150
Z59 1s. green (1856) .. .. .. .. £100
Z60 1s. green (1862) .. .. .. .. 60·00
Z61 1s. green (1862) ("K" *variety*) .. .. .. £2000
Z62 1s. green (1865) (Plate No. 4) .. .. .. 60·00
Z63 1s. green (1867–73) (Plate Nos. 4, 5, 6, 7) .. *From* 12·00
Z64 1s. green (1873–77) .. .. .. .. *From* 35·00
Plate Nos. 8, 9, 10, 11, 12, 13.
Z65 1s. orange-brown (1880) (Plate No. 13) .. .. £180
Z66 1s. orange-brown (1881) (Plate Nos. 13, 14) *From* 42·00
Z67 2s. blue (1867) .. .. .. .. £120
Z68 5s. rose (1867) (Plate No. 1) .. .. .. £600

**1880.**
Z69 ½d. deep green .. .. .. .. 14·00
Z70 ½d. pale green .. .. .. .. 14·00
Z71 1d. Venetian red .. .. .. .. 14·00
Z72 1½d. Venetian red .. .. .. ..
Z73 2d. pale rose .. .. .. .. 60·00
Z74 2d. deep rose .. .. .. ..
Z75 5d. indigo .. .. .. ..

**1881.**
Z76 1d. lilac (14 *dots*) .. .. .. .. 18·00
Z77 1d. lilac (16 *dots*) .. .. .. .. 8·00

**1884.**
Z78 ½d. slate-blue .. .. .. ..
Z79 2d. lilac .. .. .. ..
Z80 2½d. lilac .. .. .. ..
Z81 3d. lilac .. .. .. ..
Z82 4d. dull green .. .. .. ..
Z83 6d. dull green .. .. .. ..

POSTAL FISCAL
Z83*a* 1d. purple (Die 4) (1878) *wmk* Small Anchor £600
Z84 1d. purple (1881), *wmk* Orb .. .. .. £1100

| PRICES FOR STAMPS ON COVER TO 1945 | |
|---|---|
| Nos. 1/7 | *from* ×10 |
| Nos. 8/33 | *from* ×6 |
| Nos. 39/45 | *from* ×5 |
| Nos. 46/109 | *from* ×3 |
| Nos. 110/13 | *from* ×4 |
| Nos. 114/17 | *from* ×3 |
| Nos. 118/20 | *from* ×5 |
| Nos. 121/31 | *from* ×3 |

**GIBRALTAR**
(1)

**1886** (1 Jan). *Contemporary types of Bermuda optd with T* **1** *by D.L.R. Wmk Crown CA. P* 14.
1 **9** ½d. dull green .. .. .. 6·50 6·00
2 **1** 1d. rose-red .. .. .. 25·00 5·00
3 **2** 2d. purple-brown .. .. .. 75·00 70·00
4 **11** 2½d. ultramarine .. .. .. 90·00 2·75
a. Optd in blue-black .. .. £500 £150
5 **10** 4d. orange-brown .. .. .. 95·00 85·00
6 **4** 6d. deep lilac .. .. .. £200 £180
7 **5** 1s. yellow-brown .. .. .. £400 £350
1/7 .. .. .. *Set of* 7 £750 £650
1/3, 4a/7 Optd "Specimen" .. *Set of* 7 £2000

**PRINTER.** All Gibraltar stamps to No. 109 were typographed by De La Rue & Co, Ltd.

2

3

4

5

**1886** (Nov)–**87**. *Wmk Crown CA. P* 14.
8 **2** ½d. dull green (1.87) .. .. .. 3·75 2·75
9 **3** 1d. rose (12.86) .. .. .. 22·00 3·00
10 **4** 2d. brown-purple (12.86) .. .. 28·00 17·00
11 **5** 2½d. blue .. .. .. .. 55·00 2·25
12 **4** 4d. orange-brown (16.4.87) .. .. 60·00 60·00
13 6d. lilac (16.4.87) .. .. .. 85·00 85·00
14 1s. bistre (2.87) .. .. .. £180 £180
8/14 .. .. .. *Set of* 7 £375 £325
8/14 Optd "Specimen" .. *Set of* 7 £450
See also Nos. 39 to 45.

**5 CENTIMOS**
(6)

7

**1889** (1 Aug). *Surch as T* **6**.
15 **2** 5 c. on ½d. green .. .. .. 8·00 13·00
16 **3** 10 c. on 1d. rose .. .. .. 7·00 6·50
17 **4** 25 c. on 2d. brown-purple .. .. 4·00 5·00
a. Small "I" (R.6/2) .. .. £110 £140
b. Broken "N" (R.10/5) .. .. £110 £140
18 **5** 25 c. on 2½d. bright blue .. .. 24·00 1·25
a. Small "I" (R.6/2) .. .. £275 £100
b. Broken "N" (R.10/5) .. .. £275 £100
19 **4** 40 c. on 4d. orange-brown .. .. 55·00 70·00
20 50 c. on 6d. bright lilac .. .. 55·00 60·00
21 75 c. on 1s. bistre .. .. .. 55·00 70·00
15/21 .. .. .. *Set of* 7 £180 £200
15/21 Optd "Specimen" .. *Set of* 7 £300

10 c., 40 c. and 50 c. values from this issue and that of 1889–96 are known bisected and used for half their value from various post offices in Morocco (*price on cover from* £650). These bisects were never authorised by the Gibraltar Post Office.

Two varieties of the figure "5" of the 5 c., 25 c., 50 c. and 75 c. may be found.

**1889** (Nov)–**96**. *Issue in Spanish currency. Wmk Crown CA. P* 14.
22 **7** 5 c. green .. .. .. 2·00 45
23 10 c. carmine .. .. .. 1·50 45
b. Value omitted .. .. £4500
24 20 c. olive-green and brown (2.1.96) .. 16·00 10·00
25 20 c. olive-green (8.7.96) .. .. 7·00 25·00
26 25 c. ultramarine .. .. .. 12·00 70
*a. Deep ultramarine* .. .. 20·00 80
27 40 c. orange-brown .. .. .. 2·50 2·25
28 50 c. bright lilac (1890) .. .. 2·00 1·50
29 75 c. olive-green (1890) .. .. 25·00 32·00
30 1 p. bistre (11.89) .. .. .. 65·00 20·00
31 1 p. bistre and ultramarine (6.95) .. 3·50 3·25
32 2 p. black and carmine (2.1.96) .. 7·00 24·00
33 5 p. slate-grey (12.89) .. .. 40·00 75·00
22/33 .. .. .. *Set of* 12 £160 £170
22/33 (excluding No. 25). Optd "Specimen" *Set of* 11 £300

**1898** (1 Oct). *Reissue in Sterling currency. Wmk Crown CA. P* 14.
39 **2** ½d. grey-green .. .. .. 1·25 1·25
40 **3** 1d. carmine .. .. .. 2·00 35
41 **4** 2d. brown-purple and ultramarine .. 7·00 1·50
42 **5** 2½d. bright ultramarine .. .. 9·00 40
43 **4** 4d. orange-brown and green .. .. 9·00 8·00
44 6d. violet and red .. .. .. 23·00 20·00
45 1s. bistre and carmine .. .. 23·00 16·00
39/45 .. .. .. *Set of* 7 65·00 42·00
39/45 Optd "Specimen" .. *Set of* 7 £225

No. 39 is greyer than No. 8, No. 40 brighter and deeper than No. 9 and No. 42 much brighter than No. 11.

8

9

½ ½
Normal Large "2"
2½d.

This occurs on R.10/1 in each pane of 60. The diagonal stroke is also longer.

**1903** (1 May). *Wmk Crown CA. P* 14.
46 **8** ½d. grey-green and green .. .. 4·50 4·75
47 1d. dull purple/*red* .. .. .. 17·00 60
48 2d. grey-green and carmine .. .. 11·00 16·00
49 2½d. dull purple and black/*blue* .. .. 1·50 60
a. Large "2" in "½" .. .. 80·00 65·00
50 6d. dull purple and violet .. .. 10·00 17·00
51 1s. black and carmine .. .. .. 23·00 26·00
52 **9** 2s. green and blue .. .. .. 65·00 80·00
53 4s. dull purple and green .. .. 60·00 90·00
54 8s. dull purple and black/*blue* .. .. 80·00 £100
55 £1 dull purple and black/*red* .. .. £475 £550
46/55 .. .. .. *Set of* 10 £650 £800
46/55 Optd "Specimen" .. *Set of* 10 £450

**1904–8**. *Wmk Mult Crown CA. Ordinary paper* (½*d. to* 2*d. and* 6*d. to* 2*s.*) *or chalk-surfaced paper* (*others*). *P* 14
56 **8** ½d. dull and bright green (16.4.04*) .. 3·00 1·75
a. Chalk-surfaced paper (10.05) .. 4·50 2·75
57 1d. dull purple/*red* (6.9.04*) .. .. 2·25 40
a. Bisected (½d.) (on card) .. .. † £1200
b. Chalk-surfaced paper (16.9.05) .. 1·50 55
58 2d. grey-green and carmine (9.1.05) .. 4·25 2·25
a. Chalk-surfaced paper (2.07) .. 3·75 2·50
59 2½d. purple and black/*blue* (4.5.07) .. 24·00 60·00
a. Large "2" in "½" .. .. £225 £400
60 6d. dull purple and violet (19.4.06) .. 7·00 10·00
a. Chalk-surfaced paper (4.08) .. 7·50 8·00
61 1s. black and carmine (13.10.05) .. 22·00 10·00
a. Chalk-surfaced paper (4.06) .. 26·00 10·00
62 **9** 2s. green and blue (2.2.05) .. .. 48·00 55·00
a. Chalk-surfaced paper (10.07) .. 48·00 55·00
63 4s. deep purple and green (6.08) .. £120 £150
64 £1 deep purple and black/*red* (15.3.08) £500 £550
56/64 .. .. .. *Set of* 9 £650 £750
*Earliest known date of use.

**1907–12**. *Colours changed. Wmk Mult Crown CA. Chalk-surfaced paper* (6*d. to* 8*s.*). *P* 14.
66 **8** ½d. blue-green (1907) .. .. .. 1·75 80
67 1d. carmine (1.07) .. .. .. 1·25 45
a. Wmk sideways .. .. .. † £2500
68 2d. greyish slate (5.10) .. .. .. 5·50 9·00
69 2½d. ultramarine (6.07) .. .. .. 3·25 1·25
a. Large "2" in "½" .. .. .. £100 75·00

70 **8** 6d. dull and bright purple (3.12) .. £110 £325
71 1s. black/*green* (1910) .. .. 18·00 18·00
72 **9** 2s. purple and bright blue/*blue* (4.10) .. 35·00 45·00
73 4s. black and carmine (4.10) .. 65·00 85·00
74 8s. purple and green (1911) .. £180 £180
66/74 .. .. .. *Set of* 9 £375 £600
67/74 Optd "Specimen" .. .. *Set of* 8 £450

10

11

**WAR TAX**

(12)

**1912** (17 July)–**24**. *Wmk Mult Crown CA. Ordinary paper* (½d. *to* 2½d) *or chalk-surfaced paper (others). P* 14.
76 **10** ½d. blue-green .. .. .. .. 60 45
*a. Yellow-green* (4.17) .. .. 1·25 50
77 1d. carmine-red .. .. .. 2·00 55
*a. Scarlet* (6.16) .. .. .. 2·75 55
78 2d. greyish slate .. .. .. 3·00 1·25
79 2½d. deep bright blue .. .. .. 3·25 1·75
a. Large "2" in "½" .. .. 70·00 60·00
*b. Pale ultramarine* (1917) .. .. 6·00 2·00
ba. Large "2" in "½" .. .. £130 75·00
80 6d. dull purple and mauve .. .. 7·00 8·50
81 1s. black/*green* .. .. .. 5·50 6·00
a. Ordinary paper (8.18) .. ..
*b. On blue-green, olive back* (1919) .. 12·00 20·00
*c. On emerald surface* (12.23) (Optd S. £45) .. .. .. 16·00 45·00
*d. On emerald back* (3.24) .. .. 11·00 45·00
82 **11** 2s. dull purple and blue/*blue* .. .. 16·00 3·00
83 4s. black and carmine .. .. .. 26·00 50·00
84 8s dull purple and green .. .. 50·00 60·00
85 £1 dull purple and black/*red* .. .. £160 £190
76/85 .. .. .. *Set of* 10 £225 £275
76/85 Optd "Specimen" .. *Set of* 10 £400

**1918** (15 Apr). *Optd with T* **12** *by Beanland, Malin & Co, Gibraltar*.
86 **10** ½d. green .. .. .. .. .. 30 80
a. Opt double .. .. .. .. £500

Two printings of this overprint exist, the second being in slightly heavier type on a deeper shade of green.

**3 PENCE** (I)    **THREE PENCE** (II)

**1921–27**. *Wmk Mult Script CA. Chalk-surfaced paper* (6d. *to* 8s.). *P* 14.
89 **10** ½d. green (25.4.27) .. .. .. 30 35
90 1d. carmine-red (2.21) .. .. .. 1·00 50
91 1½d. chestnut (1.12.22) .. .. .. 75 40
*a. Pale chestnut* (7.24) .. .. 75 30
93 2d. grey (17.2.21) .. .. .. 1·25 85
94 2½d. bright blue (2.21) .. .. .. 11·00 20·00
a. Large "2" in "½" .. .. £130 £190
95 3d. bright blue (I) (1.1.22) .. .. 2·50 4·25
*a. Ultramarine* .. .. .. 1·40 1·50
97 6d. dull purple and mauve (1.23) .. 5·50 3·75
*a. Bright purple & magenta* (22.7.26) 1·60 4·50
98 1s. black/*emerald* (20.6.24) .. .. 7·00 9·50
99 **11** 2s. grey-purple and blue/*blue* (20.6.24) 16·00 50·00
*a. Reddish purple and blue/blue* (1925) 4·75 28·00
100 4s. black and carmine (20.6.24) .. 42·00 70·00
101 8s. dull purple and green (20.6.24) .. £170 £275
89/101 .. .. .. *Set of* 11 £200 £350
89/101 Optd "Specimen" .. *Set of* 11 £425

The ½d. exists in coils constructed from normal sheets.

**1925** (15 Oct)–**32**. *New values and colours changed. Wmk Mult Script CA. Chalk-surfaced paper. P* 14.
102 **10** 1s. sage-green and black (8.1.29) .. 10·00 17·00
*a. Olive and black* (1932) .. .. 10·00 12·00
103 **11** 2s. red-brown and black (8.1.29) .. 8·00 27·00
104 2s. 6d. green and black .. .. 7·00 16·00
105 5s. carmine and black .. .. 12·00 40·00
106 10s. deep ultramarine and black .. 32·00 50·00
107 £1 red-orange and black (16.11.27) .. £140 £180
108 £5 violet and black (Optd S. £700) .. £1600 £2750
102/7 .. .. .. *Set of* 6 £190 £275
102/7 Optd/Perf "Specimen" .. *Set of* 6 £375

**1930** (12 Apr). *T* **10** *inscribed* "THREE PENCE". *Wmk Mult Script CA. P* 14.
109 3d. ultramarine (II) (Perf S. £70) .. .. 6·50 2·00

**13** The Rock of Gibraltar

(Des Capt. H. St. C. Garrood. Recess D.L.R.)

**1931–33**. *T* **13**. *Wmk Mult Script CA. A. P* 14. *B. P* 13½ × 14.

| | | | A | | B | |
|---|---|---|---|---|---|---|
| 110 | 1d. scarlet (1.7.31) .. .. | | 1·25 | 1·75 | 9·00 | 3·50 |
| 111 | 1½d. red-brown (1.7.31) .. .. | | 1·00 | 2·00 | 8·00 | 3·50 |
| 112 | 2d. pale grey (1.11.32) .. | | 2·75 | 1·00 | 11·00 | 2·25 |
| 113 | 3d. blue (1.6.33) .. .. | | 4·00 | 3·25 | 16·00 | 20·00 |
| 110/13 | .. .. | *Set of* 4 | 8·00 | 7·00 | 40·00 | 26·00 |
| 110/13 Perf "Specimen" | | *Set of* 4 | £150 | | | |

Figures of value take the place of both corner ornaments at the base of the 2d. and 3d.

**1935** (6 May). *Silver Jubilee. As Nos.* 91/4 *of Antigua but ptd by B.W. P* 11 × 12.
114 2d. ultramarine and grey-black .. .. 1·60 2·50
a. Extra flagstaff .. .. .. 60·00
b. Short extra flagstaff .. .. 70·00
c. Lightning conductor .. .. 50·00
d. Flagstaff on right-hand turret .. 80·00
e. Double flagstaff .. .. .. 70·00
115 3d. brown and deep blue .. .. 3·25 3·50
a. Extra flagstaff .. .. .. £300
b. Short extra flagstaff .. .. £250
c. Lightning conductor .. .. £225
116 6d. green and indigo .. .. .. 7·50 8·00
a. Extra flagstaff .. .. .. £225
b. Short extra flagstaff .. .. £225
c. Lightning conductor .. .. £160
117 1s. slate and purple .. .. .. 7·50 8·50
a. Extra flagstaff .. .. .. £200
b. Short extra flagstaff .. .. £200
c. Lightning conductor .. .. £150
114/17 .. .. .. *Set of* 4 18·00 20·00
114/17 Perf "Specimen" .. *Set of* 4 £160

For illustrations of plate varieties see Catalogue Introduction.

**1937** (12 May). *Coronation. As Nos.* 95/7 *of Antigua. P* 11×11½.
118 ½d. green .. .. .. .. 25 10
119 2d. grey-black .. .. .. 80 60
120 3d. blue .. .. .. .. 2·00 90
118/20 .. .. .. *Set of* 3 2·75 1·40
118/20 Perf "Specimen" .. *Set of* 3 75·00

**14** King George VI

**15** Rock of Gibraltar

**16** The Rock (North Side)

Broken second "R" in "GIBRALTAR" (Frame Pl.2 R.9/4)

(Des Captain H. St. C. Garrood. Recess D.L.R.)

**1938** (25 Feb)–**51**. *Designs as T* **14/16**. *Wmk Mult Script CA*.
121 ½d. deep green (*p* 13½ × 14) .. .. 10 15
122 1d. yellow-brown (*p* 14) .. .. 13·00 2·25
a. Perf 13½ .. .. .. 16·00 2·00
ab. Perf 13½. Wmk sideways .. 2·50 6·00
b. Perf 13. Wmk sideways. *Red-brn* (1942) 40 55
c. Perf 13. Wmk sideways. *Deep brn* (1944) 20 3·00
d. Perf 13, *Red-brown* (1949) .. 70 1·10
123 1½d. carmine (*p* 14) .. .. 24·00 75
a. Perf 13½ .. .. .. £225 32·00
123*b* 1½d. slate-violet (*p* 13) (1.1.43) .. 20 65
124 2d. grey (*p* 14) .. .. .. 15·00 50
a. Perf 13½ .. .. .. 30 35
ab. Perf 13½. Wmk sideways .. £475 35·00
b. Perf 13. Wmk sideways (1943) .. 30 85
124*c* 2d. carmine (*p* 13) (*wmk sideways*) (15.7.44) 30 35
125 3d. light blue (*p* 13½) .. .. 12·00 40
a. Perf 14 .. .. .. 75·00 7·50
b. Perf 13 (1942) .. .. 30 30
*ba. Greenish blue* (2.51) .. .. 1·25 2·50
125*c* 5d. red-orange (*p* 13) (1.10.47) .. 70 1·25
126 6d. carmine and grey-violet (*p* 13½) (16.3.38) 32·00 3·00
a. Perf 14 .. .. .. £120 1·00
b. Perf 13 (1942) .. .. 1·75 1·25
c. Perf 13. *Scarlet and grey-violet* (1945) .. 4·25 2·10
127 1s. black and green (*p* 14) (16.3.38) .. 30·00 16·00
a. Perf 13½ .. .. .. 50·00 5·50
b. Perf 13 (1942) .. .. 2·50 2·75
ba. Broken "R" .. .. .. 40·00
128 2s. black and brown (*p* 14) (16.3.38) .. 60·00 25·00
a. Perf 13½ .. .. .. 95·00 30·00
b. Perf 13 (1942) .. .. 2·75 4·00
ba. Broken "R" .. .. .. 50·00
129 5s. black and carmine (*p* 14) (16.3.38) .. 80·00 £110
a. Perf 13½ .. .. .. 26·00 17·00
b. Perf 13 (1944) .. .. 10·00 14·00
ba. Broken "R" .. .. .. 70·00
130 10s. black and blue (*p* 14) (16.3.38) .. 55·00 80·00
a. Perf 13 (1943) .. .. 35·00 25·00
ab. Broken "R" .. .. .. £120
131 £1 orange (*p* 13½×14) (16.3.38) .. 27·00 38·00
121/31 .. .. .. *Set of* 14 95·00 80·00
121/31 Perf "Specimen" .. *Set of* 14 £425

Designs:—½d., £1, Type **14**. *Horiz as T* **15/16**—1d., 1½d. (*both*), Type **15**; 2d. (*both*), Type **16**; 3d., 5d. Europa Point; 6d. Moorish Castle; 1s. Southport Gate; 2s. Eliott Memorial; 5s. Government House; 10s. Catalan Bay.

The ½d., 1d. and both colours of the 2d. exist in coils constructed from normal sheets. These were originally joined vertically, but, because of technical problems, the 1d. and 2d. grey were subsequently issued in horizontal coils. The 2d. carmine only exists in the horizontal version.

**1946** (12 Oct). *Victory. As Nos.* 110/11 *of Antigua*.
132 ½d. green .. .. .. .. 10 10
133 3d. ultramarine .. .. .. 20 20
132/3 Perf "Specimen" .. *Set of* 2 60·00

**1948** (1 Dec). *Royal Silver Wedding. As Nos.* 112/13 *of Antigua*.
134 ½d. green .. .. .. .. 60 20
135 £1 brown-orange .. .. .. 60·00 42·00

**1949** (10 Oct). *75th Anniv of Universal Postal Union. As Nos.* 114/17 *of Antigua*.
136 2d. carmine .. .. .. .. 1·75 75
137 3d. deep blue .. .. .. .. 2·00 85
138 6d. purple .. .. .. .. 2·00 85
139 1s. blue-green .. .. .. 2·75 1·50
136/9 .. .. .. *Set of* 4 7·50 3·50

NEW
CONSTITUTION
1950
(23)

**1950** (1 Aug). *Inauguration of Legislative Council. Nos.* 124c, 125b, 126b *and* 127b *optd as T* **23**.
140 **16** 2d. carmine .. .. .. .. 30 75
141 – 3d. light blue .. .. .. 30 75
142 – 6d. carmine and grey-violet .. .. 40 75
a. Opt double .. .. .. £475 £600
143 – 1s. black and green (R.) .. .. 40 1·25
a. Broken "R" .. .. .. 25·00
140/3 .. .. .. *Set of* 4 1·25 3·25

On stamps from the lower part of the sheet of No. 142a the two impressions are almost coincident.

**1953** (2 June). *Coronation. As No.* 120 *of Antigua*.
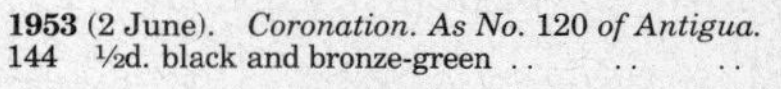
144 ½d. black and bronze-green .. .. .. 20 30

**24** Cargo and Passenger Wharves

**25** Tower of Homage, Moorish Castle

**26** Arms of Gibraltar

Major re-entry causing doubling of "ALTA" in "GIBRALTAR" (R. 4/6)

(Des N. Cummings. Recess (except £1, centre litho) De La Rue)

**1953** (19 Oct)–**59**. *T* **24/26** *and similar designs. Wmk Mult Script CA. P* 13.
145 ½d. indigo and grey-green .. .. 15 30
146 1d. bluish green .. .. .. 80 30
*a. Deep bluish green* (31.12.57) .. 80 30
147 1½d. black .. .. .. .. 90 65
148 2d. deep olive-brown .. .. 1·00 30
*a. Sepia* (18.6.58) .. .. 2·00 50
149 2½d. carmine .. .. .. 2·00 50
*a. Deep carmine* (11.9.56) .. .. 1·50 30
150 3d. light blue .. .. .. 2·00 10
*a. Deep greenish blue* (8.6.55) .. 3·00 10
*b. Greenish blue* (18.6.58) .. .. 2·75 15
151 4d. ultramarine .. .. .. 2·25 1·25
*a. Blue* (17.6.59) .. .. .. 4·50 3·00
152 5d. maroon .. .. .. 35 50
a. Major re-entry .. .. .. 8·00
*b. Deep maroon* (31.12.57) .. .. 1·25 1·25
ba. Major re-entry .. .. .. 10·00
153 6d. black and pale blue .. .. 30 30
*a. Black and blue* (24.4.57) .. .. 80 45
*b. Black and grey-blue* (17.6.59) .. 1·25 80
154 1s. pale blue and red-brown .. .. 30 45
*a. Pale blue and deep red-brown* (27.3.56) 30 35
155 2s. orange and reddish violet .. .. 18·00 2·75
*a. Orange and violet* (17.6.59) .. 16·00 1·75
156 5s. deep brown .. .. .. 24·00 12·00
157 10s. reddish brown and ultramarine .. 70·00 35·00
158 £1 scarlet and orange-yellow .. .. 75·00 38·00
145/58 .. .. .. *Set of* 14 £170 80·00

Designs: *Horiz as T* **24**—1d. South View from Straits; 1½d. Tunney Fishing Industry; 2d. Southport Gate; 2½d. Sailing in the Bay 3d; *Saturnia* (liner); 4d. Coaling wharf; 5d. Airport; 6d. Europa Point; 1s. Straits from Buena Vista; 2s. Rosia Bay and Straits; 5s. Main Entrance, Government House.

Nos. 145/6, 148 and 150 exist in coils, constructed from normal sheets.

**1954** (10 May). *Royal Visit. As No.* 150 *but inscr* "ROYAL VISIT 1954" *at top*.
159 3d. greenish blue .. .. .. 15 20

38 Gibraltar Candytuft

40 Rock and Badge of Gibraltar Regiment

39 Moorish Castle

(Des J. Celecia (½d., 2d., 2½d., 2s., 10s.), N. A. Langdon (1d., 3d., 6d., 7d., 9d., 1s.), M. Bonilla (4d.), L. V. Gomez (5s.), Sgt. T. A. Griffiths (£1). Recess (£1) or photo (others) D.L.R.)

**1960** (29 Oct)–**62**. *Designs as T* **38/9**, *and T* **40**. *W w* **12** *(upright). P* 14 (£1) *or* 13 *(others).*

160 ½d. bright purple and emerald-green .. 15 30
161 1d. black and yellow-green .. .. 10 10
162 2d. indigo and orange-brown .. .. 15 15
163 2½d. black and blue .. .. 35 35
a. *Black and grey-blue* (16.10.62) .. 15 15
164 3d. deep blue and red-orange .. 30 10
165 4d. deep red-brown and turquoise .. 2·75 55
166 6d. sepia and emerald .. .. 70 30
167 7d. indigo and carmine-red .. .. 70 75
168 9d. grey-blue and greenish blue .. 50 50
169 1s. sepia and bluish green .. .. 90 30
170 2s. chocolate and ultramarine .. 13·00 2·00
171 5s. turquoise-blue and olive-brown .. 8·00 5·00
172 10s. yellow and blue .. .. 14·00 9·00
173 £1 black and brown-orange .. 23·00 14·00
160/73 .. .. .. .. *Set of* 14 55·00 30·00

Designs: *Horiz*—2d. St. George's Hall; 3d. The Rock by moonlight; 4d. Catalan Bay; 1s. Barbary Ape; 2s. Barbary Partridge; 5s. Blue Rock Thrush. *Vert*—2½d. The Keys; 6d. Map of Gibraltar; 7d. Air terminal; 9d. American War Memorial; 10s. Rock Lily (*Narcissus niveus*).

Vignette cylinders 2A and 2B, used for printings of the 9d. from 13 March 1962 onwards, had a finer screen (250 dots per inch instead of the 200 of the original printing).

Nos. 160/2, 164 and 166 exist in coils, constructed from normal sheets.

See also No. 199.

**1963** (4 June). *Freedom from Hunger. As No.* 146 *of Antigua.*
174 9d. sepia .. .. .. .. 11·00 2·00

**1963** (2 Sept). *Red Cross Centenary. As Nos.* 147/8 *of Antigua.*
175 1d. red and black .. .. .. 50 50
176 9d. red and blue .. .. .. 12·00 2·75

**1964** (23 Apr). *400th Birth Anniv of William Shakespeare. As No.* 164 *of Antigua.*
177 7d. bistre-brown .. .. .. 40 20

**NEW CONSTITUTION 1964.**

(52)

53 Bream

**1964** (16 Oct). *New Constitution. Nos.* 164 *and* 166 *optd with T* **52**.
178 3d. deep blue and red-orange .. .. 15 10
179 6d. sepia and emerald .. .. 15 20
a. No stop after "1964" (R.2/5) .. 12·00 17·00

**1965** (17 May). *I.T.U. Centenary. As Nos.* 166/7 *of Antigua.*
180 4d. light emerald and yellow .. .. 5·00 50
181 2s. apple-green and deep blue .. .. 12·00 2·50

**1965** (25 Oct). *International Co-operation Year. As Nos.* 168/9 *of Antigua.*
182 ½d. deep bluish green and lavender .. .. 20 45
183 4d. reddish purple and turquoise-green .. 1·00 80

The value of the ½d. stamp is shown as "1/2".

**1966** (24 Jan). *Churchill Commemoration. As Nos.* 170/3 *of Antigua.*
184 ½d. new blue .. .. .. .. 20 40
185 1d. deep green .. .. .. .. 30 10
186 4d. brown .. .. .. .. 1·50 10
187 9d. bluish violet .. .. .. .. 1·75 1·40
184/7 .. .. .. .. *Set of* 4 3·25 1·75

**1966** (1 July). *World Cup Football Championships. As Nos.* 176/7 *of Antigua.*
188 2½d. violet, yellow-green, lake & yellow-brn 75 30
189 6d. chocolate, blue-green, lake & yellow-brn 1·00 50

**PRINTERS.** All stamps from here to No. 239 were printed in photogravure by Harrison and Sons Ltd, London.

(Des A. Ryman)

**1966** (27 Aug). *European Sea Angling Championships, Gibraltar. T* **53** *and similar designs. W w* **12** *(sideways on* 1s.*). P* 13½ × 14 (1s.) *or* 14 × 13½ *(others).*
190 4d. rosine, bright blue and black .. .. 20 10
191 7d. rosine, deep olive-green and black .. 20 20
a. Black (value and inscr) omitted .. .. £650
192 1s. lake-brown, emerald and black .. .. 20 20
190/2 .. .. .. .. *Set of* 3 55 45

Designs: *Horiz*—7d. Scorpion Fish. *Vert*—1s. Stone Bass.

**1966** (20 Sept). *Inauguration of W.H.O. Headquarters, Geneva. As Nos.* 178/9 *of Antigua.*
193 6d. black, yellow-green and light blue .. 3·00 1·50
194 9d. black, light purple and yellow-brown .. 4·00 1·50

56 "Our Lady of Europa"

57 H.M.S. *Victory*

(Des A. Ryman)

**1966** (15 Nov). *Centenary of Re-enthronement of "Our Lady of Europa". W w* **12**. *P* 14 × 14½.
195 **56** 2s. bright blue and black .. .. 30 50

**1966** (1 Dec). *20th Anniv of U.N.E.S.C.O. As Nos.* 196/8 *of Antigua.*
196 2d. slate-violet, red, yellow and orange .. 25 10
197 7d. orange-yellow, violet and deep olive .. 60 10
198 5s. black, bright purple and orange .. 2·50 1·75
196/8 .. .. .. .. *Set of* 3 3·00 1·75

**1966** (23 Dec). *As No.* 165 *but wmk w* **12** *sideways.*
199 4d. deep red-brown and turquoise .. .. 30 40

(Des A. Ryman)

**1967** (3 Apr)–**69**. *Horiz designs as T* **57**. *Multicoloured. W w* **12**. *P* 14 × 14½.
200 ½d. Type **57** .. .. .. 10 15
a. Grey omitted .. .. .. .. £275
201 1d. S.S. *Arab* .. .. .. .. 10 10
202 2d. H.M.S. *Carmania* .. .. .. 15 10
a. Grey-blue (hull) omitted .. .. £1400
203 2½d. M.V. *Mons Calpe* .. .. .. 30 30
204 3d. S.S. *Canberra* .. .. .. 20 10
205 4d. H.M.S. *Hood* .. .. .. 30 10
205*a* 5d. Cable Ship *Mirror* (7.7.69) .. 2·75 45
206 6d. Xebec (sailing vessel) .. .. 30 30
207 7d. *Amerigo Vespucci* (training vessel) .. 30 35
208 9d. T.V. *Raffaello* .. .. .. 30 50
209 1s. *Royal Katherine* .. .. .. 30 35
210 2s. H.M.S. *Ark Royal* .. .. .. 2·25 1·50
211 5s. H.M.S. *Dreadnought* .. .. 3·50 4·00
212 10s. S.S. *Neuralia* .. .. .. 14·00 16·00
213 £1 *Mary Celeste* (sailing vessel) .. 14·00 16·00
200/13 .. .. .. .. *Set of* 15 35·00 35·00

The ½d., 1d., 2d., 3d., 6d., 2s., 5s. and £1 exist with PVA gum as well as gum arabic, but the 5d. exists with PVA gum only.

Nos. 201/2, 204/5 and 206 exist in coils constructed from normal sheets.

58 Aerial Ropeway

(Des A. Ryman)

**1967** (15 June). *International Tourist Year. T* **58** *and similar designs but horiz. Multicoloured. W w* **12** *(sideways on 7d.). P* 14½ × 14 (7d.) *or* 14 × 14½ *(others).*
214 7d. Type **58** .. .. .. .. 10 10
215 9d. Shark fishing .. .. .. .. 10 10
216 1s. Skin-diving .. .. .. .. 15 15
214/16 .. .. .. .. *Set of* 3 30 30

59 Mary, Joseph and Child Jesus

60 Church Window

**1967** (1 Nov). *Christmas. W w* **12** *(sideways on* 6d.*). P* 14.
217 **59** 2d. multicoloured .. .. .. 10 10
218 **60** 6d. multicoloured .. .. .. 10 10

61 Gen. Eliott and Route Map

62 Eliott directing Rescue Operations

(Des A. Ryman)

**1967** (11 Dec). *250th Birth Anniv of General Eliott. Multicoloured designs as T* **61** (4d. *to* 1s.) *or T* **62**. *W w* **12** *(sideways on horiz designs). P* 14 × 15 (1s.) *or* 15 × 14 *(others).*
219 4d. Type **61** .. .. .. .. .. 10 10
220 9d. Heathfield Tower and Monument, Sussex (38 × 22 *mm*) .. .. .. .. 10 10
221 1s. General Eliott (22 × 38 *mm*) .. .. 10 10
222 2s. Type **62** .. .. .. .. .. 30 15
219/22 .. .. .. .. *Set of* 4 45 30

65 Lord Baden-Powell

(Des A. Ryman)

**1968** (27 Mar). *60th Anniv of Gibraltar Scout Association. T* **65** *and similar horiz designs. W w* **12**. *P* 14 × 14½.
223 4d. buff and bluish violet .. .. .. 15 10
224 7d. ochre and blue-green .. .. .. 15 10
225 9d. bright blue, yellow-orange and black .. 20 10
226 1s. greenish yellow and emerald .. .. 20 15
223/6 .. .. .. .. *Set of* 4 65 35

Designs:—7d. Scout Flag over the Rock; 9d. Tent, scouts and salute; 1s. Scout badges.

66 Nurse and W.H.O. Emblem

68 King John signing Magna Carta

(Des A. Ryman)

**1968** (1 July). *20th Anniv of World Health Organization. T* **66** *and similar horiz design. W w* **12**. *P* 14 × 14½.
227 2d. ultramarine, black and yellow .. .. 10 10
228 4d. slate, black and pink .. .. .. 10 10

Design:—4d. Doctor and W.H.O. emblem.

(Des A. Ryman)

**1968** (26 Aug). *Human Rights Year. T* **68** *and similar vert design. W w* **12** *(sideways). P* 13½ × 14.
229 1s. yellow-orange, brown and gold .. .. 15 10
230 2s. myrtle and gold .. .. .. .. 15 20

Design:—2s. "Freedom" and Rock of Gibraltar.

70 Shepherd, Lamb and Star

72 Parliament Houses

(Des A. Ryman)

**1968** (1 Nov). *Christmas. T* **70** *and similar vert design. Multicoloured. W w* **12**. *P* 14½ × 13½.
231 4d. Type **70** .. .. .. .. 10 10
a. Gold (star) omitted .. .. .. £110
232 9d. Mary holding Holy Child .. .. .. 10 10

(Des A. Ryman)

**1969** (26 May). *Commonwealth Parliamentary Association Conference. T* **72** *and similar designs. W* w **12** (*sideways on 2s.*). *P* 14 × 14½ (*2s.*) *or* 14½ × 14 (*others*).
233 4d. green and gold .. .. .. .. 10 10
234 9d. bluish violet and gold .. .. .. 10 10
235 2s. multicoloured .. .. .. .. 15 20
233/5 .. .. .. .. *Set of* 3 30 30

Designs: *Horiz*—9d. Parliamentary emblem and outline of "The Rock". *Vert*—2s. Clock Tower, Westminster (Big Ben) and arms of Gibraltar.

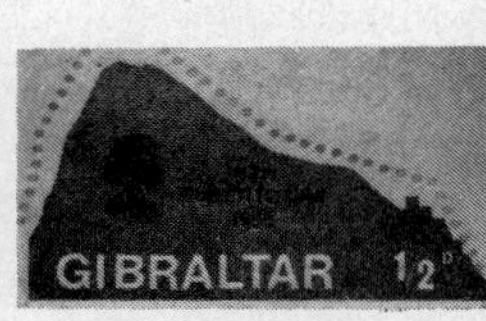

**75** Silhouette of Rock, and Queen Elizabeth

**77** Soldier and Cap Badge, Royal Anglian Regiment, 1969

(Des A. Ryman)

**1969** (30 July). *New Constitution. W* w **12**. *P* 14 × 13½ (*in addition, the outline of the Rock is perforated*).
236 **75** ½d. gold and orange .. .. .. 10 10
237 5d. silver and bright green .. .. 10 10
a. Portrait and inscr in gold and silver*
238 7d. silver and bright purple .. .. 10 10
239 5s. gold and ultramarine .. .. 35 70
236/9 .. .. .. .. *Set of* 4 50 85

*No. 237a was first printed with the head and inscription in gold and then in silver but displaced slightly to lower left.

(Des A. Ryman. Photo D.L.R.)

**1969** (6 Nov). *Military Uniforms* (*1st series*). *T* **77** *and similar vert designs. Multicoloured. W* w **12**. *P* 14.
240 1d. Royal Artillery officer, 1758 and modern cap badge .. .. .. .. .. 20 10
241 6d. Type **77** .. .. .. .. 55 20
242 9d. Royal Engineers' Artificer, 1786 and modern cap badge .. .. .. 75 30
243 2s. Private, Fox's Marines, 1704 and modern Royal Marines cap badge .. .. 4·00 1·60
240/3 .. .. .. .. *Set of* 4 5·00 2·00

Nos. 240/3 have a short history of the Regiment printed on the reverse side over the gum, therefore, once the gum is moistened the history disappears.

See also Nos. 248/51, 290/3, 300/3, 313/16, 331/4, 340/3 and 363/6.

**80** "Madonna of the Chair" (detail, Raphael)

**83** Europa Point

(Des A. Ryman. Photo Enschedé)

**1969** (1 Dec). *Christmas. T* **80** *and similar vert designs. Multicoloured. W* w **12** (*sideways*). *P* 14 × *Roulette* 9.
244 5d. Type **80** .. .. .. .. 10 10
a. Strip of 3. Nos. 244/6 .. .. 35
245 7d. "Virgin and Child" (detail, Morales) .. 15 15
246 1s. "The Virgin of the Rocks" (detail, Leonardo da Vinci) .. .. .. .. 15 20
244/6 .. .. .. .. *Set of* 3 35 40

Nos. 244/6 were issued together in *se-tenant* strips of three throughout the sheet.

(Des A. Ryman. Photo Enschedé)

**1970** (8 June). *Europa Point. W* w **12**. *P* 13½.
247 **83** 2s. multicoloured .. .. .. 30 30

(Des A. Ryman. Photo D.L.R.)

**1970** (28 Aug). *Military Uniforms* (*2nd series*). *Vert designs as T* **77**. *Multicoloured. W* w **12**. *P* 14.
248 2d. Royal Scots officer, 1839 and cap badge .. 40 10
249 5d. South Wales Borderers private, 1763 and cap badge .. .. .. .. 80 10
250 7d. Queen's Royal Regiment private, 1742 and cap badge .. .. .. 90 15
251 2s. Royal Irish Rangers piper, 1969 and cap badge .. .. .. .. .. 4·50 1·75
248/51 .. .. .. .. *Set of* 4 6·00 1·90

Nos. 248/51 have a short history of the Regiment printed on the reverse side under the gum.

**MINIMUM PRICE**

The minimum price quote is 10p which represents a handling charge rather than a basis for valuing common stamps. For further notes about prices see introductory pages.

**88** No. 191a and Rock of Gibraltar

(Des A. Ryman. Litho D.L.R.)

**1970** (18 Sept). *"Philympia 1970" Stamp Exhibition, London. T* **88** *and similar horiz design. W* w **12** (*sideways*). *P* 13.
252 1s. vermilion and bronze-green .. .. 10 10
253 2s. bright blue and magenta .. .. 20 25

Design:—2s. Victorian stamp (No. 23b) and Moorish Castle.

The stamps shown in the designs are well-known varieties with values omitted.

**90** "The Virgin Mary" (stained-glass window by Gabriel Loire)

(Photo Enschedé)

**1970** (1 Dec). *Christmas. W* w **12**. *P* 13 × 14.
254 **90** 2s. multicoloured .. .. .. 30 30

**(New Currency: 100 pence = £1)**

**91** Saluting Battery, Rosia

**92** Saluting Battery, Rosia, Modern View

(Des A. Ryman. Litho Questa)

**1971** (15 Feb). *Decimal Currency. Designs as T* **91/2**. *W* w **12** (*sideways on horiz designs*). *P* 14.
255 ½p. multicoloured .. .. .. .. 15 20
a. Pair. Nos. 255/6 .. .. .. 30 40
256 ½p. multicoloured .. .. .. .. 15 20
257 1p. multicoloured .. .. .. .. 80 30
a. Pair. Nos. 257/8 .. .. .. 1·60 60
258 1p. multicoloured .. .. .. .. 80 30
259 1½p. multicoloured .. .. .. .. 20 25
a. Pair. Nos. 259/60 .. .. .. 40 50
260 1½p. multicoloured .. .. .. .. 20 25
261 2p. multicoloured .. .. .. .. 1·50 90
a. Pair. Nos. 261/2 .. .. .. 3·00 1·75
262 2p. multicoloured .. .. .. .. 1·50 90
263 2½p. multicoloured .. .. .. .. 20 25
a. Pair. Nos. 263/4 .. .. .. 40 50
264 2½p. multicoloured .. .. .. .. 20 25
265 3p. multicoloured .. .. .. .. 20 15
a. Pair. Nos. 265/6 .. .. .. 40 30
266 3p. multicoloured .. .. .. .. 20 15
267 4p. multicoloured .. .. .. .. 2·00 1·50
a. Pair. Nos. 267/8 .. .. .. 4·00 3·00
268 4p. multicoloured .. .. .. .. 2·00 1·50
269 5p. multicoloured .. .. .. .. 30 20
a. Pair. Nos. 269/70 .. .. .. 60 40
270 5p. multicoloured .. .. .. .. 30 20
271 7p. multicoloured .. .. .. .. 65 65
a. Pair. Nos. 271/2 .. .. .. 1·25 1·25
272 7p. multicoloured .. .. .. .. 65 65
273 8p. multicoloured .. .. .. .. 70 70
a. Pair. Nos. 273/4 .. .. .. 1·40 1·40
274 8p. multicoloured .. .. .. .. 70 70
275 9p. multicoloured .. .. .. .. 70 70
a. Pair. Nos. 275/6 .. .. .. 1·40 1·40
276 9p. multicoloured .. .. .. .. 70 70
277 10p. multicoloured .. .. .. .. 80 80
a. Pair. Nos. 277/8 .. .. .. 1·60 1·60
278 10p. multicoloured .. .. .. .. 80 80
279 12½p. multicoloured .. .. .. .. 1·00 1·25
a. Pair. Nos. 279/80 .. .. .. 2·00 2·50
280 12½p. multicoloured .. .. .. .. 1·00 1·25
281 25p. multicoloured .. .. .. .. 1·40 1·40
a. Pair. Nos. 281/2 .. .. .. 2·75 2·75
282 25p. multicoloured .. .. .. .. 1·40 1·40
283 50p. multicoloured .. .. .. .. 1·40 2·50
a. Pair. Nos. 283/4 .. .. .. 2·75 5·00
284 50p. multicoloured .. .. .. .. 1·40 2·50
285 £1 multicoloured .. .. .. .. 2·75 4·00
a. Pair. Nos. 285/6 .. .. .. 5·50 8·00
286 £1 multicoloured .. .. .. .. 2·75 4·00
255/86 .. .. .. .. *Set of* 32 26·00 28·00

Designs (the two versions of each value show the same Gibraltar view taken from an early 19th-century print (first design) or modern photograph (second design): *Horiz*—1p. Prince George of Cambridge Quarters and Trinity Church; 1½p. The Wellington Bust, Alameda Gardens; 2p. Gibraltar from the North Bastion; 2½p. Catalan Bay; 3p. Convent Garden; 4p. The Exchange and Spanish Chapel; 5p. Commercial Square and Library; 7p. South Barracks and Rosia Magazine; 8p. Moorish Mosque and Castle; 9p. Europa Pass Road; 10p. South Barracks from Rosia Bay; 12½p. Southport Gates; 25p. Trooping the Colour, The Alameda. *Vert*—50p. Europa Pass Gorge; £1 Prince Edward's Gate.

The two designs of each value were printed together, *se-tenant* in horizontal and vertical pairs throughout.

See also Nos. 317/20 and 344/5.

**93**

**94** Regimental Arms

(Des A. Ryman. Photo Harrison)

**1971** (15 Feb). *Coil Stamps. W* w **12**. *P* 14½ × 14.
287 **93** ½p. red-orange .. .. .. .. 15 3
a. Coil strip (287 × 2, 288 × 2 and 289 *se-tenant*) .. .. .. .. 1·25
288 1p. blue .. .. .. .. .. 15 3
289 2p. bright green .. .. .. 65 1·1
287/9 .. .. .. .. *Set of* 3 90 1·5

(Des A. Ryman. Litho Questa)

**1971** (6 Sept). *Military Uniforms* (*3rd series*). *Multicoloured designs as T* **77**, *showing uniform and cap-badge. W* w **12**. *P* 14.
290 1p. The Black Watch (1845) .. .. .. 45 2
291 2p. Royal Regt of Fusiliers (1971) .. .. 85 3
292 4p. King's Own Royal Border Regt (1704) .. 1·75 7
293 10p. Devonshire and Dorset Regt (1801) .. 5·00 2·5
290/3 .. .. .. .. *Set of* 4 7·50 3·2

Nos. 290/3 have a short history of the Regiment printed on the reverse side under the gum.

(Des A. Ryman. Litho Harrison)

**1971** (25 Sept). *Presentation of Colours to the Gibraltar Regiment W* w **12** (*sideways*). *P* 12½ × 12.
294 **94** 3p. black, gold and red .. .. .. 30 30

**95** Nativity Scene

**96** Soldier Artificer, 1773

(Des A. Ryman. Photo Enschedé)

**1971** (1 Dec). *Christmas. T* **95** *and similar horiz design. Multicoloured. W* w **12**. *P* 13 × 13½.
295 3p. Type **95** .. .. .. .. 45 35
296 5p. Mary and Joseph going to Bethlehem .. 55 40

(Des A. Ryman. Litho Questa)

**1972** (6 Mar). *Bicentenary of Royal Engineers in Gibraltar. T* **96** *and similar multicoloured designs. W* w **12** (*sideways on* 1 *and* 3*p.*). *P* 13½ × 14 (*5p.*) *or* 14 × 13½ (*others*).
297 1p. Type **96** .. .. .. .. 40 20
298 3p. Modern tunneller .. .. .. 60 50
299 5p. Old and new uniforms and badge (*horiz*) 75 65
297/9 .. .. .. .. *Set of* 3 1·60 1·25

(Des A. Ryman. Litho Questa)

**1972** (19 July). *Military Uniforms* (*4th series*). *Multicoloured designs as T* **77**. *W* w **12** (*sideways*). *P* 14.
300 1p. Duke of Cornwall's Light Infantry, 1704 60 20
301 3p. King's Royal Rifle Corps, 1830 .. .. 1·75 50
302 7p. Officer, 37th North Hampshire, 1825 .. 2·50 1·25
303 10p. Royal Navy, 1972 .. .. .. 3·00 2·00
300/3 .. .. .. .. *Set of* 4 7·00 3·50

Nos. 300/303 have a short history of the Regiment printed on the reverse side under the gum.

**97** "Our Lady of Europa"

**98** Keys of Gibraltar and *Narcissus niveus*

(Des A. Ryman. Litho Harrison)

972 (4 Oct). *Christmas. W* w **12** *(sideways). P* 14½ × 14.

| | | | | |
|---|---|---|---|---|
| 04 | **97** | 3p. multicoloured | 10 | 10 |
| 05 | | 5p. multicoloured | 10 | 20 |

These stamps have an inscription printed on the reverse side.

(Des (from photograph by D. Groves) and photo Harrison)

972 (20 Nov). *Royal Silver Wedding. Multicoloured; background colour given. W* w **12.** *P* 14 × 14½.

| | | | | |
|---|---|---|---|---|
| 06 | **98** | 5p. carmine-red | 20 | 20 |
| 07 | | 7p. deep grey-green | 20 | 20 |

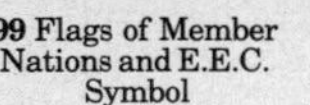

**99** Flags of Member Nations and E.E.C. Symbol

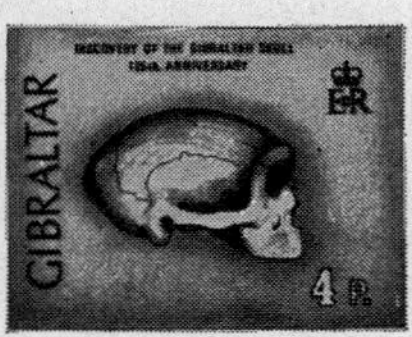


**100** Skull

(Des A. Ryman. Litho Questa)

973 (22 Feb). *Britain's Entry into E.E.C. W* w **12** *(sideways). P* 14½ × 14.

| | | | | |
|---|---|---|---|---|
| 08 | **99** | 5p. multicoloured | 40 | 30 |
| 09 | | 10p. multicoloured | 60 | 50 |

(Des A. Ryman. Litho B.W.)

1973 (22 May). *125th Anniv of Gibraltar Skull Discovery. T* **100** *and similar horiz designs. Multicoloured. W* w **12.** *P* 13 *(10p.) or* 13½ *(others).*

| | | |
|---|---|---|
| 310   4p. Type **100** | 1·00 | 50 |
|    a. Gold ("GIBRALTAR") omitted | £900 | |
| 311   6p. Prehistoric man | 1·00 | 70 |
| 312   10p. Prehistoric family (40×26 *mm*) | 1·50 | 1·25 |
| 310/12 . . *Set of* 3 | 3·25 | 2·25 |

Four mint examples of No. 310a have been found in presentation packs.

(Des A. Ryman. Litho Questa)

1973 (22 Aug). *Military Uniforms (5th series). Multicoloured designs as T* **77.** *W* w **12** *(sideways). P* 14.

| | | |
|---|---|---|
| 313   1p. King's Own Scottish Borderers, 1770 | 40 | 20 |
| 314   4p. Royal Welch Fusiliers, 1800 | 1·25 | 1·00 |
| 315   6p. Royal Northumberland Fusiliers, 1736 | 2·00 | 1·50 |
| 316   10p. Grenadier Guards, 1898 | 3·00 | 2·50 |
| 313/16 . . *Set of* 4 | 6·00 | 4·75 |

Nos. 313/16 have a short history of the Regiment printed on the reverse side under the gum.

1973 (12 Sept). *As Nos.* 261/2 *and* 267/8 *but W* w **12** *upright.*

| | | |
|---|---|---|
| 317   2p. multicoloured | 75 | 1·25 |
|    a. Pair. Nos. 317/18 | 1·50 | 2·50 |
| 318   2p. multicoloured | 75 | 1·25 |
| 319   4p. multicoloured | 1·00 | 1·25 |
|    a. Pair. Nos. 319/20 | 2·00 | 2·50 |
| 320   4p. multicoloured | 1·00 | 1·25 |
| 317/20 . . *Set of* 4 | 3·25 | 4·50 |

**101** "Nativity" (Danckerts)

**102** Victorian Pillar-box

(Des and litho Enschedé)

1973 (17 Oct). *Christmas. W* w **12.** *P* 12½ × 12.

| | | | | |
|---|---|---|---|---|
| 321 | **101** | 4p. violet and Venetian red | 25 | 15 |
| 322 | | 6p. magenta and turquoise-blue | 35 | 45 |

1973 (14 Nov). *Royal Wedding. As Nos.* 165/6 *of Anguilla. Centre multicoloured. W* w **12** *(sideways). P* 13½.

| | | |
|---|---|---|
| 323   6p. turquoise | 10 | 10 |
| 324   14p. yellow-green | 20 | 20 |

(Des A. Ryman. Litho Walsall)

1974 (2 May). *Centenary of Universal Postal Union. T* **102** *and similar vert designs. Multicoloured. (a) W* w **12** *(sideways). P* 14½.

| | | |
|---|---|---|
| 325   2p. Type **102** | 15 | 20 |
| 326   6p. Pillar-box of George VI | 25 | 30 |
| 327   14p. Pillar-box of Elizabeth II | 40 | 65 |
| 325/7 . . *Set of* 3 | 70 | 1·00 |

*(b) No wmk. Imperf × roul* 5*. *Self-adhesive (from booklets)*

| | | |
|---|---|---|
| 328   2p. Type **102** | 25 | 90 |
|    a. Booklet pane Nos. 328/30 *se-tenant* | 4·50 | |
|    b. Booklet pane Nos. 328 × 3 and 329 × 3 | 2·00 | |
| 329   6p. As No. 326 | 45 | 1·00 |
| 330   14p. As No. 327 | 5·00 | 7·50 |
| 328/30 . . *Set of* 3 | 5·25 | 8·50 |

*Nos. 328/30 were separated by various combinations of rotary-knife (giving a straight edge) and roulette.

(Des A. Ryman. Litho Questa)

**1974** (21 Aug). *Military Uniforms (6th series). Multicoloured designs as T* **77.** *W* w **12** *(sideways). P* 14.

| | | |
|---|---|---|
| 331   4p. East Lancashire Regt, 1742 | 50 | 50 |
| 332   6p. Somerset Light Infantry, 1833 | 70 | 70 |
| 333   10p. Royal Sussex Regt, 1790 | 1·00 | 1·25 |
| 334   16p. R.A.F. officer, 1974 | 2·25 | 2·50 |
| 331/4 . . *Set of* 4 | 4·00 | 4·50 |

Nos. 331/4 have a short history of the regiment printed on the reverse side under the gum.

**103** "Madonna with the Green Cushion" (Solario)

**104** Churchill and Houses of Parliament

(Des A. Ryman and M. Infante. Litho Questa)

**1974** (5 Nov). *Christmas. T* **103** *and similar vert design. Multicoloured. W* w **14.** *P* 14.

| | | |
|---|---|---|
| 335   4p. Type **103** | 40 | 30 |
| 336   6p. "Madonna of the Meadow" (Bellini) | 60 | 60 |

(Des L. Curtis. Litho Harrison)

**1974** (30 Nov). *Birth Centenary of Sir Winston Churchill. T* **104** *and similar horiz design. W* w **12.** *P* 14 × 14½.

| | | |
|---|---|---|
| 337   6p. black, reddish purple and light lavender | 25 | 15 |
| 338   20p. brownish black, lake-brown and light orange-red | 50 | 50 |
| **MS**339   114 × 93 mm. Nos. 337/8. W w **12** (sideways). P 14 | 4·00 | 4·25 |

Design:—20p. Churchill and *King George V* (battleship).

(Des A. Ryman. Litho Questa)

**1975** (14 Mar). *Military Uniforms (7th series). Multicoloured designs as T* **77.** *W* w **14.** *P* 14.

| | | |
|---|---|---|
| 340   4p. East Surrey Regt, 1846 | 30 | 30 |
| 341   6p. Highland Light Infantry, 1777 | 50 | 50 |
| 342   10p. Coldstream Guards, 1704 | 70 | 80 |
| 343   20p. Gibraltar Regt, 1974 | 1·25 | 1·50 |
| 340/3 . . *Set of* 4 | 2·40 | 2·75 |

Nos. 340/3 have a short history of each regiment printed on the reverse side under the gum.

**1975** (9 July). *As Nos.* 257/8 *but W* w **14** *(sideways).*

| | | |
|---|---|---|
| 344   1p. multicoloured | 90 | 1·25 |
|    a. Pair. Nos. 344/5 | 1·75 | 2·50 |
| 345   1p. multicoloured | 90 | 1·25 |

**105** Girl Guides' Badge

**106** Child at Prayer

(Des A. Ryman. Litho Harrison)

**1975** (10 Oct). *50th Anniv of Gibraltar Girl Guides. W* w **12.** *P* 13 × 13½.

| | | |
|---|---|---|
| 346 **105**   5p. gold, light blue and dull violet | 30 | 40 |
|    a. *Tête-bêche* (pair) | 60 | 80 |
| 347   7p. gold, sepia and light lake-brown | 40 | 50 |
|    a. *Tête-bêche* (pair) | 80 | 1·00 |
| 348 –   15p. silver, brownish black & yellow-brn | 65 | 85 |
|    a. *Tête-bêche* (pair) | 1·25 | 1·60 |
|    b. Silver omitted | † | — |
| 346/8 . . *Set of* 3 | 1·25 | 1·60 |

No. 348 is as T **105** but shows a different badge.

Nos. 346/8 were each issued in sheets of 25 (5×5) with each horizontal row containing three upright stamps and two inverted.

(Des A. Ryman. Litho Walsall)

**1975** (26 Nov). *Christmas. T* **106** *and similar vert designs. Multicoloured. W* w **14** *(sideways). P* 14.

| | | |
|---|---|---|
| 349   6p. Type **106** | 40 | 45 |
|    a. Block of 6. Nos. 349/54 | 2·10 | |
| 350   6p. Angel with lute | 40 | 45 |
| 351   6p. Child singing carols | 40 | 45 |
| 352   6p. Three children | 40 | 45 |
| 353   6p. Girl at prayer | 40 | 45 |
| 354   6p. Boy and lamb | 40 | 45 |
| 349/54 . . *Set of* 6 | 2·10 | 2·40 |

Nos. 349/54 were issued together *se-tenant* in small sheets of six (3 × 2) with the usual plate numbers and marginal inscriptions.

## NEW INFORMATION

The editor is always interested to correspond with people who have new information that will improve or correct the Catalogue.

**107** Bruges Madonna

**108** Bicentennial Emblem and Arms of Gibraltar

(Des Jennifer Toombs. Litho Walsall)

**1975** (17 Dec). *500th Birth Anniv of Michelangelo. T* **107** *and similar vert designs. Multicoloured. (a) W* w **14** *(sideways). P* 14.

| | | |
|---|---|---|
| 355   6p. Type **107** | 15 | 25 |
| 356   9p. Taddei Madonna | 20 | 35 |
| 357   15p. Pietà | 30 | 65 |
| 355/7 . . *Set of* 3 | 60 | 1·10 |

*(b) No wmk. Imperf × roul* 5*. *Self-adhesive (from booklets)*

| | | |
|---|---|---|
| 358   6p. Type **107** | 25 | 25 |
|    a. Booklet pane Nos. 358/60 *se-tenant* | 1·25 | |
|    b. Booklet pane Nos. 358 × 2, 359 × 2 and 360 × 2 | 2·50 | |
| 359   9p. As No. 356 | 40 | 40 |
| 360   15p. As No. 357 | 70 | 70 |
| 358/60 . . *Set of* 3 | 1·25 | 1·25 |

*Nos. 358/60 were separated by various combinations of rotary knife (giving a straight edge) and roulette.

(Des A. Ryman. Litho Walsall)

**1976** (28 May). *Bicentenary of American Revolution. W* w **14** *(inverted). P* 14.

| | | |
|---|---|---|
| 361 **108**   25p. multicoloured | 50 | 50 |
| **MS**362   85 × 133 mm. No. 361 × 4 | 5·50 | 5·50 |

The edges of **MS**362 are rouletted.

(Des A. Ryman. Litho Walsall)

**1976** (21 July). *Military Uniforms (8th series). Multicoloured designs as T* **77.** *W* w **14** *(inverted). P* 14.

| | | |
|---|---|---|
| 363   1p. Suffolk Regt, 1795 | 15 | 15 |
| 364   6p. Northamptonshire Regt, 1779 | 30 | 30 |
| 365   12p. Lancashire Fusiliers, 1793 | 55 | 55 |
| 366   25p. Ordnance Corps, 1896 | 1·10 | 1·10 |
| 363/6 . . *Set of* 4 | 1·90 | 1·90 |

Nos. 363/6 have a short history of each regiment printed on the reverse side under the gum.

**109** The Holy Family

**110** Queen Elizabeth II, Royal Arms and Gibraltar Arms

(Des A. Ryman. Litho Questa)

**1976** (3 Nov). *Christmas. T* **109** *and similar vert designs showing stained-glass windows in St. Joseph's Church, Gibraltar. Multicoloured. W* w **14.** *P* 14.

| | | |
|---|---|---|
| 367   6p. Type **109** | 25 | 15 |
| 368   9p. Madonna and Child | 30 | 25 |
| 369   12p. St. Bernard | 45 | 45 |
| 370   20p. Archangel Michael | 70 | 80 |
| 367/70 . . *Set of* 4 | 1·50 | 1·50 |

(Des A. Ryman. Litho J.W.)

**1977** (7 Feb). *Silver Jubilee. W* w **14.** *P* 13½.

| | | |
|---|---|---|
| 371 **110**   6p. multicoloured | 25 | 20 |
| 372   £1 multicoloured | 1·75 | 2·25 |
| **MS**373   124 × 115 mm. Nos. 371/2. P 13 | 2·40 | 3·00 |

The outer edges of the miniature sheet are either guillotined or rouletted.

**111** Toothed Orchid (*Orchis tridentata*)

(Des A. Ryman. Litho Questa)

**1977** (1 Apr)–**82.** *Multicoloured designs as T* **111.** *W* w **14** *(sideways on horiz designs; inverted on £5). Chalk-surfaced paper (15p., £5). P* 14.

| | | |
|---|---|---|
| 374   ½p. Type **111** | 40 | 50 |
|    a. Chalk-surfaced paper (22.2.82) | 1·50 | 1·75 |

375 1p. Red Mullet (*Mullus surmuletus*) (*horiz*) .. .. .. 10 10
376 2p. *Maculinea arion* (butterfly) (*horiz*) .. 30 30
377 2½p. Sardinian Warbler (*Sylvia melanocephala*) .. .. .. .. 40 35
378 3p. Giant Squill (*Scilla peruviana*) .. 20 10
379 4p. Grey Wrasse (*Crenilabrus cinereus*) (*horiz*) .. .. .. .. 30 10
b. Chalk-surfaced paper (21.4.81) .. 55 30
380 5p. *Vanessa atalanta* (butterfly) (*horiz*) 50 60
381 6p. Black Kite (*Milvus migrans*) .. 45 30
382 9p. Shrubby Scorpion-vetch (*Coronilla valentina*) .. .. .. .. 90 70
383 10p. John Dory (fish) (*Zeus faber*) (*horiz*) .. 40 20
a. Chalk-surfaced paper (21.4.81) .. 70 80
384 12p. *Colias crocea* (butterfly) (*horiz*) .. 1·00 35
a. Chalk-surfaced paper (21.4.81) .. 2·50 1·75
384*b* 15p. Winged Asparagus Pea (*Tetragonolobus purpureus*) (12.11.80) .. .. 2·25 40
385 20p. Audouin's Gull (*Larus audouinii*) .. 1·25 1·25
386 25p. Barbary Nut (iris) (*Iris sisyrinchium*) 1·25 1·50
a. Chalk-surfaced paper (21.4.81) .. 2·00 2·00
387 50p. Swordfish (*Xiphias gladius*) (*horiz*) .. 2·00 95
a. Chalk-surfaced paper (21.4.81) .. 4·00 3·25
388 £1 *Papilio machaon* (butterfly) (*horiz*) .. 4·75 4·00
389 £2 Hoopoe (*Upupa epops*) .. .. 7·50 10·00
389*a* £5 Arms of Gibraltar (16.5.79) .. .. 10·00 10·00
374/89*a* .. .. .. .. *Set of* 18 30·00 28·00

The ½p. to £2 values have a descriptive text printed on the reverse, beneath the gum.

The 9p. from the above issue exists with different dates in the imprint below the design.

**112** "Our Lady of Europa" Stamp

(Des J. Cooter. Litho Questa)

**1977** (27 May). *"Amphilex 77" Stamp Exhibition. Amsterdam. T* **112** *and similar vert designs. Multicoloured. W w* **14** *(sideways on 6p.; inverted on 12p.). P* 13½.

390 6p. Type **112** .. .. .. .. .. 10 20
391 12p. "Europa Point" stamp .. .. 20 30
392 25p. "E.E.C. Entry" stamp .. .. 30 50
390/2 .. .. .. .. *Set of* 3 55 90

**113** "The Annunciation" (Rubens)

**114** Aerial View of Gibraltar

(Des A. Ryman. Litho Enschedé)

**1977** (2 Nov). *Christmas and Rubens' 400th Birth Anniv. T* **113** *and similar multicoloured designs. W w* **14** *(sideways on 12p.). P* 13½.

393 3p. Type **113** .. .. .. .. 10 10
394 9p. "The Adoration of the Magi" .. .. 20 20
395 12p. "The Adoration of the Magi" (*horiz*) .. 25 30
396 15p. "The Holy Family under the Apple Tree" 30 40
393/6 .. .. .. .. *Set of* 4 75 85
**MS**397 110 × 200 mm. Nos. 393/6 (wmk upright) .. 3·00 3·50

(Des A. Ryman. Litho Enschedé)

**1978** (3 May). *Gibraltar from Space. P* 13½.

398 **114** 12p. multicoloured .. .. .. 25 40
a. Horiz pair imperf 3 sides
**MS**399 148×108 mm. 25p. multicoloured .. 80 80

Design:—25p. Aerial view of Straits of Gibraltar.

No. 398a occurs on the bottom pair from two sheets of 10 (2×5) and shows the stamps perforated at top only.

**115** Holyroodhouse

(Des and litho Walsall)

**1978** (12 June). *25th Anniv of Coronation. T* **115** *and similar horiz designs. Multicoloured. (a) From sheets. P* 13½ × 14.

400 6p. Type **115** .. .. .. .. 20 15
401 9p. St. James's Palace .. .. .. 25 15
402 12p. Sandringham .. .. .. .. 30 25
403 18p. Balmoral .. .. .. .. 40 40
400/3 .. .. .. .. *Set of* 4 1·00 85

(*b*) *From booklets. Imperf × roul 5*. Self-adhesive*

404 12p. As No. 402 .. .. .. 35 75
a. Booklet pane. Nos. 404/5, each × 3 .. 2·00
405 18p. As No. 403 .. .. .. .. 40 90
406 25p. Windsor Castle .. .. .. 70 1·10
a. Booklet pane of 1 .. .. .. 70
404/6 .. .. .. .. *Set of* 3 1·25 2·50

*Nos. 404/5 were separated by various combinations of rotary-knife (giving a straight edge) and roulette. No. 406 exists only with straight edges.

**116** "Sunderland", 1938–58

**117** "Madonna with Animals"

(Des A. Theobald. Litho Harrison)

**1978** (6 Sept). *60th Anniv of Royal Air Force. T* **116** *and similar horiz designs. Multicoloured. W w* **14** *(sideways). P* 14.

407 3p. Type **116** .. .. .. .. 15 10
408 9p. "Caudron", 1918 .. .. .. 35 35
409 12p. "Shackleton", 1953–66 .. .. .. 40 40
410 16p. "Hunter", 1954–77 .. .. .. 45 50
411 18p. "Nimrod", 1969–78 .. .. .. 50 60
407/11 .. .. .. .. *Set of* 5 1·75 1·75

(Des A. Ryman. Litho Questa)

**1978** (1 Nov). *Christmas. Paintings by Dürer. T* **117** *and similar vert designs. Multicoloured. W w* **14**. *P* 14.

412 5p. Type **117** .. .. .. .. 10 10
413 9p. "The Nativity" .. .. .. 15 15
414 12p. "Madonna of the Goldfinch" .. .. 20 25
415 15p. "Adoration of the Magi" .. .. 30 40
412/15 .. .. .. .. *Set of* 4 65 80

**118** Sir Rowland Hill and 1d. Stamp of 1886

(Des A. Ryman. Litho Format)

**1979** (7 Feb). *Death Centenary of Sir Rowland Hill. T* **118** *and similar horiz designs. W w* **14** *(sideways). P* 13½ × 14.

416 3p. multicoloured .. .. .. .. 15 10
417 9p. multicoloured .. .. .. .. 30 15
418 12p. multicoloured .. .. .. .. 35 20
419 25p. black, dull claret and yellow .. .. 50 50
416/19 .. .. .. .. *Set of* 4 1·10 80

Designs:—9p. Sir Rowland Hill and 1p. coil stamp of 1971; 12p. Sir Rowland Hill and Post Office Regulations document, 1840; 25p. Sir Rowland Hill and "G" cancellation.

**119** Posthorn, Dish Antenna and Early Telephone

**120** African Child

(Des A. Ryman. Litho Format)

**1979** (16 May). *Europa. Communications. W w* **14** *(sideways). P* 13½.

420 **119** 3p. green and pale green .. .. 30 10
421 9p. lake-brown and ochre .. .. 80 90
422 12p. ultramarine and dull violet-blue .. 1·00 1·10
420/2 .. .. .. .. *Set of* 3 1·90 2·00

(Des G. Hutchins. Litho Walsall)

**1979** (14 Nov). *Christmas. International Year of the Child. T* **120** *and similar vert designs. Multicoloured. W w* **14** *(sideways). P* 14.

423 12p. Type **120** .. .. .. .. 25 30
a. Block of 6. Nos. 423/8 .. .. 1·40
424 12p. Asian child .. .. .. .. 25 30
425 12p. Polynesian child .. .. .. 25 30
426 12p. American Indian child .. .. .. 25 30
427 12p. Children of different races and Nativity scene .. .. .. .. 25 30
428 12p. European child .. .. .. 25 30
423/8 .. .. .. .. *Set of* 6 1·40 1·60

Nos. 423/8 were printed together, *se-tenant*, in blocks of 6, with margin separating the two blocks in each sheet.

**121** Early Policemen

**122** Peter Amigo (Archbishop)

(Des C. Abbott. Litho Questa)

**1980** (5 Feb). *150th Anniv of Gibraltar Police Force. T* **121** *an similar horiz designs. Multicoloured. W w* **14** *(sideways). P* 14.

429 3p. Type **121** .. .. .. .. 20 1
430 6p. Policemen of 1895, early 1900s and 1980 20 1
431 12p. Policeman and police ambulance .. 25 2
432 37p. Policewoman and police motor-cyclist 55 8
429/32 .. .. .. .. *Set of* 4 1·10 1·1

(Des A. Ryman. Litho Questa)

**1980** (6 May). *Europa. Personalities. T* **122** *and similar ve designs. Multicoloured. W w* **14** *(inverted on No. 434 P* 14½ × 14.

433 12p. Type **122** .. .. .. .. 20 2
434 12p. Gustavo Bacarisas (artist) .. .. 20 2
435 12p. John Mackintosh (philanthropist) .. 20 2
433/5 .. .. .. .. *Set of* 3 55 7

**123** Queen Elizabeth the Queen Mother

**124** "Horatio Nelson" (J. F. Rigaud)

(Des Harrison. Litho Questa)

**1980** (4 Aug). *80th Birthday of Queen Elizabeth the Queen Mother W w* **14** *(sideways). P* 14.

436 **123** 15p. multicoloured .. .. .. 25 2

(Des BG Studio. Litho Questa)

**1980** (20 Aug). *175th Death Anniv of Nelson. Paintings. T* **124** *an similar multicoloured designs. W w* **14** *(sideways on 9 and 40p. P* 14.

437 3p. Type **124** .. .. .. .. 15 1
438 9p. "H.M.S. *Victory*" (*horiz*) .. .. 25 2
439 15p. "Horatio Nelson" (Sir William Beechey) 35 3
440 40p. "H.M.S. *Victory* being towed into Gibraltar" (Clarkson Stanfield) (*horiz*) .. 80 1·0
437/40 .. .. .. .. *Set of* 4 1·40 1·5
**MS**441 159 × 99 mm. No. 439 .. .. 75 1·0

**125** Three Kings

**126** Hercules creating Mediterranean Sea

(Des A. Ryman. Litho Questa)

**1980** (12 Nov). *Christmas. T* **125** *and similar horiz design, each i deep brown and orange-yellow. W w* **14** *(sideways). P* 14½.

442 15p. Type **125** .. .. .. .. 25 3
a. Horiz pair. Nos. 442/3 .. .. 50 7
443 15p. Nativity scene .. .. .. 25 3

Nos. 442/3 were printed together, *se-tenant*, in horizontal pair throughout the sheet.

(Des G. Vasarhelyi. Litho Enschedé)

**1981** (24 Feb). *Europa. Folklore. T* **126** *and similar vert design Multicoloured. W w* **14**. *P* 13½ × 13.

444 9p. Type **126** .. .. .. .. 20 1
445 15p. Hercules and Pillars of Hercules (Straits of Gibraltar) .. .. .. .. 25 3

**127** Dining-room

**128** Prince Charles and Lady Diana Spencer

(Des A. Ryman. Litho Harrison)

**981** (22 May). *450th Anniv of The Convent (Governor's Residence). T* **127** *and similar square designs. Multicoloured. W* w **14** *(sideways). P* 14½ × 14.
46 4p. Type **127** .. 10 10
47 14p. King's Chapel .. 20 20
48 15p. The Convent .. 20 20
49 55p. Cloister .. 85 1·10
46/9 .. *Set of* 4 1·10 1·40

(Des A. Ryman. Litho Questa)

**981** (27 July). *Royal Wedding. W* w **14** *(sideways). P* 14½.
50 **128** £1 multicoloured .. 1·50 1·75

**129**

**130** Paper Aeroplane

(Des A. Ryman. Litho Questa)

**981** (2 Sept). *Booklet stamps. W* w **14**. *P* 13½×14.
51 **129** 1p. black .. 10 10
a. Booklet pane. Nos. 451/2 and 453 × 3 plus printed label .. 90
b. Booklet pane. Nos. 451/2 × 2 and 453 × 6 plus two printed labels .. 1·75
52 4p. Prussian blue .. 10 10
53 15p. light green .. 25 30
51/3 .. *Set of* 3 35 45

(Des A. Ryman. Litho Walsall)

**981** (29 Sept*). *50th Anniv of Gibraltar Airmail Service. T* **130** *and similar horiz designs. Multicoloured. W* w **14** *(sideways). P* 14½ × 14.
54 14p. Type **130** .. 20 20
55 15p. Airmail letters, post box and aircraft tail fin .. 20 20
56 55p. Aircraft circling globe .. 80 90
54/6 .. *Set of* 3 1·10 1·10
*This is the local release date. The Crown Agents released the amps on 21 September.

**131** Carol Singers

**132** I.Y.D.P. Emblem and Stylised Faces

(Des Clive Torres (15p.); Peter Parody (55p.); adapted G. Vasarhelyi. Litho Questa)

**981** (19 Nov). *Christmas. Children's Drawings. T* **131** *and similar multicoloured design. W* w **14** *(sideways on* 15p.). *P* 14.
457 15p. Type **131** .. 30 15
458 55p. Postbox (*vert*) .. 1·00 85

(Des A. Ryman. Litho Questa)

**981** (19 Nov). *International Year For Disabled Persons. W* w **14** *(sideways). P* 14 × 14½.
459 **132** 14p. multicoloured .. 30 30

**133** Douglas "DC 3"

**134** Crest, H.M.S. *Opossum*

(Des A. Theobald. Litho J.W.)

**982** (10 Feb). *Aircraft. Horiz designs as T* **133**. *Multicoloured. W* w **14**. *P* 14.
60 1p. Type **133** .. 25 30
61 2p. Vickers "Viking" .. 30 30
62 3p. Airspeed "Ambassador" .. 30 30
63 4p. Vickers "Viscount" .. 40 15
64 5p. Boeing "727" .. 60 30
65 10p. Vickers "Vanguard" .. 75 30
66 14p. Short "Solent" .. 85 60
67 15p. Fokker "F.27 (Friendship)" .. 1·00 30
68 17p. Boeing "737" .. 1·00 45
69 20p. BAC "One-eleven" .. 75 40
70 25p. Lockheed "Constellation" .. 1·50 1·00
71 50p. De Havilland "Comet 4B" .. 2·75 1·75
72 £1 Saro "Windhover" .. 4·00 2·00
73 £2 Hawker Siddeley "Trident 2" .. 4·50 4·75
74 £5 D.H. "89A (Dragon Rapide)" .. 9·00 13·00
60/74 .. *Set of* 15 25·00 23·00
No. 469 exists with two different imprint dates.
For 2p. and 5p. values watermarked w **16** see Nos. 549 and 52.

(Des A. Ryman. Litho Questa)

**1982** (14 Apr). *Naval Crests (1st series). T* **134** *and similar vert designs. Multicoloured. W* w **14**. *P* 14.
475 ½p. Type **134** .. 10 10
476 15½p. H.M.S. *Norfolk* .. 45 50
477 17p. H.M.S. *Fearless* .. 50 55
478 60p. H.M.S. *Rooke* .. 1·25 1·60
475/8 .. *Set of* 4 2·10 2·40
See also Nos. 493/6, 510/13, 522/5, 541/4, 565/8, 592/5, 616/19, 638/41 and 651/4.

**135** "Spitfires" at Gibraltar

**136** Gibraltar Chamber of Commerce Centenary

(Des A. Ryman. Litho Questa)

**1982** (11 June). *Europa. Operation Torch. T* **135** *and similar horiz design. Multicoloured. W* w **14** *(sideways). P* 14.
479 14p. Type **135** .. 25 40
480 17p. General Giraud, General Eisenhower and Gibraltar .. 35 45

(Des A. Ryman. Litho Questa)

**1982** (22 Sept). *Anniversaries. T* **136** *and similar vert designs. Multicoloured. W* w **14** *(sideways). P* 14½.
481 ½p. Type **136** .. 10 10
482 15½p. British Forces Postal Service centenary .. 30 25
483 60p. 75th anniv of Gibraltar Scout Association .. 1·10 1·25
481/3 .. *Set of* 3 1·25 1·40

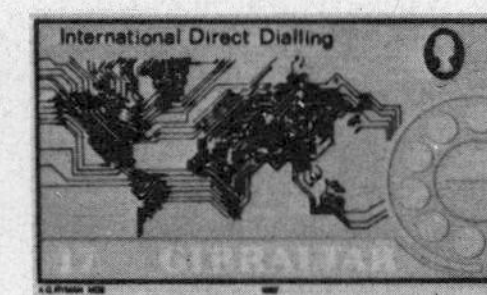


**137** Printed Circuit forming Map of World

(Des A. Ryman. Litho Harrison)

**1982** (1 Oct). *International Direct Dialling. W* w **14** *(sideways). P* 14½.
484 **137** 17p. black, pale blue and bright orange 35 35

**138** Gibraltar illuminated at Night and Holly

(Des A. Ryman. Litho Questa)

**1982** (18 Nov). *Christmas. T* **138** *and similar horiz design. Multicoloured. W* w **14** *(sideways). P* 14 × 14½.
485 14p. Type **138** .. 45 30
486 17p. Gibraltar illuminated at night and Mistletoe .. 50 35

**139** Yacht Marina

(Des Olympia Reyes. Litho Questa)

**1983** (14 Mar). *Commonwealth Day. T* **139** *and similar multicoloured designs. W* w **14** *(sideways on* 4, 14p.). *P* 14.
487 4p. Type **139** .. 10 10
488 14p. Scouts and Guides Commonwealth Day Parade .. 30 35
489 17p. Flag of Gibraltar (*vert*) .. 35 40
490 60p. Queen Elizabeth II (from photo by Tim Graham) (*vert*) .. 1·25 1·40
487/90 .. *Set of* 4 1·75 2·00

**140** St George's Hall Gallery

(Des A. Ryman. Litho Harrison)

**1983** (21 May). *Europa. T* **140** *and similar horiz design. W* w **14** *(sideways). P* 13½ × 13.
491 16p. black and brown-ochre .. 30 35
492 19p. black and pale blue .. 40 40
Design:—19p. Water catchment slope.

(Des A. Ryman. Litho Questa)

**1983** (1 July). *Naval Crests (2nd series). Vert designs as T* **134**. *Multicoloured. W* w **14**. *P* 14.
493 4p. H.M.S. *Faulknor* .. 20 10
494 14p. H.M.S. *Renown* .. 50 35
495 17p. H.M.S. *Ark Royal* .. 60 40
496 60p. H.M.S. *Sheffield* .. 1·75 1·50
493/6 .. *Set of* 4 2·75 2·10

**141** Landport Gate, 1729

(Des Olympia Reyes. Litho Enschedé)

**1983** (13 Sept). *Fortress Gibraltar in the 18th Century. T* **141** *and similar horiz designs. Multicoloured. W* w **14** *(sideways). P* 13 × 13½.
497 4p. Type **141** .. 20 10
498 17p. Koehler Gun, 1782 .. 60 45
499 77p. King's Bastion, 1779 .. 2·00 1·75
497/9 .. *Set of* 3 2·50 2·00
**MS**500 97 × 145 mm. Nos. 497/9 .. 2·50 2·25

**142** "Adoration of the Magi" (Raphael)

**143** 1932 2d. Stamp and Globe

(Des A. Ryman. Litho Questa)

**1983** (17 Nov). *Christmas. 500th Birth Anniv of Raphael. T* **142** *and similar multicoloured designs. W* w **14** *(sideways on* 4p.). *P* 14.
501 4p. Type **142** .. 25 10
502 17p. "Madonna of Foligno" (*vert*) .. 70 35
503 60p. "Sistine Madonna" (*vert*) .. 1·75 1·40
501/3 .. *Set of* 3 2·40 1·60

(Des E. Field. Litho Walsall)

**1984** (6 Mar). *Europa. Posts and Telecommunications. T* **143** *and similar vert design. Multicoloured. W* w **14**. *P* 14½ × 14.
504 17p. Type **143** .. 35 40
505 23p. Circuit board and globe .. 45 50

**144** Hockey

**145** Mississippi River Boat Float

(Des A. Ryman. Litho Walsall)

**1984** (25 May). *Sports. T* **144** *and similar horiz designs. Multicoloured. W* w **14** *(sideways). P* 14 × 14½.
506 20p. Type **144** .. 40 50
507 21p. Basketball .. 40 50
508 26p. Rowing .. 55 70
509 29p. Football .. 60 75
506/9 .. *Set of* 4 1·75 2·25

(Des A. Ryman. Litho Walsall)

**1984** (21 Sept). *Naval Crests (3rd series). Vert designs as T* **134**. *Multicoloured. W* w **14**. *P* 13½ × 13.
510 20p. H.M.S. *Active* .. 1·00 80
511 21p. H.M.S. *Foxhound* .. 1·00 80
512 26p. H.M.S. *Valiant* .. 1·25 1·00
513 29p. H.M.S. *Hood* .. 1·40 1·50
510/13 .. *Set of* 4 4·25 3·75

(Des A. Ryman. Litho Questa)

**1984** (7 Nov). *Christmas. Epiphany Floats. T* **145** *and similar horiz design. Multicoloured. W* w **14** *(sideways). P* 14 × 14½.
514 20p. Type **145** .. 40 50
515 80p. Roman Temple float .. 1·60 2·00

## OMNIBUS ISSUES

Details, together with prices for complete sets, of the various Omnibus issues from the 1935 Silver Jubilee series to date are included in a special section following Zululand at the end of the catalogue.

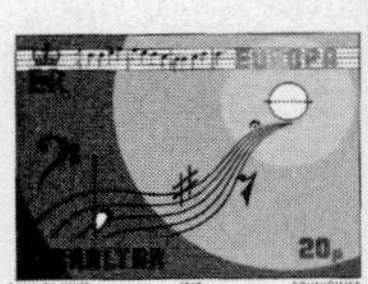

**146** Musical Symbols, and Score from Beethoven's 9th (Choral) Symphony

**147** Globe and Stop Polio Campaign Logo

(Des Olympia Reyes. Photo Courvoisier)

**1985** (26 Feb). *Europa. European Music Year. T* **146** *and similar horiz design. Multicoloured. Granite paper. P* 12½.

516 **146** 20p. multicoloured .. .. .. .. 50 50
517 – 29p. multicoloured .. .. .. .. 75 1·00

The 29p. is as T **146** but shows different symbols.

(Des E. Field. Litho J.W.)

**1985** (3 May). *Stop Polio Campaign. Vert designs as T* **147**. *Multicoloured. W* w **14** *(inverted). P* 13 × 13½.

518 26p. multicoloured (Type **147**) .. .. 60 60
a. Horiz strip of 4. Nos. 518/21 .. .. 2·25
519 26p. multicoloured ("ST" visible) .. .. 60 60
520 26p. multicoloured ("STO" visible) .. .. 60 60
521 26p. multicoloured ("STOP" visible) .. .. 60 60
518/21 .. .. .. .. .. *Set of* 4 2·25 2·25

Nos 518/21 were printed in horizontal *se-tenant* strips of four within the sheet. Each design differs in the position of the logo across the centre of the globe. On the left hand stamp in the strip only the letter "S" is visible, on the next "ST", on the next "STO" and on the last "STOP".

Other features of the design also differ, so that the word "Year" moves towards the top of the stamp and on No. 521 the upper logo is omitted.

(Des A. Ryman. Litho Questa)

**1985** (3 July). *Naval Crests (4th series). Vert designs as T* **134**. *Multicoloured. W* w **16**. *P* 14.

522 4p. H.M.S. *Duncan* .. .. .. .. .. 25 10
523 9p. H.M.S. *Fury* .. .. .. .. .. 40 40
524 21p. H.M.S. *Firedrake* .. .. .. .. 90 90
525 80p. H.M.S. *Malaya* .. .. .. .. .. 2·75 3·25
522/5 .. .. .. .. .. *Set of* 4 4·00 4·25

**148** I.Y.Y. Logo

**149** St. Joseph

(Des Olympia Reyes. Litho Walsall)

**1985** (6 Sept). *International Youth Year. T* **148** *and similar horiz designs. Multicoloured. W* w **14** *(sideways). P* 14 × 14½.

526 4p. Type **148** .. .. .. .. .. .. 25 10
527 20p. Hands passing diamond .. .. .. 95 80
528 80p. 75th anniv logo of Girl Guide Movement 2·50 2·75
526/8 .. .. .. .. .. *Set of* 3 3·25 3·25

(Des A. Ryman (4p.), Olympia Reyes (80p.). Litho Cartor, France)

**1985** (25 Oct). *Christmas. Centenary of St. Joseph's Parish Church. T* **149** *and similar vert designs. Multicoloured. W* w **16**. *P* 13½*.

529 4p. Type **149** .. .. .. .. .. .. 20 20
a. Vert pair. Nos. 529/30 .. .. .. 40 40
530 4p. St. Joseph's Parish Church .. .. 20 20
531 80p. Nativity crib .. .. .. .. .. 1·75 2·00
529/31 .. .. .. .. .. *Set of* 3 2·00 2·25

*Nos. 529/30 were printed together in panes of 25; No. 529 on rows 1, 3 and 5, and No. 530 on rows 2 and 4. *Se-tenant* vertical pairs from rows 1/2 and 3/4, forming composite designs, have the stamps separated by a line of roulettes instead of perforations. Examples of No. 529 from row 5 have perforations on all four sides.

**150** *Papilio machaon* (butterfly) and The Convent.

**151** 1887 Queen Victoria 6d. Stamp

(Des E. Field. Litho Walsall)

**1986** (10 Feb). *Europa. Nature and the Environment. T* **150** *and similar horiz design. Multicoloured. W* w **16** *(sideways). P* 13 × 13½.

532 22p. Type **150** .. .. .. .. .. .. 1·00 50
533 29p. Herring Gull and Europa Point .. .. 1·50 2·25

(Des A. Ryman. Litho Walsall)

**1986** (26 Mar). *Centenary of First Gibraltar Postage Stamps. T* **151** *and similar vert designs showing stamps. Multicoloured. W* w **16**. *P* 14 × 13½ *(44p.) or* 13½ × 13 *(others)*.

534 4p. Type **151** .. .. .. .. .. .. 25 10
535 22p. 1903 Edward VII 2½d. .. .. .. 85 75
536 32p. 1912 George V 1d. .. .. .. .. 1·25 1·40
537 36p. 1938 George VI £1 .. .. .. .. 1·40 1·60
538 44p. 1953 Coronation ½d. (29 × 46 *mm*) .. 1·75 2·00
534/8 .. .. .. .. .. *Set of* 5 5·00 5·25
**MS**539 102 × 73 mm. 29p. 1886 "GIBRALTAR" overprint on Bermuda 1d. .. .. .. .. 1·25 1·40

**152** Queen Elizabeth II in Robes of Order of the Bath

**153** Prince Andrew and Miss Sarah Ferguson

(Des A. Ryman. Litho Walsall)

**1986** (22 May). *60th Birthday of Queen Elizabeth II. W* w **16**. *P* 14 × 13½.

540 **152** £1 multicoloured .. .. .. .. .. 2·00 3·00

(Des A. Ryman. Litho Questa)

**1986** (28 Aug). *Naval Crests (5th series). Vert designs as T* **134**. *Multicoloured. W* w **16**. *P* 14.

541 22p. H.M.S. *Lightning* .. .. .. .. 1·00 75
542 29p. H.M.S. *Hermione* .. .. .. .. 1·25 1·00
543 32p. H.M.S. *Laforey* .. .. .. .. 1·50 1·75
544 44p. H.M.S. *Nelson* .. .. .. .. 1·75 2·25
541/4 .. .. .. .. .. *Set of* 4 5·00 5·25

(Des A. Ryman. Litho Questa)

**1986** (28 Aug). *Royal Wedding. Sheet* 115 × 85 *mm. W* w **16**. *P* 14½.

**MS**545 **153** 44p. multicoloured .. .. .. .. 1·10 1·40

**154** Three Kings and Cathedral of St. Mary the Crowned

**155** Neptune House

(Des M. Infante. Litho Walsall)

**1986** (14 Oct). *Christmas. International Peace Year. T* **154** *and similar vert design. Multicoloured. W* w **16**. *P* 14.

546 18p. Type **154** .. .. .. .. .. .. 1·00 40
547 32p. St. Andrew's Church .. .. .. .. 1·50 1·75

(Litho Questa)

**1986** (12 Dec)–**87**. *As Nos. 461 and 464, but W* w **16** *(sideways)*. *P* 14.

549 2p. Vickers "Viking" .. .. .. .. .. 1·00 1·25
552 5p. Boeing "727" (2.1.87) .. .. .. .. 1·40 1·75

(Des M. Infante. Litho Questa)

**1987** (17 Feb). *Europa. Architecture. T* **155** *and similar horiz design. Multicoloured. W* w **16**. *P* 14½.

563 22p. Type **155** .. .. .. .. .. .. 1·25 50
564 29p. Ocean Heights .. .. .. .. .. 2·00 1·40

(Des A. Ryman. Litho Walsall)

**1987** (15 Apr). *Naval Crests (6th series). Vert designs as T* **134**. *Multicoloured. W* w **16**. *P* 13½ × 13.

565 18p. H.M.S. *Wishart* (destroyer) .. .. 1·25 75
566 22p. H.M.S. *Charybdis* (cruiser) .. .. 1·40 95
567 32p. H.M.S. *Antelope* (destroyer) .. .. 1·90 2·25
568 44p. H.M.S. *Eagle* (aircraft carrier) .. .. 2·50 3·00
565/8 .. .. .. .. .. *Set of* 4 6·50 6·50

---

## NEW INFORMATION

The editor is always interested to correspond with people who have new information that will improve or correct the Catalogue.

**156** 13-inch Mortar, 1783

**157** Victoria Stadium

(Des A. Ryman. Litho Format)

**1987** (1 June). *Guns. T* **156** *and similar horiz designs. Multicoloured. W* w **14**. *P* 12½.

569 1p. Type **156** .. .. .. .. .. .. 10 10
570 2p. 6-inch coastal gun, 1909 .. .. .. 10 10
571 3p. 8-inch howitzer, 1783 .. .. .. .. 10 10
572 4p. Bofors "L40/70" AA gun, 1951 .. .. 10 10
573 5p. 100 ton rifled muzzle-loader, 1882 .. 10 15
574 10p. 5.25-inch heavy AA gun, 1953 .. .. 20 25
575 18p. 25-pounder gun-how, 1943 .. .. 35 40
576 19p. 64-pounder rifled muzzle-loader, 1873 .. 40 45
577 22p. 12-pounder gun, 1758 .. .. .. 45 50
578 50p. 10-inch rifled muzzle-loader, 1870 .. 1·00 1·10
579 £1 Russian 24-pounder gun, 1854 .. .. 2·00 2·10
580 £3 9.2-inch "Mk.10" coastal gun, 1935 .. 6·00 6·25
581 £5 24-pounder gun, 1779 .. .. .. 10·00 10·50
569/81 .. .. .. .. .. *Set of* 13 19·00 20·00

(Des A. Ryman. Litho Walsall)

**1987** (16 Sept). *Bicentenary of Royal Engineers' Royal Warrant. T* **157** *and similar vert designs. Multicoloured. W* w **14**. *P* 14½.

582 18p. Type **157** .. .. .. .. .. .. 1·00 65
583 32p. Freedom of Gibraltar scroll and casket 1·50 1·75
584 44p. Royal Engineers' badge .. .. .. 1·75 2·50
582/4 .. .. .. .. .. *Set of* 3 3·75 4·50

**158** The Three Kings

(Des Olympia Reyes. Litho Walsall)

**1987** (12 Nov). *Christmas. T* **158** *and similar horiz designs. Multicoloured. W* w **16** *(sideways)*. *P* 14½.

585 4p. Type **158** .. .. .. .. .. .. 15 10
586 22p. The Holy Family .. .. .. .. 75 75
587 44p. The Shepherds .. .. .. .. 1·40 1·60
585/7 .. .. .. .. .. *Set of* 3 2·10 2·25

**159** Liner passing Gibraltar

**160** European Bee Eater

(Des Olympia Reyes. Litho Format)

**1988** (16 Feb). *Europa. Transport and Communications. T* **159** *and similar horiz designs. Multicoloured. W* w **14**. *P* 14½ × 14 × *roul between se-tenant pairs*.

588 22p. Type **159** .. .. .. .. .. .. 1·25 1·50
a. Horiz pair. Nos. 588/9 .. .. .. 2·50 3·00
589 22p. Ferry, dish aerial and aircraft .. .. 1·25 1·50
590 32p. Horse-drawn carriage and modern coach 1·75 2·00
a. Horiz pair. Nos. 590/1 .. .. .. 3·50 4·00
591 32p. Car, telephone and Rock of Gibraltar .. 1·75 2·00
588/91 .. .. .. .. .. *Set of* 4 5·50 6·25

The two designs for each value were printed in sheets of ten, each containing five horizontal *se-tenant* pairs in which the stamps were rouletted between vertically.

(Des A. Ryman. Litho Walsall)

**1988** (7 Apr). *Naval Crests (7th series). Vert designs as T* **134**. *W* w **16**. *P* 13½ × 13.

592 18p. multicoloured .. .. .. .. .. 90 65
593 22p. black, brownish black and gold .. .. 1·10 90
594 32p. multicoloured .. .. .. .. .. 1·50 1·75
595 44p. multicoloured .. .. .. .. .. 2·00 2·50
592/5 .. .. .. .. .. *Set of* 4 5·00 5·25

Designs:—18p. H.M.S. *Clyde*; 22p. H.M.S. *Foresight*; 32p. H.M.S. *Severn*; 44p. H.M.S. *Rodney*.

(Des Olympia Reyes. Litho B.D.T.)

**1988** (15 June). *Birds. T* **160** *and similar horiz designs. Multicoloured. W* w **14** *(sideways)*. *P* 13½.

596 4p. Type **160** .. .. .. .. .. .. 30 15
597 22p. Atlantic Puffin .. .. .. .. .. 80 80
598 32p. Honey Buzzard .. .. .. .. .. 1·00 1·25
599 44p. Blue Rock Thrush .. .. .. .. 1·40 2·00
596/9 .. .. .. .. .. *Set of* 4 3·25 3·75

161 *Zebu* (brigantine)

162 "Snowman" (Rebecca Falero)

(Des A. Ryman. Litho B.D.T.)

**1988** (14 Sept). *Operation Raleigh. T* **161** *and similar horiz designs. Multicoloured.* W w **14**. *P* 13.

600 19p. Type **161** .. .. .. .. .. 55 60
601 22p. Miniature of Sir Walter Raleigh and logo .. .. .. .. .. 60 70
602 32p. *Sir Walter Raleigh* (expedition ship) and world map .. .. .. .. 85 1·25
600/2 .. .. .. .. .. *Set of* 3 1·75 2·25
**MS**603 135×86 mm. 22p. As No. 601; 44p. *Sir Walter Raleigh* (expedition ship) passing Gibraltar .. .. .. .. .. 3·00 3·00

(Des A. Ryman. Litho Questa)

**1988** (2 Nov). *Christmas. Children's Paintings. T* **162** *and similar multicoloured designs.* W w **16** (*sideways*). *P* 14½ (*44p.*) *or* 14 (*others*).

604 4p. Type **162** .. .. .. .. .. 15 10
605 22p. "The Nativity" (Dennis Penalver) .. 55 60
606 44p. "Father Christmas" (Gavin Key) (23×31 *mm*) .. .. .. .. 1·00 1·25
604/6 .. .. .. .. *Set of* 3 1·50 1·75

163 Soft Toys and Toy Train

164 Port Sergeant with Keys

(Des Olympia Reyes. Litho Walsall)

**1989** (15 Feb). *Europa. Children's Toys. T* **163** *and similar horiz design. Multicoloured.* W w **16** (*sideways*). *P* 13 × 13½.

607 25p. Type **163** .. .. .. .. 1·00 60
608 32p. Soft toys, toy boat and doll's house .. 1·25 1·40

(Des A. Ryman. Litho Walsall)

**1989** (28 Apr). *50th Anniv of Gibraltar Regiment. T* **164** *and similar vert designs. Multicoloured.* W w **14**. *P* 13½×13.

609 4p. Type **164** .. .. .. .. .. 25 10
610 22p. Regimental badge and colours .. .. 80 80
611 32p. Drum major .. .. .. .. 1·25 1·50
609/11 .. .. .. .. *Set of* 3 2·10 2·25
**MS**612 124×83 mm. 22p. As No. 610; 44p. Former Gibraltar Defence Force badge .. 2·00 2·00

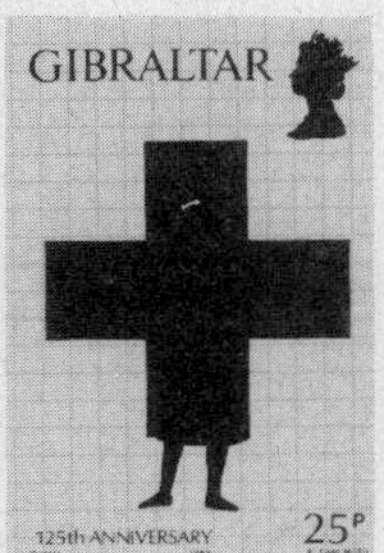

165 Nurse and Baby

166 One Penny Coin

(Des E. Field. Litho Questa)

**1989** (7 July). *125th Anniv of International Red Cross. T* **165** *and similar vert designs.* W w **16**. *P* 15×14½.

613 25p. black, bright scarlet and grey-brown .. 60 60
614 32p. black, bright scarlet and grey-brown .. 75 80
615 44p. black, bright scarlet and grey-brown .. 1·00 1·40
613/15 .. .. .. .. *Set of* 3 2·10 2·50

Designs:—32p. Famine victims; 44p. Accident victims.

(Des A. Ryman. Litho B.D.T.)

**1989** (7 Sept). *Naval Crests* (*8th series*). *Vert designs as T* **134**. W w **16**. *P* 14×13½.

616 22p. multicoloured .. .. .. .. 75 65
617 25p. black and gold .. .. .. .. 85 75
618 32p. gold, black and bright scarlet .. .. 1·10 1·40
619 44p. multicoloured .. .. .. .. 1·50 1·75
616/19 .. .. .. .. *Set of* 4 3·75 4·00

Designs:—22p. H.M.S. *Blankney;* 25p. H.M.S. *Deptford;* 32p. H.M.S. *Exmoor;* 44p. H.M.S. *Stork.*

(Des A. Ryman. Litho Questa)

**1989** (11 Oct). *New Coinage. T* **166** *and similar vert designs in two miniature sheets.* W w **16** (*sideways*). *P* 14½.

**MS**620 72×94 mm. 4p. bronze, black & dull verm (Type **166**); 4p. bronze, blk & dp brn (two pence); 4p. silver, blk & greenish yellow (ten pence); 4p. silver, black and emerald (five pence) .. .. 50 60
**MS**621 100×95 mm. 22p. silver, black & reddish orge (fifty pence); 22p. gold, black & ultram (five pounds); 22p. gold, blk & orge-brn (two pounds); 22p. gold, blk & brt emer (one pound); 22p. gold, blk & brt reddish vio (obverse of coin series); 22p. silver, black and pale violet-blue (twenty pence) 2·50 2·75

167 Father Christmas in Sleigh

168 General Post Office Entrance

(Des M. Infante. Litho Questa)

**1989** (11 Oct). *Christmas. T* **167** *and similar horiz designs. Multicoloured.* W w **16** (*sideways*). *P* 14½.

622 4p. Type **167** .. .. .. .. 15 10
623 22p. Shepherds and sheep .. .. .. 60 70
624 32p. The Nativity .. .. .. .. 90 1·10
625 44p. The Three Wise Men .. .. .. 1·40 1·75
622/5 .. .. .. .. *Set of* 4 2·75 3·25

(Des Olympia Reyes. Litho Questa)

**1990** (6 Mar). *Europa. Post Office Buildings. T* **168** *and similar vert designs. Multicoloured. P* 14½×*roul between se-tenant pairs.*

626 22p. Type **168** .. .. .. .. 65 70
a. Horiz pair. Nos. 626/7 .. .. 1·25 1·40
627 22p. Interior of General Post Office .. .. 65 70
628 32p. Interior of South District Post Office 1·00 1·25
a. Horiz pair. Nos. 628/9 .. .. 2·00 2·50
629 32p. South District Post Office .. .. 1·00 1·25
626/9 .. .. .. .. *Set of* 4 3·00 3·50

Nos. 626/7 and 628/9 were printed in *se-tenant* horizontal pairs within separate sheets of eight, the stamps in each pair being divided by a line of roulettes.

169 19th-century Firemen

170 Henry Corbould (artist) and Penny Black

(Des D. Gonzalez. Litho Questa)

**1990** (2 Apr). *125th Anniv of Gibraltar Fire Service. T* **169** *and similar multicoloured designs. P* 14½×14 (*vert*) *or* 14×14½ (*horiz*).

630 4p. Type **169** .. .. .. .. 20 10
631 20p. Early fire engine (*horiz*) .. .. .. 70 60
632 42p. Modern fire engine (*horiz*) .. .. 1·25 1·50
633 44p. Fireman in breathing apparatus .. 1·40 1·60
630/3 .. .. .. .. *Set of* 4 3·25 3·50

(Des A. Ryman. Litho Questa)

**1990** (3 May). *150th Anniv of the Penny Black. T* **170** *and similar vert designs. Multicoloured. P* 13½×14.

634 19p. Type **170** .. .. .. .. 55 50
635 22p. Bath Royal Mail coach .. .. .. 65 60
636 32p. Sir Rowland Hill and Penny Black .. 95 1·00
634/6 .. .. .. .. *Set of* 3 1·90 1·90
**MS**637 145×95 mm. 44p. Penny Black with Maltese Cross cancellation. P 14½×14 .. 1·40 1·40

(Des A. Ryman. Litho Questa)

**1990** (10 July). *Naval Crests* (*9th series*). *Vert designs as T* **134**. *Multicoloured. P* 14.

638 22p. H.M.S. *Calpe* .. .. .. .. 65 60
639 25p. H.M.S. *Gallant* .. .. .. .. 75 75
640 32p. H.M.S. *Wrestler* .. .. .. .. 1·00 1·10
641 44p. H.M.S. *Greyhound* .. .. .. 1·50 1·60
638/41 .. .. .. .. *Set of* 4 3·50 3·50

171 Model of Europort Development

172 Candle and Holly

(Des A. Ryman. Litho Questa)

**1990** (10 Oct). *Development Projects. T* **171** *and similar horiz designs. Multicoloured. P* 14½.

642 22p. Type **171** .. .. .. .. .. 65 65
643 23p. Construction of building material factory .. .. .. .. .. 65 65
644 25p. Land reclamation .. .. .. .. 80 80
642/4 .. .. .. .. *Set of* 3 1·90 1·90

(Des D. Gonzalez. Litho B.D.T.)

**1990** (10 Oct). *Christmas. T* **172** *and similar vert designs. Multicoloured. P* 13½.

645 4p. Type **172** .. .. .. .. .. 15 10
646 22p. Father Christmas .. .. .. .. 65 65
647 42p. Christmas Tree .. .. .. .. 1·25 1·40
648 44p. Nativity crib .. .. .. .. 1·25 1·40
645/8 .. .. .. .. *Set of* 4 3·00 3·25

173 Space Laboratory and Spaceplane (Colombus Development Programme)

174 Shag

(Des D. Gonzalez. Litho B.D.T.)

**1991** (26 Feb). *Europa. Europe in Space. T* **173** *and similar horiz design. Multicoloured. P* 13½×13.

649 25p. Type **173** .. .. .. .. .. 75 60
650 32p. "ERS-1" earth resources remote sensing satellite .. .. .. .. 1·00 1·25

(Des A. Ryman. Litho Walsall)

**1991** (9 Apr). *Naval Crests* (*10th series*). *Vert designs as T* **134**. *P* 13½×13.

651 4p. black, new blue and gold .. .. 15 10
652 21p. multicoloured .. .. .. .. 65 65
653 22p. multicoloured .. .. .. .. 70 70
654 62p. multicoloured .. .. .. .. 2·00 2·25
651/4 .. .. .. .. *Set of* 4 3·25 3·25

Designs:—4p. H.M.S. *Hesperus;* 21p. H.M.S. *Forester;* 22p. H.M.S. *Furious;* 62p. H.M.S. *Scylla.*

(Des Olympia Reyes. Litho B.D.T.)

**1991** (30 May). *Endangered Species. Birds. T* **174** *and similar horiz designs. Multicoloured. P* 13½.

655 13p. Type **174** .. .. .. .. 45 50
a. Block of 4. Nos. 655/8 .. .. 1·60
656 13p. Barbary Partridge .. .. .. 45 50
657 13p. Egyptian Vulture .. .. .. 45 50
658 13p. Black Stork .. .. .. .. 45 50
655/8 .. .. .. .. *Set of* 4 1·60 1·75

Nos. 655/8 were printed together, *se-tenant*, in differently arranged blocks of 4 throughout the sheet of 16.

**£1.05**

(175)

176 "North View of Gibraltar" (Gustavo Bacarisas)

**1991** (30 May). *No. 580 surch with T* **175**.

659 £1.05 on £3 9.2-inch "Mk.10" coastal gun, 1935 .. .. .. .. .. .. 2·10 2·25

(Des A. Ryman. Litho B.D.T.)

**1991** (10 Sept). *Local Paintings. T* **176** *and similar multicoloured designs. P* 14×15 (*42p.*) *or* 15×14 (*others*).

660 22p. Type **176** .. .. .. .. .. 45 50
661 26p. "Parson's Lodge" (Elena Mifsud) .. 50 55
662 32p. "Governor's Parade" (Jacobo Azagury) 65 70
663 42p. "Waterport Wharf" (Rudesindo Mannia) (*vert*) .. .. .. .. 85 90
660/3 .. .. .. .. *Set of* 4 2·25 2·40

177 "Once in Royal David's City"

178 *Danaus chrysippus*

(Des D. Gonzalez. Litho Questa)

**1991** (15 Oct). *Christmas. Carols. T* **177** *and similar horiz designs. Multicoloured. P* 14×14½.

664 4p. Type **177** .. .. .. .. .. 10 10
665 24p. "Silent Night" .. .. .. .. 50 55
666 25p. "Angels We have Heard on High" .. 50 55
667 49p. "O Come All Ye Faithful" .. .. 1·00 1·10
664/7 .. .. .. .. *Set of* 4 1·90 2·10

(Des A. Ryman. Litho Questa)

**1991** (15 Nov). *"Philanippon '91" International Stamp Exhibition, Tokyo. Sheet* 116×91 *mm. P* 14½.
**MS**668 **178** £1.05, multicoloured .. .. 2·50 2·75

**179** Columbus and *Santa Maria*

(Des Olympia Reyes. Litho Walsall)

**1992** (6 Feb). *Europa. 500th Anniv of Discovery of America by Columbus. T* **179** *and similar horiz designs. Multicoloured. P* 14½.

| | | | | |
|---|---|---|---|---|
| 669 | 24p. Type **179** .. .. .. .. | | 50 | 55 |
| | a. Horiz pair. Nos. 669/70 .. .. | | 1·00 | 1·10 |
| 670 | 24p. Map of Old World and *Nina* .. .. | | 50 | 55 |
| 671 | 34p. Map of New World and *Pinta* .. .. | | 70 | 75 |
| | a. Horiz pair. Nos. 671/2 .. .. | | 1·40 | 1·50 |
| 672 | 34p. Map of Old World and look-out .. | | 70 | 75 |
| 669/72 | .. .. .. .. | *Set of* 4 | 2·10 | 2·50 |

The two designs of each value were printed together, *se-tenant*, in sheets of eight, the background to each horizontal pair forming a composite design.

(Des D. Miller. Litho Questa (54p), B.D.T. (others))

**1992** (6 Feb). *40th Anniv of Queen Elizabeth II's Accession. Horiz designs as T* **143** *of Ascension. Multicoloured. W w* **14** *(sideways). P* 14.

| | | | | |
|---|---|---|---|---|
| 673 | 4p. Gibraltar from North .. .. .. | | 10 | 10 |
| 674 | 20p. R.N. frigate and Gibraltar from South | | 40 | 45 |
| 675 | 24p. Southport Gates .. .. .. .. | | 50 | 55 |
| 676 | 44p. Three portraits of Queen Elizabeth .. | | 90 | 95 |
| 677 | 54p. Queen Elizabeth II .. .. .. | | 1·10 | 1·25 |
| 673/7 | .. .. .. .. | *Set of* 5 | 2·75 | 3·00 |

POSTAGE DUE STAMPS

D 1

D 2

D 3 Gibraltar Coat of Arms

(Typo D.L.R.)

**1956** (1 Dec). *Chalk-surfaced paper. Wmk Mult Script CA. P* 14.

| | | | | | |
|---|---|---|---|---|---|
| D1 | D 1 | 1d. green .. .. .. .. | | 2·00 | 2·75 |
| D2 | | 2d. sepia .. .. .. .. | | 2·50 | 3·75 |
| D3 | | 4d. blue .. .. .. .. | | 3·00 | 5·50 |
| D1/3 | | .. .. .. .. | *Set of* 3 | 6·75 | 11·00 |

**1971** (15 Feb). *As Nos.* D1/3 *but inscr in decimal currency. W w* **12**. *P* 17½ × 18.

| | | | | | |
|---|---|---|---|---|---|
| D4 | D 1 | ½p. green .. .. .. .. | | 55 | 80 |
| D5 | | 1p. sepia .. .. .. .. | | 55 | 70 |
| D6 | | 2p. blue .. .. .. .. | | 65 | 80 |
| D4/6 | | .. .. .. .. | *Set of* 3 | 1·60 | 2·10 |

(Des A. Ryman. Litho Questa)

**1976** (13 Oct). *W w* **14**. *P* 14 × 13½.

| | | | | | |
|---|---|---|---|---|---|
| D 7 | D 2 | 1p. light red-orange .. .. .. | | 15 | 25 |
| D 8 | | 3p. bright blue .. .. .. | | 15 | 40 |
| D 9 | | 5p. orange-vermilion .. .. .. | | 20 | 50 |
| D10 | | 7p. reddish violet .. .. .. | | 25 | 60 |
| D11 | | 10p. greenish slate .. .. .. | | 35 | 60 |
| D12 | | 20p. green .. .. .. | | 70 | 95 |
| D7/12 | | .. .. .. .. | *Set of* 6 | 1·60 | 3·00 |

(Des A. Ryman. Litho Irish Security Stamp Ptg Ltd)

**1984** (2 July). *W w* **14** *(sideways)*. *P* 15 × 14.

| | | | | | |
|---|---|---|---|---|---|
| D13 | D 3 | 1p. black .. .. .. .. | | 10 | 10 |
| D14 | | 3p. vermilion .. .. .. .. | | 10 | 10 |
| D15 | | 5p. ultramarine .. .. .. | | 10 | 15 |
| D16 | | 10p. new blue .. .. .. | | 20 | 25 |
| D17 | | 25p. deep mauve .. .. .. | | 50 | 55 |
| D18 | | 50p. reddish orange .. .. .. | | 1·00 | 1·10 |
| D19 | | £1 blue-green .. .. .. | | 2·00 | 2·10 |
| D13/19 | | .. .. .. .. | *Set of* 7 | 3·50 | 3·75 |

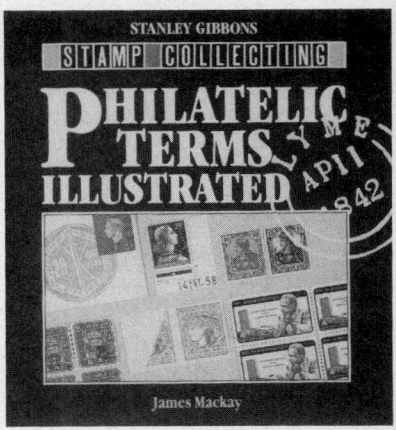

# Gilbert and Ellice Islands

The stamps of NEW ZEALAND, with face values up to 2s., were used at the New Zealand Postal Agencies on Fanning Island (27 November 1902 to 13 February 1939) and Washington Island (1 February 1921 to 30 March 1934).

| PRICES FOR STAMPS ON COVER TO 1945 | |
|---|---|
| Nos. 1/7 | *from* × 5 |
| Nos. 8/11 | *from* × 8 |
| Nos. 12/24 | *from* × 5 |
| Nos. 26/35 | *from* × 6 |
| Nos. 36/9 | *from* × 4 |
| Nos. 40/2 | *from* × 12 |
| Nos. 43/54 | *from* × 4 |
| Nos. D1/8 | *from* × 5 |

## BRITISH PROTECTORATE

GILBERT&ELLICE

PROTECTORATE

(1)

**2** Pandanus Pine

**1911** (1 Jan). *Stamps of Fiji optd with T* **1**. *Wmk Mult Crown CA. Chalk-surfaced paper* (5*d. to* 1*s.*).
**23** ½d. green 4·50 27·00
1d. red 45·00 32·00
**24** 2d. grey 6·00 12·00
**23** 2½d. ultramarine 12·00 23·00
5d. purple and olive-green 30·00 50·00
**24** 6d. dull and bright purple 20·00 38·00
**23** 1s. black/*green* (R.) 17·00 35·00
/7 *Set of* 7 £120 £180
/7 Optd "Specimen" *Set of* 7 £350
The 2d. to 6d. are on special printings which were not issued without overprint.

(Recess D.L.R.)

**911.** *Wmk Mult Crown CA. P* 14.
8 **2** ½d. green 3·25 9·00
9 1d. carmine 2·00 5·50
0 2d. grey 1·50 5·50
1 2½d. blue 1·50 7·50
/11 *Set of* 4 7·50 25·00
/11 Optd "Specimen" *Set of* 4 £140

**3**

WAR TAX

**(5)**

(Typo D.L.R.)

**912–24**. *Wmk Mult Crown CA. Chalk-surfaced paper* (3*d. to* £1). *P* 14.
2 **3** ½d. green 30 3·00
*a. Yellow-green* (1914) 2·50 4·50
3 1d. carmine 65 2·25
*a. Scarlet* (1916) 3·25 8·00
4 2d. greyish slate (1916) 8·00 16·00
5 2½d. bright blue (1916) 1·75 8·50
6 3d. purple/*yellow* (1919) 90 5·50
7 4d. black and red/*yellow* 60 3·50
8 5d. dull purple and sage-green 1·40 7·00
9 6d. dull and bright purple 1·25 7·50
0 1s. black/*green* 1·25 5·50
1 2s. purple and blue/*blue* 14·00 24·00
2 2s. 6d. black and red/*blue* 10·00 23·00
3 5s. green and red/*yellow* 22·00 45·00
4 £1 pur & blk/*red* (Die II) (1924) (S. £350) £800 £1400
2/24 *Set of* 13 £800 £1400
2/23 Optd "Specimen" *Set of* 12 £375

## CROWN COLONY

**918** (June). *Optd with T* **5**.
6 **3** 1d. red (Optd S. £60) 30 3·00

**922–27**. *Wmk Mult Script CA. Chalk-surfaced paper* (10*s.*). *P* 14.
7 **3** ½d. green (1923) 45 1·25
8 1d. violet (1927) 1·25 2·00
9 1½d. scarlet (1924) 75 1·00
0 2d. slate-green 2·50 8·50
5 10s. green and red/*emerald* (1924) £180 £275
7/35 Optd "Specimen" *Set of* 5 £300

**935** (6 May). *Silver Jubilee. As Nos.* 91/4 *of Antigua, but ptd by B.W. P* 11 × 12.
6 1d. ultramarine and grey-black 1·75 5·00
d. Flagstaff on right-hand turret 80·00
e. Double flagstaff 80·00
7 1½d. deep blue and scarlet 1·50 2·50
d. Flagstaff on right-hand turret 75·00
e. Double flagstaff 75·00
8 3d. brown and deep blue 5·00 6·50
d. Flagstaff on right-hand turret £130
e. Double flagstaff £130
39 1s. slate and purple 27·00 24·00
d. Flagstaff on right-hand turret £225
e. Double flagstaff £225
36/9 *Set of* 4 32·00 35·00
36/9 Perf "Specimen" *Set of* 4 £110
For illustrations of plate varieties see Catalogue Introduction.

**1937** (12 May). *Coronation. As Nos.* 95/7 *of Antigua, but ptd by D.L.R. P* 14.
40 1d. violet 30 20
41 1½d. scarlet 40 20
42 3d. bright blue 55 30
40/2 *Set of* 3 1·10 70
40/2 Perf "Specimen" *Set of* 3 65·00

**6** Great Frigate Bird

**7** Pandanus Pine

**8** Canoe crossing Reef

(Recess B.W. (½d., 2d., 2s. 6d.), Waterlow (1d., 5d., 6d., 2s., 5s.), D.L.R. (1½d., 2½d., 3d., 1s.))

**1939** (14 Jan)–**55.** *T* **6/8** *and similar horiz designs. Wmk Mult Script CA* (*sideways on* ½*d.*, 2*d. and* 2*s.* 6*d.*).
43 ½d. slate-blue & blue-green (*p* 11½ × 11) 20 35
44 1d. emerald-green and purple (*p* 12½) 20 70
45 1½d. black and carmine (*p* 13½) 30 75
46 2d. red-brown and black (*p* 11½ × 11) 20 80
47 2½d. black and olive-green (*p* 13½) 20 45
48 3d. black and ultramarine (*p* 13½) 45 80
a. Perf 12. *Black and bright blue* (24.8.55) 40 1·50
49 5d. bright blue and sepia (*p* 12½) 2·25 70
50 6d. olive-green and violet (*p* 12½) 40 40
51 1s. black and turquoise-blue (*p* 13½) 2·50 90
a. Perf 12 (8.5.51) 7·50 10·00
52 2s. bright blue and vermilion (*p* 12½) 11·00 6·50
53 2s. 6d. blue & emerald-green (*p* 11½ × 11) 13·00 11·00
54 5s. scarlet and bright blue (*p* 12½) 14·00 12·00
43/54 *Set of* 12 40·00 32·00
43/54 Perf "Specimen" *Set of* 12 £250
Designs: *As T* **6**—2d. Canoe and boat-house; 2s. 6d. Gilbert Islands canoe. *As T* **7**—5d. Ellice Islands canoe; 6d. Coconut palms; 2s. H.M.C.S. *Nimanoa*; 5s. Coat of arms. *As T* **8**—2½d. Native house; 3d. Seascape; 1s. Cantilever jetty, Ocean Island.

**1946** (16 Dec). *Victory. As Nos.* 110/11 *of Antigua.*
55 1d. purple 15 15
56 3d. blue 15 15
55/6 Perf "Specimen" *Set of* 2 55·00

**1949** (29 Aug). *Royal Silver Wedding. As Nos.* 112/13 *of Antigua.*
57 1d. violet 40 50
58 £1 scarlet 15·00 17·00

**1949** (10 Oct). *75th Anniv of U.P.U. As Nos.* 114/17 *of Antigua.*
59 1d. purple 55 45
60 2d. grey-black 1·25 60
61 3d. deep blue 1·50 75
62 1s. blue 2·25 95
59/62 *Set of* 4 5·00 2·50

**1953** (2 June). *Coronation. As No.* 120 *of Antigua.*
63 2d. black and grey-black 45 1·25

**18** Great Frigate Bird

**19** Loading Phosphate from Cantilever

(Recess B.W. (½d., 2d., 2s. 6d.), Waterlow (1d., 5d., 6d., 2s., 5s.), D.L.R. (2½d., 3d., 1s., 10s.) and after 1962, 1d., 5d.)

**1956** (1 Aug)–**62**. *Designs previously used for King George VI issue; but with portrait of Queen Elizabeth II as in T* **18**. *Wmk Mult Script CA. P* 11½×11 (½*d.*, 2*d.*, 2*s.* 6*d.*), 12½ (1*d.*, 5*d.*, 6*d.*, 2*s.*, 5*s.*) *or* 12 (2½*d.*, 3*d.*, 1*s.*, 10*s.*).
64 ½d. black and deep bright blue 35 60
65 1d. brown-olive and deep violet 40 20
66 2d. bluish green and deep purple 90 1·00
*a. Bluish green and purple* (30.7.62) 4·50 4·25
67 2½d. black and myrtle-green 50 60
68 3d. black and carmine-red 50 45
69 5d. ultramarine and red-orange 6·00 1·50
*a. Ultramarine & brn-orge* (DLR) (30.7.62) 10·00 9·00
70 6d. chestnut and black-brown 55 65
71 1s. black and bronze-green 55 50
72 2s. deep bright blue and sepia 7·00 3·50
73 2s. 6d. scarlet and deep blue 8·50 4·50
74 5s. greenish blue and bluish green 12·00 6·00
75 10s. black and turquoise 21·00 14·00
64/75 *Set of* 12 50·00 30·00
Designs: *Horiz* (30 × 22½ *mm*)—1d. Pandanus pine; 5d. Ellice Islands canoe; 6d. Coconut palms; 2s. H.M.C.S. *Nimanoa*; 5s. Coat of arms. (35½ × 22½ *mm*)—2d. Canoe and boat-house; 2½d. Native house; 3d. Seascape; 1s. Cantilever jetty, Ocean Island; 2s. 6d. Gilbert Islands canoe; 10s. Canoe crossing reef.
See also Nos. 85/6.

(Des R. Turrell (2d.), M. Thoma (2½d), M. A. W. Hook and A. Larkins (1s.). Photo D.L.R.)

**1960** (1 May). *Diamond Jubilee of Phosphate Discovery at Ocean Island. T* **19** *and similar horiz designs. W* w **12.** *P* 12.
76 2d. green and carmine-rose 50 15
77 2½d. black and olive-green 50 15
78 1s. black and deep turquoise 60 25
76/8 *Set of* 3 1·40 50
Designs:—2½d. Phosphate rock; 1s. Phosphate mining.

**1963** (1 Aug). *Freedom from Hunger. As No.* 146 *of Antigua.*
79 10d. ultramarine 3·00 30

**1963** (5 Oct). *Red Cross Centenary. As Nos.* 147/8 *of Antigua.*
80 2d. red and black 1·50 30
81 10d. red and blue 3·50 1·25

**22** D.H. "Heron" Aircraft and Route Map

**24** D.H. "Heron" Aircraft over Tarawa Lagoon

**23** Eastern Reef Heron in Flight

(Des Margaret Barwick. Litho Enschedé)

**1964** (20 July). *First Air Service. W* w **12** (*sideways*, 3*d.*, 3*s.* 7*d.*). *P* 11 × 11½ (1*s.*) *or* 11½ × 11 (*others*).
82 **22** 3d. blue, black and light blue 30 10
83 **23** 1s. light blue, black and deep blue 55 10
84 **24** 3s. 7d. deep green, black and light emerald 80 35
82/4 *Set of* 3 1·50 50

(Recess B.W. (2d.), D.L.R. (6d.))

**1964** (30 Oct)–**65.** *As Nos.* 66 *and* 70 *but wmk* w **12**.
85 2d. bluish green and purple 1·00 1·50
86 6d. chestnut and black-brown (26.4.65)* 1·50 2·25
*Earliest known postmark date.

**1965** (4 June). *I.T.U. Centenary. As Nos.* 166/7 *of Antigua.*
87 3d. red-orange and deep bluish green 20 10
88 2s. 6d. turquoise-blue and light purple 80 20

**25** Maneaba and Gilbertese Man blowing Bu Shell

**26** Gilbertese Women's Dance

(Des V. Whiteley from drawings by Margaret Barwick. Litho B.W.)

**1965** (16 Aug). *Vert designs as T* **25** (½*d. to* 2*s.*) *or horiz designs as T* **26** (3*s.* 7*d. to* £1). *Centres multicoloured. W* w **12.** *P* 12 × 11 (½*d. to* 2*s.*) *or* 11 × 12 (3*s.* 7*d. to* £1).
89 ½d. turquoise-green 10 10
90 1d. deep violet-blue 10 10
91 2d. bistre 10 10
92 3d. rose-red 10 10
93 4d. purple 15 10
94 5d. cerise 20 10
95 6d. turquoise-blue 20 10
96 7d. bistre-brown 25 10
97 1s. bluish violet 40 10
98 1s. 6d. lemon 1·00 65
99 2s. yellow-olive 1·00 1·25
100 3s. 7d. new blue 2·25 65
101 5s. light yellow-olive 2·25 80
102 10s. dull green 4·00 1·25
103 £1 light turquoise-blue 4·50 2·50
89/103 *Set of* 15 15·00 6·50
Designs:—1d. Ellice Islanders reef fishing by flare; 2d. Gilbertese girl weaving head garland; 3d. Gilbertese woman performing Ruoia; 4d. Gilbertese man performing Kamei; 5d. Gilbertese girl drawing water; 6d. Ellice islander performing a Fatele; 7d. Ellice youths performing spear dance; 1s. Gilbertese girl tending Ikaroa Babai plant; 1s. 6d. Ellice islanders dancing a Fatele; 2s. Ellice islanders pounding Pulaka; 5s. Gilbertese boys playing stick game; 10s. Ellice youths beating the box for the Fatele; £1 Coat of arms.

**1965** (25 Oct). *International Co-operation Year. As Nos.* 168/9 *of Antigua.*
104 ½d. reddish purple and turquoise-green 10 10
105 3s. 7d. deep bluish green and lavender 60 15

**1966** (24 Jan). *Churchill Commemoration. As Nos. 170/3 of Antigua.*

106 ½d. new blue . . . . . . . . . . . . 10 10
107 3d. deep green . . . . . . . . . . 30 10
108 3s. brown . . . . . . . . . . . . 65 25
109 3s. 7d. bluish violet . . . . . . . . . . 65 25
106/9 . . . . . . . . . . *Set of* 4 1·50 60

**(New Currency. 100 cents = $1 Australian)**

≡2ᶜ

(40)

**41** H.M.S. *Royalist*

**1966** (14 Feb). *Decimal currency. Nos. 89/103 surch as T* **40**.

110 1 c. on 1d. deep violet-blue . . . . . . . . 10 10
111 2 c. on 2d. bistre . . . . . . . . 10 10
112 3 c. on 3d. rose-red . . . . . . . . 10 10
113 4 c. on ½d. turquoise-green . . . . . . . . 10 10
114 5 c. on 6d. turquoise-blue . . . . . . . . 15 10
115 6 c. on 4d. purple . . . . . . . . 15 10
116 8 c. on 5d. cerise . . . . . . . . 15 10
117 10 c. on 1s. bluish violet . . . . . . . . 15 10
118 15 c. on 7d. bistre-brown . . . . . . . . 80 30
119 20 c. on 1s. 6d. lemon . . . . . . . . 45 25
120 25 c. on 2s. yellow-olive . . . . . . . . 45 20
121 35 c. on 3s. 7d. new blue . . . . . . . . 1·25 20
122 50 c. on 5s. light yellow-olive . . . . . . . . 75 35
123 $1 on 10s. dull green . . . . . . . . 75 40
124 $2 on £1 light turquoise-blue . . . . . . 1·50 1·25
110/24 . . . . . . . . *Set of* 15 6·00 3·00

**1966** (1 July). *World Cup Football Championships. As Nos. 176/7 of Antigua.*

125 3 c. violet, yellow-green, lake & yellow-brn . . 15 10
126 35 c. chocolate, blue-green, lake & yell-brn . . 45 20

**1966** (20 Sept). *Inauguration of W.H.O. Headquarters, Geneva. As Nos. 178/9 of Antigua.*

127 3 c. black, yellow-green and light blue . . 30 10
128 12 c. black, light purple and yellow-brown . . 60 40

**1966** (1 Dec). *20th Anniv of U.N.E.S.C.O. As Nos. 196/8 of Antigua.*

129 5 c. slate-violet, red, yellow and orange . . 60 10
130 10 c. orange-yellow, violet and deep olive . . 80 10
131 20 c. black, bright purple and orange . . . . 1·75 45
129/31 . . . . . . *Set of* 3 2·75 55

(Des V. Whiteley. Photo Harrison)

**1967** (1 Sept). *75th Anniv of the Protectorate. T* **41** *and similar horiz designs. W* w **12**. *P* 14½.

132 3 c. red, blue and myrtle-green . . . . 20 15
133 10 c. multicoloured . . . . . . 10 10
134 35 c. sepia, orange-yellow & dp bluish green . . 25 15
132/4 . . . . . . *Set of* 3 50 30

Designs:—10 c. Trading Post; 35 c. Island family.

**44** Gilbertese Women's Dance

**1968** (1 Jan). *Decimal Currency. Designs as Nos. 89/103 but with values inscr in decimal currency as T* **44**. *W* w **12** *(sideways on horiz designs). P* 12 × 11 *(vert) or* 11 × 12 *(horiz).*

135 1 c. deep violet-blue (as 1d.) . . . . . . 10 10
136 2 c. bistre (as 2d.) . . . . . . . . 15 10
137 3 c. rose-red (as 3d.) . . . . . . . . 15 10
138 4 c. turquoise-green (as ½d.) . . . . . . 15 10
139 5 c. turquoise-blue (as 6d.) . . . . . . 15 10
140 6 c. purple (as 4d.) . . . . . . . . 20 10
141 8 c. cerise (as 5d.) . . . . . . . . 20 10
142 10 c. bluish violet (as 1s.) . . . . . . 20 10
143 15 c. bistre-brown (as 7d.) . . . . . . 50 20
144 20 c. lemon (as 1s. 6d.) . . . . . . 65 15
145 25 c. yellow-olive (as 2s.) . . . . . . 1·25 20
146 35 c. new blue . . . . . . . . 1·50 20
147 50 c. light yellow-olive (as 5s.) . . . . 1·50 1·25
148 $1 dull green (as 10s.) . . . . . . 1·50 2·00
149 $2 light turquoise-blue (as £1) . . . . 4·00 2·00
135/49 . . . . . . *Set of* 15 11·00 5·50

**45** Map of Tarawa Atoll

(Des V. Whiteley. Photo D.L.R.)

**1968** (21 Nov). *25th Anniv of the Battle of Tarawa. T* **45** *and similar designs. Multicoloured. W* w **12** *(sideways). P* 14.

150 3 c. Type **45** . . . . . . . . 15 10
151 10 c. Marines landing . . . . . . . . 15 10
152 15 c. Beach-head assault . . . . . . 20 10
153 35 c. Raising U.S. and British flags . . . . 35 15
150/3 . . . . . . *Set of* 4 75 40

**46** Young Pupil against outline of Abemama Island

**47** "Virgin and Child" in Pacific Setting

(Des J.W. (from original designs by Mrs V. J. Anderson and Miss A. Loveridge). Litho D.L.R.)

**1969** (2 June). *End of Inaugural Year of South Pacific University. T* **46** *and similar horiz designs. W* w **12** *(sideways). P* 12½.

154 3 c. multicoloured . . . . . . . . 10 10
155 10 c. multicoloured . . . . . . . . 10 10
156 35 c. black, brown and grey-green . . . . 15 20
154/6 . . . . . . *Set of* 3 30 30

Designs:—10 c. Boy and girl students and Tarawa atoll; 35 c. University graduate and South Pacific islands.

(Des Jennifer Toombs. Litho B.W.)

**1969** (20 Oct). *Christmas. W* w **12** *(sideways). P* 11½.

157 – 2 c. olive-grn & multicoloured *(shades)* 15 20
158 **47** 10 c. olive-grn & multicoloured *(shades)* 15 10

Design:—2 c. As T **47** but foreground has grass instead of sand.

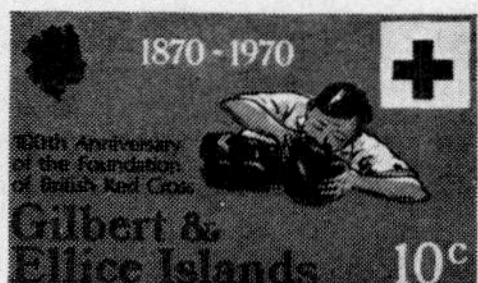


**48** "The Kiss of Life"

(Des Manate Tenang Manate. Litho J.W.)

**1970** (9 Mar*). *Centenary of British Red Cross. W* w **12** *(sideways). P* 14.

159 **48** 10 c. multicoloured . . . . . . 20 10
160 – 15 c. multicoloured . . . . . . 25 10
161 – 35 c. multicoloured . . . . . . 45 20
159/61 . . . . . . *Set of* 3 80 30

Nos. 160/1 are as T **48**, but arranged differently.

*The above were released by the Crown Agents on 2 March, but not sold locally until the 9 March.

**49** Foetus and Patients

(Des Jennifer Toombs. Litho Enschedé)

**1970** (26 June). *25th Anniv of United Nations. T* **49** *and similar horiz designs. W* w **12** *(sideways). P* 12½ × 13.

162 5 c. multicoloured . . . . . . . . 15 10
163 10 c. black, grey and red . . . . . . 15 10
164 15 c. multicoloured . . . . . . . . 20 10
165 35 c. new blue, black and turquoise-green . . 30 15
162/5 . . . . . . *Set of* 4 70 35

Designs:—10 c. Nurse and surgical instruments; 15 c. X-ray plate and technician; 35 c. U.N. emblem and map.

**53** Map of Gilbert Islands

**57** "Child with Halo" (T. Collis)

(Des G. Vasarhelyi. Litho Harrison)

**1970** (1 Sept). *Centenary of Landing in Gilbert Islands by London Missionary Society. T* **53** *and similar designs. W* w **12** *(sideways on vert designs). P* 14½ × 14 *(2 c., 35 c.) or* 14 × 14½ *(others).*

166 2 c. multicoloured . . . . . . . . 15 20
167 10 c. black and pale green . . . . . . 20 10
168 25 c. chestnut and cobalt . . . . . . 20 10
169 35 c. turquoise-blue, black and red . . . . 30 20
166/9 . . . . . . *Set of* 4 75 50

Designs: *Vert*—10 c. Sailing-ship *John Williams III*; 25 c. Rev. S. J. Whitmee. *Horiz*—35 c. M.V. *John Williams VII*.

(Des L. Curtis. Litho Format)

**1970** (3 Oct). *Christmas. Sketches. T* **57** *and similar vert designs. Multicoloured. W* w **12**. *P* 14½.

170 2 c. Type **57** . . . . . . . . . . 10 15
171 10 c. "Sanctuary, Tarawa Cathedral" (Mrs. A. Burroughs) . . . . . . . . 10 10
172 35 c. "Three ships inside star" (Mrs. C. Barnett) 20 20
170/2 . . . . . . *Set of* 3 35 35

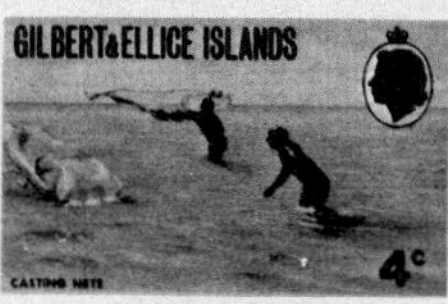


**60** Casting Nets

(Des G. Drummond. Litho Walsall)

**1971** (31 May). *Multicoloured designs as T* **60**. *W* w **12** *(sideways on* 2, 3, 4, 5, 20, 25 *and* 35 *c.). P* 14.

173 1 c. Cutting toddy *(vert)* . . . . . . 10 10
174 2 c. Lagoon fishing . . . . . . . . 15 20
175 3 c. Cleaning pandanus leaves . . . . 15 15
176 4 c. Type **60** . . . . . . . . 20 25
177 5 c. Gilbertese canoe . . . . . . . . 35 15
178 6 c. De-husking coconuts *(vert)* . . . . 30 35
179 8 c. Weaving pandanus fronds *(vert)* . . . . 35 15
180 10 c. Weaving a basket *(vert)* . . . . . . 40 15
181 15 c. Tiger shark and fishermen *(vert)* . . 3·75 1·50
182 20 c. Beating a rolled pandanus leaf . . . . 2·00 90
183 25 c. Loading copra . . . . . . . . 2·00 1·00
184 35 c. Fishing at night . . . . . . . . 2·00 50
185 50 c. Local handicrafts *(vert)* . . . . . . 1·75 1·25
186 $1 Weaving coconut screens *(vert)* . . . . 2·50 2·25
187 $2 Coat of Arms *(vert)* . . . . . . 10·00 10·00
173/87 . . . . . . *Set of* 15 23·00 17·00

See also Nos. 203/7.

**61** House of Representatives

**62** Pacific Nativity Scene

(Des V. Whiteley. Litho J.W.)

**1971** (1 Aug). *New Constitution. T* **61** *and similar horiz design. Multicoloured. W* w **12** *(sideways). P* 14.

188 3 c. Type **61** . . . . . . . . 10 20
189 10 c. Maneaba Betio (Assembly hut) . . . . 20 10

(Des L. Curtis and T. Collis. Litho Questa)

**1971** (1 Oct). *Christmas. T* **62** *and similar vert designs. W* w **12**. *P* 14 × 14½.

190 3 c. black, yellow and ultramarine . . . . 10 10
191 10 c. black, gold and turquoise-blue . . . . 10 10
192 35 c. black, gold and magenta . . . . . . 25 20
190/2 . . . . . . *Set of* 3 40 35

Designs:—10 c. Star and palm leaves; 35 c. Outrigger canoe and star.

**63** Emblem and Young Boys

(Des G. Vasarhelyi. Litho Questa)

**1971** (11 Dec). *25th Anniv of UNICEF. T* **63** *and similar horiz designs, showing UNICEF emblem and young boys. W* w **12** *(sideways). P* 14.

193 3 c. multicoloured . . . . . . . . 10 10
194 10 c. multicoloured . . . . . . . . 15 10
195 35 c. multicoloured . . . . . . . . 45 35
193/5 . . . . . . *Set of* 3 60 45

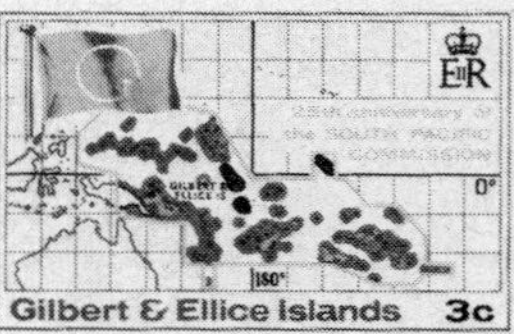


**64** Flag and Map of South Pacific

(Des A. New. Litho Questa)

**1972** (21 Feb). *25th Anniv of South Pacific Commission. T* **64** *and similar horiz designs. Multicoloured. W* w **12**. *P* 13½.

196 3 c. Type **64** . . . . . . . . . . 10 20
197 10 c. Flag and native boats . . . . . . 15 10
198 35 c. Flags of member nations . . . . . . 15 55
196/8 . . . . . . *Set of* 3 30 70

65 *Alveopora* 66 Star of Peace

(Des Sylvia Goaman after original designs by H. Wickison. Litho Questa)

**1972** (26 May). *Coral. T* **65** *and similar horiz designs. Multi-coloured. W w* **12** *(sideways). P* 14.

199 3 c. Type **65** .. .. 25 20
200 10 c. *Euphyllia* .. .. 35 10
201 15 c. *Melithea* .. .. 55 20
202 35 c. *Spongodes* .. .. 1·00 35
199/202 .. *Set of* 4 2·00 75

**1972** (7 Sept)–**73**. *As Nos.* 174, 177/8 *and* 181/2 *but W w* **12** *upright on* 2, 5 *and* 20 *c.; sideways on* 6 *and* 15 *c.*

203 2 c. Lagoon fishing (13.6.73) .. 8·50 8·50
204 5 c. Gilbertese canoe .. .. 4·00 4·00
205 6 c. De-husking coconuts (13.6.73) .. 9·00 9·00
206 15 c. Tiger shark and fishermen .. 6·00 6·00
207 20 c. Beating a rolled pandanus leaf .. 6·00 6·00
203/7 .. *Set of* 5 30·00 30·00

(Des T. Matarena (35 c.), Father Bermond (others); adapted by Jennifer Toombs. Litho Questa)

**1972** (15 Sept). *Christmas. T* **66** *and similar multicoloured designs. W w* **12** *(sideways on* 3 *and* 10 *c.). P* 13½.

208 3 c. Type **66** .. .. 10 10
209 10 c. "The Nativity" .. .. 10 10
210 35 c. Baby in "manger" *(horiz)* .. 20 20
208/10 .. *Set of* 3 30 30

67 Floral Head-dresses

(Des (from photograph by D. Groves) and photo Harrison)

**1972** (20 Nov). *Royal Silver Wedding. Multicoloured; background colour given. W w* **12**. *P* 14 × 14½.

211 **67** 3 c. brown-olive .. .. 10 15
212 35 c. lake-brown .. .. 25 15

68 Funafuti ("The Land of Bananas") 69 Dancer

(Des H. Wickison; adapted J. Cooter. Litho Walsall)

**1973** (5 Mar). *Legends of Island Names (1st series). T* **68** *and similar horiz designs. Multicoloured. W w* **12**. *P* 14½ × 14.

213 3 c. Type **68** .. .. 10 15
214 10 c. Butaritari ("The Smell of the Sea") .. 15 10
215 25 c. Tarawa ("The Centre of the World") .. 25 20
216 35 c. Abemama ("The Land of the Moon") .. 30 20
213/16 .. *Set of* 4 65 50

See also Nos. 252/5.

(Des Sister Juliette (3 c.), R. P. Turner (10 and 35 c.), C. Potts (50 c.); adapted Jennifer Toombs. Litho Questa)

**1973** (24 Sept). *Christmas. T* **69** *and similar vert designs. Multi-coloured. W w* **12** *(sideways). P* 14.

217 3 c. Type **69** .. .. 10 10
218 10 c. Canoe and lagoon .. .. 10 10
219 35 c. Lagoon at evening .. .. 20 10
220 50 c. Map of Christmas Island .. 30 45
217/20 .. *Set of* 4 60 60

**1973** (14 Nov). *Royal Wedding. As Nos.* 165/6 *of Anguilla. Centre multicoloured. W w* **12** *(sideways). P* 13½.

221 3 c. pale green .. .. 10 15
222 35 c. Prussian blue .. .. 20 15

## OMNIBUS ISSUES

Details, together with prices for complete sets, of the various Omnibus issues from the 1935 Silver Jubilee series to date are included in a special section following Zimbabwe at the end of Volume 2.

70 Meteorological Observation

(Des E. S. Cheek; adapted PAD Studio. Litho Questa)

**1973** (26 Nov). *I.M.O./W.M.O. Centenary. T* **70** *and similar horiz designs. Multicoloured. W w* **12**. *P* 14.

223 3 c. Type **70** .. .. 80 30
224 10 c. Island observing-station .. 80 20
225 35 c. Wind-finding radar .. .. 1·50 40
226 50 c. World weather watch stations .. 2·00 1·50
223/6 .. *Set of* 4 4·50 2·25

71 Te Mataaua Crest

(Des J. Cooter. Litho Questa)

**1974** (4 Mar). *Canoe Crests. T* **71** *and similar horiz designs showing sailing craft and the canoe crests given. Multicoloured. W w* **12**. *P* 13½.

227 3 c. Type **71** .. .. 10 10
228 10 c. Te Nimta-wawa .. .. 15 10
229 35 c. Tara-tara-venei-na .. .. 25 10
230 50 c. Te Bou-uoua .. .. 35 50
227/30 .. *Set of* 4 75 65
**MS**231 154 × 130 mm. Nos. 227/30 .. 2·50 5·00

72 £1 Stamp of 1924 and Te Koroba (canoe)

(Des E. S. Cheek; adapted J. Cooter. Litho Questa)

**1974** (10 June). *Centenary of Universal Postal Union. T* **72** *and similar horiz designs. W w* **12**. *P* 14.

232 4 c. multicoloured .. .. 10 10
233 10 c. multicoloured .. .. 10 10
234 25 c. multicoloured .. .. 15 15
235 35 c. light vermilion and black .. 20 20
232/5 .. *Set of* 4 40 35

Designs:—10 c. 5s. stamp of 1939 and sailing vessel *Kiakia*; 25 c. $2 stamp of 1971 and B.A.C. "1-11"; 35 c. U.P.U. emblem.

73 Toy Canoe 74 North Front Entrance, Blenheim Palace

(Des H. Wickison and G. J. Hayward; adapted J. Cooter. Litho Questa)

**1974** (5 Sept). *Christmas. T* **73** *and similar horiz designs. Multi-coloured. W w* **12** *(sideways). P* 14.

236 4 c. Type **73** .. .. 10 10
237 10 c. Toy windmill .. .. 10 10
238 25 c. Coconut "ball" .. .. 15 15
239 35 c. Canoes and constellation Pleiades .. 20 15
236/9 .. *Set of* 4 45 35

(Des J. Cooter. Litho Questa)

**1974** (30 Nov). *Birth Centenary of Sir Winston Churchill. T* **74** *and similar vert designs. Multicoloured. W w* **14**. *P* 14.

240 4 c. Type **74** .. .. 10 10
241 10 c. Churchill painting .. .. 10 10
242 35 c. Churchill's statue, London .. 25 15
240/2 .. *Set of* 3 40 30

75 Barometer Crab

(Des J. Cooter. Litho Questa)

**1975** (27 Jan). *Crabs. T* **75** *and similar horiz designs. Multi-coloured. W w* **12** *(sideways). P* 14.

243 4 c. Type **75** .. .. 25 15
244 10 c. *Ranina ranina* .. .. 35 10
245 25 c. Pelagic Swimming Crab .. 70 25
246 35 c. Ghost Crab .. .. 85 45
243/6 .. *Set of* 4 2·00 80

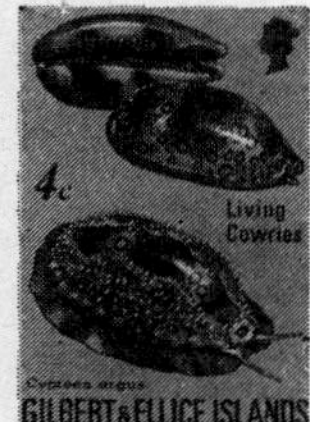

76 Eyed Cowrie 77 "Christ is Born"

(Des E. S. Cheek; adapted J. Cooter. Litho Questa)

**1975** (26 May). *Cowrie Shells. T* **76** *and similar vert designs. Multicoloured. W w* **14**. *P* 14.

247 4 c. Type **76** .. .. 40 15
248 10 c. Sieve Cowrie .. .. 70 10
249 25 c. Mole Cowrie .. .. 1·50 55
250 35 c. Map Cowrie .. .. 1·75 75
247/50 .. *Set of* 4 4·00 1·40
**MS**251 146 × 137 mm. Nos. 247/50 .. 10·00 11·00

(Des J. Cooter. Litho Questa)

**1975** (1 Aug). *Legends of Island Names (2nd series). Horiz designs as T* **68**. *Multicoloured. W w* **12** *(sideways). P* 14.

252 4 c. Beru ("The Bud") .. .. 10 10
253 10 c. Onotoa ("Six Giants") .. .. 10 10
254 25 c. Abaiang ("Land to the North") .. 20 15
255 35 c. Marakei ("Fish-trap floating on eaves") 30 20
252/5 .. *Set of* 4 60 40

(Des C. J. Barnett (4 and 25 c.), Philatelic Advisory Committee (10 c.), P. T. Burangke (35 c.); adapted J. Cooter. Litho Questa)

**1975** (22 Sept). *Christmas. T* **77** *and similar vert designs. Multi-coloured. W w* **14**. *P* 14.

256 4 c. Type **77** .. .. 10 10
257 10 c. Protestant Chapel, Tarawa .. 10 10
258 25 c. Catholic Church, Ocean Island .. 20 40
259 35 c. Fishermen and star .. .. 25 45
256/9 .. *Set of* 4 50 90

### POSTAGE DUE STAMPS

D 1

(Typo B.W.)

**1940** (Aug). *Wmk Mult Script CA. P* 12.

D1 D 1 1d. emerald-green .. .. 6·00 8·00
D2 2d. scarlet .. .. 7·00 9·00
D3 3d. brown .. .. 9·50 12·00
D4 4d. blue .. .. 12·00 20·00
D5 5d. grey-green .. .. 16·00 21·00
D6 6d. purple .. .. 16·00 22·00
D7 1s. violet .. .. 18·00 32·00
D8 1s. 6d. turquoise-green .. .. 35·00 65·00
D1/8 .. *Set of* 8 £110 £170
D1/8 Perf "Specimen" .. *Set of* 8 £160

Stamps for the Gilbert and Ellice Islands were withdrawn on 31 December 1975 when the separate colonies of KIRIBATI (GILBERT ISLANDS) and TUVALU were created.

**Gilbert Islands**
***see* Kiribati**

**Gold Coast**
***see* Ghana**

# Grenada

The earliest recorded postmark of the British administration of Grenada dates from 1784, and, although details of the early period are somewhat sparse, it would appear that the island's postal service was operated as a branch of the British G.P.O. In addition to a Packet Agency at St. George's, the capital, it is known that a further agency existed at Carriacou, in the Grenadines, for a few years after 1842.

Stamps of Great Britain were supplied to the St. George's office from 1858 until the colony assumed responsibility for the postal service in September 1860. Following the take-over the crowned-circle handstamp, No. CC2, was again used until the Grenada adhesives were issued in 1861.

There was no internal postal service before 1861.

For illustrations of the handstamp and postmark types see BRITISH POST OFFICE ABROAD notes, following GREAT BRITAIN.

### CARRIACOU

CROWNED-CIRCLE HANDSTAMPS

CC1 CC 1 CARRIACOU (13.11.1846) . . . . . . . . †

Although recorded in the G.P.O. proof book no example of No. CC1 has been reported used from Grenada.

### ST. GEORGE'S

CROWNED-CIRCLE HANDSTAMPS

CC2 CC 1 GRENADA (R.) (24.10.1850) *Price on cover* £750

*Stamps of* GREAT BRITAIN *cancelled* "A 15" *as Type* **2**

**1858** *to* **1860**.
Z1 1d. rose-red (1857), *perf* 14 . . . . . . . . £325
Z2 2d. blue (1858) (Plate No. 7) . . . . . . . . £600
Z3 4d. rose (1857) . . . . . . . . £200
Z4 6d. lilac (1856) . . . . . . . . £120
Z5 1s. green (1856) . . . . . . . . £600

| PRICES FOR STAMPS ON COVER TO 1945 | |
|---|---|
| Nos. 1/3 | *from* × 10 |
| Nos. 4/13 | *from* × 5 |
| Nos. 14/19 | *from* × 6 |
| Nos. 20/3 | *from* × 8 |
| Nos. 24/7 | *from* × 10 |
| No. 28 | — |
| No. 29 | *from* × 5 |
| Nos. 30/6 | *from* × 8 |
| Nos. 37/9 | *from* × 4 |
| No. 40 | *from* × 20 |
| Nos. 41/7 | *from* × 4 |
| Nos. 48/101 | *from* × 3 |
| Nos. 109/11 | *from* × 5 |
| Nos. 112/48 | *from* × 3 |
| Nos. 149/51 | *from* × 6 |
| Nos. 152/63 | *from* × 2 |
| Nos. D1/3 | *from* × 25 |
| Nos. D4/7 | *from* × 12 |
| Nos. D8/14 | *from* × 20 |

### CROWN COLONY

**PRINTERS.** Types **1** and **5** recess-printed by Perkins, Bacon and Co.

1

2 Small Star

(Eng C. H. Jeens)

**1861** (June)–**62**. *No wmk. Wove paper. (a) Rough perf* 14 *to* 16.
1 1 1d. bluish green . . . . . . £3000 £275
2 1d. green (5.62) . . . . . . 50·00 38·00
a. Imperf between (horiz pair) . .
3 6d. rose (*shades*) . . . . . . £800 90·00
*(b) Perf* 11 *to* 12½
3*a* 1 6d. lake-red (5.62) . . . . . . £750

No. 3*a* is only known unused, and has also been seen on laid paper. (*Price* £1100).

**SIDEWAYS WATERMARK.** W **2/3** when sideways show two points of star downwards.

**1863–71** W **2** (*Small Star*). *Rough perf* 14 *to* 16.
4 1 1d. green (3.64) . . . . . . 60·00 12·00
5 1d. yellowish green . . . . . . 95·00 22·00
6 6d. rose (*shades*) (5.63) . . . . £600 12·00
7 6d. orange-red (*shades*) (5.66) . . £650 12·00
8 6d. dull rose-red (wmk sideways) . . £3000 £225
9 6d. vermilion (5.71) . . . . £650 12·00
a. Double impression . . . . — £1800

The sideways wmk is an identifying aid to the rare shade, No. 8. Normally in this issue the wmk is upright, but it also exists sideways.

**1873** (Jan). W **2** (*Small Star sideways*). *Clean-cut perf* 15.
10 1 1d. deep green . . . . . . 70·00 24·00
a. Bisected diag (on cover) . . . . † £6000
b. Imperf between (pair) . . . . — £3000

3 Large Star

4 Broad-pointed Star

**1873** (Sept)–**74**. W **3** (*Large Star*). *Intermediate perf* 15.
11 1 1d. blue-green (wmk sideways) (2.74) . . 60·00 16·00
a. Double impression . . . .
12 6d. orange-vermilion (upright wmk) . . £600 25·00

5

POSTAGE

ONE SHILLING

(6)

**NOTE.** The early ½d., 2½d., 4d. and 1s. postage stamps were made by surcharging the undenominated Type **5** design.

The surcharges were from two founts of type—one about 1½ mm high, the other 2 mm high—so there are short and tall letters on the same stamp; also the spacing varies considerably, so that the length of the words varies.

Examples of Type **5** with surcharges, but without the "POSTAGE" inscription, are revenue stamps.

**1875** (July). *Surch with T* **6**. W **3**. *P* 14.
13 5 1s. deep mauve (B.) . . . . . . £650 9·00
a. "SHLLIING" . . . . . . — £700
b. "NE SHILLING" . . . . . . — £2500
c. Inverted "S" in "POSTAGE" . . £3500 £500
d. "OSTAGE" . . . . . .

**1875** (Dec.) W **3** (*Large Star, upright*).
14 1 1d. green *to* yellow-green (*p* 14) . . 55·00 5·00
a. Bisected diag (on cover) . . . . † £6000
15 1d. green (*p* 15) . . . . . . £7000 £2000

No. 14 was perforated at Somerset House. 40 sheets of No. 15 were perforated by Perkins, Bacon to replace spoilages and to complete the order.

**1878** (Sept). W **2** (*Small Star, sideways*). *Intermediate perf* 15.
16 1 1d. green . . . . . . £225 25·00
17 6d. deep vermilion . . . . . . £750 25·00
a. Double impression . . . . . . — £1500

**1879** (Dec). W **2** (*Small Star, upright*). *Rough perf* 15.
18 1 1d. pale green (*thin paper*) . . . . £300 17·00
a. Double impression . . . .

**1881** (April). W **2** (*Small Star, sideways*). *Rough perf* 14½.
19 1 1d. green . . . . . . £110 5·50
a. Bisected diag (on cover) . . . . † £6000

POSTAGE POSTAGE POSTAGE

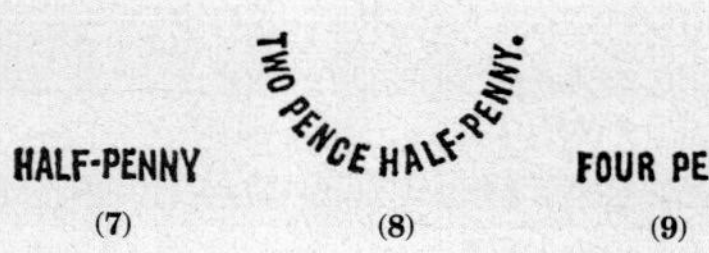


HALF-PENNY FOUR PENCE

(7) (8) (9)

**1881** (April). *Surch with T* **7/9**. *P* 14½. *(a) Wmk Large Star, T* **3**.
20 5 ½d. pale mauve . . . . . . 28·00 10·00
21 ½d. deep mauve . . . . . . 10·00 5·50
a. Imperf (pair) . . . . . . £275
ab. Ditto. "OSTAGE" (R.9/4.) . . £3000
b. Surch double . . . . . . £275
c. "OSTAGE" (R.9/4) . . . . £150 £130
d. No hyphen . . . . . . £140 £110
e. "ALF-PENNY" . . . . . . £2500
f. Wmk upright . . . . . . £550 £250
g. Ditto. "OSTAGE" (R.9/4) . . — £2000
22 2½d. rose-lake . . . . . . 40·00 5·50
a. Imperf (pair) . . . . . . £325
b. Imperf between (horiz pair) . . £1900
c. No stop . . . . . . £170 95·00
d. "PENCF" (R.8/12) . . . . £300 £180
23 4d. blue . . . . . . 90·00 8·00

The watermark is normally *sideways* on the ½d.

*(b) Wmk Broad-pointed Star, T* **4**
24 5 2½d. rose-lake . . . . . . £130 40·00
a. No stop . . . . . . £550 £200
b. "PENCF" (R.8/12) . . . . £650 £250
25 2½d. claret . . . . . . £400 £120
a. No stop . . . . . . £1000 £475
b. "PENCF" (R.8/12) . . . . £1400 £600
25*c* 2½d. deep claret . . . . . . £600 £225
d. No stop . . . . . . £2250 £900
e. "PENCF" (R.8/12) . . . . £2750 £1100
26 4d. blue . . . . . . £225 £180

Examples of the "F" for "E" error on the 2½d. value should not be confused with a somewhat similar broken "E" variety. The latter is always without the stop and shows other damage to the "E". The authentic error always occurs with the full stop shown.

The "no stop" variety occurs on R.3/4, R.6/2, R.8/3 and R.9/7.

ONE PENNY POSTAGE. POSTAGE / POSTAGE

(10) (11) (12)

**1883** (Jan). *Revenue stamps (T* **5** *with green surcharge as in T* **10**) *optd for postage.* W **2** (*Small Star*). *P* 14½.

*(a) Optd horizontally with T* **11**.
27 5 1d. orange . . . . . . £225 45·0
a. "POSTAGE" inverted . . . . £1600 £110
b. "POSTAGE" double . . . . £1200 £110
c. Inverted "S" in "POSTAGE" . . £550 £50
d. Bisected diag (on cover) . . . . † £275

*(b) Optd diagonally with T* **11** *twice on each stamp, the stamp being cut and each half used as* ½d.
28 5 Half of 1d. orange . . . . £550 £30
a. Unsevered pair . . . . £3500 £130
b. "POSTAGE" inverted . . . . — £110

*(c) Optd with T* **12**, *the stamps divided diagonally and each half used as* ½d.
29 5 Half of 1d. orange . . . . £170 £12
a. Unsevered pair . . . . £1200 £60

Nos. 27/9 exist with wmk either upright or sideways.

1d. Revenue stamps are known with "POSTAGE" written by hand, in red or black. These were apparently used, but not officially authorised.

13

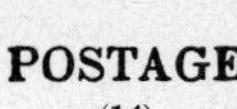
d.
1
POSTAGE.
(14)

15

(Typo D.L.R.)

**1883**. *Wmk Crown CA. P* 14.
30 13 ½d. dull green (February) . . . . 90 6
a. *Tête-bêche* (pair) . . . . 4·00 14·0
31 1d. carmine (February) . . . . 50·00 3·2
a. *Tête-bêche* (pair) . . . . £200 £22
32 2½d. ultramarine (May) . . . . 6·50 5
a. *Tête-bêche* (pair) . . . . 23·00 48·0
33 4d. greyish slate (May) . . . . 4·50 1·7
a. *Tête-bêche* (pair) . . . . 17·00 45·0
34 6d. mauve (May) . . . . 3·50 3·7
a. *Tête-bêche* (pair) . . . . 18·00 55·0
35 8d. grey-brown (February) . . . . 8·00 12·0
a. *Tête-bêche* (pair) . . . . 32·00 75·0
36 1s. pale violet (April) . . . . 90·00 55·0
a. *Tête-bêche* (pair) . . . . £550
30/36 . . . . *Set of* 7 £140 65·0

Types **13** and **15** were printed in rows *tête-bêche* in the sheets.

**1886**. *Revenue stamps (T* **5** *with green surch as T* **10**), *surch with T* **14**. *P* 14. *(a) Wmk Large Star, T* **3**.
37 5 1d. on 1½d. orange (October) . . 30·00 24·0
a. Surch inverted . . . . £225 £22
b. Surch double . . . . £225 £22
c. "THRFE" . . . . £250 £22
d. "PFNCE" . . . . £250 £22
e. "HALH" . . . . £250 £22
f. Bisected diag (on cover) . . . . † £150
38 1d. on 1s. orange (December) . . 30·00 30·0
a. "POSTAGE" (no stop) . . £225
b. "SHILLNG" . . . . £400 £35
c. Wide space (3½ mm) between "ONE" and "SHILLING" . . £400 £35
d. Bisected diag (on cover) . . . . † £150
*(b) Wmk Small Star, T* **2**
39 5 1d. on 4d. orange (November) . . £120 80·0

**1887** (Jan). *Wmk Crown CA. P* 14.
40 15 1d. carmine (Optd S. £50) . . 50 2
a. *Tête-bêche* (pair) . . . . 1·75 16·0

4d. POSTAGE (16) HALF PENNY POSTAGE (17)

**1888** (31 Mar)–**91**. *Revenue stamps (T* **5** *with green surch as T* **10**) *further surcharged.* W **2**. *P* 14½, *and No.* 35.

I. *Surch with T* **16**.
*(a) 4 mm between value and "POSTAGE"*
41 5 4d. on 2s. orange . . . . 26·00 16·00
a. Upright "d" (R. 5/6) . . £375 £275
b. Wide space (2¼ mm) between "TWO" and "SHILLINGS" . . £150 £110
c. First "S" in "SHILLINGS" inverted £300 £300
d. Imperf between (horiz pair)
*(b) 5 mm between value and "POSTAGE"*
42 5 4d. on 2s. orange . . . . 45·00 28·00
a. Wide space . . . . £225 £225
b. "S" inverted . . . . £550 £550

II. *Surch as T* **17** (December 1889)
43 5 ½d. on 2s. orange . . . . 12·00 17·00
a. Surch double . . . . £300 £325
b. Wide space . . . . £110 £120
c. "S" inverted . . . . £275 £275

POSTAGE d. AND 1 REVENUE (18) | POSTAGE AND REVENUE 1d. (19) | 2½d. (20)

III. *Surch with T* **18** (December 1890)

| | | | | |
|---|---|---|---|---|
| 4 | **5** | 1d. on 2s. orange | 70·00 | 70·00 |
| | | a. Surch inverted | £325 | |
| | | b. Wide space | £275 | £275 |
| | | c. "S" inverted | £500 | |

IV. *Surch with T* **19** (January 1891)

| | | | | |
|---|---|---|---|---|
| 5 | **5** | 1d. on 2s. orange | 45·00 | 45·00 |
| | | a. No stop after "1d" (R. 3/8) | £250 | |
| | | b. Wide space | £225 | |
| | | c. "S"" inverted | £450 | |
| 6 | **13** | 1d. on 8d. grey-brown | 9·00 | 11·00 |
| | | a. *Tête-bêche* (pair) | 50·00 | |
| | | b. Surch inverted | £250 | £250 |
| | | c. No stop after "1d" (R. 6/5) | £225 | £225 |

V. *Surch with T* **20** (December 1891)

| | | | | |
|---|---|---|---|---|
| 7 | **13** | 2½d. on 8d. grey-brown (Optd S. £65) | 8·00 | 11·00 |
| | | a. *Tête-bêche* (pair) | 70·00 | |
| | | b. Inverted surcharge | | |
| | | c. Double surcharge | £550 | £650 |
| | | d. Double surcharge, one inverted | £350 | £350 |
| | | e. Treble surcharge | — | £850 |

The wide space between "TWO" and "SHILLINGS" occurs on R. 1/4 and 10/3 of the original 2s. Revenue stamp which was printed in sheets of 120 (12×10).

The surcharges, Types **16/19**, were applied to half sheets as a setting of 60 (12×5).

There are two varieties of fraction in Type **20**, which each occur 30 times in the setting; in one the "1" has horizontal serif and the "2" commences in a ball; in the other the "I" has sloping serif and the "2" is without ball.

See also D4/7.

**21**

**22**

**23** Flagship of Columbus. (Columbus named Grenada "La Concepcion")

(Type D.L.R.)

**1895** (6 Sept)–**99**. *Wmk Crown CA. P* 14.

| | | | | |
|---|---|---|---|---|
| 48 | **22** | ½d. mauve and green (9.99) | 1·25 | 50 |
| 49 | **21** | 1d. mauve and carmine (5.96) | 2·75 | 20 |
| 50 | | 2d. mauve and brown ((9.99) | 28·00 | 32·00 |
| 51 | | 2½d. mauve and ultramarine | 5·00 | 60 |
| 52 | **22** | 3d. mauve and orange | 6·50 | 14·00 |
| 53 | **21** | 6d. mauve and green | 5·00 | 8·00 |
| 54 | **22** | 8d. mauve and black | 12·00 | 24·00 |
| 55 | | 1s. green and orange | 14·00 | 20·00 |
| 48/55 | | *Set of* 8 | 65·00 | 90·00 |
| 48/55 Optd "Specimen" | | *Set of* 8 | £140 | |

(Recess D.L.R.)

**1898** (15 Aug). 400*th Anniv of Discovery of Grenada by Columbus. Wmk Crown CC. P* 14

| | | | | |
|---|---|---|---|---|
| 56 | **23** | 2½d. ultramarine (Optd S. £85) | 10·00 | 5·00 |
| | | a. Bluish paper | 32·00 | 40·00 |

**24**

**25**

(Typo D.L.R.)

**1902.** *Wmk Crown CA. P* 14.

| | | | | |
|---|---|---|---|---|
| 57 | **24** | ½d. dull purple and green | 1·25 | 30 |
| 58 | **25** | 1d. dull purple and carmine | 1·50 | 20 |
| 59 | | 2d. dull purple and brown | 2·25 | 6·50 |
| 60 | | 2½d. dull purple and ultramarine | 2·50 | 1·25 |
| 61 | **24** | 3d. dull purple and orange | 2·25 | 4·00 |
| 62 | **25** | 6d. dull purple and green | 2·00 | 10·00 |
| 63 | **24** | 1s. green and orange | 3·25 | 14·00 |
| 64 | | 2s. green and ultramarine | 14·00 | 38·00 |
| 65 | **25** | 5s. green and carmine | 35·00 | 48·00 |
| 66 | **24** | 10s. green and purple | 95·00 | £170 |
| 57/66 | | *Set of* 10 | £140 | £250 |
| 57/66 Optd "Specimen" | | *Set of* 10 | £200 | |

**1904–6.** *Wmk Mult Crown CA. Ordinary paper. P* 14.

| | | | | |
|---|---|---|---|---|
| 67 | **24** | ½d. purple and green (1905) | 14·00 | 18·00 |
| 68 | **25** | 1d. purple and carmine | 8·00 | 2·50 |
| 69 | | 2d. purple and brown (1905) | 38·00 | 55·00 |
| 70 | | 2½d. purple and ultramarine (1905) | 38·00 | 55·00 |
| 71 | **24** | 3d. purple and orange (1905) | 2·00 | 3·50 |
| | | a. Chalk-surfaced paper | 2·25 | 4·50 |
| 72 | **25** | 6d. purple and green (1906) | 2·50 | 3·75 |
| | | a. Chalk-surfaced paper | 3·00 | 7·50 |
| 73 | **24** | 1s. green and orange (1905) | 6·00 | 18·00 |
| 74 | | 2s. green and ultramarine (1906) | 22·00 | 50·00 |
| | | a. Chalk-surfaced paper | 22·00 | 55·00 |
| 75 | **25** | 5s. green and carmine (1906) | 45·00 | 65·00 |
| 76 | **24** | 10s. green and purple (1906) | £130 | £225 |
| 67/76 | | *Set of* 10 | £275 | £425 |

**26** Badge of the Colony **27**

(Recess D.L.R.)

**1906.** *Wmk Mult Crown CA. P*14.

| | | | | |
|---|---|---|---|---|
| 77 | **26** | ½d. green | 70 | 20 |
| 78 | | 1d. carmine | 50 | 10 |
| 79 | | 2d. orange | 1·50 | 3·00 |
| 80 | | 2½d. blue | 3·00 | 1·25 |
| | | *a. Ultramarine* | 7·00 | 3·50 |

(Typo D.L.R.)

**1908.** *Wmk Crown CA. Chalk-surfaced paper. P* 14.

| | | | | |
|---|---|---|---|---|
| 82 | **27** | 1s. black/*green* | 15·00 | 23·00 |
| 83 | | 10s. green and red/*green* | 70·00 | £130 |

**1908–11.** *Wmk Mult Crown CA. Chalk-surfaced paper. P* 14.

| | | | | |
|---|---|---|---|---|
| 84 | **27** | 3d. dull purple/*yellow* | 1·50 | 1·75 |
| 85 | | 6d. dull purple and purple | 14·00 | 23·00 |
| 86 | | 1s. black/*green* (1911) | 2·50 | 3·75 |
| 87 | | 2s. blue and purple/*blue* | 12·00 | 12·00 |
| 88 | | 5s. green and red/*yellow* | 42·00 | 55·00 |
| 77/88 | | *Set of* 11 | £140 | £225 |
| 77/80, 82/5, 87/8 Optd "Specimen" | | *Set of* 10 | £200 | |

**28**

WAR TAX (29) | WAR TAX (30

(Typo D.L.R.)

**1913** (3 Jan)–**22**. *Wmk Mult Crown CA. Chalk-surfaced paper* (3*d. to* 10*s.*). *P* 14.

| | | | | |
|---|---|---|---|---|
| 89 | **28** | ½d. yellow-green | 35 | 70 |
| 90 | | ½d. green | 35 | 40 |
| 91 | | 1d. red | 70 | 15 |
| 92 | | 1d. scarlet (1916) | 70 | 35 |
| 93 | | 2d. orange | 45 | 25 |
| 94 | | 2½d. bright blue | 80 | 1·75 |
| 95 | | 2½d. dull blue (1920) | 3·00 | 3·75 |
| 96 | | 3d. purple/*yellow* | 40 | 85 |
| | | *a. White back* (3.14) (Optd S. £30) | 30 | 1·50 |
| | | *b. On lemon* (1917) | 2·00 | 7·00 |
| | | *c. On pale yellow* (1921) | 4·00 | 17·00 |
| 97 | | 6d. dull and bright purple | 90 | 6·50 |
| 98 | | 1s. black/*green* | 85 | 5·00 |
| | | *a. White back* (3.14) (Optd S. £30) | 70 | 4·50 |
| | | *b. On blue-green, olive back* (1917) | 42·00 | 60·00 |
| | | *c. On emerald surface* | 1·25 | 6·50 |
| | | *d. On emerald back* (6.22) (Optd S. £30) | 85 | 6·50 |
| 99 | | 2s. purple and blue/*blue* | 3·00 | 8·50 |
| 100 | | 5s. green and red/*yellow* | 12·00 | 40·00 |
| | | *a. On pale yellow* (1921) (Optd S. £45) | 20·00 | 55·00 |
| 101 | | 10s. green and red/*green* | 42·00 | 55·00 |
| | | *a. On emerald back* (6.22) (Optd S. £55) | 50·00 | 90·00 |
| 89/101 | | *Set of* 10 | 55·00 | £110 |
| 89/101 Optd "Specimen" | | *Set of* 10 | £150 | |
| 98 Optd in black instead of red | | | 30·00 | |

**1916** (1 June). *Optd by Govt Press, St. George's. With T* **29**.

| | | | | |
|---|---|---|---|---|
| 109 | **28** | 1d. red (*shades*) (H/S S. £50) | 2·00 | 2·00 |
| | | a. Opt inverted | £275 | |
| | | b. "T△X" | 50·00 | 70·00 |

A small "A" in "WAR", 2 mm high is found on Nos. 29, 38 and 48 of the setting of 60 and a very small "A" in "TAX", 1½ mm high, on No. 11. Value about twice normal. The normal "A" is 2¼ mm high.

No. 109b is on No. 56 of the setting.

**1916** (1 Sept)–**18.** *Optd with T* **30** *in London.*

| | | | | |
|---|---|---|---|---|
| 111 | **28** | 1d. scarlet | 15 | 20 |
| | | *a. Carmine-red/bluish* (5.18) | 2·50 | 2·25 |
| 111 Optd "Specimen" | | | 40·00 | |

**1921–32.** *Wmk Mult Script CA. Chalk-surfaced paper* (3*d.* (*No.* 122) *to* 10*s.*) *P* 14.

| | | | | |
|---|---|---|---|---|
| 112 | **28** | ½d. green | 45 | 15 |
| 113 | | 1d. carmine-red | 30 | 20 |
| 114 | | 1d. brown (1923) | 40 | 15 |
| 115 | | 1½d. rose-red (6.22) | 1·00 | 60 |
| 116 | | 2d. orange | 50 | 15 |
| 117 | | 2d. grey (1926) | 2·00 | 1·75 |
| 117*a* | | 2½d. dull blue | 1·00 | 65 |
| 118 | | 2½d. grey (6.22) | 75 | 5·00 |
| 119 | | 2½d. bright blue (1926) | 1·25 | 2·50 |
| 120 | | 2½d. ultramarine (1931) | 3·75 | 6·50 |
| 120*a* | | 2½d. chalky blue and blue (1932) | 32·00 | 45·00 |
| 121 | | 3d. bright blue (6.22) | 1·00 | 5·00 |
| 122 | | 3d. purple/*yellow* (1926) | 1·00 | 3·50 |
| 123 | | 4d. black and red/*yellow* (1926) | 50 | 3·25 |
| 124 | | 5d. dull purple & sage-green (27.12.22) | 85 | 3·50 |
| 125 | | 6d. dull and bright purple | 1·10 | 9·00 |
| 126 | | 6d. black and carmine (1926) | 1·75 | 2·50 |
| 127 | | 9d. dull purple and black (27.12.22) | 2·25 | 6·00 |
| 128 | | 1s. black/*emerald* (1923) | 2·25 | 20·00 |
| 129 | | 1s. chestnut (1926) | 3·00 | 12·00 |
| 130 | | 2s. purple and blue/*blue* (1922) | 5·00 | 8·00 |
| 131 | | 2s. 6d. black and carmine/*blue* (1929) | 6·00 | 14·00 |
| 132 | | 3s. green and violet (27.12.22) | 6·00 | 24·00 |
| 133 | | 5s. green and red/*pale yellow* (1923) | 12·00 | 26·00 |
| 134 | | 10s. green and red/*emerald* (1923) | 48·00 | 95·00 |
| 112/19, 121/34 | | *Set of* 22 | 85·00 | £225 |
| 112/34 Optd/Perf "Specimen" | | *Set of* 23 | £375 | |

**31** Grand Anse Beach

**32** Badge of the Colony

**33** Grand Etang

**34** St. George's

(Recess Waterlow)

**1934** (23 Oct)–**36**. *Wmk Mult Script CA* (*sideways on T* **32**). *P* 12½.

| | | | | |
|---|---|---|---|---|
| 135 | **31** | ½d. green | 15 | 40 |
| | | a. Perf 12½ × 13½ (1936) | 2·25 | 22·00 |
| 136 | **32** | 1d. black and sepia | 70 | 1·25 |
| | | a. Perf 13½ × 12½ (1936) | 65 | 35 |
| 137 | **33** | 1½d. black and scarlet | 2·50 | 1·25 |
| | | a. Perf 12½ × 13½ (1936) | 1·25 | 55 |
| 138 | **32** | 2d. black and orange | 70 | 40 |
| 139 | **34** | 2½d. blue | 30 | 30 |
| 140 | **32** | 3d. black and olive-green | 35 | 90 |
| 141 | | 6d. black and purple | 70 | 1·10 |
| 142 | | 1s. black and brown | 80 | 2·50 |
| 143 | | 2s. 6d. black and ultramarine | 6·50 | 15·00 |
| 144 | | 5s. black and violet | 26·00 | 32·00 |
| 135/144 | | *Set of* 10 | 35·00 | 48·00 |
| 135/44 Perf "Specimen" | | *Set of* 10 | £160 | |

**1935** (6 May). *Silver Jubilee. As T* **13** *of Antigua but ptd by Waterlow. P* 11 × 12.

| | | | |
|---|---|---|---|
| 145 | ½d. black and green | 30 | 20 |
| | j. Kite and vertical log | 22·00 | |
| | k. Kite and horizontal log | 22·00 | |
| 146 | 1d. ultramarine and grey | 40 | 60 |
| | k. Kite and horizontal log | 27·00 | |
| 147 | 1½d. deep blue and scarlet | 50 | 45 |
| | k. Kite and horizontal log | 35·00 | |
| 148 | 1s. slate and purple | 4·00 | 8·75 |
| | k. Kite and horizontal log | 75·00 | |
| 145/8 | *Set of* 4 | 4·75 | 9·00 |
| 145/8 Perf "Specimen" | *Set of* 4 | 70·00 | |

For illustrations of plate varieties see Catalogue Introduction.

**1937** (12 May). *Coronation. As Nos.* 95/7 *of Antigua. P* 11x11½.

| | | | |
|---|---|---|---|
| 149 | 1d. violet | 20 | 15 |
| 150 | 1½d. carmine | 20 | 15 |
| 151 | 2½d. blue | 50 | 30 |
| 149/51 | *Set of* 3 | 80 | 55 |
| 149/51 Perf "Specimen" | *Set of* 3 | 50·00 | |

**35** King George VI

(Photo Harrison)

**1937** (12 July)–**50**. *Wmk Mult Script CA. Chalk-surfaced paper. P* 15×14.

| | | | | |
|---|---|---|---|---|
| 152 | **35** | ¼d. brown | 15 | 10 |
| | | a. Ordinary paper (11.42) | 15 | 15 |
| | | b. Ordinary paper. *Chocolate* (1.45) | 10 | 10 |
| | | c. Chalk-surfaced paper. *Chocolate* (8.50) | 15 | 30 |

The ordinary paper is thick, smooth and opaque.

**36** Grand Anse Beach

**40** Badge of the Colony

Colon flaw (R. 5/8. Corrected on ptg of Nov 1950)

(Recess D.L.R. (10s.), Waterlow (others))

**1938** (16 Mar)–**50**. *As T* **31/4** *(but portrait of King George VI as in T* **36**) *and T* **40**. *Wmk Mult Script CA (sideways on T* **32**). *P* 12½ *or* 12 × 13 (10s.).

153 **36** ½d. yellow-green .. .. .. .. 3·50 55
a. Perf 12½ × 13½ (1938) .. .. 2·75 80
b. Perf 12½. *Blue-green* .. .. 15 40
ba. Perf 12½ × 13½. *Blue-green* .. 2·50 3·25
154 **32** 1d. black and sepia .. .. .. 20 20
a. Perf 13½ × 12½ (1938) .. .. 30 10
155 **33** 1½d. black and scarlet .. .. .. 40 10
a. Perf 12½ × 13½ (1938) .. .. 2·25 20
156 **32** 2d. black and orange .. .. .. 20 20
a. Perf 13½ × 12½ (1938) .. .. 50 20
157 **34** 2½d. bright blue .. .. .. .. 20 15
a. Perf 12½ × 13½ (?March 1950) .. £3500 £200
158 **32** 3d. black and olive-green .. .. 5·50 1·25
a. Perf 13½ × 12½ (16.3.38) .. .. 3·75 70
ab. Perf 13½ × 12½. *Black and brown-olive* (1942) .. .. .. .. 30 70
b. Perf 12½. *Black and brown-olive* (16.8.50) .. .. .. .. 30 90
ba. Colon flaw .. .. .. .. 17·00
159 6d. black and purple .. .. .. 45 20
a. Perf 13½ × 12½ (1942) .. .. 40 30
160 1s. black and brown .. .. .. 40 30
a. Perf 13½ × 12½ (1941) .. .. 90 60
161 2s. black and ultramarine .. .. 7·50 1·00
a. Perf 13½ × 12½ (1941) .. .. 10·00 1·00
162 5s. black and violet .. .. .. 2·00 1·50
a. Perf 13½ × 12½ (1947) .. .. 2·50 5·50
163 **40** 10s. steel blue and carmine *(narrow)* (*p* 12 × 13) .. .. .. .. 42·00 8·00
a. Perf 14. *Steel blue and bright carmine (narrow)* .. .. .. 95·00 42·00
b. Perf 14. *Slate-blue and bright carmine (narrow)* (1943) .. .. £110 75·00
c. Perf 12. *Slate-blue and bright carmine (narrow)* (1943) .. .. £350 £425
d. Perf 14. *Slate-blue and carmine-lake (wide)* (1944) .. .. .. 55·00 6·00
e. Perf 14. *Blue-black and carmine (narrow)* (1943) .. .. .. 20·00 7·00
f. Perf 14. *Blue-black and bright carmine (wide)* (1947) .. .. 20·00 22·00
152/163b .. .. .. .. *Set of* 12 28·00 9·50
152/63 Perf "Specimen" .. .. *Set of* 12 £225

In the earlier printings of the 10s. the paper was dampened before printing and the subsequent shrinkage produced narrow frames 23½ to 23¾ mm wide. Later printings were made on dry paper producing wide frames 24¼ mm wide.

No. 163a is one of the earlier printings line perf 13.8 × 14.1.

No. 163b is line-perf 14.1.

Nos. 163b/c show a blurred centre caused by the use of a worn plate.

Nos. 163a and 163b may be found with gum more or less yellow due to local climatic conditions.

**1946** (25 Sept). *Victory. As Nos.* 110/11 *of Antigua.*

164 1½d. carmine .. .. .. .. .. 10 10
165 3½d. blue .. .. .. .. .. 10 10
164/5 Perf "Specimen" .. .. *Set of* 2 50·00

**1948** (27 Oct). *Royal Silver Wedding. As Nos.* 112/13 *of Antigua.*

166 1½d. scarlet .. .. .. .. .. 10 10
167 10s. slate-green .. .. .. .. 6·00 12·00

**(New Currency. 100 cents = 1 West Indian dollar)**

**1949** (10 Oct). *75th Anniv of Universal Postal Union. As Nos.* 114/17 *of Antigua.*

168 5 c. ultramarine .. .. .. .. 15 10
169 6 c. olive .. .. .. .. .. 25 30
170 12 c. magenta .. .. .. .. 25 20
171 24 c. red-brown .. .. .. .. 25 20
168/71 .. .. .. .. *Set of* 4 80 70

**41** King George VI  **42** Badge of the Colony  **43** Badge of the Colony

(Recess B.W. (T **41**), D.L.R. (others))

**1951** (8 Jan). *Wmk Mult Script CA. P* 11½ (*T* **41**), 11½ × 12½ (*T* **42**), *and* 11½ × 13 (*T* **43**).

172 **41** ½ c. black and red-brown .. .. 15 1·00
173 1 c. black and emerald-green .. .. 15 25
174 2 c. black and brown .. .. .. 15 25
175 3 c. black and rose-carmine .. .. 15 10
176 4 c. black and orange .. .. .. 35 40
177 5 c. black and violet .. .. .. 20 10
178 6 c. black and olive .. .. .. 30 50
179 7 c. black and light blue .. .. 1·00 10
180 12 c. black and purple .. .. .. 1·50 30
181 **42** 25 c. black and sepia .. .. .. 2·25 50
182 50 c. black and blue .. .. .. 3·50 40
183 $1.50, black and yellow-orange .. 7·50 3·00
184 **43** $2.50, slate-blue and carmine .. 4·75 3·50
172/184 .. .. .. .. *Set of* 13 20·00 9·00

**1951** (16 Feb). *Inauguration of B.W.I. University College. As Nos.* 118/19 *of Antigua.*

185 3 c. black and carmine .. .. .. 15 10
186 6 c. black and olive .. .. .. .. 15 10

**NEW CONSTITUTION**

**1951**

(44)

**1951** (21 Sept). *New Constitution. Optd with T* **44** *by B.W.*

187 **41** 3 c. black and rose-carmine .. .. 10 10
188 4 c. black and orange .. .. .. 10 10
189 5 c. black and violet (R.) .. .. 10 10
190 12 c. black and purple .. .. .. 10 15
187/90 .. .. .. .. *Set of* 4 30 40

**1953** (3 June). *Coronation. As No.* 120 *of Antigua.*

191 3 c. black and carmine-red .. .. .. 10 10

**45** Queen Elizabeth II  **46** Badge of the Colony  **47** Badge of the Colony

(Recess B.W. (T **45**), D.L.R. (T **46/7**))

**1953** (15 June)–**59**. *Wmk Mult Script CA. P* 11½ (*T* **45**), 11½ × 12½ (*T* **46**), *or* 11½ × 13 (*T* **47**).

192 **45** ½ c. black and brown (28.12.53) .. 10 10
193 1 c. black and deep emerald .. .. 10 10
194 2 c. black and sepia (15.9.53) .. .. 20 10
195 3 c. black and carmine-red (22.2.54) .. 10 10
196 4 c. black and brown-orange (22.2.54) .. 10 10
197 5 c. black and deep violet (22.2.54) .. 10 10
198 6 c. black and olive-green (28.12.53) .. 35 15
199 7 c. black and blue (6.6.55) .. .. 60 10
200 12 c. black and reddish purple .. .. 20 10
201 **46** 25 c. black and sepia (10.1.55) .. .. 55 20
202 50 c. black and deep blue (2.12.55) .. 3·75 40
203 $1.50, black & brown-orange (2.12.55) 8·00 5·50
204 **47** $2.50, slate-blue & carmine (16.11.59) 12·00 3·25
192/204 .. .. .. *Set of* 13 23·00 9·00

On 23 December 1965, No. 203 was issued surcharged "2" but this was intended for fiscal and revenue purposes and it was not authorised to be used postally, although some are known to have passed through the mail.

**1958** (22 Apr). *Inauguration of British Caribbean Federation. As Nos.* 135/7 *of Antigua.*

205 3 c. deep green .. .. .. .. 15 10
206 6 c. blue .. .. .. .. .. 20 20
207 12 c. scarlet .. .. .. .. 30 10
205/7 .. .. .. .. *Set of* 3 60 30

**48** Queen Victoria, Queen Elizabeth II, Mail Van and Post Office, St. George's

(Photo Harrison)

**1961** (1 June). *Grenada Stamp Centenary. T* **48** *and similar horiz designs. W w* **12**. *P* 14½ × 14.

208 3 c. crimson and black .. .. .. 10 10
209 8 c. bright blue and orange .. .. 30 15
210 25 c. lake and blue .. .. .. 30 15
208/10 .. .. .. .. *Set of* 3 60 30

Designs:—8 c. Queen Victoria, Queen Elizabeth II and flagship of Columbus; 25 c. Queen Victoria, Queen Elizabeth II, R.M.S.P. *Solent* and "Dakota" aircraft.

**1963** (4 June). *Freedom from Hunger. As No.* 146 *of Antigua.*

211 8 c. bluish green .. .. .. .. 30 15

**1963** (2 Sept). *Red Cross Centenary. As Nos.* 147/8 *of Antigua.*

212 3 c. red and black .. .. .. .. 10 15
213 25 c. red and blue .. .. .. .. 20 15

**1964** (12 May)–**66**. *As Nos.* 194/8, 201/1, *but wmk* w **12**.

214 **45** 2 c. black and sepia .. .. .. 10 10
215 3 c. black and carmine-red .. .. 15 10
216 4 c. black and brown-orange .. .. 15 20
217 5 c. black and deep violet .. .. 15 10
218 6 c. black and olive-green (4.1.66) .. £160 55·00
219 12 c. black and reddish purple .. .. 20 10
220 **46** 25 c. black and sepia .. .. .. 80 15
214/20 .. .. .. *Set of* 7 £160 55·00

**1965** (17 May). *I.T.U. Centenary. As Nos.* 166/7 *of Antigua.*

221 2 c. red-orange and yellow-olive .. .. 10 10
222 50 c. lemon and light red .. .. .. 25 20

**1965** (25 Oct). *International Co-operation Year. As Nos.* 168/9 *of Antigua*

223 1 c. reddish purple and turquoise-green .. 10 15
224 25 c. deep bluish green and lavender .. 20 15

**1966** (24 Jan). *Churchill Commemoration. As Nos.* 170/3 *of Antigua.*

225 1 c. new blue .. .. .. .. .. 10 15
226 3 c. deep green .. .. .. .. 10 15
227 25 c. brown .. .. .. .. .. 15 10
228 35 c. bluish violet .. .. .. .. 25 15
225/8 .. .. .. .. *Set of* 4 45 40

**1966** (4 Feb). *Royal Visit. As Nos.* 174/5 *of Antigua.*

229 3 c. black and ultramarine .. .. .. 15 15
230 35 c. black and magenta .. .. .. 40 15

**52** Hillsborough, Carriacou  **53** Badge of the Colony

**54** Queen Elizabeth II  **55** Map of Grenada

(Des V. Whiteley. Photo Harrison)

**1966** (1 Apr). *Horiz designs as T* **52**, *and T* **53/5**. *Multicoloured W* w **12**. *P* 14½ ($1, $2, $3) *or* 14½ × 13½ *(others).*

231 1 c. Type **52** .. .. .. .. .. 10 10
232 2 c. Bougainvillea .. .. .. .. 10 10
233 3 c. Flamboyant plant .. .. .. 10 10
234 5 c. Levera beach .. .. .. .. 10 10
235 6 c. Carenage, St. George's .. .. .. 15 10
236 8 c. Annandale Falls .. .. .. .. 15 10
237 10 c. Cocoa pods .. .. .. .. 10 10
238 12 c. Inner Harbour .. .. .. .. 10 10
239 15 c. Nutmeg .. .. .. .. .. 15 10
240 25 c. St. George's .. .. .. .. 20 10
241 35 c. Grand Anse beach .. .. .. 30 10
242 50 c. Bananas .. .. .. .. .. 80 80
243 $1 Type **53** .. .. .. .. .. 2·75 1·00
244 $2 Type **54** .. .. .. .. .. 3·75 2·25
245 $3 Type **55** .. .. .. .. .. 4·00 6·50
231/45 .. .. .. .. *Set of* 15 11·00 10·00

**1966** (1 July). *World Cup Football Championships. As Nos.* 176/7 *of Antigua.*

246 5 c. violet, yellow-green, lake & yellow-brn 10 10
247 50 c. chocolate, blue-green, lake & yelllow-brn 25 20

**1966** (20 Sept). *Inauguration of W.H.O. Headquarters, Geneva. As Nos.* 178/9 *of Antigua.*

248 8 c. black, yellow-green and light blue .. 10 10
249 25 c. black, light purple and yellow-brown .. 25 20

**1966** (1 Dec). *20th Anniv of U.N.E.S.C.O. As Nos.* 196/8 *of Antigua.*

250 2 c. slate-violet, red, yellow and orange .. 10 10
251 15 c. orange-yellow, violet and deep olive .. 15 10
252 50 c. black, bright purple and orange .. .. 30 25
250/2 .. .. .. .. *Set of* 3 45 30

**ASSOCIATED STATEHOOD**

ASSOCIATED STATEHOOD 1967

(67)

expo67 MONTREAL CANADA 1c

(68)

**1967** (3 Mar). *Statehood. Nos.* 232/3, 236 *and* 240 *optd with T* **67**, *in silver*

253 2 c. Bougainvillea .. .. .. .. 10 15
254 3 c. Flamboyant plant .. .. .. 10 10
255 8 c. Annandale Falls .. .. .. .. 15 10
256 25 c. St. George's .. .. .. .. 15 15
253/6 .. .. .. .. *Set of* 4 30 30

**1967** (June). *World Fair, Montreal. Nos.* 232, 237, 239 *and* 243/4 *surch as T* **68** *or optd with "Expo" emblem only.*

257 1 c. on 15 c. Nutmeg .. .. .. 10 15
a. Surch and opt albino .. .. .. 14·00
258 2 c. Bougainvillea .. .. .. .. 10 15
259 3 c. on 10 c. Cocoa pods .. .. .. 10 15
260 $1 Type **53** .. .. .. .. .. 30 20
261 $2 Type **54** .. .. .. .. .. 45 25
257/61 .. .. .. .. *Set of* 5 70 80

(69)

70 Kennedy and Local Flower

**1967** (Oct). *Statehood. Nos. 231/45 optd with T* **69**.

| No. | | Description | Mint | Used |
|---|---|---|---|---|
| 262 | 1 c. | Type **52** | 10 | 10 |
| 263 | 2 c. | Bougainvillea | 10 | 10 |
| 264 | 3 c. | Flamboyant plant | 10 | 10 |
| 265 | 5 c. | Levera beach | 10 | 10 |
| 266 | 6 c. | Carenage, St. George's | 10 | 10 |
| 267 | 8 c. | Annandale Falls | 10 | 10 |
| 268 | 10 c. | Cocoa pods | 10 | 10 |
| 269 | 12 c. | Inner Harbour | 10 | 10 |
| 270 | 15 c. | Nutmeg | 15 | 10 |
| 271 | 25 c. | St. George's | 20 | 10 |
| 272 | 35 c. | Grand Anse beach | 55 | 10 |
| 273 | 50 c. | Bananas | 70 | 20 |
| 274 | $1 | Type **53** | 70 | 60 |
| 275 | $2 | Type **54** | 1·25 | 2·25 |
| 276 | $3 | Type **55** | 2·25 | 2·50 |
| 262/76 | | *Set of* 15 | 5·50 | 5·50 |

See also No. 295

(Des M. Shamir. Photo Harrison)

**1968** (13 Jan). *50th Birth Anniv of President Kennedy. T* **70** *and similar horiz designs. Multicoloured. P* 14½ × 14.

| No. | | Description | Mint | Used |
|---|---|---|---|---|
| 277 | 1 c. | Type **70** | 10 | 15 |
| 278 | 15 c. | Type **70** | 10 | 10 |
| 279 | 25 c. | Kennedy and strelitzia | 10 | 10 |
| 280 | 35 c. | Kennedy and roses | 10 | 10 |
| 281 | 50 c. | As 25 c. | 15 | 15 |
| 282 | $1 | As 35 c. | 25 | 30 |
| 277/82 | | *Set of* 6 | 55 | 55 |

73 Scout Bugler

76 "Near Antibes"

(Des K. Plowitz. Photo Govt Printer, Israel)

**1968** (17 Feb). *World Scout Jamboree, Idaho. T* **73** *and similar vert designs. Multicoloured. P* 13 × 13½.

| No. | | Description | Mint | Used |
|---|---|---|---|---|
| 283 | 1 c. | Type **73** | 10 | 10 |
| 284 | 2 c. | Scouts camping | 10 | 10 |
| 285 | 3 c. | Lord Baden-Powell | 10 | 10 |
| 286 | 35 c. | Type **73** | 20 | 10 |
| 287 | 50 c. | As 2 c. | 25 | 20 |
| 288 | $1 | As 3 c. | 40 | 30 |
| 283/8 | | *Set of* 6 | 85 | 55 |

(Des G. Vasarhelyi. Photo Harrison)

**1968** (23 Mar). *Paintings by Sir Winston Churchill. T* **76** *and similar horiz designs. Multicoloured. P* 14 × 14½.

| No. | | Description | Mint | Used |
|---|---|---|---|---|
| 289 | 10 c. | Type **76** | 10 | 10 |
| 290 | 12 c. | "The Mediterranean" | 10 | 10 |
| 291 | 15 c. | "St. Jean Cap Ferratt" | 15 | 10 |
| 292 | 25 c. | Type **76** | 15 | 10 |
| 293 | 35 c. | As 15 c. | 20 | 10 |
| 294 | 50 c. | Sir Winston painting | 30 | 25 |
| 289/94 | | *Set of* 6 | 85 | 45 |

CHILDREN NEED MILK

$5

(80)

2cts. + 3cts.

(81)

CHILDREN NEED MILK

1c. + 3cts.

(82)

**1968** (18 May). *No. 275 surch with T* **80**

| No. | Type | Description | Mint | Used |
|---|---|---|---|---|
| 295 | 54 | $5 on $2 multicoloured | 1·50 | 2·25 |

**1968** (22 July–19 Aug). *"Children Need Milk".*

(*a*) *Nos. 244/5 surch locally as T* **81** (22 July)

| No. | Type | Description | Mint | Used |
|---|---|---|---|---|
| 296 | 54 | 2 c. + 3 c. on $2 multicoloured | 10 | 10 |
| 297 | 55 | 3 c. + 3 c. on $3 multicoloured | 10 | 10 |
| | | a. Surch inverted | 50·00 | 25·00 |
| | | b. Surch double | 30·00 | |

(*b*) *Nos. 243/4 surch locally as T* **82** (19 Aug)

| No. | Type | Description | Mint | Used |
|---|---|---|---|---|
| 298 | 53 | 1 c. + 3 c. on $1 multicoloured | 10 | 40 |
| | | a. Surch on No. 274 | 70·00 | 70·00 |
| | | b. Surch double | 50·00 | |
| 299 | 54 | 2 c. + 3 c. on $2 multicoloured | 17·00 | 38·00 |
| | | a. Surch on No. 275 | 80·00 | |
| 296/9 | | *Set of* 4 | 17·00 | 38·00 |

83 Edith McGuire (U.S.A.)

86 Hibiscus

(Des M. Shamir. Photo Harrison)

**1968** (24 Sept). *Olympic Games, Mexico. T* **83** *and similar square designs. P* 12½.

| No. | | Description | Mint | Used |
|---|---|---|---|---|
| 300 | 1 c. | brown, black and blue | 10 | 10 |
| 301 | 2 c. | orange, brown, blue and lilac | 10 | 10 |
| | | a. Orange (badge, etc.) omitted | | |
| 302 | 3 c. | scarlet, brown and dull green | 10 | 10 |
| | | a. Scarlet (rings, "MEXICO" etc.) omitted | | |
| 303 | 10 c. | brown, black, blue and vermilion | 10 | 10 |
| 304 | 50 c. | orange, brown, blue and turquoise | 25 | 30 |
| 305 | 60 c. | scarlet, brown and red-orange | 30 | 35 |
| 300/5 | | *Set of* 6 | 65 | 70 |

Designs:—2, 50 c. Arthur Wint (Jamaica); 3, 60 c. Ferreira da Silva (Brazil); 10 c. Type **83**.

Nos. 300/2 and 303/5 were issued in separate composite sheets containing three strips of three, with three *se-tenant* labels showing Greek athlete (Nos. 300/2) or Discobolos (Nos. 303/5). (*Price for two sheets £6 mint, £8 used.*)

(Des G. Vasarhelyi (No. 314*a*), V. Whiteley (75 c.), M. Shamir (others). Litho Format (Nos. 314*a* and 317*a*). Photo Harrison (others) )

**1968** (Oct)–**71**. *Multicoloured designs as T* **86**. *P* 13½ (*Nos. 314a and 317a*), 13½ × 14½ (*vert except No. 314a*) *or* 14½ × 13½ (*horiz except No. 317a*).

| No. | | Description | Mint | Used |
|---|---|---|---|---|
| 306 | 1 c. | Type **86** | 10 | 10 |
| 307 | 2 c. | Strelitzia | 10 | 10 |
| 308 | 3 c. | Bougainvillea (1.7.69) | 10 | 10 |
| 309 | 5 c. | Rock Hind (*horiz*) (4.2.69) | 10 | 10 |
| 310 | 6 c. | Sailfish | 10 | 10 |
| 311 | 8 c. | Snapper (*horiz*) (1.7.69) | 10 | 30 |
| 312 | 10 c. | Marine Toad (*horiz*) (4.2.69) | 10 | 10 |
| 313 | 12 c. | Turtle | 15 | 10 |
| 314 | 15 c. | Tree Boa (*horiz*) | 70 | 60 |
| 314*a* | 15 c. | Thunbergia (1970) | 4·25 | 2·50 |
| 315 | 25 c. | Greater Trinidadian Murine Opossum (4.2.69) | 30 | 10 |
| 316 | 35 c. | Nine-banded Armadillo (*horiz*) (1.7.69) | 35 | 10 |
| 317 | 50 c. | Mona Monkey | 45 | 25 |
| 317*a* | 75 c. | Yacht in St. George's Harbour (*horiz*) (9.10.71) | 8·50 | 6·50 |
| 318 | $1 | Bananaquit | 2·00 | 1·50 |
| 319 | $2 | Brown Pelican (4.2.69) | 3·00 | 5·00 |
| 320 | $3 | Magnificent Frigate Bird | 4·00 | 4·50 |
| 321 | $5 | Bare-eyed Thrush (1.7.69) | 4·00 | 11·00 |
| 306/21 | | *Set of* 18 | 25·00 | 29·00 |

Nos. 314*a*, 317*a* and the dollar values are larger—29 × 45½, 44 × 28½ and 25½ × 48 mm respectively.

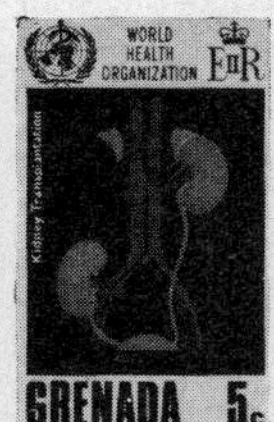


102 Kidney Transplant

106 "The Adoration of the Kings" (Veronese)

(Des M. Shamir. Litho B.W.)

**1968** (25 Nov). *20th Anniv of World Health Organization. T* **102** *and similar vert designs. Multicoloured. P* 13 × 13½.

| No. | | Description | Mint | Used |
|---|---|---|---|---|
| 322 | 5 c. | Type **102** | 10 | 10 |
| 323 | 25 c. | Heart transplant | 20 | 10 |
| 324 | 35 c. | Lung transplant | 20 | 10 |
| 325 | 50 c. | Eye transplant | 25 | 20 |
| 322/5 | | *Set of* 4 | 65 | 30 |

(Photo Harrison)

**1968** (3 Dec). *Christmas. T* **106** *and similar square designs. P* 12½.

| No. | | Description | Mint | Used |
|---|---|---|---|---|
| 326 | 5 c. | multicoloured | 10 | 10 |
| 327 | 15 c. | multicoloured | 10 | 10 |
| 328 | 35 c. | multicoloured | 10 | 10 |
| 329 | $1 | multicoloured | 30 | 40 |
| 326/9 | | *Set of* 4 | 40 | 45 |

Designs:—15 c. "Madonna and Child with Sts. John and Catherine" (Titian); 35 c. "Adoration of the Kings" (Botticelli); $1 "A Warrior Adoring" (Catena).

VISIT CARIFTA EXPO '69
April 5-30

5c

(110)

**1969** (Feb). *Caribbean Free Trade Area Exhibition. Nos. 300/5 surch in red as T* **110**.

| No. | | Description | Mint | Used |
|---|---|---|---|---|
| 330 | 5 c. | on 1 c. brown, black and blue | 10 | 10 |
| | | a. Surch double | | |
| 331 | 8 c. | on 2 c. orange, brown, blue and lilac | 10 | 10 |
| | | a. Surch double | | |
| 332 | 25 c. | on 3 c. scarlet, brown and dull green | 10 | 10 |
| | | a. Surch double | | |
| 333 | 35 c. | on 10 c. brown, black, blue and vermilion | 10 | 10 |
| 334 | $1 | on 50 c. orange, brown, blue & turquoise | 20 | 25 |
| 335 | $2 | on 60 c. scarlet, brown and red-orange | 35 | 40 |
| | | a. Scarlet (rings, "MEXICO" etc) omitted | † | — |
| 330/5 | | *Set of* 6 | 65 | 70 |

The centre of the composite sheets is also overprinted with a commemorative inscription publicising CARIFTA EXPO 1969 (*Price for two sheets £11 mint or used*).

111 Dame Hylda Bynoe (Governor) and Island Scene

(Des and litho D.L.R.)

**1969** (1 May). *Carifta Expo 1969. T* **111** *and similar horiz designs. Multicoloured. P* 13 × 13½.

| No. | | Description | Mint | Used |
|---|---|---|---|---|
| 336 | 5 c. | Type **111** | 10 | 10 |
| 337 | 15 c. | Premier E. M. Gairy and Island scene | 10 | 10 |
| 338 | 50 c. | Type **111** | 10 | 15 |
| 339 | 60 c. | Emblems of 1958 and 1967 World's Fairs | 10 | 20 |
| 336/9 | | *Set of* 4 | 30 | 40 |

114 Dame Hylda Bynoe

115 "Balshazzar's Feast" (Rembrandt)

(Photo Enschedé)

**1969** (8 June). *Human Rights Year. T* **114/15** *and similar multi-coloured design. P* 12½ × 13 ($1) *or* 13 × 12½ (*others*).

| No. | | Description | Mint | Used |
|---|---|---|---|---|
| 340 | 5 c. | Type **114** | 10 | 10 |
| 341 | 25 c. | Dr. Martin Luther King (*vert*) | 10 | 10 |
| 342 | 35 c. | Type **114** | 10 | 10 |
| 343 | $1 | Type **115** | 20 | 25 |
| 340/3 | | *Set of* 4 | 30 | 30 |

117 Batsman and Wicket-keeper

(Des M. Shamir and L. W. Denyer. Photo Harrison)

**1969** (1 Aug). *Cricket. T* **117** *and similar horiz designs. P* 14 × 14½.

| No. | | Description | Mint | Used |
|---|---|---|---|---|
| 344 | 3 c. | yellow, brown and ultramarine | 25 | 35 |
| | | a. Yellow (caps and wicket) omitted | | |
| 345 | 10 c. | multicoloured | 30 | 15 |
| 346 | 25 c. | brown, ochre and myrtle-green | 60 | 50 |
| 347 | 35 c. | multicoloured | 80 | 65 |
| 344/7 | | *Set of* 4 | 1·75 | 1·50 |

Designs:—10 c. Batsman playing defensive stroke; 25 c. Batsman sweeping ball; 35 c. Batsman playing on-drive.

Nos. 344/7 were each issued in small sheets of 9 (3 × 3) with decorative borders.

129 Astronaut handling Moon Rock

(Des G. Vasarhelyi. Photo)

**1969** (24 Sept). *First Man on the Moon. T* **129** *and similar multi-coloured designs. P* 13½ (½ c.) *or* 12½ (*others*).

| No. | | Description | Mint | Used |
|---|---|---|---|---|
| 348 | ½ c. | As Type **129** but larger (56 × 35 *mm*) | 10 | 10 |
| 349 | 1 c. | Moon rocket and moon | 10 | 10 |
| 350 | 2 c. | Module landing | 10 | 10 |
| 351 | 3 c. | Declaration left on moon | 10 | 10 |
| 352 | 8 c. | Module leaving rocket | 10 | 10 |
| 353 | 25 c. | Rocket lifting-off (*vert*) | 15 | 10 |
| 354 | 35 c. | Spacecraft in orbit (*vert*) | 15 | 10 |
| 355 | 50 c. | Capsule with parachutes (*vert*) | 20 | 10 |
| 356 | $1 | Type **129** | 35 | 30 |
| 348/56 | | *Set of* 9 | 85 | 55 |
| **MS**357 | | 115 × 90 mm. Nos. 351 and 356. Imperf | 90 | 1·50 |

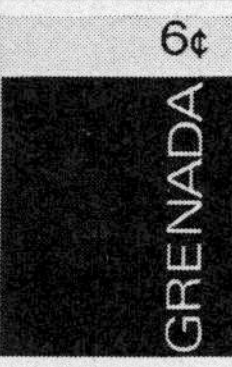


**130** Gandhi

(Des A. Robledo. Litho B.W.)

**1969** (8 Oct). *Birth Centenary of Mahatma Gandhi. T* **130** *and similar designs. P* 11½.
358 **130** 6 c. multicoloured . . . . . . 15 10
359 – 15 c. multicoloured . . . . . . 20 10
360 – 25 c. multicoloured . . . . . . 30 10
361 – $1 multicoloured . . . . . . 1·00 60
358/61 . . . . . . *Set of* 4 1·50 75
**MS**362 155 × 122 mm. Nos. 358/61. Imperf . . 2·50 3·50
Designs: *Vert*—15 c. Gandhi standing; 25 c. Gandhi walking. *Horiz*—$1 Head of Gandhi.

2c

(**134**)

**135** "Blackbeard" (Edward Teach)

**1969** (23 Dec). *Christmas. Nos. 326/9 surch with T* **134** *in black (2 c.) or optd with new date only in silver (others).*
363 2 c. on 15 c. multicoloured . . . . 10 10
a. Surch inverted . . . . 50·00
364 5 c. multicoloured . . . . 10 10
365 35 c. multicoloured . . . . 10 10
a. Opt inverted . . . . 50·00
b. Horiz pair, one with opt omitted . . £250
366 $1 multicoloured . . . . 35 70
a. Opt inverted . . . . 50·00
363/6 . . . . *Set of* 4 45 80

(Des K. Plowitz. Recess B.W.)

**1970** (2 Feb). *Pirates. T* **135** *and similar vert designs. P* 13½.
367 15 c. black . . . . 35 10
368 25 c. dull green . . . . 50 10
369 50 c. lilac . . . . 90 20
370 $1 carmine . . . . 1·50 75
367/70 . . . . *Set of* 4 3·00 1·00
Designs:—25 c. Anne Bonney; 50 c. Jean Lafitte; $1 Mary Read.

5c (**139**)    5c (**140**)

**1970** (18 Mar). *No. 348 surch with T* **139**.
371 5 c. on ½ c. multicoloured . . . . 10 10
a. Surch double . . . . 55·00
b. Surch with T **140** . . . . 90 90

**141** "The Last Supper" (detail, **142** Del Sarto)

(Des and litho B.W.)

**1970** (13 Apr). *Easter. Paintings. T* **141/2** *and similar vert designs. Multicoloured. P* 11½.
372 5 c. } Type **141/2** . . . . 10 10
373 5 c. } . . . . 10 10
374 15 c. } "Christ crowned with Thorns" (detail, . . 15 10
375 15 c. } Van Dyck) . . . . 15 10
376 25 c. } "The Passion of Christ" (detail, . . 20 10
377 25 c. } Memling) . . . . 20 10
378 60 c. } "Christ in the Tomb" (detail, Rubens) . . 25 30
379 60 c. } . . 25 30
372/9 . . . . *Set of* 8 1·25 85
**MS**380 120 × 140 mm. Nos. 376/9 . . 85 1·25
Nos. 372/9 were issued with each design spread over two *se-tenant* stamps of the same denomination.

**149** Girl with Kittens in Pram

(Des A. Robledo. Litho Questa)

**1970** (27 May). *Birth Bicentenary of William Wordsworth (poet). "Children and Pets". T* **149** *and similar horiz designs. Multicoloured. P* 11.
381 5 c. Type **149** . . . . 15 10
382 15 c. Girl with puppy and kitten . . . . 20 10
383 30 c. Boy with fishing rod and cat . . . . 35 15
384 60 c. Boys and girls with cats and dogs . . 55 30
381/4 . . . . *Set of* 4 1·10 60
**MS**385 Two sheets each 114 × 126 mm. Nos. 381, 383 and Nos. 382, 384. Imperf . . . . 1·60 2·00

**153** Parliament of India

(Des G. Vasarhelyi. Litho Questa)

**1970** (15 June). *Seventh Regional Conference of Commonwealth Parliamentary Association. T* **153** *and similar horiz designs. Multicoloured. P* 14
386 5 c. Type **153** . . . . 10 10
387 25 c. Parliament of Great Britain, Westminster . . . . 10 10
388 50 c. Parliament of Canada . . . . 15 15
389 60 c. Parliament of Grenada . . . . 15 15
386/9 . . . . *Set of* 4 40 35
**MS**390 126 × 90 mm. Nos. 386/9 . . . . 50 90

**157** Tower of the Sun

(Litho Kyodo Printing Co, Tokyo)

**1970** (8 Aug). *World Fair, Osaka. T* **157** *and similar multicoloured designs. P* 13.
391 1 c. Type **157** . . . . 10 10
392 2 c. Livelihood and Industry Pavilion (*horiz*) 10 10
393 3 c. Flower painting, 1634 . . . . 10 10
394 10 c. "Adam and Eve" (Tintoretto) (*horiz*) . . 10 10
395 25 c. O.E.C.D. (Organisation for Economic Co-operation and Development) Pavilion (*horiz*) . . . . 15 10
396 50 c. San Francisco Pavilion . . . . 35 20
391/6 . . . . *Set of* 6 60 35
**MS**397 121 × 91 mm. $1 Japanese Pavilion (56 × 34 *mm*) . . . . 55 1·10

**164** Roosevelt and "Raising U.S. Flag on Iwo Jima"

(Litho Questa)

**1970** (3 Sept). *25th Anniv of Ending of World War II. T* **164** *and similar horiz designs. Multicoloured. P* 11.
398 ½ c. Type **164** . . . . 10 10
399 5 c. Zhukov and "Fall of Berlin" . . . . 30 15
400 15 c. Churchill and "Evacuation at Dunkirk" 60 25
401 25 c. De Gaulle and "Liberation of Paris" . . 90 45
402 50 c. Eisenhower and "D-Day Landing" . . 1·25 90
403 60 c. Montgomery and "Battle of Alamein" . . 1·50 1·75
398/403 . . . . *Set of* 6 4·25 3·25
**MS**404 163 × 113 mm. Nos. 398, 400, 402/3 . . 3·00 6·50
a. Brown (panel) on 60 c. value omitted . .

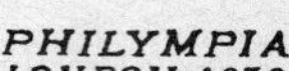


(**169**)

**170** U.P.U. Emblem, Building and Transport

**1970** (18 Sept). *"Philympia 1970" Stamp Exhibition, London Nos. 353/6 optd with T* **169**
405 25 c. Rocket lifting-off . . . . 10 10
a. Albino opt . . . . 6·00
b. Opt inverted . . . .
406 35 c. Spacecraft in orbit . . . . 10 10
a. Opt inverted . . . . 40·00
407 50 c. Capsule with parachutes . . . . 15 15
a. Albino opt . . . . 1·50
408 $1 Type **129** (Sil.) (optd vert upwards) . . 20 30
a. Albino opt . . . . 10·00
405/8 . . . . *Set of* 4 40 50
The miniature sheet was also overprinted but we understand that only 300 of these were put on sale in Grenada.

(Litho Questa)

**1970** (17 Oct). *New U.P.U. Headquarters Building. T* **170** *and similar multicoloured designs. P* 14.
409 15 c. Type **170** . . . . 15 10
410 25 c. As Type **170**, but modern transport . . 20 10
411 50 c. Sir Rowland Hill and U.P.U. Building . . 30 15
412 $1 Abraham Lincoln and U.P.U. Building . . 55 50
409/12 . . . . *Set of* 4 1·10 70
**MS**413 79 × 85 mm. Nos. 411/12 . . . . 1·25 3·00
The 50 c. and $1 are both vertical designs.

**171** "The Madonna of the Goldfinch" (Tiepolo)

CENTENARY OF THE BRITISH RED CROSS
GRENADA 1870 1970

**172** 19th-Century Nursing

(Des G. Vasarhelyi. Litho Questa)

**1970** (5 Dec). *Christmas. T* **171** *and similar vert designs. Multicoloured. P* 13½.
414 ½ c. Type **171** . . . . 10 10
415 ½ c. "The Virgin and Child with St. Peter and St. Paul" (Bouts) . . . . 10 10
416 ½ c. "The Virgin and Child" (Bellini) . . 10 10
417 2 c. "The Madonna of the Basket" (Correggio) 10 10
418 3 c. Type **171** . . . . 10 10
419 35 c. As No. 415 . . . . 30 10
420 50 c. As 2 c. . . . . 45 15
421 $1 As No. 416 . . . . 75 35
414/21 . . . . *Set of* 8 1·50 70
**MS**422 102 × 87 mm. Nos. 420/1 . . . . 1·75 2·75

(Des G. Vasarhelyi. Litho Questa)

**1970** (12 Dec). *Centenary of British Red Cross. T* **172** *and similar horiz designs. Multicoloured. P* 14½ × 14.
423 5 c. Type **172** . . . . 10 10
424 15 c. Military Ambulance, 1918 . . . . 20 10
425 25 c. First-Aid Post, 1941 . . . . 35 10
426 60 c. Red Cross Transport, 1970 . . . . 80 60
423/6 . . . . *Set of* 4 1·25 70
**MS**427 113 × 82 mm. Nos. 423/6 . . . . 1·50 1·60
a. Error. Imperf . . . . 22·00

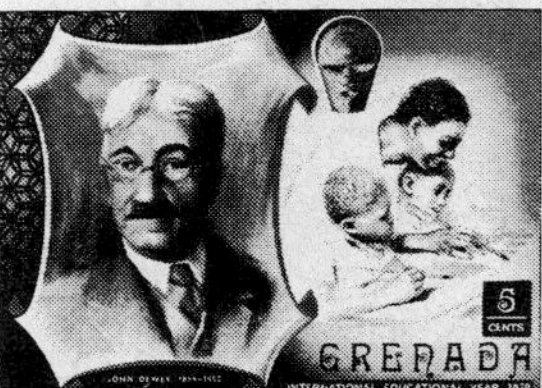


**173** John Dewey and Art Lesson

(Des G. Vasarhelyi. Litho Questa)

**1971** (1 May). *International Education Year* (1970). *T* **173** *and similar horiz designs. Multicoloured. P* 13½.
428 5 c. Type **173** . . . . 10 10
429 10 c. Jean-Jacques Rousseau and "Alphabetisation" . . . . 15 10
430 50 c. Maimonides and laboratory . . . . 50 15
431 $1 Bertrand Russell and mathematics class 95 40
428/31 . . . . *Set of* 4 1·50 55
**MS**432 90 × 98 mm. Nos. 430/1 . . . . 1·40 2·00

**NEW INFORMATION**

The editor is always interested to correspond with people who have new information that will improve or correct the Catalogue.

174 Jennifer Hosten and outline of Grenada

176 "Napolean reviewing the Guard" (E. Detaille)

175 French and Canadian Scouts

(Des local artist; adapted G. Drummond. Litho Format)

**1971** (1 June). *Winner of "Miss World" Competition* (1970). *P* 13½.

433 **174** 5 c. multicoloured .. .. .. .. 10 10
434 10 c. multicoloured .. .. .. .. 15 10
435 15 c. multicoloured .. .. .. .. 15 10
436 25 c. multicoloured .. .. .. .. 15 10
437 35 c. multicoloured .. .. .. .. 20 10
438 50 c. multicoloured .. .. .. .. 45 55
433/8 .. .. .. .. .. .. *Set of* 6 1·10 75
**MS**439 92 × 89 mm. **174** 50 c. multicoloured. Printed on silk. Imperf .. .. .. .. .. 75 1·75

(Litho Format)

**1971** (11 Sept). *13th World Scout Jamboree, Asagiri, Japan. T* **175** *and similar horiz designs. Multicoloured. P* 11.

440 5 c. Type **175** .. .. .. .. .. .. 10 10
441 35 c. German and American scouts .. .. 30 25
442 50 c. Australian and Japanese scouts .. .. 50 50
443 75 c. Grenada and British scouts .. .. 65 75
440/3 .. .. .. .. .. .. *Set of* 4 1·40 1·40
**MS**444 101 × 114 mm. Nos. 442/3 .. .. .. 1·60 2·50

(Des G. Vasarhelyi. Litho Questa)

**1971** (9 Oct). *150th Death Anniversary of Napoleon Bonaparte. T* **176** *and similar vert designs showing paintings. Multi-coloured. P* 13½.

445 5 c. Type **176** .. .. .. .. .. .. 15 15
446 15 c. "Napoleon before Madrid" (Vernet) .. 25 15
447 35 c. "Napoleon crossing Mt St. Bernard" (David) .. .. .. .. .. .. 30 15
448 $2 "Napoleon in his Study" (David) .. 1·25 1·75
445/8 .. .. .. .. .. .. *Set of* 4 1·75 2·00
**MS**449 101 × 76 mm. No. 447. Imperf .. .. 2·00 1·60

177 1d. Stamp of 1861 and Badge of Grenada

(Des R. Granger Barrett. Litho Questa)

**1971** (6 Nov). *110th Anniv of the Postal Service. T* **177** *and similar horiz designs. Multicoloured. W w* **12** (*sideways**). *P* 11.

450 5 c. Type **177** .. .. .. .. .. .. 10 15
451 15 c. 6d. stamp of 1861 and Queen Elizabeth II 15 15
452 35 c. 1d. and 6d. stamps of 1861 and badge of Grenada .. .. .. .. .. .. 30 20
453 50 c. Scroll and 1d. stamp of 1861 .. .. 45 70
450/3 .. .. .. .. .. .. *Set of* 4 90 1·10
**MS**454 96 × 114 mm. Nos. 452/3 .. .. .. 75 1·00

* This issue is printed on thick paper and consequently the watermark is very faint.

178 Apollo Splashdown

(Des R. Granger Barrett. Litho Questa)

**1971** (13 Nov). *Apollo Moon Exploration Series. T* **178** *and similar multicoloured designs. P* 11.

455 1 c. Type **178** .. .. .. .. .. .. 10 10
456 2 c. Recovery of Apollo 13 .. .. .. .. 10 10
457 3 c. Separation of Lunar Module from Apollo 14 .. .. .. .. .. .. 10 10
458 10 c. Shepard and Mitchell taking samples of moon rock .. .. .. .. .. 20 10
459 25 c. Moon Buggy .. .. .. .. .. 55 20
460 $1 Apollo 15 blast-off (*vert*) .. .. .. 1·75 1·50
455/60 .. .. .. .. .. .. *Set of* 6 2·50 1·75
**MS**461 77 × 108 mm. 50 c. as $1 .. .. .. 1·10 1·50

179 67th Regiment of Foot, 1787

180 "The Adoration of the Kings" (Memling)

(Des G. Vasarhelyi. Litho Format)

**1971** (11 Dec). *Military Uniforms. T* **179** *and similar vert designs. Multicoloured. P* 13½.

462 ½ c. Type **179** .. .. .. .. .. .. 10 10
463 1 c. 45th Regiment of Foot, 1792 .. .. 10 10
464 2 c. 29th Regiment of Foot, 1794 .. .. 10 10
465 10 c. 9th Regiment of Foot, 1801 .. .. 45 20
466 25 c. 2nd Regiment of Foot, 1815 .. .. 85 35
467 $1 70th Regiment of Foot, 1764 .. .. 2·25 2·00
462/7 .. .. .. .. .. .. *Set of* 6 3·25 2·25
**MS**468 108 × 99 mm. Nos. 466/7. P 15 .. .. 3·50 3·75

(Des G. Vasarhelyi. Litho Questa)

**1972** (15 Jan). *Christmas* (1971). *T* **180** *and similar vert designs. Multicoloured. P* 14 × 13½.

469 15 c. Type **180** .. .. .. .. .. .. 10 10
470 25 c. "Madonna and Child" (Michelangelo) .. 20 10
471 35 c. "Madonna and Child" (Murillo) .. .. 25 10
472 50 c. "The Virgin with the Apple" (Memling) 30 40
469/72 .. .. .. .. .. .. *Set of* 4 75 60
**MS**473 105 × 80 mm. $1 "The Adoration of the Kings" (Mostaert) .. .. .. .. .. 75 1·25

35c

WINTER OLYMPICS
FEB. 3-13, 1972
SAPPORO, JAPAN

(181)

VOTE
FEB. 28 1972

(182)

**1972** (3 Feb). *Winter Olympic Games, Sapporo, Japan. Nos.* 462/4 *and* **MS**468 *surch or optd only* (**MS**475).

(*a*) *Postage. As T* **181**

474 $2 on 2 c. multicoloured .. .. .. .. 60 90
**MS**475 108 × 99 mm. Nos. 466/7 (R.) .. .. 1·00 1·60

(*b*) *Air. As T* **181**, *but additionally surch* "AIR MAIL"

476 35 c. on ½ c. multicoloured .. .. .. 20 25
477 50 c. on 1 c. multicoloured .. .. .. 25 35

**1972** (25 Feb). *General Election. Nos.* 307/8, 310 *and* 315 *optd with T* **182**.

478 2 c. multicoloured .. .. .. .. .. 10 10
479 3 c. multicoloured .. .. .. .. .. 10 10
a. Opt inverted .. .. .. .. ..
480 6 c. multicoloured .. .. .. .. .. 10 15
481 25 c. multicoloured .. .. .. .. .. 15 30
478/81 .. .. .. .. .. .. *Set of* 4 40 60

183 King Arthur

(Litho Questa)

**1972** (4 Mar). *U.N.I.C.E.F. T* **183** *and similar multicoloured designs. P* 14.

482 ½ c. Type **183** .. .. .. .. .. .. 10 10
483 1 c. Robin Hood .. .. .. .. .. 10 10
484 2 c. Robinson Crusoe (*vert*) .. .. .. 10 10
485 25 c. Type **183** .. .. .. .. .. .. 10 10
486 50 c. As No. 483 .. .. .. .. .. 25 35
487 75 c. As No. 484 .. .. .. .. .. 30 50
488 $1 Mary and her little lamb (*vert*) .. .. 45 70
482/8 .. .. .. .. .. .. *Set of* 7 1·10 1·60
**MS**489 65 × 98 mm. No. 488 .. .. .. .. 55 80

INTERPEX
1972

(184)

12¢

(185)

AIR MAIL

(186)

**1972** (17 Mar). *"Interpex" Stamp Exhibition, New York. Nos.* 433/9 *optd with T* **184**.

490 **174** 5 c. multicoloured .. .. .. .. 10 10
491 10 c. multicoloured .. .. .. .. 10 10
492 15 c. multicoloured .. .. .. .. 10 10
493 25 c. multicoloured .. .. .. .. 10 10
494 35 c. multicoloured .. .. .. .. 15 15
495 50 c. multicoloured .. .. .. .. 25 30
a. Vert pair, top stamp with opt omitted £100
490/5 .. .. .. .. .. .. *Set of* 6 60 65
**MS**496 92 × 89 mm. **174** 50 c. multicoloured. Printed on silk. Imperf .. .. .. .. .. 7·50 12·00

**1972** (20 Apr). *Nos.* 306/8 *surch with T* **185**, *and No.* 433 *surch similarly, but with obliterating bars under* "12c".

497 12 c. on 1 c. Type **88** .. .. .. .. 30 45
498 12 c. on 2 c. Strelitzia .. .. .. .. 30 45
499 12 c. on 3 c. Bougainvillea .. .. .. .. 30 45
a. Horiz pair, left stamp with surch omitted .. .. .. .. ..
500 12 c. on 5 c. Type **174** .. .. .. .. 30 45
497/500 .. .. .. .. .. .. *Set of* 4 1·10 1·60

**1972**. *Air.* (*a*) *Nos.* 306/12, 314*a*/17 *and* 318/21 *optd as T* **186** *or surch in addition* (2 May)

501 5 c. Rock Hind .. .. .. .. .. 10 10
a. Opt double .. .. .. .. ..
502 8 c. Snapper .. .. .. .. .. .. 15 10
a. Opt double .. .. .. .. ..
503 10 c. Marine Toad .. .. .. .. .. 15 10
a. Opt double .. .. .. .. .. 40·00
504 15 c. Thunbergia .. .. .. .. .. 30 10
505 25 c. Greater Trinidadian Murine Opossum 35 20
a. Horiz pair, one without opt .. .. £130
506 30 c. on 1 c. Type **86** .. .. .. .. 40 25
507 35 c. Nine-banded Armadillo .. .. .. 40 25
508 40 c. on 2 c. Strelitzia .. .. .. .. 50 25
509 45 c. on 3 c. Bougainvillea .. .. .. 55 35
510 50 c. Mona Monkey .. .. .. .. .. 55 35
a. Horiz pair, one without opt .. .. 90·00
b. Opt double .. .. .. .. .. £180
511 60 c. on 5 c. Rock Hind .. .. .. .. 60 40
512 70 c. on 6 c. Sailfish .. .. .. .. 70 50
513 $1 Bananaquit .. .. .. .. .. 3·00 60
514 $1.35 on 8 c. Snapper .. .. .. .. 3·00 1·25
515 $2 Brown Pelican .. .. .. .. .. 4·25 3·00
516 $3 Magnificent Frigate Bird .. .. .. 5·00 3·50
517 $5 Bare-eyed Thrush .. .. .. .. 6·00 6·50

(*b*) *Nos.* 440/3 *optd as T* **186** (5 June)

518 **175** 5 c. multicoloured .. .. .. .. 40 10
519 – 35 c. multicoloured .. .. .. .. 1·00 30
520 – 50 c. multicoloured .. .. .. .. 1·25 45
521 – 75 c. multicoloured .. .. .. .. 1·75 1·00
501/21 .. .. .. .. .. .. *Set of* 21 27·00 17·00

187 Yachting

(Litho Format)

**1972** (8 Sept) *Olympic Games, Munich. T* **187** *and similar multi-coloured designs. P* 14. (*a*) *Postage.*

522 ½ c. Type **187** .. .. .. .. .. .. 10 10
523 1 c. Show-jumping .. .. .. .. .. 10 10
524 2 c. Running (*vert*) .. .. .. .. .. 10 10
525 35 c. As 2 c. .. .. .. .. .. .. 40 20
526 50 c. As 1 c. .. .. .. .. .. .. 55 40

(*b*) *Air*

527 25 c. Boxing .. .. .. .. .. .. 30 15
528 $1 As 25 c. .. .. .. .. .. .. 90 75
522/8 .. .. .. .. .. .. *Set of* 7 2·00 1·40
**MS**529 82 × 85 mm. 60 c. as 25 c. and 70 c. as 1 c. 1·00 1·40

188 Badge of Grenada and Nutmegs

(Des (from photographs by D. Groves) and photo Harrison)

**1972** (20 Nov). *Royal Silver Wedding. Multicoloured; background colour given. W w* **12**. *P* 14 × 14½.

530 **188** 8 c. olive-brown .. .. .. .. 10 10
531 $1 ultramarine .. .. .. .. 45 55

## COVER PRICES

Cover factors are quoted at the beginning of each country for most issues to 1945. An explanation of the system can be found on page x. The factors quoted do not, however, apply to philatelic covers.

189 Boy Scout Saluting

190 Madonna and Child

(Des R. Granger Barrett. Litho Questa)

**1972** (2 Dec). *65th Anniv of Boy Scouts. T* **189** *and similar horiz designs. Multicoloured. P* 14. *(a) Postage.*

532 ½ c. Type **189** .. .. .. .. .. .. 10 10
533 1 c. Scouts knotting ropes .. .. .. .. 10 10
534 2 c. Scouts shaking hands .. .. .. .. 10 10
535 3 c. Lord Baden-Powell .. .. .. .. 10 10
536 75 c. As 2 c. .. .. .. .. .. .. 1·40 1·90
537 $1 As 3 c. .. .. .. .. .. .. 1·60 2·00

*(b) Air*

538 25 c. Type **189** .. .. .. .. .. .. 50 40
539 35 c. As 1 c. .. .. .. .. .. .. 70 50
532/9 .. .. .. .. .. *Set of* 8 4·00 4·50
**MS**540 87 × 88 mm. 60 c. as 3 c., and 70 c. as 2 c. 1·50 2·00

(Des V. Whiteley. Litho Format)

**1972** (9 Dec). *Christmas. T* **190** *and similar vert designs. Multicoloured. P* 13½.

541 1 c. Type **190** .. .. .. .. .. .. 10 10
542 3 c. The Three Kings .. .. .. .. .. 10 10
543 5 c. The Nativity .. .. .. .. .. 10 10
544 25 c. Type **190** .. .. .. .. .. .. 15 15
545 35 c. As 3 c. .. .. .. .. .. .. 20 20
546 $1 As 5 c. .. .. .. .. .. .. 60 60
541/6 .. .. .. .. .. *Set of* 6 1·00 1·00
**MS**547 102 × 76 mm. 60 c. Type **190** and 70 c. as 3 c. P 15 .. .. .. .. .. .. 60 80

191 Greater Flamingoes

(Des M. and G. Shamir. Litho Questa)

**1973** (26 Jan). *National Zoo. T* **191** *and similar horiz designs. Multicoloured. P* 14½.

548 25 c. Type **191** .. .. .. .. .. .. 70 35
549 35 c. Brazilian Tapir .. .. .. .. .. 80 45
550 60 c. Blue and Yellow Macaw, and Scarlet Macaw .. .. .. .. .. .. 1·40 1·00
551 70 c. Ocelot .. .. .. .. .. .. 1·50 1·25
548/51 .. .. .. .. .. *Set of* 4 3·75 2·75

192 Class II Racing Yacht

(Des V. Whiteley. Litho Format)

**1973** (26 Feb). *Yachting. T* **192** *and similar horiz designs. Multicoloured. P* 13½.

552 25 c. Type **192** .. .. .. .. .. .. 35 15
553 35 c. Harbour, St George's .. .. .. .. 40 15
554 60 c. Yacht *Bloodhound* .. .. .. .. 55 55
555 70 c. St. George's .. .. .. .. .. 70 75
552/5 .. .. .. .. .. *Set of* 4 1·75 1·40

193 Helios (Greek god) and Earth orbiting the Sun

(Des G. Vasarhelyi. Litho Format)

**1973** (6 July). *I.M.O./W.M.O. Centenary. T* **193** *and similar horiz designs showing Greek Gods. Multicoloured. P* 13½.

556 ½ c. Type **193** .. .. .. .. .. .. 10 10
557 1 c. Poseidon and "Normad" storm detector 10 10
558 2 c. Zeus and radarscope .. .. .. .. 10 10
559 3 c. Iris and weather balloon.. .. .. .. 10 10
560 35 c. Hermes and "ATS-3" satellite .. .. 40 10
561 50 c. Zephyrus and diagram of pressure zones 55 25
562 75 c. Demeter and space photo .. .. .. 75 50
563 $1 Selene and rainfall diagram .. .. .. 80 80
556/63 .. .. .. .. .. *Set of* 8 2·25 1·50
**MS**564 123 × 92 mm. $2 Computer weather map (42 × 31 *mm*). P 13½. .. .. .. .. 90 1·25

194 Racing Class Yachts

195 Ignatius Semmelweis (obstetrician)

(Des G. Drummond. Litho Format)

**1973** (3 Aug). *Carriacou Regatta. T* **194** *and similar horiz designs. Multicoloured. P* 13½.

565 ½ c. Type **194** .. .. .. .. .. .. 10 10
566 1 c. Cruising Class Yacht .. .. .. .. 10 10
567 2 c. Open-decked sloops .. .. .. .. 10 10
568 35 c. *Mermaid* (sloop).. .. .. .. .. 35 20
569 50 c. St. George's Harbour .. .. .. .. 50 35
570 75 c. Map of Carriacou .. .. .. .. 70 60
571 $1 Boat-building .. .. .. .. .. 90 80
565/71 .. .. .. .. .. *Set of* 7 2·40 1·90
**MS**572 109 × 88 mm. $2 End of Race .. .. 1·25 1·75

(Des G. Vasarhelyi. Litho Format)

**1973** (17 Sept). *25th Anniv of W.H.O. T* **195** *and similar vert designs. Multicoloured. P* 14½.

573 ½ c. Type **195** .. .. .. .. .. .. 10 10
574 1 c. Louis Pasteur .. .. .. .. .. 10 10
575 2 c. Edward Jenner .. .. .. .. .. 10 10
576 3 c. Sigmund Freud .. .. .. .. .. 10 10
577 25 c. Emil Von Behring (bacteriologist) .. 55 10
578 35 c. Carl Jung .. .. .. .. .. 65 20
579 50 c. Charles Calmette (bacteriologist) .. 90 30
580 $1 William Harvey .. .. .. .. .. 1·25 75
573/80 .. .. .. .. .. *Set of* 8 3·00 1·40
**MS**581 105 × 80 mm. $2 Marie Curie .. .. 2·00 2·00

196 Princess Anne and Capt. Mark Phillips

197 "Virgin and Child" (Maratti)

(Des G. Drummond. Litho Format)

**1973** (14 Nov). *Royal Wedding. P* 13½.

582 **196** 25 c. multicoloured .. .. .. .. 10 10
583 $2 multicoloured .. .. .. .. 45 55
**MS**584 79 × 100 mm. 75 c. and $1 as Nos. 582/3 .. 40 30

Nos. 582/3 were each issued in small sheets of five stamps and one stamp-size label.

(Litho Format)

**1973** (10 Dec). *Christmas. T* **197** *and similar vert designs. Multicoloured. P* 14½.

585 ½ c. Type **197** .. .. .. .. .. .. 10 10
586 1 c. "Madonna and Child" (Crivelli) .. .. 10 10
587 2 c. "Virgin and Child with Two Angels" (Verrocchio) .. .. .. .. .. 10 10
588 3 c. "Adoration of the Shepherds" (Roberti) .. 10 10
589 25 c. "The Holy Family with the Infant Baptist" (Baroccio) .. .. .. .. 15 10
590 35 c. "The Holy Family" (Bronzino) .. .. 20 10
591 75 c. "Mystic Nativity" (Botticelli) .. .. 30 20
592 $1 "Adoration of the Kings" (Geertgen) .. 40 30
585/92 .. .. .. .. .. *Set of* 8 1·00 60
**MS**593 89 × 89 mm. $2 "Adoration of the Kings" (Mostaert) (30 × 45 *mm*). P 13½ .. .. 1·00 1·10

**INDEPENDENT**

INDEPENDENCE
7TH FEB. 1974

(198)

199 Creative Arts Theatre, Jamaica Campus

**1974** (7 Feb). *Independence. Nos.* 306/9, 311/13, 315/16 *and* 317*a*/21 *optd as T* **198**

594 1 c. Hibiscus .. .. .. .. .. .. 10 10
595 2 c. Strelitzia .. .. .. .. .. .. 10 10
596 3 c. Bougainvillea .. .. .. .. .. 10 10
597 5 c. Rock Hind .. .. .. .. .. .. 10 10
598 8 c. Snapper .. .. .. .. .. .. 15 10
599 10 c. Marine Toad .. .. .. .. .. 20 15
600 12 c. Turtle .. .. .. .. .. .. 20 15
601 25 c. Greater Trinidadian Murine Opossum .. 45 35
602 35 c. Nine-banded Armadillo .. .. .. 75 50
603 75 c. Yacht in St. George's Harbour .. .. 2·00 1·25
604 $1 Bananaquit .. .. .. .. .. 3·75 1·50
605 $2 Brown Pelican .. .. .. .. .. 6·00 3·50
606 $3 Magnificent Frigate Bird .. .. .. 10·00 5·00
607 $5 Bare-eyed Thrush .. .. .. .. 15·00 9·50
594/607 .. .. .. .. .. *Set of* 14 35·00 20·00

(Des G. Drummond. Litho Format)

**1974** (10 Apr). *25th Anniv of University of West Indies. T* **199** *and similar multicoloured designs. P* 13½ × 14.

608 10 c. Type **199** .. .. .. .. .. .. 10 10
609 25 c. Marryshow House .. .. .. .. 10 10
610 50 c. Chapel, Jamaica Campus (*vert*) .. .. 20 10
611 $1 University arms (*vert*) .. .. .. 30 30
608/11 .. .. .. .. .. *Set of* 4 55 50
**MS**612 69 × 86 mm. $2 as No. 611 .. .. .. 50 90

200 Nutmeg Pods and Scarlet Mace

201 Footballers (West Germany v Chile)

(Des G. Drummond. Litho Format)

**1974** (19 Aug). *Independence.* T **200** *and similar vert designs. Multicoloured. P* 13½.

613 3 c. Type **200** .. .. .. .. .. .. 10 10
614 8 c. Map of Grenada .. .. .. .. .. 10 10
615 25 c. Prime Minister Eric Gairy .. .. .. 15 10
616 35 c. Grand Anse Beach and flag .. .. .. 15 10
617 $1 Coat of arms .. .. .. .. .. 35 40
613/17 .. .. .. .. .. *Set of* 5 70 60
**MS**618 91 × 125 mm. $2 as $1 .. .. .. 55 90

(Des G. Vasarhelyi. Litho Format)

**1974** (3 Sept). *World Cup Football Championships, West Germany. T* **201** *and similar multicoloured designs showing footballers of the countries given. P* 14½.

619 ½ c. Type **201** .. .. .. .. .. .. 10 10
620 1 c. East Germany v Australia .. .. .. 10 10
621 2 c. Yugoslavia v Brazil .. .. .. .. 10 10
622 10 c. Scotland v Zaire .. .. .. .. .. 10 10
623 25 c. Netherlands v Uruguay .. .. .. .. 15 10
624 50 c. Sweden v Bulgaria .. .. .. .. 20 10
625 75 c. Italy v Haiti .. .. .. .. .. 35 15
626 $1 Poland v Argentina .. .. .. .. 50 25
619/26 .. .. .. .. .. *Set of* 8 1·25 60
**MS**627 114 × 76 mm. $2 Country flags. P 13 .. 90 1·75

202 Early U.S. Mail-trains and "Concorde"

(Des G. Vasarhelyi. Litho Format)

**1974** (8 Oct). *Centenary of Universal Postal Union. T* **202** *and similar horiz designs. Multicoloured. P* 14½.

628 ½ c. Type **202** .. .. .. .. .. .. 10 10
629 1 c. Mailboat *Caesar* (1839) and helicopter .. 10 10
630 2 c. Airmail transport .. .. .. .. 10 10
631 8 c. Pigeon post (1480) and telephone dial .. 15 10
632 15 c. 18th-century bellman and tracking antenna .. .. .. .. .. .. 25 10
633 25 c. Messenger (1450) and satellite .. .. 30 15
634 35 c. French pillar-box (1850) and mail-boat .. 65 25
635 $1 18th-century German postman and mail-train of the future .. .. .. .. 1·75 1·75
628/35 .. .. .. .. .. *Set of* 8 3·00 2·25
**MS**636 105 × 66 mm. $2 St. Gotthard mail-coach (1735). P 13 .. .. .. .. .. 1·25 1·75

203 Sir Winston Churchill

204 "Madonna and Child of the Eucharist" (Botticelli)

(Des G. Vasarhelyi. Litho Format)

**1974** (28 Oct). *Birth Centenary of Sir Winston Churchill. T* **203** *and similar portrait design. P* 13½.

637 **203** 35 c. multicoloured .. .. .. .. 15 10
638 – $2 multicoloured .. .. .. .. 45 50
**MS**639 129 × 96 mm. 75 c. as 35 c. and $1 as $2 65 75

(Des. M. Shamir. Litho Format)

**1974** (18 Nov). *Christmas. T* **204** *and similar vert designs, showing "The Madonna and Child" by the artists given. Multicoloured. P* 14½.

640 ½ c. Type **204** .. .. .. .. .. .. 10 10
641 1 c. Niccolo di Pietro .. .. .. .. .. 10 10
642 2 c. Van der Weyden .. .. .. .. .. 10 10

643 3 c. Bastiani .. .. .. .. .. .. 10 10
644 10 c. Giovanni .. .. .. .. .. .. 10 10
645 25 c. Van der Weyden .. .. .. .. .. 15 10
646 50 c. Botticelli .. .. .. .. .. .. 25 20
647 $1 Mantegna .. .. .. .. .. 45 50
640/7 .. .. .. .. .. .. *Set of* 8 90 80
**MS**648 117 × 96 mm. $2 as 1 c. P 13 .. .. 60 90

**205** Yachts, Port Saline

(Des G. Drummond. Litho Format)

**1975** (13 Jan)–**78**. *Multicoloured designs as* T **205**. A. *P* 14½ (½ *to* 50 *c.*) *or* 13½ (75 *c. to* $10). B. *P* 13.

| | | A | | B | |
|---|---|---|---|---|---|
| 649 | ½ c. Type **205** (*inscr* "POINT SALINE") .. .. .. | 10 | 10 | † | |
| | a. Inscr "POINT SALINES" .. | 50·00 | — | † | |
| 650 | 1 c. Yacht club race .. .. | 10 | 10 | 10 | 30 |
| 651 | 2 c. Carenage taxi .. .. | 10 | 10 | 10 | 30 |
| 652 | 3 c. Large working boats .. | 10 | 10 | 10 | 30 |
| 653 | 5 c. Deep-water dock .. .. | 10 | 10 | 10 | 15 |
| 654 | 6 c. Cocoa beans in drying trays | 10 | 10 | 10 | 20 |
| 655 | 8 c. Nutmegs .. .. .. | 10 | 10 | † | |
| 656 | 10 c. Rum distillery, River Antoine Estate, *c* 1785 .. | 10 | 10 | 15 | 15 |
| 657 | 12 c. Cocoa tree .. .. .. | 10 | 10 | † | |
| 658 | 15 c. Fishermen at Fontenoy .. | 10 | 10 | 15 | 25 |
| 659 | 20 c. Parliament Building, St. George's .. .. .. | 15 | 15 | 20 | 30 |
| 660 | 25 c. Fort George cannons .. | 20 | 15 | 25 | 35 |
| 661 | 35 c. Pearls Airport .. .. | 20 | 15 | † | — |
| 662 | 50 c. General Post Office .. | 25 | 30 | 45 | 55 |
| 663 | 75 c. Carib's Leap, Sauteurs Bay (45 × 28 *mm*) .. .. | 45 | 50 | † | |
| 664 | $1 Carenage, St. George's (45 × 28 mm) .. .. | 65 | 70 | † | |
| 665 | $2 St. George's Harbour by night (45 × 28 mm) .. | 1·00 | 1·50 | † | |
| 666 | $3 Grand Anse Beach (45 × 28 *mm*) .. .. .. | 1·25 | 2·00 | † | |
| 667 | $5 Canoe Bay and Black Bay from Point Saline Lighthouse (45 × 28 *mm*) .. | 1·75 | 2·75 | † | |
| 668 | $10 Sugar-loaf Island from Levera Beach (45 × 28 *mm*) | 4·50 | 6·50 | † | |
| 649/68 | .. .. .. *Set of* 20 | 10·00 | 13·00 | † | |

No. 649a occurs on R. 6/1 and 7/1 from plate 1A and R. 10/5 from plate 1C. It is believed that the plate was originally produced showing the incorrect inscription ("POINT SALINES") on every stamp. Each position was then individually corrected, but those noted were missed.

Dates of issue:—13.1.75, Nos. 649A/62A; 22.1.75, 663A/7A; 26.3.75, No. 668A; 1978, Nos. 650B/4B, 656B, 658B/62B.

**206** Sail-fish

(Des V. Whiteley. Litho Format)

**1975** (3 Feb). *Big Game Fishing.* T **206** *and similar horiz designs. Multicoloured. P* 14½.

669 ½ c. Type **206** .. .. .. .. .. .. 10 10
670 1 c. Blue Marlin .. .. .. .. .. 10 10
671 2 c. White Marlin .. .. .. .. .. 10 10
672 10 c. Yellowfin Tuna .. .. .. .. .. 10 10
673 25 c. Wahoo .. .. .. .. .. .. 25 10
674 50 c. Dolphin .. .. .. .. .. .. 40 15
675 70 c. Grouper .. .. .. .. .. .. 60 20
676 $1 Great Barracuda .. .. .. .. .. 80 35
669/76 .. .. .. .. .. *Set of* 8 2·00 70
**MS**677 107 × 80 mm. $2 Blue Pointer or Mako Shark. P 13 .. .. .. .. .. 1·00 1·25

**207** Granadilla Barbadine    **208** Dove, Grenada Flag and U.N. Emblem

(Des G. Vasarhelyi. Litho Format)

**1975** (26 Feb). *Flowers.* T **207** *and similar horiz designs. Multicoloured. P* 14½.

678 ½ c. Type **207** .. .. .. .. .. 10 10
679 1 c. Bleeding Heart (Easter Lily) .. .. 10 10
680 2 c. Poinsettia .. .. .. .. .. 10 10
681 3 c. Cocoa flower .. .. .. .. .. 10 10
682 10 c. Gladioli .. .. .. .. .. 10 10
683 25 c. Redhead/Yellowhead .. .. .. 25 10
684 50 c. Plumbago .. .. .. .. .. 45 15
685 $1 Orange flower .. .. .. .. 70 25
678/85 .. .. .. .. .. *Set of* 8 1·40 55
**MS**686 102 × 82 mm. $2 Barbados Gooseberry. P 13 .. .. .. .. .. .. 1·10 1·25

(Des G. Drummond. Litho Format)

**1975** (19 Mar). *Grenada's Admission to the U.N.* (1974). T **208** *and similar vert designs. Multicoloured. P* 14½.

687 ½ c. Type **208** .. .. .. .. .. 10 10
688 1 c. Grenada and U.N. flags .. .. .. 10 10
689 2 c. Grenada coat of arms .. .. .. 10 10
690 35 c. U.N. emblem over map of Grenada .. 15 10
691 50 c. U.N. buildings and flags .. .. .. 20 15
692 $2 U.N. emblem and scroll .. .. .. 45 45
687/92 .. .. .. .. *Set of* 6 80 70
**MS**693 122 × 91 mm. 75 c. Type **208** and $1 as 2 c. P 13 .. .. .. .. .. .. .. 65 90

**CANCELLED REMAINDERS*.** Some of the following issues have been remaindered, cancelled-to-order, at a fraction of their face-value. For all practical purposes these are indistinguishable from genuine postally used copies. Our used quotations which are indicated by an asterisk are the same for cancelled-to-order or postally used copies.

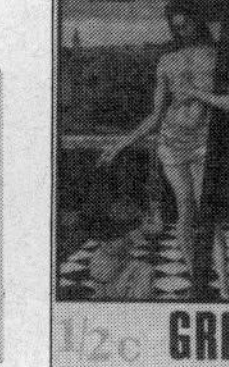


**209** Paul Revere's Midnight Ride    **210** "Blood of the Redeemer" (G. Bellini)

(Des J. Cornel (½ to 10 c.), PAD Studio (40 c. to $1), J.W. (**MS**704). Litho Format)

**1975** (6 May). *Bicentenary of American Revolution* (1st issue). T **209** *and similar multicoloured designs. P* 14½.

(*a*) *Postage. Horiz designs*

694 ½ c. Type **209** .. .. .. .. .. 10 10*
695 1 c. Crispus Attucks .. .. .. .. 10 10*
696 2 c. Patrick Henry .. .. .. .. 10 10*
697 3 c. Franklin visits Washington .. .. 10 10*
698 5 c. Rebel troops .. .. .. .. 10 10*
699 10 c. John Paul Jones .. .. .. .. 10 10*

(*b*) *Air. Vert designs*

700 40 c. "John Hancock" (Copley) .. .. 30 10*
701 50 c. "Benjamin Franklin" (Roslin) .. .. 45 15*
702 75 c. "John Adams" (Copley) .. .. .. 60 15*
703 $1 "Lafayette" (Casanova) .. .. .. 75 20*
694/703 .. .. .. .. *Set of* 10 2·00 60*
**MS**704 Two sheets 131 × 102 mm: $2 Grenada arms and U.S. seal; $2 Grenada and U.S. flags. P 13½ .. .. .. .. .. .. 3·00 60*

Stamps from **MS**704 are horiz and larger: 47½ × 35mm.

Nos. 694/703 also exist perf 13 (*Price for set of* 10 £2 *mint or used*) from additional sheetlets of 5 stamps and 1 label. Stamps perforated 14½ are from normal sheets of 40.

See also Nos. 785/92.

(Des M. Shamir. Litho Format)

**1975** (21 May). *Easter.* T **210** *and similar vert designs. Multicoloured. P* 14½.

705 ½ c. Type **210** .. .. .. .. .. 10 10*
706 1 c. "Pietà" (Bellini) .. .. .. .. 10 10*
707 2 c. "The Entombment" (Van der Weyden) .. 10 10*
708 3 c. "Pietà" (Bellini) .. .. .. .. 10 10*
709 35 c. "Pietà" (Bellini) .. .. .. .. 30 10*
710 75 c. "The Dead Christ" (Bellini) .. .. 45 10*
711 $1 "The Dead Christ supported by Angels" (Procaccini) .. .. .. .. .. 55 10*
705/11 .. .. .. .. .. *Set of* 7 1·25 30*
**MS**712 117 × 100 mm. $2 "Pietà" (Botticelli). P 13 1·00 30*

**211** Wildlife Study    **212** Leafy Jewel Box

(Des J.W. Litho Format)

**1975** (2 July). *14th World Scout Jamboree, Norway.* T **211** *and similar horiz designs. Multicoloured. P* 14.

713 ½ c. Type **211** .. .. .. .. .. 10 10*
714 1 c. Sailing .. .. .. .. .. 10 10*
715 2 c. Map-reading .. .. .. .. .. 10 10*
716 35 c. First-aid .. .. .. .. .. 40 10*
717 40 c. Physical training .. .. .. .. 45 10*
718 75 c. Mountaineering .. .. .. .. 70 10*
719 $2 Sing-song .. .. .. .. .. 1·60 20*
713/19 .. .. .. .. .. *Set of* 7 3·00 40*
**MS**720 106 × 80 mm. $1 Boat-building .. .. 90 30*

(Des J.W. Litho Questa)

**1975** (1 Aug). *Seashells.* T **212** *and similar vert designs. Multicoloured. P* 14.

721 ½ c. Type **212** .. .. .. .. .. 10 10*
722 1 c. Emerald Nerite .. .. .. .. 10 10*
723 2 c. Yellow Cockle .. .. .. .. 10 10*
724 25 c. Purple Sea Snail .. .. .. .. 55 10*
725 50 c. Turkey Wing .. .. .. .. 1·00 10*
726 75 c. West Indian Fighting Conch .. .. 1·50 10*
727 $1 Noble Wentletrap .. .. .. .. 1·75 15*
721/7 .. .. .. .. .. *Set of* 7 4·50 50*
**MS**728 102 × 76 mm. $2 Music Volute .. .. 1·60 50*

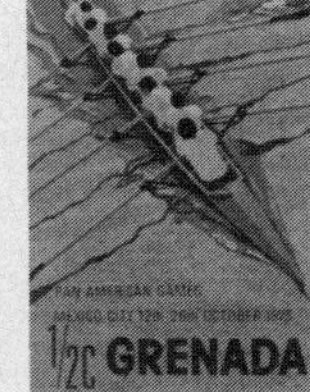


**213** *Lycorea ceres*    **214** Rowing

(Des J.W. Litho Format)

**1975** (22 Sept). *Butterflies.* T **213** *and similar vert designs. Multicoloured. P* 14.

729 ½ c. Type **213** .. .. .. .. .. 10 10*
730 1 c. *Adelpha cytherea* .. .. .. .. 10 10*
731 2 c. *Atlides polybe* .. .. .. .. 10 10*
732 35 c. *Anteos maerula* .. .. .. .. 50 10*
733 45 c. *Parides neophilus* .. .. .. .. 55 10*
734 75 c. *Nymula orestes* .. .. .. .. 85 15*
735 $2 *Euptychia cephus* .. .. .. .. 1·75 20*
729/35 .. .. .. .. .. *Set of* 7 3·25 50*
**MS**736 108×83 mm. $1 *Papilio astyalus* (sub-species *lycophron*) .. .. .. .. 90 40*

(Des J.W. Litho Questa)

**1975** (13 Oct). *Pan-American Games, Mexico City.* T **214** *and similar vert designs. Multicoloured. P* 14.

737 ½ c. Type **214** .. .. .. .. .. 10 10*
738 1 c. Swimming .. .. .. .. .. 10 10*
739 2 c. Show-jumping .. .. .. .. .. 10 10*
740 35 c. Gymnastics .. .. .. .. .. 15 10*
741 45 c. Football .. .. .. .. .. 15 10*
742 75 c. Boxing .. .. .. .. .. 25 15*
743 $2 Cycling .. .. .. .. .. 65 20*
737/43 .. .. .. .. .. *Set of* 7 1·10 40*
**MS**744 106 × 81 mm. $1 Yachting .. .. .. 1·00 40*

**215** "The Boy David" (Michelangelo)    **216** "Madonna and Child" (Filippino Lippi)

(Des M. and G. Shamir. Litho J.W.)

**1975** (3 Nov). *500th Birth Anniv of Michelangelo.* T **215** *and similar vert designs. Multicoloured. P* 14.

745 ½ c. Type **215** .. .. .. .. .. 10 10*
746 1 c. "Young Man" (detail) .. .. .. .. 10 10*
747 2 c. "Moses" .. .. .. .. .. 10 10*
748 40 c. "Prophet Zachariah" .. .. .. .. 20 10*
749 50 c. "St John the Baptist" .. .. .. 20 10*
750 75 c. "Judith and Holofernes" .. .. .. 35 15*
751 $2 "Doni Madonna" (detail from "Holy Family") .. .. .. .. .. .. 70 20*
745/51 .. .. .. .. .. *Set of* 7 1·40 50*
**MS**752 104 × 89 mm. $1 "Madonna" (head from Pietà) .. .. .. .. .. .. 70 30*

The sculpture on No. 749 though ascribed to Michelangelo, shows a work by Francesco Sangallo.

(Des M. Shamir. Litho Questa)

**1975** (8 Dec). *Christmas.* T **216** *and similar vert designs showing "Virgin and Child". Multicoloured. P* 14.

753 ½ c. Type **216** .. .. .. .. .. 10 10*
754 1 c. Mantegna .. .. .. .. .. 10 10*
755 2 c. Luis de Morales .. .. .. .. 10 10*
756 35 c. G. M. Morandi .. .. .. .. 15 10*
757 50 c. Antonello da Messina .. .. .. 20 10*
758 75 c. Dürer .. .. .. .. .. 25 10*
759 $1 Velasquez .. .. .. .. .. 35 10*
753/9 .. .. .. .. .. *Set of* 7 90 35*
**MS**760 125 × 98 mm. $2 Bellini .. .. .. 75 30*

**217** Bananaquit    **218** Carnival Time

(Des G. Drummond. Litho Questa)

**1976** (20 Jan). *Flora and Fauna. T* **217** *and similar multicoloured designs. P* 14.

| No. | Description | | |
|---|---|---|---|
| 761 | ½ c. Type **217** | 10 | 10 |
| 762 | 1 c. Brazilian Agouti | 10 | 10 |
| 763 | 2 c. Hawksbill Turtle (*horiz*) | 10 | 10 |
| 764 | 5 c. Dwarf Poinciana | 10 | 10 |
| 765 | 35 c. Albacore (*horiz*) | 90 | 45 |
| 766 | 40 c. Cardinal's Guard | 95 | 50 |
| 767 | $2 Nine-banded Armadillo (*horiz*) | 3·00 | 2·25 |
| 761/7 | *Set of* 7 | 4·50 | 3·00 |
| **MS**768 | 82 × 89 mm. $1 Belted Kingfisher | 3·50 | 2·00 |

(Des G. Drummond. Litho Questa)

**1976** (25 Feb). *Tourism. T* **218** *and similar horiz designs. Multicoloured. P* 14.

| No. | Description | | |
|---|---|---|---|
| 769 | ½ c. Type **218** | 10 | 10 |
| 770 | 1 c. Scuba diving | 10 | 10 |
| 771 | 2 c. Cruise Ship *Southward* at St. George's | 10 | 10 |
| 772 | 35 c. Game fishing | 55 | 20 |
| 773 | 50 c. St. George's Golf Course | 1·50 | 60 |
| 774 | 75 c. Tennis | 1·75 | 1·25 |
| 775 | $1 Ancient rock carvings at Mount Rich | 2·00 | 1·75 |
| 769/75 | *Set of* 7 | 5·50 | 3·50 |
| **MS**776 | 100 × 73 mm. $2 Small boat sailing | 1·50 | 2·50 |

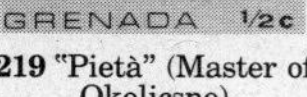


**219** "Pietà" (Master of Okolicsno)

**220** Sharpshooters

(Des M. and G. Shamir. Litho Questa)

**1976** (29 Mar). *Easter. T* **219** *and similar vert designs by the artists listed. Multicoloured. P* 14.

| No. | Description | | |
|---|---|---|---|
| 777 | ½ c. Type **219** | 10 | 10 |
| 778 | 1 c. Correggio | 10 | 10 |
| 779 | 2 c. Van der Weyden | 10 | 10 |
| 780 | 3 c. Dürer | 10 | 10 |
| 781 | 35 c. Master of the Holy Spirit | 15 | 10 |
| 782 | 75 c. Raphael | 30 | 40 |
| 783 | $1 Raphael | 35 | 50 |
| 777/83 | *Set of* 7 | 85 | 1·10 |
| **MS**784 | 108 × 86 mm. $2 Crespi | 70 | 1·25 |

(Des J.W. Litho Questa)

**1976** (15 Apr). *Bicentenary of American Revolution (2nd issue). T* **220** *and similar vert designs. Multicoloured. P* 14.

| No. | Description | | |
|---|---|---|---|
| 785 | ½ c. Type **220** | 10 | 10 |
| 786 | 1 c. Defending the Liberty Pole | 10 | 10 |
| 787 | 2 c. Loading muskets | 10 | 10 |
| 788 | 35 c. The fight for Liberty | 30 | 15 |
| 789 | 50 c. Peace Treaty, 1783 | 50 | 40 |
| 790 | $1 Drummers | 1·00 | 90 |
| 791 | $3 Gunboat | 2·50 | 2·50 |
| 785/91 | *Set of* 7 | 4·00 | 3·50 |
| **MS**792 | 93 × 79 mm. 75 c. as 35 c. and $2 as 50 c. | 1·50 | 2·50 |

**221** Nature Study

**222** Volleyball

(Des G. Vasarhelyi. Litho Questa)

**1976** (1 June). *50th Anniv of Girl Guides in Grenada. T* **221** *and similar vert designs. Multicoloured. P* 14.

| No. | Description | | |
|---|---|---|---|
| 793 | ½ c. Type **221** | 10 | 10 |
| 794 | 1 c. Campfire cooking | 10 | 10 |
| 795 | 2 c. First Aid | 10 | 10 |
| 796 | 50 c. Camping | 55 | 35 |
| 797 | 75 c. Home economics | 85 | 70 |
| 798 | $2 First Aid | 2·50 | 2·50 |
| 793/8 | *Set of* 6 | 3·50 | 3·25 |
| **MS**799 | 111 × 85 mm. $1 Painting | 1·25 | 2·25 |

(Des J.W. Litho Questa)

**1976** (21 June). *Olympic Games, Montreal. T* **222** *and similar vert designs. Multicoloured. P* 14.

| No. | Description | | |
|---|---|---|---|
| 800 | ½ c. Type **222** | 10 | 10 |
| 801 | 1 c. Cycling | 10 | 10 |
| 802 | 2 c. Rowing | 10 | 10 |
| 803 | 35 c. Judo | 15 | 10 |
| 804 | 45 c. Hockey | 20 | 30 |
| 805 | 75 c. Gymnastics | 35 | 60 |
| 806 | $1 High jump | 50 | 85 |
| 800/6 | *Set of* 7 | 1·10 | 1·75 |
| **MS**807 | 106 × 81 mm. $3 Equestrian event | 1·25 | 2·50 |

**223** "Cha-U-Kao at the Moulin Rouge"

**224** Piper "Apache"

(Des M. Shamir. Litho Questa)

**1976** (20 July). *75th Death Anniv of Toulouse Lautrec. T* **223** *and similar vert designs. Multicoloured. P* 14.

| No. | Description | | |
|---|---|---|---|
| 808 | ½ c. Type **223** | 10 | 10 |
| 809 | 1 c. "Quadrille at the Moulin Rouge" | 10 | 10 |
| 810 | 2 c. "Profile of a Woman" | 10 | 10 |
| 811 | 3 c. "Salon in the Rue des Moulins" | 10 | 10 |
| 812 | 40 c. "The Laundryman" | 40 | 35 |
| 813 | 50 c. "Marcelle Lender dancing the Bolero" | 50 | 40 |
| 814 | $2 "Signor Boileau at the Cafe" | 1·25 | 1·50 |
| 808/14 | *Set of* 7 | 2·00 | 2·25 |
| **MS**815 | 152 × 125 mm. $1 "Woman with Boa" | 85 | 1·25 |

**1976** (26 July). *West Indian Victory in World Cricket Cup. As Nos.* 559/60 *of Barbados.*

| No. | Description | | |
|---|---|---|---|
| 816 | 35 c. Map of the Caribbean | 1·25 | 35 |
| 817 | $1 The Prudential Cup | 2·75 | 2·75 |

(Des J.W. Litho Questa)

**1976** (18 Aug). *Aeroplanes. T* **224** *and similar horiz designs. Multicoloured. P* 14.

| No. | Description | | |
|---|---|---|---|
| 818 | ½ c. Type **224** | 10 | 10 |
| 819 | 1 c. Beech "Twin Bonanza" | 10 | 10 |
| 820 | 2 c. D.H. "Twin Otter" | 10 | 10 |
| 821 | 40 c. Britten Norman "Islander" | 70 | 50 |
| 822 | 50 c. D.H. "Heron" | 75 | 60 |
| 823 | $2 H.S. "748" | 2·50 | 2·75 |
| 818/23 | *Set of* 6 | 3·50 | 3·50 |
| **MS**824 | 75 × 83 mm. $3 B.A.C. "1-11" | 2·50 | 4·00 |

**225** Satellite Assembly

**226** S.S. *Geestland*

(Des PAD Studio. Litho Questa)

**1976** (1 Sept). *Viking and Helios Space Missions. T* **225** *and similar multicoloured designs. P* 14.

| No. | Description | | |
|---|---|---|---|
| 825 | ½ c. Type **225** | 10 | 10 |
| 826 | 1 c. Helios satellite | 10 | 10 |
| 827 | 2 c. Helios encapsulation | 10 | 10 |
| 828 | 15 c. Systems test | 10 | 10 |
| 829 | 45 c. Viking lander (*horiz*) | 20 | 20 |
| 830 | 75 c. Lander on Mars | 35 | 60 |
| 831 | $2 Viking encapsulation | 90 | 1·60 |
| 825/31 | *Set of* 7 | 1·40 | 2·25 |
| **MS**832 | 110 × 85 mm. $3 Orbiter and lander | 1·00 | 2·00 |

(Des J.W. Litho Format)

**1976** (3 Nov). *Ships. T* **226** *and similar horiz designs. Multicoloured. P* 14½.

| No. | Description | | |
|---|---|---|---|
| 833 | ½ c. Type **226** | 10 | 10 |
| 834 | 1 c. M. V. *Federal Palm* | 10 | 10 |
| 835 | 2 c. H.M.S. *Blake* | 10 | 10 |
| 836 | 25 c. M. V. *Vistafjord* | 35 | 15 |
| 837 | 75 c. S.S. *Canberra* | 90 | 80 |
| 838 | $1 S.S. *Regina* | 1·25 | 90 |
| 839 | $5 S.S. *Arandora Star* | 4·50 | 4·75 |
| 833/39 | *Set of* 7 | 6·50 | 6·00 |
| **MS**840 | 91 × 78 mm. $2 *Santa Maria* | 2·00 | 3·25 |

**227** "Altarpiece of San Barnaba" (Botticelli)

(Des PAD Studio. Litho Questa)

**1976** (8 Dec). *Christmas. T* **227** *and similar horiz designs. Multicoloured. P* 14.

| No. | Description | | |
|---|---|---|---|
| 841 | ½ c. Type **227** | 10 | 10 |
| 842 | 1 c. "Annunciation" (Botticelli) | 10 | 10 |
| 843 | 2 c. "Madonna of Chancellor Rolin" (Jan van Eyck) | 10 | 10 |
| 844 | 35 c. "Annunciation" (Fra Filippo Lippi) | 15 | 10 |
| 845 | 50 c. "Madonna of the Magnificat" (Botticelli) | 20 | 20 |
| 846 | 75 c. "Madonna of the Pomegranate" (Botticelli) | 30 | 30 |
| 847 | $3 "Madonna with St. Cosmas and Other Saints" (Botticelli) | 1·00 | 1·75 |
| 841/7 | *Set of* 7 | 1·50 | 2·25 |
| **MS**848 | 71 × 57 mm. $2 "Gypsy Madonna" (Titian) | 75 | 1·75 |

**228** Alexander Graham Bell and Telephones

**229** Coronation Scene

(Des G. Vasarhelyi. Litho Questa)

**1976** (17 Dec). *Telephone Centenary. T* **228** *and similar horiz designs. Multicoloured. P* 14.

| No. | Description | | |
|---|---|---|---|
| 849 | ½ c. Type **228** | 10 | 10 |
| 850 | 1 c. Telephone-users within globe | 10 | 10 |
| 851 | 2 c. Telephone satellite | 10 | 10 |
| 852 | 18 c. Telephone viewer and console | 15 | 15 |
| 853 | 40 c. Satellite and tracking stations | 35 | 45 |
| 854 | $1 Satellite transmitting to ships | 65 | 85 |
| 855 | $2 Dish aerial and modern telephone | 1·10 | 1·40 |
| 849/55 | *Set of* 7 | 2·00 | 2·75 |
| **MS**856 | 107 × 80 mm. $5 Globe encircled by flags | 2·25 | 3·75 |

(Des J.W. Litho Questa (Nos. 857/62), Walsall (863/6))

**1977** (8 Feb). *Silver Jubilee. T* **229** *and similar vert designs. Multicoloured.* (a) *Sheet stamps. P* 13½ × 14.

| No. | Description | | |
|---|---|---|---|
| 857 | ½ c. Type **229** | 10 | 10 |
| 858 | 1 c. Sceptre and orb | 10 | 10 |
| 859 | 35 c. Queen on horseback | 15 | 10 |
| 860 | $2 Spoon and ampulla | 60 | 60 |
| 861 | $2.50 Queen and Prince Philip | 65 | 60 |
| 857/61 | *Set of* 5 | 1·25 | 1·10 |
| **MS**862 | 103 × 79 mm. $5 Royal Visit to Grenada | 1·00 | 2·00 |

Nos. 857/61 also exist perf 11½ × 12 (*Price for set of* 5 £1·25 *mint or used*) from additional sheetlets of 5 stamps and 1 label. They also have different frame colours to those perforated 13½ × 14, which come from normal sheets of 40.

(*b*) *Booklet stamps. Roul* 5 × *imperf*. Self-adhesive*

| No. | Description | | |
|---|---|---|---|
| 863 | 35 c. As No. 861 | 25 | 25 |
| | a. Booklet pane of 6 | 1·50 | |
| 864 | 50 c. As No. 860 | 55 | 70 |
| | a. Booklet pane. Nos. 864/6 | 4·00 | |
| 865 | $1 As No. 858 | 1·00 | 1·50 |
| 866 | $3 As No. 859 | 2·75 | 3·75 |
| 863/6 | *Set of* 4 | 4·00 | 5·75 |

*No. 863/6 are separated by various combinations of rotary knife (giving a straight edge) and roulette.

**230** Water Skiing

(Des G. Drummond. Litho Questa)

**1977** (Apr). *Easter Water Parade. T* **230** *and similar horiz designs. Multicoloured. P* 14.

| No. | Description | | |
|---|---|---|---|
| 867 | ½ c. Type **230** | 10 | 10 |
| 868 | 1 c. Speedboat race | 10 | 10 |
| 869 | 2 c. Row boat race | 10 | 10 |
| 870 | 22 c. Swimming | 15 | 15 |
| 871 | 35 c. Work boat race | 25 | 20 |
| 872 | 75 c. Water polo | 50 | 60 |
| 873 | $2 Game fishing | 1·40 | 2·00 |
| 867/73 | *Set of* 7 | 2·25 | 2·75 |
| **MS**874 | 115 × 85 mm. $3 Yacht race | 1·50 | 2·75 |

**231** Meeting Place, Grand Anse Beach

(Litho Questa)

**1977** (14 June). *Seventh Meeting of Organization of American States. P* 14.

| No. | Description | | |
|---|---|---|---|
| 875 **231** | 35 c. multicoloured | 10 | 10 |
| 876 | $1 multicoloured | 25 | 60 |
| 877 | $2 multicoloured | 40 | 1·25 |
| 875/7 | *Set of* 3 | 65 | 1·75 |

**232** Rafting

(Des G. Drummond. Litho Questa)

**1977** (6 Sept). *Caribbean Scout Jamboree, Jamaica. T* **232** *and similar horiz designs. Multicoloured. P* 14.

| | | | |
|---|---|---|---|
| 878 | ½ c. Type **232** | 10 | 10 |
| 879 | 1 c. Tug-of-war | 10 | 10 |
| 880 | 2 c. Sea Scouts regatta | 10 | 10 |
| 881 | 18 c. Camp fire | 25 | 15 |
| 882 | 40 c. Field kitchen | 50 | 30 |
| 883 | $1 Scouts and sea scouts | 1·25 | 1·00 |
| 884 | $2 Hiking and map reading | 1·75 | 2·25 |
| 878/84 | *Set of* 7 | 3·50 | 3·50 |
| **MS**885 | 107 × 85 mm. $3 Semaphore | 2·00 | 3·25 |

233 Angel and Shepherd

Royal Visit W. I. 1977

(234)

(Des G. Vasarhelyi. Litho Questa)

**1977** (3 Nov). *Christmas. T* **233** *and similar horiz designs showing ceiling panels from the church of St. Martin in Zillis. Multicoloured. P* 14.

| | | | |
|---|---|---|---|
| 886 | ½ c. Type **233** | 10 | 10 |
| 887 | 1 c. St. Joseph | 10 | 10 |
| 888 | 2 c. Virgin and Child Fleeing to Egypt | 10 | 10 |
| 889 | 22 c. Angel | 10 | 10 |
| 890 | 35 c. A Magus on horseback | 15 | 10 |
| 891 | 75 c. Three horses | 20 | 30 |
| 892 | $2 Virgin and Child | 50 | 1·10 |
| 886/92 | *Set of* 7 | 85 | 1·50 |
| **MS**893 | 85 × 112 mm. $3 Magus offering gifts | 1·00 | 2·00 |

**1977** (10 Nov). *Royal Visit. Nos.* 857/62 *optd with T* **234**. *P* 13½ × 14 (35 c., $2, $2.50) *or* 11½ × 12 (*others*).

| | | | |
|---|---|---|---|
| 894 | ½ c. Type **229** | 10 | 10 |
| 895 | 1 c. Sceptre and orb | 10 | 10 |
| 896 | 35 c. Queen on horseback | 15 | 10 |
| 897 | $2 Spoon and ampulla | 40 | 40 |
| 898 | $2.50, Queen and Prince Philip | 45 | 45 |
| 894/8 | *Set of* 5 | 1·00 | 85 |
| **MS**899 | 103 × 79 mm. $5 Royal Visit to Grenada | 1·00 | 1·50 |

Nos. 894/5 only exist perforated 11½ × 12, but the remaining three values come perforated 13½ × 14 or 11½ × 12 (*Nos.* 896/8 *perf* 11½ × 12. *Price for set of* 3 £1.50 *mint or used.*)

235 Christjaan Eijkman (Medicine)

236 Count von Zeppelin and First Zeppelin Airship

(Des J.W. Litho Questa)

**1978** (25 Jan). *Nobel Prize Winners. T* **235** *and similar vert designs. Multicoloured. P* 14.

| | | | |
|---|---|---|---|
| 900 | ½ c. Type **235** | 10 | 10 |
| 901 | 1 c. Sir Winston Churchill (Literature) | 10 | 10 |
| 902 | 2 c. Woodrow Wilson (Peace) | 10 | 10 |
| 903 | 35 c. Frederic Passy (Peace) | 15 | 10 |
| 904 | $1 Albert Einstein (Physics) | 55 | 40 |
| 905 | $3 Carl Bosch (Chemistry) | 1·75 | 1·50 |
| 900/5 | *Set of* 6 | 2·25 | 2·00 |
| **MS**906 | 114 × 99 mm. $2 Alfred Nobel | 70 | 1·00 |

(Des G. Vasarhelyi. Litho Questa)

**1978** (13 Feb). *75th Anniv of First Zeppelin Flight and 50th Anniv of Lindbergh's Transatlantic Flight. T* **236** *and similar horiz designs. Multicoloured. P* 14.

| | | | |
|---|---|---|---|
| 907 | ½ c. Type **236** | 10 | 10 |
| 908 | 1 c. Lindbergh with *Spirit of St. Louis* | 10 | 10 |
| 909 | 2 c. Airship *Deutschland* | 10 | 10 |
| 910 | 22 c. Lindbergh's arrival in France | 15 | 10 |
| 911 | 75 c. Lindbergh and *Spirit of St. Louis* in flight | 40 | 30 |
| 912 | $1 Zeppelin over Alps | 50 | 40 |
| 913 | $3 Zeppelin over White House | 1·25 | 1·10 |
| 907/13 | *Set of* 7 | 2·25 | 1·75 |
| **MS**914 | 103 × 85 mm. 35 c. Lindbergh in cockpit; $2 Count von Zeppelin and airship | 1·10 | 1·40 |

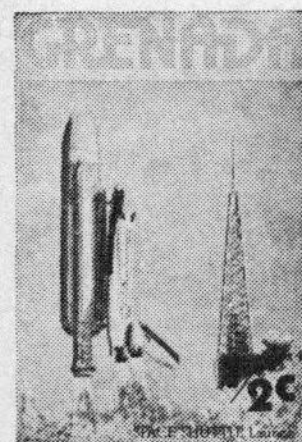
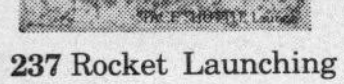

237 Rocket Launching

238 Black-headed Gull

(Des J.W. Litho Questa)

**1978** (28 Feb). *Space Shuttle. T* **237** *and similar vert designs. Multicoloured. P* 14.

| | | | |
|---|---|---|---|
| 915 | ½ c. Type **237** | 10 | 10 |
| 916 | 1 c. Booster jettison | 10 | 10 |
| 917 | 2 c. External tank jettison | 10 | 10 |
| 918 | 18 c. Space shuttle in orbit | 15 | 15 |
| 919 | 75 c. Satellite placement | 35 | 35 |
| 920 | $2 Landing approach | 1·00 | 1·00 |
| 915/20 | *Set of* 6 | 1·40 | 1·40 |
| **MS**921 | 103 × 85 mm. $3 Shuttle after landing | 1·10 | 1·25 |

(Des G. Drummond. Litho Questa)

**1978** (9 Mar). *Wild Birds of Grenada. T* **238** *and similar vert designs. Multicoloured. P* 14.

| | | | |
|---|---|---|---|
| 922 | ½ c. Type **238** | 10 | 10 |
| 923 | 1 c. Wilson's Petrel | 10 | 10 |
| 924 | 2 c. Killdeer Plover | 10 | 10 |
| 925 | 50 c. White-necked Jacobin | 1·50 | 30 |
| 926 | 75 c. Blue-faced Booby | 2·00 | 45 |
| 927 | $1 Broad-winged Hawk | 3·00 | 75 |
| 928 | $2 Red-necked Pigeon | 4·00 | 1·75 |
| 922/8 | *Set of* 7 | 9·50 | 3·00 |
| **MS**929 | 103 × 94 mm. $3 Scarlet Ibis | 5·00 | 4·00 |

239 "The Landing of Marie de Medici at Marseilles"

240 Ludwig van Beethoven

(Des PAD Studio. Litho Questa)

**1978** (30 Mar). *400th Birth Anniv of Rubens. T* **239** *and similar vert designs showing paintings. Multicoloured. P* 13½ × 14.

| | | | |
|---|---|---|---|
| 930 | 5 c. Type **239** | 10 | 10 |
| 931 | 15 c. "Rubens and Isabella Brandt" | 10 | 10 |
| 932 | 18 c. "Marchesa Brigida Spindola-Doria" | 10 | 10 |
| 933 | 25 c. "Ludovicus Nonninus" | 10 | 10 |
| 934 | 45 c. "Helene Fourment and her Children" | 15 | 15 |
| 935 | 75 c. "Clara Serena Rubens" | 25 | 25 |
| 936 | $3 "Le Chapeau de Paille" | 60 | 80 |
| 930/6 | *Set of* 7 | 1·10 | 1·40 |
| **MS**937 | 65 × 100 mm. $5 "Self Portrait" | 1·25 | 2·00 |

(Des PAD Studio. Litho Questa)

**1978** (24 Apr). *150th Death Anniv of Beethoven. T* **240** *and similar multicoloured designs. P* 14.

| | | | |
|---|---|---|---|
| 938 | 5 c. Type **240** | 10 | 10 |
| 939 | 15 c. Woman violinist (*horiz*) | 15 | 10 |
| 940 | 18 c. Musical instruments (*horiz*) | 20 | 15 |
| 941 | 22 c. Piano (*horiz*) | 20 | 15 |
| 942 | 50 c. Violins | 40 | 30 |
| 943 | 75 c. Piano and sonata score | 60 | 45 |
| 944 | $3 Beethoven's portrait and home (*horiz*) | 2·25 | 1·75 |
| 938/44 | *Set of* 7 | 3·50 | 2·75 |
| **MS**945 | 83 × 62 mm. $2 Beethoven and score | 1·50 | 2·00 |

241 King Edward's Chair

242 Queen Elizabeth II taking Salute at Trooping the Colour

(Des J.W. Litho Questa. (Nos. 946/9). Manufactured by Walsall. (Nos. 950/2))

**1978** (2 May–14 June). *25th Anniv of Coronation. Multicoloured.*

(*a*) *Sheet stamps. Vert designs as T* **241**. *P* 14 (14 June)

| | | | |
|---|---|---|---|
| 946 | 35 c. Type **241** | 15 | 10 |
| 947 | $2 Queen with regalia | 50 | 50 |
| 948 | $2.50, St. Edward's Crown | 60 | 50 |
| 946/8 | *Set of* 3 | 1·10 | 1·00 |
| **MS**949 | 102 × 76 mm. $5 Queen and Prince Philip | 1·50 | 1·40 |

(*b*) *Booklet stamps. Vert designs as T* **242**. *Roul* 5 × *imperf**. *Self-adhesive* (2 May)

| | | | |
|---|---|---|---|
| 950 | 25 c. Type **242** | 15 | 15 |
| | a. Booklet pane. Nos. 950/1, each × 3 | 80 | |
| 951 | 35 c. Queen taking part in Maundy Thursday ceremony | 15 | 25 |
| 952 | $5 Queen and Prince Philip at Opening of Parliament | 2·00 | 2·75 |
| | a. Booklet pane of 1 | 2·00 | |
| 950/2 | *Set of* 3 | 2·00 | 2·75 |

Nos. 946/8 also exist perf 12 (*Price for set of* 3 £1·10 *mint or used*) from additional sheetlets of 3 stamps and 1 label, issued 2 June. These have different frame colours from the stamps perforated 14, which come from normal sheets of 50.

*Nos. 950/1 are separated by various combinations of rotary-knife (giving a straight edge) and roulette. No. 952 exists only with straight edges.

243 Goalkeeper reaching for Ball

244 Aerial Phenomena, Germany, 1561 and U.S.A., 1952

(Des M. Rubin. Litho Format)

**1978** (1 Aug). *World Cup Football Championship, Argentina. T* **243** *and similar vert designs showing goalkeeper reaching for ball. P* 14½.

| | | | |
|---|---|---|---|
| 953 | 40 c. multicoloured | 10 | 10 |
| 954 | 60 c. multicoloured | 15 | 20 |
| 955 | 90 c. multicoloured | 25 | 30 |
| 956 | $2 multicoloured | 60 | 60 |
| 953/6 | *Set of* 4 | 1·00 | 1·10 |
| **MS**957 | 130 × 97 mm. $2.50, multicoloured | 1·25 | 1·10 |

(Des G. Vasarhelyi. Litho Format)

**1978** (17 Aug). *U.F.O. Research. T* **244** *and similar horiz designs. Multicoloured. P* 14½.

| | | | |
|---|---|---|---|
| 958 | 5 c. Type **244** | 15 | 10 |
| 959 | 35 c. Various aerial phenomena, 1950 | 35 | 25 |
| 960 | $3 U.F.O.'s, 1965 | 2·00 | 1·75 |
| 958/60 | *Set of* 3 | 2·25 | 1·90 |
| **MS**961 | 112 × 89 mm. $2 Sir Eric Gairy and U.F.O. research laboratory | 1·25 | 1·25 |

245 Wright Glider, 1902

(Des G. Vasarhelyi. Litho Questa)

**1978** (28 Aug). *75th Anniv of Powered Flight. T* **245** *and similar horiz designs. Multicoloured. P* 14.

| | | | |
|---|---|---|---|
| 962 | 5 c. Type **245** | 10 | 10 |
| 963 | 15 c. *Flyer* 1, 1903 | 10 | 10 |
| 964 | 18 c. *Flyer* 3 | 10 | 10 |
| 965 | 22 c. *Flyer* 3 from above | 15 | 10 |
| 966 | 50 c. Orville Wright and *Flyer* | 25 | 20 |
| 967 | 75 c. *Flyer* 3 in Pau, France, 1908 | 35 | 25 |
| 968 | $3 Wilbur Wright and glider | 1·10 | 70 |
| 962/8 | *Set of* 7 | 1·90 | 1·25 |
| **MS**969 | 114 × 85 mm. $2 Wright glider | 1·50 | 1·25 |

246 Cook and Hawaiian Feast

247 "Paumgartner Altarpiece" (detail)

(Des G. Vasarhelyi. Litho Questa)

**1978** (5 Dec). *Bicentenary of Discovery of Hawaii and 250th Birth Anniv of Captain Cook. T* **246** *and similar horiz designs. Multicoloured. P* 14.

| | | | |
|---|---|---|---|
| 970 | 18 c. Type **246** | 55 | 15 |
| 971 | 35 c. Cook and Hawaiian warriors | 75 | 25 |
| 972 | 75 c. Cook and Honolulu Harbour | 1·50 | 1·00 |
| 973 | $3 Cook (statue) and H.M.S. *Resolution* | 3·50 | 3·25 |
| 970/3 | *Set of* 4 | 5·75 | 4·25 |
| **MS**974 | 116 × 88 mm. $4 Cook and death scene | 3·50 | 3·75 |

(Des M. Rubin. Litho Questa)

**1978** (20 Dec). *Christmas. Paintings by Dürer. T* **247** *and similar vert designs. Multicoloured. P* 14.

| | | | |
|---|---|---|---|
| 975 | 40 c. Type **247** | 25 | 15 |
| 976 | 60 c. "The Adoration of the Magi" | 30 | 20 |
| 977 | 90 c. "The Virgin and Child" | 40 | 20 |
| 978 | $2 "Virgin and Child with St. Anne" (detail) | 75 | 55 |
| 975/8 | *Set of* 4 | 1·50 | 1·00 |
| **MS**979 | 113 × 83 mm. $4 "Madonna and Child" | 1·10 | 1·50 |

## MINIMUM PRICE

The minimum price quote is 10p which represents a handling charge rather than a basis for valuing common stamps. For further notes about prices see introductory pages.

248 National Convention and Cultural Centre (interior)

249 *Acalypha hispida*

(Des BG Studio. Litho Questa)

**1979** (8 Feb). *5th Anniv of Independence. T* **248** *and similar vert designs. Multicoloured. P* 14.
980 5 c. Type **248** .. .. .. .. .. .. 10 10
981 18 c. National Convention and Cultural Centre (exterior) .. .. .. .. .. 10 10
982 22 c. Easter Water Parade, 1978 .. .. 10 10
983 35 c. Sir Eric M. Gairy (Prime Minister) .. 15 10
984 $3 The Cross, Fort Frederick .. .. 60 80
980/4 .. .. .. .. .. *Set of* 5 80 90

(Des J.W. Litho Questa)

**1979** (26 Feb). *Flowers. T* **249** *and similar vert designs. Multicoloured. P* 14.
985 18 c. Type **249** .. .. .. .. .. .. 10 10
986 50 c. *Hibiscus rosa sinensis* .. .. .. 30 15
987 $1 *Thunbergia grandiflora* .. .. .. 55 25
988 $3 *Nerium oleander* .. .. .. .. 1·60 1·10
985/8 .. .. .. .. .. *Set of* 4 2·25 1·40
**MS**989 115 × 90 mm. $2 *Lagerstroemia speciosa* 1·00 1·40

250 Birds in Flight

251 Children playing Cricket

(Des M. Rubin. Litho Questa)

**1979** (15 Mar). *30th Anniv of Declaration of Human Rights. T* **250** *and similar vert design. Multicoloured. P* 14.
990 15 c. Type **250** .. .. .. .. .. .. 10 10
991 $2 Bird in flight .. .. .. .. .. 55 65

(Des J.W. Litho Questa)

**1979** (23 April). *International Year of the Child. T* **251** *and similar vert designs. Multicoloured. P* 14.
992 18 c. Type **251** .. .. .. .. .. .. 20 15
993 22 c. Children playing baseball .. .. 25 20
994 $5 Children playing in tree .. .. .. 3·75 4·50
992/4 .. .. .. .. .. *Set of* 3 3·75 4·50
**MS**995 114 × 92 mm. $4 Children with model spaceship .. .. .. .. .. .. .. 2·25 2·25

252 "Around the World in 80 Days"

(Des G. Vasarhelyi. Litho Questa)

**1979** (4 May). *150th Birth Anniv of Jules Verne (author). T* **252** *and similar horiz designs showing scenes from his books and modern technological developments. Multicoloured. P* 14.
996 18 c. Type **252** .. .. .. .. .. .. 25 10
997 35 c. "20,000 Leagues under the Sea" .. .. 35 15
998 75 c. "From the Earth to the Moon" .. .. 50 25
999 $3 "Master of the World" .. .. .. 1·10 80
996/9 .. .. .. .. .. *Set of* 4 2·00 1·10
**MS**1000 110 × 85 mm. $4 "Clipper of the Clouds" 1·40 1·75

253 Mail Runner, Africa (early 19th-century)

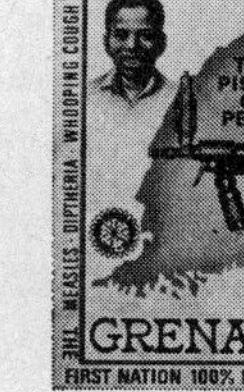

254 "The Pistol of Peace" (vaccination gun), Map of Grenada and Children

(Des J.W. Litho Questa)

**1979** (23 July). *Death Centenary of Sir Rowland Hill. T* **253** *and similar horiz designs. Multicoloured. P* 14.
1001 20 c. Type **253** .. .. .. .. .. 10 10
1002 40 c. Pony Express, America (mid 19th-century) .. .. .. .. .. .. 15 10
1003 $1 Pigeon post .. .. .. .. .. 35 25
1004 $3 Mail coach, Europe (18th-19th-century) 90 80
1001/4 .. .. .. .. .. *Set of* 4 1·25 1·10
**MS**1005 127 × 100 mm. $5 Sir Rowland Hill and 1891 1d. on 8d. *tête-bêche* block of 4 .. 1·25 1·75

Nos. 1001/4 also exist perf 12 (*Price for set of* 4 £1·25 *mint or used*) from additional sheetlets of 5 stamps and 1 label, issued 8 August. These have different background colours from the stamps perforated 14, which come from normal sheets of 40.

(Des G. Vasarhelyi. Litho Questa)

**1979** (20 Aug). *International Year of the Child. "Grenada—First Nation 100% Immunized". P* 14.
1006 **254** 5 c. multicoloured .. .. .. .. 30 30
1007 $1 multicoloured .. .. .. .. 1·40 1·75

255 Reef Shark

(Des G. Drummond. Litho Questa)

**1979** (22 Aug). *Marine Wildlife. T* **225** *and similar horiz designs. Mutlicoloured. P* 14.
1008 40 c. Type **255** .. .. .. .. .. 35 20
1009 45 c. Spotted Eagle Ray .. .. .. .. 35 20
1010 50 c. Manytooth Conger .. .. .. .. 40 30
1011 60 c. Golden Olive (shell) .. .. .. 60 35
1012 70 c. West Indian Murex (shell) .. .. 70 40
1013 75 c. Giant Tun (shell) .. .. .. .. 75 40
1014 90 c. Brown Booby .. .. .. .. 1·40 60
1015 $1 Magnificent Frigate Bird .. .. 1·50 70
1008/15 .. .. .. .. *Set of* 8 5·50 2·75
**MS**1016 109 × 78 mm. $2.50, Sooty Tern .. 2·00 1·75

256 The Flight into Egypt

(Des W. Grout. Litho Questa)

**1979** (19 Oct). *Christmas. Religious Tapestries. T* **256** *and similar multicoloured designs. P* 14.
1017 6 c. Type **256** .. .. .. .. .. 10 10
1018 25 c. The Flight into Egypt (detail) .. .. 10 10
1019 30 c. Angel (*vert*) .. .. .. .. .. 15 10
1020 40 c. Doge Marino Grimani (detail) (*vert*) .. 15 15
1021 90 c. The Annunciation to the Shepherds (*vert*) 40 30
1022 $1 The Flight into Egypt (Rome) (*vert*) .. 45 35
1023 $2 The Virgin in Glory (*vert*) .. .. 75 60
1017/23 .. .. .. .. *Set of* 7 1·75 1·50
**MS**1024 111 × 148 mm. $4 Doge Marino Grimani (*vert*) .. .. .. .. .. .. .. 1·00 1·40

257 Mickey Mouse playing Baseball

258 Paul Harris (founder)

(Litho Format)

**1979** (2 Nov). *International Year of the Child. Walt Disney Cartoon Characters. T* **257** *and similar vert designs showing characters playing sports. Multicoloured. P* 11.
1025 ½ c. Type **257** .. .. .. .. .. 10 10
1026 1 c. Donald Duck high-jumping .. .. 10 10
1027 2 c. Goofy playing basketball .. .. 10 10
1028 3 c. Goofy hurdling .. .. .. .. 10 10
1029 4 c. Donald Duck playing golf .. .. 10 10
1030 5 c. Mickey Mouse playing cricket .. .. 10 10
1031 10 c. Mickey Mouse playing football .. .. 10 10
1032 $2 Mickey Mouse playing tennis .. .. 2·25 2·00
1033 $2.50, Minnie Mouse riding horse .. .. 2·25 2·00
1025/33 .. .. .. .. *Set of* 9 4·50 4·00
**MS**1034 125 × 100 mm. $3 Goofy in riding gear. P 13½. .. .. .. .. .. .. .. 2·25 1·60

(Des J.W. Litho Questa)

**1980** (25 Feb). *75th Anniv of Rotary International. T* **258** *an*
*similar vert designs. Multicoloured. P* 14.
1035 6 c. Type **258** .. .. .. .. 10 1
1036 30 c. "Health" .. .. .. .. .. 15 1
1037 90 c. "Hunger" .. .. .. .. .. 30 3
1038 $2 "Humanity" .. .. .. .. 70 8
1035/8 .. .. .. .. *Set of* 4 1·00 1·1
**MS**1039 104 × 89 mm. $4 Rotary International emblem .. .. .. .. .. .. 1·00 1·6

## PEOPLE'S REVOLUTION
## 13 MARCH 1979

(259)

**1980** (28 Feb–8 Apr). *1st Anniv of Revolution* (*1st issue*). *Nos* 651A/2A, 654A/7A, 659A, 660B *and* 662A/8A *optd with T* **259**.
1040 2 c. Carenage taxi .. .. .. .. 10 1
a. Optd on No. 651B .. .. .. 8·50
1041 3 c. Large working boats .. .. .. 10 1
a. Optd on No. 652B .. .. .. 8·50
1042 6 c. Cocoa beans in drying trays .. .. 10 1
1043 8 c. Nutmegs .. .. .. .. .. 10 1
1044 10 c. River Antoine Estate Rum Distillery, *c.* 1785 .. .. .. .. .. 10 1
1045 12 c. Cocoa Tree .. .. .. .. .. 10 1
1046 20 c. Parliament Building, St. George's .. 10 1
1047 25 c. Fort George cannons (8.4.80) .. .. 30 3
1048 50 c. General Post Office .. .. .. 30 3
1049 75 c. Caribs Leap, Sauteurs Bay .. .. 50 4
1050 $1 Carenage, St. George's .. .. .. 60 6
1051 $2 St. George's Harbour by night .. .. 1·25 2·0
1052 $3 Grand Anse Beach .. .. .. 2·00 3·2
1053 $5 Canoe Bay and Black Bay from Point Saline Lighthouse .. .. .. .. 3·25 5·0
1054 $10 Sugar Loaf Island from Levera Beach .. 4·75 7·5
1040/54 .. .. .. .. *Set of* 15 12·00 18·0
See also Nos. 1069/73.

260 Boxing

261 Tropical Kingbird

(Des Design Images Inc. Litho Questa)

**1980** (24 Mar). *Olympic Games, Moscow. T* **260** *and similar horiz designs. Multicoloured. P* 14.
1055 25 c. Type **260** .. .. .. .. .. 10 1
1056 40 c. Cycling .. .. .. .. .. 15 10
1057 90 c. Show-jumping .. .. .. .. 20 25
1058 $2 Running .. .. .. .. .. 40 70
1055/8 .. .. .. .. *Set of* 4 75 1·00
**MS**1059 128 × 95 mm. $4 Sailing .. .. .. 80 1·40

(Des G. Drummond. Litho Questa)

**1980** (8 Apr). *Wild Birds. T* **261** *and similar vert designs. Multicoloured. P* 14.
1060 20 c. Type **261** .. .. .. .. .. 60 15
1061 40 c. Rufous-breasted Hermit .. .. .. 75 20
1062 $1 Troupial .. .. .. .. .. 1·25 1·00
1063 $2 Ruddy Quail Dove .. .. .. 2·00 2·25
1060/3 .. .. .. .. *Set of* 4 4·25 3·25
**MS**1064 85 × 114 mm. $3 Prairie Warbler .. 2·75 2·75

**LONDON 1980**

(262)

263 Free Hot Lunch at Schools

**1980** (6 May). *"London* 1980*" International Stamp Exhibition. Nos.* 1001/4 *optd with T* **262**. *P* 12.
1065 20 c. Type **253** .. .. .. .. .. 20 20
1066 40 c. Pony Express, America (mid 19th-century) .. .. .. .. .. .. 30 30
1067 $1 Pigeon Post .. .. .. .. .. 60 60
1068 $3 Mail coach, Europe (18th-19th-century) 1·75 1·75
1065/8 .. .. .. .. *Set of* 4 2·50 2·50

(Des M. Diamond. Litho Questa)

**1980** (19 May). *1st Anniv of Revolution* (*2nd issue*). *T* **263** *and similar horiz designs. Multicoloured. P* 14.
1069 10 c. Type **263** .. .. .. .. .. 10 10
1070 40 c. "From tree to can" (agro-industry) .. 15 20
1071 $1 National Health care .. .. .. 40 45
1072 $2 New housing projects .. .. .. 75 90
1069/72 .. .. .. .. *Set of* 4 1·25 1·40
**MS**1073 110 × 85 mm. $5 Prime Minister Maurice Bishop (*vert*) .. .. .. .. .. 1·00 1·75

**264** Jamb Statues, West Portal, Chartres Cathedral

(Des J.W. Litho Questa)

**1980** (15 July). *Famous Works of Art. T* **264** *and similar horiz designs. Multicoloured. P* 13½.

| No. | Description | Unused | Used |
|---|---|---|---|
| 1074 | 8 c. Type **264** | 10 | 10 |
| 1075 | 10 c. "Les Demoiselles D'Avignon" (painting by Picasso) | 10 | 10 |
| 1076 | 40 c. Winged Victory of Samothrace (statue) | 20 | 20 |
| 1077 | 50 c. "The Night Watch" (painting by Rembrandt) | 20 | 20 |
| 1078 | $1 "Portrait of Edward VI as a Child" (painting by Holbein the Younger) | 35 | 45 |
| 1079 | $3 Portrait head of Queen Nefertiti (carving) | 1·00 | 1·25 |
| 1074/9 | *Set of* 6 | 1·60 | 2·00 |
| **MS**1080 | 101 × 101 mm. $4 "Weier Haws" (detail of painting by Dürer) (*vert*) | 75 | 1·00 |

**265** Carib Canoes

(Des G. Drummond. Litho Questa)

**1980** (9 Sept)–**84**. *Shipping. Horiz designs as T* **265**. *Multicoloured*. A. *Without imprint date. P* 14.

| No. | Description | Unused | Used |
|---|---|---|---|
| 1081A | ½ c. Type **265** | 10 | 10 |
| 1082A | 1 c. Boat building | 10 | 10 |
| 1083A | 2 c. Small working boat | 15 | 10 |
| 1084A | 4 c. Columbus' *Santa Maria* | 30 | 10 |
| 1085A | 5 c. West Indiaman barque, *circa* 1840 | 30 | 10 |
| 1086A | 6 c. R.M.S.P. *Orinoco, circa* 1851 | 30 | 10 |
| 1087A | 10 c. Working schooner | 30 | 10 |
| 1088A | 12 c. Trimaran at Grand Anse anchorage | 35 | 10 |
| 1089A | 15 c. Spice Island cruising yacht *Petite Amie* | 40 | 10 |
| 1090A | 20 c. Fishing pirogue | 50 | 10 |
| 1091A | 25 c. Harbour police launch | 75 | 15 |
| 1092A | 30 c. Grand Anse speed-boat | 75 | 20 |
| 1093A | 40 c. M.V. *Seimstrand* | 75 | 25 |
| 1094A | 50 c. Three-masted schooner *Ariadne* | 80 | 35 |
| 1095A | 90 c. M.V. *Geestide* | 1·25 | 50 |
| 1096A | $1 M.V. *Cunard Countess* | 1·50 | 70 |
| 1097A | $3 Rum-runner | 3·25 | 2·75 |
| 1098A | $5 S.S. *Statendam* off St. George's | 5·50 | 5·00 |
| 1099A | $10 Coast-guard patrol boat | 9·50 | 10·00 |
| 1081A/99A | *Set of* 19 | 24·00 | 19·00 |

B. *With imprint date at foot of design. P* 14 ($1) *or* 12 (*others*)

| No. | Description | Unused | Used |
|---|---|---|---|
| 1081B | ½ c. Type **265** (1982) | 30 | 50 |
| 1085B | 5 c. West Indiaman barque, *circa* 1840 (1982) | 60 | 30 |
| 1087B | 10 c. Working schooner (1982) | 60 | 20 |
| | a. Perf 14 | † | — |
| 1090B | 20 c. Fishing pirogue (1982) | 90 | 30 |
| 1091B | 25 c. Harbour police launch (1982) | 1·00 | 40 |
| | a. Perf 14 | 2·50 | 1·25 |
| 1092B | 30 c. Grand Anse speed-boat (1982) | 1·00 | 60 |
| | a. Perf 14 | 3·25 | 1·25 |
| 1093B | 40 c. M.V. *Seimstrand* (1982) | 1·25 | 60 |
| 1094B | 50 c. Three-masted schooner *Ariadne* (1.84) | 50 | 30 |
| | a. Perf 14 (1984) | 55 | 40 |
| 1096B | $1 M.V. *Cunard Countess* (1982) | 11·00 | 5·00 |
| 1097B | $3 Rum-runner (1982) | 3·50 | 3·50 |
| 1098B | $5 S.S. *Statendam* off St. George's (1982) | 5·50 | 6·00 |
| 1099B | $10 Coast-guard patrol boat (1.84) | 8·00 | 8·50 |
| 1081B/99B | *Set of* 12 | 30·00 | 24·00 |

(Litho Walsall)

**1980** (25 Sept). *Christmas. Walt Disney Cartoon Scenes from "Snow White and the Seven Dwarfs". Horiz designs as T* **257**. *Multicoloured. P* 11.

| No. | Description | Unused | Used |
|---|---|---|---|
| 1100 | ½ c. Snow White at well | 10 | 10 |
| 1101 | 1 c. The Wicked Queen | 10 | 10 |
| 1102 | 2 c. Snow White singing to animals | 10 | 10 |
| 1103 | 3 c. Snow White doing housework for Dwarfs | 10 | 10 |
| 1104 | 4 c. The Seven Dwarfs | 10 | 10 |
| 1105 | 5 c. Snow White with Dwarfs | 10 | 10 |
| 1106 | 10 c. Witch offering Snow White apple | 10 | 10 |
| 1107 | $2.50, Snow White with Prince, and Dwarfs | 2·75 | 1·25 |
| 1108 | $3 Snow White and Prince | 3·25 | 1·75 |
| 1100/8 | *Set of* 9 | 6·00 | 3·00 |
| **MS**1109 | 127 × 102 mm. $4 Snow White sleeping (*vert*) | 2·50 | 1·90 |

(Litho Format)

**1981** (19 Jan). *50th Anniv of Walt Disney's Cartoon Character, Pluto. Vert designs as T* **257**. *Multicoloured. P* 13½.

| No. | Description | Unused | Used |
|---|---|---|---|
| 1110 | $2 Pluto with birthday cake | 1·25 | 1·00 |
| **MS**1111 | 127 × 102 mm. $4 Pluto in scene from film *Pueblo Pluto* | 2·10 | 2·25 |

No. 1110 was printed in small sheets of 8 stamps.

**266** Revolution and Grenada Flags

**1981** (13 Mar). *Festival of the Revolution. T* **266** *and similar triangular designs. Multicoloured. Litho. P* 12½.

| No. | Description | Unused | Used |
|---|---|---|---|
| 1112 | 5 c. Type **266** | 10 | 10 |
| 1113 | 10 c. Teacher, pupil, book and pencil ("education") | 10 | 10 |
| 1114 | 15 c. Food processing plant ("industry") | 10 | 10 |
| 1115 | 25 c. Selection of fruits and farm scene ("agriculture") | 15 | 15 |
| 1116 | 40 c. Crawfish and boat ("fishing") | 20 | 20 |
| 1117 | 90 c. *Cunard Countess* arriving at St. George's Harbour ("shipping") | 50 | 50 |
| 1118 | $1 Straw-work ("native handicrafts") | 60 | 60 |
| 1119 | $3 Map of Caribbean with expanded view of Grenada | 1·75 | 1·75 |
| 1112/19 | *Set of* 8 | 3·00 | 3·00 |

(Litho Format)

**1981** (7 Apr). *Easter. Walt Disney Cartoon Characters. Vert designs as T* **257**. *Multicoloured. P* 11.

| No. | Description | Unused | Used |
|---|---|---|---|
| 1120 | 35 c. Mickey Mouse and Goofy | 25 | 25 |
| 1121 | 40 c. Donald Duck, Chip and Daisy Duck | 25 | 25 |
| 1122 | $2 Minnie Mouse | 1·40 | 1·25 |
| 1123 | $2.50, Pluto and Mickey Mouse | 1·60 | 1·40 |
| 1120/3 | *Set of* 4 | 3·25 | 2·75 |
| **MS**1124 | 127 × 101 mm. $4 Goofy. P 13½ | 3·00 | 2·50 |

**267** "Woman-Flower"

**268** Prince Charles playing Polo

(Des J.W. Litho Questa)

**1981** (28 Apr). *Birth Centenary of Picasso. T* **267** *and similar vert designs. Multicoloured. P* 13½ × 14.

| No. | Description | Unused | Used |
|---|---|---|---|
| 1125 | 25 c. Type **267** | 15 | 15 |
| 1126 | 30 c. "Portrait of Madame" | 20 | 15 |
| 1127 | 90 c. "Cavalier with Pipe" | 45 | 45 |
| 1128 | $4 "Large Heads" | 2·00 | 1·75 |
| 1125/8 | *Set of* 4 | 2·50 | 2·25 |
| **MS**1129 | 128 × 103 mm. $5 "Woman on the Banks of the Seine" (after Courbet). Imperf | 3·75 | 3·00 |

(Des J.W. Litho Format)

**1981** (16 June). *Royal Wedding. T* **268** *and similar vert designs. Multicoloured.* (*a*) *P* 15.

| No. | Description | Unused | Used |
|---|---|---|---|
| 1130 | 50 c. Prince Charles and Lady Diana Spencer | 30 | 30 |
| 1131 | $2 Holyrood House | 1·00 | 1·00 |
| 1132 | $4 Type **268** | 1·75 | 2·25 |
| | a. Imperf (pair) | £400 | |
| 1130/2 | *Set of* 3 | 2·75 | 3·25 |
| **MS**1133 | 98 × 84 mm. $5 Glass Coach | 2·40 | 2·50 |

(*b*) *P* 15 × 14½

| No. | Description | Unused | Used |
|---|---|---|---|
| 1134 | 30 c. As 50 c. | 20 | 20 |
| 1135 | 40 c. As $2 | 30 | 30 |

The 30 and 40 c. values were each printed in small sheets of 6 including one *se-tenant* stamp-size label.

The $4 value, with changed background colour, also exists perforated 15 × 14½ (*price* £1.50 *mint or used*) from similar sheetlets in addition to the original version issued in sheets of 40.

**269** Lady Diana Spencer

**270** "The Bath" (Mary Cassatt)

(Manufactured by Walsall)

**1981** (16 June). *Royal Wedding. Booklet stamps. T* **269** *and similar vert designs. Multicoloured. Roul* 5 × *imperf*. Self-adhesive.*

| No. | Description | Unused | Used |
|---|---|---|---|
| 1136 | $1 Type **269** | 50 | 65 |
| | a. Booklet pane. Nos. 1136/7 each × 3 | 3·50 | |
| 1137 | $2 Prince Charles | 75 | 1·00 |
| 1138 | $5 Prince Charles and Lady Diana Spencer | 2·00 | 2·50 |
| | a. Booklet pane of 1 | 2·00 | |
| 1136/8 | *Set of* 3 | 3·00 | 3·75 |

*The $1 and $2 values were each separated by various combinations of rotary knife (giving a straight edge) and roulette. The $5 value exists only with straight edges.

(Des BG Studio. Litho Questa)

**1981** (Oct). *"Decade for Women". Paintings. T* **270** *and similar multicoloured designs. P* 14.

| No. | Description | Unused | Used |
|---|---|---|---|
| 1139 | 15 c. Type **270** | 10 | 10 |
| 1140 | 40 c. "Mademoiselle Charlotte du Val d'Ognes" (Constance Marie Charpentier) | 25 | 20 |
| 1141 | 60 c. "Self-portrait" (Mary Beale) | 40 | 30 |
| 1142 | $3 "Woman in White Stockings" (Suzanne Valadon) | 1·50 | 1·25 |
| 1139/42 | *Set of* 4 | 2·00 | 1·75 |
| **MS**1143 | 101 × 77 mm. $5 "The Artist hesitating between the Arts of Music and Painting" (Angelica Kauffman) (*horiz*) | 2·75 | 2·75 |

(Litho Questa)

**1981** (Nov). *Christmas. Horiz designs as T* **257** *showing scenes from Walt Disney's cartoon film "Cinderella". P* 13½.

| No. | Description | Unused | Used |
|---|---|---|---|
| 1144 | ½ c. multicoloured | 10 | 10 |
| 1145 | 1 c. multicoloured | 10 | 10 |
| 1146 | 2 c. multicoloured | 10 | 10 |
| 1147 | 3 c. multicoloured | 10 | 10 |
| 1148 | 4 c. multicoloured | 10 | 10 |
| 1149 | 5 c. multicoloured | 10 | 10 |
| 1150 | 10 c. multicoloured | 10 | 10 |
| 1151 | $2.50, multicoloured | 2·75 | 1·50 |
| 1152 | $3 multicoloured | 3·00 | 1·75 |
| 1144/52 | *Set of* 9 | 5·75 | 3·25 |
| **MS**1153 | 127 × 103 mm. $5 multicoloured | 4·00 | 2·75 |

**271** Landing

**272** West German Footballer and Flag

(Des M. Brodie. Litho Format)

**1981** (12 Nov). *Space Shuttle Project. T* **271** *and similar vert designs. Multicoloured. P* 14½.

| No. | Description | Unused | Used |
|---|---|---|---|
| 1154 | 30 c. Type **271** | 20 | 15 |
| 1155 | 60 c. Working in space | 40 | 30 |
| 1156 | 70 c. Lift off | 45 | 35 |
| 1157 | $3 Separation | 1·40 | 1·25 |
| 1154/7 | *Set of* 4 | 2·25 | 1·75 |
| **MS**1158 | 117 × 89 mm. $5 In orbit | 2·50 | 2·50 |

(Des Clover Mill. Litho Format)

**1981** (30 Nov.) *World Cup Football Championship, Spain* (1982). *T* **272** *and similar multicoloured designs. P* 14.

| No. | Description | Unused | Used |
|---|---|---|---|
| 1159 | 25 c. + 10 c. Type **272** | 55 | 30 |
| 1160 | 40 c. + 20 c. Argentinian footballer and flag | 70 | 40 |
| 1161 | 50 c. + 25 c. Brazilian footballer and flag | 80 | 50 |
| 1162 | $1 + 50 c. English footballer and flag | 1·25 | 95 |
| 1159/62 | *Set of* 4 | 3·00 | 1·90 |
| **MS**1163 | 141 × 128 mm. $5 + 50 c. Spanish orange mascot and Jules Rimet Trophy (*vert*) | 4·00 | 3·00 |

Nos. 1159/62 were each printed in sheetlets of 12 on an overall background design showing a football.

**273** General Post Office, St. George's

**274** Artist without Hands

(Des J.W. Litho Format)

**1981** (10 Dec). *Centenary of U.P.U. Membership. T* **273** *and similar horiz designs. Multicoloured. P* 15.

| No. | Description | Unused | Used |
|---|---|---|---|
| 1164 | 25 c. Type **273** | 20 | 15 |
| 1165 | 30 c. 1861 1d. stamp | 25 | 20 |
| 1166 | 90 c. 1970 New U.P.U. Headquarters Building 25 c. commemorative | 75 | 50 |
| 1167 | $4 1961 Stamp Centenary 25 c. commemorative | 2·25 | 2·00 |
| 1164/7 | *Set of* 4 | 3·00 | 2·50 |
| **MS**1168 | 113 × 87 mm. $5 1974 Centenary of U.P.U. ½ c. commemorative | 3·25 | 2·50 |

(Litho Questa)

**1982** (4 Feb). *International Year for the Disabled* (1981). *T* **274** *and similar vert designs. Multicoloured. P* 14.

| No. | Description | Unused | Used |
|---|---|---|---|
| 1169 | 30 c. Type **274** | 55 | 15 |
| 1170 | 40 c. Computer operator without hands | 60 | 20 |
| 1171 | 70 c. Blind schoolteacher teaching braille | 85 | 35 |
| 1172 | $3 Midget playing drums | 2·40 | 1·40 |
| 1169/72 | *Set of* 4 | 4·00 | 1·90 |
| **MS**1173 | 101 × 72 mm. $4 Auto mechanic confined to wheelchair | 3·25 | 2·75 |

**275** Tending Vegetable Patch  **276** *Dryas julia*

(Des Design Images. Litho Format)

**1982** (19 Feb). *75th Anniv of Boy Scout Movement and 125th Birth Anniv of Lord Baden-Powell. T* **275** *and similar horiz designs. Multicoloured. P* 14½.

1174 70 c. Type **275** . . . . . . . . . . 50 45
1175 90 c. Map-reading . . . . . . . . . . 55 50
1176 $1 Bee-keeping . . . . . . . . . . 65 60
1177 $4 Hospital reading . . . . . . . . 2·25 2·25
1174/7 . . . . . . . . *Set of* 4 3·50 3·50
**MS**1178 100 × 71 mm. $5 Presentation of trophies 2·75 3·25

(Des G. Drummond. Litho Questa)

**1982** (24 Mar). *Butterflies. T* **276** *and similar vert designs. Multicoloured. P* 14.

1179 10 c. Type **276** . . . . . . . . . . 75 20
1180 60 c. *Phoebis agarithe* . . . . . . . . 2·00 60
1181 $1 *Anartia amathea* . . . . . . . . 2·50 1·25
1182 $3 *Battus polydamas* . . . . . . . . 4·00 4·50
1179/82 . . . . . . . . *Set of* 4 8·50 6·00
**MS**1183 111×85 mm. $5 *Junonia evarete* . . 5·00 5·50

**277** "Saying Grace"  **278** Kensington Palace

(Des M.B.I. Studio. Litho Questa)

**1982** (14 Apr). *Norman Rockwell (painter) Commemoration. T* **277** *and similar vert designs. Multicoloured. P* 14 × 13½.

1184 15 c. Type **277** . . . . . . . . . . 30 10
1185 30 c. "Card Tricks" . . . . . . . . . . 50 15
1186 60 c. "Pharmacist" . . . . . . . . . . 80 25
1187 70 c. "Pals" . . . . . . . . . . 85 35
1184/7 . . . . . . . . *Set of* 4 2·25 75

(Des PAD Studio. Litho Questa)

**1982** (1 July). *21st Birthday of Princess of Wales. T* **278** *and similar vert designs. Multicoloured. P* 14½ × 14.

1188 50 c. Type **278** . . . . . . . . . . 30 35
1189 60 c. Type **278** . . . . . . . . . . 45 35
1190 $1 Prince and Princess of Wales . . . . 80 75
1191 $2 As $1 . . . . . . . . . . 1·25 1·00
1192 $3 Princess of Wales . . . . . . . . 1·75 2·00
1193 $4 As $3 . . . . . . . . . . 2·00 2·00
1188/93 . . . . . . . . *Set of* 6 6·00 5·75
**MS**1194 103 × 75 mm. $5 Princess Diana (*different*) . . . . . . . . . . 2·40 2·50

Nos. 1188, 1190 and 1192 come from sheetlets of 5 stamps and 1 label.

**279** Mary McLeod Bethune appointed Director of Negro Affairs, 1942

(Des Design Images. Litho Questa)

**1982** (27 July). *Birth Centenary of Franklin D. Roosevelt. T* **279** *and similar horiz designs. Multicoloured. P* 14.

1195 10 c. Type **279** . . . . . . . . . . 10 10
1196 60 c. Huddie Ledbetter ("Leadbelly") in concert (Works Progress administration) 35 30
1197 $1.10, Signing bill No. 8802, 1941 (Fair Employment committee) . . . . . . 65 55
1198 $3 Farm Security administration . . . . 1·40 1·25
1195/8 . . . . . . . . *Set of* 4 2·25 1·90
**MS**1199 100 × 70 mm. $5 William Hastie, first Negro judicial appointee . . . . . . . . 2·40 2·50

**1982** (30 Aug). *Birth of Prince William of Wales. Nos.* 1188/94 *optd with T* **171** *of Antigua.*

1200 50 c. Type **278** . . . . . . . . . . 25 30
1201 60 c. Type **278** . . . . . . . . . . 30 35
1202 $1 Prince and Princess of Wales . . . . 50 55
1203 $2 As $1 . . . . . . . . . . 95 1·00
1204 $3 Princess of Wales . . . . . . . . 1·60 1·75
1205 $4 As $3 . . . . . . . . . . 1·75 1·90
1200/5 . . . . . . . . *Set of* 6 4·75 5·50
**MS**1206 103 × 75 mm. $5 Princess Diana (*different*) . . . . . . . . . . 2·40 2·50

Nos. 1200, 1202 and 1204 come from sheetlets of 5 stamps and 1 label.

**280** Apostle and Tormentor

(Des Clover Mill. Litho Format)

**1982** (2 Sept). *Easter. Details from Painting "The Way to Calvary" by Raphael. T* **280** *and similar multicoloured designs. P* 14 × 14½ (40 c.) *or* 14½ × 14 (*others*).

1207 40 c. Type **280** . . . . . . . . . . 50 20
1208 70 c. Captain of the guards (*vert*) . . . . 75 35
1209 $1.10, Christ and apostle (*vert*) . . . . 1·00 45
1210 $4 Mourners (*vert*) . . . . . . . . 2·75 1·75
1207/10 . . . . . . . . *Set of* 4 4·50 2·50
**MS**1211 102 × 126 mm. $5 Christ falls beneath the cross (*vert*) . . . . . . . . . . 3·50 2·50

**281** "Orient Express"

(Des Artists International. Litho Format)

**1982** (4 Oct). *Famous Trains of the World. T* **281** *and similar horiz designs. Multicoloured. P* 15 × 14½.

1212 30 c. Type **281** . . . . . . . . . . 60 20
1213 60 c. "Trans-Siberian Express" . . . . . . 80 35
1214 70 c. "Golden Arrow" . . . . . . . . 1·00 45
1215 90 c. "Flying Scotsman" . . . . . . . . 1·25 55
1216 $1 German Federal Railways . . . . . . 1·50 1·00
1217 $3 German National Railways . . . . . . 3·00 3·00
1212/17 . . . . . . . . *Set of* 6 7·50 5·00
**MS**1218 109 × 81 mm. $5 "20th Century Limited" 3·00 3·50

**282** Footballers  **283** Killer Whale

(Des D. Miller. Litho Questa)

**1982** (2 Dec). *World Cup Football Championship Winners. T* **282** *and similar horiz designs. P* 14 × 13½.

1219 60 c. multicoloured . . . . . . . . . . 35 35
1220 $4 multicoloured . . . . . . . . . . 2·00 2·00
**MS**1221 93×119 mm. $5 multicoloured . . 2·50 2·75

(Litho Questa)

**1982** (14 Dec). *Christmas. Horiz designs as T* **257** *depicting scenes from Walt Disney's cartoon film "Robin Hood". P* 13½.

1222 ½ c. multicoloured . . . . . . . . . . 10 10
1223 1 c. multicoloured . . . . . . . . . . 10 10
1224 2 c. multicoloured . . . . . . . . . . 10 10
1225 3 c. multicoloured . . . . . . . . . . 10 10
1226 4 c. multicoloured . . . . . . . . . . 10 10
1227 5 c. multicoloured . . . . . . . . . . 10 10
1228 10 c. multicoloured . . . . . . . . . . 10 10
1229 $2.50, multicoloured . . . . . . . . 1·25 1·00
1230 $3 multicoloured . . . . . . . . . . 1·40 1·25
1222/30 . . . . . . . . *Set of* 9 2·50 2·25
**MS**1231 121 × 96 mm. $5 multicoloured . . . . 4·00 3·00

(Des Artists International. Litho Questa)

**1983** (10 Jan). *Save the Whales. T* **283** *and similar vert designs. Multicoloured. P* 14.

1232 15 c. Type **283** . . . . . . . . . . 75 20
1233 40 c. Sperm Whale . . . . . . . . . . 1·50 45
1234 70 c. Blue Whale . . . . . . . . . . 2·25 1·75
1235 $3 Common Dolphin . . . . . . . . . . 3·25 4·00
1232/5 . . . . . . . . *Set of* 4 7·00 5·75
**MS**1236 84 × 74 mm. $5 Humpback Whale . . 3·50 4·00

**284** "Construction of Ark"

(Des Design Images. Litho Format)

**1983** (15 Feb). *500th Birth Anniv of Raphael. T* **284** *and similar horiz designs showing painting details. Multicoloured. P* 13½.

1237 25 c. Type **284** . . . . . . . . . . 15 15
1238 30 c. "Jacob's Vision" . . . . . . . . . . 15 20
1239 90 c. "Joseph interprets the Dreams to his Brothers" . . . . . . . . . . 40 45
1240 $4 "Joseph interprets Pharaoh's Dreams" 1·90 2·00
1237/40 . . . . . . . . *Set of* 4 2·25 2·50
**MS**1241 128 × 100 mm. $5 "Creation of the Animals" . . . . . . . . . . 2·50 2·75

**285** Dentistry at Health Centre

(Des J.W. Litho Questa)

**1983** (14 Mar). *Commonwealth Day. T* **285** *and similar horiz designs. Multicoloured. P* 14.

1242 10 c. Type **285** . . . . . . . . . . 10 10
1243 70 c. Airport runway construction . . . . 35 35
1244 $1.10, Tourism . . . . . . . . . . 55 55
1245 $3 Boat-building . . . . . . . . . . 1·40 1·40
1242/5 . . . . . . . . *Set of* 4 2·10 2·10

**286** Maritime Communications via Satellite

(Des G. Vasarhelyi. Litho Questa)

**1983** (29 Mar). *World Communications Year. T* **286** *and similar horiz designs. Multicoloured. P* 14.

1246 30 c. Type **286** . . . . . . . . . . 15 15
1247 40 c. Rural telephone installation . . . . 20 20
1248 $2.50, Satellite weather map . . . . . . 1·25 1·25
1249 $3 Airport control room . . . . . . . . 1·40 1·40
1246/9 . . . . . . . . *Set of* 4 2·75 2·75
**MS**1250 111 × 85 mm. $5 Communications satellite . . . . . . . . . . 2·50 3·00

**287** Franklin Sport Sedan, 1928

(Des J. Mendola. Litho Format)

**1983** (4 May). *75th Anniv of Model "T" Ford Car. T* **287** *and similar horiz designs showing cars of the 20th century. Multicoloured. P* 14½.

1251 6 c. Type **287** . . . . . . . . . . 10 10
1252 10 c. Delage "D8", 1933 . . . . . . . . 10 10
1253 40 c. Alvis, 1938 . . . . . . . . . . 20 25
1254 60 c. Invicta "S-type" tourer, 1931 . . . . 30 35
1255 70 c. Alfa-Romeo "1750 Gran Sport", 1930 . . 35 40
1256 90 c. Isotta Fraschini, 1930 . . . . . . 40 45
1257 $1 Bugatti "Royale Type 41" . . . . . . 45 50
1258 $2 BMW "328", 1938 . . . . . . . . 95 1·00
1259 $3 Marmon "V16", 1931 . . . . . . . . 1·40 1·50
1260 $4 Lincoln "K8" saloon, 1932 . . . . . . 1·90 2·00
1251/60 . . . . . . . . *Set of* 10 5·50 6·00
**MS**1261 114 × 90 mm. $5 Cougar "XR 7", 1972 . . 2·50 3·00

Nos. 1251/60 were each issued in sheets of eight stamps with a stamp-size label in the centre position.

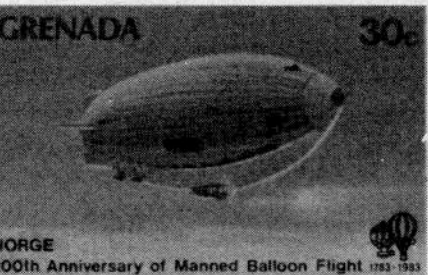


**288** *Norge* (airship)

(Des W. Wright. Litho Questa)

**1983** (18 July). *Bicentenary of Manned Flight. T* **288** *and similar multicoloured designs. P* 14.

1262 30 c. Type **288** . . . . . . . . . . 50 20
1263 60 c. Gloster "VI" seaplane . . . . . . . . 70 45
1264 $1.10, Curtiss "NC-4" flying boat . . . . 1·25 1·00
1265 $4 Dornier "Do 18" flying boat . . . . . . 3·00 2·75
1262/5 . . . . . . . . *Set of* 4 5·00 4·00
**MS**1266 114 × 85 mm. $5 Modern hot-air balloon (*vert*) . . . . . . . . . . 2·75 3·00

**289** Morty

(Litho Format)

**1983** (7 Nov). *Christmas. T* **289** *and similar vert designs showing Disney cartoon characters in scenes from "It's beginning to look a lot like Christmas" (song). Multicoloured. P* 11.

1267 ½ c. Type **289** .. .. .. .. 10 10
1268 1 c. Ludwig von Drake .. .. .. 10 10
1269 2 c. Gyro Gearloose .. .. .. .. 10 10
1270 3 c. Pluto and Figaro .. .. .. 10 10
1271 4 c. Morty and Ferdie .. .. .. 10 10
1272 5 c. Mickey Mouse and Goofy .. .. 10 10
1273 10 c. Chip'n Dale .. .. .. .. 10 10
1274 $2.50, Mickey and Minnie Mouse .. .. 2·50 1·40
1275 $3 Donald and Grandma Duck .. .. 2·75 1·75
1267/75 .. .. .. *Set of* 9 5·25 3·25
**MS**1276 127 × 102 mm. $5 Goofy with Christmas tree. P 13½ .. .. .. .. .. 3·50 3·25

**290** Daisy Duck on Pommel Horse **291** William I

(Litho Questa)

**1984** (17 Jan–May). *Olympic Games, Los Angeles. T* **290** *and similar horiz designs showing Disney cartoon characters in Olympic events. Multicoloured. A. Inscr.* "1984 LOS ANGELES". *P* 14 × 13½. *B. Inscr.* "1984 OLYMPICS LOS ANGELES" *and Olympic emblem. P* 12 (May).

| | | A | | B | |
|---|---|---|---|---|---|
| 1277 | ½ c. Type **290** .. .. | 10 | 10 | 10 | 10 |
| 1278 | 1 c. Mickey Mouse boxing | 10 | 10 | 10 | 10 |
| 1279 | 2 c. Daisy Duck in archery event | 10 | 10 | 10 | 10 |
| 1280 | 3 c. Clarabelle Cow on uneven bars | 10 | 10 | 10 | 10 |
| 1281 | 4 c. Mickey and Minnie Mouse in hurdles race | 10 | 10 | 10 | 10 |
| 1282 | 5 c. Donald Duck with Chip and Dale weightlifting.. .. | 10 | 10 | 10 | 10 |
| 1283 | $1 Little Hiawatha in single kayak .. .. | 90 | 70 | 90 | 70 |
| 1284 | $2 The Tortoise and the Hare in marathon .. .. | 1·50 | 1·25 | 1·50 | 1·25 |
| 1285 | $3 Mickey Mouse pole-vaulting .. .. | 2·00 | 1·75 | 2·00 | 1·75 |
| 1277/85 | .. .. *Set of* 9 | 4·25 | 3·75 | 4·25 | 3·75 |
| **MS**1286 | 127 × 101 mm. $5 Donald Duck in medley relay (*vert*). P 13½ × 14 .. .. .. .. | 2·75 | 3·00 | 4·00 | 3·00 |

**1984** (25 Jan). *British Monarchs. T* **291** *and similar vert designs. Multicoloured. Litho. P* 14.

1287 $4 Type **291** .. .. .. .. 2·50 2·75
a. Sheetlet. Nos. 1287/93 .. .. 18·00
1288 $4 William II .. .. .. .. 2·50 2·75
1289 $4 Henry I .. .. .. .. 2·50 2·75
1290 $4 Stephen .. .. .. .. 2·50 2·75
1291 $4 Henry II .. .. .. .. 2·50 2·75
1292 $4 Richard I .. .. .. .. 2·50 2·75
1293 $4 John .. .. .. .. 2·50 2·75
1294 $4 "Henry III" .. .. .. .. 2·50 2·75
a. Sheetlet. Nos. 1294/1300 .. .. 18·00
1295 $4 Edward I .. .. .. .. 2·50 2·75
1296 $4 Edward II .. .. .. .. 2·50 2·75
1297 $4 Edward III .. .. .. .. 2·50 2·75
1298 $4 Richard II .. .. .. .. 2·50 2·75
1299 $4 Henry IV .. .. .. .. 2·50 2·75
1300 $4 Henry V .. .. .. .. 2·50 2·75
1301 $4 Henry VI .. .. .. .. 2·50 2·75
a. Sheetlet. Nos. 1301/7 .. .. 18·00
1302 $4 Edward IV .. .. .. .. 2·50 2·75
1303 $4 Edward V .. .. .. .. 2·50 2·75
1304 $4 Richard III .. .. .. .. 2·50 2·75
1305 $4 Henry VII .. .. .. .. 2·50 2·75
1306 $4 Henry VIII .. .. .. .. 2·50 2·75
1307 $4 Edward VI .. .. .. .. 2·50 2·75
1308 $4 Lady Jane Grey .. .. .. 2·50 2·75
a. Sheetlet. Nos. 1308/14 .. .. 18·00
1309 $4 Mary I .. .. .. .. 2·50 2·75
1310 $4 Elizabeth I .. .. .. .. 2·50 2·75
1311 $4 James I .. .. .. .. 2·50 2·75
1312 $4 Charles I .. .. .. .. 2·50 2·75
1313 $4 Charles II .. .. .. .. 2·50 2·75
1314 $4 James II .. .. .. .. 2·50 2·75
1315 $4 William III .. .. .. .. 2·50 2·75
a. Sheetlet. Nos. 1315/21 .. .. 18·00
1316 $4 Mary II .. .. .. .. 2·50 2·75
1317 $$ Anne .. .. .. .. 2·50 2·75

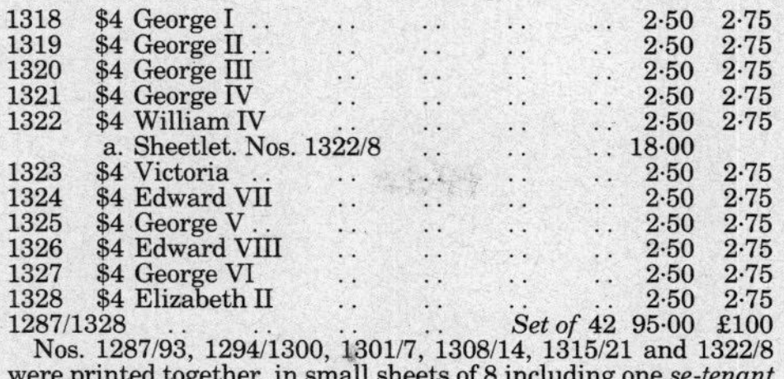

1318 $4 George I .. .. .. .. 2·50 2·75
1319 $4 George II .. .. .. .. 2·50 2·75
1320 $4 George III .. .. .. .. 2·50 2·75
1321 $4 George IV .. .. .. .. 2·50 2·75
1322 $4 William IV .. .. .. .. 2·50 2·75
a. Sheetlet. Nos. 1322/8 .. .. 18·00
1323 $4 Victoria .. .. .. .. 2·50 2·75
1324 $4 Edward VII .. .. .. .. 2·50 2·75
1325 $4 George V .. .. .. .. 2·50 2·75
1326 $4 Edward VIII .. .. .. .. 2·50 2·75
1327 $4 George VI .. .. .. .. 2·50 2·75
1328 $4 Elizabeth II .. .. .. .. 2·50 2·75
1287/1328 .. .. .. *Set of* 42 95·00 £100

Nos. 1287/93, 1294/1300, 1301/7, 1308/14, 1315/21 and 1322/8 were printed together, in small sheets of 8 including one *se-tenant* stamp-size label.

Although inscribed "Henry III" the portrait on No. 1294 is actually of Edward I.

Although announced as all being issued on 25 January 1984 the different sheetlets were distributed at monthly intervals.

**292** Lantana

(Des P.U.B. Graphics. Litho Format)

**1984** (9 Apr). *Flowers. T* **292** *and similar horiz designs. Multicoloured. P* 15.

1329 25 c. Type **292** .. .. .. .. 20 15
1330 30 c. Plumbago .. .. .. .. 25 20
1331 90 c. Spider Lily .. .. .. .. 70 60
1332 $4 Giant Alocasia .. .. .. .. 2·50 3·00
1329/32 .. .. .. *Set of* 4 3·25 3·50
**MS**1333 108 × 90 mm. $5 Orange Trumpet Vine 3·50 3·75

**293** Blue Parrot Fish 19th U.P.U CONGRESS - HAMBURG (**294**)

(Litho Questa)

**1984** (21 May). *Coral Reef Fishes. T* **293** *and similar horiz designs. Multicoloured. P* 14.

1334 10 c. Type **293** .. .. .. .. 65 20
1335 30 c. Flame-back Cherub Fish .. .. 1·25 50
1336 70 c. Painted Wrasse .. .. .. 2·00 2·00
1337 90 c. Straight-tailed Razor Fish .. .. 2·50 2·50
1334/7 .. .. .. *Set of* 4 5·75 4·75
**MS**1338 81 × 85 mm. $5 Spanish Hogfish .. 4·50 4·75

**1984** (19 June). *Universal Postal Union Congress, Hamburg. Nos.* 1331/3 *optd with T* **294**.

1339 90 c. Spider Lily .. .. .. 60 65
1340 $4 Giant Alocasia .. .. .. 2·50 3·00
**MS**1341 108 × 90 mm. $5 Orange Trumpet Vine 3·25 3·50

**295** Freighter **296** "The Night" (detail) (Correggio)

(Des Artists International. Litho Format)

**1984** (16 July). *Ships. T* **295** *and similar horiz designs. Multicoloured. P* 15.

1342 40 c. Type **295** .. .. .. .. 1·25 55
1343 70 c. *Queen Elizabeth 2* .. .. .. 1·50 1·00
1344 90 c. Sailing boats .. .. .. 1·90 1·40
1345 $4 *Amerikanis* .. .. .. .. 6·00 6·50
1342/5 .. .. .. *Set of* 4 9·50 8·50
**MS**1346 107×80 mm. $5 Spanish galleon .. 7·00 6·00

(Litho Questa)

**1984** (22 Aug). *450th Death Anniv of Correggio (painter). T* **296** *and similar vert designs showing paintings. Multicoloured. P* 14.

1347 10 c. Type **296** .. .. .. .. 35 15
1348 30 c. "The Virgin adoring the Child".. .. 60 35
1349 90 c. "The Mystical Marriage of St. Catherine with St. Sebastian" .. .. .. 1·50 1·00
1350 $4 "The Madonna and the Fruit Basket" .. 3·50 4·50
1347/50 .. .. .. *Set of* 4 5·50 5·50
**MS**1351 54 × 73 mm. $5 "The Madonna at the Spring" .. .. .. .. 3·25 3·75

**297** "L'Absinthe" (Degas) **298** Train on "Puffing Billy" Line, Victoria

(Litho Questa)

**1984** (22 Aug). *150th Birth Anniv of Edgar Degas (painter). T* **297** *and similar multicoloured designs showing paintings. P* 14.

1352 25 c. Type **297** .. .. .. .. 50 20
1353 70 c. "Pouting" (*horiz*) .. .. .. 1·00 75
1354 $1.10, "The Millinery Shop" .. .. 1·60 1·50
1355 $3 "The Bellelli Family" (*horiz*) .. .. 3·00 3·50
1352/5 .. .. .. *Set of* 4 5·50 5·50
**MS**1356 84 × 54 mm. $5 "The Cotton Market" .. 3·25 3·75

(Des Bonny Redecker. Litho Questa)

**1984** (21 Sept). *"Ausipex" International Stamp Exhibition, Melbourne. T* **298** *and similar vert designs. Multicoloured. P* 14.

1357 $1.10, Type **298** .. .. .. .. 2·00 1·50
1358 $4 Yacht *Australia II* (winner of America's Cup) .. .. .. .. 4·50 4·50
**MS**1359 107 × 76 mm. $5 Melbourne tram .. 3·75 4·50

OPENING OF POINT SALINE INT'L AIRPORT

**299** *Locomotion* (1825) (**300**)

(Des J.W. Litho Format)

**1984** (3 Oct). *Railway Locomotives. T* **299** *and similar horiz designs. Multicoloured. P* 15.

1360 30 c. Type **299** .. .. .. .. 80 35
1361 40 c. *Novelty* (1829) .. .. .. 95 40
1362 60 c. *Washington Farmer* (1836) .. .. 1·10 55
1363 70 c. French Crampton type (1859) .. .. 1·25 70
1364 90 c. Dutch State Railways (1873) .. .. 1·50 1·00
1365 $1.10, *Champion* (1882) .. .. .. 1·75 1·50
1366 $2 Webb Compound type (1893) .. .. 2·25 2·50
1367 $4 Berlin "No. 74" (1900) .. .. .. 3·75 4·50
1360/7 .. .. .. *Set of* 8 12·00 10·50
**MS**1368 Two sheets, each 100 × 70 mm. (a) $5 Crampton *Phoenix* (1863); (b) $5 Mikado type (1897) .. .. .. .. .. 8·00 8·50

**1984** (28 Oct). *Opening of Point Saline International Airport (1st issue). Nos.* 1247 *and* 1249/50 *optd as T* **300**.

1369 40 c. Rural telephone installation .. .. 25 30
1370 $3 Airport control room .. .. .. 1·75 1·90
**MS**1371 111×85 mm. $5 Communications satellite .. .. .. .. .. 3·00 3·25

On No. **MS**1371 the overprint, 54 × 8 mm., appears in two lines on the sheet margin only.

See also Nos. 1393/6.

**301** Donald Duck as Father Christmas looking into Mirror

(Litho Questa)

**1984** (26 Nov). *Christmas. Walt Disney Cartoon Characters. T* **301** *and similar vert designs. Multicoloured. P* 12 ($2) *or* 13½ × 14 (*others*).

1372 45 c. Type **301** .. .. .. .. 1·00 40
1373 60 c. Donald Duck filling stocking with presents .. .. .. .. .. 1·25 45
1374 90 c. As Father Christmas pulling a sleigh .. 1·50 75
1375 $2 As Father Christmas decorating Christmas tree .. .. .. .. 2·50 2·25
1376 $4 Donald Duck and nephews singing carols 3·50 3·75
1372/6 .. .. .. *Set of* 5 8·75 7·00
**MS**1377 127 × 102 mm. $5 As Father Christmas in sleigh .. .. .. .. .. 5·50 4·00

No. 1375 was printed in sheetlets of 8 stamps.

(Litho Questa)

**1985** (11 Feb). *Birth Bicentenary of John J. Audubon (ornithologist) (1st issue). Multicoloured designs as T* **198** *of Antigua showing original paintings. P* 14.
1378 50 c. Clapper Rail (*vert*) .. .. .. 1·00 50
1379 70 c. Hooded Warbler (*vert*) .. .. .. 1·25 75
1380 90 c. Common Flicker (*vert*) .. .. .. 1·75 1·10
1381 $4 Bohemian Waxwing (*vert*) .. .. 4·00 4·50
1378/81 .. .. .. .. *Set of* 4 7·25 6·25
**MS**1382 82×112 mm. $5 Merlin ("Pigeon Hawk") .. .. .. .. .. .. 5·50 4·00
See also Nos. 1480/4.

**302** Honda "XL500R"

(Des R. Sentnor. Litho Questa)

**1985** (11 Mar). *Centenary of the Motor Cycle. T* **302** *and similar horiz designs. Multicoloured. P* 14.
1383 25 c. Type **302** .. .. .. .. 65 40
1384 50 c. Suzuki "GS1100ES" .. .. .. 90 70
1385 90 c. Kawasaki "KZ700" .. .. .. 1·40 1·40
1386 $4 BMW "K100" .. .. .. .. 4·00 4·50
1383/6 .. .. .. .. *Set of* 4 6·25 6·25
**MS**1387 109×81 mm. $5 Yamaha "500CC V Four" 3·00 3·50

**303** "Explorer"

(Des Susan David. Litho Questa)

**1985** (15 Apr). *75th Anniv of Girl Guide Movement. T* **303** *and similar horiz designs, showing work for Guide badges. Multicoloured. P* 14.
1388 25 c. Type **303** .. .. .. .. 20 20
1389 60 c. "Cook" .. .. .. .. 45 40
1390 90 c. "Musician" .. .. .. .. 60 55
1391 $3 "Home nurse" .. .. .. .. 1·75 2·00
1388/91 .. .. .. .. *Set of* 4 2·75 2·75
**MS**1392 97×70 mm. $5 Flags of Girl Guides and Grenada .. .. .. .. .. .. 2·75 3·00

**304** Avro "748" on Inaugural Flight from Barbados

(Des Susan David. Litho Questa)

**1985** (30 Apr). *Opening of Point Saline International Airport (1984) (2nd issue). T* **304** *and similar horiz designs. Multicoloured. P* 14.
1393 70 c. Type **304** .. .. .. .. 1·50 65
1394 $1 Pan Am "L1011" on inaugural flight from New York .. .. .. 2·00 1·25
1395 $4 "Tri-Star" on inaugural flight to Miami .. .. .. .. .. 4·25 4·50
1393/5 .. .. .. .. *Set of* 3 7·00 5·75
**MS**1396 101×72 mm. $5 Point Saline Airport terminal and Avro "748" on tarmac .. .. 3·25 3·75

**305** McDonnell Douglas "DC-8"

(Des BG Studio. Litho Questa)

**1985** (15 May). *40th Anniv of International Civil Aviation Organization. T* **305** *and similar horiz designs. Multicoloured. P* 14.
1397 10 c. Type **305** .. .. .. .. 15 15
1398 50 c. "Super Constellation" .. .. .. 40 35
1399 60 c. Vickers "Vanguard" .. .. .. 45 45
1400 $4 De Haviland "Twin Otter" .. .. 2·75 3·00
1397/400 .. .. .. *Set of* 4 3·25 3·50
**MS**1401 102×64 mm. $5 Avro "748" turboprop .. 2·75 3·00

***ALTERED CATALOGUE NUMBERS***

Any Catalogue numbers altered from the last edition are shown as a list in the introductory pages.

**306** Model Boat Racing

**307** Bird of Paradise (flower)

(Litho Format)

**1985** (15 June). *Water Sports. T* **306** *and similar horiz designs. Multicoloured. P* 15.
1402 10 c. Type **306** .. .. .. .. 15 10
1403 50 c. Scuba diving, Carriacou .. .. 35 30
1404 $1.10, Windsurfers on Grand Anse Beach 75 75
1405 $4 Windsurfing .. .. .. .. 2·25 2·50
1402/5 .. .. .. .. *Set of* 4 3·25 3·25
**MS**1406 107×77 mm. $5 Beach scene .. .. 2·75 3·00

(Des Mary Walters. Litho Questa)

**1985** (1 July)–**88**. *Native Flowers. T* **307** *and similar vert designs. Multicoloured. Chalk-surfaced paper.* A. *Without imprint date. P* 14. B. *Without imprint date. P* 12.

| | | A | | B | |
|---|---|---|---|---|---|
| 1407 | ½ c. Type **307** .. .. | 15 | 15 | 10 | 20 |
| 1408 | 1 c. Passion Flower .. .. | 20 | 15 | 10 | 20 |
| 1409 | 2 c. Oleander .. .. | 20 | 15 | 10 | 20 |
| 1410 | 4 c. Bromeliad .. .. | 30 | 15 | 10 | 20 |
| 1411 | 5 c. Anthurium .. .. | 30 | 15 | 10 | 20 |
| 1412 | 6 c. Bougainvillea .. .. | 30 | 15 | 10 | 20 |
| 1413 | 10 c. Hibiscus .. .. .. | 40 | 15 | 10 | 20 |
| 1414 | 15 c. Ginger .. .. .. | 50 | 15 | 10 | 20 |
| 1415 | 25 c. Poinsettia .. .. | 60 | 25 | 10 | 20 |
| 1416 | 30 c. Mexican Creeper .. | 70 | 40 | 10 | 20 |
| 1417 | 40 c. Angel's Trumpet .. | 80 | 40 | 15 | 30 |
| 1418 | 50 c. Amaryllis .. .. | 80 | 40 | 20 | 30 |
| 1419 | 60 c. Prickly Pear .. .. | 90 | 60 | 25 | 40 |
| 1420 | 70 c. Chenille Plant .. .. | 90 | 60 | 30 | 50 |
| 1420*c* | 75 c. Cordia .. .. .. | 50 | 75 | † | |
| 1421 | $1 Periwinkle .. .. | 1·75 | 1·00 | 40 | 70 |
| 1422 | $1.10, Ixora .. .. .. | 2·00 | 1·50 | 45 | 75 |
| 1423 | $3 Shrimp Plant .. .. | 3·50 | 3·50 | 1·25 | 2·00 |
| 1424 | $5 Plumbago .. .. | 4·50 | 4·50 | 2·00 | 3·25 |
| 1425 | $10 *Lantana camara* .. | 4·75 | 6·50 | 4·00 | 6·50 |
| 1425*c* | $20 Peregrina .. .. | 8·50 | 13·00 | † | |
| | cd. Ordinary paper .. .. | 9·00 | 13·00 | † | |
| 1407A/25cA | .. .. *Set of* 21 | 29·00 | 30·00 | † | |
| 1407B/25B | .. .. *Set of* 19 | † | | 9·00 | 15·00 |

C. *With imprint date. P* 14.
1413C 10 c. Hibiscus .. .. .. .. 90 90
1416C 30 c. Mexican Creeper .. .. .. 20 30
1418C 50 c. Amaryllis .. .. .. .. 30 45
1419C 60 c. Prickly Pear .. .. .. .. 30 50
1421C $1 Periwinkle .. .. .. .. 35 70
1413C/21C .. .. .. *Set of* 5 1·90 2·50
Dates of issue:—1.7.85, Nos. 1407A/24A; 11.11.85, No. 1425A; 3.86, Nos. 1407B/12B, 1414B/19B, 1421B/3B; 7.86, Nos. 1413B, 1420B, 1424B; 1.8.86, No. 1425cA; 12.86, No. 1425B; 5.8.87, No. 1425cdA; 1987, Nos. 1416C, 1418C/19C, 1421C; 7.88, No. 1413C; 1.12.88, No. 1420cA.

**308** The Queen Mother at Royal Opera House, London

**309** Youth Gardening (Horticulture)

(Des J.W. Litho Questa)

**1985** (3 July). *Life and Times of Queen Elizabeth the Queen Mother. T* **308** *and similar multicoloured designs. P* 14.
1426 $1 Type **308** .. .. .. .. 55 60
1427 $1.50, The Queen Mother playing snooker at London Press Club (*horiz*) .. .. 80 85
1428 $2.50, At Epsom Races, 1960 .. .. 1·40 1·50
1426/8 .. .. .. .. *Set of* 3 2·50 2·75
**MS**1429 56×85 mm. $5 With Prince of Wales on 80th Birthday .. .. .. .. .. 2·75 3·00
Stamps as Nos. 1426/8, but with face values of 90 c., $1 and $3, exist from additional sheetlets of 5 plus a label issued December 1985. These also have changed background colours and are perforated 12½×12 ($1) or 12×12½ (others) (*Price for set of 3 stamps £2 mint*).

(Des Liane Fried. Litho Format)

**1985** (21 Aug). *International Youth Year. T* **309** *and similar vert designs. Multicoloured. P* 15.
1430 25 c. Type **309** .. .. .. .. 20 20
1431 50 c. Young people on beach (Leisure) .. 40 30
1432 $1.10, Girls in classroom (Education) .. 80 80
1433 $3 Nurse and young patient (Health Care) .. .. .. .. .. 1·75 2·00
1430/3 .. .. .. .. *Set of* 4 2·75 3·00
**MS**1434 111×80 mm. $5 Children of different races .. .. .. .. .. .. 2·75 3·25

(Des Susan David. Litho Questa)

**1985** (3 Sept). *300th Birth Anniv of Johann Sebastian Bach (composer). Vert designs as T* **206** *of Antigua. P* 14.
1435 25 c. multicoloured .. .. .. .. 45 20
1436 70 c. multicoloured .. .. .. .. 80 60
1437 $1 multicoloured .. .. .. .. 1·25 1·00
1438 $3 multicoloured .. .. .. .. 2·50 2·75
1435/8 .. .. .. .. *Set of* 4 4·50 4·25
**MS**1439 104×74 mm. $5 black, lavender-grey and cinnamon .. .. .. .. .. 3·50 3·75
Designs:—25 c. Crumhorn; 70 c. Oboe d'amore; $1 Violin; $3 Harpsichord; $5 Johann Sebastian Bach.

**310** Cub Scouts Camping

(Des A. DiLorenzo. Litho Questa)

**1985** (5 Sept). *4th Caribbean Cuboree. T* **310** *and similar multicoloured designs. P* 14.
1440 10 c. Type **310** .. .. .. .. 20 15
1441 50 c. Cub scouts swimming ("Physical Fitness") .. .. .. .. .. 45 4
1442 $1 Stamp collecting .. .. .. 80 8
1443 $4 Birdwatching .. .. .. .. 2·75 3·0
1440/3 .. .. .. .. *Set of* 4 3·75 4·0
**MS**1444 103×75 mm. $5 Cub scouts saluting leader (*vert*) .. .. .. .. .. 3·00 3·5

(Des Mary Walters. Litho Format)

**1985** (4 Nov). *Royal Visit. Multicoloured designs as T* **207** *of Antigua. P* 14½.
1445 50 c. Flags of Great Britain and Grenada .. 60 35
1446 $1 Queen Elizabeth II (*vert*) .. .. 1·25 1·00
1447 $4 Royal Yacht *Britannia* .. .. 3·50 4·25
1445/7 .. .. .. .. *Set of* 3 4·75 5·00
**MS**1448 111×83 mm. $5 Map of Grenada .. 5·00 3·75

(Des Walt Disney Productions. Litho Questa)

**1985** (4 Nov). *150th Birth Anniv of Mark Twain (author). Horiz designs as T* **118** *of Anguilla showing Walt Disney cartoon characters in scenes from "The Prince and the Pauper". Multicoloured. P* 14×13½.
1449 25 c. Mortie as Tom meeting the Prince (Ferdie) .. .. .. .. .. 20 2
1450 50 c. Tom and the Prince exchanging clothes .. .. .. .. .. 35 3
1451 $1.10, The Prince with John Cantry .. 70 65
1452 $1.50, The Prince knights Mike Hendon (Goofy) .. .. .. .. .. 95 85
1453 $2 Tom and the Whipping Boy .. .. 1·40 1·25
1449/53 .. .. .. .. *Set of* 5 3·25 3·0
**MS**1454 124×100 mm. $5 The Prince, Tom and Mike Hendon .. .. .. .. .. 2·75 3·0

(Des Walt Disney Productions. Litho Questa)

**1985** (4 Nov). *Birth Bicentenaries of Grimm Brothers (folklorists). Horiz designs as T* **119** *of Anguilla, showing Walt Disney cartoon characters in scenes from "The Fisherman and his Wife". Multicoloured. P* 14×13½.
1455 30 c. The Fisherman (Goofy) catching enchanted fish .. .. .. .. 15 20
1456 60 c. The Fisherman scolded by his Wife (Clarabelle) .. .. .. .. 35 40
1457 70 c. The Fisherman's Wife with dream cottage .. .. .. .. .. 40 55
1458 $1 The Fisherman's Wife as King .. 60 80
1459 $3 The Fisherman and Wife in their original shack .. .. .. .. 1·75 2·50
1455/9 .. .. .. .. *Set of* 5 3·00 4·00
**MS**1460 126×100 mm. $5 The Fisherman in boat .. .. .. .. .. .. 3·00 4·00

**311** Redspotted Hawkfish

(Des R. Sauber. Litho Questa)

**1985** (15 Nov). *Marine Life. T* **311** *and similar horiz designs. Multicoloured. P* 14.
1461 25 c. Type **311** .. .. .. .. 65 30
1462 50 c. Spotfin Butterflyfish .. .. .. 1·00 70
1463 $1.10, Fire Coral and Orange Sponges .. 1·75 2·00
1464 $3 Pillar Coral .. .. .. .. 3·50 4·00
1461/4 .. .. .. .. *Set of* 4 6·25 6·25
**MS**1465 127×100 mm. $5 Bigeye .. .. 3·50 4·00

(Litho Format)

**1985** (22 Nov). *40th Anniv of United Nations Organization. Multicoloured designs as T* **208** *of Antigua showing United Nations (New York) stamps. P* 14½.
1466 50 c. Mary McLeod Bethune (educationist) and 1975 International Women's Year 10 c. .. .. .. .. .. .. 50 30
1467 $2 Maimonides (physician) and 1966 W.H.O. 5 c. .. .. .. .. .. 2·50 2·00
1468 $2.50, Alexander Graham Bell (telephone inventor) and 1956 I.T.U. 3 c. .. 2·75 2·75
1466/8 .. .. .. .. *Set of* 3 5·25 4·50
**MS**1469 110×85 mm. $5 Dag Hammarskjold (Secretary-General) (*vert*) .. .. .. 2·50 2·75

312 "The Adoration of the Shepherds" (Mantegna)

VISIT OF
PRES REAGAN
20 FEB. 1986
(313)

(Des Mary Walters. Litho Format)

**1985** (23 Dec). *Christmas. Religious Paintings. T* **312** *and similar horiz designs. Multicoloured. P* 15.
1470 25 c. Type **312** .. .. .. .. 35 15
1471 60 c. "Journey of the Magi" (Sassetta) .. 70 55
1472 90 c. "Madonna and Child enthroned with Saints" (Raphael) .. .. .. 1·00 85
1473 $4 "Nativity" (Monaco) .. .. .. 3·25 4·00
1470/3 .. .. .. .. *Set of* 4 4·75 5·00
**MS**1474 107×81 mm. $5 "Madonna and Child enthroned with Saints" (Gaddi) .. .. .. 2·50 2·75

(Des J. Iskowitz. Litho Questa)

**1986** (6 Jan). *Centenary of Statue of Liberty* (1*st issue*). *Multicoloured designs as T* **211** *of Dominica. P* 15.
1475 5 c. Columbus Monument, 1893 (*vert*) .. 15 20
1476 25 c. Columbus Monument, 1986 (*vert*) .. 30 20
1477 40 c. Mounted police, Central Park, 1895 .. 1·00 60
1478 $4 Mounted police, 1986 .. .. .. 4·50 4·50
1475/8 .. .. .. .. *Set of* 4 5·50 5·00
**MS**1479 104×76 mm. $5 Statue of Liberty (*vert*) 2·50 3·25
See also Nos. 1644/52.

(Litho Questa)

**1986** (20 Jan). *Birth Bicentenary of John J. Audubon (ornithologist)* (2*nd issue*). *Multicoloured designs as T* **198** *of Antigua. P* 12×12½.
1480 50 c. Snowy Egret .. .. .. .. 70 45
1481 90 c. Greater Flamingo .. .. .. 1·25 80
1482 $1.10, Canada Goose .. .. .. 1·40 1·00
1483 $3 Smew .. .. .. .. .. 2·25 2·50
1480/3 .. .. .. .. *Set of* 4 5·00 4·25
**MS**1484 103×72 mm. $5 Brent Goose (*horiz*). P 14 .. .. .. .. .. .. 6·00 6·50
Nos. 1480/3 were each issued in sheetlets of five stamps and one stamp-size label, which appears in the centre of the bottom row.

**1986** (20 Feb). *Visit of President Reagan. Nos.* 1418A *and* 1424A *optd with T* **313**.
1485 50 c. Amaryllis .. .. .. .. .. 25 30
1486 $5 Plumbago .. .. .. .. .. 2·50 3·00

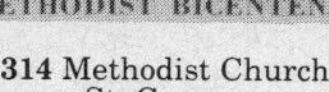

314 Methodist Church, St. Georges

315 Player with Ball

(Litho Format)

**1986** (24 Feb). *Bicentenary of Methodist Church in Grenada. T* **314** *and similar horiz design. Multicoloured. P* 15.
1487 60 c. Type **314** .. .. .. .. .. 50 60
**MS**1488 102×73 mm. $5 St. Georges .. .. 3·50 4·25

(Des N. Waldman. Litho Questa)

**1986** (6 Mar). *World Cup Football Championship, Mexico. T* **315** *and similar vert designs. Multicoloured. P* 14.
1489 50 c. Type **315** .. .. .. .. 50 40
1490 70 c. Player heading ball .. .. .. 70 60
1491 90 c. Player controlling ball .. .. 85 70
1492 $4 Player controlling ball with right foot 4·00 3·25
1489/92 .. .. .. .. *Set of* 4 5·50 4·50
**MS**1493 101×71 mm. $5 Player tackling .. 3·75 4·25

(Des W. Hanson. Litho Questa)

**1986** (20 Mar). *Appearance of Halley's Comet* (1*st issue*). *Horiz designs as T* **123** *of Anguilla. Multicoloured. P* 14.
1494 5 c. Clyde Tombaugh (astronomer) and Dudley Observatory, New York .. 15 15
1495 20 c. N.A.S.A. – U.S.A.F. "X-24B" Space Shuttle prototype, 1973 .. .. 15 15
1496 40 c. German comet medal, 1618 .. .. 30 30
1497 $4 Destruction of Sodom and Gomorrah, 1949 B.C. .. .. .. .. .. 2·25 2·75
1494/7 .. .. .. .. *Set of* 4 2·50 3·00
**MS**1498 102×70 mm. $5 Halley's Comet over Grenada .. .. .. .. .. .. 4·50 4·75
See also Nos. 1533/7 and 1980/4.

(Litho Questa)

**1986** (21 Apr). *60th Birthday of Queen Elizabeth II. Vert designs as T* **125** *of Anguilla. P* 14.
1499 2 c. black and yellow .. .. .. 10 15
1500 $1.50, multicoloured .. .. .. 75 90
1501 $4 multicoloured .. .. .. .. 2·00 2·75
1499/1501 .. .. .. *Set of* 3 2·50 3·50
**MS**1502 120×85 mm. $5 black and grey-brown .. 3·00 3·75
Designs:—2 c. Princess Elizabeth in 1951; $1.50, Queen presenting trophy at polo match, Windsor, 1965; $4 At Epsom, Derby Day, 1977; $5 King George VI and family, 1939.

(Des Walt Disney Productions. Litho Format)

**1986** (22 May). *"Ameripex" International Stamp Exhibition, Chicago. Horiz designs as T* **212** *of Dominica, showing Walt Disney cartoon characters playing baseball. Multicoloured. P* 11.
1503 1 c. Goofy as pitcher .. .. .. 10 10
1504 2 c. Goofy as catcher .. .. .. 10 10
1505 3 c. Mickey Mouse striking ball and Donald Duck as catcher .. .. .. .. 10 10
1506 4 c. Huey forcing out Dewey .. .. 10 10
1507 5 c. Chip n'Dale chasing flyball .. .. 10 10
1508 6 c. Mickey Mouse, Donald Duck and Clarabelle in argument .. .. .. .. 10 10
1509 $2 Minnie Mouse and Donald Duck reading baseball rules .. .. .. .. 1·40 1·40
1510 $3 Ludwig von Drake as umpire with Goofy and Pete colliding .. .. 1·75 2·00
1503/10 .. .. .. .. *Set of* 8 3·00 3·25
**MS**1511 Two sheets, each 126×101 mm. (a) $5 Donald Duck striking ball. (b) $5 Minnie and Mickey Mouse running between bases. P 14×13½ .. .. *Set of* 2 *sheets* 9·00 9·50

(Litho Questa)

**1986** (1 July). *Royal Wedding. Vert designs as T* **213** *of Antigua. Multicoloured. P* 14.
1512 2 c. Prince Andrew and Miss Sarah Ferguson .. .. .. .. .. .. 10 15
1513 $1.10, Prince Andrew .. .. .. 70 70
1514 $4 Prince Andrew with H.M.S. *Brazen's* helicopter .. .. .. .. 2·50 3·00
1512/14 .. .. .. .. *Set of* 3 3·00 3·50
**MS**1515 88×88 mm. $5 Prince Andrew and Miss Sarah Ferguson (*different*) .. .. .. 3·50 4·25

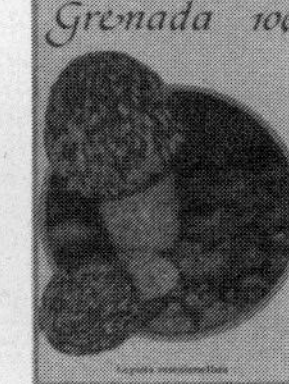


316 Brown-lined Latirus

317 *Lepiota roseolamellata*

(Des L. Birmingham. Litho Format)

**1986** (15 July). *Sea Shells. T* **316** *and similar horiz designs. Multicoloured. P* 15.
1516 25 c. Type **316** .. .. .. .. 30 20
1517 60 c. Lamellose Wentletrap .. .. .. 55 45
1518 70 c. Turkey Wing .. .. .. .. 65 50
1519 $4 Rooster Tail Conch .. .. .. 2·50 3·00
1516/19 .. .. .. .. *Set of* 4 3·50 3·75
**MS**1520 110×75 mm. $5 Angular Triton .. 3·25 4·25

(Des R. Sauber. Litho Format)

**1986** (1 Aug). *Mushrooms. T* **317** *and similar vert designs. Multicoloured. P* 15.
1521 10 c. Type **317** .. .. .. .. 40 20
1522 60 c. *Lentinus bertieri* .. .. .. 1·25 85
1523 $1 *Lentinus retinervis* .. .. .. 2·00 1·25
1524 $4 *Eccilia cystiophorus* .. .. .. 4·50 4·50
1521/4 .. .. .. .. *Set of* 4 7·50 6·25
**MS**1525 127×100 mm. $5 *Cystolepiota eriophora* 8·50 8·50

**1986** (15 Sept). *World Cup Football Championship Winners, Mexico. Nos.* 1489/93 *optd with T* **216** *of Antigua in gold.*
1526 50 c. Type **315** .. .. .. .. 30 35
1527 70 c. Player heading ball .. .. .. 40 45
1528 90 c. Player controlling ball .. .. 50 60
1529 $4 Player controlling ball with right foot 2·25 2·75
1526/9 .. .. .. .. *Set of* 4 3·00 3·75
**MS**1530 101×71 mm. $5 Player tackling .. 3·00 4·00

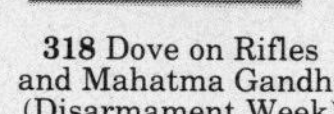

318 Dove on Rifles and Mahatma Gandhi (Disarmament Week)

319 Cockerel and Hen

(Des Mary Walters. Litho Format)

**1986** (15 Sept). *International Events. T* **318** *and similar multicoloured design. P* 15.
1531 60 c. Type **318** .. .. .. .. 50 50
1532 $4 Hands passing olive branch and Martin Luther King (International Peace Year) (*horiz*) .. .. .. .. 2·00 2·50

**1986** (15 Oct). *Appearance of Halley's Comet* (2*nd issue*). *Nos.* 1494/8 *optd with T* **218** *of Antigua* (*in silver on* $5).
1533 5 c. Clyde Tombaugh (astronomer) and Dudley Observatory, New York .. 30 30
1534 20 c. N.A.S.A.—U.S.A.F. "X-24B" Space Shuttle prototype, 1973 .. .. 55 30
1535 40 c. German comet medal, 1618 .. .. 70 45
1536 $4 Destruction of Sodom and Gomorrah, 1949 B.C. .. .. .. .. .. 3·50 4·00
1533/6 .. .. .. .. *Set of* 4 4·50 4·50
**MS**1537 102×70 mm. $5 Halley's Comet over Grenada .. .. .. .. .. .. 2·75 3·50

(Des Walt Disney Co. Litho Format)

**1986** (3 Nov). *Christmas. Multicoloured designs as T* **220** *of Antigua showing Walt Disney cartoon characters. P* 11.
1538 30 c. Mickey Mouse asleep in armchair (*vert*) .. .. .. .. .. .. 20 20
1539 45 c. Young Mickey Mouse with Father Christmas (*vert*) .. .. .. 30 30
1540 60 c. Donald Duck with toy telephone .. 40 35
1541 70 c. Pluto with pushcart .. .. .. 45 45
1542 $1.10, Daisy Duck with doll .. .. 70 75
1543 $2 Goofy as Father Christmas (*vert*) .. 1·25 1·50
1544 $2.50, Goofy singing carols at piano (*vert*) 1·60 1·75
1545 $3 Mickey Mouse, Donald Duck and nephew riding toy train .. .. 2·00 2·25
1538/45 .. .. .. .. *Set of* 8 6·25 6·75
**MS**1546 Two sheets, each 127×101 mm. (a) $5 Donald Duck, Goofy and Mickey Mouse delivering presents (*vert*). P 13½×14. (b) $5 Father Christmas playing toy piano. P 14×13½ *Set of* 2 *sheets* 5·50 6·50

(Litho Questa)

**1986** (17 Nov). *Fauna and Flora. T* **319** *and similar horiz designs. Multicoloured. P* 14.
1547 10 c. Type **319** .. .. .. .. 20 10
1548 30 c. Fish-eating Bat .. .. .. 35 20
1549 60 c. Goat .. .. .. .. .. 55 35
1550 70 c. Cow .. .. .. .. .. 60 40
1551 $1 Anthurium .. .. .. .. 1·50 1·25
1552 $1.10, Royal Poinciana .. .. .. 1·50 1·25
1553 $2 Frangipani .. .. .. .. 2·25 2·50
1554 $4 Orchid .. .. .. .. .. 5·50 6·00
1547/54 .. .. .. .. *Set of* 8 11·00 11·00
**MS**1555 Two sheets, each 104×73 mm. (a) $5 Grenada landscape. (b) $5 Horse *Set of* 2 *sheets* 10·00 11·00

320 Maserati "Biturbo" (1984)

321 Pole Vaulting

(Des J. Martin. Litho Format)

**1986** (20 Nov). *Centenary of Motoring. T* **320** *and similar horiz designs. Multicoloured. P* 15.
1556 10 c. Type **320** .. .. .. .. 20 20
1557 30 c. AC "Cobra" (1960) .. .. .. 30 30
1558 60 c. Corvette (1963) .. .. .. 50 50
1559 70 c. Dusenberg "SJ7" (1932) .. .. 60 60
1560 90 c. Porsche (1957) .. .. .. .. 75 75
1561 $1.10, Stoewer (1930) .. .. .. 85 85
1562 $2 Volkswagen "Beetle" (1957) .. .. 1·40 1·40
1563 $3 Mercedes "600 Limo" (1963) .. .. 1·90 2·00
1556/63 .. .. .. .. *Set of* 8 6·00 6·00
**MS**1564 Two sheets, each 106 × 77 mm. (a) $5 Stutz (1914). (b) $5 Packard (1941) *Set of* 2 *sheets* 5·00 6·00

(Des BG Studio. Litho Format)

**1986** (1 Dec). *Olympic Games, Seoul, South Korea* (1988). *T* **321** *and similar vert designs. Multicoloured. P* 15.
1565 10 c.+5 c. Type **321** .. .. .. 10 20
1566 50 c.+20 c. Gymnastics .. .. .. 35 45
1567 70 c.+30 c. Putting the shot .. .. 50 65
1568 $2+$1 High jumping .. .. .. 1·50 2·00
1565/8 .. .. .. .. *Set of* 4 2·25 3·00
**MS**1569 80 × 100 mm. $3 + $1 Swimming .. 2·00 2·75
The premiums on Nos. 1565/9 were to support the participation of the Grenada team.

(Litho Questa)

**1986** (19 Dec). *Birth Centenary of Marc Chagall (artist). Designs as T* **225** *of Antigua, showing various paintings. P* 13½×14 (*vert*) *or* 14×13½ (*horiz*).
1570/1609 $1×40 multicoloured .. *Set of* 40 16·00 18·00
**MS**1610 Ten sheets, each 110×95 mm. $5×10 multicoloured (*each* 104×89 *mm*). Imperf *Set of* 10 *sheets* 20·00 22·00
Although announced as all being released on 19 December 1986 the issue was distributed in ten parts, each of four stamps and one miniature sheet, at monthly intervals.

(Des J. Iskowitz. Litho Format)

**1987** (5 Feb). *America's Cup Yachting Championship. Vert designs as T* **222** *of Antigua. Multicoloured. P* 15.
1611 10 c. *Columbia*, 1958 .. .. .. 10 10
1612 60 c. *Resolute*, 1920 .. .. .. 35 35
1613 $1.10, *Endeavor*, 1934 .. .. .. 70 75
1614 $4 *Rainbow*, 1934 .. .. .. 1·90 2·50
1611/14 .. .. .. .. *Set of* 4 2·75 3·25
**MS**1615 113×84 mm. $5 *Weatherly*, 1962 .. 2·25 3·00

322 Virgin Mary and Outline Map of Grenada

323 Black Grouper

(Des G. Hamilton (10, 30, 50 c.), Mary Walters (others). Litho Format)

**1987** (27 Apr). *500th Anniv of Discovery of America by Columbus* (1992) (*1st issue*). *T* **322** *and similar multicoloured designs. P* 15.

1616 10 c. Type **322** .. .. .. .. 15 15
1617 30 c. *Santa Maria, Pinta* and *Nina* (*horiz*) .. 20 15
1618 50 c. Columbus and outline map of Grenada 25 30
1619 60 c. Christopher Columbus .. .. 25 30
1620 90 c. King Ferdinand and Queen Isabella of Spain (*horiz*) .. .. .. 40 45
1621 $1.10, Map of Antilles by Columbus .. 50 60
1622 $2 Caribs with sailing raft (*horiz*) .. 90 1·25
1623 $3 Columbus in the New World, 1493 (contemporary drawing) .. .. 1·40 1·60
1616/23 .. .. .. .. *Set of* 8 3·50 4·25
**MS**1624 Two sheets, each 104×72 mm. (a) $5 Route map and Columbus' signature. (b) $5 Columbus carrying Christ Child *Set of* 2 *sheets* 4·50 5·50

See also Nos. 2051/5 and 2091/9.

(Des W. Wright. Litho Questa)

**1987** (18 May). *Milestones of Transportation. Horiz designs as T* **226** *of Antigua. Multicoloured. P* 14.

1625 10 c. Cornu's first helicopter, 1907 .. 15 15
1626 15 c. *Monitor* and *Merrimack* (first battle between ironclad warships), 1862 .. 20 20
1627 30 c. "LZ1" (first Zeppelin), 1900 .. .. 30 30
1628 50 c. S.S. *Sirius* (first transatlantic steamship crossing), 1838 .. .. 35 35
1629 60 c. Steam locomotive on Trans-Siberian Railway (longest line).. .. .. 35 35
1630 70 c. U.S.S. *Enterprise* (largest aircraft carrier), 1960 .. .. .. .. 40 40
1631 90 c. Blanchard's Balloon (first balloon across English Channel), 1785 .. 55 55
1632 $1.50, U.S.S. *Holland 1* (first steam-powered submarine), 1900 .. .. 90 90
1633 $2 S.S. *Oceanic* (first luxury liner), 1871 1·40 1·40
1634 $3 Lamborghini "Countach" (fastest commercial car), 1984 .. .. .. 1·75 1·75
1625/34 .. .. .. .. *Set of* 10 5·75 5·75

(Des J. Martin. Litho Format)

**1987** (15 June). *"Capex '87" International Stamp Exhibition, Toronto. Game Fishes. T* **323** *and similar multicoloured designs. P* 15.

1635 10 c. Type **323** .. .. .. .. 30 15
1636 30 c. Blue Marlin (*horiz*) .. .. .. 40 15
1637 60 c. White Marlin .. .. .. .. 60 45
1638 70 c. Big Eye Thresher Shark (*horiz*) .. 70 60
1639 $1 Bonefish (*horiz*) .. .. .. 90 80
1640 $1.10, Wahoo (*horiz*) .. .. .. 1·00 90
1641 $2 Sailfish (*horiz*).. .. .. .. 1·75 2·00
1642 $4 Albacore (*horiz*) .. .. .. 2·75 3·00
1635/42 .. .. .. .. *Set of* 8 7·50 7·25
**MS**1643 Two sheets, each 100×70 mm. (a) $5 Yellowfin Tuna. (b) $5 Barracuda (*horiz*) *Set of* 2 *sheets* 4·50 5·50

(Litho Questa)

**1987** (5 Aug). *Centenary of Statue of Liberty* (1986) (*2nd issue*). *Multicoloured designs as T* **227** *of Antigua. P* 14.

1644 10 c. Computer projections of Statue and base (*horiz*) .. .. .. .. 15 10
1645 25 c. Statue and fireworks (*horiz*) .. .. 20 15
1646 50 c. Statue and fireworks (*different*) (*horiz*) 35 35
1647 60 c. Statue and boats .. .. .. 35 35
1648 70 c. Computer projections of top of Statue (*horiz*) .. .. .. .. 40 40
1649 $1 Rear view of Statue and fireworks .. 60 60
1650 $1.10, Aerial view of Statue .. .. 70 70
1651 $2 Statue and flotilla .. .. .. 1·10 1·40
1652 $4 *Queen Elizabeth 2* in New York Harbour .. .. .. .. 2·00 2·25
1644/52 .. .. .. .. *Set of* 9 5·25 5·75

**324** Alice and the Rabbit Hole

(Des Walt Disney Co. Litho Questa)

**1987** (9 Sept). *50th Anniv of First Full-Length Disney Cartoon Film. T* **324** *and similar designs. P* 14×13½.

1653/1706 30 c. × 54 multicoloured *Set of* 54 6·00 6·50
**MS**1707 Six sheets, each 127×102 mm. $5×6 multicoloured. P 13½×14 (*vert*) or 14×13½ (*horiz*) .. .. .. *Set of* 6 *sheets* 12·00 12·50

Nos. 1653/1706 (issued as six sheetlets each of nine different designs) and No. **MS**1707 depict scenes from *Alice in Wonderland, Cinderella, Peter Pan, Pinocchio, Sleeping Beauty* and *Snow White and the Seven Dwarfs*.

**325** Isaac Newton holding Apple (Law of Gravity)

(Litho Questa)

**1987** (9 Sept). *Great Scientific Discoveries. T* **325** *and similar horiz designs. Multicoloured. P* 14.

1708 50 c. Type **325** .. .. .. .. 55 45
1709 $1.10, John Jacob Berzelius and symbols of chemical elements .. .. .. 95 95
1710 $2 Robert Boyle (law of Pressure and Volume) .. .. .. .. 1·75 1·75
1711 $3 James Watt and drawing of steam engine .. .. .. .. 2·40 2·50
1708/11 .. .. .. .. *Set of* 4 5·00 5·00
**MS**1712 105×75 mm. $5 *Voyager* (experimental aircraft) and *Flyer 1* .. .. .. 2·50 3·25

No. 1711 is inscribed "RUDOLF DIESEL" in error.

**326** Wade Boggs (Boston Red Sox)

International Social Security Association

(**327**)

(Des W. Storozuk. Litho Questa)

**1987** (2 Nov). *All-Star Baseball Game, Oakland, California. Sheet* 114×82 *mm, containing T* **326** *and similar horiz design. Multicoloured. P* 14×13½.

**MS**1713 $1 Type **326**; $1 Eric Davis (Cincinnati Reds) .. .. .. .. .. 1·00 1·50

**1987** (2 Nov). *60th Anniv of International Social Security Association. Nos.* 1413A, 1418A *and* 1423A *optd with T* **327**.

1714 10 c. Hibiscus .. .. .. .. 10 15
1715 50 c. Amaryllis .. .. .. .. 25 30
1716 $3 Shrimp Plant .. .. .. .. 1·40 2·00
1714/16 .. .. .. .. *Set of* 3 1·50 2·25

(Litho Questa)

**1987** (2 Nov). *Bicentenary of U.S. Constitution. Multicoloured designs as T* **232** *of Antigua. P* 14.

1717 15 c. Independence Hall, Philadelphia (*vert*) 10 10
1718 50 c. Benjamin Franklin (Pennsylvania delegate) (*vert*).. .. .. .. 25 30
1719 60 c. State Seal, Massachusetts .. .. 25 30
1720 $4 Robert Morris (Pennsylvania delegate) (*vert*) .. .. .. .. 1·75 2·40
1717/20 .. .. .. .. *Set of* 4 2·10 2·75
**MS**1721 105×75 mm. $5 James Madison (Virginia delegate) (*vert*) .. .. .. 2·25 3·00

Nos. 1717/20 were each issued in sheetlets of five stamps and one stamp-size label, which appears in the centre of the bottom row.

**328** Goofy in "The Shadow"

**329** "The Annunciation" (Fra Angelico)

(Des Walt Disney Co. Litho Questa)

**1987** (16 Nov). *"Hafnia '87" International Stamp Exhibition, Copenhagen. T* **328** *and similar vert designs showing Walt Disney cartoon characters in scenes from Hans Christian Andersen's fairy tales. Multicoloured. P* 13½×14.

1722 25 c. Type **328** .. .. .. .. 15 15
1723 30 c. Mother Stork and brood in "The Storks" .. .. .. .. .. 15 15
1724 50 c. King Richard, Robin Hood and Little John (from *Robin Hood*) in "The Emperor's New Clothes" .. .. .. 25 30
1725 60 c. Goofy and Pluto in "The Tinderbox" .. 25 30
1726 70 c. Daisy and Donald Duck in "The Shepherdess and the Chimney Sweep" .. 30 35
1727 $1.50, Mickey and Minnie Mouse in "The Little Mermaid" .. .. .. 70 80
1728 $3 Clarabelle and Goofy in "The Princess and the Pea" .. .. .. 1·40 1·75
1729 $4 Minnie Mouse and Pegleg Pete in "The Marsh King's Daughter" .. .. 1·75 2·00
1722/9 .. .. .. .. *Set of* 8 4·50 5·25
**MS**1730 Two sheets, each 127×102 mm. (a) $5 Goofy in "The Flying Trunk". (b) $5 Goofy as "The Sandman" .. .. *Set of* 2 *sheets* 6·00 7·00

(Litho Questa)

**1987** (15 Dec). *Christmas. T* **329** *and similar vert designs showing religious paintings. Multicoloured. P* 14.

1731 15 c. Type **329** .. .. .. .. 30 10
1732 30 c. "The Annunciation" (attr. Hubert van Eyck) .. .. .. .. 45 30
1733 60 c. "The Adoration of the Magi" (Januarius Zick) .. .. .. .. 80 60
1734 $4 "The Flight into Egypt" (Gerard David) 3·00 3·50
1731/4 .. .. .. .. *Set of* 4 4·00 4·00
**MS**1735 99×75 mm. $5 "The Circumcision" (Giovanni Bellini studio).. .. .. 5·00 5·50

**330** T. Albert Marryshow

(Litho Questa)

**1988** (22 Jan). *Birth Centenary of T. Albert Marryshow (nationalist). P* 14.

1736 **330** 25 c. reddish brown, chestnut & brt crim 20 20

(Des and litho Questa)

**1988** (15 Feb). *Royal Ruby Wedding. Vert designs as T* **234** *of Antigua. Multicoloured. P* 14.

1737 15 c. deep brown, black and bright new blue 20 10
1738 50 c. multicoloured .. .. .. .. 45 30
1739 $1 deep brown and black.. .. .. 75 60
1740 $4 multicoloured .. .. .. .. 2·25 2·40
1737/40 .. .. .. .. *Set of* 4 3·25 3·00
**MS**1741 76×100 mm. $5 multicoloured.. .. 2·25 2·75

Designs:—15 c. Wedding photograph, 1947; 50 c. Queen Elizabeth II with Prince Charles and Princess Anne, *c*. 1955; $1 Queen with Princess Anne, *c*. 1957; $4 Queen Elizabeth (from photo by Tim Graham), 1980; $5 Princess Elizabeth in wedding dress, 1947.

**331** Goofy and Daisy Duck lighting Olympic Torch, Olympia

**332** Scout fishing from Boat

(Des Walt Disney Company. Litho Questa)

**1988** (13 Apr). *Olympic Games, Seoul. T* **331** *and similar vert designs showing Walt Disney cartoon characters. Multicoloured. P* 13½×14.

1742 1 c. Type **331** .. .. .. .. 10 10
1743 2 c. Donald and Daisy Duck carrying Olympic torch .. .. .. 10 10
1744 3 c. Donald Duck, Goofy and Mickey Mouse carrying flags of U.S., Korea and Spain .. .. .. .. 10 10
1745 4 c. Donald Duck releasing doves .. 10 10
1746 5 c. Mickey Mouse flying with rocket belt 10 10
1747 10 c. Morty and Ferdie carrying banner with Olympic motto .. .. .. 10 10
1748 $6 Donald Duck, Minnie Mouse and Hodori the Tiger (mascot of Seoul Games) .. .. .. .. 2·75 3·25
1749 $7 Pluto, Hodori and old post office, Seoul 3·25 3·75
1742/9 .. .. .. .. *Set of* 8 5·75 6·50
**MS**1750 Two sheets, each 127×101 mm. (a) $5 Mickey Mouse taking athlete's oath. (b) $5 Donald and Daisy Duck as athletes at Closing Ceremony .. .. .. *Set of* 2 *sheets* 4·50 5·50

**1988** (19 Apr). *Stamp Exhibitions. Nos.* 1631/4 *optd as T* **241** *of Antigua with various emblems.*

1751 90 c. Blanchard's Balloon, 1785 (optd "OLYMPHILEX '88", Seoul) .. 40 45
1752 $1.50, U.S.S. *Holland 1*, 1900 (optd "INDEPENDENCE 40", Israel) .. 60 75
1753 $2 S.S. *Oceanic*, 1871 (optd "FINLANDIA 88", Helsinki) .. .. 80 1·00
1754 $3 Lamborghini "Countach", 1984 (optd "Praga 88", Prague) .. .. .. 1·25 1·60
1751/4 .. .. .. .. *Set of* 4 2·75 3·50

(Des J. Martin. Litho Questa)

**1988** (3 May). *World Scout Jamboree, Australia. T* **332** *and similar multicoloured designs. P* 14.

1755 20 c. Type **332** .. .. .. .. 20 15
1756 70 c. Scouts hiking through forest (*horiz*) .. 70 60
1757 90 c. Practicing first aid (*horiz*) .. .. 90 80
1758 $3 Shooting rapids in inflatable canoe .. 2·25 2·50
1755/8 .. .. .. .. *Set of* 4 3·50 3·50
**MS**1759 114×80 mm. $5 Scout with Koala .. 2·10 2·75

## PRICES OF SETS

Set prices are given for many issues, generally those containing three stamps or more. Definitive sets include one of each value or major colour change, but do not cover different perforations, die types or minor shades. Where a choice is possible the set prices are based on the cheapest versions of the stamps included in the listings.

**333** *Santa Maria de Guia* (Columbus), 1498, and Map of Rotary District

**334** Roseate Tern

(Des W. Hanson. Litho Questa)

**1988** (5 May). *Rotary District 405 Conference, St. George's. T* **333** *and similar multicoloured design. P* 13½×14.
1760 $2 Type **333** .. .. .. .. 80 1·00
**MS**1761 133×90 mm. $10 Rotary emblem (*horiz*). P 14×13½ .. .. .. .. 4·25 4·75

(Des Mary Walters. Litho Questa)

**1988** (31 May). *Birds. T* **334** *and similar vert designs. Multicoloured. P* 14.
1762 10 c. Type **334** .. .. .. .. 20 15
1763 25 c. Laughing Gull .. .. .. .. 30 20
1764 50 c. Osprey .. .. .. .. 50 35
1765 60 c. Rose-breasted Grosbeak .. .. 50 35
1766 90 c. Purple Gallinule .. .. .. 55 45
1767 $1.10, White-tailed Tropic Bird .. .. 60 70
1768 $3 Blue-faced Booby .. .. .. 1·40 1·75
1769 $4 Common Shoveler .. .. .. 1·75 2·25
1762/9 .. .. .. .. *Set of* 8 5·25 5·75
**MS**1770 Two sheets, each 100×71 mm. (a) $5 Belted Kingfisher. (b) $5 Brown-crested Flycatcher ("Rusty-tailed Flycatcher") *Set of* 2 *sheets* 4·25 4·75

**335** Vauxhall Type "OE 30/98", 1925

**336** *Graf Zeppelin* over Chicago World's Fair, 1933

(Des W. Wright. Litho B.D.T.)

**1988** (1 June). *Cars. T* **335** *and similar vert designs. Multicoloured. P* 13.
1771 $2 Type **335** .. .. .. .. 80 85
a. Sheetlet. Nos. 1771/80 .. .. 8·00
1772 $2 Wills "Sainte Claire", 1926 .. .. 80 85
1773 $2 Bucciali, 1928 .. .. .. 80 85
1774 $2 Irving Napier "Golden Arrow", 1929 80 85
1775 $2 Studebaker "President", 1930 .. 80 85
1776 $2 Thomas "Flyer", 1907 .. .. 80 85
1777 $2 Isotta-Fraschini "Tipo J", 1908 .. 80 85
1778 $2 Fiat 10/14HP, 1910 .. .. .. 80 85
1779 $2 Mercer "Type 35 Raceabout", 1911 .. 80 85
1780 $2 Marmon "Model 34 Cloverleaf", 1917 80 85
1781 $2 Tatra "Type 77", 1934 .. .. 80 85
a. Sheetlet. Nos. 1781/90 .. .. 8·00
1782 $2 Rolls-Royce "Phantom III", 1938 .. 80 85
1783 $2 Studebaker "Champion Starlight", 1947 .. .. .. .. 80 85
1784 $2 Porsche "Gmund", 1948 .. .. 80 85
1785 $2 Tucker, 1948 .. .. .. 80 85
1786 $2 Peerless "V-16", 1931 .. .. 80 85
1787 $2 Minerva "AL", 1931 .. .. 80 85
1788 $2 Reo "Royale", 1933 .. .. 80 85
1789 $2 Pierce Arrow "Silver Arrow", 1933 .. 80 85
1790 $2 Hupmobile "Aerodynamic", 1934 .. 80 85
1791 $2 Peugeot "404", 1965 .. .. .. 80 85
a. Sheetlet. Nos. 1791/1800 .. .. 8·00
1792 $2 Ford "Capri", 1969 .. .. .. 80 85
1793 $2 Ferrari "312T", 1975 .. .. 80 85
1794 $2 Lotus "T-79", 1978 .. .. .. 80 85
1795 $2 Williams-Cosworth "FW07", 1979 .. 80 85
1796 $2 H.R.G. "1500 Sports", 1948 .. .. 80 85
1797 $2 Crosley "Hotshot", 1949 .. .. 80 85
1798 $2 Volvo "PV444", 1955 .. .. 80 85
1799 $2 Maserati "Tipo 61", 1960 .. .. 80 85
1800 $2 Saab "96", 1963 .. .. .. 80 85
1771/1800 .. .. .. *Set of* 30 22·00 23·00
Nos. 1771/80, 1781/90 and 1791/1800 were each printed together, *se-tenant*, in sheetlets of 10.

(Litho Questa)

**1988** (15 June). 500*th Birth Anniv of Titian (artist). Multicoloured designs as T* **238** *of Antigua. P* 13½×14.
1801 10 c. "Lavinia Vecellio" .. .. 10 10
1802 20 c. "Portrait of a Man" .. .. 10 10
1803 25 c. "Andrea de Franceschi" .. .. 10 15
1804 90 c. "Head of a Soldier" .. .. .. 40 45
1805 $1 "Man with a Flute" .. .. .. 45 50
1806 $2 "Lucrezia and Tarquinius" .. .. 80 85
1807 $3 "Duke of Mantua with Dog" .. .. 1·25 1·40
1808 $4 "La Bella di Tiziano" .. .. .. 1·60 1·75
1801/8 .. .. .. .. *Set of* 8 4·25 4·75
**MS**1809 Two sheets, each 110×95 mm. (a) $5 "Allegory of Alfonso D'Avalos (detail). P 13½×14. (b) $5 "Fall of Man" (detail) (*horiz*). P 14×13½ .. .. .. *Set of* 2 *sheets* 4·25 5·00

(Des W. Hanson. Litho Questa)

**1988** (1 July). *Airships. T* **336** *and similar multicoloured designs. P* 14.
1810 10 c. Type **336** .. .. .. .. 10 10
1811 15 c. LZ-1 over Lake Constance, 1901 (*horiz*) .. .. .. .. 10 10
1812 25 c. *Washington* (balloon) and balloon barge, 1862 .. .. .. .. 10 15
1813 45 c. *Hindenberg* and Maybach "Zeppelin" car (*horiz*) .. .. .. 20 25
1814 50 c. Goodyear airship in Statue of Liberty Centenary Race, 1986 .. .. 20 25
1815 60 c. *Hindenberg* over Statue of Liberty, 1937 (*horiz*) .. .. .. 25 30
1816 90 c. Aircraft docking experiment with *Hindenberg* 1936 (*horiz*) .. .. 40 45
1817 $2 *Hindenberg* over Olympic Stadium, Berlin, 1936 .. .. .. 80 1·00
1818 $3 *Hindenberg* over Christ of the Andes Monument, 1937 .. .. 1·25 1·60
1819 $4 *Hindenberg* and *Bremen* (liner), 1936 (*horiz*) .. .. .. 1·60 2·00
1810/19 .. .. .. .. *Set of* 10 4·50 5·50
**MS**1820 (a) 75×95 mm. $5 *Graf Zeppelin*, 1930 (*horiz*). (b) 95×75 mm. $5 Zeppelin, 1935 (*horiz*) *Set of* 2 *sheets* 4·25 5·00

**337** Tasmanian Wolf, Mickey Mouse and Pluto

**338** Pineapple

(Des Walt Disney Co. Litho Questa)

**1988** (1 Aug). *"Sydpex '88" National Stamp Exhibition, Sydney and 60th Birthday of Mickey Mouse. T* **337** *and similar horiz designs. Multicoloured. P* 14×13½.
1821 1 c. Type **337** .. .. .. .. 10 10
1822 2 c. Mickey Mouse feeding wallabies .. 10 10
1823 3 c. Mickey Mouse and Goofy with kangaroo .. .. .. .. 10 10
1824 4 c. Mickey and Minnie Mouse riding emus .. .. .. .. 10 10
1825 5 c. Mickey and Minnie Mouse with wombat .. .. .. .. 10 10
1826 10 c. Mickey Mouse and Donald Duck watching platypus .. .. .. 10 10
1827 $5 Mickey Mouse and Goofy photographing kookaburra .. .. 2·50 3·00
1828 $6 Mickey Mouse and Koala on map of Australia .. .. .. 2·75 3·25
1821/8 .. .. .. .. *Set of* 8 5·00 6·25
**MS**1829 Two sheets, each 127 × 102 mm. (a) $5 Mickey Mouse with birthday cake. (b) $5 Mickey and Minnie Mouse with parrots .. *Set of* 2 *sheets* 5·00 6·00

(Des J. Martin. Litho Questa)

**1988** (11 Aug). 10*th Anniv of International Fund for Agricultural Development. T* **338** *and similar multicoloured designs. P* 14.
1830 25 c. Type **338** .. .. .. .. 15 15
1831 75 c. Bananas .. .. .. .. 40 40
1832 $3 Mace and nutmeg (*horiz*) .. .. 1·50 2·00
1830/2 .. .. .. .. *Set of* 3 1·90 2·25

**339** Lignum Vitae

(Des W. Wright. Litho Questa)

**1988** (30 Sept). *Flowering Trees and Shrubs. T* **339** *and similar horiz designs. Multicoloured. P* 14.
1833 15 c. Type **339** .. .. .. .. 15 15
1834 25 c. Saman .. .. .. .. 20 15
1835 35 c. Red Frangipani .. .. .. 25 20
1836 45 c. Flowering Maple .. .. .. 30 25
1837 60 c. Yellow Poui .. .. .. .. 40 30
1838 $1 Wild Chestnut .. .. .. 60 60
1839 $3 Mountain Immortelle .. .. 1·50 2·00
1840 $4 Queen of Flowers .. .. .. 1·75 2·25
1833/40 .. .. .. .. *Set of* 8 4·50 5·50
**MS**1841 Two sheets, each 117 × 88 mm. (a) $5 Flamboyant. (b) $5 Orchid Tree .. *Set of* 2 *sheets* 4·25 5·00

**340** Mickey Mantle (New York Yankees)

(Des Rosemary De Figlio. Litho Questa)

**1988** (28 Nov). *Major League Baseball Players (1st series). T* **340** *and similar horiz designs showing portraits or league emblems. P* 14 × 13½.
1842/1922 30 c. × 81 multicoloured .. *Set of* 81 8·75 9·00
Nos. 1842/1922 were issued as nine sheetlets, each of nine different designs.
One sheetlet was subsequently reissued with the Pete Rose stamp replaced by a label inscribed "U.S. BASEBALL SERIES I".

(Des Walt Disney Co. Litho Questa)

**1988** (1 Dec). *Christmas. "Mickey's Christmas Eve". Vert designs as T* **246** *of Antigua showing Walt Disney cartoon characters. Multicoloured. P* 13½ × 14.
1923 $1 Donald Duck's nephew on mantelpiece 45 50
a. Sheetlet. Nos. 1923/30 .. .. 3·25
1924 $1 Goofy with string of popcorn .. 45 50
1925 $1 Chip n' Dale decorating Christmas tree .. .. .. .. 45 50
1926 $1 Father Christmas in sleigh .. .. 45 50
1927 $1 Donald's nephew with stocking .. 45 50
1928 $1 Donald's nephew unpacking Xmas decorations .. .. .. .. 45 50
1929 $1 Donald Duck with present .. .. 45 50
1930 $1 Mickey Mouse with present .. .. 45 50
1923/30 .. .. .. .. *Set of* 8 3·25 3·50
**MS**1931 Two sheets, each 127 × 102 mm. (a) $5 Ferdie leaving drink for Father Christmas. (b) $5 Mordie and Ferdie asleep .. *Set of* 2 *sheets* 4·25 4·75

**341** Tina Turner

**342** Canada Atlantic Railway No. 2, 1889

(Litho Questa)

**1988** (5 Dec). *Entertainers. T* **341** *and similar vert designs. Multicoloured. P* 14.
1932 10 c. Type **341** .. .. .. .. 15 15
1933 25 c. Lionel Ritchie .. .. .. 20 20
1934 45 c. Whitney Houston .. .. .. 30 30
1935 60 c. Joan Armatrading .. .. .. 45 45
1936 75 c. Madonna .. .. .. .. 55 55
1937 $1 Elton John .. .. .. .. 70 75
1938 $3 Bruce Springsteen .. .. .. 1·90 2·25
1939 $4 Bob Marley .. .. .. .. 2·50 3·00
1932/9 .. .. .. .. *Set of* 8 6·00 7·00
**MS**1940 115×155 mm. 55 c.×2 Yoko Minamino; $1×2 Yoko Minamino (*different*) .. .. 1·90 2·50
No. 1935 is incorrectly inscribed "JOAN AMMERTRADING".

(Des T. Hadley and W. Wright. Litho B.D.T.)

**1989** (23 Jan). *North American Railway Locomotives. T* **342** *and similar vert designs. Multicoloured. P* 13.
1941 $2 Type **342** .. .. .. .. 95 1·00
a. Sheetlet. Nos. 1941/50 .. .. 9·50
1942 $2 Virginia & Truckee Railroad "J. W. Bowker" type, 1875 .. .. .. 95 1·00
1943 $2 Philadelphia & Reading Railway *Ariel*, 1872 .. .. .. .. 95 1·00
1944 $2 Chicago & Rock Island Railroad "America" type, 1867 .. .. .. 95 1·00
1945 $2 Lehigh Valley Railroad Consolidation No. 63, 1866 .. .. .. 95 1·00
1946 $2 Great Western Railway *Scotia*, 1860 95 1·00
1947 $2 Grand Trunk Railway "Birkenhead" Class, 1854 .. .. .. .. 95 1·00
1948 $2 Camden & Amboy Railroad *Monster*, 1837 .. .. .. .. 95 1·00
1949 $2 Baltimore & Ohio Railroad "Grasshopper" Class, 1834 .. .. .. 95 1·00
1950 $2 Baltimore & Ohio Railroad *Tom Thumb*, 1829 .. .. .. 95 1·00
1951 $2 United Railways of Yucatan *Yucatan*, 1925 .. .. .. .. 95 1·00
a. Sheetlet. Nos. 1951/60 .. .. 9·50
1952 $2 Canadian National Railways Class "T2", 1924 .. .. .. .. 95 1·00
1953 $2 St. Louis—San Francisco Railroad "Light Mikado" class, 1919 .. .. 95 1·00
1954 $2 Atlantic Coast Line Railroad "Light Pacific" class, 1919 .. .. .. 95 1·00
1955 $2 Edaville Railroad No. 7, 1913 .. 95 1·00
1956 $2 Denver & Rio Grande Western Railroad Class "K27", 1903 .. .. 95 1·00
1957 $2 Pennsylvania Railroad Class "E-2" No. 7002, 1902 .. .. .. 95 1·00

1958 $2 Pennsylvania Railroad Class "H6", 1899 .. .. .. .. .. .. 95 1·00
1959 $2 Mohawk & Hudson Railroad *De Witt Clinton*, 1831 .. .. .. .. 95 1·00
1960 $2 St. Clair Tunnel Company No. 598, 1891 .. .. .. .. .. .. 95 1·00
1961 $2 Chesapeake & Ohio Railroad Class "M-1" No. 500 steam turbine electric, 1947 .. .. .. .. .. .. 95 1·00
a. Sheetlet. Nos. 1961/70 .. .. 9·50
1962 $2 Rutland Railroad No. 93, 1946 .. 95 1·00
1963 $2 Pennsylvania Railroad Class "T1", 1942 .. .. .. .. .. .. 95 1·00
1964 $2 Chesapeake & Ohio Railroad Class "H-8", 1942 .. .. .. .. .. 95 1·00
1965 $2 Atchison, Topeka & Santa Fe Railway Model "FT" diesel, 1941 .. .. 95 1·00
1966 $2 Gulf, Mobile & Ohio Railroad Models "S-1" & "S-2" diesel, 1940 .. .. 95 1·00
1967 $2 New York, New Haven & Hartford Railroad Class "15", 1937 .. .. 95 1·00
1968 $2 Seaboard Air Line Railroad Class "R", 1936 .. .. .. .. .. .. 95 1·00
1969 $2 Newfoundland Railway Class "R-2", 1930 .. .. .. .. .. .. 95 1·00
1970 $2 Canadian National Railway diesel No. 9000, 1928 .. .. .. .. 95 1·00
1941/70 .. .. .. .. .. *Set of* 30 25·00 27·00

Nos. 1941/50, 1951/60 and 1961/70 were each printed together, *se-tenant*, in sheetlets of 10.

**343** Women's Long Jump (Jackie Joyner-Kersee, U.S.A.)

**344** Nebulae

(Des L. Fried. Litho B.D.T.)

**1989** (6 Apr). *Olympic Gold Medal Winners, Seoul* (1988). *T* **343** *and similar vert designs. Multicoloured. P* 14.

1971 10 c. Type **343** .. .. .. .. 10 10
1972 25 c. Women's Singles Tennis (Steffi Graf, West Germany) .. .. .. 10 15
1973 45 c. Men's 1500 metres (Peter Rono, Kenya) .. .. .. .. .. 20 25
1974 75 c. Men's 1000 metres single kayak (Greg Barton, U.S.A.) .. .. .. 30 35
1975 $1 Women's team foil (Italy) .. .. 40 45
1976 $2 Women's 100 metres freestyle swimming (Kristin Otto, East Germany) .. .. .. .. .. 85 90
1977 $3 Men's still rings gymnastics (Holger Behrendt, East Germany) .. .. 1·25 1·40
1978 $4 Synchronized swimming pair (Japan) 1·75 1·90
1971/8 .. .. .. .. .. *Set of* 8 4·50 5·00

**MS**1979 Two sheets, each 76×100 mm. (a) $6 Olympic flame. (b) $6 Runner with Olympic torch .. .. .. .. *Set of 2 sheets* 5·00 5·25

(Litho Questa)

**1989** (25 Apr). *Appearance of Halley's Comet* (1986) (3*rd issue*). *T* **344** *and similar horiz designs. P* 14.

1980 25 c. + 5 c. multicoloured .. .. .. 10 15
1981 75 c. + 5 c. black and turquoise-green .. 35 40
1982 90 c. + 5 c. multicoloured .. .. .. 40 45
1983 $2 + 5 c. multicoloured .. .. .. 85 90
1980/3 .. .. .. .. .. *Set of* 4 1·50 1·75

**MS**1984 111×78 mm. $5 + 5 c. multicoloured. Imperf .. .. .. .. .. .. 2·10 2·25

Designs: (*As T* 344)—75 c. + 5 c. Marine astronomical experiments; 90 c. + 5 c. Moon's surface; $2 + 5 c. Edmond Halley, Sir Isaac Newton and his book *Principia*. (102×69 *mm*)—$5 + 5 c. 17th-century warships and astrological signs.

(Litho Questa)

**1989** (15 May). *Japanese Art. Paintings by Hiroshige. Horiz designs as T* **250** *of Antigua. Multicoloured. P* 14×13½.

1985 10 c. "Shinagawa on Edo Bay" .. .. 10 10
1986 25 c. "Pine Trees on the Road to Totsuka" 10 15
1987 60 c. "Kanagawa on Edo Bay" .. .. 25 30
1988 75 c. "Crossing Banyu River to Hiratsuka" 30 35
1989 $1 "Windy Shore at Odawara" .. .. 40 45
1990 $2 "Snow-Covered Post Station of Mishima" .. .. .. .. .. 85 90
1991 $3 "Full Moon at Fuchu" .. .. 1·25 1·40
1992 $4 "Crossing the Stream at Okitsu" .. 1·75 1·90
1985/92 .. .. .. .. .. *Set of* 8 4·50 5·00

**MS**1993 Two sheets, each 102×76 mm. (a) $5 "Mountain Pass at Nissaka". (b) $5 "Mt Uzu at Okabe" .. .. .. .. *Set of 2 sheets* 4·25 4·50

Nos. 1985/92 were each printed in sheetlets of 10 containing two horizontal strips of 5 stamps separated by printed labels commemorating Emperor Hirohito.

**345** Great Blue Heron

(Des D. Bruckner. Litho Questa)

**1989** (6 June)–**90**. *Birds. T* **345** *and similar multicoloured designs. P* 14.

1994 5 c. Type **345** .. .. .. .. 10 10
1995 10 c. Green Heron .. .. .. .. 10 10
1996 15 c. Turnstone .. .. .. .. 10 10
1997 25 c. Blue-winged Teal .. .. .. 10 15
1998 35 c. Ringed Plover (*vert*) .. .. .. 15 20
1999 45 c. Green-throated Carib ("Emerald-throated Hummingbird") (*vert*) .. 20 25
2000 50 c. Rufous-breasted Hermit (*vert*) .. 20 25
2001 60 c. Lesser Antillean Bullfinch (*vert*) .. 25 30
2002 75 c. Brown Pelican (*vert*) .. .. .. 30 35
2003 $1 Black-crowned Night Heron (*vert*) .. 40 45
2004 $3 American Kestrel ("Sparrow Hawk") (*vert*) .. .. .. .. .. 1·25 1·40
2005 $5 Barn Swallow (*vert*) .. .. .. 2·10 2·25
2006 $10 Red-billed Tropic Bird (*vert*) (13.11.89) 4·25 4·50
2007 $20 Barn Owl (*vert*) (22.1.90) .. .. 8·50 8·75
1994/2007 .. .. .. .. *Set of* 14 15·00 16·00

(Des D. Bruckner. Litho B.D.T.)

**1989** (12 June). *World Cup Football Championship, Italy* (1990). *Vert designs as T* **252** *of Antigua. Multicoloured. P* 14.

2008 10 c. Scotland player .. .. .. 10 10
2009 25 c. England and Brazil players .. .. 10 15
2010 60 c. Paolo Rossi (Italy) .. .. .. 25 30
2011 75 c. Jairzinho (Brazil) .. .. .. 30 35
2012 $1 Sweden striker .. .. .. 40 45
2013 $2 Péle (Brazil) .. .. .. .. 85 90
2014 $3 Mario Kempes (Argentina) .. .. 1·25 1·40
2015 $4 Pat Jennings (Northern Ireland) .. 1·75 1·90
2008/15 .. .. .. .. *Set of* 8 4·50 5·00

**MS**2016 Two sheets. (a) 70×93 mm. $6 Players jumping for ball. (b) 82×71 mm. $6 Goalkeeper *Set of 2 sheets* 5·00 5·25

**346** Xebec and Sugar Cane

(Des T. Agans. Litho B.D.T.)

**1989** (7 July). *"Philexfrance 89" International Stamp Exhibition, Paris. T* **346** *and similar horiz designs showing French sailing vessels and plantation crops. Multicoloured. P* 14.

2017 25 c. Type **346** .. .. .. .. 10 15
2018 75 c. Lugger and cotton .. .. .. 30 35
2019 $1 Full-rigged ship and cocoa .. .. 40 45
2020 $4 Ketch and coffee .. .. .. 1·75 1·90
2017/20 .. .. .. .. *Set of* 4 2·25 2·50

**MS**2021 114×70 mm. $6 "View of Fort and Town of St. George, 1779" (105×63 *mm*). Imperf .. 2·50 2·75

**347** Alan Shepard and "Freedom 7" Spacecraft, 1961 (first American in Space)



**348** *Hygrocybe occidentalis*

(Des L. Birmingham. Litho Questa)

**1989** (20 July). *20th Anniv of First Manned Landing on Moon. T* **347** *and similar horiz designs. Multicoloured. P* 14.

2022 15 c. Type **347** .. .. .. .. 10 10
2023 35 c. "Friendship 7" spacecraft, 1962 (first manned earth orbit) .. .. .. 15 20
2024 45 c. "Apollo 8" orbiting Moon, 1968 (first manned lunar orbit) .. .. .. 20 25
2025 70 c. "Apollo 15" lunar rover, 1972 .. 30 35
2026 $1 "Apollo 11" emblem and lunar module *Eagle* on Moon, 1969 .. .. .. 40 45
2027 $2 "Gemini 8" and "Agena" rocket, 1966 (first space docking) .. .. .. 85 90
2028 $3 Edward White in space, 1965 (first U.S. space walk) .. .. .. 1·25 1·40
2029 $4 "Apollo 7" emblem .. .. .. 1·75 1·90
2022/9 .. .. .. .. *Set of* 8 4·50 5·00

**MS**2030 Two sheets, each 101×71 mm. (a) $5 Moon and track of "Apollo 11", 1969. (b) $5 Armstrong and Aldrin raising U.S. flag on Moon, 1969 .. .. .. .. *Set of 2 sheets* 4·25 4·50

(Des J. Cooter. Litho B.D.T.)

**1989** (17 Aug). *Fungi. T* **348** *and similar vert designs. Multicoloured. P* 14.

2031 15 c. Type **348** .. .. .. .. 10 10
2032 40 c. *Marasmius haematocephalus* .. .. 15 20
2033 50 c. *Hygrocybe hypohaemacta* .. .. 20 25
2034 70 c. *Lepiota pseudoignicolor* .. .. 30 35
2035 90 c. *Cookeina tricholoma* .. .. 40 45
2036 $1.10, *Leucopaxillus gracillimus* .. .. 45 50
2037 $2.25, *Hygrocybe nigrescens* .. .. 95 1·00
2038 $4 *Clathrus crispus* .. .. .. 1·75 1·90
2031/8 .. .. .. .. *Set of* 8 3·75 4·25

**MS**2039 Two sheets, each 57×70 mm. (a) $6 *Mycena holoporphyra*. (b) $6 *Xeromphalina tenuipes* .. .. .. .. *Set of 2 sheets* 5·00 5·25

**349** Y.W.C.A. Logo and Grenada Scenery

**350** *Historis odius*

(Litho Questa)

**1989** (11 Sept). *Centenary of Young Women's Christian Association. T* **349** *and similar multicoloured design. P* 14.

2040 50 c. Type **349** .. .. .. .. 20 25
2041 75 c. Y.W.C.A. logo and town (*horiz*) .. 30 35

(Des Deborah Dudley Max. Litho B.D.T.)

**1989** (2 Oct). *Butterflies. T* **350** *and similar horiz designs. Multicoloured. P* 14.

2042 6 c. Type **350** .. .. .. .. 10 10
2043 30 c. *Marpesia petreus* .. .. .. 10 15
2044 40 c. *Danaus gilippus* .. .. .. 15 20
2045 60 c. *Dione juno* .. .. .. .. 25 30
2046 $1.10, *Agraulis vanillae* .. .. .. 45 50
2047 $1.25, *Danaus plexippus* .. .. .. 50 55
2048 $4 *Papilio androgeus* (inscr "*Battus polydamas*") .. .. .. .. 1·75 1·90
2049 $5 *Dryas julia* .. .. .. .. 2·10 2·25
2042/9 .. .. .. .. *Set of* 8 4·75 5·25

**MS**2050 Two sheets, each 87×115 mm. (a) $6 *Anartia jatrophae*. (b) $6 *Strymon simaethis* *Set of 2 sheets* 5·00 5·25

**351** Amerindian Hieroglyph

**352** Amos leaving Home

(Litho Questa)

**1989** (16 Oct). *500th Anniv of Discovery of America by Columbus* (1992) (2*nd issue*). *T* **351** *and similar vert designs showing different hieroglyphs. P* 14.

2051 45 c. brownish black, black and new blue 20 25
2052 60 c. brownish black, black & bright green 25 30
2053 $1 brownish black, black & dp reddish vio 40 45
2054 $4 brownish black, black & orange-brn 1·75 1·90
2051/4 .. .. .. .. *Set of* 4 2·40 2·50

**MS**2055 74×86 mm. $6 brownish black, black and vermilion .. .. .. .. .. 2·50 2·75

(Des Walt Disney Co. Litho Questa)

**1989** (20 Nov). *"World Stamp Expo '89" International Stamp Exhibition, Washington. T* **352** *and similar multicoloured designs showing Walt Disney cartoon characters in scenes from* Ben and Me. *P* 14×13½.

2056 1 c. Type **352** .. .. .. .. 10 10
2057 2 c. Meeting of Benjamin Franklin and Amos .. .. .. .. .. 10 10
2058 3 c. The Franklin stove .. .. .. 10 10
2059 4 c. Ben and Amos with bi-focals .. 10 10
2060 5 c. Amos on page of *Pennsylvania Gazette* 10 10
2061 6 c. Ben working printing press .. .. 10 10
2062 10 c. Conducting experiment with electricity .. .. .. .. .. 10 10
2063 $5 Ben disembarking in England .. 2·10 2·25
2064 $6 Ben with Document of Agreement .. 2·50 2·75
2056/64 .. .. .. .. *Set of* 9 4·50 4·75

**MS**2065 Two sheets, each 127×101 mm. (a) $6 Benjamin Franklin teaching (*vert*). P 13½×14. (b) $6 Signatories of Declaration of Independence. P 14×13½ .. .. *Set of 2 sheets* 5·00 5·25

(Litho Questa)

**1990** (4 Jan). *Christmas. Paintings by Rubens. Vert designs as T* **259** *of Antigua. Multicoloured. P* 14.

2066 20 c. "Christ in the House of Mary and Martha" .. .. .. .. .. 10 10
2067 35 c. "The Circumcision" .. .. .. 15 20
2068 60 c. "Trinity adored by Duke of Mantua and Family" .. .. .. .. 25 30
2069 $2 "Holy Family with St. Francis" .. 85 90
2070 $3 "The Ildefonso Altarpiece" .. .. 1·25 1·40
2071 $4 "Madonna and Child with Garland and Putti" .. .. .. .. 1·75 1·90
2066/71 .. .. .. .. *Set of* 6 4·00 4·25

**MS**2072 Two sheets, each 70×95 mm. (a) $5 "Adoration of the Magi". (b) $5 "Virgin and Child adored by Angels" .. .. *Set of 2 sheets* 4·25 4·50

## COVER PRICES

Cover factors are quoted at the beginning of each country for most issues to 1945. An explanation of the system can be found on page x. The factors quoted do not, however, apply to philatelic covers.

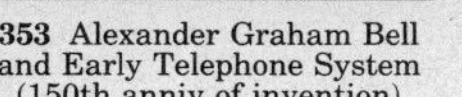

**353** Alexander Graham Bell and Early Telephone System (150th anniv of invention)

**354** *Odontoglossum triumphans*

(Des J. Genzo. Litho B.D.T.)

**1990** (12 Feb). *Anniversaries. T* **353** *and similar horiz designs. Multicoloured. P* 14.

2073 10 c. Type **353** .. .. .. .. .. 10 10
2074 25 c. George Washington and Capitol (bicent of presidential inauguration) 10 15
2075 35 c. Shakespeare and birthplace, Stratford (425th birth anniv) .. .. .. 15 20
2076 75 c. Nehru and Gandhi (birth cent of Nehru) .. .. .. .. 30 35
2077 $1 Dr. Hugo Eckener, Ferdinand von Zeppelin and Zeppelin *Delag* (80th anniv of first passenger Zeppelin) 40 45
2078 $2 Charlie Chaplin (birth cent) .. .. 85 90
2079 $3 Container ship in Hamburg Harbour (800th anniv) .. .. .. 1·25 1·40
2080 $4 Friedrich Ebert (first President) and Heidelberg gate (70th anniv of German Republic) .. .. 1·75 1·90
2073/80 .. .. .. .. .. *Set of* 8 4·25 4·75
**MS**2081 Two sheets, each 100×72 mm. (a) $6 13th-century ships in Hamburg Harbour (*vert*) (800th anniv). (b) $6 "Concorde" (20th anniv of first test flight) .. .. .. *Set of* 2 *sheets* 5·00 5·25

No. 2080 is inscribed "40th Anniversary of German Republic" in error.

(Des L. Nelson. Litho Questa)

**1990** (6 Mar). *"EXPO 90" International Garden and Greenery Exhibition, Osaka. Caribbean Orchids. T* **354** *and similar vert designs. Multicoloured. P* 14.

2082 1 c. Type **354** .. .. .. .. 10 10
2083 25 c. *Oncidium splendidum* .. .. 10 15
2084 60 c. *Laelia anceps* .. .. .. 25 30
2085 75 c. *Cattleya trianaei* .. .. .. 30 35
2086 $1 *Odontoglossum rossii* .. .. 40 45
2087 $2 *Brassia gireoudiana* .. .. 85 90
2088 $3 *Cattleya dowiana* .. .. .. 1·25 1·40
2089 $4 *Sobralia macrantha* .. .. 1·75 1·90
2082/9 .. .. .. .. .. *Set of* 8 4·50 5·00
**MS**2090 Two sheets, each 97×68 mm. (a) $6 *Oncidium lanceanum*. (b) $6 *Laelia rubescens* *Set of* 2 *sheets* 5·00 5·25

(Des Mary Walters. Litho Questa)

**1990** (16 Mar). *500th Anniv of Discovery of America by Columbus* (1992) (3*rd issue*). *New World Natural History – Butterflies. Vert designs as T* **260** *of Antigua. Multicoloured. P* 14.

2091 15 c. *Marpesia petreus* .. .. .. 10 10
2092 25 c. *Junonia evarete* .. .. .. 10 15
2093 75 c. *Siproeta stelenes* .. .. .. 30 35
2094 90 c. *Historis odius* .. .. .. 40 45
2095 $1 *Mestra cana* .. .. .. .. 40 45
2096 $2 *Biblis hyperia* .. .. .. 85 90
2097 $3 *Dryas julia* .. .. .. .. 1·25 1·40
2098 $4 *Anartia amathea* .. .. .. 1·75 1·90
2091/8 .. .. .. .. .. *Set of* 8 4·50 5·00
**MS**2099 Two sheets, each 101×69 mm. (a) $6 *Pseudolycaena marsyas*. (b) $6 *Phoebis philea* *Set of* 2 *sheets* 5·00 5·25

(Des J. Barbaris. Litho B.D.T.)

**1990** (3 Apr). *Local Fauna. Multicoloured designs as T* **254** *of Antigua. P* 14.

2100 10 c. Caribbean Monk Seal .. .. 10 10
2101 15 c. Little Brown Bat .. .. .. 10 10
2102 45 c. Brown Rat .. .. .. .. 20 25
2103 60 c. Common Rabbit .. .. .. 25 30
2104 $1 Water Opossum .. .. .. 40 45
2105 $2 White-nosed Ichneumon .. .. 85 90
2106 $3 Little Big-eared Bat (*vert*) .. .. 1·25 1·40
2107 $4 Mouse Opossum .. .. .. 1·75 1·90
2100/7 .. .. .. .. .. *Set of* 8 4·25 4·75
**MS**2108 Two sheets, each 107×80 mm. (a) $6 Common Rabbit (*different*). (b) $6 Water Opossum (*different*) .. .. *Set of* 2 *sheets* 5·00 5·25

(Des W. Wright. Litho Questa)

**1990** (30 Apr). *50th Anniv of Second World War. Horiz designs as T* **274** *of Antigua. Multicoloured. P* 14.

2109 25 c. British tanks during Operation Battleaxe, 1941 .. .. .. .. 10 10
2110 35 c. Allied tank in southern France, 1944 15 20
2111 45 c. U.S. forces landing on Guadalcanal, 1942 .. .. .. .. .. 20 25
2112 50 c. U.S. attack in New Guinea, 1943 .. 20 25
2113 60 c. Hoisting U.S. flag on Leyte, Phillippines, 1944 .. .. .. 25 30
2114 75 c. U.S. tanks entering Cologne, 1945 .. 30 35
2115 $1 Anzio offensive, 1944 .. .. 40 45
2116 $2 Battle of the Bismarck Sea, 1943 .. 85 90
2117 $3 U.S. battle fleet, 1944 .. .. 1·25 1·40
2118 $4 German fighter attacking Salerno landing, 1943 .. .. .. 1·75 1·90
2109/18 .. .. .. .. *Set of* 10 5·00 5·50
**MS**2119 111×83 mm. $6 German *U-30* submarine, 1939 .. .. .. .. 2·50 2·75

(Des Walt Disney Co. Litho Questa)

**1990** (21 June). *"Stamp World London 90" International Stamp Exhibition* (1*st issue*). *Multicoloured designs as T* **193** *of Gambia showing Walt Disney cartoon characters and British trains. P* 14×13½.

2120 5 c. Mickey Mouse driving "King Arthur" Class locomotive, 1925 (*horiz*) .. 10 10
2121 10 c. Mickey and Minnie Mouse with *Puffing Billy*, 1813 (*horiz*) .. .. 10 10
2122 20 c. Mickey Mouse with Pluto pulling Durham colliery waggon, 1765 (*horiz*) 10 10
2123 45 c. Mickey Mouse timing locomotive No. 2509, *Silver Link*, 1935 (*horiz*) .. 20 25
2124 $1 Mickey Mouse and Donald Duck with locomotive No. 60149, *Amadis*, 1948 (*horiz*) .. .. .. .. .. 40 45
2125 $2 Goofy and Mickey Mouse with Liverpool & Manchester Railway locomotive, 1830 (*horiz*) .. .. 85 90
2126 $4 Goofy and Donald Duck with *Flying Scotsman*, 1870 (*horiz*) .. .. 1·75 1·90
2127 $5 Mickey Mouse and Gyro the Mechanic with Advanced Passenger Train, 1972 (*horiz*) .. .. .. .. .. 2·10 2·25
2120/7 .. .. .. .. .. *Set of* 8 5·00 5·25
**MS**2128 Two sheets, each 127×101 mm. (a) $6 Minnie Mouse, Donald and Daisy Duck in Trevithick's *Catch-Me-Who-Can*, 1808 (*horiz*). P 14×13½. (b) $6 Donald Duck and Stockton and Darlington Railway locomotive, 1825. P 13½×14 .. .. .. *Set of* 2 *sheets* 5·00 5·25

See also No. **MS**2146.

**355** U.S. Paratroop Drop over Grenada

(Litho B.D.T.)

**1990** (3 July). *50th Anniv of United States' Airborne Forces. T* **355** *and similar horiz designs. Multicoloured. P* 14.

2129 75 c. Type **355** .. .. .. .. 30 35
**MS**2130 Two sheets, each 115×87 mm. (a) $2.50, Paratrooper landing. (b) $6 Paratroop uniforms of 1940 and 1990 .. .. *Set of* 2 *sheets* 3·50 3·75

(Des Young Phillips Studio. Litho Questa)

**1990** (5 July). *90th Birthday of Queen Elizabeth the Queen Mother. Vert designs as T* **194** *of Gambia showing photographs, 1960–69. Multicoloured. P* 14.

2131 $2 Queen Mother in coat and hat .. 85 90
a. Strip of 3. Nos. 2131/3 .. .. 2·25
2132 $2 Queen Mother in evening dress .. 85 90
2133 $2 Queen Mother in Garter robes .. 85 90
2131/3 .. .. .. .. .. *Set of* 3 2·25 2·40
**MS**2134 90×75 mm. $6 Queen Mother (as No. 2131) .. .. .. .. .. 2·50 2·75

Nos. 2131/3 were printed together, horizontally and vertically *se-tenant*, in sheetlets of 9 (3×3).

(Des B. Grout. Litho Questa)

**1990** (9 July). *Olympic Games, Barcelona* (1992). *Vert designs as T* **268** *of Antigua. Multicoloured. P* 14.

2135 10 c. Men's steeplechase .. .. 10 10
2136 15 c. Dressage .. .. .. .. 10 10
2137 45 c. Men's 200 m butterfly swimming .. 20 25
2138 50 c. Men's hockey .. .. .. 20 25
2139 65 c. Women's beam gymnastics .. 25 30
2140 75 c. "Flying Dutchman" class yachting .. 30 35
2141 $2 Freestyle wrestling .. .. 85 90
2142 $3 Men's springboard diving .. 1·25 1·40
2143 $4 Women's 1000 m sprint cycling .. 1·75 1·90
2144 $5 Men's basketball .. .. 2·10 2·25
2135/44 .. .. .. .. *Set of* 10 6·25 7·00
**MS**2145 Two sheets, each 101×70 mm. (a) $8 Equestrian three-day event. (b) $8 Men's 10000 metres .. .. .. .. *Set of* 2 *sheets* 6·75 7·00

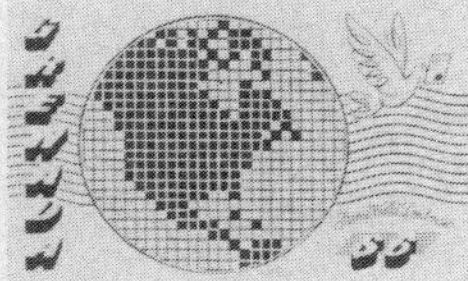

**356** Map of North America and Logo

(Des M. Pollard. Litho Questa)

**1990** (12 July). *"Stamp World London 90" International Stamp Exhibition* (2*nd issue*). *Sheet* 97×75 *mm. P* 14.

**MS**2146 **356** $6 deep mauve .. .. .. 2·50 2·75

**357** Yellow Goatfish

(Des Mary Walters. Litho B.D.T.)

**1990** (8 Aug). *Coral Reef Fishes. T* **357** *and similar horiz designs. Multicoloured. P* 14.

2147 10 c. Type **357** .. .. .. .. 10 10
2148 25 c. Black Margate .. .. .. 10 15
2149 65 c. Bluehead Wrasse .. .. .. 25 30
2150 75 c. Pudding Wife .. .. .. 30 35
2151 $1 Foureye Butterflyfish .. .. 40 45
2152 $2 Honey Damselfish .. .. .. 85 90
2153 $3 Queen Angelfish .. .. .. 1·25 1·40
2154 $5 Cherubfish .. .. .. .. 2·10 2·25
2147/54 .. .. .. .. *Set of* 8 4·75 5·25
**MS**2155 Two sheets, each 103×72 mm. (a) $6 Smooth Trunkfish. (b) $6 Sergeant Major *Set of* 2 *sheets* 5·00 5·25

**358** Tropical Mockingbird

(Des J. Anderton. Litho B.D.T.)

**1990** (10 Sept). *Birds. T* **358** *and similar horiz designs. Multicoloured. P* 14.

2156 15 c. Type **358** .. .. .. .. 10 10
2157 25 c. Grey Kingbird .. .. .. 10 15
2158 65 c. Bare-eyed Thrush .. .. .. 25 30
2159 75 c. Antillean Crested Hummingbird .. 30 35
2160 $1 House Wren .. .. .. .. 40 45
2161 $2 Purple Martin .. .. .. 85 90
2162 $4 Hooded Tanager .. .. .. 1·75 1·90
2163 $5 Scaly-breasted Ground Dove .. 2·10 2·25
2156/63 .. .. .. .. *Set of* 8 5·25 5·75
**MS**2164 Two sheets, each 101×72 mm. (a) $6 Fork-tailed Flycatcher. (b) $6 Smooth-billed Ani *Set of* 2 *sheets* 5·00 5·25

**359** Coral Crab

**360** Cameroun Player

(Des Deborah Dudley Max. Litho Questa)

**1990** (17 Sept). *Crustaceans. T* **359** *and similar horiz designs. Multicoloured. P* 14.

2165 5 c. Type **359** .. .. .. .. 10 10
2166 10 c. Smoothtail Spiny Lobster .. .. 10 10
2167 15 c. Flamestreaked Box Crab .. .. 10 10
2168 25 c. Spotted Swimming Crab .. .. 10 15
2169 75 c. Sally Lightfoot Rock Crab .. .. 30 35
2170 $1 Spotted Spiny Lobster .. .. 40 45
2171 $3 Longarm Spiny Lobster .. .. 1·25 1·40
2172 $20 Caribbean Spiny Lobster .. .. 8·50 8·75
2165/72 .. .. .. .. *Set of* 8 9·75 10·00
**MS**2173 Two sheets, 106×75 mm. (a) $6 Copper Lobster. (b) $6 Spanish Lobster .. *Set of* 2 *sheets* 5·00 5·25

(Des Young Phillips Studio. Litho Questa)

**1990** (24 Sept). *World Cup Football Championship, Italy* (2*nd issue*). *T* **360** *and similar vert designs. Multicoloured. P* 14.

2174 10 c. Type **360** .. .. .. .. 10 10
2175 25 c. Michel (Spain) .. .. .. 10 15
2176 $1 Brehme (West Germany) .. .. 40 45
2177 $5 Nevin (Scotland) .. .. .. 2·10 2·25
2174/7 .. .. .. .. *Set of* 4 2·40 2·50
**MS**2178 Two sheets, each 95×90 mm. (a) $6 Giannini (Italy). (b) $6 Perdomo (Uruguay) *Set of* 2 *sheets* 5·00 5·25

1990 W GERMANY 1 ARGENTINA 0

(**361**)

**1990** (30 Nov). *World Cup Football Championship, Italy* (1990) (3*rd issue*). *No.* **MS**2016*a optd with T* **361**.

**MS**2179 70×93 mm. $6 Players jumping for ball 2·50 2·75

No. **MS**2179 shows the overprint, Type **361**, added to the list of match results in the sheet margin.

(Litho Questa)

**1990** (31 Dec). *Christmas. Paintings by Raphael. Multicoloured designs as T* **272** *of Antigua, but vert. P* 13½×14.

2180 10 c. "The Ansidei Madonna" .. .. 10 10
2181 15 c. "The Sistine Madonna" .. .. 10 10
2182 $1 "The Madonna of the Baldacchino" .. 40 45
2183 $2 "The Large Holy Family" (detail) .. 85 90
2184 $5 "Madonna in the Meadow" .. .. 2·10 2·25
2180/4 .. .. .. .. *Set of* 5 3·00 3·25
**MS**2185 Two sheets, each 71×101 mm. (a) $6 "Madonna of the Diadem" (detail). (b) $6 "The Madonna of the Veil" (detail) .. *Set of* 2 *sheets* 5·00 5·25

(Litho Questa)

**1991** (31 Jan). *350th Death Anniv of Rubens. Horiz designs as T* **273** *of Antigua. Multicoloured. P* 14×13½.
2186 5 c. "The Brazen Serpent" (detail) .. 10 10
2187 10 c. "The Garden of Love" .. .. 10 10
2188 25 c. "Head of Cyrus" (detail) .. .. 10 15
2189 75 c. "Tournament in Front of a Castle" .. 30 35
2190 $1 "The Brazen Serpent" (different detail) .. .. .. .. 40 45
2191 $2 "Judgement of Paris" (detail) .. 85 90
2192 $4 "The Brazen Serpent" .. .. 1·75 1·90
2193 $5 "The Karmesse" (detail) .. .. 2·10 2·25
2186/93 .. .. .. .. *Set of* 8 5·00 5·50
**MS**2194 Two sheets, each 101×70 mm. (a) $6 "Anger of Neptune" (detail). (b) $6 "The Prodigal Son" (detail) .. .. .. *Set of* 2 *sheets* 5·00 5·25

**362** "The Sorcerer's Apprentice"

(Des Walt Disney Co. Litho Questa)

**1991** (4 Feb). *50th Anniv of* Fantasia *(cartoon film). T* **362** *and similar horiz designs. Multicoloured. P* 14×13½.
2195 5 c. Type **362** .. .. .. .. 10 10
2196 10 c. Dancing mushrooms ("The Nutcracker Suite") .. .. .. 10 10
2197 20 c. Pterodactyls ("The Rite of Spring") .. 10 10
2198 45 c. Centaurs ("The Pastoral Symphony") 20 25
2199 $1 Bacchus and Jacchus ("The Pastoral Symphony") .. .. .. .. 40 45
2200 $2 Dancing ostrich ("Dance of the Hours") .. .. .. .. 85 90
2201 $4 Elephant ballet ("Dance of the Hours") 1·75 1·90
2202 $5 Diana ("The Pastoral Symphony") .. 2·10 2·25
2195/202 .. .. .. .. *Set of* 8 5·00 5·25
**MS**2203 Two sheets, each 122×102 mm. (a) $6 Mickey Mouse as the Sorcerer's Apprentice; (b) $6 Mickey Mouse with Leopold Stokowski (conductor) .. .. *Set of* 2 *sheets* 5·00 5·25
**MS**2204 176×213 mm. $12 Mickey Mouse as the Sorcerer's Apprentice (*vert*). P 13½×14 .. 5·00 5·25

**363** *Adelpha iphicla*

(Des W. Wright. Litho Questa)

**1991** (8 Apr). *Butterflies. T* **363** *and similar horiz designs. Multicoloured. P* 14.
2205 5 c. Type **363** .. .. .. 10 10
2206 25 c. *Marpesia corinna* .. .. .. 10 10
2207 45 c. *Morpho rhetenor* .. .. .. 20 25
2208 50 c. *Dismorphia spio* .. .. .. 20 25
2209 60 c. *Prepona omphale* .. .. .. 25 30
2210 75 c. *Marpesia iole* .. .. .. 30 35
2211 $3 *Danaidae plexippus* .. .. .. 1·25 1·50
2212 $4 *Morpho achilleana* .. .. .. 1·75 1·90
2205/12 .. .. .. *Set of* 8 3·75 4·50
**MS**2213 Two sheets, each 118×80 mm. (a) $6 *Anteos clorinde*. (b) $6 *Haetera piera* *Set of* 2 *sheets* 4·50 4·75

(Des T. Agans. Litho Questa)

**1991** (29 April). *500th Anniv of Discovery of America by Columbus (1992). History of Exploration. Multicoloured designs as T* **194** *of British Virgin Islands. P* 14.
2214 5 c. Vitus Bering in Bering Sea, 1728–29 10 10
2215 10 c. De Bougainville off Pacific island, 1766–69 .. .. .. .. 10 10
2216 25 c. Polynesian canoe .. .. .. 10 10
2217 50 c. De Mendana off Solomon Islands, 1567–69 .. .. .. .. 20 25
2218 $1 Darwin's H.M.S. *Beagle*, 1831–35 .. 40 45
2219 $2 Cook's H.M.S. *Endeavour*, 1768–71 85 90
2220 $4 Willem Schouten in LeMaire Strait, 1615–17 .. .. .. .. 1·75 1·90
2221 $5 Tasman off New Zealand, 1642–44 .. 2·10 2·25
2214/21 .. .. .. .. *Set of* 8 5·00 5·50
**MS**2222 Two sheets, each 116×77 mm. (a) $6 *Santa Maria* sinking. (b) $6 Bow of *Santa Maria* (*vert*) .. .. .. .. *Set of* 2 *sheets* 4·50 4·75

(Des Walt Disney Co. Litho Questa)

**1991** (6 May). *"Philanippon '91" International Stamp Exhibition, Tokyo. Multicoloured designs as T* **248** *of Dominica showing Walt Disney cartoon characters at Japanese festivals. P* 14×13½.
2223 5 c. Minnie Mouse and Daisy Duck at Dolls festival .. .. .. 10 10
2224 10 c. Morty and Ferdie with Boys' Day display .. .. .. .. 10 10
2225 20 c. Mickey and Minnie Mouse at Star festival .. .. .. .. 10 10
2226 45 c. Minnie and Daisy folk-dancing .. 20 25
2227 $1 Huey, Dewey and Louie wearing Eboshi headdresses .. .. .. 40 45
2228 $2 Mickey and Goofy pulling decorated cart at Gion festival .. .. .. 85 90
2229 $4 Minnie and Daisy preparing rice broth, Seven Plants festival .. 1·75 1·90
2230 $5 Huey and Dewey with straw boat at Lanterns festival .. .. .. 2·10 2·25
2223/30 .. .. .. .. *Set of* 8 5·00 5·50
**MS**2231 Three sheets, each 127×101 mm. (a) $6 Minnie Mouse in kimono (*vert*). P 13½×14. (b) $6 Mickey taking photo. P 14×13½. (c) $6 Goofy behind fair stall. P 14×13½ .. *Set of* 3 *sheets* 6·75 7·00

(Litho Walsall)

**1991** (13 May). *Death Centenary of Vincent van Gogh (artist) (1990). Multicoloured designs as T* **195** *of British Virgin Islands. P* 13½.
2232 20 c. "Blossoming Almond Branch in Glass" (*vert*) .. .. .. .. 10 10
2233 25 c. "La Mousmé sitting" (*vert*) .. .. 10 10
2234 30 c. "Still Life with Red Cabbages and Onions" .. .. .. .. 10 15
2235 $1 "The Painter on his Way to Work" (*vert*) .. .. .. .. 40 45
2236 $2 "Portrait of Pére Tanguy" (*vert*) .. 85 90
2237 $4 "Still Life: Bottle, Lemons and Oranges" .. .. .. .. 1·75 1·90
2238 $5 "Orchard with Blossoming Apricot Trees" .. .. .. .. 2·10 2·25
2232/8 .. .. .. .. *Set of* 7 5·00 5·25
**MS**2239 Two sheets. (a) 76×102 mm. $6 "Roubine du Roi Canal with Washerwoman" (73×99 *mm*). (b) 102×76 mm. $6 "Farmhouse in a Wheatfield" (99×73 *mm*). Imperf. *Set of* 2 *sheets* 4·50 4·75

## POSTAGE DUE STAMPS

D 1

**1d.**
**SURCHARGE POSTAGE**

(D 2)

(Typo D.L.R.)

**1892** (18 Apr–Oct). (*a*) *Type* D 1. *Wmk Crown CA. P* 14.
D1 D 1 1d. blue-black .. .. .. .. 14·00 1·50
D2 2d. blue-black .. .. .. .. 80·00 1·50
D3 3d. blue-black .. .. .. .. 90·00 2·50
D1/3 .. .. .. .. *Set of* 3 £170 5·00

(*b*) *Nos. 34 and 35 surch locally as Type* D **2**
D4 13 1d. on 6d. mauve (10.92) .. .. 42·00 1·25
a. *Tête-bêche* (pair) .. .. .. £300
b. Surch double .. .. .. — 95·00
D5 1d. on 8d. grey-brown (8.92) .. .. £275 3·25
a. *Tête-bêche* (pair) .. .. £1200
D6 2d. on 6d. mauve (10.92) .. .. 80·00 2·50
a. *Tête-bêche* (pair) .. .. .. £500
D7 2d. on 8d. grey-brown (8.92) .. .. £550 9·00
a. *Tête-bêche* (pair) .. .. £2000 £1500

Nos. D4/7 were in use from August to November 1892. As supplies of Nos. D1/3 were available from April or May of that year it would not appear that they were intended for postage due purposes. There was a shortage of 1d. postage stamps in July and August, but this was alleviated by Nos. 44/5 which were still available. The provisionals *may* have been intended for postal purposes, but the vast majority appear to have been used philatelically.

**1906** (July)–**11**. *Wmk Mult Crown CA. P* 14.
D 8 D 1 1d. blue-black (1911) .. .. .. 2·00 3·75
D 9 2d. blue-black .. .. .. .. 5·50 1·75
D10 3d. blue-black (9.06) .. .. .. 9·00 5·50
D8/10 .. .. .. .. *Set of* 3 15·00 10·00

**1921** (Dec)–**22**. *As Type* D 1, *but inscr* "POSTAGE DUE". *Wmk Mult Script CA. P* 14.
D11 1d. black .. .. .. .. 90 1·00
D12 1½d. black (15.12.22) .. .. .. 6·00 9·25
D13 2d. black .. .. .. .. 2·00 1·75
D14 3d. black .. .. .. .. 2·00 3·50
D11/14 .. .. .. *Set of* 4 9·75 14·00
D11/14 Optd "Specimen" .. *Set of* 4 80·00

**1952** (1 Mar). *As Type* D 1, *but inscr* "POSTAGE DUE". *Value in cents. Chalk-surfaced paper. Wmk Mult Script CA. P* 14.
D15 2 c. black .. .. .. .. 30 3·75
a. Error. Crown missing. W **9***a* .. 60·00
b. Error. St. Edward Crown. W **9***b* .. 32·00
D16 4 c. black .. .. .. .. 30 7·00
a. Error. Crown missing. W **9***a* .. 60·00
b. Error. St. Edward Crown. W **9***b* .. 32·00
D17 6 c. black .. .. .. .. 45 8·50
a. Error. Crown missing. W **9***a* .. 70·00
b. Error. St. Edward Crown. W **9***b* .. 48·00
D18 8 c. black .. .. .. .. 75 8·50
a. Error. Crown missing. W **9***a* .. £110
b. Error. St. Edward Crown. W **9***b* .. 75·00
D15/18 .. .. .. .. *Set of* 4 1·60 24·00

## OFFICIAL STAMPS

**P.R.G.**

(O 1)

(= People's Revolutionary Government)

**1982** (June). *Various stamps optd with Type* O 1.

(*a*) *Nos.* 1085A/97A *and* 1099A
O 1 5 c. West Indiaman barque, *circa* 1840 15 10
O 2 6 c. R.M.S.P. *Orinoco*, *circa* 1851 .. .. 15 10
O 3 10 c. Working Schooner .. .. .. 15 10
O 4 12 c. Trimaran at Grand Anse anchorage .. 15 10
O 5 15 c. Spice Island cruising yacht *Petite Amie* 20 15
O 6 20 c. Fishing pirogue .. .. .. .. 25 15
O 7 25 c. Harbour police launch .. .. .. 30 20
O 8 30 c. Grand Anse speedboat .. .. .. 30 25
O 9 40 c. M.V. *Seimstrand* .. .. .. 35 30
O10 50 c. Three-masted schooner *Ariadne* .. 40 30
O11 90 c. M.V. *Geestide* .. .. .. .. 70 70
O12 $1 M.V. *Cunard Countess* .. .. .. 70 70
O13 $3 Rum-runner .. .. .. .. 2·00 3·25
O14 $10 Coast-guard patrol boat .. .. .. 6·00 11·00

(*b*) *Nos.* 1130/2 *and* 1134/5
O15 30 c. Prince Charles and Lady Diana Spencer 1·75 2·25
O16 40 c. Holyrood House .. .. .. .. 2·25 2·75
O17 50 c. Prince Charles and Lady Diana Spencer 1·25 1·75
O18 $2 Holyrood House .. .. .. .. 2·75 3·50
O19 $4 Type **268** .. .. .. .. 6·50 8·00
O1/19 .. .. .. .. *Set of* 19 23·00 32·00

The $4 from sheetlets, perforated 14½ × 14 and with changed background colour, also exists with this overprint (*Price* £8.50 *mint*, £9 *used*).

## GRENADINES OF GRENADA

Part of a group of islands north of Grenada, the most important of which is Carriacou. The Grenadine islands further north are administered by St. Vincent, and their stamps are listed after that country.

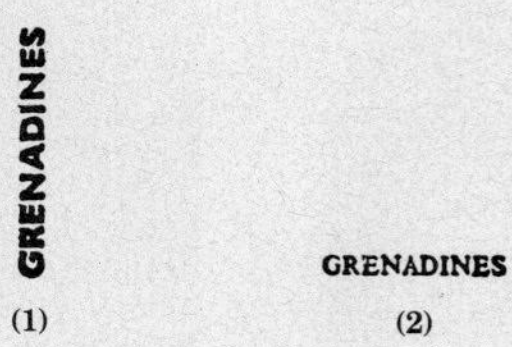

(1) (2)

**1973** (29 Dec). *Royal Wedding. Nos. 582/4 of Grenada optd with T* 1.
1 **196** 25 c. multicoloured 20 10
2 $2 multicoloured 70 50
a. Albino opt
**MS**3 79 × 100 mm. 75 c. and $1 as Nos. 1/2 1·25 50

**1974** (29 May). *Nos. 306 etc of Grenada optd with T* 2.
4 1 c. multicoloured 10 10
5 2 c. multicoloured 10 10
6 3 c. multicoloured 10 10
7 5 c. multicoloured 10 10
8 8 c. multicoloured 10 10
9 10 c. multicoloured 10 10
10 12 c. multicoloured 15 10
11 25 c. multicoloured 25 10
12 $1 multicoloured 1·75 45
13 $2 multicoloured 2·50 1·00
14 $3 multicoloured 2·50 1·50
15 $5 multicoloured 3·50 1·75
4/15 *Set of* 12 10·00 4·50

**1974** (17 Sept). *World Cup Football Championships. As Nos. 619/27 of Grenada but additionally inscr* "GRENADINES".
16 ½ c. Type **201** 10 10
17 1 c. East Germany *v* Australia 10 10
18 2 c. Yugoslavia *v* Brazil 10 10
19 10 c. Scotland *v* Zaire 10 10
20 25 c. Netherlands *v* Uruguay 10 10
21 50 c. Sweden *v* Bulgaria 15 15
22 75 c. Italy *v* Haiti 20 20
23 $1 Poland *v* Argentina 25 25
16/23 *Set of* 8 70 70
**MS**24 114 × 76 mm. $2 Country flags 65 80

**1974** (8 Oct). *Centenary of Universal Postal Union. Designs as Nos. 628 etc of Grenada, but additionally inscr* "GRENADINES".
25 8 c. Mailboat *Caesar* (1839) and helicopter 10 10
26 25 c. Messenger (1450) and satellite 15 10
27 35 c. Airmail transport 15 10
28 $1 Type **202** 50 40
25/8 *Set of* 4 80 60
**MS**29 172 × 109 mm. $1 Bellman and antenna; $2 18th-century postman and mail-train of the future. P 13 80 1·00

**1974** (11 Nov). *Birth Centenary of Sir Winston Churchill. As Nos. 637/9 of Grenada but additionally inscr* "GRENADINES".
30 **203** 35 c. multicoloured 15 10
31 – $2 multicoloured 40 45
**MS**32 129 × 96 mm. 75 c. as 35 c. and $1 as $2 35 70

**1974** (27 Nov). *Christmas. As Nos. 640/8 of Grenada but additionally inscr* "GRENADINES".
33 ½ c. Type **204** 10 10
34 1 c. Niccolo di Pietro 10 10
35 2 c. Van der Weyden 10 10
36 3 c. Bastiani 10 10
37 10 c. Giovanni 10 10
38 25 c. Van der Weyden 10 10
39 50 c. Botticelli 15 15
40 $1 Mantegna 30 25
33/40 *Set of* 8 65 60
**MS**41 117 × 96 mm. $2 as 1 c. 45 60

**CANCELLED REMAINDERS***. Some of the following issues have been remaindered, cancelled-to-order, at a fraction of their face value. For all practical purposes these are indistinguishable from genuine postally used copies. Our used quotations, which are indicated by an asterisk, are the same for cancelled-to-order or postally used copies.

**1975** (17 Feb). *Big Game Fishing. As Nos. 669 etc of Grenada, but additionally inscr* "GRENADINES" *and background colours changed.*
42 ½ c. Type **206** 10 10
43 1 c. Blue Marlin 10 10
44 2 c. White Marlin 10 10
45 10 c. Yellow Tuna 10 10
46 25 c. Wahoo 15 10
47 50 c. Dolphin 20 15
48 70 c. Grouper 25 20
49 $1 Great Barracuda 35 35
42/9 *Set of* 8 90 85
**MS**50 107 × 80 mm. $2 Blue Pointer or Mako Shark 60 90

**1975** (11 Mar). *Flowers. As Nos. 678 etc of Grenada, but additionally inscr.* "GRENADINES".
51 ½ c. Type **207** 10 10
52 1 c. Bleeding Heart (Easter Lily) 10 10
53 2 c. Poinsettia 10 10
54 3 c. Cocoa flower 10 10
55 10 c. Gladioli 10 10
56 25 c. Redhead/Yellowhead 10 10
57 50 c. Plumbago 20 15
58 $1 Orange flower 30 20
51/8 *Set of* 8 65 50
**MS**59 102 × 82 mm. $2 Barbados Gooseberry 60 70

**3** "Christ Crowned with Thorns" (Titian)

**4** "Dawn" (detail from Medici Tomb)

(Des M. Shamir. Litho Format)

**1975** (24 June). *Easter. T* **3** *and similar vert designs showing Crucifixion and Deposition scenes by the artists listed. Multicoloured. P* 14½.
60 ½ c. Type **3** 10 10*
61 1 c. Giotto 10 10*
62 2 c. Tintoretto 10 10*
63 3 c. Cranach 10 10*
64 35 c. Caravaggio 10 10*
65 75 c. Tiepolo 10 10*
66 $2 Velasquez 30 15*
60/6 *Set of* 7 55 30*
**MS**67 105 × 90 mm. $1 Titian. P 13 40 30

(Des M. Shamir. Litho Format)

**1975** (16 July). *500th Birth Anniv of Michelangelo. T* **4** *and similar vert designs. Multicoloured. P* 14½.
68 ½ c. Type **4** 10 10*
69 1 c. "Delphic Sibyl" 10 10*
70 2 c. "Giuliano de Medici" 10 10*
71 40 c. "The Creation" (detail) 25 10*
72 50 c. "Lorenzo de Medici" 25 10*
73 75 c. "Persian Sibyl" 25 10*
74 $2 "Head of Christ" 50 15*
68/74 *Set of* 7 1·25 35*
**MS**75 118 × 96 mm. $1 "The Prophet Jeremiah". P 13 50 30

**1975** (12 Aug). *Butterflies. Designs as Nos. 729 etc of Grenada, but additionally inscr* "GRENADINES". *P* 14½.
76 ½ c. *Morpho peleides* 10 10
77 1 c. *Danaus eresimus* ("*Danaus gilippus*") 10 10
78 2 c. *Dismorphia amphione* 10 10
79 35 c. *Hamadryas feronia* 35 15
80 45 c. *Philaethria dido* 45 15
81 75 c. *Phoebis argante* 70 25
82 $2 *Prepona laertes* 1·40 70
76/82 *Set of* 7 2·75 1·25
**MS**83 104×77 mm. $1 *Siproeta stelenes*. P 13 2·00 1·40

**5** Progress "Standard" Badge

(Des J.W. Litho Format)

**1975** (22 Aug). *14th World Scout Jamboree, Norway. T* **5** *and similar horiz designs. Multicoloured. P* 14½.
84 ½ c. Type **5** 10 10*
85 1 c. Boatman's badge 10 10*
86 2 c. Coxswain's badge 10 10*
87 35 c. Interpreter's badge 25 10*
88 45 c. Ambulance badge 25 10*
89 75 c. Chief Scout's award 35 10*
90 $2 Queen's Scout award 70 15*
84/90 *Set of* 7 1·40 35*
**MS**91 106 × 80 mm. $1 Venture award. P 13 55 30*

**6** The Surrender of Lord Cornwallis

(Des J.W. Litho Questa)

**1975** (30 Sept)–**76**. *Bicentenary of American Revolution (1st issue). Multicoloured.* (a) *Horiz designs as T* **6**. *P* 14.
92 ½ c. Type **6** 10 10*
93 1 c. Minute-men 10 10*
94 2 c. Paul Revere's ride 10 10*
95 3 c. Battle of Bunker Hill 10 10*
96 5 c. Fifer and drummers 10 10*
97 45 c. Backwoodsman 50 10*
98 75 c. Boston Tea Party 65 10*
99 $2 Naval engagement 1·50 10*

(b) *Larger designs. P* 11 (16.1.76)
100 $2 George Washington (35 × 60 *mm*) 1·50 1·00
101 $2 White House and flags (60 × 35 *mm*) 1·50 1·00
92/101 *Set of* 10 5·00 2·25
**MS**102 Two sheets 113 × 128 mm containing No. 100, and 128 × 113 mm containing No. 101. Imperf 2·50 2·00
See also Nos. 176/**MS**183

**7** Fencing

**8** "Madonna and Child" (Dürer)

(Des J.W. Ltd. Litho Format)

**1975** (27 Oct). *Pan-American Games, Mexico City. T* **7** *and similar horiz designs. Multicoloured. P* 14½.
103 ½ c. Type **7** 10 10*
104 1 c. Hurdling 10 10*
105 2 c. Pole-vaulting 10 10*
106 35 c. Weightlifting 15 10*
107 45 c. Throwing the javelin 15 10*
108 75 c. Throwing the discus 15 10*
109 $2 Diving 35 15*
103/109 *Set of* 7 75 35*
**MS**110 78 × 104 mm. $1 Sprinter. P 13 40 20*

**1975** (5 Nov)–**76**. *As Nos. 649A/68A of Grenada but additionally inscribed* "GRENADINES". *Multicoloured.*
111 ½ c. Yachts, Port Saline 10 20
112 1 c. Yacht Club race, St. George's 10 15
113 2 c. Carenage taxi 10 15
114 3 c. Large working boats 10 15
115 5 c. Deep-water dock, St. George's 10 15
116 6 c. Cocoa beans in drying trays 10 15
117 8 c. Nutmegs 10 15
118 10 c. Rum distillery, River Antoine Estate, *circa* 1785 10 15
119 12 c. Cocoa tree 10 15
120 15 c. Fishermen landing catch at Fontenoy 10 15
121 20 c. Parliament Building, St. George's 10 15
122 25 c. Fort George cannons 10 15
123 35 c. Pearls Airport 10 15
124 50 c. General Post Office 20 30
125 75 c. Caribs Leap, Sauteurs Bay 40 50
126 $1 Carenage, St. George's 60 70
127 $2 St. George's Harbour by night 1·25 1·75
128 $3 Grand Anse beach 1·75 2·25
129 $5 Canoe Bay and Black Bay from Point Saline Lighthouse 3·00 4·25
130 $10 Sugar-loaf Island from Levera Beach (1.76) 5·00 5·50
111/30 *Set of* 20 12·00 15·00

(Des M. Shamir. Litho Questa)

**1975** (17 Dec). *Christmas. T* **8** *and similar vert designs showing "Virgin and Child". Multicoloured. P* 14.
131 ½ c. Type **8** 10 10*
132 1 c. Dürer 10 10*
133 2 c. Correggio 10 10*
134 40 c. Botticelli 10 10*
135 50 c. Niccolo da Cremona 10 10*
136 75 c. Correggio 15 10*
137 $2 Correggio 30 15*
131/7 *Set of* 7 60 35*
**MS**138 114 × 102 mm. $1 Bellini 30 30*

**9** Bleeding Tooth

(Des J.W. Litho Questa)

**1976** (13 Jan). *Shells. T* **9** *and similar horiz designs. Multicoloured. P* 14.
139 ½ c. Type **9** 10 10*
140 1 c. Wedge Clam 10 10*
141 2 c. Hawk Wing Conch 10 10*
142 3 c. *Distorsio clathrata* 10 10*
143 25 c. Scotch Bonnet 20 10*
144 50 c. King Helmet 40 10*
145 75 c. Queen Conch 65 15*
139/45 *Set of* 7 1·25 30*
**MS**146 79 × 105 mm. $2 Atlantic Triton 1·00 50*

**10** Cocoa Thrush

(Des J.W. Litho Questa)

**1976** (4 Feb). *Flora and Fauna. T* **10** *and similar horiz designs. Multicoloured. P* 14.
147 ½ c. *Lignum vitae* 10 10
148 1 c. Type **10** 10 10
149 2 c. *Eurypelma* sp (spider) 10 10
150 35 c. Hooded Tanager 80 40
151 50 c. *Nyctaginaceae* 90 70
152 75 c. Grenada Dove 2·00 1·50
153 $1 Marine Toad 2·00 1·75
147/53 *Set of* 7 5·50 4·00
**MS**154 108 × 84 mm. $2 Blue-hooded Euphonia 3·75 4·50

11 Hooked Sailfish

(Des G. Drummond. Litho Questa)

**1976** (17 Feb). *Tourism. T* **11** *and similar horiz designs. Multicoloured. P* 14.

155 ½ c. Type **11** . . . . . . . . 10 10
156 1 c. Careened schooner, Carriacou . . . . 10 10
157 2 c. Carriacou Annual Regatta . . . . 10 15
158 18 c. Boat building on Carriacou . . . . 15 15
159 22 c. Workboat race, Carriacou Regatta . . 15 15
160 75 c. Cruising off Petit Martinique . . . . 30 45
161 $1 Water skiing . . . . . . 40 65
155/61 . . . . . . *Set of* 7 90 1·50
**MS**162 105 × 87 mm. $2 Yacht racing at Carriacou 70 1·25

12 Making a Camp Fire 13 "Christ Mocked" (Bosch)

(Des G. Vasarhelyi. Litho Questa)

**1976** (17 Mar). *50th Anniv of Girl Guides in Grenada. T* **12** *and similar horiz designs. Multicoloured. P* 14.

163 ½ c. Type **12** . . . . . . . . 10 10
164 1 c. First aid . . . . . . . . 10 10
165 2 c. Nature study . . . . . . 10 10
166 50 c. Cookery . . . . . . . . 40 50
167 $1 Sketching . . . . . . . . 80 1·25
163/7 . . . . . . *Set of* 5 1·25 1·75
**MS**168 85 × 110 mm. $2 Guide playing guitar . . 1·00 2·00

(Des PAD Studio. Litho Questa)

**1976** (28 Apr). *Easter. T* **13** *and similar vert designs. Multicoloured. P* 14.

169 ½ c. Type **13** . . . . . . . . 10 10
170 1 c. "Christ Crucified" (Antonello da Messina) 10 10
171 2 c. "Adoration of the Trinity" (Dürer) . . 10 10
172 3 c. "Lamentation of Christ" (Dürer) . . 10 10
173 35 c. "The Entombment" (Van der Weyden) . . 15 10
174 $3 "The Entombment" (Raphael) . . 60 1·25
169/74 . . . . . . *Set of* 6 70 1·40
**MS**175 57 × 72 mm. $2 "Blood of the Redeemer" (G. Bellini) . . . . . . . . 50 1·25

14 Frigate *South Carolina*

(Des J.W. Litho Questa)

**1976** (18 May). *Bicentenary of American Revolution* (2nd issue). *T* **14** *and similar horiz designs. Multicoloured. P* 14.

176 ½ c. Type **14** . . . . . . . . 10 15
177 1 c. Schooner *Lee* . . . . . . 10 15
178 2 c. H.M.S. *Roebuck* . . . . . . 10 15
179 35 c. *Andrea Doria* . . . . . . 60 55
180 50 c. Sloop *The Providence* . . . . 80 1·00
181 $1 American frigate *Alfred* . . . . 2·00 2·25
182 $2 Frigate *Confederacy* . . . . 3·25 3·75
176/82 . . . . . . *Set of* 7 6·00 7·25
**MS**183 72 × 85 mm. $3 Cutter *Revenge* . . . . 2·50 4·75

15 Piper "Apache"

(Des J.W. Litho Format)

**1976** (10 June). *Aeroplanes. T* **15** *and similar horiz designs. Multicoloured. P* 14.

184 ½ c. Type **15** . . . . . . . . 10 10
185 1 c. Beech "Twin Bonanza" . . . . 10 10
186 2 c. D.H. "Twin Otter" . . . . . . 10 10
187 40 c. Britten Norman "Islander" . . . . 30 40
188 50 c. D.H. "Heron" . . . . . . 40 45
189 $2 H.S. "748" . . . . . . 1·25 2·00
184/9 . . . . . . *Set of* 6 1·75 2·75
**MS**190 71 × 85 mm. $3 B.A.C. "1-11" . . . . 1·75 2·50

16 Cycling 17 "Virgin and Child" (Cima)

(Des J.W. Litho Format)

**1976** (1 July). *Olympic Games, Montreal. T* **16** *and similar horiz designs. Multicoloured. P* 14.

191 ½ c. Type **16** . . . . . . . . 10 10
192 1 c. Pommel horse . . . . . . 10 10
193 2 c. Hurdling . . . . . . . . 10 10
194 35 c. Shot putting . . . . . . 10 10
195 45 c. Diving . . . . . . . . 15 15
196 75 c. Sprinting . . . . . . . . 15 20
197 $2 Rowing . . . . . . . . 35 65
191/7 . . . . . . *Set of* 7 70 1·10
**MS**198 101 × 76 mm. $3 Sailing . . . . 80 1·40

(Litho Format)

**1976** (19 Oct). *Christmas. T* **17** *and similar multicoloured designs. P* 13½.

199 ½ c. Type **17** . . . . . . . . 10 10
200 1 c. "The Nativity" (Romanino) . . . . 10 10
201 2 c. "The Nativity" (Romanino) (*different*) . . 10 10
202 35 c. "Adoration of the Kings" (Bruegel) . . 10 10
203 50 c. "Madonna and Child" (Girolamo) . . 15 20
204 75 c. "Adoration of the Magi" (Giorgione) (*horiz*) . . . . . . . . 15 25
205 $2 "Adoration of the Kings" (School of Fra Angelico) (*horiz*) . . . . . . 30 70
199/205 . . . . . . *Set of* 7 70 1·40
**MS**206 120 × 100 mm. $3 "The Holy Family" (Garofalo) . . . . . . . . 60 1·60

18 Alexander Graham Bell and First Telephone

(Des G. Vasarhelyi. Litho Questa)

**1977** (28 Jan). *Telephone Centenary* (1976). *T* **18** *and similar horiz designs showing Alexander Graham Bell and telephone. Multicoloured. P* 14.

207 ½ c. Type **18** . . . . . . . . 10 10
208 1 c. Telephone, 1895 . . . . . . 10 10
209 2 c. Telephone, 1900 . . . . . . 10 10
210 35 c. Telephone, 1915 . . . . . . 15 10
211 75 c. Telephone, 1920 . . . . . . 30 40
212 $1 Telephone, 1929 . . . . . . 50 75
213 $2 Telephone, 1963 . . . . . . 75 1·40
207/13 . . . . . . *Set of* 7 1·60 2·50
**MS**214 107 × 78 mm. $3 Telephone, 1976 . . 1·10 2·50

19 Coronation Coach 20 Royal Visit

(Des Jennifer Toombs. Litho and embossed Walsall. (Nos. 215/18). Des and litho Walsall (Nos. 219/22))

**1977** (7 Feb). *Silver Jubilee. Multicoloured.*

(*a*) *Sheet stamps. Horiz designs as T* **19**. *P* 13½

215 35 c. Type **19** . . . . . . . . 10 10
216 $2 Queen entering Abbey . . . . 30 20
217 $4 Queen crowned . . . . . . 55 45
215/17 . . . . . . *Set of* 3 80 65
**MS**218 100 × 70 mm. $5 The Mall on Coronation Night . . . . . . . . 80 1·25

Nos. 215/17 also exist perf 11 (*Price for set of* 3 £1 *mint or used*) from additional sheetlets of 3 stamps and 1 label. These have different background colours from the stamps perforated 13½, which come from normal sheets of 25.

(*b*) *Booklet stamps. Vert designs as T* **20**. *Roul* 5 × *imperf.** *Self-adhesive*

219 35 c. Type **20** . . . . . . . . 15 20
a. Booklet pane of 6. . . . . . . 1·00
220 50 c. Crown of St. Edward . . . . 40 80
a. Booklet pane. Nos. 220/2. . . . . . 3·00
221 $2 The Queen and Prince Charles . . . . 1·50 1·60
222 $5 Royal Standard . . . . . . 1·60 1·75
219/22 . . . . . . *Set of* 4 3·25 4·00

*Nos. 219/22 are separated by various combinations of rotary knife (giving a straight edge) and roulette.

21 "Disrobing of Christ" (Fra Angelico) 22 "The Virgin adoring the Child" (Correggio)

(Des J.W. Litho Questa)

**1977** (5 July). *Easter. Vert designs as T* **21** *showing paintings by the artists given. Multicoloured. P* 14.

223 ½ c. Type **21** . . . . . . . . 10 10
224 1 c. Fra Angelico . . . . . . 10 10
225 2 c. El Greco . . . . . . . . 10 10
226 18 c. El Greco . . . . . . . . 10 10
227 35 c. Fra Angelico . . . . . . 10 10
228 50 c. Giottino . . . . . . . . 15 30
229 $2 Antonello da Messina . . . . 40 85
223/9 . . . . . . *Set of* 7 65 1·40
**MS**230 121 × 94 mm. $3 Fra Angelico . . . . 60 2·00

(Des J.W. Litho Questa)

**1977** (17 Nov). *Christmas. T* **22** *and similar vert designs. Multicoloured. P* 14.

231 ½ c. Type **22** . . . . . . . . 10 10
232 1 c. "Virgin and Child" (Giorgione) . . . . 10 10
233 2 c. "Virgin and Child" (Morales) . . . . 10 10
234 18 c. "Madonna della Tenda" (Raphael) . . 10 10
235 35 c. "Rest on the Flight into Egypt" (Van Dyck) . . . . . . . . 10 10
236 50 c. "Madonna and Child" (Lippi) . . . . 15 30
237 $2 "Virgin and Child" (Lippi) (*different*) . . 40 85
231/7 . . . . . . *Set of* 7 65 1·40
**MS**238 114 × 99 mm. $3 "Virgin and Child with Angels and Saints" (Ghirlandaio). . . . 60 1·75

ROYAL VISIT W.I. 1977

(23)

**1977** (23 Nov). *Royal Visit. Nos.* 215/18 *optd with T* **23**. *P* 13½.

239 35 c. Type **19** . . . . . . . . 15 10
240 $2 Queen entering Abbey . . . . 40 30
241 $4 Queen crowned . . . . . . 70 50
239/41 . . . . . . *Set of* 3 1·10 75
**MS**242 100 × 70 mm. $5 The Mall on Coronation Night . . . . . . . . 1·25 1·25

This overprint also exists on the stamps perforated 11, mentioned below No. **MS**218 (*price for set of* 3 £1·75 *mint or used*).

24 Life-saving

(Des G. Drummond. Litho Questa)

**1977** (7 Dec). *Caribbean Scout Jamboree, Jamaica. T* **24** *and similar horiz designs. Multicoloured. P* 14.

243 ½ c. Type **24** . . . . . . . . 10 10
244 1 c. Overnight hike . . . . . . 10 10
245 2 c. Cubs tying knots . . . . . . 10 10
246 22 c. Erecting a tent . . . . . . 15 10
247 35 c. Gang show limbo dance . . . . 25 10
248 75 c. Campfire cooking . . . . . . 50 55
249 $3 Sea Scouts' yacht race . . . . 1·75 3·25
243/9 . . . . . . *Set of* 7 2·50 3·50
**MS**250 109 × 85 mm. $2 Pioneering project —Spring bridge . . . . . . . . 1·40 2·25

25 Blast-off

(Des J.W. Litho Questa)

**1978** (3 Feb). *Space Shuttle. T* **25** *and similar horiz designs. Multicoloured. P* 14.

251 ½ c. Type **25** . . . . . . . . 10 10
252 1 c. Booster jettison . . . . . . 10 10
253 2 c. External tank jettison . . . . 10 10
254 22 c. Working in orbit . . . . . . 15 15
255 50 c. Shuttle re-entry . . . . . . 30 30
256 $3 Shuttle landing . . . . . . 1·25 1·00
251/6 . . . . . . *Set of* 6 1·60 1·40
**MS**257 85 × 103 mm. $2 Shuttle being towed . . 60 85

**26** Alfred Nobel and Physiology/Medicine Medal

(Des J.W. Litho Questa)

**1978** (22 Feb). *Nobel Prize Awards. T* **26** *and similar horiz designs. Multicoloured. P* 14.

258 ½ c. Type **26** . . 10 10
259 1 c. Physics and Chemistry medal . . 10 10
260 2 c. Peace medal . . 10 10
261 22 c. Nobel Institute, Oslo . . 15 15
262 75 c. Peace Prize committee . . 45 45
263 $3 Literature medal . . 1·25 1·25
258/63 *Set of* 6 1·75 1·75
MS264 127 × 103 mm. $2 Peace medal and Nobel's will . . 50 60

**27** German Zeppelin Stamp of 1930

(Des J.W. Litho Questa)

**1978** (15 Mar). *75th Anniv of First Zeppelin Flight and 50th Anniv of Lindbergh's Trans-atlantic Flight. T* **27** *and similar horiz designs. Multicoloured. P* 14 × 13½.

265 5 c. Type **27** . . 15 10
266 15 c. French "Concorde" stamp, 1970 . . 20 10
267 25 c. Liechtenstein Zeppelin stamp, 1931 . . 25 10
268 35 c. Panama Lindbergh stamp, 1928 . . 25 10
269 50 c. Russian airship stamp, 1931 . . 35 20
270 $3 Spanish Lindbergh stamp, 1930 . . 1·25 1·10
265/70 *Set of* 6 2·25 1·25
MS271 140 × 79 mm. 75 c. U.S.A. Lindbergh stamp, 1927; $2 German *Hindenburg* stamp, 1936 1·10 1·60

**28** Coronation Ring

**29** Drummer, Royal Regiment of Fusiliers.

(Des J.W. Litho Questa (Nos. 272/5). Manufactured by Walsall (Nos. 276/8))

**1978** (12 Apr). *25th Anniv of Coronation. Multicoloured.*

(*a*) *Sheet stamps. Horiz designs as T* **28.** *P* 14

272 50 c. Type **28** . . 20 15
273 $2 Queen's Orb . . 50 40
274 $2.50, Imperial State Crown . . 55 45
272/4 . . *Set of* 3 1·10 90
MS275 97 × 67 mm. $5 Queen Elizabeth II . . 1·00 1·00

Nos. 272/4 also exist perf 12 (*Price for set of* 3 £1·50 *mint or used*) from additional sheetlets of 3 stamps and 1 label, issued 2 June. These have different background colours from the stamps perforated 14, which come from normal sheets of 50.

(*b*) *Booklet stamps. Vert designs as T* **29.** *Roul* 5 × *imperf.**
*Self-adhesive*

276 18 c. Type **29** . . 25 35
a. Booklet pane. Nos. 276/7 × 3 . . 1·25
277 50 c. Drummer, Royal Anglian Regiment . . 25 45
278 $5 Drum Major, Queen's Regiment . . 2·25 3·00
a. Booklet pane of 1 . . 2·25
276/8 . . *Set of* 3 2·50 3·50

*Nos. 276/7 are separated by various combinations of rotary-knife (giving a straight edge) and roulette. No. 278 exists only with straight edges.

**30** "Le Chapeau de Paille"

**31** Wright *Flyer*

(Litho Questa)

**1978** (18 May). *400th Birth Anniv of Rubens. T* **30** *and similar vert designs. Multicoloured. P* 14.

279 5 c. Type **30** . . 10 10
280 15 c. "Achilles slaying Hector" . . 10 10
281 18 c. "Helene Fourment and her Children" . . 10 10
282 22 c. "Rubens and Isabella Brandt" . . 15 10
283 35 c. "The Ildefonso Altarpiece" . . 15 10
284 $3 "Heads of Negroes" (detail) . . 80 80
279/84 *Set of* 6 1·00 1·00
MS285 85 × 127 mm. $2 "Self-portrait" . . 45 80

(Des BG Studio. Litho Questa)

**1978** (10 Aug). *75th Anniv of Powered Flight. T* **31** *and similar designs. P* 14.

286 5 c. black, chestnut and pale blue . . 10 10
287 15 c. black, vermilion and yellow-ochre . . 10 10
288 18 c. black, vermilion and yellow-ochre . . 10 10
289 25 c. multicoloured . . 10 10
290 35 c. black, purple and magenta . . 15 10
291 75 c. multicoloured . . 25 25
292 $3 black, magenta and new blue . . 75 75
286/92 *Set of* 7 1·10 1·10
MS293 126 × 83 mm. $2 black, blue and bright blue-green . . 1·40 1·40

Designs: *Vert*—15 c. Orville Wright; 18 c. Wilbur Wright. *Horiz*—25, 75 c., $3, Wright *Flyer* (*all different*); 35 c. Wright glider; $2, Various Wright aircraft.

**32** Audubon's Shearwater

**33** Players with Ball

(Des Jennifer Toombs. Litho Questa)

**1978** (28 Sept). *Birds. T* **32** *and similar multicoloured designs. P* 14.

294 5 c. Type **32** . . 40 10
295 10 c. Semipalmated Plover . . 60 10
296 18 c. Purple-throated Carib (*horiz*) . . 85 15
297 22 c. Red-billed Whistling Duck (*horiz*) . . 1·00 20
298 40 c. Caribbean Martin (*horiz*) . . 1·25 35
299 $1 White-tailed Tropic Bird . . 2·25 1·10
300 $2 Long-billed Curlew . . 3·25 1·50
294/300 *Set of* 7 8·50 3·00
MS301 78 × 78 mm. $5 Snowy Egret . . 4·50 4·50

(Des G. Vasarhelyi. Litho Questa)

**1978** (2 Nov). *World Cup Football Championship, Argentina. T* **33** *and similar vert designs showing football scenes. P* 14.

302 15 c. multicoloured . . 10 10
303 35 c. multicoloured . . 20 10
304 50 c. multicoloured . . 25 20
305 $3 multicoloured . . 80 80
302/5 . . *Set of* 4 1·10 90
MS306 114 × 85 mm. $2 multicoloured . . 65 90

**34** Captain Cook and Kalaniopu (king of Hawaii), 1778

**35** "Virgin at Prayer"

(Des BG Studio. Litho Questa)

**1978** (13 Dec). *250th Birth Anniv of Captain Cook and Bicentenary of Discovery of Hawaii. T* **34** *and similar horiz designs. Multicoloured. P* 14.

307 18 c. Type **34** . . 45 10
308 22 c. Captain Cook and native of Hawaii . . 50 15
309 50 c. Captain Cook and death scene, 14 February 1779 . . 85 30
310 $3 Captain Cook and offering ceremony . . 2·25 1·75
307/10 *Set of* 4 3·50 2·00
MS311 171 × 113 mm. $4 H.M.S. *Resolution* (*vert*) 2·50 3·25

(Des M. Rubin. Litho Questa)

**1978** (20 Dec). *Christmas. Paintings by Dürer. T* **35** *and similar vert designs. Multicoloured. P* 14.

312 40 c. Type **35** . . 15 10
313 60 c. "The Dresden Altarpiece" . . 15 15
314 90 c. "Madonna and Child with St. Anne" . . 20 15
315 $2 "Madonna and Child with Pear" . . 40 50
312/15 *Set of* 4 80 80
MS316 114 × 84 mm. $4 "Salvator Mundi" . . 80 1·40

**36** *Strelitzia reginae*

**37** Children with Pig

(Des J.W. Litho Questa)

**1979** (15 Feb). *Flowers. T* **36** *and similar vert designs. Multicoloured. P* 14.

317 22 c. Type **36** . . 15 10
318 40 c. *Euphorbia pulcherrima* . . 25 15
319 $1 *Heliconia humilis* . . 55 30
320 $3 *Thunbergia alata* . . 1·25 80
317/20 *Set of* 4 2·00 1·10
MS321 114 × 90 mm. $2 *Bougainvillea glabra* . . 75 1·00

(Des G. Drummond. Litho Questa)

**1979** (22 Mar). *International Year of the Child. T* **37** *and similar horiz designs. Multicoloured. P* 14.

322 18 c. Type **37** . . 10 10
323 50 c. Children with donkey . . 25 25
324 $1 Children with goats . . 30 35
325 $3 Children fishing . . 1·00 1·10
322/5 . . *Set of* 4 1·50 1·60
MS326 104 × 86 mm. $4 Child with coconuts . . 1·00 1·90

**38** *20,000 Leagues Under the Sea*

(Des G. Vasarhelyi. Litho Questa)

**1979** (20 Apr). *150th Birth Anniv of Jules Verne (author). T* **38** *and similar horiz designs showing scenes from his books and modern technological developments. Multicoloured. P* 14.

327 18 c. Type **38** . . 20 10
328 38 c. *From the Earth to the Moon* . . 30 20
329 75 c. *From the Earth to the Moon* (*different*) . . 55 35
330 $3 *Five Weeks in a Balloon* . . 1·25 1·00
327/30 *Set of* 4 2·10 1·50
MS331 111 × 86 mm. $4 *Around the World in 80 days* . . 1·00 1·60

**39** Sir Rowland Hill and Mail Van

(Des BG Studio. Litho Questa)

**1979** (30 July). *Death Centenary of Sir Rowland Hill. T* **39** *and similar horiz designs showing Sir Rowland Hill and mail transport. Multicoloured. P* 14.

332 15 c. Type **39** . . 10 10
333 $1 Cargo liner . . 45 35
334 $2 Diesel mail train . . 85 50
335 $3 "Concorde" . . 1·40 80
332/5 . . *Set of* 4 2·50 1·60
MS336 85 × 67 mm. $4 Sir Rowland Hill . . 1·00 1·25

Nos. 332/5 also exist perf 12 (*Price for set of* 4 £2·25 *mint or used*) from additional sheetlets of 5 stamps and 1 label issued 6 September. These have different background colours to the stamps perforated 14, which come from normal sheets of 40.

**40** "Virgin and Child Enthroned" (11th-century Byzantine)

**41** Great Hammerhead Shark

(Des G. Vasarhelyi. Litho Questa)

**1979** (23 Oct). *Christmas. Sculptures. T* **40** *and similar vert designs. Multicoloured. P* 14.

337 6 c. Type **40** . . 10 10
338 25 c. "Presentation in the Temple" (Andre Beauneveu) . . 10 10
339 30 c. "Flight to Egypt", Utrecht, *circa* 1510 . . 10 10
340 40 c. "Madonna and Child" (Jacopo della Quercia) . . 10 10
341 90 c. "Madonna della Mela" (Luca della Robbia) . . 15 15
342 $1 "Madonna and Child" (Antonio Rossellino) . . 20 20
343 $2 "Madonna", Antwerp, 1700 . . 35 35
337/43 *Set of* 7 80 80
MS344 125 × 95 mm. $4 "Virgin", Krumau . . 65 1·10

(Des J.W. Litho Questa)

**1979** (9 Nov). *Marine Life. T* **41** *and similar horiz designs. Multicoloured. P* 14 × 13½.

345 40 c. Type **41** . . 35 25
346 45 c. Banded Butterflyfish . . 35 25
347 50 c. Permit (fish) . . 35 30
348 60 c. Threaded Turban (shell) . . 50 35
349 70 c. Milk Conch (shell) . . 55 40
350 75 c. Great Blue Heron . . 65 40
351 90 c. Coloured Atlantic Natica (shell) . . 70 50

352 $1 Red-footed Booby .. .. .. .. 95 55
345/52 .. .. .. .. *Set of* 8 4·00 2·75
**MS**353 99 × 86 mm. $2.50 Collared Plover .. 1·25 1·25

42 Goofy as Doctor

43 Classroom

(Litho Format)

**1979** (12 Dec). *International Year of the Child. Walt Disney Cartoon Characters. T* **42** *and similar multicoloured designs showing characters at various occupations. P* 11.
354 ½ c. Type **42** .. .. .. .. 10 10
355 1 c. Mickey Mouse as admiral .. .. 10 10
356 2 c. Goofy as fireman .. .. .. 10 10
357 3 c. Minnie Mouse as nurse .. .. .. 10 10
358 4 c. Mickey Mouse as drum major .. .. 10 10
359 5 c. Donald Duck as policeman .. .. 10 10
360 10 c. Donald Duck as pilot .. .. .. 10 10
361 $2 Goofy as postman (*horiz*) .. .. 1·75 1·00
362 $2.50, Donald Duck as train driver (*horiz*) .. 2·00 1·00
354/62 .. .. .. .. *Set of* 9 3·75 2·00
**MS**363 128 × 102 mm. $3 Mickey Mouse as fireman. P 13½ .. .. .. .. 1·75 1·75

**1980** (10 Mar). *1st Anniv of Revolution. Nos.* 116 *and* 119/30 *optd with T* **258** *of Grenada.*
364 6 c. Cocoa beans in drying trays .. .. 10 10
365 12 c. Cocoa Tree .. .. .. .. 10 10
366 15 c. Fishermen landing catch at Fontenoy .. 10 10
367 20 c. Parliament Building, St. George's .. 10 10
368 25 c. Fort George cannons .. .. .. 15 10
369 35 c. Pearls Airport .. .. .. 20 10
370 50 c. General Post Office .. .. .. 35 15
371 75 c. Caribs Leap, Sauteurs Bay .. .. 40 20
372 $1 Carenage, St. George's .. .. 55 30
373 $2 St. George's Harbour by night .. .. 85 70
374 $3 Grand Anse Beach .. .. .. 1·60 1·60
375 $5 Canoe Bay and Black Bay from Point Saline Lighthouse .. .. .. 2·25 2·50
376 $10 Sugar Loaf Island from Levera Beach .. 3·75 4·25
364/76 .. .. .. .. *Set of* 13 9·50 9·00

(Des BG Studio. Litho Questa)

**1980** (12 Mar). *75th Anniv of Rotary International. T* **43** *and similar horiz designs. Multicoloured. P* 14.
377 6 c. Type **43** .. .. .. .. 10 10
378 30 c. Rotary International emblem encircled by people of different races .. .. 20 10
379 60 c. Rotary International executive presenting doctor with cheque .. .. 40 20
380 $3 Nurses with young patients .. .. 1·50 75
377/80 .. .. .. .. *Set of* 4 2·00 1·00
**MS**381 85 × 72 mm. $4 Paul P. Harris (founder) 1·00 1·60

44 Yellow-bellied Seedeater

45 Running

(Des G. Drummond. Litho Questa)

**1980** (14 Apr). *Wild Birds. T* **44** *and similar vert designs. Multicoloured. P* 14.
382 25 c. Type **44** .. .. .. .. 50 15
383 40 c. Blue-hooded Euphonia .. .. 55 20
384 90 c. Yellow Warbler .. .. .. 1·25 65
385 $2 Tropical Mockingbird .. .. 1·75 1·25
382/5 .. .. .. .. *Set of* 4 3·50 2·00
**MS**386 83 × 110 mm. $3 Barn Owl .. .. 2·75 2·50

(Des G. Vasarhelyi. Litho Questa)

**1980** (21 Apr). *Olympic Games, Moscow. T* **45** *and similar horiz designs. Multicoloured. P* 14.
387 30 c. Type **45** .. .. .. .. 15 15
388 40 c. Football .. .. .. .. 15 20
389 90 c. Boxing .. .. .. .. 30 35
390 $2 Wrestling .. .. .. .. 60 75
387/90 .. .. .. .. *Set of* 4 1·00 1·25
**MS**391 104 × 75 mm. $4 Athletes in silhouette .. 75 1·10

LONDON 1980

(46)

47 Longspine Squirrelfish

**1980** (6 May). *"London 1980" International Stamp Exhibition. Nos.* 332/5 *optd with T* **46**. *P* 12.
392 15 c. Type **39** .. .. .. .. 15 15
393 $1 Cargo liner .. .. .. .. 65 35
394 $2 Diesel mail train .. .. .. 1·25 80
395 $3 "Concorde" .. .. .. .. 1·90 2·25
392/5 .. .. .. .. *Set of* 4 3·50 2·25

(Des G. Drummond. Litho Questa)

**1980** (6 Aug)–**84**. *Fishes. Horiz designs as T* **47**. *Multicoloured. P* 14. A. *Without imprint date.*
396 ½ c. Type **47** .. .. .. .. 10 10
397 1 c. Blue Chromis .. .. .. 10 10
398 2 c. Foureye Butterfly Fish .. .. 10 10
399 4 c. Sergeant Major .. .. .. 10 10
400 5 c. Yellowtail Snapper .. .. .. 10 10
401 6 c. Mutton Snapper .. .. .. 10 10
402 10 c. Cocoa Damselfish .. .. .. 10 10
403 12 c. Royal Gramma .. .. .. 10 10
404 15 c. Cherubfish .. .. .. .. 15 10
405 20 c. Blackbar Soldierfish .. .. 15 10
406 25 c. Comb Grouper .. .. .. 15 15
407 30 c. Longsnout Butterflyfish .. .. 20 20
408 40 c. Pudding Wife .. .. .. 25 25
409 50 c. Midnight Parrotfish .. .. .. 35 35
410 90 c. Redspotted Hawkfish .. .. .. 65 55
411 $1 Hogfish .. .. .. .. 70 60
412 $3 Beau Gregory .. .. .. 1·75 2·00
413 $5 Rock Beauty .. .. .. 2·75 3·00
414 $10 Barred Hamlet .. .. .. 6·00 7·00
396A/414A .. .. .. *Set of* 19 12·00 13·00

B. *With imprint date at foot of design.*
396B ½ c. Type **47** (*p* 12) (1982) .. .. .. 7·00
402B 10 c. Cocoa Damselfish (1984) .. .. 30 30

(Litho Walsall)

**1980** (7 Oct). *Christmas. Walt Disney Cartoon Scenes from "Bambi". Horiz designs as T* **42**. *Multicoloured. P* 11.
415 ½ c. Bambi with Mother .. .. .. 10 10
416 1 c. Bambi with quails .. .. .. 10 10
417 2 c. Bambi meets Thumper the rabbit .. 10 10
418 3 c. Bambi meets Flower the skunk .. .. 10 10
419 4 c. Bambi and Faline .. .. .. 10 10
420 5 c. Bambi with his father .. .. 10 10
421 10 c. Bambi on ice .. .. .. 10 10
422 $2.50, Faline with foals .. .. 1·25 85
423 $3 Bambi and Faline .. .. .. 1·25 1·00
415/23 .. .. .. .. *Set of* 9 2·50 1·90
**MS**424 127 × 102 mm. $4 Bambi as Prince of the Forest (*vert*) .. .. .. .. 1·00 1·10

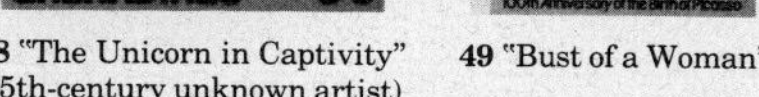

48 "The Unicorn in Captivity" (15th-century unknown artist)

49 "Bust of a Woman"

(Litho Format)

**1981** (25 Jan). *Paintings. T* **48** *and similar multicoloured designs. P* 13½.
425 6 c. Type **48** .. .. .. .. 10 10
426 10 c. "The Fighting *Temeraire*" (Turner) (*horiz*) 10 10
427 25 c. "Sunday Afternoon on the Ile de la Grande-Jatte" (Georges-Pierre Seurat) (*horiz*) .. .. .. .. 15 15
428 90 c. "Max Schmitt in a Single Scull" (Thomas Eakins) (*horiz*) .. .. .. 45 45
429 $2 "The Burial of the Count of Orgaz" (El Greco) .. .. .. .. 85 85
430 $3 "George Washington" (Gilbert Stuart) .. 1·10 1·10
425/30 .. .. .. .. *Set of* 6 2·40 2·40
**MS**431 66 × 101 mm. $5 "Kaiser Karl de Grosse" (detail, Dürer) .. .. .. .. 1·40 2·00

(Litho Format)

**1981** (26 Jan). *50th Anniv of Walt Disney's Cartoon Character, Pluto. Vert designs as T* **42**. *Multicoloured. P* 13½.
432 $2 Mickey Mouse serving birthday cake to Pluto .. .. .. .. 90 80
**MS**433 127 × 101 mm. $4 Pluto in scene from film *Pluto's Dream House* .. .. .. 2·00 2·10
No. 432 was printed in small sheets of 8 stamps.

(Litho Format)

**1981** (14 Apr). *Easter. Walt Disney Cartoon Characters. Vert designs as T* **42**. *Multicoloured. P* 11.
434 35 c. Chip .. .. .. .. 25 25
435 40 c. Dewey .. .. .. .. 25 25
436 $2 Huey .. .. .. .. 80 80
437 $2.50, Mickey Mouse .. .. .. 1·10 1·10
434/7 .. .. .. .. *Set of* 4 2·25 2·25
**MS**438 126 × 102 mm. $4 Jiminy Cricket. P 13½ 2·10 2·25

(Des J.W. Litho Questa)

**1981** (5 May). *Birth Centenary of Picasso. T* **49** *and similar vert designs. Multicoloured. P* 14.
439 6 c. Type **49** .. .. .. .. 10 10
440 40 c. Woman (study for "Les Demoiselles d'Avignon") .. .. .. 40 15
441 90 c. "Nude with raised Arms (The Dancer of Avignon)" .. .. .. 70 30
442 $4 "The Dryad" .. .. .. 2·00 1·25
439/42 .. .. .. .. *Set of* 4 2·75 1·50
**MS**443 103 × 128 mm. $5 "Les Demoiselles d'Avignon". Imperf .. .. .. 2·75 2·00

50 Balmoral Castle

51 Lady Diana Spencer

(Des J.W. Litho Format)

**1981** (16 June). *Royal Wedding. T* **50** *and similar vert designs. Multicoloured.* (a) *P* 15.
444 40 c. Prince Charles and Lady Diana Spencer 25 25
445 $2 Type **50** .. .. .. .. 65 65
446 $4 Prince Charles as parachutist .. .. 1·00 1·00
**MS**447 97 × 84 mm. $5 Royal Coach .. .. 1·50 1·50

(b) *P* 15 × 14½
448 30 c. As No. 444 .. .. .. .. 25 25
449 40 c. Type **50** .. .. .. .. 30 30
444/9 .. .. .. .. *Set of* 5 2·25 2·25

The 30 and 40 c. values were each printed in small sheets of 6 including one *se-tenant* stamp-size label.

The $4 value, with changed background colour, also exists perforated 15 × 14½ (*price* £1.50 *mint or used*) from similar sheetlets in addition to the original version from sheets of 40.

(Manufactured by Walsall)

**1981** (16 June). *Royal Wedding. Booklet stamps. T* **51** *and similar multicoloured designs. Roul* 5 × *imperf*. Self-adhesive.*
450 $1 Type **51** .. .. .. .. 45 70
a. Booklet pane. Nos. 450/1 each × 3 .. 3·00
451 $2 Prince Charles .. .. .. 70 1·10
452 $5 Prince Charles and Lady Diana Spencer (*horiz*) .. .. .. .. 2·00 2·50
a. Booklet pane of 1 .. .. .. 2·00
450/2 .. .. .. .. *Set of* 3 2·75 4·00

*The $1 and $2 values were each separated by various combinations of rotary knife (giving a straight edge) and roulette. The $5 value exists only with straight edges.

52 Amy Johnson (1st solo flight, Britain to Australia by Woman, May 1930)

53 "747" Carrier

(Des BG Studio. Litho Questa)

**1981** (13 Oct). *"Decade for Women". Famous Female Aviators. T* **52** *and similar vert designs. Multicoloured. P* 14.
453 30 c. Type **52** .. .. .. .. 35 15
454 70 c. Mme la Baronne de Laroche (1st qualified woman pilot, March 1910) .. .. 55 30
455 $1.10, Ruth Nichols (solo Atlantic flight attempt, June 1931) .. .. .. 85 40
456 $3 Amelia Earhart (1st North Atlantic solo flight by woman, May 1932) .. .. 1·75 1·10
453/6 .. .. .. .. *Set of* 4 3·25 1·75
**MS**457 90 × 85 mm. $5 Valentina Nikolayeva-Tereshkova (1st woman in space, June 1963) .. 2·00 2·00

(Litho Questa)

**1981** (2 Nov). *Christmas. Horiz designs as T* **42** *showing scenes from Walt Disney's cartoon film "Lady and the Tramp". P* 13½.
458 ½ c. multicoloured .. .. .. .. 10 10
459 1 c. multicoloured .. .. .. .. 10 10
460 2 c. multicoloured .. .. .. .. 10 10
461 3 c. multicoloured .. .. .. .. 10 10
462 4 c. multicoloured .. .. .. .. 10 10
463 5 c. multicoloured .. .. .. .. 10 10
464 10 c. multicoloured .. .. .. .. 10 10
465 $2.50, multicoloured .. .. .. 1·25 1·00
466 $3 multicoloured .. .. .. .. 1·50 1·25
458/66 .. .. .. .. *Set of* 9 2·75 2·25
**MS**467 128 × 103 mm. $5 multicoloured .. .. 2·00 2·00

(Des M. Brodie. Litho Format)

**1981** (2 Nov). *Space Shuttle Project, T* **53** *and similar horiz designs. Multicoloured. P* 14½.
468 10 c. Type **53** .. .. .. .. 30 10
469 40 c. Re-entry .. .. .. .. 55 15
470 $1.10, External tank separation .. .. 1·25 45
471 $3 Touchdown .. .. .. .. 2·00 1·00
468/71 .. .. .. .. *Set of* 4 3·75 1·50
**MS**472 117 × 89 mm. $5 Launch .. .. .. 3·50 2·75

## OMNIBUS ISSUES

Details, together with prices for complete sets, of the various Omnibus issues from the 1935 Silver Jubilee series to date are included in a special section following Zimbabwe at the end of Volume 2.

54 Footballer

55 Mail Van and Stage-Coach

(Des Clover Mill. Litho Questa)

**1981** (30 Nov). *World Cup Football Championship, Spain* (1982). *T* **54** *and similar vert designs showing footballers. P* 14.

| No. | Description | | |
|---|---|---|---|
| 473 | 20 c. multicoloured | 10 | 10 |
| 474 | 40 c. multicoloured | 20 | 20 |
| 475 | $1 multicoloured | 45 | 45 |
| 476 | $2 multicoloured | 75 | 75 |
| 473/6 | *Set of* 4 | 1·40 | 1·40 |
| **MS**477 | 106 × 128 mm. $4 multicoloured | 2·75 | 2·00 |

Nos. 473/6 were each printed in small sheets of 6 including one *se-tenant* stamp-size label.

(Des G. Vasarhelyi. Litho Format)

**1982** (13 Jan). *Centenary of U.P.U. Membership. T* **55** *and similar horiz designs. Multicoloured. P* 14½.

| No. | Description | | |
|---|---|---|---|
| 478 | 30 c. Type **55** | 40 | 15 |
| 479 | 40 c. U.P.U. emblem | 45 | 20 |
| 480 | $2.50, *Queen Elizabeth 2* (liner) and sailing ship | 2·00 | 90 |
| 481 | $4 Airliner and biplane | 2·75 | 1·60 |
| 478/81 | *Set of* 4 | 5·00 | 2·50 |
| **MS**482 | 117 × 78 mm. $5 Streamlined diesel-electric, and steam trains | 5·00 | 3·25 |

56 National Sports Meeting

(Des M. Diamond. Litho Format)

**1982** (19 Feb). *75th Anniv of Boy Scout Movement and 125th Birth Anniv of Lord Baden-Powell. T* **56** *and similar horiz designs. Multicoloured. P* 14½.

| No. | Description | | |
|---|---|---|---|
| 483 | 6 c. Type **56** | 15 | 10 |
| 484 | 90 c. Sea scouts sailing | 65 | 30 |
| 485 | $1.10, Handicraft | 90 | 60 |
| 486 | $3 Animal tending | 1·90 | 1·40 |
| 483/6 | *Set of* 4 | 3·25 | 2·10 |
| **MS**487 | 100 × 71 mm. $5 Music around campfire | 2·75 | 3·00 |

57 *Anartia jatrophae*

58 Prince and Princess of Wales

(Des J.W. Litho Questa)

**1982** (24 Mar). *Butterflies. T* **57** *and similar horiz designs. Multicoloured. P* 14.

| No. | Description | | |
|---|---|---|---|
| 488 | 30 c. Type **57** | 65 | 30 |
| 489 | 40 c. *Chioides vintra* | 70 | 35 |
| 490 | $1.10, *Cynthia cardui* | 1·25 | 75 |
| 491 | $3 *Historis odius* | 2·25 | 1·60 |
| 488/91 | *Set of* 4 | 4·25 | 2·75 |
| **MS**492 | 103×77 mm. $5 *Dione juno* | 3·25 | 3·75 |

(Des PAD Studio. Litho Questa)

**1982** (1 July). *21st Birthday of Princess of Wales. T* **58** *and similar vert designs. Multicoloured. P* 14½ × 14.

| No. | Description | | |
|---|---|---|---|
| 493 | 50 c. Blenheim Palace | 50 | 30 |
| 494 | 60 c. As 50 c. | 60 | 35 |
| 495 | $1 Type **58** | 70 | 60 |
| 496 | $2 Type **58** | 1·50 | 1·25 |
| 497 | $3 Princess of Wales | 2·00 | 1·75 |
| 498 | $4 As $3 | 2·25 | 2·00 |
| 493/8 | *Set of* 6 | 6·75 | 5·25 |
| **MS**499 | 103 × 75 mm. $5 Princess Diana (*different*) | 2·75 | 2·75 |

Nos. 493, 495 and 497 come from sheetlets of 5 stamps and 1 label.

## PRICES OF SETS

Set prices are given for many issues, generally those containing three stamps or more. Definitive sets include one of each value or major colour change, but do not cover different perforations, die types or minor shades. Where a choice is possible the set prices are based on the cheapest versions of the stamps included in the listings.

59 "New Deal"—Soil Conservation

60 "Presentation of Christ in the Temple"

(Des M. Diamond. Litho Questa)

**1982** (27 July). *Birth Centenary of Franklin D. Roosevelt. T* **59** *and similar horiz designs. Multicoloured. P* 14.

| No. | Description | | |
|---|---|---|---|
| 500 | 30 c. Type **59** | 25 | 15 |
| 501 | 40 c. Roosevelt and George Washington Carver (scientist) | 35 | 15 |
| 502 | 70 c. Civilian conservation corps and reafforestation | 65 | 35 |
| 503 | $3 Roosevelt with Pres. Barclay of Liberia, Casablanca Conference, 1943 | 2·00 | 1·25 |
| 500/3 | *Set of* 4 | 3·00 | 1·90 |
| **MS**504 | 100 × 72 mm. $5 Roosevelt delivering address at Howard University | 2·00 | 2·10 |

**1982** (30 Aug). *Birth of Prince William of Wales. Nos.* 493/9 *optd with T* **171** *of Antigua.*

| No. | Description | | |
|---|---|---|---|
| 505 | 50 c. Blenheim Palace | 40 | 40 |
| 506 | 60 c. As 50 c. | 45 | 45 |
| 507 | $1 Type **58** | 60 | 60 |
| 508 | $2 Type **58** | 1·25 | 1·25 |
| 509 | $3 Princess of Wales | 1·75 | 1·75 |
| 510 | $4 As $3 | 2·00 | 2·00 |
| 505/10 | *Set of* 6 | 5·75 | 5·75 |
| **MS**511 | 103 × 75 mm. $5 Princess Diana (*different*) | 2·10 | 2·25 |

Nos. 505, 507 and 509 come from sheetlets of 5 stamps and 1 label.

(Des Clover Mill. Litho Format)

**1982** (2 Sept). *Easter. T* **60** *and similar vert designs depicting Easter paintings by Rembrandt. Multicoloured. P* 14½.

| No. | Description | | |
|---|---|---|---|
| 512 | 30 c. Type **60** | 40 | 15 |
| 513 | 60 c. "Descent from the Cross" | 55 | 20 |
| 514 | $2 "Raising of the Cross" | 1·75 | 1·00 |
| 515 | $4 "Resurrection of Christ" | 2·75 | 2·00 |
| 512/15 | *Set of* 4 | 5·00 | 3·00 |
| **MS**516 | 101 × 126 mm. $5 "The Risen Christ" | 3·00 | 2·40 |

61 "Santa Fe"

(Des Artists International. Litho Format)

**1982** (4 Oct). *Famous Trains of the World. T* **61** *and similar vert designs. Multicoloured. P* 15.

| No. | Description | | |
|---|---|---|---|
| 517 | 10 c. Type **61** | 50 | 15 |
| 518 | 40 c. "Mistral" | 1·00 | 20 |
| 519 | 70 c. "Rheingold" | 1·25 | 45 |
| 520 | $1 "ET 403" | 1·50 | 55 |
| 521 | $1.10, Steam locomotive *Mallard* | 1·75 | 70 |
| 522 | $2 "Tokaido" | 2·00 | 1·25 |
| 517/22 | *Set of* 6 | 7·25 | 3·00 |
| **MS**523 | 121 × 95 mm. $5 "Settebello" | 2·75 | 3·00 |

62 Footballers

(Des D. Miller. Litho Questa)

**1982** (2 Dec). *World Cup Football Championship Winners. T* **62** *and similar horiz designs. P* 14 × 13½.

| No. | Description | | |
|---|---|---|---|
| 524 | 60 c. multicoloured | 35 | 35 |
| 525 | $4 multicoloured | 1·75 | 1·75 |
| **MS**526 | 92 × 134 mm. $5 multicoloured | 2·00 | 2·00 |

(Litho Questa)

**1982** (14 Dec). *Christmas. Horiz designs as T* **42** *showing scenes from Walt Disney's cartoon film "The Rescuers". P* 13½.

| No. | Description | | |
|---|---|---|---|
| 527 | ½ c. multicoloured | 10 | 10 |
| 528 | 1 c. multicoloured | 10 | 10 |
| 529 | 2 c. multicoloured | 10 | 10 |
| 530 | 3 c. multicoloured | 10 | 10 |
| 531 | 4 c. multicoloured | 10 | 10 |
| 532 | 5 c. multicoloured | 10 | 10 |
| 533 | 10 c. multicoloured | 10 | 10 |
| 534 | $2.50, multicoloured | 1·00 | 1·00 |
| 535 | $3 multicoloured | 1·25 | 1·25 |
| 527/35 | *Set of* 9 | 2·25 | 2·25 |
| **MS**536 | 120 × 96 mm. $5 multicoloured | 2·25 | 2·25 |

63 Short-finned Pilot Whale

(Des Artists International. Litho Questa)

**1983** (10 Jan). *Save the Whales. T* **63** *and similar horiz designs. Multicoloured. P* 14.

| No. | Description | | |
|---|---|---|---|
| 537 | 10 c. Type **63** | 75 | 30 |
| 538 | 60 c. Dall's Porpoise | 1·75 | 80 |
| 539 | $1.10, Humpback Whale | 2·25 | 1·40 |
| 540 | $3 Bowhead Whale | 3·50 | 3·25 |
| 537/40 | *Set of* 4 | 7·50 | 5·25 |
| **MS**541 | 113×84 mm. $5 Spotted Dolphin | 3·50 | 4·00 |

64 "David and Goliath"

(Des Design Images. Litho Format)

**1983** (15 Feb). *500th Birth Anniv of Raphael. T* **64** *and similar horiz designs showing painting details. Multicoloured. P* 13½.

| No. | Description | | |
|---|---|---|---|
| 542 | 25 c. Type **64** | 20 | 15 |
| 543 | 30 c. "David sees Bathsheba" | 20 | 20 |
| 544 | 90 c. "Triumph of David" | 50 | 45 |
| 545 | $4 "Anointing of Solomon" | 1·60 | 1·75 |
| 542/5 | *Set of* 4 | 2·25 | 2·25 |
| **MS**546 | 126 × 101 mm. $5 "Anointing of David" | 1·75 | 2·00 |

65 Voice and Visual Communication

(Des Artists International. Litho Questa)

**1983** (7 Apr). *World Communications Year. T* **65** *and similar horiz designs. Multicoloured. P* 14.

| No. | Description | | |
|---|---|---|---|
| 547 | 30 c. Type **65** | 15 | 15 |
| 548 | 60 c. Ambulance | 25 | 25 |
| 549 | $1.10, Helicopters | 45 | 45 |
| 550 | $3 Satellite | 1·25 | 1·25 |
| 547/50 | *Set of* 4 | 1·90 | 1·90 |
| **MS**551 | 127×85 mm. $5 Diver and Bottle-nosed Dolphin | 2·25 | 2·50 |

66 Chrysler "Imperial Roadster", 1931

(Des R. Sauber. Litho Format)

**1983** (4 May). *75th Anniv of Model "T" Ford Car. T* **66** *and similar horiz designs showing cars of the 20th century. Multicoloured. P* 14½.

| No. | Description | | |
|---|---|---|---|
| 552 | 10 c. Type **66** | 10 | 10 |
| 553 | 30 c. Doble steam car, 1925 | 15 | 20 |
| 554 | 40 c. Ford "Mustang", 1965 | 20 | 25 |
| 555 | 60 c. Packard tourer, 1930 | 30 | 35 |
| 556 | 70 c. Mercer "Raceabout" 1913 | 35 | 40 |
| 557 | 90 c. Corvette "Stingray", 1963 | 40 | 45 |
| 558 | $1.10, Auburn "851 Supercharger Speedster", 1935 | 50 | 55 |
| 559 | $2.50, Pierce-Arrow "Silver Arrow", 1933 | 90 | 1·00 |
| 560 | $3 Duesenberg dual cowl phaeton, 1929 | 1·25 | 1·40 |
| 561 | $4 Mercedes-Benz "SSK", 1928 | 1·60 | 1·75 |
| 552/61 | *Set of* 10 | 5·00 | 5·75 |
| **MS**562 | 119 × 90 mm. $5 McFarlan "Knicker-bocker" cabriolet, 1923 | 2·00 | 2·50 |

Nos. 552/61 were each issued in sheets of eight stamps with a stamp-size label in the centre position.

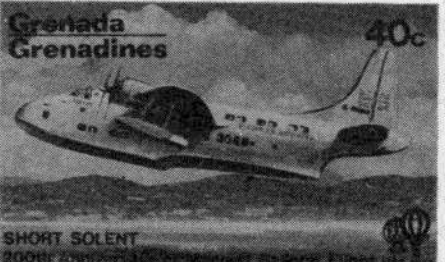


67 Short "Solent" Flying Boat

(Des W. Wright. Litho Questa)

**1983** (18 July). *Bicentenary of Manned Flight. T* **67** *and similar horiz designs. Multicoloured. P* 14.

563 40 c. Type **67** .. .. .. .. 60 20
564 70 c. Curtiss "R3C-2" seaplane .. .. .. 75 35
565 90 c. Hawker "Nimrod" biplane .. .. .. 90 40
566 $4 Montgolfier balloon .. .. .. 2·75 2·75
563/6 .. .. .. .. *Set of* 4 4·50 3·25
**MS**567 112 × 85 mm. $5 *Viktoria Luise* (airship) .. 2·75 3·00

**68** Goofy

**69** Weightlifting

(Litho Walsall)

**1983** (7 Nov). *Christmas. T* **68** *and similar vert designs showing Disney cartoon characters in scenes from "Jingle Bells" (Christmas carol). Multicoloured. P* 11.

568 ½ c. Type **68** .. .. .. .. 10 10
569 1 c. Clarabelle Cow .. .. .. .. 10 10
570 2 c. Donald Duck .. .. .. .. 10 10
571 3 c. Pluto .. .. .. .. 10 10
572 4 c. Morty and Ferdie .. .. .. .. 10 10
573 5 c. Huey, Dewey and Louie .. .. .. 10 10
574 10 c. Daisy and Chip 'n Dale .. .. .. 10 10
575 $2.50, Big Bad Wolf .. .. .. .. 2·75 2·75
576 $3 Mickey Mouse .. .. .. .. 3·25 3·25
568/76 .. .. .. .. *Set of* 9 6·00 6·00
**MS**577 102 × 124 mm. $5 Donald Duck in sleigh. P 13½ .. .. .. .. 5·00 4·50

(Des N. Waldman. Litho Questa)

**1984** (9 Jan). *Olympic Games, Los Angeles. T* **69** *and similar vert designs. Multicoloured. P* 14.

578 30 c. Type **69** .. .. .. .. 15 15
579 60 c. Gymnastics .. .. .. .. 35 35
580 70 c. Archery .. .. .. .. 40 40
581 $4 Sailing .. .. .. .. 1·75 1·90
578/81 .. .. .. .. *Set of* 4 2·40 2·50
**MS**582 70 × 102 mm. $5 Basketball .. .. 1·75 2·25

**70** Frangipani

**71** Goofy

(Des J. Cooter. Litho Questa)

**1984** (9 Apr). *Flowers. T* **70** *and similar vert designs. Multicoloured. P* 15.

583 15 c. Type **70** .. .. .. .. 15 10
584 40 c. Dwarf Poinciana .. .. .. .. 30 25
585 70 c. Walking Iris .. .. .. .. 55 45
586 $4 Lady's Slipper .. .. .. .. 2·25 2·50
583/6 .. .. .. .. *Set of* 4 3·00 3·00
**MS**587 66 × 57 mm. $5 Brazilian Glory Vine .. 2·75 3·00

(Litho Format)

**1984** (1 May). *Easter. T* **71** *and similar vert designs showing Disney cartoon characters with Easter hats. Multicoloured. P* 11.

588 ½ c. Type **71** .. .. .. .. 10 10
589 1 c. Chip and Dale .. .. .. .. 10 10
590 2 c. Daisy Duck and Huey .. .. .. 10 10
591 3 c. Daisy Duck .. .. .. .. 10 10
592 4 c. Donald Duck .. .. .. .. 10 10
593 5 c. Merlin and Madam Mim .. .. .. 10 10
594 10 c. Flower .. .. .. .. 10 10
595 $2 Minnie and Mickey Mouse .. .. .. 1·25 1·40
596 $4 Minnie Mouse .. .. .. .. 2·00 2·25
588/96 .. .. .. .. *Set of* 9 3·25 3·50
**MS**597 126 × 100 mm. $5 Minnie Mouse (*different*). P 13½ × 14 .. .. .. 2·75 3·00

**72** Bobolink

19TH U.P.U CONGRESS
HAMBURG

(**73**)

(Litho Questa)

**1984** (21 May). *Songbirds. T* **72** *and similar horiz designs. Multicoloured. P* 14.

598 40 c. Type **72** .. .. .. .. 1·40 90
599 50 c. Eastern Kingbird .. .. .. .. 1·60 1·10
600 60 c. Barn Swallow .. .. .. .. 1·75 1·25
601 70 c. Yellow Warbler .. .. .. .. 1·75 1·40
602 $1 Rose-breasted Grosbeak .. .. .. 2·00 1·60
603 $1.10, Yellowthroat .. .. .. .. 2·25 2·00
604 $2 Catbird .. .. .. .. 3·00 3·50
598/604 .. .. .. .. *Set of* 7 12·50 10·50
**MS**605 71 × 65 mm. $5 Fork-tailed Flycatcher .. 6·50 4·75

**1984** (19 June). *Universal Postal Union Congress, Hamburg. Nos.* 585/7 *optd with T* **73**.

606 70 c. Walking Iris .. .. .. .. 1·00 50
607 $4 Lady's Slipper .. .. .. .. 3·50 3·00
**MS**608 66 × 57 mm. $5 Brazilian Glory Vine .. 2·75 3·00

**74** *Geeststar*

(Litho Format)

**1984** (16 July). *Ships. T* **74** *and similar horiz designs. Multicoloured. P* 15.

609 30 c. Type **74** .. .. .. .. 1·00 40
610 60 c. *Daphne* .. .. .. .. 1·50 75
611 $1.10, *Southwind* .. .. .. .. 2·00 1·50
612 $4 *Oceanic* .. .. .. .. 4·50 4·50
609/12 .. .. .. .. *Set of* 4 8·00 6·50
**MS**613 108 × 80 mm. $5 Pirate ship .. .. 3·50 4·00

(Litho Questa)

**1984** (22 Aug). *450th Death Anniv of Correggio (painter). Multicoloured designs as T* **296** *of Grenada showing paintings. P* 14.

614 10 c. "The Hunt—Blowing the Horn" .. .. 10 10
615 30 c. "St. John the Evangelist" (*horiz*) .. 15 15
616 90 c. "The Hunt—The Deer's Head" .. .. 50 50
617 $4 "The Virgin crowned by Christ" (*horiz*) .. 2·00 2·00
614/17 .. .. .. .. *Set of* 4 2·50 2·50
**MS**618 73 × 63 mm. $5 "Martyrdom of the Four Saints" .. .. .. .. 2·40 3·00

(Litho Questa)

**1984** (22 Aug). *150th Birth Anniv of Edgar Degas (painter). Vert designs as T* **297** *of Grenada showing paintings. Multicoloured. P* 14.

619 25 c. "The Song of the Dog" .. .. .. 35 15
620 70 c. "Cafe-concert" .. .. .. .. 60 35
621 $1.10, "The Orchestra of the Opera" .. .. 1·25 1·00
622 $3 "The Dance Lesson" .. .. .. 2·50 2·25
619/22 .. .. .. .. *Set of* 4 4·25 3·25
**MS**623 53 × 73 mm. $5 "Madame Camus at the Piano" .. .. .. .. 2·40 3·00

(Des Bonny Redecker. Litho Questa)

**1984** (21 Sept). *"Ausipex" International Stamp Exhibition, Melbourne. Horiz designs as T* **298** *of Grenada. Multicoloured. P* 14.

624 $1.10, Queen Victoria Gardens, Melbourne 50 50
625 $4 Ayers Rock .. .. .. .. 2·00 2·00
**MS**626 107 × 76 mm. $5 River Yarra, Melbourne 2·50 3·00

**75** Col. Steven's Model (1825)

**76** Kawasaki "750" (1972)

(Des Bonny Redecker. Litho Format)

**1984** (3 Oct). *Railway Locomotives. T* **75** *and similar horiz designs. Multicoloured. P* 15.

627 20 c. Type **75** .. .. .. .. 65 25
628 50 c. *Royal George* (1827) .. .. .. 1·00 50
629 60 c. *Stourbridge Lion* (1829) .. .. .. 1·10 60
630 70 c. *Liverpool* (1830) .. .. .. .. 1·25 70
631 90 c. *South Carolina* (1832) .. .. .. 1·50 85
632 $1.10, *Monster* (1836) .. .. .. 1·75 1·00
633 $2 *Lafayette* (1837) .. .. .. .. 2·50 1·75
634 $4 *Lion* (1838) .. .. .. .. 4·00 3·25
627/34 .. .. .. .. *Set of* 8 12·50 8·00
**MS**635 Two sheets, each 100×70 mm. (a) $5 Sequin's locomotive (1829); (b) $5 *Der Adler* (1835) .. .. .. *Set of* 2 *sheets* 7·00 8·00

**1984** (28 Oct). *Opening of Point Saline International Airport. Nos.* 547, 549 *and* **MS**551 *optd as T* **300** *of Grenada.*

636 30 c. Type **65** .. .. .. .. 20 25
637 $1.10, Helicopters .. .. .. .. 70 75
**MS**638 127 × 85 mm. $5 Diver and dolphin .. 3·00 3·50

The overprint on No. **MS**638 appears on the sheet margin as for No. **MS**1371 of Grenada.

(Litho Questa)

**1984** (26 Nov). *Christmas. Walt Disney Cartoon Characters. Vert designs as T* **301** *of Grenada. Multicoloured. P* 12 ($2) *or* 13½ × 14 (*others*).

639 45 c. Donald Duck, and nephews knitting Christmas stockings .. .. .. 30 30
640 60 c. Donald Duck and nephews sitting on sofa .. .. .. .. 40 40
641 90 c. Donald Duck getting out of bed .. 55 55
642 $2 Donald Duck putting presents in wardrobe .. .. .. .. 1·25 1·25
643 $4 Nephews singing carols outside Donald Duck's window .. .. .. 2·25 2·25
639/43 .. .. .. .. *Set of* 5 4·25 4·25
**MS**644 126×102 mm. $5 Donald Duck filming nephews .. .. .. .. 3·50 3·00

No. 642 was printed in sheetlets of 8 stamps.

(Litho Questa)

**1985** (11 Feb). *Birth Bicentenary of John J. Audubon (ornithologist) (1st issue). Multicoloured designs as T* **198** *of Antigua showing original paintings. P* 14.

645 50 c. Blue-winged Teal .. .. .. 1·00 30
646 90 c. White Ibis .. .. .. .. 1·50 60
647 $1.10, Swallow-tailed Kite .. .. .. 2·00 1·25
648 $3 Moorhen ("Common Gallinule") .. .. 2·75 2·50
645/8 .. .. .. .. *Set of* 4 6·50 4·25
**MS**649 82 × 111 mm. $5 Mangrove Cuckoo (*vert*) 3·25 3·75

See also Nos. 736/40.

(Des BG Studio. Litho Questa)

**1985** (11 Mar). *Centenary of the Motor Cycle. T* **76** *and similar multicoloured designs. P* 14.

650 30 c. Type **76** .. .. .. .. 25 20
651 60 c. Honda "Goldwing GL1000" (1974) (*horiz*) .. .. .. .. 45 40
652 70 c. Kawasaki "Z650" (1976) (*horiz*) .. .. 55 45
653 $4 Honda "CBX" (1977) .. .. .. 2·40 2·25
650/3 .. .. .. .. *Set of* 4 3·25 3·00
**MS**654 113×76 mm. $5 BMW "R100RS" (1978) .. 2·75 3·00

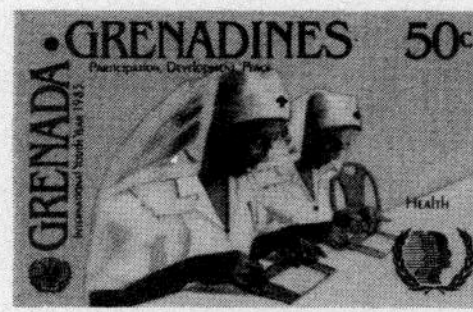


**77** Nursing Cadets folding Bandages (Health)

(Des Susan David. Litho Questa)

**1985** (15 Apr). *International Youth Year. T* **77** *and similar horiz designs. Multicoloured. P* 14.

655 50 c. Type **77** .. .. .. .. 45 35
656 70 c. Scuba diver and turtle (Environment) .. 60 50
657 $1.10, Yachting (Leisure) .. .. .. 1·00 90
658 $3 Boys playing chess (Education) .. .. 3·25 2·25
655/8 .. .. .. .. *Set of* 4 4·75 3·50
**MS**659 98 × 70 mm. $5 Hands touching globe .. 2·75 3·00

(Des BG Studio. Litho Questa)

**1985** (30 Apr). *40th Anniv of International Civil Aviation Organization. Horiz designs as T* **305** *of Grenada. Multicoloured. P* 14.

660 5 c. Lockheed "Lodestar" .. .. .. 20 10
661 70 c. Avro "748" Turboprop .. .. .. 1·00 45
662 $1.10, Boeing "727" .. .. .. .. 1·50 85
663 $3 Boeing "707" .. .. .. .. 2·75 2·25
660/3 .. .. .. .. *Set of* 4 5·00 3·25
**MS**664 87 × 68 mm. $4 Pilatus Britten-Norman "Islander" .. .. .. .. 3·00 3·00

**78** Lady Baden-Powell (founder) and Grenadian Guide Leaders

(Des D. Francis. Litho Questa)

**1985** (30 May). *75th Anniv of Girl Guide Movement. T* **78** *and similar multicoloured designs. P* 14.

665 30 c. Type **78** .. .. .. .. 25 20
666 50 c. Guide leader and guides on botany field trip .. .. .. .. 45 30
667 70 c. Guide leader and guides camping (*vert*) 70 45
668 $4 Guides sailing (*vert*) .. .. .. 2·50 2·25
665/8 .. .. .. .. *Set of* 4 3·50 3·00
**MS**669 100 × 73 mm. $5 Lord and Lady Baden-Powell (*vert*) .. .. .. .. 3·50 4·00

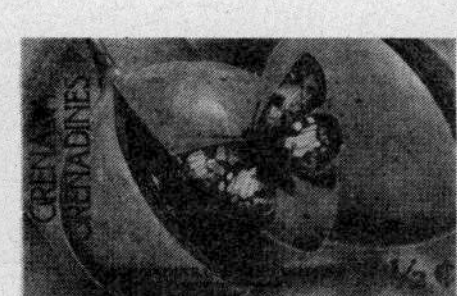

79 *Chiomara asychis*

80 The Queen Mother before Prince William's Christening

(Des I. MacLaury. Litho Questa)

**1985** (17 June)–**86**. *Butterflies. T* **79** *and similar horiz designs. Multicoloured. A. P* 14. *B. P* 12.

| | | A | | B | |
|---|---|---|---|---|---|
| 670 | ½ c. Type **79** | 10 | 10 | 10 | 10 |
| 671 | 1 c. *Anartia amathea* | 10 | 10 | 10 | 10 |
| 672 | 2 c. *Pseudolycaena marsyas* | 10 | 10 | 10 | 10 |
| 673 | 4 c. *Urbanus proteus* | 10 | 10 | 10 | 10 |
| 674 | 5 c. *Polygonus manueli* | 10 | 10 | 10 | 10 |
| 675 | 6 c. *Battus polydamas* | 10 | 10 | 10 | 10 |
| 676 | 10 c. *Eurema daira* | 10 | 10 | 10 | 10 |
| 677 | 12 c. *Phoebis agarithe* | 10 | 10 | 10 | 10 |
| 678 | 15 c. *Aphrissa statira* | 10 | 10 | 10 | 10 |
| 679 | 20 c. *Strymon simaethis* | 10 | 10 | 10 | 10 |
| 680 | 25 c. *Mestra cana* | 10 | 15 | 10 | 15 |
| 681 | 30 c. *Agraulis vanillae* | 10 | 15 | 10 | 15 |
| 682 | 40 c. *Junonia evarete* | 15 | 20 | 15 | 20 |
| 683 | 60 c. *Dryas julia* | 25 | 30 | 25 | 30 |
| 684 | 70 c. *Philaethria dido* | 30 | 35 | 30 | 35 |
| 685 | $1.10, *Hamadryas feronia* | 45 | 50 | 45 | 50 |
| 686 | $2.50, *Strymon rufofusca* | 1·00 | 1·10 | 1·00 | 1·10 |
| 687 | $5 *Appias drusilla* | 2·10 | 2·25 | 2·10 | 2·25 |
| 688 | $10 *Polites dictynna* | 4·25 | 4·50 | 4·25 | 4·50 |
| 688c | $20 *Euptychia cephus* | 8·50 | 8·75 | 8·50 | 8·75 |
| 670/88c | *Set of* 20 | 15·00 | 16·00 | 15·00 | 16·00 |

Dates of issue: 17.6.85, Nos. 670A/87A; 11.11.85, No. 688A; 1986, Nos. 670B/85B, 687B; 1.8.86, No. 688cA; 9.86, Nos. 686B, 688B; 5.89, No. 688cB.

(Des J.W. Litho Questa)

**1985** (3 July). *Life and Times of Queen Elizabeth the Queen Mother. T* **80** *and similar multicoloured designs. P* 14.

689 $1 Type **80** .. 55 60
690 $1.50, In winner's enclosure at Ascot (*horiz*) 80 85
691 $2.50, With Prince Charles at Garter ceremony, Windsor Castle .. 1·25 1·50
689/91 .. *Set of* 3 2·40 2·75
**MS**692 56×85 mm. $5 At opening of Royal York Hospice, London .. 2·75 3·00

Stamps as Nos. 689/91, but with face values of 70 c., $1.10 and $3, exist from additional sheetlets of 5 plus a label issued 28 January 1986. These also have changed background colours and are perforated 12½×12 ($1.10) or 12×12½ (others) (*Price for set of 3 stamps £2.10 mint*).

81 Scuba Diving

82 Queen Conch

(Des Marlise Nakaja. Litho Format)

**1985** (15 July). *Water Sports. T* **81** *and similar vert designs. Multicoloured. P* 15.

693 15 c. Type **81** .. 20 10
694 70 c. Boys playing in waterfall .. 55 45
695 90 c. Water skiing .. 65 55
696 $4 Swimming .. 2·25 2·25
693/6 .. *Set of* 4 3·25 3·00
**MS**697 103×78 mm. $5 Scuba diver .. 3·25 3·25

(Des Mary Walters. Litho Questa)

**1985** (1 Aug). *Marine Life. T* **82** *and similar horiz designs. Multicoloured. P* 14.

698 60 c. Type **82** .. 50 40
699 90 c. Porcupine Fish and Fire Coral .. 65 55
700 $1.10, Ghost Crab .. 80 70
701 $4 West Indies Spiny Lobster .. 2·25 2·25
698/701 .. *Set of* 4 3·75 3·50
**MS**702 299×70 mm. $5 Long-spined Urchin .. 3·50 3·75

(Des Susan David. Litho Questa)

**1985** (3 Sept). *300th Birth Anniv of Johann Sebastian Bach (composer). Vert designs as T* **206** *of Antigua. Multicoloured. P* 14.

703 15 c. Natural trumpet .. 30 10
704 60 c. Bass viol .. 60 40
705 $1.10, Flute .. 95 70
706 $3 Double flageolet .. 1·75 1·75
703/6 .. *Set of* 4 3·25 2·75
**MS**707 110×75 mm. $5 Johann Sebastian Bach 3·25 3·50

(Litho Format)

**1985** (4 Nov). *Royal Visit. Multicoloured designs as T* **207** *of Antigua. P* 14½.

708 10 c. Arms of Great Britain and Grenada .. 20 15
709 $1 Queen Elizabeth II (*vert*) .. 1·25 1·25
710 $4 Royal Yacht *Britannia* .. 3·75 3·75
708/10 .. *Set of* 3 4·75 4·75
**MS**711 111×83 mm. $5 Map of Grenada Grenadines .. 3·75 3·25

(Litho Format)

**1985** (22 Nov). *40th Anniv of United Nations Organization. Multicoloured designs as T* **208** *of Antigua showing United Nations (New York) stamps. P* 14½.

712 $1 Neil Armstrong (first man on Moon) and 1982 Peaceful Uses of Outer Space 20 c. .. 1·00 75
713 $2 Gandhi and 1971 Racial Equality Year 13 c. .. 2·50 1·90
714 $2.50, Maimonides (physician) and 1956 World Health Organization 3 c. .. 3·75 2·75
712/14 .. *Set of* 3 6·50 5·00
**MS**715 110×85 mm. $5 U.N. Under-Secretary Ralph Bunche (*vert*) .. 2·75 3·00

(Des Walt Disney Productions. Litho Questa)

**1985** (27 Nov). *150th Birth Anniv of Mark Twain (author). Horiz designs as T* **118** *of Anguilla showing Walt Disney cartoon characters illustrating scenes from "Letters from Hawaii". Multicoloured. P* 14×13½.

716 25 c. Minnie Mouse dancing the hula .. 15 20
717 50 c. Donald Duck surfing .. 30 35
718 $1.50, Donald Duck roasting marshmallow in volcano .. 90 95
719 $3 Mickey Mouse and Chip'n'Dale canoeing .. 1·75 1·90
716/19 .. *Set of* 4 2·75 3·00
**MS**720 127×102 mm. $5 Mickey Mouse with cat 3·00 3·25

(Des Walt Disney Productions. Litho Questa)

**1985** (27 Nov). *Birth Bicentenaries of Grimm Brothers (folklorists). Designs as T* **119** *of Anguilla, but vert, showing Walt Disney cartoon characters in scenes from "The Elves and the Shoemaker". Multicoloured. P* 13½×14.

721 30 c. Mickey Mouse as the unsuccessful Shoemaker .. 35 35
722 60 c. Two elves making shoes .. 60 60
723 70 c. The Shoemaker discovering the new shoes .. 70 70
724 $4 The Shoemaker's wife (Minnie Mouse) making clothes for the elves .. 2·75 2·75
721/4 .. *Set of* 4 4·00 4·00
**MS**725 126×101 mm. $5 The Shoemaker and his wife waving .. 3·25 3·50

83 "Madonna and Child" (Titian)

VISIT OF PRES. REAGAN

20 FEBRUARY 1986

(84)

(Des Mary Walters. Litho Format)

**1985** (23 Dec). *Christmas. Religious Paintings. T* **83** *and similar vert designs. Multicoloured. P* 15.

726 50 c. Type **83** .. 45 35
727 70 c. "Madonna and Child with St. Mary and John the Baptist" (Bugiardini) .. 55 45
728 $1.10, "Adoration of the Magi" (Di Fredi) .. 90 90
729 $3 "Madonna and Child with Young St. John the Baptist" (Bartolomeo) .. 2·25 2·50
726/9 .. *Set of* 4 3·75 3·75
**MS**730 112×81 mm. $5 "The Annunciation" (Botticelli) .. 3·00 3·75

(Des J. Iskowitz. Litho Questa)

**1986** (6 Jan). *Centenary of the Statue of Liberty. Multicoloured designs as T* **211** *of Dominica. P* 15.

731 5 c. Croton Reservoir, New York (1875) .. 10 10
732 10 c. New York Public Library (1986) .. 10 10
733 70 c. Old Boathouse, Central Park (1894) .. 35 40
734 $4 Boating in Central Park (1986) .. 2·00 2·10
731/4 .. *Set of* 4 2·25 2·40
**MS**735 103×76 mm. $5 Statue of Liberty (*vert*) .. 2·50 3·00

(Litho Questa)

**1986** (28 Jan). *Birth Bicentenary of John J. Audubon (ornithologist) (2nd issue). Horiz designs as T* **198** *of Antigua. Multicoloured. P* 12½×12.

736 50 c. Louisiana Heron .. 1·25 80
737 70 c. Black-crowned Night Heron .. 1·75 1·00
738 90 c. American Bittern .. 2·00 1·10
739 $4 Glossy Ibis .. 3·50 4·00
736/9 .. *Set of* 4 7·75 6·25
**MS**740 103×74 mm. $5 King Eider. P 14 .. 4·25 4·75

Nos. 736/9 were each issued in sheetlets of five stamps and one stamp-size label, which appears in the centre of the bottom row.

**1986** (20 Feb). *Visit of President Reagan of U.S.A. Nos.* 684A *and* 687A *optd with T* **84**.

741 70 c. *Philaethria dido* .. 1·00 1·00
742 $5 *Appias drusilla* .. 5·00 5·50

85 Two Footballers

86 *Hygrocybe firma*

(Des BG Studio. Litho Questa)

**1986** (18 Mar). *World Cup Football Championship, Mexico. Vert designs as T* **85** *showing footballers. P* 14.

743 10 c. multicoloured .. 20 15
744 70 c. multicoloured .. 90 80
745 $1 multicoloured .. 1·25 95
746 $4 multicoloured .. 3·75 3·75
743/6 .. *Set of* 4 5·50 4·75
**MS**747 86×104 mm. $5 multicoloured .. 3·50 4·00

(Des W. Hanson. Litho Questa)

**1986** (26 Mar). *Appearance of Halley's Comet (1st issue). Horiz designs as T* **123** *of Anguilla. Multicoloured. P* 14.

748 5 c. Nicholas Copernicus (astronomer) and Earl of Rosse's six foot reflector telescope .. 10 10
749 20 c. "Sputnik I" (first satellite) orbiting Earth, 1957 .. 20 20
750 40 c. Tycho Brahe's notes and sketch of 1577 Comet .. 30 30
751 $4 Edmond Halley and 1682 Comet .. 2·25 2·75
748/51 .. *Set of* 4 2·50 3·00
**MS**752 101×70 mm. $5 Halley's Comet .. 2·50 3·00

The captions of Nos. 750/1 are transposed.

(Litho Questa)

**1986** (21 Apr). *60th Birthday of Queen Elizabeth II. Vert designs as T* **125** *of Anguilla. P* 14.

753 2 c. black and yellow .. 10 15
754 $1.50, multicoloured .. 1·00 1·00
755 $4 multicoloured .. 2·25 2·50
753/5 .. *Set of* 3 3·00 3·25
**MS**756 120×85 mm. $5 black and grey-brown .. 3·00 3·50

Designs:—2 c. Princesses Elizabeth and Margaret, Windsor Park, 1933; $1.50, Queen Elizabeth; $4 In Sydney, Australia, 1970; $5 The Royal Family, Coronation Day, 1937.

(Des Walt Disney Productions. Litho Format)

**1986** (22 May). *"Ameripex '86" International Stamp Exhibition, Chicago. Horiz designs as T* **212** *of Dominica showing Walt Disney cartoon characters. Multicoloured. P* 11.

757 30 c. Donald Duck riding mule in Grand Canyon .. 45 45
758 60 c. Daisy Duck, Timothy Mouse and Dumbo on Golden Gate Bridge, San Francisco .. 70 70
759 $1 Mickey Mouse and Goofy in fire engine and Chicago Watertower .. 1·25 1·25
760 $3 Mickey Mouse as airmail pilot and White House .. 3·00 3·00
757/60 .. *Set of* 4 5·00 5·00
**MS**761 126×101 mm. $5 Donald Duck and Mickey Mouse watching Halley's Comet over Statue of Liberty. P 14×13½ .. 3·50 4·00

(Litho Questa)

**1986** (1 July). *Royal Wedding. Vert designs as T* **213** *of Antigua. Multicoloured. P* 14.

762 60 c. Prince Andrew and Miss Sarah Ferguson .. 45 45
763 70 c. Prince Andrew in car .. 55 55
764 $4 Prince Andrew with naval helicopter .. 2·50 2·50
762/4 .. *Set of* 3 3·25 3·25
**MS**765 88×88 mm. $5 Prince Andrew and Miss Sarah Ferguson (*different*) .. 5·00 5·00

(Des BG Studio. Litho Format)

**1986** (15 July). *Mushrooms of the Lesser Antilles. T* **86** *and similar vert designs. Multicoloured. P* 15.

766 15 c. Type **86** .. 60 20
767 50 c. *Xerocomus coccolobae* .. 1·40 60
768 $2 *Volvariella cubensis* .. 3·00 2·25
769 $3 *Lactarius putidus* .. 4·25 3·50
766/9 .. *Set of* 4 8·50 6·00
**MS**770 76×80 mm. $5 *Leptonia caeruleocapitata* 7·50 7·50

87 Giant Atlantic Pyram

88 Common Opossum

(Des L. Birmingham. Litho Format)

**1986** (1 Aug). *Sea Shells. T* **87** *and similar multicoloured designs. P* 15.

771 15 c. Type **87** .. 60 20
772 50 c. Beau's Murex .. 1·40 60
773 $1.10, West Indian Fighting Conch .. 2·25 1·90
774 $4 Alphabet Coral shell .. 4·50 4·25
771/4 .. *Set of* 4 8·00 6·25
**MS**775 109×75 mm. $5 Brown-lined Paper Bubble (*horiz*) .. 7·00 7·50

**1986** (15 Sept). *World Cup Football Championship Winners, Mexico. Nos.* 743/7 *optd with T* **216** *of Antigua in gold.*

776 **85** 10 c. multicoloured .. 20 20
777 – 70 c. multicoloured .. 65 65
778 – $1 multicoloured .. 85 85
779 – $4 multicoloured .. 2·75 3·00
776/9 .. *Set of* 4 4·00 4·25
**MS**780 86×104 mm. $5 multicoloured .. 7·00 7·50

(Des Dot and S. Barlowe. Litho Format)

**1986** (15 Sept). *Wildlife. T* **88** *and similar multicoloured designs. P* 15.
781 10 c. Type **88** .. .. .. .. .. 20 20
782 30 c. Giant Toad .. .. .. .. .. 40 40
783 60 c. Land Tortoise (*Testudo denticulata*) .. 80 80
784 70 c. Murine Opossum (*vert*) .. .. .. 85 85
785 90 c. Burmese Mongoose (*vert*) .. .. 90 90
786 $1.10, Nine-banded Armadillo .. .. 1·00 1·00
787 $2 Agouti .. .. .. .. .. 1·75 2·00
788 $3 Humpback Whale .. .. .. 3·50 3·75
781/8 .. .. .. .. .. *Set of* 8 8·50 9·00
**MS**789 Two sheets, each 103×72 mm. (a) $5 Mona Monkey (*vert*) (b) $5 Iguana *Set of 2 sheets* 11·00 12·00

**1986** (15 Oct). *Appearance of Halley's Comet (2nd issue). Nos.* 748/52 *optd with T* **218** *of Antigua (in silver on* 20 *c.,* $4 *and* $5).
790 5 c. Nicholas Copernicus (astronomer) and Earl of Rosse's six foot reflector telescope .. .. .. .. .. 30 25
791 20 c. "Sputnik I" (first satellite) orbiting Earth, 1957 .. .. .. .. .. 50 35
792 40 c. Tycho Brahe's notes and sketch of 1577 Comet .. .. .. .. .. 65 45
793 $4 Edmond Halley and 1682 Comet .. 3·00 3·50
790/3 .. .. .. .. .. *Set of* 4 4·00 4·00
**MS**794 102×70 mm. $5 Halley's Comet .. 3·75 4·25

(Des Walt Disney Co. Litho Format)

**1986** (3 Nov). *Christmas. Multicoloured designs as T* **220** *of Antigua showing Walt Disney cartoon characters. P* 11.
795 25 c. Chip n'Dale with hummingbird .. 15 15
796 30 c. Robin delivering card to Mickey Mouse (*vert*) .. .. .. .. .. 15 20
797 50 c. Piglet, Pooh and Jose Carioca on beach 25 30
798 60 c. Grandma Duck feeding birds (*vert*) .. 30 35
799 70 c. Cinderella and birds with mistletoe (*vert*) .. .. .. .. .. 35 40
800 $1.50, Huey, Dewey and Louie windsurfing 75 80
801 $3 Mickey Mouse and Morty on beach with turtle .. .. .. .. .. 1·50 1·75
802 $4 Kittens playing on piano (*vert*) .. 2·00 2·25
795/802 .. .. .. .. .. *Set of* 8 5·00 5·50
**MS**803 Two sheets, each 127×102 mm. (a) $5 Mickey Mouse and Willie the Whale. P 14×13½. (b) $5 Bambi, Thumper and Blossom in snow (*vert*). P 13½×14 *Set of 2 sheets* 8·00 8·50

**89** Cycling **90** Aston-Martin "Volanté" (1984)

(Des BG Studio. Litho Format)

**1986** (18 Nov). *Olympic Games, Seoul, South Korea* (1988). *T* **89** *and similar vert designs. Multicoloured. P* 15.
804 10 c.+5 c. Type **89** .. .. .. .. 25 30
805 50 c.+20 c. Sailing .. .. .. .. 60 70
806 70 c.+30 c. Gymnastics .. .. .. 75 85
807 $2+$1 Horse trials .. .. .. 2·25 2·50
804/7 .. .. .. .. .. *Set of* 4 3·50 4·00
**MS**808 80×100 mm. $3+$1 Marathon .. .. 3·50 4·00
The premiums on Nos. 804/8 were to support the participation of the Grenada team.

(Des W. Wright. Litho Format)

**1986** (20 Nov). *Centenary of Motoring. T* **90** *and similar horiz designs. Multicoloured. P* 15.
809 10 c. Type **90** .. .. .. .. .. 20 20
810 30 c. Jaguar "Mk V" (1948) .. .. .. 30 30
811 60 c. Nash "Ambassador" (1956) .. .. 45 45
812 70 c. Toyota "Supra" (1984) .. .. .. 50 50
813 90 c. Ferrari "Testarossa" (1985) .. .. 65 65
814 $1 BMW "501B" (1955) .. .. .. 70 70
815 $2 Mercedes-Benz "280 SL" (1968) .. .. 1·25 1·25
816 $3 Austro-Daimler "ADR8" (1932) .. .. 1·75 1·75
809/16 .. .. .. .. .. *Set of* 8 5·25 5·25
**MS**817 Two sheets, each 116 × 85 mm. (a) $5 Morgan "+8" (1977). (b) $5 Checker taxi *Set of 2 sheets* 8·50 9·00

(Litho Questa)

**1986** (19 Dec). *Birth Centenary of Marc Chagall (artist). Designs as T* **225** *of Antigua, showing various paintings. P* 13½×14 (*vert*) *or* 14×13½ (*horiz*).
818/57 $1.10×40 multicoloured .. *Set of* 40 18·00 19·00
**MS**858 Ten sheets, each 110×95 mm. $5×10 multicoloured (*each* 104×89 *mm*). Imperf *Set of* 10 *sheets* 20·00 22·00
Although announced as all being released on 19 December 1986 the issue was distributed in ten parts, each of four stamps and one miniature sheet, at monthly intervals.

(Des J. Iskowitz. Litho Format)

**1987** (5 Feb). *America's Cup Yachting Championship. Multicoloured designs as T* **222** *of Antigua. P* 15.
859 25 c. *Defender*, 1895 .. .. .. .. 40 25
860 45 c. *Caletea*, 1886 .. .. .. .. 55 35
861 70 c. *Azzurra*, 1981 .. .. .. .. 70 55
862 $4 *Australia II*, 1983 .. .. .. 2·00 2·50
859/62 .. .. .. .. .. *Set of* 4 3·25 3·25
**MS**863 113×83 mm. $5 *Columbia* defeating *Shamrock*, 1899 (*horiz*) .. .. .. 5·00 5·50

(Des Mary Walters. Litho Format)

**1987** (27 Apr). 500*th Anniv of Discovery of America by Columbus* (1992) (1*st issue*). *Vert designs as T* **322** *of Grenada. Multicoloured. P* 15.
864 15 c. Christopher Columbus .. .. .. 20 20
865 30 c. Queen Isabella of Castile .. .. 20 20
866 50 c. *Santa Maria* .. .. .. .. 35 35
867 60 c. Claiming the New World for Spain .. 35 35
868 90 c. Early Spanish map of Lesser Antilles .. 55 55
869 $1 King Ferdinand of Aragon .. .. 60 60
870 $2 Fort La Navidad (drawing by Columbus) 1·25 1·25
871 $3 Galley and Caribs, Hispaniola (drawing by Columbus) .. .. .. .. 1·75 1·75
864/71 .. .. .. .. .. *Set of* 8 4·75 4·75
**MS**872 Two sheets, 104×72 mm. (a) $5 Caribs pearl fishing. (b) $5 *Santa Maria* at anchor *Set of 2 sheets* 7·50 8·50
See also Nos. 1191/5 and 1224/32.

(Des W. Wright. Litho Questa)

**1987** (18 May). *Milestones of Transportation. Horiz designs as T* **226** *of Antigua. Multicoloured. P* 14.
873 10 c. Saunders Roe "SR-N1" (first hovercraft), 1959 .. .. .. .. .. 10 10
874 15 c. Bugatti "Royale" (largest car), 1931 .. 15 15
875 30 c. Aleksei Leonov and "Voskhod II" (first spacewalk), 1965 .. .. .. .. 25 25
876 50 c. C.S.S. *Hunley* (first submarine to sink enemy ship), 1864 .. .. .. .. 35 35
877 60 c. Rolls Royce "Flying Bedstead" (first VTOL aircraft), 1954 .. .. .. .. 40 40
878 70 c. *Jenny Lind* (first mass produced locomotive class), 1847 .. .. .. .. 45 45
879 90 c. Duryea "Buggvaut" (first U.S. petrol-driven car), 1893 .. .. .. .. 55 55
880 $1.50, Steam locomotive, Metropolitan Railway, London (first underground line), 1863 .. .. .. .. .. 1·00 1·00
881 $2 S.S. *Great Britain* (first transatlantic crossing by screw-steamship), 1843 .. 1·25 1·25
882 $3 "Budweiser Rocket" (fastest car), 1979 1·75 1·75
873/82 .. .. .. .. .. *Set of* 10 5·50 5·50

(Des Susan Barrasi. Litho Format)

**1987** (15 June). *"Capex '87" International Stamp Exhibition, Toronto. Game Fishes. Multicoloured designs as T* **323** *of Grenada, but horiz. P* 15.
883 6 c. Yellow Chub .. .. .. .. 15 15
884 30 c. Kingfish .. .. .. .. .. 35 25
885 50 c. Mako Shark .. .. .. .. 45 45
886 60 c. Dolphinfish .. .. .. .. 50 50
887 90 c. Bonito .. .. .. .. .. 65 65
888 $1.10, Cobia .. .. .. .. .. 90 90
889 $3 Great Tarpon .. .. .. .. 2·00 2·25
890 $4 Swordfish .. .. .. .. 2·50 2·75
883/90 .. .. .. .. .. *Set of* 8 6·75 7·25
**MS**891 100×70 mm. (a) $5 Jewfish. (b) $5 Amberjack .. .. .. *Set of 2 sheets* 8·50 9·00

(Litho Questa)

**1987** (5 Aug). *Centenary of Statue of Liberty* (1986) (2*nd issue*). *Multicoloured designs as T* **227** *of Antigua. P* 14.
892 10 c. Cleaning face of Statue .. .. 10 10
893 15 c. Commemorative lapel badges .. .. 15 15
894 25 c. Band playing and Statue .. .. 25 25
895 30 c. Band on parade and Statue .. .. 25 25
896 45 c. Face of Statue .. .. .. .. 40 40
897 50 c. Cleaning head of Statue (*horiz*) .. 45 45
898 60 c. Models of Statue (*horiz*) .. .. 50 50
899 70 c. Small boat flotilla (*horiz*) .. .. 55 55
900 $1 Unveiling ceremony .. .. .. 75 75
901 $1.10, Statue and Manhattan skyline .. 80 80
902 $2 Parade of warships .. .. .. 1·40 1·40
903 $3 Making commemorative flags .. .. 1·75 1·75
892/903 .. .. .. .. .. *Set of* 12 6·50 6·50

(Litho Questa)

**1987** (9 Sept). *Great Scientific Discoveries. Horiz designs as T* **325** *of Grenada. Multicoloured. P* 14.
904 60 c. Newton medal .. .. .. .. 55 40
905 $1 Louis Daguerre (inventor of daguerreotype) .. .. .. .. .. 80 65
906 $2 Antoine Lavoisier and apparatus .. 1·60 1·75
907 $3 Rudolf Diesel and diesel engine .. 3·25 3·50
904/7 .. .. .. .. .. *Set of* 4 5·50 5·50
**MS**908 105×75 mm. $5 Halley's comet .. .. 5·50 6·00
No. 907 is inscribed "JAMES WATT" in error.

(Litho Questa)

**1987** (1 Nov). *Bicentenary of U.S. Constitution. Multicoloured designs as T* **232** *of Antigua. P* 14.
909 10 c. Washington addressing delegates, Constitutional Convention .. .. .. .. 20 15
910 50 c. Flag and State Seal, Georgia .. .. 60 50
911 60 c. Capitol, Washington (*vert*) .. .. 60 50
912 $4 Thomas Jefferson (statesman) (*vert*) .. 3·00 3·25
909/12 .. .. .. .. .. *Set of* 4 4·00 4·00
**MS**913 105×75 mm. $5 Alexander Hamilton (New York delegate) (*vert*) .. .. .. 3·00 3·75
Nos. 909/12 were each issued in sheetlets of five stamps and one stamp-size label, which appears in the centre of the bottom row.

(Des Walt Disney Co. Litho Questa)

**1987** (16 Nov). *"Hafnia '87" International Stamp Exhibition, Copenhagen. Designs as T* **328** *of Grenada, but horiz, illustrating Hans Christian Andersen's fairy tales. Multicoloured. P* 14×13½.
914 25 c. Donald and Daisy Duck in "The Swineherd" .. .. .. .. .. 20 20
915 30 c. Mickey Mouse, Donald and Daisy Duck in "What the Good Man Does is Always Right" .. .. .. .. .. 20 20
916 50 c. Mickey and Minnie Mouse in "Little Tuk" .. .. .. .. .. 35 35
917 60 c. Minnie Mouse and Ferdie in "The World's Fairest Rose" .. .. .. 35 35
918 70 c. Mickey Mouse in "The Garden of Paradise" .. .. .. .. .. 45 45
919 $1.50, Goofy and Mickey Mouse in "The Naughty Boy" .. .. .. .. 90 90
920 $3 Goofy in "What the Moon Saw" .. .. 1·75 1·75
921 $4 Alice as "Thumbelina" .. .. .. 2·25 2·25
914/21 .. .. .. .. .. *Set of* 8 5·75 5·75
**MS**922 Two sheets, each 127×101 mm. (a) $5 Daisy Duck in "Hans Clodhopper". (b) $5 Aunt Matilda and Mickey Mouse in "Elder-Tree Mother" .. .. .. *Set of 2 sheets* 8·50 9·00

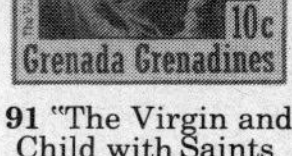

**91** "The Virgin and Child with Saints Martin and Agnes" **92** Scout signalling with Semaphore Flags

(Litho Questa)

**1987** (15 Dec). *Christmas. Religious Paintings by El Greco. T* **91** *and similar vert designs. Multicoloured. P* 14.
923 10 c. Type **91** .. .. .. .. .. 20 15
924 50 c. "St. Agnes" (detail from "The Virgin and Child with Saints Martin and Agnes") .. .. .. .. .. 60 50
925 60 c. "The Annunciation" .. .. .. 60 50
926 $4 "The Holy Family with St. Anne" .. 3·50 4·00
923/6 .. .. .. .. .. *Set of* 4 4·50 4·75
**MS**927 75×101 mm. $5 "The Adoration of the Shepherds" .. .. .. .. .. 6·00 6·50

(Des and litho Questa)

**1988** (15 Feb). *Royal Ruby Wedding. Vert designs as T* **234** *of Antigua. Multicoloured. P* 14.
928 20 c. deep brown, black and light green .. 20 15
929 30 c. deep brown and black .. .. .. 25 20
930 $2 multicoloured .. .. .. .. 1·40 1·60
931 $3 multicoloured .. .. .. .. 2·00 2·25
928/31 .. .. .. .. .. *Set of* 4 3·50 3·75
**MS**932 76×100 mm. $5 multicoloured .. .. 3·75 4·25
Designs:—20 c. Queen Elizabeth II with Princess Anne, *c.* 1957; 30 c. Wedding photograph, 1947; $2 Queen with Prince Charles and Princess Anne, *c.* 1955; $3 Queen Elizabeth (from photo by Tim Graham), 1980; $5 Princess Elizabeth in wedding dress, 1947.

(Des Walt Disney Company. Litho Questa)

**1988** (13 Apr). *Olympic Games, Seoul. Multicoloured designs as T* **331** *of Grenada, showing Walt Disney cartoon characters as Olympic competitors. P* 14×13½.
933 1 c. Minnie Mouse as rhythmic gymnast (*horiz*) .. .. .. .. .. 10 10
934 2 c. Pete and Goofy as pankration wrestlers (*horiz*) .. .. .. .. .. 10 10
935 3 c. Huey and Dewey as synchronized swimmers (*horiz*) .. .. .. .. 10 10
936 4 c. Huey, Dewey and Louey in hoplite race (*horiz*) .. .. .. .. .. 10 10
937 5 c. Clarabelle and Daisy Duck playing baseball (*horiz*) .. .. .. .. 10 10
938 10 c. Goofy and Donald Duck in horse race (*horiz*) .. .. .. .. .. 10 10
939 $6 Donald Duck and Uncle Scrooge McDuck windsurfing (*horiz*) .. .. 2·75 3·00
940 $7 Mickey Mouse in chariot race (*horiz*) .. 3·25 3·50
933/40 .. .. .. .. .. *Set of* 8 5·75 6·25
**MS**941 Two sheets, each 127×101 mm. (a) $5 Mickey Mouse throwing discus in pentathlon. (b) $5 Donald Duck playing tennis. P 13½×14 *Set of 2 sheets* 4·75 5·50

(Des J. Martin. Litho Questa)

**1988** (3 May). *World Scout Jamboree, Australia. T* **92** *and similar multicoloured designs. P* 14.
942 50 c. Type **92** .. .. .. .. .. 30 35
943 70 c. Canoeing .. .. .. .. .. 35 40
944 $1 Cooking over campfire (*horiz*) .. .. 50 55
945 $3 Scouts around campfire (*horiz*) .. .. 1·60 2·00
942/5 .. .. .. .. .. *Set of* 4 2·50 3·00
**MS**946 110×77 mm. $5 Erecting tent (*horiz*) .. 2·75 3·25

(Des Mary Walters. Litho Questa)

**1988** (31 May). *Birds. Designs as T* **334** *of Grenada, but horiz. Multicoloured. P* 14.
947 20 c. Yellow-crowned Night Heron .. .. 30 25
948 25 c. Brown Pelican .. .. .. .. 30 25
949 45 c. Audubon's Shearwater .. .. .. 40 35
950 60 c. Red-footed Booby .. .. .. 50 40
951 70 c. Bridled Tern .. .. .. .. 55 45
952 90 c. Red-billed Tropic Bird .. .. .. 70 60
953 $3 Blue-winged Teal .. .. .. 1·75 2·00
954 $4 Sora Rail .. .. .. .. .. 2·00 2·50
947/54 .. .. .. .. .. *Set of* 8 6·00 6·25
**MS**955 Two sheets, each 105×75 mm. (a) $5 Purple-throated Carib. (b) $5 Little Blue Heron *Set of 2 sheets* 4·75 6·00

(Litho Questa)

**1988** (15 June). 500*th Birth Anniv of Titian (artist). Vert designs as T* **238** *of Antigua. Multicoloured. P* 13½×14.
956 15 c. "Man with Blue Eyes" .. .. .. 10 10
957 30 c. "The Three Ages of Man" (detail) .. 15 15
958 60 c. "Don Diego Mendoza" .. .. .. 25 30
959 75 c. "Emperor Charles V seated" .. .. 35 40
960 $1 "A Young Man in a Fur" .. .. .. 45 50
961 $2 "Tobias and the Angel" .. .. .. 90 95
962 $3 "Pietro Bembo" .. .. .. .. 1·40 1·50
963 $4 "Pier Luigi Farnese" .. .. .. 1·75 1·90
956/63 .. .. .. .. .. *Set of* 8 4·75 5·25
**MS**964 110×95 mm. (a) $5 "Sacred and Profane Love" (detail). (b) $5 "Venus and Adonis" (detail) *Set of 2 sheets* 6·50 7·50

(Des W. Hanson. Litho Questa)

**988** (1 July). *Airships. Multicoloured designs as T* **336** *of Grenada. P* 14.
65 10 c. *Hindenberg* over Sugarloaf Mountain, Rio de Janeiro, 1937 (*horiz*) .. .. 10 10
66 20 c. *Hindenberg* over New York, 1937 (*horiz*) .. .. .. .. 10 10
67 30 c. U.S. Navy airships on Atlantic escort duty, 1944 (*horiz*) .. .. 15 15
68 40 c. *Hindenberg* approaching Lakehurst, 1937 .. .. .. .. 20 25
69 60 c. *Graf Zeppelin* and *Hindenberg* over Germany, 1936 .. .. .. 25 30
70 70 c. *Hindenberg* and *Los Angeles* moored at Lakehurst, 1936 (*horiz*) .. .. 30 35
71 $1 *Graf Zeppelin II* over Dover, 1939 .. 45 50
72 $2 *Deutschland* on scheduled passenger flight, 1912 (*horiz*) .. .. 80 1·00
73 $3 *Graf Zeppelin* over Dome of the Rock, Jerusalem, 1931 (*horiz*) .. .. 1·25 1·50
74 $4 *Hindenberg* over Olympic stadium, Berlin, 1936 (*horiz*) .. .. 1·60 1·90
65/74 .. .. .. .. *Set of* 10 4·50 5·50
**IS**975 Two sheets (a) 76×95 mm. $5 *Graf Zeppelin*, 1933. (b) 95×76 mm. $5 *Graf Zeppelin*, 1931 (*horiz*) .. .. .. *Set of* 2 *sheets* 5·50 6·00

**93** Bambi and his Mother

(Des Walt Disney Co. Litho Questa)

**988** (25 July). *Disney Animal Cartoon Films. T* **93** *and similar designs. P* 14×13½.
76/1029 30 c.×54 multicoloured .. *Set of* 54 6·50 8·00
**IS**1030 Six sheets, each 127×102 mm. $5×6 multicoloured. P 14×13½ (*horiz*) or 13½×14 (*vert*) .. .. .. *Set of* 6 *sheets* 13·00 14·00
Nos. 976/1029 (issued as six sheetlets each of nine different esigns) and No. **MS**1030 depict scenes from *Bambi*, *Dumbo* ($5 ert), *Lady and The Tramp* ($5 vert), *The Aristocats*, *The Fox nd the Hound* and *101 Dalmatians*.

(Des Walt Disney Co. Litho Questa)

**988** (1 Aug). *"Sydpex '88" National Stamp Exhibition, Sydney and 60th Birthday of Mickey Mouse. Horiz designs as T* **337** *of Grenada. Multicoloured. P* 14×13½.
031 1 c. Mickey Mouse conducting at Sydney Opera House .. .. .. 10 10
032 2 c. Mickey Mouse and Donald Duck at Ayers Rock .. .. .. 10 10
033 3 c. Goofy and Mickey Mouse on sheep station .. .. .. 10 10
034 4 c. Goofy and Mickey Mouse at Lone Pine Koala Sanctuary .. .. 10 10
035 5 c. Mickey Mouse, Donald Duck and Goofy playing Australian football .. 10 10
036 10 c. Mickey Mouse and Goofy camel racing 10 10
037 $5 Donald Duck and his nephews bowling .. .. .. .. 2·40 2·75
038 $6 Mickey Mouse with America's Cup trophy and *Australia II* (yacht) .. 2·75 3·25
031/8 .. .. .. .. *Set of* 8 5·00 6·00
**MS**1039 Two sheets, each 127×102 mm. (a) $5 Goofy diving on Great Barrier Reef. (b) $5 Donald Duck, Mickey and Minnie Mouse at beach barbecue .. .. .. *Set of* 2 *sheets* 4·50 5·00

(Des W. Wright. Litho Questa)

**988** (30 Sept). *Flowering Trees and Shrubs. Multicoloured designs as T* **339** *of Grenada. P* 14.
040 10 c. Potato Tree (*vert*) .. .. .. 15 15
041 20 c. Wild Cotton .. .. .. .. 15 15
042 30 c. Shower of Gold (*vert*) .. .. 20 20
043 60 c. Napoleon's Button (*vert*) .. .. 35 30
044 90 c. Geiger Tree .. .. .. .. 60 55
045 $1 Fern Tree .. .. .. .. 70 65
046 $2 French Cashew .. .. .. 1·25 1·50
047 $4 Amherstia (*vert*) .. .. .. 2·00 2·50
040/7 .. .. .. .. *Set of* 8 5·00 5·50
**IS**1048 Two sheets, each 117×88 mm. (a) $5 African Tulip Tree (*vert*). (b) $5 Swamp Immortelle .. .. .. *Set of* 2 *sheets* 4·25 4·75

(Des W. Wright. Litho B.D.T.)

**988** (7 Oct). *Cars. Vert designs as T* **335** *of Grenada. Multicoloured. P* 13.
049 $2 Doble "Series E", 1925 .. .. 1·00 1·00
a. Sheetlet. Nos. 1049/58 .. .. 9·00
050 $2 Alvis "12/50", 1926 .. .. 1·00 1·00
051 $2 Sunbeam 3-litre, 1927 .. .. 1·00 1·00
052 $2 Franklin "Airman", 1928 .. .. 1·00 1·00
053 $2 Delage "D8S", 1929 .. .. 1·00 1·00
054 $2 Mors, 1897 .. .. .. 1·00 1·00
055 $2 Peerless "Green Dragon", 1904 .. 1·00 1·00
056 $2 Pope-Hartford, 1909 .. .. 1·00 1·00
057 $2 Daniels "Submarine Speedster", 1920 1·00 1·00
058 $2 McFarlan 9.3 litre, 1922 .. .. 1·00 1·00
059 $2 Frazer Nash "Lemans" replica, 1949 1·00 1·00
a. Sheetlet. Nos. 1059/68 .. .. 9·00
060 $2 Pegaso "Z102", 1953 .. .. 1·00 1·00
061 $2 Siata "Spyder V-8", 1953 .. .. 1·00 1·00
1062 $2 Kurtis-Offenhauser, 1953 .. .. 1·00 1·00
1063 $2 Kaiser-Darrin, 1954 .. .. 1·00 1·00
1064 $2 Tracta, 1930 .. .. .. 1·00 1·00
1065 $2 Maybach "Zeppelin", 1932 .. .. 1·00 1·00
1066 $2 Railton "Light Sports", 1934 .. .. 1·00 1·00
1067 $2 Hotchkiss, 1936 .. .. .. 1·00 1·00
1068 $2 Mercedes-Benz "W163", 1939 .. 1·00 1·00
1069 $2 Aston Martin "Vantage V8", 1982 .. 1·00 1·00
a. Sheetlet. Nos. 1069/78 .. .. 9·00
1070 $2 Porsche "956", 1982 .. .. 1·00 1·00
1071 $2 Lotus "Esprit Turbo", 1983 .. .. 1·00 1·00
1072 $2 McLaren "MP4/2", 1984 .. .. 1·00 1·00
1073 $2 Mercedes-Benz "190E 2.3-16", 1985 .. 1·00 1·00
1074 $2 Ferrari "250 GT Lusso", 1963 .. 1·00 1·00
1075 $2 Porsche "904", 1964 .. .. 1·00 1·00
1076 $2 Volvo "P1800", 1967 .. .. 1·00 1·00
1077 $2 McLaren-Chevrolet "M8D", 1970 .. 1·00 1·00
1078 $2 Jaguar "XJ6", 1981 .. .. 1·00 1·00
1049/78 .. .. .. .. *Set of* 30 27·00 27·00
Nos. 1049/58, 1059/68 and 1069/78 were each printed together, *se-tenant*, in sheetlets of 10.

(Des Walt Disney Co. Litho Questa)

**1988** (1 Dec). *"Mickey's Christmas Parade". Multicoloured designs as T* **246** *of Antigua showing Walt Disney cartoon characters. P* 13½×14.
1079 $1 Dumbo .. .. .. .. 45 50
a. Sheetlet. Nos. 1079/86 .. .. 3·25
1080 $1 Goofy as Father Christmas .. .. 45 50
1081 $1 Minnie Mouse waving from window .. 45 50
1082 $1 Clarabelle, Mordie and Ferdie watching parade .. .. .. 45 50
1083 $1 Donald Duck's nephews .. .. 45 50
1084 $1 Donald Duck as drummer .. .. 45 50
1085 $1 Toy soldiers .. .. .. .. 45 50
1086 $1 Mickey Mouse on wooden horse .. 45 50
1079/86 .. .. .. .. *Set of* 8 3·25 3·50
**MS**1087 Two sheets, each 127 × 102 mm. (a) $7 Peter Pan and Captain Hook on float (*horiz*). (b) $7 Mickey Mouse as Father Christmas and Donald Duck in carnival train (*horiz*). P 14 × 13½ .. .. .. *Set of* 2 *sheets* 6·50 7·00

**94** Middleweight Boxing (Gold, Henry Maske, East Germany)

**95** Launch of "Apollo 11"

(Des L. Fried. Litho B.D.T.)

**1989** (13 Apr). *Olympic Medal Winners, Seoul* (1988). *T* **94** *and similar horiz designs. Multicoloured. P* 14.
1088 15 c. Type **94** .. .. .. .. 10 10
1089 50 c. Freestyle wrestling (130 kg) (Bronze, Andreas Schroeder, East Germany) .. 20 25
1090 60 c. Women's team gymnastics (Bronze, East Germany) .. .. .. 25 30
1091 75 c. Platform diving (Gold, Greg Louganis, U.S.A.) .. .. .. .. 30 35
1092 $1 Freestyle wrestling (52 kg) (Gold, Mitsuru Sato, Japan) .. .. 40 45
1093 $2 Men's freestyle 4×200 metres relay swimming (Bronze, West Germany) .. 85 90
1094 $3 Men's 5000 metres (Silver, Dieter Baumann, West Germany) .. .. 1·25 1·40
1095 $4 Women's heptathlon (Gold, Jackie Joyner-Kersee, U.S.A.) .. .. 1·75 1·90
1088/95 .. .. .. .. *Set of* 8 4·50 5·00
**MS**1096 Two sheets, each 70×100 mm. (a) $6 Weightlifting (67.5 kg) (Gold, Joachim Kunz, East Germany). (b) $6 Team Three-Day Event (Gold, West Germany) .. .. *Set of* 2 *sheets* 5·00 5·25

(Litho Questa)

**1989** (15 May). *Japanese Art. Paintings by Hiroshige. Horiz designs as T* **250** *of Antigua. Multicoloured. P* 14×13½.
1097 15 c. "Crossing the Oi at Shimada by Ferry" 10 10
1098 20 c. "Daimyo and Entourage at Arai" .. 10 10
1099 45 c. "Cargo Portage through Goyu" .. 20 25
1100 75 c. "Snowfall at Fujigawa" .. .. 30 35
1101 $1 "Horses for the Emperor at Chirifu" .. 40 45
1102 $2 "Rainfall at Tsuchiyama" .. .. 85 90
1103 $3 "An Inn at Ishibe" .. .. .. 1·25 1·40
1104 $4 "On the Shore of Lake Biwa at Otsu" 1·75 1·90
1097/104 .. .. .. .. *Set of* 8 4·50 4·75
**MS**1105 Two sheets, each 102×78 mm. (a) $5 "Fishing Village of Yokkaichi on the Mie". (b) $5 "Pilgrimage to Atsuta Shrine at Miya" *Set of* 2 *sheets* 4·25 4·50
Nos. 1097/104 were each printed in sheetlets of 10 containing two horizontal strips of 5 stamps separated by printed labels commemorating Emperor Hirohito.

(Des D. Bruckner. Litho B.D.T.)

**1989** (12 June). *World Cup Football Championship, Italy* (1990). *Multicoloured designs as T* **252** *of Antigua. P* 14.
1106 15 c. World Cup trophy .. .. .. 10 10
1107 20 c. Flags of Argentina (winners 1986) and International Federation of Football Associations (F.I.F.A.) (*horiz*) .. 10 10
1108 45 c. Franz Beckenbauer (West Germany) with World Cup, 1974 .. .. 20 25
1109 75 c. Flags of Italy (winners 1982) and F.I.F.A. (*horiz*) .. .. .. 30 35
1110 $1 Péle (Brazil) with Jules Rimet trophy 40 45
1111 $2 Flags of West Germany (winners 1974) and F.I.F.A. (*horiz*) .. .. 85 90
1112 $3 Flags of Brazil (winners 1970) and F.I.F.A. (*horiz*) .. .. .. 1·25 1·40
1113 $4 Jules Rimet trophy and Brazil players 1·75 1·90
1106/13 .. .. .. .. *Set of* 8 4·50 4·75
**MS**1114 (a) 100×81 mm. $6 Goalkeeper (*horiz*). (b) 66×95 mm. $6 Péle with Jules Rimet trophy *Set of* 2 *sheets* 5·00 5·25

(Des W. Wright. Litho B.D.T.)

**1989** (28 June). *North American Railway Locomotives. Vert designs as T* **342** *of Grenada. Multicoloured. P* 13.
1115 $2 Morris & Essex Railroad *Dover*, 1841 85 90
a. Sheetlet. Nos. 1115/24 .. .. 8·50
1116 $2 Baltimore & Ohio Railroad *Memmon* No. 57, 1848 .. .. .. 85 90
1117 $2 Camden & Amboy Railroad *John Stevens*, 1849 .. .. .. 85 90
1118 $2 Lawrence Machine Shop *Lawrence*, 1853 .. .. .. .. 85 90
1119 $2 South Carolina Railroad *James S. Corry*, 1859 .. .. .. 85 90
1120 $2 Mine Hill & Schuylkill Haven Railroad Flexible Beam No. 3 type, 1860 .. .. .. .. 85 90
1121 $2 Delaware, Lackawanna & Western Railroad *Montrose*, 1861 .. .. 85 90
1122 $2 Central Pacific Railroad *Pequop* No. 68, 1868 .. .. .. 85 90
1123 $2 Boston & Providence Railroad *Daniel Nason*, 1863 .. .. .. 85 90
1124 $2 Morris & Essex Railroad *Joe Scranton*, 1870 .. .. .. 85 90
1125 $2 Central Railroad of New Jersey No. 124, 1871 .. .. .. 85 90
a. Sheetlet. Nos. 1125/34 .. .. 8·50
1126 $2 Baldwin tramway steam locomotive, 1876 .. .. .. .. 85 90
1127 $2 Lackawanna & Bloomsburg Railroad *Luzerne*, 1878 .. .. .. 85 90
1128 $2 Central Mexicano Railroad No. 150, 1892 .. .. .. .. 85 90
1129 $2 Denver, South Park & Pacific Railroad *Breckenridge* No. 15, 1879 .. 85 90
1130 $2 Miles Planting & Manufacturing Company plantation locomotive *Daisy*, 1894 .. .. .. .. 85 90
1131 $2 Central of Georgia Railroad Baldwin "854" No. 1136, 1895 .. .. 85 90
1132 $2 Savannah, Florida & Western Railroad No. 111, 1900 .. .. 85 90
1133 $2 Douglas, Gilmore & Company contractors locomotive No. 3, 1902 .. 85 90
1134 $2 Lehigh Valley Coal Company compressed air locomotive No. 900, 1903 .. .. .. .. 85 90
1135 $2 Morgan's Louisiana & Texas Railroad McKeen diesel locomotive, 1908 .. 85 90
a. Sheetlet. Nos. 1135/44 .. .. 8·50
1136 $2 Clear Lake Lumber Company Type "B Climax" locomotive No. 6, 1910 .. 85 90
1137 $2 Blue Jay Lumber Company Heisler locomotive No. 10, 1912 .. .. 85 90
1138 $2 Stewartstown Railroad gasoline locomotive No. 6, 1920s .. .. 85 90
1139 $2 Bangor & Aroostock Railroad Class "G" No. 186, 1921 .. .. 85 90
1140 $2 Hammond Lumber Company No. 6, 1923 .. .. .. .. 85 90
1141 $2 Central Railroad of New Jersey diesel locomotive No. 1000, 1925 .. 85 90
1142 $2 Atchison, Topeka & Santa Fe Railroad "Super Chief" diesel express, 1935 .. 85 90
1143 $2 Norfolk & Western Railroad Class "Y-6", 1948 .. .. .. 85 90
1144 $2 Boston & Maine Railroad Budd diesel railcar, 1949 .. .. .. 85 90
1115/44 .. .. .. .. *Set of* 30 23·00 24·00
Nos. 1115/24, 1125/34 and 1135/44 were each printed together, *se-tenant*, in sheetlets of 10.

(Des Walt Disney Co. Litho Questa)

**1989** (7 July). *"Philexfrance 89" International Stamp Exhibition, Paris. Multicoloured designs as T* **251** *of Antigua showing Walt Disney cartoon characters in Paris. P* 14×13½ (*horiz*) *or* 13½×14 (*vert*).
1145 1 c. Mickey Mouse and Donald Duck at Ecole Militaire inflating balloon .. 10 10
1146 2 c. Mickey and Minnie Mouse on river boat passing Conciergerie .. .. 10 10
1147 3 c. Mickey Mouse at Hotel de Ville (*vert*) 10 10
1148 4 c. Mickey Mouse at Genie of the Bastille monument (*vert*) .. .. .. 10 10
1149 5 c. Mickey and Minnie Mouse arriving at Opera House .. .. .. 10 10
1150 10 c. Mickey and Minnie Mouse on tandem in Luxembourg Gardens .. .. 10 10
1151 $5 Mickey Mouse in aeroplane over L'Arch de la Defense (*vert*) .. .. 2·40 2·75
1152 $6 Mickey Mouse at Place Vendome (*vert*) .. .. .. .. 2·75 3·25
1145/52 .. .. .. .. *Set of* 8 5·00 5·75
**MS**1153 Two sheets, each 127×102 mm. (a) $6 Mickey and Minnie Mouse on scooter in Place de la Concorde. (b) $6 Donald Duck, Mickey and Minnie Mouse in balloon over Versailles. P 14×13½ .. .. .. *Set of* 2 *sheets* 5·00 5·25

(Des L. Birmingham. Litho Questa)

**1989** (20 July). *20th Anniv of First Manned Landing on Moon. T* **95** *and similar multicoloured designs. P* 14.
1154 25 c. Type **95** .. .. .. .. 10 15
1155 50 c. Splashdown (*horiz*) .. .. 20 25
1156 60 c. Modules in space .. .. .. 25 30
1157 75 c. Aldrin setting up experiment (*horiz*) 30 35
1158 $1 "Apollo 11" leaving Earth orbit (*horiz*) 40 45

1159 $2 Moving "Apollo 11" to launch site .. 85 90
1160 $3 Lunar module *Eagle* leaving Moon (*horiz*) .. .. .. .. 1·25 1·40
1161 $4 *Eagle* landing on Moon .. .. 1·75 1·90
1154/61 .. .. .. .. *Set of* 8 4·50 5·25
**MS**1162 (a) 71×100 mm. $5 Armstrong stepping onto Moon. (b) 101×72 mm. $5 Armstrong's footprint on Moon .. .. *Set of* 2 *sheets* 4·25 4·50

(Des J. Cooter. Litho B.D.T.)

**1989** (17 Aug). *Fungi. Vert designs as T* **348** *of Grenada. Multicoloured. P* 14.
1163 6 c. *Agaricus purpurellus* (incorrectly inscr *Collybia aurea*) .. .. 10 10
1164 10 c. *Podaxis pistillaris* .. .. 10 10
1165 20 c. *Hygrocybe firma* .. .. .. 10 10
1166 30 c. *Agaricus rufoaurantiacus* .. .. 10 15
1167 75 c. *Leptonia howellii* .. .. .. 30 35
1168 $2 *Marasmiellus purpureus* .. .. 85 90
1169 $3 *Marasmius trinitatis* .. .. 1·25 1·40
1170 $4 *Collybia aurea* (incorrectly inscr *Hygrocybe martinicensis*) .. .. 1·75 1·90
1163/70 .. .. .. .. *Set of* 8 4·00 4·50
**MS**1171 Two sheets, each 56×71 mm. (a) $6 *Lentinus crinitus* (incorrectly inscr *Agaricus purpurellus*). (b) $6 *Hygrocybe martinicensis* (incorrectly inscr *Lentinus crinitus*) *Set of* 2 *sheets* 5·00 5·25

(Des Deborah Dudley Max. Litho B.D.T.)

**1989** (2 Oct). *Butterflies. Horiz designs as T* **350** *of Grenada. Multicoloured. P* 14.
1172 25 c. *Battus polydamas* (inscr "*Papilio androgeus*") .. .. .. 10 15
1173 35 c. *Phoebis sennae* .. .. .. 15 20
1174 45 c. *Hamadryas feronia* .. .. .. 20 25
1175 50 c. *Cynthia cardui* .. .. .. 20 25
1176 75 c. *Ascia monuste* .. .. .. 30 35
1177 90 c. *Eurema lisa* .. .. .. 40 45
1178 $2 *Aphrissa statira* .. .. .. 85 90
1179 $3 *Hypolimnas misippus* .. .. 1·25 1·40
1172/9 .. .. .. .. *Set of* 8 3·00 3·50
**MS**1180 Two sheets, each 87×115 mm. (a) $6 *Anartia amathea*. (b) $6 *Pseudolycaena marsyas* *Set of* 2 *sheets* 5·00 5·25

**96** Ethel Barrymore **97** Buddy Holly

(Des J. Genzo. Litho B.D.T.)

**1989** (9 Oct). 425*th Birth Anniv of Shakespeare. Shakespearean Actors. T* **96** *and similar horiz designs. Multicoloured. P* 14.
1181 15 c. Type **96** .. .. .. .. 10 10
1182 $1.10, Richard Burton .. .. .. 45 50
1183 $2 John Barrymore .. .. .. 85 90
1184 $3 Paul Robeson .. .. .. 1·25 1·40
1181/4 .. .. .. .. *Set of* 4 2·40 2·50
**MS**1185 103×77 mm. $6 Bando Tamasaburo and Nakamura Kanzaburo .. .. .. 2·50 2·75

(Des J. Genzo. Litho B.D.T.)

**1989** (9 Oct). *Musicians. T* **97** *and similar vert designs. Multicoloured. P* 14.
1186 10 c. Type **97** .. .. .. .. 10 10
1187 25 c. Jimmy Hendrix .. .. .. 10 15
1188 75 c. Mighty Sparrow .. .. .. 30 35
1189 $4 Katsutoji Kineya .. .. .. 1·75 1·90
1186/9 .. .. .. .. *Set of* 4 2·00 2·25
**MS**1190 103×77 mm. $6 Kurt Weill .. .. 2·50 2·75

(Des D. Miller. Litho Questa)

**1989** (16 Oct). 500*th Anniv of Discovery of America by Columbus* (1992) (2*nd issue*). *Pre-Columbian Arawak Society. Vert designs as T* **247** *of Antigua. Multicoloured. P* 14.
1191 15 c. Arawaks canoeing .. .. .. 10 10
1192 75 c. Family and campfire .. .. .. 30 35
1193 90 c. Using stone tools .. .. .. 40 45
1194 $3 Eating and drinking .. .. 1·25 1·40
1191/4 .. .. .. .. *Set of* 4 1·75 2·00
**MS**1195 84×87 mm. $6 Making fire .. .. 2·50 2·75

(Des Walt Disney Co. Litho Questa)

**1989** (17 Nov). *"World Stamp Expo '89" International Stamp Exhibition, Washington. Multicoloured designs as T* **352** *of Grenada showing Walt Disney cartoon characters illustrating proverbs from* Poor Richard's Almanack. *P* 14×13½.
1196 1 c. Scrooge McDuck with gold coins in sinking boat .. .. .. 10 10
1197 2 c. Robin Hood shooting apple off Friar Tuck .. .. .. .. 10 10
1198 3 c. Winnie the Pooh with honey .. .. 10 10
1199 4 c. Goofy, Minnie Mouse and Donald Duck exercising .. .. .. 10 10
1200 5 c. Pinnochio holding Jimminy Cricket .. 10 10
1201 6 c. Huey and Dewey putting up wallpaper .. .. .. .. 10 10
1202 8 c. Mickey Mouse asleep in storm .. .. 10 10
1203 10 c. Mickey Mouse as Benjamin Franklin selling *Pennsylvania Gazette* .. .. 10 10
1204 $5 Mickey Mouse with chicken, recipe book and egg .. .. .. 2·10 2·25
1205 $6 Mickey Mouse missing carriage .. .. 2·50 2·75
1196/1205 .. .. .. *Set of* 10 4·50 4·75
**MS**1206 Two sheets, each 127×102 mm. (a) $6 Mickey Mouse bowing. P 14×13½. (b) $6 Mickey Mouse delivering basket of food (*vert*). P 13½×14 .. .. .. *Set of* 2 *sheets* 5·00 5·25

(Litho Questa)

**1990** (4 Jan). *Christmas. Paintings by Rubens. Vert designs as T* **259** *of Antigua. Multicoloured. P* 14.
1207 10 c. "The Annunciation" .. .. .. 10 10
1208 15 c. "The Flight of the Holy Family into Egypt" .. .. .. .. 10 10
1209 25 c. "The Presentation in the Temple" .. 10 15
1210 45 c. "The Holy Family under the Apple Tree" .. .. .. .. 20 25
1211 $2 "Madonna and Child with Saints" .. 85 90
1212 $4 "The Virgin and Child enthroned with Saints" .. .. .. .. 1·75 1·90
1213 $5 "The Holy Family" .. .. .. 2·10 2·25
1207/13 .. .. .. .. *Set of* 7 4·50 5·00
**MS**1214 Two sheets, each 70×95 mm. (a) $5 "The Adoration of the Magi" (sketch). (b) $5 "The Adoration of the Magi" .. .. *Set of* 2 *sheets* 4·25 4·50

(Des L. Nelson. Litho Questa)

**1990** (6 Mar). *"EXPO 90" International Garden and Greenery Exhibition, Osaka. Caribbean Orchids. Vert designs as T* **354** *of Grenada. Multicoloured. P* 14.
1215 15 c. *Brassocattleya* Thalie .. .. 10 10
1216 20 c. *Odontocidium* Tigersun .. .. 10 10
1217 50 c. *Odontioda* Hambuhren .. .. 20 25
1218 75 c. *Paphiopedilum* Delrosi .. .. 30 35
1219 $1 *Vuylstekeara* Yokara .. .. 40 45
1220 $2 *Paphiopedilum* Geelong .. .. 85 90
1221 $3 *Wilsonara* Tigerwood .. .. 1·25 1·40
1222 $4 *Cymbidium* Ormoulu .. .. 1·75 1·90
1215/22 .. .. .. .. *Set of* 8 4·50 4·75
**MS**1223 Two sheets, each 98×68 mm. (a) $6 *Odontonia* Sappho. (b) $6 *Cymbidium* Vieux Rose .. .. .. .. *Set of* 2 *sheets* 5·00 5·25

(Des Mary Walters. Litho Questa)

**1990** (16 Mar). 500*th Anniv of Discovery of America by Columbus* (1992) (3*rd issue*). *New World Natural History – Insects. Designs as T* **260** *of Antigua, but horiz. Multicoloured. P* 14.
1224 35 c. *Dynastes hercules* (beetle) .. .. 15 20
1225 40 c. *Chalcolepidius porcatus* (beetle) .. 15 20
1226 50 c. *Acrocinus longimanus* (beetle) .. 20 25
1227 60 c. *Battus polydamas* (butterfly) .. 25 30
1228 $1 *Orthemis ferruginea* (skimmer) .. 40 45
1229 $2 *Psiloptera variolosa* (beetle) .. 85 90
1230 $3 *Hypolimnas misippus* (butterfly) .. 1·25 1·40
1231 $4 Scarab Beetle .. .. .. 1·75 1·90
1224/31 .. .. .. .. *Set of* 8 4·50 5·00
**MS**1232 Two sheets, each 102×70 mm. (a) $6 *Calpodes ethlius* (butterfly). (b) $6 *Danaus plexippus* (butterfly) .. .. *Set of* 2 *sheets* 5·00 5·25

(Des J. Barbaris. Litho B.D.T.)

**1990** (3 Apr). *Wildlife. Horiz designs as T* **254** *of Antigua. Multicoloured. P* 14.
1233 5 c. West Indies Giant Rice Rat .. .. 10 10
1234 25 c. Agouti .. .. .. .. 10 15
1235 30 c. Humpback Whale .. .. .. 10 15
1236 40 c. Pilot Whale .. .. .. 15 20
1237 $1 Spotted Dolphin .. .. .. 40 45
1238 $2 Egyptian Mongoose .. .. .. 85 90
1239 $3 Brazilian Tree Porcupine .. .. 1·25 1·40
1240 $4 American Manatee .. .. .. 1·75 1·90
1233/40 .. .. .. .. *Set of* 8 4·25 4·75
**MS**1241 Two sheets, each 107×80 mm. (a) $6 Caribbean Monk Seal. (b) $6 Egyptian Mongoose (*different*) .. .. .. *Set of* 2 *sheets* 5·00 5·25

(Des W. Wright. Litho Questa)

**1990** (30 Apr). 50*th Anniv of Second World War. Horiz designs as T* **274** *of Antigua. Multicoloured. P* 14.
1242 6 c. British Tanks in France, 1939 .. 10 10
1243 10 c. Operation "Crusader", North Africa, 1941 .. .. .. .. 10 10
1244 20 c. Retreat of the Afrika Corps, 1942 .. 10 10
1245 45 c. American landing on Aleutian Islands, 1943 .. .. .. 20 25
1246 50 c. U.S. marines landing on Tarawa, 1943 20 25
1247 60 c. U.S. army entering Rome, 1944 .. 25 30
1248 75 c. U.S. tanks crossing River Seine, 1944 30 35
1249 $1 Battle of the Bulge, 1944 .. .. 40 45
1250 $5 American infantry in Italy, 1945 .. 2·10 2·25
1251 $6 *Enola Gay* dropping atomic bomb on Hiroshima, 1945 .. .. .. 2·50 2·75
1242/51 .. .. .. .. *Set of* 10 5·50 6·00
**MS**1252 112×84 mm. $6 St. Paul's Cathedral in London Blitz, 1940 .. .. .. 2·50 2·75

(Des Walt Disney Company. Litho Questa)

**1990** (3 May). *"Stamp World London 90" International Stamp Exhibition* (1*st issue*). *Multicoloured designs as T* **193** *of Gambia showing Walt Disney cartoon characters at Shakespeare sites. P* 14×13½ (15, 60 *c.*, $1, $5) *or* 13½×14 (*others*).
1253 15 c. Daisy Duck at Ann Hathaway's Cottage (*horiz*) .. .. .. 10 10
1254 30 c. Minnie and Bill Mouse at Shakespeare's birthplace, Stratford 10 15
1255 50 c. Minnie Mouse in front of Mary Arden's house, Wilmcote .. 20 25
1256 60 c. Mickey Mouse leaning on hedge in New Place gardens, Stratford (*horiz*) 25 30
1257 $1 Mickey Mouse walking in New Place gardens, Stratford (*horiz*) .. 40 45
1258 $2 Mickey Mouse carrying books in Scholars Lane, Stratford .. 85 90
1259 $4 Mickey Mouse and Royal Shakespeare Theatre, Stratford .. .. .. 1·75 1·90
1260 $5 Ludwig von Drake teaching Mickey Mouse at the Stratford Grammar School (*horiz*) .. .. .. 2·10 2·2
1253/60 .. .. .. .. *Set of* 8 5·25 5·7
**MS**1261 Two sheets, each 126×101 mm. (a) $6 Mickey Mouse as Shakespeare. P 13½×14. (b) $6 Mickey and Minnie Mouse in rowing boat on River Avon, Stratford (*horiz*). P 14×13½ *Set of* 2 *sheets* 5·00 5·2

(Des Young Phillips Studio. Litho Questa)

**1990** (5 July). 90*th Birthday of Queen Elizabeth the Queen Mother. Vert designs as T* **194** *of Gambia, showing photographs*, 1970–79. *Multicoloured. P* 14.
1262 $2 Queen Mother in pink hat and coat .. 85 9
a. Strip of 3. Nos. 1262/4 .. .. 2·25
1263 $2 Prince Charles and Queen Mother at Garter ceremony .. .. .. 85 9
1264 $2 Queen Mother in blue floral outfit .. 85 9
1262/4 .. .. .. .. *Set of* 3 2·25 2·4
**MS**1265 90×75 mm. $6 Queen Mother in Garter robes .. .. .. .. .. .. 2·50 2·7
Nos. 1262/4 were printed together, horizontally and verticall *se-tenant*, in sheetlets of 9 (3×3).

(Des M. Pollard. Litho Questa)

**1990** (12 July). *"Stamp World London* 90*" International Stam Exhibition* (2*nd issue*). *Sheet* 97×75 *mm containing hori design as T* **356** *of Grenada. P* 14.
**MS**1266 $6 blue-green .. .. .. .. 2·50 2·7
Design:—$6 Map of South America and logo.

(Des J. Anderton. Litho B.D.T.)

**1990** (10 Sept). *Birds. Multicoloured designs as T* **358** *o Grenada, but vert. P* 14.
1267 25 c. Yellow-bellied Seedeater .. .. 10 1
1268 45 c. Carib Grackle .. .. .. 20 2
1269 50 c. Black-whiskered Vireo .. .. 20 2
1270 75 c. Bananaquit .. .. .. .. 30 3
1271 $1 Collared Swift .. .. .. 40 4
1272 $2 Yellow-bellied Elaenia .. .. 85 9
1273 $3 Blue-hooded Euphonia .. .. 1·25 1·4
1274 $5 Eared Dove .. .. .. .. 2·10 2·2
1267/74 .. .. .. .. *Set of* 8 4·75 5·5
**MS**1275 Two sheets, each 101×72 mm. (a) $6 Mangrove Cuckoo. (b) $6 Scaly-breasted Thrasher .. .. .. *Set of* 2 *sheets* 5·00 5·2

(Des Deborah Dudley Max. Litho Questa)

**1990** (17 Sept). *Crustaceans. Horiz designs as T* **359** *o Grenada. Multicoloured. P* 14.
1276 10 c. Slipper Lobster .. .. .. 10 1
1277 25 c. Green Reef Crab .. .. .. 10 1
1278 65 c. Caribbean Lobsterette .. .. 25 3
1279 75 c. Blind Deep Sea Lobster .. .. 30 3
1280 $1 Flattened Crab .. .. .. 40 4
1281 $2 Ridged Slipper Lobster .. .. 85 9
1282 $3 Land Crab .. .. .. .. 1·25 1·4
1283 $4 Mountain Crab .. .. .. 1·75 1·9
1276/83 .. .. .. .. *Set of* 8 4·50 5·0
**MS**1284 Two sheets, each 108×76 mm. (a) $6 Caribbean King Crab. (b) $6 Purse Crab *Set of* 2 *sheets* 5·00 5·2

**98** Lineker, England **99** Angel with Star and Lantern

**1990** (24 Sept). *World Cup Football Championship, Italy. T* **9** *and similar vert designs. Multicoloured. P* 14.
1285 15 c. Type **98** .. .. .. .. 10 1
1286 45 c. Burruchaga, Argentina .. .. 20 2
1287 $2 Hysen, Sweden .. .. .. 85 9
1288 $4 Sang Ho, South Korea .. .. 1·75 1·9
1285/8 .. .. .. .. *Set of* 4 2·50 2·7
**MS**1289 Two sheets, each 76×90 mm. (a) $6 Ramos, U.S.A. (b) $6 Stojkovic, Yugoslavia *Set of* 2 *sheets* 5·00 5·2

(Des B. Grout. Litho Questa)

**1990** (1 Nov). *Olympic Games, Barcelona* (1992). *Vert design as T* **268** *of Antigua. Multicoloured. P* 14.
1290 10 c. Boxing .. .. .. .. 10 1
1291 25 c. Olympic flame .. .. .. 10 1
1292 50 c. Football .. .. .. .. 20 2
1293 75 c. Discus throwing .. .. .. 30 3
1294 $1 Pole vaulting .. .. .. 40 4
1295 $2 Show jumping .. .. .. 85 9
1296 $4 Women's basketball .. .. .. 1·75 1·9
1297 $5 Men's gymnastics .. .. .. 2·10 2·2
1290/7 .. .. .. .. *Set of* 8 5·25 5·7
**MS**1298 Two sheets. (a) 101×70 mm. $6 Sailboards. (b) 70×101 mm. $6 Decathlon *Set of* 2 *sheets* 5·00 5·2

(Litho Questa)

**991** (31 Jan). *350th Death Anniv of Rubens. Multicoloured designs as T* **273** *of Antigua. P* 13½×14 (*vert*) *or* 14×13½ (*horiz*).

299 5 c. "Adam and Eve" (Eve detail) (*vert*) .. 10 10
300 15 c. "Esther before Ahasuerus" (detail) .. 10 10
301 25 c. "Adam and Eve" (Adam detail) (*vert*) 10 15
302 50 c. "Expulsion from Eden" .. .. 20 25
303 $1 "Cain slaying Abel" (detail) (*vert*) .. 40 45
304 $2 "Lot's Flight" .. .. .. 85 90
305 $4 "Samson and Delilah" (detail) .. 1·75 1·90
306 $5 "Abraham and Melchizedek" .. 2·10 2·25
299/306 .. .. .. .. *Set of* 8 5·00 5·50
**1S1307** Two sheets, each 101×71 mm. (a) $6 "The Meeting of David and Abigail" (detail). (b) $6 "Daniel in the Lions' Den" (detail) *Set of* 2 *sheets* 5·00 5·25

(Des Mary Walters. Litho B.D.T.)

**991** (5 Feb). *Coral Reef Fishes. Horiz designs as T* **357** *of Grenada. Multicoloured. P* 14.

308 15 c. Barred Hamlet .. .. .. 10 10
309 35 c. Squirrelfish .. .. .. 15 20
310 45 c. Redspotted Hawkfish .. .. 20 35
311 75 c. Bigeye .. .. .. 30 35
312 $1 Spiny Puffer .. .. .. 40 45
313 $2 Smallmouth Grunt .. .. .. 85 90
314 $3 Harlequin Bass .. .. .. 1·25 1·40
315 $4 Creole Fish .. .. .. 1·75 1·90
308/15 .. .. .. .. *Set of* 8 4·50 5·00
**1S1316** Two sheets, each 103×72 mm. (a) $6 Copper Sweeper. (b) $6 Fairy Basslet *Set of* 2 *sheets* 5·00 5·25

(Litho Questa)

**991** (1 Mar). *Christmas* (1990). *Hummel Figurines. T* **99** *and similar vert designs. Multicoloured. P* 14.

317 10 c. Type **99** .. .. .. 10 10
318 15 c. Christ Child and Angel playing mandolin .. .. .. 10 10
319 25 c. Shepherd .. .. .. 10 15
320 50 c. Angel with trumpet and lantern .. 20 25
321 $1 Nativity scene .. .. .. 40 45
322 $2 Christ Child and Angel holding candle 85 90
323 $4 Angel with baskets .. .. .. 1·75 1·90
324 $5 Angels singing .. .. .. 2·10 2·25
317/24 .. .. .. .. *Set of* 8 5·00 5·50
**MS1325** Two sheets, each 99×122 mm. (a) 5 c. As No. 1318; 40 c. As No. 1320; 60 c. As No. 1321; $3 As No. 1324. (b) 20 c. As Type **99**; 30 c. As No. 1319; 75 c. As No. 1322; $6 As No. 1323 *Set of* 2 *sheets* 4·75 5·00

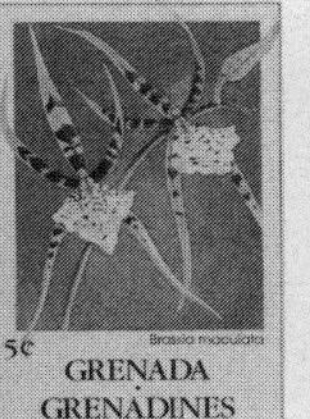

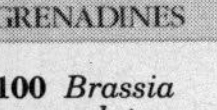


**100** *Brassia maculata*

**101** Donald and Daisy Duck with Solar-powered Car

(Des S. Barlowe. Litho Walsall)

**1991** (1 Apr). *Orchids. T* **100** *and similar vert designs. Multicoloured. P* 14.

1326 5 c. Type **100** .. .. .. 10 10
1327 10 c. *Oncidium lanceanum* .. .. 10 10
1328 15 c. *Broughtonia sanguinea* .. .. 10 10
1329 25 c. *Diacrium bicornutum* .. .. 10 15
1330 35 c. *Cattleya labiata* .. .. 15 20
1331 45 c. *Epidendrum fragrans* .. .. 20 25
1332 50 c. *Oncidium papilio* .. .. 20 25
1333 75 c. *Neocogniauxia monophylla* .. 30 35
1334 $1 *Epidendrum polybulbon* .. .. 40 45
1335 $2 *Spiranthes speciosa* .. .. 85 90
1336 $4 *Epidendrum ciliare* .. .. 1·75 1·90
1337 $5 *Phais tankervilliae* .. .. 2·10 2·25
1326/37 .. .. .. .. *Set of* 12 5·50 6·25

(Des W. Wright. Litho Questa)

**1991** (8 Apr). *Butterflies. Horiz designs as T* **363** *of Grenada. Multicoloured. P* 14.

1340 20 c. *Dynastor napoleon* .. .. 10 10
1341 25 c. *Pieridae callinira* .. .. 10 10
1342 30 c. *Anartia amathea* .. .. 10 15
1343 35 c. *Heliconiidae dido* .. .. 15 20
1344 50 c. *Nymphalidae praeneste* .. .. 20 25
1345 75 c. *Dryas julia* .. .. .. 30 35
1346 $3 *Papilionidae paeon* .. .. 1·25 1·50
1347 $4 *Morpho cypris* .. .. 1·75 1·90
1340/7 .. .. .. .. *Set of* 8 3·50 4·00
**MS1348** Two sheets, each 118×80 mm. (a) $6 *Danaus plexippus*. (b) $6 *Caligo idomenides* *Set of* 2 *sheets* 4·50 4·75

(Des Walt Disney Co. Litho Questa)

**1991** (22 Apr). *Ecology Conservation. T* **101** *and similar multicoloured designs showing Walt Disney cartoon characters. P* 14×13½.

1349 10 c. Type **101** .. .. .. 10 10
1350 15 c. Goofy saving water .. .. 10 10
1351 25 c. Donald and Daisy on nature hike .. 10 10
1352 45 c. Donald Duck returning chick to nest 20 25
1353 $1 Donald Duck and balloons .. .. 40 45
1354 $2 Minnie Mouse and Daisy Duck on hot day .. .. .. .. 85 90
1355 $4 Mickey's nephews cleaning beach .. 1·75 1·90
1356 $5 Donald Duck on pedal generator .. 2·10 2·25
1349/56 .. .. .. .. *Set of* 8 5·00 5·50
**MS1357** Three sheets, each 127×102 mm. (a) $6 Hiawatha and felled forest. P 14×13½. (b) $6 Donald Duck recycling (*vert*). P 13½×14. (c) $6 Mickey Mouse with Arbor Day notice. P 14×13½ .. .. .. *Set of* 3 *sheets* 6·75 7·00

(Des T. Agans. Litho Questa)

**1991** (29 Apr). *500th Anniv of Discovery of America by Columbus* (1992). *History of Exploration. Multicoloured designs as T* **194** *of British Virgin Islands. P* 14.

1358 15 c. Magellan rounding Cape Horn, 1519–21 .. .. .. 10 10
1359 20 c. Drake's *Golden Hind*, 1577–80 .. 10 10
1360 50 c. Cook's H.M.S. *Resolution*, 1768–71 .. 20 25
1361 60 c. Douglas World Cruiser seaplane, 1924 25 30
1362 $1 *Sputnik 1* satellite, 1957 .. .. 40 45
1363 $2 Gagarin's space flight, 1961 .. .. 85 90
1364 $4 Glenn's space flight, 1962 .. .. 1·75 1·90
1365 $5 Space shuttle, 1981 .. .. .. 2·10 2·25
1358/65 .. .. .. .. *Set of* 8 5·25 5·75
**MS1366** Two sheets, (a) 105×78 mm. $6 Bow of *Pinta* (*vert*). (b) 78×105 mm. $6 Fleet of Columbus .. .. .. *Set of* 2 *sheets* 4·50 4·75

(Des Walt Disney Co. Litho Questa)

**1991** (6 May). *"Philanippon '91" International Stamp Exhibition, Tokyo. Multicoloured designs as T* **248** *of Dominica showing Walt Disney cartoon characters in Japanese scenes. P* 14×13½.

1367 15 c. Minnie Mouse with silkworms .. 10 10
1368 30 c. Mickey, Minnie, Morty and Ferdie at Torii Gate .. .. .. 10 15
1369 50 c. Donald Duck and Mickey Mouse trying origami .. .. .. 20 25
1370 60 c. Mickey and Minnie diving for pearls 25 30
1371 $1 Minnie Mouse in kimono .. .. 40 45
1372 $2 Mickey making masks .. .. 85 90
1373 $4 Donald and Mickey making paper .. 1·75 1·90
1374 $5 Minnie and Pluto making pottery .. 2·10 2·25
1367/74 .. .. .. .. *Set of* 8 5·25 5·75
**MS1375** Four sheets, each 122×102 mm. (a) $6 Mickey flower-arranging (*vert*). (b) $6 Mickey carving a netsuke (*vert*). (c) $6 Mickey at tea ceremony (*vert*). (d) $6 Mickey making printing plate (*vert*). P 13½×14 .. .. *Set of* 4 *sheets* 10·00 10·50

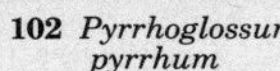

**102** *Pyrrhoglossum pyrrhum*

**103** Queen, Prince Philip, Prince Charles and Prince William at Trooping the Colour, 1990

(Des Mary Walters. Litho Questa)

**1991** (1 June). *Mushrooms. T* **102** *and similar vert designs. Multicoloured. P* 14.

1376 5 c. Type **102** .. .. .. 10 10
1377 45 c. *Agaricus purpurellus* .. .. 20 25
1378 50 c. *Amanita craseoderma* .. .. 20 25
1379 90 c. *Hygrocybe acutoconica* .. .. 40 45
1380 $1 *Limacella guttata* .. .. 40 45
1381 $2 *Lactarius hygrophoroides* .. .. 80 90
1382 $4 *Boletellus cubensis* .. .. 1·75 1·90
1383 $5 *Psilocybe caerulescens* .. .. 2·10 2·25
1376/83 .. .. .. .. *Set of* 8 5·50 6·00
**MS1384** Two sheets, each 100×70 mm. (a) $6 *Marasmius haematocephalus*. (b) $6 *Lepiota spiculata* .. .. .. *Set of* 2 *sheets* 4·50 4·75

(Des D. Miller. Litho Walsall)

**1991** (5 July). *65th Birthday of Queen Elizabeth II. T* **103** *and similar horiz designs. Multicoloured. P* 14.

1385 20 c. Type **103** .. .. .. 10 10
1386 25 c. Queen and Prince Charles at polo match, 1985 .. .. .. 10 10
1387 $2 Queen and Prince Philip at Maundy service, 1989 .. .. .. 85 90
1388 $4 Queen with Queen Mother on her 87th birthday, 1987 .. .. 1·75 1·90
1385/8 .. .. .. .. *Set of* 4 2·50 2·75
**MS1389** 68×90 mm. $5 The Queen at Caen Hill, 1990, and Prince Philip at R.A.F. Benson, 1989 2·10 2·25

(Des D. Miller. Litho Walsall)

**1991** (5 July). *10th Wedding Anniv of Prince and Princess of Wales. Horiz designs as T* **103**. *Multicoloured. P* 14.

1390 5 c. Prince and Princess of Wales kissing, 1987 .. .. .. 10 10
1391 60 c. Portraits of Prince, Princess and sons 25 30
1392 $1 Prince Henry in 1988 and Prince William in 1987 .. .. .. 40 45
1393 $5 Princess Diana in 1990 and Prince Charles in 1988 .. .. .. 2·10 2·25
1390/3 .. .. .. .. *Set of* 4 2·50 2·75
**MS1394** 68×90 mm. $5 Princess with Prince Henry in Majorca, and Prince and Princess with Prince Henry at polo match .. .. .. 2·10 2·25

OFFICIAL STAMPS

**1982** (June). *Various stamps optd with Type* O 1 *of Grenada.*

(*a*) *Nos.* 400/12 *and* 414

O 1 5 c. Yellowtail Snapper .. .. .. 10 15
O 2 6 c. Mutton Snapper .. .. .. 10 15
O 3 10 c. Cocoa Damselfish .. .. .. 10 15
O 4 12 c. Royal Gramma .. .. .. 10 15
O 5 15 c. Cherubfish .. .. .. 10 15
O 6 20 c. Blackbar Soldierfish .. .. .. 10 20
O 7 25 c. Comb Grouper .. .. .. 10 20
O 8 30 c. Longsnout Butterflyfish .. .. 15 20
O 9 40 c. Pudding Wife .. .. .. 15 25
O10 50 c. Midnight Parrotfish .. .. .. 20 30
O11 90 c. Redspotted Hawkfish .. .. .. 40 55
O12 $1 Hogfish .. .. .. .. 40 60
O13 $3 Beau Gregory .. .. .. 1·25 2·25
O14 $10 Barred Hamlet .. .. .. 4·25 6·00

(*b*) *Nos.* 444/6 *and* 448/9

O15 30 c. Prince Charles and Lady Diana Spencer 2·00 2·00
O16 40 c. Prince Charles and Lady Diana Spencer 1·60 1·60
O17 40 c. Type **50** .. .. .. .. 2·00 2·75
O18 $2 Type **50** .. .. .. .. 2·50 3·50
O19 $4 Prince Charles as parachutist .. 6·50 8·50

The Royal Wedding $4 from sheetlets, perforated 14½ × 14 and with changed background colour, also exists with this overprint (*Price* £8.50 *mint*, £9 *used*).

(*c*) *Nos.* 473/6

O20 **54** 20 c. multicoloured .. .. .. 10 20
O21 – 40 c. multicoloured .. .. .. 15 25
O22 – $1 multicoloured .. .. .. 35 70
O23 – $2 multicoloured .. .. .. 70 1·40
O1/23 .. .. .. .. *Set of* 23 20·00 29·00

## Griqualand West *see* South Africa

# Guyana
**(*formerly* British Guiana)**

## BRITISH GUIANA

The postal service from what was to become British Guiana dates from the last years of the 18th-century, being placed on a more regular basis after the final British occupation.

An inland postal system was organised in 1850, using the adhesive stamps of British Guiana, but, until 1 May 1860, overseas mails continued to be the province of the British G.P.O. The stamps of Great Britain being supplied for use on such letters from 11 May 1858.

For illustration of the handstamp and postmark type see BRITISH POST OFFICES ABROAD notes, following GREAT BRITAIN.

### CROWNED-CIRCLED HANDSTAMPS

The provision of a handstamp, probably as Type CC 1, inscribed "DEMERARA", is recorded in the G.P.O. proof book under 1 March 1856. No examples have been reported. A further handstamp, as Type CC **6**, recorded in the proof book on 17 February 1866, is known used as a cancellation in at least two instances, *circa* 1868.

### GEORGETOWN (DEMERARA)

*Stamps of* GREAT BRITAIN *cancelled* "A 03" *as Type* **2**.

**1858** to **1860**.

| No. | Description | Price |
|---|---|---|
| Z1 | 1d. rose-red (1857), *perf* 14 | £130 |
| Z2 | 4d. rose (1857) | £120 |
| Z3 | 6d. lilac (1856) | £100 |
| | a. Azure paper | |
| Z4 | 1s. green (1856) | £1000 |

### NEW AMSTERDAM (BERBICE)

*Stamps of* GREAT BRITAIN *cancelled* "A 04" *as Type* **2**.

**1858** to **1860**.

| No. | Description | Price |
|---|---|---|
| Z5 | 1d. rose-red (1857), *perf* 14 | |
| Z6 | 2d. blue (1858) (Plate Nos. 7, 8) | £350 |
| Z7 | 4d. rose (1857) | £250 |
| Z8 | 6d. lilac (1856) | £180 |
| Z9 | 1s. green (1856) | £1100 |

**PRICES FOR STAMPS ON COVER TO 1945**

| | |
|---|---|
| Nos. 1/21 | *from* × 3 |
| No. 23 | † |
| Nos. 24/7 | *from* × 3 |
| Nos. 29/115 | *from* × 4 |
| Nos. 116/24 | *from* × 6 |
| Nos. 126/36 | *from* × 5 |
| Nos. 137/59 | *from* × 6 |
| Nos. 162/5 | *from* × 8 |
| Nos. 170/4 | *from* × 5 |
| Nos. 175/89 | *from* × 6 |
| No. 192 | *from* × 20 |
| Nos. 193/210 | *from* × 4 |
| Nos. 213/15 | *from* × 5 |
| Nos. 216/21 | *from* × 3 |
| Nos. 222/4 | *from* × 8 |
| Nos. 233/50 | *from* × 3 |
| No. 251 | — |
| Nos. 252/7 | *from* × 3 |
| Nos. 259/82 | *from* × 4 |
| Nos. 283/7 | *from* × 5 |
| Nos. 288/300 | *from* × 4 |
| Nos. 301/4 | *from* × 5 |
| Nos. 305/7 | *from* × 6 |
| Nos. 308/19 | *from* × 5 |
| Nos. D1/4 | *from* × 12 |
| Nos. O1/12 | *from* × 12 |

### CROWN COLONY

1

2

(Set up and printed at the office of the *Royal Gazette*, Georgetown, British Guiana)

**1850** (1 July)–**51**. *Type-set. Black impression. (a) Medium wove paper. Prices are for—I. Cut square. II. Cut round.*

| No. | Type | Description | I Used | II Used |
|---|---|---|---|---|
| 1 | 1 | 2 c. *rose* (1.3.51) | — | £55000 |
| 2 | | 4 c. *orange* | £16000 | £2750 |
| 3 | | 4 c. *lemon-yellow* (1851) | £27000 | £3250 |
| 4 | | 8 c. *green* | £9000 | £2000 |
| 5 | | 12 c. *blue* | £4000 | £1700 |
| 6 | | 12 c. *indigo* | £9000 | £2000 |
| 7 | | 12 c. *pale blue* (1851) | £8000 | £2250 |
| | | a. "2" of "12" with straight foot | — | £4000 |
| | | b. "1" of "12" omitted | † | £26000 |

*(b) Pelure paper* (1851)

| No. | Type | Description | I Used | II Used |
|---|---|---|---|---|
| 8 | 1 | 4 c. *pale yellow* | £32000 | £3250 |

These stamps were initialled by the postmaster, or the Post Office clerks, before they were issued. The initials are—E. T. E. D(alton), E. D. W(ight), J. B. S(mith), H. A. K(illikelley), and W. H. L(ortimer). There are several types of each value and it has been suggested that the setting contained one horizontal row of four slightly different impressions.

Ten examples of No. 1 have been recorded, including three pairs on separate covers.

(Litho Waterlow)

**1852** (1 Jan). *Surface-coloured paper. Imperf.*

| No. | Type | Description | Un | Used |
|---|---|---|---|---|
| 9 | 2 | 1 c. black/*magenta* | £8500 | £4250 |
| 10 | | 4 c. black/*deep blue* | £10000 | £4500 |

There are two types of each value.

Reprints, on thicker paper and perf $12^1/_2$, were made in 1865 (*Price £12 either value*).

Such reprints with the perforations removed are sometimes offered as genuine originals.

**CONDITION.** Prices for Nos. 9 to 21 are for fine copies. Poor to medium specimens can be supplied when in stock at much lower rates.

3

4

5

(Dies eng and stamps litho Waterlow)

**1853–59**. *Imperf. (a) Original printing.*

| No. | Type | Description | Un | Used |
|---|---|---|---|---|
| 11 | 3 | 1 c. vermilion | £3000 | £1000 |

This 1 c. in *reddish brown* is probably a proof (*Price £650*).

ONE CENT — A; ONE CENT — B; ONE CENT — C; ONE CENT — D

A. "O" large and 1 mm from left corner.
B. "O" small and ¾ mm from left corner.
C. "O" small and ¾ mm from left corner. "NT" widely spaced.
D. "ONE" close together, "O" 1¼ mm from left corner.

*(b) Fresh lithographic transfers from the 4 c. with varying labels of value. White line above value* (1857–59).

| No. | Type | Description | Un | Used |
|---|---|---|---|---|
| 12 | 3 | 1 c. dull red (A) | £2000 | £800 |
| 13 | | 1 c. brownish red (A) | £4250 | £800 |
| 14 | | 1 c. dull red (B) | £2500 | £850 |
| 15 | | 1 c. brownish red (B) | £4250 | £850 |
| 16 | | 1 c. dull red (C) | £2500 | £850 |
| 17 | | 1 c. dull red (D) | £4500 | £2500 |

**1853–59**. *Imperf.*

| No. | Type | Description | Un | Used |
|---|---|---|---|---|
| 18 | 4 | 4 c. deep blue | £1100 | £425 |
| | | a. Retouched | £1900 | £800 |
| 19 | | 4 c. blue (1855) | £900 | £400 |
| 20 | | 4 c. pale blue (1859) | £800 | £300 |
| | | a. Retouched | £1500 | £550 |

The 4 c. value was produced from transfers from the original 1 c., with the bottom inscription removed, teamed with a new face value. The join often shows as a white line or traces of it above the label of value and lower corner figures. In some stamps on the sheet this line is missing, owing to having been retouched, and in these cases a line of colour usually appears in its place.

The 1 c. and 4 c. stamps were reprinted in 1865 from fresh transfers of five varieties. These are on thin paper and perf $12^1/_2$ (*Price £10 each unused*).

**1860** (May). *Figures in corners framed. Imperf.*

| No. | Type | Description | Un | Used |
|---|---|---|---|---|
| 21 | 5 | 4 c. blue | £2500 | £425 |

6

(Type-set and printed at the *Official Gazette* by Baum and Dallas, Georgetown).

**1856**. *(a) Surface-coloured paper.*

| No. | Type | Description | Un | Used |
|---|---|---|---|---|
| 23 | 6 | 1 c. black/*magenta* | | |
| 24 | | 4 c. black/*magenta* (Feb) | — | £5500 |
| 25 | | 4 c. black/*rose-carmine* (Sept) | — | £7500 |
| 26 | | 4 c. black/*blue* (Oct) | — | £32000 |

*(b) Paper coloured through*

| No. | Type | Description | Un | Used |
|---|---|---|---|---|
| 27 | 6 | 4 c. black/*deep blue* (Aug) | — | £42000 |

Since only one example of No. 23 is known, no market price can be given. This celebrated stamp frequently termed "the world's rarest", was last on the market in 1980.

These stamps, like those of the first issue, were initialled before being issued; the initials are—E.T.E.D., E.D.W., C.A. W(atson), and W.H.L.

The 4 c. is known in four types, differing in the position of the inscriptions.

**PAPERMAKERS' WATERMARKS**. Seven different paper makers' watermarks were used in the period 1860 to 1875 and stamps bearing portions of these are worth a premium.

7

6 ONE CENT 0 — A

B

C

D

6 XII CENTS 0 — E

F

(Dies eng and litho Waterlow)

**1860** (July)–**63**. *Tablets of value as illustrated. Thick paper. P* 12.

| No. | Type | Description | Un | Used |
|---|---|---|---|---|
| 29 | 7 | 1 c. pale rose | £900 | £170 |
| 30 | | 2 c. deep orange (8.60) | £120 | 38·00 |
| 31 | | 2 c. pale orange | £120 | 38·00 |
| 32 | | 4 c. deep blue (8.60) | £300 | 50·00 |
| 33 | | 4 c. blue | £250 | 45·00 |
| 34 | | 8 c. brownish rose | £325 | 55·00 |
| 35 | | 8 c. pink | £275 | 50·00 |
| 36 | | 12 c. lilac (12.60) | £425 | 32·00 |
| 37 | | 12 c. grey-lilac | £350 | 32·00 |
| 38 | | 24 c. deep green (6.63) | £850 | 70·00 |
| 39 | | 24 c. green | £800 | 65·00 |

The 1 c. was reprinted in 1865 on *thin* paper, P $12^1/_2$–13, and in a different shade. *Price* £10.

The 12 c. in both shades is frequently found surcharged with a large "5d" in *red*; this is to denote the proportion of postage repayable by the colony to Great Britain for overseas letters.

**1861** (1 Nov). *Colour changed. Thick paper P* 12.

| No. | Type | Description | Un | Used |
|---|---|---|---|---|
| 40 | 7 | 1 c. reddish brown | £250 | 75·00 |

**1862–65**. *(a) Thin paper. P* 12.

| No. | Type | Description | Un | Used |
|---|---|---|---|---|
| 41 | 7 | 1 c. brown | £350 | £150 |
| 42 | | 1 c. black (1863) | 80·00 | 38·00 |
| 43 | | 2 c. orange | 80·00 | 27·00 |
| 44 | | 4 c. blue | 80·00 | 27·00 |
| 45 | | 4 c. pale blue | 75·00 | 20·00 |
| 46 | | 8 c. pink (1863) | £110 | 40·00 |
| 47 | | 12 c. dull purple (1863) | £100 | 18·00 |
| 48 | | 12 c. purple | £100 | 20·00 |
| 49 | | 12 c. lilac | £110 | 27·00 |
| 50 | | 24 c. green | £550 | 70·00 |

*(b) Thin paper. P* $12^1/_2$–13 (1863)

| No. | Type | Description | Un | Used |
|---|---|---|---|---|
| 51 | 7 | 1 c. black | 50·00 | 15·00 |
| 52 | | 2 c. orange | 70·00 | 15·00 |
| 53 | | 4 c. blue | 75·00 | 17·00 |
| 54 | | 8 c. pink | £150 | 60·00 |
| 55 | | 12 c. brownish lilac | £400 | 85·00 |
| 56 | | 24 c. green | £500 | 55·00 |

Copies are found on *pelure* paper.

*(c) Medium paper. P* $12^1/_2$–13

| No. | Type | Description | Un | Used |
|---|---|---|---|---|
| 57 | 7 | 1 c. black (1864) | 42·00 | 23·00 |
| 58 | | 2 c. deep orange (1864) | 60·00 | 17·00 |
| 59 | | 2 c. orange | 65·00 | 14·00 |
| 60 | | 4 c. greyish blue (1864) | 70·00 | 14·00 |
| 61 | | 4 c. blue | 70·00 | 20·00 |
| 62 | | 8 c. pink (1864) | £120 | 38·00 |
| 63 | | 12 c. brownish lilac (1865) | £325 | 65·00 |
| 64 | | 24 c. green (1864) | £130 | 50·00 |
| 65 | | 24 c. deep green | £275 | 55·00 |

*(d) Medium paper. P* 10 (Nov 1865)

| No. | Type | Description | Un | Used |
|---|---|---|---|---|
| 65a | 7 | 12 c. grey-lilac | £275 | 55·00 |

8

9

G

H

I

K

New transfers for the 1 c., 2 c., 8 c., and 12 c. with the spaces between values and the word "CENTS" about 1 mm.

**863–75.** *Medium paper (a) P 12½–13 (1863–68).*
6 8 1 c. black (1866) . . . . 24·00 15·00
7 2 c. orange-red (1865) . . 32·00 3·50
8 2 c. orange . . 28·00 3·50
9 9 6 c. blue (1865) . . 90·00 38·00
0 6 c. greenish blue . . 90·00 40·00
1 6 c. deep blue . . 95·00 38·00
2 6 c. milky blue . . 95·00 38·00
3 8 8 c. pink (1868) . . £110 12·00
4 8 c. carmine . . £120 12·00
5 12 c. grey-lilac (1867) . . £325 18·00
6 12 c. brownish purple . . £400 23·00
7 9 24 c. green (*perf* 12) . . £200 19·00
8 24 c. yellow-green (*perf* 12) . . £100 8·00
9 24 c. yellow-green (*perf* 12½–13) . . £110 7·50
0 24 c. green (*perf* 12½–13) (1864) . . £110 9·00
1 24 c. blue-green (*perf* 12½–13) . . £150 18·00
2 48 c. pale red . . £130 42·00
3 48 c. deep red . . £130 42·00
4 48 c. carmine-rose . . £250 45·00

The 4 c. corresponding to this issue can only be distinguished rom that of the previous issue by minor plating flaws.

There is a variety of the 6 c. with stop before "VICISSIM".

Varieties of most of the values of issues of 1863–64 and 1866 are o be found on both very thin and thick papers.

*(b) P 10 (1866–71)*
85 8 1 c. black (1869) . . 7·50 2·00
86 1 c. grey-black . . 8·50 4·25
87 2 c. orange (1868) . . 13·00 1·25
88 2 c. reddish orange . . 22·00 2·50
89 4 c. slate-blue . . 60·00 11·00
90 4 c. blue . . 65·00 6·00
a. Bisected (on cover) . . † £3500
b. Ditto Imperf (on cover) . . † —
91 4 c. pale blue . . 70·00 8·50
92 9 6 c. milky blue (1867) . . £100 24·00
93 6 c. ultramarine . . £100 38·00
94 6 c. dull blue . . £100 32·00
95 8 8 c. pink (5.71) . . 95·00 12·00
96 8 c. brownish pink . . £100 12·00
96*a* 8 c. carmine . . £100 14·00
97 12 c. pale lilac (1867) . . £190 12·00
98 12 c. grey-lilac . . £110 12·00
99 12 c. brownish grey . . £100 15·00
00 12 c. lilac . . £100 15·00
01 9 24 c. deep green . . £180 9·00
02 24 c. bluish green . . — 8·00
03 24 c. yellow-green . . £130 7·50
04 48 c. crimson (1867) . . £275 24·00
05 48 c. red . . £275 22·00
04 Handstamped "Specimen" . . £170
04 Perf "Specimen" . . £120

*(c) P 15 (1875–76)*
06 8 1 c. black . . 27·00 7·50
07 2 c. orange-red . . £120 8·50
08 2 c. orange . . £120 8·50
09 4 c. bright blue . . £200 70·00
11 9 6 c. ultramarine . . £275 65·00
12 8 8 c. deep rose (1876) . . £170 60·00
13 12 c. lilac . . £400 42·00
14 9 24 c. yellow-green . . £475 35·00
15 24 c. deep green . . £500 40·00

There is a variety of the 48 c. with stop after "P" in PETIMUSQUE".

Imperforate stamps of this and of the previous issue are onsidered to be proofs.

**PRICES** for stamps of the 1862 issue are for good average copies. Copies with roulettes on all sides very seldom occur and do not exist n marginal positions.

10 11 12
13 14 15

(Type-set and printed at the Office of the *Royal Gazette*, Georgetown)

**1862** (Sept). *Black on coloured paper. Roul* 6.
116 10 1 c. *rose* . . £1200 £225
a. Unsigned . . £150
b. Wrong ornament (as T 13) at left (R. 1/1) . . — £375
c. "1" for "I" in "BRITISH" (R. 1/5) . . — £375
117 11 1 c. *rose* . . £1600 £300
a. Unsigned . . £160
b. Narrow "T" in "CENTS" (R. 3/1) . . — £375
c. Wrong ornament (as T 15) at top (R. 3/3) . . — £375
d. "1" for "I" in "BRITISH" and italic "S" in "POSTAGE" (R. 3/5) . . — £375
118 12 1 c. *rose* . . £2500 £400
a. Unsigned . . £325
b. "1" for "I" in "GUIANA" (R. 4/4) . . — £400
c. Wrong ornament (as T 15) at left (R. 4/5) . . — £400
d. "C" for "O" in "POSTAGE" (R. 4/6) — £400
119 10 2 c. *yellow* . . £1200 £200
a. Unsigned . . £160
b. Wrong ornament (as T 13) at left (R. 1/1) . . — £350
c. "1" for "I" in "BRITISH" (R. 1/5) . . — £350
120 11 2 c. *yellow* . . £1600 £275
a. Unsigned . . £170
b. "C" for "O" in "TWO" and narrow "T" in "CENTS" (R. 3/1) . . — £350
c. Wrong ornament (as T 15) at top (R. 3/3) . . — £350
d. "1" for "I" in "BRITISH" and italic "S" in "POSTAGE" (R. 3/5) . . — £350
e. Italic "T" in "TWO" (R. 3/6) . . — £350
121 12 2 c. *yellow* . . £2500 £375
a. Unsigned . . £350
b. "1" for "I" in "GUIANA" (R. 4/4) . . — £375
c. Wrong ornament (as T 15) at left (R. 4/5) . . — £375
d. "C" for "O" in "POSTAGE" (R. 4/6) — £375
122 13 4 c. *blue* . . £1300 £250
a. Unsigned . . £250
b. Wrong ornament (as T 15) at left (R. 1/6) . . — £400
c. Wrong ornament (as T 15) at top and italic "S" in "CENTS" (R. 2/2) . . — £400
d. Ornament omitted at right (R. 2/4) — £400
123 14 4 c. *blue* . . £1600 £350
a. Unsigned . . £275
b. With inner frame lines (as in T 10/13) (R. 2/5–6) . . £2750 £1300
ba. "1" for "I" in "BRITISH" (R. 2/5) . . £2750 £1300
c. "1" for "I" in "BRITISH" and "GUIANA" (R. 4/1) . . — £400
124 15 4 c. *blue* . . £1600 £350
a. Unsigned . . £275
b. Wrong ornament (as T 12) at foot (R. 3/1) . . — £400
c. Italic "S" in "CENTS" (R. 3/2) . . — £400
d. Italic "S" in "BRITISH" (R. 3/3) . . — £400

Stamps were initialled across the centre before use by the Acting Receiver-General, Robert Mather. Black was used on the 1 c., red for the 2 c. and an ink which appears white for the 4 c.

The three values of this provisional were each printed in sheets of 24 (6 × 4). The 1 c. and 2 c. were produced from the same setting of the border ornaments which contained 12 examples as Type **10** (Rows 1 and 2), 8 as Type **11** (R. 3/1 to R. 4/2) and 4 as Type **12** (R. 4/3–6).

The setting of the 4 c. contained 10 examples as Type **13** (R. 1/1 to R. 2/4), 8 as Type **14** (R. 2/5–6 and Row 4) and 6 as Type **15** (Row 3).

16 (17)

(Typo D.L.R.)

**1876** (1 July)–**79**. *Wmk Crown CC. (a) P* 14.
126 16 1 c. slate . . 2·75 1·40
127 2 c. orange . . 32·00 1·00
128 4 c. blue . . £110 7·00
129 6 c. brown . . 70·00 6·00
130 8 c. rose . . £100 75
131 12 c. pale violet . . 50·00 1·25
132 24 c. emerald-green . . 60·00 3·00
133 48 c. red-brown . . £100 14·00
134 96 c. olive-bistre . . £425 £250
126/134 . . *Set of* 9 £850 £250
126/132, 134 Handstamped/Perf "Specimen" *Set of* 8 £500

*(b) P* 12½ (1877)
135 16 4 c. blue . . £1200 £200

*(c) Perf compound of* 14 × 12½ (1879)
136 16 1 c. slate . . — £200

**1878.** *Provisionals. Various stamps with old values ruled through with thick bars, in black ink, the bars varying in depth of colour.*

*(a) With two horiz bars* (17 Apr)
137 16 (1 c.) on 6 c. brown . . 38·00 65·00

*(b) Official stamps with horiz bars across* "OFFICIAL" (end Aug)
138 8 1 c. black . . £120 70·00
139 16 1 c. slate . . £110 50·00
140 2 c. orange . . £130 65·00

*(c) With horiz and vert bars as T* 17 (6 Nov)
141 9 (1 c.) on 6 c. ultramarine (93) . . £130 80·00
142 16 (1 c.) on 6 c. brown . . £180 75·00

*(d) Official stamps with bars across* "OFFICIAL" (23 Nov)

*(i) With two horiz bars and one vert*
144 16 (1 c.) on 4 c. blue . . £130 70·00
145 (1 c.) on 6 c. brown . . £150 75·00
146 8 (2 c.) on 8 c. rose . . £275 £110

*(ii) With one horiz bar and one vert*
147 16 (1 c.) on 4 c. blue . . † £1500
148 (2 c.) on 8 c. rose . . £225 85·00

1 2 2
(18) (19) (20)

**1881** (21 Dec). *No. 134 with old value ruled through with bar in black ink and surch.*
149 18 1 on 96 c. olive-bistre . . 3·50 5·00
a. Bar in red
b. Bar omitted
150 19 2 on 96 c. olive-bistre . . 4·00 8·50
a. Bar in red
b. Bar omitted
151 20 2 on 96 c. olive-bistre . . 40·00 40·00

In the setting of 60 Type 19 occurs on the first five vertical rows and Type 20 on the sixth.

1 2 2
(21) (23) (24)

**1881** (28 Dec). *Various stamps with old value ruled with bar and surch. (a) On No.* 105.
152 21 1 on 48 c. red . . 32·00 5·00
a. Bar omitted . . — £400

*(b) On Official stamps (including unissued 48 c. optd with Type O 2)*
153 21 1 on 12 c. brownish purple (O4) . . £100 60·00
154 1 on 48 c. red-brown . . £120 80·00
155 23 2 on 12 c. pale violet (O11) . . 60·00 20·00
a. Horiz pair. Nos. 155/6 . . £450
b. Surch double . . £600 £375
c. Surch double (T **23** + **24**) . .
d. Extra bar through "OFFICIAL" . .
156 24 2 on 12 c. pale violet (O11) . . £225 £140
157 23 2 on 24 c. emerald-green (O12) . . 65·00 30·00
a. Horiz pair. Nos. 157/8 . . £500
b. Surch double . . £700
158 24 2 on 24 c. emerald-green (O12) . . £325 £325
159 19 2 on 24 c. green (O5) . . £180 95·00

On Nos. 149/59 the bar is found in various thicknesses ranging from 1 to 4 mm.

26

27

(Type-set, Baldwin & Co. Georgetown)

**1882** (9 Jan). *Black impression. P* 12. *Perforated with the word "SPECIMEN" diagonally.*
162 26 1 c. *magenta* . . 35·00 28·00
a. Imperf between (horiz pair) . .
b. Without "SPECIMEN" . . £250 £225
c. "1" with foot . . 70·00 60·00
163 2 c. *yellow* . . 55·00 45·00
a. Without "SPECIMEN" . . £250 £250
b. Small "2" . . 55·00 45·00
164 27 1 c. *magenta* . . 35·00 28·00
a. Without "SPECIMEN" . . £250 £225
b. "1" with foot . . 70·00 60·00
165 2 c. *yellow* . . 50·00 40·00
a. Bisected diagonally (1 c.) . .
b. Without "SPECIMEN" . . £250 £250
c. Small "2" . . 85·00 75·00

These stamps were perforated "SPECIMEN" as a precaution against fraud. Stamps are known with "SPECIMEN" double.

The 1 c. and 2 c. stamps were printed in separate sheets; but utilising the same clichés, these being altered according to the face value required. Two settings were used, common to both values:—

1st setting. Four rows of three, T **26** being Nos. 5, 6, 7, 8, 11 and 12, and T **27** the remainder.

From this setting there were two printings of the 2 c., but only one of the 1 c.

2nd setting. Six rows of two, T **26** being Nos. 3, 7, 8, 9, 11 and 12, and T **27** the remainder.

There were two printings of each value from this setting.

*Se-tenant* pairs are worth about 20% more.

The "1" with foot occurs on T **27** on No. 9 in the first setting and on T **26** on No. 7 in the first printing only of the second setting.

The small "2" appears on T **26** in the first setting on Nos. 6, 7, 8 and 12 in the first printing and on Nos. 7, 8 and 12 only in the second printing: in the second setting it comes on Nos. 3, 9 and 12 in the first printing and on Nos. 9, 11 and 12 in the second printing. On T **27** the variety occurs in the first setting on No. 9 of the second printing only and in the second setting on No. 10 in both printings.

(Typo D.L.R.)

**1882.** *Wmk Crown CA. P* 14.
170 16 1 c. slate (27 Jan) . . 7·50 20
171 2 c. orange (27 Jan) . . 20·00 15
a. Value doubly printed . .
172 4 c. blue . . 75·00 5·00
173 6 c. brown . . 5·00 6·50
174 8 c. rose . . 80·00 40
170/4 . . *Set of* 5 £170 11·00
170/4 Perf "Specimen" . . *Set of* 5 £250

INLAND 4 CENTS 4 CENTS
(*a*) (*b*)
Two types of "4"

2 CENTS
REVENUE
(28)

6 6
(*c*) (*d*)
Two types of "6"

**1888–89.** *T* 16 *(without value in lower label) optd.* "INLAND REVENUE", *and surch with value as T* 28, *by D.L.R. Wmk Crown CA. P* 14.
175 1 c. dull purple (8.89) . . 60 20
176 2 c. dull purple (25.5.89) . . 1·25 30
177 3 c. dull purple . . 60 20
178 4 c. dull purple (*a*) . . 2·50 30
a. Larger figure "4" (*b*) . . 23·00 9·00
179 6 c. dull purple (*c*) . . 2·50 1·75
a. Figure 6 with straight top (*d*) . . 18·00 3·50
180 8 c. dull purple (8.89) . . 1·50 25
181 10 c. dull purple . . 6·00 2·50
182 20 c. dull purple . . 17·00 10·00
183 40 c. dull purple . . 20·00 17·00
184 72 c. dull purple (1.10.88) . . 32·00 32·00
185 $1 green (1.10.88) . . £400 £325

186 $2 green (1.10.88) .. .. .. .. £180 £160
187 $3 green (1.10.88) .. .. .. .. £110 90·00
188 $4 green (*a*) (1.10.88) .. .. .. £325 £325
a. Larger figure "4" (*b*) .. .. £900 £900
189 $5 green (1.10.88) .. .. .. .. £225 £160
175/189 .. .. .. .. *Set of* 15 £1200 £1000

Nos. 175/89 were surcharged in settings of 60 (6×10). No. 178a occurs on all stamps in the third vertical row, No. 179a in the fourth and sixth vertical rows and No. 188a in the second vertical row.

**2**

(29)

30

INLAND
One
Cent
~~1 DOLLAR~~
REVENUE

(31)

**1889** (6 June). *No.* 176 *surch with T* **29** *in red by* Official Gazette.
192 "2" on 2 c. dull purple .. .. .. 60 15

The varieties with figure "2" *inverted* or *double* were made privately by a postal employee in Demerara.

**1889** (Sept). *Wmk Crown CA. P* 14.
193 **30** 1 c. dull purple and slate-grey .. .. 1·50 90
194 2 c. dull purple and orange .. .. 1·25 10
195 4 c. dull purple and ultramarine .. 4·00 1·50
196 4 c. dull purple and cobalt .. .. 10·00 2·25
197 6 c. dull purple and brown .. .. 22·00 7·50
198 6 c. dull purple and maroon .. .. 6·00 3·75
199 8 c. dull purple and rose .. .. 6·50 60
200 12 c. dull purple and bright purple .. 15·00 1·00
200*a* 12 c. dull purple and mauve .. .. 8·50 2·00
201 24 c. dull purple and green .. .. 7·50 2·50
202 48 c. dull purple and orange-red .. .. 13·00 9·00
203 72 c. dull purple and red-brown .. .. 23·00 29·00
204 72 c. dull purple and yellow-brown .. 65·00 75·00
205 96 c. dull purple and carmine .. .. 65·00 70·00
206 96 c. dull purple and rosine .. .. 75·00 80·00
193/205 .. .. .. .. *Set of* 10 £120 £110
193/205 Optd "Specimen" .. .. *Set of* 10 £150

**1890** (15 July). *Stamps of* 1888–89 *surch locally* "One Cent", *in red, as in T* **31**.
207 1 c. on $1 (No. 185) .. .. .. .. 90 35
a. Surch double .. .. .. .. — 75·00
208 1 c. on $2 (No. 186) .. .. .. .. 50 60
a. Surch double .. .. .. .. 75·00
209 1 c. on $3 (No. 187) .. .. .. .. 1·40 1·25
a. Surch double .. .. .. .. 60·00
210 1 c. on $4 (No. 188) .. .. .. .. 2·00 4·50
a. Surch double .. .. .. .. 65·00
b. Larger figure "4" (*b*) .. .. .. 10·00 22·00
207/10 .. .. .. .. *Set of* 4 4·25 6·00

**1890–91.** *Colours changed. Wmk Crown CA. P* 14
213 **30** 1 c. sea-green (12.90) .. .. .. 30 10
214 5 c. ultramarine (1.91) .. .. .. 2·50 10
215 8 c. dull purple and greenish black (10.90) .. .. .. .. 2·50 2·75
213/15 .. .. .. .. *Set of* 3 4·75 2·75
213/215 Optd "Specimen" .. .. *Set of* 3 60·00

**32** Mount Roraima

**33** Kaieteur Falls

(Recess D.L.R.)

**1898** (18 July). *Queen Victoria's Jubilee. Wmk Crown CC (sideways on T* **32**). *P* 14.
216 **32** 1 c. blue-black and carmine .. .. 2·75 25
217 **33** 2 c. brown and indigo .. .. .. 5·00 90
a. Imperf between (horiz pair) .. £3250
218 2 c. brown and blue .. .. .. 12·00 90
219 **32** 5 c. green and sepia .. .. .. 18·00 2·00
a. Imperf between (horiz pair) ..
220 **33** 10 c. blue-black and orange-red .. .. 15·00 20·00
221 **32** 15 c. red-brown and blue .. .. .. 18·00 16·00
216/21 .. .. .. .. *Set of* 5 55·00 35·00
216/21 Optd "Specimen" .. .. *Set of* 5 90·00

A second plate was later used for the 1 c. on which the lines of shading on the mountains in the background are strengthened, and those along the ridge show distinct from each other, whereas, in the original, they are more or less blurred. In the second plate the shading of the sky is less pronounced.

TWO CENTS.

(34)

35

(Surch at Printing Office of the *Daily Chronicle*, Georgetown)

**1899** (22 Feb–15 June). *Surch with T* **34**.
222 **32** 2 c. on 5 c. (No. 219) (15 June) .. .. 1·60 1·10
a. No stop after "CENTS" (R. 9/5) .. 50·00 45·00
b. Comma after "CENTS" (R. 7/2) ..
c. "CINTS" (R. 4/1) .. .. ..
223 **33** 2 c. on 10 c. (No. 220) .. .. .. 60 1·40
a. No stop after "CENTS" (R.5/5 or 2/9) 20·00 45·00
b. "GENTS" for "CENTS" (R. 5/7) .. 50·00 60·00
c. Surch inverted .. .. .. £300 £325
224 **32** 2 c. on 15 c. (No. 221) .. .. .. 1·25 1·25
a. No stop after "CENTS" (R. 9/2 1st setting only) .. .. .. 50·00 55·00
b. Surch double .. .. .. £425 £500
c. Surch double, one without stop ..
d. Surch inverted .. .. .. £300 £350
222/4 .. .. .. .. *Set of* 3 3·00 3·25

No. 222c was caused by damage to the first "E" of "CENTS" which developed during surcharging. The listing is for an example with only the upright stroke of the letter visible.

There were two settings of No. 223 with the no stop varieties occurring on R. 5/5 of the first and R. 2/9 of the second.

Only one example of No. 224c is known.

**1900–7.** *T* **30**. *Wmk Crown CA. P* 14
233 1 c. grey-green (1907) .. .. .. 3·50 2·00
234 2 c. dull purple and carmine .. .. 3·25 25
235 2 c. dull purple and black/*red* (1901) .. 1·00 10
236 6 c. grey-black and ultramarine (1902) .. 6·50 11·00
237 48 c. grey and purple-brown (1901) .. 45·00 32·00
*a. Brownish grey and brown* (1907) .. 24·00 28·00
238 60 c. green and rosine (1903) .. .. 55·00 £140
233/8 .. .. .. .. *Set of* 6 85·00 £160
233/8 Optd "Specimen" .. .. *Set of* 6 90·00

No. 233 is a reissue of No. 213 in non-fugitive ink.

**1905–7.** *Wmk Multiple Crown CA. Ordinary paper* (1 c. *to* 60 c.) *or chalk-surfaced paper* (72, 96 c.).
240 **30** 1 c. grey-green .. .. .. .. 1·40 30
a. Chalk-surfaced paper .. .. 2·75 30
241 2 c. purple and black/*red* .. .. 5·00 10
a. Chalk-surfaced paper .. .. 2·25 10
242 4 c. dull purple and ultramarine .. 7·00 6·50
a. Chalk-surfaced paper .. .. 6·00 8·00
243 5 c. dull pur & bl/*bl* (1.5.05) (Optd S. £20) 6·50 3·50
a. Chalk-surfaced paper .. .. 3·50 3·75
244 6 c. grey-black and ultramarine .. 16·00 28·00
a. Chalk-surfaced paper .. .. 15·00 29·00
245 12 c. dull and bright purple .. .. 22·00 30·00
a. Chalk-surfaced paper .. .. 22·00 35·00
246 24 c. dull purple and green (1906) .. 5·00 6·00
a. Chalk-surfaced paper .. .. 3·75 4·50
247 48 c. grey and purple-brown .. .. 18·00 25·00
a. Chalk-surfaced paper .. .. 13·00 20·00
248 60 c. green and rosine .. .. .. 24·00 55·00
a. Chalk-surfaced paper .. .. 14·00 55·00
249 72 c. purple and orange-brown (1907) .. 26·00 48·00
250 96 c. black & vermilion/*yellow* (20.11.05) (Optd S. £30) .. .. .. 35·00 45·00
240/50 .. .. .. .. *Set of* 11 £130 £225

**1905.** *Optd* "POSTAGE AND REVENUE". *Wmk Multiple Crown CA. Chalk-surfaced paper. P* 14.
251 **35** $2.40 green and violet (S. £75) .. .. £160 £250

**1907–10.** *Colours changed. Wmk Mult Crown CA. P* 14
252 **30** 1 c. blue-green .. .. .. .. 3·75 2·25
253 2 c. rose-red .. .. .. .. 6·00 10
a. Redrawn (1910) .. .. .. 6·00 10
254 4 c. brown and purple .. .. .. 2·25 60
255 5 c. ultramarine .. .. .. 3·00 70
256 6 c. grey and black .. .. .. 13·00 7·00
257 12 c. orange and mauve .. .. .. 4·00 4·00
252/7 .. .. .. .. *Set of* 6 29·00 13·00
253/7 Optd "Specimen" .. .. *Set of* 5 75·00

In No. 253a the flag at the main truck is close to the mast, whereas in the original type it appears to be flying loose from halyards. There are two background lines above the value "2 CENTS" instead of three and the "S" is further away from the end of the tablet.

37

War
Tax

(38)

(Typo D.L.R.)

**1913–21.** *Wmk Mult Crown CA. Chalk-surfaced paper* (4 c. *and* 48 c. *to* 96 c.). *P* 14.
259 **37** 1 c. yellow-green .. .. .. 1·00 70
*a. Blue-green* (1917) .. .. .. 1·25 25
260 2 c. carmine .. .. .. .. 50 10
*a. Scarlet* (1916) .. .. .. 90 10
b. Wmk sideways .. .. .. † £1500
261 4 c. brown and bright purple (1914) .. 1·50 25
*a. Deep brown and purple* .. .. 2·00 25
262 5 c. bright blue .. .. .. .. 60 85
263 6 c. grey and black .. .. .. 75 85
264 12 c. orange and violet .. .. .. 70 90
265 24 c. dull purple and green (1915) .. 2·25 4·00
266 48 c. grey and purple-brown (1914) .. 8·50 10·00
267 60 c. green and rosine (1915) .. .. 13·00 38·00
268 72 c. purple and orange-brown (1915) .. 38·00 48·00
269 96 c. black and vermilion/*yellow* (1915) .. 28·00 45·00
*a. White back* (1913) .. .. .. 14·00 29·00
*b. On lemon* (1916) (Optd S. £20) .. 16·00 32·00
*c. On pale yellow* (1921) (Optd S. £20) 18·00 50·00
259/69*a* .. .. .. .. *Set of* 11 70·00 £120
259/69*a* Optd "Specimen" .. .. *Set of* 11 £130

**1918** (4 Jan). *No.* 260*a optd with T* **38**, *by D.L.R.*
271 **37** 2 c. scarlet .. .. .. .. 15 15

The relative position of the words "WAR" and "TAX" vary considerably in the sheet.

**1921–27.** *Wmk Mult Script CA. Chalk-surfaced paper* (24 c. t 96 c.). *P* 14.
272 **37** 1 c. green (1922) .. .. .. 1·50 2
273 2 c. rose-carmine .. .. .. 1·00 2
274 2 c. bright violet (1923) .. .. 50 1
275 4 c. brown and bright purple (1922) .. 1·50 1
276 6 c. bright blue (1922) .. .. .. 2·00 2
277 12 c. orange and violet (1922) .. .. 1·50 1·5
278 24 c. dull purple and green .. .. 1·50 4·5
279 48 c. black and purple (1926) .. .. 8·00 3·5
280 60 c. green and rosine (1926) .. .. 6·50 30·0
281 72 c. dull purple and orange-brown (1923) 7·00 30·0
282 96 c. black and red/*yellow* (1927) .. 13·00 32·0
272/82 .. .. .. .. *Set of* 11 40·00 90·0
272/82 Optd "Specimen" .. .. *Set of* 11 £150

**39** Ploughing a Rice Field

**40** Indian shooting Fish

(Recess Waterlow)

**1931** (21 July). *Centenary of County Union T* **39/40** *and simila designs. Wmk Mult Script CA. P* 12½.
283 1 c. emerald-green .. .. .. .. 1·00 7
284 2 c. brown .. .. .. .. .. 1·00 1
285 4 c. carmine .. .. .. .. .. 1·75 3
286 6 c. blue .. .. .. .. .. 1·25 2·5
287 $1 violet .. .. .. .. .. 18·00 35·0
283/7 .. .. .. .. *Set of* 5 21·00 35·0
283/7 Perf "Specimen" .. .. *Set of* 5 75·00

Designs: *Vert*—4 c., $1 Kaieteur Falls. *Horiz*—6 c. Public buildings, Georgetown.

**43** Ploughing a Rice Field

**44** Gold Mining

(Recess Waterlow)

**1934** (1 Oct)–**51**. *T* **40** (*without dates at top of frame*), **43/4** *an similar designs. Wmk Mult Script CA* (*sideways on hori designs*). *P* 12½.
288 **43** 1 c. green .. .. .. .. .. 40 3
289 **40** 2 c. red-brown .. .. .. .. 1·00 1
290 **44** 3 c. scarlet .. .. .. .. .. 15 1
aa. Wmk error. Crown missing .. ..
a. Perf 12½×13½ (30.12.43) .. .. 30 1
b. Perf 13×14 (28.4.49) .. .. 30 1
291 – 4 c. slate-violet .. .. .. .. 1·50 3
a. Imperf between (vert pair) .. .. † £900
b. Imperf horiz (vert pair) .. .. £5500 £600
292 – 6 c. deep ultramarine .. .. .. 2·50 1·7
293 – 12 c. red-orange .. .. .. .. 10 1
a. Perf 14×13 (16.4.51) .. .. 10 4
294 – 24 c. purple .. .. .. .. .. 1·75 2·5
295 – 48 c. black .. .. .. .. .. 6·50 6·5
296 – 50 c. green .. .. .. .. .. 9·00 13·0
297 – 60 c. red-brown .. .. .. .. 25·00 26·0
298 – 72 c. purple .. .. .. .. .. 1·25 7
299 – 96 c. black .. .. .. .. .. 20·00 28·0
300 – $1 bright violet .. .. .. .. 32·00 24·0
288/300 .. .. .. .. *Set of* 13 90·00 90·0
288/300 Perf "Specimen" .. .. *Set of* 13 £140

Designs: *Vert*—4 c., 50 c. Kaieteur Falls (as No. 285, but wit dates omitted); 96 c. Sir Walter Raleigh and his son. *Horiz*—6 Shooting logs over falls; 12 c. Stabroek Market 24 c. Sugar cane i punts; 48 c. Forest road; 60 c. Victoria Regia Lilies; 72 c. Moun Roraima; $1 Botanical Gardens.

**1935** (6 May). *Silver Jubilee. As T* **13** *of Antigua.*
301 2 c. ultramarine and grey .. .. .. 15 1
f. Diagonal line by turret .. .. 18·00
h. Dot by flagstaff .. .. .. 18·00
302 6 c. brown and deep blue .. .. .. 80 3
f. Diagonal line by turret .. .. 35·00
g. Dot to left of chapel .. .. .. 35·00
303 12 c. green and indigo .. .. .. 1·25 3·7
f. Diagonal line by turret .. .. 45·00
h. Dot by flagstaff .. .. .. 45·00
304 24 c. slate and purple .. .. .. 3·50 4·7
h. Dot by flagstaff .. .. .. 75·00
301/4 .. .. .. .. *Set of* 4 5·25 8·0
301/4 Perf "Specimen" .. .. *Set of* 4 70·00

For illustrations of plate varieties see Catalogue Introduction.

**1937** (12 May). *Coronation. As Nos.* 110/11 *of Antigua, but ptd by D.L.R. P* 14.
305 2 c. yellow-brown .. .. .. .. 15 1
306 4 c. grey-black .. .. .. .. 50 1
307 6 c. bright blue .. .. .. .. 75 7
305/7 .. .. .. .. *Set of* 3 1·25 9
305/7 Perf "Specimen" .. .. *Set of* 3 50·00

**MINIMUM PRICE**

The minimum price quote is 10p which represents a handling charge rather than a basis for valuing common stamps. For further notes about prices see introductory pages.

**53** South America **54** Victoria Regia Lilies

(Recess Waterlow)

**38** (1 Feb)–**1952**. *As earlier types but with portrait of King George VI as in T* **53/4**. *Wmk Mult Script CA. P* 12½

| | | | | |
|---|---|---|---|---|
| 08 | **43** | 1 c. yellow-green .. .. .. .. | 5·50 | 35 |
| | | *aa. Green* (1944) .. .. .. .. | 10 | 10 |
| | | a. Perf 14×13 (1949) .. .. .. | 10 | 50 |
| 09 | – | 2 c. slate-violet .. .. .. | 30 | 10 |
| | | a. Perf 13×14 (28.4.49) .. .. | 30 | 10 |
| 10 | **53** | 4 c. scarlet and black .. .. | 40 | 10 |
| | | a. Imperf horiz (vert pair) .. .. | £6500 | £5000 |
| | | b. Perf 13×14 (1952) .. .. .. | 35 | 10 |
| 11 | **40** | 6 c. deep ultramarine .. .. .. | 25 | 10 |
| | | a. Perf 13×14 (24.10.49) .. .. | 30 | 30 |
| 12 | – | 24 c. blue-green .. .. .. .. | 18·00 | 8·50 |
| | | a. Wmk sideways .. .. .. | 1·00 | 10 |
| 13 | – | 36 c. bright violet (7.3.38).. .. .. | 1·00 | 10 |
| | | a. Perf 13×14 (13.12.51) .. .. | 1·75 | 30 |
| 14 | – | 48 c. orange .. .. .. .. | 50 | 30 |
| | | a. Perf 14×13 (14.6.51) .. .. | 1·25 | 1·25 |
| 15 | – | 60 c. red-brown .. .. .. .. | 4·75 | 2·50 |
| 16 | – | 96 c. purple .. .. .. .. .. | 2·00 | 2·00 |
| | | a. Perf 12½×13½ (1944) .. .. | 1·75 | 3·25 |
| | | b. Perf 13×14 (8.2.51) .. .. .. | 2·25 | 4·25 |
| 17 | – | $1 bright violet .. .. .. .. | 5·50 | 35 |
| | | a. Perf 14×13(1951) .. .. .. | £200 | £275 |
| 18 | – | $2 purple (11.6.45) .. .. .. | 4·00 | 8·00 |
| | | a. Perf 14×13 (9.8.50) .. .. .. | 6·00 | 8·00 |
| 19 | **54** | $3 red-brown (2.7.45) .. .. .. | 23·00 | 20·00 |
| | | *a. Bright red-brown* (12.46) .. .. | 26·00 | 28·00 |
| | | b. Perf 14×13. *Red-brown* (29.10.52) .. | 23·00 | 40·00 |
| 08a/19 | | .. .. .. .. *Set of* 12 | 38·00 | 30·00 |
| 08/19 Perf "Specimen" | | .. .. *Set of* 12 | £200 | |

Designs: *Vert*—2 c., 36 c. Kaieteur Falls; 96 c. Sir Walter aleigh and his son. *Horiz*—24 c. Sugar cane in punts; 48 c. Forest ad; 60 c. Shooting logs over falls; $1 Botanical Gardens; $2 Mount oraima.

**46** (1 Oct). *Victory. As Nos.* 110/11 *of Antigua.*

| | | | |
|---|---|---|---|
| 20 | 3 c. carmine .. .. .. .. .. | 10 | 10 |
| 21 | 6 c. blue .. .. .. .. .. | 10 | 10 |
| 20/1 Perf "Specimen" | .. .. *Set of* 2 | 48·00 | |

**48** (20 Dec). *Royal Silver Wedding. As Nos.* 112/13 *of Antigua, but $3 in recess.*

| | | | |
|---|---|---|---|
| 22 | 3 c. scarlet .. .. .. .. .. | 10 | 20 |
| 23 | $3 red-brown .. .. .. .. .. | 9·00 | 13·00 |

**49** (10 Oct). *75th Anniv of Universal Postal Union. As Nos.* 114/17 *of Antigua.*

| | | | |
|---|---|---|---|
| 24 | 4 c. carmine .. .. .. .. .. | 20 | 15 |
| 25 | 6 c. deep blue .. .. .. .. .. | 25 | 35 |
| 26 | 12 c. orange .. .. .. .. .. | 25 | 30 |
| 27 | 24 c. blue-green .. .. .. .. .. | 25 | 45 |
| 24/7 | .. .. .. .. .. *Set of* 4 | 85 | 1·10 |

**51** (16 Feb). *University College of B.W.I. As Nos.* 118/19 *of Antigua.*

| | | | |
|---|---|---|---|
| 28 | 3 c. black and carmine .. .. .. .. | 15 | 10 |
| 29 | 6 c. black and blue .. .. .. .. | 25 | 10 |

**53** (2 June). *Coronation. As No.* 120 *of Antigua.*

| | | | |
|---|---|---|---|
| 30 | 4 c. black and scarlet .. .. .. .. | 10 | 10 |

**55** G.P.O. Georgetown **62** Felling Greenheart.

Centre litho, frame recess ($1); recess (others). Waterlow (until 1961), then D.L.R.)

**954** (1 Dec)–**63**. *T* **55**, **62** *and similar designs. Wmk Mult Script CA. P* 12½×13* (*horiz*) *or* 13 (*vert*).

| | | | |
|---|---|---|---|
| 31 | 1 c. black .. .. .. .. .. | 10 | 10 |
| 32 | 2 c. myrtle-green .. .. .. .. | 10 | 10 |
| 33 | 3 c. brown-olive and red-brown .. .. | 1·75 | 10 |
| 34 | 4 c. violet .. .. .. .. .. | 10 | 10 |
| | a. D.L.R. ptg (5.12.61) .. .. .. | 4·50 | 1·75 |
| | *ab. Deep violet* (3.1.63) .. .. .. | 2·75 | 45 |
| 35 | 5 c. scarlet and black .. .. .. | 20 | 10 |
| 36 | 6 c. yellow-green .. .. .. .. | 10 | 10 |
| | a. D.L.R. ptg. *Green* (22.5.62) .. .. | 30 | 40 |
| 37 | 8 c. ultramarine .. .. .. .. | 10 | 10 |
| | a. D.L.R. ptg. *Blue* (19.9.61) .. .. | 2·75 | 30 |
| 38 | 12 c. black and reddish brown .. .. | 30 | 10 |
| | *a. Black and light brown* (13.6.56) .. | 15 | 10 |
| | b. D.L.R. ptg. *Black and brown* (11.7.61) | 2·75 | 55 |
| 39 | 24 c. black and brownish orange .. .. | 2·50 | 10 |
| | *a. Black and orange* (13.6.56) .. .. | 2·50 | 10 |
| 40 | 36 c. rose-carmine and black .. .. | 55 | 30 |
| 41 | 48 c. ultramarine and brown-lake .. .. | 60 | 50 |
| | *a. Brt ultram & pale brn-lake* (13.6.56) | 40 | 40 |
| | ab. D.L.R. ptg (19.9.61) .. .. .. | 20·00 | 13·00 |
| 42 | 72 c. carmine and emerald .. .. | 6·50 | 2·75 |
| | a. D.L.R. ptg (17.7.62) .. .. .. | 10·00 | 14·00 |

| | | | |
|---|---|---|---|
| 343 | $1 pink, yellow, green and black .. .. | 11·00 | 1·40 |
| 344 | $2 deep mauve .. .. .. .. | 8·50 | 2·50 |
| | a. D.L.R. ptg. *Reddish mauve* (11.7.61) | 16·00 | 4·75 |
| 345 | $5 ultramarine and black .. .. | 11·00 | 10·00 |
| | a. D.L.R. ptg (19.9.61) .. .. | 40·00 | 23·00 |
| 331/45 | .. .. .. .. *Set of* 15 | 38·00 | 16·00 |

Designs: *Horiz*—2 c. Botanical Gardens; 3 c. Victoria Regia Lilies; 5 c. Map of Caribbean; 6 c. Rice combine-harvester; 8 c. Sugar cane entering factory; 24 c. Mining for bauxite; 36 c. Mount Roraima; $1 Channel-billed Toucan; $2 Dredging gold. *Vert*—4 c. Amerindian shooting fish; 48 c. Kaieteur Falls; 72 c. Arapaima; $5 Arms of British Guiana.

The separately listed De La Rue printings are identifiable as singles by the single wide-tooth perfs at each side at the bottom of the stamps. In the Waterlow these wide teeth are at the top.

*All the Waterlow printing and early De La Rue printings of the horizontal designs measure 12.3 × 12.8, but De La Rue printings of 22 May 1962 and all later printings (including those on the Block CA watermark) measure 12.3 × 12.6.

See also Nos. 354/65.

**SELF-GOVERNMENT**

**70**

(Photo Harrison)

**1961** (23 Oct). *History and Culture Week. W* w **12** *P* 14½ × 14.

| | | | | |
|---|---|---|---|---|
| 346 | **70** | 5 c. sepia and orange-red .. .. | 10 | 10 |
| 347 | | 6 c. sepia and blue-green .. .. | 10 | 10 |
| 348 | | 30 c. sepia and yellow-orange .. | 20 | 20 |
| 346/8 | | .. .. .. .. *Set of* 3 | 30 | 30 |

**1963** (14 July). *Freedom from Hunger. As No.* 146 *of Antigua.*

| | | | |
|---|---|---|---|
| 349 | 20 c. reddish violet .. .. .. .. | 30 | 10 |

**1963** (2 Sept). *Red Cross Centenary. As Nos.* 147/8 *of Antigua.*

| | | | |
|---|---|---|---|
| 350 | 5 c. red and black .. .. .. .. | 10 | 15 |
| 351 | 20 c. red and blue .. .. .. .. | 35 | 25 |

**1963–65.** *As Nos.* 333/44, *but wmk* w **12**.

| | | | |
|---|---|---|---|
| 354 | 3 c. brown-olive and red-brown (12.65) .. | 4·00 | 4·25 |
| 356 | 5 c. scarlet and black (28.5.64) .. | 30 | 10 |
| 359 | 12 c. black and yellowish brown (6.10.64) .. | 20 | 10 |
| 360 | 24 c. black and bright orange (10.12.63) .. | 1·50 | 10 |
| 361 | 36 c. rose-carmine and black (10.12.63) .. | 60 | 40 |
| 362 | 48 c. bright ultramarine and Venetian red (25.11.63) .. .. .. | 1·25 | 2·00 |
| 363 | 72 c. carmine and emerald (25.11.63) .. | 4·00 | 13·00 |
| 364 | $1 pink, yellow, green and black (10.12.63) | 6·50 | 90 |
| 365 | $2 reddish mauve (10.12.63) .. .. | 6·50 | 14·00 |
| 354/65 | .. .. .. .. *Set of* 9 | 22·00 | 30·00 |

There was no London release of No. 354.

For 1 c. value, see No. 393aA of Guyana.

**71** Weightlifting

(Photo D.L.R.)

**1964** (1 Oct). *Olympic Games, Tokyo. W* w **12**. *P* 13 × 13½.

| | | | | |
|---|---|---|---|---|
| 367 | **71** | 5 c. orange .. .. .. .. | 10 | 10 |
| 368 | | 8 c. blue .. .. .. .. .. | 10 | 10 |
| 369 | | 25 c. magenta .. .. .. .. | 20 | 20 |
| 367/9 | | .. .. .. .. *Set of* 3 | 30 | 30 |

**1965** (17 May). *I.T.U. Centenary. As Nos.* 166/7 *of Antigua.*

| | | | |
|---|---|---|---|
| 370 | 5 c. emerald and yellow-olive .. .. | 10 | 15 |
| 371 | 25 c. light blue and magenta .. .. | 20 | 15 |

**1965** (25 Oct). *International Co-operation Year. As Nos.* 168/9 *of Antigua.*

| | | | |
|---|---|---|---|
| 372 | 5 c. reddish purple and turquoise-green .. | 10 | 10 |
| 373 | 25 c. deep bluish green and lavender .. | 25 | 20 |

**72** St. George's Cathedral, Georgetown

(Des Jennifer Toombs, Photo Harrison)

**1966** (24 Jan). *Churchill Commemoration. W* w **12**. *P* 14 × 14½.

| | | | | |
|---|---|---|---|---|
| 374 | **72** | 5 c. black, crimson and gold .. .. | 30 | 10 |
| 375 | | 25 c. black, blue and gold .. .. | 1·10 | 40 |

**1966** (3 Feb). *Royal Visit. As Nos.* 174/5 *of Antigua.*

| | | | |
|---|---|---|---|
| 376 | 3 c. black and ultramarine .. .. .. | 50 | 15 |
| 377 | 25 c. black and magenta .. .. .. | 1·50 | 60 |

## GUYANA

British Guiana became independent as Guyana on 25 May 1966.

**GUYANA**
**INDEPENDENCE**
**1966**

**(73)**

**1966** (26 May)–**67**. *Various stamps as Nos.* 311/45 *optd with T* **73** *by De La Rue.* (i) *Wmk Mult Script CA.*

| | | | |
|---|---|---|---|
| 379 | 2 c. myrtle-green .. .. .. .. | 10 | 10 |
| 380 | 3 c. brown-olive and red-brown .. .. | 3·00 | 3·25 |
| 381 | 4 c. violet .. .. .. .. .. | 10 | 10 |
| 383 | 6 c. yellow-green .. .. .. .. | 10 | 10 |
| 384 | 8 c. ultramarine .. .. .. .. | 10 | 10 |
| 385 | 12 c. black and reddish brown .. .. | 10 | 15 |
| 392 | $5 ultramarine and black .. .. .. | 27·00 | 32·00 |
| 379/92 | .. .. .. .. *Set of* 7 | 27·00 | 32·00 |

(ii) *Wmk w* **12**. A. *Upright.* B. *Sideways*

| | | A | | B | |
|---|---|---|---|---|---|
| 393 | 1 c. .. .. .. .. | 10 | 10 | 10 | 10 |
| | a. Opt omitted .. .. | 85·00 | — | † | |
| 395 | 3 c. .. .. .. .. | 10 | 10 | † | |
| 396 | 4 c. .. .. .. .. | 10 | 10 | 10 | 10 |
| 397 | 5 c. .. .. .. .. | 10 | 10 | † | |
| 398 | 6 c. .. .. .. .. | 10 | 10 | † | |
| 399 | 8 c. .. .. .. .. | 10 | 30 | 10 | 10 |
| 400 | 12 c. .. .. .. .. | 10 | 10 | 10 | 10 |
| 401 | 24 c. .. .. .. .. | 1·40 | 10 | 1·40 | 20 |
| 402 | 36 c. .. .. .. .. | 25 | 25 | 20 | 35 |
| 403 | 48 c. .. .. .. .. | 5·00 | 7·50 | 30 | 30 |
| 404 | 72 c. .. .. .. .. | 30 | 50 | 65 | 1·00 |
| 405 | $1 .. .. .. .. | 35 | 35 | 1·50 | 1·00 |
| 406 | $2 .. .. .. .. | 1·00 | 75 | 1·00 | 1·40 |
| 407 | $5 .. .. .. .. | 1·00 | 1·75 | 1·75 | 2·75 |
| 393A/407A | .. .. *Set of* 14 | 9·00 | 11·00 | | |
| 393B/407B | .. .. *Set of* 11 | | | 6·00 | 6·50 |

Dates of issue: Of the above, the 1 c., 4 c., 6 c. (W w **12** upright) and the 12 c., 36 c., 72 c., $2 and $5 (W w **12** sideways) were issued on 28.2.67; the 8 c. upright wmk and the $1 sideways wmk, on 14.3.67; the rest on 26.5.66.

No. 393a is listed here as an error as there is no evidence of the 1 c. basic stamp having been issued as a printing with Block CA watermark.

See also Nos. 420/40.

**74** Flag and Map **75** Arms of Guyana

(Des V. Whiteley. Photo Harrison)

**1966** (26 May). *Independence. P* 14½.

| | | | | |
|---|---|---|---|---|
| 408 | **74** | 5 c. multicoloured .. .. .. | 10 | 10 |
| 409 | | 15 c. multicoloured .. .. .. | 10 | 10 |
| 410 | **75** | 25 c. multicoloured .. .. .. | 10 | 10 |
| 411 | | $1 multicoloured .. .. .. | 20 | 25 |
| 408/11 | | .. .. .. .. *Set of* 4 | 30 | 30 |

**76** Bank Building

(Des R. Granger Barrett. Photo Enschedé)

**1966** (11 Oct). *Opening of Bank of Guyana. P* 13½ × 14.

| | | | | |
|---|---|---|---|---|
| 412 | **76** | 5 c. multicoloured .. .. .. | 10 | 10 |
| 413 | | 25 c. multicoloured .. .. .. | 10 | 10 |

**CANCELLED REMAINDERS.*** In 1969 remainders of some issues were put on the market cancelled-to-order in such a way as to be indistinguishable from genuine postally used copies for all practical purposes. Our used quotations which are indicated by an asterisk are the same for cancelled-to-order or postally used copies.

**77** British Guiana One Cent Stamp of 1856

(Des V. Whiteley. Litho D.L.R.)

**1967** (23 Feb). *World's Rarest Stamp Commemoration. P* 12½.
414 **77** 5 c. black, magenta, silver & light ochre .. 10 10*
415 25 c. black, magenta, gold and light green .. 10 10*

**78** Château Margot

**GUYANA**
**INDEPENDENCE**
**1966**
(82)

(Des R. Granger Barrett. Photo Harrison)

**1967** (26 May). *First Anniv of Independence. T* **78** *and similar multicoloured designs. P* 14 (6 c.), 14½ × 14 (15 c.) *or* 14 × 14½ (*others*).
416 6 c. Type **78** .. .. .. .. .. 10 10*
417 15 c. Independence Arch .. .. .. 10 10*
418 25 c. Fort Island (*horiz*) .. .. .. 10 10*
419 $1 National Assembly (*horiz*) .. .. 20 15
416/19 .. .. .. .. *Set of* 4 20 15

**1967–68.** *Stamps as Nos.* 331/45 *optd with T* **82** *locally.*

(i) *Wmk Mult Script CA*
420 1 c. black (3.10.67) .. .. .. 10 10
a. Opt inverted .. .. .. 28·00
b. Date misplaced 5 mm .. .. 8·00
c. Date misplaced 2 mm .. .. 8·00
421 2 c. myrtle-green (3.10.67) .. .. 10 10
a. "1966" for "GUYANA" .. .. 17·00
b. Date misplaced 5 mm .. .. 8·00
c. Date misplaced 2 mm .. .. 8·00
422 3 c. brown-olive and red-brown (3.10.67) 30 10
a. "1966" for "GUYANA" .. .. 12·00
b. Vert pair, one without opt .. £300
c. Date misplaced 2 mm .. .. 8·00
423 4 c. violet (10.67) .. .. .. 10 10
*a. Deep violet* .. .. .. 20 20
b. Opt inverted .. .. .. 38·00
424 6 c. yellow-green (11.67) .. .. 10 10
a. "1966" for "GUYANA" .. .. 18·00
b. Opt inverted .. .. .. 35·00
c. Opt double .. .. ..
425 8 c. ultramarine (12.67) .. .. 10 10
426 12 c. black and brown (12.67) .. .. 10 10
426*a* 24 c. black and orange (date?) .. £170 75·00
427 $2 reddish mauve (12.67) .. .. 80 1·40
428 $5 ultramarine and black (12.67) .. 1·50 2·25

(ii) *Wmk w* **12** (*upright*)
429 1 c. black (2.68) .. .. .. 10 10
430 2 c. myrtle-green (2.68) .. .. 20 20
431 3 c. brown-olive and red-brown (3.10.67) 30 10
a. "1966" for "GUYANA" .. .. 75·00
b. Opt inverted .. .. .. 20·00
432 4 c. violet (2.68) .. .. .. 10 10
433 5 c. scarlet and black (3.10.67) .. 2·00 80
*a. Deep scarlet and black* .. .. 30 40
c. Date misplaced 2 mm .. .. 8·00
434 6 c. yellow-green (2.68) .. .. 10 10
a. Opt double, one diagonal .. 50·00
435 24 c. black and bright orange (11.12.67) .. 1·25 10
a. Opt double, one diagonal (horiz pair) £180
436 36 c. rose-carmine and black (12.67) .. 30 10
437 48 c. bright ultramarine and Venetian red (12.67) .. .. .. .. 30 40
a. Opt inverted .. .. .. 35·00
438 72 c. carmine and emerald (12.67) .. 80 40
439 $1 pink, yellow, green and black (12.67) 2·50 50
440 $2 reddish mauve (12.67) .. .. 2·50 2·50
420/40 (*excl.* 426*a*) .. .. *Set of* 21 10·50 8·00

The "1966" errors occurred on R. 7/10 and were later corrected. Nos. 425/8 and 436/40 were issued in mid-December, but some were cancelled-to-order with a November date in error.

On Nos. 420b and 421b the "1" of "1966" is below the second "D" of "INDEPENDENCE" (R. 6/3). On Nos. 420c, 421c, 422c and 433c it is below the second "E" (R. 6/1).

No. 433*a* is from a printing made specially for this overprint.

**83** "Millie" (Blue and Yellow Macaw)

**84** Wicket-keeping

(Des V. Whiteley. Photo Harrison)

**1967–68.** *Christmas. P* 14½ × 14. (*a*) *First issue* (6 Nov 1967).
441 **83** 5 c. yellow, new blue, blk & bronze-grn 10 10*
442 25 c. yellow, new blue, black and violet .. 15 10*

(*b*) *Second issue. Colours changed* (22 Jan 1968)
443 **83** 5 c. yellow, new blue, black and red .. 10 10*
444 25 c. yellow, new blue, blk & apple-grn .. 15 10*

(Des V. Whiteley. Photo Harrison)

**1968** (8 Jan). *M.C.C.'s West Indies Tour. T* **84** *and similar vert designs. P* 14.
445 5 c. Type **84** .. .. .. .. 10 10*
a. Strip of 3. Nos. 445/7 .. .. 70
446 6 c. Batting .. .. .. .. 10 10*
447 25 c. Bowling .. .. .. .. 30 10*
445/7 .. .. .. .. *Set of* 3 70 15*

Nos. 445/7 were issued in small sheets of 9 containing three *se-tenant* strips.

**87** Sunfish

**102** "Christ of St John of the Cross" (Salvador Dali)

(Des R. Granger Barrett. Photo Harrison)

**1968** (4 Mar). *Multicoloured designs as T* **87**, *showing fish* (1 *to* 6 *c.*), *birds* (10 *to* 40 *c.*) *or animals* (*others*). *No wmk. P* 14 × 14½.
448 1 c. Type **87** .. .. .. .. 10 10
449 2 c. Pirai .. .. .. .. 10 10
450 3 c. Lukunani .. .. .. .. 10 10
451 5 c. Hassar .. .. .. .. 10 10
452 6 c. Patua .. .. .. .. 20 10
453 10 c. Spix's Guan (*vert*) .. .. .. 40 10
454 15 c. Harpy Eagle (*vert*) .. .. .. 75 10
455 20 c. Hoatzin (*vert*) .. .. .. 50 10
456 25 c. Guianan Cock of the Rock (*vert*) .. 50 10
457 40 c. Great Kiskadee (*vert*) .. .. 60 20
458 50 c. Brazilian Agouti ("Accouri") .. 80 40
459 60 c. White-lipped Peccary .. .. 80 10
460 $1 Paca ("Labba") .. .. .. 1·00 10
461 $2 Nine-banded Armadillo .. .. 1·50 2·00
462 $5 Ocelot .. .. .. .. 2·00 3·00
448/62 .. .. .. *Set of* 15 8·00 5·50

For Nos. 448/62 with W **106** see Nos. 485/99.

(Des and photo Harrison)

**1968** (25 Mar). *Easter. P* 14.
463 **102** 5 c. multicoloured .. .. .. 10 10*
464 25 c. multicoloured .. .. .. 10 10*

**103** "Efficiency Year"

**104** "Savings Bonds"

(Des W. Starzmann. Litho B.W.)

**1968** (22 July). *"Savings Bonds and Efficiency". P* 14.
465 **103** 6 c. multicoloured .. .. .. 10 10*
466 25 c. multicoloured .. .. .. 10 10*
467 **104** 30 c. multicoloured .. .. .. 10 10*
468 40 c. multicoloured .. .. .. 10 10*
465/8 .. .. .. .. *Set of* 4 20 15*

**105** Open Book, Star and Crescent

(Des R. Gates. Photo D.L.R.)

**1968** (9 Oct). *1400th Anniv of the Holy Quran. P* 14.
469 **105** 6 c. black, gold and flesh .. .. 10 10*
470 25 c. black, gold and lilac .. .. 10 10*
471 30 c. black, gold and light apple-green .. 10 10*
472 40 c. black, gold and cobalt .. .. 10 10*
469/72 .. .. .. .. *Set of* 4 30 15*

## ALTERED CATALOGUE NUMBERS

Any Catalogue numbers altered from the last edition are shown as a list in the introductory pages.

**106** Lotus Blossoms

**107** Broadcasting Greetings

(Des L. Pritchard; adapted G. Vasarhelyi. Litho D.L.R.)

**1968** (11 Nov). *Christmas. T* **107** *and similar vert design. W* **1**[illegible] *P* 14.
473 6 c. brown, blue and green .. .. .. 10 1
474 25 c. brown, reddish violet and green .. 10 1
475 30 c. blue-green and turquoise-green .. 10 1
476 40 c. red and turquoise-green .. .. 10 1
473/6 .. .. .. .. *Set of* 4 30 1

Designs:—25 c. Type **107**; 30, 40 c. Map showing radio lin[illegible] Guyana–Trinidad.

**109** Festival Ceremony

(Des J. Cooter. Litho P.B.)

**1969** (26 Feb). *Hindu Festival of Phagwah. T* **109** *and simil*[illegible] *horiz design. Multicoloured. W* **106** (*sideways*). *P* 13½.
477 6 c. Type **109** .. .. .. .. 10
478 25 c. Ladies spraying scent .. .. 10
479 30 c. Type **109** .. .. .. .. 10
480 40 c. As 25 c. .. .. .. .. 10
477/80 .. .. .. .. *Set of* 4 30

**111** "Sacrament of the Last Supper" (Dali)

**112** Map showing "CARIFTA" Countries

(Photo D.L.R.)

**1969** (10 Mar). *Easter. W* **106** (*sideways*). *P* 13½ × 13.
481 **111** 6 c. multicoloured .. .. .. 10
482 25 c. multicoloured .. .. .. 10
483 30 c. multicoloured .. .. .. 10
484 40 c. multicoloured .. .. .. 10
481/4 .. .. .. .. *Set of* 4 30

**1969–71.** *As Nos.* 448/62, *but Wmk* **106** (*sideways on* 1 *to* 6 *c. a*[illegible] 50 *c. to* $5). *Chalk-surfaced paper.*
485 1 c. Type **87** .. .. .. .. 10
486 2 c. Pirai .. .. .. .. 10
487 3 c. Lukunani .. .. .. .. 10
488 5 c. Hassar .. .. .. .. 10
489 6 c. Patua .. .. .. .. 10
490 10 c. Spix's Guan .. .. .. .. 25
a. Glazed paper (21.12.71) .. .. 75 1·[illegible]
491 15 c. Harpy Eagle .. .. .. .. 30
a. Glazed paper (21.12.71) .. .. 1·00 1·[illegible]
492 20 c. Hoatzin .. .. .. .. 30
493 25 c. Guianan Cock of the Rock .. .. 30
a. Glazed paper (21.12.71) .. .. 1·25 2·[illegible]
494 40 c. Great Kiskadee .. .. .. 60
495 50 c. Brazilian Agouti ("Accouri") .. .. 35
496 60 c. White-lipped Peccary .. .. 35
497 $1 Paca ("Labba") .. .. .. 70
a. Glazed paper (21.12.71) .. .. 2·50 6·[illegible]
498 $2 Nine-banded Armadillo .. .. 1·00 3·[illegible]
499 $5 Ocelot .. .. .. .. 1·50 5·[illegible]
485/99 .. .. .. *Set of* 15 5·00 10·[illegible]

These were put on sale by the Crown Agents on 25 March 19[illegible] but although supplies were sent to Guyana in time they were n[illegible] released there until needed as ample supplies remained of th[illegible] stamps without watermark. It is understood that the 3 c. and 5 [illegible] were put on sale in early May 1969 followed by the 25 c. but the[illegible] are no records of when the remainder were released.

(Des J. Cooter. Litho P.B.)

**1969** (30 Apr). *First Anniv of CARIFTA* (*Caribbean Free Tra*[illegible] *Area*). *T* **112** *and similar design. W* **106** (*sideways on* 25 *c*[illegible] *P* 13½.
500 6 c. rose-red, ultramarine and turquoise-blue 10
501 25 c. lemon, brown and rose-red .. .. 10

Design: *Horiz*—25 c. "Strength in Unity".

114 Building *Independence* (first aluminium ship)    116 Scouts raising Flag

(Des R. Gates. Litho B.W.)

**1969** (30 Apr). *50th Anniv of International Labour Organization. T* **114** *and similar design. W* **106** *(sideways on 40 c.). P* 12 × 11 (30 c.) *or* 11 × 12 (40 c.).

502 30 c. turquoise-blue, black and silver .. .. 20 10
503 40 c. multicoloured .. .. .. .. 20 10

Design: *Horiz*—40 c. Bauxite processing plant.

(Des Jennifer Toombs. Litho B.W.)

**1969** (13 Aug). *Third Caribbean Scout Jamboree and Diamond Jubilee of Scouting in Guyana. T* **116** *and similar horiz design. Multicoloured. W* **106** *(sideways). P* 13.

504 6 c. Type **116** .. .. .. .. .. 10 10
505 8 c. Camp-fire cooking .. .. .. .. 10 10
506 25 c. Type **116** .. .. .. .. .. 10 10
507 30 c. As 8 c. .. .. .. .. .. 10 10
508 50 c. Type **116** .. .. .. .. .. 15 15
504/8 .. .. .. .. .. *Set of* 5 30 30

118 Gandhi and Spinning-wheel    119 "Mother Sally Dance Troupe"

(Des G. Drummond. Litho Format)

**1969** (1 Oct). *Birth Centenary of Mahatma Gandhi. W* **106** *(sideways). P* 14½.

509 **118** 6 c. black, brown and yellowish olive .. 15 20
510 15 c. black, brown and lilac .. .. 20 25

(Des V. Whiteley (5, 25 c.), J.W. (others). Litho B.W. (5, 25 c.), D.L.R. (others))

**1969** (17 Nov). *Christmas. T* **119** *and similar vert design. Multicoloured. No wmk* (5, 25 c.) *or W* **106**. *P* 13½ (5, 25 c.) *or* 13 × 13½ *(others).*

511 5 c. Type **119** .. .. .. .. .. 10 10
a. Opt omitted .. .. .. .. .. 28·00
b. Opt double .. .. .. .. .. 25·00
512 6 c. City Hall, Georgetown (*horiz*) .. .. 10 10
a. Opt omitted .. .. .. .. .. 28·00
b. Opt inverted .. .. .. .. .. 30·00
513 25 c. Type **119** .. .. .. .. .. 10 10
a. Opt omitted .. .. .. .. .. 28·00
514 60 c. As 6 c. .. .. .. .. .. 20 25
511/14 .. .. .. .. .. *Set of* 4 30 30

Nos. 511/14 are previously unissued stamps optd as in T **119** by Guyana Lithographic Co, Ltd.

## REPUBLIC

121 Forbes Burnham and Map    125 "The Descent from the Cross"

(Des L. Curtis. Litho D.L.R.)

**1970** (23 Feb). *Republic Day. T* **121** *and similar designs. W* **106** *(sideways on 15 and 25 c.). P* 14.

515 5 c. sepia, ochre and pale blue .. .. 10 10
516 6 c. multicoloured .. .. .. .. 10 10
517 15 c. multicoloured .. .. .. .. 10 10
518 25 c. multicoloured .. .. .. .. 10 10
515/18 .. .. .. .. .. *Set of* 4 20 20

Designs: *Vert*—6 c. "Rural Self-help". *Horiz*—15 c. University of Guyana; 25 c. Guyana House.

(Des J. Cooter. Litho Questa)

**1970** (24 Mar). *Easter. Paintings by Rubens. T* **125** *and similar vert design. Multicoloured. W* **106** *(inverted). P* 14 × 14½.

519 5 c. Type **125** .. .. .. .. .. 10 10
520 6 c. "Christ on the Cross" .. .. .. 10 10
521 15 c. Type **125** .. .. .. .. .. 10 10
522 25 c. As 6 c. .. .. .. .. .. 10 10
519/22 .. .. .. .. .. *Set of* 4 20 20

127 "Peace" and U.N. Emblem    128 "Mother and Child" (Philip Moore)

(Des and litho Harrison)

**1970** (26 Oct). *25th Anniv of United Nations. T* **127** *and similar horiz design. Multicoloured. W* **106** *(inverted). P* 14.

523 5 c. Type **127** .. .. .. .. .. 10 10
524 6 c. U.N. Emblem, Gold-panning and Drilling 10 10
525 15 c. Type **127** .. .. .. .. .. 10 10
526 25 c. As 6 c. .. .. .. .. .. 10 10
523/6 .. .. .. .. .. *Set of* 4 20 20

(Des Harrison. Litho J.W.)

**1970** (8 Dec). *Christmas. W* **106**. *P* 13½.

527 **128** 5 c. multicoloured .. .. .. 10 10
528 6 c. multicoloured .. .. .. 10 10
529 15 c. multicoloured .. .. .. 10 15
530 25 c. multicoloured .. .. .. 10 15
527/30 .. .. .. .. .. *Set of* 4 20 30

129 National Co-operative Bank    130 Racial Equality Symbol

(Des E. Samuels. Litho J.W.)

**1971** (23 Feb). *Republic Day. W* **106** *(sideways). P* 14.

531 **129** 6 c. multicoloured .. .. .. 10 10
532 15 c. multicoloured .. .. .. 10 10
533 25 c. multicoloured .. .. .. 10 10
531/3 .. .. .. .. .. *Set of* 3 20 20

(Des E. Samuels. Litho Harrison)

**1971** (22 Mar). *Racial Equality Year. W* **106** *(sideways). P* 14.

534 **130** 5 c. multicoloured .. .. .. 10 10
535 6 c. multicoloured .. .. .. 10 10
536 15 c. multicoloured .. .. .. 10 15
537 25 c. multicoloured .. .. .. 10 15
534/7 .. .. .. .. .. *Set of* 4 20 30

131 Young Volunteer felling Tree (from painting by J. Criswick).    132 Yellow Allamanda

(Des and litho Harrison)

**1971** (19 July). *First Anniv of Self-help Road Project. W* **106**. *P* 14.

538 **131** 5 c. multicoloured .. .. .. 10 10
539 20 c. multicoloured .. .. .. 15 10
540 25 c. multicoloured .. .. .. 20 10
541 50 c. multicoloured .. .. .. 30 65
538/41 .. .. .. .. .. *Set of* 4 65 80

Two types of 25 c.:

I Flowers facing up. Value in centre.

II Flowers facing down. Value to right. Colours changed.

(Des V. Whiteley (1 to 40 c.), PAD Studio (others). Litho D.L.R. (1 to 6 c.), J.W. (10 c. to 40 c.), Format (50 c. to $5))

**1971** (17 Sept)–**76**. *Flowering Plants. Vert designs as T* **132**. *Multicoloured. W* **106** *(sideways on* 1 c. *to* 40 c.). *P* 13 × 13½ (1 *to* 6 c.) *or* 13½ (10 c. *to* $5).

542 1 c. Pitcher Plant of Mt Roraima (15.1.72) 10 10
543 2 c. Type **132** .. .. .. .. .. 10 10
544 3 c. Hanging Heliconia .. .. .. .. 10 10
545 5 c. Annatto tree .. .. .. .. .. 10 10
546 6 c. Cannon-ball tree .. .. .. .. 10 10
547 10 c. Cattleya (18.9.72) .. .. .. 1·25 10
a. Perf 13 (28.1.76) .. .. .. .. 1·50 10
548 15 c. Christmas Orchid (18.9.72) .. .. 80 10
a. Perf 13 (3.9.76) .. .. .. .. 65 10
549 20 c. *Paphinia cristata* (18.9.72) .. .. 1·00 20
a. Perf 13 (28.1.76) .. .. .. .. 1·75 20
550 25 c. Marabunta (I) (18.9.72) .. .. 90 3·00
550*a* 25 c. Marabunta (II) (*wmk upright*) (20.8.73) .. .. .. .. .. 30 50
ab. Perf 13 (*wmk sideways*) (3.9.76) .. 45 10
551 40 c. Tiger Beard (18.9.72) .. .. .. 1·50 10
552 50 c. *Guzmania lingulata* (3.9.73) .. .. 40 50
553 60 c. Soldier's Cap (3.9.73) .. .. .. 40 50
554 $1 *Chelonanthus uliginoides* (3.9.73) .. 40 45
555 $2 *Norantea guianensis* (3.9.73) .. 60 1·50
556 $5 *Odontadenia grandiflora* (3.9.73) .. 1·00 1·50
542/56 .. .. .. .. *Set of* 16 8·00 7·75

The watermark is often indistinct, particularly on the early printings.

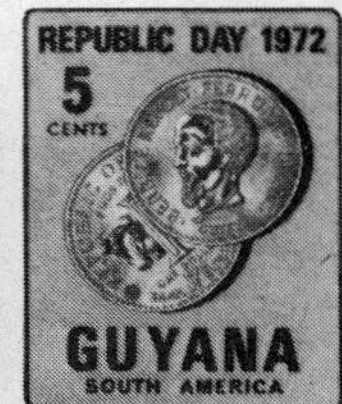


133 Child praying at Bedside    134 Obverse and Reverse of Guyana $1 Coin

(Des V. Bassoo (T **133**), M. Austin (25, 50 c.). Litho J.W.)

**1971** (29 Nov). *Christmas. T* **133** *and similar vert design. Multicoloured. W* **106** *(sideways on* 5 c. *and* 20 c.). *P* 13½.

557 5 c. Type **133** .. .. .. .. .. 10 10
558 20 c. Type **133** .. .. .. .. .. 10 10
559 25 c. Carnival Masquerader .. .. .. 10 10
560 50 c. As 25 c. .. .. .. .. .. 20 30
557/60 .. .. .. .. .. *Set of* 4 35 50

(Des G. Drummond. Litho Questa)

**1972** (23 Feb). *Republic Day. T* **134** *and similar vert design. W* **106** *(sideways). P* 14½ × 14.

561 **134** 5 c. silver, black and orange-red .. 10 10
562 – 20 c. silver, black and magenta .. .. 15 10
563 **134** 25 c. silver, black and ultramarine .. 15 15
564 – 50 c. silver, black and yellow-green .. 25 30
561/4 .. .. .. .. .. *Set of* 4 55 55

Design:—20, 50 c. Reverse and obverse of Guyana $1 coin.

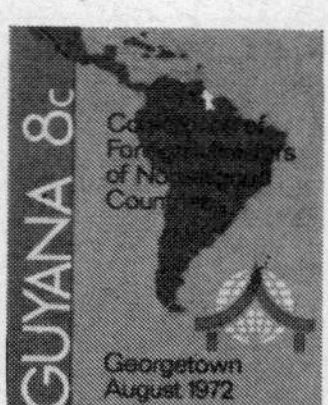


135 Hands and Irrigation Canal    136 Map and Emblem

(Des J. Criswick. Litho J.W.)

**1972** (3 Apr). *Youman Nabi (Mohammed's Birthday). W* **106**. *P* 14.

565 **135** 5 c. multicoloured .. .. .. 10 10
566 25 c. multicoloured .. .. .. 10 10
567 30 c. multicoloured .. .. .. 10 10
568 60 c. multicoloured .. .. .. 20 20
565/8 .. .. .. .. .. *Set of* 4 35 35

(Des J. Criswick. Litho J.W.)

**1972** (20 July). *Conference of Foreign Ministers of Non-aligned Countries. W* **106**. *P* 13½.

569 **136** 8 c. multicoloured .. .. .. 10 10
570 25 c. multicoloured .. .. .. 10 10
571 40 c. multicoloured .. .. .. 15 15
572 50 c. multicoloured .. .. .. 20 20
569/72 .. .. .. .. .. *Set of* 4 40 40

137 Hand reaching for Sun    138 Joseph, Mary, and the Infant Jesus

(Des G. Bowen. Litho J.W.)

**1972** (25 Aug). *First Caribbean Festival of Arts.* W **106** (*inverted on* 40, 50 c.). P 13½.

| | | | | |
|---|---|---|---|---|
| 573 | **137** | 8 c. multicoloured | 10 | 10 |
| 574 | | 25 c. multicoloured | 10 | 10 |
| 575 | | 40 c. multicoloured | 15 | 20 |
| 576 | | 50 c. multicoloured | 20 | 25 |
| 573/6 | | *Set of* 4 | 45 | 55 |

(Des Megan Anderson. Litho B.W.)

**1972** (18 Oct). *Christmas.* W **106**. P 13 × 13½.

| | | | | |
|---|---|---|---|---|
| 577 | **138** | 8 c. multicoloured | 10 | 10 |
| 578 | | 25 c. multicoloured | 10 | 10 |
| 579 | | 40 c. multicoloured | 15 | 25 |
| 580 | | 50 c. multicoloured | 15 | 25 |
| 577/80 | | *Set of* 4 | 40 | 60 |

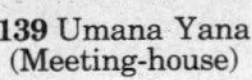

**139** Umana Yana (Meeting-house)

**140** Pomegranate

(Des J. Cooter. Litho Questa)

**1973** (23 Feb). *Republic Day. T* **139** *and similar vert design. Multicoloured.* W **106** (*inverted on* 8 c.). P 14.

| | | | |
|---|---|---|---|
| 581 | 8 c. Type **139** | 10 | 10 |
| 582 | 25 c. Bethel Chapel | 10 | 10 |
| 583 | 40 c. As 25 c. | 15 | 20 |
| 584 | 50 c. Type **139** | 20 | 20 |
| 581/4 | *Set of* 4 | 45 | 50 |

(Des E. Samuels. Litho Format)

**1973** (19 Apr). *Easter. T* **140** *and similar multicoloured design.* W **106** (*sideways on* 25 *and* 40 c.). P 14½ (8, 50 c.) *or* 13½ (*others*).

| | | | |
|---|---|---|---|
| 585 | 8 c. Type **140** | 10 | 10 |
| 586 | 25 c. Cross and map (34 × 47 *mm*) | 10 | 10 |
| 587 | 40 c. As 25 c. | 10 | 10 |
| 588 | 50 c. Type **140** | 15 | 15 |
| 585/8 | *Set of* 4 | 35 | 35 |

**141** Stylized Blood Cell

**142** Steel-Band Players

(Des S. Greaves. Litho Harrison)

**1973** (1 Oct). *25th Anniv of Guyana Red Cross.* W **106**. P 14.

| | | | | |
|---|---|---|---|---|
| 589 | **141** | 8 c. vermilion and black | 10 | 10 |
| 590 | | 25 c. vermilion and bright purple | 20 | 15 |
| 591 | | 40 c. vermilion and ultramarine | 30 | 45 |
| 592 | | 50 c. vermilion and blackish olive | 40 | 70 |
| 589/92 | | *Set of* 4 | 85 | 1·25 |

(Des E. Samuels; adapted J. Cooter. Litho Questa)

**1973** (20 Nov). *Christmas. T* **142** *and similar vert design. Multicoloured.* W **106**. P 14 (8, 25 c.) *or* 13½ (*others*).

| | | | |
|---|---|---|---|
| 593 | 8 c. Type **142** | 10 | 10 |
| 594 | 25 c. Type **142** | 15 | 10 |
| 595 | 40 c. "Virgin and Child" (stained-glass window) (34 × 47 *mm*) | 30 | 40 |
| 596 | 50 c. As 40 c. | 30 | 40 |
| 593/6 | *Set of* 4 | 75 | 90 |

**143** Symbol of Progress

8c

(**144**)

(Des PAD Studio. Litho Questa)

**1974** (23 Feb). *Republic Day. T* **143** *and similar vert design. Multicoloured.* W **106**. P 13½.

| | | | |
|---|---|---|---|
| 597 | 8 c. Type **143** | 10 | 10 |
| 598 | 25 c. Wai-Wai Indian | 10 | 10 |
| 599 | 40 c. Type **143** | 15 | 25 |
| 600 | 50 c. As 25 c. | 15 | 30 |
| 597/600 | *Set of* 4 | 40 | 65 |

**1974** (18 Mar). *No.* 546 *surch with T* **144**.

| | | | |
|---|---|---|---|
| 601 | 8 c. on 6 c. Cannon-ball tree | 10 | 10 |

See also No. 620.

**145** Kite with Crucifixion Motif

**146** British Guiana 24 c. Stamp of 1874

(Des R. Savory; adapted J. Cooter. Litho Questa)

**1974** (8 Apr). *Easter. T* **145** *and similar vert design.* W **106**. P 13½.

| | | | | |
|---|---|---|---|---|
| 602 | **145** | 8 c. multicoloured | 10 | 10 |
| 603 | – | 25 c. black and dull green | 10 | 10 |
| 604 | – | 40 c. black and magenta | 10 | 15 |
| 605 | **145** | 50 c. multicoloured | 15 | 25 |
| 602/5 | | *Set of* 4 | 35 | 50 |

Design:—Nos. 603/4, "Crucifixion" in pre-Columbian style.

(Des R. Savory. Litho Harrison)

**1974** (18 June). *Centenary of Universal Postal Union. T* **146** *and similar horiz design.* W **106** (*sideways on* 8 *and* 40 c.). P 13½ × 14 (8, 40 c.) *or* 14 (*others*).

| | | | | |
|---|---|---|---|---|
| 606 | **146** | 8 c. multicoloured | 15 | 10 |
| 607 | – | 25 c. bright yellow-green, deep slate-violet and black | 20 | 10 |
| 608 | **146** | 40 c. multicoloured | 20 | 20 |
| 609 | – | 50 c. bright yellow-green, reddish chestnut and black | 25 | 25 |
| 606/9 | | *Set of* 4 | 70 | 55 |

Design (42 × 25 *mm*):—25 c., 50 c. U.P.U. emblem and Guyana postman.

**147** Guides with Banner

**148** Buck Toyeau

(Des M. Broodhagen; adapted J. Cooter. Litho Questa)

**1974** (1 Aug). *Girl Guides' Golden Jubilee. T* **147** *and similar horiz design. Multicoloured.* W **106** (*sideways*). P 14½.

| | | | |
|---|---|---|---|
| 610 | 8 c. Type **147** | 15 | 10 |
| 611 | 25 c. Guides in camp | 30 | 15 |
| 612 | 40 c. As 25 c. | 45 | 40 |
| 613 | 50 c. Type **147** | 45 | 45 |
| 610/13 | *Set of* 4 | 1·25 | 1·00 |
| MS614 | 170 × 137 mm. Nos. 610/13 | 1·40 | 1·75 |

(Des S. Greaves and R. Granger Barrett. Litho Enschedé)

**1974** (18 Nov). *Christmas. T* **148** *and similar vert designs. Multicoloured.* W **106**. P 13½ × 13.

| | | | |
|---|---|---|---|
| 615 | 8 c. Type **148** | 10 | 10 |
| 616 | 35 c. Five-fingers and awaras | 10 | 10 |
| 617 | 50 c. Pawpaw and tangerine | 15 | 10 |
| 618 | $1 Pineapple and sapodilla | 30 | 60 |
| 615/18 | *Set of* 4 | 55 | 70 |
| MS619 | 127 × 94 mm. Nos. 615/18 | 90 | 1·75 |

**1975** (20 Jan). *No.* 544 *surch as T* **144**.

| | | | |
|---|---|---|---|
| 620 | 8 c. on 3 c. Hanging Heliconia | 10 | 10 |

**149** Golden Arrow of Courage

**150** Old Sluice Gate

(Des L. Curtis. Litho D.L.R.)

**1975** (23 Feb). *Republic Day. Guyana Orders and Decorations. T* **149** *and similar vert designs.* W **106**. P 13½.

| | | | |
|---|---|---|---|
| 621 | 10 c. Type **149** | 10 | 10 |
| 622 | 35 c. Cacique's Crown of Honour | 10 | 15 |
| 623 | 50 c. Cacique's Crown of Valour | 15 | 20 |
| 624 | $1 Order of Excellence | 35 | 60 |
| 621/4 | *Set of* 4 | 60 | 90 |

(Des E. Samuels; adapted PAD Studio. Litho Questa)

**1975** (2 May). *Silver Jubilee of International Commission on Irrigation and Drainage. T* **150** *and similar horiz design. Multicoloured.* W **106** (*sideways on* 35 c. *and* $1). P 14.

| | | | |
|---|---|---|---|
| 625 | 10 c. Type **150** | 10 | 10 |
| 626 | 35 c. Modern sluice gate | 10 | 15 |
| 627 | 50 c. Type **150** | 15 | 30 |
| 628 | $1 As 35 c. | 35 | 60 |
| 625/8 | *Set of* 4 | 60 | 1·00 |
| MS629 | 162 × 121 mm. Nos. 625/8. Wmk sideways | 1·10 | 1·90 |

**151** I.W.Y. Emblem and Rock Drawing

**152** Freedom Monument

(Des C. Henriques; adapted PAD Studio. Litho Questa)

**1975** (1 July). *International Women's Year. T* **151** *and similar horiz designs showing different rock drawings.* W **106** (*sideways*). P 14.

| | | | | |
|---|---|---|---|---|
| 630 | **151** | 10 c. grey-green and yellow | 10 | 10 |
| 631 | – | 35 c. reddish violet and greenish blue | 20 | 10 |
| 632 | – | 50 c. royal blue and orange | 25 | 15 |
| 633 | – | $1 brown and bright blue | 45 | 45 |
| 630/3 | | *Set of* 4 | 85 | 65 |
| MS634 | | 178 × 89 mm. Nos. 630/3 | 1·40 | 2·00 |

(Des PAD Studio. Litho Questa)

**1975** (26 Aug). *Namibia Day. T* **152** *and similar vert design. Multicoloured.* W **106**. P 14.

| | | | |
|---|---|---|---|
| 635 | 10 c. Type **152** | 10 | 10 |
| 636 | 35 c. Unveiling of Monument | 15 | 10 |
| 637 | 50 c. Type **152** | 25 | 15 |
| 638 | $1 As 35 c. | 35 | 35 |
| 635/8 | *Set of* 4 | 70 | 60 |

**153** G.N.S. Emblem

**154** Court Building, 1875 and Forester's Badge

(Des C. Henriques; adapted PAD Studio. Litho Questa)

**1975** (1 Oct*). *First Anniv of National Service.* W **106**. P 14.

| | | | | |
|---|---|---|---|---|
| 639 | **153** | 10 c. greenish yellow, light green and light reddish violet | 10 | 10 |
| 640 | – | 35 c. orange, lt green & reddish violet | 10 | 10 |
| 641 | – | 50 c. light violet-blue, light green and light yellow-brown | 15 | 15 |
| 642 | – | $1 light mauve, dull green & lt emerald | 40 | 40 |
| 639/42 | | *Set of* 4 | 60 | 60 |
| MS643 | | 196 × 133 mm. Nos. 639/42. W **106** (inverted) | 1·10 | 1·50 |

*This is the local date of issue; the Crown Agents released the stamps a day later.

Nos. 640/2 are as T **153** but have different symbols within the circle.

(Des R. Savory; adapted PAD Studio. Litho Questa)

**1975** (14 Nov). *Centenary of Guyanese Ancient Order of Foresters. T* **154** *and similar horiz designs. Multicoloured.* W **106** (*sideways*). P 14.

| | | | |
|---|---|---|---|
| 644 | 10 c. Type **154** | 10 | 10 |
| 645 | 35 c. Rock drawing of hunter and quarry | 10 | 10 |
| 646 | 50 c. Crossed axes and bugle-horn | 15 | 10 |
| 647 | $1 Bow and arrow | 40 | 40 |
| 644/7 | *Set of* 4 | 60 | 50 |
| MS648 | 129 × 97 mm. Nos. 644/7 | 1·00 | 1·75 |

35c

(155)

**156** Shoulder Flash

**1976** (10 Feb). *No. 553 surch with T* **155**.
649 35 c. on 60 c. Soldier's Cap .. .. .. 20 25

(Des C. Henriques; adapted J.W. Litho Questa)

**1976** (29 Mar). *50th Anniv of the St. John's Ambulance in Guyana. T* **156** *and similar vert designs. W* **106**. *P* 14.
650 **156** 8 c. silver, black and magenta .. .. 10 10
651 – 15 c. silver, black and orange .. .. 10 10
652 – 35 c. silver, black and green .. .. 20 20
653 – 40 c. silver, black and new blue .. .. 25 25
650/3 .. .. .. .. .. *Set of* 4 55 50
Nos. 651/3 are as T **156** but show different shoulder flashes.

**157** Triumphal Arch

**158** Flame in Archway

(Des C. Henriques. Litho J.W.)

**1976** (25 May). *Tenth Anniv of Independence. T* **157** *and similar vert designs. Multicoloured. W* **106**. *P* 13½.
654 8 c. Type **157** .. .. .. .. 10 10
655 15 c. Stylised Victoria Regia lily .. .. 10 10
656 35 c. "Onward to Socialism" .. .. 15 15
657 40 c. Worker pointing the way .. .. 15 15
654/7 .. .. .. .. .. *Set of* 4 35 35
**MS**658 120×100 mm. Nos. 654/7. Wmk inverted. P 14½ .. .. .. .. .. .. 50 1·00

**1976** (3 Aug). *West Indian Victory in World Cricket Cup. As Nos. 559/60 of Barbados.*
659 15 c. Map of the Caribbean .. .. .. 1·25 1·50
660 15 c. Prudential Cup .. .. .. .. 1·25 1·50

(Des G. Vasarhelyi. Litho J.W.)

**1976** (21 Oct). *Deepavali Festival. T* **158** *and similar vert designs. Multicoloured. W* **106**. *P* 14.
661 8 c. Type **158** .. .. .. .. 10 10
662 15 c. Flame in hand .. .. .. .. 10 10
663 35 c. Flame in bowl .. .. .. .. 15 20
664 40 c. Goddess Latchmi .. .. .. .. 15 25
661/4 .. .. .. .. .. *Set of* 4 35 50
**MS**665 94 × 109 mm. Nos. 661/4 .. .. .. 50 1·00

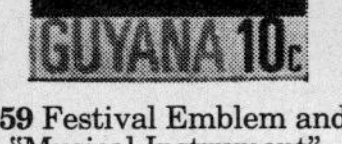


**159** Festival Emblem and "Musical Instrument"

**160** 1 c. and 5 c. Coins

(Des C. Henriques. Litho Questa)

**1977** (1 Feb). *Second World Black and African Festival of Arts and Culture, Nigeria. W* **106**. *P* 14.
666 **159** 10 c. dull red, black and gold .. .. 10 10
667 35 c. deep violet, black and gold .. .. 20 10
668 50 c. ultramarine, black and gold .. .. 25 25
669 $1 blue-green, black and gold .. .. 60 75
666/9 .. .. .. .. .. *Set of* 4 1·00 1·00
**MS**670 90 × 157 mm. Nos. 666/9 .. .. 1·50 2·50
The above were scheduled for release in 1975, and when finally issued had the original inscription obliterated and a new one applied by overprinting. Examples of Nos. 666/70 are known without overprint.

(Des J.W. Litho Questa)

**1977** (26 May). *New Coinage. T* **160** *and similar horiz designs. W* **106**. *P* 14.
671 8 c. multicoloured .. .. .. .. 15 10
672 15 c. yellow-brown, grey and black .. .. 20 10
673 35 c. bright yellow-green, grey and black .. 35 30
674 40 c. carmine-red, grey and black .. .. 40 35
675 $1 multicoloured .. .. .. .. 80 90
676 $2 multicoloured .. .. .. .. 1·40 2·00
671/6 .. .. .. .. .. *Set of* 6 3·00 3·25
Designs:—15 c. 10 and 25 c. coins; 35 c. 50 c. and $1 coins; 40 c. $5 and $10 coins; $1 $50 and $100 coins; $2 Reverse of $1 coin.

**161** Hand Pump, *circa* 1850

**162** Cuffy Monument

(Des J. Porteous Wood. Litho Harrison)

**1977** (15 Nov). *National Fire Prevention Week. T* **161** *and similar horiz designs. Multicoloured. W* **106**. *P* 14 × 14½.
677 8 c. Type **161** .. .. .. .. 15 10
678 15 c. Steam engine, *circa* 1860 .. .. 30 10
679 35 c. Fire engine, *circa* 1930 .. .. 50 40
680 40 c. Fire engine, 1977 .. .. .. 60 55
677/80 .. .. .. .. .. *Set of* 4 1·40 1·00

(Des BG Studio. Litho Questa)

**1977** (7 Dec). *Cuffy Monument (commemorating 1763 Slave Revolt). W* **106**. *P* 14.
681 **162** 8 c. multicoloured .. .. .. 10 10
682 – 15 c. multicoloured .. .. .. 10 10
683 **162** 35 c. multicoloured .. .. .. 15 20
684 – 40 c. multicoloured .. .. .. 15 30
681/4 .. .. .. .. .. *Set of* 4 35 55
Nos. 682 and 684 show a different view of the monument.

**163** American Manatee

(Des BG Studio. Litho Questa)

**1978** (15 Feb). *Wildlife Conservation. T* **163** *and similar multicoloured designs. W* **106** *(sideways on 8 and 15 c.). P* 14.
685 8 c. Type **163** .. .. .. .. 35 10
686 15 c. Giant sea turtle .. .. .. .. 50 15
687 35 c. Harpy Eagle (*vert*) .. .. .. 1·50 1·25
688 40 c. Iguana (*vert*) .. .. .. .. 1·50 1·25
685/8 .. .. .. .. .. *Set of* 4 3·50 2·50

**164** L. F. S. Burnham (Prime Minister) and Parliament Buildings, Georgetown

**165** Dr. George Giglioli (scientist and physician)

(Des Walsall. Litho Questa)

**1978** (27 Apr). *25th Anniv of Prime Minister's Entry into Parliament. T* **164** *and similar horiz designs. W* **106** *(sideways). P* 13½ × 14.
689 8 c. black, violet and bluish grey .. .. 10 10
690 15 c. black, light violet-blue and bluish grey .. 10 10
691 35 c. black, red and bluish grey .. .. 15 20
692 40 c. black, red-orange and bluish grey .. 15 20
689/92 .. .. .. .. .. *Set of* 4 40 45
**MS**693 176 × 118 mm. Nos. 689/92 .. .. 55 1·00
Designs:—15 c. Burnham, graduate and children ("Free Education"); 35 c. Burnham and industrial works (Nationalization of Bauxite industry); 40 c. Burnham and village scene ("The Co-operative Village").

(Des J.W. Litho Harrison)

**1978** (4 Sept). *National Science Research Council. T* **165** *and similar multicoloured designs. W* **106** *(sideways on 10 and 50 c.). P* 13½ × 14 (10, 50 *c.*) *or* 14 × 13½ (*others*).
694 10 c. Type **165** .. .. .. .. 10 10
695 30 c. Institute of Applied Science and Technology (*horiz*) .. .. .. .. 15 15
696 50 c. Emblem of National Science Research Council .. .. .. .. 25 25
697 60 c. Emblem of Commonwealth Science Council (commemorating the 10th Meeting) (*horiz*) .. .. .. 25 25
694/7 .. .. .. .. .. *Set of* 4 60 60

## OMNIBUS ISSUES

Details, together with prices for complete sets, of the various Omnibus issues from the 1935 Silver Jubilee series to date are included in a special section following Zimbabwe at the end of Volume 2.

**166** *Prepona pheridamas*

**167** *Agrias claudina*

(Des J. Cooter. Litho J.W.)

**1978** (1 Oct)–**80**. *Butterflies. Horiz designs as T* **166** (5 *to* 60 *c.*) *or vert as T* **167** ($1 *to* $10). *Multicoloured. W* **106**. *P* 14 × 13½ (5 *to* 60 *c.*) *or* 13 ($1 *to* $10).
698 5 c. Type **166** .. .. .. .. 50 10
699 10 c. *Archonias bellona* .. .. .. 50 10
700 15 c. *Eryphanis polyxena* .. .. .. 60 10
701 20 c. *Helicopis cupido* .. .. .. 60 10
702 25 c. *Nessaea batesii* .. .. .. .. 70 10
702*a* 30 c. *Nymphidium mantus* (25.1.80) .. .. 70 60
703 35 c. *Anaea galanthis* .. .. .. 80 10
704 40 c. *Morpho rhetenor* (male) .. .. 80 10
705 50 c. *Hamadryas amphinome* .. .. 80 10
705*a* 60 c. *Papilio androgeus* (25.1.80) .. .. 80 60
706 $1 Type **167** .. .. .. .. 2·25 15
707 $2 *Morpho rhetenor* (female) .. .. 3·25 35
708 $5 *Morpho deidamia* .. .. .. 5·00 90
708*a* $10 *Elbella patrobas* (25.1.80) .. .. 6·50 3·75
698/708*a* .. .. .. .. *Set of* 14 21·00 6·00

**168** Amerindian Stone-chip Grater in Preparation

**169** Dish Aerial by Night

(Des L. Curtis. Litho Questa)

**1978** (18 Dec). *National/International Heritage Year. T* **168** *and similar vert designs. Multicoloured. W* **106**. *P* 14.
709 10 c. Type **168** .. .. .. .. 10 10
710 30 c. Cassiri and decorated Amerindian jars .. 15 10
711 50 c. Fort Kyk-over-al .. .. .. .. 20 15
712 60 c. Fort Island .. .. .. .. 20 20
709/12 .. .. .. .. *Set of* 4 55 45

(Des L. Curtis. Litho Questa)

**1979** (7 Feb). *Satellite Earth Station. T* **169** *and similar horiz designs. Multicoloured. W* **106** *(sideways). P* 14 × 14½.
713 10 c. Type **169** .. .. .. .. 10 10
714 30 c. Dish aerial by day .. .. .. 20 15
715 50 c. Satellite with solar veins .. .. 30 15
716 $3 Cylinder satellite .. .. .. 1·50 90
713/16 .. .. .. .. *Set of* 4 1·90 1·10

**170** Sir Rowland Hill and British Guiana 1850 12 c. "Cottonreel" Stamp

**171** "Me and my Sister"

(Des and litho J.W.)

**1979** (11 June). *Death Centenary of Sir Rowland Hill. T* **170** *and similar multicoloured designs. W* **106** *(sideways on* 10 *and* 50 *c.). P* 14.
717 10 c. Type **170** .. .. .. .. 10 10
718 30 c. British Guiana 1856 1 c. black on magenta stamp (*vert*) .. .. .. 20 15
719 50 c. British Guiana 1898 1 c. stamp .. .. 30 25
720 $3 Printing press used for early British Guiana stamps (*vert*) .. .. .. 1·00 1·50
717/20 .. .. .. .. *Set of* 4 1·40 1·75

(Des J.W. Litho Questa)

**1979** (20 Aug). *International Year of the Child. Paintings by local children. T* **171** *and similar multicoloured designs. W* **106** *(sideways on* 30, 50 *c. and* $3). *P* 13½.
721 10 c. Type **171** .. .. .. .. 10 10
722 30 c. "Fun with the Fowls" (*horiz*) .. .. 15 15
723 50 c. "Two Boys catching Ducks" (*horiz*) .. 20 20
724 $3 "Mango Season" (*horiz*) .. .. .. 65 1·25
721/4 .. .. .. .. *Set of* 4 90 1·50

172 "An 8 Hour Day"

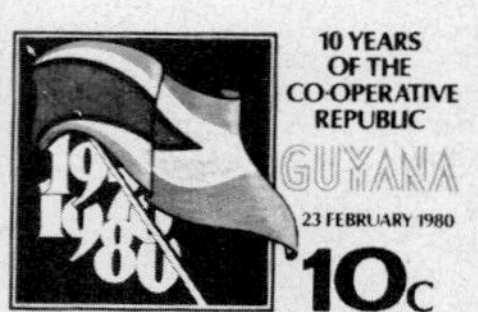


173 Guyana Flag

(Des C. Rodriguez. Litho Walsall)

**1979** (27 Sept). *60th Anniv of Guyana Labour Union. T* **172** *and similar multicoloured designs. W* **106** *(sideways on 30 c.). P* 14 × 14½ *(30 c.) or* 14½ × 14 *(others).*

725 10 c. Type **172** .. .. .. .. .. 10 10
726 30 c. "Abolition of Night Baking" (*horiz*) .. 10 10
727 50 c. "Introduction of the Workmen's Compensation Ordinance" .. .. .. 15 15
728 $3 H. N. Critchlow (founder) .. .. 55 90
725/8 .. .. .. .. .. *Set of* 4 75 1·10

(Des BG Studio. Litho Questa)

**1980** (23 Feb). *10th Anniv of Republic. T* **173** *and similar horiz designs. W* **106** *(sideways). P* 14.

729 10 c. multicoloured .. .. .. .. 10 10
730 35 c. black and red-orange .. .. .. 20 10
731 60 c. multicoloured .. .. .. .. 35 20
732 $3 multicoloured .. .. .. .. 70 90
729/32 .. .. .. .. *Set of* 4 1·25 1·10

Designs:—35 c. View of Demerara River Bridge; 60 c. Kaieteur Falls; $3 "Makanaima the Great Ancestral Spirit of the Amerindians".

174 Snoek

175 Children's Convalescent Home (Community Service)

(Des J.W. Litho Questa)

**1980** (6 May). *"London 1980" International Stamp Exhibition. Fishes. T* **174** *and similar horiz designs. Multicoloured. W* **106** *(sideways). P* 14½.

733 35 c. Type **174** .. .. .. .. .. 25 25
a. Block of 12. Nos. 733/44 .. .. .. 2·75
734 35 c. Haimara .. .. .. .. .. 25 25
735 35 c. Electric Eel .. .. .. .. 25 25
736 35 c. Golden Rivulus .. .. .. .. 25 25
737 35 c. Pencil Fish .. .. .. .. 25 25
738 35 c. Four-eyed Fish .. .. .. .. 25 25
739 35 c. Pirai or Carib Fish .. .. .. 25 25
740 35 c. Smoking Hassar .. .. .. .. 25 25
741 35 c. Devil Ray .. .. .. .. .. 25 25
742 35 c. Flying Patwa .. .. .. .. 25 25
743 35 c. Arapaima Pirariucii .. .. .. 25 25
744 35 c. Lukanani .. .. .. .. .. 25 25
733/44 .. .. .. .. *Set of* 12 2·75 2·75

Nos. 733/44 were printed together, *se-tenant*, in a block of 12 within the sheetlet containing one of each design.

(Des local artist; adapted J.W. Litho Walsall)

**1980** (23 June). *75th Anniv of Rotary International. T* **175** *and similar multicoloured designs. P* 14.

745 10 c. Type **175** .. .. .. .. .. 10 10
746 30 c. Rotary Club of Georgetown and Rotary emblems .. .. .. .. .. 10 10
747 50 c. District 404 emblem (*vert*) .. .. 20 20
748 $3 Rotary anniversary emblem (*vert*) .. 80 80
745/8 .. .. .. .. .. *Set of* 4 1·00 1·10

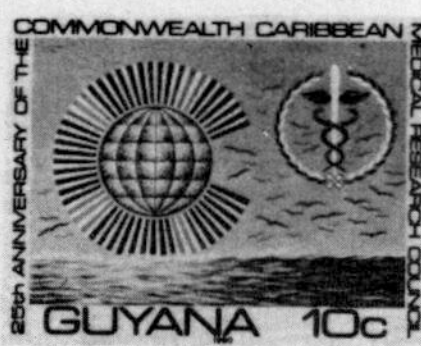


176 "C" encircling Globe, Caduceus Emblem and Sea

177 *Virola surinamensis*

(Des L. Curtis. Litho Enschedé)

**1980** (23 Sept). *25th Anniv of Commonwealth Caribbean Medical Research Council. T* **176** *and similar horiz designs. Multicoloured. W* **106** *(sideways). P* 13.

749 10 c. Type **176** .. .. .. .. .. 10 10
750 60 c. Researcher with microscope, Caduceus emblem, stethoscope and beach scene .. 40 20
751 $3 Caduceus emblem, "C" encircling researcher and island silhouettes .. 1·10 1·00
749/51 .. .. .. .. *Set of* 3 1·40 1·10

(Des L. Curtis. Litho Format)

**1980** (1 Dec). *Christmas. Trees and Foliage. T* **177** *and similar horiz designs. Multicoloured. W* **106** *(sideways). P* 13½.

752 10 c. Type **177** .. .. .. .. .. 10 10
753 30 c. *Hymenaea courbaril* .. .. .. 20 10
754 50 c. *Mora excelsa* .. .. .. .. 30 15
755 $3 *Peltogyne venosa* .. .. .. .. 1·25 1·10
752/5 .. .. .. .. .. *Set of* 4 1·75 1·25

178 Brazilian Tree Porcupine

1981
CONFERENCE
$1·05 X
(179)

(Des G. Drummond. Litho Questa)

**1981** (2 Mar). *Wildlife. T* **178** *and similar horiz designs. Multicoloured. W* **106** *(sideways). P* 14.

756 30 c. Type **178** .. .. .. .. .. 40 40
a. Sheetlet of 12. Nos. 756/67 .. .. 4·25
757 30 c. Red Howler .. .. .. .. 40 40
758 30 c. Common Squirrel-Monkey .. .. 40 40
759 30 c. Two-toed Sloth .. .. .. .. 40 40
760 30 c. Brazilian Tapir .. .. .. .. 40 40
761 30 c. Collared Peccary .. .. .. .. 40 40
762 30 c. Six-banded Armadillo .. .. .. 40 40
763 30 c. Tamandua ("Ant Eater") .. .. 40 40
764 30 c. Giant Anteater .. .. .. .. 40 40
765 30 c. Murine Opossum .. .. .. .. 40 40
766 30 c. Brown Four-eyed Opossum .. .. 40 40
767 30 c. Brazilian Agouti .. .. .. .. 40 40
756/67 .. .. .. .. *Set of* 12 4·25 4·25

Nos. 756/67 were printed together, *se-tenant*, within the sheet of 12.

See also No. 852.

**1981** (4 May). *Liberation of Southern Africa Conference. No.* 635 *surch with T* **179** *by Govt Printer.*

768 $1.05 on 10 c. Type **152** .. .. .. 40 50

ROYAL
WEDDING
1981
$3·60
X X
(180)

181 Map of Guyana

7·20
(182)

**1981** (6 May). *Royal Wedding (1st issue). Nos.* 554 *and* 556 *surch as T* **180** *by Govt Printer. A. In blue. B. In black.*

| | | A | | B | |
|---|---|---|---|---|---|
| 769 | $3.60 on $5 *Odontadenia grandiflora* .. .. | 2·25 | 3·50 | 1·25 | 1·00 |
| | a. Surch inverted .. .. | £100 | — | † | |
| | b. Surch double .. .. | 40·00 | — | † | |
| 770 | $7.20 on $1 *Chelonanthus uliginoides* .. .. | 1·75 | 2·00 | 2·50 | 2·25 |
| | a. Surch on No. 556 .. .. | † | | 40·00 | — |
| | b. Surch double .. .. | 45·00 | — | † | |
| | c. Surch triple .. .. | | | | |

See also Nos. 841/3 and 930/6.

(Surch by Govt Printer)

**1981** (11 May). *W* **106** *(sideways). P* 13.

771 **181** 10 c. on 3 c. black, ind & Venetian red .. 40 10
772 30 c. on 2 c. black, ind & greenish grey .. 45 15
773 50 c. on 2 c. black, ind & greenish grey .. 55 25
774 60 c. on 2 c. black, ind & greenish grey .. 70 30
775 75 c. on 3 c. black, ind & Venetian red .. 70 45
a. Surch double .. .. .. .. 40·00
b. Surch triple .. .. .. .. 60·00
771/5 .. .. .. .. *Set of* 5 2·50 1·10

Nos. 771/5 are fiscal stamps surcharged for postal use.
See also Nos. 940/76, 988/9 and 1029.

**1981** (11 May). *No.* 544 *surch with T* **182** *by Govt Printer.*

775c 720 c. on 3 c. Hanging Heliconia .. .. 50·00 15·00
ca. Surch quadruple .. .. ..

1981
(183)

**1981** (8 June). *Optd with T* **183** *by Bovell's Printery.*

776 **105** 25 c. black, gold and lilac (R.) .. .. 10 10
777 30 c. black, gold & lt apple-green (R.) .. 15 15
778 – 35 c. multicoloured (No. 645) (R.) .. 15 15
779 – $1 multicoloured (No. 554) .. .. 1·00 75
776/9 .. .. .. .. .. *Set of* 4 1·25 1·10

210
7 (184) X (185)
ESSEQUIBO IS OURS 15 (186)
ESSEQUIBO IS OURS 15 (186*a*)

**1981** (8 June–1 July) *Nos.* 545 *and* 556 *surch with T* **184** *(No. 780) or as T* **185**, *all by Bovell's Printery.*

780 75 c. on 5 c. Annatto tree .. .. .. 50 30
781 210 c. on $5 *Odontadenia grandiflora* .. .. 80 70
781a 220 c. on 5 c. Annatto tree .. .. .. 55·00 8·00

**1981** (8 June). *Nos. D8/11 surch in black (15 c.) or red (others). A. As T* **186**. *B. As T* **186***a*. *Both by Bovell's Printery.*

| | | A | | B | |
|---|---|---|---|---|---|
| 782 D 2 | 10 c. on 2 c. black .. | 25 | 10 | 50 | 10 |
| | c. Surch omitted (in vert pair with normal) .. | — | — | † | |
| 783 | 15 c. on 12 c. bright scarlet | 25 | 15 | 60 | 25 |
| 784 | 20 c. on 1 c. olive .. .. | 20 | 20 | 30 | 25 |
| | a. "ESSEOUIBO" .. | † | | 25·00 | — |
| | c. Surch omitted (in vert pair with normal) .. | † | | — | — |
| 785 | 45 c. on 2 c. black .. | 75 | 25 | 1·25 | 65 |
| 786 | 55 c. on 4 c. dull ultram .. | 30 | 30 | 3·00 | 3·00 |
| | c. Surch inverted .. | — | — | — | — |
| | d. Surch double, one inverted (T **186** + T **186**) .. | — | — | † | |
| | da. Ditto, but T **186** + T **186***a* .. | — | — | † | |
| | db. Ditto, but T **186***a* + T **186** .. | † | | — | — |
| | e. Surch double (55 c. + 60 c.) .. | — | — | † | |
| 787 | 60 c. on 4 c. dull ultram .. | † | | 50 | 25 |
| | a. "ESSEOUIBO" .. | † | | 10·00 | — |
| | c. Surch omitted (in vert pair with normal) .. | † | | — | — |
| 788 | 65 c. on 2 c. black .. | 40 | 40 | 75 | 70 |
| 789 | 70 c. on 4 c. dull ultram .. | 1·00 | 1·25 | 1·50 | 1·50 |
| 790 | 80 c. on 4 c. dull ultram .. | 35 | 40 | 60 | 70 |
| | c. Surch inverted .. | — | — | † | |
| | d. Surch omitted (in vert pair with inverted) .. | — | — | † | |
| 782A/90A | .. .. *Set of* 8 | 3·25 | 2·75 | | |
| 782B/90B | .. .. *Set of* 9 | | | 8·00 | 6·50 |

With the exception of No. 787 these stamps were surcharged with a setting of eighteen (three horizontal rows) as Type **186** and twelve as Type **186***a*. The two types of surcharge can, therefore, be found as vertical *se-tenant* pairs.

No. 787 was produced from a setting of 12 containing Type **186***a* only. The same setting was also used for the bottom two rows of the 20 c. on 1 c. value. The "ESSEOUIBO" error occurs on the first stamp in the second horizontal row of this setting.

Examples of 15, 45 and 60 c. surcharges are also known on stamps with watermark w **12**.

1981 (187)
1981 (188)
1981 (189)

**1981** (8 June–1 July). *Nos.* 491, 494 *and* 555 *optd with T* **187**, **188** *or* **189**, *all by Bovell's Printery.*

791 15 c. Harpy Eagle (R.) .. .. .. .. 3·25 10
a. Opt omitted (in vert pair with normal) † —
b. Opt double .. .. .. .. ..
c. Opt inverted .. .. .. .. ..
d. Opt in black .. .. .. .. 35·00 5·00
da Opt double, one inverted .. .. ..
792 40 c. Great Kiskadee (1.7.81) .. .. 3·25 40
a. Opt double .. .. .. .. 28·00
793 $2 *Norantea guianensis* (1.7.81) .. .. 3·50 1·40
791/3 .. .. .. .. *Set of* 3 9·00 1·75

50c (190)
x 120 ■ ■ (191)

(192)

(Surch by Bovell's Printery)

**1981** (1 July). *(a) Postage. (i) No.* 545 *surch with T* **190**.

794 50 c. on 5 c. Annatto tree .. .. .. 30 20
a. Surch inverted .. .. .. .. 6·00

(ii) *No.* 554 *surch as T* **191**

795 120 c. on $1 *Chelonanthus uliginoides* .. 75 50
796 140 c. on $1 *Chelonanthus uliginoides* .. 70 50

(iii) *Nos. F7 and F9 surch as T* **192**

797 150 c. on $2 *Norantea guianensis* .. .. 75 50
798 360 c. on $2 *Norantea guianensis* .. .. 3·00 1·50
799 720 c. on 60 c. Soldier's Cap .. .. .. 3·00 2·75

(iv) *Nos.* 556 *and* 716 *surch as T* **185**

800 220 c. on $3 Cylinder satellite (surch vert – reading downwards) .. .. 1·75 75
a. Surch reading upwards .. .. ..
801 250 c. on $5 *Odontadenia grandiflora* .. 1·25 80
802 280 c. on $5 *Odontadenia grandiflora* .. 1·50 1·25
803 375 c. on $5 *Odontadenia grandiflora* .. 1·75 1·40
a. Surch inverted .. .. .. ..
b. "7" of "375" omitted .. .. ..

(b) *Air. No.* 843 *with commemorative opt cancelled by three bars*

804 $1.10 on $2 *Norantea guianensis* .. .. 17·00 15·00

No. 803b was subsequently corrected by the insertion of a very uneven "7".

100

15 (193) AIR (194)

(Surch by Bovell's Printery)

**1981** (1 July). *No.* 485 *surch. (a) Postage. With T* **193**.
805 15 c. on 1 c. Type **87** .. .. .. 10 10
a. Horiz strip of 3. Nos. 805/7 .. .. 85
b. Surch inverted .. .. ..
c. Surch double .. .. ..

*(b) Air. As T* **194**
806 100 c. on 1 c. Type **87** .. .. .. .. 35 35
807 110 c. on 1 c. Type **87** .. .. .. .. 40 40

Nos. 805/7 were printed together, *se-tenant*, within the same sheet providing 36 examples of No. 805 and 32 each of the others. No. 805 appears in the six vertical columns of Rows 3 to 8 with horizontal pairs of Nos. 806/7 in vertical columns 1, 2, 9, 10 and vertical pairs in the central six vertical columns of Rows 1, 2, 9, 10.

ESSEQUIBO IS OURS (195) ESSEQUIBO IS OURS (195*a*) 1981 (196)

**1981** (1 July). *No.* 700 *optd.* A. *With T* **195**. B. *With T* **195***a*. *Both by Bovell's Printery.*

| | | A | | B | |
|---|---|---|---|---|---|
| 808 | 15 c. *Eryphanis polyxena* .. | 30 | 10 | 40 | 15 |
| | a. "I" of "IS" omitted .. | † | | — | — |

No. 808Ba is believed to occur on either R. 5/1 or R. 5/5.

**1981** (7 July–15 Sept). *Various stamps optd with T* **196** *by Bovell's Printery.*
809 – 15 c. multicoloured (No. 548) .. .. 4·00 10
a. Opt inverted .. .. ..
810 – 15 c. multicoloured (No. 659) (opt vert —reading downwards) .. .. 3·00 20
a. Opt reading upwards .. ..
b. Opt albino .. .. ..
811 – 15 c. multicoloured (No. 660) .. .. 3·00 20
a. Opt inverted .. .. ..
b. Vert pair, one with opt omitted
811*c* – 40 c. multicoloured (No. F5) .. .. — £200
812 – 50 c. multicoloured (No. 623) .. .. 60 20
a. Opt inverted .. .. ..
813 **150** 50 c. multicoloured .. .. .. 1·00 25
814 – 50 c. royal blue and orange (No. 632) 13·00 1·00
815 – 50 c. multicoloured (No. 646) .. .. 1·50 25
816 **159** 50 c. ultramarine, black and gold .. 7·50 1·00
817 – 50 c. multicoloured (No. F6) .. .. 2·00 30
818 – 60 c. multicoloured (No. 731) (15.9.81) 60 25
819 – 60 c. multicoloured (No. 750) (15.9.81) 60 25
820 – $1 multicoloured (No. 624) .. .. 6·00 1·00
821 **159** $1 blue-green, black and gold .. 3·75 50
822 – $2 multicoloured (No. 555) .. .. 2·25 1·00
823 – $3 multicoloured (No. 732) .. .. 2·50 95
824 – $5 multicoloured (No. 556) .. .. 3·25 2·25

Overprints on Nos. 814/15 and 823 are vertical, reading upwards.

55 (197) 55 (198)

110 (199)

440 (200) 440 (201)

550 (202) 550 (203)

240 (204)

(Surch by Bovell's Printery)

**1981** (7 July–15 Sept). *(a) Various stamps surch as T* **197/203**.
825 **116** 55 c. on 6 c. multicoloured (surch T **197**) (15.9.81) .. .. .. .. 4·00 80
a. Surch with T **198** .. .. .. 11·00 3·50
b. Vert pair. Nos. 825/a .. .. 14·00 4·50
826 **111** 70 c. on 6 c. multicoloured (15.9.81) .. 70 30
827 100 c. on 6 c. multicoloured .. .. 80 35
a. Surch inverted .. .. .. 3·50 1·25
828 – 100 c. on 8 c. multicoloured (No. 505) .. 3·75 40
829 **152** 100 c. on $1.05 on 10 c. mult (No. 768) (surch vert—reading upwards) .. 23·00 3·50
a. Surch reading downwards
830 **116** 110 c. on 6 c. multicoloured .. .. 4·00 40
831 **149** 110 c. on 10 c. multicoloured (surch vert—reading downwards) .. .. 2·00 40
832 **151** 110 c. on 10 c. grey-green and yellow .. 3·75 70
833 **154** 110 c. on 10 c. multicoloured .. .. 4·00 70
834 – 125 c. on $2 multicoloured (No. 555) .. 8·50 1·00
835 **116** 180 c. on 6 c. multicoloured (15.9.81) .. 4·50 65
836 400 c. on 6 c. multicoloured .. .. 4·50 1·75
837 440 c. on 6 c. multicoloured (surch T **200**) 13·00 5·00
a. Surch with T **201** .. .. 3·50 1·75
b. Vert pair. Nos. 837/a .. .. 17·00 7·00
838 – 550 c. on $10 multicoloured (No. O21) (surch T **202**) (15.9.81) .. .. 4·50 2·00
a. Surch with T **203** .. .. 10·00 5·50
b. Vert pair. Nos. 838/a .. .. 15·00 8·00
839 – 625 c. on 40 c. multicoloured (No. F5) .. 9·50 3·00

*(b) No.* 728 *surch with T* **204**
840 – 240 c. on $3 multicoloured (15.9.81) .. 9·50 1·50

Nos. 825/a, 837/a and 838/a were each printed together, *se-tenant*, in vertical pairs throughout sheets containing five of these pairs plus an additional fifteen examples of Nos. 825, 837a and 838.

75 Royal Wedding 1981 X 60 (205) Royal Wedding 1981 X (206)

Air Mail X 1.10 Royal Wedding 1981 (207)

(Surch by Bovell's Printery)

**1981** (22 July). *Royal Wedding (2nd issue). (a) Postage. Nos.* 544 *and* 556 *surch with T* **205/6**.
841 60 c. on 3 c. Hanging Heliconia .. .. 70 80
a. Surch inverted .. .. .. 75·00
b. "Royal Wedding" diagonal (as T **206**) .. 75·00
c. Surch double (T **205** + T **206**) .. .. 45·00
d. Surch T **205** double .. .. 90·00
842 75 c. on $5 *Odontadenia grandiflora* .. .. 80 90

*(b) Air. No.* 555 *surch with T* **207**
843 $1.10 on $2 *Norantea guianensis* .. .. 1·25 1·40
a. Surch double .. .. .. 60·00
b. Surch inverted .. .. .. £100
841/3 .. .. .. .. *Set of* 3 2·50 2·75

It is believed No. 841b comes from trial sheets which were accidentally included in supplies of the normal No. 841.

Espana 82 (208) 1831-1981 Von Stephan 330 (209)

**1981** (22 July). *World Cup Football Championship, Spain* (1982) (1*st issue*). *No.* 781a *optd with T* **208** *by Bovell's Printery.*
844 220 c. on 5 c. Annatto tree .. .. .. 1·25 90

See also Nos. 937/9.

**1981** (22 July). 150*th Birth Anniv of Heinrich von Stephan* (*founder of U.P.U.*). *No.* 720 *surch with T* **209**.
845 330 c. on $3 Printing press used for early British Guiana stamps.. .. .. 1·50 1·25

12 (211)

**1981** (24 Aug). *No.* 452 *surch as T* **211** *by Bovell's Printery.*
847 12 c. on 12 c. on 6 c. Patua .. .. 20 25
a. Large surch omitted .. .. 17·00
b. Strip of 3. Nos. 847/9 .. .. 50
c. Strip of 3. Nos. 847, 850/1 .. .. 50
848 15 c. on 10 c. on 6 c. Patua .. .. 15 10
849 15 c. on 30 c. on 6 c. Patua .. .. 15 10
a. Small surch omitted .. .. 25·00
850 15 c. on 50 c. on 6 c. Patua .. .. .. 15 10
851 15 c. on 60 c. on 6 c. Patua .. .. .. 15 10

Nos. 847/51 are further surcharges on previously unissued stamps.

No. 847 exists with the smaller of the two 12 c. surcharges printed by either lithography or typography.

Nos. 847/9 and 847, 850/1 were each printed together, *se-tenant*, within the sheets providing 36 examples of No. 847 and 30 each of Nos. 848/9 or 850/1. Each sheet also contained four stamps cancelled with a black diagonal cross. In each instance No. 847 appeared in the six central vertical columns of Rows 3 to 8 with horizontal pairs of Nos. 848/9 or 850/1 in vertical columns 1, 2, 9, 10 and vertical pairs in R. 1/4–8, R. 2/4–8, R. 9/3–7 and R. 10/3–7.

**1981** (1 Sept). *As No.* 762 *but perf* 12.
852 30 c. Six-banded Armadillo .. .. .. 45 15

No. 852 was printed in sheets of 50.

**214** Coromantyn Free Negro Armed Ranger, *circa* 1772 and Cuffy Monument

**215** Louis Braille

(Des G. Drummond. Litho Rosenbaum Bros, Vienna)

**1981** (1 Oct). 16*th Anniv of Guyana Defence Force. T* **214** *and similar vert designs. Multicoloured. W* **106** *(inverted on* $1). *P* 13½.
853 15 c. on 10 c. Type **214**. .. .. .. .. 30 10
854 50 c. Private, 27th Foot Regiment, *circa* 1825 40 30
855 $1 on 30 c. Private, Col. Fourgeoud's Marines, *circa* 1775 .. .. .. 60 50
856 $1.10 on $3 W.O. and N.C.O., Guyana Defence Force, 1966 .. .. 1·50 75
853/6 .. .. .. .. *Set of* 4 2·50 1·50

The 15 c., $1 and $1.10 values are surcharged on previously unissued stamps.

(Des G. Vasarhelyi. Litho Questa)

**1981** (2 Nov). *International Year for Disabled Persons. Famous Disabled People. T* **215** *and similar horiz designs. Multicoloured. W* **106** *(sideways). P* 13½ × 14.
857 15 c. on 10 c. Type **215**. .. .. .. 30 10
858 50 c. Helen Keller and Rajkumari Singh .. 75 55
859 $1 on 60 c. Beethoven and Sonny Thomas .. 80 60
860 $1.10 on $3 Renoir .. .. .. .. 90 70
857/60 .. .. .. .. *Set of* 4 2·50 1·75

The 15 c., $1 and $1.10 values are surcharged, by Bovell's Printery, on previously unissued stamps. Examples of Nos. 857, 859 and 860 are known without surcharge.

12 X (216) 50 AIR (217)

(Surch by Bovell's Printery)

**1981** (10 Nov). *Nos.* 452 *and* 489 *surch. (a) Postage. With T* **216**.

| | | A. On No. 452 | | B. On No. 489 | |
|---|---|---|---|---|---|
| 861 | 12 c. on 6 c. Patua .. .. | 15 | 10 | 15 | 10 |
| | a. Strip of 3. Nos. 861/3 .. | 1·25 | — | 1·10 | — |
| | *(b) Air. As T* **217** | | | | |
| 862 | 50 c. on 6 c. Patua .. .. | 25 | 15 | 20 | 15 |
| 863 | $1 on 6 c. Patua .. .. | 50 | 30 | 50 | 30 |

Nos. 861/3 were printed together, *se-tenant*, throughout the sheet. All sheets of Nos. 861B/3B and about half of Nos. 861A/3A contained 36 examples of the 12 c., 35 of the 50 c. and 29 of the $1. On the remainder of the unwatermarked sheets there were the same number of the 12 c., but 34 of the 50 c. and 30 of the $1. No. 861 appeared in the six central vertical columns of Rows 3 to 8 with horizontal pairs of Nos. 862/3 in vertical columns 1, 2, 9, 10 and vertical pairs in the six central vertical columns of Rows 1, 2, 9, 10. The additional $1 value on the second stage of the setting occurred on R. 9/1.

1981 (218)

**1981** (14 Nov). *Nos.* 548 *and* 554/5 *optd with T* **218** *in red by Bovell's Printery.*
864 15 c. Christmas Orchid .. .. .. 2·50 10
a. Optd on No. 548a. .. .. .. 3·75
865 $1 *Chelonanthus uliginoides* .. .. 40 35
866 $2 *Norantea guianensis* .. .. .. 90 95

110 (219) 110 (220) Nov 81 50c (221)

**1981** (14 Nov). *(a) Nos.* 601, 620, 644, *and* O13 *surch with T* **219/20** *in blue by Bovell's Printery.*
867 110 c. on 10 c. Type **154** (surch T **219**) .. .. 2·00 45
868 110 c. on 110 c. on 8 c. on 3 c. Hanging Heliconia (surch T **219** + **220**) .. .. 2·25 60
a. Type **220** albino .. .. 25·00
869 110 c. on 110 c. on 8 c. on 6 c. Cannon-ball tree (surch T **219**+ **220**) .. .. .. 2·25 75
869*a* 110 c. on 10 c. on 25 c. Marabunta (surch T **219** vert) .. .. .. .. .. 2·00 75

*(b) Nos.* 717, 720, 728, 749, 751 *and* 755 *surch with T* **220** *by Bovell's Printery*
870 110 c. on 10 c. Type **170** (R.) .. .. .. 1·25 40
a. Surch albino .. .. .. 15·00
871 110 c. on 10 c. Type **176** (B.) .. .. .. 4·50 90
872 110 c. on $3 Printing press used for early British Guiana stamps (R.) (surch vert) 1·25 45
873 110 c. on $3 H.N. Critchlow (B.) (surch vert) 4·50 70
874 110 c. on $3 Caduceus emblem, "C" encircling researcher, and island silhouettes (B.) 1·40 45
a. Surch in red .. .. .. 3·00 1·25
875 110 c. on $3 *Peltogyne venosa* (B.) .. 3·00 80
a. Surch in red .. .. .. 48·00 6·00

*(c) No.* 698 *surch with T* **221** *by Herald Printing-Kitty*
876 50 c. on 5 c. Type **166** .. .. .. 2·00 20

222 Yellow Allamanda (*Allamanda cathartica*)

X X
Human Rights
Day
1981
110 AIR
(223)

**1981** (14 Nov)–**82.** *Flowers. Coil stamps. Vert designs as T* **222**. *W* **106**. *P* 15 × 14.
877 15 c. on 2 c. grey-lilac, blue & turquoise-green 15 15
a. Vert pair. Nos. 877/8 .. .. 50 45
b. New blue surch (12.82) .. .. 20 10
ba. Vert pair. Nos. 877b/8b .. .. 65 50
878 15 c. on 8 c. grey-lilac, blue and mauve .. 15 15
b. New blue surch (12.82) .. .. 20 10
Design:—15 c. on 8 c. Mazaruni Pride (*Sipanea prolensis*).
Nos. 877/8 are surcharges on previously unissued stamps and were printed together, *se-tenant*, in vertical pairs throughout the coil.

**1981** (14 Nov). *Air. Human Rights Day. No.* 748 *surch with T* **223** *in blue by Bovell's Printery.*
879 110 c. on $3 Rotary anniversary emblem .. 1·75 1·50

U.N.I.C.E.F.
1946 - 1981
125 XX
(224)

**1981** (14 Nov). *35th Anniv of U.N.I.C.E.F. No.* 724 *surch with T* **224** *by Bovell's Printery.*
880 125 c. on $3 "Mango Season" .. .. .. 1·00 60

Cancun 81
50c
(224*a*)

**1981** (14 Nov). *"Cancun 81" International Conference. No.* 698 *surch with T* **224***a* *by Herald Printing-Kitty.*
880*a* 50 c. on 5 c. Type **166** .. .. .. 1·50 60

225 Tape Measure and Guyana Metrication Board Van

1982
(226)

(Des local artist; adapted A. Theobald. Litho Questa)

**1982** (18 Jan). *Metrication. T* **225** *and similar vert designs. Multicoloured. W* **106**. *P* 14½ × 14.
881 15 c. Type **225** .. .. .. .. 15 15
a. Sheetlet of 6. Nos. 881/6 .. .. 80
882 15 c. "Metric man" .. .. .. 15 15
883 15 c. "Postal service goes metric" .. 15 15
884 15 c. Weighing child on metric scales .. .. 15 15
885 15 c. Canje Bridge .. .. .. 15 15
886 15 c. Tap filling litre bucket .. .. 15 15
881/6 .. .. .. *Set of* 6 80 80
Nos. 881/6 were printed together, *se-tenant*, in a sheetlet of 6.

**1982** (8 Feb). *Various stamps optd with T* **226** *in blue by Autoprint.*
887 – 20 c. multicoloured (No. 549) .. .. 2·00 20
a. Optd on No. 549a .. .. 4·50 1·50
888 **105** 25 c. black, gold and lilac .. .. 60 25
889 – 25 c. multicoloured (No. 550*a*) .. .. 2·50 35
a. Optd on No. 550 .. .. 11·00 3·00
b. Optd on No. 550ab .. .. 7·50 2·00
See also Nos. 914/17, 919/21, 923/4, 977, 992/8, 1001, 1004, 1006/8, 1015, 1017, 1059, 1117 and OP3/4.

20c
(227)

20
(228)

POSTAGE
(229)

**1982** (8 Feb). *Nos.* 506, 546 *and* 601 *surch or optd as T* **227/9** *by Bovell's Printery (No. 890) or Autoprint (others).*
890 20 c. on 6 c. Cannon-ball tree (surch T **227**) (G.) .. .. .. .. .. 35 20
891 20 c. on 6 c. Cannon-ball tree (surch T **228**) (B.) .. .. .. .. .. 35 20
892 25 c. Type **116** (optd T **229**) (B.) .. 1·00 10
893 125 c. on 8 c. on 6 c. Cannon-ball tree (surch T **228**) (B.) .. .. .. .. 35 35

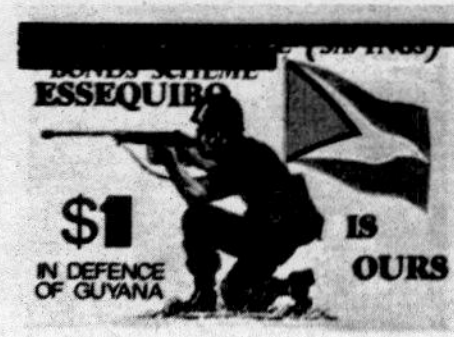

230 Guyana Soldier and Flag

**1982** (8 Feb). *Savings Campaign. W* **106** *(sideways). P* 14×14½.
894 **230** $1 multicoloured .. .. .. 30 30
No. 894 is a fiscal stamp overprinted, by Bovell's Printery, for postal use.

110 X
BADEN POWELL
1857 - 1982
(231)

**1982** (15–22 Feb). *125th Birth Anniv of Lord Baden-Powell and 75th Anniv of Boy Scout Movement. Nos.* 543, 545 *and* 601 *surch as T* **231** *by Bovell's Printery.*
895 15 c. on 2 c. Type **132** (surch T **231**) (22 Feb) 10 10
a. Sheetlet of 25. Nos. 895/6, each × 8, Nos. 897/8, each × 4 and No. 899 .. 8·00
896 15 c. on 2 c. Type **132** (surch "Scout Movement 1907–1982") (22 Feb) .. .. 10 10
897 15 c. on 2 c. Type **132** (surch "1907–1982") (22 Feb) .. .. .. .. 15 15
898 15 c. on 2 c. Type **132** (surch "1857–1982") (22 Feb) .. .. .. .. 15 15
899 15 c. on 2 c. Type **132** (surch "1982") (22 Feb) 10 10
900 110 c. on 5 c. Annatto tree (surch T **231**) .. 1·00 40
a. Sheetlet of 25. Nos. 900/1, each × 8, Nos. 902/3, each × 4, and No. 904 (22 Feb) 12·00
901 110 c. on 5 c. Annatto tree (surch "Scout Movement 1907–1982") .. .. .. 60 40
902 110 c. on 5 c. Annatto tree (surch "1907–1982") (22 Feb) .. .. .. .. 1·25 80
903 110 c. on 5 c. Annatto tree (surch "1857–1982") (22 Feb) .. .. .. .. 1·25 80
904 110 c. on 5 c. Annatto tree (surch "1982") (22 Feb) .. .. .. .. 60 40
a. "110" larger .. .. .. 95·00
905 125 c. on 8 c. on 6 c. Cannon-ball tree (surch T **231**) (G.) .. .. .. .. 1·00 50
a. Sheetlet of 25. Nos. 905/6, each × 8, Nos. 907/8, each × 4, and No. 909 (22 Feb) 16·00
906 125 c. on 8 c. on 6 c. Cannon-ball tree (surch "Scout Movement 1907–1982") (G.) .. 1·00 50
907 125 c. on 8 c. on 6 c. Cannon-ball tree (surch "1907–1982") (G.) (22 Feb) .. 1·50 90
908 125 c. on 8 c. on 6 c. Cannon-ball tree (surch "1857–1982") (G.) (22 Feb) .. 1·50 90
909 125 c. on 8 c. on 6 c. Cannon-ball tree (surch "1982") (G.) (22 Feb) .. .. 75 50
895/909 .. .. .. *Set of* 15 9·00 6·00
In addition to the sheetlets of 25, Nos. 895a, 900a and 905a, Nos. 899/901, 904/6 and 909 also come from sheets containing one type of surcharge only.
No. 904a occurs in the printing of sheets containing this surcharge only. The "110" is in the same size as the surcharge on Type **241**.

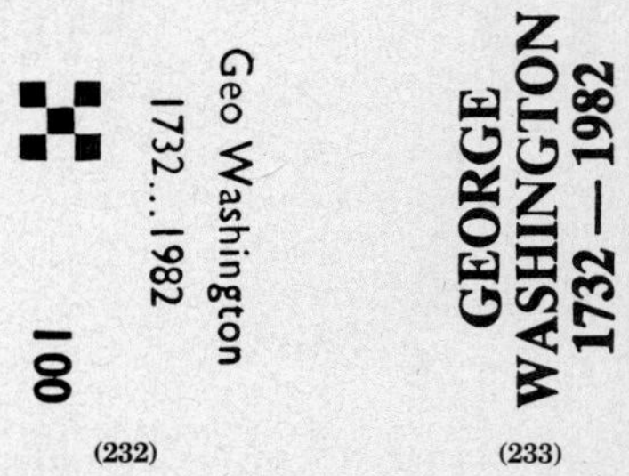

(232) (233)

**1982** (15 Feb). *250th Birth Anniv of George Washington. Nos.* 708, 718 *and* 720 *surch as T* **232** *by Herald Printing-Kitty or optd only with T* **233** *by Autoprint.*
910 100 c. on $3 Printing press used for early British Guiana stamps. .. .. .. 45 50
911 400 c. on 30 c. British Guiana 1856 1 c. black on magenta stamp .. .. .. 1·60 1·90
a. Surch inverted .. .. .. .. 20·00
912 $5 *Morpho deidamia* (B.) .. .. .. 4·50 2·25
910/12 .. .. .. .. *Set of* 3 6·00 4·25

**1982** (3 Mar). *Savings Campaign. Horiz design as T* **230.** *Multicoloured. W* **106.** *P* 14 × 14½.
913 110 c. on $5 Guyana male and female soldiers with flag .. .. .. .. 50 35
No. 913 is a fiscal stamp surcharged, by Bovell's Printery, for postal use.
See also No. 990.

45 (234)
20 (235)
210 (236)

**1982** (15 Mar). *Easter. Nos.* 481/4 *optd with T* **226**, *in blue, or surch as T* **234**, *all by Autoprint.*
914 **111** 25 c. multicoloured .. .. .. 35 20
915 30 c. multicoloured .. .. .. 30 15
916 45 c. on 6 c. multicoloured (B.) .. .. 45 35
917 75 c. on 40 c. multicoloured (R.) .. .. 75 35
914/17 .. .. .. .. *Set of* 4 1·75 95
No. 917 exists with the surcharge either at the right or in the centre of the design.

**1982** (15 Mar). *No.* 703 *surch with T* **235** *by Herald Printing-Kitty.*
918 20 c. on 35 c. *Anaea galanthis* .. .. 60 10

**1982** (8 Apr). *No.* F5 *optd with T* **226** *and surch as T* **228** *in blue, both by Autoprint.*
919 180 c. on 40 c. Tiger Beard .. .. .. 3·25 60

**1982** (23 Apr). *Nos.* 555/6 *optd with T* **226** *in blue by Autoprint.*
920 $2 *Norantea guianensis* .. .. .. 80 70
921 $5 *Odontadenia grandiflora* .. .. 1·40 1·60

**1982** (23 Apr). *No.* 542 *surch as T* **228** *in blue by Autoprint.*
922 220 c. on 1 c. Pitcher Plant of Mt Roraima .. 1·25 60

**1982** (27 Apr). *Nos.* 472 *and* 684 *optd with T* **226** *in blue by Autoprint.*
923 **105** 40 c. black, gold and cobalt .. .. 35 20
924 – 40 c. multicoloured .. .. .. 50 40

**1982** (27 Apr). *Nos.* 469, 751, 842 *and* 843 *surch as T* **228**, *vertically (Nos. 925/7), or as T* **236** *(others), all in blue by Autoprint.*
925 **105** 80 c. on 6 c. black, gold and flesh .. 30 35
926 85 c. on 6 c. black, gold and flesh .. 50 35
927 – 160 c. on $1.10 on $2 multicoloured (No. 843) .. .. .. .. 1·00 55
928 – 210 c. on $3 multicoloured (No. 751) (surch reading up) .. .. 2·50 70
a. Surch reading down .. .. 12·00
929 – 235 c. on 75 c. on $5 multicoloured (No. 842) .. .. .. .. 9·00 2·00
The surcharge on No. 929 is as Type **236**, but horizontal.

85 (237)
130 (238)

(239)

(Surch by Herald Printing-Kitty)

**1982** (27 Apr–May). *Royal Wedding (3rd issue). Coil stamps. Nos.* 841/3 *surch as T* **237** *(No. 930),* **238** *(Nos. 931/2, 934/5) or* **239** *(others).*
930 85 c. on 60 c. on 3 c. Hanging Heliconia .. 1·25 35
931 130 c. on 60 c. on 3 c. Hanging Heliconia .. 1·25 55
a. Surch (as T **238**) inverted .. £100
932 160 c. on $1.10 on $2 *Norantea guianensis* (vert surch) .. .. .. .. 2·00 2·00
a. Surch (as T **238**) double .. .. 50·00

33 170 c. on $1.10 on $2 *Norantea guianensis* .. 7·00 4·00
34 210 c. on 75 c. on $5 *Odontadenia grandiflora* (B.) .. .. .. .. .. 1·25 90
a. Surch (as T **238**) inverted .. .. 45·00
35 235 c. on 75 c. on $5 *Odontadenia grandiflora* 1·50 1·50
a. Surch (T **206**) omitted .. .. ..
b. Surch (as T **238**) double .. .. ..
36 330 c. on $1.10 on $2 *Norantea guianensis* .. 6·00 1·50
30/6 .. .. .. .. .. .. *Set of* 7 18·00 9·75

ESPANA
1982

(240)

220 AIR
Princess
of Wales
1961 - 1982

(241)

982 (15 May). *World Cup Football Championship, Spain (2nd issue). Nos.* 544, 546 *and* 554 *optd with T* **240** *or surch also as T* **228**, *both by Autoprint.*
37 $1 *Chelonanthus uliginoides* .. .. 75 60
38 110 c. on 3 c. Hanging Heliconia (B.) .. .. 75 40
39 250 c. on 6 c. Cannon-ball tree (B.) .. 1·00 90
37/9 .. .. .. .. .. *Set of* 3 2·25 1·75
See also No. 1218.

(Optd Govt Printer and surch by Autoprint )

1982 (17 May). *W* **106** *(sideways). P* 13.
40 **181** 15 c. on 2 c. black, ind & greenish grey 50 15
a. Opt ("ESSEQUIBO etc") omitted 18·00
41 20 c. on 2 c. black, ind & greenish grey 1·50 30
42 25 c. on 2 c. black, ind & greenish grey 3·25 20
43 30 c. on 2 c. black, ind & greenish grey 40 15
44 40 c. on 2 c. black, ind & greenish grey 1·50 30
a. Surch inverted .. .. .. 20·00
45 45 c. on 2 c. black, ind & greenish grey 1·75 45
46 50 c. on 2 c. black, ind & greenish grey 1·00 30
a. Opt ("ESSEQUIBO etc") omitted 18·00
47 60 c. on 2 c. black, ind & greenish grey 3·25 20
48 75 c. on 2 c. black, ind & greenish grey 2·00 25
49 80 c. on 2 c. black, ind & greenish grey 1·25 20
50 85 c. on 2 c. black, ind & greenish grey 75 25
51 100 c. on 3 c. black, ind and Venetian red 75 35
52 110 c. on 3 c. black, ind and Venetian red 80 30
53 120 c. on 3 c. black, ind and Venetian red 3·75 35
54 125 c. on 3 c. black, ind and Venetian red 1·50 35
55 130 c. on 3 c. black, ind and Venetian red 90 35
a. Surch inverted .. .. .. 17·00
b. Error. Nos. 952 and 955 *se-tenant*
c. Error. Nos. 955 and 956 *se-tenant*
956 150 c. on 3 c. black, ind and Venetian red 3·50 40
957 160 c. on 3 c. black, ind and Venetian red 2·00 40
958 170 c. on 3 c. black, ind and Venetian red 1·40 45
959 175 c. on 3 c. black, ind and Venetian red 3·00 45
960 180 c. on 3 c. black, ind and Venetian red 2·00 50
961 200 c. on 3 c. black, ind and Venetian red 2·25 45
962 210 c. on 3 c. black, ind and Venetian red 4·50 50
963 220 c. on 3 c. black, ind and Venetian red 5·50 60
964 235 c. on 3 c. black, ind and Venetian red 4·75 60
965 240 c. on 3 c. black, ind and Venetian red 4·50 60
966 250 c. on 3 c. black, ind and Venetian red 2·25 60
967 300 c. on 3 c. black, ind and Venetian red 6·00 75
968 330 c. on 3 c. black, ind and Venetian red 2·75 90
969 375 c. on 3 c. black, ind and Venetian red 4·50 1·00
970 400 c. on 3 c. black, ind and Venetian red 6·50 1·10
971 440 c. on 3 c. black, ind and Venetian red 4·00 1·10
972 500 c. on 3 c. black, ind and Venetian red 3·50 1·40
973 550 c. on 3 c. black, ind and Venetian red 3·75 1·75
974 625 c. on 3 c. black, ind and Venetian red 2·75 2·00
975 1500 c. on 2 c. black, ind & greenish grey 10·00 4·00
976 2000 c. on 2 c. black, ind & greenish grey 11·00 5·50
940/76 .. .. .. .. .. *Set of* 37 £100 25·00

Nos. 940/76 are fiscal stamps, surcharged for postal use, as Type 181, but with the overprinted inscription and face value redrawn. On the 15 to 85 c., the surcharged face value is in blue, on the 100 to 625 c. in black, and on the 1500 and 2000 c. in red.

Nos. 955b/c come from the first printing of the 130 c. which had one cliché of the 110 c. surcharge (R. 4/1) and three of the 150 c. (R. 2/8–10) included in error.

For 25 c. and 40 c. surcharges in black see Nos. 988/9 and for the 25 c. in red, No. 1029.

1982 (7 June). *No.* 548 *optd with T* **226** *in blue by Autoprint.*
977 15 c. Christmas Orchid .. .. .. .. 3·25 10
a. Optd on No. 548a .. .. .. .. 48·00 12·00

1982 (15 June). *No.* O26 *optd with T* **229** *in blue by Autoprint.*
978 100 c. on 6 c. Type **116** .. .. .. .. 3·00 35

1982 (25 June). *Air. 21st Birthday of Princess of Wales. Nos.* 542, 545 *and* 555 *surch as T* **241** *by Bovell's Printery.*
979 110 c. on 5 c. Annatto tree (R.) .. .. .. 60 50
a. Surch in black .. .. .. 60·00
980 220 c. on 1 c. Pitcher Plant of Mt Roraima .. 1·25 80
a. Surch double .. .. .. ..
981 330 c. on $2 *Norantea guianensis* (B.) .. 1·50 1·50
a. Surch in greenish blue .. ..
ab. Surch double .. .. ..
979/81 .. .. .. .. *Set of* 3 3·00 2·50



GUYANA
H.R.H.
Prince William
21st June 1982
000
0000000000 $1.10

(242)

H.R.H.
Prince William
21st June 1982

$2.20

(243)

1982 (12 July). *Birth of Prince William of Wales. Surch as T* **242** *(50 c. and $1.10) or with T* **243** *(others), all in blue by Autoprint.*

(*a*) *On stamps of British Guiana*
982 50 c. on 2 c. myrtle-green (No. 332) .. .. 40 45
983 $1.10 on 3 c. brown-olive and red-brown (No. 354) .. .. .. .. .. .. 1·00 80
a. Surch inverted .. .. .. .. 35·00
b. Surch double .. .. .. ..
c. Surch on No. 333 .. .. .. .. 1·00 75
ca. Surch inverted .. .. .. .. 55·00
cb. Surch double .. .. .. .. 70·00
cc. Surch as T **243** (lines at foot) .. 40·00

(*b*) *On stamps of Guyana previously optd* "GUYANA INDEPENDENCE 1966"
984 50 c. on 2 c. myrtle-green (No. 430) .. .. 5·00 2·50
985 $1.10 on 3 c. brown-olive and red-brown (No. 431) .. .. .. .. .. 7·50 2·50
a. Surch on No. 422 .. .. .. .. 40·00 10·00
986 $1.25 on 6 c. yellow-green (No. 398A) .. 70 80
a. Surch inverted .. .. .. .. 50·00
b. Surch double .. .. .. .. 70·00
c. Surch on No. 434 .. .. .. .. 4·50 3·25
987 $2.20 on 24 c. black and brownish orange (No. 401B) .. .. .. .. .. 1·50 1·50
a. Surch inverted .. .. .. .. 70·00
b. Surch on No. 401A .. .. .. .. 12·00 10·00
c. Surch on No. 435 .. .. .. .. 38·00 25·00
982/7 .. .. .. .. .. *Set of* 6 14·50 7·50

Nos. 982, 983c and 985a have Mult Script CA watermark and the remainder watermark w **12** (sideways on No. 987).

1982 (13 July). *As Nos.* 942 *and* 944 *but with surcharged face values in black by Autoprint.*
988 **181** 25 c. on 2 c. black, ind & greenish grey .. 75 20
989 40 c. on 2 c. black, ind & greenish grey .. 35 15

1982 (13 July). *Savings Campaign. Coil stamp. As No.* 913 *but showing inverted comma before* "OURS" *in overprint.*
990 110 c. on $5 Guyana male and female soldiers with flag .. .. .. .. .. 5·50 50

ITALY
$2.35

(244)

50
C.A. & CARIB
GAMES
1982

(245)

1982 (15 July). *Italy's Victory in World Cup Football Championship. No.* F7 *optd as T* **240** *and surch with T* **244**, *both in blue by Autoprint.*
991 $2.35 on 180 c. on 60 c. Soldier's Cap .. 2·25 75

1982 (16 Aug). *Wildlife Protection. Nos.* 687 *and* 733/8 *optd with T* **226** *(vert on Nos.* 993/8) *in blue by Autoprint.*
992 35 c. Harpy Eagle .. .. .. .. 2·00 40
993 35 c. Type **174** .. .. .. .. .. 2·00 40
a. Block of 6. Nos. 993/8 .. .. .. 12·50
994 35 c. Haimara .. .. .. .. .. 2·00 40
995 35 c. Electric Eel .. .. .. .. 2·00 40
996 35 c. Golden Rivulus .. .. .. .. 2·00 40
997 35 c. Pencil Fish .. .. .. .. 2·00 40
998 35 c. Four-eyed Fish .. .. .. .. 2·00 40
992/8 .. .. .. .. .. *Set of* 7 12·50 2·50

1982 (16 Aug). *Central American and Caribbean Games, Havana. Nos.* 542/3 *surch as T* **245** *by Autoprint.*
999 50 c. on 2 c. Type **132** .. .. .. .. 1·00 45
a. Surch inverted .. .. .. .. † —
1000 60 c. on 1 c. Pitcher Plant of Mt Roraima .. 1·25 30

1982 (15 Sept). *No.* 730 *optd with T* **226** *vertically in blue by Autoprint.*
1001 35 c. black and red-orange .. .. .. 30 20

1982 (15 Sept). *Nos.* 841 *and* 979 *further surch as T* **228** *(No.* 1003 *has solid bar) in blue by Autoprint.*
1002 130 c. on 60 c. on 3 c. Hanging Heliconia .. 60 50
a. Surch as T **228** inverted .. .. £150
1003 170 c. on 110 c. on 5 c. Annatto tree .. 2·00 75
a. With six lines as in T **228** .. .. 90·00

1982 (15 Sept). *No.* 841 *optd with T* **226** *and surch as T* **228**, *both in blue by Autoprint.*
1004 440 c. on 60 c. on 3 c. Hanging Heliconia .. 2·75 1·50
a. T **226** and T **228** both inverted .. 65·00
b. Surch and optd on No. 841b .. .. 20·00
c. Without opt T **226** .. .. .. 15·00 2·00

No. 1004c also differs from No. 1004 by showing a "c" after the surcharge "60" on Type **205**.

Commonwealth
GAMES
AUSTRALIA
1982
1.25

(246)

INT.
FOOD DAY
1982

(247)

1982 (27 Sept). *Commonwealth Games, Brisbane, Australia. No.* 546 *surch with T* **246** *in blue by Autoprint.*
1005 $1.25 on 6 c. Cannon-ball tree .. .. 1·50 40

1982 (1 Oct). *Nos.* 552, 641 *and* 719 *optd with T* **226** *(vertically on Nos.* 1007/8) *in blue by Autoprint.*
1006 50 c. multicoloured (No. 552) .. .. .. 2·00 25
1007 50 c. light violet-blue, light green and light yellow-brown (No. 641) .. .. .. 1·50 25
1008 50 c. multicoloured (No. 719) .. .. .. 60 25

1982 (1 Oct). *Various Official stamps additionally optd for postal purposes as T* **229**, *but smaller (29 mm in length), all in blue by Autoprint.*
1009 15 c. Christmas Orchid (No. O23) (vert opt) 4·50 10
1010 50 c. *Guzmania lingulata* (No. O14) (vert opt) .. .. .. .. .. 1·25 25
1011 100 c. on $3 Cylinder satellite (No. O19) .. 1·75 50

1982 (15 Oct). *International Food Day. No.* 617 *optd with T* **247** *in blue by Autoprint.*
1012 50 c. Pawpaw and tangerine .. .. .. 14·00 1·25

INT. YEAR
OF THE
ELDERLY

(248)

Dr. R. KOCH
CENTENARY
TBC BACILLUS
DISCOVERY

(249)

F. D. ROOSEVELT
1882-1982

(250)

1982 (15 Oct). *International Year of the Elderly. No.* 747 *optd with T* **248** *in blue by Autoprint.*
1013 50 c. District 404 emblem .. .. .. 4·50 50

1982 (15 Oct). *Centenary of Robert Koch's Discovery of Tubercle Bacillus. No.* 750 *optd with T* **249** *in blue by Autoprint.*
1014 60 c. Researcher with microscope, Caduceus emblem, stethoscope and beach scene .. 2·00 30

1982 (15 Oct). *International Decade for Women. No.* 633 *optd with T* **226** *in blue by Autoprint.*
1015 $1 brown and bright blue .. .. .. 3·25 80
a. Opt inverted .. .. .. .. 17·00

1982 (15 Oct). *Birth Centenary of F. D. Roosevelt (American statesman). No.* 706 *optd with T* **250** *in blue by Autoprint.*
1016 $1 Type **167** .. .. .. .. .. 1·50 45

GAC Inaug. Flight
Georgetown—
Boa Vista, Brasil
200

(251)

(252)

1982 (15 Oct). *1st Anniv of G.A.C. Inaugural Flight Georgetown to Boa Vista, Brazil. No.* 842 *optd with T* **226** *and surch with T* **251**, *both in blue by Autoprint.*
1017 200 c. on 75 c. on $5 *Odontadenia grandiflora* 15·00 3·00

1982 (18 Nov). *CARICOM Heads of Government Conference, Kingston, Jamaica. Nos.* 881/6 *surch with T* **252** *by Herald Printing-Kitty.*
1018 50 c. on 15 c. Type **225** .. .. .. 1·00 30
a. Sheetlet of 6. Nos. 1018/23 .. .. 5·25
1019 50 c. on 15 c. "Metric man" .. .. 1·00 30
1020 50 c. on 15 c. "Postal service goes metric" .. 1·00 30
1021 50 c. on 15 c. Weighing child on metric scales 1·00 30
1022 50 c. on 15 c. Canje Bridge .. .. .. 1·00 30
1023 50 c. on 15 c. Tap filling litre bucket .. .. 1·00 30
1018/23 .. .. .. .. .. *Set of* 6 5·25 1·75

CHRISTMAS 1982 (253)   15 (254)   50 (255)

**1982** (1 Dec). *Christmas. Nos.* 895/9 *optd with T* **253** *in red by Autoprint.*

1024 15 c. on 2 c. Type **132** (surch T **231**) .. .. 20 15
a. Sheetlet of 25. Nos. 1024/5, each × 8, Nos. 1026/7, each × 4 and No. 1028 .. .. 9·00
1025 15 c. on 2 c. Type **132** (surch "Scout Movement 1907–1982") .. .. 20 15
1026 15 c. on 2 c. Type **132** (surch "1907–1982") .. 30 25
1027 15 c. on 2 c. Type **132** (surch "1857–1982") .. 30 25
1028 15 c. on 2 c. Type **132** (surch "1982") .. .. 2·50 2·50
1024/8 .. .. .. .. *Set of* 5 3·25 3·00

Nos. 1024/8 were only issued in the *se-tenant* sheetlets of 25.

**1982** (15 Dec). *As No.* 942 *but with surcharged face value in red by Autoprint.*

1029 **181** 25 c. on 2 c. black, indigo and greenish grey .. .. .. .. .. 50 10

**1982** (15 Dec). *Nos.* 543 *and* 546 *surch as T* **254** *by Autoprint.*

1030 15 c. on 2 c. Type **132** (B.) .. .. .. 15 10
1031 20 c. on 6 c. Cannon-ball tree (Blk.) .. .. 25 10

For similar surcharges in different colours see Nos. 1034/5 and 1063; and for surcharges incorporating "c" Nos. 1085/7 and 1098/9.

**1982** (15 Dec). *No.* 489 *surch as T* **255** *by Autoprint.*

1032 50 c. on 6 c. Patua .. .. .. .. .. 20 25
1033 100 c. on 6 c. Patua .. .. .. .. .. 40 45

**1983** (5 Jan). *As Nos.* 1030/1, *but with colours of surcharge changed.*

1034 15 c. on 2 c. Type **132** (Blk.) .. .. .. 10 10
1035 20 c. on 6 c. Cannon-ball tree (G.) .. .. .. 10 10

1983 (256)   POSTAGE (257)   60th BIRTHDAY ANNIVERSARY OF OUR PRESIDENT 25c ALL GUYANA OUR HERITAGE

**258** Guyana Flag (inscr "60th BIRTHDAY ANNIVERSARY")

**1983** (1 Feb). *Optd with T* **256** *by Autoprint.*

1036 – 15 c. multicoloured (No. 655) (opt vert) 6·00 2·00
1037 – 15 c. yellow-brown, grey and black (No. 672) .. .. .. .. .. 50 10
1038 – 15 c. multicoloured (No. 682) (opt vert) .. 40 10
1039 **214** 15 c. on 10 c. multicoloured (opt vert) .. 35 10
1040 **215** 15 c. on 10 c. multicoloured .. .. 15 10
1041 – 50 c. multicoloured (No. 646) .. .. 3·00 25
1042 – 50 c. multicoloured (No. 696) (opt vert) .. 3·50 25
1043 – 50 c. multicoloured (No. 719) .. .. 1·50 25
1036/43 .. .. .. .. *Set of* 8 14·00 3·00

See also Nos. 1060/1, 1069/70, 1072/9, 1096, 1101 and 1110/16.

**1983** (1 Feb). *No.* O17 *optd for postal purposes with T* **257** *in red by Autoprint.*

1044 15 c. Harpy Eagle .. .. .. .. 3·75 10

**1983** (8 Feb). *National Heritage. Nos.* 710/12 *and No.* 778 *surch as T* **234** *in black (No.* 1045*) or blue (others) by Autoprint.*

1045 90 c. on 30 c. Cassiri and decorated Amerindian jars .. .. .. .. .. 2·40 1·60
1046 90 c. on 35 c. Rock drawing of hunter and quarry .. .. .. .. .. 35 50
1047 90 c. on 50 c. Fork Kyk-over-al .. .. .. 2·40 1·60
1048 90 c. on 60 c. Fort Island .. .. .. 4·50 50
1045/8 .. .. .. .. *Set of* 4 8·75 3·75

(Des K. Everett (25 c.). Litho Format)

**1983** (19 Feb). *President Burnham's 60th Birthday and 30 Years in Parliament. T* **258** *and similar multicoloured designs. W* **106** *(sideways) (25 c., $1.30). P* 13½ *($1.30) or* 14 *(others).*

1049 25 c. Type **258** .. .. .. .. .. 15 20
a. Horiz pair. Nos. 1049/50 .. .. .. 30 40
1050 25 c. As T **258**, but position of flag reversed and inscr "30th ANNIVERSARY IN PARLIAMENT" .. .. .. .. 15 20
1051 $1.30, Youth display (41 × 25 *mm*) .. .. 75 65
1052 $6 Presidential standard (43½ × 25 *mm*) .. 2·50 2·75
1049/52 .. .. .. .. *Set of* 4 3·25 3·50

Nos. 1049/50 were printed together, *se-tenant*, in horizontal pairs throughout the sheet.

For stamps as Nos. 1049/50, but without commemorative inscriptions, see Nos. 1108/9.

**PRINTERS.** Nos. 1053/1126 were surcharged or overprinted by Autoprint, Georgetown.

FIFTY CENTS (259)   20 X (260)

**1983** (7 Mar). *Surch as T* **259**.

1053 **170** 50 c. on 10 c. mult (No. 717) (R.) .. .. 75 25
1054 – 50 c. on 400 c. on 30 c. multicoloured (No. 911) (surch vert) .. .. .. 1·00 25
1055 **152** $1 on 10 c. multicoloured (No. 635) (surch vert) .. .. .. .. 6·00 45
1056 $1 on $1.05 on 10 c. multicoloured (No. 768) (surch vert) .. .. .. 3·00 45
1056*a* – $1 on $1.10 on $2 multicoloured (No. 843) .. .. .. .. .. 2·50 2·00
1057 – $1 on 220 c. on 5 c. mult (No. 844) (B.) 7·00 1·00
1058 – $1 on 330 c. on $2 mult (No. 981) (B.) 75 45
1059 – $1 on $12 on $1.10 on $2 mult (similar to No. P3) (B.) .. .. .. 18·00 5·00
1053/9 .. .. .. .. .. *Set of* 8 35·00 9·00

Nos. 1057/9 have thin bars cancelling previous surcharges, and, in addition, No. 1059 is optd with T **226** in blue.

See also Nos. 1062 and 1080/4.

**1983** (7 Mar). *No.* 859 *optd with T* **256**.

1060 $1 on 60 c. Beethoven and Sonny Thomas .. 2·50 45

**1983** (11 Mar). *Conference of Foreign Ministers of Non-aligned Countries, New Delhi. No.* 569 *surch with T* **259** *and No.* 570 *optd with T* **256**.

1061 **136** 25 c. multicoloured (opt vert) .. .. 2·00 25
1062 50 c. on 8 c. mult (surch vert) (R.) .. 3·00 25

**1983** (14 Mar). *As No.* 1030, *but colour of surcharge changed.*

1063 15 c. on 2 c. Type **132** (R.) .. .. .. 30 10

**1983** (14 Mar). *No.* 771 *further surch with T* **260** *in blue.*

1064 **181** 20 c. on 10 c. on 3 c. black, indigo and Venetian red .. .. .. 35 10

**Commonwealth Day 14 March 1983** $1.30 (261)   $4.80 (262)

**1983** (14 Mar). *Commonwealth Day. Nos.* 398A *and* 401B *surch as T* **261** *in black (25 c., $1.30) or blue (others).*

1065 25 c.on 6 c. yellow-green .. .. .. 1·50 20
1066 $1.20 on 6 c. yellow-green .. .. .. 75 50
1067 $1.30 on 24 c. black and bright orange .. 90 55
1068 $2.40 on 24 c. black and bright orange .. 1·50 1·25
1065/8 .. .. .. .. *Set of* 4 4·25 2·25

**1983** (17 Mar). *Easter. Nos.* 482/3 *optd with T* **256**.

1069 **111** 25 c. multicoloured .. .. .. 10 10
1070 30 c. multicoloured .. .. .. 25 15

**1983** (17 Mar). *25th Anniv of International Maritime Organization. British Guiana fiscal stamp optd in red as T* **262**. *Wmk Mult Crown CA. P* 14.

1071 $4.80, bright blue and deep dull green .. 4·50 5·50

**1983** (1 Apr). *Optd with T* **256**.

1072 **152** 50 c. mult (No. 637) (opt vert) .. 1·50 25
1073 **159** 50 c. ultramarine, black and gold (No. 668) (opt vert) .. .. 5·00 25
1073*a* – 50 c. multicoloured (No. 723) ..
1074 – 50 c. mult (No. 854) (opt vert) .. 60 25
1075 – 50 c. multicoloured (No. 858) .. 30 25
1076 – $1 multicoloured (No. 628) .. 7·50 45
1077 – $1 mult (No. 638) (opt vert) .. 6·50 45
1078 – $1 multicoloured (No. 675) .. 4·00 45
1079 – $1 on 30 c. mult (No. 855) (opt vert) 1·25 45
1079*a* – $3 multicoloured (No. 720) .. 8·50 70
1079*b* – $3 multicoloured (No. 724) ..
1079*c* – $3 multicoloured (No. 748) ..

**1983** (1 Apr). *Surch with T* **259**, *vertically, in black (No.* 1082*) or blue (others).*

1080 **148** 50 c. on 8 c. multicoloured (No. 615) .. 1·75 25
1081 **162** 50 c. on 8 c. multicoloured (No. 681) .. 6·00 25
1082 **171** 50 c. on 10 c. multicoloured (No. 721) .. 3·00 25
1083 – 50 c. on 10 c. on 25 c. mult (No. O13) .. 3·50 25
1084 – 50 c. on 330 c. on $3 mult (No. 845) .. 3·00 25

**1983** (2 May). *Surch as T* **254**, *but with "c" after new face value.*

1085 **105** 15 c. on 6 c. black, gold and flesh (No. 469) (B.) .. 10 10
1086 – 20 c. on 6 c. multicoloured (No. 546) .. 10 10
1087 **111** 50 c. on 6 c. multicoloured (No. 481) .. 30 30

For No. 1085 with black overprint, see No. 1098.

$1 (263)   110 (264)   ITU 1983 25 (265)

**1983** (2 May). *No.* 489 *surch with T* **263**.

1088 $1 on 6 c. Patua .. .. .. .. .. 45 50

**1983** (2 May). *No.* 639 *surch with T* **264** *in blue.*

1089 **153** 110 c. on 10 c. greenish yellow, light green and light reddish violet .. 1·50 50
a. Error. Surch on 35 c (No. 640) 90·00

**1983** (2 May). *Nos.* 551 *and* 556 *surch as T* **228** *in blue.*

1090 250 c. on 40 c. Tiger Beard .. .. .. 4·50 1·2[illegible]
1091 400 c. on $5 *Odontadenia grandiflora* .. 4·50 1·9[illegible]

**1983** (17 May). *World Telecommunications and Health Day. Nos.* 842 *and* 980 *further surch as T* **265**.

1092 25 c. on 220 c. on 1 c. Pitcher Plant of Mt Roraima (surch T **265**) (R.) .. .. 20 2[illegible]
a. Sheetlet of 25. Nos. 1092/3 each × 8 and No. 1094 × 9 .. .. .. .. 4·75
b. Six bars only at top .. ..
1093 25 c. on 220 c. on 1 c. Pitcher Plant of Mt Roraima (surch "WHO 1983 25") (R.) .. 20 2[illegible]
b. Six bars only at top .. ..
1094 25 c. on 220 c. on 1 c. Pitcher Plant of Mt Roraima (surch "17 MAY '83 ITU/WHO 25") (R.) .. .. .. .. 20 2[illegible]
b. Six bars only at top .. ..
1095 $4.50 on 75 c. on $5 *Odontadenia grandiflora* (surch "ITU/WHO 17 MAY 1983") (B.) .. .. .. .. .. 11·00 3·0[illegible]
a. Surch on 235 c. on 75 c. on $5 (No. 929) .. 7·00 4·0[illegible]
1092/5 .. .. .. .. *Set of* 4 11·00 3·2[illegible]

**1983** (18 May). *30th Anniv of President's Entry into Parliament. Nos.* 690 *and* 692 *surch as T* **259**, *the former additionally optd with T* **256**.

1096 $1 on 15 c. black, light violet-blue and bluish grey .. .. .. .. .. 4·50 5[illegible]
1097 $1 on 40 c. black, red-orange and bluish grey 6·50 5[illegible]

No. **MS**693 was also reissued with examples of Nos. 1096/7 affixed over the 8 c. and 35 c. values, and an example of No. 1050 added to the righthand sheet margin. These miniature sheets revalued to $6, numbered on the reverse and cancelled with First Day of Issue postmarks, were for presentation purposes and were not available for postage.

**1983** (23 May). *Surch as T* **254**, *but with "c" after new face value.*

1098 **105** 15 c. on 6 c. black, gold and flesh (No. 469) (Blk.) .. .. .. 10 1[illegible]
1099 – 50 c. on 6 c. multicoloured (No. 489) (Blk.) 30 3[illegible]

**1983** (23 May). *No.* 546 *surch as T* **228**, *but with "c" after new face value.*

1100 20 c. on 6 c. Cannon-ball tree .. .. .. 10 1[illegible]

**1983** (23 May). *No.* 611 *optd with T* **256**.

1101 25 c. Guides in camp .. .. .. .. 35·00 1·7[illegible]

$1 (266)   120 $1.30 CANADA 1983 (267)   XXX (268)

**1983** (23 May). *No.* 489 *surch with T* **266** *in red.*

1102 $1 on 6 c. Patua .. .. .. .. .. 55 5[illegible]

**1983** (15 June). *15th World Scout Jamboree, Alberta. Nos.* 835/6 *and* O13 *additionally surch or optd as T* **267**.

1103 – $1.30 on 100 c. on 8 c. multicoloured .. 3·00 1·00
1104 **116** 180 c. on 6 c. multicoloured .. .. 3·00 2·00
1105 $3.90 on 400 c. on 6 c. multicoloured .. 3·50 3·50
1103/5 .. .. .. .. *Set of* 3 8·50 6·00

**1983** (22 June). *Nos.* 659/60 *surch as T* **254**.

1106 60 c. on 15 c. Map of the Caribbean .. .. 7·00 35
1107 $1.50 on 15 c. Prudential Cup .. .. 8·00 80

**1983** (1 July). *As Nos.* 1049/50, *but without commemorative inscr above flag. W* **106** *(sideways). P* 14.

1108 25 c. As Type **258** .. .. .. .. 15 15
a. Horiz pair. Nos. 1108/9 .. .. .. 30 30
1109 25 c. As No. 1050 .. .. .. .. 15 15

Nos. 1108/9 were printed together, *se-tenant* in horizontal pairs throughout the sheet.

**1983** (1 July). *Optd with T* **256**.

1110 **105** 30 c. black, gold and light apple-green (No. 471) .. .. .. .. 40 2[illegible]
1111 – 30 c. multicoloured (No. 695) .. .. 9·00 3[illegible]
1112 – 30 c. multicoloured (No. 718) (opt vert) .. 4·00 2[illegible]
1113 – 30 c. multicoloured (No. 722) .. .. 7·50 2[illegible]
1114 – 30 c. multicoloured (No. 746) .. .. 4·00 2[illegible]
1115 – 60 c. multicoloured (No. 697) .. .. 4·25 2[illegible]
1116 – 60 c. multicoloured (No. 731) .. .. 5·00 2[illegible]
1110/16 .. .. .. .. *Set of* 7 30·00 1·25

**1983** (1 July). *No.* 553 *optd with T* **226** *in blue.*

1117 60 c. Soldier's Cap .. .. .. .. 3·25 35

**1983** (1 July). *Surch as T* **264** *in blue.*

1118 **157** 120 c. on 8 c. multicoloured (No. 654) 3·25 60
1119 **159** 120 c. on 10 c. dull red, black and gold (No. 666) .. .. .. 3·50 60
1120 – 120 c. on 35 c. multicoloured (No. 622) 3·50 60
a. Surch reading upwards ..
1121 – 120 c. on 35 c. orange, light green and reddish violet (No. 640) .. 3·50 60

**1983** (1 July). *Nos.* 716 *and* 729 *surch as T* **268**.

1122 120 c. on 10 c. Type **173** (R.) .. .. .. 3·25 60
1123 120 c. on 375 c. on $3 Cylinder satellite .. 3·00 60

No. 1123 also carries an otherwise unissued surcharge in red, reading "INTERNATIONAL SCIENCE YEAR 1982 375". As issued much of this is obliterated by two heavy bars.

CARICOM DAY 1983

120

GUYANA 60 XXX

(269) (270)

**1983** (1 July). *British Guiana No. D1a and Guyana No. D8 surch with T* **269** *in blue.*
1124 D 1 120 c. on 1 c. deep green.. .. .. 3·25 60
1125 D 2 120 c. on 1 c. olive .. .. .. 3·25 60

**1983** (1 July). *CARICOM Day. No. 823 additionally surch with T* **270** *in red.*
1126 60 c. on $3 "Makanaima the Great Ancestral Spirit of the Amerindians" .. .. 1·75 35

**271** *Kurupukari*

(Litho Format)

**1983** (11 July*). *Riverboats. T* **271** *and similar horiz designs. W* **106**. *P* 14.
1127 30 c. black and vermilion .. .. .. 15 20
a. *Tête-bêche* (vert pair) .. .. .. 30
1128 60 c. black and bright reddish violet .. 30 35
a. *Tête-bêche* (vert pair) .. .. .. 60
1129 120 c. black and bright lemon .. .. 1·00 60
a. *Tête-bêche* (vert pair) .. .. .. 1·10
1130 130 c. black .. .. .. .. .. 60 65
a. *Tête-bêche* (vert pair) .. .. .. 1·25
1131 150 c. black and bright emerald .. .. 75 80
a. *Tête-bêche* (vert pair) .. .. .. 1·50
1127/31 .. .. .. .. *Set of* 5 2·50 2·40

Designs:—60 c. *Makouria*; 120 c. *Powis*; 130 c. *Pomeroon*; 150 c. *Lukanani*.

*Although not finally issued until 11 July First Day Covers of Nos. 1127/31 are postmarked with the intended release date of 1 July.

Nos. 1127/31 were each issued in sheets of 80 (10 × 8) with the bottom three rows inverted forming *tête-bêche* vertical pairs from Rows 5 and 6.

2.30

(272)

**1983** (22 July). *Unissued Royal Wedding surcharge, similar to No. 843, surch as T* **272** *in blue by Autoprint.*
1132 $2.30 on $1.10 on $2 *Norantea guianensis* .. 2·50 1·50
1133 $3.20 on $1.10 on $2 *Norantea guianensis* .. 3·00 1·75

BW Mont Golfier 1783-1983

(273) (274)

**1983** (5 Sept). *Bicentenary of Manned Flight and 20th Anniv of Guyana Airways. Nos. 701/2a optd as T* **273/4**, *in red (Nos. 1134/47) or blue (Nos. 1148/68) by Autoprint.*
1134 20 c. multicoloured (optd T **273**) .. .. 10 10
a. Sheetlet of 25. Nos. 1134/8 each × 4 and 1139 × 5.. .. .. .. .. 2·50
1135 20 c. multicoloured (optd "LM") .. .. 10 10
1136 20 c. multicoloured (optd "GY 1963 1983") .. 10 10
1137 20 c. multicoloured (optd "JW") .. .. 10 10
1138 20 c. multicoloured (optd "CU") .. .. 10 10
1139 20 c. multicoloured (optd T **274**) .. .. 10 10
1140 25 c. multicoloured (optd "BGI") .. .. 50 25
a. Sheetlet of 25. Nos. 1140 × 2, 1141 × 8, 1142/44 each × 2, 1145 × 5 and 1146/7 each × 2.. .. .. .. 9·00
1141 25 c. multicoloured (optd "GEO") .. .. 15 10
1142 25 c. multicoloured (optd "MIA") .. .. 50 25
1143 25 c. multicoloured (optd "BVB") .. .. 50 25
1144 25 c. multicoloured (optd "PBM") .. .. 50 25
1145 25 c. multicoloured (optd T **274**) .. .. 20 15
1146 25 c. multicoloured (optd "POS") .. .. 50 25
1147 25 c. multicoloured (optd "JFK") .. .. 50 25
1148 30 c. multicoloured (optd "AHL") .. .. 25 15
a. Sheetlet of 25. Nos. 1148/54, 1155 × 5 and 1156/68 .. .. .. .. 7·00
1149 30 c. multicoloured (optd "BCG") .. .. 25 15
1150 30 c. multicoloured (optd "BMJ") .. .. 25 15
1151 30 c. multicoloured (optd "EKE") .. .. 25 15
1152 30 c. multicoloured (optd "GEO") .. .. 25 15
1153 30 c. multicoloured (optd "GFO") .. .. 25 15
1154 30 c. multicoloured (optd "IBM") .. .. 25 15
1155 30 c. multicoloured (optd T **274**) .. .. 25 15
1156 30 c. multicoloured (optd "KAI") .. .. 25 15
1157 30 c. multicoloured (optd "KAR") .. .. 25 15
1158 30 c. multicoloured (optd "KPG") .. .. 25 15
1159 30 c. multicoloured (optd "KRG") .. .. 25 15
1160 30 c. multicoloured (optd "KTO") .. .. 25 15
1161 30 c. multicoloured (optd "LTM") .. .. 25 15
1162 30 c. multicoloured (optd "MHA") .. .. 25 15
1163 30 c. multicoloured (optd "MWJ") .. .. 25 15
1164 30 c. multicoloured (optd "MYM") .. .. 25 15
1165 30 c. multicoloured (optd "NAI") .. .. 25 15
1166 30 c. multicoloured (optd "ORJ") .. .. 25 15
1167 30 c. multicoloured (optd "USI") .. .. 25 15
1168 30 c. multicoloured (optd "VEG") .. .. 25 15
1134/68 .. .. .. .. *Set of* 35 8·00 4·50

The overprints on the 20 c. value represent airlines, on the 25 c. international airports and on the 30 c. internal airports. Those on Nos. 1150 and 1154 were incorrect and examples of the former exist with the manuscript correction "PMT".

(275) (275*a*)

**1983** (14 Sept). *No. 649 surch with T* **275** *in blue by Autoprint.*
1169 240 c. on 35 c. on 60 c. Soldier's Cap .. .. 1·25 1·00
a. Surch with T **275*a*** .. .. .. 1·25 1·00
b. Pair. Nos. 1169/a .. .. .. 2·50

Types **275** and **275*a*** occur *se-tenant* within the sheet.

FAO 1983

30

(276)

POSTAGE ONE PENNY 25c 1st. APRIL 1858 A03 . GUYANA .

**277** G.B. 1857 1d. with Georgetown "AO3" Postmark

**1983** (15 Sept). *F.A.O. Fisheries Project. Nos. 485 and 487 surch as T* **276** *in red by Autoprint.*
1170 30 c. on 1 c. Type **87** .. .. .. .. 15 15
1171 $2.60 on 3 c. Lukunani .. .. .. .. 1·50 1·75

(Des K. Everett. Litho Format)

**1983** (1 Oct). *125th Anniv of Use of Great Britain Stamps in Guyana. T* **277** *and similar square designs. W* **106**. *P* 14½.

(*a*) *Inscriptions in black*
1172 **277** 25 c. lake-brown and black .. .. 10 10
a. *Tête-bêche* (pair) .. .. .. 20
1173 – 30 c. rose-red and black .. .. 10 15
a. *Tête-bêche* (pair) .. .. .. 20
1174 – 60 c. bright violet and black .. .. 25 30
a. *Tête-bêche* (pair) .. .. .. 50
1175 – 120 c. dull green and black .. .. 50 55
a. *Tête-bêche* (pair) .. .. .. 1·00

(*b*) *Inscriptions in bright blue*
1176 **277** 25 c. lake-brown and black .. .. 10 10
a. Block of 4. Nos. 1176/9 .. .. 40
1177 – 25 c. rose-red and black .. .. 10 10
1178 – 25 c. bright violet and black .. .. 10 10
1179 – 25 c. dull green and black .. .. 10 10
1180 **277** 30 c. lake-brown and black .. .. 10 15
a. Block of 4. Nos. 1180/3 .. .. 40
1181 – 30 c. rose-red and black .. .. 10 15
1182 – 30 c. bright violet and black .. .. 10 15
1183 – 30 c. dull green and black .. .. 10 15
1184 **277** 45 c. lake-brown and black .. .. 20 25
a. Block of 4. Nos. 1184/7 .. .. 80
1185 – 45 c. rose-red and black .. .. 20 25
1186 – 45 c. bright violet and black .. .. 20 25
1187 – 45 c. dull green and black .. .. 20 25
1188 **277** 120 c. lake-brown and black .. .. 50 55
a. Block of 4. Nos. 1188/91 .. .. 2·50
1189 – 130 c. rose-red and black .. .. 55 60
1190 – 150 c. bright violet and black .. .. 65 70
1191 – 200 c. dull green and black .. .. 90 95
1172/91 .. .. .. .. *Set of* 20 4·50 5·00

Designs:—Nos. 1173, 1177, 1181, 1185, 1189, G.B. 1857 4d. rose; Nos. 1174, 1178, 1182, 1186, 1190, G.B. 1856 6d. lilac; Nos. 1175, 1179, 1183, 1187, 1191, G.B. 1856 1s. green.

Each design incorporates the "A03" postmark except Nos. 1189/91 which show mythical postmarks of the Crowned-circle type inscribed "DEMERARA", "BERBICE" or "ESSEQUIBO".

Nos. 1172/5 were each printed in sheets with the bottom row inverted, forming vertical *tête-bêche* pairs. Nos. 1176/87 were issued in sheets of 60, one for each value, with the four designs *se-tenant*. Nos. 1188/91 were issued in sheets of 20, containing five *se-tenant* blocks.

75

INT. COMMUNICATIONS YEAR 50

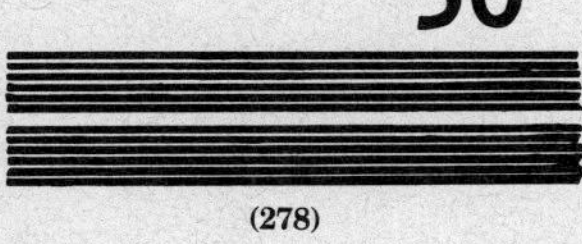

(278) (279)

**1983** (15 Oct). *International Communications Year. No. 716 surch with T* **278** *by Autoprint.*
1192 50 c. on 375 c. on $3 Cylinder satellite .. 3·50 30

No. 1192 also carries an otherwise unissued "375" surcharge. As issued much of this surcharge is obliterated by two groups of six thin horizontal lines.

**1983** (15 Oct). *St. John's Ambulance Commemoration. Nos. 650 and 653 surch as T* **279**, *vertically on No. 1194 by Autoprint.*
1193 **156** 75 c. on 8 c. silver, black and magenta .. 2·50 30
1194 – $1.20 on 40 c. silver, black and new blue 4·50 50

$1.20

Int. Food Day 1983

1918-1983

I.L.O.

(280) (281)

**1983** (15 Oct). *International Food Day. No. 616 surch with T* **280** *by Autoprint.*
1195 $1.20 on 35 c. Five-fingers and awaras .. 1·00 50

**1983** (15 Oct). *65th Anniv of I.L.O. and 25th Death Anniv. of H. N. Critchlow (founder of Guyana Labour Union). No. 840 further optd with T* **281** *by Autoprint.*
1196 240 c. on $3 H. N. Critchlow .. .. .. 1·50 1·25

25c. Human Rights Day

(282) (283)

**1983** (1 Nov). *Deepavali Festival. Nos. 661 and 663/4 surch as T* **282** *by Autoprint.*
1197 25 c. on 8 c. Type **158** .. .. .. .. 20 10
1198 $1.50 on 35 c. Flame in bowl.. .. .. 1·25 60
1199 $1.50 on 40 c. Goddess Latchmi .. .. 80 60
1197/9 .. .. .. .. *Set of* 3 2·00 1·25

On Nos. 1198/9 the original face values are obliterated by "XX" and the surcharges are horizontal.

**1983** (3 Nov). *No. 732 optd with T* **226** *and No. 798 further optd with T* **256**, *both vertically reading upwards by Autoprint.*
1200 $3 "Makanaima the Great Ancestral Spirit of the Amerindians" (B.) .. .. 1·50 1·00
a. Opt reading downwards .. .. 12·00
1201 360 c. on $2 *Norantea guianensis* .. .. 1·75 1·40

**1983** (15 Nov). *Wildlife Protection. Nos. 686 and 688 surch as T* **234**, *and No. 852 optd with T* **256** *by Autoprint.*
1202 30 c. Six-banded Armadillo .. .. .. 30 15
1203 60 c. on 15 c. Giant sea turtle .. .. .. 45 30
1204 $1.20 on 40 c. Iguana .. .. .. .. 75 50
1202/4 .. .. .. .. *Set of* 3 1·40 85

**1983** (1 Dec). *Human Rights Day. No. 1079c optd with T* **283** *by Autoprint.*
1205 $3 Rotary anniversary emblem .. .. 1·40 1·25

LOS ANGELES 1984

125 ●●●

(284)

●●● 55

(284*a*)

**1983** (6 Dec). *Olympic Games, Los Angeles (1984). Nos. 733/44 surch with T* **284** *by Herald Printing-Kitty or further surch with T* **284*a*** *by Autoprint.*
1206 55 c. on 125 c. on 35 c. Type **174** .. .. 25 25
a. Block of 12. Nos. 1206/17 .. .. 3·50
1207 55 c. on 125 c. on 35 c. Haimara .. .. 25 25
1208 55 c. on 125 c. on 35 c. Electric Eel.. .. 25 25
1209 55 c. on 125 c. on 35 c. Golden Rivulus .. 25 25
1210 55 c. on 125 c. on 35 c. Pencil Fish .. .. 25 25
1211 55 c. on 125 c. on 35 c. Four-eyed Fish .. 25 25
1212 55 c. on 125 c. on 35 c. Pirai or Carib Fish 25 25
1213 55 c. on 125 c. on 35 c. Smoking Hassar .. 25 25
1214 55 c. on 125 c. on 35 c. Devil Ray .. .. 25 25
1215 55 c. on 125 c. on 35 c. Flying Patwa .. 25 25
1216 55 c. on 125 c. on 35 c. Arapaima Pirariucii 25 25
1217 55 c. on 125 c. on 35 c. Lukanani .. .. 25 25
1217*a* 125 c. on 35 c. Type **174** .. .. 1·50
ab. Block of 12. Nos. 1217*a/l* .. .. 18·00
1217*b* 125 c. on 35 c. Haimara .. .. 1·50
1217*c* 125 c. on 35 c. Electric Eel .. .. 1·50
1217*d* 125 c. on 35 c. Golden Rivulus .. .. 1·50
1217*e* 125 c. on 35 c. Pencil Fish .. .. 1·50
1217*f* 125 c. on 35 c. Four-eyed Fish .. .. 1·50
1217*g* 125 c. on 35 c. Pirai or Carib Fish .. 1·50
1217*h* 125 c. on 35 c. Smoking Hassar .. .. 1·50
1217*i* 125 c. on 35 c. Devil Ray .. .. 1·50
1217*j* 125 c. on 35 c. Flying Patwa .. .. 1·50
1217*k* 125 c. on 35 c. Arapaima Pirariucii.. .. 1·50
1217*l* 125 c. on 35 c. Lukanani .. .. 1·50

**1983** (14 Dec). *No. F7 with unissued "ESPANA 1982" surch, as Nos. 938/9 in blue, further optd with T* **256** *vertically by Autoprint.*
1218 180 c. on 60 c. Soldier's Cap .. .. 1·00 65
a. Opt (T **256**) omitted .. ..

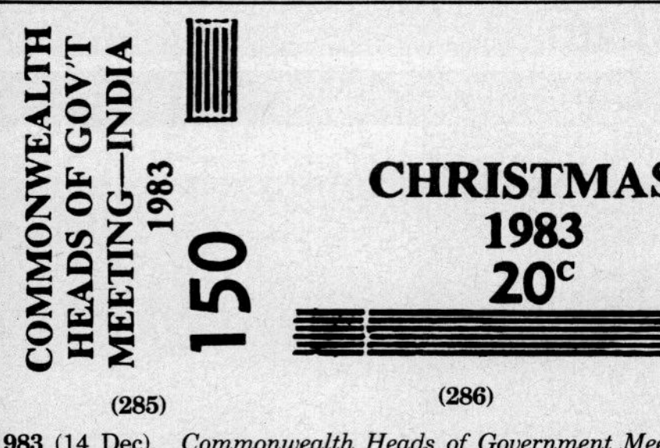


(285) (286)

**1983** (14 Dec). *Commonwealth Heads of Government Meeting, New Delhi. No.* 542 *surch with T* **285** *by Autoprint.*
1219 150 c. on 1 c. Pitcher Plant of Mt Roraima .. 1·00 60

**1983** (14 Dec). *Christmas. Nos.* 861A/B *further surch with T* **286** *by Autoprint.*

A. *No wmk* B. *Wmk* **106**

1220 20 c. on 12 c. on 6 c. Patua .. 35 10 35 10

**1984** (8 Jan). *Nos.* 838 *and* F9 *optd as T* **229**, *but smaller* 24 × 6 *mm, vertically in blue by Autoprint.*
1221 $2 *Norantea guianensis* .. .. 2·00 70
1221*a* 550 c. on $10 *Elbella patrobas* .. .. 4·50 4·25

17 ¢

(287)

**1984** (Jan). *Flowers. Unissued coil stamps as T* **222** *handstamped with T* **287** *in blue.*
1222 17 c. on 2 c. grey-lilac, blue & turquoise-green 25 25
a. Vert pair. Nos. 1222/3 .. .. .. 50 50
1223 17 c. on 8 c. grey-lilac, blue and mauve .. 25 25

Nos. 1222/3 were intended for use on 8 c. postal stationery envelopes to uprate them to the new price of 25 c.

ALL OUR HERITAGE ● 25 (288)

1984 ● 25 (289)

1984 ● 25 (290)

● 25 (291)

**1984** (24 Feb). *Republic Day. No.* 703 *surch as T* **288/91** *in black and No.* 705*a optd as T* **288/9** *in blue by Autoprint.*
1224 25 c. on 35 c. multicoloured (surch T **288**) .. 10 10
a. Sheetlet of 25. No. 1224 × 6, Nos. 1225/7 each × 4, Nos. 1228/30 each × 2 and No. 1231 .. .. .. .. .. 2·50
1225 25 c. on 35 c. multicoloured (surch T **289**) .. 10 10
1226 25 c. on 35 c. multi (surch "REPUBLIC DAY") 10 10
1227 25 c. on 35 c. multicoloured (surch T **290**) .. 10 10
1228 25 c. on 35 c. multi (surch "BERBICE") .. 20 15
1229 25 c. on 35 c. multi (surch "DEMERARA") .. 20 15
1230 25 c. on 35 c. multi (surch "ESSEQUIBO") .. 20 15
1231 25 c. on 35 c. multicoloured (surch T **291**) .. 40 35
1232 60 c. multicoloured (opt T **288**) .. .. 25 30
a. Sheetlet of 25. Nos. 1232/3 each × 8 and No. 1234 × 9 .. .. .. .. 5·75
1233 60 c. multicoloured (opt "REPUBLIC DAY") 25 30
1234 60 c. multicoloured (opt T **289**) .. .. 25 30
1224/34 .. .. .. .. *Set of* 11 1·90 1·75

25 ¢ POSTAGE (+ 2.25 SURTAX) OLYMPIC GAMES 84

(292)

**1984** (1 Mar). *Guyana Olympic Committee Appeal. Nos.* 841/3 *handstamped with T* **292** *in blue.*
1235 25 c. +2.25 c. on 60 c. on 3 c. Hanging Heliconia 4·00 4·00
1236 25 c. +2.25 c. on 75 c. on $5 *Odontadenia grandiflora* .. .. .. .. 4·00 4·00
1237 25 c. +2.25 c. on $1.10 on $2 *Norantea guianensis* .. .. .. .. 4·00 4·00
1235/7 .. .. .. .. *Set of* 3 11·00 11·00

Nos. 1235/7 come from stamp booklets, the $2.25 charity premium on each stamp being donated to the local Olympic Committee Appeal Fund. All examples of these handstamps are inverted.

**PRINTERS.** Nos. 1238/97 and 1302/27 were overprinted or surcharged by Autoprint, Georgetown.

Protecting Our Heritage (293)

XXXXX 90 (294)

**1984** (5 Mar). *Nature Protection. Various stamps optd with T* **293** *in black (except for No.* 1239 *in blue) with some additionally surch as T* **272** *(Nos.* 1238/40, 1250/1 *and* 1254/5) *or as T* **294** *(Nos.* 1242, 1247 *and* 1252/3) *all in blue.*
1238 20 c. on 15 c. multicoloured (No. 491) (opt + surch vert) .. .. .. .. 2·50 10
a. Opt T **293** in blue .. .. .. 13·00 50
1239 20 c. on 15 c. multicoloured (No. 791) (opt + surch vert) .. .. .. .. 2·50 10
a. Surch on No. 791a (pair) .. ..
1240 20 c. on 15 c. multicoloured (No. 1044) (opt + surch vert) .. .. .. .. 24·00 1·50
a. Opt T **293** in blue .. .. .. 5·50 1·00
1241 25 c. multicoloured (No. 550*a*) .. .. 5·00 10
a. On No. 550ab .. .. .. 35·00 3·25
1242 30 c. on 15 c. multicoloured (No. 548) .. 6·50 20
1243 40 c. multicoloured (No. 494) (opt vert) .. 3·00 20
1244 50 c. multicoloured (No. 552) .. .. 60 25
1245 50 c. multicoloured (No. F6) .. .. .. 60 25
a. Opt Type F 1 double .. .. 23·00
1246 60 c. multicoloured (No. 459) .. .. 5·50 30
a. On No. 496 .. .. .. 50·00 4·00
1247 90 c. on 40 c. multicoloured (No. 551) .. 4·00 40
a. On No. F5 .. .. .. 70·00 6·00
1248 180 c. on 40 c. multicoloured (No. 919) .. 4·00 70
1249 $2 multicoloured (No. 461) .. .. 32·00 1·25
1250 225 c. on 10 c. multicoloured (No. 490a) (opt + surch vert) .. .. .. .. 8·00 90
1251 260 c. on $1 multicoloured (No. 497a) .. 5·50 1·00
1252 320 c. on 40 c. multicoloured (No. 551) .. 3·25 1·25
1253 350 c. on 40 c. multicoloured (No. 551) .. 6·50 1·50
1254 390 c. on 50 c. multicoloured (No. 495) .. 3·25 1·75
a. On No. 458 .. .. .. 75·00 20·00
1255 450 c. on $5 multicoloured (No. 499) .. .. 3·50 1·90
1238/55 .. .. .. .. *Set of* 18 90·00 10·00

1984 (295)

(296)

**1984** (17 Mar). *Easter. Nos.* 483 *and* 916/17 *optd with T* **295**, *and No.* 481 *surch as T* **272**, *but without decimal point, all in blue.*
1256 **111** 30 c. multicoloured .. .. .. 20 20
1257 45 c. on 6 c. multicoloured .. .. 25 25
1258 75 c. on 40 c. multicoloured .. .. 35 35
1259 130 c. on 6 c. multicoloured .. .. 65 60
1256/9 .. .. .. .. *Set of* 4 1·40 1·25

No. 1258 exists with the previous surcharge either at the right or in the centre of the design.

**1984** (2 Apr). *Nos.* 937/9 *and* 991 *surch as T* **294**.
1260 75 c. on $1 *Chelonanthus uliginoides* .. 6·00 35
1261 75 c. on 110 c. on 3 c. Hanging Heliconia .. 7·00 35
1262 225 c. on 250 c. on 6 c. Cannon-ball tree .. 2·00 1·25
1263 230 c. on $2.35 on 180 c. on 60 c. Soldier's Cap 2·00 1·75

**1984** (2 May). *Nos.* 899/901, 904/6 *and* 909 *surch as T* **294**.
1264 20 c. on 15 c. on 2 c. Type **132** (No. 899) .. 75 15
1265 75 c. on 110 c. on 5 c. Annatto tree (No. 904) 6·00 60
1266 90 c. on 110 c. on 5 c. Annatto tree (No. 900) (B.) .. .. .. .. .. 4·00 75
1267 90 c. on 110 c. on 5 c. Annatto tree (No. 901) (B.) .. .. .. .. .. 5·00 75
1268 120 c. on 125 c. on 8 c. on 6 c. Cannon-ball tree (No. 905) .. .. .. .. 5·00 90
1269 120 c. on 125 c. on 8 c. on 6 c. Cannon-ball tree (No. 906) .. .. .. .. 5·00 90
1270 120 c. on 125 c. on 8 c. on 6 c. Cannon-ball tree (No. 909) .. .. .. .. 2·25 90
1264/70 .. .. .. .. *Set of* 7 25·00 4·50

Nos. 1264/70 were surcharged on the sheets which contained one type of the previous surcharge only.

**1984** (17 May). *World Telecommunications and Health Day. Nos.* 802 *and* 980 *surch as T* **296** *in blue.*
1271 25 c. on 220 c. on 1 c. Pitcher Plant of Mt Roraima (surch T **296**) .. .. 20 20
a. Sheetlet of 25. Nos. 1271/2 each × 8 and No. 1273 × 9 .. .. .. .. 4·50
1272 25 c. on 220 c. on 1 c. Pitcher Plant of Mt Roraima (surch "WHO DAY 1984") .. 20 20
1273 25 c. on 220 c. on 1 c. Pitcher Plant of Mt Roraima (surch "ITU/WHO DAY 1984") 20 20
1274 $4.50 on 280 c. on $5 *Odontadenia grandiflora* (surch "ITU/WHO DAY 1984") .. 1·75 1·75
1271/4 .. .. .. .. *Set of* 4 2·10 2·10

The surcharge is horizontal on No. 1274 and vertical on the others.

**1984** (11 June). *No.* 1005 *surch vertically as T* **272**, *but without decimal point.*
1275 120 c. on $1.25 on 6 c. Cannon-ball tree .. 4·50 55

**1984** (15 June). *World Forestry Conference. Nos.* 752/5 *surch as T* **272**, *but without decimal point, or optd with T* **295** *($3), and No.* 875 *surch as T* **294**.
1276 55 c. on 30 c. *Hymenaea courbaril* .. .. 2·00 30
1277 75 c. on 110 c. on $3 *Peltogyne venosa* (B.) .. 40 35
1278 160 c. on 50 c. *Mora excelsa* (B.) .. .. 75 70
1279 260 c. on 10 c. Type **177** (B.) .. .. 1·25 1·25
1280 $3 *Peltogyne venosa* (B.) .. .. 1·40 1·40
1276/80 .. .. .. .. *Set of* 5 5·25 3·50

**1984** (18 June). *No.* 625 *surch vertically as T* **294**.
1281 55 c. on 110 c. on 10 c. Type **150** .. .. 30 30
1282 90 c. on 110 c. on 10 c. Type **150** (B.) .. .. 40 45

Nos. 1281/2 also carry an otherwise unissued 110 c. surcharge in blue as Type **264**.

UPU Congress 1984 Hamburg (297)

60 (298)

**1984** (19 June). *U.P.U. Congress, Hamburg. Nos.* 1188/91 *optd with T* **297**.
1283 120 c. lake-brown and black .. .. 50 55
a. Block of 4. Nos. 1283/6 .. .. .. 2·25
1284 130 c. rose-red and black .. .. .. 55 60
1285 150 c. bright violet and black .. .. 60 65
1286 200 c. dull green and black .. .. .. 80 85
1283/6 .. .. .. .. *Set of* 4 2·25 2·40

**1984** (21 June). *Nos.* 982/3 *and* 986/7 *surch with T* **298** *(60 c.) or as T* **272**, *but without the decimal point (others).*
1287 45 c. on 50 c. on 2 c. myrtle-green .. .. 20 25
1288 60 c. on $1.10 on 3 c. brown-olive and red-brown (B.) .. .. .. .. .. 75 30
a. Surch on No. 983c .. .. .. 1·50 30
1289 120 c. on $1.25 on 6 c. yellow-green .. .. 50 55
1290 200 c. on $2.20 on 24 c. black and brownish orange (B.) .. .. .. .. 80 85

**1984** (30 June). *Nos.* 979/80 *and* 1003 *surch as T* **294**, *and No.* 981 *optd vertically with T* **295**.
1291 75 c. on 110 c. on 5 c. Annatto tree .. .. 30 35
1292 120 c. on 170 c. on 110 c. on 5 c. Annatto tree 50 55
1293 200 c. on 220 c. on 1 c. Pitcher Plant of Mt Roraima (B.) .. .. .. .. 4·50 85
1294 330 c. on $2 *Norantea guianensis* (B.) .. .. 1·40 1·75

CARICOM DAY 1984 60 XX

(299)

**1984** (30 June). *CARICOM Day. No.* 1200 *additionally surch with T* **299**.
1295 60 c. on $3 "Makanaima the Great Ancestral Spirit of the Amerindians" .. .. 30 30

**1984** (30 June). *No.* 544 *surch as T* **275** *in blue.*
1296 150 c. on 3 c. Hanging Heliconia .. .. 60 65

60 CARICOM HEADS OF GOV'T CONFERENCE JULY 1984 X

(300)

**301** Children and Thatched School

**1984** (2 July). *CARICOM Heads of Government Conference. No.* 544 *surch with T* **300** *in blue.*
1297 60 c. on 3 c. Hanging Heliconia .. .. 30 30

(Litho Format)

**1984** (16 July). *Centenary of Guyana Teachers' Association. T* **301** *and similar horiz designs. Multicoloured. W* **106** *(sideways). P* 14.
1298 25 c. Type **301** .. .. .. .. 10 15
a. Block of 4. Nos. 1298/301 .. .. 35
1299 25 c. Torch and graduates .. .. .. 10 15
1300 25 c. Torch and target emblem .. .. 10 15
1301 25 c. Teachers of 1884 and 1984 in front of school .. .. .. .. .. 10 15
1298/301 .. .. .. .. *Set of* 4 35 55

Nos. 1298/301 were printed together, *se-tenant*, in blocks of 4 throughout the sheet.

INT. CHESS FED. 1924-1984 25 XX

(302)

25 TRACK AND FIELD

(303)

**1984** (20 July). *50th Anniv of International Chess Federation. No.* 1048 *optd or surch as T* **302** *or optd with T* **295**, *all in blue.*
1302 25 c. on 90 c. on 60 c. Fort Island (surch T **302**) 20 15
a. Sheetlet of 25. No. 1302 × 16 and No. 1303 × 9 .. .. .. .. .. 7·00
1303 25 c. on 90 c. on 60 c. Fort Island (opt T **295**) .. 50 15
1304 75 c. on 90 c. on 60 c. Fort Island (surch T **302**) 50 35
a. Sheetlet of 25. No. 1304 × 16 and No. 1305 × 9 .. .. .. .. .. 13·00

1305 75 c. on 90 c. on 60 c. Fort Island (opt T **295**) 75 35
1306 90 c. on 60 c. Fort Island (opt T **302**) 60 45
a. Sheetlet of 25. No. 1306 × 16 and No. 1307 × 9 17·00
1307 90 c. on 60 c. Fort Island (opt T **295**) 1·00 45
1302/7 *Set of* 6 3·25 1·60

Overprints as Type **295** occur in the central horizontal and vertical rows of each sheet.

**1984** (28 July). *Olympic Games, Los Angeles. No.* 1051 *surch as T* **303** *in blue.*
1308 25 c. on $1.30, multicoloured (surch T **303**) 20 25
a. Booklet pane of 10. No. 1308 × 4 and Nos. 1309/10, each × 3 2·00
b. Coil strip of 5. Nos. 1308 × 2, 1311 × 2 and 1312 1·00
1309 25 c. on $1.30, mult (surch "BOXING") 20 25
1310 25 c. on $1.30, mult (surch "OLYMPIC GAMES 1984 LOS ANGELES") 20 25
1311 25 c. on $1.30, mult (surch "CYCLING") 40 25
1312 25 c. on $1.30, mult (surch "OLYMPIC GAMES 1984") 2·50 50
1313 $1.20 on $1.30, multicoloured (surch T **303**) 1·00 1·10
a. Booklet pane of 10. No. 1313 × 4 and Nos. 1314/15 each × 3 10·00
b. Coil strip of 5. Nos. 1313 × 2, 1316 × 2 and 1317 5·00
1314 $1.20 on $1.30, mult (surch "BOXING") 1·00 1·10
1315 $1.20 on $1.30, mult (surch "OLYMPIC GAMES 1984 LOS ANGELES") 1·00 1·10
1316 $1.20 on $1.30, mult (surch "CYCLING") 1·50 1·10
1317 $1.20 on $1.30, multicoloured (surch "OLYMPIC GAMES 1984") 3·00 1·50
1308/17 *Set of* 10 10·00 6·50

Nos. 1308 and 1313 come from booklets and coils, Nos. 1309/10 and 1314/15 from booklets only, and Nos. 1311/12 and 1316/17 from coils only.

The coils were constructed from normal sheets with coil joins on every fifth stamp.

25

GIRL GUIDES 1924-1984

(304)

**1984** (15 Aug). *60th Anniv of Girl Guide Movement in Guyana. Nos.* 900/9 *surch with T* **304** *in blue.*
1318 25 c. on 110 c. on 5 c. Annatto tree (No. 900) 10 15
a. Sheetlet of 25. Nos. 1318/19, each × 8, Nos. 1320/1, each × 4 and No. 1322 3·00
1319 25 c. on 110 c. on 5 c. Annatto tree (No. 901) 10 15
1320 25 c. on 110 c. on 5 c. Annatto tree (No. 902) 10 15
1321 25 c. on 110 c. on 5 c. Annatto tree (No. 903) 10 15
1322 25 c. on 110 c. on 5 c. Annatto tree (No. 904) 75 40
1323 25 c. on 125 c. on 8 c. on 6 c. Cannon-ball tree (No. 905) 10 15
a. Sheetlet of 25. Nos. 1323/4, each × 8, Nos. 1325/6, each × 4 and No. 1327 3·00
1324 25 c. on 125 c. on 8 c. on 6 c. Cannon-ball tree (No. 906) 10 15
1325 25 c. on 125 c. on 8 c. on 6 c. Cannon-ball tree (No. 907) 10 15
1326 25 c. on 125 c. on 8 c. on 6 c. Cannon-ball tree (No. 908) 10 15
1327 25 c. on 125 c. on 8 c. on 6 c. Cannon-ball tree (No. 909) 75 40
1318/27 *Set of* 10 1·90 1·75

— 25 130 1984

(305) (306) (307)

1984 1984

(308) (309)

**1984** (Sept–Nov). *Various stamps surch or optd.*

(*a*) *As T* **294** *or as T* **298** (60 *c.*)
1328 20 c. on 15 c. on 2 c. Type **132** (No. 1030) 30 10
1329 20 c. on 15 c. on 2 c. Type **132** (No. 1034) 65 10
1330 20 c. on 15 c. on 2 c. Type **132** (No. 1063) 40 10
1331 60 c. on 110 c. on 8 c. on 3 c. Hanging Heliconia (as No. 868, but without T **219**) (two vert obliterating panels) 27·00
a. One vert obliterating panel* 85·00
1332 120 c. on 125 c. on 8 c. on 6 c. Cannon-ball tree (No. 893) 2·50 50
1333 120 c. on 125 c. on $2 *Norantea guianensis* (No. 834) 27·00
1334 120 c. on 125 c. on $2 *Norantea guianensis* (No. O20) 1·25 50
1335 120 c. on 140 c. on $1 *Chelonanthus uliginoides* (No. 796) 3·50 50
1336 200 c. on 220 c. on 1 c. Pitcher Plant of Mt Roraima (No. 922) (B.) 2·00 85
1337 320 c. on $1.10 on $2 *Norantea guianensis* (No. 804) (B.) 3·25 1·50
1338 350 c. on 375 c. on $5 *Odontadenia grandiflora* (No. 803) (B.) 2·25 1·60
1339 390 c. on 400 c. on $5 *Odontadenia grandiflora* (No. 1091) (B.) 3·00 2·00
1340 450 c. on $5 *Odontadenia grandiflora* (No. O16) (B.) 3·25 2·50

*The small original printing of the 60 c. surcharge has the "8 c" and "110" values obliterated by a single vertical block of six lines. On the vast majority of the supply these features were covered by two vertical blocks of six lines each.

(*b*) *As T* **305** (*figures surch, bar in ballpoint pen*)
1341 25 c. on 10 c. Cattleya (No. 547) 13·00 2·00
a. Surch on No. 547a 40·00
1342 25 c. on 15 c. Christmas Orchid (No. 864a) 3·25 15
1342*a* 25 c. on 35 c. on 60 c. Soldier's Cap (No. 649) 75·00

(*c*) *As T* **306** (*on Nos.* 1343/8 *the original face value is obliterated by a fleur-de-lys*
1343 25 c. on 15 c. Christmas Orchid (No. 548) 90·00
1344 25 c. on 15 c. Christmas Orchid (No. 809) 45·00
1345 25 c. on 15 c. Christmas Orchid (No. 864) 8·00 1·75
1346 25 c. on 15 c. Christmas Orchid (No. 977) 2·75 10
a. Surch on No. 977a 90·00
1347 25 c. on 15 c. Christmas Orchid (No. 1009) 2·75 10
1348 25 c. on 15 c. Christmas Orchid (No. O23) 2·75 10
1349 130 c. on 110 c. on $2 *Norantea guianensis* (No. 804) 70·00
1350 130 c. on 110 c. on $2 *Norantea guianensis* (No. O22) 8·50 2·50
1351 600 c. on $7.20 on $1 *Chelonanthus uliginoides* (No. 770A) 11·00 2·50
a. With two fleur-de-lys over original opt 2·25 1·25
b. Surch on No. 770B 13·00 3·00
ba. With two fleur-de-lys over original opt 2·25

(*d*) *With T* **307** (*Nov*)
1352 20 c. *Paphinia cristata* (No. 549) 6·50 10
a. Optd on No. 549a 85·00
1353 $3.60 on $5 *Odontadenia grandiflora* (No. 769A) 3·50 2·00
a. Optd on No. 769B 7·50 1·50

(*e*) *With T* **308** *vertically in blue* (*Nov*)
1354 50 c. on 8 c. Type **136** (No. 1062) 6·00 25
1355 60 c. on 1 c. Pitcher Plant of Mt Roraima (No. 1000) 55 25
1356 $2 *Norantea guianensis* (No. O33) 1·75 1·00

(*f*) *With T* **309**
1357 20 c. *Paphinia cristata* (No. 549) 40·00
a. Optd on No. 549a 90·00
1357*b* 20 c. *Paphina cristata* (No. 887a) ("1984" omitted)
1358 25 c. Marabunta (No. 550) 65·00
1358*a* 25 c. Marabunta (No. 889) ("1984" omitted)
1358*b* 25 c. Marabunta (No. 889b) ("1984" omitted)
1359 25 c. Marabunta (No. F4) 3·25 50
a. Optd on No. F4a 1·75 10
1360 $3.60 on $5 *Odontadenia grandiflora* (No. 769A) 2·25 1·50
a. Optd on No. 769B 2·75

ICAO ICAO

(310) (311)

**1984** (6 Sept). *40th Anniv of International Civil Aviation Organization. Nos.* 981 (*with previously unissued surcharge*), 1017 *and* 1148/68 *optd as T* **310** (30 *c.*) *or T* **311** (200 *c.*), *all in blue by Autoprint.*
1361 30 c. multicoloured (No. 1148) 10 15
a. Sheetlet of 25. Nos. 1361/71, 1372 × 2 and 1373/84 2·50
1362 30 c. multicoloured (No. 1149) 10 15
1363 30 c. multicoloured (No. 1150) 10 15
1364 30 c. multicoloured (No. 1151) 10 15
1365 30 c. multicoloured (No. 1152) 10 15
1366 30 c. multicoloured (No. 1153) 10 15
1367 30 c. mult (No. 1154) (optd "IMB/ICAO") 10 15
1368 30 c. mult (No. 1155) (optd "KCV/ICAO") 10 15
1369 30 c. mult (No. 1156) (optd "KAI/ICAO") 10 15
1370 30 c. multicoloured (No. 1157) 10 15
1371 30 c. multicoloured (No. 1158) 10 15
1372 30 c. mult (No. 1155) (optd "1984") 10 15
1373 30 c. mult (No. 1155) (optd "KPM/ICAO") 10 15
1374 30 c. multicoloured (No. 1159) 10 15
1375 30 c. multicoloured (No. 1160) 10 15
1376 30 c. multicoloured (No. 1161) 10 15
1377 30 c. mult (No. 1155) (optd "PMT/ICAO") 10 15
1378 30 c. multicoloured (No. 1162) 10 15
1379 30 c. multicoloured (No. 1163) 10 15
1380 30 c. multicoloured (No. 1164) 10 15
1381 30 c. multicoloured (No. 1165) 10 15
1382 30 c. multicoloured (No. 1166) 10 15
1383 30 c. multicoloured (No. 1167) 10 15
1384 30 c. multicoloured (No. 1168) 10 15
1385 200 c. on 330 c. on $2 mult (No. 981) 65 70
a. Opt T **311** omitted
1386 200 c. on 75 c. on $5 mult (No. 1017) 2·50 1·50
1361/86 *Set of* 26 5·00 5·25

No. 1385 also carries an otherwise unissued surcharge "G.A.C. Inaug. Flight Georgetown—Toronto 200" in black.

## COVER PRICES

Cover factors are quoted at the beginning of each country for most issues to 1945. An explanation of the system can be found on page x. The factors quoted do not, however, apply to philatelic covers.

1984 $1.50

(312) (313) (314)

**1984** (15 Sept). *Wildlife Protection. Nos.* 756/67 *optd with T* **312** *by Autoprint.*
1387 30 c. Type **178** 15 20
a. Sheetlet of 12. Nos. 1387/98 1·60
1388 30 c. Red Howler 15 20
1389 30 c. Common Squirrel-Monkey 15 20
1390 30 c. Two-toed Sloth 15 20
1391 30 c. Brazilian Tapir 15 20
1392 30 c. Collared Peccary 15 20
1393 30 c. Six-banded Armadillo 15 20
1394 30 c. Tamandua ("Ant Eater") 15 20
1395 30 c. Giant Anteater 15 20
1396 30 c. Murine Opossum 15 20
1397 30 c. Brown Four-eyed Opossum 15 20
1398 30 c. Brazilian Agouti 15 20
1387/98 *Set of* 12 1·60 2·25

**1984** (1 Oct). *Nos. D6/7 and D10/11 surch with T* **269** *in blue by Autoprint.*
1399 D **2** 120 c. on 4 c. dp ultramarine (No. D6) 4·00 45
1400 120 c. on 4 c. dull ultram (No. D10) 15·00 75
1401 120 c. on 12 c. reddish scarlet (No. D7) 4·00 45
1402 120 c. on 12 c. bright scarlet (No. D11) 4·00 45
1399/402 *Set of* 4 24·00 1·90

**1984** (15 Oct). *175th Birth Anniv of Louis Braille (inventor of alphabet for the blind). No.* 1040 *surch with T* **313** *in blue by Autoprint.*
1403 $1.50 on 15 c. on 10 c. Type **215** 3·50 55

**1984** (15 Oct). *International Food Day. No.* 1012 *surch with T* **314** *by Tip Torres.*
1404 150 c. on 50 c. Pawpaw and tangerine 50 55

Type **314** places a "1" alongside the original face value and obliterates the "1982" date on the previous overprint.

**1984** (15 Oct). *Birth Centenary of H. N. Critchlow (founder of Guyana Labour Union). No.* 873, *surch horizontally as T* **236**, *and No.* 1196, *both optd with T* **312** *by Autoprint.*
1405 240 c. on 110 c. on $3 H. N. Critchlow (No. 873) 1·00 85
1406 240 c. on $3 H. N. Critchlow (No. 1196) 5·50 85

**1984** (22 Oct). *Nos.* 910/12 *surch as T* **272**, *but vertically and without the decimal point, and Nos.* 1184/7 *surch as T* **234** *by Autoprint.*
1407 **277** 25 c. on 45 c. lake-brown and black 15 15
a. Block of 4. Nos. 1407/10 55
1408 – 25 c. on 45 c. rose-red and black (No. 1185) 15 15
1409 – 25 c. on 45 c. bright violet and black (No. 1186) 15 15
1410 – 25 c. on 45 c. dull green and black (No. 1187) 15 15
1411 – 120 c. on 100 c. on $3 multicoloured (No. 910) 3·75 45
1412 – 120 c. on 400 c. on 30 c. multicoloured (No. 911) 55 45
1413 – 320 c. on $5 mult (No. 912) (B.) 5·50 1·25
1407/13 *Set of* 7 9·25 2·50

25 X

MAHA SABHA 1934-1984 — Philatelic Exhibition New York 1984

(315) (316)

**1984** (1 Nov). *Deepavali Festival. Nos.* 544/5 *surch as T* **315** *in blue by Autoprint.*
1414 25 c. on 5 c. Annatto tree 10 10
1415 $1.50 on 3 c. Hanging Heliconia 50 55

**1984** (15 Nov). *A.S.D.A. Philatelic Exhibition, New York. Nos.* 1188/91 *optd with T* **316** *in red by Autoprint.*
1416 **277** 120 c. lake-brown and black 40 45
a. Block of 4. Nos. 1416/19 1·90
1417 – 130 c. rose-red and black 45 50
1418 – 150 c. bright violet and black 50 55
1419 – 200 c. dull green and black 70 75
1416/19 *Set of* 4 1·90 2·00

(Litho Format)

**1984** (16 Nov). *Olympic Games, Los Angeles* (2*nd issue*). *Design as No.* 1051, *but with Olympic rings and inscr* "OLYMPIC GAMES 1984 LOS ANGELES". *P* 13½.
1420 $1.20, Youth display (41 × 25 *mm*) 1·50 45

No. 1420 also exists from coils of 500 or 1,000 with numbers on the reverse of each stamp.

**X 20**

(317)

**318** Pair of Swallow-tailed Kites on Tree

**1984** (24 Nov). *Nos.* 847, 861B, 1099 *and* 1102 *surch as T* **317**.
1421 20 c. on 12 c. on 12 c. on 6 c. multicoloured (No. 847) .. .. .. 35 10
1422 20 c. on 12 c. on 6 c. mult (No. 861B) .. 60·00
1423 25 c. on 50 c. on 6 c. mult (No. 1099) .. 10 10
1424 60 c. on $1 on 6 c. mult (No. 1102).. .. 20 25

No. 1423 shows the previous surcharge obliterated by horizontal parallel lines.

(Litho Questa)

**1984** (3 Dec). *Christmas. Swallow-tailed Kites. T* **318** *and similar horiz designs. Multicoloured.* W **106** *(sideways). P* 14 × 14½.
1425 60 c. Type **318** .. .. .. .. .. 1·00 1·00
a. Horiz strip of 5. Nos. 1425/9 .. .. 4·50
1426 60 c. Swallow-tailed Kite on branch .. 1·00 1·00
1427 60 c. Kite in flight with wings raised .. 1·00 1·00
1428 60 c. Kite in flight with wings lowered .. 1·00 1·00
1429 60 c. Kite gliding .. .. .. .. .. 1·00 1·00
1425/9 .. .. .. .. *Set of* 5 4·50 4·50

Nos. 1425/9 were printed together, *se-tenant*, in horizontal strips of 5 throughout the sheet with the backgrounds forming a composite design. Each stamp is inscribed "CHRISTMAS 1982".

**319** St. George's Cathedral, Georgetown

(Litho Format)

**1985** (8 Feb–Oct). *Georgetown Buildings. T* **319** *and similar horiz designs, each black and stone.* W **106** *(sideways). P* 14.
1430 25 c. Type **319** .. .. .. .. .. 10 10
1431 60 c. Demerara Mutual Life Assurance Building .. .. .. .. .. 20 25
1432 120 c. As No. 1431 .. .. .. .. .. 40 45
a. Horiz strip of 3. Nos. 1432/4 .. 1·25
b. No wmk (10.85) .. .. .. .. 40 45
ba. Horiz strip of 3. Nos. 1432b/4b .. 1·25
1433 120 c. Town Hall .. .. .. .. .. 40 45
b. No wmk (10.85) .. .. .. .. 40 45
1434 120 c. Victoria Law Courts .. .. .. .. 40 45
b. No wmk (10.85) .. .. .. .. 40 45
1435 200 c. As No. 1433 .. .. .. .. .. 70 75
1436 300 c. As No. 1434 .. .. .. .. .. 1·00 1·10
1430/6 .. .. .. .. *Set of* 7 3·00 3·25

Nos. 1432/4 were printed together, *se-tenant*, in horizontal strips of 3 within the sheet, forming a composite design.

International
Youth Year 1985

(320)

**Republic Day 1970-1985**

(321)

**1985** (15 Feb). *International Youth Year. As No.* 1420, *but* W **106** *(sideways), optd with T* **320** *by Tip Torres.*
1437 $1.20, Youth display .. .. .. .. 1·25 45

Examples used for this overprint all show the second line of the original inscription as "LOS ANGELLES".

**1985** (22 Feb). *Republic Day. Nos* 1049/50 *and* 1052 *optd or surch as T* **321** *in red by Autoprint.*
1438 25 c. Type **238** .. .. .. .. .. 10 10
a. Horiz pair. Nos. 1438/9 .. .. 20 20
1439 25 c. Flag (inscr "30th ANNIVERSARY IN PARLIAMENT") .. .. .. 10 10
1440 120 c. on $6 Presidential standard.. .. 40 45
1441 130 c. on $6 Presidential standard.. .. 45 50
1438/41 .. .. .. .. *Set of* 4 1·00 1·00

Examples of Nos. 1438/9 overprinted "1980–1985" in error come from stock dispersed by the liquidator of Format International Security Printers Ltd.

**322** Young Ocelot on Branch

**International Youth Year 1985**

(323)

(Des K. Everett. Litho Format)

**1985** (11 Mar)–**87**. *Wildlife Protection. T* **322** *and similar multicoloured designs.* W **106** *inverted.* A. *P* 14½ *(320 c., 330 c.) or* 12½ *(others). Without imprint.* B. *P* 14. *With imprint date at foot* (18.2.87).

| | | A | | B | |
|---|---|---|---|---|---|
| 1442 | 25 c. Type **322** (grey-olive background) .. .. | 1·00 | 10 | † | |
| 1443 | 60 c. Young Ocelot (*different*) (yell-brn background).. .. | 20 | 25 | † | |
| 1444 | 120 c. As No. 1443 .. .. | 50 | 45 | 15 | 20 |
| | a. Vert strip of 3. Nos. 1444/6 .. .. .. | 1·50 | | 40 | |
| 1445 | 120 c. Type **322** .. .. | 50 | 45 | 15 | 20 |
| 1446 | 120 c. Young Ocelot (*diff*) (red-brown background) .. | 50 | 45 | 15 | 20 |
| 1447 | 130 c. As No. 1446 .. .. | 45 | 50 | † | |
| 1448 | 320 c. Scarlet Macaw (28 × 46 *mm*) .. .. .. | 2·75 | 1·25 | † | |
| 1449 | 330 c. Young Ocelot reaching for branch (28×46 *mm*) | 1·25 | 1·25 | † | |
| 1442/9 | .. .. .. *Set of* 8 | 6·50 | 4·25 | † | |

Nos. 1444/6 were printed together, *se-tenant*, in vertical strips of 3 throughout the sheet.

Examples of the 25 c. with imprint date and perforated 14 come from stock dispersed by the liquidator of Format International Security Printers Ltd.

**1985** (11 Mar–11 Apr). *No.* 940 *and Revenue stamp, as T* **181**, *surch as T* **305** *with fleur-de-lys over existing value, by Tip Torres, and Nos.* 912, 1016 *and* O 24 *surch as T* **272**, *but without the decimal point, by Autoprint.*
1450 30 c. on 50 c. multicoloured (No. O24) (B.) 20 10
1451 55 c. on 2 c. black, indigo & greenish grey 30 20
a. Opt "ESSEQUIBO etc" omitted .. 10·00
1452 55 c. on 15 c. on 2 c. black, indigo and greenish grey (No. 940) .. .. 30 20
1453 90 c. on $1 multicoloured (No. 1016) (B.) .. 1·25 30
1454 225 c. on $5 multicoloured (No. 912) (11.4) 1·75 70
1455 230 c. on $5 multicoloured (No. 912) (B.) .. 1·50 75
1456 260 c. on $5 multicoloured (No. 912) (B.) .. 1·50 80
1450/6 .. .. .. .. *Set of* 7 6·25 2·75

On Nos. 1454/6 the surcharges are sideways.

**1985** (15 Apr). *International Youth Year Save the Children Fund Campaign. Nos.* 880, 1073*a*, 1079*b and* 1082 *optd or surch as T* **323** *in blue by Autoprint.*
1457 50 c. "Two Boys catching Ducks" (No. 1073*a*).. .. .. .. .. 1·50 20
1458 50 c. on 10 c. Type **171** (No. 1082) .. 3·25 20
1459 120 c. on 125 c. on $3 "Mango Season" (No. 880) .. .. .. .. 1·50 45
1460 $3 "Mango Season" (No. 1079*b*) .. 1·50 1·10
a. Opt Type **256** ("1983") omitted .. 12·00
1457/60 .. .. .. .. *Set of* 4 7·00 1·75

On Nos. 1457 and 1459/60 the overprints and surcharge as Type **323** are sideways.

**Airy Hall**

**25**

(324)

**1985**

(325)

**1985** (2 May). *125th Anniv of British Guiana Post Office* (1*st issue*). *No.* 699 *surch as T* **324** *in blue by Autoprint.*
1461 25 c. on 10 c. multicoloured (surch T **324**) .. 15 10
a. Sheetlet of 25. Nos. 1461/85 .. 3·25
1462 25 c. on 10 c. multicoloured (surch "Belfield Arab. Coast") .. .. .. .. 15 10
1463 25 c. on 10 c. multicoloured (surch "Belfield E. C. Dem.") .. .. .. .. 15 10
1464 25 c. on 10 c. mult (surch "Belladrum") .. 15 10
1465 25 c. on 10 c. multicoloured (surch "Beterver-wagting") .. .. .. .. 15 10
1466 25 c. on 10 c. multicoloured (surch "Blairmont Ferry") .. .. .. .. 15 10
1467 25 c. on 10 c. mult (surch "Boeraserie") .. 15 10
1468 25 c. on 10 c. mult (surch "Brahm") .. 15 10
1469 25 c. on 10 c. mult (surch "Bushlot") .. 15 10
1470 25 c. on 10 c. mult (surch "De Kinderen") .. 15 10
1471 25 c. on 10 c. multicoloured (surch "Fort Wellington") .. .. .. .. 15 10
1472 25 c. on 10 c. mult (surch "Georgetown") .. 15 10
1473 25 c. on 10 c. mult (surch "Hague").. .. 15 10
1474 25 c. on 10 c. mult (surch "Leguan") .. 15 10
1475 25 c. on 10 c. mult (surch "Mahaica") .. 15 10
1476 25 c. on 10 c. mult (surch "Mahaicony") .. 15 10
1477 25 c. on 10 c. multicoloured (surch "New Amsterdam") .. .. .. .. 15 10
1478 25 c. on 10 c. mult (surch "Plaisance") .. 15 10
1479 25 c. on 10 c. multicoloured (surch "No. 6 Police Station") .. .. .. .. 15 10
1480 25 c. on 10 c. mult (surch "Queenstown") .. 15 10
1481 25 c. on 10 c. mult (surch "Vergenoegen") .. 15 10
1482 25 c. on 10 c. mult (surch "Vigilance") .. 15 10
1483 25 c. on 10 c. mult (surch "Vreed-en-Hoop") 15 10
1484 25 c. on 10 c. mult (surch "Wakenaam") .. 15 10
1485 25 c. on 10 c. mult (surch "Windsor Castle") 15 10
1461/85 .. .. .. .. *Set of* 25 3·25 2·25

The surcharged names are those of the post offices and postal agencies open in 1860.

See also Nos. 1694/717 and 2140/64.

**1985** (17 May). *I.T.U./W.H.O. Day. Nos.* 1148/68 *optd with T* **325**, *or with single capital letter, in red by Autoprint.*
1486 30 c. multicoloured (No. 1148) .. .. 10 15
a. Sheetlet of 25. Nos. 1486/510.. .. 2·25
1487 30 c. multicoloured (No. 1149) .. .. 10 15
1488 30 c. multicoloured (No. 1150) .. .. 10 15
1489 30 c. multicoloured (No. 1151) .. .. 10 15
1490 30 c. multicoloured (No. 1152) .. .. 10 15
1491 30 c. multicoloured (No. 1153) .. .. 10 15
1492 30 c. multicoloured (No. 1154) (optd "I") .. 10 15
1493 30 c. multicoloured (No. 1155) (optd "T") .. 10 15
1494 30 c. multicoloured (No. 1156) (optd "U") .. 10 15
1495 30 c. multicoloured (No. 1157) .. .. 10 15
1496 30 c. multicoloured (No. 1158) .. .. 10 15
1497 30 c. multicoloured (No. 1155) (optd "W") .. 10 15
1498 30 c. multicoloured (No. 1155) (optd "H") .. 10 15
1499 30 c. multicoloured (No. 1155) (optd "O") .. 10 15
1500 30 c. multicoloured (No. 1159) .. .. 10 15
1501 30 c. multicoloured (No. 1160) .. .. 10 15
1502 30 c. multicoloured (No. 1161) (optd "D") .. 10 15
1503 30 c. multicoloured (No. 1155) (optd "A") .. 10 15
1504 30 c. multicoloured (No. 1162) (optd "Y") .. 10 15
1505 30 c. multicoloured (No. 1163) .. .. 10 15
1506 30 c. multicoloured (No. 1164) .. .. 10 15
1507 30 c. multicoloured (No. 1165) .. .. 10 15
1508 30 c. multicoloured (No. 1166) .. .. 10 15
1509 30 c. multicoloured (No. 1167) .. .. 10 15
1510 30 c. multicoloured (No. 1168) .. .. 10 15
1486/1510 .. .. .. *Set of* 25 2·25 3·25

**20**

**60**

**CARDI 1975-1985**

(326) (327)

**1985** (21 May). *No.* 861B *surch with T* **326** *by Autoprint.*
1511 20 c. on 12 c. on 6 c. Patua .. .. .. 10 10
a. Surch on No. 861A (no wmk).. .. 6·00

For a similar surcharge, but with new face value at right see Nos. 1655/6.

**1985** (29 May). *10th Anniv of Caribbean Agricultural Research Development Institute. No.* 544 *surch with T* **327** *in blue by Autoprint.*
1512 60 c. on 3 c. Hanging Heliconia .. .. 30 25

**1985** (3 June). *No.* 839 *surch as Type* O **10** *by Autoprint, but with two blocks of obliterating bars over the previous surch.*
1513 600 c. on 625 c. on 40 c. Tiger Beard .. 5·50 2·25

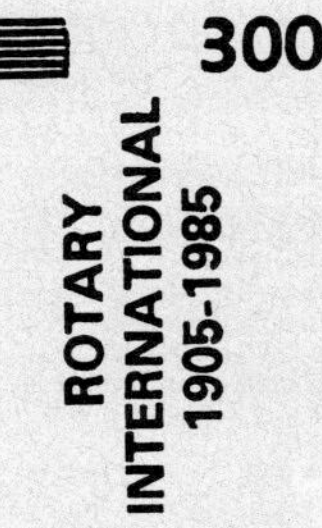


(328)

**1985** (21 June). *80th Anniv of Rotary International. Nos.* 707 *and* 879 *surch as T* **328** *in red by Autoprint.*
1514 120 c. on 110 c. on $3 Rotary anniversary emblem .. .. .. .. .. 5·50 45
1515 300 c. on $2 *Morpho rhetenor* .. .. 1·75 1·10

No. 1205 exists with a similar 120 c. horizontal surcharge. A limited quantity was available mint, but examples are mainly found on First Day Covers (*Price £8 on First Day Cover*).

**CARICOM DAY 1985**

**60** **XX**

(329)

**1985** (28 June). *CARICOM Day. No.* 1200 *surch with T* **329** *in red.*
1516 60 c. on $3 "Makanaima the Great Ancestral Spirit of the Amerindians" .. 30 30

**135th Anniversary Cotton Reel 1850-1985**

**120**

(330)

**1985** (28 June). *135th Anniv of First British Guiana Stamps. No.* 870 *surch with T* **330** *in red.*
1517 120 c. on 110 c. on 10 c. Type **170** .. .. 50 55

**"REICHENBACHIA" ISSUES.** Due to the proliferation of these designs the catalogue uses the book plate numbers as description for each design. The following index gives the species on each plate and the stamp numbers on which they occur.

**Series 1**

Plate No. 1 – *Odontoglossum crispum* – 1578, 2112
Plate No. 2 – *Cattleya percivaliana* – 1519, 2026, 2394
Plate No. 3 – *Cypripedium sanderianum* – 1525, 2084
Plate No. 4 – *Odontoglossum rossi* – 1533, **MS**1539, 2095, **MS**2105
Plate No. 5 – *Cattleya dowiana aurea* – 1667, 1779, 1942/3, 2030, 2464
Plate No. 6 – *Coelogyne cristata maxima* – 1526, **MS**1685, 1759, 2085, 2093, 2119, **MS**2234, 2519
Plate No. 7 – *Odontoglossum insleayi splendens* – 1520, 1967
Plate No. 8 – *Laelia euspatha* – 1571, 1933, 1950
Plate No. 9 – *Dendrobium wardianum* – 1552, 1763, 1979/80, 1996, 2002, 2005, 2017, 2022, 2138/9, 2387
Plate No. 10 – *Laelia autumnalis xanthotropis* – 1521, 1968, 2027
Plate No. 11 – *Phalaenopsis grandiflora aurea* – 1579, 2113
Plate No. 12 – *Cattleya lawrenceana* – 1518, 1935
Plate No. 13 – *Masdevallia shuttleworthii* and *M. xanthocorys* – 1527, 1684, 1760, 2092, 2107, 2110, 2120, 2233, 2448, 2520
Plate No. 14 – *Aeranthus sesquipedalis* – 1584, 2096, 2472
Plate No. 15 – *Cattleya mendelii* Duke of Marlborough – 1752, 1804, 2009, 2050, 2259, 2532
Plate No. 16 – *Zygopetalum intermedium* – 1559, 2090
Plate No. 17 – *Phaius humblotii* – 1732, 1792, 1885, 1965, 2062, 2393
Plate No. 18 – *Chysis bractescens* – 1528, 1536, 2087, 2133
Plate No. 19 – *Masdevallia backhousiana* – 1522, 1969, 2028
Plate No. 20 – *Cattleya citrina* – 1529, **MS**1570, 1761, 2086, 2094, **MS**2106, 2121, 2449, 2521
Plate No. 21 – *Oncidium jonesianum* and *Oncidium jonesianum phaeanthum* – 1585, 2097, 2129
Plate No. 22 – *Saccolabium giganteum* – 1553, **MS**1619, 1764, 1940/1, 1989, 1997, 2006, 2018, 2023, **MS**2232, 2388, **MS**2531
Plate No. 23 – *Cypripedium io* – 1572, 1936
Plate No. 24 – *Odontoglossum blandum* – 1635, 1774, 1864/5, 1931, 1961, 2019, 2047, 2344, 2527, 2529
Plate No. 25 – *Maxillaria sanderiana* – 1530, 1762, 2108, 2111, 2122, 2522
Plate No. 26 – *Odontoglossum* Edward II – 1633, 2137, 2258, 2450
Plate No. 27 – *Vanda teres* – 1524, 2438
Plate No. 28 – *Odontoglossum hallii xanthoglossum* – 1580, 2114
Plate No. 29 – *Odontoglossum crispum hrubyanum* – 1531, 1537, 2088, 2134
Plate No. 30 – *Oncidium concolor* – 1532, 1538, 2089, 2135
Plate No. 31 – *Trichopilia suavis alba* – 1523, 1970, 2029
Plate No. 32 – *Cattleya superba splendens* – 1561, 2512
Plate No. 33 – *Odontoglossum luteo-purpureum* – 1634, 2098, 2342, 2479
Plate No. 34 – *Cypripedium niveum* – 1562
Plate No. 35 – *Stanhopea shuttleworthii* – 1563
Plate No. 36 – *Laelia anceps percivaliana* – 1558, 2439
Plate No. 37 – *Odontoglossum hebraicum* – 1627, 2115, 2440
Plate No. 38 – *Cypripedium oenanthum superbum* – 1560, 2445
Plate No. 39 – *Dendrobium superbiens* – 1737, 1797, 1985, 2063, 2104, 2414, 2515
Plate No. 40 – *Laelia harpophylla* – 1581, 1767, 2123, 2126, 2523
Plate No. 41 – *Lycaste skinneri* and *alba* – 1564
Plate No. 42 – *Phalaenopsis stuartiana* – 1582, 1657, 1768, 1993, 2125, 2127, 2524
Plate No. 43 – *Cattleya trianaei ernesti* – 1586, 1658, 1770, 2099, 2130/1, 2525
Plate No. 44 – *Sobralia xantholeuca* – 1556, 1971
Plate No. 45 – *Odontoglossum crispum kinlesideanum* – 1583, 1769, 2124, 2128, 2526
Plate No. 46 – *Cattleya trianaei schroederiana* – 1628, 2116, 2476
Plate No. 47 – *Epidendrum vitellinum* – 1557, 1972
Plate No. 48 – *Laelia anceps stella* and *barkeriana* – 1565
Plate No. 49 – *Odontoglossum harryanum* – 1554, 1765, 1912, 1964, 1966, 1994, 2003, 2007, 2015, 2024
Plate No. 50 – *Dendrobium leechianum* – 1672, 1784, 2031, 2403, 2496, 2558
Plate No. 51 – *Phalaenopsis speciosa* – 1573, 1934
Plate No. 52 – *Laelia elegans schilleriana* – 1551, 1949
Plate No. 53 – *Zygopetalum wendlandi* – 1621, 1771, 1930, 1954, 1962, 1983, 1986, 2020, 2048, 2361, 2364, E4
Plate No. 54 – *Cypripedium selligerum majus* – 1664, 1776, 2032, 2381, 2404
Plate No. 55 – *Angraecum articulatum* – 1597, 1625, 1772, 1927, 1990, 2046, 2265, 2463, 2465
Plate No. 56 – *Laelia anceps sanderiana* – 1629, 2117, 2441
Plate No. 57 – *Vanda coerulea* – 1622, 1973, 2395/6
Plate No. 58 – *Dendrobium nobile sanderianum* – 1630, 2118, 2442
Plate No. 59 – *Laelia gouldiana* – 1620, 2243, 2359
Plate No. 60 – *Odontoglossum grande* – 1682, 1789, 1944, 2038, 2514, 2528
Plate No. 61 – *Cypripedium rothschildianum* – 1574, 2356
Plate No. 62 – *Vanda sanderiana* – 1566, 2513
Plate No. 63 – *Dendrobium aureum* – 1575, 2357
Plate No. 64 – *Oncidium macranthum* – 1555, 1766, 1913, 1981/2, 1995, 2004, 2008, 2016, 2025
Plate No. 65 – *Cypripedium tautzianum* – 1598, 1626, 1773, 1963, 2021, 2049, 2221, 2434, 2437, 2530, E1
Plate No. 66 – *Cymbidium mastersi* – 1632, 2091, 2136, 2257, 2446
Plate No. 67 – *Angraecum caudatum* – 1631, 2132, 2256, 2443
Plate No. 68 – *Laelia albida* – 1734, 1794, 1884, 1937, 2056, 2378/9, 2435
Plate No. 69 – *Odontoglossum roezlii* – 1680, 1787, 2033, 2405, 2444
Plate No. 70 – *Oncidium ampliatum majus* – 1576, 2358
Plate No. 71 – *Renanthera lowii* – 1679, 1786, 1952, 1976, 2034, 2360
Plate No. 72 – *Cattleya warscewiczii* – 1577, 1951, 2429
Plate No. 73 – *Oncidium lanceanum* – 1623, 1974, 2397
Plate No. 74 – *Vanda hookeriana* – 1736, 1796, 1984, 2064, 2103, 2415, 2454
Plate No. 75 – *Cattleya labiata gaskelliana* – 1624, 1975, 2398/9
Plate No. 76 – *Epidendrum prismatocarpum* – 1751, 1803, 2058, 2453
Plate No. 77 – *Cattleya guttata leopoldi* – 1663, 1775, 1955, 1958, 2042, 2372/3
Plate No. 78 – *Oncidium splendidum* – 1669, 1781, 1959, 2043, 2451
Plate No. 79 – *Odontoglossum hebraicum aspersum* – 1670, 1782, 2035, 2100, 2343, 2406, 2473
Plate No. 80 – *Cattleya dowiana* var *chrysotoxa* – 1754, 1806, 2059, 2517
Plate No. 81 – *Cattleya trianae alba* – 1748, 1800, 1957, 2010, 2051, 2382
Plate No. 82 – *Odontoglossum humeanum* – 1753, 1805, 2011, 2052, 2260, 2516
Plate No. 83 – *Cypripedium argus* – 1671, 1783, 2039, 2466, 2480
Plate No. 84 – *Odontoglossum luteo-purpureum prionopetalum* – 1668, 1780, 2044, 2421
Plate No. 85 – *Cattleya rochellensis* – 1673, 1785, 1960, 2045, 2497, 2518
Plate No. 86 – *Odontoglossum triumphans* – 1731, 1791, 1847, 1868, 1953, 1956, 2055, 2055a, 2264, 2362, 2377, E2, E2a, E11, (Nos. 1847, 2055a, 2264, E2 and E11 are inscr "ONTOGLOSSUM" in error)
Plate No. 87 – *Phalaenopsis casta* – 1681, 1788, 1977, 2036, 2452, 2474, 2478
Plate No. 88 – *Oncidium tigrinum* – 1750, 1802, 2060, 2436
Plate No. 89 – *Cypripedium lemoinierianum* – 1749, 1801, 1978, 2012, 2053, 2422
Plate No. 90 – *Catasetum bungerothii* – 1738, 1798, 1932, 1938, 1947/8, 1988, 2014, 2057, 2380, 2433
Plate No. 91 – *Cattleya ballantiniana* – 1735, 1795, 1822, 1987, 2013, 2054, 2109, 2375/6, 2447
Plate No. 92 – *Dendrobium brymerianum* – 1665, 1777, 1939, 1945, 2040, 2384
Plate No. 93 – *Cattleya eldorado crocata* – 1733, 1793, 1991/2, 2065, 2401, 2416
Plate No. 94 – *Odontoglossum sanderianum* – 1683, 1790, 2037, 2345, 2407, 2484
Plate No. 95 – *Cattleya labiata warneri* – 1666, 1778, 2041, 2400, 2467
Plate No. 96 – *Odontoglossum schroderianum* – 1747, 1799, 2061, 2374

**Series 2**

Plate No. 1 – *Cypripedium morganiae burfordiense* – 2178, 2556
Plate No. 2 – *Cattleya bowringiana* – 1886, 1929, 2102, 2426
Plate No. 3 – *Dendrobium formosum* – 1919, 1998, 2389
Plate No. 4 – *Phaius tuberculosus* – 1813, 2428, 2500
Plate No. 5 – *Odontoglossum crispum mundyanum* – 1815, 2475
Plate No. 6 – *Laelia praestans* – 1881, 1999, 2390, 2624/6
Plate No. 7 – *Dendrobium phalaenopsis* var *statterianum* – 1917, 2365
Plate No. 8 – *Cypripedium boxalli atratum* – 1811, 2408
Plate No. 9 – *Odontoglossum wattianum* – 1816, 2101, 2409/10
Plate No. 10 – *Cypripedium lathamianum inversum* – 1869, 1880, 2423, 2482
Plate No. 11 – *Paphinia rugosa* and *Zygopetalum xanthinum* – 2503, E6
Plate No. 12 – *Dendrobium melanodiscus* – 1817, 2411/12, **MS**2590
Plate No. 13 – *Laelia anceps schroderiana* – 1877, 1907, 2385, 2424
Plate No. 14 – *Phaius hybridus cooksonii* – 1920, 2366/7
Plate No. 15 – *Disa grandiflora* – 1918, 1926, 2386, 2419
Plate No. 16 – *Selenipedium hybridum grande* – 2314, 2331
Plate No. 17 – *Cattleya schroederae alba* – 1872, 2413, 2610/11
Plate No. 18 – *Lycaste skinnerii armeniaca* – 1923, 1928, 1946, 2420, 2557
Plate No. 19 – *Odontoglossum excellens* – 2175
Plate No. 20 – *Laelio-cattleya elegans* var *blenheimensis* – 1916, 2000, 2391
Plate No. 21 – *Odontoglossum coradinei* – 1810, 2383
Plate No. 22 – *Odontoglossum wilckeanum* var *rothschildianum* – 1922, 2368
Plate No. 23 – *Cypripedium lawrenceanum hyeanum* – 2504, 2601, O65
Plate No. 24 – *Cattleya intermedia punctatissima* – 1887, 1914, 2418
Plate No. 25 – *Laelia purpurata* – 2067, 2576
Plate No. 26 – *Masdevallia harryana splendens* – 2505, 2596, O59
Plate No. 27 – *Selenipedium hybridum nitidissimum* – 1874, 1915, 2402, 2425
Plate No. 28 – *Cattleya mendelii* var *measuresiana* – 1924, 2369/70
Plate No. 29 – *Odontoglossum vexillarium* (*miltonia vexillaria*) – 1818, 2485
Plate No. 30 – *Saccolabium coeleste* – 1809, 2363, 2430
Plate No. 31 – *Cypripedium hybridum youngianum* – 2324, 2594, O57
Plate No. 32 – *Miltonia* (*hybrida*) *bleuana* – 1921, 2001, 2392
Plate No. 33 – *Laelia grandis* – 1873, 2616/19
Plate No. 34 – *Cattleya labiata* var *lueddemanniana* – 1819, 2431, 2481
Plate No. 35 – *Odontoglossum coronarium* – 2511, E9
Plate No. 36 – *Cattleya granulosa* var *schofieldiana* – 2316, 2592, O55
Plate No. 37 – *Odontoglossum* (*hybridum*) *leroyanum* – 2174
Plate No. 38 – *Cypripedium* (*hybridum*) *laucheanum* and *eyermanianum* – 1814, 2477, 2580
Plate No. 39 – *Cychnoches chlorochilon* – 2172
Plate No. 40 – *Cattleya O'Brieniana* – 2276
Plate No. 41 – *Odontoglossum ramosissimum* – 2066, 2581
Plate No. 42 – *Dendrobium phalaenopsis* var – 1812, 2427, 2499
Plate No. 43 – *Cypripedium* (*hybridum*) *pollettianum* and *maynardii* – 2216, 2593, O56
Plate No. 44 – *Odontoglossum naevium* – 1878, 2498, 2656
Plate No. 45 – *Cypripedium* (*hybridium*) *castleanum* – 1876, 1925, 2371, 2417
Plate No. 46 – *Odontoglossum cervantesii decorum* – **MS**2275, **MS**2332
Plate No. 47 – *Cattleya amethystoglossa* – 2171
Plate No. 48 – *Cattleya* (*hybrida*) *arnoldiana* – 2217, O53
Plate No. 49 – *Cattleya labiata* – 2239, 2605, 2614/15, 2646/7
Plate No. 50 – *Dendrobium* (*hybridum*) *venus* and *cassiope* – 1879, 2501, 2620/1
Plate No. 51 – *Selenipedium* (*hybridum*) *weidlichianum* – 2177, 2502
Plate No. 52 – *Cattleya mossiae* var. *reineckiana* – 2072, 2577
Plate No. 53 – *Cymbidium lowianum* – 2236, 2585, 2606
Plate No. 54 – *Oncidium loxense* – 2176, 2579
Plate No. 55 – *Cattleya* (*hybrida*) *hardyana* – **MS**2275, **MS**2332
Plate No. 56 – *Coelogyne sanderae* – 1875, 2612/13, 2627
Plate No. 57 – *Cypripedium leeanum* var *giganteum* – **MS**2275, **MS**2332
Plate No. 58 – *Coelogyne pandurata* – 2173, 2582
Plate No. 59 – *Schomburgkia sanderiana* – 2323, 2595, O61
Plate No. 60 – *Oncidium superbiens* – 2227, 2607
Plate No. 61 – *Dendrobium johnsoniae* – 2235, O58
Plate No. 62 – *Laelia hybrida behrensiana* – 2322, 2509, 2622/3
Plate No. 63 – Hybrid *Calanthes Victoria Regina, Bella* and *Burfordiense* – 2510, E8
Plate No. 64 – *Cattleya mendelii* Quorndon House var – 2238, 2608
Plate No. 65 – *Arachnanthe clarkei* – 2073, 2578
Plate No. 66 – *Zygopetalum burtii* – 2240, 2583
Plate No. 67 – *Cattleya* (*hybrida*) *parthenia* – 2318, 2584
Plate No. 68 – *Phalaenopsis sanderiana* and *intermedia portei* – 2225, 2597, O60
Plate No. 69 – *Phaius blumei* var *assamicus* – 2317, 2598, O62
Plate No. 70 – *Angraecum humblotii* – 2470, 2602, O67
Plate No. 71 – *Odontoglossum pescatorei* – 2471, 2603, O68
Plate No. 72 – *Cattleya rex* – 2193
Plate No. 73 – *Zygopetalum crinitum* – 2315, 2329,
Plate No. 74 – *Cattleya lueddemanniana alba* – 2219/20, 2222/3, 2328
Plate No. 75 – *Cymbidium* (*hybridum*) *winnianum* – 2506, O64
Plate No. 76 – Hybrid *Masdevallias courtauldiana, geleniana* and *measuresiana* – 2242
Plate No. 77 – *Cypripedium* (*hybridum*) *calypso* – 2191
Plate No. 78 – *Masdevallia chimaera* var *mooreana* – 2325
Plate No. 79 – *Miltonia phalaenopsis* – 2241, 2508
Plate No. 80 – *Lissochilus giganteus* – 2190
Plate No. 81 – *Aerides savageanum* – **MS**2275, **MS**2332
Plate No. 82 – *Thunia brymeriana* – 2069, 2483
Plate No. 83 – *Miltonia moreliana* – 2182
Plate No. 84 – *Oncidium kramerianum* – 2469, 2604, O69
Plate No. 85 – *Cattleya Victoria Regina* – 2068
Plate No. 86 – *Zygopetalum klabochorum* – 2180
Plate No. 87 – *Laelia autumnalis alba* – 2070, 2432
Plate No. 88 – *Spathoglottis kimballiana* – 2071
Plate No. 89 – *Laelio-cattleya* ("The Hon. Mrs. Astor") – 2181
Plate No. 90 – *Phaius hybridus amabilis* and *marthiae* – 2468, 2599, O63
Plate No. 91 – *Zygopetalum rostratum* – 2277
Plate No. 92 – *Coelogyne swaniana* – 2218, 2591, O54
Plate No. 93 – *Laelio-cattleya* (*hybrida*) *phoebe* – 2507, E7
Plate No. 94 – *Epidendrum atro-purpureum* var *randianum* – 2192
Plate No. 95 – *Dendrobium imperatrix* – 2226, 2600, O66
Plate No. 96 – *Vanda parishii* var *marriottiana* – 2237, 2330

**331** *Cattleya lawrenceana* (Plate No. 12 (Series 1))

**332** Arms of Guyana

(Litho Format)

**1985** (9 July). *Centenary of Publication of Sanders'* Reichenbachia *(1st issue). T* **331** *and similar vert designs showing orchids. Multicoloured. No wmk. P* 13½×14.

| | | | |
|---|---|---|---|
| 1518 | 25 c. Type **331** | 40 | 30 |
| 1519 | 60 c. Plate No. 2 (Series 1) | 50 | 35 |
| 1520 | 60 c. Plate No. 7 (Series 1) | 50 | 35 |
| 1521 | 60 c. Plate No. 10 (Series 1) | 50 | 35 |
| 1522 | 60 c. Plate No. 19 (Series 1) | 50 | 35 |
| 1523 | 60 c. Plate No. 31 (Series 1) | 50 | 35 |
| 1524 | 120 c. Plate No. 27 (Series 1) | 75 | 55 |
| 1525 | 130 c. Plate No. 3 (Series 1) | 75 | 55 |
| 1526 | 130 c. Plate No. 6 (Series 1) | 1·10 | 55 |
| 1527 | 130 c. Plate No. 13 (Series 1) | 75 | 55 |
| 1528 | 130 c. Plate No. 18 (Series 1) | 1·50 | 55 |
| 1529 | 130 c. Plate No. 20 (Series 1) | 1·00 | 55 |
| 1530 | 130 c. Plate No. 25 (Series 1) | 75 | 55 |
| 1531 | 130 c. Plate No. 29 (Series 1) | 1·25 | 55 |
| 1532 | 130 c. Plate No. 30 (Series 1) | 1·25 | 55 |
| 1533 | 200 c. Plate No. 4 (Series 1) | 1·25 | 85 |
| 1518/33 | *Set of* 16 | 12·00 | 7·00 |

Nos. 1518/33 were printed in four sheets each of 16 orchid stamps, arranged as blocks of four of each design, and 9 examples of Type **332** which appear on the vertical and horizontal gutters between the blocks.

For 130 c. stamps as Nos. 1526/7 and 1529/30, but with watermark **106** see Nos. 1759/62.

(Litho Format)

**1985** (9 July–16 Sept). *Booklet and Coil Stamps. No wmk.*

| | | | | |
|---|---|---|---|---|
| 1534 | **332** | 25 c. multicoloured (*imperf* × *p* 14) | 15 | 15 |
| 1534*a* | | 25 c. multicoloured (*imperf* × *p* 13½) (16 Sept) | 15 | 15 |
| 1534*b* | | 25 c. multicoloured (*p* 13½×14) | 15 | 15 |
| 1535 | | 25 c. multicoloured (*p* 13½×*imperf*) | 15 | 15 |
| 1535*a* | | 25 c. mult (*p* 14×*imperf*) (16 Sept) | 15 | 15 |
| 1535*b* | | 25 c. mult (*p* 14×13½) (16 Sept) | 15 | 15 |
| 1534/5*b* | | *Set of* 6 | 80 | 80 |

See note below No. 1533. Examples of Nos. 1534/5*b* were cut from the gutters of the orchid sheets and the white area surrounding the design varies considerably in size. Nos. 1534, 1534*b* and 1535 occur from sheets with vertical orchid designs and Nos. 1534*a* and 1535*a*/*b* from those with horizontal designs.

See also Nos. 1807/8*b* (watermarked **106**), 1820/1*a* (additionally inscribed "1966–1986") and 2183/4*c* (within frame).

(333) (334)

**1985** (9 July). *85th Birthday of Queen Elizabeth the Queen Mother (1st issue). Nos.* 1528 *and* 1531/3 *optd with T* **333** *(in two lines on No.* 1538) *or with similar opts (No.* **MS**1539), *all in blue by Format.*

| | | | |
|---|---|---|---|
| 1536 | 130 c. Plate No. 18 (Series 1) | 45 | 50 |
| 1537 | 130 c. Plate No. 29 (Series 1) | 45 | 50 |
| 1538 | 130 c. Plate No. 30 (Series 1) | 45 | 50 |
| 1536/8 | *Set of* 3 | 1·25 | 1·40 |
| **MS**1539 | 100×126 mm. 200 c.×4 Plate No. 4 (Series 1) | 4·00 | 4·75 |

The four stamps in No. **MS**1539 are overprinted "LADY BOWES-LYON 1900–1923", "DUCHESS OF YORK 1923–1937", "QUEEN ELIZABETH 1937–1952" or "QUEEN MOTHER 1952–1985", all reading upwards.

See also No. **MS**1570.

**1985** (18 July). *International Youth Year. Nos.* 900/4 *surch with T* **334** *in red by Autoprint.*

| | | | |
|---|---|---|---|
| 1540 | 25 c. on 110 c. on 5 c. mult (No. 900) | 10 | 10 |
| | a. Sheetlet of 25. Nos. 1540/1, each × 8, Nos. 1542/3, each × 4 and No. 1544 | 4·00 | |
| 1541 | 25 c. on 110 c. on 5 c. mult (No. 901) | 10 | 10 |
| 1542 | 25 c. on 110 c. on 5 c. mult (No. 902) | 25 | 10 |
| 1543 | 25 c. on 110 c. on 5 c. mult (No. 903) | 25 | 10 |
| 1544 | 25 c. on 110 c. on 5 c. mult (No. 904) | 80 | 15 |
| 1540/4 | *Set of* 5 | 1·40 | 50 |

In addition to the sheetlet containing the five different original surcharges, Type **334** can also be found on the sheets of No. 900.

(335) (336)

**1985** (26 July). *75th Anniv of Girl Guide Movement. No.* 612 *surch with T* **335** *by Tip Torres.*

| | | | |
|---|---|---|---|
| 1545 | 225 c. on 350 c. on 225 c. on 40 c. Guides in camp | 5·00 | 90 |
| | a. Inverted "L"'s for 1's in surcharged dates | | |

No. 1545a occurs on all stamps in the bottom row.

In addition to Type **335** No. 1545 also carries two otherwise unissued surcharges at top right.

Nos. 610 and 613 also exist surcharged with Type **335**. A limited quantity was available mint, but examples were mainly found on First Day Covers (*Price £25 per pair on First Day Cover*).

**1985** (26 July). *Birth Bicentenary of John J. Audubon (ornithologist). No.* 992 *surch with T* **336** *by Tip Torres.*

| | | | |
|---|---|---|---|
| 1546 | 240 c. on 35 c. Harpy Eagle | 6·00 | 1·75 |

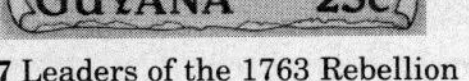

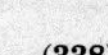

**337** Leaders of the 1763 Rebellion (338)

(Des K. Everett (150 c.). Litho Format)

**1985** (29 July). *150th Anniv of Abolition of Slavery* (1984) *(1st issue). T* **337** *and similar horiz designs. P* 14.

| | | | |
|---|---|---|---|
| 1547 | 25 c. black and bluish grey | 50 | 10 |
| 1548 | 60 c. black and mauve | 25 | 25 |
| 1549 | 130 c. black and light greenish blue | 50 | 50 |
| 1550 | 150 c. black and rose-lilac | 60 | 55 |
| 1547/50 | *Set of* 4 | 1·60 | 1·25 |

Designs:—60 c. Damon and Parliament Buildings, Georgetown; 130 c. Quamina and Demerara, 1823; 150 c. *Den Arendt* (slave ship), 1627.

Nos. 1549/50 exist imperforate from stock dispersed by the liquidator of Format International Security Printers Ltd.

For these designs in changed colours see Nos. 2552/5.

(Litho Format)

**1985** (1 Aug). *Centenary of Publication of Sanders'* Reichenbachia *(2nd issue). Vert designs as T* **331** *showing orchids. Multicoloured. No wmk. P* 13½×14.

| | | | |
|---|---|---|---|
| 1551 | 25 c. Plate No. 52 (Series 1) | 40 | 25 |
| 1552 | 55 c. Plate No. 9 (Series 1) | 50 | 35 |
| 1553 | 55 c. Plate No. 22 (Series 1) | 50 | 35 |
| 1554 | 55 c. Plate No. 49 (Series 1) | 50 | 25 |
| 1555 | 55 c. Plate No. 64 (Series 1) | 50 | 35 |
| 1556 | 60 c. Plate No. 44 (Series 1) | 50 | 35 |
| 1557 | 60 c. Plate No. 47 (Series 1) | 50 | 35 |
| 1558 | 120 c. Plate No. 36 (Series 1) | 75 | 55 |
| 1559 | 130 c. Plate No. 16 (Series 1) | 75 | 55 |
| 1560 | 130 c. Plate No. 38 (Series 1) | 75 | 55 |
| 1561 | 150 c. Plate No. 32 (Series 1) | 75 | 55 |
| 1562 | 150 c. Plate No. 34 (Series 1) | 75 | 55 |
| 1563 | 150 c. Plate No. 35 (Series 1) | 75 | 55 |
| 1564 | 150 c. Plate No. 41 (Series 1) | 75 | 55 |
| 1565 | 150 c. Plate No. 48 (Series 1) | 75 | 55 |
| 1566 | 150 c. Plate No. 62 (Series 1) | 75 | 55 |
| 1551/66 | *Set of* 16 | 9·00 | 6·50 |

Nos. 1551/66 were printed in a similar sheet format to Nos. 1518/33.

For 55 c. stamps as Nos. 1552/5, but with watermark **106** see Nos. 1763/6.

For 50 c. stamps in designs of Nos. 1554/5 see Nos. 1912/13.

**1985** (16 Aug). *Signing of Guyana—Libya Friendship Treaty. No.* 621 *surch with T* **338** *by Autoprint.*

| | | | |
|---|---|---|---|
| 1567 | 150 c. on 10 c. Type **149** | 7·50 | 2·75 |

**ALTERED CATALOGUE NUMBERS**

Any Catalogue numbers altered from the last edition are shown as a list in the introductory pages.

(339) (340) (341)

**1985** (16 Aug). *Namibia Day. No.* 636 *surch with T* **339** *in deep carmine by Tip Torres.*

| | | | |
|---|---|---|---|
| 1568 | 150 c. on 35 c. Unveiling of Monument | 1·75 | 55 |

**1985** (16 Aug). *World Cup Football Championship, Mexico* (1966) *(1st issue). No.* F2 *surch with T* **340** *by Autoprint.*

| | | | |
|---|---|---|---|
| 1569 | 275 c. on 3 c. Hanging Heliconia | 1·75 | 95 |

See also No. 1727.

**1985** (12 Sept). *85th Birthday of Queen Elizabeth the Queen Mother (2nd issue). Sheet* 120×129 *mm containing No.* 1529×4 *optd as No.* **MS**1539, *each stamp surch with T* **341** *by Tip Torres.*

| | | | |
|---|---|---|---|
| **MS**1570 | 200 c. on 130 c. × 4 Plate No. 20 (Series 1) | 8·00 | 6·00 |

(Litho Format)

**1985** (16 Sept). *Centenary of Publication of Sanders'* Reichenbachia *(3rd issue). Multicoloured designs as T* **331** *showing orchids. No wmk. P* 13½×14 *(Nos.* 1571/7 *and* 1584) *or* 14×13½ *(others).*

| | | | |
|---|---|---|---|
| 1571 | 25 c. Plate No. 8 (Series 1) | 30 | 20 |
| 1572 | 25 c. Plate No. 23 (Series 1) | 30 | 20 |
| 1573 | 25 c. Plate No. 51 (Series 1) | 30 | 20 |
| 1574 | 25 c. Plate No. 61 (Series 1) | 30 | 20 |
| 1575 | 25 c. Plate No. 63 (Series 1) | 30 | 20 |
| 1576 | 25 c. Plate No. 70 (Series 1) | 30 | 20 |
| 1577 | 25 c. Plate No. 72 (Series 1) | 30 | 20 |
| 1578 | 120 c. Plate No. 1 (Series 1) (*horiz*) | 75 | 55 |
| 1579 | 120 c. Plate No. 11 (Series 1) (*horiz*) | 75 | 55 |
| 1580 | 120 c. Plate No. 28 (Series 1) (*horiz*) | 75 | 55 |
| 1581 | 150 c. Plate No. 40 (Series 1) (*horiz*) | 80 | 65 |
| 1582 | 150 c. Plate No. 42 (Series 1) (*horiz*) | 80 | 65 |
| 1583 | 150 c. Plate No. 45 (Series 1) (*horiz*) | 80 | 65 |
| 1584 | 200 c. Plate No. 14 (Series 1) | 1·00 | 80 |
| 1585 | 200 c. Plate No. 21 (Series 1) (*horiz*) | 1·00 | 80 |
| 1586 | 200 c. Plate No. 43 (Series 1) (*horiz*) | 1·00 | 80 |
| 1571/86 | *Set of* 16 | 8·75 | 6·75 |

Nos. 1571/86 were printed in a similar sheet format to Nos. 1518/33.

For 150 c. and 200 c. stamps as Nos. 1581/3 and 1586, but with watermark **106** see Nos. 1767/70.

(342) (343)

**1985** (23 Sept). *30th Anniv of Commonwealth Caribbean Medical Research Council. Nos.* 819, 871, 874/*a*, 928*a and* 1014 *surch or optd (vertically reading upwards on Nos.* 1587/8) *as T* **342** *by Autoprint.*

| | | | | |
|---|---|---|---|---|
| 1587 | – | 60 c. multicoloured (No. 819) | 20 | 25 |
| 1588 | – | 60 c. multicoloured (No. 1014) | 20 | 25 |
| 1589 | **176** | 120 c. on 110 c. on 10 c. multicoloured (No. 871) | 40 | 45 |
| 1590 | – | 120 c. on 110 c. on $3 mult (No. 874) | 40 | 45 |
| 1591 | – | 120 c. on 110 c. on $3 mult (No. 874a) | 40 | 45 |
| 1592 | – | 120 c. on 210 c. on $3 mult (No. 928a) | 40 | 45 |
| 1587/92 | | *Set of* 6 | 1·75 | 2·10 |

**1985** (30 Sept). *20th Anniv of Guyana Defence Force. No.* 856 *surch as T* **343** *by Autoprint.*

| | | | |
|---|---|---|---|
| 1593 | 25 c. on $1.10 on $3 W.O. and N.C.O., Guyana Defence Force, 1966 | 20 | 10 |
| 1594 | 225 c. on $1.10 on $3 W.O. and N.C.O., Guyana Defence Force, 1966 | 1·10 | 75 |

**1985** (5 Oct). *Fire Prevention. Nos.* 678 *and* 680 *optd with T* **325** *and surch as T* **255** *by Autoprint.*

| | | | |
|---|---|---|---|
| 1595 | 25 c. on 40 c. Fire engine, 1977 | 3·00 | 10 |
| 1596 | 320 c. on 15 c. Steam engine, *circa* 1860 | 7·00 | 2·25 |

(Litho Format)

**1985** (7 Oct). *Centenary of Publication of Sanders'* Reichenbachia *(4th issue). Vert design as T* **331**. *Multicoloured. No wmk. P* 13½×14.

| | | | |
|---|---|---|---|
| 1597 | 60 c. Plate No. 55 (Series 1) | 60 | 30 |

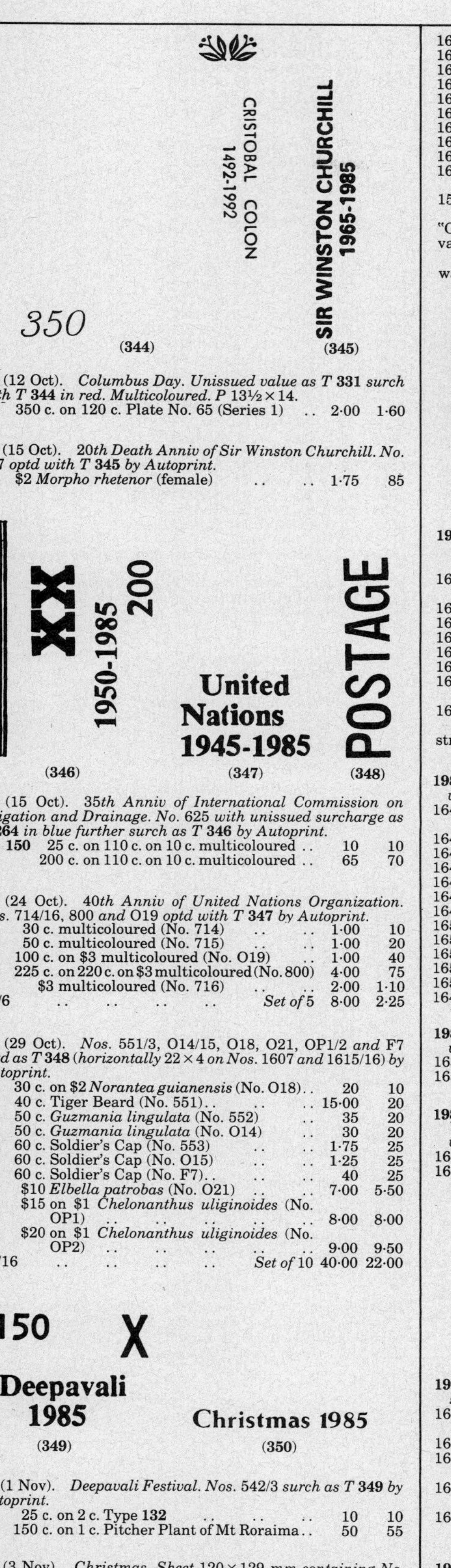


(344) (345)

**1985** (12 Oct). *Columbus Day. Unissued value as T* **331** *surch with T* **344** *in red. Multicoloured. P* 13½ × 14.
1598 350 c. on 120 c. Plate No. 65 (Series 1) .. 2·00 1·60

**1985** (15 Oct). *20th Death Anniv of Sir Winston Churchill. No.* 707 *optd with T* **345** *by Autoprint.*
1599 $2 *Morpho rhetenor* (female) .. .. 1·75 85

(346) (347) (348)

**1985** (15 Oct). *35th Anniv of International Commission on Irrigation and Drainage. No.* 625 *with unissued surcharge as T* **264** *in blue further surch as T* **346** *by Autoprint.*
1600 **150** 25 c. on 110 c. on 10 c. multicoloured .. 10 10
1601 200 c. on 110 c. on 10 c. multicoloured .. 65 70

**1985** (24 Oct). *40th Anniv of United Nations Organization. Nos.* 714/16, 800 *and* O19 *optd with T* **347** *by Autoprint.*
1602 30 c. multicoloured (No. 714) .. .. 1·00 10
1603 50 c. multicoloured (No. 715) .. .. 1·00 20
1604 100 c. on $3 multicoloured (No. O19) .. 1·00 40
1605 225 c. on 220 c. on $3 multicoloured (No. 800) 4·00 75
1606 $3 multicoloured (No. 716) .. .. 2·00 1·10
1602/6 .. .. .. .. .. *Set of* 5 8·00 2·25

**1985** (29 Oct). *Nos.* 551/3, O14/15, O18, O21, OP1/2 *and* F7 *optd as T* **348** *(horizontally* 22 × 4 *on Nos.* 1607 *and* 1615/16) *by Autoprint.*
1607 30 c. on $2 *Norantea guianensis* (No. O18) .. 20 10
1608 40 c. Tiger Beard (No. 551) .. .. .. 15·00 20
1609 50 c. *Guzmania lingulata* (No. 552) .. 35 20
1610 50 c. *Guzmania lingulata* (No. O14) .. 30 20
1611 60 c. Soldier's Cap (No. 553) .. .. 1·75 25
1612 60 c. Soldier's Cap (No. O15) .. .. 1·25 25
1613 60 c. Soldier's Cap (No. F7) .. .. 40 25
1614 $10 *Elbella patrobas* (No. O21) .. .. 7·00 5·50
1615 $15 on $1 *Chelonanthus uliginoides* (No. OP1) .. .. .. .. .. 8·00 8·00
1616 $20 on $1 *Chelonanthus uliginoides* (No. OP2) .. .. .. .. .. 9·00 9·50
1607/16 .. .. .. .. .. *Set of* 10 40·00 22·00

(349) (350)

**1985** (1 Nov). *Deepavali Festival. Nos.* 542/3 *surch as T* **349** *by Autoprint.*
1617 25 c. on 2 c. Type **132** .. .. .. 10 10
1618 150 c. on 1 c. Pitcher Plant of Mt Roraima .. 50 55

**1985** (3 Nov). *Christmas. Sheet* 120 × 129 *mm containing No.* 1553 × 4 *optd as T* **350** *in red by Format.*
**MS**1619 55 c. × 4 Plate No. 22 (Series 1), each with a different overprint (Type **350**, "Happy New Year", "Merry Christmas" or "Happy Holidays") .. .. .. .. .. 80 85

(Litho Format)

**1985** (4 Nov). *Centenary of Publication of Sanders'* Reichenbachia *(5th issue). Multicoloured designs as T* **331** *showing orchids. No wmk. P* 14 × 13½ *(60, 200 c.) or* 13½ × 14 *(others).*
1620 25 c. Plate No. 59 (Series 1) .. .. 30 20
1621 30 c. Plate No. 53 (Series 1) .. .. 30 20
1622 60 c. Plate No. 57 (Series 1) *(horiz)* .. 50 35
1623 60 c. Plate No. 73 (Series 1) *(horiz)* .. 50 35
1624 60 c. Plate No. 75 (Series 1) *(horiz)* .. 50 35
1625 75 c. Plate No. 55 (Series 1) .. .. 55 40
1626 100 c. Plate No. 65 (Series 1) .. .. 65 50
1627 120 c. Plate No. 37 (Series 1) .. .. 75 55
1628 120 c. Plate No. 46 (Series 1) .. .. 75 55
1629 120 c. Plate No. 56 (Series 1) .. .. 75 55
1630 120 c. Plate No. 58 (Series 1) .. .. 75 55
1631 120 c. Plate No. 67 (Series 1) .. .. 75 55
1632 130 c. Plate No. 66 (Series 1) .. .. 80 65
1633 150 c. Plate No. 26 (Series 1) .. .. 90 75
1634 200 c. Plate No. 33 (Series 1) *(horiz)* .. 1·00 85
1635 225 c. Plate No. 24 (Series 1) .. .. 1·25 95
1620/35 .. .. .. .. *Set of* 16 10·00 7·50
Nos. 1620/35 were printed in a similar sheet format to Nos. 1518/33.
The 30, 75, 100 and 225 c. values show face values and "Guyana" in blue. Examples of these four stamps with face values and "Guyana" in black were prepared, but not issued.
For stamps as Nos. 1621, 1625/6 and 1635, but with watermark **106** see Nos. 1771/4.
For 50 c. in design of No. 1625 see No. 1927.

REICHENBACHIA 1886-1986

**351** Clive Lloyd (cricketer) (**352**)

(Litho Format)

**1985** (7 Nov). *Clive Lloyd's Testimonial Year. T* **351** *and similar vert designs. Multicoloured. W* **106** *(sideways on* $3.50). *P* 14½ × 14 (25 c.), 12½ ($3.50) *or* 14 *(others).*
1636 25 c. Type **351** .. .. .. .. 50 20
a. Horiz strip of 3. Nos. 1636/8 .. .. 1·40
1637 25 c. Clive Lloyd, bat and wicket .. .. 50 20
1638 25 c. Cricket equipment .. .. 50 20
1639 60 c. As No. 1638 (25 × 33 *mm*) .. .. 75 30
1640 $1.30, As No. 1637 (25 × 33 *mm*) .. 1·25 60
1641 $2.25, Type **351** (25 × 33 *mm*) .. .. 2·00 90
1642 $3.50, Clive Lloyd with the Prudential Cup (36 × 56 *mm*) .. .. .. 2·50 1·50
1636/42 .. .. .. .. *Set of* 7 7·25 3·50
Nos. 1636/8 were printed together, *se-tenant*, in horizontal strips of 3 throughout the sheet.

**1985** (15 Nov). *Wildlife Protection. Nos.* 756/67 *optd with T* **325** *vertically in red by Autoprint.*
1643 30 c. Type **178** .. .. .. .. 30 30
a. Sheetlet of 12. Nos. 1643/54 .. .. 3·25
1644 30 c. Red Howler .. .. .. .. 30 30
1645 30 c. Common Squirrel Monkey .. .. 30 30
1646 30 c. Two-toed Sloth .. .. .. 30 30
1647 30 c. Brazilian Tapir .. .. .. 30 30
1648 30 c. Collared Peccary .. .. .. 30 30
1649 30 c. Six-banded Armadillo .. .. 30 30
1650 30 c. Tamandua ("Ant Eater") .. .. 30 30
1651 30 c. Giant Anteater .. .. .. 30 30
1652 30 c. Murine Opossum .. .. .. 30 30
1653 30 c. Brown Four-eyed Opossum .. .. 30 30
1654 30 c. Brazilian Agouti .. .. .. 30 30
1643/54 .. .. .. .. *Set of* 12 3·25 3·25

**1985** (23 Dec). *Nos.* 847 *and* 861B *surch as T* **326**, *but with face value of surch at right.*
1655 20 c. on 12 c. on 12 c. on 6 c. Patua (No. 847) 30 15
1656 20 c. on 12 c. on 6 c. Patua (No. 861B) .. 30 15

**1986** (13 Jan). *Centenary of the Appearance of* Reichenbachia *Volume I. Nos.* 1582 *and* 1586 *optd with T* **352** *in reddish violet.*
1657 150 c. Plate No. 42 (Series 1) .. .. 60 60
1658 200 c. Plate No. 43 (Series 1) .. .. 75 75

Republic Day

1986 1986

(**353**) (**354**)

**1986** (22 Feb). *Republic Day. Nos.* 1108/9 *and* 1052 *optd or surch as T* **353** *by Autoprint.*
1659 25 c. As Type **258** .. .. .. .. 10 10
a. Horiz pair. Nos. 1659/60 .. .. 15 20
1660 25 c. As No. 1050 .. .. .. .. 10 10
1661 120 c. on $6 Presidential standard (surch vert) .. .. .. .. .. 40 45
1662 225 c. on $6 Presidential standard (surch vert) .. .. .. .. .. 70 75
1659/62 .. .. .. .. *Set of* 4 1·10 1·25

(Litho Format)

**1986** (26 Feb). *Centenary of Publication of Sanders'* Reichenbachia *(6th issue). Vert designs as T* **331**. *Multicoloured. No wmk. P* 13½ × 14.
1663 40 c. Plate No. 77 (Series 1) .. .. 35 20
1664 45 c. Plate No. 54 (Series 1) .. .. 35 25
1665 50 c. Plate No. 92 (Series 1) .. .. 35 25
1666 60 c. Plate No. 95 (Series 1) .. .. 40 30
1667 75 c. Plate No. 5 (Series 1) .. .. 45 35
1668 90 c. Plate No. 84 (Series 1) .. .. 55 40
1669 150 c. Plate No. 78 (Series 1) .. .. 75 60
1670 200 c. Plate No. 79 (Series 1) .. .. 90 80
1671 300 c. Plate No. 83 (Series 1) .. .. 1·50 1·25
1672 320 c. Plate No. 50 (Series 1) .. .. 1·60 1·40
1673 360 c. Plate No. 85 (Series 1) .. .. 1·75 1·50
1663/73 .. .. .. .. *Set of* 11 8·00 6·50
Nos. 1663/73 were printed in a similar sheet format to Nos. 1518/33.
For stamps as Nos. 1663/73, but with watermark **106** see Nos. 1775/85.

**1986** (24 Mar). *Easter. No.* 481 *optd with T* **354** *and surch as T* **317**, *but without the "X", both by Autoprint.*
1674 **111** 25 c. on 6 c. multicoloured .. .. 25 10
1675 50 c. on 6 c. multicoloured .. .. 40 20
1676 100 c. on 6 c. multicoloured .. .. 65 40
1677 200 c. on 6 c. multicoloured .. .. 1·25 70
1674/7 .. .. .. .. *Set of* 4 2·25 1·25

1926 1986 1926

150 X

1986 QUEEN ELIZABETH

(**355**) (**356**)

**1986** (27 Mar). *60th Anniv of St. John's Ambulance in Guyana. No.* 652 *surch with T* **355** *by Autoprint.*
1678 150 c. on 35 c. silver, black and green .. 1·50 55

(Litho Format)

**1986** (4 Apr). *Centenary of Publication of Sanders'* Reichenbachia *(7th issue). Multicoloured designs as T* **331**. *No wmk. P* 13½ × 14 *(225 c.) or* 14 × 13½ *(others).*
1679 25 c. Plate No. 71 (Series 1) *(horiz)* .. 40 20
1680 120 c. Plate No. 69 (Series 1) *(horiz)* .. 1·00 55
1681 150 c. Plate No. 87 (Series 1) *(horiz)* .. 1·25 65
1682 225 c. Plate No. 60 (Series 1) .. .. 1·50 90
1683 350 c. Plate No. 94 (Series 1) *(horiz)* .. 2·00 1·50
1679/83 .. .. .. .. *Set of* 5 5·50 3·50
Nos. 1679/83 were printed in a similar sheet format to Nos. 1518/33.
For stamps as Nos. 1679/83, but with watermark **106** see Nos. 1786/90.

**1986** (21 Apr). *60th Birthday of Queen Elizabeth II. Nos.* 1526/7 *optd or surch as T* **356** *by Tip Torres.*
1684 130 c. Plate No. 13 (Series 1) .. .. 60 50
**MS**1685 100 × 126 mm. 130 c. on 130 c., 200 c. on 130 c., 260 c. on 130 c., 330 c. on 130 c., Plate No. 6 (Series 1) .. .. .. .. .. 3·00 3·25
The original face values on No. **MS** 1685 are obliterated by a floral pattern.

Protect the

GUYANA INDEPENDENCE 1966-1986

60 25

(**357**) (**358**)

**1986** (3 May). *Wildlife Protection. Nos.* 685, 739/44 *and* 993/8 *surch as T* **357** *by Tip Torres.*
1686 60 c. on 35 c. Type **174** .. .. 25 25
a. Block of 6. Nos. 1686/91 .. .. 1·40
1687 60 c. on 35 c. Haimara .. .. 25 25
1688 60 c. on 35 c. Electric Eel .. .. 25 25
1689 60 c. on 35 c. Golden Rivulus .. .. 25 25
1690 60 c. on 35 c. Pencil Fish .. .. 25 25
1691 60 c. on 35 c. Four-eyed Fish .. .. 25 25
1691*a* 60 c. on 35 c. Pirai or Carib fish .. .. 25 25
ab. Block of 6. Nos. 1691*a/f* .. .. 1·40
1691*b* 60 c. on 35 c. Smoking Hassar .. .. 25 25
1691*c* 60 c. on 35 c. Devil Ray .. .. 25 25
1691*d* 60 c. on 35 c. Flying Patwa .. .. 25 25
1691*e* 60 c. on 35 c. Arapaima Pirariucii .. 25 25
1691*f* 60 c. on 35 c. Lukanani .. .. 25 25
1692 $6 on 8 c. Type **163** .. .. 1·75 1·75
1686/92 .. .. .. .. *Set of* 13 4·00 4·00
Nos. 1686/91 were previously overprinted with Type **226**.
On No. 1692 the previous value is covered by a fleur-de-lys.

**1986** (5 May). *No.* 799 *surch as T* **326** *by Autoprint.*
1693 600 c. on 720 c. on 60 c. Soldier's Cap .. 2·50 75

**1986** (15 May). *125th Anniv of British Guiana Post Office (2nd issue). No.* 702a *surch as T* **324** *by Autoprint.*
1694 25 c. on 30 c. multicoloured (surch "Abary") 15 15
a. Sheetlet of 25. Nos. 1694/1704, 1705 × 2, 1706/17 .. .. .. 3·25
1695 25 c. on 30 c. mult (surch "Anna Regina") 15 15
1696 25 c. on 30 c. mult (surch "Aurora") .. 15 15
1697 25 c. on 30 c. mult (surch "Bartica Grove") 15 15
1698 25 c. on 30 c. mult (surch "Bel Air") .. 15 15
1699 25 c. on 30 c. mult (surch "Belle Plaine") 15 15
1700 25 c. on 30 c. multicoloured (surch "Clonbrook") .. .. .. .. 15 15
1701 25 c. on 30 c. multicoloured (surch "T.P.O. Dem. Railway") .. .. .. 15 15
1702 25 c. on 30 c. mult (surch "Enmore") .. 15 15
1703 25 c. on 30 c. multicoloured (surch "Fredericksburg") .. .. .. 15 15
1704 25 c. on 30 c. mult (surch "Good Success") 15 15
1705 25 c. on 30 c. multicoloured (surch "1986") 15 15
1706 25 c. on 30 c. mult (surch "Mariabba") .. 15 15
1707 25 c. on 30 c. multicoloured (surch "Massaruni") .. .. .. .. 15 15
1708 25 c. on 30 c. multicoloured (surch "Nigg") 15 15
1709 25 c. on 30 c. multicoloured (surch "No. 50") 15 15

1710 25 c. on 30 c. mult (surch "No. 63 Benab") 15 15
1711 25 c. on 30 c. multicoloured (surch "Philadelphia") .. .. .. 15 15
1712 25 c. on 30 c. mult (surch "Sisters") .. 15 15
1713 25 c. on 30 c. mult (surch "Skeldon") .. 15 15
1714 25 c. on 30 c. mult (surch "Suddie") .. 15 15
1715 25 c. on 30 c. multicoloured (surch "Taymouth Manor") .. .. .. 15 15
1716 25 c. on 30 c. multicoloured (surch "Wales") 15 15
1717 25 c. on 30 c. multicoloured (surch "Whim") 15 15
1694/717 .. .. .. .. *Set of* 24 3·25 3·25

The surcharged names are those of postal agencies opened between 1860 and 1880.

**1986** (26 May). *20th Anniv of Independence. (a) No.* 332 *of British Guiana, Nos* 398A, 401B *of Guyana surch as T* **358** *by Autoprint and No.* 656 *surch as T* **339** *by Tip Torres.*

1718 25 c. on 2 c. myrtle-green (No. 332) .. 15 10
1719 25 c. on 35 c. multicoloured (No. 656) .. 15 10
1720 60 c. on 2 c. myrtle-green (No. 332) .. 20 10
1721 120 c. on 6 c. yellow-green (No. 398A) .. 35 20
1722 130 c. on 24 c. black & brt orange (No. 401B) 45 20

(*b*) *Nos.* 1188/91 *surch as T* **358**, *but without* "GUYANA", *by Autoprint.*

1723 **277** 25 c. on 120 c. lake-brown, black and bright blue (No. 1188) .. .. 15 10
a. Block of 4. Nos. 1723/6 .. .. 90
1724 – 25 c. on 130 c. rose-red, black and bright blue (No. 1189) .. .. 15 10
1725 – 25 c. on 150 c. bright violet, black and bright blue (No. 1190) .. .. 15 10
1726 – 225 c. on 200 c. dull green, black and bright blue (No. 1191) .. .. 50 50
1718/26 .. .. .. .. *Set of* 9 2·00 1·25

On Nos. 1721/2 "1986" has been added below the existing overprint.

Nos. 1718 and 1720 have Mult Script CA watermark, No. 1721 watermark w **12** upright and No. 1722 watermark w **12** sideways.

MEXICO
1986

(359)

225

CARICOM
DAY 1986

(360)

**1986** (31 May). *World Cup Football Championship, Mexico (2nd issue). No.* 544 *surch with T* **359** *in blue by Autoprint.*

1727 225 c. on 3 c. Hanging Heliconia .. .. 1·50 45

**1986** (28 June). *CARICOM Day. No.* 705*a optd with T* **360** *in blue by Autoprint.*

1728 60 c. *Papilio androgeus* .. .. .. 40 15

CARICOM
HEADS OF GOV'T
CONFERENCE
JULY 1986
60

(361)

INT. YEAR
OF PEACE
25

(362)

**1986** (1 July). *CARICOM Heads of Government Conference, Georgetown. Nos.* 544 *and* 601 *surch as T* **361** *in blue by Autoprint.*

1729 25 c. on 8 c. on 6 c. Cannon-ball Tree .. 20 10
1730 60 c. on 3 c. Hanging Heliconia .. .. 40 25

(Litho Format)

**1986** (10 July). *Centenary of Publication of Sanders'* Reichenbachia *(8th issue). Vert designs as T* **331**. *Multicoloured. No wmk. P* 13½ × 14.

1731 30 c. Plate No. 86 (Series 1) .. .. 25 15
1732 55 c. Plate No. 17 (Series 1) .. .. 40 20
1733 60 c. Plate No. 93 (Series 1) .. .. 40 20
1734 100 c. Plate No. 68 (Series 1) .. .. 55 20
1735 130 c. Plate No. 91 (Series 1) .. .. 60 30
1736 250 c. Plate No. 74 (Series 1) .. .. 90 60
1737 260 c. Plate No. 39 (Series 1) .. .. 90 60
1738 375 c. Plate No. 90 (Series 1) .. .. 1·25 85
1731/8 .. .. .. .. *Set of* 8 4·75 2·75

Nos. 1731/8 were printed in a similar sheet format to Nos. 1518/33.

For stamps as Nos. 1731/8, but with watermark **106** see Nos. 1791/8.

For these designs with different face values see Nos. 1822, 1868 and 1884/5.

**1986** (14 July). *International Peace Year. Nos.* 542 *and* 546 *surch as T* **362** *in blue (No.* 1739) *or black (others).*

1739 25 c. on 1 c. Pitcher Plant of Mt Roraima .. 10 10
a. Sheetlet of 25. No. 1739 × 24 and one label .. .. .. 1·25
1740 60 c. on 6 c. Cannon-ball Tree .. .. 10 10
a. Sheetlet of 25. Nos. 1740/3, each × 4, and nine labels .. .. 2·25
1741 120 c. on 6 c. Cannon-ball Tree .. .. 15 20
1742 130 c. on 6 c. Cannon-ball Tree .. .. 15 20
1743 150 c. on 6 c. Cannon-ball Tree .. .. 20 25
1739/43 .. .. .. .. *Set of* 5 55 70

As surcharged the sheet of No. 1739 contained a stamp without face value, overprinted "1986", in the centre position.

Nos. 1740/3 were each surcharged in blocks of four from the corner positions of the same sheet. Stamps in the central horizontal and vertical rows were without value and were overprinted with one letter of "PEACE".

**363** Halley's Comet and British Guiana 1907 2 c. Stamp

(Litho Format)

**1986** (19 July). *Appearance of Halley's Comet. T* **363** *and similar vert design. P* 13½ × 14.

1744 **363** 320 c. rosine, black & deep reddish lilac 60 60
a. Horiz pair. Nos. 1744/5 .. .. 1·10 1·10
ab. Imperf between (horiz pair) ..
1745 – 320 c. multicoloured .. .. .. 60 60
**MS**1746 76 × 50 mm. Nos. 1744/5. Imperf .. 90 1·00

Design:—No. 1745, Guyana 1985 320 c. Macaw stamp.

(Litho Format)

**1986** (24 July). *Centenary of Publication of Sanders'* Reichenbachia *(9th issue). Vert designs as T* **331**. *Multicoloured. No wmk. P* 13½ × 14.

1747 40 c. Plate No. 96 (Series 1) .. .. 25 15
1748 45 c. Plate No. 81 (Series 1) .. .. 25 15
1749 90 c. Plate No. 89 (Series 1) .. .. 45 20
1750 100 c. Plate No. 88 (Series 1) .. .. 45 20
1751 150 c. Plate No. 76 (Series 1) .. .. 60 35
1752 180 c. Plate No. 15 (Series 1) .. .. 70 40
1753 320 c. Plate No. 82 (Series 1) .. .. 85 55
1754 330 c. Plate No. 80 (Series 1) .. .. 1·00 70
1747/54 .. .. .. .. *Set of* 8 4·00 2·40

Nos. 1747/54 were printed in a similar sheet format to Nos. 1518/33.

For stamps as Nos. 1747/54, but with watermark **106** see Nos. 1799/1806.

**1986** (28 July). *No.* 489 *surch as T* **317**, *but without the* "X".

1755 20 c. on 6 c. Patua .. .. .. .. 30 15

GUSIA
1936-1986

(364)

REGIONAL
PHARMACY
CONFERENCE
1986
130

(365)

**1986** (15 Aug). *50th Anniv of Guyana United Sadr Islamic Association. Nos.* 469/70 *optd or surch as T* **364** *by Autoprint.*

1756 **105** 25 c. black, gold and lilac .. .. 20 10
1757 $1.50 on 6 c. black, gold and flesh .. 65 40

**1986** (19 Aug). *Regional Pharmacy Conference. No.* 545 *surch with T* **365** *in blue.*

1758 130 c. on 5 c. Annatto Tree .. .. .. 70 30

**1986** (21 Aug)–**87**. *As previous* Reichenbachia *issues, but W* **106** *(sideways on horiz designs). P* 13½×14 *(vert) or* 14×13½ *(horiz).*

(*a*) *As Nos.* 1526/7 *and* 1529/30

1759 130 c. Plate No. 6 (Series 1) .. .. 35 20
1760 130 c. Plate No. 13 (Series 1) .. .. 35 20
1761 130 c. Plate No. 20 (Series 1) .. .. 35 20
1762 130 c. Plate No. 25 (Series 1) .. .. 35 20
1759/62 .. .. .. .. *Set of* 4 1·25 70

(*b*) *As Nos.* 1552/5

1763 55 c. Plate No. 9 (Series 1) .. .. 25 10
1764 55 c. Plate No. 22 (Series 1) .. .. 25 10
1765 55 c. Plate No. 49 (Series 1) .. .. 25 10
1766 55 c. Plate No. 64 (Series 1) .. .. 25 10
1763/6 .. .. .. .. *Set of* 4 90 30

(*c*) *As Nos.* 1581/3 *and* 1586

1767 150 c. Plate No. 40 (Series 1) (*horiz*) .. 35 20
1768 150 c. Plate No. 42 (Series 1) (*horiz*) .. 35 20
1769 150 c. Plate No. 45 (Series 1) (*horiz*) .. 35 20
1770 200 c. Plate No. 43 (Series 1) (*horiz*) .. 45 30
1767/70 .. .. .. .. *Set of* 4 1·40 80

(*d*) *As Nos.* 1621, 1625/6 *and* 1635

1771 30 c. Plate No. 53 (Series 1) (10.86) .. 10 10
1772 75 c. Plate No. 55 (Series 1) (1.87) .. 20 15
1773 100 c. Plate No. 65 (Series 1) (1.87) .. 25 15
1774 225 c. Plate No. 24 (Series 1) (10.86) .. 35 35
1771/4 .. .. .. .. *Set of* 4 75 60

(*e*) *As Nos.* 1663/73 (1987)

1775 40 c. Plate No. 77 (Series 1) .. .. 1·50 1·50
1776 45 c. Plate No. 54 (Series 1) .. .. 1·50 1·50
1777 50 c. Plate No. 92 (Series 1) .. .. 1·50 1·50
1778 60 c. Plate No. 95 (Series 1) .. .. 2·00 2·00
1779 75 c. Plate No. 5 (Series 1) .. .. 2·50 2·50
1780 90 c. Plate No. 84 (Series 1) .. .. 3·00 3·00
1781 150 c. Plate No. 78 (Series 1) .. .. 5·00 5·00
1782 200 c. Plate No. 79 (Series 1) .. .. 6·50 6·50
1783 300 c. Plate No. 83 (Series 1) .. .. 10·00 10·00
1784 320 c. Plate No. 50 (Series 1) .. .. 11·00 11·00
1785 360 c. Plate No. 85 (Series 1) .. .. 12·50 12·50
1775/85 .. .. .. .. *Set of* 11 50·00 50·00

(*f*) *As Nos.* 1679/83 (1987)

1786 25 c. Plate No. 71 (Series 1) .. .. 1·50 1·50
1787 120 c. Plate No. 69 (Series 1) .. .. 6·00 6·00
1788 150 c. Plate No. 87 (Series 1) .. .. 7·00 7·00
1789 225 c. Plate No. 60 (Series 1) .. .. 8·50 8·50
1790 350 c. Plate No. 94 (Series 1) .. .. 15·00 15·00
1786/90 .. .. .. .. *Set of* 5 32·00 32·00

(*g*) *As Nos.* 1731/8 (1987)

1791 30 c. Plate No. 86 (Series 1) .. .. 1·00 1·00
1792 55 c. Plate No. 17 (Series 1) .. .. 1·50 1·50
1793 60 c. Plate No. 93 (Series 1) .. .. 1·50 1·50
1794 100 c. Plate No. 68 (Series 1) .. .. 2·00 2·00
1795 130 c. Plate No. 91 (Series 1) .. .. 2·50 2·50
1796 250 c. Plate No. 74 (Series 1) .. .. 5·00 5·00
1797 260 c. Plate No. 39 (Series 1) .. .. 5·00 5·00
1798 375 c. Plate No. 90 (Series 1) .. .. 7·00 7·00
1791/8 .. .. .. .. *Set of* 8 20·00 20·00

(*h*) *As Nos.* 1747/54 (1987)

1799 40 c. Plate No. 96 (Series 1) .. .. 1·00 1·00
1800 45 c. Plate No. 81 (Series 1) .. .. 1·00 1·00
1801 90 c. Plate No. 89 (Series 1) .. .. 2·00 2·00
1802 100 c. Plate No. 88 (Series 1) .. .. 2·00 2·00
1803 150 c. Plate No. 76 (Series 1) .. .. 3·00 3·00
1804 180 c. Plate No. 15 (Series 1) .. .. 4·00 4·00
1805 320 c. Plate No. 82 (Series 1) .. .. 5·50 5·50
1806 330 c. Plate No. 80 (Series 1) .. .. 6·50 6·50
1799/1806 .. .. .. .. *Set of* 8 22·00 22·00

Nos. 1759/1806 were printed in a similar sheet format to Nos. 1518/33.

These stamps, together with other unwatermarked values from the 1st to the 9th issues, also exist made up into two small books which reproduce the order of the plates in the original volumes.

**1986** (21 Aug). *Booklet and Coil Stamps. As Nos.* 1534/5*b*, *but W* **106** (*sideways on Nos.* 1807*a*, 1808*a*/*b*).

1807 **332** 25 c. multicoloured (*imperf* × *p* 14) 15 15
1807*a* 25 c. multicoloured (*imperf* × *p* 13½) 15 15
1807*b* 25 c. multicoloured (*p* 13½×14) .. 15 15
1808 25 c. multicoloured (*p* 13½×*imperf*) 15 15
1808*a* 25 c. multicoloured (*p* 14×*imperf*) .. 15 15
1808*b* 25 c. multicoloured (*p* 14×13½) .. 15 15
1807/8*b* .. .. .. .. *Set of* 6 80 80

The note below Nos. 1534/5*b* also applies to Nos. 1807/8*b*.

(Litho Format)

**1986** (23 Sept). *Centenary of Publication of Sanders'* Reichenbachia (10*th issue*). *Multicoloured designs as T* **331**. *No wmk. P* 14 × 13½ (*Nos.* 1810, 1812, 1815, 1818) *or* 13½ × 14 (*others*).

1809 30 c. Plate No. 30 (Series 2) .. .. 25 15
1810 45 c. Plate No. 21 (Series 2) (*horiz*) .. 30 15
1811 75 c. Plate No. 8 (Series 2) .. .. 55 15
1812 80 c. Plate No. 42 (Series 2) (*horiz*) .. 55 15
1813 90 c. Plate No. 4 (Series 2) .. .. 65 25
1814 130 c. Plate No. 38 (Series 2) .. .. 70 35
1815 160 c. Plate No. 5 (Series 2) (*horiz*) .. 85 40
1816 200 c. Plate No. 9 (Series 2) .. .. 1·00 50
1817 320 c. Plate No. 12 (Series 2) .. .. 1·75 70
1818 350 c. Plate No. 29 (Series 2) (*horiz*) .. 2·00 70
1819 360 c. Plate No. 34 (Series 2) .. .. 2·00 70
1809/19 .. .. .. .. *Set of* 11 9·50 3·75

Nos. 1809/19, together with Nos. 1820/1*a*, were printed in a similar sheet format to Nos. 1518/33.

(Litho Format)

**1986** (23 Sept). *20th Anniv of Independence (2nd issue). Booklet and Coil Stamps. T* **332** *additionally inscr* "1966–1986" *at foot. No wmk.*

1820 25 c. multicoloured (*imperf*×*p* 14) .. 15 15
1821 25 c. multicoloured (*p* 13½×*imperf*) .. 15 15
1821*a* 25 c. multicoloured (*p* 13½×14) .. 15 15
1820/1*a* .. .. .. .. *Set of* 3 40 40

Nos. 1820/1*a* together with Nos. 1809/19, were printed in the sheet format described beneath No. 1533.

(Litho Format)

**1986** (26 Sept). *Centenary of Publication of Sanders'* Reichenbachia (11*th issue*). *Design as No.* 1735, *but with different face value. Multicoloured. No wmk. P* 13½ × 14.

1822 40 c. Plate No. 91 (Series 1) .. .. 70 15

120

(366)

650
12th World Orchid Conference
TOKYO JAPAN MARCH 1987

(367)

**1986** (3 Oct). *Nos.* 1361/84 *surch with T* **366** *by Autoprint.*

1823 120 c. on 30 c. multicoloured (No. 1361) .. 30 30
a. Sheetlet of 25. Nos. 1823/33, 1834 × 2 and 1835/46 .. .. .. .. 6·75
1824 120 c. on 30 c. multicoloured (No. 1362) .. 30 30
1825 120 c. on 30 c. multicoloured (No. 1363) .. 30 30

1826 120 c. on 30 c. multicoloured (No. 1364) .. 30 30
1827 120 c. on 30 c. multicoloured (No. 1365) .. 30 30
1828 120 c. on 30 c. multicoloured (No. 1366) .. 30 30
1829 120 c. on 30 c. multicoloured (No. 1367) .. 30 30
1830 120 c. on 30 c. multicoloured (No. 1368) .. 30 30
1831 120 c. on 30 c. multicoloured (No. 1369) .. 30 30
1832 120 c. on 30 c. multicoloured (No. 1370) .. 30 30
1833 120 c. on 30 c. multicoloured (No. 1371) .. 30 30
1834 120 c. on 30 c. multicoloured (No. 1372) .. 30 30
1835 120 c. on 30 c. multicoloured (No. 1373) .. 30 30
1836 120 c. on 30 c. multicoloured (No. 1374) .. 30 30
1837 120 c. on 30 c. multicoloured (No. 1375) .. 30 30
1838 120 c. on 30 c. multicoloured (No. 1376) .. 30 30
1839 120 c. on 30 c. multicoloured (No. 1377) .. 30 30
1840 120 c. on 30 c. multicoloured (No. 1378) .. 30 30
1841 120 c. on 30 c. multicoloured (No. 1379) .. 30 30
1842 120 c. on 30 c. multicoloured (No. 1380) .. 30 30
1843 120 c. on 30 c. multicoloured (No. 1381) .. 30 30
1844 120 c. on 30 c. multicoloured (No. 1382) .. 30 30
1845 120 c. on 30 c. multicoloured (No. 1383) .. 30 30
1846 120 c. on 30 c. multicoloured (No. 1384) .. 30 30
1823/46 .. .. .. .. *Set of* 24 6·50 6·50

**1986** (6 Oct). *12th World Orchid Conference, Tokyo (1st issue). Unissued design as No.* 1731, *but with different face value, surch with T* **367** *by Tip Torres.*
1847 650 c. on 40 c. Plate No. 86 (Series 1) .. 2·50 1·75
No. 1847 is inscribed "ONTOGLOSSUM TRIUMPHANS" in error.
See also Nos. 2138/9.

1492-1992 CHRISTOPHER COLUMBUS 320

(368)

**1986** (10–30 Oct). *Columbus Day. Unissued design as No.* 1635, *but with different face value, surch with T* **368** *by Tip Torres.*
1864 320 c. on 150 c. Plate No. 24 (Series 1) (surch in black (figures and obliterating device) and red) .. .. .. .. 75 45
1865 320 c. on 150 c. Plate No. 24 (Series 1) (entire surch in red) (30 Oct) .. 75 45

1986 50

(369)

AIR UNICEF 1946-1986 120

(370)

**1986** (15 Oct). *International Food Day. Nos.* 1170/1 *further surch as T* **369** *by Autoprint.*
1866 50 c. on 30 c. on 1 c. Type **87** .. .. 20 15
1867 225 c. on $2.60 on 3 c. Lukunani .. .. 60 45

(Litho Format)

**1986** (23 Oct). *Centenary of Publication of Sanders'* Reichenbachia *(12th issue). Vert designs as T* **331**, *one as No.* 1731 *with different face value. Multicoloured. No wmk. P* 13½ × 14.
1868 40 c. Plate No. 86 (Series 1) .. .. 40 15
1869 90 c. Plate No. 10 (Series 2) .. .. 70 30

**1986** (24 Oct). *Air. 40th Annivs of U.N.I.C.E.F. and U.N.E.S.C.O. No.* 706 *surch as T* **370** *by Autoprint.*
1870 120 c. on $1 Type **167** (surch T **370**) .. 35 35
a. Pair. Nos. 1870/1 .. 70 70
1871 120 c. on $1 Type **167** (surch "UNESCO 1946–1986") .. .. 35 35
Nos. 1870/1 were surcharged together, *se-tenant*, in horizontal and vertical pairs throughout the sheet.

(Litho Format)

**1986** (30 Oct). *Centenary of Publication of Sanders'* Reichenbachia *(13th issue). Vert designs as T* **331**. *Multicoloured. No wmk. P* 13½ × 14.
1872 45 c. Plate No. 17 (Series 2) .. .. 30 15
1873 50 c. Plate No. 33 (Series 2) .. .. 30 15
1874 60 c. Plate No. 27 (Series 2) .. .. 45 15
1875 75 c. Plate No. 56 (Series 2) .. .. 55 20
1876 85 c. Plate No. 45 (Series 2) .. .. 55 20
1877 90 c. Plate No. 13 (Series 2) .. .. 70 20
1878 200 c. Plate No. 44 (Series 2) .. .. 1·00 45
1879 300 c. Plate No. 50 (Series 2) .. .. 1·60 60
1880 320 c. Plate No. 10 (Series 2) .. .. 1·75 70
1881 390 c. Plate No. 6 (Series 2) .. .. 2·00 95
1872/81 .. .. .. *Set of* 10 8·25 3·25
Nos. 1872/81 were printed in a similar sheet format to Nos. 1518/33.
For these designs with different face values see Nos. 1907, 1915 and 1925.

25 Deepavali 1986

(371)

X CHRISTMAS 1986 20

(372)

**1986** (3 Nov). *Deepavali Festival. Nos.* 543 *and* 601 *surch as T* **371** *by Autoprint.*
1882 25 c. on 2 c. Type **132** .. .. .. 15 10
1883 200 c. on 8 c. on 6 c. Cannon-ball Tree .. 55 40

(Litho Format)

**1986** (25 Nov). *Centenary of Publication of Sanders'* Reichenbachia *(14th issue). Vert designs as T* **331**, *two as Nos.* 1732 *and* 1734 *with different face values. Multicoloured. No wmk. P* 13½ × 14.
1884 40 c. Plate No. 68 (Series 1) .. .. 30 15
1885 80 c. Plate No. 17 (Series 1) .. .. 60 25
1886 200 c. Plate No. 2 (Series 2) .. .. 1·25 60
1887 225 c. Plate No. 24 (Series 2) .. .. 1·50 70
1884/7 .. .. .. .. *Set of* 4 3·25 1·50
Nos. 1884/7 were printed in a similar sheet format to Nos. 1518/33.
For these designs with different face values see Nos. 1914 and 1929.

**1986** (26 Nov). *Christmas. No.* 452 *surch with T* **372** *and previously unissued miniature sheet containing Nos.* 1425/9, *each surch as T* **342**, *but without dates, all in red by Autoprint.*
1888 20 c. on 6 c. Patua .. .. .. 10 10
**MS**1889 215×75 mm. 120 c. on 60 c. × 5 Nos. 1425/9 .. .. .. .. .. .. 2·50 2·50

1986

(373)

$15

(374)

**1986** (26 Nov). *Wildlife Protection. Nos.* 756/67 *optd with T* **373** *in blue by Autoprint.*
1894 30 c. Type **178** .. .. .. .. 25 25
a. Sheetlet of 12. Nos. 1894/905 .. .. 2·75
1895 30 c. Red Howler .. .. .. .. 25 25
1896 30 c. Common Squirrel-Monkey .. .. 25 25
1897 30 c. Two-toed Sloth .. .. .. 25 25
1898 30 c. Brazilian Tapir .. .. .. 25 25
1899 30 c. Collared Peccary .. .. .. 25 25
1900 30 c. Six-banded Armadillo .. .. .. 25 25
1901 30 c. Tamandua ("Ant Eater") .. .. 25 25
1902 30 c. Giant Anteater .. .. .. 25 25
1903 30 c. Murine Opossum .. .. .. 25 25
1904 30 c. Brown Four-eyed Opossum .. .. 25 25
1905 30 c. Brazilian Agouti .. .. .. 25 25
1894/905 .. .. .. .. *Set of* 12 2·75 2·75

**1986** (1 Dec). *No.* 1642 *surch with T* **374** *in red by Autoprint.*
1906 $15 on $3.50, Clive Lloyd with the Prudential Cup .. .. .. .. .. .. 7·00 6·00

(Litho Format)

**1986** (3 Dec). *Centenary of Publication of Sanders'* Reichenbachia *(15th issue). Design as No.* 1877, *but with different face value. Multicoloured. No wmk. P* 13½ × 14.
1907 50 c. Plate No. 13 (Series 2) .. .. 55 15

GUYANA 25c

375 Memorial

GPOC $10 1977 1987

(376)

(Litho Format)

**1986** (13 Dec). *President Burnham Commemoration. T* **375** *and similar multicoloured designs. P* 12½.
1908 25 c. Type **375** .. .. .. .. 10 10
1909 120 c. Map of Guyana and flags .. .. 35 20
1910 130 c. Parliament Buildings and mace .. 35 20
1911 $6 L. F. Burnham and Georgetown mayoral chain *(vert)* .. .. .. .. 1·25 1·25
1908/11 .. .. .. .. *Set of* 4 1·90 1·60

(Litho Format)

**1986** (15–22 Dec). *Centenary of Publication of Sanders'* Reichenbachia *(16th issue). Multicoloured designs as Nos.* 1554/5, 1874 *and* 1887 *with different face values. W* **106** *(Nos.* 1912/13*) or no wmk (others). P* 13½ × 14.
1912 50 c. Plate No. 49 (Series 1) (22.12) .. 30 15
1913 50 c. Plate No. 64 (Series 1) .. .. 30 15
1914 85 c. Plate No. 24 (Series 2) .. .. 55 25
1915 90 c. Plate No. 27 (Series 2) .. .. 55 25
1912/15 .. .. .. .. *Set of* 4 1·50 70

(Litho Format)

**1986** (27 Dec). *Centenary of Publication of Sanders'* Reichenbachia *(17th issue). Vert designs as T* **331**. *Multicoloured. No wmk. P* 13½ × 14.
1916 25 c. Plate No. 20 (Series 2) .. .. 25 15
1917 40 c. Plate No. 7 (Series 2) .. .. 25 15
1918 85 c. Plate No. 15 (Series 2) .. .. 40 20
1919 90 c. Plate No. 3 (Series 2) .. .. 40 20
1920 120 c. Plate No. 14 (Series 2) .. .. 55 30
1921 130 c. Plate No. 32 (Series 2) .. .. 55 30
1922 150 c. Plate No. 22 (Series 2) .. .. 70 35
1923 320 c. Plate No. 18 (Series 2) .. .. 1·00 55
1924 330 c. Plate No. 28 (Series 2) .. .. 1·00 70
1916/24 .. .. .. .. *Set of* 9 4·50 2·75
Nos. 1916/24 were printed in a similar sheet format to Nos. 1518/33.
For these designs with different face values see Nos. 1926 and 1928.

(Litho Format)

**1987** (5–16 Jan). *Centenary of Publication of Sanders'* Reichenbachia *(18th issue). Multicoloured designs as Nos.* 1625, 1876, 1886, 1918 *and* 1923 *with different face values. W* **106** *(No.* 1927*) or no wmk (others). P* 13½ × 14.
1925 35 c. Plate No. 45 (Series 2) .. .. 30 15
1926 50 c. Plate No. 15 (Series 2) .. .. 30 15
1927 50 c. Plate No. 55 (Series 1) (16.1) .. 30 15
1928 85 c. Plate No. 18 (Series 2) .. .. 55 25
1929 90 c. Plate No. 2 (Series 2) .. .. 55 25
1925/9 .. .. .. .. *Set of* 5 1·75 85
Nos. 1925/9 were printed in a similar sheet format to Nos. 1518/33.

**1987** (19 Jan). *10th Anniv of Guyana Post Office Corporation (1st issue). Unissued designs as Nos.* 1621 *and* 1635, *but with different face values, surch or optd as T* **376** *by Tip Torres.*
1930 $2.25, Plate No. 53 (Series 1) .. .. 75 35
1931 $10 on 150 c. Plate No. 24 (Series 1) .. 2·25 2·50
See also Nos. 2074/80.

200

200

(377)

(378)

200

TWO DOLLARS

(379)

(380)

1987

15.00

(381)

225
(382)

120
(383)

120
(384)

**1987** (9 Feb–Sept). *Various* Reichenbachia *issues surch as T* **377/84**.

*(a) As T* **377** *in red by Tip Torres* (9 Feb)

1932 200 c. on 40 c. Plate No. 90 (Series 1) .. 40 40

*(b) As T* **378** *by Tip Torres* (6 Mar)

1933 200 c. on 25 c. Plate No. 8 (Series 1) (No. 1571) .. 40 40
1934 200 c. on 25 c. Plate No. 51 (Series 1) (No. 1573) .. 40 40

*(c) As T* **379** *by Tip Torres (No. 1935 without ornament)* (6 Mar)

1935 $2 on 25 c. Plate No. 12 (Series 1) (No. 1518) .. 40 40
1936 $2 on 25 c. Plate No. 23 (Series 1) (No. 1572) .. 40 40

*(d) As T* **380** *by Tip Torres* (17 Mar)

1937 200 c. on 40 c. Plate No. 68 (Series 1) (No. 1884) (ornament inverted) .. 40 40
a. Ornament upright .. 40 40
1938 200 c. on 40 c. Plate No. 90 (Series 1) .. 40 40
1939 200 c. on 50 c. Plate No. 92 (Series 1) (No. 1665) .. 40 40
1940 200 c. on 50 c. Plate No. 22 (Series 1) (*wmkd*) .. 40 40
1941 200 c. on 55 c. Plate No. 22 (Series 1) (No. 1764) (*wmkd*) .. 40 40
1942 200 c. on 60 c. Plate No. 5 (Series 1) (ornament inverted) .. 40 40
1943 200 c. on 75 c. Plate No. 5 (Series 1) (No. 1667) (ornament inverted) .. 40 40
1944 200 c. on 75 c. Plate No. 60 (Series 1) .. 40 40
1945 200 c. on 75 c. Plate No. 92 (Series 1) .. 40 40
1946 200 c. on 85 c. Plate No. 18 (Series 2) (No. 1928) .. 40 40
1947 200 c. on 375 c. Plate No. 90 (Series 1) (No. 1738) .. 40 40
1948 200 c. on 375 c. Plate No. 90 (Series 1) (No. 1798) (*wmkd*) .. 40 40
1937/48 .. *Set of* 12 4·25 4·25

*(e) As T* **377** *by Tip Torres* (March)

1949 200 c. on 25 c. Plate No. 52 (Series 1) (No. 1551) .. 40 40
1950 200 c. on 25 c. Plate No. 8 (Series 1) (No. 1571) .. 40 40
1951 200 c. on 25 c. Plate No. 72 (Series 1) (No. 1577) .. 40 40
1952 200 c. on 25 c. Plate No. 71 (Series 1) (No. 1679) (surch vert – reading downwards) .. 40 40
1953 200 c. on 30 c. Plate No. 86 (Series 1) (No. 1731) .. 40 40
1954 200 c. on 30 c. Plate No. 53 (Series 1) (No. 1771) (*wmkd*) .. 40 40
1955 200 c. on 40 c. Plate No. 77 (Series 1) (No. 1663) .. 40 40
1956 200 c. on 40 c. Plate No. 86 (Series 1) (No. 1868) .. 40 40
1957 200 c. on 45 c. Plate No. 81 (Series 1) (No. 1748) .. 40 40
1958 200 c. on 45 c. Plate No. 77 (Series 1) .. 40 40
1959 200 c. on 45 c. Plate No. 78 (Series 1) .. 40 40
1960 200 c. on 45 c. Plate No. 85 (Series 1) .. 40 40
1961 200 c. on 50 c. Plate No. 24 (Series 1) (*wmkd*) .. 40 40
1962 200 c. on 50 c. Plate No. 53 (Series 1) (*wmkd*) .. 40 40
1963 200 c. on 50 c. Plate No. 65 (Series 1) (*wmkd*) .. 40 40
1964 200 c. on 55 c. Plate No. 49 (Series 1) (No. 1554) .. 40 40
1965 200 c. on 55 c. Plate No. 17 (Series 1) (No. 1732) .. 40 40
1966 200 c. on 55 c. Plate No. 49 (Series 1) (No. 1765) (*wmkd*) .. 40 40
1967 200 c. on 60 c. Plate No. 7 (Series 1) (No. 1520) .. 40 40
1968 200 c. on 60 c. Plate No. 10 (Series 1) (No. 1521) .. 40 40
1969 200 c. on 60 c. Plate No. 19 (Series 1) (No. 1522) .. 40 40
1970 200 c. on 60 c. Plate No. 31 (Series 1) (No. 1523) .. 40 40
1971 200 c. on 60 c. Plate No. 44 (Series 1) (No. 1556) .. 40 40
1972 200 c. on 60 c. Plate No. 47 (Series 1) (No. 1557) .. 40 40
1973 200 c. on 60 c. Plate No. 57 (Series 1) (No. 1622) (surch vert – reading down) .. 40 40
1974 200 c. on 60 c. Plate No. 73 (Series 1) (No. 1623) (surch vert – reading up) .. 40 40
1975 200 c. on 60 c. Plate No. 75 (Series 1) (No. 1624) (surch vert – reading down) .. 40 40
1976 200 c. on 60 c. Plate No. 71 (Series 1) (surch vert – reading down) .. 40 40
1977 200 c. on 60 c. Plate No. 87 (Series 1) (surch vert – reading down) .. 40 40
1978 225 c. on 90 c. Plate No. 89 (Series 1) (No. 1749) .. 40 40
1949/78 .. *Set of* 30 11·00 11·00

*(f) As T* **381** *by Gardy Ptg* (March)

1979 120 c. on 50 c. Plate No. 9 (Series 1) (*wmkd*) 30 30
1980 120 c. on 55 c. Plate No. 9 (Series 1) (No. 1552) .. 30 30
1981 120 c. on 55 c. Plate No. 64 (Series 1) (No. 1555) .. 30 30
1982 120 c. on 55 c. Plate No. 64 (Series 1) (No. 1766) (*wmkd*) .. 30 30
1983 $10 on 25 c. Plate No. 53 (Series 1) 1·75 1·75
1984 $12 on 80 c. Plate No. 74 (Series 1) .. 2·00 2·00
1985 $15 on 80 c. Plate No. 39 (Series 1) .. 2·50 2·50
1986 $25 on 25 c. Plate No. 53 (Series 1) .. 4·00 4·00
1979/86 .. *Set of* 8 10·00 10·00

Nos. 1979/82 do not show a date as part of the surcharge. On No. 1986 the surcharge is achieved by a dollar sign in front of the original face value.

*(g) With T* **382** *by Gardy Ptg* (June)

1987 225 c. on 40 c. Plate No. 91 (Series 1) (No. 1822) .. 50 50
1988 225 c. on 40 c. Plate No. 90 (Series 1) .. 50 50
1989 225 c. on 50 c. Plate No. 22 (Series 1) (*wmkd*) .. 50 50
1990 225 c. on 60 c. Plate No. 55 (Series 1) (No. 1597) .. 50 50
1991 225 c. on 60 c. Plate No. 93 (Series 1) (No. 1733) .. 50 50
1992 225 c. on 80 c. Plate No. 93 (Series 1) .. 50 50
1993 225 c. on 150 c. Plate No. 42 (Series 1) (No. 1657) (surch vert – reading down) 50 50
1987/93 .. *Set of* 7 3·25 3·25

*(h) As T* **383** (July)

1994 120 c. on 50 c. Plate No. 49 (Series 1) (No. 1912) (*wmkd*) .. 30 30
1995 120 c. on 50 c. Plate No. 64 (Series 1) (No. 1913) (*wmkd*) .. 30 30
1996 120 c. on 50 c. Plate No. 9 (Series 1) (*wmkd*) 30 30
1997 120 c. on 50 c. Plate No. 22 (Series 1) (*wmkd*) .. 30 30
1998 120 c. on 50 c. Plate No. 3 (Series 2) .. 30 30
1999 120 c. on 50 c. Plate No. 6 (Series 2) .. 30 30
2000 120 c. on 50 c. Plate No. 20 (Series 2) .. 30 30
2001 120 c. on 50 c. Plate No. 32 (Series 2) .. 30 30
2002 120 c. on 55 c. Plate No. 9 (Series 1) (No. 1552) .. 30 30
2003 120 c. on 55 c. Plate No. 49 (Series 1) (No. 1554) .. 30 30
2004 120 c. on 55 c. Plate No. 64 (Series 1) (No. 1555) .. 30 30
2005 120 c. on 55 c. Plate No. 9 (Series 1) (No. 1763) (*wmkd*) .. 30 30
2006 120 c. on 55 c. Plate No. 22 (Series 1) (No. 1764) (*wmkd*) .. 30 30
2007 120 c. on 55 c. Plate No. 49 (Series 1) (No. 1765) (*wmkd*) .. 30 30
2008 120 c. on 55 c. Plate No. 64 (Series 1) (No. 1766) (*wmkd*) .. 30 30
2009 120 c. on 55 c. Plate No. 15 (Series 1) .. 30 30
2010 120 c. on 55 c. Plate No. 81 (Series 1) .. 30 30
2011 120 c. on 55 c. Plate No. 82 (Series 1) .. 30 30
2012 120 c. on 55 c. Plate No. 89 (Series 1) .. 30 30
1994/2012 .. *Set of* 19 5·25 5·25

*(i) As T* **384** *by Gardy Ptg* (Sept)

2013 120 c. on 40 c. Plate No. 91 (Series 1) (No. 1822) .. 30 30
2014 120 c. on 40 c. Plate No. 90 (Series 1) .. 30 30
2015 120 c. on 50 c. Plate No. 49 (Series 1) (No. 1912) (*wmkd*) .. 30 30
2016 120 c. on 50 c. Plate No. 64 (Series 1) (No. 1913) (*wmkd*) .. 30 30
2017 120 c. on 50 c. Plate No. 9 (Series 1) (*wmkd*) 30 30
2018 120 c. on 50 c. Plate No. 22 (Series 1) (*wmkd*) .. 30 30
2019 120 c. on 50 c. Plate No. 24 (Series 1) (*wmkd*) .. 30 30
2020 120 c. on 50 c. Plate No. 53 (Series 1) (*wmkd*) .. 30 30
2021 120 c. on 50 c. Plate No. 65 (Series 1) (*wmkd*) .. 30 30
2022 120 c. on 55 c. Plate No. 9 (Series 1) (No. 1763) (*wmkd*) .. 30 30
2023 120 c. on 55 c. Plate No. 22 (Series 1) (No. 1764) (*wmkd*) .. 30 30
2024 120 c. on 55 c. Plate No. 49 (Series 1) (No. 1765) (*wmkd*) .. 30 30
2025 120 c. on 55 c. Plate No. 64 (Series 1) (No. 1766) (*wmkd*) .. 30 30
2026 120 c. on 60 c. Plate No. 2 (Series 1) (No. 1519) .. 30 30
2027 120 c. on 60 c. Plate No. 10 (Series 1) (No. 1521) .. 30 30
2028 120 c. on 60 c. Plate No. 19 (Series 1) (No. 1522) .. 30 30
2029 120 c. on 60 c. Plate No. 31 (Series 1) (No. 1523) .. 30 30
2030 120 c. on 60 c. Plate No. 5 (Series 1) .. 30 30
2031 120 c. on 60 c. Plate No. 50 (Series 1) .. 30 30
2032 120 c. on 60 c. Plate No. 54 (Series 1) .. 30 30
2033 120 c. on 60 c. Plate No. 69 (Series 1) (surch vert – reading down) .. 30 30
2034 120 c. on 60 c. Plate No. 71 (Series 1) (surch vert – reading up) .. 30 30
a. Surch reading down .. 30 30
2035 120 c. on 60 c. Plate No. 79 (Series 1) .. 30 30
2036 120 c. on 60 c. Plate No. 87 (Series 1) (surch vert – reading up) .. 30 30
a. Surch reading down .. 30 30
2037 120 c. on 60 c. Plate No. 94 (Series 1) (surch vert – reading down) .. 30 30
2038 120 c. on 75 c. Plate No. 60 (Series 1) .. 30 30
2039 120 c. on 75 c. Plate No. 83 (Series 1) .. 30 30
2040 120 c. on 75 c. Plate No. 92 (Series 1) .. 30 30
2041 120 c. on 75 c. Plate No. 95 (Series 1) .. 30 30
2042 200 c. on 45 c. Plate No. 77 (Series 1) .. 30 30
2043 200 c. on 45 c. Plate No. 78 (Series 1) .. 30 30
2044 200 c. on 45 c. Plate No. 84 (Series 1) .. 30 30
2045 200 c. on 45 c. Plate No. 85 (Series 1) .. 30 30
2046 200 c. on 50 c. Plate No. 55 (Series 1) (No. 1927) (*wmkd*) .. 40 40
2047 200 c. on 50 c. Plate No. 24 (Series 1) (*wmkd*) .. 40 40
2048 200 c. on 50 c. Plate No. 53 (Series 1) (*wmkd*) .. 40 40
2049 200 c. on 50 c. Plate No. 65 (Series 1) (*wmkd*) .. 40 40
2050 200 c. on 55 c. Plate No. 15 (Series 1) .. 40 40
2051 200 c. on 55 c. Plate No. 81 (Series 1) .. 40 40
2052 200 c. on 55 c. Plate No. 82 (Series 1) .. 40 40
2053 200 c. on 55 c. Plate No. 89 (Series 1) .. 40 40
2054 225 c. on 40 c. Plate No. 91 (Series 1) (No. 1822) .. 50 50
2055 225 c. on 40 c. Plate No. 86 (Series 1) (No. 1868) .. 50 50
a. Inscr "ONTOGLOSSUM TRIUMPHANS" in error .. 50 50
2056 225 c. on 40 c. Plate No. 68 (Series 1) (No. 1884) .. 50 50
2057 225 c. on 40 c. Plate No. 90 (Series 1) .. 50 50
2058 225 c. on 65 c. Plate No. 76 (Series 1) .. 50 50
2059 225 c. on 65 c. Plate No. 80 (Series 1) .. 50 50
2060 225 c. on 65 c. Plate No. 88 (Series 1) .. 50 50
2061 225 c. on 65 c. Plate No. 96 (Series 1) .. 50 50
2062 600 c. on 80 c. Plate No. 17 (Series 1) (No. 1885) .. 1·25 1·25
2063 600 c. on 80 c. Plate No. 39 (Series 1) .. 1·25 1·25
2064 600 c. on 80 c. Plate No. 74 (Series 1) .. 1·25 1·25
2065 600 c. on 80 c. Plate No. 93 (Series 1) .. 1·25 1·25
2013/65 .. *Set of* 53 20·00 20·00

Initially some values were surcharged in sheets of sixteen orchid stamps together with nine examples of No. 2081. Subsequently, however, the surcharges appeared in the individual blocks of 4 with the arms design issued separately as Nos. 2082/3.

For 600 c. on 900 c. with surcharge as T **384** see No. 2219.

(Litho Format)

**1987** (16 Feb). *Centenary of Publication of Sanders'* Reichenbachia *(19th issue). Vert designs as T* **331**. *Multicoloured. No wmk. P* 13½×14.

2066 180 c. Plate 41 (Series 2) .. 75 40
2067 230 c. Plate 25 (Series 2) .. 85 50
2068 300 c. Plate 85 (Series 2) .. 1·10 65
2069 330 c. Plate 82 (Series 2) .. 1·25 70
2070 425 c. Plate 87 (Series 2) .. 1·50 85
2071 440 c. Plate 88 (Series 2) .. 1·50 85
2072 590 c. Plate 52 (Series 2) .. 1·75 1·25
2073 650 c. Plate 65 (Series 2) .. 2·25 1·50
2066/73 .. *Set of* 8 10·00 6·00

Nos. 2066/73 were printed in a similar sheet format to Nos. 1518/33.

(385) (386)

**1987** (17 Feb). *10th Anniv of Guyana Post Office Corporation (2nd issue). Nos. 543, 545, 548a and 601 surch as T* **385** *in blue by Autoprint.*

2074 25 c. on 2 c. Type **132** .. 15 10
2075 25 c. on 5 c. Annatto tree .. 15 10
2076 25 c. on 8 c on 6 c. Cannon-ball tree .. 15 10
2077 25 c. on 15 c. Christmas Orchid .. 15 10
2078 60 c. on 15 c. Christmas Orchid .. 35 10
2079 $1.20 on 2 c. Type **132** .. 50 40
2080 $1.30 on 15 c. Christmas Orchid .. 50 40
2074/80 .. *Set of* 7 1·75 1·10

**1987** (6 Mar). *Nos.* 1534/5 *surch with T* **386** *by Tip Torres*

2081 **332** 200 c. on 25 c. mult (*p* 13½ × 14) .. 50 40
2082 200 c. on 25 c. mult (*imperf* × *p* 14) .. 50 40
2083 200 c. on 25 c. mult (*p* 13½ × *imperf*) .. 50 40
2081/3 .. *Set of* 3 1·40 1·10

See note below No. 2065.

1987 (387) 1987 (388) 1987 (389) 1987 (390)

**1987** (6 Mar–Dec). *Various* Reichenbachia *issues optd as T* **387/90**.

*(a) With T* **387** *by Tip Torres* (March)

2084 130 c. Plate No. 3 (Series 1) (No. 1525) .. 30 30
2085 130 c. Plate No. 6 (Series 1) (No. 1526) .. 30 30
2086 130 c. Plate No. 20 (Series 1) (No. 1529) .. 30 30
2087 130 c. Plate No. 18 (Series 1) (No. 1536) .. 30 30
2088 130 c. Plate No. 29 (Series 1) (No. 1537) .. 30 30
2089 130 c. Plate No. 30 (Series 1) (No. 1538) .. 30 30
2090 130 c. Plate No. 16 (Series 1) (No. 1559) .. 30 30
2091 130 c. Plate No. 66 (Series 1) (No. 1632) .. 30 30
2092 130 c. Plate No. 13 (Series 1) (No. 1684) .. 30 30
2093 130 c. Plate No. 6 (Series 1) (No. 1759) (*wmkd*) .. 30 30
2094 130 c. Plate No. 20 (Series 1) (No. 1761) (*wmkd*) .. 30 30
2095 200 c. Plate No. 4 (Series 1) (No. 1533) .. 40 40
2096 200 c. Plate No. 14 (Series 1) (No. 1584) 40 40
2097 200 c. Plate No. 21 (Series 1) (No. 1585) (opt vert – reading down) .. 40 40
2098 200 c. Plate No. 33 (Series 1) (No. 1634) (opt vert – reading down) .. 40 40
2099 200 c. Plate No. 43 (Series 1) (No. 1658) (opt vert – reading down) .. 40 40
2100 200 c. Plate No. 79 (Series 1) (No. 1670) .. 40 40
2101 200 c. Plate No. 9 (Series 2) (No. 1816) .. 40 40
2102 200 c. Plate No. 2 (Series 2) (No. 1886) .. 40 40
2103 250 c. Plate No. 74 (Series 1) (No. 1736) .. 50 50

2104 260 c. Plate No. 39 (Series 1) (No. 1737) .. 50 50
2084/2104 .. .. .. .. *Set of* 21 6·75 6·75
**MS**2105 100×129 mm. 200 c.×4 Plate 4 (Series 1) (No. **MS**1539) .. .. .. .. 1·50 1·50
**MS**2106 100×129 mm. 200 c. on 130 c.×4 Plate 20 (Series 1) (No. **MS**1570) .. .. .. 1·50 1·50

*(b) With T* **388** *by Gardy Ptg* (March)
2107 130 c. Plate No. 13 (Series 1) (No. 1527) .. 30 30
2108 130 c. Plate No. 25 (Series 1) (No. 1530) .. 30 30
2109 130 c. Plate No. 91 (Series 1) (No. 1735) .. 30 30
2110 130 c. Plate No. 13 (Series 1) (No. 1760) (*wmkd*) .. .. .. .. 30 30
2111 130 c. Plate No. 25 (Series 1) (No. 1762) (*wmkd*) .. .. .. .. 30 30
2107/11 .. .. .. .. *Set of* 5 1·40 1·40

*(c) With T* **389** *by Gardy Ptg* (July)
2112 120 c. Plate No. 1 (Series 1) (No. 1578) (opt vert – reading down) .. .. 30 30
2113 120 c. Plate No. 11 (Series 1) (No. 1579) (opt vert – reading down) .. .. 30 30
2114 120 c. Plate No. 28 (Series 1) (No. 1580) (opt vert – reading down) .. .. 30 30
2115 120 c. Plate No. 37 (Series 1) (No. 1627) .. 30 30
2116 120 c. Plate No. 46 (Series 1) (No. 1628) .. 30 30
2117 120 c. Plate No. 56 (Series 1) (No. 1629) .. 30 30
2118 120 c. Plate No. 58 (Series 1) (No. 1630) .. 30 30
2119 130 c. Plate No. 6 (Series 1) (No. 1759) (*wmkd*) .. .. .. .. 30 30
2120 130 c. Plate No. 13 (Series 1) (No. 1760) (*wmkd*) .. .. .. .. 30 30
2121 130 c. Plate No. 20 (Series 1) (No. 1761) (*wmkd*) .. .. .. .. 30 30
2122 130 c. Plate No. 25 (Series 1) (No. 1762) (*wmkd*) .. .. .. .. 30 30
2123 150 c. Plate No. 40 (Series 1) (No. 1581) (opt vert–reading down) .. .. 40 40
2124 150 c. Plate No. 45 (Series 1) (No. 1583) (opt vert–reading down) .. .. 40 40
2125 150 c. Plate No. 42 (Series 1) (No. 1657) (opt vert–reading down) .. .. 40 40
2126 150 c. Plate No. 40 (Series 1) (No. 1767) (*wmkd*) (opt vert–reading up) .. 40 40
2127 150 c. Plate No. 42 (Series 1) (No. 1768) (*wmkd*) (opt vert–reading up) .. 40 40
2128 150 c. Plate No. 45 (Series 1) (No. 1769) (*wmkd*) (opt vert–reading up) .. 40 40
2129 200 c. Plate No. 21 (Series 1) (No. 1585) (opt vert–reading down) .. .. 50 50
2130 200 c. Plate No. 43 (Series 1) (No. 1658) (opt vert–reading down) .. .. 50 50
2131 200 c. Plate No. 43 (Series 1) (No. 1770) (*wmkd*) (opt vert–reading up) .. 50 50
2112/31 .. .. .. .. *Set of* 20 6·50 6·50

*(d) With T* **390** *by Gardy Ptg* (Dec)
2132 120 c. Plate No. 67 (Series 1) (No. 1631) .. 30 30
2133 130 c. Plate No. 18 (Series 1) (No. 1536) .. 30 30
2134 130 c. Plate No. 29 (Series 1) (No. 1537) .. 30 30
2135 130 c. Plate No. 30 (Series 1) (No. 1538) .. 30 30
2136 130 c. Plate No. 66 (Series 1) (No. 1632) .. 30 30
2137 150 c. Plate No. 26 (Series 1) (No. 1633) .. 40 40
2132/7 .. .. .. .. *Set of* 6 1·75 1·75

650
12th World Orchid Conference
TOKYO JAPAN
(391)

28 MARCH 1927
PAA
GEO-POS
(392)

**1987** (12 Mar). *12th World Orchid Conference, Tokyo (2nd issue). Nos.* 1552 *and* 1763 *surch with T* **391** *by Tip Torres.*
2138 650 c. on 55 c. Plate No. 9 (Series 1) (No. 1552) .. .. .. .. 1·50 1·25
2139 650 c. on 55 c. Plate No. 9 (Series 1) (No. 1763) .. .. .. .. 1·50 1·25

**1987** (17 Mar). *125th Anniv of British Guiana Post Office (3rd issue). No.* 699 *surch as T* **324** *by Autoprint.*
2140 25 c. on 10 c. mult (surch "AGRICOLA") .. 15 15
a. Sheetlet of 25. Nos. 2140/64 .. 3·25
2141 25 c. on 10 c. mult (surch "BAGOTVILLE") 15 15
2142 25 c. on 10 c. mult (surch "BOURDA") .. 15 15
2143 25 c. on 10 c. mult (surch "BUXTON") .. 15 15
2144 25 c. on 10 c. mult (surch "CABACABURI") 15 15
2145 25 c. on 10 c. multicoloured (surch "CARMICHAEL STREET") .. 15 15
2146 25 c. on 10 c. multicoloured (surch "COTTON TREE") .. .. .. 15 15
2147 25 c. on 10 c. mult (surch "DUNOON") .. 15 15
2148 25 c. on 10 c. mult (surch "FELLOWSHIP") 15 15
2149 25 c. on 10 c. mult (surch "GROVE") .. 15 15
2150 25 c. on 10 c. mult (surch "HACKNEY") .. 15 15
2151 25 c. on 10 c. mult (surch "LEONORA") .. 15 15
2152 25 c. on 10 c. multicoloured (surch "1987") 15 15
2153 25 c. on 10 c. mult (surch "MALLALI") .. 15 15
2154 25 c. on 10 c. mult (surch "PROVIDENCE") 15 15
2155 25 c. on 10 c. mult (surch "RELIANCE") .. 15 15
2156 25 c. on 10 c. mult (surch "SPARTA") .. 15 15
2157 25 c. on 10 c. multicoloured (surch "STEWARTVILLE") .. .. 15 15
2158 25 c. on 10 c. mult (surch "TARLOGY") .. 15 15
2159 25 c. on 10 c. multicoloured (surch "T.P.O. BERBICE RIV.") .. .. .. 15 15
2160 25 c. on 10 c. multicoloured (surch "T.P.O. DEM. RIV.") .. .. .. 15 15
2161 25 c. on 10 c. multicoloured (surch "T.P.O. ESSEO. RIV.") .. .. .. 15 15
2162 25 c. on 10 c. multicoloured (surch "T.P.O. MASSARUNI RIV.") .. .. 15 15
2163 25 c. on 10 c. multicoloured (surch "TUSCHEN (De VRIENDEN)") .. 15 15
2164 25 c. on 10 c. multicoloured (surch "ZORG") 15 15
2140/64 .. .. .. .. *Set of* 25 3·25 3·25

The surcharged names are those of postal agencies opened by 1885.

**1987** (28 Mar). *50th Anniv of First Georgetown to Port-of-Spain Flight by P.A.A. No.* 708*a optd with T* **392** *by Autoprint.*
2165 $10 *Elbella patrobas* .. .. .. 2·00 2·50

**1987** (6 Apr). *No.* 704 *surch with figures only as T* **324** *by Autoprint.*
2166 25 c. on 40 c. *Morpho rhetenor* (male) .. 30 10

1987
120
(393)

1987
(394)

CAPEX '87
(395)

**1987** (21 Apr). *Easter. Nos.* 481/2 *and* 484 *optd or surch as T* **393** *by Autoprint.*
2167 **111** 25 c. multicoloured .. .. .. 15 10
2168 120 c. on 6 c. multicoloured .. .. 20 20
2169 320 c. on 6 c. multicoloured .. .. 50 45
2170 500 c. on 40 c. multicoloured .. .. 75 70
2167/70 .. .. .. .. *Set of* 4 1·40 1·25

(Litho Format)

**1987** (24 Apr). *Centenary of Publication of Sanders' Reichenbachia (20th issue). Multicoloured designs as T* **331**. *No wmk. P* 13½×14 (240, 260, 500, 560 *c.) or* 13½×14 (*others*).
2171 240 c. Plate No. 47 (Series 2) .. .. 80 45
2172 260 c. Plate No. 39 (Series 2) .. .. 90 55
2173 275 c. Plate No. 58 (Series 2) (*horiz*) .. 90 55
2174 390 c. Plate No. 37 (Series 2) (*horiz*) .. 1·10 70
2175 450 c. Plate No. 19 (Series 2) (*horiz*) .. 1·50 90
2176 460 c. Plate No. 54 (Series 2) (*horiz*) .. 1·50 90
2177 500 c. Plate No. 51 (Series 2) .. .. 1·75 1·10
2178 560 c. Plate No. 1 (Series 2) .. .. 2·00 1·50
2171/8 .. .. .. .. *Set of* 8 9·50 6·00

Nos. 2171/8 were printed in a similar sheet format to Nos. 1518/33.

**1987** (Apr). *No.* 706 *optd with T* **394** *by Autoprint.*
2179 **167** $1 multicoloured .. .. .. 40 15

(Litho Format)

**1987** (2 June). *Centenary of Publication of Sanders' Reichenbachia (21st issue). Vert designs as T* **331**. *Multicoloured. No wmk. P* 13½×14.
2180 500 c. Plate No. 86 (Series 2) .. .. 1·75 1·10
2181 520 c. Plate No. 89 (Series 2) .. .. 1·90 1·25
2182 $20 Plate No. 83 (Series 2) .. .. 6·00 6·50
2180/2 .. .. .. .. *Set of* 3 8·75 8·00

Nos. 2180/2 were printed in a similar sheet format to Nos. 1518/33, but included Nos. 2183/4 instead of Nos. 1534/5.

Two types of bird in coat of arms:

A B

(Litho Format)

**1987** (2 June–29 Sept). *Booklet and Coil Stamps. As T* **332**, *but within frame. No wmk. A. Bird with short tail. B. Bird with crest and long tail* (29 Sept).

| | | A | | B | |
|---|---|---|---|---|---|
| 2183 | 25 c. mult (*imperf×p* 14) .. | 15 | 15 | 15 | 15 |
| 2183*c* | 25 c. mult (*p* 13½×14) .. | 15 | 15 | 15 | 15 |
| 2184 | 25 c. mult (*p* 13½×*imperf*) | 15 | 15 | 15 | 15 |
| 2184*c* | 25 c. mult (*p* 14×13½) .. | † | | 15 | 15 |

Nos. 2183/4*c* were cut from the gutters of the orchid stamps as detailed in the note below No. 1533.

**1987** (10 June). *"Capex '87" International Stamp Exhibition, Toronto. Nos.* 1744/5 *optd with T* **395**.
2185 **363** 320 c. rosine, black and dp reddish lilac 40 45
a. Horiz pair. Nos. 2185/6 .. 80 90
ab. Imperf between (horiz pair) .. 80 90
2186 – 320 c. multicoloured .. .. 40 45

**1987** (15 July). *Commonwealth Heads of Government Meeting, Vancouver. Nos.* 1066/8 *further optd with T* **394**.
2187 $1.20 on 6 c. yellow-green .. .. 15 20
2188 $1.30 on 24 c. black and bright orange .. 15 20
2189 $2.40 on 24 c. black and bright orange .. 30 35
2187/9 .. .. .. *Set of* 3 55 70

(Litho Format)

**1987** (22 July). *Centenary of Publication of Sanders' Reichenbachia (22nd issue). Vert designs as T* **331**. *Multicoloured. No wmk. P* 13½×14.
2190 400 c. Plate No. 80 (Series 2) .. .. 1·25 80
2191 480 c. Plate No. 77 (Series 2) .. .. 1·50 1·00
2192 600 c. Plate No. 94 (Series 2) .. .. 2·00 1·50
2193 $25 Plate No. 72 (Series 2) .. .. 6·50 7·00
2190/3 .. .. .. .. *Set of* 4 10·00 9·25

Nos. 2190/3 were printed in a similar sheet format to Nos. 1518/33.

**396** Steam Locomotive *Alexandra*

FAIREY NICHOLL
8 AUG 1927
GEO-MAZ
(397)

(Litho Format)

**1987** (3 Aug–4 Dec). *Guyana Railways. T* **396** *and similar horiz designs. No wmk. P* 12½ ($10, $12) *or* 15 (*others*).
2194 **396** $1.20, bronze-green .. .. 25 25
a. Block of 4. Nos. 2194/7 .. 90
2195 – $1.20, bronze-green .. .. 25 25
2196 – $1.20, bronze-green .. .. 25 25
2197 – $1.20, bronze-green .. .. 25 25
2198 **396** $1.20, maroon (4 Dec) .. .. 25 25
a. Block of 4. Nos. 2198/201 90
2199 – $1.20, maroon (4 Dec) .. .. 25 25
2200 – $1.20, maroon (4 Dec) .. .. 25 25
2201 – $1.20, maroon (4 Dec) .. .. 25 25
2202 **396** $3.20, deep dull blue .. .. 60 60
a. Block of 5. Nos. 2202/6 .. 2·75
2203 – $3.20, deep dull blue .. .. 60 60
2204 – $3.20, deep dull blue .. .. 60 60
2205 – $3.20, deep dull blue .. .. 60 60
2206 – $3.20, deep dull blue .. .. 60 60
2207 – $3.30, brownish black (4 Dec) .. 60 60
a. Block of 5. Nos. 2207/11 .. 2·75
2208 **396** $3.30, brownish black (4 Dec) .. 60 60
2209 – $3.30, brownish black (4 Dec) .. 60 60
2210 – $3.30, brownish black (4 Dec) .. 60 60
2211 – $3.30, brownish black (4 Dec) .. 60 60
2212 – $10 multicoloured (4 Dec) .. 1·50 1·50
2213 – $12 multicoloured .. .. 1·75 1·75
2194/213 .. .. .. *Set of* 20 9·50 9·50

Designs: (*As T* **396**)—Nos. 2195, 2199, 2203, 2207, Front view of diesel locomotive; Nos. 2196, 2200, 2204, 2210, Steam locomotive with searchlight; Nos. 2197, 2201, 2205, 2209, Side view of diesel locomotive. (82×55 *mm*)—Nos. 2206, Molasses warehouses and early locomotive; No. 2211, Diesel locomotive and passenger train. (88×39 *mm*)—No. 2212, Cattle train; No. 2213, Molasses train.

Nos. 2194/7 and 2198/201 were each printed together, *se-tenant*, in blocks of 4, within the sheets of 40.

Nos. 2202/6 and 2207/11 were each printed together, *se-tenant*, in blocks of 5 within the sheets of 25. The order of the stamps as Type **396** differs in the $3.30 block.

**1987** (7 Aug). *50th Anniv of First Flights from Georgetown to Massaruni and Mabaruma. No.* 706 *optd as T* **397** *by Autoprint.*
2214 **167** $1 multicoloured (optd T **397**) .. 15 15
a. Pair. Nos. 2214/15 .. .. 30 30
2215 $1 mult (optd "FAIREY NICHOLL 15 AUG 1927 GEO- MAB") .. 15 15

Nos. 2214/15 were overprinted together, *se-tenant*, in vertical or horizontal pairs within the sheet.

(Litho Format)

**1987** (29 Sept). *Centenary of Publication of Sanders' Reichenbachia (23rd issue). Vert designs as T* **331**. *Multicoloured. No wmk. P* 13½×14.
2216 200 c. Plate No. 43 (Series 2) .. .. 75 45
2217 200 c. Plate No. 48 (Series 2) .. .. 75 45
2218 200 c. Plate No. 92 (Series 2) .. .. 75 45
2216/18 .. .. .. .. *Set of* 3 2·00 1·25

Nos. 2216/18 were printed in a similar sheet format to Nos. 1518/33.

(Litho Format)

**1987** (9 Oct). *Centenary of Publication of Sanders' Reichenbachia (24th issue). Vert design as T* **331**, *optd as T* **384** *by Gardy Ptg* (600 *c.*). *Multicoloured. No wmk. P* 13½ × 14.
2219 600 c. on 900 c. Plate No. 74 (Series 2) .. 2·00 2·00
a. Pair. Nos. 2219/20 .. .. 4·00 4·00
2220 900 c. Plate No. 74 (Series 2) .. .. 2·00 2·00

Nos. 2219/20 were printed in a similar sheet format to Nos. 1518/33 with the surcharge on the first and last stamp of each block of four.

950
CRISTOVÃO COLOMBO
1492 — 1992
(398)

THE PASSING OF HALLEY'S COMET:
PROPHESY OF THE ARRIVAL OF
HERNAN CORTES 1519.
V CENTENARY OF THE LANDING OF
CHRISTOPHER COLUMBUS
$ 20.00 IN THE AMERICAS

(399)

**1987** (9 Oct). *Columbus Day. No.* 1598 *further surch with T* **382**, *No.* 2220 *surch as T* **398** *and No.* **MS**1746 *surch with T* **399**.

2221 225 c. on 350 c. on 120 c. Plate No. 65 (Series 1) .. .. .. .. 30 35
2222 950 c. on 900 c. Plate No. 74 (Series 2) (surch with T **398**) .. .. .. 1·25 1·40
a. Horiz pair. Nos. 2222/3 .. .. 2·50 2·75
2223 950 c. on 900 c. Plate No. 74 (Series 2) (surch "950 CHRISTOPHE COLOMB 1492 — 1992") .. .. 1·25 1·40
2221/3 .. .. .. .. *Set of* 3 2·50 2·75
**MS**2224 76 × 50 mm. $20 on 320 c. × 2 Nos. 1744/5 .. .. .. .. .. 5·00 5·25

Nos. 2222/3 were surcharged together, *se-tenant*, in horizontal pairs in the sheetlet of 4.

(Litho Format)

**1987** (26 Oct). *Centenary of Publication of Sanders'* Reichenbachia (25*th issue*). *Multicoloured designs as T* **331**. *No wmk. P* 13½ × 14 (575 *c.*) *or* 14 × 13½ (*others*).

2225 325 c. Plate No. 68 (Series 2) (*horiz*) .. 1·25 70
2226 420 c. Plate No. 95 (Series 2) (*horiz*) .. 1·50 90
2227 575 c. Plate No. 60 (Series 2) .. .. 1·75 1·25
2225/7 .. .. .. .. *Set of* 3 4·00 2·50

Nos. 2225/7, together with No. E7, were printed in a similar sheet format to Nos. 1518/33.

DEEPAVALI
1987
25

(400)

**1987** (2 Nov). *Deepavali Festival. Nos.* 544/5 *surch as T* **400**.

2228 25 c. on 3 c. Hanging Heliconia .. .. 10 10
2229 $3 on 5 c. Annatto tree .. .. 40 45

120

CHRISTMAS
1987
20 1987

(401) (402)

**1987** (9 Nov). *Christmas. No.* 452 *surch with T* **401** *in red, previously unissued miniature sheet containing Nos.* 1425/9 *each surch with T* **402** *in blue and No.* **MS**1619 *with each stamp surch with T* **382**.

2230 20 c. on 6 c. Patua .. .. .. .. 10 10
**MS**2231 215 × 75 mm. 120 c. on 60 c. × 5 Nos. 1425/9 .. .. .. .. .. 80 85
**MS**2232 120 × 129 mm. 225 c. on 55 c. × 4 Plate No. 22 (Series 1), each with a different overprint (Type **350**, "Happy New Year", "Merry Christmas" or "Happy Holidays") .. .. 1·10 1·25

**1987** (20 Nov). *Royal Ruby Wedding. Nos.* 1684/5 *optd with T* **390** (130 *c.*) *or surch as T* **384** *by Gardy Ptg.*

2233 130 c. Plate No. 13 (Series 1) .. .. 15 20
**MS**2234 600 c. on 130 c. on 130 c., 600 c. on 200 c. on 130 c., 600 c. on 260 c. on 130 c., 600 c. on 330 c. on 130 c., Plate No. 6 (Series 1) .. .. 3·00 3·25

(Litho Format)

**1987** (23 Nov). *Centenary of Publication of Sanders'* Reichenbachia (26*th issue*). *Vert designs as T* **331**. *Multicoloured. No wmk. P* 13½ × 14.

2235 255 c. Plate No. 61 (Series 2) .. .. 1·75 1·00
2236 290 c. Plate No. 53 (Series 2) .. .. 2·00 1·25
2237 375 c. Plate No. 96 (Series 2) .. .. 2·50 1·40
2238 680 c. Plate No. 64 (Series 2) .. .. 3·50 2·25
2239 720 c. Plate No. 49 (Series 2) .. .. 4·00 3·50
2240 750 c. Plate No. 66 (Series 2) .. .. 4·00 3·50
2241 800 c. Plate No. 79 (Series 2) .. .. 4·50 4·00
a. Face value omitted .. ..
2242 850 c. Plate No. 76 (Series 2) .. .. 4·50 4·00
a. Face value omitted .. ..
2235/42 .. .. .. .. *Set of* 8 24·00 19·00

Nos. 2235/42 were printed in a similar sheet format to Nos. 1518/33.

Nos. 2241a and 2242a occurred in the same sheet as Nos. 2276a and 2277a.

AIR

75

(403)

**1987** (Nov). *Air. No.* 1620 *surch with T* **403** *by Gardy Ptg.*

2243 75 c. on 25 c. Plate No. 59 (Series 1) .. 30 15

Protect our Heritage '87

320

PROTECT OUR
HERITAGE '87

(404) (405)

**1987** (9 Dec). *Wildlife Protection. Nos.* 756/67 *optd vertically with T* **394**, *Nos.* 1432b/4b *surch with T* **404** *in red and Nos.* 1631/3, 1752/3 *and* 1847 *optd with T* **405**.

2244 30 c. Type **178** .. .. .. 15 15
a. Sheetlet of 12. Nos. 2244/55 .. 1·60
2245 30 c. Red Howler .. .. .. 15 15
2246 30 c. Common Squirrel-Monkey .. .. 15 15
2247 30 c. Two-toed Sloth .. .. .. 15 15
2248 30 c. Brazilian Tapir .. .. .. 15 15
2249 30 c. Collared Peccary .. .. .. 15 15
2250 30 c. Six-banded Armadillo .. .. 15 15
2251 30 c. Tamandua ("Ant Eater") .. .. 15 15
2252 30 c. Giant Anteater .. .. .. 15 15
2253 30 c. Murine Opossum .. .. .. 15 15
2254 30 c. Brown Four-eyed Opossum .. .. 15 15
2255 30 c. Brazilian Agouti .. .. .. 15 15
2256 120 c. Plate No. 67 (Series 1) .. .. 30 30
2257 130 c. Plate No. 66 (Series 1) .. .. 30 30
2258 150 c. Plate No. 26 (Series 1) .. .. 35 35
2259 180 c. Plate No. 15 (Series 1) .. .. 40 40
2260 320 c. Plate No. 82 (Series 1) .. .. 60 60
2261 320 c. on 120 c. Demerara Mutual Life Assurance Building .. .. 60 60
a. Horiz strip of 3. Nos. 2261/3 .. 1·60
b. Surch on No. 1432 .. ..
ba. Horiz strip of 3. Nos. 2261b/3b ..
2262 320 c. on 120 c. Town Hall .. .. 60 60
b. Surch on No. 1433 .. ..
2263 320 c. on 120 c. Victoria Law Courts .. 60 60
b. Surch on No. 1434 .. ..
2264 650 c. on 40 c. Plate No. 86 (Series 1) .. 1·25 1·25
2244/64 .. .. .. .. *Set of* 21 6·00 6·00

AIR

(406)

**1987** (Dec). *Air. No.* 1597 *optd with T* **406**.

2265 60 c. Plate No. 55 (Series 1) .. .. 30 30

No. 2265 was only issued in $15 stamp booklets.

★ AUSTRALIA ★
1987 JAMBOREE 1988

(407)

* AUSTRALIA *

$10
1987 Jamboree 1988

(408)

**1988** (7 Jan). *World Scout Jamboree, Australia. Nos.* 830, 837/a *and* 1104 *handstamped with T* **407** (*No.* 2266) *or surch with T* **408** *by Tip Torres* (*others*), *all in red.*

2266 **116** 440 c. on 6 c. multicoloured (No. 837a) (surch T **201**) .. .. 30 30
a. On No. 837 (surch T **200**) .. 6·00
2267 $10 on 110 c. on 6 c. mult (No. 830) 60 60
2268 $10 on 180 c. on 6 c. mult (No. 1104) 60 60
2269 $10 on 440 c. on 6 c. mult (No. 837) 60 60
a. On No. 837a .. .. .. 60 60
2266/9 .. .. .. .. *Set of* 4 1·90 1·90

IFAD
For a World
Without Hunger
25

Republic
Day
1988
25

(409) (410)

**1988** (26 Jan). *10th Anniv of International Fund for Agricultural Development. Nos.* 485 *and* 487 *surch as T* **409** *by Autoprint.*

2270 25 c. on 1 c. Type **87** .. .. .. 10 10
2271 $5 on 3 c. Lukunani .. .. .. 20 25

**1988** (23 Feb). *Republic Day. Nos.* 545, 548a *and* 555 *surch as T* **410** *in blue.*

2272 25 c. on 5 c. Annatto tree .. .. 10 10
2273 120 c. on 15 c. Christmas Orchid .. .. 15 10
2274 $10 on $2 *Noranthea guianensis* .. 55 60
2272/4 .. .. .. .. *Set of* 3 70 70

(Litho Format)

**1988** (26 Feb). *Centenary of Publication of Sanders'* Reichenbachia (27*th issue*). *Four sheets, each* 102×127 *mm, containing vert designs as T* **331**. *Multicoloured. No wmk. P* 13½×14.

**MS**2275 (a) 320 c. Plate No. 46 (Series 2); 330 c. Plate No. 55 (Series 2); 350 c. Plate No. 57 (Series 2); 500 c. Plate No. 81 (Series 2). (b) 320 c. Plate No. 55 (Series 2); 330 c. Plate No. 46 (Series 2); 350 c. Plate No. 81 (Series 2); 500 c. Plate No. 57 (Series 2). (c) 320 c. Plate No. 57 (Series 2); 330 c. Plate No. 81 (Series 2); 350 c. Plate No. 46 (Series 2); 500 c. Plate No. 55 (Series 2). (d) 320 c. Plate No. 81 (Series 2); 330 c. Plate No. 57 (Series 2); 350 c. Plate No. 55 (Series 2); 500 c. Plate No. 46 (Series 2) *Set of* 4 *sheets* 15·00 12·00

(Litho Format)

**1988** (24 Mar). *Centenary of Publication of Sanders'* Reichenbachia (28*th issue*). *Vert designs as T* **331**. *Multicoloured. No wmk. P* 13½×14.

2276 $10 Plate No. 40 (Series 2) .. .. 1·75 1·75
a. Face value omitted .. ..
2277 $12 Plate No. 91 (Series 2) .. .. 1·75 1·75
a. Face value omitted .. ..

Nos. 2276/7 were printed in a similar sheet format to Nos. 1518/33.

Nos. 2276a/7a occurred in the same sheet as Nos. 2241a and 2242a.

**1988** (5 Apr). *125th Anniv of British Guiana Post Office* (4*th issue*). *No.* 702a *surch as T* **324** *by Autoprint.*

2278 25 c. on 30 c. mult (surch "Albouystown") .. 15 15
a. Sheetlet of 25. Nos. 2278/88, 2289×2, 2290/301 .. .. .. 3·25
2279 25 c. on 30 c. mult (surch "Anns Grove") .. 15 15
2280 25 c. on 30 c. mult (surch "Amacura") .. 15 15
2281 25 c. on 30 c. mult (surch "Arakaka") .. 15 15
2282 25 c. on 30 c. mult (surch "Baramanni") .. 15 15
2283 25 c. on 30 c. mult (surch "Cuyuni") .. 15 15
2284 25 c. on 30 c. mult (surch "Hope Placer") .. 15 15
2285 25 c. on 30 c. mult (surch "H M P S") .. 15 15
2286 25 c. on 30 c. multicoloured (surch "Kitty") 15 15
2287 25 c. on 30 c. mult (surch "M'M'Zorg") .. 15 15
2288 25 c. on 30 c. mult (surch "Maccaseema") 15 15
2289 25 c. on 30 c. multicoloured (surch "1988") 15 15
2290 25 c. on 30 c. mult (surch "Morawhanna") 15 15
2291 25 c. on 30 c. mult (surch "Naamryck") .. 15 15
2292 25 c. on 30 c. multicoloured (surch "Purini") 15 15
2293 25 c. on 30 c. mult (surch "Potaro Landing") 15 15
2294 25 c. on 30 c. mult (surch "Rockstone") .. 15 15
2295 25 c. on 30 c. mult (surch "Rosignol") .. 15 15
2296 25 c. on 30 c. mult (surch "Stanleytown") .. 15 15
2297 25 c. on 30 c. mult (surch "Santa Rosa") .. 15 15
2298 25 c. on 30 c. mult (surch "Tumatumari") .. 15 15
2299 25 c. on 30 c. mult (surch "Weldaad") .. 15 15
2300 25 c. on 30 c. mult (surch "Wismar") .. 15 15
2301 25 c. on 30 c. multicoloured (surch "TPO Berbice Railway") .. .. 15 15
2278/301 .. .. .. .. *Set of* 24 3·25 3·25

The surcharged names are those of postal agencies opened between 1886 and 1900.

120

Olympic
Games
1988

(411)

Caricom Day
1988
25

(412)

**1988** (3 May). *Olympic Games, Seoul. Nos.* 1206/17 *further surch with T* **411**.

2302 120 c. on 55 c. on 125 c. on 35 c. Type **174** 15 15
a. Block of 12. Nos. 2302/13 .. .. 1·60
2303 120 c. on 55 c. on 125 c. on 35 c. Haimara .. 15 15
2304 120 c. on 55 c. on 125 c. on 35 c. Electric Eel 15 15
2305 120 c. on 55 c. on 125 c. on 35 c. Golden Rivulus .. .. .. .. 15 15
2306 120 c. on 55 c. on 125 c. on 35 c. Pencil Fish 15 15
2307 120 c. on 55 c. on 125 c. on 35 c. Four-eyed Fish .. .. .. .. 15 15
2308 120 c. on 55 c. on 125 c. on 35 c. Pirai or Carib Fish .. .. .. .. 15 15
2309 120 c. on 55 c. on 125 c. on 35 c. Smoking Hassar .. .. .. .. 15 15
2310 120 c. on 55 c. on 125 c. on 35 c. Devil Ray 15 15
2311 120 c. on 55 c. on 125 c. on 35 c. Flying Patwa .. .. .. .. 15 15
2312 120 c. on 55 c. on 125 c. on 35 c. Arapaima Pirariucii .. .. .. .. 15 15
2313 120 c. on 55 c. on 125 c. on 35 c. Lukanani 15 15
2302/13 .. .. .. .. *Set of* 12 1·60 1·60

(Litho Format)

**1988** (1 June). *Centenary of Publication of Sanders' Reichenbachia (29th issue). Vert designs as T* **331**. *Multicoloured. No wmk. P* $13^{1}/_{2}\times14$.

2314 320 c. Plate No. 16 (Series 2) .. .. 55 40
2315 475 c. Plate No. 73 (Series 2) .. .. 80 50
2316 525 c. Plate No. 36 (Series 2) .. .. 1·00 65
2317 530 c. Plate No. 69 (Series 2) .. .. 1·00 65
2318 $15 Plate No. 67 (Series 2) .. .. 2·75 2·25
2314/18 .. .. .. .. *Set of* 5 5·50 4·00

Nos. 2314/18 were printed in a similar sheet format to Nos. 1518/33.

**1988** (15 June). *CARICOM Day. Nos. 545/6 and 555 surch as T* **412**.

2319 25 c. on 5 c. Annatto tree .. .. 10 10
2320 $1.20 on 6 c. Cannon-ball tree .. .. 10 10
2321 $10 on $2 *Norantea guianensis* .. .. 45 50
2319/21 .. .. .. .. *Set of* 3 60 65

(Litho Format)

**1988** (15 June). *Centenary of Publication of Sanders' Reichenbachia (30th issue). Vert designs as T* **331**. *Multicoloured. No wmk. P* $13^{1}/_{2}\times14$.

2322 700 c. Plate No. 62 (Series 2) .. .. 1·00 65
2323 775 c. Plate No. 59 (Series 2) .. .. 1·25 70
2324 875 c. Plate No. 31 (Series 2) .. .. 1·50 85
2325 950 c. Plate No. 78 (Series 2) .. .. 1·75 90
2322/5 .. .. .. .. *Set of* 4 5·00 2·75

Nos. 2322/5 were printed in a similar sheet format to Nos. 1518/33.

**WHO 1948-1988** (413) — **1988** (414)

**1988** (17 June). *40th Anniv of World Health Day. No. 705a optd with T* **413** *or T* **414** *by Autoprint.*

2326 60 c. *Papilio androgeus* (T **413**) .. .. 2·50 3·00
a. Sheetlet of 25. Nos. 2326 and 2327×24 .. .. 3·00
2327 60 c. *Papilio androgeus* (T **414**) .. .. 10 10

Nos. 2326 and 2327 were overprinted together, *se-tenant*, in a sheetlet of 25 showing a single example of No. 2326 in the central position.

(Litho Format)

**1988** (22 June). *Centenary of Publication of Sanders' Reichenbachia (31st issue). Vert design as T* **331**. *No wmk. P* $13^{1}/_{2}\times14$.

2328 350 c. Plate No. 74 (Series 2) .. .. 35 30

No. 2328 was printed in a similar sheet format to Nos. 1518/33.

(Litho Format)

**1988** (9 July). *Centenary of Publication of Sanders Reichenbachia (32nd issue). Vert designs as T* **331**, *with Nos. 2329/31 additional inscr "1985 – 1988". No wmk. P* $13^{1}/_{2}\times14$.

2329 130 c. Plate No. 73 (Series 2) .. .. 40 25
2330 200 c. Plate No. 96 (Series 2) .. .. 50 30
2331 260 c. Plate No. 16 (Series 2) .. .. 70 35
2329/31 .. .. .. .. *Set of* 3 1·40 80
**MS**2332 Four sheets, each 102×127 mm. (a) 120 c. Plate No. 81 (Series 2); 120 c. Plate No. 57 (Series 2); 120 c. Plate No. 55 (Series 2); 120 c. Plate No. 46 (Series 2). (b) 150 c. Plate No. 57 (Series 2); 150 c. Plate No. 81 (Series 2); 150 c. Plate No. 46 (Series 2); 150 c. Plate No. 55 (Series 2). (c) 225 c. Plate No. 46 (Series 2); 225 c. Plate No. 55 (Series 2); 225 c. Plate No. 57 (Series 2); 225 c. Plate No. 81 (Series 2). (d) 305 c. Plate No. 55 (Series 2); 305 c. Plate No. 46 (Series 2); 305 c. Plate No. 81 (Series 2); 305 c. Plate No. 57 (Series 2) .. .. *Set of 4 sheets* 6·00 4·50

CONSERVE TREES (415) — CONSERVE WATER (416)

**1988** (15 July). *Conservation of Resources.*

(a) *Nos. 1444B/6B optd as T* **415** *by Gardy Ptg*

2333 120 c. Young Ocelot (No. 1444B) (opt T **415**) 10 10
a. Block of 9. Nos. 2333/41 .. .. 90
2334 120 c. Young Ocelot (No. 1444B) (opt "CONSERVE ELECTRICITY") .. .. 10 10
2335 120 c. Young Ocelot (No. 1444B) (opt "CONSERVE WATER") .. .. 10 10
2336 120 c. Type **322** (opt "CONSERVE ELECTRICITY") .. .. 10 10
2337 120 c. Type **322** (opt "CONSERVE WATER") .. .. 10 10
2338 120 c. Type **322** (opt T **415**) .. .. 10 10
2339 120 c. Young Ocelot (No. 1446B) (opt "CONSERVE WATER") .. .. 10 10
2340 120 c. Young Ocelot (No. 1446B) (opt T **415**) 10 10
2341 120 c. Young Ocelot (No. 1446B) (optd "CONSERVE ELECTRICITY") .. .. 10 10

(b) *Nos. 1634, 1670, 1683 and 1774 optd with T* **416** *(opt vert–reading upwards on Nos. 2342, 2345) by Tip Torres.*

2342 200 c. Plate No. 33 (Series 1) .. .. 10 10
2343 200 c. Plate No. 79 (Series 1) .. .. 10 10
2344 225 c. Plate No. 24 (Series 1) .. .. 10 10
2345 350 c. Plate No. 94 (Series 1) .. .. 15 20
2333/45 .. .. .. .. *Set of* 13 1·25 1·25

The three different overprints as T **415** were applied, *se-tenant*, in strips of three, both horizontally and vertically, on blocks of nine.

BEWARE OF ANIMALS (417) — 120 (418)

**1988** (15 July). *Road Safety Campaign. Nos. 2194/201 optd as T* **417** *by Gardy Ptg.*

2346 **396** $1.20, bronze-green (opt T **417**) .. 20 20
a. Block of four. Nos. 2346/9 .. 70
2347 – $1.20, bronze-green (No. 2195) (opt "BEWARE OF CHILDREN") .. 20 20
2348 – $1.20, bronze-green (No. 2196) (opt "DRIVE SAFELY") .. .. 20 20
2349 – $1.20, bronze-green (No. 2197) (opt "DO NOT DRINK AND DRIVE") 20 20
2350 **396** $1.20, maroon (opt T **417**) .. .. 20 20
a. Block of four. Nos. 2350/3 .. 70
2351 – $1.20, maroon (No. 2199) (opt "BEWARE OF CHILDREN") .. 20 20
2352 – $1.20, maroon (No. 2200) (opt "DRIVE SAFELY") .. .. 20 20
2353 – $1.20, maroon (No. 2201) (opt "DO NOT DRINK AND DRIVE") .. 20 20
2346/53 .. .. .. .. *Set of* 8 1·40 1·40

**1988** (July). *No. 706 optd with T* **414** *or surch with T* **418**, *both by Autoprint.*

2354 $1 Type **167** .. .. .. .. 15 15
2355 120 c. on $1 Type **167** .. .. .. 15 15

120 (419)

120 (420) — 240 (421)

**1988** (July–Oct). *Various Reichenbachia issues surch by Gardy Ptg.*

(a) *As T* **419**

2356 120 c. on 25 c. Plate No. 61 (Series 1) (No. 1574) .. .. .. .. 15 15
2357 120 c. on 25 c. Plate No. 63 (Series 1) (No. 1575) .. .. .. .. 15 15
2358 120 c. on 25 c. Plate No. 70 (Series 1) (No. 1576) .. .. .. .. 15 15
2359 120 c. on 25 c. Plate No. 59 (Series 1) (No. 1620) .. .. .. .. 15 15
2360 120 c. on 25 c. Plate No. 71 (Series 1) (No. 1679) (surch vert - reading down) 15 15
2361 120 c. on 30 c. Plate No. 53 (Series 1) (No. 1621) .. .. .. .. 15 15
2362 120 c. on 30 c. Plate No. 86 (Series 1) (No. 1731) .. .. .. .. 15 15
2363 120 c. on 30 c. Plate No. 30 (Series 2) (No. 1809) .. .. .. .. 15 15
a. Horiz pair, one without surch ..
2364 120 c. on 30 c. Plate No. 53 (Series 1) (No. 1771) (*wmkd*) .. .. 15 15
2365 120 c. on 30 c. Plate No. 7 (Series 2) .. 15 15
2366 120 c. on 30 c. Plate No. 14 (Series 2) ("120" at foot) .. .. .. 15 15
2367 120 c. on 30 c. Plate No. 14 (Series 2) ("120" at top below bars) .. .. 15 15
2368 120 c. on 30 c. Plate No. 22 (Series 2) .. 15 15
2369 120 c. on 30 c. Plate No. 28 (Series 2) ("120" at bottom right) .. .. 15 15
2370 120 c. on 30 c. Plate No. 28 (Series 2) ("120" at top left) .. .. .. 15 15
2371 120 c. on 35 c. Plate No. 45 (Series 2) (No. 1925) .. .. .. .. 15 15
a. Horiz pair, one without surch ..
2372 120 c. on 40 c. Plate No. 77 (Series 1) (No. 1663) ("120" at bottom right) 15 15
2373 120 c. on 40 c. Plate No. 77 (Series 1) (No. 1663) ("120" at top left) .. 15 15
2374 120 c. on 40 c. Plate No. 96 (Series 1) (No. 1747) .. .. .. .. 15 15
2375 120 c. on 40 c. Plate No. 91 (Series 1) (No. 1822) ("120" at bottom right) 15 15
2376 120 c. on 40 c. Plate No. 91 (Series 1) (No. 1822) ("120" at top left) .. 15 15
2377 120 c. on 40 c. Plate No. 86 (Series 1) (No. 1868) .. .. .. .. 15 15
2378 120 c. on 40 c. Plate No. 68 (Series 1) (No. 1884) ("120" at top left) .. 15 15
2379 120 c. on 40 c. Plate No. 68 (Series 1) (No. 1884) ("120" at bottom left) .. 15 15
2380 120 c. on 40 c. Plate No. 90 (Series 1) .. 15 15
2381 120 c. on 45 c. Plate No. 54 (Series 1) (No. 1664) .. .. .. .. 15 15
2382 120 c. on 45 c. Plate No. 81 (Series 1) (No. 1748) .. .. .. .. 15 15
2383 120 c. on 45 c. Plate No. 21 (Series 2) (No. 1810) .. .. .. .. 15 15
a. Vert pair, one without surch
2384 120 c. on 50 c. Plate No. 92 (Series 1) (No. 1665) .. .. .. .. 15 15
2385 120 c. on 50 c. Plate No. 13 (Series 2) (No. 1907) .. .. .. .. 15 15
a. Horiz pair, one without surch
2386 120 c. on 50 c. Plate No. 15 (Series 2) (No. 1926) .. .. .. .. 15 15
a. Horiz pair, one without surch ..
2387 120 c. on 50 c. Plate No. 9 (Series 1) (*wmkd*) 15 15
2388 120 c. on 50 c. Plate No. 22 (Series 1) (*wmkd*) .. .. .. .. 15 15
2389 120 c. on 50 c. Plate No. 3 (Series 2) .. 15 15
2390 120 c. on 50 c. Plate No. 6 (Series 2) .. 15 15
2391 120 c. on 50 c. Plate No. 20 (Series 2) .. 15 15
2392 120 c. on 50 c. Plate No. 32 (Series 2) .. 15 15
2393 120 c. on 55 c. Plate No. 17 (Series 1) (No. 1732) .. .. .. .. 15 15
2394 120 c. on 60 c. Plate No. 2 (Series 1) (No. 1519) .. .. .. .. 15 15
2395 120 c. on 60 c. Plate No. 57 (Series 1) (No. 1622) (surch vert at top - reading down) .. .. .. .. 15 15
2396 120 c. on 60 c. Plate No. 57 (Series 1) (No. 1622) (surch vert at foot - reading down) .. .. .. .. 15 15
2397 120 c. on 60 c. Plate No. 73 (Series 1) (No. 1623) (surch vert - reading up) .. 15 15
2398 120 c. on 60 c. Plate No. 75 (Series 1) (No. 1624) (surch vert at top - reading down) .. .. .. .. 15 15
2399 120 c. on 60 c. Plate No. 75 (Series 1) (No. 1624) (surch vert at foot - reading down) .. .. .. .. 15 15
2400 120 c. on 60 c. Plate No. 95 (Series 1) (No. 1666) .. .. .. .. 15 15
2401 120 c. on 60 c. Plate No. 93 (Series 1) (No. 1733) .. .. .. .. 15 15
2402 120 c. on 60 c. Plate No. 27 (Series 2) (No. 1874) .. .. .. .. 15 15
a. Horiz pair, one without surch ..
2403 120 c. on 60 c. Plate No. 50 (Series 1) .. 15 15
2404 120 c. on 60 c. Plate No. 54 (Series 1) .. 15 15
2405 120 c. on 60 c. Plate No. 69 (Series 1) (surch vert–reading up) .. .. .. 15 15
2406 120 c. on 60 c. Plate No. 79 (Series 1) .. 15 15
2407 120 c. on 60 c. Plate No. 94 (Series 1) (surch vert - reading down) .. .. 15 15
2408 120 c. on 70 c. Plate No. 8 (Series 2) .. 15 15
2409 120 c. on 70 c. Plate No. 9 (Series 2) ("120" at foot above bars) .. .. 15 15
2410 120 c. on 70 c. Plate No. 9 (Series 2) ("120" at top right) .. .. .. 15 15
2411 120 c. on 70 c. Plate No. 12 (Series 2) ("120" at foot above bars) .. .. 15 15
2412 120 c. on 70 c. Plate No. 12 (Series 2) "120" at top left) .. .. .. 15 15
2413 120 c. on 70 c. Plate No. 17 (Series 2) .. 15 15
2414 120 c. on 80 c. Plate No. 39 (Series 1) .. 15 15
2415 120 c. on 80 c. Plate No. 74 (Series 1) .. 15 15
2416 120 c. on 80 c. Plate No. 93 (Series 1) .. 15 15
2417 120 c. on 85 c. Plate No. 45 (Series 2) (No. 1876) .. .. .. .. 15 15
2418 120 c. on 85 c. Plate No. 24 (Series 2) (No. 1914) .. .. .. .. 15 15
a. Horiz pair, one without surch ..
2419 120 c. on 85 c. Plate No. 15 (Series 2) (No. 1918) .. .. .. .. 15 15
2420 120 c. on 85 c. Plate No. 18 (Series 2) (No. 1928) .. .. .. .. 15 15
a. Horiz pair, one without surch ..
2421 120 c. on 90 c. Plate No. 84 (Series 1) (No. 1668 .. .. .. .. 15 15
2422 120 c. on 90 c. Plate No. 89 (Series 1) (No. 1749) .. .. .. .. 15 15
2423 120 c. on 90 c. Plate No. 10 (Series 2) (No. 1869) .. .. .. .. 15 15
a. Horiz pair, one without surch ..
2424 120 c. on 90 c. Plate No. 13 (Series 2) (No. 1877) .. .. .. .. 15 15
2425 120 c. on 90 c. Plate No. 27 (Series 2) (No. 1915) .. .. .. .. 15 15
2426 120 c. on 90 c. Plate No. 2 (Series 2) (No. 1929) .. .. .. .. 15 15
a. Horiz pair, one without surch ..
2427 200 c. on 80 c. Plate No. 42 (Series 2) (No. 1812) (surch vert–reading down) .. 15 15
2428 200 c. on 90 c. Plate No. 4 (Series 2) (No. 1813) .. .. .. .. 15 15

(b) *As T* **420** (Sept)

2429 120 c. on 25 c. Plate No. 72 (Series 1) (No. 1577) .. .. .. .. 15 15

(c) *As T* **421** (Oct)

2430 240 c. on 140 c. Plate No. 30 (Series 2) .. 15 15
2431 240 c. on 140 c. Plate No. 34 (Series 2) .. 15 15
2432 240 c. on 425 c. Plate No. 87 (Series 2) (No. 2070) .. .. .. .. 15 15
2433 260 c. on 375 c. Plate No. 90 (Series 1) (No. 1738) .. .. .. .. 15 15
2356/433 .. .. .. .. *Set of* 78 10·50 10·50

Nos. 2363, 2371, 2383, 2385/6, 2402, 2418, 2420, 2423 and 2426 come from sheetlets of four on which the surcharge was applied to two of the stamps only.

On No. 2433 there are no bars and the surcharge is placed over the original face value.

CONSERVE OUR RESOURCES (422) — + (423) — AIR (424)

**1988** (July). *Conservation of Resources. Various* Reichen-*bachia issues optd with T* **422** *by Gardy Ptg.*

2434 100 c. Plate No. 65 (Series 1) (No. 1626) 15 15
2435 100 c. Plate No. 68 (Series 1) (No. 1734) 15 15
2436 100 c. Plate No. 88 (Series 1) (No. 1750) 15 15
2437 100 c. Plate No. 65 (Series 1) (No. 1773) (*wmkd*) .. .. .. .. 15 15

2438 120 c. Plate No. 27 (Series 1) (No. 1524) .. 15 15
2439 120 c. Plate No. 36 (Series 1) (No. 1558) .. 15 15
2440 120 c. Plate No. 37 (Series 1) (No. 1627) .. 15 15
2441 120 c. Plate No. 56 (Series 1) (No. 1629) .. 15 15
2442 120 c. Plate No. 58 (Series 1) (No. 1630) .. 15 15
2443 120 c. Plate No. 67 (Series 1) (No. 1631) .. 15 15
2444 120 c. Plate No. 69 (Series 1) (No. 1680) (opt vert - reading down) .. .. 15 15
2445 130 c. Plate No. 38 (Series 1) (No. 1560) .. 15 15
2446 130 c. Plate No. 66 (Series 1) (No. 1632) .. 15 15
2447 130 c. Plate No. 91 (Series 1) (No. 1735) .. 15 15
2448 130 c. Plate No. 13 (Series 1) (No. 1760) (*wmkd*) .. .. .. .. .. 15 15
a. Opt inverted .. ..
2449 130 c. Plate No. 20 (Series 1) (No. 1761) (*wmkd*) .. .. .. .. .. 15 15
2450 150 c. Plate No. 26 (Series 1) (No. 1633) .. 15 15
2451 150 c. Plate No. 78 (Series 1) (No. 1669) .. 15 15
2452 150 c. Plate No. 87 (Series 1) (No. 1681) (opt vert - reading down) .. .. 15 15
2453 150 c. Plate No. 76 (Series 1) (No. 1751) .. 15 15
2454 250 c. Plate No. 74 (Series 1) (No. 1736) .. 15 15
2434/54 .. .. .. .. *Set of* 21 2·75 2·75

The 130 c., No. 2448, exists in equal quantities with the overprint either upright or inverted.

**1988** (3 Aug). *125th Anniv of International Red Cross. Nos.* 2202/5 *and* 2207/10 *optd with T* **423** *in red by Gardy Ptg.*

2455 **396** $3. 20, deep dull blue .. .. 15 20
a. Vert pair. Nos. 2455 and 2457 .. 30 40
2456 – $3. 20, deep dull blue (No. 2203) .. 15 20
a. Vert pair. Nos. 2456 and 2458 .. 30 40
2457 – $3. 20, deep dull blue (No. 2204) .. 15 20
2458 – $3. 20, deep dull blue (No. 2205) .. 15 20
2459 – $3. 30, brownish black (No. 2207) .. 15 20
a. Vert pair. Nos. 2459 and 2461 .. 30 40
2460 **396** $3. 30, brownish black .. 15 20
a. Vert pair. Nos. 2460 and 2462 .. 30 40
2461 – $3. 30, brownish black (No. 2209) .. 15 20
2462 – $3. 30, brownish black (No. 2210) .. 15 20
2455/62 .. .. .. .. *Set of* 8 1·10 1·40

Nos. 2455/62 were issued in vertical strips of ten, each strip containing two designs *se-tenant*.

**1988** (Aug). *Air. Various* Reichenbachia *issues optd with T* **424** *by Gardy Ptg.*

2463 75 c. Plate No. 55 (Series 1) (No. 1625) .. 15 15
2464 75 c. Plate No. 5 (Series 1) (No. 1667) .. 15 15
2465 75 c. Plate No. 55 (Series 1) (No. 1772) (*wmkd*) .. .. .. .. .. 15 15
2466 75 c. Plate No. 83 (Series 1) .. .. 15 15
2467 75 c. Plate No. 95 (Series 1) .. .. 15 15
2463/7 .. .. .. .. *Set of* 5 65 65

(Litho Format)

**1988** (15 Aug). *Centenary of Publication of Sanders'* Reichenbachia *(33rd issue). Multicoloured designs as T* **331**. *P* 13½×14 *(270 c., 360 c.) or* 14×13½ *(others).*

2468 270 c. Plate No. 90 (Series 2) .. .. 70 60
2469 360 c. Plate No. 84 (Series 2) .. .. 1·00 75
2470 550 c. Plate No. 70 (Series 2) (*horiz*) .. 1·75 1·10
2471 670 c. Plate No. 71 (Series 2) (*horiz*) .. 2·25 1·40
2468/71 .. .. .. .. *Set of* 4 5·25 3·50

Nos. 2468/71 were printed in a similar sheet format to Nos. 1518/33.

A further small book similar to those described under Nos. 1767/1806, containing stamps showing plate numbers 1 to 48 of the second series, was issued on 23 August 1988.

1928 — 1988
CRICKET
JUBILEE

(425)

**1988** (5 Sept). *60th Anniv of Cricket in Guyana. Nos.* 1584, 1670, 1681 *and* 1815 *optd as T* **425** *or surch also by Gardy Ptg.*

2472 200 c. Plate No. 14 (Series 1) .. .. 30 30
2473 200 c. Plate No. 79 (Series 1) .. .. 30 30
2474 800 c. on 150 c. Plate No. 87 (Series 1) .. 1·25 1·25
2475 800 c. on 160 c. Plate No. 5 (Series 2) .. 1·25 1·25
2472/5 .. .. .. .. *Set of* 4 2·75 2·75

Nos. 2472 and 2474 were only issued in $20 stamp booklets.

OLYMPIC GAMES
1988

(426)

KOREA 1988

150

(427)

**1988** (16 Sept). *Olympic Games, Seoul. (a) Nos.* 1628, 1634, 1671, 1681, 1683, 1814, 1818/19, 1880 *and* 2069 *optd as T* **426** *or surch also by Gardy Ptg.*

2476 120 c. Plate No. 46 (Series 1) .. .. 10 10
2477 130 c. Plate No. 38 (Series 2) .. .. 10 10
2478 150 c. Plate No. 87 (Series 1) .. .. 10 10
2479 200 c. Plate No. 33 (Series 1) .. .. 10 10
2480 300 c. Plate No. 83 (Series 1) .. .. 15 20
2481 300 c. on 360 c. Plate No. 34 (Series 2) .. 15 20
2482 320 c. Plate No. 10 (Series 2) .. .. 15 20
2483 330 c. Plate No. 82 (Series 2) .. .. 15 20
2484 350 c. Plate No. 94 (Series 1) (opt vert - reading up) .. .. .. .. 15 20
2485 350 c. Plate No. 29 (Series 2) .. .. 15 20

(*b*) *Design as No.* 1420, *but incorrectly inscr* "LOS ANGELLES", *optd or surch as T* **427**, *inscr* "OLYMPICS 1988" (A) *or* "KOREA 1988" (B), *by Gardy Ptg.*

2486 $1.20, multicoloured (A) .. .. 10 10
a. Horiz strip of 5. Nos. 2486, 2488, 2490, 2492 and 2494 .. .. 40
b. Booklet pane of 10. Nos. 2486/95 .. 80
2487 $1.20, multicoloured (B) .. .. 10 10
2488 130 c. on $1.20, multicoloured (A) .. 10 10
2489 130 c. on $1.20, multicoloured (B) .. 10 10
2490 150 c. on $1.20, multicoloured (A) .. 10 10
2491 150 c. on $1.20, multicoloured (B) .. 10 10
2492 200 c. on $1.20, multicoloured (A) .. 10 10
2493 200 c. on $1.20, multicoloured (B) .. 10 10
2494 350 c. on $1.20, multicoloured (A) .. 15 20
2495 350 c. on $1.20, multicoloured (B) .. 15 20
2476/95 .. .. .. .. *Set of* 20 1·75 1·90

Nos. 2486/95 were issued in $20 stamp booklets which included pane No. 2486b. Nos. 2486, 2488, 2490, 2492 and 2494 were also available from sheets containing horizontal *se-tenant* strips of 5. All values later appeared in coils of 500 or 1,000.

V CENTENARY OF
THE LANDING OF
CHRISTOPHER COLUMBUS
IN THE AMERICAS

(428)

**1988** (12 Oct). *Columbus Day. Nos.* 1672/3 *optd or surch as T* **428** *by Gardy Ptg.*

2496 320 c. Plate No. 50 (Series 1) .. .. 15 20
2497 $15 on 360 c. Plate No. 85 (Series 1) .. 65 70

(Litho Format)

**1988** (3 Nov). *Centenary of Publication of Sanders'* Reichenbachia *(34th issue). Multicoloured designs as T* **331**. *P* 14×13½ *(130 c.) or* 13¼×14 *(others).*

2498 100 c. Plate No. 44 (Series 2) .. .. 70 55
2499 130 c. Plate No. 42 (Series 2) (*horiz*) .. 70 55
2500 140 c. Plate No. 4 (Series 2) .. .. 90 65
2501 160 c. Plate No. 50 (Series 2) .. .. 90 65
2502 175 c. Plate No. 51 (Series 2) .. .. 1·10 75
2503 200 c. Plate No. 11 (Series 2) .. .. 1·10 75
2504 200 c. Plate No. 23 (Series 2) .. .. 1·10 75
2505 200 c. Plate No. 26 (Series 2) .. .. 1·10 75
2506 200 c. Plate No. 75 (Series 2) .. .. 1·10 75
2507 200 c. Plate No. 93 (Series 2) .. .. 1·10 75
2508 250 c. Plate No. 79 (Series 2) .. .. 1·40 90
2509 280 c. Plate No. 62 (Series 2) .. .. 1·40 1·00
2510 285 c. Plate No. 63 (Series 2) .. .. 1·50 1·00
2511 380 c. Plate No. 35 (Series 2) .. .. 1·75 1·25
2498/511 .. .. .. .. *Set of* 14 14·50 12·50

Nos. 2498/511 were printed in a similar sheet format to Nos. 1518/33.

SEASON'S
GREETINGS

SEASON'S
GREETINGS

(429)

120

(430)

SEASON'S
GREETINGS

SEASON'S
GREETINGS
1988

(431)

240

(432)

**1988** (10 Nov). *Christmas (1st issue). Various* Reichenbachia *issues optd or surch by Gardy Ptg*

(*a*) *With T* **429**

2512 150 c. Plate No. 32 (Series 1) (No. 1561) 20 25
2513 150 c. Plate No. 62 (Series 1) (No. 1566) 20 25
2514 225 c. Plate No. 60 (Series 1) (No. 1682) 30 35
2515 260 c. Plate No. 39 (Series 1) (No. 1737) 35 40
2516 320 c. Plate No. 82 (Series 1) (No. 1753) 40 45
2517 330 c. Plate No. 80 (Series 1) (No. 1754) 45 50
2518 360 c. Plate No. 85 (Series 1) (No. 1673) 45 50

(*b*) *As T* **430** *in blue*

2519 120 c. on 100 c. Plate No. 6 (Series 1) (*wmkd*) .. .. .. .. 15 20
2520 120 c. on 100 c. Plate No. 13 (Series 1) (*wmkd*) .. .. .. .. 15 20
2521 120 c. on 100 c. Plate No. 20 (Series 1) (*wmkd*) .. .. .. .. 15 20
2522 120 c. on 100 c. Plate No. 25 (Series 1) (*wmkd*) .. .. .. .. 15 20
2523 120 c. on 100 c. Plate No. 40 (Series 1) (*horiz*) (*wmkd*) .. .. .. 15 20
2524 120 c. on 100 c. Plate No. 42 (Series 1) (*horiz*) (*wmkd*) .. .. .. 15 20
2525 120 c. on 100 c. Plate No. 43 (Series 1) (*horiz*) (*wmkd*) .. .. .. 15 20
2526 120 c. on 100 c. Plate No. 45 (Series 1) (*horiz*) (*wmkd*) .. .. .. 15 20

(*c*) *With T* **431** *in blue*

2527 225 c. Plate No. 24 (Series 1) (No. 1635) 30 35
2528 225 c. Plate No. 60 (Series 1) (No. 1682) 30 35
2529 225 c. Plate No. 24 (Series 1) (No. 1774) (*wmkd*) .. .. .. .. 30 35
2530 225 c. on 350 c. on 120 c. Plate No. 65 (Series 1) (No. 2221) .. .. 30 35
**MS**2531 120×129 mm. 225 c. on 55 c.×4 Plate No. 22 (Series 1) each with a different overprint (Type **350**, "Happy New Year", "Merry Christmas" or "Happy Holidays") (No. **MS**2232) 1·10 1·25

(*d*) *With T* **432**

2532 240 c. on 180 c. Plate No. 15 (Series 1) (No. 1752) .. .. .. .. 30 35
2512/30 *and* 2532 .. .. *Set of* 20 4·50 5·50

CHRISTMAS
1988
20

(433)

Protect yourself
from AIDS.
Better safe
than sorry.

(434)

**1988** (16 Nov). *Christmas (2nd issue). Nos.* 489, 1188/91 *and* 1449 *surch or optd as T* **433** *by Autoprint.*

2533 – 20 c. on 6 c. mult (No. 489) (R.) .. 10 10
2534 **277** 120 c. lake-brown, black & bright blue 15 20
a. Block of 4. Nos. 2534/7 .. 60
2535 – 120 c. on 130 c. rose-red, black and bright blue (No. 1189) .. 15 20
2536 – 120 c. on 150 c. bright violet, black and bright blue (No. 1190) .. 15 20
2537 – 120 c. on 200 c. dull green, black and bright blue (No. 1191) .. 15 20
2538 – 500 c. on 330 c. mult (No. 1449) (R.) 65 70
2533/8 .. .. .. .. *Set of* 6 1·10 1·40

No. 2538 shows "CHRISTMAS 1988" vertical, reading up.

**1988** (1 Dec). *AIDS Information Campaign. Nos.* 707/8*a optd as T* **434** *or surch also.*

2539 120 c. on $5 *Morpho deidamia* (A) .. 30 30
a. Strip of 5. Nos. 2539/43 .. .. 1·40
2540 120 c. on $5 *Morpho deidamia* (B) .. 30 30
2541 120 c. on $5 *Morpho deidamia* (C) .. 30 30
2542 120 c. on $5 *Morpho deidamia* (D) .. 30 30
2543 120 c. on $5 *Morpho deidamia* (Type **434**) 30 30
2544 120 c. on $10 *Elbella patrobas* (A) .. 30 30
a. Strip of 5. Nos. 2544/8 .. .. 1·40
2545 120 c. on $10 *Elbella patrobas* (B) .. 30 30
2546 120 c. on $10 *Elbella patrobas* (C) .. 30 30
2547 120 c. on $10 *Elbella patrobas* (D) .. 30 30
2548 120 c. on $10 *Elbella patrobas* (Type **434**) 30 30
2549 $2 *Morpho rhetenor* (female) (Type **434**) 40 40
2550 $5 *Morpho deidamia* (Type **434**) .. 90 90
2551 $10 *Elbella patrobas* (Type **434**) .. 1·75 1·75
2539/51 .. .. .. .. *Set of* 13 5·25 5·25

Nos. 2539/43 and 2544/8 were surcharged horizontally and vertically *se-tenant* with Type **434** and four other slogans: (A) "Be compassionate towards AIDS victims."; (B) "Get information on AIDS. it may save your life."; (C) "Get the facts. Education helps to prevent AIDS."; (D) "Say no to Drugs and limit the spread of AIDS.".

(Des K. Everett (150 c.). Litho Format)

**1988** (16 Dec). *150th Anniv of Abolition of Slavery* (1984) (2*nd issue). Designs as Nos.* 1547/50, *but colours changed. P* 14.

2552 **337** 25 c. black and bistre-brown .. 10 10
2553 – 60 c. black and brown-lilac .. 10 10
2554 – 130 c. black and blue-green .. 15 20
2555 – 150 c. black and dull blue .. 20 25
2552/5 .. .. .. .. *Set of* 4 30 40

Nos. 2552/5 exist imperforate from stock dispersed by the liquidator of Format International Security Printers Ltd.

1050

SALUTING WINNERS
OLYMPIC GAMES
1988

(435)

**1989** (3 Jan). *Olympic Medal Winners, Seoul. Nos.* 1672, 192 *and* 2178 *surch as T* **435** *by Gardy Ptg.*

2556 550 c. on 560 c. Plate No. 1 (Series 2) .. 70 7
2557 900 c. on 320 c. Plate No. 18 (Series 2) 1·10 1·2
2558 1050 c. on 320 c. Plate No. 50 (Series 1) 1·40 1·5
2556/8 .. .. .. .. *Set of* 3 3·00 3·2

A further small book, similar to these described under Nos 1767/1806, containing stamps showing plate numbers 49 to 96 c the second series, was issued on 3 January 1989.

REPUBLIC DAY 1989 (436)

$5.00 (437)

**1989** (22 Feb). *Republic Day. Nos.* 2194/201 *and* 2212 *optd with T* **436** *in red by Gardy Ptg.*

2559 **396** $1.20, bronze-green .. .. 15 20
a. Block of 4. Nos. 2559/62 .. 60
2560 – $1.20, bronze-green (No. 2195) .. 15 20
2561 – $1.20, bronze-green (No. 2196) .. 15 20
2562 – $1.20, bronze-green (No. 2197) .. 15 20
2563 **396** $1.20, maroon .. .. .. 15 20
a. Block of 4. Nos. 2563/6 .. .. 60
2564 – $1.20, maroon (No. 2199) .. .. 15 20
2565 – $1.20, maroon (No. 2200) .. .. 15 20
2566 – $1.20, maroon (No. 2201) .. .. 15 20
2567 – $10 multicoloured .. .. .. 1·25 1·40
2559/67 .. .. .. .. *Set of* 9 2·25 2·75

**1989** (22 Feb). *Nos.* 2202/5 *and* 2207/10 *surch with T* **437** *in red.*

2568 **396** $5 on $3.20, deep dull blue .. 65 70
a. Vert pair. Nos. 2568 and 2570 .. 1·25
2569 – $5 on $3.20, deep dull blue (No. 2203) 65 70
a. Vert pair. Nos. 2569 and 2571 .. 1·25
2570 – $5 on $3.20, deep dull blue (No. 2204) 65 70
2571 – $5 on $3.20, deep dull blue (No. 2205) 65 70
2572 – $5 on $3.30, brownish blk (No. 2207) 65 70
a. Vert pair. Nos. 2572 and 2574 .. 1·25
2573 **396** $5 on $3.30, brownish black .. 65 70
a. Vert pair. Nos. 2573 and 2575 .. 1·25
2574 – $5 on $3.30, brownish blk (No. 2209) 65 70
2575 – $5 on $3.30, brownish blk (No. 2210) 65 70
2568/75 .. .. .. .. *Set of* 8 4·50 5·00

Nos. 2568/75 were issued in vertical strips of ten, each strip containing two designs *se-tenant.*

**1989** (22 Feb–Mar). *Various* Reichenbachia *issues surch by Gardy Ptg.*

(*a*) *As T* **420** *in red*

2576 120 c. on 140 c. Plate No. 25 (Series 2) .. 15 20
2577 120 c. on 140 c. Plate No. 52 (Series 2) .. 15 20
2578 120 c. on 140 c. Plate No. 65 (Series 2) .. 15 20
2579 120 c. on 175 c. Plate No. 54 (Series 2) (surch vert–reading down) .. 15 20

(*b*) *As T* **421**, *but with two bars only*

2580 120 c. on 140 c. Plate No. 38 (Series 2) .. 15 20
2581 120 c. on 140 c. Plate No. 41 (Series 2) .. 15 20
2582 170 c. on 175 c. Plate No. 58 (Series 2) (Mar) .. .. .. .. 20 25
2583 250 c. on 280 c. Plate No. 66 (Series 2) (Mar) .. .. .. .. 30 35
2584 250 c. on 280 c. Plate No. 67 (Series 2) (Mar) .. .. .. .. 30 35
2585 300 c. on 290 c. Plate No. 53 (Series 2) (No. 2236) (Mar) .. .. .. 40 45
2576/85 .. .. .. .. *Set of* 10 1·75 2·25

TEN DOLLARS

$10.00 (438)

TEN DOLLARS (439)

**1989** (22 Feb). *Nos.* 1744/5 *and* 2185/6 *surch with T* **438** (*Nos.* 2586, 2588) *or T* **439** (*Nos.* 2587, 2589), *both in red.*

2586 **363** $10 on 320 c. rosine, black and deep reddish violet (No. 1744) .. 1·25 1·40
a. Horiz pair. Nos. 2586/7 .. 2·50
2587 – $10 on 320 c. multicoloured (No. 1745) 1·25 1·40
2588 **363** $10 on 320 c. rosine, black and deep reddish violet (No. 2185) .. 1·25 1·40
a. Horiz pair. Nos. 2588/9 .. 2·50
2589 – $10 on 320 c. multicoloured (No. 2186) 1·25 1·40
2586/9 .. .. .. .. *Set of* 4 4·50 5·00

EASTER 125 (440)

POSTAGE (441)

**1989** (22 Mar). *Easter. No.* 1817 *in block of four surch as T* **440**.

**MS**2590 97×124 mm. 125 c. on 320 c., 250 c. on 320 c., 300 c. on 320 c., 350 c. on 320 c., Plate No. 12 (Series 2) .. .. .. .. .. 1·25 1·40

**1989** (Mar). *Nos.* O54/7, O59/63 *and* O65/9 *optd with T* **441** *or surch additionally as T* **421** *with two bars only by Gardy Ptg.*

2591 125 c. on 130 c. Plate No. 92 (Series 2) .. 10 10
2592 125 c. on 140 c. Plate No. 36 (Series 2) .. 10 10
2593 150 c. Plate No. 43 (Series 2) .. .. 10 10
2594 150 c. on 175 c. Plate No. 31 (Series 2) .. 10 10
2595 250 c. Plate No. 59 (Series 2) .. .. 10 10
2596 250 c. on 225 c. Plate No. 26 (Series 2) (surch at top) .. .. .. .. 10 10
a. Surch at foot .. .. .. .. 10 10
2597 250 c. on 230 c. Plate No. 68 (Series 2) .. 10 10
2598 250 c. on 260 c. Plate No. 69 (Series 2) (surch at top) .. .. .. .. 10 10
a. Surch in centre .. .. .. 10 10
2599 300 c. on 275 c. Plate No. 90 (Series 2) .. 10 15
2600 350 c. Plate No. 95 (Series 2) (opt vert – reading up) .. .. .. .. 15 20
a. Opt vert – reading down .. .. 15 20
2601 350 c. on 330 c. Plate No. 23 (Series 2) .. 15 20
2602 600 c. Plate No. 70 (Series 2) (opt vert – reading up) .. .. .. .. 25 30
2603 $12 Plate No. 71 (Series 2) (opt vert – reading up) .. .. .. .. 50 55
2604 $15 Plate No. 84 (Series 2) .. .. 60 65
2591/604 .. .. .. .. *Set of* 14 2·50 3·00

**1989** (Mar). *Centenary of Publication of Sanders'* Reichenbachia (35*th issue*). *Vert designs as T* **331**. *Multicoloured. P* $13^1/_2$×14.

2605 200 c. Plate No. 49 (Series 2) .. .. 10 10
2606 200 c. Plate No. 53 (Series 2) .. .. 10 10
2607 200 c. Plate No. 60 (Series 2) .. .. 10 10
2608 200 c. Plate No. 64 (Series 2) .. .. 10 10
2605/8 .. .. .. .. *Set of* 4 20 20

Nos. 2605/8 were printed in a similar sheet format to Nos. 1518/33.

250 (442)

**1989** (Mar). *As No.* 1442, *but with imprint date, surch with T* **442**. *P* 14.

2609 **322** 250 c. on 25 c. multicoloured .. .. 10 10

375 RED CROSS 1948 1988 (443)

**1989** (Apr). 40*th Anniv of Guyana Red Cross. No.* 1872 *surch as T* **443**.

2610 375 c. on 45 c. Plate No. 17 (Series 2) .. 15 20
2611 425 c. on 45 c. Plate No. 17 (Series 2) .. 15 20

HEALTH FOR ALL 250 (444)

**1989** (3 Apr). *World Health Day. Nos.* 1875 *and* 2239 *surch as T* **444**.

2612 250 c. on 75 c. Plate No. 56 (Series 2) (surch T **444**) .. .. .. .. 10 10
a. Pair. Nos. 2612/13 .. .. 20 25
2613 250 c. on 75 c. Plate No. 56 (Series 2) (surch "ALL FOR HEALTH") .. .. 10 10
2614 675 c. on 720 c. Plate No. 49 (Series 2) (surch "ALL FOR HEALTH") .. 30 35
a. Pair. Nos. 2614/15 .. .. 60 70
2615 675 c. on 720 c. Plate No. 49 (Series 2) (surch as T **444**) .. .. 30 35
2612/15 .. .. .. .. *Set of* 4 70 80

Nos. 2612/13 and 2614/15 were each issued, *se-tenant*, in horizontal and vertical pairs, within the sheets of four.

BOY SCOUTS 1909 1989 (445)

PHOTOGRAPHY 1839 - 1989 550 (446)

**1989** (11 Apr). *Scouting Anniversaries. Nos.* 1873, 1879, 2322, 2509 *and unissued value as No.* 1873 *optd or surch as T* **445**.

2616 250 c. on 50 c. Plate No. 33 (Series 2) (surch T **445**) .. .. .. .. 10 10
a. Pair. Nos. 2616/17 .. .. .. 20 25
2617 250 c. on 50 c. Plate No. 33 (Series 2) (surch "GIRL GUIDES 1924 1989") .. 10 10
2618 250 c. on 100 c. Plate No. 33 (Series 2) (surch as T **445**) .. .. .. 10 10
a. Pair. Nos. 2618/19 .. .. .. 20 25
2619 250 c. on 100 c. Plate No. 33 (Series 2) (surch "GIRL GUIDES 1924 1989") 10 10
2620 300 c. Plate No. 50 (Series 2) (optd as T **445**) 10 15
a. Pair. Nos. 2620/1 .. .. .. 20 30
2621 300 c. Plate No. 50 (Series 2) (optd "GIRL GUIDES 1924 1989") .. .. 10 15
2622 $25 on 280 c. Plate No. 62 (Series 2) (surch "LADY BADEN POWELL 1889 – 1989") .. .. .. 1·00 1·10
2623 $25 on 700 c. Plate No. 62 (Series 2) (surch "LADY BADEN POWELL 1889 – 1989") .. .. .. 1·00 1·10
2616/23 .. .. .. .. *Set of* 8 2·25 2·75

The events commemorated are the 80th anniversary of Boy Scout Movement in Guyana, 65th anniversary of Girl Guide Movement in Guyana and birth centenary of Lady Baden-Powell.

On Nos. 2616/17 the surcharge is a "2" applied in front of the original face value to form "250".

Nos. 2616/17, 2618/19 and 2620/1 were each issued, *se-tenant*, in horizontal and vertical pairs within the sheets of four.

**1989** (15 Apr). 150 *Years of Photography. No.* 1881 *surch as T* **446**.

2624 550 c. on 390 c. Plate No. 6 (Series 2) .. 20 25
a. Pair. Nos. 2624/5 .. .. .. 45 55
2625 650 c. on 390 c. Plate No. 6 (Series 2) (original value cancelled by two bars) 25 30
2626 650 c. on 390 c. Plate No. 6 (Series 2) (original value cancelled by six bars) 25 30
2624/6 .. .. .. .. *Set of* 3 65 75

No. 2624 exists either as complete sheets of four or horizontally and vertically *se-tenant* with No. 2625. No. 2626 only comes as sheets of four all showing the same surcharge.

I.L.O. 1919-1989 300 (447)

**1989** (2 May). 70*th Anniv of International Labour Organization. No.* 1875 *surch with T* **447**.

2627 300 c. on 75 c. Plate No. 56 (Series 2) .. 10 15

80c (448)

$6.40 (449)

$5

$2.55 (450)

X (451)

$6.40 (452)

**1989** (8 May–16 Aug). *Various stamps surch*

(*a*) *As T* **448** *with short obliterating bars over original value*
2628 80 c. on 6 c. Patua (No. 452) .. .. 10 10
2629 $1 on 2 c. Type **132** (15 June) .. .. 10 10
2630 $2.05 on 3 c. Hanging Heliconia (No. 544) (15 June) .. .. .. 10 10
2631 $2.55 on 5 c. Annatto tree (No. 545) (15 June) .. .. .. 10 15
2632 $3.25 on 6 c. Cannon-ball tree (No. 546) (15 June) .. .. .. 15 20
2633 $5 on 6 c. Type **111** (16 Aug) .. .. 20 25
2634 $6.40 on 10 c. *Archonias bellona* (No. 699) (18 May) .. .. .. 25 30
2635 $8.90 on 60 c. *Papilio androgeus* (No. 705*a*) (26 May) .. .. .. 35 40

(*b*) *As T* **449** (*larger figures on 80 c.*) *without any obliterating bars*
2636 80 c. on 6 c. Patua (No. 452) .. .. 10 10
2637 $6.40 on 10 c. *Archonias bellona* (No. 699) (18 May) .. .. .. 25 30
2638 $7.65 on 40 c. *Morpho rhetenor* (male) (No. 704) (18 May) .. .. .. 30 35
2639 $8.90 on 60 c. *Papilio androgeus* (No. 705*a*) (26 May) .. .. .. 35 40

(*c*) *As T* **450** (*larger figures on $1*) *with "X" over original value*
2640 $1 on 2 c. Type **132** (15 June) .. .. 10 10
2641 $2.55 on 5 c. Annatto tree (No. 545) (15 June) .. .. .. 10 15
2642 $3.25 on 6 c. Cannon-ball tree (No. 546)
2643 $50 on $2 *Morpho rhetenor* (female) (No. 707) (B.) (5 June) .. .. 2·00 2·10
2644 $100 on $2 *Morpho rhetenor* (female) (No. 707) (5 June) .. .. .. 4·00 4·25

(*d*) *With T* **451**
2645 $5 on 6 c. Type **111** (16 Aug) .. .. 20 25

(*e*) *As T* **421**, *but two obliterating bars only*
2646 640 c. on 675 c. on 720 c. Plate No. 49 (Series 2) (surch "ALL FOR HEALTH") (No. 2614) .. .. 25 30
a. Pair. Nos. 2646/7 .. .. .. 50 60
2647 640 c. on 675 c. on 720 c. Plate No. 49 (Series 2) (surch "HEALTH FOR ALL") (No. 2615) .. .. .. 25 30

(*f*) *As T* **452**
2648 – $6.40 on $3.30, brownish black (No. 2207) .. .. .. .. 25 30
a. Vert pair. Nos. 2648 and 2650 .. 50 60
2649 **396** $6.40 on $3.30, brownish black .. 25 30
a. Vert pair. Nos. 2649 and 2651 .. 50 60
2650 – $6.40 on $3.30, brownish black (No. 2209) .. .. .. .. 25 30
2651 – $6.40 on $3.30, brownish black (No. 2210) .. .. .. .. 25 30
2652 **396** $7.65 on $3.20, deep dull blue .. 30 35
a. Vert pair. Nos. 2652 and 2654 .. 60 70
2653 – $7.65 on $3.20, dp dull blue (No. 2203) 30 35
a. Vert pair. Nos. 2653 and 2655 .. 60 70
2654 – $7.65 on $3.20, dp dull blue (No. 2204) 30 35
2655 – $7.65 on $3.20, dp dull blue (No. 2205) 30 35
2628/55 .. .. .. .. *Set of* 28 10·50 11·50

CARICOM
DAY

125

(453)

**454** *Stalachtis calliope*

**1989** (26 June). *CARICOM Day. No.* 1878 *surch with T* **453**.
2656 125 c. on 200 c. Plate No. 44 (Series 2) .. 10 10

(Des Mary Walters. Litho Questa)

**1989** (7 Sept). *Butterflies. T* **454** *and similar vert designs. Multicoloured. P* 14.
2657 80 c. Type **454** .. .. .. .. 10 10
2658 $2.25, *Morpho rhetenor* .. .. .. 10 10
2659 $5 *Agrias claudia* .. .. .. 20 25
2660 $6.40, *Marpesia marcella* .. .. .. 25 30
2661 $7.65, *Papilio zagreus* .. .. .. 30 35
2662 $8.90, *Chorinea faunus* .. .. .. 35 40
2663 $25 *Euptychia cephus* .. .. .. 1·00 1·10
2664 $100 *Nessaea regina* .. .. .. 4·00 4·15
2657/64 .. .. .. .. *Set of* 8 5·50 6·25
For miniature sheets accompanying this issue see Nos. EMS18/19.

**455** Kathryn Sullivan (first U.S woman to walk in space)

AHMADIYYA
CENTENARY
1889-1989
$8·90

(456)

(Des M. Dorfman. Litho Questa)

**1989** (8 Nov). *25 Years of Women in Space. T* **455** *and similar vert designs. Multicoloured. P* 14.
2665 $6.40, Type **455** .. .. .. .. 25 30
2666 $12.80, Svetlana Savitskaya (first Soviet woman to walk in space) .. .. 50 55
2667 $15.30, Judy Resnik and Christa McAuliffe with *Challenger* logo .. 60 65
2668 $100 Sally Ride (first U.S woman astronaut) .. .. .. .. .. 4·00 4·25
2665/8 .. .. .. .. *Set of* 4 4·75 5·25
For miniature sheet accompanying this issue see No. EMS20.

**1989** (22 Nov). *Centenary of Ahmadiyya (Moslem organization). Nos.* 543/5 *surch as T* **456**.
2669 80 c. on 2 c. Type **132** .. .. .. 10 10
2670 $6.40 on 3 c. Hanging Heliconia .. 25 30
2671 $8.90 on 5 c. Annatto tree .. .. 35 40
2669/71 .. .. .. .. *Set of* 3 65 75

**457** Head of Harpy Eagle

**458** Channel-billed Toucan

(Des J. Barbaris. Litho Questa)

**1990** (23 Jan). *Endangered Species. Harpy Eagle. T* **457** *and similar vert designs. Multicoloured. P* 14.
2672 $2.25, Type **457** .. .. .. .. 10 10
2673 $5 Harpy Eagle with monkey prey .. 20 25
2674 $8.90, Eagle on branch (facing right) .. 35 40
2675 $30 Eagle on branch (facing left) .. 1·25 1·40
2672/5 .. .. .. .. *Set of* 4 1·75 1·90

(Des J. Barbaris. Litho Questa)

**1990** (23 Jan). *Birds of Guyana. T* **458** *and similar multicoloured designs. P* 14.
2676 $15 Type **458** .. .. .. .. 60 65
2677 $25 Blue and Yellow Macaw .. .. 1·00 1·10
2678 $50 Wattled Jacana (*horiz*) .. .. 2·00 2·25
2679 $60 Hoatzin (*horiz*) .. .. .. 2·40 2·50
2676/9 .. .. .. .. *Set of* 4 5·50 5·75
**MS**2680 Two sheets, each 110×80 mm. (a) $100 Great Kiskadee. (b) $100 Amazon Kingfisher *Set of* 2 *sheets* 8·00 8·50

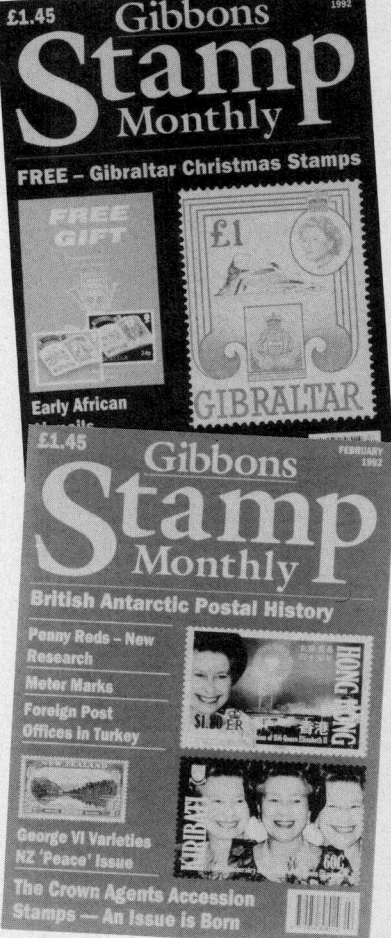

EXPRESS LETTER STAMPS

$12.00

EXPRESS

(E 1)

**1986** (10 Nov). *Various stamps surch as Type* E 1 *by Tip Torres.*

E1 $12 on 350 c. on 120 c. mult (No. 1598) .. 2·50 2·50
E2 $15 on 40 c. multicoloured (as No. 1868, but inscr "ONTOGLOSSUM") .. .. 3·00 3·00
a. Surch on No. 1868 (inscr "ODONTOGLOSSUM") .. .. 3·00 3·00
E3 $20 on $6.40, multicoloured (No. **MS**1746) 3·50 3·50
E4 $25 on 25 c. multicoloured (as No. 1621, but value changed) .. .. 4·00 4·00
E1/4 .. .. .. .. .. *Set of* 4 14·50 14·50

The surcharges on Nos. E2/3 include a pattern of leaves over the original value. On No. E4 a dollar sign has been added in front of the original value and a small maltese cross overprinted above "EXPRESS" at bottom right.

**1987** (3 Mar). *No.* E3 *additionally optd with small Maltese cross above surch.*

E5 $20 on $6.40, multicoloured .. .. 3·25 3·25
a. With additional "2" optd at bottom left .. 3·25 3·25

(Litho Format)

**1987** (1 Sept)–**88**. *Centenary of Publication of Sanders' Reichenbachia. Vert designs as T* **331** *additionally inscr* "EXPRESS". *Multicoloured. No wmk. P* 13½×14.

E6 $15 Plate No. 11 (Series 2) (29.9.87) .. 2·25 2·25
E7 $20 Plate No. 93 (Series 2) (17.5.88) .. 2·50 2·75
E8 $25 Plate No. 63 (Series 2) (26.10.87) .. 3·00 3·50
E9 $45 Plate No. 35 (Series 2) .. .. 6·00 6·50
E6/9 .. .. .. .. .. *Set of* 4 12·50 13·50

Nos. E6/9, in conjunction with postage issues, were printed in a similar sheet format to Nos. 1518/33.

EXPRESS

FORTY DOLLARS

(E 2) *(Illustration reduced. Actual size of surcharge* 64 × 36 *mm)*

**1987** (Nov). *No.* 1744ab *surch with Type* E **2** *by Gardy Ptg.*

E10 $40 on $6.40, multicoloured .. .. 7·00 7·50

**1987** (Dec). *No.* E 2 *additionally optd with T* **390** *by Gardy Ptg.*

E11 $15 on 40 c. multicoloured (inscr "ONTOGLOSSUM" .. .. .. .. 2·75 3·00

SPECIAL DELIVERY

$40-00

(E 3)
*(Illustration reduced. Actual size of surcharge* 80×45 *mm)*

**1988** (10 Aug). *Nos.* 2206 *and* 2211 *surch as Type* E 3 *in red by Gardy Ptg.*

E12 $40 on $3.20, deep dull blue .. .. 5·50 6·50
E13 $45 on $3.30, brownish black .. .. 6·00 7·00

Nos. E12/13 were only issued in vertical strips of five, being the remainders of the sheets utilised to produce Nos. 2455/62.

***MINIMUM PRICE***

The minimum price quote is 10p which represents a handling charge rather than a basis for valuing common stamps. For further notes about prices see introductory pages.

EXPRESS

FORTY DOLLARS

(E 4)

**1989** (Mar). *Nos.* 1744ab *and* 2185ab *surch with Type* E 4 *in red.*

E14 $40 on $6.40, multicoloured (No. 1744ab) 1·60 1·75
E15 $40 on $6.40, multicoloured (No. 2185ab) 1·60 1·75

**1989** (May). *Nos.* 2206 *and* 2211 *surch as Type* E **3**.

E16 $190 on $3.30, brownish black .. .. 7·50 8·00
E17 $225 on $3.20, deep dull blue .. .. 8·50 9·00

Nos. E16/17 were surcharged on the remains of the sheets utilized for Nos. 2648/55.

EXPRESS

(E 5)

(E 6)

(Des Mary Walters. Litho Questa)

**1989** (7 Sept). *Butterflies. Two sheets, each* 97×67 *mm, containing vert designs as T* **454** *optd with Type* E **5**. *Multicoloured. P* 14.

EMS18 $130 *Phareas coeleste* .. .. .. 3·25 3·50
EMS19 $190 *Papilio torquatus* .. .. .. 7·50 8·00

(Des M. Dorfman. Litho Questa)

**1989** (8 Nov). *Women in Space. Sheet,* 92×67 *mm, containing vert design as T* **455** *optd with Type* E **5**. *Multicoloured. P* 14.

EMS20 $190 Valentina Tereshkova (first woman cosmonaut) .. .. .. 7·50 8·00

**1989** (17 Nov). *"World Stamp Expo '89" International Stamp Exhibition, Washington. Nos.* **EMS**18/19 *optd with Type* E **6**.

EMS21 $130 *Phareas coeleste* .. .. .. 3·25 3·50
EMS22 $190 *Papilio torquatus* .. .. .. 7·50 8·00

Nos. EMS21/22 show additional overprints on sheet margins.

PARCEL POST STAMPS

PARCEL POST

X X PARCEL POST

$15.00 $15.00 $12.00

(P 1) (P 2)

**1981** (8 June). *No.* 554 *surch as Type* P 1 *by Bovell's Printery.*

P1 $15 on $1 *Chelonanthus uliginoides* .. .. 8·50 5·50
P2 $20 on $1 *Chelonanthus uliginoides* .. .. 10·00 8·50

**1983** (15 Jan). *No.* 843 *surch with Type* P **2** *in blue by Autoprint.*

P3 $12 on $1.10 on $2 *Norantea guianensis* .. 10·00 4·00

Parcel Post
$12.00

(P 3)

**1983** (14 Sept). *Unissued Royal Wedding surch, similar to No.* 843, *further surch with Type* P 3 *in blue by Autoprint.*

P4 $12 on $1.10 on $2 *Norantea guianensis* .. 1·75 2·00

TWENTY FIVE DOLLARS
PARCEL POST 25.00

(P 4)

**1985** (25 Apr). *No.* 673 *surch with Type* P 4 *in red by Tip. Torres.*

P5 $25 on 35 c. bright yellow-green, grey & black 12·00 12·00

POSTAGE DUE STAMPS

D 1 D 2

(Typo D.L.R.)

**1940** (Mar)–**55**. *Wmk Mult Script CA. Chalk-surfaced paper* (4 *c.*). *P* 14.

D1 D 1 1 c. green .. .. .. .. .. 1·60 4·50
a. Chalk-surfaced paper. *Deep green,* (30.4.52) .. .. .. .. 75 3·75
ab. W9*a* (Crown missing) .. .. £100
ac. W9*b* (St. Edward's Crown) .. 50·00
D2 2 c. black .. .. .. .. .. 8·00 2·50
a. Chalk-surfaced paper (30.4.52) .. 75 2·75
ab. W9*a* (Crown missing) .. .. 90·00
ac. W9*b* (St. Edward's Crown) .. 45·00
D3 4 c. bright blue (1.5.52) .. .. 30 4·25
a. W9*a* (Crown missing) .. .. 85·00
b. W9*b* (St. Edward's Crown) .. 45·00
D4 12 c. scarlet .. .. .. .. 14·00 8·50
a. Chalk-surfaced paper (19.7.55) .. 8·00 14·00
D1a/4a .. .. .. .. .. *Set of* 4 9·00 22·00
D1, D2 and D4 Perf "Specimen" .. *Set of* 3 50·00

(Typo D.L.R.)

**1967–8**. *Chalk-surfaced paper. W* w **12**. *P* 14.

D5 D 2 2 c. black (11.12.68) .. .. .. 50 6·00
D6 4 c. deep ultramarine .. .. .. 30 2·00
D7 12 c. reddish scarlet .. .. .. 30 3·00
D5/7 .. .. .. .. .. *Set of* 3 1·00 10·00

**1973** (24 May). *Glazed, ordinary paper. W* **106**. *P* 14.

D 8 D 2 1 c. olive .. .. .. .. 15 1·50
D 9 2 c. black .. .. .. .. 15 1·50
D10 4 c. dull ultramarine .. .. .. 15 1·50
D11 12 c. bright scarlet .. .. .. 20 1·75
D8/11 .. .. .. .. .. *Set of* 4 60 5·50

OFFICIAL STAMPS

OFFICIAL OFFICIAL OFFICIAL

(O 1) (O 1*a*) (O 2)

**1875**. *Optd with Type* O 1 (1 *c.*) *or* O 1*a* (*others*) *by litho. P* 10.

O1 8 1 c. black (R.) .. .. .. .. 26·00 11·00
a. Imperf between (horiz pair) .. — £2750
O2 2 c. orange .. .. .. .. £100 14·00
O3 8 c. rose .. .. .. .. .. £250 95·00
O4 7 12 c. brownish purple .. .. .. £950 £400
O5 9 24 c. green .. .. .. .. £650 £180

Two types of the word "OFFICIAL" are found on each value. On the 1 c., the word is either 16 or 17 mm long. On the other values the chief difference is in the shape and position of the letter "o" in "OFFICIAL". In one case the "o" is upright, in the other it slants to the left.

**1877**. *Optd with Type* O 2 *by typo. Wmk Crown CC. P* 14.

O 6 16 1 c. slate .. .. .. .. £150 55·00
a. Imperf between (vert pair) .. — £4750
O 7 2 c. orange .. .. .. .. 70·00 13·00
O 8 4 c. blue .. .. .. .. .. 75·00 20·00
O 9 6 c. brown .. .. .. .. £1700 £400
O10 8 c. rose .. .. .. .. .. £1600 £325

*Prepared for use, but not issued*

O11 16 12 c. pale violet .. .. .. .. £800
O12 24 c. green .. .. .. .. £950

The "OFFICIAL" overprints have been extensively forged.

The use of Official stamps was discontinued in June 1878, but was resumed in June 1981.

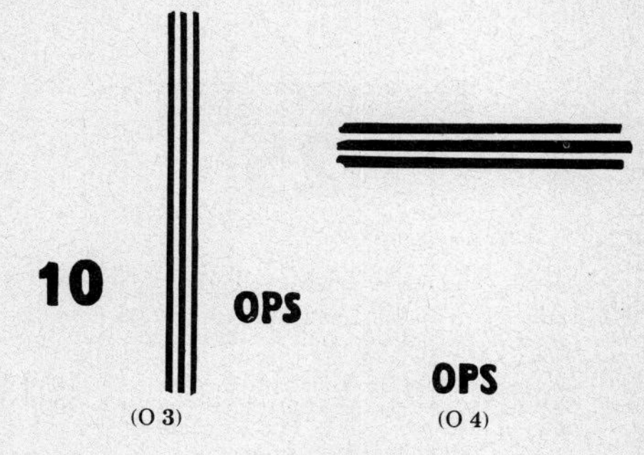


(O 3) (O 4)

OPS

(O 5)

**1981** (8 June). *Nos.* 556, F4a *and* F6/7 *surch or optd with Types* O 3/5 *by Bovell's Printery.*

O13 10 c. on 25 c. Marabunta (Blk. + R.) .. 1·50 1·40
O14 50 c. *Guzmania lingulata* (R.) .. .. 1·60 50
O15 60 c. Soldier's Cap (R.) .. .. .. 1·25 30
O16 $5 *Odontadenia grandiflora* (opt Type O 5) (R.) .. .. .. .. 4·50 2·50
O13/16 .. .. .. .. .. *Set of* 4 8·00 4·25

OPS

(O 6)

OPS
100

(O 7)

**1981** (1 July). *(a) Postage. Nos.* 491, 708*a*, 716, 834 *and* F9 *optd or surch as Types* O **5/7** *or additionally surch as T* **227**.

| | | | |
|---|---|---|---|
| O17 | 15 c. Harpy Eagle (opt Type O **6**) . . . . | 3·50 | 30 |
| O18 | 30 c. on $2 *Norantea guianensis* (No. F9) (opt Type O **5**) (Blk. + R.) . . . . | 45 | 30 |
| O19 | 100 c. on $3 Cylinder satellite (surch Type O **7**) (Blk. + R.) . . . . | 3·00 | 60 |
| O20 | 125 c. on $2 *Norantea guianensis* (opt Type O **5**) (R.) . . . . | 3·00 | 65 |
| O21 | $10 *Elbella patrobas* (opt Type O **5**) . . | 5·00 | 5·50 |
| | *(b) Air. No.* 804 *optd with Type* O **5** *in red* | | |
| O22 | $1.10 on $2 *Norantea guianensis* . . . . | 3·00 | 3·50 |
| | a. Opt Type O **5** double . . . . | £110 | |
| O17/22 | . . . . . . . . *Set of* 6 | 16·00 | 9·75 |

**1981** (7 July). *Nos.* 548, 719, 828 *and* 830 *optd with Type* O **5**.

| | | | |
|---|---|---|---|
| O23 | 15 c. Christmas Orchid . . . . | 4·00 | 1·00 |
| O24 | 50 c. British Guiana 1898 1 c. stamp . . | 1·25 | 35 |
| O25 | 100 c. on 8 c. Camp-fire cooking . . . . | 3·75 | 50 |
| O26 | 110 c. on 6 c. Type **116** . . . . | 4·50 | 75 |

OPS

OPS (O 8)

250 (O 9)

(Surch or optd by Autoprint)

**1982** (17 May). *(a) Postage. (i) Various stamps optd with Type* O **8** *in blue*

| | | | | |
|---|---|---|---|---|
| O27 | – | 20 c. multicoloured (No. 701). . | 30 | 20 |
| O28 | **136** | 40 c. multicoloured . . . . | 75 | 25 |
| O29 | – | 40 c. carmine-red, grey & blk (No. 674) | 1·00 | 25 |
| O30 | – | $2 multicoloured (No. 676). . | 6·00 | 1·00 |
| O27/30 | | . . . . *Set of* 4 | 7·25 | 1·50 |
| | | *(ii) No.* 911 *additionally surch with Type* O **9** *in blue* | | |
| O31 | – | 250 c. on 400 c. on 30 c. multicoloured . . | 80 | 80 |
| | | *(b) Air. No.* 980 *additionally optd with Type* O **8** *in blue* | | |
| O32 | – | 220 c. on 1 c. multicoloured . . . . | 3·00 | 1·00 |

**1982** (12 July). *No.* F9 *optd with Type* O **5** *in red by Bovell's Printery*.

| | | | |
|---|---|---|---|
| O33 | $2 *Norantea guianensis* . . . . | 12·00 | 2·00 |

**1982** (15 Sept). *Air. No.* 979 *optd with Type* O **8** *by Autoprint*.

| | | | |
|---|---|---|---|
| O34 | 110 c. on 5 c. Annatto tree . . . . | 3·00 | 1·00 |

**1984** (2 Apr). *No.* 912 *surch as Type* O **9** *vertically, in blue (except for No.* O37 *which has "OPS" in blue and "225" in black) by Autoprint*.

| | | | |
|---|---|---|---|
| O35 | 150 c. on $5 multicoloured . . . . | 70 | 70 |
| O36 | 200 c. on $5 multicoloured . . . . | 85 | 85 |
| O37 | 225 c. on $5 multicoloured . . . . | 1·00 | 1·00 |
| O38 | 230 c. on $5 multicoloured . . . . | 1·00 | 1·00 |
| O39 | 260 c. on $5 multicoloured . . . . | 1·25 | 1·25 |
| O40 | 320 c. on $5 multicoloured . . . . | 1·50 | 1·50 |
| O41 | 350 c. on $5 multicoloured . . . . | 1·60 | 1·60 |
| O42 | 600 c. on $5 multicoloured . . . . | 2·50 | 2·50 |
| O35/42 | . . . . . . . . *Set of* 8 | 9·25 | 9·25 |

25

(O 10)

(Surch or optd by Autoprint)

**1984** (25 June). *Nos.* O32 *and* O34 *surch as Type* O **10** *(25 c., 60 c.) or as T* **294** *(others), and No.* 981 *optd vertically with Type* O **8**.

| | | | |
|---|---|---|---|
| O43 | 25 c. on 110 c. on 5 c. Annatto tree . . . . | 15 | 15 |
| O44 | 30 c. on 110 c. on 5 c. Annatto tree (B.) . . | 20 | 20 |
| O45 | 45 c. on 220 c. on 1 c. Pitcher Plant of Mt Roraima . . . . | 20 | 20 |
| O46 | 55 c. on 110 c. on 5 c. Annatto tree . . . . | 25 | 25 |
| O47 | 60 c. on 220 c. on 1 c. Pitcher Plant of Mt Roraima . . . . | 25 | 25 |
| O48 | 75 c. on 220 c. on 1 c. Pitcher Plant of Mt Roraima . . . . | 30 | 30 |
| O49 | 90 c. on 220 c. on 1 c. Pitcher Plant of Mt Roraima (B.) . . . . | 40 | 40 |
| O50 | 120 c. on 220 c. on 1 c. Pitcher Plant of Mt Roraima . . . . | 50 | 50 |
| O51 | 130 c. on 220 c. on 1 c. Pitcher Plant of Mt Roraima (B.) . . . . | 55 | 55 |
| O52 | 330 c. on $2 *Norantea guianensis* (B.) . . | 1·40 | 1·60 |
| O43/52 | . . . . . . . . *Set of* 10 | 3·75 | 4·00 |

(Litho Format)

**1987** (5 Oct)–**88**. *Centenary of Publication of Sanders'* Reichenbachia. *Multicoloured designs as T* **331** *additionally inscr* "OFFICIAL". *No wmk. P* $14\times13^{1}/_{2}$ *(230, 350, 600 c., $12) or* $13^{1}/_{2}\times14$ *(others)*.

| | | | |
|---|---|---|---|
| O53 | 120 c. Plate No. 48 (Series 2) . . . . | 25 | 25 |
| O54 | 130 c. Plate No. 92 (Series 2) . . . . | 25 | 25 |
| O55 | 140 c. Plate No. 36 (Series 2) (5.10.88) . . | 25 | 25 |
| O56 | 150 c. Plate No. 43 (Series 2) . . . . | 25 | 25 |
| O57 | 175 c. Plate No. 31 (Series 2) (5.10.88) . . | 30 | 30 |
| O58 | 200 c. Plate No. 61 (Series 2) . . . . | 35 | 35 |
| O59 | 225 c. Plate No. 26 (Series 2) . . . . | 35 | 35 |
| O60 | 230 c. Plate No. 68 (Series 2) *(horiz)* . . | 35 | 35 |
| O61 | 250 c. Plate No. 59 (Series 2) (5.10.88) . . | 40 | 40 |
| O62 | 260 c. Plate No. 69 (Series 2) (5.10.88) . . | 40 | 40 |
| O63 | 275 c. Plate No. 90 (Series 2) . . . . | 40 | 40 |
| O64 | 320 c. Plate No. 75 (Series 2) . . . . | 50 | 50 |
| O65 | 330 c. Plate No. 23 (Series 2) . . . . | 60 | 60 |
| O66 | 350 c. Plate No. 95 (Series 2) *(horiz)* . . | 60 | 60 |
| O67 | 600 c. Plate No. 70 (Series 2) *(horiz)* . . | 95 | 95 |
| O68 | $12 Plate No. 71 (Series 2) *(horiz)* . . | 1·75 | 1·75 |
| O69 | $15 Plate No. 84 (Series 2) . . . . | 2·00 | 2·00 |
| O53/69 | . . . . . . *Set of* 17 | 9·00 | 9·00 |

Nos. O53/69 were printed in a similar sheet format to Nos. 1518/33.

OFFICIAL PARCEL POST STAMPS

**1981** (8 June). *Nos.* P1/2 *optd with Type* O **5** *in red by Bovell's Printery*.

| | | | |
|---|---|---|---|
| OP1 | $15 on $1 *Chelonanthus uliginoides* . . . . | 7·50 | 4·00 |
| | a. Opt in black . . . . . . | 60·00 | 8·00 |
| OP2 | $20 on $1 *Chelonanthus uliginoides* . . . . | 9·50 | 5·50 |

OPS

Parcel Post
$12.00

(OP 1)

**1983** (15 Jan). *No.* 843 *surch with Type* OP **1**, *and optd with T* **226**, *both in blue by Autoprint*.

| | | | |
|---|---|---|---|
| OP3 | $12 on $1.10 on $2 *Norantea guianensis* . . | 50·00 | 15·00 |
| | a. Surch Type OP1 omitted . . . . | | |

**1983** (22 Aug). *As No.* OP3, *but additionally optd with Type* O **8** *by Autoprint*.

| | | | |
|---|---|---|---|
| OP4 | $12 on $1.10 on $2 *Norantea guianensis* . . | 22·00 | 6·50 |

**1983** (3 Nov). *No.* P4 *additionally optd with Type* O **8** *in blue by Autoprint*.

| | | | |
|---|---|---|---|
| OP5 | $12 on $1.10 on $2 *Norantea guianensis* . . | 11·00 | 5·00 |

POSTAL FISCAL STAMPS

REVENUE
ONLY
*

(F 1)

**1975** (1 Nov). *Nos.* 543/5 *and* 550*a*/56 *optd with Type* F **1**.

| | | | |
|---|---|---|---|
| F 1 | 2 c. Type **132** . . . . . . | 30 | 30 |
| F 2 | 3 c. Hanging Heliconia . . . . . . | 30 | 30 |
| F 3 | 5 c. Annatto tree . . . . . . | 50 | 30 |
| F 4 | 25 c. Marabunta (Type II) . . . . . . | 60 | 30 |
| | a. Optd on No. 550 (Type I). . . . | 15·00 | 13·00 |
| F 5 | 40 c. Tiger Beard . . . . . . | 30 | 30 |
| F 6 | 50 c. *Guzmania lingulata* . . . . . . | 35 | 40 |
| F 7 | 60 c. Soldier's Cap . . . . . . | 50 | 50 |
| F 8 | $1 *Chelonanthus uliginoides* . . . . | 85 | 1·00 |
| F 9 | $2 *Norantea guianensis* . . . . | 1·75 | 2·25 |
| F10 | $5 *Odontadenia grandiflora* . . . . | 5·50 | 7·50 |
| F1/F10 | . . . . . . *Set of* 10 | 10·00 | 12·00 |

Although intended for fiscal use Nos. F1/10 were allowed, by the postal authorities, as "an act of grace" to do duty as postage stamps until 30 June 1976.

# Heligoland

Stamps of HAMBURG (see Part 7 (*Germany*) of this catalogue) were used in Heligoland until 16 April 1867. The Free City of Hamburg ran the Heligoland postal service between 1796 and 1 June 1866. Its stamps continued in use on the island until replaced by Heligoland issues.

| PRICES FOR STAMPS ON COVER | |
|---|---|
| Nos. 1/19 | *from* × 3 |

**PRINTERS.** All the stamps of Heligoland were typographed at the Imperial Printing Works, Berlin.

**REPRINTS**. Many of the stamps of Heligoland were subsequently reprinted at Berlin (between 1875 and 1885), Leipzig (1888) and Hamburg (1892 and 1895). Of these only the Berlin productions are difficult to distinguish from the originals so separate notes are provided for the individual values. Leipzig reprints can be identified by their highly surfaced paper and those from Hamburg by their 14 perforation. All of these reprints are worth much less than the original stamps priced below.

There was, in addition, a small reprinting of Nos. 13/19, made by the German government in 1890 for exchange purposes, but examples of this printing are far scarcer than the original stamps.

Forgeries, printed by lithography instead of typography, also exist for Nos. 1/4, 6 and 8 perforated 12½ or 13. Forged cancellations can also be found on originals and, on occasion, genuine postmarks on reprints.

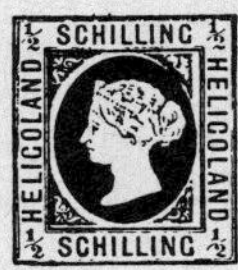

1

Three Dies of Embossed Head for Types **1** and **2**:

Die I Die II

Die III

Die I. Blob instead of curl beneath the chignon. Outline of two jewels at top of diadem.
Die II. Curl under chignon. One jewel at top of diadem.
Die III. Shorter curl under chignon. Two jewels at top of diadem.

(Des Wedding. Die eng E. Schilling)

**1867** (Mar)–**68**. *Head Die I embossed in colourless relief. Roul.*

| | | | | |
|---|---|---|---|---|
| 1 | **1** | ½ sch. blue-green and rose .. .. .. | £300 | £800 |
| | | a. Head Die II (7.68) .. .. .. | £700 | £1100 |
| 2 | | 1 sch. rose and blue-green (21.3.67) .. | £160 | £180 |
| 3 | | 2 sch. rose and grass-green (21.3.67) .. | 8·00 | 50·00 |
| 4 | | 6 sch. green and rose .. .. .. | 10·00 | £250 |

For Nos. 1/4 the second colour given is that of the spandrels on the ½ and 1 sch., and of the spandrels and central background for the 2 and 6 sch.

All four values exist from the Berlin, Leipzig and Hamburg reprintings. The following points are helpful in identifying originals from Berlin reprints; for Leipzig and Hamburg reprints see general note above:

- ½ sch. – Reprints are all in yellowish green and show Head Die II
- 1 sch. – All reprints are Head Die III
- 2 sch. – Berlin reprints are in dull rose with a deeper blue-green
- 6 sch. – Originals show white specks in green. Berlin reprints have a more solid bluish green

**1869** (Apr)–**73**. *Head embossed in colourless relief. P* 13½×14½.

| | | | | |
|---|---|---|---|---|
| 5 | 1 | ¼ sch. rose and green (background) (I) (*quadrillé paper*) (8.73) .. .. | 21·00 | £1500 |
| | | a. Error. Green and rose (background) (9.73) .. .. .. .. | £100 | £3000 |
| | | *b. Deep rose and pale green* (background) (11.73) .. .. .. | 80·00 | £1500 |
| 6 | | ½ sch. blue-green and rose (II) .. .. | £190 | £200 |
| | | *a. Yellow-green and rose* (7.71) .. | £140 | £190 |
| | | b. Quadrillé paper (6.73) .. .. | 90·00 | £150 |
| 7 | | ¾ sch. green and rose (I) (*quadrillé paper*) (12.73) .. .. .. .. | 24·00 | £1100 |
| 8 | | 1 sch. rose and yellow-green (III) (7.71) .. | £130 | £180 |
| | | a. Quadrillé paper. *Rose and pale blue-green* (6.73) .. .. .. | £110 | £180 |
| 9 | | 1½ sch. grn & rose (I) (*quadrillé paper*) (9.73) | 55·00 | £250 |

For Nos. 5/9 the second colour given is that of the spandrels on the ½ and 1 sch., of the central background on the ¼ and 1½ sch., and of the central background, side labels and side marginal lines of the ¾ sch.

No. 5a was a printing of the ¼ sch. made in the colour combination of the 1½ sch. by mistake.

All five values exist from the Berlin, Leipzig and Hamburg reprintings. The following points are helpful in identifying originals from Berlin reprints; for Leipzig and Hamburg reprints see general note above:

- ¼ sch. – All Berlin and some Hamburg reprints are Head Die II
- ½ sch. – Berlin reprints on thinner paper with solid colour in the spandrels.
- ¾ sch. – Berlin reprints on thinner, non-quadrillé paper
- 1 sch. – Berlin reprints are on thinner paper or show many breaks in the rose line beneath "SCHILLING" at the top of the design or in the line above it at the foot.
- 1½ sch. – All Berlin and some Hamburg reprints are Head Die II

Berlin, Leipzig and Hamburg reprints also exist of the 2 and 6 sch., but these values do not come as perforated originals.

2

3

4

5

(Des H. Gätke. Die eng E. Schilling (T **2**), A. Schiffner (others)

**1875** (Feb)–**90**. *Head Die II on T* **2** *embossed in colourless relief. P* 13½×14½.

| | | | | |
|---|---|---|---|---|
| 10 | **2** | 1 pf. (¼d.) deep green and rose .. .. | 8·00 | £500 |
| 11 | | 2 pf. (½d.) deep rose and deep green .. | 8·00 | £600 |
| 12 | **3** | 3 pf. (⅝d.) pale green, red & yellow (6.76) | £225 | £1100 |
| | | *a. Green, red and orange* (6.77) .. | £160 | £850 |
| 13 | **2** | 5 pf. (¾d.) deep yellow-green and rose .. | 8·00 | 18·00 |
| | | *a. Deep green and rose* (6.90) .. .. | 9·50 | 40·00 |
| 14 | | 10 pf. (1½d.) deep rose and deep green .. | 30·00 | 20·00 |
| | | *a. Scarlet and pale blue-green* (5.87) .. | 7·50 | 20·00 |
| 15 | **3** | 20 pf. (2½d.) rose, green and yellow (6.76) | £200 | £120 |
| | | *a. Rose-carmine, dp green & orge* (4.80) | £130 | 50·00 |
| | | *b. Dull red, pale green and lemon* (7.88) | 11·00 | 28·00 |
| | | *c. Aniline verm, brt grn & lemon* (6.90) | 11·00 | 50·00 |
| 16 | **2** | 25 pf. (3d.) deep green and rose .. .. | 10·00 | 26·00 |
| 17 | | 50 pf. (6d.) rose and green .. .. | 16·00 | 32·00 |
| 18 | **4** | 1 m. (1s.) dp green, scarlet & black (8.79) | £140 | £200 |
| | | a. Perf 11½ .. .. .. .. | £800 | |
| | | *b. Dp green, aniline rose & black* (5.89) | £140 | £200 |
| 19 | **5** | 5 m. (5s.) dp grn, aniline rose & blk (8.79) | £110 | £950 |
| | | a. Perf 11½ .. .. .. .. | £800 | |
| | | ab. Imperf between (pair) .. .. | £2500 | |

For stamps as Type **2** the first colour is that of the central background and the second that of the frame. On the 3 pf. the first colour is of the frame and the top band of the shield, the second is the centre band and the third the shield border. The 20 pf. is similar, but has the centre band in the same colour as the frame and the upper band on the shield in the second colour.

The 1, 2 and 3 pf. exist from the Berlin, Leipzig and Hamburg reprintings. There were no such reprints for the other values. The following points are helpful in identifying originals from Berlin reprints; for Leipzig and Hamburg reprints see general note above:

- 1 pf. – Berlin printings show a peculiar shade of pink
- 2 pf. – All reprints are much lighter in shade than the deep rose and deep green of the originals
- 3 pf. – Berlin reprints either show the band around the shield in brownish orange, or have this feature in deep yellow with the other two colours lighter.

Heligoland was ceded to Germany on 9 August 1890.

## PRICES OF SETS

Set prices are given for many issues, generally those containing three stamps or more. Definitive sets include one of each value or major colour change, but do not cover different perforations, die types or minor shades. Where a choice is possible the set prices are based on the cheapest versions of the stamps included in the listings.

# Hong Kong

### CROWN COLONY

The Hong Kong Post Office was established in February 1841, when much of the business previously transacted through the Macao postal agency was transferred to the island. The first cancellation is known from April 1842, but local control of the posts was shortlived as the Hong Kong Post Office became a branch of the British G.P.O. following the ratification of the Treaty of Nanking on 26 June 1843.

The colonial authorities resumed control of the postal service on 1 May 1860, although the previously established postal agencies in the Chinese Treaty Ports remained part of the British G.P.O. system until 1 May 1868.

For illustrations of the handstamp types see BRITISH POST OFFICES ABROAD notes, following GREAT BRITAIN.

CROWNED-CIRCLE HANDSTAMPS

| | | | |
|---|---|---|---|
| CC1 | CC1 | HONG KONG (R.) (17.10.1843) | *Price on cover* £550 |
| CC2 | CC1b | HONG KONG (R.) (21.8.1844) | *Price on cover* £375 |
| CC3 | CC3 | HONG KONG (R.) (16.6.1852) | *Price on cover* £200 |

We no longer list the Great Britain stamps with obliteration "B 62" within oval. The Government notification dated 29 November 1862 stated that only the Hong Kong stamps to be issued on 8 December would be available for postage and the stamps formerly listed were all issued in Great Britain later than the date of the notice.

| PRICES FOR STAMPS ON COVER TO 1945 | |
|---|---|
| Nos. 1/27 | *from* × 6 |
| Nos. 28/36 | *from* × 4 |
| Nos. 37/9 | *from* × 5 |
| Nos. 40/4 | *from* × 4 |
| Nos. 45/8 | *from* × 10 |
| Nos. 49/50 | *from* × 4 |
| No. 51 | *from* × 15 |
| Nos. 52/61 | *from* × 5 |
| Nos. 62/99 | *from* × 4 |
| Nos. 100/32 | *from* × 3 |
| Nos. 133/6 | *from* × 2 |
| Nos. 137/9 | *from* × 4 |
| Nos. 140/68 | *from* × 2 |
| Nos. D1/12 | *from* × 8 |
| Nos. F1/11 | *from* × 4 |
| No. F12 | *from* × 3 |
| Nos. P1/3 | *from* × 2 |

**PRINTERS.** All definitive issues up to 1960 were typographed by De La Rue & Co.

**CONDITION.** Mint or fine used specimens of the earlier Hong Kong stamps are rarely met with and are worth considerably more than our prices which are for stamps in average condition. Inferior specimens can be supplied at much lower prices.

1

2

3

**1862** (8 Dec). *No wmk. P* 14.

| | | | | |
|---|---|---|---|---|
| 1 | **1** | 2 c. brown .. .. .. .. | £170 | 45·00 |
| | | *a. Deep brown* .. .. .. | £275 | 50·00 |
| 2 | | 8 c. yellow-buff .. .. .. | £300 | 30·00 |
| 3 | | 12 c. pale greenish blue.. .. .. | £225 | 30·00 |
| 4 | **3** | 18 c. lilac .. .. .. .. | £250 | 25·00 |
| 5 | | 24 c. green .. .. .. .. | £500 | 55·00 |
| 6 | | 48 c. rose .. .. .. .. | £1400 | £170 |
| 7 | | 96 c. brownish grey .. .. .. | £1800 | £180 |

**1863–71**. *Wmk Crown CC. P* 14.

| | | | | |
|---|---|---|---|---|
| 8 | **1** | 2 c. deep brown (1865).. .. .. | £110 | 15·00 |
| | | *a. Brown* .. .. .. .. | 55·00 | 3·75 |
| | | *b. Pale yellowish brown* .. .. | 65·00 | 5·50 |
| 9 | **2** | 4 c. grey (1863) .. .. .. | 55·00 | 7·00 |
| | | *a. Slate* .. .. .. .. | 55·00 | 3·25 |
| | | *b. Deep slate* .. .. .. .. | 75·00 | 5·00 |
| | | *c. Greenish grey* .. .. .. | £130 | 23·00 |
| | | *d. Bluish slate* .. .. .. | £225 | 12·00 |
| | | e. Perf 12½ (1870) .. .. .. | £3250 | £250 |
| 10 | | 6 c. lilac (1863) .. .. .. | £180 | 4·50 |
| | | *a. Mauve* .. .. .. .. | £190 | 5·50 |
| 11 | **1** | 8 c. pale dull orange (1865) .. .. | £200 | 4·50 |
| | | *a. Brownish orange* .. .. .. | £170 | 4·50 |
| | | *b. Bright orange* .. .. .. | £190 | 4·00 |
| 12 | | 12 c. pale greenish blue (1864?) .. | £400 | 17·00 |
| | | *a. Pale blue* .. .. .. .. | 12·00 | 3·00 |
| | | *b. Deep blue* .. .. .. .. | 90·00 | 5·50 |
| 13 | **3** | 18 c. lilac (1866) .. .. .. | £1600 | £200 |
| 14 | | 24 c. green (1865) .. .. .. | £190 | 5·00 |
| | | *a. Pale green* .. .. .. .. | £300 | 8·50 |
| | | *b. Deep green* .. .. .. .. | £400 | 16·00 |
| 15 | **2** | 30 c. vermilion (1863) .. .. .. | £350 | 7·50 |
| | | *a. Orange-vermilion* .. .. .. | £275 | 8·50 |
| 16 | | 30 c. mauve (14.8.71) .. .. .. | 85·00 | 2·25 |
| 17 | | 48 c. pale rose (1865) .. .. .. | £400 | 20·00 |
| | | *a. Rose-carmine* .. .. .. | £425 | 11·00 |
| | | *b. Bright claret* .. .. .. | † | — |

18 2 96 c. olive-bistre (1865) .. .. .. £10000 £425
19 96 c. brownish grey (1866) .. .. £425 19·00
*a. Brownish black* .. .. £550 17·00

There is a wide range of shades in this issue, of which we can only indicate the main groups.

No. 12 is the same shade as No. 3 without wmk, the impression having a waxy appearance.

Only one used copy of No. 17*b* is known.

See also Nos. 22 and 28/31.

**16 cents.** (4) *28 cents.* (5) 5 cents. (6) **10 cents.** (7)

**ts.**

No. 20b

**1876.** *Nos.* 13 *and* 16 *surch with T* 4 *or* 5 *by Noronha and Sons, Hong Kong.*

20 3 16 c. on 18 c. lilac (June?) .. .. £850 £120
a. Space between "n" and "t" .. .. £2500 £375
b. Space between "s" and stop .. £2500 £375
21 2 28 c. on 30 c. mauve (July?) .. .. £500 40·00

**1877** (Aug). *New value. Wmk Crown CC. P* 14.

22 3 16 c. yellow .. .. .. .. £475 42·00

**1880** (Mar–Sept). *Surch with T* 6 *or* 7.

23 1 5 c. on 8 c. bright orange (No. 11*b*) (Sept) .. .. .. £275 50·00
a. Surch inverted .. .. .. — £5500
b. Surch double .. .. .. — £8500
24 3 5 c. on 18 c. lilac (No. 13) .. .. £225 35·00
25 1 10 c. on 12 c. pale blue (No. 12*a*) .. £275 42·00
*a. Blue* .. .. .. .. £375 48·00
26 3 10 c. on 16 c. yellow (No. 22) (August) £1000 75·00
a. Surch inverted .. .. .. —£13000
27 10 c. on 24 c. green (No. 14) (June) .. £400 50·00

**1880.** *Colours changed and new values. Wmk Crown CC. P* 14.

28 1 2 c. dull rose (July) .. .. .. 60·00 8·50
*a. Rose* .. .. .. .. .. 70·00 10·00
29 2 5 c. blue (Nov) .. .. .. .. £110 13·00
30 10 c. mauve (Nov) .. .. .. £130 6·50
31 3 48 c. brown .. .. .. .. £325 48·00

**1882–96.** *Wmk Crown CA. P* 14.

32 1 2 c. rose-lake .. .. .. .. 60·00 13·00
*a. Rose-pink* .. .. .. .. 75·00 22·00
b. Perf 12 .. .. .. .. £10000
33 1 2 c. carmine (1883) .. .. .. 10·00 30
*a. Aniline carmine* .. .. .. 11·00 30
34 2 4 c. slate-grey (1896) .. .. .. 3·50 20
35 5 c. pale blue .. .. .. .. 4·50 30
*a. Blue* .. .. .. .. .. 4·50 30
36 10 c. dull mauve .. .. .. .. £275 4·00
37 10 c. green (1883) .. .. .. .. 65·00 60
*a. Deep blue-green* .. .. .. £750 22·00
38 10 c. purple/*red* (1.1.91) .. .. .. 4·50 20
39 30 c. yellowish green (1.1.91) .. .. 65·00 23·00
*a. Grey-green* .. .. .. .. 16·00 9·00
38, 39a Optd "Specimen" .. *Set of* 2 £200

Examples of No. 39 should not be confused with washed or faded stamps from the grey-green shade which tend to turn to a very yellow-green when dampened.

For other stamps with this watermark, but in colours changed to the U.P.U. scheme see Nos. 56/61.

**20 CENTS** (8) **50 CENTS** (9) **1 DOLLAR** (10)

**1885** (June). *As Nos.* 15, 19 *and* 31, *but wmkd Crown CA, surch with T* 8 *to* 10 *by De La Rue.*

40 2 20 c. on 30 c. orange-red .. .. .. 38·00 2·00
a. Surch double .. .. ..
41 3 50 c. on 48 c. yellowish brown .. .. £140 9·50
42 $1 on 96 c. grey-olive .. .. .. £200 23·00
40/2 Optd "Specimen" .. .. *Set of* 3 £400

**7 cents.** (11) **14 cents.** (12)

弍 (13) (20 c.) 五十 (14) (50 c.) 壹員 (15) ($1)

**1891** (1 Jan–Mar). (*a*) *Nos.* 16 *and* 37 *surch with T* 11 *or* 12 *by Noronha and Sons, Hong Kong*

43 2 7 c. on 10 c. green .. .. .. .. 42·00 5·50
a. Antique "t" in "cents" (R.1/1) .. £425 £140
b. Surch double .. .. .. .. £3500 £1000
44 14 c. on 30 c. mauve (Feb) .. .. .. 75·00 42·00
a. Antique "t" in "cents" (R.1/1) .. £1700 £850

(*b*) *As Nos.* 40/2 (*surch with T* 8 *to* 10 *by De La Rue*), *but colours changed*

45 2 20 c. on 30 c. yellowish green (No. 39) .. £100 60·00
*a. Grey-green* (No. 39*a*) .. .. 55·00 50·00
46 3 50 c. on 48 c. dull purple .. .. .. £180 £120
47 $1 on 96 c. purple/*red* .. .. .. £300 £120
45a/7 Optd "Specimen" .. .. *Set of* 3 £300

(*c*) *Nos.* 45/7 *with further surch, T* 13/15, *in Chinese characters, handstamped locally* (Mar)

48 2 20 c. on 30 c. yellowish green .. .. 32·00 3·00
*a. Grey-green* .. .. .. .. 11·00 1·50
49 3 50 c. on 48 c. dull purple .. .. .. 30·00 2·50
50 $1 on 96 c. purple/*red* .. .. .. £140 10·00

The true antique "t" variety (Nos. 43a and 44a) should not be confused with a small "t" showing a short foot. In the antique "t" the crossbar is accurately bisected by the vertical stroke, which is thicker at the top. The lower curve bends towards the right and does not turn upwards to the same extent as on the normal.

The handstamped surcharges on Nos. 48/50 were applied over the original Chinese face values. The single character for "2" was intended to convert "30 c." to "20 c.". There were six slightly different versions of the "2" handstamp and three for the "50 c.".

A used example of No. 48 in the Royal Philatelic Collection shows surcharge Type **8** double.

The errors of the Chinese surcharges previously listed on the above issue and also on Nos. 52 and 55 are now omitted as being outside the scope of the catalogue. While some without doub possess philatelic merit, it is impossible to distinguish between the genuine errors and the clandestine copies made to order with the original chops. No. 55c is retained as this represents a distinctly different chop which was used for the last part of the printing.

**1841 Hong Kong JUBILEE 1891** (16) **10 CENTS** (17) 拾 (18) 拾 (19)

**1891** (22 Jan). *50th Anniversary of Colony. Optd with T* **16**.

51 1 2 c. carmine (No. 33) .. .. .. £150 60·00
a. Short "J" in "JUBILEE" .. .. £250 90·00
b. Short "U" in "JUBILEE" .. .. £250 90·00
c. Broken "1" in "1891" .. .. £350 £130
d. Tall narrow "K" in "KONG" .. £500 £300
e. Opt double .. .. .. .. £7000 £5500
f. Space between "O" and "N" of "HONG" .. .. .. £1000 £450

This overprint was applied in a setting of 12 during a number of printings and other less marked varieties therefore exist.

The prices quoted for No. 51e are for examples on which the two impressions are distinctly separated. Examples on which the two impressions are almost coincidental are worth considerably less.

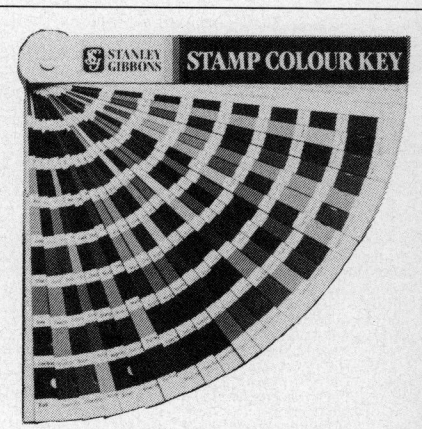

898 (1 Apr). *Wmk Mult Crown CA. P 14. (a) Surch with T* **10**, *and handstamped Chinese characters as T* **15**

52 **3** $1 on 96 c. black .. .. .. .. .. 48·00 15·00
 *a. Grey-black* .. .. .. .. .. 48·00 15·00

*(b) Surch with T* **10** *only*

53 **3** $1 on 96 c. black .. .. .. .. .. £325 £550
 *a. Grey-black* (Optd S. £200) .. .. .. £325 £550

898 (Apr). *(a) Surch with T* **17**.

4 **2** 10 c. on 30 c. grey-green (No. 39*a*) .. .. £225 £350
 a. Figures "10" widely spaced ($1^1/_2$ mm) £1000

Type **17** was applied in a setting of 12, No. 54a appearing on position 12.

*(b) As No. 54, but with Chinese character, T* **18**, *in addition*

55 **2** 10 c. on 30 c. grey-green (No. 39*a*) (H/S S. £100) .. .. .. .. 16·00 35·00
 *a. Yellowish green* (Optd S. £100) .. 60·00
 b. Figures "10" widely spaced ($1^1/_2$ mm) £200 £250
 c. Chinese character large (Type **19**) .. £400 £300

1900 (Aug)–01. *Wmk Crown CA. P 14.*

56 **1** 2 c. dull green .. .. .. .. .. 6·00 20
57 **2** 4 c. carmine .. .. .. .. .. 3·50 20
58 5 c. yellow .. .. .. .. .. 5·50 2·75
59 10 c. ultramarine .. .. .. .. .. 11·00 55
60 **1** 12 c. blue (1901) .. .. .. .. .. 9·00 27·00
61 **2** 30 c. brown (12.01) .. .. .. .. .. 6·00 13·00
56/61 .. .. .. .. *Set of* 6 38·00 40·00
56/9, 61 Optd "Specimen" .. .. *Set of* 5 £250

20

21

22

23

1903. *Wmk Crown CA. P 14.*

62 **20** 1 c. dull purple and brown .. .. 60 15
63 2 c. dull green .. .. .. .. 1·75 70
64 **21** 4 c. purple/*red* .. .. .. .. 2·25 10
65 5 c. dull green and brown-orange .. .. 3·75 3·50
66 8 c. slate and violet .. .. .. 3·00 60
67 **20** 10 c. purple and blue/*blue* .. .. 10·00 30
68 **23** 12 c. green and purple/*yellow* .. .. 4·50 2·00
69 20 c. slate and chestnut .. .. .. 11·00 80
70 **22** 30 c. dull green and black .. .. 14·00 4·75
71 **23** 50 c. dull green and magenta .. .. 11·00 11·00
72 **20** $1 purple and sage-green .. .. 38·00 9·50
73 **23** $2 slate and scarlet .. .. .. 80·00 90·00
74 **22** $3 slate and dull blue .. .. .. 80·00 £110
75 **23** $5 purple and blue-green .. .. £140 £150
76 **22** $10 slate and orange/*blue* .. .. £375 £275
62/76 .. .. .. .. *Set of* 15 £700 £600
62/76 Optd "Specimen" .. .. *Set of* 15 £600

1904–6. *Wmk Mult Crown CA. Chalk-surfaced paper (8, 12 c., $3, $5) or ordinary paper (others). P 14.*

77 **20** 2 c. dull green .. .. .. .. 60 35
 a. Chalk-surfaced paper (1906) .. .. 1·50 90
78 **21** 4 c. purple/*red* .. .. .. .. 2·00 15
 a. Chalk-surfaced paper (1906) .. .. 1·25 10
79 5 c. dull green and brown-orange .. .. 4·50 1·75
 a. Chalk-surfaced paper (1906) .. .. 3·00 1·75
80 8 c. slate and violet (1906) .. .. 3·50 1·25
81 **20** 10 c. purple and blue/*blue* .. .. 4·00 40
82 **23** 12 c. green and purple/*yellow* (1906) .. 4·50 4·25
83 20 c. slate and chestnut .. .. .. 7·00 1·00
 a. Chalk-surfaced paper (1906) .. .. 5·00 90
84 **22** 30 c. dull green and black .. .. 9·50 4·50
 a. Chalk-surfaced paper (1906) .. .. 14·00 5·50
85 **23** 50 c. green and magenta .. .. .. 13·00 3·00
 a. Chalk-surfaced paper (1906) .. .. 12·00 4·00
86 **20** $1 purple and sage-green .. .. 38·00 6·50
 a. Chalk-surfaced paper (1906) .. .. 38·00 6·50
87 **23** $2 slate and scarlet .. .. .. 80·00 48·00
 a. Chalk-surfaced paper (1905) .. .. 65·00 45·00
88 **22** $3 slate and dull blue (1905) .. .. 70·00 90·00
89 **23** $5 purple and blue-green (1905) .. £130 £150
90 **22** $10 slate and orange/*blue* .. .. £550 £375
 a. Chalk-surfaced paper (1906) .. .. £500 £375
77/90 .. .. .. .. *Set of* 14 £750 £600

1907–11. *Colours changed and new value. Wmk Mult Crown CA. Chalk-surfaced paper (6 c. and 20 c. to $2). P 14.*

91 **20** 1 c. brown (1910) .. .. .. .. 1·00 75
92 2 c. deep green .. .. .. .. 9·00 60
 *a. Green* .. .. .. .. .. 7·00 50
93 **21** 4 c. carmine-red .. .. .. .. 1·50 25
94 **22** 6 c. orange-vermilion and purple .. .. 7·00 2·50
95 **20** 10 c. bright ultramarine .. .. .. 5·00 30
96 **23** 20 c. purple and sage-green (1911) .. 25·00 23·00
97 **22** 30 c. purple and orange-yellow (1911) .. 29·00 12·00
98 **23** 50 c. black/*green* (1911) .. .. .. 17·00 6·00
99 $2 carmine-red and black (1910) .. £100 90·00
91/9 .. .. .. .. *Set of* 9 £170 £120
91, 93/9 Optd "Specimen" .. .. *Set of* 8 £325

24 25 26

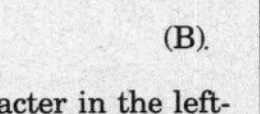

27 28 (A) (B)

In Type A of the 25 c. the upper Chinese character in the left-hand label has a short vertical stroke crossing it at the foot. In Type B this stroke is absent.

1912 (Nov)–21. *Wmk Mult Crown CA. Chalk-surfaced paper (12 c. to $10). P 14.*

100 **24** 1 c. brown .. .. .. .. .. 75 30
 *a. Black-brown* .. .. .. .. 2·00 85
 b. Crown broken at right (R.9/2) .. £130 £110
101 2 c. deep green .. .. .. .. 1·75 25
 *a. Green* .. .. .. .. 1·75 25
102 **25** 4 c. carmine-red .. .. .. .. 1·50 20
 *a. Scarlet* .. .. .. .. 6·00 90
103 **26** 6 c. yellow-orange .. .. .. .. 2·25 60
 *a. Brown-orange* .. .. .. .. 2·00 80
104 **25** 8 c. grey (1915) .. .. .. .. 12·00 3·25
 *a. Slate* .. .. .. .. 19·00 3·25
105 **24** 10 c. ultramarine .. .. .. .. 19·00 25
 *a. Deep bright ultramarine* .. .. 14·00 20
106 **27** 12 c. purple/*yellow* .. .. .. .. 1·00 3·25
 *a. White back* (Optd S. £50) (5.14) .. 3·50 7·00
107 20 c. purple and sage-green .. .. .. 1·75 60
108 **28** 25 c. purple and magenta (Type A) (1.14) 6·00 9·00
109 25 c. purple and magenta (Type B) (8.19) 40·00 32·00
110 **26** 30 c. purple and orange-yellow .. .. 20·00 3·50
 *a. Purple and orange* .. .. .. 9·00 3·00
111 **27** 50 c. black/*blue-green* .. .. .. 4·50 50
 *a. White back* (Optd S. £70) (5.14) .. 3·75 2·50
 *b. On blue-green, olive back* (1917) .. £170 9·00
 *c. On emerald surface* (9.19) .. .. 8·00 10·00
 *d. On emerald back* (Optd S. £70) (7.12.21) .. .. .. .. 8·50 4·00
112 **24** $1 purple and blue/*blue* .. .. 10·00 90
113 **27** $2 carmine-red and grey-black .. .. 55·00 17·00
114 **26** $3 green and purple .. .. .. 80·00 32·00
115 **27** $5 green and red/*green* .. .. £150 85·00
 *a. White back* (Optd S. £90) (5.14) .. £150 80·00
 *b. On blue-green, olive back* (Optd S. £100) (1917) .. .. .. £325 65·00
116 **26** $10 purple and black/*red* .. .. £170 45·00
100/16 .. .. .. .. *Set of* 17 £500 £190
100/16 Optd "Specimen" .. .. *Set of* 17 £750

1921 (Jan)–37. *Wmk Mult Script CA. Chalk-surfaced paper (12 c. to $5). P 14.*

117 **24** 1 c. brown .. .. .. .. .. 30 25
 b. Crown broken at right (R.9/2) ..
118 2 c. blue-green .. .. .. .. 65 20
 *a. Yellow-green* .. .. .. .. 3·00 20
118*b* 2 c. grey (14.4.37) .. .. .. .. 6·00 3·25
119 **25** 3 c. grey (8.10.31) .. .. .. .. 1·50 40
120 4 c. carmine-rose .. .. .. .. 80 30
 *a. Carmine-red* .. .. .. .. 55 15
 b. Top of lower Chinese characters at right broken off .. .. .. 80·00 60·00
121 5 c. violet (16.10.31) .. .. .. 1·25 15
122 8 c. grey .. .. .. .. .. 4·50 25·00
123 8 c. orange (7.12.21) .. .. .. 80 70
124 **24** 10 c. bright ultramarine .. .. .. 60 10
124*a* **27** 12 c. purple/*yellow* (3.4.33) .. .. 4·25 40
125 20 c. purple and sage-green (7.12.21) .. 1·50 10
126 **28** 25 c. purple and magenta (B) (7.12.21) .. 80 30
127 **26** 30 c. purple and chrome-yellow (7.12.21) 3·50 1·25
 *a. Purple and orange-yellow* .. .. 13·00 3·00
128 **27** 50 c. black/*emerald* (1924) .. .. 3·25 10
129 **24** $1 purple and blue/*blue* (7.12.21) .. 7·00 50
130 **27** $2 carmine-red & grey-black (7.12.21) 35·00 1·75
131 **26** $3 green and dull purple (1926) .. 80·00 20·00
132 **27** $5 green and red/*emerald* (1925) .. £120 21·00
117/32 .. .. .. .. *Set of* 18 £225 70·00
117/32 Optd/Perf "Specimen" .. *Set of* 18 £600

1935 (6 May). *Silver Jubilee. As Nos. 91/4 of Antigua, but ptd by B.W. P 11 × 12.*

133 3 c. ultramarine and grey-black .. .. 1·75 2·00
 c. Lightning conductor .. .. .. £120
134 5 c. green and indigo .. .. .. 4·00 1·50
 a. Extra flagstaff .. .. .. .. £190 £200
 b. Short extra flagstaff .. .. .. £140
 c. Lightning conductor .. .. .. £130
 d. Flagstaff on right-hand turret .. .. £140
135 10 c. brown and deep blue .. .. .. 4·00 1·00
136 20 c. slate and purple .. .. .. 16·00 4·00
 b. Short extra flagstaff .. .. .. £200
 d. Flagstaff on right-hand turret .. .. £200
 e. Double flagstaff .. .. .. £200
133/6 .. .. .. .. *Set of* 4 23·00 7·75
133/6 Perf "Specimen" .. .. *Set of* 4 95·00

For illustrations of plate varieties see Catalogue Introduction.

1937 (12 May). *Coronation. As Nos. 95/7 of Antigua. P 11×11½.*

137 4 c. green .. .. .. .. .. 1·25 1·00
138 15 c. carmine .. .. .. .. .. 2·75 2·00
139 25 c. blue .. .. .. .. .. 3·75 1·50
137/9 .. .. .. .. *Set of* 3 7·00 4·00
137/9 Perf "Specimen" .. .. *Set of* 3 70·00

**29** King George VI

1938–52. *Wmk Mult Script CA. Chalk-surfaced paper (80 c., $1 (No. 155), $2 (No. 157), $5 (No. 159), $10 (No. 161)). P 14.*

140 **29** 1 c. brown (24.5.38) .. .. .. 40 40
 *a. Pale brown* (27.2.52) .. .. .. 30 2·50
141 2 c. grey (5.4.38) .. .. .. .. 30 15
 a. Perf $14^1/_2$×14 (1942) .. .. .. 65 2·75
142 4 c. orange (5.4.38) .. .. .. 60 70
 a. Perf $14^1/_2$×14 (28.9.45) .. .. 2·75 2·25
143 5 c. green (24.5.38) .. .. .. 35 10
 a. Perf $14^1/_2$×14 (12.41) .. .. .. 80 2·25
144 8 c. red-brown (1.11.41) .. .. .. 35 1·75
 a. Imperf (pair) .. .. .. .. £13000
145 10 c. bright violet (13.4.38) .. .. 15·00 60
 a. Perf $14^1/_2$×14. *Dull violet* (12.41) 1·75 10
 *b. Dull reddish violet* (9.4.46) .. .. 2·25 30
 *c. Reddish lilac* (9.4.47) .. .. .. 3·25 15
146 15 c. scarlet (13.4.38) .. .. .. 30 15
147 20 c. black (1.2.46) .. .. .. .. 20 15
148 20 c. scarlet-vermilion (1.4.48) .. .. 1·50 20
 *a. Rose-red* (25.4.51) .. .. .. 4·00 2·75
149 25 c. bright blue (5.4.38) .. .. .. 4·50 45
150 25 c. pale yellow-olive (9.4.46) .. .. 70 1·25
151 30 c. yellow-olive (13.4.38) .. .. £110 85
 a. Perf $14^1/_2$×14. *Yellowish olive* (12.41) .. .. .. .. 5·50 6·00
152 30 c. blue (9.4.46) .. .. .. .. 1·25 10
153 50 c. reddish purple (13.4.38) .. .. 7·50 30
 a. Perf $14^1/_2$×14. *Dp magenta* (12.41) 2·00 50
 b. Chalk-surfaced paper. *Brt purple* (9.4.47) .. .. .. .. 1·25 10
154 80 c. carmine (2.2.48) .. .. .. 1·00 50
155 $1 dull lilac and blue (*chalk-surfaced paper*) (27.4.38) .. .. .. 4·50 1·50
 a. Ordinary paper. *Pale reddish lilac and blue* (11.41) .. .. .. 6·00 2·50
156 $1 red-orange and green (9.4.46) .. 2·75 10
 a. Chalk-surfaced paper (21.6.48) .. 8·00 1·00
 b. Chalk-surfaced paper. *Yellow-orge and green* (6.11.52) .. .. .. 23·00 11·00
157 $2 red-orange and green (24.5.38) .. 50·00 9·00
158 $2 reddish violet and scarlet (9.4.46) 3·00 40
 a. Chalk-surfaced paper (9.4.47) .. 8·00 35
159 $5 dull lilac and scarlet (2.6.38) .. 35·00 38·00
160 $5 green and violet (9.4.46) .. .. 25·00 3·50
 *a. Yellowish green and violet* (9.4.46) 48·00 4·00
 ab. Chalk-surfaced paper (9.4.47) .. 48·00 2·50
161 $10 green and violet (2.6.38) .. .. £325 48·00
162 $10 bright lilac and blue (9.4.46) .. 50·00 15·00
 a. Chalk-surfaced paper. *Reddish violet and blue* (9.4.47) .. .. 80·00 18·00
140/62 .. .. .. .. *Set of* 23 £450 £110
140/62 Perf "Specimen" .. .. *Set of* 23 £1200

The varieties perf 14½ × 14 with the exception of the 4 c. were printed and perforated by Bradbury, Wilkinson & Co, Ltd, from De La Rue plates and are on rough-surfaced paper. The dates quoted for these are London release dates and it is believed that supplies did not reach Hong Kong before the Japanese occupation.

Nos. 142a and 144 were printed by Harrison & Sons in 1941 and issued in sheets of 120 (12 × 10) instead of two panes of 60 (6 × 10).

Also in 1941 Williams, Lea & Co printed the $1 and $2 perf 14 from De La Rue plates.

Nos. 160/*a* were separate printings released in Hong Kong on the same day.

No. 144a. One imperforate sheet was found and most of the stamps were sold singly to the public at a branch P.O. and used for postage.

**30** Street Scene

**31** *Empress of Japan* (liner) and Junk

(Des W. E. Jones. Recess B.W.)

1941 (26 Feb). *Centenary of British Occupation. T* **30/1** *and similar designs. Wmk Mult Script CA (sideways on horiz designs). P 13½ × 13 (2 c. and 25 c.) or 13 × 13½ (others).*

163 2 c. orange and chocolate .. .. .. 1·25 1·00
164 4 c. bright purple and carmine .. .. 2·25 1·00
165 5 c. black and green .. .. .. .. 80 30
166 15 c. black and scarlet .. .. .. .. 3·00 60
167 25 c. chocolate and blue .. .. .. 4·00 1·00
168 $1 blue and orange .. .. .. .. 8·50 4·00
163/168 .. .. .. .. *Set of* 6 18·00 7·00
163/8 Perf "Specimen" .. .. *Set of* 6 £170

Designs: *Horiz*—5 c. The University; 15 c. The Harbour; $1 China Clipper and Seaplane. *Vert*—25 c. The Hong Kong Bank.

Hong Kong was under Japanese occupation from 25 December 1941 until 30 August 1945. The Japanese post offices in the colony were closed on 31 August and mail was carried free, marked with cachets reading "PASSED FREE/OF POSTAGE" or "HONG KONG/1945/POSTAGE PAID", until Hong Kong stamps were re-introduced on 28 September 1945.

**NEW INFORMATION**

The editor is always interested to correspond with people who have new information that will improve or correct the Catalogue.

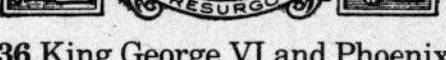

36 King George VI and Phoenix

37 Queen Elizabeth II

Extra character (R. 1/2)

(Des W. E. Jones. Recess D.L.R.)

**1946** (29 Aug). *Victory. Wmk Mult Script CA. P 13.*
169 **36** 30 c. blue and red (*shades*) 1·00 30
a. Extra character 22·00
170 $1 brown and red 1·00 30
a. Extra character 24·00
169/70 Perf "Specimen' *Set of 2* £100

HONG KONG

Spur on "N" of "KONG" (R. 2/9)

**1948** (22 Dec). *Royal Silver Wedding. As Nos.* 112/13 *of Antigua.*
171 10 c. violet 60 40
a. Spur on "N" 22·00
172 $10 carmine 65·00 25·00

**1949** (10 Oct). *75th Anniv of Universal Postal Union. As Nos.* 114/17 *of Antigua.*
173 10 c. violet 1·00 25
174 20 c. carmine-red 4·00 50
175 30 c. deep blue 3·75 75
176 80 c. bright reddish purple 5·50 1·75
173/6 *Set of 4* 13·00 3·00

**1953** (2 June) *Coronation. As No.* 120 *of Antigua.*
177 10 c. black and slate-lilac 1·50 15

**1954** (5 Jan)–**62**. *Chalk-surfaced paper* (20 c. *to* $10). *Wmk Mult Script CA. P* 14.
178 **37** 5 c. orange 35 10
a. Imperf (pair) £850
179 10 c. lilac 80 10
*a. Reddish violet* (18.7.61) 2·00 10
180 15 c. green 1·50 30
*a. Pale green* (6.12.55) 1·50 20
181 20 c. brown 1·75 15
182 25 c. scarlet 1·00 50
*a. Rose-red* (26.5.58) 70 15
183 30 c. grey 2·00 10
*a. Pale grey* (26.2.58) 2·50 10
184 40 c. bright blue 1·25 10
*a. Dull blue* (10.1.61) 4·50 30
185 50 c. reddish purple 1·75 10
186 65 c. grey (20.6.60) 13·00 6·00
187 $1 orange and green 3·75 10
188 $1.30, blue and red (20.6.60) 16·00 90
*a. Bright blue and red* (23.1.62) 24·00 1·50
189 $2 reddish violet and scarlet 6·00 30
*a. Lt reddish violet & scarlet* (26.2.58) 6·00 30
190 $5 green and purple 28·00 1·00
*a. Yellowish green and purple* (7.3.61) 45·00 1·50
191 $10 reddish violet and bright blue 28·00 4·25
*a. Lt reddish violet & brt blue* (26.2.58) 32·00 4·25
178/91 *Set of 14* 90·00 12·00
No. 178a. One sheet was found: 90 stamps imperf, 10 perf three sides only.

38 University Arms

39 Statue of Queen Victoria

(Des and photo Harrison)

**1961** (11 Sept). *Golden Jubilee of Hong Kong University. W* w **12**. *P* 11½ × 12.
192 **38** $1 multicoloured 2·50 80
a. Gold ptg omitted £600

(Des Cheung Yat-man. Photo Harrison)

**1962** (4 May). *Stamp Centenary. W* w **12**. *P* 14½.
193 **39** 10 c. black and magenta 20 10
194 20 c. black and light blue 60 55
195 50 c. black and bistre 70 20
193/5 *Set of 3* 1·40 75

40 Queen Elizabeth II (after Annigoni) 41

(Photo Harrison)

**1962** (4 Oct)–**73**. *W* w **12** (*upright*). *Chalk-surfaced paper. P* 15 × 14 (5 *c. to* $1) *or* 14 × 14½ (*others*).
196 **40** 5 c. red-orange 10 20
197 10 c. bright reddish violet 65 10
*a. Reddish violet* (19.11.71) 1·25 10
ab. Glazed paper (14.4.72) 3·25 55
198 15 c. emerald 1·00 20
199 20 c. red-brown 60 20
*a. Brown* (13.12.71) 2·00 70
ab. Glazed paper (27.9.72) 4·25 1·50
200 25 c. cerise 1·25 55
201 30 c. deep grey-blue 1·00 10
*a. Chalky blue* (19.11.71) 1·75 30
ab. Glazed paper (27.9.72) 4·50 70
202 40 c. deep bluish green 60 15
203 50 c. scarlet 40 10
*a. Vermilion* (13.12.71) 2·00 40
ab. Glazed paper (27.9.72) 4·50 55
204 65 c. ultramarine 8·50 1·25
205 $1 sepia 9·00 10
206 **41** $1.30, multicoloured 2·00 10
a. Pale yellow omitted† 17·00
b. Pale yellow inverted £1500
c. Ochre (sash) omitted 17·00
d. Glazed paper (3.2.71) 6·50 85
da. Ochre (sash) omitted
207 $2 multicoloured 3·25 15
a. Pale yellow omitted† 17·00
b. Ochre (sash) omitted 18·00
c. Pale yellow† and ochre (sash) omitted 75·00
d. Glazed paper (1973)* 75·00 4·50
208 $5 multicoloured 7·00 60
a. Ochre (sash) omitted 22·00
b. Glazed paper (3.2.71) 20·00 6·50
209 $10 multicoloured 16·00 1·50
a. Ochre (sash) omitted 70·00
b. Pale yellow† and ochre (sash) omitted £100
c. Glazed paper (1973)* £275 35·00
210 $20 multicoloured 32·00 10·00
196/210 *Set of 15* 75·00 13·00
*These are from printings which were sent to Hong Kong in March 1973 but not released in London.
†This results in the Queen's face appearing pinkish.
It is believed that No. 206b comes from the last two vertical rows of a sheet, the remainder of which had the pale yellow omitted.
The $1.30 to $20 exist with PVA gum as well as gum arabic. The glazed paper printings are with PVA gum only.
See also Nos. 222, etc.

**1963** (4 June). *Freedom from Hunger. As No.* 146 *of Antigua, but additionally inscr in Chinese characters.*
211 $1.30, bluish green 13·00 3·75

**1963** (2 Sept). *Red Cross Centenary. As Nos.* 147/8 *of Antigua, but additionally inscr in Chinese characters at right.*
212 10 c. red and black 2·50 15
213 $1.30, red and blue 6·50 2·50

**1965** (17 May). *I.T.U. Centenary. As Nos.* 166/7 *of Antigua.*
214 10 c. light purple and orange-yellow 2·50 15
215 $1.30, olive-yellow and deep bluish green 8·50 75

**1965** (25 Oct). *International Co-operation Year. As Nos.* 168/9 *of Antigua.*
216 10 c. reddish purple and turquoise-green 2·00 10
217 $1.30, dp bluish green & lavender (*shades*) 6·50 65

**1966** (24 Jan). *Churchill Commemoration. As Nos.* 170/3 *of Antigua but additionally inscr in Chinese characters.*
218 10 c. new blue 1·75 10
219 50 c. deep green 2·25 15
220 $1.30, brown 5·00 1·25
221 $2 bluish violet 5·50 4·00
218/21 *Set of 4* 13·00 5·00

**1966** (Aug)–**72**. *As Nos.* 196/208 *and* 210 *but wmk W* w **12** (*sideways*). *Chalk-surfaced paper* (5 *c. to* $1) *or glazed, ordinary paper* ($1.30 *to* $20).
222 **40** 5 c. red-orange (5.12.66) 20 20
223 10 c. reddish violet (31.3.67)* 25 15
224 15 c. emerald (31.3.67)* 35 35
225 20 c. red-brown 40 30
a. Glazed, ordinary paper (14.4.72) 2·00 1·25
226 25 c. cerise (31.3.67)* 50 1·00
a. Glazed, ordinary paper (14.4.72) 3·50 3·50
227 30 c. deep grey-blue (31.3.70) 3·75 30
a. Glazed ordinary paper (14.4.72) 4·00 1·25
228 40 c. deep bluish green (1967) 60 40
a. Glazed, ordinary paper (14.4.72) 4·50 3·50
229 50 c. scarlet (31.3.67)* 60 20
230 65 c. ultramarine (29.3.67)* 2·50 3·50
*a. Bright blue* (16.7.68) 2·00 3·25
231 $1 sepia (29.3.67)* 6·00 60
232 **41** $1.30, multicoloured (14.4.72) 6·00 1·25
233 $2 multicoloured (13.12.71) 8·00 2·00
a. Ochre (sash) omitted
234 $5 multicoloured (13.12.71) 40·00 6·50
236 $20 multicoloured (14.4.72) 75·00 42·00
222/36 *Set of 14* £130 50·00
*Earliest known postmark dates.
The 5 c. to 25 c., 40 c. and 50 c. exist with PVA gum as well as gum arabic, but the 30 c., and all stamps on glazed paper exist with PVA gum only.

**1966** (20 Sept). *Inauguration of W.H.O. Headquarters, Geneva. As Nos.* 178/9 *of Antigua, but additionally inscr in Chinese characters.*
237 10 c. black, yellow-green and light blue 1·50 10
238 50 c. black, light purple and yellow-brown 2·00 60

**1966** (1 Dec). *20th Anniv of U.N.E.S.C.O. As Nos.* 196/8 *of Antigua, but additionally inscr in Chinese characters.*
239 10 c. slate-violet, red, yellow and orange 2·00 10
240 50 c. orange-yellow, violet and deep olive 5·50 40
241 $2 black, light purple and orange 18·00 6·50
239/41 *Set of 3* 23·00 6·50

42 Rams' Heads on Chinese Lanterns

(Des V. Whiteley. Photo Harrison)

**1967** (17 Jan). *Chinese New Year ("Year of the Ram"). T* **42** *and similar horiz design. W* w **12** (*sideways*). *P* 14½.
242 10 c. rosine, olive-green and light yellow-olive 75 15
243 $1.30, emerald, rosine and light yellow-olive 4·00 3·00
Design:—$1.30, Three rams.

44 Cable Route Map

(Des V. Whiteley. Photo Harrison)

**1967** (30 Mar). *Completion of Malaysia–Hong Kong Link of SEACOM Telephone Cable. W* w **12**. *P* 12½.
244 **44** $1.30, new blue and red 1·75 1·25

45 Rhesus Macaques in Tree ("Year of the Monkey")

(Des R. Granger Barrett. Photo Harrison)

**1968** (23 Jan). *Chinese New Year ("Year of the Monkey"). T* **45** *and similar horiz design. W* w **12** (*sideways*). *P* 14½.
245 10 c. gold, black and scarlet 2·00 15
246 $1.30, gold, black and scarlet 4·00 4·00
Design:—$1.30, Family of Rhesus Macaques.

47 *Iberia* (liner) at Ocean Terminal

(Des and litho D.L.R.)

**1968** (24 Apr). *Sea Craft. T* **47** *and similar horiz designs. P* 13.
247 10 c. multicoloured 70 10
a. Dull orange and new blue omitted £325
248 20 c. cobalt-blue, black and brown 1·25 45
249 40 c. orange, black and mauve 2·75 3·75
250 50 c. orange-red, black and green 3·25 50
a. Green omitted £325
251 $1 greenish yellow, black and red 4·75 2·25
252 $1.30, Prussian blue, black and pink 6·00 1·75
247/52 *Set of 6* 17·00 8·00
Designs:—20 c. Pleasure launch; 40 c. Car ferry; 50 c. Passenger ferry; $1, Sampan; $1.30, Junk.

53 *Bauhinia blakeana*

54 Arms of Hong Kong

(Des V. Whiteley. Photo Harrison)

**1968** (25 Sept)–**73**. *W* w **12**. *P* 14 × 14½.
(*a*) *Upright wmk. Chalk-surfaced paper*
253 **53** 65 c. multicoloured 2·00 30
a. Glazed ordinary paper (3.73) 22·00 4·50
254 **54** $1 multicoloured 2·00 30
(*b*) *Sideways wmk. Glazed, ordinary paper*
254*a* **53** 65 c. multicoloured (27.9.72) 17·00 5·00
254*b* **54** $1 multicoloured (13.12.71) 2·00 1·00
Nos. 253/4 exist with PVA gum as well as gum arabic; Nos. 254*a*/*b* with PVA gum only.

55 "Aladdin's Lamp" and Human Rights Emblem

(Des R. Granger Barrett. Litho B.W.)

**1968** (20 Nov). *Human Rights Year. W w* **12** *(sideways). P* 13½.
255 **55** 10 c. orange, black and myrtle-green .. 25 10
256 50 c. yellow, black & dp reddish purple .. 45 1·00

56 Cockerel

(Des R. Granger Barrett. Photo Enschedé)

**1969** (11 Feb). *Chinese New Year ("Year of the Cock"). T* **56** *and similar multicoloured design. P* 13½.
257 10 c. Type **56** .. .. .. .. .. 1·00 15
a. Red omitted .. .. .. .. 65·00
258 $1.30, Cockerel (*vert*) .. .. .. 7·50 4·50

58 Arms of Chinese University 59 Earth Station and Satellite

(Des V. Whiteley. Photo Govt Ptg Bureau, Tokyo)

**1969** (26 Aug). *Establishment of Chinese University of Hong Kong. P* 13½.
259 **58** 40 c. violet, gold and pale turquoise-blue 50 75

(Des V. Whiteley. Photo Harrison)

**1969** (24 Sept). *Opening of Communications Satellite Tracking Station. W w* **12**. *P* 14½.
260 **59** $1 multicoloured .. .. .. 2·00 1·75

60 Chow's Head 62 "Expo 70" Emblem

(Des R. Granger Barrett. Photo D.L.R.)

**1970** (28 Jan). *Chinese New Year ("Year of the Dog"). T* **60** *and similar design. W w* **12** *(sideways on* $1.30). *P* 14½×14 (10 c.) *or* 14×14½ ($1.30).
261 10 c. lemon-yellow, orange-brown and black .. 2·00 25
262 $1.30, multicoloured .. .. .. 11·00 3·75
Design: *Horiz*—$1.30, Chow standing.

(Des and litho B.W.)

**1970** (14 Mar). *World Fair, Osaka. T* **62** *and similar multicoloured design. W w* **12** *(sideways on 25 c.). P* 13½ × 13 (15 c.) *or* 13 × 13½ (25 c.).
263 15 c. Type **62** .. .. .. .. .. 15 40
264 25 c. Expo '70 Emblem and Junks (*horiz*) .. 15 50

64 Plaque in Tung Wah Hospital 65 Symbol

(Des M. F. Griffith. Photo Harrison)

**1970** (9 Apr). *Centenary of Tung Wah Hospital. W w* **12** *(sideways). P* 14½.
265 **64** 10 c. multicoloured .. .. .. 15 10
266 50 c. multicoloured .. .. .. 20 30

(Des J. Cooter. Litho B.W.)

**1970** (5 Aug). *Asian Productivity Year. W w* **12**. *P* 14 × 13½.
267 **65** 10 c. multicoloured .. .. .. 15 15

66 Pig

(Des Kan Tai-Keung. Photo Govt Ptg Bureau, Tokyo)

**1971** (20 Jan). *Chinese New Year ("Year of the Pig"). P* 13½.
268 **66** 10 c. multicoloured .. .. .. 1·25 25
269 $1.30, multicoloured .. .. .. 4·25 4·25

67 "60" and Scout Badge 68 Festival Emblem

(Des Kan Tai-Keung. Litho Harrison)

**1971** (23 July). *Diamond Jubilee of Scouting in Hong Kong. W w* **12** *(sideways). P* 14×15.
270 **67** 10 c. black, scarlet and yellow .. .. 15 10
271 50 c. black, green and blue .. .. 80 45
272 $2 black, magenta and bluish violet .. 3·00 5·50
270/2 .. .. .. .. .. *Set of* 3 3·50 5·50

(Des Kan Tai-Keung. Litho J.W.)

**1971** (2 Nov). *Hong Kong Festival. T* **68** *and similar designs. W w* **12** *(sideways on 10 c. and 50 c.). P* 14 (10 c.) *or* 14½ *(others).*
273 **68** 10 c. orange and purple .. .. .. 45 10
274 – 50 c. multicoloured .. .. .. 70 50
275 – $1 multicoloured .. .. .. 1·90 3·00
273/5 .. .. .. .. .. *Set of* 3 2·75 3·25
Designs: *Horiz* (39 × 23 *mm*)—50 c. Coloured streamers. *Vert* (23 × 39 *mm*)—$1 "Orchid".

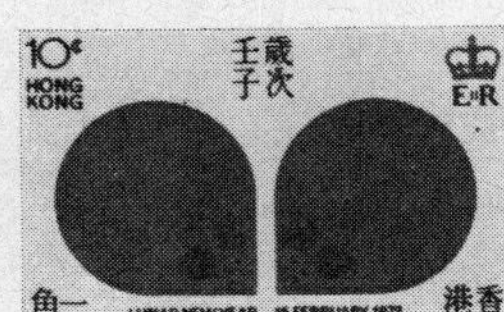

69 Stylised Rats

(Des Kan Tai-Keung. Photo D.L.R.)

**1972** (8 Feb). *Chinese New Year ("Year of the Rat"). W w* **12**. *P* 13½.
276 **69** 10 c. red, gold and black .. .. .. 75 25
277 $1.30, gold, red and black .. .. 4·00 4·00

70 Tunnel Entrance

(Des G. Drummond from painting by G. Baxter. Litho Harrison)

**1972** (20 Oct). *Opening of Cross-Harbour Tunnel. W w* **12**. *P* 14×15.
278 **70** $1 multicoloured .. .. .. 1·75 1·50

71 Phoenix and Dragon 72 Ox

(Des (from photograph by D. Groves) and photo Harrison)

**1972** (20 Nov). *Royal Silver Wedding. W w* **12**. *P* 14×15.
279 **71** 10 c. multicoloured .. .. .. 10 10
a. Gold omitted .. .. .. £325
280 50 c. multicoloured .. .. .. 45 70

(Des R. Granger Barrett. Photo Harrison)

**1973** (25 Jan). *Chinese New Year ("Year of the Ox"). W w* **12** *(sideways on* 10 c.). *P* 14½.
281 **72** 10 c. reddish orange, brown and black .. 50 10
282 – $1.30, lt yellow, yellow-orange & black 2·25 4·00
Design:—$1.30, similar to 10 c., but horiz.

73 Queen Elizabeth II 74

(Des from coinage. Photo ($10 and $20 also embossed) Harrison)

**1973** (12 June). *W w* **12** *(sideways on* 15, 30, 40 *c.*, $1.30, 2, 5, 10, $20). *P* 14½ × 14 *(Nos.* 283/91) *or* 14 × 14½ (292/6).
283 **73** 10 c. bright orange .. .. .. 55 20
a. Wmk sideways (from coils) .. .. 55 40
284 15 c. yellow-green .. .. .. 4·75 2·75
285 20 c. reddish violet .. .. .. 35 10
286 25 c. lake-brown .. .. .. 4·75 3·00
287 30 c. ultramarine .. .. .. 90 20
288 40 c. turquoise-blue .. .. .. 2·25 1·00
289 50 c. light orange-vermilion .. .. 1·25 20
290 65 c. greenish bistre .. .. .. 5·50 6·50
291 $1 bottle-green .. .. .. 2·00 40
292 **74** $1.30, pale yellow and reddish violet .. 4·00 45
293 $2 pale green and reddish brown .. 4·50 60
294 $5 pink and royal blue .. .. 5·00 2·00
295 $10 pink and deep blackish olive .. 8·00 4·25
296 $20 pink and brownish black .. .. 14·00 17·00
283/96 .. .. .. .. *Set of* 14 50·00 35·00
Nos. 295/6 are known with embossing omitted, but it has been reported that such errors can be faked.
See also Nos. 311/24*c* and 340/53.

**1973** (14 Nov). *Royal Wedding. As Nos.* 165/6 *of Anguilla, but additionally inscr in Chinese characters.*
297 50 c. ochre .. .. .. .. .. 25 15
298 $2 bright mauve .. .. .. .. 65 80

75 Festival Symbols forming Chinese Character

(Des Kan Tai-Keung. Litho B.W.)

**1973** (23 Nov). *Hong Kong Festival. T* **75** *and similar horiz designs. W w* **12**. *P* 14½.
299 **75** 10 c. brownish red and bright green .. 15 10
300 – 50 c. deep magenta and reddish orange .. 40 35
301 – $1 bright green and deep mauve .. 90 1·60
299/301 .. .. .. .. *Set of* 3 1·25 1·75
Each value has the festival symbols arranged to form a Chinese character. "Hong" on the 10 c.; "Kong" on the 50 c.; "Festival" on the $1.

76 Tiger 77 Chinese Mask

(Des R. Granger Barrett. Litho Harrison)

**1974** (8 Jan). *Chinese New Year ("Year of the Tiger"). W w* **12** *(sideways on* $1.30). *P* 14½.
302 **76** 10 c. multicoloured .. .. .. 1·50 15
303 – $1.30, multicoloured .. .. .. 5·50 7·00
Design:—$1.30, Similar to T **76**, but vert.

(Des R. Hookham. Litho Enschedé)

**1974** (1 Feb). *Arts Festival. Vert designs as T* **77** *showing Chinese opera masks. W w* **12** *(sideways). P* 12 × 12½.
304 **77** 10 c. multicoloured .. .. .. 40 10
305 – $1 multicoloured .. .. .. 1·50 2·75
306 – $2 multicoloured .. .. .. 1·75 3·75
304/6 .. .. .. .. *Set of* 3 3·25 6·00
**MS**307 159 × 94 mm. Nos. 304/6. Wmk upright. P 14 × 13 .. .. .. .. .. 14·00 22·00

78 Pigeons with Letters

(Des Kan Tai-Keung. Litho Harrison)

**1974** (9 Oct). *Centenary of Universal Postal Union. T* **78** *and similar horiz designs.* W w **12** (*sideways on* 10 *and* 50 *c.*). *P* 14½.
308 10 c. light greenish blue, light yellow-green and slate-black .. .. .. .. .. 15 10
a. No wmk .. .. .. .. .. 35·00
309 50 c. deep mauve, orange and slate-black .. 30 25
310 $2 multicoloured .. .. .. .. 60 2·25
308/10 .. .. .. .. *Set of* 3 95 2·25
Designs:—50 c. Globe within letter; $2 Hands holding letters.

**1975** (21 Jan)–**82**. *New values* (60, 70, 80 *and* 90 *c.*) *or as Nos.* 283/96 *but* W w **14** (*sideways on* 10, 20, 25, 50, 65 *c., and* $1).
311 **73** 10 c. bright orange (21.2.75) .. .. 55 20
a. Wmk upright (from coils) (10.78) 1·25 2·00
312 15 c. yellow-green (21.1.75) .. .. 7·50 4·00
313 20 c. reddish violet (19.3.75) .. .. 15 10
*a. Deep reddish mauve* (21.6.77) .. 40 10
*b. Deep reddish purple* (22.6.79) .. 40 10
314 25 c. lake-brown (19.3.75) .. .. 7·50 4·00
315 30 c. ultramarine (9.4.75) .. .. 40 20
*a. Deep ultramarine* (20.4.78) .. 90 30
316 40 c. turquoise-blue (19.3.75) .. .. 50 70
317 50 c. light orange-vermilion (19.3.75) .. 85 30
318 60 c. lavender (4.5.77) .. .. .. 80 75
319 65 c. greenish bistre (19.3.75) .. .. 8·00 8·00
320 70 c. yellow (4.5.77) .. .. .. 1·00 20
*a. Chrome-yellow* (24.1.80) .. .. 1·25 50
321 80 c. bright magenta (4.5.77) .. .. 1·00 50
*a. Magenta* (24.1.80) .. .. 1·40 70
321*b* 90 c. sepia (1.10.81) .. .. .. 4·50 90
322 $1 bottle-green (19.3.75) .. .. 2·00 40
*a. Blackish olive* (24.1.80) .. .. 1·50 50
323 **74** $1.30, pale yell & reddish vio (19.3.75) 1·60 30
324 $2 pale green & reddish brn (19.3.75) 1·75 80
*a. Pale green and brown* (10.5.82) .. 3·00 1·00
324*b* $5 pink and royal blue (20.4.78) .. 2·00 75
*ba. Pink & deep ultramarine* (10.5.82) 3·25 1·50
324*c* $10 pink & deep blackish olive (20.4.78) 2·00 2·50
324*d* $20 pink and brownish black (20.4.78) 4·00 5·00
311/24*d* .. .. .. .. *Set of* 18 40·00 26·00
Nos. 324*c*/*d* are known with the embossing omitted. See note after No. 296.

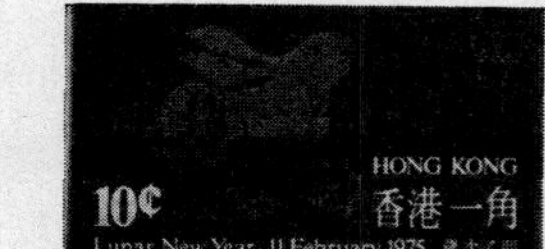

**79** Stylized Hare

(Des Kan Tai-Keung. Litho Harrison)

**1975** (5 Feb). *Chinese New Year* ("*Year of the Hare*"). *T* **79** *and similar horiz design. P* 14½. (*a*) *No wmk.*
325 **79** 10 c. silver and light red .. .. .. 50 25
326 – $1.30, gold and light green .. .. 3·25 4·50
(*b*) W w **12**
327 **79** 10 c. silver and light red .. .. .. 50 25
328 – $1.30, gold and light green .. .. 3·25 4·50
Design:—$1.30, Pair of hares.

**80** Queen Elizabeth II, the Duke of Edinburgh and Hong Kong Arms

**81** Mid-Autumn Festival

(Des PAD Studio. Litho Questa)

**1975** (30 Apr). *Royal Visit.* W w **14** (*sideways*). *P* 13½×14.
329 **80** $1.30, multicoloured .. .. .. .. 1·25 1·75
330 $2 multicoloured .. .. .. .. 1·50 2·50

(Des Tao Ho. Litho De La Rue, Bogotá)

**1975** (31 July). *Hong Kong Festivals of* 1975. *T* **81** *and similar vert designs. Multicoloured. No wmk. P* 14.
331 50 c. Type **81** .. .. .. .. 50 20
332 $1 Dragon-boat Festival .. .. .. 1·25 2·00
333 $2 Tin Hau Festival .. .. .. .. 1·75 2·75
331/3 .. .. .. .. *Set of* 3 3·25 4·50
**MS**334 102 × 83 mm. Nos. 331/3 .. .. .. 6·00 11·00

**82** Hwamei

**83** Dragon

(Des C. Kuan. Litho Harrison)

**1975** (29 Oct). *Birds. T* **82** *and similar vert designs. Multicoloured.* W w **14**. *P* 14½.
335 50 c. Type **82** .. .. .. .. 1·25 30
336 $1.30, Chinese Bulbul .. .. .. 3·50 4·00
337 $2 Black-capped Kingfisher .. .. 4·00 5·00
335/7 .. .. .. .. *Set of* 3 8·00 8·50

(Des Kan Tai-Keung. Litho Questa)

**1976** (21 Jan). *Chinese New Year* ("*Year of the Dragon*"). *T* **83** *and similar horiz design.* W w **14** (*sideways*). *P* 14½.
338 **83** 20 c. mauve, dull lake and gold .. .. 35 10
339 – $1.30, light yellow-green, lt red & gold 1·40 2·50
No. 339 is as T **83** but has the design reversed.

**1976** (20 Feb–19 Mar). *As Nos.* 283, 285, 287 *and* 293/6 *but without wmk.*
340 **73** 10 c. bright orange (coil stamp) (19.3.76) 11·00 8·00
342 20 c. reddish violet .. .. .. 2·75 40
a. Imperf (pair) .. .. .. £300
344 30 c. ultramarine .. .. .. 4·50 1·25
350 **74** $2 pale green and reddish brown .. 5·00 2·75
351 $5 pink and royal blue .. .. .. 7·00 7·00
352 $10 pink and deep blackish olive (19.3.76) .. .. .. 25·00 23·00
353 $20 pink and brownish black (19.3.76) 48·00 38·00
340/53 .. .. .. .. *Set of* 7 90·00 70·00
No. 353 is known with the embossing omitted. See note after No. 296.

**84** "60" and Girl Guides Badge

**85** "Postal Services" in Chinese Characters

(Des P. Ma. Photo Harrison)

**1976** (23 Apr). *Girl Guides Diamond Jubilee. T* **84** *and similar horiz design. Multicoloured.* W w **12**. *P* 14½.
354 20 c. Type **84** .. .. .. .. 30 10
355 $1.30, Badge, stylised diamond and "60" .. 1·50 2·25

(Des Tao Ho. Litho Harrison)

**1976** (11 Aug). *Opening of new G.P.O. T* **85** *and similar vert designs.* W w **14**. *P* 14½.
356 20 c. yellow-green, lt greenish grey & black .. 15 10
357 $1.30, reddish orge, lt greenish grey & blk .. 60 1·00
358 $2 yellow, light greenish grey and black .. 80 1·75
356/8 .. .. .. .. *Set of* 3 1·40 2·50
Designs:—$1.30, Old G.P.O.; $2 New G.P.O.

**86** Tree Snake on Branch

(Des Jennifer Wong. Litho J.W.)

**1977** (6 Jan). *Chinese New Year* ("*Year of the Snake*"). *T* **86** *and similar horiz design.* W w **14** (*sideways*). *P* 13½.
359 **86** 20 c. multicoloured .. .. .. 35 10
360 – $1.30, multicoloured .. .. .. 2·25 3·50
The $1.30 shows a snake facing left.

**87** Presentation of the Orb

**88** Tram Cars

(Des Hong Kong Govt Services Dept; adapted J.W. Litho Harrison)

**1977** (7 Feb). *Silver Jubilee. T* **87** *and similar multicoloured designs.* W w **14** (*sideways on* $2). *P* 14½ × 14 ($2) *or* 14 × 14½ (*others*).
361 20 c. Type **78** .. .. .. .. 20 10
362 $1.30, Queen's visit, 1975 .. .. .. 70 1·10
363 $2 The Orb (*vert*) .. .. .. .. 80 1·10
361/3 .. .. .. .. *Set of* 3 1·50 2·00

(Des Tao Ho. Litho J.W.)

**1977** (30 June). *Tourism. T* **88** *and similar vert designs. Multicoloured.* W w **14**. *P* 13½.
364 20 c. Type **88** .. .. .. .. 40 10
365 60 c. Star Ferryboat .. .. .. 1·00 1·25
366 $1.30, The Peak Railway .. .. .. 1·25 1·50
367 $2 Junk and sampan .. .. .. 1·25 2·25
364/7 .. .. .. .. *Set of* 4 3·50 4·50

**89** Buttercup Orchid

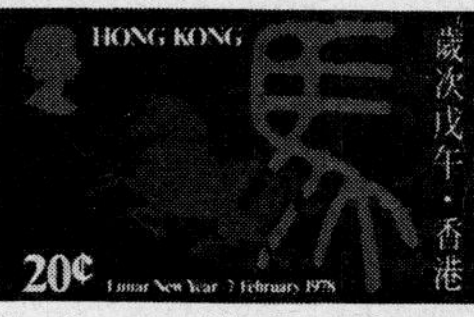

**90** Horse

(Des Beryl Walden. Litho Questa)

**1977** (12 Oct). *Orchids. T* **89** *and similar vert designs. Multicoloured.* W w **14**. *P* 14½.
368 20 c. Type **89** .. .. .. .. 75 10
369 $1.30, Lady's Slipper Orchid .. .. 1·75 1·50
370 $2 Susan Orchid .. .. .. .. 2·00 2·50
368/70 .. .. .. .. *Set of* 3 4·00 3·75

(Des Graphic Atelier Ltd, Hong Kong. Litho Harrison)

**1978** (26 Jan). *Chinese New Year* ("*Year of the Horse*"). W w **14** (*sideways*). *P* 14½.
371 **90** 20 c. magenta, yellow-olive & brn-olive .. 30 10
372 $1.30, orange, yellow-brn & reddish brn 1·25 2·40

**91** Queen Elizabeth II

**92** Girl and Boy holding Hands

(Des G. Vasarhelyi. Litho Harrison)

**1978** (2 June). *25th Anniv of Coronation.* W w **14**. *P* 14 × 14½.
373 **91** 20 c. magenta and ultramarine .. .. 20 10
374 $1.30, ultramarine and magenta .. 70 1·25

(Des Annette Walker. Litho Harrison)

**1978** (8 Nov). *Centenary of Po Leung Kuk* (*child care organisation*). *T* **92** *and similar horiz design. Multicoloured.* W w **14** (*sideways*). *P* 14½.
375 20 c. Type **92** .. .. .. .. 15 10
376 $1.30, Ring of children .. .. .. 60 1·00

**93** Electronics Industry

**94** *Precis orithya*

(Litho Harrison)

**1979** (9 Jan). *Industries. T* **93** *and similar horiz designs.* W w **14** (*sideways*). *P* 14½.
377 20 c. orange-yellow, olive-yellow & yell-olive 10 10
378 $1.30, multicoloured .. .. .. 60 90
379 $2 multicoloured .. .. .. .. 60 1·10
377/9 .. .. .. .. *Set of* 3 1·25 1·90
Designs:—$1.30, Toy industry; $2, Garment industry.

(Des Jane Thatcher. Photo Harrison)

**1979** (20 June). *Butterflies. T* **94** *and similar vert designs. Multicoloured. No wmk. P* 14½.
380 20 c. Type **94** .. .. .. .. 35 10
381 $1 *Graphium sarpedon* .. .. .. 70 70
382 $1.30, *Heliophorus epicles* .. .. 85 1·10
383 $2 *Danus genutia* .. .. .. 1·10 2·50
380/3 .. .. .. .. *Set of* 4 2·75 4·00

**95** Diagrammatic view of Railway Station

**96** Tsui Shing Lau Pagoda

(Des Tao Ho. Litho J.W.)

**1979** (1 Oct). *Mass Transit Railway. T* **95** *and similar horiz designs. Multicoloured.* W w **14** (*sideways*). *P* 13½.

384 20 c. Type **95** .. .. .. .. .. 15 10
385 $1.30, Diagrammatic view of car .. .. 50 50
386 $2 Plan showing route of railway .. .. 60 70
384/6 .. .. .. .. .. *Set of* 3 1·10 1·10

(Des D. Leonard. Litho J.W.)

**1980** (14 May). *Rural Architecture. T* **96** *and similar designs.* W w **14** (*sideways on* $1.30 *and* $2). *P* 13 × 13½ (20 c.) *or* 13½ × 13 (*others*).

387 20 c. black, magenta and yellow .. .. 10 10
388 $1.30, multicoloured .. .. .. 60 85
389 $2 multicoloured .. .. .. .. 75 1·60
387/9 .. .. .. .. .. *Set of* 3 1·25 2·25

Designs: *Horiz*—$1.30, Village House, Sai O; $2, Ching Chung Koon Temple.

**97** Queen Elizabeth the Queen Mother

**98** Botanical Gardens

(Des Harrison. Litho Questa)

**1980** (4 Aug). *80th Birthday of Queen Elizabeth the Queen Mother.* W w **14** (*sideways*). *P* 14.

390 **97** $1.30, multicoloured .. .. .. 55 70

(Des D. Chan. Litho J.W.)

**1980** (12 Nov). *Parks. T* **98** *and similar vert designs. Multicoloured.* W w **14**. *P* 13½.

391 20 c. Type **98** .. .. .. .. .. 10 10
392 $1 Ocean Park .. .. .. .. 30 45
393 $1.30, Kowloon Park .. .. .. 40 75
394 $2 Country Parks .. .. .. .. 55 1·25
391/4 .. .. .. .. .. *Set of* 4 1·25 2·25

**99** *Epinephelus akaara*

**100** Wedding Bouquet from Hong Kong

(Des Jane Thatcher. Litho J.W.)

**1981** (28 Jan). *Fishes. T* **99** *and similar horiz designs. Multicoloured.* W w **14** (*sideways*). *P* 13½.

395 20 c. Type **99** .. .. .. .. .. 15 10
396 $1 *Nemipterus virgatus* .. .. .. 45 45
397 $1.30, *Choerodon azurio* .. .. .. 55 60
398 $2 *Scarus ghobban* .. .. .. .. 65 1·10
395/8 .. .. .. .. .. *Set of* 4 1·60 2·00

(Des J.W. Photo Harrison)

**1981** (29 July). *Royal Wedding. T* **100** *and similar vert designs. Multicoloured.* W w **14** (*sideways*). *P* 14.

399 20 c. Type **100** .. .. .. .. .. 10 10
400 $1.30, Prince Charles in Hong Kong .. .. 35 35
401 $5 Prince Charles and Lady Diana Spencer 1·25 1·50
399/401 .. .. .. .. .. *Set of* 3 1·50 1·75

**101** Suburban Development

**102** "Victoria from the Harbour, *c* 1855"

(Des Tao Ho. Litho J.W.)

**1981** (14 Oct). *Public Housing. T* **101** *and similar vert designs showing suburban development.* W w **14** (*inverted on No.* **MS**406). *P* 13½.

402 20 c. multicoloured .. .. .. .. 10 10
a. Red (jacket and trousers) omitted .. 75·00
403 $1 multicoloured .. .. .. .. 25 30
404 $1.30, multicoloured .. .. .. .. 35 40
405 $2 multicoloured .. .. .. .. 50 60
402/5 .. .. .. .. .. *Set of* 4 1·10 1·25
**MS**406 148 × 105 mm. Nos. 402/5 .. .. 1·75 3·00

(Des R. Solley. Litho Questa)

**1982** (5 Jan). *Port of Hong Kong, Past and Present. T* **102** *and similar horiz designs. Multicoloured.* W w **14**. *P* 14½.

407 20 c. Type **102** .. .. .. .. .. 15 10
408 $1 "West Point, Hong Kong, 1847" .. .. 45 45
409 $1.30, Fleet of Junks .. .. .. 60 65
410 $2 Liner *Queen Elizabeth 2* at Hong Kong .. 80 1·25
407/10 .. .. .. .. .. *Set of* 4 1·75 2·25

**103** Large Indian Civet

(Des Karen Phillipps. Litho Harrison)

**1982** (4 May). *Wild Animals. T* **103** *and similar horiz designs.* W w **14** (*sideways*). *P* 14½.

411 20 c. black, salmon-pink and olive-bistre .. 20 10
412 $1 multicoloured .. .. .. .. 70 60
413 $1.30, black, emerald and yellow-orange .. 80 90
414 $5 black, orange-brown and greenish yellow 1·40 2·50
411/14 .. .. .. .. .. *Set of* 4 2·75 3·75

Designs:—$1 Chinese Pangolin; $1.30, Chinese Porcupine; $5 Indian Muntjac ("Barking Deer").

**104** Queen Elizabeth II **105**

(Des and photo ($5 to $50 also embossed) Harrison)

**1982** (30 Aug). W w **14** (*sideways on Nos.* 427/30). *P* 14½ × 14 (*Nos.* 415/26) *or* 14 × 14½ (*others*).

415 **104** 10 c. bright carmine, carmine and lemon 40 20
416 20 c. bluish violet, violet and lavender .. 45 15
417 30 c. bluish violet, violet and salmon .. 60 20
418 40 c. vermilion and pale blue .. .. 60 20
419 50 c. chestnut, orange-brn & sage-green 70 20
420 60 c. bright purple and brownish grey .. 1·25 60
421 70 c. dp grey-grn, myrtle-grn & orge-yell 1·25 30
422 80 c. bistre-brown, lt brown & sage-grn 1·50 60
423 90 c. bottle-green, deep grey-green and pale turquoise-green .. .. 1·50 20
424 $1 reddish orge, red-orge & pale rose .. 1·50 30
425 $1.30, turquoise-blue and mauve .. 2·50 30
426 $2 ultramarine and flesh .. .. 3·00 65
427 **105** $5 dp magenta, brt purple & olive-yell 3·50 2·00
428 $10 sepia and grey-brown .. .. 3·75 4·00
429 $20 deep claret and pale blue .. .. 8·00 11·00
430 $50 deep claret and brownish grey .. 13·00 21·00
415/30 .. .. .. .. *Set of* 16 38·00 38·00

Nos. 415/30 come with a fluorescent security marking, "Hong Kong" in Chinese characters encircled by the same in English, printed over the central oval of the design.

Nos. 415 and 424 also exist from coils.

No. 428 is known with the embossing omitted. See note after No. 296.

For similar stamps without watermark see Nos. 471/87.

**106** Table Tennis

**107** Dancing

(Des A. Wong. Litho J.W.)

**1982** (20 Oct). *Sport for the Disabled. T* **106** *and similar horiz designs. Multicoloured.* W w **14**. *P* 14 × 14½.

431 30 c. Type **106** .. .. .. .. .. 20 10
432 $1 Racing .. .. .. .. .. 35 45
433 $1.30, Basketball .. .. .. .. 60 80
434 $5 Archery .. .. .. .. .. 1·40 2·50
431/4 .. .. .. .. .. *Set of* 4 2·25 3·50

(Des Tao Ho. Litho J.W.)

**1983** (26 Jan). *Performing Arts. T* **107** *and similar vert designs.* W w **14** (*sideways*). *P* 14½×14.

435 30 c. cobalt and deep grey-blue .. .. 20 10
436 $1.30, rose and brown-purple .. .. 60 80
437 $5 bright green and deep green .. .. 1·60 2·75
435/7 .. .. .. .. .. *Set of* 3 2·25 3·25

Designs:—$1.30, "Theatre"; $5 "Music".

## NEW INFORMATION

The editor is always interested to correspond with people who have new information that will improve or correct the Catalogue.

**108** Aerial View of Hong Kong

(Des local artist. Litho Enschedé)

**1983** (14 Mar). *Commonwealth Day. T* **108** *and similar horiz designs. Multicoloured.* W w **14** (*sideways*). *P* 14½×13.

438 30 c. Type **108** .. .. .. .. .. 20 10
439 $1 *Liverpool Bay* (container ship) .. .. 45 65
440 $1.30, Hong Kong flag .. .. .. 55 80
441 $5 Queen Elizabeth II and Hong Kong .. 1·25 2·25
438/41 .. .. .. .. .. *Set of* 4 2·25 3·50

**109** Victoria Harbour

(Des Tao Ho. Litho Harrison)

**1983** (17 Aug). *Hong Kong by Night. T* **109** *and similar horiz designs. Multicoloured.* W w **14** (*sideways*). *P* 14½.

442 30 c. Type **109** .. .. .. .. .. 30 10
443 $1 Space Museum, Tsim Sha Tsui Cultural Centre .. .. .. .. .. 65 1·00
444 $1.30, Fireworks display .. .. .. 75 1·25
a. Silver (value and inscr) omitted .. £550
445 $5 *Jumbo*, floating restaurant .. .. 2·00 3·50
a. Silver (value and inscr) omitted .. £650
442/5 .. .. .. .. .. *Set of* 4 3·25 5·25

**110** Old and New Observatory Buildings

(Des C. Shun Wah. Litho Harrison)

**1983** (23 Nov). *Centenary of Hong Kong Observatory. T* **110** *and similar horiz designs.* W w **14** (*sideways*). *P* 14½.

446 40 c. yellow-orange, bistre-brown and black .. 30 10
447 $1 reddish mauve, deep mauve and black .. 65 1·00
448 $1.30, new blue, steel-blue and black .. 75 1·25
449 $5 olive-yellow, brown-olive and black .. 2·00 3·50
446/9 .. .. .. .. .. *Set of* 4 3·25 5·25

Designs:—$1 Wind-measuring equipment; $1.30, Thermometer; $5 Ancient and modern seismometers.

**111** "DH 86" *Dorado* (Hong Kong-Penang Service, 1936)

(Des M. Harris. Litho J.W.)

**1984** (7 Mar). *Aviation in Hong Kong. T* **111** *and similar multicoloured designs.* W w **14** (*sideways on* 40 c. *to* $1.30, *inverted on* $5). *P* 13½.

450 40 c. Type **111** .. .. .. .. .. 35 10
451 $1 Sikorsky "S-42B" (San Francisco-Hong Kong Service, 1937) .. .. .. 65 1·00
452 $1.30, Cathay-Pacific "Jumbo" jet leaving Kai Tak Airport .. .. .. .. 75 1·25
453 $5 Baldwin brothers' balloon, 1891 (*vert*) .. 2·00 3·50
450/3 .. .. .. .. .. *Set of* 4 3·25 5·25

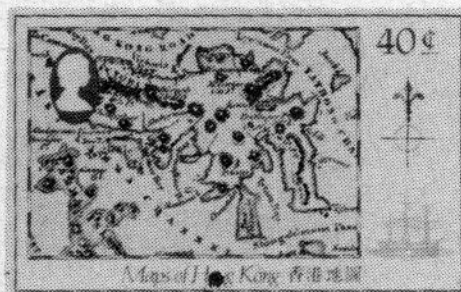


**112** Map by Capt E. Belcher, 1836

(Des R. Solley. Litho B.D.T.)

**1984** (21 June). *Maps of Hong Kong. T* **112** *and similar horiz designs. Multicoloured.* W w **14** (*sideways*). *P* 14.

454 40 c. Type **112** .. .. .. .. .. 35 15
455 $1 Bartholomew map of 1929 .. .. 55 1·00
456 $1.30, Early map of Hong Kong waters .. 65 1·25
457 $5 Chinese-style map of 1819 .. .. 1·75 3·50
454/7 .. .. .. .. .. *Set of* 4 3·00 5·25

**113** Cockerel

(Des J. Yim. Litho Cartor, France)

**1984** (6 Sept). *Chinese Lanterns. T* **113** *and similar horiz designs showing stylised animals as lanterns. Multicoloured. W w* **14** *(sideways). P* 13½ × 13.

| | | | |
|---|---|---|---|
| 458 | 40 c. Type **113** | 20 | 15 |
| 459 | $1 Dog | 35 | 55 |
| 460 | $1.30, Butterfly | 40 | 75 |
| 461 | $5 Fish | 1·40 | 3·00 |
| 458/61 | *Set of* 4 | 2·10 | 4·00 |

**114** Jockey on Horse and Nurse with Baby ("Health Care")

(Des M. Harris. Litho Walsall)

**1984** (21 Nov). *Centenary of Royal Hong Kong Jockey Club. T* **114** *and similar horiz designs showing aspects of Club's charity work. Multicoloured. W w* **14** *(sideways). P* 14½.

| | | | |
|---|---|---|---|
| 462 | 40 c. Type **114** | 20 | 15 |
| 463 | $1 Disabled man playing handball ("Support for Disabled") | 40 | 70 |
| 464 | $1.30, Ballerina ("The Arts") | 45 | 1·00 |
| 465 | $5 Humboldt Penguins ("Ocean Park") | 1·75 | 3·25 |
| 462/5 | *Set of* 4 | 2·50 | 4·75 |
| **MS**466 | 178 × 98 mm. Nos. 462/5 | 3·00 | 5·00 |

**115** Hung Sing Temple

(Des M. Harris. Litho J.W.)

**1985** (14 Mar). *Historic Buildings. T* **115** *and similar horiz designs. Multicoloured. P* 13½.

| | | | |
|---|---|---|---|
| 467 | 40 c. Type **115** | 25 | 20 |
| 468 | $1 St. John's Cathedral | 50 | 80 |
| 469 | $1.30, The Old Supreme Court Building | 55 | 1·00 |
| 470 | $5 Wan Chai Post Office | 1·75 | 3·50 |
| 467/70 | *Set of* 4 | 2·75 | 5·00 |

**1985** (13 June)–**87**. *As Nos.* 415/16, 418/30 *and new value* ($1.70). *No wmk. P* 14½ × 14 (10 *c. to* $2) *or* 14 × 14½ (*others*).

| | | | | |
|---|---|---|---|---|
| 471 | **104** | 10 c. brt carm, carm & lemon (23.10.85) | 20 | 20 |
| 472 | | 20 c. bluish violet, vio & lavender (6.87) | 3·00 | 3·50 |
| 474 | | 40 c. vermilion and pale blue (23.10.85) | 40 | 20 |
| 475 | | 50 c. chestnut orange-brown and sage-green (23.10.85) | 40 | 30 |
| 476 | | 60 c. brt purple & brnish grey (23.10.85) | 65 | 50 |
| 477 | | 70 c. deep grey-green, myrtle-green and orange-yellow (23.10.85) | 70 | 35 |
| 478 | | 80 c. bistre-brown, light brown and sage-green (23.10.85) | 80 | 70 |
| 479 | | 90 c. bottle-green, deep grey-green and pale turquoise-green (23.10.85) | 80 | 40 |
| 480 | | $1 reddish orange, red-orange and pale rose (23.10.85) | 85 | 40 |
| 481 | | $1.30, turquoise-blue and mauve | 1·25 | 45 |
| 482 | | $1.70, dull ultramarine, bright blue and bright green (2.9.85) | 1·00 | 1·00 |
| 483 | | $2 ultramarine and flesh (23.10.85) | 1·50 | 1·00 |
| 484 | **105** | $5 deep magenta, bright purple and olive-yellow (23.10.85) | 2·00 | 2·50 |
| 485 | | $10 sepia and grey-brown (23.10.85) | 2·50 | 3·50 |
| 486 | | $20 deep claret and pale blue (23.10.85) | 3·00 | 5·00 |
| 487 | | $50 dp claret & brownish grey (23.10.85) | 10·00 | 18·00 |
| 471/87 | | *Set of* 16 | 26·00 | 35·00 |

**116** Prow of Dragon Boat

**117** The Queen Mother with Prince Charles and Prince William, 1984

(Des R. Hookham. Litho Cartor S.A., France)

**1985** (19 June). 10*th International Dragon Boat Festival. T* **116** *and similar horiz designs showing different parts of dragon boat. Multicoloured. P* 13½ × 13.

| | | | |
|---|---|---|---|
| 488 | 40 c. Type **116** | 20 | 15 |
| 489 | $1 Drummer and rowers | 30 | 55 |
| 490 | $1.30, Rowers | 35 | 65 |
| 491 | $5 Stern of boat | 1·25 | 2·50 |
| 488/91 | *Set of* 4 | 1·90 | 3·50 |
| **MS**492 | 190 × 100 mm. Nos. 488/91. P 13 × 12 | 1·90 | 3·50 |

(Des C. Abbott. Litho Questa)

**1985** (7 Aug). *Life and Times of Queen Elizabeth the Queen Mother. T* **117** *and similar vert designs. Multicoloured. P* 14½ × 14.

| | | | |
|---|---|---|---|
| 493 | 40 c. At Glamis Castle, aged 7 | 35 | 10 |
| 494 | $1 Type **117** | 65 | 50 |
| 495 | $1.30, The Queen Mother, 1970 (from photo by Cecil Beaton) | 65 | 70 |
| 496 | $5 With Prince Henry at his christening (from photo by Lord Snowdon) | 1·40 | 2·25 |
| 493/6 | *Set of* 4 | 2·75 | 3·25 |

**118** Melastoma

(Des N. Jesse. Litho B.D.T.)

**1985** (25 Sept). *Native Flowers. T* **118** *and similar horiz designs. Multicoloured. P* 13½.

| | | | |
|---|---|---|---|
| 497 | 40 c. Type **118** | 40 | 15 |
| 498 | 50 c. Chinese Lily | 40 | 25 |
| 499 | 60 c. Grantham's Camellia | 40 | 35 |
| 500 | $1.30, Narcissus | 70 | 75 |
| 501 | $1.70, Bauhinia | 80 | 1·25 |
| 502 | $5 Chinese New Year Flower | 2·00 | 3·25 |
| 497/502 | *Set of* 6 | 4·25 | 5·50 |

**119** Hong Kong Academy for Performing Arts

(Des N. Jesse. Litho Format)

**1985** (27 Nov). *New Buildings. T* **119** *and similar multi-coloured designs. P* 15.

| | | | |
|---|---|---|---|
| 503 | 50 c. Type **119** | 35 | 15 |
| 504 | $1.30, Exchange Square (*vert*) | 65 | 45 |
| 505 | $1.70, Hong Kong Bank Headquarters (*vert*) | 85 | 75 |
| 506 | $5 Hong Kong Coliseum | 1·50 | 1·75 |
| 503/6 | *Set of* 4 | 3·00 | 2·75 |

**120** Halley's Comet in the Solar System

(Des A. Chan. Litho Cartor S.A., France)

**1986** (26 Feb). *Appearance of Halley's Comet. T* **120** *and similar horiz designs. Multicoloured. P* 13½ × 13.

| | | | |
|---|---|---|---|
| 507 | 50 c. Type **120** | 20 | 15 |
| 508 | $1.30, Edmond Halley and Comet | 35 | 50 |
| 509 | $1.70, Comet over Hong Kong | 40 | 80 |
| 510 | $5 Comet passing the Earth | 1·25 | 2·75 |
| 507/10 | *Set of* 4 | 2·00 | 3·75 |
| **MS**511 | 135 × 80 mm. Nos. 507/10 | 2·00 | 3·75 |

(Des A. Theobald. Litho Harrison)

**1986** (21 Apr). 60*th Birthday of Queen Elizabeth II. Vert designs as T* **110** *of Ascension. Multicoloured. P* 14½ × 14.

| | | | |
|---|---|---|---|
| 512 | 50 c. At wedding of Miss Celia Bowes-Lyon, 1931 | 25 | 10 |
| 513 | $1 Queen in Garter procession, Windsor Castle, 1977 | 40 | 30 |
| 514 | $1.30, In Hong Kong, 1975 | 45 | 40 |
| 515 | $1.70, At Royal Lodge, Windsor, 1980 (from photo by Norman Parkinson) | 45 | 60 |
| 516 | $5 At Crown Agents Head Office, London, 1983 | 1·00 | 2·00 |
| 512/16 | *Set of* 5 | 2·25 | 3·00 |

**121** Train, Airliner and Map of World

(Des Agay Ng Kee Chuen. Litho B.D.T.)

**1986** (18 July). *"Expo '86" World Fair, Vancouver. T* **121** *and similar horiz designs. Multicoloured. P* 13½.

| | | | |
|---|---|---|---|
| 517 | 50 c. Type **121** | 25 | 15 |
| 518 | $1.30, Hong Kong Bank Headquarters and map of world | 50 | 45 |
| 519 | $1.70, Container ship and map of world | 70 | 85 |
| 520 | $5 Dish aerial and map of world | 1·75 | 2·50 |
| 517/20 | *Set of* 4 | 3·00 | 3·50 |

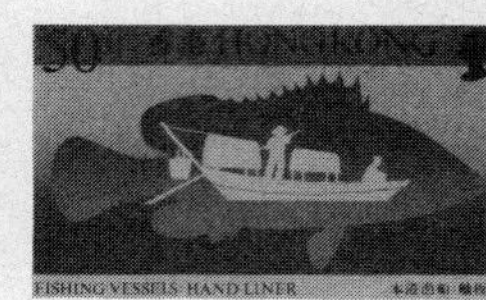

**122** Hand-liner Sampan

**123** "The Second Puan Khequa" (attr Spoilum)

(Des Graphic Communications Ltd. Litho B.D.T.)

**1986** (24 Sept). *Fishing Vessels. T* **122** *and similar horiz designs, each showing fishing boat and outline of fish. Multicoloured. P* 13½.

| | | | |
|---|---|---|---|
| 521 | 50 c. Type **122** | 20 | 15 |
| 522 | $1.30, Stern trawler | 50 | 50 |
| 523 | $1.70, Long liner junk | 70 | 90 |
| 524 | $5 Junk trawler | 1·75 | 2·50 |
| 521/4 | *Set of* 4 | 2·75 | 3·50 |

(Des R. Solley. Litho B.D.T.)

**1986** (9 Dec). 19*th-century Hong Kong Portraits. T* **123** *and similar vert designs. Multicoloured. P* 14 × 13½.

| | | | |
|---|---|---|---|
| 525 | 50 c. Type **123** | 20 | 15 |
| 526 | $1.30, "Chinese Lady" (19th-century copy) | 50 | 45 |
| 527 | $1.70, "Lamqua" (self-portrait) | 60 | 70 |
| 528 | $5 "Wife of Wo Hing Qua" (attr G. Chinnery) | 1·75 | 2·00 |
| 525/8 | *Set of* 4 | 2·75 | 3·00 |

**MACHINE LABELS.** A single machine operated at the G.P.O. from 30 December 1986 issuing 10, 50 c., $1.30 and $1.70 labels, each inscribed "O1". The original design depicted a carp, but this was changed to a rabbit on 18 August 1987 when a second machine was installed at Tsim Sha Tsui post office which issues labels coded "O2".

It is the intention that the label design should change each year to reflect the Chinese calendar and labels showing a dragon were provided for both machines from 23 March 1988. Values were changed to 10 c., 60 c., $1.40 and $1.80 on 1 September 1988.

The same face values were used for the Year of the Snake labels, introduced on 24 February 1989 and for the Year of the Horse from 21 February 1990. These showed an amended overall background pattern.

**124** Rabbit

(Des Kan Tai-Keung. Litho B.D.T.)

**1987** (21 Jan). *Chinese New Year ("Year of the Rabbit"). T* **124** *and similar horiz designs showing stylized rabbits. P* 13½.

| | | | |
|---|---|---|---|
| 529 | 50 c. multicoloured | 20 | 10 |
| 530 | $1.30, multicoloured | 35 | 30 |
| 531 | $1.70, multicoloured | 40 | 35 |
| 532 | $5 multicoloured | 1·00 | 1·10 |
| 529/32 | *Set of* 4 | 1·75 | 1·75 |
| **MS**533 | 133 × 84 mm. Nos. 529/32 | 2·00 | 3·00 |

Nos. 530/1 have the "0" omitted from their face values.

## PRICES OF SETS

Set prices are given for many issues, generally those containing three stamps or more. Definitive sets include one of each value or major colour change, but do not cover different perforations, die types or minor shades. Where a choice is possible the set prices are based on the cheapest versions of the stamps included in the listings.

**125** "Village Square, Hong Kong Island, 1838" (Auguste Borget)

**126** Queen Elizabeth II and Central Victoria

(Des J. Yim. Litho B.D.T.)

**1987** (23 Apr). *19th-century Hong Kong Scenes. T* **125** *and similar horiz designs. Multicoloured. P* 14.

534 50 c. Type **125** . . . . . . 25 10
535 $1.30, "Boat Dwellers, Kowloon Bay, 1838" (Auguste Borget) . . 45 35
536 $1.70, "Flagstaff House, 1846" (Murdoch Bruce) . . . . 55 60
537 $5 "Wellington Street, late 19th-century" (C. Andrasi) . . . . 1·00 1·50
534/7 . . . . *Set of* 4 2·00 2·25

Two types of Nos. 538/52.

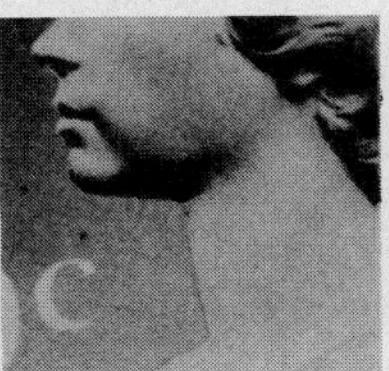
I. Heavy shading under mouth and cheek

II. Lighter shading

(Des W. Hookham. Litho Leigh-Mardon Ltd, Melbourne)

**1987** (13 July)–**88**. *T* **126** *and similar vert designs, each showing Queen Elizabeth II and Hong Kong skyline. P* 14½ × 14 (10 c. *to* $2) *or* 14 ($5 *to* $50). A. *Shading as Type* I. B. *Shading as Type* II (1.9.88).

| | | | A | | B | |
|---|---|---|---|---|---|---|
| 538 | **126** | 10 c. multicoloured | 35 | 30 | 30 | 20 |
| 539 | | 40 c. multicoloured | 55 | 30 | 45 | 25 |
| 540 | | 50 c. multicoloured | 60 | 20 | 45 | 30 |
| 541 | | 60 c. multicoloured | 65 | 30 | 45 | 35 |
| 542 | | 70 c. multicoloured | 75 | 35 | 55 | 40 |
| 543 | | 80 c. multicoloured | 75 | 35 | 55 | 40 |
| 544 | | 90 c. multicoloured | 80 | 30 | 70 | 35 |
| 545 | | $1 multicoloured | 80 | 35 | 70 | 45 |
| 546 | | $1.30, multicoloured | 1·00 | 45 | 1·00 | 50 |
| 546*c* | | $1.40, multicoloured | | † | 1·50 | 1·25 |
| 547 | | $1.70, multicoloured | 1·00 | 50 | 1·00 | 60 |
| 547*c* | | $1.80, multicoloured | | † | 1·50 | 1·50 |
| 548 | | $2 multicoloured | 1·00 | 60 | 1·00 | 60 |
| 549 | – | $5 multicoloured | 1·75 | 1·40 | 1·50 | 1·25 |
| 550 | – | $10 multicoloured | 2·50 | 2·50 | 3·00 | 2·50 |
| 551 | – | $20 multicoloured | 4·00 | 4·50 | 3·75 | 4·00 |
| 552 | – | $50 multicoloured | 8·50 | 12·00 | 9·50 | 11·00 |
| 538A/52A | | *Set of* 15 | 23·00 | 22·00 | | † |
| 538B/52B | | *Set of* 17 | | † | 25·00 | 23·00 |

Designs (25 × 31 *mm*): $5 Kowloon; $10 Victoria Harbour; $20 Legislative Council Building; $50 Government House.

Nos. 538/52 carry the fluorescent security markings as described beneath Nos. 415/30 with the $5 to $50 values showing an additional vertical fluorescent bar at right.

For these stamps as Type II, but with imprint dates, see Nos. 600/15.

**127** Hong Kong Flag

**128** Alice Ho Miu Ling Nethersole Hospital, 1887

(Des R. Hookham. Photo Enschedé)

**1987** (13 July)–**89**. *Coil Stamps. T* **127** *and similar vert design. P* 14½×14. A. *Without imprint date*. B. *With imprint date* (1.8.89).

| | | A | | B | |
|---|---|---|---|---|---|
| 553 | 10 c. multicoloured | 40 | 50 | 10 | 10 |
| 554 | 50 c. bistre, lake and black | 1·10 | 1·40 | 10 | 10 |

Design:—50 c. Map of Hong Kong.

Nos. 553/4 carry the fluorescent security marking as described beneath Nos. 415/30.

The printing with imprint date has every fifth stamp in the roll of 1,000 numbered on the reverse.

Nos. 553B/4B exist with different imprint dates at foot.

(Des A. Fung. Litho Walsall)

**1987** (8 Sept). *Hong Kong Medical Centenaries. T* **128** *and similar horiz designs. Multicoloured. P* 14½.

555 50 c. Type **128** . . . . . . 20 10
556 $1.30, Matron and nurses, Nethersole Hospital, 1891 . . . . 35 35
557 $1.70, Scanning equipment, Faculty of Medicine . . . . . . 45 50
558 $5 Nurse and patient, Faculty of Medicine 1·10 1·40
555/8 . . . . *Set of* 4 1·90 2·10

**129** Casual Dress with Fringed Hem, 220–589

(Des Sumiko Davies. Litho CPE Australia Ltd, Melbourne)

**1987** (18 Nov). *Historical Chinese Costumes. T* **129** *and similar horiz designs. Multicoloured. P* 13½.

559 50 c. Type **129** . . . . . . 15 10
560 $1.30, Two-piece dress and wrap, 581–960 30 35
561 $1.70, Formal dress, Song Dynasty, 960–1279 . . . . . . 35 45
562 $5 Manchu empress costume, 1644–1911 . . 90 1·25
559/62 . . . . *Set of* 4 1·50 1·90

**130** Dragon

**131** White-breasted Kingfisher

(Des Kan Tai-Keung. Litho CPE Australia Ltd, Melbourne)

**1988** (27 Jan). *Chinese New Year ("Year of the Dragon"). T* **130** *and similar horiz designs showing dragons. P* 13½.

563 50 c. multicoloured . . . . 25 15
564 $1.30, multicoloured . . . . 45 50
565 $1.70, multicoloured . . . . 60 75
566 $5 multicoloured . . . . 1·40 2·25
563/6 . . . . *Set of* 4 2·40 3·25
**MS**567 134 × 88 mm. Nos. 563/6 . . . . 3·25 3·75

(Des Karen Phillipps. Litho CPE Australia Ltd, Melbourne)

**1988** (20 Apr). *Hong Kong Birds. T* **131** *and similar vert designs. Multicoloured. P* 13½.

568 50 c. Type **131** . . . . . . 20 10
569 $1.30, Fukien Niltava . . . . 40 35
570 $1.70, Black Kite . . . . 45 50
571 $5 Pied Kingfisher . . . . 1·00 1·40
568/71 . . . . *Set of* 4 1·90 2·10

**132** Chinese Banyan

**133** Lower Terminal, Peak Tramway

(Des A. Chan. Litho B.D.T.)

**1988** (16 June). *Trees of Hong Kong. T* **132** *and similar vert designs. Multicoloured. P* 13½.

572 50 c. Type **132** . . . . . . 15 10
573 $1.30, Hong Kong Orchid Tree . . . . 25 25
574 $1.70, Cotton Tree . . . . 30 30
575 $5 Schima . . . . 80 90
572/5 . . . . *Set of* 4 1·25 1·40
**MS**576 135×85 mm. Nos. 572/5 . . . . 1·40 1·75

(Des Lilian Tang. Litho Leigh-Mardon Ltd, Melbourne)

**1988** (4 Aug). *Centenary of The Peak Tramway. T* **133** *and similar vert designs. Multicoloured. P* 14½×15.

577 50 c. Type **133** . . . . . . 15 10
578 $1.30, Tram on incline . . . . 25 45
579 $1.70, Peak Tower Upper Terminal . . 30 45
580 $5 Tram . . . . . . 80 1·00
577/80 . . . . *Set of* 4 1·25 1·75
**MS**581 160×90 mm. Nos. 577/80 . . . . 1·40 2·00

**134** Hong Kong Catholic Cathedral

**135** Deaf Girl

(Des C. Buendia. Litho CPE Australia Ltd, Melbourne)

**1988** (30 Sept). *Centenary of Hong Kong Catholic Cathedral. P* 14.

582 **134** 60 c. multicoloured . . . . 20 20

(Des M. Tucker. Litho Harrison)

**1988** (30 Nov). *Community Chest Charity. T* **135** *and similar vert designs. P* 14½.

583 60 c. + 10 c. brownish black, vermilion and greenish blue . . . . 15 15
584 $1.40 + 20 c. brownish black, vermilion and bright green . . . . 25 30
585 $1.80 + 30 c. brownish black, vermilion and bright orange . . . . 30 35
586 $5 + $1 brownish blk, verm and yell-brn 90 95
583/6 . . . . *Set of* 4 1·40 1·50

Designs:—$1.40, Elderly woman; $1.80, Blind boy using braille typewriter; $5 Mother and baby.

**136** Snake

**137** Girl and Doll

(Des Kan Tai-keung. Litho Enschedé)

**1989** (18 Jan). *Chinese New Year ("Year of the Snake"). T* **136** *and similar horiz designs. Multicoloured. P* 13½ × 14.

587 60 c. Type **136** . . . . . . 10 15
a. Booklet pane. Nos. 587 and 589, each ×5 . . . . . . 1·75
588 $1.40, Snake and fish . . . . 20 25
589 $1.80, Snake on branch . . . . 25 30
590 $5 Coiled snake . . . . 75 80
587/90 . . . . *Set of* 4 1·10 1·40
**MS**591 135×85 mm. Nos. 587/90 . . . . 1·50 1·75

(Des M. Tucker. Litho B.D.T.)

**1989** (4 May). *Cheung Chau Bun Festival. T* **137** *and similar vert designs. Multicoloured. P* 13½.

592 60 c. Type **137** . . . . . . 15 15
593 $1.40, Girl in festival costume . . 30 30
594 $1.80, Paper effigy of god Taai Si Wong . . 45 45
595 $5 Floral gateway . . . . 1·00 1·10
592/5 . . . . *Set of* 4 1·75 1·75

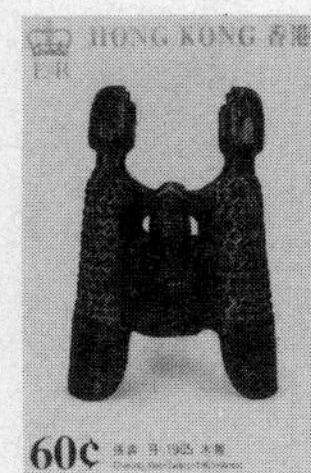

**138** "Twins" (wood carving, Cheung Yee)

**139** Lunar New Year Festivities

(Des Kan Tai-keung. Litho Enschedé)

**1989** (19 July). *Modern Art. T* **138** *and similar vert designs. Multicoloured. P* 12×12½.

596 60 c. Type **138** . . . . . . 15 15
597 $1.40, "Figures" (acrylic on paper, Chan Luis) . . . . . . 30 30
598 $1.80, "Lotus" (copper sculpture, Van Lau) 45 45
599 $5 "Zen Painting" (ink and colour on paper, Lui Shou-kwan) . . . . 1·00 1·10
596/9 . . . . *Set of* 4 1·75 1·75

**1989** (1 Aug)–**91**. *As Nos.* 538B/52B, *and new values, with imprint date added to designs. P* 14½×14 (10 c. *to* $2.30) *or* 14 ($5 *to* $50).

600 **126** 10 c. multicoloured . . . . 10 10
601 40 c. multicoloured . . . . 10 10
602 50 c. multicoloured . . . . 10 10
603 60 c. multicoloured . . . . 10 10
604 70 c. multicoloured . . . . 10 10
605 80 c. multicoloured . . . . 10 10
606 90 c. multicoloured . . . . 10 15

| | | | | |
|---|---|---|---|---|
| 607 | 126 | $1 multicoloured | 15 | 20 |
| 607*a* | | $1.20, multicoloured (2.4.91) | 20 | 25 |
| 608 | | $1.30, multicoloured | 20 | 25 |
| 609 | | $1.40, multicoloured | 20 | 25 |
| 609*a* | | $1.70, multicoloured (2.4.91) | 25 | 30 |
| 610 | | $1.80, multicoloured | 25 | 30 |
| 611 | | $2 multicoloured | 30 | 35 |
| 611*a* | | $2.30, multicoloured (2.4.91) | 35 | 40 |
| 612 | – | $5 multicoloured | 75 | 80 |
| 613 | – | $10 multicoloured | 1·50 | 1·60 |
| 614 | – | $20 multicoloured | 3·00 | 3·25 |
| 615 | – | $50 multicoloured | 7·50 | 7·75 |
| 600/15 | | *Set of* 19 | 13·75 | 14·75 |

All values except Nos. 607*a*, 609*a* and 611*a* exist with different imprint dates.

For miniature sheets containing No. 613 see Nos. **MS**646 and **MS**684/5.

(Des Sumiko Davies. Litho Enschedé)

**1989** (6 Sept). *Hong Kong People. T* **139** *and similar vert designs. Multicoloured. P* 13×14½.

| | | | |
|---|---|---|---|
| 616 | 60 c. Type **139** | 10 | 10 |
| 617 | $1.40, Shadow boxing and horse racing | 20 | 25 |
| 618 | $1.80, Foreign-exchange dealer and traditional builder | 30 | 35 |
| 619 | $5 Multi-racial society | 80 | 85 |
| 616/19 | *Set of* 4 | 1·25 | 1·40 |

**140** University of Science and Technology

(Des I. Leung. Litho CPE Australia Ltd, Melbourne)

**1989** (5 Oct). *Building for the Future. T* **140** *and similar square designs. P* 13.

| | | | |
|---|---|---|---|
| 620 | 60 c. blue-black, orange-yellow & yellow-brn | 10 | 10 |
| 621 | 70 c. black, pale rose and rose | 10 | 15 |
| 622 | $1.30, black, brt yellow-green & blue-grn | 20 | 25 |
| 623 | $1.40, black, azure and bright blue | 20 | 25 |
| 624 | $1.80, brownish black, pale turquoise-green and turquoise-blue | 30 | 35 |
| 625 | $5 agate, pale red-orange and orange-red | 80 | 85 |
| 620/5 | *Set of* 6 | 1·50 | 1·60 |

Designs:—70 c. Cultural Centre; $1.30, Eastern Harbour motorway interchange; $1.40, New Bank of China Building; $1.80, Convention and Exhibition Centre; $5 Light Rail Transit train.

**141** Prince and Princess of Wales and Hong Kong Skyline

**142**

(Des Ng Kee-chuen. Litho Leigh-Mardon Ltd, Melbourne)

**1989** (8 Nov). *Royal Visit. T* **141** *and similar vert designs, each showing portrait and different view. Multicoloured. W* **142** *(sideways). P* 14½.

| | | | |
|---|---|---|---|
| 626 | 60 c. Type **141** | 10 | 10 |
| 627 | $1.40, Princess of Wales | 20 | 25 |
| 628 | $1.80, Prince of Wales | 30 | 35 |
| 629 | $5 Prince and Princess of Wales in evening dress | 80 | 85 |
| 626/9 | *Set of* 4 | 1·25 | 1·40 |
| **MS**630 | 128×75 mm. No. 629 | 1·10 | 1·10 |

**143** Horse

**144** Chinese Lobster Dish

(Des Kan Tai-Keung. Litho Enschedé)

**1990** (23 Jan). *Chinese New Year ("Year of the Horse"). T* **143** *and similar horiz designs. P* 13½×12½.

| | | | |
|---|---|---|---|
| 631 | 60 c. multicoloured | 15 | 15 |
| | a. Booklet pane. Nos. 631 and 633, each×3 | 1·50 | |
| 632 | $1.40, multicoloured | 30 | 30 |
| 633 | $1.80, multicoloured | 40 | 40 |
| 634 | $5 multicoloured | 1·00 | 1·00 |
| 631/4 | *Set of* 4 | 1·75 | 1·75 |
| **MS**635 | 135×85 mm. Nos. 631/4 | 1·90 | 2·00 |

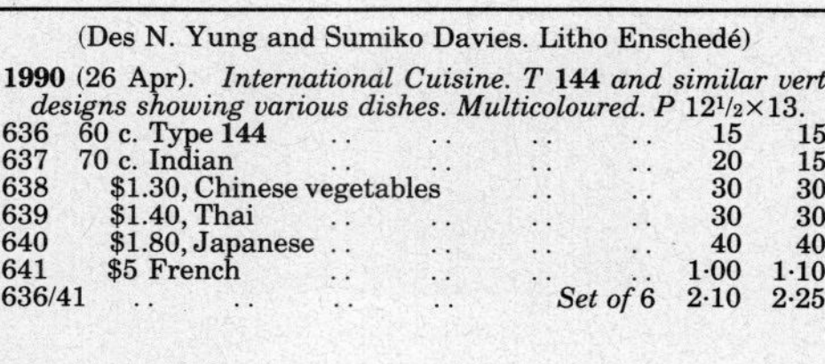

(Des N. Yung and Sumiko Davies. Litho Enschedé)

**1990** (26 Apr). *International Cuisine. T* **144** *and similar vert designs showing various dishes. Multicoloured. P* 12½×13.

| | | | |
|---|---|---|---|
| 636 | 60 c. Type **144** | 15 | 15 |
| 637 | 70 c. Indian | 20 | 15 |
| 638 | $1.30, Chinese vegetables | 30 | 30 |
| 639 | $1.40, Thai | 30 | 30 |
| 640 | $1.80, Japanese | 40 | 40 |
| 641 | $5 French | 1·00 | 1·10 |
| 636/41 | *Set of* 6 | 2·10 | 2·25 |

**145** Air Pollution and Clean Air

**146** Street Lamp and Des Voeux Road, 1890

(Litho Leigh-Mardon Ltd, Melbourne)

**1990** (5 June). *United Nations World Environment Day. T* **145** *and similar vert designs. Multicoloured. P* 14½.

| | | | |
|---|---|---|---|
| 642 | 60 c. Type **145** | 15 | 15 |
| 643 | $1.40, Noise pollution and music | 30 | 25 |
| 644 | $1.80, Polluted and clean water | 35 | 30 |
| 645 | $5 Litter on ground and in bin | 95 | 1·00 |
| 642/5 | *Set of* 4 | 1·60 | 1·50 |

(Des R. Hookham and I. Leung. Litho Leigh-Mardon Ltd, Melbourne)

**1990** (24 Aug). *"New Zealand 1990" International Stamp Exhibition, Auckland. Sheet* 130×75 *mm containing No.* 613. *P* 14.

| | | | |
|---|---|---|---|
| **MS**646 | $10 multicoloured | 6·00 | 7·00 |

The stamp in No. **MS**646 shows the imprint date changed to "1990".

(Des M. Tucker. Litho Leigh-Mardon Ltd, Melbourne)

**1990** (2 Oct). *Centenary of Electricity Supply. T* **146** *and similar horiz designs. P* 14½.

| | | | |
|---|---|---|---|
| 647 | 60 c. black, olive-bistre & pale orange-brown | 15 | 10 |
| 648 | $1.40, multicoloured | 30 | 25 |
| 649 | $1.80, black, olive-bistre and deep cobalt | 35 | 30 |
| 650 | $5 multicoloured | 1·00 | 1·00 |
| 647/50 | *Set of* 4 | 1·60 | 1·50 |
| **MS**651 | 155×85 mm. Nos. 648 and 650 | 1·25 | 1·75 |

Designs:—$1.40, Street lamp and *Jumbo* (floating restaurant), 1940; $1.80, Street lamp and pylon, 1960; $5 Street lamp and Hong Kong from harbour, 1980.

**147** Christmas Tree and Skyscrapers

(Litho Leigh-Mardon Ltd, Melbourne)

**1990** (8 Nov). *Christmas. T* **147** *and similar horiz designs. Multicoloured. P* 14½.

| | | | |
|---|---|---|---|
| 652 | 50 c. Type **147** | 15 | 10 |
| 653 | 60 c. Dove with holly | 15 | 15 |
| 654 | $1.40, Firework display | 30 | 30 |
| 655 | $1.80, Father Christmas hat on sky-scraper | 35 | 40 |
| 656 | $2 Children with Father Christmas | 40 | 45 |
| 657 | $5 Candy stick with bow and Hong Kong skyline | 1·10 | 1·40 |
| 652/7 | *Set of* 6 | 2·25 | 2·50 |

**148** Ram

**149** Letter "A", Clock, Teddy Bear and Building Bricks (Kindergarten)

(Des Kan Tai-keung. Litho Enschedé)

**1991** (24 Jan). *Chinese New Year ("Year of the Ram"). T* **148** *and similar horiz designs. P* 13½×12½.

| | | | |
|---|---|---|---|
| 658 | 60 c. multicoloured | 15 | 10 |
| | a. Booklet pane. Nos. 658 and 660, each × 3, with margins all round | 1·50 | |
| 659 | $1.40, multicoloured | 35 | 30 |
| 660 | $1.80, multicoloured | 40 | 40 |
| 661 | $5 multicoloured | 1·10 | 1·40 |
| 658/61 | *Set of* 4 | 1·75 | 2·00 |
| **MS**662 | 135×85 mm. Nos. 658/61 | 1·75 | 2·25 |

(Litho Enschedé)

**1991** (18 Apr). *Education. T* **149** *and similar vert designs. Multicoloured. P* 13½×13.

| | | | |
|---|---|---|---|
| 663 | 80 c. Type **149** | 15 | 15 |
| 664 | $1.80, Globe, laboratory flask and mathematical symbols (Primary and Secondary) | 35 | 35 |
| 665 | $2.30, Machinery (Vocational) | 55 | 65 |
| 666 | $5 Mortar board, computer and books (Tertiary) | 1·25 | 1·50 |
| 663/6 | *Set of* 4 | 2·10 | 2·40 |

**150** Rickshaw

**151** Victorian Pillar Box and Cover of 1888

(Des C. Tillyer. Litho B.D.T.)

**1991** (6 June). 100 *Years of Public Transport. T* **150** *and similar square designs. Multicoloured. P* 14.

| | | | |
|---|---|---|---|
| 667 | 80 c. Type **150** | 15 | 15 |
| 668 | 90 c. Double-decker bus | 15 | 15 |
| 669 | $1.70, Harbour ferry | 40 | 40 |
| 670 | $1.80, Tram | 40 | 45 |
| 671 | $2.30, Mass Transit Railway train | 60 | 70 |
| 672 | $5 Jetfoil | 1·25 | 1·40 |
| 667/72 | *Set of* 6 | 2·75 | 3·00 |

(Des H. Choi. Litho B.D.T.)

**1991** (25 Aug). *150th Anniv of Hong Kong Post Office. T* **151** *and similar vert designs. Multicoloured. P* 14.

| | | | |
|---|---|---|---|
| 673 | 80 c. Type **151** | 15 | 15 |
| 674 | $1.70, Edwardian pillar box and cover | 40 | 40 |
| 675 | $1.80, King George V pillar box and cover of 1935 | 40 | 45 |
| 676 | $2.30, King George VI pillar box and cover of 1938 | 55 | 60 |
| 677 | $5 Queen Elizabeth II pillar box and cover of 1989 | 1·10 | 1·25 |
| 673/7 | *Set of* 5 | 2·40 | 2·50 |
| **MS**678 | 130×75 mm. $10 As No. 676 | 2·40 | 2·50 |

**152** Bronze Buddha, Lantau Island

**153** Monkey

(Litho Questa)

**1991** (24 Oct). *Landmarks. T* **152** *and similar vert designs. P* 14.

| | | | |
|---|---|---|---|
| 679 | 80 c. rosine and black | 15 | 15 |
| 680 | $1.70, bright emerald and black | 35 | 40 |
| 681 | $1.80, reddish violet and black | 35 | 40 |
| 682 | $2.30, new blue and black | 50 | 60 |
| 683 | $5 bright yellow-orange and black | 1·00 | 1·25 |
| 679/83 | *Set of* 5 | 2·10 | 2·50 |

Designs:—$1.70, Peak Pavilion; $1.80, Clock Tower; $2.30, Catholic Cathedral; $5 Wong Tai Sin Temple.

(Des Kan Tai-keung. Litho Leigh-Mardon Ltd, Melbourne)

**1991** (16 Nov). *"Philanippon '91" International Stamp Exhibition, Tokyo. Sheet* 130×75 *mm containing No.* 613. *P* 14.

| | | | |
|---|---|---|---|
| **MS**684 | $10 multicoloured | 2·25 | 2·50 |

The stamp in No. **MS**684 shows the imprint date changed to "1991".

(Des K. Li. Litho Leigh-Mardon Ltd, Melbourne)

**1991** (4 Dec). *Olympic Games, Barcelona* (1992). *Sheet* 130×75 *mm. containing No.* 613. *P* 14.

| | | | |
|---|---|---|---|
| **MS**685 | $10 multicoloured | 1·50 | 1·75 |

The stamp in No. **MS**685 shows the imprint date changed to "1991".

(Des Kan Tai-keung. Litho Leigh-Mardon Ltd, Melbourne)

**1992** (22 Jan). *Chinese New Year ("Year of the Monkey").* *T* **153** *and similar horiz designs. P* 14½.

| | | | |
|---|---|---|---|
| 686 | 80 c. multicoloured .. .. .. | 10 | 15 |
| | a. Booklet pane. Nos. 686 and 688, each × 3, with margins all round .. .. | 1·40 | |
| 687 | $1.80, multicoloured .. .. .. | 25 | 30 |
| 688 | $2.30, multicoloured .. .. .. | 35 | 40 |
| 689 | $5 multicoloured .. .. .. | 75 | 80 |
| 686/9 | .. .. .. .. *Set of* 4 | 1·25 | 1·50 |
| **MS**690 | 135×85 mm. Nos. 686/9 .. .. | 1·50 | 1·60 |

(Des D. Miller. Litho Leigh-Mardon Ltd, Melbourne)

**1992** (11 Feb). *40th Anniv of Queen Elizabeth II's Accession. Horiz designs as T* **143** *of Ascension. Multicoloured. P* 14½.

| | | | |
|---|---|---|---|
| 691 | 80 c. Royal barge in Hong Kong harbour .. | 10 | 15 |
| 692 | $1.70, Queen watching dancing display .. | 25 | 30 |
| 693 | $1.80, Fireworks display .. .. .. | 25 | 30 |
| 694 | $2.30, Three portraits of Queen Elizabeth | 35 | 40 |
| 695 | $5 Queen Elizabeth II .. .. .. | 75 | 80 |
| 691/5 | .. .. .. .. *Set of* 5 | 1·50 | 1·75 |

## POSTAGE DUE STAMPS

**PRINTERS.** Nos. D1/23 were typographed by De La Rue & Co.

D 1 Post-office Scales

D 2

**1923** (Dec)–**56.** *Wmk Mult Script CA. Ordinary paper. P 14.*

| | | | | |
|---|---|---|---|---|
| D1 | D 1 | 1 c. brown | 1·25 | 65 |
| | | a. Wmk sideways (1931) | 90 | 2·00 |
| | | ab. Chalk-surfaced paper (21.3.56) | 15 | 70 |
| D2 | | 2 c. green | 10·00 | 4·75 |
| | | a. Wmk sideways (1928) | 8·00 | 4·75 |
| D3 | | 4 c. scarlet | 21·00 | 6·00 |
| | | a. Wmk sideways (1928) | 23·00 | 6·00 |
| D4 | | 6 c. yellow | 22·00 | 13·00 |
| | | a. Wmk sideways (1931) | 26·00 | 18·00 |
| D5 | | 10 c. bright ultramarine | 19·00 | 7·50 |
| | | a. Wmk sideways (1934) | 45·00 | 13·00 |
| D1/5 | | *Set of* 5 | 65·00 | 28·00 |
| D1a/5a | | *Set of* 5 | 90·00 | 38·00 |
| D1/5 Optd "Specimen" | | *Set of* 5 | £160 | |

**1938** (Feb)–**63.** *Wmk Mult Script CA (sideways). Ordinary paper. P 14.*

| | | | | |
|---|---|---|---|---|
| D 6 | D 1 | 2 c. grey | 7·50 | 7·50 |
| | | a. Chalk-surfaced paper (21.3.56) | 70 | 8·00 |
| D 7 | | 4 c. orange | 10·00 | 5·50 |
| | | a. Chalk-surfaced paper. *Orange-yellow* (23.5.61) | 2·00 | 7·50 |
| D 8 | | 6 c. scarlet | 8·00 | 6·00 |
| D 9 | | 8 c. chestnut (26.2.46) | 4·50 | 26·00 |
| D10 | | 10 c. violet | 11·00 | 45 |
| | | a. Chalk-surfaced paper (17.9.63) | 6·00 | 3·50 |
| D11 | | 20 c. black (26.2.46) | 6·00 | 3·00 |
| D12 | | 50 c. blue (7.47) | 22·00 | 14·00 |
| D6a/12 | | *Set of* 7 | 45·00 | 55·00 |
| D6/12 Perf "Specimen" | | *Set of* 7 | £250 | |

**1965** (15 Apr)–**72.** *Chalk-surfaced paper. P 14.*

(a) *Wmk w* **12** *(sideways)*

| | | | | |
|---|---|---|---|---|
| D13 | D 1 | 4 c. yellow-orange | 3·50 | 17·00 |
| D14 | | 5 c. red (13.5.69) | 2·25 | 3·75 |
| | | a. Glazed paper (17.11.72) | 9·00 | 23·00 |
| D15 | | 10 c. violet (27.6.67) | 1·50 | 3·25 |
| D16 | | 20 c. black (1965) | 2·50 | 3·25 |
| D17 | | 50 c. deep blue (1965) | 8·50 | 9·00 |
| | | *a. Blue* (13.5.69) | 8·00 | 9·00 |
| D13/17 | | *Set of* 5 | 16·00 | 32·00 |

(b) *Wmk w* **12** *(upright)*

| | | | | |
|---|---|---|---|---|
| D18 | D 1 | 5 c. red (20.7.67) | 1·00 | 4·00 |
| D19 | | 50 c. deep blue (26.8.70) | 8·50 | 10·00 |

The 5 c. is smaller, 21 × 18 mm.

**1972** (17 Nov)–**74.** *Glazed, ordinary paper. W* w **12** *(sideways).*

(a) *P* 14 × 14½

| | | | | |
|---|---|---|---|---|
| D20 | D 1 | 10 c. bright reddish violet | 3·00 | 3·25 |
| D21 | | 20 c. grey-black | 3·50 | 5·00 |
| D22 | | 50 c. deep dull blue | 3·00 | 9·50 |

(b) *P* 13½ × 14

| | | | | |
|---|---|---|---|---|
| D23 | D 1 | 5 c. brown-red (1.5.74) | 1·75 | 4·50 |
| D20/3 | | *Set of* 4 | 10·00 | 20·00 |

(Typo Walsall)

**1976** (19 Mar*)–**78.** *Smaller design (21 × 17 mm) with redrawn value-tablet. Glazed, ordinary paper. W* w **14**. *P* 14.

| | | | | |
|---|---|---|---|---|
| D25 | D 1 | 10 c. bright reddish violet | 30 | 3·00 |
| | | a. Chalk-surfaced paper (15.12.78) | 20 | 1·00 |
| D26 | | 20 c. grey-black | 45 | 3·25 |
| | | a. Chalk-surfaced paper (15.12.78) | 25 | 1·25 |
| D27 | | 50 c. deep dull blue | 50 | 3·75 |
| | | a. Chalk-surfaced paper (15.12.78) | 50 | 1·75 |
| D28 | | $1 yellow (1.4.76) | 6·50 | 7·00 |
| | | a. Chalk-surfaced paper (15.12.78) | 40 | 2·00 |
| D25/8 | | *Set of* 4 | 7·00 | 15·00 |
| D25a/8a | | *Set of* 4 | 1·25 | 5·50 |

*This is the London release date. It is believed that the stamps were not released locally until 14 April.

(Typo Walsall)

**1986** (11 Jan). *As Nos.* D27a/8a, *but without watermark. P* 14.

| | | | | |
|---|---|---|---|---|
| D29 | D 1 | 50 c. slate-blue | 1·00 | 3·00 |
| D30 | | $1 lemon | 1·25 | 3·50 |

(Des A. Chan. Litho B.D.T.)

**1987** (25 Mar). *P* 14×15.

| | | | | |
|---|---|---|---|---|
| D31 | D 2 | 10 c. light green | 10 | 10 |
| D32 | | 20 c. red-brown | 10 | 10 |
| D33 | | 50 c. bright violet | 10 | 10 |
| D34 | | $1 yellow-orange | 15 | 20 |
| D35 | | $5 dull ultramarine | 75 | 80 |
| D36 | | $10 bright rose-red | 1·50 | 1·60 |
| D31/6 | | *Set of* 6 | 2·25 | 2·50 |

### MINIMUM PRICE

The minimum price quote is 10p which represents a handling charge rather than a basis for valuing common stamps. For further notes about prices see introductory pages.

## POSTCARD STAMPS

Stamps specially surcharged for use on Postcards

3
CENTS
(P 1)

THREE
(P 2)

**1879** (1 April). *Nos. 22 and 13 surch as Type* P 1.

| | | | | |
|---|---|---|---|---|
| P1 | 3 | 3 c. on 16 c. yellow (No. 22) | £160 | £250 |
| P2 | | 5 c. on 18 c. lilac (No. 13) | £140 | £250 |

**1879** (Nov). *No.* P2 *surch with Type* P 2.

| | | | | |
|---|---|---|---|---|
| P3 | 3 | 3 c. on 5 c. on 18 c. lilac | £2000 | £3000 |

## POSTAL FISCAL STAMPS

I. Stamps inscribed "STAMP DUTY"

**NOTE.** The dated circular "Hong Kong" cancellation with "PAID ALL" in lower segment normally indicates fiscal, not postal, use, but a few instances are known where it was applied *in red*, for postal purposes.

F 1

F 2

F 3

**1874–1902.** *Wmk Crown CC.* (a) *P* 15½ × 15.

| | | | | |
|---|---|---|---|---|
| F1 | F 1 | $2 olive-green | £150 | 30·00 |
| | | a. Thin paper | £200 | 45·00 |
| F2 | F 2 | $3 dull violet | £110 | 25·00 |
| | | a. Thin paper | £200 | 32·00 |
| | | b. Bluish paper | | |
| F3 | F 3 | $10 rose-carmine | £3000 | £375 |

(b) *P* 14

| | | | | |
|---|---|---|---|---|
| F4 | F 1 | $2 dull bluish green (12.90) | £130 | 80·00 |
| F5 | F 2 | $3 dull mauve (3.02) | £170 | £120 |
| | | a. Bluish paper | £900 | |
| F6 | F 3 | $10 grey-green (1.92) | £1900 | |
| F4/5 Optd "Specimen" | | *Set of* 2 | £250 | |

12
CENTS.
(F 4)

F 5

**1881** (Feb). *No.* F3 *surch with Type* F 4.

| | | | | |
|---|---|---|---|---|
| F7 | F 3 | 12 c. on $10 rose-carmine | £375 | £120 |

**1890** (24 Dec). *Wmk Crown CA. P* 14.

| | | | | |
|---|---|---|---|---|
| F8 | F 5 | 2 c. dull purple | 27·00 | 9·00 |

No. F8 was authorised for postal use between 24 and 30 December 1890.

5
DOLLARS
(F 6)

(F 7)

F 8

**1891** (1 Jan). *Surch with Type* F **6**. *Wmk Crown CA. P* 14.

| | | | | |
|---|---|---|---|---|
| F9 | F 3 | $5 on $10 purple/*red* (Optd S. £100) | £150 | 60·00 |

**1897** (Sept). *Surch with Type* F **7**.

| | | | | |
|---|---|---|---|---|
| F10 | F 1 | $1 on $2 olive-green (No. F1) | 75·00 | 50·00 |
| | | a. Chinese surch wholly omitted | £750 | £650 |
| F11 | | $1 on $2 dull bluish green (No. F4) (H/S S. £90) | £110 | 75·00 |
| | | a. Chinese surch wholly omitted | £500 | £350 |
| | | b. Diagonal portion of Chinese surch omitted | £5000 | |

**1938** (11 Jan). *Wmk Mult Script CA. P* 14.

| | | | | |
|---|---|---|---|---|
| F12 | F 8 | 5 c. green | 38·00 | 7·50 |

Authorised for postal use on mail posted between 11 and 20 January 1938 (both dates inclusive).

II. Stamps overprinted "S.O." (Stamp Office), or "S.D." (Stamp Duty)

S. O.
印 厘
(S 1)

S. D.
印 厘
(S 2)

**1891** (1 Jan). *Optd with Types* S 1 *or* S 2.

| | | | | |
|---|---|---|---|---|
| S1 | S 1 | 2 c. carmine (No. 33) | £300 | £130 |
| S2 | S 2 | 2 c. carmine (No. 33) | £200 | 80·00 |
| | | a. Opt inverted | † | £1500 |
| S3 | S 1 | 10 c. purple/*red* (No. 38) | £400 | £200 |

Examples of No. S1 exist with the "O" amended to "D" in manuscript.

Other fiscal stamps are found apparently postally used, but there is no evidence that this use was authorised.

## JAPANESE OCCUPATION OF HONG KONG

Hong Kong surrendered to the Japanese on 25 December 1941. The postal service was not resumed until 22 January 1942 when the G.P.O. and Kowloon Central Office re-opened.

Initially six values (1, 2, 3, 4, 10 and 30 s.) of the current Japanese definitive set were on sale, but the range was gradually expanded to cover all values between ½ s. and 10 y. Supply of these Japanese stamps was often interrupted and, during the period between 28 July 1942 and 21 August 1943, circular "Postage Paid" handstamps were sometimes used. A substantial increase in postage rates during April 1945 led to the issue of the local surcharges, Nos. J1/3.

| PRICES FOR STAMPS ON COVER | |
|---|---|
| Nos. J1/3 | *from* × 7 |

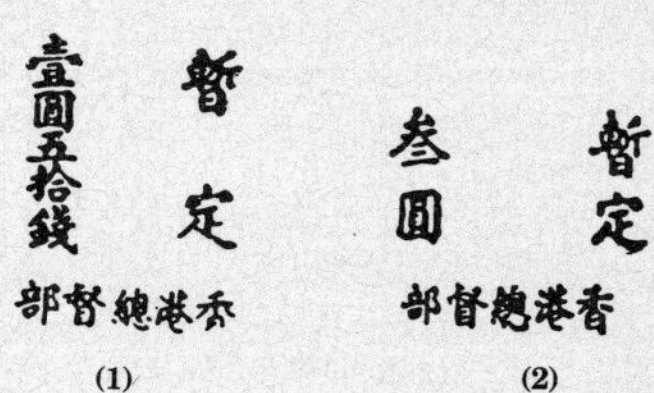


(1) (2)

**1945** (16 Apr). *Stamps of Japan surch with T* 1 *(No. J1) or as T* 2.

| | | | |
|---|---|---|---|
| J1 | 1.50 yen on 1 s. brown | 18·00 | 16·00 |
| J2 | 3 yen on 2 s. scarlet | 11·00 | 14·00 |
| J3 | 5 yen on 5 s. claret | £400 | 70·00 |

Designs (18½ × 22 *mm*):—1 s. Girl Worker; 2 s. Gen. Nogi; 5 s. Admiral Togo.

No. J3 has four characters of value similarly arranged but differing from T 2.

## BRITISH POST OFFICES IN CHINA

Under the terms of the 1842 Treaty of Nanking China granted Great Britain and its citizens commercial privileges in five Treaty Ports, Amoy, Canton, Foochow, Ningpo and Shanghai. British Consuls were appointed to each Port and their offices, as was usual during this period, collected and distributed mail for the British community. This system was formally recognised by a Hong Kong Government notice published on 16 April 1844. Mail from the consular offices was postmarked when it passed through Hong Kong.

The number of Chinese Treaty Ports was increased to sixteen by the ratification of the Treaty of Peking in 1860 with British postal facilities being eventually extended to the Ports of Chefoo, Hankow, Kiungchow (Hoihow), Swatow, Tainan (Anping) and Tientsin.

As postal business expanded the consular agencies were converted into packet agencies or post offices which passed under the direct control of the Hong Kong postal authorities on 1 May 1868.

In May 1898 the British Government leased the territory of Wei Hai Wei from China for use as a naval station to counter the Russian presence at Port Arthur.

The opening of the Trans-Siberia Railway and the extension of Imperial Penny Postage to the Treaty Port agencies resulted in them becoming a financial burden on the colonial post office. Control of the agencies reverted to the G.P.O., London, on 1 January 1911.

The pre-adhesive postal markings of the various agencies are a fascinating, but complex, subject. Full details can be found in *Hong Kong & the Treaty Ports of China & Japan* by F. W. Webb (Royal Philatelic Society, London—out of print) and in various publications of the Hong Kong Study Circle.

From 15 October 1864 the use of Hong Kong stamps on mail from the Treaty Ports became compulsory, although such stamps were, initially, not cancelled (with the exception of Amoy) until they reached Hong Kong where the "B62" killer was applied. Cancellation of mail at the actual Ports commenced during 1866 at Shanghai and Ningpo, spreading to all the agencies during the next ten years. Shanghai had previously used a c.d.s. on adhesives during 1863 and again in 1865–66.

The main types of cancellation used between 1866 and 1930 are illustrated below. The illustrations show the style of each postmark and no attempt has been made to cover differences in type letters or figures, arrangement, diameter or colour.

Until 1885 the vertical and horizontal killers were used to obliterate the actual stamps with an impression of one of the circular date stamps shown elsewhere on the cover. Many of the early postmarks were also used as backstamps or transit marks and, in the notes which follow, references to use are for the first appearance of the mark, not necessarily its first use as an obliterator.

Illustrations in this section are taken from *Hong Kong & the Treaty Ports of China & Japan* by F. W. Webb and are reproduced with the permission of the Royal Philatelic Society, London.

Postmark Types

Type A
Vertical killer

Type B
Horizontal killer

Type C
Name horizontal

Type D
Name curved

Type E
Double circle Name at top

Type F
Double circle Name at foot

Type G
Single circle Name at top

### AMOY

One of the five original Treaty Ports, opened to British trade by the Treaty of Nanking in 1842. A consular postal agency was established in 1844 which later expanded into two separate offices, one on the off-shore island of Ku Lang Seu and the other in Amoy itself.

Amoy "PAID" (*supplied* 1858) *used* 1859–67
Type **A** ("A1") (*supplied* 1866) *used at Ku Lang Seu* 1869–82
Type **D** (*supplied* 1866) *used* 1867–1922
Type **B** ("D27") (*supplied* 1876) *used at Amoy* 1876–84
Type **C** *used* 1876–94
Type **F** (*supplied* 1913) *used* 1916–22

### ANPING

Anping is the port for Tainan, on the island of Formosa, opened to British trade in 1860. A British Vice-consulate operated in the port and mail is known postmarked there between 1889 and 1895. Formosa passed under Japanese control in 1895 and British Treaty Port rights then lapsed.

Type **D** *used* 1889–95

### CANTON

A British postal service was organised in Canton from 1834, but was closed when the foreign communities were evacuated in 1839. The city was one of the original Treaty Ports and a consular agency was opened there in 1844. The consulate closed during the riots of 1858, being replaced by a temporary postal agency at Whampoa, further down river. When British forces reached Canton a further temporary agency was set up in 1859, but both closed in 1863 when the consulate was re-established.

Type **A** ("C1") (*supplied* 1866) *used* 1875–84
Type **C** (*supplied* 1866) *used* 1866–1901
Type **D** *used* 1890–1922

### CHEFOO

Chefoo was opened to British trade in 1860. Although a consulate was established in 1861 no organised postal agency was provided until 1903 when one was opened at the premises of Curtis Brothers, a commercial firm.

Type **E** (*supplied* 1902) *used* 1903–20
Type **D** (*supplied* 1907) *used* 1907–13
Type **F** *used* 1916–22

### FOOCHOW

Foochow, originally known as Foochowfoo, was one of the original Treaty Ports opened to British trade in 1842. A British consulate and postal agency was established in June 1844.

Type **A** ("F1") (*supplied* 1866) *used* 1873–84
Type **D** (inscr "FOOCHOWFOO") (*supplied* 1866) *used* 1867–1905
Type **D** (inscr "FOOCHOW") (*supplied* 1894) *used* 1894–1917
Type **E** (inscr "B.P.O.") *used* 1906–10
Type **F** *used* 1915–22

### HANKOW

Hankow, on the Yangtse River 600 miles from the sea, became a Treaty Port in 1860. A British consulate opened the following year, but no organised British postal agency was established until 1872.

Type **D** (*supplied* 1874) *used* 1874–1916
Type **B** ("D29") (*supplied* 1876) *used* 1878–83
Type **F** *used* 1916–22

### KIUNGCHOW (HOIHOW)

Kiungchow, a city on the island of Hainan, and its port of Hoihow was added to the Treaty Port system in 1860. A consular postal agency was opened at Kiungchow in 1876, being transferred to Hoihow in 1878. A second agency was opened at Kiungchow in 1879.

Type **B** ("D28") (*supplied* 1876) *used* 1876–83
Type **D** (inscr "KIUNG-CHOW") (*supplied* 1876) *used* 1879–81

"REGISTERED KIUNG-CHOW" with "REGISTERED" removed (*originally supplied* 1876) *used* 1884–85
Type **D** (inscr "HOIHOW") *used* 1885–1922

### NINGPO

Ningpo was one of the 1842 Treaty Ports and a consular postal agency was established there in 1844.

Type **A** ("N1") (*supplied* 1866) *used* 1870–82
Type **C** (*supplied* 1866) *used* 1870–99
Type **D** *used* 1895–1922

### SHANGHAI

Shanghai was one of the original Treaty Ports of 1842 and a packet agency was opened at the British consulate in 1844. It moved to separate premises in 1861 and was upgraded to a Post Office in 1867.

British military post offices operated in Shanghai from 1927 until 1940.

Type **D** (inscr "SHANGHAE") (*supplied* 1861) *used* 1862–99

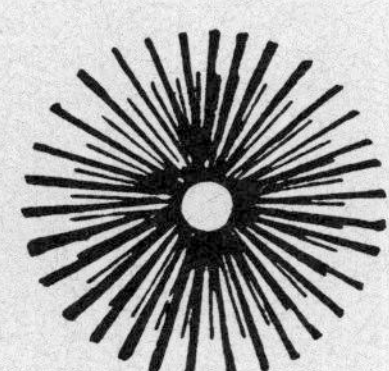

Sunburst *used* 1864–65
Type **A** ("S1") (*supplied* 1866) *used* 1866–85
Type **D** (inscr "SHANGHAI") (*supplied* 1885) *used* 1886–1906
Type **G** (inscr "B.P.O." at foot) (*supplied* 1904) *used* 1904–17
Type **G** (inscr "Br.P.O." at foot) (*supplied* 1907) *used* 1907–22
Type **E** (figures "I" to "VIII" at foot) *used* 1912–22

### SWATOW

Swatow became a Treaty Port in 1860 and a consular packet agency was opened in the area made available for foreign firms during the same year. In 1867 the original agency was transferred to the Chinese city on the other side of the Han river, but a second agency was subsequently opened in the foreign concession during 1883.

Type **A** ("S2") (*supplied* 1866) *used* 1875–85
Type **C** (*supplied* 1866) *used* 1866–89
Type **D** (*supplied* 1883) *used* 1884–1922
Type **F** *used* 1916–22

### TIENTSIN

Tientsin became a Treaty Port in 1860. A British consulate was established in 1861, but no formal postal agency was organised there until 1882. It was not, however, very successful and was closed during 1890. The British Post Office reopened on 1 October 1906 under the management of the Chinese Engineering and Mining Company.

British military post offices operated in Tientsin from 1927 until 1940.

Type **E** *used* 1906–13
Type **G** (supplied 1907) *used* 1907–22

### WEI HAI WEI

The territory of Wei Hai Wei was leased from the Chinese by the British Government from 24 May 1898. At that time there were no organised postal services from the area, although a private local post did operate between the port and Chefoo from December 1898 until March 1899. A Chinese Imperial post office opened in March 1899 to be followed by a British postal agency on the offshore island of Liu Kung Tau on 1 September 1899. A second British agency opened at Port Edward on 1 April 1904.

Liu Kung Tau oval *used* 1899–1901
Type **D** (inscr "LIU KUNG TAU") (*supplied* 1899) *used* 1901–30

Port Edward rectangle *used* 1904–08
Type **D** (inscr "PORT EDWARD") (*supplied* 1907) *used* 1907–30

| PRICES FOR STAMPS ON COVER | |
|---|---|
| Nos. 1/14 | *from* × 10 |
| Nos. 15/17 | — |
| Nos. 18/28 | *from* × 12 |

## CHINA

**(1)**

**1917** (1 Jan)–**21.** *Stamps of Hong Kong,* 1912–21 (*wmk Mult Crown CA*), *optd with T* **1**, *at Somerset House.*

| No. | Description | Unused | Used |
|---|---|---|---|
| 1 | 1 c. brown | 50 | 75 |
| | *a. Black-brown* | 55 | 1·50 |
| | b. Crown broken at side | £120 | £150 |
| | c. Wmk sideways | † | £2000 |
| 2 | 2 c. green | 25 | 15 |
| 3 | 4 c. carmine-red | 50 | 10 |
| 4 | 6 c. orange | 1·00 | 45 |
| 5 | 8 c. slate | 2·00 | 60 |
| 6 | 10 c. ultramarine | 1·00 | 10 |
| 7 | 12 c. purple/*yellow* | 1·75 | 1·75 |
| 8 | 20 c. purple and sage-green | 3·25 | 30 |
| 9 | 25 c. purple and magenta (A) | 4·00 | 12·00 |
| 11 | 30 c. purple and orange-yellow | 10·00 | 3·50 |
| 12 | 50 c. black/*blue-green* (*olive back*) | 16·00 | 75 |
| | *a. On emerald surface* (1917?) | 9·50 | 4·00 |
| | *b. On emerald back* (1919) | 7·50 | 2·50 |
| | *c. On white back* (1920) | 50·00 | 18·00 |
| 13 | $1 reddish purple and bright blue/*blue* | 25·00 | 1·75 |
| | *a. Grey-purple and blue/blue* (1921) | 24·00 | 3·25 |
| 14 | $2 carmine-red and grey-black | 70·00 | 35·00 |
| 15 | $3 green and purple | £110 | 85·00 |
| 16 | $5 green and red/*blue-green* (*olive back*) | £120 | 85·00 |
| 17 | $10 purple and black/*red* | £400 | £200 |
| 1/17 | *Set of* 16 | £650 | £375 |
| 12/17 | H/S "Specimen" *Set of* 6 | £800 | |

**1922** (Mar)–**27.** *As last, but wmk Mult Script CA.*

| No. | Description | Unused | Used |
|---|---|---|---|
| 18 | 1 c. brown | 35 | 1·25 |
| 19 | 2 c. green | 65 | 80 |
| 20 | 4 c. carmine-rose | 1·25 | 75 |
| | a. Lower Chinese character at right broken at top | 70·00 | 60·00 |
| 21 | 6 c. orange-yellow | 75 | 2·25 |
| 22 | 8 c. grey | 90 | 8·50 |
| 23 | 10 c. bright ultramarine | 75 | 1·00 |
| 24 | 20 c. purple and sage-green | 2·50 | 2·75 |
| 25 | 25 c. purple and magenta (B) | 7·50 | 38·00 |
| 26 | 50 c. black/*emerald* (1927) (H/S S. £200) | 23·00 | 65·00 |
| 27 | $1 purple and blue/*blue* | 15·00 | 17·00 |
| 28 | $2 carmine-red and grey-black | £100 | £120 |
| 18/28 | *Set of* 11 | £140 | £225 |

The overprinted stamps Nos. 1/17 were introduced on 1 January 1917 for use in the then-existing agencies of Amoy,

Canton, Chefoo, Foochow, Hankow, Hoihow, Ningpo, Shanghai, Swatow and Tientsin. They were also supplied to the British naval base of Wei Hai Wei.

The British P.O.s in the Treaty Ports closed by agreement with the Chinese on 30 November 1922, but the above overprinted issues continued in use at the Wei Hai Wei offices until they in turn closed on 30 September 1930.

## BRITISH POST OFFICES IN JAPAN

Under the terms of the Anglo-Japanese Treaty of Yedo, signed on 26 August 1858, five Japanese ports were opened to British trade. British consulates were established at Decima (Nagasaki), Kanagawa (Yokohama), Hiogo (Kobe) and Hakodadi (Hakodate). The postage stamps of Hong Kong became available at the Yokohama and Nagasaki consulates during October 1864 and at Hiogo in 1869, although cancellation of mail did not commence until 1866 at Yokohama and Nagasaki or 1876 at Hiogo. Japan became a member of the U.P.U. on 1 June 1877 and all of the British Postal Agencies were closed by the end of 1879.

For illustrations of postmark types see BRITISH POST OFFICES IN CHINA.

### YOKOHAMA

The British Consulate opened in Kanagawa on 21 July 1859, but was relocated to Yokohama where it provided postal services from 1 July 1860 until a separate Post Office was established in 1867. The British Post Office in Yokohama closed on 31 December 1879.

Type **A** ("Y1") (*supplied* 1866) *used* 1868–79
Type **D** (*supplied* 1866) *used* 1866–79

### NAGASAKI

The British Consulate opened in Nagasaki on 14 June 1859, but, with few British residents at the port, the consular staff found it inconvenient to carry out postal duties so that few Nagasaki c.d.s. or "N2" cancellations exist. The postal service was terminated on 30 September 1879.

Type **A** ("N2") (*supplied* 1866) *used* 1876–79
Type **D** (*supplied* 1866) *used* 1876–79

### HIOGO

The Port of Hiogo (Kobe) was first opened to foreigners on 1 January 1868. The British Consular mail service at Hiogo commenced during 1869 to serve the foreigners at Hiogo, Kobe and Osaka. The cities of Hiogo and Kobe later merged to become the single city of Kobe. The consular office at Hiogo closed on 30 November 1879.

Type **B** ("D30") (*supplied* 1876) *used* 1876–79
Type **D** (*supplied* 1876) *used* 1876–79

### HAKODATE

A British consular office existed at Hakodate, but it was never issued with a c.d.s., obliterator or Hong Kong stamps. No British covers are recorded from this consulate prior to opening of the Japanese Post Office.

# India

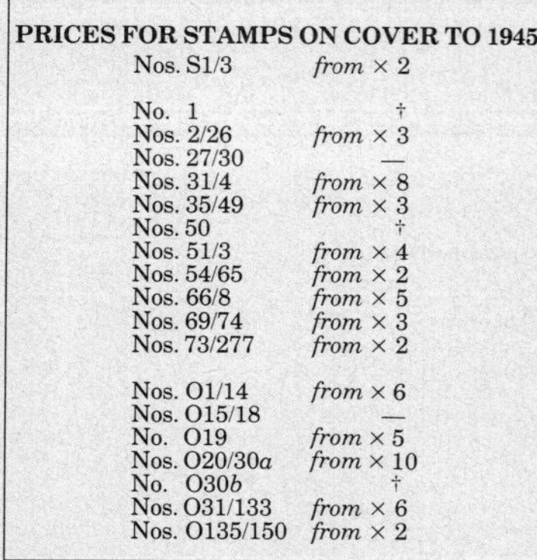

**PRICES FOR STAMPS ON COVER TO 1945**

| | |
|---|---|
| Nos. S1/3 | *from* × 2 |
| No. 1 | † |
| Nos. 2/26 | *from* × 3 |
| Nos. 27/30 | — |
| Nos. 31/4 | *from* × 8 |
| Nos. 35/49 | *from* × 3 |
| Nos. 50 | † |
| Nos. 51/3 | *from* × 4 |
| Nos. 54/65 | *from* × 2 |
| Nos. 66/8 | *from* × 5 |
| Nos. 69/74 | *from* × 3 |
| Nos. 73/277 | *from* × 2 |
| Nos. O1/14 | *from* × 6 |
| Nos. O15/18 | — |
| No. O19 | *from* × 5 |
| Nos. O20/30*a* | *from* × 10 |
| No. O30*b* | † |
| Nos. O31/133 | *from* × 6 |
| Nos. O135/150 | *from* × 2 |

**(12 pies = 1 anna; 16 annas = 1 rupee)**

### ISSUE FOR SIND PROVINCE

1

**1852** (1 July). "Scinde Dawk." *Embossed.*

| | | | | |
|---|---|---|---|---|
| S1 | 1 | ½ a. white | £4250 | £800 |
| S2 | | ½ a. blue | £10000 | £3250 |
| S3 | | ½ a. scarlet | — | £7000 |

These stamps were issued under the authority of Sir Bartle Frere, Commissioner in Sind. They were suppressed in October 1854.

No. S3 is on sealing wax (usually cracked). Perfect copies are very rare.

### EAST INDIA COMPANY ADMINISTRATION

**2** (*Much reduced*)

3

The ½ a., 1 a. and 4 a. were lithographed in Calcutta at the office of the Surveyor-General. The die was engraved by Mr Maniruddin (spelling uncertain). *Ungummed* paper watermarked as T **2** (the "No. 4" paper) with the Arms of the East India Co in the sheet. The watermark is sideways on the ½ a. and 1 a., and upright on the 4 a. where the paper was trimmed so that only the central portion showing the oval and the arms was used. Imperforate.

**1854** (April).

| | | | |
|---|---|---|---|
| 1 | 3 | ½ a. vermilion | £800 |
| | | *a. Deep vermilion* | £1000 |

This stamp, with 9½ arches in the side border, was prepared for use and a supply was sent to Bombay, but was not officially issued.

The vermilion shade is normally found on toned paper and the deep vermilion on white.

**ILLUSTRATIONS.** Types 4/8 are shown twice actual size.

4

**1854** (1 Oct). *Die I.*

| | | | | |
|---|---|---|---|---|
| 2 | 4 | ½ a. blue | 40·00 | 12·00 |
| | | a. Printed on both sides | † | £6500 |
| 3 | | ½ a. pale blue | 60·00 | 12·00 |
| 4 | | ½ a. deep blue | 50·00 | 16·00 |
| 5 | | ½ a. indigo | £140 | 48·00 |

We give the official date of issue, but copies are known which were put on sale as much as a fortnight earlier.

These stamps were printed between 5 May and 29 July 1854 (Printing 30 millions).

4*a*

*Die II*

| | | | | |
|---|---|---|---|---|
| 6 | 4*a* | ½ a. blue | 40·00 | 75·00 |
| 7 | | ½ a. indigo | 48·00 | 75·00 |

The bulk were printed between 1 and 12 August 1854, with some extra sheets on or before 2 November (Printing about 2 millions).

## COVER PRICES

Cover factors are quoted at the beginning of each country for most issues to 1945. An explanation of the system can be found on page x. The factors quoted do not, however, apply to philatelic covers.

5

*Die III*

| | | | | |
|---|---|---|---|---|
| 8 | 5 | ½ a. pale blue | £600 | 35·00 |
| 8*a* | | ½ a. blue | £600 | 35·00 |
| 9 | | ½ a. greenish blue | £1000 | £150 |
| 10 | | ½ a. deep blue | £700 | 60·00 |

These stamps were printed between 3 July and 25 August 1855 (Printing about 4¾ millions).

### THE THREE DIES OF THE ½ ANNA

DIE I. *Chignon shading* mostly solid blobs of colour. *Corner ornaments,* solid blue stars with long points, always conspicuous. *Band below diadem* always heavily shaded. *Diadem and jewels.* The middle and right-hand jewels usually show a clearly defined cross. *Outer frame lines.* Stamps with white or faintly shaded chignons and weak frame lines are usually Die I (worn state).

DIE II. *Chignon* normally shows much less shading. A strong line of colour separates hair and chignon. *Corner ornaments.* The right blue star is characteristic (see illustration) but tends to disappear. It never obliterates the white cross. *Band below diadem.* As Die I but heavier, sometimes solid. *Diadem and jewels.* As Die I but usually fainter. *Outer frame lines.* Always strong and conspicuous.

DIE III. *Chignon shading* shows numerous fine lines, often blurred. *Corner ornaments* have a small hollow blue star with short points, which tends to disappear as in Die II. *Band below diadem,* shows light shading or hardly any shading. *Diadem and jewels.* Jewels usually marked with a solid squat star. The ornaments between the stars appear in the shape of a characteristic white "w". *Frame lines* variable.

The above notes give the general characteristics of the three Dies, but there are a few exceptions due to retouching, etc.

**6** (*See note below No.* 14)

*Die I*

| | | | | |
|---|---|---|---|---|
| 11 | 6 | 1 a. deep red | £225 | 38·00 |
| 12 | | 1 a. red | £170 | 32·00 |

Printing of these stamps commenced on 26 July 1854, and continued into August (Printing, see note below No. 14).

7

*Die II: With more lines in the chignon than in Die I, and with white curved line where chignon joins head**

| | | | | |
|---|---|---|---|---|
| 13 | 7 | 1 a. deep red | £100 | 42·00 |
| 14 | | 1 a. dull red | 35·00 | 35·00 |

*Very worn printings of Die II may be found with chignon nearly as white as in Die I.

In stamps of Die I, however, the small blob of red projecting from the hair into the chignon is always visible.

These stamps were printed in August and September 1854 (Total printing, Dies I and II together, about 7¾ millions).

8

*Die III. With pointed bust*

| | | | | |
|---|---|---|---|---|
| 15 | 8 | 1 a. red | £900 | £130 |
| 16 | | 1 a. dull red | £950 | £150 |

These stamps were printed between 7 July and 25 August 1855 (Printing, about 1½ millions).

9

**NOTE.** Our catalogue prices for Four Annas stamps are for cut-square specimens, with clear margins and in good condition. Cut-to-shape copies are worth from 3% to 20% of these prices according to condition.

Four Dies of the Head:—

I II

DIE I. Band of diadem and chignon strongly shaded.

DIE II. Lines in band of diadem worn. Few lines in the upper part of the chignon, which, however, shows a strong drawn comma-like mark.

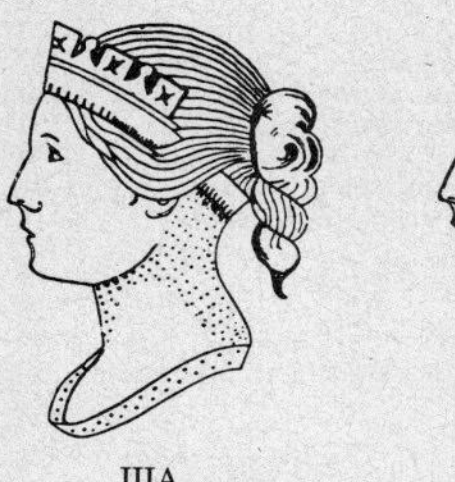

IIIA

III

DIE IIIA. Upper part of chignon partly redrawn, showing two short, curved vertical lines in the NE corner. "Comma" has disappeared.

DIE III. Upper part of chignon completely redrawn, but band of diadem shows only a few short lines.

Two Dies of the Frame:—

Die I. Outer frame lines weak. Very small dots of colour, or none at all, in the "R" and "A's". The white lines to the right of "INDIA" are separated, by a line of colour, from the inner white circle.

Die II. Outer frame lines strengthened. Dots in the "R" and "A's" strong. White lines to right of "INDIA" break into inner white circle.

(Des Capt. H. Thuillier)

**1854** (15 Oct). *W* **2** *upright, central portion only. Imperf.*
*1st Printing. Head Die I. Frame Die I. Stamps widely spaced and separated by blue wavy line.*

| | | | Un. | Used | Us pr |
|---|---|---|---|---|---|
| 17 | 9 | 4 a. indigo and red | £3250 | £475 | £1600 |
| 18 | | 4 a. blue and pale red | £3250 | £425 | £1500 |
| | | a. Head inverted | | †£23000/ £75000 | † |

This printing was made between 13 and 28 Oct 1854 (Printing, 206,040).

**Twenty-seven confirmed examples of No. 18a are now known, only three of which are cut-square. The range of prices quoted reflects the difference in value between a sound cut-to-shape stamp and the finest example known.**

*2nd Printing. Head Die II. Frame Die I. Stamps widely spaced and separated by blue wavy line.*

| | | | | | |
|---|---|---|---|---|---|
| 19 | 9 | 4 a. blue and red | £3250 | £275 | £1000 |
| 20 | | 4 a. indigo and deep red | £3250 | £325 | £1100 |

This printing was made between 1 and 13 Dec 1854 (Printing, 393,960).
This is known with head double.

*3rd Printing. Head Dies II, IIIA and III. Frame Dies I and II. Stamps widely spaced and separated by wavy line.*

| | | | | | |
|---|---|---|---|---|---|
| 21 | 9 | 4 a. bright blue and bright red (Head III, Frame I) | £6500 | £1100 | £3500 |
| | | a. Head II, Frame I | — | £1600 | £5000 |
| | | b. Head IIIA, Frame I | — | £1600 | £4750 |
| | | c. Head III, Frame II | — | — | £7000 |

This printing was made between 10 March and 2 April 1855 (Printing, 138,960).

*4th Printing. Head Die III. Frame Die II. Stamps closely spaced 2 to 2½ mm without separating line.*

| | | | | | |
|---|---|---|---|---|---|
| 22 | 9 | 4 a. deep blue and red | £1900 | £275 | £850 |
| 23 | | 4 a. blue and red | £1800 | £225 | £750 |
| 24 | | 4 a. pale blue and pale red | £1900 | £275 | £850 |

This printing was made between 3 April and 9 May 1855 (Printing, 540,960).
This is known with head double.

*5th Printing. Head Die III. Frame Die II. Stamps spaced 4 to 6 mm without separating line.*

| | | | | | |
|---|---|---|---|---|---|
| 25 | 9 | 4 a. blue and rose-red | £3000 | £375 | £1400 |
| 26 | | 4 a. deep blue and red | £3000 | £375 | £1400 |

This printing was made between 4 Oct and 3 Nov 1855 (Printing, 380,064).

*Serrated perf about 18, or pin-perf*

| | | | | |
|---|---|---|---|---|
| 27 | ½ a. blue (Die I) | | | |
| 28 | 1 a. red (Die I) | | | |
| 29 | 1 a. red (Die II) | — | £1200 | — |
| 30 | 4 a. blue and red (Die II) | — | £5000 | — |

This is believed to be an unofficial perforation. Most of the known specimens bear Madras circle postmarks (C122 to C126), but some are known with Bombay postmarks. Beware of fakes.

**BISECTS.** The bisected stamps for issues between 1854 and 1860 were used exclusively in the Straits Settlements during shortages of certain values. Prices quoted are for those with Singapore "B 172" cancellations. Penang marks are considerably rarer.

10

11

(Plate made at Mint, Calcutta. Typo Stamp Office)

**1854** (6 Oct). *Sheet wmk sideways, as W* **2** *but with* "No. 3" *at top left.* Imperf.*

| | | | | |
|---|---|---|---|---|
| 31 | 10 | 2 a. green (*shade*) | 85·00 | 22·00 |
| | | a. Bisected (1 a.) (1857) (on cover) | † | — |
| 34 | | 2 a. emerald-green | £850 | |

The 2 a. was also printed on paper with sheet watermark incorporating the words "STAMP OFFICE. One Anna", etc. (*Price £300 unused, £275 used*).

Apart from the rare emerald-green shade, there is a range of shades of No. 31 varying from bluish to yellowish green.

Many stamps show traces of lines external to the design shown in our illustration. Stamps with this frame on all four sides are scarce.

Many reprints of the ½, 1, 2, and 4 a. exist.

**PRINTERS.** All Indian stamps from No. 35 to 200 were typographed by De La Rue & Co.

**1855** (Oct). *Blue glazed paper. No wmk. P* 14.

| | | | | |
|---|---|---|---|---|
| 35 | 11 | 4 a. black | £250 | 12·00 |
| | | a. Imperf (pair) | £1400 | £1400 |
| | | b. Bisected (2 a.) (1859) (on cover) | † | £4250 |
| 36 | | 8 a. carmine (Die I) | £225 | 10·00 |
| | | a. Imperf (pair) | £1200 | |
| | | b. Bisected (4 a.) (1859) (on cover) | † | £18000 |

The first supply of the 4 a. was on white paper, but it is difficult to distinguish it from No. 45.

In the 8 a. the paper varies from deep blue to almost white.

For difference between Die I and Die II in the 8 a., see illustrations above No. 73.

**1856–64.** *No wmk. Paper yellowish to white. P* 14.

| | | | | |
|---|---|---|---|---|
| 37 | 11 | ½ a. blue (Die I) | 19·00 | 1·25 |
| | | a. Imperf (pair) | £275 | £700 |
| 38 | | ½ a. pale blue (Die I) | 18·00 | 1·00 |
| 39 | | 1 a. brown | 11·00 | 1·25 |
| | | a. Imperf between (vert pair) | | |
| | | b. Imperf (pair) | £650 | £900 |
| | | c. Bisected (½ a.) (1859) (on cover) | † | £17000 |
| 40 | | 1 a. deep brown | 20·00 | 1·75 |
| 41 | | 2 a. dull pink | £160 | 12·00 |
| | | a. Imperf (pair) | £1200 | |
| 42 | | 2 a. yellow-buff | 70·00 | 11·00 |
| | | a. Imperf (pair) | £800 | £1100 |
| 43 | | 2 a. yellow | 70·00 | 12·00 |
| 44 | | 2 a. orange | 85·00 | 12·00 |
| | | a. Imperf (pair) | | |
| 45 | | 4 a. black | 75·00 | 6·00 |
| | | a. Bisected diagonally (2 a.) (1859) (on cover) | † | £6000 |
| | | b. Imperf (pair) | £1200 | £1400 |
| 46 | | 4 a. grey-black | 70·00 | 4·75 |
| 47 | | 4 a. green (1864) | £325 | 24·00 |
| 48 | | 8 a. carmine (Die I) | 65·00 | 7·50 |
| 49 | | 8 a. pale carmine (Die I) | 65·00 | 7·50 |
| | | a. Bisected (4 a.) (1859) (on cover) | † | £17000 |

*Prepared for use, but not officially issued*

| | | | | |
|---|---|---|---|---|
| 50 | 11 | 2 a. yellow-green | £500 | £600 |
| | | a. Imperf (pair) | £1200 | |

This stamp is known with trial obliterations, and a few are known postally used. It also exists *imperf*, but is not known used thus.

For difference between Die I and Die II in the ½ a., see illustrations above No. 73.

## CROWN COLONY

On the 1 November 1858, Her Majesty Queen Victoria assumed the government of the territories in India "heretofore administered in trust by the Honourable East India Company".

12

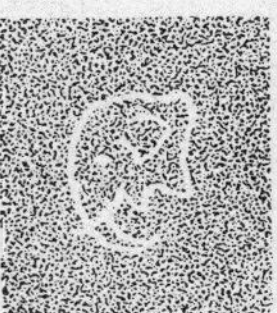

13

**1860** (9 May). *No wmk. P* 14.

| | | | | |
|---|---|---|---|---|
| 51 | 12 | 8 p. purple/*bluish* | £150 | 65·00 |
| 52 | | 8 p. purple/*white* | 16·00 | 4·50 |
| | | a. Bisected diagonally (4 p.) (1862) (on cover) | † | £18000 |
| | | b. Imperf (pair) | £1200 | £1500 |
| 53 | | 8 p. mauve | 16·00 | 5·00 |

**1865.** *Paper yellowish to white. W* **13**. *P* 14.

| | | | | |
|---|---|---|---|---|
| 54 | 11 | ½ a. blue (Die I) | 2·75 | 40 |
| | | a. Imperf | † | £600 |
| 55 | | ½ a. pale blue (Die I) | 3·25 | 40 |
| 56 | 12 | 8 p. purple | 7·50 | 7·00 |
| 57 | | 8 p. mauve | 5·50 | 7·00 |
| 58 | 11 | 1 a. pale brown | 2·50 | 30 |
| 59 | | 1 a. deep brown | 2·25 | 30 |
| 60 | | 1 a. chocolate | 8·00 | 50 |
| 61 | | 2 a. yellow | 24·00 | 4·00 |
| 62 | | 2 a. orange | 24·00 | 1·10 |
| | | a. Imperf | † | £1200 |
| 63 | | 2 a. brown-orange | 16·00 | 2·75 |
| 64 | | 4 a. green | £180 | 18·00 |
| 65 | | 8 a. carmine (Die I) | £800 | 75·00 |

The 8 p. mauve, No. 57, is found variously surcharged "NINE" or "NINE PIE" by local postmasters, to indicate that it was being sold for 9 pies, as was the case during 1874. Such surcharges were made without Government sanction.

The stamps of India, wmk Elephant's Head, surcharged with a crown and value in "cents", were used in the Straits Settlements.

14

POSTAGE

(15)

POSTACE

(16)

**1866** (28 June). *Fiscal stamps as T* **14** *optd. Wmk Crown over* "INDIA". *P* 14 (*at sides only*). (*a*) *As T* **15**.

| | | | |
|---|---|---|---|
| 66 | 6 a. purple (G.) | £500 | £110 |
| | a. Overprint inverted | † | £8000 |

There are 20 different types of this overprint.

(*b*) *With T* **16**

| | | | |
|---|---|---|---|
| 68 | 6 a. purple (G.) | £800 | £130 |

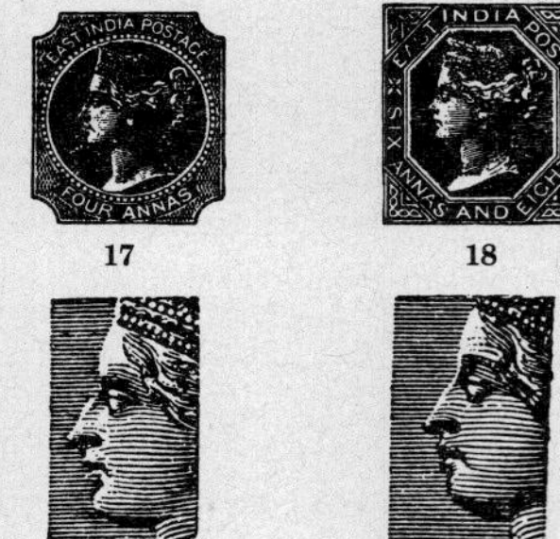

17 18

Die I Die II

Two Dies of 4 a:—

Die I.—Mouth closed, line from corner of mouth downwards only. Pointed chin.

Die II.—Mouth slightly open; lips, chin, and throat defined by line of colour. Rounded chin.

**1866** (Sept)–**1878.** *W* **13.** *P* 14.

| | | | | |
|---|---|---|---|---|
| 69 | **17** | 4 a. green (Die I) | 30·00 | 80 |
| 70 | | 4 a. deep green (Die I) | 30·00 | 70 |
| 71 | | 4 a. blue-green (Die II) (1878) | 9·50 | 55 |
| 72 | **18** | 6 a. 8 p. slate (5.67) | 23·00 | 18·00 |
| | | a. Imperf (pair) | £1200 | |

Die I (8 a.)

(Die I (½ a.)

Die II (8 a.)

Die II (½ a.)

**1868** (1 Jan). *Die II. Profile redrawn and different diadem. W* **13.** *P* 14.

| | | | | |
|---|---|---|---|---|
| 73 | **11** | 8 a. rose (Die II) | 15·00 | 3·75 |
| 74 | | 8 a. pale rose (Die II) | 15·00 | 3·75 |

**1873.** *Die II. Features, especially the mouth, more firmly drawn. W* **13.** *P* 14.

| | | | | |
|---|---|---|---|---|
| 75 | **11** | ½ a. deep blue (Die II) | 1·25 | 30 |
| 76 | | ½ a. blue (Die II) | 1·60 | 40 |

19

20

**1874** (18 July–1 Sept). *W* **13.** *P* 14.

| | | | | |
|---|---|---|---|---|
| 77 | **19** | 9 p. bright mauve (18.7.74) | 6·50 | 6·50 |
| 78 | | 9 p. pale mauve | 6·50 | 6·50 |
| 79 | **20** | 1 r. slate (1.9.74) | 23·00 | 12·00 |

21

22

**1876** (19 Aug). *W* **13.** *P* 14.

| | | | | |
|---|---|---|---|---|
| 80 | **21** | 6 a. olive-bistre | 4·75 | 2·00 |
| 81 | | 6 a. pale brown | 5·00 | 1·50 |
| 82 | **22** | 12 a. Venetian red | 6·00 | 13·00 |

## EMPIRE

Queen Victoria assumed the title of Empress of India in 1877, and the inscription on the stamps was altered from "EAST INDIA" to "INDIA".

23 24 25 26 27 28

29 30 31 32 33 34

**1882** (1 Jan)–**88.** *W* **34.** *P* 14.

| | | | | |
|---|---|---|---|---|
| 84 | **23** | ½ a. deep blue-green (1883) | 2·00 | 10 |
| 85 | | ½ a. blue-green | 2·00 | 10 |
| | | a. Double impression | £275 | |
| 86 | **24** | 9 p. rose (1883) | 50 | 1·50 |
| 87 | | 9 p. aniline carmine | 70 | 1·75 |
| 88 | **25** | 1 a. brown-purple (1883) | 2·25 | 10 |
| 89 | | 1 a. plum | 2·25 | 10 |
| 90 | **26** | 1 a. 6 p. sepia | 50 | 70 |
| 91 | **27** | 2 a. pale blue (1883) | 2·75 | 20 |
| 92 | | 2 a. blue | 2·75 | 20 |
| | | a. Double impression | £450 | £600 |
| 93 | **28** | 3 a. orange | 11·00 | 4·50 |
| 94 | | 3 a. brown-orange | 5·00 | 45 |
| 95 | **29** | 4 a. olive-green (6.85) | 8·00 | 30 |
| 96 | | 4 a. slate-green | 7·00 | 30 |
| 97 | **30** | 4 a. 6 p. yellow-green (1.5.86) | 9·50 | 5·00 |
| 98 | **31** | 8 a. dull mauve (1883) | 12·00 | 2·00 |
| 99 | | 8 a. magenta | 15·00 | 1·75 |
| 100 | **32** | 12 a. purple/*red* (1.4.88) | 4·50 | 2·00 |
| 101 | **33** | 1 r. slate (1883) | 11·00 | 4·25 |
| 84/101 | | *Set of* 11 | 50·00 | 14·00 |
| 97, 100 | | Handstamped "Specimen" *Set of* 2 | 75·00 | |

No. 92a is from a sheet of 2 a. stamps with a very marked double impression issued in Karachi in 1896–97. Most of the stamps were used on telegrams.

(35) 36

37

**1891** (1 Jan). *No.* 97 *surch with T* **35** *by Govt Press, Calcutta.*

| | | | | |
|---|---|---|---|---|
| 102 | **30** | 2½ a. on 4½ a. yellow-green | 1·50 | 60 |

There are several varieties in this surcharge due to variations in the relative positions of the letters and figures.

**1892** (Jan)–**97.** *W* **34.** *P* 14.

| | | | | |
|---|---|---|---|---|
| 103 | **36** | 2½ a. yellow-green | 1·00 | 40 |
| 104 | | 2½ a. pale blue-green (1897) | 2·25 | 80 |
| 105 | **37** | 1 r. green and rose | 14·00 | 4·25 |
| 106 | | 1 r. green and aniline carmine | 5·50 | 2·00 |

38

¼

(39)

40

**USED HIGH VALUES.** It is necessary to emphasise that used prices quoted for the following and all later high value stamps are for postally used copies.

(Head of Queen from portrait by von Angeli)

**1895** (1 Sept). *W* **34.** *P* 14.

| | | | | |
|---|---|---|---|---|
| 107 | **38** | 2 r. carmine and yellow-brown | 32·00 | 10·00 |
| 107*a* | | 2 r. carmine and brown | 38·00 | 12·00 |
| 108 | | 3 r. brown and green | 25·00 | 10·00 |
| 109 | | 5 r. ultramarine and violet | 30·00 | 22·00 |
| 107/9 | | *Set of* 3 | 80·00 | 38·00 |

**1898** (1 Oct). *No.* 85 *surch with T* **39** *by Govt Press, Calcutta.*

| | | | | |
|---|---|---|---|---|
| 110 | **23** | ¼ on ½ a. blue-green | 10 | 30 |
| | | a. Surch double | 90·00 | |
| | | b. Double impression of stamp | £180 | |

**1899.** *W* **34.** *P* 14.

| | | | | |
|---|---|---|---|---|
| 111 | **40** | 3 p. aniline carmine | 10 | 10 |

**1900** (1 Oct)–**02.** *W* **34.** *P* 14.

| | | | | |
|---|---|---|---|---|
| 112 | **40** | 3 p. grey | 10 | 40 |
| 113 | **23** | ½ a. pale yellow-green | 45 | 30 |
| 114 | | ½ a. yellow-green | 60 | 30 |
| 115 | **25** | 1 a. carmine | 50 | 15 |
| 116 | **27** | 2 a. pale violet | 3·25 | 50 |
| 117 | | 2 a. mauve (1902) | 5·00 | 1·75 |
| 118 | **36** | 2½ a. ultramarine | 3·00 | 3·75 |
| 112/18 | | *Set of* 5 | 6·50 | 4·50 |

41

42

43

44

45

46

47

48

49

50

51

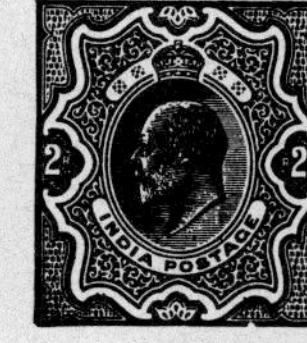

52

**1902** (9 Aug)–**11.** *W* **34.** *P* 14.

| | | | | |
|---|---|---|---|---|
| 119 | **41** | 3 p. grey | 35 | 10 |
| 120 | | 3 p. slate-grey (1904) | 30 | 10 |
| 121 | **42** | ½ a. yellow-green | 35 | 10 |
| 122 | | ½ a. green | 45 | 10 |
| 123 | **43** | 1 a. carmine | 45 | 10 |
| 124 | **44** | 2 a. violet (13.5.03) | 1·50 | 35 |
| 125 | | 2 a. mauve | 1·50 | 10 |
| 126 | **45** | 2½ a. ultramarine (1902) | 3·25 | 15 |
| 127 | **46** | 3 a. orange-brown (1902) | 3·25 | 15 |
| 128 | **47** | 4 a. olive (20.4.03) | 3·00 | 25 |
| 129 | | 4 a. pale olive | 3·00 | 30 |
| 130 | | 4 a. olive-brown | 8·50 | 3·00 |
| 131 | **48** | 6 a. olive-bistre (6.8.03) | 10·00 | 4·25 |
| 132 | | 6 a. maize | 10·00 | 4·25 |
| 133 | **49** | 8 a. purple (*shades*) (8.5.03) | 7·50 | 1·00 |
| 134 | | 8 a. claret (1910) | 9·00 | 1·00 |
| 135 | **50** | 12 a. purple/*red* (1903) | 7·50 | 2·00 |
| 136 | **51** | 1 r. green and carmine (1903) | 6·00 | 70 |
| 137 | | 1 r. green and scarlet (1911) | 26·00 | 1·75 |
| 138 | **52** | 2 r. rose-red and yellow-brown (1903) | 23·00 | 3·50 |
| 139 | | 2 r. carmine and yellow-brown | 23·00 | 3·25 |
| 140 | | 3 r. brown and green (1904) | 20·00 | 19·00 |
| 141 | | 3 r. red-brown and green (1911) | 27·00 | 22·00 |
| 142 | | 5 r. ultramarine and violet (1904) | 50·00 | 35·00 |
| 143 | | 5 r. ultramarine and deep lilac (1911) | 60·00 | 40·00 |
| 144 | | 10 r. green and carmine (1909) | 75·00 | 18·00 |
| 146 | | 15 r. blue and olive-brown (1909) | £130 | 42·00 |
| 147 | | 25 r. brownish orange and blue (1909) | £750 | £800 |
| 119/147 | | *Set of* 17 | £900 | £800 |

No. 147 can often be found with telegraph cancellation; these can be supplied at one third of the price given above.

**1905** (2 Feb). *No.* 122 *surch with T* **39.**

| | | | | |
|---|---|---|---|---|
| 148 | **42** | ¼ on ½ a. green | 30 | 10 |
| | | a. Surch inverted | — | £550 |

It is doubtful if No. 148a exists unused with genuine surcharge.

53 54

**1906** (Dec)–**07.** *W* **34.** *P* 14.

| | | | | |
|---|---|---|---|---|
| 149 | **53** | ½ a. green (12.06) | 1·00 | 10 |
| 150 | **54** | 1 a. carmine (1.07) | 60 | 10 |

55 56

57

58* 59

60

61 62 63 64 65 66

67

*T 58. Two types of the 1½ a.; (A) As illustrated. (B) Inscribed "1½ As". "ONE AND A HALF ANNAS".

**1911** (Dec)–**22**. *W* **34**. *P* 14.

| No. | Type | Description | Unused | Used |
|---|---|---|---|---|
| 151 | **55** | 3 p. pale grey (1912) | 30 | 10 |
| 152 | | 3 p. grey | 15 | 10 |
| 153 | | 3 p. slate-grey | 15 | 10 |
| 154 | | 3 p. blue-slate (1922) | 1·25 | 30 |
| 155 | **56** | ½ a. yellow-green (1912) | 30 | 10 |
| | | a. Double print | £180 | |
| 156 | | ½ a. pale blue-green | 30 | 10 |
| 159 | **57** | 1 a. rose-carmine | 1·25 | 15 |
| 160 | | 1 a. carmine | 1·25 | 15 |
| 161 | | 1 a. aniline carmine | 1·10 | 10 |
| 162 | | 1 a. pale rose-carmine, C (1918) | 1·75 | 30 |
| 163 | **58** | 1½ a. chocolate (Type A) (1919) | 1·50 | 30 |
| 164 | | 1½ a. grey-brown (Type A) | 6·00 | 1·75 |
| 165 | | 1½ a. chocolate (Type B) (1921) | 1·50 | 2·25 |
| 166 | **59** | 2 a. dull purple | 1·00 | 15 |
| 167 | | 2 a. mauve | 1·00 | 15 |
| 168 | | 2 a. violet | 3·50 | 30 |
| 169 | | 2 a. bright purple (Jan 1919) | 3·50 | 30 |
| 170 | **60** | 2½ a. ultramarine (1912) | 1·75 | 2·00 |
| 171 | **61** | 2½ a. ultramarine (1913) | 1·00 | 20 |
| 172 | **62** | 3 a. dull orange | 3·75 | 35 |
| 173 | | 3 a. orange-brown | 2·50 | 20 |
| 174 | **63** | 4 a. deep olive (1912) | 3·25 | 30 |
| 175 | | 4 a. olive-green | 3·00 | 15 |
| 176 | **64** | 6 a. bistre (1912) | 3·75 | 90 |
| 177 | | 6 a. yellow-bistre | 3·75 | 1·00 |
| 178 | | 6 a. deep bistre-brown | 11·00 | 2·50 |
| 179 | **65** | 8 a. purple (1912) | 6·00 | 60 |
| 180 | | 8 a. mauve | 11·00 | 75 |
| 181 | | 8 a. deep lilac | 11·00 | 80 |
| 182 | | 8 a. bright aniline mauve | 16·00 | 2·50 |
| 183 | **66** | 12 a. dull claret (1912) | 9·00 | 1·50 |
| 184 | | 12 a. claret | 7·00 | 1·50 |
| 185 | **67** | 1 r. brown and green (1913) | 16·00 | 1·50 |
| 186 | | 1 r. red-brown and blue-green | 9·50 | 80 |
| 187 | | 2 r. carmine and brown (1913) | 13·00 | 1·10 |
| 188 | | 5 r. ultramarine and violet (1913) | 38·00 | 4·00 |
| 189 | | 10 r. green and scarlet (1913) | 55·00 | 9·00 |
| 190 | | 15 r. blue and olive (1913) | 90·00 | 13·00 |
| 191 | | 25 r. orange and blue (1913) | £160 | 26·00 |
| 151/191 | | *Set of* 17 | £350 | 50·00 |

A variety of the 3 pies exists with line joining "P" and "S" of the value at right, sometimes described as "3 Rs".

**FORGERIES.**—Collectors are warned against forgeries of all the later surcharges of India, and particularly the errors.

**NINE**

**PIES**

(68)

**1921.** *T* **57** *surch with T* **68**.

| No. | Description | Unused | Used |
|---|---|---|---|
| 192 | 9 p. on 1 a. rose-carmine | 20 | 15 |
| | a. Error. "NINE NINE" | 45·00 | 75·00 |
| | b. Error. "PIES PIES" | 45·00 | 75·00 |
| | c. Surch double | £100 | £120 |
| 193 | 9 p. on 1 a. carmine-pink | 70 | 45 |
| 194 | 9 p. on 1 a. aniline carmine | 1·75 | 75 |

In the initial setting of the surcharge No. 192a occurred on R. 2/13–16 of the fourth pane and No. 192b on R. 4/13–16 of the third. For the second setting No. 192a was corrected. Examples of No. 192b still occur but on R. 2/13–16 of the third pane. Later printings showed this corrected also.

**1922.** *T* **56** *surch with T* **39**.

| No. | Description | Unused | Used |
|---|---|---|---|
| 195 | ¼ a. on ½ a. yellow-green | 30 | 20 |
| | a. Surch inverted | 8·00 | |
| | b. Surch omitted (in horiz pair with normal) | £130 | |
| 196 | ¼ a. on ½ a. blue-green | 40 | 40 |

**1922–26.** *W* **34**. *P* 14.

| No. | Type | Description | Unused | Used |
|---|---|---|---|---|
| 197 | **57** | 1 a. chocolate | 30 | 10 |
| 198 | **58** | 1½ a. rose-carmine (Type B) | 80 | 30 |
| 199 | **61** | 2½ a. orange | 4·25 | 4·25 |
| 200 | **62** | 3 a. ultramarine | 12·00 | 60 |
| 197/200 | | *Set of* 4 | 15·00 | 4·75 |

69 70 71

**PRINTERS.** The following issues of postage and contemporary official stamps were all printed by the Security Printing Press, Nasik, *unless otherwise stated.*

**1926–33.** *Typo. W* **69**. *P* 14.

| No. | Type | Description | Unused | Used |
|---|---|---|---|---|
| 201 | **55** | 3 p. slate | 20 | 10 |
| 202 | **56** | ½ a. green | 40 | 10 |
| 203 | **57** | 1 a. chocolate | 40 | 10 |
| | | a. *Tête-bêche* (pair) (1932) | 1·25 | 8·00 |
| 204 | **58** | 1½ a. rose-carmine (Type B) (1929) | 1·25 | 10 |
| 205 | **59** | 2 a. bright purple | 3·75 | 5·00 |
| 206 | **70** | 2 a. purple | 90 | 10 |
| | | a. *Tête-bêche* (pair) (1933) | 7·50 | 28·00 |
| 207 | **61** | 2½ a. orange (1929) | 75 | 10 |
| 208 | **62** | 3 a. ultramarine | 4·50 | 90 |
| 209 | | 3 a. blue (1928) | 4·50 | 10 |
| 210 | **63** | 4 a. pale sage-green | 1·50 | 10 |
| 211 | **71** | 4 a. sage-green | 5·00 | 10 |
| 212 | **65** | 8 a. reddish purple | 4·00 | 10 |
| 213 | **66** | 12 a. claret | 5·00 | 20 |
| 214 | **67** | 1 r. chocolate and green | 5·00 | 20 |
| | | a. Chocolate (head) omitted | £1700 | |
| 215 | | 2 r. carmine and orange | 7·50 | 45 |
| 216 | | 5 r. ultramarine and purple | 20·00 | 1·25 |
| 217 | | 10 r. green and scarlet (1927) | 35·00 | 2·25 |
| 218 | | 15 r. blue and olive (1928) | 24·00 | 24·00 |
| 219 | | 25 r. orange and blue (1928) | 90·00 | 24·00 |
| 201/219 | | *Set of* 16 | £180 | 50·00 |

72 D.H. "Hercules"

Missing tree-top (R. 11/6 of 8 a.)

(Des R. Grant. Litho)

**1929** (22 Oct). *Air. W* **69** (*sideways*). *P* 14.

| No. | Type | Description | Unused | Used |
|---|---|---|---|---|
| 220 | **72** | 2 a. deep blue-green | 1·50 | 50 |
| 221 | | 3 a. blue | 1·00 | 1·25 |
| 222 | | 4 a. olive-green | 2·25 | 65 |
| 223 | | 6 a. bistre | 2·25 | 90 |
| 224 | | 8 a. purple | 2·50 | 1·00 |
| | | a. Missing tree-top | 50·00 | 35·00 |
| 225 | | 12 a. rose-red | 7·50 | 4·00 |
| 220/225 | | *Set of* 6 | 15·00 | 7·50 |

**73** Purana Qila

(Des H. W. Barr. Litho)

**1931** (9 Feb). *Inauguration of New Delhi. T* **73** *and similar horiz designs. W* **69** (*sideways*). *P* 13½ × 14.

| No. | Description | Unused | Used |
|---|---|---|---|
| 226 | ¼ a. olive-green and orange-brown | 50 | 1·00 |
| 227 | ½ a. violet and green | 50 | 40 |
| 228 | 1 a. mauve and chocolate | 75 | 20 |
| 229 | 2 a. green and blue | 1·25 | 90 |
| 230 | 3 a. chocolate and carmine | 2·50 | 2·50 |
| 231 | 1 r. violet and green | 5·00 | 13·00 |
| 226/231 | *Set of* 6 | 9·50 | 16·00 |

Designs:—No. 227, War Memorial Arch; No. 228, Council House; No. 229, The Viceroy's House; No. 230, Government of India Secretariat; No. 231, Dominion Columns and the Secretariat.

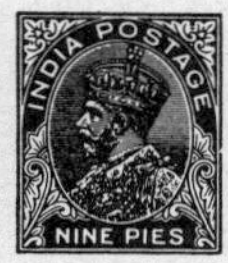

79 80 81

82 83

(T **82/3** des T. I. Archer. 9 p. litho and typo; 1¼ a., 3½ a. litho; others typo)

**1932–36.** *W* **69**. *P* 14.

| No. | Type | Description | Unused | Used |
|---|---|---|---|---|
| 232 | **79** | ½ a. green (1934) | 35 | 10 |
| 233 | **80** | 9 p. deep green (22.4.32) | 30 | 10 |
| 234 | **81** | 1 a. chocolate (1934) | 1·00 | 10 |
| 235 | **82** | 1¼ a. mauve (22.4.32) | 30 | 10 |
| 236 | **70** | 2 a. vermilion | 8·00 | 3·50 |
| 236*a* | **59** | 2 a. vermilion (1934) | 3·75 | 50 |
| 236*b* | | 2 a. vermilion (*small die*) (1936) | 4·50 | 30 |
| 237 | **62** | 3 a. carmine | 80 | 10 |
| 238 | **83** | 3½ a. ultramarine (22.4.32) | 1·25 | 10 |
| 239 | **64** | 6 a. bistre (1935) | 7·00 | 1·50 |
| 232/239 | | *Set of* 9 | 20·00 | 5·00 |

No. 236*a* measures 19 × 22.6 mm and No. 236*b* 18.4 × 21.8 mm.

**84** Gateway of India, Bombay

**1935** (6 May). *Silver Jubilee, T* **84** *and similar horiz designs. Litho W* **69** (*sideways*). *P* 13½ × 14.

| No. | Description | Unused | Used |
|---|---|---|---|
| 240 | ½ a. black and yellow-green | 30 | 10 |
| 241 | 9 p. black and grey-green | 30 | 10 |
| 242 | 1 a. black and brown | 30 | 10 |
| 243 | 1¼ a. black and bright violet | 30 | 10 |
| 244 | 2½ a. black and orange | 45 | 45 |
| 245 | 3½ a. black and dull ultramarine | 2·00 | 1·25 |
| 246 | 8 a. black and purple | 2·00 | 1·75 |
| 240/246 | *Set of* 7 | 5·00 | 3·50 |

Designs:—9 p. Victoria Memorial, Calcutta; 1 a. Rameswaram Temple, Madras; 1¼ a. Jain Temple, Calcutta; 2½ a. Taj Mahal, Agra; 3½ a. Golden Temple, Amritsar; 8 a. Pagoda in Mandalay.

**91** King George VI

**92** Dak Runner

**93** King George VI

**1937** (23 Aug–15 Dec). *Typo. W* **69**. *P* 13½ × 14 *or* 14 × 13½ (*T* **93**).

| No. | Type | Description | Unused | Used |
|---|---|---|---|---|
| 247 | **91** | 3 p. slate | 40 | 10 |
| 248 | | ½ a. red-brown | 40 | 10 |
| 249 | | 9 p. green (23.8.37) | 2·00 | 20 |
| 250 | | 1 a. carmine (23.8.37) | 15 | 10 |
| | | a. *Tête-bêche* (vert pair) | 30 | 1·25 |
| 251 | **92** | 2 a. vermilion | 1·25 | 20 |
| 252 | – | 2½ a. bright violet | 60 | 10 |
| 253 | – | 3 a. yellow-green | 2·75 | 20 |
| 254 | – | 3½ a. bright blue | 1·60 | 50 |
| 255 | – | 4 a. brown | 9·50 | 10 |
| 256 | – | 6 a. turquoise-green | 7·50 | 30 |
| 257 | – | 8 a. slate-violet | 4·00 | 20 |
| 258 | – | 12 a. lake | 16·00 | 50 |
| 259 | **93** | 1 r. grey and red-brown | 1·00 | 15 |
| 260 | | 2 r. purple and brown | 3·75 | 15 |
| 261 | | 5 r. green and blue | 13·00 | 20 |
| 262 | | 10 r. purple and claret | 15·00 | 50 |
| 263 | | 15 r. brown and green | 55·00 | 55·00 |
| 264 | | 25 r. slate-violet and purple | 60·00 | 11·00 |
| 247/264 | | *Set of* 18 | £170 | 60·00 |

Designs: *Horiz as T* **92**—2½ a. Dak bullock cart; 3 a. Dak tonga; 3½ a. Dak camel; 4 a. Mail train; 6 a. *Strathnaver* (liner); 8 a. Mail lorry; 12 a. Mail plane (small head).

**100***a* King George VI

**101** King George VI **102**

**103** Mail Plane (large head)

(*T* **100***a*/**102** des T. I. Archer. Typo)

**1940–43.** *W* **69**. *P* 13½ × 14.

| No. | Type | Description | Unused | Used |
|---|---|---|---|---|
| 265 | **100***a* | 3 p. slate | 25 | 10 |
| 266 | | ½ a. purple (1.10.42) | 40 | 10 |
| 267 | | 9 p. green | 40 | 10 |
| 268 | | 1 a. carmine (1.4.43) | 40 | 10 |
| 269 | **101** | 1 a. 3 p. yellow-brown | 50 | 10 |
| 269*a* | | 1½ a. dull violet (9.42) | 40 | 10 |
| 270 | | 2 a. vermilion | 45 | 10 |

| | | | | |
|---|---|---|---|---|
| 271 | 101 | 3 a. bright violet (1942) | 40 | 10 |
| 272 | | 3½ a. bright blue | 70 | 10 |
| 273 | 102 | 4 a. brown | 45 | 10 |
| 274 | | 6 a. turquoise-green | 65 | 10 |
| 275 | | 8 a. slate-violet | 1·00 | 10 |
| 276 | | 12 a. lake | 2·50 | 15 |
| 277 | 103 | 14 a. purple (15.10.40) | 4·50 | 30 |
| 265/277 | | *Set of* 14 | 12·00 | 75 |

The 1½ a. and 3 a. were at first printed by lithography and were of finer execution and without Jubilee lines in the sheet margins.

105 "Victory" and King George VI

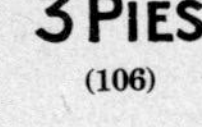


(106)

**1946** (2 Jan). *Victory. Litho. W* **69**. *P* 13.

| | | | | |
|---|---|---|---|---|
| 278 | 105 | 9 p. yellow-green (8.2.46) | 25 | 10 |
| 279 | | 1½ a. dull violet | 25 | 10 |
| 280 | | 3½ a. bright blue | 75 | 50 |
| 281 | | 12 a. claret (8.2.46) | 1·25 | 55 |
| 278/81 | | *Set of* 4 | 2·25 | 1·10 |

**1946** (8 Aug). *Surch with T* **106**.

| | | | | |
|---|---|---|---|---|
| 282 | 101 | 3 p. on 1 a. 3 p. yellow-brown | 10 | 10 |

## DOMINION

**301** Asokan Capital (Inscr reads "Long Live India")

**302** Indian National Flag

**303** Douglas DC4

(Des T. I. Archer. Litho)

**1947** (21 Nov–15 Dec). *Independence. W* **69**. *P* 14 × 13½ (1½ *a.*) *or* 13½ × 14 (*others*).

| | | | | |
|---|---|---|---|---|
| 301 | 301 | 1½ a. grey-green (15 Dec) | 15 | 10 |
| 302 | 302 | 3½ a. orange-red, blue and green | 25 | 30 |
| 303 | 303 | 12 a. ultramarine (15 Dec) | 1·00 | 1·00 |
| 301/3 | | *Set of* 3 | 1·25 | 1·25 |

**304** Lockheed "Constellation"

(Des T. I. Archer. Litho)

**1948** (29 May). *Air. Inauguration of India-U.K. Air Service. W* **69**. *P* 13½ × 14.

| | | | | |
|---|---|---|---|---|
| 304 | 304 | 12 a. black and ultramarine | 90 | 1·00 |

**305** Mahatma Gandhi **306**

(Photo Courvoisier)

**1948** (15 Aug). *First Anniv of Independence. P* 11½.

| | | | | |
|---|---|---|---|---|
| 305 | 305 | 1½ a. brown | 1·00 | 30 |
| 306 | | 3½ a. violet | 4·00 | 1·25 |
| 307 | | 12 a. grey-green | 5·00 | 60 |
| 308 | 306 | 10 r. purple-brown and lake | 55·00 | 40·00 |
| 305/8 | | *Set of* 4 | 60·00 | 40·00 |

**307** Ajanta Panel

**308** Konarak Horse

**309** Trimurti

**310** Bodhisattva

**311** Nataraja

**312** Sanchi Stupa, East Gate

**313** Bodh Gaya Temple

**314** Bhuvanesvara

**315** Gol Gumbad, Bijapur

**316** Kandarya Mahadeva Temple

**317** Golden Temple, Amritsar

**318** Victory Tower, Chittorgarh

**319** Red Fort, Delhi

**320** Taj Mahal, Agra

**321** Qutb Minar, Delhi

**322** Satrunjaya Temple, Palitana

(Des T. I. Archer and I. M. Das. Typo (low values), litho (rupee values))

**1949** (15 Aug). *W* **69** (*sideways on* 6 *p.*, 1 *r. and* 10 *r.*). *P* 14 (3 *p. to* 2 *a.*), 13½ (3 *a. to* 12 *a.*), 14×13½ (1 *r. and* 10 *r.*), 13½×14 (2 *r. and* 5 *r.*), 13 (15 *r.*).

| | | | | |
|---|---|---|---|---|
| 309 | 307 | 3 p. slate-violet | 15 | 10 |
| 310 | 308 | 6 p. purple-brown | 25 | 10 |
| 311 | 309 | 9 p. yellow-green | 40 | 10 |
| 312 | 310 | 1 a. turquoise | 60 | 10 |
| 313 | 311 | 2 a. carmine | 80 | 10 |
| 314 | 312 | 3 a. brown-orange | 1·50 | 10 |
| 315 | 313 | 3½ a. bright blue | 3·00 | 2·50 |
| 316 | 314 | 4 a. lake | 5·00 | 10 |
| 317 | 315 | 6 a. violet | 2·00 | 10 |
| 318 | 316 | 8 a. turquoise-green | 2·00 | 10 |
| 319 | 317 | 12 a. dull blue | 1·75 | 10 |
| 320 | 318 | 1 r. dull violet and green | 9·00 | 10 |
| 321 | 319 | 2 r. claret and violet | 8·00 | 15 |
| 322 | 320 | 5 r. blue-green and red-brown | 22·00 | 50 |
| 323 | 321 | 10 r. purple-brown and deep blue | 30·00 | 3·25 |
| | | *a. Purple-brown and blue* | 55·00 | 3·25 |
| 324 | 322 | 15 r. brown and claret | 12·00 | 12·00 |
| 309/324 | | *Set of* 16 | 85·00 | 17·00 |

For T **310** with statue reversed, see No. 333.

**323** Globe and Asokan Capital

**1949** (10 Oct). *75th Anniv of U.P.U. Litho. W* **69**. *P* 13.

| | | | | |
|---|---|---|---|---|
| 325 | 323 | 9 p. green | 75 | 75 |
| 326 | | 2 a. rose | 1·00 | 1·25 |
| 327 | | 3½ a. bright blue | 1·75 | 2·25 |
| 328 | | 12 a. brown-purple | 3·50 | 2·50 |
| 325/8 | | *Set of* 4 | 6·00 | 6·00 |

## REPUBLIC

**324** Rejoicing Crowds

**328** As T **310**, but statue reversed

(Des D. J. Keymer & Co. Litho)

**1950** (26 Jan). *Inauguration of Republic. T* **324** *and similar designs. W* **69** (*sideways on* 3½ *a.*). *P* 13.

| | | | | |
|---|---|---|---|---|
| 329 | | 2 a. scarlet | 70 | 15 |
| 330 | | 3½ a. ultramarine | 1·50 | 2·75 |
| 331 | | 4 a. violet | 1·50 | 40 |
| 332 | | 12 a. maroon | 3·00 | 2·25 |
| 329/32 | | *Set of* 4 | 6·00 | 5·00 |

Designs: *Vert*—3½ a. Quill, ink-well and verse. *Horiz*—4 a. Ear of corn and plough; 12 a. Spinning-wheel and cloth.

**1950** (15 July)–**51**. *Typo. W* **69**. *P* 14 (1 *a.*), 13½ (*others*).

| | | | | |
|---|---|---|---|---|
| 333 | 328 | 1 a. turquoise | 2·50 | 10 |
| 333*a* | 313 | 2½ a. lake (30.4.51) | 2·25 | 1·25 |
| 333*b* | 314 | 4 a. bright blue (30.4.51) | 5·25 | 10 |
| 333/*b* | | *Set of* 3 | 9·00 | 1·25 |

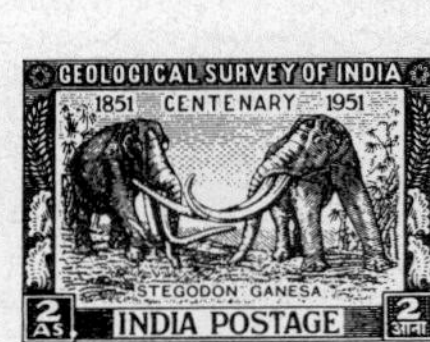


**329** *Stegodon ganesa*

**330** Torch

**1951** (13 Jan). *Centenary of Geological Survey of India. Litho. W* **69**. *P* 13.

| | | | | |
|---|---|---|---|---|
| 334 | 329 | 2 a. black and claret | 1·00 | 15 |

**1951** (4 Mar). *First Asian Games, New Delhi. Litho. W* **69** (*sideways*). *P* 14.

| | | | | |
|---|---|---|---|---|
| 335 | 330 | 2 a. reddish purple and brown-orange | 75 | 20 |
| 336 | | 12 a. chocolate and light blue | 4·00 | 90 |

**PROCESS.** All the following issues were printed in photogravure, *except where otherwise stated.*

**331** Kabir

**332** Locomotives in 1853 and 1953

**1952** (1 Oct). *Indian Saints and Poets. T* **331** *and similar vert designs. W* **69**. *P* 14.

| | | | | |
|---|---|---|---|---|
| 337 | | 9 p. bright emerald-green | 30 | 15 |
| 338 | | 1 a. carmine | 30 | 10 |
| 339 | | 2 a. orange-red | 60 | 10 |
| 340 | | 4 a. bright blue | 1·25 | 15 |
| 341 | | 4½ a. bright mauve | 30 | 10 |
| 342 | | 12 a. brown | 1·50 | 60 |
| 337/42 | | *Set of* 6 | 3·75 | 1·00 |

Designs:—1 a. Tulsidas; 2 a. Meera; 4 a. Surdas; 4½ a. Ghalib; 12 a. Tagore.

**1953** (16 Apr). *Railway Centenary. W* **69**. *P* 14½ × 14.

| | | | | |
|---|---|---|---|---|
| 343 | 332 | 2 a. black | 40 | 10 |

**333** Mount Everest

**1953** (2 Oct). *Conquest of Mount Everest.* W **69**. *P* 14½ × 14.
344 **333** 2 a. bright violet .. .. .. .. 40 10
345 14 a. brown .. .. .. .. 3·00 25

**334** Telegraph Poles of 1851 and 1951

**1953** (1 Nov). *Centenary of Indian Telegraphs.* W **69**. *P* 14½ × 14.
346 **334** 2 a. blue-green .. .. .. .. .. 30 10
347 12 a. blue .. .. .. .. .. 3·00 40

**335** Postal Transport, 1854

**1954** (1 Oct). *Stamp Centenary. T* **335** *and similar horiz designs.* W **69**. *P* 14½ × 14.
348 1 a. reddish purple .. .. .. .. .. 25 10
349 2 a. cerise .. .. .. .. .. 30 10
350 4 a. orange-brown .. .. .. .. .. 1·75 15
351 14 a. blue .. .. .. .. .. 1·50 40
348/51 .. .. .. .. *Set of* 4 3·50 60
Designs:—2, 14 a. "Airmail"; 4 a. Postal transport, 1954.

**338** U.N. Emblem and Lotus

**1954** (24 Oct). *United Nations Day.* W **69** *(sideways). P* 13.
352 **338** 2 a. turquoise-green .. .. .. 30 10

**339** Forest Research Institute

**1954** (11 Dec). *Fourth World Forestry Congress, Dehra Dun.* W **69**. *P* 14½ × 14.
353 **339** 2 a. ultramarine .. .. .. 15 10

**340** Tractor

**344** Woman Spinning

**347** "Malaria Control" (Mosquito and Staff of Aesculapius)

**1955** (26 Jan). *Five Year Plan. T* **340, 344, 347** *and similar designs.* W **69** *(sideways on small horiz designs). P* 14 × 14½ *(small horiz) or* 14½ × 14 *(others).*
354 3 p. bright purple .. .. .. .. .. 20 10
355 6 p. violet .. .. .. .. .. 20 10
356 9 p. orange-brown .. .. .. .. .. 20 10
357 1 a. blue-green .. .. .. .. .. 35 10
358 2 a. light blue .. .. .. .. .. 20 10
359 3 a. pale blue-green .. .. .. .. .. 40 10
360 4 a. rose-carmine .. .. .. .. .. 40 10
361 6 a. yellow-brown .. .. .. .. .. 70 10
362 8 a. blue .. .. .. .. .. 4·25 10
363 10 a. turquoise-green .. .. .. .. .. 70 70
364 12 a. bright blue .. .. .. .. .. 50 10
365 14 a. bright green .. .. .. .. .. 1·50 20
366 1 r. deep dull green .. .. .. .. .. 4·00 10
367 1 r. 2 a. grey .. .. .. .. .. 1·75 2·75
368 1 r. 8 a. reddish purple .. .. .. .. .. 6·00 3·50
369 2 r. cerise .. .. .. .. .. 4·00 10
370 5 r. brown .. .. .. .. .. 14·00 30
371 10 r. orange .. .. .. .. .. 14·00 2·00
354/71 .. .. .. .. *Set of* 18 48·00 8·75
Designs: *Horiz (as T* **340**)—6 p. Power loom; 9 p. Bullock-driven well; 1 a. Damodar Valley Dam; 4 a. Bullocks; 8 a. Chittaranjan Locomotive Works; 12 a. Hindustan Aircraft Factory, Bangalore; 1 r. Telephone engineer; 2 r. Rare Earth Factory, Alwaye; 5 r. Sindri Fertiliser Factory; 10 r. Steel plant. *(As T* **347**)—10 a. Marine Drive, Bombay; 14 a. Kashmir landscape; 1 r. 2 a. Cape Comorin; 1 r. 8 a. Mt Kangchenjunga. *Vert (as T* **344**)—3 a. Woman weaving with hand loom.
For stamps as Nos. 366, 369/71 but W **374** see Nos. 413/16.

**358** Bodhi Tree

**359** Round Parasol and Bodhi Tree

(Des C. Pakrashi (2 a.), R. D'Silva (14 a.))

**1956** (24 May). *Buddha Jayanti.* W **69** *(sideways on 14 a.). P* 13 × 13½ *(2 a.) or* 13½ × 13 *(14 a.).*
372 **358** 2 a. sepia .. .. .. .. .. 30 10
373 **359** 14 a. vermilion .. .. .. .. .. 3·00 2·50

**360** Lokmanya Bal Gangadhar Tilak

**361** Map of India

**1956** (23 July). *Birth Centenary of Tilak (journalist).* W **69**. *P* 13 × 13½.
374 **360** 2 a. chestnut .. .. .. .. .. 10 10

**(New Currency 100 n(aye) p(aise) = 1 rupee.)**

**1957** (1 Apr)–**58**. W **69** *(sideways). P* 14 × 14½.
375 **361** 1 n.p. blue-green .. .. .. 10 10
376 2 n.p. light brown .. .. .. 10 10
377 3 n.p. deep brown .. .. .. 10 10
378 5 n.p. bright green .. .. .. 4·25 10
379 6 n.p. grey .. .. .. 10 10
379*a* 8 n.p. light blue-green (7.5.58) .. .. 2·25 80
380 10 n.p. deep dull green .. .. .. 4·25 10
381 13 n.p. bright carmine-red .. .. .. 30 10
381*a* 15 n.p. violet (16.1.58) .. .. .. 50 10
382 20 n.p. blue .. .. .. 30 10
383 25 n.p. ultramarine .. .. .. 30 10
384 50 n.p. orange .. .. .. 2·25 10
385 75 n.p. reddish purple .. .. .. 1·25 10
385*a* 90 n.p. bright purple (16.1.58) .. .. 70 40
375/85*a* .. .. .. .. *Set of* 14 14·50 1·25
The 8, 15 and 90 n.p. have their value expressed as "nP".
For similar stamps but W **374** see Nos. 399/412.

**362** The Rani of Jhansi

**363** Shrine

**1957** (15 Aug). *Indian Mutiny Centenary.* W **69**. *P* 14½ × 14 *(15 n.p.) or* 13 × 13½ *(90 n.p.).*
386 **362** 15 n.p. brown .. .. .. .. 15 10
387 **363** 90 n.p. reddish purple .. .. .. .. 1·50 40

**364** Henri Dunant and Conference Emblem

**365** "Nutrition"

**1957** (28 Oct). *19th International Red Cross Conference, New Delhi.* W **69** *(sideways). P* 13½ × 13.
388 **364** 15 n.p. deep grey and carmine .. .. 10 10

**1957** (14 Nov). *Children's Day. T* **365** *and similar designs.* W **69** *(sideways on 90 n.p.). P* 14×13½ *(90 n.p.) or* 13½×14 *(others).*
389 8 n.p. reddish purple .. .. .. .. 10 15
390 15 n.p. turquoise-green .. .. .. .. 10 10
391 90 n.p. orange-brown .. .. .. .. 25 15
389/91 .. .. .. .. *Set of* 3 30 30
Designs: *Horiz*—15 n.p. "Education". *Vert*—90 n.p. "Recreation".

## ALTERED CATALOGUE NUMBERS

Any Catalogue numbers altered from the last edition are shown as a list in the introductory pages.

**368** Bombay University

**369** Calcutta University

**1957** (31 Dec). *Centenary of Indian Universities. T* **368/9** *and similar design.* W **69** *(sideways on T* **368**). *P* 14 × 14½ *(No. 392) or* 13½ × 14 *(others).*
392 10 n.p. violet .. .. .. .. .. 10 10
393 10 n.p. grey .. .. .. .. .. 10 10
394 10 n.p. light brown .. .. .. .. .. 15 10
392/4 .. .. .. .. *Set of* 3 30 25
Design: *Horiz as T* **369**—No. 394, Madras University.

**371** J. N. Tata (founder) and Steel Plant

**372** Dr. D. K. Karve

**1958** (1 Mar). *50th Anniv of Steel Industry.* W **69**. *P* 14½ × 14.
395 **371** 15 n.p. orange-red .. .. .. .. 10 10

**1958** (18 Apr). *Birth Centenary of Karve (educationalist).* W **69** *(sideways). P* 14.
396 **372** 15 n.p. orange-brown .. .. .. 10 10

**373** "Wapiti" and "Hunter" Aircraft

**374** Asokan Capital

**1958** (30 Apr). *Silver Jubilee of Indian Air Force.* W **69**. *P* 14½ × 14.
397 **373** 15 n.p. blue .. .. .. .. .. 40 10
398 90 n.p. ultramarine .. .. .. .. .. 85 90

**ASOKAN CAPITAL WATERMARK.** When the watermark was originally introduced in 1958 the base of each individual capital was 10 mm wide. During 1985 a modified version, with the capital base measurement reduced to 8 mm, was introduced. Examples have been seen on Nos. 921a, 922a, 923a and 928a.

**1958–63.** *As Nos.* 366, 369/71 *and* 375/85*a but* W **374**.
399 **361** 1 n.p. blue-green (1960) .. .. 30 10
a. Imperf (pair) .. .. .. £100
400 2 n.p. light brown (27.10.58) .. .. 10 10
401 3 n.p. deep brown (1958) .. .. 10 10
402 5 n.p. bright green (27.10.58) .. .. 10 10
403 6 n.p. grey (1963) .. .. .. 15 2·75
404 8 n.p. light blue-green (1958) .. .. 40 10
405 10 n.p. deep dull green (27.10.58) .. .. 15 10
a. Imperf (pair) .. .. † —
406 13 n.p. bright carmine-red (1963) .. .. 20 2·50
407 15 n.p. violet (10.60) .. .. .. 40 10
408 20 n.p. blue (27.10.58) .. .. .. 30 10
409 25 n.p. ultramarine (27.10.58) .. .. 30 10
410 50 n.p. orange (1959) .. .. .. 30 10
411 75 n.p. reddish purple (1959) .. .. 40 10
412 90 n.p. bright purple (1960) .. .. 3·75 10
413 – 1 r. deep dull green (1959) .. .. 2·75 10
414 – 2 r. cerise (1959) .. .. .. 4·50 10
415 – 5 r. brown (1959) .. .. .. 9·00 30
416 – 10 r. orange (1959) .. .. .. 19·00 3·50
399/416 .. .. .. .. *Set of* 18 38·00 8·50
The 5, 10, 15, 20, 25 and 50 n.p. with serial numbers on the back are coil stamps prepared from sheets for experimenting with coil machines. In the event the machines were not purchased and the stamps were sold over the counter.

**375** Bipin Chandra Pal

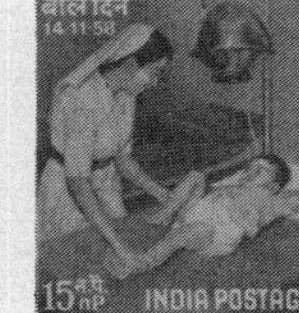

**376** Nurse with Child Patient

**1958** (7 Nov). *Birth Centenary of Pal (patriot).* W **374**. *P* 14 × 13½.
418 **375** 15 n.p. deep dull green .. .. .. 10 10

**1958** (14 Nov). *Children's Day.* W **374**. *P* 14×13½.
419 **376** 15 n.p. violet .. .. .. .. .. 10 10

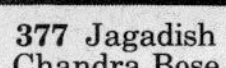

**377** Jagadish Chandra Bose

**378** Exhibition Gate

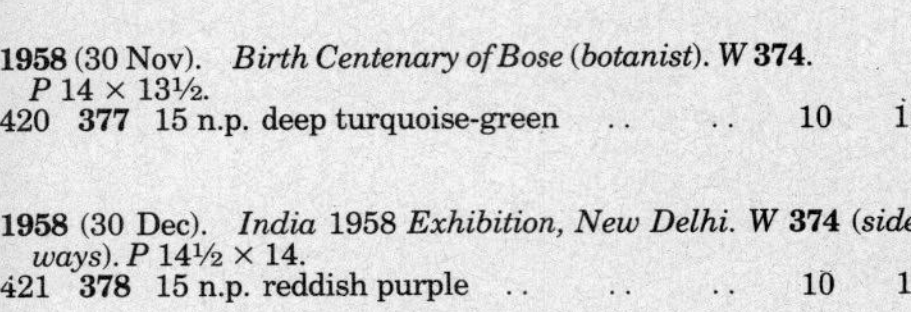

**1958** (30 Nov). *Birth Centenary of Bose (botanist).* W **374**. *P* 14 × 13½.
420 **377** 15 n.p. deep turquoise-green .. .. .. 10 10

**1958** (30 Dec). *India* 1958 *Exhibition, New Delhi.* W **374** (*sideways*). *P* 14½ × 14.
421 **378** 15 n.p. reddish purple .. .. .. .. 10 10

**379** Sir Jamsetjee Jejeebhoy

**380** "The Triumph of Labour" (after Chowdhury)

**1959** (15 Apr). *Death Centenary of Jejeebhoy (philanthropist).* W **374**. *P* 14 × 13½.
422 **379** 15 n.p. brown .. .. .. .. .. 10 10

**1959** (15 June). *40th Anniv of International Labour Organization.* W **374** (*sideways*). *P* 14½ × 14.
423 **380** 15 n.p. dull green .. .. .. .. 10 10

**381** Boys awaiting admission to Children's Home

**382** "Agriculture"

**1959** (14 Nov). *Children's Day.* W **374**. *P* 14×14½.
424 **381** 15 n.p. deep dull green .. .. .. 10 10
a. Imperf (pair) .. .. .. £550

**1959** (30 Dec). *First World Agricultural Fair, New Delhi.* W **374**. *P* 13½ × 13.
425 **382** 15 n.p. grey .. .. .. .. .. 10 10

**383** Thiruvalluvar (philosopher)

**1960** (15 Feb). *Thiruvalluvar Commemoration.* W **374**. *P* 14 × 13½.
426 **383** 15 n.p. reddish purple .. .. .. .. 10 10

**384** Yaksha pleading with the Cloud (from the "Meghaduta")

**385** Shakuntala writing a letter to Dushyanta (from the "Shakuntala")

**1960** (22 June). *Kalidasa (poet) Commemoration.* W **374**. *P* 13.
427 **384** 15 n.p. grey .. .. .. .. .. .. 15 10
428 **385** 1 r. 3 n.p. pale yellow and brown .. 70 20

**386** S. Bharati (poet)

**387** Dr. M. Visvesvaraya

**1960** (11 Sept). *Subramania Bharati Commemoration.* W **374**. *P* 14 × 13½.
429 **386** 15 n.p. blue .. .. .. .. .. 10 10

**1960** (15 Sept). *Birth Centenary of Dr. M. Visvesvaraya (engineer).* W **374**. *P* 13 × 13½.
430 **387** 15 n.p. brown and bright carmine .. 10 10

**388** "Children's Health"

**1960** (14 Nov). *Children's Day.* W **374**. *P* 13½ × 13.
431 **388** 15 n.p. deep dull green .. .. .. .. 10 10

**389** Children greeting U.N. Emblem

**390** Tyagaraja

**1960** (11 Dec). *U.N.I.C.E.F. Day.* W **374**. *P* 13½ × 13.
432 **389** 15 n.p. orange-brown and olive-brown 10 10

**1961** (6 Jan). *114th Death Anniv of Tyagaraja (musician).* W **374**. *P* 14×13½.
433 **390** 15 n.p. greenish blue .. .. .. 10 10

**391** "First Aerial Post" cancellation

**392** "Air India" Boeing 707 jetliner and Humber-Sommer plane

**1961** (18 Feb). *50th Anniv of First Official Airmail Flight, Allahabad-Naini.* T **391/2** *and similar design.* W **374**. *P* 14 (*5 n.p.*) *or* 13 × 13½ (*others*).
434 5 n.p. olive-drab .. .. .. .. .. 85 20
435 15 n.p. deep green and grey .. .. .. 90 30
436 1 r. purple and grey .. .. .. 3·75 1·00
434/6 .. .. .. .. .. *Set of* 3 5·00 1·40
Design: *Horiz as T* **392**—1 r. H. Pecquet flying Humber-Sommer plane and "Aerial Post" cancellation.

**394** Shivaji on horseback

**395** Motilal Nehru (politician)

**1961** (17 Apr). *Chatrapati Shivaji (Maratha ruler) Commemoration.* W **374**. *P* 13×13½.
437 **394** 15 n.p. brown and green .. .. 30 15

**1961** (6 May). *Birth Centenary of Pandit Motilal Nehru.* W **374**. *P* 14.
438 **395** 15 n.p. olive-brown and brown-orange .. 10 10

**396** Tagore (poet)

**397** All India Radio Emblem and Transmitting Aerials

**1961** (7 May). *Birth Centenary of Rabindranath Tagore.* W **374**. *P* 13 × 13½.
439 **396** 15 n.p. yellow-orange and blue-green .. 30 15

**1961** (8 June). *Silver Jubilee of All India Radio.* W **374**. *P* 13½ × 13.
440 **397** 15 n.p. ultramarine .. .. .. .. 10 10

**398** Prafulla Chandra Ray

**399** V. N. Bhatkande

**1961** (2 Aug). *Birth Centenary of Ray (social reformer).* W **374**. *P* 14×13½.
441 **398** 15 n.p. grey .. .. .. .. .. 10 10

**1961** (1 Sept). *Birth Centenary of Bhatkande (composer)* (1960). W **374**. *P* 13×13½.
442 **399** 15 n.p. olive-brown .. .. .. .. 10 10

**400** Child at Lathe

**401** Fair Emblem and Main Gate

**1961** (14 Nov). *Children's Day.* W **374**. *P* 14 × 13½.
443 **400** 15 n.p. brown .. .. .. .. .. 10 10

**1961** (14 Nov). *Indian Industries Fair, New Delhi.* W **374**. *P* 14 × 14½.
444 **401** 15 n.p. blue and carmine .. .. .. 10 10

**402** Indian Forest

**1961** (21 Nov). *Centenary of Scientific Forestry.* W **374**. *P* 13 × 13½.
445 **402** 15 n.p. green and brown.. .. .. 10 10

**403** Pitalkhora: Yaksha

**404** Kalibangan Seal

**1961** (14 Dec). *Centenary of Indian Archaeological Survey.* W **374**. *P* 14 × 13½ (*15 n.p.*) *or* 13½ × 14 (*90 n.p.*).
446 **403** 15 n.p. orange-brown .. .. .. 15 10
447 **404** 90 n.p. yellow-olive and light brown .. 30 15

## MINIMUM PRICE

The minimum price quote is 10p which represents a handling charge rather than a basis for valuing common stamps. For further notes about prices see introductory pages.

405 M. M. Malaviya

406 Gauhati Refinery

**1961** (24 Dec). *Birth Centenary of Malaviya (educationist).* W **374**. *P* 14×13½.
448 **405** 15 n.p. deep slate .. .. .. .. 10 10

**1962** (1 Jan). *Inauguration of Gauhati Oil Refinery.* W **374**. *P* 13×13½.
449 **406** 15 n.p. blue .. .. .. .. 15 10

407 Bhikaiji Cama

408 Village Panchayati and Parliament Building

**1962** (26 Jan). *Birth Centenary of Bhikaiji Cama (patriot).* W **374**. *P* 14.
450 **407** 15 n.p. reddish purple .. .. .. .. 10 10

**1962** (26 Jan). *Inauguration of Panchayati System of Local Government.* W **374**. *P* 13×13½.
451 **408** 15 n.p. bright purple .. .. .. .. 10 10

409 D. Saraswati (religious reformer)

410 G. S. Vidhyarthi (journalist)

**1962** (4 Mar). *Dayanard Saraswati Commemoration.* W **374**. *P* 14.
452 **409** 15 n.p. orange-brown .. .. .. .. 10 10

**1962** (25 Mar). *Ganesh Shankar Vidhyarthi Commemoration.* W **374**. *P* 14×13½.
453 **410** 15 n.p. red-brown .. .. .. .. 10 10

411 Malaria Eradication Emblem

412 Dr. R. Prasad

**1962** (7 Apr). *Malaria Eradication.* W **374**. *P* 13 × 13½.
454 **411** 15 n.p. yellow and claret .. .. .. 10 10

**1962** (13 May). *Retirement of President Dr. Rajendra Prasad.* W **374**. *P* 13.
455 **412** 15 n.p. bright purple (*shades*) .. .. 15 10

413 Calcutta High Court

416 Ramabai Ranade

**1962.** *Centenary of Indian High Courts. T* **413** *and similar horiz designs.* W **374**. *P* 14.
456 15 n.p. dull green (1 July) .. .. .. 15 15
457 15 n.p. red-brown (6 August) .. .. .. 15 15
458 15 n.p. slate (14 August) .. .. .. 15 15
456/8 .. .. .. .. .. *Set of* 3 40 40
Designs:—No. 457, Madras High Court; No. 458, Bombay High Court.

**1962** (15 Aug). *Birth Centenary of Ramabai Ranade (social reformer).* W **374**. *P* 14 × 13½
459 **416** 15 n.p. orange-brown .. .. .. .. 10 10

417 Indian Rhinoceros

418 "Passing the Flag to Youth"

**1962** (1 Oct). *Wild Life Week.* W **374**. *P* 13½ × 14.
460 **417** 15 n.p. red-brown and deep turquoise .. 30 10

**INSCRIPTIONS.** From No. 461 onwards all designs are inscribed "BHARAT" in Devanagri, in addition to "INDIA" in English.

**1962** (14 Nov). *Children's Day.* W **374**. *P* 13½ × 13.
461 **418** 15 n.p. orange-red and turquoise-green 10 10

419 Human Eye within Lotus Blossom

420 S. Ramanujan

**1962** (3 Dec). *19th International Ophthalmology Congress, New Delhi.* W **374**. *P* 13½ × 13.
462 **419** 15 n.p. deep olive-brown .. .. .. 10 10

**1962** (22 Dec). *75th Birth Anniv of Srinivasa Ramanujan (mathematician).* W **374**. *P* 13½×14.
463 **420** 15 n.p. deep olive-brown .. .. .. 20 15

421 S. Vivekananda

Re.1

(422)

**1963** (17 Jan). *Birth Centenary of Vivekananda (philosopher).* W **374**. *P* 14 × 14½.
464 **421** 15 n.p. orange-brown and yellow-olive .. 15 15

**1963** (2 Feb). *No. 428 surch with T* **422**.
465 **385** 1 r. on 1 r. 3 n.p. pale yellow & brn 30 10

423 Hands reaching for F.A.O. Emblem

424 Henri Dunant (founder) and Centenary Emblem

**1963** (21 Mar). *Freedom from Hunger.* W **374**. *P* 13.
466 **423** 15 n.p. grey-blue .. .. .. .. 75 30

**1963** (8 May). *Red Cross Centenary.* W **374**. *P* 13.
467 **424** 15 n.p. red and grey .. .. .. 1·75 30
a. Red (cross) omitted .. .. £2250

425 Artillery and Helicopter

**1963** (15 Aug). *Defence Campaign. T* **425** *and similar horiz design.* W **374**. *P* 14.
468 15 n.p. grey-green .. .. .. .. 30 10
469 1 r. red-brown .. .. .. .. 55 45
Design:—1 r. Sentry and parachutists.

427 D. Naoroji (parliamentarian)

428 Annie Besant (patriot and theosophist)

**1963** (4 Sept). *Dadabhoy Naoroji Commemoration.* W **374**. *P* 13.
470 **427** 15 n.p. grey .. .. .. .. 10 10

**1963** (1 Oct). *Annie Besant Commemoration.* W **374**. *P* 13½×14.
471 **428** 15 n.p. turquoise-green .. .. .. 10 10
No 471 is incorrectly dated "1837". Mrs. Besant was born in 1847.

429 Gaur

430 Lesser Panda

**1963** (7 Oct). *Wild Life Preservation. T* **429/30** *and similar designs.* W **374**. *P* 13½ × 14 (10 *n.p.*) *or* 13 (*others*).
472 10 n.p. black and yellow-orange .. .. 60 1·50
473 15 n.p. orange-brown and green .. .. 1·00 50
474 30 n.p. slate and yellow-ochre .. .. 3·25 1·50
475 50 n.p. orange and deep grey-green .. 2·75 60
476 1 r. light brown and blue .. .. 2·50 50
472/6 .. .. .. .. .. *Set of* 5 9·00 4·25
Designs: *Vert*—30 n.p. Indian elephant. *Horiz* (*as T* **430**)—50 n.p. Tiger; 1 r. Lion.

434 "School Meals"

435 Eleanor Roosevelt at Spinning-wheel

**1963** (14 Nov). *Children's Day.* W **374**. *P* 14 × 13½.
477 **434** 15 n.p. bistre-brown .. .. .. .. 10 10

**1963** (10 Dec). *15th Anniv of Declaration of Human Rights.* W **374**. *P* 13½ × 13.
478 **435** 15 n.p. reddish purple .. .. .. 10 10

436 Dipalakshmi (bronze)

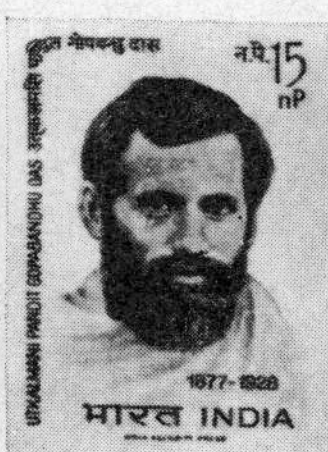

437 Gopabandhu Das (social reformer)

**1964** (4 Jan). *26th International Orientalists Congress, New Delhi.* W **374**. *P* 13 × 13½.
479 **436** 15 n.p. deep ultramarine .. .. 10 10

**1964** (4 Jan). *Gopabandhu Das Commemoration.* W **374**. *P* 13 × 13½.
480 **437** 15 n.p. deep dull purple .. .. .. 10 10

438 Purandaradasa

**1964** (14 Jan). *400th Death Anniv of Purandaradasa (composer). W* **374**. *P* 13×13½.
481 **438** 15 n.p. light brown . . . . . . 10 10

**439** S. C. Bose and I. N. A. Badge **440** Bose and Indian National Army

**1964** (23 Jan). *67th Birth Anniv of Subhas Chandra Bose (nationalist). W* **374**. *P* 13.
482 **439** 15 n.p. yellow-bistre . . . . . . 30 15
483 **440** 55 n.p. black, orange and orange-red . . 40 35

**441** Sarojini Naidu **442** Kasturba Gandhi

**1964** (13 Feb). *85th Birth Anniv of Sarojini Naidu (poetess). W* **374**. *P* 14.
484 **441** 15 n.p. deep grey-green and purple . . 10 10

**1964** (22 Feb). *20th Death Anniv of Kasturba Gandhi. W* **374**. *P* 14 × 13½.
485 **442** 15 n.p. orange-brown . . . . . . 10 10

**443** Dr. W. M. Haffkine (immunologist) **444** Jawaharlal Nehru (statesman)

**1964** (16 Mar). *Haffkine Commemoration. W* **374**. *P* 13.
486 **443** 15 n.p. deep purple-brown/*buff* . . . . 10 10

**(Value expressed as paisa instead of naye paise.)**

**1964** (12 June). *Nehru Mourning Issue. No wmk. P* 13½ × 13.
487 **444** 15 p. deep slate . . . . . . 10 10

**445** Sir Asutosh Mookerjee **446** Sri Aurobindo

**1964** (29 June). *Birth Centenary of Sir Asutosh Mookerjee (education reformer). W* **374**. *P* 13½ × 13.
488 **445** 15 p. bistre-brown and yellow-olive . . 10 10

**1964** (15 Aug). *92nd Birth Anniv of Sri Aurobindo (religious teacher). W* **374**. *P* 13×13½.
489 **446** 15 p. dull purple . . . . . . 10 10

**447** Raja R. Roy (social reformer) **448** I.S.O. Emblem and Globe

**1964** (27 Sept). *Raja Rammohun Roy Commemoration. W* **374**. *P* 13 × 13½.
490 **447** 15 n.p. brown . . . . . . 10 10

**1964** (9 Nov). *Sixth International Organization for Standardization General Assembly, Bombay. No wmk. P* 13 × 13½.
491 **448** 15 p. carmine . . . . . . 10 15

**449** Jawaharlal Nehru (from 1 r. commemorative coin) **450** St. Thomas (after statue, Ortona Cathedral, Italy)

**1964** (14 Nov). *Children's Day. No wmk. P* 14 × 13½.
492 **449** 15 p. slate . . . . . . 10 10

**1964** (2 Dec). *St. Thomas Commemoration. No wmk. P* 14 × 13½.
493 **450** 15 p. reddish purple . . . . . . 10 20
No. 493 was issued on the occasion of Pope Paul's visit to India.

**451** Globe **452** J. Tata (industrialist)

**1964** (14 Dec). *22nd International Geological Congress. W* **374**. *P* 14 × 13½.
494 **451** 15 p. blue-green . . . . . . 15 20

**1965** (7 Jan). *Jamsetji Tata Commemoration. No wmk. P* 13½ × 13.
495 **452** 15 p. dull-purple and orange . . . . 10 20

**453** Lala Lajpat Rai **454** Globe and Congress Emblem

**1965** (28 Jan). *Birth Centenary of Lala Lajpat Rai (social reformer). No wmk. P* 13×13½.
496 **453** 15 p. light brown . . . . . . 10 10

**1965** (8 Feb). *20th International Chamber of Commerce Congress, New Delhi. No wmk. P* 13½ × 13.
497 **454** 15 p. grey-green and carmine . . . . 10 15

**455** Freighter *Jalausha* and Visakhapatnam **456** Abraham Lincoln

**1965** (5 Apr). *National Maritime Day. W* **374** *(sideways). P* 14½ × 14.
498 **455** 15 p. blue . . . . . . 15 20

**1965** (15 Apr). *Death Centenary of Abraham Lincoln. W* **374**. *P* 13.
499 **456** 15 p. brown and yellow-ochre . . . . 10 10

**457** I.T.U. Emblem and Symbols **458** "Everlasting Flame"

**1965** (17 May). *I.T.U. Centenary. W* **374** *(sideways). P* 14½ × 14.
500 **457** 15 p. reddish purple . . . . . . 75 30

**1965** (27 May). *First Anniv of Nehru's Death. W* **374**. *P* 13.
501 **458** 15 p. carmine and blue . . . . . . 10 10

**459** I.C.Y. Emblem **460** Climbers on Summit

**1965** (26 June). *International Co-operation Year. P* 13½×13.
502 **459** 15 p. deep olive and yellow-brown . . 60 40

**1965** (15 Aug). *Indian Mount Everest Expedition. P* 13.
503 **460** 15 p. deep reddish purple . . . . 10 10

**461** Bidri Vase **462** Brass Lamp **466** Electric Locomotive

**474** Medieval Sculpture **475** Dal Lake, Kashmir

**1965–75.** *T* **461/2, 466, 474/5** *and similar designs.*

(*a*) *W* **374** (*sideways on* 2, 3, 5, 6, 8, 30, 50, 60 *p.*, 2, 5, 10 *r.*). *P* 14 × 14½ (4, 10, 15, 20, 40, 70 *p.*, 1 *r.*) *or* 14½ × 14 (*others*)
504 2 p. red-brown (16.10.67) . . . . 10 30
505 3 p. brown-olive (16.10.67) . . . . 10 70
505*a* 4 p. lake-brown (15.5.68) . . . . 10 1·00
506 5 p. cerise (16.10.67) . . . . . . 10 10
a. Imperf (pair) . . . . . . £180
507 6 p. grey-black (1.7.66) . . . . . . 10 1·25
508 8 p. red-brown (15.3.67) . . . . . . 30 2·50
509 10 p. new blue (1.7.66) . . . . . . 30 10
510 15 p. bronze-green (15.8.65) . . . . 60 10
511 20 p. purple (16.10.67) . . . . . . 60 10
512 30 p. sepia (15.3.67) . . . . . . 15 10
513 40 p. maroon (2.10.68) . . . . . . 15 10
514 50 p. blue-green (15.3.67) . . . . . . 20 10
515 60 p. deep grey (16.10.67) . . . . 35 10
516 70 p. chalky blue (15.3.67) . . . . 60 10
517 1 r. red-brown and plum (1.7.66) . . 60 10
518 2 r. new blue & deep slate-violet (15.3.67) 2·00 10
519 5 r. deep slate-violet and brown (15.3.67) 2·50 25
520 10 r. black and bronze-green (14.11.65) . . 12·00 80
504/20 . . . . . . . . *Set of* 18 18·00 6·50

(*b*) *No wmk. P* 14½ × 14
520*a* 5 p. cerise (12.5.74) . . . . . . 15 10

(*c*) *Wmk Large Star and* "INDIA GOVT"† *in sheet. P* 14½ × 14
521 2 p. red-brown (1.3.75) . . . . . . 15 50
521*a* 5 p. cerise (1.3.75) . . . . . . 15 10

Designs: *Horiz* (*as T* **466**)—4 p. Coffee berries; 15 p. Plucking tea; 20 p. Folland "Gnat" fighter aircraft; 40 p. Calcutta G.P.O.; 70 p. Hampi Chariot (sculpture). (*As T* **475**)—5 r. Bhakra Dam, Punjab; 10 r. Atomic Reactor, Trombay. *Vert* (*as T* **461/2**)—5 p. "Family Planning"; 6 p. Konarak Elephant; 8 p. Spotted Deer ("Chital"); 30 p. Indian dolls; 50 p. Mangoes; 60 p. Somnath Temple.

†The arrangement of this watermark in the sheet results in the words and the star appearing upright, inverted or sideways.

Two different postal forgeries exist of No. 511, both printed in lithography and without watermark. The cruder version is roughly perforated 15, but the more sophisticated is perforated 14×14½.

See also Nos. 721/38.

**479** G. B. Pant (statesman) **480** V. Patel

**1965** (10 Sept). *Govind Ballabh Pant Commemoration. P* 13.
522 **479** 15 p. brown and deep green . . . . 10 15

**1965** (31 Oct). *90th Birth Anniv of Vallabhbhai Patel (statesman). P* 14 × 13½.
523 **480** 15 p. blackish brown .. .. .. 10 20

**481** C. Das **482** Vidyapati (poet)

**1965** (5 Nov). *95th Birth Anniv of Chittaranjan Das (lawyer and patriot). P* 13.
524 **481** 15 p. yellow-brown .. .. .. 10 10

**1965** (17 Nov). *Vidyapati Commemoration. P* 14 × 14½.
525 **482** 15 p. yellow-brown .. .. .. 10 10

**483** Sikandra, Agra **484** Soldier, Fighters and Cruiser *Mysore*

**1966** (24 Jan). *Pacific Area Travel Association Conference. New Delhi. P* 13½ × 14.
526 **483** 15 p. slate .. .. .. .. 10 10

**1966** (26 Jan). *Indian Armed Forces. P* 14
527 **484** 15 p. violet .. .. .. .. 30 15

**485** Lal Bahadur Shastri (statesman) **486** Kambar (poet)

**1966** (26 Jan). *Shastri Mourning Issue. P* 13 × 13½.
528 **485** 15 p. black .. .. .. .. 10 10

**1966** (5 Apr). *Kambar Commemoration. P* 14 × 14½.
529 **486** 15 p. grey-green .. .. .. .. 10 10

**487** B. R. Ambedkar **488** Kunwar Singh (patriot)

**1966** (14 Apr). *75th Birth Anniv of Dr. Bhim Rao Ambedkar (lawyer). P* 14 × 13½.
530 **487** 15 p. purple-brown .. .. .. 10 10

**1966** (23 Apr). *Kunwar Singh Commemoration. P* 14 × 13½.
531 **488** 15 p. chestnut .. .. .. .. 10 10

**489** G. K. Gokhale **490** Acharya Dvivedi (poet)

**1966** (9 May). *Birth Centenary of Gopal Krishna Gokhale (patriot). P* 13½ × 13.
532 **489** 15 p. brown-purple and pale yellow .. 10 10

**1966** (15 May). *Dvivedi Commemoration. P* 13½ × 14.
533 **490** 15 p. drab .. .. .. .. .. 10 10

## NEW INFORMATION

The editor is always interested to correspond with people who have new information that will improve or correct the Catalogue.

**491** Maharaja Ranjit Singh (warrior) **492** Homi Bhabha (scientist) and Nuclear Reactor

**1966** (28 June). *Maharaja Ranjit Singh Commemoration. P* 14 × 13½.
534 **491** 15 p. purple .. .. .. .. 15 10

**1966** (4 Aug). *Dr. Homi Bhabha Commemoration. P* 14½ × 14.
535 **492** 15 p. dull purple .. .. .. 10 30

**493** A. K. Azad (scholar) **494** Swami Tirtha

**1966** (11 Nov). *Abul Kalam Azad Commemoration. P* 13½ × 14.
536 **493** 15 p. chalky blue .. .. .. .. 10 10

**1966** (11 Nov). *60th Death Anniv of Swami Rama Tirtha (social reformer). P* 13 × 13½.
537 **494** 15 p. turquoise-blue .. .. .. 10 20

**495** Infant and Dove Emblem **496** Allahabad High Court

(Des C. Pakrashi)

**1966** (14 Nov). *Children's Day. P* 13 × 13½.
538 **495** 15 p. bright purple .. .. .. 20 15

**1966** (25 Nov). *Centenary of Allahabad High Court. P* 14½ × 14.
539 **496** 15 p. dull purple .. .. .. .. 15 30

**497** Indian Family **498** Hockey Game

**1966** (12 Dec). *Family Planning. P* 13.
540 **497** 15 p. brown .. .. .. .. 10 10

**1966** (31 Dec). *India's Hockey Victory in Fifth Asian Games. P* 13.
541 **498** 15 p. new blue .. .. .. .. 70 30

**499** "Jai Kisan" **500** Voter and Polling Booth

**1967** (11 Jan). *First Anniv of Shastri's Death. P* 13½ × 14.
542 **499** 15 p. yellow-green .. .. .. 10 15

**1967** (13 Jan). *Indian General Election. P* 13½ × 14.
543 **500** 15 p. red-brown .. .. .. .. 10 10

**501** Gurudwara Shrine, Patna **502** Taj Mahal, Agra

**1967** (17 Jan). *300th Birth Anniv (1966) of Guru Gobind Singh (Sikh religious leader). P* 14 × 13½.
544 **501** 15 p. bluish violet .. .. .. 15 10

**1967** (19 Mar). *International Tourist Year. P* 14½ × 14.
545 **502** 15 p. bistre-brown and orange .. .. 10 10

**503** Nandalal Bose and "Garuda" **504** Survey Emblem and Activities

**1967** (16 Apr). *First Death Anniv of Nandalal Bose (painter). P* 14 × 13½.
546 **503** 15 p. bistre-brown .. .. .. 10 10

**1967** (1 May). *Survey of India Bicentenary. P* 13½ × 13.
547 **504** 15 p. reddish lilac .. .. .. 10 15

**505** Basaveswara **506** Narsinha Mehta (poet)

**1967** (11 May). *800th Death Anniv of Basaveswara (reformer and statesman). P* 13½ × 14.
548 **505** 15 p. orange-red .. .. .. .. 10 10

**1967** (30 May). *Narsinha Mehta Commemoration. P* 14 × 13½.
549 **506** 15 p. blackish brown .. .. .. 10 10

**507** Maharana Pratap **508** Narayana Guru

**1967** (11 June). *Maharana Pratap (Rajput leader) Commemoration. P* 14 × 14½.
550 **507** 15 p. red-brown .. .. .. .. 10 10

**1967** (21 Aug). *Narayana Guru (philosopher) Commemoration. P* 14.
551 **508** 15 p. brown .. .. .. .. 10 10

**509** President Radhakrishnan **510** Martyrs' Memorial, Patna

**1967** (5 Sept). *75th Birth Anniv of Sarvepalli Radhakrishnan (former President). P* 13.
552 **509** 15 p. claret .. .. .. .. 20 10

**1967** (1 Oct). *25th Anniv of "Quit India" Movement. P* 14½ × 14.
553 **510** 15 p. lake .. .. .. .. 10 10

**511** Route Map **512** Wrestling

**1967** (9 Nov). *Centenary of Indo-European Telegraph Service. P* 13½ × 14.
554 **511** 15 p. black and light blue .. .. 10 15

**1967** (12 Nov). *World Wrestling Championships, New Delhi. P* 13½ × 14.
555 **512** 15 p. purple and light orange-brown .. 15 15

**513** Nehru leading Naga Tribesmen

**514** Rashbehari Basu (nationalist)

**1967** (1 Dec). *4th Anniv of Nagaland as a State of India. P* 13×13½.
556 **513** 15 p. ultramarine .. .. .. .. 10 10

**1967** (26 Dec). *Rashbehari Basu Commemoration. P* 14.
557 **514** 15 p. maroon .. .. .. .. .. 10 15

**515** Bugle, Badge and Scout Salute

**1967** (27 Dec). *60th Anniv of Scout Movement in India. P* 14½×14.
558 **515** 15 p. chestnut .. .. .. .. .. 40 20

**516** Men embracing Universe

**517** Globe and Book of Tamil

**1968** (1 Jan). *Human Rights Year. P* 13.
559 **516** 15 p. bronze-green .. .. .. .. 20 15

**1968** (3 Jan). *International Conference-Seminar of Tamil Studies, Madras. P* 13.
560 **517** 15 p. reddish lilac .. .. .. .. 20 10

**518** U.N. Emblem and Transport

**519** Quill and Bow Symbol

**1968** (1 Feb). *United Nations Conference on Trade and Development, New Delhi. P* 14½×14.
561 **518** 15 p. turquoise-blue .. .. .. .. 20 10

**1968** (20 Feb). *Centenary of* Amrita Bazar Patrika *(newspaper). P* 13½×14.
562 **519** 15 p. sepia and orange-yellow .. .. .. 10 10

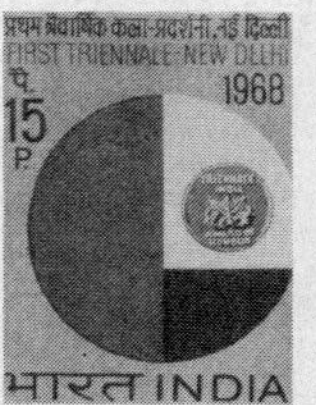


**520** Maxim Gorky

**521** Emblem and Medal

**1968** (28 Mar). *Birth Centenary of Maxim Gorky. P* 13½.
563 **520** 15 p. plum .. .. .. .. .. 10 15

**1968** (31 Mar). *First Triennale Art Exhibition, New Delhi. P* 13.
564 **521** 15 p. orange, royal blue and light blue 20 15
a. Orange omitted .. .. .. £500

**522** Letter-box and "100,000"

**523** Stalks of Wheat, Agricultural Institute and Production Graph

(Des C. Pakrashi)

**1968** (1 July). *Opening of 100,000th Indian Post Office. P* 13.
565 **522** 20 p. red, blue and black .. .. .. 10 10

**1968** (17 July). *Wheat Revolution. P* 13.
566 **523** 20 p. bluish green and orange-brown .. 15 15

**524** "Self-portrait"

**525** Lakshminath Bezbaruah

(Des from self-portrait)

**1968** (17 Sept). *30th Death Anniv of Gaganendranath Tagore (painter). P* 13.
567 **524** 20 p. brown-purple and ochre .. .. 20 10

**1968** (5 Oct). *Birth Centenary of Lakshminath Bezbaruah (writer). P* 13½ × 14.
568 **525** 20 p. blackish brown .. .. .. 15 10

**526** Athlete's Legs and Olympic Rings

**1968** (12 Oct). *Olympic Games, Mexico. P* 14½ × 14.
569 **526** 20 p. brown and grey .. .. .. 10 15
570 1 r. sepia and brown-olive .. .. .. 30 15

**527** Bhagat Singh and Followers

**528** Azad Hind Flag, Swords and Chandra Bose (founder)

**1968** (19 Oct). *61st Birth Anniv of Bhagat Singh (patriot). P* 13.
571 **527** 20 p. yellow-brown .. .. .. .. 20 15

**1968** (21 Oct). *25th Anniv of Azad Hind Government. P* 14 × 14½.
572 **528** 20 p. deep blue .. .. .. .. 15 15

**529** Sister Nivedita

**530** Marie Curie and Radium Treatment

**1968** (27 Oct). *Birth Centenary of Sister Nivedita (social reformer). P* 14×14½.
573 **529** 20p. deep bluish green .. .. .. 20 20

**1968** (6 Nov). *Birth Centenary of Marie Curie. P* 14½ × 14.
574 **530** 20 p. slate-lilac .. .. .. .. 60 30

**531** Map of the World

**532** Cochin Synagogue

**1968** (1 Dec). *21st International Geographical Congress, New Delhi. P* 13.
575 **531** 20 p. new blue .. .. .. .. 10 10

**1968** (15 Dec). *400th Anniv of Cochin Synagogue. P* 13.
576 **532** 20 p. blue and carmine .. .. .. 30 15

**533** I.N.S. *Nilgiri* (frigate)

**534** Red-billed Blue Magpie

**1968** (15 Dec). *Navy Day. P* 13.
577 **533** 20 p. grey-blue .. .. .. .. .. 50 30

**1968** (31 Dec). *Birds. T* **534** *and similar designs. P* 14 × 14½ (1 *r.) or* 14½ × 14 *(others).*
578 20 p. multicoloured .. .. .. .. .. 55 30
579 50 p. scarlet, black and turquoise-green .. 1·10 55
580 1 r. deep blue, yellow-brown and pale blue .. 1·75 1·00
581 2 r. multicoloured .. .. .. .. 1·75 1·40
578/81 .. .. .. .. *Set of* 4 4·50 3·00

Designs: *Horiz*—50 p. Brown-fronted Pied Woodpecker; 2 r. Yellow-backed Slaty-headed Sunbird. *Vert*—1 r. Scimitar Babbler.

**538** Bankim Chandra Chatterjee

**539** Dr. Bhagavan Das

**1969** (1 Jan). *130th Birth Anniv of Bankim Chandra Chatterjee (writer). P* 13½.
582 **538** 20 p. ultramarine .. .. .. .. 10 15

**1969** (12 Jan). *Birth Centenary of Dr. Bhagavan Das (philosopher). P* 13½.
583 **539** 20 p. pale chocolate .. .. .. .. 10 10

**540** Dr. Martin Luther King

**541** Mirza Ghalib and Letter Seal

**1969** (25 Jan). *Martin Luther King Commemoration. P* 13½.
584 **540** 20 p. deep olive-brown .. .. .. .. 20 15

**1969** (17 Feb). *Death Centenary of Mirza Ghalib (poet). P* 14½ × 14.
585 **541** 20 p. sepia, brown-red and flesh .. .. 10 15

**542** Osmania University

**1969** (15 Mar). *50th Anniv of Osmania University. P* 14½ × 14.
586 **542** 20 p. olive-green .. .. .. .. .. 10 15

**543** Rafi Ahmed Kidwai and Mail Plane

**1969** (1 Apr). *20th Anniv of "ALL-UP" Air Mail Scheme. P* 13.
587 **543** 20 p. deep blue .. .. .. .. .. 30 15

**544** I.L.O. Badge and Emblem

**545** Memorial, and Hands dropping Flowers

**1969** (11 Apr). *50th Anniv of International Labour Organisation. P* 14½ × 14.
588 **544** 20 p. chestnut .. .. .. .. .. 10 15

**1969** (13 Apr). *50th Anniv of Jallianwala Bagh Massacre, Amritsar. P* 14×13½.
589 **545** 20 p. rose-carmine .. .. .. .. 10 15

546 K. Nageswara Rao Pantulu (journalist)

547 Ardaseer Cursetjee Wadia, and Ships

**1969** (1 May). *Kasinadhuni Nageswara Rao Pantulu Commemoration. P* 13½ × 14.
590 **546** 20 p. brown .. .. .. .. .. 10 15

**1969** (27 May). *Ardaseer Cursetjee Wadia (ship-builder) Commemoration. P* 14½×14.
591 **547** 20 p. turquoise-green .. .. .. .. 10 15

548 Serampore College

549 Dr. Zakir Husain

**1969** (7 June). *150th Anniv of Serampore College. P* 13½.
592 **548** 20 p. plum .. .. .. .. .. 10 15

**1969** (11 June). *President Dr. Zakir Husain Commemoration. P* 13.
593 **549** 20 p. sepia .. .. .. .. .. 10 15

550 Laxmanrao Kirloskar

**1969** (20 June). *Birth Centenary of Laxmanrao Kirloskar (agriculturalist). P* 13.
594 **550** 20 p. grey-black .. .. .. .. .. 10 10

551 Gandhi and his Wife

552 Gandhi's Head and Shoulders

553 Gandhi walking (woodcut)

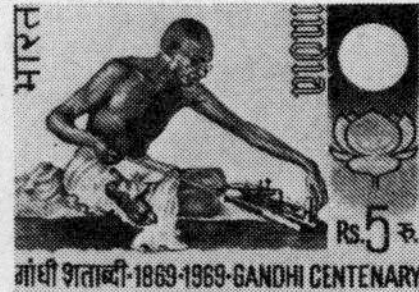


554 Gandhi with Charkha

(Des Suraj Sadan (20 p.), P. Chitnis (75 p.), Indian Security Press (1 r.) and C. Pakrashi (5 r.))

**1969** (2 Oct). *Birth Centenary of Mahatma Gandhi. P* 13½ × 14 *(20 p.), 14 × 14½ (1 r.) or 13 (others).*
595 **551** 20 p. blackish brown .. .. .. 30 15
596 **552** 75 p. cinnamon and drab.. .. .. 85 70
597 **553** 1 r. blue .. .. .. .. .. 1·00 65
598 **554** 5 r. greyish brown and red-orange .. 4·00 5·00
595/8 .. .. .. .. .. .. *Set of* 4 5·50 6·00

555 *Ajanta* (tanker) and I.M.C.O. Emblem

**1969** (14 Oct). *10th Anniv of Inter-Governmental Maritime Consultative Organization. P* 13.
599 **555** 20 p. violet-blue .. .. .. .. .. 40 20

556 Outline of Parliament Building and Globe

557 Astronaut walking beside Space Module on Moon

**1969** (30 Oct). *57th Inter-Parliamentary Conference, New Delhi. P* 14½ × 14.
600 **556** 20 p. new blue .. .. .. .. .. 10 15

**1969** (19 Nov). *First Man on the Moon. P* 14 × 14½.
601 **557** 20 p. olive-brown.. .. .. .. .. 10 15

558 Gurudwara Nankana Sahib (birthplace)

559 Tiger's Head and Hands holding Globe

**1969** (23 Nov). *500th Anniv of Guru Nanak Dev (Sikh religious leader). P* 13½.
602 **558** 20 p. slate-violet .. .. .. .. .. 10 15

**1969** (24 Nov). *International Union for the Conservation of Nature and Natural Resources Conference, New Delhi. P* 14½ × 14.
603 **559** 20 p. orange-brown and bronze-green .. 30 20

560 Sadhu Vaswani

561 Thakkar Bapa

**1969** (25 Nov). *90th Birth Anniv of Sadhu Vaswani (educationist). P* 14 × 14½.
604 **560** 20 p. grey.. .. .. .. .. .. 10 10

**1969** (29 Nov). *Birth Centenary of Thakkar Bapa (humanitarian). P* 13½.
605 **561** 20 p. chocolate .. .. .. .. .. 10 15

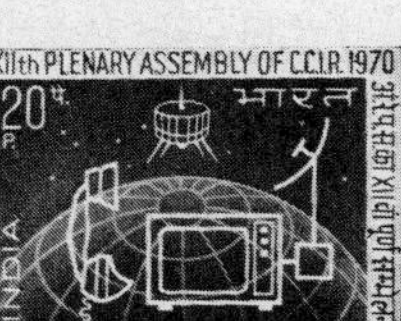


562 Satellite, Television, Telephone and Globe

563 C. N. Annadurai

**1970** (21 Jan). *12th Plenary Assembly of International Radio Consultative Committee. P* 13.
606 **562** 20 p. Prussian blue .. .. .. .. 10 15

**1970** (3 Feb). *First Death Anniv of Conjeevaram Natrajan Annadurai (statesman). P* 13.
607 **563** 20 p. reddish purple and royal blue .. 10 10

564 M. N. Kishore and Printing Press

565 Nalanda College

**1970** (19 Feb). *75th Death Anniv of Munshi Newal Kishore (publisher). P* 13.
608 **564** 20 p. lake.. .. .. .. .. .. 10 15

**1970** (27 Mar). *Centenary of Nalanda College. P* 14½ × 14.
609 **565** 20 p. brown .. .. .. .. .. 30 30

566 Swami Shraddhanand (social reformer)

567 Lenin

**1970** (30 Mar). *Swami Shraddhanand Commemoration. P* 14 × 13½.
610 **566** 20 p. yellow-brown .. .. .. .. 30 20

**1970** (22 Apr). *Birth Centenary of Lenin. P* 13.
611 **567** 20 p. orange-brown and sepia .. .. 10 15

568 New U.P.U. H.Q. Building

569 Sher Shah Suri (15th-century ruler)

**1970** (20 May). *New U.P.U. Headquarters Building, Berne. P* 13.
612 **568** 20 p. emerald, grey and black .. .. 10 15

**1970** (22 May). *Sher Shah Suri Commemoration. P* 13.
613 **569** 20 p. deep bluish green .. .. .. .. 10 15

570 V. D. Savarkar (patriot) and Cellular Jail, Andaman Islands

571 "UN" and Globe

**1970** (28 May). *Vinayak Damodar Savarkar Commemoration. P* 13.
614 **570** 20 p. orange-brown .. .. .. .. 10 15

**1970** (26 June). *25th Anniv of United Nations. P* 13.
615 **571** 20 p. light new blue .. .. .. .. 20 15

572 Symbol and Workers

**1970** (18 Aug). *Asian Productivity Year. P* 14½ × 14.
616 **572** 20 p. violet .. .. .. .. .. 15 15

573 Dr. Montessori and I.E.Y. Emblem

**1970** (31 Aug). *Birth Centenary of Dr. Maria Montessori (educationist). P* 13.
617 **573** 20 p. dull purple .. .. .. .. .. 30 20

574 J. N. Mukherjee (revolutionary) and Horse

575 V. S. Srinivasa Sastri

**1970** (9 Sept). *Jatindra Nath Mukherjee Commemoration. P* 14½ × 14.
618 **574** 20 p. chocolate .. .. .. .. .. 40 20

**1970** (22 Sept). *Srinivasa Sastri (educationist) Commemoration. P* 13×13½.
619 **575** 20 p. yellow and brown-purple .. .. 25 20

576 I. C. Vidyasagar

577 Maharishi Valmiki

**1970** (26 Sept). *150th Birth Anniv of Iswar Chandra Vidyasagar (educationist). P* 13.
620 **576** 20 p. brown and purple .. .. 20 20

**1970** (14 Oct). *Maharishi Valmiki (ancient author) Commemoration. P* 13.
621 **577** 20 p. purple .. .. .. .. 15 15

578 Calcutta Port

**1970** (17 Oct). *Centenary of Calcutta Port Trust. P* 13½ × 13.
622 **578** 20 p. greenish blue .. .. .. 30 15

579 University Building

**1970** (29 Oct). *50th Anniv of Jamia Millia Islamia University. P* 14½ × 14.
623 **579** 20 p. yellow-green .. .. .. 20 20

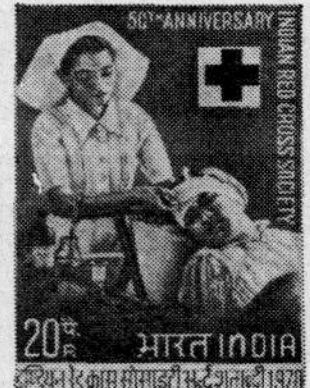


580 Jamnalal Bajaj 581 Nurse and Patient

**1970** (4 Nov). *Jamnalal Bajaj (industrialist) Commemoration. W* **374**. *P* 13½×13.
624 **580** 20 p. olive-grey .. .. .. .. 10 15

**1970** (5 Nov). *50th Anniv of Indian Red Cross. W* **374** *(sideways). P* 13 × 13½.
625 **581** 20 p. red and greenish blue .. .. 20 20

582 Sant Namdeo 583 Beethoven

**1970** (9 Nov). *700th Birth Anniv of Sant Namdeo (mystic). W* **374**. *P* 13.
626 **582** 20 p. orange .. .. .. .. 10 15

**1970** (16 Dec). *Birth Bicentenary of Beethoven. P* 13.
627 **583** 20 p. orange and greyish black .. .. 80 30

584 Children examining Stamps 585 Girl Guide

**1970** (23 Dec). *Indian National Philatelic Exhibition, New Dehli. T* **584** *and similar horiz design. P* 13.
628 20 p. orange and myrtle-green .. .. 30 10
629 1 r. orange-brown and pale yellow-brown .. 1·25 80
Design:—1 r. Gandhi commemorative through magnifier.

**1970** (27 Dec). *Diamond Jubilee of Girl Guide Movement in India. P* 13.
630 **585** 20 p. maroon .. .. .. .. 30 20

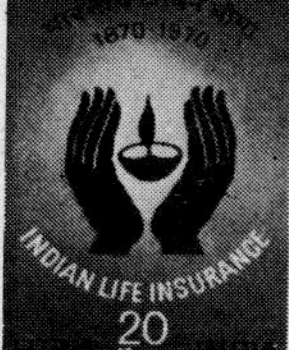


586 Hands and Lamp (Emblem)

587 Vidyapith Building

**1971** (11 Jan). *Centenary of Indian Life Insurance. P* 13.
631 **586** 20 p. sepia and crimson .. .. 15 20

**1971** (10 Feb). *50th Anniv of Kashi Vidyapith University. P* 14½×14.
632 **587** 20 p. blackish brown .. .. .. 15 20

588 Sant Ravidas 589 C. F. Andrews

**1971** (10 Feb). *Sant Ravidas (15th-cent mystic) Commemoration. P* 13.
633 **588** 20 p. lake .. .. .. .. .. 15 20

**1971** (12 Feb). *Birth Centenary of Charles Freer Andrews (missionary). P* 13×13½.
634 **589** 20 p. chestnut .. .. .. .. 35 20

590 Acharya Narendra Deo (scholar)

591 Crowd and "100"

**1971** (19 Feb). *15th Death Anniv of Acharya Narendra Deo. P* 13.
635 **590** 20 p. dull green .. .. .. .. 15 20

**1971** (10 Mar). *Centenary of Decennial Census. P* 13.
636 **591** 20 p. brown and blue .. .. .. 20 20

592 Sri Ramana Maharishi (mystic)

593 Raja Ravi Varma and "Damayanti and the Swan"

**1971** (14 Apr). *21st Death Anniv of Ramana Maharishi. P* 13½.
637 **592** 20 p. orange and sepia .. .. .. 15 20

**1971** (29 Apr). *65th Death Anniv of Ravi Varma (artist). P* 13.
638 **593** 20 p. green .. .. .. .. 15 20

594 Dadasaheb Phalke and Camera

595 "Abhisarika" (Tagore)

**1971** (30 Apr). *Birth Centenary of Dadasaheb Phalke (cinematographer). P* 13½×13.
639 **594** 20 p. deep maroon .. .. .. 40 20

**1971** (7 Aug). *Birth Centenary of Abanindranath Tagore (painter). P* 14×14½.
640 **595** 20 p. grey, buff-yellow & blackish brown 20 20

596 Swami Virjanand (Vedic scholar)

597 Cyrus the Great and Procession

**1971** (14 Sept). *Swami Virjanand Commemoration. P* 13½.
641 **596** 20 p. chestnut .. .. .. .. 15 20

**1971** (12 Oct). *2500th Anniv of Charter of Cyrus the Great. P* 13.
642 **597** 20 p. blackish brown .. .. .. 35 30

598 Globe and Money Box

**1971** (31 Oct). *World Thrift Day. P* 14½ × 14.
643 **598** 20 p. blue-grey .. .. .. .. 15 15

599 Ajanta Caves Painting 600 "Women at Work" (Geeta Gupta)

**1971** (4 Nov). *25th Anniv of U.N.E.S.C.O. P* 13.
644 **599** 20 p. red-brown .. .. .. .. 65 30

(Des from painting by Geeta Gupta)

**1971** (14 Nov). *Children's Day. P* 14 × 14½.
645 **600** 20 p. scarlet .. .. .. .. 15 20

REFUGEE RELIEF
शरणार्थी
सहायता
(601)

Refugee
Relief
(602)

शरणार्थी
सहायता
REFUGEE
RELIEF
(603)

REFUGEE
RELIEF
(604)

REFUGEE
RELIEF
(605)

Refugee Relief
(606)

Refugee
relief
(606*a*)

शरणार्थी
सहायता
Refugee
Relief
(606*b*)

607 Refugees

**1971.** *Obligatory Tax. Refugee Relief.*

*(a) Provisional issues. No. 506 variously optd*

*(i) For all India, optd at Nasik*
646 **601** 5 p. cerise (15 Nov) .. .. .. 10 10
a. Opt double .. .. .. .. 2·50

*(ii) For various areas*
647 **602** 5 p. Bangalore .. .. .. .. 1·00 30
a. Opt double, one inverted .. ..
648 **603** 5 p. Jaipur .. .. .. .. 2·75 40
649 **604** 5 p. Rajasthan .. .. .. .. 1·75 40
a. Error. "RELIEF REFUGEE" .. 12·00
b. Opt inverted .. .. .. ..
650 **605** 5 p. New Delhi .. .. .. .. 6·00 90
a. Opt inverted .. .. .. .. 7·00
650*b* **606** 5 p. Goa .. .. .. .. 6·00 1·50
650*c* **606*a*** 5 p. Jabalpur .. .. .. .. 3·25 1·00
650*d* **606*b*** 5 p. Alwar .. .. .. ..

*(b) Definitive issue. W* **374**. *P* 14 × 14½
651 **607** 5 p. carmine (1 Dec) .. .. .. 10 10

From 15 November 1971 until 31 March 1973, the Indian Government levied a 5 p. surcharge on all mail, except postcards and newspapers, for the relief of refugees from the former East Pakistan.

As supplies of the provisional overprint could not be sent to all Indian post offices in time, local postmasters were authorised to make their own overprints. Most of these were applied by rubber stamps and so we do not list them. Those listed have typographed overprints and No. 649 also has a rubber handstamp in native language. Some of the above overprints were also used in areas other than those where they were produced.

**608** C. V. Raman (scientist) and Light Graph

**1971** (12 Nov). *First Death Anniv of Chandrasekhara Venkata Raman. P* 13.
652 **608** 20 p. orange and deep brown .. .. 30 20

**609** Visva Bharati Building and Rabindranath Tagore (founder)

**1971** (24 Dec). *50th Anniv of Visva Bharati University. P* 14½×14.
653 **609** 20 p. sepia and yellow-brown .. .. 15 25

**610** Cricketers **611** Map and Satellite

**1971** (30 Dec). *Indian Cricket Victories. P* 14½ × 14.
654 **610** 20 p. green, myrtle-green and sage-green 1·75 65

**1972** (26 Feb). *First Anniv of Arvi Satellite Earth Station. P* 13½.
655 **611** 20 p. plum .. .. .. .. 15 20

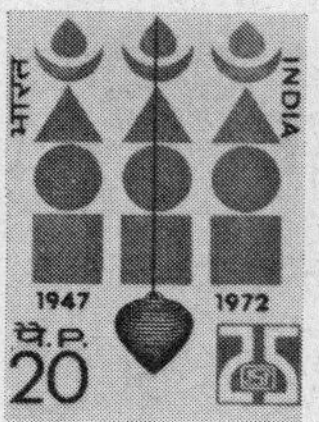

**612** Elemental Symbols and Plumb-line **613** Signal-box Panel

**1972** (29 May). *25th Anniv of Indian Standards Institution. P* 13.
656 **612** 20 p. turquoise-grey and black .. .. 15 30

**1972** (30 June). *50th Anniv of International Railways Union. P* 13.
657 **613** 20 p. multicoloured .. .. .. 40 40
a. Blue omitted .. .. .. 50·00

**614** Hockey-player **615** Symbol of Sri Aurobindo

**1972** (10 Aug). *Olympic Games, Munich. T* **614** *and similar horiz design. P* 13.
658 20 p. deep bluish violet .. .. .. 30 15
659 1 r. 45, light turquoise-green & brown-lake 95 1·75
Design:—1 r. 45, Various sports.

**1972** (15 Aug). *Birth Centenary of Sri Aurobindo (religious teacher). P* 13½.
660 **615** 20 p. yellow and new blue .. .. 15 20

**616** Celebrating Independence Day in front of Parliament **617** Inter-Services Crest

**1972** (15 Aug). *25th Anniversary of Independence (1st issue). P* 13.
661 **616** 20 p. multicoloured .. .. .. 15 20
See also Nos. 673/4.

**1972** (15 Aug). *Defence Services Commemoration. P* 13.
662 **617** 20 p. multicoloured .. .. .. 30 20

**618** V. O. Chidambaram Pillai (trade union leader) and Ship **619** Bhai Vir Singh

**1972** (5 Sept). *Birth Centenary of V. O. Chidambaram Pillai. P* 13.
663 **618** 20 p. new blue and purple-brown .. 30 30

**1972** (16 Oct). *Birth Centenary of Bhai Vir Singh (poet). P* 13.
664 **619** 20 p. plum .. .. .. .. 30 30

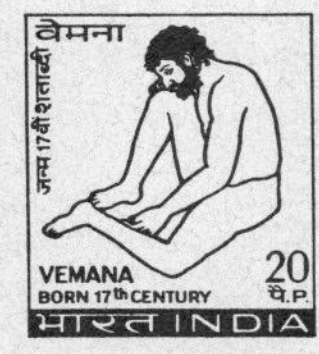


**620** T. Prakasam **621** Vemana

**1972** (16 Oct). *Birth Centenary of Tanguturi Prakasam (lawyer). P* 13.
665 **620** 20 p. brown .. .. .. .. 15 30

**1972** (16 Oct). *300th Birth Anniv of Vemana (poet). W* **374**. *P* 13½ × 14.
666 **621** 20 p. black .. .. .. .. 15 30

**622** Bertrand Russell **623** Symbol of "Asia 72"

**1972** (16 Oct). *Birth Centenary of Bertrand Russell (philosopher). P* 13½ × 14.
667 **622** 1 r. 45, black .. .. .. 2·50 2·75

**1972** (3 Nov). *"Asia '72" (Third Asian International Trade Fair), New Delhi. T* **623** *and similar vert design. W* **374**. *P* 13.
668 20 p. black and orange .. .. .. 10 20
669 1 r. 45, orange and slate-black .. .. 60 1·75
Design:—1 r. 45, Hand of Buddha.

**624** V. A. Sarabhai and Rocket **625** Flag of U.S.S.R. and Kremlin Tower

**1972** (30 Dec). *First Death Anniv of Vikram A. Sarabhai (scientist). P* 13.
670 **624** 20 p. brown and myrtle-green .. .. 15 30

**1972** (30 Dec). *50th Anniv of U.S.S.R. P* 13.
671 **625** 20 p. light yellow and red .. .. 15 30

**626** Exhibition Symbol **627** "Democracy"

**1973** (8 Jan). *"Indipex '73" Stamp Exhibition (1st issue). P* 13.
672 **626** 1 r. 45, light mauve, gold and black .. 45 1·25
See also Nos. 701/**MS**704.

**1973** (26 Jan). *25th Anniv of Independence (2nd issue). T* **627** *and similar multicoloured design. P* 13 (20 p.) *or* 14½ × 14 (1 r. 45).
673 20 p. Type **627** .. .. .. .. .. 15 15
674 1 r. 45, "Gnat" fighters over India Gate (38 × 20 *mm*) .. .. .. .. 85 1·60

**628** Sri Ramakrishna Paramahamsa (religious leader) **629** Postal Corps Emblem

**1973** (18 Feb). *Sri Ramakrishna Paramahamsa Commemoration. P* 13.
675 **628** 20 p. light brown .. .. .. .. 15 30

**1973** (1 Mar). *First Anniv of Army Postal Service Corps. P* 13.
676 **629** 20 p. deep ultramarine and vermilion .. 40 40

**630** Flag and Map of Bangladesh **631** Kumaran Asan

(Des C. Pakrashi)

**1973** (10 Apr). *"Jai Bangla" (Inauguration of First Bangladesh Parliament). P* 13.
677 **630** 20 p. multicoloured .. .. .. 15 30

**1973** (12 Apr). *Birth Centenary of Kumaran Asan (writer and poet). P* 13.
678 **631** 20 p. sepia .. .. .. .. 20 45

**632** Flag and Flames **633** Dr. B. R. Ambedkar (lawyer)

(Des C. Pakrashi)

**1973** (13 Apr). *Homage to Martyrs for Independence. P* 13.
679 **632** 20 p. multicoloured .. .. .. 15 30

(Des Charanjit Lal)

**1973** (14 Apr). *Bhim Rao Ambedkar Commemoration. P* 13.
680 **633** 20 p. bronze-green and deep purple .. 15 50

**634** "Radha-Kishangarh" (Nihal Chand) **635** Mount Everest

**1973** (5 May). *Indian Miniature Paintings. T* **634** *and similar vert designs. Multicoloured. P* 13.
681 20 p. Type **634** .. .. .. .. 30 35
682 50 p. "Dance Duet" (Aurangzeb's period) .. 60 1·50
683 1 r. "Lovers on a Camel" (Nasir-ud-din) .. 1·50 2·50
684 2 r. "Chained Elephant" (Zain-al-Abidin) .. 2·00 3·00
681/4 .. .. .. .. .. *Set of* 4 4·00 6·50

**1973** (15 May). *15th Anniv of Indian Mountaineering Foundation. P* 13.
685 **635** 20 p. blue .. .. .. .. .. 30 40

636 Tail of Boeing "747"

637 Cross, Church of St. Thomas' Mount, Madras

(Des Air-India Art Studies from photograph by Jehangir Gazdar)

**1973** (8 June). *25th Anniv of Air-India's International Services. P* 13.
686 **636** 1 r. 45, indigo and carmine-red .. 3·50 3·50

**1973** (3 July). *19th Death Centenary of St. Thomas. P* 13.
687 **637** 20 p. blue-grey and agate .. .. 15 35

638 Michael Madhusudan Dutt (poet—Death Centenary)

639 A. O. Hume

**1973** (21 July). *Centenaries. T* **638** *and similar horiz designs. P* 13.
688 20 p. sage-green and orange-brown .. .. 70 50
a. Orange-brown omitted .. .. .. £350
689 30 p. red-brown .. .. .. .. 70 1·50
690 50 p. deep brown .. .. .. .. 90 1·75
691 1 r. dull violet and orange-vermilion .. 90 1·50
688/91 .. .. .. .. *Set of* 4 3·00 4·75
Designs:—30 p. Vishnu Digambar Paluskar (musician—birth centenary); 50 p. Dr G. A. Hansen (centenary of discovery of leprosy bacillus); 1 r. Nicolaus Copernicus (astronomer—5th birth centenary).

**1973** (31 July). *Allan Octavian Hume (founder of Indian National Congress) Commemoration. P* 13.
692 **639** 20 p. grey .. .. .. .. 15 30

640 Gandhi and Nehru

641 R. C. Dutt

(Des C. Pakrashi from photograph)

**1973** (15 Aug). *Gandhi and Nehru Commemoration. P* 13.
693 **640** 20 p. multicoloured .. .. .. 15 20

**1973** (27 Sept). *Romesh Chandra Dutt (writer) Commemoration. P* 13.
694 **641** 20 p. brown .. .. .. .. 15 30

642 K. S. Ranjitsinhji

643 Vithalbhai Patel

**1973** (27 Sept). *K. S. Ranjitsinhji (cricketer) Commemoration. P* 13.
695 **642** 30p. myrtle-green .. .. .. 3·00 1·50

**1973** (27 Sept). *Vithalbhai Patel (lawyer) Commemoration. P* 13.
696 **643** 50 p. light red-brown .. .. .. 20 40

## ALTERED CATALOGUE NUMBERS

Any Catalogue numbers altered from the last edition are shown as a list in the introductory pages.

644 Sowar of President's Bodyguard

645 Interpol Emblem

**1973** (30 Sept). *Bicentenary of President's Bodyguard. P* 13.
697 **644** 20 p. multicoloured .. .. .. 35 40

**1973** (9 Oct). *50th Anniv of Interpol. P* 13.
698 **645** 20 p. brown .. .. .. .. 30 40

646 Syed Ahmad Khan (social reformer)

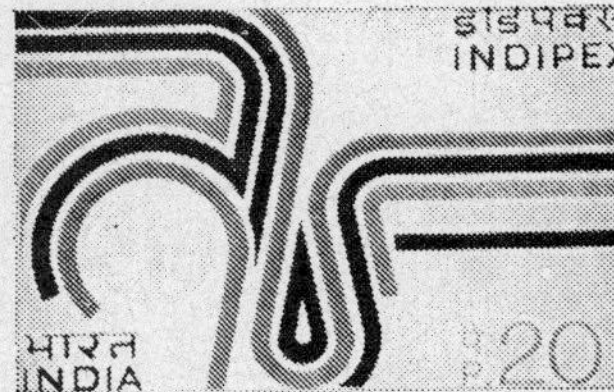


647 "Children at Play" (Bela Raval)

**1973** (17 Oct). *Syed Ahmad Khan Commemoration. P* 13.
699 **646** 20 p. sepia .. .. .. .. 15 40

**1973** (14 Nov). *Children's Day. P* 13.
700 **647** 20 p. multicoloured .. .. .. 15 20

648 Indipex Emblem

**1973** (14 Nov). *"Indipex '73" Philatelic Exhibition, New Delhi (2nd issue). T* **648** *and similar multicoloured designs. P* 13½ × 13 (2 *r.*) *or* 13 × 13½ *(others).*
701 20 p. Type **648** .. .. .. .. 20 30
702 1 r. Ceremonial elephant and 1½ a. stamp of 1947 *(vert)* .. .. .. 1·00 1·75
703 2 r. Common Peafowl *(vert)* .. .. 1·50 2·25
701/3 .. .. .. .. *Set of* 3 2·50 4·00
**MS**704 127 × 127 mm. Nos. 672 and 701/3. Imperf 4·75 8·00

649 Emblem of National Cadet Corps

650 C. Rajagopalachari (statesman)

**1973** (25 Nov). *25th Anniv of National Cadet Corps. P* 13.
705 **649** 20 p. multicoloured .. .. .. 20 30

**1973** (25 Dec). *Chakravarti Rajagopalachari Commemoration. P* 13.
706 **650** 20 p. olive-brown .. .. .. 15 40

651 "Sun" Mask

652 Chhatrapati

**1974** (15 Apr). *Indian Masks. T* **651** *and similar multicoloured designs. P* 13.
707 20 p. Type **651** .. .. .. .. 15 15
708 50 p. "Moon" mask .. .. .. 30 55
709 1 r. "Narasimha" .. .. .. 80 1·25
710 2 r. "Ravana" *(horiz)* .. .. .. 1·25 2·00
707/10 .. .. .. .. *Set of* 4 2·25 3·50
**MS**711 109 × 135 mm. Nos. 707/10 .. .. 3·75 6·00

**1974** (2 June). *300th Anniv of Coronation of Chhatrapati Shri Shivaji Maharaj. P* 13.
712 **652** 25 p. multicoloured .. .. .. 30 30

653 Maithili Sharan Gupta (poet)

654 Kandukuri Veeresalingam (social reformer)

**1974** (3 July). *Indian Personalities (1st series). T* **653** *and similar vert designs. P* 13.
713 25 p. chestnut .. .. .. .. 15 30
714 25 p. deep brown .. .. .. .. 15 30
715 25 p. sepia .. .. .. .. 15 30
713/15 .. .. .. .. *Set of* 3 40 80
Portraits:—No. 714, Jainarain Vyas (politician and journalist); No. 715, Utkal Gourab Madhusudan Das (social reformer).

**1974** (15 July). *Indian Personalities (2nd series). T* **654** *and similar vert designs. P* 13.
716 25 p. lake-brown .. .. .. .. 25 40
717 50 p. dull purple .. .. .. .. 55 1·50
718 1 r. chestnut-brown .. .. .. 70 1·50
716/18 .. .. .. .. *Set of* 3 1·40 3·00
Portraits:—50 p. Tipu Sultan; 1 r. Max Mueller (Sanskrit scholar).

655 Kamala Nehru

(Des Charanjit Lal)

**1974** (1 Aug). *Kamala Nehru Commemoration. P* 14½ × 14.
719 **655** 25 p. multicoloured .. .. .. 35 40

656 W. P. Y. Emblem

**1974** (14 Aug). *World Population Year. P* 13½.
720 **656** 25 p. maroon and buff .. .. .. 15 20

**LARGE STAR AND INDIA GOVT WATERMARK.** Two types exist of this sheet watermark. The initial arrangement resulted in the stars appearing upright, inverted and sideways, in either direction, within the same sheet.

Printings issued from the beginning of 1980 shows a second type on which the stars in each sheet all point in the same direction. All commemoratives with this watermark used the second type.

657 Spotted Deer

657*b* Bidri Vase

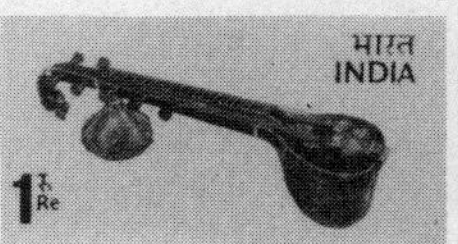


657*a* Vina

Two types of No. 732:

I II

Type I. Left shoulder cut quare. Top of Hindi inscription aligns vith edge of shoulder.

Type II. Shoulder ends in point. Top of English inscription aligns with edge of shoulder. Portrait redrawn slightly smaller.

Two types of No. 736:

I II

ype I. "INDIA" inscription lls below foot of main design. istance between foot of "2" in ce value and top of Hindi scription 11 mm.

Type II. "INDIA" above foot of design. Distance between "2" and inscription 10½ mm. Inscription redrawn slightly smaller.

**974** (20 Aug)–**83.** *P* 14 × 14½ (10, 20, 50 *p.*) *or* 14½ × 14 (*others*).

(*a*) *Various designs with values expressed with* "p" *or* "Re" *as T* **657**/*a*. *W* **374** (*sideways*)

21 – 15 p. blackish brown (deep background) (1.10.74) .. .. .. .. 1·75 30
22 **657** 25 p. sepia (20.8.74) .. .. .. 75 30
a. Imperf (pair) .. .. .. £170
23 **657*a*** 1 r. red-brown and black (1.10.74) .. 2·50 30
a. Black (face value and inscr) omitted £100

)) *Various designs with values expressed in numerals only as in T* **657*b***

(i) *Wmk Large Star and* "INDIA GOVT" *in sheet**

24 **657*b*** 2 p. red-brown (*photo*) (1.11.76) .. 30 70
24*a* 2 p. pale reddish brown (*litho*) (15.3.79) 30 70
25 – 5 p. cerise (as No. 506) (1.11.76) .. 20 10
27 **466** 10 p. new blue (5.7.79) .. .. .. 1·50 20

(ii) *W* **374** (*sideways on* 15, 25, 30, 60 *p.*, 1, 2, 5, 10 *r.*)

29 **466** 10 p. new blue (1.11.76) .. .. .. 30 15
a. Imperf (pair) .. .. .. £100
30 – 15 p. blackish brown (light background) (15.7.75) .. .. .. .. 1·25 10
31 – 20 p. deep dull green (15.7.75) .. .. 10 10
a. Imperf (horiz pair) .. .. .. £250
32 – 25 p. reddish brown (I) (25.10.78) .. 2·25 50
a. Type II (31.5.79) .. .. .. 2·50 50
32*b* – 30 p. sepia (as No. 512) (1.5.79) .. 1·25 30
33 – 50 p. deep violet (15.7.75) .. .. 1·75 10
34 – 60 p. deep grey (as No. 515) (1.11.76) .. 50 60
35 **657*a*** 1 r. red-brown and grey-black (15.7.75) 3·25 10
36 – 2 r. violet and blackish brown (I) (15.7.75) .. .. .. .. 7·50 30
a. Type II (1977) .. .. .. 7·50 30
37 – 5 r. deep slate-violet and brown (as No. 519) (1.11.76) .. .. .. 1·25 80
38 – 10 r. slate and bronze-green (as No. 520) (1.11.76) .. .. .. .. 1·25 1·25
b. Wmk upright .. .. .. 1·25 1·25
c. Perf 13 (22.10.83) .. .. .. 1·10 1·10
ca. Wmk upright .. .. .. 1·10 1·10
21/38 .. .. .. .. *Set of* 18 25·00 6·00

Designs: *Vert as T* **657**, **657*b***:—15 p. Tiger; 25 p. Gandhi. *Ioriz* (20×17 *mm*)—20 p. Handicrafts toy; 50 p. Great Egret in ight. *Horiz as T* **657*a***:—2 r. Himalayas.

*See note below No. 720. Nos. 724*a* and 727 exist on both ypes of watermark, Nos. 724 and 725 on the first type only.

No. 724*a* can be easily identified by the background of orizontal lines.

From early in 1976 Nos. 730, 731 and 735 were printed from ew cylinders, which produced stamps with a slightly smaller esign area than that of the original issue.

The 2 r. value with the blackish brown omitted is a chemically roduced fake.

For stamps as No. 732, but with face value changed to 30 p., 5 p., 50 p., 60 p. or 1 r. see Nos. 968, 979, 1073, 1320 and 1436.

**NEW INFORMATION**

The editor is always interested to correspond with eople who have new information that will improve or correct the Catalogue.

**658** President V. Giri

**659** U.P.U. Emblem

(Des Charanjit Lal)

**1974** (24 Aug). *Retirement of Pres. Giri. P* 13.
739 **658** 25 p. multicoloured .. .. .. .. 10 15

(Des C. Pakrashi (25 p.), A. Ramachandran (1 r.), Jyoti Bhatt (2 r.))

**1974** (3 Oct). *Centenary of Universal Postal Union. T* **659** *and similar designs. P* 13.
740 25 p. violet-blue, royal blue and black .. 30 10
741 1 r. multicoloured .. .. .. .. 1·75 1·75
742 2 r. multicoloured .. .. .. .. 2·00 2·25
a. Red (inscr etc) omitted .. .. £225
740/2 .. .. .. .. .. *Set of* 3 3·50 3·50
**MS**743 108 × 108 mm. Nos. 740/2 .. .. 4·00 8·50

Designs: *Horiz*—1 r. Birds and nest, "Madhubani" style. *Vert*—2 r. Arrows around globe.

**660** Woman Flute-player (sculpture)

**661** Nicholas Roerich (medallion by H. Dropsy)

(Des Benoy Sarkar)

**1974** (9 Oct). *Centenary of Mathura Museum. T* **660** *and similar vert design. P* 13½.
744 25 p. chestnut and blackish brown .. .. 40 20
a. Horiz pair. Nos. 744/5 .. .. 80 1·00
745 25 p. chestnut and blackish brown .. .. 40 20

Design:—No. 745, Vidyadhara with garland.

Nos. 744/5 were printed together within the sheet, horizontally *se-tenant*.

**1974** (9 Oct). *Birth Centenary of Professor Roerich (humanitarian). P* 13.
746 **661** 1 r. deep blue-green and greenish yellow 50 55

**662** Pavapuri Temple

**663** "Cat" (Rajesh Bhatia)

(Des Benoy Sarkar)

**1974** (13 Nov). *2,500th Anniv of Bhagwan Mahavira's attainment of Nirvana. P* 13.
747 **662** 25 p. indigo .. .. .. .. .. 40 15

**1974** (14 Nov). *Children's Day. P* 13.
748 **663** 25 p. multicoloured .. .. .. .. 40 30

**664** "Indian Dancers" (Amita Shah)

**665** Territorial Army Badge

**1974** (14 Nov). *25th Anniv of UNICEF in India. P* 14½ × 14.
749 **664** 25 p. multicoloured .. .. .. 35 30
a. Black (name and value) omitted £250

On No. 749a the background is in greenish black instead of the intense black of the normal.

(Des Benoy Sarkar)

**1974** (16 Nov). *25th Anniv of Indian Territorial Army. P* 13.
750 **665** 25 p. black, bright yellow and emerald .. 50 30

**666** Krishna as Gopal Bal with Cows (Rajasthan painting on cloth)

**667** Symbols and Child's Face

**1974** (2 Dec). *19th International Dairy Congress, New Delhi. P* 13½.
751 **666** 25 p. brown-purple and brown-ochre .. 40 20

(Des Benoy Sarkar)

**1974** (8 Dec). *Help for Retarded Children. P* 13.
752 **667** 25 p. red-orange and black .. .. 20 30

**668** Marconi

**669** St. Francis Xavier's Shrine, Goa

**1974** (12 Dec). *Birth Centenary of Guglielmo Marconi (radio pioneer). P* 13.
753 **668** 2 r. deep slate .. .. .. .. 1·50 1·25

**1974** (24 Dec). *St Francis Xavier Celebration. P* 13.
754 **669** 25 p. multicoloured .. .. .. 15 30

**670** Saraswati (Deity of Language and Learning)

**671** Parliament House, New Delhi

**1975** (10 Jan). *World Hindi Convention, Nagpur. P* 14 × 14½.
755 **670** 25 p. slate and carmine-red .. .. 30 30

For similar stamp see No. 761.

**1975** (26 Jan). *25th Anniv of Republic. P* 13.
756 **671** 25 p. grey-black, silver and azure .. 30 30

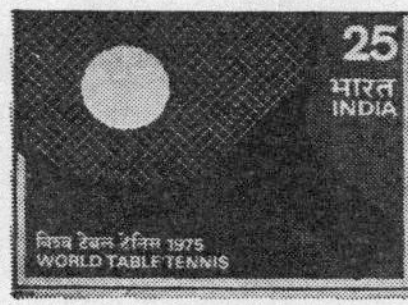

**672** Table-tennis Bat

**1975** (6 Feb). *World Table-tennis Championships, Calcutta. P* 13.
757 **672** 25 p. black, vermilion and yellow-olive 55 15

**673** "Equality, Development and Peace"

**674** Stylised Cannon

(Des Shyama Sarabhai)

**1975** (16 Feb). *International Women's Year. P* 13.
758 **673** 25 p. multicoloured .. .. .. 90 45

(Des Benoy Sarkar)

**1975** (8 Apr). *Bicentenary of Indian Army Ordnance Corps. P* 13.
759 **674** 25 p. multicoloured .. .. .. 55 35

**675** Arya Samaj Emblem **676** Saraswati

**1975** (11 Apr). *Centenary of Arya Samaj Movement. P* 13.
760 **675** 25 p. light red-orange & brownish black .. 30 30

**1975** (12 Apr). *World Telugu Language Conference, Hyderabad. P* 14 × 14½.
761 **676** 25 p. black and deep bluish green .. 45 30

**677** Satellite "Aryabhata"

**1975** (20 Apr). *Launch of First Indian Satellite. P* 13.
762 **677** 25 p. lt blue, deep indigo & dull purple .. 40 40

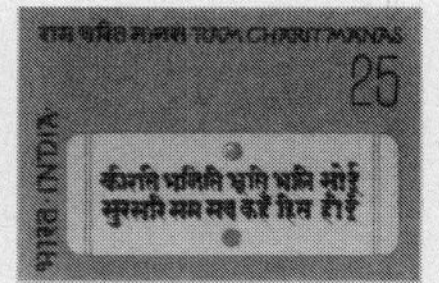


**678** Blue-winged Pitta **679** Page from "Ramcharitmanas" Manuscript

(Des J. P. Irani)

**1975** (28 Apr). *Indian Birds. T* **678** *and similar multicoloured designs. P* 13.
763 25 p. Type **678** .. .. .. .. .. 45 15
764 50 p. Asian Black-headed Oriole .. .. .. 90 1·00
765 1 r. Western Tragopan (*vert*).. .. .. .. 2·00 2·75
766 2 r. Himalayan Monal Pheasant (*vert*) .. 2·50 3·75
763/6 .. .. .. .. .. *Set of* 4 5·25 7·00

(Des R. K. Joshi)

**1975** (24 May). *4th Centenary of* Ramcharitmanas *(epic poem by Goswami Tulsidas). P* 13.
767 **679** 25 p. black, orange-yellow and vermilion 40 15

**680** Young Women within Y.W.C.A. Badge **681** "The Creation"

(Des Benoy Sarkar)

**1975** (20 June). *Centenary of Indian Y.W.C.A. P* 13.
768 **680** 25 p. multicoloured .. .. .. .. 20 30

**1975** (28 June). *500th Birth Anniv of Michelangelo. T* **681** *and similar designs showing "Creation" frescoes from Sistine Chapel. P* 14 × 13½.
769 50 p. multicoloured .. .. .. .. 50 60
a. Block of 4. Nos 769/72 .. .. .. 1·75
ab. Black (inscr & face value) omitted .. £300
770 50 p. multicoloured .. .. .. .. 50 60
771 50 p. multicoloured .. .. .. .. 50 60
772 50 p. multicoloured .. .. .. .. 50 60
769/72 .. .. .. .. *Set of* 4 1·75 2·25

T **681** illustrates No. 769. Nos. 770 and 772 are horizontal designs, size 49 × 34 mm.

Nos. 769/72 were printed in *se-tenant* blocks of four within the sheet, forming two composite designs in horizontal pairs.

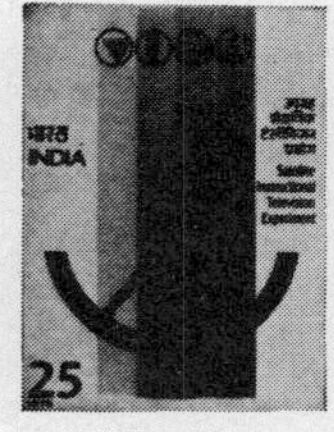


**682** Commission Emblem **683** Stylised Ground Antenna

**1975** (28 July). *25th Anniv of International Commission on Irrigation and Drainage. P* 13½.
773 **682** 25 p. multicoloured .. .. .. 40 20

(Des Benoy Sarkar)

**1975** (1 Aug). *Inauguration of Satellite Instructional Television Experiment. P* 13.
774 **683** 25 p. multicoloured .. .. .. 40 20

**684** St. Arunagirinathar **685** Commemorative Text

**1975** (14 Aug). *600th Birth Anniv of St. Arunagirinathar. P* 13½.
775 **684** 50 p. dull purple and slate-black .. 1·00 1·00

**1975** (26 Aug). *Namibia Day. P* 13½.
776 **685** 25 p. grey-black and rose-red .. .. 40 40

**686** Mir Anees (poet) **687** Memorial Temple to Ahilyabai Holkar (ruler)

**1975** (4 Sept). *Indian Celebrities. P* 13½ *(No.* 777) *or* 13 *(No.* 778).
777 **686** 25 p. blackish green .. .. .. 25 40
778 **687** 25 p. chestnut .. .. .. .. 25 40

**688** Bharata Natyam **689** Ameer Khusrau

**1975** (20 Oct). *Indian Dances. T* **688** *and similar vert designs. Multicoloured. P* 13.
779 25 p. Type **668** .. .. .. .. .. 55 20
780 50 p. Orissi .. .. .. .. .. 85 80
a. Turquoise-green (dress) omitted .. 45·00
781 75 p. Kathak .. .. .. .. .. 1·00 1·00
782 1 r. Kathakali .. .. .. .. .. 1·25 1·25
783 1 r. 50, Kuchipudi .. .. .. .. 2·00 2·50
784 2 r. Manipuri .. .. .. .. .. 2·25 3·25
779/84 .. .. .. .. *Set of* 6 7·25 8·00

**1975** (24 Oct). *650th Death of Anniv of Ameer Khusrau (poet). P* 13.
785 **689** 50 p. reddish brown and buff .. .. 70 1·00

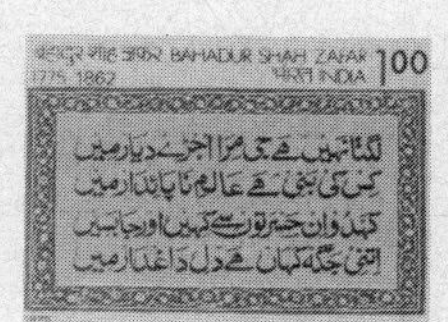

**690** V. K. Krishna Menon **691** Text of Poem

**1975** (24 Oct). *First Death Anniv of V. K. Krishna Menon (statesman). P* 13 × 13½.
786 **690** 25 p. olive .. .. .. .. .. 40 40

(Des R. K. Joshi)

**1975** (24 Oct). *Birth Bicentenary of Emperor Bahadur Shah Zafar. P* 13½×13.
787 **691** 1 r. black, stone and yellow-brown .. 65 90

**692** Sansadiya Soudha, New Delhi **693** V. Patel

**1975** (28 Oct). *21st Commonwealth Parliamentary Conferenc New Delhi. P* 14½ × 14.
788 **692** 2 r. olive .. .. .. .. .. 2·00 2·5

**1975** (31 Oct). *Birth Centenary of Vallabhbhai Patel (statesman P* 13 × 13½.
789 **693** 25 p. slate-green .. .. .. .. .. 15 3

**694** N. C. Bardoloi **695** "Cow" (Sanjay Nathubhai Patel)

**1975** (3 Nov). *Birth Centenary of Nabin Chandra Bardolc (politician). P* 13 × 13½.
790 **694** 25 p. reddish brown .. .. .. 20 4

**1975** (14 Nov). *Children's Day. P* 13½ × 13.
791 **695** 25 p. multicoloured .. .. .. 50 4

**696** Original Printing Works, Nasik Road **697** Gurdwara Sisganj (site of martyrdom)

**1975** (13 Dec). *50th Anniv of India Security Press. P* 13.
792 **696** 25 p. multicoloured .. .. .. 30 3

**1975** (16 Dec). *Tercentenary of the Martyrdom of Guru Teg Bahadur (Sikh leader). P* 13.
793 **697** 25 p. multicoloured .. .. .. 30 3

**698** Theosophical Society Emblem **699** Weather Cock

**1975** (20 Dec). *Centenary of the Theosophical Society. P* 13.
794 **698** 25 p. multicoloured .. .. .. 40 4

(Des Benoy Sarkar)

**1975** (24 Dec). *Centenary of the Indian Meteorological Depart ment. P* 13 × 13½.
795 **699** 25 p. multicoloured .. .. .. 40 4

**700** Early Mail Cart **701** L. N. Mishra (politician)

(Des Benoy Sarkar)

**1975** (25 Dec). *"Inpex 75" National Philatelic Exhibition, Calcutta T* **700** *and similar vert design. P* 13.
796 **700** 25 p. black and lake-brown .. .. 50 3
797 – 2 r. grey-brown, brown-purple & black 2·25 3·0
Design:—2 r. Indian Bishop Mark, 1775.

**1976** (3 Jan). *First Death Anniv of Lalit Narayan Mishra. P* 13.
798 **701** 25 p. olive-sepia .. .. .. .. 30 30

**702** Tiger **703** Painted Storks

**1976** (24 Jan). *Birth Centenary of Jim Corbett (naturalist). P* 13.
799 **702** 25 p. multicoloured .. .. .. .. 70 40

(Des Charanjit Lal)

**1976** (10 Feb). *Keoladeo Ghana Bird Sanctuary, Bharatpur. P* 13.
800 **703** 25 p. multicoloured .. .. .. .. 70 40

**704** Vijayanta Tank

**705** Alexander Graham Bell

**1976** (4 Mar). *Bicentenary of 16th Light Cavalry Regt. P* 13.
801 **704** 25 p. multicoloured .. .. .. .. 80 30

**1976** (10 Mar). *Alexander Graham Bell Commemoration. P* 13.
802 **705** 25 p. grey-black and yellow-ochre .. 70 40

**706** Muthuswami Dikshitar

**707** Eye and Red Cross

**1976** (18 Mar). *Birth Bicentenary of Dikshitar (composer). P* 13½.
803 **706** 25 p. purple .. .. .. .. .. 60 40

(Des Benoy Sarkar)

**1976** (7 Apr). *World Health Day. Prevention of Blindness. P* 13.
804 **707** 25 p. reddish brown and dull vermilion .. 50 40

**708** "Industries"

**709** Diesel Locomotive, 1963

(Des Benoy Sarkar)

**1976** (30 Apr). *Industrial Development. P* 13.
805 **708** 25 p. multicoloured .. .. .. .. 30 30

**1976** (15 May). *Locomotives. T* **709** *and similar horiz designs. Multicoloured. P* 14½ × 14.

| | | | |
|---|---|---|---|
| 806 | 25 p. Type **709** .. .. .. .. | 55 | 10 |
| 807 | 50 p. Steam locomotive, 1895 .. .. | 1·25 | 55 |
| 808 | 1 r. Steam locomotive, 1963 .. .. | 2·25 | 1·25 |
| 809 | 2 r. Steam locomotive, 1853 .. .. | 3·00 | 2·50 |
| 806/9 | .. .. .. .. *Set of* 4 | 6·50 | 4·00 |

**710** Nehru

**711**

**712**

Three types of Nehru portrait (*illustrated actual size*)
**Type 710.** Portrait measures 24 mm at base. First character above "NEHRU" has two prongs.
**Type 711.** Whole portrait is larger, measuring 25½ mm at base. Character above "NEHRU" has three prongs.
**Type 712.** Small portrait, 23 mm at base, with smaller inscription. Character above "NEHRU" has three prongs.

**1976.** *T* **710/12** *and similar vert design. W* **374.** *P* 13½.

| | | | | |
|---|---|---|---|---|
| 810 | **710** | 25 p. dull violet (27.5.76) .. .. .. | 3·50 | 60 |
| 810*a* | **711** | 25 p. dull violet (9.76) .. .. .. | 3·00 | 60 |
| 810*b* | **712** | 25 p. dull violet (14.11.76) .. .. | 2·75 | 60 |
| 811 | – | 25 p. red-brown (2.10.76) .. .. .. | 1·00 | 30 |
| | | a. Imperf (pair) .. .. .. | | |

Design:—No. 811, Gandhi.
For these designs in a smaller size see Nos. 732, 968/9, 979/80 and 1073/4 and 1320.

**713** "Spirit of 76" (Willard)

**714** K. Kamaraj (politician)

**1976** (29 May). *Bicentenary of American Revolution. P* 13.
812 **713** 2 r. 80, multicoloured .. .. .. 1·25 1·25

**1976** (15 July). *Kumaraswamy Kamaraj Commemoration. P* 13.
813 **714** 25 p. sepia .. .. .. .. .. 15 15

**715** "Shooting"

**716** Subhadra Kumari Chauhan (poetess)

(Des Gopi Gajwani (25 p., 1 r.), Sukumar Shankar (1 r. 50), India Security Press (2 r. 80))

**1976** (17 July). *Olympic Games, Montreal. T* **715** *and similar vert designs. P* 13.

| | | | |
|---|---|---|---|
| 814 | 25 p. deep violet and vermilion .. .. | 30 | 10 |
| 815 | 1 r. multicoloured .. .. .. | 1·00 | 90 |
| 816 | 1 r. 50, deep mauve and grey-black .. | 1·50 | 2·00 |
| 817 | 2 r. 80, multicoloured .. .. | 1·60 | 2·25 |
| 814/17 | .. .. .. .. *Set of* 4 | 4·00 | 4·75 |

Designs:—1 r. Shot-put; 1 r. 50, Hockey; 2 r. 80, Sprinting.

**1976** (6 Aug). *S. K. Chauhan Commemoration. P* 13.
818 **716** 25 p. grey-blue .. .. .. .. 15 30

**717** Param Vir Chakra Medal

**718** University Building, Bombay

(Des Benoy Sarkar)

**1976** (15 Aug). *Param Vir Chakra Commemoration. P* 13.
819 **717** 25 p. multicoloured .. .. .. 15 30
Examples of No. 819 are found pre-released at Jodhpur on 28 July 1976.

**1976** (3 Sept). *60th Anniv of Shreemati Nathibai Damodar Thackersey Women's University. P* 13½.
820 **718** 25 p. bluish violet .. .. .. 30 30

**719** Bharatendu Harischandra (writer)

**720** S. C. Chatterji

**1976** (9 Sept). *Harischandra Commemoration. P* 13.
821 **719** 25 p. agate .. .. .. .. .. 15 30

**1976** (15 Sept). *Birth Centenary of Sarat Chandra Chatterji (writer). P* 13.
822 **720** 25 p. grey-black .. .. .. .. 15 30

**721** Planned Family

**722** Maharaja Agrasen and Coins

(Des A. K. Nagar)

**1976** (22 Sept). *Family Planning. P* 14 × 14½.
823 **721** 25 p. multicoloured .. .. .. 15 30

**1976** (24 Sept). *Maharaja Agrasen Commemoration. P* 13.
824 **722** 25 p. red-brown .. .. .. .. .. 15 30

**723** Swamp Deer

**724** Hands holding Hearts

(Des from photos by Rajesh Bedi)

**1976** (1 Oct). *Wildlife. T* **723** *and similar multicoloured designs. P* 14 × 14½ (25, 50 *p.*) *or* 14½ × 14 (*others*).

| | | | |
|---|---|---|---|
| 825 | 25 p. Type **723** .. .. .. | 45 | 40 |
| | a. Black (name and year date) omitted .. | | |
| 826 | 50 p. Lion .. .. .. .. .. | 1·25 | 1·75 |
| 827 | 1 r. Leopard (*horiz*) .. .. .. | 1·75 | 2·00 |
| 828 | 2 r. Caracal (*horiz*) .. .. .. | 2·00 | 3·00 |
| 825/8 | .. .. .. .. *Set of* 4 | 5·00 | 6·50 |

(Des B. G. Varma)

**1976** (1 Oct). *Voluntary Blood Donation. P* 13.
829 **724** 25 p. yellow-ochre, scarlet and black .. 30 40

**725** Suryakant Tripathi ("Nirala")

**726** "Loyal Mongoose" (H. D. Bhatia)

**1976** (15 Oct). *80th Birth Anniv of "Nirala" (poet). P* 13.
830 **725** 25 p. deep blue .. .. .. .. 15 30

**1976** (14 Nov). *Children's Day. P* 13½ × 14.
831 **726** 25 p. multicoloured .. .. .. 40 40

**727** Hiralal Shastri (social reformer)

**728** Dr. Hari Singh Gour (lawyer)

**1976** (24 Nov). *Shastri Commemoration. P* 13.
832 **727** 25 p. sepia .. .. .. .. .. 20 30

**1976** (26 Nov). *Dr. Gour Commemoration. P* 13.
833 **728** 25 p. deep reddish purple .. .. 20 30

**729** A 300 B2 Airbus

**730** Hybrid Coconut Palm

**1976** (1 Dec). *Inauguration of Indian Airlines' Airbus Service. P* $14^{1}/_{2}\times14$.
834 **729** 2 r. multicoloured .. .. .. 2·25 2·25

**1976** (27 Dec). *Diamond Jubilee of Coconut Research. P* 13.
835 **730** 25 p. multicoloured .. .. .. 20 30

**731** First Stanza of *Vande Mataram*

**1976** (30 Dec). *Centenary of "Vande Mataram" (patriotic song by B. C. Chatterjee). P* 13.
836 **731** 25 p. multicoloured .. .. .. 20 30

**732** Globe and Film Strip **733** Seismograph and Crack in Earth's Crust

**1977** (3 Jan). *Sixth International Film Festival of India, New Delhi. P* 13.
837 **732** 2 r. multicoloured .. .. .. 1·50 2·00

**1977** (10 Jan). *Sixth World Conference on Earthquake Engineering, New Delhi. P* 13.
838 **733** 2 r. deep plum .. .. .. .. 1·40 2·00

**734** Tarun Ram Phookun **735** Paramahansa Yogananda (religious leader)

**1977** (22 Jan). *Birth Centenary of Tarun Ram Phookun (politician). P* 13.
839 **734** 25 p. blackish brown .. .. .. 15 30

**1977** (7 Mar). *Yogananda Commemoration. P* 13.
840 **735** 25 p. reddish orange .. .. .. 25 30

**736** Asian Regional Red Cross Emblem **737** Fahkruddin Ali Ahmed

**1977** (9 Mar). *First Asian Regional Red Cross Conference, New Delhi. P* 13.
841 **736** 2 r. pink, deep blue and scarlet.. .. 1·75 2·25

**1977** (22 Mar). *Death of President Ahmed. P* 13.
842 **737** 25 p. multicoloured .. .. .. 35 35

**738** Emblem of Asian-Oceanic Postal Union

**1977** (1 Apr). *15th Anniv of Asian-Oceanic Postal Union. P* 13.
843 **738** 2 r. multicoloured .. .. .. 1·50 2·00

**739** Narottam Morarjee and *Loyalty* (liner) **740** Makhanlal Chaturvedi (writer and poet)

**1977** (2 Apr). *Birth Centenary of Morarjee (ship owner). P* 13.
844 **739** 25 p. greenish blue .. .. .. 40 40

**1977** (4 Apr). *Chaturvedi Commemoration. P* 13.
845 **740** 25 p. lake-brown .. .. .. .. 15 30

**741** Mahaprabhu Vallabhacharya (philosopher) **742** Federation Emblem

**1977** (14 Apr). *Vallabhacharya Commemoration. P* 13.
846 **741** 1 r. sepia .. .. .. .. 30 40

**1977** (23 Apr). *50th Anniv of Federation of Indian Chambers of Commerce and Industry. P* 13.
847 **742** 25 p. dull purple, brown-ochre and buff .. 15 40

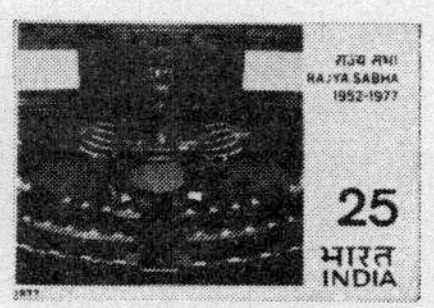

**744** "Environment Protection" **745** Rajya Sabha Chamber

**1977** (5 July). *World Environment Day. P* 13.
848 **744** 2 r. multicoloured .. .. .. 60 1·25

**1977** (21 June). *25th Anniv of Rajya Sabha (Upper House of Parliament). P* 13.
849 **745** 25 p. multicoloured .. .. .. 15 30

**746** Lotus

(Des from paintings by J. P. Irani)

**1977** (1 July). *Indian Flowers. T* **746** *and similar multicoloured designs. P* $14^{1}/_{2}\times14$ *(25 p., 2 r.) or* $14\times14^{1}/_{2}$ *(others).*
850 25 p. Type **746** .. .. .. .. 25 15
a. Black (inscription) omitted .. .. £250
851 50 p. Rhododendron (*vert*) .. .. .. 45 70
852 1 r. Kadamba (*vert*) .. .. .. 75 1·00
853 2 r. Gloriosa Lily .. .. .. 1·00 2·00
850/3 .. .. .. .. *Set of* 4 2·25 3·50

**747** Berliner Gramophone **748** Coomaraswamy and Siva

(Des Benoy Sarkar)

**1977** (20 July). *Centenary of Sound Recording. P* 13.
854 **747** 2 r. yellow-brown and black .. .. 1·00 1·75

**1977** (22 Aug). *Birth Centenary of Ananda Kentish Coomaraswamy (art historian). P* 13.
855 **748** 25 p. multicoloured .. .. .. 40 40

**749** Ganga Ram and Hospital **750** Dr. Samuel Hahnemann (founder of homeopathy)

**1977** (4 Sept). *50th Death Anniv of Sir Ganga Ram (social reformer). P* $14^{1}/_{2}\times14$.
856 **749** 25 p. maroon .. .. .. .. 20 30

**1977** (6 Oct). *32nd International Homeopathic Congress, New Delhi. P* 13.
857 **750** 2 r. black and green .. .. .. 2·50 2·50

**751** Ram Manohar Lohia (politician) **752** Early Punjabi Postman

**1977** (12 Oct). *R. M. Lohia Commemoration. P* 13.
858 **751** 25 p. red-brown .. .. .. .. 30 30

**1977** (12 Oct). *"Inpex-77" Philatelic Exhibition. Bangalore. T* **752** *and similar horiz design. P 13 (25 p.) or* $13^{1}/_{2}\times14$ *(2 r.).*
859 25 p. multicoloured .. .. .. .. 45 30
860 2 r. olive-grey/*flesh* .. .. .. 1·75 2·50
Design:—2 r. "Lion and Palm" essay, 1853.

**753** Scarlet "Scinde Dawks" of 1852 **754** "Mother and Child" (Khajuraho sculpture)

**1977** (19 Oct). *"Asiana 77" Philatelic Exhibition, Bangalore. T* **753** *and similar horiz design. P* 13.
861 1 r. orange, black and yellow .. .. 1·00 1·00
862 3 r. orange, black and light blue .. .. 2·00 2·50
Design:—3 r. Foreign mail arriving at Ballard Pier, Bombay, 1927.

**1977** (23 Oct). *15th International Congress of Pediatrics, New Delhi. P* 13.
863 **754** 2 r. reddish brown and grey .. .. 2·25 2·75

**755** Statue of Kittur Rani Channamma, Belgaum **756** Symbolic Sun

**1977** (23 Oct). *Kittur Rani Channamma (ruler) Commemoration. P* 13.
864 **755** 25 p. grey-green .. .. .. 60 40

**1977** (8 Nov). *Union Public Service Commission Commemoration. P* 13.
865 **756** 25 p. multicoloured .. .. .. 35 30

**757** Ear of Corn **758** "Cats" (Nikur Dilipbhai Mody)

(Des Benoy Sarkar)

**1977** (13 Nov). *"Agriexpo 77" Agricultural Exhibition, New Delhi.* W **374** (*sideways*). *P* 13.
866 **757** 25 p. blue-green .. .. .. .. 40 40

**1977** (14 Nov). *Children's Day. T* **758** *and similar horiz design. Multicoloured. P* 13.
867 25 p. Type **758** .. .. .. .. .. 50 30
868 1 r. "Friends" (Bhavsar Ashish Ramanlal) .. 2·50 3·00

759 Jotirao Phooley (social reformer)

760 Diagram of Population Growth

**1977** (28 Nov). *Indian Personalities. T* **759** *and similar vert design. W* **374** (*sideways*). *P* 13.
869 25 p. brown-olive .. .. .. .. 30 40
870 25 p. chestnut .. .. .. .. 30 40
Portrait:—No. 870, Senapti Bapat (patriot).

**1977** (13 Dec). *41st Session of International Statistical Institute, New Delhi. P* 13.
871 **760** 2 r. blue-green and red .. .. .. 85 1·40

761 Kamta Prasad Guru and Vyakarna (Hindi Grammar)

762 Kremlin Tower and Soviet Flag

**1977** (25 Dec). *Kamta Prasad Guru (writer) Commemoration. W* **374** (*sideways*). *P* 13½×14.
872 **761** 25 p. deep brown .. .. .. .. 15 30

**1977** (30 Dec). *60th Anniv of October Revolution. P* 13.
873 **762** 1 r. multicoloured .. .. .. 45 75

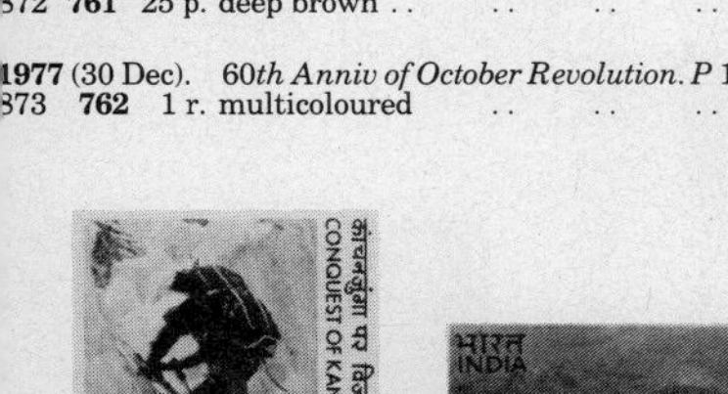

763 Climber crossing a Crevice

764 "Shikara" on Lake Dal, Kashmir

**1978** (15 Jan). *Conquest of Kanchenjunga* (1977). *T* **763** *and similar horiz design. Multicoloured. P* 13
874 25 p. Type **763** .. .. .. .. 10 10
875 1 r. Indian flag near summit .. .. .. 45 80

**1978** (23 Jan). *27th Pacific Area Travel Association Conference, New Delhi. P* 13.
876 **764** 1 r. multicoloured .. .. .. 1·50 1·25

765 Children in Library

766 Mother-Pondicherry

**1978** (11 Feb). *Third World Book Fair, New Delhi. P* 13.
877 **765** 1 r. chestnut and slate .. .. .. 45 80

**1978** (21 Feb). *Birth Centenary of Mother-Pondicherry (philosopher). P* 13.
878 **766** 25 p. brown and light grey .. .. 15 30

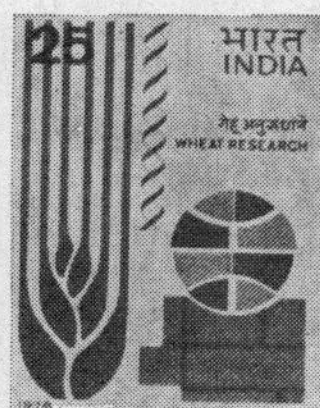

767 Wheat and Globe

768 Nanalal Dalpatram Kavi (poet)

**1978** (23 Feb). *Fifth International Wheat Genetics Symposium, New Delhi. P* 13.
879 **767** 25 p. yellow and blue-green .. .. 15 30

**1978** (16 Mar). *Nanalal Kavi Commemoration. W* **374** (*sideways*). *P* 13.
880 **768** 25 p. red-brown .. .. .. .. 15 30

769 Surjya Sen (revolutionary)

770 "Two Vaishnavas" (Jamini Roy)

**1978** (22 Mar). *Surjya Sen Commemoration. W* **374** (*sideways*). *P* 13.
881 **769** 25 p. sepia and orange-red .. .. 15 30

**1978** (23 Mar). *Modern Indian Paintings. T* **770** *and similar vert designs. Multicoloured. P* 14.
882 25 p. Type **770** .. .. .. .. 20 30
a. Black (face value and inscr) omitted .. £200
883 50 p. "The Mosque" (Sailoz Mookherjea) .. 40 1·25
884 1 r. "Head" (Rabindranath Tagore) .. .. 70 1·50
885 2 r. "Hill Women" (Amrita Sher Gil) .. 90 2·00
882/5 .. .. .. .. .. *Set of* 4 2·00 4·50

771 "Self-portrait" (Rubens)

772 Charlie Chaplin

**1978** (4 Apr). *400th Birth Anniv of Rubens. P* 13.
886 **771** 2 r. multicoloured .. .. .. 2·00 3·00

**1978** (16 Apr). *Charlie Chaplin Commemoration. P* 13.
887 **772** 25 p. Prussian blue and gold .. .. 75 35

773 Deendayal Upadhyaya (politician)

774 Syama Prasad Mookerjee

**1978** (5 May). *Deendayal Upadhyaya Commemoration. P* 13.
888 **773** 25 p. olive-brown and pale orange .. 15 30

**1978** (6 July). *Syama Prasad Mookerjee (politician) Commemoration. P* 13×13½.
889 **774** 25 p. brown-olive .. .. .. 30 40

775 Airavat (mythological elephant), Jain Temple, Gujerat (Kachchh Museum)

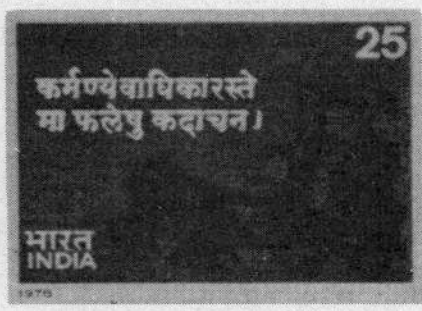

776 Krishna and Arjuna in Battle Chariot

**1978** (27 July). *Treasures from Indian Museums. T* **775** *and similar multicoloured designs. P* 13 × 13½ (25, 50 *p.*) *or* 13½ × 13 (*others*).
890 25 p. Type **775** .. .. .. .. .. 30 30
891 50 p. Kalpadruma (magical tree), Besnagar (Indian Museum) .. .. .. 65 1·00
892 1 r. Obverse and reverse of Kushan gold coin (National Museum) (*horiz*) .. .. 85 1·50
893 2 r. Dagger and knife of Emperor Jehangir, Mughal (Salar Jung Museum) (*horiz*) .. 1·25 2·00
890/3 .. .. .. .. .. *Set of* 4 2·75 4·25

**1978** (25 Aug). *Bhagawadgeeta (Divine Song of India) Commemoration. P* 13.
894 **776** 25 p. gold and vermilion .. .. 15 30

777 Bethune College

778 E. V. Ramasami

**1978** (4 Sept). *Centenary of Bethune College, Calcutta. P* 13.
895 **777** 25 p. deep brown and deep green .. 15 30

**1978** (17 Sept). *E. V. Ramasami (social reformer) Commemoration. P* 13.
896 **778** 25 p. black .. .. .. .. .. 15 15

779 Uday Shankar

780 Leo Tolstoy

**1978** (26 Sept). *Uday Shankar (dancer) Commemoration. P* 13.
897 **779** 25 p. reddish brown and stone .. .. 15 30

**1978** (2 Oct). *150th Birth Anniv of Leo Tolstoy (writer). P* 13.
898 **780** 1 r. multicoloured .. .. .. 30 30

781 Vallathol Narayana Menon

782 "Two Friends" (Dinesh Sharma)

**1978** (15 Oct). *Birth Centenary of Vallathol Narayana Menon (poet). P* 13.
899 **781** 25 p. bright purple and brown .. .. 15 30

**1978** (14 Nov). *Children's Day. P* 13.
900 **782** 25 p. multicoloured .. .. .. 15 30

783 Machine Operator

784 Sowars of Skinner's Horse

**1978** (17 Nov). *National Small Industries Fair, New Delhi. P* 13½.
901 **783** 25 p. bronze-green .. .. .. .. 15 30

**1978** (25 Nov). *175th Anniv of Skinner's Horse (cavalry regiment). P* 13.
902 **784** 25 p. multicoloured .. .. .. 40 50

**785** Mohammad Ali Jauhar

**786** Chakravarti Rajagopalachari

**1978** (10 Dec). *Birth Centenary of Mohammad Ali Jauhar (patriot). P* 13.
903 **785** 25 p. olive-green .. .. .. .. .. 15 30

**1978** (10 Dec). *Birth Centenary of Chakravarti Rajagopalachari (first post-independence Governor-General). P* 13.
904 **786** 25 p. lake-brown .. .. .. .. .. 15 30

**787** Wright Brothers and *Flyer*

**788** Ravenshaw College

**1978** (23 Dec). *75th Anniv of Powered Flight. W* **374** *(sideways). P* 13 × 13½.
905 **787** 1 r. purple and yellow-ochre .. .. 45 30

**1978** (24 Dec). *Centenary of Ravenshaw College, Cuttack. P* 14.
906 **788** 25 p. lake and deep green .. .. 15 30

**789** Schubert

**790** Uniforms of 1799, 1901 and 1979 with Badge

**1978** (25 Dec). *150th Death Anniv of Franz Schubert (composer). P* 13.
907 **789** 1 r. multicoloured .. .. .. 40 55
a. Black (face value) omitted .. ..
Two black cylinders were used for the design of No. 907. No. 907a shows the black still present on the portrait.

(Des Charanjit Lal)

**1979** (20 Feb). *Fourth Reunion of Punjab Regiment. P* 13.
908 **790** 25 p. multicoloured .. .. .. 70 60

**791** Bhai Parmanand

**792** Gandhi with Young Boy

**1979** (24 Feb). *Bhai Parmanand (scholar) Commemoration. P* 13.
909 **791** 25 p. deep violet-blue .. .. .. .. 15 30

**1979** (5 Mar). *International Year of the Child. T* **792** *and similar vert design. P* 13.
910 25 p. reddish brown and scarlet-vermilion .. 40 30
911 1 r. reddish brown and yellow-orange .. 85 1·50
Design:—1 r. Indian I.Y.C. emblem.

During October 1979 two stamps inscribed "HAPPY CHILD NATION'S PRIDE" with face values of 50 p. and 1 r. were issued to post offices. These were intended for sale as charity labels, without postal validity, the proceeds going to a Child Welfare fund. It would seem that the instructions issued were unclear, however, as some post offices sold these labels as postage stamps and accepted mail franked with them.

**793** Albert Einstein

**794** Rajarshi Shahu Chhatrapati

**1979** (14 Mar). *Birth Centenary of Albert Einstein (physicist). P* 13.
912 **793** 1 r. blue-black .. .. .. .. .. 30 50

**1979** (1 May). *Rajarshi Shahu Chhatrapati (ruler of Kolhapur State, 1874–1922, and precursor of social reform in India) Commemoration. P* 13.
913 **794** 25 p. deep dull purple .. .. .. 15 30

**795** Exhibition Logo

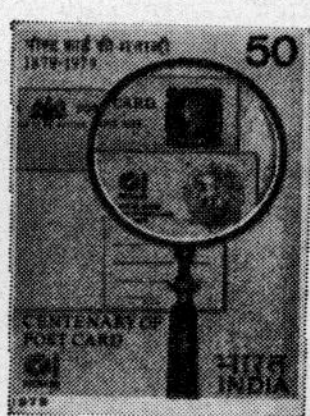

**796** Postcards under Magnifying Glass

**1979** (2 July). *"India 80" International Stamp Exhibition (1st issue). P* 13.
914 **795** 30 p. deep green and orange .. .. 15 30
See also Nos. 942/5 and 955/8.

**1979** (2 July). *Centenary of Indian Postcards. P* 13.
915 **796** 50 p. multicoloured .. .. .. 15 40

**797** Raja Mahendra Pratap

**798** Flounder, Herring and Prawn

**799** Rubber Tapping

**1979** (15 Aug). *Raja Mahendra Pratap (patriot) Commemoration. P* 13.
916 **797** 30 p. brown-olive .. .. .. .. 15 40

**1979** (3 Sept)–**88**. *Designs as T* **798/9**. *P* 14½ × 14 (15, 20, 35 *p.*, 1, 2 *r.*), 13 (5*p.* (*No.* 938), 25*p.* (*No.* 925*b*), 3 *r.* 25, 10 *r.*) *or* 14 × 14½ (*others*).

(*a*) *Photo. Wmk Large Star and* "INDIA GOVT" *in sheet**
917 2 p. slate-violet (31.3.80) .. .. .. 30 75
918 5 p. new blue (26.11.79) .. .. .. 1·00 20
919 15 p. deep bluish green (10.3.80) .. .. 1·25 15

(*b*) *Photo. W* **374**† (*sideways on* 15, 20, 35 *p.*, 1, 2 *r.*, 2 *r.* 25, 2 *r.* 80, 3 *r.* 25, *and* 10 *r.*)
920 2 p. slate-violet (25.3.81) .. .. 10 10
921 5 p. new blue (25.3.81) .. .. .. 10 10
a. Perf 13 (5.7.82) .. .. .. 10 10
ab. Wmk sideways (1988) .. .. 10 10
922 10 p. deep green (25.1.82) .. .. 30 10
a. Perf 13 (5.7.82) .. .. .. 10 10
ab. Printed double .. .. ..
ac. Wmk sideways (1988) .. .. 10 10
923 15 p. deep bluish green (25.3.81) .. .. 10 10
a. Perf 13 (5.7.82) .. .. .. 10 10
ab. Wmk upright .. .. .. 20 10
924 20 p. Indian red (25.3.81) .. .. 30 10
a. Perf 13 (5.7.82) .. .. .. 10 10
ab. Wmk upright (1988) .. .. 10 10
925 25 p. red-brown (26.11.79) .. .. 50 10
a. Perf 13 (5.7.82) .. .. .. 30 10
925*b* 25 p. deep blue-green (5.9.85) .. .. 10 10
ba. Wmk sideways (1988) .. .. 10 10
926 30 p. yellowish green .. .. .. 45 10
a. Perf 13 (6.9.82) .. .. .. 10 10
ab. Wmk sideways (1987) .. .. 10 10
927 35 p. cerise (15.9.80) .. .. .. 40 10
a. Perf 13 (5.7.82) .. .. .. 50 15
ab. Wmk upright .. .. .. 20 10
928 50 p. deep violet (25.1.82) .. .. 50 10
a. Imperf (pair) .. .. .. 30·00
b. Perf 13 (5.7.82) .. .. .. 10 10
ba. Wmk sideways (1988) .. .. 10 10
929 1 r. bistre-brown (17.6.80) .. .. 30 10
a. Imperf (pair) .. .. .. 75·00
b. Perf 13 (10.11.83) .. .. .. 10 10
ba. Wmk upright (1987) .. .. 10 10
932 2 r. deep rose-lilac (7.12.80) .. .. 50 10
a. Perf 13 (10.11.83) .. .. 10 15
ab. Wmk upright (1987) .. .. 10 15
933 2 r. 25, red and blue-green (25.3.81) .. 30 15
a. Wmk upright .. .. .. 30 15
ab. Perf 13 (1983) .. .. .. 10 10
b. Perf 13 (*wmk sideways*) (1987) .. 10 10
934 2 r. 80, red and blue-green (25.3.81) .. 15 20
a. Wmk upright .. .. .. 15 20
934*b* 3 r. 25, reddish orange & bl-grn (28.12.82) 15 20
ba. Wmk upright .. .. .. 15 20
935 5 r. red and emerald (23.11.80) .. .. 3·50 30
a. Wmk sideways .. .. .. 3·50 30
b. Perf 13×12½ (*wmk upright*) (11.8.83) 60 40
ba. Wmk sideways .. .. .. 75 40
936 10 r. maroon and bright green (24.2.84) .. 50 55
a. Imperf (pair) .. .. ..
b. Wmk upright (1988) .. .. 50 55
920/36 .. .. .. .. *Set of* 17 2·25 1·90

(*c*) *Litho. Wmk Large Star and* "INDIA GOVT" *in sheet** (2 *p.*) *or* W **374** (5*p.*)
937 2 p. slate-violet (2.2.81) .. .. .. 10 10
938 5 p. new blue (29.11.82) .. .. .. 10 10
Designs: *Horiz as T* **798**—2 p. Adult education class; 10 p. Irrigation canal; 25 p. (No. 925) Chick hatching from egg; 25 p. (No. 925*b*) Village, wheat and tractor; 30 p. Harvesting maize; 50 p. Woman dairy farmer, cows and milk bottles. (36 × 19 *mm*)—10 r. Forest and hillside. *Vert as T* **798**—15 p. Farmer and agriculture symbols; 20 p. Mother feeding child; 35 p. "Family". (17 × 28 *mm*)—1 r. Cotton plant; 2 r. Weaving. *Vert as T* **799**—2 r. 25, Cashew; 2 r. 80, Apples; 3 r. 25, Oranges.

*See note concerning this watermark below No. 720. The 2 p. and 5 p. exist on both types of this watermark, the others on the second type only.

†For notes on the amended version of W **374** see above No. 399. The changes in watermark position from 1987 onwards show the reduced size base.

Nos. 920/1 and 923/4 were originally intended for issue on 9 March 1981 and First Day Covers showing this date are known from at least one post office.

At least one sheet of No. 924a exists without an impression from the ink cylinder on the first horizontal row.

No. 937 can be easily identified by the background of horizontal lines.

For 75 p. in same design as No. 927 see No. 1214.

**800** Jatindra Nath Das

**802** Early and Modern Lightbulbs

**801** De Havilland "Puss Moth" Aeroplane

**1979** (13 Sept). *50th Death Anniv of Jatindra Nath Das (revolutionary). P* 13.
941 **800** 30 p. blackish brown .. .. .. 15 30

**1979** (15 Oct). *Air. "India 80" International Stamp Exhibition (2nd issue). Mail-carrying Aircraft. T* **801** *and similar horiz designs. Multicoloured. P* 14½ × 14.
942 30 p. Type **801** .. .. .. .. 25 25
943 50 p. Indian Air Force "Chetak" helicopter .. 40 45
944 1 r. Indian Airlines Boeing "737" airliner .. 55 75
945 2 r. Air India Boeing "747" airliner .. 75 95
942/5 .. .. .. .. .. *Set of* 4 1·75 2·25

**804** Hirakud Dam, Orissa

**803** Gilgit Record

**1979** (21 Oct). *Centenary of Electric Lightbulb. P* 13.
946 **802** 1 r. brown-purple .. .. .. 15 30

**1979** (23 Oct). *International Archives Week. P* 14½×14.
947 **803** 30 p. yellow-ochre and sepia .. .. 15 40

**805** Fair Emblem

**1979** (29 Oct). *50th Anniv, and 13th Congress, of International Commission on Large Dams. P* 13.
948 **804** 30 p. lake-brown and deep blue-green .. 15 30

**1979** (10 Nov). *India International Trade Fair, New Delhi. P* 13.
949 **805** 1 r. grey-black and salmon .. .. 15 30

**806** Child learning to Read

979 (10 Nov). *International Children's Book Fair, New Delhi. P* 14½ × 14.
50 **806** 30 p. multicoloured .. .. .. .. 15 30

**807** Dove with Olive Branch and I.A.E.A. Emblem

979 (4 Dec). *23rd I.A.E.A. (International Atomic Energy Agency) Conference, New Delhi. P* 13.
51 **807** 1 r. multicloured .. .. .. .. 20 45

**808** "Hindustan Pushpak" Aeroplane and "Rohini-1" Glider
**809** Gurdwara Baoli Sahib Temple, Goindwal, Amritsar District

(Des R. N. Pasricha)

1979 (10 Dec). *Flying and Gliding. P* 13.
952 **808** 30 p. black, orange-brown and blue .. 60 50

1979 (21 Dec). *500th Birth Anniv of Guru Amar Das (Sikh leader). P* 13.
953 **809** 30 p. multicoloured .. .. .. .. 15 30

**810** Ring of People encircling U.N. Emblem and Cog-wheel
**811** Army Post Office and Postmarks

1980 (21 Jan). *3rd U.N.I.D.O. (United Nations Industrial Development Organisation) General Conference, New Delhi. P* 13.
954 **810** 1 r. multicoloured .. .. .. .. 15 30

(Des Benoy Sarkar (30, 50 p.), India Security Press (others))

1980 (25 Jan). *"India 80" International Stamp Exhibition (3rd issue).* T **811** *and similar vert designs. No wmk* (1 r.) *or Large Star and "INDIA GOVT" in sheet* (others). P* 13.
955 30 p. grey-olive .. .. .. .. 30 30
956 50 p. bistre-brown and dull olive-bistre .. 50 75
957 1 r. Venetian red .. .. .. .. 60 80
958 2 r. olive-brown .. .. .. .. 60 1·25
955/8 .. .. .. .. .. *Set of* 4 1·75 2·75
Designs:—50 p. Money order transfer document, 1879; 1 r. Copper prepayment ticket, 1774; 2 r. Sir Rowland Hill and birthplace at Kidderminster.
*See note below No. 720.

**812** Energy Symbols
**813** Uniforms of 1780 and 1980, Crest and Ribbon

(Des C. Pakrashi)

1980 (17 Feb). *Institution of Engineers (India) Commemoration. Wmk Large Star and "INDIA GOVT" in sheet. P* 13.
959 **812** 30 p. gold and blue .. .. .. 15 30

1980 (26 Feb). *Bicentenary of Madras Sappers. P* 13.
960 **813** 30 p. multicoloured .. .. .. 40 40

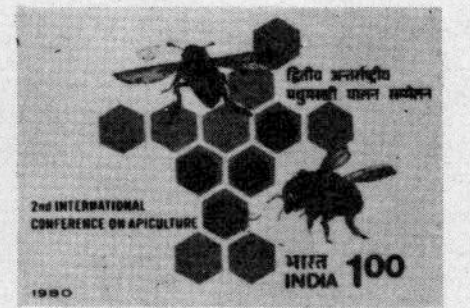


**814** Books
**815** Bees and Honey-comb

(Des J. Gupta)

1980 (29 Feb). *4th World Book Fair, New Delhi. Wmk Large Star and "INDIA GOVT" in sheet. P* 13.
961 **814** 30 p. new blue .. .. .. .. 30 30

(Des M. Bardhan)

1980 (29 Feb). *2nd International Apiculture Conference, New Delhi. P* 13.
962 **815** 1 r. deep brown and olive-bistre .. 30 45

**816** Welthy Fisher and Saksharta Nicketan (Literacy House), Lucknow
**817** Darul-Uloom, Deoband

(Des M. Choudhury)

1980 (18 Mar). *Welthy Fisher (teacher) Commemoration. Wmk Large Star and "INDIA GOVT" in sheet. P* 13.
963 **816** 30 p. chalky blue .. .. .. .. 30 30

(Des Charanjit Lal)

1980 (21 Mar). *Darul-Uloom (college), Deoband Commemoration. Wmk Large Star and "INDIA GOVT" in sheet. P* 13.
964 **817** 30 p. deep grey-green .. .. .. 15 30

**818** Keshub Chunder Sen
**819** Chhatrapati Shivaji Maharaj

1980 (15 Apr). *Keshub Chunder Sen (religious and social reformer) Commemoration. Wmk. Large Star and "INDIA GOVT" in sheet. P* 13.
965 **818** 30 p. bistre-brown .. .. .. 15 30

1980 (21 Apr). *300th Death Anniv of Chhatrapati Shivaji Maharaj (warrior). P* 13.
966 **819** 30 p. multicoloured .. .. .. 15 30

**820** Table Tennis
**821** N. M. Joshi

1980 (9 May). *5th Asian Table Tennis Championships, Calcutta. Wmk Large Star and "INDIA GOVT" in sheet. P* 13.
967 **820** 30 p. deep reddish purple .. .. 20 30

1980 (27 May). *Designs as Nos.* 732 *and* 810*b. Size* 17 × 20 *mm.* W **374** *(sideways). P* 14½ × 14.
968 30 p. red-brown (Gandhi) .. .. .. 1·25 40
969 30 p. dull violet (Nehru) .. .. .. 30 20

1980 (5 June). *Narayan Malhar Joshi (trade-unionist) Commemoration. Wmk Large Star and "INDIA GOVT" in sheet. P* 13.
970 **821** 30 p. magenta .. .. .. .. 40 40

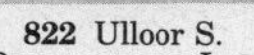

**822** Ulloor S. Parameswara Iyer
**823** S. M. Zamin Ali

1980 (6 June). *Ulloor S. Parameswara Iyer (poet) Commemoration. Wmk Large Star and "INDIA GOVT" in sheet. P* 13.
971 **822** 30 p. maroon .. .. .. .. 50 40

1980 (25 June). *Syed Mohammed Zamin Ali (educationist and poet) Commemoration. Wmk Large Star and "INDIA GOVT" in sheet. P* 13.
972 **823** 30 p. bronze-green .. .. .. 15 40

**824** Helen Keller
**825** High-jumping

1980 (27 June). *Birth Centenary of Helen Keller (campaigner for the handicapped). P* 13.
973 **824** 30 p. black and dull orange .. .. 40 30

1980 (19 July). *Olympic Games, Moscow.* T **825** *and similar vert design. Multicoloured. P* 13½ × 14.
974 1 r. Type **825** .. .. .. .. 40 40
975 2 r. 80, Horse-riding .. .. .. .. 85 1·40

**826** Prem Chand
**827** Mother Teresa and Nobel Peace Prize Medallion

1980 (31 July). *Birth Centenary of Prem Chand (novelist). Wmk Large Star and "INDIA GOVT" in sheet. P* 13.
976 **826** 30 p. red-brown .. .. .. .. 15 30

1980 (27 Aug). *Award of 1979 Nobel Peace Prize to Mother Teresa. Wmk Large Star and "INDIA GOVT" in sheet. P* 13.
977 **827** 30 p. bluish violet .. .. .. 30 30

**828** Lord Mountbatten
**829** Scottish Church College, Calcutta

1980 (28 Aug). *Lord Mountbatten Commemoration. P* 13.
978 **828** 2 r. 80, multicoloured .. .. .. 1·60 2·25

1980 (1 Sept)–82. *As Nos.* 968/9, *but new face value.*
979 35 p. red-brown (Gandhi) (16.9.80) .. .. 40 30
a. Perf 13 (5.7.82) .. .. .. 40 30
980 35 p. dull violet (Nehru) .. .. .. 30 20
a. Perf 13 (5.7.82) .. .. .. 30 20

(Des C. Pakrashi)

1980 (27 Sept). *150th Anniv of Scottish Church College, Calcutta. Wmk Large Star and "INDIA GOVT" in sheet. P* 13.
981 **829** 35 p. deep rose-lilac .. .. .. 15 30

**830** Rajah Annamalai Chettiar
**831** Gandhi marching to Dandi

1980 (30 Sept). *Rajah Annamalai Chettiar (banker and educationist) Commemoration. P* 14×14½.
982 **830** 35 p. deep lilac .. .. .. .. 15 30

(Des S. Ramachandran)

1980 (2 Oct). *50th Anniv of "Dandi March" (Gandhi's defiance of Salt Tax Law).* T **831** *and similar vert design. P* 14½×14.
983 35 p. black, turquoise-blue and gold .. .. 15 45
a. Horiz pair. Nos. 983/4 .. .. 30 90
984 35 p. black, deep mauve and gold .. .. 15 45
Design:—No. 983, Type **831**; No. 984, Gandhi picking up handful of salt at Dandi.

No. 984 with the deep mauve omitted is a chemically produced fake.

Nos. 983/4 were printed together, *se-tenant*, in horizontal pairs throughout the sheet.

**832** Jayaprakash Narayan **833** Great Indian Bustard

(Des Directorate of Advertising and Visual Publicity, New Delhi)

**1980** (8 Oct). *Jayaprakash Narayan (socialist) Commemoration. Wmk Large Star and "INDIA GOVT" in sheet. P* 14×14½.
985 **832** 35 p. chocolate .. .. .. .. .. 40 40

(Des J. Irani)

**1980** (1 Nov). *International Symposium on Bustards, Jaipur. P* 13.
986 **833** 2 r. 30, multicoloured .. .. .. .. 1·00 1·75

**834** Arabic Commemorative Inscription

(Des B. Makhmoor)

**1980** (3 Nov). *Moslem Year* 1400 *A.H. Commemoration. P* 13.
987 **834** 35 p. multicoloured .. .. .. .. 15 30

**835** "Girls Dancing" (Pampa Paul) **836** Dhyan Chand

**1980** (14 Nov). *Children's Day. P* 13½ × 13.
988 **835** 35 p. multicoloured .. .. .. .. 40 40

**1980** (3 Dec). *Dhyan Chand (hockey player) Commemoration. P* 14 × 14½.
989 **836** 35 p. red-brown .. .. .. .. .. 70 50

**837** Gold Mining **838** M. A. Ansari

**1980** (20 Dec). *Centenary of Kolar Gold Fields, Karnataka. P* 13.
990 **837** 1 r. multicoloured .. .. .. .. 40 30

**1980** (25 Dec). *Mukhtayar Ahmad Ansari (medical practitioner and politician) Commemoration. Wmk Large Star and "INDIA GOVT" in sheet. P* 14×14½.
991 **838** 35 p. dull olive .. .. .. .. .. 30 30

**839** India Government Mint, Bombay **840** Bride from Tamil Nadu

**1980** (27 Dec). *150th Anniv of India Government Mint. Bombay. P* 13.
992 **839** 35 p. black, silver and dull blue .. .. 15 30

**1980** (30 Dec). *Brides in Traditional Costume. T* **840** *and similar vert designs. Multicoloured. P* 13.
993 1 r. Type **840** .. .. .. .. .. 40 55
994 1 r. Bride from Rajasthan .. .. .. .. 40 55
995 1 r. Bride from Kashmir .. .. .. .. 40 55
996 1 r. Bride from Bengal .. .. .. .. 40 55
993/6 .. .. .. .. .. *Set of* 4 1·40 2·00

**841** Mazharul Haque **842** St. Stephen's College

**1981** (2 Jan). *Mazharul Haque (journalist) Commemoration. Wmk Large Star and "INDIA GOVT" in sheet. P* 14×14½.
997 **841** 35 p. chalky blue .. .. .. .. .. 15 40

**1981** (1 Feb). *Centenary of St. Stephen's College, Delhi. Wmk Large Star and "INDIA GOVT" in sheet. P* 14 × 14½.
998 **842** 35 p. dull scarlet .. .. .. .. .. 15 40

**843** Gommateshwara **844** G. V. Mavalankar

**1981** (9 Feb). *Millenium of Gommateshwara (statue at Shravanabelgola. P* 14 × 14½.
999 **843** 1 r. multicoloured .. .. .. .. 15 30

**1981** (27 Feb). *25th Death Anniv of Ganesh Vasudeo Mavalankar (parliamentarian). P* 14×14½.
1000 **844** 35 p. Venetian red .. .. .. .. 15 40

**845** Flame of Martyrdom **846** Heinrich von Stephan and U.P.U. Emblem

(Des D. Dey)

**1981** (23 Mar). *"Homage to Martyrs". P* 14 × 14½.
1001 **845** 35 p. multicoloured .. .. .. .. 15 30

**1981** (8 Apr). *150th Birth Anniv of Heinrich von Stephan (founder of U.P.U.). P* 14½ × 14.
1002 **846** 1 r. red-brown and new blue .. .. 15 50

**847** Disabled Child being helped by Able-bodied Child **848** Bhil

(Des K. Raha)

**1981** (20 Apr). *International Year for Disabled Persons. P* 14½ × 14.
1003 **847** 1 r. black and blue .. .. .. .. 15 30

(Des from photographs by A. Pareek (No. 1004), S. Dutta (No. 1005). S. Theodore Baskaran (No. 1006), Kikrumielie Angami (No. 1007))

**1981** (30 May). *Tribes of India. T* **848** *and similar vert designs. Multicoloured. P* 14.
1004 1 r. Type **848** .. .. .. .. .. 25 25
1005 1 r. Dandami Maria .. .. .. .. 25 25
1006 1 r. Toda .. .. .. .. .. 25 25
1007 1 r. Khlamngam Naga .. .. .. .. 25 25
1004/7 .. .. .. .. .. *Set of* 4 90 90

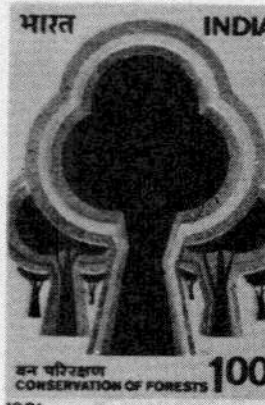

**849** Stylised Trees **850** Nilmoni Phukan

(Des M. Bardhan)

**1981** (15 June). *Conservation of Forests. P* 14 × 14½.
1008 **849** 1 r. multicoloured .. .. .. .. 15 20

**1981** (22 June). *Nilmoni Phukan (poet) Commemoration. P* 14 × 14½.
1009 **850** 35 p. red-brown .. .. .. .. .. 15 30

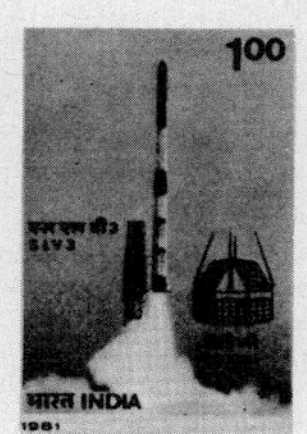


**851** Sanjay Gandhi **852** Launch of "SLV 3" and Diagram of "Rohini"

(Des C. Pakrashi)

**1981** (23 June). *First Death Anniv of Sanjay Gandhi (politician). P* 13.
1010 **851** 35 p. multicoloured .. .. .. .. 20 30

**1981** (18 July). *Launch of "SLV 3" Rocket with "Rohini" Satellite. P* 14 × 14½.
1011 **852** 1 r. black, pink and pale blue .. .. 20 20

**853** Games Logo **854** Flame of the Forest

(Des M. Chaudhury (No. 1013) )

**1981** (28 July). *Asian Games, New Delhi (1st issue). T* **853** *and similar horiz design. Multicoloured. P* 13½ × 13.
1012 1 r. Type **853** .. .. .. .. .. 65 35
1013 1 r. Games emblem and stylised hockey players .. .. .. .. .. 65 35

See also Nos. 1026, 1033, 1057, 1059 and 1061/6.

(Des from photographs by K. Vaid (35 p., 2 r.), R. Bedi (others))

**1981** (1 Sept). *Flowering Trees. T* **854** *and similar vert designs. Multicoloured. P* 13 × 13½.
1014 35 p. Type **854** .. .. .. .. .. 25 15
1015 50 p. Crateva .. .. .. .. .. 35 40
1016 1 r. Golden Shower .. .. .. .. 45 40
1017 2 r. Bauhinia .. .. .. .. .. 65 75
1014/17 .. .. .. .. *Set of* 4 1·50 1·50

**855** W.F.D. Emblem and Wheat **856** *Stichophthalma camadeva*

(Des M. Bardhan)

**1981** (16 Oct). *World Food Day. P* 14 × 14½.
1018 **855** 1 r. greenish yellow and Prussian blue 20 20

(Des from paintings by M. Mandal)

**1981** (20 Oct). *Butterflies. T* **856** *and similar multicoloured designs. P* 13.
1019 35 p. Type **856** .. .. .. .. .. 50 15
1020 50 p. *Cethosia biblis* .. .. .. .. 80 40
1021 1 r. *Cyrestis achates* (*vert*) .. .. .. 1·10 40
1022 2 r. *Teinopalpus imperialis* (*vert*) .. .. 1·25 1·50
1019/22 .. .. .. .. *Set of* 4 3·25 2·25

**857** Bellary Raghava  **858** Regimental Colour

981 (31 Oct). *Bellary Raghava (actor) Commemoration. P 14½ × 14.*
.023 **857** 35 p. brown-olive .. .. .. .. 30 20

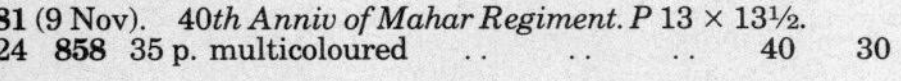

981 (9 Nov). *40th Anniv of Mahar Regiment. P 13 × 13½.*
024 **858** 35 p. multicoloured .. .. .. .. 40 30

**859** "Toyseller" (Kumari Ruchita Sharma)  **860** Rajghat Stadium

981 (14 Nov). *Children's Day. P 14×14½.*
025 **859** 35 p. multicoloured .. .. .. .. 30 20

1981 (19 Nov). *Asian Games, New Delhi (2nd issue). P 13½ × 13.*
1026 **860** 1 r. multicoloured .. .. .. .. 65 30

**861** Kashi Prasad Jayasawal and Yaudheya Coin  **862** India and P.L.O. Flags, and People

1981 (27 Nov). *Birth Centenary of Kashi Prasad Jayasawal (lawyer and historian). P 14 × 14½.*
1027 **861** 35 p. chalky blue .. .. .. .. 30 20

(Des B. Makhmoor)

1981 (29 Nov). *Palestinian Solidarity. P 14½ × 14.*
1028 **862** 1 r. multicoloured .. .. .. .. 1·25 40

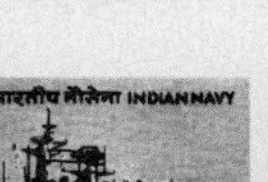

**863** I.N.S. *Taragiri* (frigate)  **864** Henry Heras and Indus Valley Seal

1981 (4 Dec). *Indian Navy Day. P 14½ × 14.*
1029 **863** 35 p. multicoloured .. .. .. .. 1·00 65

1981 (14 Dec). *Henry Heras (historian) Commemoration. P 14½ × 14.*
1030 **864** 35 p. deep rose-lilac .. .. .. .. 45 20

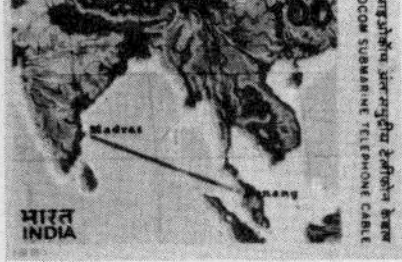


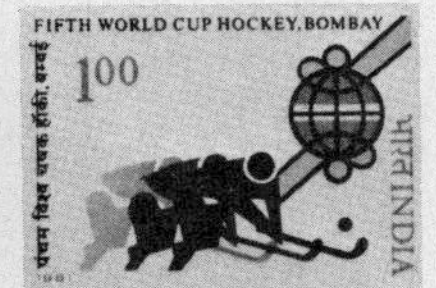


**865** Map of South-East Asia showing Cable Route  **866** Stylised Hockey-players and Championship Emblem

1981 (24 Dec). *Inauguration of I.O.C.O.M. (Indian Ocean Commonwealth Cable) Submarine Telephone Cable. P 13½×13.*
1031 **865** 1 r. multicoloured .. .. .. .. 1·00 35

(Des C. Lal)

1981 (29 Dec). *World Cup Hockey Championship, Bombay. P 13½ × 13.*
1032 **866** 1 r. multicoloured .. .. .. .. 50 30

**867** Jawaharlal Nehru Stadium  **868** Early and Modern Telephones

1981 (30 Dec). *Asian Games, New Delhi (3rd issue). P 13½ × 13.*
1033 **867** 1 r. multicoloured .. .. .. .. 30 15

(Des C. Pakrashi)

1982 (28 Jan). *Centenary of Telephone Services. P 13.*
1034 **868** 2 r. black, new blue and olive-grey .. 30 30

**869** Map of World  **870** Sir J. J. School of Art

1982 (8 Feb). *International Soil Science Congress, New Delhi. P 13.*
1035 **869** 1 r. multicoloured .. .. .. .. 30 15

(Des M. Patel)

1982 (2 Mar). *125th Anniv of Sir J. J. School of Art, Bombay. P 14 × 14½.*
1036 **870** 35 p. multicoloured .. .. .. .. 20 20

**871** "Three Musicians"  **872** Deer (stone carving), 5th-century A.D.

1982 (15 Mar). *Birth Centenary of Picasso (1981). P 14.*
1037 **871** 2 r. 85, multicoloured .. .. .. .. 35 40

1982 (23 Mar). *Festival of India. Ancient Sculpture. T* **872** *and similar vert design. Multicoloured. P 14 × 14½.*
1038 2 r. Type **872** .. .. .. .. .. 20 40
1039 3 r. 05, Kaliya Mardana (bronze statue), 9th-century A.D. .. .. .. .. .. 35 60

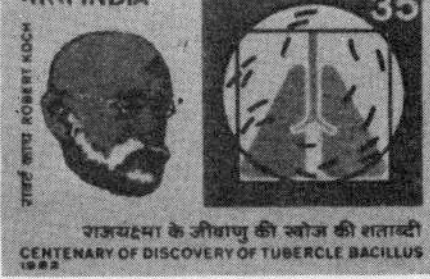


**873** Radio Telescope, Ooty  **874** Robert Koch and Symbol of Disease

1982 (23 Mar). *Festival of India. Science and Technology. P 13½ × 13.*
1040 **873** 3 r. 05, multicoloured .. .. .. .. 35 40

(Des A. Ramachandran)

1982 (24 Mar). *Centenary of Robert Koch's Discovery of Tubercle Bacillus. P 13½ × 13.*
1041 **874** 35 p. deep rose-lilac .. .. .. .. 50 30

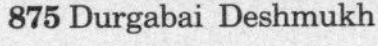

**875** Durgabai Deshmukh  **876** Blue Poppy

1982 (9 May). *First Death Anniv of Durgabai Deshmukh (social reformer). P 14½ × 14.*
1042 **875** 35 p. blue .. .. .. .. .. 30 40

1982 (29 May). *Himalayan Flowers. T* **876** *and similar vert designs. Multicoloured. P 14.*
1043 35 p. Type **876** .. .. .. .. .. 25 15
1044 1 r. Showy Inula .. .. .. .. .. 50 20
1045 2 r. Cobra Lily .. .. .. .. .. 75 1·00
1046 2 r. 85, Brahma Kamal .. .. .. .. 1·00 1·50
1043/6 .. .. .. .. *Set of 4* 2·25 2·50

**877** "Apple" Satellite  **878** Bidhan Chandra Roy

1982 (19 June). *1st Anniv of "Apple" Satellite Launch. P 13½ × 13.*
1047 **877** 2 r. multicoloured .. .. .. .. 40 80

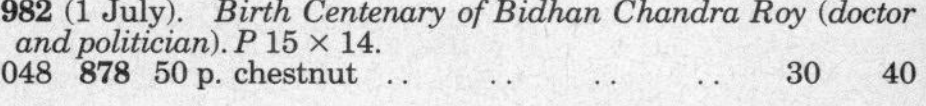

1982 (1 July). *Birth Centenary of Bidhan Chandra Roy (doctor and politician). P 15 × 14.*
1048 **878** 50 p. chestnut .. .. .. .. .. 30 40

**879** Oil Rig *Sagar Samrat*  **880** "Bindu" (S. H. Raza)

1982 (14 Aug). *25th Anniv of Oil and Natural Gas Commission. P 13½ × 13.*
1049 **879** 1 r. multicoloured .. .. .. .. 30 30

1982 (17 Sept). *Festival of India. Contemporary Paintings. T* **880** *and similar vert design. Multicoloured. P 14×14½.*
1050 2 r. Type **880** .. .. .. .. .. 30 50
1051 3 r. 05, "Between the Spider and the Lamp" (M. F. Hussain) .. .. 45 1·25

**881** Red Deer Stag, Kashmir  **882** "Wapiti" and "Mig-25" Aircraft

1982 (1 Oct). *Wildlife Conservation. P 13 × 13½.*
1052 **881** 2 r. 85, multicoloured .. .. .. .. 50 50

1982 (8 Oct). *50th Anniv of Indian Air Force. P 13½ × 13.*
1053 **882** 1 r. multicoloured .. .. .. .. 1·00 40

**883** J. Tata with "Puss Moth"  **884** Police Patrol

1982 (15 Oct). *50th Anniv of Civil Aviation in India. P 13½ × 13.*
1054 **883** 3 r. 25, multicoloured .. .. .. .. 1·25 70

(Des B. Prakash)

1982 (21 Oct). *Police Commemoration Day. P 13.*
1055 **884** 50 p. bronze-green .. .. .. .. 40 20

**885** Coins and Economic Symbols  **886** Wrestling Bout

(Des S. Jha)

**1982** (23 Oct). *Centenary of Post Office Savings Bank. P* 13.
1056 **885** 50 p. brown and cinnamon .. .. 20 20

(Des A. Ramachandran)

**1982** (30 Oct). *Asian Games, New Delhi* (4*th issue*). *P* 13½ × 14.
1057 **886** 1 r. multicoloured .. .. .. 20 20

**887** Troposcatter Communication Link

**888** Arjuna shooting Arrow at Fish

**1982** (2 Nov). 1*st Anniv of Troposcatter Communication Link between India and U.S.S.R. P* 13.
1058 **887** 3 r. 05, multicoloured .. .. .. 30 40

(Des A. Ramachandran)

**1982** (6 Nov). *Asian Games, New Delhi* (5*th issue*). *P* 13½ × 14.
1059 **888** 1 r. multicoloured .. .. .. 50 20

**889** "Mother and Child" (Deepak Sharma)

**890** Stylised Cyclists

**1982** (14 Nov). *Children's Day. P* 14 × 14½.
1060 **889** 50 p. multicoloured .. .. .. 20 20

(Des C. Pakrashi (50 p.), B. Prakash (3 r. 25))

**1982** (19 Nov). *Asian Games, New Delhi* (6*th issue*). *T* **890** *and similar horiz designs. Multicoloured. P* 13.
1061 50 p. Type **890** .. .. .. 10 10
1062 2 r. Javelin-throwing .. .. .. 25 30
1063 2 r. 85, Discus-throwing .. .. .. 30 45
1064 3 r. 25, Football .. .. .. 40 55
1061/4 .. .. .. *Set of* 4 90 1·25

**891** Yachting

**892** Chetwode Building

(Des C. Pakrashi)

**1982** (25 Nov). *Asian Games, New Delhi* (7*th issue*). *T* **891** *and similar horiz design. Multicoloured. P* 13.
1065 2 r. Type **891** .. .. .. 25 30
1066 2 r. 85, Rowing .. .. .. 30 40

**1982** (10 Dec). 50*th Anniv of Indian Military Academy, Dehradun. P* 13.
1067 **892** 50 p. multicoloured .. .. .. 20 30

**893** Purushottamdas Tandon

**894** Darjeeling Himalayan Railway

**1982** (15 Dec). *Birth Centenary of Purushottamdas Tandon* (*politician*). *P* 12½×13.
1068 **893** 50 p. yellow-brown .. .. .. 20 40

**1982** (18 Dec). *Centenary of Darjeeling Himalayan Railway. P* 13.
1069 **894** 2 r. 85, multicoloured .. .. .. 1·75 2·25

**895** Vintage Rail Coach and Silhouette of Steam Engine

**896** Antarctic Camp

(Des C. Pakrashi)

**1982** (30 Dec). *"Inpex 82" Stamp Exhibition. T* **895** *and similar multicoloured design. P* 13 (50 *p.*) *or* 13½ × 14 (2 *r.*).
1070 50 p. Type **895** .. .. .. 30 50
1071 2 r. 1854 ½ a. stamp and 1947 3½ a. Independence commemorative (33 × 44 *mm*) 60 1·25

**1983** (9 Jan). *First Indian Antarctic Expedition. P* 13.
1072 **896** 1 r. multicoloured .. .. .. 1·25 1·25

**1983** (25 Jan). *As Nos.* 968/9, *but new face value. W* **374** (*sideways*). *P* 12½ × 13.
1073 50 p. red-brown (Gandhi) .. .. .. 1·25 45
a. Wmk upright .. .. .. 1·00 30
1074 50 p. deep ultramarine (Nehru) .. .. 1·25 45
a. Wmk upright .. .. .. 40 10

**897** Roosevelt with Stamp Collection

**898** "Siberian (Great White) Cranes at Bharatpur" (Diane Pierce)

**1983** (30 Jan). *Birth Centenary of Franklin D. Roosevelt* (*American statesman*) (1982). *P* 12½ × 13.
1075 **897** 3 r. 25, bistre-brown .. .. .. 45 1·00

1983 (7 Feb). *International Crane Workshop, Bharatpur. P* 13.
1076 **898** 2 r. 85, multicoloured .. .. .. 1·10 1·60

**899** Jat Regiment Uniforms Past and Present

**900** Non-aligned Summit Logo

(Des C. Lal)

**1983** (16 Feb). *Presentation of Colours to Battalions of the Jat Regiment. P* 13.
1077 **899** 50 p. multicoloured .. .. .. 40 50

(Des N. Srivastava)

**1983** (7 Mar). 7*th Non-aligned Summit Conference, New Delhi. T* **900** *and similar horiz design. P* 13.
1078 1 r. bistre, orange-brown and black .. .. 20 30
1079 2 r. multicoloured .. .. .. 30 95
Design:—2 r. Nehru.

**901** Shore Temple, Mahabalipuram

**902** Acropolis and Olympic Emblems

(Des R. Pasricha)

**1983** (14 Mar). *Commonwealth Day. T* **901** *and similar horiz design. Multicoloured. P* 13.
1080 1 r. Type **901** .. .. .. 15 30
1081 2 r. Gomukh, Gangotri Glacier .. .. 30 95

(Des B. Makhmoor)

**1983** (25 Mar). *International Olympic Committee Session, New Delhi. P* 13.
1082 **902** 1 r. multicoloured .. .. .. 20 30

**903** "St. Francis and Brother Falcon" (statue by Giovanni Collina)

**904** Karl Marx and *Das Kapital*

**1983** (4 Apr). 800*th Birth Anniv of St. Francis of Assisi. P* 13.
1083 **903** 1 r. bistre-brown .. .. .. 20 30

**1983** (5 May). *Death Centenary of Karl Marx. P* 13.
1084 **904** 1 r. brown .. .. .. 20 30

**905** Darwin and Map of Voyage

(Des M. Mandal)

**1983** (18 May). *Death Centenary* (1982) *of Charles Darwin* (*naturalist*). *P* 13.
1085 **905** 2 r. multicoloured .. .. .. 75 1·25

**906** Swamp Deer

**907** Globe and Satellite

**1983** (30 May). 50*th Anniv of Kanha National Park. P* 13.
1086 **906** 1 r. multicoloured .. .. .. 30 40

(Des M. Mandal)

**1983** (18 July). *World Communications Year. P* 13 × 12½.
1087 **907** 1 r. multicoloured .. .. .. 30 40

**908** Simon Bolivar

**1983** (24 July). *Birth Bicentenary of Simon Bolivar* (*South American statesman*). *P* 12½ × 13.
1088 **908** 2 r. multicoloured .. .. .. 50 1·00

**909** Meera Behn

**910** Ram Nath Chopra

(Des C. Pakrashi (No. 1091))

**1983** (9 Aug–28 Dec). *India's Struggle for Freedom* (1*st series*). *T* **909** *and similar designs. P* 14×13½ (*No.* 1091) *or* 13 (*others*).
1089 50 p. dull vermilion and dull green .. 30 65
a. Horiz pair. Nos. 1089/90 .. .. 60 1·25
1090 50 p. lt brown, dull green & dull vermilion 30 65
1091 50 p. multicoloured .. .. .. 30 45
1092 50 p. reddish brn, yell-grn & red-orge (18.10) 10 15
1093 50 p. olive-sepia, green and orange (18.10).. 10 15
1094 50 p. olive-green, yellow-grn & orge (28.12) 10 15
1089/94 .. .. .. *Set of* 6 1·10 1·90

Designs: *Vert*—No. 1089, Type **909**; No. 1090, Mahadev Desai; No. 1092, Hemu Kalani (revolutionary); No. 1093, Acharya Vinoba Bhave (social reformer); No. 1094, Surendranath Banerjee (political reformer). *Horiz* (43×31 *mm*)—No. 1091, Quit India Resolution.

Nos. 1089/90 were printed together, *se-tenant*, in horizontal pairs throughout the sheet.

See also Nos. 1119/24, 1144/9, 1191/4, 1230/5, 1287/96 and 1345/9.

**1983** (17 Aug). *Ram Nath Chopra* (*pharmacologist*) *Commemoration. P* 12½ × 13.
1095 **910** 50 p. Venetian red .. .. .. 25 50

**911** Nanda Devi Mountain

**912** Great Indian Hornbill

**1983** (27 Aug). 25*th Anniv of Indian Mountaineering Federation. P* 13.
1096 **911** 2 r. multicoloured .. .. .. 50 70

(Des J. Irani)

**1983** (15 Sept). *Centenary of Natural History Society, Bombay. P* 13.
1097 **912** 1 r. multicoloured .. .. .. 45 35

**913** View of Garden  **914** Golden Langur

**1983** (23 Sept). *Rock Garden, Chandigarh. P* 13.
1098 **913** 1 r. multicoloured .. .. .. .. 30 30

**1983** (1 Oct). *Indian Wildlife. Monkeys. T* **914** *and similar horiz design. Multicoloured. P* 13.
1099 1 r. Type **914** .. .. .. .. .. 25 20
1100 2 r. Liontail Macaque .. .. .. .. 45 65

**915** Ghats of Varanasi  **916** Krishna Kanta Handique

**1983** (3 Oct). *Fifth General Assembly of World Tourism Organization. P* 14 × 13½.
1101 **915** 2 r. multicoloured .. .. .. .. 30 30

**1983** (7 Oct). *Krishna Kanta Handique (scholar) Commemoration. P* 13 × 12½.
1102 **916** 50 p. deep blue .. .. .. .. 20 40

**918** Woman and Child (from "Festival" by Kashyap Premsawala)  **920** *Udan Khatola*, First Indian Hot Air Balloon

**1983** (14 Nov). *Children's Day. P* 13 × 13½.
1103 **918** 50 p. multicoloured .. .. .. .. 20 30

**1983** (21 Nov). *Bicentenary of Manned Flight. T* **920** *and similar vert design. Multicoloured. P* 13.
1104 1 r. Type **920** .. .. .. .. .. 20 20
1105 2 r. Montgolfier balloon .. .. .. .. 30 35

**921** Tiger  **922** Commonwealth Logo

**1983** (22 Nov). *Ten Years of "Project Tiger". P* 13 × 13½.
1106 **921** 2 r. multicoloured .. .. .. .. 70 1·00

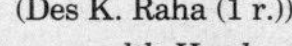
(Des K. Raha (1 r.))

**1983** (23 Nov). *Commonwealth Heads of Government Meeting, New Delhi. T* **922** *and similar vert design. Multicoloured. P* 13 × 12½.
1107 1 r. Type **922** .. .. .. .. .. 10 15
1108 2 r. Early 19th-century Goanese couple .. 25 30

**923** "Pratiksha"  **925** Lancer in Ceremonial Uniform

**1983** (5 Dec). *Birth Cent of Nanda Lal Bose (artist). P* 13 × 12½.
1109 **923** 1 r. multicoloured .. .. .. .. 20 20

**1984** (7 Jan). *Bicentenary of 7th Light Cavalry Regiment. P* 13 × 12½.
1110 **925** 1 r. multicoloured .. .. .. .. 1·25 40

**926** Troopers in Ceremonial Uniform, and Tank  **927** Society Building and William Jones (founder)

**1984** (9 Jan). *Presentation of Regimental Guidon to the Deccan Horse. P* 13 × 13½.
1111 **926** 1 r. multicoloured .. .. .. .. 1·25 65

**1984** (15 Jan). *Bicentenary of Asiatic Society. P* 13.
1112 **927** 1 r. emerald and bright purple .. .. 30 40

**928** Insurance Logo  **929** "Sea Harrier" Aircraft

(Des S. Jha)

**1984** (1 Feb). *Centenary of Postal Life Insurance. P* 13 × 13½.
1113 **928** 1 r. multicoloured .. .. .. .. 30 30

(Des Capt. A. Dhir and S. Dheer)

**1984** (12 Feb). *President's Review of the Fleet. T* **929** *and similar horiz designs. Multicoloured. P* 13½ × 13.
1114 1 r. Type **929** .. .. .. .. .. 20 40
a. Block of 4. Nos. 1114/17 .. .. 70
1115 1 r. I.N.S. *Vikrant* (aircraft carrier) .. 20 40
1116 1 r. I.N.S. *Vela* (submarine) .. .. 20 40
1117 1 r. Destroyer .. .. .. .. 20 40
1114/17 .. .. .. .. *Set of* 4 70 1·40
Nos. 1114/7 were printed in *se-tenant* blocks of four within the sheet, forming a composite design.

**930** I.L.A. Logo and Hemispheres

(Des J. Irani)

**1984** (20 Feb). *12th International Leprosy Congress. P* 13.
1118 **930** 1 r. multicoloured .. .. .. .. 30 30

(Des C. Pakrashi (Nos. 1119, 1121/4))

**1984** (21 Feb–10 May). *India's Struggle for Freedom (2nd series). Vert portraits as T* **909**. *P* 13.
1119 50 p. dp brownish olive, yell-grn & brt orge 15 20
1120 50 p. bistre-brown, emerald & brt orge (23.4) 15 20
1121 50 p. multicoloured (10.5) .. .. .. 15 20
1122 50 p. multicoloured (10.5) .. .. .. 15 20
1123 50 p. multicoloured (10.5) .. .. .. 15 20
1124 50 p. multicoloured (10.5) .. .. .. 15 20
1119/24 .. .. .. .. *Set of* 6 80 1·10
Designs:—No. 1119, Vasudeo Balvant Phadke (revolutionary); No. 1120, Baba Kanshi Ram (revolutionary); No. 1121, Tatya Tope; No. 1122, Nana Sahib; No. 1123, Begum Hazrat Mahal; No. 1124, Mangal Pandey.

**932** "Salyut 7"

(Des R. Pasricha)

**1984** (3 Apr). *Indo-Soviet Manned Space Flight. P* 14.
1125 **932** 3 r. multicoloured .. .. .. .. 45 45

**935** G. D. Birla  **936** Basketball

**1984** (11 June). *90th Birth Anniv of G. D. Birla (industrialist). P* 13.
1126 **935** 50 p. chocolate .. .. .. .. 20 50

(Des K. Reha and S. Jha)

**1984** (28 July). *Olympic Games, Los Angeles. T* **936** *and similar multicoloured designs. P* 13.
1127 50 p. Type **936** .. .. .. .. .. 15 15
1128 1 r. High jumping .. .. .. .. 20 20
1129 2 r. Gymnastics (*horiz*) .. .. .. 40 60
1130 2 r. 50, Weightlifting (*horiz*) .. .. 50 80
1127/30 .. .. .. .. *Set of* 4 1·10 1·60

**937** Gwalior  **938** B.V. Paradkar and Newspaper

**1984** (3 Aug). *Forts. T* **937** *and similar multicoloured designs. P* 13½ × 13 (50 *p.*, 2 *r.*) *or* 13 × 13½ (*others*).
1131 50 p. Type **937** .. .. .. .. .. 35 25
1132 1 r. Vellore (*vert*) .. .. .. .. 40 25
1133 1 r. 50, Simhagad (*vert*) .. .. .. 60 75
1134 2 r. Jodphur .. .. .. .. .. 80 1·25
1131/4 .. .. .. .. *Set of* 4 1·90 2·25

**1984** (14 Sept). *B. V. Paradkar (journalist) Commemoration. P* 13 × 13½.
1135 **938** 50 p. reddish brown .. .. .. 20 30

**939** Dr. D. N. Wadia and Institute of Himalayan Geology, Dehradun  **940** "Herdsman and Cattle in Forest" (H. Kassam)

**1984** (23 Oct). *Birth Centenary* (1983) *of Dr. D. N. Wadia (geologist). P* 13.
1136 **939** 1 r. multicoloured .. .. .. 30 30

**1984** (14 Nov). *Children's Day. P* 13 × 13½.
1137 **940** 50 p. multicoloured .. .. .. 30 45

**941** Indira Gandhi

(Des C. Lal)

**1984** (19 Nov). *Prime Minister Indira Gandhi Commemoration (1st issue). P* 15 × 14.
1138 **941** 50 p. black, lavender and bright orange 50 50
See also Nos. 1151, 1167 and 1170.

**942** Congress Emblem **943** Dr. Rajendra Prasad at Desk

**1984** (20 Nov). *12th World Mining Congress, New Delhi. P* 13 × 13½.
1139 **942** 1 r. black and orange-yellow .. 30 30

**1984** (3 Dec). *Birth Centenary of Dr. Rajendra Prasad (former President). P* 13.
1140 **943** 50 p. multicoloured .. .. .. .. 35 35

**944** Mrinalini (rose) **945** "Fergusson College" (Gopal Deuskar)

**1984** (23 Dec). *Roses. T* **944** *and similar vert design. Multicoloured. P* 13.
1141 1 r. 50, Type **944** .. .. .. .. .. 60 60
1142 2 r. Sugandha .. .. .. .. .. 80 80

**1985** (2 Jan). *Centenary of Fergusson College, Pune. P* 13.
1143 **945** 1 r. multicoloured .. .. .. .. 30 30

**1985** (10 Jan–24 Dec). *India's Struggle for Freedom* (3rd *series*). *Portraits as T* **909**. *P* 13.
1144 50 p. chestnut, deep green & bright orange 25 30
1145 50 p. chocolate, emerald & brt orange (21.7) 25 30
1146 50 p. reddish brown, emer & red-orge (22.7) 25 30
1147 50 p. olive-sepia, emer & reddish orge (2.12) 25 30
1148 50 p. royal blue, emerald & brt orge (23.12) 25 30
1149 50 p. grey-black, emerald & brt orge (24.12) 25 30
1144/9 .. .. .. .. .. .. *Set of* 6 1·40 1·60

Designs: *Vert*—No. 1144, Narhar Vishnu Gadgil (politician); No. 1145, Jairamdas Doulatram (journalist); No. 1147, Kakasaheb Kalelkar (author); No. 1148, Master Tara Singh (politician); No. 1149, Ravishankar Maharaj (politician). *Horiz*—No. 1146, Jatindra and Nellie Sengupta (politicians).

**947** Gunner and Howitzer from Mountain Battery

**1985** (15 Jan). *50th Anniv of Regiment of Artillery. P* 13½ × 13.
1150 **947** 1 r. multicoloured .. .. .. 1·50 1·00

**948** Indira Gandhi making speech

(Des R. Chopra)

**1985** (31 Jan). *Indira Gandhi Commemoration* (2nd *issue*). *P* 14.
1151 **948** 2 r. multicoloured .. .. .. 90 1·25

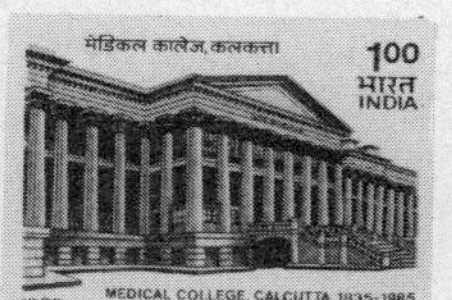

**949** Minicoy Lighthouse **950** Medical College Hospital

**1985** (2 Feb). *Centenary of Minicoy Lighthouse. P* 13.
1152 **949** 1 r. multicoloured .. .. .. 1·25 40

**1985** (20 Feb). *150th Anniv of Medical College, Calcutta. P* 13½ × 13.
1153 **950** 1 r. yellow, reddish brown and deep reddish purple .. .. .. 50 30

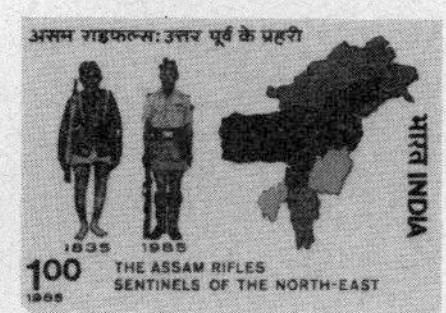

**951** Medical College, Madras

**952** Riflemen of 1835 and 1985, and Map of North-East India

**1985** (6 Mar). *150th Anniv of Medical College, Madras. P* 13½ × 13.
1154 **951** 1 r. yellow-brown and reddish brown .. 60 30

(Des A. Sharma)

**1985** (29 Mar). *150th Anniv of Assam Rifles. P* 13½ × 13.
1155 **952** 1 r. multicoloured .. .. .. 1·25 75

**953** Potato Plant

**954** Baba Jassa Singh Ahluwalia

(Des Indian Council of Agricultural Research)

**1985** (1 Apr). *50th Anniv of Potato Research in India. P* 13.
1156 **953** 50 p. deep brown and grey-brown .. 50 50

**1985** (4 Apr). *Death Bicentenary* (1983) *of Baba Jassa Singh Ahluwalia (Sikh leader). P* 13.
1157 **954** 50 p. deep reddish purple .. .. 45 50

**955** St. Xavier's College

**956** White-winged Wood Duck

**1985** (12 Apr). *125th Anniv of St. Xavier's College, Calcutta. P* 13.
1158 **955** 1 r. multicoloured .. .. .. 30 40

**1985** (18 May). *Wildlife Conservation. White-winged Wood Duck. P* 14.
1159 **956** 2 r. multicoloured .. .. .. 2·25 2·00

**957** "Mahara"

**958** Yaudheya Copper Coin, c 200 B.C.

**1985** (5 June). *Bougainvillea. T* **957** *and similar vert design. Multicoloured. P* 13.
1160 50 p. Type **957** .. .. .. .. .. 30 30
1161 1 r. "H. B. Singh" .. .. .. .. .. 40 40

**1985** (7 June). *Festival of India* (1st *issue*). *P* 13.
1162 **958** 2 r. multicoloured .. .. .. 75 75

**MINIMUM PRICE**

The minimum price quote is 10p which represents a handling charge rather than a basis for valuing common stamps. For further notes about prices see introductory pages.

**959** Statue of Didarganj Yakshi (deity) **962** Swami Haridas

**1985** (13 June). *Festival of India* (2nd *issue*). *P* 13.
1163 **959** 1 r. multicoloured .. .. .. 30 30

**1985** (19 Sept). *Swami Haridas (philosopher) Commemoration. P* 13.
1164 **962** 1 r. multicoloured .. .. .. 60 50

Although not officially issued until 19 September 1985 examples of No. 1164 are known to have circulated from 27 November 1984, the date on which it was originally scheduled for release.

**963** Stylised Mountain Road

**1985** (10 Oct). *25th Anniv of Border Roads Organization. P* 13.
1165 **963** 2 r. brt carmine, bluish violet & black 60 60

**964** Nehru addressing General Assembly

**1985** (24 Oct). *40th Anniv of United Nations Organization. P* 13.
1166 **964** 2 r. multicoloured .. .. .. 40 40

**965** Indira Gandhi with Crowd

**1985** (31 Oct). *Indira Gandhi Commemoration* (3rd *issue*). *P* 14.
1167 **965** 2 r. brownish black and black .. 80 1·00

**966** Girl using Home Computer **967** Halley's Comet

**1985** (14 Nov). *Children's Day. P* 13½ × 13.
1168 **966** 50 p. multicoloured .. .. .. 30 40

**1985** (19 Nov). *19th General Assembly of International Astronomical Union, New Delhi. P* 13 × 13½.
1169 **967** 1 r. multicoloured .. .. .. 40 50

**968** Indira Gandhi **969** St. Stephen's Hospital

**1985** (19 Nov). *Indira Gandhi Commemoration (4th issue). P 14.*
1170 **968** 3 r. multicoloured .. .. .. .. 1·25 1·25

**1985** (25 Nov). *Centenary of St. Stephen's Hospital, Delhi. P 13.*
1171 **969** 1 r. black and buff .. .. .. .. 30 30

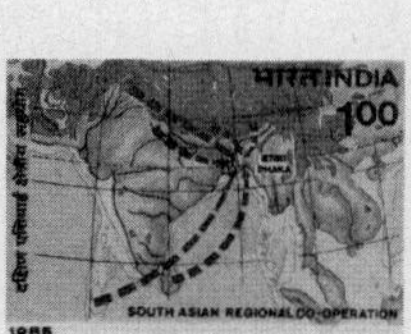

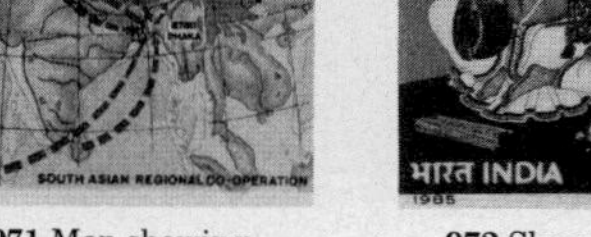

**971** Map showing Member States **972** Shyama Shastri

**1985** (8 Dec). *1st Summit Meeting of South Asian Association for Regional Co-operation, Dhaka, Bangladesh. T* **971** *and similar multicoloured design. P* 13½ × 13 (1 r.) *or* 14 (3 r.).
1172 1 r. Type **971** .. .. .. .. .. .. 40 20
1173 3 r. Flags of member nations (44 × 32 *mm*) .. 1·25 1·40

**1985** (21 Dec). *Shyama Shastri (composer) Commemoration. P 13.*
1174 **972** 1 r. multicoloured .. .. .. .. 75 40

**975** Young Runners and Emblem

(Des J. Irani)

**1985** (24 Dec). *International Youth Year. P* 13½ × 13.
1175 **975** 2 r. multicoloured .. .. .. .. 40 40

**976** Handel and Bach

**1985** (27 Dec). *300th Birth Annivs of George Frederick Handel and Johann Sebastian Bach (composers). P* 13 × 13½.
1176 **976** 5 r. multicoloured .. .. .. .. 1·50 90

**977** A. O. Hume (founder) and Early Congress Presidents **978** Bombay and Duncan Dry Docks, Bombay

(Des C. Pakrashi)

**1985** (28 Dec). *Centenary of Indian National Congress. T* **977** *and similar vert designs showing miniature portraits of Congress Presidents. P 14.*
1177 **977** 1 r. black, bright orange, lt green & grey 40 40
a. Block of 4. Nos. 1177/80 .. .. 1·40
1178 – 1 r. black, bright orange and light green 40 40
1179 – 1 r. black, bright orange and light green 40 40
1180 – 1 r. black, bright orange, lt green & grey 40 40
1177/80 .. .. .. .. .. *Set of* 4 1·40 1·40

Nos. 1178/80 each show sixteen miniature portraits. The individual stamps can be distinguished by the position of the face value and inscription which are at the top on Nos. 1177/8 and at the foot on Nos. 1179/80. No. 1180 shows a portrait of Prime Minister Rajiv Gandhi in a grey frame at bottom right.

(Des Capt. A. Dhir)

**1986** (11 Jan). *250th Anniv of Naval Dockyard, Bombay. P* 13½ × 13.
1181 **978** 2 r. 50, multicoloured .. .. .. 1·50 1·50

**979** Hawa Mahal and Jaipur 1904 2 a. Stamp **980** I.N.S. *Vikrant* (aircraft carrier)

**1986** (14 Feb). *"INPEX '86" Philatelic Exhibition, Jaipur. T* **979** *and similar horiz design. Multicoloured. P* 13½ × 13.
1182 50 p. Type **979** .. .. .. .. .. 50 30
1183 2 r. Mobile camel post office, Thar Desert 90 1·10

(Des A. Sharma)

**1986** (16 Feb). *Completion of 25 Years Service by I.N.S. Vikrant. P* 13 × 13½.
1184 **980** 2 r. multicoloured .. .. .. 1·75 1·75

**981** Humber-Sommer Biplane and Later Mail Planes **982** Triennale Emblem

(Des R. Pasricha)

**1986** (18 Feb). *75th Anniversary of First Official Airmail Flight, Allahabad – Naini. T* **981** *and similar horiz design. Multicoloured. P* 13½ × 13 (50 *p.*) *or* 13 (3 *r.*).
1185 50 p. Type **981** .. .. .. .. .. 75 50
1186 3 r. Modern Air India mail plane and Humber-Sommer biplane (37 × 24 *mm*) 2·00 2·50

**1986** (22 Feb). *6th Triennale Art Exhibition, New Delhi. P* 13 × 13½.
1187 **982** 1 r. black, brt purple & orange-yellow 60 40

**983** Chaitanya Mahaprabhu **984** Main Building, Mayo College

**1986** (13 Mar). *500th Birth Anniv of Chaitanya Mahaprabhu (religious leader). P 13.*
1188 **983** 2 r. multicoloured .. .. .. 1·50 1·75

**1986** (12 Apr). *Mayo College (public school), Ajmer, Commem. P* 13½ × 13.
1189 **984** 1 r. multicoloured .. .. .. 65 40

**985** Two Footballers **987** Swami Sivananda

(Des Vandana Joshi)

**1986** (31 May). *World Cup Football Championship, Mexico. P 13.*
1190 **985** 5 r. multicoloured .. .. .. 2·00 2·00

**1986** (14 Aug–30 Dec). *India's Struggle for Freedom (4th series). Vert portraits as T* **909**. *P* 13.
1191 50 p. sepia, emerald and orange-red .. 50 50
1192 50 p. olive-sepia, emerald & orge-red (26.12) 50 50
1193 50 p. slate-blk, emer & reddish orge (29.12) 50 50
1194 50 p. red-brown, emerald & orge-red (30.12) 50 50
1191/4 .. .. .. .. *Set of* 4 1·75 1·75

Designs:—No. 1191, Bhim Sen Sachar; No. 1192, Alluri Seeta Rama Raju; No. 1193, Sagarmal Gopa; No. 1194, Veer Surendra Sai.

**1986** (8 Sept). *Birth Centenary of Swami Sivananda (spiritual leader). P 13.*
1195 **987** 2 r. multicoloured .. .. .. 1·75 1·25

**988** Volleyball **989** Madras G.P.O.

(Des Mohinder Dhadwal)

**1986** (16 Sept). *Asian Games, Seoul, South Korea. T* **988** *and similar vert design. Multicoloured. P* 13 × 13½.
1196 1 r. 50, Type **988** .. .. .. .. 1·00 75
1197 3 r. Hurdling .. .. .. .. 1·75 2·00

**1986** (9 Oct). *Bicentenary of Madras G.P.O. P 13.*
1198 **989** 5 r. black and Indian red .. .. 2·50 2·75

**990** Parachutist **991** Early and Modern Policemen

(Des Nenu Bagga)

**1986** (17 Oct). *225th Anniv of 8th Battalion of Coast Sepoys (now 1st Battalion Parachute Regiment). P* 13 × 13½.
1199 **990** 3 r. multicoloured .. .. .. 2·50 3·00

(Des A. Ali)

**1986** (21 Oct). *125th Anniv of Indian Police. T* **991** *and similar vert design showing early and modern police. P* 13 × 13½.
1200 1 r. 50, multicoloured .. .. .. 1·50 2·00
a. Horiz pair. Nos. 1200/1 .. .. .. 3·00 4·00
1201 2 r. multicoloured .. .. .. .. 1·50 2·00

Nos. 1200/1 were printed together, *se-tenant*, in horizontal pairs with the 2 r. at left, each pair forming a composite design.

**992** Hand holding Flower and World Map **993** "Girl Rock Climber" (Sujasha Dasgupta)

(Des B. Raj)

**1986** (24 Oct). *International Peace Year. P* 13½ × 13.
1202 **992** 5 r. multicoloured .. .. .. 1·25 85

**1986** (14 Nov). *Children's Day. P* 13 × 13½.
1203 **993** 50 p. multicoloured .. .. .. 1·00 75

**994** Windmill

**1986** (15 Nov)–**91**. *Science and Technology. T* **994** *and similar designs. W* **374** *(sideways on 75 p., 5, 50 r.). P 13. (a) Photo.*
1211 35 p. vermilion (27.2.87) .. .. .. 10 10
a. Wmk sideways .. .. .. .. 10 10
1212 40 p. rose-red (15.10.88) .. .. .. 10 10
1213 60 p. emerald and scarlet (27.2.87) .. 10 10
a. Wmk sideways .. .. .. .. 10 10
1214 75 p. orange-vermilion (20.11.90) .. 10 10
a. Wmk upright .. .. .. .. 10 10
1217 5 r. deep brown & reddish orange (1.1.88) 20 25
a. Wmk upright .. .. .. .. 20 25
1218 20 r. bistre-brown and blue (30.11.88) .. 80 85
a. Wmk sideways .. .. .. ..
1219 50 r. black, turquoise-blue and cerise .. 2·00 2·10
a. Wmk upright .. .. .. .. 2·00 2·10

(b) *Litho.*

1220 40 p. rose-red (1991) .. .. .. .. 10 10
1211/20 .. .. .. .. .. *Set of* 7 3·00 3·00

Designs: *Horiz* (20×17 *mm*)—35 p. Family planning. (37×20 *mm*)—60 p. Indian family; 20 r. Bio gas production. *Vert* (17×20 *mm*)—40 p. Television set, dish aerial and transmitter; 75 p. "Family" (as No. 927). (20×37 *mm*)—5 r. Solar energy.

Numbers have been left for further values in this new definitive series.

A postal forgery of the 5 r., No. 1217, has been reported on unwatermarked paper and perforated 10½ line.

**995** Growth Monitoring **996** Tansen

**1986** (11 Dec). *40th Anniv of United Nations Children's Fund. T* **995** *and similar horiz design. Multicoloured. P* 13½×13.

1221 50 p. Type **995** .. .. .. .. .. 75 60
1222 5 r. Immunization .. .. .. .. .. 2·25 2·50

**1986** (12 Dec). *Tansen (musician and composer) Commem. P* 13.

1223 **996** 1 r. multicoloured .. .. .. 1·00 30

**997** Indian Elephant **998** St. Martha's Hospital

(Des Pratibha Pandey)

**1986** (15 Dec). *50th Anniv of Corbett National Park. T* **997** *and similar horiz design. Multicoloured. P* 13½×13.

1224 1 r. Type **997** .. .. .. .. .. .. 1·75 70
1225 2 r. Gharial .. .. .. .. .. .. 2·50 3·00

**1986** (30 Dec). *Centenary of St. Martha's Hospital, Bangalore. P* 13½×13.

1226 **998** 1 r. Prussian blue, vermilion and black 1·00 70

**999** Yacht *Trishna* and Route Map **1000** Map of Southern Africa and Logo

**1987** (10 Jan). *Indian Army Round the World Yacht Voyage, 1985–7. P* 13½×13.

1227 **999** 6 r. 50, multicoloured .. .. .. 2·50 1·75

**1987** (25 Jan). *Inauguration of AFRICA Fund. P* 14.

1228 **1000** 6 r. 50, black .. .. .. .. .. 2·50 2·25

**1001** Emblem **1002** Blast Furnace

**1987** (11 Feb). *29th Congress of International Chamber of Commerce, New Delhi. P* 13×13½.

1229 **1001** 5 r. bluish violet, new blue and rosine 2·25 1·25

**1987** (13 Feb–12 Dec). *India's Struggle for Freedom (5th series). Vert portraits as T* **909**. *P* 13.

1230 60 p. bistre-brown, emerald & reddish orge 20 20
1231 60 p. deep violet, emerald & orge-red (18.3) 20 20
1232 60 p. red-brown, dp green & orge-red (21.3) 20 20
1233 60 p. bl, yellowish grn & reddish orge (25.4) 20 20
1234 60 p. yellowish brn, emer & orge-red (17.6) 20 20
1235 60 p. brown, emerald and orange-red (22.8) 20 20
1236 60 p. brown-red, emerald and reddish orange (31.12) .. .. .. 20 20
1230/6 .. .. .. .. .. *Set of* 7 1·25 1·25

Designs:—No. 1230, Hakim Ajmal Khan; No. 1231, Lala Har Dayal; No. 1232, M. N. Roy; No. 1233, Tripuraneni Ramaswamy Chowdary; No. 1234, Dr. Kailas Nath Katju; No. 1235, S. Satyamurti; No. 1236, Pandit Hriday Nath Kunzru.

(Des P. Biswas)

**1987** (28 Mar). *Centenary of South Eastern Railway. T* **1002** *and similar multicoloured designs. P* 13×13½ *(vert) or* 13½×13 *(horiz).*

1237 1 r. Type **1002** .. .. .. .. .. 40 15
1238 1 r. 50, Metre-gauge tank locomotive, No. 691, 1887 *(horiz)* .. .. .. .. 45 35
1239 2 r. Electric train on viaduct, 1987 .. 55 50
1240 4 r. Steam locomotive, *c* 1900 *(horiz)* .. 80 1·00
1237/40 .. .. .. .. *Set of* 4 2·00 1·75

**1003** Kalia Bhomora Bridge, Tezpur, Assam **1004** Madras Christian College

**1987** (14 Apr). *Inauguration of Brahmaputra Bridge. P* 13½×13.

1241 **1003** 2 r. multicoloured .. .. .. 30 30

**1987** (16 Apr). *150th Anniv of Madras Christian College. P* 13.

1242 **1004** 1 r. 50, black and brown-lake .. .. 20 20

**1005** Shree Shree Ma Anandamayee **1006** "Rabindranath Tagore" (self-portrait)

**1987** (1 May). *Shree Shree Ma Anandamayee (Hindu spiritual leader) Commem. P* 13×13½.

1243 **1005** 1 r. bistre-brown .. .. .. .. 20 15

**1987** (8 May). *Rabindranath Tagore (poet) Commem. P* 14.

1244 **1006** 2 r. multicoloured .. .. .. .. 30 30

**1007** Garwhal Rifles Uniforms of 1887 **1008** J. Krishnamurti

**1987** (10 May). *Centenary of Garwhal Rifles Regiment. P* 13×13½.

1245 **1007** 1 r. multicoloured .. .. .. 40 15

**1987** (11 May). *J. Krishnamurti (philosopher) Commem. P* 13×13½.

1246 **1008** 60 p. sepia .. .. .. .. 40 55

**1009** Regimental Uniforms of 1887 **1010** Hall of Nations, Pragati Maidan, New Delhi

**1987** (3 June). *Centenary of 37th Dogra Regt (now 7th Battalion (1 Dogra)), Mechanised Infantry Regt. P* 13½×13.

1247 **1009** 1 r. multicoloured .. .. .. 40 15

(Des P. Biswas (Nos. 1248/9), Nenu Bagga (No. **MS**1250)

**1987** (15 June)–**89**. *"India–89" International Stamp Exhibition, New Delhi (1st issue). T* **1010** *and similar horiz design. Multicoloured. P* 13½×13.

1248 50 p. Exhibition logo .. .. .. .. 10 15
a. Booklet pane. No. 1248×4 (20.1.89) 15
1249 5 r. Type **1010** .. .. .. .. .. 45 50
a. Booklet pane. No. 1249×4 (20.1.89) 1·50
**MS**1250 156×58 mm. Nos. 1248/9 *(sold at* 8 *r.)* 70 1·00

See also Nos. 1264/8, 1333/4, 1341/2 and 1358/61.

**1011** "Sadyah-Snata" Sculpture, Sanghol **1012** Flag and Stylized Birds with "40" in English and Hindi

**1987** (3 July). *Festival of India, U.S.S.R. P* 13.

1251 **1011** 6 r. 50, multicoloured .. .. .. .. 1·00 75

**1987** (15 Aug). *40th Anniv of Independence. P* 13×13½.

1252 **1012** 60 p. reddish orange, dp green & new bl 15 15

**1013** Sant Harchand Singh Longowal **1014** Guru Ghasidas

**1987** (20 Aug). *Sant Harchand Singh Longowal (Sikh leader) Commemoration. P* 13×13½.

1253 **1013** 1 r. multicoloured .. .. .. 30 15

**1987** (1 Sept). *Guru Ghasidas (Hindu leader) Commemoration. P* 13.

1254 **1014** 60 p. deep Indian red .. .. .. 15 15

**1015** Thakur Anukul Chandra **1016** University of Allahabad

**1987** (2 Sept). *Thakur Anukul Chandra (spiritual leader) Commemoration. P* 13×13½.

1255 **1015** 1 r. multicoloured .. .. .. 40 15

**1987** (23 Sept). *Centenary of Allahabad University. P* 13.

1256 **1016** 2 r. multicoloured .. .. .. 30 40

**1017** Pankha Offering **1018** Chhatrasal on Horseback

**1987** (1 Oct). *Phoolwalon Ki Sair Festival, Delhi. P* 13×13½.

1257 **1017** 2 r. multicoloured .. .. .. 30 40

**1987** (2 Oct). *Chhatrasal (Bundela ruler) Commemoration. P* 14.

1258 **1018** 60 p. chestnut .. .. .. .. 30 20

**1019** Family and Stylized Houses **1020** Map of Asia and Logo

**1987** (5 Oct). *International Year of Shelter for the Homeless. P* 13½×13.

1259 **1019** 5 r. multicoloured .. .. .. .. 45 60

**1987** (14 Oct). *Asia Regional Conference of Rotary International. T* **1020** *and similar horiz design. P* 13½×13.

1260 60 p. chestnut and emerald .. .. .. 15 15
1261 6 r. 50, multicoloured .. .. .. 60 80

Design:—6 r. 50, Oral Polio vaccination.

**1021** Blind Boy, Braille Books and Computer — **1022** Iron Pillar, Delhi

**1987** (15 Oct). *Centenary of Service to Blind. T* **1021** *and similar horiz design. P* 13½×13.
1262 1 r. multicoloured .. .. .. .. 15 15
1263 2 r. deep blue and new blue .. .. 35 30
Design:—2 r. Eye donation.

**1987** (17 Oct)–89. *"India–89" International Stamp Exhibition, New Delhi (2nd issue). Delhi Landmarks. T* **1022** *and similar horiz designs. Multicoloured. P* 13½×13.
1264 60 p. Type **1022** .. .. .. .. 10 15
a. Booklet pane. No. 1264×4 (20.1.89) 20
1265 1 r. 50, India Gate .. .. .. 15 20
a. Booklet pane. No. 1265×4 (20.1.89) 45
1266 5 r. Dewan-e-Khas, Red Fort .. .. 45 50
a. Booklet pane. No. 1266×4 (20.1.89) 1·50
1267 6 r. 50, Old Fort .. .. .. .. 60 65
a. Booklet pane. No. 1267×4 (20.1.89) 2·00
1264/7 .. .. .. .. *Set of* 4 1·10 1·40
**MS**1268 100×86 mm. Nos. 1264/7 (*sold at* 15 *r.*) 1·40 1·75

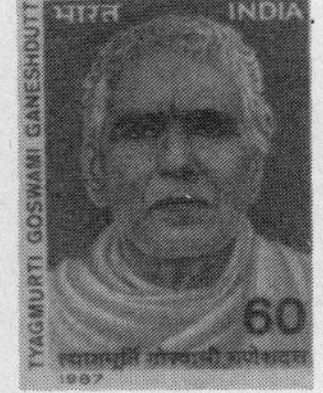
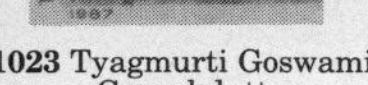

**1023** Tyagmurti Goswami Ganeshdutt — **1024** "My Home" (Siddharth Deshprabha)

**1987** (2 Nov). *Tyagmurti Goswami Ganeshdutt (spiritual leader and social reformer) Commemoration. P* 13×13½.
1269 **1023** 60 p. brown-red .. .. .. 15 15

**1987** (14 Nov). *Children's Day. P* 13½×13.
1270 **1024** 60 p. multicoloured .. .. .. 30 15

**1025** Chinar — **1026** Logo (from sculpture "Worker and Woman Peasant" by V. Mukhina)

(Des O. Ravindran, A. Mehta, T. D. Singh, Sudha Chowdhary)

**1987** (19 Nov). *Indian Trees. T* **1025** *and similar multicoloured designs. P* 13×13½ (*vert*) *or* 13½×13 (*horiz*).
1271 60 p. multicoloured .. .. .. .. 15 15
1272 1 r. 50, multicoloured .. .. .. 20 20
1273 5 r. black, dull yellow-green and chestnut 55 65
1274 6 r. 50, brown, carmine-red & yellow-green 80 80
1271/4 .. .. .. .. *Set of* 4 1·40 1·60
Designs: *Horiz*—1 r. 50, Pipal; 6 r. 50, Banyan. *Vert*—5 r. Sal.

**1987** (21 Nov). *Festival of U.S.S.R., India. P* 14.
1275 **1026** 5 r. multicoloured .. .. .. 50 50

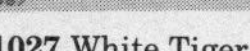

**1027** White Tiger — **1028** Execution of Veer Narayan Singh

**1987** (29 Nov). *Wildlife. T* **1027** *and similar multicoloured design. P* 13×13½ (1 *r.*) *or* 13½×13 (5 *r.*).
1276 1 r. Type **1027** .. .. .. .. 30 15
1277 5 r. Snow Leopard (*horiz*) .. .. .. 70 85

(Des S. Samanta)

**1987** (10 Dec). *Veer Narayan Singh (patriot) Commemoration. P* 13½×13.
1278 **1028** 60 p. deep brown .. .. .. 15 15

**1029** Rameshwari Nehru — **1030** Father Kuriakose Elias Chavara

**1987** (10 Dec). *Rameshwari Nehri (women's rights campaigner) Commemoration. P* 13×13½.
1279 **1029** 60 p. red-brown .. .. .. 15 15

**1987** (20 Dec). *Father Kuriakose Elias Chavara (founder of Carmelites of Mary Immaculate) Commemoration. P* 13×13½.
1280 **1030** 60 p. bistre-brown .. .. .. 15 15

**1031** Dr. Rajah Sir Muthiah Chettiar — **1032** Golden Temple, Amritsar

**1987** (21 Dec). *Dr. Rajah Sir Muthiah Chettiar (politician) Commemoration. P* 13.
1281 **1031** 60 p. slate .. .. .. .. .. 15 15

**1987** (26 Dec). 400*th Anniv of Golden Temple, Amritsar. P* 13×13½.
1282 **1032** 60 p. multicoloured .. .. .. 30 15

**1033** Rukmini Devi and Dancer — **1034** Dr. Hiralal

**1987** (27 Dec). *Rukmini Devi (Bharatanatyam dance pioneer) Commemoration. P* 13½×13.
1283 **1033** 60 p. deep rose-red .. .. .. 30 15

**1987** (31 Dec). *Dr. Hiralal (historian) Commemoration. P* 13×13½.
1284 **1034** 60 p. deep violet-blue .. .. .. 15 15

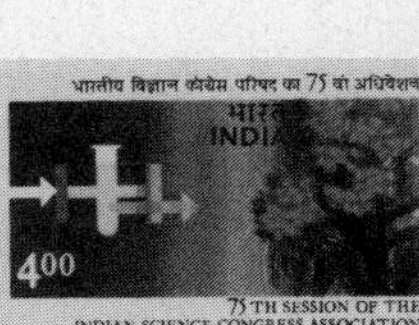

**1035** Light Frequency Experiment and Bodhi Tree — **1036** Rural Patient

**1988** (7 Jan). 75*th Session of Indian Science Congress Association. P* 13.
1285 **1035** 4 r. multicoloured .. .. .. 50 60

(Des M. Sharma)

**1988** (28 Jan). 13*th Asian Pacific Dental Congress. P* 13×13½.
1286 **1036** 4 r. multicoloured .. .. .. 50 50

**1988** (2 Feb–6 Oct). *India's Struggle for Freedom (6th series). Vert portraits as T* **909**. *P* 13.
1287 60 p. black, emerald and reddish orange .. 15 15
1288 60 p. chestnut, emerald & brt orange (4.2) 15 15
1289 60 p. brt carmine, emer & orge-red (27.2) .. 15 15
1290 60 p. blackish purple, emer & brt orge (7.3) 15 15
1291 60 p. plum, dp green & reddish orge (18.6) 15 15
1292 60 p. slate-blk, dp grn & reddish orge (19.6) 15 15
1293 60 p. deep lilac, dp green & orge-red (28.6) 15 15
1294 60 p. dp bluish green, grn & orge-red (6.9) 15 15
1295 60 p. red-brown, emerald & orge-red (6.10) 15 15
1296 60 p. magenta, dp green & brt orange (5.12) 20 15
1287/96 .. .. .. .. *Set of* 10 1·40 1·40
Designs:—No. 1287, Mohan Lal Sukhadia; No. 1288, Dr. S. K. Sinha; No. 1289, Chandra Shekhar Azad; No. 1290, G. B. Pant; No. 1291, Dr. Anugrah Narain Singh; No. 1292, Kuladhor Chaliha; No. 1293, Shivprasad Gupta; No. 1294, Sarat Chandra Bose; No. 1295, Baba Kharak Singh; No. 1296, Sheikh Mohammad Abdullah.

**1037** U Tirot Singh — **1038** Early and Modern Regimental Uniforms

**1988** (3 Feb). *U Tirot Singh (Khasis leader) Commemoration. P* 13×13½.
1297 **1037** 60 p. bistre-brown .. .. .. 15 15

**1988** (19 Feb). *Bicentenary of 4th Battalion of the Kumaon Regiment. P* 14.
1298 **1038** 1 r. multicoloured .. .. .. 30 15

**1039** Balgandharva — **1040** Soldiers and Infantry Combat Vehicle

**1988** (22 Feb). *Birth Centenary of Balgandharva (actor). P* 13×13½.
1299 **1039** 60 p. bistre-brown .. .. .. 20 15

**1988** (24 Feb). *Presentation of Colours to Mechanised Infantry Regiment. P* 13½×13.
1300 **1040** 1 r. multicoloured .. .. .. 35 15

**1041** B. N. Rau — **1042** Mohindra Government College

**1988** (26 Feb). *B. N. Rau (constitutional lawyer) Commemoration. P* 13.
1301 **1041** 60 p. grey-black .. .. .. 15 15

**1988** (14 Mar). *Mohindra Government College, Patiala. P* 13×13½.
1302 **1042** 1 r. cerise .. .. .. .. 15 15

**1043** Dr. D. V. Gundappa — **1044** Rani Avantibai

**1988** (17 Mar). *Dr. D. V. Gundappa (scholar) Commemoration. P* 13½×13.
1303 **1043** 60 p. slate .. .. .. .. 15 15

**1988** (20 Mar). *Rani Avantibai of Ramgarh Commemoration. P* 13×13½.
1304 **1044** 60 p. cerise .. .. .. .. 15 15

**1045** *Malayala Manorama* Office, Kottayam — **1046** Maharshi Dadhichi

**1988** (23 Mar). *Centenary of* Malayala Manorama *(newspaper). P* 13.
1305 **1045** 1 r. black and new blue .. .. 15 15

**1988** (26 Mar). *Maharshi Dadhichi (Hindu saint) Commemoration. P* 13×13½.
1306 **1046** 60 p. Indian red .. .. .. 15 15

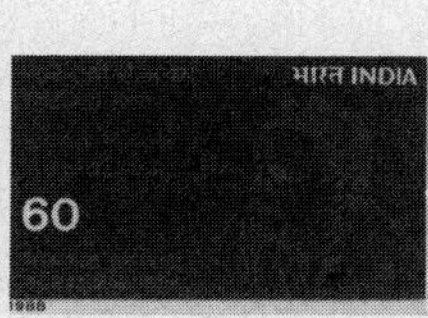


**1047** Mohammad Iqbal

**1048** Samarth Ramdas

(Des Alka Sharma)

**1988** (21 Apr). *50th Death Anniv of Mohammad Iqbal (poet). P* 13.
1307 **1047** 60 p. gold and rosine .. .. .. 15 15

**1988** (1 May). *Samarth Ramdas (Hindu spiritual leader) Commem. P* 13.
1308 **1048** 60 p. deep yellow-green .. .. 15 15

**1049** Swati Tirunal Rama Varma

**1050** Bhaurao Patil and Class

**1988** (2 May). *175th Birth Anniv of Swati Tirunal Rama Varma (composer). P* 13×13½.
1309 **1049** 60 p. deep mauve .. .. .. 20 15

**1988** (9 May). *Bhaurao Patil (educationist) Commemoration. P* 13½×13.
1310 **1050** 60 p. reddish brown .. .. .. 15 15

**1051** "Rani Lakshmi Bai" (M. F. Husain)

**1988** (9 May). *Martyrs from First War of Independence. P* 13×13½.
1311 **1051** 60 p. multicoloured .. .. .. 15 15
a. Myrtle-green (lowest stripe of flag, date, etc) omitted ..

**1052** Broad Peak

**1053** Child with Grandparents

(Des R. Pasricha (1 r. 50, 4 r.), N. Roerich (5 r.))

**1988** (19 May). *Himalayan Peaks. T* **1052** *and similar horiz designs. P* 13½×13.
1312 1 r. 50, reddish lilac, deep violet and blue 25 25
1313 4 r. multicoloured .. .. .. 50 50
1314 5 r. multicoloured .. .. .. 60 60
1315 6 r. 50, multicoloured .. .. .. 70 70
1312/15 .. .. .. .. .. *Set of* 4 1·90 1·90
Designs:—4 r. K 2 (Godwin Austen); 5 r. Kanchenjunga; 6 r.50, Nanda Devi.

(Des Neeta Verma)

**1988** (24 May). *"Love and Care for Elders". P* 13×13½.
1316 **1053** 60 p. multicoloured .. .. .. 15 15

**1054** Victoria Terminus, Bombay

**1055** Lawrence School, Lovedale

**1988** (30 May). *Centenary of Victoria Terminus Station, Bombay. P* 13½×13.
1317 **1054** 1 r. multicoloured .. .. .. 20 15

**1988** (31 May). *130th Anniv of Lawrence School, Lovedale. P* 13.
1318 **1055** 1 r. red-brown and deep green .. 15 15

**1056** Khejri Tree

**1988** (5 June). *World Environment Day. P* 14.
1319 **1056** 60 p. multicoloured .. .. .. 20 15

**1988** (15 June). *As No.* 732, *but new face value. W* **374**. *P* 12½ × 13.
1320 60 p. grey-black (Gandhi) .. .. .. 10 10
a. Wmk sideways .. .. .. 10 10

**1057** Rani Durgawati

**1058** Acharya Shanti Dev

**1988** (24 June). *Rani Durgawati (Gondwana ruler) Commemoration. P* 13.
1322 **1057** 60 p. deep rose-red .. .. .. 15 15

**1988** (28 July). *Acharya Shanti Dev (Buddhist scholar) Commemoration. P* 13×13½.
1323 **1058** 60 p. red-brown .. .. .. 15 15

**1059** Y. S. Parmar

**1988** (4 Aug). *Dr. Yashwant Singh Parmar (former Chief Minister of Himachal Pradesh) Commemoration. P* 13×13½.
1324 **1059** 60 p. slate-violet .. .. .. 15 15

**1060** Arm pointing at Proclamation in Marathi

(Des Contract Advertising (India) Ltd)

**1988** (16 Aug). *40th Anniv of Independence. Bal Gangadhar Tilak (patriot) Commemoration. T* **1060** *and similar horiz design. Multicoloured. P* 13×13½.
1325 60 p. Type **1060** .. .. .. 15 15
a. Vert pair. Nos. 1325/6 .. .. 30 30
1326 60 p. Battle scene .. .. .. 15 15
Nos. 1325/6 were printed together, *se-tenant*, in vertical pairs throughout the sheet, each pair forming a composite design showing a painting by M. F. Husain.

**1061** Durgadas Rathore

**1062** Gopinath Kaviraj

**1988** (26 Aug). *150th Birth Anniv of Durgadas Rathore (Regent of Marwar). P* 13×13½.
1327 **1061** 60 p. reddish brown .. .. .. 15 15

**1988** (7 Sept). *Gopinath Kaviraj (scholar) Commemoration. P* 13×13½.
1328 **1062** 60 p. bistre-brown .. .. .. 15 15

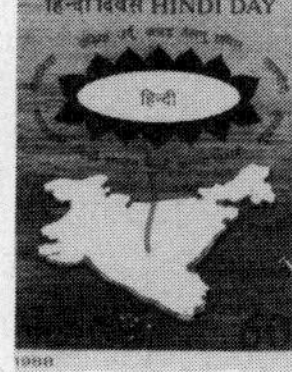


**1063** Lotus and Outline Map of India

**1064** Indian Olympic Association Logo

**1988** (14 Sept). *Hindi Day. P* 13×13½.
1329 **1063** 60 p. orange-verm, grn & reddish brn 15 15

(Des C. Parameswaran (5 p.))

**1988** (17 Sept). *"Sports–1988" and Olympic Games, Seoul. T* **1064** *and similar design. P* 13.
1330 60 p. brown-purple .. .. .. 15 15
1331 5 r. multicoloured .. .. .. 40 45
Design: *Horiz*—5 r. Various sports.

**1065** Jerdon's Courser

**1066** *Times of India* Front Page

**1988** (7 Oct). *Wildlife Conservation. Jerdon's Courser. P* 13×13½.
1332 **1065** 1 r. multicoloured .. .. .. 50 20

(Des C. Pakrashi (4 r.), C. Meena (5 r.))

**1988** (9 Oct)–**89**. *"India–89" International Stamp Exhibition, New Delhi (3rd issue). General Post Offices. Horiz designs as T* **1022**. *Multicoloured. P* 13½×13.
1333 4 r. Bangalore G.P.O. .. .. .. 40 35
a. Booklet pane. No. 1333×6 (20.1.89) 2·25
1334 5 r. Bombay G.P.O. .. .. .. 50 45
a. Booklet pane. No. 1334×6 (20.1.89) 2·75

(Des A. Nath)

**1988** (3 Nov). *150th Anniv of* The Times of India. *P* 14.
1335 **1066** 1 r. 50, black, gold and lemon .. 15 15

**1067** "Maulana Abul Kalam Azad" (K. Hebbar)

**1988** (11 Nov). *Birth Centenary of Maulana Abul Kalam Azad (politician). P* 13½×13.
1336 **1067** 60 p. multicoloured .. .. .. 15 15

1068 Nehru

**1988** (14 Nov). *Birth Centenary of Jawaharlal Nehru* (1989) (*1st issue*). *T* **1068** *and similar design. P* 13×13½ (60 *p.*) or 13½×13 (1 *r.*).
1337 60 p. grey-black, red-orange & deep green 20 15
1338 1 r. multicoloured .. .. .. 25 15
Design: *Vert*—1 r. "Jawaharlal Nehru" (Svetoslav Roerich).
See also No. 1393

1069 Birsa Munda

(Des S. Samantha)

**1988** (15 Nov). *Birsa Munda (Munda leader) Commemoration. P* 13½ × 13.
1339 **1069** 60 p. reddish brown .. .. .. 15 15

1070 Bhakra Dam

**1988** (15 Dec). *25th Anniv of Dedication of Bhakra Dam. P* 14.
1340 **1070** 60 p. bright carmine .. .. .. 35 40

1071 Dead Letter Office Cancellations of 1886

1072 K. M. Munshi

**1988** (20 Dec)–**89**. *"India–89" International Stamp Exhibition, New Delhi (4th issue). Postal Cancellations. T* **1071** *and similar horiz design. P* 13½×13.
1341 60 p. dp cinnamon, black & carm-vermilion 25 15
a. Booklet pane. No. 1341×6 (20.1.89) 1·40
1342 6 r. 50, orange-brown and black .. .. 1·00 1·00
a. Booklet pane. No. 1342×6 (20.1.89) 5·50
Design:—6 r. 50, Travelling post office handstamp of 1864.

**1988** (30 Dec). *Birth Centenary of K. M. Munshi (author and politician)* (1987). *P* 13½ × 13.
1343 **1072** 60 p. deep olive .. .. .. 15 15

1073 Mannathu Padmanabhan

1074 Lok Sabha Secretariat

**1989** (2 Jan). *Mannathu Padmanabhan (social reformer) Commemoration. P* 13 × 13½.
1344 **1073** 60 p. olive-brown .. .. .. 15 15

**1989** (2 Jan–11 May). *India's Struggle for Freedom (7th series). Vert portraits as T* **909**. *P* 13.
1345 60 p. blk, dull yellowish grn & reddish orge 20 20
1346 60 p. red-orange, dp grn & dp lilac (8.3.89) 20 20
1347 60 p. grey-black, bottle-green and bright orange (13.4.89) .. .. 20 20
1348 60 p. bistre-brown, emerald and reddish orange (13.4.89) .. .. 20 20
1349 60 p. brown, dp green & orge-red (11.5.89) 20 20
1345/9 .. .. .. .. *Set of* 5 90 90
Designs:—No. 1345, Hare Krushna Mahtab; No. 1346, Balasaheb Gangadhar Kher; No. 1347, Raj Kumari Amrit Kaur; No. 1348, Saifuddin Kitchlew; No. 1349, Asaf Ali.

**1989** (10 Jan). *60th Anniv of Lok Sabha Secretariat (formerly Legislative Assembly Department). P* 13½ × 13.
1355 **1074** 60 p. brown-olive .. .. .. 15 15

1075 Goddess Durga seated on Lion (5th-cent terracotta plaque)

1076 Baldev Ramji Mirdha

**1989** (11 Jan). *125th Anniv of Lucknow Museum. P* 14.
1356 **1075** 60 p. deep blue and new blue .. .. 15 15

**1989** (17 Jan). *Birth Centenary of Baldev Ramji Mirdha (nationalist). P* 13 × 13½.
1357 **1076** 60 p. slate-green .. .. .. 15 15

1077 Girl with Stamp Collection

1078 St. John Bosco and Boy

(Des K. Radhakrishnan (60 p.), M. Jain (1 r. 50))

**1989** (20 Jan). *"India–89" International Stamp Exhibition, New Delhi (5th issue). Philately. T* **1077** *and similar horiz designs. P* 13½×13.
1358 60 p. orge-yellow, rose-red & dp violet-blue 15 10
a. Booklet pane. No. 1358×6 .. .. 80
1359 1 r. 50, brownish grey, orge-yellow & blk 20 15
a. Booklet pane. No. 1359×6 .. .. 1·10
1360 5 r. dull vermilion and blue .. .. 60 50
a. Booklet pane. No. 1360×6 .. .. 3·25
1361 6 r. 50, black, red-brown & turquoise-blue 70 60
a. Booklet pane. No. 1361×6 .. .. 3·75
1358/61 .. .. .. .. *Set of* 4 1·50 1·25
Designs:—1 r. 50, Dawk gharry, *c.* 1842; 5 r. Travancore 1888 2 ch. conch shell stamp; 6 r. 50, Early Indian philatelic magazines.

**1989** (31 Jan). *St. John Bosco (founder of Salesian Brothers) Commemoration. P* 13.
1362 **1078** 60 p. carmine .. .. .. 15 15

1079 Modern Tank and 19th-century Sowar

1080 Dargah Sharif, Ajmer

(Des P. Biswas)

**1989** (8 Feb). *Third Cavalry Regiment. P* 13½ × 13.
1363 **1079** 60 p. multicoloured .. .. .. 30 15

**1989** (13 Feb). *Dargah Sharif (Sufi shrine), Ajmer. P* 13½ × 13.
1364 **1080** 1 r. multicoloured .. .. .. 20 20

1081 Task Force and Indian Naval Ensign

**1989** (15 Feb). *President's Review of the Fleet. P* 14.
1365 **1081** 6 r. 50, multicoloured .. .. 1·25 1·00

## COVER PRICES

Cover factors are quoted at the beginning of each country for most issues to 1945. An explanation of the system can be found on page x. The factors quoted do not, however, apply to philatelic covers.

1082 Shaheed Laxman Nayak and Barbed Wire Fence

1083 Rao Gopal Singh

**1989** (29 Mar). *Shaheed Laxman Nayak Commemoration. P* 13½×13.
1366 **1082** 60 p. dp brown, dp green & red-orange 15 15

**1989** (30 Mar). *Rao Gopal Singh Commemoration. P* 13×13½.
1367 **1083** 60 p. olive-brown .. .. .. 15 15

1084 Sydenham College

1085 Bishnu Ram Medhi

**1989** (19 Apr). *75th Anniv of Sydenham College, Bombay* (1988). *P* 13½×13.
1368 **1084** 60 p. grey-black .. .. .. 30 15

**1989** (24 Apr). *Birth Centenary of Bishnu Ram Medhi (politician)* (1988). *P* 13.
1369 **1085** 60 p. yellowish green, deep blue-green and orange-red .. .. 30 15

1086 Dr. N. S. Hardikar

1087 "Advaita" in Devanagari Script

**1989** (13 May). *Birth Centenary of Dr. Narayana Subbarao Hardikar (nationalist). P* 13×13½.
1370 **1086** 60 p. orange-brown .. .. .. 15 15

**1989** (17 May). *Sankaracharya (philosopher) Commemoration. P* 14.
1371 **1087** 60 p. multicoloured .. .. .. 20 20

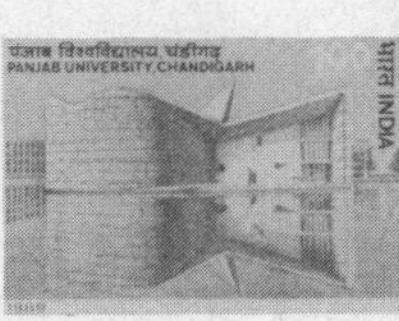
1088 Gandhi Bhavan, Punjab University

1089 Scene from Film *Raja Harischandra*

**1989** (19 May). *Punjab University, Chandigarh. P* 13½×13.
1372 **1088** 1 r. light brown and turquoise-blue .. 15 15

**1989** (30 May). *75 Years of Indian Cinema. P* 14.
1373 **1089** 60 p. black and yellow .. .. 20 15

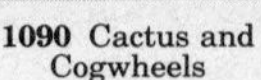
1090 Cactus and Cogwheels

1091 Early Class and Modern University Students

**1989** (20 June). *Centenary of Kirloskar Brothers Ltd (engineering group). P* $13^1/_2\times13$.
1374 **1090** 1 r. multicoloured .. .. .. 15 15

**1989** (27 June). *Centenary of First D.A.V. College. P* $13^1/_2\times13$.
1375 **1091** 1 r. multicoloured .. .. .. 15 15

**1092** Post Office, Dakshin Gangotri Base, Antarctica

**1093** First Allahabad Bank Building

(Des S. Samantha)

**1989** (11 July). *Opening of Post Office, Dakshin Gangotri Research Station, Antarctica. P* 14.
1376 **1092** 1 r. multicoloured .. .. .. 30 15

**1989** (19 July). *125th Anniv of Allahabad Bank* (1990). *P* 14.
1377 **1093** 60 p. maroon and new blue .. .. 15 15

**1094** Nehru inspecting Central Reserve Police, Neemuch, 1954

**1095** Dairy Cow

**1989** (27 July). *50th Anniv of Central Reserve Police Force (formerly Crown Representative's Police). P* $13^1/_2\times13$.
1378 **1094** 60 p. brown .. .. .. .. .. 20 20

**1989** (18 Aug). *Centenary of Military Farms. P* $13^1/_2\times13$.
1379 **1095** 1 r. multicoloured .. .. .. 20 15

**1096** Mustafa Kemal Atatürk

**1097** Dr. S. Radhakrishnan

**1989** (30 Aug). *50th Death Anniv of Mustafa Kemal Atatürk (Turkish statesman)* (1988). *P* $13\times13^1/_2$.
1380 **1096** 5 r. multicoloured .. .. .. 40 45

**1989** (11 Sept). *Birth Centenary of Dr. Sarvepalli Radhakrishnan (former President)* (1988). *P* $13^1/_2\times13$.
1381 **1097** 60 p. grey-black .. .. .. 15 15

**1098** Football Match

**1099** Dr. P. Subbarayan

**1989** (23 Sept). *Centenary of Mohun Bagan Athletic Club. P* $13^1/_2\times13$.
1382 **1098** 1 r. multicoloured .. .. .. 20 15

**1989** (30 Sept). *Birth Centenary of Dr. P. Subbarayan (politician). P* $13\times13^1/_2$.
1383 **1099** 60 p. orange-brown .. .. .. 15 15

**1100** Shyamji Krishna Varma

**1101** Sayajirao Gaekwad III

**1989** (4 Oct). *Shyamji Krishna Varma (nationalist) Commemoration. P* 13.
1384 **1100** 60 p. purple-brown, dp grn & orge-red 15 15

**1989** (6 Oct). *50th Death Anniv of Maharaja Sayajirao Gaekwad III of Baroda. P* $13\times13^1/_2$.
1385 **1101** 60 p. brownish grey .. .. .. 15 15

**1102** Symbolic Bird with Letter

**1103** Namakkal Kavignar

**1989** (14 Oct). *"Use Pincode" Campaign. P* 14.
1386 **1102** 60 p. multicoloured .. .. .. 15 15

**1989** (19 Oct). *Namakkal Kavignar (writer) Commemoration. P* $13\times13^1/_2$.
1387 **1103** 60 p. brownish black .. .. .. 15 15

**1104** Diagram of Human Brain

**1105** Pandita Ramabai and Original Sharada Sadan Building

**1989** (21 Oct). *18th International Epilepsy Congress and 14th World Congress on Neurology, New Delhi. P* $13^1/_2\times13$.
1388 **1104** 6 r. 50, multicoloured .. .. 60 65

**1989** (26 Oct). *Pandita Ramabai (women's education pioneer) Commemoration. P* $13^1/_2\times13$.
1389 **1105** 60 p. light brown .. .. .. 15 15

**1106** Releasing Homing Pigeons

**1107** Acharya Narendra Deo

**1989** (3 Nov). *Orissa Police Pigeon Post. P* $13^1/_2\times13$.
1390 **1106** 1 r. Indian red .. .. .. 20 15

**1989** (6 Nov). *Birth Centenary of Acharya Narendra Deo (scholar). P* 13.
1391 **1107** 60 p. brown, emerald and red-orange 15 15

**1108** Acharya Kripalani

**1989** (11 Nov). *Acharya Kripalani (politician) Commemoration. P* $13^1/_2\times13$.
1392 **1108** 60 p. grey-blk, myrtle-grn & orge-red 15 15

**1109** Nehru

(Des S. Debnath)

**1989** (14 Nov). *Birth Centenary of Jawaharlal Nehru (2nd issue). P* $14\times15$.
1393 **1109** 1 r. dull brown, purple-brown and buff 20 15

**1110** Meeting Logo

**1111** Sir Gurunath Bewoor

**1989** (19 Nov). *8th Asian Track and Field Meeting, New Delhi. P* 14.
1394 **1110** 1 r. black, reddish orge & yellowish grn 15 15

**1989** (20 Nov). *Sir Gurunath Bewoor (former Director-General, Posts and Telegraphs) Commemoration. P* $13\times13^1/_2$.
1395 **1111** 60 p. light brown .. .. .. 15 15

**1112** Balkrishna Sharma Navin

**1113** Abstract Painting of Houses

**1989** (8 Dec). *Balkrishna Sharma Navin (politician and poet) Commemoration. P* $13\times13^1/_2$.
1396 **1112** 60 p. black .. .. .. .. 15 15

**1989** (15 Dec). *Centenary of Bombay Art Society* (1988). *P* $13^1/_2\times13$.
1397 **1113** 1 r. multicoloured .. .. .. 15 15

**1114** Likh Florican

**1115** Centenary Logo

**1989** (20 Dec). *Wildlife Conservation. Likh Florican. P* $13\times13^1/_2$.
1398 **1114** 2 r. multicoloured .. .. .. 35 30

**1989** (29 Dec). *Centenary of Indian Oil Production. P* 14.
1399 **1115** 60 p. red-brown .. .. .. 20 15

**1116** Dr. M. G. Ramachandran

**1117** Volunteers working at Sukhna Lake, Chandigarh

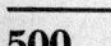

**1990** (17 Jan). *Dr. M. G. Ramachandran (former Chief Minister of Tamil Nadu) Commemoration. P* 13×13½.
1400 **1116** 60 p. reddish brown . . . . . . 15 15

(Des T. Bedi and S. Singh)

**1990** (29 Jan). *Save Sukhna Lake Campaign. P* 13½×13.
1401 **1117** 1 r. multicoloured . . . . . . 15 15

**1118** Gallantry Medals

**1990** (21 Feb). *Presentation of New Colours to Bombay Sappers. P* 15×14*.
1402 **1118** 60 p. multicoloured . . . . . . 20 20
*On No. 1402 the left hand side of the triangle is perforated 15 and the remaining two sides 14.

**1119** Conch Shell and Logo

**1120** Penny Black and Envelope

**1990** (2 May). *23rd Annual General Meeting of Asian Development Bank, New Delhi. P* 14.
1403 **1119** 2 r. black, brt orange & greenish yell 15 15

(Des M. Deogawanka)

**1990** (6 May). *150th Anniv of the Penny Black. P* 13×13½.
1404 **1120** 6 r. multicoloured . . . . . . 50 40

**1121** Ho Chi-Minh and Vietnamese House

**1122** Chaudhary Charan Singh

**1990** (17 May). *Birth Centenary of Ho Chi-Minh (Vietnamese leader). P* 13½×13.
1405 **1121** 2 r. reddish brown and yellowish green 15 15

**1990** (29 May). *3rd Death Anniv of Chaudhary Charan Singh (former Prime Minister). P* 13.
1406 **1122** 1 r. orange-brown . . . . . . 10 10

**1123** Armed Forces' Badge and Map of Sri Lanka

**1124** Wheat

**1990** (30 July). *Indian Peace-keeping Operations in Sri Lanka. P* 13.
1407 **1123** 2 r. multicoloured . . . . . . 10 10

**1990** (31 July). *60th Anniv of Indian Council of Agricultural Research (1989). P* 14.
1408 **1124** 2 r. blk, brt yellow-grn & dp bluish grn 10 10

**1125** Khudiram Bose

**1126** "Life in India" (Tanya Vorontsova)

**1990** (11 Aug). *Khudiram Bose (patriot) Commemoration. P* 13×13½.
1409 **1125** 1 r. dull vermilion, dull grn & brn-red 10 10

**1990** (16 Aug). *Indo-Soviet Friendship. Children's Paintings. T* **1126** *and similar horiz design. Multicoloured. P* 14.
1410 1 r. Type **1126** . . . . . . 10 20
a. Horiz pair. Nos. 1410/11 . . . . 45 90
1411 6 r. 50, "St. Basil's Cathedral and Kremlin, Moscow" (Sanjay Adhikari) 40 70
Nos. 1410/11 were printed together, *se-tenant*, in horizontal pairs throughout the sheet.
Stamps in similar designs were also issued by U.S.S.R.

**1127** K. Kelappan

**1128** Girl in Garden

**1990** (24 Aug). *K. Kelappan (social reformer) Commemoration. P* 13×13½
1412 **1127** 1 r. reddish brown . . . . . . 10 10

**1990** (5 Sept). *Year of the Girl Child. P* 13×13½
1413 **1128** 1 r. multicoloured . . . . . . 10 10

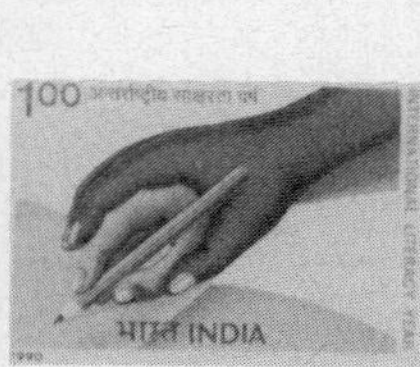


**1129** Hand guiding Child's Writing

**1130** Woman using Water Pump

**1990** (8 Sept). *International Literacy Year. P* 13½×13.
1414 **1129** 1 r. multicoloured . . . . . . 10 10

**1990** (10 Sept). *Safe Drinking Water Campaign. P* 13×13½.
1415 **1130** 4 r. black, scarlet-verm & dp bluish grn 30 30

**1131** Sunder Lal Sharma

**1132** Kabbadi

**1990** (28 Sept). *50th Death Anniv of Sunder Lal Sharma (patriot). P* 13×13½.
1416 **1131** 60 p. lake . . . . . . 10 10

(Des C. Pakrashi (Nos. 1418/19), R. Pasricha (No. 1420))

**1990** (29 Sept). *11th Asian Games, Peking. T* **1132** *and similar vert designs. Multicoloured. P* 13×13½.
1417 1 r. Type **1132** . . . . . . 15 15
1418 4 r. Athletics . . . . . . 40 40
1419 4 r. Cycling . . . . . . 40 40
1420 6 r. 50, Archery . . . . . . 70 70
1417/20 . . . . . . *Set of* 4 1·50 1·50

**1133** A. K. Gopalan

**1134** Gurkha Soldier

**1990** (1 Oct). *Ayillyath Kuttiari Gopalan (social reformer) Commemoration. P* 13×13½.
1421 **1133** 1 r. red-brown . . . . . . 10 10

(Des R. Pasricha)

**1990** (1 Oct). *50th Anniv of 3rd and 5th Battalions, 5th Gurkha Rifles. P* 13.
1422 **1134** 2 r. black and ochre . . . . . . 30 20

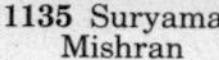


**1135** Suryamall Mishran

**1136** "Doll and Cat" (Subhash Kumar Nagarajan)

**1990** (19 Oct). *75th Birth Anniv of Suryamall Mishran (poet). P* 13 × 13½.
1423 **1135** 2 r. brown and pale orange . . . . 10 10

**1990** (14 Nov). *Children's Day. P* 13½×13.
1424 **1136** 1 r. multicoloured . . . . . . 10 10

**1137** Security Post and Border Guard on Camel

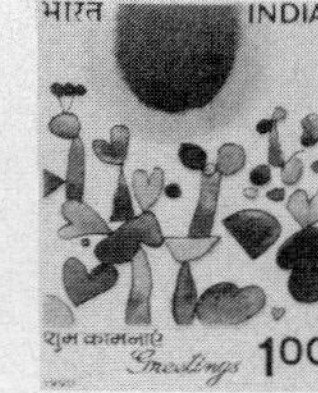


**1138** Hearts and Flowers

**1990** (30 Nov). *25th Anniv of Border Security Force. P* 13½×13.
1425 **1137** 5 r. greenish blue, yellow-brown & blk 30 35

(Des R. Pasricha (1 r.))

**1990** (17 Dec). *Greetings Stamps. T* **1138** *and similar multicoloured design. P* 13×13½ *(1 r.) or* 13½×13 *(4 r.)*.
1426 1 r. Type **1138** . . . . . . 15 10
1427 4 r. Ceremonial elephants (*horiz*) . . 35 40

**1139** Bikaner

**1140** Bhakta Kanakadas and Udipi Temple

(Des R. Pasricha (4, 5 r.), P. Biswas (6 r. 50))

**1990** (24 Dec). *Cities of India. T* **1139** *and similar horiz designs. Multicoloured. P* 13½×13.
1428 4 r. Type **1139** . . . . . . 35 35
1429 5 r. Hyderabad . . . . . . 45 45
1430 6 r. 50, Cuttack . . . . . . 60 60
1428/30 . . . . . . *Set of* 3 1·25 1·25

**1990** (26 Dec). *Bhakta Kanakadas (mystic and poet) Commemoration. P* 14.
1431 **1140** 1 r. orange-red . . . . . . 15 15

## NEW INFORMATION

The editor is always interested to correspond with people who have new information that will improve or correct the Catalogue.

1141 Shaheed Minar Monument

1142 Dnyaneshwar (poet) and Manuscript

**1990** (26 Dec). *300th Anniv of Calcutta. T* **1141** *and similar design. P* 14.
1432 1 r. multicoloured .. .. .. 10 10
1433 6 r. black, ochre and rosine .. .. 45 50
Design: *Horiz* (44×36 *mm*)—6 r. Eighteenth-century shipping on the Ganges.

**1990** (31 Dec). *700th Anniv of Dnyaneshwari (spiritual epic). P* 13×13½.
1434 **1142** 2 r. multicoloured .. .. .. 10 15

1143 Madan Mohan Malaviya (founder) and University

1144 Road Users

**1991** (20 Jan). *75th Anniv of Banaras Hindu University. P* 13½×13.
1435 **1143** 1 r. brown-lake .. .. .. 10 10

**1991** (30 Jan). *As No.* 732, *but new face value. W* **374**. *P* 13.
1436 1 r. orange-brown (Gandhi) .. .. 10 10

(Des J. Das)

**1991** (30 Jan). *International Traffic Safety Conference, New Delhi. P* 13½×13.
1437 **1144** 6 r. 50, black, dp blue & orge-vermilion 40 45

1145 Exhibition Emblem

1146 Jagnnath Sunkersett and Central Railways Headquarters

**1991** (12 Feb). *7th Triennale Art Exhibition, New Dehli. P* 13×13½.
1438 **1145** 6 r. 50, multicoloured .. .. 40 45

**1991** (15 Feb). *98th Birth Anniv of Jagnnath Sunkersett (educationist and railway pioneer). P* 13×13½.
1439 **1146** 2 r. royal blue and Indian red .. 10 15

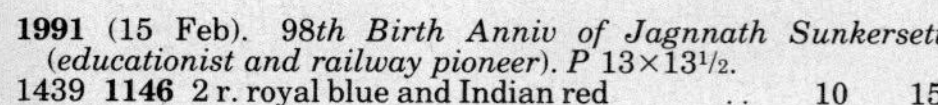

1147 Tata Memorial Centre

1148 River Dolphin

**1991** (28 Feb). *50th Anniv of Tata Memorial Medical Centre. P* 13½×13.
1440 **1147** 2 r. light brown and stone .. .. 10 15

**1991** (4 Mar). *Endangered Marine Mammals. T* **1148** *and similar horiz design. P* 13½×13.
1441 4 r. red-brown, turquoise-blue & brt green 35 35
1442 6 r. 50, multicoloured .. .. .. 55 55
Design:—6 r. 50, Sea Cow.

1149 Drugs

1150 Hand, Bomb Explosion and Dove

(Des J. Irani)

**1991** (5 Mar). *International Conference on Drug Abuse, Calcutta. P* 13×13½.
1443 **1149** 5 r. bluish violet and bright scarlet .. 50 50

(Des J. Das)

**1991** (7 Mar). *World Peace. P* 13×13½.
1444 **1150** 6 r. 50, black, cinnamon & orge-brown 55 60

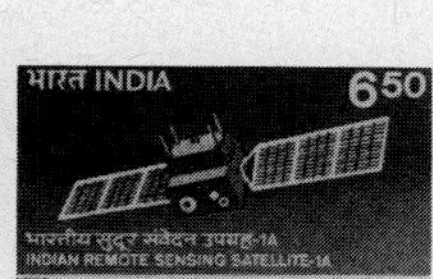
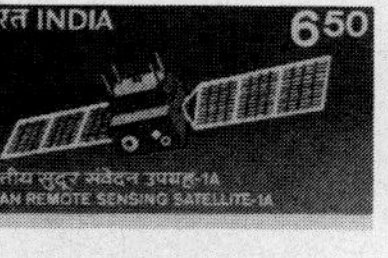


1151 Remote Sensing Satellite "1A"

1152 Babu Jagjivan Ram

**1991** (18 Mar). *Launch of Indian Remote Sensing Satellite "1A". P* 14.
1445 **1151** 6 r. 50, chestnut and deep violet-blue 25 30

**1991** (5 Apr). *Babu Jagjivan Ram (politician) Commemoration. P* 13×13½.
1446 **1152** 1 r. yellow-brown .. .. .. 10 10

1153 Dr. B. R. Ambedkar and Demonstration

1154 Valar Dance

**1991** (14 Apr). *Birth Centenary of Dr. Bhimrao Ramji Ambedkar (social reformer). P* 13½×13.
1447 **1153** 1 r. reddish brown and deep dull blue 10 10

**1991** (30 Apr). *Tribal Dances. T* **1154** *and similar horiz designs. Multicoloured. P* 13½×13.
1448 2 r. 50, Type **1154** .. .. .. 10 15
1449 4 r. Kayang .. .. .. .. 15 20
1450 5 r. Hozagiri .. .. .. .. 20 25
1451 6 r. 50, Velakali .. .. .. .. 25 30
1448/51 .. .. .. .. *Set of* 4 65 80

1155 Ariyakudi Ramanuja Iyengar and Temples

1156 Karpoori Thakur

(Des J. Sharma)

**1991** (18 May). *Ariyakudi Ramanuja Iyengar (singer and composer) Commemoration. P* 13½×13.
1452 **1155** 2 r. red-brown and deep bluish green 10 15

(Des L. Sahu)

**1991** (30 May). *Jan Nayak Karpoori Thakur (politician and social reformer) Commemoration. P* 13×13½.
1453 **1156** 1 r. reddish brown .. .. .. 10 10

### MINIMUM PRICE

The minimum price quote is 10p which represents a handling charge rather than a basis for valuing common stamps. For further notes about prices see introductory pages.

1157 Emperor Penguins

1158 Rashtrapati Bhavan Building, New Delhi

**1991** (23 June). *30th Anniv of Antarctic Treaty. T* **1157** *and similar horiz design. Multicoloured. P* 13½×13.
1454 5 r. Type **1157** .. .. .. .. 20 25
a. Horiz pair. Nos. 1454/5 .. .. 45 55
1455 6 r. 50, Antarctic map and pair of Gentoo Penguins .. .. .. .. 25 30
Nos. 1454/5 were printed together, *se-tenant*, in horizontal pairs throughout the sheet, each pair forming a composite design.

(Des P. Biswas)

**1991** (25 June). *60th Anniv of New Delhi. T* **1158** *and similar horiz designs. Multicoloured. P* 13½×13.
1456 5 r. Type **1158** .. .. .. .. 20 25
a. Horiz pair. Nos. 1456/7 .. .. 25 55
1457 6 r. 50, New Delhi monuments .. .. 25 30
Nos. 1456/7 were printed together, *se-tenant*, in horizontal pairs throughout the sheet, each pair forming a composite design.

1159 Sri Ram Sharma Acharya

1160 "Shankar awarded Padma Vibhushan" (cartoon)

**1991** (27 June). *Sri Ram Sharma Acharya (social reformer) Commemoration. P* 13½×13.
1458 **1159** 1 r. turquoise-green and rosine .. 10 10

**1991** (31 July). *Keshav Shankar Pillai (cartoonist) Commemoration. T* **1160** *and similar design. P* 13½×13 (4 *r.*) *or* 13×13½ (6 *r.* 50).
1459 4 r. light brown .. .. .. .. 15 20
1460 6 r. 50, deep rose-lilac .. .. .. 25 30
Design: *Vert*—6 r. 50, "The Big Show".

1161 Sriprakash and Kashi Vidyapith University

1162 Gopinath Bardoloi

**1991** (3 Aug). *20th Death Anniv of Sriprakash (politician). P* 13½×13.
1461 **1161** 2 r. red-brown and light brown .. 10 10

**1991** (5 Aug). *Birth Centenary of Gopinath Bardoloi (Assamese politician)* (1990). *P* 13×13½.
1462 **1162** 1 r. deep reddish lilac .. .. 10 10

1163 Rajiv Gandhi

(Des R. Chopra)

**1991** (20 Aug). *Rajiv Gandhi (Congress Party leader) Commemoration. P* 13.
1463 **1163** 1 r. multicoloured .. .. .. 10 10

**1164** Muni Mishrimalji and Memorial

**1165** Mahadevi Verma (poetess) and "Varsha"

**1991** (24 Aug). *Birth Centenary of Muni Mishrimalji (Jain religious leader). P* 13½×13.
1464 **1164** 1 r. yellow-brown .. .. .. 10 10

(Des S. Samant)

**1991** (16 Sept). *Hindu Writers. T* **1165** *and similar horiz design. P* 13½×13.
1465 **1165** 2 r. black and light blue .. .. 10 10
a. Horiz pair. Nos. 1465/6 .. 15 15
1466 – 2 r. black and light blue .. .. 10 10
Design:—No. 1466, Jayshankar Prasad (poet and dramatist) and scene from "Kamayani".
Nos. 1465/6 were printed together, *se-tenant,* in horizontal pairs throughout the sheet.

**1166** Parliament House and C.P.A. Emblem

**1167** Frog

(Des P. Biswas)

**1991** (27 Sept). *37th Commonwealth Parliamentary Association Conference, New Delhi. P* 13½×13.
1467 **1166** 6 r. 50, blue and reddish brown .. 25 30

**1991** (30 Sept). *Greetings Stamps. T* **1167** *and similar vert design. P* 13×13½.
1468 1 r. emerald and deep rose-red .. .. 10 10
a. Horiz pair. Nos. 1468/9 .. .. 30 35
1469 6 r. 50, deep rose-red and emerald .. 25 30
Design:—6 r. 50, Symbolic bird carrying flower.
Nos. 1468/9 were printed together, *se-tenant,* in horizontal pairs throughout the sheet.

**1168** *Cymbidium aloifolium*

**1169** Gurkha Soldier in Battle Dress

(Des O. Ravindran)

**1991** (12 Oct). *Orchids. T* **1168** *and similar vert designs. Multicoloured. P* 13×13½.
1470 1 r. Type **1168** .. .. .. .. 10 10
1471 2 r. 50, *Paphiopedilum venustum* .. 10 15
1472 3 r. *Aerides crispum* .. .. .. 10 15
1473 4 r. *Cymbidium bicolour* .. .. 15 20
1474 5 r. *Vanda spathulata* .. .. .. 20 25
1475 6 r. 50, *Cymbidium devonianum* .. 25 30
1470/5 .. .. .. .. .. *Set of* 6 75 1·00

(Des R. Pasricha)

**1991** (18 Oct). *90th Anniv of 2nd Battalion, Third Gorkha Rifles. P* 13½×13.
1476 **1169** 4 r. multicoloured .. .. .. 15 20

**1170** Couple on Horse (embroidery)

**1171** Chithiru Tirunal and Temple Sculpture

**1991** (29 Oct). *3rd Death Anniv of Kamaladevi Chattopadhyaya, (founder of All India Handicrafts Board). T* **1170** *and similar vert design. P* 13×13½.
1477 1 r. carmine-lake, crimson and yellow .. 10 10
1478 6 r. 50, multicoloured .. .. .. 25 30
Design:—6 r. 50, Traditional puppet.

**1991** (7 Nov). *Chithiru Tirunal Bala Rama Varma (former Maharaja of Travancore) Commemoration. P* 13½×13.
1479 **1171** 2 r. slate-violet .. .. .. 10 15

**1172** "Children in Traditional Costume" (Arpi Snehalbhai Shah)

**1173** Mounted Sowar and Tanks

**1991** (14 Nov). *Children's Day. P* 13×13½.
1480 **1172** 1 r. multicoloured .. .. .. 10 10

(Des R. Pasricha)

**1991** (14 Nov). *70th Anniv of the 18th Cavalry Regiment (1992). P* 13½×13.
1481 **1173** 6 r. 50, multicoloured .. .. 25 30

**1174** Kites

**1175** Sports on Bricks

**1991** (15 Nov). *India Tourism Year. P* 13½×13.
1482 **1174** 6 r. 50, multicoloured .. .. 25 30
It was originally intended to release No. 1482 on 28 January 1991, but the issue was postponed until 15 November. Examples are known used from Jaipur on the original date.

**1991** (18 Nov). *International Conference on Youth Tourism, New Delhi. P* 13×13½.
1483 **1175** 6 r. 50, multicoloured .. .. 25 30

**1176** "Mozart at Piano" (unfinished painting, J. Lange)

**1177** Homeless Family

**1991** (5 Dec). *Death Bicentenary of Mozart. P* 13×13½.
1484 **1176** 6 r. 50, multicoloured .. .. 25 30

(Des N. Srivastav)

**1991** (7 Dec). *South Asian Association for Regional Co-operation Year of Shelter. P* 13½×13.
1485 **1177** 4 r. lake-brown and ochre .. .. 15 20

**1178** People running on Heart

**1179** "Sidhartha with an Injured Bird" (Asit Kumar Haldar)

**1991** (11 Dec). *"Run for Your Heart" Marathon, New Delhi. P* 13½×13.
1486 **1178** 1 r. black, slate and bright scarlet .. 10 10

**1991** (28 Dec). *Birth Centenary of Asit Kumar Haldar (artist) (1990). P* 13×13½.
1487 **1179** 2 r. yellow, Indian red and black .. 10 10

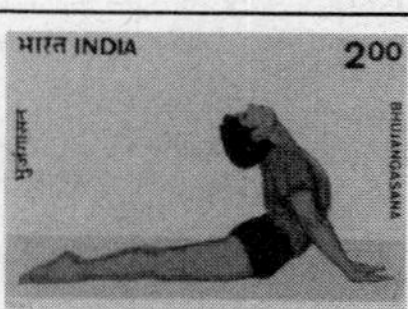

**1180** Bhujangasana

**1991** (30 Dec). *Yoga Exercises. T* **1180** *and similar horiz designs. Multicoloured. P* 13½×13.
1488 2 r. Type **1180** .. .. .. .. 10 10
1489 5 r. Dhanurasana .. .. .. .. 20 25
1490 6 r. 50, Ustrasana .. .. .. .. 25 30
1491 10 r. Utthita trikonasana .. .. .. 45 50
1488/91 .. .. .. .. *Set of* 4 90 1·00

## Index to Indian Stamp Designs from 1947

The following index is intended to facilitate the identification of all Indian stamps from 1947 onwards. Portrait stamps are usually listed under surnames only, views under the name of the town or city and other issues under the main subject or a prominent word and date chosen from the inscription. Simple abbreviations have occasionally been resorted to and when the same design or subject appears on more than one stamp, only the first of each series is indicated.


Abdullah 1296
Acharya 1458
AFRICA Fund 1228
Agrasen 824
Agriculture and Fish 917
"Agriexpo 77" 866
Ahluwalia 1157
Ahmed 842
Air India 304, 686
Airbus 834
Aircraft 304, 397, 434, 511, 686, 834, 952, 1053, 1054, 1185
Ajmer 1364
Ali, A. 1349
Ali, S. M. Z 972
All India Radio 440
"All Up" Air Mail 587
Allahabad Bank 1377
Allahabad High Court 539
Allahabad University 1256
Ambedkar 530, 680, 1447
American Revolution 812
*Amrita Bazar Patrika* 562
Anandamayee 1243
Ancient Sculpture 1038
Andrews 634
Anees 777
Annadurai 607
Ansari 991
Antarctica 1072, 1376, 1454
Apiculture Conference 962
Archaeological Survey 446
Architecture 314, 515
Army Ordnance Corps 759
Army Postal Corps 676
Artillery Regiment 1150
Arunagirinathar 775
Arvi Satellite Station 655
Arya Samaj 760
Aryabhata Satellite 762
Asan 678
"Asia 72" 668
Asian Development Bank 1403
Asian Games 335, 541, 1012, 1026, 1033, 1057, 1059, 1061, 1196, 1417
Asian-Oceanic Postal Union 843
Asian Pacific Dental Congress 1286
Asian Productivity Year 616
Asian Track and Field Meeting 1394
"Asiana 77" 861
Asiatic Society 1112
Assam Rifles 1155
Atatürk 1380
Atomic Reactor 520, 535, 738
Aurobindo 489, 660
Avantibai 1304
Azad, A. K. 536, 1336
Azad, C. S. 1289
Azad Hind 572

Bach 1176
Bahadur 793
Bai 1311
Bajaj 624
Balgandharva 1299
Balloon 1104
Banaras Hindu University 1435
Banerjee, S. 1094
Bangalore G.P.O. 1333
Bapa 605
Bapat 870
Bardoloi, G. 1462
Bardoloi, N. C. 790
Basaveswara 548
Basu 557
Beethoven 627
Behn 1089
Bell 802
Besant 471
Bethune College 895
Bewoor 1395
Bezbaruah 568
Bhabha 535
Bhagwadgeeta 894
Bhakra Dam 519, 737, 1340
Bharati 429
Bhatkande 442
Bhave 1093
Bhuvanesvara 316
Bikaner 1428
Bio Gas 1218
Bird Sanctuary 800
Birds 578, 733, 763, 800, 986, 1076, 1097, 1159, 1332, 1398, 1469
Birla 1126
Blind 1262
Bodh Gaya 315
Bolivar 1088
Bombay Art Society 1397
Bombay G.P.O. 1334
Bombay Sappers 1402
Border Roads 1165
Border Security Force 1425
Bose, J. C 420
Bose, K. 1409
Bose, N. L. 546, 1109
Bose, Sarat C. 1294
Bose, Subhas C. 482
Bougainvillea 1160
Brahmaputra Bridge 1241
Brides 993
Buddha Jayanti 372
Buildings and Mythology 309, 333, 513
Bullocks 356
Bustard 986
Butterflies 1019

Cable 1031
Calcutta 1432
Calcutta G.P.O. 513
Calcutta Port 622
Cama 450
Camel Post Office 1183
C.C.I.R. Assembly 606
Census 636
Central Reserve Police 1378
Chakra 819
Chaliha 1292
Chamber of Commerce 497, 847
Chand, D. 989
Chand, P. 976
Chandigarh 1372
Chandra 1256
Channamma 864
Chaplin 887
Chatterjee, B. C. 582
Chatterji, S. C. 822
Chattopadhyaya 1477
Chaturvedi 845
Chauhan 818
Chavara 1280
Chettiar, A. 982
Chettiar, M. 1281
Chhatrapati (ruler) 712
Chhatrapati, R. S. 913
Chhatrasal 1258
Children's Day 389, 419, 424, 431, 443, 461, 477, 492, 538, 645, 700, 748, 791, 831, 867, 900, 988, 1025, 1060, 1103, 1137, 1168, 1203, 1270, 1424, 1480
Chopra 1095
Chowdary 1233
Cinema 1373
Civil Aviation 1054
Cochin Synagogue 576
Coconut Research 835
Coffee Berries 505a
Commonwealth Day 1080
Commonwealth Heads of Govt. 1107
Commonwealth Parl Assn Conf 1467
Conservation of Nature 603
Coomaraswamy 855
Copernicus 691
Corbett 799, 1224
Council of Agricultural Research 1408
Cricket 654
Curie 574
Cuttack 1430
Cyprus the Great Charter 642

Dadhichi 1306
Dairy Congress 751
Dakshin Gangotri Base 1376
Dal Lake 518
Dam 357, 519
Dances 779, 1448
Dandi March 983
Dargah Sharif 1364
Darjeeling Railway 1069
Darul Uloom College 964
Darwin 1085
Das, A. 953
Das, B. 583
Das, C. 524
Das, G. 480
Das, J. N. 941
Das, U. G. M. 715
D.A.V. College 1375
Dawk Gharry 1359
Dayal 1231
Deccan Horse 1111
Deer 508, 722
Deo 635, 1391
Desai 1090
Deshmukh 1042
Dev 1323
Devi 1283
Dikshitar 803
Dnyaneshwari 1434
Dogra Regt 1247
Doulatram 1145
Drug Abuse Conf 1443
Dunant 388, 467
Durgawati 1322
Dutt, M. M. 688
Dutt, R. C. 694
Dvivedi 533

Earthquake Engineering 838
Eighteenth Cavalry 1481
Einstein 912
Elders 1316
Electric Lightbulb 946
Elephant 507, 1427
Epilepsy Congress 1388
"Everlasting Flame" 501

Factory 369, 414
Family Planning 506, 540, 725, 823, 1211
Fergusson College 1143
Festival of India 1040, 1050, 1162, 1163, 1251
Festival of U.S.S.R. 1275
Film Festival 837
First Aerial Post 434, 1185
Fish & Agriculture 917
Fisher 963
Five Year Plan 354, 413
Flowering Trees 1014
Flowers 850, 1043, 1426
Flying & Gliding 952
Football 1382
Forest Conservation 1008
Forestry 445
Forts of India 1131
Freedom from Hunger 466
Frog 1468
Fruit 514, 933

Gadgil 1144
Gaekwad of Baroda 1385
Gandhi, Indira 1138, 1151, 1167, 1170
Gandhi, K. 485
Gandhi, M. K. 305, 595, 693, 732, 811, 968, 979, 983, 1073, 1320, 1436
Gandhi, R. 1463
Gandhi, S. 1010
Ganeshdutt 1269
Garwhal Rifles 1245
Gauhati Refinery 449
General Election 543
Geographical Congress 575
Geological Congress 494
Geological Survey 334
Ghalib 585
Ghasidas 1254
Ghats of Varanasi 1101
Gil, A. S. 885
Giri 739
Girl Guides Jubilee 630
Gokhale 532
Gol Gumbad 317
Gold Mining 990
Golden Temple, Amritsar 319, 1282
Gommateshwara 999
Gopa 1193
Gopalan 1421
Gorky 563
Gour 833
Gramophone 854
Greetings Stamps 1426, 1468
"Greetings to our Forces" 662
Gundappa 1303
Gupta, M. S. 713
Gupta, S. 1293
Gurka Rifles 1422, 1476
Guru, K. P. 872
Guru Nanak Dev 602

Haffkine 486
Haldar 1487
Halley's Comet 1169
Hampi Chariot 516
Handel 1176
Handicrafts 504, 724
Handique 1102
Hansen 690
Haque 997
Hardikar 1370
Haridas 1164
Harishchandra 821
Hawa Mahal 1182
Heras 1030
High Courts 456, 539
"Hijri" 987
Himalayas 736, 1312
Hindi Convention 755
Hindi Day 1329
Hirakud Dam 948
Hiralal 1284
Ho Chi-Minh 1405
Hockey 541, 658, 1032
Holkar Temple 778
Homage to Martyrs 679, 1001
Homeopathic Congress 857
Human Rights 478, 559
Hume 692
Husain 593
Hyderabad 1429

I.A.E.A. Conference 951
I.M.C.O. 10th Anniversary 599
Inauguration of Republic 329
Independence 301, 661, 673, 1252, 1311
"India 1958" Exhibition 421
"India 80" 914, 942, 955
"India-89" 1248, 1264, 1333, 1341, 1358
India Govt Mint 992
India Security Press 792
Indian Air Force 397, 1053
Indian Industries Fair 444
Indian Life Insurance 631
Indian Military Academy 1067
Indian Mountaineering 685, 1096
Indian Mutiny 386, 1311
Indian National Congress 1177
Indian Science Congress 1285
Indian Standards Inst 656
"Indipex '73" 672, 701
Indo-Soviet Friendship 1410
Indo-Soviet Manned Space Flight 1125
Industries 805
"Inpex 75" 796
"Inpex 77" 859
"Inpex 82" 1070
"Inpex 86" 1182
Institution of Engineers 959
Int Astronomical Union 1169
Int Chamber of Commerce 1229
Int Children's Book Fair 950
Int Co-operation Year 502
Int Labour Organization 423, 588
Int Literacy Year 1414
Int Peace Year 1202
Int Railways Union 657
Int Statistical Inst. 871
Int Tourist Year 545
Int Trade Fair 949
Int Traffic Safety Conference 1437
Int Women's Year 758
Int Year of Disabled 1003
Int Year of Shelter for Homeless 1259
Int Year of the Child 910
Int Youth Tourism Conf 1483
Int Youth Year 1175
Inter-Parlimentary Conf 698
Interpol 695
Iqbal 1307
Irrigation and Drainage 773
Islamia University 623
I.T.U. 500
Iyengar 1452
Iyer 971

"Jai Bangla" 677
"Jai Jawan" 527
"Jai Kisan" 542
Jallianwala Bagh 589
Jat Regiment 1077
Jauhar 903
Jayasawal 1027
Jejeebhoy 422
Jerdon's Courser 1332
Joshi 970

Kalani 1092
Kalelkar 1147
Kalidasa 427, 465
Kamaraj 813
Kambar 529
Kanakadas 1431
Kanchenjunga 874
Kandarya Mahadeva 318
Kanha National Park 1086
Karve 396
Katju 1234
Kaur 1347
Kavi 880
Kavignar 1387
Kaviraj 1328
Kelappan 1412
Keller 973
Khan, H. A. 1230
Khan, S. A. 699
Kher 1346
Khusrau 785
King, M. L. 584
Kirloskar 594
Kirloskar Brothers Ltd 1374
Kishore 608
Kitchlew 1348
Koch 1041
Kripalani 1392
Krishnamurti 1246
Kumaon Regt 1298
Kunwar Singh 531
Kunzru 1236

Landscapes 363
Lawrence School 1318
Lenin 611
Leprosy Congress 1118
Light Cavalry 1110
Light Cavalry Regiment 801
Lincoln 499
Locomotives 509, 727, 806
Lohia 858
Lok Sabha Secretariat 1355
Longowal 1253
Loom 355
Lucknow Museum 1356

Madras Christian College 1242
Madras G.P.O. 1198
Madras Sappers 960
Mahal 1123
Mahaprabhu, C. 1188
Mahar Regiment 1024
Maharaj, C. S. 966
Maharaj, R. 1149
Maharishi 637
Mahtab 1345
Malaria Control 361
Malaria Eradication 454
Malaviya 448
*Malayala Manorama* (newspaper) 1305
Man on the Moon 601
Man's First Flight, Bicent. 1104
Map of India 375, 399
Marconi 753
Marx 1084
Masks 707
Mathura Museum 744
Mavalankar 1000
Mayo College 1189
Mechanised Infantry Regt 1300
Medhi 1369
Medical College 1153, 1154
Medieval Sculpture 517
Menon, V. K. K. 786
Menon, V. N. 899
Michelangelo 769
Military Farms 1379
Minicoy Lighthouse 1152
Mirdha 1357
Mishra 798
Mishran 1423
Mishrimalji 1464
Mohindra Govt College 1302
Mohun Bagan Athletic Club 1382
Monkeys 1099
Montessori 617
Mookerjee, Sir A. 488
Mookerjee, S.P. 889
Mookherjea, S. 883
Morarjee 844
Mother-Pondicherry 878
Mother Teresa 977
Mount Everest 344, 503
Mountains 1162
Mountbatten 978
Mozart 1484
Mueller 718

Mukherjee 618
Munda 1339
Museum Treasures 890
Munshi 1343
Musical Instruments 723
Mythology & Temples 309, 333, 515, 734, 778

Naidu 484
Nalanda College 609
Namdeo 626
Namibia Day 776
Nana Sahib 1122
Naoroji 470
Narayan 985
Narayana Guru 551
National Archives 947
National Cadet Corps 705
Natural History Society 1097
Naval Dockyard, Bombay 1181
Navin 1396
Navy 577, 1029, 1114, 1365
Nayak 1366
Nehru, J. 487, 492, 501, 556, 693, 810, 969, 980, 1074, 1079, 1166, 1337, 1378, 1393
Nehru, K. 719
Nehru, P. M. 438
Nehru, R. 1279
Neurology Congress 1388
New Delhi 564, 1456
*Nilgiri* (ship) 577
Nirala 830
Nirvana 747
Nivedita 573
Non-Aligned Summit 1078

October Revolution 873
Oil Exploration and Production 1049, 1399
Olympics 569, 658, 814, 974, 1082, 1127, 1330
Ophthalmology 462
Orchids 1470
Orientalists' Congress 479
Orissa Pigeon Post 1390
Osmania University 586

Pacific Area Travel 526, 876
Padmanabhan 1344
Paintings 681, 882
Pal 418
Palestinian Solidarity 1028
Paluskar 689
Panchayati Councils 451
Pandey 1124
Pant 522, 1290
Pantulu 590
Parachute Regiment 1199
Paradkar 1135
Paramahamsa 675
Parliamentary Conference 788
Parmanand 909
Parmar 1324
Patel, Vallabhbhai 523, 789
Patel, Vithalbhai 696
Patil 1310
Peace-keeping Operations 1407
Pediatrics Congress 863
Penny Black 1404
Personalities 713
Phadke 1119
Phalke 639
Philatelic Exhibition 628, 672, 701, 796, 859, 861, 914, 942, 955, 1070
Phookun 839
Phooley 869
Phoolwalon Ki Sair 1257
Phukan 1009
Picasso 1037
Pillai, K. S. 1459
Pallai, V. O. C. 663
Pincode 1386
Plucking Tea 510
Plumbline and Symbols 656

Police 1055, 1200, 1378, 1390
Postmarks 1341
Post Office 513, 565
Post Office Savings Bank 1056
Postal Life Insurance 1113
Postcard Centenary 915
Potato Research 1156
Powered Flight 905
Prakasam 665
Prasad, J. 1466
Prasad, R. 455, 1140
Pratap, M. 550
Pratap, R. N. 916
President's Bodyguard 697
President's Review 1365
"Project Tiger" 1106
Punjab Regiment 908
Punjab University 1372
Purandaradasa 481

"Quit India" 553, 1091
Qutb Minar 323

Radhakrishnan 552, 1381
Raghava 1023
Rai 496
Railway Centenary 343, 1237
Rajagopalachari 706, 904
Raju 1192
Rajya Sabha 849
Ram, B. J. 1446
Ram, B. K. 1120
Ram, G. 856
Ramabai 1389
Ramachandran 1400
Raman 652
Ramanujan 463
Ramasami 896
Ramcharitmanas 767
Ramdas 1308
Ranade 459
Ranjit Singh 534
Ranjitsinhji 695
Rathore 1327
Rau 1301
Ravenshaw College 906
Ravidas 633
Ray 441
Red Cross 388, 467, 625, 841
Red Fort 321
Refugee Relief 646
Republic Anniversary 756
Retarded Children 752
Review of the Fleet 1114
Rhinoceros 460
River Dolphin 1441
Rock Garden 1098
Roerich 746
Roosevelt 1075
Roses 1206
Rotary Int 1260
Route Map 554
Roy, B. C. 1048
Roy, J. 882
Roy, M. N. 1232
Roy, R. R. 490
Rubens 886
Run for Your Heart Marathon 1486
Russell 667

Sachar 1191
Safe Drinking Water 1415
Sai 1194
St Francis 1083
St John Bosco 1362
St Martha's Hospital 1226
St Stephen's College 998
St Stephen's Hospital 1171
St Thomas 493, 687
St Xavier's College 1158
Saints & Poets 337
Sanchi Stupa 314
Sankaracharya 1371
Sarabhai 670
Saraswati 452

Sastri 619
Satellite 1047, 1445
Satrunjaya 324
Savarkar 614
Sayamurti 1235
Schubert 907
Scottish Church College 981
Scout Jubilee 558
Sculpture 516
Sea Cow 1442
Sen, K. C. 965
Sen, S. 881
Sengupta 1146
Serampore College 592
Shankar 897
Sharma 1416
Shastri, H. 832
Shastri, L. B. 528
Shastri, S. 1174
Sher Shah Suri 613
Shivaji 437
Shraddhanand 610
Siberian Crane 1076
Singh, A. N. 1291
Singh, Baba 1295
Singh, Bhagat 571
Singh, Bhai 664
Singh, C. C. 1406
Singh, Guru G. 544
Singh, Master Tara 1148
Singh, R. G. 1367
Singh, U. T. 1297
Singh, V. N. 1278
Sinha 1288
Sivananda 1195
Sir J. J. School of Art 1036
Skinner's Horse 902
SLV 3 Rocket 1011
Small Industries Fair 901
Soil Science Congress 1035
Solar energy 1217
South Asian Regional Co-operation 1172
South Eastern Railway 1237
Spinning 358
"Sports 1988" 1330
Sri Lanka 1407
Sriprakash 1461
Stamp Centenary 348
Stamp Collecting 1358
Standardization 491
Steel Industry 395
Subbarayan 1383
Sukhadia 1287
Sukhna Lake 1401
Sunkersett 1439
Survey of India 547
Sydenham College 1368

Table Tennis 757, 967
Tagore, A. 640
Tagore, G. 567
Tagore, R. 439, 653, 884, 1244
Taj Mahal 322
Tamil Conference 560
Tandon 1068
Tansen 1223
Tata 395, 495
Tata Memorial Medical Centre 1440
Telecommunications 1212
Telegraph Centenary 346, 554
Telephone 1034
Telephone Engineer 366, 413
Television Experiment 774
Telugu Conference 761
Territorial Army 750
Thakur 1453
Theosophical Society 794
"They Defend" 468
Third Cavalry Regt 1363
Third World Book Fair 877
Thiruvallivar 426
Tiger 721
Tilak 374, 1325
*Times of India* (newspaper) 1335
Tipu Sultan 717

Tirtha 537
Tolstoy 898
Tope 1121
Tourism Year 1482
Tractor 354, 925*b*
Trade and Development 561
Trains 509, 727
Trees 1271
Tribes 1004
Triennale Art Exhibition 1187, 1438
*Trishna* (yacht) 1227
Troposcatter Link 1058
Tyagaraja 433

UNESCO 644
UNICEF 432, 479, 1221
UNIDO Conference 954
Union Public Service Comm. 865
United Nations 352, 615, 1166
Universities 392
Upadhyaya 888
UPU 325, 612, 740
USSR Jubilee 671

Vallabhacharya 846
Valmiki 621
"Vande Mataram" 836
Varma, C. T. B. R. 1479
Varma, R. 638
Varma, S. K. 1384
Varma, S. T. R. 1309
Vaswani 604
Veersalingam 716
Vemana 666
Verma 1465
Victoria Station, Bombay 1317
Victory 278
Victory Tower 320
Vidhyarthi 453
Vidyapati 525
Vidyapith 632
Vidyasagar 620
*Vikrant* (aircraft carrier) 1184
Virjanand 641
Visakhapatnam 498
Visva Bharati 653
Visvesvaraya 430
Vivekananda 464
Voluntary Blood Donation 829
Von Stephan 1002
Vyas 714

Wadia, A. C. 591
Wadia, D. N. 1136
Weather Services 795
Weaving 359, 932
Wheat Research 879
Wheat Revolution 566, 925*b*
Wild Animals 721, 1276, 1332
Wildlife Preservation 472, 825, 1052, 1099, 1159, 1224, 1398
Windmill 1219
Womens University 820
Wood Duck 1155
World Agricultural Fair 425
World Book Fair 961
World Communications Year 1087
World Cup Football Championships 1190
World Environment Day 848, 1319
World Food Day 1018
World Forestry Congress 353
World Health Day 804
World Mining Congress 1139
World Peace 1444
World Population Year 720
World Thrift Day 643
Wrestling 555

Xavier 754

Yacht Voyage 1227
Year of Shelter 1485
Year of the Girl Child 1413
Yoga 1488
Yogananda 840
YWCA 768

Zafar 787

## OFFICIAL STAMPS

Stamps overprinted "POSTAL SERVICE" or "I.P.N." were not used as postage stamps, and are therefore omitted.

**Service.**

(O 1)

(Optd by the Military Orphanage Press, Calcutta)

**1866** (1 Aug)–**72**. *Optd with Type* O 1. *P* 14. *(a) No wmk.*

O 1 **11** ½ a. blue — £130
O 2 ½ a. pale blue £650 85·00
a. Optd inverted
O 3 1 a. brown — 90·00
O 4 1 a. deep brown — 85·00
O 5 8 a. carmine 9·50 19·00

*(b) Wmk Elephant's Head, T* 13

O 6 **11** ½ a. blue £110 19·00
O 7 ½ a. pale blue £110 12·00
a. Opt inverted
b. No dot on "i" (No. 50 on pane) — £250
c. No stop (No. 77 on pane) — £200
O 8 **12** 8 p. purple (1.72) 17·00 32·00
a. No dot on "i" £180
b. No stop £180
O 9 **11** 1 a. brown £110 15·00
O10 1 a. deep brown £110 30·00
a. No dot on "i" — £400
b. No stop — £350
O11 2 a. orange £110 45·00
O12 2 a. yellow £110 45·00
a. Opt inverted
b. Imperf
O13 4 a. green £110 50·00
a. Opt inverted
O14 **17** 4 a. green (Die I) £750 £200

A variety with wide and more open capital "S" occurs six times in sheets of all values except No. O8. Price four times the normal.

Reprints exist of Nos. O6, O9 and O14; the latter is Die II instead of Die I.

Reprints of the overprint have also been made, in different setting, on the 8 pies, purple, no watermark.

O 2 O 6

O 3 O 4

(No. O15 surch at Calcutta, others optd at Madras)

**1866** (Oct). *Fiscal stamps, Nos. O15/18 with top and bottom inscrs removed, surch or optd. Wmk Crown over "INDIA".*

*(a) Surch as in Type O 2. Thick blue glazed paper. Imperf × perf* 14

O15 O 2 2 a. purple £350 £225

*(b) Optd "SERVICE POSTAGE" in two lines as in Types O 3/4 and similar type. Imperf × perf* 14

O16 O 3 2 a. purple (G.) £700 £375
O17 O 4 4 a. purple (G.) £2000 £900
O18 – 8 a. purple (G.) £3750 £2000
a. Optd on complete stamp (inscr "FOREIGN BILL") — £6500

*(c) Optd "SERVICE POSTAGE" in semi-circle. Wmk Large Crown. P* 15½ × 15

O19 O 6 ½ a. mauve/*lilac* (G.) £325 80·00
a. Opt double £1900

So-called reprints of Nos. O15 to O18 are known, but in these the surcharge differs entirely in the spacing, etc., of the words; they are more properly described as Government imitations. The imitations of No. O15 have surcharge in *black* or in *green*. No. O19 exists with reprinted overprint which has a full stop after "POSTAGE".

**PRINTERS.** The following stamps up to No. O108 were overprinted by De La Rue and thereafter Official stamps were printed or overprinted by the Security Printing Press at Nasik.

**Service.** (O 7)

**On H. M. S.** (O 8)

**On H. S. M.** (O 9)

**1867–73.** *Optd with Type* O 7. *Wmk Elephant's Head. T* 13. *P* 14.

O20 **11** ½ a. blue (Die I) 14·00 40
O21 ½ a. pale blue (Die I) 17·00 75
O22 ½ a. blue (Die II) (1873) £100 35·00
O23 1 a. brown 14·00 45
O24 1 a. deep brown 17·00 80
O25 1 a. chocolate 20·00 90
O26 2 a. yellow 6·50 2·50
O27 2 a. orange 4·50 2·25
O28 **17** 4 a. pale green (Die I) 8·00 2·00
O29 4 a. green (Die I) 3·00 1·50
O30 **11** 8 a. rose (Die II) (1868) 3·25 1·50
O30*a* 8 a. pale rose (Die II) 3·25 1·50

*Prepared for use, but not issued*

O30*b* **18** 6 a. 8 p. slate £160

**1874–82.** *Optd with Type* O 8. *(a) In black.*

O31 **11** ½ a. blue (Die II) 4·50 20
O32 1 a. brown 6·00 20
O33 2 a. yellow 19·00 6·00
O33*a* 2 a. orange 18·00 4·50
O34 **17** 4 a. green (Die I) 4·75 2·50
O35 **11** 8 a. rose (Die II) 3·50 1·75

*(b) Optd in blue-black*

O36 **11** ½ a. blue (Die II) (1882) £225 30·00
O37 1 a. brown (1882) £425 95·00

**1883–99.** *Wmk Star, T* 34. *P* 14. *Optd with Type* O 9.

O37*a* **40** 3 p. aniline carmine (1899) 20 10
O38 **23** ½ a. deep blue-green 35 10
a. Opt double † £650
O39 ½ a. blue-green 20 10
O40 **25** 1 a. brown-purple 50 10
a. Opt inverted £300 £400
b. Opt double † £650
c. Opt omitted (in horiz pair with normal) £700
O41 1 a. plum 30 10
O42 **27** 2 a. pale blue 1·75 20
O43 2 a. blue 2·25 20
O44 **29** 4 a. olive-green 3·75 20
O44*a* 4 a. slate-green 3·25 20
O45 **31** 8 a. dull mauve 8·00 70
O46 8 a. magenta 4·50 40
O47 **37** 1 r. green and rose (1892) 20·00 2·00
O48 1 r. green and carmine (1892) 3·50 40
O37*a*/48 *Set of* 7 12·50 1·40

**1900** *Colours changed. Optd with Type* O 9.

O49 **23** ½ a. pale yellow-green 70 35
O49*a* ½ a. yellow-green 90 40
ab. Opt double £500
O50 **25** 1 a. carmine 1·25 10
a. Opt inverted † £600
b. Opt double † £650
O51 **27** 2 a. pale violet 15·00 40
O52 2 a. mauve 18·00 45
O49/52 *Set of* 3 15·00 70

**1902–9.** *Stamps of King Edward VII optd with Type* O 9.

O54 **41** 3 p. grey (1903) 70 30
O55 3 p. slate-grey (1905) 80 40
a. No stop after 'M' 55·00 40·00
O56 **42** ½ a. green 90 30
O57 **43** 1 a. carmine 70 10
O58 **44** 2 a. violet 3·00 20
O59 2 a. mauve 1·75 10
O60 **47** 4 a. olive 3·00 15
O61 4 a. pale olive 3·50 15
O62 **48** 6 a. olive-bistre (1909) 1·50 10
O63 **49** 8 a. purple (*shades*) 6·00 70
O64 8 a. claret 7·50 60
O65 **51** 1 r. green and carmine (1905) 4·00 30
O54/65 *Set of* 8 17·00 1·60

**1906.** *New types. Optd with Type* O 9.

O66 **53** ½ a. green 30 10
a. No stop after 'M' 40·00 28·00
O67 **54** 1 a. carmine 80 10
a. No stop after 'M' 55·00 38·00

**On H. S. M.**

(O 9*a*)

**1909.** *Optd with Type* O 9*a*.

O68 **52** 2 r. carmine and yellow-brown 7·50 60
O68*a* 2 r. rose-red and yellow-brown 7·00 80
O69 5 r. ultramarine and violet 14·00 1·50
O70 10 r. green and carmine 16·00 8·50
O70*a* 10 r. green and scarlet 42·00 7·00
O71 15 r. blue and olive-brown 55·00 28·00
O72 25 r. brownish orange and blue £140 60·00
O68/72 *Set of* 5 £200 85·00

**SERVICE** (O 10) (14 mm)

**SERVICE** (O 11) (21½ mm)

**NINE PIES** (O 12)

**1912–13.** *Stamps of King George V (wmk Single Star, T* 34) *optd with Type* O 10 *or* O 11 *(rupee values).*

O73 **55** 3 p. grey 15 10
O74 3 p. slate-grey 15 10
O75 3 p. blue-slate 1·00 10
a. Opt omitted (in pair with normal)
O76 **56** ½ a. yellow-green 15 10
a. Overprint double 95·00
O77 ½ a. pale blue-green 20 10
O80 **57** 1 a. rose-carmine 60 10
O81 1 a. carmine 50 10
O82 1 a. aniline carmine 50 10
a. Overprint double † £550
O83 **59** 2 a. mauve 45 10
O84 2 a. purple 45 10
O85 **63** 4 a. deep olive 1·00 10
O86 4 a. olive-green 1·00 10
O87 **64** 6 a. yellow-bistre 1·50 1·75
O88 6 a. deep bistre-brown 3·25 2·75
O89 **65** 8 a. purple 2·25 35
O89*a* 8 a. mauve 2·25 35
O90 8 a. bright aniline mauve 15·00 1·75
O91 **67** 1 r. red-brown and blue-green (1913) 2·25 35
O92 2 r. rose-carmine and brown (1913) 3·00 2·00
O93 5 r. ultramarine and violet (1913) 11·00 9·50
O94 10 r. green and scarlet (1913) 27·00 28·00
O95 15 r. blue and olive (1913) 70·00 85·00
O96 25 r. orange and blue (1913) £170 £110
O73/96 *Set of* 13 £250 £200

**1921.** *No.* O80 *surch with Type* O 12.

O97 **57** 9 p. on 1 a. rose-carmine 30 30

**1922.** *No.* 197 *optd with Type* O 10.

O98 **57** 1 a. chocolate 40 10

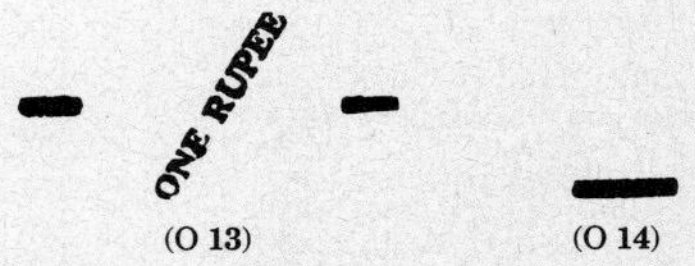


(O 13) (O 14)

**1925.** *Official stamps surcharged.*

*(a) Issue of* 1909, *as Type* O 13

O 99 **52** 1 r. on 15 r. blue and olive 4·25 2·50
O100 1 r. on 25 r chestnut and blue 17·00 42·00
O101 2 r. on 10 r green and scarlet 3·75 3·00
O101*a* 2 r. on 10 r. green and carmine £180 48·00

*(b) Issue of* 1912, *with Type* O 14

O102 **67** 1 r. on 15 r. blue and olive 17·00 45·00
O103 1 r. on 25 r. orange and blue 5·00 7·00
a. Surch inverted £425

*(c) Issue of* 1912, *as Type* O 13

O104 **67** 2 r. on 10 r. green and scarlet £650

Examples of the above showing other surcharge errors are believed to be of clandestine origin.

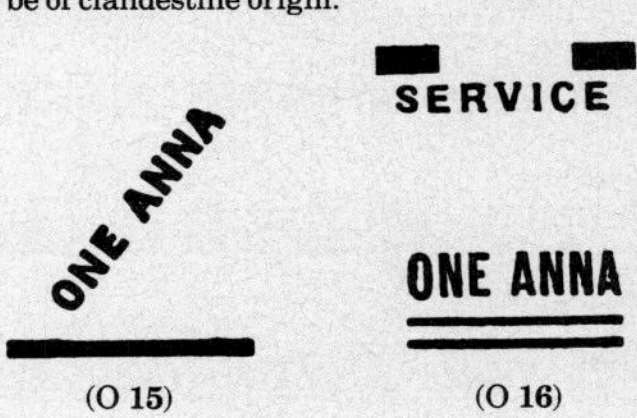


(O 15) (O 16)

**1926.** *No.* O62 *surch with Type* O 15.

O105 **48** 1 a. on 6 a. olive-bistre 30 30

**1926.** *Postage stamps of* 1911–22 *(wmk. Single Star), surch as Type* O **16**.

O106 **58** 1 a. on 1½ a. chocolate (A) 20 10
O107 1 a. on 1½ a. chocolate (B) 45 60
a. Error. On 1 a. chocolate (197) £160
O108 **61** 1 a. on 2½ a. ultramarine 60 1·25

The surcharge on No. O108 has no bars at top.

Examples of Nos. O106/7 with inverted or double surcharges are believed to be of clandestine origin.

**SERVICE** (O 17) (13½ mm)

**SERVICE** (O 18) (19½ mm)

**1926–31.** *Stamps of King George V (wmk Multiple Star, T* 69) *optd with Types* O 17 *or* O 18 *(rupee values).*

O109 **55** 3 p. slate (1.10.29) 15 10
O110 **56** ½ a. green (1931) 80 20
O111 **57** 1 a. chocolate 15 10
O112 **70** 2 a. purple 20 10
O113 **71** 4 a. sage-green 25 10
O115 **65** 8 a. reddish purple 60 10
O116 **66** 12 a. claret (1927) 60 45
O117 **67** 1 r. chocolate and green (1930) 1·25 45
O118 2 r. carmine and orange (1930) 6·00 4·50
O120 10 r. green and scarlet (1931) 65·00 45·00
O109/20 *Set of* 10 65·00 45·00

**1930.** *As No.* O111, *but optd as Type* O 10 *(14 mm).*

O125 **57** 1 a. chocolate 50·00 4·00

**1932–36.** *Stamps of King George V (wmk Mult Star, T* 69) *optd with Type* O 17.

O126 **79** ½ a. green (1935) 50 10
O127 **80** 9 p. deep green 20 10
O127*a* **81** 1 a. chocolate (1936) 60 10
O128 **82** 1¼ a. mauve 20 10
O129 **70** 2 a. vermilion 75 60
O130 **59** 2 a. vermilion (1935) 1·25 1·25
O130*a* 2 a. vermilion (*small die*) (1936) 75 10
O131 **61** 2½ a. orange (22.4.32) 15 10
O132 **63** 4 a. sage-green (1935) 75 10
O133 **64** 6 a. bistre (1936) 15·00 5·50
O126/33 *Set of* 9 17·00 5·75

**1937–39.** *Stamps of King George VI optd as Types* O **17** *or* O **18** *(rupee values).*

O135 **91** ½ a. red-brown (1938) 7·00 15
O136 9 p. green (1937) 7·00 10
O137 1 a. carmine (1937) 1·00 10
O138 **93** 1 r. grey and red-brown (5.38) 50 20
O139 2 r. purple and brown (5.38) 1·50 1·40
O140 5 r. green and blue (10.38) 2·50 2·75
O141 10 r. purple and claret (1939) 13·00 4·75
O135/41 *Set of* 7 29·00 8·50

(O 19)

(O 20)

**1939** (May). *Stamp of King George V, surch with Type* O **19**.

O142 **82** 1 a. on 1¼ a. mauve 4·50 20

(Des T. I. Archer)

**1939** (1 June)–**42**. *Typo. W* **69**. *P* 14.

O143 O **20** 3 p. slate 20 10
O144 ½ a. red-brown 75 10
O144*a* ½ a. purple (1942) 20 10
O145 9 p. green 30 10
O146 1 a. carmine 30 10
O146*a* 1 a. 3 p. yellow-brown (1941) 2·75 40
O146*b* 1½ a. dull violet (1942) 65 10
O147 2 a. vermilion 60 10
O148 2½ a. bright violet 60 15
O149 4 a. brown 60 10
O150 8 a. slate-violet 90 20
O143/50 *Set of* 11 7·00 90

**1948** (15 Aug). *First Anniv of Independence. Nos.* 305/8 *optd as Type* O **17**.

O150*a* **305** 1½ a. brown 42·00 30·00
O150*b* 3½ a. violet £600 £350
O150*c* 12 a. grey-green £1400 £1400
O150*d* **306** 10 r. purple-brown and lake £8500

Nos. O150*a/d* were only issued to the Governor-General's Secretariat.

O 21

Asokan Capital

O 22

(Des T. I. Archer)

**1950** (2 Jan)–**51**. *Typo* (O **21**) *or litho* (O **22**). *W* **69**. *P* 14.

O151 O **21** 3 p. slate-violet (1.7.50) 10 10
O152 6 p. purple-brown (1.7.50) 10 10
O153 9 p. green (1.7.50) 20 10
O154 1 a. turquoise (1.7.50) 45 10
O155 2 a. carmine (1.7.50) 70 10
O156 3 a. red-orange (1.7.50) 2·50 70
O157 4 a. lake (1.7.50) 7·00 10
O158 4 a. ultramarine (1.10.51) 40 10
O159 6 a. bright violet (1.7.50) 2·00 40
O160 8 a. red-brown (1.7.50) 1·50 10
O161 O **22** 1 r. violet 1·75 10
O162 2 r. rose-carmine 1·00 30
O163 5 r. bluish green 2·00 1·50
O164 10 r. reddish brown 4·00 10·00
O151/64 *Set of* 14 21·00 12·00

**1957** (1 Apr)–**58**. *Value in naye paise. Typo* (*t*) *or litho* (*l*). *W* **69**. *P* 14.

O165 O **21** 1 n.p. slate (*l*) 10 10
*a. Slate-black* (*l*) 10 10
*b. Greenish slate* (*t*) 10 10
O166 2 n.p. blackish violet (*t*) 10 10
O167 3 n.p. chocolate (*t*) 10 10
O168 5 n.p. green (*l*) 10 10
*a. Deep emerald* (*t*) 10 10
O169 6 n.p. turquoise-blue (*t*) 10 10
O170 13 n.p. scarlet (*t*) 10 10
O171 15 n.p. reddish violet (*l*) (6.58) 60 60
*a. Reddish violet* (*t*) 35 65
O172 20 n.p. red (*l*) 10 10
*a. Vermilion* (*t*) 30 10
O173 25 n.p. violet-blue (*l*) 15 10
*a. Ultramarine* (*t*) 60 10
O174 50 n.p. red-brown (*l*) 30 10
*a. Reddish brown* (*t*) 60 40
O165/74 *Set of* 10 1·25 1·10

**1958–71.** *As Nos.* O165/74*a and* O161/4 *but W* **374** *(upright). Litho* (*l*) *or typo* (*t*). *P* 14.

O175 O **21** 1 n.p. slate-black (*t*) (1.59) 10 10
O176 2 n.p. blackish violet (*t*) (1.59) 10 10
O177 3 n.p. chocolate (*t*) (11.58) 10 10
O178 5 n.p. deep emerald (*t*) (11.58) 10 10
O179 6 n.p. turquoise-blue (*t*) (5.59) 10 10
O180 10 n.p. deep grey-green (*l*) (1963) 40 40
*a. Deep grey-green* (*t*) (1966?) 75 65
O181 13 n.p. scarlet (*t*) (1963) 15 2·00
O182 15 n.p. deep violet (*t*) (11.58) 10 10
*a. Light reddish violet* (*t*) (1961) 35 10
O183 20 n.p. vermilion (*t*) (5.59) 10 10
*a. Red* (*t*) (1966?) 90 45
O184 25 n.p. ultramarine (*t*) (7.59) 10 10
O185 50 n.p. reddish brown (*t*) (6.59) 15 10
*a. Chestnut* (*l*) (1966?) 90 60
O186 O **22** 1 r. reddish violet (*l*) (2.59) 15 10
O187 2 r. rose-carmine (*l*) (1960) 25 10
a. Wmk sideways. *Pale rose-carmine* (*l*) (1969?) 35 60
O188 O **22** 5 r. slate-green (*l*) (7.59) 50 55
a. Wmk sideways. *Deep grey-green* (*l*) (1969?) 70 80
O189 10 r. brown-lake (*l*) (7.59) 1·25 80
a. Wmk sideways (*l*) (1971) 2·25 2·50
O175/89 *Set of* 15 3·00 4·00

O **23** *(see also Type* O **26**)

शरणार्थी
सहायता
REFUGEE
RELIEF
(O 24)

O 25

**1967** (20 Mar)–**73**? *Photo. W* **374** *(sideways). P* 15×14.

O190 O **23** 2 p. violet (1973?) 15 30
O191 5 p. green (1973?) 20 10
O192 10 p. myrtle-green (2.7.73) 40 15
O193 15 p. plum (2.7.73) 75 30
O194 20 p. red (2.7.73) 3·00 2·75
O195 30 p. ultramarine (1973) 1·25 55
O196 50 p. chestnut (2.7.73) 1·75 1·75
O197 1 r. dull purple (20.3.67) 30 10
*a. Deep slate-purple* (1969) 50 10
O190/7 *Set of* 8 7·00 5·50

**1967** (15 Nov)–**74**(?). *Wmk Large Star and "INDIA GOVT" in sheet*. Photo. P* 15 × 14. *No gum.*

O200 O **23** 2 p. violet 10 30
O201 3 p. chocolate 10 40
O202 5 p. green 10 10
*a. Yellowish green* (1969) 10 10
O203 6 p. turquoise-blue 45 70
O204 10 p. myrtle-green 10 20
*a. Bronze-green* (1969) 50 35
O205 15 p. plum 10 20
O206 20 p. red 10 20
O207 25 p. carmine-red (1974?) 3·00 2·75
O208 30 p. ultramarine 10 20
O209 50 p. chestnut 10 20
O200/9 *Set of* 10 3·50 4·75

*The arrangement of this watermark in the sheet results in the words and the star appearing upright, inverted or sideways.

**1971.** *Obligatory Tax. Refugee Relief.*

(*a*) *Provisional issue. No.* O202 *optd with Type* O **24**.

O210 O **23** 5 p. yellowish green (15.11) 20 20
*a. Green* 20 20

(*b*) *Issue for Bangalore. No.* O202 *optd with T* **602**

O211 O **23** 5 p. yellowish green 80 40
a. Opt inverted 3·00

(*c*) *Issue for Goa. No.* O202 *optd with T* **606**

O212 O **23** 5 p. yellowish green

(*d*) *Definitive issue. Wmk Large Star and "INDIA GOVT" in sheet*. Litho. P* 15 × 14. *No gum.*

O213 O **25** 5 p. yellowish green (1.12) 15 15
*a. Yellow-green* 15 15

*See note below No. O209.

The surcharge on mail for the relief of refugees from the former East Pakistan referred to in the note after No. 651 also applied to official mail. The cost of the stamps used by each Government Department was charged against its budget and the additional charge for refugee stamps meant that each Department had to spend less to keep within its budget.

O 26

O 27

O 28

**1976** (1 Apr)–**80**. *Redrawn, showing face-value in figures only and smaller Capital with Hindi motto beneath. P* 14 (2, 5, 10 *r.*) *or* 15 × 14 (*others*). (*a*) *Wmk Large Star and "INDIA GOVT" in sheet.* No gum.*

O214 O **26** 2 p. deep violet-blue 20 50
O215 5 p. yellowish green 10 15
O216 10 p. myrtle-green 15 40
*a. Deep dull green* (1978) 10 30
O217 15 p. deep purple 10 20
O218 20 p. Indian red 15 35
O219 25 p. rose-carmine 40 70
*a. Bright crimson* (1978) 50 80
O220 30 p. chalky blue (1.5.79) 70 70
O221 35 p. violet (6.12.80) 30 10
O222 50 p. chestnut 65 65
O223 1 r. deep brownish purple (13.8.80) 1·25 40

(*b*) *W* **374** (*sideways*)

O224 O **26** 1 r. deep brownish purple 65 65
O225 – 2 r. rose-red (date?) 1·25 1·25
a. Wmk upright 40 90
O226 – 5 r. deep green (date?) 2·00 2·50
a. Wmk upright (1978) 60 1·50
O227 – 10 r. brown-lake (date?) 1·25 2·75
a. Wmk upright 2·50 3·50
O214/27 *Set of* 14 6·00 9·00

The 2, 5 and 10 r. are larger, size as Type O **22**.

*See note below No. 720. The 2 p. value is only known on the first type of watermark, the 35, 50 p. and 1 r. values on the second and the remaining values on both.

**1981** (14 Feb). *Redrawn showing revised border design and inscriptions, with face value figures now in bottom corners. Wmk Large Star and "INDIA GOVT" in sheet. P* 15×14.

O228 O **27** 2 r. rose-red 40 45
O229 5 r. deep green 50 55
O230 10 r. brown-lake 1·25 1·25
O228/30 *Set of* 3 1·90 2·00

**1981** (10 Dec). *As Nos.* O215/19, O221/3 *and* O228/30 *but printed on cream paper with simulated perforations as Type* O **28**. *Unwatermarked. Imperf.*

O231 O **28** 5 p. dull yellowish green 30 30
O232 10 p. deep green 35 35
O233 15 p. deep reddish violet 35 35
O234 20 p. dull vermilion 40 40
O235 25 p. bright rose 90 65
O236 35 p. violet 50 30
O237 50 p. orange-brown 90 60
O238 1 r. deep dull purple 1·00 60
O239 2 r. orange-vermilion 1·25 1·75
O240 5 r. deep dull green 1·50 2·25
O241 10 r. lake-brown 2·00 3·25
O231/41 *Set of* 11 8·50 9·75

Some values have been seen unofficially pin-perforated.

**1982** (22 Nov). *As Nos.* 215/23 *and* 228/30. *Wmk Large Star and "INDIA GOVT" in sheet. P* 12½ × 13.

O242 O **26** 5 p. light green 15 30
O243 10 p. deep dull green 15 40
O244 15 p. blackish purple 15 40
O245 20 p. Indian red 15 40
O246 25 p. cerise 20 50
O247 30 p. deep ultramarine 20 50
O248 35 p. bluish violet 20 30
O249 50 p. reddish brown 30 50
O250 1 r. deep purple-brown 40 50
O251 O **27** 2 r. rose-red 55 1·00
O252 5 r. grey-green 80 1·90
O253 10 r. chocolate 1·40 3·25
O242/53 *Set of* 12 4·25 9·00

**1984** (16 Apr)–**88**. *As Nos.* O215/23, O228/30 *and new values. W* **374** *(sideways). P* 13.

O254 O **26** 5 p. yellowish green 10 10
a. Wmk upright 10 10
O255 10 p. deep dull green 10 10
a. Wmk upright 10 10
O256 15 p. blackish purple 10 10
a. Wmk upright 10 10
O257 20 p. Indian red 10 10
a. Wmk upright 10 10
O258 25 p. rose-carmine (1986) 10 10
a. Wmk upright 10 10
O259 30 p. deep ultramarine 10 10
a. Wmk upright 10 10
O260 35 p. bluish violet 10 10
a. Wmk upright 10 10
O261 40 p. bright violet (15.10.88) 10 10
a. Wmk upright 10 10
O262 50 p. reddish brown 10 10
a. Wmk upright 10 10
O263 60 p. deep brown (15.4.88) 10 10
a. Wmk upright 10 10
O264 1 r. deep purple-brown 10 10
a. Wmk upright 10 10
O265 O **27** 2 r. rose-red 10 15
a. Wmk upright 10 15
O266 5 r. grey-green 20 25
a. Wmk upright 20 25
O267 10 r. chocolate 40 45
O254/67 *Set of* 14 1·10 1·25

Printings from 20 July 1990 were on ungummed paper. Mint prices are the same for stamps with or without gum.

## INDIA USED ABROAD

In the years following 1858 the influence of the Indian Empire, political, military and economic, extended beyond its borders into neighbouring states, the Arabian Gulf, East Africa and the Far East. Such influence often led to the establishment of Indian civil post offices in the countries concerned where unoverprinted stamps of India were used.

Such offices operated in the following countries. An * indicates that details will be found under that heading elsewhere in the catalogue.

### ADEN (SOUTH ARABIAN FEDERATION)*

Unoverprinted stamps of India used from 1854 until 1937.

### BAHRAIN*

Unoverprinted stamps of India used from 1884 until 1933.

### BRITISH EAST AFRICA (KENYA, UGANDA AND TANGANYIKA)*

Unoverprinted stamps of India used during August and September 1890.

### FRENCH INDIAN SETTLEMENTS

The first Indian post office, at Chandernagore, was open by 1784 to be followed by offices in the other four Settlements. By an agreement with the French, dating from 1814, these offices handled mail destined for British India, Great Britain, the British Empire and most other foreign destinations except France and the French colonies. In later years the system was expanded by a number of sub-offices and it continued to operate until the French territories were absorbed into India on 2 May 1950 (Chandernagore) or 1 November 1954.

Chandernagore. Open by 1784. Used numeral cancellations "B86" or "86".
Sub-offices:
Gondalpara (opened 1906)
Lakhiganj (opened 1909)
Temata (opened 1891)
Karikal. Open by 1794. Used numeral cancellations "C147", "147" or "6/M–21".
Sub-offices:
Ambagarattur (opened 1904)
Kottuchari (opened 1901)
Nedungaon (opened 1903)
Puraiyar Road (opened 1901)
Settur (opened 1905)
Tirumalrayapatnam (opened 1875 – used numeral cancellation "6/M-21/1")
Tiramilur (opened 1898)
Mahe. Open by 1795. Used numeral cancellations "C192" or "9/M-14".

Pondicherry. Opened 1787. Used numeral cancellations "C111", "111" (also used elsewhere), "6/M-19" (also used elsewhere) or "6/M-20".
Sub-offices:
Ariyankuppam (opened 1904)
Bahoor (opened 1885)
Mudaliarpet (opened 1897)
Muthialpet (opened 1885)
Pondicherry Bazaar (opened 1902)
Pondicherry Railway Station (opened 1895)
Olugarai (opened 1907)
Vallinur (opened 1875) – used numeral cancellation "M-19/1"
Yanam. Opened 1876. Used numeral cancellation "5/M-4".

## IRAN

The British East Company was active in the Arabian Gulf from the early years of the 17th century with their first factory (trading centre) being established at Jask in 1619. After 1853 this commercial presence was converted into a political arm of the Indian Government culminating in the appointment of a Political Resident to Bushire in 1862.

The first Indian post office in Iran (Persia) opened at Bushire on 1 May 1864 with monthly mail services operating to the Resident there and to the British Legation at Tehran. Further offices in the other Gulf ports followed, but, unless otherwise stated below, all were closed on 1 April 1923.

Abadan. Opened during First World War.
Ahwaz. Opened March 1915.
Bandar Abbas. Opened 1 April 1867. Used numeral cancellations "22" or "1/K-5"
Bushire. Opened 1 May 1864. Used numeral cancellations "140", "308", "26" (also used elsewhere) or "K-5".
Chabbar. Opened August 1913. Closed 1920.
Henjam. Opened 1913.
Jask. Opened 1880.
Linga. Opened 1 April 1867. Used numeral cancellations "21" or "2/K-5".
Mohammera. Opened 19 July 1892.
Maidan-i-Naphtun. Opened during First World War. Closed 1920.

## IRAQ*

Unoverprinted stamps of India used from 1868 until 1918.

## KUWAIT*

Unoverprinted stamps of India used from 1904 until 1923.

## MALAYSIA (STRAITS SETTLEMENTS)*

Unoverprinted stamps of India used from 1854 until 1867.

## MUSCAT*

Unoverprinted stamps of India used from 1864 until 1947.

## NEPAL

A post office was opened in the British Residency at Kathmandu in 1816 following the end of the Gurkha War. Stamps of India were used from 1854, initially with "B137", "137" or "C-37" numeral cancellations. The Residency Post Office continued to provide the overseas mail service after Nepal introduced its own issues in 1881.

In 1920 the Residency Post Office became the British Legation Post Office. On the independence of India in 1947 the service was transferred to the Indian Embassy and continued to function until 1965.

## PORTUGUESE INDIA

A British post office was open in Damaun by 1823 and Indian stamps were used there until November 1883, some with "13" and "3/B-19" numeral cancellations.

No other British post offices were opened in the Portuguese territories, but from 1854 Indian stamps were sold by the local post offices. Between 1871 and 1877 mail intended for, or passing through, British India required combined franking of India and Portuguese India issues. After 1877 the two postal administrations accepted the validity of each other's stamps.

## SOMALILAND PROTECTORATE*

Unoverprinted stamps of India used from 1887 until 1903.

## TIBET

The first Indian post office in Tibet accompanied the Tibetan Frontier Commission in 1903. The Younghusband Military Expedition to Lhasa in the following year operated a number of Field Post Offices which were replaced by civil post offices at Gartok (opened 23 September 1906), Gyantse (opened March 1905), Pharijong (opened 1905) and Yatung (opened 1905). All Indian post offices in Tibet closed on 1 April 1955 except Gyantse which, it is believed, did not operate after 1943.

## TRUCIAL STATES (DUBAI)*

Unoverprinted stamps of India used from 1909 until 1947.

## ZANZIBAR (TANZANIA)*

Unoverprinted stamps of India used from 1875 until 1895.

# CHINA EXPEDITIONARY FORCE

Following the outbreak of the Boxer Rising in North China the Peking Legations were besieged by the rebels in June 1900. An international force, including an Indian Army division, was assembled for their relief. The Legations were relieved on 14 August 1900, but operations against the Boxers continued in North China with Allied garrisons at key cities and along the Peking–Tientsin–Shanhaikwan railway. The last Indian Army battalion did not leave North China until 1923.

Field Post Offices accompanied the Indian troops and commenced operations on 23 July 1900 using unoverprinted Indian postage and official stamps. The unoverprinted postage issues were replaced in mid-August by stamps overprinted "C.E.F." to prevent currency speculation. The use of unoverprinted official stamps continued as they were not valid for public postage.

**PRICES FOR STAMPS ON COVER**

| | |
|---|---|
| Nos. C1/10 | *from* × 15 |
| No. C10*a* | † |
| Nos. C11/22 | *from* × 8 |
| Nos. C23/34 | *from* × 20 |

**C. E. F.**

(C 1)

***Stamps of India overprinted with Type* C 1, *in black***

**1900** (Aug). *Stamps of Queen Victoria.*

| No. | Type | Description | Unused | Used |
|---|---|---|---|---|
| C 1 | **40** | 3 p. carmine | 20 | 35 |
| | | a. No stop after "C" (R. 1/2) | | |
| | | b. No stop after "F" | | |
| C 2 | **23** | ½ a. green | 30 | 30 |
| | | a. Opt double | | |
| | | b. No stop after "F" | | |
| C 3 | **25** | 1 a. brown-purple | 1·25 | 75 |
| | | a. No stop after "F" | | |
| C 4 | **27** | 2 a. ultramarine | 1·75 | 3·00 |
| | | a. No stop after "F" | | |
| C 5 | **36** | 2½ a. green | 2·25 | 6·50 |
| | | a. No stop after "F" | | |
| C 6 | **28** | 3 a. orange | 2·50 | 9·00 |
| | | a. Opt double, one albino | £100 | |
| | | b. No stop after "F" | | |
| C 7 | **29** | 4 a. olive-green | 2·00 | 4·75 |
| | | a. Opt double, one albino | £100 | |
| | | b. No stop after "F" | | |
| C 8 | **31** | 8 a. magenta | 2·00 | 7·50 |
| | | a. No stop after "F" | | |
| C 9 | **32** | 12 a. purple/*red* | 4·50 | 12·00 |
| | | a. Opt double, one albino | £100 | |
| | | b. No stop after "F" | £200 | |
| C10 | **37** | 1 r. green and carmine | 5·50 | 8·50 |
| | | a. No stop after "F" | | |
| C1/10 | | *Set of* 10 | 20·00 | 48·00 |

*Prepared, but not issued*

| No. | Type | Description | Unused | Used |
|---|---|---|---|---|
| C10*a* | **26** | 1 a. 6 p. sepia | £180 | |

The missing stop after "F" variety occurs in the ninth row of the upper pane.

**1904** (27 Feb).

| No. | Type | Description | Unused | Used |
|---|---|---|---|---|
| C11 | **25** | 1 a. carmine | 21·00 | 6·00 |

**1904.** *Stamps of King Edward VII.*

| No. | Type | Description | Unused | Used |
|---|---|---|---|---|
| C12 | **41** | 3 p. grey | 1·25 | 2·00 |
| | | a. Opt double, one albino | £140 | |
| | | b. Opt triple, one albino | £275 | |
| | | *c. Slate-grey* | 1·40 | 2·50 |
| C13 | **43** | 1 a. carmine | 1·25 | 60 |
| | | a. Opt double, one albino | £100 | |
| C14 | **44** | 2 a. mauve | 6·00 | 1·50 |
| | | a. Opt double, one albino | £100 | |
| C15 | **45** | 2½ a. ultramarine | 2·50 | 5·00 |
| C16 | **46** | 3 a. orange-brown | 3·00 | 4·00 |
| C17 | **47** | 4 a. olive-green | 7·00 | 11·00 |
| C18 | **49** | 8 a. claret | 6·00 | 7·00 |
| | | *a. Purple* | 50·00 | |
| C19 | **50** | 12 a. purple/*red* | 9·00 | 19·00 |
| C20 | **51** | 1 r. green and carmine | 9·00 | 22·00 |
| C12/20 | | *Set of* 9 | 40·00 | 65·00 |

**1909.** "POSTAGE & REVENUE."

| No. | Type | Description | Unused | Used |
|---|---|---|---|---|
| C21 | **53** | ½ a. green (No. 149) | 1·40 | 50 |
| | | a. Opt double, one albino | £100 | |
| C22 | **54** | 1 a. carmine (No. 150) | 1·00 | 25 |

**1913–21.** *Stamps of King George V. Wmk Star.*

| No. | Type | Description | Unused | Used |
|---|---|---|---|---|
| C23 | **55** | 3 p. slate-grey (1913) | 1·00 | 7·00 |
| C24 | **56** | ½ a. green | 1·00 | 2·25 |
| C25 | **57** | 1 a. aniline carmine | 1·40 | 1·00 |
| C26 | **58** | 1½ a. chocolate (Type A) | 11·00 | 35·00 |
| | | a. Opt double, one albino | £100 | |
| C27 | **59** | 2 a. mauve | 3·50 | 24·00 |
| | | a. Opt triple | £325 | |
| C28 | **61** | 2½ a. bright blue | 5·50 | 13·00 |
| C29 | **62** | 3 a. orange-brown | 14·00 | 60·00 |
| C30 | **63** | 4 a. olive-green | 16·00 | 90·00 |
| C32 | **65** | 8 a. mauve | 14·00 | £160 |
| C33 | **66** | 12 a. claret | 14·00 | 80·00 |
| C34 | **67** | 1 r. red-brown and blue-green | 42·00 | £140 |
| C23/34 | | *Set of* 11 | £110 | £550 |

On No. C27a two of the overprints are only lightly inked.

**BRITISH RAILWAY ADMINISTRATION**

As a vital communications link the North China Railway (Peking – Tientsin – Shanhaikwan) was captured by Russian forces during operations against the Boxers. Control of the line was subsequently, in February 1901, assigned to the China Expeditionary Force and a British Railway Administration was set up to run it. By international agreement the line was to provide postal services for the other national contingents and also, to a lesser extent, for the civilian population. Travelling post offices were introduced and, on 20 April 1901, a late letter service for which an additional fee of 5 c. was charged.

Type **32** of China

**B.R.A.**
**5**
**Five Cents**

(BR 35)

**1901** (20 Apr). *No.* 108 *of China surch with Type* BR **35**.

| No. | Type | Description | Unused | Used |
|---|---|---|---|---|
| BR133 | **32** | 5 c. on ½ c. brown (Bk.) | £200 | 85·00 |
| | | a. Surch inverted | £6500 | £1700 |
| | | b. Surch in green | £170 | 3110 |
| | | ba. Imperf between (horiz pair) | † | £11000 |

No. BR133 was used for the collection of the 5 c. late letter fee and was affixed to correspondence by a postal official at the railway station. It was cancelled with a violet circular postmark showing "RAILWAY POST OFFICE" at top and the name of the station (PEKING, TIENTSIN, TONGKU, TONGSHAN or SHANHAIKWAN) at foot. With the exception of official mail it could only be used in combination with Indian stamps overprinted "C.E.F.", stamps from the other allied contingents or of the Chinese Imperial Post (*Price used on cover*: No. BR133 *from* £170, No. BR133b *from* £225).

The late fee charge was abolished on 20 May 1901 and No. BR133 was then withdrawn. The British Railway Administration continued to run the line, and its travelling post offices, until it was returned to its private owners in September 1902.

# INDIAN EXPEDITIONARY FORCES 1914–22

**PRICES FOR STAMPS ON COVER**
Nos. E1/13 *from* × 10

**I. E. F.**

(E 1)

**1914.** *Stamps of India (King George V) optd with Type* E 1.

| No. | Type | Description | Unused | Used |
|---|---|---|---|---|
| E 1 | **55** | 3 p. slate-grey | 15 | 25 |
| | | a. No stop after "F" | 20·00 | 20·00 |
| | | b. No stop after "E" | 60·00 | 60·00 |
| | | c. Opt double | 35·00 | 25·00 |
| E 2 | **56** | ½ a. yellow-green | 20 | 20 |
| | | a. No stop after "F" | 50·00 | 50·00 |
| | | b. Opt double | £160 | £250 |
| E 3 | **57** | 1 a. aniline carmine | 30 | 20 |
| | | a. No stop after "F" | 28·00 | 28·00 |
| E 4 | | 1 a. carmine | 1·25 | 1·00 |
| E 5 | **59** | 2 a. mauve | 50 | 30 |
| | | a. No stop after "F" | 50·00 | 60·00 |
| | | b. No stop after "E" | £140 | £160 |
| E 6 | **61** | 2½ a. ultramarine | 70 | 1·00 |
| | | a. No stop after "F" | £140 | £150 |
| E 7 | **62** | 3 a. orange-brown | 70 | 60 |
| | | a. No stop after "F" | £130 | £140 |
| E 8 | **63** | 4 a. olive-green | 60 | 60 |
| | | a. No stop after "F" | £180 | £190 |
| E 9 | **65** | 8 a. purple | 1·00 | 1·00 |
| | | a. No stop after "F" | £190 | £200 |
| E10 | | 8 a. mauve | 6·50 | 8·00 |
| E11 | **66** | 12 a. dull claret | 6·50 | 9·00 |
| | | a. No stop after "F" | £225 | £225 |
| | | b. Opt double, one albino | 55·00 | |
| E12 | | 12 a. claret | 2·25 | 5·00 |
| E13 | **67** | 1 r. red-brown and blue-green | 2·50 | 4·00 |
| | | a. Opt double, one albino | £100 | |
| E1/13 | | *Set of* 10 | 8·00 | 12·00 |

# INDIAN CUSTODIAN FORCES IN KOREA

**भारतीय**
**संरक्षा कटक**
**कोरिया**

(K 1)

**1953** (17 Oct). *Stamps of India optd with Type* K 1.

| No. | Type | Description | Unused | Used |
|---|---|---|---|---|
| K 1 | **307** | 3 p. slate-violet | 70 | 3·00 |
| K 2 | **308** | 6 p. purple-brown | 70 | 3·00 |
| K 3 | **309** | 9 p. yellow-green | 70 | 3·00 |
| K 4 | **328** | 1 a. turquoise | 70 | 3·00 |
| K 5 | **311** | 2 a. carmine | 90 | 3·00 |
| K 6 | **313** | 2½ a. lake | 1·00 | 4·00 |
| K 7 | **312** | 3 a. brown-orange | 1·25 | 4·00 |
| K 8 | **314** | 4 a. bright blue | 1·75 | 4·50 |
| K 9 | **315** | 6 a. violet | 6·50 | 8·50 |
| K10 | **316** | 8 a. turquoise-green | 3·25 | 8·50 |
| K11 | **317** | 12 a. dull blue | 4·50 | 16·00 |
| K12 | **318** | 1 r. dull violet and green | 6·00 | 17·00 |
| K1/12 | | *Set of* 12 | 24·00 | 70·00 |

# INDIAN U.N. FORCE IN CONGO

**U.N. FORCE**
**(INDIA)**
**CONGO**

(U 1)

**1962** (15 Jan). *Stamps of India optd with Type* U 1. *W* **69** *(sideways)* (13 *n.p.*) *or W* **374** *(others).*

| No. | Type | Description | Unused | Used |
|---|---|---|---|---|
| U1 | **361** | 1 n.p. blue-green | 60 | 1·25 |
| U2 | | 2 n.p. light brown | 60 | 70 |
| U3 | | 5 n.p. bright green | 60 | 45 |
| U4 | | 8 n.p. light blue-green | 65 | 30 |
| U5 | | 13 n.p. bright carmine-red | 70 | 40 |
| U6 | | 50 n.p. orange | 70 | 70 |
| U1/6 | | *Set of* 6 | 3·50 | 3·50 |

# INDIAN U.N. FORCE IN GAZA (PALESTINE) UNEF

**UNEF**

(G 1)

**1965** (15 Jan). *No.* 492 *of India optd with Type* G 1.

| No. | Type | Description | Unused | Used |
|---|---|---|---|---|
| G1 | **449** | 15 p. slate (C.) | 40 | 2·00 |

## INTERNATIONAL COMMISSION IN INDO-CHINA

The International Control Commissions for Indo-China were established in August 1954 as part of the Geneva Declaration which partitioned Vietnam and sought to achieve stable settlements in Cambodia and Laos. The three supervisory commissions were chaired by India with Canada and Poland as the other members. Joint inspection teams of servicemen from the three countries were also provided.

The Indian contingent included a postal unit which handled mail for the three commissions and the inspection teams. The unit arrived in Indo-China on 3 September 1954 and opened field post offices at Saigon (F.P.O. 742), Hanoi (F.P.O. 743), Vientiane (F.P.O. 744) and Pnom Penh (F.P.O. 745).

| अन्तर्राष्ट्रीय आयोग कम्बोज | अन्तर्राष्ट्रीय आयोग लाओस | अन्तर्राष्ट्रीय आयोग वियत नाम |
|---|---|---|
| (N 1) | (N 2) | (N 3) |

**1954** (1 Dec). *Stamps of India. W* **69**.

| | | | | |
|---|---|---|---|---|
| | | *(a) Optd as Type* N **1**, *for use in Cambodia* | | |
| N 1 | **307** | 3 p. slate-violet | 60 | 2·50 |
| N 2 | **328** | 1 a. turquoise | 90 | 75 |
| N 3 | **311** | 2 a. carmine | 90 | 80 |
| N 4 | **316** | 8 a. turquoise-green | 2·00 | 3·50 |
| N 5 | **317** | 12 a. dull blue | 2·25 | 4·00 |
| | | *(b) Optd as Type* N **2**, *for use in Laos* | | |
| N 6 | **307** | 3 p. slate-violet | 60 | 2·50 |
| N 7 | **328** | 1 a. turquoise | 90 | 75 |
| N 8 | **311** | 2 a. carmine | 90 | 80 |
| N 9 | **316** | 8 a. turquoise-green | 2·00 | 3·50 |
| N10 | **317** | 12 a. dull blue | 2·25 | 4·00 |
| | | *(c) Optd as Type* N **3**, *for use in Vietnam* | | |
| N11 | **307** | 3 p. slate-violet | 60 | 2·50 |
| N12 | **328** | 1 a. turquoise | 90 | 75 |
| N13 | **311** | 2 a. carmine | 90 | 80 |
| N14 | **316** | 8 a. turquoise-green | 2·00 | 3·50 |
| N15 | **317** | 12 a. dull blue | 2·25 | 4·00 |
| N1/15 | | *Set of* 15 | 17·00 | 30·00 |

**1957** (1 Apr). *Stamps of India. W* **69** *(sideways)*.

| | | | | |
|---|---|---|---|---|
| | | *(a) Optd as Type* N **1**, *for use in Cambodia* | | |
| N16 | **361** | 2 n.p. light brown | 40 | 30 |
| N17 | | 6 n.p. grey | 35 | 30 |
| N18 | | 13 n.p. bright carmine-red | 50 | 40 |
| N19 | | 50 n.p. orange | 1·75 | 1·25 |
| N20 | | 75 n.p. reddish purple | 1·75 | 1·25 |
| | | *(b) Optd as Type* N **2**, *for use in Laos* | | |
| N21 | **361** | 2 n.p. light brown | 40 | 30 |
| N22 | | 6 n.p. grey | 35 | 30 |
| N23 | | 13 n.p. bright carmine-red | 50 | 40 |
| N24 | | 50 n.p. orange | 1·75 | 1·25 |
| N25 | | 75 n.p. reddish purple | 1·75 | 1·25 |
| | | *(c) Optd as Type* N **3**, *for use in Vietnam* | | |
| N26 | **361** | 2 n.p. light brown | 40 | 30 |
| N27 | | 6 n.p. grey | 35 | 30 |
| N28 | | 13 n.p. bright carmine-red | 50 | 40 |
| N29 | | 50 n.p. orange | 1·75 | 1·25 |
| N30 | | 75 n.p. reddish purple | 1·75 | 1·25 |
| N16/30 | | *Set of* 15 | 12·50 | 9·50 |

F.P.O. 744 (Vientiane) was closed on 25 July 1958 and F.P.O. 745 (Pnom Penh) on 26 June 1958.

**1960** (Sept)–**65**. *Stamps of India. W* **374**.

| | | | | |
|---|---|---|---|---|
| | | *(a) Optd as Type* N **1**, *for use in Cambodia* | | |
| N32 | **361** | 2 n.p. light brown (1962) | 15 | 2·25 |
| | | *(b) Optd as Type* N **2**, *for use in Laos* | | |
| N38 | **361** | 2 n.p. light brown (1962) | 15 | 2·25 |
| N39 | | 3 n.p. deep brown (1.8.63) | 10 | 20 |
| N40 | | 5 n.p. bright green (1.8.63) | 10 | 15 |
| N41 | | 50 n.p. orange (1965) | 2·50 | 2·25 |
| N42 | | 75 n.p. reddish purple (1965) | 2·50 | 2·50 |
| | | *(c) Optd as Type* N **3**, *for use in Vietnam* | | |
| N43 | **361** | 1 n.p. blue-green | 10 | 20 |
| N44 | | 2 n.p. light brown (1962) | 15 | 2·25 |
| N45 | | 3 n.p. deep brown (1963) | 10 | 20 |
| N46 | | 5 n.p. bright green (1963) | 10 | 15 |
| N47 | | 50 n.p. orange (1965) | 2·50 | 2·25 |
| N48 | | 75 n.p. reddish-purple (1965) | 2·50 | 2·50 |
| N32/48 | | *Set of* 12 | 9·50 | 15·00 |

F.P.O. 744 (Vientiane) re-opened on 22 May 1961.

| अंनिआ ICC | ICC |
|---|---|
| (N 4) | (N 5) |

**1965** (15 Jan). *No.* 492 *of India optd with Type* N **4**, *for use in Laos and Vietnam.*

| | | | | |
|---|---|---|---|---|
| N49 | **449** | 15 p. slate (C.) | 30 | 2·00 |

F.P.O. 743 (Hanoi) was closed in 1966.

**1968** (2 Oct). *Nos.* 504/5, 506, 509/10, 515 *and* 517/18 *etc of India optd as Type* N **5**, *in red, for use in Laos and Vietnam.*

| | | | |
|---|---|---|---|
| N50 | 2 p. red-brown | 10 | 80 |
| N51 | 3 p. brown-olive | 10 | 80 |
| N52 | 5 p. cerise | 10 | 40 |
| N53 | 10 p. new blue | 75 | 75 |
| N54 | 15 p. bronze-green | 50 | 75 |
| N55 | 60 p. deep grey | 35 | 90 |
| N56 | 1 r. red-brown and plum | 50 | 1·40 |
| N57 | 2 r. new blue and deep slate-violet | 1·00 | 4·25 |
| N50/7 | *Set of* 8 | 3·00 | 9·00 |

The final two field post offices, No. 742 (Saigon) and No. 744 (Vientiane) closed at the end of 1968 when the inspection teams withdrew.

### *COVER PRICES*

Cover factors are quoted at the beginning of each country for most issues to 1945. An explanation of the system can be found on page x. The factors quoted do not, however, apply to philatelic covers.

## INDIAN NATIONAL ARMY

The following are stated to have been used in the Japanese-occupied areas of India during the drive on Imphal. Issued by the Indian National Army.

Typo. No gum. Perf 11½ or imperf. 1 p. violet, 1 p. maroon, 1 a. green.

## JAPANESE OCCUPATION OF THE ANDAMAN AND NICOBAR ISLANDS

The Andaman Islands in the Bay of Bengal were occupied on the 23 March 1942 and the Nicobar Islands in July 1942. Civil administration was resumed in October 1945.

The following Indian stamps were surcharged with large figures preceded by a decimal point:—

*Postage stamps*—.3 on ½ a. (No. 248), .5 on 1 a. (No. 250), .10 on 2 a. (No. 236*b*), .30 on 6 a. (No. 274).

*Official stamps*—.10 on 1 a. 3 p. (No. O146*b*), .20 on 3 p. (No. O143) from booklet panes, .20 in red on 3 p. (No. O143).

## INDIAN CONVENTION STATES

The following issues resulted from a series of postal conventions agreed between the Imperial Government and the state administrations of Patiala (1 October 1884), Gwalior, Jind and Nabha (1 July 1885), and Chamba and Faridkot (1 January 1887).

Under the terms of these conventions the British Indian Post Office supplied overprinted British India issues to the state administrations which, in turn, had to conform to a number of conditions covering the issue of stamps, rates of postage and the exchange of mail.

Such overprinted issues were valid for postage within the state of issue, to other "Convention States" and to destinations in British India.

Stamps of Chamba, Gwalior, Jind, Nabha and Patiala ceased to be valid for postage on 1 January 1951, when they were replaced by those of the Republic of India, valid from 1 April 1950.

***Stamps of India overprinted***

In the Queen Victoria issues we omit varieties due to broken type, including the numerous small "A" varieties which may have come about through damaged type. We do, however, list the small "G", small "R" and tall "R" in "GWALIOR" as these were definitely the result of the use of type of the wrong size.

Variations in the length of the words due to unequal spacing when setting are also omitted.

### CHAMBA

| PRICES FOR STAMPS ON COVER | |
|---|---|
| Nos. 1/27 | *from* × 15 |
| Nos. 28/120 | *from* × 10 |
| Nos. O1/86 | *from* × 20 |

| CHAMBA STATE | CHAMBA |
|---|---|
| (1) | (2) |

**1886–95.** *Queen Victoria. Optd with T* **1**.

| | | | | |
|---|---|---|---|---|
| 1 | **23** | ½ a. blue-green | 10 | 25 |
| | | a. "CHMABA" | £160 | £200 |
| | | b. "8TATE" | £250 | |
| | | c. Opt double | | |
| 2 | **25** | 1 a. brown-purple | 20 | 40 |
| | | a. "CHMABA" | £300 | £375 |
| | | b. "8TATE" | £425 | |
| 3 | | 1 a. plum | 55 | 45 |
| 4 | **26** | 1½ a. sepia (1895) | 60 | 4·00 |
| 5 | **27** | 2 a. dull blue | 35 | 65 |
| | | b. "CHMABA" | £850 | £1000 |
| | | c. "8TATE" | £950 | |
| 6 | | 2 a. ultramarine | 50 | 85 |
| 7 | **36** | 2½ a. green (1895) | 14·00 | 40·00 |
| 8 | **28** | 3 a. orange (1887) | 3·50 | 10·00 |
| 9 | | 3 a. brown-orange (1891) | 40 | 2·00 |
| | | a. "CHMABA" | £1900 | £1900 |
| | | b. Opt inverted | | |
| 10 | **29** | 4 a. olive-green | 60 | 2·25 |
| | | a. "CHMABA" | £750 | £850 |
| | | b. "8TATE" | £1100 | |
| 11 | | 4 a. slate-green | 1·25 | 3·00 |
| 12 | **21** | 6 a. olive-bistre (1890) | 90 | 3·25 |
| 13 | | 6 a. bistre-brown | 2·50 | 4·75 |
| 14 | **31** | 8 a. dull mauve (1887) | 2·50 | 5·00 |
| | | a. "CHMABA" | £1700 | £1800 |
| 15 | | 8 a. magenta (1895) | 1·25 | 4·50 |
| 16 | **32** | 12 a. purple/*red* (1890) | 1·75 | 4·00 |
| | | a. "CHMABA" | £2500 | |
| | | b. "SLATE" | £2750 | |
| 17 | **33** | 1 r. slate (1887) | 19·00 | 55·00 |
| | | a. "CHMABA" | £4000 | |
| 18 | **37** | 1 r. green and carmine (1895) | 1·60 | 4·25 |
| 19 | **38** | 2 r. carmine and yellow-brown (1895) | 50·00 | £110 |
| 20 | | 3 r. brown and green (1895) | 55·00 | £100 |
| 21 | | 5 r. ultramarine and violet (1895) | 65·00 | £140 |
| | | a. Opt double, one albino | £110 | |
| 1/21 | | *Set of* 15 | £190 | £400 |

**1900–4.** *Colours changed.*

| | | | | |
|---|---|---|---|---|
| 22 | **40** | 3 p. carmine | 10 | 20 |
| 23 | | 3 p. grey (1904) | 15 | 65 |
| | | a. Opt inverted | 55·00 | |
| 24 | **23** | ½ a. pale yellow-green (1902) | 15 | 60 |
| 25 | | ½ a. yellow-green (1903) | 10 | 30 |
| 26 | **25** | 1 a. carmine (1902) | 10 | 20 |
| 27 | **27** | 2 a. pale violet (1903) | 5·00 | 13·00 |
| 22/7 | | *Set of* 5 | 5·00 | 11·00 |

**1903–5.** *King Edward VII. Optd with T* **1**.

| | | | | |
|---|---|---|---|---|
| 28 | **41** | 3 p. pale grey | 10 | 50 |
| 29 | | 3 p. slate-grey (1905) | 10 | 50 |
| 30 | **42** | ½ a. green | 10 | 20 |
| 31 | **43** | 1 a. carmine | 15 | 20 |
| 32 | **44** | 2 a. pale violet (1904) | 30 | 80 |
| 33 | | 2 a. mauve | 30 | 70 |
| 34 | **46** | 3 a. orange-brown (1905) | 70 | 2·00 |
| 35 | **47** | 4 a. olive (1904) | 90 | 3·50 |
| 36 | **48** | 6 a. olive-bistre (1905) | 1·40 | 5·50 |
| 37 | **49** | 8 a. purple (*shades*) (1904) | 1·25 | 4·50 |
| 38 | | 8 a. claret | 3·00 | 9·00 |
| 39 | **50** | 12 a. purple/*red* (1905) | 1·75 | 6·00 |
| 40 | **51** | 1 r. green and carmine (1904) | 2·00 | 7·00 |
| 28/40 | | *Set of* 10 | 8·00 | 27·00 |

**1907.** *Nos.* 149/50 *of India optd with T* **1**.

| | | | | |
|---|---|---|---|---|
| 41 | **53** | ½ a. green | 20 | 90 |
| 42 | **54** | 1 a. carmine | 25 | 90 |

**1913.** *King George V optd with T* **1**.

| | | | | |
|---|---|---|---|---|
| 43 | **55** | 3 p. slate-grey | 10 | 30 |
| 44 | **56** | ½ a. green | 10 | 30 |
| 45 | **57** | 1 a. rose-carmine | 75 | 1·25 |
| 46 | | 1 a. aniline carmine | 10 | 50 |
| 47 | **59** | 2 a. mauve | 30 | 1·50 |

48 **62** 3 a. orange-brown .. .. .. 55 2·25
49 **63** 4 a. olive .. .. .. 65 1·60
50 **64** 6 a. olive-bistre .. .. .. 65 2·00
51 **65** 8 a. purple .. .. .. 90 3·50
52 **66** 12 a. dull claret .. .. .. 1·40 7·00
53 **67** 1 r. brown and green .. .. 4·00 7·50
a. Opt double, one albino .. .. 25·00
43/53 .. .. .. .. *Set of* 10 8·00 24·00

**1921**. *No.* 192 *of India optd with T* **2**.
54 **57** 9 p. on 1 a. rose-carmine .. .. 80 7·50

**1923–27**. *Optd with T* **1**. *New values, etc.*
55 **57** 1 a. chocolate .. .. .. 15 80
56 **58** 1½ a. chocolate (Type A) .. .. 14·00 50·00
57 1½ a. chocolate (Type B) (1924) .. 30 2·75
58 1½ a. rose-carmine (Type B) (1927) .. 60 5·50
59 **61** 2½ a. ultramarine .. .. .. 50 2·75
60 2½ a. orange (1927) .. .. 70 4·25
61 **62** 3 a. ultramarine (1924) .. .. 1·10 5·00
55/61 .. .. .. .. *Set of* 7 15·00 65·00
Nos. 58 and 60 with inverted overprint are of clandestine origin.

CHAMBA STATE (3) CHAMBA STATE (4)

**1927–37**. *King George V (Nasik printing, wmk Mult Star). Optd at Nasik with T* **3** *or* **4** *(1 r.).*
62 **55** 3 p. slate (1928) .. .. .. 10 35
63 **56** ½ a. green (1928) .. .. .. 10 45
64 **80** 9 p. deep green (1932) .. .. 45 2·50
65 **57** 1 a. chocolate .. .. .. 15 10
66 **82** 1¼ a. mauve (1932) .. .. .. 30 1·00
67 **58** 1½ a. rose-carmine (B) (1932) .. .. 80 1·75
68 **70** 2 a. purple (1928) .. .. .. 30 55
69 **61** 2½ a. orange (1932) .. .. .. 40 3·50
70 **62** 3 a. bright blue (1928) .. .. 60 3·50
71 **71** 4 a. sage-green (1928) .. .. 40 1·40
72 **64** 6 a. bistre (1937) .. .. 24·00 75·00
73 **65** 8 a. reddish purple (1928) .. .. 60 3·50
74 **66** 12 a. claret (1928) .. .. .. 85 4·75
75 **67** 1 r. chocolate and green (1928) .. 2·50 7·50
62/75 .. .. .. .. *Set of* 14 28·00 95·00
The 9 p. exists printed by lithography or typography.

**1935–36**. *New types and colours. Optd with T* **3**.
76 **79** ½ a. green .. .. .. 30 2·00
77 **81** 1 a. chocolate .. .. .. 40 40
78 **59** 2 a. vermilion (No. 236*a*) .. .. 30 5·50
79 2 a. vermilion (*small die*, No. 236*b*) .. 80·00 90·00
80 **62** 3 a. carmine .. .. .. 1·00 3·00
81 **63** 4 a. sage-green (1936) .. .. 80 2·50
76/81 .. .. .. .. *Set of* 6 80·00 95·00

CHAMBA STATE (5) CHAMBA (6) CHAMBA (7)

**1938**. *King George VI. Nos.* 247/64 *optd with T* **3** *(3 p. to 1 a.), T* **5** *(2 a. to 12 a.) or T* **4** *(rupee values).*
82 **91** 3 p. slate .. .. .. 1·75 3·75
83 ½ a. red-brown .. .. .. 60 2·25
84 9 p. green .. .. .. 1·75 8·00
85 1 a. carmine .. .. .. 90 65
86 **92** 2 a. vermilion .. .. .. 1·40 3·75
87 – 2½ a. bright violet .. .. .. 1·50 7·00
88 – 3 a. yellow-green .. .. .. 4·00 9·00
89 – 3½ a. bright blue .. .. .. 2·25 9·00
90 – 4 a. brown .. .. .. 6·00 5·50
91 – 6 a. turquoise-green .. .. 7·50 19·00
92 – 8 a. slate-violet .. .. .. 6·50 15·00
93 – 12 a. lake .. .. .. 3·25 20·00
94 **93** 1 r. grey and red-brown .. .. 16·00 24·00
95 2 r. purple and brown .. .. 28·00 85·00
96 5 r. green and blue .. .. 50·00 £140
97 10 r. purple and claret .. .. £110 £275
98 15 r. brown and green .. .. £225 £425
99 25 r. slate-violet and purple .. £325 £550
82/99 .. .. .. .. *Set of* 18 £700 £1400

**1942–47**. *Optd with T* **6** *(to 12 a.), "CHAMBA" only, as in T* **5** *(14 a.) or T* **7** *(rupee values). (a) Stamps of* 1937.
100 **91** ½ a. red-brown .. .. .. 6·50 8·00
101 1 a. carmine .. .. .. 9·00 9·00
102 **93** 1 r. grey and red-brown .. .. 19·00 25·00
103 2 r. purple and brown .. .. 24·00 80·00
104 5 r. green and blue .. .. 55·00 £120
105 10 r. purple and claret .. .. 90·00 £225
106 15 r. brown and green .. .. £225 £375
107 25 r. slate-violet and purple .. £325 £500
100/107 .. .. .. .. *Set of* 8 £650 £1200

(*b*) *Stamps of* 1940–43
108 **100*a*** 3 p. slate .. .. .. 40 1·75
109 ½ a. purple (1943) .. .. 60 1·00
110 9 p. green .. .. .. 50 3·50
111 1 a. carmine (1943) .. .. 90 1·25
112 **101** 1½ a. dull violet (1943) .. .. 60 2·75
113 2 a. vermilion (1943) .. .. 1·40 3·50
114 3 a. bright violet .. .. 2·00 5·50
115 3½ a. bright blue .. .. 2·50 12·00
116 **102** 4 a. brown .. .. .. 3·00 4·75
117 6 a. turquoise-green .. .. 7·50 18·00
118 8 a. slate-violet .. .. 8·50 22·00
119 12 a. lake .. .. .. 15·00 30·00
120 **103** 14 a. purple (1947) .. .. 4·00 3·00
108/120 .. .. .. .. *Set of* 13 42·00 £100
The 3 a. exists printed by lithography or typography.

OFFICIAL STAMPS

SERVICE

CHAMBA STATE (O 1)

**1886–98**. *Queen Victoria. Optd with Type* O **1**.
O 1 **23** ½ a. blue-green .. .. .. 10 10
a. "CHMABA" .. .. .. £120 £130
b. "SERV CE" .. .. .. £750
c. "8TATE" .. .. .. £275
O 2 **25** 1 a. brown-purple .. .. .. 20 25
a. "CHMABA" .. .. .. £200 £225
b. "SERV CE" .. .. .. £750
c. "8TATE" .. .. .. £400
d. "SERVICE" double .. .. £450 £450
O 3 **25** 1 a. plum .. .. .. 25 10
O 4 **27** 2 a. dull blue .. .. .. 55 70
a. "CHMABA" .. .. .. £550 £700
O 5 2 a. ultramarine (1887) .. .. 45 70
O 6 **28** 3 a. orange (1890) .. .. ..
O 7 3 a. brown-orange (1891) .. .. 1·25 4·00
a. "CHMABA" .. .. .. £1200 £1400
O 8 **29** 4 a. olive-green .. .. .. 45 1·40
a. "CHMABA" .. .. .. £550 £700
b. "SERV CE" .. .. .. £1300
c. "8TATE" .. .. .. £1200
O 9 4 a. slate-green .. .. .. 70 1·75
O10 **21** 6 a. olive-bistre (1890) .. .. 1·50 4·00
O11 6 a. bistre-brown .. .. ..
O12 **31** 8 a. dull mauve (1887) .. .. 80 2·00
a. "CHMABA" .. .. .. £1800 £1900
O13 8 a. magenta (1895) .. .. 70 1·25
O14 **32** 12 a. purple/*red* (1890) .. .. 7·00 20·00
a. "CHMABA" .. .. .. £2250
b. "SLATE" .. .. .. £2500
O15 **33** 1 r. slate (1890) .. .. 11·00 42·00
a. "CHMABA" .. .. .. £1800
O16 **37** 1 r. green and carmine (1898) .. 5·00 12·00
O1/16 .. .. .. .. *Set of* 10 25·00 75·00
Printings up to and including that of December 1895 had the "SERVICE" overprint applied to sheets of stamps already overprinted with Type 1. From the printing of September 1898 onwards both "SERVICE" and "CHAMBA STATE" were overprinted at the same time. Nos. O6, O8 and O12 only exist using the first method, and No. O16 was only printed using the second.

**1902–4**. *Colours changed. Optd as Type* O **1**.
O17 **40** 3 p. grey (1904) .. .. .. 15 40
O18 **23** ½ a. pale yellow-green .. .. 15 1·25
O19 ½ a. yellow-green .. .. .. 75 40
O20 **25** 1 a. carmine .. .. .. 30 40
O21 **27** 2 a. pale violet (1903) .. .. 6·00 13·00
O17/21 .. .. .. .. *Set of* 4 6·00 13·00

**1903–5**. *King Edward VII. Stamps of India optd as Type* O **1**.
O22 **41** 3 p. pale grey .. .. .. 15 15
O23 3 p. slate-grey (1905) .. .. 10 50
O24 **42** ½ a. yellow-green .. .. .. 10 10
O25 **43** 1 a. carmine .. .. .. 15 20
O26 **44** 2 a. pale violet (1904) .. .. 1·00 50
O27 2 a. mauve .. .. .. 40 40
O28 **47** 4 a. olive (1905) .. .. .. 1·50 4·75
O29 **49** 8 a. purple (1905) .. .. 1·60 5·00
O30 8 a. claret .. .. .. 4·00 8·00
O31 **51** 1 r. green and carmine (1905) .. 1·25 3·50
O22/31 .. .. .. .. *Set of* 7 4·50 12·50
The 2 a. mauve King Edward VII, overprinted "On H.M.S.", was discovered in Calcutta, but was not sent to Chamba, and is an unissued variety (*Price un.* £22).

**1907**. *Nos.* 149/50 *of India, optd with Type* O **1**.
O32 **53** ½ a. green .. .. .. 20 50
a. Opt inverted .. .. .. £1700 £1700
O33 **54** 1 a. carmine .. .. .. 50 40
The error, No. O32a was due to an inverted cliché which was corrected after a few sheets had been printed.

**1913–14**. *King George V Official stamps (wmk Single Star) optd with T* **1**.
O34 **55** 3 p. slate-grey .. .. .. 20 40
O35 3 p. grey .. .. .. 20 30
O36 **56** ½ a. yellow-green .. .. .. 10 10
O37 ½ a. pale blue-green .. .. 35 15
O38 **57** 1 a. aniline carmine .. .. 10 10
O39 1 a. rose-carmine .. .. 1·50 30
O40 **59** 2 a. mauve (1914) .. .. 75 3·75
O41 **63** 4 a. olive .. .. .. 75 2·50
O42 **65** 8 a. purple .. .. .. 1·25 3·75
O43 **67** 1 r. brown and green (1914) .. 2·75 8·00
a. Opt double, one albino
O34/43 .. .. .. .. *Set of* 7 5·25 17·00
No. O36 with inverted overprint and No. O39 with double or inverted overprint (on gummed side) are of clandestine origin.

**1914**. *King George V. Optd with Type* O **1**.
O44 **59** 2 a. mauve .. .. .. 6·00
O45 **63** 4 a. olive .. .. .. 9·00

**1921**. *No.* O97 *of India optd with T* **2** *at top.*
O46 **57** 9 p. on 1 a. rose-carmine .. .. 15 1·75

**1925**. *As* 1913–14. *New colour.*
O47 **57** 1 a. chocolate .. .. .. 40 40

CHAMBA STATE SERVICE (O 2) CHAMBA STATE SERVICE (O 3)

**1927–39**. *King George V (Nasik printing, wmk Mult Star), optd at Nasik with Type* O **2** *or* O **3** *(rupee values).*
O48 **55** 3 p. slate (1928) .. .. .. 20 25
O49 **56** ½ a. green (1928) .. .. .. 30 15
O50 **80** 9 p. deep green (1932) .. .. 35 3·00
O51 **57** 1 a. chocolate .. .. .. 10 10
O52 **82** 1¼ a. mauve (1932) .. .. 1·50 40
O53 **70** 2 a. purple (1928) .. .. 40 40
O54 **71** 4 a. sage-green (1928) .. .. 40 40
O55 **65** 8 a. reddish purple (1930) .. .. 1·40 4·00
O56 **66** 12 a. claret (1928) .. .. 1·25 7·00
O57 **67** 1 r. chocolate and green (1930) .. 6·00 11·00
O58 2 r. carmine and orange (1939) .. 12·00 75·00
O59 5 r. ultramarine and purple (1939) .. 28·00 £120
O60 10 r. green and scarlet (1939) .. 38·00 £120
O48/60 .. .. .. .. *Set of* 13 80·00 £300

**1935–39**. *New types and colours. Optd with Type* O **2**.
O61 **79** ½ a. green .. .. .. 30 30
O62 **81** 1 a. chocolate .. .. .. 50 30
O63 **59** 2 a. vermilion .. .. .. 1·25 80
O64 2 a. vermilion (*small die*) (1939) .. 70 3·50
O65 **63** 4 a. sage-green (1936) .. .. 85 1·00
O61/5 .. .. .. .. *Set of* 5 3·25 5·25

**1938–40**. *King George VI. Optd with Type* O **2** *or* O **3** *(rupee values).*
O66 **91** 9 p. green .. .. .. 3·75 8·50
O67 1 a. carmine .. .. .. 2·75 1·00
O68 **93** 1 r. grey and red-brown (1940?) .. £650 £750
O69 2 r. purple and brown (1939) .. 45·00 £130
O70 5 r. green and blue (1939) .. 70·00 £200
O71 10 r. purple and claret (1939) .. £130 £325
O66/71 .. .. .. .. *Set of* 6 £800 £1300

CHAMBA SERVICE (O 4)

**1940–43**. (*a*) *Official stamps optd with T* **6**.
O72 **O 20** 3 p. slate .. .. .. 60 40
O73 ½ a. red-brown .. .. .. 6·50 1·75
O74 ½ a. purple (1943) .. .. 60 60
O75 9 p. green .. .. .. 1·00 1·50
O76 1 a. carmine (1941) .. .. 60 50
O77 1 a. 3 p. yellow-brown (1941) .. 25·00 10·00
O78 1½ a. dull violet (1943) .. .. 3·50 2·00
O79 2 a. vermilion (1941) .. .. 2·50 1·50
O80 2½ a. bright violet (1941) .. .. 1·25 7·00
O81 4 a. brown .. .. .. 3·00 4·00
O82 8 a. slate-violet .. .. .. 5·50 11·00

(*b*) *Postage stamps optd with Type* O **4**.
O83 **93** 1 r. grey and red-brown (1942) .. 28·00 60·00
O84 2 r. purple and brown (1942) .. 42·00 £100
O85 5 r. green and blue (1942) .. 80·00 £170
O86 10 r. purple and claret (1942) .. £140 £300
O72/86 .. .. .. .. *Set of* 15 £300 £600

## FARIDKOT

For earlier issues, see under INDIAN FEUDATORY STATES

| PRICES FOR STAMPS ON COVER | |
|---|---|
| Nos. 1/17 | *from* × 25 |
| Nos. O1/15 | *from* × 30 |

FARIDKOT STATE (1)

**1887** (1 Jan)–**1900**. *Queen Victoria. Optd with T* **1**.
1 **23** ½ a. deep green .. .. .. 20 30
a. "ARIDKOT" .. .. ..
b. "FAR DKOT" .. .. .. — £500
2 **25** 1 a. brown-purple .. .. .. 35 85
3 1 a. plum .. .. .. 50 60
4 **27** 2 a. blue .. .. .. 1·50 2·25
5 2 a. deep blue .. .. .. 1·60 3·00
6 **28** 3 a. orange .. .. .. 2·50 3·50
7 3 a. brown-orange (1893) .. .. 1·00 1·75
8 **29** 4 a. olive-green .. .. .. 2·00 4·50
a. "ARIDKOT" .. .. .. £550
9 4 a. slate-green .. .. .. 2·25 7·50
10 **21** 6 a. olive-bistre .. .. .. 7·00 15·00
a. "ARIDKOT" .. .. .. £700
11 6 a. bistre-brown .. .. .. 1·75 6·50
12 **31** 8 a. dull mauve .. .. .. 3·25 12·00
a. "ARIDKOT" .. .. .. £1100
13 8 a. magenta .. .. .. 5·50 30·00
14 **32** 12 a. purple/*red* (1900) .. .. 25·00 £150
15 **33** 1 r. slate .. .. .. 22·00 £130
a. "ARIDKOT" .. .. .. £1600
16 **37** 1 r. green and carmine (1893) .. 17·00 26·00
1/16 .. .. .. .. *Set of* 10 65·00 £300
The ½ a., 1 a., 2 a., 3 a., 4 a., 8 a. and 1 r. (No. 16) are known with broken "O" (looking like a "C") in "FARIDKOT".

**1900**. *Optd with T* **1**.
17 **40** 3 p. carmine .. .. .. 50 12·00

OFFICIAL STAMPS

SERVICE

FARIDKOT STATE (O 1)

**1886–98**. *Queen Victoria. Optd with Type* O **1**.
O 1 **23** ½ a. deep green .. .. .. 15 30
a. "SERV CE" .. .. .. £650
b. "FAR DKOT" .. .. ..
c. Thin seriffed "I" in "SERVICE" .. 65·00
O 2 **25** 1 a. brown-purple .. .. .. 40 75
a. Thin seriffed "I" in "SERVICE" .. 80·00
O 3 1 a. plum .. .. .. 45 55
a. "SERV CE" .. .. .. £800
O 4 **27** 2 a. dull blue .. .. .. 90 4·00
a. "SERV CE" .. .. .. £900
O 5 2 a. deep blue .. .. .. 70 5·00
O 6 **28** 3 a. orange .. .. .. 3·25 3·25
O 7 3 a. brown-orange (12.98) .. .. 1·00 10·00
a. Thin seriffed "I" in "SERVICE" .. £180
O 8 **29** 4 a. olive-green .. .. .. 1·40 5·50
a. "SERV CE" .. .. .. £1000
b. "ARIDKOT" .. .. ..
O 9 4 a. slate-green .. .. .. 3·00 12·00

O10 **21** 6 a. olive-bistre .. .. .. 18·00 35·00
a. "ARIDKOT" .. .. .. £550
b. "SERVIC" .. .. .. .. £850
O11 6 a. bistre-brown .. .. .. 10·00 13·00
O12 **31** 8 a. dull mauve .. .. .. 2·50 7·50
a. "SERV CE" .. .. .. £1100
O13 8 a. magenta .. .. .. 5·50 30·00
O14 **33** 1 r. slate .. .. .. 25·00 65·00
O15 **37** 1 r. green and carmine (12.98) .. 42·00 £160
a. Thin seriffed "I" in "SERVICE" ..
O1/15 .. .. .. .. *Set of* 9 75·00 £225

The ½ a., 1 a., 2 a., 3 a., 4 a., 8 a. and 1 r. (No. O15) are known with the broken "O".

Printings up to and including that of November 1895 had the "SERVICE" overprint applied to sheets already overprinted with Type 1. From December 1898 onwards "SERVICE" and "FARIDKOT STATE" were overprinted at one operation to provide fresh supplies of Nos. O1/3, O7 and O15.

The thin seriffed "I" variety occurs on the December 1898 overprinting only.

This State ceased to use overprinted stamps after 31 March 1901.

## GWALIOR

**PRICES FOR STAMPS ON COVER**

| | |
|---|---|
| Nos. 1/3 | *from* × 10 |
| Nos. 4/11 | — |
| Nos. 12/66 | *from* × 5 |
| Nos. 67/128 | *from* × 4 |
| Nos. 129/37 | *from* × 5 |
| Nos. O1/94 | *from* × 12 |

**OVERPRINTS.** From 1885 to 1926 these were applied by the Government of India Central Printing Press, Calcutta, and from 1927 at the Security Press, Nasik, *unless otherwise stated.*

गवालियर

GWALIOR
(1)

GWALIOR
गवालियर
(2)

GWALIOR
Small "G"

GWALIOR
Small "R"

GWALIOP
Tall "R"
(original state)

GWALIOR
Tall "R"
(damaged state)

**OVERPRINT VARIETIES OF TYPE 2.**

Small "G"—Occurs on R.7/11 from June 1900 printing of ½, 1, 2, 3, 4 a. and 3 p. (No. 38), and on an unknown position from May 1901 printing of 2, 3 and 5 r.

Small "R"—Occurs on R. 9/3 from June 1900 printing of 3 p. to 4 a. and on R.2/3 from May 1901 printing of 2, 3 and 5 r.

Tall "R" —Occurs on R.20/2 from printings between June 1900 and May 1907. The top of the letter is damaged on printings from February 1903 onwards.

**1885–97.** *Queen Victoria. I. Optd. with T* **1**.

(*a*) *Space between two lines of overprint* 13 *mm. Hindi inscription* 13 *to* 14 *mm long* (May 1885)

1 **23** ½ a. blue-green .. .. .. 48·00 11·00
2 **25** 1 a. brown-purple .. .. .. 45·00 17·00
3 **27** 2 a. dull blue .. .. .. 35·00 11·00
1/3 .. .. .. .. *Set of* 3 £110 35·00

A variety exists of the ½ a. in which the space between the two lines of overprint is only 9½ mm but this is probably from a proof sheet.

(*b*) *Space between two lines of overprint* 15 *mm on* 4 *a. and* 6 *a. and* 16 *to* 17 *mm on other values* (June 1885)

A. *Hindi inscription* 13 *to* 14 *mm long*
B. *Hindi inscription* 15 *to* 15½ *mm long*

| No. | Type | Value | A | | B | |
|---|---|---|---|---|---|---|
| 4 | **23** | ½ a. blue-green .. | 24·00 | — | 48·00 | — |
| 5 | **25** | 1 a. brown-purple .. | 28·00 | — | 55·00 | — |
| 6 | **26** | 1½ a. sepia .. | 38·00 | — | 70·00 | — |
| 7 | **27** | 2 a. dull blue .. | 28·00 | — | 55·00 | — |
| 8 | **17** | 4 a. green .. | 42·00 | — | 85·00 | — |
| 9 | **21** | 6 a. olive-bistre .. | 42·00 | — | 85·00 | — |
| 10 | **31** | 8 a. dull mauve .. | 38·00 | — | 80·00 | — |
| 11 | **33** | 1 r. slate .. | 38·00 | — | 80·00 | — |
| 4/11 | | *Set of* 8 | £250 | — | £500 | — |

The two types of overprint on these stamps occur in the same settings, with about a quarter of the stamps in each sheet showing the long inscription (B). Nos. 4/7 and 10/11 were overprinted in sheets of 240 and Nos. 8/9 in sheets of 320. *Se-tenant* pairs exist and are rare.

II. *Optd with T* **2**

A. *Hindi inscription* 13 *to* 14 *mm long*
B. *Hindi inscription* 15 *to* 15½ *mm long*

(*a*) *In red* (Sept 1885)

| No. | Type | Value | A | | B | |
|---|---|---|---|---|---|---|
| 12 | **23** | ½ a. blue-green .. | 20 | 20 | 35 | 50 |
| 13 | **27** | 2 a. dull blue .. | 6·50 | 7·50 | 16·00 | 18·00 |
| 14 | **17** | 4 a. green .. | 12·00 | 9·00 | 48·00 | 40·00 |
| 15 | **33** | 1 r. slate .. | 7·50 | 11·00 | 20·00 | 30·00 |
| 12/15 | | *Set of* 4 | 23·00 | 25·00 | 75·00 | 80·00 |

No. 14 was overprinted in sheets of 320, about 80 stamps being Type B. The remaining three values were from a setting of 240 containing 166 as Type A and 74 as Type B.

Reprints have been made of Nos. 12 to 15, but the majority of the specimens have the word "REPRINT" overprinted upon them.

(*b*) *In black* (1885–97)

| No. | Type | Value | A | | B | |
|---|---|---|---|---|---|---|
| 16 | **23** | ½ a. blue-green (1889) .. | 35 | 45 | 15 | 10 |
| | | a. Opt double .. | — | — | — | — |
| | | b. "GWALICR" .. | † | | 60·00 | 70·00 |
| | | c. Small "G" .. | † | | 40·00 | 40·00 |
| | | d. Small "R" .. | † | | 40·00 | — |
| | | e. Tall "R" .. | † | | 40·00 | 40·00 |
| 17 | **24** | 9 p. carmine (1891) .. | 26·00 | 45·00 | 40·00 | 55·00 |
| 18 | **25** | 1 a. brown-purple .. | 20 | 15 | 50 | 20 |
| 19 | | 1 a. plum .. | † | | 40 | 10 |
| | | a. Small "G" .. | † | | 45·00 | 45·00 |
| | | d. Small "R" .. | † | | 45·00 | — |
| | | e. Tall "R" .. | † | | 48·00 | — |
| 20 | **26** | 1½ a. sepia .. | 25 | 45 | 25 | 30 |
| 21 | **27** | 2 a. dull blue .. | 1·90 | 70 | 35 | 10 |
| | | a. "R" omitted .. | † | | £300 | — |
| 22 | | 2 a. deep blue .. | 2·50 | 1·25 | 90 | 20 |
| | | a. Small "G" .. | † | | 90·00 | 90·00 |
| | | d. Small "R" .. | † | | 90·00 | — |
| | | e. Tall "R" .. | † | | £100 | £100 |
| 23 | **36** | 2½ a. yellow-green (1896) .. | † | | 2·75 | 8·00 |
| | | a. "GWALICR" .. | † | | £375 | — |
| 24 | **28** | 3 a. orange .. | 2·75 | 3·25 | 20·00 | 13·00 |
| 25 | | 3 a. brown-orange .. | 2·50 | 1·25 | 30 | 15 |
| | | a. Small "G" .. | † | | £120 | £120 |
| | | d. Small "R" .. | † | | £160 | — |
| | | e. Tall "R" .. | † | | 90·00 | 90·00 |
| 26 | **29** | 4 a. olive-green (1889) .. | 1·50 | 75 | 1·60 | 1·00 |
| 27 | | 4 a. slate-green .. | 1·60 | 75 | 60 | 30 |
| | | a. Small "G" .. | † | | £190 | £160 |
| | | d. Small "R" .. | † | | £190 | — |
| | | e. Tall "R" .. | † | | £120 | — |
| 28 | **21** | 6 a. olive-bistre .. | 2·25 | 3·50 | 1·75 | 3·25 |
| 29 | | 6 a. bistre-brown .. | 60 | 2·25 | 85 | 2·25 |
| 30 | **31** | 8 a. dull mauve .. | 5·50 | 12·00 | 55 | 55 |
| 31 | | 8 a. magenta (1897) .. | † | | 3·50 | 3·25 |
| 32 | **32** | 12 a. purple/*red* (1891) .. | 3·00 | 7·50 | 1·00 | 55 |
| | | a. Pair, with and without opt .. | † | | — | — |
| | | e. Tall "R" .. | † | | £300 | £275 |
| 33 | **33** | 1 r. slate (1889) .. | 60·00 | £140 | 65 | 70 |
| 34 | **37** | 1 r. green and carmine (1896) .. | † | | 2·25 | 2·75 |
| | | a. "GWALICR" .. | † | | £475 | £550 |
| 35 | **38** | 2 r. carmine and yellow-brown (1896) .. | † | | 5·00 | 3·00 |
| | | a. Small "G" .. | † | | £150 | £110 |
| | | d. Small "R" .. | † | | £150 | £120 |
| 36 | | 3 r. brown and green (1896) | † | | 7·00 | 3·50 |
| | | a. Small "G" .. | † | | £160 | £120 |
| | | d. Small "R" .. | † | | £170 | £130 |
| 37 | | 5 r. ultramarine and violet (1896) .. | † | | 12·00 | 6·50 |
| | | a. Small "G" .. | † | | £180 | £140 |
| | | d. Small "R" .. | † | | £190 | £150 |
| 16/37 | | *Set of* 16 | | | 50·00 | 60·00 |

Printings to 1891 continued to use the setting showing both types, but subsequently a new setting containing Type B overprints only was used.

The ½ a., 1 a., 2 a. and 3 a. exist with space between "I" and "O" of "GWALIOR".

The "GWALICR" error occurs on R.1/5 in the May 1896 printing only.

**1899–1911.** (*a*) *Optd with T* **2** (B).

38 **40** 3 p. carmine .. .. .. 10 20
a. Opt inverted .. .. .. £400 £250
b. Small "G" .. .. .. 40·00 40·00
d. Small "R" .. .. .. 40·00
e. Tall "R" .. .. .. 26·00
39 3 p. grey (1904) .. .. .. 5·50 45·00
e. Tall "R" .. .. .. £150
40 **23** ½ a. pale yellow-green (1901) .. 10 45
e. Tall "R" .. .. .. 48·00
40*f* ½ a. yellow-green (1903) .. .. 60 1·40
fe. Tall "R" .. .. .. 65·00
41 **25** 1 a. carmine (1901) .. .. 20 35
e. Tall "R" .. .. .. 55·00
42 **27** 2 a. pale violet (1903) .. .. 35 1·50
e. Tall "R" .. .. .. 75·00
43 **36** 2½ a. ultramarine (1903) .. .. 65 1·50
e. Tall "R" .. .. .. £100
38/43 .. .. .. .. *Set of* 6 6·25 45·00

(*b*) *Optd as T* **2**, *but "GWALIOR"* 13 *mm long. Optd spaced* 2¾ *mm*

44 **38** 3 r. brown and green (1911) .. .. 85·00 £100
45 5 r. ultramarine and violet (1910) .. 50·00 55·00

**1903–11.** *King Edward VII. Optd as T* **2**.

A. "GWALIOR" 14 *mm long. Overprint spaced* 1¾ *mm*
B. "GWALIOR" 13 *mm long. Overprint spaced* 2¾ *mm* (1908–11)

| No. | Type | Value | A | | B | |
|---|---|---|---|---|---|---|
| 46 | **41** | 3 p. pale grey .. | 15 | 15 | 50 | 10 |
| | | e. Tall "R" .. | 16·00 | 18·00 | † | |
| | | *f. Slate-grey* (1905) .. | 15 | 15 | 60 | 20 |
| | | fe. Tall "R" .. | 20·00 | 22·00 | † | |
| 48 | **42** | ½ a. green .. | 10 | 10 | † | |
| | | e. Tall "R" .. | 16·00 | 17·00 | † | |
| 49 | **43** | 1 a. carmine .. | 10 | 10 | 85 | 50 |
| | | e. Tall "R" .. | 19·00 | 20·00 | † | |
| 50 | **44** | 2 a. pale violet (1904) .. | 50 | 40 | † | |
| | | e. Tall "R" .. | 40·00 | — | † | |
| | | *f. Mauve* .. | 45 | 15 | 50 | 10 |
| | | fe. Tall "R" .. | 45·00 | — | † | |
| 52 | **45** | 2½ a. ultramarine (1904) .. | 8·50 | 25·00 | 45 | 4·00 |
| | | e. Tall "R" .. | £275 | | † | |
| 53 | **46** | 3 a. orange-brown (1904) .. | 50 | 15 | 1·00 | 15 |
| | | e. Tall "R" .. | 75·00 | — | † | |
| 54 | **47** | 4 a. olive .. | 1·10 | 40 | † | |
| | | e. Tall "R" .. | 85·00 | 75·00 | † | |
| | | *f. Pale olive* .. | 2·50 | 75 | 2·00 | 50 |
| | | fe. Tall "R" .. | £100 | — | † | |
| 56 | **48** | 6 a. olive-bistre (1904) .. | 2·25 | 2·50 | 2·50 | 70 |
| | | e. Tall "R" .. | £250 | — | † | |
| 57 | **49** | 8 a. purple (*shades*) (1905) .. | 1·60 | 1·10 | 3·00 | 1·25 |
| | | e. Tall "R" .. | £130 | — | † | |
| | | *f. Claret* .. | † | | 7·00 | 1·50 |
| 59 | **50** | 12 a. purple/*red* (1905) .. | 2·00 | 5·50 | 1·75 | 3·25 |
| | | e. Tall "R" .. | £275 | — | † | |
| 60 | **51** | 1 r. green & carmine (1905) .. | 1·40 | 1·75 | 1·90 | 1·00 |
| | | e. Tall "R" .. | £275 | — | † | |
| 61 | **52** | 2 r. carmine and yellow-brown (1906) .. | 30·00 | 42·00 | 8·50 | 12·00 |
| 62 | | 3 r. brown and green (1910) | † | | 22·00 | 32·00 |
| | | *a. Red-brown and green* .. | † | | 38·00 | 45·00 |
| 63 | | 5 r. ultram & vio (1911) | † | | 16·00 | 23·00 |
| 46/63 | | *Set of* 14 | | | 50·00 | 65·00 |

**1907–08.** *Nos.* 149 *and* 150 *of India optd as T* **2**.

(*a*) *"GWALIOR"* 14 *mm long. Overprint spaced* 1¾ *mm*

64 **53** ½ a. green .. .. .. .. 10 20
e. Tall "R" .. .. .. .. 27·00

(*b*) *"GWALIOR"* 13 *mm long. Overprint spaced* 2¾ *mm* (1908)

65 **53** ½ a. green .. .. .. .. 20 10
66 **54** 1 a. carmine .. .. .. .. 30 10

**1912–14.** *King George V. Optd as T* **2**.

67 **55** 3 p. slate-grey .. .. .. 10 10
a. Opt double .. .. .. † £400
68 **56** ½ a. green .. .. .. 15 10
a. Opt inverted .. .. .. — £275
69 **57** 1 a. aniline carmine .. .. 15 10
a. Opt double .. .. .. 25·00
70 **59** 2 a. mauve .. .. .. 30 10
71 **62** 3 a. orange-brown .. .. .. 40 15
72 **63** 4 a. olive (1913) .. .. .. 40 40
73 **64** 6 a. olive-bistre .. .. .. 65 75
74 **65** 8 a. purple (1913) .. .. .. 60 30
75 **66** 12 a. dull claret (1914) .. .. 85 1·40
76 **67** 1 r. brown and green (1913) .. 1·25 40
a. Opt double, one albino .. 30·00
b. Opt double .. .. .. £350
77 2 r. carmine-rose and brown (1913) .. 4·50 2·25
a. Opt double one albino .. 50·00
78 5 r. ultramarine and violet (1913) .. 16·00 6·50
a. Opt double, one albino .. 60·00
67/78 .. .. .. .. *Set of* 12 23·00 11·00

GWALIOR
(3)

**1921.** *No.* 192 *of India optd with T* **3**.

79 **57** 9 p. on 1 a. rose-carmine .. .. 10 35

No. 79 with inverted overprint is of clandestine origin.

**1923–7.** *Optd as T* **2**. *New colours and values.*

80 **57** 1 a. chocolate .. .. .. 15 10
81 **58** 1½ a. chocolate (B) (1925) .. .. 55 50
82 1½ a. rose-carmine (B) (1927) .. 10 15
83 **61** 2½ a. ultramarine (1925) .. .. 75 1·40
84 2½ a. orange (1927) .. .. 20 30
85 **62** 3 a. ultramarine (1924) .. .. 35 50
80/5 .. .. .. .. *Set of* 6 1·90 2·75

No. 82 with inverted overprint is of clandestine origin.

GWALIOR
गवालियर
(4)

GWALIOR
गवालियर
(5)

**1928–36.** *King George V (Nasik printing, wmk Mult Star), optd at Nasik with T* **4** *or* **5** *(rupee values).*

86 **55** 3 p. slate (1932) .. .. .. 30 10
87 **56** ½ a. green (1930) .. .. .. 30 10
88 **80** 9 p. deep green (1932) .. .. 1·25 20
89 **57** 1 a. chocolate .. .. .. 15 10
90 **82** 1¼ a. mauve (1936) .. .. .. 20 10
91 **70** 2 a. purple .. .. .. 20 15
92 **62** 3 a. bright blue .. .. .. 40 40
93 **71** 4 a. sage-green .. .. .. 70 80
94 **65** 8 a. reddish purple .. .. 90 1·00
95 **66** 12 a. claret .. .. .. 85 1·60
96 **67** 1 r. chocolate and green .. .. 1·00 1·50
97 2 r. carmine and orange .. .. 2·50 2·50
98 5 r. ultramarine and purple (1929) .. 10·00 18·00
99 10 r. green and scarlet (1930) .. 26·00 30·00
100 15 r. blue and olive (1930) .. .. 45·00 48·00
101 25 r. orange and blue (1930) .. 80·00 85·00
86/101 .. .. .. .. *Set of* 16 £150 £170

The 9 p. exists printed by lithography or typography.

**1935–36.** *New types and colours. Optd with T* **4**.

102 **79** ½ a. green (1936) .. .. .. 20 10
103 **81** 1 a. chocolate .. .. .. 10 10
104 **59** 2 a. vermilion (1936) .. .. 30 1·00
102/4 .. .. .. .. *Set of* 3 50 1·10

**1938–48.** *King George VI. Nos.* 247/50, 253, 255/6, *and* 259/64 *optd with T* **4** *or* **5** *(rupee values).*

105 **91** 3 p. slate .. .. .. 2·75 10
106 ½ a. red-brown .. .. .. 2·25 10
107 9 p. green (1939) .. .. .. 28·00 2·50
108 1 a. carmine .. .. .. 3·25 15
109 – 3 a. yellow-green (1939) .. .. 4·00 2·50
110 – 4 a. brown .. .. .. 22·00 1·25
111 – 6 a. turquoise-green (1939) .. .. 2·25 4·25
112 **93** 1 r. grey and red-brown (1942) .. 2·75 1·50
113 2 r. purple and brown (1948) .. 10·00 6·00
114 5 r. green and blue (1948) .. .. 40·00 25·00
115 10 r. purple and claret (1948) .. 38·00 35·00
116 15 r. brown and green (1948) .. £120 £130
117 25 r. slate-violet and purple (1948) .. £110 £110
105/117 .. .. .. .. *Set of* 13 £350 £275

**1942–5.** *King George VI. Optd with T* **4**.

118 **100*a*** 3 p. slate .. .. .. 45 10
119 ½ a. purple (1943) .. .. 45 10
120 9 p. green .. .. .. 45 10
121 1 a. carmine (1943) .. .. 40 10
a. Opt double .. .. .. — £100
122 **101** 1½ a. dull violet .. .. .. 2·00 20
123 2 a. vermilion .. .. .. 55 20
124 3 a. bright violet .. .. .. 1·25 30
125 **102** 4 a. brown .. .. .. 75 20
126 6 a. turquoise-green (1945) .. 17·00 14·00
127 8 a. slate-violet (1944) .. .. 2·75 2·75
128 12 a. lake (1943) .. .. .. 5·50 11·00
118/128 .. .. .. .. *Set of* 11 28·00 26·00

The 1½ a. and 3 a. exist printed by lithography or typography.

## GWALIOR

गवालियर
(6)

**1949.** *King George VI. Optd with T* **6** *at the Alizah Printing Press, Gwalior.*
129 **100a** 3 p. slate .. .. .. .. 60 50
130 ½ a. purple .. .. .. .. 60 50
131 1 a. carmine .. .. .. .. 75 60
132 **101** 2 a. vermilion .. .. .. .. 9·00 1·50
133 3 a. bright violet .. .. .. .. 27·00 16·00
134 **102** 4 a. brown .. .. .. .. 2·00 2·50
135 6 a. turquoise-green .. .. .. .. 27·00 29·00
136 8 a. slate-violet .. .. .. .. 75·00 42·00
137 12 a. lake .. .. .. .. £190 90·00
129/137 .. .. .. .. *Set of* 9 £300 £160

OFFICIAL STAMPS

गवालियर

गवालियर

सरविस (O 1) सरविस (O 2)

**1895–96.** *Queen Victoria. Optd with Type* O **1**.
O 1 **23** ½ a. blue-green .. .. .. .. 10 10
a. Hindi characters transposed .. 22·00 22·00
b. 4th Hindi character omitted .. £170 35·00
c. Opt double .. .. .. .. † £475
O 2 **25** 1 a. brown-purple .. .. .. .. 3·25 40
O 3 1 a. plum .. .. .. .. 65 10
a. Hindi characters transposed .. 32·00 32·00
b. 4th Hindi character omitted .. — 48·00
O 4 **27** 2 a. dull blue .. .. .. .. 70 20
O 5 2 a. deep blue .. .. .. .. 90 20
a. Hindi characters transposed .. 50·00 60·00
b. 4th Hindi character omitted .. 65·00 85·00
O 6 **29** 4 a. olive-green .. .. .. .. 1·50 60
a. Hindi characters transposed .. £250 £250
b. 4th Hindi character omitted .. £750 £500
O 7 4 a. slate-green .. .. .. .. 1·00 45
a. Hindi characters transposed .. £200
O 8 **31** 8 a. dull mauve .. .. .. .. 1·40 1·40
O 9 8 a. magenta .. .. .. .. 80 70
a. Hindi characters transposed .. £700 £750
b. 4th Hindi character omitted ..
O10 **37** 1 r. green and carmine (1896) .. .. 2·75 3·00
a. Hindi characters transposed .. £1500
O1/10 .. .. .. .. *Set of* 6 5·25 4·00

In the errors listed above it is the last two Hindi characters that are transposed, so that the word reads "Sersiv". The error occurs on R.19/1 in the sheet from the early printings up to May 1896.

**1901–04.** *Colours changed.*
O23 **40** 3 p. carmine (1902) .. .. .. .. 20 30
O24 3 p. grey (1904) .. .. .. .. 75 1·25
O25 **23** ½ a. pale yellow-green .. .. .. .. 1·10 15
O26 ½ a. yellow-green .. .. .. .. 15 10
O27 **25** 1 a. carmine .. .. .. .. 1·50 10
O28 **27** 2 a. pale violet (1903) .. .. .. .. 55 1·50
O23/8 .. .. .. .. *Set of* 5 2·75 3·00

**1903–08.** *King Edward VII. Optd as Type* O **1**.

*(a) Overprint spaced* 10 *mm* (1903–5)
O29 **41** 3 p. pale grey .. .. .. .. 30 10
*a. Slate-grey* (1905) .. .. .. .. 30 10
O31 **42** ½ a. green .. .. .. .. 90 10
O32 **43** 1 a. carmine .. .. .. .. 35 10
O33 **44** 2 a. pale violet (1905) .. .. .. .. 1·00 40
*a. Mauve* .. .. .. .. 60 15
O35 **47** 4 a. olive (1905) .. .. .. .. 5·00 80
O36 **49** 8 a. purple (1905) .. .. .. .. 2·75 70
*a. Claret* .. .. .. .. 4·00 2·00
O38 **51** 1 r. green and carmine (1905) .. .. 1·90 1·10
O29/38 .. .. .. .. *Set of* 7 10·50 2·75

*(b) Overprint spaced* 8 *mm* (1907–8)
O39 **41** 3 p. pale grey .. .. .. .. 1·60 15
*a. Slate-grey* .. .. .. .. 2·50 50
O41 **42** ½ a. green .. .. .. .. 1·40 10
O42 **43** 1 a. carmine .. .. .. .. 40 10
O43 **44** 2 a. mauve .. .. .. .. 5·50 45
O44 **47** 4 a. olive .. .. .. .. 2·50 70
O45 **49** 8 a. purple .. .. .. .. 2·75 3·00
O46 **51** 1 r. green and carmine (1908) .. .. 10·00 5·00
O39/46 .. .. .. .. *Set of* 7 22·00 8·50

**1907–08.** *Nos. 149 and 150 of India optd as Type* O **1**.

*(a) Overprint spaced* 10 *mm* (1908)
O47 **53** ½ a. green .. .. .. .. 2·00 10
O48 **54** 1 a. carmine .. .. .. .. 2·00 10

*(b) Overprint spaced* 8 *mm* (1907)
O49 **53** ½ a. green .. .. .. .. 60 10
O50 **54** 1 a. carmine .. .. .. .. 27·00 3·00

**1913–23.** *King George V. Optd with Type* O **1**.
O51 **55** 3 p. slate-grey .. .. .. .. 20 10
O52 **56** ½ a. green .. .. .. .. 20 10
a. Opt double .. .. .. .. 65·00
O53 **57** 1 a. rose-carmine .. .. .. .. 2·50 30
*a. Aniline carmine* .. .. .. .. 20 10
ab. Opt double .. .. .. .. 55·00
O54 1 a. chocolate (1923) .. .. .. .. 1·50 10
O55 **59** 2 a. mauve .. .. .. .. 35 10
O56 **63** 4 a. olive .. .. .. .. 45 35
O57 **65** 8 a. purple .. .. .. .. 55 60
O58 **67** 1 r. brown and green .. .. .. .. 6·50 7·50
O51/58 .. .. .. .. *Set of* 8 9·00 8·00

**1921.** *No.* O97 *of India optd with T* **3**.
O59 **57** 9 p. on 1 a. rose-carmine .. .. 10 15

**1927–35.** *King George V (Nasik printing, wmk Mult Star), optd at Nasik as Type* O **1** *(but top line measures* 13 *mm instead of* 14 *mm) or with Type* O **2** *(rupee values).*
O61 **55** 3 p. slate .. .. .. .. 10 10
O62 **56** ½ a. green .. .. .. .. 10 15
O63 **80** 9 p. deep green (1932) .. .. .. 10 15
O64 **57** 1 a. chocolate .. .. .. .. 10 10
O65 **82** 1¼ a. mauve (1933) .. .. .. .. 40 15
O66 **70** 2 a. purple .. .. .. .. 15 15
O67 **71** 4 a. sage-green .. .. .. .. 40 30
O68 **65** 8 a. reddish purple (1928) .. .. .. 40 30
O69 **67** 1 r. chocolate and green .. .. .. 60 70
O70 2 r. carmine and orange (1935) .. .. 2·25 4·00
O71 5 r. ultramarine and purple (1932) .. 10·00 50·00
O72 10 r. green and scarlet (1932) .. .. 48·00 £100
O61/72 .. .. .. .. *Set of* 12 55·00 £140

**1936–37.** *New types. Optd as Type* O **1** *(13 mm).*
O73 **79** ½ a. green .. .. .. .. 15 15
O74 **81** 1 a. chocolate .. .. .. .. 15 15
O75 **59** 2 a. vermilion .. .. .. .. 20 30
O76 2 a. vermilion *(small die)* .. .. .. 1·90 1·00
O77 **63** 4 a. sage-green (1937) .. .. .. 30 35
O73/7 .. .. .. .. *Set of* 5 2·40 1·75

**1938.** *King George VI. Optd as Type* O **1** *(13 mm).*
O78 **91** ½ a. red-brown .. .. .. .. 5·50 25
O79 1 a. carmine .. .. .. .. 1·10 15

गवालियर (O 3) 1A———1A (O 4)

**1940–42.** *Official stamps optd with Type* O **3**.
O80 O **20** 3 p. slate .. .. .. .. 50 10
O81 ½ a. red-brown .. .. .. .. 3·50 25
O82 ½ a. purple (1942) .. .. .. .. 50 10
O83 9 p. green (1942) .. .. .. .. 70 45
O84 1 a. carmine .. .. .. .. 3·00 10
O85 1 a. 3 p. yellow-brown (1942) .. .. 9·00 1·60
O86 1½ a. dull violet (1942) .. .. .. 80 30
O87 2 a. vermilion .. .. .. .. 80 30
O88 4 a. brown (1942) .. .. .. .. 90 1·00
O89 8 a. slate-violet (1942) .. .. .. 2·25 3·25
O80/9 .. .. .. .. *Set of* 10 20·00 6·75

**1942.** *Stamp of 1932 (King George V) optd with Type* O **1** *and surch with Type* O **4**.
O90 **82** 1 a. on 1¼ a. mauve .. .. .. 12·00 2·25

**1942–47.** *King George VI. Optd with Type* O **2**.
O91 **93** 1 r. grey and red-brown .. .. .. 8·00 7·50
O92 2 r. purple and brown .. .. .. 17·00 32·00
O93 5 r. green and blue (1943) .. .. .. 45·00 £150
O94 10 r. purple and claret (1947) .. .. £120 £300
O91/4 .. .. .. .. *Set of* 4 £170 £450

## JIND

For earlier issues, see under INDIAN FEUDATORY STATES

| PRICES FOR STAMPS ON COVER | |
|---|---|
| Nos. 1/4 | *from* × 20 |
| Nos. 5/16 | — |
| Nos. 17/40 | *from* × 15 |
| Nos. 41/149 | *from* × 8 |
| Nos. O1/86 | *from* × 15 |

JHIND STATE (1) JEEND STATE (2) JHIND STATE (3)

**1885.** *Queen Victoria. Optd with T* **1**.
1 **23** ½ a. blue-green .. .. .. .. 50 1·10
a. Opt inverted .. .. .. .. 65·00 70·00
2 **25** 1 a. brown-purple .. .. .. .. 9·50 13·00
a. Opt inverted .. .. .. .. £400 £450
3 **27** 2 a. dull blue .. .. .. .. 4·00 6·50
a. Opt inverted .. .. .. .. £250 £275
4 **17** 4 a. green .. .. .. .. 26·00 38·00
5 **31** 8 a. dull mauve .. .. .. .. £200
a. Opt inverted .. .. .. .. £3000
6 **33** 1 r. slate .. .. .. .. £180
a. Opt inverted .. .. .. .. £3000
1/6 .. .. .. .. *Set of* 6 £375

The overprint inverted errors occurred on R.10/8 in the setting of 120, although it is believed that one pane of the ½ a. had the overprint inverted on the entire pane. Examples of inverted overprints on the ½ a., 1 a. and 2 a. with the lines much less curved are thought to come from a trial printing.

All six values exist with reprinted overprint. This has the words "JHIND" and "STATE" 8 and 9 mm in length respectively, whereas in the originals the words are 9 and 9½ mm.

**1885.** *Optd with T* **2**.
7 **23** ½ a. blue-green (R.) .. .. .. .. 42·00
8 **25** 1 a. brown-purple .. .. .. .. 42·00
9 **27** 2 a. dull blue (R.) .. .. .. .. 55·00
10 **17** 4 a. green (R.) .. .. .. .. 70·00
11 **31** 8 a. dull mauve .. .. .. .. 75·00
12 **33** 1 r. slate (R.) .. .. .. .. 80·00
7/12 .. .. .. .. *Set of* 6 £325

**1886.** *Optd with T* **3**, *in red.*
13 **23** ½ a. blue-green .. .. .. .. 15·00
a. "JEIND" for "JHIND" .. .. £650
14 **27** 2 a. dull blue .. .. .. .. 16·00
a. "JEIND" for "JHIND" .. .. £750
15 **17** 4 a. green .. .. .. .. 22·00
a. Opt double, one albino .. .. 32·00
16 **33** 1 r. slate .. .. .. .. 32·00
a. "JEIND" for "JHIND" .. .. £1100
13/16 .. .. .. .. *Set of* 4 75·00

**1886–99.** *Optd with T* **3**.
17 **23** ½ a. blue-green .. .. .. .. 10 10
a. Opt inverted .. .. .. .. £180
18 **25** 1 a. brown-purple .. .. .. .. 20 15
a. "JEIND" for "JHIND" .. .. £300
19 1 a. plum (1899) .. .. .. .. 75 50
20 **26** 1½ a. sepia (1896) .. .. .. .. 50 1·00
21 **27** 2 a. dull blue .. .. .. .. 40 40
22 2 a. ultramarine .. .. .. .. 40 45
23 **28** 3 a. brown-orange (1891) .. .. .. 40 45
24 **29** 4 a. olive-green .. .. .. .. 1·10 1·00
25 4 a. slate-green .. .. .. .. 1·50 1·75
26 **21** 6 a. olive-bistre (1891) .. .. .. 2·50 4·75
27 6 a. bistre-brown .. .. .. .. 50 2·75
28 **31** 8 a. dull mauve .. .. .. .. 1·25 4·75
a. "JEIND" for "JHIND" .. .. £1000
29 8 a. magenta (1897) .. .. .. .. 2·00 5·50
30 **32** 12 a. purple/*red* (1896) .. .. .. 1·60 6·00
31 **33** 1 r. slate .. .. .. .. 6·00 22·00
32 **37** 1 r. green and carmine (1897) .. .. 5·00 18·00
33 **38** 2 r. carmine and yellow-brown (1896) .. £140 £300
34 3 r. brown and green (1896) .. .. £225 £350
35 5 r. ultramarine and violet (1896) .. £275 £400
17/35 .. .. .. .. *Set of* 14 £600 £1000

Varieties exist in which the word "JHIND" measures 10½ mm and 9¾ mm instead of 10 mm. Such varieties are to be found on Nos. 17, 18, 21, 24, 28 and 31.

**1900–4.** *Colours changed.*
36 **40** 3 p. carmine .. .. .. .. 20 85
37 3 p. grey (1904) .. .. .. .. 10 1·00
38 **23** ½ a. pale yellow-green (1902) .. .. 70 1·75
39 ½ a. yellow-green (1903) .. .. .. 2·50 4·00
40 **25** 1 a. carmine (1902) .. .. .. .. 15 2·25
36/40 .. .. .. .. *Set of* 4 1·00 5·25

**1903–9.** *King Edward VII. Optd with T* **3**.
41 **41** 3 p. pale grey .. .. .. .. 10 10
42 3 p. slate-grey (1905) .. .. .. .. 10 35
43 **42** ½ a. green .. .. .. .. 10 50
44 **43** 1 a. carmine .. .. .. .. 40 50
45 **44** 2 a. pale violet .. .. .. .. 70 90
46 2 a. mauve (1906) .. .. .. .. 35 55
47 **45** 2½ a. ultramarine (1909) .. .. .. 30 2·75
48 **46** 3 a. orange-brown .. .. .. .. 30 35
a. Opt double .. .. .. .. 95·00 £150
49 **47** 4 a. olive .. .. .. .. 1·50 2·75
50 4 a. pale olive .. .. .. .. 1·00 2·75
51 **48** 6 a. bistre (1905) .. .. .. .. 1·40 4·75
52 **49** 8 a. purple *(shades)* .. .. .. .. 1·50 4·50
53 8 a. claret .. .. .. .. 4·00 7·00
54 **50** 12 a. purple/*red* (1905) .. .. .. 1·50 4·75
55 **51** 1 r. green and carmine (1905) .. .. 1·75 4·75
41/55 .. .. .. .. *Set of* 11 8·00 24·00

**1907–9.** *Nos. 149/50 of India optd with T* **3**.
56 **53** ½ a. green .. .. .. .. 10 15
57 **54** 1 a. carmine (1909) .. .. .. .. 10 40

**1913.** *King George V. Optd with T* **3**.
58 **55** 3 p. slate-grey .. .. .. .. 10 1·00
59 **56** ½ a. green .. .. .. .. 10 60
60 **57** 1 a. aniline carmine .. .. .. .. 10 35
61 **59** 2 a. mauve .. .. .. .. 15 1·75
62 **62** 3 a. orange-brown .. .. .. .. 1·50 6·00
63 **64** 6 a. olive-bistre .. .. .. .. 3·25 13·00
58/63 .. .. .. .. *Set of* 6 4·75 20·00

JIND STATE (4) JIND STATE (5) JIND STATE (6)

**1914–27.** *King George V. Optd with T* **4**.
64 **55** 3 p. slate-grey .. .. .. .. 15 20
65 **56** ½ a. green .. .. .. .. 30 15
66 **57** 1 a. aniline carmine .. .. .. .. 15 15
67 **58** 1½ a. chocolate (Type A) (1922) .. .. 35 1·60
68 1½ a. chocolate (Type B) (1924) .. .. 30 1·50
69 **59** 2 a. mauve .. .. .. .. 30 45
70 **61** 2½ a. ultramarine (1922) .. .. .. 30 2·25
71 **62** 3 a. orange-brown .. .. .. .. 30 1·25
72 **63** 4 a. olive .. .. .. .. 30 1·75
73 **64** 6 a. olive-bistre .. .. .. .. 45 3·50
74 **65** 8 a. purple .. .. .. .. 70 2·25
75 **66** 12 a. dull claret .. .. .. .. 55 3·50
76 **67** 1 r. brown and green .. .. .. .. 2·50 4·75
a. Opt double, one albino .. .. 25·00
77 2 r. carmine and yellow-brown (1927) .. 4·00 25·00
78 5 r. ultramarine and violet (1927) .. 24·00 85·00
64/78 .. .. .. .. *Set of* 15 30·00 £120

No. 71 with inverted overprint is of clandestine origin.

**1922.** *No. 192 of India optd "JIND" in block capitals.*
79 **57** 9 p. on 1 a. rose-carmine .. .. .. 1·50 8·50

**1924–27.** *Optd with T* **4**. *New colours.*
80 **57** 1 a. chocolate .. .. .. .. 50 50
81 **58** 1½ a. rose-carmine (Type B) (1927) .. 20 1·50
82 **61** 2½ a. orange (1927) .. .. .. .. 30 3·25
83 **62** 3 a. bright blue (1925) .. .. .. 50 3·25
80/3 .. .. .. .. *Set of* 4 1·40 7·75

Nos. 81/2 with inverted overprint are of clandestine origin.

**1927–37.** *King George V (Nasik printing, wmk Mult Star), optd at Nasik with T* **5** *or* **6** *(rupee values).*
84 **55** 3 p. slate .. .. .. .. 10 10
85 **56** ½ a. green (1929) .. .. .. .. 10 20
86 **80** 9 p. deep green (1932) .. .. .. 15 40
87 **57** 1 a. chocolate (1928) .. .. .. .. 10 10
88 **82** 1¼ a. mauve (1932) .. .. .. .. 15 30
89 **58** 1½ a. rose-carmine (Type B) (1930) .. 30 1·00
90 **70** 2 a. purple (1928) .. .. .. .. 30 25
91 **61** 2½ a. orange (1930) .. .. .. .. 30 3·00
92 **62** 3 a. bright blue (1930) .. .. .. 35 2·50
93 **83** 3½ a. ultramarine (1937) .. .. .. 35 4·75
94 **71** 4 a. sage-green (1928) .. .. .. 45 80
95 **64** 6 a. bistre (1937) .. .. .. .. 40 5·50
96 **65** 8 a. reddish purple (1930) .. .. .. 60 1·90
97 **66** 12 a. claret (1930) .. .. .. .. 85 6·00

| No. | Type | Description | Unused | Used |
|---|---|---|---|---|
| 98 | 67 | 1 r. chocolate and green (1930) | 80 | 1·90 |
| 99 | | 2 r. carmine and orange (1930) | 8·00 | 32·00 |
| 00 | | 5 r. ultramarine and purple (1928) | 9·00 | 18·00 |
| 01 | | 10 r. green and carmine (1928) | 12·00 | 18·00 |
| 02 | | 15 r. blue and olive (1929) | 50·00 | £160 |
| 03 | | 25 r. orange and blue (1929) | 75·00 | £250 |
| 4/103 | | *Set of* 20 | £140 | £450 |

**934.** *New types and colours. Optd with T* **5**.

| No. | Type | Description | Unused | Used |
|---|---|---|---|---|
| 04 | 79 | ½ a. green | 15 | 15 |
| 05 | 81 | 1 a. chocolate | 20 | 15 |
| 06 | 59 | 2 a. vermilion | 30 | 40 |
| 07 | 62 | 3 a. carmine | 40 | 40 |
| 08 | 63 | 4 a. sage-green | 45 | 65 |
| 04/8 | | *Set of* 5 | 1·25 | 1·60 |

**937–38.** *King George VI. Nos. 247/64 optd with T* **5** *or T* **6** *(rupee values).*

| No. | Type | Description | Unused | Used |
|---|---|---|---|---|
| 09 | 91 | 3 p. slate | 1·75 | 75 |
| 10 | | ½ a. red-brown | 40 | 1·25 |
| 11 | | 9 p. green (1937) | 50 | 1·50 |
| 12 | | 1 a. carmine (1937) | 30 | 35 |
| 13 | 92 | 2 a. vermilion | 1·00 | 5·50 |
| 14 | – | 2½ a. bright violet | 70 | 5·50 |
| 15 | – | 3 a. yellow-green | 1·75 | 5·50 |
| 16 | – | 3½ a. bright blue | 75 | 6·00 |
| 17 | – | 4 a. brown | 2·50 | 6·00 |
| 18 | – | 6 a. turquoise-green | 1·00 | 7·50 |
| 19 | – | 8 a. slate-violet | 2·00 | 8·50 |
| 20 | – | 12 a. lake | 1·60 | 9·50 |
| 21 | 93 | 1 r. grey and red-brown | 10·00 | 12·00 |
| 22 | | 2 r. purple and brown | 15·00 | 38·00 |
| 23 | | 5 r. green and blue | 30·00 | 35·00 |
| 24 | | 10 r. purple and claret | 55·00 | 50·00 |
| 25 | | 15 r. brown and green | £180 | £425 |
| 26 | | 25 r. slate-violet and purple | £250 | £475 |
| 09/126 | | *Set of* 18 | £475 | £1000 |

**JIND**

(7)

**941–43.** *King George VI. Optd with T* **7**. *(a) Stamps of* 1937.

| No. | Type | Description | Unused | Used |
|---|---|---|---|---|
| .27 | 91 | 3 p. slate | 6·50 | 7·50 |
| .28 | | ½ a. red-brown | 1·00 | 30 |
| .29 | | 9 p. green | 5·50 | 7·00 |
| .30 | | 1 a. carmine | 1·00 | 2·00 |
| .31 | 93 | 1 r. grey and red-brown | 6·00 | 11·00 |
| .32 | | 2 r. purple and brown | 11·00 | 14·00 |
| .33 | | 5 r. green and blue | 30·00 | 40·00 |
| .34 | | 10 r. purple and claret | 50·00 | 50·00 |
| .35 | | 15 r. brown and green | £120 | £110 |
| .36 | | 25 r. slate-violet and purple | £160 | £300 |
| .27/136 | | *Set of* 10 | £350 | £475 |
| | | *(b) Stamps of* 1940–43 | | |
| .37 | 100*a* | 3 p. slate (1942) | 40 | 50 |
| .38 | | ½ a. purple (1943) | 40 | 50 |
| .39 | | 9 p. green (1942) | 40 | 80 |
| .40 | | 1 a. carmine (1942) | 50 | 45 |
| .41 | 101 | 1 a. 3 p. yellow-brown | 85 | 1·75 |
| 42 | | 1½ a. dull violet (1942) | 2·75 | 1·75 |
| .43 | | 2 a. vermilion | 1·00 | 1·25 |
| .44 | | 3 a. bright violet (1942) | 4·00 | 1·75 |
| .45 | | 3½ a. bright blue | 2·00 | 3·25 |
| .46 | 102 | 4 a. brown | 2·00 | 1·75 |
| .47 | | 6 a. turquoise-green | 2·50 | 4·50 |
| .48 | | 8 a. slate-violet | 2·00 | 4·50 |
| .49 | | 12 a. lake | 6·00 | 6·00 |
| .37/149 | | *Set of* 13 | 22·00 | 26·00 |

The 1½ a. and 3 a. exist printed by lithography or typography.

OFFICIAL STAMPS

SERVICE

3ERVICE (O 14) — SERVICE (O 15) — JHIND STATE (O 16)

**885.** *Queen Victoria. Nos. 1/3 of Jind optd with Type* O **14**.

| No. | Type | Description | Unused | Used |
|---|---|---|---|---|
| O1 | 23 | ½ a. blue-green | 30 | 30 |
| | | a. Opt Type 1 inverted | 65·00 | 40·00 |
| O2 | 25 | 1 a. brown-purple | 20 | 10 |
| | | a. Opt Type 1 inverted | 9·00 | 7·00 |
| O3 | 27 | 2 a. dull blue | 20·00 | 24·00 |
| | | a. Opt Type 1 inverted | £475 | |

The three values have had the overprint reprinted in the same way as the ordinary stamps of 1885. See note after No. 6.

**885.** *Nos. 7/9 of Jind optd with Type* O **15**.

| No. | Type | Description | Unused | Used |
|---|---|---|---|---|
| O7 | 23 | ½ a. blue-green (R.) | 50·00 | |
| O8 | 25 | 1 a. brown-purple | 50·00 | |
| O9 | 27 | 2 a. dull blue (R.) | 55·00 | |
| O7/9 | | *Set of* 3 | £140 | |

**886.** *Optd with Type* O **16**, *in red.*

| No. | Type | Description | Unused | Used |
|---|---|---|---|---|
| O10 | 23 | ½ a. blue-green | 11·00 | |
| | | a. "ERVICE" | £1400 | |
| | | b. "JEIND" | £375 | |
| O11 | 27 | 2 a. dull blue | 15·00 | |
| | | a. "ERVICE" | £1400 | |
| | | b. "JEIND" | £550 | |

**886–1902.** *Optd with Type* O **16**.

| No. | Type | Description | Unused | Used |
|---|---|---|---|---|
| O12 | 23 | ½ a. blue-green | 40 | 10 |
| O13 | 25 | 1 a. brown-purple | 11·00 | |
| | | a. "ERVICE" | | |
| | | b. "JEIND" | £300 | |
| O14 | | 1 a. plum (1902) | 3·00 | 15 |
| O15 | 27 | 2 a. dull blue | 75 | 45 |
| O16 | | 2 a. ultramarine | 45 | 30 |
| O17 | 29 | 4 a. olive-green (1892) | 40 | 35 |
| O18 | | 4 a. slate-green | 1·25 | 1·10 |
| O19 | 31 | 8 a. dull mauve (1892) | 1·50 | 2·00 |
| O20 | | 8 a. magenta (1897) | 2·00 | 4·00 |
| O21 | 37 | 1 r. green and carmine (1896) | 6·00 | 16·00 |
| O12/21 | | *Set of* 6 | 10·00 | 17·00 |

Varieties mentioned in note after No. 35 exist on Nos. O12, O15, O17 and O20.

Printings up to and including that of October 1897 had the "SERVICE" overprint. Type O 15, applied to sheets already overprinted with Type 3. From the printing of December 1899 onwards "SERVICE" and "JHIND STATE" were overprinted at one operation, as Type O 16, to provide fresh supplies of Nos. O12, O14 and O21.

**1902.** *Colour changed. Optd with Type* O **16**.

| No. | Type | Description | Unused | Used |
|---|---|---|---|---|
| O22 | 23 | ½ a. yellow-green | 30 | 15 |

**1903–6.** *King Edward VII stamps of India optd with Type* O **16**.

| No. | Type | Description | Unused | Used |
|---|---|---|---|---|
| O23 | 41 | 3 p. pale grey | 10 | 10 |
| O24 | | 3 p. slate-grey (1906) | 10 | 10 |
| O25 | 42 | ½ a. green | 1·40 | 10 |
| | | a. "HIND" | £750 | £200 |
| O26 | 43 | 1 a. carmine | 60 | 10 |
| | | a. "HIND" | — | £170 |
| O27 | 44 | 2 a. pale violet | 70 | 35 |
| O28 | | 2 a. mauve | 20 | 10 |
| O29 | 47 | 4 a. olive | 40 | 45 |
| O30 | 49 | 8 a. purple (*shades*) | 7·00 | 5·00 |
| O31 | | 8 a. claret | 2·25 | 1·50 |
| O32 | 51 | 1 r. green and carmine (1906) | 2·50 | 2·25 |
| O23/32 | | *Set of* 7 | 6·50 | 4·00 |

**1907.** *Nos. 149/50 of India optd with Type* O **16**.

| No. | Type | Description | Unused | Used |
|---|---|---|---|---|
| O33 | 53 | ½ a. green | 15 | 10 |
| O34 | 54 | 1 a. carmine | 20 | 10 |

**1914–27.** *King George V. Official stamps of India optd with T* **4**.

| No. | Type | Description | Unused | Used |
|---|---|---|---|---|
| O35 | 55 | 3 p. slate-grey | 10 | 10 |
| O36 | 56 | ½ a. green | 10 | 10 |
| O37 | 57 | 1 a. aniline carmine | 10 | 10 |
| O38 | | 1 a. pale rose-carmine | 15 | 10 |
| O39 | 59 | 2 a. mauve | 15 | 10 |
| O40 | 63 | 4 a. olive | 20 | 15 |
| O41 | 64 | 6 a. yellow-bistre (1927) | 40 | 2·25 |
| O42 | 65 | 8 a. purple | 30 | 85 |
| O43 | 67 | 1 r. brown and green | 90 | 1·50 |
| O44 | 67 | 2 r. carmine and yellow-brown (1927) | 5·50 | 25·00 |
| O45 | | 5 r. ultramarine and violet (1927) | 16·00 | 55·00 |
| O35/45 | | *Set of* 10 | 21·00 | 75·00 |

No. O40 with double overprint is of clandestine origin.

**1924.** *As 1914-27. New colour.*

| No. | Type | Description | Unused | Used |
|---|---|---|---|---|
| O46 | 57 | 1 a. chocolate | 20 | 10 |

JIND STATE SERVICE (O 17) — JIND STATE SERVICE (O 18) — JIND SERVICE (O 19)

**1927–37.** *King George V (Nasik printing, wmk Mult Star), optd with Types* O **17** *or* O **18** *(rupee values).*

| No. | Type | Description | Unused | Used |
|---|---|---|---|---|
| O47 | 55 | 3 p. slate (1928) | 10 | 15 |
| O48 | 56 | ½ a. green (1929) | 10 | 50 |
| O49 | 80 | 9 p. deep green (1932) | 30 | 15 |
| O50 | 57 | 1 a. chocolate | 10 | 10 |
| O51 | 82 | 1¼ a. mauve (1932) | 15 | 15 |
| O52 | 70 | 2 a. purple (1929) | 15 | 15 |
| O53 | 61 | 2½ a. orange (1937) | 30 | 4·00 |
| O54 | 71 | 4 a. sage-green (1929) | 20 | 20 |
| O55 | 64 | 6 a. bistre (1937) | 40 | 5·00 |
| O56 | 65 | 8 a. reddish purple (1929) | 35 | 1·25 |
| O57 | 66 | 12 a. claret (1928) | 50 | 4·00 |
| O58 | 67 | 1 r. chocolate and green (1928) | 1·00 | 2·00 |
| O59 | | 2 r. carmine and orange (1930) | 12·00 | 11·00 |
| O60 | | 5 r. ultramarine and purple (1929) | 10·00 | 60·00 |
| O61 | | 10 r. green and carmine (1928) | 19·00 | 35·00 |
| O47/61 | | *Set of* 15 | 40·00 | £110 |

The 9 p. exists printed by lithography or typography.

**1934.** *Optd with Type* O **17**.

| No. | Type | Description | Unused | Used |
|---|---|---|---|---|
| O62 | 79 | ½ a. green | 15 | 10 |
| O63 | 81 | 1 a. chocolate | 15 | 10 |
| O64 | 59 | 2 a. vermilion | 20 | 15 |
| O65 | 63 | 4 a. sage-green | 1·75 | 30 |
| O62/5 | | *Set of* 4 | 2·00 | 60 |

**1937–40.** *King George VI. Optd with Types* O **17** *or* O **18** *(rupee values).*

| No. | Type | Description | Unused | Used |
|---|---|---|---|---|
| O66 | 91 | ½ a. red-brown (1938) | 40·00 | 30 |
| O67 | | 9 p. green | 70 | 2·25 |
| O68 | | 1 a. carmine | 45 | 30 |
| O69 | 93 | 1 r. grey and red-brown (1940) | 18·00 | 25·00 |
| O70 | | 2 r. purple and brown (1940) | 32·00 | 75·00 |
| O71 | | 5 r. green and blue (1940) | 70·00 | £130 |
| O72 | | 10 r. purple and claret (1940) | £120 | £300 |
| O66/72 | | *Set of* 7 | £250 | £475 |

**1939–43.** *(a) Official stamps optd with T* **7**.

| No. | Type | Description | Unused | Used |
|---|---|---|---|---|
| O73 | O 20 | 3 p. slate | 45 | 20 |
| O74 | | ½ a. red-brown | 2·00 | 60 |
| O75 | | ½ a. purple (1943) | 45 | 30 |
| O76 | | 9 p. green | 1·75 | 2·50 |
| O77 | | 1 a. carmine | 1·75 | 15 |
| O78 | | 1½ a. dull violet (1942) | 2·75 | 40 |
| O79 | | 2 a. vermilion | 65 | 30 |
| O80 | | 2½ a. bright violet | 75 | 2·75 |
| O81 | | 4 a. brown | 1·10 | 75 |
| O82 | | 8 a. slate-violet | 1·40 | 1·60 |
| | | *(b) Postage stamps optd with Type* O **19** | | |
| O83 | 93 | 1 r. grey and red-brown (1942) | 16·00 | 24·00 |
| O84 | | 2 r. purple and brown (1942) | 27·00 | 60·00 |
| O85 | | 5 r. green and blue (1942) | 65·00 | £130 |
| O86 | | 10 r. purple and claret (1942) | £120 | £200 |
| O73/86 | | *Set of* 14 | £200 | £375 |

## NABHA

**PRICES FOR STAMPS ON COVER**

| | |
|---|---|
| Nos. 1/3 | *from* × 15 |
| Nos. 4/6 | — |
| Nos. 10/36 | *from* × 12 |
| Nos. 37/117 | *from* × 7 |
| Nos. O1/68 | *from* × 15 |

NABHA STATE (1) — NABHA STATE (2)

**1885** (May). *Queen Victoria. Optd with T* **1**.

| No. | Type | Description | Unused | Used |
|---|---|---|---|---|
| 1 | 23 | ½ a. blue-green | 75 | 1·75 |
| 2 | 25 | 1 a. brown-purple | 15·00 | 42·00 |
| 3 | 27 | 2 a. dull blue | 7·00 | 17·00 |
| 4 | 17 | 4 a. green | 40·00 | 75·00 |
| 5 | 31 | 8 a. dull mauve | £225 | |
| 6 | 33 | 1 r. slate | £180 | |
| 1/6 | | *Set of* 6 | £425 | |

All six values have had the overprint reprinted. On the reprints the words "NABHA" and "STATE" both measure 9¼ mm in length, whereas on the originals these words measure 11 and 10 mm respectively. The varieties with overprint double come from the reprints.

**1885** (Nov)–**1900**. *Optd with T* **2**. *(a) In red.*

| No. | Type | Description | Unused | Used |
|---|---|---|---|---|
| 10 | 23 | ½ a. blue-green | 15 | 40 |
| 11 | 27 | 2 a. dull blue | 60 | 1·00 |
| 12 | 17 | 4 a. green | 20·00 | 65·00 |
| 13 | 33 | 1 r. slate | 60·00 | £100 |
| 10/13 | | *Set of* 4 | 75·00 | £150 |
| | | *(b) In black* (Nov 1885–97) | | |
| 14 | 23 | ½ a. blue-green (1888) | 10 | 10 |
| 15 | 24 | 9 p. carmine (1892) | 35 | 1·60 |
| 16 | 25 | 1 a. brown-purple | 40 | 30 |
| 17 | | 1 a. plum | 30 | 20 |
| 18 | 26 | 1½ a. sepia (1891) | 30 | 85 |
| | | a. "ABHA" for "NABHA" | £225 | |
| 19 | 27 | 2 a. dull blue (1888) | 40 | 50 |
| 20 | | 2 a. ultramarine | 30 | 50 |
| 21 | 28 | 3 a. orange (1889) | 2·25 | 5·50 |
| 22 | | 3 a. brown-orange | 75 | 50 |
| 23 | 29 | 4 a. olive-green (1888) | 60 | 75 |
| 24 | | 4 a. slate-green | 60 | 60 |
| 25 | 21 | 6 a. olive-bistre (1889) | 1·75 | 3·50 |
| 26 | | 6 a. bistre-brown | 80 | 1·75 |
| 27 | 31 | 8 a. dull mauve | 65 | 1·40 |
| 28 | 32 | 12 a. purple/*red* (1889) | 1·00 | 2·00 |
| | | a. Opt double, one albino | 25·00 | |
| 29 | 33 | 1 r. slate (1888) | 5·50 | 18·00 |
| 30 | 37 | 1 r. green and carmine (1893) | 3·75 | 3·75 |
| | | a. "N BHA" for "NABHA" | | |
| 31 | 38 | 2 r. carmine and yellow-brown (1897) | 75·00 | £120 |
| 32 | | 3 r. brown and green (1897) | 75·00 | £120 |
| 33 | | 5 r. ultramarine and violet (1897) | 85·00 | £150 |
| 14/33 | | *Set of* 15 | £225 | £375 |
| | | *(c) New value. In black* (Nov 1900) | | |
| 36 | 40 | 3 p. carmine | 10 | 15 |

**1903–09.** *King Edward VII. Optd with T* **2**.

| No. | Type | Description | Unused | Used |
|---|---|---|---|---|
| 37 | 41 | 3 p. pale grey | 10 | 15 |
| 37*a* | | 3 p. slate-grey (1906) | 10 | 15 |
| 38 | 42 | ½ a. green | 10 | 30 |
| | | a. "NABH" | £550 | |
| 39 | 43 | 1 a. carmine | 15 | 30 |
| 40 | 44 | 2 a. pale violet | 30 | 60 |
| 40*a* | | 2 a. mauve | 50 | 20 |
| 40*b* | 45 | 2½ a. ultramarine (1909) | 18·00 | 50·00 |
| 41 | 46 | 3 a. orange-brown | 30 | 30 |
| 42 | 47 | 4 a. olive | 60 | 1·75 |
| 43 | 48 | 6 a. olive-bistre | 60 | 3·75 |
| 44 | 49 | 8 a. purple | 1·50 | 4·50 |
| 44*a* | | 8 a. claret | 3·00 | 6·00 |
| 45 | 50 | 12 a. purple/*red* | 1·10 | 6·00 |
| 46 | 51 | 1 r. green and carmine | 2·00 | 4·50 |
| 37/46 | | *Set of* 11 | 22·00 | 65·00 |

**1907.** *Nos. 149/50 of India optd with T* **2**.

| No. | Type | Description | Unused | Used |
|---|---|---|---|---|
| 47 | 53 | ½ a. green | 30 | 60 |
| 48 | 54 | 1 a. carmine | 35 | 70 |

**1913.** *King George V. Optd with T* **2**.

| No. | Type | Description | Unused | Used |
|---|---|---|---|---|
| 49 | 55 | 3 p. slate | 10 | 10 |
| 50 | 56 | ½ a. green | 10 | 10 |
| 51 | 57 | 1 a. aniline carmine | 15 | 10 |
| 52 | 59 | 2 a. mauve | 20 | 30 |
| 53 | 62 | 3 a. orange-brown | 30 | 35 |
| 54 | 63 | 4 a. olive | 35 | 65 |
| 55 | 64 | 6 a. olive-bistre | 50 | 1·75 |
| 56 | 65 | 8 a. purple | 70 | 1·75 |
| 57 | 66 | 12 a. dull claret | 80 | 4·75 |
| 58 | 67 | 1 r. brown and green | 2·00 | 2·50 |
| | | a. Opt double, one albino | 29·00 | |
| 49/58 | | *Set of* 10 | 4·75 | 11·00 |

**1924.** *As 1913. New colour.*

| No. | Type | Description | Unused | Used |
|---|---|---|---|---|
| 59 | 57 | 1 a. chocolate | 90 | 90 |

No. 59 with inverted or double overprint is of clandestine origin.

NABHA STATE (3) — NABHA STATE (4)

**1927–36.** *King George V (Nasik printing, wmk Mult Star), optd as T* **3** *or* **4** *(rupee values).*

| No. | Type | Description | Unused | Used |
|---|---|---|---|---|
| 60 | 55 | 3 p. slate (1932) | 15 | 15 |
| 61 | 56 | ½ a. green (1928) | 15 | 20 |
| 61*a* | 80 | 9 p. deep green (1934) | 40 | 1·10 |
| 62 | 57 | 1 a. chocolate | 15 | 15 |
| 63 | 82 | 1¼ a. mauve (1936) | 20 | 1·25 |
| 64 | 70 | 2 a. purple (1932) | 55 | 35 |
| 65 | 61 | 2½ a. orange (1932) | 30 | 2·25 |
| 66 | 62 | 3 a. bright blue (1930) | 40 | 1·00 |
| 67 | 71 | 4 a. sage-green (1932) | 1·25 | 1·00 |
| 71 | 67 | 2 r. carmine and orange (1932) | 11·00 | 35·00 |
| 72 | | 5 r. ultramarine and purple (1932) | 42·00 | 90·00 |
| 60/72 | | *Set of* 11 | 50·00 | £120 |

The 9 p. exists printed by lithography or typography.

**1936–37.** *New types and colours. Optd as T* **3**.

| No. | Type | Description | Unused | Used |
|---|---|---|---|---|
| 73 | 79 | ½ a. green | 15 | 25 |
| 74 | 81 | 1 a. chocolate | 15 | 30 |
| 75 | 62 | 3 a. carmine (1937) | 1·00 | 3·00 |
| 76 | 63 | 4 a. slate-green (1937) | 90 | 1·25 |
| 73/6 | | *Set of* 4 | 2·00 | 4·25 |

NABHA STATE (5)  NABHA (6)

**1938.** *King George VI. Nos. 247/64 optd as T* **3** *(3 p. to 1 a.), T* **5** *(2 a. to 12 a.) or T* **4** *(rupee values).*

77 **91** 3 p. slate .. 4·50 30
78 ½ a. red-brown .. 1·50 30
79 9 p. green .. 14·00 3·00
80 1 a. carmine .. 1·00 30
81 **92** 2 a. vermilion .. 75 2·50
82 – 2½ a. bright violet .. 85 3·25
83 – 3 a. yellow-green .. 95 2·75
84 – 3½ a. bright blue .. 1·00 6·50
85 – 4 a. brown .. 1·75 3·00
86 – 6 a. turquoise-green .. 1·50 6·50
87 – 8 a. slate-violet .. 1·75 7·00
88 – 12 a. lake .. 2·25 8·50
89 **93** 1 r. grey and red-brown .. 9·00 12·00
90 2 r. purple and brown .. 14·00 45·00
91 5 r. green and blue .. 42·00 £100
92 10 r. purple and claret .. 80·00 £225
93 15 r. brown and green .. £180 £375
94 25 r. slate-violet and purple .. £200 £425
77/94 .. *Set of* 18 £500 £1100

**1941–45.** *King George VI. Optd with T* **6**. *(a) Stamps of 1937.*

95 **91** 3 p. slate (1942) .. 24·00 1·50
96 ½ a. red-brown (1942) .. 60·00 2·00
97 9 p. green (1942) .. 10·00 6·00
98 1 a. carmine (1942) .. 12·00 2·00
95/8 .. *Set of* 4 95·00 10·50

*(b) Stamps of 1940-43*

105 **100a** 3 p. slate (1942) .. 60 40
106 ½ a. purple (1943) .. 1·90 40
107 9 p. green (1942) .. 1·40 40
108 1 a. carmine (1945) .. 70 1·50
109 **101** 1 a. 3 p. yellow-brown .. 70 70
110 1½ a. dull violet (1942) .. 80 60
111 2 a. vermilion (1943) .. 70 1·40
112 3 a. bright violet (1943) .. 1·40 2·50
113 3½ a. bright blue (1944) .. 5·00 12·00
114 **102** 4 a. brown .. 1·50 75
115 6 a. turquoise-green (1943) .. 4·00 14·00
116 8 a. slate-violet (1943) .. 4·00 11·00
117 12 a. lake (1943) .. 4·25 14·00
105/117 .. *Set of* 13 24·00 55·00

The 1½ a. exists printed by lithography or typography.

OFFICIAL STAMPS

SERVICE

SERVICE (O 8)  NABHA STATE (O 9)

**1885** (May). *Nos. 1/3 of Nabha optd with Type* O **8**.

O1 **23** ½ a. blue-green .. 60 30
O2 **25** 1 a. brown-purple .. 20 15
a. Opt Type O 8 double .. † £600
O3 **27** 2 a. dull blue .. 32·00 55·00
O1/3 .. *Set of* 3 32·00 55·00

The three values have had the overprint reprinted in the same way as the ordinary stamps of 1885.

**1885** (Nov)–**97**. *Optd with Type* O **9**. *(a) In red.*

O 4 **23** ½ a. blue-green .. 2·00 2·00
O 5 **27** 2 a. deep blue .. 45 55

*(b) In black (Nov 1885–97)*

O 6 **23** ½ a. blue-green (1888) .. 10 10
a. "SERVICE." with stop .. 90·00 2·25
b. "S ATE" for "STATE" ..
O 7 **25** 1 a. brown-purple .. 20 15
O 8 1 a. plum .. 20 15
a. "SERVICE." with stop .. 4·50 75
b. "NABHA STATE" double .. † £225
O 9 **27** 2 a. dull blue (1888) .. 35 30
O10 2 a. ultramarine .. 60 60
O11 **28** 3 a. orange (1889) .. 9·00 22·00
O12 3 a. brown-orange .. 8·00 18·00
O13 **29** 4 a. olive-green (1888) .. 50 35
O14 4 a. slate-green .. 60 40
O15 **21** 6 a. olive-bistre (1889) .. 9·00 9·00
O16 6 a. bistre-brown .. £300
O17 **31** 8 a. dull mauve (1889) .. 60 70
O18 **32** 12 a. purple/*red* (1889) .. 4·00 7·50
O19 **33** 1 r. slate (1889) .. 21·00 85·00
O20 **37** 1 r. green and carmine (1.97) .. 18·00 32·00
O6/20 .. *Set of* 10 55·00 £140

Printings up to and including that of August 1895 had the "SERVICE" overprint applied to sheets of stamps already overprinted with Type **2**. From the printing of January 1897 onwards the two parts of the overprint were applied at one operation. This method was only used for printings of the ½ a., 1 a. and 1 r. (O20).

**1903–06.** *King Edward VII stamps of India optd with Type* O **9**.

O24 **41** 3 p. pale grey (1906) .. 1·75 4·00
O25 3 p. slate-grey (1906) .. 65 2·75
O26 **42** ½ a. green .. 30 10
O27 **43** 1 a. carmine .. 15 10
O28 **44** 2 a. pale violet .. 40 40
O29 2 a. mauve .. 45 40
O30 **47** 4 a. olive .. 1·10 45
O32 **49** 8 a. purple (*shades*) .. 90 90
O33 8 a. claret .. 3·75 2·25
a. Opt double, one albino .. 25·00
O34 **51** 1 r. green and carmine .. 1·50 2·00
O24/34 .. *Set of* 7 4·50 6·00

**1907.** *Nos. 149/50 of India optd with Type* O **9**.

O35 **53** ½ a. green .. 10 10
O36 **54** 1 a. carmine .. 15 20

**1913.** *King George V. Optd with Type* O **9**.

O37 **63** 4 a. olive .. 10·00
O38 **67** 1 r. brown and green .. 50·00
a. Opt double, one albino .. 80·00

**1913.** *Official stamps of India optd with T* **2**.

O39 **55** 3 p. slate-grey .. 20 2·50
O39*a* 3 p. bluish slate .. 20 2·50
O40 **56** ½ a. green .. 15 10
O41 **57** 1 a. aniline carmine .. 15 10
O42 **59** 2 a. mauve .. 25 15
O43 **63** 4 a. olive .. 35 30
O44 **65** 8 a. dull mauve .. 60 60
O46 **67** 1 r. brown and green .. 1·75 1·75
O39/46 .. *Set of* 7 3·00 4·50

NABHA STATE SERVICE (O 10)  NABHA SERVICE (O 11)

**1932–42?.** *King George V (Nasik printing, wmk Mult Star), optd at Nasik with Type* O **10**.

O47 **55** 3 p. slate .. 10 15
O50 **81** 1 a. chocolate (1935) .. 10 15
O50*a* **63** 4 a. sage-green (1942?) .. 13·00 2·00
O51 **65** 8 a. reddish purple (1937) .. 85 1·75
O47/51 .. *Set of* 4 13·00 3·75

**1938.** *King George VI. Optd as Type* O **10**.

O54 **91** 9 p. green .. 1·25 1·75
O55 1 a. carmine .. 3·75 30

**1940–43.** *(a) Official stamps optd with T* **6**.

O56 **O 20** 3 p. slate (1942) .. 45 35
O57 ½ a. red-brown (1942) .. 60 30
O57*a* ½ a. purple (1943) .. 80 30
O58 9 p. green .. 80 20
O59 1 a. carmine (1942) .. 40 20
O61 1½ a. dull violet (1942) .. 50 40
O62 2 a. vermilion (1942) .. 50 45
O64 4 a. brown (1942) .. 1·75 1·75
O65 8 a. slate-violet (1942) .. 2·50 5·50

*(b) Postage stamps optd with Type* O **11**.

O66 **93** 1 r. grey and red-brown (1942) .. 7·50 21·00
O67 2 r. purple and brown (1942) .. 21·00 75·00
O68 5 r. green and blue (1942) .. £150 £225
O56/68 .. *Set of* 11 £170 £300

## PATIALA

| PRICES FOR STAMPS ON COVER | |
|---|---|
| Nos. 1/6 | *from* × 10 |
| Nos. 7/34 | *from* × 6 |
| Nos. 35/45 | *from* × 8 |
| Nos. 46/115 | *from* × 4 |
| Nos. O1/84 | *from* × 15 |

PUTTIALLA STATE (1)  PUTTIALLA STATE (2)  PATIALA STATE (3)

**1884.** *Queen Victoria. Optd with T* **1**, *in red.*

1 **23** ½ a. blue-green .. 80 70
a. Opt double, one sideways .. £700 £400
2 **25** 1 a. brown-purple .. 22·00 18·00
a. Opt double ..
b. Optd in red and in black .. £375
3 **27** 2 a. dull blue .. 5·00 5·00
4 **17** 4 a. green .. 20·00 22·00
5 **31** 8 a. dull mauve .. £150 £350
a. Opt inverted .. £2750
b. Optd in red and in black .. 42·00
ba. Ditto. Opts inverted .. £1700
6 **33** 1 r. slate .. 75·00 £160
1/6 .. *Set of* 6 £225 £500

Nos. 5a and 5ba each occur once in the setting of 120. The 8 a. value also exists with a trial overprint (showing the words more curved) reading downwards (*Price £250 unused*), which should not be confused with No. 5a.

**1885.** *Optd with T* **2**. *(a) In red.*

7 **23** ½ a. blue-green .. 30 20
a. "AUTTIALLA" .. 10·00 12·00
b. "STATE" only ..
c. Wide spacing between lines .. 1·60 1·90
8 **27** 2 a. dull blue .. 95 35
a. "AUTTIALLA" .. 19·00
b. Wide spacing between lines .. 6·50 6·50
9 **17** 4 a. green .. 1·00 1·10
a. Optd in red and in black .. £140
b. Wide spacing between lines .. 65·00
10 **33** 1 r. slate .. 4·75 23·00
a. "AUTTIALLA" .. £250
b. Wide spacing between lines .. 70·00

*(b) In black*

11 **25** 1 a. brown-purple .. 15 15
a. Optd in red and in black .. 3·00 20·00
b. "AUTTIALLA" .. 30·00
ba. Ditto. Optd in red and in black .. £750
c. Opt double .. £130 £140
d. Wide spacing between lines .. 30·00
12 **31** 8 a. dull mauve .. 7·50 13·00
a. "AUTTIALLA" .. £200
b. Opt double, one albino .. 45·00
c. Wide spacing between lines .. 65·00
7/12 .. *Set of* 6 13·00 35·00

The ½, 2 and 4 a. (T **29**), and 1 r. (all overprinted in black), are proofs.

All six values exist with reprinted overprints, and the error "AUTTIALLA STATE" has been reprinted in complete sheets on all values and in addition in black on the ½, 2, 4 a., and 1 r. Nearly all these however, are found with the word "REPRINT" overprinted upon them. On the genuine "AUTTIALLA" errors, which occur on R. 9/12 in the setting of 120, the word "STATE" is 8½ mm long; on the reprints only 7¾ mm.

Nos. 7/8 and 10/12 exist with error "PUTTILLA", but their status is uncertain.

**1891–96.** *Optd with T* **3**.

13 **23** ½ a. blue-green (1892) .. 10 10
14 **24** 9 p. carmine .. 25 60
15 **25** 1 a. brown-purple .. 30 15
16 1 a. plum .. 45 30
a. "PATIALA" omitted .. £130 £160
b. "PA" omitted ..
c. "PATIA" omitted ..
d. "PATIAL" omitted ..
17 **26** 1½ a. sepia .. 30 45
18 **27** 2 a. dull blue (1896) .. 40 20
19 2 a. ultramarine .. 60 40
20 **28** 3 a. brown-orange .. 40 35
21 **29** 4 a. olive-green (1896) .. 40 40
a. "PATIALA" omitted .. £225 £160
22 4 a. slate-green .. 40 40
23 **21** 6 a. bistre-brown .. 40 2·00
24 6 a. olive-bistre .. 1·25 5·50
25 **31** 8 a. dull mauve ..
26 8 a. magenta (1896) .. 65 2·50
27 **32** 12 a. purple/*red* .. 65 3·00
28 **37** 1 r. green and carmine (1896) .. 3·50 11·00
29 **38** 2 r. carmine and yellow-brown (1895) .. 80·00 £225
30 3 r. brown and green (1895) .. 95·00 £250
31 5 r. ultramarine and violet (1895) .. £110 £275
13/31 .. *Set of* 14 £250 £700

The errors on the 1 a. plum and 4 a. olive-green occur on R.19/1 in the December 1898 printing. Nos. 16b/d are early stages of the error before the entire word was omitted.

**1899–1902.** *Colours changed and new value. Optd with T* **3**.

32 **40** 3 p. carmine (1899) .. 10 10
a. Pair, one without opt ..
33 **23** ½ a. pale yellow-green .. 20 15
34 **25** 1 a. carmine .. 35 20
32/4 .. *Set of* 3 60 40

**1903–06.** *King Edward VII. Optd with T* **3**.

35 **41** 3 p. pale grey .. 10 10
a. Additional albino opt of Jind Type **3**
36 3 p. slate-grey (1906) .. 10 10
37 **42** ½ a. green .. 30 10
38 **43** 1 a. carmine .. 10 10
a. Horiz pair, one without opt .. £600
39 **44** 2 a. pale violet .. 30 30
*a. Mauve* .. 2·25 40
40 **46** 3 a. orange-brown .. 30 20
41 **47** 4 a. olive (1905) .. 1·10 60
42 **48** 6 a. olive-bistre (1905) .. 70 2·25
43 **49** 8 a. purple (1906) .. 1·50 90
44 **50** 12 a. purple/*red* (1906) .. 1·75 4·50
45 **51** 1 r. green and carmine (1905) .. 1·25 1·75
35/45 .. *Set of* 10 6·75 9·75

**1912.** *Nos. 149/50 of India optd with T* **3**.

46 **53** ½ a. green .. 10 10
47 **54** 1 a. carmine .. 25 25

**1912–26.** *King George V. Optd with T* **3**.

48 **55** 3 p. slate-grey .. 10 10
49 **56** ½ a. green .. 15 10
50 **57** 1 a. aniline carmine .. 20 10
51 **58** 1½ a. chocolate (Type A) (1922) .. 30 50
52 **59** 2 a. mauve .. 20 20
53 **62** 3 a. orange-brown .. 45 60
54 **63** 4 a. olive .. 70 85
55 **64** 6 a. yellow-brown .. 1·60 1·90
*a. Yellow-bistre* .. 60 1·25
56 **65** 8 a. purple .. 65 65
57 **66** 12 a. dull claret .. 85 2·50
58 **67** 1 r. brown and green .. 2·50 4·25
a. Opt double, one albino .. 29·00
59 2 r. carmine and yellow-brown (1926) .. 6·00 38·00
60 5 r. ultramarine and violet (1926) .. 16·00 40·00

**1923–6.** *As 1912–26. New colours.*

61 **57** 1 a. chocolate .. 30 10
62 **62** 3 a. ultramarine (1926) .. 35 1·75
48/62 .. *Set of* 15 26·00 80·00

PATIALA STATE (4)  PATIALA STATE (5)

**1928–34.** *King George V (Nasik printing, wmk Mult Star) optd at Nasik with T* **4** *or* **5** *(rupee values).*

63 **55** 3 p. slate (1932) .. 35 10
64 **56** ½ a. green .. 15 10
65 **80** 9 p. deep green (1934) .. 20 20
66 **57** 1 a. chocolate .. 20 15
67 **82** 1¼ a. mauve (1932) .. 50 15
68 **70** 2 a. purple .. 20 20
69 **61** 2½ a. orange (1934) .. 60 1·00
70 **62** 3 a. bright blue (1929) .. 40 75
71 **71** 4 a. sage-green .. 75 65
72 **65** 8 a. reddish purple (1933) .. 1·50 1·40
73 **67** 1 r. chocolate and green (1929) .. 1·75 2·75
74 2 r. carmine and orange .. 3·25 17·00
63/74 .. *Set of* 12 9·00 22·00

The 9 p. exists printed by lithography or typography.

**1935–7.** *Optd with T* **4**.

75 **79** ½ a. blue-green (1937) .. 20 10
76 **81** 1 a. chocolate (1936) .. 20 10
77 **59** 2 a. vermilion (No. 236a) (1936) .. 15 20
78 **62** 3 a. carmine .. 1·25 1·50
79 **63** 4 a. sage-green .. 40 85
75/9 .. *Set of* 5 2·00 2·50

PATIALA STATE (6)  PATIALA (7)  PATIALA (8)

**1937–8.** *King George VI. Nos. 247/64 optd with T* **4** *(3 p. to 1 a.), T* **6** *(2 a. to 12 a.), or T* **5** *(rupee values).*

80 **91** 3 p. slate .. .. .. .. 23·00 30
81 ½ a. red-brown .. .. .. .. 3·75 20
82 9 p. green (1937) .. .. .. 1·60 40
83 1 a. carmine (1937) .. .. .. 60 20
84 **92** 2 a. vermilion .. .. .. .. 1·00 2·75
85 – 2½ a. bright violet .. .. .. 1·40 6·00
86 – 3 a. yellow-green .. .. .. 1·40 3·00
87 – 3½ a. bright blue .. .. .. 1·75 8·50
88 – 4 a. brown .. .. .. .. 6·00 6·00
89 – 6 a. turquoise-green .. .. .. 9·50 13·00
90 – 8 a. slate-violet .. .. .. 9·50 13·00
91 – 12 a. lake .. .. .. .. 9·50 17·00
92 **93** 1 r. grey and red-brown .. .. 15·00 22·00
93 2 r. purple and brown .. .. 20·00 45·00
94 5 r. green and blue .. .. .. 32·00 75·00
95 10 r. purple and claret .. .. 55·00 £140
96 15 r. brown and green .. .. 95·00 £225
97 25 r. slate-violet and purple .. .. £140 £300
80/97 .. .. .. .. .. *Set of* 18 £375 £800

**1941–6.** *King George VI. Optd with T* **7** *or* **8** *(rupee value).*

*(a) Stamps of* 1937

98 **91** 3 p. slate .. .. .. .. 7·50 50
99 ½ a. red-brown .. .. .. .. 7·50 20
100 9 p. green .. .. .. .. 75·00 2·50
101 1 a. carmine .. .. .. .. 15·00 50
102 **93** 1 r. grey and red-brown (1946) .. 7·00 25·00
98/102 .. .. .. .. *Set of* 5 £100 25·00

*(b) Stamps of* 1940-43

103 **100a** 3 p. slate (1942) .. .. .. 60 15
104 ½ a. purple (1943) .. .. .. 60 15
105 9 p. green (1942) .. .. .. 60 15
a. Vert pair, one without opt .. £1700
106 1 a. carmine (1944) .. .. .. 40 10
107 **101** 1 a. 3 p. yellow-brown .. .. 1·40 1·00
108 1½ a. violet (1942) .. .. .. 2·50 45
109 2 a. vermilion (1944) .. .. .. 2·50 20
110 3 a. bright violet (1944) .. .. 1·75 70
111 3½ a. bright blue (1944) .. .. 6·50 11·00
112 **102** 4 a. brown (1944) .. .. .. 1·75 70
113 6 a. turquoise-green (1944) .. .. 1·75 7·00
114 8 a. slate-violet (1944) .. .. 2·25 4·50
115 12 a. lake (1945) .. .. .. 4·75 13·00
103/15 .. .. .. .. *Set of* 13 25·00 35·00

The 1½ a. exists printed by lithography or typography.

## OFFICIAL STAMPS

SERVICE (O 2) SERVICE (O 3)

**1884.** *Nos. 1/3 of Patiala optd with Type* O **2**, *in black.*

O1 **23** ½ a. blue-green .. .. .. 4·25 15
O2 **25** 1 a. brown-purple .. .. .. 30 10
a. Opt Type 1 inverted .. .. £550 £150
b. Opt Type 1 double .. .. .. † 80·00
c. "SERVICE" double .. .. £550 £250
d. "SERVICE" inverted .. .. † £550
O3 **27** 2 a. dull blue .. .. .. £1800 50·00

**1885–90.** *(a) No. 7 of Patiala optd with Type* O **2**, *in black.*

O4 **23** ½ a. blue-green .. .. .. 20 10
a. "SERVICE" double .. .. † £375
b. "AUTTIALLA" .. .. .. 50·00 14·00

*(b) No. 11 of Patiala optd with Type* O **2**, *in black*

O5 **25** 1 a. brown-purple .. .. .. 30 10
a. "SERVICE" double .. .. £500
b. "SERVICE" double, one inverted .. † £325
c. "AUTTIALLA" .. .. £300 40·00
d. "PUTTIALLA STATE" double † £400

*(c) As No. 7 of Patiala, but optd in black, and No. 8, optd with Type* O **3**

O6 **23** ½ a. blue-green (Bk.) (1890) .. 40 10
O7 **27** 2 a. dull blue (R.) .. .. .. 15 10
a. "SERVICE" double, one inverted .. 30·00

There are reprints of Nos. O4, O5 and O7. The first has the word "SERVICE" in the large type in *red* instead of the small type in *black*, and the second has the word in the large type in *black* in place of the small type. The 2 a. with Type O 3, in *black*, is a proof. The ½ a. "AUTTIALLA" has also been reprinted, but nearly all the above have been overprinted "REPRINT".

No. O7 exists with error "PUTTILLA", but its status is uncertain.

SERVICE

PATIALA STATE (O 4) PATIALA STATE SERVICE (O 5) PATIALA STATE SERVICE (O 6)

**1891** (Nov)–**1900**. *Optd with Type* O **4**, *in black.*

O 8 **23** ½ a. blue-green (9.95) .. .. 10 10
a. "SERVICE" inverted .. .. 50·00
b. "I" of "SERVICE" omitted .. £475
c. First "T" of "STATE" omitted .. £180 £180
O 9 **25** 1 a. plum (10.1900) .. .. 1·50 10
a. "SERVICE" inverted .. .. 55·00
O10 **27** 2 a. dull blue (12.98) .. .. 1·50 60
*a. Deep blue* .. .. .. 1·25 90
b. "SERVICE" inverted .. .. 55·00
c. Thin seriffed "I" in "SERVICE" .. 70·00
O12 **28** 3 a. brown-orange .. .. .. 20 70
a. "I" of "SERVICE" omitted ..
O13 **29** 4 a. olive-green .. .. .. 20 45
*a. Slate-green* (9.95) .. .. 20 15
b. "I" of "SERVICE" omitted ..
O15 **21** 6 a. bistre-brown .. .. .. 60 35
O16 **31** 8 a. dull mauve .. .. .. 55 55
*a. Magenta* (12.98) .. .. .. 45 55
b. "I" of "SERVICE" omitted .. £1300
c. Thin seriffed "I" in "SERVICE" ..
O18 **32** 12 a. purple/*red* .. .. .. 45 50
a. "I" of "SERVICE" omitted ..
O19 **33** 1 r. slate .. .. .. .. 55 55
a. "I" of "SERVICE" omitted ..
O8/19 .. .. .. .. *Set of* 9 4·75 3·25

Stamps from the first printing of November 1891 (Nos. O12/13, O15/16, O18/19) had the "SERVICE" overprint, as Type O **3**, applied to sheets already overprinted with Type **3**. Subsequent printings of Nos. O8/10*a*, O13*a* and O16*a* had both overprints applied at one operation as shown on Type O 4.

The errors with "SERVICE" inverted occur from a trial printing, in two operations, during 1894, which was probably not issued. Some of the "I" omitted varieties may also come from the same trial printing.

**1902** (Jan)–**03**. *Optd with Type* O **4**.

O20 **25** 1 a. carmine .. .. .. .. 10 10
O21 **37** 1 r. green and carmine (5.03) .. .. 5·00 9·00

**1903–10.** *King Edward VII stamps of India optd with Type* O **4**.

O22 **41** 3 p. pale grey .. .. .. 10 10
*a. Slate-grey* (1909) .. .. .. 10 10
O24 **42** ½ a. green .. .. .. .. 10 10
O25 **43** 1 a. carmine .. .. .. .. 10 10
O26 **44** 2 a. pale violet (1905) .. .. 20 20
*a. Mauve* .. .. .. .. 15 10
O28 **46** 3 a. orange-brown .. .. .. 1·25 1·50
O29 **47** 4 a. olive (1905) .. .. .. 30 20
O30 **49** 8 a. purple (*shades*) .. .. .. 45 50
*a. Claret* (1910) .. .. .. 1·25 60
O32 **51** 1 r. green and carmine (1906) .. 70 70
O22/32 .. .. .. .. *Set of* 8 2·75 2·75

**1907.** *Nos. 149/50 of India optd with Type* O **4**.

O33 **53** ½ a. green .. .. .. .. 10 10
O34 **54** 1 a. carmine .. .. .. .. 10 10

**1913–26.** *King George V. Official stamps of India optd with T* **3**.

O35 **55** 3 p. slate-grey .. .. .. 10 10
*a. Bluish slate* (1926) .. .. 15 10
O36 **56** ½ a. green .. .. .. .. 10 10
O37 **57** 1 a. carmine .. .. .. .. 10 10
O38 1 a. brown (1925) .. .. .. 1·90 45
O39 **59** 2 a. mauve .. .. .. .. 30 15
O40 **63** 4 a. olive .. .. .. .. 20 30
O41 **64** 6 a. yellow-bistre (1926) .. .. 45 1·75
O42 **65** 8 a. purple .. .. .. .. 35 40
O43 **67** 1 r. brown and green .. .. 1·00 1·40
O44 2 r. carmine and yellow-brown (1926) .. 4·50 17·00
O45 5 r. ultramarine and violet (1926) .. 8·00 17·00
O35/45 .. .. .. .. *Set of* 11 15·00 35·00

**1927–36.** *King George V (Nasik printing, wmk Mult Star), optd at Nasik with Type* O **5** *or Type* O **6** *(rupee values).*

O47 **55** 3 p. slate .. .. .. .. 10 10
a. Blue opt .. .. .. .. 60 60
O48 **56** ½ a. green (1932) .. .. .. 15 30
O49 **57** 1 a. chocolate .. .. .. 10 10
O50 **82** 1¼ a. mauve (1932) .. .. .. 15 10
O51 **70** 2 a. purple .. .. .. .. 15 25
O52 2 a. vermilion (1933) .. .. .. 30 30
O53 **61** 2½ a. orange (1933) .. .. .. 30 30
O54 **71** 4 a. sage-green (1935) .. .. 30 30
O55 **65** 8 a. reddish purple (1929) .. .. 50 55
O56 **67** 1 r. chocolate and green (1929) .. 1·60 1·10
O57 2 r. carmine and orange (1936) .. 3·25 14·00
O47/57 .. .. .. .. *Set of* 11 6·25 16·00

**1935–9.** *New types. Optd with Type* O **5**.

O58 **79** ½ a. green (1936) .. .. .. 10 10
O59 **81** 1 a. chocolate (1936) .. .. .. 10 20
O60 **59** 2 a. vermilion .. .. .. .. 15 15
O61 2 a. vermilion (*small die*) (1939) .. 3·00 60
O62 **63** 4 a. sage-green (1936) .. .. 30 20
O58/62 .. .. .. .. *Set of* 5 3·25 1·10

**1937–39.** *King George VI. Optd with Types* O **5** *or* O **6** *(rupee values).*

O63 **91** ½ a. red-brown (1938) .. .. 1·00 20
O64 9 p. green (1938) .. .. .. 13·00 42·00
O65 1 a. carmine .. .. .. .. 1·00 20
O66 **93** 1 r. grey and red-brown (1939) .. 2·00 3·50
O67 2 r. purple and brown (1939) .. 8·00 5·00
O68 5 r. green and blue (1939) .. .. 20·00 40·00
O63/8 .. .. .. .. *Set of* 6 40·00 80·00

1A 1A (O 7) 1A SERVICE 1A (O 8) PATIALA SERVICE (O 9)

**1939–40.** *Stamp of* 1932 *(King George V).*

*(a) Optd with Types* O **5** *and* O **7**

O69 **82** 1 a. on 1¼ a. mauve .. .. .. 3·00 1·40

*(b) Optd with T* **4** *and* O **8**

O70 **82** 1 a. on 1¼ a. mauve (1940) .. .. 1·50 1·40

"SERVICE" measures 9¼ mm on No. O69 but only 8¾ mm on O70.

**1939–44.** *(a) Official stamps optd with T* **7**.

O71 O **20** 3 p. slate (1940) .. .. .. 30 10
O72 ½ a. red-brown .. .. .. 1·25 10
O73 ½ a. purple (1942) .. .. .. 30 10
O74 9 p. green .. .. .. .. 30 15
O75 1 a. carmine .. .. .. .. 40 10
O76 1 a. 3 p. yellow-brown (1941) .. 60 25
O77 1½ a. dull violet (1944) .. .. 1·00 15
O78 2 a. vermilion (1940) .. .. 2·50 15
O79 2½ a. bright violet (1940) .. .. 50 60
O80 4 a. brown (1943) .. .. .. 60 40
O81 8 a. slate-violet (1944) .. .. 1·10 2·25

*(b) Postage stamps optd with Type* O **9**

O82 **93** 1 r. grey and red-brown (1943) .. 7·50 4·00
O83 2 r. purple and brown (1944) .. 13·00 25·00
O84 5 r. green and blue (1944) .. .. 20·00 42·00
O71/84 .. .. .. .. *Set of* 14 45·00 70·00

## INDIAN FEUDATORY STATES

These stamps were only valid for use within their respective states, *unless otherwise indicated.*

Postage stamps of the Indian States, current at that date, were replaced by those of the Republic of India on 1 April 1950.

*Unless otherwise stated,* all became obsolete on 1 May 1950 (with the exception of the "Anchal" stamps of Travancore-Cochin, which remained current until 1 July 1951 or Sept 1951 for the Official issues).

### ALWAR

**PRICES FOR STAMPS ON COVER**

| | |
|---|---|
| Nos. 1/2 | *from* × 25 |
| No. 3 | *from* × 50 |
| No. 4 | — |
| No. 5 | *from* × 50 |

1 (1 a.).

**1877.** *Litho. Rouletted.*

1 1 ¼ a. grey-blue .. .. .. .. 2·25 50
a. *Ultramarine* .. .. .. 2·00 50
b. Imperf between (pair) .. .. — 40·00
c. *Bright greenish blue* .. .. 12·00 7·00
2 1 a. brown .. .. .. .. 2·50 90
a. Imperf between (pair) .. .. 45·00 45·00
b. *Red-brown* .. .. .. .. 1·40 60
c. *Chocolate* .. .. .. .. 9·00 8·00

**1899–1901.** *Redrawn. P 12. (a) Wide margins between stamps.*

3 1 ¼ a. slate-blue .. .. .. .. 4·50 2·00
a. Imperf between (horiz pair) .. £300 £325
b. Imperf between (vert pair) .. .. £350
4 ¼ a. emerald-green .. .. .. £550

*(b) Narrower margins* (1901)

5 1 ¼ a. emerald-green .. .. .. 2·00 1·50
a. Imperf between (horiz pair) .. £190
b. Imperf between (vert pair) .. .. £190 £200
c. Imperf horiz (vert pair) .. .. £200
d. Imperf (pair) .. .. .. £225
e. *Pale yellow-green* .. .. .. 5·00 1·90
ea. Imperf (pair) .. .. .. £275
eb. Imperf between (horiz pair) .. † £375

In the redrawn type only the bottom outer frameline is thick, whereas in the original 1877 issue the left-hand frameline is also thick, as shown in Type 1.

The stamps of Alwar became obsolete on 1 July 1902.

### BAHAWALPUR

*See after* PAKISTAN

### BAMRA

**PRICES FOR STAMPS ON COVER**

| | |
|---|---|
| Nos. 1/6 | — |
| Nos. 8/40 | *from* × 25 |

**Raja Sir Sudhal Deo, 1869–1903**

**GUM.** The stamps of Bamra were issued without gum.

1 (¼ a.) 1*a* 2 (½ a.)

3 (1 a.) 4 (2 a.) 5 (4 a.)

6 (8 a.)

*(illustrations actual size)*

(Typo Jagannata Ballabh Press, Deogarh)

**1888.** *Imperf.*

1 1 ¼ a. black/*yellow* .. .. .. £140
a. "g" inverted (R.5/1) .. .. .. £1600
b. Last native character inverted .. £1700
c. Last native character as Type 1*a* .. £1700
2 2 ½ a. black/*rose* .. .. .. 70·00
a. "g" inverted (R.5/1) .. .. .. £1400
3 3 1 a. black/*blue* .. .. .. 42·00
a. "g" inverted (R.5/1) .. .. .. £1300
b. Scroll inverted (R.8/4) .. .. £1100
4 4 2 a. black/*green* .. .. .. .. 65·00 £140
a. "a" omitted (R.8/3) .. .. .. £1400
b. Scroll inverted (R.8/4) .. .. £1200
5 5 4 a. black/*yellow* .. .. .. 48·00
a. "a" omitted (R.8/3) .. .. .. £1300
b. Scroll inverted (R.8/4) .. .. £1100
6 6 8 a. black/*rose* .. .. .. 38·00
a. "a" omitted (R.8/3) .. .. .. £1200
b. Horiz pair, one printed on back .. £350
c. Scroll inverted (R.8/4) .. .. £1000

These stamps were all printed from the same plate of 96 stamps, 12 × 8, but for some values only part of the plate was used. There are 96 varieties of the ½, 4 and 8 a., 72 of the 1 a., 80 of the 2 a. and not less than 88 of the ¼ a.

The scroll ornament can be found pointing to either the right or the left.

There are two forms of the third native character. In the first five horizontal rows it is as in T 1 and in the last three rows as in T 4.

These stamps have been reprinted: the ¼ a. and ½ a. in blocks of 8 varieties (all showing scroll pointing to right), and all the values in blocks of 20 varieties (all showing scroll pointing to left). On the reprints the fourth character is of a quite different shape.

8

**1890** (July)–**93.** *Black on coloured paper. Nos. 24/5 and 39/40 show face value as "One Rupee". (a) "Postage" with capital "P".*

8 8 ¼ a. on *rose-lilac* .. .. .. 1·40 2·00
a. "Eeudatory" (R. 2/4) .. .. 10·00 15·00
b. "Quatrer" (R. 1/3) .. .. .. 10·00 15·00
c. Inverted "e" in "Postage" (R. 2/3) .. 10·00 15·00
9 ¼ a. on *bright rose* .. .. .. 60 90
10 ¼ a. on *reddish purple* .. .. .. 80 1·00
a. First "a" in "anna" inverted (R. 3/3) 27·00 30·00
b. "AMRA" inverted (R. 4/4) .. .. 42·00 42·00
c. "M" and second "A" in "BAMRA" inverted (R. 4/4) .. .. .. 50·00 50·00
11 ½ a. on *dull green* .. .. .. 1·00 1·25
a. "Eeudatory" (R. 2/4) .. .. 32·00 35·00
12 ½ a. on *blue-green* .. .. .. 1·75 1·75
13 1 a. on *bistre-yellow* .. .. .. 1·60 1·25
a. "Eeudatory" (R. 2/4) .. .. 65·00 70·00
14 1 a. on *orange-yellow* .. .. .. 32·00 32·00
a. "annas" for "anna" .. .. .. 90·00 90·00
15 2 a. on *rose-lilac* .. .. .. 7·00 12·00
a. "Eeudatory" (R. 2/4) .. .. £100 £120
16 2 a. on *bright rose* .. .. .. 1·60 1·60
17 2 a. on *dull rose* .. .. .. 4·25 2·75
18 4 a. on *rose-lilac* .. .. .. £375 £450
a. "Eeudatory" (R. 2/4) .. .. £1400 £1400
19 4 a. on *dull rose* .. .. .. 3·50 2·50
a. "Eeudatory" (R. 2/4) .. .. £400 £400
b. "BAMBA" (R. 2/1) .. .. .. £400 £400
20 4 a. on *bright rose* .. .. .. 2·25 3·50
20*a* 4 a. on *deep pink* .. .. .. 12·00 10·00
21 8 a. on *rose-lilac* .. .. .. 14·00 28·00
a. "Foudatory" and "Postagc" (R. 1/2) £140 £150
b. "BAMBA" (R. 2/1) .. .. .. £140 £150
22 8 a. on *bright rose* .. .. .. 7·00 8·00
23 8 a. on *dull rose* .. .. .. 9·00 10·00
24 1 r. on *rose-lilac* .. .. .. 32·00 48·00
a. "Eeudatory" (R. 2/4) .. .. £325 £350
b. "BAMBA" (R. 2/1) .. .. .. £190 £200
c. "Postagc" (R. 1/2) .. .. .. £190 £200
25 1 r. on *bright rose* .. .. .. 15·00 18·00
a. Small "r" in "rupee" .. .. £170 £170

*(b) "postage" with small "p"* (1891–93)

26 8 ¼ a. on *bright rose* .. .. .. 60 90
27 ¼ a. on *reddish purple* .. .. .. 60 65
28 ½ a. on *dull green* .. .. .. 1·00 1·25
a. First "a" in "anna" inverted (R. 3/3) 17·00 18·00
29 ½ a. on *blue-green* .. .. .. 1·90 1·90
a. First "a" in "anna" inverted (R. 3/3) 17·00 18·00
30 1 a. on *bistre-yellow* .. .. .. 1·60 1·25
31 1 a. on *orange-yellow* .. .. .. 32·00 32·00
32 2 a. on *bright rose* .. .. .. 1·60 2·00
33 2 a. on *dull rose* .. .. .. 4·00 1·50
34 4 a. on *dull rose* .. .. .. 4·50 2·75
35 4 a. on *bright rose* .. .. .. 3·75 4·50
35*a* 4 a. on *deep pink* .. .. .. 15·00 12·00
36 8 a. on *rose-lilac* .. .. .. 27·00 42·00
37 8 a. on *bright rose* .. .. .. 7·00 8·00
38 8 a. on *dull rose* .. .. .. 9·00 10·00
39 1 r. on *rose-lilac* .. .. .. 42·00 65·00
40 1 r. on *bright rose* .. .. .. 20·00 22·00
a. Small "r" in "rupee" .. .. £225 £225
b. Small "r" in "rupee" and native characters in the order 2, 3, 1, 4, 5 (R. 4/4) .. .. .. £1400 £1400

There are 10 settings of Type **8.** The first setting (of 20 (4×5)) has capital "P" throughout. The remaining settings (of 16 (4×4)) have capital "P" and small "p" mixed.

For the first setting the 8 a. and 1 r. values were printed within the same block, the ten lefthand stamps being 8 a. values and the ten righthand stamps 1 r.

The various stamps were distributed between the settings as follows:

Setting I—Nos. 8/c, 11/a, 13/a, 15/a, 18/19a, 21, 24/a
Setting II—Nos. 19, 19b, 21/b, 24, 24b/c, 34, 36, 39
Setting III—Nos. 9, 11, 13, 16, 26, 28, 30, 32
Setting IV—Nos. 20, 22, 25, 35, 37, 40
Setting V—Nos. 10, 10b/c, 20*a*, 27, 35*a*
Setting VI—Nos. 11, 12, 28, 28a, 29/a
Setting VII—Nos. 10/a, 12, 17, 19, 23, 25a, 27, 29, 33/4, 38, 40a/b
Setting VIII—Nos. 17, 33
Setting IX—Nos. 10/a, 12, 14/a, 17, 19, 23, 27, 29, 31, 33/4, 38
Setting X—Nos. 19, 34

There are 4 sizes of the central ornament, which represents an elephant's trunk holding a stick:—(*a*) 4 mm long; (*b*) 5 mm; (*c*) 6½ mm; (*d*) 11 mm. These ornaments are found pointing to right or left, either upright or inverted.

Ornaments (*a*) are found in all settings; (*b*) in all settings from Settings III to X; (*c*) in Settings I and II; and (*d*) only in Setting I.

The stamps of Bamra have been obsolete since 1 January 1895.

### BARWANI

**PRICES FOR STAMPS ON COVER**

| | |
|---|---|
| Nos. 1/2 | *from* × 3 |
| Nos. 3/43 | *from* × 5 |

**PROCESS.** All Barwani stamps are typographed from clichés, and are in sheets of 4, *unless otherwise indicated.*

Issues to about 1930 were printed by the Barwani State Printing Press, and subsequently by the *Times of India* Press, Bombay.

**GUM.** Nos. 1/31 were issued without gum.

**BOOKLET PANES.** Those stamps which were printed in sheets of 4 were issued in stamp booklets, binding holes appearing in the side margin.

1 Rana Ranjitsingh 2 Rana Ranjitsingh 3

**1921** (Mar?). *Clear impression. Medium wove paper. P 7 all round.*

1 1 ¼ a. blue-green (dull *to* deep) .. .. 65·00 £140
2 ½ a. dull blue .. .. .. .. £150 £200
a. Imperf (pair) .. .. .. — £750

**1921** (June?). *Blurred impression. Soft wove paper. P 7 on two or three sides.*

3 1 ¼ a. green (*shades*) .. .. .. 11·00 40·00
4 ½ a. ultramarine (dull *to* pale) .. .. 16·00 60·00

**NOTE.** As the small sheets of Barwani stamps were often not perforated all round, many of the earlier stamps are perforated on two or three sides only. Owing to the elementary method of printing, the colours vary greatly in depth, even within a single sheet.

**1921.** *Clear impression. Vertically laid bâtonné paper. Imperf.*

5 1 ¼ a. green (*shades*) .. .. .. 8·50
6 ½ a. green (*shades*) .. .. .. 3·00
a. Perf 11 at top or bottom only .. 3·00

It is suggested that No. 5 may be an error due to printing from the wrong plate.

**1922** (?). *Clear impression. Thickish glazed wove paper. P 7 on two or three sides.*

7 1 ¼ a. dull blue .. .. .. .. 65·00

**1922.** *Smooth, soft medium wove paper. P 7 on two or three sides.*

*(a) Clear impression*

8 1 ¼ a. deep grey-blue .. .. .. 19·00

*(b) Poor impression*

9 1 ¼ a. steel blue .. .. .. .. 9·50

Examples of No. 9 exist with perforations on all four sides.

**1922.** *P 11 on two or three sides.*

*(a) Thick, glazed white wove paper*

10 2 1 a. vermilion (*shades*) .. .. .. 1·40 10·00
a. Imperf between (vert pair) .. £150
b. Doubly printed .. .. ..
11 2 a. purple (*to* violet) .. .. .. 1·75 10·00
a. Doubly printed .. .. .. £150
b. Imperf between (pair) .. .. £120 £140

*(b) Thick, toned wove paper*

12 2 2 a. purple .. .. .. .. 9·50 25·00

**1922.** *Poor impression. Thin, poor wove paper. Pin-perf 8½ on two or three sides.*

13 1 ¼ a. grey (*to* grey-blue) .. .. .. 1·40
a. Imperf (pair) .. .. .. £130
b. Imperf between (vert pair) .. .. £110

**1923.** *Thin, smooth, unglazed wove paper. P 11 on two or three sides.*

14 1 ½ a. green (pale *to* deep) .. .. .. 1·25 9·00
a. Imperf between (pair) .. .. £200
15 2 1 a. brown-red .. .. .. .. £1700 £1700

**1923.** *Poor impression. Thick, soft wove paper. P 7 on two or three sides.*

16 1 ½ a. green (pale *to* deep) .. .. .. 22·00

No. 16 also exists perforated on all four sides.

**1923** (Mar?). *Poor quality wove paper. P 7 on two or three sides.*

17 1 ¼ a. black .. .. .. .. 42·00 £100
a. Imperf between (horiz pair) .. £800

**1923** (May?). *Horizontally laid bâtonné paper. P 12.*

18 1 ¼ a. rose (*shades*) .. .. .. 80 5·50
a. Imperf between (vert or horiz pair) .. £200
b. Pin perf 6 .. .. .. 65·00 32·00
c. Perf compound of 12 and 6 .. .. 26·00
d. Perf 7 .. .. .. .. £130
da. On wove paper .. .. .. £500

No. 18 was issued in sheets of 12 (3 panes of 4) and was printed on paper showing a sheet watermark of Britannia and a double-lined inscription. No. 18d was only issued in booklet panes of 4.

**1925** (?). *Vertically laid bâtonné paper. P 11.*

19 1 ¼ a. blue (pale *to* deep) .. .. .. 80 5·50
a. *Tête-bêche* (horiz pair) .. .. £1400

No. 19 was issued in sheets of 8 and was printed on paper with a sheet watermark of a shell and an inscription "SHELL" in double-lined capitals.

**1927.** *Very poor impression. Thin, brittle wove paper. P* 7.
20 1 ¼ a. milky blue (*shades*) .. .. .. 9·00 20·00
21 ½ a. yellow-green (*shades*) .. .. 10·00
a. Imperf between (horiz pair) .. £375
22 3 4 a. orange-brown .. .. 60·00
a. Imperf between (horiz pair) .. £600
20/2 .. .. .. *Set of* 3 70·00
On Nos. 20/1 the portrait is nearly invisible.

**1927.** *Thick wove paper. Sewing maching perf* 6–10.
23 3 4 a. yellow-brown .. .. .. 70·00
a. Imperf between (horiz pair) ..
b. Perf 7 .. .. .. .. 20·00
c. *Orange-brown* .. .. .. 85·00

**1928–32** (?). *Thick glazed paper.* (a) *P* 7.
24 1 ¼ a. deep bright blue .. .. 8·50
25 ½ a. bright yellow-green .. .. 11·00
(*b*) *P* 10½ (*rough*) (Nov 1928)
26 1 ¼ a. ultramarine .. .. .. 3·25
a. *Tête-bêche* (horiz pair) .. .. 8·00
b. Horiz pair, one stamp printed on reverse .. .. ..
27 ½ a. apple-green .. .. .. 3·75
a. *Tête-bêche* (vert pair) .. .. 8·00
(*c*) *P* 11 (*clean-cut*) (1929-32?)
28 1 ¼ a. bright blue .. .. .. 1·75 5·50
a. *Indigo* .. .. .. 1·75 5·50
ab. Imperf between (horiz pair) .. 40·00
b. *Deep dull blue* .. .. 1·25 5·50
ba. Imperf between (vert pair) .. £100
c. *Ultramarine* .. .. 2·00 7·50
29 ½ a. myrtle-green .. .. 1·50 6·00
a. Imperf between (horiz pair) .. 90·00
b. *Turquoise-green* .. .. 3·25 7·50
ba. Imperf between (vert pair) .. £170
30 2 1 a. rose-carmine (1931) .. .. 10·00 18·00
a. Imperf between (vert pair) .. — £450
31 3 4 a. salmon (*to orange*) (1931) .. 45·00 70·00
a. Imperf between (horiz pair) .. £700
28/31 .. .. .. *Set of* 4 48·00 80·00

No. 26 was printed in sheets of 8 (4 × 2) with the two centre pairs *tête-bêche* while No. 27 in similar sheets, had the two horizontal rows *tête-bêche*. Both sheets are always found with one long side imperforate.

Nos. 28/31 were printed in sheets of 8 the two lower values existing either 4 × 2 or 2 × 4 and the two higher values 4 × 2 only. No *tête-bêche* pairs were included in these printings. It is believed that a small printing of No. 31 was produced in sheets of 4, but details are uncertain.

4 Rana Devi Singh 5

**1932** (Oct)**–47.** *Medium to thick wove paper.*

A. *Close setting* (2½–4½ *mm*). *P* 11, 12 *or compound* (1932–41)
B. *Wide setting* (6–7 *mm*). *P* 11 (1945–47)

| | | | A | | B | |
|---|---|---|---|---|---|---|
| 32 | 4 | ¼ a. slate | 80 | 7·50 | 2·25 | 10·00 |
| 33 | | ½ a. blue-green | 1·40 | 7·50 | 2·25 | 8·00 |
| 34 | | 1 a. brown | 1·60 | 7·50 | 6·00 | 8·50 |
| | | a. Imperf between (horiz pair) | £1000 | — | † | |
| | | b. *Chocolate.* Perf 8½ (1947) | † | | 10·00 | 20·00 |
| 35 | | 2 a. purple (*shades*) | 3·00 | 12·00 | † | |
| | | a. *Rose-carmine* (1945) | † | | £100 | £150 |
| 36 | | 4 a. olive-green | 6·00 | 18·00 | 16·00 | 22·00 |
| 32A/6A | | *Set of* 5 | 11·00 | 42·00 | | |

The measurements given in the heading indicate the vertical spacing between impressions. There are eight settings of this interesting issue: four "Close" where the over-all stamp dimensions from centre to centre of perfs vary in width from 21½ to 23 mm and in height from 25 to 27½ mm; three "Wide", width 23–23½ mm and height 29–30 mm and one "Medium" (26½ × 31 mm) (No. 34*b* only).

**1933–47.** *P* 11.

A. *Close setting* (3–4½ *mm*). *Thick, cream-surfaced wove paper* (1933 *and* 1941 (*No.* 38*a*A)
B *Wide setting* (7–10 *mm*). *Medium to thick wove paper* (1939–47)

| | | | A | | B | |
|---|---|---|---|---|---|---|
| 37 | 1 | ¼ a. black | 1·60 | — | 2·50 | 13·00 |
| 38 | | ½ a. blue-green | 10·00 | 14·00 | † | |
| | | a. *Yellowish green* (1941) | 6·00 | 11·00 | 3·75 | 14·00 |
| 39 | 2 | 1 a. brown (*shades*) | 9·00 | 12·00 | 7·00 | 11·00 |
| | | a. Perf 8½ (5 mm) (1947) | † | | 9·00 | 20·00 |
| 40 | | 2 a. bright purple (1939) | † | | 45·00 | 90·00 |
| 41 | | 2 a. rose-carmine (1945) | † | | 19·00 | 55·00 |
| 42 | 3 | 4 a. sage-green | 19·00 | 32·00 | 17·00 | 26·00 |
| | | a. *Pale sage-green* (1939) | † | | 9·00 | 18·00 |

There were two "Close" settings (over-all stamp size 25×29 mm) and five "Wide" settings with over-all sizes 26½–31½ × 31–36½ mm. There was also one "Medium" setting (26½×31 mm) but this was confined to the 1 a. perf 8½, No. 39a.

**1938.** *P* 11.
43 5 1 a. brown .. .. .. 15·00 30·00
Stamps printed in red with designs similar to Types 3 and 5 were intended for fiscal use.

The stamps of Barwani became obsolete on 1 July 1948.

## *MINIMUM PRICE*

The minimum price quote is 10p which represents a handling charge rather than a basis for valuing common stamps. For further notes about prices see introductory pages.

## BHOPAL

**PRICES FOR STAMPS ON COVER**
Nos. 1/100 *from* × 10
Nos. O301/57 *from* × 15

The correct English inscription on these stamps is "H.H. NAWAB SHAH JAHAN BEGAM". In the case of Nos. 22 and 23 the normal stamps are spelt "BEGAN" and specimens with "BEGAM" are "errors".

As the stamps were printed from lithographic stones on which each unit was drawn separately by hand, numerous errors of spelling occurred. These are constant on all sheets and are listed. Some of our illustrations inadvertently include errors of spelling.

**ILLUSTRATIONS.** Types **1/3***a* and **6/12***a* are shown actual size.

**EMBOSSING.** Nos. 1/99 were only valid for postage when embossed with the device, in Urdu, of the ruling Begam. On T **1/3** and **6** to **12***a*. this was intended to fill the central part of the design. Almost all varieties can be found with the embossing inverted or sideways, as well as upright.

Shah Jahan

Sultan Jahan

(*actual size*)

The various basic types were often in concurrent use but for greater convenience the following list is arranged according to types instead of being in strict chronological order.

**GUM.** Nos. 1/99 were issued without gum.

**Nawab Shah Jahan Begam, 16 November 1868–15 June 1901**

1 (¼ a.)

**1872.** *Litho.* (*a*) *Double frame. Sheets of* 20 (5 × 4)
1 1 ¼ a. black .. .. .. £250 £250
a. "BFGAM" (R.3/1) .. .. £1000 £1000
b. "BEGAN" (R.2/2, R.4/4) .. .. £600 £600
c. "EGAM" (R.4/5) .. .. £1000 £1000
2 ½ a. red .. .. .. 11·00 22·00
a. "BFGAM" (R.3/1) .. .. 60·00 80·00
b. "BEGAN" (R.2/2, R.4/4) .. .. 40·00 55·00
c. "EGAM" (R.4/5) .. .. 60·00 80·00

2 (½ a.)

(*b*) *Single frame. Sheets of* 20 (4 × 5)
3 2 ¼ a. black .. .. .. — £3500
4 ½ a. red .. .. .. 9·00 14·00
a. "NWAB" (R.2/2) .. .. 45·00 60·00

3 (¼ a.)

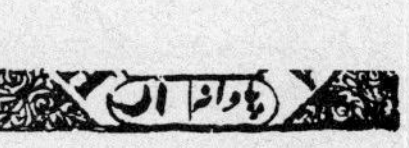

3*a* (¼ a.)

**1878** (Jan). *All lettered* "EEGAM" *for* "BEGAM". *Sheets of* 20 (4 × 5).
(*a*) *Plate* 1. *Frame lines extend horiz and vert between stamps throughout sheet*
5 3 ¼ a. black .. .. .. 2·25 5·50
(*b*) *Plate* 2. *Frame lines normal*
5*a* 3*a* ¼ a. black .. .. .. 2·25 5·50

Apart from the frame line difference between Types 3 and 3*a* the stamps can also be distinguished by the differences in the value tablets, notably the thin vertical line in the centre in Type 3*a* compared with the slightly diagonal and heavier line in Type 3.

4 (¼ a.)

5 (½ a.)

**1878** (June?)**–79.** *Value in parenthesis* (*Nos.* 6/7). *Sheets of* 32 (4 × 8). *Imperf.*
6 4 ¼ a. green (1879) .. .. .. 6·00 8·50
7 ¼ a. green (*perf*) (1879) .. .. 7·00 10·00
8 5 ½ a. red .. .. .. 3·50 5·00
a. "JAHN" (R.5/2) .. .. 24·00
b. "NWAB" (R.3/2, R.4/2) .. .. 15·00
c. "EEGAM" (R.1/3) .. .. 24·00
9 ½ a. brown .. .. .. 19·00 26·00
a. "JAHN" (R.5/2) .. .. £120
b. "NWAB" (R.3/2, R.4/2) .. .. 75·00
c. "EEGAM" (R.1/3) .. .. £120

The ¼ a. shows the "N" of "NAWAB" reversed on R.6/4 and the "N" of "JAHAN" reversed on R.1/2–4 and R.2/2–4.

**1880.** *T* 5 *redrawn; value not in parenthesis. Sheets of* 32 (4 × 8)
(*a*) *Imperf*
10 ¼ a. blue-green .. .. .. 4·00
a. "NAWA" (R.2/2–4) .. .. 22·00
b. "CHAH" (R.8/3) .. .. 50·00
11 ½ a. brown-red .. .. .. 7·50 11·00
(*b*) *Perf*
12 ¼ a. blue-green .. .. .. 5·00
a. "NAWA" (R.2/2–4) .. .. 30·00
b. "CHAH" (R.8/3) .. .. 70·00
13 ½ a. brown-red .. .. .. 4·50

The ¼ a. shows the "N" of "NAWAB" reversed on R.8/4.
Nos. 12/13 sometimes come with gum.

**1884.** *T* 5 *again redrawn. Sheets of* 32 (4 × 8), *some with value in parenthesis, others not. Perf.*
14 ¼ a. greenish blue .. .. .. 2·50 5·50
a. "ANAWAB" (R.8/1–4) .. .. 16·00

In this plate there is a slanting dash under and to left of the letters "JA" of "JAHAN," instead of a character like a large comma, as on all previous varieties of this design. With the exception of R.1/1 all stamps in the sheet show "N" of "JAHAN" reversed.

**1895.** *T* 5 *again redrawn. Sheets of* 8 (2 × 4). *Laid paper.*
15 ¼ a. red (*imperf*) .. .. .. 1·50 1·00
16 ¼ a. red (*perf*) .. .. .. — £225

In these cases where the same design has been redrawn several times, and each time in a number of varieties of type, it is not easy to distinguish the various issues. Nos. 6 and 7 may be distinguished from Nos. 10 and 12 by the presence or absence of the parenthesis marks (); 8, 9 and 11 differ principally in colour; 8 and 15 are very much alike, but differ in the value as well as in paper.

6 (1 a.)

**1881.** *Sheets of* 24 (4 × 6). *Imperf.*
17 6 ¼ a. black .. .. .. 1·40 4·75
a. "NWAB" (R.6/2–4) .. .. 4·75
18 ½ a. red .. .. .. 1·60 4·00
a. "NWAB" (R.6/2–4) .. .. 4·75
19 1 a. brown .. .. .. 1·40 4·25
a. "NWAB" (R.6/2–4) .. .. 4·75
20 2 a. blue .. .. .. 1·00 4·25
a. "NWAB" (R.6/2–4) .. .. 4·50
21 4 a. buff .. .. .. 6·00 18·00
a. "NWAB" (R.6/2–4) .. .. 22·00
17/21 .. .. .. *Set of* 5 9·50 30·00

In this issue all values were produced from the same drawing, and therefore show exactly the same varieties of type. The value at foot in this and all the following issues is given in only one form.

7 (½ a.)

**1886.** *Similar to T* 6 *but normally lettered* (*incorrectly*) "BEGAN"; *larger lettering. Sheets of* 32 (4 × 8). (*a*) *Imperf.*
22 7 ½ a. pale red .. .. .. 70 3·50
a. "BEGAM" (R.2/1) .. .. 7·50
b. "NWAB" (R.3/4) .. .. 7·50
(*b*) *Perf*
23 7 ½ a. pale red .. .. .. £130
a. "BEGAM" (R.2/1) .. .. £400
b. "NWAB" (R.3/4) .. .. £400

8 (4 a.)

**1886.** *T* **8**. *T* **6** *redrawn. Sheets of* 24 (4 × 6). *The* "M" *of* "BEGAM" *is an inverted* "W". *The width of the stamps is rather greater than the height.* (a) *Wove paper. Imperf.*

24 **8** 4 a. yellow .. .. .. .. £350
a. "EEGAM" (R.2/3–4, R.3/3–4, R.4/2, R.4/4, R.6/1) .. .. .. £450

(b) *Laid paper*

25 **8** 4 a. yellow (*imperf*) .. .. .. 5·00
a. "EEGAM" (R.2/3–4, R.3/3–4, R.4/2, R.4/4, R.6/1) .. .. .. 10·00
26 4 a. yellow (*perf*) .. .. .. 2·50 8·00
a. "EEGAM" (R.2/3–4, R.3/3–4, R.4/2, R.4/4, R.6/1) .. .. .. 5·00 12·00

**1889.** *T* **6** *again redrawn. Sheets of* 32 (4 × 8) *lettered* "BEGAN."

27 ¼ a. black (*perf*) .. .. .. .. 80 1·75
a. "EEGAN" (R.7/3) .. .. .. 9·00 13·00
28 ¼ a. black (*imperf*) .. .. .. 1·10 1·75
a. "EEGAN" (R.7/3) .. .. .. 12·00 15·00

9 (¼ a.)

**1889–90.** *T* **9**. *T* **6** *again redrawn. Sheets of* 24 (4 × 6), *all with* "M" *like an inverted* "W". *Wove paper.* (a) *Imperf.*

29 **9** ¼ a. black .. .. .. .. 55 70
30 1 a. brown .. .. .. .. 85 1·60
a. "EEGAM" (R.2/3) .. .. .. 8·50 12·00
b. "BBGAM" (R.3/1) .. .. .. 8·50 12·00
31 2 a. blue .. .. .. .. 75 90
a. "BBEGAM" (R.1/2) .. .. .. 6·50 8·00
b. "NAWAH" (R.4/2) .. .. .. 6·50 8·00
32 4 a. orange-yellow .. .. .. 1·25 1·75
29/32 .. .. .. .. *Set of* 4 3·00 4·25

(b) *Perf*

33 **9** ¼ a. black .. .. .. .. 70 1·10
34 1 a. brown .. .. .. .. 1·25 2·00
a. "EEGAM" (R.2/3) .. .. .. 11·00 15·00
b. "BBGAM" (R.3/1) .. .. .. 11·00 15·00
35 2 a. blue .. .. .. .. 75 1·25
a. "BBEGAM" (R.1/2) .. .. .. 6·50 10·00
b. "NAWAH" (R.4/2) .. .. .. 6·50 10·00
36 4 a. orange-yellow .. .. .. 1·50 3·00
33/6 .. .. .. .. *Set of* 4 3·75 6·25

Nos. 32 and 36 are nearly square, in many cases rather larger in height than in width.

**1891.** *As last, but sheets of* 32 (4 × 8).

37 **9** ½ a. red (*imperf*) .. .. .. 85 1·10
38 ½ a. red (*perf*) .. .. .. 75 1·60

**1894–98.** *T* **6** *again redrawn;* (a) *Sheets of* 24 (4 × 6), *almost all showing a character inside the octagon below, as in T* **9**. *Wove paper.*

39 1 a. deep brown (*imperf*) .. .. .. 2·25 1·25
*a. Red-brown* .. .. .. 22·00
b. Printed both sides .. .. .. — £350
41 1 a. deep brown (*perf*) .. .. .. 2·25 1·75

10 (1 a.)

(b) *As Nos.* 39/41, *but printed from a fresh transfer* (?), *showing the lines blurred and shaky. Wove paper. Imperf* (1898)

42 **10** 1 a. purple-brown .. .. .. 2·00 2·75
a. "NAWAH" (R.4/1) .. .. .. 13·00 16·00
43 1 a. purple-brown/*buff* .. .. .. 2·00 2·75
a. "NAWAH" (R.4/1) .. .. .. 13·00 16·00
b. Printed on both sides .. ..

The above are known without embossing.

11 (¼ a.)

**1895.** *Sheets of* 8 (2 × 4), *lettered* "EEGAM". *White laid paper.*

44 **11** ¼ a. black (*imperf*) .. .. .. 1·60 1·10
a. "A" inserted (R.4/2) .. .. .. 6·00 5·00
45 ¼ a. black (*perf*) .. .. .. 30·00 14·00
a. "NAW B" (R.4/2) .. .. .. £225 £150

On the perf stamp the second "A" in "NAWAB" was missing on R.4/2 in the setting. This letter was later inserted for the imperf printing varying progressively from small to large.

12 (½ a.)

**1895.** *Narrow label at bottom. Sheets of* 8 (2 × 4), *lettered* "W W" *for* "H H". *Laid paper.*

46 **12** ½ a. black (*imperf*) .. .. .. 80 1·10

12*a*

**1895.** *Sheets of* 8 (2 × 4). *Laid paper.*

47 **12*a*** ½ a. red (*imperf*) .. .. .. 90 90

No. 47 is a combination of Types **1** and **6**, having the double outer frame to the octagon and the value in one form only.

13 (¼ a.) (14 (¼ a.)

**1884.** *Sheets of* 32 (4 × 8). *Perf.*

48 **13** ¼ a. blue-green .. .. .. £120 £150
a. "JAN" (R.2/1–2, R.3/1, R3/3–4, R.4/1–3, R.5/1–3) .. .. £120
b. "BEGM" (R.2/3–4) .. .. .. £350
c. "NWAB" and "JAN" (R.3/2) .. .. £600
ca. "NWAB" and "JN" (R.5/4) .. .. £600
d. "SHAHAN" (R.4/4) .. .. .. £600
e. "JAHA" (R.6/2–4) .. .. .. £275

**1895.** *T* **14**, *double-lined frame round each stamp. Sheets of* 6 (2 × 3), *lettered* "JAN". *Laid paper.*

49 **14** ¼ a. bright green (*imperf*) .. .. 1·60 3·50

15 (½ a.) 16 (¼ a.)

**1884.** *Sheets of* 32 (4 × 8). *Laid paper.*

50 **15** ¼ a. blue-green (*imperf*) .. .. .. 55·00 65·00
a. "NWAB" (R.1/1) .. .. .. £250
b. "SAH" (R.1/4) .. .. .. £250
c. "NAWA" and "JANAN" (R.3/2) .. .. £250
51 ¼ a. blue-green (*perf*) .. .. .. 30 1·00
a. "NWAB" (R.1/1) .. .. .. 3·00
b. "SAH" (R.1/4) .. .. .. 3·00
c. "NAWA" and "JANAN" (R.3/2) .. .. 3·00
d. Imperf between (vert pair) .. .. £170
52 ½ a. black (*imperf*) .. .. .. 60 60
a. "NWAB" (R.1/1) .. .. .. 5·50
b. "SAH" (R.1/4) .. .. .. 5·50
c. "NAWA" and "JANAN" (R.3/2) .. .. 5·50
53 **15** ½ a. black (*perf*) .. .. .. 30 1·00
a. "NWAB" (R.1/1) .. .. .. 3·00
b. "SAH" (R.1/4) .. .. .. 3·00
c. "NAWA" and "JANAN" (R.3/2) .. .. 3·00

The ¼ a. of this issue is in *blue-green*, or *greenish blue*. Both values were printed from the same stone, the value alone being altered. There are therefore the same varieties of each. These are the only stamps of this design on laid paper.

Both values show the "N" of "NAWAB" reversed on R.1/1–4, R.2/1–4, R.3/1–4 and the "N" of "JAHAN" reversed on R.1/1–4, R.2/1–4, R.3/4.

**1886.** *T* **15** *redrawn. Sheets of* 32 (4 × 8). *Wove paper.*

54 ¼ a. green (*imperf*) .. .. .. 30 1·10
a. "NAWA" (R.6/3–4) .. .. .. 1·50
b. "NWAB" (R.1/1) .. .. .. 2·50
c. "NWABA" (R.7/4) .. .. .. 2·50
d. "NAWAA" (R.6/2) .. .. .. 2·50
e. "BEGAAM" and "NWABA" (R.7/3) .. 2·50
55 ¼ a. green (*perf*) .. .. .. 65 1·60
a. "NAWA" (R.6/3–4) .. .. .. 4·50
b. "NWAB" (R.1/1) .. .. .. 6·50
c. "NWABA" (R.7/4) .. .. .. 6·50
d. "NAWAA" (R.6/2) .. .. .. 6·50
e. "BEGAAM" and "NWABA" (R.7/3) .. 6·50
56 ½ a. red (*imperf*) .. .. .. 40 50
a. "SAH" (R.1/4) .. .. .. 3·50
b. "NAWABA" (R.6/3–4) .. .. .. 2·75

The ¼ a. varies from *yellow-green* to *deep green*.

All examples of the ¼ a. value show the "N" of "NAWAB" reversed. On the same value the "N" of "JAHAN" is reversed on all positions except R.3/2, R.4/1, R.4/3. On the ½ a. both "N"s are always reversed.

**1888.** *T* **15** *again redrawn. Sheets of* 32 (4 × 8), *letters in upper angles smaller.* "N" *of* "NAWAB" *correct. Wove paper.*

57 ¼ a. deep green (*imperf*) .. .. .. 35 55
a. "SAH" (R.6/2) .. .. .. 3·50
b. "NAWA" (R.4/4) .. .. .. 3·50
58 ¼ a. deep green (*perf*) .. .. .. 45 70
a. "SAH" (R.6/2) .. .. .. 4·00
b. "NAWA" (R.4/4) .. .. .. 4·00

Nos. 50 to 58 have the dash under the letter "JA" as in No. 14.

**1891.** *T* **15** *again redrawn. Sheets of* 32 (4 × 8), *lettered* "NWAB." *Wove paper.* (a) *Imperf.*

59 ½ a. red .. .. .. .. 40 50
a. "SAH" (R.2/4) .. .. .. 3·00

(b) *P* 3 *to* 4½, *or about* 7

60 ½ a. red .. .. .. .. 60 70
a. "SAH" (R.2/4) .. .. .. 4·50

Nos. 59 and 60 have the comma under "JA". The "N" of "JAHAN" is reversed on R.1/1–3, R.2/1–2.

**1894.** *T* **15** *again redrawn; letters in corners larger than in* 1888, *value in very small characters. Sheets of* 32 (4 × 8), *all with* "G" *in left-hand lower corner. Wove paper.*

61 ¼ a. green (*imperf*) .. .. .. 55 60
a. "NAWAH" (R.4/4) .. .. .. 5·50
b. Value in brackets (R.1/1) .. .. 5·50
62 ¼ a. green (*perf*) .. .. .. 85 95
a. "NAWAH" (R.4/4) .. .. .. 8·00
b. Value in brackets (R.1/1) .. .. 8·00

Nos. 61 and 62 have neither the dash nor the comma under "JA".

**1896.** *T* **16**; *oval narrower, stops after* "H.H.", *space after* "NAWAB". *The line down the centre is under the first* "H" *of* "SHAH" *or between* "HA" *instead of being under the second* "H" *or between* "AH". *Sheets of* 32 (4 × 8). *Wove paper. Imperf.*

63 **16** ¼ a. bright green .. .. .. 30 30
a. "SHAN" (R.1/1) .. .. .. 3·00
64 ¼ a. pale green .. .. .. 30 30
a. "SHAN" (R.1/1) .. .. .. 3·00
65 ¼ a. black .. .. .. 30 30
a. "SHAN" (R.1/1) .. .. .. 3·00

**1899.** *T* **15** *redrawn. Sheets of* 32 (4 × 8), *the first* "A" *of* "NAWAB" *always absent. Numerous defective and malformed letters. Wove paper. Imperf.*

66 ½ a. black .. .. .. .. 1·60 2·50
a. "NWASBAHJANNI" (R.2/4) .. .. 10·00 13·00
b. "SBAH" (R.3/3, R.4/3–4, R.5/1–2, R.6/4) 5·00 7·00
c. "SBAN" (R.8/2) .. .. .. 10·00 13·00
d. "NWIB" (R.3/2) .. .. .. 10·00 13·00
e. "BEIAM" (R.4/4) .. .. .. 10·00 13·00
f. "SHH" (R.6/3) .. .. .. 10·00 13·00
g. "SBAH" and "BBGAM" (R.3/4) .. .. 10·00 13·00
h. "BBGAM" (R.1/3) .. .. .. 10·00 13·00

17 (8 a.) (18 (¼ a.)

**1890.** *T* **17**. *Sheets of* 10 (2 × 5). *Single-line frame to each stamp.*

(a) *Wove paper*

67 **17** 8 a. slate-green (*imperf*) .. .. 24·00 40·00
a. "HAH" (R.3/1, R.4/1, R.5/1) .. .. 42·00
b. "JABAN" (R.2/2) .. .. .. 42·00
68 8 a. slate-green (*perf*) .. .. 24·00 40·00
a. "HAH" (R.3/1, R.4/1, R.5/1) .. .. 42·00
b. "JABAN" (R.2/2) .. .. .. 42·00

(b) *Thin laid paper*

69 **17** 8 a. green-black (*imperf*) .. .. 35·00 50·00
a. "HAH" (R.3/1, R.4/1, R.5/1) .. .. 50·00
b. "JABAN" (R.2/2) .. .. .. 50·00
70 8 a. green-black (*perf*) .. .. 35·00 50·00
a. "HAH" (R.3/1, R.4/1, R.5/1) .. .. 50·00
b. "JABAN" (R.2/2) .. .. .. 50·00

The "N" of "NAWAB" is reversed on R.5/2 and the "N" of "JAHAN" on R.1/1–2, R.2/2, R.3/2, R.4/2 and R.5/2.

**1893.** *T* 17 *redrawn. No frame to each stamp, but a frame to the sheet. Sheets of* 10 (2 × 5). (a) *Wove paper.*

71 8 a. green-black (*imperf*) .. .. .. 14·00 15·00
72 8 a. green-black (*perf*) .. .. .. 18·00 24·00

(*b*) *Thin laid paper. Imperf*

73 8 a. green-black .. .. .. .. 95·00 £110

**1898.** *Defective transfer from the stone of 1893. Lettering irregular. Sheets of* 10 (2 × 5). *Wove paper. Imperf.*

74 8 a. green-black .. .. .. .. 24·00 28·00
a. Reversed "E" in "BEGAM" (R.1/2, R.3/2) 55·00
75 8 a. black .. .. .. .. 24·00 28·00
a. Reversed "E" in "BEGAM" (R.1/2, R.3/2) 55·00

**1896–1901.** *Sheets of* 32 (4 × 8). (*a*) *Wove paper. Imperf.*

76 18 ¼ a. black .. .. .. .. 50 50

(*b*) *Printed from a fresh transfer* (?), *lines shaky* (1899)

77 18 ¼ a. black .. .. .. .. 1·25 1·25

(*c*) *The same, on thick wove paper* (1901)

78 18 ¼ a. black .. .. .. .. £250 £250

**Nawab Sultan Jahan Begam, 16 June 1901–17 May 1926**

19 (¼ a.) 20

**1902.** *T* 19. *With the octagonal embossed device of the previous issues. Sheets of* 16 (4 × 4) ¼ *a. or* 8 (2 × 4) *others. Thin, yellowish wove paper. Imperf.*

79 19 ¼ a. rose .. .. .. .. 2·75 4·50
80 ¼ a. rose-red .. .. .. .. 1·50 3·00
81 ½ a. black .. .. .. .. 2·00 4·00
a. Printed both sides .. .. .. £325
82 1 a. brown .. .. .. .. 2·50 6·50
83 1 a. red-brown .. .. .. .. 2·50 6·50
84 2 a. blue .. .. .. .. 6·50 8·00
85 4 a. orange .. .. .. .. 38·00 60·00
86 4 a. yellow .. .. .. .. 28·00 48·00
87 8 a. lilac .. .. .. .. 45·00 80·00
88 1 r. rose .. .. .. .. £110 £130
79/88 .. .. .. .. *Set of* 7 £160 £225

**1903.** *With a circular embossed device. Sheets of* 16 (4 × 4) ¼ *a. (two plates) or* 8 (2 × 4) (*others*).

A. *Wove paper.* B. *Laid paper*

| | | | A | | B | |
|---|---|---|---|---|---|---|
| 89 | 19 | ¼ a. rose-red | 75 | 1·75 | 50 | — |
| 90 | | ¼ a. red | 65 | 1·40 | 30 | 1·75 |
| 91 | | ½ a. black | 50 | 1·75 | 60 | 2·75 |
| 92 | | 1 a. brown | 1·00 | 3·00 | 27·00 | — |
| 93 | | 1 a. red-brown | 2·25 | — | — | — |
| 94 | | 2 a. blue | 2·50 | 9·50 | 50·00 | — |
| 95 | | 4 a. orange | † | | £110 | £110 |
| 96 | | 4 a. yellow | 14·00 | 35·00 | 65·00 | 65·00 |
| 97 | | 8 a. lilac | 32·00 | 60·00 | £400 | — |
| 98 | | 1 r. rose | 42·00 | 75·00 | £400 | — |
| 89A/98A | | *Set of* 7 | 80·00 | £150 | | |

**1903.** *No. 71 optd with initial of the new Begam, either 6 or 11 mm long, in red.*

99 8 a. green-black .. .. .. .. 48·00 50·00
a. Opt inverted .. .. .. .. £120 £120

Some of the previous stamps remained on sale (and probably in use) after the issue of the series of 1902, and some of these were afterwards put on sale with the new form of embossing; fresh plates were made of some of the old designs, in imitation of the earlier issues, and impressions from these were also sold with the new embossed device. We no longer list these doubtful items.

(Recess Perkins, Bacon & Co)

**1908.** *P* 13½.

100 20 1 a. green .. .. .. .. 1·50 1·10
a. Printed both sides .. .. .. £100
b. Imperf (pair) .. .. ..

The ordinary postage stamps of Bhopal became obsolete on 1 July 1908.

## OFFICIAL STAMPS

SERVICE (O 1) SERVICE (O 2)

(Recess and optd Perkins, Bacon)

**1908–11.** *As T* 20, *but inscribed* "H.H. BEGUM'S SERVICE" *at left. No wmk. P* 13 *to* 14. *Overprinted.* (*a*) *With Type* O 1.

O301 ½ a. yellow-green .. .. .. .. 1·25 10
a. Imperf (pair) .. .. .. 85·00
b. Pair, one without overprint .. £200
c. Opt double, one inverted .. .. £100
ca. Ditto. Imperf (pair) .. .. .. £120
d. Opt inverted .. .. .. £100 £100
e. Imperf between (horiz pair) .. £325
O302 1 a. carmine-red .. .. .. .. 1·75 20
a. Opt inverted .. .. .. 70·00 70·00
b. Imperf (pair) .. .. .. 85·00
c. *Red* .. .. .. .. 2·50 10
O303 2 a. ultramarine .. .. .. .. 14·00 10
a. Imperf (pair) .. .. .. 50·00
O304 4 a. brown (1911) .. .. .. 8·00 15
O301/4 .. .. .. .. *Set of* 4 21·00 40

(*b*) *With Type* O 2

O305 ½ a. yellow-green .. .. .. .. 3·75 20
O306 1 a. carmine-red .. .. .. .. 6·00 90
O307 2 a. ultramarine .. .. .. .. 3·00 30
a. Opt inverted .. .. .. .. 25·00
O308 4 a. brown (1911) .. .. .. .. 65·00 30
a. Opt inverted .. .. .. .. 20·00 60·00
b. Opt double .. .. .. .. 80·00
c. Imperf (pair) .. .. .. .. 75·00
d. Imperf (pair) and opt inverted .. 75·00
O305/8 .. .. .. .. *Set of* 4 70·00 1·50

The two overprints differ in the shape of the letters, noticeably in the "R".

**Nawab Mohammad Hamidullah. Khan**
**17 May 1926 to transfer of administration to India, 1 June 1949**

SERVICE
(O 3) (O 4)

(Des T. I. Archer. Litho Indian Govt Ptg Wks, Nasik)

**1930** (1 July)–**31.** *Type* O 4 (25½ × 30½ *mm*) *optd with Type* O 3. *P* 14.

O309 O 4 ½ a. sage-green (1931) .. .. .. 2·25 20
O310 1 a. carmine-red .. .. .. 3·50 15
O311 2 a. ultramarine .. .. .. 3·50 15
O312 4 a. chocolate .. .. .. 3·00 20
O309/12 .. .. .. *Set of* 4 11·00 60

The ½ a., 2 a. and 4 a. are inscribed "POSTAGE" at left.

(Litho Perkins, Bacon)

**1932–34.** *As Type* O 4 (21 × 25 *mm*), *but inscr* "POSTAGE" *at left. Optd with Type* O 1. (*a*) "BHOPAL STATE" *at right. P* 13.

O313 ¼ a. orange .. .. .. .. 1·60 30
a. Perf 11½ (1933) .. .. .. 3·50 20
b. Perf 14 (1934) .. .. .. 9·00 30
c. Perf 13½ (1934) .. .. .. 9·00 30
ca. Vert pair, one without opt .. .. 95·00

(*b*) "BHOPAL GOVT" *at right. P* 13½

O314 ½ a. yellow-green .. .. .. .. 2·25 10
O315 1 a. carmine-red .. .. .. .. 3·50 10
a. Vert pair, one without opt .. £170
O316 2 a. ultramarine .. .. .. .. 4·25 45
O317 4 a. chocolate .. .. .. .. 3·25 60
a. Perf 14 (1934) .. .. .. 9·00 40
O313/17 .. .. .. *Set of* 5 13·00 1·10

No. O317 is comb-perforated and No. O317a line-perforated.

¼A (O 5) THREE PIES (O 6) ONE ANNA (O 7)

**1935–36.** *Nos.* O314, O316 *and* O317 *surch as Types* O 5 *to* O 7.

O318 O 5 ¼ a. on ½ a. yellow-green (R.) .. 11·00 5·00
a. Surch inverted .. .. .. 80·00 60·00
b. Vert pair. Nos. O318/19 .. 17·00 10·00
ba. Ditto. Surch inverted .. .. £150 £120
O319 O 6 3 p. on ½ a. yellow-green (R.) .. 1·25 1·25
a. "THEEE PIES" (R. 7/10) .. 38·00 38·00
b. "THRFE for "THREE" (R. 10/6) 38·00 38·00
c. Surch inverted .. .. 40·00 35·00
O320 O 5 ¼ a. on 2 a. ultramarine (R.) .. 9·00 5·00
a. Surch inverted .. .. .. 80·00 60·00
b. Vert pair. Nos. O320/1 .. 15·00 8·00
ba. Ditto. Surch inverted .. .. £150 £120
O321 O 6 3 p. on 2 a. ultramarine (R.) .. 65 90
a. Surch inverted .. .. .. 40·00 35·00
b. "THEEE PIES" (R. 7/10) .. 35·00 35·00
ba. Ditto. Surch inverted .. .. £275 £275
c. "THRFE" for "THREE" (R. 10/6) 35·00 35·00
ca. Ditto. Surch inverted .. .. £275 £275
O322 O 5 ¼ a. on 4 a. chocolate (R.) .. £375 £110
a. Vert pair. Nos O322 and O324 £500 £180
O323 ¼ a. on 4 a. chocolate (No. O317a) (Blk.) (25.5.36) .. .. 24·00 10·00
a. Vert pair. Nos. O323 and O325 40·00 18·00
O324 O 6 3 p. on 4 a. chocolate (R.) .. 42·00 27·00
a. "THEEE PIES" (R. 7/10) .. £225 £225
c. "THRFE" for "THREE" (R. 10/6) £225 £225
O325 3 p. on 4 a. chocolate (No. O317a) (Blk.) (25.5.36) .. .. 1·75 1·25
a. "THRER" for "THREE" (R. 8/2) £130 95·00
b. "FHREE" for "THREE" (R.3/10, 10/1) .. .. .. £140 £100
c. "PISE" for "PIES" (R. 10/10) .. £180 £160
d. "PIFS" for "PIES" (R. 7/9) .. £130 95·00
O326 O 7 1 a. on ½ a. yellow-green (V.) .. 75 1·00
a. Surch inverted .. .. .. 38·00 38·00
b. First "N" in "ANNA" inverted (R. 4/5) .. .. .. 42·00 42·00
ba. Ditto. Surch inverted .. .. £275 £275
O327 1 a. on 2 a. ultramarine (R.) .. 90 55
a. Surch inverted .. .. .. 40·00 32·00
b. First "N" in "ANNA" inverted (R. 4/5) .. .. .. 42·00 42·00
ba. Ditto. Surch inverted .. .. £275 £275
O327*d* 1 a. on 2 a. ultramarine (V.) .. 40·00 40·00
da. Surch inverted .. .. .. 85·00 85·00
db. First "N" in "ANNA" inverted (R. 4/5) .. .. .. £275 £275
dc. Ditto. Surch inverted .. .. £425 £425
O328 1 a. on 2 a. ultram (Blk.) (25.5.36) 60 65
a. "ANNO" .. .. .. .. £700
O329 1 a. on 4 a. chocolate (B.) .. .. 1·25 1·40
a. First "N" in "ANNA" inverted (R. 4/5) .. .. .. 42·00 42·00
b. Perf 14 .. .. .. .. 3·75 2·00
ba. Ditto. First "N" in "ANNA" inverted (R. 4/5) .. .. .. 80·00 65·00

Nos. O318 to O325 are arranged in composite sheets of 100 (10 × 10). The two upper horizontal rows of each value are surcharged as Type O 5 and the next five rows as Type O 6. The remaining three rows are also surcharged as Type O 6 but in a slightly narrower setting.

The surcharge on No. O323 differs from Type O 5 in the shape of the figures and letter.

O 8

(Des T. I. Archer. Litho Indian Govt Ptg Wks, Nasik (No. O330). Typo Bhopal Govt Ptg Wks (others) )

**1935–39.** *As Type* O 8.

(*a*) *Litho. Inscr* "BHOPAL GOVT POSTAGE". *Optd* "SERVICE" (13½ *mm*). *P* 13½

O330 1 a. 3 p. blue and claret .. .. .. 40 20

(*b*) *Typo. Inscr* "BHOPAL STATE POSTAGE". *Optd* "SERVICE" (11 *mm*). *P* 12

O331 1 a. 6 p. blue and claret (1937) .. .. 40 20
a. Imperf between (pair) .. .. 85·00 85·00
b. Opt omitted .. .. .. 75·00 65·00
c. Opt double, one inverted .. .. £160 £160
d. Imperf (pair) .. .. .. — 75·00
e. Blue printing double .. .. — 70·00
O332 1 a. 6 p. claret (1939) .. .. .. 1·25 30
a. Imperf between (pair) .. .. 85·00 85·00
b. Opt omitted .. .. .. — £160
c. Opt double, one inverted .. .. — £160
d. Opt double .. .. .. — £160

**PRINTERS.** From No. O333 all issues were printed by the Bhopal Govt Ptg Wks in typography.

O 9 O 10 The Moti Mahal

**1936** (July)–**38.** *Optd* "SERVICE". *P* 12.

O333 O 9 ¼ a. orange (Br.) .. .. .. 35 15
a. Imperf between (vert pair) .. 95·00
b. Opt inverted .. .. .. £110 £110
c. Black opt .. .. .. 6·50 75
ca. Opt inverted .. .. .. — £150
cb. Opt double .. .. .. — £150
O334 ¼ a. yellow (Br.) (1938) .. .. 50 10
O335 1 a. scarlet .. .. .. .. 40 10
a. Imperf between (horiz pair) .. 55·00 55·00
b. Imperf between (vert pair) .. — 90·00
c. Imperf between (block of four) .. £150 £150

**1936–49.** *As Type* O 10 (*various palaces*). *P* 12.

(*a*) *Optd* "SERVICE" (13½ *mm*)

O336 ½ a. purple-brown and yellow-green .. 45 20
a. Imperf between (vert pair) .. — 80·00
ab. Imperf between (horiz pair) .. — 80·00
b. Opt double .. .. .. £110 80·00
c. Frame double .. .. .. 55·00 15·00
*d. Purple-brown and green* (1938) .. 45 20

(*b*) *Optd* "SERVICE" (11 *mm*)

O337 2 a. brown and blue (1937) .. .. 55 20
a. Imperf between (vert pair) .. — 95·00
ab. Imperf between (horiz pair) .. — 80·00
b. Opt inverted .. .. .. £100 £100
c. Pair, one without opt .. .. £170
d. As c. but opt inverted .. .. £325
O338 2 a. green and violet (1938) .. .. 2·25 20
a. Imperf between (vert pair) .. — 80·00
b. Imperf between (vert strip of 3) .. 60·00 65·00
c. Frame double .. .. .. — 80·00
d. Centre double .. .. .. — 80·00
O339 4 a. blue and brown (1937) .. .. 1·00 50
a. Imperf between (horiz pair) .. — £190
b. Opt omitted .. .. .. — £120
c. Opt double .. .. .. — £100
*d. Blue and reddish brown* (1938) .. 1·40 50
da. Frame double .. .. .. — £100
O340 8 a. bright purple and blue (1938) .. 1·60 65
a. Imperf between (vert pair) .. — £140
b. Opt omitted .. .. .. — 80·00
c. Opt double .. .. .. — 90·00
d. Imperf vert (horiz pair) and opt omitted .. .. .. — £110
e. Imperf (pair) and opt omitted .. — £110
O341 1 r. blue and reddish purple (Br.) (1938) .. 4·00 2·25
a. Imperf horiz (vert pair) .. .. — £500
b. Opt in black (1942) .. .. 9·00 5·00
*ba. Light blue and bright purple* .. 27·00 27·00
bb. Laid paper .. .. .. £225
O336/41 .. .. .. *Set of* 6 9·00 3·50

(*c*) *Optd* "SERVICE" (11½ *mm*) *with serifs*

O342 1 r. dull blue and bright purple (Blk.) (1949) .. .. .. 30·00 45·00
a. "SREVICE" for "SERVICE" (R. 6/6) 90·00 £120
b. "SERVICE" omitted .. .. £325

(*d*) *Optd* "SERVICE" (13½ *mm*) *with serifs*

O343 8 a. bright purple and blue (1949) .. 42·00 60·00
a. "SERAICE" for "SERVICE" (R. 6/5) £170 £200
b. Fig "1" for "I" in "SERVICE" (R. 7/1) £170 £200

The ½ a. is inscr "BHOPAL GOVT" below the arms, other values have "BHOPAL STATE".

Designs:—(37½ × 22½ *mm*) 2 a. The Moti Masjid; 4 a. Taj Mahal and Be-Nazir Palaces. (39 × 24 *mm*)—8 a. Ahmadabad Palace. (45½ × 27½ *mm*)—1 r. Rait Ghat.

O 11 Tiger

O 13 The Moti Mahal

**1940**. *As Type* O 11 (*animals*). *P* 12.
O344 ¼ a. bright blue .. .. .. .. .. 2·00 30
O345 1 a. bright purple (Spotted Deer) .. .. 8·50 40

**1941**. *As Type* O 8 *but coloured centre inscr* "SERVICE"; *bottom frame inscr* "BHOPAL STATE POSTAGE". *P* 12.
O346 1 a. 3 p. emerald-green .. .. .. .. 30 30
a. Imperf between (pair) .. .. .. £170 £170

**1944–47**. *As Type* O **13** (*various palaces*). *P* 12.
O347 ½ a. green .. .. .. .. .. 40 30
a. Imperf (pair) .. .. .. .. — 40·00
b. Imperf between (vert pair) .. .. — 75·00
c. Doubly printed .. .. .. — 60·00
O348 2 a. violet .. .. .. .. .. 2·75 1·25
a. Imperf (pair) .. .. .. .. — 40·00
c. *Bright purple* (1945) .. .. .. 75 90
d. *Mauve* (1947) .. .. .. .. 6·50 4·50
e. Error. Chocolate (imperf) .. .. 80·00 80·00
O349 4 a. chocolate .. .. .. .. 2·25 60
a. Imperf (pair) .. .. .. .. — 50·00
b. Imperf vert (horiz pair) .. .. — 90·00
c. Doubly printed .. .. .. — 70·00
O347/9 .. .. .. .. *Set of* 3 3·00 1·60
Design inscr "BHOPAL STATE":—2 a. The Moti Masjid; 4 a. Be-Nazir Palaces.

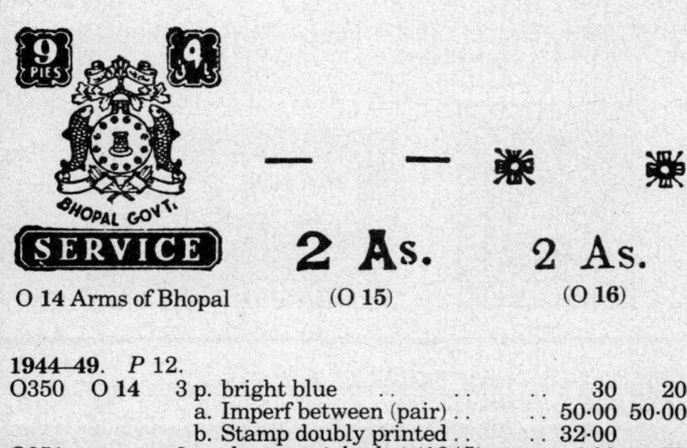


O 14 Arms of Bhopal (O 15) (O 16)

**1944–49**. *P* 12.
O350 O 14 3 p. bright blue .. .. .. 30 20
a. Imperf between (pair) .. .. 50·00 50·00
b. Stamp doubly printed .. .. 32·00
O351 9 p. chestnut (*shades*) (1945) .. 4·00 75
a. Imperf (pair) .. .. .. — 80·00
b. *Orange-brown* .. .. .. 1·50 2·00
O352 1 a. purple (1945) .. .. .. 1·50 20
a. Imperf horiz (vert pair) .. .. — £110
b. *Violet* (1946) .. .. .. 2·00 70
O353 1½ a. claret (1945) .. .. .. 75 30
a. Imperf between (pair) .. .. — £100
O354 3 a. yellow .. .. .. .. 2·50 2·25
a. Imperf (pair) .. .. .. — 80·00
b. Imperf horiz (vert pair) .. .. — 95·00
c. Imperf vert (horiz pair) .. ..
d. *Orange-brown* (1949) .. .. 38·00 32·00
O355 6 a. carmine (1945) .. .. .. 6·00 16·00
a. Imperf (pair) .. .. .. — 85·00
b. Imperf horiz (vert pair) .. .. — 95·00
c. Imperf vert (horiz pair) .. .. — 95·00
O350/5 .. .. .. .. *Set of* 6 11·00 18·00

**1949** (July). *Surch with Type* O **15**. *P* 12.
O356 O 14 2 a. on 1½ a. claret .. .. .. 1·25 2·75
a. Stop omitted .. .. .. 9·00 12·00
b. Imperf (pair) .. .. .. £130 £140
ba. Stop omitted (pair) .. .. £325 £350
c. "2" omitted (in pair with normal) £200
The "stop omitted" variety occurs on positions 60 and 69 in the sheet of 81.

**1949**. *Surch with Type* O **16**. *Imperf.*
O357 O 14 2 a. on 1½ a. claret .. .. £275 £325
a. Perf 12 .. .. .. .. £350 £325
Three different types of "2" occur in the setting of Type O **16**.

## BHOR

**PRICES FOR STAMPS ON COVER**

| | |
|---|---|
| Nos. 1/2 | *from* × 40 |
| No. 3 | *from* × 6 |

**GUM**. The stamps of Bhor were issued without gum.

1

2

**1879**. *Handstamped. Very thick to thin native paper. Imperf.*
1 1 ½ a. carmine (*shades*) .. .. .. 1·75 3·25
a. *Tête-bêche* (pair) .. .. .. £375
2 2 1 a. carmine (*shades*) .. .. .. 2·50 4·50

3 Pant Sachiv Shankarro Chimnaji

**1901**. *Typo. Wove paper. Imperf.*
3 3 ½ a. red .. .. .. .. .. .. 6·00 28·00

## BIJAWAR

**PRICES FOR STAMPS ON COVER**

The stamps of Bijawar are very rare used on cover.

1 Maharaja Sir Sarwant Singh Bahadur 2

(Typo Lakshmi Art Ptg Works, Bombay)

**1935** (1 July)–**36**. (*a*) *P* 11.
1 1 3 p. brown .. .. .. .. .. 1·50 1·00
a. Imperf (pair) .. .. .. .. 5·50
b. Imperf between (vert pair) .. .. 60·00
2 6 p. carmine .. .. .. .. 1·00 1·00
a. Imperf (pair) .. .. .. .. 65·00
b. Imperf between (vert or horiz pair) 60·00
3 9 p. violet .. .. .. .. 1·00 1·50
a. Imperf (pair) .. .. .. .. £100
b. Imperf between (vert or horiz pair) 60·00
4 1 a. blue .. .. .. .. .. 1·40 1·90
a. Imperf (pair) .. .. .. .. 65·00
b. Imperf between (vert or horiz pair) 65·00
c. Imperf vert (horiz strip of 3) .. 90·00
5 2 a. deep green .. .. .. .. 1·75 2·75
a. Imperf (pair) .. .. .. .. 95·00
b. Imperf horiz (vert pair) .. .. 11·00
c. Imperf between (vert pair) .. .. 30·00
d. Imperf between (horiz pair) .. .. 45·00
1/5 .. .. .. .. .. *Set of* 5 6·00 7·00

(*b*) *Roul* 7 (1936)
6 1 3 p. brown .. .. .. .. .. 50 1·25
a. Printed on gummed side .. .. £275
7 6 p. carmine .. .. .. .. 80 3·00
8 9 p. violet .. .. .. .. 3·00 20·00
9 1 a. blue .. .. .. .. 3·25 25·00
10 2 a. deep green .. .. .. .. 3·25 30·00
6/10 .. .. .. .. .. *Set of* 5 10·00 70·00

**1937** (May). *Typo. P* 9.
11 **2** 4 a. orange .. .. .. .. .. 3·00 35·00
a. Imperf between (vert pair) .. .. £140
b. Imperf (pair) .. .. .. .. £225
12 6 a. lemon .. .. .. .. .. 3·00 35·00
a. Imperf between (vert pair) .. .. £140
b. Imperf (pair) .. .. .. .. £225
13 8 a. emerald-green .. .. .. .. 3·50 42·00
a. Imperf (pair) .. .. .. .. £225
14 12 a. greenish blue .. .. .. .. 4·50 48·00
a. Imperf (pair) .. .. .. .. £250
15 1 r. bright violet .. .. .. .. 18·00 75·00
a. "1 Rs" for "1 R" (R. 1/2) .. .. 45·00 £225
b. Imperf (pair) .. .. .. .. £300
ba. "1 Rs" for "1 R" (R. 1/2) .. .. £700
11/15 .. .. .. .. .. *Set of* 5 29·00 £200

The stamps of Bijawar were withdrawn in 1941.

## BUNDI

**PRICES FOR STAMPS ON COVER**

| | |
|---|---|
| No. 1 | *from* × 2 |
| No. 2 | *from* × 4 |
| Nos. 3/53 | *from* × 10 |
| Nos. 54/63 | *from* × 5 |
| Nos. 64/78 | *from* × 2 |
| Nos. 79/92 | *from* × 10 |
| Nos. O1/52 | *from* × 15 |
| Nos. O53/9 | *from* × 20 |

**GUM**. Nos. 1/17 were issued without gum.

**ILLUSTRATIONS**. Types **1/10** and **12/19** are shown actual size.

In Nos. 1 to 17 characters denoting the value are below the dagger, except in Nos. 2a, 11 and 17.
All Bundi stamps until 1914 are imperforate.

1

**1894** (May). *Each stamp with a distinct frame and the stamps not connected by the framing lines. Three vertical lines on dagger. Laid or wove paper.*
1 1 ½ a. slate-grey .. .. .. .. .. £3500 £1500
a. Last two letters of value below the rest .. .. .. .. .. — £3000

2 (Block of four stamps)

**1894** (Dec). *Stamps joined together, with no space between them. Two vertical lines on dagger. Thin wove paper.*
2 2 ½ a. slate-grey .. .. .. .. .. 22·00 22·00
a. Value at top, name below .. .. £170 £170
b. Right upper ornament omitted .. £700 £700
c. Last two letters of value below the rest .. .. .. .. .. £650 £650
d. Left lower ornament omitted .. £700 £700

3

**1896** (Nov). *Dagger shorter, lines thicker. Stamps separate. Laid paper.*
3 3 ½ a. slate-grey .. .. .. .. 3·50 5·50
a. Last two letters of value below the rest .. .. .. .. .. £300 £300

4 (1 anna)

5 (2 annas)

6 (2 annas)

**1897–98**. *No shading in centre of blade of dagger. The stamps have spaces between them, but are connected by the framing lines, both vertically and horizontally. Laid paper.*

I. *Blade of dagger comparatively narrow, and either triangular, as in T* **4** *and* **6**, *or with the left-hand corner not touching the bar behind it, as in T* **5** (1897-98)
4 4 1 a. Indian red .. .. .. .. 7·50 12·00
5 5 1 a. red .. .. .. .. .. 7·50 12·00
6 2 a. green .. .. .. .. .. 9·00 15·00
7 6 2 a. yellow-green .. .. .. .. 9·00 15·00
8 5 4 a. green .. .. .. .. .. 25·00 32·00
9 8 a. Indian red .. .. .. .. 50·00 80·00
10 1 r. yellow/*blue* .. .. .. .. £100 £140
4/10 .. .. .. .. .. *Set of* 5 £160 £225

7

I. *Blade varying in shape, but as a rule not touching the bar; value above and name below the dagger, instead of the reverse* (Jan 1898)

11 7 4 a. emerald-green .. .. .. 18·00
a. *Yellow-green* .. .. .. 10·00

8 (½ anna)

9 (8 annas)

II. *Blade wider and (except on the ½ a.) almost diamond shaped; it nearly always touches the bar* (1898–1900)

12 8 ½ a. slate-grey (5.2.98) .. .. .. 1·25 1·50
13 9 1 a. Indian red (7.98) .. .. .. 1·40 1·50
14 2 a. pale green (9.11.98) .. .. .. 6·50 7·50
a. First two characters of value (= two) omitted .. .. .. £700 £700
15 8 a. Indian red (7.98) .. .. .. 4·50 7·50
16 1 r. yellow/*blue* (7.98) .. .. .. 8·50 16·00
a. On wove paper .. .. .. 7·50 16·00
12/16 .. .. .. *Set of* 5 18·00 27·00

10

IV. *Inscriptions as on No.* 11; *point of dagger to left* (9.11.98)

17 10 4 a. green .. .. .. 12·00 15·00
a. *Yellow-green* .. .. .. 7·00 10·00

All the above stamps are lithographed in large sheets, containing as many varieties of type as there are stamps in the sheets.

11 Raja protecting Sacred Cows

Type 11 was produced from separate clichés printed as a block of four. The same clichés were used for all values, but not necessarily in the same order within the block. The Devanagri inscriptions, "RAJ BUNDI" at top and the face value at bottom, were inserted into the basic clichés as required so that various differences exist within the 58 settings which have been identified.

The denominations may be identified from the following illustrations. The ½ a., 3 a. and rupee values can be easily distinguished by their colours.

Bottom tablets:—

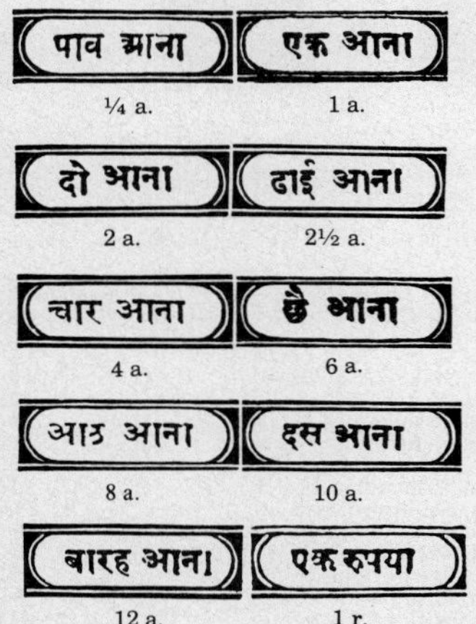

¼ a. 1 a. 2 a. 2½ a. 4 a. 6 a. 8 a. 10 a. 12 a. 1 r.

The nine versions of the inscriptions are as follows:

A B

Top tablet

Type A. Top tablet has inscription in two separate words with a curved line over the first character in the second. The second word has three characters.
Bottom tablet has short line above the first character in the second word.

Type B. Top tablet as Type A, but without the curved line over the first character in the second word.
Bottom tablet as Type A.

C

Type C. Top tablet as Type B, but with large loop beneath the first character in the second word. This loop is usually joined to the main character, but is sometimes detached as in the illustration.
Bottom tablet as Type A.

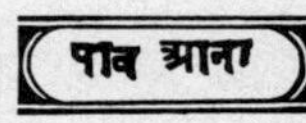

D Top tablet E Bottom tablet

Type D. Top tablet in thinner lettering with the inscription shown as one word of six characters. The fourth character has a curved line above it, as in Type A, and a loop beneath, as in Type C.
Bottom tablet as Type A, but thinner letters.

Type E. Top tablet as Type C.
Bottom tablet shows a redrawn first character to the second word. This has the line at top extending over the entire character.

F
Bottom tablet

Type F. Top tablet as Type B.
Bottom tablet as Type E, but first character in second word differs.

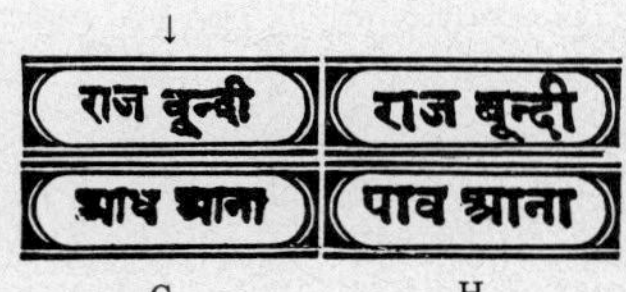

G H

Type G. Top tablet as Type C, but without dot over first character in second word. There are now four characters in the second word.
Bottom tablet as Type E.

Type H. Top tablet as Type G, but with characters larger and bolder.
Bottom tablet as Type E, but with characters larger and bolder.

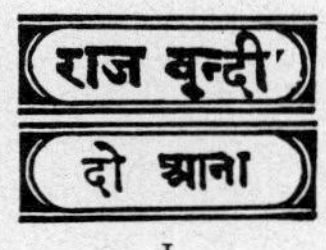

I

Type I. Top tablet as Type H.
Bottom tablet as Type E.

Some settings contained more than one inscription type within the block of four so that *se-tenant* examples are known of Type B with Type C (¼, 1, 2, 4, 8, 10 and 12 a.), Type C with Type E (¼, ½ and 4 a.) and Type E with Type F (½ and 4 a.). Type F only exists from this mixed setting.

**1914** (Oct)–**41.** *T* **11.** *Typo. Ungummed paper except for Nos.* 73/8.

I. *Rouletted in colour*

(*a*) *Inscriptions as Type* A. *Thin wove paper* (1916–23)

18 ½ a. black .. .. .. 2·00 10·00
19 1 a. vermilion .. .. .. 2·50 10·00
20 2 a. emerald .. .. .. 2·00
a. *Deep green* (*coarse ptg on medium wove paper*) (1923) .. .. 1·60 7·00
21 2½ a. chrome-yellow (*shades*) (1917) .. .. 4·50 15·00
22 3 a. chestnut (1917) .. .. .. 7·00 17·00
23 4 a. yellow-green .. .. .. 17·00
24 6 a. cobalt (1917) .. .. .. 12·00 35·00
25 1 r. reddish violet (1917) .. .. 15·00 48·00

A special printing of the 1 a. took place in late 1917 in connection with the "OUR DAY" Red Cross Society Fund. This had the "RAJ BUNDI" inscription in the bottom tablet with the face value below it. The top tablet carried four Devanagri characters for "OUR DAY". No evidence has been found to suggest that this 1 a. stamp was used for postal purposes (*Price*, £160 *unused*).

(*b*) *Inscriptions as Type* B. *Thin wove or pelure paper* (1914–23)

25*a* ¼ a. cobalt (1916) .. .. .. 2·25 9·00
26 ¼ a. ultramarine (*shades*) (1917) .. .. 1·75 4·00
a. *Indigo* (1923) .. .. .. 1·60 4·00
b. Error. Black (1923) .. ..
27 ½ a. black .. .. .. 2·50 4·25
28 1 a. vermilion (1915) .. .. .. 2·75
a. *Carmine* (1923) .. .. .. 3·75 5·50
b. *Red* (*shades*) (1923) .. .. 4·00
29 2 a. emerald (*shades*) (1915) .. .. 3·75 10·00
30 2½ a. olive-yellow (1917) .. .. 5·00 15·00
31 3 a. chestnut (1917) .. .. .. 4·50 14·00
32 4 a. apple-green (1915) .. .. 3·50 18·00
32*a* 4 a. olive-yellow (1917) .. .. 85·00 £110
33 6 a. pale ultramarine (*shades*) (1917) .. 8·00 30·00
a. *Deep ultramarine* (1917) .. .. 7·00
34 8 a. orange (1915) .. .. .. 7·50 35·00
35 10 a. olive-sepia (1917) .. .. £190
36 12 a. sage-green (1917) .. .. £375
36*a* 1 r. lilac (*shades*) (1915) .. .. 22·00

(*c*) *Inscriptions as Type* C. *Thin to medium wove paper* (1917–41)

37 ¼ a. ultramarine (*shades*) (1923) .. .. 2·50 4·25
a. *Indigo* (1923) .. .. .. 2·50 4·25
b. Error. Black (1923) .. ..
c. *Cobalt* (*medium wove paper*) (1937) .. 7·50 8·00
38 ½ a. black .. .. .. 1·25 2·75
39 1 a. orange-red .. .. .. 6·50 9·00
a. *Carmine* (1923) .. .. .. 5·50 8·00
b. *Deep red* (*medium wove paper*) (1936) .. 7·00 8·00
40 2 a. emerald .. .. .. 6·00 11·00
a. *Sage-green* .. .. .. 6·50
41 4 a. yellow-green (*shades*) .. .. 24·00 42·00
a. *Olive-yellow* .. .. .. 70·00 90·00
b. *Bright apple-green* (*medium wove paper*) (1936) .. .. £100 £100
42 8 a. reddish orange .. .. .. 9·00 32·00
43 10 a. brown-olive .. .. .. 16·00 35·00
a. *Olive-sepia* .. .. .. 35·00
b. *Yellow-brown* .. .. .. 35·00
44 12 a. sage-green .. .. .. 6·00 35·00
45 1 r. lilac .. .. .. 22·00 55·00
46 2 r. red-brown and black .. .. 40·00 85·00
a. *Chocolate and black* (*medium wove paper*) (1936) .. .. 48·00 £100
47 3 r. blue and red-brown .. .. 70·00 £140
a. *Grey-blue and chocolate* (*medium wove paper*) (1941) .. .. 90·00
ab. Chocolate (inscriptions) inverted .. £3500
48 4 r. emerald and scarlet .. .. £150 £250
49 5 r. scarlet and emerald .. .. £160 £275

(*d*) *Inscriptions as Type* D. *Thin wove paper* (1918?)

50 2½ a. buff (*shades*) .. .. .. 11·00 24·00
51 3 a. red-brown .. .. .. 16·00 16·00
a. Semi-circle and dot omitted from 4th character .. .. .. 35·00 35·00
52 10 a. bistre .. .. .. 24·00 50·00
a. 4th character turned to left instead of downwards .. .. .. 45·00
53 12 a. grey-olive .. .. .. 32·00 55·00
a. 4th character turned to left instead of downwards .. .. .. 60·00

(*e*) *Inscriptions as Type* E. (i) *Medium wove paper* (1930–37)

54 ¼ a. deep slate .. .. .. 14·00 13·00
54*a* ¼ a. indigo (*thin wove paper*) (1935) .. 7·00 11·00
b. *Cobalt* (1937) .. .. .. 11·00 11·00
55 ½ a. black .. .. .. 9·00 11·00
56 1 a. carmine-red .. .. .. 16·00 18·00
57 3 a. chocolate (*shades*) (1936) .. .. 10·00 18·00
58 4 a. yellow-olive (1935) .. .. £200 £110
a. *Bright apple-green* (1936) .. .. £200 £110

(ii) *Very thick wove paper* (1930–32)

59 ¼ a. indigo (1932) .. .. .. 8·50 11·00
60 ½ a. black .. .. .. 35·00
61 1 a. bright scarlet (1931) .. .. 8·00 11·00
a. *Carmine-red* .. .. .. 35·00

(iii) *Thin horizontally laid paper* (1935)

62 ¼ a. indigo .. .. .. 4·00 8·00
63 1 a. scarlet-vermilion .. .. .. 6·50 13·00

Nos. 62 and 63 exist in *tête-bêche* blocks of four on the same or opposite sides of the paper.

(*f*) *Inscriptions as Type* F. *Medium wove paper* (1935)

63*a* ½ a. black .. .. .. 30·00
63*b* 4 a. yellow-olive .. .. .. £325 £225

(*g*) *Inscriptions as Type* G. (i) *Horizontally laid paper* (1935)

64 ½ a. black .. .. .. 80·00 80·00
a. Vert laid paper .. .. .. 75·00 75·00
65 1 a. scarlet .. .. .. 70·00 50·00
66 4 a. bright green .. .. .. 20·00 35·00

(ii) *Medium wove paper* (1936)

66*a* ½ a. black .. .. .. 4·00 15·00
66*b* 4 a. yellow-green .. .. .. £375 £300

(*h*) *Inscriptions as Type* H. *Medium wove paper* (1935–41)

67 ¼ a. ultramarine .. .. .. 1·25 7·00
68 ½ a. black (1938) .. .. .. 75·00 75·00
69 1 a. deep red .. .. .. 5·00 16·00
a. *Rosine* (1938) .. .. .. 7·50 18·00
70 4 a. emerald (1938) .. .. .. 17·00 27·00
71 4 r. yellow-green and vermilion (1941) .. £180
72 5 r. vermilion and yellow-green (1941) .. £250

No. 70 shows the currency spelt as "ANE" with the last letter missing and an accent over the Devanagri "N".

II. *P* 11.

(*a*) *Inscriptions as Type* H. *Medium wove paper with gum* (1939–41)

| | | | |
|---|---|---|---|
| 73 | ¼ a. ultramarine | 25·00 | 38·00 |
| | *a. Greenish blue* (1941) | 1·75 | 35·00 |
| 74 | ½ a. black | 24·00 | 24·00 |
| 75 | 1 a. scarlet-vermilion (1940) | £120 | 60·00 |
| | *a. Rose* (1940) | 12·00 | 30·00 |
| 76 | 2 a. yellow-green (1941) | 15·00 | 65·00 |

(*b*) *Inscriptions as Type* I. *Medium wove paper with gum* (1940)

| | | | |
|---|---|---|---|
| 77 | ½ a. black | £120 | 95·00 |
| 78 | 2 a. bright apple-green | 42·00 | 42·00 |

**FISCAL USE.** Collectors are warned that the low values of the later settings of Type **11** were extensively used for fiscal purposes. Stamps which have been fraudulently cleaned of pen-cancels, regummed or provided with forged postmarks are frequently met with. Particular care should be exercised with examples of Nos. 64/5, 68/70, 74/5*a* and 77.

20

**1941–44.** *Typo. P* 11.

| | | | | |
|---|---|---|---|---|
| 79 | **20** | 3 p. bright blue | 75 | 2·50 |
| 80 | | 6 p. deep blue | 90 | 2·75 |
| 81 | | 1 a. orange-red | 1·00 | 3·00 |
| 82 | | 2 a. chestnut | 4·00 | 8·00 |
| | | *a. Deep brown* (*no gum*) (1944) | 10·00 | 12·00 |
| 83 | | 4 a. bright green | 6·00 | 24·00 |
| 84 | | 8 a. dull green | 10·00 | 70·00 |
| 85 | | 1 r. deep blue | 19·00 | 85·00 |
| 79/85 | | *Set of* 7 | 38·00 | £180 |

The first printing only of Nos. 79/85 is usual with gum; all further printings, including No. 82*a*, are without gum.

21 Maharao Rajah Bahadur Singh

22 Bundi

(Typo *Times of India* Press, Bombay)

**1947.** *P* 11.

| | | | | |
|---|---|---|---|---|
| 86 | **21** | ¼ a. blue-green | 55 | 13·00 |
| 87 | | ½ a. violet | 45 | 13·00 |
| 88 | | 1 a. yellow-green | 45 | 13·00 |
| 89 | – | 2 a. vermilion | 1·00 | 25·00 |
| 90 | – | 4 a. orange | 1·25 | 35·00 |
| 91 | **22** | 8 a. ultramarine | 2·25 | |
| 92 | | 1 r. chocolate | 10·00 | |
| 86/92 | | *Set of* 7 | 14·00 | |

On the 2 and 4 a. the Rajah is in Indian dress.

OFFICIAL STAMPS

**PRICES.** Prices for Nos. O1/52 are for unused examples. Used stamps are generally worth a small premium over the prices quoted.

बूंदी (O 1) — BUNDI SERVICE (O 2)

सरविस

BUNDI SERVICE (O 3)

**1915–41.** *T* **11** *handstamped as Types* O 1/3. *Ungummed paper except Nos.* O47/52.

A. *Optd with Type* O 1. B. *Optd with Type* O 2. C. *Optd with Type* O 3.

I. *Rouletted in colour*

(*a*) *Inscriptions as Type* A. *Thin wove paper.*

| | | A | B | C |
|---|---|---|---|---|
| O 1 | ½ a. black | £120 | † | † |
| | a. Red opt | 90·00 | † | † |
| O 1*b* | 2 a. emerald | 1·75 | † | † |
| | *ba. Deep green (coarse ptg on medium wove paper)* | 6·50 | 11·00 | £100 |
| | bb. Red opt | 10·00 | 11·00 | † |
| O 2 | 2½ a. chrome-yellow (*shades*) | 2·00 | 5·50 | £100 |
| | a. Red opt | 65·00 | 75·00 | † |
| O 3 | 3 a. chestnut | 2·50 | 14·00 | † |
| | a. Green opt | 60·00 | † | † |
| | b. Red opt | 85·00 | 85·00 | † |
| O 4 | 6 a. cobalt | 24·00 | 24·00 | £110 |
| | a. Red opt | £100 | £110 | £120 |
| O 5 | 1 r. reddish violet | 32·00 | 32·00 | † |
| | a. Red opt | £130 | £140 | † |

(*b*) *Inscriptions as Type* B. *Thin wove or pelure paper*

| | | A | B | C |
|---|---|---|---|---|
| O 6 | ¼ a. ultramarine (*shades*) | 1·10 | 1·60 | 7·50 |
| | a. Red opt | 1·25 | 4·00 | 65·00 |
| O 7 | ½ a. black | 3·00 | 4·50 | 20·00 |
| | a. Red opt | 3·00 | 11·00 | 70·00 |
| O 8 | 1 a. vermilion | 4·00 | † | † |
| | a. Red opt | — | † | † |
| | *b. Carmine* | 7·00 | 7·00 | 30·00 |
| | *c. Red* (*shades*) | — | 6·00 | — |
| O 9 | 2 a. emerald (*shades*) | 13·00 | 18·00 | † |
| | a. Red opt | — | 45·00 | † |
| O 9*b* | 3 a. chestnut (R.) | — | † | † |
| O10 | 4 a. apple-green | 12·00 | 38·00 | † |
| | a. Red opt | 95·00 | † | † |
| O10*b* | 4 a. olive-yellow | £110 | £120 | † |
| | ba. Red opt | — | £225 | † |
| O11 | 6 a. pale ultramarine (*shades*) | 11·00 | 60·00 | † |
| | a. Red opt | £100 | £100 | † |
| | *b. Deep ultramarine* | 40·00 | 55·00 | † |
| | ba. Red opt | £100 | £100 | † |
| O12 | 8 a. orange | 38·00 | 50·00 | £120 |
| | a. Red opt | £120 | † | † |
| O13 | 10 a. olive-sepia | £130 | £160 | £200 |
| | a. Red opt | £250 | £275 | £300 |
| O14 | 12 a. sage-green | £140 | £170 | £200 |
| | a. Red opt | † | † | £300 |
| O14*b* | 1 r. lilac | £180 | † | † |

(*c*) *Inscriptions as Type* C. *Thin to medium wove paper.*

| | | A | B | C |
|---|---|---|---|---|
| O15 | ¼ a. ultramarine (*shades*) | 1·25 | 1·50 | 8·50 |
| | a. Red opt | 75 | 5·00 | † |
| | b. Green opt | 2·50 | 18·00 | † |
| | *c. Cobalt* (*medium wove paper*) | 35·00 | 38·00 | £120 |
| | ca. Red opt | 24·00 | 18·00 | 80·00 |
| O16 | ½ a. black | 3·50 | 2·50 | 8·50 |
| | a. Red opt | 75 | 8·00 | 65·00 |
| | b. Green opt | 1·75 | † | † |
| O17 | 1 a. orange-red | 1·25 | — | † |
| | *a. Carmine* | 13·00 | 5·00 | 12·00 |
| | *b. Deep red* (*medium wove paper*) | 24·00 | 29·00 | 55·00 |
| O18 | 2 a. emerald | 4·50 | 8·00 | † |
| | a. Red opt | † | 35·00 | † |
| | *b. Sage-green* | 7·00 | 13·00 | 50·00 |
| O19 | 4 a. yellow-green (*shades*) | 8·00 | 26·00 | † |
| | b. Red opt | — | † | † |
| | *c. Olive-yellow* | 70·00 | 80·00 | † |
| | ca. Red opt | £130 | £130 | † |
| O20 | 8 a. reddish orange | 14·00 | 24·00 | £110 |
| | a. Red opt | £100 | † | † |
| O21 | 10 a. brown-olive | 30·00 | 48·00 | £130 |
| | a. Red opt | £130 | £140 | £160 |
| O22 | 12 a. sage-green | 32·00 | 50·00 | £140 |
| | a. Red opt | † | † | £200 |
| O23 | 1 r. lilac | £110 | † | † |
| | a. Red opt | £160 | † | † |
| O24 | 2 r. red-brown and black | £225 | £180 | † |
| | a. Red opt | † | £375 | † |
| | *b. Chocolate and black* (*medium wove paper*) | £300 | £300 | † |
| O25 | 3 r. blue and red-brown | £250 | £200 | † |
| | a. Red opt | £425 | † | † |
| | *b. Grey-blue and chocolate* (*medium wove paper*) | £400 | £400 | † |
| | ba. Red opt | £425 | † | † |
| O26 | 4 r. emerald and scarlet | £275 | £300 | † |
| O27 | 5 r. scarlet and emerald | £275 | £300 | † |

(*d*) *Inscriptions as Type* D. *Thin wove paper*

| | | A | B | C |
|---|---|---|---|---|
| O28 | 2½ a. buff (*shades*) | 15·00 | 18·00 | † |
| | b. Red opt | 95·00 | — | † |
| O29 | 3 a. red-brown | 20·00 | 24·00 | † |
| | a. Variety as No. 51a | 38·00 | 45·00 | † |
| | b. Red opt | † | £140 | † |
| O30 | 10 a. bistre | 28·00 | 50·00 | £170 |
| | a. Variety as No. 52a | 60·00 | £110 | £275 |
| | b. Red opt | £170 | † | † |
| O31 | 12 a. grey-olive | 35·00 | 60·00 | £170 |
| | a. Variety as No. 53a | 70·00 | £120 | £275 |
| | b. Red opt | £170 | £200 | † |

(*e*) *Inscriptions as Type* E. (i) *Medium wove paper*

| | | A | B | C |
|---|---|---|---|---|
| O32 | ¼ a. deep slate | 30·00 | 15·00 | † |
| | a. Red opt | 27·00 | 27·00 | † |
| O32*b* | ¼ a. indigo (*thin wove paper*) | 14·00 | 27·00 | † |
| | ba. Red opt | 22·00 | 24·00 | † |
| | bb. Green opt | 25·00 | 30·00 | † |
| | *c. Cobalt* | 48·00 | 45·00 | £120 |
| | ca. Red opt | 35·00 | 30·00 | 80·00 |
| O33 | ½ a. black | 25·00 | 13·00 | † |
| | a. Red opt | 22·00 | 10·00 | † |
| | b. Green opt | † | £100 | † |
| O34 | 1 a. carmine-red | 28·00 | 28·00 | £110 |
| O35 | 3 a. chocolate (*shades*) | £100 | 90·00 | £130 |
| | a. Red opt | £170 | £180 | † |
| O35*b* | 4 a. yellow-olive | † | £225 | † |

(ii) *Very thick wove paper*

| | | A | B | C |
|---|---|---|---|---|
| O36 | ¼ a. indigo | 9·00 | 11·00 | † |
| | a. Red opt | 14·00 | 17·00 | † |
| | b. Green opt | 30·00 | † | † |
| O37 | ½ a. black | 38·00 | 38·00 | † |
| O38 | 1 a. bright scarlet | 13·00 | 11·00 | 95·00 |

(iii) *Thin horizontally laid paper*

| | | A | B | C |
|---|---|---|---|---|
| O39 | ¼ a. indigo | 42·00 | 50·00 | † |
| | a. Red opt | 5·00 | 8·00 | 90·00 |
| O40 | 1 a. scarlet-vermilion | 20·00 | 20·00 | † |
| | a. Red opt | £120 | £130 | † |

Nos. O39/40a exist in *tête-bêche* blocks of four on the same or opposite sides of the paper.

(*f*) *Inscriptions as Type* F. *Medium wove paper*

| | | A | B | C |
|---|---|---|---|---|
| O40*b* | ½ a. black | — | — | † |
| | ba. Red opt | £150 | — | † |
| O40*c* | 4 a. yellow-olive | † | £300 | † |

(*g*) *Inscriptions as Type* G. (i) *Horizontally laid paper*

| | | A | B | C |
|---|---|---|---|---|
| O41 | ½ a. black (red opt) | £110 | £110 | † |
| | a. Vert laid paper | £100 | £110 | † |
| | ab. Red opt | £100 | 60·00 | £150 |
| O42 | 4 a. bright green | £120 | £140 | † |
| | a. Red opt | £140 | £160 | † |

(ii) *Medium wove paper*

| | | A | B | C |
|---|---|---|---|---|
| O42*b* | ½ a. black | 90·00 | £100 | † |
| | ba. Red opt | £150 | £150 | † |

(*h*) *Inscriptions as Type* H. *Medium wove paper*

| | | A | B | C |
|---|---|---|---|---|
| O43 | ¼ a. ultramarine | 30·00 | 75·00 | † |
| | a. Red opt | £150 | £170 | † |
| O44 | ½ a. black | £120 | £130 | † |
| | a. Red opt | £100 | † | £200 |
| O45 | 1 a. rosine | 95·00 | 90·00 | £170 |
| O46 | 4 a. emerald | £130 | £160 | £225 |
| | a. Red opt | £180 | † | £250 |

II. *P* 11. (*a*) *Inscriptions as Type* H. *Medium wove paper with gum*

| | | A | B | C |
|---|---|---|---|---|
| O47 | ¼ a. ultramarine | 45·00 | 75·00 | 95·00 |
| | a. Red opt | 60·00 | 85·00 | † |
| | *b. Greenish blue* | 70·00 | 70·00 | 95·00 |
| | c. Ditto. Red opt | £110 | † | † |
| O48 | ½ a. black | 45·00 | 55·00 | £130 |
| | a. Red opt | 60·00 | £120 | £120 |
| O49 | 1 a. scarlet-vermilion | £200 | £250 | £275 |
| | *a. Rose* | 95·00 | 80·00 | £130 |
| O50 | 2 a. yellow-green | £140 | £100 | £100 |

(*b*) *Inscriptions as Type* I. *Medium wove paper with gum*

| | | A | B | C |
|---|---|---|---|---|
| O51 | ½ a. black | £110 | £150 | £170 |
| | a. Red opt | £140 | £160 | † |
| O52 | 2 a. bright apple-green | £160 | £160 | † |

Until 1941 it was the general practice to carry official mail free but some of the above undoubtedly exist postally used.

**1941.** *Nos.* 79 *to* 85 *optd* "SERVICE".

| | | | | |
|---|---|---|---|---|
| O53 | **20** | 3 p. bright blue (R.) | 2·25 | 4·50 |
| O54 | | 6 p. deep blue (R.) | 5·00 | 6·00 |
| O55 | | 1 a. orange-red | 5·00 | 6·50 |
| O56 | | 2 a. brown | 7·00 | 8·50 |
| O57 | | 4 a. bright green | 24·00 | 65·00 |
| O58 | | 8 a. dull green | 65·00 | £140 |
| O59 | | 1 r. deep blue (R.) | 90·00 | £160 |
| O53/9 | | *Set of* 7 | £180 | £350 |

On 25 March 1948 Bundi became part of the Rajasthan Union.

## BUSSAHIR (BASHAHR)

| PRICES FOR STAMPS ON COVER | |
|---|---|
| Nos. 1/21 | *from* × 8 |
| Nos. 22/23 | *from* × 2 |
| Nos. 24/43 | *from* × 8 |

1

2

3

4

5

6

7

8

(9)

The initials are those of the Tika Raghunath Singh, son of the then Raja, who was the organiser and former director of the State Post Office.

(Litho at the Bussahir Press by Maulvi Karam Bakhsh, Rampur)

**1895** (20 June). *Laid paper. Optd with T* **9** *in pale greenish blue* (B.), *rose* (R.), *mauve* (M.) *or lake* (L.). *With or without gum.*

(*a*) *Imperf.*

| | | | | |
|---|---|---|---|---|
| 1 | **1** | ¼ a. pink (R.M.) (1.9.95) | £425 | |
| 2 | **2** | ½ a. grey (R.M.) | £190 | |
| 3 | **3** | 1 a. vermilion (M.) | 80·00 | |
| 4 | **4** | 2 a. orange-yellow (R.M.L.) | 24·00 | 75·00 |
| 5 | **5** | 4 a. slate-violet (R.M.L.) | 35·00 | |
| | | a. Without monogram | £110 | |
| 6 | **6** | 8 a. red-brown (B.M.L.) | 35·00 | 75·00 |
| | | a. Without monogram | 95·00 | |
| | | b. Thick paper | 60·00 | |
| 7 | **7** | 12 a. green (L.) | £120 | |
| 8 | **8** | 1 r. ultramarine (R.M.L.) | 40·00 | |
| | | a. Without monogram | £110 | |

) *Perf with a sewing machine; gauge and size of holes varying between 7 and 11½*

1 ¼ a. pink (B.M.) .. 22·00 65·00
a. Without monogram .. £110 90·00
2 ½ a. grey (R.) .. 14·00 65·00
a. Without monogram .. £180
3 1 a. vermilion (M.) .. 14·00 65·00
4 2 a. orange-yellow (B.R.M.) .. 20·00 65·00
a. Without monogram .. — £130
5 4 a. slate-violet (B.R.M.) .. 15·00 70·00
a. Without monogram .. 60·00
6 8 a. red-brown (B.R.M.) .. 15·00 70·00
a. Without monogram .. 75·00
7 12 a. green (R.M.L.) .. 40·00 75·00
a. Without monogram .. 95·00
8 1 r. ultramarine (R.M.) .. 24·00 70·00
a. Without monogram .. £100
16 .. *Set of* 8 £150 £475

99. *As 1895, but pin-perf or rouletted.*
3 1 a. vermilion (M.) .. £120 £150
4 2 a. orange-yellow (M.L.) .. 35·00 75·00
a. Without monogram .. £120
5 4 a. slate-violet (B.R.M.L.) .. £120
7 12 a. green (R.) .. £225
8 1 r. ultramarine (R.) .. £225

Nos. 1 to 21 were in sheets of 24. They seem to have been overinted and perforated as required. Those first issued for use were rforated, but they were subsequently supplied imperf, both to llectors and for use. Nos. 17 to 21 were some of the last supplies. o rule seems to have been observed as to the colour of the overinted monogram; pale blue, rose and mauve were used from the st. The pale blue varies to greenish blue or blue-green, and pears quite green on the yellow stamps. The lake is possibly a xture of the mauve and the rose—it is a quite distinct colour and parently later than the others. Specimens without overprint are her remainders left in the Treasury or copies that have escaped cidentally; they have been found sticking to the backs of others at bore the overprint.

Varieties may also be found doubly overprinted, in two different lours.

10

11

12

11. Lines of shading above and at bottom left and right of shield.
12. White dots above shield and ornaments in bottom corners.

13

14

15

16

(Printed at the Bussahir Press by Maulvi Karam Bakhsh)

896–97. *Wove paper. Optd with monogram "R.S.", T 9, in rose. Recess singly from line-engraved dies. With or without gum. Various perfs.*
2 10 ¼ a. deep violet (1897) .. — £325
3 11 ½ a. grey-blue .. £350 £120
3a ½ a. deep blue (1897) .. — £190

No. 23 exists sewing-machine perf about 10 and also perf 4½–16. Nos. 22 and 23a are pin-perf.

896–1900. *As Nos. 22/3, but lithographed in sheets of various sizes. No gum.*

(*a*) *Imperf*
4 10 ¼ a. slate-violet (B.R.M.L.) .. 2·50
5 11 ½ a. blue (*shades*) (R.M.L.) .. 2·50 10·00
a. Without monogram ..
b. Laid paper (B.L.) .. 38·00
6 13 1 a. olive (*shades*) (R.M.L.) .. 9·00 16·00

(*b*) *Pin-perf or rouletted*
7 10 ¼ a. slate-violet (R.M.L.) .. 5·00 8·00
8 11 ½ a. blue (*shades*) (R.M.L.) .. 8·00 16·00
9 13 1 a. olive (*shades*) (R.M.L.) .. 12·00 18·00
0 14 2 a. orange-yellow (B.) .. £225 £250

The ¼ a. and ½ a. are in sheets of 24, the 1 a. and 2a. in blocks f 4.

900–01. *¼ a., 1 a, colours changed; ½ a. redrawn type; 2 a. with dash before "STATE" and characters in lower left label; 4 a. new value. No gum.*

(*a*) *Imperf*
1 10 ¼ a. vermilion (B.M.) .. 1·25 3·00
a. Without monogram ..
1b 12 ½ a. blue (M.) .. 5·00
ba. Without monogram .. 22·00
2 13 1 a. vermilion (B.M.) .. 2·00 4·50
a. Without monogram .. 18·00
3 15 2 a. ochre (M.) (9.00) .. 17·00
4 2 a. yellow (B.M.) (11.00) .. 17·00
a. Without monogram .. 28·00
5 2 a. orange (B.M.) (1.01) .. 16·00
a. Without monogram .. 28·00
6 16 4 a. claret (B.R.M.) .. 21·00 48·00
a. Without monogram .. 28·00

(*b*) *Pin-perf or rouletted*
37 10 ¼ a. vermilion (B.M.) .. 1·25 4·00
37a 12 ½ a. blue (M.) .. 14·00 22·00
38 13 1 a. vermilion (B.M.) .. 1·25 5·00
39 1 a. brown-red (M.) (3.01) .. — £100
40 15 2 a. ochre (B.M.) (9.00) .. 17·00
41 2 a. yellow (B.R.M.) (11.00) .. 18·00 32·00
42 2 a. orange (B.M.) (1.01) .. 18·00 32·00
43 16 4 a. claret (B.R.M.) .. 24·00

The ¼ a., ½ a. and 1 a. are in sheets of 24; the 2 a. in sheets of 50 differing throughout in the dash and the characters added at lower left; the 4 a. in sheets of 28.

(17)

The stamps formerly catalogued with large overprint "R.N.S." (T 17) are now believed never to have been issued for use.

Remainders are also found with overprint "P.S.", the initials of Padam Singh who succeeded Raghunath Singh in the direction of the Post Office, and with the original monogram "R.S." in a damaged state, giving it the appearance of a double-lined "R."

The stamps of Bussahir have been obsolete since 1 April 1901. Numerous remainders were sold after this date, and all values were later reprinted in the colours of the originals, or in fancy colours, from the original stones, or from new ones. Printings were also made from new types, similar to those of the second issue of the 8 a., 12 a., and 1 r. values, in sheets of 8.

Reprints are frequently found on laid paper.

Collectors are warned against obliterated copies bearing the Rampur postmark with date "19 MA 1900." Many thousand remainders and reprints were thus obliterated for export after the closing of the State Post Office.

## CHARKHARI

**PRICES FOR STAMPS ON COVER**

| | |
|---|---|
| Nos. 1/4 | *from* × 2 |
| Nos. 5/26 | *from* × 20 |
| Nos. 27/44 | *from* × 3 |
| Nos. 45/53 | *from* × 100 |
| Nos. 54/5 | *from* × 5 |
| No. 56 | *from* × 2 |

1

¼ ½ 1 2 4
¼ ½ 1 2 4

The top row shows the figures of value used in the stamps of 1894–97, and the bottom row those for the 1904 issue. In the 4 a. the figure slopes slightly to the right in the first issue, and to the left in the second.

1894. *Typo from a single die. No gum. Imperf.*
1 1 ¼ anna, rose .. £900 £700
2 1 annas, dull green .. £1600 £2250
3 2 annas, dull green .. £1800
4 4 annas, dull green .. £1200

Nos. 1/2 are known pin-perforated.

1897. *Inscr "ANNA". No gum. Imperf.*
5 1 ¼ a. magenta .. 25·00 30·00
*a. Purple* .. 1·75 2·50
*b. Violet* .. 1·75 2·50
6 ½ a. purple .. 2·25 3·50
*a. Violet* .. 3·50 4·00
7 1 1 a. blue-green .. 4·00 5·00
*a. Turquoise-blue* .. 4·00 4·50
*b. Indigo* .. 9·00 11·00
8 2 a. blue-green .. 7·00 10·00
*a. Turquoise-blue* .. 7·00 8·00
*b. Indigo* .. 9·00 13·00
9 4 a. blue-green .. 6·00 11·00
*a. Turquoise-blue* .. 6·00 9·00
*b. Indigo* .. 17·00 22·00
ba. Figure of value sideways ..
5/9 .. *Set of* 5 19·00 25·00

Minor varieties may be found with the first "A" in "ANNA" not printed.

All values are known on various coloured papers, but these are proofs or trial impressions.

1904. *Numerals changed as illustrated above. No gum.*
10 1 ¼ a. violet .. 2·50 3·50
11 ½ a. violet .. 3·50 4·50
12 1 a. green .. 8·00 12·00
13 2 a. green .. 18·00 20·00
14 4 a. green .. 15·00 22·00
10/14 .. *Set of* 5 42·00 55·00

Stamps of this issue can be found showing part of the papermarker's watermark. "Mercantile Script Extra Strong John Haddon & Co.".

2 (Right-hand sword over left)

POSTAGE STAMP
Type I

POSTAGE STAMP
Type II

Type I. "P" of "POSTAGE" in same size as other letters. "E" small with long upper and lower arms. White dot often appears on one or both of the sword hilts.

Type II. "P" larger than the other letters. "E" large with short upper and lower arms. No dots occur on the hilts.

1909–19. *Litho in Calcutta. Wove paper. P* 11. (*a*) *Type* I.
15 2 1 p. chestnut .. 32·00 40·00
*a. Pale chestnut* .. 1·75 35·00
*b. Orange-brown* .. 3·00 35·00
16 1 p. turquoise-blue .. 30 45
a. Imperf between (horiz pair) .. £140
*b. Greenish blue* (1911) .. 35 50
*c. Pale turquoise-green* .. 60 70
17 ½ a. vermilion .. 90 90
*a. Deep rose-red* .. 75 90
18 1 a. sage-green .. 1·40 1·40
*a. Yellow-olive* .. 95 1·10
19 2 a. grey-blue .. 2·00 3·00
*a. Dull violet-blue* .. 3·00 3·00
20 4 a. deep green .. 2·75 4·00
21 8 a. brown-red .. 3·50 12·00
22 1 r. pale chestnut .. 7·00 16·00
15a/22 .. *Set of* 8 17·00 65·00

(*b*) *Type* II
24 2 1 p. turquoise-blue .. 1·00 1·00
25 ½ a. vermilion .. 70 80
a. Imperf (pair) .. £300
*b. Deep rose-red* .. 1·50 1·75
26 1 a. yellow-olive (1919) .. 1·25 1·50
*a. Sage-green* .. 1·25 1·50
24/6 .. *Set of* 3 2·75 3·00

No. 15, from the original printing, shows an upstroke to the "1", not present on other brown printings of this value.

See also Nos. 31/44.

POSTAGE STAMP CHARKHARI STATE C.I. JI INDIA BUNDELKHAND 1 PICE
3

4

"ᒧI" below Swords Right sword overlaps left. Double frame lines.

"JI" below Swords. Left sword overlaps right. Single frame line.

1912–17. *Handstamped. Wove paper. No gum. Imperf.*
27 3 1 p. violet .. — 70·00
*a. Dull purple* .. — 70·00
28 4 1 p. violet (1917) .. 8·00 6·00
*a. Dull purple* .. 9·00 6·00
b. *Tête-bêche* (pair) .. 60·00 60·00
c. Laid paper .. — £120

5 (*actual size* 63 × 25 *mm*)

6 (Left-hand sword over right)

1922. *Handstamped. No gum.* (*a*) *Wove paper. Imperf.*
29 5 1 a. violet .. 60·00 75·00
*a. Dull purple* .. 70·00 80·00

(*b*) *Laid paper. P* 11
30 5 1 a. violet .. 60·00 85·00
a. Imperf .. £110 £120

(Typo State Ptg Press, Charkhari)

1930–45. *No gum. Imperf.*
31 6 1 p. deep blue .. 35 6·50
a. Vert pair, top ptd inverted on back, bottom normal upright .. 12·00
b. *Tête-bêche* (pair) .. £110
32 1 p. dull *to* light green (*pelure*) (1943) .. 35·00 85·00
33 1 p. violet (1943) .. 11·00 65·00
a. *Tête-bêche* (pair) .. 48·00
34 ½ a. deep olive .. 30 6·50
35 ½ a. red-brown (1940) .. 1·50 15·00
a. *Tête-bêche* (pair) .. £200
36 ½ a. black (*pelure*) (1943) .. 40·00 85·00
37 ½ a. red (1943) .. 14·00 30·00
a. *Tête-bêche* (pair) .. 40·00
38 ½ a. grey-brown .. 60·00 75·00
39 1 a. green .. 50 6·50
*a. Emerald* .. 14·00 26·00
40 1 a. chocolate (1940) .. 2·25 15·00
a. *Tête-bêche* (pair) .. 70·00
*b. Lake-brown* .. — 24·00
41 1 a. red (1940) .. 50·00 55·00
*a. Carmine* .. — 55·00
42 2 a. light blue .. 1·25 8·50
a. *Tête-bêche* (pair) .. 9·00
43 2 a. greenish grey (1941?) .. 28·00 42·00
a. *Tête-bêche* (pair) .. 60·00
43b 2 a. yellow-green (1945) .. — £275
44 4 a. carmine .. 4·00 12·00
a. *Tête-bêche* (pair) .. 14·00

7 Imlia Palace

½ As.

(8)

(Typo Batliboi Litho Works, Bombay)

**1931** (25 June). *T 7 and similar designs. P 11, 11½, 12 or compound.*

45 ½ a. blue-green .. .. .. .. .. 40 10
a. Imperf between (horiz or vert pair) .. 25·00 11·00
46 1 a. blackish brown .. .. .. .. 40 10
a. Imperf between (horiz or vert pair) .. 10·00 8·00
47 2 a. violet .. .. .. .. .. 30 10
a. Imperf between (horiz or vert pair) .. 22·00 22·00
b. Doubly printed .. .. .. .. 8·50
48 4 a. olive-green .. .. .. .. 30 10
a. Imperf between (vert pair) .. .. 45·00
49 8 a. magenta .. .. .. .. 35 10
a. Imperf between (horiz or vert pair) .. 28·00 12·00
50 1 r. green and rose .. .. .. .. 1·10 15
a. Imperf between (vert pair) .. .. 90·00 90·00
b. Green (centre) omitted .. .. .. — 75·00
51 2 r. red and brown .. .. .. .. 1·25 20
a. Imperf horiz (vert pair) .. .. 48·00 14·00
52 3 r. chocolate and blue-green .. .. 2·50 25
a. Imperf between (horiz pair) .. .. — £100
b. *Tête-bêche* (pair) .. .. .. 90·00 18·00
c. Chocolate (centre) omitted .. .. 18·00
53 5 r. turquoise and purple .. .. .. 3·00 45
a. Imperf between (horiz pair) .. .. £100
b. Centre inverted .. .. .. 32·00 22·00
c. Centre doubly printed .. .. .. — 30·00
45/53 .. .. .. .. .. *Set of* 9 8·50 1·25

Designs:—½ a. The Lake; 2 a. Industrial School; 4 a. Bird's-eye view of City; 8 a. The Fort; 1 r. Guest House. 2 r. Palace Gate; 3 r. Temples at Rainpur; 5 r. Goverdhan Temple.

This issue was the subject of speculative manipulation, large stocks being thrown on the market cancelled-to-order at very low prices and unused at less than face value. The issue was an authorized one but was eventually withdrawn by the State authorities.

**1940**. *Nos. 21/2 surch as T* 8.

54 2 ½ a. on 8 a. brown-red .. .. .. 24·00 75·00
a. No space between "½" and "As." .. 29·00 75·00
b. Surch inverted .. .. .. £225
c. "1" of "½" inverted .. .. .. £200
55 1 a. on 1 r. chestnut .. .. .. 55·00 £120
a. Surch inverted .. .. .. £250
56 "1 ANNA" on 1 r. chestnut .. .. £325 £375

## COCHIN

**(6 puttans = 5 annas. 12 pies = 1 anna; 16 annas = 1 rupee)**

Stamps of Cochin were also valid for postage in Travancore.

**PRICES FOR STAMPS ON COVER**

| | |
|---|---|
| Nos. 1/3 | *from* × 30 |
| Nos. 4/5 | *from* × 10 |
| Nos. 6/6*b* | *from* × 3 |
| Nos. 7/9 | *from* × 20 |
| Nos. 11/22 | *from* × 15 |
| Nos. 26/128 | *from* × 8 |
| Nos. O1/105 | *from* × 15 |

1

2

(Dies eng P. Orr & Sons, Madras; typo Cochin Govt, Ernakulam)

**1892** (1 April). *No wmk, or wmk large Umbrella in the sheet. P* 12.

1 1 ½ put. buff .. .. .. .. 1·25 1·40
*a. Orange-buff* .. .. .. .. 1·25 1·10
*b. Yellow* .. .. .. .. 1·75 1·50
c. Imperf (pair) .. .. .. ..
2 1 put. purple .. .. .. .. 1·50 1·00
3 2 2 put. deep violet .. .. .. .. 1·00 1·25
1/3 .. .. .. .. .. *Set of* 3 3·25 3·00

**1896** (End). *Similar to T* 1, *but* 28 × 33 *mm. P* 12.

*(a) Wmk Arms and inscription in sheet*

4 1 put. violet .. .. .. .. .. 30·00 42·00

*(b) Wmk Conch Shell to each stamp*

5 1 put. deep violet .. .. .. .. 16·00 22·00

This stamp was originally printed for provisional use as a fiscal; afterwards it was authorized for postal use.

*(c) On laid paper*

6 1 ½ put. orange-buff .. .. .. .. £400 £110
*a. Orange* .. .. .. .. — £110
*b. Yellow* .. .. .. .. — £110

WATERMARKS. Prior to the 1911–23 issue, printed by Perkins, Bacon & Co, little attention was paid to the position of the watermark. Inverted and sideways watermarks are frequently found in the 1898 and 1903 issues.

**1897**. *Wmk a small Umbrella on each stamp. P* 12.

7 1 ½ put. buff .. .. .. .. .. 2·25 1·50
*a. Orange* .. .. .. .. 1·50 1·00
ab. *Orange*. Imperf (pair) .. ..
*b. Yellow* .. .. .. .. 2·00 1·00
8 1 put. purple .. .. .. .. 3·00 2·00
9 2 2 put. deep violet .. .. .. .. 2·50 2·25
a. Imperf (pair) .. .. ..
b. Doubly printed .. .. .. † —
c. Printed both sides .. .. ..
d. *Tête-bêche* (pair) .. .. .. £2250
7/9 .. .. .. .. .. *Set of* 3 6·25 4·75

The paper watermarked with a small umbrella is more transparent than that of the previous issue. The wmk is not easy to distinguish.

The 1 put. in deep violet was a special printing for fiscal use only.

3

4

(5)

5

6

**1898**. *Thin yellowish paper. Wmk small Umbrella on each stamp. With or without gum. P* 12.

11 3 3 pies, blue .. .. .. .. .. 1·00 50
a. Imperf between (horiz pair) .. £325
b. Imperf between (vert pair) .. £450
c. Doubly printed .. .. ..
12 4 ½ put. green .. .. .. .. 1·50 40
a. Imperf between (horiz pair) ..
b. Stamp sideways (in pair) .. ..
13 5 1 put. pink .. .. .. .. .. 2·00 60
a. *Tête-bêche* (pair) .. .. .. £1800 £1800
b. Laid paper .. .. .. † £1600
ba. Laid paper. *Tête-bêche* (pair) .. † £5500
*c. Red* .. .. .. .. 1·75 50
*d. Carmine-red* .. .. .. 2·50 60
14 6 2 put. deep violet .. .. .. .. 3·00 1·00
a. Imperf between (vert pair) .. £300
11/14 .. .. .. .. .. *Set of* 4 6·50 2·00

**1903**. *Thick white paper. Wmk small Umbrella on each stamp. With or without gum. P* 12.

16 3 3 pies, blue .. .. .. .. .. 30 10
a. Doubly printed .. .. .. — £180
b. Imperf between (horiz pair) .. .. † £350
17 4 ½ put. green .. .. .. .. 75 10
a. Stamp sideways (in pair) .. .. £650 £650
b. Doubly printed .. .. .. — £180
18 5 1 put. pink .. .. .. .. 1·25 10
a. *Tête-bêche* (pair) .. .. .. † £2250
19 6 2 put. deep violet .. .. .. .. 1·40 20
a. Doubly printed .. .. .. £375 £180
16/19 .. .. .. .. .. *Set of* 4 3·25 40

**2** (7) **2** (7*a*)

**1909**. *T* 3 *(paper and perf of* 1903*), surch with T* 7. *Wmk is always sideways. No gum.*

22 3 2 on 3 pies, rosy mauve .. .. .. 15 30
a. Surch T 7 inverted .. .. .. 70·00 70·00
b. Surch T 7*a* .. .. .. .. £350 £225
c. Stamps *tête-bêche* .. .. .. £100 £100
d. Stamps and surchs *tête-bêche* .. .. £140 £140

Varieties a, c and d were caused by the inversion of one stamp (No. 7) in the plate and the consequent inversion of the corresponding surcharge to correct the error.

8 Raja Sir Sri Rama Varma I

8*a*

(Recess Perkins, Bacon & Co)

**1911–13**. *Currency in pies and annas. W* 8*a*. *P* 14.

26 8 2 p. brown .. .. .. .. .. 30 10
a. Imperf (pair) .. .. ..
27 3 p. blue .. .. .. .. .. 30 10
a. Perf 14 × 12½ .. .. .. 25·00 2·50
28 4 p. green .. .. .. .. .. 90 10
28*a* 4 p. apple-green .. .. .. .. 2·50 40
29 9 p. carmine .. .. .. .. 1·10 10
a. Wmk sideways .. .. ..
30 1 a. brown-orange .. .. .. .. 1·60 10
31 1½ a. purple .. .. .. .. 3·75 40
32 2 a. grey (1913) .. .. .. .. 7·50 40
33 3 a. vermilion (1913) .. .. .. 28·00 32·00
26/33 .. .. .. .. .. *Set of* 8 38·00 32·00

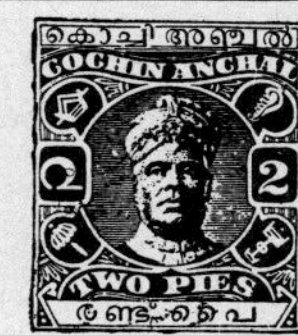


9 Maharaja Sir Sri Rama Varma II 10

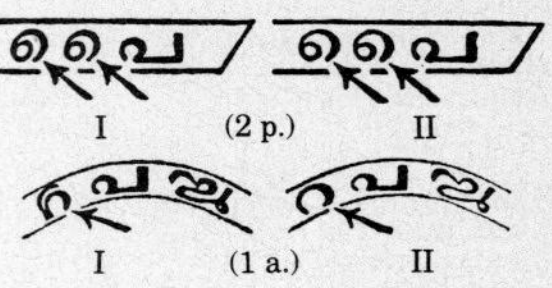


(Recess Perkins, Bacon & Co)

**1916–30**. *W* 8*a*. *P* 13½ *to* 14.

35 10 2 p. brown (Die I) *(a) (b) (c)* .. .. 2·50 10
a. Imperf (pair) .. .. ..
b. Die II *(b) (c)* (1930) .. .. 75 10
36 4 p. green *(a) (b)* .. .. .. 95 10
37 6 p. red-brown *(a) (b) (c)* (1922) .. 1·00 10
38 8 p. sepia *(b)* (1923) .. .. .. 1·40 10
39 9 p. carmine *(a)* .. .. .. 7·00 15
40 10 p. blue *(b)* (1923) .. .. .. 1·40 10
41 9 1 a. orange (Die I) *(a)* .. .. 5·00 30
a. Die II *(a) (b)* (1922) .. .. 8·00 30
42 10 1½ a. purple *(b)* (1923) .. .. 2·25 10
43 2 a. grey *(a) (b) (d)* .. .. .. 3·75 10
44 2¼ a. yellow-green *(a) (d)* (1922) .. 3·75 50
45 3 a. vermilion *(a) (b)* .. .. .. 11·00 35
35/45 .. .. .. .. *Set of* 11 35·00 1·50

Four different perforating heads were used for this issue: *(a)* comb 13.9; *(b)* comb 13.6; *(c)* line 13.8; *(d)* line 14.2. Values on which each perforation occur are shown above. Stamps with perforation *(a)* are on hand-made paper, while the other perforations are on softer machine-made paper with a horizontal mesh.

2 Two pies (11) 2 Two pies (12) 2 Two pies (13)

2 Two Pies (14) 2 Two Pies (15)

**1922–29**. *T* 8 *(P* 14*), surch with T* 11/15.

46 11 2 p. on 3 p. blue .. .. .. .. 40 30
a. Surch double .. .. .. £200 £200
47 12 2 p. on 3 p. blue .. .. .. .. 1·50 60
a. Surch double .. .. .. £350
b. Capital "P" in "Pies" .. .. 24·00 16·00
ba. Surch double .. .. ..
48 13 2 p. on 3 p. blue (6.24) .. .. .. 2·50 30
a. Capital "P" in "Pies" .. .. 30·00 12·00
b. Perf 14 × 12½ .. .. .. 14·00 16·00
ba. Ditto. Capital "P" in "Pies" .. .. £170 £170
49 14 2 p. on 3 p. blue (1929) .. .. .. 2·00 2·50
a. Surch double .. .. .. £200
b. Surch with Type 15 .. .. .. 65·00 75·00
ba. Ditto. Surch double .. .. ..

There are four settings of these overprints. The first (July 1922) consisted of 39 stamps with Type 11, and 9 with Type 12, and in Type 11 the centre of the "2" is above the "o" of "Two". In the second setting (May 1924) there were 36 of Type 11 and 12 of Type 12, and the centre of the figure is above the space between "Two" and "Pies". The third setting (June 1924) consists of stamps with Type 13 only.

The fourth setting (1929) was also in sheets of 48, No. 49b being the first stamp in the fourth row.

ONE ANNA
ഒരു അണ
ANCHAL &
REVENUE
(16)

Three Pies
൩ 3
മൂന്നു പൈ
(17)

**1928**. *Surch with T* 16.

50 10 1 a. on 2¼ a. yellow-green *(a)* .. .. 5·00 12·00
a. "REVENUF" for "REVENUE" .. 45·00 65·00
b. Surch double .. .. ..

**932–33.** *Surch as T* **17**. *W* **8***a*. *P* 13½.

| | | | | |
|---|---|---|---|---|
| 1 | **10** | 3 p. on 4 p. green (*b*) | 1·00 | 75 |
| 2 | | 3 p. on 8 p. sepia (*b*) | 1·00 | 1·40 |
| 3 | | 9 p. on 10 p. blue (*b*) | 1·50 | 1·25 |
| 1/3 | | *Set of* 3 | 3·00 | 3·00 |

**18** Maharaja Sir Sri Rama Varma III

(Recess Perkins, Bacon & Co)

**933–38.** *T* **18** (*but frame and inscription of* 1 a. *as T* **9**). *W* **8***a*. *P* 13 × 13½.

| | | | | |
|---|---|---|---|---|
| 4 | **18** | 2 p. brown (1936) | 50 | 10 |
| 5 | | 4 p. green | 60 | 10 |
| 6 | | 6 p. red-brown | 70 | 10 |
| 7 | – | 1 a. brown-orange | 70 | 10 |
| 8 | **18** | 1 a. 8 p. carmine | 3·00 | 2·25 |
| 9 | | 2 a. grey (1938) | 1·75 | 10 |
| 0 | | 2¼ a. yellow-green | 1·50 | 10 |
| 1 | | 3 a. vermilion (1938) | 3·00 | 40 |
| 2 | | 3 a. 4 p. violet | 1·50 | 1·25 |
| 3 | | 6 a. 8 p. sepia | 1·75 | 4·50 |
| 4 | | 10 a. blue | 3·00 | 5·50 |
| 4/64 | | *Set of* 11 | 16·00 | 12·50 |

For stamps in this design, but lithographed, see Nos. 67/71.

**934.** *Surcharged as T* **14**. *W* **8***a*. *P* 13½.

| | | | | |
|---|---|---|---|---|
| 5 | **10** | 6 p. on 8 p. sepia (R.) (*b*) | 75 | 50 |
| 6 | | 6 p. on 10 p. blue (R.) (*b*) | 1·75 | 65 |

**"DOUBLE PRINTS".** The errors previously listed under this description are now identified as blanket offsets, a type of variety outside the scope of this catalogue. Examples occur on issues from 1938 onwards.

**SPACING OF OVERPRINTS AND SURCHARGES.** The typeset overprints and surcharges issued from 1939 onwards show considerable differences in spacing. Except for specialists, however, these differences have little significance as they occur within the same settings and do not represent separate printings.

(Litho The Associated Printers, Madras)

**1938.** *W* **8***a* (A) *P* 11 *or* (B) *P* 13 × 13½.

| | | | A | | B | |
|---|---|---|---|---|---|---|
| 67 | **18** | 2 p. brown | 1·00 | 15 | 5·50 | 40 |
| 68 | | 4 p. green | 85 | 10 | 8·00 | 5·00 |
| 69 | | 6 p. red-brown | 2·25 | 10 | † | £1300 |
| 70 | | 1 a. brown-orange | 45·00 | 50·00 | 50·00 | 55·00 |
| 71 | | 2¼ a. sage-green | 6·00 | 10 | 12·00 | 1·60 |
| 67/71 | | *Set of* 5 | 50·00 | 50·00 | † | |

Most examples of Nos. 70A/B were used fiscally. Collectors are warned against examples which have been cleaned and regummed or provided with forged postmarks.

**ANCHAL**
(19)

**THREE PIES**
(20)

**SURCHARGED**
**ANCHAL**

**ONE ANNA THREE PIES**
(21)

**NINE PIES**
(22)

**ANCHAL**
**ANCHAL**

**NINE PIES**
(23)

**SURCHARGED NINE PIES**
(24)

**ANCHAL**
(25)

**939–44.** *T* **18** *variously optd or surch.*

I. *Recess-printed stamps. Nos.* 57/8

| | | | |
|---|---|---|---|
| 2 | 3 p. on 1 a. 8 p. carmine (T **20**) | £110 | 50·00 |
| 3 | 3 p. on 1 a. 8 p. carmine (T **21**) | 2·00 | 4·50 |
| 4 | 6 p. on 1 a. 8 p. carmine (T **20**) | 2·00 | 12·00 |
| 5 | 1 a. brown-orange (T **19**) | 1·50 | 15 |
| 6 | 1 a. 3 p. on 1 a. 8 p. carmine (T **21**) | 1·00 | 30 |
| 2/6 | *Set of* 5 | £110 | 60·00 |

I. *Lithographed stamps. Nos.* 68 *and* 70. A. *P* 11. B. *P* 13 × 13½

| | | A | | B | |
|---|---|---|---|---|---|
| 77 | 3 p. on 4 p. (T **21**) | 5·00 | 1·25 | 12·00 | 1·50 |
| 78 | 6 p. on 1 a. (T **22**) | £160 | £110 | † | |
| 79 | 6 p. on 1 a. (T **23**) | £160 | £110 | 40·00 | 24·00 |
| 30 | 9 p. on 1 a. (T **22**) | 55·00 | 65·00 | † | |
| 31 | 9 p. on 1 a. (T **23**) | † | | 95·00 | 19·00 |
| 32 | 9 p. on 1 a. (T **24**) | † | | 11·00 | 1·50 |
| 33 | 1 a. (T **19**) | £130 | 30 | — | £120 |
| 34 | 1 a. (T **25**) | 1·00 | 1·50 | 10·00 | 50 |

**26** Maharaja Sri Kerala Varma I

**27** (*The actual measurement of this wmk is* 6¼ × 3⅝ *in.*)

(Litho The Associated Printers, Madras)

**1943.** *Frame of* 1 *a. inscr* "ANCHAL & REVENUE". A. *P* 11. B. *P* 13 × 13½. (*a*) *W* **8***a*.

| | | | A | | B | |
|---|---|---|---|---|---|---|
| 85 | **26** | 2 p. grey-brown | † | £850 | 1·00 | 20 |
| 85*a* | | 4 p. green | † | | £225 | £140 |
| 85*b* | | 1 a. brown-orange | † | | 65·00 | 75·00 |
| 85/*b* | | *Set of* 3 | † | | £225 | £180 |

(*b*) *W* **27**

| | | | A | | B | |
|---|---|---|---|---|---|---|
| 86 | **26** | 2 p. grey-brown | † | £850 | 24·00 | 30 |
| 87 | | 4 p. green | 3·00 | 1·25 | 7·00 | 9·00 |
| 88 | | 6 p. red-brown | 8·00 | 1·00 | 1·00 | 10 |
| 89 | | 9 p. ultramarine | 16·00 | 1·00 | † | |
| | | a. Imperf between (horiz pair) | £800 | — | † | |
| 90 | | 1 a. brown-orange | 20·00 | 30·00 | £180 | £110 |
| 91 | | 2¼ a. yellow-green | 24·00 | 5·00 | 11·00 | 40 |

Part of W **27** appears on many stamps in each sheet, while others are entirely without wmk.

Most examples of Nos. 85*b* and 90A/B were used fiscally. Collectors are warned against examples which have been cleaned and regummed or provided with forged postmarks.

**1944.** *T* **26** *variously opt or surch.* A. *P* 11. B. *P* 13 × 13½

(*a*) *W* **8***a*.

| | | A | | B | |
|---|---|---|---|---|---|
| 92 | 3 p. on 4 p. (T **21**) | † | | 42·00 | 8·00 |
| 92*a* | 9 p. on 1 a. (T **23**) | † | | 4·00 | 65 |
| 92*b* | 9 p. on 1 a. (T **24**) | † | | 1·10 | 1·00 |
| 92*c* | 1 a. 3 p. on 1 a. (T **21**) | † | | — | £2250 |

(*b*) *W* **27**

| | | A | | B | |
|---|---|---|---|---|---|
| 93 | 2 p. on 6 p. (T **20**) | 75 | 1·25 | 75 | 1·25 |
| 94 | 3 p. on 4 p. (T **20**) | 1·25 | 10 | † | |
| 95 | 3 p. on 4 p. (T **21**) | † | | 1·40 | 10 |
| 96 | 3 p. on 6 p. (T **20**) | 80 | 15 | 80 | 15 |
| 97 | 4 p. on 6 p. (T **20**) | † | | 2·50 | 5·00 |

**28** Maharaja Sri Ravi Varma **29**

I

II

(Litho The Associated Printers, Madras)

**1944–48.** *W* **27**. *No gum.* (*a*) *Type* I. *P* 11.

| | | | | |
|---|---|---|---|---|
| 98 | **28** | 9 p. ultramarine (1944) | 6·00 | 1·25 |

(*b*) *Type* II. *P* 13

| | | | | |
|---|---|---|---|---|
| 98*a* | **28** | 9 p. ultramarine (1946) | 4·00 | 5·50 |
| | | ab. Perf 13 × 13½ | 12·00 | 1·25 |
| 99 | | 1 a. 3 p. magenta (1948) | 6·00 | 4·50 |
| | | a. Perf 13 × 13½ | 65·00 | 14·00 |
| 100 | | 1 a. 9 p. ultramarine (*shades*) (1948) | 10·00 | 5·00 |
| 98*a*/100 | | *Set of* 3 | 18·00 | 9·75 |

Nos. 98*a*/100 are line-perforated, Nos. 98ab and 99a comb-perforated.

(Litho The Associated Printers, Madras)

**1946–48.** *Frame of* 1 *a. inscr* "ANCHAL & REVENUE". *W* **27**. *No gum* (*except for stamps perf* 11). *P* 13.

| | | | | |
|---|---|---|---|---|
| 101 | **29** | 2 p. chocolate | 75 | 10 |
| | | a. Imperf horiz (vert pair) | £800 | £800 |
| | | c. Perf 11 | 8·00 | 60 |
| | | d. Perf 11 × 13 | £275 | £120 |
| 102 | | 3 p. carmine | 50 | 10 |
| 103 | | 4 p. grey-green | £1000 | 65·00 |
| 104 | | 6 p. red-brown (1947) | 15·00 | 1·75 |
| | | a. Perf 11 | £130 | 1·25 |
| 105 | | 9 p. ultramarine | 50 | 10 |
| | | a. Imperf between (horiz pair) | † | £850 |
| 106 | **29** | 1 a. orange (1948) | 5·00 | 14·00 |
| | | a. Perf 11 | £375 | |
| 107 | | 2 a. black | 55·00 | 1·75 |
| | | a. Perf 11 | 95·00 | 3·50 |
| 108 | | 3 a. vermilion | 35·00 | 40 |
| 101/8 | | *Set of* 8 | £1000 | 75·00 |

**30** Maharaja Sri Kerala Varma II

(Litho The Associated Printers, Madras)

**1948–50.** *W* **27**. *P* 11.

| | | | | |
|---|---|---|---|---|
| 109 | **30** | 2 p. grey-brown | 75 | 10 |
| | | a. Imperf vert (horiz pair) | † | £700 |
| 110 | | 3 p. carmine | 75 | 10 |
| | | a. Imperf between (vert pair) | † | £700 |
| 111 | | 4 p. green | 3·75 | 15 |
| | | a. Imperf vert (horiz pair) | £250 | £275 |
| 112 | | 6 p. chestnut | 6·50 | 10 |
| | | a. Imperf vert (horiz pair) | £700 | |
| 113 | | 9 p. ultramarine | 1·10 | 10 |
| 114 | | 2 a. black | 21·00 | 30 |
| 115 | | 3 a. orange-red | 29·00 | 35 |
| | | a. Imperf vert (horiz pair) | £1100 | |
| 116 | | 3 a. 4 p. violet (1950) | £100 | £275 |
| 109/16 | | *Set of* 8 | £140 | £275 |

**31** Chinese Nets

**32** Dutch Palace

(Litho The Associated Printers, Madras)

**1949.** *W* **27**. *P* 11.

| | | | | |
|---|---|---|---|---|
| 117 | **31** | 2 a. black | 60 | 2·25 |
| | | a. Imperf vert (horiz pair) | £400 | |
| 118 | **32** | 2¼ a. green | 60 | 2·50 |
| | | a. Imperf vert (horiz pair) | £400 | |

**SIX PIES**

ആറു പൈ
(33)

പൈ Normal

പൈ Error

Due to similarities between two Malayalam characters some values of the 1948 provisional issue exist with an error in the second word of the Malayalam surcharge. On Nos. 119, 122 and O103 this occurs twice in the setting of 48. No. 125 shows four examples and No. O104b one. Most instances are as illustrated above, but in two instances on the setting for No. 125 the error occurs on the second character.

**1949.** *Surch as T* **33**. (i) *On* 1944–48 *issue*. *P* 13.

| | | | | |
|---|---|---|---|---|
| 119 | **28** | 6 p. on 1 a. 3 p. magenta | 1·25 | 90 |
| | | a. Incorrect character | 13·00 | 8·50 |
| 120 | | 1 a. on 1 a. 9 p. ultramarine (R.) | 75 | 40 |

(ii) *On* 1946–48 *issue*

| | | | | |
|---|---|---|---|---|
| 121 | **29** | 3 p. on 9 p. ultramarine | 4·00 | 8·00 |
| 122 | | 6 p. on 1 a. 3 p. magenta | 5·00 | 5·50 |
| | | a. Surch double | † | £300 |
| | | b. Incorrect character | 38·00 | 38·00 |
| 123 | | 1 a. on 1 a. 9 p. ultramarine (R.) | 3·00 | 50 |
| | | a. Surch in black | † | £950 |
| | | b. Black surch with smaller native characters 7½ mm instead of 10 mm long | † | £1200 |

(iii) *On* 1948–50 *issue*

| | | | | |
|---|---|---|---|---|
| 124 | **30** | 3 p. on 9 p. ultramarine | 1·75 | 1·50 |
| | | a. Larger native characters 20 mm instead of 16½ mm long | 1·75 | 40 |
| | | ab. Imperf between (vert pair) | † | £750 |
| | | b. Surch double | £300 | |
| 125 | | 3 p. on 9 p. ultramarine (R.) | 2·00 | 60 |
| | | a. Incorrect character | 11·00 | 5·00 |
| 126 | | 6 p. on 9 p. ultramarine (R.) | 75 | 40 |
| 119/26 | | *Set of* 8 | 17·00 | 14·00 |

Nos. 122/3 were not issued without surcharge.

**1949.** *Surch as T* **20**. *W* **27**. *P* 13.

127 **29** 6 p. on 1 a. orange . . . . . . . . 48·00 80·00
128 9 p. on 1 a. orange . . . . . . . . 32·00 70·00

From 1 July 1949 Cochin became part of the combined state of Travancore-Cochin.

## OFFICIAL STAMPS

On C G S (O 1) — ON C G S (O 2 Small "ON") — ON C G S (O 3 "G" without serif)

**1913.** *Optd with Type* O **1** (3 *p.*) *or* O **2** (*others*).

O1 **8** 3 p. blue (R.) . . . . . . . . 80·00 10
a. Black opt . . . . † £700
b. Inverted "S" . . . . — 42·00
O2 4 p. green (*wmk sideways*) . . . . 8·00 10
a. Opt inverted . . . . — £190
O3 9 p. carmine . . . . . . 45·00 10
a. Wmk sideways . . . . 13·00 10
O4 $1^1/_2$ a. purple . . . . . . 22·00 10
a. Opt double . . . . £300
O5 2 a. grey . . . . . . 13·00 10
O6 3 a. vermilion . . . . . . 28·00 15
O7 6 a. violet . . . . . . 24·00 2·00
O8 12 a. ultramarine . . . . . . 26·00 5·00
O9 $1^1/_2$ r. deep green . . . . . . 22·00 28·00
O1/9 . . . . . . *Set of* 9 £200 32·00

**1919–33.** *Optd as Type* O **3**.

O10 **10** 4 p. green (*a*) (*b*) . . . . 3·25 10
a. Opt double . . . . £300
O11 6 p. red-brown (*a*) (*b*) (1922) . . . . 5·00 10
a. Opt double . . . . £300
O12 8 p. sepia (*b*) (1923) . . . . 10·00 10
O13 9 p. carmine (*a*) (*b*) . . . . 25·00 10
O14 10 p. blue (*b*) (1923) . . . . 10·00 10
O15 $1^1/_2$ a. purple (*a*) (*b*) (1921) . . . . 5·50 10
O16 2 a. grey (*b*) (1923) . . . . 30·00 10
O17 $2^1/_4$ a. yellow-green (*a*) (*b*) (1922) . . . . 8·00 10
a. Opt double . . . . † £300
O18 3 a. vermilion (*a*) (*b*) (*c*) . . . . 13·00 25
a. Opt inverted . . . . † £300
O19 6 a. violet (*a*) (*b*) (1924) . . . . 24·00 50
O19*a* 12 a. ultramarine (*a*) (*b*) (1929) . . . . 15·00 2·75
O19*b* $1^1/_2$ r. deep green (*a*) (*b*) (1933) . . . . 22·00 50·00
O10/19*b* . . . . *Set of* 12 £150 50·00

8 Eight pies (O 4 $27^1/_2$ mm high) — ON C G S (O 5 Straight back to "C") — ON C G S (O 6 Circular "O"; "N" without serifs)

**1923** (Jan)–**24.** *T* **8** *and* **10** *surch with Type* O **4**.

O20 8 p. on 9 p. carmine (No. O3) . . . . £225 20
a. "Pies" for "pies" (R. 4/8) . . . . £475 45·00
b. Wmk sideways . . . . £110 15
ba. "Pies" for "pies" (R. 4/8) . . . . £275 16·00
c. Surch double . . . . † £275
O21 8 p. on 9 p. carmine (*a*) (*b*) (No. O13) (11.24) . . . . 70·00 10
a. "Pies" for "pies" (R. 4/8) . . . . £180 11·00
b. Surch double . . . . † £275

Varieties with smaller "i" or "t" in "Eight" and small "i" in "Pies" are also known from a number of positions in the setting.

**1925** (Apr). *T* **10** *surch as Type* O **4**.

O22 10 p. on 9 p. carmine (*b*) (No. O13) . . . . 65·00 30
a. Surch inverted . . . .
b. Surch double . . . . † £275
c. Surch 25 mm high (*a*) . . . . £120 75
ca. Surch double . . . . † £300

**1929.** *T* **8** *surch as Type* O **4**.

O23 10 p. on 9 p. carmine (No. O3a) . . . . £400 7·00
a. Surch double . . . . † £300

**1929–31.** *Optd with Type* O **5**.

O24 **10** 4 p. green (*b*) (1931) . . . . 22·00 1·10
a. Inverted "S" . . . . 80·00 9·00
O25 6 p. red-brown (*b*) (*c*) (*d*) (1930) . . . . 10·00 10
a. Inverted "S" . . . . 55·00 3·50
O26 8 p. sepia (*b*) (1930) . . . . 6·00 10
a. Inverted "S" . . . . 35·00 3·50
O27 10 p. blue (*b*) . . . . 6·00 10
a. Inverted "S" . . . . 35·00 4·00
O28 2 a. grey (*b*) (1930) . . . . 14·00 10
a. Inverted "S" . . . . 60·00 5·00
O29 3 a. vermilion (*b*) (1930) . . . . 8·00 15
a. Inverted "S" . . . . 50·00 6·00
O30 6 a. violet (*b*) (*d*) (1930) . . . . 55·00 3·00
a. Inverted "S" . . . . £200 50·00
O24/30 . . . . *Set of* 7 £110 4·00

Pies

No. O32b

**1933.** *Nos.* O26/7 *surch as T* **14**, *in red.*

O32 **10** 6 p. on 8 p. sepia (*b*) . . . . 1·75 10
a. Inverted "S" . . . . 13·00 3·50
b. "3" for "S" in "Pies" . . . .
O33 6 p. on 10 p. blue (*b*) . . . . 4·00 10
a. Inverted "S" . . . . 30·00 3·50

The inverted "S" varieties occur on R.2/1 of one setting of this overprint only.

**1933–38.** *Recess-printed stamps of* 1933–38 *optd.*

(*a*) *With Type* O **5**

O34 **18** 4 p. green . . . . 1·75 10
O35 6 p. red-brown (1934) . . . . 1·75 10
O36 1 a. brown-orange . . . . 8·00 10
O37 1 a. 8 p. carmine . . . . 2·00 10
O38 2 a. grey . . . . 8·00 10
O39 $2^1/_4$ a. yellow-green . . . . 4·00 10
O40 3 a. vermilion . . . . 20·00 10
O41 3 a. 4 p. violet . . . . 1·50 15
O42 6 a. 8 p. sepia . . . . 1·50 15
O43 10 a. blue . . . . 1·50 20
O34/43 . . . . *Set of* 10 45·00 90

(*b*) *With Type* O **6** (*typo*)

O44 **18** 1 a. brown-orange (1937) . . . . 35·00 20
O45 2 a. grey-black (1938) . . . . 15·00 35
O46 3 a. vermilion (1938) . . . . 10·00 40
O44/6 . . . . *Set of* 3 55·00 85

ON C G S (O 7 Curved back to "c") — ON C G S (O 8)

ON C G S (O 9 Circular "O"; N with serifs) — ON C G S (O 10 Oval "O") — ON C G S (O 11)

**1938–44.** *Lithographed stamps of* 1938. *W* **8a**, *optd.*

(*a*) *With Type* O **7** *or* O **8** (1 *a*). I. *P* 11. II. *P* 13 × $13^1/_2$.

| | | | I | | II | |
|---|---|---|---|---|---|---|
| O47 | **18** | 4 p. green | 11·00 | 60 | 11·00 | 1·25 |
| | | a. Inverted "S" | 12·00 | 70 | † | |
| O48 | | 6 p. red-brown | 8·00 | 20 | † | |
| | | a. Inverted "S" | 8·50 | 25 | † | |
| O49 | | 1 a. brown-orange | £200 | 2·50 | † | |
| O50 | | 2 a. grey-black | 6·00 | 30 | † | |
| | | a. Inverted "S" | 6·50 | 35 | † | |

(*b*) *With Type* O **9** (*litho*) *or* O **10** (6 *p.*)

| | | | I | | II | |
|---|---|---|---|---|---|---|
| O51 | **18** | 6 p. red-brown | † | | 3·50 | 90 |
| O52 | | 1 a. brown-orange | 1·00 | 10 | † | |
| O53 | | 3 a. vermilion | 2·75 | 35 | † | |

(*c*) *With Type* O **11**

| | | | I | | II | |
|---|---|---|---|---|---|---|
| O53*a* | **18** | 6 p. red-brown | £650 | £275 | † | |

The inverted "S" varieties, Nos. O47a, O48a and O50a, occur 21 times in the setting of 48.

**1942–43.** *Unissued stamps optd with Type* O **10**. *Litho. W* **27**. I. *P* 11. II. *P* 13×$13^1/_2$.

| | | | I | | II | |
|---|---|---|---|---|---|---|
| O54 | **18** | 4 p. green | 60·00 | 10·00 | 70 | 50 |
| O55 | | 6 p. red-brown | 80·00 | 10·00 | 16·00 | 90 |
| | | a. Optd both sides | † | | † | 80·00 |
| O56 | | 1 a. brown-orange | 16·00 | 5·00 | 1·25 | 2·50 |
| | | a. Optd both sides | † | | — | — |
| O56*b* | | 2 a. grey-black (1943) | 42·00 | 50 | † | |
| | | ba. Opt omitted | † | £600 | † | |
| O56c | | $2^1/_4$ a. sage-green (1943) | £550 | 3·00 | † | |
| O56*d* | | 3 a. vermilion (1943) | 10·00 | 3·00 | † | |

**1943.** *Official stamps variously surch with T* **20** *or* **21**.

(i) *On* $1^1/_2$ *a. purple, of* 1919–33

O57 **10** 9 p. on $1^1/_2$ a. (*b*) (T **20**) . . . . £180 10·00

(ii) *On recess-printed* 1 *a.* 8 *p. carmine of* 1933–44 (*Type* O **5** *opt*)

O58 3 p. on 1 a. 8 p. (T **21**) . . . . 1·00 30
O59 9 p. on 1 a. 8 p. (T **20**) . . . . 90·00 21·00
O60 1 a. 9 p. on 1 a. 8 p. (T **20**) . . . . 80 80
O61 1 a. 9 p. on 1 a. 8 p. (T **21**) . . . . 70 30

(iii) *On lithographed stamps of* 1938–44. *T* **18**. I. *P* 11. II. *P* 13 × $13^1/_2$

(*a*) *W* **8a**

| | | I | | II | |
|---|---|---|---|---|---|
| O62 | 3 p. on 4 p. (Types O **7** and **20**) | † | | 11·00 | 2·75 |
| | a. Surch double | † | | £225 | £130 |
| O63 | 3 p. on 4 p. (Types O **7** and **21**) | † | | 60·00 | 32·00 |
| O64 | 3 p. on 1 a. (Types O **9** and **20**) | 1·75 | 60 | † | |
| O65 | 9 p. on 1 a. (Types O **9** and **20**) | £140 | 35·00 | † | |
| O66 | 1 a. 3 p. on 1 a. (Types O **9** and **21**) | £140 | 75·00 | † | |

(*b*) *W* **27**

| | | I | | II | |
|---|---|---|---|---|---|
| O67 | 3 p. on 4 p. (Types O **10** and **20**) | † | | 55·00 | 35·00 |
| O67*a* | 3 p. on 4 p. (Types O **10** and **21**) | † | | £200 | — |
| O67*b* | 3 p. on 1 a. (Types O **10** and **20**) | 95·00 | 55·00 | 75·00 | 45·00 |

**1944.** *Optd with Type* O **10**. *W* **27**. *P* 13 × $13^1/_2$.

O68 **26** 4 p. green . . . . 8·00 7
a. Perf 11 . . . . 65·00 2·5
b. Perf 13 . . . . £150 40·0
O69 6 p. red-brown . . . . 70 1
a. Opt double . . . . — 55·0
b. Perf 11 . . . . 60 1
c. Perf 13 . . . . 7·00 2·0
O70 1 a. brown-orange . . . . £1100 40·0
O71 2 a. black . . . . 1·25 2
O72 $2^1/_4$ a. yellow-green . . . . 1·50 3
a. Optd both sides . . . . † 90·0
O73 3 a. vermilion . . . . 2·25 4
a. Perf 11 . . . . 2·50 4

Stamps perforated 13 × $13^1/_2$ are from a comb machine; those perforated 13 from a line perforator.

**1944.** *Optd with Type* O **10** *and variously surch as Types* **20** *and* **21**. *W* **27**.

| | | | I | | II | |
|---|---|---|---|---|---|---|
| O74 | **26** | 3 p. on 4 p. (T **20**) | 5·00 | 40 | 1·00 | 10 |
| | | b. Optd Type O **10** on both sides | † | 90·00 | † | |
| O75 | | 3 p. on 4 p. (T **21**) | £275 | £120 | 3·00 | 30 |
| O76 | | 3 p. on 1 a. (T **20**) | † | | 8·00 | 1·40 |
| O77 | | 9 p. on 6 p. (T **20**) | † | | 4·00 | 35 |
| | | a. Stamp printed both sides | † | | — | |
| O78 | | 9 p. on 6 p. (T **21**) | † | | 1·50 | 15 |
| O79 | | 1 a. 3 p. on 1 a. (T **20**) | † | | 3·00 | 20 |
| O80 | | 1 a. 3 p. on 1 a. (T **21**) | † | | 2·25 | 10 |
| O74/80 | | *Set of* 7 | † | | 20·00 | 2·00 |

**1946–47.** *Stamps of* 1944-48 *optd with Type* O **10**. *Type* II. *P* 13.

O81 **28** 9 p. ultramarine . . . . 75 10
a. Stamp printed both sides . . . . † £170
b. Perf 13 × $13^1/_2$ . . . . 1·40 10
O82 1 a. 3 p. magenta (1947) . . . . 45 15
a. Opt double . . . . 17·00 12·00
b. Optd both sides, opt double on reverse . . . . 30·00
O83 1 a. 9 p. ultramarine (1947) . . . . 35 15
a. Opt double . . . .
O81b/83 . . . . *Set of* 3 1·40 30

**1948.** *Stamps of* 1946–48 *and unissued values optd with Type* O **2**. *P* 13.

O84 **29** 3 p. carmine . . . . 30 10
a. Stamp printed both sides . . . . † —
O85 4 p. grey-green . . . . 13·00 4·00
O86 6 p. red-brown . . . . 3·00 20
O87 9 p. ultramarine . . . . 75 10
O88 1 a. 3 p. magenta . . . . 1·25 20
O89 1 a. 9 p. ultramarine . . . . 1·40 40
O90 2 a. black . . . . 10·00 1·50
O91 $2^1/_4$ a. yellow-green . . . . 11·00 1·25
O84/91 . . . . *Set of* 8 38·00 7·00

**1949.** *Stamps of* 1948–50 *and unissued values optd with Type* O **7**.

O92 **30** 3 p. carmine . . . . 30 10
a. "C" for "G" in opt . . . . 5·00 2·50
O93 4 p. green . . . . 50 15
a. Imperf between (pair) . . . . † £650
b. Optd on reverse . . . . 45·00 45·00
c. "C" for "G" in opt . . . . 7·00 2·50
O94 6 p. chestnut . . . . 1·00 10
a. Imperf between (vert pair) . . . . † £800
b. "C" for "G" in opt . . . . 10·00 2·50
O95 9 p. ultramarine . . . . 50 10
a. "C" for "G" in opt . . . . 7·00 2·50
O96 2 a. black . . . . 60 15
a. "C" for "G" in opt . . . . 8·00 3·00
O97 $2^1/_4$ a. yellow-green . . . . 1·25 1·75
a. "C" for "G" in opt . . . . 12·00 12·00
O98 3 a. orange-red . . . . 1·10 30
a. "C" for "G" in opt . . . . 11·00 5·00
O99 3 a. 4 p. violet . . . . 10·00 12·00
a. "C" for "G" in opt . . . . 85·00 85·00
O92/9 . . . . *Set of* 8 14·00 13·00

The "C" for "G" variety occurs on R. 1/4. Nos. O92/9, O103/4 and O104b also exist with a flat back to "G" which occurs twice on the sheet.

**1949.** *Official stamps surch as T* **33**. (i) *On 1944 issue.*

O100 **28** 1 a. on 1 a. 9 p. ultramarine (R.) . . . . 60 15

(ii) *On 1948 issue*

O101 **29** 1 a. on 1 a. 9 p. ultramarine (R.) . . . . 9·00 6·00

(iii) *On 1949 issue*

O103 **30** 6 p. on 3 p. carmine . . . . 30 30
a. Imperf between (vert pair) . . . . † £550
b. Surch double . . . . † £250
c. "C" for "G" in opt . . . . 5·00 5·00
d. Incorrect character . . . . 5·50 5·50
O104 9 p. on 4 p. green (18 *mm long*) . . . . 50 50
a. Imperf between (horiz pair) . . . . £450
b. Larger native characters, 22 mm long . . . . 60 40
ba. Ditto. Imperf between (horiz pair) . . . . £450 £450
bb. Incorrect character . . . . 8·00 8·00
c. "C" for "G" in opt . . . . 7·00 7·00
ca. Ditto. Larger native characters, 22 mm long . . . . 7·00 7·00
O100/4 . . . . *Set of* 4 9·50 6·25

**1949.** *No.* 124*a*, *but with lines of surch* $17^1/_2$ *mm apart, optd* "SERVICE".

O105 **30** 3 p. on 9 p. ultramarine . . . . 60 40

For later issues see TRAVANCORE-COCHIN

## DHAR

**PRICES FOR STAMPS ON COVER**
The stamps of Dhar are rare used on cover.

1

2

अर्धा बलड. No. 1c — अर्धा लबड. No. 1d — आर्धा डबल. No. 2

**1897–1900.** *Type-set. Colour-fugitive paper. With oval handstamp in black. No gum. Imperf.*
1 1 ½ p. black/*red* (three characters at bottom left) .. .. .. .. 80 80
a. Handstamp omitted .. .. .. £140
b. Line below upper inscription (R.2/2) 55·00 55·00
c. Character transposed (R.2/3) .. 14·00 15·00
d. Character transposed (R.2/5) .. 55·00
2 ½ p. black/*red* (four characters at bottom left) .. .. .. .. .. 70 1·00
a. Handstamp omitted .. .. .. £120
3 ¼ a. black/*orange* .. .. .. 1·00 1·75
a. Handstamp omitted .. .. .. £140
4 ½ a. black/*magenta* .. .. .. 1·10 1·90
a. Handstamp omitted .. .. .. £140 £140
b. Line below upper inscription (R.2/2) 85·00 95·00
5 1 a. black/*green* .. .. .. .. 2·75 5·00
a. Handstamp omitted .. .. .. £225
b. Printed both sides .. .. ..
c. Line below upper inscription (R.2/2) £130 £140
6 2 a. black/*yellow* .. .. .. 15·00 30·00
e. Top right corner ornament transposed with one from top of frame (R.2/5) .. .. .. .. £100 £130
1/6 .. .. .. .. .. *Set of* 6 19·00 38·00

Nos. 1/6 were each issued in sheets of 10 (5 × 2), but may, on the evidence of a single sheet of the ½ pice value, have been printed in sheets of 20 containing two of the issued sheets *tête-bêche*.

Research has identified individual characteristics for stamps printed from each position in the sheet.

The same research suggests that the type remained assembled during the entire period of production, being amended as necessary to provide the different values. Seven main settings have been identified with changes sometimes occurring during their use which form sub-settings.

The distribution of stamps between the main settings was as follows:
Setting I—½ p.
Setting II—½ a., 1 a.
Setting III—1 a.
Setting IV—½ p., ½ a., 1 a.
Setting V—½ p.
Setting VI—½ p. (No. 2), ¼ a.
Setting VII—2 a.

The listed constant errors all occurred during Setting IV.

In No. 1c the three characters forming the second word in the lower inscription are transposed to the order (2) (3) (1) and in No. 1d to the order (3) (2) (1).

On Nos. 1b, 4b and 5c the line which normally appears above the upper inscription is transposed so that it appears below the characters.

All values show many other constant varieties including mistakes in the corner and border ornaments, and also both constant and non-constant missing lines, dots and characters.

Examples of complete forgeries and faked varieties on genuine stamps exist.

(Typo at Bombay)

**1898–1900.** *P* 11 *to* 12.
7 2 ½ a. carmine .. .. .. .. 1·25 2·50
a. Imperf (pair) .. .. .. .. 35·00
*b. Deep rose* .. .. .. .. 90 2·25
8 1 a. claret .. .. .. .. 90 2·25
9 1 a. reddish violet .. .. .. 2·00 6·50
a. Imperf between (horiz pair) .. .. £350
b. Imperf (pair) .. .. .. .. £100
10 2 a. deep green .. .. .. .. 3·25 12·00
7/10 .. .. .. .. .. *Set of* 4 6·50 21·00

The stamps of Dhar have been obsolete since 31 March 1901.

## DUNGARPUR

**PRICES FOR STAMPS ON COVER**
Nos. 1/15 *from* × 2

1 State Arms

(Litho Shri Lakshman Bijaya Printing Press, Dungarpur)

**1933–48.** *P* 11.
1 1 ¼ a. bistre-yellow .. .. .. .. — 65·00
2 ¼ a. rose (1935) .. .. .. .. — £150
3 ¼ a. red-brown (1937) .. .. .. — £130
4 1 a. pale turquoise-blue .. .. .. — 65·00
5 1 a. rose (1938) .. .. .. .. — £450
6 1 a. 3 p. deep reddish violet (1935) .. .. — 90·00
7 2 a. deep dull green (1947) .. .. — £110
8 4 a. rose-red (1934) .. .. .. — £160

Nos. 2 and 5 are known in a *se-tenant* strip of 3, the centre stamp being the 1 a. value.

2

3

4

Maharawal Sir Shri Lakshman Singh Bahadur

Two dies of ½ a.:
Die I. Large portrait. Width of face 5 mm.
Die II. Small portrait. Width of face 4.5 mm.

(Typo L. V. Indap & Co, Bombay)

**1932–46.** *T* **2** (*various frames*) *and* **3**/**4**. *Various perfs.*
9 2 ¼ a. orange (*p* 12, 11, 10½ *or* 10) (1939) .. £170 26·00
10 ½ a. vermilion (Die I) (*p* 12, 11 *or* 10½) .. £110 24·00
a. Die II (*p* 10) (1944) .. .. £110 24·00
b. Imperf between (vert pair) .. .. † —
11 1 a. deep blue (*p* 12, 11, 10½ *or* 10) (1936) £110 16·00
12 3 1 a. 3 p. bright mauve (*p* 10½ *or* 10) (1944) £225 75·00
13 4 1½ a. deep violet (*p* 10) (1946) .. .. £225 85·00
14 2 2 a. bright green (*p* 12) (1943) .. .. £275 £150
15 4 a. brown (*p* 12, 10½ *or* 10) (1941) .. £225 60·00

Stamps perforated 12, 11 and 10½ were printed in sheets of 12 (4×3) which were imperforate along the top, bottom and, sometimes, at right so that examples exist with one or two adjacent sides imperforate. Stamps perforated 10 were printed in sheets of 4 either imperforate at top, bottom and right-hand side or fully perforated.

## DUTTIA (DATIA)

**PRICES FOR STAMPS ON COVER**
Nos. 1/15 —
Nos. 16/40 *from* × 30

All the stamps of Duttia were impressed with a circular handstamp (as a rule in *blue*) before issue.

This handstamp shows the figure of Ganesh in the centre, surrounded by an inscription in Devanagari reading "DATIYA STET POSTAJ 1893". Stamps could not be used for postage without this control mark.

**PROCESS.** Nos. 1/15 were type-set and printed singly. Nos. 16/40 were typo from plates comprising 8 or more clichés.

**GUM.** The stamps of Duttia (*except No.* 25b) were issued without gum.

1 (4 a.) Ganesh.

2 (½ a.)

2*a* (2 a.)

**1893.** *Each with control handstamp in blue as shown on T* **2**. *Imperf.*
1 1 ¼ a. black/*orange* .. .. .. .. £1900
a. Without handstamp .. .. .. £1500
2 ½ a. black/*blue-green* .. .. .. £2250
a. Without handstamp .. .. .. £1500
3 2 1 a. red .. .. .. .. £1900
a. Handstamp in black .. .. .. £1900
4 1 2 a. black/*yellow* .. .. .. £1700
5 4 a. black/*rose* .. .. .. £1300

**1896?** *Rosettes in lower corners. Imperf.*
5*a* 2*a* ½ a. black/*green* (blue handstamp) .. £3750
5*b* 2 a. grey-blue/*yellow* (black handstamp) £2250

Only two examples of No. 5*a* have been reported. As originally printed an incorrect third character transformed the face value into eight annas, but this was corrected to half anna in manuscript.

**1897?** *Imperf.*
6 2 ½ a. black/*green* .. .. .. .. 13·00 75·00
a. *Tête-bêche* (vert pair) .. .. £450
b. Value in one group .. .. .. 27·00
ba. *Tête-bêche* (horiz pair) .. .. £400
7 1 a. black/*white* .. .. .. .. 50·00 95·00
a. *Tête-bêche* (pair) .. .. .. £600
b. Laid paper .. .. .. .. 10·00
8 2 a. black/*yellow* .. .. .. .. 17·00 80·00
9 2 a. black/*lemon* .. .. .. .. 24·00
10 4 a. black/*rose* .. .. .. .. 15·00 70·00
a. *Tête-bêche* (pair) .. .. .. £140

3 (½ a.)

4 (¼ a.)

**1897.** *Name spelt* "DATIA." *Imperf.*
12 3 ½ a. black/*green* .. .. .. .. 50·00
13 1 a. black/*white* .. .. .. .. £110
14 2 a. black/*yellow* .. .. .. .. 60·00
a. *Tête-bêche* (vert pair) .. .. .. £1000
15 4 a. black/*rose* .. .. .. .. 55·00
a. *Tête-bêche* (vert pair) .. .. .. £1000
12/15 .. .. .. .. .. *Set of* 4 £250

**1899–1906.**
(*a*) *Rouletted in colour or in black, horizontally and at end of rows*
16 4 ¼ a. vermilion .. .. .. .. 1·75
*a. Rose-red* .. .. .. .. 1·25
*b. Pale rose* .. .. .. .. 1·10
*c. Lake* .. .. .. .. 1·25 4·50
*d. Carmine* .. .. .. .. 2·00
*e. Brownish red* .. .. .. .. 4·50
ea. *Tête-bêche* (pair) .. .. .. £2500
17 ½ a. black/*blue-green* .. .. .. 1·40 4·50
*a. On deep green* .. .. .. 2·00
*b. On yellow-green (pelure)* .. .. 2·25 5·50
*c. On dull green* (1906) .. .. .. 1·25
18 1 a. black/*white* .. .. .. .. 1·10 4·50
19 2 a. black/*lemon-yellow* .. .. .. 2·50
*a. On orange-yellow* .. .. .. 3·75
*b. On buff-yellow* .. .. .. 1·75 6·50
*c. On pale yellow* (1906) .. .. .. 2·25 6·50
20 4 a. black/*deep rose* .. .. .. 1·40 6·50
a. *Tête-bêche* (pair) .. .. ..

(*b*) *Rouletted in colour between horizontal rows, but imperf at top and bottom and at ends of rows*
20*b* 4 ¼ a. brownish red .. .. .. .. 17·00
21 1 a. black/*white* .. .. .. .. 10·00

**1904–5.** *Without rouletting.*
22 4 ¼ a. red .. .. .. .. 1·75
23 ½ a. black/*green* .. .. .. .. 7·50
24 1 a. black (1905) .. .. .. .. 5·00 14·00

**1911.** *P* 13½. *Stamps very wide apart.*
25 4 ¼ a. carmine .. .. .. .. 2·50
a. Imperf horiz (vert pair) .. .. £130
b. Stamps closer together (with gum) 4·25 12·00
c. As b. Imperf vert (horiz pair) .. £100
25*d* 1 a. black .. .. .. .. £500

**1912?** *Printed close together.* (*a*) *Coloured roulette × imperf.*
26 4 ½ a. black/*green* .. .. .. .. 5·50

(*b*) *Printed wide apart. P* 13½ × *coloured roulette.* (¼ a.) *or* 13½ × *imperf* (½ a.)
27 4 ¼ a. carmine .. .. .. .. 2·50
28 ½ a. black/*dull green* .. .. .. 6·00 15·00

**1916.** *Colours changed. Imperf.*
29 4 ¼ a. deep blue .. .. .. .. 3·00 8·00
30 ½ a. green .. .. .. .. 2·75 10·00
31 1 a. purple .. .. .. .. 3·50 11·00
a. *Tête-bêche* (pair) .. .. .. 18·00
32 2 a. brown .. .. .. .. 7·00 16·00
33 2 a. lilac .. .. .. .. 5·00 16·00
34 4 a. Venetian red (date?) .. .. .. 60·00

**1918.** *Colours changed.* (*a*) *Imperf.*
35 4 ½ a. blue .. .. .. .. 1·00 5·00
36 1 a. pink .. .. .. .. 1·40 6·50

(*b*) *P* 11½
37 4 ¼ a. black .. .. .. .. 3·50 8·00

**1920.** *Rouletted.*
38 4 ¼ a. blue .. .. .. .. 1·00 4·50
a. Roul × perf 7 .. .. .. 28·00 28·00
39 ½ a. pink .. .. .. .. 1·25 6·00
a. Roul × perf 7 .. .. .. 85·00

**1920?** *Rough perf about* 7.
40 4 ½ a. dull red .. .. .. .. 4·00 11·00

## FARIDKOT

**PRICES FOR STAMPS ON COVER**
Nos. N1/4 *from* × 10
Nos. N5/8 *from* × 30

**GUM.** The stamps of Faridkot (Nos. N1/8) were issued without gum.

N 1 (1 folus)

N 2 (1 paisa)

N 3

**1879–86.** *Rough, handstamped impression. Imperf.*

*(a) Native thick laid paper*

N1 N 1 1 f. ultramarine .. .. .. .. 27·00 30·00
N2 N 2 1 p. ultramarine .. .. .. .. 65·00 70·00

*(b) Ordinary laid paper*

N3 N 1 1 f. ultramarine .. .. .. .. 14·00 16·00
N4 N 2 1 p. ultramarine .. .. .. .. 42·00 55·00

*(c) Wove paper, thick to thinnish*

N5 N 1 1 f. ultramarine .. .. .. .. 1·00 1·50
a. *Tête-bêche* (pair) .. .. .. .. £160
N6 N 2 1 p. ultramarine .. .. .. .. 1·50 3·75
a. Pair, one stamp sideways .. .. £400

*(d) Thin wove whity brown paper*

N7 N 2 1 p. ultramarine .. .. .. .. 16·00 18·00

*(e) Wove paper*

N8 N 3 1 p. ultramarine .. .. .. .. 1·25
a. *Tête-bêche* (pair) .. .. .. .. £160

It is doubtful whether stamps of Type N 3 were ever used for postage.

Impressions of these types in various colours, the ½ a. labels, and the later printings from re-engraved dies, were never in circulation at all.

Faridkot became a convention state and from 1887 used the Indian stamps overprinted which are listed under the Convention States.

## HYDERABAD

**PRICES FOR STAMPS ON COVER**

| | |
|---|---|
| Nos. 1/3 | *from* × 10 |
| Nos. 4/12 | — |
| Nos. 13/60 | *from* × 5 |
| Nos. O1/53 | *from* × 10 |

The official title of the State in English was The Dominions of the Nizam and in Urdu "Sarkar-i-Asafia" (State of the successors of Asaf). This Urdu inscription appears in many of the designs.

1

2

(Eng Mr. Rapkin. Plates by Nissen & Parker, London. Recess Mint, Hyderabad)

**1869** (8 Sept). *P* 11½.

1 1 1 a. olive-green .. .. .. .. 8·50 6·00
a. Imperf between (horiz pair) .. £110
b. Imperf horiz (vert pair) .. .. £120 £100
c. Imperf (pair) .. .. .. .. £130 £130

Reprints in the colour of the issue, and also in fancy colours, were made in 1880 on white wove paper, perforated 12½.

**1870** (16 May). *Locally engraved; 240 varieties of each value; wove paper. Recess. P* 11½.

2 2 ½ a. brown .. .. .. .. .. 4·00 4·00
3 2 a. sage-green .. .. .. .. .. 35·00 30·00

Stamps exist showing traces of lines in the paper, but they do not appear to be printed on true laid paper.

Reprints of both values were made in 1880 on white wove paper, perforated 12½: the ½ a. in grey-brown, yellow-brown, sea-green and dull blue, and the 2 a. in bright green and in blue-green.

3

A Normal 2 a. B Variety

In A the coloured lines surrounding each of the four labels join a coloured circle round their inner edge, in B this circle is missing.

C 3 a. D

C. Normal
D. Character ‸ omitted

(Plates by Bradbury, Wilkinson & Co. Recess Mint, Hyderabad)

**1871–1909.** *(a) No wmk. (i) Rough perf* 11½.

4 3 ½ a. red-brown .. .. .. .. 16·00 16·00
5 1 a. purple-brown .. .. .. .. 75·00 80·00
6 2 a. green (A) .. .. .. .. £300
7 3 a. ochre-brown .. .. .. .. 27·00 30·00
8 4 a. slate .. .. .. .. 90·00 95·00
9 8 a. deep brown .. .. .. ..
10 12 a. dull blue .. .. .. .. £180

*(ii) Pin-perf* 8–9

11 3 ½ a. red-brown .. .. .. .. — £150
12 1 a. drab .. .. .. .. £170 £100

*(iii) P* 12½

13 3 ½ a. orange-brown .. .. .. 30 10
a. Imperf vert (horiz pair) .. .. † 65·00
ab. Imperf horiz (vert pair) .. .. † £130
b. *Brick-red* .. .. .. 30 10
ba. Imperf vert (horiz pair) .. .. † 65·00
bb. Doubly printed .. .. .. † 80·00
c. *Rose-red* .. .. .. 30 10
d. Error. Magenta .. .. .. 35·00 8·00
14 1 a. purple-brown .. .. .. 1·75 2·25
a. Doubly printed .. .. .. 95·00
b. *Drab* .. .. .. 30 10
ba. Imperf (pair) .. .. .. — £140
bb. Doubly printed .. .. .. 95·00
c. *Grey-black* .. .. .. 30 10
d. *Black* (1909) .. .. .. 30 10
da. Doubly printed .. .. .. 95·00
db. Imperf vert (horiz pair) .. .. † £140
dc. Imperf horiz (vert pair) .. .. † £140
15 2 a. green (A) .. .. .. 65 10
a. *Deep green* (A) .. .. .. 95 15
b. *Blue-green* (A) .. .. .. 80 30
ba. *Blue-green* (B) .. .. .. 75·00 55·00
c. *Pale green* (A) .. .. .. 85 10
ca. *Pale green* (B) .. .. .. 65·00 45·00
d. *Sage-green* (A) (1909) .. .. 65 20
da. *Sage-green* (B) .. .. .. — 42·00
16 3 a. ochre-brown (C) .. .. .. 90 50
a. *Chestnut* (C) .. .. .. 40 45
aa. Character omitted (D) .. .. 95·00 55·00
17 4 a. slate .. .. .. 2·00 1·10
a. Imperf horiz (vert pair) .. .. £350 £350
b. *Greenish grey* .. .. .. 1·00 70
ba. Imperf vert (horiz pair) .. .. £375
c. *Olive-green* .. .. .. 2·00 1·00
18 8 a. deep brown .. .. .. 1·25 1·25
a. Imperf vert (horiz pair) .. .. £400
19 12 a. pale ultramarine .. .. .. 2·25 2·50
a. *Grey-green* .. .. .. 2·00 2·25
13/19 .. .. .. .. *Set of* 7 5·25 4·50

*(b) W* **7**. *P* 12½

19*b* 3 1 a. black (1909) .. .. .. 70·00 5·50
19*c* 2 a. sage-green (A) (1909) .. .. — 28·00
*ca. Sage-green* (B) .. .. ..

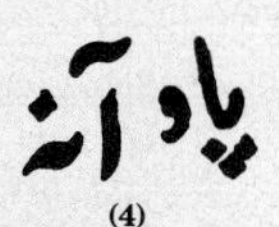

(4)

5

**1898.** *Surch with T* **4**. *P* 12½.

20 3 ¼ a. on ½ a. orange-brown .. .. 50 75
a. Surch inverted .. .. .. 25·00 20·00
b. Pair, one without surcharge .. £200

(Des Khusrat Ullah. Recess Mint, Hyderabad)

**1900** (20 Sept). *P* 12½.

21 5 ¼ a. deep blue .. .. .. .. 3·00 1·90
*a. Pale blue* .. .. .. .. 3·00 1·90

6

7

(Plates by Allan G. Wyon, London. Recess Mint, Hyderabad.)

**1905** (7 Aug). *Wmk T* **7**. *P* 12½.

22 6 ¼ a. dull blue .. .. .. .. 1·25 30
a. Imperf (pair) .. .. .. 28·00 50·00
b. *Dull ultramarine* .. .. .. 4·00 60
ba. Perf 11 × 12½ .. .. .. 15·00 15·00
c. *Pale blue-green* .. .. .. 9·00 1·25
23 ½ a. orange .. .. .. .. 2·50 30
a. Perf 11 .. .. .. ..
b. *Vermilion* .. .. .. .. 1·50 25
ba. Imperf (pair) .. .. .. 26·00 50·00
c. *Yellow* .. .. .. .. 50·00 15·00

**1908–11.** *W* **7**. *Various perfs, also compound.*

A. *Perf* 12½. B. *Perf* 11½, 12

| No. | Type | | A | | B | |
|---|---|---|---|---|---|---|
| 24 | 6 | ¼ a. grey .. .. .. | 45 | 10 | 2·00 | 15 |
| | | a. Imperf between (horiz pair) .. .. | 95·00 | 95·00 | † | |
| | | b. Imperf between (vert pair) .. .. | † | 95·00 | † | |
| 25 | | ½ a. green .. .. .. | 90 | 10 | 2·25 | 10 |
| | | a. *Pale green* .. .. | 90 | 20 | 2·25 | 10 |
| | | b. *Blue-green* .. .. | 5·00 | 90 | † | |
| | | c. Imperf between (vert pair) .. .. | 95·00 | — | † | |
| 26 | 6 | 1 a. carmine .. .. | 1·00 | 10 | 2·25 | 30 |
| | | a. Double impression, Perf 12½ × 11 .. | — | — | † | |
| 27 | | 2 a. lilac .. .. | 75 | 10 | 3·00 | 60 |
| 28 | | 3 a. brown-orange (1909) .. | 1·10 | 20 | 5·50 | 1·25 |
| 29 | | 4 a. olive-green (1909) .. | 1·00 | 20 | 6·50 | 2·00 |
| 30 | | 8 a. purple (1911) .. .. | 3·00 | 2·50 | — | — |
| 31 | | 12 a. blue-green (1911) .. | 27·00 | 14·00 | 4·00 | 5·00 |

C. *Perf* 11. D. *Perf* 13½

| No. | Type | | C | | D | |
|---|---|---|---|---|---|---|
| 24 | 6 | ¼ a. grey .. .. .. | 24·00 | 13·00 | † | |
| 25 | | ½ a. green .. .. | † | | 45·00 | 22·00 |
| 26 | | 1 a. carmine .. .. | 16·00 | 8·00 | † | |
| 27 | | 2 a. lilac .. .. | 2·50 | 35 | 1·40 | 10 |
| | | a. Imperf between (horiz pair) .. .. | † | | † | £120 |
| | | b. *Rose-lilac* .. .. | † | | 1·10 | 10 |
| 28 | | 3 a. brown-orange (1909) .. | 85 | 30 | 1·25 | 20 |
| 29 | | 4 a. olive-green (1909) .. | 16·00 | 4·00 | 85 | 20 |
| | | a. Imperf between (pair) | £180 | £180 | † | |
| 30 | | 8 a. purple (1911) .. .. | 1·75 | 1·25 | 1·10 | 30 |
| 31 | | 12 a. blue-green (1911) .. | — | — | 3·00 | 75 |

**1912.** *New plates eng by Bradbury, Wilkinson & Co. Perfs as before, or compound.*

| No. | Type | | A | | B | |
|---|---|---|---|---|---|---|
| 32 | 6 | ¼ a. grey-black .. .. | 80 | 10 | 50 | 20 |
| | | a. Imperf horiz (vert pair) | † | 95·00 | † | |
| 34 | | ½ a. deep green .. .. | 40 | 10 | 2·25 | 30 |
| | | a. Imperf between (pair) | † | 95·00 | † | |
| | | b. Laid paper. Imperf (pair) .. .. .. | 55·00 | 55·00 | † | |

| No. | Type | | C | | D | |
|---|---|---|---|---|---|---|
| 32 | 6 | ¼ a. grey-black .. .. | 70 | 10 | 30 | 10 |
| | | b. Imperf between (horiz pair) .. .. | † | 95·00 | † | |
| | | c. Imperf between (vert pair) .. .. | † | 95·00 | † | |
| 33 | | ¼ a. brown-purple (*shades*) | † | | 30 | 10 |
| | | a. Imperf horiz (vert pair) | † | | † | 95·00 |
| 34 | | ½ a. deep green .. .. | 2·50 | 10 | — | — |
| | | a. Imperf between (pair) | — | — | — | — |

In Wyon's ¼ a. stamp the fraction of value is closer to the end of the label than in the B.W. issue. In the Wyon ¼ a. and ½ a. the value in English and the label below are further apart than in the B.W.

Wyon's ¼ a. measures 19½ × 20 mm and the ½ a. 19½ × 20½ mm; both stamps from the Bradbury plates measure 19¾ × 21½ mm.

8 Symbols

9

**1915.** *Inscr* "Post & Receipt". *Various perfs as above, and compound.*

| No. | Type | | A | | C | |
|---|---|---|---|---|---|---|
| 35 | 8 | ½ a. green .. .. | 5·00 | 35 | 60 | 10 |
| | | a. Imperf between (pair) .. | — | — | † | 85·00 |
| | | b. Imperf (pair) .. .. | 70·00 | 50·00 | † | |
| 36 | | 1 a. carmine .. .. | 5·50 | 85 | 75 | 20 |
| | | a. Imperf between (pair) .. | — | — | † | |
| | | b. Imperf (pair) .. .. | 80·00 | 65·00 | † | |
| | | c. Perf 12½ × 11 .. | 5·50 | 3·50 | † | |
| | | d. *Scarlet* .. .. | — | — | — | 10·00 |

D

35 8 ½ a. green .. .. .. .. 60 10
a. Imperf between (pair) .. .. 42·00 42·00
c. *Emerald-green* .. .. .. 3·00 1·00
36 1 a. carmine .. .. .. .. 75 10
a. Imperf between (pair) .. .. 85·00
d. *Scarlet* .. .. .. .. 1·00 10
da. Imperf between (horiz pair) .. † 85·00
db. Imperf horiz (vert pair) .. .. † 85·00

For ½ a. claret, see No. 58.

**1927** (1 Feb). *As W* **7** *but larger. P* 13½.

37 9 1 r. yellow .. .. .. .. 9·00 11·00

چارپائی

**10** (4 pies)

آٹھ پائی

**11** (8 pies)

**1930** (6 May). *Surch as T* **10** *and* **11**. *W* **7**. *P* 13½.

38 6 4 p. on ¼ a. grey-black (R.) .. .. 38·00 11·00
a. Perf 11 .. .. .. .. † £150
b. Perf 12½ .. .. .. .. † 55·00
39 4 p. on ¼ a. brown-purple (R.) .. 10 10
a. Imperf between (pair) .. .. £275 £275
b. Surch double .. .. .. † —
c. Perf 11 .. .. .. .. † £300
d. Black surch .. .. .. £300 £300
40 8 8 p. on ½ a. green (R.) .. .. .. 10 10
a. Imperf between (horiz pair) .. † £100
b. Perf 11 .. .. .. .. £150 £100
c. Perf 12½ .. .. .. .. † £200

12 Symbols

13 The Char Minar

14 Bidar College

(Plates by De La Rue. Recess Stamps Office, Hyderabad)

**931** (12 Nov)–**47.** *T* **12** *to* **14** *(and similar types).* *W* **7**. *Wove paper.* *P* 13½.

1 12 4 p. black .. .. .. .. 20 10
a. Laid paper (1947) .. .. .. 2·50 4·00
b. Imperf (pair) .. .. .. 48·00 65·00
2 8 p. green .. .. .. .. 30 10
a. Imperf between (vert pair) .. .. — £550
b. Imperf (pair) .. .. .. 60·00 80·00
c. Laid paper (1947) .. .. .. 3·00 3·50
3 13 1 a. brown *(shades)* .. .. .. 20 10
a. Imperf between (horiz pair) .. .. — £550
4 – 2 a. violet *(shades)* .. .. .. 1·00 10
a. Imperf (pair) .. .. .. £130 £170
5 – 4 a. ultramarine .. .. .. 90 15
a. Imperf (pair) .. .. .. £160 £200
6 – 8 a. orange .. .. .. 2·00 1·10
*a. Yellow-orange* (1944) .. .. 42·00 26·00
7 14 12 a. scarlet .. .. .. 3·00 4·50
8 – 1 r. yellow .. .. .. 3·00 2·50
1/8 .. .. .. .. *Set of* 8 9·50 7·50

Designs *(as T* **14**): *Horiz*—2 a. High Court of Justice; 4 a. Osman agar Reservoir. *Vert*—8 a. Entrance to Ajanta Caves; 1 r. Victory ower, Daulatabad.

Nos. 41a and 42c have a large sheet watermark "NIZAM's OVERNMENT" and arms, but this does not appear on all stamps.

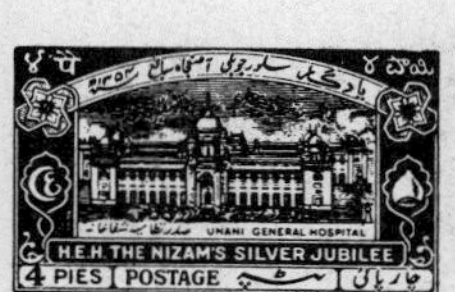

15 Unani General Hospital

16 Family Reunion

(Litho Indian Security Printing Press, Nasik)

**937** (13 Feb). *Various horiz designs as T* **15**, *inscr* "H.E.H. THE NIZAM'S SILVER JUBILEE". *P* 14.

9 4 p. slate and violet .. .. .. 15 30
0 8 p. slate and brown .. .. .. 20 40
1 1 a. slate and orange-yellow .. .. 30 30
2 2 a. slate and green .. .. .. 50 1·10
9/52 .. .. .. *Set of* 4 1·00 1·90

Designs:—8 p. Osmania General Hospital; 1 a. Osmania University; 2 a. Osmania Jubilee Hall.

(Des T. I. Archer. Typo)

**945** (6 Dec). *Victory.* *W* **7** *(very faint).* *Wove paper.* *P* 13½.

53 16 1 a. blue .. .. .. .. 10 10
a. Imperf between (vert pair) .. .. £475
b. Laid paper .. .. .. 30 35

No. 53b has a large sheet wmk reading "HYDERABAD GOVERNMENT", in circular frame, but parts of this do not appear on all stamps.

17 Town Hall

18 Power House, Hyderabad

(Des. T. I. Archer. Litho Government Press)

**947** (17 Feb). *Reformed Legislature.* *P* 13½.

54 17 1 a. black .. .. .. 30 30
a. Imperf between (pair) .. .. — £650

(Des T. I. Archer. Typo)

**1947–49.** *As T* **18** *(inscr* "H. E. H. THE NIZAM'S GOVT. POSTAGE"). *W* **7**. *P* 13½.

55 1 a. 4 p. green .. .. .. 40 50
56 3 a. greenish blue .. .. .. 40 65
*a. Bluish green* .. .. .. 50 65
57 6 a. sepia .. .. .. 3·00 5·00
*a. Red-brown* (1949) .. .. 18·00 22·00
ab. Imperf (pair) .. .. .. 80·00
55/7 .. .. .. *Set of* 3 3·50 5·50

Designs:—3 a. Kaktyai Arch, Warangal Fort; 6 a. Golkunda Fort.

**1947.** *As 1915 issue but colour changed.* *P* 13½.

58 8 ½ a. claret .. .. .. 50 50
a. Imperf between (horizontal pair) .. — £275
b. Imperf between (vert pair) .. — £300

An Independence commemorative set of four, 4 p., 8 p., 1 a. and 2 a., was prepared in 1947, but not issued.

**1948.** *As T* **12** ("POSTAGE" *at foot*). *Recess.* *W* **7**. *P* 13½.

59 6 p. claret .. .. .. 2·50 2·00

Following intervention by the forces of the Dominion of India during September 1948 the Hyderabad postal system was taken over by the Dominion authorities, operating as an agency of the India Post Office.

**1949.** *T* **12** ("POSTAGE" *at top*). *Litho.* *W* **7**. *P* 13½.

60 12 2 p. bistre-brown .. .. .. 1·00 1·10
a. Imperf between (horizontal pair) .. † £475
b. Imperf (pair) .. .. .. £475 £475

No. 60 was prepared by altering a plate of No. 41, each impression being amended individually.

## OFFICIAL STAMPS

Official stamps became valid for postage within India from 1910.

سرکاری (O 1) سرکاری (O 1a) سرکاری (O 2)

**1873.** I. *Handstamped as Type* O **1**. A. *In red.* B. *In black.*

| | | | A | | B | |
|---|---|---|---|---|---|---|
| O1 1 | 1 a. olive-green .. | .. | 30·00 | 16·00 | — | — |
| O2 2 | ½ a. brown .. | .. | — | £100 | — | 75·00 |
| O3 | 2 a. sage-green .. | .. | — | £180 | — | 95·00 |

Varieties of Type O 1 occur.

Imitations of these overprints on genuine stamps and on reprints are found horizontally or vertically in various shades of red, in magenta and in black.

II. *T* **3** *optd as Type* O **1**. A. *In red.* B. *In black.*
*(a) Rough perf* 11½.

| | | A | | B | |
|---|---|---|---|---|---|
| O 4 | ½ a. red-brown .. | — | — | — | — |
| O 5 | 1 a. purple-brown .. | — | — | £110 | £110 |
| O 6 | 2 a. green (A) .. | — | — | — | £350 |
| O 7 | 4 a. slate .. | — | — | — | — |
| O 8 | 8 a. deep brown .. | — | — | — | £400 |

*(b) Pin perf* 8–9

| | | A | | B | |
|---|---|---|---|---|---|
| O 8*a* | 1 a. drab .. | † | | 6·50 | 70·00 |

*(c) P* 12½

| | | A | | B | |
|---|---|---|---|---|---|
| O 9 | ½ a. red-brown .. | 3·25 | 2·50 | 2·25 | 1·00 |
| | a. Opt inverted .. | † | | — | — |
| O11 | 1 a. purple-brown .. | 20·00 | 15·00 | — | 5·00 |
| O12 | 1 a. drab .. | 4·50 | — | 1·25 | 85 |
| | a. Opt inverted .. | † | | — | — |
| O13 | 2 a. green *(to deep)* (A) .. | 7·50 | 7·50 | 2·25 | 2·25 |
| | a. Opt inverted .. | † | | — | — |
| | b. Inner circle missing (B) | † | | 75·00 | — |
| O14 | 3 a. ochre-brown .. | — | — | 6·50 | 6·50 |
| O15 | 4 a. slate .. | 17·00 | 13·00 | 4·25 | 4·25 |
| O16 | 8 a. deep brown .. | 23·00 | — | 14·00 | 9·50 |
| | a. Imperf between (pair) .. | £400 | — | † | |
| O17 | 12 a. blue .. | 27·00 | — | 16·00 | — |

The use of Official Stamps (Sarkari) was discontinued in 1878, but was resumed in 1909, when the current stamps were overprinted from a new die.

**1909–11.** *Optd with Type* O **1a**. *(a) On Type* **3**. *P* 12½.

O18 ½ a. orange-brown .. .. .. 40·00 4·00
a. Opt inverted .. .. ..
O19 1 a. black .. .. .. 24·00 10
O20 2 a. sage-green (A) .. .. 24·00 20
a. Optd on No. 15*da* (B) .. .. — 10·00
b. Stamp doubly printed .. .. † 85·00
O20*c* 3 a. ochre-brown .. .. .. 2·00 70
O20*d* 4 a. olive-green .. .. .. — 3·25
O20*e* 8 a. deep brown .. .. .. — 24·00
O20*f* 12 a. grey-green .. .. .. — 42·00

*(b) On Type* **6**. A. *Perf* 12½. B. *Perf* 11½, 12. C. *Perf* 11

| | | A | | B | |
|---|---|---|---|---|---|
| O21 | ½ a. orange .. | — | 1·25 | † | |
| | *a. Vermilion* .. | 40·00 | 15 | † | |
| | b. Opt inverted .. | † | £110 | † | |
| | c. Imperf between (vert pair) | † | £110 | † | |
| O22 | ½ a. green (W.) .. | 6·00 | 10 | 7·50 | 20 |
| | *a. Pale green* (W.) .. | 6·00 | 10 | 7·50 | 20 |
| | b. Opt inverted .. | † | 50·00 | † | 42·00 |
| | c. Imperf between (vert pair) | † | 85·00 | † | |
| | d. Imperf between (horiz pair) | † | 80·00 | † | |
| | e. Stamp doubly printed .. | † | 75·00 | † | |
| | f. Perf 13½ .. | — | 30·00 | † | |
| O23 | 1 a. carmine .. | 18·00 | 15 | 25·00 | 30 |
| | a. Opt double .. | 75·00 | — | † | |
| | b. Perf 12½×11 .. | — | 3·00 | † | |
| | c. Stamp doubly printed .. | † | | — | 75·00 |
| O24 | 2 a. lilac .. | 24·00 | 20 | 35·00 | 1·00 |
| O25 | 3 a. brown-orange .. | 42·00 | 9·00 | 70·00 | 14·00 |
| | a. Opt inverted .. | † | 80·00 | † | |
| | b. Perf 13½ .. | — | 38·00 | † | |
| O26 | 4 a. olive-green (1911) .. | 18·00 | 20 | 32·00 | 2·25 |
| O27 | 8 a. purple (1911) .. | 13·00 | 50 | 30·00 | 2·75 |
| O28 | 12 a. blue-green (1911) .. | 14·00 | 50 | 14·00 | 1·00 |
| | a. Perf 12×12½ .. | † | | — | — |
| | b. Imperf between (horiz pair) .. | — | £350 | † | |

| | | C | |
|---|---|---|---|
| O22 | ½ a. green (W.) .. | | |
| | *a. Pale green* (W.) .. | | |
| O22*g* | ½ a. deep green (B.W.) .. | 75·00 | |
| O23 | 1 a. carmine .. | — | 4·50 |
| O24 | 2 a. lilac .. | | |
| O25 | 3 a. brown-orange .. | — | 18·00 |
| O26 | 4 a. olive-green (1911) .. | — | 7·00 |
| O28 | 12 a. blue-green (1911) .. | | |

The Wyon and Bradbury, Wilkinson stamps are distinguished above and below by the use of the letters (W.) and (B.W.) respectively.

**1911–12.** *T* **6** *optd with Type* O **2**. *Various perfs, also compound.*
A. *Perf* 12½. B. *Perf* 11½, 12

| | | A | | B | |
|---|---|---|---|---|---|
| O29 | ¼ a. grey (W.) .. | 22·00 | 50 | 16·00 | 20 |
| O30 | ¼ a. grey-black (B.W.) .. | 1·00 | 15 | 2·50 | 30 |
| | a. Opt inverted .. | † | 50·00 | — | — |
| | b. Pair, one without opt | — | — | — | — |
| | c. Imperf between (vert pair) | † | 85·00 | † | |
| O32 | ½ a. pale green (W.) .. | 15·00 | 40 | — | 15 |
| O33 | ½ a. deep green (B.W.) .. | 1·00 | 10 | — | 30 |
| | a. Opt inverted .. | — | 18·00 | † | |
| | c. Perf 11 × 12½ .. | 25·00 | 25·00 | † | |
| O34 | 1 a. carmine .. | 75 | 10 | 3·25 | 15 |
| | a. Opt inverted .. | — | 27·00 | † | |
| | b. Perf 11 × 12½ .. | 25·00 | 25·00 | † | |
| | c. Imperf horiz (vert pair) .. | † | £100 | † | |
| O35 | 2 a. lilac .. | 2·00 | 20 | 8·00 | 1·25 |
| O36 | 3 a. brown-orange .. | 6·00 | 70 | 6·00 | 1·00 |
| | a. Opt inverted .. | † | 60·00 | † | |
| O37 | 4 a. olive-green .. | 5·00 | 80 | 3·25 | 60 |
| | a. Opt inverted .. | — | 60·00 | — | — |
| O38 | 8 a. purple .. | — | — | — | — |
| O39 | 12 a. blue-green .. | — | — | — | — |

C. *Perf* 11. D. *Perf* 13½

| | | C | | D | |
|---|---|---|---|---|---|
| O29 | ¼ a. grey (W.) .. | 35·00 | 20·00 | — | — |
| O30 | ¼ a. grey-black (B.W.) .. | 45 | 20 | 70 | 10 |
| | d. Imperf between (horiz pair) | † | | † | 85·00 |
| O31 | ¼ a. brown-pur *(shades)* (B.W.) | — | — | 50 | 10 |
| | a. Imperf horiz (vert pair) .. | † | | † | 85·00 |
| | b. Imperf between (horiz pair) | † | | † | 95·00 |
| O32 | ½ a. pale green (W.) .. | † | | — | — |
| O33 | ½ a. deep green (B.W.) .. | 90 | 10 | 70 | 10 |
| | a. Opt inverted .. | — | 20·00 | † | |
| | b. Imperf between (horiz pair) | † | | † | 70·00 |
| | d. Imperf horiz (vert pair) .. | † | 95·00 | † | |
| | *e. Yellow-green* .. | † | | — | 50 |
| O34 | 1 a. carmine .. | 75 | 10 | — | — |
| O35 | 2 a. lilac .. | 85 | 15 | 3·25 | 10 |
| | a. Imperf between (horiz pair) | † | | † | £120 |
| | *b. Rose-lilac* .. | † | | 1·75 | 10 |
| O36 | 3 a. brown-orange .. | 9·00 | 50 | 9·00 | 20 |
| | a. Opt inverted .. | † | 65·00 | † | 60·00 |
| O37 | 4 a. olive-green .. | 1·75 | 30 | 1·40 | 10 |
| | a. Opt inverted .. | † | | † | 60·00 |
| O38 | 8 a. purple .. | — | 17·00 | 2·25 | 20 |
| O39 | 12 a. blue-green .. | — | — | 4·00 | 30 |

**1917–20.** *T* **8** *optd with Type* O **2**. *Various perfs as above, also compound.*

| | | A | | C | |
|---|---|---|---|---|---|
| O40 | ½ a. green .. | — | 3·50 | 2·75 | 30 |
| | a. Opt inverted .. | † | | † | 20·00 |
| | b. Pair, one without opt .. | † | | — | — |
| O41 | 1 a. carmine .. | — | 3·50 | 3·50 | 15 |
| | a. Opt inverted .. | † | | † | 15·00 |
| | *e. Scarlet* (1920) .. | † | | — | 16·00 |

| | | D | |
|---|---|---|---|
| O40 | ½ a. green .. | 80 | 10 |
| | a. Opt inverted .. | † | 19·00 |
| | b. Pair, one without opt .. | † | 80·00 |
| | c. Imperf between (horiz pair) .. | † | 65·00 |
| | d. Imperf between (vert pair) .. | † | 75·00 |
| | e. Perf 11×13½ or 13½×11 .. | 25·00 | 25·00 |
| | *f. Emerald-green* .. | 2·50 | 40 |
| O41 | 1 a. carmine .. | 1·00 | 10 |
| | a. Opt inverted .. | † | 24·00 |
| | b. Opt double .. | † | 55·00 |
| | c. Imperf horiz (vert pair) .. | † | 85·00 |
| | d. Stamp printed double .. | † | 70·00 |
| | *e. Scarlet* (1920) .. | 60 | 10 |
| | ea. Stamp printed double .. | † | 75·00 |
| | eb. Imperf between (horiz pair) .. | † | 75·00 |
| | ec. Imperf between (vert pair) .. | † | 75·00 |

**1930–34.** *T* **6** *and* **8** *optd as Type* O **2** *and surch at top of stamp, in red, as T* **10** *or* **11**.

O42 4 p. on ¼ a. grey-black (O30) (1934) .. £100 17·00
O43 4 p. on ¼ a. brown-purple (O31) .. 50 10
b. Imperf between (horiz pair) .. † 90·00
c. Imperf between (vert pair) .. † 90·00
d. Imperf horiz (vert pair) .. † 90·00
e. Red surch double .. .. † 50·00
f. Black opt double .. .. † £110
O44 8 p. on ½ a. green (O40) .. .. 45 10
c. Imperf between (horiz pair) .. † 90·00
ca. Imperf between (vert pair) .. † 90·00
d. Red surch double .. .. † 50·00
e. Stamp doubly printed .. .. † 90·00
f. Black opt double .. .. † £110
O45 8 p. on ½ a. yellow-green (O33e) .. 35·00 45·00

For Nos. O42/5 the red surcharge was intended to appear on the upper part of the stamp, above the official overprint, Type O 2, but surcharge and overprint are not infrequently found superimposed on one another.

**1934–44.** *Nos.* 41/8 *optd with Type* O **2**.

O46 4 p. black .. .. .. 60 10
a. Imperf (pair) .. .. .. 60·00
b. Imperf between (vert pair) .. £500 £500
c. Imperf between (horiz pair) .. — £500
O47 8 p. green .. .. .. 30 10
a. Opt inverted .. .. .. † £150
b. Imperf between (horiz pair) .. — £500
c. Opt double .. .. .. † £120
d. Imperf (pair) .. .. .. £100 £130
O48 1 a. brown .. .. .. 30 10
a. Imperf between (vert pair) .. £400 £400
b. Imperf between (horiz pair) .. — £400
c. Imperf (pair) .. .. .. £150 £180
d. Opt double .. .. .. — £150
O49 2 a. violet .. .. .. 2·00 10
a. Imperf between (horiz pair) .. — £550
O50 4 a. ultramarine .. .. .. 1·00 10
O51 8 a. orange (1935) .. .. .. 5·00 50
*a. Yellow-orange* (1944) .. .. — 38·00
O52 12 a. scarlet (1935) .. .. .. 4·25 1·25
O53 1 r. yellow (1935) .. .. .. 6·00 2·00
O46/53 .. .. .. *Set of* 8 17·00 3·75

**1947.** *No.* 58 *optd with Type* O 2.
O54 8 ½ a. claret .. .. .. .. .. 6·50 3·50
a. Pair, one without opt .. ..

**1949.** *No.* 60 *optd with Type* O 2.
O55 12 2 p. bistre-brown .. .. .. 5·50 4·00

**1950.** *No.* 59 *optd with Type* O 2.
O56 6 p. claret .. .. .. .. .. .. 7·00 7·50

## IDAR

**PRICES FOR STAMPS ON COVER**
Nos. 1/2*b* *from* × 2
Nos. 3/6 *from* × 3

1 Maharaja Shri Himatsinhji 2

(Typo M. N. Kothari & Sons, Bombay)

**1939** (21 Feb). *P* 11. (*a*) *White panels.*
1 1 ½ a. emerald .. .. .. .. 6·00 12·00
a. Imperf between (pair) .. .. .. £500
*b. Yellow-green* .. .. .. .. 5·50 12·00
ba. Imperf between (horiz pair) .. .. £500
*c. Pale yellow-green* (thick paper) .. 9·00 14·00

(*b*) *Coloured panels*
2 1 ½ a. emerald .. .. .. .. 6·50 14·00
*a. Yellow-green* .. .. .. .. 5·50 14·00
*b. Pale yellow-green* (thick paper) .. 14·00 16·00

In No. 2 the whole design is composed of half-tone dots. In No. 1 the dots are confined to the oval portrait.

Covers have been seen which indicate that No. 1 may have been issued as early as 1934.

(Typo Purshottum Ghellaji Mehta & Co., Himmatnagar)

**1944** (21 Oct). *P* 12.
3 2 ½ a. blue-green .. .. .. .. 85 24·00
a. Imperf between (vert pair) .. .. £130
*b. Yellow-green* .. .. .. .. 85 28·00
ba. Imperf between (vert pair) .. .. 12·00
4 1 a. violet .. .. .. .. .. 65 24·00
a. Imperf (pair) .. .. .. .. £200
b. Imperf vert (horiz pair) .. .. £225
5 2 a. blue .. .. .. .. .. 1·00 32·00
a. Imperf between (vert pair) .. 60·00
b. Imperf between (horiz pair) .. £100
6 4 a. vermilion .. .. .. .. 2·40 40·00
a. Doubly printed .. .. .. £275
3/6 .. .. .. .. .. *Set of* 4 4·25 £110

Nos. 1 to 6 are from booklet panes of 4 stamps, producing single stamps with one or two adjacent sides imperf.

The 4 a. violet is believed to be a colour trial.

## INDORE

**(HOLKAR STATE)**

**PRICES FOR STAMPS ON COVER**
Nos. 1/15 *from* × 20
Nos. 16/43 *from* × 6
Nos. S1/7 *from* × 40

1 Maharaja Tukoji Rao II Holkar XI

(Litho Waterlow & Sons)

**1886** (6 Jan). *P* 15. (*a*) *Thick white paper.*
1 1 ½ a. bright mauve .. .. .. .. 4·00 5·00

(*b*) *Thin white or yellowish paper*
2 1 ½ a. pale mauve .. .. .. .. 1·25 1·10
*a. Dull mauve* .. .. .. .. 1·25 1·50

2 Type I 2*a* Type II

**TYPES 2 AND 2a.** In addition to the difference in the topline character (marked by arrow), the two Types can be distinguished by the difference in the angles of the 6-pointed stars and the appearance of the lettering. In Type I the top characters are smaller and more cramped than the bottom; in Type II both are in the same style and similarly spaced.

**1889.** *Handstamped. No gum. Imperf.*
3 2 ½ a. black/*pink* .. .. .. .. 13·00 13·00
4 2*a* ½ a. black/*pink* .. .. .. .. 1·50 1·75
a. *Tête-bêche* (pair) .. .. .. £130

3 Maharaja Shivaji Rao Holkar XII 4 Maharaja Tukoji Rao III Holkar XIII 5

(Recess Waterlow)

**1889–92.** *Medium wove paper. P* 14 *to* 15.
5 3 ¼ a. orange (9.2.92) .. .. .. 30 30
a. Imperf between (horiz pair) .. — £500
b. Very thick wove paper .. .. 70 45
*c. Yellow* .. .. .. .. 30 30
6 ½ a. dull violet .. .. .. 1·00 60
*a. Brown-purple* .. .. .. 30 15
b. Imperf between (vert pair) .. £450
7 1 a. green (7.2.92) .. .. .. 65 50
a. Imperf between (pair) .. .. £600 £600
b. Very thick wove paper .. ..
8 2 a. vermilion (7.2.92) .. .. 1·60 1·00
a. Very thick wove paper .. .. 4·75 3·00
5/8 .. .. .. .. .. *Set of* 4 2·50 1·60

(Recess Perkins, Bacon & Co)

**1904–20.** *P* 13½, 14.
9 4 ¼ a. orange .. .. .. .. 30 10
10 5 ½ a. lake (1909) .. .. .. 5·50 10
*a. Brown-lake (shades)* .. .. 6·50 15
b. Imperf (pair) .. .. .. 16·00
11 1 a. green .. .. .. .. 1·60 10
a. Imperf (pair) .. .. .. £120
b. Perf 12½ (1920) .. .. .. † 42·00
12 2 a. brown .. .. .. .. 5·00 30
a. Imperf (pair) .. .. .. 75·00
13 3 a. violet .. .. .. .. 6·50 2·00
14 4 a. ultramarine .. .. .. 6·00 1·10
*a. Dull blue* .. .. .. .. 5·00 1·00
9/14 .. .. .. .. .. *Set of* 6 21·00 3·25

**पाव आना.**

(6)

7 Maharaja Yeshwant Rao II Holkar XIV

**1905** (June). *No.* 6*a surch* "QUARTER ANNA" *in Devanagari, as T* 6.
15 3 ¼ a. on ½ a. brown-purple .. .. 1·50 11·00

**NOTE.** From 1 March 1908 the use of Indore stamps was restricted to official mail. Nos. S1/7 were withdrawn and replaced by Nos. 9/14.

(Recess Perkins, Bacon & Co)

**1927–37.** *P* 13 *to* 14.
16 7 ¼ a. orange (*a*) (*d*) (*e*) .. .. .. 30 10
17 ½ a. claret (*a*) (*d*) (*e*) .. .. .. 30 10
18 1 a. green (*a*) (*d*) (*e*) .. .. .. 50 10
19 1¼ a. green (*c*) (*d*) (1933) .. .. 50 15
20 2 a. sepia (*a*) .. .. .. .. 2·50 80
21 2 a. bluish green (*d*) (1936) .. .. 4·50 60
a. Imperf (pair) .. .. .. 25·00 70·00
22 3 a. deep violet (*a*) .. .. .. 1·50 5·50
23 3 a. Prussian blue (*d*) (1935?) .. 12·00
a. Imperf (pair) .. .. .. 30·00 £130
24 3½ a. violet (*d*) (1934) .. .. .. 4·00 8·00
a. Imperf (pair) .. .. .. 40·00 £130
25 4 a. ultramarine (*a*) .. .. .. 3·25 2·25
26 4 a. yellow-brown (*d*) (1937) .. .. 13·00 1·50
a. Imperf (pair) .. .. .. 30·00 £110
27 8 a. slate-grey (*a*) .. .. .. 5·50 5·00
28 8 a. red-orange (*d*) (1937) .. .. 10·00 9·00
29 12 a. carmine (*d*) (1934) .. .. .. 5·00 10·00
30 – 1 r. black and light blue (*b*) .. .. 8·00 14·00
31 – 2 r. black and carmine (*b*) .. .. 30·00 30·00
32 – 5 r. black & brown-orange (*b*) .. .. 42·00 42·00

Nos. 30/32 are as Type **7**, but larger, size 23 × 28 mm.

Five different perforating heads were used for this issue: (*a*) comb 13·6; (*b*) comb 13·9; (*c*) line 13·2; (*d*) line 13·8; (*e*) line 14·2. Values on which each perforation occur are indicated above.

Nos. 21a, 23a, 24a and 26a are plate proofs which were provisionally used for postage *circa* 1938–42. A plate proof of the 1 r. in green and carmine is also known postally used (*Price for pair £30 unused, £160 used*).

(8)

9

**1940** (1 Aug). *Surch in words as T* 8.
33 7 ¼ a. on 5 r. black and brown-orange (*b*) 2·50 30
a. Surch double (Blk. + G.) .. .. — £400
34 ½ a. on 2 r. black and carmine (*b*) .. 4·00 75
35 1 a. on 1¼ a. green (*c*) (*d*) (*e*) .. .. 4·75 35
b. Surch inverted (*d*) .. .. .. 80·00
c. Surch double (*c*) .. .. .. £300
33/5 .. .. .. .. *Set of* 3 10·00 1·25

(Typo "*Times of India*" Press, Bombay)

**1941–46.** *P* 11.
36 9 ¼ a. red-orange .. .. .. .. 1·50 10
37 ½ a. claret .. .. .. .. .. 1·00 10
38 1 a. green .. .. .. .. .. 4·25 10
39 1¼ a. yellow-green .. .. .. .. 8·50 30
a. Imperf (pair) .. .. .. .. £190
40 2 a. turquoise-blue .. .. .. .. 8·00 1·00
41 4 a. yellow-brown (1946) .. .. .. 9·00 7·00

*Larger size* (23 × 28 *mm*)
42 2 r. black and carmine (1943) .. .. 10·00 70·00
43 5 r. black and yellow-orange (1943) .. 12·00 85·00
36/43 .. .. .. .. .. *Set of* 8 48·00 £150

OFFICIAL STAMPS

**SERVICE** **SERVICE**

(S 1) (S 2)

**1904–6.** (*a*) *Optd with Type* S 1.
S1 4 ¼ a. orange (1906) .. .. .. .. 10 30
S2 5 ½ a. lake .. .. .. .. .. 10 10
a. Opt inverted .. .. .. .. 15·00 22·00
b. Opt double .. .. .. .. 17·00
c. Imperf (pair) .. .. .. .. 35·00
*d. Brown-lake* .. .. .. .. 10 10
da. Opt inverted .. .. .. .. 15·00
e. Pair, one without opt .. .. .. £350
S3 1 a. green .. .. .. .. .. 10 15
S4 2 a. brown (1905) .. .. .. .. 30 20
a. Pair, one without opt .. .. .. £550
S5 3 a. violet (1906) .. .. .. .. 1·75 1·25
a. Imperf (pair) .. .. .. .. £300
S6 4 a. ultramarine (1905) .. .. .. 2·25 1·40

(*b*) *Optd with Type* S 2
S7 5 ½ a. lake .. .. .. .. .. 10 35
a. Opt double .. .. .. .. £160
S1/7 .. .. .. .. *Set of* 6 4·00 3·00

Types S 1 and S 2 differ chiefly in the shape of the letter "R".

## JAIPUR

**PRICES FOR STAMPS ON COVER**
No. 1 *from* × 3
No. 2 *from* × 2
Nos. 3/5 *from* × 10
Nos. 6/70 *from* × 4
Nos. 71/80 *from* × 6

Nos. O1/34 *from* × 8

1 Chariot of the Sun God, Surya 2

½ a. 36 varieties (2 plates). Plate I, 12 stamps 2½ mm apart horizontally; Plate II, 24 stamps 4½ mm apart.
1 a. and 2 a. 12 varieties.

**1904.** *Litho.*
(*a*) *Value at sides in small letters and characters. Roughly perf* 14
1 1 ½ a. pale blue (Plate I) .. .. .. 50·00 85·00
*a. Ultramarine* .. .. .. .. 80·00 £100
b. Imperf, *ultramarine* .. .. .. £350
2 ½ a. grey-blue (Plate II) .. .. .. £750 £200
a. Imperf .. .. .. .. £350 £450
*b. Ultramarine* .. .. .. .. — £275
3 1 a. dull red .. .. .. .. .. 2·75 7·50
*a. Scarlet* .. .. .. .. .. 3·00 7·50
4 2 a. pale green .. .. .. .. 2·50 9·00
*a. Emerald-green* .. .. .. .. 3·50

(*b*) *Value in larger letters and characters. 24 varieties on one plate. Roughly perf* 14
5 2 ½ a. pale blue .. .. .. .. 2·75 3·50
*a. Deep blue* .. .. .. .. 3·00 3·75
*b. Ultramarine* .. .. .. .. 3·00 3·75
c. Imperf .. .. .. .. .. £300 £300

Nos. 1b, 2a and 5c are on gummed paper. Imperforate plate proofs also exist for Nos. 1/5, but these are ungummed.

3 Chariot of the Sun God, Surya

(Recess Perkins, Bacon & Co)

**1904.** *P* 12.
6 3 ½ a. blue .. .. .. .. .. 3·00 4·00
a. Perf 12½ .. .. .. .. .. 12·00 8·50
b. Perf comp of 12 and 12½ .. .. 14·00 14·00

7 3 1 a. brown-red .. .. .. .. 38·00 38·00
a. Perf 12½ .. .. .. .. 70·00 70·00
b. Perf comp of 12 and 12½ .. .. £120 £120
*c. Carmine* .. .. .. .. 2·25 2·25
ca. Imperf between (vert pair) .. .. £325 £425
cb. Perf comp of 12 and 12½ .. .. 10·00 10·00
8 2 a. deep green .. .. .. .. 5·50 8·00
a. Perf 12½ .. .. .. .. 70·00 55·00
b. Perf comp of 12 and 12½ .. .. 25·00 25·00

Nos. 6b, 7b, 7cb and 8b occur on the bottom two rows of sheets otherwise perforated 12.

**1905–8.** *Wmk* "JAs WRIGLEY & SON Ld. 219" "SPECIAL POSTAGE PAPER LONDON" *or* "PERKINS BACON & Co Ld LONDON" *in sheet. P* 13½.

9 3 ¼ a. olive-yellow (1906) .. .. .. 20 20
10 ½ a. blue .. .. .. .. 80 80
*a. Indigo* .. .. .. .. 40 40
11 1 a. brown-red (1906) .. .. .. 4·25 4·25
*a. Bright red* (1908) .. .. .. 70 40
12 2 a. deep green .. .. .. .. 1·00 75
13 4 a. chestnut .. .. .. .. 2·50 2·00
14 8 a. bright violet .. .. .. .. 3·00 2·75
15 1 r. yellow .. .. .. .. 8·00 8·50
*a. Orange-yellow* .. .. .. 8·00 9·50
*b. Yellow-ochre* .. .. .. 11·00 13·00
9/15 .. .. .. .. *Set of* 7 14·00 13·50

4 Chariot of the Sun God, Surya

३ आना

(5)

(Typo Jail Press, Jaipur)

**1911.** *Thin wove paper. No gum. Imperf. Six varieties of each value.*

16 4 ¼ a. green .. .. .. .. 1·25 1·60
a. Printed double .. .. .. 5·00
ab. Ditto, one inverted .. ..
b. "¼" inverted at right upper corner 5·00
c. No stop after "STATE" .. .. 5·00
17 ¼ a. greenish yellow .. .. .. 30 40
a. Printed double .. .. .. 2·00
b. "¼" inverted in right upper corner 1·50
c. No stop after "STATE" .. .. 1·50
18 ½ a. ultramarine .. .. .. 30 40
a. Printed double .. .. .. 2·00
b. No stop after "STATE" .. .. 75
c. Large "J" in "JAIPUR" .. .. 75
d. "⅓" for "½" at lower left .. .. 1·50
19 ½ a. grey-blue .. .. .. 90 90
a. No stop after "STATE" .. .. 1·75
b. Large "J" in "JAIPUR" .. .. 1·75
c. "⅓" for "½" at lower left .. .. 2·75
20 1 a. rose-red .. .. .. 30 40
a. Printed double .. .. .. £120
21 2 a. greyish green .. .. .. 2·00 5·50
*a. Deep green* .. .. .. 2·00 5·50
ab. Printed double .. .. .. £120

One sheet of the ¼ a. is known in blue.

(Typo Jail Press, Jaipur)

**1913–18.** *Paper-maker's wmk* "DORLING & CO. LONDON" *in sheet. P* 11.

22 3 ¼ a. pale olive-yellow .. .. .. 20 30
a. Imperf horiz (vert pair) .. .. £200 £200
b. Imperf vert (horiz pair) .. .. — £200
23 ¼ a. olive .. .. .. .. 20 40
a. Imperf between (horiz pair) .. £190
b. Imperf vert (horiz pair) .. .. £200
c. Imperf horiz (vert pair) .. .. £200
24 ¼ a. bistre .. .. .. .. 20 35
a. Imperf between (horiz pair) .. £190
b. Imperf between (vert pair) .. † £225
c. Imperf horiz (vert pair) .. .. † £225
d. Doubly printed .. .. .. † —
25 ½ a. pale ultramarine .. .. .. 20 30
a. Imperf vert (horiz pair) .. .. † £300
*b. Blue* .. .. .. .. 30 30
ba. Imperf between (horiz pair) .. £250
26 1 a. carmine (1918) .. .. .. 1·25 1·25
a. Imperf between (vert pair) .. † £275
b. Imperf horiz (vert pair) .. .. † £275
27 1 a. rose-red .. .. .. .. 1·60 3·75
a. Imperf between (vert pair) .. £300
28 1 a. scarlet .. .. .. .. 35 75
a. Imperf between (vert pair) .. £300 £300
29 2 a. green (1918) .. .. .. 85 1·40
30 4 a. chocolate .. .. .. .. 1·25 2·75
31 4 a. pale brown .. .. .. .. 1·75 3·00
a. Imperf vert (horiz pair) .. .. £325
22/31 .. .. .. .. *Set of* 5 2·50 5·00

**1926.** *Surch with T* 5.

32 3 3 a. on 8 a. bright violet (R.) .. .. 90 1·40
a. Surch inverted .. .. .. £170 £140
33 3 a. on 1 r. yellow (R.) .. .. .. 1·10 2·00
a. Surch inverted .. .. .. £170 £140
*c. Yellow-ochre* .. .. .. 4·50

**1928.** *As* 1913–18 *issue. Wmk* "DORLING & CO. LONDON" (½ *a.*, 1 *a.*, 2 *a.*) *or* "OVERLAND BANK" (*all values*) *in sheet. No gum. P* 12.

34 3 ½ a. ultramarine .. .. .. 3·00 4·00
a. Perf comp of 12 and 11 .. .. 12·00 7·50
35 1 a. rose-red .. .. .. .. 18·00 13·00
a. Imperf between (vert pair) .. .. £325
36 1 a. scarlet .. .. .. .. 23·00 12·00
a. Perf comp of 12 and 11 .. .. 32·00 20·00
37 2 a. green .. .. .. .. 50·00 24·00
a. Perf comp of 12 and 11 .. .. 95·00 55·00
38 3 8 a. bright violet .. .. .. .. £200 £250
39 1 r. orange-vermilion .. .. .. £200 £250

The "OVERLAND BANK" paper has a coarser texture. The ½ a. and 2 a. values also exist on this paper perforated 11, but such stamps are difficult to distinguish from examples of Nos. 25 and 29.

6 Chariot of the Sun God, Surya

7 Maharaja Sir Man Singh Bahadur

8 Sowar in Armour

(Des T. I. Archer. Litho Indian Security Printing Press, Nasik)

**1931** (14 Mar). *Investiture of Maharaja. T* 6/8 *and similar designs. No wmk. P* 14.

40 ¼ a. black and deep lake .. .. .. 45 45
41 ½ a. black and violet .. .. .. .. 20 10
42 1 a. black and blue .. .. .. .. 3·25 3·50
43 2 a. black and buff .. .. .. .. 3·25 3·50
44 2½ a. black and carmine .. .. .. 25·00 29·00
45 3 a. black and myrtle .. .. .. 10·00 24·00
46 4 a. black and olive-green .. .. .. 11·00 26·00
47 6 a. black and deep blue .. .. .. 6·00 26·00
48 8 a. black and chocolate .. .. .. 9·00 40·00
49 1 r. black and pale olive .. .. .. 22·00 75·00
50 2 r. black and yellow-green .. .. 15·00 85·00
51 5 r. black and purple .. .. .. 26·00 95·00
40/51 .. .. .. .. *Set of* 12 £110 £375

Designs: *Vert*—1 a. Elephant and state banner; 2½ a. Common Peafowl; 8 a. Sireh-Deorhi Gate. *Horiz*—3 a. Bullock carriage; 4 a. Elephant carriage; 6 a. Albert Museum; 1 r. Chandra Mahal; 2 r. Amber Palace; 5 r. Maharajas Jai Singh and Sir Man Singh.

Eighteen of these sets were issued for presentation purposes with a special overprint "INVESTITURE–MARCH 14, 1931" in red (*Price for set of* 12 £2500, *unused*).

10 Maharaja Sir Man Singh Bahadur

One Rupee

(11)

(Des T. I. Archer. Litho Indian Security Printing Press, Nasik)

**1932–46.** *P* 14. (*a*) *Inscr* "POSTAGE & REVENUE".

52 10 1 a. black and blue .. .. .. 30 20
53 2 a. black and buff .. .. .. 45 40
54 4 a. black and grey-green .. .. .. 1·60 2·25
55 8 a. black and chocolate .. .. .. 2·50 3·75
56 1 r. black and yellow-bistre .. .. 12·00 40·00
57 2 r. black and yellow-green .. .. 48·00 £150
52/7 .. .. .. .. *Set of* 6 60·00 £180

(*b*) *Inscr* "POSTAGE"

58 7 ¼ a. black and brown-lake .. .. 30 10
59 ¾ a. black and brown-red (1943?) .. 1·75 1·00
60 1 a. black and blue (1943?) .. .. 2·25 45
61 2 a. black and buff (1943?) .. .. 2·25 1·00
62 2½ a. black and carmine .. .. .. 55 40
63 3 a. black and green .. .. .. 55 35
64 4 a. black and grey-green (1943?) .. 5·50 30·00
65 6 a. black and deep blue .. .. 1·40 9·00
*a. Black and pale blue* (1946) .. .. 3·25 25·00
66 8 a. black and chocolate (1946) .. .. 6·50 35·00
67 1 r. black and yellow-bistre (1946) .. 13·00 50·00
58/67 .. .. .. .. *Set of* 10 30·00 £110

**1936.** *Nos.* 57 *and* 51 *surch with T* 11.

68 10 1 r. on 2 r. black and yellow-green (R.) 2·50 25·00
69 – 1 r. on 5 r. black and purple .. .. 2·50 20·00

पाव आना

(12)

13 Maharaja and Amber Palace

**1938** (Dec). *No.* 41 *surch* "QUARTER ANNA" *in Devanagari, T* 12.

70 7 ¼ a. on ½ a. black and violet (R.) .. 3·25 6·00

(Recess D.L.R.)

**1947** (Dec)–**48.** *Silver Jubilee of Maharaja's Accession to Throne. Various designs as T* 13. *P* 13½ × 14.

71 ¼ a. red-brown and green (5.48) .. .. 15 90
72 ½ a. green and violet .. .. .. 15 90
73 ¾ a. black and lake (5.48) .. .. .. 15 1·25
74 1 a. red-brown and ultramarine .. .. 30 1·10
75 2 a. violet and scarlet .. .. .. 20 1·10
76 3 a. green and black (5.48) .. .. 30 1·75
77 4 a. ultramarine and brown .. .. 45 1·10
78 8 a. vermilion and brown .. .. .. 60 1·75
79 1 r. purple and green (5.48) .. .. 1·00 5·50
71/9 .. .. .. .. *Set of* 9 2·75 14·00

Designs:—¼ a. Palace Gate; ¾ a. Map of Jaipur; 1 a. Observatory; 2 a. Wind Palace; 3 a. Coat of Arms; 4 a. Amber Fort Gate; 8 a. Chariot of the Sun; 1 r. Maharaja's portrait between State flags.

3 PIES

(14)

**1947** (Dec). *No.* 41 *surch with T* 14.

80 7 3 p. on ½ a. black and violet (R.) .. 7·00 14·00
a. "PIE" for "PIES" .. .. .. 30·00 45·00
b. Bars at left vertical .. .. .. 35·00 50·00
c. Surch inverted .. .. .. 30·00 28·00
d. Surch inverted and "PIE" for "PIES" £120 £100
e. Surch double, one inverted .. .. 42·00 40·00
f. As variety e, but inverted surch showing "PIE" for "PIES" .. .. £200 £180

OFFICIAL STAMPS

SERVICE (O 1)

SERVICE (O 2)

**1928** (13 Nov)–**31.** *T* 3 *typographed. No gum* (*except for Nos. O6/a*). *P* 11, 12, *or compound. Wmk* "DORLING & CO. LONDON" (4 *a.*) *or* "OVERLAND BANK" (*others*). (*a*) *Optd with Type* O 1.

O 1 ¼ a. olive .. .. .. .. 55 90
*a. Bistre* .. .. .. .. 40 40
O 2 ½ a. pale ultramarine (Blk.) .. .. 30 10
a. Imperf between (horiz pair) .. £225 £225
b. Imperf between (vert pair) .. † £275
c. Opt inverted .. .. .. † £250
d. Opt double (R. and Blk.) .. .. † £350
O 3 ½ a. pale ultramarine (R.) (13.10.30) .. 2·25 15
a. Imperf horiz (vert pair) .. ..
b. Stamp doubly printed .. ..
O 3c 1 a. rose-red .. .. .. 35 20
d. Imperf between (horiz pair) .. † £275
O 4 1 a. scarlet .. .. .. .. 75 50
a. Opt inverted .. .. .. £275 £275
b. Imperf between (horiz pair) .. † £275
O 5 2 a. green .. .. .. .. 40 40
a. Imperf between (vert pair) .. † £300
b. Imperf between (horiz pair) .. £300 £300
O 6 4 a. pale brown (with gum) .. .. 2·00 1·75
*a. Chocolate* (*with gum*) .. .. 2·00 1·75
O 7 8 a. bright violet (R.) (13.10.30) .. 18·00 42·00
O 8 1 r. orange-vermilion .. .. .. 35·00 £110

(*b*) *Optd with Type* O 2

O 9 ½ a. ultramarine (Blk.) (11.2.31) .. £110 15
a. Imperf vert (horiz pair) .. .. † £350
O10 ½ a. ultramarine (R.) (15.10.30) .. £120 15
a. Imperf between (vert pair) .. † £350
O11 8 a. bright violet (11.2.31) .. .. £225 £140
O12 1 r. orange-vermilion (11.2.31) .. £225 £170

SERVICE (O 3)

आध आना (O 4)

**1931–7.** *Nos.* 41/3 *and* 46 *optd at Nasik with Type* O 3, *in red.*

O13 7 ½ a. black and violet .. .. .. 20 10
O14 – 1 a. black and blue .. .. .. £170 1·50
O15 8 2 a. black and buff (1936) .. .. 2·00 2·25
O16 – 4 a. black and olive-green (1937) .. 10·00 10·00
O13/16 .. .. .. .. *Set of* 4 £170 12·50

**1932.** *No.* O5 *surch with Type* O 4.

O17 3 ½ a. on 2 a. green .. .. .. £100 40

**1932–7.** *Nos.* 52/6 *optd at Nasik with Type* O 3, *in red.*

O18 10 1 a. black and blue .. .. .. 60 10
O19 2 a. black and buff .. .. .. 60 10
O20 4 a. black and grey-green (1937) .. £150 3·50
O21 8 a. black and chocolate .. .. .. 1·90 1·10
O22 1 r. black and yellow-bistre .. .. 7·50 8·50
O18/22 .. .. .. .. *Set of* 5 £150 12·00

**1936–46.** *Stamps of* 1932–46, *inscr* "POSTAGE".

(*a*) *Optd at Nasik with Type* O 3, *in red*

O23 7 ¼ a. black and brown-lake (1936) .. 30 10
O24 ¾ a. black and brown-red (1944) .. 1·10 30
O25 1 a. black and blue (1941?) .. .. 4·25 30
O26 2 a. black and buff (date?) .. .. 3·75 50
O27 2½ a. black and carmine (1946) .. 6·00 27·00
O28 4 a. black and grey-green (1942) .. 3·25 1·50
O29 8 a. black and chocolate (1943) .. 2·75 2·50
O30 1 r. black and yellow-bistre (date?) .. £200
O23/9 .. .. .. .. *Set of* 7 19·00 30·00

(*b*) *Optd locally as Type* O 2 (16 *mm long*), *in black*

O31 7 ¼ a. black and red-brown (1936) .. 50·00 45·00

## 9 PIES

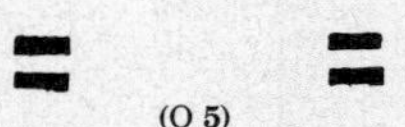

(O 5)

**1947.** *No.* O25 *surch with Type* O **5**, *in red.*

| | | | | |
|---|---|---|---|---|
| O32 | **7** | 9 p. on 1 a. black and blue .. .. | 50 | 60 |

**1947** (Dec). *No.* O13 *surch as T* **14**, *but "3 PIES" placed higher.*

| | | | | |
|---|---|---|---|---|
| O33 | **7** | 3 p. on ½ a. black and violet (R.) | 1·75 | 4·75 |
| | | a. Surch double, one inverted .. | 35·00 | 35·00 |
| | | ab. "PIE" for "PIES" in inverted surcharge .. .. .. .. | £180 | £180 |
| | | c. Surch inverted .. .. .. | £650 | £650 |

**1949.** *No.* O13 *surch* "THREE-QUARTER ANNA" *in Devanagari, as T* **12**, *but with two bars on each side.*

| | | | | |
|---|---|---|---|---|
| O34 | **7** | ¾ a. on ½ a. black and violet (R.) .. | 6·50 | 7·00 |
| | | a. Surch double .. .. .. | £650 | £650 |

There are three different types of surcharge in the setting of 30, which vary in one or other of the Devanagari characters.

On 30 March 1949 Jaipur became part of the Rajasthan Union.

## JAMMU AND KASHMIR

**PRICES FOR STAMPS ON COVER**

| | |
|---|---|
| Nos. 1/49 | *from* × 4 |
| No. 50 | *from* × 2 |
| Nos. 52/88 | *from* × 3 |
| Nos. 90/101 | *from* × 10 |
| Nos. 101*b*/23 | *from* × 5 |
| Nos. 124/36 | *from* × 10 |
| Nos. 138/9 | *from* × 100 |
| Nos. 140/61*a* | *from* × 15 |
| Nos. 162/8 | *from* × 5 |
| Nos. O1/18 | *from* × 30 |

**ILLUSTRATIONS.** Designs of Jammu and Kashmir are illustrated actual size.

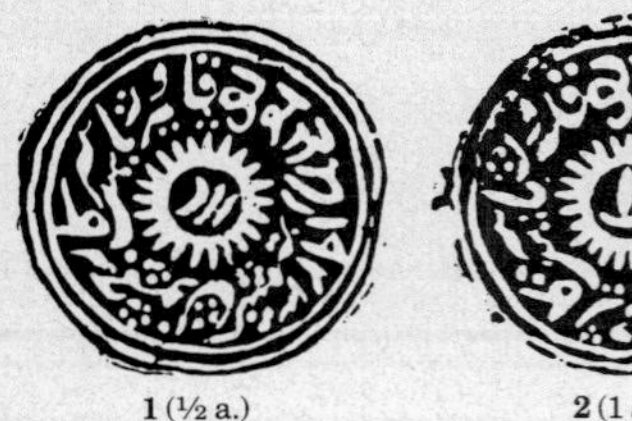

1 (½ a.) 2 (1 a.)

3 (4 a.)

Characters denoting the value (on the circular stamps only) are approximately as shown in the central circles of the stamps illustrated above.

These characters were taken from Punjabi merchants' notation and were not familiar to most of the inhabitants of the state. Type **1** was certainly the ½ anna value, but there has long been controversy over the correct face values of Types **2** and **3**.

The study of surviving material suggests that, to some extent, this confusion involved contemporary post office officials. Although covers posted at Jammu, where the stamps were in use for twelve years, show Type **2** used as the 1 a. value and Type **3** as the 4 a., those originating from Srinagar (Kashmir) during 1866–68 show both Types **2** and **3** used as 1 a. stamps.

In the following listing we have followed contemporary usage at Jammu and this reflects the prevailing opinion amongst modern authorities.

**GUM.** The stamps of Jammu and Kashmir were issued without gum.

**PRICES.** Prices for the circular stamps, Nos. 1/49, are for cut-square examples. Cut-to-shape examples are worth from 10% to 20% of these prices, according to condition.

A. *Handstamped in watercolours*

**1866** (23 Mar)–**67.** *Native paper, thick to thin, usually having the appearance of laid paper and tinted grey or brown. For Jammu and Kashmir.*

| | | | | |
|---|---|---|---|---|
| 1 | **1** | ½ a. grey-black .. .. .. .. | £120 | 65·00 |
| 2 | **2** | 1 a. grey-black .. .. .. .. | £350 | |
| 3 | **3** | 4 a. grey-black .. .. .. .. | £300 | |
| 4 | **2** | 1 a. royal blue .. .. .. .. | £450 | £275 |
| 4*a* | **1** | ½ a. ultramarine .. .. .. .. | | |
| 5 | **2** | 1 a. ultramarine .. .. .. .. | £225 | 65·00 |
| 6 | **3** | 4 a. ultramarine .. .. .. .. | £475 | £200 |
| 7 | | 4 a. indigo (1867) .. .. .. .. | £1300 | £475 |

**1869–72.** *Reissued for use in Jammu only.*

| | | | | |
|---|---|---|---|---|
| 8 | **1** | ½ a. red .. .. .. .. | 50·00 | |
| 9 | **2** | 1 a. red .. .. .. .. | 90·00 | |
| 10 | **3** | 4 a. red .. .. .. .. | 40·00 | 50·00 |
| 11 | **1** | ½ a. orange-red .. .. .. .. | £120 | |
| 12 | **2** | 1 a. orange-red .. .. .. .. | £130 | |
| 13 | **3** | 4 a. orange-red .. .. .. .. | 65·00 | |
| 13*a* | | 4 a. carmine-red .. .. .. | | |
| 13*b* | | 4 a. orange (1872) .. .. .. | | |

**1869–76.** *Special Printings.*

| | | | | |
|---|---|---|---|---|
| 14 | **1** | ½ a. deep black .. .. .. .. | 17·00 | |
| 15 | **2** | 1 a. deep black .. .. .. .. | £150 | |
| 16 | **3** | 4 a. deep black .. .. .. .. | £110 | |
| 17 | **1** | ½ a. bright blue .. .. .. .. | £100 | |
| 18 | **2** | 1 a. bright blue .. .. .. .. | 90·00 | |
| 19 | **3** | 4 a. bright blue .. .. .. .. | £100 | |
| 20 | **1** | ½ a. emerald-green .. .. .. .. | 65·00 | |
| 21 | **2** | 1 a. emerald-green .. .. .. .. | 70·00 | |
| 22 | **3** | 4 a. emerald-green .. .. .. .. | 75·00 | |
| 23*a* | **1** | ½ a. yellow .. .. .. .. | £350 | |
| 24 | **2** | 1 a. yellow .. .. .. .. | £375 | |
| 25 | **3** | 4 a. yellow .. .. .. .. | £350 | |
| 25*a* | | 4 a. deep blue-black (1876) .. .. | £475 | £275 |

These special printings were available for use, but little used.

B. *Handstamped in oil colours. Heavy blurred prints*

**1877–78.** (*a*) *Native paper.*

| | | | | |
|---|---|---|---|---|
| 26 | **1** | ½ a. red .. .. .. .. | 23·00 | 32·00 |
| 27 | **2** | 1 a. red .. .. .. .. | 25·00 | |
| 28 | **3** | 4 a. red .. .. .. .. | £140 | £400 |
| 29 | **1** | ½ a. black .. .. .. .. | 19·00 | 32·00 |
| 32 | | ½ a. slate-blue .. .. .. .. | 80·00 | |
| 34 | **2** | 1 a. slate-blue .. .. .. .. | 19·00 | |
| 35 | **1** | ½ a. sage-green .. .. .. .. | £100 | |
| 36 | **2** | 1 a. sage-green .. .. .. .. | £110 | |
| 37 | **3** | 4 a. sage-green .. .. .. .. | £110 | |

(*b*) *European laid paper, medium to thick*

| | | | | |
|---|---|---|---|---|
| 38 | **1** | ½ a. red .. .. .. .. | — | £275 |
| 39 | **3** | 4 a. red .. .. .. .. | £325 | |
| 41 | **1** | ½ a. black .. .. .. .. | 18·00 | 32·00 |
| 44 | | ½ a. slate-blue .. .. .. .. | 18·00 | |
| 45 | **2** | 1 a. slate-blue .. .. .. .. | 38·00 | |
| 46 | **3** | 4 a. slate-blue .. .. .. .. | £275 | |
| 47 | | 4 a. sage-green .. .. .. .. | £800 | |
| 48 | **1** | ½ a. yellow .. .. .. .. | 95·00 | |

(*c*) *Thick yellowish wove paper*

| | | | | |
|---|---|---|---|---|
| 49 | **1** | ½ a. red (1878) .. .. .. .. | — | £425 |

Forgeries exist of the ½ a. and 1 a. in types which were at one time supposed to be authentic.

Reprints and imitations (of which some of each were found in the official remainder stock) exist in a great variety of fancy colours, both on native paper, usually thinner and smoother than that of the originals, and on various thin European *wove* papers, on which the originals were never printed.

The imitations, which do not agree in type with the above illustrations, are also to be found on *laid* paper.

All the reprints, etc. are in oil colours or printer's ink. The originals in oil colour are usually blurred, particularly when on native paper. The reprints, etc. are usually clear.

(3*a*)

**1877.** *Provisional. Seal obliterator of Jammu handstamped in red watercolour on pieces of native paper, and used as a ½ anna stamp.*

| | | | | |
|---|---|---|---|---|
| 50 | **3*a*** | (½ a.) rose-red .. .. .. .. | — | £550 |

### FOR USE IN JAMMU

½ a. ½ a.

1 a. 4 ½ a.

T **4** to **11** have a star at the top of the oval band; the characters denoting the value are in the upper part of the inner oval. All are dated 1923, corresponding with A.D. 1866.

*T* **4.** *Printed in blocks of four, three varieties of ½ anna and one of 1 anna.*

**1867.** *In watercolour on native paper.*

| | | | | |
|---|---|---|---|---|
| 52 | ½ a. grey-black .. .. .. .. | £180 | 85·0 |
| 53 | 1 a. grey-black .. .. .. .. | £850 | £35 |
| 54 | ½ a. indigo .. .. .. .. | 90·00 | £10 |
| 55 | 1 a. indigo .. .. .. .. | £120 | 85·0 |
| 56 | ½ a. deep ultramarine .. .. .. | 90·00 | 80·0 |
| 57 | 1 a. deep ultramarine .. .. .. | £130 | 95·0 |
| 58 | ½ a. deep violet-blue .. .. .. | 80·00 | 60·0 |
| 59 | 1 a. deep violet-blue .. .. .. | £180 | £12 |

**1868–77.** *In watercolour on native paper.*

| | | | |
|---|---|---|---|
| 60 | ½ a. red (*shades*) .. .. .. .. | 3·00 | 2·5 |
| 61 | 1 a. red (*shades*) .. .. .. .. | 5·00 | 5·0 |
| 62 | ½ a. orange-red .. .. .. .. | 90·00 | 28·0 |
| 63 | 1 a. orange-red .. .. .. .. | £120 | 42·0 |
| 64 | ½ a. orange .. .. .. .. | 85·00 | 80·0 |
| 65 | 1 a. orange .. .. .. .. | £350 | £27 |

**1874–6.** *Special printings; in watercolour on native paper.*

| | | | |
|---|---|---|---|
| 66 | ½ a. bright blue .. .. .. .. | £250 | £13 |
| 67 | 1 a. bright blue .. .. .. .. | £120 | £13 |
| 68 | ½ a. emerald-green .. .. .. .. | £900 | £70 |
| 69 | 1 a. emerald-green .. .. .. .. | £1500 | £100 |
| 69*a* | ½ a. jet-black .. .. .. .. | 95·00 | £12 |
| 69*b* | 1 a. jet-black .. .. .. .. | £650 | £55 |

**1877.** *In oil colour.* (*a*) *Native paper.*

| | | | |
|---|---|---|---|
| 70 | ½ a. red .. .. .. .. | 8·00 | 5·00 |
| 71 | 1 a. red .. .. .. .. | 17·00 | 13·00 |
| 72 | ½ a. brown-red .. .. .. .. | — | 28·00 |
| 73 | 1 a. brown-red .. .. .. .. | — | 80·00 |
| 74 | ½ a. black .. .. .. .. | — | £300 |
| 75 | 1 a. black .. .. .. .. | — | £450 |
| 76 | ½ a. deep blue-black .. .. .. | — | £650 |
| 77 | 1 a. deep blue-black .. .. .. | — | £2500 |

(*b*) *Laid paper* (*medium or thick*)

| | | | |
|---|---|---|---|
| 78 | ½ a. red .. .. .. .. | — | £375 |

(*c*) *Thick wove paper*

| | | | |
|---|---|---|---|
| 79 | ½ a. red .. .. .. .. | — | £325 |
| 80 | 1 a. red .. .. .. .. | | |

(*d*) *Thin laid, bâtonné paper*

| | | | |
|---|---|---|---|
| 84 | ½ a. red .. .. .. .. | — | £90 |
| 85 | 1 a. red .. .. .. .. | — | £275 |

The circular and rectangular stamps listed under the heading "Special Printings' did not supersede those in *red*, which was the normal colour for Jammu down to 1878. It is not known for what reason other colours were used during that period, but these stamps were printed in 1874 or 1875 and were certainly put into use. The rectangular stamps were again printed in *black* (jet-black, as against the greyish black of the 1867 printings) at that time, and impressions of the two periods can also be distinguished by the obliterations, which until 1868 were in *magenta* and after that in *black*.

There are reprints of these, in *oil* colour, *brown-red* and *bright blue*, on native paper; they are very clearly printed, which is not the case with the originals in *oil* colour.

### FOR USE IN KASHMIR

5

**1866** (Sept(?)). *Printed from a single die. Native laid paper.*

| | | | | |
|---|---|---|---|---|
| 86 | **5** | ½ a. black .. .. .. .. | £1200 | £275 |

Forgeries of this stamp are commonly found, copied from an illustration in *Le Timbre-Poste*.

6 (½ a.) 7 (1 a.)

**1867.** *Native laid paper.*

| | | | | |
|---|---|---|---|---|
| 87 | **6** | ½ a. black .. .. .. .. | £800 | 95·00 |
| 88 | **7** | 1 a. black .. .. .. .. | £1400 | £225 |

Printed in sheets of 25 (5 × 5), the four top rows being ½ a. and the bottom row 1 a.

8 (¼ a.) 9 (2 a.)

10 (4 a.)

11 (8 a.)

**1867.** *Native laid paper.*

90 8 ¼ a. black .. .. .. .. .. 70 70
91 6 ½ a. ultramarine .. .. .. .. 1·00 70
92 ½ a. violet-blue .. .. .. .. .. 1·25 90
93 7 1 a. ultramarine .. .. .. .. £2500 £1000
94 1 a. orange .. .. .. .. .. 6·00 5·00
95 1 a. brown-orange .. .. .. .. 6·00 5·00
96 1 a. orange-vermilion .. .. .. .. 6·00 5·00
97 9 2 a. yellow .. .. .. .. .. 7·00 6·00
98 2 a. buff .. .. .. .. .. 8·00 6·00
99 10 4 a. emerald-green .. .. .. .. 16·00 14·00
a. *Tête-bêche* (pair) .. .. .. .. £500
100 4 a. sage-green .. .. .. .. .. £100 45·00
100a 4 a. myrtle-green .. .. .. .. £500 £500
101 11 8 a. red .. .. .. .. .. 17·00 16·00
a. *Tête-bêche* (pair) .. .. .. .. £500

Of the above, the ½ a. and 1 a. were printed from the same plate of 25 as Nos. 87/8, the ¼ a. and 2 a. from a new plate of 10 (5 × 2), the top row being ¼ a. and the lower 2 a., and the 4 a. and 8 a. from single dies. Varieties at one time catalogued upon European papers were apparently never put into circulation, though some of them were printed while these stamps were still in use.

Nos. 86 to 101 are in watercolour.

### FOR USE IN JAMMU AND KASHMIR

In the following issues there are 15 varieties on the sheets of the ⅛ a., ¼ a. and ½ a.; 20 varieties of the 1 a. and 2 a. and 8 varieties of the 4 a. and 8 a. The value is in the lower part of the central oval.

12 (¼ a.)

13 (½ a.)

14 (1 a.)

15 (2 a.)

16 (4 a.)

17 (8 a.)

**1878–79.** *Provisional printings.*

I. *Ordinary white laid paper, of varying thickness*

(*a*) *Rough perf* 10 *to* 12 (i) *or* 13 *to* 16 (ii)

101b 12 ¼ a. red (i) .. .. .. .. ..
102 13 ½ a. red (i) .. .. .. .. .. 12·00 10·00
103 14 1 a. red (ii) .. .. .. .. .. £750
104 13 ½ a. slate-violet (i) .. .. .. .. 48·00 45·00
104a 14 1 a. violet (ii) .. .. .. .. ..

(*b*) *Imperf*

105 13 ½ a. slate-violet (*shades*) .. .. .. 13·00 12·00
106 14 1 a. slate-purple .. .. .. .. 18·00 18·00
107 1 a. mauve .. .. .. .. .. 21·00 21·00
108 15 2 a. violet .. .. .. .. .. 19·00 19·00
109 2 a. bright mauve .. .. .. .. 21·00 21·00
110 2 a. slate-blue .. .. .. .. 28·00 28·00
111 2 a. dull blue .. .. .. .. 40·00 40·00
112 12 ¼ a. red .. .. .. .. .. 14·00 13·00
113 13 ½ a. red .. .. .. .. .. 6·00 6·00
114 14 1 a. red .. .. .. .. .. 6·50 6·50
115 15 2 a. red .. .. .. .. .. 40·00 48·00
116 16 4 a. red .. .. .. .. .. 60·00 55·00

II. *Medium wove paper.* (*a*) *Rough perf* 10 *to* 12

117 13 ½ a. red .. .. .. .. .. — 80·00

(*b*) *Imperf*

117b 12 ¼ a. red .. .. .. .. ..
118 13 ½ a. red .. .. .. .. .. 6·00 4·50
119 14 1 a. red .. .. .. .. .. 6·50 6·50
120 15 2 a. red .. .. .. .. .. 35·00 10·00

III. *Thick wove paper. Imperf*

121 13 ½ a. red .. .. .. .. .. 22·00
122 14 1 a. red .. .. .. .. .. 30·00 13·00
123 15 2 a. red .. .. .. .. .. 12·00 13·00

**1879.** *Definitive issue. Thin wove paper, fine to coarse.*

(*d*) *Rough perf* 10 *to* 12

124 13 ½ a. red .. .. .. .. .. 90·00 70·00

(*b*) *Imperf*

125 12 ¼ a. red .. .. .. .. .. 1·25 1·50
126 13 ½ a. red .. .. .. .. .. 50 55
127 14 1 a. red .. .. .. .. .. 1·25 1·50
a. Bisected (½ a.) (on cover) .. .. † £2750
128 15 2 a. red .. .. .. .. .. 1·90 2·25
129 16 4 a. red .. .. .. .. .. 4·00 4·50
130 17 8 a. red .. .. .. .. .. 4·50 5·00

**1880** (Mar). *Provisional printing in watercolour on thin bâtonné paper. Imperf.*

130a 12 ¼ a. ultramarine .. .. .. .. £550 £400

**1881–83.** *As Nos.* 124 *to* 130. *Colour changed.*

(*a*) *Rough perf* 10 *to* 12

130b 13 ½ a. orange .. .. .. .. ..

(*b*) *Imperf*

131 12 ¼ a. orange .. .. .. .. .. 6·00 5·00
132 13 ½ a. orange .. .. .. .. .. 18·00 12·00
133 14 1 a. orange .. .. .. .. .. 13·00 7·00
a. Bisected (½ a.) (on cover) .. .. † £2750
134 15 2 a. orange .. .. .. .. .. 14·00 7·00
135 16 4 a. orange .. .. .. .. .. 20·00
136 17 8 a. orange .. .. .. .. .. 35·00

No. 127a was used at Leh in April 1883 and No. 133a was used there later.

Nos. 125/30 and 132/6 were re-issued between 1890 and 1894 and used concurrently with the stamps which follow. Such re-issues can be identified by the "three-circle" cancellations, introduced in December 1890.

18 (⅛ a.)

**1883–94.** *New colours. Thin wove papers, toned, coarse to fine, or fine white* (1889). *Imperf.*

138 18 ⅛ a. yellow-brown .. .. .. .. 20 30
139 ⅛ a. yellow .. .. .. .. .. 20 30
140 12 ¼ a. sepia .. .. .. .. .. 35 20
141 ¼ a. brown .. .. .. .. .. 30 20
a. Double impression .. .. .. .. £1100
142 ¼ a. pale brown .. .. .. .. .. 30 20
a. Error. Green .. .. .. .. 40·00
143 13 ½ a. dull blue .. .. .. .. .. 4·00
144 ½ a. bright blue .. .. .. .. 40·00
145 ½ a. vermillion .. .. .. .. .. 55 30
146 ½ a. rose .. .. .. .. .. 55 45
147 ½ a. orange-red .. .. .. .. .. 50 30
148 14 1 a. greenish grey .. .. .. .. 35 35
149 1 a. bright green .. .. .. .. 45 50
a. Double impression .. .. .. ..
150 1 a. dull green .. .. .. .. .. 35 35
151 1 a. blue-green .. .. .. .. .. 65
152 15 2 a. red/*yellow* .. .. .. .. 55 55
153 2 a. red/*yellow-green* .. .. .. 80 1·00
154 2 a. red/*deep green* .. .. .. 4·50 4·50
155 16 4 a. deep green .. .. .. .. 1·75 2·25
156 4 a. green .. .. .. .. .. 1·75 2·25
157 4 a. pale green .. .. .. .. 2·00 2·50
158 4 a. sage-green .. .. .. .. 2·00
159 17 8 a. pale blue .. .. .. .. 4·00 5·00
159a 8 a. deep blue .. .. .. .. 6·00 6·50
160 8 a. bright blue .. .. .. .. 5·50 6·50
161 8 a. indigo-blue .. .. .. .. 7·50 8·50
161a 8 a. slate-lilac .. .. .. .. 10·00 12·00

Well-executed forgeries of the ¼ a. to 8 a. have come from India, mostly postmarked; they may be detected by the type, which does not agree with any variety on the genuine sheets, and also, in the low values, by the margins being filled in with colour, all but a thin white frame round the stamp. The forgeries of the 8 a. are in sheets of eight like the originals.

Other forgeries of nearly all values also exist, showing all varieties of type. All values are on thin, coarse wove paper.

In February 1890, a forgery, in watercolour, of the ½ a. orange appeared, and many have been found genuinely used (*Price* £3).

Nos. 143 and 144 were never issued.

Examples of the ¼ a. brown, ½ a. orange-red and 1 a. green on wove paper exist with clean-cut perf 12.

There is a reference in the Jammu and Kashmir State Administration Report covering 1890–91 to the re-introduction of perforating and the machine-gumming of paper at the Jammu printing works.

The few known examples, the ¼ a. being only recorded used, the others unused or used, would appear to date from this period, but there is, as yet, no direct confirmation as to their status.

**1887–94.** *Thin creamy laid paper. Imperf.*

162 18 ⅛ a. yellow .. .. .. .. .. 16·00 17·00
163 12 ¼ a. brown .. .. .. .. .. 9·00 6·00
164 13 ½ a. brown-red (March 1887) .. .. — 42·00
165 ½ a. orange-red .. .. .. .. 6·00 4·75
166 14 1 a. grey-green .. .. .. .. £120 £110
168 17 8 a. blue (*Printed in watercolour*) .. £150 £150
a. On wove paper .. .. .. £100 £100

19

T **19** represents a ¼ a. stamp, which exists in sheets of twelve varieties, in *red* and *black*, on thin wove and laid papers, also in *red* on native paper, but which does not appear ever to have been issued for use. It was first seen in 1886.

The ¼ a. *brown*, and the 4 a. *green*, exist on ordinary white laid paper; the ½ a. *red* on native paper; the ¼ a. in *bright green*, on thin white wove (this may be an error in the colour of the 4 a.); and the 8 a. in *lilac* on thin white wove. None of these are known to have been in use.

### OFFICIAL STAMPS

**1878.** I. *White laid paper.* (*a*) *Rough perf* 10 *to* 12.

O1 13 ½ a. black .. .. .. .. ..

(*b*) *Imperf*

O2 13 ½ a. black .. .. .. .. 45·00 45·00
O3 14 1 a. black .. .. .. .. 50·00 50·00
O4 15 2 a. black .. .. .. .. 50·00 55·00

II. *Medium wove paper. Imperf*

O5 14 1 a. black .. .. .. .. ..

**1880–94.** *Thin wove papers, toned, coarse to fine, or fine white* (1889). *Imperf.*

O 6 12 ¼ a. black .. .. .. .. 30 30
a. Double print .. .. .. .. £120
O 7 13 ½ a. black .. .. .. .. 15 20
O 8 14 1 a. black .. .. .. .. 20 20
O 9 15 2 a. black .. .. .. .. 30 30
O10 16 4 a. black .. .. .. .. 35 50
O11 17 8 a. black .. .. .. .. 50 60

**1887–94.** *Thin creamy laid paper. Imperf.*

O12 12 ¼ a. black .. .. .. .. 2·50 3·00
O13 13 ½ a. black .. .. .. .. 1·90 2·50
O14 14 1 a. black .. .. .. .. 1·50 2·00
O15 15 2 a. black .. .. .. .. 12·00
O16 16 4 a. black .. .. .. .. 38·00 42·00
O17 17 8 a. black .. .. .. .. 28·00 40·00

**1889.** *Stout white wove paper. Imperf.*

O18 12 ¼ a. black .. .. .. .. 90·00

The stamps of Jammu and Kashmir have been obsolete since 1 November 1894.

## JASDAN

**PRICES FOR STAMPS ON COVER**

| | |
|---|---|
| Nos. 1/2 | *from* × 2 |
| No. 3 | *from* × 3 |
| Nos. 4/6 | *from* × 5 |

1 Sun

(Typo L. V. Indap & Co, Bombay)

**1942** (15 Mar)–**47**(?). *Stamps from booklet panes. Various perfs.*

1 1 1 a. myrtle-green (*p* 10½×*imperf*) .. £275 £275
2 1 a. light green (*p* 12×*imperf*) .. £250 £275
3 1 a. light green (*p* 10½×*imperf*) .. 60·00 80·00
4 1 a. pale yellow-green (*p* 8½×*imperf*) 5·50 45·00
5 1 a. dull yellow-green (*p* 10) .. 8·00 50·00
6 1 a. bluish green (*p* 9) .. .. 7·00 45·00

Nos. 1/4 were issued in panes of four with the stamps imperforate on one or two sides; Nos. 5/6 were in panes of eight perforated all round.

A 1 a. rose with the arms of Jasdan in the centre is a fiscal stamp.

Jasdan was merged with the United State of Kathiawar on 15 February 1948 and renamed the United State of Saurashtra.

## JHALAWAR

**PRICES FOR STAMPS ON COVER**

Nos. 1/2 *from* × 25

(Figure of an Apsara, "RHEMBA", a dancing nymph of the Hindu Paradise)

1 (1 paisa) 2 (¼ anna)

**1887–90.** *Typo in horizontal strips of* 12. *Laid paper. No gum.*

| No. | Type | Description | Unused | Used |
|---|---|---|---|---|
| 1 | 1 | 1 p. yellow-green | 1·25 | 4·25 |
| | | *a. Blue-green* | 32·00 | 15·00 |
| 2 | 2 | ¼ a. green (*shades*) | 60 | 1·25 |

The stamps formerly listed as on wove paper are from sheets on laid paper, with the laid lines almost invisible.

The stamps of Jhalawar have been obsolete since 1 November 1900.

## JIND

**PRICES FOR STAMPS ON COVER**
Nos. J1/34 *from* × 50

**ILLUSTRATIONS.** Designs of Jind are illustrated actual size.

J 1 (½ a.)

J 2 (1 a.)

J 3 (2 a.)

J 4 (4 a.)

J 5 (8 a.)

(The letter "R" on stamp is the initial of Raghbir Singh, at one time Rajah)

(Litho Jind State Rajah's Press, Sungroor)

**1874.** *Thin yellowish paper. Imperf.*

| No. | Type | Description | Unused | Used |
|---|---|---|---|---|
| J1 | J 1 | ½ a. blue | 4·00 | 2·00 |
| | | a. No frame to value. (Retouched all over) | £225 | £140 |
| J2 | J 2 | 1 a. rosy mauve | 7·00 | 6·00 |
| J3 | J 3 | 2 a. yellow | 1·00 | 2·50 |
| J4 | | 2 a. brown-buff | 50·00 | 35·00 |
| J5 | J 4 | 4 a. green | 18·00 | 5·00 |
| J6 | J 5 | 8 a. dull purple | £300 | 80·00 |
| J6*a* | | 8 a. bluish violet | £140 | 60·00 |
| J7 | | 8 a. slate-blue | £130 | 60·00 |

**1876.** *Bluish laid card-paper. No gum. Imperf.*

| No. | Type | Description | Unused | Used |
|---|---|---|---|---|
| J 8 | J 1 | ½ a. blue | 30 | 1·50 |
| J 9 | J 2 | 1 a. purple | 1·25 | 3·50 |
| J10 | J 3 | 2 a. brown | 70 | 4·50 |
| J11 | J 4 | 4 a. green | 1·00 | 5·00 |
| J11*a* | J 5 | 8 a. bluish violet | 8·00 | 14·00 |
| J12 | | 8 a. slate-blue | 7·00 | 10·00 |
| J13 | | 8 a. steel-blue | 9·00 | 15·00 |

Stocks of the ½ a. (No. J8) and 2 a. (No. J4) were perforated 12 in 1885 for use as fiscal stamps.

J 6 (¼ a.)

J 7 (½ a.)

J 8 (1 a.)

J 9 (2 a.)

J 10 (4 a.)

J 11 (8 a.)

(Litho Jind State Rajah's Press, Sungroor)

**1882–85.** *Types* J **6** *to* J **11**. 25 *varieties of each value. No gum.* A. *Imperf* (1882–4). B. *P* 12 (1885). (*a*) *Thin yellowish wove paper.*

| No. | Description | A | | B | |
|---|---|---|---|---|---|
| J15 | ¼ a. buff (*shades*) | 30 | 95 | 40 | 95 |
| J16 | ¼ a. red-brown | 30 | 70 | 1·60 | — |
| | a. Doubly printed | 42·00 | — | † | |
| J17 | ½ a. lemon | 50 | 50 | 50·00 | 50·00 |
| J18 | ½ a. buff | 75 | 1·00 | 40 | 1·60 |
| J19 | ½ a. brown-buff | 70 | 60 | 1·60 | 2·25 |
| J20 | 1 a. brown (*shades*) | 1·00 | 2·00 | 1·10 | 2·25 |
| J21 | 2 a. blue | 1·25 | 3·00 | 1·40 | 3·50 |
| J22 | 2 a. deep blue | 90 | 1·00 | 2·25 | 2·50 |
| J23 | 4 a. sage-green | 80 | 90 | 3·00 | 4·00 |
| J24 | 4 a. blue-green | 1·40 | 1·90 | 2·00 | — |
| | a. Imperf between (pair) | † | | £475 | — |
| J25 | 8 a. red | 3·00 | 3·00 | 6·50 | — |
| | (*b*) *Various thick laid papers* | | | | |
| J26 | ¼ a. brown-buff | 1·50 | — | 6·00 | — |
| J27 | ½ a. lemon | 1·50 | — | 40·00 | 20·00 |
| J27*a* | ½ a. brown-buff | — | — | † | |
| J28 | 1 a. brown | 1·50 | 2·50 | 2·00 | — |
| J29 | 2 a. blue | 18·00 | 20·00 | 18·00 | 20·00 |
| J30 | 8 a. red | 2·50 | 6·50 | 2·50 | 5·50 |
| | (*c*) *Thick white wove paper* | | | | |
| J31 | ¼ a. brown-buff | 9·00 | — | † | |
| J32 | ½ a. brown-buff | 20·00 | — | † | |
| J33 | 1 a. brown | 3·50 | — | — | — |
| J34 | 8 a. red | 4·50 | 6·00 | 6·50 | — |

The perforated stamps ceased to be used for postal purposes in July 1885, but were used as fiscals to at least the mid-1920s. Other varieties exist, but they must either be fiscals or reprints, and it is not quite certain that all those listed above were issued as early as 1885.

Jind became a Convention State and from 1 July 1885 used overprinted Indian stamps.

## KISHANGARH

**PRICES FOR STAMPS ON COVER**
Nos. 1/3 —
Nos. 4/91 *from* × 8
Nos. O1/32 *from* × 30

**GUM.** The stamps of Kishangarh were issued without gum, *except for* Nos. 42/50 and O 17/24.

1

**1899.** *Medium wove paper. Typo from a plate of eight impressions.*

| No. | Type | Description | Unused | Used |
|---|---|---|---|---|
| 1 | 1 | 1 a. green (*imperf*) | 18·00 | 40·00 |
| 2 | | 1 a. green (*pin-perf*) | 42·00 | |

**1900.** *Thin white wove paper. Printed from a single die. Imperf.*

| No. | Type | Description | Unused | Used |
|---|---|---|---|---|
| 3 | 1 | 1 a. blue | £375 | |

**ILLUSTRATIONS.** Types **2** to **10***a* are shown actual size.

**2** (¼ a.)

**3** (½ a.)

**4** (1 a.)

**5** (2 a.)
Maharaja Sardul Singh

**6** (4 a.)

**7** (1 r.)

**8** (2 r.)

**9** (5 r.)

**1899–1901.** *Thin white wove paper.* (*a*) *Imperf.*

| No. | Type | Description | Unused | Used |
|---|---|---|---|---|
| 4 | 2 | ¼ a. green | £250 | |
| 5 | | ¼ a. carmine | 3·00 | |
| | | *a. Rose-pink* | 30 | 1·00 |
| 6 | | ¼ a. magenta | 5·00 | |
| | | a. Doubly printed | 75·00 | |
| 7 | 3 | ½ a. lilac | 55·00 | 80·00 |
| 8 | | ½ a. red | £900 | £600 |
| 9 | | ½ a. green | 22·00 | 25·00 |
| 10 | | ½ a. pale yellow-olive | 30·00 | 30·00 |
| | | *a. Bistre-brown* | 30·00 | 30·00 |
| 11 | | ½ a. slate-blue | 12·00 | 14·00 |
| | | a. Pair, one stamp sideways | £1000 | |
| | | *b. Deep blue* | 2·75 | 3·25 |
| | | *c. Light blue* | 60 | 80 |
| 12 | 4 | 1 a. slate | 3·25 | 4·00 |
| | | a. Laid paper | 32·00 | |
| 12*b* | | 1 a. pink | 50·00 | £110 |
| 13 | | 1 a. mauve | 3·25 | 2·75 |
| | | a. Laid paper | 30·00 | |
| 14 | | 1 a. brown-lilac | 1·10 | 90 |
| | | a. Laid paper | 27·00 | |
| 15 | 5 | 2 a. dull orange | 4·00 | 4·50 |
| | | a. Laid paper | £225 | £225 |
| 16 | 6 | 4 a. chocolate | 4·25 | |
| | | *a. Lake-brown* | 4·25 | 6·50 |
| | | *b. Chestnut* | 4·25 | 6·50 |
| | | c. Laid paper (*shades*) | 50·00 | 50·00 |
| 17 | 7 | 1 r. brown-lilac | 20·00 | 25·00 |
| 18 | | 1 r. dull green | 17·00 | |
| 19 | 8 | 2 r. brown-red | 60·00 | |
| | | a. Laid paper | 55·00 | |
| 20 | 9 | 5 r. mauve | 50·00 | |
| | | a. Laid paper | 60·00 | |
| | | (*b*) *Pin-perf* 12½ *or* 14 | | |
| 21 | 2 | ¼ a. green | £140 | £225 |
| | | a. Imperf between (pair) | £475 | |
| 22 | | ¼ a. carmine | 1·40 | 2·25 |
| | | *a. Rose-pink* | 25 | 40 |
| | | ab. *Tête-bêche* (horiz pair) | £275 | |
| | | *b. Rose* | | |
| 23 | | ¼ a. magenta | 5·00 | 7·00 |
| | | *a. Bright purple* | | |
| | | ab. Doubly printed | | |
| 24 | 3 | ½ a. green | 17·00 | 21·00 |
| | | a. Imperf between (pair) | £160 | |
| 25 | | ½ a. pale yellow-olive | 12·00 | 15·00 |
| | | a. Imperf vert (horiz pair) | £160 | |
| | | *b. Bistre-brown* | 12·00 | 15·00 |
| 26 | | ½ a. deep blue | 1·40 | 1·75 |
| | | *a. Light blue* | 40 | 40 |
| | | ab. Doubly printed | 70·00 | 70·00 |
| 27 | 4 | 1 a. slate | 3·25 | 1·60 |
| | | a. Laid paper | 30·00 | 16·00 |
| 27*b* | | 1 a. pink | 60·00 | £120 |
| 28 | | 1 a. mauve | 80 | 1·00 |
| | | a. Laid paper | 30·00 | 13·00 |
| 29 | | 1 a. brown-lilac | 75 | 60 |
| | | a. Laid paper | 30·00 | 13·00 |
| 30 | 5 | 2 a. dull orange | 4·00 | 5·00 |
| 31 | 6 | 4 a. chocolate | 2·00 | 3·75 |
| | | *a. Lake-brown* | 2·50 | 3·75 |
| | | *b. Chestnut* | 3·50 | 4·25 |
| | | c. Laid paper (*shades*) | 40·00 | 40·00 |
| 32 | 7 | 1 r. dull green | 10·00 | 14·00 |
| | | a. Laid paper | 70·00 | |
| 33 | | 1 r. pale olive-yellow | £250 | £250 |
| 34 | 8 | 2 r. brown-red | 35·00 | 42·00 |
| | | a. Laid paper | 40·00 | |
| 35 | 9 | 5 r. mauve | 30·00 | 42·00 |
| | | a. Laid paper | 60·00 | |

All the above, both imperf and pin-perf, exist in vertical *tête-bêche* pairs imperf between from the centre of the sheet. *Prices from* 3 × *normal, unused.* No. 22ab is an error.

**FISCAL STAMPS.** Many of the following issues were produced in different colours for fiscal purposes. Such usage is indicated by the initials "M.C.", punched hole or violet Stamp Office handstamp.

10 (¼ a.)

10*a* (1 r.)

901. *Toned wove paper. Pin-perf.*
6 10 ¼ a. dull pink .. .. .. .. .. 8·00 6·00
7 4 1 a. violet .. .. .. .. .. 38·00 27·00
8 10*a* 1 r. dull green .. .. .. .. .. 14·00 15·00
6/8 .. .. .. .. *Set of* 3 55·00 42·00

These were printed from plates: Nos. 36 and 37 in sheets of 24, No. 38 in sheets of 16. All the others, except Nos. 1, 2 and 3, were printed singly, sometimes on paper with spaces ruled in pencil.
The 1 a. (No. 37) differs from T 4 in having an inscription in native characters below the words "ONE ANNA".

11 (½ a.)

12 Maharaja Sardul Singh

903. *Litho. Thick white wove glazed paper. Imperf.*
9 11 ½ a. pink .. .. .. .. .. 4·00 3·00
a. Printed both sides .. .. .. .. † £900
0 12 2 a. dull yellow .. .. .. .. .. 3·00 4·00

12*a* (8 a.)

904. *Printed singly. Thin paper. Pin-perf.*
1 12*a* 8 a. grey .. .. .. .. .. 5·00 7·50
a. *Tête-bêche* (pair) .. .. .. 24·00
b. Doubly printed .. .. .. .. 90·00

13 Maharaja Madan Singh 14

(Recess Perkins Bacon & Co)

904–5. *With gum. P* 12½.
2 13 ¼ a. carmine .. .. .. .. .. 40 35
a. Perf 13½ .. .. .. .. .. 40 35
3 ½ a. chestnut .. .. .. .. .. 60 65
a. Perf 13½ .. .. .. .. .. 30 30
4 1 a. blue .. .. .. .. .. 1·60 1·10
a. Perf 13½ .. .. .. .. .. 40 60
5 2 a. orange-yellow .. .. .. .. 8·00 7·00
a. Perf 13½ .. .. .. .. 16·00 10·00
6 4 a. brown .. .. .. .. .. 10·00 8·50
a. Perf 13½ .. .. .. .. 8·00 8·00
b. Perf 12 .. .. .. .. 24·00 24·00
7 8 a. violet (1905) .. .. .. .. 6·00 10·00
8 1 r. green .. .. .. .. .. 12·00 15·00
9 2 r. olive-yellow .. .. .. .. 14·00 42·00
0 5 r. purple-brown .. .. .. .. 21·00 40·00
2/50 .. .. .. .. .. *Set of* 9 60·00 £130

Stamps in other colours, all perforated 13½, are colour trials.

912. *Printed from half-tone blocks. No ornaments to left and right of value in English; large ornaments on either side of value in Hindi. Small stop after "STATE". (a) Thin wove paper. Rouletted.*
1 14 2 a. deep violet ("TWO ANNA") .. 3·00 6·00
a. *Tête-bêche* (vert pair) .. .. 7·00
b. Imperf (pair) .. .. .. £140

No. 51 is printed in four rows, each inverted in respect to that above and below it.

*(b) Thick white chalk-surfaced paper. Rouletted*
2 14 2 a. lilac ("TWO ANNA") .. .. £350 £200

*c) Thick white chalk-surfaced paper. Rouletted in colour (Medallion only in half-tone)*
3 14 ¼ a. ultramarine .. .. .. .. 8·00 10·00

913. *No ornaments on either side of value in English. Small ornaments in bottom label. With stop after "STATE". Thick white chalk-surfaced paper. Rouletted.*
4 14 2 a. purple ("TWO ANNAS") .. .. 2·50 5·00

15

पाव आना

No. 59e. This occurs on R. 3/3 on one setting only

2 TWO ANNAS 2 — No. 60. Small figures

2 TWO ANNAS 2 — No. 60b. Large figures

(Typo Diamond Soap Works, Kishangarh)

1913 (Aug). *Thick surfaced paper. Half-tone centre. Type-set inscriptions. Rouletted. Inscr "KISHANGARH".*
59 15 ¼ a. pale blue .. .. .. .. 20 30
a. Imperf (pair) .. .. .. .. 7·00
b. Roul × imperf (horiz pair) .. .. 22·00
c. "OUARTER" .. .. .. .. 5·00 5·50
ca. As last, imperf (pair) .. .. 28·00
cb. As last, roul × imperf .. .. 50·00
d. "KISHANGAHR" .. .. .. 5·00 5·50
da. As last, imperf (pair) .. .. 28·00
db. As last, roul × imperf .. .. 50·00
e. Character omitted .. .. .. 7·00 7·00
ea. As last, imperf (pair) .. .. 32·00
60 2 a. purple .. .. .. .. 7·00 16·00
a. "KISHANGAHR" .. .. .. 60·00 85·00
b. Large figures "2" .. .. .. 32·00 50·00

1913–16. *Stamps printed far apart, horizontally and vertically, otherwise as No. 54, except as noted below.*
63 14 ¼ a. blue .. .. .. .. .. 20 40
64 ½ a. green (1915) .. .. .. 20 55
a. Printed both sides .. .. .. £140
b. Imperf (pair) .. .. .. £130 £130
*c. Emerald-green* (1916) .. .. 1·75 2·75
65 1 a. red .. .. .. .. 1·00 1·75
a. Without stop* .. .. .. 1·25 2·50
ab. Imperf (pair) .. .. .. £150
66 2 a. purple ("TWO ANNAS") (1915) .. 6·00 7·00
67 4 a. bright blue .. .. .. .. 6·00 8·00
68 8 a. brown .. .. .. .. 7·00 28·00
69 1 r. mauve .. .. .. .. 12·00 55·00
70 2 r. deep green .. .. .. .. 42·00 £100
71 5 r. brown .. .. .. .. 85·00 £180
63/71 .. .. .. .. .. *Set of* 9 £140 £350

*For this issue, ornaments were added on either side of the English value (except in the ¼ a.) and the inscription in the right label was without stop, except in the case of No. 65.
In Nos. 70 and 71 the value is expressed as "RUPIES" instead of "RUPEES".
Initial printings of the ¼ a., 1 a. and 4 a. values were in sheets of 20 containing two pairs of 10 separated by a central gutter margin. Stamps from these sheets measure 20 × 25½ mm and have heavier screening dots on the perforation margins than on the designs. Subsequent printings of these stamps, and of the other values in the set, were from single pane sheets of 20 on which the designs measured 19½ × 24¾ mm and with the screening dots uniform across the sheet.

16 Maharaja Yagyanarain Singhji 17

1928–36. *Thick surfaced paper. Typo. Pin-perf.*
72 16 ¼ a. light blue .. .. .. .. 35 1·40
73 ½ a. yellow-green .. .. .. .. 50 60
*a. Deep green* .. .. .. .. 1·25 1·50
ab. Imperf (pair) .. .. .. 45·00 45·00
ac. Imperf between (vert or horiz pair) 48·00 48·00
74 17 1 a. carmine .. .. .. .. 60 1·00
a. Imperf (pair) .. .. .. 70·00 70·00
75 2 a. purple .. .. .. .. 3·00 6·50
75*a* 2 a. magenta (1936) .. .. .. 5·00 10·00
ab. Imperf (pair) .. .. .. 95·00
76 16 4 a. chestnut .. .. .. .. 1·25 1·75
a. Imperf (pair) .. .. ..
77 8 a. violet .. .. .. .. 3·50 15·00
78 1 r. light green .. .. .. .. 7·50 30·00
79 2 r. lemon-yellow (1929) .. .. 22·00 65·00
80 5 r. claret (1929) .. .. .. 25·00 80·00
a. Imperf (pair) .. .. .. £100
72/80 .. .. .. .. .. *Set of* 9 55·00 £180

The 4 a. to 5 r. are slightly larger than, but otherwise similar to, the ¼ a. and ½ a. The 8 a. has a dotted background covering the whole design.

1943–47. *As last, but thick, soft, unsurfaced paper. Poor impression. Typo. Pin-perf.*
81 16 ¼ a. pale dull blue (1945) .. .. 1·40 3·50
a. Imperf (pair) .. .. .. 28·00
82 ¼ a. greenish blue (1947) .. .. 1·10 3·00
a. Imperf (pair) .. .. .. 28·00
83 ½ a. deep green (1944) .. .. .. 80 1·10
a. Imperf (pair) .. .. .. 25·00 25·00
b. Imperf between (vert or horiz pair) 35·00
84 ½ a. yellow-green (1946) .. .. 2·75 3·25
a. Imperf (pair) .. .. .. 25·00 25·00
b. Imperf between (vert or horiz pair) 35·00
85 17 1 a. carmine-red (1944) .. .. .. 3·00 2·00
a. Double print .. .. ..
b. Imperf (pair) .. .. .. 25·00 25·00
c. Imperf between (vert or horiz pair) 35·00
*d. Red-orange* (1947) .. .. .. 27·00 18·00
da. Imperf (pair) .. .. .. 55·00 55·00

86 2 a. bright magenta .. .. .. 5·50 8·50
a. Imperf (pair) .. .. .. 40·00 40·00
87 2 a. maroon (1947) .. .. .. 40·00 15·00
a. Imperf (pair) .. .. .. 42·00 42·00
b. Imperf between (vert or horiz pair) 60·00
88 16 4 a. brown (1944) .. .. .. 21·00 16·00
a. Imperf (pair) .. .. ..
89 8 a. violet (1945) .. .. .. 38·00 70·00
90 1 r. green (1945) .. .. .. 45·00 90·00
a. Imperf (pair) .. .. .. £150 £200
90*b* 2 r. yellow (date?) .. .. ..
ba. Imperf (pair) .. .. .. £325
91 5 r. claret (1945) .. .. .. £275 £325
a. Imperf (pair) .. .. .. £275

OFFICIAL STAMPS

(O 1)

1918. *Handstamped with Type* O 1.

*(a) Stamps of* 1899–1901. (i) *Imperf*
O 1 2 ¼ a. green .. .. .. .. — £100
O 2 ¼ a. rose-pink .. .. .. .. — 5·00
O 3 4 1 a. mauve .. .. .. .. — 32·00
O 3a 1 a. brown-lilac .. .. .. .. 27·00 4·75
O 4 6 4 a. chocolate .. .. .. .. — 45·00

(ii) *Pin-perf*
O 5 2 ¼ a. green .. .. .. .. — 85·00
O 6 ¼ a. rose-pink .. .. .. .. 1·50 60
O 7 3 ½ a. light blue .. .. .. .. — 28·00
O 8 4 1 a. mauve .. .. .. .. 16·00 1·50
O 9 1 a. brown-lilac .. .. .. .. 14·00 1·50
O10 5 2 a. dull orange .. .. .. .. — 90·00
O11 6 4 a. chocolate .. .. .. .. 23·00 16·00
O12 7 1 r. dull green .. .. .. .. 80·00 75·00
O13 8 2 r. brown-red .. .. .. .. — £600
O14 9 5 r. mauve .. .. .. .. — £750

*(b) Stamps of* 1903 *and* 1904
O15 12 2 a. dull yellow .. .. .. .. 25·00 7·00
a. Stamp printed both sides .. .. † £475
b. Red opt .. .. .. .. £120 85·00
O16 12*a* 8 a. grey .. .. .. .. 30·00 22·00
a. Red opt .. .. .. .. — 75·00

(c) *Stamps of* 1904–5. *P* 13½ (¼ *a. to* 4 *a.) or* 12½ *(others)*
O17 13 ¼ a. carmine .. .. .. .. — £100
O18 ½ a. chestnut .. .. .. .. 65 35
O19 1 a. blue .. .. .. .. 7·00 4·00
a. Red opt .. .. .. .. 11·00 7·00
O20 2 a. orange-yellow .. .. .. .. — £450
O21 4 a. brown .. .. .. .. 27·00 18·00
a. Red opt .. .. .. .. 32·00 21·00
O22 8 a. violet .. .. .. .. £140 £110
a. Red opt .. .. .. .. — £110
O23 1 r. green .. .. .. .. £275 £250
a. Red opt .. .. .. .. — £225
O24 5 r. purple-brown .. .. .. ..

*(d) Stamps of* 1913
O25 15 ¼ a. pale blue .. .. .. .. 6·00
a. "OUARTER" .. .. .. .. 22·00
b. "KISHANGAHR" .. .. .. 22·00
c. Character omitted .. .. .. 22·00
d. Imperf (pair) .. .. .. 75·00
O26 14 2 a. purple (No. 54) .. .. .. — 45·00
a. Red opt .. .. .. .. 70·00 20·00
O27 15 2 a. purple .. .. .. .. £160 £170
a. "KISHANGAHR" .. .. .. £325
b. Large figures "2" .. .. .. £250

*(e) Stamps of* 1913–16
O28 14 ¼ a. blue .. .. .. .. 50 50
a. Red opt .. .. .. .. 1·75 1·75
O29 ½ a. green .. .. .. .. 75 75
a. Red opt .. .. .. .. 2·00 1·50
O30 1 a. red .. .. .. .. 3·50 3·50
a. Without stop .. .. .. 1·00 1·00
ab. Red opt .. .. .. .. — 55·00
O31 2 a. purple .. .. .. .. 5·50 4·00
a. Red opt .. .. .. .. 65·00 35·00
O32 4 a. bright blue .. .. .. .. 20·00 15·00
a. Red opt .. .. .. .. — 30·00
O33 8 a. brown .. .. .. .. 65·00 40·00
a. Red opt .. .. .. .. — 75·00
O34 1 r. lilac .. .. .. .. £180 £180
O35 2 r. deep green .. .. .. ..
O36 5 r. brown .. .. .. .. £750

This overprint is found inverted as often as it is upright; and many other "errors" exist.
On 25 March 1948 Kishangarh became part of the Rajasthan Union.

## LAS BELA

| PRICES FOR STAMPS ON COVER | |
|---|---|
| Nos. 1/12 | *from* × 8 |

1

2

(Litho Thacker & Co, Bombay)

**1897–98.** *Thick paper. Pin-perf.*
1 1 ½ a. black on *white* .. .. .. 9·00 6·00

**1898–1900.** *Pin-perf.*
2 1 ½ a. black on *greyish blue* (1898) .. .. 7·50 4·50
3 ½ a. black on *greenish grey* (1899) .. .. 6·50 4·00
a. "BFLA" for "BELA" .. .. .. 70·00
b. Imperf between (horiz strip of 3)
4 ½ a. black on *thin white surfaced paper* (1899) .. .. .. .. .. 15·00
5 ½ a. black on *slate* (1900) .. .. .. 20·00
a. Imperf between (pair) .. .. .. £325

**1901–2.** *Pin-perf.*
6 1 ½ a. black on *pale grey* .. .. .. 7·00 6·00
a. "BFLA" for "BELA" .. .. 65·00
7 ½ a. black on *pale green* (1902) .. .. 12·00 13·00
8 2 1 a. black on *orange* .. .. .. 10·00 11·00

There are at least 14 settings of the above ½ a. stamps, the sheets varying from 16 to 30 stamps.

**1904.** *Stamps printed wider apart. Pin-perf.*
11 1 ½ a. black on *pale blue* .. .. .. 7·00 6·00
a. Imperf between (pair) .. .. £350
12 ½ a. black on *pale green* .. .. .. 7·00 6·00

There are three plates of the above two stamps, each consisting of 18 varieties.

All the coloured papers of the ½ a. show coloured fibres, similar to those in granite paper.

The stamps of Las Bela have been obsolete since 1 April 1907.

## MORVI

**PRICES FOR STAMPS ON COVER**
Nos. 1/19 *from* × 6

1

2

3

Maharaja Sir Lakhdirji Waghji

**1931** (1 April). *Typo. P* 12.

(*a*) *Printed in blocks of four. Stamps 10 mm apart (Nos. 1/2) or 6½ mm apart (No. 3). Perf on two or three sides*
1 1 3 p. deep red .. .. .. .. 3·00 8·50
2 ½ a. blue .. .. .. .. 16·00 22·00
3 2 a. yellow-brown .. .. .. 70·00
1/3 .. .. .. .. .. *Set of* 3 80·00

(*b*) *Printed in two blocks of four. Stamps 5½ mm apart. Perf on four sides*
4 1 3 p. bright scarlet .. .. .. 3·00 8·00
a. Error. Dull blue .. .. .. 3·75 11·00
b. Ditto. Double print .. .. .. £325
c. Ditto. Printed on gummed side .. £325
5 ½ a. dull blue .. .. .. 1·75 4·50
6 1 a. brown-red .. .. .. 2·75 9·50
7 2 a. yellow-brown .. .. .. 4·00 13·00
4/7 .. .. .. .. *Set of* 4 9·00 32·00

Nos. 1/3 were supplied to post offices in panes of four sewn into bundles with interleaving.

**1932–33.** *Horizontal background lines wider apart and portrait smaller than in T* 1. *Typo. P* 11.
8 2 3 p. carmine-rose (*shades*) .. .. 75 2·50
9 6 p. green .. .. .. .. 90 3·25
a. Imperf between (horiz pair) .. £1200
*b. Emerald-green* .. .. .. 60 2·75
10 1 a. ultramarine (*to deep*) .. .. 1·25 5·50
a. Imperf between (vert pair) .. .. £900
11 2 a. bright violet (1933) .. .. 10·00 18·00
a. Imperf between (vert pair) .. .. £900
8/11 .. .. .. .. *Set of* 4 11·00 26·00

**1934.** *Typo. London ptg. P* 14.
12 3 3 p. carmine .. .. .. 70 1·00
13 6 p. emerald-green .. .. .. 60 2·25
14 1 a. purple-brown .. .. .. 1·00 4·00
a. Imperf between (horiz pair) .. † £850
15 2 a. bright violet .. .. .. 2·00 7·00
12/15 .. .. .. .. *Set of* 4 3·50 13·00

**1935–48.** *Typo. Morvi Press ptg. Rough perf* 11.
16 3 3 p. scarlet (*shades*) .. .. .. 40 1·25
a. Imperf between (horiz pair) .. £850
17 6 p. grey-green .. .. .. 60 1·90
*a. Emerald-green* .. .. .. 4·25 13·00
18 1 a. brown .. .. .. 12·00 14·00
*a. Pale yellow-brown* .. .. 15·00 22·00
*b. Chocolate* .. .. .. 16·00 22·00
19 2 a. dull violet (*to deep*) .. .. 2·50 10·00
16/19 .. .. .. .. *Set of* 4 14·00 25·00

Nos. 17*a*, 18*a* and 18*b* were issued between 1944 and 1948.

Morvi was incorporated in the Union of Saurashtra on 15 February 1948.

## *MINIMUM PRICE*

The minimum price quote is 10p which represents a handling charge rather than a basis for valuing common stamps. For further notes about prices see introductory pages.

## NANDGAON

**PRICES FOR STAMPS ON COVER**
The stamps of Nandgaon are very rare used on cover.

**GUM.** The stamps of Nandgaon were issued without gum.

1

**1892** (Feb). *Litho. Imperf.*
1 1 ½ a. blue .. .. .. .. .. 1·60 75·00
*a. Dull blue* .. .. .. .. 2·50
b. Optd with T 2 .. .. .. £120
2 2 a. rose .. .. .. .. .. 11·00 £150

Collectors are warned against copies of T 1 with faked postmarks. Genuinely used they are very rare.

(2)

3 (2 a.)

("M.B.D." = Rajah Machant Balram Das)

**1893–94.** *Typo.*

(i) *Printed wide apart on the sheet, no wavy lines between stamps*

(*a*) *Optd with T* 2 *in purple or grey*
3 3 2 a. red .. .. .. .. .. 15·00

(*b*) *Without overprint*
4 3 ½ a. green .. .. .. .. 8·00 30·00
5 2 a. red .. .. .. .. .. 4·00 30·00

(ii) *Printed closer together, wavy lines between stamps*

(*a*) *Optd with T* 2 *in purple or grey*
6 3 ½ a. green .. .. .. .. 2·75 5·00
*a. Sage-green* .. .. .. .. 2·75
7 1 a. rose (*laid paper*) .. .. .. 12·00 42·00
8 1 a. rose (*wove paper*) .. .. .. 5·00 14·00
9 2 a. dull carmine .. .. .. 5·50 14·00

(*b*) *Without overprint*
10 3 ½ a. green .. .. .. .. 13·00 27·00
11 1 a. rose (*laid paper*) .. .. .. £140
12 1 a. rose (*wove paper*) .. .. .. 24·00 48·00

It has been stated that no stamps were regularly issued for postal use without the "control" mark, T 2, but it is very doubtful if this is correct. The overprint probably indicates official use.

The 1 a. exists in *ultramarine* and in *brown*, but these appear to be reprints.

The stamps of Nandgaon have been obsolete since 1 January 1895.

## NAWANAGAR

**PRICES FOR STAMPS ON COVER**
The stamps of Nawanagar are very rare used on cover.

**GUM.** The stamps of Nawanagar were issued without gum.

1 (1 docra)

2 (2 docra)

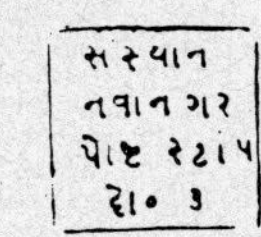
3 (3 docra)

**1877.** *Typo in sheets of* 32 (4×8 *or* 8×4). *Laid paper.* (*a*) *Imperf*
1 1 1 doc. blue (*shades*) .. .. .. 40 17·00
a. *Tête-bêche* (pair) .. .. .. £1000
b. Doubly printed .. .. .. 80·00

(*b*) *Perf* 12½ (*line*) *or* 11 (*harrow*)
2 1 1 doc. slate-blue .. .. .. 45·00 80·00
a. *Tête-bêche* (pair) (*p* 11) .. .. £1300

**1877.** *T* 2 *and* 3. *Type-set in black. Wove paper. Thick horizontal and vertical frame lines.*
A. *Stamp* 14½–15 *mm wide.* B. *Stamp* 16 *mm wide.* C. *Stamp* 19 *mm wide.*

| | | A | B | C |
|---|---|---|---|---|
| 2*b* | 1 doc. *deep mauve* .. .. .. | £130 | £130 | † £110 |
| 2*c* | 2 doc. *green* .. .. .. | † | † | † £1100 |
| 2*d* | 3 doc. *yellow* .. .. .. | † | † | † £1800 £1200 |

Prices for the 1 doc. and 2 doc. values are for used, no unused examples being known.

**1880.** *As last, but thin frame lines, as illustrated.* D. *Stamp* 15 *to* 18 *mm wide.* E. *Stamp* 14 *mm wide.*

| | | D | | E | |
|---|---|---|---|---|---|
| 3 | 1 doc. *deep mauve* .. .. .. | 1·00 | 4·00 | † | |
| | *a. On rose* .. .. .. | 1·00 | — | 1·00 | 2·50 |
| 4 | 1 doc. *magenta* .. .. .. | † | | 1·00 | — |
| 5 | 2 doc. *yellow-green* .. .. | 1·50 | 6·00 | 1·50 | 5·00 |
| | *a. On blue-green* .. .. | 3·00 | — | 4·00 | — |
| | b. Error. Yellow .. .. | £300 | — | † | |
| 6 | 3 doc. *orange-yellow* .. .. | 3·50 | — | † | |
| | *a. On yellow* .. .. | 5·50 | 10·00 | 3·00 | 7·00 |
| | *ab. On yellow.* Laid paper .. | 80·00 | — | 40·00 | — |

There are several different settings of each value of this series.

No. 5b occurs in the sheet of the 3 doc. value from one setting only.

4 (1 docra)

**1893.** *Typo in sheets of* 36. *P* 12. (*a*) *Thick paper.*
8 4 1 doc. black .. .. .. .. .. 1·10
a. Imperf (pair) .. .. .. .. £350
9 3 doc. orange .. .. .. .. 2·25

(*b*) *Thick laid paper*
10 4 1 doc. black .. .. .. .. .. £225

(*c*) *Thin wove paper*
11 4 1 doc. black *to* grey .. .. .. 50 2·00
a. Imperf between (pair) .. .. £350
b. Imperf (pair) .. .. .. £300
12 2 doc. green .. .. .. .. 50 2·25
a. Imperf (pair) .. .. .. £325
b. Imperf between (vert pair) .. .. £350
13 3 doc. orange-yellow .. .. .. 1·00 3·50
a. Imperf between (pair) .. .. £350
*b. Orange* .. .. .. .. 60 3·50
ba. Imperf (pair) .. .. .. £325
bb. Imperf vert (horiz pair) .. .. £350

(*d*) *Thin, soft wove paper*
14 4 1 doc. black .. .. .. ..
15 2 doc. deep green .. .. .. 3·00
16 3 doc. brown-orange .. .. .. 4·00

Cancellations for postal purposes were intaglio seals, applied in black. Other forms of cancellation were only used on remainders.

The stamps of Nawanagar became obsolete on 1 January 1895.

## NEPAL

Nepal being an independent state, its stamps will be found listed in Part 21 (*South-East Asia*) of this catalogue.

## ORCHHA

**PRICES FOR STAMPS ON COVER**

| | |
|---|---|
| Nos. 1/2 | — |
| Nos. 3/7 | *from* × 8 |
| Nos. 8/30 | *from* × 50 |
| Nos. 31/45 | *from* × 4 |

A set of four stamps, ½ a. red, 1 a. violet, 2 a. yellow and 4 a. deep blue-green, in a design similar to T 2, was prepared in 1897 with State authority but not put into use. These exist both imperforate and pin-perforated.

1

2

(T 1/2 litho Shri Pratap Prabhakar)

**1913.** *Background to arms unshaded. Very blurred impression. Wove paper. No gum. Imperf.*
1 1 ½ a. green .. .. .. .. 18·00 40·00
2 1 a. red .. .. .. .. 19·00

**1914–17.** *Background shaded with short horizontal lines. Clearer impression. Wove paper. No gum. Imperf.*
3 2 ¼ a. bright ultramarine .. .. .. 60 2·50
*a. Grey-blue* .. .. .. 35 2·00
*b. Deep blue* .. .. .. 1·50 2·00
ba. Laid paper .. .. .. £325
4 ½ a. green (*shades*) .. .. .. 40 2·00
*a. Dull green* .. .. .. 1·50 2·50
*b. Apple-green* .. .. .. 2·00 2·50
5 1 a. scarlet .. .. .. 1·75 3·25
a. Laid paper .. .. .. — £160
*b. Indian red* .. .. .. 1·75 6·50
*c. Carmine* .. .. .. 2·50 3·00
ca. Laid paper .. .. .. £140
6 2 a. red-brown (1916) .. .. .. 4·50 11·00
*a. Light brown* .. .. .. 8·50 11·00
*b. Chestnut* .. .. .. 11·00 13·00
7 4 a. ochre (1917) .. .. .. 8·00 16·00
*a. Yellow-orange* .. .. .. 8·00 16·00
*b. Yellow* .. .. .. 8·00 16·00
3/7 .. .. .. .. *Set of* 5 13·00 30·00

There are two sizes of T 2 in the setting of 8 (4 × 2). In each value stamps from the upper row are slightly taller than those from the lower.

**3** Maharaja Vir Singh Deo Bahadur **4**

(Typo Lakshmi Art Ptg Wks, Bombay)

**35** (1 Apr). *Thick, chalk-surfaced wove paper. P* 9½, 10, 10 × 9½, 11, 11 × 9½, 11½, 11½ × 11, 11½ × 12, 12 *or* 12 × 11.

| | Type | | Unused | Used |
|---|---|---|---|---|
| | **3** | ¼ a. purple and slate | 30 | 45 |
| | | a. Ordinary paper | 20 | 40 |
| | | ab. Imperf between (vert pair) | 10·00 | |
| | | ac. Imperf vert (horiz pair) | 35·00 | |
| | | ½ a. olive-grey and emerald | 40 | 40 |
| | | a. Imperf (pair) | | |
| | | ¾ a. magenta and deep myrtle-green | 40 | 40 |
| | | 1 a. myrtle-green and purple-brown | 40 | 40 |
| | | a. Imperf (pair) | — | 48·00 |
| | | 1¼ a. slate and mauve | 40 | 40 |
| | | a. Imperf (pair) | — | £110 |
| | | 1½ a. brown and scarlet | 40 | 40 |
| | | a. Imperf between (vert pair) | 60·00 | |
| | | b. Imperf between (horiz pair) | 60·00 | |
| | | 2 a. blue and red-orange | 40 | 40 |
| | | a. Imperf (pair) | 10·00 | |
| | | 2½ a. olive-brown and dull orange | 50 | 50 |
| | | a. Imperf (pair) | 10·00 | |
| | | 3 a. bright blue and magenta | 50 | 50 |
| | | 4 a. deep reddish purple and sage-green | 50 | 75 |
| | | a. Imperf (pair) | 7·50 | |
| | | 6 a. black and pale ochre | 50 | 80 |
| | | a. Imperf (pair) | 7·50 | |
| | | 8 a. brown and purple | 60 | 80 |
| | | a. Imperf (pair) | 7·50 | |
| | | 12 a. bright emerald and bright purple | 70 | 1·00 |
| | | a. Imperf (pair) | 7·50 | |
| | | 12 a. pale greenish blue and bright purple | 14·00 | 20·00 |
| | | 1 r. chocolate and myrtle-green | 70 | 1·25 |
| | | a. Imperf (pair) | 8·00 | |
| | | b. Imperf between (horiz pair) | 60·00 | |
| | **4** | 1 r. chocolate and myrtle-green | 1·75 | 3·00 |
| | | a. Imperf (pair) | | |
| | **3** | 2 r. purple-brown and bistre-yellow | 1·25 | 2·00 |
| | | a. Imperf (pair) | 9·00 | |
| | | 3 r. black and greenish blue | 1·25 | 2·25 |
| | | a. Imperf (pair) | 9·00 | |
| | | 4 r. black and brown | 1·60 | 2·75 |
| | | a. Imperf (pair) | 9·00 | |
| | | 5 r. bright blue and plum | 2·50 | 3·75 |
| | | a. Imperf (pair) | 9·00 | |
| | | 10 r. bronze-green and cerise | 5·00 | 8·50 |
| | | a. Imperf (pair) | 10·00 | |
| | | b. Imperf between (horiz pair) | 75·00 | |
| | | 15 r. black and bronze-green | 8·50 | 16·00 |
| | | a. Imperf (pair) | 11·00 | |
| | | 25 r. red-orange and blue | 11·00 | 19·00 |
| | | a. Imperf (pair) | 14·00 | |
| 20, 22/30 | | *Set of* 22 | 35·00 | 60·00 |

Values to 5 r. except the 1 a., are inscribed "POSTAGE", and the maining values "POSTAGE & REVENUE".

The central portrait of Type **3** is taken from a half-tone block and nsists of large square dots. The portrait of Type **4** has a back-ound of lines.

Owing to a lack of proper State control considerable quantities these stamps circulated at below face value and the issue was bsequently withdrawn, supplies being exchanged for the 939–42 issue. We are, however, now satisfied that the lower lues at least did genuine postal duty until 1939.

Used prices are for stamps cancelled-to-order, postally used amples being worth considerably more.

**5** H.H. The Maharaja of Orchha **6**

(Litho Indian Security Printing Press, Nasik)

**39–42**? *P* 13½ × 14 (*T* **5**) *or* 14 × 13½ (*T* **6**).

| Type | | Unused | Used |
|---|---|---|---|
| **5** | ¼ a. chocolate | 1·00 | 24·00 |
| | ½ a. yellow-green | 1·00 | 17·00 |
| | ¾ a. bright blue | 1·00 | 30·00 |
| | 1 a. scarlet | 1·00 | 7·50 |
| | 1¼ a. blue | 1·00 | 30·00 |
| | 1½ a. mauve | 1·40 | 38·00 |
| | 2 a. vermilion | 1·40 | 24·00 |
| | 2½ a. turquoise-green | 1·40 | |
| | 3 a. slate-violet | 2·00 | 35·00 |
| | 4 a. slate | 2·50 | 12·00 |
| | 8 a. magenta | 4·75 | 55·00 |
| **6** | 1 r. grey-green | 8·00 | |
| | 2 r. bright violet | 19·00 | |
| | 5 r. yellow-orange | 65·00 | |
| | 10 r. turquoise-green (1942) | £200 | |
| | 15 r. slate-lilac (date ?) | £1600 | |
| | 25 r. claret (date ?) | £1600 | |

## POONCH

**PRICES FOR STAMPS ON COVER**

| | |
|---|---|
| Nos. 1/2 | *from* × 3 |
| Nos. 3/62 | *from* × 10 |
| Nos. O1/10 | *from* × 30 |

**GUM.** The stamps of Poonch were issued without gum, except for some examples of Nos. 7/10.

The stamps of Poonch are all imperforate, and handstamped in watercolours.

**ILLUSTRATIONS.** Designs of Poonch are illustrated actual size.

**1**

**2**

**1876.** *T* **1** (22 × 21 *mm*). *Yellowish white, wove paper.*

| No. | Type | | Unused | Used |
|---|---|---|---|---|
| 1 | **1** | 6 p. red | £2000 | 85·00 |

**1877.** *As T* **1** (19 × 17 *mm*). *Same paper.*

| No. | | Unused | Used |
|---|---|---|---|
| 1*a* | ½ a. red | £3750 | £1200 |

**1879.** *T* **2** (21 × 19 *mm*). *Same paper.*

| No. | | Unused | Used |
|---|---|---|---|
| 2 | ½ a. red | — | £950 |

**3** (½ a.)

**4** (1 a.)

**5** (2 a.)

**6** (4 a.)

**1880.** *Yellowish white, wove paper.*

| No. | Type | | Unused | Used |
|---|---|---|---|---|
| 3 | **3** | ½ a. red | 22·00 | 11·00 |
| 4 | **4** | 1 a. red | 30·00 | 17·00 |
| 5 | **5** | 2 a. red | 35·00 | 30·00 |
| 6 | **6** | 4 a. red | 38·00 | 32·00 |

**1884.** *Toned wove bâtonné paper.*

| No. | Type | | Unused | Used |
|---|---|---|---|---|
| 7 | **3** | ½ a. red | 4·00 | 4·00 |
| 8 | **4** | 1 a. red | 7·00 | |
| 9 | **5** | 2 a. red | 8·00 | 8·50 |
| 10 | **6** | 4 a. red | 13·00 | 13·00 |

These are sometimes found gummed.

**7** (1 pice)

**1884–87.** *Various papers.* (*a*) *White laid bâtonné or ribbed bâtonné.*

| No. | Type | | Unused | Used |
|---|---|---|---|---|
| 11 | **7** | 1 p. red | 8·00 | 9·00 |
| | | a. Pair, one stamp sideways | 70·00 | |
| 12 | **3** | ½ a. red | 1·25 | 2·00 |
| 13 | **4** | 1 a. red | 1·40 | |
| 14 | **5** | 2 a. red | 2·75 | 3·50 |
| 15 | **6** | 4 a. red | 6·50 | |
| | | (*b*) *Thick white laid paper* | | |
| 22 | **7** | 1 p. red | 12·00 | |
| 23 | **3** | ½ a. red | 24·00 | |
| 24 | **4** | 1 a. red | 32·00 | |
| 25 | **5** | 2 a. red | 38·00 | |
| 26 | **6** | 4 a. red | 42·00 | |
| | | (*c*) *Yellow wove bâtonné* | | |
| 27 | **7** | 1 p. red | 2·25 | 2·00 |
| | | a. Pair, one stamp sideways | | |
| 28 | **3** | ½ a. red | 2·50 | 2·75 |
| 29 | **4** | 1 a. red | 11·00 | |
| 30 | **5** | 2 a. red | 3·00 | 3·75 |
| 31 | **6** | 4 a. red | 2·25 | 2·25 |
| | | (*d*) *Orange-buff wove bâtonné* | | |
| 32 | **7** | 1 p. red | 40 | 80 |
| | | a. Pair, one stamp sideways | 14·00 | |
| 33 | **3** | ½ a. red | 10·00 | |
| 34 | **5** | 2 a. red | 22·00 | |
| 35 | **6** | 4 a. red | 8·00 | |
| | | (*e*) *Yellow laid paper* | | |
| 36 | **7** | 1 p. red | 1·00 | 1·40 |
| 37 | **3** | ½ a. red | 2·00 | |
| 38 | **4** | 1 a. red | 11·00 | |
| 39 | **5** | 2 a. red | 14·00 | 16·00 |
| 40 | **6** | 4 a. red | 18·00 | |
| | | (*f*) *Yellow laid bâtonné* | | |
| 41 | **7** | 1 p. red | 6·00 | 4·50 |
| | | (*g*) *Buff laid or ribbed bâtonné paper thicker than* (*d*) | | |
| 42 | **4** | 1 a. red | 24·00 | |
| 43 | **6** | 4 a. red | 32·00 | |
| | | (*h*) *Blue-green laid paper* (1887) | | |
| 44 | **3** | ½ a. red | 14·00 | |
| 45 | **4** | 1 a. red | 2·00 | 2·75 |
| 46 | **5** | 2 a. red | 11·00 | |
| 47 | **6** | 4 a. red | 20·00 | |
| | | (*i*) *Yellow-green laid paper* | | |
| 48 | **3** | ½ a. red | | |
| | | (*j*) *Blue-green wove bâtonné* | | |
| 49 | **7** | 1 p. red | 20·00 | 21·00 |
| 50 | **4** | 1 a. red | 40 | 75 |
| | | (*k*) *Lavender wove bâtonné* | | |
| 51 | **4** | 1 a. red | 27·00 | |
| 52 | **5** | 2 a. red | 60 | 1·00 |
| | | (*l*) *Various coloured papers* | | |
| 53 | **7** | 1 p. red/*grey-blue laid* | 3·75 | 3·00 |
| 54 | | 1 p. red/*lilac laid* | 45·00 | 48·00 |
| 55 | | 1 p. red/*blue wove bâtonné* | 70 | 45 |
| | | a. Pair, one stamp sideways | | |

**1888.** *Printed in aniline rose on various papers.*

| No. | Type | | Unused | Used |
|---|---|---|---|---|
| 56 | **7** | 1 p. on *blue wove bâtonné* | 2·00 | |
| 57 | | 1 p. on *buff laid* | 3·50 | |
| 58 | **3** | ½ a. on *white laid* | 6·00 | |
| 59 | **4** | 1 a. on *green laid* | 9·00 | 9·00 |
| 60 | | 1 a. on *green wove bâtonné* | 3·50 | 3·00 |
| 61 | **5** | 2 a. on *lavender wove bâtonné* | 3·50 | 3·00 |
| 62 | **6** | 4 a. on *yellow laid* | 7·50 | 7·50 |

OFFICIAL STAMPS

**1888.** (*a*) *White laid bâtonné paper.*

| No. | Type | | Unused | Used |
|---|---|---|---|---|
| O 1 | **7** | 1 p. black | 80 | 90 |
| | | a. Pair, one stamp sideways | 10·00 | |
| | | b. *Tête-bêche* (pair) | 13·00 | |
| O 2 | **3** | ½ a. black | 80 | 1·25 |
| O 3 | **4** | 1 a. black | 70 | 1·00 |
| O 4 | **5** | 2 a. black | 1·25 | 1·25 |
| O 5 | **6** | 4 a. black | 3·00 | 3·50 |
| | | (*b*) *White toned wove bâtonné paper* | | |
| O 6 | **7** | 1 p. black | 1·60 | |
| O 7 | **3** | ½ a. black | 2·25 | 2·00 |
| | | a. Pair, one stamp sideways | £475 | |
| O 8 | **4** | 1 a. black | 7·50 | 7·50 |
| O 9 | **5** | 2 a. black | 4·00 | 4·00 |
| O10 | **6** | 4 a. black | 8·00 | |

The stamps of Poonch have been obsolete since 1894.

## RAJASTHAN

Rajasthan was formed in 1948–49 from a number of States in Rajputana; these included Bundi, Jaipur and Kishangarh, whose posts continued to function more or less separately until ordered by the Indian Government to close on 1 April 1950.

**PRICES FOR STAMPS ON COVER**

| | |
|---|---|
| Nos. 1/7 | *from* × 15 |
| Nos. 8/10 | — |
| Nos. 11/12 | *from* × 5 |
| Nos. 13/14 | — |
| Nos. 15/25 | *from* × 4 |
| Nos. 26/42 | *from* × 3 |
| No. 43 | *from* × 5 |
| Nos. 44/60 | *from* × 3 |
| No. 61 | *from* × 5 |
| Nos. 62/5 | — |

### BUNDI

(1)

**1949.** *Nos.* 86/92 *of Bundi.* (*a*) *Handstamped with T* **1**.

A. *In black.* B. *In violet.* C. *In blue*

| No. | | A | B | C |
|---|---|---|---|---|
| 1 | ¼ a. blue-green | 2·25 | 2·25 | 15·00 |
| | a. Pair, one without opt | 70·00 | † | † |
| 2 | ½ a. violet | 2·25 | 2·25 | 14·00 |
| | a. Pair, one without opt | † | 80·00 | † |
| 3 | 1 a. yellow-green | 2·25 | 8·00 | 16·00 |
| | a. Pair, one without opt | † | 80·00 | † |
| 4 | 2 a. vermilion | 5·00 | 18·00 | — |
| 5 | 4 a. orange | 17·00 | 9·00 | 32·00 |
| 6 | 8 a. ultramarine | 2·75 | 2·50 | 22·00 |
| 7 | 1 r. chocolate | — | £110 | 38·00 |

The above prices are for unused, used stamps being worth about three times the unused prices. Most of these handstamps are known, sideways, inverted or double.

(*b*) *Machine-printed as T* **1** *in black*

| No. | | | |
|---|---|---|---|
| 8 | ¼ a. blue-green | | |
| 9 | ½ a. violet | | |
| 10 | 1 a. yellow-green | | |

11 2 a. vermilion .. .. .. .. .. .. 1·75 22·00
a. Opt inverted .. .. .. .. .. £140
12 4 a. orange .. .. .. .. .. .. 2·00 22·00
a. Opt double .. .. .. .. .. £140
13 8 a. ultramarine .. .. .. .. .. 40·00
a. Opt inverted .. .. .. .. .. £180
14 1 r. chocolate .. .. .. .. .. .. 7·00

JAIPUR

राजस्थान

## RAJASTHAN

(2)

**1950** (26 Jan). *T 7 of Jaipur optd with T* **2**.
15 ¼ a. black and brown-lake (No. 58) (B.) .. 3·00 7·50
16 ½ a. black and violet (No. 41) (R.) .. 2·50 7·50
17 ¾ a. black and brown-red (No. 59) (Blue-blk.) 3·00 8·00
a. Opt in pale blue .. .. .. 8·00 18·00
18 1 a. black and blue (No. 60) (R.) .. 3·50 13·00
19 2 a. black and buff (No. 61) (R.) .. 3·25 14·00
20 2½ a. black and carmine (No. 62) (B.) .. 4·25 11·00
21 3 a. black and green (No. 63) (R.) .. 4·25 24·00
22 4 a. black and grey-green (No. 64) (R.) .. 4·25 28·00
23 6 a. black and pale blue (No. 65*a*) (R.) .. 5·50 35·00
24 8 a. black and chocolate (No. 66) (R.) .. 8·00 45·00
25 1 r. black and yellow-bistre (No. 67) (R.) .. 10·00 65·00
15/25 .. .. .. .. .. *Set of* 11 45·00 £225

KISHANGARH

**1948–49.** *Various stamps of Kishangarh handstamped with T* 1 *in red.*

(*a*) *On stamps of* 1899–1901
26 ¼ a. rose-pink (No. 5*a*) (B.) .. .. .. 80·00
26*a* ¼ a. rose-pink (No. 22*a*) .. .. .. — 70·00
27 ½ a. deep blue (No. 26) .. .. .. 85·00
28 1 a. lilac (No. 29) .. .. .. 25·00
29 1 a. brown-lilac (No. 29*b*) .. .. .. 14·00 27·00
b. Imperf (pair) .. .. .. 40·00 60·00
c. Violet handstamp .. .. .. — £100
d. Black handstamp .. .. .. — £130
30 4 a. chocolate (No. 31) .. .. .. 32·00 45·00
a. Violet handstamp .. .. .. — £160
31 1 r. dull green (No. 32) .. .. .. 95·00 £100
31*a* 2 r. brown-red (No. 34) .. .. .. £120
32 5 r. mauve (No. 35) .. .. .. .. £120 £120

(*b*) *On stamps of* 1904–05
33 13 ½ a. chestnut .. .. .. .. — 45·00
33*a* 1 a. blue .. .. .. .. — 65·00
34 4 a. brown .. .. .. .. 12·00
a. Blue handstamp .. .. .. 95·00
35 12*a* 8 a. grey .. .. .. .. 45·00 70·00
36 13 8 a. violet .. .. .. .. 11·00
37 1 r. green .. .. .. .. 11·00
38 2 r. olive-yellow .. .. .. .. 17·00
39 5 r. purple-brown .. .. .. .. 17·00
a. Blue handstamp .. .. .. £130

(*c*) *On stamps of* 1912–16
40 14 ½ a. green (No. 64) .. .. .. — 50·00
41 1 a. red .. .. .. .. — 50·00
42 2 a. deep violet (No. 51) .. .. .. 80·00
43 2 a. purple (No. 66) .. .. .. 1·40 5·00
44 4 a. bright blue .. .. .. .. — £160
45 8 a. brown .. .. .. .. 5·00
46 1 r. mauve .. .. .. .. 10·00
47 2 r. deep green .. .. .. .. 10·00
48 5 r. brown .. .. .. .. £130

(*d*) *On stamps of* 1928–36
49 16 ½ a. yellow-green .. .. .. .. 45·00
49*a* 2 a. magenta .. .. .. .. — 90·00
50 4 a. chestnut .. .. .. .. 60·00
51 8 a. violet .. .. .. .. 6·00 35·00
52 1 r. light green .. .. .. .. 18·00
53 2 r. lemon-yellow .. .. .. .. 14·00
54 5 r. claret .. .. .. .. 14·00

(*e*) *On stamps of* 1943–47
55 16 ¼ a. pale dull blue .. .. .. .. 27·00 27·00
56 ¼ a. greenish blue .. .. .. .. 27·00 27·00
a. Imperf (pair) .. .. .. 90·00
57 ½ a. deep green .. .. .. .. 14·00 14·00
a. Violet handstamp .. .. .. — 70·00
57*b* ½ a. yellow-green .. .. .. .. 21·00 21·00
ba. Imperf (pair) .. .. .. 90·00
bb. Blue handstamp .. .. .. — 70·00
58 17 1 a. carmine-red .. .. .. .. 17·00 17·00
a. Violet handstamp .. .. .. — 80·00
58*b* 1 a. orange-red (*imperf*) .. .. .. 55·00
ba. Blue handstamp .. .. .. 65·00
59 2 a. bright magenta .. .. .. .. 42·00 42·00
60 2 a. maroon (*imperf*) .. .. .. 50·00
61 16 4 a. brown .. .. .. .. 1·75 5·00
62 8 a. violet .. .. .. .. 14·00 35·00
63 1 r. green .. .. .. .. 6·00
64 2 r. yellow .. .. .. .. £110
65 5 r. claret .. .. .. .. 50·00

A 1 a. value in deep violet-blue was issued for revenue purposes, but is known postally used (*Price* £45 *used*).

## *NEW INFORMATION*

The editor is always interested to correspond with people who have new information that will improve or correct the Catalogue.

## RAJPIPLA

**PRICES FOR STAMPS ON COVER**

The stamps of Rajpipla are very rare used on cover.

1 (1 pice)

2 (2 a.)

3 (4 a.)

**1880.** *Litho. With or without gum* (1 *p.*) *or no gum* (*others*). *P* 11 (1 *p.*) *or* 12½.
1 1 1 p. blue .. .. .. .. .. 60 12·00
2 2 2 a. green .. .. .. .. .. 11·00 32·00
a. Imperf between (pair) .. .. £550 £550
3 3 4 a. red .. .. .. .. .. 4·25 20·00
1/3 .. .. .. .. *Set of* 3 14·00 60·00

These stamps became obsolete in 1886.

## SHAHPURA

**PRICES FOR STAMPS ON COVER**

Nos. 1/5 *from* × 2

RAJ
SHAHPURA
Postage 1 pice

1

RAJ
SHAHPURA
1 pice

2

**1914–17.** *Typo.*
1 1 1 p. carmine/*bluish grey* (*p* 11) .. .. — £110
2 1 p. carmine/*drab* (*imperf*) (1917) .. .. — £160

**1919–28.** *Typo. Imperf.*
3 2 1 p. carmine/*drab* (1928) .. .. .. — £225
4 1 a. black/*pink* .. .. .. .. — £225

POSTAL FISCAL

F 1

**1932–47.** *Typo. P* 11, 11½ *or* 12.
F1 F 1 1 a. red (*shades*) .. .. .. 11·00 55·00
a. Pin-perf 7 (1947) .. ..

Nos. F1/a were used for both fiscal and postal purposes. Manuscript cancellations must be assumed to be fiscal, unless on cover showing other evidence of postal use. The design was first issued for fiscal purposes in 1898.

## SIRMOOR

**PRICES FOR STAMPS ON COVER**

The stamps of Sirmoor are very rare used on cover.

1 (1 pice)

2

3 Raja Sir Shamsher Parkash

**1876** (June)–**80.** *Litho. P* 11½.
1 1 1 p. pale green .. .. .. .. 5·00
2 1 p. blue (on *laid* paper) (1880) .. .. 4·00 70·00
a. Imperf between (pair) .. .. £170
b. Imperf (pair) .. .. .. £170

(Litho at Calcutta)

**1892.** *Thick wove paper. P* 11½.
3 2 1 p. yellow-green .. .. .. .. 45 50
a. Imperf between (pair) .. .. 70·00
b. *Deep green* .. .. .. .. 35 40
ba. Imperf between (pair) .. .. 70·00 70·00
4 1 p. blue .. .. .. .. 45 45
a. Imperf between (pair) .. .. 60·00 60·00
b. Imperf (pair) .. .. .. 75·00

These were originally made as reprints, about 1891, to supply collectors, but there being very little demand for them they were put into use. The design was copied (including the perforations) from an illustration in a dealer's catalogue.

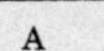

A

B

C

D

There were seven printings of the 3 and 6 pies, six of the 1 anna and four of the 2 annas, the last being used overprinted for officia use (Nos. 99/102), all in sheets of seventy, made up of groups c transfers showing two or more minor varieties. There are tw distinct varieties of the 3 p. and 6 p., as shown in Types A and B, ( and D. Of these B and D are the types of the sixth printing of thos values, and A and C those of all the other printings.

A and C have large white dots evenly placed between the ends c the upper and lower inscriptions; B has small white dots, and les space between the ends of the inscriptions; D has large spaces, an large white dots *not* in the centres of the spaces, especially at th left side.

The last printing of each value is only known with the Waterlov overprint, T 18.

Roman figures denote printings.

(Litho Waterlow & Sons)

**1885–96.** *P* 14 *to* 15.
5 3 3 p. chocolate (A), I, IV .. .. .. 35 2
6 3 p. brown (B), VI .. .. .. 15 2
7 3 p. orange (A), II, III, IV, V .. .. 70 1
8 3 p. orange (B), VI .. .. .. 15 1
a. Imperf (pair) .. .. £450
9 6 p. blue-green (C), I .. .. .. 2·00 8
10 6 p. bright green (C), III .. .. .. 38·00 38·0
11 6 p. green (C), II, IV .. .. .. 70 4
12 6 p. deep green (C), V .. .. .. 30 2
13 6 p. yellowish green (D), VI .. .. 40 9
14 1 a. bright blue, I .. .. .. 65 9
15 1 a. dull blue, III .. .. .. 5·50 4·5
16 1 a. steel-blue, IV .. .. .. 55·00 55·0
17 1 a. grey-blue, V .. .. .. 1·60 6
18 1 a. slate-blue, VI .. .. .. 50 1·2
19 2 a. pink, I .. .. .. 4·00 7·0
20 2 a. carmine, V .. .. .. 3·50 3·0
21 2 a. rose-red, VI .. .. .. 3·25 3·7

3 p. orange Printings III and IV are rare, being worth at least si times the value of other printings.

4 Indian Elephant

5 Raja Sir Shamsher Parkash

(Recess Waterlow & Sons)

**1895–99.** *P* 12 *to* 15 *and compounds.*
22 4 3 p. orange-brown .. .. .. 50 3
23 6 p. green .. .. .. .. 50 3
a. Imperf between (vert pair) .. £1200
24 1 a. blue .. .. .. .. 1·10 3
25 2 a. rose .. .. .. .. 1·00 1·0
26 3 a. yellow-green .. .. .. 7·00 12·0
27 4 a. deep green .. .. .. 4·50 6·5
28 8 a. deep blue .. .. .. 6·00 8·0
29 1 r. vermilion .. .. .. 13·00 25·0
22/9 .. .. .. .. *Set of* 8 30·00 48·0

(Recess Waterlow & Sons)

**1899.** *P* 13 *to* 15.
30 5 3 a. yellow-green .. .. .. 1·25 10·0
31 4 a. deep green .. .. .. 1·75 7·0
32 8 a. deep blue .. .. .. 2·25 8·5
33 1 r. vermilion .. .. .. 4·25 15·0
30/3 .. .. .. .. *Set of* 4 8·50 38·0

OFFICIAL STAMPS

**NOTE.** The varieties occurring in the machine-printed "On S.S.S. overprints may, of course, also be found in the inverted and doubl overprints, and many of them are known thus.

Roman figures denote printings of the basic stamps (Nos 7/21). Where more than one printing was overprinted the price quoted are for the commonest.

I. MACHINE-PRINTED

On
S. S.
S.

(11)

**890.** *Optd with T* **11**. (*a*) *In black.*
0 3 6 p. green, II .. .. .. .. £400 £400
a. Stop before first "S" .. ..
1 2 a. pink, I .. .. .. .. 48·00 75·00
a. Stop before first "S" .. .. £120

(*b*) *In red*
2 3 6 p. green, II .. .. .. .. 7·00 1·75
a. Stop before first "S" .. .. 45·00 25·00
3 1 a. bright blue, I .. .. .. 23·00 9·00
a. Stop before first "S" .. .. 80·00 60·00
b. Opt inverted .. .. .. † £350

(*c*) *Doubly optd in red and in black*
3*c* 3 6 p. green, II .. .. .. .. £900 £900
ca. Stop before first "S" (R.) .. ..

(12) (13)

**891.** *Optd with T* **12**. (*a*) *In black.*
4 3 3 p. orange, II .. .. .. .. 1·25 10·00
a. Opt inverted .. .. .. .. £225
5 6 p. green, II .. .. .. .. 1·50 1·50
a. Opt double .. .. .. .. £120
b. No stop after lower "S" .. .. 20·00 20·00
c. Raised stop before lower "S" .. 45·00 45·00
6 1 a. bright blue, I .. .. .. £150 £150
7 2 a. pink, I .. .. .. .. .. 11·00 30·00

(*b*) *In red*
8 3 6 p. green, II .. .. .. .. 15·00 3·00
a. Opt inverted .. .. .. .. £130 £110
b. Opt double .. .. .. .. £130 £110
9 1 a. bright blue, I .. .. .. .. 12·00 19·00
a. Opt inverted .. .. .. .. — £190
b. Opt double .. .. .. .. — £190
c. No stop after lower "S" .. .. 75·00 85·00

**892–97.** *Optd with T* **13**. (*a*) *In black.*
0 3 3 p. orange, III, V, VI .. .. .. 40 40
a. Opt inverted .. .. .. .. £160
b. First "S" inverted and stop raised .. 5·00 5·00
c. No stop after lower "S" .. .. 5·00 5·00
d. Raised stop after second "S" .. 17·00 12·00
1 6 p. green, IV, V. .. .. .. 1·40 50
a. First "S" inverted and stop raised .. 17·00 8·00
b. Raised stop after second "S" .. 17·00 8·00
2 1 a. blue, IV, V .. .. .. .. 7·00 1·00
a. Opt double .. .. .. .. £190
b. First "S" inverted and stop raised .. 20·00 10·00
c. No stop after lower "S" .. .. 55·00 55·00
d. Raised stop after second "S" .. 30·00 12·00
3 2 a. pink, I, V .. .. .. .. 7·00 7·00
a. Opt inverted .. .. .. .. £275 £275
b. First "S" inverted and stop raised .. 35·00 35·00
c. No stop after lower "S" .. .. 35·00 35·00
d. Raised stop after second "S" .. 55·00 55·00

(*b*) *In red*
4 3 6 p. green, II, III, IV .. .. .. 1·75 50
a. Opt inverted .. .. .. .. 85·00 85·00
b. First "S" inverted and stop raised .. 12·00 5·00
5 1 a. blue, I, IV .. .. .. .. 6·50 1·00
a. Opt inverted .. .. .. .. £120 85·00
b. Opt double .. .. .. .. £150
c. First "S" inverted and stop raised .. 18·00 8·00
d. No stop after lower "S" .. .. 18·00 8·00

(*c*) *Doubly overprinted in black and red*
5*e* 3 6 p. bright green, III .. .. ..

There are six settings of this overprint. The inverted "S" occurs n the 2nd and 5th settings, and the missing stop in the 2nd setting f all values except the 6 p. In the 5th setting occurs the raised stop fter second "S".

(14) (15)

**896.** *Optd as T* **14**.
6 3 3 p. orange, VI .. .. .. .. 5·50 1·25
a. Comma after first "S". .. .. 38·00 30·00
b. Opt inverted .. .. .. ..
c. Opt double .. .. .. .. † £275
7 6 p. green, V, VI .. .. .. .. 5·50 60
a. Comma after first "S". .. .. 40·00 18·00
b. Comma after lower "S" .. .. 40·00 18·00
c. "S" at right inverted .. .. .. 55·00 38·00
8 1 a. grey-blue, V .. .. .. .. 5·50 1·25
a. Comma after first "S". .. .. 50·00 22·00
b. Comma after lower "S" .. .. 50·00 22·00
c. "S" at right inverted .. .. .. — 40·00
9 2 a. carmine, V .. .. .. .. 15·00 14·00
a. Comma after first "S". .. .. £100 £100

There are four settings of this overprint, (1) 23 mm high, ncludes the comma after lower "S"; (2) and (3) 25 mm high, with ariety, comma after first "S"; (4) 25 mm high, with variety, "S" right inverted.

**1898** (Nov). *Optd with T* **15**.
70 3 6 p. green, V, VI .. .. .. .. 90·00 5·50
a. Small "S" at right .. .. .. — 25·00
b. Comma after lower "S" .. .. — 50·00
c. Lower "S" inverted and stop raised — 50·00
71 1 a. grey-blue, V .. .. .. .. £100 8·00
a. Small "S" at right .. .. .. — 40·00
b. Small "S" without stop .. .. — 70·00

There are two settings of this overprint. Nos. 70a and 71a/b occur in the first setting, and Nos. 70b/c in the second setting.

(16) (17)

**1899.** *Optd with T* **16**.
72 3 3 p. orange, VI .. .. .. .. £110 6·00
73 6 p. deep green, V .. .. .. .. — 12·00

**1899** (Dec)–**1900.** *Optd as T* **17**.
74 3 3 p. orange, VI .. .. .. .. — 4·00
a. Raised stop after lower "S" .. .. — 45·00
75 6 p. green, V, VI .. .. .. .. — 4·00
a. Raised stop after lower "S" .. .. — 45·00
b. Comma after first "S". .. .. — 55·00
76 1 a. blue, I, V, VI .. .. .. .. — 5·00
a. Raised stop after lower "S" .. .. — 65·00
77 2 a. carmine, V .. .. .. .. — 80·00
a. Raised stop after lower "S" .. .. — £275

There are two settings of this overprint: (1) 22 mm high, with raised stop variety; (2) 23 mm high, with "comma" variety on the 6 pies.

(18) (19)

(Optd by Waterlow & Sons)

**1900.** *Optd with T* **18**.
78 3 3 p. orange .. .. .. .. 1·00 2·50
79 6 p. green .. .. .. .. 40 45
80 1 a. blue .. .. .. .. .. 35 50
81 2 a. carmine .. .. .. .. 3·25 15·00

Nos. 78/81 were from printing VII which was not issued without the overprint.

## II. HANDSTAMPED

The words "On" and each letter "S" struck separately (except for Type **22** which was applied at one operation).

**1894.** *Handstamped with T* **19**. (*a*) *In black.*
82 3 3 p. orange, V .. .. .. .. 3·00 3·50
a. "On" sideways.. .. .. .. 60·00
83 6 p. green, IV, V .. .. .. .. 5·00 6·00
a. "On" only .. .. .. .. 60·00 60·00
84 1 a. blue, I, III, IV, V .. .. .. 7·00 7·50
85 2 a. carmine, V .. .. .. .. 13·00 14·00
a. "On" only .. .. .. .. 60·00
b. "On" sideways.. .. .. .. 70·00

(*b*) *In red*
86 3 6 p. green, IV .. .. .. .. 50·00 55·00
86*a* 1 a. grey-blue, V .. .. .. .. £130 £130

**1896.** *Handstamped with letters similar to those of T* **13**, *with stops, but irregular.*
87 3 3 p. orange, III, V, VI .. .. .. 55·00 45·00
88 6 p. green, II, IV, V .. .. .. 55·00 45·00
a. "On" omitted .. .. .. .. 90·00
88*b* 1 a. grey-blue, V .. .. .. .. 65·00 65·00
89 2 a. carmine, V .. .. .. .. 90·00

**1897.** *Handstamped with letters similar to those of T* **14**, *with stops, but irregular.*
90 3 3 p. orange, VI .. .. .. .. 8·00 12·00
a. "On" double .. .. .. .. 65·00
91 6 p. deep green, V .. .. .. .. 30·00 32·00
a. "On" only .. .. .. .. — 75·00
92 1 a. grey-blue, V .. .. .. .. 80·00 80·00
a. "On" only .. .. .. .. — 75·00
93 2 a. carmine, V .. .. .. .. 55·00 60·00

In No. 90a the second "On" is over the lower "S".

(20) (21)

**1896.** (*a*) *Handstamped with T* **20**.
94 3 3 p. orange, V .. .. .. .. 50·00 50·00
95 2 a. carmine, V .. .. .. .. 55·00 55·00

(*b*) *Handstamped with T* **21**
96 3 3 p. orange, V .. .. .. .. 90·00 90·00
97 6 p. green .. .. .. .. ..
98 1 a. blue, I, III .. .. .. .. £100
98*a* 2 a. carmine, V .. .. .. .. £110

(22) (23)

(*c*) *Handstamped with T* **22**.
99 3 3 p. orange, VI .. .. .. .. £100
100 6 p. deep green, V .. .. .. .. £140
101 1 a. grey-blue, V .. .. .. .. £200
101*a* 2 a. carmine, V .. .. .. .. £250

**1899.** *Handstamped with T* **23**.
102 3 3 p. orange, IV, V, VI .. .. .. 13·00 7·00
103 6 p. green, IV, V, VI .. .. .. 14·00 14·00
104 1 a. blue, I, V .. .. .. .. 29·00 25·00
105 2 a. rose-red, I, V, VI .. .. .. 24·00 20·00

(24)

**1901** (?). *Handstamped with T* **24**.
105*a* 3 6 p. yellowish green, VI .. .. .. — £140

## III. MIXED MACHINE-PRINTED AND HANDSTAMPED

**1896.** (i) *Handstamped "On" as in T* **19**, *and machine-printed opt T* **13** *complete.*
106 3 6 p. deep green, V .. .. ..

(ii) *Handstamped opt as T* **14**, *and machine-printed opt T* **13**, *complete*
107 3 6 p. deep green, V .. .. ..

Various other types of these handstamps are known to exist, but in the absence of evidence of their authenticity we do not list them. It is stated that stamps of T 4 were never officially overprinted.

The stamps of Sirmoor have been obsolete since 1 April 1902.

## SORUTH

| PRICES FOR STAMPS ON COVER | |
|---|---|
| Nos. 1/15 | *from* × 5 |
| Nos. 16/57 | *from* × 10 |
| Nos. O1/13 | *from* × 20 |
| Nos. 58/61 | *from* × 10 |
| Nos. O14/22 | *from* × 10 |

The name "Saurashtra" corrupted to "Sorath" or "Soruth", was originally used for all the territory later known as Kathiawar. Strictly speaking the name should have been applied only to a portion of Kathiawar including the state of Junagadh. As collectors have known these issues under the heading of "Soruth" for so long, we retain the name.

The currency was 40 docras = 1 koree but early stamps are inscribed in "annas of a koree", one "anna" being a sixteenth of a koree.

**GUM.** Nos. 1/47 of Soruth were issued without gum.

### A. JUNAGADH

1

(="Saurashtra Post 1864–65")

**1864** (Nov). *Handstamped in water-colour. Imperf.*
1 1 (1 a.) black/*azure* (laid) .. .. .. £650 40·00
2 (1 a.) black/*grey* (laid) .. .. .. £650 40·00
3 (1 a.) black/*azure* (wove) .. .. .. — £150
4 (1 a.) black/*cream* (wove) .. .. .. — £450
4*a* (1 a.) black/*cream* (laid) .. .. .. † £600

### COVER PRICES

Cover factors are quoted at the beginning of each country for most issues to 1945. An explanation of the system can be found on page x. The factors quoted do not, however, apply to philatelic covers.

**ILLUSTRATIONS.** Types **2** to **11** are shown actual size.

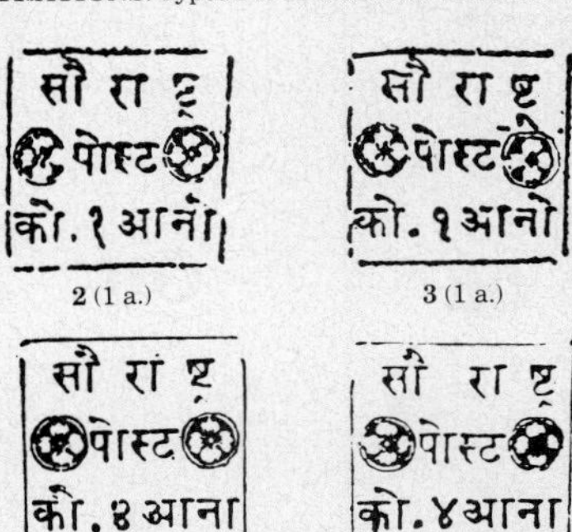

2 (1 a.) 3 (1 a.)

4 (4 a.) 5 (4 a.)

(Type-set at Junagadh Sarkari Saurashtra Nitiprakash Ptg Press)

**1868–75.** *T* **2** *to* **5** *(two characters, Devanagri and Gujerati respectively for "1" and "4" as shown in the illustrations). Imperf.*

*A. Inscriptions in Gujerati characters*

5 1 a. black/*yellowish* (wove) .. .. .. † £3500

B. *Inscriptions in Devanagri characters (as in the illustrations)*

I. *Accents over first letters in top and bottom lines. Wove paper*

6 1 a. red/*green* .. .. .. † £1500
7 1 a. red/*blue* .. .. .. † £1500
8 1 a. black/*pink* .. .. .. £300 60·00
9 2 a. black/*yellow* (1869) .. .. † £1600

II. *Accents over second letters in top and bottom lines* (1869–75).

*(a) Wove paper*

10 **2** 1 a. black/*pink* .. .. £180 42·00
a. Printed both sides .. .. † —
b. First two characters in last word of bottom line omitted (R. 4/1) .. .. — £150

*(b) Laid paper*

10c **2** 1 a. black/*white* .. .. † £2000
11 1 a. black/*azure* (1870) .. 50·00 8·00
a. Final character in both top and bottom lines omitted (R. 1/1) ..
b. First two characters in last word of bottom line omitted (R. 4/1) .. — 60·00
12 **3** 1 a. black/*azure* .. .. £110 16·00
a. Printed both sides .. .. † —
b. Final character in bottom line omitted (R. 1/1) .. .. — 60·00
c. Accent omitted from last word in bottom line (R. 5/2, 5/4) .. — 45·00
d. Large numeral (R. 4/1) .. £250 75·00
13 1 a. red/*white* (1875) .. 12·00 14·00
a. First two characters in bottom line omitted (R. 5/1) .. 50·00 60·00
14 **4** 4 a. black/*white* .. .. £100 £120
a. Final character in bottom line omitted (R. 1/1) .. £250
15 **5** 4 a. black/*white* .. .. £140 £150
a. First two characters in last word of bottom line omitted (R. 4/1) .. £500
b. Final character in bottom line omitted (R. 5/2) .. .. £600

Nos. 10/15 were printed in sheets of 20 (4×5). The same type was used throughout, but changes made to produce the different values resulted in five different settings:

Setting I Nos. 10*b*, 11, 15
Setting II Nos. 11/12, 14
Setting III Nos. 11/12, 14
Setting IV Nos. 11/12, 15
Setting V No. 13

The Devanagari (Type **2**) and Gujerati (Type **3**) numerals were mixed in settings II to IV of the 1 a. value, so that *se-tenant* pairs of Nos. 11/12 exist. Horizontally laid paper was used for setting II; vertically laid for settings I and III to V.

Official imitations, consisting of 1 a. carmine-red on white wove and white laid, 1 a. black on blue wove, 4 a. black on white wove, 4 a. black on blue wove, 4 a. red on white laid—all imperforate; 1 a. carmine-red on white laid, 1 a. black on blue wove, 4 a. black on white laid and blue wove—all perforated 12, were made in 1890. Entire sheets of originals have 20 stamps (4×5), the imitations only 4 or 16.

6

7

(Dies eng John Dickinson & Co Ltd, London. Typo Junagadh Sarkari Saurashtra Nitiprakash Ptg Press)

**1877.** *Imperf.*

*(a) Medium laid paper, lines wide apart*
*(b) Thick laid paper, lines wide apart*
*(c) Thick laid paper, lines close together*

16 **6** 1 a. green (*a*) .. .. 30 30
17 1 a. green (*b*) .. .. 30 30
18 1 a. green (*c*) .. .. 30 30
a. Printed both sides .. £300
19 **7** 4 a. vermilion (*a*) .. .. 80 1·00
20 4 a. vermilion/*toned* (*b*) .. 80 1·00
a. Printed both sides .. £300
21 4 a. scarlet/*bluish* (*b*) .. .. 80 1·00

**1886.** *P* 12. *(a) Wove paper.*

22 **6** 1 a. green .. .. 65 65
a. Imperf (pair) .. 35·00 40·00
b. Error. Blue .. — £600
c. Imperf horiz (vert pair) .. 60·00
23 **7** 4 a. red .. .. 3·00 3·00
a. Imperf (pair) .. 75·00 85·00

*(b) Toned laid paper*

24 **6** 1 a. green .. .. 15 15
a. Imperf vert (horiz pair) .. 55·00
25 1 a. emerald-green .. .. 95 65
a. Error. Blue .. £600 £600
26 **7** 4 a. red .. .. 90 60
27 4 a. carmine .. .. 1·40 1·25

*(c) Bluish white laid paper*

28 **6** 1 a. green .. .. 1·00 1·50
a. Imperf between (pair) .. 80·00
29 4 a. scarlet .. .. 3·25 5·50

There is a very wide range of colours in both values. The laid paper is found both vertical and horizontal.

The 1 a. was issued in sheets of 20 varieties, with marginal inscriptions; the 4 a. is in horizontal strips of 5 varieties.

**(Indian currency)**

**Three pies.** ત્રણ પાઇ. (8)

**One anna.** એક આનો. (9)

**1913.** *Surch in Indian currency with T* **8** *or* **9**. *P* 12.

*(a) On yellowish wove paper*

34 **6** 3 p. on 1 a. emerald .. 10 15
a. Imperf (pair) ..

*(b) On white wove paper*

35 **6** 3 p. on 1 a. emerald .. 10 15
a. Imperf between (pair) .. £120 £120
b. Surch inverted .. 35·00 20·00
c. Surch double .. † —
36 **7** 1 a. on 4 a. carmine .. 1·50 2·50
a. Imperf (pair)
b. Surch both sides .. £450
c. Capital "A" in "Anna" .. 11·00

*(c) On white laid paper*

37 **6** 3 p. on 1 a. emerald .. 60·00 30·00
a. Imperf (pair) .. — £120
38 **7** 1 a. on 4 a. red .. 7·00 18·00
a. Capital "A" in "Anna" .. 85·00
b. Surch inverted .. £400
c. Surch double .. £400
d. Surch double, one inverted .. £400

*(d) On toned wove paper*

39 **7** 1 a. on 4 a. red .. 90 2·00
a. Imperf (pair)
b. Capital "A" in "Anna" .. 6·00
c. Surch inverted .. £400
d. Imperf between (horiz pair) ..

10

11

(Dies eng Thacker & Co, Bombay. Typo Junagadh State Press)

**1914** (1 Sept). *New plates. T* **6/7** *redrawn as T* **10/11**. *Wove paper. P* 12.

40 **10** 3 p. bright green .. 35 35
a. Imperf (pair) .. 2·25 4·50
b. Imperf vert (horiz pair) .. 38·00
c. Laid paper .. 2·00 1·50
ca. Imperf (pair) .. 6·50 8·50
41 **11** 1 a. red .. 60 60
a. Imperf (pair) .. 12·00 22·00
b. Imperf between (pair) .. £190
c. Laid paper .. 50·00 25·00

**12** Nawab Sir Mahabatkhanji III **13**

(Dies eng Popatlal Bhimji Pandya. Typo Junagadh State Press)

**1923** (1 Sept). *Blurred impression. Laid paper. Pin-perf* 12.

42 **12** 1 a. red .. .. 3·00 5·00

Sheets of 16 stamps (8 × 2).

ત્રણ પાઇ (14) ત્રણ પાઈ (14*a*)

**1923** (1 Sept). *Surch with T* **14**.

43 **12** 3 p. on 1 a. red .. 2·50 6·00
a. Surch with T **14***a* .. 3·25 7·50

Four stamps in the setting have surch. T **14***a*, i.e. with top of last character curved to right.

**1923** (Oct). *Blurred impression. Wove paper. Pin-perf* 12, *small holes.*

44 **13** 3 p. mauve .. .. 35 40

**1924.** *Clear impression. P* 12, *large holes. Wove paper.*

45 **13** 3 p. mauve (1.24) .. .. 50 35
46 **12** 1 a. red (4.24) .. .. 3·00 3·75
a. Imperf (pair) .. 35·00 70·0[0]
b. Pin perf .. 2·00 2·50

The first plate of the 3 p., which printed No. 44, produced unsatisfactory impressions, so it was replaced by a second plate, from which No. 45 comes. Sheets printed from the first plate had very large margins.

The 1 a. is also from a new plate, giving a clearer impression. Sheets of 16 stamps (4 × 4).

**1929.** *Clear impression. P* 12, *large holes. Laid paper.*

47 **13** 3 p. mauve .. .. 1·25 1·0[0]
a. Imperf (pair) .. 2·75 7·5[0]
b. Perf 11 .. 1·75 1·7[5]
ba. Imperf between (horiz pair) .. 3·00 8·5[0]

The laid paper shows a sheet watermark of the State Arms within a circular inscription.

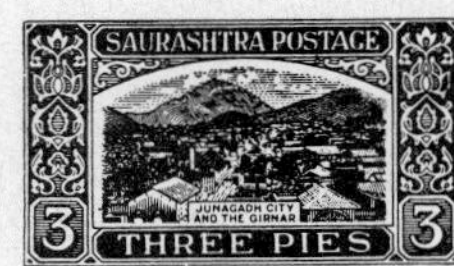



**15** Junagadh City

**16** Lion

**17** Nawab Sir Mahabatkhanji III

**18** Kathi Horse

(Litho Indian Security Printing Press, Nasik)

**1929** (1 Oct). *P* 14. *Inscr* "POSTAGE".

49 **15** 3 p. black and blackish green .. 50 1[0]
50 **16** ½ a. black and deep blue .. 4·50 1[0]
51 **17** 1 a. black and carmine .. 2·75 8[0]
52 **18** 2 a. black and dull orange .. 6·50 1·4[0]
*a. Grey and dull yellow* .. 25·00 1·1[0]
53 **15** 3 a. black and carmine .. 2·00 2·5[0]
54 **16** 4 a. black and purple .. 9·00 10·0[0]
55 **18** 8 a. black and yellow-green .. 10·00 12·0[0]
56 **17** 1 r. black and pale blue .. 2·75 11·0[0]
49/56 .. *Set of* 8 35·00 32·0[0]

**1936.** *As T* **17**, *but inscr* "POSTAGE AND REVENUE". *P* 14.

57 **17** 1 a. black and carmine .. 2·50 9[0]

OFFICIAL STAMPS

**SARKARI**

(O 1)

**1929 (1 Oct).** *Optd with Type* O **1**, *in vermilion, at Nasik.*

O1 **15** 3 p. black and blackish green .. 50 1[0]
a. Red opt .. 50 1[0]
O2 **16** ½ a. black and deep blue .. 1·25 1[0]
a. Red opt .. 2·00 1[…]
O3 **17** 1 a. black and carmine (No. 51) .. 1·00 1[0]
a. Red opt .. 1·25 1[…]
O4 **18** 2 a. black and dull orange .. 2·00 3[…]
*a. Grey and dull yellow* .. 10·00 6[…]
b. Red opt .. 12·00 1·2[5]
O5 **15** 3 a. black and carmine .. 60 2[…]
a. Red opt .. 7·50 1·5[0]
O6 **16** 4 a. black and purple .. 1·50 4[…]
a. Red opt .. 11·00 1·0[0]
O7 **18** 8 a. black and yellow-green .. 1·75 8[…]
O8 **17** 1 r. black and pale blue .. 2·25 8·5[0]
O1/8 .. *Set of* 8 9·50 9·5[0]

**SARKARI** (O 2) **SARKARI** (O 3)

**1932.** *Optd with Types* O **2** (3 *a.*, 1 *r.*) *or* O **3** (*others*), *all in red, a[t] Junagadh State Press.*

O 9 **15** 3 a. black and carmine .. 40·00 7·0[0]
a. Optd with Type O **3** .. 12·00 12·0[0]
O10 **16** 4 a. black and purple .. 15·00 15·0[0]
O11 **18** 8 a. black and yellow-green .. 20·00 16·0[0]
O12 **17** 1 r. black and pale blue .. 65·00 65·0[0]
a. Optd with Type O **3** .. 20·00 38·0[0]

**1938.** *No.* 57 *optd with Type* O **1**, *in vermilion.*

O13 **17** 1 a. black and carmine .. 4·50 6[…]
a. Brown-red opt .. 4·50 6[…]

The state was occupied by Indian troops on 9 November 1947.

### B. UNITED STATE OF SAURASHTRA

Under the new Constitution of India the United State of ıurashtra was formed on 15 February 1948, comprising 31 former ates and 191 estates of Kathiawar, including Jasdan, Morvi, ıawanagar and Wadhwan. A referendum was held in Junagadh ıich then joined the United State on 20 January 1949. However, is believed that the following issues were in use only in ınagadh.

The following issues were surcharged at the Junagadh State ess.

**POSTAGE & REVENUE**

**ONE ANNA**

(19)

**Postage & Revenue**

**ONE ANNA**

(20)

49. *Stamps of 1929 surch. (a) With T 19 in red.*
16 1 a. on ½ a. black and deep blue (6.49) .. 5·50 2·75
 a. Surch double .. .. .. .. — £200
 b. "AFNA" for "ANNA" and inverted "N" in "REVENUE" .. .. £850
 c. Larger first "A" in "ANNA" .. 80·00 60·00

*(b) With T 20 in green*
18 1 a. on 2 a. grey and dull yellow (2.49) 3·75 12·00

No. 58c occurs on position 10.

A number of other varieties occur on No. 58, including: small "V" "REVENUE" (No. 8); small "N" in "REVENUE" (Nos. 9, 13 and ); small "E" in "POSTAGE" (No. 12); thick "A" in "POSTAGE" o. 19); inverted "N" in "REVENUE" and small second "A" in NNA" (No. 25); small "O" in "ONE" (No. 26); small "V" and "U" "REVENUE" (No. 28); small "N" in "ONE" (No. 37).

In No. 59 no stop after "ANNA" is known on Nos. 4, 17, 25, 34 and and small "N" in "ONE" on Nos. 9, 11, 26 and 31.

21

(Typo Waterlow)

49 (Sept). *Court Fee stamps of Bhavnagar state optd "SAURASHTRA" and further optd "U.S.S. REVENUE & POSTAGE" as in T 21, in black. Typo. P 11.*
21 1 a. purple .. .. .. .. 5·00 5·00
 a. "POSTAGE" omitted .. .. £200 £180
 b. Opt double .. .. .. .. £225 £250

Minor varieties include small "S" in "POSTAGE" (Nos. 9 and 49); all "N" in "REVENUE" (Nos. 15 and 55); small "U" in EVENUE" (Nos. 18 and 58); small "V" in "REVENUE" (Nos. 24, 64 and 77); and small "O" in "POSTAGE" (Nos. 31 and 71).

Various missing stop varieties also occur.

**POSTAGE & REVENUE**
**ONE ANNA**

(22)

50 (Mar). *Stamp of 1929 surch with T 22.*
15 1 a. on 3 p. black and blackish green .. 30·00 30·00
 a. "P" of "POSTAGE" omitted .. £250 £250
 b. "O" of "ONE" omitted .. .. £300

Other minor varieties include small "S" in "POSTAGE" with ıall "V" in "REVENUE" (Nos. 14 and 26) and small "V" in EVENUE" (No. 11).

OFFICIAL STAMPS

48–49. *Nos. O4/O7 surch "ONE ANNA" (2¼ mm high).*
14 18 1 a. on 2 a. grey & dull yell (B.) (7.48) £2000 18·00
15 15 1 a. on 3 a. black and carmine (8.48) £1700 32·00
 a. Surch double .. .. .. † £950
16 16 1 a. on 4 a. black and purple (1.49) .. £170 24·00
 a. "ANNE" for "ANNA" .. .. £1700 £325
 b. "ANNN" for "ANNA" .. .. £1700 £325
17 18 1 a. on 8 a. black and yellow-green (1.49) £170 20·00
 a. "ANNE" for "ANNA" .. .. £1700 £275
 b. "ANNN" for "ANNA" .. .. £1700 £275

Numerous minor varieties of fount occur in this surcharge.

The spelling errors occur on positions 24 ("ANNE") and 35 ANNN").

48 (Nov). *Handstamped "ONE ANNA" (4 mm high).*
18 17 1 a. on 1 r. (No. O8) .. .. £450 23·00
19 1 a. on 1 r. (No. O12a) .. .. £180 27·00
 a. Optd on No. O12 .. .. — 42·00

A used copy of No. O12a is known surcharged in black as on ıs. O14/17. This may have come from a proof sheet.

49 (Jan). *Postage stamps optd with Type O 3, in red.*
20 15 3 p. black and blackish green .. .. £170 7·50
21 16 ½ a. black and deep blue .. .. £300 7·50
22 18 1 a. on 2 a. grey and dull yellow (No. 59) 32·00 10·00

Various wrong fount letters occur in the above surcharges.

**MANUSCRIPT OVERPRINTS.** Nos. 49, 50, 57, 58, 59 and 60 are known with manuscript overprints reading "Service" or "SARKARI" (in English or Gujerati script), usually in red. Such provisionals were used at Gadhda and Una between June and December 1949 *(Price from £70 each, used on piece).*

The United State of Saurashtra posts were integrated with the Indian Postal Service on 1 April 1950.

## TRAVANCORE

| PRICES FOR STAMPS ON COVER | |
|---|---|
| Nos. 1/77 | *from* × 10 |
| Nos. O1/108 | *from* × 15 |

**(16 cash = 1 chuckram; 28 chuckrams = 1 rupee)**

"Anchel" or "Anchal" = Post Office Department.

The stamps of Travancore were valid on mail posted to Cochin.

**PRINTERS.** All stamps of Travancore were printed by the Stamp Manufactory, Trivandrum, *unless otherwise stated.*

**PRINTING METHODS.** The dies were engraved on brass from which electrotypes were made and locked together in a forme for printing the stamps. As individual electrotypes became worn they were replaced by new ones and their positions in the forme were sometimes changed. This makes it difficult to plate the early issues. From 1901 plates were made which are characterised by a frame (or "Jubilee" line) round the margins of the sheets.

Up to the 6 cash of 1910 the dies were engraved by Dharmalingham Asari.

**SHADES.** We list only the main groups of shades but there are many others in view of the large number of printings and the use of fugitive inks. Sometimes shade variation is noticeable within the same sheet.

1 Conch or Chank Shell

1888 (16 Oct). *As T 1, but each value differs slightly. Laid paper. P 12.*
1 1 1 ch. ultramarine *(shades)* .. .. 1·50 1·60
2 2 ch. red .. .. .. .. 3·00 4·75
3 4 ch. green .. .. .. .. 8·00 8·00
1/3 .. .. .. .. *Set of 3* 11·00 13·00

The paper bears a large sheet watermark showing a large conch shell surmounted by "GOVERNMENT" in large outline letters, in an arch with "OF TRAVANCORE" at foot in a straight line. Many stamps in the sheet are without watermark.

These stamps on laid paper in abnormal colours are proofs.

2

Three forms of watermark Type 2.
*(as seen from the back of the stamp)*

**WATERMARKS AND PAPERS.**

Type A appeared upright on early printings of the 1, 2 and 4 ch. values on odd-sized sheets which did not fit the number of shells. Later it was always sideways with 15 mm between the shells on standard-sized sheets of 84 (14 × 6) containing 60 shells (10 × 6). It therefore never appears centred on the stamps and it occurs on hand-made papers only.

Type B is similar in shape but can easily be distinguished as it is invariably upright, with 11 mm between the shells, and is well centred on the stamps. It also occurs only on handmade papers. It was introduced in 1904 and from 1914, when Type A was brought back into use, it was employed concurrently until 1924.

Type C is quite different in shape and occurs on machine-made papers. There are two versions. The first, in use from 1924 to 1939, has 84 shells 11 mm apart and is always upright and well centred. The second, introduced in 1929 and believed not to have been used after 1930, has 60 shells (12 × 5) 15 mm apart and is invariably badly centred so that some stamps in the sheet are without watermark. This second version is normally found upright, but a few sideways watermark varieties are known and listed as Nos. 35g, 37c, O31j and O32i. We do not distinguish between the two versions of Type C in the lists, but stamps known to exist in the second version are indicated in footnotes. The machine-made paper is generally smoother and of more even texture.

**NO WATERMARK VARIETIES.** Some of these were formerly listed but we have now decided to omit them as they do not occur in full sheets. They arise in the following circumstances: *(a)* on sheets with wmk A; *(b)* on sheets with the wide-spaced form of wmk C; and *(c)* on late printings of the pictorial issues of 1939–46. They are best collected in pairs, with and without watermark.

**DATES OF ISSUE.** In the absence of more definite information the dates quoted usually refer to the first reported date of new printings on different watermarks but many were not noted at the time and the dates of these are indicated by a query. Dated postmarks on single stamps are difficult to find.

3 4 5

6 7 8

1889–1904. *Wove paper. Wmk A (upright or sideways). P 12 (sometimes rough).*
4 1 ½ ch. slate-lilac (1894) .. .. 75 20
 a. Doubly printed .. .. † £120
 *b. Reddish lilac* .. .. .. 40 10
 ba. Imperf between (vert pair) .. £120 £120
 bb. Doubly printed .. .. .. † £120
 *c. Purple* (1899) .. .. .. 55 10
 ca. Doubly printed .. .. .. † £120
 *d. Dull purple* (1904) .. .. 75 10
5 5 ¾ ch. black (14.3.01) .. .. .. 85 15
6 1 1 ch. ultramarine .. .. .. 60 15
 a. *Tête-bêche* (pair) .. .. .. £2000 £2000
 b. Doubly printed .. .. .. † £180
 c. Imperf vert (horiz pair) .. .. † £180
 *d. Pale ultramarine* (1892) .. .. 1·50 15
 *e. Violet-blue* (1901) .. .. 1·75 30
7 2 ch. salmon (1890) .. .. .. 1·90 30
 *a. Rose* (1891) .. .. .. 1·60 15
 ab. Imperf (pair) .. .. .. † £180
 *b. Pale pink* (1899) .. .. 1·50 30
 ba. Imperf between (vert pair) .. 95·00
 bb. Doubly printed .. .. .. £170
 *c. Red* (1904) .. .. .. 1·10 15
 ca. Imperf between (horiz pair) .. † £140
8 4 ch. green .. .. .. .. 1·50 40
 *a. Yellow-green* (1901) .. .. 1·50 40
 *b. Dull green* (1904) .. .. 3·75 50
 ba. Doubly printed .. .. .. † £180

Nos. 6, 6*d*, 7 and 8 occur with the watermark upright and sideways. No. 7*a* is known only with the watermark upright. The remainder exist only with the watermark sideways.

The sheet sizes were as follows:

½ ch. 56 (14 × 4) except for No. 4*d* which was 84 (14 × 6), initially without border, later with border.

¾ ch. 84 (14 × 6) with border.

1 ch. No. 6, 80 (10 × 8) and later 84 (14 × 6) without border and then with border; No. 6*d*, 96 (16 × 6); No. 6*e*, 84 (14 × 6) with border.

2 ch. No. 7, 80 (10 × 8); No. 7*a*, 70 (10 × 7); Nos. 7*b*, 7*c*, 60 (10 × 6).

4 ch. No. 8, 60 (10 × 6); Nos. 8*a*/*b*, 84 (14 × 6) with border.

After 1904 all stamps in Types 3 to 8 were in standard-sized sheets of 84 (14 × 6) with border.

For later printings watermarked Type A, see Nos. 23/30.

1904–20. *Wmk B, upright (centred). P 12, sometimes rough.*
9 3 4 ca. pink (11.08) .. .. .. .. 10 10
 a. Imperf between (vert pair) .. £100 £100
10 1 6 ca. chestnut (2.10) .. .. .. 30 10
 a. Imperf between (horiz pair) .. † £100
11 ½ ch. reddish lilac .. .. .. 20 10
 *a. Reddish violet* (6.10) .. .. 15 10
 *b. Lilac* .. .. .. .. 35 15
 c. "CHUCRRAM" .. .. .. 3·50 3·00
12 4 10 ca. pink (1920) .. .. .. 15·00 3·75
13 5 ¾ ch. black .. .. .. .. 50 10
14 1 1 ch. bright blue .. .. .. ..
 *a. Blue* .. .. .. .. 1·60 25
 *b. Deep blue* .. .. .. 1·60 25
 *c. Indigo* (8.10) .. .. .. 40 10
 *d. Chalky blue* (1912) .. .. 2·00 30
15 1¼ ch. claret *(shades)* (10.14) .. .. 30 20
 a. Imperf between (horiz pair) .. £110 £110
16 2 ch. salmon .. .. .. .. 10·00 4·00
 *a. Red* (8.10) .. .. .. 40 10
17 6 3 ch. violet (11.3.11) .. .. .. 1·10 10
 a. Imperf between (vert pair) .. £100 £100
 b. Imperf between (vert strip of 3) .. † £150
18 1 4 ch. dull green .. .. .. 4·50 2·00
 *a. Slate-green* .. .. .. 1·10 35
19 7 7 ch. claret (1916) .. .. .. 1·60 40
 a. Error. Carmine-red .. .. — 50·00
20 8 14 ch. orange-yellow (1916) .. .. 2·40 90
 a. Imperf vert (horiz strip of 3) .. £200

$\frac{1}{4}$ (9)   1 C (10)

**1906.** *Surch as T* **9**. *Wmk* B.
21 1 ¼ on ½ ch. reddish lilac .. .. .. 10 10
a. *Reddish violet* .. .. 10 10
b. *Lilac* .. .. .. .. 20 15
c. "CHUCRRAM" .. .. 3·00 3·00
d. Surch inverted .. .. 25·00 20·00
22 ⅜ on ½ ch. reddish lilac .. .. .. 20 20
a. *Reddish violet* .. .. 10 20
b. *Lilac* .. .. .. .. 10 20
c. "CHUCRRAM" .. .. 3·00 3·00
d. Surch inverted .. .. — 30·00
e. Surch double .. .. ..
f. "8" omitted .. .. .. — 40·00

**1914–22.** *Reversion to wmk* A *(sideways). P* 12 *(sometimes rough).*
23 3 4 ca. pink (1915) .. .. 3·75 30
24 4 5 ca. olive-bistre (30.10.21) .. .. 30 10
a. Imperf between (horiz pair) .. 40·00 40·00
b. Imperf between (horiz strip of 3) .. 85·00 85·00
c. "TRAVANCOPE" .. .. — 8·00
25 1 6 ca. orange-brown (2.15) .. .. 2·25 20
26 ½ ch. reddish violet (12.14) .. .. 1·10 15
a. "CHUCRRAM" .. .. 5·00 3·25
b. Imperf between (horiz pair) .. 85·00
27 4 10 ca. pink (26.10.21) .. .. 30 10
28 1 1 ch. grey-blue (5.22) .. .. 4·00 50
a. *Deep blue* .. .. .. 4·00 50
29 1¼ ch. claret (12.19) .. .. 5·00 20
30 6 3 ch. reddish lilac (8.22) .. .. 5·00 50

**1921** (Mar). *Surch as T* **10**. *Wmk* A.
31 3 1 c. on 4 ca. pink .. .. .. 10 15
a. Surch inverted .. .. 14·00 8·00
32 1 5 c. on 1 ch. grey-blue (R.) .. .. 10 10
a. *Deep blue* .. .. .. 10 10
b. Stamp printed both sides .. ..
c. Imperf between (vert pair) .. .. † £100
d. Surch inverted .. .. 12·00 7·00
e. Surch double .. .. 24·00 16·00
f. On wmk B. *Deep blue* .. .. 12·00 12·00

**ALBINO OVERPRINT VARIETIES.** Stamps with overprint double, one albino are frequently found in the provisional and official issues of Travancore, and are only worth a small premium over the normal prices.

**1924–39.** *Wmk* C. *Machine-made paper. P* 12.
33 4 5 ca. olive-bistre (18.6.25) .. .. 5·00 1·10
a. Imperf between (horiz pair) .. 70·00
b. "TRAVANCOPE" .. .. — 7·00
34 5 ca. chocolate (1930) .. .. 90 20
a. Imperf between (horiz pair) .. 30·00
b. Imperf between (vert pair) .. † 75·00
35 1 6 ca. brown-red (3.24) .. .. 3·00 10
a. Imperf between (horiz pair) .. 19·00 19·00
b. Imperf between (vert pair) .. 60·00 60·00
c. Printed both sides .. .. 50·00
d. Perf 12½ .. .. .. 4·00 50
e. Perf comp of 12 and 12½ .. 8·00 4·00
f. Perf 12½ × 11 .. .. — 55·00
g. Wmk sideways .. .. — 9·50
36 ½ ch. reddish violet (date?) .. .. 4·25 4·25
a. "CHUCRRAM" .. .. 30·00
37 4 10 ca. pink (8.24) .. .. 90 10
a. Imperf between (horiz pair) .. 65·00
b. Imperf between (vert pair) .. 17·00 19·00
c. Wmk sideways (16.9.28) .. — 3·50
38 5 ¾ ch. black (4.10.32) .. .. 4·75 40
39 ¾ ch. mauve (16.11.32) .. .. 30 10
a. Imperf between (horiz pair) .. † 70·00
b. Perf 12½ (8.37) .. .. 5·00 70
ba. Imperf between (horiz pair) .. 65·00
c. Perf comp of 12 and 12½ .. 9·50 4·50
40 ¾ ch. reddish violet (1939) .. .. 1·10 30
a. Perf 12½ .. .. .. 4·00 70
b. Perf comp of 12 and 12½ .. 6·50 2·00
c. Perf 11 .. .. .. — 55·00
d. Perf comp of 12 and 11 .. — 55·00
41 1 1 ch. slate-blue (8.26) .. .. 1·40 10
a. *Indigo* .. .. .. 2·25 10
b. Imperf between (horiz pair) .. † 90·00
c. Imperf between (vert pair) .. † 90·00
d. Perf 12½ .. .. .. 8·00 90
42 1½ ch. rose (1932) .. .. 80 10
a. Imperf between (horiz strip of 3) .. 90·00
b. Perf 12½ .. .. .. 14·00 2·75
c. Perf comp of 12 and 12½ .. — 18·00
43 2 ch. carmine-red (4.6.29) .. .. 5·50 30
44 6 3 ch. violet (4.25) .. .. 3·00 15
a. Imperf between (vert pair) .. 70·00 70·00
b. Perf 12½ .. .. .. — 8·50
c. Perf comp of 12 and 12½ .. — 15·00
45 1 4 ch. grey-green (5.4.34) .. .. 5·00 40
46 7 7 ch. claret (1925) .. .. 6·00 1·40
a. Doubly printed .. .. † £160
b. *Carmine-red* (date?) .. .. 60·00 55·00
c. *Brown-purple* (1932) .. .. 8·50 2·75
ca. Perf. 12½ .. .. .. 8·00 8·00
cb. Perf comb of 12 and 12½ .. 8·00 8·00
46*d* 8 14 ch. orange-yellow (*p* 12½) (date?) .. £100

It is believed that the 12½ perforation and the perf 12 and 12½ compound were introduced in 1937 and that the 11 perforation came later, probably in 1939.

The 5 ca. chocolate, 6 ca., 10 ca. and 3 ch. also exist on the wide-spaced watermark (60 shells to the sheet of 84).

**11** Sri Padmanabha Shrine

**12** State Chariot

**13** Maharaja Sir Bala Rama Varma

(Des M. R. Madhawan Unnithan. Plates by Calcutta Chromotype Co. Typo Stamp Manufactory, Trivandrum)

**1931** (6 Nov). *Coronation. Cream or white paper. Wmk* C. *P* 11½, 12.
47 11 6 ca. black and green .. .. 30 35
a. Imperf between (horiz pair) .. £180 £200
48 12 10 ca. black and ultramarine. .. 30 30
49 13 3 ch. black and purple .. .. 40 45
47/9 .. .. .. .. *Set of* 3 90 1·00

1 C (14)   1 C (15)

**16** Maharaja Sir Bala Rama Varma and Subramania Shrine

**1932** (14 Jan). (i) *Surch as T* **14**. (*a*) *Wmk* A *(sideways).*
50 1 1 c. on 1¼ ch. claret .. .. 10 15
a. Imperf between (horiz pair) .. 70·00
b. Surch inverted .. .. 4·25 6·00
c. Surch double .. .. 24·00 24·00
d. Pair, one without surch .. 70·00 80·00
e. "c" omitted .. .. 45·00 45·00
51 2 c. on 1¼ ch. claret .. .. 10 10
a. Surch inverted .. .. 4·25 6·00
b. Surch double .. .. 24·00
c. Surch double, one inverted. .. 55·00
d. Surch treble .. .. 55·00
e. Surch treble, one inverted .. 70·00 70·00
f. Pair, one without surch .. 75·00 75·00
g. "2" omitted .. .. 45·00 45·00
h. "c" omitted .. .. 45·00 45·00
i. Imperf between (horiz pair) .. 70·00

(*b*) *Wmk* B *(upright)*
52 1 1 c. on 1¼ ch. claret .. .. 75 75
a. Surch inverted .. .. 17·00
b. Surch double .. .. 26·00
53 2 c. on 1¼ ch claret .. .. 2·25 2·50

(*c*) *Wmk* C
54 1 1 c. on 1¼ ch. claret .. .. 6·50 6·50
a. Surch inverted .. .. 32·00 32·00
55 2 c. on 1¼ ch. claret .. .. 8·00 5·50

(ii) *Surch as T* **10**. *Wmk* B
56 1 2 c. on 1¼ ch. claret .. .. 4·25 8·00

**1932** (5 Mar) *Surch as T* **15**. *Wmk* C.
57 4 1 c. on 5 ca. chocolate .. .. 10 10
a. Imperf between (horiz pair) .. 85·00
b. Surch inverted .. .. 7·50 10·00
c. Surch inverted on back only .. 38·00
d. Pair, one without surch .. 70·00
e. "1" omitted .. .. 38·00
f. "C" omitted .. .. — 38·00
g. "TRAVANCOPE" .. .. 8·50
58 1 c. on 5 ca. slate-purple .. .. 30 15
a. Surch inverted .. .. † 90·00
b. "1" inverted .. .. 50·00 50·00
59 2 c. on 10 ca. pink .. .. 10 10
a. Imperf between (horiz pair) .. 75·00
b. Surch inverted .. .. 5·00 7·00
c. Surch double .. .. 16·00 18·00
d. Surch double, one inverted. .. 42·00 42·00
e. Surch double, both inverted .. 30·00

No. 58 was not issued without the surcharge.

(Plates by Indian Security Printing Press, Nasik. Typo Stamp Manufactory, Trivandrum)

**1937** (29 Mar). *Temple Entry Proclamation. T* **16** *and similar horiz designs. Wmk* C. *P* 12.
60 6 ca. carmine .. .. .. 30 30
a. Imperf between (horiz strip of 3) .. £325
b. Perf 12½ .. .. .. 90 90
c. Compound perf .. .. 17·00 17·00
61 12 ca. bright blue .. .. 60 15
a. Perf 12½ .. .. .. 80 40
ab. Imperf between (vert pair) .. £300
b. Compound perf .. .. 24·00
62 1½ ch. yellow-green .. .. 40 30
a. Imperf between (vert pair) .. £225
b. Perf 12½ .. .. .. 10·00 3·50
c. Compound perf .. ..
63 3 ch. violet .. .. .. 1·25 50
a. Perf 12½ .. .. .. 1·40 70
60/3 .. .. .. .. *Set of* 4 2·25 1·10

Designs:—Maharaja's portrait and temples—12 ca. Sri Padmanabha; 1½ ch. Mahadeva; 3 ch. Kanyakumari.

**COMPOUND PERFS.** This term covers stamps perf compound o 12½ and 11, 12 and 11 or 12 and 12½, and where two or more combinations exist the prices are for the commonest. Such compounds can occur on values which do not exist perf 12 all round

**17** Lake Ashtamudi

**18** Maharaja Sir Bala Rama Varma

(Des Nilakantha Pellai. Plates by Indian Security Printing Press Nasik. Typo Stamp Manufactory, Trivandrum)

**1939** (9 May). *Maharaja's 27th Birthday. T* **17/18** *and simila designs. Wmk* C. *P* 12½.
64 1 ch. yellow-green .. .. 90 1
a. Imperf between (horiz pair) .. 16·00
b. Perf 11 .. .. .. 3·00 1
ba. Imperf between (vert pair) .. 14·00 18·0
bb. Imperf between (vert strip of 3) .. 16·00
c. Perf 12 .. .. .. 5·00 5
ca. Imperf between (horiz pair) .. 16·00
cb. Imperf between (vert pair) .. 16·00
d. Compound perf .. .. 6·00 1·5
da. Imperf between (vert pair) .. 45·00
65 1½ ch. scarlet .. .. .. 50 6
a. Doubly printed .. .. 85·00
b. Imperf between (horiz pair) .. 18·00
c. Imperf between (vert pair) .. 16·00
d. Perf 11 .. .. .. 3·00 7·5
da. Imperf horiz (vert pair) .. 8·00
e. Perf 12 .. .. .. 9·00 2·5
f. Perf 13½ .. .. .. 10·00 24·0
g. Compound perf .. .. 15·00 3·5
h. Imperf (pair) .. .. 20·00
66 2 ch. orange .. .. .. 1·25 3
a. Perf 11 .. .. .. 6·50 3
b. Perf 12 .. .. .. 25·00 3·7
c. Compound perf .. .. 25·00 4·0
67 3 ch. brown .. .. .. 1·40 1
a. Doubly printed .. .. — 50·0
b. Imperf between (horiz pair) .. 20·00 26·0
c. Perf 11 .. .. .. 7·00 3
ca. Doubly printed .. .. 32·00 32·0
d. Perf 12 .. .. .. 11·00 1·0
da. Imperf between (vert pair) .. 60·00 60·0
e. Compound perf .. .. 7·50 1·0
68 4 ch. red .. .. .. 90 4
a. Perf 11 .. .. .. 10·00 5
b. Perf 12 .. .. .. 11·00 2·0
c. Compound perf .. .. 40·00 40·0
69 7 ch. pale blue .. .. .. 2·25 5·5
a. Perf 11 .. .. .. 25·00 11·0
*ab. Blue* .. .. .. 25·00 11·0
b. Compound perf .. .. 30·00 13·0
70 14 ch. turquoise-green .. .. 3·00 13·0
a. Perf 11 .. .. .. 4·25 24·0
64/70 .. .. .. .. *Set of* 7 9·00 18·0

Designs: *Vert as T* **18**—1½ ch., 3 ch. Portraits of Maharaja i different frames. *Horiz as T* **17**—4 ch. Sri Padmanabha Shrine 7 ch. Cape Comorin; 14 ch. Pachipari Reservoir.

**19** Maharaja and Aruvikara Falls   2 CASH (20)

(Des Nilakantha Pellai. Plates by Indian Security Printing Press Nasik. Typo Stamp Manufactory, Trivandrum)

**1941** (20 Oct). *Maharaja's 29th Birthday. T* **19** *and similar hori design. Wmk* C. *P* 12½.
71 6 ca. blackish violet .. .. 1·75 1
a. Perf 11 .. .. .. 2·50 1
ab. Imperf between (vert pair) .. 16·00
ac. Imperf horiz (vert pair) .. 20·00
b. Perf 12 .. .. .. 6·50 1·0
ba. Imperf between (horiz pair) .. 15·00
bb. Imperf between (vert pair) .. 17·00
bc. Imperf between (vert strip of 3) .. 16·00
c. Compound perf .. .. 2·25 7
72 ¾ ch. brown .. .. .. 1·75
a. Perf 11 .. .. .. 3·00
ab. Imperf between (horiz pair) .. 50·00
ac. Imperf between (vert pair) .. 15·00 20·0
ad. Imperf between (vert strip of 3) .. 15·00
ae. Block of four imperf between (horiz and vert) .. .. 60·00
b. Perf 12 .. .. .. 13·00 3·5
c. Compound perf .. .. 4·25 1·1

Design:—¾ ch. Maharaja and Marthanda Varma Bridg Alwaye.

**1943** (17 Sept). *Nos.* 65, 71 *(colour changed) and* 72 *surch as T* **2** *P* 12½.
73 2 ca. on 1½ ch. scarlet .. .. 30
a. Imperf between (vert pair) .. 23·00
b. "2" omitted .. .. £100 £1
c. "CA" omitted .. .. £140
d. "ASH" omitted .. .. £140
e. Perf 11 .. .. .. 20
ea. "CA" omitted .. .. £140
f. Compound perf .. .. 55
fa. Imperf between (vert pair) .. 50·00
fb. "2" omitted .. .. £100
74 4 ca. on ¾ ch. brown .. .. 1·50
a. Perf 11 .. .. .. 1·25
b. Perf 12 .. .. .. — 45·
c. Compound perf .. .. 2·50 1·

5 8 ca. on 6 ca. scarlet 1·25 10
a. Perf 11 75 10
ab. Imperf between (horiz pair) 21·00
b. Perf 12 — 35·00
c. Compound perf 5·50 3·75
/5 *Set of* 3 2·00 25

21 Maharaja Sir Bala Rama Varma

SPECIAL

(22)

es Nilakantha Pellai. Plates by Indian Security Printing Press, Nasik. Typo Stamp Manufactory, Trivandrum)

**46** (24 Oct). *Maharaja's 34th Birthday. Wmk C. P* 12½.
21 8 ca. carmine 6·00 1·75
a. Perf 11 50 50
b. Perf 12 12·00 3·00
ba. Imperf between (horiz pair) 24·00 30·00
bb. Imperf between (horiz strip of 3) 38·00
c. Compound perf

**46.** *No.* O103 *revalidated for ordinary postage with opt T* **22**, *in orange. P* 12½.
7 19 6 ca. blackish violet 4·25 1·50
a. Perf 11 14·00 4·25
b. Compound perf 5·50 2·25

## OFFICIAL STAMPS

**UM.** Soon after 1911 the Official stamps were issued without um. Thus only the initial printings of the 1, 2, 3 and 4 ch. values ere gummed. As Nos. O38/9, O41/2 and O95 were overprinted on amps intended for normal postage these, also, have gum.

**RINTINGS.** Sometimes special printings of postage stamps were ade specifically for overprinting for Official use, thus accounting r Official stamps appearing with watermarks or in shades not sted in the postage issues.

**ETTINGS.** These are based on the study of complete sheets of 84, d the measurements given are those of the majority of stamps on e sheet. Examples are known showing different measurements each overprint was set individually in loose type, but these are ot included in the listings.

On S S (O 1) On S S (O 2)

Rounded "O"

**11** (16 Aug)–**26.** *Contemporary stamps optd with Type* O **1** (*13 mm wide*). *P* 12, *sometimes rough.* (*a*) *Wmk B* (*upright*) (16.8.11–21).
1 3 4 ca. pink (1916) 10 10
a. Opt inverted † 38·00
b. Opt double 60·00 45·00
c. "S S" inverted 15·00 8·00
d. Imperf (pair) 95·00 95·00
2 1 6 ca. chestnut (date ?) 25·00 25·00
3 ½ ch. reddish lilac (R.) (1919) 70 35
a. "CHUCRRAM" 7·50 4·50
4 4 10 ca. pink (1921) 8·50 2·25
a. "O" inverted 23·00 8·00
b. Left "S" inverted 23·00 8·00
c. Right "S" inverted 23·00 8·00
5 1 1 ch. chalky blue (R.) 35 10
a. Imperf between (vert pair) † 90·00
b. Opt inverted 7·00 4·25
c. Opt double 55·00 48·00
d. "nO" for "On" 75·00 75·00
e. "O" inverted 4·50 1·25
f. Left "S" inverted 4·50 1·25
g. Right "S" inverted 4·50 1·25
h. "S S" inverted — 22·00
6 2 ch. red 30 10
a. Opt inverted 8·00 8·00
b. "O" inverted 6·00 1·25
c. Left "S" inverted 5·50 1·10
d. Right "S" inverted 6·00 1·25
7 2 ch. red (B.) (date ?) — 40·00
8 6 3 ch. violet 30 10
a. Imperf between (vert pair) 80·00 80·00
b. Imperf vert (horiz pair) 80·00
c. Opt inverted 10·00 10·00
d. Opt double 55·00 55·00
e. Right "S" inverted 4·50 1·00
f. Right "S" omitted 55·00 55·00
g. Left "S" omitted 55·00 55·00
9 3 ch. violet (B.) (date ?) 55·00 28·00
0 1 4 ch. slate-green 55 10
a. Imperf between (pair) 85·00 85·00
b. Opt inverted 24·00 11·00
c. Opt double 65·00 65·00
d. "O" inverted 8·00 2·40
e. Left "S" inverted 7·00 2·40
f. Right "S" inverted 8·00 2·75
g. Left "S" omitted 55·00 55·00
1 4 ch. slate-green (B.) (1921) — 21·00
a. "O" inverted — 50·00
b. Left "S" inverted — 50·00
c. Right "S" inverted — 50·00

(*b*) *Wmk A* (*sideways*) (1919–25)
O12 3 4 ca. pink 2·50 15
a. Imperf (pair) £110 £110
b. Opt inverted 30·00 15·00
c. "O" inverted 15·00 4·50
d. Left "S" inverted 15·00 4·50
e. Right "S" inverted 15·00 4·50
O13 4 ca. pink (B.) (1921) 16·00 75
a. "O" inverted — 14·00
O14 4 5 ca. olive-bistre (1921) 30 10
a. Opt inverted 11·00 8·50
b. "O" inverted 3·00 1·25
c. Left "S" inverted 3·00 1·25
d. Right "S" inverted 3·00 1·25
O15 1 6 ca. orange-brown (1921) 15 10
a. Imperf between (vert pair) † 85·00
b. Opt inverted 10·00 8·00
c. Opt double 38·00 38·00
d. "O" inverted 4·00 1·00
e. Left "S" inverted 3·75 90
f. Right "S" inverted 4·00 1·00
O16 6 ca. orange-brown (B.) (1921) 7·50 1·25
a. Opt inverted 60·00 60·00
b. "O" inverted 32·00 12·00
c. Left "S" inverted 32·00 12·00
d. Right "S" inverted 32·00 12·00
O17 ½ ch. reddish violet (R.) (date?) 35 10
a. *Reddish lilac* (date?) 35 10
b. Imperf between (horiz pair) 60·00 60·00
c. Imperf between (vert pair) 42·00 42·00
d. Stamp doubly printed 48·00
e. Opt inverted 9·00 3·00
f. Opt double, both inverted 65·00
g. "CHUCRRAM" 4·00 2·75
h. "On" omitted — 65·00
i. Right "S" inverted — 13·00
j. Right "S" omitted — 65·00
O18 4 10 ca. pink (3.21) 30 10
a. *Scarlet* (1925?) — 7·50
b. Opt inverted — 11·00
c. Opt double 50·00 40·00
d. "O" inverted 4·50 1·75
e. Left "S" inverted 4·00 1·50
f. Right "S" inverted 4·50 1·75
g. Imperf between (horiz pair) — 70·00
O19 10 ca. pink (B.) (date ?) 23·00 6·00
a. Opt inverted — 45·00
b. "O" inverted — 24·00
O20 1 1 ch. grey-blue (R.) (date ?) 2·00 60
a. *Deep blue* 2·00 60
b. "O" inverted 16·00 6·00
c. Left "S" inverted 16·00 6·00
d. "On" omitted
O21 1¼ ch. claret (12.19) 35 10
a. Stamp doubly printed — £120
b. Opt inverted 9·00 8·00
c. Opt double 45·00
d. "O" inverted 8·00 1·75
e. Left "S" inverted 9·00 2·25
f. Right "S" inverted 9·00 2·25
g. Error. Carmine 50·00
O22 1¼ ch. claret (B.) (1921) — 32·00
a. "O" inverted — 70·00
b. Left "S" inverted — 70·00
c. Right "S" inverted — 70·00

(*c*) *Wmk C* (1925–30)
O23 4 5 ca. olive-bistre (1926) 30 15
a. Imperf between (horiz pair) 85·00 85·00
b. Opt inverted 11·00 10·00
c. "O" inverted 3·00 1·40
d. Left "S" inverted 3·00 1·40
e. Right "S" inverted 3·00 1·40
O23*f* 5 ca. chocolate (1930) 28·00
fa. Opt inverted — 75·00
O24 10 ca. pink (1926) 1·60 15
a. Imperf between (vert pair) † 80·00
b. Opt inverted 40·00 40·00
c. "O" inverted 13·00 2·00
d. Left "S" inverted 13·00 2·25
e. Right "S" inverted 13·00 2·25
f. Stamp doubly printed
O25 1 1¼ ch. claret (1926) 5·00 40
a. "O" inverted 22·00 3·00
b. Left "S" inverted 25·00 4·00
c. Right "S" inverted 25·00 4·00
d. Opt double † 55·00
O26 7 7 ch. claret 1·50 30
a. "O" inverted 12·00 2·50
b. Left "S" inverted 12·00 2·50
c. Right "S" inverted 12·00 2·50
d. Error. Carmine-red 60·00
O27 8 14 ch. orange-yellow 1·75 40
a. "O" inverted 13·00 3·00
b. Left "S" inverted 13·00 3·00
c. Right "S" inverted 13·00 3·00

**1926–30.** *Contemporary stamps optd with Type* O **2** (16½ *mm wide*). *Wmk C. P* 12.
O28 4 5 ca. olive-bistre 1·50 25
a. Right "S" inverted 8·50 3·00
O29 5 ca. chocolate (1930) 15 20
a. Imperf between (vert pair) † £100
b. Opt inverted 16·00
c. "O" inverted 2·00 2·00
d. Left "S" inverted 2·00 2·00
O30 1 6 ca. brown-red (date?) 2·50 80
a. "O" inverted 13·00 4·50
b. Left "S" inverted 13·00 4·50
c. Opt double † 80·00
O31 4 10 ca. pink 30 10
a. Imperf between (horiz pair) 42·00 42·00
b. Imperf between (vert pair) 32·00 32·00
c. Imperf vert (horiz strip of 3) † 70·00
d. Opt inverted 9·00 9·00
e. "Ou" for "On" 32·00 32·00
f. "O" inverted 4·00 1·50
g. Left "S" inverted 3·50 1·40
h. Right "S" inverted 3·50 1·25
i. Left "S" omitted 25·00 25·00
j. Wmk sideways — 5·00

O32 1 1¼ ch. claret (*shades*) 1·60 30
a. Imperf between (horiz pair) 60·00 65·00
b. Imperf between (vert pair) 60·00 65·00
c. Opt inverted 18·00 18·00
d. "O" inverted 13·00 2·75
e. Left "S" inverted 13·00 2·75
f. Right "S" inverted 13·00 2·75
g. Left "S" omitted 60·00 60·00
h. Right "S" omitted 60·00 60·00
i. Wmk sideways — 7·00
O33 6 3 ch. violet 7·00 70
a. Opt inverted † 70·00
b. "O" inverted 28·00 16·00
c. "O" omitted 55·00 55·00
d. "Ou" for "On" 75·00 75·00
e. Left "S" inverted — 20·00
O34 7 7 ch. claret (date?) 55·00 1·75
O35 8 14 ch. orange-yellow 24·00 85
a. Imperf between (vert pair) £180
b. "O" inverted 55·00 7·00

The 5 ca. olive-bistre, 3 ch. and 7 ch. exist only with the normal watermark spaced 11 mm; the 5 ca. chocolate and 14 ch. exist only with the wide 15 mm spacing; the 6 ca., 10 ca. and 1¼ ch. exist in both forms.

On S S (O 3) On S S (O 4) On *S S* (O 5)

Italic "S S"

**1930.** *Wmk C. P* 12. (*a*) *Optd with Type* O 3.
O36 4 10 ca. pink 85·00 65·00
O37 1 1¼ ch. carmine-rose 3·00 2·50

(*b*) *Optd with Type* O 4
O38 5 ¾ ch. black (R.) 30 10
a. Left "S" omitted 42·00
b. Right "S" omitted 42·00
c. Large roman "S" at left — 40·00

(*c*) *Optd with Type* O 5
O39 5 ¾ ch. black (R.) 30 10
a. Opt inverted † 90·00
b. "n" omitted 45·00 45·00
O40 1 4 ch. slate-green (R.) 21·00 9·00

On S S (O 6) On S S (O 7) On S S (O 8)

Oval "O"

**1930–39** (?). *Contemporary stamps overprinted. P* 12.

(*a*) *With Type* O **6** (*16 mm high*) (i) *Wmk A*
O41 3 4 ca. pink 10·00 18·00
a. Large right "S" as Type O **2** 50·00 65·00

(ii) *Wmk B*
O42 3 4 ca. pink 13·00 22·00
a. Large right "S" as Type O **2** 60·00 75·00

(iii) *Wmk C*
O43 1 6 ca. brown-red (1932) 30 10
a. Opt inverted 16·00
b. Opt double 35·00 35·00
c. "O" inverted 8·00 5·00
O44 4 10 ca. pink 1·50 1·10
O45 5 ¾ ch. mauve (1933) 1·10 10
a. Imperf between (horiz pair) 50·00 40·00
b. Imperf between (horiz strip of 3) † 65·00
c. Imperf between (vert pair) † 50·00
d. Stamp doubly printed † 80·00
e. Perf 12½ 3·75 40
f. Perf comp of 12 and 12½ 7·50 1·25
g. Right "S" inverted — 13·00
O46 1 1¼ ch. carmine-rose 9·50 1·75
a. Opt double 75·00 55·00
b. Large right "S" as Type O **2** 60·00 32·00
O47 4 ch. grey-green 1·50 2·25
O48 4 ch. grey-green (R.) (27.10.30) 70 15
a. Imperf between (horiz pair) 60·00 60·00
b. Opt double 24·00 24·00
c. "O" inverted 20·00 13·00
d. Large right "S" as Type O **2** 27·00 20·00
e. Imperf between (vert pair) 60·00
O49 8 14 ch. orange-yellow (1931) 3·25 1·00
a. Imperf between (vert pair) † 70·00

For the 1½ ch. and 3 ch., and for Nos. O43 and O48/9 but perf 12½, see Nos. O66/70 (new setting combining Types O **6** and O **8**).

(*b*) *With Type* O **7** (*14 mm high*). *Wmk C*
O50 3 4 ca. pink 7·00 13·00
a. "O" inverted 30·00 42·00
O51 4 5 ca. chocolate (1932) 12·00 9·00
a. Opt inverted 65·00 65·00
O52 1 6 ca. brown-red 15 10
a. Imperf between (vert pair) 45·00 45·00
b. Opt inverted 25·00
c. Opt double † 38·00
d. "nO" for "On" 70·00 70·00
e. Right "S" inverted 10·00 7·00
f. Left "S" omitted — 60·00
g. Large "n" as Type O **5** 16·00 10·00
h. Large italic left "S" as Type O **5** 16·00 10·00
i. Perf 12½ — 4·50
j. Perf compound of 12 and 12½ — 9·00

O53 1 ½ ch. reddish violet (1932) 30 15
a. "CHUCRRAM" 7·50 5·50
b. "Ou" for "On" 38·00 38·00
c. Left "S" omitted — 60·00
d. "O" of "On" omitted 80·00
O54 ½ ch. reddish violet (R.) (1935) 15 10
a. Imperf between (vert pair) 55·00 55·00
b. "CHUCRRAM" 3·00 3·00
c. Left "S" inverted — 12·00
O55 4 10 ca. pink (date?) 1·50 75
a. Imperf between (horiz pair) 10·00 11·00
b. Imperf between (vert pair) 10·00 11·00
c. "O" inverted 16·00 12·00
d. Right "S" inverted 16·00 12·00
O56 5 ¾ ch. mauve (1933?) 30 10
a. Imperf between (vert pair) † 60·00
b. "Ou" for "On" 38·00 38·00
c. "O" inverted 12·00 10·00
d. Right "S" inverted — 10·00
e. Opt double † 60·00
f. Perf comp of 12 and 12½ 16·00 9·00
O57 1 1 ch. deep blue (R.) (1935) 85 15
*a. Slate-blue* 80 15
b. Imperf between (horiz pair) 50·00 50·00
c. Imperf between (vert pair) 25·00 25·00
d. Perf 12½ 7·00 2·00
e. Perf comp of 12 and 12½ 11·00 3·25
O58 1¼ ch. claret 1·10 50
O59 1½ ch. rose (1933) 35 10
a. Imperf between (vert pair) † 65·00
b. Opt double 50·00 50·00
c. "O" inverted 3·75 2·50
e. Large "n" as type O 5 28·00 16·00
f. Large italic left "S" as Type O 5 28·00 16·00
g. Left "S" inverted — 14·00
h. Perf 12½ — 6·50
i. Perf comp of 12 and 12½ — 8·50
ia. Stamp doubly printed † 90·00
O60 6 3 ch. reddish violet (1933) 1·10 40
a. "O" inverted 12·00 7·00
O61 3 ch. violet (R.) (1934) 60 10
a. Imperf between (horiz pair) 45·00 32·00
b. Imperf between (vert pair) 45·00 32·00
c. Opt inverted † 32·00
d. "O" inverted 12·00 8·00
e. Perf 12½ — 1·90
ea. Imperf between (vert pair) † 80·00
f. Perf comp of 12 and 12½ — 5·00
fa. Imperf between (horiz pair) † 80·00
O62 1 4 ch. grey-green (1934) — £130
O63 4 ch. grey-green (R.) (1935?) 80 15
a. "Ou" for "On" 35·00 35·00
O64 7 7 ch. claret (*shades*) 1·10 30
a. Imperf between (vert pair) 24·00 24·00
b. "O" inverted 26·00 13·00
c. Left "S" inverted 26·00 13·00
d. Perf 12½ — 4·00
e. Perf comp of 12 and 12½ — 6·00
ea. Imperf between (vert pair) † 48·00
eb. Imperf between (vert strip of 3) 60·00 60·00
O65 8 14 ch. orange (1933) 1·50 40
a. Imperf between (horiz pair) 26·00 32·00
b. Imperf between (vert pair) 65·00
c. Opt inverted † £130

(c) *New setting combining Type O 8 (18 mm high) in top row with Type O 6 (16 mm high) for remainder. Wmk C (dates?)*

A. *Type* O 8. B. *Type* O 6

| | | | A | | B | |
|---|---|---|---|---|---|---|
| O66 | 1 | 6 ca. brown-red | 5·00 | 2·25 | † | |
| | | a. Perf 12½ | 5·00 | 2·25 | 1·75 | 50 |
| | | ab. Imperf between (vert pair) | † | | 55·00 | 55·00 |
| | | ac. "O" inverted | † | | 14·00 | 8·00 |
| | | g. Perf comp of 12 and 12½ | † | | — | 9·00 |
| O67 | | 1½ ch. rose | 14·00 | 4·25 | 3·00 | 35 |
| | | a. Perf 12½ | 20·00 | 5·00 | 6·00 | 45 |
| | | ab. "O" inverted | † | | 25·00 | 10·00 |
| | | c. Perf comp of 12 and 12½ | † | | — | 12·00 |
| O68 | 6 | 3 ch. violet (R.) | 24·00 | 7·00 | 4·00 | 65 |
| | | a. Perf 12½ | 30·00 | 8·50 | 8·00 | 75 |
| | | b. Perf comp of 12 and 12½ | 45·00 | 12·00 | 15·00 | 3·00 |
| O69 | 1 | 4 ch. grey-green (R.) | 30·00 | 17·00 | † | |
| | | a. Perf 12½ | 22·00 | 11·00 | 6·00 | 2·00 |
| | | ab. Imperf between (horiz pair) | † | | † | 85·00 |
| O70 | 8 | 14 ch. orange-yellow | 24·00 | 8·00 | † | |
| | | a. Perf 12½ | 22·00 | 8·00 | 5·00 | 75 |

Nos. O66B and O69/70B naturally exist but are not distinguishable from Nos. O43 and O48/9.

Nos. O66/70A/B in vertical *se-tenant* pairs are very scarce.

As with the postage issues it is believed that the 12½ and compound perforations were issued between 1937 and 1939.

1 ch

8 c (O 9) 1 ch Wrong fount "1 c"

**1932.** *Official stamps surch as T* 14 *or with Type* O 9. *P* 12.

(a) *With opt Type* O 1 (i) *Wmk* A

O71 4 6 c. on 5 ca. olive-bistre 16·00 8·00
a. "O" inverted 48·00 22·00
b. Left "S" inverted 48·00 22·00
c. Right "S" inverted 48·00 22·00

(ii) *Wmk* C

O72 4 6 c. on 5 ca. olive-bistre 7·00 2·50
a. "O" inverted 22·00 8·00
b. Left "S" inverted 22·00 8·00
c. Right "S" inverted 22·00 8·00
O73 12 c. on 10 ca. pink 45·00

(b) *With opt Type* O 2. *Wmk* C

O74 4 6 c. on 5 ca. olive-bistre 1·40 50
a. Opt and surch inverted 32·00
b. Surch inverted 28·00
c. Left "S" inverted 10·00 4·25
d. Right "S" inverted 10·00 4·25
e. "6" omitted — 45·00
O75 6 c. on 5 ca. chocolate 15 15
a. Surch inverted 9·00 9·00
b. Surch double 55·00
c. Surch double, one inverted 55·00
d. "O" inverted 2·50 2·50
e. Left "S" inverted 2·50 2·50
O76 12 c. on 10 ca. pink 30 15
a. Opt inverted 6·50 6·50
b. Surch inverted 7·00 7·00
c. Opt and surch inverted 22·00 22·00
d. Pair, one without surch £160
e. "O" inverted 3·00 2·50
f. Left "S" inverted 2·25 1·75
g. "Ou" for "On" 42·00 42·00
i. "c" omitted 32·00 32·00
O77 1 1 ch. 8 c. on 1¼ ch. claret 75 25
a. Surch inverted † 38·00
b. "O" inverted 5·50 2·25
c. Left "S" inverted 5·50 2·25
d. Right "S" inverted 5·50 2·25
e. Wrong fount "1 c" 17·00 12·00

(c) *With opt Type* O 3. *Wmk* C

O78 4 12 c. on 10 ca. pink † £180
O79 1 1 ch. 8 c. on 1¼ ch. carmine-rose 32·00 20·00
a. "n" omitted £120
b. Wrong fount "1 c" £100 70·00

(d) *With opt Type* O 6. *Wmk* C

O80 4 12 c. on 10 ca. pink 27·00 7·50
O81 1 1 ch. 8 c. on 1¼ ch. carmine-rose 42·00 12·00
a. Wrong fount "1 c" £110 48·00
b. "h" omitted
*c. Brown-red* — 12·00

(e) *With opt Type* O 7. *Wmk* C

O82 4 6 c. on 5 ca. chocolate 15 15
a. Opt inverted 35·00 35·00
b. Surch inverted 11·00 12·00
c. Right "S" omitted 55·00 55·00
d. Two quads for right "S" £450
e. Right "S" inverted 16·00
O83 12 c. on 10 ca. pink 15 15
a. Opt inverted 7·00 7·00
b. Surch inverted 6·00 6·00
c. Opt and surch inverted 30·00 30·00
d. Opt double † 55·00
e. "O" inverted 9·00 9·00
f. Right "S" inverted 9·00 9·00
g. "On" omitted — 50·00
h. "n" omitted — 50·00
i. "c." omitted 24·00 24·00
j. Surch double † 48·00
O84 1 1 ch. 8 c. on 1¼ ch. claret 35 25
a. Imperf between (vert pair) † £110
b. Opt omitted † £180
c. Surch inverted 14·00 14·00
d. Surch double 38·00
e. "O" inverted 4·00 2·50
f. Wrong fount "1 c" 14·00 12·00

SERVICE (O 10) 13 mm — SERVICE (O 11) 13½ mm — SERVICE 8 CASH (O 12)

**1939–41.** *Nos.* 35 *and* 40 *with type-set opt, Type* O 10. *P* 12½.

O85 1 6 ca. brown-red (1941) 70 10
a. Perf 11 1·10 45
b. Perf 12 70 30
c. Compound perf 70 70
O86 5 ¾ ch. reddish violet 35·00 22·00
a. Perf 12 9·00 80
b. Compound perf 45·00 28·00

**1939** (9 Nov). *Maharaja's 27th Birthday. Nos.* 64/70 *with type-set opt, Type* O 10. *P* 12½.

O87 1 ch. yellow-green 1·40 20
O88 1½ ch. scarlet 1·40 50
a. "SESVICE" 42·00 23·00
b. Perf 12 9·00 2·50
ba. "SESVICE" — 55·00
bb. Imperf between (horiz pair) † 75·00
c. Compound perf 5·00 1·25
O89 2 ch. orange 1·25 1·25
a. "SESVICE" 60·00 60·00
b. Compound perf 30·00 30·00
O90 3 ch. brown 1·75 10
a. "SESVICE" 32·00 18·00
b. Perf 12 3·25 40
ba. "SESVICE" 60·00 27·00
c. Compound perf 4·25 1·60
O91 4 ch. red 3·00 1·10
O92 7 ch. pale blue 4·50 1·40
O93 14 ch. turquoise-green 5·50 1·25
O87/93 *Set of* 7 17·00 5·00

**1940** (?)–**45.** *Nos.* 40*a and* 42*b optd with Type* O 11. *P* 12½.

O94 5 ¾ ch. reddish violet 5·50 15
a. Imperf between (horiz pair) 60·00
b. Perf 11 18·00 1·00
c. Perf 12 5·00 15
d. Compound perf 14·00 75
O95 1 1½ ch. rose (1945) 10·00 7·50
a. Perf 12 2·75 1·00
b. Compound perf 12·00 11·00

**1942** (?). *Nos.* 64/70 *optd with Type* O 11. *P* 12½.

O 96 1 ch. yellow-green 35 1
a. Imperf between (vert pair) 30·00 30·0
b. Opt inverted † 22·0
c. Opt double 20·00
d. Perf 11 45 1
da. Imperf between (vert pair) 17·00
db. Opt double 42·00 42·0
e. Perf 12 1·90 3
ea. Imperf between (vert pair) 45·00 45·0
eb. Stamp doubly printed 85·00
ec. Opt inverted † 42·0
ed. Opt double 18·00
f. Compound perf 2·75 1·0
g. "S" inverted — 25·0
O 97 1½ ch. scarlet 85 1
a. Imperf between (horiz pair) 38·00
b. Perf 11 85 1
ba. Imperf between (vert pair) 45·00 45·0
bb. Imperf between (vert strip of 3) 38·00
bc. Imperf between (horiz pair) † 50·0
c. Perf 12 1·90 3
ca. Imperf between (vert strip of 3) 65·00
d. Compound perf 1·50 3
e. Imperf (pair) 25·00
O 98 2 ch. orange 75 3
a. Perf 11 2·50 5
ab. Imperf between (vert pair)
b. Perf 12 30·00 30·0
ba. Imperf between (vert pair) £120 £12
c. Compound perf 32·00 32·0
O 99 3 ch. brown 40 1
a. Imperf between (vert pair)
b. Perf 11 85 1
c. Perf 12 1·90 5
ca. Imperf between (vert pair) £100 £10
d. Compound perf 8·00 7
O100 4 ch. red 75 3
a. Perf 11 1·60 4
b. Perf 12 6·50 2·2
c. Compound perf 30·00 17·0
O101 7 ch. pale blue 2·25 3
a. Perf 11 3·75 1·7
b. Perf 12 8·50 5·0
c. Compound perf 12·00 4·0
*d. Blue (p 11)* 4·00 2·2
da. Perf 12 4·00 2·2
db. Compound perf 16·00 8·0
O102 14 ch. turquoise-green 5·00 7
a. Perf 11 5·50 1·5
b. Perf 12 5·50 2·4
c. Compound perf 32·00 5·0
O96/102 *Set of* 7 9·00 1·7

**1942.** *Maharaja's 29th Birthday. Nos* 71/2 *optd with Type* O 11. *P* 12½.

O103 6 ca. blackish violet 30 1
a. Perf 11 70 3
b. Perf 12 15·00 2·2
c. Compound perf 1·50 7
O104 ¾ ch. brown 1·00 1
a. Imperf between (vert pair) † £10
b. Perf 11 2·50 1
c. Perf 12 14·00 1·2
d. Compound perf 3·00 8

**1943.** *Surch with Type* O 12. *P* 12½.

O105 19 8 ca. on 6 ca. scarlet 75 1
a. Perf 11 1·10 1
ab. Surch inverted † £40
b. Compound perf 3·25 1·2

**1945.** *Nos.* 73/4 *optd with Type* O 11. *P* 12½.

O106 2 ca. on 1½ ch. scarlet 40 2
a. Perf 11 35 1
ab. Pair, one without surch £130
b. Compound perf 70 7
ba. "2" omitted £100 £10
O107 4 ca. on ¾ ch. brown 70 1
a. Perf 11 40 1
b. Compound perf 1·10 7

**1947.** *Maharaja's 34th Birthday. Optd with Type* O 11. *P* 11.

O108 21 8 ca. carmine 1·10 7
a. Imperf between (horiz pair) 35·00
ab. Imperf between (vert pair) † 70·0
b. Opt double † 95·0
c. Perf 12½ 3·00 1·
ca. Stamp doubly printed 30·00
d. Perf 12 3·50 1·
da. Stamp doubly printed 32·00

From 1 July 1949 Travancore formed part of the new State of Travancore-Cochin and stamps of Travancore surcharged in Indian currency were used.

## TRAVANCORE-COCHIN

On 1 July 1949 the United State of Travancore and Cochin was formed ("U.S.T.C.") and the name was changed to State of Travancore-Cochin ("T.C.") by the new constitution of India on 26 January 1950.

| PRICES FOR STAMPS ON COVER | |
|---|---|
| Nos. 1/13 | *from* × 8 |
| Nos. O1/17 | *from* × 15 |

**NO WATERMARK VARIETIES.** These were formerly listed but we have now decided to omit them as they do not occur in full sheets. They are best collected in pairs, with and without watermarks.

**COMPOUND PERFS.** The notes above Type 17 of Travancore also apply here.

**ALIDITY OF STAMPS.** From 6 June 1950 the stamps of ravancore-Cochin were valid on mail from both Indian and state ost offices to destinations in India and abroad.

ONE ANNA
ഒരണ
(1)

2 p. on 6 ca.

രണ്ടു പൈസ   രണ്ടു പൈസ

Normal — Variety: 1st character of 2nd group as 1st character of 1st group

49 (1 July). *Stamps of Travancore surch in "PIES" or "ANNAS" as T* 1. *P* 12½.
19 2 p. on 6 ca. blackish violet (R.) .. .. 60 20
a. Surch inverted .. 22·00
b. Character error .. 55·00 45·00
c. "O" inverted .. 15·00 11·00
d. Perf 11 .. 40 15
da. Imperf between (vert pair) .. 50·00 50·00
db. Pair, one without surch .. 55·00
dc. Character error .. 48·00 42·00
dd. "O" inverted ..
e. Perf 12 .. 20 10
ea. Imperf between (horiz pair) .. 18·00
eb. Imperf between (vert pair) .. 5·00 8·50
ec. Surch inverted .. 40·00
ed. Character error .. 55·00 45·00
ee. Imperf between (vert strip of 3) .. 20·00
ef. Block of four imperf between (horiz and vert) .. 24·00
eg. "O" inverted .. 15·00 11·00
f. Perf 14 .. † £250
g. Imperf (pair) .. 8·50 £250
h. Compound perf .. — 22·00
21 4 p. on 8 ca. carmine .. 60 10
a. Surch inverted .. 24·00
b. "S" inverted .. 40·00 30·00
c. Perf 11 .. 40 10
ca. Imperf between (vert pair) .. 60·00 60·00
cb. Surch inverted .. 42·00
cc. Pair, one without surch .. 60·00 60·00
cd. "FOUP" for "FOUR" .. 60·00 48·00
ce. "S" inverted .. 40·00 30·00
d. Perf 12 .. 30 30
da. Imperf between (vert pair) .. 14·00
db. Pair, one without surch .. 55·00
dc. "FOUP" for "FOUR" .. 60·00 48·00
dd. "S" inverted .. 45·00 32·00
de. Surch inverted .. 55·00
c. Imperf (pair) .. 55·00
f. Compound perf .. — 22·00
g. Perf 13½ .. † £250
17 ½ a. on 1 ch. yellow-green .. 75 30
a. "NANA" for "ANNA" .. 65·00 55·00
b. Inverted "H" in "HALF" .. — 45·00
c. Imperf between (vert pair) .. † 50·00
d. Perf 11 .. 60 15
da. Imperf between (vert pair) .. 16·00
db. Surch inverted .. † 60·00
dc. "NANA" for "ANNA" .. 75·00 55·00
dd. Inverted "H" in "HALF" .. — 45·00
e. Perf 12 .. 35 15
ea. Imperf between (horiz pair) .. 14·00 17·00
eb. Imperf between (vert pair) .. 4·50 7·50
ec. Surch inverted .. 5·00
ed. "NANA" for "ANNA" .. 75·00 55·00
ee. Block of four imperf between (horiz and vert) .. 24·00
f. Perf 14 .. † £250
g. Imperf (pair) .. 8·50 13·00
h. Compound perf .. — 22·00
18 1 a. on 2 ch. orange .. 90 30
a. Perf 11 .. 30 20
ab. Surch double .. 45·00
b. Perf 12 .. 1·10 30
ba. Imperf between (horiz pair) .. 4·25
bb. Imperf between (vert pair) .. 4·25 7·50
bc. Block of four imperf between (horiz and vert) .. 24·00
c. Perf 13½ .. 70·00 2·00
d. Imperf (pair) .. 8·50
e. Compound perf .. 24·00 16·00
– 2 a. on 4 ch. red (68) .. 1·00 35
a. Surch inverted .. † £130
b. "O" inverted .. 16·00 10·00
c. Perf 11 .. 90 35
ca. "O" inverted .. — 13·00
d. Perf 12 .. 1·25 55
da. "O" inverted .. 22·00 14·00
e. Compound perf .. 22·00 22·00
18 3 a. on 7 ch. pale blue (69) .. 5·50 2·50
a. Perf 11 .. 4·00 1·50
*ab. Blue* .. 24·00 4·00
ac. "3" omitted .. † —
b. Perf 12 .. 4·25 2·50
c. Compound perf .. — 24·00
*ca. Blue* .. — 32·00
– 6 a. on 14 ch. turquoise-green (70) .. 5·50 8·00
a. Accent omitted from native surch .. 80·00 80·00
b. Perf 11 .. 4·00 7·00
ba. Accent omitted from native surch .. 80·00 80·00
c. Perf 12 .. 6·50 9·00
ca. Accent omitted from native surch .. 90·00 90·00
d. Compound perf .. 15·00 15·00
da. Accent omitted from native surch .. £110
e. Imperf (pair)
.. *Set of* 7 9·00 8·50

There are two settings of the ½ a. surcharge. In one the first tive character is under the second downstroke of the "H" and in e other it is under the first downstroke of the "A" of "HALF". They ur on stamps perf 12½, 11 and 12 equally commonly and also the Official stamps.

. S. T. C. (2)   T.-C. (3)   SIX PIES (4)

**1949.** *No.* 106 *of Cochin optd with T* 2.
8 29 1 a. orange .. 4·50 40·00
a. No stop after "S" (R. 1/6) .. 48·00
b. Raised stop after "T" (R. 4/1) .. 48·00

**1950** (1 Apr). *No.* 106 *of Cochin optd with T* 3.
9 29 1 a. orange .. 5·50 35·00
a. No stop after "T" .. 45·00
b. Opt inverted .. £160
ba. No stop after "T" .. £1500

The no stop variety occurs on No. 5 in the sheet and again on No. 8 in conjunction with a short hyphen.

**1950** (1 Apr). *No.* 9 *surch as T* 4.
10 29 6 p. on 1 a. orange .. 1·60 10·00
a. No stop after "T" (R. 1/5) .. 17·00
b. Error. Surch on No. 8 .. 40·00
ba. No stop after "S" .. £250
bb. Raised stop after "T" .. £250
11 9 p. on 1 a. orange .. 1·40 10·00
a. No stop after "T" (R. 1/5) .. 17·00
b. Error. Surch on No. 8 .. £120
ba. No stop after "S" .. £475
bb. Raised stop after "T" .. £475

5 Conch or Chank Shell   6 Palm Trees

(Litho Indian Security Printing Press, Nasik)

**1950.** *W* **69** *of India. P* 14.
12 5 2 p. rose-carmine .. 45 1·10
13 6 4 p. ultramarine .. 70 3·00

The ordinary issues of Travancore-Cochin became obsolete on 1 July 1951.

OFFICIAL STAMPS

**VALIDITY.** Travancore-Cochin official stamps were valid for use throughout India from 30 September 1950.

SERVICE (O 1)   SERVICE (O 2)

**1949–51.** *Stamps of Travancore surch with value as T* 1 *and optd* "SERVICE". *No gum. P* 12½. (a) *With Type* O 1.

(i) *Wmk C of Travancore*
O 1 19 2 p. on 6 ca. blackish violet (R.) .. 30 15
a. Imperf between (vert pair) .. 60·00 60·00
b. Character error .. 24·00 20·00
c. "O" inverted .. 13·00 9·00
d. Pair, one without surch .. 65·00
e. Perf 11 .. 35 10
ea. Imperf between (vert pair) .. 60·00 60·00
eb. Character error .. 32·00 26·00
ec. "O" inverted .. 13·00 9·00
f. Perf 12 .. 20 20
fa. Imperf between (horiz pair) .. 6·00 11·00
fb. Imperf between (vert pair) .. 6·00
fc. Character error .. 28·00 24·00
fd. "O" inverted .. 13·00
fe. Block of four imperf between (horiz and vert) .. 22·00
g. Imperf (pair) .. 8·00 12·00
ga. Character error .. £120
O 2 21 4 p. on 8 ca. carmine .. 70 30
a. "FOUB" for "FOUR" .. 75·00 50·00
b. Perf 11 .. 1·00 20
ba. "FOUB" for "FOUR" .. 60·00 32·00
c. Perf 12 .. 1·00 30
ca. "FOUB" for "FOUR" .. 60·00 42·00
d. Compound perf .. 14·00 14·00
O 3 17 ½ a. on 1 ch. yellow-green .. 30 15
a. Pair, one without surch .. 42·00
b. Surch inverted .. 18·00
c. "NANA" for "ANNA" .. 85·00 45·00
d. Perf 11 .. 80 15
da. Pair, one without surch .. 65·00
db. Surch inverted .. 55·00
dc. "NANA" for "ANNA" .. 85·00 50·00
e. Perf 12 .. 3·75 1·25
ea. "NANA" for "ANNA" .. £120 85·00
eb. Pair, one without surch .. 55·00
f. Compound perf .. — 18·00
O 4 18 1 a. on 2 ch. orange .. 9·50 5·00
a. Surch inverted .. 70·00
b. Pair, one without surch .. £300
c. Perf 11 .. 8·50 6·00
O 5 – 2 a. on 4 ch. red (68) .. 65 40
b. Perf 11 .. 2·50 45
ba. Surch inverted .. £225
c. Perf 12 .. 3·00 1·50
ca. O inverted .. — 28·00
cb. Pair, one without surch .. £120
d. Compound perf .. — 25·00
e. Imperf (pair) .. 12·00
O 6 – 3 a. on 7 ch. pale blue (69) .. 2·25 70
a. Imperf between (vert pair) .. 14·00
*b. Blue* .. 14·00 4·00
c. Perf 11 .. 1·90 60
*ca. Blue* .. 14·00 4·00
d. Perf 12 .. 1·75 1·75
da. Imperf between (horiz pair) .. 10·00
db. Imperf between (vert pair) .. 8·00
dc. Block of four imperf between (horiz and vert) .. 22·00
*dd. Blue* .. 13·00 3·75
e. Imperf (pair) .. 11·00
O 7 – 6 a. on 14 ch. turquoise-green (70) .. 5·50 2·00
a. Imperf between (vert pair) .. 24·00
b. Perf 11 .. 5·00 1·40
c. Perf 12 .. 16·00 5·00
ca. Imperf between (horiz pair) .. 21·00
cb. Imperf between (vert pair) .. 25·00
cc. Block of four imperf between (horiz and vert) .. 45·00
d. Imperf (pair) .. 14·00
O1/7 .. *Set of* 7 15·00 7·00

(ii) *W* **27** *of Cochin*
O 8 19 2 p. on 6 ca. blackish violet (R.) .. 10 30
a. Type O 1 double .. 16·00
b. Perf 11 .. 30 50
c. Perf 12 .. 40 60
O 9 – 2 a. on 4 ch. red (68) .. 50 35
a. Perf 11 .. 40 35
ab. Imperf between (vert pair) .. £100 £100
b. Compound perf .. — 28·00

(b) *With Type* O 2

(i) *Wmk C of Travancore*
O10 21 4 p. on 8 ca. carmine .. 15 10
a. "FOUB" for "FOUR" .. 65·00 32·00
b. 2nd "E" of "SERVICE" in wrong fount .. — 40·00
c. "S" in "PIES" inverted .. — 40·00
d. Imperf between (vert pair) .. † 55·00
e. Perf 11 .. 15 10
ea. Imperf between (horiz pair) .. 4·50
eb. Imperf between (vert pair) .. 18·00
ec. "FOUB" for "FOUR" .. 60·00 32·00
ed. 2nd "E" of "SERVICE" in wrong fount .. — 40·00
ee. "S" in "PIES" inverted .. — 40·00
ef. Block of four imperf between (horiz and vert) .. 24·00
f. Perf 12 .. 15 15
fa. Imperf between (horiz pair) .. 2·00
fb. Imperf between (vert pair) .. 2·00
fc. Block of four imperf between (horiz and vert) .. 9·00 13·00
fd. "FOUB" for "FOUR" .. 65·00 30·00
ff. 2nd "E" of "SERVICE" in wrong fount .. 60·00 38·00
g. Perf 13½ .. 2·50 1·25
h. Compound perf .. 8·00 8·00
i. Imperf (pair) .. 6·00
ia. 2nd "E" of "SERVICE" in wrong fount .. 85·00
O11 17 ½ a. on 1 ch. yellow-green .. 30 10
a. "AANA" for "ANNA" .. 75·00 45·00
b. Perf 11 .. 10 10
ba. Imperf between (horiz pair) .. 25·00 25·00
bb. Imperf between (vert pair) .. 5·50
bc. Block of four imperf between (horiz and vert) .. 29·00
bd. "AANA" for "ANNA" .. 65·00 40·00
c. Perf 12 .. 30 10
ca. Imperf between (horiz pair) .. 3·50
cb. Imperf between (vert pair) .. 3·50 5·50
cc. "AANA" for "ANNA" .. 65·00 42·00
cd. Block of four imperf between (horiz and vert) .. 20·00
d. Compound perf .. 14·00 10·00
da. "AANA" for "ANNA" .. — 80·00
e. Imperf (pair) .. 6·00 9·00
O12 18 1 a. on 2 ch. orange .. 20 20
a. Imperf between (vert pair) .. † 55·00
b. Perf 11 .. 80 50
ba. Imperf between (horiz pair) .. 5·50 9·00
bb. Imperf between (vert pair) .. 27·00 27·00
c. Perf 12 .. 30 20
ca. Imperf between (horiz pair) .. 3·50
cb. Imperf between (vert pair) .. 3·00 6·50
cc. Block of four imperf between (horiz and vert) .. 16·00
d. Compound perf .. 15·00 13·00
e. Imperf (pair) .. 14·00
O13 – 2 a. on 4 ch. red (68) .. 1·75 80
a. "O" inverted .. 32·00 24·00
b. Perf 11 .. 1·10 1·10
ba. "O" inverted .. 28·00 24·00
c. Perf 12 .. 4·50 1·10
ca. Imperf between (vert pair) .. 90·00 95·00
cb. "O" inverted .. 50·00 24·00
d. Compound perf .. 17·00 13·00
O14 – 3 a. on 7 ch. pale blue (69) .. 2·75 75
a. "S" inverted in "SERVICE" .. 50·00 32·00
b. First "E" inverted .. £100 85·00
c. "C" inverted .. 75·00 65·00
d. Second "E" inverted .. 95·00 80·00
e. Perf 11 .. 1·10 75
ea. "S" inverted in "SERVICE" .. 45·00 32·00
f. Perf 12 .. 3·00 1·25
fa. "S" inverted in "SERVICE" .. 65·00 45·00
g. Compound perf .. — 27·00
h. Imperf (pair) .. 32·00
O15 – 6 a. on 14 ch. turquoise-green (70) .. 1·10 1·60
a. Accent omitted from native surch .. 16·00 12·00
b. "S" inverted in "SERVICE" .. 60·00 40·00
c. Perf 11 .. 8·00 2·25
ca. Accent omitted from native surch .. 50·00 22·00
cb. "S" inverted in "SERVICE" .. 90·00 48·00
d. Perf 12 .. 22·00 3·25
da. Accent omitted from native surch .. 85·00 27·00
db. "S" inverted in "SERVICE" .. £120 55·00
e. Compound perf .. 32·00 32·00
O10/15 .. *Set of* 6 3·25 3·25

(ii) *W* **27** *of Cochin*

| | | | | |
|---|---|---|---|---|
| O16 | **17** | ½ a. on 1 ch. yellow-green | 30 | 30 |
| | | a. Perf 11 | 10 | 10 |
| | | b. Perf 12 | 12·00 | 6·50 |
| | | c. Compound perf. | 8·00 | 3·50 |
| O17 | **18** | 1 a. on 2 ch. orange | 30 | 30 |
| | | a. Perf 11 | 50 | 40 |
| | | b. Perf 12 | 10·00 | 5·00 |
| | | c. Perf 13½ | 2·50 | 1·50 |
| | | d. Compound perf | 4·00 | 3·75 |

Nos. O2, O10, O12 and O17 have the value at top in English and at bottom in native characters with "SERVICE" in between. All others have "SERVICE" below the surcharge.

Type O **2** was overprinted at one operation with the surcharges.

The Official stamps became obsolete in September 1951.

## WADHWAN

| PRICES FOR STAMPS ON COVER | |
|---|---|
| No. 1 | *from* × 50 |
| No. 2 | – |
| Nos. 3/5 | *from* × 50 |

1

**1888–94.** *Litho. (a) Thin toned wove paper*

| | | | | |
|---|---|---|---|---|
| 1 | 1 | ½ pice, black (I, III) (*p* 12½ *large holes*) | 8·00 | 30·00 |
| | | a. Imperf between (vert pair) (I) | | |
| | | b. Pin-perf 6½ irregular (I) | 45·00 | |
| | | c. Compound of 12½ and pin-perf 6½ (I) | | |
| 2 | | ½ pice, black (II) (*p* 12½ *irregular small holes*) | 20·00 | |

(*b*) *Medium toned wove paper*

| | | | | |
|---|---|---|---|---|
| 3 | 1 | ½ pice, black (III) (*p* 12½) | 6·00 | 22·00 |
| 4 | | ½ pice, black (V) (*p* 12) | 5·00 | 6·00 |

(*c*) *Thick off-white or toned wove paper*

| | | | | |
|---|---|---|---|---|
| 5 | 1 | ½ pice, black (IV, VI) (*p* 12) (7.92) | 4·00 | 4·50 |
| | | a. Perf compound of 12 and 11 (IV) | 11·00 | 22·00 |
| 6 | | ½ pice, black (VII) (*fine impression*) (*p* 12) (1894) | 4·00 | 16·00 |

Sheets from the Stone IV printing had at least one horizontal line of perforations gauging 11, normally between the bottom two rows of the sheet.

These stamps were lithographed from seven different stones taken from a single die. Brief details of the individual stones are as follows:

- Stone I – No. 1. Sheet size not known, but possibly 28 (4×7). Sheet margins imperforate
- Stone II – No. 2. Sheets of 42 (7×6) with imperforate margins
- Stone III – Nos. 1 (thin paper) and 3 (medium paper). Sheets of 40 (4×10) with imperforate margins
- Stone IV – Nos. 5/a. Sheets of 32 (4×8) with imperforate margins at top and right
- Stone V – No. 4. Sheets of 20 (4×5) with imperforate margins at top, right and bottom
- Stone VI – No. 5. Sheets of 30 (5×6) with all margins perforated
- Stone VII – No. 6. Sheets of 32 (4×8) with all margins perforated. Much finer impression than the other stones

Stamps from stones I and II come with or without the dot before "STATE". Those from the later stones always show the dot. The shading on the pennant above the shield can also be used in stone identification. Stamps from stones I to III show heavy shading on the pennant, but this is less evident on stone IV and reduced further to a short line or dot on stones V to VII. There is a ")" hairline after "HALF" on the majority of stamps from Stone III.

The stamps of Wadhwan became obsolete on 1 January 1895.

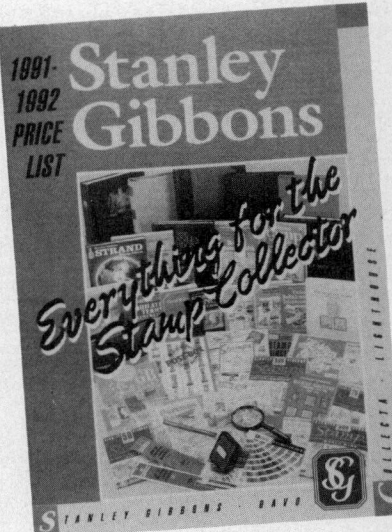

# Ionian Islands

The British occupation of the Ionian Islands was completed in 14 and the archipelago was placed under the protection of Great itain by the Treaty of Paris in 1815. The United States of the nian Islands were given local self-government, which included sponsibility for the postal services. Crowned-circle handstamps ere, however, supplied in 1844, although it is believed these were tended for use on prepaid mail to foreign destinations.

Examples of the Great Britain 1855 1d. red-brown stamp are own used at Corfu, but there is little information available ncerning such usage.

For illustrations of the handstamp types see BRITISH POST FICES ABROAD notes, following GREAT BRITAIN.

### CEPHALONIA

CROWNED-CIRCLE HANDSTAMPS

:1 CC 1 CEPHALONIA (19.4.1844) .. *Price on cover* £1000

### CORFU

CROWNED-CIRCLE HANDSTAMPS

:2 CC 1 CORFU (19.4.1844) .. .. *Price on cover* £500
:3 CC 1 CORFU (G. or B.) (1844) .. *Price on cover* —

*amps of* GREAT BRITAIN *cancelled with No.* CC2.
1d. red-brown (1855) Die II, *wmk* Large Crown, *perf* 14 .. .. .. .. .. .. £700

### ZANTE

CROWNED-CIRCLE HANDSTAMPS

:4 CC 1 ZANTE (G. or B.) (19.4.1844) .. *Price on cover* £1000

Nos. CC1/2 were later, *circa* 1860/1, struck in green (Cephalonia) red (Corfu).

It is believed that examples of No. CC4 in black are from an authorised use of this handstamp. A similar handstamp, but thout "PAID AT" was introduced in 1861.

| PRICES FOR STAMPS ON COVER | |
|---|---|
| Nos. 1/3 | *from* × 10 |

1

(Recess Perkins, Bacon & Co)

59 (15 June). *Imperf.*
1 (½d.) orange (no wmk) .. .. .. 70·00 £500
(1d.) blue (wmk "2") .. .. .. 20·00 £180
(2d.) carmine (wmk "1") .. .. .. 15·00 £180

On 30 May 1864, the islands were ceded to Greece, and these mps became obsolete.

Great care should be exercised in buying used stamps, on or off er, as forged postmarks are plentiful.

# Iraq

Indian post offices were opened at Baghdad and Basra, then t of the Turkish Empire, on 1 January 1868. Unoverprinted mps of India were used, Baghdad being allocated numeral cellations "356", "18" and "K-6", and Basra (also spelt ssorah, Busreh, Busrah, Busra) "357", "19" and "1/K-6".

Both offices closed in November 1914, but Basra re-opened the owing month when Indian stamps overprinted "I.E.F." were d.

**(Currency. 16 annas = 1 rupee)**

## I. ISSUES FOR BAGHDAD

| PRICES FOR STAMPS ON COVER | |
|---|---|
| Nos 1/25 | *from* × 6 |

### BRITISH OCCUPATION

British and Indian troops occupied the port of Basra on 22 vember 1914 to protect the oil pipeline. They then advanced up rivers, and after a hard campaign took Baghdad from the Turks 11 March 1917.

IN BRITISH BAGHDAD OCCUPATION 2 Ans

(1)

17 (1 Sept). *Stamps of Turkey, surch as T* 1 *in three operations.*

(a) *Pictorial designs of* 1914. *T* **32**, *etc., and* **31**
**32** ¼ a. on 2 pa. claret (Obelisk) .. .. 80·00 90·00
a. "IN BRITISH" omitted .. .. £4250
2 **34** ¼ a. on 5 pa. dull purple (Leander's Tower 55·00 60·00
a. Value omitted .. .. .. £4000
3 **36** ½ a. on 10 pa. green (Lighthouse garden) £550 £600
4 **31** ½ a. on 10 pa. green (Mosque of Selim) .. £850 £1000
5 **37** 1 a. on 20 pa. red (Castle) .. .. £300 £300
a. "BAGHDAD" double .. .. £1300
6 **38** 2 a. on 1 pi. bright blue (Mosque) .. .. 90·00 £110

(b) *As (a), but overprinted with small five-pointed Star*
7 **37** 1 a. on 20 pa. red (B.) .. .. .. £170 £180
a. "OCCUPATION" omitted .. .. £3250
b. "BAGHDAD" double
8 **38** 2 a. on 1 pi. bright blue (R.) .. .. £2250 £3000

(c) *Postal Jubilee stamps (Old G.P.O.). P* 12½
9 **60** ½ a. on 10 pa. carmine .. .. .. £275 £300
a. Perf 13½ .. .. .. £450 £475
10 1 a. on 20 pa. blue .. .. .. £900 £950
a. Value omitted .. .. .. £4750
b. Perf 13½ .. .. .. £650 £750
11 2 a. on 1 pi. black and violet .. .. 85·00 95·00
a. "BAGHDAD" omitted .. .. £3000
b. Perf 13½ .. .. .. 55·00 65·00

(d) *T* **30** *(G.P.O., Constantinople) with opt T* **26**.
12 **30** 2 a. on 1 pi. ultramarine .. .. £250 £325

(e) *Stamps optd with six-pointed Star and Arabic date "1331" within Crescent. T* **53** *(except No. 16, which has five-pointed Star and Arabic "1332", T* **57**)
13 **30** ½ a. on 10 pa. green (R.) .. .. 55·00 60·00
14 1 a. on 20 pa. rose .. .. .. £300 £325
a. Value omitted .. .. .. £3750 £3750
b. Optd with T **26** (Arabic letter "B") also .. .. .. .. £4250 £4250
15 **23** 1 a. on 20 pa. rose (No. 554a) .. .. £300 £325
a. Value omitted .. .. .. £4500
16 **21** 1 a. on 20 pa. carmine (No. 732) .. £2500 £3250
17 **30** 2 a. on 1 pi. ultramarine (R.) .. .. 65·00 75·00
a. "BAGHDAD" omitted .. .. † —
18 **21** 2 a. on 1 pi. dull blue (No. 543) (R.) .. £110 £120
a. "OCCUPATION" omitted

(f) *Stamps with similar opt, but date between Star and Crescent (Nos. 19 and 22, T* **54**; *others T* **55**, *five-pointed Star)*
19 **23** ½ a. on 10 pa. grey-green (No. 609a) (R.) 70·00 75·00
a. "OCCUPATION" omitted .. .. £3500
20 **60** ½ a. on 10 pa. carmine (*p* 12½) (B.) .. £100 £110
a. Perf 13½ .. .. .. £200 £200
21 **30** 1 a. on 20 pa. rose .. .. .. 65·00 75·00
22 **28** 1 a. on 20 pa. rose (Plate II) (No. 617) .. £275 £300
23 **15** 1 a. on 10 pa. on 20 pa. claret (No. 630) £140 £140
a. "OCCUPATION" omitted .. .. £3000 £3000
24 **30** 2 a. on 1 pi. ultramarine (R.) .. .. £120 £130
a. "OCCUPATION" omitted .. .. £4000
b. "BAGHDAD" omitted .. .. £4000
25 **28** 2 a. on 1 pi. ultramarine (Pl. II) (No. 645) £950 £1100

The last group (*f*) have the Crescent obliterated by hand in violet-black ink, as this included the inscription, "Tax for the relief of children of martyrs".

## II. ISSUES FOR MOSUL

| PRICES FOR STAMPS ON COVER | |
|---|---|
| Nos. 1/8 | *from* × 40 |

### BRITISH OCCUPATION

A British and Indian force, designated Indian Expeditionary Force "D", occupied Mosul on 1 November 1918.

POSTAGE

I.E.F. 'D'

1 Anna (1) 4 I 4 II

Two types of tougra in central design:
(a) Large "tougra" or sign-manual of El Ghazi 7 mm high.
(b) Smaller "tougra" of Sultan Rechad 5½ mm high.

Two types of 4 a. surcharge:
I. Normal "4". Apostrophes on D 3½ mm apart.
II. Small "4" Apostrophes on D 4½ mm apart.

**1919** (1 Feb). *Turkish Fiscal stamps surch as T* 1 *by Govt Press, Baghdad. P* 11½ (½ a.), 12 (1 a.), *or* 12½ (*others*).
1 ½ a. on 1 pi. green and red .. .. 1·40 1·40
2 1 a. on 20 pa. black/*red* (a) .. .. 1·40 1·75
a. Imperf between (horiz pair) .. .. £600
b. Surch double .. .. .. £500
c. "A" of "Anna" omitted
3 1 a. on 20 pa. black/*red* (b) .. .. 4·00 3·00
b. Surch double .. .. .. £600
4 2½ a. on 1 pi. mauve and yellow (*b*) .. 1·50 1·50
a. No bar to fraction (R. 2/4) .. .. 25·00 35·00
b. Surch double .. .. .. £650
5 3 a. on 20 pa. green (*a*) .. .. 1·60 2·25
6 3 a. on 20 pa. green and orange (*b*) .. 25·00 42·00
7 4 a. on 1 pi. deep violet (*a*) (I) .. .. 3·00 3·50
a. "4" omitted .. .. .. £1400
c. Surch double .. .. .. £750
7d 4 a. on 1 pi. deep violet (*a*) (II) .. .. 4·25 5·50
da. Surch double, one with "4" omitted .. £2250
8 8 a. on 10 pa. lake (*a*) .. .. .. 4·00 4·75
a. Surch inverted .. .. .. £550 £550
b. Surch double .. .. .. £550 £550
c. No apostrophe after "D" (R. 1/5) .. 22·00 32·00
d. Surch inverted. No apostrophe after "D" .. .. ..
e. "na" of "Anna" omitted .. ..
f. Error. 8 a. on 1 pi. deep violet .. £1700

No. 4a occurs on some sheets only. No. 8c comes from the first setting only.

In December 1925 the League of Nations awarded the vilayet of Mosul to Iraq.

## III. ISSUES FOR IRAQ

| PRICES FOR STAMPS ON COVER | |
|---|---|
| Nos. 1/18 | *from* × 4 |
| Nos. 41/154 | *from* × 2 |
| Nos. O19/171 | *from* × 2 |

### BRITISH OCCUPATION

IN BRITISH IRAQ OCCUPATION 1An.

(1)

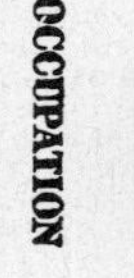

A

B

**1918** (1 Sept)–**21**. *Turkish pictorial issue of* 1914, *surch as T* 1 *by Bradbury Wilkinson. P* 12.

(a) *No wmk. Tougra as* A (1 Sept 1918–20)
1 **34** ¼ a. on 5 pa. dull purple .. .. 25 45
2 **36** ½ a. on 10 pa. green .. .. .. 25 15
3 **37** 1 a. on 20 pa. red .. .. .. 25 10
4 **34** 1½ a. on 5 pa. dull purple (1920) .. 1·40 50
5 **38** 2½ a. on 1 pi. bright blue .. .. 80 70
a. Surch inverted .. .. .. £3000
6 **39** 3 a. on 1½ pi. grey and rose .. .. 50 25
a. Surch double (Bk. + R.) .. .. £1700 £2250
7 **40** 4 a. on 1¾ pi. red-brown and grey .. 50 25
a. Centre inverted .. .. .. † £9000
8 **41** 6 a. on 2 pi. black and green .. .. 1·25 1·25
9 **42** 8 a. on 2½ pi. green and orange .. 90 60
a. Surch inverted .. .. .. † £5000
10 **43** 12 a. on 5 pi. deep lilac .. .. 1·50 1·25
11 **44** 1 r. on 10 pi. red-brown .. .. 2·00 1·40
12 **45** 2 r. on 25 pi. yellow-green .. .. 6·00 2·50
13 **46** 5 r. on 50 pi. rose .. .. .. 20·00 14·00
14 **47** 10 r. on 100 pi. indigo .. .. 29·00 17·00
1/14 .. .. .. .. *Set of* 14 60·00 35·00
1/3, 5/14 Perf "Specimen" .. .. *Set of* 13 £250

(b) *No wmk. Tougra as* B *(one device instead of two)* (1921)
15 **44** 1 r. on 10 pi. red-brown .. .. 90·00 19·00

(c) *Wmk Mult Script CA* (1921)
16 **36** ½ a. on 10 pa. green .. .. .. 40 60
17 **34** 1½ a. on 5 pa. dull purple .. .. 70 60
18 **45** 2 r. on 25 pi. yellow-green .. .. 11·00 7·50
16/18 .. .. .. .. *Set of* 3 11·00 8·00
16/18 Optd "Specimen" .. .. *Set of* 3 50·00

Designs: *Horiz*—5 pa. Leander's Tower; 10 pa. Lighthouse-garden, Stamboul; 20 pa. Castle of Europe; 1 pi. Mosque of Sultan Ahmed; 1½ pi. Martyrs of Liberty Monument; 1¾ pi. Fountains of Suleiman; 2 pi. Cruiser *Hamidiye*; 2½ pi. Candilli, Bosphorus; 5 pi. Former Ministry of War; 10 pi. Sweet Waters of Europe; 25 pi. Suleiman Mosque; 50 pi. Bosphorus at Rumeli Hisar; 100 pi. Sultan Ahmed's Fountain.

No. 7a is only recorded with telegraph cancellation.

The original settings of Nos. 1/18 showed the surcharge 27 mm wide, except for the 2½ a. (24 mm), 4 a. (26½ mm), 6 a. (32 mm), 8 a. (30½ mm), 12 a. (33 mm), 1 r. (31½ mm), 2 r. (30 mm) and 5 r. (32 mm). The 6 a., 8 a. and 5 r. also exist from a subsequent setting on which the surcharge was 27½ mm wide.

### LEAGUE OF NATIONS MANDATE

On 25 April 1920 the Supreme Council of the Allies assigned to the United Kingdom a mandate under the League of Nations to administer Iraq.

The Emir Faisal, King of Syria in 1920, was proclaimed King of Iraq on 23 August 1921.

**King Faisal I**
**23 August 1921–8 September 1933**

2 Sunni Mosque, Muadhdham

3 Winged Cherub

4 Allegory of Date Palm

(Des Miss Edith Cheesman (½ a., 1 a., 4 a., 6 a., 8 a., 2 r., 5 r., 10 r.), Mrs. C. Garbett (Miss M. Maynard) (others). Typo (1 r.) or recess (others) Bradbury, Wilkinson)

**1923** (May)–**25**. *T* 2/4 *and similar designs. Wmk Mult Script CA (sideways on* 1½ *a.,* 4 *a.,* 8 *a.,* 5 *r.). P* 12.
41 **2** ½ a. olive-green .. .. .. .. 15 10
42 – 1 a. brown .. .. .. .. 20 10

| No. | Type | Description | Unused | Used |
|---|---|---|---|---|
| 43 | 3 | 1½ a. lake | 25 | 10 |
| 44 | – | 2 a. orange-buff | 30 | 15 |
| 45 | – | 3 a. grey-blue | 50 | 15 |
| 46 | – | 4 a. violet | 80 | 25 |
| 47 | – | 6 a. greenish blue | 90 | 30 |
| 48 | – | 8 a. olive-bistre | 1·00 | 30 |
| 49 | 4 | 1 r. brown and blue-green | 2·00 | 70 |
| 50 | 2 | 2 r. black | 10·00 | 7·00 |
| 51 | | 2 r. olive-bistre (1925) | 16·00 | 3·25 |
| 52 | – | 5 r. orange | 21·00 | 13·00 |
| 53 | – | 10 r. lake | 27·00 | 20·00 |
| 41/53 | | *Set of* 13 | 70·00 | 40·00 |
| 41/53 Optd "Specimen" | | *Set of* 13 | £225 | |

Designs: *Horiz* (*as T* 2)—1 a. Gufas on the Tigris; 2 a. Bull from Babylonian wall-sculpture; 3 a. Arch of Ctesiphon; 6 a., 10 r. Shiar Mosque, Kadhimain. *Vert* (*as T* 3)—4 a., 8 a., 5 r. Tribal Standard, Dulaim Camel Corps.

With the exception of Nos. 49 and 50, later printings of these stamps and of No. 78 are on a thinner paper.

10

11
King Faisal I

12

(Recess Bradbury, Wilkinson)

**1927.** *Wmk Mult Script CA. P* 12.

| No. | Type | Description | Unused | Used |
|---|---|---|---|---|
| 78 | 10 | 1 r. red-brown (Optd S. £30) | 4·00 | 50 |

See note below No. 53.

(Recess Bradbury, Wilkinson)

**1931** (17 Feb). *Wmk Mult Script CA. P* 12.

| No. | Type | Description | Unused | Used |
|---|---|---|---|---|
| 80 | 11 | ½ a. green | 20 | 10 |
| 81 | | 1 a. red-brown | 20 | 10 |
| 82 | | 1½ a. scarlet | 40 | 30 |
| 83 | | 2 a. orange | 30 | 10 |
| 84 | | 3 a. blue | 45 | 10 |
| 85 | | 4 a. slate-purple | 80 | 70 |
| 86 | | 6 a. greenish blue | 80 | 60 |
| 87 | | 8 a. deep green | 1·00 | 70 |
| 88 | 12 | 1 r. chocolate | 2·50 | 90 |
| 89 | | 2 r. yellow-brown | 4·50 | 2·50 |
| 90 | | 5 r. orange | 18·00 | 25·00 |
| 91 | | 10 r. scarlet | 45·00 | 65·00 |
| 92 | 10 | 25 r. violet | £500 | £650 |
| 80/91 | | *Set of* 12 | 65·00 | 85·00 |
| 80/92 Perf "Specimen" | | *Set of* 13 | £500 | |

**(New Currency. 1000 fils = 1 dinar)**

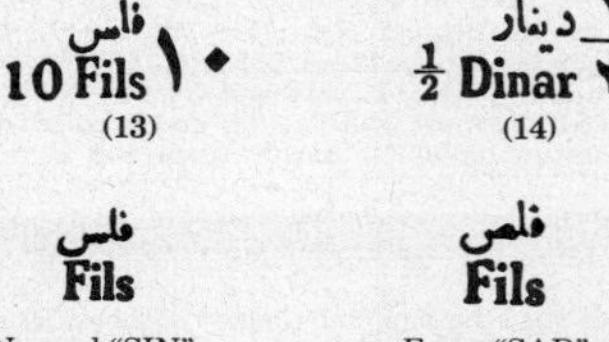
(13) (14)

Normal "SIN" — Error "SAD" (R. 8/16 of second setting)

(Surcharged at Govt Ptg Wks, Baghdad)

**1932** (1 Apr). *Nos.* 80/92 *and* 46 *surch in* "Fils" *or* "Dinar" *as T* 13 *or* 14.

| No. | Type | Description | Unused | Used |
|---|---|---|---|---|
| 106 | 11 | 2 f. on ½ a. green (R.) | 15 | 10 |
| 107 | | 3 f. on ½ a. green | 15 | 10 |
| | | a. Surch double | £140 | |
| | | b. Surch inverted | £140 | |
| | | c. Arabic letter "SAD" instead of "SIN" | | |
| 108 | | 4 f. on 1 a. red-brown (G.) | 40 | 25 |
| 109 | | 5 f. on 1 a. red-brown | 25 | 10 |
| | | a. Inverted Arabic "5" (R. 8/11) | 27·00 | 32·00 |
| 110 | | 8 f. on 1½ a. scarlet | 35 | 30 |
| | | a. Surch inverted | £140 | |
| 111 | | 10 f. on 2 a. orange | 35 | 10 |
| | | a. Inverted Arabic "1" (R. 8/13) | 18·00 | 18·00 |
| | | b. No space between "10" and "Fils" | | |
| 112 | | 15 f. on 3 a. blue | 35 | 1·00 |
| 113 | | 20 f. on 4 a. slate-purple | 1·00 | 1·00 |
| | | a. Surch inverted | | |
| 114 | – | 25 f. on 4 a. violet (No. 46) | 1·00 | 1·50 |
| | | a. "Flis" for "Fils" (R. 2/1, 10/8, 10/15) | £300 | £350 |
| | | b. Inverted Arabic "5" (R. 10/7, 10/14) | £300 | £350 |
| | | c. Vars a and b in *se-tenant* pair | £800 | |
| | | d. Error. 20 f. on 4 a. violet (R. 10/1, 10/9) | | |
| 115 | 11 | 30 f. on 6 a. greenish blue | 1·25 | 60 |
| | | a. Error. 80 f. on 6 a. greenish blue | | |
| 116 | | 40 f. on 8 a. deep green | 2·25 | 1·75 |
| 117 | 12 | 75 f. on 1 r. chocolate | 1·75 | 1·75 |
| | | a. Inverted Arabic "5" | 27·00 | 35·00 |
| 118 | | 100 f. on 2 r. yellow-brown | 5·50 | 3·75 |
| 119 | | 200 f. on 5 r. orange | 11·00 | 8·50 |
| 120 | | ½ d. on 10 r. scarlet | 35·00 | 45·00 |
| | | a. No bar in English "½" | £600 | £650 |
| | | *b. Scarlet-vermilion* | | |
| 121 | 10 | 1 d. on 25 r. violet | 80·00 | £110 |
| 106/121 | | *Set of* 16 | £120 | £150 |

Nos. 106/13 and 115/16 were in sheets of 160 (16×10), No. 114 sheets of 150 (15×10) and Nos. 117/21 sheets of 100 (10×10). There were three settings of the surcharge for the 3 f. and two settings for the 5, 10, 25, 40, 100 and 200 f. Nos. 109a and 111a come from the first setting and Nos. 107c, 111b and 114a/b come from the second.

No. 109a can be easily identified as it shows the point of the Arabic numeral at the foot of the surcharge.

All 10 f. stamps from the second setting are as No. 111b except for R.4/7–8 and 15–16 where the spacing is the same as for the first setting (Type 13).

No. 114d shows "20" handstamped over a faint English "25". Most examples of this error were removed from the sheets before issue. The Arabic value "25" was unaltered.

No. 115a shows the error in the English face value only.

No. 117a occurs on R. 1/2, 1/7 and a third position in the first vertical row not yet identified.

No. 120a occurs on R. 10/1, one position in the first horizontal row and another in the second.

No. 120b was a special printing of No. 91 which does not exist unsurcharged.

15

**1932** (9 May). *T* 10 *to* 12, *but with values altered to* "FILS" *or* "DINAR" *as in T* 15. *Wmk Mult Script CA. P* 12.

| No. | Type | Description | Unused | Used |
|---|---|---|---|---|
| 138 | 11 | 2 f. ultramarine | 30 | 10 |
| 139 | | 3 f. green | 30 | 10 |
| 140 | | 4 f. brown-purple | 30 | 10 |
| 141 | | 5 f. grey-green | 30 | 10 |
| 142 | | 8 f. scarlet | 30 | 10 |
| 143 | | 10 f. yellow | 30 | 10 |
| 144 | | 15 f. blue | 30 | 10 |
| 145 | | 20 f. orange | 45 | 20 |
| 146 | | 25 f. mauve | 45 | 15 |
| 147 | | 30 f. bronze-green | 60 | 15 |
| 148 | | 40 f. violet | 60 | 55 |
| 149 | 12 | 50 f. brown | 60 | 20 |
| 150 | | 75 f. dull ultramarine | 1·60 | 1·25 |
| 151 | | 100 f. deep green | 2·50 | 50 |
| 152 | | 200 f. scarlet | 10·00 | 2·75 |
| 153 | 10 | ½ d. deep blue | 27·00 | 20·00 |
| 154 | | 1 d. claret | 60·00 | 55·00 |
| 138/154 | | *Set of* 17 | 95·00 | 75·00 |
| 138/54 Perf "Specimen" | | *Set of* 17 | £180 | |

## OFFICIAL STAMPS

ON STATE SERVICE
(O 1)

**1920** (1 May)–**23.** *As Nos.* 1/18, *but surch includes additional wording* "ON STATE SERVICE" *as Type* O 1 *in black.*

(*a*) *No wmk. Tougra as* A (1920)

| No. | Type | Description | Unused | Used |
|---|---|---|---|---|
| O19 | 36 | ½ a. on 10 pa. blue-green | 75 | 30 |
| O20 | 37 | 1 a. on 20 pa. red | 75 | 20 |
| O21 | 34 | 1½ a. on 5 pa. purple-brown | 1·75 | 40 |
| O22 | 38 | 2½ a. on 1 pi. blue | 80 | 1·00 |
| O23 | 39 | 3 a. on 1½ pi. black and rose | 2·00 | 50 |
| O24 | 40 | 4 a. on 1¾ pi. red-brown and grey-blue | 2·25 | 80 |
| O25 | 41 | 6 a. on 2 pi. black and green | 4·00 | 2·00 |
| O26 | 42 | 8 a. on 2½ pi. yellow-green & orge-brn | 2·75 | 1·75 |
| O27 | 43 | 12 a. on 5 pi. purple | 2·75 | 2·25 |
| O28 | 44 | 1 r. on 10 pi. red-brown | 3·50 | 2·75 |
| O29 | 45 | 2 r. on 25 pi. olive-green | 12·00 | 8·00 |
| O30 | 46 | 5 r. on 50 pi. rose-carmine | 26·00 | 18·00 |
| O31 | 47 | 10 r. on 100 pi. slate-blue | 48·00 | 48·00 |
| O19/31 | | *Set of* 13 | 95·00 | 75·00 |

(*b*) *No wmk. Tougra as* B (*No.* 15) (1922)

| No. | Type | Description | Unused | Used |
|---|---|---|---|---|
| O32 | 44 | 1 r. on 10 pi. red-brown | 12·00 | 7·00 |

(*c*) *Wmk Mult Script CA* (1921–23)

| No. | Type | Description | Unused | Used |
|---|---|---|---|---|
| O33 | 36 | ½ a. on 10 pa. green | 15 | 20 |
| O34 | 37 | 1 a. on 20 pa. red | 35 | 20 |
| O35 | 34 | 1½ a. on 5 pa. purple-brown | 35 | 35 |
| O36 | 40 | 4 a. on 1¾ pi. red-brown and grey-blue | 75 | 75 |
| O37 | 41 | 6 a. on 2 pi. black and green (1923) | 7·50 | 28·00 |
| O38 | 42 | 8 a. on 2½ pi. yellow-green & orge-brn | 1·50 | 1·50 |
| O39 | 43 | 12 a. on 5 pi. purple (1923) | 6·00 | 23·00 |
| O40 | 45 | 2 r. on 25 pi. olive-green (1923) | 22·00 | 45·00 |
| O33/40 | | *Set of* 8 | 35·00 | 90·00 |
| O33/40 Optd "Specimen" | | *Set of* 8 | £120 | |

Nos. O25/6, O30 and O37/8 only exist from the setting with the surcharge 27½ mm wide.

ON STATE SERVICE
(O 2)

ON STATE SERVICE
(O 3)

**1923.** *Optd with Types* O 2 (*horiz designs*) *or* O 3 (*vert designs*).

| No. | Type | Description | Unused | Used |
|---|---|---|---|---|
| O54 | 2 | ½ a. olive-green | 50 | 10 |
| O55 | – | 1 a. brown | 50 | 10 |
| O56 | 3 | 1½ a. lake | 1·50 | 35 |
| O57 | – | 2 a. orange-buff | 1·00 | 20 |
| O58 | – | 3 a. grey-blue | 2·25 | 35 |
| O59 | – | 4 a. violet | 2·25 | 40 |
| O60 | – | 6 a. greenish blue | 3·25 | 1·25 |
| O61 | – | 8 a. olive-bistre | 3·50 | 1·00 |
| O62 | 4 | 1 r. brown and blue-green | 3·25 | 1·25 |
| O63 | 2 | 2 r. black (R.) | 14·00 | 6·50 |
| O64 | – | 5 r. orange | 38·00 | 19·00 |
| O65 | – | 10 r. lake | 55·00 | 48·00 |
| O54/65 | | *Set of* 12 | £110 | 70·00 |
| O54/65 Optd "Specimen" | | *Set of* 12 | £200 | |

ON STATE SERVICE رسمي
(O 4)

ON STATE SERVICE رسمي
(O 5)

**1924–25.** *Optd with Types* O 4 (*horiz designs*) *or* O 5 (*vert designs*

| No. | Type | Description | Unused | Used |
|---|---|---|---|---|
| O66 | 2 | ½ a. olive-green | 20 | 1 |
| O67 | – | 1 a. brown | 20 | 1 |
| O68 | 3 | 1½ a. lake | 30 | 1 |
| O69 | – | 2 a. orange-buff | 45 | 1 |
| O70 | – | 3 a. grey-blue | 45 | 1 |
| O71 | – | 4 a. violet | 1·00 | 1 |
| O72 | – | 6 a. greenish blue | 1·00 | 2 |
| O73 | – | 8 a. olive-bistre | 1·25 | 3 |
| O74 | 4 | 1 r. brown and blue-green | 6·00 | 1·0 |
| O75 | 2 | 2 r. olive-bistre (1925) | 15·00 | 3·7 |
| O76 | – | 5 r. orange | 38·00 | 28·0 |
| O77 | – | 10 r. lake | 55·00 | 42·0 |
| O66/77 | | *Set of* 12 | £110 | 65·0 |
| O66/77 Optd "Specimen" | | *Set of* 12 | £200 | |

**1927.** *Optd with Type* O 5.

| No. | Type | Description | Unused | Used |
|---|---|---|---|---|
| O79 | 10 | 1 r. red-brown (Optd S. £30) | 3·50 | 8 |

ON STATE SERVICE

ON STATE SERVICE رسمي
(O 6)

رسمي
(O 7)

**1931.** *Optd.* (*a*) *As Type* O 6.

| No. | Type | Description | Unused | Used |
|---|---|---|---|---|
| O 93 | 11 | ½ a. green | 15 | 1·6 |
| O 94 | | 1 a. red-brown | 20 | 1 |
| O 95 | | 1½ a. scarlet | 4·50 | 9·5 |
| O 96 | | 2 a. orange | 50 | 1 |
| O 97 | | 3 a. blue | 85 | 5 |
| O 98 | | 4 a. slate-purple | 95 | 4 |
| O 99 | | 6 a. greenish blue | 2·75 | 8·0 |
| O100 | | 8 a. deep green | 2·75 | 8·0 |

(*b*) *As Type* O 7, *horizontally*

| No. | Type | Description | Unused | Used |
|---|---|---|---|---|
| O101 | 12 | 1 r. chocolate | 6·00 | 9·0 |
| O102 | | 2 r. yellow-brown | 12·00 | 26·0 |
| O103 | | 5 r. orange | 28·00 | 55·0 |
| O104 | | 10 r. scarlet | 55·00 | 90·0 |

(*c*) *As Type* O 7, *vertically upwards*

| No. | Type | Description | Unused | Used |
|---|---|---|---|---|
| O105 | 10 | 25 r. violet | £550 | £70 |
| O93/104 | | *Set of* 12 | £100 | £19 |
| O93/105 Perf "Specimen" | | *Set of* 13 | £500 | |

**1932** (1 Apr). *Official issues of* 1924–25 *and* 1931 *surch in* "FILS *or* "DINAR", *as T* 13 *or* 14.

| No. | Type | Description | Unused | Used |
|---|---|---|---|---|
| O122 | 11 | 3 f. on ½ a. green | 1·25 | 1·5 |
| | | a. Pair, one without surch | £250 | |
| O123 | | 4 f. on 1 a. red-brown (G.) | 1·00 | 1 |
| O124 | | 5 f. on 1 a. red-brown | 80 | 1 |
| | | a. Inverted Arabic "5" (R. 8/11) | 27·00 | 23·0 |
| O125 | 3 | 8 f. on 1½ a. lake (No. O68) | 1·25 | 4 |
| O126 | 11 | 10 f. on 2 a. orange | 1·25 | 1 |
| | | a. Inverted Arabic "1" (R. 8/13) | 17·00 | 17·0 |
| | | b. "10" omitted | † | – |
| | | c. No space between "10" and "Fils" | | |
| O127 | | 15 f. on 3 a. blue | 1·50 | 3 |
| O128 | | 20 f. on 4 a. slate-purple | 1·25 | 4 |
| O129 | | 25 f. on 4 a. slate-purple | 1·75 | 5 |
| O130 | – | 30 f. on 6 a. greenish blue (No. O72) | 1·75 | 8 |
| O131 | 11 | 40 f. on 8 a. deep green | 1·75 | 1·5 |
| | | a. "Flis" for "Fils" (R. 7/5, 7/13) | £180 | £25 |
| O132 | 12 | 50 f. on 1 r. chocolate | 1·75 | 1·7 |
| | | a. Inverted Arabic "5" (R. 1/2) | 45·00 | 45·0 |
| O133 | | 75 f. on 1 r. chocolate | 3·50 | 4·5 |
| | | a. Inverted Arabic "5" | 40·00 | 45·0 |
| O134 | 2 | 100 f. on 2 r. olive-bistre (surch at top) | 3·50 | 2·7 |
| | | a. Surch at foot | | |
| O135 | – | 200 f. on 5 r. orange (No. O76) | 9·50 | 12·0 |
| O136 | – | ½ d. on 10 r. lake (No. O77) | 40·00 | 50·0 |
| | | a. No bar in English "½" (R. 2/10) | £400 | £45 |
| O137 | 10 | 1 d. on 25 r. violet | 80·00 | £12 |
| O122/37 | | *Set of* 16 | £130 | £17 |

Nos. O122/4, O126/9 and O131 were in sheets of 160 (16×10) Nos. O130, O134 and O136 150 (10×15), No. O135 150 (15×10 and Nos. O125, O132/3 and O137 in sheets of 100 (10×10). There was a second setting of the surcharge for the 3 f (equivalent to the third postage setting), 10 f. to 25 f., 40 f. t 100 f. and 1 d. Nos. O126c, O131a and O134a come from th second setting.

All 100 f. stamps from the second setting are as No. O134a. For notes on other varieties see below No. 121.

**1932** (9 May). *Optd.* (*a*) *As Type* O 6.

| No. | Type | Description | Unused | Used |
|---|---|---|---|---|
| O155 | 11 | 2 f. ultramarine | 60 | 1 |
| O156 | | 3 f. green | 60 | 1 |
| O157 | | 4 f. brown-purple | 80 | 1 |
| O158 | | 5 f. grey-green | 80 | 1 |
| O159 | | 8 f. scarlet | 80 | 1 |
| O160 | | 10 f. yellow | 1·25 | 1 |
| O161 | | 15 f. blue | 1·75 | 1 |
| O162 | | 20 f. orange | 1·75 | 1 |
| O163 | | 25 f. mauve | 1·50 | 1 |
| O164 | | 30 f. bronze-green | 2·50 | 2 |
| O165 | | 40 f. violet | 3·25 | 2 |

(*b*) *As Type* O 7, *horizontally*

| No. | Type | Description | Unused | Used |
|---|---|---|---|---|
| O166 | 12 | 50 f. brown | 2·00 | 2 |
| O167 | | 75 f. dull ultramarine | 1·75 | 9 |
| O168 | | 100 f. deep green | 5·00 | 3 |
| O169 | | 200 f. scarlet | 12·00 | 5·5 |

(*c*) *As Type* O 7, *vertically upwards*

| No. | Type | Description | Unused | Used |
|---|---|---|---|---|
| O170 | 10 | ½ d. deep blue | 11·00 | 16·0 |
| O171 | | 1 d. claret | 45·00 | 55·0 |
| O155/71 | | *Set of* 17 | 80·00 | 70·0 |
| O155/71 Perf "Specimen" | | *Set of* 17 | £300 | |

The British Mandate was given up on 3 October 1932 and Ira became an independent kingdom. Later issues will be found liste in Part 19 (*Middle East*) of this catalogue.

# Ireland (Republic)

All the issues of Ireland are listed together here, in this section the Gibbons Catalogue, purely as a matter of convenience to lectors.

| PRICES FOR STAMPS ON COVER TO 1945 | |
|---|---|
| Nos. 1/15 | from × 5 |
| Nos. 17/21 | from × 3 |
| Nos. 22/5a | from × 4 |
| Nos. 26/9a | from × 5 |
| Nos. 30/43 | from × 4 |
| Nos. 44/6 | — |
| Nos. 47/63 | from × 5 |
| Nos. 64/6 | from × 3 |
| Nos. 67/70 | from × 6 |
| Nos. 71/82 | from × 2 |
| Nos. 83/8 | from × 3 |
| Nos. 89/98 | from × 2 |
| Nos. 99/104 | from × 3 |
| Nos. 105/37 | from × 2 |
| Nos. D1/4 | from × 7 |
| Nos. D5/14 | from × 6 |

## PROVISIONAL GOVERNMENT

16 January—6 December 1922

*tamps of Great Britain overprinted. T* **104/8**, *W* **100**; *T* **109**, *W* **110**

Rialtar Sealadac na héireann 1922

(1)

Rialtar Sealadac na héireann 1922.

(2)

Rialtar Sealadac na héireann 1922

(3)

("Provisional Government of Ireland, 1922")

**22** (17 Feb). *T* **104** *to* **108** (*W* **100**) *and* **109** *of Great Britain overprinted in black.*

(*a*) *With T* **1**, *by Dollard Printing House, Ltd. Optd in black**

**105** ½d. green .. .. .. .. 40 40
a. Opt inverted .. .. .. £400 £550
**104** 1d. scarlet .. .. .. .. 45 35
a. Opt inverted .. .. .. £250 £300
b. Opt double, both inverted, one albino £350
1d. carmine-red .. .. .. 1·00 50
2½d. bright blue .. .. .. .. 1·00 4·50
**106** 3d. bluish violet .. .. .. 2·75 3·75
4d. grey-green .. .. .. .. 2·50 6·50
**107** 5d. yellow-brown .. .. .. 3·50 8·50
**108** 9d. agate .. .. .. .. 9·00 17·00
10d. turquoise-blue .. .. .. 7·00 15·00
.. .. .. .. .. .. *Set of* 8 24·00 50·00

*All values except 2½d. and 4d. are known with greyish black erprint, but these are difficult to distinguish.

The ½d. with red overprint is a trial or proof printing (*Price* 50).

Bogus inverted T **1** overprints exist on the 2d., 4d., 9d. and 1s. lues.

(*b*) *With T* **2**, *by Alex Thom & Co, Ltd*

**105** 1½d. red-brown .. .. .. .. 1·75 75
a. Error. "PENCF" .. .. .. £350 £275
**106** 2d. orange (Die I) .. .. .. 1·50 60
a. Opt inverted .. .. .. £180 £250
2d. orange (Die II) .. .. .. 1·75 70
a. Opt inverted .. .. .. £300 £400
**107** 6d. reddish purple, **C** .. .. .. 8·50 6·00
**108** 1s. bistre-brown .. .. .. 11·00 9·00
/15 .. .. .. .. .. .. *Set of* 5 22·00 15·00

Varieties occur throughout the T **2** overprint in the relative sitions of the lines of the overprint, the "R" of "Rialtas" being over her the "Se" or "S" of "Sealadac" or intermediately.

(*c*) *With T* **3**

**109** 2s. 6d. chocolate-brown .. .. .. 30·00 60·00
2s. 6d. sepia-brown .. .. .. 50·00 70·00
5s. rose-red .. .. .. .. 55·00 95·00
10s. dull grey-blue .. .. .. £120 £225
'21 .. .. .. .. .. .. *Set of* 3 £180 £350

**22** (1 April–July). *Optd by Dollard with T* **1**, *in red or carmine.*

**104** 2½d. bright blue (R.) .. .. .. 85 2·50
**106** 4d. grey-green (R.) .. .. .. 7·00 15·00
4d. grey-green (C.) (July) .. .. 40·00 60·00
**108** 9d. agate (R.) .. .. .. .. 12·00 17·00
*a* 9d. agate (C.) (July) .. .. .. 80·00 85·00
/5 .. .. .. .. .. .. *Set of* 3 17·00 30·00

**22** (19 June–Aug). *Optd as T* **2**, *in black, by Harrison & Sons, for use in horiz and vert coils.*

**105** ½d. green .. .. .. .. 2·00 9·50
**104** 1d. scarlet .. .. .. .. 1·25 4·75
**105** 1½d. red-brown (21.6) .. .. .. 3·75 28·00
**106** 2d. bright orange (Die I) .. .. 14·00 30·00
*a* 2d. bright orange (Die II) (August) .. 15·00 22·00
/9*a* .. .. .. .. .. .. *Set of* 5 32·00 85·00

The Harrison overprint measures 15 × 17 mm (maximum) against the 14½ × 16 mm of T **2** (Thom printing) and is a much bolder black than the latter, while the individual letters are taller, the "i" of "Rialtas" being specially outstanding.

The "R" of "Rialtas" is always over the "Se" of "Sealadac".

**1922.** *Optd by Thom.*

(*a*) *As T* **2** *but bolder, in dull to shiny blue-black or red* (June–Nov)

30 **105** ½d. green .. .. .. .. 1·60 80
31 **104** 1d. scarlet .. .. .. .. 50 40
a. "Q" for "O" (No. 357ab) .. .. £1200 £1100
b. Reversed "Q" for "O" (No. 357ac) .. £350 £250
32 **105** 1½d. red-brown .. .. .. .. 3·00 3·25
33 **106** 2d. orange (Die I) .. .. .. 17·00 2·50
34 2d. orange (Die II) .. .. .. 2·50 70
35 **104** 2½d. blue (R.) .. .. .. .. 7·00 17·00
36 **106** 3d. violet .. .. .. .. 2·00 2·75
37 4d. grey-green (R.) .. .. .. 2·25 4·00
38 **107** 5d. yellow-brown .. .. .. 3·50 6·50
39 6d. reddish purple, **C** .. .. .. 6·50 2·50
40 **108** 9d. agate (R.) .. .. .. .. 11·00 14·00
41 9d. olive-green (R.) .. .. .. 4·50 16·00
42 10d. turquoise-blue .. .. .. 25·00 45·00
43 1s. bistre-brown .. .. .. 7·50 8·50
30/43 .. .. .. .. .. .. *Set of* 14 80·00 £110

Both 2d. stamps exist with the overprint inverted but there remains some doubt as to whether they were issued.

These Thom printings are distinguishable from the Harrison printings by the size of the overprint, and from the previous Thom printings by the intensity and colour of the overprint, the latter being best seen when the stamp is looked through with a strong light behind it.

(*b*) *As with T* **3**, *but bolder, in shiny blue-black* (Oct–Dec)

44 **109** 2s. 6d. chocolate-brown .. .. .. £180 £225
45 5s. rose-red .. .. .. £170 £250
46 10s. dull grey-blue .. .. .. £850 £950
44/6 .. .. .. .. .. .. *Set of* 3 £1100 £1300

The above differ from Nos. 17/21 not only in the bolder impression and colour of the ink but also in the "h" and "é" of "héireann" which are closer together.

Rialtar Sealadac na héireann 1922.

(4)

Saorstát Éireann 1922

(5 Wide date)
("Irish Free State 1922")

**1922** (21 Nov–Dec). *Optd by Thom with T* **4** (*wider setting*) *in shiny blue-black.*

47 **105** ½d. green .. .. .. .. 1·00 1·75
a. Opt in jet-black .. .. .. £100 90·00
48 **104** 1d. scarlet .. .. .. .. 2·00 2·50
49 **105** 1½d. red-brown (4 December) .. .. 3·00 7·50
50 **106** 2d. orange (Die II) .. .. .. 9·00 6·00
51 **108** 1s. olive-bistre (4 December) .. .. 40·00 48·00
47/51 .. .. .. .. .. .. *Set of* 5 50·00 60·00

The overprint T **4** measures 15¾ × 16 mm (maximum).

## IRISH FREE STATE

6 December 1922—29 December 1937

**1922** (Dec)–**23.**

(*a*) *Optd by Thom with T* **5**, *in dull to shiny blue-black or red*

52 **105** ½d. green .. .. .. .. 30 30
a. No accent in "Saorstat" .. .. £1000 £900
b. Accent inserted by hand .. .. 85·00 95·00
53 **104** 1d. scarlet .. .. .. .. 30 35
aa. No accent in "Saorstat" .. .. £7000 £5000
a. No accent and final "t" missing .. £6000 £4500
b. Accent inserted by hand .. .. £130 £150
c. Accent and "t" inserted .. .. £225 £250
d. Reversed "Q" for "O" (No. 357ac) .. £300 £250
54 **105** 1½d. red-brown .. .. .. .. 2·50 8·50
55 **106** 2d. orange (Die II) .. .. .. 1·00 2·00
56 **104** 2½d. bright blue (R.) (6.1.23) .. .. 3·00 6·50
a. No accent .. .. .. .. £140 £170
57 **106** 3d. bluish violet (6.1.23) .. .. 3·50 13·00
a. No accent .. .. .. .. £250 £275
58 4d. grey-green (R.) (16.1.23) .. .. 2·50 4·50
a. No accent .. .. .. .. £150 £170
59 **107** 5d. yellow-brown .. .. .. 3·00 4·75
60 6d. reddish pur (*chalk-surfaced paper*) 2·00 1·75
a. Accent inserted by hand .. .. £700 £700
61 **108** 9d. olive-green (R.) .. .. .. 3·00 5·50
a. No accent .. .. .. .. £250 £275
62 10d. turquoise-blue .. .. .. 15·00 32·00
63 1s. bistre-brown .. .. .. 9·00 9·50
a. No accent .. .. .. .. £5500 £6500
b. Accent inserted by hand .. .. £600 £650
64 **109** 2s. 6d. chocolate-brown .. .. .. 35·00 55·00
a. Major Re-entry .. .. .. £850 £950
b. No accent .. .. .. .. £350 £400
c. Accent reversed .. .. .. £425 £475
65 5s. rose-red .. .. .. .. 60·00 £110
a. No accent .. .. .. .. £450 £500
b. Accent reversed .. .. .. £550 £600
66 10s. dull grey-blue .. .. .. £140 £250
a. No accent .. .. .. .. £2000 £2500
b. Accent reversed .. .. .. £2750 £3500
52/66 .. .. .. .. .. .. *Set of* 15 £250 £450

The accents inserted by hand are in dull black. The reversed accents are grave (thus "à") instead of acute ("á"). A variety with "S" of "Saorstat" directly over "é" of "éireann", instead of to left, may be found in all values except the 2½d. and 4d. In the 2s. 6d., 5s. and 10s. it is very slightly to the left in the "S" over "é" variety, bringing the "á" of "Saorstat" directly above the last "n" of "éireann".

(*b*) *Optd with T* **5**, *in dull or shiny blue-black, by Harrison, for use in horiz or vert coils* (7.3.23)

67 ½d. green .. .. .. .. 1·75 9·00
a. Long "1" in "1922" .. .. .. 20·00 45·00
68 1d. scarlet .. .. .. .. 3·75 8·50
a. Long "1" in "1922' .. .. .. 75·00 £140
69 1½d. red-brown .. .. .. .. 7·50 38·00
a. Long "1" in "1922" .. .. .. 85·00 £225
70 2d. orange (Die II) .. .. .. 3·75 8·50
a. Long "1" in "1922" .. .. .. 18·00 42·00
67/70 .. .. .. .. .. .. *Set of* 4 15·00 55·00

In the Harrison overprint the characters are rather bolder than those of the Thom overprint, and the foot of the "1" of "1922" is usually rounded instead of square. The long "1" in "1922" has a serif at foot. The second "e" of "éireann" appears to be slightly raised.

**PRINTERS.** The following and all subsequent issues to No. 148 were printed at the Government Printing Works, Dublin, *unless otherwise stated.*

6 "Sword of Light"

7 Map of Ireland

8 Arms of Ireland

9 Celtic Cross

10

(Des J. J. O'Reilly, T **6**; J. Ingram, T **7**; Miss M. Girling, T **8**; and Miss L. Williams, T **9**. Typo. Plates made by Royal Mint, London)

**1922** (6 Dec)–**34.** *W* **10.** *P* 15 × 14.

71 **6** ½d. bright green (20.4.23) .. .. 40 30
a. Imperf × perf 14, wmk sideways (11.34) .. .. .. .. .. 27·00 42·00
72 **7** 1d. carmine (23.2.23) .. .. .. 30 10
a. Perf 15 × imperf (single perf) (1933) 85·00 £160
c. Perf 15 × imperf (7.34) .. .. 18·00 40·00
d. Booklet pane. Three stamps plus three printed labels (21.8.31) .. £190
73 1½d. claret (2.2.23) .. .. .. 1·25 1·75
74 2d. grey-green (6.12.22) .. .. 40 10
a. Imperf × perf 14, wmk sideways (11.34) .. .. .. .. .. 48·00 70·00
b. Perf 15 × imperf (1934) .. .. £8500 £1500
75 **8** 2½d. red-brown (7.9.23) .. .. .. 3·00 3·00
76 **9** 3d. ultramarine (16.3.23) .. .. 1·00 75
77 **8** 4d. slate-blue (28.9.23) .. .. .. 2·00 3·25
78 **6** 5d. deep violet (11.5.23) .. .. 9·50 9·00
79 6d. claret (21.12.23) .. .. .. 3·50 3·50
80 **8** 9d. deep violet (26.10.23) .. .. 15·00 13·00
81 **9** 10d. brown (11.5.23) .. .. .. 9·00 17·00
82 **6** 1s. light blue (15.6.23) .. .. .. 28·00 4·50
71/82 .. .. .. .. .. .. *Set of* 12 65·00 50·00

No. 72a is imperf vertically except for a single perf at each top corner. It was issued for use in automatic machines.

See also Nos. 111/22 and 227/8.

Saorstát Éireann 1922

(11 Narrow Date)

12 Daniel O'Connell

**1925** (Aug)–**28.** *T* **109** *of Great Britain* (*Bradbury, Wilkinson printing*) *optd at the Government Printing Works, Dublin or by Harrison and Sons.* (*a*) *With T* **11** *in black or grey-black* (25.8.25).

83 2s. 6d. chocolate-brown .. .. .. 35·00 65·00
a. Wide and narrow date (pair) (1927) .. £250
84 5s. rose-red .. .. .. .. 50·00 £100
a. Wide and narrow date (pair) (1927) .. £400
85 10s. dull grey-blue .. .. .. £110 £225
a. Wide and narrow date (pair) (1927) .. £1100
83/5 .. .. .. .. .. .. *Set of* 3 £180 £350

The varieties with wide and narrow date *se-tenant* are from what is known as the "composite setting," in which some stamps showed the wide date, as T **5**, while in others the figures were close together, as in T **11**.

Single specimens of this printing with wide date may be distinguished from Nos. 64 to 66 by the colour of the ink, which is black or grey-black in the composite setting and blue-black in the Thom printing.

The type of the "composite" overprint usually shows distinct signs of wear.

(*b*) *As T* **5** (*wide date*) *in black* (1927–28)

86 2s. 6d. chocolate-brown (9.12.27) .. .. 38·00 40·00
a. Circumflex accent over "a" .. .. £200 £250
b. No accent over "a" .. .. .. £350 £375
c. Flat accent on "a" .. .. .. £300 £350
87 5s. rose-red (2.28) .. .. .. 60·00 80·00
a. Circumflex accent over "a" .. .. £325 £375
c. Flat accent on "a" .. .. .. £400 £450
88 10s. dull grey-blue (15.2.28) .. .. £140 £150
a. Circumflex accent over "a" .. .. £800 £900
c. Flat accent on "a" .. .. .. £900 £1000
86/8 .. .. .. .. .. .. *Set of* 3 £200 £225

This printing can be distinguished from the Thom overprints in dull black, by the clear, heavy impression (in deep black) which often shows in relief on the back of the stamp.

The variety showing a circumflex accent over the "a" occurred on R.9/2. The overprint in this position finally deteriorated to such an extent that some examples of the 2s. 6d. were without accent (No. 86b). A new cliché was then introduced with the accent virtually flat and which also showed damage to the "a" and the crossbar of the "t".

(Des L. Whelan. Typo)

29 (22 June). *Catholic Emancipation Centenary.* W10. P 15 × 14.

| | | | | |
|---|---|---|---|---|
| 12 | 2d. grey-green | .. | 40 | 35 |
| | 3d. blue | .. | 4·00 | 8·50 |
| | 9d. bright violet | .. | 4·00 | 4·00 |
| '91 | .. | *Set of* 3 | 7·50 | 11·50 |

13 Shannon Barrage 14 Reaper

(Des E. L. Lawrenson. Typo)

30 (15 Oct). *Completion of Shannon Hydro-Electric Scheme.* W 10. P 15 × 14.

| | | | |
|---|---|---|---|
| 13 | 2d. agate | 60 | 30 |

(T 14 and 15 des G. Atkinson. Typo)

31 (12 June). *Bicentenary of the Royal Dublin Society.* W 10. P 15 × 14.

| | | | |
|---|---|---|---|
| 14 | 2d. blue | 45 | 20 |

The Cross of Cong 16 Adoration of the Cross 17 Hurler

32 (12 May). *International Eucharistic Congress.* W 10. P 15 × 14.

| | | | |
|---|---|---|---|
| 15 | 2d. grey-green | 50 | 25 |
| | 3d. blue | 2·25 | 5·00 |

(T 16 to 19 des R. J. King. Typo)

33 (18 Sept). *"Holy Year".* W 10. P 15 × 14.

| | | | |
|---|---|---|---|
| 16 | 2d. grey-green | 50 | 15 |
| | 3d. blue | 2·25 | 2·00 |

34 (27 July). *Golden Jubilee of the Gaelic Athletic Association.* W 10. P 15 × 14.

| | | | |
|---|---|---|---|
| 17 | 2d. green | 60 | 15 |

35 (Mar–July). *T 109 of Great Britain (Waterlow printings) optd as T 5 (wide date), at the Government Printing Works, Dublin.*

| | | | | |
|---|---|---|---|---|
| 9 | 109 | 2s. 6d. chocolate (No. 450) | 45·00 | 48·00 |
| | | a. Flat accent on "a" (R. 9/2) | £225 | £200 |
| 0 | | 5s. bright rose-red (No. 451) | 80·00 | 80·00 |
| | | a. Flat accent on "a" (R. 9/2) | £300 | £250 |
| 1 | | 10s. indigo (No. 452) | £350 | £350 |
| | | a. Flat accent on "a" (R. 9/2) | £900 | £750 |
| /101 | | *Set of* 3 | £425 | £425 |

18 St. Patrick 19 Ireland and New Constitution

37 (8 Sept). W 10. P 14 × 15.

| | | | | |
|---|---|---|---|---|
| 2 | 18 | 2s. 6d. emerald-green | £140 | 65·00 |
| 3 | | 5s. maroon | £180 | £110 |
| 4 | | 10s. deep blue | £140 | 50·00 |
| 2/4 | | *Set of* 3 | £425 | £200 |

See also Nos. 123/5.

## EIRE

29 December 1937—17 April 1949

37 (29 Dec). *Constitution Day.* W 10. P 15 × 14.

| | | | | |
|---|---|---|---|---|
| 5 | 19 | 2d. claret | 75 | 20 |
| 6 | | 3d. blue | 4·00 | 3·25 |

For similar stamps see Nos. 176/7.

20 Father Mathew

(Des S. Keating. Typo)

38 (1 July). *Centenary of Temperance Crusade.* W 10. P 15 × 14.

| | | | | |
|---|---|---|---|---|
| 7 | 20 | 2d. black | 1·50 | 30 |
| 8 | | 3d. blue | 10·00 | 6·00 |

21 George Washington, American Eagle and Irish Harp

22

(Des G. Atkinson. Typo)

**1939** (1 Mar). *150th Anniv of U.S. Constitution and Installation of First U.S. President.* W 10. P 15 × 14.

| | | | | |
|---|---|---|---|---|
| 109 | 21 | 2d. scarlet | 1·50 | 40 |
| 110 | | 3d. blue | 4·50 | 3·75 |

**SIZE OF WATERMARK.** T 22 can be found in various sizes from about 8 to 10 mm high. This is due to the use of two different dandy rolls supplied by different firms and to the effects of paper shrinkage and other factors such as pressure and machine speed.

White line above left value tablet joining horizontal line to ornament (R. 3/7)

**1940–68.** *Typo.* W 22. P 15 × 14 *or* 14 × 15 (2s. 6d. *to* 10s.).

| | | | | |
|---|---|---|---|---|
| 111 | 6 | ½d. bright green (24.11.40) | 1·50 | 40 |
| 112 | 7 | 1d. carmine (26.10.40) | 30 | 10 |
| | | a. From coils. Perf 14×imperf (9.40) | 55·00 | 65·00 |
| | | b. From coils. Perf 15×imperf (20.3.46) | 32·00 | 14·00 |
| | | c. Booklet pane. Three stamps plus three printed labels | £950 | |
| 113 | | 1½d. claret (1.40) | 12·00 | 30 |
| 114 | | 2d. grey-green (1.40) | 30 | 10 |
| 115 | 8 | 2½d. red-brown (3.41) | 8·50 | 15 |
| 116 | 9 | 3d. blue (12.40) | 40 | 10 |
| 117 | 8 | 4d. slate-blue (12.40) | 40 | 10 |
| 118 | 6 | 5d. deep violet (7.40) | 65 | 10 |
| 119 | | 6d. claret (3.42) | 1·25 | 30 |
| | | aa. Chalky paper (1967) | 1·25 | 20 |
| 119a | | 8d. scarlet (12.9.49) | 80 | 50 |
| 120 | 8 | 9d. deep violet (7.40) | 1·25 | 50 |
| 121 | 9 | 10d. brown (7.40) | 60 | 35 |
| 121a | | 11d. rose (12.9.49) | 1·25 | 1·50 |
| 122 | 6 | 1s. light blue (6.40) | £110 | 17·00 |
| 123 | 18 | 2s. 6d. emerald-green (10.2.43) | 32·00 | 1·25 |
| | | a. Chalk-surfaced paper (1968?) | 1·50 | 2·00 |
| 124 | | 5s. maroon (15.12.42) | 30·00 | 2·50 |
| | | a. Line flaw | | |
| | | b. Chalk-surfaced paper (1968?) | 6·00 | 3·25 |
| | | *ba. Purple* | 3·50 | 3·75 |
| | | bb. Line flaw | 35·00 | |
| 125 | | 10s. deep blue (7.45) | 55·00 | 5·00 |
| | | a. Chalk-surfaced paper (1968) | 14·00 | 7·50 |
| | | *ab. Blue* | 8·00 | 9·00 |
| 111/25 | | *Set of* 25 | £130 | 27·00 |

There is a wide range of shades and also variation in paper used in this issue.

See also Nos. 227/8.

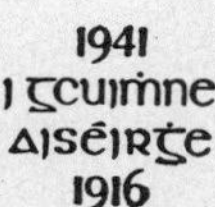


(23 *Trans* "In memory of the rising of 1916")

24 Volunteer and G.P.O., Dublin

**1941** (12 Apr). *25th Anniv of Easter Rising (1916). Provisional issue.* T 7 *and* 9 *(2d. in new colour), optd with* T 23.

| | | | | |
|---|---|---|---|---|
| 126 | 7 | 2d. orange (G.) | 2·00 | 30 |
| 127 | 9 | 3d. blue (V.) | 38·00 | 9·00 |

(Des V. Brown. Typo)

**1941** (27 Oct). *25th Anniv of Easter Rising (1916). Definitive issue.* W 22. P 15 × 14.

| | | | | |
|---|---|---|---|---|
| 128 | 24 | 2½d. blue-black | 70 | 20 |

25 Dr. Douglas Hyde

26 Sir William Rowan Hamilton

27 Bro. Michael O'Clery

(Des S. O'Sullivan. Typo)

**1943** (31 July). *50th Anniv of Founding of Gaelic League.* W 22. P 15 × 14.

| | | | | |
|---|---|---|---|---|
| 129 | 25 | ½d. green | 40 | 30 |
| 130 | | 2½d. claret | 60 | 10 |

(Des S. O'Sullivan from a bust by Hogan. Typo)

**1943** (13 Nov). *Centenary of Announcement of Discovery of Quaternions.* W 22. P 15 × 14.

| | | | | |
|---|---|---|---|---|
| 131 | 26 | ½d. green | 40 | 40 |
| 132 | | 2½d. brown | 1·00 | 10 |

(Des R. J. King. Typo)

**1944** (30 June). *Tercentenary of Death of Michael O'Clery. (Commemorating the "Annals of the Four Masters").* W 22 *(sideways).* P 14 × 15.

| | | | | |
|---|---|---|---|---|
| 133 | 27 | ½d. emerald-green | 10 | 10 |
| 134 | | 1s. red-brown | 45 | 10 |

Although issued as commemoratives these two stamps were kept in use as part of the current issue, replacing Nos. 111 and 122.

28 Edmund Ignatius Rice

29 "Youth Sowing Seeds of Freedom"

(Des S. O'Sullivan. Typo)

**1944** (29 Aug). *Death Centenary of Edmund Rice (founder of Irish Christian Brothers).* W 22. P 15 × 14.

| | | | | |
|---|---|---|---|---|
| 135 | 28 | 2½d. slate | 50 | 15 |

(Des R. J. King. Typo)

**1945** (15 Sept). *Centenary of Death of Thomas Davis (founder of Young Ireland Movement).* W 22. P 15 × 14.

| | | | | |
|---|---|---|---|---|
| 136 | 29 | 2½d. blue | 75 | 25 |
| 137 | | 6d. claret | 7·00 | 3·75 |

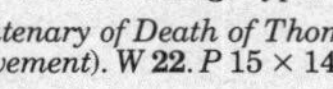

30 "Country and Homestead"

(Des R. J. King. Typo)

**1946** (16 Sept). *Birth Centenaries of Davitt and Parnell (land reformers).* W 22. P 15 × 14.

| | | | | |
|---|---|---|---|---|
| 138 | 30 | 2½d. scarlet | 75 | 15 |
| 139 | | 3d. blue | 2·75 | 2·75 |

31 Angel Victor over Rock of Cashel

(Des R. J. King. Recess Waterlow (1d. to 1s. 3d. until 1961), D.L.R. (8d., 1s. 3d. from 1961 and 1s. 5d.))

**1948** (7 Apr)–**65.** *Air.* T 31 *and similar horiz designs.* W 22. P 15 (1s. 5d.) *or* 15 × 14 (*others*).

| | | | | |
|---|---|---|---|---|
| 140 | 31 | 1d. chocolate (4.4.49) | 2·25 | 3·00 |
| 141 | – | 3d. blue | 4·50 | 2·25 |
| 142 | – | 6d. magenta | 1·00 | 1·00 |
| 142a | – | 8d. lake-brown (13.12.54) | 5·50 | 4·50 |
| 143 | – | 1s. green (4.4.49) | 1·75 | 1·00 |
| 143a | 31 | 1s. 3d. red-orange (13.12.54) | 5·50 | 1·25 |
| 143b | | 1s. 5d. deep ultramarine (1.4.65) | 3·50 | 1·00 |
| 140/143b | | *Set of* 7 | 22·00 | 12·50 |

Designs:—3d., 8d. Lough Derg; 6d. Croagh Patrick; 1s. Glendalough.

35 Theobald Wolfe Tone

(Des K. Uhlemann. Typo)

**1948** (19 Nov). *150th Anniv of Insurrection.* W 22. P 15 × 14.

| | | | | |
|---|---|---|---|---|
| 144 | 35 | 2½d. reddish purple | 1·25 | 10 |
| 145 | | 3d. violet | 3·75 | 3·25 |

## REPUBLIC OF IRELAND

18 April 1949

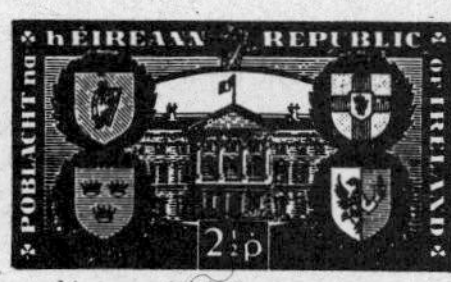

36 Leinster House and Arms of Provinces

37 J. C. Mangan

(Des Muriel Brandt. Typo)

**1949** (21 Nov). *International Recognition of Republic.* W 22. P 15 × 14.

| | | | | |
|---|---|---|---|---|
| 146 | 36 | 2½d. reddish brown | 1·25 | 10 |
| 147 | | 3d. bright blue | 4·50 | 3·00 |

(Des R. J. King. Typo)

**1949** (5 Dec). *Death Centenary of James Clarence Mangan (poet).* W 22. P 15 × 14.

| | | | | |
|---|---|---|---|---|
| 148 | 37 | 1d. green | 1·50 | 20 |

38 Statue of St. Peter, Rome

39 Thomas Moore

40 Irish Harp

(Recess Waterlow & Sons)

**1950** (11 Sept). *Holy Year*. W **22**. P 12½.

| | | | | |
|---|---|---|---|---|
| 149 | **38** | 2½d. violet | 60 | 40 |
| 150 | | 3d. blue | 8·00 | 8·00 |
| 151 | | 9d. brown | 9·00 | 9·50 |
| 149/51 | | *Set of 3* | 16·00 | 16·00 |

**PRINTERS.** Nos. 152 to 200 were recess-printed by De La Rue & Co, Dublin, *unless otherwise stated.*

(Eng W. Vacek)

**1952** (10 Nov). *Death Centenary of Thomas Moore (poet)*. W **22**. P 13.

| | | | | |
|---|---|---|---|---|
| 152 | **39** | 2½d. reddish purple | 50 | 10 |
| 153 | | 3½d. deep olive-green | 1·50 | 2·75 |

(Des F. O'Ryan. Typo Government Printing Works, Dublin)

**1953** (9 Feb). *"An Tostal" (Ireland at Home) Festival*. W **22** (*sideways*). P 14 × 15.

| | | | | |
|---|---|---|---|---|
| 154 | **40** | 2½d. emerald-green | 1·00 | 35 |
| 155 | | 1s. 4d. blue | 17·00 | 24·00 |

41 Robert Emmet

42 Madonna and Child (Della Robbia)

43 Cardinal Newman (first Rector)

(Eng L. Downey)

**1953** (21 Sept). *150th Death Anniv of Emmet (patriot)*. W **22**. P 13.

| | | | | |
|---|---|---|---|---|
| 156 | **41** | 3d. deep bluish green | 3·00 | 15 |
| 157 | | 1s. 3d. carmine | 55·00 | 9·00 |

(Eng A. R. Lane)

**1954** (24 May). *Marian Year*. W **22**. P 15.

| | | | | |
|---|---|---|---|---|
| 158 | **42** | 3d. blue | 2·00 | 10 |
| 159 | | 5d. myrtle-green | 3·50 | 5·50 |

(Des L. Whelan. Typo Govt Printing Works, Dublin)

**1954** (19 July). *Centenary of Founding of Catholic University of Ireland*. W **22**. P 15 × 14.

| | | | | |
|---|---|---|---|---|
| 160 | **43** | 2d. bright purple | 1·50 | 10 |
| 161 | | 1s. 3d. blue | 14·00 | 6·00 |

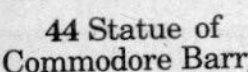


44 Statue of Commodore Barry

45 John Redmond

46 Thomas O'Crohan

(Des and eng H. Woyty-Wimmer)

**1956** (16 Sept). *Barry Commemoration*. W **22**. P 15.

| | | | | |
|---|---|---|---|---|
| 162 | **44** | 3d. slate-lilac | 1·50 | 10 |
| 163 | | 1s. 3d. deep blue | 6·00 | 8·00 |

**1957** (11 June). *Birth Centenary of John Redmond (politician)*. W **22**. P 14 × 15.

| | | | | |
|---|---|---|---|---|
| 164 | **45** | 3d. deep blue | 1·25 | 10 |
| 165 | | 1s. 3d. brown-purple | 8·50 | 9·50 |

**1957** (1 July). *Birth Centenary of Thomas O'Crohan (author)*. W **22**. P 14 × 15.

| | | | | |
|---|---|---|---|---|
| 166 | **46** | 2d. maroon | 1·75 | 15 |
| | | a. Wmk sideways | † | — |
| 167 | | 5d. violet | 1·75 | 5·50 |

47 Admiral Brown

48 "Father Wadding" (Ribera)

49 Tom Clarke

(Des S. O'Sullivan. Typo Govt Printing Works, Dublin)

**1957** (23 Sept). *Death Centenary of Admiral William Brown*. W **22**. P 15 × 14.

| | | | | |
|---|---|---|---|---|
| 168 | **47** | 3d. blue | 3·00 | 20 |
| 169 | | 1s. 3d. carmine | 32·00 | 12·00 |

**1957** (25 Nov). *300th Death Anniv of Father Luke Wadding (theologian)*. W **22**. P 15.

| | | | | |
|---|---|---|---|---|
| 170 | **48** | 3d. deep blue | 2·00 | 10 |
| 171 | | 1s. 3d. lake | 15·00 | 7·00 |

**1958** (28 July). *Birth Centenary of Thomas J. ("Tom") Clarke (patriot)*. W **22**. P 15.

| | | | | |
|---|---|---|---|---|
| 172 | **49** | 3d. deep green | 2·50 | 10 |
| 173 | | 1s. 3d. red-brown | 6·50 | 13·00 |

50 Mother Mary Aikenhead

51 Arthur Guinness

(Eng Waterlow. Recess Imprimerie Belge de Securité, Brussels subsidiary of Waterlow & Sons)

**1958** (20 Oct). *Death Centenary of Mother Mary Aikenhead (foundress of Irish Sisters of Charity)*. W **22**. P 15 × 14.

| | | | | |
|---|---|---|---|---|
| 174 | **50** | 3d. Prussian blue | 1·00 | 10 |
| 175 | | 1s. 3d. rose-carmine | 15·00 | 10·00 |

(Typo Govt Printing Works, Dublin)

**1958** (29 Dec). *21st Anniv of the Irish Constitution*. W**22**. P 15 × 14.

| | | | | |
|---|---|---|---|---|
| 176 | **19** | 3d. brown | 1·00 | 10 |
| 177 | | 5d. emerald-green | 2·25 | 4·50 |

**1959** (20 July). *Bicentenary of Guinness Brewery*. W **22**. P 15.

| | | | | |
|---|---|---|---|---|
| 178 | **51** | 3d. brown-purple | 4·00 | 10 |
| 179 | | 1s. 3d. blue | 12·00 | 8·50 |

52 "The Flight of the Holy Family"

(Des K. Uhlemann)

**1960** (20 June). *World Refugee Year*. W **22**. P 15.

| | | | | |
|---|---|---|---|---|
| 180 | **52** | 3d. purple | 35 | 10 |
| 181 | | 1s. 3d. sepia | 55 | 3·00 |

53 Conference Emblem

(Des P. Rahikainen)

**1960** (19 Sept). *Europa*. W **22**. P 15.

| | | | | |
|---|---|---|---|---|
| 182 | **53** | 6d. light brown | 3·00 | 1·00 |
| 183 | | 1s. 3d. violet | 12·00 | 15·00 |

The ink of No. 183 is fugitive.

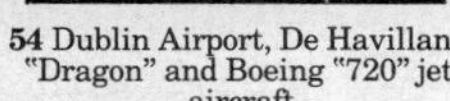


54 Dublin Airport, De Havilland "Dragon" and Boeing "720" jet aircraft

55 St. Patrick

(Des J. Flanagan and D. R. Lowther)

**1961** (26 June). *25th Anniv of Aer Lingus*. W **22**. P 15.

| | | | | |
|---|---|---|---|---|
| 184 | **54** | 6d. blue | 1·00 | 3·00 |
| 185 | | 1s. 3d. green | 1·50 | 4·50 |

(Recess B.W.)

**1961** (25 Sept). *Fifteenth Death Centenary of St. Patrick*. W **22**. P 14½.

| | | | | |
|---|---|---|---|---|
| 186 | **55** | 3d. blue | 1·00 | 10 |
| 187 | | 8d. purple | 1·75 | 3·00 |
| 188 | | 1s. 3d. green | 2·00 | 1·25 |
| 186/8 | | *Set of 3* | 4·25 | 4·00 |

**NEW INFORMATION**

The editor is always interested to correspond with people who have new information that will improve or correct the Catalogue.

56 J. O'Donovan and E. O'Curry

(Recess B.W.)

**1962** (26 Mar). *Death Centenaries of O'Donovan and O'Curry (scholars)*. W **22**. P 15.

| | | | | |
|---|---|---|---|---|
| 189 | **56** | 3d. carmine | 40 | 10 |
| 190 | | 1s. 3d. purple | 2·50 | 2·50 |

57 Europa "Tree"

(Des L. Weyer)

**1962** (17 Sept). *Europa*. W **22**. P 15.

| | | | | |
|---|---|---|---|---|
| 191 | **57** | 6d. carmine-red | 50 | 1·00 |
| 192 | | 1s. 3d. turquoise | 1·25 | 1·50 |

58 Campaign Emblem

(Des K. Uhlemann)

**1963** (21 Mar). *Freedom from Hunger*. W **22**. P 15.

| | | | | |
|---|---|---|---|---|
| 193 | **58** | 4d. deep violet | 50 | 10 |
| 194 | | 1s. 3d. scarlet | 1·75 | 2·00 |

59 "Co-operation"

(Des A. Holm)

**1963** (16 Sept). *Europa*. W **22**. P 15.

| | | | | |
|---|---|---|---|---|
| 195 | **59** | 6d. carmine | 75 | 50 |
| 196 | | 1s. 3d. blue | 3·00 | 3·00 |

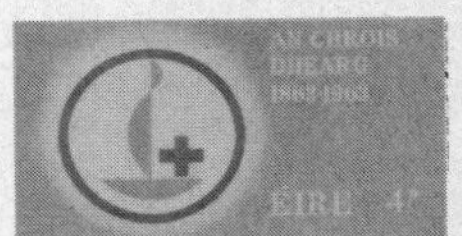


60 Centenary Emblem

(Des P. Wildbur. Photo Harrison & Sons)

**1963** (2 Dec). *Centenary of Red Cross*. W **22**. P 14½ × 14.

| | | | | |
|---|---|---|---|---|
| 197 | **60** | 4d. red and grey | 50 | 10 |
| 198 | | 1s. 3d. red, grey and light emerald | 1·00 | 1·50 |

61 Wolfe Tone

(Des P. Wildbur)

**1964** (13 Apr). *Birth Bicentenary of Wolfe Tone (revolutionary)*. W **22**. P 15.

| | | | | |
|---|---|---|---|---|
| 199 | **61** | 4d. black | 75 | 1( |
| 200 | | 1s. 3d. ultramarine | 2·25 | 1·5( |

62 Irish Pavilion at Fair

(Des A. Devane. Photo Harrison & Sons)

**1964** (20 July). *New York World's Fair*. W **22**. P 14½ × 14.

| | | | | |
|---|---|---|---|---|
| 201 | **62** | 5d. blue-grey, brown, violet & yellow-ol | 60 | 1 |
| | | a. Brown omitted* | £1000 | |
| 202 | | 1s. 5d. blue-grey, brown, turquoise-blue and light yellow-green | 2·25 | 2·5 |

*No. 201a comes from the top row of a sheet and shows part of th brown cross which would appear in the sheet margin. As the secon horizontal row was normal it would appear that the brown cylinde was incorrectly registered.

63 Europa "Flower" 64 "Waves of Communication"

(Des G. Bétemps. Photo Harrison)

)64 (14 Sept). *Europa. W* **22** *(sideways). P* 14 × 14½.
)3 **63** 8d. olive-green and blue . . . . 1·25 1·00
)4 1s. 5d. red-brown and orange . . . . 3·25 2·50

(Des P. Wildbur. Photo Harrison)

)65 (17 May). *I.T.U. Centenary. W* **22.** *P* 14½ × 14.
)5 **64** 3d. blue and green . . . . . . . . 40 10
)6 8d. black and green . . . . . . . . 1·75 2·00

**RINTERS.** Nos. 207 onwards were photogravure-printed by ıe Stamping Branch of the Revenue Commissioners, Dublin *nless otherwise stated.*

65 W. B. Yeats (poet) 66 I.C.Y. Emblem

(Des R. Kyne, from drawing by S. O'Sullivan)

)65 (14 June). *Yeats' Birth Centenary. W* **22** *(sideways). P* 15.
)7 **65** 5d. black, orange-brown and deep green 60 10
)8 1s. 5d. black, grey-green and brown . . 4·00 1·75

)65 (16 Aug). *International Co-operation Year. W* **22.** *P* 15.
)9 **66** 3d. ultramarine and new blue . . . . 75 10
ı0 10d. deep brown and brown . . . . 1·25 3·50

67 Europa "Sprig"

(Des H. Karlsson)

)65 (27 Sept). *Europa. W* **22.** *P* 15.
11 **67** 8d. black and brown-red . . . . 1·00 75
12 1s. 5d. purple and light turquoise-blue 3·00 1·75

68 James Connolly

69 "Marching to Freedom"

)es E. Delaney (No. 216), R. Kyne, after portraits by S. O'Sullivan (others))

)66 (12 Apr). *50th Anniv of Easter Rising. T* **68/9** *and similar horiz portraits. W* **22.** *P* 15.
13 3d. black and greenish blue . . . . . . 20 10
a. Horiz pair. Nos. 213/14 . . . . . . 50 3·00
14 3d. black and bronze-green . . . . . . 20 10
15 5d. black and yellow-olive . . . . . . 30 10
a. Horiz pair. Nos. 215/16 . . . . . . 75 3·00
16 5d. black, orange and blue-green . . . . 30 10
17 7d. black and light orange-brown . . . . 65 2·25
a. Horiz pair. Nos. 217/18 . . . . . . 1·75 11·00
18 7d. black and blue-green . . . . . . 65 2·25
19 1s. 5d. black and turquoise . . . . . . 90 1·50
a. Horiz pair. Nos. 219/20 . . . . . . 3·00 11·00
20 1s. 5d. black and bright green . . . . 90 1·50
13/20 . . . . . . *Set of* 8 5·50 7·00

Designs:—No. 213, Type **68**; No. 214, Thomas J. Clarke; No. 215, . H. Pearse; No. 216, Type **69**; No. 217, Eamonn Ceannt; No. 218, ean MacDiarmada; No. 219, Thomas MacDonagh; No. 220, oseph Plunkett.

Nos. 213/14, 215/16, 217/18 and 219/20 were each printed ›gether, *se-tenant*, in horizontal pairs throughout the sheet.

76 R. Casement 77 Europa "Ship"

(Des R. Kyne)

**1966** (3 Aug). *50th Death Anniv of Roger Casement (patriot). W* **22** *(sideways). P* 15.
221 **76** 5d. black . . . . . . . . . . 10 10
222 1s. red-brown . . . . . . . . . . 20 45

(Des R. Kyne, after G. and J. Bender)

**1966** (26 Sept). *Europa. W* **22** *(sideways). P* 15.
223 **77** 7d. emerald and orange . . . . 40 40
224 1s. 5d. emerald and light grey . . . . 1·00 1·00

78 Interior of Abbey (from lithograph) 79 Cogwheels

**1966** (8 Nov). *750th Anniv of Ballintubber Abbey. W* **22.** *P* 15.
225 **78** 5d. red-brown . . . . . . . . . . 10 10
226 1s. black . . . . . . . . . . 20 25

**1966–67.** *As Nos. 116, 118 but photo. Smaller design (17 × 21 mm). Chalk-surfaced paper. W* **22.** *P* 15.
227 **9** 3d. blue (1.8.67) . . . . . . 50 15
228 **6** 5d. bright violet (1.12.66) . . . . . . 30 15

No. 228 was only issued in booklets at first but was released in sheets on 1.4.68 in a slightly brighter shade. In the sheet stamps the lines of shading are more regular.

(Des O. Bonnevalle)

**1967** (2 May). *Europa. W* **22** *(sideways). P* 15.
229 **79** 7d. light emerald, gold and pale cream 30 40
230 1s. 5d. carmine-red, gold and pale cream 70 1·00

80 Maple Leaves

(Des P. Hickey)

**1967** (28 Aug). *Canadian Centennial. W* **22.** *P* 15.
231 **80** 5d. multicoloured . . . . . . 10 10
232 1s. 5d. multicoloured . . . . . . 20 60

81 Rock of Cashel (from photo by Edwin Smith)

**1967** (25 Sept). *International Tourist Year. W* **22** *(inverted). P* 15.
233 **81** 7d. sepia . . . . . . . . . . 15 20
234 10d. slate-blue . . . . . . . . . . 15 40

82 1 c. Fenian Stamp Essay 83 24 c. Fenian Stamp Essay

**1967** (23 Oct). *Centenary of Fenian Rising. W* **22** *(sideways). P* 15.
235 **82** 5d. black and light green . . . . 15 10
236 **83** 1s. black and light pink . . . . 15 25

84 Jonathan Swift 85 Gulliver and Lilliputians

(Des M. Byrne)

**1967** (30 Nov). *300th Birth Anniv of Jonathan Swift. W* **22** *(sideways). P* 15.
237 **84** 3d. black and olive-grey . . . . 10 10
238 **85** 1s. 5d. blackish brown and pale blue . . 20 20

86 Europa "Key"

(Des H. Schwarzenbach and M. Biggs)

**1968** (29 Apr). *Europa. W* **22.** *P* 15.
239 **86** 7d. brown-red, gold and brown. . . . 30 50
240 1s. 5d. new blue, gold and brown . . 60 1·00

87 St Mary's Cathedral, Limerick

(Des from photo by J. J. Bambury. Recess B.W.)

**1968** (26 Aug). *800th Anniv of St. Mary's Cathedral, Limerick. W* **22.** *P* 15.
241 **87** 5d. Prussian blue . . . . . . 10 10
242 10d. yellow-green . . . . . . 20 60

88 Countess Markievicz 89 James Connolly

**1968** (23 Sept). *Birth Centenary of Countess Markievicz (patriot). W* **22.** *P* 15.
243 **88** 3d. black . . . . . . . . 10 10
244 1s. 5d. deep blue and blue . . . . 20 20

**1968** (23 Sept). *Birth Centenary of James Connolly (patriot). W* **22** *(sideways). P* 15.
245 **89** 6d. deep brown and chocolate . . . . 15 30
246 1s. blksh grn, apple-grn & myrtle-grn 15 10

90 Stylised Dog (brooch) 91 Stag

92 Winged Ox (Symbol of St. Luke)

93 Eagle (Symbol of St. John The Evangelist)

(Des H. Gerl)

**1968–70.** *Pence values expressed with* "p". *W* **22** (*sideways on* ½d. *to* 1s. 9d.). *P* 15.

| No. | Type | Description | | |
|---|---|---|---|---|
| 247 | **90** | ½d. red-orange (7.6.69) .. .. .. | 10 | 30 |
| 248 | | 1d. pale yellow-green (7.6.69) .. .. | 15 | 10 |
| | | a. Coil stamp. Perf 14 × 15 (8.70?) .. | 90 | 3·00 |
| 249 | | 2d. light ochre (14.10.68) .. .. | 30 | 10 |
| | | a. Coil stamp. Perf 14 × 15 (8.70?) .. | 90 | 3·75 |
| 250 | | 3d. blue (7.6.69) .. .. .. .. | 35 | 10 |
| | | a. Coil stamp. Perf 14 × 15 (8.70?) .. | 90 | 3·75 |
| 251 | | 4d. deep brown-red (31.3.69) .. .. | 25 | 10 |
| 252 | | 5d. myrtle-green (31.3.69) .. .. | 30 | 35 |
| 253 | | 6d. bistre-brown (24.2.69) .. .. | 20 | 10 |
| 254 | **91** | 7d. brown and yellow (7.6.69) .. .. | 45 | 3·00 |
| 255 | | 8d. chocolate & orange-brown (14.10.68) | 45 | 1·00 |
| 256 | | 9d. slate-blue and olive-green (24.2.69) | 50 | 10 |
| 257 | | 10d. chocolate and bluish violet (31.3.69) | 1·00 | 75 |
| 258 | | 1s. chocolate and red-brown (31.3.69) .. | 40 | 10 |
| 259 | | 1s. 9d. black & lt turquoise-bl (24.2.69) | 4·00 | 70 |
| 260 | **92** | 2s. 6d. multicoloured (14.10.68) .. | 2·25 | 30 |
| 261 | | 5s. multicoloured (24.2.69) .. .. | 3·75 | 70 |
| 262 | **93** | 10s. multicoloured (14.10.68) .. .. | 7·50 | 2·50 |
| 247/62 | | .. .. .. .. .. *Set of* 16 | 20·00 | 9·00 |

The 1d., 2d., 3d., 5d., 6d., 9d., 1s. and 2s. 6d. exist with PVA gum as well as gum arabic. The coil stamps exist on PVA only, and the rest on gum arabic only.

See also Nos. 287/301, 339/59 and 478/83.

**94** Human Rights Emblem

**95** Dail Eireann Assembly

**1968** (4 Nov). *Human Rights Year. W* **22** (*sideways*). *P* 15.

| No. | Type | Description | | |
|---|---|---|---|---|
| 263 | **94** | 5d. yellow, gold and black .. .. | 15 | 10 |
| 264 | | 7d. yellow, gold and red .. .. | 15 | 35 |

(Des M. Byrne)

**1969** (21 Jan). *50th Anniv of Dail Eireann (First National Parliament). W* **22** (*sideways*). *P* 15 × 14½.

| No. | Type | Description | | |
|---|---|---|---|---|
| 265 | **95** | 6d. myrtle-green .. .. .. | 15 | 10 |
| 266 | | 9d. Prussian blue .. .. .. | 15 | 30 |

**96** Colonnade

**97** Quadruple I.L.O. Emblems

(Des L. Gasbarra and G. Belli; adapted Myra Maguire)

**1969** (28 Apr). *Europa. W* **22**. *P* 15.

| No. | Type | Description | | |
|---|---|---|---|---|
| 267 | **96** | 9d. grey, ochre and ultramarine .. | 50 | 1·00 |
| 268 | | 1s. 9d. grey, gold and scarlet .. .. | 75 | 1·25 |

(Des K. C. Dābczewski)

**1969** (14 July). *50th Anniv of International Labour Organization. W* **22** (*sideways*). *P* 15.

| No. | Type | Description | | |
|---|---|---|---|---|
| 269 | **97** | 6d. black and grey .. .. .. | 15 | 10 |
| 270 | | 9d. black and yellow .. .. .. | 15 | 25 |

**98** "The Last Supper and Crucifixion" (Evie Hone Window, Eton Chapel)

(Des R. Kyne)

**1969** (1 Sept). *Contemporary Irish Art (1st issue). W* **22** (*sideways*). *P* 15 × 14½.

| No. | Type | Description | | |
|---|---|---|---|---|
| 271 | **98** | 1s. multicoloured .. .. .. | 30 | 1·50 |

See also Nos. 280, 306, 317, 329, 362, 375, 398, 408, 452, 470 and 498.

**99** Mahatma Gandhi

**1969** (2 Oct). *Birth Centenary of Mahatma Gandhi. W* **22**. *P* 15.

| No. | Type | Description | | |
|---|---|---|---|---|
| 272 | **99** | 6d. black and green .. .. .. | 20 | 10 |
| 273 | | 1s. 9d. black and yellow .. .. | 30 | 90 |

**100** Symbolic Bird in Tree

(Des D. Harrington)

**1970** (23 Feb). *European Conservation Year. W* **22**. *P* 15.

| No. | Type | Description | | |
|---|---|---|---|---|
| 274 | **100** | 6d. bistre and black .. .. .. | 15 | 10 |
| 275 | | 9d. slate-violet and black .. .. | 15 | 70 |

**101** "Flaming Sun"

(Des L. le Brocquy)

**1970** (4 May). *Europa. W* **22**. *P* 15.

| No. | Type | Description | | |
|---|---|---|---|---|
| 276 | **101** | 6d. bright violet and silver .. .. | 25 | 10 |
| 277 | | 9d. brown and silver .. .. .. | 55 | 1·00 |
| 278 | | 1s. 9d. deep olive-grey and silver .. | 1·25 | 1·40 |
| 276/8 | | .. .. .. .. .. *Set of* 3 | 1·90 | 2·25 |

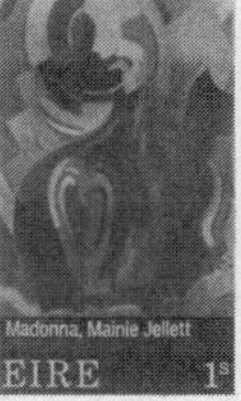


**102** "Sailing Boats" (Peter Monamy)

**103** "Madonna of Eire" (Mainie Jellett)

(Des P. Wildbur and P. Scott)

**1970** (13 July). *250th Anniv of Royal Cork Yacht Club. W* **22**. *P* 15.

| No. | Type | Description | | |
|---|---|---|---|---|
| 279 | **102** | 4d. multicoloured .. .. .. | 15 | 10 |

**1970** (1 Sept). *Contemporary Irish Art (2nd issue). W* **22** (*sideways*). *P* 15.

| No. | Type | Description | | |
|---|---|---|---|---|
| 280 | **103** | 1s. multicoloured .. .. .. | 15 | 20 |

**104** Thomas MacCurtain

**106** Kevin Barry

(Des P. Wildbur)

**1970** (26 Oct). *50th Death Anniversaries of Irish Patriots. T* **104** *and similar vert design. W* **22** (*sideways*). *P* 15.

| No. | Type | Description | | |
|---|---|---|---|---|
| 281 | | 9d. black, bluish violet and greyish black .. | 35 | 25 |
| | | a. Pair. Nos. 281/2 .. .. .. | 1·25 | 2·00 |
| 282 | | 9d. black, bluish violet and greyish black .. | 35 | 25 |
| 283 | | 2s. 9d. black, new blue and greyish black .. | 85 | 1·50 |
| | | a. Pair. Nos. 283/4 .. .. .. | 4·50 | 13·00 |
| 284 | | 2s. 9d. black, new blue and greyish black .. | 85 | 1·50 |
| 281/4 | | .. .. .. .. .. *Set of* 4 | 5·25 | 3·25 |

Designs:—Nos. 281 and 283, Type **104**; others, Terence MacSwiney.

Nos. 281/2 and 283/4 were each printed together, *se-tenant*, in horizontal and vertical pairs throughout the sheet.

(Des P. Wildbur)

**1970** (2 Nov). *50th Death Anniv of Kevin Barry (patriot). W* **22** (*inverted*). *P* 15.

| No. | Type | Description | | |
|---|---|---|---|---|
| 285 | **106** | 6d. olive-green .. .. .. | 20 | 10 |
| 286 | | 1s. 2d. royal blue .. .. .. | 30 | 1·00 |

**106a** Stylized Dog (Brooch)

**107** "Europa Chain"

Two types of 10 p.:
I. Outline and markings of the ox in lilac.
II. Outline and markings in brown.

**1971** (15 Feb)–**75.** *Decimal Currency. Designs as Nos.* 247/62 *bu[t] with* "p" *omitted as in T* **106a**. *W* **22** (*sideways on* 10, 12, 20 *an[d]* 50 *p.*). *P* 15.

| No. | Type | Description | | |
|---|---|---|---|---|
| 287 | **106a** | ½p. bright green .. .. .. | 10 | 1 |
| | | a. Wmk sideways .. .. | 8·00 | 10·0 |
| | | ab. Booklet pane of 6 .. .. | 42·00 | |
| 288 | | 1p. blue .. .. .. .. | 60 | 1 |
| | | a. Coil stamp. Perf 14×14½ .. | 75 | 6 |
| | | b. Coil strip. Nos. 288a, 289a and 291a *se-tenant* .. .. | 2·00 | |
| | | c. Wmk sideways .. .. | 35 | 4 |
| | | ca. Booklet pane of 6 .. .. | 2·00 | |
| | | cb. Booklet pane. No. 288c×5 plus one *se-tenant* label (11.3.74) .. | 2·00 | |
| 289 | | 1½p. lake-brown .. .. .. | 20 | 1 |
| | | a. Coil stamp. Perf 14×14½ .. | 40 | 4 |
| | | b. Coil strip. Nos. 289a, 291a, 294a and 290a *se-tenant* (24.2.72) .. | 2·00 | |
| | | c. Coil strip. Nos. 289a×2, 290a and 295ab *se-tenant* (29.1.74) | 2·00 | |
| 290 | | 2p. myrtle-green .. .. .. | 20 | 1 |
| | | a. Coil stamp. Perf 14×14½ (24.2.72) .. .. .. | 40 | 4 |
| | | b. Wmk sideways (27.1.75) .. | 45 | 5 |
| | | ba. Booklet pane. No. 290b×5 plus one *se-tenant* label (27.1.75) .. | 2·25 | |
| 291 | | 2½p. sepia .. .. .. .. | 25 | 1 |
| | | a. Coil stamp. Perf 14×14½ (20.2.71) .. .. .. | 50 | 6 |
| | | b. Wmk sideways .. .. | 80 | 1·2 |
| | | ba. Booklet pane of 6 .. .. | 4·25 | |
| 292 | | 3p. cinnamon .. .. .. | 15 | 1 |
| 293 | | 3½p. orange-brown .. .. .. | 15 | 1 |
| 294 | | 4p. pale bluish violet .. .. | 15 | 1 |
| | | a. Coil stamp. Perf 14×14½ (24.2.72) .. .. .. | 1·50 | 6 |
| 295 | **91** | 5p. brown and yellow-olive .. | 70 | 2 |
| 295a | **106a** | 5p. bright yellow-green (29.1.74) .. | 2·25 | 4 |
| | | ab. Coil stamp. Perf 14×14½ (29.1.74) .. .. .. | 1·25 | 9 |
| | | ac. Wmk sideways (11.3.74) .. | 70 | 8 |
| | | ad. Booklet pane. No. 295ac×5 plus one *se-tenant* label (11.3.74) .. | 3·50 | |
| | | ae. Booklet pane. No. 295ac×6 (11.3.74) .. .. .. | 13·00 | |
| 296 | **91** | 6p. blackish brown and slate .. | 3·00 | 30 |
| 296a | | 7p. indigo and olive-green (29.1.74) | 4·75 | 1·00 |
| 297 | | 7½p. chocolate and reddish lilac .. | 50 | 40 |
| 298 | | 9p. black and turquoise-green .. | 1·50 | 35 |
| 299 | **92** | 10p. multicoloured (I) .. .. | 14·00 | 7·50 |
| 299a | | 10p. multicoloured (II) .. .. | 14·00 | 70 |
| 299b | | 12p. multicoloured (29.1.74) .. | 1·50 | 70 |
| 300 | | 20p. multicoloured .. .. .. | 2·00 | 10 |
| 301 | **93** | 50p. multicoloured .. .. .. | 4·00 | 65 |
| 287/301 | | .. .. .. .. *Set of* 18 | 30·00 | 5·00 |

The ½, 1, 2, 2½p. and 5 p. (No. 295*a*) with watermark sideways all come from stamp booklets and exist with one or two sides imperforate.

See also Nos. 339/59 and 478/83.

(Des H. Haflidason; adapted P. Wildbur)

**1971** (3 May). *Europa. W* **22** (*sideways*). *P* 15.

| No. | Type | Description | | |
|---|---|---|---|---|
| 302 | **107** | 4p. sepia and olive-yellow .. .. | 35 | 1 |
| 303 | | 6p. black and new blue.. .. .. | 2·00 | 2·0 |

**108** J. M. Synge

**109** "An Island Man" (Jack B. Yeats)

(Des R. Kyne from a portrait by Jack B. Yeats)

**1971** (19 July). *Birth Centenary of J. M. Synge (playwright). W* **22** *P* 15.

| No. | Type | Description | | |
|---|---|---|---|---|
| 304 | **108** | 4p. multicoloured .. .. .. | 15 | 1 |
| 305 | | 10p. multicoloured .. .. .. | 40 | 7 |

(Des P. Wildbur)

**1971** (30 Aug). *Contemporary Irish Art (3rd issue). Birth Centenary of J. B. Yeats (artist). W* **22**. *P* 15.

| No. | Type | Description | | |
|---|---|---|---|---|
| 306 | **109** | 6p. multicoloured .. .. .. | 55 | 5 |

## OMNIBUS ISSUES

Details, together with prices for complete sets of the various Omnibus issues from the 1935 Silver Jubilee series to date are included in a special section following Zimbabwe at the end of Volume 2.

110 Racial Harmony Symbol

111 "Madonna and Child" (statue by J. Hughes)

(Des P. Wildbur. Litho Harrison)

**971** (18 Oct). *Racial Equality Year. No wmk. P* 14 × 14½.
07 **110** 4p. red .. .. .. .. .. .. 20 10
08 10p. black .. .. .. .. .. 70 75

(Des R. Kyne)

**971** (15 Nov). *Christmas.* **W 22.** *P* 15.
09 **111** 2½p. black, gold and deep bluish green 10 10
10 6p. black, gold and ultramarine .. 45 65

112 Heart

(Des L. le Brocquy)

**972** (7 Apr). *World Health Day.* **W 22** *(sideways). P* 15.
.1 **112** 2½p. gold and brown .. .. .. 30 15
.2 12p. silver and grey .. .. .. 1·10 1·75

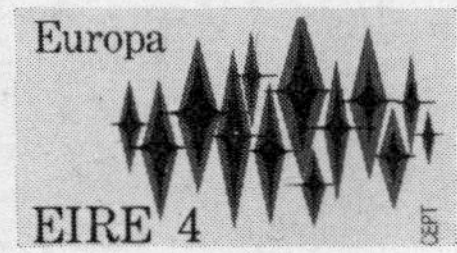


113 "Communications"

(Des P. Huovinen and P. Wildbur)

**972** (1 May). *Europa.* **W 22** *(sideways). P* 15.
13 **113** 4p. orange, black and silver .. .. 1·50 25
14 6p. blue, black and silver .. .. 4·00 3·75

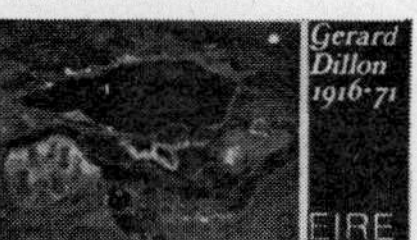


114 Dove and Moon

115 "Black Lake" (Gerard Dillon)

(Des P. Scott)

**972** (1 June). *The Patriot Dead,* 1922–23. **W 22.** *P* 15.
15 **114** 4p. grey-blue, light orange & deep blue 15 10
16 6p. dp yellow-grn, lemon & dp dull grn 55 40

(Des P. Wildbur)

**972** (10 July). *Contemporary Irish Art* (4*th issue*). **W 22** *(sideways). P* 15.
17 **115** 3p. multicoloured .. .. .. .. 55 35

116 "Horseman" (Carved Slab)

117 Madonna and Child (from Book of Kells)

(Des P. Scott)

**972** (28 Aug). *50th Anniv of Olympic Council of Ireland.* **W 22.** *P* 15.
18 **116** 3p. bright yellow, black and gold .. 10 10
19 6p. salmon, black and gold .. .. 30 60

**VATERMARK.** All issues from here onwards are on unwatermarked paper.

(Des P. Scott)

**1972** (16 Oct). *Christmas. P* 15.
320 **117** 2½p. multicoloured *(shades)* .. .. 15 10
321 4p. multicoloured .. .. .. 30 10
322 12p. multicoloured .. .. .. 75 65
320/2 .. .. .. .. .. *Set of* 3 1·10 70

118 2d. Stamp of 1922

119 Celtic Head Motif

(Des Stamping Branch of the Revenue Commissioners, Dublin)

**1972** (6 Dec). *50th Anniv of the First Irish Postage Stamp. P* 15.
323 **118** 6p. light grey and grey-green .. .. 30 40
**MS**324 72 × 104 mm. No. 323 × 4 .. .. 8·50 12·00

(Des L. le Brocquy)

**1973** (1 Jan). *Entry into European Communities. P* 15.
325 **119** 6p. multicoloured .. .. .. 50 90
326 12p. multicoloured .. .. .. 75 1·10



120 Europa "Posthorn"

(Des L. Anisdahl; adapted R. Kyne)

**1973** (30 Apr). *Europa. P* 15.
327 **120** 4p. bright blue .. .. .. .. 50 10
328 6p. black .. .. .. .. 2·00 1·75

121 "Berlin Blues II" (W. Scott)

122 Weather Map

(Adapted by R. Scott)

**1973** (9 Aug). *Contemporary Irish Art* (5*th issue*). *P* 15 × 14½.
329 **121** 5p. ultramarine and grey-black .. 40 20

(Des R. Ballagh)

**1973** (4 Sept). *I.M.O./W.M.O. Centenary. P* 14½ × 15.
330 **122** 3½p. multicoloured .. .. .. 30 10
331 12p. multicoloured .. .. .. 1·40 1·50

123 Tractor ploughing

124 "Flight into Egypt" (Jan de Cock)

(Des P. Scott)

**1973** (5 Oct). *World Ploughing Championships, Wellington Bridge. P* 15 × 14½.
332 **123** 5p. multicoloured .. .. .. 15 10
333 7p. multicoloured .. .. .. 60 50

(Des D. Kiely)

**1973** (1 Nov). *Christmas. P* 15.
334 **124** 3½p. multicoloured .. .. .. 15 10
335 12p. multicoloured .. .. .. 1·10 1·00

125 Daunt Island Lightship and Ballycotton Lifeboat, 1936

126 "Edmund Burke" (statue by J. H. Foley)

(Des M. Byrne from painting by B. Gribble)

**1974** (28 Mar). *150th Anniv of Royal National Lifeboat Institution. P* 15 × 14½.
336 **125** 5p. multicoloured .. .. .. 30 15

(Des P. Wildbur)

**1974** (29 Apr). *Europa. P* 14½ × 15.
337 **126** 5p. black and pale violet-blue .. .. 75 10
338 7p. black and light emerald .. .. 2·25 2·00

Two types of 50p.:

Type I. Fine screen (Cyls 1)

Type II. Coarse screen (Cyls 2)

**1974–83.** *Designs as Nos.* 287 *etc. No wmk. P* 15.
339 **106*a*** ½p. bright green (5.6.78) .. .. 20 10
340 1p. blue (14.2.75) .. .. .. 10 10
a. Coil stamp. Perf 14×14½ (21.3.77) .. .. .. 40 50
b. Coil strip. Nos. 340a, 341a×2 and 344a *se-tenant* (21.3.77) .. 1·40
341 2p. myrtle-green (7.4.76) .. .. 10 10
a. Coil stamp. Perf 14×14½ (21.3.77) .. .. .. 40 40
342 3p. cinnamon (14.2.75) .. .. 10 10
343 3½p. orange-brown (9.10.74) .. 4·50 4·50
344 5p. bright yellow-green (16.8.74) .. 40 10
a. Coil stamp. Perf 14 × 14½ (21.3.77) .. .. .. 85 85
345 **91** 6p. blackish brn & slate (16.10.74) 3·00 1·25
346 **106*a*** 6p. slate (17.6.75) .. .. .. 20 10
347 **91** 7p. indigo and olive-green (27.9.74) 2·25 35
348 **106*a*** 7p. deep yellow-green (17.6.75) .. 35 10
a. Booklet pane. No. 348 × 5 plus *se-tenant* label (21.3.77) .. 11·00
349 **91** 8p. dp brown & dp orge-brn (17.6.75) 1·50 50
350 **106*a*** 8p. chestnut (14.7.76) .. .. 30 10
351 **91** 9p. black & turquoise-green (12.74) 2·50 30
352 **106*a*** 9p. greenish slate (14.7.76) .. 30 10
352*a* 9½p. vermilion (3.12.79) .. .. 35 10
353 **92** 10p. multicoloured (II) (12.74) .. 4·00 30
354 **91** 10p. black and violet-blue (14.7.76) 1·75 10
354*a* **106*a*** 10p. deep mauve (8.6.77) .. .. 70 10
355 **91** 11p. black and rose-carmine (14.7.76) 45 20
355*a* 12p. black and bright green (8.6.77) 1·25 10
355*b* **106*a*** 12p. yellowish green (26.3.80) .. 30 10
355*c* **91** 13p. reddish brn & red-brn (26.3.80) 40 60
356 **92** 15p. multicoloured (17.6.74) .. 1·00 40
356*a* **106*a*** 15p. ultramarine (10.7.80) .. .. 40 10
356*b* **91** 16p. black & dull yellow-grn (10.7.80) 40 30
356*c* **92** 17p. multicoloured (8.6.77) .. .. 90 20
357 20p. multicoloured (13.6.74) .. 1·25 10
358 **93** 50p. multicoloured (I) (12.74) .. 1·25 30
a. Type II (1983) .. .. .. 1·50 1·75
359 £1 multicoloured (17.6.75) .. 1·75 30
339/59 .. .. .. .. *Set of* 29 28·00 9·50

For 18p., 19p., 22p., 24p., 26p. and 29p. values printed by lithography, see Nos. 478/83.
Stamps with one or two sides imperf come from the booklet pane.

**127** "Oliver Goldsmith" (statue by J. H. Foley)
**128** "Kitchen Table" (Norah McGuiness)

(Des P. Wildbur)

**1974** (24 June). *Death Bicentenary of Oliver Goldsmith (writer). P* 14½ × 15.
360 **127** 3½p. black and olive-yellow .. .. 25 10
361 12p. black and bright yellowish green .. 1·25 1·00

(Design adapted by Norah McGuiness. Photo Harrison)

**1974** (19 Aug). *Contemporary Irish Art* (*6th issue*). *P* 14 × 14½.
362 **128** 5p. multicoloured .. .. .. 35 15

**129** Rugby Players
**130** U.P.U. "Postmark"

(Design adapted from Irish Press photograph. Eng C. Slania. Recess (3½p.) or recess and photo (12p.) Harrison)

**1974** (9 Sept). *Centenary of Irish Rugby Football Union. P* 14½ × 14.
363 **129** 3½p. greenish black .. .. .. 30 10
*a. Deep greenish blue* .. .. 6·50 2·75
364 12p. multicoloured .. .. .. 2·00 1·75
No. 363a is from a second printing using a recut plate on which the engraving was deeper.

(Des R. Ballagh)

**1974** (9 Oct). *Centenary of Universal Postal Union. P* 14½ × 15.
365 **130** 5p. light yellowish green and black .. 30 10
366 7p. light ultramarine and black .. 40 50

**131** "Madonna and Child" (Bellini)
**132** "Peace"

(Des P. Wildbur)

**1974** (14 Nov). *Christmas. P* 14½ × 15.
367 **131** 5p. multicoloured .. .. .. 15 10
368 15p. multicoloured .. .. .. 1·10 70

(Des Alexandra Wejchert)

**1975** (24 Mar). *International Women's Year. P* 14½ × 15.
369 **132** 8p. brt reddish purple & ultramarine .. 25 75
370 15p. ultramarine and bright green .. 50 1·25

**133** "Castletown Hunt" (R. Healy)

(Des R. Kyne)

**1975** (28 Apr). *Europa. P* 15 × 14½.
371 **133** 7p. grey-black .. .. .. 75 15
372 9p. dull blue-green .. .. .. 1·50 1·75

**134** Putting

(Des from photographs by J. McManus)

**1975** (26 June). *Ninth European Amateur Golf Team Championship, Killarney. P* 15 × 14½.
373 **134** 6p. multicoloured (*shades*) .. .. 75 45
374 – 9p. multicoloured (*shades*) .. .. 1·50 1·25
The 9p. is similar to T **134** but shows a different view of the putting green.

**135** "Bird of Prey" (sculpture by Oisin Kelly)
**136** Nano Nagle (founder) and Waifs

(Design adapted by the artist)

**1975** (28 June). *Contemporary Irish Art* (*7th issue*). *P* 15 × 14½.
375 **135** 15p. yellow-brown .. .. .. 55 60

(Des Kilkenny Design Workshops)

**1975** (1 Sept). *Bicentenary of Presentation Order of Nuns. P* 14½ × 15.
376 **136** 5p. black and pale blue.. .. .. 20 10
377 7p. black and light stone .. .. 30 30

**137** Tower of St. Anne's Church, Shandon
**138** St. Oliver Plunkett (commemorative medal by Imogen Stuart)

(Des P. Scott)

**1975** (6 Oct). *European Architectural Heritage Year. T* **137** *and similar vert design. P* 12½.
378 **137** 5p. blackish brown .. .. .. 20 10
379 6p. multicoloured .. .. .. 40 85
380 – 7p. steel-blue .. .. .. 40 10
381 – 9p. multicoloured .. .. .. 45 80
378/81 .. .. .. .. *Set of* 4 1·25 1·75
Design:—Nos. 380/1, Interior of Holycross Abbey, Co. Tipperary.

(Design adapted by the artist. Recess Harrison)

**1975** (13 Oct). *Canonisation of Oliver Plunkett. P* 14 × 14½.
382 **138** 7p. black .. .. .. .. 15 10
383 15p. chestnut .. .. .. .. 55 45

**139** "Madonna and Child" (Fra Filippo Lippi)
**140** James Larkin (from a drawing by Sean O'Sullivan)

(Des P. Wildbur)

**1975** (13 Nov). *Christmas. P* 15.
384 **139** 5p. multicoloured .. .. .. 15 10
385 7p. multicoloured .. .. .. 15 10
386 10p. multicoloured .. .. .. 45 30
384/6 .. .. .. .. *Set of* 3 65 40

(Des P. Wildbur)

**1976** (21 Jan). *Birth Centenary of James Larkin (Trade Union leader). P* 14½ × 15.
387 **140** 7p. deep bluish green and pale grey .. 20 10
388 11p. sepia and yellow-ochre .. 80 40

**141** Alexander Graham Bell
**142** 1847 Benjamin Franklin Essay

(Des R. Ballagh)

**1976** (10 Mar). *Telephone Centenary. P* 14½ × 15.
389 **141** 9p. multicoloured .. .. .. 20
390 15p. multicoloured .. .. .. 45

(Des L. le Brocquy; graphics by P. Wildbur. Litho Irish Securi[t]
Stamp Printing Ltd)

**1976** (17 May). *Bicentenary of American Revolution. T* **142** *an*[d]
*similar horiz designs. P* 14½ × 14.
391 7p. ultramarine, light red and silver .. 20
a. Silver (inscr) omitted .. .. .. † £20
392 8p. ultramarine, light red and silver .. 35
393 9p. violet-blue, orange and silver .. .. 35
394 15p. light rose-red, grey-blue and silver .. 55
a. Silver (face-value and inscr) omitted .. £500 £60
391/4 .. .. .. .. .. *Set of* 4 1·25 1·6
**MS**395 95 × 75 mm. Nos. 391/4 .. .. .. 5·50 8·0
a. Silver omitted .. .. .. .. £1500
Designs:—7p. Thirteen stars; 8p. Fifty stars; 9, 15p. Type **142**.
No. **MS**395 exists with the sheet margins overprinted in blue
commemorate "Stampa 76", the Irish National Stamp Exhibition

**143** Spirit Barrel

(Des P. Hickey)

**1976** (1 July). *Europa. Irish Delft. T* **143** *and similar horiz desig*[ns].
*Multicoloured. P* 15 × 14.
396 9p. Type **143** .. .. .. .. .. 30 1
397 11p. Dish .. .. .. .. .. 70 7

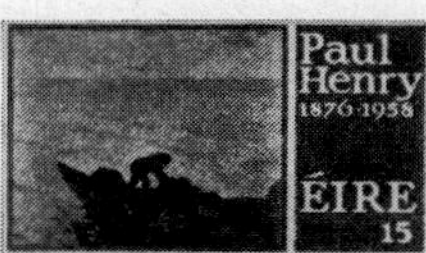


**144** "The Lobster Pots, West of Ireland" (Paul Henry)

(Des R. McGrath)

**1976** (30 Aug). *Contemporary Irish Art* (*8th issue*). *P* 15.
398 **144** 15p. multicoloured .. .. .. 50

**145** Radio Waves

(Des G. Shepherd and A. O'Donnell. Litho De La Rue Smurfit Ltd
Dublin)

**1976** (5 Oct). *50th Anniv of Irish Broadcasting Service. T* **145** *an*[d]
*similar vert design. P* 14½ × 14 (*9p.*) *or* 14 × 14½ (*11p.*).
399 9p. light new blue and bottle-green .. .. 20 1
400 11p. agate, orange-red and light new blue .. 60 1·0
Design:—11p. Transmitter, radio waves and globe.

**146** "The Nativity" (Lorenzo Monaco)

(Des R. McGrath)

**1976** (11 Nov). *Christmas. P* 15 × 14½.
401 **146** 7p. multicoloured .. .. .. 15 1
402 9p. multicoloured .. .. .. 15 1
403 15p. multicoloured .. .. .. 55 55
401/3 .. .. .. .. .. *Set of* 3 75 65

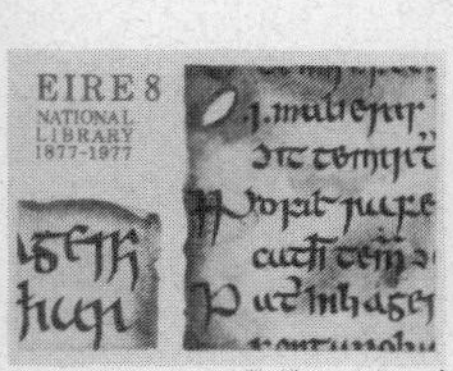

**147** 16th Century Manuscript **148** Ballynahinch, Galway

(Des P. Hickey)

77 (9 May). *Centenaries of National Library* (8p.) *and National Museum* (10p.). *T* **147** *and similar horiz design. Multicoloured. P* 15 × 14½.

4 8p. Type **147** .. .. .. .. .. .. 30 30

5 10p. Prehistoric stone .. .. .. .. .. 40 35

Des E. van der Grijn. Litho Irish Security Stamp Printing Ltd)

77 (27 June). *Europa. T* **148** *and similar vert design. Multicoloured. P* 14 × 15.

6 10p. Type **148** .. .. .. .. .. 30 25

7 12p. Lough Tay, Wicklow .. .. .. .. 80 1·25

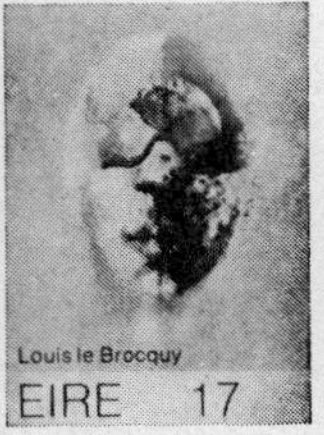

**149** "Head" (Louis le Brocquy) **150** Guide and Tents

)esign adapted by the artist. Litho Irish Security Stamp Ptg Ltd)

77 (8 Aug). *Contemporary Irish Art (9th issue). P* 14 × 14½.

8 **149** 17p. multicoloured .. .. .. .. 45 60

(Des R. Ballagh)

77 (22 Aug). *Scouting and Guiding. T* **150** *and similar horiz design. Multicoloured. P* 15 × 14½.

9 8p. Type **150** .. .. .. .. .. .. 40 10

0 17p. Tent and Scout saluting .. .. .. .. 1·00 1·50

**151** "The Shanachie" (drawing by Jack B. Yeats) **152** "Electricity" (Golden Jubilee of Electricity Supply Board)

es L. Miller (10p.), R. Ballagh (12p.). Litho Irish Security Stamp Printing Ltd)

977 (12 Sept). *Anniversaries. T* **151** *and similar horiz design. P* 14 × 14½ (10*p.*) *or* 14½ × 14 (12*p.*).

1 10p. black .. .. .. .. .. .. 30 15

2 12p. black .. .. .. .. .. .. 50 1·00

Designs and events:—10p. Type **151** (Golden Jubilee of Irish olklore Society); 12p. The philosopher Eriugena (1100th Death nniv).

)es R. Ballagh (10p.), P. Hickey (12p.), B. Blackshaw (17p.). Photo Stamping Branch of the Revenue Commissioners (12p.); Litho Irish Security Stamp Ptg Ltd (others))

977 (10 Oct). *Golden Jubilees. T* **152** *and similar horiz designs. P* 15 × 14½ (12*p.*) *or* 15 × 14 (*others*).

3 10p. multicoloured .. .. .. .. .. 15 10

4 12p. multicoloured .. .. .. .. .. 45 1·25

5 17p. grey-black and grey-brown .. .. .. 50 80

3/15 .. .. .. .. .. *Set of* 3 1·00 1·90

Designs:—12p. Bulls (from contemporary coinage) (Jubilee Agricultural Credit Corporation); 17p. Greyhound (Jubilee of reyhound Track Racing).

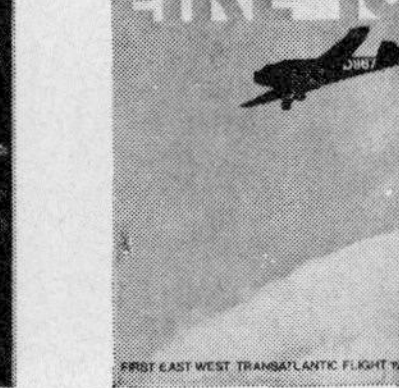


**153** "The Holy Family" (Giorgione) **154** *Bremen* in Flight

(Des R. McGrath)

**1977** (3 Nov). *Christmas. P* 14½ × 15.

416 **153** 8p. multicoloured .. .. .. .. 15 10

417 10p. multicoloured .. .. .. .. 15 10

418 17p. multicoloured .. .. .. .. 50 80

416/18 .. .. .. .. .. *Set of* 3 70 90

(Des R. Ballagh. Litho Irish Security Stamp Ptg Ltd)

**1978** (13 Apr). *50th Anniv of First East–West Transatlantic Flight. P* 14 × 14½.

419 **154** 10p. bright blue and black .. .. .. 20 15

420 – 17p. olive-brown and black .. .. .. 55 75

The 17p. is as T **154**, but shows a different sky and sea.

**155** Spring Gentian **156** Catherine McAuley

(Des Wendy Walsh. Litho Irish Security Stamp Ptg Ltd)

**1978** (12 June). *Wild Flowers. T* **155** *and similar vert designs. Multicoloured. P* 14 × 15.

421 8p. Type **155** .. .. .. .. .. .. 30 30

422 10p. Strawberry tree .. .. .. .. .. 40 15

423 11p. Large-flowered Butterwort .. .. .. 55 60

424 17p. St. Dabeoc's Heath .. .. .. .. 95 1·75

421/4 .. .. .. .. .. *Set of* 4 2·00 2·50

(Des R. Ballagh (10p.), R. Kyne (11p.), E. van der Grijn (17p.). Litho Irish Security Stamp Ptg Ltd)

**1978** (18 Sept). *Anniversaries and Events. T* **156** *and similar multicoloured designs. P* 14½ × 14 (11*p.*) *or* 14 × 14½ (*others*).

425 10p. Type **156** .. .. .. .. .. 25 10

426 11p. Doctor performing vaccination (*horiz*) .. 40 60

427 17p. "Self Portrait" .. .. .. .. .. 50 85

425/7 .. .. .. .. .. *Set of* 3 1·00 1·40

Events:—10p. Birth bicentenary of Catherine McAuley (founder of Sisters of Mercy); 11p. Global Eradication of Smallpox; 17p. Birth centenary of Sir William Orpen (painter).

**157** Diagram of Drilling Rig **158** Farthing

(Des R. Ballagh. Litho Irish Security Stamp Ptg Ltd)

**1978** (18 Oct). *Arrival Onshore of Natural Gas. P* 14 × 14½.

428 **157** 10p. maroon, turquoise-green and bistre 20 20

(Des P. Wildbur and R. Mercer)

**1978** (26 Oct). *50th Anniv of Irish Currency. T* **158** *and similar horiz designs. P* 15 × 14½.

429 8p. black, copper and deep bluish green .. 20 20

430 10p. black, silver and blue-green .. .. 30 10

431 11p. black, copper and chocolate .. .. 35 50

432 17p. black, silver and deep blue .. .. 60 1·00

429/32 .. .. .. .. .. *Set of* 4 1·25 1·60

Designs:—10p. Florin; 11p. Penny; 17p. Half-crown.

**159** "The Virgin and Child" (Guercino) **160** Conolly Folly, Castletown

(Des P. Wildbur)

**1978** (16 Nov). *Christmas. P* 14½ × 15.

433 **159** 8p. purple-brown, gold and pale turquoise-green .. .. .. 20 10

434 10p. purple-brown, chocolate and pale turquoise-green .. .. .. 20 10

435 17p. purple-brown, deep blue-green and pale turquoise-green .. .. .. 50 90

433/5 .. .. .. .. .. *Set of* 3 80 95

(Des R. McGrath)

**1978** (6 Dec). *Europa. Architecture. T* **160** *and similar horiz design. P* 15 × 14½.

436 10p. lake-brown and red-brown .. .. .. 30 15

437 11p. green and deep green .. .. .. .. 35 60

Design:—11p. Dromoland Belvedere.

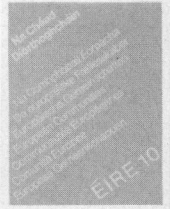


**161** Athletes in Cross-country Race **162** "European Communities" (in languages of member nations)

(Des R. Mercer. Litho Irish Security Stamp Ptg Ltd)

**1979** (20 Aug). *7th World Cross-country Championships, Limerick. P* 14½ × 14.

438 **161** 8p. multicoloured .. .. .. .. 15 30

(Des P. Wildbur)

**1979** (20 Aug). *First Direct Elections to European Assembly. P* 14½ × 15.

439 **162** 10p. dull turquoise-green .. .. .. 15 15

440 11p. reddish violet .. .. .. 15 35

**163** Sir Rowland Hill **164** Winter Wren (*Troglodytes troglodytes*)

(Des C. Harrison. Litho Irish Security Stamp Ptg Ltd)

**1979** (20 Aug). *Death Centenary of Sir Rowland Hill. P* 14 × 14½.

441 **163** 17p. black, brownish grey and red .. 30 60

(Des Wendy Walsh. Litho Irish Security Stamp Ptg Ltd)

**1979** (30 Aug). *Birds. T* **164** *and similar horiz designs. Multicoloured. P* 14½ × 14.

442 8p. Type **164** .. .. .. .. .. .. 40 50

443 10p. Great Crested Grebe (*Podiceps cristatus*) 50 15

444 11p. White-fronted Goose (*Anser albifrons flavirostris*) .. .. .. 50 55

445 17p. Peregrine Falcon (*Falco peregrinus*) .. 80 1·60

442/5 .. .. .. .. .. *Set of* 4 2·00 2·50

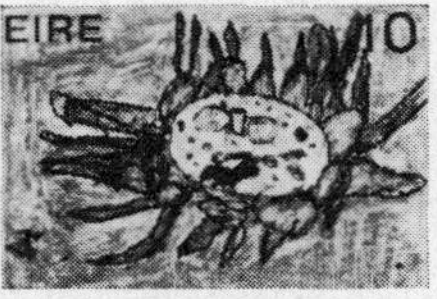


**165** "A Happy Flower" (David Gallagher)

(Des P. Wildbur. Litho Irish Security Stamp Ptg Ltd)

**1979** (13 Sept). *International Year of the Child. Paintings by Children. T* **165** *and similar multicoloured designs. P* 14 × 14½ (11*p.*) *or* 14½ × 14 (*others*).

446 10p. Type **165** .. .. .. .. .. 20 10

447 11p. "Myself and My Skipping Rope" (Lucy Norman) (*vert*) .. .. .. .. 25 50

448 17p. "Swans on a Lake" (Nicola O'Dwyer) .. 35 75

446/8 .. .. .. .. .. *Set of* 3 70 1·25

**166** Pope John Paul II

(Des P. Byrne. Litho Irish Security Stamp Ptg Ltd)

**1979** (29 Sept). *Visit of Pope John Paul II. P* 14½ × 14.

449 **166** 12p. multicoloured .. .. .. .. 30 20

**167** Brother and Child

(Des R. Kyne (9½p.), P. Scott (11p.), R. Mercer (20p.). Photo Stamping Branch of the Revenue Commissioners, Dublin (11p.), Litho Irish Security Stamp Ptg Ltd (others))

**1979** (4 Oct). *Commemorations. T* **167** *and similar designs. P* 14½ × 14 (9½*p.*), 14½ × 15 (11*p.*) *or* 14 × 14½ (*others*).
450 9½p. black and pale claret .. .. .. .. 20 10
451 11p. black, reddish orange and bright blue .. 20 55
452 20p. multicoloured .. .. .. .. 40 1·40
450/2 .. .. .. .. .. *Set of* 3 70 1·90

Designs and commemorations: *Horiz*—9½p. Type **167** (centenary of Hospitaller Order of St. John of God in Ireland); 20p. "Seated Figure" (sculpture by F. E. McWilliam) (Contemporary Irish Art (10th issue)). *Vert*—11p. Windmill and Sun (International Energy Conservation Month).

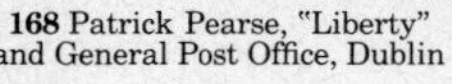

**168** Patrick Pearse, "Liberty" and General Post Office, Dublin

**169** Madonna and Child (panel painting from Domnach Airgid Shrine)

(Des R. Ballagh)

**1979** (10 Nov). *Birth Centenary of Patrick Pearse (patriot). P* 15 × 14½.
453 **168** 12p. multicoloured .. .. .. .. 35 15

(Des Ewa Gargulinska)

**1979** (15 Nov). *Christmas. P* 14½ × 15.
454 **169** 9½p. multicoloured .. .. .. .. 15 10
455 20p. multicoloured .. .. .. .. 30 55

**170** Bianconi Long Car, 1836

**171** John Baptist de la Salle (founder)

(Des P. Wildbur. Litho Irish Security Stamp Ptg Ltd)

**1979** (6 Dec). *Europa. Communications. T* **170** *and similar horiz design. Multicoloured. P* 14½ × 14.
456 12p. Type **170** .. .. .. .. 30 30
457 13p. Transatlantic cable, Valentia, 1866 .. 40 1·10

(Des P. Wildbur. Litho Irish Security Stamp Ptg Ltd)

**1980** (19 Mar). *Centenary of arrival of De La Salle Order. P* 14 × 14½.
458 **171** 12p. multicoloured .. .. .. .. 30 20

**172** George Bernard Shaw

**173** Stoat

(Des P. Byrne. Litho Irish Security Stamp Ptg Ltd)

**1980** (7 May). *Europa. Personalities. T* **172** *and similar multicoloured design. P* 14 × 14½.
459 12p. Type **172** .. .. .. .. 40 30
460 13p. Oscar Wilde (28 × 38 *mm*) .. .. 40 95

(Des Wendy Walsh. Litho Irish Security Stamp Ptg Ltd)

**1980** (30 July). *Wildlife. T* **173** *and similar vert designs. Multicoloured. P* 14 × 14½.
461 12p. Type **173** .. .. .. .. .. 30 20
462 15p. Arctic Hare .. .. .. .. .. 35 15
463 16p. Red Fox .. .. .. .. .. 45 30
464 25p. Red Deer .. .. .. .. .. 60 85
461/4 .. .. .. .. *Set of* 4 1·50 1·40
**MS**465 73 × 97 mm. Nos. 461/4 .. .. .. 2·50 3·50

No. **MS**465 exists with the sheet margins overprinted to commemorate "STAMPA 80", the Irish National Stamp Exhibition, in black or red.

**174** Playing Bodhran and Whistle

**175** Sean O'Casey

(Des J. Dixon and P. Wildbur. Litho Irish Security Stamp Ptg Ltd)

**1980** (25 Sept). *Traditional Music and Dance. T* **174** *and similar vert designs. Multicoloured. P* 14 × 14½.
466 12p. Type **174** .. .. .. .. .. 15 10
467 15p. Playing Uilleann pipes .. .. .. 20 15
468 25p. Dancing .. .. .. .. .. 35 80
466/8 .. .. .. .. .. *Set of* 3 65 95

(Des P. Wildbur (12p.), P. Scott (25p.). Litho Irish Security Stamp Ptg Ltd)

**1980** (23 Oct). *Commemorations. T* **175** *and similar vert design. P* 14 × 14½.
469 12p. multicoloured .. .. .. .. 15 10
470 25p. black, buff and drab .. .. .. 30 55

Designs and commemorations:—12p. Type **175** (Birth centenary of Sean O'Casey (playwright)); 25p. "Gold Painting No. 57" (Patrick Scott) (Contemporary Irish Art (11th issue)).

**176** Nativity Scene (painting by Geraldine McNulty)

**177** Boyle Air-pump, 1659

(Des P. Wildbur)

**1980** (13 Nov). *Christmas. P* 14½ × 15.
471 **176** 12p. multicoloured .. .. .. .. 20 10
472 15p. multicoloured .. .. .. .. 20 10
473 25p. multicoloured .. .. .. .. 55 90
471/3 .. .. .. .. .. *Set of* 3 85 95

(Des P. Wildbur. Litho Irish Security Stamp Ptg Ltd)

**1981** (12 Mar). *Irish Science and Technology. T* **177** *and similar vert designs. Multicoloured. P* 14 × 14½.
474 12p. Type **177** .. .. .. .. 30 10
475 15p. Ferguson tractor, 1936 .. .. .. 30 10
476 16p. Parsons turbine, 1884 .. .. .. 35 60
477 25p. Holland submarine, 1878 .. .. .. 45 75
474/7 .. .. .. .. .. *Set of* 4 1·25 1·40

(Litho Irish Security Stamp Ptg Ltd)

**1981** (27 Apr)–**82**. *No wmk. P* 14 × 14½.
478 **106a** 18p. dull claret .. .. .. .. 45 15
479 19p. light blue .. .. .. .. 55 80
480 22p. dull turquoise-blue (1.9.81) .. .. 65 10
481 24p. drab (29.10.81) .. .. .. 75 50
482 26p. blue-green (1.4.82) .. .. .. 2·00 30
483 29p. purple (1.4.82) .. .. .. 2·00 2·00
478/83 .. .. .. .. *Set of* 6 5·75 3·50

**178** "The Legend of the Cock and the Pot"

**179** Cycling

(Des P. Byrne. Litho Irish Security Stamp Ptg Ltd)

**1981** (4 May). *Europa. Folklore. Paintings by Maria Simonds-Gooding. T* **178** *and similar vert design. P* 14 × 14½.
491 18p. black, orange-yellow and carmine .. 40 10
492 19p. black, yellow-orange and yellow .. 50 60

Design:—19p. "The Angel with the Scales of Judgement".

(Des R. Ballagh. Litho Irish Security Stamp Ptg Ltd)

**1981** (24 June). *50th Anniv of "An Óige" (Irish Youth Hostel Association). T* **179** *and similar multicoloured designs. P* 14 × 14½ (15, 30*p.*) *or* 14½ × 14 (*others*).
493 15p. Type **179** .. .. .. .. 35 35
494 18p. Hill-walking (*horiz*) .. .. .. 40 10
495 19p. Mountaineering (*horiz*) .. .. .. 40 60
496 30p. Rock-climbing .. .. .. .. 65 65
493/6 .. .. .. .. *Set of* 4 1·60 1·50

**180** Jeremiah O'Donovan Rossa

**181** "Railway Embankment" (W. J. Leech)

(Des C. Harrison. Litho Irish Security Stamp Ptg Ltd)

**1981** (31 Aug). *150th Birth Anniv of Jeremiah O'Donovan Ross (politician). P* 14 × 14½.
497 **180** 15p. multicoloured .. .. .. 30 2

(Des P. Wildbur. Litho Irish Security Stamp Ptg Ltd)

**1981** (31 Aug). *Contemporary Irish Art (12th issue). P* 14½ × 1
498 **181** 30p. multicoloured .. .. .. 60 5

**182** James Hoban and White House

**183** "Arkle" (steeplechaser)

(Des B. Thompson. Litho Irish Security Stamp Ptg Ltd)

**1981** (29 Sept). *150th Death Anniv of James Hoban (White Hous architect). P* 14½ × 14.
499 **182** 18p. multicoloured .. .. .. 30 2

(Des Wendy Walsh and P. Wildbur. Litho Irish Security Stamp Pt Ltd)

**1981** (23 Oct). *Famous Irish Horses. T* **183** *and similar hor designs. Multicoloured. Ordinary paper (18p.) or chalk-su faced paper (others). P* 14½ × 14.
500 18p. Type **183** .. .. .. .. 65 6
a. Pair. Nos. 500/1 .. .. .. .. 1·25 1·2
501 18p. "Boomerang" (showjumper) .. .. 65 6
502 22p. "King of Diamonds" (Draught horse) .. 70 3
503 24p. "Ballymoss" (flatracer) .. .. .. 70 6
504 36p. "Coosheen Finn" (Connemara pony) .. 90 9
500/4 .. .. .. .. *Set of* 5 3·25 2·7

The 18p values were printed together, *se-tenant*, in horizonta and vertical pairs throughout the sheet.

**184** "Nativity" (F. Barocci)

**185** Eviction Scene

(Des P. Wildbur. Litho Irish Security Stamp Ptg Ltd)

**1981** (19 Nov). *Christmas. Chalk-surfaced paper. P* 14 × 14½
505 **184** 18p. multicoloured .. .. .. 35 1(
506 22p. multicoloured .. .. .. 40 1(
507 36p. multicoloured .. .. .. 90 1·4(
505/7 .. .. .. .. *Set of* 3 1·50 1·4(

(Des R. Mercer (18p.), P. Wildbur (22p.). Litho Irish Security Stam Ptg Ltd)

**1981** (10 Dec). *Anniversaries. T* **185** *and similar multicoloure design. Chalk-surfaced paper. P* 14 × 14½ (18*p.*) *or* 14½ × 1 (22*p.*).
508 18p. Type **185** .. .. .. .. 35 2
509 22p. Royal Dublin Society emblem (*horiz*) .. 40 3

Anniversaries—18p. Centenary of Land Law (Ireland) Act; 22p 250th of Royal Dublin Society (organization for the advancemen of agriculture, industry, art and science).

**186** Upper Lake, Killarney National Park

**187** "The Stigmatization of St Francis" (Sassetta)

(Des P. Wildbur. Litho Irish Security Stamp Ptg Ltd)

**982** (26 Feb). *50th Anniv of Killarney National Park. T* **186** *and similar horiz design. Multicoloured. P* 14½ × 14.

10 18p. Type **186** .. .. .. .. .. 40 20
11 36p. Eagle's Nest .. .. .. .. .. 85 1·10

Des P. Wildbur (22p.), M. Craig (24p.). Litho Irish Security Stamp Ptg Ltd)

**982** (2 Apr). *Religious Anniversaries. T* **187** *and similar horiz design. Chalk-surfaced paper. P* 14 × 14½ *(22p.) or* 14½ × 14 *(24p.).*

12 22p. multicoloured .. .. .. .. .. 60 15
13 24p. olive-brown .. .. .. .. .. 90 65

Designs and anniversaries:—22p. Type **187** (800th birth anniv f St Francis of Assisi (founder of Franciscan Order)); 24p. 'rancis Makemie (founder of American Presbyterianism) and ld Presbyterian Church, Ramelton, Co Donegal (300th anniv of rdination).

**188** The Great Famine, 1845–50

**189** Pádraic Ó Conaire (writer) (Birth Centenary)

(Des P. Wildbur. Litho Irish Security Stamp Ptg Ltd)

**982** (4 May). *Europa. Historic Events. T* **188** *and similar design. Chalk-surfaced paper. P* 14 × 14½ *(26p.) or* 14½ × 14 *(29p.).*

14 26p. black and stone .. .. .. .. .. 90 40
15 29p. multicoloured .. .. .. .. .. 95 1·00

Design: *Horiz*—29p. The coming of Christianity to Ireland.

(Des P. Wildbur. Litho Irish Security Stamp Ptg Ltd)

**982** (16 June). *Anniversaries of Cultural Figures. T* **189** *and similar vert designs. Chalk-surfaced paper. P* 14 × 14½.

16 22p. black and light blue .. .. .. .. 50 30
17 26p. black and sepia .. .. .. .. 70 30
18 29p. black and blue .. .. .. .. 80 1·00
19 44p. black and greenish grey .. .. .. 1·25 1·40
16/19 .. .. .. .. .. *Set of* 4 3·00 2·75

Designs and anniversaries:—26p. James Joyce (writer) (birth entenary); 29p. John Field (musician) (birth bicentenary); 44p. 'harles Kickham (writer) (death centenary).

**190** Porbeagle Shark (*Lamna nasus*)

**191** Galway Hooker

Des Wendy Walsh and P. Wildbur. Litho Irish Security Stamp Ptg Ltd)

**982** (29 July). *Marine Life. T* **190** *and similar horiz designs. Multicoloured. Chalk-surfaced paper. P* 14½ × 14.

20 22p. Type **190** .. .. .. .. .. 60 1·00
21 22p. Oyster (*Ostrea edulis*) .. .. .. .. 60 1·00
22 26p. Salmon (*Salmo salár*) .. .. .. .. 70 30
23 29p. Dublin Bay prawn (*Nephrops norvegicus*) 90 1·75
20/3 .. .. .. .. .. *Set of* 4 2·50 3·50

(Des P. Wildbur. Litho Irish Security Stamp Ptg Ltd)

**982** (21 Sept). *Irish Boats. T* **191** *and similar multicoloured designs. Ordinary paper (26p.) or chalk-surfaced paper (others). P* 14 × 14½ *(Nos. 524 and 527) or* 14½ × 14 *(others).*

24 22p. Type **191** .. .. .. .. .. 85 1·00
25 22p. Currach (*horiz*) .. .. .. .. 85 1·00
26 26p. *Asgard II* (*horiz*). .. .. .. 85 30
27 29p. Howth 17-Footer .. .. .. .. 1·00 1·75
24/7 .. .. .. .. .. *Set of* 4 3·25 3·50

**192** "Irish House of Commons" (painting by Francis Wheatley)

**193** "Madonna and Child" (sculpture)

(Des P. Wildbur (22p.) or R. Ballagh (26p.). Litho Irish Security Stamp Ptg Ltd)

**1982** (14 Oct). *Bicentenary of Grattan's Parliament (22p.) and Birth Centenary of Éamon de Valera (26p.). T* **192** *and similar multicoloured design. P* 14½ × 14 *(22p.) or* 14 × 14½ *(26p.).*

528 22p. Type **192** .. .. .. .. .. 60 85
529 26p. Éamon de Valera (*vert*) .. .. .. 65 40

(Des P. Wildbur. Litho Irish Security Stamp Ptg Ltd)

**1982** (11 Nov). *Christmas. P* 14 × 14½.

530 **193** 22p. multicoloured .. .. .. .. 40 40
531 26p. multicoloured .. .. .. .. 45 30

**194** Aughnanure Castle

**195** Ouzel Galley Goblet

(Des M. Craig and P. Wildbur. Litho Irish Security Stamp Ptg Ltd)

**1982** (15 Dec)–**90**. *Irish Architecture. T* **194** *and similar designs. Chalk-surfaced paper (24, 28, 32, 37, 39, 46p., £1 (No. 550b), £2) or ordinary paper (others). P* 15×14 *(15, 20, 22, 23, 24, 26, 39, 46, 50p., £1 (No. 550), £2, £5) or* 14×15 *(others).*

532 1p. dull violet-blue (6.7.83) .. .. 10 10
a. Chalk-surfaced paper (9.87) .. .. 10 10
533 2p. deep yellow-green (6.7.83) .. .. 15 10
a. Chalk-surfaced paper (27.6.85) .. 15 10
ab. Booklet pane. Nos. 533a, 543a and 545a, each × 2 .. .. .. 3·00
ac. Booklet pane. Nos. 533a, 543a and 545a, each × 4 .. .. .. 6·00
ad. Booklet pane. Nos. 533a×2, 535b×3, 544a×3 and 545c×4 (8.9.86) .. 5·00
ae. Booklet pane. Nos. 533a×4, 535b, 544a×2 and 545c×5 (24.11.88) .. 5·00
534 3p. black (6.7.83) .. .. .. 15 10
a. Chalk-surfaced paper (2.88) .. 20 20
535 4p. maroon (16.3.83) .. .. .. 10 10
a. Booklet pane. Nos. 535×3, 543×4 and 1 label (15.8.83) .. .. .. 2·50
b. Chalk-surfaced paper (9.7.84) .. 15 10
ba. Booklet pane. Nos. 535b×3, 543a×5 and 545a×4 .. .. .. 5·75
c. Perf 13½ (3.5.90) .. .. .. 1·25 1·50
ca. Booklet pane. Nos. 535c×3, 545b, 752ab×2 and 754ab×2 .. .. 7·00
536 5p. olive-sepia (6.7.83) .. .. .. 15 10
a. Chalk-surfaced paper (8.87) .. .. 15 15
537 6p. deep grey-blue (16.3.83) .. .. 20 15
a. Chalk-surfaced paper (11.85) .. 30 30
538 7p. dull yellow-green (16.3.83) .. .. 20 15
a. Chalk-surfaced paper (3.88) .. 75 75
539 10p. black (6.7.83) .. .. .. 20 20
a. Chalk-surfaced paper (3.87) .. 20 30
540 12p. purple-brown (6.7.83) .. .. 30 30
a. Chalk-surfaced paper (5.87) .. 1·75 1·75
541 15p. deep yellow-green (6.7.83) .. .. 45 35
542 20p. deep brown-purple (16.3.83) .. .. 50 45
a. Chalk-surfaced paper (12.84) .. 55 55
543 22p. chalky blue .. .. .. .. 50 20
a. Chalk-surfaced paper (9.7.84) .. 60 30
544 23p. yellow-green (16.3.83) .. .. 60 60
544*a* 24p. bistre-brown (27.6.85) .. .. 75 35
ab. Ordinary paper (9.87) .. .. 90 80
545 26p. blackish brown .. .. .. 65 25
a. Chalk-surfaced paper (9.7.84) .. 75 25
b. Perf 13½ (3.5.90) .. .. .. 1·25 1·50
545*c* 28p. maroon (27.6.85) .. .. .. 65 45
ca. Ordinary paper (10.87) .. .. 2·00 2·00
546 29p. deep yellow-green .. .. .. 80 65
547 30p. black (16.3.83) .. .. .. 70 30
a. Chalk-surfaced paper (3.87) .. 70 80
b. Perf 13½ (3.5.90) .. .. .. 1·25 1·50
ba. Booklet pane. Nos. 547b, 754ab and 774a/5a .. .. .. .. 6·50
bb. Booklet pane. Nos. 547b×2, 754ab×2 and 774a .. .. .. .. 6·50
547*c* 32p. bistre-brown (1.5.86) .. .. 1·25 1·00
ca. Ordinary paper (9.90) .. .. 3·00 3·50
547*d* 37p. chalky blue (27.6.85) .. .. 90 90
547*e* 39p. maroon (1.5.86) .. .. .. 1·25 1·25
548 44p. black and grey .. .. .. 90 90
a. Chalk-surfaced paper (4.85) .. 1·40 1·40
548*b* 46p. olive-green and brownish grey (1.5.86) 2·00 1·25
ba. Ordinary paper (9.87) .. .. 2·50 2·25
549 50p. dull ultramarine and grey (16.3.83) 1·00 1·00
a. Chalk-surfaced paper (12.84) .. 1·50 1·25
550 £1 bistre-brown and grey .. .. 5·50 3·00
a. Chalk-surfaced paper (9.84) .. 8·00 6·00
550*b* £1 chalky blue & brownish grey (27.6.85) 2·50 1·50
ba. Ordinary paper (1.88) .. .. 3·50 1·75
550*c* £2 grey-olive and black (26.7.88) .. 4·00 4·00
551 £5 crimson and grey .. .. .. 10·00 5·00
a. Chalk-surfaced paper (8.87) .. 13·00 8·50
532/51 .. .. .. .. *Set of* 28 32·00 23·00

Designs: *Horiz (as T* **194**)—1p. to 5p. Central Pavilion, Dublin Botanic Gardens; 6p. to 12p. Dr. Steevens' Hospital, Dublin; 28p. to 37p. St. MacDara's Church. (37×21 *mm*)—46p., £1 (No. 550) Cahir Castle: 50p., £2 Casino, Marino; £5 Central Bus Station, Dublin. *Vert (as T* **194**)— 15p. to 22p. Type **194**; 23p. to 26p., 39p. Cormac's Chapel. (21×37 *mm*)—44p., £1 (No. 550b) Killarney Cathedral.

The following stamps first appeared in booklet panes, but were later issued in sheets: Nos. 533a (7.86), 535b (7.85), 543a (10.84) and 545a (1.85).

Nos. 533ab/ae and 535a/ba show the horizontal edges of the panes imperforate so that 2, 22 and 26p. values from them exist imperforate at top, bottom, left or right, the 4p. at top or bottom the 24p. at right and the 28p. at top.

No. 535ba comes from a £2 Discount booklet and shows "Booklet Stamp" printed over the gum on the reverse of each stamp.

Nos. 535c, 545b and 547b are on ordinary paper and come from the 1990 150th Anniversary of the Penny Black £6 booklet. Examples of Nos. 535c, 545b and 752ab from the right-hand column of booklet pane No. 535ca are imperforate at right (4p.) or top (others). In booklet pane No. 547bb Nos. 547b and 754ab are imperforate at right.

Booklet pane No. 547ba exists with the margins overprinted to commemorate "New Zealand 1990" International Stamp Exhibition Auckland, and No. 547bb with the margins overprinted in blue for "STAMPA 90", the Irish National Stamp Exhibition.

(Des P. Wildbur (22p.), C. Harrison (26p.). Litho Irish Security Stamp Ptg Ltd)

**1983** (23 Feb). *Bicentenaries of Dublin Chamber of Commerce (22p.) and Bank of Ireland (26p.). T* **195** *and similar multicoloured design. P* 14 × 14½ *(22p.) or* 14½ × 14 *(26p.).*

552 22p. Type **195** .. .. .. .. .. 30 45
553 26p. Bank of Ireland building (*horiz*).. .. 35 35

**196** Pádraig O Siochfhradha (writer and teacher) (Birth cent)

**197** Neolithic Carved Pattern, Newgrange Tomb

(Des C. Harrison (26p.), R. Ballagh (29p.). Litho Irish Security Stamp Ptg Ltd)

**1983** (7 Apr). *Anniversaries. T* **196** *and similar vert design. Multicoloured. P* 14 × 14½.

554 26p. Type **196** .. .. .. .. .. 60 60
555 29p. Young Boys' Brigade member (Centenary) .. .. .. .. 80 1·40

(Des L. le Brocquy (26p.), P. Wildbur (29p.). Litho Irish Security Stamp Ptg Ltd)

**1983** (4 May). *Europa. T* **197** *and similar horiz design. P* 14½ × 14.

556 26p. grey-black and gold .. .. .. 2·00 40
557 29p. black, blackish brown and gold .. .. 4·00 3·25

Design:—29p. Sir William Rowan Hamilton's formulae for the multiplication of quaternions.

**198** Kerry Blue Terrier

(Des Wendy Walsh and L. Miller. Litho Irish Security Stamp Ptg Ltd)

**1983** (23 June). *Irish Dogs. T* **198** *and similar horiz designs. Multicoloured. P* 14½ × 14.

558 22p. Type **198** .. .. .. .. .. 60 35
559 26p. Irish Wolfhound .. .. .. .. 70 35
560 26p. Irish Water Spaniel .. .. .. 70 35
561 29p. Irish Terrier .. .. .. .. 90 1·25
562 44p. Irish Setters .. .. .. .. 1·25 1·60
558/62 .. .. .. .. *Set of* 5 3·75 3·50
**MS**563 142 × 80 mm. Nos. 558/62 .. .. .. 5·50 7·00

No. **MS**563 exists with the sheet margins overprinted in blue to commemorate "STAMPA 83", the Irish National Stamp Exhibition.

**199** Animals (Irish Society for the Prevention of Cruelty to Animals)

**200** Postman with Bicycle

(Des Wendy Walsh (No. 564), B. Murphy (No. 566), K. Uhlemann (No. 567), R. Ballagh (others). Litho Irish Security Stamp Ptg Ltd)

**1983** (11 Aug). *Anniversaries and Commemorations. T* **199** *and similar designs. P* 14½ × 14 *(Nos. 564, 566) or* 14 × 14½ *(others).*

564 **199** 22p. multicoloured .. .. .. 70 80
565 – 22p. multicoloured .. .. .. 70 80
566 – 26p. multicoloured .. .. .. 80 45
567 – 26p. multicoloured .. .. .. 80 45
568 – 44p. grey-blue and black .. .. 1·40 1·60
564/8 .. .. .. .. *Set of* 5 4·00 3·75

Designs: *Vert*—No. 565, Sean Mac Diarmada (patriot) (birth cent); No. 567, "St. Vincent de Paul in the Streets of Paris" (150th anniv of Society of St. Vincent de Paul); No. 568, "Andrew Jackson" (Frank McKelvey) (President of the United States). *Horiz*—No. 566, "100" (Centenary of Industrial Credit Company).

(Des R. Ballagh. Litho Irish Security Stamp Ptg Ltd)

**1983** (15 Sept). *World Communications Year. T* **200** *and similar vert design. Multicoloured. P* 14 × 14½.
569 22p. Type **200** .. .. .. .. .. .. 75 55
570 29p. Dish antenna .. .. .. .. .. 1·25 1·50

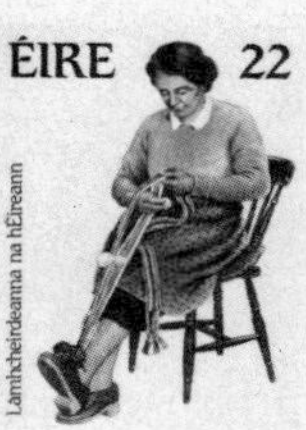


**201** Weaving

**202** "La Natividad" (R. van der Weyden)

(Des R. Mercer. Litho Irish Security Stamp Ptg Ltd)

**1983** (13 Oct). *Irish Handicrafts. T* **201** *and similar vert designs. Multicoloured. P* 14 × 14½.
571 22p. Type **201** .. .. .. .. .. .. 60 60
572 26p. Basketmaking .. .. .. .. .. 70 45
573 29p. Irish crochet .. .. .. .. .. 1·00 1·25
574 44p. Harpmaking .. .. .. .. .. 1·50 1·75
571/4 .. .. .. .. .. *Set of* 4 3·50 3·50

(Des and litho Irish Security Stamp Ptg Ltd)

**1983** (30 Nov). *Christmas. P* 14 × 14½.
575 **202** 22p. multicoloured .. .. .. .. 65 30
576 26p. multicoloured .. .. .. .. 85 30

**203** *Princess* (Dublin and Kingstown Railway)

(Des C. Rycroft. Litho Irish Security Stamp Ptg Ltd)

**1984** (30 Jan). *150th Anniv of Irish Railways. T* **203** *and similar horiz designs. Multicoloured. Ordinary paper (26p., miniature sheet) or chalk-surfaced paper (others). P* 15 × 14.
577 23p. Type **203** .. .. .. .. .. 1·00 1·00
578 26p. *Macha* (Great Southern Railway) .. 1·00 35
579 29p. *Kestrel* (Great Northern Railway) .. 1·25 1·25
580 44p. Two-car electric unit (Coras Iompair Eireann) .. .. .. .. .. 1·50 1·50
577/80 .. .. .. .. *Set of* 4 4·25 3·75
**MS**581 129 × 77 mm. Nos. 577/80 .. .. .. 5·00 5·50
No. **MS**581 exists with the sheet margins overprinted in black to commemorate "STAMPA 84", the Irish National Stamp Exhibition.

**204** *Sorbus hibernica*

(Des Wendy Walsh and P. Wildbur. Litho Irish Security Stamp Ptg Ltd)

**1984** (1 Mar). *Irish Trees. T* **204** *and similar horiz designs. Multicoloured. P* 15 × 14.
582 22p. Type **204** .. .. .. .. .. 85 60
583 26p. *Taxus baccata fastigiata* .. .. .. 95 40
584 29p. *Salix hibernica* .. .. .. .. 1·25 1·50
585 44p. *Betula pubescens* .. .. .. .. 1·40 2·00
582/5 .. .. .. .. .. *Set of* 4 4·00 4·00

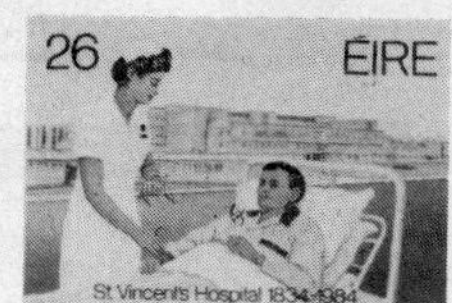


**205** St. Vincent's Hospital, Dublin

(Des B. Donegan, adapted by C. Vis (26p.), B. Murphy (44p.). Litho Irish Security Stamp Ptg Ltd)

**1984** (12 Apr). *150th Anniv of St. Vincent's Hospital and Bicentenary of Royal College of Surgeons. T* **205** *and similar horiz design. Multicoloured. P* 15 × 14.
586 26p. Type **205** .. .. .. .. .. 50 30
587 44p. Royal College and logo .. .. .. .. 90 1·25

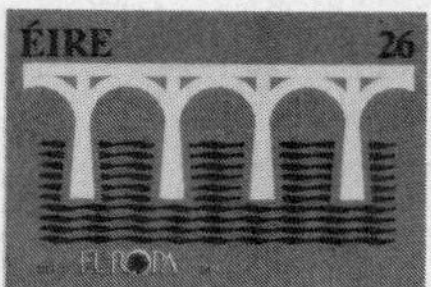


**206** C.E.P.T. 25th Anniversary Logo

(Des J. Larrivière. Litho Irish Security Stamp Ptg Ltd)

**1984** (10 May). *Europa. P* 15 × 14.
588 **206** 26p. blue, deep dull blue and black .. 1·25 40
589 29p. light green, blue-green and black .. 1·75 2·00

**207** Flags on Ballot Box

**208** John McCormack

(Des R. Ballagh. Litho Irish Security Stamp Ptg Ltd)

**1984** (10 May). *Second Direct Elections to European Assembly. P* 15 × 14.
590 **207** 26p. multicoloured .. .. .. .. 70 50

(Des R. Mercer and J. Sharpe. Litho Irish Security Stamp Ptg Ltd)

**1984** (6 June). *Birth Centenary of John McCormack (tenor). P* 14 × 15.
591 **208** 22p. multicoloured .. .. .. .. 70 65

**209** Hammer-throwing

(Des L. le Brocquy and P. Wildbur. Litho Irish Security Stamp Ptg Ltd)

**1984** (21 June). *Olympic Games, Los Angeles. T* **209** *and similar horiz designs. P* 15 × 14.
592 22p. deep mauve, black and gold .. .. 40 55
593 26p. violet, black and gold .. .. .. 50 55
594 29p. bright blue, black and gold .. .. 65 1·00
592/4 .. .. .. .. .. *Set of* 3 1·40 1·90
Designs:—26p. Hurdling; 29p. Running.

**210** Hurling

**211** Galway Mayoral Chain (500th Anniv of Mayoral Charter)

(Des C. Harrison. Litho Irish Security Stamp Ptg Ltd)

**1984** (23 Aug). *Centenary of Gaelic Athletic Association. T* **210** *and similar multicoloured design. P* 15 × 14 *(22p.) or* 14 × 15 *(26p.).*
595 22p. Type **210** .. .. .. .. .. 50 60
596 26p. Irish football (*vert*) .. .. .. .. 60 65

(Des P. Wildbur. Litho Irish Security Stamp Ptg Ltd)

**1984** (18 Sept). *Anniversaries. T* **211** *and similar multicoloured design. P* 14 × 15 *(26p.) or* 15 × 14 *(44p.).*
597 26p. Type **211** .. .. .. .. .. 60 40
598 44p. St. Brendan (from 15th-cent Bodleian manuscript) (1500th birth anniv) (*horiz*) 1·25 1·10

**212** Hands passing Letter

**213** "Virgin and Child" (Sassoferrato)

(Litho Irish Security Stamp Ptg Ltd)

**1984** (19 Oct). *Bicentenary of the Irish Post Office. P* 15 × 14.
599 **212** 26p. multicoloured .. .. .. .. 55 55

(Des O'Connor O'Sullivan Advertising (17p.), P. Wildbur (others Litho Irish Security Stamp Ptg Ltd)

**1984** (26 Nov). *Christmas. T* **213** *and similar multicolour design. Chalk-surfaced paper. P* 15×14 *(17p.) or* 14× *(others).*
600 17p. Christmas star (*horiz*) .. .. .. 50 5
601 22p. Type **213** .. .. .. .. .. 50 7
602 26p. Type **213** .. .. .. .. .. 70 3
600/2 .. .. .. .. .. *Set of* 3 1·50 1·4
No. 600 represented a special concession rate for Christmas ca postings to addresses within Ireland and Great Britain between November and 8 December 1984.

**214** "Love" and Heart-shaped Balloon

**215** Dunsink Observatory (Bicentenary)

(Des Susan Dubsky (22p.), Patricia Jorgensen (26p.). Litho Iris Security Stamp Ptg Ltd)

**1985** (31 Jan). *Greetings Stamps. T* **214** *and similar mult coloured design. Chalk-surfaced paper. P* 15×14 *(22p.)* 14×15 *(26p.).*
603 22p. Type **214** .. .. .. .. .. 50 3
604 26p. Bouquet of hearts and flowers (*vert*) .. 60 3

(Des R. Ballagh (22, 44p.), K. Thomson (26p.), M. Lunt (37p.). Lith Irish Security Stamp Ptg Ltd)

**1985** (14 Mar). *Anniversaries. T* **215** *and similar designs. Mul coloured. Chalk-surfaced paper. P* 15×14 *(26p.) or* 14×1 *(others).*
605 22p. Type **215** .. .. .. .. .. 50 5
606 26p. "A Landscape at Tivoli, Cork, with Boats" (Nathanial Grogan) (800th anniv of city of Cork) (*horiz*) .. .. .. .. 60 3
607 37p. Royal Irish Academy (Bicentenary) .. 90 1·2
608 44p. Richard Crosbie's balloon flight (Bicentenary of first aeronautic flight by an Irishman) .. .. .. .. 1·10 1·5
605/8 .. .. .. .. .. *Set of* 4 2·75 3·2

**216** *Polyommatus icarus*

**217** Charles Villiers Stanford (composer)

(Des I. Loe. Litho Irish Security Stamp Ptg Ltd)

**1985** (11 Apr). *Butterflies. T* **216** *and similar vert design Multicoloured. Chalk-surfaced paper. P* 14×15.
609 22p. Type **216** .. .. .. .. 1·00 7
610 26p. *Vanessa atalanta* .. .. .. 1·10 5
611 28p. *Gonepteryx rhamni* .. .. .. 1·25 1·7
612 44p. *Eurodryas aurinia* .. .. .. 2·00 2·2
609/12 .. .. .. .. *Set of* 4 4·75 4·7

(Des P. Hickey and J. Farrar. Litho Irish Security Stamp Pt Ltd)

**1985** (16 May). *Europa. Irish Composers. T* **217** *and simila horiz design. Multicoloured. Chalk-surfaced paper. P* 15×14
613 26p. Type **217** .. .. .. .. .. 1·25 3
614 37p. Turlough Carolan (composer and lyricist) .. .. .. .. .. 2·50 3·0

**218** George Frederick Handel

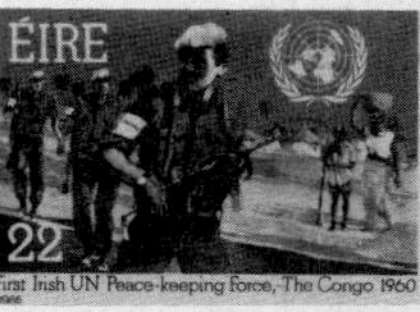


**219** U.N. Patrol of Irish Soldiers, Congo, 1960 (25th Anniv. of Irish Participation in U.N. Peace-keeping Force)

(Des K. Uhlemann and J. Farrar. Litho Irish Security Stamp Pt Ltd)

**1985** (16 May). *European Music Year. Composers. T* **218** *an similar vert designs. Multicoloured. Chalk-surfaced paper P* 14×15.
615 22p. Type **218** .. .. .. .. .. 1·00 1·2
a. Pair. Nos. 615/16 .. .. .. 2·00 2·5
616 22p. Guiseppe Domenico Scarlatti .. .. 1·00 1·2
617 26p. Johann Sebastian Bach .. .. .. 1·00 3
615/17 .. .. .. .. *Set of* 3 2·75 2·5
Nos. 615/16 were printed together, *se-tenant*, in horizontal an vertical pairs throughout the sheet.

es B. Donegan and J. Farrar (22p.), R. Ballagh (26p.), B. Donegan (44p.). Litho Irish Security Stamp Ptg Ltd)

**85** (20 June). *Anniversaries. T* **219** *and similar multi-coloured designs. Chalk-surfaced paper. P* 15 × 14 (22p.) *or* 14 × 15 (*others*).
8 22p. Type **219** .. .. .. .. .. .. 85 60
9 26p. Thomas Ashe (patriot) (birth cent) (*vert*) .. .. .. .. .. .. 90 50
0 44p. "Bishop George Berkeley" (James Lathan) (philosopher, 300th birth anniv) (*vert*) .. .. .. .. .. 1·50 2·25
8/20 .. .. .. .. .. *Set of* 3 3·00 3·00

**220** Group of Young People

es J. Farrar and N. Mooney. Litho Irish Security Stamp Ptg Ltd)

**85** (1 Aug). *International Youth Year. T* **220** *and similar multicoloured design. Chalk-surfaced paper. P* 15 × 14 (22p.) *or* 14 × 15 (26p.).
1 22p. Type **220** .. .. .. .. .. .. 75 50
2 26p. Students and young workers (*vert*) .. 75 50

**221** Visual Display Unit

es B. Donegan (44p.), C. Rycraft (others). Litho Irish Security Stamp Ptg Ltd)

**85** (3 Oct). *Industrial Innovation. T* **221** *and similar horiz designs. Multicoloured. Chalk-surfaced paper. P* 15 × 14.
3 22p. Type **221** .. .. .. .. .. .. 65 50
4 26p. Turf cutting with hand tool and with modern machinery .. .. .. .. 70 45
5 44p. "The Key Man" (Sean Keating) (150th anniv of Institution of Engineers of Ireland) .. .. .. .. .. 1·25 1·25
3/5 .. .. .. .. .. *Set of* 3 2·40 2·00

**22** Lighted Candle and Holly **223** "Virgin and Child in a Landscape" (Adrian van Ijsenbrandt)

Des R. Mahon (No. 626). Litho Irish Security Stamp Ptg Ltd)

**85** (26 Nov). *Christmas. T* **222** *and designs as T* **223** *showing paintings. Multicoloured. Chalk-surfaced paper. P* 15 × 14 (26p.) *or* 14 × 15 (*others*).
6 22p. Type **222** .. .. .. .. .. .. 75 60
a. Sheetlet. No. 626 × 16 .. .. .. .. 11·00
7 22p. Type **223** .. .. .. .. .. .. 90 1·40
a. Pair. Nos. 627/8 .. .. .. .. 1·75 2·75
8 22p. "The Holy Family" (Murillo) .. .. .. 90 1·40
9 26p. "The Adoration of the Shepherds" (Louis le Nain) (*horiz*) .. .. .. 90 25
6/9 .. .. .. .. .. *Set of* 4 3·00 3·25
No. 626 was only issued in sheetlets of 16 sold at £3, providing discount of 52p. off the face value of the stamps.
Nos. 627/8 were printed together, *se-tenant*, in horizontal and ertical pairs throughout the sheet.

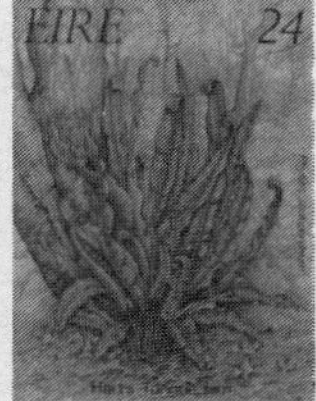


**224** Stylised Love Bird with Letter **225** Hart's Tongue Fern

Des R. Hoek (22p.), T. Monaghan (26p.). Litho Irish Security Stamp Ptg Ltd)

**986** (30 Jan). *Greetings Stamps. T* **224** *and similar vert design. Multicoloured. Chalk-surfaced paper. P* 14 × 15.
30 22p. Type **224** .. .. .. .. .. 1·00 90
31 26p. Heart-shaped pillar-box .. .. .. 1·10 70

(Des I. Loe. Litho Irish Security Stamp Ptg Ltd)

**1986** (20 Mar). *Ferns. T* **255** *and similar vert designs. Multi-coloured. Chalk-surfaced paper. P* 14 × 15.
632 24p. Type **225** .. .. .. .. .. .. 80 70
633 28p. Rusty-back Fern .. .. .. .. .. 90 70
634 46p. Killarney Fern .. .. .. .. .. 1·60 1·60
632/4 .. .. .. .. .. *Set of* 3 3·00 2·75

**226** "Harmony between Industry and Nature" **227** Boeing "747" over Globe showing Aer Lingus Routes

(Des G. van Gelderen. Litho Irish Security Stamp Ptg Ltd)

**1986** (1 May). *Europa. Protection of the Environment. T* **226** *and similar multicoloured design. Chalk-surfaced paper. P* 14 × 15 (28p.) *or* 15 × 14 (39p.).
635 28p. Type **226** .. .. .. .. .. .. 1·50 40
636 39p. *Vanessa atalanta* (butterfly) and tractor in field ("Preserve hedgerows") (*horiz*) .. .. .. .. .. 2·25 3·00

(Des R. Ballagh. Litho Irish Security Stamp Ptg Ltd)

**1986** (27 May). *50th Anniv of Aer Lingus (airline). T* **227** *and similar horiz design. Multicoloured. Chalk-surfaced paper. P* 15 × 14.
637 28p. Type **227** .. .. .. .. .. .. 1·40 50
638 46p. De Havilland "Dragon" *Iolar* (first aircraft) .. .. .. .. .. .. 1·90 2·00

**228** Grand Canal at Robertstown **229** *Severn* (19th-century paddle-steamer)

(Des B. Matthews. Litho Irish Security Stamp Ptg Ltd)

**1986** (27 May). *Irish Waterways. T* **228** *and similar multi-coloured designs. Chalk-surfaced paper. P* 14 × 15 (28p.) *or* 15 × 14 (*others*).
639 24p. Type **228** .. .. .. .. .. .. 1·00 80
640 28p. Fishing in County Mayo (*vert*) .. .. 1·25 80
641 30p. Motor cruiser on Lough Derg .. .. 1·50 2·00
639/41 .. .. .. .. .. *Set of* 3 3·25 3·25

(Des C. Rycraft. Litho Irish Security Stamp Ptg Ltd)

**1986** (10 July). *150th Anniv of British and Irish Steam Packet Company. T* **229** *and similar horiz design. Multicoloured. P* 15 × 14.
642 24p. Type **229** .. .. .. .. .. .. 75 80
643 28p. M.V. *Leinster* (modern ferry) .. .. 85 60

**230** Kish Lighthouse and Helicopter **231** J. P. Nannetti (first president) and Linotype Operator (Dublin Council of Trade Unions centenary)

(Des R. Ballagh. Litho Irish Security Stamp Printing Ltd)

**1986** (10 July). *Irish Lighthouses. T* **230** *and similar vert design. Multicoloured. P* 14 × 15.
644 24p. Type **230** .. .. .. .. .. .. 75 75
645 30p. Fastnet Lighthouse .. .. .. .. 1·25 1·25

(Des R. Ballagh (Nos. 646/7), M. Cameron (No. 648), A. Mazer (Nos. 649/50). Litho Irish Security Stamp Ptg Ltd)

**1986** (21 Aug). *Anniversaries and Commemorations. T* **231** *and similar designs. Ordinary paper* (24p.) *or chalk-surfaced paper* (*others*). *P* 14 × 15 (*Nos.* 646/7, 649) *or* 15 × 14 (*others*).
646 24p. multicoloured .. .. .. .. .. 70 70
647 28p. black and brownish grey .. .. .. 80 70
648 28p. multicoloured .. .. .. .. .. 80 70
649 30p. multicoloured .. .. .. .. .. 85 80
650 46p. multicoloured .. .. .. .. .. 1·25 1·40
646/50 .. .. .. .. .. *Set of* 5 4·00 4·00
Designs: *Vert*—No. 647, Arthur Griffith (statesman); No. 649, Clasped hands (International Peace Year). *Horiz*—No. 648, Woman surveyor (Women in Society); No. 650, Peace dove (International Peace Year).

**232** William Mulready and his Design for 1840 Envelope **233** "The Adoration of the Shepherds" (Francesco Pascucci)

(Des C. Harrison (24p.), A. Mazer from aquatints by M. A. Hayes (others). Litho Irish Security Stamp Ptg Ltd)

**1986** (2 Oct). *Birth Bicentenaries of William Mulready (artist)* (24p). *and Charles Bianconi (originator of Irish mail coach service)* (*others*). *T* **232** *and similar multicoloured designs. Chalk-surfaced paper. P* 14 × 15 (28p.) *or* 15 × 14 (*others*).
651 24p. Type **232** .. .. .. .. .. .. 65 70
652 28p. Bianconi car outside Hearns Hotel, Clonmel (*vert*) .. .. .. .. .. 75 55
653 39p. Bianconi car on the road .. .. .. 1·25 1·25
651/3 .. .. .. .. .. *Set of* 3 2·40 2·25

(Des C. O'Neill (21p.). Litho Irish Security Stamp Ptg Ltd)

**1986** (20 Nov). *Christmas. T* **233** *and similar multicoloured design. Chalk-surfaced paper. P* 15 × 14 (21p.) *or* 14 × 15 (28p.).
654 21p. Type **233** .. .. .. .. .. .. 85 85
a. Sheetlet. No. 654 × 12 .. .. .. .. 9·00
655 28p. "The Adoration of the Magi" (Frans Francken III) (*vert*) .. .. .. .. 90 55
No. 654 was only issued in sheetlets of 12 sold at £2.50, providing a discount of 2p. off the face value of the stamps.

**234** "Butterfly and Flowers" (Tara Collins) **235** Cork Electric Tram

(Litho Irish Security Stamp Ptg Ltd)

**1987** (27 Jan) *Greetings Stamps. Children's Paintings. T* **234** *and similar multicoloured design. Chalk-surfaced paper. P* 15 × 14 (24p.) *or* 14 × 15 (28p.).
656 24p. Type **234** .. .. .. .. .. .. 80 75
657 28p. "Postman on Bicycle delivering Hearts" (Brigid Teehan) (*vert*) .. .. .. .. 95 75

(Des C. Rycraft. Litho Irish Security Stamp Ptg Ltd)

**1987** (4 Mar). *Irish Trams. T* **235** *and similar horiz designs. Multicoloured. Chalk-surfaced paper. P* 15 × 14.
658 24p. Type **235** .. .. .. .. .. .. 65 55
659 28p. Dublin Standard tram .. .. .. .. 70 55
660 30p. Howth (G.N.R.) tram .. .. .. .. 80 1·00
661 46p. Galway horse tram .. .. .. .. 1·40 1·60
658/61 .. .. .. .. .. *Set of* 4 3·25 3·25
**MS**662 131 × 85 mm. Nos. 658/61 .. .. .. 4·75 5·50

**236** Ships from Crest (Bicentenary of Waterford Chamber of Commerce) **237** Bord na Mona Headquarters and "The Turf Cutter" sculpture (John Behan), Dublin

(Des K. Uhlemann (24p.), J Farrer (28p.), A. Mazer and Wendy Walsh (30p.), M. Cameron (39p.). Litho Irish Security Stamp Ptg Ltd)

**1987** (9 Apr). *Anniversaries. T* **236** *and similar designs. Chalk-surfaced paper. P* 14 × 15 (30p.) *or* 15 × 14 (*others*).
663 24p. black, ultramarine and deep grey-green 80 60
664 28p. multicoloured .. .. .. .. .. 90 60
665 30p. multicoloured .. .. .. .. .. 95 1·40
666 39p. multicoloured .. .. .. .. .. 1·25 1·60
663/6 .. .. .. .. .. *Set of* 4 3·50 3·75
Designs: *Horiz*—28p. Canon John Hayes and symbols of agriculture and development (birth centenary and 50th anniv of Muintir na Tire programme); 39p. Mother Mary Martin and International Missionary Training Hospital, Drogheda (50th anniv of Medical Missionaries of Mary). *Vert*—30p. *Calceolaria burbidgei* and College crest (300th anniv of Trinity College Botanic Gardens, Dublin).

(Des M. Lunt. Litho Harrison)

**1987** (14 May). *Europa. Modern Architecture. T* **237** *and similar horiz design. Multicoloured. P* 15 × 14.
667 28p. Type **237** .. .. .. .. .. .. 1·25 60
668 39p. St. Mary's Church, Cong .. .. .. 2·50 3·00

## COVER PRICES

Cover factors are quoted at the beginning of each country for most issues to 1945. An explanation of the system can be found on page x. The factors quoted do not, however, apply to philatelic covers.

238 Kerry Cow

239 Fleadh Nua, Ennis

(Des B. Driscoll. Litho Irish Security Stamp Ptg Ltd)

**1987** (2 July). *Irish Cattle. T* **238** *and similar horiz designs. Multicoloured. Chalk-surfaced paper. P* 15 × 14.
669 24p. Type **238** .. .. .. .. .. .. 65 60
670 28p. Friesian cow and calf .. .. .. .. 80 60
671 30p. Hereford bullock .. .. .. .. 85 1·40
672 39p. Shorthorn bull .. .. .. .. 1·10 1·60
669/72 .. .. .. .. *Set of* 4 3·00 3·75

(Des R. Ballagh. Litho Irish Security Stamp Ptg Ltd)

**1987** (27 Aug). *Festivals. T* **239** *and similar multicoloured designs. Chalk-surfaced paper. P* 14 × 15 *(vert) or* 15 × 14 *(horiz).*
673 24p. Type **239** .. .. .. .. .. .. 75 60
674 28p. Rose of Tralee International Festival .. 85 60
675 30p. Wexford Opera Festival (*horiz*) .. 1·00 1·50
676 46p. Ballinasloe Horse Fair (*horiz*) .. .. 1·40 1·60
673/6 .. .. .. .. .. *Set of* 4 3·50 4·00

240 Flagon (1637), Arms and Anniversary Ornament (1987) (350th Anniv of Dublin Goldsmiths' Company)

241 Scenes from "The Twelve Days of Christmas" (carol)

(Des B. Donegan (No. 677), R. Ballagh (No. 678), A. Mazer and Breda Mathews (No. 679), Libby Carton (No. 680). Litho Harrison (46p.) or Irish Security Stamp Ptg Ltd (others))

**1987** (1 Oct). *Anniversaries and Commemorations. T* **240** *and similar designs. Ordinary paper (46p.) or chalk-surfaced paper (others). P* 15 × 14 *(horiz) or* 14 × 15 *(vert).*
677 **240** 24p. multicoloured .. .. .. .. 55 70
678 – 24p. grey and black .. .. .. .. 55 70
679 – 28p. multicoloured .. .. .. .. 65 60
680 – 46p. multicoloured .. .. .. .. 1·00 1·00
677/80 .. .. .. .. *Set of* 4 2·50 2·75
Designs: *Vert*—24p. (No. 678) Cathal Brugha (statesman); 46p. Woman chairing board meeting (Women in Society). *Horiz*—28p. Arms of Ireland and inscription (50th anniv of Constitution).

(Des M. Cameron (21p.), A. Mazer (others). Litho Irish Security Stamp Ptg Ltd)

**1987** (17 Nov). *Christmas. T* **241** *and similar multicoloured designs. Chalk-surfaced paper. P* 15 × 14 *(21p.) or* 14 × 15 *(others).*
681 21p. Type **241** .. .. .. .. .. 60 50
a. Sheetlet. No. 681 × 14 .. .. .. .. 7·50
682 24p. The Nativity (detail, late 15th-cent Waterford Vestments) (*vert*) .. .. 60 60
683 28p. Figures from Neapolitan crib, *c* 1850 (*vert*) .. .. .. .. .. .. 75 65
681/3 .. .. .. .. .. *Set of* 3 1·75 1·60
No. 681 represents a special rate for greetings cards within Ireland and to all E.E.C. countries. It was only issued in sheetlets of 14 stamps and 1 label sold at £2.90, providing an additional discount of 4p. off the face value of the stamps.

242 Acrobatic Clowns spelling "LOVE"

243 "Robert Burke" (Sidney Nolan) and Map of Burke and Wills Expedition Route

(Des M. Cameron (24p.), Aislinn Adams (28p.). Litho Irish Security Stamp Ptg Ltd)

**1988** (27 Jan). *Greetings Stamps. T* **242** *and similar multi-coloured design. Chalk-surfaced paper. P* 15 × 14 *(24p.) or* 14 × 15 *(28p.).*
684 24p. Type **242** .. .. .. .. .. .. 75 50
685 28p. Pillar box and hearts (*vert*) .. .. .. 85 55

(Des A. Mazer. Litho Irish Security Stamp Ptg Ltd)

**1988** (1 Mar). *Bicentenary of Australian Settlement. T* **243** *and similar horiz design. Multicoloured. Chalk-surfaced paper. P* 15 × 14.
686 24p. Type **243** .. .. .. .. .. 65 60
687 46p. "Eureka Stockade" (mural detail, Sidney Nolan) .. .. .. .. .. 1·40 1·40

244 Past and Present Buildings of Dublin

245 Showjumping

(Des S. Conlin. Litho Irish Security Stamp Ptg Ltd)

**1988** (1 Mar). *Dublin Millennium. Chalk-surfaced paper. P* 15 × 14.
688 **244** 28p. multicoloured .. .. .. .. 60 55
a. Booklet pane. No. 688 × 4 .. .. 2·25
No. 688a was printed with either Irish or English inscriptions in the centre of the pane and came from £2.24 stamp booklets. Loose panes could also be purchased from the Philatelic Bureau, Dublin, and its agents.

(Des Ann Flynn Litho Irish Security Stamp Ptg Ltd)

**1988** (7 Apr). *Olympic Games, Seoul. T* **245** *and similar horiz design. Multicoloured. Chalk-surfaced paper. P* 15 × 14.
689 28p. Type **245** .. .. .. .. .. 1·00 1·25
a. Sheetlet. Nos. 689/90, each × 5 .. 9·00
690 28p. Cycling .. .. .. .. .. 1·00 1·25
Nos. 689/90 were printed together, *se-tenant*, in a sheetlet containing five of each design and two stamp-size labels.

246 William T. Cosgrave (statesman)

247 Air Traffic Controllers and "A320" Airbus

(Des R. Ballagh (24p.), J. Farrer (30p.), K. Uhlemann (50p.). Litho Irish Security Stamp Ptg Ltd)

**1988** (7 Apr). *Anniversaries and Events. T* **246** *and similar designs. Chalk-surfaced paper. P* 14×15 *(vert) or* 15×14 *(horiz).*
691 24p. brownish grey and black .. .. .. 60 45
692 30p. multicoloured .. .. .. .. 1·00 75
693 50p. multicoloured .. .. .. .. 1·25 2·00
691/3 .. .. .. .. *Set of* 3 2·50 2·00
Designs: *Horiz*—30p. Members with casualty and ambulance (50th anniv of Order of Malta Ambulance Corps). *Vert*—50p. Barry Fitzgerald (actor) (birth centenary).

(Des C. Rycraft (28p.), M. Cameron (39p.). Litho Irish Security Stamp Ptg Ltd)

**1988** (12 May). *Europa. Transport and Communications. T* **247** *and similar horiz design. Multicoloured. Chalk-surfaced paper. P* 15×14.
694 28p. Type **247** .. .. .. .. .. 75 55
695 39p. Globe with stream of letters from Ireland to Europe .. .. .. .. 1·25 1·25

248 *Sirius* (paddle-steamer) (150th anniv of regular transatlantic steamship services)

249 Cottonweed

(Des C. Rycraft. Litho Irish Security Stamp Ptg Ltd)

**1988** (12 May). *Transatlantic Transport Anniversaries. T* **248** *and similar horiz design. Multicoloured. Chalk-surfaced paper. P* 15×14.
696 24p. Type **248** .. .. .. .. .. 60 45
697 46p. *Mercury* and *Maia* (Short-Mayo composite aircraft) in Foynes Harbour (50th anniv of first commercial transatlantic flight) .. .. .. .. 1·00 1·25

(Des Frances Poskitt. Litho Irish Security Stamp Ptg Ltd)

**1988** (21 June). *Endangered Flora of Ireland. T* **249** *and similar vert designs. Multicoloured. Chalk-surfaced paper. P* 14×15.
698 24p. Type **249** .. .. .. .. .. 65 55
699 28p. Hart's Saxifrage .. .. .. .. 75 55
700 46p. Purple Milk-Vetch .. .. .. .. 1·10 1·25
698/700 .. .. .. .. *Set of* 3 2·25 2·10

**NEW INFORMATION**
The editor is always interested to correspond with people who have new information that will improve or correct the Catalogue.

250 Garda on Duty

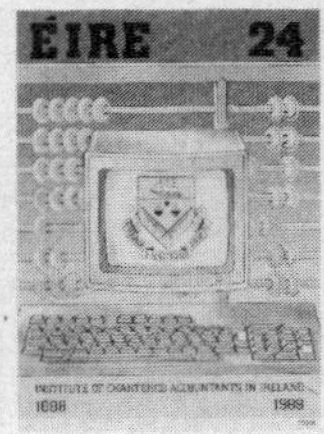

251 Computer and Abacus (Institute of Chartered Accountants in Ireland Centenary)

(Des D. Teskey. Litho Irish Security Stamp Ptg Ltd)

**1988** (23 Aug). *Irish Security Forces. T* **250** *and similar hor designs. Multicoloured. Chalk-surfaced paper. P* 15×14.
701 28p. Type **250** .. .. .. .. .. 75 7
a. Strip of 4. Nos. 701/4 .. .. .. 2·75
702 28p. Army unit with personnel carrier .. 75 7
703 28p. Navy and Air Corps members with fisheries control ship .. .. .. 75 7
704 28p. Army and navy reservists .. .. 75 7
701/4 .. .. .. .. *Set of* 4 2·75 2·7
Nos. 701/4 were printed together, both horizontally an vertically *se-tenant*, throughout the sheet of 20 (4 × 5).

(Des C. Rycraft (24p.), K. King and A. Mazer (46p.). Litho Iris Security Stamp Ptg Ltd)

**1988** (6 Oct). *Anniversaries. T* **251** *and similar multicoloure design. Chalk-surfaced paper. P* 14×15 *(24p.) or* 15×14 *(46p.*
705 24p. Type **251** .. .. .. .. .. 50 4
706 46p. *Duquesa Santa Ana* off Donegal (*horiz*) (400th anniv of Spanish Armada) .. 1·50 1·2

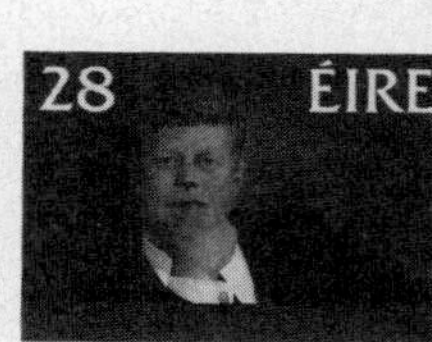

252 "President Kennedy" (James Wyeth)

Nollaig '88
EIRE 21
253 St. Kevin's Church, Glendalough

(Des A. Mazer. Litho Irish Security Stamp Ptg Ltd)

**1988** (24 Nov). *25th Death Anniv of John F. Kenned (American statesman). Chalk-surfaced paper. P* 15×14.
707 **252** 28p. multicoloured .. .. .. .. 70 7

(Des Ann Flynn (21p.), B. Donegan (others). Litho Irish Securit Stamp Ptg Ltd)

**1988** (24 Nov). *Christmas. T* **253** *and similar vert designs Multicoloured. Chalk-surfaced paper. P* 14×15.
708 21p. Type **253** .. .. .. .. .. 60 5
a. Sheetlet. No. 708 × 14 .. .. .. 7·50
709 24p. The Adoration of the Magi .. .. 55 5
710 28p. The Flight into Egypt .. .. .. 70 5
711 46p. The Holy Family .. .. .. 1·00 1·0
708/11 .. .. .. .. *Set of* 4 2·50 2·2
No. 708 represents a special rate for greetings cards withi Ireland and to all E.E.C. countries. It was only issued i sheetlets of 14 stamps and 1 label sold at £2.90, providing a additional discount of 4p. off the face value of the stamps.
The designs of Nos. 709/11 are from a 15th-century Frenc Book of Hours.

254 Spring Flowers spelling "Love" in Gaelic

255 Italian Garden, Garinish Island

(Des Susan Dubsky (24p.), A. Mazer (28p.). Litho Irish Security Stamp Ptg Ltd)

**1989** (24 Jan). *Greetings Stamps. T* **254** *and similar multicoloured design. Chalk-surfaced paper. P* 15×14 *(24p. or* 14×15 *(28p.).*
712 24p. Type **254** .. .. .. .. .. 50 5
713 28p. "The Sonnet" (William Mulready) (*vert*) 60 5

(Des Frances Poskitt. Litho Irish Security Stamp Ptg Ltd)

**1989** (11 Apr). *National Parks and Gardens. T* **255** *and simila horiz designs. Multicoloured. Chalk-surfaced paper. P* 15×14
714 24p. Type **255** .. .. .. .. .. 75 5
715 28p. Lough Veagh, Glenveagh National Park .. .. .. .. .. .. 85 5
716 32p. Barnaderg Bay, Connemara National Park .. .. .. .. .. .. 90 1·2
717 50p. St. Stephen's Green, Dublin .. .. 1·50 1·7
714/17 .. .. .. .. *Set of* 4 3·50 3·7

256 "Silver Stream", 1908

257 Ring-a-ring-a-roses

(Des C. Rycraft. Litho Irish Security Stamp Ptg Ltd)

989 (11 Apr). *Classic Irish Cars. T* **256** *and similar horiz designs. Multicoloured. Chalk-surfaced paper. P* 15×14.

18 24p. Type **256** .. .. .. .. 50 45
a. Booklet pane. Nos. 718/19, each ×2 .. 2·00
b. Booklet pane. Nos. 718/21 .. .. 3·00
19 28p. Benz "Comfortable", 1898 .. .. 50 55
20 39p. "Thomond", 1929 .. .. .. 1·00 1·25
21 46p. Chambers' 8 h.p. model, 1905 .. .. 1·40 1·50
18/21 .. .. .. .. *Set of* 4 3·00 3·25

Booklet panes Nos. 718a/b come from £2.41 stamp booklets nd stamps from them have one or two adjacent sides nperforate. Such panes were also available loose from the hilatelic Bureau, Dublin, and its agents

(Des C. Harrison. Litho Irish Security Stamp Ptg Ltd)

989 (11 May). *Europa. Children's Games. T* **257** *and similar horiz design. Multicoloured. Chalk-surfaced paper. P* 15×14.

22 28p. Type **257** .. .. .. .. 1·00 65
23 39p. Hopscotch .. .. .. .. 1·40 1·25

Nos. 722/3 were each issued in sheets of 10 showing additional ustrations in the left-hand sheet margin.

258 Irish Red Cross Flag (50th anniv)

259 Saints Kilian, Totnan and Colman (from 12th-century German manuscript)

)es Q Design (24p.), R. Hoek (28p.). Litho Irish Security Stamp Ptg Ltd)

989 (11 May). *Anniversaries and Events. T* **258** *and similar vert design. Chalk-surfaced paper. P* 14×15.

24 24p. vermilion and black .. .. .. 55 60
25 28p. new blue, black and lemon .. .. 1·10 1·10

Design:—28p. Circle of twelve stars (third direct elections to uropean Parliament).

(Des P. Effert. Litho Irish Security Stamp Ptg Ltd)

989 (15 June). *1300th Death Anniv of Saints Kilian, Totnan and Colman. Chalk-surfaced paper. P* 13½.

26 **259** 28p. multicoloured .. .. .. 80 90
a. Booklet pane. No. 726×4 with margins all round .. .. 3·00

A stamp in a similar design was issued by West Germany.
No. 726a exists with text in Irish, English, German or Latin n the pane margin.

260 19th-century Mail Coach passing Cashel

261 Crest and 19th-century Dividers (150th anniv of Royal Institute of Architects of Ireland)

)es Katie O'Sullivan and B. Donegan. Litho Irish Security Stamp Ptg Ltd)

989 (27 July). *Bicentenary of Irish Mail Coach Service. Chalk-surfaced paper. P* 15×14.

27 **260** 28p. multicoloured .. .. .. 1·00 75

)es R. Ballagh (24p.), A. Mazer (28p.), K. Uhlemann (30p.), Carey Clarke (46p.). Litho Irish Security Stamp Ptg Ltd)

989 (27 July). *Anniversaries and Commemorations. T* **261** *and similar designs. Chalk-surfaced paper. P* 15×14 *(30p.) or* 14×15 *(others).*

28 24p. grey and black .. .. .. 60 55
29 28p. multicoloured .. .. .. 65 55
30 30p. multicoloured .. .. .. 1·40 1·25
31 46p. orange-brown .. .. .. 1·60 1·40
28/31 .. .. .. .. *Set of* 4 3·75 3·25

Designs: *Vert*—24p. Sean T. O'Kelly (statesman) (drawing by ean O'Sullivan); 46p. Jawaharlal Nehru (birth centenary). *'oriz*—30p. Margaret Burke-Sheridan (soprano) (portrait by De ennaro) and scene from *La Bohème* (birth centenary)

262 "*NCB Ireland* rounding Cape Horn" (Des Fallon)

263 Willow Red Grouse

(Des I. Caulder. Litho Irish Security Stamp Ptg Ltd)

**1989** (31 Aug). *First Irish Entry in Whitbread Round the World Yacht Race. Chalk-surfaced paper. P* 15×14.

732 **262** 28p. multicoloured .. .. .. 1·00 90

(Des R. Ward. Litho Irish Security Stamp Ptg Ltd)

**1989** (5 Oct). *Game Birds. T* **263** *and similar square designs. Multicoloured. Chalk-surfaced paper. P* 13½.

733 24p. Type **263** .. .. .. .. 80 55
734 28p. Lapwing .. .. .. .. 90 55
735 39p. Woodcock .. .. .. .. 1·25 1·50
736 46p. Ring-necked Pheasant .. .. 1·40 1·75
733/6 .. .. .. .. *Set of* 4 4·00 4·00
**MS**737 128×92 mm. Nos. 733/6 .. .. 4·00 4·00

No. **MS**737 exists overprinted on the margins to commemorate "STAMPA 89", the Irish National Stamp Exhibition.

264 "The Annunciation"

265 Logo (Ireland's Presidency of the European Communities)

(Des Jacinta Fitzgerald (21p.), J. McEvoy from 13th-century Flemish Psalter (others). Litho Irish Security Stamp Ptg Ltd)

**1989** (14 Nov). *Christmas. T* **264** *and similar vert designs. Multicoloured. Chalk-surfaced paper. P* 14×15.

738 21p. Children decorating crib .. .. 65 65
a. Sheetlet. No. 738×14 .. .. .. 8·00
739 24p. Type **264** .. .. .. .. 75 45
740 28p. "The Nativity" .. .. .. 85 55
741 46p. "The Adoration of the Magi" .. .. 1·50 2·00
738/41 .. .. .. .. *Set of* 4 3·25 3·25

No. 738 represents a special rate for greetings cards within Ireland and to all E.E.C. countries. It was only issued in sheetlets of 14 stamps and 1 label sold at £2.90, providing an additional discount of 4p. off the face value of the stamps.

(Des B. Donegan (30p.), Q Design (50p.). Litho Irish Security Stamp Ptg Ltd)

**1990** (9 Jan). *European Events. T* **265** *and similar horiz design. Multicoloured. Chalk-surfaced paper. P* 15×14.

742 30p. Type **265** .. .. .. .. 80 60
743 50p. Logo and outline map of Ireland (European Tourism Year) .. .. 1·60 1·90

266 Dropping Messages from Balloon

267 Silver Kite Brooch

(Des Aislinn Adams (26p.), Patricia Sleeman and R. Vogel (30p.). Litho Irish Security Stamp Ptg Ltd)

**1990** (30 Jan). *Greetings Stamps. T* **266** *and similar vert design. Chalk-surfaced paper. P* 14×15.

744 26p. multicoloured .. .. .. 70 70
745 30p. rosine, pale buff and reddish brown .. 80 80

Design:—30p. Heart and "Love" drawn in lipstick.

(Des M. Craig and Q Design. Litho Irish Security Stamp Ptg Ltd)

**1990** (8 Mar)–**91**. *Irish Heritage and Treasures. T* **267** *and similar designs. Chalk-surfaced paper (5, 20, 26, 28, 30, 32, 37, 38, 41, 44, 50, 52p., £1, £5) or ordinary paper (others). P* 14×15 *(10, 20, 30, 32p., £5) or* 15×14 *(others).*

746 1p. black and light new blue (26.7.90) .. 10 10
a. Chalk-surfaced paper (10.91) .. .. 10 10
747 2p. black and bright red-orange (26.7.90) 10 10
a. Chalk-surfaced paper (15.11.90) .. 10 10
ab. Booklet pane. Nos. 747a, 748a×3, 752 and 754×2 plus label .. .. 1·60
ac. Booklet pane. Nos. 747a×2, 755×2 and 820 (17.10.91) .. .. .. 1·90
748 4p. black and bluish violet (26.7.90) .. 10 10
a. Chalk-surfaced paper (15.11.90) .. 10 10
ab. Booklet pane. Nos. 748a×3, 753×4 plus label (17.10.91) .. .. 2·50
749 5p. black and bright green (29.1.91) .. 10 10
750 10p. black and bright red-orange (26.7.90) 20 25
751 20p. black and lemon (29.1.91) .. .. 35 40
752 26p. black and bright violet .. .. 50 25
a. Ordinary paper (5.90) .. .. 55 60
ab. Perf 13½ (3.5.90) .. .. .. 1·25 1·50
753 28p. black and bright red-orange (3.4.91) .. 50 55
a. Ordinary paper (5.91) .. .. 50 55
754 30p. black and new blue .. .. .. 55 30
a. Ordinary paper (5.90) .. .. 65 55
ab. Perf 13½ (3.5.90) .. .. .. 1·25 1·50
755 32p. black and light green .. .. 60 40
a. Ordinary paper (5.90) .. .. 60 40
756 34p. black and lemon (26.7.90) .. .. 60 65
757 37p. brownish black & bright green (3.4.91) 70 75
a. Ordinary paper (11.91) .. .. 70 75
758 38p. black and bright violet (3.4.91) .. 70 75
759 41p. black and bright red orange .. .. 75 80
a. Ordinary paper (10.90) .. .. 90 1·00
760 44p. agate and lemon (3.4.91) .. .. 80 85
761 50p. black and lemon .. .. .. 1·00 1·10
a. Ordinary paper (5.90) .. .. 90 95
762 52p. black and new blue (3.4.91) .. .. 95 1·00
763 £1 black and lemon .. .. .. 1·90 2·00
a. Ordinary paper (5.90) .. .. 2·25 2·50
764 £2 black and bright green (26.7.90) .. 3·75 4·00
765 £5 black and new blue (29.1.91) .. .. 9·25 9·50
746/65 .. .. .. .. *Set of* 20 20·00 21·00

Designs: *Vert (as T* **267**)—1p., 2p. Type **267**; 4p., 5p. Dunamase Food Vessel; 26p., 28p. Lismore Crozier; 34p., 37p., 38p. Gleninsheen Collar; 41p., 44p. Silver thistle brooch; 50p., 52p. Broighter Boat. (22×38 *mm*)—£5 St. Patrick's Bell Shrine. *Horiz (as T* **267**)— 10p. Derrinboy Armlets; 20p. Gold dress fastener; 30p. Enamelled latchet brooch; 32p. Broighter Collar. (38×22 *mm*)—£1 Ardagh Chalice; £2 Tara Brooch.

Nos. 747a and 748a were initially only available from booklet pane No. 747ab, but were subsequently issued in sheet form during March (4p.) and October (2p.) 1991.

The three outer edges of booklet pane No. 747ab are imperforate so that No. 747a is imperforate at left, No. 748a at left or right, No. 752 at left and foot, and No. 754 at top or top and right.

In No. 747ac the 2p. is imperforate at foot and the 32p. imperforate at right. In No. 748b two of each value are imperforate at foot.

Nos. 752ab and 754ab come from the 1990 150th Anniversary of the Penny Black £6 stamp booklets and occur in *se-tenant* panes, Nos. 535ca and 547ba/bb. One example of No. 752ab from pane No. 535ca is imperforate at top and both examples of No. 754ab from pane No. 547bb are imperforate at right.

For 4, 28 and 32p. stamps in same design as Nos. 748, 753 and 755, but printed in photogravure, see Nos. 808/10.

For 32p. value as No. 755, but 27×20 mm and self-adhesive see No. 823.

268 Posy of Flowers

269 Player heading Ball

(Des M. Cameron. Litho Irish Security Stamp Ptg Ltd)

**1990** (22 Mar). *Greetings Stamps. T* **268** *and similar vert designs. Multicoloured. P* 14×15.

766 26p. Type **268** .. .. .. .. 70 80
a. Booklet pane. Nos. 766/9 .. .. 2·50
767 26p. Birthday presents .. .. .. 70 80
768 30p. Flowers, ribbon and horseshoe .. .. 70 80
769 30p. Balloons .. .. .. .. 70 80
766/9 .. .. .. .. *Set of* 4 2·50 3·00

Nos. 766/9 come from £1.98 discount stamp booklets.

Booklet pane No. 766a exists with the 26p. values at left or right and the right-hand stamp (either No. 767 or 769) imperforate at right. The booklet pane also contains 8 small greetings labels.

(Des C. Harrison. Litho Irish Security Stamp Ptg Ltd)

**1990** (5 Apr). *World Cup Football Championship, Italy. T* **269** *and similar vert design. Multicoloured. Chalk-surfaced paper. P* 14×15.

770 30p. Type **269** .. .. .. .. 1·25 1·25
a. Sheetlet. Nos. 770/1, each × 4 .. 9·00
771 30p. Tackling .. .. .. .. 1·25 1·25

Nos. 770/1 were printed together, *se-tenant*, in a sheetlet of 8 stamps and 1 central stamp-size label.

270 Battle of the Boyne, 1690

(Des S. Conlin. Litho Irish Security Stamp Ptg Ltd)

**1990** (5 Apr). *300th Anniv of the Williamite Wars (1st issue).* **T 270** *and similar horiz designs. Multicoloured. Chalk-surfaced paper. P* 13½.
772 30p. Type **270** .. .. .. .. 1·00 90
a. Pair. Nos. 772/3 .. .. .. 2·00 1·75
773 30p. Siege of Limerick, 1690 .. .. 1·00 90
Nos. 772/3 were printed together, *se-tenant*, in horizontal and vertical pairs throughout the sheet.
See also Nos. 806/7.

**271** 1990 Irish Heritage 30p. Stamp and 1840 Postmark

**272** General Post Office, Dublin

(Des Q Design. Litho Irish Security Stamp Ptg Ltd)

**1990** (3 May). *150th Anniv of the Penny Black.* **T 271** *and similar horiz designs. Multicoloured. Chalk-surfaced paper. P* 15×14.
774 30p. Type **271** .. .. .. .. 70 80
a. Ordinary paper .. .. .. 1·50 1·75
ab. Booklet pane. Nos. 774a/5a, each × 2 8·00
775 50p. Definitive stamps of 1922, 1969, 1982 and 1990 .. .. .. .. 1·40 1·50
a. Ordinary paper .. .. .. 2·50 3·00
Nos. 774a and 775a were only issued in booklets.
In booklet pane No. 774ab one example of each value is imperforate at right.
Booklet pane No. 774ab exists with the margins overprinted in red in connection with "STAMPA 90", the Irish National Stamp Exhibition.
For other booklet panes containing Nos. 774a/5a see Nos. 547ba/bb.

(Des P. Keogh. Litho Irish Security Stamp Ptg Ltd)

**1990** (3 May). *Europa. Post Office Buildings.* **T 272** *and similar vert design. Multicoloured. P* 14 × 15.
776 30p. Type **272** .. .. .. .. 1·00 60
777 41p. Westport Post Office, County Mayo .. 1·40 1·50
Nos. 776/7 were each printed in sheets of 10 stamps and 2 stamp-size labels.

**273** Medical Missionary giving Injection

**274** Narcissus "Foundling" and Japanese Gardens, Tully

(Des I. Calder (26, 50p.), R. Ballagh (30p.). Litho Irish Security Stamp Ptg Ltd)

**1990** (21 June). *Anniversaries and Events.* **T 273** *and similar designs. P* 15×14 (*horiz*) *or* 14×15 (*vert*).
778 26p. multicoloured .. .. .. .. 75 55
779 30p. black .. .. .. .. .. 80 90
780 50p. multicoloured .. .. .. .. 1·40 1·50
778/80 .. .. .. .. *Set of* 3 2·75 2·75
Designs: *Vert*—30p. Michael Collins (statesman) (birth centenary). *Horiz*—50p. Missionaries working at water pump (Irish missionary service).

(Des I. Loe. Litho Irish Security Stamp Ptg Ltd)

**1990** (30 Aug). *Garden Flowers.* **T 274** *and similar vert designs. Multicoloured. P* 14×15.
781 26p. Type **274** .. .. .. .. 70 55
a. Booklet pane. Nos. 781/2, each × 2 .. 2·75
b. Booklet pane. Nos. 781/4 .. .. 3·75
782 30p. *Rosa x hibernica* and Malahide Castle gardens .. .. .. .. 75 70
783 41p. *Primula* "Rowallane Rose" and Rowallane garden .. .. .. 1·25 90
784 50p. *Erica erigena* "Irish Dusk" and Palm House, National Botanical Gardens .. 1·40 1·25
781/4 .. .. .. .. *Set of* 4 3·75 3·00
Both booklet panes show the stamps as horizontal rows of four imperforate at top and at right. Stamps from the right of the pane, 30p. on No. 781a, 50p. on No. 781b, are imperforate at top and right with the other values imperforate at top only.

Frama label

Klussendorf label

Amiel Pitney/Bowes label

**MACHINE LABELS.** For a trial period of three months from 8 October 1990 labels in the above designs, ranging in value from 1p. to £99.99, were available from the head post offices at Dublin (Frama), Limerick (Klussendorf) and Cork (Amiel Pitney/Bowes). The Amiel Pitney/Bowes machine (Cork) was taken out of service on 31 January 1991. The other two machines were withdrawn on 31 May 1991.

**275** *Playboy of the Western World* (John Synge)

**276** Nativity

(Des R. Ballagh. Litho Irish Security Stamp Ptg Ltd)

**1990** (18 Oct). *Irish Theatre.* **T 275** *and similar horiz designs. Multicoloured. P* 13½.
785 30p. Type **275** .. .. .. .. 80 80
a. Horiz strip of 4. Nos. 785/8 .. .. 3·00
786 30p. *Juno and the Paycock* (Sean O'Casey) 80 80
787 30p. *The Field* (John Keane) .. .. 80 80
788 30p. *Waiting for Godot* (Samuel Beckett) .. 80 80
785/8 .. .. .. .. *Set of* 4 3·00 3·00
Nos. 785/8 were printed together in sheets of 20 (4×5), producing horizontal *se-tenant* strips of 4 and vertical *se-tenant* pairs of Nos. 785 and 788 or 786/7.

(Des Pamela Leonard (No. 789), B. Cronin (others). Litho Irish Security Stamp Ptg Ltd)

**1990** (15 Nov). *Christmas.* **T 276** *and similar vert designs. Multicoloured. Chalk-surfaced paper* (50p.) *or ordinary paper* (*others*). *P* 14×15.
789 26p. Child praying by bed .. .. 70 65
a. Sheetlet. No. 789×12 .. .. 7·50
790 26p. Type **276** .. .. .. .. 70 60
791 30p. Madonna and Child .. .. .. 80 70
792 50p. Adoration of the Magi .. .. 1·40 1·60
789/92 .. .. .. .. *Set of* 4 3·25 3·25
No. 789 was only issued in sheetlets of 12 sold at £2.86, providing a discount of 26p. off the face value of the stamps.

**277** Hearts in Mail Sack and Postman's Cap

**278** Starley "Rover" Bicycle, 1886

(Des Liz Manning (26p.), Louise Mullally (30p.). Litho Irish Security Stamp Ptg Ltd)

**1991** (29 Jan). *Greetings Stamps.* **T 277** *and similar vert design. Multicoloured. Chalk-surfaced paper. P* 14×15.
793 26p. Type **277** .. .. .. .. 70 70
794 30p. Boy and girl kissing .. .. .. 80 80

(Des E. Patton. Litho Irish Security Stamp Ptg Ltd)

**1991** (5 Mar). *Early Bicycles.* **T 278** *and similar vert designs. Multicoloured. Chalk-surfaced paper. P* 14×15.
795 26p. Type **278** .. .. .. .. 65 60
796 30p. Child's horse tricycle, 1875 .. .. 75 70
797 50p. "Penny Farthing", 1871 .. .. 1·40 1·50
795/7 .. .. .. .. *Set of* 3 2·75 3·00
**MS**798 113×72 mm. Nos. 795/7 .. .. 2·50 2·50
No. **MS**798 exists with a privately-applied marginal overprint for the "Collectorex 91" Exhibition, Dublin.

**279** Cuchulainn (statue by Oliver Sheppard) and Proclamation

**280** Scene from *La Traviata* (50th anniv of Dublin Grand Opera Society)

(Des I. Calder. Litho Irish Security Stamp Ptg Ltd)

**1991** (3 Apr). *75th Anniv of Easter Rising. Chalk-surfaced paper. P* 15×14.
799 **279** 32p. multicoloured .. .. .. 85 8

(Des K. Uhlemann (28p.), M. Craig and I. Calder (32p.), M. Craig (44p.), M. Craig and Q Design (52p.). Litho Irish Security Stamp Ptg Ltd)

**1991** (11 Apr). *"Dublin 1991 European City of Culture".* **T 280** *and similar horiz designs. Multicoloured. Chalk-surfaced paper. P* 13½ (52p.) *or* 15×14 (*others*).
800 28p. Type **280** .. .. .. .. 65 6
a. Booklet pane. Nos. 800/2 .. .. 2·50
b. Booklet pane. Nos. 800/3 .. .. 3·75
801 32p. City Hall and European Community emblem .. .. .. .. 85 8
802 44p. St. Patrick's Cathedral (800th anniv) 1·25 1·2
803 52p. Custom House (bicent) (41×24 *mm*) 1·40 1·4
800/3 .. .. .. .. *Set of* 4 3·75 3·7

**281** *Giotto* Spacecraft approaching Halley's Comet

(Des C. Rycraft. Litho Irish Security Stamp Ptg Ltd)

**1991** (14 May). *Europa. Europe in Space.* **T 281** *and similar horiz design. Multicoloured. P* 15×14.
804 32p. Type **281** .. .. .. .. 85 8
805 44p. Hubble Telescope orbiting Earth .. 1·25 1·2
Nos. 804/5 were each issued in sheetlets of 10 (2×5) with illustrations of space launches on enlarged left hand margins.

**282** Siege of Athlone

**283** John A. Costello (statesman)

(Des S. Conlin. Litho Irish Security Stamp Ptg Ltd)

**1991** (14 May). *300th Anniv of the Williamite Wars (2nd issue).* **T 282** *and similar horiz design. Multicoloured. P* 15×14.
806 28p. Type **282** .. .. .. .. 75 7
a. Pair. Nos. 806/7 .. .. .. 1·50 1·5
807 28p. Generals Ginkel and Sarsfield (signatories of Treaty of Limerick) .. 75 7
Nos. 806/7 were printed together, *se-tenant*, in horizontal and vertical pairs throughout the sheet.

**1991** (14 May). *Booklet stamps. As Nos.* 748, 753 *and* 755, *but printed in photogravure by Enschedé. Chalk-surfaced paper P* 14×15.
808 4p. black and bluish violet .. .. 10 1
a. Booklet pane. Nos. 808×2, 809 and 810×2 plus label .. .. .. 1·90
809 28p. black and reddish orange .. .. 50 5
810 32p. black and light green .. .. .. 60 6
808/10 .. .. .. .. *Set of* 3 1·00 1·1
Booklet pane No. 808a has imperforate outer edges giving stamps imperforate at left or right (4p.), at left and foot (28p.) and at top or top and right (32p.).

(Des R. Ballagh (28p.), Q Design (others). Litho Irish Security Stamp Ptg, Ltd)

**1991** (2 July). *Anniversaries.* **T 283** *and similar designs. Chalk-surfaced paper* (28p.). *P* 15×14 (52p.) *or* 14×15 (*others*).
811 28p. black .. .. .. .. .. 70 7
812 32p. multicoloured .. .. .. .. 85 8
813 52p. multicoloured .. .. .. .. 1·40 1·5
811/13 .. .. .. .. *Set of* 3 2·75 2·7
Designs: *Vert*—28p. Type **283** (birth centenary) (drawing by Sean O'Sullivan); 32p. "Charles Stewart Parnell" (Sydney Hall) (death centenary). *Horiz*—52p. Meeting of United Irishmen (bicentenary).

**284** Player on Green, Portmarnock (Walker Cup)

**285** Wicklow Cheviot

(Des E. Patton. Litho Irish Security Stamp Ptg Ltd)

**91** (3 Sept). *Golf Commemorations. T* **284** *and similar multicoloured design. Chalk-surfaced paper* (32p.). *P* 15×14 (28p.) *or* 14×15 (32p.).

4 28p. Type **284** .. .. .. .. 50 55
5 32p. Logo and golfer of 1900 (centenary of Golfing Union of Ireland) (*vert*) .. 60 65

(Des Pamela Leonard. Litho Irish Security Stamp Ptg Ltd)

**91** (3 Sept). *Irish Sheep. T* **285** *and similar multicoloured designs. Chalk-surfaced paper. P* 15×14 (52p.) *or* 14×15 (others).

6 32p. Type **285** .. .. .. .. 60 65
7 38p. Donegal Blackface .. .. .. 70 75
8 52p. Galway (*horiz*) .. .. .. 95 1·00
6/18 .. .. .. .. *Set of* 3 2·00 2·10

**286** Boatyard

**287** The Annunciation

(Des C. Rycraft. Litho Irish Security Stamp Ptg Ltd)

91 (17 Oct). *Fishing Fleet. T* **286** *and similar horiz designs. Multicoloured. Chalk-surfaced paper. P* 15×14.

9 28p. Type **286** .. .. .. .. 50 55
a. Booklet pane. Nos. 819/22 .. .. 2·50
b. Booklet pane. Nos. 819/20 each × 2 .. 2·25
0 32p. Traditional inshore trawlers .. .. 60 65
1 44p. Inshore lobster pot boat .. .. 80 85
2 52p. Modern factory ship .. .. .. 95 1·00
9/22 .. .. .. .. *Set of* 4 2·50 2·75

In booklet pane No. 819a the 32p. and 52p. values are perforate at right.

Booklet pane No. 819a exists with the gutter margin erprinted in connection with the "Philanippon '91" ternational Stamp Exhibition, Tokyo.

For a further booklet pane including No. 820 see No. 747ac.

(Litho Printset Pty Ltd, Australia)

**91** (31 Oct). *As No.* 755, *but larger,* 27×20 *mm, and self-adhesive. P* 11½.

3 32p. black and light green .. .. .. 60 65

No. 823 was only available in coils of 100, or as strips of 3 from e Philatelic Bureau, each stamp, with die-cut perforations, ing separate on the imperforate backing paper.

es Q. Design (No. 827), T. Gayer (others). Litho Irish Security Stamp Ptg Ltd)

**91** (14 Nov). *Christmas. T* **287** *and similar vert designs. Chalk-surfaced paper. P* 14×15.

7 28p. multicoloured .. .. .. .. 55 60
a. Sheetlet. No. 827×13 .. .. .. 6·50
8 28p. dull ultramarine, sage-green and black 55 60
9 32p. scarlet and black .. .. .. 60 65
0 52p. multicoloured .. .. .. .. 90 95
7/30 .. .. .. .. *Set of* 4 2·25 2·50

Designs:—No. 827, Three Kings; No. 828, Type **287**; No. 829, e Nativity; No. 830, Adoration of the Kings.

No. 827 was only issued in sheetlets of 13 stamps and two bels (at the centre of rows 1 and 2) sold at £3.36 providing a scount of 28p. off the face value of the stamps.

**288** Multicoloured Heart

es T. Monaghan (28p.), R. Ballagh (32p.). Litho Irish Security Stamp Ptg Ltd)

**92** (28 Jan). *Greetings Stamps. T* **288** *and similar multicoloured design. P* 15×14 (28p.) *or* 14×15 (32p.).

1 28p. Type **288** .. .. .. .. 55 60
2 32p. "LOVE" at end of rainbow (*vert*) .. 60 65

POSTAGE DUE STAMPS

From 1922 to 1925 Great Britain postage due stamps in both script and block watermarks were used without overprint.

D 1

D 2

D 3

(Des Ruby McConnell. Typo Govt Printing Works, Dublin)

**1925** (20 Feb). *W* **10**. *P* 14 × 15.

| No. | Type | Description | Unused | Used |
|---|---|---|---|---|
| D1 | D 1 | ½d. emerald-green | 10·00 | 16·00 |
| D2 | | 1d. carmine | 14·00 | 2·25 |
| | | a. Wmk sideways | £200 | 90·00 |
| D3 | | 2d. deep green | 22·00 | 5·00 |
| | | a. Wmk sideways | 40·00 | 14·00 |
| D4 | | 6d. plum | 6·00 | 6·00 |
| D1/4 | | *Set of* 4 | 48·00 | 26·00 |

**1940–70.** *W* **22**. *P* 14 × 15.

| No. | Type | Description | Unused | Used |
|---|---|---|---|---|
| D 5 | D 1 | ½d. emerald-green (1942) | 35·00 | 20·00 |
| D 6 | | 1d. carmine (1941) | 1·00 | 50 |
| D 7 | | 1½d. vermilion (1953) | 1·75 | 6·50 |
| D 8 | | 2d. deep green (1940) | 2·25 | 50 |
| D 9 | | 3d. blue (10.11.52) | 1·75 | 1·00 |
| D10 | | 5d. blue-violet (3.3.43) | 3·00 | 3·00 |
| D11 | | 6d. plum (21.3.60) | 2·25 | 1·50 |
| | | a. Wmk sideways (1968) | 70 | 85 |
| D12 | | 8d. orange (30.10.62) | 7·50 | 7·00 |
| D13 | | 10d. bright purple (27.1.65) | 8·00 | 7·50 |
| D14 | | 1s. apple-green (10.2.69) | 7·50 | 8·00 |
| | | a. Wmk sideways (1970) | 50·00 | 8·50 |
| D5/14 | | *Set of* 10 | 60·00 | 50·00 |

**1971** (15 Feb). *As Nos.* D5/14, *but with values in decimal currency and colours changed. W* **22**. *P* 14 × 15.

| No. | Type | Description | Unused | Used |
|---|---|---|---|---|
| D15 | D 1 | 1p. sepia | 30 | 40 |
| | | a. Wmk sideways | 1·50 | 1·50 |
| D16 | | 1½p. light emerald | 40 | 1·25 |
| D17 | | 3p. stone | 90 | 1·50 |
| D18 | | 4p. orange | 90 | 1·25 |
| D19 | | 5p. greenish blue | 95 | 2·00 |
| D20 | | 7p. bright yellow | 40 | 2·00 |
| D21 | | 8p. scarlet | 40 | 1·50 |
| D15/21 | | *Set of* 7 | 3·75 | 9·00 |

**1978** (20 Mar). *As Nos.* D17/19, *but no wmk. P* 14 × 15.

| No. | Type | Description | Unused | Used |
|---|---|---|---|---|
| D22 | D 1 | 3p. stone | 2·00 | 5·00 |
| D23 | | 4p. orange | 5·00 | 8·00 |
| D24 | | 5p. greenish blue | 2·00 | 4·00 |
| D22/4 | | *Set of* 3 | 8·00 | 15·00 |

The above are on whiter paper and the colours are brighter.

**1980** (11 June)–**85**. *Photo. Chalk-surfaced paper. P* 15.

| No. | Type | Description | Unused | Used |
|---|---|---|---|---|
| D25 | D 2 | 1p. apple green | 10 | 30 |
| D26 | | 2p. dull blue | 10 | 30 |
| D27 | | 4p. myrtle-green | 15 | 30 |
| D28 | | 6p flesh | 20 | 45 |
| D29 | | 8p. chalky blue | 25 | 50 |
| D30 | | 18p. green | 50 | 80 |
| D31 | | 20p. Indian red (22.8.85) | 1·50 | 2·25 |
| D32 | | 24p. bright yellowish green | 60 | 1·25 |
| D33 | | 30p. deep violet blue (22.8.85) | 2·00 | 3·00 |
| D34 | | 50p. cerise (22.8.85) | 3·50 | 4·25 |
| D25/34 | | *Set of* 10 | 8·00 | 12·00 |

(Des Q Design. Litho Irish Security Stamp Ptg Ltd)

**1988** (6 Oct). *Chalk-surfaced paper. P* 14 × 15.

| No. | Type | Description | Unused | Used |
|---|---|---|---|---|
| D35 | D 3 | 1p. black, orange-vermilion & lemon | 10 | 10 |
| D36 | | 2p. black, orange-verm & purple-brn | 10 | 10 |
| D37 | | 3p. black, orange-vermilion and plum | 10 | 10 |
| D38 | | 4p. black, orange-vermilion & brt vio | 10 | 10 |
| D39 | | 5p. black, orge-vermilion & royal blue | 10 | 15 |
| D40 | | 17p. black, orange-verm & dp yell-grn | 30 | 35 |
| D41 | | 20p. black, orange-vermilion & slate-bl | 35 | 40 |
| D42 | | 24p. black, orange-verm & dp turq-grn | 45 | 50 |
| D43 | | 30p. black, orange-vermilion & dp grey | 55 | 60 |
| D44 | | 50p. black, orge-verm & brownish grey | 90 | 95 |
| D45 | | £1 black, orge-vermilion & bistre-brn | 1·90 | 2·00 |
| D35/45 | | *Set of* 11 | 4·25 | 4·75 |

## THOMOND AND LONG ISLAND

Labels inscribed "Principality of Thomond" appeared on the philatelic market in the early 1960s. Thomond is the name of a district in western Ireland. The area does not have its own administration or postal service and the labels were not recognised by the Department of Posts & Telegraphs, Dublin.

Local carriage labels were issued for Long Island, County Cork in April 1973; they were intended to cover the cost of taking mail from the island to the nearest mainland post office. A local service operated for a few weeks before it was suppressed by the Irish Post Office. As the stamps were not accepted for national or international mail they are not listed here.

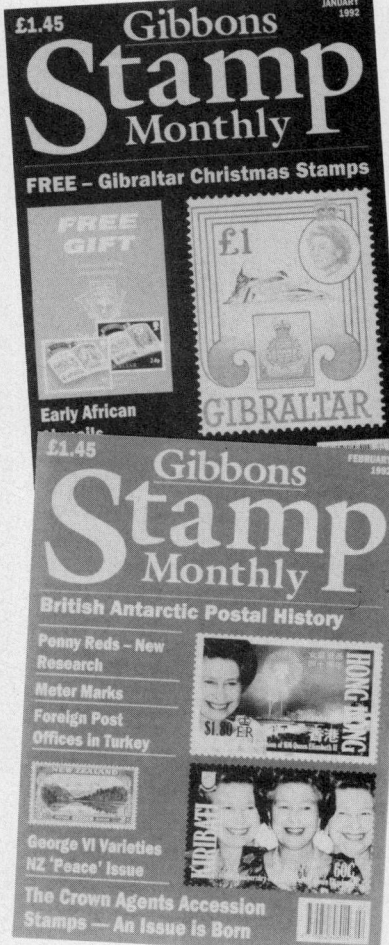

# Addenda

## ANTIGUA

**275** Locomotive *Prince Regent*, Middleton Colliery, 1812

(Des W. Hanson Studio. Litho Walsall)

**991** (18 Mar). *Cog Railways. T* **275** *and similar multicoloured designs. P* 14.

| | | | |
|---|---|---|---|
| 485 | 25 c. Type **275** .. .. .. .. | 10 | 10 |
| 486 | 30 c. Snowdon Mountain Railway .. .. | 10 | 10 |
| 487 | 40 c. First railcar at Hell Gate, Manitou & Pike's Peak Railway, U.S.A. .. .. | 15 | 20 |
| 488 | 60 c. Pnka rack railway, Amberawa, Java | 25 | 30 |
| 489 | $1 Green Mountain Railway, Maine, 1883 .. .. .. .. .. | 40 | 45 |
| 490 | $2 Cog locomotive *Pike's Peak*, 1891 .. | 85 | 90 |
| 491 | $4 Vitznau-Rigi Railway, Switzerland, and Mt Rigi hotel local post stamp .. | 1·75 | 1·90 |
| 492 | $5 Leopoldina Railway, Brazil .. .. | 2·10 | 2·25 |
| 485/92 | .. .. .. .. *Set of* 8 | 5·25 | 5·75 |
| S1493 | Two sheets, each 100×70 mm. (a) $6 Electric donkey locomotives, Panama Canal. (b) $6 Gornergrat Railway, Switzerland (*vert*) *Set of* 2 *sheets* | 5·00 | 5·25 |

## ASCENSION

**144** Compass Rose and *Eye of the Wind* (cadet ship)

(Des R. Watton. Litho Walsall)

**992** (18 Feb). *500th Anniv of Discovery of America by Columbus and Re-enactment Voyages. T* **144** *and similar horiz designs. Multicoloured. W w* **14** (*sideways*). *P* 13½×14.

| | | | |
|---|---|---|---|
| 74 | 9p. Type **144** .. .. .. .. .. | 20 | 25 |
| 75 | 18p. Map of re-enactment voyages and *Soren Larsen* (cadet ship) .. .. | 35 | 40 |
| 76 | 25p. *Santa Maria, Pinta* and *Nina* .. .. | 50 | 55 |
| 77 | 70p. Columbus and *Santa Maria* .. .. | 1·40 | 1·50 |
| 74/7 | .. .. .. .. *Set of* 4 | 2·25 | 2·50 |

## BAHAMAS

(Des A. Lowe and L. Curtis. Litho Questa)

**992** (17 Mar). *500th Anniv of Discovery of America by Columbus (5th issue). Vert designs as T* **173**. *Multicoloured. W w* **16**. *P* 14½×14.

| | | | |
|---|---|---|---|
| 33 | 15 c. Lucayans sighting fleet .. .. | 15 | 20 |
| 34 | 40 c. *Santa Maria* and dolphins .. .. | 45 | 50 |
| 35 | 55 c. Lucayan canoes approaching ships .. | 65 | 70 |
| 36 | 60 c. Columbus giving thanks for landfall | 70 | 75 |
| 33/6 | .. .. .. .. *Set of* 4 | 1·75 | 2·00 |
| S937 | 61×57 mm. $1.50, Children at Columbus Monument .. .. .. .. .. | 1·75 | 2·00 |

## BANGLADESH

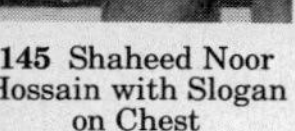

**145** Shaheed Noor Hossain with Slogan on Chest

**146** Bronze Stupa

(Des K. Mustafa. Litho State Security Ptg Press, Gazipur)

**991** (10 Nov). *4th Death Anniv of Shaheed Noor Hossain (democrat). P* 14.

| | | | |
|---|---|---|---|
| 00 **145** | 2 t. multicoloured .. .. .. .. | 10 | 10 |

(Des M. Akond. Litho State Security Ptg Press, Gazipur)

**1991** (26 Nov). *Archaeological Relics from Mainamati. T* **146** *and similar horiz designs. Multicoloured. P* 13½.

| | | | |
|---|---|---|---|
| 401 | 4 t. Type **146** .. .. .. .. .. | 10 | 10 |
| | a. Horiz strip of 5. Nos. 401/5 .. .. | 55 | |
| 402 | 4 t. Earthenware and bronze pitchers .. | 10 | 10 |
| 403 | 4 t. Remains of Salban Vihara Monastery | 10 | 10 |
| 404 | 4 t. Gold coins .. .. .. .. | 10 | 10 |
| 405 | 4 t. Terracotta plaque .. .. .. | 10 | 10 |
| 401/5 | .. .. .. .. *Set of* 5 | 55 | 60 |

Nos. 401/5 were printed together, *se-tenant*, in horizontal strips of 5 throughout the sheet.

**147** Demonstrators

**148** Munier Chowdhury

(Des. M. Muniruzzaman. Litho State Security Ptg Press, Gazipur)

**1991** (6 Dec). *1st Anniv of Mass Uprising. P* 13½.

| | | | |
|---|---|---|---|
| 406 **147** | 4 t. multicoloured .. .. .. .. | 10 | 10 |

(Litho State Security Ptg Press, Gazipur)

**1991** (14 Dec). *20th Anniv of Independence. Martyred Intellectuals. T* **148** *and similar vert designs. Each reddish brown and grey-black. P* 13½.

| | | | |
|---|---|---|---|
| 407 | 2 t. Type **148** .. .. .. .. | 10 | 10 |
| | a. Sheetlet. Nos. 407/16 .. .. | 60 | |
| 408 | 2 t. Ghyasuddin Ahmad .. .. .. | 10 | 10 |
| 409 | 2 t. Rashidul Hasan .. .. .. | 10 | 10 |
| 410 | 2 t. Muhammad Anwar Pasha .. .. | 10 | 10 |
| 411 | 2 t. Dr. Muhammad Mortaza .. .. | 10 | 10 |
| 412 | 2 t. Shahid Saber .. .. .. .. | 10 | 10 |
| 413 | 2 t. Fazlur Rahman Khan .. .. | 10 | 10 |
| 414 | 2 t. Ranada Prasad Saha .. .. | 10 | 10 |
| 415 | 2 t. Adhyaksha Joges Chandra Ghose .. | 10 | 10 |
| 416 | 2 t. Santosh Chandra Bhattacharyya .. | 10 | 10 |
| 417 | 2 t. Dr. Gobinda Chandra Deb .. .. | 10 | 10 |
| | a. Sheetlet. Nos. 417/26 .. .. | 60 | |
| 418 | 2 t. A. Muniruzzaman .. .. .. | 10 | 10 |
| 419 | 2 t. Mufazzal Haider Chaudhury .. .. | 10 | 10 |
| 420 | 2 t. Dr. Abdul Alim Choudhury .. .. | 10 | 10 |
| 421 | 2 t. Sirajuddin Hossain .. .. .. | 10 | 10 |
| 422 | 2 t. Shahidulla Kaiser .. .. .. | 10 | 10 |
| 423 | 2 t. Altaf Mahmud .. .. .. | 10 | 10 |
| 424 | 2 t. Dr. Jyotirmay Guha Thakurta .. | 10 | 10 |
| 425 | 2 t. Dr. Muhammad Abul Khair .. .. | 10 | 10 |
| 426 | 2 t. Dr. Serajul Haque Khan .. .. | 10 | 10 |
| 427 | 2 t. Dr. Mohammad Fazle Rabbi .. .. | 10 | 10 |
| | a. Sheetlet. Nos. 427/36 .. .. | 60 | |
| 428 | 2 t. Mir Abdul Quyyum .. .. .. | 10 | 10 |
| 429 | 2 t. Golam Mostafa .. .. .. | 10 | 10 |
| 430 | 2 t. Dhirendranath Dutta .. .. | 10 | 10 |
| 431 | 2 t. S. Mannan .. .. .. .. | 10 | 10 |
| 432 | 2 t. Nizamuddin Ahmad .. .. .. | 10 | 10 |
| 433 | 2 t. Abul Bashar Chowdhury .. .. | 10 | 10 |
| 434 | 2 t. Selina Parveen .. .. .. | 10 | 10 |
| 435 | 2 t. Dr. Abul Kalam Azad .. .. | 10 | 10 |
| 436 | 2 t. Saidul Hassan .. .. .. | 10 | 10 |
| 407/36 | .. .. .. .. *Set of* 30 | 1·60 | 1·75 |

Nos. 407/16, 417/26 and 427/36 were printed together, *se-tenant*, in sheetlets of 10, the two horizontal rows in each sheetlet being separated by a row of inscribed labels.

**149** *Penaeus monodon*

(Litho State Security Ptg Pres, Gazipur)

**1991** (31 Dec). *Shrimps. T* **149** *and similar horiz design. Multicoloured. P* 14×13½.

| | | | |
|---|---|---|---|
| 437 | 6 t. Type **149** .. .. .. .. | 20 | 25 |
| | a. Horiz pair. Nos. 437/8 .. .. | 40 | |
| 438 | 6 t. *Metapenaeus monoceros* .. .. | 20 | 25 |

Nos. 437/8 were printed together, *se-tenant*, in horizontal pairs throughout the sheet.

### PRICES OF SETS

Set prices are given for many issues, generally those containing three stamps or more. Definitive sets include one of each value or major colour change, but do not cover different perforations, die types or minor shades. Where a choice is possible the set prices are based on the cheapest versions of the stamps included in the listings.

## BRITISH VIRGIN ISLANDS

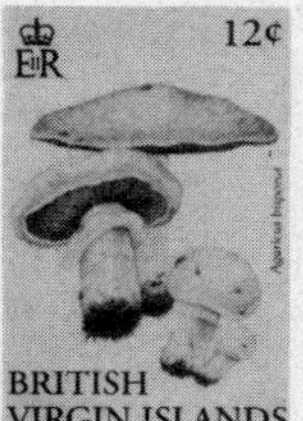


**197** *Agaricus bisporus*

(Litho Questa)

**1992** (15 Jan). *Fungi. T* **197** *and similar multicoloured designs. P* 14.

| | | | |
|---|---|---|---|
| 808 | 12 c. Type **197** .. .. .. .. | 10 | 10 |
| 809 | 30 c. *Lentinus edodes* (*horiz*) .. .. | 35 | 40 |
| 810 | 45 c. *Hyrocybe acutoconica* .. .. .. | 50 | 55 |
| 811 | $1 *Gymnopilus chrysopellus* (*horiz*) .. | 1·10 | 1·25 |
| 808/11 | .. .. .. .. *Set of* 4 | 2·00 | 2·10 |
| **MS**812 | 94×68mm. $2 *Pleurotus ostreatus* (*horiz*) | 2·25 | 2·50 |

**Note.** The first Supplement recording new stamps not in this Catalogue or the Addenda appeared in the July 1992 number of *Gibbons Stamp Monthly*.

# Index


page

'reface iii
ddresses iv
tamps Added and Numbers Altered vi
pecialist Philatelic Societies vii
ieneral Philatelic Information viii
bbreviations xvi
elect Bibliography xix

*'ountry*

bu Dhabi 1
den (South Arabian Federation) *see Vol. 2*
itutaki (Cook Islands) 273
lderney (Guernsey) GB77
lwar (Indian States) 516
ndaman and Nicobar Islands (Japanese Occupation) (India) 509
nguilla 1
ntigua 11
scension 39
ustralia 48
ustralian Antarctic Territory 103

aghdad (Iraq) 547
ahamas 105
ahawalpur (Pakistan) *see Vol. 2*
ahrain 116
amra (Indian States) 516
angkok (British P.O. in Siam) 179
angladesh 117
arbados 125
arbuda (Antigua) 28
arwani (Indian States) 516
asutoland (Lesotho) *see Vol. 2*
atum (British Occupation) 136
echuanaland (Botswana) 162
echuanaland Protectorate (Botswana) 160
elize 136
ermuda 149
hopal (Indian States) 517
hor (Indian States) 520
iafra (Nigeria) *see Vol. 2*
ijawar (Indian States) 520
otswana 160
.M.A. Malaya (Malaysia) *see Vol. 2*
ritish Antarctic Territory 170
ritish Bechuanaland (Botswana) 160
ritish Central Africa (Malawi) *see Vol. 2*
ritish Columbia (Canada) 201
ritish Columbia and Vancouver Island (Canada) 201
ritish Commonwealth Occupation Force (Japan) (Australia) 102
ritish Commonwealth Omnibus Issues *see Vol. 2*
ritish Consular Mail (Madagascar) *see Vol. 2*
ritish East Africa (Kenya, Uganda and Tanganyika) *see Vol. 2*
ritish Forces in Egypt (Egypt) 323
ritish Guiana (Guyana) 424
ritish Honduras (Belize) 136
ritish Indian Ocean Territory 173
ritish Kaffraria (South Africa) *see Vol. 2*
ritish Levant 175
ritish Military Administration, Malaya (Malaysia) *see Vol. 2*
ritish New Guinea (Papua New Guinea) *see Vol. 2*
ritish North Borneo (Malaysia) *see Vol. 2*
ritish Occupation of Iraq 547
ritish Occupation of Italian Colonies 177
ritish P.O.s Abroad GB95
ritish P.O.s in China (Hong Kong) 466
ritish P.O.s in Crete 179
ritish P.O.s in Japan (Hong Kong) 468
ritish P.O.s in Morocco (Morocco Agencies) *see Vol. 2*

*Country* *page*

British P.O. in Siam 179
British Postal Agencies in Eastern Arabia 179
British Solomon Islands Protectorate (Solomon Islands) *see Vol. 2*
British Somaliland (Somaliland Protectorate) *see Vol. 2*
British South Africa Company (Rhodesia) *see Vol. 2*
British Virgin Islands 180
Brunei 190
Brunei (Japanese Occupation) 197
Bundi (Indian States) 520, 537
Burma 198
Burma (Japanese Occupation) 199
Bushire (British Occupation) 201
Bussahir (Indian States) 522

Caicos Islands (Turks and Caicos Islands) *see Vol. 2*
Cameroons (British Occupation) 201
Canada 201
Cape of Good Hope (South Africa) *see Vol. 2*
Cayes of Belize (Belize) 148
Cayman Islands 241
C.E.F. (Cameroons) 201
C.E.F. (*on* India) 508
Ceylon (Sri Lanka) *see Vol. 2*
Chamba (Indian States) 509
Channel Islands GB68
Charkhari (Indian States) 523
China (British P.O.s) 466
China Expeditionary Force (India) 508
Christmas Island 250
Cochin (Indian States) 524
Cocos (Keeling) Islands 255
Cook Islands 259
Crete (British Administration) 179
Crowned-circle handstamps GB95
Cyprus 286
Cyrenaica (British Occupation of Italian Colonies) 178

Datia (Duttia) (Indian States) 527
Dhar (Indian States) 527
Dominica 305
Dungarpur (Indian States) 527
Duttia (Indian States) 527

East Africa Forces (E.A.F.) (British Occupation of Italian Colonies) 178
East Africa & Uganda (Kenya, Uganda and Tanganyika) *see Vol. 2*
East India (India Nos. 35 etc.) 469
E.E.F. (Palestine) *see Vol. 2*
Egypt 320
Eire (Ireland) 551
Eritrea (M.E.F. and B.M.A.) (British Occupation of Italian Colonies) 178

Falkland Islands 323
Falkland Islands Dependencies 333
Faridkot (Indian States) 510, 527
Federated Malay States (Malaysia) *see Vol. 2*
Fiji 335

Gambia 346
G.E.A. (Tanzania) *see Vol. 2*
Ghana 359
Gibraltar 379
Gilbert and Ellice Islands 389
Gilbert Islands (Kiribati) *see Vol. 2*
Gold Coast (Ghana) 359
Graham Land (Falkland Islands) 333
Great Britain GB1
Great Britain (Channel Islands) GB68
Great Britain (Island Issues) GB68
Great Britain (Official Stamps) GB66
Great Britain (Postage Due Stamps) GB66
Great Britain (Postal Fiscals) GB67
Great Britain (Regional Stamps) GB64
Great Britain (Used Abroad) GB95

*Country* *page*

Grenada 392
Grenadines (Grenada *and* St. Vincent) 413 and *see Vol. 2*
Griqualand West (South Africa) *see Vol. 2*
Guernsey GB68
Guyana 424
Gwalior (Indian States) 511

Hadhramaut (South Arabian Federation) *see Vol. 2*
Heligoland 455
Holkar (Indore) (Indian States) 530
Hong Kong 455
Hong Kong (Japanese Occupation) 466
Hyderabad (Indian States) 528

Idar (Indian States) 530
I.E.F. (India) 508
I.E.F. 'D' (Iraq) 547
India 468
Indian Convention States 509
Indian Custodian Forces in Korea 508
Indian Expeditionary Forces, 1914–22 508
Indian Feudatory States 516
Indian National Army 509
Indian U.N. Force in Congo 508
Indian U.N. Force in Gaza (Palestine) 508
Indore (Indian States) 530
International Commission in Indo-China 509
Ionian Islands 547
Iraq 547
Ireland (Republic) 549
Isle of Man GB78

Jaipur (Indian States) 530, 538
Jamaica *see Vol. 2*
Jammu and Kashmir (Indian States) 532
Japan (British P.O.s) (Hong Kong) 468
Japanese Occupation of Andaman and Nicobar Islands (India) 509
Japanese Occupation of Brunei 197
Japanese Occupation of Burma 199
Japanese Occupation of Hong Kong 466
Japanese Occupation of Kelantan (Malaysia) *see Vol. 2*
Japanese Occupation of Malaya (Malaysia) *see Vol. 2*
Japanese Occupation of North Borneo (Malaysia) *see Vol. 2*
Japanese Occupation of Sarawak (Malaysia) *see Vol. 2*
Jasdan (Indian States) 533
Jersey GB86
Jhalawar (Indian States) 533
Jind (Indian States) 512, 534
Johore (Malaysia) *see Vol. 2*
Junagadh (Soruth) (Indian States) 539

Kashmir and Jammu (Indian States) 532
Kathiri State of Seiyun (South Arabian Federation) *see Vol. 2*
Kedah (Malaysia) *see Vol. 2*
Kelantan (Malaysia) *see Vol. 2*
Kelantan (Japanese Occupation) (Malaysia) *see Vol. 2*
Kelantan (Thai Occupation) (Malaysia) *see Vol. 2*
Kenya *see Vol. 2*
Kenya, Uganda and Tanganyika *see Vol. 2*
King Edward VII Land (New Zealand) *see Vol. 2*
Kiribati *see Vol. 2*
Kishangarh (Indian States) 534, 538
Korea (Indian Custodian Forces) 508
Kuwait *see Vol. 2*

Labuan (Malaysia) *see Vol. 2*
Lagos (Nigeria) *see Vol. 2*
Las Bela (Indian States) 535
Leeward Islands *see Vol. 2*
Lesotho *see Vol. 2*

| Country | page |
|---|---|
| Levant (British) | 175 |
| Long Island | *see Vol. 2* |
| Lydenburg (Transvaal) (South Africa) | *see Vol. 2* |
| | |
| Madagascar (British Consular Mail) | *see Vol. 2* |
| Mafeking Siege Stamps (Cape of Good Hope) (South Africa) | *see Vol. 2* |
| Mafia (Tanzania) | *see Vol. 2* |
| Mahra Sultanate of Qishn and Socotra (South Arabian Federation) | *see Vol. 2* |
| Malacca (Malaysia) | *see Vol. 2* |
| Malawi | *see Vol. 2* |
| Malaya (B.M.A.) (Malaysia) | *see Vol. 2* |
| Malaya (Japanese Occupation) (Malaysia) | *see Vol. 2* |
| Malaya (Thai Occupation) (Malaysia) | *see Vol. 2* |
| Malayan Federation (Malaysia) | *see Vol. 2* |
| Malayan Postal Union (Malaysia) | *see Vol. 2* |
| Malaysia | *see Vol. 2* |
| Malaysian Federal Territory | *see Vol. 2* |
| Malaysian States | *see Vol. 2* |
| Maldive Islands | *see Vol. 2* |
| Malta | *see Vol. 2* |
| Mauritius | *see Vol. 2* |
| Middle East Forces (M.E.F.) (British Occupation of Italian Colonies) | 177 |
| Montserrat | *see Vol. 2* |
| Morocco Agencies (British Post Offices) | *see Vol. 2* |
| Morvi (Indian States) | 536 |
| Mosul (Iraq) | 547 |
| Muscat | *see Vol. 2* |
| | |
| Nabha (Indian States) | 513 |
| Namibia | *see Vol. 2* |
| Nandgaon (Indian States) | 536 |
| Natal (South Africa) | *see Vol. 2* |
| Nauru | *see Vol. 2* |
| Nawanagar (Indian States) | 536 |
| Negri Sembilan (Malaysia) | *see Vol. 2* |
| Nevis (St. Kitts-Nevis) | *see Vol. 2* |
| New Brunswick (Canada) | 203 |
| New Carlisle, Gaspé (Canada) | 201 |
| Newfoundland (Canada) | 204 |
| New Guinea (Papua New Guinea) | *see Vol. 2* |
| New Hebrides (Vanuatu) | *see Vol. 2* |
| New Republic (South Africa) | *see Vol. 2* |
| New South Wales (Australia) | 48 |
| New Zealand | *see Vol. 2* |
| Niger Coast Protectorate (Nigeria) | *see Vol. 2* |
| Niger Company Territories (Nigeria) | *see Vol. 2* |
| Nigeria | *see Vol. 2* |
| Niuafo'ou (Tonga) | *see Vol. 2* |
| Niue | *see Vol. 2* |
| Norfolk Island | *see Vol. 2* |
| North Borneo (Malaysia) | *see Vol. 2* |
| North Borneo (Japanese Occupation) (Malaysia) | *see Vol. 2* |
| Northern Ireland | GB64 |
| Northern Nigeria (Nigeria) | *see Vol. 2* |
| Northern Rhodesia (Zambia) | *see Vol. 2* |
| North West Pacific Islands (Papua New Guinea) | *see Vol. 2* |
| Nova Scotia (Canada) | 209 |
| Nyasaland Protectorate (Malawi) | *see Vol. 2* |
| Nyasaland–Rhodesian Force (N.F.) (Tanganyika) | *see Vol. 2* |
| | |
| Oil Rivers (Nigeria) | *see Vol. 2* |
| Omnibus Issues | *see Vol. 2* |
| Orange Free State (South Africa) | *see Vol. 2* |
| Orange River Colony (South Africa) | *see Vol. 2* |
| Orchha (Indian States) | 536 |
| | |
| Pahang (Malaysia) | *see Vol. 2* |
| Pakistan | *see Vol. 2* |
| Palestine (British Mandate) | *see Vol. 2* |
| Papua (Papua New Guinea) | *see Vol. 2* |
| Papua New Guinea | *see Vol. 2* |
| Patiala (Indian States) | 514 |
| Penang (Malaysia) | *see Vol. 2* |
| Penrhyn Island (Cook Islands) | 280 |
| Perak (Malaysia) | *see Vol. 2* |
| Perlis (Malaysia) | *see Vol. 2* |
| Pietersburg (Transvaal) (South Africa) | *see Vol. 2* |
| Pitcairn Islands | *see Vol. 2* |
| Poonch (Indian States) | 537 |
| Prince Edward Island (Canada) | 211 |
| Puttiala (Patiala) (Indian States) | 514 |
| | |
| Qatar | *see Vol. 2* |
| Qu'aiti State in Hadhramaut (South Arabian Federation) | *see Vol. 2* |
| Queensland (Australia) | 53 |
| | |
| Rajasthan (Indian States) | 537 |
| Rajpipla (Indian States) | 538 |
| Rarotonga (Cook Islands, No. 50, etc.) | 259 |
| Redonda (Antigua) | 37 |
| Rhodesia | *see Vol. 2* |
| Rhodesia and Nyasaland | *see Vol. 2* |
| Ross Dependency (New Zealand) | *see Vol. 2* |
| Rustenburg (Transvaal) (South Africa) | *see Vol. 2* |
| | |
| Sabah (Malaysia) | *see Vol. 2* |
| St. Christopher (St.Kitts-Nevis) | *see Vol. 2* |
| St. Christopher, Nevis and Anguilla (St. Kitts-Nevis) | *see Vol. 2* |
| St. Helena | *see Vol. 2* |
| St. Kitts (St. Kitts-Nevis) | *see Vol. 2* |
| St. Kitts–Nevis | *see Vol. 2* |
| St. Lucia | *see Vol. 2* |
| St. Vincent | *see Vol. 2* |
| Salonica (British Levant) | 177 |
| Samoa | *see Vol. 2* |
| Sarawak (Malaysia) | *see Vol. 2* |
| Sarawak (Japanese Occupation) (Malaysia) | *see Vol. 2* |
| Saurashtra (Soruth) (Indian States) | 541 |
| Schweizer Renecke (Transvaal) (South Africa) | *see Vol. 2* |
| Scinde (India) | 468 |
| Scotland | GB64 |
| Seiyun (South Arabian Federation) | *see Vol. 2* |
| Selangor (Malaysia) | *see Vol. 2* |
| Seychelles | *see Vol. 2* |
| Shahpura (Indian States) | 538 |
| Shihr and Mukalla (South Arabian Federation) | *see Vol. 2* |
| Sierra Leone | *see Vol. 2* |
| Singapore | *see Vol. 2* |
| Sirmoor (Indian States) | 538 |
| Solomon Islands | *see Vol. 2* |
| Somalia (British Occupation of Italian Colonies) | 178 |
| Somaliland Protectorate | *see Vol. 2* |
| Soruth (Indian States) | 539 |
| South Africa | *see Vol. 2* |
| South African Republic (Transvaal) (South Africa) | *see Vol. 2* |
| South Arabian Federation | *see Vol. 2* |
| South Australia (Australia) | 56 |
| Southern Cameroons | *see Vol. 2* |
| Southern Nigeria (Nigeria) | *see Vol. 2* |
| Southern Rhodesia (Zimbabwe) | *see Vol. 2* |
| South Georgia (Falkland Islands) | 333 |
| South Georgia and South Sandwich Islands | *see Vol. 2* |
| South Orkneys (Falkland Islands) | 333 |
| South Shetlands (Falkland Islands) | 333 |
| South West Africa (Namibia) | *see Vol. 2* |
| Sri Lanka | *see Vol. 2* |
| Stellaland (Botswana) | 160 |
| Straits Settlements (Malaysia) | *see Vol. 2* |
| Sudan | *see Vol. 2* |
| Sungei Ujong (Malaysia) | *see Vol. 2* |
| Swaziland | *see Vol. 2* |
| | |
| Tanganyika (Tanzania) | *see Vol. 2* |
| Tangier (Morocco Agencies) | *see Vol. 2* |
| Tanzania | *see Vol. 2* |
| Tasmania (Australia) | 60 |
| Thai Occupation of Kelantan (Malaysia) | *see Vol. 2* |
| Thai Occupation of Malaya (Malaysia) | *see Vol. 2* |
| Thai Occupation of Trengganu (Malaysia) | *see Vol. 2* |
| Tobago (Trinidad and Tobago) | *see Vol. 2* |
| Togo (Anglo-French Occupation) | *see Vol. 2* |
| Tokelau (New Zealand) | *see Vol. 2* |
| Tonga | *see Vol. 2* |
| Transjordan | *see Vol. 2* |
| Transvaal (South Africa) | *see Vol. 2* |
| Travancore (Indian States) | 541 |
| Travancore-Cochin (Indian States) | 544 |
| Trengganu (Malaysia) | *see Vol. 2* |
| Trengganu (Thai Occupation) (Malaysia) | *see Vol. 2* |
| Trinidad (Trinidad and Tobago) | *see Vol. 2* |
| Trinidad and Tobago | *see Vol. 2* |
| Tripolitania (M.E.F. and B.M.A.) (British Occupation of Italian Colonies) | 179 |
| Tristan da Cunha | *see Vol. 2* |
| Trucial States | *see Vol. 2* |
| Turkish Cypriot Posts (Cyprus) | 299 |
| Turkish Empire (British P.O.) (British Levant) | 175 |
| Turks Islands (Turks and Caicos Islands) | *see Vol. 2* |
| Turks and Caicos Islands | *see Vol. 2* |
| Tuvalu | *see Vol. 2* |
| | |
| Uganda | *see Vol. 2* |
| | |
| Vancouver Island (British Columbia) | 201 |
| Van Diemen's Land (Tasmania) (Australia) | 60 |
| Vanuatu | *see Vol. 2* |
| Victoria (Australia) | 63 |
| Victoria Land (New Zealand) | *see Vol. 2* |
| Virgin Islands (British Virgin Islands) | 180 |
| Volksrust (Transvaal) (South Africa) | *see Vol. 2* |
| Vryburg (Cape of Good Hope) (South Africa) | *see Vol. 2* |
| | |
| Wadhwan (Indian States) | 546 |
| Wales | GB64 |
| Western Australia (Australia) | 72 |
| Western Samoa (Samoa) | *see Vol. 2* |
| Wolmaransstad (Transvaal) (South Africa) | *see Vol. 2* |
| | |
| Zambia | *see Vol. 2* |
| Zanzibar (Tanzania) | *see Vol. 2* |
| Zil Elwannyen (Elwagne, Eloigne) Sesel (Seychelles) | *see Vol. 2* |
| Zimbabwe | *see Vol. 2* |
| Zululand (South Africa) | *see Vol. 2* |
| | |
| **Addenda** | 567 |

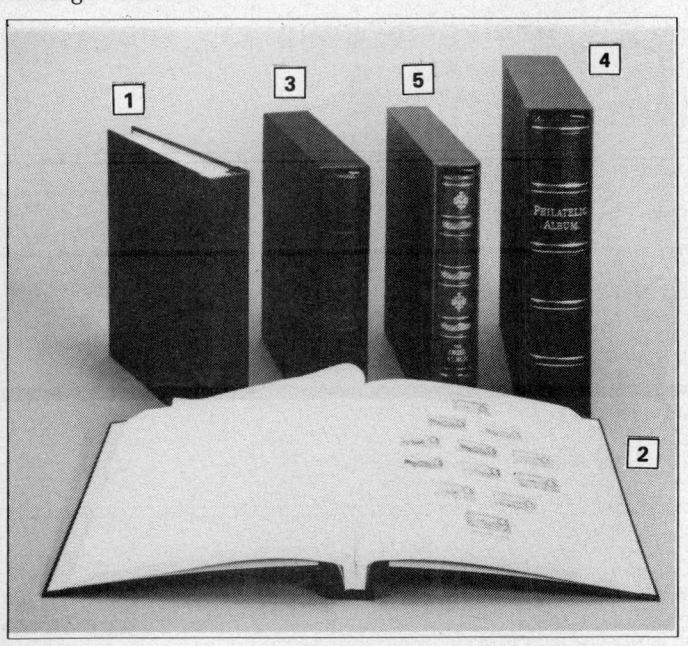

# STOCKBOOKS

We are pleased to announce that Stanley Gibbons are now offering a selected range of Lighthouse stockbooks in addition to the popular S.G. branded junior style. Fastbound with stout linen-hinged leaves, all come with glassine interleaving to ensure complete protection for your stamps and will give years of use.

**1. Junior Stockbooks**

With a bright full-colour, stamps design cover these stockbooks have white leaves with glassine strips and interleaving – ideal for the younger collector.

| | Size (ins) | No. of Pages | No. of Strips |
|---|---|---|---|
| **Item 2659** | 8½ × 6⅝ | 8 | 48 |
| **Item 2650** | 11 × 8¾ | 8 | 72 |

**2. Lighthouse Stockbooks**

A variety of bright single colour covers with gold blocking on the front and spine.

| | Size (ins) | No. of Pages | No. of Strips |
|---|---|---|---|
| **Item 2679** | 6¼ × 4⅝ | 16 | 64 |
| **Item 2651** | 9 × 7 | 16 | 96 |
| **Item 2631** | 9 × 7 | 32 | 192 |

For further details visit your favourite stamp shop or write to:

**Stanley Gibbons Publications Ltd.,**
**5 Parkside, Christchurch Road,**
**Ringwood, Hampshire BH24 3SH**
**Telephone 0425 472363**

The larger page size stockbooks feature a luxury leather look binding and have double glassine interleaving for even greater protection. NOTE the new 48-page stockbook (item 2662) has double linen hinged 'lay flat' leaves.

| | Size (ins) | No. of pages | No. of Strips |
|---|---|---|---|
| **Item 2652** | 12 × 9 | 16 | 144 |
| **Item 2653** | 12 × 9 | 32 | 288 |
| **Item 2662** | 12 × 9 | 48 | 432 |

**3.** Two stylish stockbooks with binding as above but with black leaves and crystal clear acetate strips. Double glassine interleaving.

| | | | |
|---|---|---|---|
| **Item 2664** | 12 × 9 | 16 | 144 |
| **Item 2665** | 12 × 9 | 32 | 288 |

**4.** The 'King Size' member of the S.G. Stock-book range! Cover Specifications as above with 64 double linen-hinged leaves to ensure that the book lies absolutely flat when open. White leaves with glassine strips and double interleaving. Definitely the top of the range and a luxury stockbook any collector would be proud to own.

| | | | |
|---|---|---|---|
| **Item 2678** | 12 × 9 | 64 | 576 |

# ACCESSORIES

From Stamp Hinges to Ultra Violet Lamps; from Tweezers and Magnifiers to Colour Keys and Watermark Detectors – Stanley Gibbons accessories are the answer to every collector's requirements.

The range has been completely revised with an improved selection of tweezers and the addition of a drying book and photo mounts for cover and postcard collectors.

A new range of magnifiers has been introduced which allows a wider variety of choice with each item having been carefully selected for its quality and value for money.

Current details of our superb range are available direct from Stanley Gibbons or your favourite supplier.

**Stanley Gibbons Publications Ltd.,**
**5 Parkside, Christchurch Road,**
**Ringwood, Hampshire BH24 3SH**

**Telephone 0425 472363**

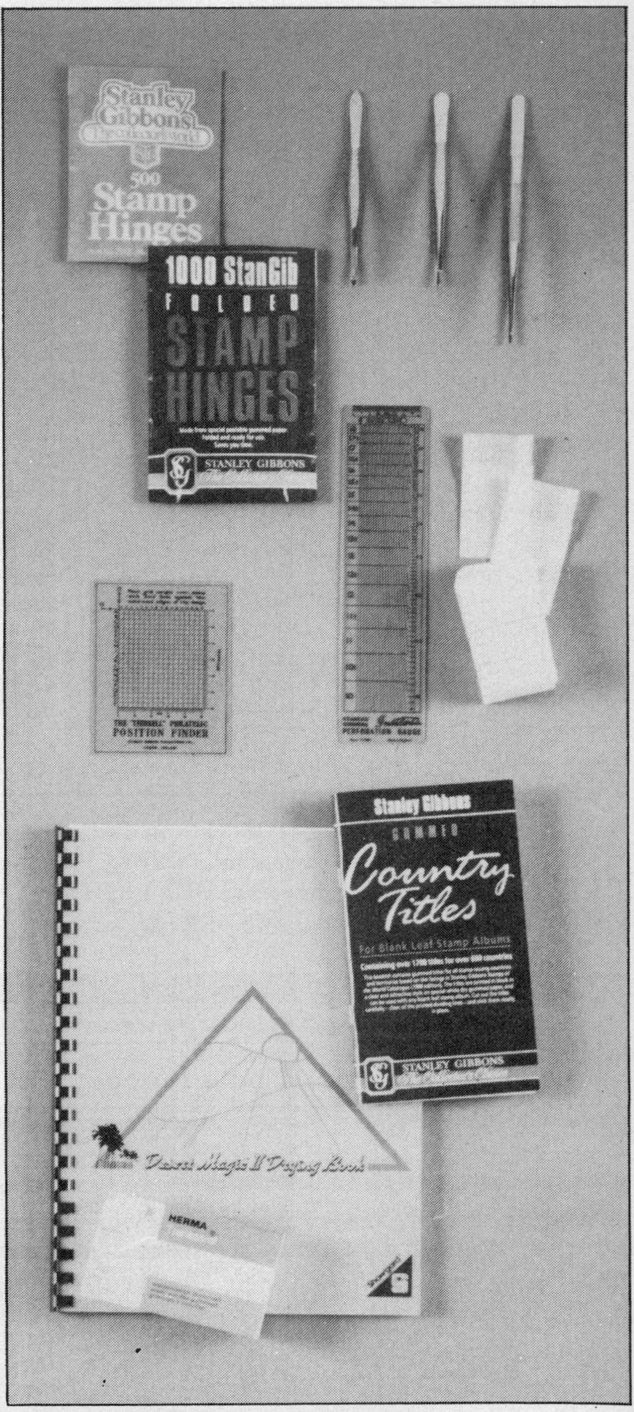